DIRECTORY
of
Nursing
Homes

3rd Edition

**Administrators ▪ Medical Directors
Directors of Nursing ▪ Licensure ▪ Capacity
Certification ▪ Chain Ownership ▪ Affiliation
Admissions Requirements ▪ Staff
Facilities ▪ Activities**

Phoenix ▪ New York
ORYX PRESS
1988

The rare Arabian Oryx is believed to have inspired the myth of the unicorn. This desert antelope became virtually extinct in the early 1960s. At that time several groups of international conservationists arranged to have 9 animals sent to the Phoenix Zoo to be the nucleus of a captive breeding herd. Today the Oryx population is nearly 800, and over 400 have been returned to reserves in the Middle East.

Copyright © 1988 by The Oryx Press
2214 North Central at Encanto
Phoenix, Arizona 85004-1483

Published simultaneously in Canada

Printed and Bound in the United States of America

Library of Congress Cataloging-in-Publication Data
Main entry under title:

Directory of nursing homes.

    Includes index.
    1. Nursing homes—United States—Directories.
2. Long-term care facilities—United States—Directories.
I. Mongeau, Sam, 1951–
RA997.A2D49   1984   362.1′6′02573   84-18994
ISBN 0-89774-414-4
ISSN 0888-7624

DIRECTORY
of
Nursing Homes

3rd Edition

TABLE OF CONTENTS

Introduction   vii

Funding Long-Term Care: Structuring Public/Private Partnerships *by* Paul R. Willging   ix

Funding Long-Term Care: Devising Private Insurance Mechanisms *by* Sheldon Goldberg   xiii

List of Abbreviations   xvi

State-by-State Listing of Facilities   1

Affiliation Index   1162

Alphabetical Listing of Facilities   1176

Corporate Nursing Home Headquarters   1259

INTRODUCTION

A recently enacted federal law, set to take effect over the next two and one-half years, strengthens the rights of nursing home residents, and specifically addresses the residents' ability to participate in choosing treatment style, drugs, and physicians, as well as guaranteeing each resident's right to privacy, including the right to receive notice before any change in room or roommate, a right to meet with other patients in organized groups, a right to "voice grievances" about care, and a right to have such grievances addressed promptly by the nursing facility.

The new law also prescribes standards for the training and staffing requirements of nursing home employees. For example, the new law mandates minimum standards for the training of nurses aides, who provide the bulk of the care in nursing homes, in both nursing care and patients' rights.

Failure by the nursing facility to adhere to the law will be costly. Civil penalties of up to $10,000 a day may be assessed if the nursing facility is found to be in violation of any portion of the new federal legislation.

Some of the most significant requirements of the new law are:

- Nursing homes must maintain or enhance the "quality of life of each resident."
- At least once a year nursing homes must conduct a comprehensive assessment of each patient's ability to perform such everyday activities as bathing, eating, and walking. Results of such assessments will be used to prepare a written plan of care, describing how the resident's medical, psychological, and social needs will be met.
- Every nurse's aide must receive at least 75 hours training in nursing skills and residents' rights. Nursing homes are responsible for making sure that nurses aides are competent to perform the tasks they are assigned.
- A nursing home must not admit any patient who is mentally ill or mentally retarded unless a state agency first certifies that the person requires the type of care provided in the nursing home. The state agency must also determine whether the person needs "active treatment" for the mental illness or retardation.

- A nursing home must have licensed nurses on duty around the clock and must have a registered nurse on duty for at least eight hours a day, seven days a week. State officials may grant an exemption if the nursing home can show that it was unable to recruit the necessary personnel and that the exemption would not endanger the health or safety of the residents.
- Any nursing home with more than 120 beds must have at least one full-time social worker with at least a bachelor's degree in social work or similar qualifications.
- Nursing homes must ordinarily give 30 days' notice before discharging or transferring a resident. The resident may challenge such decisions by filing an appeal under procedures to be established by each state.
- Nursing homes must permit "immediate access" to any resident by relatives and by federal and state officials, including specially designated ombudsmen. Every state has an ombudsman to investigate complaints about long-term care facilities. Patients, their relatives and lawyers may file complaints.
- If a nursing home fails to meet federal standards, the government may deny payment under Medicaid and Medicare and may appoint new managers to operate the facility. Payment must be withheld if the facility is found to be substandard in three consecutive annual surveys.

Chain Ownership Highlighted

The revised and expanded *Directory of Nursing Homes, 3rd Edition* lists detailed information for more than 16,000 licensed nursing facilities in the United States, Puerto Rico, and the Virgin Islands. Information was compiled by means of a questionnaire survey sent to all facilities. Those facilities that did not respond to the questionnaire were checked against state licensing directories to verify that information listed is the most accurate and current to date. These facilities have an asterisk (*) adjacent to their name. New features for this edition include listing the names of the owners of chain-owned nursing homes in the entry of the chain-owned facilities, and an Appendix listing the names and addresses of nursing home chains in alphabetical order.

Much of the information listed in this directory was compiled before the legislation determining patients' rights and employee training standards was enacted, and entries should not be used to measure any facility's compliance with the new legislation. Furthermore, users of this directory should bear in mind that all information has been supplied either by the facility or through public sources. The editors have assumed all information supplied by facilities to be factual and accurate. Listings are not meant to be comparative in nature nor is a listing in this directory meant of be an endorsement of any facility by the editors of The Oryx Press.

The editors caution all users to visit and compare facilities before either becoming a resident or placing a loved one in a long-term care facility. If conditions make a personal visit impossible, potential residents should consult a qualified professional who is familiar with the facility to determine whether it would meet their needs.

Arranged alphabetically by state, then city, each entry contains core information including name, address, telephone, number of beds, level of care provided and Medicaid, Medicare, and/or Medi-Cal* certification. Additionally, entries may include the name of the facility administrator, medical director and/or director of nursing, ownership type (corporate, private, nonprofit corporation, nonprofit organization/ foundation, public), languages spoken, full- and part-time staff members, admissions requirements including age and/or gender restrictions, religious and or fraternal affiliation, and detailed lists of special facilities and activities offered at each facility. Also included is an Affiliations Index, which lists facilities that are sponsored by religious or fraternal organizations. The Affiliations Index is arranged alphabetically

by state, then by sponsor. Following the Affiliations Index is an alphabetical listing of all facilities which is followed by the alphabetical listing of corporate nursing home headquarters.

A directory of this size is impossible to compile and publish without the dedicated and enthusiastic participation by a great number of people. The significant contributions of Susan Johnson, Linda Archer, Anne Rhodes, Susan Sims, Sandi Bourelle, Linda Vespa, Laurie Pacult, Priscilla Wiggins, Jim Defazio, Mary O'Connor, Gene Price, Mary Blackwell, John Wagner, and many others have added greatly to this publication.

Inquiries concerning the directory should be addressed to: The Editors, *Directory of Nursing Homes,* The Oryx Press, 2214 N Central at Encanto, Phoenix, Arizona 85004-1483.

Articles Highlight Insurance Issues

Another new feature for this edition is the presentation of opinion articles, written by respected, distinguished members of the health care community, which present the concerns, opinions, and forecasts of the authors on a topic of concern to the industry. In this edition, the Oryx Press is very proud to present two articles that discuss financing long-term care in the future. "Funding Long-Term Care: Structuring Public/Private Partnerships," by Dr. Paul R. Willging, executive vice president of The American Health Care Association, and "Funding Long-Term Care: Devising Private Insurance Mechanisms," by Sheldon Goldberg, president of The American Association of the Homes for the Aging, suggest actions that need to be taken to avoid costly problems for the elderly in the future.

---

*Medi-Cal is the name of the Medicaid program in California.

FUNDING LONG-TERM CARE:
Structuring Public/Private Partnerships

Paul R. Willging

I am pleased to introduce this directory of our nation's nursing homes, because the issues associated with providing and financing long-term care to the elderly and chronically ill are so significant. And as we look to the decades ahead, these issues will become even more significant.

The trends are clear: at a time when the American population is aging and increasingly in need of nursing home services—federal and state governments are unable or unwilling to pay for those services.

Currently, formal mechanisms for the financing of nursing home care are rooted in the public sector. Before the creation of the Medicare and Medicaid programs, even institutions providing long term care were primarily public. While Titles XVIII and XIX of the Social Security Act stimulated a dramatic growth in the private sector's involvement in long-term care, these programs shifted the country's reliance from public delivery systems to public financing.

Indeed, public financing has been the key to ensuring the availability of nursing home services to our nation's elderly. However, with pressure mounting to control government spending, policymakers have begun to realize that—as a nation—we cannot continue to rely on traditional approaches to financing long-term care. In fact, budget debates notwithstanding, the elderly should not be forced to rely on basic welfare mechanisms to insure protection against the often catastrophic costs of nursing home services.

While policymakers, consumers, and providers agree that a more rational and human approach to financing long-term care is essential, viable proposals have yet to be seriously debated in the policy arena. But they will. The demographics demand it. And given the current budgetary limitations, a public-private sector initiative must emerge through which the elderly will be offered protection against the potentially catastrophic costs of long-term nursing home care.

Demographics of an Aging Population

People *are* living longer. Decreasing mortality rates have had and will continue to have a significant impact on the need for long-term care. From 1940 to 1980, the age-adjusted death rates for the elderly decreased by 38 percent. Examination of mortality trends by the leading causes of death also reveals substantial declines—the largest for individuals between the ages of 65 and 69 and for those over 85.

The resulting increases in life expectancy are affecting long-term care in two important ways. First, and most publicly recognized, is that more people are surviving to age 65. In fact, 41 percent of the people born between 1900 and 1902 reached age 65, while 76 percent of those born in 1978 can expect to survive to their 65th birthday. The second consequence is the lengthening of the post age 65 period—a period of increasing vulnerability and frailty.

Exactly how will these mortality trends affect the need for long-term care?

Census Bureau statistics show that in a mere 12 years, the 75 to 84 age group will increase from 7.7 to 12.2 million, while the 85 and over population will more than double—from 2.2 to 5.1 million. By the year 2040, 13.3 million Americans will be over 85.

Statistics also show that the rate of nursing home use increases dramatically with age. For individuals over 85, the utilization rate is 25 percent; for the 75 to 84 age group, the rate is six percent; and for the 65 to 74 population, utilization is two percent. These rates reflect the fact that the "old old" are prone to chronic disabilities and therefore have a greater need for supportive and medical services.

Health Care Expenses of the Elderly

The elderly's higher need for and use of health care services are reflected in the level of their personal health care expenditures.

In 1981 the elderly averaged 1.75 more visits to physicians' offices and nearly twice as many hospital discharges per 1,000 compared to the population as a whole. In 1982 the elderly's average hospital stay was 2.6 days longer than the national average for the nonelderly. On a per capita basis, the elderly typically spend approximately three times more on health care services than the rest of the population.

Perhaps most revealing is the fact that in 1984 health expenditures for the over-65 age group was $119 billion, while total health care expenditures for those under age 65 were $267 billion. Nursing home care represented the elderly's second largest expenditure category and, by far, the largest category of out-of-pocket expenditures.

Catastrophic health care proposals currently pending in Congress were developed in an effort to protect the elderly from potential financial disaster as a result of catastrophic illness. However, with both Democrats and Republicans reluctant to even discuss proposals that could be viewed as budget busters, the proposals have added only incrementally to existing programs. Medicare—which provides primarily acute care coverage—is the prime target.

In the area of long-term care, the proposals would affect no more than three percent of nursing home residents. As a result, the plans have fallen victim to intense criticism by lawmakers, consumer advocates, providers, and even the press. At the heart of the criticism is a fundamental question related to defining a "catastrophic" health care event. Do catastrophic expenses occur when medical bills exceed a specified out-of-pocket amount such as $2,000, $5,000, or $10,000 in a given year, or is an individual faced with a catastrophic situation when expenses exceed a percentage of family income?

While the definitional debate may never be settled, it seems clear that no matter how "catastrophic" is defined, current proposals ignore the greatest emotional and financial catastrophe related to health care faced by the elderly—financing long-term care.

Almost inevitably, long term care leads to catastrophic expenses—by anyone's definition. The costs of long-term nursing home treatment are high, and the insurance protection available is minimal. In fact, in 1984, when nursing home expenditures totaled $32 billion, families and patients paid 50 percent of the bill out-of-pocket. Medicaid paid 43 percent of total costs, while Medicare paid for less than two percent and private insurance paid for less than one percent.

Furthermore, for elderly individuals with out-of-pocket health care expenses exceeding $2,000 a year, nursing home care was responsible for more than 80 percent of the costs. Hospital care, on the other hand, accounted for 10 percent, while physician services accounted for less than six percent.

Problems with Current Public Financing

The major problem with the current financing system is rooted in the fact that Medicaid is the primary public payor for nursing home services. The tragedy of the Medicaid system is that it is a welfare program which pays for care only after individuals have exhausted their savings.

While Medicaid covers a wide range of services, eligibility is based on income and assets. Therefore, the great majority of Americans needing long-term care become eligibile for assistance when their out-of-pocket costs have sufficiently impoverished them, thereby qualifying them for coverage.

Unfortunately, impoverishment comes quickly to elderly individuals receiving nursing home care. According to a 1987 report prepared by the staff of the House Select Committee on Aging, seven in ten elderly living alone spend down to the federal poverty level after only 13 weeks in a nursing home. Within one year of entering a nursing home, more than 90 percent of these elderly are impoverished.

Geographic variation in the Medicaid program is another major concern. States have considerable flexibility in setting income limits for eligibility. Consequently, people with incomes near the poverty level are eligible if they live in some states but not others. In addition, the long-term care services that Medicaid covers vary considerably from state to state, in part because their coverage is at the state's option.

Further complicating the current financing situation is the fact that many individuals believe that Medicare provides protection against nursing home care expenses. In truth, Medicare coverage of nursing home services is intentionally focused on the costs associated with rehabilitative placements in skilled nursing facilities immediately following hospitalization.

Availability of Private Insurance

Private insurance for long-term care is increasingly recognized as an untapped method for enabling public program financing to cope with population growth and for preventing the elderly from spending down to Medicaid eligibility levels.

Insurers' interest in offering long-term care coverage continues to grow, and progressive new products are being designed. Currently, approximately 70 companies offer nursing home insurance products, and more than 40,000 policies are in force. Policies typically offer indemnity benefits ranging from $10 to $100 per day—with up to four years of coverage. Premiums, which range from $100 to $2,000 annually, are based on age and vary by the indemnity level and waiting period chosen.

Estimates based on existing and prototype policies show that a fairly high percentage of the elderly could afford long-term care insurance premiums. In fact, the Employee Benefits Research Institute suggests that in 1984 long-term care insurance premiums were less than five percent of cash income for 21 percent of families with a member over age 65.

Despite the relative affordability of premiums, marketing long-term care insurance remains a problem. First of all, the public is unfamiliar with the long-term care financing system. According to the American Association of Retired Persons, more than 80 percent of respondents to a survey said they believed that Medicare or private insurance covered the cost of long-term nursing home care. Obviously, education will be crucial to stimulating consumer interest in the private insurance market.

Secondly, long-term care insurance is sold primarily to individuals rather than to groups. While the federal government and some state governments have expressed interest in including long-term care coverage as part of employee health benefits packages, no significant action has spurred widespread movement in this area.

Finally, because of limited actuarial experience in long-term care, insurers have been very cautious in designing and offering coverage. As a result, benefits typically are medically oriented, targeted to low-risk populations, and provide partial indemnity rather than complete service coverage.

On the positive side, efforts are under way to remove some of these barriers and stimulate the market. Insurance companies are gaining in experience. Federal legislation has been proposed to encourage policy development, and state governments are purging their insurance laws of provisions that discourage industry interest in the long-term care market.

Policy Options for Financing Long Term Care

It is clear that substantial changes in policy and better public understanding of the problems inherent in current financing mechanisms are essential to developing an efficient and humane financing system for long-term care.

The options are obvious.

At one pole is a nationally uniform government entitlement program. At the opposite pole is an option that relies totally on the private sector for solutions. Between these extremes is the most viable option, one that would require innovative policy-making: a private-public sector partnership.

The advantages to the public sector option are numerous. Such a program would be similar to Medicare and provide uniform coverage for long-term care services. Financing for this form of coverage would be achieved through either of two mechanisms:

- Social insurance using an involuntary contribution method, such as payroll taxes or
- General revenues with some premium support, as is used in Medicare part B.

However, legislative proposals following this approach have received little attention—even in the context of active debate. Why? Cost is a major stumbling block. Estimates range as high as $60 billion annually for a federal program providing comprehensive long-term care services. Given the current fiscal climate, the entitlement approach is not viable.

At the other end of the spectrum is a more reasonable approach, which relies heavily on private sector initiatives. This would translate into a federally mandated private long-term care insurance program.

Under such an approach, policymakers could design a program requiring all employers to offer insurance to employees. While such an approach would result in considerable participation, the self-employed and unemployed would remain at risk. Medicaid, therefore, would continue to play a large role in financing long-term care by subsidizing premiums, coinsurance, and deductibles for low-wage or non-wage earners and by offering assistance to uninsured individuals who have spent down to Medicaid eligibilty.

At the mid-point of this continuum is perhaps the most promising option: the public-private partnership. Approaches of this type are based on the premise that applying the combined resources of the public and private sectors may enable more comprehensive solutions than either sector could achieve independently.

There are two principal ways in which a public-private partnership could be structured. The approach most often discussed would establish a government insurance program for beneficiaries that would provide coverage after a certain threshold was reached. Possibilities range from using a dollar amount, such as a $100,000 deductible, as the trigger for coverage, to using length of stay, such as two years of nursing home care. Either way, the notion is that all Americans would be entitled to participate in this government program once the trigger threshold was reached. Except for those Americans presently covered under Medicaid and Medicare, private insurance coverage would be expected to fill in any gaps short of the threshold.

It would be possible, however, to establish a partnership strategy without creating an explicit government entitlement program. The same effect could be achieved by using a so called "stop-loss" approach whereby the primary insurer covers all claims up to a predetermined limit, and the government covers all costs above that limit. In most cases, the second insurer—in this case the government—would set an upper limit of expenditures to limit risk.

Conclusion

As pressure mounts to control government spending, many policymakers have abandoned efforts to develop a system of financing long-term care that is both cost effective and dignified. Cost, they say, is prohibitive.

Cost, however, should not be an excuse for inaction. The resources are available. With a different application of resources, including the personal resources available to the elderly themselves, a new and more effective system can be developed. While a new federal program may represent a part of the answer, private sector initiatives must be an integral part of any new approach. The expansion of private long-term care insurance undoubtedly will represent one link in the long-term care chain.

The purpose of such a program would be singular: to recognize the need of America's frail and infirm elderly for quality long-term care services—without fear of financial calamity.

About the Author

Dr. Paul R. Willging was named executive vice president and chief staff officer of the American Health Care Association on October 15, 1985. In this capacity he serves as the principal spokesman for the nation's only federation of long-term care providers and frequently represents the industry at hearings on Capitol Hill, at news conferences, and before allied professional societies.

FUNDING LONG-TERM CARE:
Devising Private Insurance Mechanisms

Sheldon Goldberg

The extended cost of long-term health care is the greatest catastrophic illness expense that many elderly are likely ever to face. The editors at The Oryx Press are to be commended, therefore, for their foresight in inviting examination of the long-term care financing issue up front in this edition of *The Directory of Nursing Homes.* As president of the American Association of Homes for the Aging, I am especially pleased to have this opportunity to express not-for-profit providers' views on the subject.

Proposals to protect the elderly from the financial burden of devastating illness are gaining attention at the federal level. Yet while acknowledging the dimensions of the problem, the White House and key members of Congress remain divided on how to solve it. Presently, it is the private, not the public, sector that is spearheading innovations in long-term care financing. Ultimately, it will require a commitment from both sectors to make long-term nursing home and at-home care affordable for the increasing numbers of elderly persons who will need these services in years to come.

National deliberations over the expansion of Medicare coverage for catastrophic illness expenses have intensified the debate regarding public versus private sector responsibilities for financing long-term care (LTC) services. Advocates of a social insurance approach argue that a public sector program holds the greatest potential for ensuring universal coverage and equal access and for offering coverage at reasonable costs through broad-based risk pooling which minimizes the potential for adverse selection. They also contend that supply and demand factors will continue to inhibit private insurance markets, thereby limiting the potential of private insurance as a solution to the LTC financing dilemma.

Barriers to the supply of insurance coverage are found in the carriers' reluctance to market policies offering meaningful protection due to the fear of adverse selection, open-ended liability, and insurance-induced demand. Insufficient demand to motivate market expansion is traced to the consumer's ignorance of the need for LTC protection, overestimation of existing coverage under Medicare and Medigap policies, and inability to afford insurance premiums. Furthermore, employers are reluctant to offer financial contributions to LTC insurance due to current unfunded liabilities of $500 billion to $1 trillion for postretirement acute care benefits.

Proponents of private sector interventions contend that the enactment of a social insurance program is neither politically nor economically feasible in the near future, given a growing national debt, and that the private sector must intervene now to develop viable strategies for financing LTC. Proponents also suggest that consumers and providers alike will fare better under a private system, which will promote consumer choice and access to preferred services, lead to more innovative financing and delivery mechanisms, and guarantee providers greater certainty with respect to reimbursement levels.

Market Potential of LTC Insurance

The American Association of Homes for the Aging (AAHA) has long advocated a strong partnership between the public and private sectors in identifying creative solutions to the financing problem, especially given the magnitude of expenditures required to fund chronic care services for a growing older population and the apparent absence of political will to enact a national system of LTC insurance. Despite this support of a joint effort, several factors argue persuasively for the market potential of private LTC insurance.

First, demographic projections forecast a dramatic growth in the over 65 population in the next several decades. By the year 2040, the over 65 population will grow by 300 percent and the over 85 population by 1,000 percent. Health care and related services must be expanded substantially to accommodate the current and future needs of the elderly. Since services are driven by financing, financial protection will be critical to ensure that services are available and accessible.

A second factor supporting the potential for private insurance relates to the long-standing absence of adequate financing for chronic care services. The elderly currently pay 50 percent of total national nursing home expenditures directly out-of-pocket, while Medicare contributes less than 2 percent and private insurance about 1.4 percent. Medicaid, which accounts for the bulk of the remaining expenditures, is not an insurance program and only becomes available after individuals have depleted their personal resources. Private insurance, on the other hand, would provide individuals protection against catastrophic chronic care expenditures and could reduce pressure on state Medicaid budgets by protecting consumers from depleting their assets.

A third factor is the public sector's reluctance to offer insurance protection for LTC services. The current debate regarding the expansion of Medicare protection for catastrophic illness paints a grim picture relative to public sector financing. The failure of the President and Congress to expand Medicare protection to include chronic care benefits makes clear the absence of government support for a social insurance program. Given this lack of support it is incumbent upon the private sector to fill the gaps.

While the financial capacity of the elderly to pay for LTC protection has posed roadblocks to the private market in the past, research indicates that this situation is changing and the elderly's ability to fund LTC benefits will continue to improve. According to a study conducted by Brandeis University, 50 to 80 percent of the elderly could afford to purchase *some* level of LTC protection, depending on the amount of discretionary income spent. Furthermore, the type of insurance protection purchased by the elderly will significantly affect the amount of protection they can obtain for the same cost. For example, elderly in high-income categories can afford to purchase private indemnity policies or enter continuing care retirement communities that offer full health care guarantees. Individuals with more limited resources could gain access to a richer benefit package through delivery settings such as social health maintenance organizations or life care at home programs. Both of these models represent prepaid case-managed care with access to a broad range of chronic care services.

Effective LTC Insurance Alternatives

One of the most critical issues affecting LTC insurance market expansion relates to the insurability of LTC services. Public and private sector hesitation to insure LTC services can be attributed to the lack of reliable information regarding LTC risks and utilization. Insurance companies need such data to project costs, structure benefits, and price policies. Sufficient data on costs and utilization now exist, however, to develop sound LTC protection without causing undue liability to insurers. Research conducted by Brandeis University on the lifetime risks and costs of nursing home use among the elderly demonstrates that LTC utilization is extremely skewed—much more so than acute care utilization. Approximately 15 percent of the elderly population account for almost 90 percent of total national nursing home expenditures. Moreover, almost 50 percent of these expenditures are incurred by 4 percent of the population—those individuals with nursing home stays in excess of five years. While Medicare beneficiaries entering nursing homes will stay, on average, for about 16 months and will incur lifetime costs in the $36,000 range, spreading this risk across the entire Medicare population would reduce average lifetime costs to $16,000 or approximately $1,500 per elderly person annually. These data clearly suggest that broad-based risk pooling can protect individuals against catastrophic expenditures for LTC services.

Equally promising data on LTC utilization controls have been generated by the Social HMO demonstrations. Midterm results from the four demonstrations strongly suggest the potential for increasing chronic care services without substantial increases to systemwide costs. This can be achieved by shifting savings from reductions in acute care utilization to chronic care benefits, substituting lower-cost alternatives to traditional services, and using effective care-management strategies focusing on preventive health care and effective targeting of service utilization. Continuing care, or life care, retirement communities provide further evidence of the ability to insure LTC services. Continuing care communities represent a self-insurance model where communities pool entry and monthly fees to prefund a full array of chronic care services.

This research and experience demonstrate that chronic care services can be insured effectively without causing undue liability to insurers if the following strategies are employed:

1. Prefunding of health care liability allowing sufficient time to build health care reserves prior to utilization;
2. Pooling health care risks across a broad population to prevent adverse selection;
3. Employing lower cost alternatives to traditional services and controlling health care utilization through case-management strategies that promote

preventive health care and effective targeting of services; and

4. Encouraging providers to share risk with insurance carriers for health care utilization to reduce premium levels.

Several traditional delivery settings demonstrate the potential to successfully employ these strategies and to expand protection of chronic care services. For example, continuing care retirement communities offer a full continuum of chronic care services. They also have the ability to prefund and pool health care risks across a sizeable population of residents and to control utilization through careful case management. Traditional continuing care communities may choose to reinsure liability for health care service guaranteed in resident contracts. Continuing care retirement communities providing health care services on a fee-for-service basis can use commercial insurance to provide residents catastrophic protection while shifting health care risks to a commercial insurer. Housing facilities can employ commercial insurance as a vehicle for expanding protection for supportive services. Moreover, by employing their own allied health staff and paraprofessionals, housing administrators can provide supportive services more cost-effectively than by subcontracting through community-based agencies.

Insurance may also be "wrapped around" a series of services to create a single system of financing and delivery. For example, Group Health of Puget Sound, an HMO located in Washington State, has joined forces with the Metropolitan Life Insurance Company to recreate the Social HMO. By integrating commercial insurance for chronic care benefits with an HMO operating under a Medicare risk contract that provides enhanced acute care benefits, Group Health and the Metropolitan are providing a benefit package to older people that exceeds the level of chronic care protection offered by the Social HMO. Furthermore, the use of private insurance to cover chronic care benefits eliminates the need for federal and state waivers of Medicare and Medicaid eligibility criteria as currently required under the Social HMO.

The public sector is also beginning to explore the potential for using private insurance as part of a public/private partnership in funding chronic care services. At the national level, legislation has been introduced to create a Medicare "stop-loss" program. Under this approach, individuals would be responsible for funding first-dollar coverage through private insurance. Medicare coverage would become available after individuals satisfied an up-front deductible. The size of the deductible to be covered by private insurance would be related to income, with a view toward providing Medicare coverage at the point when chronic care benefits become catastrophic based on what the individual can afford.

The success of the Medicare stop-loss approach depends, in part, on the availability of private LTC coverage and individuals' willingness to purchase insurance to cover service utilization during the deductible period. In this regard, legislation has been introduced to amend the federal tax code to encourage the promotion of the private insurance market. Such legislation would: (1) provide to individuals tax credits for insurance premiums and tax-free withdrawal of income from IRAs for premium payments; (2) provide employers the same tax advantages for contributions to LTC benefit plans as they currently enjoy for contributions for accident and health insurance; and (3) create an exemption for interest earned on LTC reserves by insurance carriers.

At the state level, proposals are being explored to provide LTC insurance premium subsidies to low-income individuals as a strategy to promote the purchase of private insurance and prevent the spending down of their resources to Medicaid eligibility levels. Selected states also are considering the amendment of Medicaid eligibility criteria as a strategy for promoting private coverage. As such, individuals purchasing private insurance providing at least two years of nursing home benefits could become eligible for Medicaid without exhausting all of their resources.

As indicated above, assistance from the public and private sectors must be brought to bear on the LTC financing dilemma. Private LTC insurance as a stand-alone product remains a costly proposition. The provider-based models described here illustrate how insurance premiums can be reduced and benefits expanded by integrating commercial coverage into case-managed, provider-based LTC systems. The Medicare stop-loss approach represents a strategy for expanding federal insurance protection for LTC while limiting federal liability. State subsidies for private insurance may reduce the growth of state spending for chronic care services by preventing the impoverishment of individuals. Notwithstanding the potential for private insurance, however, continued pressure must be applied to the public sector to help finance chronic care expenses for those who cannot benefit from any of these approaches.

About the Author

Sheldon L. Goldberg is president of the American Association of Homes for the Aging (AAHA). He has been AAHA's chief staff executive since 1982. Prior to his position with AAHA, Mr. Goldberg served as executive director of the Wisconsin Association of Homes for the Aging. He formerly served as budget policy analyst for the Wisconsin Department of Health and Human Services and as director of health and human services for the Wisconsin County Boards Association.

LIST OF ABBREVIATIONS

Ave	Avenue	N	North
Blvd	Boulevard	NE	Northeast
Ct	Court	NW	Northwest
DO	Doctor of Osteopathy	Pkwy	Parkway
DON	Director of Nursing	PO	Post Office
Dr	Doctor, Drive	pt	part-time
E	East	Rd	Road
Ext	Extension	Rev	Reverend
ft	full-time	RN	Registered Nurse
Fwy	Freeway	RR	Rural Route
Hwy	Highway	Rte	Route
ICF	Intermediate Care Facility	S	South
		SE	Southeast

ICF   Intermediate Care Facility

A certified facility that meets federal standards and provides less extensive health related care and services. It has regular nursing service, but not around the clock. Most intermediate care facilities carry on rehabilitation programs, with an emphasis on personal care and social services. Mainly, these homes serve people who are not fully capable of living by themselves, yet are not necessarily ill enough to need 24-hour nursing care.

SNF   Skilled Nursing Facility

A facility that has been certified as meeting federal standards within the meaning of the Social Security Act. It provides the level of care that comes closest to hospital care with 24-hour nursing services. Regular medical supervision and rehabilitation therapy are also provided. Generally, a skilled nursing facility cares for convalescent patients and those with long-term illnesses.

ICF/MR	Intermediate Care Facility for Mentally Retarded	Sr	Sister, Senior
Jr	Junior	St	Street
Ln	Lane	SW	Southwest
LPN	Licensed Practical Nurse	W	West
MD	Medical Doctor		

STATE-BY-STATE
LISTING OF FACILITIES

ALABAMA

ABBEVILLE

Henry County Hospital & Nursing Home*
Dothan Rd, Abbeville, AL, 36310
(205) 585-2241
Admin J Juanita Ham.
Licensure Skilled care. *Beds* 60. *Certified*
Medicaid; Medicare.
Owner Proprietary Corp (Healthcare
Management).

ALABASTER

Briarcliff Nursing Home Inc*
850 NW 9th St, Alabaster, AL, 35007
(205) 663-3859
Admin Mary Alice Edmonds. *Medical Dir/Dir
of Nursing* Harry Phillips MD.
Licensure Skilled care; Intermediate care. *Beds*
SNF 188; ICF 38. *Certified* Medicaid;
Medicare.
Owner Nonprofit Corp.
Admissions Requirements Minimum age 18;
Medical examination; Physician's request.
Staff RNs 4 (ft); LPNs 16 (ft), 9 (pt);
Orderlies 3 (ft); Physical therapists; Speech
therapists; Activities coordinators 2 (ft);
Dietitians; Podiatrists.
Facilities Dining room; Activities room;
Crafts room; Laundry room; Barber/Beauty
shop; Library.
Activities Arts & crafts; Cards; Games;
Reading groups; Prayer groups; Movies;
Shopping trips; Social/Cultural gatherings.

ALBERTVILLE

Albertville Nursing Home Inc
PO Box 749, Hwy 75 N, Albertville, AL,
35950
(205) 878-1398
Admin Audrey Cole. *Medical Dir/Dir of
Nursing* Dr A Lynn Luther; Becky Brown
RN.
Licensure Skilled care; Intermediate care. *Beds*
SNF 67; ICF 66. *Certified* Medicaid;
Medicare.
Owner Proprietary Corp.
Admissions Requirements Medical
examination; Physician's request.
Staff RNs 2 (ft), 1 (pt); LPNs 9 (ft), 3 (pt);
Orderlies 4 (ft); Nurses aides 39 (ft), 19 (pt);
Activities coordinators 3 (ft).
Facilities Dining room; Activities room;
Chapel; Laundry room; Barber/Beauty shop.
Activities Arts & crafts; Cards; Games;
Reading groups; Prayer groups; Movies;
Shopping trips; Social/Cultural gatherings;
Baby day; Bus rides; Pet shows.

ALEXANDER CITY

Adams Nursing Home
1423 Hillabee St, Alexander City, AL, 35010
(205) 329-0847
Admin Ray Hills. *Medical Dir/Dir of Nursing*
Edvin Larson MD; Chris McGill RN DON.

Licensure Skilled care; Intermediate care. *Beds*
SNF 44; ICF 44. *Certified* Medicaid;
Medicare.
Owner Proprietary Corp.
Admissions Requirements Medical
examination; Physician's request.
Staff RNs 2 (ft); LPNs 9 (ft); Orderlies 2 (ft);
Nurses aides 24 (ft); Activities coordinators
1 (ft).
Facilities Dining room; Activities room;
Crafts room; Laundry room; Barber/Beauty
shop.
Activities Arts & crafts; Cards; Games;
Reading groups; Prayer groups; Movies.

Brown Nursing Home
PO Box 1056, 1451 Washington St, Alexander
City, AL, 35010
(205) 329-9061
Admin Rosemary Misencik. *Medical Dir/Dir
of Nursing* James P Temple MD; Angela
Meigs DON.
Licensure Skilled care; Intermediate care. *Beds*
SNF 48; ICF. *Certified* Medicaid; Medicare.
Owner Proprietary Corp.
Admissions Requirements Minimum age 18;
Medical examination; Physician's request.
Staff Physicians 1 (pt); RNs 1 (ft), 2 (pt);
LPNs 4 (ft), 1 (pt); Orderlies 1 (pt); Nurses
aides 14 (ft), 6 (pt); Activities coordinators 1
(ft); Dietitians 1 (pt).
Facilities Dining room; Activities room;
Laundry room; Barber/Beauty shop.
Activities Arts & crafts; Games; Reading
groups; Prayer groups; Movies; Social/
Cultural gatherings.

Chapman Nursing Home Inc*
Rte 5, Box 283, Dadeville Hwy, Alexander
City, AL, 35010
(205) 234-6366
Admin Margaret S Chapman.
Licensure Skilled care. *Beds* 147. *Certified*
Medicaid; Medicare.
Owner Proprietary Corp.

ALICEVILLE

Aliceville Manor Nursing Home*
17th St NW, Aliceville, AL, 35442
(205) 373-6307
Admin Mary Ellen Wheat.
Licensure Skilled care; Intermediate care. *Beds*
SNF 59; ICF 21. *Certified* Medicaid;
Medicare.
Owner Proprietary Corp.

ALTOONA

Altoona Health Care Center
PO Box 68, Walnut Grove Rd, Altoona, AL,
35952
(205) 589-6394
Admin Lee Guyton. *Medical Dir/Dir of
Nursing* M Bailey.
Licensure Skilled care; Intermediate care. *Beds*
SNF 50; ICF. *Certified* Medicaid; Medicare.
Owner Proprietary Corp.

Admissions Requirements Medical
examination.
Staff RNs 1 (ft), 2 (pt); LPNs 4 (ft), 2 (pt);
Nurses aides 20 (ft), 10 (pt); Activities
coordinators 1 (ft); Dietitians 1 (ft).
Facilities Dining room; Activities room;
Laundry room; Barber/Beauty shop.
Activities Arts & crafts; Cards; Games;
Reading groups; Prayer groups; Movies;
Shopping trips; Social/Cultural gatherings.

ANDALUSIA

Columbia Regional Nursing Home
200 Hillcrest Dr, Andalusia, AL, 36420
(205) 222-4141
Admin Robert Jones. *Medical Dir/Dir of
Nursing* Merle Neese RN.
Licensure Skilled care. *Beds* SNF 48. *Certified*
Medicaid; Medicare.
Owner Proprietary Corp (Healthcare
Management).
Admissions Requirements Medical
examination; Physician's request.
Staff Physicians 1 (ft), 5 (pt); RNs 1 (ft), 4
(pt); LPNs 5 (ft), 2 (pt); Orderlies 2 (ft);
Nurses aides 18 (ft); Activities coordinators
2 (ft).
Facilities Dining room; Activities room;
Chapel; Crafts room; Laundry room; Barber/
Beauty shop.
Activities Arts & crafts; Cards; Games; Prayer
groups; Movies; Shopping trips; Social/
Cultural gatherings.

ANNISTON

Anniston Nursing Home*
PO Box 1825, 500 Leighton Ave, Anniston,
AL, 36201
(205) 237-8053
Admin Carolyn H Beck.
Licensure Skilled care. *Beds* 85. *Certified*
Medicaid.
Owner Proprietary Corp.

Golden Springs Nursing Facility Inc*
Coleman Rd, PO Box 1790, Anniston, AL,
36201
(205) 831-5730
Admin Becky Helton. *Medical Dir/Dir of
Nursing* Dr Robert Lokey.
Licensure Skilled care; Intermediate care. *Beds*
114. *Certified* Medicaid; Medicare.
Owner Proprietary Corp (National Health
Corp).
Admissions Requirements Medical
examination; Physician's request.
Staff Physicians 1 (pt); RNs 3 (ft), 2 (pt);
LPNs 7 (ft), 9 (pt); Orderlies 2 (ft), 2 (pt);
Nurses aides 24 (ft), 15 (pt); Physical
therapists 1 (ft); Activities coordinators 1
(ft); Dietitians 1 (ft).
Facilities Dining room; Physical therapy
room; Activities room; Laundry room;
Barber/Beauty shop; Library.

Activities Arts & crafts; Cards; Games;
Reading groups; Prayer groups; Movies;
Shopping trips; Social/Cultural gatherings.

ARAB

Nursing Home of Arab Inc*
209 2nd St SE, Arab, AL, 35016
(205) 586-3111
Admin Suzanne Shelton.
Licensure Skilled care; Intermediate care. *Beds*
SNF 40; ICF 27. *Certified* Medicaid;
Medicare.
Owner Proprietary Corp.
Facilities Dining room; Activities room;
Chapel; Laundry room; Barber/Beauty shop.
Activities Arts & crafts; Cards; Games; Prayer
groups; Movies; Social/Cultural gatherings.

ASHLAND

Clay County Hospital & Nursing Home*
544 E 1st Ave, Ashland, AL, 36251
(205) 354-2131
Admin Jane M Williams.
Licensure Skilled care; Intermediate care. *Beds*
SNF 59; ICF 4. *Certified* Medicaid;
Medicare.
Owner Publicly owned.

ASHVILLE

Ashville-Whitney Nursing Home Inc
PO Box 130, Ashville, AL, 35953
(205) 594-5148
Admin Jimmy T Terrell. *Medical Dir/Dir of
Nursing* Dr Lynn Luther; Anna Engle.
Licensure Intermediate care. *Beds* 43.
Certified Medicaid.
Owner Proprietary Corp.
Admissions Requirements Medical
examination; Physician's request.
Staff RNs 1 (pt); LPNs 5 (ft); Nurses aides 24
(ft); Activities coordinators 1 (ft); Dietitians
1 (ft).
Facilities Dining room; Laundry room;
Barber/Beauty shop.
Activities Arts & crafts; Cards; Reading
groups; Prayer groups; Shopping trips;
Social/Cultural gatherings.

ATHENS

Athens Convalescent Center Inc*
611 W Market St, Athens, AL, 35611
(205) 232-1620
Admin John L Wallace.
Licensure Skilled care; Intermediate care. *Beds*
SNF 64; ICF 28. *Certified* Medicaid;
Medicare.
Owner Proprietary Corp.

Limestone Health Facility
1600 W Hobbs St, Athens, AL, 35611
(205) 232-3461
Admin Bill R Hunt. *Medical Dir/Dir of
Nursing* Dr W K Shannon; Nancy P Louell
RN.
Licensure Skilled care; Intermediate care. *Beds*
SNF 86; ICF 50. *Certified* Medicaid;
Medicare.
Owner Proprietary Corp.
Staff RNs 4 (ft); LPNs 13 (ft), 7 (pt);
Orderlies 1 (ft); Nurses aides 32 (ft), 20 (pt);
Physical therapists 1 (pt); Reality therapists
2 (ft); Recreational therapists 2 (ft);
Activities coordinators 2 (ft); Dietitians 1
(ft).
Facilities Dining room; Activities room;
Chapel; Crafts room; Laundry room; Barber/
Beauty shop.
Activities Arts & crafts; Cards; Games;
Reading groups; Prayer groups; Movies.

ATMORE

Atmore Nursing Care Center*
715 E Laurel St, PO Box 589, Atmore, AL,
36504
(205) 368-9121
Admin Virginia Johns. *Medical Dir/Dir of
Nursing* Harold Q Wilson MD.
Licensure Skilled care; Intermediate care. *Beds*
100. *Certified* Medicaid; Medicare.
Owner Proprietary Corp (Unicare).
Admissions Requirements Medical
examination; Physician's request.
Staff Physicians 8 (pt); RNs 5 (ft), 2 (pt);
LPNs 18 (ft), 10 (pt); Nurses aides 40 (ft),
20 (pt); Recreational therapists 1 (ft);
Activities coordinators 1 (ft); Dietitians 2
(pt); Social workers 1 (ft).
Facilities Dining room; Activities room;
Chapel; Crafts room; Laundry room; Barber/
Beauty shop.
Activities Arts & crafts; Reading groups;
Prayer groups; Movies; Shopping trips;
Social/Cultural gatherings.

ATTALLA

Attalla Nursing Home Inc*
Rte 2, PO Box 239, 900 Stewart Ave, Attalla,
AL, 35954
(205) 538-7852
Admin Ted H Cook.
Licensure Skilled care; Intermediate care. *Beds*
SNF 106; ICF 59. *Certified* Medicaid;
Medicare.
Owner Proprietary Corp.

BESSEMER

Jones Valley Nursing Home*
PO Box 297, Bessemer, AL, 35020
(205) 425-4359
Admin Carrie Phillips.
Licensure Skilled care; Intermediate care. *Beds*
SNF 34; ICF 12. *Certified* Medicaid;
Medicare.
Owner Proprietary Corp.

Livingston Nursing Home Inc*
4201 Bessemer Super Hwy, Bessemer, AL,
35020
(205) 428-3249
Admin Betty V Duncan.
Licensure Skilled care; Intermediate care. *Beds*
SNF 63; ICF 6. *Certified* Medicaid;
Medicare.
Owner Proprietary Corp.

Meadowood Nursing Home*
820 Golf Course Rd, Bessemer, AL, 35020
(205) 425-5241
Admin Nella A Gossett.
Licensure Skilled care; Intermediate care. *Beds*
SNF 90; ICF 90. *Certified* Medicaid;
Medicare.
Owner Proprietary Corp (Beverly Enterprises).

Ruby Hill Nursing Home Inc
507 Whitmore Dr, Bessemer, AL, 35020
(205) 428-3292
Admin Frankie H Jones. *Medical Dir/Dir of
Nursing* Dr Dodson Curry; Veronica
Scarbrough DON.
Licensure Skilled care; Intermediate care. *Beds*
SNF 25; ICF 50. *Certified* Medicaid;
Medicare.
Owner Privately owned.
Admissions Requirements Medical
examination; Physician's request.
Staff RNs 1 (ft), 2 (pt); LPNs 5 (ft), 4 (pt);
Nurses aides 17 (ft), 12 (pt); Activities
coordinators 1 (ft), 2 (pt).
Facilities Dining room; Activities room;
Crafts room; Laundry room.
Activities Arts & crafts; Cards; Games;
Reading groups; Prayer groups; Movies.

Southgate Village
325 Selma Rd, Bessemer, AL, 35020
(205) 428-9383
Admin Gerry Ann Howton. *Medical Dir/Dir
of Nursing* Dr Jerry McLane; Louise G
Parker RN.
Licensure Skilled care; Intermediate care. *Beds*
SNF 63; ICF 18. *Certified* Medicaid;
Medicare.
Owner Proprietary Corp (American Health
Care Inc).
Admissions Requirements Medical
examination; Physician's request.
Staff RNs; LPNs; Orderlies; Nurses aides;
Activities coordinators; Dietitians.
Facilities Dining room; Activities room;
Chapel; Laundry room.
Activities Arts & crafts; Games; Reading
groups.

BIRMINGHAM

Avonwood Rest Home Inc*
4246 5th Ave S, Birmingham, AL, 35222
(205) 592-8101
Admin Eugene Lamberth.
Licensure Intermediate care. *Beds* 56.
Owner Proprietary Corp.

Burgess Nursing Home*
1532 Bankhead Hwy W, Birmingham, AL,
35214
(205) 798-3871
Admin William H Burgess Jr.
Licensure Skilled care. *Beds* 53. *Certified*
Medicaid; Medicare.
Owner Proprietary Corp.

Civic Center Nursing Home*
1201 N 22nd St, Birmingham, AL, 35234
(205) 251-5271
Admin Annette Lee Malloy.
Licensure Skilled care; Intermediate care. *Beds*
SNF 85; ICF 10. *Certified* Medicaid;
Medicare.
Owner Nonprofit Corp.

East Lake Health Care*
7110 1st Ave N, Birmingham, AL, 35206
(205) 836-5226
Admin John Mitchell Rutoskey.
Licensure Skilled care; Intermediate care. *Beds*
SNF 31; ICF 31. *Certified* Medicaid;
Medicare.
Owner Proprietary Corp.

Estes Health Care Center—East*
733 Mary Vann Ln, Birmingham, AL, 35215
(205) 854-1361
Admin Michael Dray.
Licensure Skilled care; Intermediate care. *Beds*
SNF 102; ICF 18. *Certified* Medicaid;
Medicare.
Owner Proprietary Corp.

Estes Health Care Center—Riverchase*
2500 Riverhaven Dr, Birmingham, AL, 35244
(205) 823-6760
Admin Dennis Lee.
Licensure Skilled care; Intermediate care. *Beds*
SNF 102; ICF 18. *Certified* Medicaid;
Medicare.
Owner Proprietary Corp.

Estes Oak Knoll Nursing Facility
824 6th Ave W, Birmingham, AL, 35064
(205) 787-2619
Admin Jack D Barnes, Jr.
Licensure Skilled care; Intermediate care. *Beds*
SNF 72; ICF 28. *Certified* Medicaid;
Medicare.
Owner Proprietary Corp (Northport Health
Services).
Staff Physicians; RNs; LPNs; Nurses aides;
Speech therapists; Activities coordinators.
Facilities Dining room; Physical therapy
room; Activities room; Crafts room; Barber/
Beauty shop.

Fairview Nursing & Convalescent Home*
1028 Bessemer Rd, Birmingham, AL, 35228
(205) 923-1777
Admin David B Johnston.
Licensure Skilled care; Intermediate care. *Beds*
SNF 154; ICF 11. *Certified* Medicaid;
Medicare.
Owner Proprietary Corp (Vari-Care Inc).

Forestdale Health Care Center
1000 Dugan Ave, Birmingham, AL, 35214
(205) 798-8780
Admin Carol Grubis.
Licensure Skilled care; Intermediate care. *Beds*
SNF 60; ICF 60. *Certified* Medicaid;
Medicare.
Owner Proprietary Corp (Beverly Enterprises).

A G Gaston Home for Senior Citizens
PO Box 697, 9225 Airport Rd, Birmingham,
AL, 35201-0697
(205) 849-2273
Admin Loretha Chappell. *Medical Dir/Dir of
Nursing* Dr C R Hixon.
Licensure Skilled care; Intermediate care. *Beds*
SNF 39; ICF 12. *Certified* Medicare.
Owner Proprietary Corp.
Admissions Requirements Medical
examination; Physician's request.
Staff Physicians 1 (ft); RNs 1 (ft), 3 (pt);
LPNs 5 (ft), 3 (pt); Orderlies 4 (ft), 1 (pt);
Nurses aides 9 (ft), 3 (pt); Activities
coordinators 1 (ft); Dietitians 1 (pt); Dentists
1 (pt).
Facilities Dining room; Activities room;
Laundry room.
Activities Arts & crafts; Games; Prayer groups;
Shopping trips; Social/Cultural gatherings.

Hanover House*
39 Hanover Circle, Birmingham, AL, 35205
(205) 933-1828
Admin Ray R Wood.
Licensure Skilled care. *Beds* 80.
Owner Proprietary Corp.

**Hillhaven Convalescent Center & Nursing
Home***
2728 10th Ave S, Birmingham, AL, 35205
(205) 933-7010
Admin Yolanda Brewer. *Medical Dir/Dir of
Nursing* Dr John Buckingham.
Licensure Skilled care; Intermediate care. *Beds*
114. *Certified* Medicaid; Medicare.
Owner Proprietary Corp (Hillhaven Corp).
Admissions Requirements Medical
examination; Physician's request.
Staff RNs 5 (ft); LPNs 8 (ft), 5 (pt); Orderlies
1 (ft), 1 (pt); Nurses aides 27 (ft), 13 (pt);
Physical therapists 1 (ft); Activities
coordinators 1 (ft); Dietitians 1 (ft).
Facilities Dining room; Physical therapy
room; Activities room; Barber/Beauty shop.
Activities Arts & crafts; Cards; Games;
Reading groups; Prayer groups; Movies;
Shopping trips; Social/Cultural gatherings.

Jefferson County Home*
200 N Pine Hill Rd, Birmingham, AL, 35217
(205) 841-5533
Admin Lillian V Holmes.
Licensure Skilled care; Intermediate care. *Beds*
SNF 148; ICF 312. *Certified* Medicaid;
Medicare.
Owner Publicly owned.

Kirkwood by the River*
3605 Ratliff Rd, Birmingham, AL, 36210
(205) 956-2184
Admin Duke Bradford.
Licensure Skilled care. *Beds* 51.
Owner Nonprofit Corp.

Lakeview Nursing Home
8017 2nd Ave S, Birmingham, AL, 35206
(205) 836-4231
Admin Mary Mann. *Medical Dir/Dir of
Nursing* William Doggett Jr MD.

Licensure Skilled care. *Beds* SNF 54. *Certified*
Medicare.
Owner Nonprofit Corp.
Admissions Requirements Medical
examination.
Staff RNs 2 (ft), 1 (pt); LPNs 5 (ft), 4 (pt);
Nurses aides 13 (ft), 9 (pt); Activities
coordinators 1 (ft).
Facilities Dining room; Activities room;
Crafts room; Laundry room; Barber/Beauty
shop; Library; Sitting room.
Activities Arts & crafts; Cards; Games;
Reading groups; Prayer groups; Movies;
Shopping trips; Social/Cultural gatherings.

Lakeview Nursing Home Inc
8017 2nd Ave S, Birmingham, AL, 35206
(205) 836-4231
Admin Mary Mann.
Licensure Skilled care; Intermediate care. *Beds*
SNF 54. *Certified* Medicare.
Owner Proprietary Corp.

Mary Lewis Convalescent Center Inc*
2600 Highland Ave, Birmingham, AL, 35205
(205) 252-4397
Admin Clarence A Shelton III. *Medical Dir/
Dir of Nursing* Joseph Lee MD.
Licensure Skilled care; Intermediate care. *Beds*
SNF 20; ICF 27. *Certified* Medicaid;
Medicare.
Owner Proprietary Corp.
Staff RNs 1 (ft), 1 (pt); LPNs 3 (ft), 3 (pt);
Nurses aides 10 (ft), 5 (pt); Activities
coordinators 1 (ft); Dietitians 1 (pt).
Facilities Dining room; Activities room;
Crafts room; Laundry room; Barber/Beauty
shop.
Activities Arts & crafts; Cards; Games;
Reading groups; Prayer groups; Movies;
Shopping trips; Social/Cultural gatherings.

Macdel Health Care Inc*
2211 18th St SW, Birmingham, AL, 35211
(205) 925-6484
Admin Rebecca J Etheridge.
Licensure Skilled care; Intermediate care. *Beds*
SNF 42; ICF 31. *Certified* Medicaid;
Medicare.
Owner Proprietary Corp.

Methodist Home for the Aging*
1424 Montclair Rd, Birmingham, AL, 35201
(205) 956-4150
Admin A Wray Tomlin.
Licensure Skilled care; Intermediate care. *Beds*
SNF 105; ICF 16. *Certified* Medicaid;
Medicare.
Owner Nonprofit Corp.
Affiliation Methodist

Northway Convalescent Center*
1424 N 25 St, Birmingham, AL, 35234
(205) 328-5870
Admin Karen Waldrop.
Licensure Skilled care; Intermediate care. *Beds*
SNF 60; ICF 53. *Certified* Medicaid;
Medicare.
Owner Proprietary Corp.

Rose Manor Health Care*
7755 4th Ave S, Birmingham, AL, 35206
(205) 833-0146
Admin Sarah J McKinney. *Medical Dir/Dir of
Nursing* Henry L Darnell Jr MD.
Licensure Skilled care; Intermediate care. *Beds*
SNF 100; ICF 12. *Certified* Medicaid;
Medicare.
Owner Proprietary Corp.
Admissions Requirements Medical
examination; Physician's request.
Staff Physicians 1 (pt); RNs 2 (ft); LPNs 9
(ft), 3 (pt); Orderlies 3 (ft); Nurses aides 30
(ft); Physical therapists 1 (pt); Reality
therapists 1 (pt); Recreational therapists 1
(ft); Occupational therapists 1 (pt); Speech
therapists 1 (pt); Activities coordinators 1

(ft); Dietitians 1 (ft); Dentists 1 (pt);
Ophthalmologists 1 (pt); Podiatrists 1 (pt);
Audiologists 1 (pt).
Facilities Dining room; Activities room;
Chapel; Crafts room; Barber/Beauty shop.
Activities Arts & crafts; Cards; Games;
Reading groups; Prayer groups; Movies;
Shopping trips.

St Lukes Nursing Home*
1220 S 17th St, Birmingham, AL, 35205
(205) 933-2180
Admin Terry L Durham.
Licensure Skilled care; Intermediate care. *Beds*
SNF 42; ICF 41. *Certified* Medicaid;
Medicare.
Owner Proprietary Corp.

St Martins-in-the-Pines
4941 Montevallo Rd, Birmingham, AL, 35210
(205) 956-1831
Admin Jack K Holloway. *Medical Dir/Dir of
Nursing* Dr Charles Colvin.
Licensure Skilled care. *Beds* 107.
Owner Nonprofit Corp.
Admissions Requirements Minimum age 65;
Medical examination.
Staff RNs 3 (ft), 2 (pt); LPNs 10 (ft), 2 (pt);
Orderlies 3 (ft), 1 (pt); Nurses aides 70 (ft);
Physical therapists 1 (pt); Activities
coordinators 3 (ft); Dietitians 1 (ft).
Affiliation Episcopal
Facilities Dining room; Physical therapy
room; Activities room; Chapel; Crafts room;
Laundry room; Barber/Beauty shop; Library.
Activities Arts & crafts; Cards; Games;
Reading groups; Prayer groups; Movies;
Shopping trips; Social/Cultural gatherings.

South Haven Nursing Home*
3141 Old Columbiana Rd, Birmingham, AL,
35226
(205) 822-1580
Admin Rheta S Skelton. *Medical Dir/Dir of
Nursing* Dr W C Browne.
Licensure Skilled care; Intermediate care. *Beds*
SNF 75; ICF 36. *Certified* Medicaid;
Medicare.
Owner Proprietary Corp.
Admissions Requirements Minimum age 65;
Medical examination; Physician's request.
Staff Physicians; RNs 5 (ft); LPNs 11 (ft);
Nurses aides 40 (ft), 10 (pt); Recreational
therapists; Speech therapists; Activities
coordinators 1 (ft); Dietitians 1 (pt); Dentists
1 (pt); Podiatrists 1 (pt); Medical records
person 1 (pt).
Facilities Dining room; Physical therapy
room; Activities room; Chapel; Crafts room;
Laundry room; Barber/Beauty shop; Library;
TV rooms.
Activities Arts & crafts; Cards; Games;
Reading groups; Prayer groups; Movies;
Shopping trips; Social/Cultural gatherings;
Ceramics.

BOAZ

The Nursing Home of Boaz*
PO Box 368, Corley Ave, Boaz, AL, 35957
(205) 593-8380
Admin William E Hill.
Licensure Skilled care; Intermediate care. *Beds*
SNF 47; ICF 33. *Certified* Medicaid;
Medicare.
Owner Proprietary Corp.

BREWTON

New Hope Manor*
Pineview St & 3rd Ave, Brewton, AL, 36426
(205) 867-6077
Admin Randolph M McDowell.
Licensure Skilled care; Intermediate care. *Beds*
SNF 82; ICF 22. *Certified* Medicaid;
Medicare.
Owner Proprietary Corp.

BUTLER

Rush Nursing Center Butler Inc
PO Box 677, Hwy 10 E, Butler, AL, 36904
(205) 459-2394
Admin Grace Morgan. *Medical Dir/Dir of Nursing* Douglas Smith MD; Linda Sims RN DON.
Licensure Skilled care; Intermediate care; Domiciliary. *Beds* SNF 39; ICF 10; Domiciliary 14. *Certified* Medicaid; Medicare.
Owner Proprietary Corp (Truco Inc).
Admissions Requirements Physician's request.
Staff Physicians 4 (ft); RNs 2 (ft); LPNs 5 (ft); Orderlies 5 (ft); Nurses aides 11 (ft); Activities coordinators 1 (ft).
Facilities Dining room; Activities room; Laundry room; Barber/Beauty shop.
Activities Arts & crafts; Cards; Games; Prayer groups; Movies; Shopping trips.

CAMDEN

Camden Nursing Facility
PO Box 486, Camden, AL, 36726
(205) 682-4231
Admin Patsy H Tate. *Medical Dir/Dir of Nursing* Dr Sumpter Blackman; Juilie C Tait.
Licensure Skilled care 10B. *Beds* 75. *Certified* Medicaid; Medicare.
Owner Privately owned.
Admissions Requirements Medical examination; Physician's request.
Staff Physicians 3 (ft); RNs 4 (ft); LPNs 6 (ft), 1 (pt); Nurses aides 23 (ft), 4 (pt); Activities coordinators 1 (ft); Dietitians 1 (ft).
Facilities Dining room; Activities room; Chapel; Crafts room; Laundry room; Barber/ Beauty shop; Library.
Activities Arts & crafts; Cards; Games; Reading groups; Prayer groups; Movies; Shopping trips; Social/Cultural gatherings.

CARBON HILL

Carbon Hill Health Care Inc
516 E 4th Ave, Carbon Hill, AL, 35549
(205) 924-9940
Admin Sandra E Talley.
Licensure Intermediate care. *Beds* 49.
Owner Proprietary Corp.

CENTRE

Cherokee County Nursing Home
PO Box 199, Hospital Ave, Centre, AL, 35960
(205) 927-5778
Admin Carol Peace. *Medical Dir/Dir of Nursing* C Clark Smeltzer Jr; Sue Estes RN.
Licensure Skilled care. *Beds* 53. *Certified* Medicare.
Owner Publicly owned.
Admissions Requirements Medical examination.
Staff RNs 1 (ft), 2 (pt); LPNs 6 (ft), 1 (pt); Nurses aides 17 (ft), 12 (pt); Activities coordinators 1 (ft), 1 (pt).
Facilities Dining room; Activities room; Chapel; Crafts room; Laundry room; Barber/ Beauty shop.
Activities Arts & crafts; Cards; Games; Reading groups; Prayer groups; Movies.

CENTREVILLE

Bibb Medical Center Hospital & Nursing Home*
164 Pierson Ave, Centreville, AL, 35042
(205) 926-7251
Admin Terry J Smith. *Medical Dir/Dir of Nursing* William O Owings MD.
Licensure Skilled care; Intermediate care. *Beds* SNF 62; ICF 41. *Certified* Medicaid; Medicare.

Owner Publicly owned.
Staff Physicians 4 (pt); RNs 2 (ft); LPNs 10 (ft), 2 (pt); Orderlies 7 (ft), 1 (pt); Nurses aides 25 (ft), 7 (pt); Physical therapists 1 (pt); Activities coordinators 1 (ft); Dietitians 1 (ft); Dentists 1 (pt); Ophthalmologists 1 (pt).
Facilities Dining room; Physical therapy room; Chapel; Barber/Beauty shop.
Activities Cards; Games; Reading groups; Prayer groups.

CHATOM

Washington County Infirmary
PO Box 597, Saint Stephens Ave, Chatom, AL, 36539
(205) 847-2223
Admin Thomas J Owens. *Medical Dir/Dir of Nursing* Paul Petcher; Dorothy Whigham.
Licensure Skilled care; Intermediate care. *Beds* 103. *Certified* Medicaid; Medicare.
Owner Nonprofit Corp.
Staff Physicians; RNs; LPNs; Orderlies; Nurses aides; Physical therapists; Activities coordinators; Dietitians.
Facilities Dining room; Physical therapy room; Activities room; Crafts room; Laundry room; Barber/Beauty shop; Library.
Activities Arts & crafts; Games; Movies.

CITRONELLE

Citronelle Convalescent Center
PO Drawer 38, 108 N 4th St, Citronelle, AL, 36522
(205) 866-5509
Admin June Keller. *Medical Dir/Dir of Nursing* John H Prine MD; Marsha Reid DON.
Licensure Skilled care; Intermediate care. *Beds* SNF 56; ICF 13. *Certified* Medicaid; Medicare.
Owner Proprietary Corp.
Admissions Requirements Minimum age 21; Medical examination; Physician's request.
Staff RNs 1 (ft), 1 (pt); LPNs 5 (ft), 1 (pt); Nurses aides 19 (ft), 5 (pt); Dietitians 1 (ft).
Facilities Dining room; Physical therapy room; Activities room; Laundry room; Barber/Beauty shop.
Activities Arts & crafts; Cards; Games; Reading groups; Prayer groups; Movies.

CLANTON

Clanton Health Care Center Inc*
1705 Lay Dam Rd, Clanton, AL, 35045
(205) 755-4384
Admin Billy R Hatley. *Medical Dir/Dir of Nursing* Dr Kent Johns.
Licensure Skilled care; Intermediate care. *Beds* SNF 40; ICF 10. *Certified* Medicaid; Medicare.
Owner Proprietary Corp.
Staff RNs 1 (ft), 3 (pt); LPNs 2 (ft), 3 (pt); Orderlies 2 (ft), 1 (pt); Nurses aides 10 (ft), 9 (pt); Activities coordinators 1 (pt); Dietitians 1 (ft).
Facilities Dining room; Activities room; Crafts room; Barber/Beauty shop.
Activities Arts & crafts; Cards; Games; Reading groups; Prayer groups; Movies; Social/Cultural gatherings.

Hatley Health Care Inc
300 Medical Ctr Dr, Clanton, AL, 30545
(205) 755-4960
Admin Bill R Hatley. *Medical Dir/Dir of Nursing* Kent Johns MD; Betty Creest DON.
Licensure Skilled care; Intermediate care. *Beds* 119. *Certified* Medicaid; Medicare.
Owner Privately owned.
Staff RNs; LPNs; Orderlies; Nurses aides; Recreational therapists; Activities coordinators; Dietitians.

Facilities Dining room; Activities room; Crafts room; Barber/Beauty shop.
Activities Arts & crafts; Cards; Games; Reading groups; Prayer groups; Movies; Social/Cultural gatherings.

COLLINSVILLE

Collinsville Nursing Home Inc*
Drawer G, US Hwy 11, Collinsville, AL, 35961
(205) 524-2117
Admin Vera A Gressler.
Licensure Skilled care; Intermediate care. *Beds* SNF 94; ICF 26. *Certified* Medicaid; Medicare.
Owner Proprietary Corp.

COOK SPRINGS

Baptist Home for Senior Citizens Inc
PO Box 10, Off I-20, Cook Springs, AL, 35052
(205) 338-2221
Admin Jerry W Moss. *Medical Dir/Dir of Nursing* Dr E H Edwards; Susan L Moss RN.
Licensure Skilled care; Intermediate care. *Beds* SNF 93; ICF 33. *Certified* Medicaid; Medicare; VA.
Owner Proprietary Corp (Northport Health Services).
Admissions Requirements Minimum age 62; Medical examination; Physician's request.
Staff Physicians 1 (pt); RNs 2 (ft), 2 (pt); LPNs 16 (ft); Orderlies 41 (ft); Nurses aides; Physical therapists 1 (pt); Speech therapists 1 (pt); Activities coordinators 1 (ft); Dietitians 1 (ft); Ophthalmologists 1 (pt).
Affiliation Baptist
Facilities Dining room; Physical therapy room; Activities room; Chapel; Crafts room; Laundry room; Barber/Beauty shop.
Activities Arts & crafts; Cards; Games; Reading groups; Prayer groups; Movies; Social/Cultural gatherings.

CORDOVA

Cordova Health Care Center
200 Highland St, Cordova, AL, 35550
(205) 483-9282
Admin Kenneth Hoffman. *Medical Dir/Dir of Nursing* George H Weaver MD; Virgina Telle RN DON.
Licensure Skilled care; Intermediate care. *Beds* SNF 94; ICF 10. *Certified* Medicaid; Medicare.
Owner Proprietary Corp (Northport Health Services).
Admissions Requirements Medical examination; Physician's request.
Staff Physicians 1 (ft); RNs 2 (ft), 1 (pt); LPNs 9 (ft), 5 (pt); Nurses aides 30 (ft), 10 (pt); Activities coordinators 1 (ft); Dietitians 1 (ft).
Facilities Dining room; Activities room; Laundry room; Barber/Beauty shop.
Activities Arts & crafts; Cards; Games; Reading groups; Prayer groups.

CROSSVILLE

Crossville Nursing Home Inc
PO Box 97, Hwy 227, Crossville, AL, 35962
(205) 528-7844
Admin Gerald Bell. *Medical Dir/Dir of Nursing* Raymond C Ufford MD; Mary Colley RN DON.
Licensure Skilled care; Intermediate care. *Beds* SNF 118; ICF. *Certified* Medicaid; Medicare.
Owner Proprietary Corp.
Admissions Requirements Medical examination; Physician's request.

Staff Physicians 1 (ft), 2 (pt); RNs 3 (ft); LPNs 8 (ft), 1 (pt); Nurses aides 45 (ft), 6 (pt); Activities coordinators 1 (ft), 1 (pt); Dietitians 1 (ft).
Facilities Dining room; Physical therapy room; Activities room; Chapel; Crafts room; Laundry room; Barber/Beauty shop.
Activities Arts & crafts; Cards; Games; Reading groups; Prayer groups; Movies; Shopping trips; Social/Cultural gatherings.

CULLMAN

Cullman Health Care Center
1607 Main Ave NE, Cullman, AL, 35055
(205) 734-8745
Admin Edith R Sinyard. *Medical Dir/Dir of Nursing* Dr George Lyrene; Robin Self RN.
Licensure Skilled care; Intermediate care. *Beds* 165. *Certified* Medicaid; Medicare.
Owner Proprietary Corp.
Admissions Requirements Medical examination; Physician's request.
Staff RNs 4 (ft); LPNs 18 (ft), 2 (pt); Physical therapists 1 (ft); Activities coordinators 2 (ft); Dietitians 12 (ft).
Facilities Dining room; Physical therapy room; Activities room; Chapel; Crafts room; Laundry room; Barber/Beauty shop; Library.
Activities Arts & crafts; Cards; Games; Reading groups; Prayer groups; Movies; Shopping trips; Social/Cultural gatherings; Exercise.

DADEVILLE

Dadeville Convalescent Home*
237 Lafayette St, Dadeville, AL, 36853
(205) 825-9244
Admin Betty S Chapman.
Licensure Skilled care; Intermediate care. *Beds* SNF 71; ICF 40. *Certified* Medicaid; Medicare.
Owner Proprietary Corp.

Easterwood Nursing Home*
300 Columbus St, Dadeville, AL, 36853
(205) 825-7883
Admin Emma M Swindall. *Medical Dir/Dir of Nursing* Dr Jerry Swindall.
Licensure Skilled care. *Beds* 29. *Certified* Medicaid; Medicare.
Owner Proprietary Corp.
Staff Physicians 1 (ft); RNs 1 (ft), 1 (pt); LPNs 2 (ft), 6 (pt); Nurses aides 6 (ft), 3 (pt); Recreational therapists 1 (pt); Activities coordinators 1 (pt).
Facilities Dining room; Activities room; Crafts room; Laundry room.
Activities Arts & crafts; Cards; Games; Reading groups; Prayer groups; Shopping trips.

Wilder Nursing Home*
PO Box 217, Lafayette St, Dadeville, AL, 36853
(205) 825-7881
Admin Frances Marie Melton.
Licensure Skilled care; Intermediate care. *Beds* SNF 47; ICF 17. *Certified* Medicaid; Medicare.
Owner Proprietary Corp.

DAPHNE

Mercy Medical
PO Box 1090, 101 Villa Dr, Daphne, AL, 36526
(205) 626-2694
Admin Sr Mary Eileen Wilhelm. *Medical Dir/Dir of Nursing* Dr Samuel Eichold; Betty Bentley DON.
Licensure Skilled care; Specialized hospital. *Beds* SNF; Specialized hospital 137. *Certified* Medicare.
Owner Nonprofit Corp.
Admissions Requirements Physician's request.

Staff Physicians 1 (pt); RNs 21 (ft), 12 (pt); LPNs 18 (ft), 3 (pt); Nurses aides 22 (ft), 5 (pt); Physical therapists 2 (ft); Recreational therapists 1 (ft); Occupational therapists 1 (ft); Speech therapists 1 (pt); Dietitians 1 (pt).
Affiliation Roman Catholic
Facilities Dining room; Physical therapy room; Activities room; Chapel; Crafts room; Laundry room; Barber/Beauty shop.
Activities Arts & crafts; Cards; Games; Reading groups; Prayer groups; Movies; Shopping trips; Social/Cultural gatherings.

DECATUR

Flint City Nursing Home Inc*
Rte 4, Box 500, Hwy 31 S, Decatur, AL, 35601
(205) 355-2418
Admin Berneal McKennie.
Licensure Skilled care; Intermediate care. *Beds* SNF 46; ICF 30. *Certified* Medicaid; Medicare.
Owner Proprietary Corp.

Medical Park Convalescent Center Inc
1350 14th Ave SE, Decatur, AL, 35601
(205) 355-6911
Admin Mac Prittich.
Licensure Skilled care; Intermediate care. *Beds* SNF 75; ICF 108. *Certified* Medicaid; Medicare.
Owner Proprietary Corp.

West Morgan Health Care Center
PO Box 1215, Decatur, AL, 35602
(205) 353-5567
Admin Linda Robertson. *Medical Dir/Dir of Nursing* Dr Lane B Thompson; Hazel Sparks DON.
Licensure Skilled care. *Beds* SNF 20; ICF 23. *Certified* Medicaid; Medicare.
Owner Proprietary Corp.
Admissions Requirements Physician's request.
Staff RNs 1 (ft), 1 (pt); LPNs 4 (ft), 2 (pt); Orderlies 1 (ft); Nurses aides 15 (ft), 3 (pt); Activities coordinators 1 (ft); Dietitians 6 (ft), 1 (pt).
Facilities Dining room; Activities room; Barber/Beauty shop.
Activities Arts & crafts; Cards; Games; Reading groups; Prayer groups; Movies; Shopping trips; Social/Cultural gatherings.

DEMOPOLIS

Woodhaven Manor Nursing Home*
105 W Windsor St, Demopolis, AL, 36732
(205) 289-2741
Admin Alice Hawkins.
Licensure Skilled care; Intermediate care. *Beds* SNF 35; ICF 40. *Certified* Medicaid; Medicare.
Owner Proprietary Corp.

DOTHAN

Extendicare Health Center*
814 S Saint Andrews St, Dothan, AL, 36301
(205) 793-1177
Admin Helen Harrell.
Licensure Skilled care; Intermediate care. *Beds* SNF 52; ICF 57. *Certified* Medicaid; Medicare.
Owner Proprietary Corp.

Wesley Manor Methodist Home for the Aging
210 Honeysuckle Rd, Dothan, AL, 36301
(205) 792-0921
Admin W J Mathis Jr. *Medical Dir/Dir of Nursing* Lewe West MD.
Licensure Skilled care; Intermediate care. *Beds* SNF 62; ICF 54. *Certified* Medicaid; Medicare.
Owner Nonprofit Corp (Meth Homes for Aging).

Admissions Requirements Minimum age 62; Medical examination.
Affiliation Methodist
Facilities Dining room; Physical therapy room; Activities room; Chapel; Crafts room; Laundry room; Barber/Beauty shop; Library.
Activities Arts & crafts; Cards; Games; Reading groups; Prayer groups; Movies; Shopping trips; Social/Cultural gatherings; Ceramics.

DOUBLE SPRINGS

Double Springs Health Care Center
Box 286, Rte 1, Hwy 33 N, Double Springs, AL, 35553
(205) 489-2136
Admin Eunell S Handy. *Medical Dir/Dir of Nursing* Dr T M Blake; Faye Donaldson RN.
Licensure Skilled care; Intermediate care. *Beds* SNF 100; ICF. *Certified* Medicaid; Medicare.
Owner Proprietary Corp (Beverly Enterprises).
Admissions Requirements Medical examination; Physician's request.
Staff RNs 2 (ft), 2 (pt); LPNs 8 (ft), 6 (pt); Orderlies 1 (pt); Nurses aides 22 (ft), 8 (pt); Recreational therapists 1 (ft); Activities coordinators 1 (ft).
Facilities Dining room; Physical therapy room; Activities room; Laundry room.
Activities Arts & crafts; Cards; Games; Reading groups; Prayer groups; Movies.

EIGHT MILE

Estes Health Care Center—Oakridge*
4525 Saint Stephens Rd, Eight Mile, AL, 36613
(205) 452-0996
Admin Donald E Henle.
Licensure Skilled care; Intermediate care. *Beds* SNF 86; ICF 86. *Certified* Medicaid; Medicare.
Owner Proprietary Corp.

ELBA

Elba General Hospital & Nursing Home*
987 Drayton St, Elba, AL, 36323
(205) 897-2257
Admin Steven A Nadeau. *Medical Dir/Dir of Nursing* John Mason Kimmey MD.
Licensure Skilled care. *Beds* SNF 71. *Certified* Medicaid; Medicare.
Owner Proprietary Corp (National Healthcare).
Admissions Requirements Medical examination; Physician's request.
Staff Physicians 3 (pt); RNs 3 (ft); LPNs 8 (ft); Orderlies 5 (ft); Nurses aides 19 (ft); Physical therapists 1 (ft); Activities coordinators 1 (ft); Dietitians 1 (pt).
Facilities Dining room; Physical therapy room; Activities room; Laundry room; Barber/Beauty shop.
Activities Arts & crafts; Games; Reading groups; Prayer groups; Movies; Shopping trips; Social/Cultural gatherings; television.

ENTERPRISE

Enterprise Hospital & Nursing Home
Dothan Hwy 84 E, Enterprise, AL, 36330
(205) 347-9541
Admin J Alan Kent. *Medical Dir/Dir of Nursing* David Rhyne MD; Marie Lepore RN DON.
Licensure Skilled care; Intermediate care. *Beds* SNF 110; ICF 41. *Certified* Medicaid; Medicare.
Owner Publicly owned.
Admissions Requirements Medical examination; Physician's request.

Staff RNs 2 (ft); LPNs 13 (ft); Orderlies 6 (ft); Nurses aides 48 (ft); Activities coordinators 4 (ft); Dietitians 1 (pt).
Facilities Dining room; Activities room; Crafts room; Barber/Beauty shop.
Activities Arts & crafts; Cards; Games; Reading groups; Prayer groups; Movies; Shopping trips; Social/Cultural gatherings.

EUFAULA

Eufaula Geriatric Center
430 Rivers Ave, Eufaula, AL, 36027
(205) 687-6627
Admin C W Null. *Medical Dir/Dir of Nursing* Tim Shaw MD; Laura Perry RN.
Licensure Skilled care; Intermediate care. *Beds* SNF 120; ICF 60. *Certified* Medicaid; Medicare.
Owner Proprietary Corp (Beverly Enterprises).
Admissions Requirements Physician's request.
Staff Physicians 1 (pt); RNs 4 (ft), 1 (pt); LPNs 20 (ft), 3 (pt); Orderlies 6 (ft), 2 (pt); Nurses aides 50 (ft), 8 (pt); Activities coordinators 2 (ft); Dietitians 1 (pt); Social service 1 (ft).
Affiliation Baptist
Facilities Dining room; Activities room; Crafts room; Laundry room; Barber/Beauty shop.
Activities Arts & crafts; Games; Reading groups; Prayer groups; Movies.

EUTAW

Greene County Hospital & Nursing Home*
509 Wilson Ave, Eutaw, AL, 35462
(205) 372-3388
Admin John L Solomon. *Medical Dir/Dir of Nursing* Dr Rucker Staggers.
Licensure Skilled care; Intermediate care. *Beds* SNF 40; ICF 12. *Certified* Medicaid; Medicare.
Owner Publicly owned.
Admissions Requirements Physician's request.
Staff Physicians 5 (ft), 1 (pt); RNs 1 (ft), 1 (pt); LPNs 6 (ft), 1 (pt); Orderlies 4 (ft); Nurses aides 14 (ft), 10 (pt); Physical therapists 1 (pt); Activities coordinators 1 (ft); Dietitians 1 (ft).
Facilities Dining room; Physical therapy room; Laundry room; Barber/Beauty shop.
Activities Arts & crafts; Cards; Games; Reading groups; Social/Cultural gatherings.

EVERGREEN

Evergreen Nursing Home Inc*
PO Box 391, Knoxville St, Evergreen, AL, 36401
(205) 578-3783
Admin James A Ansley.
Licensure Skilled care; Intermediate care. *Beds* SNF 41; ICF 10. *Certified* Medicaid; Medicare.
Owner Proprietary Corp.

FAIRFIELD

Fairfield Health Care Center*
6825 Grasselli Rd, Fairfield, AL, 35064
(205) 780-3920
Admin Lee O'Dell. *Medical Dir/Dir of Nursing* Jack C Whites MD.
Licensure Skilled care; Intermediate care. *Beds* SNF 115; ICF 75. *Certified* Medicaid; Medicare.
Owner Proprietary Corp.
Admissions Requirements Minimum age 21; Medical examination; Physician's request.
Staff Physicians 1 (pt); RNs 3 (ft); LPNs 25 (ft), 10 (pt); Nurses aides 40 (ft), 20 (pt); Physical therapists 1 (pt); Recreational therapists 1 (pt); Occupational therapists 1

(pt); Speech therapists 1 (pt); Activities coordinators 1 (pt); Dietitians 1 (pt); Dentists 1 (pt); Podiatrists 1 (pt); Audiologists 1 (pt).
Facilities Dining room; Physical therapy room; Activities room; Chapel; Crafts room; Laundry room; Barber/Beauty shop; Treatment room.
Activities Arts & crafts; Cards; Games; Reading groups; Prayer groups; Movies; Shopping trips; Social/Cultural gatherings.

FAIRHOPE

Estes Health Care Center—Fairhope*
108 S Church St, Fairhope, AL, 36532
(205) 928-2153
Admin Donna Tucker.
Licensure Skilled care; Intermediate care. *Beds* SNF 66; ICF 70. *Certified* Medicaid; Medicare.
Owner Proprietary Corp.

FALKVILLE

Falkville Nursing Home Inc
3rd St, PO Box 409, Falkville, AL, 35622
(205) 784-5291
Admin Phillip Rollins. *Medical Dir/Dir of Nursing* Dinfsh Gandhi MD.
Licensure Skilled care; Intermediate care. *Beds* SNF 75; ICF 30. *Certified* Medicaid; Medicare.
Owner Proprietary Corp (National Healthcare).
Staff Physicians 5 (pt); RNs 4 (ft); LPNs 8 (ft), 1 (pt); Orderlies 5 (ft), 1 (pt); Nurses aides 35 (ft), 2 (pt); Physical therapists 1 (pt); Speech therapists 1 (pt); Activities coordinators 1 (ft), 1 (pt); Dietitians 1 (pt); Dentists 1 (pt).
Facilities Dining room; Physical therapy room; Activities room; Chapel; Laundry room; Barber/Beauty shop.
Activities Arts & crafts; Cards; Games; Prayer groups; Shopping trips.

Summerford Nursing Home Inc
Rte 2, Box 18, Hwy 31 North, Falkville, AL, 35622
(205) 784-5275
Admin Robert O Summerford. *Medical Dir/Dir of Nursing* John Summerford MD; Barbara Pruett.
Licensure Skilled care; Intermediate care. *Beds* SNF 163; ICF 33. *Certified* Medicaid; Medicare.
Owner Proprietary Corp.
Staff Physicians 3 (pt); RNs 3 (ft), 1 (pt); LPNs 19 (ft), 4 (pt); Orderlies 5 (ft), 3 (pt); Nurses aides 56 (ft), 6 (pt); Physical therapists 1 (pt); Occupational therapists 1 (ft); Speech therapists 1 (pt); Activities coordinators 5 (ft); Dietitians 1 (pt).
Facilities Dining room; Physical therapy room; Activities room; Chapel; Crafts room; Laundry room; Barber/Beauty shop.
Activities Arts & crafts; Cards; Games; Reading groups; Prayer groups.

FAYETTE

Fayette County Nursing Home
PO Drawer 878, 1653 Temple Ave N, Fayette, AL, 35555
(205) 932-5966
Admin Barbara Flynn. *Medical Dir/Dir of Nursing* Henry G Hodo Jr MD; Barbara Flynn RN.
Licensure Skilled care; Intermediate care. *Beds* SNF 85; ICF 16. *Certified* Medicaid; Medicare.
Owner Nonprofit organization/foundation.
Admissions Requirements Physician's request.
Staff Physicians 8 (ft), 1 (pt); RNs 2 (ft), 2 (pt); LPNs 11 (ft), 5 (pt); Orderlies 2 (ft), 1 (pt); Nurses aides 15 (ft), 12 (pt);

Occupational therapists 1 (pt); Activities coordinators 1 (ft); Dietitians 2 (ft);; Social Service 1 (ft); Dentist 1 (pt).
Facilities Dining room; Activities room; Crafts room; Laundry room; Barber/Beauty shop; Library.
Activities Arts & crafts; Cards; Games; Reading groups; Prayer groups; Movies; Shopping trips; Social/Cultural gatherings; Church services.

FLORENCE

El Reposo Sanitarium
Box 530, Rte 5, Florence, AL, 35630
(205) 757-2143
Admin R Wayne Hayward. *Medical Dir/Dir of Nursing* Ramona Clarke RN.
Licensure Intermediate care. *Beds* ICF 40. *Certified* Medicaid.
Owner Nonprofit Corp.
Admissions Requirements Medical examination; Physician's request.
Staff RNs 1 (ft); LPNs 2 (ft), 2 (pt); Nurses aides 9 (ft), 7 (pt); Activities coordinators 1 (ft);; Dietitians 1 (ft).
Facilities Dining room; Activities room; Lounge.
Activities Games; Prayer groups; Movies; Bus rides.

Eliza Memorial Hospital Mitchell Hollingsworth Annex
PO Box 818, Flagg Circle, Florence, AL, 35631
(205) 767-9401
Admin J T Whetstone. *Medical Dir/Dir of Nursing* L L Hibbett MD; J L Shelton DON.
Licensure Skilled care; Intermediate care. *Beds* 202. *Certified* Medicaid; Medicare.
Owner Nonprofit Corp.
Admissions Requirements Medical examination; Physician's request.
Staff RNs 7 (ft), 2 (pt); LPNs 25 (ft), 1 (pt); Orderlies 10 (ft), 1 (pt); Nurses aides 60 (ft), 6 (pt); Physical therapists 1 (ft), 1 (pt); Recreational therapists 2 (pt); Activities coordinators 1 (ft); Dietitians 1 (ft); Dentist 1 (pt).
Facilities Dining room; Physical therapy room; Activities room; Crafts room; Laundry room; Barber/Beauty shop; Library.
Activities Arts & crafts; Cards; Games; Social/Cultural gatherings; Exercise class.

Glenwood Convalescent Center*
210 Ana Dr, Florence, AL, 35630
(205) 766-8963
Admin Timothy L Morrow.
Licensure Skilled care. *Beds* 114. *Certified* Medicaid; Medicare.
Owner Proprietary Corp.

FOLEY

Foley Nursing Home*
1700 N Alston St, Foley, AL, 36535
(205) 943-2781
Admin Paul W Philips Jr.
Licensure Skilled care; Intermediate care. *Beds* SNF 74; ICF 80. *Certified* Medicaid; Medicare.
Owner Proprietary Corp (Beverly Enterprises).

FORT PAYNE

Mountain Manor Nursing Home Inc
403 13th St NW, Fort Payne, AL, 35967
(205) 845-5990
Admin Robert Morrow. *Medical Dir/Dir of Nursing* Dr William Holtlin.
Licensure Skilled care; Intermediate care. *Beds* SNF 94; ICF 29. *Certified* Medicaid; Medicare.
Owner Proprietary Corp.
Admissions Requirements Physician's request.

Staff Physicians 4 (pt); RNs 3 (ft), 1 (pt); LPNs 9 (ft), 6 (pt); Orderlies 3 (ft); Nurses aides 44 (ft), 4 (pt); Activities coordinators 1 (ft); Dietitians 1 (pt).
Facilities Dining room; Activities room; Laundry room; Barber/Beauty shop; Two living rooms.
Activities Arts & crafts; Games; Reading groups; Prayer groups; Movies; Shopping trips.

GADSDEN

Gadsden Health Care Center Inc*
1945 Davis Dr, Gadsden, AL, 35901
(205) 547-4938
Admin W R Lester. *Medical Dir/Dir of Nursing* Dr John B Keeling.
Licensure Skilled care; Intermediate care. *Beds* 152. *Certified* Medicaid; Medicare.
Owner Proprietary Corp.
Facilities Dining room; Physical therapy room; Activities room; Chapel; Crafts room; Laundry room; Barber/Beauty shop.
Activities Arts & crafts; Cards; Games; Reading groups; Prayer groups; Movies; Shopping trips; Social/Cultural gatherings.

McGuffey Health Care Center Inc
2301 Rainbow Dr, Gadsden, AL, 35999-35901
(205) 543-3467
Admin Laurence A Baird. *Medical Dir/Dir of Nursing* Dr Myron Hawkins; Janet Jacobs RN.
Licensure Skilled care; Intermediate care. *Beds* SNF 147; ICF 62. *Certified* Medicaid; Medicare; VA.
Owner Proprietary Corp.
Admissions Requirements Medical examination; Physician's request.
Staff Physicians; RNs; LPNs; Orderlies; Nurses aides; Physical therapists; Recreational therapists; Occupational therapists; Speech therapists; Activities coordinators; Dietitians; Social worker.
Facilities Dining room; Physical therapy room; Activities room; Crafts room; Barber/Beauty shop.
Activities Arts & crafts; Cards; Games; Reading groups; Prayer groups; Movies; Shopping trips; Social/Cultural gatherings.

Physicians Care Center*
700 Hutchins St, Gadsden, AL, 35901
(205) 543-7101
Admin Carroll Crane.
Licensure Skilled care. *Beds* 71. *Certified* Medicaid; Medicare.
Owner Proprietary Corp.

GARDENDALE

Gardendale Nursing Home Inc
420 Dean Lane, Gardendale, AL, 35071
(205) 631-8709
Admin Faith M Hammock. *Medical Dir/Dir of Nursing* Sue Gibson RN DON.
Licensure Skilled care. *Beds* 148. *Certified* Medicaid; Medicare.
Owner Proprietary Corp.
Admissions Requirements Minimum age 18; Medical examination; Physician's request.
Staff RNs 3 (ft), 1 (pt); LPNs 13 (ft), 4 (pt); Nurses aides 52 (ft), 17 (pt); Recreational therapists 1 (ft), 2 (pt); Activities coordinators 1 (ft).
Facilities Dining room; Physical therapy room; Activities room; Chapel; Laundry room; Barber/Beauty shop.
Activities Arts & crafts; Cards; Games; Prayer groups; Movies.

GENEVA

Wiregrass Nursing Home
1200 W Maple Ave, Geneva, AL, 36340
(205) 684-3655

Admin Roger Mayers. *Medical Dir/Dir of Nursing* Dr John Simmons; Sue Paschall RN.
Licensure Skilled care; Intermediate care. *Beds* SNF 74; ICF 12. *Certified* Medicaid; Medicare.
Owner Nonprofit Corp.
Admissions Requirements Physician's request.
Staff Physicians 1 (pt); RNs 5 (ft); LPNs 9 (ft); Nurses aides 28 (ft), 2 (pt); Activities coordinators 2 (ft), 1 (pt); Dietitians 1 (pt); Houskeepers 5 (ft).
Facilities Dining room; Activities room; Crafts room; Laundry room; Barber/Beauty shop.
Activities Arts & crafts; Cards; Games; Reading groups; Prayer groups; Movies; Shopping trips; Social/Cultural gatherings.

GEORGIANA

Georgiana Nursing Facility
PO Box 189, Georgiana, AL, 36033
(205) 376-2267
Admin Alice Newton. *Medical Dir/Dir of Nursing* Dr Jeffrey Voreis; Sheridan Hanks.
Licensure Skilled care; Intermediate care. *Beds* SNF 56; ICF 5. *Certified* Medicaid; Medicare.
Owner Nonprofit Corp.
Admissions Requirements Medical examination; Physician's request.
Staff Physicians 1 (ft); RNs 1 (ft), 2 (pt); LPNs 5 (ft), 1 (pt); Orderlies 3 (ft), 1 (pt); Nurses aides 10 (ft), 3 (pt); Recreational therapists 1 (ft); Activities coordinators 1 (ft); Dietitians 1 (ft).
Facilities Dining room; Physical therapy room; Activities room; Chapel; Crafts room; Laundry room; Barber/Beauty shop; Library.
Activities Arts & crafts; Cards; Games; Reading groups; Prayer groups; Movies; Shopping trips; Church outings.

GLENCOE

Coosa Valley Healthcare Inc
426 Pineview Ave, Glencoe, AL, 35905
(205) 492-5350
Admin M Andrew Cook.
Licensure Skilled care; Intermediate care. *Beds* SNF 94; ICF 30. *Certified* Medicaid; Medicare.
Owner Proprietary Corp.

GOODWATER

Goodwater Nursing Home
100 Mountain St, Goodwater, AL, 35072
(205) 839-6711
Admin John R Chapman Jr. *Medical Dir/Dir of Nursing* Dr John James; Janey Cox RN.
Licensure Skilled care; Intermediate care. *Beds* SNF 42; ICF. *Certified* Medicaid; Medicare.
Owner Proprietary Corp.
Staff Physicians 1 (ft); RNs 1 (ft), 2 (pt); LPNs 3 (ft), 3 (pt); Orderlies 1 (ft); Nurses aides 14 (ft), 1 (pt); Activities coordinators 1 (ft), 1 (pt); Dietitians 3 (ft), 4 (pt).
Facilities Dining room; Activities room; Chapel; Crafts room; Laundry room; Barber/Beauty shop; Library.
Activities Arts & crafts; Cards; Games; Reading groups; Prayer groups; Movies; Shopping trips; Social/Cultural gatherings.

GRAND BAY

Grand Bay Convalescent Home*
PO Box 328, Hwy 90 W, Grand Bay, AL, 36541
(205) 865-6443
Admin Marlene H Hart.
Licensure Intermediate care. *Beds* 53. *Certified* Medicaid.
Owner Proprietary Corp.

GREENSBORO

Greensboro Health Care Inc
626 Armory St, Greensboro, AL, 36744
(205) 624-3054
Admin Margaret Kynard. *Medical Dir/Dir of Nursing* Chester Singleton MD; Rebekah Bonds.
Licensure Skilled care. *Beds* 102. *Certified* Medicaid; Medicare.
Owner Proprietary Corp.
Admissions Requirements Medical examination; Physician's request.
Staff RNs; LPNs; Orderlies; Nurses aides; Physical therapists; Speech therapists; Activities coordinators; Dietitians.
Facilities Dining room; Activities room; Crafts room; Laundry room; Barber/Beauty shop.
Activities Arts & crafts; Cards; Games; Reading groups; Prayer groups; Movies; Social/Cultural gatherings.

GREENVILLE

Greenville Nursing Home*
408 Country Club Dr, Greenville, AL, 36037
(205) 382-2693
Admin Jacob L Curfton Jr.
Licensure Skilled care; Intermediate care. *Beds* SNF 66; ICF 52. *Certified* Medicaid; Medicare.
Owner Proprietary Corp.

GUIN

Marion Sunset Manor
1201 W 14th Ave, Guin, AL, 35563
(205) 468-3331
Admin Stan Junkin. *Medical Dir/Dir of Nursing* Dianna B Junkin.
Licensure Skilled care; Intermediate care. *Beds* SNF 33; ICF 18. *Certified* Medicaid; Medicare.
Owner Proprietary Corp.
Admissions Requirements Medical examination.
Staff Physicians 1 (pt); RNs 1 (ft), 1 (pt); LPNs 3 (ft), 3 (pt); Orderlies 2 (ft), 2 (pt); Nurses aides 11 (ft), 10 (pt); Activities coordinators 1 (ft); Dietitians 1 (ft).
Facilities Dining room; Crafts room; Laundry room; Barber/Beauty shop.
Activities Arts & crafts; Games; Prayer groups; Movies; Fishing trips; Picnics.

GUNTERSVILLE

Barfield Health Care Inc
PO Box 167, Star Rte 62, Guntersville, AL, 35976
(205) 582-3112
Admin E B Barfield Jr. *Medical Dir/Dir of Nursing* Dr Dalton Diamond; Lorraine Hall RN DON.
Licensure Skilled care; Intermediate care. *Beds* SNF 38; ICF 65. *Certified* Medicaid; Medicare.
Owner Privately owned.
Admissions Requirements Medical examination.
Staff RNs 3 (ft); LPNs 7 (ft), 2 (pt); Orderlies 3 (ft); Nurses aides 30 (ft); Activities coordinators 1 (ft); Dietitians 1 (ft).
Facilities Dining room; Activities room; Chapel; Crafts room; Laundry room; Barber/Beauty shop.
Activities Arts & crafts; Games; Prayer groups; Movies; Shopping trips; Social/Cultural gatherings; Resident council.

HALEYVILLE

Crestview Manor*
2201 11th Ave, Haleyville, AL, 35565
(205) 486-9478

Admin Alton Anderson.
Licensure Skilled care; Intermediate care. *Beds* SNF 67; ICF 30. *Certified* Medicaid; Medicare.
Owner Proprietary Corp.
Staff RNs 2 (ft), 2 (pt); LPNs 13 (ft), 2 (pt); Orderlies 1 (ft); Nurses aides 50 (ft), 5 (pt); Activities coordinators 1 (ft); Dietitians 1 (ft), 1 (pt).
Facilities Dining room; Activities room; Crafts room; Laundry room; Barber/Beauty shop; Library.
Activities Arts & crafts; Cards; Games; Reading groups; Prayer groups; Movies; Shopping trips; Social/Cultural gatherings.

HAMILTON

Marion County Nursing Home
1315 Military St South, Hamilton, AL, 35570
(205) 921-2183
Admin Brenda Ray. *Medical Dir/Dir of Nursing* Charles Pyle MD; Geri Gilliland RN.
Licensure Skilled care; Intermediate care. *Beds* 69. *Certified* Medicaid; Medicare.
Owner Proprietary Corp.
Admissions Requirements Physician's request.
Staff RNs 2 (ft); LPNs 5 (ft), 5 (pt); Orderlies 7 (ft), 1 (pt); Nurses aides 13 (ft), 11 (pt); Physical therapists 1 (pt); Recreational therapists 1 (ft); Activities coordinators 1 (ft).

HANCEVILLE

Hanceville Nursing Home*
PO Box 409, US Highway 31 N, Hanceville, AL, 35077
(205) 352-2251
Admin James D Moody.
Licensure Skilled care; Intermediate care. *Beds* SNF 136; ICF 20. *Certified* Medicaid; Medicare.
Owner Proprietary Corp.

HEFLIN

Cleburne County Hospital & Nursing Home*
411 Ross St, Heflin, AL, 36264
(205) 463-2121
Admin Carolyn Parker. *Medical Dir/Dir of Nursing* Dr David Justice.
Licensure Skilled care. *Beds* 40. *Certified* Medicare.
Owner Proprietary Corp (Healthcare Management).
Staff Physicians 3 (ft), 1 (pt); RNs 6 (ft), 4 (pt); LPNs 12 (ft), 4 (pt); Orderlies 1 (ft), 2 (pt); Nurses aides 13 (ft), 5 (pt); Activities coordinators 1 (ft).
Facilities Dining room; Activities room; Chapel; Laundry room; Barber/Beauty shop; Library.

HUEYTOWN

Hueytown Nursing Home Inc*
190 Brooklane Dr, Hueytown, AL, 35020
(205) 491-2905
Admin Charlotte Hooton. *Medical Dir/Dir of Nursing* Dr David Barthold.
Licensure Intermediate care. *Beds* 50. *Certified* Medicaid.
Owner Proprietary Corp (Vantage Healthcare).
Staff Physicians 1 (ft); RNs 1 (ft); LPNs 2 (ft), 4 (pt); Nurses aides 9 (ft), 6 (pt); Activities coordinators 1 (ft); Dietitians 4 (ft), 1 (pt).
Facilities Dining room; Activities room; Chapel; Laundry room; Barber/Beauty shop.
Activities Arts & crafts; Cards; Games; Reading groups; Prayer groups; Movies; Shopping trips; Social/Cultural gatherings.

Self Nursing Home Inc*
131 Crest Rd, Hueytown, AL, 35020
(205) 491-2411
Admin J A Self Jr.
Licensure Skilled care; Intermediate care. *Beds* SNF 75; ICF 56. *Certified* Medicaid; Medicare.
Owner Proprietary Corp.

HUNTSVILLE

Big Spring Manor*
500 Saint Clair Ave SW, Huntsville, AL, 35801
(205) 539-5111
Admin Wendell R Stidger.
Licensure Skilled care; Intermediate care. *Beds* SNF 102; ICF 30. *Certified* Medicaid; Medicare.
Owner Proprietary Corp (Convalescent Services).

Huntsville Nursing Home
4320 Judith Ln SW, Huntsville, AL, 35805
(205) 837-1730
Admin Phillip Rollins. *Medical Dir/Dir of Nursing* Lee Hardison DON.
Licensure Skilled care; Intermediate care. *Beds* SNF 19; ICF 110. *Certified* Medicaid; Medicare.
Owner Proprietary Corp (Wessex Corp).
Admissions Requirements Medical examination; Physician's request.
Staff Physicians 1 (pt); RNs 2 (ft), 1 (pt); LPNs 15 (ft); Orderlies 4 (ft); Nurses aides 50 (ft); Physical therapists 1 (ft); Speech therapists 1 (ft); Activities coordinators 1 (ft); Dietitians 1 (pt).
Facilities Dining room; Physical therapy room; Activities room; Crafts room; Barber/Beauty shop.
Activities Arts & crafts; Cards; Games; Reading groups; Prayer groups; Movies; Social/Cultural gatherings.

Parkview Village Ltd*
2004 Max Luther Dr, Huntsville, AL, 35810
(205) 852-9290
Admin Rodney McBridge. *Medical Dir/Dir of Nursing* Tulio Figarola MD.
Licensure Skilled care; Domiciliary care. *Beds* SNF 60; Domiciliary care 35. *Certified* Medicare.
Owner Proprietary Corp.
Admissions Requirements Medical examination; Physician's request.
Staff Physicians 1 (ft); RNs 5 (ft), 3 (pt); LPNs 1 (ft), 5 (pt); Nurses aides 11 (ft), 11 (pt); Physical therapists 1 (ft); Speech therapists 1 (pt); Activities coordinators 1 (ft); Dietitians 1 (pt); Dentists 1 (pt).
Facilities Dining room; Physical therapy room; Activities room; Chapel; Crafts room; Laundry room; Barber/Beauty shop; Library; Pool; Shuffle boards; Horseshoe arena; Garden plots.
Activities Arts & crafts; Cards; Games; Reading groups; Prayer groups; Movies; Shopping trips; Social/Cultural gatherings.

Whitesburg Manor Health Center
105 Teakwood Dr, Huntsville, AL, 35801
(205) 881-5000
Admin William H Birmingham Jr. *Medical Dir/Dir of Nursing* Michael McCarthy MD; Leslie Enright RN DON.
Licensure Skilled care; Intermediate care. *Beds* 159. *Certified* Medicaid; Medicare.
Owner Proprietary Corp (Hillhaven Corp).
Staff Physicians; RNs; LPNs; Nurses aides; Physical therapists; Occupational therapists; Speech therapists; Activities coordinators; Dietitians; Ophthalmologists.
Languages German, Spanish
Facilities Dining room; Physical therapy room; Activities room; Chapel; Laundry room; Barber/Beauty shop; Library; Sewing room.

Activities Arts & crafts; Cards; Games; Reading groups; Prayer groups; Movies; Shopping trips; Social/Cultural gatherings; Bingo; Garden club; Sittercise.

JACKSON

Arrington Nursing Home
PO Box 247, 2616 N College Ave, Jackson, AL, 36545-0247
(205) 246-2476
Admin Wallace D Nelson.
Licensure Skilled care; Intermediate care. *Beds* SNF 70; ICF 21. *Certified* Medicaid; Medicare.
Owner Proprietary Corp.

JACKSONVILLE

Wessex House of Jacksonville Inc
410 W Wilson St, Jacksonville, AL, 36265
(205) 435-7704
Admin M Lee O'Dell. *Medical Dir/Dir of Nursing* Thomas Bridges MD; Margaret Novak RN BSN.
Licensure Skilled care; Intermediate care; Intermediate care for mentally retarded. *Beds* SNF 121; ICF 46. *Certified* Medicaid; Medicare.
Owner Proprietary Corp (Wessex Corp).
Admissions Requirements Minimum age 21; Medical examination; Physician's request.
Staff Physicians 1 (pt); RNs 5 (ft); LPNs 21 (ft); Orderlies 3 (ft); Nurses aides 40 (ft); Physical therapists 1 (ft); Speech therapists 1 (ft); Activities coordinators 1 (ft); Dietitians 1 (ft).
Facilities Dining room; Physical therapy room; Activities room; Laundry room; Barber/Beauty shop.
Activities Arts & crafts; Cards; Games; Reading groups; Prayer groups; Movies; Shopping trips; Social/Cultural gatherings.

JASPER

Ridgeview Health Care Center Inc*
907 11th St NE, Jasper, AL, 35501
(205) 384-3402
Admin Joe W Kelley Jr.
Licensure Skilled care; Intermediate care. *Beds* SNF 48; ICF 56. *Certified* Medicaid; Medicare.
Owner Proprietary Corp.

Ridgewood Health Care Center Inc*
201 4th Ave N, Jasper, AL, 35501
(205) 221-4862
Admin J Frank Caldwell.
Licensure Skilled care. *Beds* 98. *Certified* Medicaid; Medicare.
Owner Proprietary Corp.

Shadescrest Health Care Center*
PO Box 1012, 2600 Old Parrish Hwy, Jasper, AL, 35501
(205) 384-9086
Admin Paulette Key.
Licensure Skilled care; Intermediate care. *Beds* SNF 77; ICF 30. *Certified* Medicaid; Medicare.
Owner Proprietary Corp.

KILLEN

Lauderdale Christian Nursing Home*
Rte 2, Killen, AL, 35645
(205) 757-2103
Admin Louis E Cottrell Jr.
Licensure Skilled care; Intermediate care. *Beds* SNF 38; ICF 20. *Certified* Medicaid; Medicare.
Owner Nonprofit Corp.

LAFAYETTE

Lafayette Extended Care
805 Hospital St, Lafayette, AL, 36862
(205) 864-8854
Admin Alice England. *Medical Dir/Dir of Nursing* Emma M Swindall MD; Bonnie Mcvay RN DON.
Licensure Skilled care; Intermediate care. *Beds* SNF 47. *Certified* Medicaid; Medicare.
Owner Proprietary Corp.
Admissions Requirements Medical examination.
Staff Physicians 1 (ft); RNs 1 (ft), 1 (pt); LPNs 1 (ft), 8 (pt); Nurses aides 11 (ft), 8 (pt); Activities coordinators 1 (ft).
Facilities Dining room; Activities room; Laundry room; Barber/Beauty shop; Library.
Activities Arts & crafts; Cards; Games; Reading groups; Prayer groups; Movies; Shopping trips; Social/Cultural gatherings.

LaFayette Nursing Home Inc
1st St S E, Lafayette, AL, 36862
(205) 864-9371
Admin Tommy F Pike. *Medical Dir/Dir of Nursing* Dr J M D Holmes.
Licensure Intermediate care. *Beds* ICF 45. *Certified* Medicaid.
Owner Privately owned.
Staff Physicians 1 (ft); LPNs 2 (ft), 2 (pt); Orderlies 2 (ft), 2 (pt); Nurses aides 7 (ft), 5 (pt); Activities coordinators 1 (ft); Dietitians 1 (ft).
Facilities Dining room; Laundry room.
Activities Arts & crafts; Cards; Games; Prayer groups; Social/Cultural gatherings.

LANETT

Lanett Geriatric Center Inc*
702 S 13th St, Lanett, AL, 36863
(205) 644-1111
Admin Janice Babb.
Licensure Skilled care; Intermediate care. *Beds* SNF 44; ICF 21. *Certified* Medicaid; Medicare.
Owner Proprietary Corp.

LINDEN

Marengo Nursing Home*
608 N Main St, Linden, AL, 36748
(205) 295-8631
Admin D P Philen.
Licensure Skilled care; Intermediate care. *Beds* SNF 34; ICF 26. *Certified* Medicaid; Medicare.
Owner Proprietary Corp.

LINEVILLE

Lineville Geriatric Center Inc*
Hwy 9, PO Box 545, Lineville, AL, 36266
(205) 396-2104
Admin Denise A Edwards. *Medical Dir/Dir of Nursing* George Smith MD.
Licensure Skilled care; Intermediate care. *Beds* 81. *Certified* Medicaid; Medicare.
Owner Proprietary Corp.
Staff RNs 2 (ft), 1 (pt); LPNs 8 (ft); Orderlies 7 (ft), 1 (pt); Nurses aides 12 (ft), 4 (pt); Activities coordinators 1 (ft); Dietitians 1 (ft).

LUVERNE

Luverne Geriatric Center Inc
310 W 3rd St, Luverne, AL, 36049
(205) 335-5331
Admin Dale Sasser. *Medical Dir/Dir of Nursing* Dr S P Walker; Dr Jean Senecal; Aneke Shirley.
Licensure Skilled care. *Beds* SNF 137. *Certified* Medicaid; Medicare.
Owner Proprietary Corp.

Admissions Requirements Medical examination; Physician's request.
Staff Physicians 4 (pt); RNs 2 (ft); LPNs 12 (ft), 6 (pt); Nurses aides 50 (ft), 15 (pt); Recreational therapists 1 (ft); Activities coordinators 1 (ft); Dietitians 1 (ft); Dentists 1 (pt).
Facilities Dining room; Activities room; Crafts room; Laundry room; Barber/Beauty shop.
Activities Arts & crafts; Cards; Games; Reading groups; Prayer groups; Movies; Shopping trips; Social/Cultural gatherings.

MADISON

Madison Manor Nursing Home*
PO Box 350, Wall Triana Hwy, Madison, AL, 35758
(205) 772-9243
Admin Carol Grubis.
Licensure Skilled care; Intermediate care. *Beds* SNF 49; ICF 31. *Certified* Medicaid; Medicare.
Owner Proprietary Corp.

MARBURY

Resurrection Catholic Nursing Home
PO Box 89, Marbury, AL, 36051
(205) 755-1139
Admin Sr Janet Kemmler. *Medical Dir/Dir of Nursing* Charles Quarles MD; Mary Coburn LPN.
Licensure Intermediate care. *Beds* ICF 20. *Certified* Medicaid.
Owner Nonprofit Corp.
Admissions Requirements Females only; Medical examination; Physician's request.
Staff Physicians; LPNs; Nurses aides; Activities coordinators; Dietitians.
Affiliation Roman Catholic
Facilities Dining room; Activities room; Laundry room; Library; TV room.
Activities Arts & crafts; Cards; Games; Reading groups; Prayer groups; Movies; Shopping trips.

MARION

Perry Community Hospital & Nursing Home
PO Box 149, Marion, AL, 36756
(205) 683-6111
Admin Marshall L Nero. *Medical Dir/Dir of Nursing* Sterling Haynes MD; Betty Franklin RN DON.
Licensure Skilled care; Intermediate care. *Beds* 31. *Certified* Medicaid; Medicare.
Owner Proprietary Corp (Healthcare Management).
Admissions Requirements Medical examination; Physician's request.
Staff RNs 1 (ft), 1 (pt); LPNs 3 (ft), 3 (pt); Orderlies 3 (ft), 3 (pt); Nurses aides 6 (ft), 6 (pt); Physical therapists 1 (ft); Activities coordinators 1 (ft); Dietitians 1 (pt).
Facilities Dining room; Physical therapy room; Activities room; Chapel; Crafts room; Laundry room; Barber/Beauty shop.
Activities Arts & crafts; Cards; Games; Reading groups; Prayer groups; Movies.

Southland Nursing Home*
500 Shivers Terr, Marion, AL, 36756
(205) 683-6141
Admin Bill R Bolton.
Licensure Skilled care; Intermediate care. *Beds* SNF 54; ICF 17. *Certified* Medicaid; Medicare.
Owner Proprietary Corp (Vari-Care Inc).

MCCALLA

Plantation Manor
PO Box 97, McCalla, AL, 35111
(205) 477-6161

Admin Cecil L Lee. *Medical Dir/Dir of Nursing* Cemal Goral MD.
Licensure Skilled care; Intermediate care. *Beds* SNF 57; ICF 46. *Certified* Medicaid; Medicare.
Owner Proprietary Corp.
Admissions Requirements Medical examination; Physician's request.
Staff Physicians 1 (pt); RNs 1 (ft), 1 (pt); LPNs 9 (ft), 2 (pt); Orderlies 7 (ft), 2 (pt); Nurses aides 15 (ft), 5 (pt); Physical therapists 1 (ft); Recreational therapists 1 (ft); Activities coordinators 1 (ft); Dietitians 1 (pt); Dentists 1 (pt).

MOBILE

Allen Memorial Home*
735 S Washington Ave, Mobile, AL, 36690
(205) 433-2642
Admin Sr Scholastica.
Licensure Skilled care; Intermediate care. *Beds* SNF 80; ICF 14. *Certified* Medicaid; Medicare.
Owner Proprietary Corp.

Bay Manor Health Care Center
7020 Bruns Dr, Mobile, AL, 36609
(205) 639-1588
Admin Al Hudson. *Medical Dir/Dir of Nursing* David McRae MD; Posey Look DON.
Licensure Skilled care. *Beds* SNF 120. *Certified* Medicaid; Medicare.
Owner Proprietary Corp (Beverly Enterprises).
Staff RNs 3 (ft), 3 (pt); LPNs 10 (ft), 8 (pt); Nurses aides 25 (ft), 12 (pt); Activities coordinators 1 (ft); Social worker 1 (ft).
Facilities Dining room; Activities room; Laundry room; Barber/Beauty shop.
Activities Arts & crafts; Cards; Games; Reading groups; Prayer groups; Movies; Shopping trips; Social/Cultural gatherings.

Cogburn Health Center Inc*
148 Tuscaloosa St, Mobile, AL, 36607
(205) 471-5431
Admin L Steven Roberts.
Licensure Skilled care; Intermediate care. *Beds* SNF 142; ICF 8. *Certified* Medicaid; Medicare.
Owner Proprietary Corp.

Heritage Nursing & Convalescent Center*
954 Navco Rd, Mobile, AL, 36690
(205) 473-8684
Admin John E Saad. *Medical Dir/Dir of Nursing* L D McLaughlin MD.
Licensure Skilled care. *Beds* 174. *Certified* Medicaid; Medicare.
Owner Proprietary Corp.
Staff Physicians 1 (pt); RNs 9 (ft); LPNs 25 (ft); Nurses aides 45 (ft); Physical therapists 2 (pt); Recreational therapists 2 (ft); Speech therapists 1 (pt); Dietitians 1 (pt).
Facilities Dining room; Physical therapy room; Activities room; Chapel; Crafts room; Laundry room; Barber/Beauty shop.
Activities Arts & crafts; Cards; Games; Reading groups; Prayer groups; Movies; Social/Cultural gatherings.

Hillhaven Convalescent Center*
1758 Springhill Ave, Mobile, AL, 36607
(205) 479-0551
Admin Dee B Wilcher.
Licensure Skilled care. *Beds* 174. *Certified* Medicaid; Medicare.
Owner Proprietary Corp (Hillhaven Corp).

Ideal Rest Home Inc*
1203 Government St, Mobile, AL, 36604
(205) 438-4566
Admin Mary G Turk.
Licensure Intermediate care. *Beds* 49. *Certified* Medicaid.
Owner Proprietary Corp.

Little Sisters of the Poor—Sacred Heart Home
1655 McGill Ave, Mobile, AL, 36604
(205) 476-6335
Admin Sr Catherine. *Medical Dir/Dir of Nursing* Dr James Browning; Sr Rose Marie.
Licensure Skilled care; Intermediate care. *Beds* SNF 18; ICF 91; Domiciliary 15. *Certified* Medicaid; Medicare.
Owner Nonprofit Corp.
Admissions Requirements Minimum age 60; Medical examination.
Staff Physicians; RNs; LPNs; Nurses aides; Activities coordinators; Dentists; Ophthalmologists.
Affiliation Roman Catholic
Facilities Dining room; Physical therapy room; Activities room; Chapel; Crafts room; Laundry room; Barber/Beauty shop; Library.
Activities Arts & crafts; Cards; Games; Reading groups; Prayer groups; Movies; Shopping trips; Social/Cultural gatherings.

Lynwood Nursing Home*
4164 Halls Mill Rd, Mobile, AL, 36609
(205) 661-5404
Admin James T Lutes.
Licensure Skilled care; Intermediate care. *Beds* SNF 77; ICF 50. *Certified* Medicaid; Medicare.
Owner Proprietary Corp (Wessex Corp).

Southern Medical of Springhill Nursing Home*
3717 Dauphin St, Mobile, AL, 36608
(205) 343-0909
Admin Jake Cureton. *Medical Dir/Dir of Nursing* Dr Gerald Wallace.
Licensure Skilled care; Intermediate care. *Beds* SNF 111; ICF 40. *Certified* Medicaid; Medicare.
Owner Proprietary Corp.
Staff Physicians 3 (pt); RNs 2 (ft); LPNs 12 (ft), 1 (pt); Nurses aides 23 (ft); Physical therapists 1 (ft); Recreational therapists 1 (ft); Speech therapists 1 (ft); Activities coordinators 1 (ft); Dietitians 1 (pt); Podiatrists 1 (pt); 1 (ft).
Facilities Dining room; Physical therapy room; Activities room; Crafts room; Laundry room; Barber/Beauty shop; Library.
Activities Arts & crafts; Cards; Games; Reading groups; Prayer groups; Movies; Shopping trips; Social/Cultural gatherings.

Springhill Manor Nursing Home
PO Box 8395, 3900 Old Shell Rd, Mobile, AL, 36608
(205) 342-5623
Admin Gerald B Hart. *Medical Dir/Dir of Nursing* James E Hassell; Sybile L Bradley DON.
Licensure Intermediate care for mentally retarded. *Beds* ICF 34. *Certified* Medicaid.
Owner Proprietary Corp.
Admissions Requirements Medical examination.
Staff Physicians 1 (pt); RNs 1 (pt); LPNs 5 (pt); Nurses aides 8 (ft), 6 (pt); Recreational therapists 1 (ft); Occupational therapists 1 (ft); Activities coordinators 1 (ft); Dietitians 1 (pt).
Facilities Dining room; Activities room; Crafts room; Laundry room.
Activities Arts & crafts; Cards; Games; Reading groups; Prayer groups; Movies.

Twin Oaks Nursing Home Inc*
857 Crawford Ln, Mobile, AL, 36617
(205) 476-3420
Admin Clarence M Ball Jr. *Medical Dir/Dir of Nursing* Herbert Stone MD.
Licensure Skilled care; Intermediate care. *Beds* SNF 30; ICF 80. *Certified* Medicaid; Medicare.
Owner Proprietary Corp.
Admissions Requirements Physician's request.
Staff Physicians 2 (pt); RNs 2 (ft), 2 (pt); LPNs 9 (ft), 7 (pt); Nurses aides 26 (ft), 10 (pt); Physical therapists 1 (ft); Recreational

therapists 1 (ft); Occupational therapists 1 (pt); Speech therapists 1 (pt); Activities coordinators 1 (pt); Dietitians 1 (ft); Podiatrists 1 (pt).
Facilities Dining room; Physical therapy room; Activities room; Crafts room; Laundry room.
Activities Arts & crafts; Cards; Games; Reading groups; Prayer groups; Movies; Shopping trips; Social/Cultural gatherings.

MONROEVILLE

Monroe Manor Nursing Home
236 W Claiborne St, Monroeville, AL, 36460
(205) 575-2648
Admin Debra C Rawls. *Medical Dir/Dir of Nursing* Dr Tim Jones; Wanda G Lett.
Licensure Intermediate care. *Beds* ICF 54. *Certified* Medicaid.
Owner Privately owned.
Admissions Requirements Medical examination; Physician's request.
Staff Physicians 1 (pt); RNs 1 (ft); LPNs 5 (ft), 2 (pt); Orderlies 2 (ft); Nurses aides 13 (ft), 5 (pt); Activities coordinators 1 (ft); Dietitians 1 (ft).
Facilities Dining room; Activities room; Laundry room; Barber/Beauty shop.
Activities Arts & crafts; Games; Prayer groups; Movies; Social/Cultural gatherings.

Monroe Nursing Home Inc*
Rte 2, Box 800, Monroeville, AL, 36460
(205) 575-3285
Admin Billy Jones. *Medical Dir/Dir of Nursing* Jack Whetstone MD.
Licensure Skilled care; Intermediate care. *Beds* SNF 51; ICF 24. *Certified* Medicaid; Medicare.
Owner Proprietary Corp.
Admissions Requirements Medical examination; Physician's request.
Staff RNs 2 (ft); LPNs 7 (ft), 1 (pt); Nurses aides 21 (ft), 3 (pt); Physical therapists 1 (pt); Activities coordinators 1 (ft); Dietitians 1 (pt).
Facilities Dining room; Activities room; Barber/Beauty shop.

MONTGOMERY

Capitol Hill Healthcare Center
520 S Hull St, Montgomery, AL, 36104
(205) 834-2920
Admin Patti W Turenne. *Medical Dir/Dir of Nursing* Kynard Adams MD.
Licensure Skilled care; Intermediate care. *Beds* SNF 284; ICF. *Certified* Medicaid; Medicare.
Owner Proprietary Corp.
Admissions Requirements Medical examination; Physician's request.
Staff RNs 6 (ft), 3 (pt); LPNs 42 (ft), 4 (pt); Nurses aides 114 (ft), 1 (pt); Physical therapists 2 (ft); Recreational therapists 1 (ft); Activities coordinators 4 (ft); Dietitians 1 (ft), 1 (pt).
Facilities Dining room; Physical therapy room; Activities room; Laundry room; Barber/Beauty shop.
Activities Arts & crafts; Cards; Games; Reading groups; Prayer groups; Movies; Shopping trips; Social/Cultural gatherings; Living history program; Camping; Current events; Quilting; Resident-Help-Resident program; Reminiscence resident council; Resident newsletter.

Cedar Crest
4490 Virginia Loop Rd, Montgomery, AL, 36116
(205) 281-6826
Admin Kevin J Metz. *Medical Dir/Dir of Nursing* Dr Michael Reeves; Sue Corley.
Licensure Skilled care. *Beds* 110. *Certified* Medicaid; Medicare.

Owner Proprietary Corp (Vari-Care Inc).
Admissions Requirements Minimum age 16; Medical examination; Physician's request.
Staff Physicians 10 (pt); RNs 4 (ft), 1 (pt); LPNs 7 (ft), 3 (pt); Orderlies 4 (ft); Nurses aides 30 (ft), 9 (pt); Physical therapists 1 (pt); Speech therapists 1 (pt); Activities coordinators 1 (ft); Dietitians 1 (ft), 1 (pt); Ophthalmologists 1 (pt).
Facilities Dining room; Physical therapy room; Activities room; Crafts room; Laundry room; Barber/Beauty shop; Library; Resident sitting areas.
Activities Arts & crafts; Cards; Games; Reading groups; Prayer groups; Movies; Shopping trips; Social/Cultural gatherings; Special events; Van rides.

Father Purcell Memorial Exceptional Children's Center
2048 W Fairview Ave, Montgomery, AL, 36108-4198
(205) 834-5590
Admin Frank J May Jr. *Medical Dir/Dir of Nursing* David Morrison MD; Carolyn Diehl RN.
Licensure Skilled care. *Beds* 58. *Certified* Medicaid.
Owner Nonprofit organization/foundation.
Admissions Requirements Minimum age 14; Medical examination; Physician's request.
Staff Physicians 1 (pt); RNs 5 (ft); LPNs 13 (ft); Nurses aides 18 (ft), 11 (pt); Physical therapists 1 (pt); Occupational therapists 1 (pt); Speech therapists 1 (ft); Activities coordinators 1 (pt).
Languages Spanish
Affiliation Roman Catholic
Facilities Dining room; Activities room; Homebound special education classroom.
Activities Movies; Various education.

Father Walter Memorial Child Care Center
2815 Forbes Dr, Montgomery, AL, 36199
(205) 262-6421
Admin Audrey Wright.
Licensure Skilled care. *Beds* 44. *Certified* Medicaid.
Owner Nonprofit Corp.
Admissions Requirements Medical examination; Physician's request.
Staff RNs 2 (ft), 1 (pt); LPNs 5 (ft); Orderlies 3 (ft); Nurses aides 20 (ft); Physical therapists 1 (pt); Recreational therapists 1 (pt); Dietitians 1 (pt); Dentists 1 (pt).
Affiliation Roman Catholic
Facilities Dining room; Activities room; Laundry room.
Activities Movies.

John Knox Manor Inc II*
4401 Narrow Ln Rd, Montgomery, AL, 36199
(205) 281-6336
Admin Wanda Barnidge. *Medical Dir/Dir of Nursing* Dr Donald Marshall.
Licensure Skilled care; Intermediate care. *Beds* SNF 59; ICF 39. *Certified* Medicaid; Medicare.
Owner Nonprofit Corp.
Admissions Requirements Minimum age 21; Medical examination; Physician's request.
Staff RNs 3 (ft), 1 (pt); LPNs 10 (ft), 3 (pt); Orderlies 3 (ft), 3 (pt); Nurses aides 30 (ft), 5 (pt); Physical therapists 1 (pt); Activities coordinators 2 (ft); Dietitians 1 (pt).
Affiliation Presbyterian
Facilities Dining room; Physical therapy room; Activities room; Chapel; Crafts room; Laundry room; Barber/Beauty shop.
Activities Arts & crafts; Cards; Games; Reading groups; Prayer groups; Movies; Shopping trips; Social/Cultural gatherings.

Magnolia Manor Nursing Center
1837 Upper Wetumpka Rd, Montgomery, AL, 36199
(205) 264-8416

Admin Jimmy D Prince. *Medical Dir/Dir of Nursing* Malcolm Brown; Angela Self.
Licensure Skilled care; Intermediate care; Pediatric Long-term care. *Beds* SNF 50; ICF 135. *Certified* Medicaid; Medicare; VA Contract.
Owner Proprietary Corp.
Admissions Requirements Medical examination; Physician's request.
Staff Physicians; RNs; LPNs; Orderlies; Nurses aides; Physical therapists; Reality therapists; Recreational therapists; Speech therapists; Activities coordinators; Dietitians; Ophthalmologists.
Facilities Dining room; Physical therapy room; Activities room; Chapel; Crafts room; Laundry room; Barber/Beauty shop; Library; Developed courtyards & playgrounds; Special childrens unit.
Activities Arts & crafts; Cards; Games; Reading groups; Prayer groups; Movies; Shopping trips; Social/Cultural gatherings.

Oak Hill Health Care Inc*
100 Perry Hill Rd, Montgomery, AL, 36193
(205) 272-0171
Admin Carolyn P Hopper. *Medical Dir/Dir of Nursing* Dr S J Selikoff.
Licensure Skilled care; Intermediate care. *Beds* SNF 92; ICF 38. *Certified* Medicaid; Medicare.
Owner Proprietary Corp (Wessex Corp).
Admissions Requirements Medical examination; Physician's request.
Facilities Dining room; Physical therapy room; Activities room; Laundry room; Barber/Beauty shop; Library.
Activities Arts & crafts; Cards; Games; Reading groups; Prayer groups; Movies; Shopping trips; Social/Cultural gatherings.

South Haven Manor Nursing Home*
1300 E South Blvd, Montgomery, AL, 36116
(205) 288-0122
Admin Brunese O Seaborn.
Licensure Skilled care. *Beds* 86. *Certified* Medicaid; Medicare.
Owner Proprietary Corp (Vari-Care Inc).

Tyson Manor Health Facility*
2020 N Country Club Dr, Montgomery, AL, 36106
(205) 263-1643
Admin Katie A Hester.
Licensure Skilled care; Intermediate care. *Beds* SNF 101; ICF 24. *Certified* Medicaid; Medicare.
Owner Proprietary Corp.

Woodley Manor Nursing Home Inc
3312 Woodley Rd, Montgomery, AL, 36116
(205) 288-2780
Admin Juanita C Busby. *Medical Dir/Dir of Nursing* Dr Mont Highley.
Licensure Skilled care; Intermediate care. *Beds* SNF 92; ICF 3. *Certified* Medicaid; Medicare.
Owner Proprietary Corp (Vari-Care Inc).
Admissions Requirements Minimum age 21; Medical examination; Physician's request.
Staff Physicians 1 (pt); RNs 3 (ft); LPNs 7 (ft), 1 (pt); Orderlies 1 (ft), 1 (pt); Nurses aides 35 (ft), 3 (pt); Physical therapists 1 (pt); Recreational therapists 1 (ft); Speech therapists 1 (pt); Activities coordinators 1 (ft); Dietitians 1 (ft); Ophthalmologists 1 (pt); Podiatrists 1 (pt); Social service worker.
Facilities Dining room; Physical therapy room; Activities room; Chapel; Crafts room; Laundry room; Barber/Beauty shop; Library.
Activities Arts & crafts; Cards; Games; Reading groups; Prayer groups; Movies; Shopping trips; Social/Cultural gatherings.

MONTROSE

Montrose Bay Health Care Center
PO Box 256, Montrose, AL, 36559
928-2177
Admin Roland R Garney. *Medical Dir/Dir of Nursing* Thomas Yancey MD; Pat McArthur RN DON.
Licensure Skilled care. *Beds* SNF 83. *Certified* Medicaid; Medicare; VA.
Owner Proprietary Corp (Vari-Care Inc).
Admissions Requirements Medical examination; Physician's request.
Staff RNs 2 (ft), 1 (pt); LPNs 6 (ft), 1 (pt); Nurses aides 28 (ft), 4 (pt); Physical therapists 1 (pt); Speech therapists 1 (pt); Activities coordinators 1 (ft); Dietitians 1 (pt).
Facilities Dining room; Physical therapy room; Activities room; Crafts room; Laundry room; Barber/Beauty shop.
Activities Arts & crafts; Cards; Games; Prayer groups; Movies; Shopping trips; Social/Cultural gatherings.

MOULTON

Moulton Health Care Center
PO Box 336, 300 Hospital St, Moulton, AL, 35650
(205) 974-1146
Admin Karen C Free. *Medical Dir/Dir of Nursing* Robert Rhyne MD; Wanda Hare RN DON.
Licensure Skilled care; Intermediate care. *Beds* SNF 71; ICF 65. *Certified* Medicaid; Medicare.
Owner Proprietary Corp (National Health Corp).
Admissions Requirements Medical examination; Physician's request.
Staff Physicians 3 (pt); RNs 5 (ft), 1 (pt); LPNs 9 (ft), 3 (pt); Nurses aides 65 (ft), 5 (pt); Physical therapists 1 (ft), 1 (pt); Speech therapists 1 (pt); Activities coordinators 2 (ft); Dietitians 1 (ft).
Facilities Dining room; Physical therapy room; Activities room; Crafts room; Laundry room; Barber/Beauty shop; Speech therapy; 3 outdoor patios.
Activities Arts & crafts; Cards; Games; Reading groups; Prayer groups; Movies; Social/Cultural gatherings; Activities for room-bound patients; Church services.

MOUNDVILLE

Moundville Nursing Home Inc
4th St, PO Box 607, Moundville, AL, 35474
(205) 371-2252
Admin Bertha L Madison. *Medical Dir/Dir of Nursing* Dr Larry Shelton; Kathy Fox DON.
Licensure Skilled care; Intermediate care. *Beds* SNF 52; ICF 6. *Certified* Medicaid; Medicare.
Owner Proprietary Corp.
Staff RNs 1 (ft), 3 (pt); LPNs 4 (ft), 3 (pt); Orderlies 2 (ft), 1 (pt); Nurses aides 14 (ft), 4 (pt); Activities coordinators 1 (ft); Dietitians 1 (ft).
Facilities Dining room; Activities room; Chapel; Crafts room; Laundry room; Barber/Beauty shop.
Activities Arts & crafts; Cards; Games; Reading groups; Prayer groups; Shopping trips.

MUSCLE SHOALS

Muscle Shoals Nursing Home*
200 Ala Ave, Muscle Shoals, AL, 35660
(205) 381-4330
Admin Myrtie M Ray.
Licensure Intermediate care. *Beds* 52. *Certified* Medicaid.
Owner Proprietary Corp.

NORTHPORT

Estes Health Care Center—Glen Haven*
2201 32nd St, Northport, AL, 35476
(205) 339-5700
Admin Jim Turnipseed.
Licensure Skilled care; Intermediate care. *Beds* SNF 99; ICF 66. *Certified* Medicaid; Medicare.
Owner Proprietary Corp (Northport Health Services).

Estes Health Care Center—Park Manor
Hwy 82 By-Pass, Northport, AL, 35476
(205) 339-5300
Admin Alan Hutchins. *Medical Dir/Dir of Nursing* James C Guin; Margo Gray.
Licensure Skilled care. *Beds* 152. *Certified* Medicaid; Medicare.
Owner Proprietary Corp (Northport Health Services).
Admissions Requirements Medical examination; Physician's request.
Staff RNs 2 (ft), 1 (pt); LPNs 13 (ft), 5 (pt); Nurses aides 48 (ft), 29 (pt); Activities coordinators 1 (ft).
Facilities Dining room; Activities room; Laundry room; Barber/Beauty shop; Library.
Activities Arts & crafts; Cards; Games; Reading groups; Prayer groups; Movies; Social/Cultural gatherings.

Estes Health Care—North
600 34th St, Northport, AL, 35476
(205) 339-5900
Admin David A Estes. *Medical Dir/Dir of Nursing* Dr Hayes Boyd.
Licensure Skilled care. *Beds* SNF 40; ICF 28. *Certified* Medicaid; Medicare.
Owner Proprietary Corp (Northport Health Services).
Staff RNs 1 (ft), 1 (pt); LPNs 5 (ft), 4 (pt); Nurses aides 15 (ft), 7 (pt); Activities coordinators 1 (ft); Dietitians 1 (ft).
Facilities Dining room; Activities room; Chapel; Barber/Beauty shop.
Activities Arts & crafts; Cards; Games; Reading groups; Prayer groups; Picnics.

Forest Manor Inc
2215 32nd St, Northport, AL, 35476
(205) 339-5400
Admin Donald W Peak. *Medical Dir/Dir of Nursing* J C Guin; Virginia O'Neal.
Licensure Skilled care; Intermediate care. *Beds* SNF 75; ICF 75. *Certified* Medicaid; Medicare.
Owner Proprietary Corp.
Admissions Requirements Medical examination; Physician's request.
Staff Physicians 1 (pt); RNs 2 (ft), 1 (pt); LPNs 20 (ft), 3 (pt); Orderlies 10 (ft), 3 (pt); Nurses aides 50 (ft), 12 (pt); Activities coordinators 1 (ft); Dietitians 1 (pt).
Facilities Dining room; Physical therapy room; Activities room; Chapel; Crafts room; Laundry room; Barber/Beauty shop.
Activities Arts & crafts; Cards; Games; Reading groups; Prayer groups.

ONEONTA

Oneonta Manor Nursing Home*
210 Shirley St, Oneonta, AL, 35121
(205) 274-2365
Admin Laurel Massey.
Licensure Skilled care; Intermediate care. *Beds* SNF 52; ICF 50. *Certified* Medicaid; Medicare.
Owner Proprietary Corp.

OPELIKA

Opelika Nursing Home*
1908 1/2 Pepperell Pkwy, Opelika, AL, 36801
(205) 749-1471
Admin Mary Wallace Wilson.

Licensure Skilled care; Intermediate care. *Beds* SNF 174; ICF 51. *Certified* Medicaid; Medicare.
Owner Proprietary Corp.

OPP

Covington Manor Inc*
W Covington Ave, Opp, AL, 36467
(205) 493-3096
Admin Barbara K Ward. *Medical Dir/Dir of Nursing* Dr J G Dunn.
Licensure Skilled care; Intermediate care. *Beds* SNF 73; ICF 16. *Certified* Medicaid; Medicare.
Owner Proprietary Corp.
Admissions Requirements Medical examination; Physician's request.
Staff RNs 1 (ft), 2 (pt); LPNs 8 (ft), 1 (pt); Orderlies 2 (ft), 2 (pt); Nurses aides 21 (ft), 6 (pt); Activities coordinators 1 (ft); Dietitians 1 (ft).
Facilities Dining room; Activities room; Laundry room; Barber/Beauty shop.
Activities Arts & crafts; Cards; Games; Reading groups; Prayer groups.

Lakeview Manor Inc*
Paulk Ave, Opp, AL, 36467
(205) 493-4558
Admin Eula W McCord.
Licensure Skilled care; Intermediate care. *Beds* SNF 45; ICF 45. *Certified* Medicaid; Medicare.
Owner Proprietary Corp.

OXFORD

Colonial Pines Health Care Center
1130 S Hale St, Oxford, AL, 36203
(205) 831-0481
Admin Katie A Johnston. *Medical Dir/Dir of Nursing* Dr Paul Siehl; Betty Weathington.
Licensure Skilled care; Intermediate care. *Beds* SNF 110; ICF 63. *Certified* Medicaid; Medicare.
Owner Proprietary Corp (Beverly Enterprises).
Admissions Requirements Medical examination; Physician's request.
Staff RNs; LPNs; Orderlies; Nurses aides; Speech therapists; Activities coordinators; Dietitians.
Facilities Dining room; Activities room; Chapel; Crafts room; Laundry room; Barber/ Beauty shop.
Activities Arts & crafts; Cards; Games; Reading groups; Prayer groups; Movies; Shopping trips; Social/Cultural gatherings.

OZARK

Oak View Manor Inc*
Mixon Street Rd, Ozark, AL, 36360
(205) 774-2631
Admin Ann M Galloway.
Licensure Skilled care; Intermediate care. *Beds* SNF 82; ICF 32. *Certified* Medicaid; Medicare.
Owner Proprietary Corp.

Ozark Nursing Home Inc*
201 Bryan Dr, Ozark, AL, 36360
(205) 774-2561
Admin E M Beverly.
Licensure Skilled care. *Beds* 123. *Certified* Medicaid.
Owner Proprietary Corp (Northport Health Services).

PELL CITY

Ingram Manor Inc*
510 Wolf Creek Rd N, Pell City, AL, 35125
(205) 338-3329
Admin Katherine Ponder.

Licensure Skilled care; Intermediate care. *Beds* SNF 32; ICF 42. *Certified* Medicaid; Medicare.
Owner Proprietary Corp.

Jack Cline Nursing Home*
Rte 3, Box 447, Pell City, AL, 35125
(205) 640-5212
Admin Billie Bischoff.
Licensure Intermediate care. *Beds* 49. *Certified* Medicaid.
Owner Proprietary Corp.

PHENIX CITY

Canterbury Health Facility
1720 Knowles Rd, Phenix City, AL, 36867
(205) 291-0485
Admin Julia P Compton. *Medical Dir/Dir of Nursing* Dr N S Lutou Sr, Sr W S Warr; Sharon J Mayo RN DON.
Licensure Skilled care; Intermediate care; Domicillary. *Beds* SNF 26; ICF 74; Domicillary 100. *Certified* Medicaid; Medicare; VA.
Owner Proprietary Corp (Wessex Corp).
Admissions Requirements Medical examination; Physician's request.
Staff Physicians 3 (pt); RNs 3 (ft), 1 (pt); LPNs 14 (ft), 2 (pt); Orderlies 5 (ft); Nurses aides 33 (ft), 6 (pt); Physical therapists 1 (pt); Occupational therapists 1 (pt); Speech therapists 1 (pt); Activities coordinators 1 (ft); Dietitians 1 (pt); Ophthalmologists 1 (pt).
Facilities Dining room; Physical therapy room; Activities room; Laundry room; Barber/Beauty shop; Van (9 passenger); Bus (45 passenger).
Activities Arts & crafts; Cards; Games; Reading groups; Prayer groups; Movies; Shopping trips; Social/Cultural gatherings; Special events; Bus trips.

Parkwood Health Facility Inc*
3301 Stadium Dr, Phenix City, AL, 36867
(205) 297-0237
Admin Julia P Compton.
Licensure Skilled care; Intermediate care. *Beds* SNF 39; ICF 35. *Certified* Medicaid; Medicare.
Owner Proprietary Corp.

Phenix City Nursing Home*
3900 Lakewood Dr, Phenix City, AL, 36867
(205) 298-8247
Admin Roland R Garney.
Licensure Skilled care; Intermediate care. *Beds* SNF 66; ICF 10. *Certified* Medicaid; Medicare.
Owner Proprietary Corp (Vari-Care Inc).

PIEDMONT

Piedmont Hospital & Nursing Home*
Calhoun St, PO Box 330, Piedmont, AL, 36272
(205) 447-6041
Admin Robert E Morrow. *Medical Dir/Dir of Nursing* Dr Russell Ulrich.
Licensure Skilled care; Intermediate care. *Beds* 31. *Certified* Medicaid; Medicare.
Owner Proprietary Corp (Healthcare Management).
Staff Physicians 1 (pt); RNs 1 (ft), 1 (pt); LPNs 5 (ft), 2 (pt); Orderlies 3 (ft), 2 (pt); Nurses aides 8 (ft), 3 (pt); Activities coordinators 1 (ft); Dietitians 1 (pt).

PLEASANT GROVE

Cottage Hill Nursing Home*
700 1st Ave, Pleasant Grove, AL, 35127
(205) 744-8330
Admin William G Allen Jr.

Licensure Skilled care; Intermediate care. *Beds* SNF 44; ICF 20. *Certified* Medicaid; Medicare.
Owner Proprietary Corp.

Pleasant Grove Health Care Center
30 7th St, Pleasant Grove, AL, 35127
(205) 744-8226
Admin Ruby Baker. *Medical Dir/Dir of Nursing* Bonnie Hull.
Licensure Skilled care; Intermediate care. *Beds* SNF 89; ICF 109. *Certified* Medicaid; Medicare.
Owner Proprietary Corp (Beverly Enterprises).
Staff Physicians 1 (pt); RNs 3 (ft), 1 (pt); LPNs 19 (ft), 1 (pt); Activities coordinators 2 (ft); Dietitians 2 (ft); Ophthalmologists 1 (pt); Social worker 2 (ft).

PRATTVILLE

Autauga Health Care Center
750 Wetumpka St, Prattville, AL, 36067
(205) 365-2241
Admin Donna Tillerson. *Medical Dir/Dir of Nursing* Dr William Sanders; Ann Kornschutz RN DON.
Licensure Skilled care; Intermediate care. *Beds* SNF 58; ICF 14. *Certified* Medicaid; Medicare.
Owner Proprietary Corp.
Admissions Requirements Medical examination; Physician's request.
Staff Physicians 1 (pt); RNs 4 (ft), 2 (pt); LPNs 6 (ft), 3 (pt); Nurses aides 22 (ft), 10 (pt); Activities coordinators 2 (ft), 1 (pt); Dietitians 1 (ft), 3 (pt).
Facilities Dining room; Activities room; Laundry room; Barber/Beauty shop.
Activities Arts & crafts; Cards; Games; Reading groups; Prayer groups; Movies; Shopping trips; Social/Cultural gatherings.

RED BAY

Red Bay Nursing Home
Rte 2, Box 3, 30305 10th Ave N, Red Bay, AL, 35582
(205) 356-4982
Admin Christine T Crutchfield. *Medical Dir/ Dir of Nursing* Walker Dempsey MD; Maxine Timbes RN DON.
Licensure Skilled care; Intermediate care. *Beds* SNF 52; ICF 28. *Certified* Medicaid; Medicare.
Owner Proprietary Corp.
Admissions Requirements Physician's request.
Staff RNs 3 (ft); LPNs 10 (ft); Orderlies 2 (ft); Nurses aides 21 (ft), 3 (pt); Activities coordinators 1 (ft); Dietitians 1 (ft).
Facilities Dining room; Activities room; Laundry room; Barber/Beauty shop.
Activities Arts & crafts; Cards; Games; Reading groups; Prayer groups; Movies; Social/Cultural gatherings.

REFORM

Fountain Nursing Home*
PO Box 400, 2nd Ave NW, Reform, AL, 35481
(205) 375-6379
Admin Ellen W Meyer.
Licensure Skilled care; Intermediate care. *Beds* SNF 58; ICF 27. *Certified* Medicaid; Medicare.
Owner Proprietary Corp.

ROANOKE

Rosser Nursing Home*
Seymore St, Roanoke, AL, 36274
(205) 863-4512
Admin Susie Rosser Minnifield.

Licensure Intermediate care. *Beds* 50.
Certified Medicaid.
Owner Proprietary Corp.

Traylor Nursing Home Inc
402 Yancey St, Roanoke, AL, 36274
(205) 863-6131
Admin Ronald L Traylor. *Medical Dir/Dir of
Nursing* G W Everett MD; Sarah Clemons
DON.
Licensure Skilled care; Intermediate care. *Beds*
SNF 52; ICF 50. *Certified* Medicaid;
Medicare.
Owner Proprietary Corp.
Admissions Requirements Medical
examination; Physician's request.
Staff RNs 2 (ft), 3 (pt); LPNs 8 (ft), 1 (pt);
Orderlies 1 (ft); Nurses aides 23 (ft), 5 (pt);
Activities coordinators 1 (ft), 1 (pt);
Dietitians 2 (ft).
Facilities Dining room; Activities room;
Chapel; Laundry room; Barber/Beauty shop.
Activities Arts & crafts; Cards; Games;
Reading groups; Shopping trips.

RUSSELLVILLE

Burns Nursing Home Inc
701 Monroe St, Russellville, AL, 35653
(205) 332-4110
Admin Larry M DeArman.
Licensure Skilled care; Intermediate care. *Beds*
47. *Certified* Medicaid; Medicare.
Owner Proprietary Corp.
Admissions Requirements Physician's request.
Facilities Dining room; Activities room;
Laundry room; Barber/Beauty shop.
Activities Arts & crafts; Games; Reading
groups; Prayer groups; Shopping trips;
Social/Cultural gatherings.

North Alabama Nursing Home
PO Box 608, 705 Gandy St, Russellville, AL,
35653
(205) 332-3773
Admin Floree Thurman. *Medical Dir/Dir of
Nursing* W P Hyatt MD; Rebecca Livingston
RN DON.
Licensure Skilled care; Intermediate care. *Beds*
SNF 50; ICF. *Certified* Medicaid; Medicare.
Owner Privately owned.
Staff RNs 2 (ft); LPNs 5 (ft); Orderlies 2 (ft);
Nurses aides 18 (ft); Activities coordinators
1 (ft); Dietitians 5 (ft).
Facilities Dining room; Activities room;
Crafts room; Laundry room; Barber/Beauty
shop.
Activities Arts & crafts; Cards; Games;
Reading groups; Prayer groups; Movies;
Shopping trips.

Terrace Manor Nursing Home Inc
Box 12, Rte 1, Underwood Rd, Russellville,
AL, 35653
(205) 332-3826
Admin Roland Wade. *Medical Dir/Dir of
Nursing* Wayne P Hyatt MD.
Licensure Skilled care; Intermediate care. *Beds*
SNF 43; ICF. *Certified* Medicaid; Medicare.
Owner Proprietary Corp.
Admissions Requirements Medical
examination.
Staff RNs 1 (ft), 1 (pt); LPNs 4 (ft), 1 (pt);
Nurses aides 16 (ft), 5 (pt); Recreational
therapists 1 (ft); Activities coordinators 1
(ft); Dietitians 1 (pt).
Facilities Dining room; Activities room;
Chapel; Crafts room; Laundry room; Barber/
Beauty shop.
Activities Arts & crafts; Cards; Games;
Reading groups; Prayer groups; Social/
Cultural gatherings.

SCOTTSBORO

Jackson County Hospital & Nursing Home*
Woods Cove Rd, PO Box 927, Scottsboro, AL,
35768
(205) 259-4444
Admin James K Mason.
Licensure Skilled care; Intermediate care. *Beds*
SNF 30; ICF 20. *Certified* Medicaid;
Medicare.
Owner Publicly owned.
Admissions Requirements Medical
examination; Physician's request.
Staff RNs 1 (ft), 3 (pt); LPNs 5 (ft), 3 (pt);
Orderlies 2 (ft), 1 (pt); Nurses aides 16 (ft),
4 (pt); Activities coordinators 1 (ft).
Facilities Dining room; Activities room;
Chapel; Crafts room; Barber/Beauty shop.
Activities Arts & crafts; Cards; Games;
Reading groups; Prayer groups; Movies;
Shopping trips; Social/Cultural gatherings.

Scottsboro Nursing Home*
Cloverdale Rd, Scottsboro, AL, 35768
(205) 259-1505
Admin Jerry A Taylor. *Medical Dir/Dir of
Nursing* Larry Bolton.
Licensure Skilled care; Intermediate care. *Beds*
SNF 75; ICF 20. *Certified* Medicaid;
Medicare.
Owner Proprietary Corp.
Admissions Requirements Medical
examination; Physician's request.
Staff Physicians 12 (ft); RNs 4 (ft); LPNs 6
(ft), 3 (pt); Nurses aides 25 (ft), 16 (pt);
Activities coordinators 10 (ft), 1 (pt);
Dietitians 1 (ft); Dentists 2 (pt); Social
worker 1 (ft).
Facilities Dining room; Activities room;
Chapel; Laundry room; Barber/Beauty shop;
Library; Conference-exam room; Sunrooms;
Spacious lobby; Sun patio.
Activities Arts & crafts; Games; Reading
groups; Prayer groups; Movies; Social/
Cultural gatherings; Summer outings;
Birthday & Ice cream parties; Resident
council.

SELMA

Dunn Rest Home*
515 Mabry St, Selma, AL, 36701
(205) 872-3471
Admin Ellen B Dunn. *Medical Dir/Dir of
Nursing* Dr William E Ehlert.
Licensure Skilled care; Intermediate care. *Beds*
SNF 87; ICF 6. *Certified* Medicaid;
Medicare.
Owner Proprietary Corp (Vari-Care).
Admissions Requirements Minimum age 21;
Medical examination; Physician's request.
Staff Physicians 1 (ft), 10 (pt); RNs 3 (ft), 2
(pt); Orderlies 4 (ft), 4 (pt); Nurses aides 26
(ft), 6 (pt); Physical therapists 1 (pt);
Activities coordinators 1 (ft); Dietitians 3
(ft), 1 (pt); Dentists 1 (pt).
Facilities Dining room; Activities room;
Laundry room; Barber/Beauty shop.
Activities Arts & crafts; Cards; Games;
Reading groups; Prayer groups; Movies;
Shopping trips.

Lighthouse Convalescent Home
2911 Range Line Rd, Selma, AL, 36701
(205) 875-1868
Admin John Crear. *Medical Dir/Dir of
Nursing* C L Lett MD.
Licensure Intermediate care. *Beds* ICF 48.
Certified Medicaid.
Owner Proprietary Corp.
Staff RNs 1 (ft); LPNs 4 (ft), 2 (pt); Orderlies
3 (ft), 2 (pt); Nurses aides 3 (ft), 8 (pt);
Activities coordinators 1 (ft); Dietitians 2
(ft), 4 (pt).

Facilities Dining room; Activities room;
Chapel; Crafts room.
Activities Arts & crafts; Cards; Games; Prayer
groups; Movies; Social/Cultural gatherings.

Warren Manor Nursing Home
11 Bell Rd, Selma, AL, 36701
(205) 874-7425
Admin Kevin J Metz. *Medical Dir/Dir of
Nursing* Dr Freeman Singleton.
Licensure Skilled care; Intermediate care. *Beds*
SNF 112; ICF 16. *Certified* Medicaid;
Medicare.
Owner Proprietary Corp (Vari-Care).
Admissions Requirements Minimum age 21;
Medical examination; Physician's request.
Staff Physicians 1 (pt); RNs 2 (ft), 1 (pt);
LPNs 9 (ft), 7 (pt); Orderlies 6 (ft), 3 (pt);
Nurses aides 26 (ft), 18 (pt); Physical
therapists 1 (pt); Activities coordinators 1
(ft); Dietitians 1 (ft).
Facilities Dining room; Physical therapy
room; Activities room; Crafts room; Laundry
room; Barber/Beauty shop; Library.
Activities Arts & crafts; Cards; Games;
Reading groups; Prayer groups; Movies;
Shopping trips; Social/Cultural gatherings.

SPANISH FORT

Westminster Village
500 Spanish Fort Blvd, Spanish Fort, AL,
36527
(205) 626-7007
Admin Dr Leo Fallon. *Medical Dir/Dir of
Nursing* Dr M L McBrearty; Jeannie
Blackmon.
Licensure Skilled care; Domicillary. *Beds* SNF
60; Domicillary 14. *Certified* Medicare.
Owner Nonprofit Corp.
Admissions Requirements Medical
examination; Physician's request.
Staff Physicians 3 (pt); RNs 6 (ft); LPNs 7
(ft); Orderlies 2 (ft), 2 (pt); Nurses aides 15
(ft), 20 (pt); Physical therapists 1 (pt);
Recreational therapists 1 (ft); Activities
coordinators 1 (ft); Dietitians 1 (ft);
Ophthalmologists 1 (pt); Podiatrists 1 (pt).
Facilities Dining room; Physical therapy
room; Activities room; Chapel; Crafts room;
Laundry room; Barber/Beauty shop; Library.
Activities Cards; Games; Prayer groups;
Movies; Shopping trips; Rhythm band;
Gardening; Cooking.

SYLACAUGA

Marble City Nursing Home Inc*
PO Box 1123, Fayetteville Rd, Sylacauga, AL,
35150
(205) 245-7402
Admin Robert L Sprayberry.
Licensure Skilled care; Intermediate care. *Beds*
SNF 63; ICF 50. *Certified* Medicaid;
Medicare.
Owner Proprietary Corp.

Sylacauga Hospital & Nursing Home*
W Hickory St, Sylacauga, AL, 35150
(205) 249-4921
Admin Frank G Perryman. *Medical Dir/Dir of
Nursing* Dr James G Wright.
Licensure Skilled care; Intermediate care. *Beds*
52. *Certified* Medicaid; Medicare.
Owner Publicly owned.
Staff RNs 1 (ft), 2 (pt); LPNs 6 (ft), 2 (pt);
Nurses aides 17 (ft), 8 (pt); Physical
therapists 1 (pt); Activities coordinators 1
(ft); Dietitians 1 (ft).
Facilities Dining room; Physical therapy
room; Activities room; Crafts room;
Laundry room; Barber/Beauty shop; Library.
Activities Arts & crafts; Games; Prayer groups;
Social/Cultural gatherings.

TALLADEGA

Talladega Nursing Home
616 Chaffee St, Talladega, AL, 35160
(205) 362-4197
Admin William P Patterson. *Medical Dir/Dir of Nursing* Dr L D Graves.
Licensure Skilled care; Intermediate care. *Beds* SNF 73; ICF 128. *Certified* Medicaid; Medicare.
Owner Proprietary Corp.
Admissions Requirements Medical examination; Physician's request.
Staff Physicians 10 (pt); RNs 3 (ft); LPNs 13 (ft); Nurses aides 82 (ft); Physical therapists 1 (pt); Recreational therapists 3 (ft); Activities coordinators 1 (ft); Dietitians 1 (ft).
Languages Chinese
Facilities Dining room; Physical therapy room; Activities room; Chapel; Crafts room; Laundry room; Barber/Beauty shop.
Activities Arts & crafts; Cards; Games; Reading groups; Prayer groups; Movies; Shopping trips; Social/Cultural gatherings; Bird watching & feeding; Volunteers from community.

TALLASSEE

The Nursing Home of Tallassee Inc*
Rte 2, PO Box 48A, Wetumpka Hwy, Tallassee, AL, 36078
(205) 283-3975
Admin Mellie Jones.
Licensure Skilled care; Intermediate care. *Beds* SNF 59; ICF 22. *Certified* Medicaid; Medicare.
Owner Proprietary Corp.

THOMASVILLE

Thomasville Hospital & Nursing Home*
1440 Hwy 43 N, Thomasville, AL, 36784
(205) 636-4431
Admin Rex Jackson. *Medical Dir/Dir of Nursing* Dr J L Dozier.
Licensure Skilled care. *Beds* 50. *Certified* Medicare.
Owner Publicly owned.
Staff RNs 2 (ft); LPNs 5 (ft), 2 (pt); Orderlies 2 (ft), 1 (pt); Nurses aides 14 (ft), 4 (pt); Activities coordinators 1 (ft).
Facilities Dining room; Chapel; Barber/Beauty shop; Library.
Activities Arts & crafts; Games; Prayer groups; Movies; Shopping trips.

TROY

Pike Manor Health Care Center
PO Drawer 787, Elba Hwy, Troy, AL, 36081
(205) 566-0880
Admin Ralph N Railey. *Medical Dir/Dir of Nursing* J D Colley Jr MD; Robin Self RN.
Licensure Skilled care; Intermediate care. *Beds* SNF 68; ICF 96. *Certified* Medicaid; Medicare.
Owner Proprietary Corp.
Admissions Requirements Physician's request.
Staff RNs 16 (ft), 3 (pt); Orderlies 5 (ft); Nurses aides 47 (ft), 10 (pt); Activities coordinators 1 (ft); Dietitians 2 (ft).
Facilities Dining room; Activities room; Crafts room; Barber/Beauty shop; Library.
Activities Arts & crafts; Cards; Games; Reading groups; Prayer groups.

TRUSSVILLE

Trussville Nursing Home Inc*
PO Box 65, Chalkville Rd, Trussville, AL, 35175
(205) 655-3227
Admin Joyce B McHugh.

Licensure Skilled care; Intermediate care. *Beds* SNF 102; ICF 23. *Certified* Medicaid; Medicare.
Owner Proprietary Corp (Beverly Enterprises).

TUSCALOOSA

Heritage Health Care Center
1101 Snows Mill Ave, Tuscaloosa, AL, 35406
(205) 759-5179
Admin George L Jackson. *Medical Dir/Dir of Nursing* Delores Sargent DON.
Licensure Skilled care; Intermediate care. *Beds* SNF 114; ICF 38. *Certified* Medicaid; Medicare; VA.
Owner Proprietary Corp.
Admissions Requirements Physician's request.
Facilities Dining room; Physical therapy room; Activities room; Chapel; Crafts room; Laundry room; Barber/Beauty shop.
Activities Arts & crafts; Cards; Games; Reading groups; Prayer groups; Movies; Shopping trips; Social/Cultural gatherings.

La Rocca Nursing Home
403 34th Ave E, Tuscaloosa, AL, 35404
(205) 553-1341
Admin Lyman H Hardy. *Medical Dir/Dir of Nursing* Evelyn W Hardy.
Licensure Skilled care. *Beds* SNF 75.
Owner Privately owned.
Admissions Requirements Medical examination; Physician's request.
Staff Physicians; RNs; LPNs; Nurses aides; Activities coordinators; Dietitians.
Facilities Dining room; Physical therapy room; Activities room; Chapel; Crafts room; Laundry room; Barber/Beauty shop; Library.
Activities Cards; Games; Reading groups; Prayer groups.

TUSCUMBIA

Great Hall-Riverbend Center
901 Keller Ln, Tuscumbia, AL, 35674
(205) 381-8006
Admin Terrance Ackley. *Medical Dir/Dir of Nursing* Joseph Glaister.
Licensure Intermediate care for mentally retarded. *Beds* ICF/MR 8. *Certified* Medicaid.
Owner Nonprofit Corp.
Admissions Requirements Minimum age 18.
Staff RNs 1 (pt); Nurses aides 4 (pt).
Facilities Dining room; Activities room; Crafts room; Laundry room.
Activities Arts & crafts; Cards; Games; Movies; Shopping trips; Social/Cultural gatherings; Habilitation training.

Oak Crest Nursing Home Inc
813 Keller Ln, Tuscumbia, AL, 35674
(205) 383-1535
Admin Nancy Brewer. *Medical Dir/Dir of Nursing* James Ashmore MD; Cheryl Bullard DON.
Licensure Skilled care. *Beds* 109. *Certified* Medicaid; Medicare.
Owner Proprietary Corp.
Admissions Requirements Medical examination; Physician's request.
Staff Physicians 1 (ft); RNs 2 (ft); LPNs 14 (ft); Orderlies 35 (ft); Recreational therapists 2 (ft); Activities coordinators 1 (ft); Dietitians 10 (ft); Dentist 1 (pt).
Languages Sign
Facilities Dining room; Activities room; Chapel; Crafts room; Laundry room; Barber/Beauty shop; Library.
Activities Arts & crafts; Cards; Games; Reading groups; Prayer groups; Movies; Social/Cultural gatherings.

Shoals Nursing Home*
500 Hazleton St, Tuscumbia, AL, 35674
(205) 383-4541
Admin Clyde Ray Jr.

Licensure Skilled care. *Beds* 103. *Certified* Medicaid; Medicare.
Owner Proprietary Corp.

TUSKEGEE

Magnolia Haven Nursing Home
650 Wright St, Tuskegee, AL, 36083
(205) 727-4960
Admin Reginald L Eldridge. *Medical Dir/Dir of Nursing* Calvin Dowe; Fran Norfleet DON.
Licensure Skilled care; Intermediate care. *Beds* SNF 57; ICF 10. *Certified* Medicaid; Medicare; VA.
Owner Proprietary Corp (Vari-Care).
Admissions Requirements Medical examination; Physician's request.
Staff Physicians 1 (ft); RNs 1 (ft), 3 (pt); LPNs 5 (ft), 4 (pt); Orderlies 4 (ft), 4 (pt); Nurses aides 15 (ft), 13 (pt); Physical therapists 1 (ft), 1 (pt); Recreational therapists 1 (ft); Activities coordinators 1 (ft); Dietitians 1 (ft); Social service rep 1 (ft).
Facilities Dining room; Physical therapy room; Activities room; Crafts room; Laundry room; Barber/Beauty shop.
Activities Arts & crafts; Cards; Games; Reading groups; Prayer groups; Movies; Shopping trips; Social/Cultural gatherings.

Tuskegee Health Care Inc
PO Box 659, 502 Gautier St, Tuskegee, AL, 36083
(205) 727-1945
Admin Margaret K Phillips. *Medical Dir/Dir of Nursing* Robert Story MD; Dianne Sallas DON.
Licensure Skilled care; Intermediate care. *Beds* SNF 40; ICF 102. *Certified* Medicaid; Medicare.
Owner Proprietary Corp (Wessex Corp).
Staff RNs 3 (ft), 2 (pt); LPNs 14 (ft), 4 (pt); Nurses aides 35 (ft), 10 (pt); Activities coordinators 2 (ft).

UNION SPRINGS

Bullock County Hospital & Nursing Home*
102 W Conecuh Ave, Union Springs, AL, 36089
(205) 738-3446
Admin Ray Hills.
Licensure Skilled care. *Beds* 32. *Certified* Medicaid; Medicare.
Owner Publicly owned.

VALLEY

George H Lanier Memorial Nursing Home
4800 48th St, Valley, AL, 36854
(205) 756-3111
Admin Howard D Clem Sr. *Medical Dir/Dir of Nursing* S C Simmons Jr MD; Fay Hamm RN.
Licensure Skilled care; Intermediate care. *Beds* 75. *Certified* Medicaid; Medicare.
Owner Nonprofit Corp.
Admissions Requirements Minimum age 18; Medical examination.
Staff Physicians 30 (ft); RNs 3 (ft); LPNs 11 (ft), 10 (pt); Orderlies 1 (ft); Nurses aides 26 (ft); Physical therapists 1 (pt); Activities coordinators 1 (ft); Dietitians 2 (pt); Ophthalmologists 1 (pt).
Facilities Dining room; Physical therapy room; Activities room; Chapel; Crafts room; Barber/Beauty shop.
Activities Arts & crafts; Cards; Games; Prayer groups; Social/Cultural gatherings.

VERNON

Lamar Convalescent Center Inc*
Rte 1, Box 70, Vernon, AL, 35592
(205) 695-9313

Admin J W Spearman. *Medical Dir/Dir of Nursing* Dr William C Box.
Licensure Skilled care; Intermediate care. *Beds* 83. *Certified* Medicaid; Medicare.
Owner Proprietary Corp.
Staff Physicians 3 (pt); RNs 1 (ft), 2 (pt); LPNs 8 (ft), 3 (pt); Orderlies 4 (ft), 2 (pt); Nurses aides 18 (ft), 4 (pt); Activities coordinators 1 (ft), 2 (pt); Dietitians 2 (ft).
Facilities Dining room; Activities room; Laundry room; Barber/Beauty shop.
Activities Arts & crafts; Games; Reading groups; Prayer groups; Movies; Shopping trips; Social/Cultural gatherings.

Lamar County Hospital & Nursing Home*
507 5th St SW, Vernon, AL, 35592
(205) 695-7111
Admin Robert E Morrow.
Licensure Skilled care; Intermediate care. *Beds* SNF 61; ICF 10. *Certified* Medicaid; Medicare.
Owner Publicly owned.

WETUMPKA

Valley Brook Park Inc*
208 Marshall St, Wetumpka, AL, 36092
(205) 567-5131
Admin Glenda Bobo. *Medical Dir/Dir of Nursing* Dr Dunn Jr.
Licensure Skilled care; Intermediate care. *Beds* SNF 57; ICF 23. *Certified* Medicaid; Medicare.
Owner Proprietary Corp.
Admissions Requirements Medical examination; Physician's request.
Staff Physicians 5 (pt); RNs 1 (ft), 2 (pt); LPNs 8 (ft), 2 (pt); Orderlies 6 (ft), 2 (pt); Nurses aides 20 (ft), 3 (pt); Recreational therapists 1 (ft); Activities coordinators 1 (ft); Dietitians 1 (ft).
Facilities Dining room; Activities room; Crafts room; Laundry room; Barber/Beauty shop.
Activities Arts & crafts; Games; Shopping trips; Social/Cultural gatherings.

WINFIELD

Winfield Nursing Home Inc*
Main St, Winfield, AL, 35594
(205) 487-4211
Admin Ross M Taylor Jr.
Licensure Skilled care; Intermediate care. *Beds* SNF 70; ICF 53. *Certified* Medicaid; Medicare.
Owner Proprietary Corp.

YORK

Sumter Nursing Home*
Rte 1, Box 415A, York, AL, 36925
(205) 392-5281
Admin B M Lanier.
Licensure Skilled care; Intermediate care. *Beds* SNF 90; ICF 10. *Certified* Medicaid; Medicare.
Owner Publicly owned.

ALASKA

ANCHORAGE

Hope Park Cottage*
2805 Bering St, Anchorage, AK, 99503
(907) 561-5335
Admin Stephen P Lesko.
Licensure Intermediate care for mentally
retarded. *Beds* 10.
Owner Publicly owned.

Our Lady of Compassion Care Center
4900 Eagle Street, Anchorage, AK, 99503
(907) 562-2281
Admin Tom Boling. *Medical Dir/Dir of
Nursing* Dr Mark Agnew.
Licensure Skilled care; Intermediate care. *Beds*
SNF; ICF 224. *Certified* Medicaid;
Medicare.
Owner Nonprofit organization/foundation.
Admissions Requirements Medical
examination; Physician's request.
Staff Physical therapists 3 (ft); Recreational
therapists 1 (ft); Occupational therapists 2
(ft); Speech therapists 1 (ft); Dietitians 1 (ft).
Languages Native Alaskan
Affiliation Roman Catholic
Facilities Dining room; Physical therapy
room; Activities room; Chapel; Crafts room;
Laundry room; Barber/Beauty shop; Library;
Gift shop.
Activities Reading groups; Prayer groups;
Social/Cultural gatherings Recreation; Bus
Trips.

CORDOVA

Cordova Community Hospital
PO Box 160, Cordova, AK, 99574
(907) 424-8000
Admin Edward Zeine. *Medical Dir/Dir of
Nursing* A D Tilgner MD; Patricia Ju Vette
DON.
Licensure Skilled care; Intermediate care. *Beds*
12. *Certified* Medicaid; Medicare.
Owner Publicly owned.
Staff Physicians 3 (ft); RNs 8 (ft), 6 (pt);
Nurses aides 5 (ft), 2 (pt); Physical therapists
1 (pt); Activities coordinators 1 (pt);
Dietitians 1 (pt); Dentists 1 (pt);
Ophthalmologists 1 (pt); Mental
healthalcohol therapist 1 (ft); Psychologist 1
(ft).
Facilities Dining room; Physical therapy
room; Activities room; Chapel; Crafts room;
Laundry room.
Activities Arts & crafts; Cards; Games;
Reading groups; Prayer groups; Social/
Cultural gatherings; Musical programs;
fishing trips.

FAIRBANKS

Careage North Health Care Center*
PO Box 847, Fairbanks, AK, 99707
(907) 452-1921
Admin Sharon White.

Licensure Skilled care; Intermediate care. *Beds*
101. *Certified* Medicaid; Medicare.

HOMER

South Peninsula Hospital
PO Box 275, 4300 Bartlett, Homer, AK,
99603
(907) 235-8101
Admin Michael Herring.
Licensure Skilled care; Intermediate care. *Beds*
SNF 16; ICF. *Certified* Medicaid.
Owner Nonprofit Corp.
Admissions Requirements Physician's request.
Staff RNs 3 (ft); LPNs 2 (ft); Nurses aides 4
(ft); Physical therapists 1 (pt); Occupational
therapists 1 (pt); Speech therapists 1 (pt);
Activities coordinators 1 (pt); Dietitians 1
(pt); Dentists 1 (pt); Ophthalmologists 1 (pt);
Podiatrists 1 (pt).
Activities Arts & crafts; Cards; Games;
Movies; Shopping trips; Social/Cultural
gatherings.

JUNEAU

St Ann's Nursing Home
415 6th St, Juneau, AK, 99801
(907) 586-3883
Admin Jack W Buck. *Medical Dir/Dir of
Nursing* Dr Krehlik; Edna Leamer RNC
DON.
Licensure Skilled care; Intermediate care. *Beds*
SNF 45; ICF. *Certified* Medicaid.
Owner Nonprofit Corp.
Admissions Requirements Medical
examination; Physician's request.
Staff Physicians 1 (pt); RNs 4 (ft), 3 (pt);
LPNs 3 (ft), 1 (pt); Nurses aides 25 (ft), 6
(pt); Physical therapists 1 (pt); Recreational
therapists 1 (ft); Occupational therapists 1
(pt); Speech therapists 1 (pt); Activities
coordinators 1 (ft); Dietitians 1 (pt).
Facilities Dining room; Physical therapy
room; Activities room; Chapel; Crafts room;
Laundry room; Barber/Beauty shop.
Activities Arts & crafts; Cards; Games;
Reading groups; Prayer groups; Movies;
Shopping trips.

KETCHIKAN

Island View Manor*
3100 Tongass, Ketchikan, AK, 99901
(907) 225-5171
Admin Sr Barbara Haase.
Licensure Skilled care; Intermediate care. *Beds*
44. *Certified* Medicaid; Medicare.

KODIAK

Kodiak Island Hospital
1915 E Rezanof Dr, Kodiak, AK, 99615
(907) 486-3281
Medical Dir/Dir of Nursing Kate Fitzgerald
DON.

Licensure Intermediate care. *Beds* ICF 19.
Certified Medicaid.
Owner Nonprofit Corp.
Admissions Requirements Physician's request.
Staff Physicians 12 (ft); RNs 1 (ft), 1 (pt);
LPNs 3 (ft), 2 (pt); Nurses aides 5 (ft), 4
(pt); Physical therapists 1 (ft); Activities
coordinators 1 (ft); Dietitians 1 (pt).
Affiliation Lutheran
Facilities Dining room; Physical therapy
room; Activities room; Crafts room; Laundry
room.
Activities Arts & crafts; Cards; Games;
Reading groups; Prayer groups; Movies;
Shopping trips; Social/Cultural gatherings;
Cooking events; BBQs; Van.

NOME

Norton Sound Regional Hospital*
PO Box 966, 50 & Bering, Nome, AK, 99762
(907) 443-5411
Admin Richard Conti. *Medical Dir/Dir of
Nursing* Dr Dennis Ohlragge.
Licensure Intermediate care. *Beds* 6. *Certified*
Medicaid.
Admissions Requirements Medical
examination.
Staff Physicians 4 (ft); RNs 11 (ft); Nurses
aides 4 (ft); Activities coordinators 1 (ft);
Dietitians 1 (ft); Dentists 2 (ft); Audiologists
1 (ft); Physical Therapy assistants 1 (ft);
Optometrists 1 (ft).
Facilities Dining room; Physical therapy
room; Activities room.
Activities Arts & crafts; Games; Shopping
trips.

PALMER

Valley Hospital*
PO Box 1687, 515 E Dahlia St, Palmer, AK,
99645
(907) 745-4813
Admin James G Walsh.
Licensure Acute care. *Beds* 36. *Certified*
Medicaid; Medicare.

PETERSBURG

Petersburg General Hospital
PO Box 589, Petersburg, AK, 99833
(907) 772-4291
Admin Gary W Grandy. *Medical Dir/Dir of
Nursing* T H Wood; Joy Janssen RN DON.
Licensure Skilled care; Intermediate care. *Beds*
14. *Certified* Medicaid; Medicare.
Owner Publicly owned.
Admissions Requirements Medical
examination; Physician's request.
Staff Physicians 2 (ft), 12 (pt); RNs 5 (ft), 4
(pt); LPNs 2 (ft), 1 (pt); Orderlies 1 (ft);
Nurses aides 3 (ft), 2 (pt); Physical therapists
1 (pt); Occupational therapists 1 (pt);
Activities coordinators 1 (pt); Dietitians 1
(pt); Dentists 1 (pt); Ophthalmologists 1 (pt).

Facilities Dining room; Physical therapy
room; Activities room; Barber/Beauty shop.
Activities Arts & crafts; Cards; Games;
Reading groups; Prayer groups; Shopping
trips; Social/Cultural gatherings.

SEWARD

Wesleyan Nursing Home Inc
PO Box 430, 431 1st Ave, Seward, AK, 99664
(907) 224-5241
Admin Mildred Pelch RN. *Medical Dir/Dir of
Nursing* Gerald Bell MD; Edith Hough RN
DON.
Licensure Skilled care; Intermediate care. *Beds*
SNF 66; ICF. *Certified* Medicaid.
Owner Nonprofit Corp.
Admissions Requirements Minimum age 18;
Physician's request.
Staff Physicians; RNs 5 (ft); LPNs 5 (ft);
Orderlies 4 (ft); Nurses aides 20 (ft);
Physical therapists; Reality therapists;
Recreational therapists 2 (ft); Occupational
therapists; Speech therapists; Activities
coordinators 1 (ft); Dietitians; Dentists;
Ophthalmologists; Podiatrists; Social worker
1 (ft).
Affiliation Methodist
Facilities Dining room; Activities room;
Crafts room; Laundry room; Barber/Beauty
shop.

Activities Arts & crafts; Cards; Games;
Reading groups; Prayer groups; Movies;
Shopping trips; Social/Cultural gatherings;
Bowling; Picnics.

SOLDOTNA

Heritage Place
232 Rockwell, Soldotna, AK, 99669
(907) 262-2545
Admin Mary Almen. *Medical Dir/Dir of
Nursing* Betty Bumbaugh.
Licensure Skilled care. *Beds* SNF 45. *Certified*
Medicaid; Medicare.
Owner Nonprofit organization/foundation.
Admissions Requirements Medical
examination; Physician's request.
Staff RNs; Nurses aides; Activities
coordinators.
Affiliation Lutheran
Facilities Dining room; Physical therapy
room; Activities room; Laundry room;
Barber/Beauty shop; Library.
Activities Arts & crafts; Cards; Games;
Reading groups; Prayer groups; Movies;
Shopping trips; Social/Cultural gatherings.

VALDEZ

Harborview Development Center
PO Box 487, Valdez, AK, 99686
(907) 835-4344

Admin Patrick J Londo. *Medical Dir/Dir of
Nursing* Bernard Gerard MD.
Licensure Intermediate care; Intermediate care
for mentally retarded. *Beds* ICF 16; ICF/MR
64. *Certified* Medicaid; Medicare.
Owner Publicly owned.
Staff Physicians 3 (pt); RNs 9 (ft), 4 (pt);
LPNs 1 (ft); Nurses aides 76 (ft), 6 (pt);
Physical therapists 1 (pt); Recreational
therapists 3 (ft); Occupational therapists 1
(ft); Dietitians 1 (pt); Dentists 1 (pt);
Podiatrists 1 (pt);; QMRPs 4 (ft).
Languages Yurak
Facilities Dining room; Physical therapy
room; Activities room; Crafts room; Laundry
room; Barber/Beauty shop; Library.
Activities Arts & crafts; Games; Movies;
Shopping trips; Social/Cultural gatherings;
Shopping trips.

WRANGELL

Wrangell General Hospital—LTC Facility*
PO Box 80, Wrangell, AK, 99929
(907) 874-3356
Admin John Vowell.
Licensure Skilled care; Intermediate care. *Beds*
ICF 14. *Certified* Medicaid; Medicare.

ARIZONA

BISBEE

Copper Queen Community Hospital
Cole Ave & Bisbee Rd, Bisbee, AZ, 85603
(602) 432-5383
Admin John Houston.
Licensure Intermediate care. *Beds* 21.
Owner Nonprofit Corp.

BULLHEAD CITY

Silver Ridge Village
2812 Silver Creek Rd, Bullhead City, AZ, 86430
(602) 763-0244
Admin Helen Cahill, Acting Adm. *Medical Dir/Dir of Nursing* Dr T Dallman; Alice Yeager RN DON.
Licensure Skilled care. *Beds* SNF 120.
Owner Nonprofit Corp.
Staff RNs 7 (ft), 3 (pt); LPNs 6 (ft), 3 (pt); Orderlies 3 (ft); Nurses aides 19 (ft); Dietitians 1 (ft);; Human Resources 1 (ft).

CAMP VERDE

The Arbors Nursing Center
General Crook Hwy & Salt Mine Rd, Camp Verde, AZ, 86322
(602) 567-5253
Admin Roger D Shurlow. *Medical Dir/Dir of Nursing* Henry H Kaldenbaugh MD; Joan Nitch RN BS DON.
Licensure Skilled care; Intermediate care. *Beds* SNF 60; ICF 60. *Certified* Medicare.
Owner Proprietary Corp.
Admissions Requirements Minimum age 12; Medical examination; Physician's request.
Staff Physicians 1 (pt); RNs 5 (ft), 3 (pt); LPNs 3 (ft), 3 (pt); Orderlies 1 (ft); Nurses aides 15 (ft), 5 (pt); Physical therapists 1 (pt); Reality therapists 1 (pt); Recreational therapists 1 (ft), 1 (pt); Occupational therapists 1 (pt); Speech therapists 1 (pt); Activities coordinators 1 (ft); Dietitians 1 (ft); Dentists 1 (pt); Ophthalmologists 1 (pt); Podiatrists 1 (pt).
Facilities Dining room; Physical therapy room; Activities room; Chapel; Crafts room; Laundry room; Barber/Beauty shop; Library.
Activities Arts & crafts; Cards; Games; Reading groups; Prayer groups; Movies; Shopping trips; Social/Cultural gatherings.

CASA GRANDE

Hoemako Long-Term Care*
1101 E Florence Blvd, Casa Grande, AZ, 85222
(602) 836-7401
Admin Robert Benjamin.
Licensure Skilled care. *Beds* 29.
Owner Nonprofit Corp.

CHANDLER

Chandler Health Care Center
416 S Dobson Rd, Chandler, AZ, 85224
(602) 899-6717
Admin Annette Milne. *Medical Dir/Dir of Nursing* H J Wiens MD; Kathleen Carrasco.
Licensure Skilled care. *Beds* SNF 120. *Certified* Medicare.
Owner Proprietary Corp (Beverly Enterprises).
Admissions Requirements Minimum age 18; Medical examination; Physician's request.
Staff RNs; LPNs; Orderlies; Nurses aides.
Facilities Dining room; Physical therapy room; Activities room; Chapel; Barber/Beauty shop.
Activities Arts & crafts; Cards; Games; Reading groups; Prayer groups; Movies; Shopping trips; Social/Cultural gatherings.

CHINLE

Chinle Nursing Home*
PO Box 910, Chinle, AZ, 86503
(602) 674-5216
Admin Verna Tsosie.
Licensure Skilled care. *Beds* 79. *Certified* Medicare.
Owner Nonprofit Corp.

COTTONWOOD

Rio Verde Health Care Center
197 S Williard, Cottonwood, AZ, 86326
(602) 634-5548
Admin Wilton H Syckes Jr. *Medical Dir/Dir of Nursing* Dr Welley; Winnie Bartling RN DON.
Licensure Skilled care; Intermediate care. *Beds* SNF; ICF 80. *Certified* Medicare.
Owner Proprietary Corp.
Admissions Requirements Minimum age 18; Medical examination.
Staff RNs; LPNs; Orderlies; Nurses aides; Physical therapists 1 (pt); Recreational therapists 1 (ft), 1 (pt); Occupational therapists 1 (pt); Speech therapists 1 (pt); Activities coordinators 1 (ft), 1 (pt); Dietitians 1 (pt).
Facilities Dining room; Physical therapy room; Activities room; Crafts room; Laundry room; Barber/Beauty shop.
Activities Arts & crafts; Cards; Games; Reading groups; Prayer groups; Movies; Shopping trips; Social/Cultural gatherings.

DOUGLAS

Southeast Arizona Medical Center
RR1, Box 30F, Douglas, AZ, 85607
(602) 364-7931
Admin Ray McJunkins, Acting Admin. *Medical Dir/Dir of Nursing* Ruth Kish RN.
Licensure Skilled care; Intermediate care. *Beds* SNF 43; ICF. *Certified* Medicare.
Owner Nonprofit Corp.
Admissions Requirements Physician's request.

Staff Physicians 7 (pt); RNs 2 (ft), 2 (pt); LPNs 3 (ft), 2 (pt); Orderlies 1 (ft), 1 (pt); Nurses aides 9 (ft), 5 (pt); Physical therapists 2 (ft); Activities coordinators 1 (ft), 1 (pt); Dietitians 1 (pt);; Social worker 1 (ft), 1 (pt); Physician asst 1 (pt).
Languages Spanish
Facilities Dining room; Physical therapy room; Activities room; Chapel; Crafts room; Barber/Beauty shop; Enclosed patio.
Activities Arts & crafts; Cards; Games; Reading groups; Prayer groups; Movies.

FLAGSTAFF

Los Arcos Health Care Center
800 W University Ave, Flagstaff, AZ, 86001
(602) 779-6931
Admin Mrs Johnie Bradshaw. *Medical Dir/Dir of Nursing* Dr Seeby; Mrs L Martin RN.
Licensure Skilled care; Intermediate care. *Beds* SNF 60; ICF 20. *Certified* Medicare.
Owner Proprietary Corp.
Admissions Requirements Minimum age 18; Medical examination; Physician's request.
Staff Physicians 1 (pt); RNs 8 (ft), 2 (pt); LPNs 3 (ft), 1 (pt); Orderlies 1 (ft), 1 (pt); Nurses aides 12 (ft), 4 (pt); Physical therapists 1 (pt); Recreational therapists 1 (ft); Occupational therapists 1 (pt); Speech therapists 1 (pt); Activities coordinators 1 (ft); Dietitians 1 (pt); Ophthalmologists 1 (pt).
Languages Spanish, Navajo
Facilities Dining room; Physical therapy room; Activities room; Chapel; Laundry room; Barber/Beauty shop.
Activities Arts & crafts; Cards; Games; Reading groups; Prayer groups; Movies; Shopping trips; Social/Cultural gatherings.

FLORENCE

Pinal County Nursing Center
PO Box 648, 1900 Central Ave, Florence, AZ, 85232
(602) 868-5854
Admin Charles R Stevens P D FACHCA. *Medical Dir/Dir of Nursing* O V Moreno MD; Pamela S Marquez RN DON.
Licensure Skilled care; Intermediate care; Supervisory. *Beds* SNF 52; Supervisory 55.
Owner Nonprofit organization/foundation.
Admissions Requirements Medical examination; Physician's request.
Staff RNs 4 (ft), 1 (pt); LPNs; Orderlies; Nurses aides; Physical therapists; Reality therapists; Recreational therapists 4 (ft), 1 (pt); Speech therapists; Activities coordinators 1 (ft); Dietitians 1 (ft); Dentists 1 (ft); Ophthalmologists 1 (pt); Podiatrists 1 (pt).
Languages Spanish
Facilities Dining room; Activities room; Crafts room; Laundry room; Barber/Beauty shop; Library.

Activities Arts & crafts; Cards; Games;
Reading groups; Prayer groups; Movies;
Shopping trips; Social/Cultural gatherings;
College courses.

Pinal General Hospital*
Adamsville Rd, Florence, AZ, 85232
(602) 868-5841
Admin Allan J Orler.
Licensure Intermediate care. *Beds* 21.
Certified Medicare.
Owner Publicly owned.

GLENDALE

Colter Village
5125 N 58th Ave, Glendale, AZ, 85301
(602) 931-5800
Admin Carolyn Kindler. *Medical Dir/Dir of
Nursing* Kay Hardin RN.
Licensure Skilled care; Intermediate care;
Independent Retirement; Assisted
Retirement; Personal care. *Beds* SNF 186;
ICF; Apts for retirees 105.
Owner Proprietary Corp.
Staff Physicians.

Glen Ridge Manor
5910 W Northern Ave, Glendale, AZ, 85302
(602) 937-2779
Admin Maureen R Groves. *Medical Dir/Dir of
Nursing* Jame Beech MD; Charlene Wagner
DON.
Licensure Skilled care. *Beds* SNF 135.
Owner Proprietary Corp.
Admissions Requirements Medical
examination; Physician's request.
Staff Physicians 1 (pt); RNs 9 (ft); LPNs 14
(ft), 2 (pt); Orderlies 56 (ft), 20 (pt); Nurses
aides 1 (ft), 1 (pt); Physical therapists 1 (pt);
Occupational therapists 1 (pt); Speech
therapists 1 (pt); Activities coordinators 1
(ft); Dietitians 1 (ft); Dentists 1 (pt);
Ophthalmologists 1 (pt).
Languages Spanish
Facilities Dining room; Physical therapy
room; Laundry room; Barber/Beauty shop.
Activities Arts & crafts; Cards; Games;
Reading groups; Prayer groups; Movies;
Shopping trips; Social/Cultural gatherings.

GlenCroft Care Center
8641 N 67th Ave, Glendale, AZ, 85302
(602) 939-9475
Admin Norm Klassen. *Medical Dir/Dir of
Nursing* Dr R Vito; Linda Byler RN.
Licensure Skilled care; Intermediate care;
Personal care. *Beds* SNF 161; ICF 40;
Personal 24.
Owner Nonprofit Corp.
Staff Physicians; RNs; LPNs; Orderlies;
Nurses aides; Physical therapists;
Recreational therapists; Occupational
therapists; Speech therapists; Activities
coordinators; Dietitians; Dentists;
Ophthalmologists; Podiatrists.

Glendale Care Center
4704 W Diana, Glendale, AZ, 85302
(602) 247-3949
Admin Elizabeth Holden.
Licensure Skilled care; Intermediate care;
Personal care. *Beds* SNF 98; ICF 63;
Personal 31.
Owner Nonprofit Corp (Volunteers of
America Care).

Glendale Nursing Home
7022 N 48th Ave, Glendale, AZ, 85301
(602) 934-7265
Admin Melanie S Seamans. *Medical Dir/Dir of
Nursing* Honor L Jereb.
Licensure Skilled care. *Beds* SNF 61.
Owner Proprietary Corp.
Admissions Requirements Medical
examination; Physician's request.

Staff RNs 3 (ft), 1 (pt); LPNs 8 (ft); Orderlies
2 (ft); Nurses aides 27 (ft); Activities
coordinators 1 (ft).
Languages Spanish, Hindi, German
Facilities Dining room; Activities room;
Crafts room; Laundry room.
Activities Arts & crafts; Cards; Games;
Reading groups; Prayer groups; Movies;
Shopping trips; Social/Cultural gatherings;
Parties.

GLOBE

Gila County General Hospital
1100 Monroe St, Globe, AZ, 85501
(602) 425-5721
Admin Elton J Somers. *Medical Dir/Dir of
Nursing* Efrain Pineres MD; Larry McGee
DON.
Licensure Skilled care. *Beds* SNF 69.
Owner Nonprofit organization/foundation.
Admissions Requirements Physician's request.
Staff Physicians 1 (ft); RNs 4 (ft), 1 (pt);
LPNs 4 (ft); Nurses aides 20 (ft), 3 (pt);
Physical therapists 1 (ft); Activities
coordinators 1 (ft); Dietitians 1 (ft).
Languages Spanish, Italian
Facilities Dining room; Physical therapy
room; Activities room; Chapel; Crafts room;
Barber/Beauty shop.
Activities Arts & crafts; Games; Reading
groups; Prayer groups; Movies; Social/
Cultural gatherings.

GREEN VALLEY

Santa Rita Health Care Center
150 N La Canada Dr, Green Valley, AZ,
85614
(602) 625-2500
Admin Margaret Y Mitchell. *Medical Dir/Dir
of Nursing* Dr Alex McGlamery; Audrey
Perry.
Licensure Skilled care; Personal care. *Beds*
SNF 98; Personal 19. *Certified* Medicare.
Owner Proprietary Corp.
Admissions Requirements Minimum age 16;
Medical examination; Physician's request.
Staff Physicians 7 (pt); RNs 6 (ft), 6 (pt);
LPNs 3 (ft), 3 (pt); Nurses aides 31 (ft), 17
(pt); Recreational therapists 1 (ft);
Occupational therapists 1 (pt); Speech
therapists 1 (pt); Activities coordinators 1
(ft); Dietitians 1 (pt); Dentists 1 (pt);
Ophthalmologists 1 (pt); Dentist 1 (pt).
Languages Spanish
Facilities Dining room; Activities room;
Chapel; Barber/Beauty shop; Library.
Activities Arts & crafts; Cards; Games;
Reading groups; Prayer groups; Movies;
Shopping trips.

KINGMAN

Kingman Health Care Center*
1081 Kathleen Ave, Kingman, AZ, 86401
(602) 793-2779
Admin Patsy A Hawtin.
Licensure Skilled care; Personal care. *Beds*
SNF 80; Personal 40.
Owner Proprietary Corp.

LAKE HAVASU CITY

Lake Havasu Nursing Center
3576 Kearsage, Lake Havasu City, AZ, 86403
(602) 453-1500
Admin J D Stahl. *Medical Dir/Dir of Nursing*
Margaret Lo Iacono RN DON.
Licensure Skilled care; Intermediate care;
Personal care. *Beds* SNF 60; ICF 40;
Personal 20. *Certified* Medicare.
Owner Proprietary Corp (US Care Corp).
Staff RNs 5 (ft), 5 (pt); LPNs 8 (ft), 6 (pt);
Nurses aides 40 (ft), 10 (pt); Activities
coordinators 1 (ft).

Languages Spanish, German, Navajo
Facilities Dining room; Physical therapy
room; Activities room; Chapel; Laundry
room; Barber/Beauty shop; Intermediate
dining room.
Activities Arts & crafts; Cards; Games;
Reading groups; Prayer groups; Movies;
Shopping trips; Social/Cultural gatherings;
Mohave County fine arts program.

LAVEEN

American Indian Nursing Home*
8201 W Baseline, PO Box 9, Laveen, AZ,
85339
(602) 237-3813
Admin Victor E Vallet.
Licensure Skilled care; Personal care. *Beds* 76.
Owner Nonprofit Corp.
Admissions Requirements Physician's request.
Staff RNs 5 (ft); LPNs 7 (ft); Orderlies 32 (ft);
Physical therapists 2 (ft); Reality therapists 2
(ft); Recreational therapists 2 (ft); Activities
coordinators 1 (ft); Dietitians 1 (ft).
Facilities Dining room; Physical therapy
room; Activities room; Laundry room.
Activities Arts & crafts; Cards; Games;
Reading groups; Prayer groups; Movies;
Shopping trips; Social/Cultural gatherings.

MESA

Chula Vista Nursing Home
60 S 58th St, Mesa, AZ, 85206
(602) 832-3903
Admin Jane Wagner.
Licensure Skilled care; Intermediate care. *Beds*
SNF 55; ICF 45.
Owner Proprietary Corp.

Cosada Villa Nursing Center
420 W 10th Pl, Mesa, AZ, 85201
(602) 833-4226
Admin Karen L Cooper. *Medical Dir/Dir of
Nursing* Dr R L Smith; Estelita Foley RN
DON.
Licensure Skilled care; Intermediate care. *Beds*
174. *Certified* Medicare & county.
Owner Proprietary Corp.
Admissions Requirements Minimum age 18.
Staff Physicians; RNs; LPNs; Orderlies;
Nurses aides; Physical therapists;
Recreational therapists; Occupational
therapists; Speech therapists; Activities
coordinators; Dietitians; Ophthalmologists.
Facilities Dining room; Physical therapy
room; Activities room; Crafts room; Barber/
Beauty shop.
Activities Arts & crafts; Cards; Games;
Reading groups; Prayer groups; Movies;
Shopping trips; Social/Cultural gatherings.

East Mesa Care Center
51 S 48th St, Mesa, AZ, 85206
(602) 832-8333
Admin Emmie Lester. *Medical Dir/Dir of
Nursing* Dr Richard Adamson; Lois Charette
DON.
Licensure Skilled care; Intermediate care;
Personal care. *Beds* SNF 50; ICF 49;
Personal 48. *Certified* Medicare.
Owner Proprietary Corp (American Health
Centers Inc).
Admissions Requirements Medical
examination; Physician's request.
Staff Physicians; RNs; LPNs; Orderlies;
Nurses aides; Physical therapists;
Recreational therapists; Occupational
therapists; Speech therapists; Activities
coordinators; Dietitians; Dentists;
Ophthalmologists; Podiatrists.
Languages Spanish
Facilities Dining room; Physical therapy
room; Activities room; Chapel; Crafts room;
Laundry room; Barber/Beauty shop.

Activities Arts & crafts; Games; Reading groups; Prayer groups; Movies; Social/Cultural gatherings.

Golden Mesa Nursing Home*
715 N Country Club, Mesa, AZ, 85201
(602) 969-1305
Admin William Constable.
Licensure Skilled care. *Beds* 109.
Owner Proprietary Corp.
Admissions Requirements Minimum age 21; Medical examination; Physician's request.
Staff RNs 4 (ft); LPNs 4 (ft), 2 (pt); Nurses aides 29 (ft); Activities coordinators 2 (ft).
Facilities Dining room; Physical therapy room; Activities room; Laundry room; Barber/Beauty shop; Library.
Activities Arts & crafts; Cards; Games; Reading groups; Prayer groups; Movies; Shopping trips; Social/Cultural gatherings.

Good Shephard Villa*
5848 E University Dr, Mesa, AZ, 85205
(602) 981-0098
Admin Knut H Mehl.
Licensure Skilled care; Intermediate care. *Beds* SNF 50; ICF 30.
Owner Nonprofit Corp.

Las Flores Nursing Center
6458 E Broadway, Mesa, AZ, 85206
(602) 832-5160
Admin Robin Skelton. *Medical Dir/Dir of Nursing* Joseph Chatham MD; Darlene Raszler.
Licensure Skilled care. *Beds* SNF 100. *Certified* Medicare.
Owner Proprietary Corp (Vari-Care Inc).
Admissions Requirements Minimum age 16; Medical examination; Physician's request.
Staff Physicians 3 (pt); RNs 7 (ft), 6 (pt); LPNs 7 (ft), 1 (pt); Orderlies 1 (ft); Nurses aides 41 (ft), 3 (pt); Physical therapists 1 (ft); Occupational therapists 1 (pt); Speech therapists 1 (pt); Activities coordinators 1 (ft), 1 (pt); Dietitians 1 (ft); Podiatrists 1 (pt); Social workers 1 (ft), 1 (pt); Dentist 1 (pt).
Facilities Dining room; Physical therapy room; Activities room; Crafts room; Laundry room; Barber/Beauty shop; Library.
Activities Arts & crafts; Cards; Games; Reading groups; Prayer groups; Movies; Social/Cultural gatherings.

Mesa Christian Home
255 W Brown Rd, Mesa, AZ, 85201
(602) 833-3988
Admin Sally W Worthington.
Licensure Skilled care; Intermediate care; Personal care. *Beds* SNF 112; Personal 45.
Owner Nonprofit Corp (Luth Hosp & Homes Socty).
Staff RNs 14 (ft), 5 (pt); LPNs 10 (ft), 5 (pt); Orderlies 2 (ft), 2 (pt); Nurses aides 61 (ft), 20 (pt); Recreational therapists 1 (ft); Activities coordinators 3 (ft), 1 (pt).
Facilities Dining room; Physical therapy room; Activities room; Crafts room; Laundry room; Barber/Beauty shop; Library; Resident's kitchen.
Activities Arts & crafts; Games; Reading groups; Movies; Shopping trips; Social/Cultural gatherings; Swimming.

Patterson Terrace Care Center*
1825 W Emelita Ave, Mesa, AZ, 85202
(602) 964-0562
Admin Genevieve Stratton. *Medical Dir/Dir of Nursing* Dr Benton.
Licensure Skilled care. *Beds* 64.
Owner Nonprofit Corp (Bethesda Care Centers).
Admissions Requirements Minimum age 16; Medical examination; Physician's request.

Staff RNs 1 (ft), 7 (pt); LPNs 1 (ft), 3 (pt); Nurses aides 17 (ft), 3 (pt); Activities coordinators 1 (ft); Rehabilitation Aides 1 (ft).
Facilities Dining room; Activities room; Chapel; Crafts room; Barber/Beauty shop; Library; Outdoor pool.
Activities Arts & crafts; Cards; Games; Reading groups; Prayer groups; Movies; Shopping trips; Social/Cultural gatherings; Exercise; Swimming; Resident council.

Royal Nursing Home*
108 E 2nd Ave, Mesa, AZ, 85202
(602) 834-1490
Admin Bruce Grambley.
Licensure Skilled care. *Beds* 46.
Owner Proprietary Corp.

NOGALES

Holy Cross Hospital & Health Center—Geriatric Center*
1230 Target Range Rd, Nogales, AZ, 85621
(602) 287-2771
Admin Walt Connolly.
Licensure Skilled care. *Beds* 30.
Owner Nonprofit Corp.

PAYSON

Payson Care Center
107 E Lone Pine Dr, Payson, AZ, 85541
(602) 474-6896
Admin Reid E Halpern. *Medical Dir/Dir of Nursing* Dr W Romberger MD; JoAnne Dudley RN DON.
Licensure Skilled care; Intermediate care; Personal care. *Beds* SNF 41; ICF 19; Personal 33. *Certified* Medicare.
Owner Proprietary Corp (Life Care Centers of America).
Facilities Dining room; Physical therapy room; Activities room; Chapel; Crafts room; Barber/Beauty shop.
Activities Arts & crafts; Cards; Games; Reading groups; Prayer groups; Movies; Social/Cultural gatherings.

PEORIA

Camelot Manor*
11311 N 99th Ave, Peoria, AZ, 85345
(602) 977-8373
Admin Sharon Kempton.
Licensure Personal care. *Beds* 48.
Owner Proprietary Corp.

Good Shepherd Retirement Center
10323 W Olive Ave, Peoria, AZ, 85345
(602) 974-2555
Admin Katheryn Pipho. *Medical Dir/Dir of Nursing* Peter Chan MD; Loretta Reardanz RN DON.
Licensure Skilled care; Intermediate care; Personal care. *Beds* SNF 116; ICF 77; Personal 20. *Certified* Medicaid.
Owner Nonprofit Corp (Evangelical Lutheran/Good Samaritan).
Admissions Requirements Minimum age 18; Medical examination; Physician's request.
Staff RNs 5 (ft), 6 (pt); LPNs 10 (ft), 8 (pt); Orderlies 3 (ft); Nurses aides 48 (ft), 11 (pt); Activities coordinators 3 (ft); Dietitians 1 (ft).
Languages Spanish
Affiliation Lutheran
Facilities Dining room; Physical therapy room; Activities room; Chapel; Crafts room; Barber/Beauty shop; Library.
Activities Arts & crafts; Cards; Games; Reading groups; Prayer groups; Movies; Shopping trips; Social/Cultural gatherings.

Pueblo Norte-West Nursing Center
13215 N 94th Dr, Peoria, AZ, 85345
(602) 933-7722

Admin Corinne D King MPH. *Medical Dir/Dir of Nursing* Harold Griess MD; Bee Ann Olson RN.
Licensure Skilled care; Intermediate care; Personal care. *Beds* SNF 60; ICF 60; Personal 8. *Certified* Medicare.
Owner Nonprofit Corp (Adventist Health Sys-USA).
Admissions Requirements Medical examination; Physician's request.
Staff RNs 5 (ft), 5 (pt); LPNs 6 (ft), 3 (pt); Orderlies 1 (ft), 2 (pt); Nurses aides 39 (ft), 1 (pt); Activities coordinators 1 (ft).
Affiliation Seventh-Day Adventist
Facilities Dining room; Physical therapy room; Activities room; Chapel; Laundry room; Barber/Beauty shop; Library.
Activities Arts & crafts; Cards; Games; Reading groups; Movies; Shopping trips; Social/Cultural gatherings; Music.

PHOENIX

Arizona Eastern Star Home*
4602 N 24th St, Phoenix, AZ, 85016
(602) 954-9178
Admin Hilda B Rubel.
Licensure Skilled care. *Beds* 36.
Owner Nonprofit Corp.
Admissions Requirements Minimum age 18; Medical examination.
Staff RNs 4 (ft), 4 (pt); LPNs 1 (ft), 1 (pt); Nurses aides 18 (ft), 4 (pt); Activities coordinators; Dietitians.
Affiliation Order of Eastern Star
Facilities Dining room; Activities room; Chapel; Crafts room; Laundry room; Barber/Beauty shop; Library.
Activities Arts & crafts; Cards; Games; Reading groups; Prayer groups; Movies; Shopping trips; Social/Cultural gatherings.

Beatitudes Care Center*
1712 W Glendale Ave, Phoenix, AZ, 85021
(602) 995-2611
Admin Ken H Buckwald.
Licensure Skilled care; Personal care. *Beds* SNF 156; Personal 120.
Owner Nonprofit Corp.

Bel Isle Nursing Home*
720 E Montebello, Phoenix, AZ, 85014
(602) 266-4122
Admin Daniel J Belisle.
Licensure Skilled care. *Beds* 61.
Owner Proprietary Corp.

Bells Lodge
4202 N 20th Ave, Phoenix, AZ, 85015
(602) 264-3824
Admin Kathryn G Coheen. *Medical Dir/Dir of Nursing* Dr William Morrissey; Patricia Phillips.
Licensure Skilled care. *Beds* SNF 100. *Certified* Medicaid; Medicare.
Owner Proprietary Corp (Hillhaven Corp).
Admissions Requirements Minimum age 18; Medical examination; Physician's request.
Staff RNs 8 (ft), 2 (pt); LPNs 12 (ft), 3 (pt); Nurses aides 35 (ft), 8 (pt); Activities coordinators 1 (ft), 1 (pt).
Languages Spanish
Facilities Dining room; Physical therapy room; Activities room; Laundry room; Barber/Beauty shop; Library; Lobby; Lounges; Enclosed patio.
Activities Arts & crafts; Cards; Games; Reading groups; Prayer groups; Shopping trips; Movies; Social/Cultural gatherings.

Capri Nursing Home*
1501 E Orangewood, Phoenix, AZ, 85020
(602) 944-1574
Admin William E Fay.
Licensure Skilled care. *Beds* 59.
Owner Proprietary Corp.

Christian Care Nursing Center
11812 N 19th Ave, Phoenix, AZ, 85029
(602) 861-3241
Admin Naomi Markle. *Medical Dir/Dir of
Nursing* Linda L Nelson.
Licensure Skilled care; Intermediate care. *Beds*
60.
Owner Nonprofit Corp.
Admissions Requirements Medical
examination; Physician's request.
Staff RNs 4 (ft), 1 (pt); LPNs 3 (ft), 2 (pt);
Orderlies 3 (ft); Nurses aides 26 (ft);
Activities coordinators 1 (ft);; Physical
therapy aide 1 (ft).
Facilities Dining room; Physical therapy
room; Activities room; Barber/Beauty shop.
Activities Arts & crafts; Games; Prayer groups;
Singing; Exercises.

Crestview Convalescent Lodge
2151 E Maryland, Phoenix, AZ, 85016
(602) 264-6427
Admin Michael L Fahey. *Medical Dir/Dir of
Nursing* William Dunn MD; Carol Krause
RN DON.
Licensure Skilled care. *Beds* 66.
Owner Nonprofit Corp.
Admissions Requirements Minimum age 62;
Medical examination; Physician's request.
Staff RNs 8 (ft); LPNs 4 (ft), 2 (pt); Nurses
aides 25 (ft); Activities coordinators 1 (ft).
Affiliation Roman Catholic
Facilities Dining room; Activities room;
Crafts room; Barber/Beauty shop; Library;
Social services.
Activities Arts & crafts; Cards; Games;
Reading groups; Prayer groups; Movies.

Desert Haven Nursing Center*
2645 E Thomas Rd, Phoenix, AZ, 85016
(602) 956-8000
Admin Carolyn DeBiasi. *Medical Dir/Dir of
Nursing* Dr Kienzle.
Licensure Skilled care. *Beds* 115. *Certified*
Medicare.
Owner Proprietary Corp (Vari-Care Inc).
Admissions Requirements Medical
examination; Physician's request.
Facilities Dining room; Physical therapy
room; Activities room; Laundry room;
Barber/Beauty shop.
Activities Arts & crafts; Cards; Games; Prayer
groups; Movies; Shopping trips; Social/
Cultural gatherings.

Desert Terrace Nursing Facility
2509 N 24th St, Phoenix, AZ, 85008
(602) 273-1347
Admin Ray McKisson. *Medical Dir/Dir of
Nursing* Joseph Freund MD; Sarah Brooks
RN.
Licensure Skilled care. *Beds* SNF 108.
Certified Medicare.
Owner Proprietary Corp (Vari-Care Inc).
Admissions Requirements Medical
examination; Physician's request.
Staff Physicians 10 (pt); RNs 8 (ft), 3 (pt);
LPNs 7 (ft), 3 (pt); Orderlies 40 (ft), 6 (pt);
Nurses aides 40 (ft), 6 (pt); Physical
therapists 2 (ft); Occupational therapists 1
(pt); Speech therapists 1 (pt); Activities
coordinators 2 (ft); Dietitians 1 (pt); Dentists
1 (pt); Ophthalmologists 1 (pt); Podiatrists 1
(pt).
Languages Spanish
Facilities Dining room; Physical therapy
room; Activities room; Crafts room; Laundry
room; Barber/Beauty shop; Library.
Activities Arts & crafts; Cards; Games;
Reading groups; Prayer groups; Movies;
Shopping trips; Social/Cultural gatherings.

Highland Manor Nursing Home
4635 N 14th St, Phoenix, AZ, 85014
(602) 264-9039
Admin Dee Konecki. *Medical Dir/Dir of
Nursing* Walter Neiri MD.

Licensure Skilled care. *Beds* 107. *Certified*
Medicare.
Owner Proprietary Corp (Vari-Care Inc).
Admissions Requirements Medical
examination; Physician's request.
Staff Physicians 1 (pt); RNs 10 (ft), 1 (pt);
LPNs 4 (ft), 1 (pt); Orderlies 1 (ft); Nurses
aides 42 (ft), 1 (pt); Physical therapists 3
(pt); Occupational therapists 1 (pt); Speech
therapists 1 (pt); Activities coordinators 2
(ft); Dietitians 1 (ft), 1 (pt); Dentists 1 (pt);
Ophthalmologists 1 (pt); Podiatrists 1 (pt).
Languages Sign
Facilities Dining room; Physical therapy
room; Laundry room; Barber/Beauty shop;
Library.
Activities Arts & crafts; Cards; Games;
Reading groups; Prayer groups; Movies;
Shopping trips; Social/Cultural gatherings;
Swimming.

Hillhaven Health Care Center*
531 W Thomas Rd, Phoenix, AZ, 85013
(602) 264-9651
Admin David K Niess. *Medical Dir/Dir of
Nursing* William Semmens MD.
Licensure Skilled care. *Beds* SNF 120; ICF
60; Medicare Certified 60. *Certified*
Medicare.
Owner Proprietary Corp (Hillhaven Corp).
Admissions Requirements Minimum age 16;
Physician's request.
Staff Physicians 1 (pt); RNs 15 (ft), 5 (pt);
LPNs 35 (ft), 5 (pt); Nurses aides 60 (ft), 10
(pt); Physical therapists 2 (ft), 1 (pt);
Recreational therapists 4 (ft); Occupational
therapists 1 (ft); Speech therapists 1 (pt);
Activities coordinators 1 (ft); Dietitians 1
(pt); Dentists 1 (pt); Podiatrists 1 (pt).
Facilities Dining room; Physical therapy
room; Activities room; Crafts room; Laundry
room; Barber/Beauty shop.
Activities Arts & crafts; Cards; Games; Prayer
groups; Movies; Shopping trips.

Homestead Rest Home*
343 W Lynwood Ave, Phoenix, AZ, 85003
(602) 256-6772
Admin Lena Inman.
Licensure Personal care. *Beds* 13.
Owner Proprietary Corp.

**Kivel Geriatric Center-Nursing Home-Kivel
Care Center**
3020 N 36th St, Phoenix, AZ, 85018
(602) 956-3110
Admin Meyer W Cohen. *Medical Dir/Dir of
Nursing* Jerome J Kastrul MD; Peg Bratton
RN DON.
Licensure Skilled care; Intermediate care; Sub-
Acute personal special care unit for
Alzheimer's disease & related disorders. *Beds*
152.
Owner Nonprofit Corp.
Admissions Requirements Minimum age 18;
Medical examination; Physician's request.
Staff RNs 10 (ft), 6 (pt); LPNs 15 (ft), 7 (pt);
Nurses aides 64 (ft), 4 (pt); Recreational
therapists 1 (ft); Activities coordinators 4
(ft), 1 (pt);; Occupational therapists Chaplain
1 (pt).
Affiliation Jewish
Facilities Dining room; Physical therapy
room; Activities room; Chapel; Crafts room;
Barber/Beauty shop; Library; Kiln for
ceramics.
Activities Arts & crafts; Cards; Games;
Reading groups; Prayer groups; Movies;
Shopping trips; Social/Cultural gatherings;
Cooking classes; Ceramics.

Maryland Gardens*
31 W Maryland, Phoenix, AZ, 85018
(602) 265-6834
Admin Cathy Williams. *Medical Dir/Dir of
Nursing* Noreen Readel.
Beds 39.
Owner Proprietary Corp.

Admissions Requirements Medical
examination.
Staff RNs 2 (ft); LPNs 4 (ft); Nurses aides 13
(ft), 6 (pt); Reality therapists 1 (ft);
Recreational therapists 2 (ft); Activities
coordinators 1 (ft); Dietitians 1 (ft).
Facilities Dining room; Activities room;
Crafts room; Laundry room; Library.
Activities Arts & crafts; Cards; Games;
Reading groups; Prayer groups; Movies;
Shopping trips; Social/Cultural gatherings.

Orangewood Health Center
7550 N 16th St, Phoenix, AZ, 85020
(602) 944-4455
Admin Robert O Stuewig. *Medical Dir/Dir of
Nursing* Fernando Compos MD.
Licensure Skilled care; Intermediate care. *Beds*
SNF 40; ICF 24. *Certified* Medicare.
Owner Nonprofit Corp.
Admissions Requirements Minimum age 65.
Staff Physicians; RNs 6 (ft), 2 (pt); LPNs 2
(ft), 1 (pt); Orderlies; Nurses aides 23 (ft), 1
(pt); Activities coordinators 1 (ft), 1 (pt).
Affiliation Baptist
Facilities Dining room; Physical therapy
room; Activities room; Chapel; Crafts room;
Laundry room; Barber/Beauty shop; Library;
Shop.
Activities Arts & crafts; Cards; Games;
Reading groups; Prayer groups; Movies;
Shopping trips.

Phoenix Jewish Care Center
11411 N 19th Ave, Phoenix, AZ, 85029
(602) 256-7500
Admin Dana L Brown. *Medical Dir/Dir of
Nursing* Nancy Simms DON.
Licensure Skilled care. *Beds* SNF 127.
Certified Medicare.
Owner Privately owned.
Staff RNs 10 (ft); LPNs 9 (ft); Orderlies 2 (ft);
Nurses aides 52 (ft); Physical therapists 3
(ft); Activities coordinators 2 (ft); Dietitians
1 (ft).
Languages Yiddish, Hebrew, Italian
Activities Arts & crafts; Cards; Games;
Reading groups; Prayer groups; Movies;
Shopping trips; Social/Cultural gatherings.

Phoenix Mountain Nursing Center
13232 N Tatum Blvd, Phoenix, AZ, 85032
(602) 996-5200
Admin Susan K White. *Medical Dir/Dir of
Nursing* Elizabeth Griffin RN DON.
Licensure Skilled care. *Beds* SNF 127.
Certified Medicare.
Owner Proprietary Corp.
Admissions Requirements Minimum age 16.
Staff RNs 8 (ft), 9 (pt); LPNs 6 (ft), 5 (pt);
Orderlies 4 (ft); Nurses aides 44 (ft), 8 (pt);
Physical therapists 1 (ft); Recreational
therapists 1 (pt); Occupational therapists 1
(pt); Speech therapists 1 (pt); Activities
coordinators 1 (ft); Dietitians 1 (pt);
Ophthalmologists 1 (pt).
Facilities Dining room; Physical therapy
room; Activities room; Crafts room; Laundry
room; Barber/Beauty shop; Library.
Activities Arts & crafts; Cards; Games;
Reading groups; Prayer groups; Movies;
Social/Cultural gatherings.

**Phoenix Nursing & Convalescent
Center—East***
1342 E McDowell, Phoenix, AZ, 85006
(602) 254-6568
Admin Frances Neriz. *Medical Dir/Dir of
Nursing* Sidney Axelrod MD.
Licensure Skilled care. *Beds* 136.
Owner Proprietary Corp.
Admissions Requirements Minimum age Birth;
Medical examination; Physician's request.
Staff RNs 3 (ft); LPNs 12 (ft); Orderlies 8 (ft);
Nurses aides 32 (ft); Physical therapists 1
(ft); Recreational therapists 1 (ft);
Respiratory therapists 8 (ft).

Facilities Dining room; Physical therapy room; Activities room; Crafts room; Laundry room.
Activities Arts & crafts; Cards; Games; Reading groups; Prayer groups; Movies; Shopping trips; Social/Cultural gatherings; Resident council.

Phoenix Nursing & Convalescent Center—West*
1314 E McDowell, Phoenix, AZ, 85006
(602) 254-6568
Admin Robert Gundling.
Licensure Skilled care. *Beds* 140. *Certified* Medicare.
Owner Proprietary Corp.

San Juan Gardens*
5602 N 7th St, Phoenix, AZ, 85014
(602) 248-9310
Admin Yolanda Burkholder. *Medical Dir/Dir of Nursing* Dr Robert Briggs.
Licensure Personal care. *Beds* 16.
Owner Proprietary Corp.
Staff Physicians; RNs; LPNs; Orderlies; Nurses aides; Physical therapists; Reality therapists; Recreational therapists; Occupational therapists; Speech therapists; Activities coordinators; Dietitians; Dentists; Ophthalmologists; Podiatrists; Audiologists.
Facilities Dining room; Activities room; Crafts room; Laundry room; Barber/Beauty shop; Library.
Activities Arts & crafts; Cards; Games; Reading groups; Prayer groups; Movies; Shopping trips; Social/Cultural gatherings.

South Mountain Manor*
2211 E Southern Ave, Phoenix, AZ, 85040
(602) 276-7358
Admin Peggy Ann Constable.
Licensure Intermediate care. *Beds* 115.
Owner Proprietary Corp.

Tanner Chapel Manor Nursing Home
2150 E Broadway, Phoenix, AZ, 85040
(602) 243-1735
Admin Grace Evans. *Medical Dir/Dir of Nursing* Geraldine Griffin RN.
Licensure Skilled care. *Beds* SNF 50.
Owner Nonprofit Corp.
Admissions Requirements Minimum age 18; Medical examination; Physician's request.
Staff RNs 3 (ft), 1 (pt); LPNs 2 (ft), 3 (pt); Orderlies 2 (ft); Nurses aides 18 (ft), 3 (pt); Activities coordinators 1 (ft), 1 (pt); Dietitians 1 (pt).
Languages Spanish
Facilities Dining room; Physical therapy room; Activities room; Chapel; Laundry room; Barber/Beauty shop.
Activities Arts & crafts; Cards; Games; Reading groups; Prayer groups; Movies; Shopping trips; Social/Cultural gatherings.

Vantage Convalescent Center
1856 E Thomas Rd, Phoenix, AZ, 85016
(602) 274-3508
Admin Virginia McLaren RN. *Medical Dir/Dir of Nursing* Frances Sierakowski MD; Clara Naylor RN DON.
Licensure Skilled care. *Beds* SNF 84.
Owner Proprietary Corp (Vantage Healthcare).
Admissions Requirements Minimum age 18; Medical examination; Physician's request.
Staff RNs 5 (ft), 2 (pt); LPNs 9 (ft); Orderlies; Nurses aides 30 (ft); Activities coordinators 1 (ft);; Social worker 1 (ft).
Languages Spanish
Facilities Dining room; Physical therapy room; Activities room; Crafts room; Laundry room; Barber/Beauty shop; Library.
Activities Arts & crafts; Cards; Games; Reading groups; Prayer groups; Movies; Shopping trips; Social/Cultural gatherings; Cooking classes.

Village Green*
2932 N 14th St, Phoenix, AZ, 85014
(602) 264-5274
Admin Jeanne Y Caron. *Medical Dir/Dir of Nursing* Dr Noel Smith.
Beds 80.
Owner Proprietary Corp.
Admissions Requirements Medical examination.
Facilities Dining room; Activities room; Crafts room; Laundry room; Barber/Beauty shop; Library.
Activities Arts & crafts; Cards; Games; Reading groups; Prayer groups; Movies; Shopping trips; Social/Cultural gatherings.

PRESCOTT

Prescott Samaritan Village*
1030 Scott Dr, Prescott, AZ, 86301
(602) 778-2450
Admin Dean Mertz.
Licensure Skilled care; Personal care. *Beds* SNF 60; Personal 20.
Owner Nonprofit Corp (Evangelical Lutheran/ Good Samaritan).
Admissions Requirements Medical examination; Physician's request.
Staff Physicians 1 (pt); RNs 3 (ft), 4 (pt); LPNs 5 (ft), 3 (pt); Orderlies 2 (ft), 1 (pt); Nurses aides 18 (ft), 10 (pt); Physical therapists 1 (pt); Activities coordinators 1 (ft).
Affiliation Lutheran
Facilities Dining room; Physical therapy room; Activities room; Chapel; Crafts room; Laundry room; Barber/Beauty shop; Library; Solarium.
Activities Arts & crafts; Cards; Games; Reading groups; Prayer groups; Movies; Shopping trips; Social/Cultural gatherings; Foster grandparent program.

SAFFORD

Evergreen Care Center
1706 20th Ave, Safford, AZ, 85546
(602) 428-0630
Admin Jacqueline Anderson. *Medical Dir/Dir of Nursing* Edward R Curtis MD; Dytha Doelle RN DON.
Licensure Skilled care. *Beds* 120.
Owner Proprietary Corp.
Admissions Requirements Minimum age 16; Medical examination; Physician's request.
Staff RNs 9 (ft), 1 (pt); LPNs 6 (ft); Nurses aides 39 (ft).
Facilities Dining room; Activities room; Crafts room; Laundry room; Barber/Beauty shop.
Activities Arts & crafts; Cards; Games; Prayer groups; Movies; Shopping trips.

SCOTTSDALE

Casa Delmar*
3333 N Civic Center, Scottsdale, AZ, 85251
(602) 947-7333
Admin Andrew J Kellogg. *Medical Dir/Dir of Nursing* Theodore Rudberg.
Licensure Skilled care. *Beds* 130. *Certified* Medicare.
Owner Proprietary Corp.
Admissions Requirements Minimum age 16; Medical examination; Physician's request.
Staff Physicians 2 (pt); RNs 9 (ft), 3 (pt); LPNs 9 (ft), 2 (pt); Orderlies 10 (ft); Nurses aides 27 (ft), 3 (pt); Physical therapists 1 (ft); Reality therapists 1 (pt); Recreational therapists 1 (pt); Occupational therapists 1 (pt); Speech therapists 1 (pt); Activities coordinators 1 (ft); Dietitians 1 (ft); Podiatrists 1 (pt).
Facilities Dining room; Activities room; Crafts room; Laundry room; Barber/Beauty shop.

Activities Arts & crafts; Cards; Games; Reading groups; Prayer groups; Movies; Shopping trips; Social/Cultural gatherings.

Hayden Manor Care Center
2501 N Hayden Rd, Scottsdale, AZ, 85257
(602) 949-1824
Admin Berde J Groff. *Medical Dir/Dir of Nursing* Helen Learmont.
Licensure Skilled care. *Beds* 39.
Owner Proprietary Corp (Quality Health Care Specialists Inc).
Admissions Requirements Medical examination; Physician's request.
Staff RNs 3 (ft); LPNs 1 (ft); Orderlies 2 (ft); Nurses aides 35 (ft); Activities coordinators 1 (ft); Dietitians 1 (pt);; FSM Food service 1 (ft).
Facilities Dining room; Activities room; Crafts room; Laundry room; Barber/Beauty shop.
Activities Arts & crafts; Games; Reading groups; Prayer groups; Movies; Shopping trips; Social/Cultural gatherings.

Monterey Nursing Center
7303 E Monterey Way, Scottsdale, AZ, 85251
(602) 947-7443
Admin Cheri L Allen. *Medical Dir/Dir of Nursing* Dr Theodore Rudberg; Joan Sprain DON.
Licensure Skilled care. *Beds* SNF 90; ICF. *Certified* Medicare.
Owner Proprietary Corp (Vari-Care Inc).
Admissions Requirements Minimum age 18; Medical examination; Physician's request.
Staff RNs; LPNs; Orderlies; Nurses aides; Physical therapists; Recreational therapists; Occupational therapists; Speech therapists; Activities coordinators; Dietitians; Ophthalmologists.
Languages Spanish
Facilities Dining room; Physical therapy room; Activities room; Crafts room; Laundry room; Barber/Beauty shop; Outside patio.
Activities Arts & crafts; Cards; Games; Reading groups; Movies; Shopping trips; Social/Cultural gatherings.

Pueblo Norte Nursing Center
7100 E Mescal St, Scottsdale, AZ, 85254
(602) 948-5800
Admin Marshall N Horsman. *Medical Dir/Dir of Nursing* Ruth Eckert MD; Marilynn Stabel RN DON.
Licensure Skilled care; Intermediate care. *Beds* SNF 128; ICF. *Certified* Medicare.
Owner Nonprofit Corp (Adventist Health Sys-USA).
Admissions Requirements Minimum age 21; Medical examination; Physician's request.
Staff Physicians 15 (pt); RNs 20 (ft); LPNs 8 (ft); Orderlies 5 (ft); Nurses aides 43 (ft); Physical therapists 1 (ft); Recreational therapists 2 (ft); Activities coordinators 1 (ft); Dietitians 1 (ft);; Dentist.
Affiliation Seventh-Day Adventist
Facilities Dining room (3); Physical therapy room; Activities room; Chapel; Crafts room; Laundry room; Barber/Beauty shop; Library; Dentist suite.
Activities Arts & crafts; Cards; Games; Reading groups; Prayer groups; Movies; Shopping trips.

Scottsdale Convalescent Plaza
1475 N Granite Reef Rd, Scottsdale, AZ, 85257
(602) 990-1904
Admin Vicki Bunda. *Medical Dir/Dir of Nursing* Joseph Lillo DO; Connie Engel RN DON.
Licensure Skilled care. *Beds* SNF 148. *Certified* Medicare.
Owner Proprietary Corp.
Admissions Requirements Medical examination; Physician's request.

Staff RNs 12 (ft); LPNs 16 (ft); Nurses aides 46 (ft), 1 (pt); Physical therapists 1 (pt); Occupational therapists 1 (pt); Speech therapists 1 (pt); Activities coordinators 2 (ft); Dietitians 1 (pt).
Languages Spanish
Facilities Dining room; Activities room; Barber/Beauty shop; Library; TV lounges.
Activities Arts & crafts; Cards; Games; Reading groups; Prayer groups; Movies; Shopping trips; Social/Cultural gatherings; Outside trips for meals; Fishing trips; Exercise groups.

Scottsdale Heritage Court
3339 N Civic Center Plaza, Scottsdale, AZ, 85251
(602) 948-5400
Admin Mary G Hill. *Medical Dir/Dir of Nursing* Dr Gerald Wolfey; Cynthia Jordan RN DON.
Licensure Skilled care; Intermediate care. *Beds* SNF 108; ICF. *Certified* Medicare.
Owner Proprietary Corp.
Admissions Requirements Minimum age 18; Medical examination; Physician's request.
Staff RNs 5 (ft); LPNs 7 (ft), 1 (pt); Orderlies 7 (ft); Nurses aides 29 (ft), 2 (pt); Activities coordinators 1 (ft), 1 (pt); Dietitians 1 (ft).
Facilities Dining room; Physical therapy room; Activities room; Crafts room; Laundry room; Barber/Beauty shop; Library.
Activities Arts & crafts; Cards; Games; Reading groups; Prayer groups; Movies; Social/Cultural gatherings.

Scottsdale Village Square
2620 N 68th St, Scottsdale, AZ, 85257
(602) 946-6571
Admin Paul R Friedlan. *Medical Dir/Dir of Nursing* Theodore Rudberg MD.
Licensure Skilled care; Intermediate care; Personal care. *Beds* SNF 12; ICF 66; Personal 62.
Owner Proprietary Corp.
Admissions Requirements Medical examination; Physician's request.
Staff RNs 2 (ft); LPNs 12 (ft), 6 (pt); Nurses aides 23 (ft), 20 (pt); Activities coordinators 3 (ft), 2 (pt).
Languages Spanish
Facilities Dining room; Physical therapy room; Activities room; Crafts room; Laundry room; Barber/Beauty shop; Library; Fenced-in area.
Activities Arts & crafts; Cards; Games; Reading groups; Prayer groups; Movies; Shopping trips; Social/Cultural gatherings; Fashion shows; Picnics.

Shadow Mountain Health Care Center
11150 N 92nd St, Scottsdale, AZ, 85260
(602) 860-1766
Admin Anne C Difierro. *Medical Dir/Dir of Nursing* Joseph Sandor MD; Christine Walker RN DON.
Licensure Skilled care; Intermediate care; Personal care; Post-surgery recuperative care. *Beds* 120. *Certified* Medicare.
Owner Proprietary Corp (Beverly Enterprises).
Admissions Requirements Medical examination.
Staff Physicians; RNs; LPNs; Nurses aides; Physical therapists; Reality therapists; Recreational therapists; Occupational therapists; Speech therapists; Activities coordinators; Dietitians; Dentists; Ophthalmologists; Dermatologist; Respiratory therapist; Social worker.
Languages Spanish
Facilities Dining room; Physical therapy room; Activities room; Chapel; Crafts room; Laundry room; Barber/Beauty shop; Library; Smoking lounges; Whirlpool rooms.

Activities Arts & crafts; Cards; Games; Reading groups; Prayer groups; Movies; Shopping trips; Social/Cultural gatherings; Outings; Educational courses; Resident council sessions; Cocktail hour.

SEDONA

Kachina Point Health Center
505 Jacks Canyon Rd, Sedona, AZ, 86336
(602) 284-1000
Admin Fran Crockett RN. *Medical Dir/Dir of Nursing* Ferenc Nagy MD; Caroline Nejedlo.
Licensure Skilled care; Intermediate care; SCU for Alzheimer's Patients. *Beds* SNF 76; ICF 30. *Certified* Medicaid; Medicare.
Owner Proprietary Corp (Hillhaven Corp).
Admissions Requirements Medical examination; Physician's request.
Staff Physicians; RNs; LPNs; Orderlies; Nurses aides; Physical therapists; Reality therapists; Recreational therapists; Occupational therapists; Speech therapists; Activities coordinators; Dietitians; Dentists; Ophthalmologists; Podiatrists.
Languages Spanish, Swedish, German, French
Facilities Dining room; Physical therapy room; Activities room; Crafts room; Laundry room; Barber/Beauty shop; Library.
Activities Arts & crafts; Cards; Games; Reading groups; Prayer groups; Movies; Shopping trips; Social/Cultural gatherings; Van outings.

SHOW LOW

Pueblo Norte Nursing Center
2401 E Hunt St, Show Low, AZ, 85901
(602) 537-5333
Admin Norm Allred. *Medical Dir/Dir of Nursing* Timothy Mueller MD; Elidia Walker RN.
Licensure Skilled care; Intermediate care. *Beds* SNF 100; ICF. *Certified* Medicare.
Owner Nonprofit Corp (Adventist Health Sys-USA).
Admissions Requirements Medical examination; Physician's request.
Staff RNs; LPNs; Orderlies; Nurses aides; Activities coordinators.
Affiliation Seventh-Day Adventist
Facilities Dining room; Physical therapy room; Activities room; Chapel; Crafts room; Laundry room; Barber/Beauty shop; Library.
Activities Arts & crafts; Cards; Games; Reading groups; Prayer groups; Movies; Shopping trips.

SIERRA VISTA

Sierra Vista Care Center*
660 Coronado Rd, Sierra Vista, AZ, 85635
(602) 459-4900
Admin Charles J Steck.
Licensure Skilled care; Intermediate care. *Beds* SNF 56; ICF 44.
Owner Proprietary Corp.

SUN CITY

Beverly Manor Convalescent Center
13101 N 103rd Ave, Sun City, AZ, 85351
(602) 972-1153
Admin Dennis D Cox. *Medical Dir/Dir of Nursing* D Kanefield MD; Jeannette Slack RN.
Licensure Skilled care; Intermediate care. *Beds* SNF 150; ICF 45. *Certified* Medicare.
Owner Proprietary Corp (Beverly Enterprises).
Admissions Requirements Physician's request.
Staff RNs; LPNs; Orderlies; Nurses aides; Activities coordinators; Dietitians.
Languages French, Spanish, German
Facilities Dining room; Physical therapy room; Activities room; Crafts room; Laundry room; Barber/Beauty shop; Library.

Activities Arts & crafts; Cards; Games; Reading groups; Prayer groups; Movies; Shopping trips; Social/Cultural gatherings; Variety.

Boswell Extended Care Center
10601 W Santa Fe Dr, Sun City, AZ, 85372
(602) 974-7000
Admin Roger Whitcomb. *Medical Dir/Dir of Nursing* Dr Dubrow; Colleen Strom DON.
Licensure Skilled care; Extended care. *Beds* 128. *Certified* Medicare.
Owner Nonprofit Corp.
Admissions Requirements Minimum age 18; Medical examination; Physician's request.
Facilities Dining room; Physical therapy room; Activities room; Crafts room; Laundry room; Barber/Beauty shop.
Activities Arts & crafts; Cards; Games; Reading groups; Prayer groups; Movies; Social/Cultural gatherings.

Sun Valley Lodge
12415 N 103rd Ave, Sun City, AZ, 85351
(602) 933-0137
Admin James Hilty. *Medical Dir/Dir of Nursing* Dr Phillip Turner; Carol Burden.
Licensure Skilled care; Personal care. *Beds* SNF 64; Personal 50.
Owner Nonprofit Corp.
Facilities Dining room; Physical therapy room; Activities room; Chapel; Crafts room; Laundry room; Barber/Beauty shop; Library.
Activities Arts & crafts; Cards; Games; Reading groups; Prayer groups; Movies; Shopping trips; Social/Cultural gatherings.

Wooddale Health Centre
9940 W Union Hills Dr, Sun City, AZ, 85373
(602) 933-0022
Admin Sherman M Rorvig. *Medical Dir/Dir of Nursing* Jeanette Magnus.
Licensure Skilled care; Intermediate care; Personal care. *Beds* SNF 60; ICF 30; Personal 10.
Owner Nonprofit Corp.
Admissions Requirements Medical examination.
Staff RNs 6 (ft); LPNs 7 (ft); Nurses aides 35 (ft); Physical therapists 1 (pt); Activities coordinators 1 (ft); Dietitians 1 (ft).
Affiliation Lutheran
Facilities Dining room; Physical therapy room; Activities room; Crafts room; Laundry room; Barber/Beauty shop.
Activities Arts & crafts; Cards; Games; Reading groups; Movies; Shopping trips; Social/Cultural gatherings; Bible study.

TEMPE

Friendship Village of Tempe Health Center
2645 E Southern, Tempe, AZ, 85282
(602) 831-0880
Admin Madalen Meyers. *Medical Dir/Dir of Nursing* Roger Boylan MD; Phyllis Beaudien.
Licensure Skilled care. *Beds* 120. *Certified* Medicare.
Owner Nonprofit Corp (Life Care Services Corp).
Admissions Requirements Minimum age 62; Medical examination; Physician's request.
Staff RNs 11 (ft), 1 (pt); LPNs 9 (ft), 2 (pt); Nurses aides 45 (ft), 5 (pt); Activities coordinators 2 (ft); Dietitians 1 (pt).
Facilities Dining room; Physical therapy room; Activities room; Laundry room; Barber/Beauty shop; Library.
Activities Arts & crafts; Cards; Games; Reading groups; Prayer groups; Movies; Shopping trips; Social/Cultural gatherings.

Westchester Care Center
6100 S Rural Rd, Tempe, AZ, 85283
(602) 831-8660

Admin Eliot C Higbee. *Medical Dir/Dir of Nursing* Richard O Flynn MD; Roberta Holka RN DON.
Licensure Skilled care; Intermediate care. *Beds* SNF 49; ICF 51.
Owner Nonprofit Corp (Volunteers of America Care).
Admissions Requirements Medical examination; Physician's request.
Staff RNs 6 (ft), 10 (pt); LPNs 5 (ft), 10 (pt); Nurses aides 32 (ft), 17 (pt); Physical therapists 2 (pt); Occupational therapists 1 (pt); Speech therapists 1 (pt); Activities coordinators 1 (ft), 2 (pt); Dietitians 1 (ft); Dentists 1 (pt); Podiatrists 1 (pt).
Affiliation Volunteers of America
Facilities Dining room; Physical therapy room; Activities room; Chapel; Crafts room; Laundry room; Barber/Beauty shop; Day rooms; Resident lounge.
Activities Arts & crafts; Cards; Games; Reading groups; Prayer groups; Movies; Shopping trips; Social/Cultural gatherings.

TUCSON

Arizona Elks Long-Term Care Unit*
1901 W Speedway, Tucson, AZ, 85745
(602) 623-5562
Admin Mildred V Boyd.
Licensure Intermediate care. *Beds* 46.
Owner Nonprofit Corp.
Admissions Requirements Males only; Medical examination; Physician's request.
Facilities Dining room; Physical therapy room; Activities room.

Arizona William-Wesley*
2611 N Warren Ave, Tucson, AZ, 85719
(602) 795-9574
Admin Mary Jane Lindsay. *Medical Dir/Dir of Nursing* William Farr MD.
Licensure Skilled care. *Beds* 102.
Owner Proprietary Corp.
Admissions Requirements Medical examination; Physician's request.
Staff Physicians 1 (pt); RNs 4 (ft), 2 (pt); LPNs 3 (ft), 6 (pt); Orderlies 1 (ft); Nurses aides 33 (ft), 11 (pt); Physical therapists 1 (pt); Recreational therapists 1 (pt); Occupational therapists 1 (pt); Speech therapists 1 (pt); Activities coordinators 2 (ft); Dietitians 1 (ft); Dentists 1 (pt); Ophthalmologists 1 (pt); Podiatrists 1 (pt); Audiologists 1 (pt).
Facilities Dining room; Physical therapy room; Activities room; Chapel; Crafts room; Laundry room; Barber/Beauty shop; Library.
Activities Arts & crafts; Cards; Games; Reading groups; Prayer groups; Movies; Shopping trips; Social/Cultural gatherings; Employees' musical group.

Bonnie Brae's*
5838 E Pima St, Tucson, AZ, 85712
(602) 296-7151
Admin Annie M Markel.
Licensure Skilled care. *Beds* 122.
Owner Proprietary Corp.

Desert Life Health Care*
1919 W Orange Grove, Tucson, AZ, 85704
(602) 297-8311
Admin Thomas M Henry. *Medical Dir/Dir of Nursing* John Pifre MD.
Licensure Skilled care; Intermediate care; Personal care. *Beds* SNF 120; Personal 53. *Certified* Medicare.
Owner Proprietary Corp (Hillhaven Corp).
Admissions Requirements Medical examination; Physician's request.
Staff RNs 7 (ft), 7 (pt); LPNs 20 (ft), 9 (pt); Nurses aides 64 (ft), 15 (pt); Physical therapists 2 (pt); Recreational therapists 1 (ft); Occupational therapists 1 (ft); Speech therapists 1 (ft); Activities coordinators 2 (ft), 2 (pt); Dietitians 1 (ft); Social workers 1 (ft); COTA 1 (pt); Physical therapy aides.

Facilities Dining room; Physical therapy room; Activities room; Chapel; Crafts room; Barber/Beauty shop; Library; TV lounge; Private patios; Jacuzzi; Occupational therapy room.
Activities Arts & crafts; Cards; Games; Reading groups; Prayer groups; Movies; Shopping trips; Social/Cultural gatherings; Special Olympics; Resident council; Music therapy; Reality orientation.

Devon Gables Health Center
6150 E Grant Rd, Tucson, AZ, 85712
(602) 296-6181
Admin Loris Gielczyk. *Medical Dir/Dir of Nursing* Dr Loes, Dr Clark.
Licensure Skilled care; Intermediate care; Intermediate care for mentally retarded. *Certified* Medicare.
Owner Proprietary Corp (Hillhaven Corp).
Staff Physicians 2 (pt); RNs 20 (ft); LPNs 25 (ft); Orderlies 10 (ft); Nurses aides 80 (ft); Physical therapists 1 (ft); Reality therapists 1 (ft); Recreational therapists 5 (ft); Occupational therapists 1 (ft); Speech therapists 1 (pt); Activities coordinators 1 (ft); Dietitians 1 (pt).
Languages Spanish
Facilities Dining room; Physical therapy room; Activities room; Chapel; Crafts room; Laundry room; Barber/Beauty shop; Library.
Activities Arts & crafts; Cards; Games; Reading groups; Prayer groups; Movies; Shopping trips; Social/Cultural gatherings; BBQs; Cocktail hour.

Flower Square Health Care Center
2502 N Dodge Blvd, Tucson, AZ, 85716
(602) 323-3200
Admin Mayra Mollica. *Medical Dir/Dir of Nursing* Dr John Pifer; Ersel Butz, RN DON.
Licensure Skilled care; Intermediate care; Personal care. *Beds* SNF 120; ICF 72; Personal 72.
Owner Privately owned.
Admissions Requirements Medical examination; Physician's request.
Staff RNs; LPNs; Orderlies; Nurses aides; Recreational therapists; Activities coordinators; Dietitians.
Languages Spanish
Facilities Dining room; Physical therapy room; Activities room; Chapel; Crafts room; Laundry room; Barber/Beauty shop; Library.
Activities Arts & crafts; Cards; Games; Reading groups; Prayer groups; Movies; Shopping trips; Social/Cultural gatherings; Monthly newsletter.

Handmaker Jewish Geriatric Center
2221 N Rosemont, Tucson, AZ, 85712
(602) 881-2323
Admin Richard S Lamden. *Medical Dir/Dir of Nursing* Robert Hirsch MD.
Licensure Skilled care; Intermediate care. *Beds* 161. *Certified* Medicare.
Owner Nonprofit Corp.
Admissions Requirements Minimum age 55; Medical examination; Physician's request.
Staff Physicians 3 (pt); Orderlies 2 (ft); Physical therapists 1 (ft), 2 (pt); Occupational therapists 1 (ft), 1 (pt); Speech therapists 1 (pt); Activities coordinators 1 (ft); Dietitians 1 (pt); Ophthalmologists 1 (pt); Podiatrists 1 (pt); Dentist 1 (pt).
Affiliation Jewish
Facilities Dining room; Physical therapy room; Activities room; Chapel; Crafts room; Laundry room; Barber/Beauty shop; Library; Playground.
Activities Arts & crafts; Cards; Games; Reading groups; Prayer groups; Movies; Shopping trips; Social/Cultural gatherings.

La Colina Healthcare
2900 E Ajo Way, Tucson, AZ, 85713
(602) 294-0005

Admin William A Wortley. *Medical Dir/Dir of Nursing* Cindy Kari RN DON.
Licensure Skilled care. *Beds* SNF 240. *Certified* Medicare.
Owner Proprietary Corp (Beverly Enterprises).
Admissions Requirements Physician's request.
Staff RNs 13 (ft); LPNs 15 (ft); Orderlies; Nurses aides 48 (ft); Recreational therapists 3 (ft); Speech therapists 1 (pt); Activities coordinators 1 (ft); Dietitians 9 (ft).
Languages Spanish
Facilities Dining room; Physical therapy room; Activities room; Crafts room; Laundry room; Barber/Beauty shop.
Activities Arts & crafts; Cards; Games; Reading groups; Prayer groups; Movies; Shopping trips; Social/Cultural gatherings.

La Hacienda Nursing Home
2950 N Dodge Blvd, Tucson, AZ, 85716
(602) 795-6504
Admin Janet Green. *Medical Dir/Dir of Nursing* Dr James Belitson MD; Earline Perkins RN DON.
Licensure Skilled care. *Beds* 64.
Owner Proprietary Corp.
Admissions Requirements Medical examination; Physician's request.
Staff RNs 4 (ft), 4 (pt); LPNs 4 (ft), 1 (pt); Orderlies 22 (ft), 6 (pt); Nurses aides; Activities coordinators; Dietitians.
Languages Spanish
Facilities Dining room; Activities room; Crafts room; Laundry room; Barber/Beauty shop.
Activities Arts & crafts; Cards; Games; Reading groups; Prayer groups; Movies; Shopping trips; Social/Cultural gatherings.

Leewood Nursing Home*
1020 N Woodland Ave, Tucson, AZ, 85711
(602) 327-6261
Admin Donald M Dalton.
Licensure Skilled care. *Beds* 86.
Owner Proprietary Corp.

Park Villa Convalescent Center
2001 N Park Ave, Tucson, AZ, 85719
(602) 624-8877
Admin Dee Konecki. *Medical Dir/Dir of Nursing* Judy Sue Donnelly.
Licensure Skilled care. *Beds* SNF 200. *Certified* Medicaid; Medicare.
Owner Proprietary Corp.
Admissions Requirements Minimum age 18; Medical examination; Physician's request.
Staff Physicians 1 (pt); RNs 10 (ft); LPNs 15 (ft), 3 (pt); Orderlies 10 (ft); Nurses aides 40 (ft), 7 (pt); Physical therapists 1 (pt); Occupational therapists 1 (pt); Speech therapists 1 (pt); Activities coordinators 2 (ft); Dietitians 1 (pt).
Languages Spanish
Facilities Dining room; Physical therapy room; Activities room; Crafts room; Laundry room; Barber/Beauty shop; Library.
Activities Arts & crafts; Cards; Games; Reading groups; Prayer groups; Movies; Shopping trips; Social/Cultural gatherings.

Posada Del Sol Health Care Facility*
2250 N Craycroft, Tucson, AZ, 85712
(602) 886-5481
Admin Paul Wayne Eaton.
Licensure Skilled care. *Beds* 256. *Certified* Medicare.
Owner Publicly owned.

Santa Rosa Convalescent Center
1650 N Santa Rosa Blvd, Tucson, AZ, 85712
(602) 795-1610
Admin William J Mitchell.
Licensure Skilled care. *Beds* 144. *Certified* Medicare.
Owner Proprietary Corp.

Su Casa Personal Care Residence
720 W 41st St, Tucson, AZ, 85713
(602) 624-0784

Admin Elizabeth L Stapleton. *Medical Dir/Dir of Nursing* Elizabeth L Stapleton RN.
Licensure Personal care. *Beds* 29. *Certified* Medicaid; Indian Health Services.
Owner Proprietary Corp.
Admissions Requirements Medical examination; Physician's request.
Staff RNs 1 (ft); LPNs 3 (ft), 2 (pt); Nurses aides 1 (ft), 2 (pt); Activities coordinators 1 (ft); Dietitians 1 (pt).
Languages Spanish, Papago
Facilities Dining room; Activities room; Laundry room; Living room; Fenced yard provides protective services.
Activities Arts & crafts; Cards; Games; Reading groups; Prayer groups; Shopping trips; Social/Cultural gatherings.

Valley House Health Care
5545 E Lee, Tucson, AZ, 85712
(602) 296-2306
Admin Thomas A Hines. *Medical Dir/Dir of Nursing* Dr James Belitsos; Midge Krebs RN.
Licensure Skilled care. *Beds* SNF 147. *Certified* Medicare; VA.
Owner Proprietary Corp (Hillhaven Corp).
Admissions Requirements Medical examination; Physician's request.
Staff Physicians 3 (pt); RNs 9 (ft), 15 (pt); LPNs 8 (ft), 9 (pt); Orderlies 1 (ft); Nurses aides 47 (ft), 17 (pt); Physical therapists 1 (pt); Occupational therapists 1 (pt); Speech therapists 1 (pt); Activities coordinators 2 (ft), 1 (pt); Dietitians 1 (ft); Dentist 1 (pt).
Facilities Dining room; Physical therapy room; Activities room; Crafts room; Laundry room; Barber/Beauty shop; Library.
Activities Arts & crafts; Cards; Games; Reading groups; Prayer groups; Movies; Shopping trips; Social/Cultural gatherings; Exercises; Bell ringing; Current events.

Villa Campana Health Center
6651 E Carondelet Dr, Tucson, AZ, 85710
(602) 296-6100
Admin Julie Cropp. *Medical Dir/Dir of Nursing* James Belitsos; Judy Black.
Licensure Skilled care. *Beds* SNF 120. *Certified* Medicare.
Owner Proprietary Corp (Hillhaven Corp).
Admissions Requirements Minimum age 55 (apartments only).
Staff Physicians 3 (pt); RNs 5 (ft), 4 (pt); LPNs 12 (ft), 6 (pt); Orderlies 12 (ft), 2 (pt); Nurses aides 27 (ft), 11 (pt); Physical therapists 2 (ft); Occupational therapists 1 (ft); Speech therapists 1 (pt); Activities coordinators 2 (ft); Dietitians 1 (ft), 1 (pt); Dentist 1 (pt).

Facilities Dining room; Physical therapy room; Activities room; Laundry room; Barber/Beauty shop.
Activities Arts & crafts; Cards; Games; Reading groups; Prayer groups; Movies; Shopping trips; Social/Cultural gatherings; Field trips.

Villa Maria Geriatric Center
4310 E Grant Rd, Tucson, AZ, 85712
(602) 323-9351
Admin R Kevin McFeely. *Medical Dir/Dir of Nursing* James G Belitsos MD; Vickey Johnson RN DON.
Licensure Skilled care. *Beds* SNF 93.
Owner Nonprofit Corp.
Admissions Requirements Medical examination; Physician's request.
Staff RNs 7 (ft); LPNs 5 (ft); Nurses aides 23 (ft), 2 (pt); Recreational therapists 2 (ft).
Languages Spanish
Affiliation Roman Catholic
Facilities Dining room; Activities room; Chapel; Laundry room; Barber/Beauty shop; Library.
Activities Arts & crafts; Cards; Games; Reading groups; Prayer groups; Movies; Shopping trips; Social/Cultural gatherings.

WILLCOX

Northern Cochise Nursing Home
901 W Rex Allen Dr, Willcox, AZ, 85643
(602) 384-3541
Admin Nancy A Holloway.
Licensure Skilled care. *Beds* 24.
Owner Nonprofit Corp.
Admissions Requirements Medical examination; Physician's request.
Staff RNs 1 (ft), 1 (pt); LPNs 3 (ft), 2 (pt); Nurses aides 7 (ft), 5 (pt); Physical therapists 1 (pt); Activities coordinators 1 (ft); Dietitians 1 (pt).
Languages Spanish
Facilities Dining room; Activities room; Laundry room.
Activities Arts & crafts; Cards; Games; Reading groups; Prayer groups; Movies; Social/Cultural gatherings.

WINSLOW

Winslow Convalescent Center*
116 E Hillview, Winslow, AZ, 86407
(602) 289-4678
Admin Lois Miles.
Licensure Skilled care. *Beds* 38.
Owner Proprietary Corp.

YUMA

Hillhaven Healthcare
2222 Ave A, Yuma, AZ, 85364
(602) 783-8831
Admin David Reynolds. *Medical Dir/Dir of Nursing* Roger Nutt MD, Fred Lindberg MD; Margene Nutt RN.
Licensure Skilled care; Intermediate care; Personal care; Special care for Alzheimer's patients. *Beds* 143. *Certified* Medicare.
Owner Proprietary Corp (Hillhaven Corp).
Admissions Requirements Minimum age 18; Medical examination; Physician's request.
Staff RNs 5 (ft), 4 (pt); LPNs 10 (ft), 5 (pt); Nurses aides 40 (ft), 10 (pt); Physical therapists 1 (pt); Reality therapists 1 (pt); Recreational therapists 1 (pt); Occupational therapists 1 (pt); Speech therapists 1 (pt); Activities coordinators 2 (ft); Dietitians 1 (pt); Dentists 1 (pt); Ophthalmologists 1 (pt); Podiatrists 1 (pt).
Languages Spanish
Facilities Dining room; Physical therapy room; Activities room; Chapel; Crafts room; Laundry room; Barber/Beauty shop; Library; Private dining rooms; Large family room/lounge; Facility van for transportation.
Activities Arts & crafts; Cards; Games; Reading groups; Prayer groups; Movies; Shopping trips; Social/Cultural gatherings; Pet visits; Church services; Bible study.

La Mesa Care Center
2470 S Arizona Ave, Yuma, AZ, 85364
(602) 344-8541
Admin G'Anne Degnan. *Medical Dir/Dir of Nursing* Doris Lawseth.
Licensure Skilled care; Intermediate care; Personal. *Beds* 128. *Certified* Medicare.
Owner Proprietary Corp (US Care Corp).
Admissions Requirements Medical examination; Physician's request.
Staff Physicians; RNs; LPNs; Orderlies; Nurses aides; Physical therapists; Reality therapists; Recreational therapists; Occupational therapists; Speech therapists; Activities coordinators; Dietitians; Dentists; Ophthalmologists; Podiatrists.
Languages Spanish
Facilities Dining room; Physical therapy room; Activities room; Chapel; Crafts room; Laundry room; Barber/Beauty shop; Library.
Activities Arts & crafts; Cards; Games; Reading groups; Prayer groups; Movies; Shopping trips; Social/Cultural gatherings.

ARKANSAS

ALEXANDER

Alexander Human Development Center
PO Box 320, Alexander, AR, 72002
(501) 847-3506
Admin Michael McCreight. *Medical Dir/Dir of Nursing* Etta Buckelew MD.
Licensure Intermediate care for mentally retarded. *Beds* ICF/MR 150. *Certified* Medicaid.
Owner Publicly owned.
Admissions Requirements Minimum age 21.
Staff Physicians 1 (pt); RNs 3 (ft); LPNs 9 (ft); Physical therapists 1 (pt); Recreational therapists 2 (ft); Occupational therapists 1 (pt); Speech therapists 3 (ft); Dietitians 1 (ft); Podiatrists 1 (ft); Mental retardation aides 126 (ft); Dentist 1 (pt).
Facilities Dining room; Activities room; Crafts room; Laundry room; Barber/Beauty shop; Library.
Activities Arts & crafts; Movies; Shopping trips; Social/Cultural gatherings.

ARKADELPHIA

Arkadelphia Human Developmental Center*
PO Box 70, Arkadelphia, AR, 71923
(501) 246-8011
Admin Russ Burbank.
Licensure Intermediate care for mentally retarded. *Beds* 167. *Certified* Medicaid.

Riverwood Convalescent Home*
102 Caddo St, Arkadelphia, AR, 71923
(501) 246-5566
Admin Spencer Honey.
Licensure Intermediate care. *Beds* 120. *Certified* Medicaid.
Owner Proprietary Corp (Beverly Enterprises).

Twin Rivers Medical Center*
Box 98, 1420 Pine St, Arkadelphia, AR, 71923
(501) 246-9801
Admin D W Gathright.
Licensure Intermediate care. *Beds* 42. *Certified* Medicaid.

ASH FLAT

Ash Flat Convalescent Center
Box 5A, Star Rte, Ash Flat, AR, 72513
(501) 994-2341
Admin Rebecca Frazier. *Medical Dir/Dir of Nursing* Annette Racaniello DO; Wanda Davis DON.
Licensure Skilled care. *Beds* SNF 105. *Certified* Medicaid.
Owner Proprietary Corp (Diversicare Corp).
Admissions Requirements Physician's request.
Staff Physicians 1 (ft); RNs 3 (ft); LPNs 8 (ft); Orderlies 4 (ft); Nurses aides 60 (ft); Physical therapists 1 (ft); Speech therapists 1 (ft); Activities coordinators 1 (ft); Dietitians 1 (ft).

Facilities Dining room; Activities room; Chapel; Crafts room; Laundry room; Barber/Beauty shop.
Activities Arts & crafts; Cards; Games; Reading groups; Prayer groups; Movies; Shopping trips; Social/Cultural gatherings.

ASHDOWN

Little River Nursing Home
PO Box 577, 5th & Locke St, Ashdown, AR, 71822
(501) 898-5101
Admin Judy Adams. *Medical Dir/Dir of Nursing* Effie Turner RN.
Licensure Intermediate care. *Beds* ICF 76. *Certified* Medicaid.
Owner Nonprofit Corp.
Admissions Requirements Physician's request.
Staff Physicians; RNs 1 (ft), 1 (pt); LPNs 7 (ft), 2 (pt); Orderlies; Nurses aides 17 (ft), 10 (pt); Physical therapists 1 (ft); Recreational therapists 1 (ft); Activities coordinators 1 (ft), 1 (pt); Dietitians 1 (ft).
Facilities Dining room; Physical therapy room; Activities room; Barber/Beauty shop; Living room.
Activities Arts & crafts; Games; Reading groups; Prayer groups; Shopping trips; Birthday parties.

Pleasant Manor Nursing Home Inc
750 S Locust St, Ashdown, AR, 71822
(501) 898-5001
Admin Maxine Rhodes. *Medical Dir/Dir of Nursing* Dr Wayne Reid; Judy Pickett RN DON.
Licensure Intermediate care. *Beds* ICF 53. *Certified* Medicaid.
Owner Proprietary Corp.
Admissions Requirements Medical examination; Physician's request.
Staff Physicians 1 (ft), 4 (pt); RNs 1 (ft); LPNs 5 (ft), 2 (pt); Nurses aides 16 (ft), 5 (pt); Recreational therapists 1 (ft); Activities coordinators 1 (ft).
Facilities Dining room; Physical therapy room; Activities room; Crafts room; Laundry room; Barber/Beauty shop; Library.
Activities Arts & crafts; Cards; Games; Reading groups; Prayer groups; Shopping trips; Social/Cultural gatherings.

BATESVILLE

Intermed of Batesville*
PO Box 2698, Batesville, AR, 72501
(501) 698-1853
Admin Richard L Case.
Licensure Skilled care. *Beds* 140. *Certified* Medicaid.
Owner Proprietary Corp (Beverly Enterprises).

Wood-Lawn Inc*
2901 Neeley St, Batesville, AR, 72501
(501) 793-7195
Admin Joyce Skinner.

Licensure Skilled care. *Beds* 121. *Certified* Medicaid.

BELLA VISTA

Concordia Care Center*
7 Professional Dr, Bella Vista, AR, 72714
(501) 855-3736
Admin Sarah E Bentley. *Medical Dir/Dir of Nursing* Albert E Martin MD.
Licensure Skilled care. *Beds* 82. *Certified* Medicaid; Medicare.
Staff RNs 1 (ft), 2 (pt); LPNs 7 (ft), 2 (pt); Orderlies 1 (ft), 1 (pt); Nurses aides 27 (ft), 4 (pt); Activities coordinators 1 (ft).
Facilities Dining room; Chapel; Crafts room; Laundry room; Barber/Beauty shop; Library.
Activities Arts & crafts; Cards; Games; Reading groups; Prayer groups; Movies; Shopping trips; Social/Cultural gatherings.

BENTON

Benton Services Center Nursing Home
Services Center Branch, Benton, AR, 72015
(501) 778-1111
Admin Charles L Smith.
Licensure Intermediate care. *Beds* SNF 402. *Certified* Medicaid.

Country Inn Nursing Center Inc*
PO Box 999, Benton, AR, 72015-0999
(501) 623-6811
Admin Elton Stewart PhD.
Licensure Skilled care; Intermediate care. *Beds* SNF 71; ICF 142. *Certified* Medicaid.

Rose Care Center of Benton I
3300 Military Rd, Benton, AR, 72015
(501) 778-8282
Admin Kaye Keller. *Medical Dir/Dir of Nursing* Paul Hogue MD; Teena Campbell RN DON.
Licensure Skilled care. *Beds* 103. *Certified* Medicaid.
Admissions Requirements Medical examination; Physician's request.
Staff RNs 1 (ft), 2 (pt); LPNs 10 (ft), 4 (pt); Nurses aides 48 (ft), 10 (pt); Dietitians 1 (ft); Ophthalmologists 1 (pt).
Facilities Dining room; Activities room; Laundry room; Barber/Beauty shop.
Activities Arts & crafts; Cards; Games; Reading groups; Prayer groups; Movies; Shopping trips; Social/Cultural gatherings.

Rose Care Center of Benton II
PO Box 280, 809 Kenwood Rd, Benton, AR, 72015
(501) 778-7417
Admin Paula Binns. *Medical Dir/Dir of Nursing* Samuel Taggart MD; Kathy Norwood RN DON.
Licensure Intermediate care. *Beds* ICF 140. *Certified* Medicaid.
Owner Proprietary Corp (Rose Care Inc).
Admissions Requirements Minimum age 21; Medical examination; Physician's request.

Staff Physicians 1 (ft); RNs 1 (ft), 1 (pt); LPNs 12 (ft), 1 (pt); Orderlies 2 (ft), 1 (pt); Nurses aides 38 (ft), 8 (pt); Physical therapists 1 (pt); Activities coordinators 1 (ft); Dietitians 1 (pt); Ophthalmologists 1 (pt); Home economist 1 (ft).
Languages Sign
Facilities Dining room; Activities room; Crafts room; Laundry room; Barber/Beauty shop; TV/Living room; Visitation rooms.
Activities Arts & crafts; Cards; Games; Reading groups; Prayer groups; Movies; Shopping trips; Social/Cultural gatherings; Bus rides; Picnics; Beauty contests.

BENTONVILLE

Bentonville Manor Nursing Home
224 S Main St, Bentonville, AR, 72712
(501) 273-3373
Admin Marilu A Monroe.
Licensure Skilled care. *Beds* 67. *Certified* Medicaid.
Admissions Requirements Minimum age 18; Medical examination; Physician's request.
Staff Physicians 10 (pt); RNs 1 (ft), 1 (pt); LPNs 3 (ft), 7 (pt); Nurses aides 20 (ft), 7 (pt); Physical therapists 2 (pt); Reality therapists 1 (pt); Recreational therapists 1 (pt); Occupational therapists 1 (pt); Speech therapists 1 (pt); Activities coordinators 1 (pt); Dietitians 1 (pt); Dentists 1 (pt); Ophthalmologists 1 (pt).
Facilities Dining room; Activities room; Crafts room; Laundry room; Barber/Beauty shop; Library.
Activities Arts & crafts; Cards; Games; Reading groups; Prayer groups; Movies; Shopping trips; Social/Cultural gatherings.

BERRYVILLE

Berryville Health Care Center*
Simpson Ave, Berryville, AR, 72616
(501) 423-6966
Admin Roger L Curtis.
Licensure Intermediate care. *Beds* 52. *Certified* Medicaid.

BLYTHEVILLE

Blytheville Nursing Center Inc
1400 N Division, Blytheville, AR, 72315
(501) 763-0240
Admin Rose Jackson. *Medical Dir/Dir of Nursing* Joe Jones MD; Sally Jones RN DON.
Licensure Skilled care. *Beds* SNF 105. *Certified* Medicaid.
Owner Proprietary Corp (Beverly Enterprises).
Admissions Requirements Medical examination; Physician's request.
Staff RNs 1 (ft), 2 (pt); LPNs 8 (ft), 4 (pt); Nurses aides 25 (ft), 4 (pt); Activities coordinators 1 (ft), 1 (pt).
Facilities Dining room; Barber/Beauty shop; Whirlpool bath; Shower room.
Activities Arts & crafts; Cards; Games; Reading groups; Prayer groups; Movies; Shopping trips; Social/Cultural gatherings.

Keith Acres Nursing Home
PO Box 716, 112 W Clinton, Blytheville, AR, 72315-716
(501) 763-9213
Admin Jean L Carmon. *Medical Dir/Dir of Nursing* C R Cole MD; Alice D Karr DON.
Licensure Intermediate care. *Beds* ICF 44. *Certified* Medicaid.
Owner Proprietary Corp.
Admissions Requirements Medical examination; Physician's request.
Staff Physicians 1 (pt); RNs 1 (ft); LPNs 2 (ft), 4 (pt); Nurses aides 11 (ft), 4 (pt); Activities coordinators 1 (ft); Dietitians 1 (pt).

Facilities Dining room; Laundry room.
Activities Arts & crafts; Games; Prayer groups; Social/Cultural gatherings.

Mississippi County Nursing Home
PO Box 108, Blytheville, AR, 72315
(501) 762-3220
Admin Sandra Ray. *Medical Dir/Dir of Nursing* Carol A Couch RN DON.
Licensure Intermediate care. *Beds* ICF 70.
Certified Medicaid.
Owner Publicly owned.
Admissions Requirements Physician's request.
Facilities Dining room; Activities room; Barber/Beauty shop.
Activities Arts & crafts; Cards; Games; Reading groups; Prayer groups; Movies; Shopping trips; Social/Cultural gatherings.

Parkview Manor Nursing Home—Blytheville
PO Box 664, 710 N Ruddle, Blytheville, AR, 72315
(501) 763-3654
Admin Arvell Pate. *Medical Dir/Dir of Nursing* Dr C R Cole; Tammy McCormick RN.
Licensure Intermediate care. *Beds* ICF 46.
Certified Medicaid.
Owner Proprietary Corp.
Admissions Requirements Medical examination; Physician's request.
Staff Physicians; RNs; LPNs; Nurses aides.
Facilities Dining room; Activities room; Chapel; Laundry room.
Activities Arts & crafts; Games; Prayer groups; Shopping trips; Social/Cultural gatherings.

BOONEVILLE

Booneville Human Development Center
Box 327, Booneville, AR, 72927
(501) 675-2121
Admin William Agin, Ph.D.. *Medical Dir/Dir of Nursing* James Harlison MD.
Licensure Intermediate care for mentally retarded. *Beds* ICF/MR 210. *Certified* Medicaid.
Owner Publicly owned.
Admissions Requirements Minimum age 21; Medical examination.
Staff Physicians 1 (ft).
Facilities Dining room; Physical therapy room; Activities room; Chapel; Crafts room; Laundry room; Barber/Beauty shop.
Activities Arts & crafts; Cards; Games; Reading groups; Prayer groups; Movies; Shopping trips; Social/Cultural gatherings.

Oak Manor Nursing Center*
PO Box 170, Booneville, AR, 72927
(501) 675-3763
Admin Eileen P Macklin.
Licensure Skilled care. *Beds* 101. *Certified* Medicaid.

BRINKLEY

Cla-Clif Home for the Aged*
PO Box 671, Brinkley, AR, 72021
(501) 734-3636
Admin Rev Charles F Clay.
Licensure Intermediate care. *Beds* 77.
Certified Medicaid.

St Joseph Home
509 S New York, Brinkley, AR, 72021
(501) 734-1818
Admin Sharon S Perry. *Medical Dir/Dir of Nursing* Dr William Gilli; Melinda Duggin RN.
Licensure Intermediate care. *Beds* ICF 28.
Certified Medicaid.
Owner Publicly owned.
Admissions Requirements Medical examination; Physician's request.

Staff RNs 1 (ft); LPNs 3 (ft), 1 (pt); Nurses aides 7 (ft), 3 (pt); Activities coordinators 1 (ft); Dietitians 1 (pt).
Facilities Dining room; Activities room; Laundry room; Barber/Beauty shop.
Activities Arts & crafts; Games; Prayer groups; Movies; Shopping trips; Social/Cultural gatherings.

CABOT

Cabot Manor Nursing Home Inc
615 W Main St, Cabot, AR, 72023
(501) 843-6181 or 843-7729
Admin Peggy Moody. *Medical Dir/Dir of Nursing* Jerry Chapman MD.
Licensure Skilled care. *Beds* 75. *Certified* Medicaid.
Owner Proprietary Corp.
Admissions Requirements Minimum age 18; Medical examination; Physician's request.
Staff RNs 1 (ft), 2 (pt); LPNs 5 (ft), 3 (pt); Nurses aides 20 (ft), 7 (pt); Activities coordinators 1 (ft); Dentists; Dentist.
Facilities Dining room; Activities room; Laundry room.
Activities Arts & crafts; Cards; Games; Reading groups; Prayer groups; Movies; Shopping trips; Social/Cultural gatherings.

Rollins Nursing Home
PO Box 27, 428 W Locust, Cabot, AR, 72023
(501) 843-6021, 982-7852
Admin Vickie L Vinson. *Medical Dir/Dir of Nursing* Dr Jerry Chapman; Marilyn McColgan RN.
Licensure Intermediate care. *Beds* 37.
Certified Medicaid.
Owner Privately owned.
Admissions Requirements Males only.
Staff Physicians 2 (pt); RNs 1 (ft); LPNs 2 (ft), 1 (pt); Orderlies 2 (ft); Nurses aides 10 (ft); Activities coordinators 1 (ft); Dietitians 1 (pt).
Facilities Dining room; Activities room; Laundry room.
Activities Arts & crafts; Cards; Games; Reading groups; Prayer groups; Movies; Outdoor activities; Field trips.

CALICO ROCK

White River Convalescent Home Inc*
PO Box 408, Calico Rock, AR, 72519
(501) 297-3719
Admin Dean Hudson.
Licensure Skilled care. *Beds* 91. *Certified* Medicaid.

CAMDEN

Leisure Lodge Inc*
900 Magnolia Rd, Camden, AR, 71701
(501) 836-6833
Admin Les Wallace.
Licensure Skilled care. *Beds* 106. *Certified* Medicare.
Owner Proprietary Corp (Beverly Enterprises).

Leisure Lodge Inc—Camden, Bruce Street*
515 Bruce St, Camden, AR, 71701
(501) 836-6831
Admin Terri Platt.
Licensure Intermediate care. *Beds* 70.
Certified Medicaid.
Owner Proprietary Corp (Beverly Enterprises).

Longmeadow Nursing Home—Camden*
Rte 1, Box 843, Camden, AR, 71701
(501) 836-9337
Admin Jimmie Dean Henson.
Licensure Intermediate care. *Beds* 69.
Certified Medicaid.

Ouachita Convalescent Center*
1411 Country Club Rd, Camden, AR, 71701
(501) 836-4111

Admin Annie Jo Young. *Medical Dir/Dir of Nursing* James Guthrie.
Licensure Skilled care. *Beds* 142.
Staff RNs 2 (ft); LPNs 8 (ft), 3 (pt); Nurses aides 29 (ft), 4 (pt); Activities coordinators 1 (ft); Dietitians 1 (ft).

CARAWAY

Lane's Rest Home Inc—Caraway*
PO Box 519, Caraway, AR, 72419
(501) 482-3711
Admin Flossie Lane.
Licensure Intermediate care. *Beds* 40.
Certified Medicaid.

CARLISLE

Chambers Nursing Home Inc*
Rte 1, Box 234, Carlisle, AR, 72024
(501) 552-7811
Admin Hazel J Glover.
Licensure Intermediate care. *Beds* 52.
Certified Medicaid.

J W Comer Nursing Home
Box 231, Rte 1, Carlisle, AR, 72024
(501) 552-3350
Admin Helen L Comer. *Medical Dir/Dir of Nursing* Dr B E Holmes; Betty J O'Cain RN.
Licensure Intermediate care. *Beds* ICF 22.
Certified Medicaid.
Owner Privately owned.
Admissions Requirements Males only; Medical examination; Physician's request.
Staff Physicians 1 (pt); RNs 1 (ft); LPNs 1 (ft), 1 (pt); Nurses aides 5 (ft), 3 (pt); Activities coordinators 1 (ft); Dietitians 1 (ft), 1 (pt).
Facilities Dining room; Activities room; Laundry room.
Activities Arts & crafts; Cards; Games; Reading groups; Shopping trips; Social/Cultural gatherings.

Zimmerman Nursing Home Inc
PO Box 14, Rte 1, Carlisle, AR, 72024
(501) 552-7449
Admin John F Zimmerman. *Medical Dir/Dir of Nursing* Dr Fred C Inman; Tanya Wilson.
Licensure Intermediate care. *Beds* 41.
Certified Medicaid; Medicare.
Owner Privately owned.
Admissions Requirements Minimum age 55; Medical examination.
Staff RNs 1 (ft); LPNs 3 (ft); Orderlies 2 (ft), 1 (pt); Nurses aides 10 (ft), 10 (pt); Activities coordinators 1 (ft).
Facilities Dining room; Activities room; Chapel; Crafts room; Laundry room; Barber/Beauty shop.
Activities Arts & crafts; Cards; Games; Reading groups; Shopping trips; Social/Cultural gatherings.

CARTHAGE

Carthage Nursing Home*
Hwy 48 W, PO Box 35, Carthage, AR, 71725
(501) 254-2222
Admin Morgan Treadwell. *Medical Dir/Dir of Nursing* John Delamore.
Licensure Intermediate care. *Beds* 85.
Certified Medicaid.
Staff Physicians 3 (pt); RNs 1 (ft); LPNs 3 (ft), 2 (pt); Nurses aides 42 (ft), 5 (pt); Recreational therapists 1 (ft); Activities coordinators 1 (ft); Dietitians 1 (ft); Dentists 1 (pt); Ophthalmologists 1 (pt).
Facilities Dining room; Activities room; Laundry room; Barber/Beauty shop.
Activities Cards; Games; Reading groups; Prayer groups; Shopping trips; Social/Cultural gatherings.

CHARLESTON

Greenhurst Nursing Home
PO Box 458, Charleston, AR, 72933
(501) 965-7373
Admin Erich Z Schaffer. *Medical Dir/Dir of Nursing* Martin C Schaffer RN DON.
Licensure Skilled care. *Beds* SNF 73. *Certified* Medicaid.
Owner Proprietary Corp.
Staff Physicians 4 (ft); RNs 3 (ft); LPNs 8 (ft); Nurses aides 30 (ft), 20 (pt); Physical therapists 1 (pt); Activities coordinators 1 (ft); Dietitians 1 (pt).
Languages German, Italian, French
Facilities Dining room; Activities room; Laundry room; Barber/Beauty shop.
Activities Arts & crafts; Cards; Reading groups; Prayer groups; Movies; Social/Cultural gatherings.

CLARKSVILLE

Clarksville Convalescent Home Inc*
400 Oak Court St, Clarksville, AR, 72830
(501) 754-8611
Admin Ronnie F Johnson.
Licensure Intermediate care. *Beds* 105.
Certified Medicaid.

Mickel Nursing Home*
PO Box 250, Hwy 64 E, Clarksville, AR, 72830
(501) 754-2052
Admin Mary Ann Farris.
Licensure Skilled care; Intermediate care for mentally retarded. *Beds* SNF 24; ICF/MR 53. *Certified* Medicaid.

CLINTON

Van Buren County Nursing Home
PO Box 206, Clinton, AR, 72031
(501) 745-2401
Admin Lillian B Varnell. *Medical Dir/Dir of Nursing* John A Hall MD; Joyce Thomas RN DON.
Licensure Skilled care. *Beds* SNF 104. *Certified* Medicaid.
Owner Nonprofit Corp.
Admissions Requirements Medical examination; Physician's request.
Staff Physicians 5 (ft); RNs 1 (ft), 2 (pt); LPNs 13 (ft); Orderlies 3 (ft); Nurses aides 26 (ft), 4 (pt); Activities coordinators 1 (ft); Dietitians 1 (ft).
Facilities Dining room; Activities room; Crafts room; Laundry room; Barber/Beauty shop.
Activities Arts & crafts; Cards; Games; Reading groups; Movies; Shopping trips; Social/Cultural gatherings.

COLLEGE STATION

Jean's Nursing Home*
PO Box 161, College Station, AR, 72053
(501) 490-1533
Admin Eunice Reed.
Licensure Skilled care. *Beds* 105. *Certified* Medicaid.

CONWAY

Conway Convalescent Center*
824 Salem Rd, Conway, AR, 72032
(501) 327-4421
Admin Brenda Bane. *Medical Dir/Dir of Nursing* Dr Bob Banister.
Licensure Intermediate care. *Beds* 108. *Certified* Medicaid; Medicare.
Admissions Requirements Medical examination.

Staff Physicians 1 (pt); RNs 2 (ft), 2 (pt); LPNs 5 (ft), 1 (pt); Orderlies 1 (ft); Nurses aides 50 (ft), 5 (pt); Activities coordinators 1 (ft); Dietitians 1 (pt).
Facilities Dining room; Activities room; Chapel; Laundry room; Barber/Beauty shop.
Activities Arts & crafts; Cards; Games; Reading groups; Prayer groups; Movies; Social/Cultural gatherings.

Conway Human Development Center
Siebenmorgen Rd, Conway, AR, 72032
(501) 329-6851
Admin Bob Clark. *Medical Dir/Dir of Nursing* Jim Pinkerton.
Licensure Intermediate care for mentally retarded. *Beds* 656. *Certified* Medicaid.
Owner Nonprofit organization/foundation.
Admissions Requirements Minimum age 6.
Staff Physicians 2 (ft), 2 (pt); RNs 17 (ft); LPNs 83 (ft); Nurses aides 628 (ft); Physical therapists 2 (ft), 2 (pt); Occupational therapists 6 (ft); Speech therapists 10 (ft); Activities coordinators 24 (ft); Dietitians 3 (ft); Podiatrists 1 (ft); Dentist 1 (ft).
Facilities Dining room; Physical therapy room; Activities room; Chapel; Crafts room; Laundry room; Barber/Beauty shop; Library.
Activities Cards; Games; Reading groups; Movies; Shopping trips; Social/Cultural gatherings.

Heritage Center Inc—Conway
619 Center St, Conway, AR, 72032
(501) 327-7642
Admin Janis Young. *Medical Dir/Dir of Nursing* Dr Robert Rook; Barbara Norris DON.
Licensure Intermediate care. *Beds* ICF 55. *Certified* Medicaid.
Owner Proprietary Corp.
Admissions Requirements Medical examination; Physician's request.
Staff RNs 1 (pt); LPNs 6 (pt); Orderlies 2 (pt); Nurses aides 20 (pt); Activities coordinators 1 (pt); Dietitians 1 (pt).
Facilities Dining room; Activities room; Crafts room; Barber/Beauty shop.
Activities Arts & crafts; Cards; Games; Prayer groups; Movies; Shopping trips; Exercise groups.

Johnson's Meadowlake Home Inc*
PO Box 10567, Conway, AR, 72032
(501) 329-9879
Admin Mark Johnson.
Licensure Intermediate care. *Beds* 70. *Certified* Medicaid.
Admissions Requirements Medical examination; Physician's request.
Staff RNs 1 (ft); LPNs 4 (ft), 2 (pt); Orderlies 1 (ft); Nurses aides 19 (ft), 1 (pt); Activities coordinators 1 (ft).
Facilities Dining room; Activities room; Laundry room; Barber/Beauty shop.
Activities Arts & crafts; Cards; Games; Reading groups; Prayer groups; Shopping trips; Social/Cultural gatherings; Outings.

CORNING

Corning Nursing Home*
100 W 5th & Walnut Sts, Corning, AR, 72422
(501) 857-3100
Admin Carolyn Veach.
Licensure Intermediate care. *Beds* 117. *Certified* Medicaid; Medicare.

CROSSETT

Leisure Lodge Inc—Crossett
1101 Waterwell Rd, Crossett, AR, 71635
(501) 364-5721
Admin Elaine Colvin. *Medical Dir/Dir of Nursing* Dr D L Toon; LaNell Johnson.
Licensure Skilled care. *Beds* SNF 79. *Certified* Medicaid.

Owner Proprietary Corp (Beverly Enterprises).
Admissions Requirements Physician's request.
Staff Physicians; RNs; LPNs; Nurses aides;
Activities coordinators; Dietitians.
Facilities Dining room; Activities room;
Chapel; Crafts room; Laundry room; Barber/
Beauty shop.
Activities Arts & crafts; Games; Reading
groups; Prayer groups; Movies; Shopping
trips; Social/Cultural gatherings; Zoo trips;
Tours; Luncheons.

DANVILLE

Mitchell's Nursing Home Inc
Box 10, Danville, AR, 72833
(501) 495-2914
Admin Maurine Mitchell. *Medical Dir/Dir of
Nursing* Dr Walter P Harris.
Licensure Intermediate care. *Beds* 92.
Certified Medicaid.
Admissions Requirements Minimum age 18.
Staff Physicians 7 (ft); RNs 2 (ft); LPNs 7 (ft);
Orderlies 1 (ft); Nurses aides 52 (ft);
Physical therapists 1 (pt); Reality therapists
1 (pt); Recreational therapists 1 (pt);
Occupational therapists 1 (pt); Activities
coordinators 1 (pt); Dietitians 1 (pt).
Facilities Dining room; Activities room;
Crafts room; Laundry room; Barber/Beauty
shop.
Activities Arts & crafts; Cards; Games;
Reading groups; Prayer groups; Movies;
Shopping trips.

DARDANELLE

Dardanelle Nursing Center Inc*
510 W Green St, Dardanelle, AR, 72834
(501) 229-4884
Admin Vickie Rainey. *Medical Dir/Dir of
Nursing* Dr Gene D Ring.
Licensure Skilled care. *Beds* 90. *Certified*
Medicare.
Owner Proprietary Corp (Beverly Enterprises).
Staff RNs 1 (ft), 1 (pt); LPNs 8 (ft), 1 (pt);
Orderlies 2 (ft); Nurses aides 22 (ft), 1 (pt);
Activities coordinators 1 (ft).
Facilities Dining room; Laundry room;
Barber/Beauty shop.
Activities Arts & crafts; Cards; Games;
Movies; Shopping trips; Social/Cultural
gatherings.

DEQUEEN

DeQueen Nursing Home*
PO Box 1040, DeQueen, AR, 71832
(501) 642-3317
Admin Nancy C Dossey.
Licensure Intermediate care. *Beds* 35.
Certified Medicaid.

Ridgeview Lodge Nursing Center*
PO Box 71, DeQueen, AR, 71832
(501) 642-3562
Admin Judy Ney.
Licensure Intermediate care. *Beds* 105.
Certified Medicaid.

DES ARC

Des Arc Convalescent Center*
Rte 2, Box 143-B, Des Arc, AR, 72040
(501) 256-4194
Admin Helen Mixon.
Licensure Skilled care. *Beds* 80. *Certified*
Medicaid.

DEWITT

DeWitt City Nursing Home*
Box 428, DeWitt, AR, 72042
(501) 946-4541
Admin Vivian A Meins.

Licensure Intermediate care. *Beds* 54.
Certified Medicaid.

Leisure Lodge Inc—DeWitt*
Hwy 152A, DeWitt, AR, 72042
(501) 946-3569
Admin Betty Fischer.
Licensure Intermediate care. *Beds* 140.
Certified Medicaid.
Owner Proprietary Corp (Beverly Enterprises).

DUMAS

Dumas Nursing Center*
960 E Bowles, Dumas, AR, 71639
(501) 382-6100
Admin Richard Thomas.
Licensure Skilled care. *Beds* 80. *Certified*
Medicaid.
Owner Proprietary Corp (Beverly Enterprises).

EL DORADO

East Manor Nusing Center*
100 Hargett Dr, El Dorado, AR, 71730
(501) 862-6681
Admin Rose McCallum. *Medical Dir/Dir of
Nursing* Luis Merced.
Licensure Intermediate care. *Beds* 84.
Certified Medicaid.
Owner Proprietary Corp (Beverly Enterprises).
Staff Physicians 1 (ft), 2 (pt); RNs 1 (ft), 1
(pt); LPNs 5 (ft), 1 (pt); Nurses aides 17 (ft),
3 (pt); Physical therapists 1 (pt); Activities
coordinators 1 (ft); Dietitians 1 (ft), 1 (pt);
Dentists 1 (ft); Ophthalmologists 1 (ft);
Social worker 1 (ft).
Facilities Dining room; Activities room;
Crafts room; Laundry room; Barber/Beauty
shop.
Activities Arts & crafts; Cards; Games;
Reading groups; Prayer groups; Shopping
trips; Social/Cultural gatherings.

Hillsboro Manor Nursing Home*
PO Box 728, El Dorado, AR, 71730
(501) 862-5124
Admin John Reynolds.
Licensure Skilled care. *Beds* 72. *Certified*
Medicaid.

Hudson Memorial Nursing Home
700 N College, El Dorado, AR, 71730
(501) 863-8131
Admin Mervin Mast. *Medical Dir/Dir of
Nursing* Dr George W Warren; Mrs Virginia
Ables RN.
Licensure Skilled care. *Beds* SNF 108.
Owner Nonprofit organization/foundation.
Admissions Requirements Minimum age 16;
Medical examination; Physician's request.
Staff RNs 3 (ft); LPNs 8 (ft), 3 (pt); Orderlies
2 (ft); Nurses aides 37 (ft), 8 (pt); Activities
coordinators 1 (ft); Rehabilitation aide 1 (ft).
Facilities Dining room; Physical therapy
room; Activities room; Crafts room; Laundry
room; Barber/Beauty shop; Library.
Activities Arts & crafts; Games; Reading
groups; Prayer groups; Movies; Shopping
trips; Social/Cultural gatherings.

Oak Ridge Nursing Home*
Griffin & Leon Sts, El Dorado, AR, 71730
(501) 862-5511
Admin Kleve R Bassford.
Licensure Skilled care. *Beds* 180. *Certified*
Medicaid.

ENGLAND

England Manor Nursing Home Inc*
PO Box 302, England, AR, 72046
(501) 842-2771
Admin Pattie Sue Cox. *Medical Dir/Dir of
Nursing* Dr Thomas Braswell.
Licensure Intermediate care. *Beds* 63.
Certified Medicaid.

Admissions Requirements Minimum age 18;
Medical examination; Physician's request.
Staff Physicians 3 (pt); RNs 1 (ft); LPNs 2
(ft), 1 (pt); Nurses aides 22 (ft); Activities
coordinators 1 (ft); Dietitians 1 (ft), 2 (pt);
Dentists 1 (pt); Ophthalmologists 1 (pt);
Podiatrists 1 (pt); Audiologists 1 (pt).
Facilities Dining room; Activities room;
Crafts room; Barber/Beauty shop.
Activities Arts & crafts; Cards; Games;
Reading groups; Prayer groups; Movies;
Shopping trips.

England Nursing Center
416 Rest Ave, England, AR, 72046-0325
(501) 842-3971
Admin Beth Elkins. *Medical Dir/Dir of
Nursing* Tommy Braswell MD.
Licensure Intermediate care. *Beds* ICF 76.
Certified Medicaid.
Owner Privately owned.
Admissions Requirements Physician's request.
Staff Physicians; RNs; LPNs; Orderlies;
Nurses aides; Activities coordinators;
Dietitians.
Facilities Dining room; Activities room;
Crafts room; Barber/Beauty shop.
Activities Arts & crafts; Cards; Games;
Reading groups; Prayer groups; Movies;
Shopping trips.

EUREKA SPRINGS

Eureka Springs Convalescent Center*
Rte 1, Box 23, Eureka Springs, AR, 72632
(501) 253-7038
Admin Debbie Johnson. *Medical Dir/Dir of
Nursing* Dr Jess D Green.
Licensure Skilled care. *Beds* 100. *Certified*
Medicaid.
Admissions Requirements Medical
examination; Physician's request.
Staff Physicians 8 (pt); RNs 1 (ft), 1 (pt);
LPNs 9 (ft), 1 (pt); Nurses aides 18 (ft), 4
(pt); Physical therapists 2 (pt); Recreational
therapists 1 (ft); Occupational therapists 1
(pt); Speech therapists 1 (pt); Activities
coordinators 1 (ft); Dietitians 1 (ft); Dentists
1 (pt); Ophthalmologists 1 (pt); Audiologists
1 (pt).
Facilities Dining room; Activities room;
Chapel; Laundry room; Barber/Beauty shop.
Activities Arts & crafts; Cards; Games;
Reading groups; Prayer groups; Movies;
Shopping trips; Social/Cultural gatherings.

FAYETTEVILLE

Apple Tree Inn*
3100 Old Missouri Rd, Fayetteville, AR,
72701
(501) 521-4353
Admin Ginger Bridges. *Medical Dir/Dir of
Nursing* James Patrick.
Licensure Intermediate care. *Beds* 140.
Certified Medicaid.
Admissions Requirements Medical
examination; Physician's request.
Staff RNs 4 (ft); LPNs 15 (ft); Orderlies 4 (ft);
Nurses aides 45 (ft); Physical therapists;
Speech therapists; Activities coordinators;
Dentists; Podiatrists.
Facilities Dining room; Activities room;
Laundry room; Barber/Beauty shop.
Activities Arts & crafts; Cards; Games;
Reading groups; Prayer groups; Shopping
trips; Social/Cultural gatherings.

Fayetteville City Hospital Geriatrics Center*
PO Box 1743, Fayetteville, AR, 72701
(501) 442-5100
Admin Steve Dyer.
Licensure Skilled care. *Beds* 104. *Certified*
Medicaid.

Sunrise Manor Care Center*
1001 Rochier St, Fayetteville, AR, 72701
(501) 443-5211
Admin Mary Ann Nubbie.
Licensure Skilled care. *Beds* 147. *Certified*
Medicaid.

FORDYCE

Dallas County Nursing Home*
201 Clifton, Fordyce, AR, 71742
(501) 352-3155
Admin Ellen Harrington.
Licensure Skilled care. *Beds* 34. *Certified*
Medicaid.
Owner Proprietary Corp (National
Healthcare).

Southern Nursing Home*
PO Box 472, Fordyce, AR, 71742
(501) 352-2104
Admin Janice E Roark. *Medical Dir/Dir of
Nursing* Don G Howard MD.
Licensure Skilled care. *Beds* 75. *Certified*
Medicaid; Medicare.
Staff Physicians 3 (pt); RNs 1 (ft), 1 (pt);
LPNs 6 (ft), 5 (pt); Nurses aides 20 (ft), 4
(pt); Activities coordinators 1 (ft); Dietitians
5 (ft), 5 (pt).
Facilities Dining room; Laundry room;
Barber/Beauty shop.
Activities Arts & crafts; Games; Reading
groups; Prayer groups; Shopping trips;
Social/Cultural gatherings.

FORREST CITY

Borden Nursing Home Inc*
PO Box 545, Forrest City, AR, 72335
(501) 633-5163
Admin Chambliso Satterfield.
Licensure Intermediate care. *Beds* 33.
Certified Medicaid.
Staff Physicians 1 (pt); RNs 1 (ft); LPNs 3
(ft); Nurses aides 9 (ft), 9 (pt); Activities
coordinators 1 (ft); Dietitians 1 (ft); Dentists
1 (pt); Cooks 4 (ft).
Facilities Dining room; Activities room;
Laundry room.
Activities Arts & crafts; Games; Reading
groups; Prayer groups; Shopping trips.

Crestpark Inn of Forrest City*
PO Box 1658, 503 Kittel Rd, Forrest City,
AR, 72335
(501) 633-7630
Admin Janice Heath. *Medical Dir/Dir of
Nursing* H N Cogburn MD.
Licensure Skilled care. *Beds* 88. *Certified*
Medicaid.
Admissions Requirements Medical
examination; Physician's request.
Staff Physicians 10 (pt); RNs 1 (ft), 1 (pt);
LPNs 4 (ft), 2 (pt); Nurses aides 22 (ft), 1
(pt); Activities coordinators 1 (ft); Dietitians
1 (ft), 1 (pt); Dentists 4 (pt);
Ophthalmologists 1 (pt).
Facilities Dining room; Activities room;
Crafts room; Laundry room; Barber/Beauty
shop.
Activities Arts & crafts; Cards; Games;
Reading groups; Prayer groups; Movies;
Shopping trips.

Geriatrics Nursing Center Inc—Forrest City*
PO Box 1081, Forrest City, AR, 72335
(501) 633-7500
Admin Gerald Kimbrough.
Licensure Skilled care. *Beds* 70. *Certified*
Medicaid.
Owner Proprietary Corp (Beverly Enterprises).

FORT SMITH

Armour Heights Nursing Home Inc
3900 Armour Ave, Fort Smith, AR, 72904
(501) 782-8956

Admin Betty L Kirby. *Medical Dir/Dir of
Nursing* Richard Darden MD; Fredora
Hulse RN.
Licensure Skilled care. *Beds* SNF 75. *Certified*
Medicaid.
Owner Proprietary Corp.
Staff Physicians; RNs; LPNs; Orderlies;
Nurses aides; Activities coordinators;
Dietitians; Ophthalmologists.
Facilities Dining room; Laundry room;
Barber/Beauty shop; Library.
Activities Arts & crafts; Games; Reading
groups; Prayer groups; Movies; Shopping
trips; Trips.

Brownwood Life Care Center Inc
2121 Towson Ave, Fort Smith, AR, 72901
(501) 785-2273
Admin Dave Broaddrick. *Medical Dir/Dir of
Nursing* Karen Parish DON.
Licensure Intermediate care for mentally
retarded. *Beds* ICF/MR 50. *Certified*
Medicaid.
Owner Proprietary Corp.
Staff Physicians 1 (pt); RNs 5 (ft); LPNs 12
(ft); Orderlies 2 (ft); Nurses aides 50 (ft);
Physical therapists 1 (pt); Occupational
therapists 1 (ft); Speech therapists 1 (ft);
Activities coordinators 1 (ft); Dietitians 1
(ft).
Facilities Dining room; Physical therapy
room; Activities room; Crafts room; Laundry
room; Barber/Beauty shop; Library.
Activities Arts & crafts; Games.

Medi-Home Inc—Fort Smith*
4623 Rogers Ave, Fort Smith, AR, 72903
(501) 452-1541
Admin Nancy Stein. *Medical Dir/Dir of
Nursing* Dr Mort Wilson.
Licensure Skilled care. *Beds* 157. *Certified*
Medicaid.
Admissions Requirements Medical
examination; Physician's request.
Staff RNs 3 (ft), 2 (pt); LPNs 12 (ft), 2 (pt);
Orderlies 1 (ft); Nurses aides 43 (ft), 7 (pt);
Activities coordinators 1 (ft), 1 (pt);
Dietitians 1 (pt).
Facilities Dining room; Activities room;
Chapel; Crafts room; Laundry room.
Activities Arts & crafts; Cards; Games.

Methodist Nursing Home Inc
1915 S 74th St, Fort Smith, AR, 72903-2899
(501) 452-1611
Admin Gina L Cowan. *Medical Dir/Dir of
Nursing* Lottie Klyne.
Licensure Skilled care; Intermediate care. *Beds*
SNF 145; ICF. *Certified* Medicaid.
Owner Nonprofit organization/foundation.
Admissions Requirements Medical
examination; Physician's request.
Staff RNs 3 (ft); LPNs 20 (ft); Orderlies 40
(ft); Nurses aides; Activities coordinators 1
(ft); Dietitians 15 (ft); Laundry 4 (ft);
Housekeeping 16 (ft).
Languages German
Affiliation Methodist
Facilities Dining room; Activities room;
Chapel; Crafts room; Laundry room; Barber/
Beauty shop.
Activities Arts & crafts; Cards; Games;
Reading groups; Prayer groups; Movies;
Social/Cultural gatherings.

Oaks Lodge Rest Home Inc*
3310 Waldron Rd, Fort Smith, AR, 72904
(501) 783-3101, 3102
Admin Becky Birch.
Licensure Intermediate care. *Beds* 105.
Certified Medicaid.

Parkview Nursing Home—Fort Smith*
425 N 51st St, Fort Smith, AR, 72903
(501) 452-0530
Admin Marcia Webb.
Licensure Intermediate care. *Beds* 41.
Certified Medicaid.

Rose Care Center of Fort Smith*
5301 Wheeler Ave, Fort Smith, AR, 72901
(501) 646-3454
Admin James E Milford.
Licensure Skilled care. *Beds* 187. *Certified*
Medicaid.

GLENWOOD

Glenwood Nursing Home Inc*
Box 1390, Glenwood, AR, 71943
(501) 356-3953
Admin Roger Tidwell.
Licensure Intermediate care. *Beds* 70.
Certified Medicaid.

GRAVETTE

Gravette Manor Nursing Home
PO Box 180, Gravette, AR, 72736
(501) 787-5381
Admin Bobbi R Wilks. *Medical Dir/Dir of
Nursing* Dr Billy V Hall; Kathy Mitchell
RN.
Licensure Intermediate care. *Certified*
Medicaid.
Owner Privately owned.
Admissions Requirements Medical
examination; Physician's request.
Staff RNs 1 (ft); LPNs 3 (ft), 2 (pt); Nurses
aides 26 (ft), 10 (pt); Activities coordinators
1 (ft), 1 (pt); Dietitians 1 (ft).
Facilities Dining room; Activities room;
Crafts room; Laundry room; Barber/Beauty
shop; Fenced yard with patio.
Activities Arts & crafts; Cards; Games;
Reading groups; Prayer groups; Movies;
Shopping trips; Social/Cultural gatherings;
Fishing trips; Picnics; Trips to zoo.

GREENWOOD

Pink Bud Home for the Golden Years
Hwy 71, PO Box 592, Greenwood, AR, 72936
(501) 996-4125
Admin Roger W Corbin. *Medical Dir/Dir of
Nursing* Vincy Hannaman.
Licensure Intermediate care. *Beds* 74.
Certified Medicaid.
Admissions Requirements Medical
examination.
Staff Physicians 4 (pt); RNs 2 (ft); LPNs 4
(ft), 1 (pt); Orderlies 30 (ft), 2 (pt); Nurses
aides 12 (ft), 2 (pt); Physical therapists 1
(pt); Activities coordinators 2 (ft); Dietitians
1 (pt).
Facilities Dining room; Physical therapy
room; Activities room; Crafts room; Laundry
room; Barber/Beauty shop; Lobby.
Activities Arts & crafts; Games; Reading
groups; Prayer groups; Social/Cultural
gatherings.

GURDON

Pineview Home Inc*
PO Box 10, 904 Seahorn St, Gurdon, AR,
71743
(501) 353-2566
Admin Lisa Crow.
Licensure Intermediate care. *Beds* 50.
Certified Medicaid.

HAMBURG

Leisure Lodge Inc—Hamburg*
Rte 3, Box 300, Hamburg, AR, 71646
(501) 853-8204
Admin Myrtle Kilcrease.
Licensure Skilled care. *Beds* 105. *Certified*
Medicaid.
Owner Proprietary Corp (Beverly Enterprises).

HAMPTON

Hampton Nursing Home
PO Box 538, Hampton, AR, 71744-0538
(510) 798-4272
Admin Linda Stringfellow. *Medical Dir/Dir of Nursing* Tom L Dunn MD.
Licensure Skilled care. *Beds* 74. *Certified* Medicaid.
Staff Physicians 3 (pt); RNs 1 (ft), 2 (pt); LPNs 9 (ft); Nurses aides 17 (ft), 9 (pt); Physical therapists 1 (pt); Activities coordinators 1 (ft); Dietitians 2 (ft); Dentists 1 (pt); Optometrists 1 (ft); Social workers 1 (ft), 1 (pt).
Facilities Dining room; Activities room; Crafts room; Laundry room; Barber/Beauty shop; Day room.
Activities Arts & crafts; Games; Reading groups; Prayer groups; Movies; Shopping trips; Social/Cultural gatherings; Fishing trips; Picnics; Special outing each summer; Fund raisers.

HARRISON

Harrison Nursing Center
115 Orendorff Ave, CC-6, Harrison, AR, 72601
(501) 741-3438
Admin Debbie Taylor. *Medical Dir/Dir of Nursing* Dr R H (Bob) Langston.
Licensure Skilled care. *Beds* 102. *Certified* Medicaid.
Owner Proprietary Corp (Beverly Enterprises).
Admissions Requirements Physician's request.
Staff Physicians 8 (pt); RNs 1 (ft), 1 (pt); LPNs 8 (ft), 2 (pt); Orderlies 4 (ft); Nurses aides 25 (ft), 2 (pt); Physical therapists 1 (pt); Activities coordinators 1 (ft); Dietitians 1 (ft); Dentists 1 (pt).
Facilities Dining room; Activities room; Crafts room; Laundry room; Barber/Beauty shop; Court yard.
Activities Arts & crafts; Cards; Games; Reading groups; Prayer groups; Shopping trips; Social/Cultural gatherings.

Hillcrest Home—Harrison
315 E Sherman, Harrison, AR, 72601
(501) 741-5001
Admin Frederick G Helmuth. *Medical Dir of Nursing* Susan P Steckley RN DON.
Licensure Intermediate care. *Beds* ICF 67. *Certified* Medicaid.
Owner Publicly owned.
Admissions Requirements Minimum age 18; Medical examination.
Staff RNs 3 (ft); LPNs 2 (ft), 2 (pt); Orderlies 5 (ft); Nurses aides 10 (ft); Activities coordinators 1 (ft).
Affiliation Mennonite
Facilities Dining room; Physical therapy room; Activities room; Chapel; Crafts room; Laundry room; Library; Courtyard with fountain.
Activities Arts & crafts; Games; Reading groups; Movies; Shopping trips.

Hilltop Nursing Center
202 Tims Ave, Harrison, AR, 72601
(501) 741-7667
Admin Norean Bailey. *Medical Dir/Dir of Nursing* H V Kirby MD.
Licensure Skilled care. *Beds* SNF 140. *Certified* Medicaid.
Owner Proprietary Corp (Beverly Enterprises).
Admissions Requirements Minimum age 65; Medical examination; Physician's request.
Staff Physicians 1 (pt); RNs 2 (ft), 1 (pt); LPNs 6 (ft), 3 (pt); Orderlies 8 (ft); Nurses aides 31 (ft); Physical therapists 1 (pt); Activities coordinators 1 (ft); Dietitians 1 (ft); Restorative aide 1 (ft); Social worker 1 (ft).

Facilities Dining room; Physical therapy room; Laundry room; Barber/Beauty shop.
Activities Arts & crafts; Cards; Games; Reading groups; Prayer groups; Movies; Shopping trips; Social/Cultural gatherings.

HEBER SPRINGS

Geriatrics Nursing Center Inc—Heber Springs*
1040 Weddingford Rd, Heber Springs, AR, 72543
(501) 362-8137
Admin Nancy Sue Thompson.
Licensure Skilled care. *Beds* 140. *Certified* Medicaid.
Owner Proprietary Corp (Beverly Enterprises).

Lakeland Lodge Nursing Home
600 S 11th St, Heber Springs, AR, 72543
(501) 362-3185
Admin Elaine R Hickerson. *Medical Dir/Dir of Nursing* Nathan Poff MD; Lea Branscum DON.
Licensure Skilled care. *Beds* 102. *Certified* Medicaid.
Owner Proprietary Corp (Beverly Enterprises).
Admissions Requirements Medical examination; Physician's request.
Staff RNs; LPNs; Nurses aides; Reality therapists; Activities coordinators; Dietitians.
Facilities Dining room; Activities room; Crafts room; Laundry room; Barber/Beauty shop.
Activities Arts & crafts; Cards; Games; Reading groups; Prayer groups; Movies; Shopping trips; Social/Cultural gatherings.

HELENA

Crestpark Inn of Helena—Intermediate Care Facility
PO Box 310, Hospital Drive, Helena, AR, 72342
(501) 338-3405
Admin Rita Fincher. *Medical Dir/Dir of Nursing* C P McCarty MD; Jaynie Jones RN DON.
Licensure Intermediate care. *Beds* ICF 75; ICF/MR. *Certified* Medicaid.
Owner Proprietary Corp.
Staff Physicians; RNs 1 (ft); LPNs 6 (ft), 1 (pt); Orderlies 5 (ft); Nurses aides 25 (ft); Physical therapists 1 (pt); Recreational therapists 1 (pt); Occupational therapists; Speech therapists; Activities coordinators 1 (ft); Dietitians 1 (ft), 1 (pt).
Facilities Dining room; Physical therapy room; Activities room; Chapel; Crafts room; Laundry room; Barber/Beauty shop; Library.
Activities Arts & crafts; Cards; Games; Reading groups; Prayer groups; Movies; Social/Cultural gatherings.

Crestpark Inn of Helena Skilled Nursing Facility*
PO Box 310, Helena, AR, 72342
(501) 338-9886
Admin Jeanne Crisp.
Licensure Skilled care. *Beds* 111. *Certified* Medicaid.

HOPE

Heather Manor Nursing Center*
PO Box 961, Hope, AR, 71801
(501) 777-4673
Admin Nora McRoy. *Medical Dir/Dir of Nursing* Dr J C Little.
Licensure Skilled care. *Beds* 105. *Certified* Medicaid.
Admissions Requirements Medical examination; Physician's request.
Staff Physicians 7 (pt); RNs 2 (ft); LPNs 9 (pt); Nurses aides 40 (ft); Physical therapists 1 (pt); Reality therapists 1 (pt); Recreational

therapists 1 (pt); Speech therapists 1 (pt); Activities coordinators 1 (ft); Dietitians 1 (ft); Dentists 1 (pt).
Facilities Dining room; Physical therapy room; Activities room; Chapel; Crafts room; Laundry room; Barber/Beauty shop.
Activities Arts & crafts; Cards; Games; Reading groups; Prayer groups; Movies; Shopping trips.

Parkview Skilled of Hope*
426 S Main, Hope, AR, 71801
(501) 777-4638
Admin Calvin Remy.
Licensure Skilled care. *Beds* 55. *Certified* Medicaid; Medicare.

Pinehope Nursing Home*
1900 S Walker St, Hope, AR, 71801
(501) 777-8855
Admin Ray Woodard.
Licensure Intermediate care. *Beds* 105. *Certified* Medicaid.

HOT SPRINGS

Arkansas Healthcare Nursing Center
909 Golf Links Rd, Hot Springs, AR, 71901
(501) 624-7149
Admin Harold Smith. *Medical Dir/Dir of Nursing* Dr Rheeta Stecker; Jane Tadlock RN.
Licensure Skilled care. *Beds* 152. *Certified* Medicaid; Medicare.
Owner Proprietary Corp (Beverly Enterprises).
Staff RNs 2 (ft), 1 (pt).
Facilities Dining room; Physical therapy room; Barber/Beauty shop.
Activities Arts & crafts; Games; Prayer groups; Shopping trips; Social/Cultural gatherings.

Garland Convalescent Center*
600 Carpenter Dam Rd, Hot Springs, AR, 71901
(501) 262-2571
Admin Rex Ann Waymon.
Licensure Skilled care. *Beds* 105. *Certified* Medicaid.

Hot Springs Nursing Home
1401 Park Ave, Hot Springs, AR, 71901
(501) 623-3781, 624-0616
Admin Ronald Nield. *Medical Dir/Dir of Nursing* Dr John Simpson; Cleo Thompson RN DON.
Licensure Skilled care. *Beds* SNF 140. *Certified* Medicaid.
Owner Proprietary Corp (Vantage Healthcare).
Staff RNs 2 (ft), 2 (pt); LPNs 15 (ft), 5 (pt); Orderlies 1 (ft); Nurses aides 40 (ft), 10 (pt); Activities coordinators 1 (ft); Dietitians 1 (ft).
Facilities Dining room; Activities room; Laundry room; Barber/Beauty shop.
Activities Arts & crafts; Cards; Games; Reading groups; Prayer groups; Movies; Shopping trips; Social/Cultural gatherings.

Lakewood Convalescent Home
Rte 17, Box 661, Carpenter Dam Rd, Hot Springs, AR, 71901
(501) 262-1920
Admin Dorothy Smith. *Medical Dir/Dir of Nursing* Kenneth Seifert MD; Joan Krahn RN DON.
Licensure Intermediate care. *Beds* ICF 50. *Certified* Medicaid.
Owner Nonprofit Corp.
Admissions Requirements Minimum age 60; Physician's request.
Staff Physicians 4 (pt); RNs 1 (ft), 1 (pt); LPNs 4 (ft), 2 (pt); Nurses aides 25 (ft); Physical therapists 1 (pt); Occupational therapists 1 (pt); Speech therapists 1 (pt); Activities coordinators 1 (ft); Dietitians 1 (ft), 1 (pt); Podiatrists 1 (pt); Dentist 1 (pt).

Facilities Dining room; Crafts room; Laundry room; Barber/Beauty shop.
Activities Arts & crafts; Games; Prayer groups; Movies; Shopping trips; Social/Cultural gatherings.

Nucare Convalescent Center Inc
1316 Park Ave, Hot Springs, AR, 71901
(501) 624-2516
Admin Gladys Owens. *Medical Dir/Dir of Nursing* Dr Robert Lewis; Abby Littlejohn.
Licensure Skilled care. *Beds* 100. *Certified* Medicaid.
Owner Proprietary Corp (Southeastern Health Care Inc).
Admissions Requirements Medical examination; Physician's request.
Staff Physicians 2 (ft); RNs 1 (ft), 2 (pt); LPNs 15 (ft), 2 (pt); Orderlies 1 (ft); Nurses aides 50 (ft); Physical therapists 1 (pt); Reality therapists 1 (pt); Recreational therapists 1 (pt); Occupational therapists 1 (pt); Speech therapists 1 (pt); Activities coordinators 1 (ft); Dietitians 1 (ft); Dentists 1 (pt); Ophthalmologists 1 (pt); Podiatrists 1 (pt); Psychiatrist 1 (pt).
Facilities Dining room; Activities room; Chapel; Crafts room; Laundry room; Barber/Beauty shop; Library.
Activities Arts & crafts; Cards; Games; Reading groups; Prayer groups; Movies; Shopping trips; Social/Cultural gatherings.

Quality Care Nursing Center
351 Woodfin St, Hot Springs, AR, 71901
(501) 624-5238
Admin Kevin Hodges. *Medical Dir/Dir of Nursing* Donna Guthrie RN.
Licensure Skilled care. *Beds* 113. *Certified* Medicaid.
Owner Proprietary Corp (Beverly Enterprises).
Admissions Requirements Physician's request.
Staff Physicians; RNs; LPNs; Orderlies; Nurses aides; Recreational therapists; Occupational therapists; Activities coordinators; Dietitians; Dentists; Ophthalmologists.
Facilities Dining room; Activities room; Laundry room; Barber/Beauty shop; Library.
Activities Arts & crafts; Cards; Games; Reading groups; Prayer groups; Movies; Shopping trips; Social/Cultural gatherings.

HOT SPRINGS VILLAGE

Good Samaritan Cedar Lodge
5 Cortez Rd, Hot Springs Village, AR, 71909
(501) 922-2000
Admin Jonathan Conrad. *Medical Dir/Dir of Nursing* Lorraine Hollier RN DON.
Licensure Intermediate care. *Beds* ICF 40. *Certified* Medicaid.
Owner Nonprofit Corp (Evangelical Lutheran/ Good Samaritan).
Admissions Requirements Medical examination; Physician's request.
Staff RNs 1 (ft); LPNs 3 (ft), 2 (pt); Orderlies 2 (ft); Nurses aides 6 (ft), 2 (pt); Activities coordinators 2 (pt).
Affiliation Lutheran
Facilities Dining room; Physical therapy room; Activities room; Chapel; Crafts room; Laundry room; Barber/Beauty shop; Library; Billiar room; Whirlpool spa; Wood shop; Fitness Center; Den.
Activities Arts & crafts; Cards; Games; Reading groups; Prayer groups; Movies; Movies; Social/Cultural gatherings.

HUNTSVILLE

Meadowview Lodge*
Drawer E, Huntsville, AR, 72740
(501) 738-2021
Admin George W Johnson.
Licensure Skilled care. *Beds* 70. *Certified* Medicaid.

JACKSONVILLE

Jacksonville Nursing Center
1320 W Braden St, Jacksonville, AR, 72076
(501) 982-0521
Admin Gary Gipson. *Medical Dir/Dir of Nursing* Dr Tom Wortham MD; Pat Hunter DON.
Licensure Skilled care. *Beds* 245. *Certified* Medicaid; Medicare.
Owner Proprietary Corp (Beverly Enterprises).
Admissions Requirements Physician's request.
Staff RNs; LPNs; Orderlies; Nurses aides; Physical therapists; Activities coordinators; Dietitians.
Facilities Dining room; Physical therapy room; Activities room; Crafts room; Laundry room; Barber/Beauty shop.
Activities Arts & crafts; Games; Reading groups; Movies; Shopping trips; Social/ Cultural gatherings.

Rose Care Center of Jacksonville
1701 S Hwy 161, Jacksonville, AR, 72076
(501) 982-5141
Admin Doris A Beard RN. *Medical Dir/Dir of Nursing* Kay Kwok RN.
Licensure Intermediate care. *Beds* 58. *Certified* Medicaid.
Owner Proprietary Corp (Rose Care Inc).
Admissions Requirements Minimum age 21; Medical examination; Physician's request.
Staff RNs 1 (ft); LPNs 4 (ft), 1 (pt); Nurses aides 19 (ft), 2 (pt); Activities coordinators 1 (ft).
Facilities Dining room; Activities room.
Activities Arts & crafts; Cards; Games; Reading groups; Prayer groups.

JASPER

Newton County Nursing Home*
PO Box 442, Jasper, AR, 72641
(501) 446-2204 or 446-2333
Admin Rick E. Eddings.
Licensure Intermediate care. *Beds* 42. *Certified* Medicaid.

JONESBORO

Craighead Nursing Center
Rte 9, Box 32, Jonesboro, AR, 72401
(501) 932-7677
Admin Nevin Beachy. *Medical Dir/Dir of Nursing* J F Thomas MD; John Heern RN DON.
Licensure Skilled care. *Beds* SNF 57. *Certified* Medicaid.
Owner Publicly owned.
Admissions Requirements Minimum age 40; Medical examination; Physician's request.
Staff Physicians 1 (pt); RNs 1 (ft), 2 (pt); LPNs 4 (ft), 1 (pt); Nurses aides 13 (ft); Physical therapists 1 (pt); Speech therapists 1 (pt); Activities coordinators 1 (ft); Dietitians 1 (pt).
Facilities Dining room; Activities room; Crafts room; Barber/Beauty shop.
Activities Arts & crafts; Games; Reading groups; Prayer groups; Movies; Shopping trips.

Geriatrics Nursing Center
800 Southwest Dr, Jonesboro, AR, 72401
(501) 935-7550
Admin Kathy Atchley. *Medical Dir/Dir of Nursing* Nadine Haley.
Licensure Skilled care. *Beds* SNF 103. *Certified* Medicaid.
Owner Proprietary Corp (Beverly Enterprises).
Staff RNs 3 (ft), 1 (pt); LPNs 9 (ft), 5 (pt); Nurses aides 40 (ft), 10 (pt); Activities coordinators 1 (ft).

Jonesboro Human Development Center
4701 Colony Dr, Jonesboro, AR, 72401
(501) 932-5230
Admin Jerry W Cooper. *Medical Dir/Dir of Nursing* Dr Robert Lawrence.
Licensure Intermediate care for mentally retarded. *Beds* ICF/MR 128. *Certified* Medicaid.
Owner Publicly owned.
Admissions Requirements Minimum age 6; Medical examination.
Facilities Dining room; Physical therapy room; Activities room; Chapel; Crafts room; Laundry room; Library; Classrooms.
Activities Arts & crafts; Games; Movies; Shopping trips; Social/Cultural gatherings; Active Treatment Programming.

Rose Care Center of Jonesboro*
Rte 12, Box 404, Jonesboro, AR, 72401
(501) 932-3271
Admin Vicki Moore McMillan. *Medical Dir/ Dir of Nursing* Dr Forrest Wisdom.
Licensure Skilled care. *Beds* 108. *Certified* Medicaid.
Admissions Requirements Medical examination; Physician's request.
Staff Physicians 1 (pt); RNs 2 (ft); LPNs 12 (ft); Nurses aides 24 (ft), 5 (pt); Physical therapists 1 (pt); Reality therapists 1 (pt); Speech therapists 1 (pt); Activities coordinators 1 (ft); Dietitians 1 (ft); Dentists 1 (pt); Ophthalmologists 1 (pt).
Facilities Dining room; Activities room; Crafts room; Laundry room; Barber/Beauty shop.
Activities Arts & crafts; Cards; Games; Reading groups; Prayer groups; Movies; Shopping trips; Social/Cultural gatherings.

Rose Skill Care Nursing Center of Jonesboro*
2911 Brown's Ln, Jonesboro, AR, 72401
(501) 935-8330
Admin Betty L Metz. *Medical Dir/Dir of Nursing* G D Wisdom MD.
Licensure Skilled care. *Beds* 152. *Certified* Medicaid; Medicare.
Admissions Requirements Minimum age 21; Medical examination; Physician's request.
Staff Physicians 2 (pt); RNs 1 (ft), 2 (pt); LPNs 14 (ft), 5 (pt); Nurses aides 38 (ft), 1 (pt); Speech therapists 1 (pt); Activities coordinators 1 (ft); Dietitians 1 (pt); Dentists 1 (pt).
Facilities Dining room; Physical therapy room; Laundry room; Barber/Beauty shop.
Activities Arts & crafts; Cards; Games; Prayer groups; Shopping trips; Social/Cultural gatherings.

JUDSONIA

Oakdale Nursing Home*
PO Box 670, Judsonia, AR, 72081
(501) 268-2288
Admin Leonard M Wiggins.
Licensure Skilled care. *Beds* 100. *Certified* Medicaid.

JUNCTION CITY

Junction City Nursing Home
PO Box 2, Rte 1 Maple & First, Junction City, AR, 71749
(501) 924-4522
Admin Lisa Barnette. *Medical Dir/Dir of Nursing* Sook Langston.
Licensure Skilled care. *Beds* 84. *Certified* Medicaid.
Owner Proprietary Corp (Beverly Enterprises).
Admissions Requirements Medical examination; Physician's request.
Staff RNs; LPNs; Nurses aides; Activities coordinators; Dietitians.
Facilities Dining room; Activities room; Laundry room; Barber/Beauty shop.
Activities Arts & crafts; Games; Reading groups; Prayer groups.

LAKE CITY

Lakeside Nursing Center
PO Box 578, Lake City, AR, 72437
(501) 237-8151
Admin Gaylon Gammill. *Medical Dir/Dir of Nursing* Dr R A Robbins; Verneil Gooman DON.
Licensure Skilled care. *Beds* SNF 40. *Certified* Medicaid.
Owner Proprietary Corp.
Admissions Requirements Physician's request.
Facilities Dining room; Activities room; Crafts room; Laundry room; Barber/Beauty shop; Library.
Activities Arts & crafts; Games; Reading groups; Prayer groups; Shopping trips; Social/Cultural gatherings.

LAKE VILLAGE

Leisure Lodge Inc—Lake Village*
Hwy 65 S, Lake Village, AR, 71653
(501) 265-5337
Admin Mary McCoy. *Medical Dir/Dir of Nursing* Danny Berry.
Licensure Intermediate care. *Beds* 85. *Certified* Medicaid.
Owner Proprietary Corp (Beverly Enterprises).
Staff Physicians 1 (ft); RNs 1 (ft); LPNs 8 (ft); Nurses aides 28 (ft); Activities coordinators 1 (ft); Dietitians 1 (ft); Dentists 1 (pt).
Facilities Dining room; Activities room; Laundry room; Barber/Beauty shop.
Activities Arts & crafts; Games; Prayer groups; Movies; Shopping trips; Social/Cultural gatherings.

LITTLE ROCK

Arkansas Easter Seals Residential Center
PO Box 5148, Little Rock, AR, 72225
(501) 663-8331
Admin Jim Butler. *Medical Dir/Dir of Nursing* Richard McCarthy MD; Nancy Tomosicski RN DON.
Licensure Intermediate care for mentally retarded. *Beds* ICF/MR 25. *Certified* Medicaid.
Owner Nonprofit organization/foundation.
Admissions Requirements Minimum age 3.
Staff Physicians 2 (pt); RNs 1 (ft); LPNs 5 (ft); Nurses aides 12 (ft), 2 (pt); Physical therapists 3 (ft); Recreational therapists 2 (ft); Occupational therapists 3 (ft); Speech therapists 3 (ft); Dietitians 1 (ft).
Facilities Dining room; Physical therapy room; Activities room; Laundry room; Occupational therapy.
Activities Arts & crafts; Games; Reading groups; Movies; Shopping trips.

Doctors Nursing Center Inc*
4115 W 16th St, Little Rock, AR, 72204
(501) 664-3926
Admin Deanna Crawford.
Licensure Skilled care. *Beds* 194. *Certified* Medicaid.

Fountainbleau Nursing Home*
10905 W Markham St, Little Rock, AR, 72211
(501) 225-6501
Admin James David Hightower. *Medical Dir/Dir of Nursing* Jerry D Malott MD.
Licensure Intermediate care. *Beds* 70. *Certified* Medicaid.
Admissions Requirements Medical examination; Physician's request.
Staff RNs 1 (ft); LPNs 3 (ft), 3 (pt); Nurses aides 20 (ft), 5 (pt); Activities coordinators 1 (ft).
Facilities Dining room; Activities room; Laundry room; Barber/Beauty shop.
Activities Arts & crafts; Games; Reading groups; Prayer groups.

Hillhaven of Little Rock*
5720 W Markham, Little Rock, AR, 72205
(501) 664-6200
Admin James W Ives.
Licensure Skilled care. *Beds* 174. *Certified* Medicaid; Medicare.
Owner Proprietary Corp (Hillhaven Corp).

Little Rock Nursing Center
1516 Cumberland St, Little Rock, AR, 72202
(501) 374-7565
Admin Patricia Miller. *Medical Dir/Dir of Nursing* John Wolverton MD; Majorie Ince.
Licensure Skilled care. *Beds* SNF 204. *Certified* Medicaid.
Owner Proprietary Corp (Rose Care Inc).
Admissions Requirements Minimum age 55; Physician's request.
Staff Physicians 1 (ft), 6 (pt); RNs 2 (ft), 2 (pt); LPNs 21 (ft); Orderlies 5 (ft); Nurses aides 60 (ft); Physical therapists; Reality therapists; Recreational therapists; Occupational therapists; Speech therapists; Activities coordinators 2 (ft); Dietitians 2 (ft); Dentists 1 (pt); Ophthalmologists 1 (pt).
Facilities Dining room; Physical therapy room; Activities room; Laundry room; Barber/Beauty shop; Library.
Activities Arts & crafts; Cards; Games; Reading groups; Prayer groups; Movies; Shopping trips; Social/Cultural gatherings.

Presbyterian Village Health Care Center
500 N Brookside Dr, Little Rock, AR, 72205
(501) 225-0114
Admin Nelson Reinhardt. *Medical Dir/Dir of Nursing* James Flack MD.
Licensure Skilled care; Intermediate care. *Beds* 78.
Admissions Requirements Medical examination; Physician's request.
Staff Physicians 1 (pt); RNs 5 (ft); LPNs 13 (ft); Orderlies 2 (ft); Nurses aides 45 (ft); Physical therapists 1 (ft); Reality therapists 1 (pt); Occupational therapists 1 (pt); Speech therapists 1 (pt); Dietitians 1 (pt); Ophthalmologists 1 (pt); Dentist 1 (pt).
Affiliation Presbyterian
Facilities Dining room; Physical therapy room; Activities room; Chapel; Crafts room; Laundry room; Barber/Beauty shop; Library.
Activities Arts & crafts; Cards; Games; Reading groups; Prayer groups; Movies; Shopping trips; Social/Cultural gatherings.

Riley's Oak Hill Manor South*
8701 Riley Dr, Little Rock, AR, 72205
(501) 224-2700
Admin Anne Stroud. *Medical Dir/Dir of Nursing* Dr Harold Hedges.
Licensure Skilled care. *Beds* 224.
Admissions Requirements Medical examination; Physician's request.
Staff RNs 5 (ft); LPNs 13 (ft), 2 (pt); Nurses aides 42 (ft), 6 (pt); Physical therapists 1 (pt); Recreational therapists 2 (pt); Dietitians 2 (ft); Dentists 1 (pt); Podiatrists 1 (pt); 1 (pt).
Facilities Dining room; Physical therapy room; Activities room; Chapel; Crafts room; Laundry room; Barber/Beauty shop; Library.
Activities Arts & crafts; Cards; Games; Reading groups; Movies; Shopping trips; Social/Cultural gatherings.

Rose Care Center of Little Rock*
800 Brookside Dr, Little Rock, AR, 72205
(501) 224-3940
Admin Billie Brarzseal. *Medical Dir/Dir of Nursing* Dr Michael Hendren.
Licensure Intermediate care. *Beds* 143. *Certified* Medicaid.
Staff Physicians 1 (ft); RNs 2 (ft), 2 (pt); LPNs 20 (ft), 2 (pt); Nurses aides 55 (ft), 5 (pt); Physical therapists 1 (pt); Occupational therapists 1 (pt); Activities coordinators 1

(ft); Dietitians 1 (pt); Dentists 1 (pt); Ophthalmologists 1 (pt); Podiatrists 1 (pt); Audiologists 1 (pt); Social workers 1 (ft).
Facilities Dining room; Activities room; Crafts room; Laundry room; Barber/Beauty shop; Library; Courtyard.
Activities Arts & crafts; Cards; Games; Reading groups; Prayer groups; Shopping trips; Social/Cultural gatherings; Exercise classes; Outings.

Southwest Homes*
3915 Dixon Rd, Little Rock, AR, 72206
(501) 888-4257
Admin Gerald O Geddes.
Licensure Intermediate care. *Beds* 125. *Certified* Medicaid.

Trinity Court Nursing Home*
2000 Main St, Little Rock, AR, 72206
(501) 375-9062
Admin Earnest Johnson.
Licensure Skilled care. *Beds* 160. *Certified* Medicaid.

Vantage Convalescent Center*
8500 Mize Rd, Little Rock, AR, 72209
(501) 562-2964
Admin Stormy Smith.
Licensure Skilled care. *Beds* 150. *Certified* Medicaid.
Owner Proprietary Corp (Vantage Healthcare).

Williamsburg Retirement Inn
6301 Lee Ave, Little Rock, AR, 72205
(501) 663-9461
Admin Michael A Mahan. *Medical Dir/Dir of Nursing* Carla Brakop MD.
Licensure Skilled care. *Beds* 101. *Certified* Medicaid.
Owner Proprietary Corp (Beverly Enterprises).
Admissions Requirements Medical examination; Physician's request.
Staff RNs 2 (ft); LPNs 11 (ft), 4 (pt); Nurses aides 18 (ft), 18 (pt); Activities coordinators 1 (ft); Dietitians 1 (ft).
Facilities Dining room; Laundry room; Barber/Beauty shop.
Activities Arts & crafts; Cards; Prayer groups; Movies; Social/Cultural gatherings; Music groups.

LONOKE

Golden Years Manor*
PO Box 244, 1010 Barnes, Lonoke, AR, 72086
(501) 676-3103
Admin Judy Clyburn.
Licensure Skilled care. *Beds* 101. *Certified* Medicaid.

Lonoke Nursing Home Inc
PO Box 276, 420 E Academy St, Lonoke, AR, 82086
(501) 676-2785
Admin Thelma L Shook. *Medical Dir/Dir of Nursing* Frances Carter RN.
Licensure Intermediate care. *Beds* ICF 53. *Certified* Medicaid.
Owner Proprietary Corp.
Admissions Requirements Physician's request.
Staff RNs 1 (ft); LPNs 4 (ft), 1 (pt); Nurses aides 12 (ft), 3 (pt); Activities coordinators 1 (ft).
Facilities Dining room; Laundry room.
Activities Arts & crafts; Games; Movies; Church groups visit.

MAGNOLIA

Magnolia Manor
301 S Boundry St, Magnolia, AR, 71753
(501) 234-1361
Admin Dorthay Gay. *Medical Dir/Dir of Nursing* Rodney Griffin; Stephanie Snider DON.
Licensure Skilled care. *Beds* 113. *Certified* Medicaid.

Owner Proprietary Corp (Beverly Enterprises).
Admissions Requirements Minimum age 75.
Staff RNs 10 (ft); LPNs 3 (ft); Orderlies 1 (ft); Nurses aides 50 (ft); Physical therapists 1 (ft); Recreational therapists 1 (ft).
Facilities Dining room; Activities room; Crafts room; Laundry room; Barber/Beauty shop; Library.
Activities Arts & crafts; Cards; Games; Reading groups; Prayer groups; Movies; Shopping trips; Social/Cultural gatherings.

Meadowbrook Lodge*
600 Lelia St, Magnolia, AR, 71753
(501) 234-7000
Admin Sandy Whittington.
Licensure Intermediate care. *Beds* 140.
Certified Medicaid.
Owner Proprietary Corp (Beverly Enterprises).

MALVERN

Longmeadow Nursing Home of Malvern*
PO Box 567, Malvern, AR, 72104
(501) 332-6934
Admin Mark Mitchell. *Medical Dir/Dir of Nursing* Dr N B Kersh.
Licensure Intermediate care. *Beds* 69.
Certified Medicaid.
Staff RNs 1 (ft); LPNs 2 (ft), 3 (pt); Nurses aides 20 (ft), 2 (pt); Speech therapists 1 (pt); Activities coordinators 1 (ft); Dietitians 1 (pt).
Affiliation Baptist
Facilities Dining room; Activities room; Laundry room; Barber/Beauty shop.
Activities Arts & crafts; Cards; Games; Reading groups; Prayer groups; Movies; Shopping trips; Social/Cultural gatherings.

Malvern Nursing Home*
Rte 8, Box 176, Malvern, AR, 72104
(501) 337-9581
Admin Jayne Howard West. *Medical Dir/Dir of Nursing* C F Peters MD.
Licensure Skilled care. *Beds* 95. *Certified* Medicaid.
Staff Activities coordinators 1 (ft).
Facilities Dining room; Laundry room; Barber/Beauty shop.
Activities Arts & crafts; Movies; Shopping trips.

Stillmeadow Convalescent Center
Rte 2, Box 11, Malvern, AR, 72104
(501) 332-5251
Admin Marion Cunningham. *Medical Dir/Dir of Nursing* C F Peters MD; Jackie Campbell RN DON.
Licensure Skilled care. *Beds* 104. *Certified* Medicaid.
Owner Proprietary Corp (Manor Care).
Admissions Requirements Physician's request.
Staff Physicians 10 (pt); RNs 2 (ft), 2 (pt); LPNs 5 (ft), 5 (pt); Nurses aides 41 (ft), 10 (pt); Physical therapists 1 (pt); Activities coordinators 1 (ft); Dietitians 1 (pt); Dentist 1 (pt).
Facilities Dining room; Physical therapy room; Activities room; Chapel; Crafts room; Laundry room; Barber/Beauty shop.
Activities Arts & crafts; Games; Reading groups; Prayer groups; Movies; Shopping trips; Social/Cultural gatherings.

MANILA

Manila Nursing Home*
PO Box 429, Manila, AR, 72442
(501) 561-4492
Admin Gaylon Gammill. *Medical Dir/Dir of Nursing* Eugene Shaneyfelt.
Licensure Intermediate care. *Beds* 53.
Certified Medicaid.
Staff RNs 1 (ft), 1 (pt); LPNs 2 (ft), 3 (pt); Nurses aides 12 (ft); Activities coordinators 1 (ft); Dietitians 1 (ft), 1 (pt).

Facilities Dining room; Activities room; Laundry room.
Activities Arts & crafts; Games; Prayer groups; Shopping trips.

MARIANNA

Crestpark Inn of Marianna*
PO Box 386, Marianna, AR, 72360
(501) 295-3466
Admin Alan Curtis.
Licensure Intermediate care. *Beds* 90.
Certified Medicaid.

MARKED TREE

Three Rivers Nursing Center*
PO Box 519, Marked Tree, AR, 72365
(501) 358-2432
Admin Dorothy Abbott Castro.
Licensure Intermediate care. *Beds* 112.
Certified Medicaid.

MARSHALL

Marshall Nursing Center*
PO Box 541, Marshall, AR, 72650
(501) 448-3151
Admin W Burt Glenn.
Licensure Intermediate care. *Beds* 77.
Certified Medicaid.
Admissions Requirements Medical examination; Physician's request.
Staff Physicians 3 (ft); RNs 1 (ft); LPNs 5 (ft), 1 (pt); Orderlies 2 (ft), 1 (pt); Nurses aides 23 (ft), 3 (pt); Physical therapists 1 (pt); Reality therapists 1 (ft); Recreational therapists 1 (ft); Activities coordinators 1 (ft); Dietitians 1 (pt); Dentists 2 (pt); Ophthalmologists 1 (pt).
Facilities Dining room; Activities room; Laundry room.
Activities Arts & crafts; Games; Prayer groups; Movies.

MARVELL

Cedar Lodge Nursing Home Inc*
PO Box 928, Marvell, AR, 72366
(501) 829-2361
Admin Ms B J Cooper. *Medical Dir/Dir of Nursing* Robert Miller MD.
Licensure Intermediate care. *Beds* 132.
Certified Medicaid.
Admissions Requirements Medical examination.
Staff Physicians 1 (pt); RNs 1 (ft), 1 (pt); LPNs 6 (ft), 1 (pt); Orderlies 2 (ft), 1 (pt); Nurses aides 53 (ft), 5 (pt); Activities coordinators 1 (ft); Dietitians 1 (ft).
Facilities Dining room; Laundry room; Barber/Beauty shop.
Activities Cards; Games; Prayer groups; Shopping trips; Social/Cultural gatherings.

MCCRORY

Woodruff County Nursing Home
PO Box 407, McCrory, AR, 72101
(501) 731-2543
Admin Shelley Lee. *Medical Dir/Dir of Nursing* Fred Wilson MD; Kitty Smith RN.
Licensure Skilled care. *Beds* SNF 105.
Certified Medicaid.
Owner Publicly owned.
Admissions Requirements Medical examination.
Staff Physicians 4 (ft); RNs 2 (ft), 1 (pt); LPNs 5 (ft), 6 (pt); Orderlies 3 (ft); Nurses aides 26 (ft), 5 (pt); Physical therapists 2 (ft); Speech therapists 1 (pt); Activities coordinators 1 (ft); Dietitians 1 (ft).

Facilities Dining room; Physical therapy room; Activities room; Chapel; Crafts room; Laundry room; Barber/Beauty shop; Gift shop.
Activities Arts & crafts; Cards; Games; Prayer groups; Movies; Social/Cultural gatherings; Live bands; Beauty contests.

MCGEHEE

Leisure Lodge Nursing Center*
700 Westwood Dr, McGehee, AR, 71654
(501) 222-5450
Admin Julianne McRae RN. *Medical Dir/Dir of Nursing* Robert L Prosser MD; Verle LaFarra RN.
Licensure Skilled care. *Beds* 140. *Certified* Medicaid.
Owner Proprietary Corp (Beverly Enterprises).
Admissions Requirements Medical examination; Physician's request.
Staff RNs 3 (ft); LPNs 8 (ft); Nurses aides 30 (ft); Activities coordinators 1 (ft);; Audiologists 1 (ft) Social service.
Facilities Dining room; Activities room; Chapel; Laundry room; Barber/Beauty shop.
Activities Arts & crafts; Cards; Games; Reading groups; Prayer groups; Movies; Shopping trips; Social/Cultural gatherings.

MELBOURNE

Pioneer Nursing Home Inc
PO Box 395, Melbourne, AR, 72556
(501) 368-4377, 368-4191
Admin Nancy Pratt; Opal Irene Cook. *Medical Dir/Dir of Nursing* Cindy Mason DON.
Licensure Intermediate care. *Beds* ICF 64.
Certified Medicaid.
Owner Proprietary Corp.
Staff RNs 1 (ft); LPNs 4 (ft); Nurses aides 25 (ft); Activities coordinators 1 (ft); Dietitians 1 (pt).
Facilities Dining room; Activities room; Laundry room.
Activities Arts & crafts; Cards; Games; Reading groups; Prayer groups.

MENA

Mena Manor*
100 9th St, Mena, AR, 71953
(501) 394-2617
Admin Murlene Williams Autry. *Medical Dir/Dir of Nursing* Dr Lon Sessler.
Licensure Intermediate care. *Beds* 69.
Certified Medicaid.
Admissions Requirements Medical examination; Physician's request.
Staff RNs 1 (ft); Nurses aides 48 (ft); Physical therapists 1 (ft); Activities coordinators 1 (ft); Dietitians 1 (ft).
Facilities Dining room; Activities room; Laundry room.
Activities Arts & crafts; Cards; Games; Prayer groups; Social/Cultural gatherings.

Rich Mountain Manor
504 Hornbeck, Mena, AR, 71953
(501) 394-3511
Admin Vesta Rhoades. *Medical Dir/Dir of Nursing* Calvin Austin MD; Betty Anderson DON.
Licensure Skilled care. *Beds* SNF 115.
Certified Medicaid.
Owner Proprietary Corp (Diversicare Corp).
Admissions Requirements Medical examination; Physician's request.
Staff RNs 2 (ft), 1 (pt); LPNs 7 (ft), 2 (pt); Nurses aides 30 (ft); Activities coordinators 1 (ft).
Facilities Dining room; Activities room; Chapel; Laundry room; Barber/Beauty shop.
Activities Arts & crafts; Games; Prayer groups; Movies; Shopping trips; Social/Cultural gatherings.

MONETTE

Lane's Nursing Home—Monette*
PO Box 469, Monette, AR, 72447
(501) 486-5419
Admin James Cliff Lane.
Licensure Skilled care. *Beds* 86. *Certified*
Medicaid.

MONTICELLO

Leisure Lodge Inc—Monticello
PO Box 576, Monticello, AR, 71655
(501) 367-6852
Admin Kent McRae. *Medical Dir/Dir of
Nursing* Dr A T Llana.
Licensure Skilled care. *Beds* 124. *Certified*
Medicaid; Medicare.
Owner Proprietary Corp (Beverly Enterprises).
Admissions Requirements Medical
examination.
Staff Physicians 6 (pt); RNs 2 (ft), 3 (pt);
LPNs 8 (ft), 6 (pt); Orderlies 2 (pt); Nurses
aides 28 (ft), 3 (pt); Physical therapists 1
(pt); Speech therapists 1 (pt); Activities
coordinators 1 (ft); Dietitians 1 (ft); Dentists
1 (pt); Social director 1 (ft).
Facilities Dining room; Physical therapy
room; Activities room; Crafts room; Laundry
room; Barber/Beauty shop; Library.
Activities Arts & crafts; Games; Reading
groups; Prayer groups; Shopping trips;
Social/Cultural gatherings.

MORRILTON

Morrilton Manor Nursing Home
1212 W Childress, Morrilton, AR, 72110
(501) 354-4585
Admin Judith L Havlik. *Medical Dir/Dir of
Nursing* T H Hickey.
Licensure Skilled care. *Beds* 122. *Certified*
Medicaid.
Admissions Requirements Medical
examination.
Staff Physicians 8 (pt); RNs 2 (ft), 3 (pt);
LPNs 10 (ft), 1 (pt); Nurses aides 45 (ft);
Physical therapists 1 (pt); Activities
coordinators 2 (ft); Dietitians 1 (ft).
Facilities Dining room; Barber/Beauty shop.
Activities Arts & crafts; Games; Prayer groups;
Movies; Shopping trips.

Riverview Manor Nursing Home*
1209 S Bridge St, Morrilton, AR, 72110
(501) 354-4647
Admin Vickie J Cannon Massey.
Licensure Intermediate care. *Beds* 53.
Certified Medicaid.

MOUNT IDA

Montgomery Country Nursing Home*
Ray St, PO Box 885, Mount Ida, AR, 71957
(501) 867-2156
Admin Audean Kennedy. *Medical Dir/Dir of
Nursing* James Davis MD.
Licensure Intermediate care. *Beds* 56.
Certified Medicaid.
Admissions Requirements Medical
examination.
Staff Physicians 1 (ft); RNs 2 (ft); LPNs 6 (ft),
1 (pt); Nurses aides 26 (ft); Activities
coordinators 1 (pt); Dietitians 1 (pt);
Dentists 1 (pt).
Facilities Dining room; Activities room;
Chapel; Crafts room; Laundry room; Barber/
Beauty shop; Library.
Activities Arts & crafts; Cards; Games;
Reading groups; Prayer groups; Movies;
Shopping trips; Social/Cultural gatherings;
Community gospel singing.

MOUNTAIN HOME

Baxter Manor Nursing Home
620 Hospital Dr, Mountain Home, AR, 72653
(501) 425-6203
Admin William P Flippo. *Medical Dir/Dir of
Nursing* Dr Daniel Chock; Hazel LaVerne
Johnson RN DNS.
Licensure Skilled care. *Beds* SNF 105.
Certified Medicaid.
Owner Nonprofit organization/foundation.
Admissions Requirements Physician's request.
Staff RNs 3 (ft); LPNs 12 (ft); Orderlies 1 (ft);
Nurses aides 37 (ft); Activities coordinators
1 (ft); Dietitians 1 (ft).
Facilities Dining room; Activities room;
Chapel; Laundry room; Barber/Beauty shop.
Activities Arts & crafts; Cards; Games;
Reading groups; Prayer groups; Movies;
Shopping trips.

Mountain Home Good Samaritan Village
3031 Turnage Dr, Mountain Home, AR,
72653
(501) 425-2494
Admin Arthur Rosenkotter.
Licensure Intermediate care. *Beds* 70.
Certified Medicaid; Medicare.
Owner Nonprofit Corp (Evangelical Lutheran/
Good Samaritan).

Mountain Home Nursing Center
PO Box 325, Hwy 5 N, Mountain Home, AR,
72653
(501) 425-6931
Admin Ann Marie Roper. *Medical Dir/Dir of
Nursing* John Guenthner MD; Phyllis Baxter
RN DON.
Licensure Intermediate care. *Beds* SNF 105.
Certified Medicaid.
Owner Proprietary Corp.
Admissions Requirements Medical
examination; Physician's request.
Staff Physicians 1 (ft); RNs 3 (ft); LPNs 11
(ft); Physical therapists 1 (ft); Activities
coordinators 1 (ft); Dietitians 1 (ft).
Facilities Dining room; Physical therapy
room; Laundry room; Barber/Beauty shop.
Activities Arts & crafts; Cards; Games;
Reading groups; Prayer groups; Movies;
Shopping trips; Social/Cultural gatherings;
Bingo; Outings to fish hatchery; Fishing.

Pine Lane Healthcare
1100 Pine Tree Lane, Mountain Home, AR,
72653
(501) 425-6316
Admin Jennifer Gettman. *Medical Dir/Dir of
Nursing* Dr R Burnett; Debra Humman RN.
Licensure Skilled care. *Beds* 105. *Certified*
Medicaid.
Owner Proprietary Corp (Hillhaven Corp).
Admissions Requirements Minimum age 18.
Staff RNs 6 (ft), 2 (pt); LPNs 6 (ft), 2 (pt);
Orderlies 4 (ft); Nurses aides 22 (ft), 4 (pt);
Activities coordinators 1 (ft).
Activities Arts & crafts; Cards; Games; Prayer
groups; Movies; Social/Cultural gatherings.

MOUNTAIN VIEW

Compton's Oak Grove Lodge
PO Box 930, Oak Grove St, Mountain View,
AR, 72560
(501) 269-3886
Admin Kari Henderson. *Medical Dir/Dir of
Nursing* Carrol Richardson.
Licensure Skilled care. *Beds* SNF 86. *Certified*
Medicaid.
Owner Privately owned.
Admissions Requirements Physician's request.
Staff Physicians; RNs; LPNs; Nurses aides;
Physical therapists; Activities coordinators;
Dietitians; Dentist.
Facilities Dining room; Activities room;
Crafts room; Laundry room; Barber/Beauty
shop; Library.

Activities Arts & crafts; Cards; Games; Prayer
groups; Shopping trips; Social/Cultural
gatherings; Basketball; Horseshoes;
Dominoes; Folk & gospel musicals weekly.

MURFREESBORO

Idlehour Nursing Center Inc*
PO Box 666, Murfreesboro, AR, 71958
(501) 285-2186
Admin JoAnn Brown.
Licensure Intermediate care. *Beds* 75.
Certified Medicaid.
Owner Proprietary Corp (Beverly Enterprises).

NASHVILLE

Benson's Nursing Home Inc*
1315 Hutchinson St, Nashville, AR, 71852
(501) 845-4933
Admin Willie Benson Jr. *Medical Dir/Dir of
Nursing* Dr M H Wilmoth.
Licensure Intermediate care. *Beds* 117.
Certified Medicaid; Medicare.
Admissions Requirements Physician's request.
Staff Physicians 1 (ft), 6 (pt); RNs 1 (ft), 1
(pt); LPNs 2 (ft), 2 (pt); Nurses aides 15 (ft),
9 (pt); Physical therapists 1 (pt); Activities
coordinators 1 (ft), 1 (pt); Dietitians 2 (pt);
Dentists 3 (pt); Podiatrists 1 (pt).
Facilities Dining room; Activities room;
Crafts room; Laundry room; Barber/Beauty
shop; Church annex.
Activities Arts & crafts; Cards; Games;
Reading groups; Prayer groups; Movies;
Shopping trips; Social/Cultural gatherings.

Colonial Nursing Home Inc
311 W Henderson St, Nashville, AR, 71852
(501) 845-4128
Admin Vicki Keeney. *Medical Dir/Dir of
Nursing* Sarita Floyd RN.
Licensure Intermediate care. *Beds* ICF 50.
Certified Medicaid.
Owner Proprietary Corp.
Admissions Requirements Medical
examination; Physician's request.
Staff RNs 1 (ft); LPNs 3 (ft), 3 (pt); Orderlies
1 (ft); Nurses aides 8 (ft), 5 (pt);
Recreational therapists 1 (ft); Activities
coordinators 1 (ft); Dietitians 1 (pt);
Ophthalmologists 1 (pt).
Facilities Dining room; Laundry room;
Barber/Beauty shop.
Activities Arts & crafts; Cards; Games;
Reading groups; Prayer groups; Social/
Cultural gatherings; Taped music.

Guest House of Nashville*
PO Box 1680, Nashville, AR, 71852
(501) 845-3881
Admin Willa Jean Owens.
Licensure Skilled care. *Beds* 70. *Certified*
Medicaid.

Leisure Lodge of Nashville
PO Box 812, Nashville, AR, 71852
(501) 845-2021
Admin Beverly Starr. *Medical Dir/Dir of
Nursing* Dr Joe King; Paulette Downs RN
DON.
Licensure Skilled care. *Beds* SNF 78. *Certified*
Medicaid.
Owner Proprietary Corp (Beverly Enterprises).
Admissions Requirements Minimum age 16;
Medical examination; Physician's request.
Staff Physicians 6 (pt); RNs 1 (ft), 1 (pt);
LPNs 5 (ft), 3 (pt); Nurses aides 28 (ft), 5
(pt); Activities coordinators 1 (ft); Dietitians
1 (ft).
Facilities Dining room; Activities room;
Chapel; Crafts room; Laundry room; Barber/
Beauty shop; Picnic area.
Activities Arts & crafts; Cards; Games;
Reading groups; Prayer groups; Movies;
Shopping trips; Social/Cultural gatherings.

Nashville Nursing Home*
810 N 8th, Nashville, AR, 71852
(501) 845-1616
Admin Frances Joan McCrary.
Licensure Intermediate care. *Beds* 50.
  Certified Medicaid; Medicare.
Staff RNs 1 (ft); LPNs 4 (ft), 1 (pt); Nurses
  aides 12 (ft), 4 (pt); Activities coordinators 1
  (ft); Dietitians 1 (pt).
Facilities Dining room; Activities room;
  Laundry room; Barber/Beauty shop.
Activities Arts & crafts; Games; Reading
  groups; Movies; Shopping trips.

NEWPORT

Pinedale Nursing Home
1311 N Pecan St, Newport, AR, 72112
(501) 523-5881
Admin Marion R Huckeby. *Medical Dir/Dir of
  Nursing* Guilford Dudley.
Licensure Skilled care. *Beds* 125. *Certified*
  Medicaid.
Admissions Requirements Medical
  examination; Physician's request.
Staff Physicians 1 (pt); RNs 1 (ft), 2 (pt);
  LPNs 9 (ft), 1 (pt); Orderlies 11 (ft), 4 (pt);
  Nurses aides 30 (ft), 8 (pt); Physical
  therapists 1 (pt); Recreational therapists 2
  (ft); Activities coordinators 2 (ft); Dietitians
  1 (pt); Dentists 1 (pt).
Facilities Dining room; Physical therapy
  room; Activities room; Laundry room;
  Barber/Beauty shop; Library.
Activities Arts & crafts; Cards; Games;
  Reading groups; Prayer groups; Movies;
  Shopping trips; Social/Cultural gatherings.

Regional Healthcare Inc*
Drawer J, Newport, AR, 72112
(501) 523-6539
Admin Roger Snow.
Licensure Intermediate care. *Beds* 105.
  Certified Medicaid.

NORTH LITTLE ROCK

Mercy Nursing Home Inc
6401 E 47th St, North Little Rock, AR, 72117
(501) 945-2356
Admin Geraldine Robinson. *Medical Dir/Dir
  of Nursing* Dr M J Elders; Jo Ann Curry
  DON.
Licensure Intermediate care. *Beds* 85.
  Certified Medicaid.
Owner Proprietary Corp.
Staff Physicians 2 (pt); RNs 1 (ft); LPNs 4
  (ft); Nurses aides 30 (ft); Physical therapists
  1 (pt); Occupational therapists 1 (pt);
  Activities coordinators 1 (pt); Dietitians 1
  (pt); Dentists 1 (pt).
Facilities Dining room; Physical therapy
  room; Activities room; Chapel; Laundry
  room; Barber/Beauty shop.
Activities Cards; Games; Prayer groups;
  Shopping trips; Social/Cultural gatherings.

Riley's Oak Hill Manor North*
2501 John Ashley Dr, North Little Rock, AR,
  72114
(501) 758-3800
Admin Steve Gates.
Licensure Skilled care. *Beds* 224. *Certified*
  Medicaid.

OLA

Yell County Nursing Home Inc*
PO Box 38, Ola, AR, 72853
(501) 489-5237
Admin Barry N Tippin.
Licensure Intermediate care. *Beds* 74.
  Certified Medicaid.

OSCEOLA

Osceola Nursing Home
PO Box 545, 406 S Broadway, Osceola, AR,
  72370
(501) 563-3201
Admin Debora Thomas. *Medical Dir/Dir of
  Nursing* Franc J Fenaughty MD; Linda
  Richardson RN DON.
Licensure Skilled care. *Beds* 96. *Certified*
  Medicaid.
Owner Proprietary Corp.
Admissions Requirements Medical
  examination; Physician's request.
Staff Physicians 5 (ft); RNs 1 (ft), 1 (pt);
  LPNs 8 (ft), 4 (pt); Nurses aides 25 (ft), 5
  (pt); Speech therapists 1 (ft).
Facilities Dining room; Activities room;
  Laundry room; Barber/Beauty shop.
Activities Arts & crafts; Cards; Games;
  Reading groups; Prayer groups; Movies;
  Shopping trips; Social/Cultural gatherings.

OZARK

Ozark Nursing Home Inc*
600 N 12th St, Ozark, AR, 72949
(501) 667-4791
Admin Gus S Schaffer.
Licensure Intermediate care. *Beds* 118.
  Certified Medicaid.

PARAGOULD

Greene Acres Nursing Home Inc*
PO Box 1027, Paragould, AR, 72451-1027
(501) 236-8771
Admin Larry McFadden. *Medical Dir/Dir of
  Nursing* Asa Crow MD.
Licensure Intermediate care. *Beds* 70.
  Certified Medicaid.
Owner Nonprofit Corp.
Admissions Requirements Physician's request.
Staff Physicians 14 (pt); RNs 1 (ft); LPNs 7
  (ft), 5 (pt); Nurses aides 17 (ft), 6 (pt);
  Activities coordinators 1 (ft); Dietitians 1
  (pt).
Facilities Dining room; Laundry room;
  Barber/Beauty shop.
Activities Arts & crafts; Games; Reading
  groups; Social/Cultural gatherings.

Paragould Nursing Center
Rte 3, Box 45A, Paragould, AR, 72450
(501) 236-7104
Admin Diana Goodman. *Medical Dir/Dir of
  Nursing* Dr Bennie Mitchell; Lucille Jackson.
Licensure Skilled care. *Beds* SNF 180.
  Certified Medicaid.
Owner Proprietary Corp (Beverly Enterprises).
Admissions Requirements Physician's request.
Staff RNs 2 (ft), 2 (pt); LPNs 20 (ft), 1 (pt);
  Nurses aides 54 (ft); Activities coordinators
  2 (ft).
Facilities Dining room; Activities room;
  Laundry room; Barber/Beauty shop.
Activities Arts & crafts; Games; Reading
  groups; Prayer groups; Movies; Shopping
  trips; Social/Cultural gatherings.

PARIS

Logan County Nursing Center*
PO Box 431, Paris, AR, 72855
(501) 963-6151
Admin Erma Garner.
Licensure Intermediate care. *Beds* 31.
  Certified Medicaid.

Paris Retirement Inn Inc*
513 N Roseville, Paris, AR, 72855
(501) 963-3096
Admin Nancy Davis.
Licensure Intermediate care. *Beds* 72.
  Certified Medicaid.
Owner Proprietary Corp (Beverly Enterprises).

PERRYVILLE

Perry County Nursing Center
PO Box 270, Perryville, AR, 72126
(501) 889-2400
Admin Judy Weiss. *Medical Dir/Dir of
  Nursing* Cindy Weiss.
Licensure Intermediate care. *Beds* ICF 70.
  Certified Medicaid.
Owner Privately owned.
Staff Physicians 1 (ft), 2 (pt); RNs 1 (ft), 2
  (pt); LPNs 4 (ft), 3 (pt); Nurses aides 30 (ft),
  8 (pt); Activities coordinators 1 (ft);
  Dietitians 1 (ft); Dentists 1 (ft).
Facilities Dining room; Physical therapy
  room; Activities room; Laundry room;
  Barber/Beauty shop.
Activities Arts & crafts; Cards; Games;
  Reading groups; Prayer groups; Movies;
  Shopping trips; Social/Cultural gatherings.

PIGGOTT

Piggott Nursing Center
PO Box 388, 450 S 9th St, Piggott, AR, 72454
(501) 598-2291
Admin Gaye Wiley. *Medical Dir/Dir of
  Nursing* Jerry L Muse MD; Nadine Haley
  RN.
Licensure Skilled care. *Beds* SNF 105.
  Certified Medicaid.
Owner Proprietary Corp (Beverly Enterprises).
Admissions Requirements Medical
  examination; Physician's request.
Staff Physicians 5 (pt); RNs 2 (ft), 1 (pt);
  LPNs 8 (ft), 1 (pt); Nurses aides 24 (ft), 2
  (pt); Physical therapists 1 (pt); Activities
  coordinators 1 (ft); Dietitians 1 (pt).
Facilities Dining room; Physical therapy
  room; Activities room; Crafts room; Laundry
  room; Barber/Beauty shop; Miniature golf
  course.
Activities Arts & crafts; Cards; Games;
  Reading groups; Prayer groups; Movies;
  Shopping trips; Social/Cultural gatherings.

PINE BLUFF

Davis Skilled Nursing Facility*
1111 W 12th St, Pine Bluff, AR, 71601
(501) 541-7191
Admin Robert L Dolan.
Licensure Skilled care. *Beds* 100. *Certified*
  Medicaid.

Jefferson Convalescent Home Inc
PO Box 7223, 3406 W Seventh, Pine Bluff,
  AR, 71611
(501) 534-5681
Admin Linda Manasco. *Medical Dir/Dir of
  Nursing* James Lindsey.
Licensure Intermediate care. *Beds* 50.
  Certified Medicaid.
Owner Nonprofit organization/foundation.
Admissions Requirements Medical
  examination; Physician's request.
Staff RNs 1 (ft); LPNs 5 (ft); Nurses aides 18
  (ft); Activities coordinators 1 (ft); Dietitians
  1 (ft), 1 (pt).
Facilities Dining room; Activities room;
  Laundry room; Barber/Beauty shop.
Activities Arts & crafts; Cards; Games;
  Reading groups; Prayer groups.

Loma Linda Rest Home*
PO Box 1329, Pine Bluff, AR, 71613
(501) 535-8878
Admin Carolyn A Compton.
Licensure Intermediate care. *Beds* 205.
  Certified Medicaid.

Oak Park Nursing Home Inc
PO Box 8270, Pine Bluff, AR, 71611
(501) 536-2972
Admin Nancy K Rollins. *Medical Dir/Dir of
  Nursing* Shafgat Hussain.

Licensure Intermediate care. *Beds* ICF 67. *Certified* Medicaid.
Owner Proprietary Corp.
Admissions Requirements Physician's request.
Staff RNs 1 (ft); LPNs 4 (ft), 3 (pt); Nurses aides 14 (ft), 4 (pt); Activities coordinators 1 (ft); Dietitians 1 (ft).
Facilities Dining room; Activities room; Laundry room; Barber/Beauty shop.
Activities Arts & crafts; Cards; Games; Reading groups; Prayer groups; Movies; Shopping trips; Social/Cultural gatherings.

Pine Bluff Nursing Home
PO Box 1310, 3701 S Main, Pine Bluff, AR, 71613
(501) 534-6614
Admin Robert L Wells. *Medical Dir/Dir of Nursing* Herbert Fendley; Mary Huntley.
Licensure Skilled care. *Beds* 245. *Certified* Medicaid; Medicare.
Owner Proprietary Corp.
Admissions Requirements Minimum age 40; Medical examination; Physician's request.
Staff RNs 4 (ft); LPNs 19 (ft); Nurses aides 59 (ft); Physical therapists 1 (pt); Activities coordinators 2 (ft); Dietitians 1 (ft), 1 (pt).
Facilities Dining room; Physical therapy room; Activities room; Laundry room; Barber/Beauty shop.
Activities Arts & crafts; Cards; Games; Reading groups; Prayer groups; Movies; Shopping trips; Social/Cultural gatherings.

POCAHONTAS

Randolph County Nursing Home*
1405 Hospital Dr, Pocahontas, AR, 72455
(501) 892-5214
Admin Dickie C Smith.
Licensure Skilled care. *Beds* 80. *Certified* Medicaid.

PRAIRIE GROVE

Medi-Home of Prairie Grove
PO Box 616, 621 S Mock St, Prairie Grove, AR, 72753
(501) 846-2169
Admin Maxine Thompson. *Medical Dir/Dir of Nursing* Bob G Mitchell MD; Georgia German DON.
Licensure Skilled care. *Certified* Medicaid.
Owner Privately owned.
Admissions Requirements Medical examination.
Staff RNs 1 (ft), 1 (pt); LPNs 5 (ft), 3 (pt); Orderlies 2 (ft); Nurses aides 38 (ft), 6 (pt); Activities coordinators 1 (ft).
Facilities Dining room; Laundry room; Barber/Beauty shop.
Activities Arts & crafts; Cards; Games; Reading groups; Prayer groups; Movies.

PRESCOTT

Hillcrest Nursing Home—Prescott
1421 W 2nd St North, Prescott, AR, 71857
(501) 887-3811
Admin Margie Pickett. *Medical Dir/Dir of Nursing* Joyce Hall.
Licensure Intermediate care. *Beds* ICF 70. *Certified* Medicaid.
Owner Nonprofit Corp.
Staff Physicians 1 (ft), 3 (pt); RNs 1 (ft); LPNs 8 (pt); Nurses aides 30 (ft); Activities coordinators 1 (ft); Dietitians 1 (ft).
Facilities Dining room; Activities room; Crafts room; Laundry room; Barber/Beauty shop.
Activities Arts & crafts; Cards; Games; Reading groups; Prayer groups; Movies; Shopping trips; Social/Cultural gatherings.

Prescott Nursing Center
Rte 6, Box 227, Prescott, AR, 71857
(501) 887-6639

Admin Anne K Williams.
Licensure Skilled care. *Beds* SNF 111. *Certified* Medicaid; VA.
Owner Proprietary Corp (Beverly Enterprises).
Admissions Requirements Minimum age 18; Medical examination; Physician's request.
Staff Physicians; RNs; LPNs; Nurses aides; Physical therapists; Occupational therapists; Activities coordinators; Dietitians.
Facilities Dining room; Activities room; Crafts room; Laundry room; Barber/Beauty shop.
Activities Arts & crafts; Cards; Games; Reading groups; Prayer groups; Movies; Shopping trips; Social/Cultural gatherings.

RISON

Cleveland County Nursing Home
501 E Magnolia, Rison, AR, 71665
(501) 325-6202
Admin Marilyn Reed-Hoover. *Medical Dir/Dir of Nursing* H Mark Attwood MD; Phyllis Attwood RN DON.
Licensure Skilled care. *Beds* SNF 67. *Certified* Medicaid.
Owner Proprietary Corp (Beverly Enterprises).
Staff Physicians 1 (ft); RNs 1 (ft), 2 (pt); LPNs 8 (ft), 1 (pt); Nurses aides 14 (ft), 9 (pt); Physical therapists 1 (pt); Activities coordinators 1 (ft); Dietitians 1 (ft).
Languages German
Facilities Dining room; Physical therapy room; Crafts room; Laundry room; Barber/Beauty shop; Library.
Activities Arts & crafts; Games; Reading groups; Prayer groups; Shopping trips; Social/Cultural gatherings.

ROGERS

Medi-Home of Rogers*
1603 W Walnut St, Rogers, AR, 72756
(501) 636-9334
Admin Linda L Neely. *Medical Dir/Dir of Nursing* Dr Robert Hall.
Licensure Intermediate care. *Beds* 70. *Certified* Medicaid.
Admissions Requirements Medical examination; Physician's request.
Staff RNs 1 (ft); LPNs 3 (ft); Orderlies 3 (ft); Nurses aides 18 (ft); Activities coordinators 1 (ft); Dietitians 1 (ft).
Facilities Dining room; Activities room; Laundry room; Barber/Beauty shop.
Activities Arts & crafts; Cards; Games; Prayer groups; Movies; Shopping trips; Social/Cultural gatherings.

Rogers Nursing Center
1151 W New Hope Rd, Rogers, AR, 72756
(501) 636-6290
Admin Gerald Kimbrough. *Medical Dir/Dir of Nursing* William Jennings MD; Barbara Talik RN DON.
Licensure Skilled care. *Beds* SNF 140. *Certified* Medicaid; Medicare; VA.
Owner Proprietary Corp (Beverly Enterprises).
Admissions Requirements Minimum age 18; Medical examination; Physician's request.
Staff RNs 3 (ft); LPNs 9 (ft), 5 (pt); Orderlies 4 (ft); Nurses aides 40 (ft), 20 (pt); Physical therapists 1 (pt); Activities coordinators 1 (ft); Dietitians 1 (ft); Social service coordinator 1 (ft).
Facilities Dining room; Physical therapy room; Activities room; Crafts room; Laundry room; Barber/Beauty shop.
Activities Arts & crafts; Cards; Games; Reading groups; Prayer groups; Movies; Shopping trips; Social/Cultural gatherings; Fishing trips; Outings once a month.

Rose Care Center of Rogers
1513 S Dixieland Rd, Rogers, AR, 72756
(501) 636-5841

Admin John W Krouse. *Medical Dir/Dir of Nursing* Dr Jennings.
Licensure Skilled care. *Beds* 140. *Certified* Medicaid.
Staff RNs 4 (ft), 2 (pt); LPNs 8 (ft), 1 (pt); Nurses aides 26 (ft), 3 (pt); Physical therapists 1 (pt); Recreational therapists 1 (ft); Speech therapists 1 (ft); Activities coordinators 1 (ft); Dietitians 1 (ft); Dentist 1 (pt).
Facilities Dining room; Activities room; Crafts room; Laundry room; Barber/Beauty shop; Library.
Activities Arts & crafts; Cards; Games; Reading groups; Prayer groups; Movies; Shopping trips; Social/Cultural gatherings.

RUSSELLVILLE

Legacy Lodge Nursing Home
900 W 12th St, Russellville, AR, 72801
(501) 968-5858
Admin Erby E Rowell. *Medical Dir/Dir of Nursing* Finley Turner.
Licensure Skilled care. *Beds* 122. *Certified* Medicaid.
Owner Proprietary Corp.
Admissions Requirements Physician's request.
Staff Physicians 1 (pt); RNs 3 (ft); LPNs 14 (ft); Nurses aides 28 (ft); Physical therapists 1 (pt); Activities coordinators 1 (ft); Dietitians 1 (ft); Dentists 1 (pt); Ophthalmologists 1 (pt).
Facilities Dining room; Activities room; Crafts room; Laundry room; Barber/Beauty shop.
Activities Arts & crafts; Cards; Games; Reading groups; Prayer groups; Movies; Shopping trips; Social/Cultural gatherings.

Russellville Nursing Center
1700 W "C" St, Russellville, AR, 72801
(501) 968-5256
Admin Linda Eoff. *Medical Dir/Dir of Nursing* Dennis Berner MD.
Licensure Skilled care. *Beds* SNF 92. *Certified* Medicaid.
Owner Privately owned.
Admissions Requirements Medical examination; Physician's request.
Staff RNs 1 (ft), 1 (pt); LPNs 6 (ft), 4 (pt); Nurses aides 23 (ft), 12 (pt); Activities coordinators 1 (ft); Dietitians 1 (pt).
Facilities Dining room; Laundry room; Barber/Beauty shop.
Activities Arts & crafts; Cards; Games; Reading groups; Prayer groups; Movies; Shopping trips; Social/Cultural gatherings.

Stella Manor Nursing Center
400 N Vancouver, Russellville, AR, 72901
(501) 968-4141
Admin Barbara S McCoy. *Medical Dir/Dir of Nursing* Ronda Hart DON.
Licensure Skilled care. *Beds* SNF 144. *Certified* Medicaid.
Owner Privately owned.
Admissions Requirements Physician's request.
Staff RNs 3 (ft); LPNs 14 (ft), 2 (pt); Nurses aides 60 (ft), 10 (pt).
Facilities Dining room; Activities room; Crafts room; Laundry room; Barber/Beauty shop.
Activities Arts & crafts; Cards; Games; Reading groups; Prayer groups; Movies; Shopping trips; Social/Cultural gatherings.

SALEM

Fulton County Nursing Center
PO Box 397, Salem, AR, 72576
(501) 895-3817
Admin Kay Cooper. *Medical Dir/Dir of Nursing* Linda Stevens.
Licensure Skilled care. *Beds* SNF 125. *Certified* Medicaid.
Owner Proprietary Corp.

Admissions Requirements Minimum age 55.
Staff RNs; LPNs; Nurses aides; Dietitians.
Facilities Dining room; Activities room;
  Laundry room.
Activities Arts & crafts; Cards; Games; Social/
  Cultural gatherings.

SEARCY

Byrd Haven Nursing Home*
PO Box 180, Searcy, AR, 72143
(501) 268-2324
Admin Ralph Byrd Jr.
Licensure Intermediate care. *Beds* 47.
  Certified Medicaid.

Leisure Lodge Inc—Searcy*
211 Aztec, Searcy, AR, 72143
(501) 268-6188
Admin Teresa Mattingly.
Licensure Skilled care. *Beds* 245. *Certified*
  Medicaid.
Owner Proprietary Corp (Beverly Enterprises).

SHERIDAN

Grant County Nursing Home
PO Box 100 BB, Rte 2, Sheridan, AR, 72150
(501) 942-2183, 942-2212
Admin Mary E Scott. *Medical Dir/Dir of
  Nursing* Dr Jack Irvin; Susan Damion.
Licensure Skilled care; Intermediate care. *Beds*
  SNF 110; ICF. *Certified* Medicaid.
Owner Proprietary Corp (Diversicare Corp).
Admissions Requirements Medical
  examination; Physician's request.
Staff Physicians 3 (ft); RNs 2 (ft), 1 (pt);
  LPNs 4 (ft), 6 (pt); Nurses aides 35 (ft), 5
  (pt); Activities coordinators 1 (ft); Dietitians
  1 (ft).
Languages Spanish
Facilities Dining room; Activities room;
  Crafts room; Laundry room; Barber/Beauty
  shop.
Activities Arts & crafts; Cards; Games;
  Reading groups; Prayer groups; Movies;
  Shopping trips; Social/Cultural gatherings.

SIDNEY

Sharp Nursing Home
General Delivery, Sidney, AR, 72577
(501) 283-5897
Admin James R Hollandsworth. *Medical Dir/
  Dir of Nursing* J R Baker; Marjorie Fowler.
Licensure Intermediate care. *Beds* ICF 67.
  Certified Medicaid.
Owner Nonprofit Corp.
Admissions Requirements Medical
  examination; Physician's request.
Staff Physicians 1 (pt); RNs 1 (ft); LPNs 6
  (ft), 6 (pt); Nurses aides 10 (ft), 13 (pt);
  Activities coordinators 1 (pt); Dietitians 1
  (pt).
Facilities Dining room; Activities room;
  Laundry room; Barber/Beauty shop.
Activities Arts & crafts; Cards; Games; Prayer
  groups; Movies; Social/Cultural gatherings.

SILOAM SPRINGS

Woodland Manor Inc*
811 W Elgin, Siloam Springs, AR, 72761
(501) 524-3128
Admin Montie Vest.
Licensure Skilled care. *Beds* 120. *Certified*
  Medicaid; Medicare.

SMACKOVER

Smackover Nursing Home*
PO Drawer J, Smackover, AR, 71762
(501) 725-3871
Admin Earnest E Allen. *Medical Dir/Dir of
  Nursing* Dr George W Warren.
Licensure Skilled care. *Beds* 80.

Admissions Requirements Medical
  examination.
Staff RNs 2 (ft); LPNs 5 (ft), 1 (pt); Orderlies
  1 (ft); Activities coordinators 1 (ft).
Affiliation Methodist
Facilities Dining room; Activities room;
  Laundry room; Barber/Beauty shop; Library.
Activities Arts & crafts; Cards; Games;
  Reading groups; Prayer groups; Movies;
  Shopping trips; Social/Cultural gatherings;
  Picnics; Bus rides.

SPRINGDALE

Holland Nursing Center North*
PO Box Drawer 685, Springdale, AR, 72764-
  0685
(501) 756-9000
Admin Deanna Shackelford.
Licensure Intermediate care. *Beds* 56.
  Certified Medicaid.

Holland Nursing Center West Inc*
PO Box Drawer 685, Springdale, AR, 72765-
  0685
(501) 756-1600
Admin Tommy Holland.
Licensure Intermediate care. *Beds* 30.
  Certified Medicaid.

Pleasant Valley Nursing Center*
102 N Gutensohn, Springdale, AR, 72764
(501) 756-0330
Admin Paul B Keener RN.
Licensure Skilled care. *Beds* 140. *Certified*
  Medicaid.

STAMPS

Homestead Manor Nursing Home
405 North St, Stamps, AR, 71860
(501) 533-4444
Admin Mary Jane Allen.
Licensure Skilled care. *Beds* SNF 116.
  Certified Medicaid.
Owner Proprietary Corp.
Admissions Requirements Medical
  examination; Physician's request.
Staff RNs 2 (ft); LPNs 8 (ft); Orderlies 35 (ft),
  6 (pt); Nurses aides; Activities coordinators
  1 (ft); Dietitians 1 (ft).
Facilities Dining room; Activities room;
  Crafts room; Laundry room; Barber/Beauty
  shop.
Activities Arts & crafts; Cards; Games;
  Reading groups; Prayer groups; Movies;
  Shopping trips; Social/Cultural gatherings.

STAR CITY

Gardner Nursing Home of Star City Inc*
N Drew St, Star City, AR, 71667
(501) 628-4144
Admin Annabelle Smith.
Licensure Intermediate care. *Beds* 72.
  Certified Medicaid.

Star City Nursing Center
Ford & Victory Sts, Star City, AR, 71667
(501) 628-4295
Admin Suzonne Loe.
Licensure Skilled care. *Beds* 87. *Certified*
  Medicaid.
Owner Proprietary Corp (Beverly Enterprises).

STUTTGART

Crestpark Inn of Stuttgart Inc*
PO Box 790, Stuttgart, AR, 72160
(501) 673-1657
Admin Brenda Dunbar Hardin.
Licensure Intermediate care. *Beds* 74.
  Certified Medicaid.

Rose Care Center of Stuttgart*
PO Box 426, Stuttgart, AR, 72160
(501) 673-6981

Admin Lucille Harper.
Licensure Skilled care. *Beds* 90. *Certified*
  Medicaid.

TAYLOR

Taylor Nursing Home*
Rte 2, Box 280, Taylor, AR, 71861
(501) 694-3781
Admin Ruby Pyle.
Licensure Intermediate care. *Beds* 41.
  Certified Medicaid; Medicare.
Admissions Requirements Medical
  examination; Physician's request.
Staff Physicians 3 (pt); RNs 1 (ft); LPNs 1
  (ft), 6 (pt); Nurses aides 11 (ft); Activities
  coordinators 1 (ft); Dentists 1 (pt).
Facilities Dining room; Activities room;
  Crafts room; Laundry room; Barber/Beauty
  shop.
Activities Arts & crafts; Cards; Games.

TEXARKANA

Evergreen Place
1100 E 36th St, Texarkana, AR, 75502
(501) 773-7515 or 773-7516
Admin Sue Ward. *Medical Dir/Dir of Nursing*
  Dr Russell Mayo; Linda Alford RN.
Licensure Intermediate care. *Beds* ICF 69.
  Certified Medicaid.
Owner Proprietary Corp.
Admissions Requirements Medical
  examination; Physician's request.
Staff Physicians 1 (ft); RNs 1 (ft); LPNs 8 (ft),
  1 (pt); Nurses aides 21 (ft); Activities
  coordinators 1 (ft); Dietitians 1 (ft).
Facilities Dining room; Physical therapy
  room; Activities room; Chapel; Crafts room;
  Laundry room; Barber/Beauty shop.
Activities Arts & crafts; Cards; Games;
  Reading groups; Prayer groups; Movies;
  Shopping trips.

Medicalodge Inc of Texarkana*
1621 E 42nd St, Texarkana, AR, 75502
(501) 774-3581
Admin Leo Sutterfield.
Licensure Skilled care. *Beds* 105. *Certified*
  Medicaid; Medicare.
Owner Proprietary Corp.

Oakwood Place*
307 Pinehurst, Texarkana, AR, 75501
(501) 773-2341
Admin Elanda Callahan.
Licensure Intermediate care. *Beds* 42.
  Certified Medicaid; Medicare.
Owner Proprietary Corp.

Parkview of Texarkana*
2415 Marietta St, Texarkana, AR, 75502
(501) 774-4662
Admin James Schimke.
Licensure Intermediate care. *Beds* 52.
  Certified Medicaid.

TRUMANN

Rose Care Center of Trumann
333 Melody Dr, Trumann, AR, 72472
(501) 483-7623
Admin Judy K Glasco. *Medical Dir/Dir of
  Nursing* Dr Floyd Smith; Sally Houston RN.
Licensure Skilled care. *Beds* SNF 77. *Certified*
  Medicaid.
Owner Proprietary Corp (Rose Care Inc).
Admissions Requirements Medical
  examination; Physician's request.
Staff RNs 2 (ft), 1 (pt); LPNs 7 (ft), 2 (pt);
  Nurses aides 25 (ft), 1 (pt); Activities
  coordinators 1 (ft); Dietitians 1 (ft).

Facilities Dining room; Activities room;
Laundry room; Barber/Beauty shop.
Activities Arts & crafts; Cards; Games;
Reading groups; Prayer groups; Movies;
Shopping trips; Social/Cultural gatherings;
Picnics; Various parties.

VAN BUREN

Brownwood Manor Inc
1404 N 28th St, Van Buren, AR, 72956
(501) 474-8021
Admin Berta Young.
Licensure Skilled care. *Beds* 99. *Certified*
Medicaid.
Owner Proprietary Corp.
Admissions Requirements Minimum age 21;
Medical examination; Physician's request.
Staff RNs 2 (ft); LPNs 8 (ft); Orderlies 2 (ft);
Activities coordinators 1 (ft).
Facilities Dining room; Activities room;
Crafts room; Laundry room; Barber/Beauty
shop.
Activities Arts & crafts; Cards; Games;
Reading groups; Prayer groups; Movies;
Social/Cultural gatherings.

New Haven O'Rest Inc*
2010 Alma Hwy, Van Buren, AR, 72956
(501) 474-6885
Admin Gelene Hendershot.
Licensure Skilled care. *Beds* 152. *Certified*
Medicaid.

Van Buren Nursing Center
228 Pointer Trail W, Van Buren, AR, 72956
(501) 474-5276
Admin Shelby Gorman.
Licensure Skilled care. *Beds* 105. *Certified*
Medicaid.
Owner Proprietary Corp (Beverly Enterprises).

WALDRON

Pinewood Nursing Home
PO Box Q, 11th & Washington St, Waldron,
AR, 72958
(501) 637-3171
Admin Sr Donald Mary Lynch. *Medical Dir/
Dir of Nursing* Marilyn Barr MD; Carolyn S
Pugh RN DON.
Licensure Skilled care. *Beds* SNF 89. *Certified*
Medicaid.
Owner Nonprofit Corp.
Admissions Requirements Physician's request.
Staff RNs 2 (ft); LPNs 3 (ft), 16 (pt); Nurses
aides 13 (ft), 18 (pt); Activities coordinators
1 (ft).
Affiliation Roman Catholic
Facilities Dining room; Activities room;
Laundry room; Barber/Beauty shop; Library.
Activities Arts & crafts; Cards; Games;
Reading groups; Prayer groups; Movies;
Social/Cultural gatherings.

WALNUT RIDGE

Lawrence Hall Nursing Home
1309 Hwy 25 W, Walnut Ridge, AR, 72476
(501) 886-1295
Admin Terry De Priest. *Medical Dir/Dir of
Nursing* Ralph Joseph MD; Judy Robinett
RN DON.
Licensure Skilled care. *Beds* SNF 122.
Certified Medicaid; Medicare.
Owner Publicly owned.
Staff Physicians 5 (ft); RNs 2 (ft), 4 (pt);
LPNs 12 (ft); Nurses aides 30 (ft); Activities
coordinators 1 (ft); Dietitians 1 (ft).
Facilities Dining room; Activities room;
Barber/Beauty shop; Private rooms;
Courtyard; 24 hour physician coverage.
Activities Arts & crafts; Cards; Games;
Reading groups; Prayer groups; Movies;
Shopping trips; Social/Cultural gatherings;
Bingo; Popcorn parties; Animal therapy;
Church.

Sheltering Arms Nursing Home*
311 NW 2nd St, Walnut Ridge, AR, 72476
(501) 886-3770
Admin Diann Cude. *Medical Dir/Dir of
Nursing* Robert Quevillon MD.
Licensure Intermediate care. *Beds* 36.
Certified Medicaid; Medicare.
Admissions Requirements Medical
examination; Physician's request.
Staff Physicians 1 (pt); RNs 1 (ft); LPNs 3
(ft), 1 (pt); Nurses aides 7 (ft), 3 (pt);
Physical therapists 1 (pt); Activities
coordinators 1 (ft); Dietitians 1 (pt); Dentists
1 (pt).
Facilities Dining room; Activities room;
Laundry room; Library.
Activities Arts & crafts; Cards; Games;
Reading groups; Prayer groups; Movies;
Shopping trips; Social/Cultural gatherings.

Walnut Ridge Convalescent Center*
1500 Hwy 25 W, Walnut Ridge, AR, 72476
(501) 886-9022
Admin Pamela W Murphy. *Medical Dir/Dir of
Nursing* Ralph Joseph MD.
Licensure Skilled care. *Beds* 105. *Certified*
Medicaid.
Admissions Requirements Medical
examination; Physician's request.
Staff Physicians 2 (pt); RNs 1 (ft), 1 (pt);
LPNs 8 (ft), 1 (pt); Nurses aides 33 (ft);
Physical therapists 1 (pt); Activities
coordinators 1 (ft); Dietitians 1 (pt); Dentists
1 (pt); Ophthalmologists 1 (pt).
Facilities Dining room; Chapel; Laundry
room; Barber/Beauty shop.
Activities Arts & crafts; Cards; Games;
Reading groups; Prayer groups; Movies;
Social/Cultural gatherings.

WARREN

Pine Lodge Nursing Home
730 E Church St, Warren, AR, 71671
(501) 226-5843
Admin Brenda Mercer. *Medical Dir/Dir of
Nursing* Dr Joe H Wharton; Jamison Nelson
RN.
Licensure Skilled care. *Beds* 99. *Certified*
Medicaid.
Owner Proprietary Corp (Beverly Enterprises).
Staff RNs; LPNs; Nurses aides; Activities
coordinators; Dietitians.
Facilities Dining room; Activities room;
Laundry room; Barber/Beauty shop.
Activities Arts & crafts; Cards; Games;
Reading groups; Prayer groups; Movies;
Shopping trips; Social/Cultural gatherings;
Auctions; Fair.

**Southeast Arkansas Human Development
Center**
Rte 3, 1 Center Cir, Warren, AR, 71671
(501) 226-6774
Admin Margo Green. *Medical Dir/Dir of
Nursing* Judy Adams.
Licensure Intermediate care for mentally
retarded. *Beds* ICF/MR 81. *Certified*
Medicaid.
Owner Publicly owned.
Admissions Requirements Minimum age 6;
Medical examination.
Staff Physicians 2 (pt); RNs 3 (ft); LPNs 5
(ft); Nurses aides 71 (ft); Physical therapists
1 (pt); Occupational therapists 1 (pt); Speech
therapists 1 (pt); Activities coordinators 4
(ft); Dietitians 1 (pt).
Facilities Dining room; Physical therapy
room; Activities room; Crafts room; Laundry
room; Barber/Beauty shop; Library.
Activities Arts & crafts; Cards; Games;
Movies; Shopping trips; Social/Cultural
gatherings.

Wagnon Place Inc
PO Box 230, Warren, AR, 71671
(501) 226-6766

Admin Sue Wagnon. *Medical Dir/Dir of
Nursing* George F Wynne MD; Susan
Reynolds DON.
Licensure Skilled care. *Beds* SNF 105.
Certified Medicaid.
Owner Proprietary Corp.
Admissions Requirements Medical
examination; Physician's request.
Staff Physicians 5 (ft); RNs 2 (ft), 1 (pt);
LPNs 7 (ft), 2 (pt); Nurses aides 30 (ft), 3
(pt); Activities coordinators 2 (ft).
Facilities Dining room; Activities room;
Chapel; Laundry room; Barber/Beauty shop.
Activities Arts & crafts; Cards; Games;
Reading groups; Prayer groups; Movies;
Shopping trips; Social/Cultural gatherings.

WEST MEMPHIS

**Geriatrics Nursing Center Inc—West
Memphis***
610 S Avalon St, West Memphis, AR, 72301
(501) 735-4543
Admin Eudora "Dodie" Danehower.
Licensure Skilled care. *Beds* 155. *Certified*
Medicaid.
Owner Proprietary Corp (Beverly Enterprises).

Leisure Lodge Inc—West Memphis*
111 E Jackson Ave, West Memphis, AR,
72301
(501) 735-5174
Admin Dorothy Person.
Licensure Intermediate care. *Beds* 84.
Certified Medicaid.
Owner Proprietary Corp (Beverly Enterprises).

WILMOT

Ashley Manor*
PO Box 96, Lake St, Wilmot, AR, 71676
(501) 473-2291
Admin Tony Cooper.
Licensure Intermediate care. *Beds* 68.
Certified Medicaid.

Wilmot Nursing Home*
PO Box 37, Wilmot, AR, 71676-0037
(501) 473-5505
Admin Vealetta Kellebrew.
Licensure Intermediate care. *Beds* 32.
Certified Medicaid.

WYNNE

Crestpark of Wynne, Skilled
PO Box 1127, Wynne, AR, 72396
(501) 238-7941
Admin Ollie Lou Sugg. *Medical Dir/Dir of
Nursing* Kenneth Beaton MD; Barbara Dane
RN DON.
Licensure Skilled care. *Beds* SNF 137; ICF;
ICF/MR. *Certified* Medicaid.
Owner Privately owned.
Admissions Requirements Minimum age 75;
Medical examination; Physician's request.
Staff RNs 2 (ft); LPNs 9 (ft); Nurses aides 37
(ft), 5 (pt); Physical therapists 1 (pt);
Recreational therapists 1 (ft); Activities
coordinators 1 (ft); Dietitians 1 (pt).
Facilities Dining room; Activities room;
Chapel; Crafts room; Laundry room; Barber/
Beauty shop; Library.
Activities Arts & crafts; Cards; Games;
Reading groups; Prayer groups; Movies;
Social/Cultural gatherings; Church groups.

YELLVILLE

Marion County Nursing Home*
PO Drawer 309, Yellville, AR, 72687
(501) 449-4201
Admin W Gale Dobbs.
Licensure Intermediate care. *Beds* 61.
Certified Medicaid.

CALIFORNIA

ALAMEDA

Hillhaven Alameda
516 Willow St, Alameda, CA, 94501
(415) 521-5600
Admin Mary L Lubin. *Medical Dir/Dir of Nursing* Marie Wilson RN.
Licensure Skilled care. *Beds* SNF 180. *Certified* Medicare; Medi-Cal.
Owner Proprietary Corp (Hillhaven Corp).
Admissions Requirements Medical examination; Physician's request.
Staff Physicians 1 (pt); RNs 18 (ft); LPNs 17 (ft); Nurses aides 105 (ft); Physical therapists 2 (ft); Recreational therapists 1 (ft); Occupational therapists 1 (ft); Speech therapists 1 (ft); Activities coordinators 1 (ft); Dietitians 1 (ft); Dentists 1 (pt); Podiatrists 1 (pt).
Languages Spanish, Japanese
Facilities Dining room; Physical therapy room; Activities room; Crafts room; Laundry room; Barber/Beauty shop.
Activities Arts & crafts; Cards; Games; Reading groups; Prayer groups; Movies; Shopping trips; Social/Cultural gatherings; Therapeutic recreation.

Marina Convalescent Center Inc*
3201 Fernside Blvd, Alameda, CA, 94501
(415) 523-2363
Admin Martin Neeham.
Licensure Skilled care. *Beds* 33. *Certified* Medicare.
Owner Proprietary Corp.

Prather Methodist Memorial Home*
508 Westline Dr, Alameda, CA, 94501
(415) 521-5765
Admin Gail A Miller.
Licensure Skilled care. *Beds* 151. *Certified* Medicare; Medi-Cal.
Owner Nonprofit Corp.

South Shore Convalescent Hospital*
625 Willow St, Alameda, CA, 94501
(415) 523-3772
Admin Barbara Lee Olson. *Medical Dir/Dir of Nursing* Lester Johnson MD.
Licensure Skilled care. *Beds* 26. *Certified* Medicare.
Owner Proprietary Corp.
Admissions Requirements Physician's request.
Staff RNs 1 (ft), 1 (pt); LPNs 4 (ft), 3 (pt); Orderlies 1 (ft), 1 (pt); Nurses aides 14 (ft), 6 (pt); Recreational therapists 1 (ft); Activities coordinators 1 (ft); Dietitians 1 (ft).
Facilities Dining room; Activities room; Crafts room; Laundry room.
Activities Arts & crafts; Cards; Games; Reading groups; Prayer groups; Movies.

The Waters Edge*
2401 Blanding Ave, Alameda, CA, 94501
(415) 522-1084
Admin Christian Zimmerman.

Licensure Skilled care. *Beds* 120. *Certified* Medi-Cal.
Owner Proprietary Corp.

ALHAMBRA

Alhambra Convalescent Home
415 S Garfield, Alhambra, CA, 91801
(213) 282-3151
Admin Conchita J Gasendo. *Medical Dir/Dir of Nursing* Dr Julitta Phillips.
Licensure Skilled care. *Beds* 97. *Certified* Medicare; Medi-Cal.
Owner Proprietary Corp.
Staff RNs 2 (ft), 3 (pt); LPNs 2 (ft), 6 (pt); Orderlies 3 (ft), 4 (pt); Nurses aides 19 (ft), 5 (pt); Physical therapists 1 (ft); Reality therapists 1 (pt); Recreational therapists 1 (pt); Occupational therapists 1 (pt); Speech therapists 1 (pt); Activities coordinators 1 (ft), 1 (pt); Dietitians 1 (pt); Dentists 1 (pt); Ophthalmologists 1 (pt); Podiatrists 1 (pt); Dentist 1 (pt).
Facilities Dining room; Activities room.
Activities Arts & crafts; Cards; Games; Reading groups; Prayer groups; Movies; Shopping trips; Social/Cultural gatherings; Picnics; Family council; Wheelchair exercises; Body dynamics; Pet days; One-to-one visits.

Brykirk Extended Care Hospital*
2339 W Valley Blvd, Alhambra, CA, 91803
(213) 289-7809
Admin Sheryl L Brykman.
Licensure Skilled care. *Beds* 43. *Certified* Medicare; Medi-Cal.
Owner Proprietary Corp.

California PEO Home*
700 N Stoneman Ave, Alhambra, CA, 91801
(213) 289-5284
Admin Marjorie Jackson.
Licensure Skilled care. *Beds* 44. *Certified* Medicare; Medi-Cal.
Owner Nonprofit Corp.

The Home for the Aged of the Protestant Episcopal Church of the Diocese of Los Angeles
1428 S Marengo Ave, Alhambra, CA, 91803
(818) 576-1032
Admin G W Cummings. *Medical Dir/Dir of Nursing* Russell Simpson MD, Linda Price MD; John Fraklin DON.
Licensure Skilled care; Intermediate care. *Beds* SNF 99; ICF 99; 200. *Certified* Medicaid; Medicare; Medi-Cal.
Owner Nonprofit Corp.
Admissions Requirements Minimum age 62.
Staff Physicians 1 (ft), 3 (pt); RNs 18 (ft); LPNs 6 (ft); Orderlies 7 (ft); Nurses aides 64 (ft).
Languages Spanish, Chinese
Affiliation Episcopal
Facilities Dining room; Physical therapy room; Activities room; Chapel; Crafts room; Laundry room; Barber/Beauty shop; Library.

Activities Arts & crafts; Cards; Games; Reading groups; Prayer groups; Movies; Shopping trips; Social/Cultural gatherings.

Lutheran Health Facility*
2400 S Fremont, Alhambra, CA, 91803
(213) 289-6211
Admin Jerry McConnell.
Licensure Skilled care. *Beds* 50. *Certified* Medicare; Medi-Cal.
Owner Nonprofit Corp.
Affiliation Lutheran

ALPINE

Alpine Convalescent Center*
PO Box 458, 2120 Alpine Blvd, Alpine, CA, 92001
(714) 445-2644
Admin R Patrick Doyle.
Licensure Skilled care; Intermediate care for mentally retarded. *Beds* 99. *Certified* Medi-Cal.
Owner Proprietary Corp.

ALTA LOMA

Alta Loma Convalescent Hospital*
9333 La Mesa Dr, Alta Loma, CA, 91701
(714) 987-2501
Admin Emil W Lenkey.
Licensure Skilled care. *Beds* 59. *Certified* Medicare; Medi-Cal.
Owner Proprietary Corp.

ALTADENA

Scripps Home*
2212 N El Molino, Altadena, CA, 91001
(818) 798-0934
Admin James W Graunke. *Medical Dir/Dir of Nursing* Dr Carol Thrun.
Licensure Skilled care; Intermediate care. *Beds* 49.
Owner Nonprofit Corp.
Admissions Requirements Minimum age 70; Medical examination.
Staff Physicians 1 (pt); RNs 5 (ft), 5 (pt); Nurses aides 14 (ft), 14 (pt); Physical therapists 2 (pt); Activities coordinators 1 (ft); Podiatrists 2 (pt).
Facilities Dining room; Physical therapy room; Activities room; Laundry room; Barber/Beauty shop; Library.
Activities Arts & crafts; Games; Prayer groups; Movies; Shopping trips; Social/Cultural gatherings; Current events, poetry, drama groups.

ALTURAS

Warnerview Convalescent Hospital*
225 McDowell Ave, Alturas, CA, 96101
(916) 233-3416
Admin Lawrence Eckman.

Licensure Skilled care. *Beds* 59. *Certified*
Medicare; Medi-Cal.
Owner Nonprofit Corp.

ANAHEIM

Anaheim Terrace Care Center
141 S Knott Ave, Anaheim, CA, 92804
(714) 821-7310
Admin Kelli Lockhart. *Medical Dir/Dir of
Nursing* Stanley Friedman MD; Diane
Edwards RN DON.
Licensure Skilled care. *Beds* SNF 99. *Certified*
Medicaid; Medicare; Medi-Cal.
Owner Proprietary Corp (Summit Health Ltd).
Facilities Dining room; Physical therapy
room; Activities room; Laundry room;
Barber/Beauty shop; Living room.
Activities Arts & crafts; Cards; Games;
Reading groups; Prayer groups; Movies;
Shopping trips; Social/Cultural gatherings.

Beverly Manor Convalescent Hospital*
3067 Orange Ave, Anaheim, CA, 92804
(714) 827-2440
Admin Carolyn Carlsen-Rouzier. *Medical Dir/
Dir of Nursing* Franklin Hanauer MD.
Licensure Skilled care. *Beds* 83. *Certified*
Medicare; Medi-Cal.
Owner Proprietary Corp (Beverly Enterprises).
Staff RNs 2 (ft); LPNs 6 (ft), 4 (pt); Nurses
aides 20 (ft), 20 (pt); Activities coordinators
1 (ft).
Facilities Dining room; Physical therapy
room; Activities room; Crafts room; Laundry
room; Barber/Beauty shop.
Activities Arts & crafts; Cards; Games;
Reading groups; Prayer groups; Movies;
Social/Cultural gatherings.

Buena Vista Convalescent Hospital*
1440 S Euclid St, Anaheim, CA, 92802
(714) 535-7264
Admin Jane Beaver.
Licensure Skilled care. *Beds* 99. *Certified*
Medicare; Medi-Cal.
Owner Proprietary Corp.

Casa Grande Intermediate Care Facility
3615 W Ball Rd, Anaheim, CA, 92804
(714) 826-4400
Admin Mary Bennett. *Medical Dir/Dir of
Nursing* John Hayes.
Licensure Intermediate care for mentally
retarded. *Beds* ICF/MR 91. *Certified* Medi-
Cal.
Owner Proprietary Corp (Care Enterprises).
Admissions Requirements Minimum age 18.
Staff Physicians 4 (pt); RNs 1 (ft), 2 (pt);
LPNs 6 (ft), 5 (pt); Nurses aides 50 (ft), 12
(pt); Physical therapists 1 (pt); Recreational
therapists 1 (pt); Occupational therapists 1
(pt); Speech therapists 1 (pt); Activities
coordinators 1 (ft); Dietitians 1 (pt); Dentists
1 (pt); Ophthalmologists 1 (pt); Podiatrists 1
(pt).
Facilities Dining room; Activities room;
Crafts room.
Activities Arts & crafts; Cards; Games; Prayer
groups; Movies; Shopping trips; Social/
Cultural gatherings.

Casa Pacifica Convalescent Hospital
861 S Harbor Blvd, Anaheim, CA, 92805
(714) 635-8131
Admin Pamela Burnham. *Medical Dir/Dir of
Nursing* Sultan Shah MD.
Licensure Skilled care. *Beds* SNF 99. *Certified*
Medicaid; Medicare; Medi-Cal.
Owner Proprietary Corp.
Admissions Requirements Minimum age 55.
Staff Physicians 1 (pt); RNs 2 (ft), 2 (pt);
LPNs 15 (ft); Orderlies 5 (ft); Nurses aides
29 (ft), 5 (pt); Physical therapists 1 (pt);
Occupational therapists 1 (pt); Speech
therapists 1 (pt); Activities coordinators 1
(ft), 1 (pt); Dietitians 1 (pt); Dentists 1 (pt);
Ophthalmologists 1 (pt); Podiatrists 1 (pt).

Languages Spanish, Korean, Tagalog, Hindi,
German
Facilities Dining room; Activities room;
Laundry room; Barber/Beauty shop; Library.
Activities Arts & crafts; Cards; Games;
Reading groups; Movies; Shopping trips;
Social/Cultural gatherings.

Extended Care Hospital of Anaheim*
501 S Beach Blvd, Anaheim, CA, 92804
(714) 828-7730
Admin Marc Landry.
Licensure Skilled care. *Beds* 250. *Certified*
Medicare; Medi-Cal.
Owner Proprietary Corp.

Fountainbleau Nursing Centre*
3415 W Ball Rd, Anaheim, CA, 92804
(714) 826-8950
Admin Jaime Deutsch.
Licensure Skilled care. *Beds* 152. *Certified*
Medicare; Medi-Cal.
Owner Proprietary Corp.

Grand Care Convalescent Hospital*
2040 S Euclid St, Anaheim, CA, 92802
(714) 636-2800
Admin Ronald G Stinebiser.
Licensure Skilled care. *Beds* 94. *Certified*
Medicare; Medi-Cal.
Owner Proprietary Corp (Health Care Grp).

Guidance Center Sanitarium
1135 Leisure Ct, Anaheim, CA, 92801
(714) 772-1353
Admin Dr George C Scholl. *Medical Dir/Dir
of Nursing* H Gurgis MD; Eunice Parker RN
DON.
Licensure Skilled care; Intermediate care. *Beds*
115. *Certified* Medi-Cal.
Owner Proprietary Corp.
Admissions Requirements Minimum age 18;
Medical examination.
Staff Physicians 5 (pt); RNs 8 (ft); LPNs 5
(ft); Orderlies 4 (ft); Nurses aides 25 (ft);
Physical therapists 3 (ft); Reality therapists 1
(pt); Recreational therapists 1 (pt);
Occupational therapists 1 (pt); Speech
therapists 1 (pt); Activities coordinators 3
(ft); Dietitians 1 (pt); Ophthalmologists 1
(pt);; Dentist 2 (pt).
Languages Spanish
Facilities Dining room; Activities room;
Crafts room; Laundry room; Barber/Beauty
shop; 6 large outdoor areas.
Activities Arts & crafts; Cards; Games;
Reading groups; Prayer groups; Movies;
Shopping trips; Social/Cultural gatherings;
Exercise; Music; Adult education; Therapy
groups.

Hillhaven Convalescent Hospital*
1130 W La Palma Ave, Anaheim, CA, 92801
(714) 772-7480
Admin Thomas Hines. *Medical Dir/Dir of
Nursing* Seawright Anderson MD.
Licensure Skilled care. *Beds* 72. *Certified*
Medicare; Medi-Cal.
Owner Proprietary Corp (Hillhaven Corp).
Admissions Requirements Medical
examination; Physician's request.
Staff RNs 3 (pt); Nurses aides 5 (ft), 20 (pt);
Activities coordinators 1 (ft); Dietitians 1
(pt).
Facilities Dining room; Physical therapy
room; Activities room; Laundry room;
Barber/Beauty shop; Library.
Activities Arts & crafts; Cards; Games;
Movies; Shopping trips; Social/Cultural
gatherings.

Lutheran Health Facility of Anaheim
891 S Walnut St, Anaheim, CA, 92802
(714) 776-7150, 774-1234
Admin Marion L Hopkins. *Medical Dir/Dir of
Nursing* Dr Stanley Kerkhoff.
Licensure Skilled care. *Beds* SNF 33. *Certified*
Medicaid.
Owner Nonprofit Corp.

Admissions Requirements Minimum age 65;
Medical examination; Physician's request.
Staff Physicians 1 (pt); RNs 2 (ft), 1 (pt);
LPNs 3 (ft), 3 (pt); Orderlies 1 (pt); Nurses
aides 12 (ft), 3 (pt); Physical therapists 1
(pt); Occupational therapists 1 (pt); Speech
therapists 1 (pt); Activities coordinators 1
(pt); Dietitians 1 (pt).
Affiliation Lutheran
Facilities Dining room.
Activities Arts & crafts; Games; Reading
groups; Prayer groups; Movies; Limo trips;
Walks.

Orangeview Convalescent Hospital*
1720 W Orange, Anaheim, CA, 92804
(714) 776-1720
Admin Clyde D Vineyard.
Licensure Skilled care. *Beds* 36. *Certified*
Medicare; Medi-Cal.
Owner Proprietary Corp.

Parkview Convalescent Hospital
1514 E Lincoln Ave, Anaheim, CA, 92805
(714) 774-2222
Admin Greg Goings. *Medical Dir/Dir of
Nursing* Hildie Brandt.
Licensure Skilled care. *Beds* SNF 41. *Certified*
Medicare; Medi-Cal.
Owner Proprietary Corp.
Admissions Requirements Physician's request.
Staff RNs 2 (ft), 1 (pt); LPNs 4 (ft), 1 (pt);
Nurses aides 11 (ft), 10 (pt); Activities
coordinators 1 (ft).
Languages Spanish
Facilities Dining room; Activities room;
Laundry room; Library.
Activities Arts & crafts; Cards; Games;
Reading groups; Prayer groups; Movies;
Shopping trips.

St Elizabeth Convalescent Hospital*
3435 W Ball Rd, Anaheim, CA, 92804
(714) 827-5880
Admin William Cloonan.
Licensure Skilled care. *Beds* 97. *Certified*
Medicare; Medi-Cal.
Owner Proprietary Corp.

ANDERSON

Hospitality House Nursing Home
1450 Happy Valley Rd, Anderson, CA, 96007
(916) 241-2804
Admin Shirley J Jacobsen.
Licensure Skilled care. *Beds* 34. *Certified*
Medi-Cal.
Admissions Requirements Minimum age Adult
services; Physician's request.
Facilities Dining room; Activities room;
Crafts room; Barber/Beauty shop.
Activities Arts & crafts; Cards; Games;
Reading groups; Prayer groups; Movies;
Shopping trips; Social/Cultural gatherings.

ANGWIN

Pine Breeze Convalescent Hospital*
295 Pine Breeze Dr, Angwin, CA, 94508
(707) 965-2461
Admin Merle Prusia.
Licensure Skilled care. *Beds* 59.
Owner Proprietary Corp.

ANTIOCH

Antioch Convalescent Hospital
1210 A St, Antioch, CA, 94509
(415) 757-8787
Admin Velda C Pierce. *Medical Dir/Dir of
Nursing* Raymond Stotler; Marita Pato.
Licensure Skilled care. *Beds* 99. *Certified*
Medicaid; Medicare; Medi-Cal.
Owner Proprietary Corp.
Admissions Requirements Physician's request.

Staff Physicians 1 (pt); RNs 1 (ft), 1 (pt); LPNs 7 (ft), 3 (pt); Orderlies 1 (ft); Nurses aides 25 (ft), 15 (pt); Physical therapists 1 (pt); Occupational therapists 1 (pt); Speech therapists 1 (pt); Activities coordinators 1 (ft); Dietitians 1 (pt); Ophthalmologists 1 (pt).
Facilities Dining room; Physical therapy room; Activities room; Laundry room; Barber/Beauty shop.
Activities Arts & crafts; Cards; Games; Reading groups; Prayer groups; Movies; Shopping trips; Social/Cultural gatherings.

Cavallo Convalescent Hospital*
1907 Cavallo Rd, Antioch, CA, 94509
(415) 757-5442
Admin Rilda M Scarfo. *Medical Dir/Dir of Nursing* Mark Dechter MD & Barbara Franzen MD.
Licensure Skilled care. *Beds* 38. *Certified* Medicare; Medi-Cal.
Owner Proprietary Corp.
Admissions Requirements Minimum age 18; Medical examination.
Staff Physicians 2 (ft); RNs 1 (ft), 1 (pt); LPNs 3 (ft), 2 (pt); Orderlies 1 (pt); Nurses aides 10 (ft), 4 (pt); Recreational therapists 1 (ft); Activities coordinators 1 (ft).
Facilities Dining room; Activities room; Crafts room; Laundry room; Barber/Beauty shop.
Activities Arts & crafts; Cards; Games; Reading groups; Prayer groups; Movies; Shopping trips; Social/Cultural gatherings; BBQs; Resident council; Exercise class; Mass once a month; Bible study; Adult education class..

Lone Tree Convalescent Hospital*
4001 Lone Tree Way, Antioch, CA, 94509
(415) 754-0470
Admin John Bird. *Medical Dir/Dir of Nursing* Abe Kaplan MD.
Licensure Skilled care. *Beds* 99. *Certified* Medicare; Medi-Cal.
Owner Proprietary Corp.
Staff Physicians 1 (pt); RNs 3 (ft), 1 (pt); LPNs 3 (ft), 6 (pt); Orderlies 2 (pt); Nurses aides 24 (ft), 16 (pt); Physical therapists 1 (pt); Occupational therapists 1 (pt); Speech therapists 1 (pt); Activities coordinators 2 (pt); Dietitians 1 (pt); Dentists 1 (pt); Podiatrists 1 (pt).
Facilities Dining room; Physical therapy room; Activities room; Laundry room; Barber/Beauty shop.
Activities Arts & crafts; Cards; Games; Prayer groups; Movies; Shopping trips.

ARCADIA

Arcadia Convalescent Hospital Inc
1601 S Baldwin Ave, Arcadia, CA, 91006
(818) 445-2170
Admin Orlando Clarizio. *Medical Dir/Dir of Nursing* Dr Jack Baker; Mina Villegas RN.
Licensure Skilled care. *Beds* SNF 74. *Certified* Medicare; Medi-Cal.
Owner Privately owned.
Staff Physicians; RNs; Orderlies; Nurses aides; Physical therapists; Recreational therapists; Occupational therapists; Speech therapists; Activities coordinators; Dietitians; Dentists; Ophthalmologists; Podiatrists; LVNs.
Facilities Dining room; Physical therapy room; Activities room; Crafts room; Laundry room; Barber/Beauty shop.
Activities Arts & crafts; Cards; Games; Reading groups; Prayer groups; Movies; Shopping trips; Social/Cultural gatherings.

Huntington Drive Convalescent Hospital*
400 W Huntington Dr, Arcadia, CA, 91106
(818) 445-2421
Admin Ann E Koeckeitz. *Medical Dir/Dir of Nursing* F Kunze MD.

Licensure Skilled care. *Beds* 99. *Certified* Medicare; Medi-Cal.
Owner Proprietary Corp (Beverly Enterprises).
Admissions Requirements Physician's request.
Staff RNs 4 (ft), 3 (pt); LPNs 9 (ft), 4 (pt); Nurses aides 34 (ft), 1 (pt); Activities coordinators 1 (ft).
Facilities Dining room; Physical therapy room; Activities room; Crafts room; Laundry room; Barber/Beauty shop.
Activities Arts & crafts; Games; Reading groups; Prayer groups; Movies; Social/Cultural gatherings.

ARLINGTON

Alta Vista Healthcare*
9020 Garfield Ave, Arlington, CA, 92503
(714) 688-8200
Admin Gary Dickerson.
Licensure Skilled care. *Beds* 107. *Certified* Medicare; Medi-Cal.
Owner Proprietary Corp (Hillhaven Corp).

ARROYO GRANDE

South County Convalescent Center
1212 Farroll Ave, Arroyo Grande, CA, 93420
(805) 489-8137
Admin William Sheets. *Medical Dir/Dir of Nursing* Dale Rodseth.
Licensure Skilled care. *Beds* SNF 99. *Certified* Medi-Cal.
Owner Privately owned.
Staff RNs; LPNs; Nurses aides; Activities coordinators; Dietitians.
Facilities Dining room; Activities room; Chapel; Crafts room; Laundry room; Barber/Beauty shop.
Activities Arts & crafts; Cards; Games; Reading groups; Prayer groups; Movies; Social/Cultural gatherings.

ARTESIA

Pilgrims Convalescent Hospital
11614 E 183rd St, Artesia, CA, 90701
(213) 865-5218
Admin Elroy Vander Ley. *Medical Dir/Dir of Nursing* Janet Doppenburg.
Licensure Skilled care. *Beds* SNF 59. *Certified* Medicaid; Medicare; Medi-Cal.
Owner Nonprofit Corp.
Admissions Requirements Minimum age 65; Medical examination.
Staff RNs 1 (ft), 4 (pt); LPNs 8 (ft), 2 (pt); Nurses aides 19 (ft), 5 (pt); Physical therapists 1 (pt); Speech therapists 1 (pt); Activities coordinators 2 (pt); Dietitians 1 (pt).
Affiliation Christian Reformed
Facilities Dining room; Activities room; Crafts room; Laundry room; Barber/Beauty shop.
Activities Arts & crafts; Cards; Games; Reading groups; Prayer groups; Movies; Shopping trips; Social/Cultural gatherings; Church program & outings to church luncheons; Bible classes.

Twin Palms Care Center
11900 E Artesia Blvd, Artesia, CA, 90701
(213) 865-0271
Admin Catherine M Eichberg. *Medical Dir/Dir of Nursing* James M Hilton MD; Adele Peltier RN DON.
Licensure Skilled care; Intermediate care. *Beds* SNF 222; ICF 74. *Certified* Medi-Cal.
Owner Proprietary Corp.
Admissions Requirements Minimum age IC 18; SNF 45; Medical examination.
Staff RNs 10 (ft); LPNs 22 (ft); Nurses aides 122 (ft); Activities coordinators 2 (ft).
Languages Tagalog

Facilities Dining room; Activities room; Barber/Beauty shop.
Activities Arts & crafts; Cards; Games; Reading groups; Prayer groups; Movies; Shopping trips; Social/Cultural gatherings; Nature walks; Volleyball; Basketball; Ping-pong.

ASHEVILLE

Autumnfield of Asheville
141 Hillside, Asheville, CA, 28801
(704) 253-4000
Admin Gilen R Meibaum. *Medical Dir/Dir of Nursing* Alesia Swann; Jenny Clark RN; Dave Khatri MD.
Licensure Intermediate care; Home for aged. *Beds* ICF 18; Home for aged 25. *Certified* Medicaid.
Owner Proprietary Corp.
Admissions Requirements Minimum age 21; Medical examination; Physician's request.
Staff RNs 1 (pt); LPNs 2 (ft), 5 (pt); Nurses aides 14 (ft), 2 (pt); Activities coordinators 1 (ft); Dietitians 1 (ft); Ophthalmologists 1 (pt); Podiatrists 1 (pt).
Facilities Dining room; Activities room.
Activities Bingo; Cookouts; Car shows; Educational encouragement.

ATASCADERO

Country Care Convalescent Hospital*
14900 El Camino Real, Atascadero, CA, 93422
(805) 466-0282
Admin John M Arrambide.
Licensure Skilled care. *Beds* 40. *Certified* Medicare; Medi-Cal.
Owner Nonprofit Corp.

Danish Convalescent Home*
10805 El Camino Real, Atascadero, CA, 93422
(805) 466-9254
Admin Roy B Jensen.
Licensure Skilled care. *Beds* 64. *Certified* Medicare; Medi-Cal.
Owner Proprietary Corp.

AUBERRY

Wish-I-Ah Lodge*
35680 N Wish-I-Ah Rd, Auberry, CA, 93602
(209) 855-2211
Admin Theodore Harwick.
Licensure Skilled care. *Beds* 135. *Certified* Medi-Cal.
Owner Proprietary Corp.

AUBURN

Auburn Convalescent Hospital*
260 Racetrack St, Auburn, CA, 95603
(916) 885-7051
Admin Martin C Klein.
Licensure Skilled care. *Beds* 84. *Certified* Medicare; Medi-Cal.
Owner Proprietary Corp.

Auburn Ravine Terrace*
750 Auburn Ravine Terrace, Auburn, CA, 95603
(916) 823-6131
Admin David L Ferguson.
Licensure Skilled care. *Beds* 56. *Certified* Medi-Cal.
Owner Nonprofit Corp.

Hilltop Manor Convalescent Hospital 2
PO Box 5218, 12225 Shale Ridge Ln, Auburn, CA, 95604-5218
(916) 885-7511
Admin Bradley J Wilcox.

Licensure Skilled care. *Beds* 230. *Certified* Medicare; Medi-Cal.
Owner Proprietary Corp.

BAKERSFIELD

Bakersfield Convalescent Hospital
730 34th St, Bakersfield, CA, 93301
(805) 327-7687
Admin Christopher A Monroe. *Medical Dir/Dir of Nursing* R Larwood MD.
Licensure Skilled care. *Beds* SNF 150. *Certified* Medicaid; Medicare; Medi-Cal.
Owner Proprietary Corp.
Admissions Requirements Minimum age 18; Medical examination; Physician's request.
Staff RNs 8 (ft); LPNs 17 (ft), 3 (pt); Nurses aides 33 (ft), 7 (pt); Physical therapists 2 (pt); Occupational therapists 1 (pt); Speech therapists 1 (pt); Activities coordinators 1 (ft); Dietitians 1 (pt); Ophthalmologists 1 (pt).
Languages Spanish
Facilities Dining room; Physical therapy room; Activities room; Crafts room; Laundry room; Barber/Beauty shop; Library; Private suites.
Activities Arts & crafts; Cards; Games; Reading groups; Prayer groups; Movies; Shopping trips; Social/Cultural gatherings; Outings to theater & places of interest.

Beverly Manor Convalescent Hospital*
3601 San Dimas, Bakersfield, CA, 93301
(805) 323-2894
Admin Jerome Sturz.
Licensure Skilled care. *Beds* 99. *Certified* Medicare; Medi-Cal.
Owner Proprietary Corp (Beverly Enterprises).

Colonial Convalescent Hospital*
1611 Height St, Bakersfield, CA, 93305
(805) 872-0705
Admin James Williams.
Licensure Skilled care. *Beds* 120. *Certified* Medicare; Medi-Cal.
Owner Proprietary Corp (Care Enterprises).

Crestwood Manor*
6600 Eucalyptus Dr, Bakersfield, CA, 93306
(805) 366-5757
Admin Cornel Artho. *Medical Dir/Dir of Nursing* Arthur Unger MD.
Licensure Skilled care. *Beds* 109. *Certified* Medicare.
Owner Proprietary Corp (Crestwood Hosp).
Admissions Requirements Minimum age 18.
Facilities Dining room; Activities room; Crafts room; Laundry room; Barber/Beauty shop; Library.
Activities Arts & crafts; Cards; Games; Reading groups; Prayer groups; Movies; Shopping trips; Social/Cultural gatherings.

Hilltop Convalescent Hospital
1601 Height St, Bakersfield, CA, 93305
(805) 872-2324
Admin Michael D Hagen.
Licensure Skilled care. *Beds* SNF 117. *Certified* Medicare; Medi-Cal.
Owner Proprietary Corp (Care Enterprises).
Admissions Requirements Medical examination; Physician's request.
Staff Physicians 1 (pt); RNs 5 (ft); LPNs 6 (ft); Nurses aides 35 (ft), 3 (pt); Physical therapists 1 (pt); Occupational therapists 1 (pt); Speech therapists 1 (pt); Activities coordinators 2 (ft); Dietitians 2 (pt); Ophthalmologists 1 (pt).
Languages Spanish
Facilities Dining room; Physical therapy room; Activities room; Crafts room; Laundry room; Barber/Beauty shop; Recreation areas outside.
Activities Arts & crafts; Cards; Games; Prayer groups; Movies; Shopping trips; Social/Cultural gatherings.

Manor Lodge Convalescent Hospital
2607 Mount Vernon Ave, Bakersfield, CA, 93306
(805) 871-8733
Admin Lynn Gann. *Medical Dir/Dir of Nursing* Dr Frank Chang.
Licensure Skilled care. *Beds* SNF 37. *Certified* Medi-Cal.
Owner Privately owned.
Admissions Requirements Medical examination; Physician's request.
Staff RNs 1 (ft), 1 (pt); Nurses aides 14 (ft), 3 (pt); Activities coordinators 1 (ft).
Facilities Dining room; Activities room; Laundry room; Barber/Beauty shop.
Activities Arts & crafts; Games; Reading groups; Prayer groups; Movies; Shopping trips.

Parkview Julian Convalescent Hospital*
1801 Julian Ave, Bakersfield, CA, 93304
(805) 831-9150
Admin Frank Denham. *Medical Dir/Dir of Nursing* Samuel Schreiber MD.
Licensure Skilled care. *Beds* 99. *Certified* Medicare; Medi-Cal.
Owner Proprietary Corp.
Admissions Requirements Physician's request.
Staff RNs 2 (ft); LPNs 10 (ft); Nurses aides 25 (ft).
Facilities Dining room; Physical therapy room; Activities room; Barber/Beauty shop.
Activities Arts & crafts; Cards; Games; Reading groups; Movies; Social/Cultural gatherings; Outside entertainment.

Parkview Real Convalescent Hospital*
329 N Real Rd, Bakersfield, CA, 93309
(805) 327-7107
Admin Frank Denham.
Licensure Skilled care. *Beds* 164. *Certified* Medicare; Medi-Cal.
Owner Proprietary Corp.

Riverside Cottage Rest Home
1131 S "H" St, Bakersfield, CA, 93304
(805) 831-9126
Admin Roberta Mills.
Licensure Intermediate care. *Beds* 15. *Certified* Medi-Cal.
Owner Proprietary Corp.

Rosewood Health Facility
1401 New Stine Rd, Bakersfield, CA, 93309
(805) 834-0620
Admin Jo Ann Walters; Ted Ahlem. *Medical Dir/Dir of Nursing* H C Freedman MD; Elaine Allen RN.
Licensure Skilled care. *Beds* SNF 79. *Certified* Medicare; Medi-Cal.
Owner Nonprofit Corp (American Baptist Homes W).
Admissions Requirements Medical examination; Physician's request.
Staff RNs; LPNs; Nurses aides; Physical therapists; Occupational therapists; Speech therapists; Activities coordinators; Dietitians; Ophthalmologists.
Facilities Dining room; Physical therapy room; Activities room; Chapel; Laundry room; Barber/Beauty shop; Library.
Activities Arts & crafts; Games; Reading groups; Prayer groups; Movies; Shopping trips; Social/Cultural gatherings; Dinner outings.

Shady Manor Convalescent Hospital
2901 S "H" St, Bakersfield, CA, 93304
(805) 831-0765
Admin Astrik Lott. *Medical Dir/Dir of Nursing* Louise Largeteau RN.
Licensure Skilled care. *Beds* SNF 37. *Certified* Medi-Cal.
Owner Privately owned.
Admissions Requirements Physician's request.
Staff RNs 1 (ft), 2 (pt); LPNs 2 (ft), 2 (pt); Nurses aides 9 (ft); Activities coordinators 1 (ft); Dietitians 1 (pt).

Languages Spanish
Facilities Dining room; Laundry room.
Activities Arts & crafts; Cards; Games; Reading groups; Prayer groups; Movies; Shopping trips; Social/Cultural gatherings.

Valley Convalescent Hospital*
1205 8th St, Bakersfield, CA, 93304
(805) 324-9468
Admin Carlos R Lewis. *Medical Dir/Dir of Nursing* Samuel Schrieber.
Licensure Skilled care. *Beds* 87. *Certified* Medicare; Medi-Cal.
Owner Proprietary Corp.
Staff Physicians 6 (ft); RNs 1 (ft), 2 (pt); Orderlies 1 (ft); Nurses aides 27 (ft), 8 (pt); Physical therapists 1 (pt); Recreational therapists 1 (pt); Occupational therapists 1 (pt); Speech therapists 1 (pt); Activities coordinators 1 (ft); Dietitians 1 (ft); Dentists 1 (pt); Ophthalmologists 1 (pt); Podiatrists 1 (pt); Audiologists 1 (pt).
Facilities Dining room; Physical therapy room; Activities room; Crafts room; Laundry room; Barber/Beauty shop; Library.
Activities Arts & crafts; Cards; Games; Reading groups; Prayer groups; Movies; Shopping trips; Social/Cultural gatherings.

BALDWIN PARK

Baldwin Park Convalescent Hospital*
14518 E Los Angeles St, Baldwin Park, CA, 91706
(213) 337-7229
Admin Ann M Whitefoot.
Licensure Skilled care. *Beds* 49. *Certified* Medi-Cal.
Owner Proprietary Corp (Coastal Care Centers Inc).

Baldwin Park Health Care Center*
14318 Ohio St, Baldwin Park, CA, 91706
(213) 960-1971
Admin A Rzepnick. *Medical Dir/Dir of Nursing* Ron Atturi.
Licensure Skilled care. *Beds* 98. *Certified* Medicare; Medi-Cal.
Owner Proprietary Corp.
Admissions Requirements Physician's request.
Staff Physicians 4 (pt); RNs 1 (ft); LPNs 7 (ft); Orderlies 3 (ft); Nurses aides 23 (ft); Physical therapists 1 (pt); Occupational therapists 1 (pt); Speech therapists 1 (pt); Activities coordinators 1 (ft); Dietitians 1 (ft); Dentists 1 (pt); Ophthalmologists 1 (pt); Podiatrists 1 (pt); Audiologists 1 (pt).
Facilities Dining room; Physical therapy room; Activities room; Chapel; Crafts room; Laundry room; Barber/Beauty shop; Library.
Activities Arts & crafts; Cards; Games; Reading groups; Prayer groups; Movies; Shopping trips; Adult Education.

Golden State Habilitation Convalescent Center*
1758 Big Dalton Ave, Baldwin Park, CA, 91706
(818) 962-3274
Admin Michael C O'Neil.
Licensure Skilled care; Intermediate care for mentally retarded. *Beds* 155. *Certified* Medi-Cal.
Owner Proprietary Corp (Care Enterprises).
Staff Physicians 1 (pt); RNs 8 (ft); LPNs 12 (ft); Orderlies 34 (ft); Nurses aides 40 (ft); Physical therapists 1 (pt); Occupational therapists 1 (pt); Speech therapists 1 (pt); Activities coordinators 1 (pt); Dietitians 1 (pt); Dentists 1 (pt); Ophthalmologists 1 (pt); Podiatrists 1 (pt); Audiologists 1 (pt).
Facilities Dining room; Physical therapy room; Activities room; Laundry room; Barber/Beauty shop.
Activities Arts & crafts; Cards; Games; Movies; Shopping trips; Social/Cultural gatherings.

Palm Vista Care Center
14475 Ituni St, Baldwin Park, CA, 91706
(818) 962-7095
Admin Leanne M K Martinsen. *Medical Dir/
Dir of Nursing* Arlene Bumgarner RN DON.
Licensure Skilled care. *Beds* 97. *Certified*
Medicare; Medi-Cal.
Owner Proprietary Corp (Chartham
Management).
Admissions Requirements Minimum age 40;
Medical examination; Physician's request.
Staff RNs 1 (ft), 1 (pt); LPNs 7 (ft), 2 (pt);
Nurses aides 35 (ft), 10 (pt); Activities
coordinators 1 (ft).
Languages Spanish
Facilities Dining room; Physical therapy
room; Activities room; Crafts room; Barber/
Beauty shop.
Activities Arts & crafts; Cards; Games;
Reading groups; Prayer groups; Movies;
Social/Cultural gatherings.

The Rose Convalescent Hospital
3541 Puente Ave, Baldwin Park, CA, 91706
(818) 962-1043
Admin Terry Parker. *Medical Dir/Dir of
Nursing* Dinah Closas.
Licensure Skilled care. *Beds* SNF 49. *Certified*
Medicaid; Medicare; Medi-Cal.
Owner Proprietary Corp.
Staff RNs 1 (ft), 2 (pt); LPNs 1 (ft), 4 (pt);
Orderlies 3 (ft); Nurses aides 30 (ft);
Physical therapists 1 (pt); Occupational
therapists 1 (pt); Speech therapists 1 (pt);
Dietitians 1 (pt).
Languages Spanish
Facilities Dining room; Activities room;
Laundry room.
Activities Arts & crafts; Cards; Games;
Reading groups; Movies; Baldwin Park
Adult Education.

BANNING

Banning Convalescent Hospital*
3476 Wilson, Banning, CA, 92220
(714) 849-4723
Admin Daniel Shoopman. *Medical Dir/Dir of
Nursing* Ronald Rothe MD.
Licensure Skilled care. *Beds* 64. *Certified*
Medicare; Medi-Cal.
Owner Proprietary Corp (Care Enterprises).
Staff RNs 1 (ft), 2 (pt); LPNs 4 (ft), 4 (pt);
Nurses aides 14 (ft), 12 (pt); Activities
coordinators 1 (ft); Dietitians 1 (pt).
Facilities Dining room; Physical therapy
room; Activities room; Laundry room;
Barber/Beauty shop.
Activities Arts & crafts; Cards; Games;
Reading groups; Prayer groups; Movies.

BEAUMONT

Beaumont Convalescent Hospital*
1441 N Michigan Ave, Beaumont, CA, 92223
(714) 845-1166
Admin John Parfih. *Medical Dir/Dir of
Nursing* Robert Payton MD.
Licensure Skilled care. *Beds* 87. *Certified*
Medicare; Medi-Cal.
Owner Proprietary Corp (Care Enterprises).
Admissions Requirements Medical
examination; Physician's request.
Staff RNs 2 (ft), 1 (pt); LPNs 9 (ft), 2 (pt);
Orderlies 1 (ft); Nurses aides 36 (ft), 3 (pt);
Physical therapists 1 (ft); Occupational
therapists 1 (pt); Speech therapists 1 (pt);
Activities coordinators 1 (ft); Dietitians 1
(pt); Dentists 1 (pt).
Facilities Dining room; Physical therapy
room; Activities room; Laundry room;
Barber/Beauty shop.
Activities Arts & crafts; Cards; Games; Prayer
groups; Movies; Shopping trips.

Valley View
40901 E 8th, Beaumont, CA, 92223
(714) 845-3125
Admin Ms Terry Parker. *Medical Dir/Dir of
Nursing* Dr William Beard.
Licensure Intermediate care for mentally
retarded. *Beds* ICF/MR 56. *Certified* Medi-
Cal.
Owner Proprietary Corp (Care Enterprises).
Admissions Requirements Medical
examination; Physician's request.
Staff RNs; LPNs; Orderlies; Nurses aides;
Physical therapists 1 (pt); Recreational
therapists 1 (pt); Occupational therapists 1
(pt); Speech therapists 1 (pt); Dietitians 1
(pt).
Languages Spanish
Facilities Dining room; Activities room;
Laundry room.
Activities Arts & crafts; Cards; Games;
Movies; Shopping trips.

BELL GARDENS

Bell Gardens Convalescent Center
5648 E Gotham St, Bell Gardens, CA, 90201
(213) 927-2641, 771-4448
Admin Rachel Slomovic. *Medical Dir/Dir of
Nursing* William Slomovic RN.
Licensure Skilled care. *Beds* SNF 135.
Certified Medicare; Medi-Cal.
Owner Proprietary Corp.
Admissions Requirements Minimum age 18;
Medical examination; Physician's request.
Staff Physicians; RNs; Orderlies; Nurses aides;
Physical therapists; Recreational therapists;
Occupational therapists; Speech therapists;
Activities coordinators; Dietitians; Dentists;
Ophthalmologists; Podiatrists; LVNs.
Languages Spanish
Facilities Dining room; Physical therapy
room; Activities room; Crafts room; Laundry
room; Barber/Beauty shop.
Activities Arts & crafts; Cards; Games;
Reading groups; Prayer groups; Movies;
Shopping trips; Social/Cultural gatherings;
Outings.

Del Rio Convalescent Center
7002 E Gage Ave, Bell Gardens, CA, 90201
(213) 927-6586
Admin Steven D Highland. *Medical Dir/Dir of
Nursing* Michael Platt MD; Elizabeth
Stearns RN DON.
Licensure Skilled care. *Beds* SNF 99. *Certified*
Medi-Cal; VA.
Owner Proprietary Corp.
Admissions Requirements Minimum age 40;
Physician's request.
Staff RNs 1 (ft), 1 (pt); LPNs 7 (ft), 1 (pt);
Orderlies 2 (ft); Nurses aides 36 (ft), 5 (pt);
Activities coordinators 2 (ft); Dietitians 1
(pt).
Languages Spanish
Facilities Dining room; Physical therapy
room; Activities room; Crafts room; Laundry
room; Barber/Beauty shop; Library; 4 1/2
acres fenced grounds; Canteen.
Activities Arts & crafts; Cards; Games; Prayer
groups; Movies; Shopping trips; Social/
Cultural gatherings; Outings.

Del Rio Sanitarium
7004 E Gage Ave, Bell Gardens, CA, 90201
(213) 927-6586
Admin Steven D Highland; Mahmood
Moledina. *Medical Dir/Dir of Nursing* Dr
Michael Platt; Jerry D Maxwell.
Licensure Skilled care. *Beds* SNF 84. *Certified*
Medi-Cal.
Owner Proprietary Corp.
Admissions Requirements Minimum age 40;
Medical examination; Physician's request;
must be ambulatory.

Staff RNs 1 (ft), 1 (pt); LPNs 7 (ft), 1 (pt);
Orderlies; Nurses aides 32 (ft), 5 (pt);
Activities coordinators 2 (ft); Dietitians 1
(pt).
Languages Spanish
Facilities Dining room; Physical therapy
room; Activities room; Crafts room; Laundry
room; Barber/Beauty shop; Library; 4 1/2
acres of fenced grounds.
Activities Arts & crafts; Cards; Games;
Reading groups; Prayer groups; Movies;
Shopping trips; Social/Cultural gatherings;
Outings to state fairs; Disneyland; Beaches.

BELLFLOWER

Bel Tooren Villa Convalescent Hospital
16910 Woodruff Ave, Bellflower, CA, 90706
(213) 867-1761
Admin Shirley B Schouleman. *Medical Dir/Dir
of Nursing* K P Wong MD; Vicki L Miller
RN.
Licensure Skilled care. *Beds* SNF 99. *Certified*
Medicare; Medi-Cal.
Owner Proprietary Corp (Columbia Corp).
Admissions Requirements Medical
examination; Physician's request.
Staff Physicians; RNs; LPNs; Orderlies;
Nurses aides; Physical therapists; Reality
therapists; Recreational therapists;
Occupational therapists; Speech therapists;
Activities coordinators; Dietitians; Dentists;
Ophthalmologists; Podiatrists.
Languages Spanish
Facilities Dining room; Physical therapy
room; Activities room; Crafts room; Laundry
room; Barber/Beauty shop; Library.
Activities Arts & crafts; Cards; Games;
Reading groups; Prayer groups; Movies;
Social/Cultural gatherings.

Bellflower Convalescent Hospital*
9710 E Artesia Ave, Bellflower, CA, 90706
(213) 925-2274
Admin Pompeyo Rosales.
Licensure Skilled care. *Beds* 49. *Certified*
Medicare; Medi-Cal.
Owner Proprietary Corp.

Bellflower Golden Age Convalescent Home
9028 Rose St, Bellflower, CA, 90706
(213) 925-4252
Admin Brad De Haan. *Medical Dir/Dir of
Nursing* Virginia Fernandez RN.
Licensure Skilled care. *Beds* 53. *Certified*
Medicare; Medi-Cal.
Owner Proprietary Corp (Chartham
Management).
Staff RNs 1 (pt); LPNs 3 (ft); Nurses aides 14
(ft); Physical therapists 1 (ft); Activities
coordinators 1 (ft); Dietitians 1 (pt).
Facilities Dining room; Activities room;
Barber/Beauty shop.
Activities Arts & crafts; Cards; Games;
Reading groups; Prayer groups; Movies;
Shopping trips; Social/Cultural gatherings.

Woodruff Convalescent Center*
17836 S Woodruff Ave, Bellflower, CA, 90706
(213) 925-8457
Admin Martin Simon. *Medical Dir/Dir of
Nursing* Lawrence Wallington MD.
Licensure Skilled care. *Beds* 140. *Certified*
Medicare; Medi-Cal.
Owner Proprietary Corp.
Admissions Requirements Minimum age 16;
Medical examination; Physician's request.
Staff RNs 4 (ft), 5 (pt); LPNs 6 (ft), 1 (pt);
Orderlies 1 (ft); Nurses aides 52 (ft);
Activities coordinators 2 (ft); Dietitians 1
(ft).
Facilities Dining room; Physical therapy
room; Activities room; Crafts room; Barber/
Beauty shop.
Activities Arts & crafts; Games; Prayer groups;
Movies.

BELMONT

Belmont Convalescent Hospital*
1041 Hill St, Belmont, CA, 94002
(415) 591-7181
Admin Mary Lou South. *Medical Dir/Dir of Nursing* Jonathan F Feinberg.
Licensure Skilled care. *Beds* 33.
Owner Proprietary Corp.
Admissions Requirements Medical examination.
Staff RNs 2 (ft), 2 (pt); LPNs 1 (ft), 1 (pt); Nurses aides 8 (ft), 1 (pt); Physical therapists 1 (pt); Activities coordinators 1 (pt).
Facilities Dining room; Activities room; Laundry room; Barber/Beauty shop.
Activities Arts & crafts; Cards; Games; Reading groups; Prayer groups; Movies; Van rides.

Carlmont Convalescent Hospital
2140 Carlmont Dr, Belmont, CA, 94002
(415) 591-9601
Admin George M Lamb. *Medical Dir/Dir of Nursing* Sunie B Creegan RN.
Licensure Skilled care. *Beds* SNF 59.
Owner Proprietary Corp.
Admissions Requirements Medical examination; Physician's request.
Staff RNs 3 (ft), 2 (pt); Orderlies 2 (ft); Nurses aides 26 (ft), 3 (pt); Activities coordinators 1 (ft), 1 (pt); LVNs 4 (ft), 4 (pt).
Languages Spanish, Tagalog, German, French
Facilities Dining room; Physical therapy room; Activities room; Barber/Beauty shop.
Activities Arts & crafts; Games; Reading groups; Prayer groups; Movies; Social/Cultural gatherings.

BERKELEY

Ashby Geriatric Hospital Inc*
2270 Ashby Ave, Berkeley, CA, 94705
(415) 841-9494
Admin Bradley M Besaw.
Licensure Skilled care. *Beds* 31. *Certified* Medicare; Medi-Cal.
Owner Proprietary Corp.

Berkeley Hills Convalescent Hospital*
2223 Ashby Ave, Berkeley, CA, 94705
(415) 843-7007
Admin Suellen Rideout.
Licensure Skilled care. *Beds* 36. *Certified* Medicare; Medi-Cal.
Owner Proprietary Corp.

Chaparral House
1309 Allston Way, Berkeley, CA, 94702
(415) 848-8774
Admin James M Johnson. *Medical Dir/Dir of Nursing* L Craig MD.
Licensure Intermediate care. *Beds* ICF 49. *Certified* Medi-Cal.
Owner Nonprofit organization/foundation.
Staff RNs 1 (ft), 2 (pt); LPNs 7 (ft), 2 (pt); Nurses aides 10 (ft), 4 (pt); Activities coordinators 1 (ft); Chaplain 1 (ft).
Facilities Dining room; Activities room; Crafts room; Laundry room; Barber/Beauty shop.
Activities Arts & crafts; Cards; Games; Reading groups; Prayer groups; Movies; Shopping trips.

Claremont Convalescent Hospital
2500 Ashby Ave, Berkeley, CA, 94705
(415) 841-5260
Admin Dick A Isaacs.
Licensure Skilled care. *Beds* 36. *Certified* Medicare.
Owner Nonprofit Corp (Guardian Fdn Inc).

Elmwood Convalescent Hospital
2829 Shattuck Ave, Berkeley, CA, 94705
(415) 848-3760

Admin Elizabeth Schmidt. *Medical Dir/Dir of Nursing* Frank Lucido MD; Kitti Gordon DON.
Licensure Skilled care. *Beds* SNF 81. *Certified* Medicare.
Owner Nonprofit Corp (Guardian Fdn Inc).
Admissions Requirements Minimum age Geriatric.
Staff Physicians 2 (pt); RNs 5 (ft), 1 (pt); LPNs 8 (ft); Orderlies 2 (pt); Physical therapists 1 (pt); Reality therapists 1 (pt); Recreational therapists 1 (pt); Occupational therapists 1 (pt); Speech therapists 1 (pt); Activities coordinators 1 (ft), 1 (pt); Ophthalmologists 1 (pt); Dentists 1 (pt).
Languages Spanish, Chinese, Tagalog, German
Facilities Dining room; Physical therapy room; Activities room; Crafts room; Laundry room; Barber/Beauty shop; Library; Sitting room.
Activities Arts & crafts; Cards; Games; Reading groups; Prayer groups; Movies; Shopping trips; Social/Cultural gatherings; Small group activities.

Kyakameena Skilled Nursing Facility
2131 Carleton St, Berkeley, CA, 94704
(415) 843-2131
Admin Portia H Strause. *Medical Dir/Dir of Nursing* Dr Robert D Tufft; Virginia Toby RN DON.
Licensure Skilled care. *Beds* SNF 59. *Certified* Medicare; Medi-Cal.
Owner Proprietary Corp.
Admissions Requirements Medical examination; Physician's request.
Staff RNs 1 (ft), 2 (pt); LPNs 7 (ft), 1 (pt); Nurses aides 25 (ft); Physical therapists 1 (pt); Occupational therapists 1 (pt); Speech therapists 1 (pt); Activities coordinators 1 (ft); Dietitians 1 (pt); Ophthalmologists 1 (pt); Dentist 1 (pt).
Facilities Dining room; Activities room; Laundry room; Barber/Beauty shop; Garden patio.
Activities Arts & crafts; Cards; Games; Reading groups; Prayer groups; Movies; Shopping trips; Social/Cultural gatherings; Music; Canine companion.

BIG PINE

Inyo County Sanitorium*
County Rd, Box 88, Big Pine, CA, 93513
(714) 938-2411
Admin Michael Cosenza.
Licensure Skilled care. *Beds* 45. *Certified* Medicare; Medi-Cal.
Owner Publicly owned.

BLOOMINGTON

Intercommunity Center of Bloomington*
18612 Santa Ana, Bloomington, CA, 92316
(714) 877-1201
Admin Ben Bollinger.
Licensure Intermediate care; Intermediate care for mentally retarded. *Beds* 96. *Certified* Medi-Cal.
Owner Nonprofit Corp.

BLYTHE

Blythe Convalescent Hospital*
285 W Chanslor Way, Blythe, CA, 92225
(619) 922-8176
Admin John Ryan. *Medical Dir/Dir of Nursing* William Wiley MD.
Licensure Skilled care. *Beds* 50. *Certified* Medi-Cal.
Owner Proprietary Corp.
Admissions Requirements Medical examination; Physician's request.

Staff Physicians 1 (pt); RNs 2 (ft); LPNs 3 (ft), 1 (pt); Orderlies 1 (ft); Nurses aides 13 (ft), 5 (pt); Physical therapists 1 (pt); Reality therapists 1 (pt); Recreational therapists 1 (ft); Occupational therapists 1 (pt); Activities coordinators 1 (ft); Dietitians 1 (ft); Dentists 1 (pt); Ophthalmologists 1 (pt); Podiatrists 1 (pt); Audiologists 1 (pt).
Facilities Dining room; Activities room; Crafts room; Laundry room; Barber/Beauty shop.
Activities Arts & crafts; Cards; Games; Reading groups; Prayer groups; Shopping trips; Social/Cultural gatherings.

BRAWLEY

Royal Convalescent Hospital Inc*
320 W Cattle Call Dr, Brawley, CA, 92227
(714) 344-5431
Admin Tobias Friedman.
Licensure Skilled care. *Beds* 99. *Certified* Medicare; Medi-Cal.
Owner Proprietary Corp.

BUENA PARK

Farmdale Convalescent Hospital
8520 Western Ave, Buena Park, CA, 90620
(714) 828-8222
Licensure Skilled care. *Beds* SNF 143. *Certified* Medicare; Medi-Cal.
Owner Proprietary Corp.
Admissions Requirements Physician's request.
Staff RNs 4 (ft), 3 (pt); LPNs 9 (ft), 4 (pt); Nurses aides 35 (ft), 20 (pt); Physical therapists 3 (pt); Recreational therapists 1 (pt); Occupational therapists 1 (pt); Speech therapists 1 (pt); Activities coordinators 2 (ft); Dietitians 1 (pt); Dentists 1 (pt); Ophthalmologists 1 (pt); Podiatrists 1 (pt).
Facilities Dining room; Physical therapy room; Activities room; Laundry room; Barber/Beauty shop.
Activities Arts & crafts; Games; Prayer groups; Movies; Shopping trips; Social/Cultural gatherings.

Orange West Convalescent Hospital
9021 Knott Ave, Buena Park, CA, 90620
(714) 826-2330
Admin Charlotte Dufresne, Admin. *Medical Dir/Dir of Nursing* G D Kohler MD; Ann Fredricks DON.
Licensure Skilled care. *Beds* SNF 99. *Certified* Medicare; Medi-Cal.
Owner Proprietary Corp.
Staff RNs 6 (ft), 3 (pt); LPNs 7 (ft), 4 (pt); Nurses aides 25 (ft), 6 (pt); Activities coordinators 1 (ft), 1 (pt); Dietitians 1 (ft).
Languages Spanish, Korean
Activities Arts & crafts; Cards; Games; Reading groups; Prayer groups; Movies; Shopping trips; Social/Cultural gatherings; Outings; Musical entertainment.

BURBANK

Beverly Manor
925 W Alameda Ave, Burbank, CA, 91506
(818) 843-1771
Admin Scott Carlson. *Medical Dir/Dir of Nursing* Stuart Shipco MD; Lois Wallerstein RN DON.
Licensure Skilled care. *Beds* SNF 89. *Certified* Medicaid; Medi-Cal.
Owner Proprietary Corp (Beverly Enterprises).
Admissions Requirements Minimum age 65; Medical examination; Physician's request.
Staff Physicians; RNs; LPNs; Orderlies; Nurses aides; Recreational therapists; Activities coordinators; Dietitians; Dentists; Ophthalmologists; Podiatrists.
Languages Spanish

Facilities Dining room; Activities room; Crafts room; Laundry room; Library.
Activities Arts & crafts; Cards; Games; Reading groups; Prayer groups; Movies; Shopping trips; Social/Cultural gatherings.

Beverly Manor Convalescent Hospital*
1041 S Main St, Burbank, CA, 91506
(818) 843-2330
Admin Berna-Dean Darms. *Medical Dir/Dir of Nursing* Dr Valentine Birds.
Licensure Skilled care. *Beds* 188. *Certified* Medicare; Medi-Cal.
Owner Proprietary Corp (Beverly Enterprises).
Admissions Requirements Medical examination.
Staff Physicians 32 (pt); RNs 8 (ft), 6 (pt); LPNs 11 (ft), 6 (pt); Nurses aides 67 (ft), 1 (pt); Physical therapists 2 (pt); Occupational therapists 1 (pt); Speech therapists 3 (pt); Activities coordinators 2 (ft); Dietitians 1 (pt); Dentists 1 (pt); Ophthalmologists 2 (pt); Podiatrists 3 (pt); Audiologists 1 (pt).
Facilities Dining room; Physical therapy room; Activities room; Crafts room; Laundry room; Barber/Beauty shop.
Activities Arts & crafts; Cards; Games; Reading groups; Prayer groups; Movies; Shopping trips; Social/Cultural gatherings; Grooming class; Reality class; Restorative exercise; Cooking classes; Patient council; Birthday parties; Adult education; Outings.

Burbank Convalescent Hospital
2710 W Olive Ave, Burbank, CA, 91505
(818) 848-5581
Admin Orlando Clarizo Jr. *Medical Dir/Dir of Nursing* Dr George Papkin.
Licensure Skilled care. *Beds* SNF 54. *Certified* Medicaid; Medicare.
Owner Privately owned.
Staff Physicians 3 (ft), 12 (pt); RNs 1 (ft), 1 (pt); LPNs 5 (ft), 1 (pt); Orderlies 1 (ft), 1 (pt); Nurses aides 22 (ft); Physical therapists 1 (ft); Reality therapists 1 (pt); Recreational therapists 1 (ft); Occupational therapists 1 (ft); Speech therapists 1 (ft); Activities coordinators 1 (ft); Dietitians 1 (ft); Dentists 1 (ft); Ophthalmologists 1 (ft); Podiatrists 1 (ft).
Languages Spanish, Tagalog.
Facilities Dining room; Physical therapy room; Activities room; Laundry room.
Activities Arts & crafts; Cards; Games; Reading groups; Prayer groups; Movies.

Cypress Convalescent Center*
700 N 1st St, Burbank, CA, 91502
(213) 842-8169
Admin Michael O'Neil.
Licensure Skilled care. *Beds* 70. *Certified* Medicare; Medi-Cal.
Owner Proprietary Corp.

St Joseph Medical Center Pavilion
2727 W Alameda Ave, Burbank, CA, 91505
(818) 843-7900
Admin Scott T Seamons. *Medical Dir/Dir of Nursing* Alonzo Y Olsen Jr MD; Julie Theiring RN DON.
Licensure Skilled care. *Beds* SNF 149. *Certified* Medicare; Medi-Cal.
Owner Nonprofit Corp.
Admissions Requirements Medical examination; Physician's request.
Staff RNs 1 (ft); LPNs 1 (ft); Orderlies 1 (ft); Nurses aides 1 (ft); Physical therapists 1 (ft); Recreational therapists 1 (ft); Occupational therapists 1 (ft); Speech therapists 1 (ft); Activities coordinators 1 (ft); Dietitians 1 (ft); Ophthalmologists 1 (pt); Podiatrists 1 (pt).
Affiliation Roman Catholic
Facilities Dining room; Physical therapy room; Activities room; Chapel; Crafts room; Laundry room; Barber/Beauty shop; Library.

Activities Arts & crafts; Cards; Games; Reading groups; Prayer groups; Movies; Shopping trips; Social/Cultural gatherings; Field trips.

BURLINGAME

Bayview Convalescent Hospital
1100 Trousdale Dr, Burlingame, CA, 94010
(415) 692-3758
Admin Samuel G Bergstrom. *Medical Dir/Dir of Nursing* Robert Minkowsky.
Licensure Skilled care. *Beds* 281. *Certified* Medicare; Medi-Cal.
Owner Proprietary Corp (Care Enterprises).
Admissions Requirements Physician's request.
Staff RNs 10 (ft), 10 (pt); LPNs 10 (ft), 13 (pt); Nurses aides 68 (ft), 29 (pt); Physical therapists 2 (pt); Occupational therapists 1 (pt); Speech therapists 1 (pt); Activities coordinators 4 (ft); Dietitians 1 (ft); Ophthalmologists 1 (pt); Dentist 1 (pt).
Facilities Dining room; Physical therapy room; Activities room; Crafts room; Laundry room; Barber/Beauty shop; Library.
Activities Arts & crafts; Cards; Games; Reading groups; Prayer groups; Movies; Shopping trips; Social/Cultural gatherings.

Hillhaven Convalescent Hospital*
1609 Trousdale Dr, Burlingame, CA, 94010
(415) 697-1865
Admin Sally Brown.
Licensure Skilled care. *Beds* 85. *Certified* Medicare; Medi-Cal.
Owner Proprietary Corp (Hillhaven Corp).

CALISTOGA

Calistoga Convalescent Hospital*
1715 Washington St, Calistoga, CA, 94515
(707) 942-6253
Admin Mary E Robinson. *Medical Dir/Dir of Nursing* Dr D O'Neil.
Licensure Skilled care. *Beds* 72. *Certified* Medicare; Medi-Cal.
Owner Proprietary Corp (Care Enterprises).
Admissions Requirements Physician's request.
Facilities Dining room; Physical therapy room; Activities room; Crafts room; Laundry room; Barber/Beauty shop; Library.
Activities Arts & crafts; Games; Reading groups; Prayer groups; Movies; Social/Cultural gatherings.

CAMARILLO

Camarillo Convalescent Hospital*
205 Granada St, Camarillo, CA, 93010
(805) 482-9805
Admin Margaret Devoir. *Medical Dir/Dir of Nursing* Leonard Ackland MD.
Licensure Skilled care. *Beds* 114. *Certified* Medicare; Medi-Cal.
Owner Proprietary Corp.
Admissions Requirements Physician's request.
Facilities Dining room; Activities room; Crafts room; Laundry room; Barber/Beauty shop.
Activities Arts & crafts; Games; Reading groups; Movies; Shopping trips.

CAMPBELL

Camden Convalescent Hospital*
1331 Camden Ave, Campbell, CA, 95008
(408) 377-4030
Admin Margaret Jo Randall.
Licensure Skilled care. *Beds* 59. *Certified* Medi-Cal.
Owner Proprietary Corp.

Rosscare Convalescent Hospital
238 Virginia Ave, Campbell, CA, 95008
(408) 379-8114

Admin Michael L Skaggs. *Medical Dir/Dir of Nursing* Norman Woods MD.
Licensure Skilled care. *Beds* SNF 45. *Certified* Medicaid; Medicare; Medi-Cal.
Owner Privately owned.
Admissions Requirements Minimum age 65; Females only; Physician's request.
Staff Physicians 1 (pt); RNs 4 (ft), 5 (pt); LPNs 5 (ft), 6 (pt); Nurses aides 12 (ft), 6 (pt); Physical therapists 1 (pt); Reality therapists 1 (pt); Recreational therapists 1 (pt); Occupational therapists 1 (pt); Speech therapists 1 (pt); Activities coordinators 1 (ft); Dietitians 1 (ft); Dentists 1 (pt); Ophthalmologists 1 (pt); Podiatrists 1 (pt).
Languages Spanish
Facilities Dining room; Activities room; Crafts room; Laundry room; Barber/Beauty shop.
Activities Arts & crafts; Cards; Games; Reading groups; Prayer groups; Movies; Shopping trips; Social/Cultural gatherings.

CANOGA PARK

Beverly Manor Convalescent Hospital
7940 Topanga Canyon Blvd, Canoga Park, CA, 91304
(213) 347-3800
Admin Suzanne Trotter. *Medical Dir/Dir of Nursing* Robert Watson MD.
Licensure Skilled care. *Beds* 149. *Certified* Medicare; Medi-Cal.
Owner Proprietary Corp (Beverly Enterprises).
Admissions Requirements Medical examination; Physician's request.
Staff Physicians 3 (pt); RNs 7 (ft), 1 (pt); LPNs 15 (ft); Nurses aides 42 (ft); Physical therapists 2 (ft), 3 (pt); Recreational therapists 1 (pt); Occupational therapists 1 (pt); Speech therapists 1 (pt); Activities coordinators 2 (ft); Dietitians 1 (pt); Dentists 1 (pt); Ophthalmologists 1 (pt); Podiatrists 1 (pt).
Facilities Dining room; Physical therapy room; Activities room; Chapel; Barber/Beauty shop; Music room.
Activities Arts & crafts; Cards; Games; Reading groups; Movies; Shopping trips; Social/Cultural gatherings; Dining out.

Canoga Care Center Inc
22029 Saticoy St, Canoga Park, CA, 91304
(818) 887-7050
Admin Alan L Lien, Regional Admin; Merribel Ramsey, Associate Admin. *Medical Dir/Dir of Nursing* Tess Acejo RN.
Licensure Skilled care. *Beds* SNF 200. *Certified* Medicare; Medi-Cal.
Owner Proprietary Corp.
Admissions Requirements Minimum age 55; Medical examination; Physician's request.
Staff RNs 6 (ft), 4 (pt); LPNs 10 (ft), 4 (pt); Nurses aides 60 (ft), 18 (pt); Physical therapists 1 (ft); Activities coordinators 2 (ft).
Languages Spanish, Korean, Tagalog, Indian
Facilities Dining room; Physical therapy room; Activities room; Crafts room; Laundry room; Barber/Beauty shop; Library.
Activities Arts & crafts; Cards; Games; Reading groups; Prayer groups; Movies; Shopping trips; Social/Cultural gatherings.

Golden State West Valley Convalescent Hospital*
7057 Shoup Ave, Canoga Park, CA, 91304
(213) 348-8422
Admin Marie S Mills.
Licensure Skilled care. *Beds* 99. *Certified* Medicare; Medi-Cal.
Owner Proprietary Corp.

Holiday Manor Nursitarium
20554 Roscoe Blvd, Canoga Park, CA, 91306
(818) 341-9800
Admin Hilda Wirth. *Medical Dir/Dir of Nursing* Rosemary Scislow DON.

Licensure Skilled care; Secured for wandering confused patients. *Beds* SNF 94. *Certified* Medi-Cal.
Owner Proprietary Corp.
Admissions Requirements Minimum age 55.
Staff RNs; LPNs; Orderlies; Nurses aides; Activities coordinators.
Facilities Dining room; Activities room; Crafts room; Barber/Beauty shop.
Activities Games; Reading groups; Prayer groups; Movies; Social/Cultural gatherings; Bus trips.

Topanga Terrace Convalescent Center
22125 Roscoe Blvd, Canoga Park, CA, 91304
(818) 883-7292
Admin Nicholas Deutsch. *Medical Dir/Dir of Nursing* Edwin Marcus MD; Doris Komph RN.
Licensure Skilled care. *Beds* SNF 112. *Certified* Medicare; Medi-Cal.
Owner Proprietary Corp.
Admissions Requirements Minimum age 18; Physician's request.
Staff RNs 5 (ft), 4 (pt); LPNs 5 (ft), 2 (pt); Orderlies 13 (ft), 1 (pt); Nurses aides 17 (ft), 1 (pt); Physical therapists; Occupational therapists; Speech therapists; Activities coordinators 1 (ft), 1 (pt); Dietitians 1 (pt); Dentists; Ophthalmologists; Podiatrists.
Languages Spanish, German, Hungarian, Czech
Facilities Dining room; Physical therapy room; Activities room; Chapel; Crafts room; Laundry room; Barber/Beauty shop.
Activities Arts & crafts; Cards; Games; Reading groups; Prayer groups; Movies.

CAPISTRANO BEACH

Beverly Manor Convalescent Hospital*
35410 Del Rey, Capistrano Beach, CA, 92624
(714) 496-5786
Admin Carolyn Carlsen-Rouzier. *Medical Dir/Dir of Nursing* Dr B Bundy.
Licensure Skilled care. *Beds* 127. *Certified* Medicare; Medi-Cal.
Owner Proprietary Corp (Beverly Enterprises).
Admissions Requirements Minimum age 21.
Staff RNs 20 (ft); LPNs 20 (ft); Nurses aides 90 (ft); Activities coordinators 1 (ft); Dietitians 1 (ft).
Facilities Dining room; Physical therapy room; Activities room; Crafts room; Laundry room; Barber/Beauty shop.
Activities Arts & crafts; Cards; Games; Reading groups; Prayer groups; Movies; Shopping trips.

CAPITOLA

Eldercare Convalescent Hospital*
1935 Wharf Rd, Capitola, CA, 95010
(408) 476-0770
Admin Ralph N Tisdial.
Licensure Skilled care. *Beds* 25. *Certified* Medicare; Medi-Cal.
Owner Proprietary Corp.

Golden Age Convalescent Hospital*
523 Burlingame, Capitola, CA, 95010
(408) 475-0722
Admin John Smith. *Medical Dir/Dir of Nursing* Paul Weiss MD.
Licensure Skilled care. *Beds* 40. *Certified* Medicare.
Owner Proprietary Corp.
Admissions Requirements Minimum age 56; Physician's request.
Staff Physicians 2 (pt); RNs 1 (ft), 3 (pt); LPNs 4 (ft), 3 (pt); Orderlies 2 (pt); Nurses aides 4 (ft), 9 (pt).
Facilities Dining room; Activities room; Laundry room; Barber/Beauty shop.
Activities Arts & crafts; Cards; Games; Reading groups; Prayer groups; Movies; Shopping trips; Social/Cultural gatherings.

CARLSBAD

Lutheran Health Facility of Carlsbad*
201 Grand Ave, Carlsbad, CA, 92008
(714) 729-4983
Admin Thomas K Pembleton Jr. *Medical Dir/Dir of Nursing* Dr Albert Freiberger.
Licensure Skilled care. *Beds* 59. *Certified* Medicare; Medi-Cal.
Owner Nonprofit Corp.
Admissions Requirements Physician's request.
Staff Physicians 1 (pt); RNs 4 (ft), 3 (pt); LPNs 1 (pt); Nurses aides 20 (ft), 15 (pt); Physical therapists 1 (pt); Occupational therapists 1 (pt); Speech therapists 1 (pt); Activities coordinators 1 (pt); Dietitians 1 (pt).
Affiliation Lutheran
Facilities Dining room; Physical therapy room; Activities room; Barber/Beauty shop.
Activities Arts & crafts; Cards; Games; Reading groups; Prayer groups; Movies; Social/Cultural gatherings.

CARMEL

Carmel Convalescent Hospital*
Hwy 1 at Valley Way, Carmel, CA, 93921
(408) 624-8296
Admin Tanis Clark Jr.
Licensure Skilled care. *Beds* 65. *Certified* Medicare; Medi-Cal.
Owner Proprietary Corp.

Carmel Valley Manor*
8545 Carmel Valley Rd, Carmel, CA, 93921
(408) 624-1281
Admin John P Doolittle. *Medical Dir/Dir of Nursing* David Thorngate MD.
Licensure Skilled care. *Beds* 28. *Certified* Medicare; Medi-Cal.
Owner Nonprofit Corp.
Admissions Requirements Minimum age 65; Medical examination; Physician's request.
Staff Physicians 2 (pt); RNs 3 (ft), 7 (pt); LPNs 1 (ft); Orderlies 2 (ft), 1 (pt); Nurses aides 14 (ft), 4 (pt); Physical therapists 1 (pt); Recreational therapists 1 (pt); Occupational therapists 1 (pt); Activities coordinators 1 (pt); Dietitians 1 (pt); Dentists 1 (pt); Podiatrists 1 (pt).
Affiliation Congregational
Facilities Dining room; Physical therapy room; Activities room; Chapel; Crafts room; Laundry room; Barber/Beauty shop; Library.
Activities Arts & crafts; Games; Reading groups; Prayer groups; Movies; Shopping trips; Social/Cultural gatherings; Picnics; BBQs; Scenic rides.

CARMICHAEL

Carmichael Convalescent Hospital
8336 Fair Oaks Blvd, Carmichael, CA, 95608
(916) 944-3100
Admin Carole Henry. *Medical Dir/Dir of Nursing* Otto Neubuerger MD; Jennifer Worden RN.
Licensure Skilled care. *Beds* SNF 126. *Certified* Medicaid; Medicare; Medi-Cal.
Owner Proprietary Corp.
Admissions Requirements Physician's request.
Staff RNs 8 (ft); LPNs 16 (ft); Nurses aides 53 (ft); Physical therapists 1 (ft); Recreational therapists 2 (ft); Occupational therapists 1 (ft); Speech therapists 1 (ft); Activities coordinators 1 (ft); Dietitians 1 (pt); Ophthalmologists 1 (pt); Podiatrists 1 (pt).
Languages German, Russian, Spanish, Tagalog
Facilities Dining room; Physical therapy room; Activities room; Crafts room; Laundry room; Barber/Beauty shop; Library.
Activities Arts & crafts; Cards; Games; Reading groups; Prayer groups; Movies; Social/Cultural gatherings.

Crestwood Manor—Carmichael*
4741 Engle Rd, Carmichael, CA, 95608
(916) 483-8424
Admin Rufus L McDonald. *Medical Dir/Dir of Nursing* Dr Donald N ReVille.
Beds 80. *Certified* Medi-Cal.
Owner Proprietary Corp.
Admissions Requirements Minimum age 18; Medical examination; Physician's request.
Staff Physicians 6 (pt); RNs 2 (ft), 2 (pt); LPNs 8 (ft), 5 (pt); Orderlies 10 (ft), 2 (pt); Nurses aides 7 (ft), 3 (pt); Recreational therapists 1 (pt); Activities coordinators 1 (ft); Dietitians 1 (pt).
Facilities Dining room; Activities room; Crafts room; Library.
Activities Arts & crafts; Cards; Games; Reading groups; Prayer groups; Movies; Shopping trips; Social/Cultural gatherings; Bus mobility; Vocational training.

El Camino Convalescent Hospital*
2540 Carmichael Way, Carmichael, CA, 95608
(916) 482-0465
Admin Jame Cook.
Licensure Skilled care. *Beds* 170. *Certified* Medicare; Medi-Cal.
Owner Proprietary Corp (Crestwood Hosp).

Eskaton Manzanita Manor
5318 Manzanita Ave, Carmichael, CA, 95608
(916) 331-8513
Admin John T Supplitt. *Medical Dir/Dir of Nursing* William Hicks MD; Kathy Smith RN DON.
Licensure Skilled care. *Beds* 99. *Certified* Medicaid; Medicare; Medi-Cal.
Owner Nonprofit Corp.
Staff RNs 5 (ft), 1 (pt); LPNs 12 (ft), 2 (pt); Nurses aides 35 (ft), 15 (pt); Physical therapists 1 (ft); Recreational therapists 1 (ft); Occupational therapists 1 (ft); Speech therapists 1 (ft); Dietitians 1 (pt); Ophthalmologists 1 (pt); Dentist 1 (pt).
Facilities Dining room; Physical therapy room; Activities room; Chapel; Laundry room; Barber/Beauty shop; Living room.
Activities Arts & crafts; Cards; Games; Reading groups; Prayer groups; Movies; Shopping trips; Social/Cultural gatherings.

Hillhaven Convalescent Hospital
8845 Fair Oaks Blvd, Carmichael, CA, 95608
(916) 455-3014
Admin Patricia Linn.
Licensure Skilled care. *Beds* 89. *Certified* Medicare; Medi-Cal.
Owner Proprietary Corp.

Mission Oaks Convalescent Hospital*
3630 Mission Ave, Carmichael, CA, 95608
(916) 488-1580
Admin Donald J Hunter.
Licensure Skilled care. *Beds* 138. *Certified* Medicare; Medi-Cal.
Owner Proprietary Corp.

Mt Olivette Care Center
6041 Fair Oaks Blvd, Carmichael, CA, 95608
(916) 483-8103
Admin Patrick M Jaggard. *Medical Dir/Dir of Nursing* Otto Neubuerger MD; Donna Poulter RN DON.
Licensure Skilled care. *Beds* SNF 112. *Certified* Medicare; Medi-Cal.
Owner Proprietary Corp.
Admissions Requirements Medical examination; Physician's request.
Staff Physicians 35 (pt); RNs 5 (ft), 10 (pt); LPNs 8 (ft), 3 (pt); Nurses aides 32 (ft), 9 (pt); Physical therapists 1 (pt); Occupational therapists 1 (pt); Speech therapists 1 (pt); Activities coordinators 1 (ft); Dietitians 1 (pt); Dentists 2 (pt); Ophthalmologists 1 (pt); Podiatrists 1 (pt).
Languages Chinese, Tagalog, Spanish

Facilities Dining room; Physical therapy room; Laundry room; Barber/Beauty shop.
Activities Arts & crafts; Cards; Games; Reading groups; Prayer groups; Movies; Social/Cultural gatherings.

Mountain Manor
6101 Fair Oaks Blvd, Carmichael, CA, 95608
(916) 488-7211
Admin Stuart Drake.
Licensure Intermediate care; Residential care. Beds 47; Residential 33. Certified Medi-Cal.
Owner Proprietary Corp.
Admissions Requirements Minimum age 62; Physician's request.
Staff RNs 1 (ft), 2 (pt); LPNs 3 (ft), 2 (pt); Orderlies 1 (ft); Nurses aides 10 (ft); Activities coordinators 3 (ft).
Facilities Dining room; Physical therapy room; Activities room; Crafts room; Laundry room; Barber/Beauty shop.
Activities Arts & crafts; Cards; Games; Reading groups; Prayer groups; Movies; Shopping trips; Social/Cultural gatherings; Bingo; Exercise; Ceramics.

Walnut Whitney Convalescent Hospital*
3529 Walnut Ave, Carmichael, CA, 95608
(916) 488-8601
Admin Richard L Thorpe. Medical Dir/Dir of Nursing William E Hedges MD.
Licensure Skilled care. Beds 126. Certified Medicare; Medi-Cal.
Owner Proprietary Corp.
Admissions Requirements Medical examination; Physician's request.
Staff Physicians 35 (pt); RNs 6 (ft), 6 (pt); LPNs 10 (ft), 5 (pt); Nurses aides 40 (ft), 10 (pt); Physical therapists 1 (pt); Reality therapists 1 (pt); Recreational therapists 1 (pt); Occupational therapists 1 (pt); Speech therapists 1 (pt); Activities coordinators 2 (ft); Dietitians 1 (pt); Dentists 1 (pt); Ophthalmologists 1 (pt); Podiatrists 1 (pt); Audiologists 1 (pt).

CASTRO VALLEY

Hillhaven Convalescent Hospital
20259 Lake Chabot Rd, Castro Valley, CA, 94546
(415) 351-3700
Admin Terrance J McGregor.
Licensure Skilled care. Beds SNF 95. Certified Medicaid; Medicare; Medi-Cal.
Owner Proprietary Corp (Hillhaven Corp).
Admissions Requirements Physician's request.
Staff Physicians; RNs; LPNs; Nurses aides; Physical therapists; Recreational therapists; Occupational therapists; Speech therapists; Activities coordinators; Dietitians; Dentists; Ophthalmologists; Podiatrists.
Facilities Dining room; Physical therapy room; Activities room; Crafts room; Laundry room; Barber/Beauty shop.
Activities Arts & crafts; Cards; Games; Reading groups; Prayer groups; Movies; Shopping trips; Social/Cultural gatherings.

Redwood Convalescent Hospital
22103 Redwood Rd, Castro Valley, CA, 94546
(415) 537-8848
Admin Robert J Myers. Medical Dir/Dir of Nursing Dr I Moncrief; Angie Lin RN DON.
Licensure Skilled care. Beds SNF 70. Certified Medi-Cal.
Owner Proprietary Corp.
Admissions Requirements Physician's request.
Staff Physicians 1 (pt); RNs 3 (ft), 2 (pt); LPNs 7 (ft), 3 (pt); Orderlies 1 (ft); Nurses aides 27 (ft), 2 (pt); Physical therapists 1 (pt); Activities coordinators 1 (ft), 1 (pt); Dietitians 1 (pt).
Facilities Dining room; Physical therapy room; Activities room; Chapel; Crafts room; Laundry room; Barber/Beauty shop.

Activities Arts & crafts; Cards; Games; Reading groups; Prayer groups; Movies; Shopping trips; Social/Cultural gatherings.

St Annes Convalescent Hospital
22424 Charlene Way, Castro Valley, CA, 94546
(415) 537-5944
Admin Roland Rapp. Medical Dir/Dir of Nursing Andrew May MD.
Licensure Skilled care. Beds SNF 48. Certified Medi-Cal.
Owner Proprietary Corp.
Admissions Requirements Medical examination; Physician's request.
Staff Physicians 9 (ft); RNs 1 (ft), 1 (pt); LPNs 3 (ft), 3 (pt); Orderlies 1 (ft); Nurses aides 17 (ft), 4 (pt); Physical therapists 1 (pt); Reality therapists 1 (pt); Recreational therapists 1 (pt); Occupational therapists 1 (pt); Speech therapists 1 (pt); Activities coordinators 1 (ft), 1 (pt); Dietitians 1 (ft); Dentists 1 (pt); Ophthalmologists 1 (pt); Podiatrists 1 (pt).
Languages Spanish, Tagalog
Facilities Dining room; Activities room; Crafts room; Laundry room; Barber/Beauty shop.
Activities Arts & crafts; Cards; Games; Reading groups; Prayer groups; Movies; Shopping trips; Social/Cultural gatherings; Bingo; Cooking; Gardening; Pet visits.

St John Kronstadt Convalescent Center
PO Box 2794, 4432 James Ave, Castro Valley, CA, 94546
(415) 889-7000
Admin Fred Sanciangco. Medical Dir/Dir of Nursing Andrew May MD; Rosemary Noonan RN.
Licensure Skilled care. Beds SNF 49. Certified Medicaid; Medicare; Medi-Cal.
Owner Nonprofit Corp.
Admissions Requirements Physician's request.
Staff RNs 1 (ft), 2 (pt); LPNs 4 (ft), 4 (pt); Nurses aides 20 (ft), 5 (pt); Physical therapists 1 (pt); Occupational therapists 1 (pt); Speech therapists 1 (pt); Activities coordinators 3 (ft); Dietitians 1 (pt); Ophthalmologists 1 (pt); Dentist 1 (pt).
Languages Russian
Affiliation Russian Orthodox
Facilities Dining room; Activities room; Chapel; Crafts room; Laundry room; Barber/Beauty shop; TV Room.
Activities Arts & crafts; Cards; Games; Reading groups; Prayer groups; Movies; Shopping trips; Social/Cultural gatherings.

St Joseph Convalescent Hospital Inc
18949 Redwood Rd, Castro Valley, CA, 94546
(415) 886-1101
Admin Marianne Quenneville. Medical Dir/Dir of Nursing Andrew May Jr MD; Geneva Robinson DON.
Licensure Intermediate care. Beds ICF 82. Certified Medicaid; Medi-Cal.
Owner Proprietary Corp.
Staff Physicians 1 (pt); RNs 2 (pt); LPNs 4 (ft); Nurses aides 6 (ft); Physical therapists 1 (pt); Occupational therapists 1 (pt); Speech therapists 1 (pt); Activities coordinators 2 (ft); Dietitians 1 (pt); Ophthalmologists 1 (pt); Podiatrists 1 (pt).
Languages Spanish
Facilities Dining room; Activities room; Crafts room; Laundry room; Barber/Beauty shop.
Activities Arts & crafts; Cards; Games; Reading groups; Prayer groups; Movies; Shopping trips; Social/Cultural gatherings.

Stanton Hill Convalescent Hospital Inc*
20090 Stanton Ave, Castro Valley, CA, 94546
(415) 538-8464
Admin Joy M Susko.

Licensure Skilled care. Beds 50. Certified Medicare; Medi-Cal.
Owner Proprietary Corp.

CERES

Hale Aloha Convalescent Hospital*
1711 Richland Ave, Ceres, CA, 95307
(209) 537-4581
Admin John S Poat. Medical Dir/Dir of Nursing Amos Henry MD.
Licensure Skilled care. Beds 46. Certified Medicare; Medi-Cal.
Owner Proprietary Corp.
Admissions Requirements Physician's request.
Staff RNs 1 (ft), 1 (pt); LPNs 2 (ft), 2 (pt); Orderlies 2 (ft); Nurses aides 10 (ft), 3 (pt); Activities coordinators 1 (ft).
Facilities Dining room; Laundry room.
Activities Arts & crafts; Games; Social/Cultural gatherings.

CHATSWORTH

Chatsworth Health & Rehabilitation Center*
21820 Craggy View St, Chatsworth, CA, 91311
(213) 882-8233
Admin Myra S Burman. Medical Dir/Dir of Nursing Carl M Friedman MD.
Licensure Skilled care. Beds 132. Certified Medicare.
Owner Proprietary Corp.
Admissions Requirements Minimum age 18; Physician's request.
Staff Physical therapists; Recreational therapists 15 (ft); Occupational therapists; Speech therapists; Activities coordinators 2 (ft); Dietitians.
Facilities Dining room; Activities room; Crafts room; Barber/Beauty shop; Library.
Activities Arts & crafts; Cards; Games; Reading groups; Movies; Shopping trips; Social/Cultural gatherings.

Chatsworth Park Convalescent Hospital
10610 Owensmouth, Chatsworth, CA, 91311
(818) 882-3200
Admin Marcia Fischbach. Medical Dir/Dir of Nursing Dr David Chernof; Marolyn Zieglgansberger RN DON.
Licensure Skilled care; Intermediate care. Beds SNF 94; ICF 34. Certified Medicaid; Medicare; Medi-Cal.
Owner Proprietary Corp.
Admissions Requirements Minimum age 50; Physician's request.
Staff Physicians 12 (pt); RNs 2 (ft); LPNs 11 (ft), 2 (pt); Orderlies 6 (ft); Nurses aides 27 (ft), 3 (pt); Physical therapists 1 (pt); Recreational therapists 1 (pt); Occupational therapists 1 (pt); Speech therapists 1 (pt); Activities coordinators 2 (ft); Dietitians 1 (pt); Dentists 1 (pt); Ophthalmologists 1 (pt); Podiatrists 1 (pt).
Languages Tagalog, Spanish, Yiddish, Hebrew, Portuguese
Facilities Dining room; Physical therapy room; Activities room; Crafts room; Laundry room; Barber/Beauty shop; Library.
Activities Arts & crafts; Cards; Games; Reading groups; Prayer groups; Movies; Social/Cultural gatherings.

CHERRY VALLEY

Sunset Haven Convalescent Hospital*
9246 Avenida Mira Villa, Cherry Valley, CA, 92223
(714) 845-3194
Admin Doug Padgett.
Licensure Skilled care. Beds 59. Certified Medi-Cal.
Owner Nonprofit Corp.

CHICO

Beverly Manor Convalescent Hospital*
188 Cohasset Ln, Chico, CA, 95926
(916) 343-6084
Admin Mary E Granneman.
Licensure Skilled care. *Beds* 76. *Certified*
Medicare; Medi-Cal.
Owner Proprietary Corp (Beverly Enterprises).

Chico Convalescent Hospital*
1645 The Esplanade, Chico, CA, 95926
(916) 343-6045
Admin Janet M Walston.
Licensure Skilled care. *Beds* 59. *Certified*
Medicare; Medi-Cal.

Crestwood Convalescent Hospital*
587 Rio Lindo Ave, Chico, CA, 95926
(916) 345-1306
Admin Larry E Bradley. *Medical Dir/Dir of
Nursing* Philip Morgans MD.
Licensure Skilled care. *Beds* 184. *Certified*
Medicare; Medi-Cal.
Owner Proprietary Corp (Crestwood Hosp).
Admissions Requirements Medical
examination; Physician's request.
Staff RNs 6 (ft), 4 (pt); LPNs 14 (ft), 3 (pt);
Orderlies 4 (ft); Nurses aides 59 (ft), 7 (pt);
Physical therapists 3 (pt); Recreational
therapists 1 (ft); Activities coordinators 1
(ft); Dietitians 1 (ft).
Facilities Dining room; Physical therapy
room; Activities room; Laundry room;
Barber/Beauty shop.
Activities Arts & crafts; Cards; Games;
Reading groups; Prayer groups; Movies;
Shopping trips; Social/Cultural gatherings.

Riverside Convalescent Hospital
375 Cohasset Rd, Chico, CA, 95926
(916) 343-5595
Admin Mary Ann Selak.
Licensure Skilled care. *Beds* 70. *Certified*
Medicare; Medi-Cal.
Owner Proprietary Corp.
Facilities Dining room; Physical therapy
room; Activities room; Crafts room; Laundry
room; Barber/Beauty shop; Library.
Activities Arts & crafts; Cards; Games;
Reading groups; Prayer groups; Movies;
Shopping trips; Social/Cultural gatherings.

CHOWCHILLA

Chowchilla Convalescent Hospital*
1000 Ventura St, Chowchilla, CA, 93610
(209) 665-4826
Admin Beverly P Brown. *Medical Dir/Dir of
Nursing* Thomas F Way MD.
Licensure Skilled care. *Beds* 65. *Certified*
Medicare; Medi-Cal.
Owner Proprietary Corp.
Admissions Requirements Minimum age 18;
Medical examination; Physician's request.
Staff Physicians 4 (pt); RNs 1 (ft), 2 (pt);
LPNs 6 (ft), 2 (pt); Nurses aides 27 (ft);
Physical therapists 1 (pt); Occupational
therapists 1 (pt); Speech therapists 1 (pt);
Activities coordinators 1 (ft); Dietitians 1
(pt); Dentists 1 (pt); Ophthalmologists 1 (pt);
Podiatrists 1 (pt); Audiologists 1 (pt).
Facilities Dining room; Activities room;
Crafts room; Laundry room; Barber/Beauty
shop.
Activities Arts & crafts; Cards; Games;
Reading groups; Prayer groups; Movies;
Shopping trips; Social/Cultural gatherings.

CHULA VISTA

Collingwood Manor*
553 F St, Chula Vista, CA, 92010
(714) 426-8611
Admin Mary C Norwood.

Licensure Intermediate care. *Beds* 88.
Certified Medi-Cal.
Owner Nonprofit Corp.

Fredericka Manor Convalescent Hospital
111 3rd Ave, Chula Vista, CA, 92010
(619) 427-2777
Admin Craig R Wyble. *Medical Dir/Dir of
Nursing* William Diamond MD; Louise
Moore RN DON.
Licensure Skilled care. *Beds* SNF 174.
Certified Medicare; Medi-Cal.
Owner Proprietary Corp (Pacific Homes).
Admissions Requirements Minimum age 65.
Staff Physicians 1 (pt); RNs 13 (ft), 4 (pt);
LPNs 10 (ft), 2 (pt); Nurses aides 48 (ft), 12
(pt); Physical therapists 1 (pt); Recreational
therapists 1 (pt); Occupational therapists 1
(pt); Speech therapists 1 (pt); Activities
coordinators 2 (ft), 1 (pt); Dietitians 1 (ft);
Ophthalmologists 1 (pt); Podiatrists 1 (pt);
Social worker 1 (pt).
Languages Spanish, Tagalog
Facilities Dining room; Physical therapy
room; Activities room; Chapel; Crafts room;
Barber/Beauty shop.
Activities Arts & crafts; Cards; Games;
Reading groups; Prayer groups; Movies;
Shopping trips.

CITY OF INDUSTRY

El-Encanto Convalescent Hospital*
555 El Encanto Dr, City of Industry, CA,
91744
(818) 336-1274
Admin Buck L Perkins. *Medical Dir/Dir of
Nursing* Dr Chandiah Veerappa.
Licensure Skilled care; Intermediate care for
mentally retarded. *Beds* SNF 159; ICF/MR
89. *Certified* Medi-Cal.
Owner Nonprofit Corp.
Admissions Requirements Minimum age 18.
Staff Physicians 5 (pt); RNs 4 (ft), 6 (pt);
LPNs 24 (ft), 2 (pt); Nurses aides 99 (ft);
Physical therapists 1 (ft); Occupational
therapists 1 (pt); Activities coordinators 1
(ft); Dietitians 1 (ft); Ophthalmologists 1
(pt); Audiologists Dentist 1 (pt).
Facilities Dining room; Physical therapy
room; Activities room; Crafts room; Laundry
room; Barber/Beauty shop.
Activities Arts & crafts; Cards; Games;
Reading groups; Movies; Shopping trips;
Social/Cultural gatherings.

CLAREMONT

Claremont Convalescent Hospital*
650 W Harrison Ave, Claremont, CA, 91711
(714) 626-1227
Admin Floy Biggs. *Medical Dir/Dir of Nursing*
Rinard Hart.
Licensure Skilled care. *Beds* 58. *Certified*
Medicare; Medi-Cal.
Owner Proprietary Corp (Pacific Homes).
Staff RNs 4 (ft); LPNs 6 (ft); Orderlies 1 (ft);
Nurses aides 19 (ft); Activities coordinators
1 (ft).
Facilities Dining room; Activities room;
Crafts room; Laundry room; Barber/Beauty
shop; Library; Pool room; Sewing room;
Meeting hall.
Activities Arts & crafts; Cards; Games;
Reading groups; Prayer groups; Movies.

Hillhaven Convalescent Hospital
590 S Indian Hill Blvd, Claremont, CA, 91711
(714) 624-4511
Admin Darleen M Curley. *Medical Dir/Dir of
Nursing* Rinard Hart MD; Julie Kidder
DON.
Licensure Skilled care. *Beds* SNF 99. *Certified*
Medicare; Medi-Cal.
Owner Proprietary Corp (Hillhaven Corp).
Admissions Requirements Minimum age 65;
Physician's request.

Staff Physicians 24 (ft); RNs 2 (ft); LPNs 10
(ft), 4 (pt); Orderlies 2 (ft); Physical
therapists 1 (pt); Recreational therapists 1
(pt); Occupational therapists 1 (pt); Speech
therapists 1 (pt); Activities coordinators 1
(ft); Dietitians 1 (ft); Dentists 1 (pt);
Ophthalmologists 1 (pt); Podiatrists 1 (pt).
Facilities Dining room; Physical therapy
room; Activities room; Crafts room; Laundry
room; Barber/Beauty shop; Library.
Activities Arts & crafts; Cards; Games;
Reading groups; Prayer groups; Movies;
Shopping trips; Social/Cultural gatherings;
Out to lunch, brunch, holiday festivities.

Pilgrim Place Health Services Center*
277 Harrison Ave, Claremont, CA, 91711
(714) 624-2084
Admin George Worth.
Licensure Skilled care. *Beds* 49. *Certified*
Medicare; Medi-Cal.
Owner Nonprofit Corp.

CLOVERDALE

Manzanita Manor Convalescent Hospital*
300 Cherry Creek Rd, Cloverdale, CA, 95425
(707) 894-5201
Admin Dieter Miesler.
Licensure Skilled care. *Beds* 72. *Certified*
Medicare; Medi-Cal.
Owner Proprietary Corp (Care Enterprises).

CLOVIS

Clovis Convalescent Hospital*
111 Barstow Ave, Clovis, CA, 93612
(209) 299-2591
Admin Brenda Caprioglio.
Licensure Skilled care. *Beds* 57. *Certified*
Medicare; Medi-Cal.
Owner Proprietary Corp (Beverly Enterprises).

Clovis Nursing Home*
2604 Clovis Ave, Clovis, CA, 93612
(209) 291-2173
Admin Carl Lamoreaux.
Licensure Skilled care. *Beds* 81. *Certified*
Medicare.
Owner Proprietary Corp.

COALINGA

Coalinga Convalescent Center
834 Maple Road, Coalinga, CA, 93210
(209) 935-1575
Admin Jerry A Patton. *Medical Dir/Dir of
Nursing* Vickey Keller RN.
Licensure Skilled care. *Beds* SNF 58. *Certified*
Medicare; Medi-Cal.
Owner Privately owned.
Admissions Requirements Physician's request.
Staff RNs 1 (ft), 3 (pt); LPNs 3 (ft), 4 (pt);
Nurses aides 23 (ft), 8 (pt); Physical
therapists 1 (pt); Occupational therapists 1
(pt); Speech therapists 1 (pt); Activities
coordinators 1 (ft); Dietitians 1 (pt).
Languages Spanish
Facilities Dining room; Physical therapy
room; Laundry room; Barber/Beauty shop;
Library.
Activities Arts & crafts; Games; Prayer groups;
Social/Cultural gatherings; Park activities.

COLTON

Grand Terrace Convalescent Hospital*
12000 Mount Vernon, Colton, CA, 92324
(714) 825-5221
Admin Diane Herschberg. *Medical Dir/Dir of
Nursing* Richard Neil.
Licensure Skilled care. *Beds* 59. *Certified*
Medicare; Medi-Cal.
Owner Proprietary Corp.

Staff Physicians 7 (pt); RNs 1 (ft), 4 (pt); LPNs 3 (ft), 4 (pt); Orderlies 4 (ft); Nurses aides 15 (ft), 10 (pt); Physical therapists 1 (ft); Occupational therapists 1 (pt); Speech therapists 1 (pt); Activities coordinators 1 (ft); Dietitians 1 (pt); Dentists 1 (pt); Ophthalmologists 1 (pt); Podiatrists 1 (pt).
Facilities Dining room; Physical therapy room; Activities room; Laundry room; Barber/Beauty shop; Library.
Activities Arts & crafts; Cards; Games; Reading groups; Prayer groups; Movies; Social/Cultural gatherings.

Olivewood Convalescent Hospital
23185 Washington St, Colton, CA, 92324
(714) 824-1530
Admin Valerie Shieck-Machain. *Medical Dir/ Dir of Nursing* Bernard Tilton MD.
Licensure Skilled care. *Beds* SNF 109. *Certified* Medicare; Medi-Cal.
Owner Nonprofit Corp.
Admissions Requirements Minimum age 60; Physician's request.
Facilities Dining room; Physical therapy room; Activities room; Crafts room; Laundry room; Barber/Beauty shop; Library.
Activities Arts & crafts; Cards; Games; Reading groups; Prayer groups; Movies.

COMPTON

Compton Convalescent Hospital
2309 N Santa Fe Ave, Compton, CA, 90222
(213) 639-8111
Admin Mark F Wilson. *Medical Dir/Dir of Nursing* Dan E Davis RN.
Licensure Skilled care. *Beds* 99. *Certified* Medicare; Medi-Cal.
Owner Proprietary Corp.
Admissions Requirements Minimum age 25; Physician's request.
Staff RNs 2 (ft); LPNs 10 (ft); Orderlies 6 (ft); Nurses aides 50 (ft); Physical therapists; Recreational therapists; Occupational therapists; Speech therapists; Activities coordinators; Dietitians; Dentists; Ophthalmologists; Podiatrists; Dentist.
Facilities Dining room; Physical therapy room; Activities room; Laundry room; Barber/Beauty shop.
Activities Arts & crafts; Cards; Games; Reading groups; Prayer groups; Movies; Shopping trips; Social/Cultural gatherings.

CONCORD

Bayberry Convalescent Hospital*
2151 Central St, Concord, CA, 94520
(415) 825-1300
Admin Beulah Mullin.
Licensure Skilled care. *Beds* 99. *Certified* Medicare; Medi-Cal.
Owner Nonprofit Corp.

Casa San Miguel
1050 San Miguel Rd, Concord, CA, 94518
(415) 825-4280
Admin Lenore Shenker. *Medical Dir/Dir of Nursing* Martin Stuart MD; Marilyn Eipperle RN DON.
Licensure Skilled care; Intermediate care. *Beds* SNF 150; ICF 50. *Certified* Medicare; Medi-Cal.
Owner Proprietary Corp.
Facilities Dining room; Physical therapy room; Activities room; Chapel; Crafts room; Laundry room; Barber/Beauty shop; Library.
Activities Arts & crafts; Cards; Games; Prayer groups; Movies; Shopping trips; Social/ Cultural gatherings.

Hacienda Convalescent Hospital*
3318 Willow Pass, Concord, CA, 94520
(415) 689-9222
Admin Shirley M Begovich. *Medical Dir/Dir of Nursing* D K Fisher MD.

Licensure Skilled care. *Beds* 83. *Certified* Medicare; Medi-Cal.
Owner Proprietary Corp (Hillhaven Corp).
Admissions Requirements Minimum age 65; Medical examination; Physician's request.
Staff RNs 3 (ft), 6 (pt); LPNs 5 (ft), 2 (pt); Nurses aides 30 (ft), 6 (pt); Physical therapists 1 (pt); Occupational therapists 1 (pt); Speech therapists 1 (pt); Activities coordinators 1 (ft); Podiatrists 1 (pt).
Facilities Dining room; Physical therapy room; Activities room; Laundry room; Barber/Beauty shop.
Activities Arts & crafts; Cards; Games; Reading groups; Prayer groups.

Valley Manor Convalescent Hospital*
3806 Clayton Rd, Concord, CA, 94521
(415) 689-2266
Admin Bob R Lauderdale. *Medical Dir/Dir of Nursing* Eugene B Whitney.
Licensure Skilled care; Intermediate care. *Beds* 223. *Certified* Medicare; Medi-Cal.
Owner Proprietary Corp.
Admissions Requirements Medical examination.
Staff RNs 9 (ft), 4 (pt); LPNs 15 (ft), 8 (pt); Nurses aides 72 (ft), 10 (pt); Physical therapists 1 (ft); Speech therapists 1 (pt); Activities coordinators 3 (ft); Dietitians 1 (ft); Dentists 1 (pt); Ophthalmologists 1 (pt); Podiatrists 1 (pt); Audiologists 1 (pt).
Facilities Dining room; Physical therapy room; Activities room; Crafts room; Laundry room; Barber/Beauty shop; Library.
Activities Arts & crafts; Cards; Games; Reading groups; Prayer groups; Movies; Shopping trips; Social/Cultural gatherings.

CORONA

Corona Gables Retirement Home & Convalescent Hospital*
1400 Circle City Dr, Corona, CA, 91720
(714) 735-0252
Admin Mona L Fisk.
Licensure Skilled care. *Beds* 80. *Certified* Medicare; Medi-Cal.
Owner Proprietary Corp.

COSTA MESA

Beverly Manor Convalescent Hospital
340 Victoria Ave, Costa Mesa, CA, 92627
(714) 642-0387
Admin Jeanne Beach. *Medical Dir/Dir of Nursing* Alan Greenberg MD; Sheryl Kennedy DON.
Licensure Skilled care. *Beds* SNF 79. *Certified* Medicare; Medi-Cal.
Owner Proprietary Corp (Beverly Enterprises).
Admissions Requirements Physician's request.
Staff Physicians 3 (pt); RNs 4 (ft), 2 (pt); Orderlies 5 (ft); Nurses aides 34 (ft), 5 (pt); Physical therapists 1 (ft), 1 (pt); Occupational therapists 1 (pt); Speech therapists 1 (pt); Activities coordinators 1 (ft); Dietitians 1 (pt); Dentists 1 (pt); Ophthalmologists 1 (pt); Podiatrists 1 (pt); LVNs 4 (ft), 3 (pt); Social service 1 (ft).
Languages Spanish
Facilities Dining room; Physical therapy room; Activities room; Crafts room; Laundry room; Barber/Beauty shop.
Activities Arts & crafts; Cards; Games; Reading groups; Prayer groups; Movies.

Mesa Verde Convalescent Hospital
661 Center St, Costa Mesa, CA, 92627
(714) 548-5584
Admin Barbara Wunsch. *Medical Dir/Dir of Nursing* Paul Kuhn MD; Louise McGuire DON.
Licensure Skilled care. *Beds* SNF 80. *Certified* Medicare.
Owner Proprietary Corp.

Admissions Requirements Medical examination.
Staff Physicians 4 (pt); RNs 9 (ft), 1 (pt); LPNs 8 (ft), 4 (pt); Orderlies 3 (ft), 3 (pt); Nurses aides 30 (ft), 8 (pt); Physical therapists 2 (ft); Reality therapists 1 (pt); Recreational therapists 1 (pt); Occupational therapists 1 (pt); Speech therapists 1 (pt); Activities coordinators 2 (ft); Dietitians 1 (pt); Dentists 1 (pt); Ophthalmologists 1 (pt); Podiatrists 1 (pt); Social service 1 (ft).
Facilities Dining room; Physical therapy room; Activities room; Chapel; Crafts room; Laundry room; Barber/Beauty shop; Library; Conference room.
Activities Arts & crafts; Cards; Games; Reading groups; Prayer groups; Movies; Shopping trips; Social/Cultural gatherings.

Port Mesa Convalescent Hospital
2570 Newport Blvd, Costa Mesa, CA, 92627
(714) 642-0400
Admin Ronald A Reynolds. *Medical Dir/Dir of Nursing* Korey Jorgensen MD; Vicky S Reynolds RN.
Licensure Skilled care. *Beds* 139. *Certified* Medicaid; Medicare; Medi-Cal.
Owner Proprietary Corp.
Admissions Requirements Physician's request.
Staff RNs; LPNs; Orderlies; Nurses aides; Activities coordinators 2 (ft).
Languages Spanish, Korean, Tagalog
Facilities Dining room; Physical therapy room; Activities room; Crafts room; Laundry room; Barber/Beauty shop.
Activities Arts & crafts; Cards; Games; Reading groups; Movies; Shopping trips; Social/Cultural gatherings.

COVINA

Badillo Convalescent Hospital*
519 W Badillo St, Covina, CA, 91722
(213) 332-6406
Admin Natan Gierowitz.
Licensure Skilled care. *Beds* 52. *Certified* Medicare; Medi-Cal.
Owner Proprietary Corp.

Covina Convalescent Center
261 W Badillo St, Covina, CA, 92506
(213) 339-1281
Admin Rena Kay Papp. *Medical Dir/Dir of Nursing* Dr Advincula; Carol Cook RN DON.
Licensure Skilled care. *Beds* SNF 99. *Certified* Medicare; Medi-Cal.
Owner Proprietary Corp.
Admissions Requirements Physician's request.
Staff RNs 2 (ft), 1 (pt); LPNs 12 (ft), 3 (pt); Orderlies 25 (ft), 4 (pt); Activities coordinators 1 (ft), 1 (pt); Dietitians 1 (ft).
Languages Spanish
Facilities Dining room; Physical therapy room; Activities room; Laundry room; Barber/Beauty shop.
Activities Arts & crafts; Cards; Games; Reading groups; Prayer groups; Movies; Shopping trips; Social/Cultural gatherings.

Rowland*
330 W Rowland Ave, Covina, CA, 91723
(213) 967-2741
Admin Anthony Kalomas. *Medical Dir/Dir of Nursing* E Mason MD.
Licensure Skilled care. *Beds* 126. *Certified* Medicare; Medi-Cal.
Owner Proprietary Corp.
Admissions Requirements Minimum age 65.
Staff RNs 4 (ft), 2 (pt); LPNs 7 (ft), 2 (pt); Orderlies 3 (ft); Nurses aides 47 (ft), 6 (pt); Physical therapists 1 (ft); Recreational therapists 1 (pt); Speech therapists 1 (pt); Activities coordinators 1 (ft), 1 (pt); Dietitians 1 (pt); Dentists 1 (pt); Podiatrists 1 (pt).

Facilities Dining room; Physical therapy room; Activities room; Chapel; Crafts room; Laundry room; Barber/Beauty shop; Library.
Activities Arts & crafts; Cards; Games; Reading groups; Prayer groups; Movies; Shopping trips; Social/Cultural gatherings.

CRESCENT CITY

Crescent City Convalescent Hospital*
1280 Marshall St, Crescent City, CA, 95531
(707) 464-6151
Admin Randall Brigham.
Licensure Skilled care. *Beds* 99. *Certified* Medicare; Medi-Cal.
Owner Proprietary Corp (Care Enterprises).

CULVER CITY

Marina Convalescent Hospital*
5240 Sepulveda Ave, Culver City, CA, 90230
(213) 391-7266
Admin Robert Lee. *Medical Dir/Dir of Nursing* Dr Keating.
Licensure Skilled care. *Beds* 116. *Certified* Medicare; Medi-Cal.
Owner Proprietary Corp.
Staff RNs 3 (ft), 4 (pt); LPNs 9 (ft), 2 (pt); Orderlies 5 (ft); Nurses aides 28 (ft), 5 (pt); Physical therapists 1 (pt); Recreational therapists 1 (ft); Occupational therapists 1 (pt); Speech therapists 1 (pt); Activities coordinators 1 (ft); Dietitians 1 (ft); Dentists 1 (pt); Ophthalmologists 1 (pt); Podiatrists 1 (pt); Audiologists 1 (pt).
Facilities Dining room; Physical therapy room; Activities room; Crafts room; Laundry room; Barber/Beauty shop; Staff developer.
Activities Arts & crafts; Cards; Games; Reading groups; Prayer groups; Movies.

Marycrest Manor
10664 Saint James Dr, Culver City, CA, 90230
(213) 838-2778
Admin Sr Margaret Mary. *Medical Dir/Dir of Nursing* John A Zaro MD; Mardrie White RN DON.
Licensure Skilled care. *Beds* SNF 59. *Certified* Medicare; Medi-Cal.
Owner Nonprofit Corp.
Admissions Requirements Minimum age 70; Females only; Medical examination; Physician's request.
Staff Physicians 20 (pt); RNs 2 (ft), 5 (pt); LPNs 5 (ft), 7 (pt); Nurses aides 30 (ft), 8 (pt); Physical therapists 2 (pt); Recreational therapists 1 (pt); Occupational therapists 1 (pt); Speech therapists 1 (pt); Activities coordinators 1 (ft), 2 (pt); Dietitians 1 (ft), 1 (pt); Dentists 1 (pt); Ophthalmologists 1 (pt); Podiatrists 1 (pt).
Languages Spanish, Arabic
Affiliation Roman Catholic
Facilities Dining room; Physical therapy room; Activities room; Chapel; Laundry room; Barber/Beauty shop; Library.
Activities Arts & crafts; Cards; Games; Prayer groups; Movies; Shopping trips; Parties; Visiting entertainers.

CUPERTINO

Pleasant View Convalescent Hospital
22590 Voss Ave, Cupertino, CA, 95014
(408) 253-9034
Admin Dee Haynie. *Medical Dir/Dir of Nursing* Fred W Schwertley MD; Ingrid Tillmann DON.
Licensure Skilled care. *Beds* SNF 170. *Certified* Medicare; Medi-Cal.
Owner Proprietary Corp.
Admissions Requirements Minimum age 16; Medical examination.
Staff RNs 7 (ft), 2 (pt); LPNs 8 (ft), 5 (pt); Nurses aides 65 (ft); Physical therapists 1 (ft); Activities coordinators 2 (ft); Dietitians 1 (ft).
Languages Spanish, Chinese, Tagalog, German, Arabic, Portuguese
Facilities Dining room; Physical therapy room; Activities room; Barber/Beauty shop.
Activities Arts & crafts; Cards; Games; Reading groups; Prayer groups; Movies; Shopping trips; Social/Cultural gatherings; Educational programs; Horticulture therapy; Music therapy.

Sunny View Manor
22445 Cupertino Rd, Cupertino, CA, 95014
(408) 253-4300
Admin Jan Douglas. *Medical Dir/Dir of Nursing* F W Schwertley MD; Anne Ham.
Licensure Skilled care. *Beds* SNF 45. *Certified* Medi-Cal.
Owner Nonprofit Corp.
Admissions Requirements Minimum age 62; Medical examination.
Staff RNs 2 (ft), 8 (pt); LPNs 1 (ft); Nurses aides 14 (ft), 5 (pt); Activities coordinators 1 (ft).
Languages Tagalog, Spanish
Affiliation Lutheran
Facilities Dining room; Physical therapy room; Activities room; Chapel; Crafts room; Barber/Beauty shop; Library.
Activities Arts & crafts; Games; Prayer groups; Movies; Shopping trips.

DALY CITY

St Francis Convalescent Pavilion Inc*
99 Escuela Dr, Daly City, CA, 94015
(415) 994-3200
Admin Joseph D Echelberry.
Licensure Skilled care. *Beds* 239. *Certified* Medicare; Medi-Cal.
Owner Proprietary Corp.

St Francis Heights Convalescent Hospital*
35 Escuela Dr, Daly City, CA, 94015
(415) 755-9515
Admin Susan S Edwards.
Licensure Skilled care. *Beds* 102. *Certified* Medicare; Medi-Cal.
Owner Proprietary Corp.

DANVILLE

Diablo Convalescent Hospital*
336 Diablo Rd, Danville, CA, 94526
(415) 837-5536
Admin Ann Aldenhuysen.
Licensure Skilled care. *Beds* 52. *Certified* Medi-Cal.
Owner Proprietary Corp.

DAVIS

Driftwood Convalescent Hospital*
1850 E 8th St, Davis, CA, 95616
(916) 756-1800
Admin J Craig Coogan. *Medical Dir/Dir of Nursing* S Schaffer MD.
Licensure Skilled care. *Beds* 124. *Certified* Medicare; Medi-Cal.
Owner Proprietary Corp (ARA Living Centers).
Staff Physicians 3 (pt); RNs 9 (ft), 4 (pt); LPNs 4 (ft), 1 (pt); Orderlies 6 (ft), 2 (pt); Nurses aides 34 (ft), 18 (pt); Physical therapists 1 (pt); Recreational therapists 1 (pt); Speech therapists 1 (pt); Activities coordinators 1 (ft), 1 (pt); Dietitians 1 (pt); Dentists 1 (pt); Podiatrists 1 (pt); Audiologists 1 (pt).
Facilities Dining room; Physical therapy room; Activities room; Laundry room; Barber/Beauty shop.

Activities Arts & crafts; Cards; Games; Reading groups; Prayer groups; Movies; Shopping trips; Social/Cultural gatherings.

Sierra Health Care Convalescent Hospital
715 Pole Line Rd, Davis, CA, 95616
(916) 756-4900
Admin May Turner.
Licensure Skilled care. *Beds* 132. *Certified* Medicare; Medi-Cal.
Owner Proprietary Corp (Medicrest of California).
Admissions Requirements Minimum age 18.
Staff RNs 4 (ft), 4 (pt); LPNs 7 (ft), 3 (pt); Orderlies 15 (ft), 3 (pt); Nurses aides 45 (ft), 10 (pt); Activities coordinators 2 (ft).
Languages Spanish, Vietnamese, Farsi, Egyptian, Ethiopic
Facilities Dining room; Physical therapy room; Activities room; Chapel; Crafts room; Laundry room; Barber/Beauty shop; Library.
Activities Arts & crafts; Cards; Games; Reading groups; Prayer groups; Movies; Shopping trips; Social/Cultural gatherings; Resident & family council.

DELANO

Browning Manor Convalescent Hospital
PO Box 68, 729 Browning, Delano, CA, 93215
(805) 725-2501
Admin Carolyn Johnson. *Medical Dir/Dir of Nursing* Erwood Edgar MD; Beverly Donley RN DON.
Licensure Skilled care. *Beds* SNF 53. *Certified* Medicare; Medi-Cal.
Owner Proprietary Corp.
Admissions Requirements Medical examination; Physician's request.
Staff RNs; LPNs; Orderlies; Nurses aides; Activities coordinators.
Languages Spanish, Tagalog
Facilities Dining room; Activities room; Laundry room.
Activities Arts & crafts; Cards; Games; Reading groups; Prayer groups; Movies; Social/Cultural gatherings.

DESERT HOT SPRINGS

Angel View Childrens Habilitation Center
12-379 Miracle Hill Rd, Desert Hot Springs, CA, 92240
(714) 329-6471
Admin Henry Kotzen. *Medical Dir/Dir of Nursing* Carl Reller MD; Jean Hinton RN.
Licensure Intermediate care. *Beds* 52. *Certified* Medi-Cal.
Owner Nonprofit Corp.
Admissions Requirements Minimum age 3; Medical examination.
Staff RNs 1 (ft), 3 (pt); LPNs 8 (ft), 2 (pt); Nurses aides 40 (ft); Physical therapists 1 (pt); Occupational therapists 1 (pt); Speech therapists 1 (pt); Activities coordinators 1 (ft); Dietitians 1 (pt); Dentists 1 (pt).
Facilities Dining room; Physical therapy room; Activities room; Crafts room; Barber/Beauty shop; Library; Swimming & therapy pool.
Activities Arts & crafts; Games; Reading groups; Movies; Shopping trips; Social/Cultural gatherings.

DINUBA

Dinuba Convalescent Hospital*
1730 S College, Dinuba, CA, 93618
(209) 591-3300
Admin Jimmie Evans.
Licensure Skilled care. *Beds* 99. *Certified* Medicare; Medi-Cal.
Owner Proprietary Corp (National Heritage).

DOWNEY

Downey Care Center
13007 S Paramount Blvd, Downey, CA, 90242
(213) 923-9301
Admin Adrienne Rzepnick. *Medical Dir/Dir of Nursing* Robert Tsai MD; Marie Weiler DON.
Licensure Skilled care. *Beds* SNF 99. *Certified* Medicaid; Medicare; Medi-Cal.
Owner Proprietary Corp.
Staff RNs 3 (ft); LPNs 9 (ft); Orderlies 4 (ft); Nurses aides 25 (ft); Recreational therapists 1 (ft); Activities coordinators 1 (ft).
Languages Spanish
Facilities Dining room; Activities room; Crafts room; Laundry room; Barber/Beauty shop.
Activities Arts & crafts; Cards; Games; Reading groups; Prayer groups; Movies; Shopping trips; Social/Cultural gatherings.

Downey Community Health Center*
8425 Iowa St, Downey, CA, 90241
(213) 862-4119
Admin John Hryze.
Licensure Skilled care. *Beds* 115. *Certified* Medicare; Medi-Cal.
Owner Proprietary Corp.

Lakewood Park Health Center*
12023 S Lakewood Blvd, Downey, CA, 90242
(213) 869-0978
Admin Charles E Steen.
Licensure Skilled care; Intermediate care. *Beds* SNF 207; ICF 24. *Certified* Medicare; Medi-Cal.
Owner Proprietary Corp.
Facilities Dining room; Physical therapy room; Activities room; Crafts room; Barber/Beauty shop; Library.
Activities Arts & crafts; Cards; Games; Reading groups; Prayer groups; Movies; Shopping trips; Social/Cultural gatherings.

Pico Downey Golden Age Convalescent Home*
9300 Telegraph Rd, Downey, CA, 90240
(213) 869-2567
Admin Marilyn Spaun. *Medical Dir/Dir of Nursing* Joel M Sandler MD.
Licensure Skilled care. *Beds* 70. *Certified* Medicare; Medi-Cal.
Owner Proprietary Corp (National Heritage).
Admissions Requirements Minimum age 18; Medical examination; Physician's request.
Staff RNs 1 (ft), 2 (pt); LPNs 8 (ft), 2 (pt); Nurses aides 2 (pt); Physical therapists 1 (pt); Recreational therapists 1 (pt); Occupational therapists 1 (pt); Speech therapists 1 (pt); Activities coordinators 1 (ft); Dietitians 1 (pt); Dentists 1 (pt); Ophthalmologists 1 (pt); Podiatrists 1 (pt).
Facilities Dining room; Barber/Beauty shop.

DUARTE

Buena Vista Manor
802 Buena Vista St, Duarte, CA, 91010
(213) 359-8141
Admin Steve Paterson. *Medical Dir/Dir of Nursing* William Beard MD.
Licensure Skilled care. *Beds* 59. *Certified* Medicare; Medi-Cal.
Owner Nonprofit Corp (So CA Presbyterian Hm).
Staff Physicians 3 (pt); RNs 1 (ft), 1 (pt); LPNs 7 (ft), 2 (pt); Orderlies 1 (pt); Nurses aides 22 (ft), 2 (pt); Recreational therapists 1 (ft); Occupational therapists 1 (pt); Activities coordinators 1 (pt); Dietitians 1 (ft).
Affiliation Presbyterian
Facilities Dining room; Activities room; Crafts room; Laundry room; Barber/Beauty shop; Library.

Activities Arts & crafts; Cards; Games; Reading groups; Prayer groups; Movies; Shopping trips; Social/Cultural gatherings; Teas; Exercise; Brunches.

Community Care Center*
2335 S Mountain Ave, Duarte, CA, 91010
(213) 357-3207
Admin William J Cartwright.
Licensure Skilled care. *Beds* 176. *Certified* Medi-Cal.
Owner Proprietary Corp.

Highland Convalescent Hospital
PO Box 297, 1340 Highland Ave, Duarte, CA, 91010
(818) 359-9171
Admin Bonnie A Garcia. *Medical Dir/Dir of Nursing* J Corbin MD.
Licensure Skilled care. *Beds* 58. *Certified* Medicare; Medi-Cal.
Owner Proprietary Corp.
Staff Physicians 11 (pt); RNs 1 (ft), 4 (pt); LPNs 3 (ft), 4 (pt); Nurses aides 29 (ft); Physical therapists 1 (pt); Occupational therapists 1 (pt); Speech therapists 1 (pt); Activities coordinators 1 (ft), 1 (pt); Dietitians 1 (pt); Dentists 1 (pt); Ophthalmologists 1 (pt); Podiatrists 1 (pt).
Languages Spanish, Thai, German, Hindi, Hungarian
Facilities Dining room; Physical therapy room; Activities room; Laundry room; Barber/Beauty shop; Library.
Activities Arts & crafts; Cards; Games; Reading groups; Prayer groups; Movies; Shopping trips; Social/Cultural gatherings.

Monrovia Convalescent Hospital
PO Box 216, 1220 E Huntington, Duarte, CA, 91010
(213) 359-6618
Admin Sherman Davidson.
Licensure Skilled care. *Beds* 72. *Certified* Medicare; Medi-Cal.
Owner Proprietary Corp.

Westminster Gardens Health Center
1420 Santo Domingo Ave, Duarte, CA, 91010
(818) 359-2571
Admin John Rollins. *Medical Dir/Dir of Nursing* Dr Marshall Welles; Dorothy J Kaufmann.
Licensure Skilled care. *Beds* SNF 64.
Owner Nonprofit organization/foundation.
Admissions Requirements Physician's request.
Staff RNs 3 (pt); LPNs 5 (ft), 4 (pt); Nurses aides 19 (ft), 12 (pt); Physical therapists; Speech therapists; Activities coordinators 1 (ft); Dietitians 1 (pt); Dentists; Ophthalmologists.
Languages Spanish
Affiliation Presbyterian
Facilities Dining room; Physical therapy room; Activities room; Barber/Beauty shop; Library.
Activities Arts & crafts; Cards; Games; Reading groups; Prayer groups; Movies; Social/Cultural gatherings; Bible Studies; Pet therapy; Church every Sunday morning; Hymn singing.

EL CAJON

Anza Convalescent Hospital*
622 S Anza St, El Cajon, CA, 92020
(714) 442-3391
Admin Richard Mendlen.
Licensure Skilled care. *Beds* 160. *Certified* Medicare; Medi-Cal.
Owner Proprietary Corp (Care Enterprises).

Carroll's Intermediate Care*
151 Claydelle Ave, El Cajon, CA, 92020
(714) 442-0245
Admin Joann Prather. *Medical Dir/Dir of Nursing* Dr Palmer.

Licensure Intermediate care. *Beds* 65. *Certified* Medi-Cal.
Owner Proprietary Corp.
Admissions Requirements Physician's request.
Staff LPNs 3 (ft); Nurses aides 7 (ft); Activities coordinators 1 (ft); Dietitians 1 (pt).
Facilities Dining room; Activities room; Crafts room; Laundry room; Barber/Beauty shop.
Activities Arts & crafts; Games; Reading groups; Prayer groups; Movies.

Carroll's Intermediate Care—Anza*
654 S Anza, El Cajon, CA, 92020
(714) 440-5005
Admin Roger L Caddell.
Licensure Intermediate care. *Beds* 120. *Certified* Medi-Cal.
Owner Proprietary Corp.

El Cajon Valley Convalescent Center*
510 E Washington Ave, El Cajon, CA, 92020
(714) 440-1211
Admin H A Bunn & D Bunn.
Licensure Skilled care. *Beds* 256. *Certified* Medicare; Medi-Cal.
Owner Proprietary Corp.
Facilities Dining room; Physical therapy room; Activities room; Crafts room; Laundry room; Barber/Beauty shop; Library.
Activities Arts & crafts; Games.

Helix View Nursing Home Inc*
1201 S Orange Ave, El Cajon, CA, 92020
(714) 442-0255
Admin Daniel Bunn.
Licensure Skilled care. *Beds* 66. *Certified* Medicare; Medi-Cal.
Owner Proprietary Corp.

Lo-Har Lodge Incorporated*
794 Dorothy St, El Cajon, CA, 92020
(714) 444-8270
Admin Berry T Crow.
Licensure Skilled care. *Beds* 32.
Owner Proprietary Corp.

Madison Convalescent Center*
1391 E Madison Ave, El Cajon, CA, 92021
(714) 444-1107
Admin Aleene Brown. *Medical Dir/Dir of Nursing* Frank Flint.
Licensure Skilled care. *Beds* 96. *Certified* Medicare; Medi-Cal.
Owner Proprietary Corp (Care Enterprises).
Admissions Requirements Physician's request.
Staff RNs 4 (ft); LPNs 8 (ft), 2 (pt); Orderlies 3 (ft); Nurses aides 22 (ft), 7 (pt); Physical therapists 1 (pt); Occupational therapists; Speech therapists; Activities coordinators 1 (ft); Dietitians 1 (pt).
Facilities Dining room; Physical therapy room; Activities room; Crafts room; Laundry room; Barber/Beauty shop; Library.
Activities Arts & crafts; Games; Prayer groups; Movies; Shopping trips; Bingo; Music therapy.

Magnolia Center*
635 Magnolia, El Cajon, CA, 92020
(714) 442-8826
Admin Jean M Robbins.
Licensure Skilled care. *Beds* 99. *Certified* Medicare; Medi-Cal.
Owner Proprietary Corp.

Parkside Special Care Center
444 W Lexington Ave, El Cajon, CA, 92020
(619) 442-7744
Admin Stephen F Winner. *Medical Dir/Dir of Nursing* Sally Replole RN.
Licensure Skilled care. *Beds* SNF 50. *Certified* Medi-Cal.
Owner Proprietary Corp.
Admissions Requirements Must have LPS Conservatorship & diagnosis Alzheimers.

Staff RNs 2 (ft), 2 (pt); LPNs 3 (ft); Nurses aides 24 (ft); Recreational therapists 1 (pt); Activities coordinators 1 (ft); Dietitians 1 (pt); Dentists 1 (pt); Ophthalmologists 1 (pt).
Languages Spanish
Facilities Dining room; Activities room; Crafts room; Laundry room; Barber/Beauty shop; 1 1/2 acre park next to facility with connecting secure passageway.
Activities Arts & crafts; Cards; Games; Prayer groups; Movies; Social/Cultural gatherings; Activities specialized for patients with Alzheimers disease.

The Royal Home
12436 Royal Rd, El Cajon, CA, 92021
(619) 443-3886
Admin James E Carter I. *Medical Dir/Dir of Nursing* Frank Fint MD; Tina Rahowski.
Licensure Skilled care. *Beds* SNF 19. *Certified* Medi-Cal.
Owner Proprietary Corp.
Admissions Requirements Physician's request.
Staff RNs 1 (ft), 1 (pt); LPNs 1 (ft), 3 (pt); Nurses aides 2 (ft), 4 (pt); Activities coordinators 1 (ft), 1 (pt); Dietitians 1 (ft).
Facilities Dining room; Laundry room; Patio.
Activities Arts & crafts; Cards; Games; Reading groups; Prayer groups; Shopping trips; Social/Cultural gatherings.

TLC Convalescent Hospital
1340 E Madison Ave, El Cajon, CA, 92021
(714) 442-8855
Admin Donald L Linfesty.
Licensure Skilled care. *Beds* 99. *Certified* Medicare; Medi-Cal.
Owner Proprietary Corp.

Vista Del Cerro Convalescent Center*
675 E Bradley Ave, El Cajon, CA, 92021
(714) 448-6633
Admin Clyde Prince. *Medical Dir/Dir of Nursing* Charles Miller MD.
Licensure Skilled care. *Beds* 56. *Certified* Medicare; Medi-Cal.
Owner Proprietary Corp.
Admissions Requirements Physician's request.
Staff RNs 4 (ft); LPNs 9 (ft); Nurses aides 30 (ft); Physical therapists 1 (pt); Recreational therapists 1 (pt); Activities coordinators 1 (ft); Podiatrists 1 (pt).
Facilities Dining room; Laundry room.
Activities Arts & crafts; Cards; Games; Reading groups; Prayer groups; Shopping trips.

EL CENTRO

Valley Convalescent Hospital
1700 S Imperial Ave, El Centro, CA, 92243
(619) 352-8471
Admin Annette Brinnon. *Medical Dir/Dir of Nursing* Shirley Crossman.
Licensure Skilled care. *Beds* SNF 123. *Certified* Medicare; Medi-Cal.
Owner Proprietary Corp (National Heritage).
Admissions Requirements Medical examination; Physician's request.
Staff RNs; LPNs; Orderlies; Nurses aides.
Languages Spanish, German
Facilities Dining room; Physical therapy room; Activities room; Crafts room; Barber/Beauty shop.
Activities Arts & crafts; Cards; Games; Reading groups; Prayer groups; Movies; Social/Cultural gatherings.

EL CERRITO

Shields Intermediate Care Facility
3230 Carlson Blvd, El Cerrito, CA, 94530
(415) 525-3212
Admin Carolyn L J Logan. *Medical Dir/Dir of Nursing* Otis Rounds MD; Birdie Stafford LVN.

Licensure Intermediate care. *Beds* ICF 45. *Certified* Medi-Cal.
Owner Proprietary Corp.
Admissions Requirements Medical examination; Physician's request.
Staff LPNs 3 (ft); Nurses aides 12 (ft); Activities coordinators 1 (ft).
Facilities Dining room; Activities room; Crafts room; Laundry room.
Activities Arts & crafts; Cards; Games; Prayer groups; Movies; Social/Cultural gatherings.

EL MONTE

Chandler Care Center—El Monte*
3825 N Durfee Ave, El Monte, CA, 91732
(213) 444-2535
Admin Charlotte R Ulrich.
Licensure Skilled care. *Beds* 139. *Certified* Medicare; Medi-Cal.
Owner Proprietary Corp.

Chandler Care Center—Ramona*
12036 Ramona Blvd, El Monte, CA, 91732
(213) 448-9851
Admin Danny J Amador.
Licensure Skilled care. *Beds* 99. *Certified* Medicare; Medi-Cal.
Owner Proprietary Corp.

Cherrylee Lodge Sanitarium
5053 N Peck Rd, El Monte, CA, 91732
(818) 448-4248, (213) 686-0174
Admin Lance W Comfort. *Medical Dir/Dir of Nursing* Richard Weiss MD; Shirley K Wilson DON.
Licensure Skilled care. *Beds* SNF 46. *Certified* Medicare; Medi-Cal.
Owner Proprietary Corp.
Admissions Requirements Medical examination; Physician's request.
Staff RNs 1 (ft), 3 (pt); Orderlies 1 (ft); Nurses aides 16 (ft), 1 (pt); Activities coordinators 1 (ft), 1 (pt); Dietitians 1 (ft); LVNs 3 (ft), 4 (pt).
Languages Spanish, Tagalog
Facilities Dining room; Activities room; Laundry room; Barber/Beauty shop.
Activities Arts & crafts; Cards; Games; Prayer groups; Movies; Shopping trips; Social/Cultural gatherings.

El Monte Convalescent Hospital*
4096 Easy St, El Monte, CA, 91731
(213) 442-1500
Admin Lilly P Telles. *Medical Dir/Dir of Nursing* Donald E Medanis.
Licensure Skilled care. *Beds* 99. *Certified* Medicare; Medi-Cal.
Owner Proprietary Corp.
Staff Physicians 12 (pt); RNs 3 (ft), 2 (pt); LPNs 5 (ft), 4 (pt); Orderlies 4 (ft), 2 (pt); Nurses aides 35 (ft), 9 (pt); Physical therapists 1 (pt); Occupational therapists 1 (pt); Speech therapists 1 (pt); Activities coordinators 2 (ft); Dietitians 1 (pt); Dentists 1 (pt); Podiatrists 1 (pt); Audiologists 1 (pt).
Facilities Dining room; Physical therapy room; Activities room; Crafts room; Laundry room; Barber/Beauty shop; Library.
Activities Arts & crafts; Cards; Games; Reading groups; Prayer groups; Movies; Bingo; Lunch outings.

El Monte Golden Age Convalescent Home*
11900 Ramona Blvd, El Monte, CA, 91732
(213) 442-5721
Admin Ray Fischella.
Licensure Skilled care. *Beds* 148. *Certified* Medicare.
Owner Nonprofit Corp.

Elmcrest Convalescent Hospital
3111 Santa Anita Ave, El Monte, CA, 91733
(213) 443-0218
Admin John Torrez. *Medical Dir/Dir of Nursing* Douglas Copley; Pam Chacon.

Licensure Skilled care. *Beds* 96. *Certified* Medicare; Medi-Cal.
Owner Proprietary Corp (Care Enterprises).
Admissions Requirements Physician's request.
Languages Spanish
Facilities Dining room; Physical therapy room; Activities room; Laundry room; Barber/Beauty shop.
Activities Arts & crafts; Cards; Games; Reading groups; Prayer groups; Movies; Shopping trips; Social/Cultural gatherings.

Idle Acre Sanitarium & Convalescent Hospital
5044 Buffington Rd, El Monte, CA, 91732
(213) 443-1351
Admin Barry Silberberg. *Medical Dir/Dir of Nursing* Gary Schlecter MD.
Licensure Skilled care. *Beds* 53. *Certified* Medi-Cal.
Owner Proprietary Corp.
Staff Physicians; RNs; LPNs; Nurses aides; Activities coordinators; Dietitians.
Languages Spanish
Facilities Dining room; Activities room; Laundry room; Barber/Beauty shop.
Activities Arts & crafts; Games; Prayer groups.

Sunset Manor Convalescent Hospital
2720 Nevada Ave, El Monte, CA, 91733
(818) 443-9425
Admin B E Hendrickson. *Medical Dir/Dir of Nursing* Richard Hart MD; Linda Blankenship RN.
Licensure Skilled care. *Beds* 81. *Certified* Medicare; Medi-Cal.
Owner Proprietary Corp.
Admissions Requirements Minimum age 18; Physician's request.
Staff Physicians 13 (pt); RNs 2 (ft), 2 (pt); LPNs 7 (ft), 4 (pt); Orderlies 4 (ft), 2 (pt); Nurses aides 28 (ft), 8 (pt); Physical therapists 1 (pt); Occupational therapists 1 (pt); Speech therapists 1 (pt); Activities coordinators 1 (ft), 1 (pt); Dietitians 1 (ft); Dentists 1 (pt); Ophthalmologists 1 (pt); Podiatrists 1 (pt).
Languages Sign, Spanish, Tagalog
Facilities Dining room; Physical therapy room; Activities room; Crafts room; Laundry room; Barber/Beauty shop.
Activities Arts & crafts; Cards; Games; Reading groups; Prayer groups; Movies; Senior citizen gatherings.

Wellesley Manor Convalescent Hospital
11210 Lower Azusa Rd, El Monte, CA, 91731
(818) 442-6861
Admin Ruth R Dinglasan. *Medical Dir/Dir of Nursing* R Atiga MD; Trudy Yerkes RN DON.
Licensure Skilled care. *Beds* 90. *Certified* Medicare; Medi-Cal.
Owner Proprietary Corp (Medicrest of California).
Staff Physicians 2 (ft), 1 (pt); RNs 2 (ft); LPNs 8 (ft), 2 (pt); Nurses aides 40 (ft), 20 (pt); Activities coordinators 1 (ft).
Facilities Dining room; Physical therapy room; Activities room; Crafts room; Laundry room; Barber/Beauty shop.
Activities Arts & crafts; Cards; Games; Reading groups; Prayer groups; Movies; Shopping trips; Social/Cultural gatherings.

ELK GROVE

Elk Grove Convalescent Hospital
9461 Batey Ave, Elk Grove, CA, 95624
(916) 685-9525
Admin Betty M Dever.
Licensure Skilled care. *Beds* 136. *Certified* Medicare; Medi-Cal.
Owner Nonprofit organization/foundation.

ENCINITAS

Scripps Memorial Hospital-Ocean View Convalescent
900 Santa Fe Rd, Encinitas, CA, 92024
(714) 753-6423
Admin Charles Bloom. *Medical Dir/Dir of Nursing* Dr Arthur Edwards.
Licensure Skilled care. *Beds* 99. *Certified* Medicaid; Medicare; Medi-Cal.
Owner Nonprofit organization/foundation.
Admissions Requirements Minimum age 18; Medical examination.
Staff RNs 5 (ft); LPNs 10 (ft); Nurses aides 33 (ft), 10 (pt); Physical therapists 1 (ft); Recreational therapists 1 (ft); Occupational therapists 1 (ft); Speech therapists 1 (ft); Activities coordinators 2 (pt); Dietitians 1 (pt).
Facilities Dining room; Physical therapy room; Activities room; Crafts room; Laundry room; Barber/Beauty shop; Private ocean view rooms.
Activities Arts & crafts; Cards; Games; Reading groups; Prayer groups; Movies; Shopping trips; Social/Cultural gatherings.

ESCONDIDO

Beverly Manor Convalescent Hospital
421 E Mission Ave, Escondido, CA, 92025
(714) 747-0430
Admin Vic Tose. *Medical Dir/Dir of Nursing* Raymond Dann MD.
Licensure Skilled care. *Beds* 180. *Certified* Medicaid; Medicare; Medi-Cal.
Owner Proprietary Corp (Beverly Enterprises).
Facilities Dining room; Physical therapy room; Activities room; Crafts room; Laundry room; Barber/Beauty shop; Library; TV/Living room.
Activities Arts & crafts; Cards; Games; Reading groups; Prayer groups; Movies.

Escondido Convalescent Center
201 N Fig St, Escondido, CA, 92025
(619) 746-0303
Admin Frana K Priddy RN. *Medical Dir/Dir of Nursing* Dr Thomas E Rastle; Rena Shaphard RN.
Licensure Skilled care. *Beds* SNF 74. *Certified* Medicare; Medi-Cal.
Owner Proprietary Corp (Care Enterprises).
Admissions Requirements Physician's request.
Staff RNs 3 (ft), 1 (pt); LPNs 6 (ft), 4 (pt); Nurses aides 24 (ft); Physical therapists 1 (ft); Occupational therapists 1 (ft); Speech therapists 1 (ft); Activities coordinators 1 (ft); Dietitians 1 (ft); Ophthalmologists 1 (ft); Podiatrists 1 (ft).
Languages Spanish, Tagalog
Facilities Dining room; Physical therapy room; Laundry room; Barber/Beauty shop.
Activities Arts & crafts; Games; Reading groups; Prayer groups; Movies; Shopping trips; Social/Cultural gatherings.

Hilltop Convalescent Center
1260 E Ohio St, Escondido, CA, 92027
(619) 746-1100
Admin Marie Kessler. *Medical Dir/Dir of Nursing* Dr Britton; Candace Meyer RN.
Licensure Skilled care. *Beds* 98. *Certified* Medicare; Medi-Cal.
Owner Proprietary Corp (Care Enterprises).
Admissions Requirements Minimum age 18.
Staff RNs 2 (ft); LPNs 10 (ft), 3 (pt); Nurses aides 34 (ft); Physical therapists 1 (ft); Occupational therapists 1 (ft), 1 (pt); Speech therapists 1 (pt); Activities coordinators 1 (ft); Dietitians 1 (ft).
Languages Spanish, Slavic
Facilities Dining room; Physical therapy room; Activities room; Crafts room; Barber/Beauty shop; Library.

Activities Arts & crafts; Cards; Games; Reading groups; Prayer groups; Movies; Shopping trips; Social/Cultural gatherings; Field trips.

Redwood Terrace Lutheran Home*
710 W 13th Ave, Escondido, CA, 92025
(714) 747-4306
Admin Daniel H Johnson. *Medical Dir/Dir of Nursing* Stephen D Smith MD.
Licensure Skilled care; Intermediate care. *Beds* SNF 30; ICF 29.
Owner Nonprofit Corp.
Admissions Requirements Minimum age 62; Medical examination; Physician's request.
Staff RNs 5 (ft), 7 (pt); LPNs 2 (pt); Nurses aides 17 (ft), 12 (pt); Activities coordinators 1 (ft).
Affiliation Lutheran
Facilities Dining room; Physical therapy room; Activities room; Chapel; Crafts room; Laundry room; Barber/Beauty shop; Library.
Activities Arts & crafts; Cards; Games; Reading groups; Prayer groups; Movies; Shopping trips; Social/Cultural gatherings.

Valle Vista Convalescent Hospital Inc*
1025 W 2nd St, Escondido, CA, 92025
(714) 745-1288
Admin C R Cook.
Licensure Skilled care. *Beds* 53. *Certified* Medicare; Medi-Cal.
Owner Proprietary Corp.

EUREKA

Crestwood Manor
2370 Buhne St, Eureka, CA, 95501
(707) 442-5721
Admin Cleatus V Weller. *Medical Dir/Dir of Nursing* Ken Stiver MD; Loleta Turner RN DNS.
Licensure Skilled care. *Beds* SNF 85. *Certified* Medi-Cal.
Owner Proprietary Corp (Crestwood Hosp).
Admissions Requirements Minimum age 18; Medical examination; Physician's request.
Staff RNs 4 (ft), 2 (pt); LPNs 7 (ft), 2 (pt); Nurses aides 30 (ft), 10 (pt); Recreational therapists 6 (ft), 1 (pt); Activities coordinators 1 (ft); Dietitians 1 (ft).
Facilities Dining room; Activities room; Crafts room; Laundry room; Barber/Beauty shop.
Activities Arts & crafts; Cards; Games; Reading groups; Prayer groups; Movies; Shopping trips; Social/Cultural gatherings.

Granada Convalescent Hospital
2885 Harris St, Eureka, CA, 95501
(707) 443-1627
Admin Tom E Sutton. *Medical Dir/Dir of Nursing* Ken Stiver MD; Jessie Laurendeau DON.
Licensure Skilled care. *Beds* SNF 87. *Certified* Medicaid; Medicare; Medi-Cal.
Owner Proprietary Corp (Coastal Care Centers Inc).
Admissions Requirements Minimum age 5; Physician's request.
Staff RNs 4 (ft), 1 (pt); LPNs 4 (ft), 2 (pt); Orderlies 5 (ft), 2 (pt); Nurses aides 28 (ft), 5 (pt); Physical therapists 1 (ft), 2 (pt); Recreational therapists 1 (ft); Occupational therapists 1 (pt); Speech therapists 1 (pt); Activities coordinators 1 (ft); Dietitians 1 (pt).
Facilities Dining room; Physical therapy room; Activities room; Crafts room; Laundry room; Barber/Beauty shop.
Activities Arts & crafts; Cards; Games; Reading groups; Prayer groups; Movies; Shopping trips; Social/Cultural gatherings.

Pacific Convalescent Hospital
2211 Harrison Ave, Eureka, CA, 95501
(707) 443-9767

Admin Neil Fassihger. *Medical Dir/Dir of Nursing* Ken Stiver MD; Phyllis Bowser RN DON.
Licensure Skilled care. *Beds* SNF 59. *Certified* Medicare; Medi-Cal.
Owner Proprietary Corp.
Admissions Requirements Medical examination; Physician's request.
Staff RNs 4 (ft); LPNs 5 (ft), 2 (pt); Nurses aides 25 (ft), 3 (pt); Physical therapists 1 (ft); Recreational therapists 1 (ft); Speech therapists 1 (ft); Activities coordinators 1 (ft); Dietitians 1 (ft).
Languages Spanish, Cambodian
Facilities Dining room; Physical therapy room; Activities room; Crafts room; Laundry room; Barber/Beauty shop; Deck; Patio.
Activities Arts & crafts; Cards; Games; Reading groups; Prayer groups; Movies; Shopping trips; Social/Cultural gatherings; BBQs; Outings; Contests.

Sea View Convalescent Hospital
8400 Purdue Dr, Eureka, CA, 95501
(707) 443-5668
Admin Rebecca Campbell. *Medical Dir/Dir of Nursing* Ken Stiver MD; Janice Mauney DON.
Licensure Skilled care. *Beds* 99. *Certified* Medicare; Medi-Cal.
Owner Proprietary Corp.
Admissions Requirements Medical examination; Physician's request.
Staff RNs 5 (ft); LPNs 6 (ft), 1 (pt); Orderlies 8 (ft), 2 (pt); Nurses aides 20 (ft), 6 (pt); Activities coordinators 1 (ft).
Languages Finnish, Spanish, Portuguese
Facilities Dining room; Physical therapy room; Activities room; Crafts room; Laundry room; Barber/Beauty shop.
Activities Arts & crafts; Cards; Games; Reading groups; Prayer groups; Movies; Shopping trips; Social/Cultural gatherings.

Sunset Convalescent Hospital*
2353 23rd St, Eureka, CA, 95501
(707) 443-1627
Admin Robert Bates. *Medical Dir/Dir of Nursing* Dr Ken Stiver.
Licensure Skilled care. *Beds* 99. *Certified* Medicare; Medi-Cal.
Owner Proprietary Corp (Coastal Care Centers Inc).
Admissions Requirements Medical examination; Physician's request.
Facilities Dining room; Physical therapy room; Activities room; Crafts room; Laundry room; Barber/Beauty shop; Library; Speech Therapy Room.
Activities Arts & crafts; Cards; Games; Reading groups; Prayer groups; Movies; Shopping trips; Social/Cultural gatherings.

FAIRFIELD

CareWest La Mariposa Nursing & Rehabilitation Center
1244 Travis Blvd, Fairfield, CA, 94533
(707) 422-7750
Admin Jordan. *Medical Dir/Dir of Nursing* Dr V Douglas Jodoin; Martha O'Donnell DON.
Licensure Skilled care. *Beds* SNF 99. *Certified* Medicare; Medi-Cal.
Owner Proprietary Corp (Care Enterprises).
Admissions Requirements Medical examination.
Staff Physicians 1 (pt); Physical therapists 1 (ft); Occupational therapists 1 (ft); Speech therapists 2 (pt); Activities coordinators 1 (ft), 1 (pt); Dietitians 1 (ft); Ophthalmologists 1 (pt); Podiatrists 1 (pt); Social services 1 (pt); Physical therapy aides 2 (pt).
Languages Spanish, Chinese, German, French, Italian

Facilities Dining room; Physical therapy room; Activities room; Laundry room; Barber/Beauty shop; ST room; OT room; TV room/lounge; Patio-garden.
Activities Arts & crafts; Cards; Games; Movies; Shopping trips; Social/Cultural gatherings; Church services; Music parties & performances; Discussion groups.

Fairfield Convalescent
1255 Travis Blvd, Fairfield, CA, 94533
(707) 425-0623
Admin Annette S Eugenis. *Medical Dir/Dir of Nursing* Dr Daniel Green; Lynn Holbrook RN.
Licensure Skilled care. *Beds* SNF 99. *Certified* Medicare; Medi-Cal.
Owner Proprietary Corp (American Health Care Inc).
Staff RNs; Nurses aides; Physical therapists; Recreational therapists; Occupational therapists; Speech therapists; Activities coordinators; Dietitians; Ophthalmologists; Podiatrists; LVNs.
Languages Spanish, Tagalog
Facilities Dining room; Physical therapy room; Activities room; Crafts room; Laundry room; Barber/Beauty shop.
Activities Arts & crafts; Cards; Games; Reading groups; Prayer groups; Movies; Shopping trips; Social/Cultural gatherings.

Sunny Acres Convalescent Hospital*
1260 Travis Blvd, Fairfield, CA, 94533
(707) 425-0669
Admin Annette S Eugenis. *Medical Dir/Dir of Nursing* Dr Edward Lopez.
Licensure Skilled care. *Beds* 90. *Certified* Medicare; Medi-Cal.
Owner Proprietary Corp.
Admissions Requirements Medical examination.
Staff RNs 2 (ft), 4 (pt); LPNs 5 (ft), 5 (pt); Nurses aides 29 (ft), 11 (pt); Activities coordinators 1 (ft).
Facilities Dining room; Activities room; Crafts room; Laundry room; Barber/Beauty shop.
Activities Arts & crafts; Cards; Games; Reading groups; Prayer groups; Movies; Shopping trips; Social/Cultural gatherings; Outside facility activities; Wine & cheese tasting; Nature walks; Picnics; Exercise; Residential council.

FALLBROOK

Fallbrook Convalescent Hospital
325 Potter St, Fallbrook, CA, 92028
(619) 728-2330
Admin Robert Durbin. *Medical Dir/Dir of Nursing* E B Shields MD; G Cimino DNS.
Licensure Skilled care. *Beds* SNF 54. *Certified* Medicare; Medi-Cal.
Owner Privately owned.
Admissions Requirements Minimum age 65; Medical examination; Physician's request.
Activities Arts & crafts; Cards; Games; Reading groups; Prayer groups; Movies; Shopping trips; Social/Cultural gatherings.

FILLMORE

Fillmore Convalescent Center*
118 B St, Fillmore, CA, 93015
(805) 524-0083
Admin Brad Davis. *Medical Dir/Dir of Nursing* Dinko Rosic MD.
Licensure Skilled care; Intermediate care. *Beds* SNF 89; ICF 3. *Certified* Medicare; Medi-Cal.
Owner Proprietary Corp.
Admissions Requirements Medical examination; Physician's request.
Staff Physicians 13 (pt); RNs 1 (ft), 5 (pt); LPNs 6 (ft); Physical therapists 1 (pt); Occupational therapists 1 (pt); Speech

therapists 1 (pt); Activities coordinators 1 (ft); Dietitians 1 (pt); Dentists 1 (pt); Podiatrists 1 (pt).
Facilities Dining room; Physical therapy room; Activities room; Crafts room; Laundry room; Barber/Beauty shop.
Activities Arts & crafts; Games; Reading groups; Prayer groups; Movies; Shopping trips; Social/Cultural gatherings; Resident council; Cooking; Sewing.

FOLSOM

Folsom Convalescent Hospital
510 Mill St, Folsom, CA, 95630
(916) 985-3641
Admin D V Callaway. *Medical Dir/Dir of Nursing* Dr D Gutman.
Licensure Skilled care. *Beds* 99. *Certified* Medicare; Medi-Cal.
Owner Proprietary Corp.
Staff RNs 6 (ft), 2 (pt); LPNs 6 (ft), 3 (pt); Orderlies 4 (ft), 2 (pt); Nurses aides 60 (ft), 20 (pt); Physical therapists 1 (pt); Reality therapists 1 (pt); Recreational therapists 1 (ft); Occupational therapists 1 (pt); Speech therapists 1 (pt); Activities coordinators 1 (ft); Dietitians 1 (pt); Dentists 1 (pt); Ophthalmologists 1 (pt); Podiatrists 1 (pt); 1 (pt) Dentist.
Facilities Dining room; Physical therapy room; Activities room; Crafts room; Laundry room; Barber/Beauty shop.
Activities Arts & crafts; Cards; Games; Reading groups; Prayer groups; Movies; Shopping trips; Social/Cultural gatherings.

FONTANA

Casa Maria Convalescent Hospital
17933 San Bernardino Ave, Fontana, CA, 92335
(714) 877-1555
Admin Lois Easterday. *Medical Dir/Dir of Nursing* Robert Bom MD.
Licensure Skilled care. *Beds* 57. *Certified* Medicaid; Medicare; Medi-Cal.
Owner Proprietary Corp.
Admissions Requirements Minimum age 65; Medical examination; Physician's request.
Staff Physicians 4 (ft); RNs 3 (ft); LPNs 7 (ft); Orderlies 3 (ft); Nurses aides 15 (ft); Physical therapists 1 (ft); Recreational therapists 2 (ft); Occupational therapists 1 (ft); Speech therapists 1 (ft); Activities coordinators 1 (ft); Dietitians 1 (ft); Ophthalmologists 1 (ft).
Languages Spanish
Facilities Dining room; Physical therapy room; Activities room; Crafts room; Laundry room; Barber/Beauty shop.
Activities Arts & crafts; Games; Prayer groups; Movies; Shopping trips; Social/Cultural gatherings.

Citrus Nursing Center
9440 Citrus Ave, Fontana, CA, 92335
(714) 823-3481
Admin Elaine Fickett. *Medical Dir/Dir of Nursing* Richard Neil MD; Charlotte Keefer RN DON.
Licensure Skilled care. *Beds* SNF 99. *Certified* Medicare; Medi-Cal.
Owner Proprietary Corp (Care Enterprises).
Admissions Requirements Minimum age 21; Medical examination.
Staff RNs 2 (ft), 1 (pt); LPNs 11 (ft), 1 (pt); Orderlies 6 (ft); Nurses aides 34 (ft), 2 (pt); Physical therapists 1 (ft); Occupational therapists; Speech therapists; Activities coordinators 1 (ft); Dietitians 1 (pt).
Languages Spanish
Facilities Dining room; Physical therapy room; Activities room; Laundry room; Barber/Beauty shop.

Activities Arts & crafts; Cards; Games; Reading groups; Prayer groups; Movies; Shopping trips; Social/Cultural gatherings.

Laurel Convalescent Hospital
7509 N Laurel Ave, Fontana, CA, 92335
(714) 822-8066
Admin Peter D Bennett. *Medical Dir/Dir of Nursing* William Thompson; Kathy Sexton DON.
Licensure Skilled care. *Beds* SNF 99. *Certified* Medicare; Medi-Cal.
Owner Proprietary Corp (Care Enterprises).
Admissions Requirements Minimum age 60; Medical examination; Physician's request.
Staff Physicians 12 (pt); RNs 3 (ft); LPNs 10 (ft); Orderlies 2 (ft); Nurses aides 22 (ft); Physical therapists 1 (pt); Occupational therapists 1 (pt); Speech therapists 1 (pt); Activities coordinators 1 (ft); Dietitians 1 (pt); Dentists 1 (pt); Ophthalmologists 1 (pt); Podiatrists 1 (pt); Social worker 1 (ft).
Languages Spanish
Facilities Dining room; Physical therapy room; Activities room; Barber/Beauty shop; Library; Large outdoor grounds.
Activities Arts & crafts; Cards; Games; Reading groups; Prayer groups; Movies; Shopping trips; Social/Cultural gatherings; Patient oriented council; Family council.

FORTUNA

St Luke Manor
2321 Newberg Rd, Fortuna, CA, 95540
(707) 725-4467
Admin John Henkel. *Medical Dir/Dir of Nursing* Harold Averhan MD; Joyce Osborn DON.
Licensure Skilled care. *Beds* SNF 104. *Certified* Medicare; Medi-Cal.
Owner Nonprofit Corp.
Admissions Requirements Minimum age 18; Medical examination.
Staff RNs 6 (ft), 3 (pt); LPNs 4 (ft), 2 (pt); Orderlies 4 (ft); Nurses aides 20 (ft), 26 (pt); Activities coordinators 1 (ft).
Affiliation Lutheran
Facilities Dining room; Physical therapy room; Activities room; Chapel; Laundry room; Barber/Beauty shop.
Activities Arts & crafts; Cards; Games; Reading groups; Prayer groups; Movies; Shopping trips; Social/Cultural gatherings.

FOWLER

Fowler Convalescent Hospital
306 E Tulare St, Fowler, CA, 93625
(209) 834-2542
Admin Bryan Strombom. *Medical Dir/Dir of Nursing* Bob Landford MD.
Licensure Skilled care. *Beds* 49. *Certified* Medicare; Medi-Cal.
Owner Proprietary Corp (Beverly Enterprises).
Admissions Requirements Minimum age 18.
Staff Physicians; RNs; LPNs; Orderlies; Nurses aides; Physical therapists; Reality therapists; Recreational therapists; Occupational therapists; Speech therapists; Activities coordinators; Dietitians; Ophthalmologists; Podiatrists; Dentist.
Facilities Dining room; Activities room; Crafts room; Laundry room; Barber/Beauty shop.
Activities Arts & crafts; Cards; Games; Reading groups; Prayer groups; Movies; Shopping trips; Social/Cultural gatherings.

Kings Vista Convalescent Hospital*
8448 E Adams Ave, Fowler, CA, 93625
(209) 834-2519
Admin Carrie Stauber.
Licensure Skilled care. *Beds* 49. *Certified* Medi-Cal.
Owner Proprietary Corp (Beverly Enterprises).

FREMONT

Crestwood Rehabilitation & Convalescent Hospital*
2500 Country Dr, Fremont, CA, 94536
(415) 792-4242
Admin Tom Curry. *Medical Dir/Dir of Nursing* Dr P Loeb.
Licensure Skilled care. *Beds* 126. *Certified* Medicare.
Owner Proprietary Corp (Crestwood Hosp).
Staff RNs 4 (ft), 2 (pt); LPNs 7 (ft), 5 (pt); Orderlies 5 (ft); Nurses aides 55 (ft), 5 (pt); Physical therapists 1 (pt); Reality therapists 1 (pt); Recreational therapists 1 (pt); Occupational therapists 1 (pt); Speech therapists 1 (pt); Activities coordinators 2 (ft); Dietitians 1 (ft); Dentists 1 (pt); Podiatrists 2 (pt).
Facilities Dining room; Physical therapy room; Activities room; Laundry room; Barber/Beauty shop.
Activities Arts & crafts; Cards; Games; Reading groups; Prayer groups; Movies; Shopping trips; Social/Cultural gatherings.

Driftwood Convalescent Hospital
39022 Presidio Way, Fremont, CA, 94538
(415) 792-3743
Admin Laura Eisenhart. *Medical Dir/Dir of Nursing* Ashwani Bindal MD.
Licensure Skilled care. *Beds* 122. *Certified* Medicare; Medi-Cal.
Owner Proprietary Corp (ARA Living Centers).
Admissions Requirements Physician's request.
Staff Physicians; RNs; LPNs; Nurses aides; Physical therapists; Occupational therapists; Speech therapists; Activities coordinators; Dietitians; Ophthalmologists; Podiatrists.
Facilities Dining room; Physical therapy room; Activities room; Laundry room; Barber/Beauty shop; Lounges; Sunroom.
Activities Arts & crafts; Cards; Games; Reading groups; Prayer groups; Movies; Shopping trips; Social/Cultural gatherings.

Fremont Convalescent Hospital*
2171 Mowry Ave, Fremont, CA, 94536
(415) 793-8383
Admin Imogene Ellwanger.
Licensure Skilled care. *Beds* 88. *Certified* Medicare; Medi-Cal.
Owner Proprietary Corp (Crestwood Hosp).

Park Central Convalescent Hospital*
2100 Parkside Dr, Fremont, CA, 94536
(415) 797-5300
Admin Carol Carrell. *Medical Dir/Dir of Nursing* Phillip M Loeb MD.
Licensure Skilled care. *Beds* 99. *Certified* Medicare; Medi-Cal.
Owner Proprietary Corp (Care Enterprises).
Staff RNs 3 (ft), 4 (pt); LPNs 4 (ft), 6 (pt); Nurses aides 25 (ft), 4 (pt); Physical therapists 1 (ft); Speech therapists 1 (pt); Activities coordinators 1 (ft); Dietitians 1 (ft); Dentists 1 (pt); Podiatrists 1 (pt); Audiologists 1 (pt).

Parkmont Care Center
2400 Parkside Dr, Fremont, CA, 94536
(415) 793-7222
Admin Imogene Ellwanger. *Medical Dir/Dir of Nursing* Anmol Mahal MD; Mary Ferrara RN DON.
Licensure Skilled care. *Beds* SNF 85. *Certified* Medicare; Medi-Cal.
Owner Proprietary Corp.
Admissions Requirements Medical examination; Physician's request.
Staff RNs 3 (ft), 1 (pt); LPNs 11 (ft), 3 (pt); Nurses aides 47 (ft), 9 (pt); Recreational therapists 1 (ft); Activities coordinators 1 (ft); Dietitians 1 (ft).
Languages German, Portuguese, Spanish, Tagalog, Italian, Chinese

Facilities Dining room; Activities room; Crafts room; Laundry room; Barber/Beauty shop; Library; TV room.
Activities Arts & crafts; Cards; Games; Reading groups; Prayer groups; Movies; Shopping trips; Social/Cultural gatherings; Picnics; Sing-alongs; Glamour girls; Fashion shows.

Westwood*
4303 Stevenson Blvd, Fremont, CA, 94538
(415) 657-6000
Admin Richard A Knowles.
Licensure Skilled care. *Beds* 118. *Certified* Medi-Cal.
Owner Proprietary Corp.

FRESNO

Beverly Manor Convalescent Hospital
2715 Fresno St, Fresno, CA, 93721
(209) 486-4433
Admin Ronald Kinnersley. *Medical Dir/Dir of Nursing* Diane Anthony.
Licensure Skilled care. *Beds* 232. *Certified* Medicare; Medi-Cal.
Owner Proprietary Corp (Beverly Enterprises).
Staff RNs; LPNs; Nurses aides; Recreational therapists; Activities coordinators; Dietitians.
Facilities Dining room; Physical therapy room; Activities room; Crafts room; Laundry room; Barber/Beauty shop.
Activities Arts & crafts; Cards; Games; Reading groups; Prayer groups; Movies; Shopping trips; Social/Cultural gatherings.

California Home for the Aged Inc
6720 E Kings Canyon Rd, Fresno, CA, 93727
(209) 251-8414
Admin Yuba Radojkovich. *Medical Dir/Dir of Nursing* J R Medina MD; Helen Zueleski RN.
Licensure Skilled care; Intermediate care; Community care. *Beds* SNF 66; ICF 25; Community care 37. *Certified* Medicare; Medi-Cal.
Owner Nonprofit Corp.
Admissions Requirements Minimum age 62; Medical examination.
Staff RNs 3 (ft); LPNs 11 (ft); Orderlies 9 (ft); Nurses aides 41 (ft), 3 (pt); Activities coordinators 3 (ft); 34 (ft).
Languages Armenian
Facilities Dining room; Activities room; Chapel; Crafts room; Laundry room; Barber/Beauty shop; Library.
Activities Arts & crafts; Cards; Games; Prayer groups; Movies; Shopping trips; Social/Cultural gatherings; Exercises.

Country View Convalescent Hospital*
925 N Cornelia Ave, Fresno, CA, 93706
(209) 275-4786
Admin Cheryl Mitchum. *Medical Dir/Dir of Nursing* Dr Alvin Chaffin.
Licensure Skilled care. *Beds* 59. *Certified* Medicare; Medi-Cal.
Owner Proprietary Corp (Beverly Enterprises).
Admissions Requirements Physician's request.
Staff Physicians 1 (pt); RNs 1 (ft), 2 (pt); LPNs 3 (ft), 3 (pt); Orderlies 2 (ft), 2 (pt); Nurses aides 11 (ft), 4 (pt); Physical therapists 1 (pt); Reality therapists 1 (ft); Recreational therapists 1 (ft); Occupational therapists 1 (pt); Speech therapists 1 (pt); Activities coordinators 1 (ft); Dietitians 1 (pt); Dentists 1 (pt); Ophthalmologists 1 (pt); Podiatrists 1 (pt); Audiologists 1 (pt).

Fresno Care & Guidance Center*
1715 S Cedar Ave, Fresno, CA, 93702
(209) 237-8377
Admin Hilma Mitchell.
Licensure Skilled care. *Beds* 99. *Certified* Medi-Cal.
Owner Proprietary Corp (Beverly Enterprises).

Fresno Convalescent Hospital
3003 N Mariposa St, Fresno, CA, 93703
(209) 222-7416
Admin Jean Dresslar. *Medical Dir/Dir of Nursing* Graham Ruff MD; Frances De la Torre RN DON.
Licensure Skilled care. *Beds* SNF 116. *Certified* Medicare; Medi-Cal.
Owner Nonprofit organization/foundation; Nonprofit Corp.
Admissions Requirements Medical examination; Physician's request.
Staff RNs 5 (ft), 3 (pt); LPNs 5 (ft), 2 (pt); Nurses aides 40 (ft), 20 (pt); Physical therapists 1 (pt); Speech therapists 1 (pt); Activities coordinators 1 (ft); Dietitians 1 (pt); Ophthalmologists 1 (pt).
Languages Spanish
Facilities Dining room; Physical therapy room; Activities room; Crafts room; Laundry room; Barber/Beauty shop.
Activities Arts & crafts; Games; Prayer groups; Movies; Musical programs; Exercise programs; Excursions in facility van; Visits to parks; Visits to zoo; School.

Fresno Westview Convalescent Hospital*
2772 S Fig Ave, Fresno, CA, 93706
(209) 485-3750
Admin Juanita R Basye. *Medical Dir/Dir of Nursing* E H Holvey MD.
Licensure Skilled care; Intermediate care. *Beds* SNF 120; ICF 79. *Certified* Medi-Cal.
Owner Proprietary Corp.
Admissions Requirements Minimum age 5.
Staff Physicians 3 (pt); RNs 4 (ft), 5 (pt); LPNs 13 (ft), 5 (pt); Orderlies 17 (ft), 8 (pt); Nurses aides 54 (ft), 14 (pt); Physical therapists 1 (pt); Reality therapists 2 (ft); Recreational therapists 1 (ft); Occupational therapists 1 (ft); Speech therapists 1 (pt); Activities coordinators 4 (ft), 2 (pt); Dietitians 3 (pt); Dentists 1 (pt); Ophthalmologists 4 (pt); Podiatrists 1 (pt); Audiologists 1 (pt).
Facilities Dining room; Physical therapy room; Activities room; Crafts room; Laundry room; Barber/Beauty shop.
Activities Arts & crafts; Cards; Games; Reading groups; Prayer groups; Movies; Shopping trips; Social/Cultural gatherings; Camping; Fishing; County fair.

Hillcrest Convalescent Hospital*
3672 N 1st St, Fresno, CA, 93726
(209) 227-5383
Admin Daniel A Kotyk. *Medical Dir/Dir of Nursing* W A Rohlfing MD.
Licensure Skilled care. *Beds* 65. *Certified* Medicare; Medi-Cal.
Owner Proprietary Corp (Beverly Enterprises).
Facilities Dining room; Physical therapy room; Activities room; Crafts room; Laundry room; Barber/Beauty shop; Library.
Activities Arts & crafts; Cards; Games; Reading groups; Prayer groups; Movies; Shopping trips; Social/Cultural gatherings.

Hope Manor*
1665 M St, Fresno, CA, 93721
(209) 268-5361
Admin John F Einhart. *Medical Dir/Dir of Nursing* J Malcolm Masten MD.
Licensure Skilled care; Intermediate care. *Beds* SNF 85; ICF 70. *Certified* Medicare; Medi-Cal.
Owner Proprietary Corp.
Admissions Requirements Medical examination; Physician's request.
Staff Physicians 1 (pt); RNs 2 (ft), 1 (pt); LPNs 14 (ft), 2 (pt); Orderlies 10 (ft); Nurses aides 50 (ft); Physical therapists 1 (ft), 1 (pt); Speech therapists 1 (pt); Activities coordinators 2 (ft), 2 (pt); Dietitians 1 (pt); Dentists 1 (pt); Podiatrists 1 (pt).

Facilities Dining room; Physical therapy room; Activities room; Chapel; Crafts room; Laundry room; Barber/Beauty shop; Library; Dentist office.
Activities Arts & crafts; Cards; Games; Reading groups; Prayer groups; Movies; Social/Cultural gatherings; Video games.

Hy-Lond Convalescent Hospital*
3408 E Shields Ave, Fresno, CA, 93726
(209) 227-4063
Admin Laverle A Emmerson.
Licensure Skilled care. *Beds* 121. *Certified* Medicare; Medi-Cal.
Owner Proprietary Corp (Beverly Enterprises).

Hy-Pana House Convalescent Hospital*
3510 E Shields Ave, Fresno, CA, 93726
(209) 222-4807
Admin Patrick Uribe.
Licensure Skilled care. *Beds* 112. *Certified* Medicare; Medi-Cal.
Owner Proprietary Corp (Beverly Enterprises).

Manning Gardens Convalescent Hospital*
2113 E Manning Ave, Fresno, CA, 93725
(209) 834-2586
Admin Cary J Hanson.
Licensure Skilled care. *Beds* 59. *Certified* Medicare; Medi-Cal.
Owner Proprietary Corp.
Staff Physicians 5 (pt); RNs 1 (ft), 1 (pt); LPNs 5 (ft), 2 (pt); Nurses aides 25 (ft), 5 (pt); Physical therapists 1 (pt); Speech therapists 1 (pt); Activities coordinators 1 (ft), 1 (pt); Dietitians 1 (pt); Dentists 1 (pt); Podiatrists 1 (pt).

Nazareth House
2121 N 1st St, Fresno, CA, 93703
(209) 237-2257
Admin Sr J Fidelis. *Medical Dir/Dir of Nursing* Sr Margaret Brody.
Licensure Skilled care; Intermediate care. *Beds* SNF 27; ICF 12. *Certified* Medi-Cal.
Owner Nonprofit Corp.
Admissions Requirements Minimum age 65; Medical examination; Physician's request.
Staff RNs 5 (ft), 2 (pt); LPNs 2 (ft); Nurses aides 17 (ft); Activities coordinators 1 (ft); Dietitians 1 (ft), 1 (pt); Ophthalmologists 1 (pt); Dentist 1 (pt).
Languages Spanish, Italian
Affiliation Roman Catholic
Facilities Dining room; Physical therapy room; Activities room; Chapel; Crafts room; Laundry room; Barber/Beauty shop; Library; TV.
Activities Arts & crafts; Games; Reading groups; Prayer groups; Movies; Shopping trips; Social/Cultural gatherings.

Pacific Gardens Health Care Center
577 S Peach Ave, Fresno, CA, 93727
(209) 251-8463
Admin Lisa McQuone. *Medical Dir/Dir of Nursing* Robb Smith Jr MD; Valentine DiCerto DON.
Licensure Skilled care. *Beds* SNF 180. *Certified* Medicare; Medi-Cal.
Owner Proprietary Corp (American Medical Services Inc).
Admissions Requirements Medical examination.
Staff RNs 6 (ft), 3 (pt); LPNs 15 (ft), 7 (pt); Orderlies; Nurses aides 70 (ft), 20 (pt); Physical therapists contract 1 (ft); Occupational therapists contract 1 (ft); Speech therapists 1 (ft); Activities coordinators 3 (ft); Dietitians 1 (ft); Ophthalmologists (contract) 1 (ft);; Social worker 1 (ft).
Languages Spanish
Facilities Dining room; Physical therapy room; Activities room; Laundry room; Barber/Beauty shop; Covered patio.

Activities Arts & crafts; Cards; Games; Reading groups; Prayer groups; Movies; Shopping trips; Social/Cultural gatherings; Exercise; Cooking groups; Music therapy.

Raintree Convalescent Hospital
5265 E Huntington Ave, Fresno, CA, 93727
(209) 251-8244
Admin Patrick Unibe. *Medical Dir/Dir of Nursing* Joan E Rubinstein MD; Lynn Herbert RN DON.
Licensure Skilled care. *Beds* 49. *Certified* Medicaid.
Owner Proprietary Corp (Beverly Enterprises).
Admissions Requirements Physician's request.
Languages Spanish
Facilities Dining room; Activities room; Laundry room.
Activities Arts & crafts; Cards; Games; Reading groups; Prayer groups; Movies; Shopping trips.

Riley Nursing Home
2604 Clovis Ave, Fresno, CA, 93612-3902
(209) 237-0261
Admin Angela Shoberg.
Licensure Skilled care. *Beds* 25. *Certified* Medicare; Medi-Cal.
Owner Proprietary Corp.

San Joaquin Gardens Health Facility
5555-59 N Fresno St, Fresno, CA, 93710
(209) 439-4770
Admin Leonard P Kelly. *Medical Dir/Dir of Nursing* Edwin G Wiens MD.
Licensure Skilled care; Intermediate care. *Beds* SNF 56; ICF 32. *Certified* Medicare; Medi-Cal.
Owner Nonprofit Corp (American Baptist Homes W).
Staff RNs 4 (ft), 3 (pt); LPNs 3 (ft), 5 (pt); Nurses aides 15 (ft), 23 (pt); Reality therapists 1 (pt); Recreational therapists 2 (ft).
Facilities Dining room; Activities room; Chapel; Crafts room; Laundry room; Barber/Beauty shop; Library.
Activities Arts & crafts; Games; Reading groups; Movies; Shopping trips; Social/Cultural gatherings.

Sierra View Convalescent Hospital*
668 E Bullard Ave, Fresno, CA, 93710
(209) 439-4461
Admin Charles Roy Wagner.
Licensure Skilled care; Intermediate care. *Beds* SNF 26; ICF 59. *Certified* Medi-Cal.
Owner Nonprofit Corp.

Sunnyside Convalescent Hospital*
2939 S Peach Ave, Fresno, CA, 93725
(209) 233-6248
Admin Michael L Fellen.
Licensure Skilled care; Intermediate care. *Beds* SNF 100; ICF 16. *Certified* Medi-Cal.
Owner Proprietary Corp.

Terrace Care Convalescent Hospital*
2020 N Weber Ave, Fresno, CA, 93705
(209) 237-0883
Admin Charles E Eggleston. *Medical Dir/Dir of Nursing* Dr Walter Rohlfing.
Licensure Skilled care. *Beds* 233. *Certified* Medicare; Medi-Cal.
Owner Proprietary Corp.
Admissions Requirements Medical examination; Physician's request.
Staff RNs 10 (ft), 5 (pt); LPNs 13 (ft), 6 (pt); Nurses aides 62 (ft), 28 (pt); Physical therapists 1 (ft); Occupational therapists 1 (ft); Activities coordinators 3 (ft).
Facilities Dining room; Physical therapy room; Activities room; Chapel; Crafts room; Laundry room; Barber/Beauty shop.
Activities Arts & crafts; Cards; Games; Prayer groups; Movies; Social/Cultural gatherings.

Townhouse Convalescent Hospital
1233 A St, Fresno, CA, 93706
(209) 268-6317
Admin Martha LoPresti. *Medical Dir/Dir of Nursing* Dr Kennett; Ruby Routon RN DON.
Licensure Skilled care. *Beds* SNF 80. *Certified* Medicaid; Medicare; Medi-Cal.
Owner Proprietary Corp.
Staff RNs; LPNs; Orderlies 10 (ft); Nurses aides 55 (ft); Activities coordinators 1 (ft), 1 (pt); Dietitians 1 (ft).
Languages Spanish, Chinese
Facilities Dining room; Physical therapy room; Activities room; Crafts room; Barber/Beauty shop.
Activities Arts & crafts; Cards; Games; Reading groups; Prayer groups; Movies; Shopping trips; Social/Cultural gatherings.

Twilight Haven*
1717 S Winery Ave, Fresno, CA, 93727
(209) 251-8417
Admin Leonard P Kelly. *Medical Dir/Dir of Nursing* Mrs Dadian.
Licensure Skilled care. *Beds* 43. *Certified* Medicare; Medi-Cal.
Owner Nonprofit Corp.
Admissions Requirements Minimum age 62.
Staff Physicians; RNs; LPNs; Orderlies; Nurses aides; Activities coordinators; Dietitians.
Facilities Dining room; Activities room; Chapel; Laundry room; Barber/Beauty shop.
Activities Arts & crafts; Games; Prayer groups; Movies; Shopping trips; Social/Cultural gatherings.

Valley Care & Guidance Center
9919 S Elm Ave, Fresno, CA, 93706
(209) 834-5351
Admin Carolyn Hankinson. *Medical Dir/Dir of Nursing* Dr Parayno; Dorothy Nishi DON.
Licensure Skilled care. *Beds* SNF 79. *Certified* Medi-Cal.
Owner Proprietary Corp (Beverly Enterprises).
Admissions Requirements Minimum age 18.
Staff RNs 2 (ft); LPNs 5 (ft); Orderlies 6 (ft); Nurses aides 63 (ft); Activities coordinators 1 (ft).
Languages Spanish, Japanese, Hindi
Facilities Dining room; Activities room; Chapel; Crafts room; Laundry room; Barber/Beauty shop; Library.
Activities Arts & crafts; Cards; Games; Reading groups; Prayer groups; Movies; Shopping trips; Social/Cultural gatherings.

Valley Convalescent Hospital
4840 E Tulare Ave, Fresno, CA, 93727
(209) 251-7161
Admin Robert S Stauff. *Medical Dir/Dir of Nursing* Graham Ruff MD; Angela Shoberg RN DON.
Licensure Skilled care. *Beds* SNF 99. *Certified* Medicare; Medi-Cal.
Owner Proprietary Corp (Summit Health Ltd).
Admissions Requirements Minimum age 18; Medical examination; Physician's request.
Staff Physicians 28 (ft); RNs 3 (ft), 2 (pt); LPNs 7 (ft), 6 (pt); Nurses aides 35 (ft), 14 (pt); Physical therapists 1 (ft), 1 (pt); Occupational therapists 1 (ft); Speech therapists 1 (ft); Activities coordinators 1 (ft), 2 (pt); Dietitians 1 (ft), 1 (pt); Ophthalmologists 1 (ft), 1 (pt).
Facilities Dining room; Physical therapy room; Activities room; Crafts room; Laundry room; Barber/Beauty shop; Library.
Activities Arts & crafts; Cards; Games; Reading groups; Prayer groups; Movies; Shopping trips; Social/Cultural gatherings; Cultural outings.

FULLERTON

Fairway Convalescent Center
2800 N Harbor Blvd, Fullerton, CA, 92635
(714) 871-9202 or (213) 691-2015
Admin Rhonda G Allen. *Medical Dir/Dir of Nursing* Bruce Mutter MD; Frances Kreuger DON.
Licensure Skilled care. *Beds* 59. *Certified* Medicare; Medi-Cal.
Owner Proprietary Corp.
Staff RNs 1 (ft), 2 (pt); LPNs 5 (ft), 6 (pt); Orderlies 2 (ft); Nurses 26 (ft), 6 (pt); Physical therapists 1 (pt); Recreational therapists 1 (pt); Occupational therapists 1 (pt); Speech therapists 1 (pt); Activities coordinators 1 (ft), 1 (pt); Dietitians 1 (pt); Dentists 1 (pt); Ophthalmologists 1 (pt); Podiatrists 1 (pt); 1 (pt).
Facilities Dining room; Physical therapy room; Activities room; Crafts room; Laundry room; Barber/Beauty shop; Speech therapy room; Whirlpool room.
Activities Arts & crafts; Cards; Games; Reading groups; Prayer groups; Movies; Shopping trips; Social/Cultural gatherings; Cooking classes; Music.

Fullerton Care Convalescent Hospital*
2222 N Harbor, Fullerton, CA, 92635
(714) 992-5701
Admin John R Torrez. *Medical Dir/Dir of Nursing* Bruce Mutter.
Licensure Skilled care. *Beds* 300. *Certified* Medicare; Medi-Cal.
Owner Proprietary Corp (Care Enterprises).
Admissions Requirements Physician's request.
Facilities Dining room; Physical therapy room; Activities room; Chapel; Crafts room; Laundry room; Barber/Beauty shop.
Activities Arts & crafts; Cards; Games; Reading groups; Prayer groups; Movies; Shopping trips; Social/Cultural gatherings.

Gordon Lane Convalescent Hospital
1821 E Chapman Ave, Fullerton, CA, 92631
(714) 879-7301
Admin Vada Dane. *Medical Dir/Dir of Nursing* Frank Amato MD.
Licensure Skilled care. *Beds* 99.
Owner Proprietary Corp.
Admissions Requirements Medical examination; Physician's request.
Facilities Dining room; Physical therapy room; Activities room; Crafts room; Laundry room; Barber/Beauty shop; Library.
Activities Arts & crafts; Cards; Games; Reading groups; Prayer groups; Movies; Shopping trips; Social/Cultural gatherings; Parties; Special entertainment.

Seaside Care Center
2800 N Harbor Blvd, Fullerton, CA, 92635-1727
(213) 591-8701
Admin Thomas Higgins.
Licensure Skilled care; Intermediate care for mentally retarded. *Beds* 99. *Certified* Medicare.
Owner Proprietary Corp.

Sunhaven Convalescent & Rehabilitation Hospital*
201 E Bastanchury Rd, Fullerton, CA, 92635
(714) 870-0060
Admin Sally Kuster. *Medical Dir/Dir of Nursing* J Soffice MD.
Licensure Skilled care. *Beds* 59. *Certified* Medicare; Medi-Cal.
Owner Proprietary Corp.
Admissions Requirements Medical examination; Physician's request.
Staff RNs 2 (ft); LPNs 6 (ft), 3 (pt); Orderlies 20 (ft); Nurses aides 10 (ft); Activities coordinators 1 (ft).

Facilities Dining room; Activities room; Crafts room; Barber/Beauty shop.
Activities Arts & crafts; Cards; Games; Reading groups; Prayer groups; Social/Cultural gatherings.

Sunny Hills Convalescent Hospital*
330 W Bastanchury Rd, Fullerton, CA, 92635
(714) 879-4511
Admin Kathleen Lester.
Licensure Skilled care. *Beds* 99. *Certified* Medicare; Medi-Cal.
Owner Proprietary Corp.

Wilshire Care Center
245 E Wilshire Ave, Fullerton, CA, 92632
(714) 871-6020
Admin Carol A M Hinshaw. *Medical Dir/Dir of Nursing* Dr John Cowles; Myrna Gutomen DON.
Licensure Skilled care. *Beds* SNF 99. *Certified* Medicare; Medi-Cal.
Owner Proprietary Corp.
Admissions Requirements Medical examination; Physician's request.
Staff Physicians 1 (pt); RNs 3 (ft), 2 (pt); LPNs 5 (ft), 3 (pt); Orderlies 3 (ft), 1 (pt); Nurses aides 24 (ft), 5 (pt); Activities coordinators 1 (ft), 1 (pt).
Languages Spanish
Facilities Dining room; Physical therapy room; Activities room; Crafts room; Laundry room; Barber/Beauty shop; Patio.
Activities Arts & crafts; Cards; Games; Reading groups; Prayer groups; Movies; Shopping trips; Social/Cultural gatherings; Monthly buffets; Field trips; Reality group/individual sessions.

GALT

Royal Oaks Convalescent Hospital
144 F St, Galt, CA, 95632
(209) 745-1537
Admin Margherita Fagan. *Medical Dir/Dir of Nursing* James McFarland MD; Janet Farrell RN DON.
Licensure Skilled care. *Beds* SNF 99. *Certified* Medicaid; Medicare; Medi-Cal.
Owner Proprietary Corp (Beverly Enterprises).
Admissions Requirements Minimum age 21; Medical examination; Physician's request.
Staff RNs 4 (ft), 1 (pt); LPNs 9 (ft), 1 (pt); Orderlies 2 (ft); Nurses aides 42 (ft), 2 (pt); Activities coordinators 1 (ft), 1 (pt); Dietitians 1 (ft); Ophthalmologists 1 (pt); Social service 1 (pt).
Languages Italian, Spanish, German, Chinese, Tagalog, Portuguese
Facilities Dining room; Physical therapy room; Activities room; Crafts room; Barber/Beauty shop.
Activities Arts & crafts; Cards; Games; Reading groups; Prayer groups; Movies; Shopping trips; Social/Cultural gatherings.

GARDEN GROVE

Chapman Harbor Skilled Nursing Center
12232 Chapman Ave, Garden Grove, CA, 92640
(714) 971-5517
Admin Keith T Goodell. *Medical Dir/Dir of Nursing* Dr Marcolesco.
Licensure Skilled care. *Beds* SNF 78. *Certified* Medicare; Medi-Cal.
Owner Proprietary Corp.
Admissions Requirements Minimum age 40; Medical examination; Physician's request.
Staff Physicians; RNs; Orderlies; Nurses aides; Recreational therapists; Occupational therapists; Speech therapists; Activities coordinators; Dietitians; Dentists; Ophthalmologists; Podiatrists; LVNs.
Facilities Dining room; Physical therapy room; Activities room; Chapel; Crafts room; Laundry room; Barber/Beauty shop; Library.

Activities Arts & crafts; Cards; Games; Reading groups; Prayer groups; Movies; Shopping trips; Social/Cultural gatherings.

Garden Grove Convalescent Hospital*
12882 Shackleford Ln, Garden Grove, CA, 92641
(714) 638-9470
Admin Emanuel Newman.
Licensure Skilled care. *Beds* 99. *Certified* Medicare; Medi-Cal.
Owner Proprietary Corp.

Haster Convalescent Hospital*
12681 Haster St, Garden Grove, CA, 92640
(714) 971-2153
Admin Esther Abney. *Medical Dir/Dir of Nursing* John Cowles MD.
Licensure Skilled care. *Beds* 132. *Certified* Medicare; Medi-Cal.
Owner Proprietary Corp (Care Enterprises).
Admissions Requirements Physician's request.
Staff RNs 4 (ft); LPNs 8 (ft); Activities coordinators 2 (ft).
Facilities Dining room; Physical therapy room; Activities room; Chapel; Crafts room; Laundry room; Barber/Beauty shop; Library.
Activities Arts & crafts; Cards; Games; Reading groups; Prayer groups; Movies; Shopping trips; Social/Cultural gatherings.

Hy-Lond Home*
9861 W 11 St, Garden Grove, CA, 92644
(714) 531-8741
Admin Lila Russavage.
Licensure Skilled care; Intermediate care for mentally retarded. *Beds* 159. *Certified* Medi-Cal.
Owner Proprietary Corp (Beverly Enterprises).

Meadow View Park
13392 Taft Ave, Garden Grove, CA, 92643
(714) 638-5450
Admin Kenneth Goldblatt. *Medical Dir/Dir of Nursing* Dr S Osburn.
Licensure Developmental disabled. *Beds* Developmental disabled 59. *Certified* Medicare; Medi-Cal.
Owner Proprietary Corp.
Staff Physicians 3 (pt); RNs 1 (ft), 1 (pt); LPNs 5 (ft), 4 (pt); Physical therapists 1 (pt); Occupational therapists 1 (pt); Speech therapists 1 (pt); Activities coordinators 1 (ft); Dietitians 1 (pt); Dentists 1 (pt); Ophthalmologists 1 (pt); Podiatrists 1 (pt).
Languages Spanish
Facilities Dining room; Physical therapy room; Activities room; Crafts room; Laundry room.
Activities Arts & crafts; Games; Reading groups; Movies; Shopping trips; Social/Cultural gatherings.

Orangegrove Rehabilitation Hospital*
12332 Garden Grove, Garden Grove, CA, 92643
(714) 534-1041
Admin James D Baker III. *Medical Dir/Dir of Nursing* Gordon Glasgow MD.
Licensure Skilled care. *Beds* 99. *Certified* Medicare; Medi-Cal.
Owner Proprietary Corp.
Admissions Requirements Minimum age 12; Medical examination; Physician's request.
Staff Physicians 6 (ft); RNs 8 (ft), 2 (pt); LPNs 10 (ft), 2 (pt); Orderlies 5 (ft); Nurses aides 35 (ft), 2 (pt); Physical therapists 6 (ft); Reality therapists 1 (pt); Recreational therapists 1 (pt); Occupational therapists 3 (ft); Speech therapists 1 (ft), 1 (pt); Activities coordinators 1 (ft), 1 (pt); Dietitians 1 (ft); Dentists 1 (pt); Ophthalmologists 1 (pt); Podiatrists 1 (pt); Audiologists 1 (pt).
Facilities Dining room; Physical therapy room; Activities room; Chapel; Crafts room; Laundry room; Barber/Beauty shop; Library.

Activities Arts & crafts; Cards; Games; Reading groups; Prayer groups; Movies; Shopping trips; Social/Cultural gatherings.

Pacific Haven Convalescent Home
12072 Trask Ave, Garden Grove, CA, 92643
(714) 534-1942
Admin Norman W Gunsolley. *Medical Dir/Dir of Nursing* J D Cowles MD; Juanita Bailey RN.
Licensure Skilled care. *Beds* 99. *Certified* Medicare; Medi-Cal.
Owner Nonprofit Corp.
Admissions Requirements Medical examination; Physician's request.
Staff Physicians 28 (ft); RNs 3 (ft); LPNs 10 (ft); Nurses aides 33 (ft); Activities coordinators 1 (ft); Dietitians 1 (ft).
Languages Spanish
Affiliation Reorganized Church of Jesus Christ of Latter-Day Saints
Facilities Dining room; Physical therapy room; Activities room; Chapel; Crafts room; Laundry room; Barber/Beauty shop; Library.
Activities Arts & crafts; Cards; Games; Reading groups; Prayer groups; Movies; Shopping trips; Social/Cultural gatherings; Cooking classes; Resident/family councils.

Palm Grove Care Center
13075 Blackbird St, Garden Grove, CA, 92643
(714) 530-6322
Admin Frances Hoogstad. *Medical Dir/Dir of Nursing* John Cowles MD; Marilyn Cothron DON.
Licensure Skilled care. *Beds* SNF 126. *Certified* Medicare; Medi-Cal.
Owner Proprietary Corp (Summit Health Ltd).
Admissions Requirements Minimum age Adult; Physician's request.
Staff Physicians 1 (pt); RNs 5 (ft), 2 (pt); LPNs 12 (ft), 2 (pt); Nurses aides 44 (ft); Physical therapists 2 (pt); Occupational therapists 1 (pt); Speech therapists 1 (pt); Activities coordinators 2 (ft); Dietitians 1 (pt); Dentists 1 (pt); Ophthalmologists 1 (pt); Podiatrists 1 (pt); Social service coordinator 1 (pt).
Languages Spanish
Facilities Dining room; Physical therapy room; Activities room; Crafts room; Laundry room; Barber/Beauty shop; Family/patient lounge; Outdoor patios (4).
Activities Arts & crafts; Cards; Games; Reading groups; Prayer groups; Movies; Shopping trips; Social/Cultural gatherings.

GARDENA

Alondra Nursing Home*
1140 W Rosecrans Ave, Gardena, CA, 90247
(213) 323-3194
Admin George Curtis.
Licensure Skilled care. *Beds* 99. *Certified* Medicare; Medi-Cal.
Owner Proprietary Corp (Care Enterprises).

Ayer-Lar Sanitarium
16530 S Broadway, Gardena, CA, 90248
(213) 329-7581
Admin Lee M Ayers. *Medical Dir/Dir of Nursing* George Lee MD; Sugimoto.
Licensure Skilled care. *Beds* SNF 50. *Certified* Medicaid; Medi-Cal.
Owner Proprietary Corp.
Admissions Requirements Minimum age 25.
Staff RNs 1 (ft), 2 (pt); LPNs 6 (ft), 2 (pt); Nurses aides 35 (ft).
Facilities Activities room.
Activities Arts & crafts; Cards; Games; Prayer groups; Movies.

Clear View Convalescent Center
15823 S Western Ave, Gardena, CA, 90247
(213) 770-3131

Admin Ronald W O Wong. *Medical Dir/Dir of Nursing* Magdy Salib MD; Candice Rowedder RN DON.
Beds 99. *Certified* Medi-Cal.
Owner Proprietary Corp.
Admissions Requirements Minimum age 18; Physician's request.
Staff Physicians 2 (pt); RNs 3 (ft); LPNs 10 (ft); Orderlies 2 (ft); Nurses aides 60 (ft); Physical therapists 1 (pt); Reality therapists 1 (pt); Recreational therapists 1 (pt); Occupational therapists 1 (pt); Speech therapists 1 (pt); Activities coordinators 2 (ft); Dietitians 1 (pt); Dentists 1 (pt); Ophthalmologists 1 (pt); Podiatrists 1 (pt); Dentist 1 (pt).
Facilities Dining room; Physical therapy room; Activities room; Crafts room; Laundry room; Barber/Beauty shop; Secured facility for the confused/disoriented patient; Ambulatory.
Activities Arts & crafts; Cards; Games; Reading groups; Prayer groups; Movies; Shopping trips; Social/Cultural gatherings; BBQs; Picnics; Candlelight dinners; Wine socials; AA meetings; VFW meetings; Veterans assistance.

Clear View Sanitarium
15823 S Western Ave, Gardena, CA, 90247
(213) 538-2323
Admin Ronald W O Wong. *Medical Dir/Dir of Nursing* Magdy Salib MD; Margaret Reid RN DON.
Beds 73. *Certified* Medi-Cal.
Owner Proprietary Corp.
Admissions Requirements Minimum age 18; Physician's request.
Staff Physicians 1 (pt); RNs 2 (ft); LPNs 7 (ft); Orderlies 2 (ft); Nurses aides 45 (ft); Physical therapists 1 (pt); Reality therapists 1 (pt); Recreational therapists 1 (pt); Occupational therapists 1 (pt); Speech therapists 1 (pt); Activities coordinators 1 (ft); Dietitians 1 (pt); Dentists 1 (pt); Ophthalmologists 1 (pt); Podiatrists 1 (pt); Dentist 1 (pt).
Facilities Dining room; Physical therapy room; Activities room; Crafts room; Laundry room; Barber/Beauty shop; Spacious grounds.
Activities Arts & crafts; Cards; Games; Prayer groups; Movies; Shopping trips; Social/Cultural gatherings.

Gardena Convalescent Center*
14819 S Vermont, Gardena, CA, 90247
(213) 321-6571
Admin Dorothy Bryson.
Licensure Skilled care. *Beds* 74. *Certified* Medicare; Medi-Cal.
Owner Proprietary Corp.

Las Flores Convalescent Hospital*
14165 Purche Ave, Gardena, CA, 90249
(213) 323-4570
Admin Diana Fortune. *Medical Dir/Dir of Nursing* Burton H Goldman MD.
Licensure Skilled care. *Beds* 99. *Certified* Medicare; Medi-Cal.
Owner Proprietary Corp.
Admissions Requirements Minimum age 21; Medical examination; Physician's request.
Staff RNs 1 (ft), 1 (pt); LPNs 9 (ft), 2 (pt); Nurses aides 47 (ft), 1 (pt); Physical therapists 1 (pt); Recreational therapists 1 (ft); Occupational therapists 1 (pt); Speech therapists 1 (pt); Dietitians 1 (ft), 1 (pt); Dentists 1 (pt); Ophthalmologists 1 (pt); Podiatrists 1 (pt); Audiologists 1 (pt).
Facilities Dining room; Physical therapy room; Activities room; Crafts room; Laundry room; Barber/Beauty shop.
Activities Arts & crafts; Cards; Games; Reading groups; Prayer groups; Movies; Shopping trips; Social/Cultural gatherings.

South Bay Keiro Nursing Home*
15115 S Vermont, Gardena, CA, 90247
(213) 532-0700
Admin Edwin Hiroto.
Licensure Skilled care. *Beds* 98. *Certified* Medicare.
Owner Nonprofit Corp.

GILROY

Driftwood Convalescent Hospital*
8170 Murray Ave, Gilroy, CA, 95020
(408) 842-9311
Admin Gerald E Hunter.
Licensure Skilled care. *Beds* 132. *Certified* Medicare; Medi-Cal.
Owner Proprietary Corp.

GLENDALE

Autumn Hills*
430 N Glendale Ave, Glendale, CA, 91206
(213) 246-5677
Admin Kenneth B Thompson. *Medical Dir/Dir of Nursing* Dr Donald Doty.
Licensure Skilled care. *Beds* 99. *Certified* Medicare; Medi-Cal.
Owner Proprietary Corp (ARA Living Centers).
Admissions Requirements Physician's request.
Staff Physicians 20 (pt); RNs 2 (ft), 1 (pt); Nurses aides 30 (ft); Physical therapists 1 (pt); Reality therapists 1 (pt); Recreational therapists 1 (pt); Occupational therapists 1 (pt); Speech therapists 1 (pt); Activities coordinators 1 (ft); Dietitians 1 (pt); Dentists 1 (pt); Ophthalmologists 1 (pt); Podiatrists 1 (pt); Audiologists 1 (pt).
Facilities Dining room; Physical therapy room; Activities room; Crafts room; Laundry room; Barber/Beauty shop.
Activities Arts & crafts; Cards; Games; Reading groups; Prayer groups; Movies; Shopping trips; Social/Cultural gatherings; Variety.

Beverly Manor Convalescent Hospital*
630 W Broadway, Glendale, CA, 91204
(818) 247-3345
Admin William Mathies. *Medical Dir/Dir of Nursing* Albert P Killian MD.
Licensure Skilled care; Intermediate care. *Beds* 140. *Certified* Medicare; Medi-Cal.
Owner Proprietary Corp (Beverly Enterprises).
Facilities Dining room; Physical therapy room; Activities room; Laundry room; Barber/Beauty shop; Library.
Activities Arts & crafts; Cards; Games; Reading groups; Prayer groups; Movies; Shopping trips; Social/Cultural gatherings; Wheelchair walks; Adopt-a-grandparent; Adopt-a-friend.

Broadway Manor Convalescent Hospital
605 W Broadway, Glendale, CA, 91204
(818) 246-7174
Admin Ralph M Guarino. *Medical Dir/Dir of Nursing* Albert P Killian MD; Marie Savage DON.
Licensure Skilled care. *Beds* SNF 78. *Certified* Medicare; Medi-Cal.
Owner Proprietary Corp.
Staff Physicians 16 (pt); RNs 2 (ft), 2 (pt); LPNs 6 (ft), 6 (pt); Orderlies 8 (ft), 2 (pt); Nurses aides 14 (ft), 6 (pt); Physical therapists 2 (ft), 3 (pt); Occupational therapists 1 (pt); Speech therapists 1 (pt); Activities coordinators 1 (ft); Dietitians 1 (ft); Dentists 1 (pt); Ophthalmologists 1 (pt); Podiatrists 1 (pt); Dentist 1 (pt).
Languages Spanish, Tagalog
Facilities Dining room; Physical therapy room; Activities room; Laundry room; Barber/Beauty shop.
Activities Arts & crafts; Cards; Games; Reading groups; Prayer groups; Movies; Shopping trips; Social/Cultural gatherings.

Cal Haven Convalescent Hospital*
445 W Broadway, Glendale, CA, 91204
(818) 241-2157
Admin Edward V Hamilton. *Medical Dir/Dir of Nursing* Dr A P Killian.
Licensure Skilled care. *Beds* 35. *Certified* Medicare; Medi-Cal.
Owner Proprietary Corp.
Admissions Requirements Minimum age 40; Medical examination.
Staff Physicians 1 (pt); RNs 2 (ft), 2 (pt); LPNs 3 (ft), 4 (pt); Orderlies 2 (ft), 1 (pt); Nurses aides 9 (ft), 7 (pt); Physical therapists 1 (pt); Reality therapists 1 (pt); Recreational therapists 1 (pt); Occupational therapists 1 (pt); Speech therapists 1 (pt); Activities coordinators 1 (ft), 1 (pt); Dietitians 1 (pt); Dentists 1 (pt); Ophthalmologists 1 (pt); Podiatrists 1 (pt); Audiologists 1 (pt).
Facilities Dining room; Physical therapy room; Activities room; Crafts room; Laundry room; Barber/Beauty shop; Library; Patios.
Activities Arts & crafts; Cards; Games; Reading groups; Prayer groups; Movies; Shopping trips; Social/Cultural gatherings; Walks in area.

Casa Verdugo Convalescent Lodge
1208 S Central Ave, Glendale, CA, 91204
(818) 246-5516
Admin John E Wareham. *Medical Dir/Dir of Nursing* Ethel Hamilton MD; Ruth Hull RN DON.
Licensure Skilled care. *Beds* SNF 48. *Certified* Medicare.
Owner Nonprofit Corp (So CA Presbyterian Hm).
Admissions Requirements Medical examination; Physician's request.
Staff RNs 2 (ft), 1 (pt); LPNs 5 (ft); Orderlies 5 (ft); Nurses aides 15 (ft), 10 (pt); Activities coordinators 1 (ft).
Affiliation Presbyterian
Facilities Dining room; Activities room; Laundry room; Barber/Beauty shop.
Activities Arts & crafts; Games; Reading groups; Prayer groups; Movies; Shopping trips Educational classes/Glendale College.

Chandler Convalescent Hospital*
525 S Central Ave, Glendale, CA, 91204
(213) 240-1610
Admin Henry Levine.
Licensure Skilled care. *Beds* 106. *Certified* Medicare; Medi-Cal.
Owner Proprietary Corp.

Dreiers Sanitarium*
1400 W Glenoaks Blvd, Glendale, CA, 91201
(213) 242-1183
Admin Dolores D Haedrich. *Medical Dir/Dir of Nursing* George Papkin MD.
Licensure Skilled care. *Beds* 59. *Certified* Medicare; Medi-Cal.
Owner Proprietary Corp.
Staff Physicians 1 (pt); RNs 1 (ft), 3 (pt); LPNs 2 (ft), 4 (pt); Orderlies 1 (ft), 1 (pt); Nurses aides 18 (ft), 3 (pt); Activities coordinators 1 (ft).
Facilities Dining room; Activities room; Crafts room; Laundry room; Barber/Beauty shop.
Activities Arts & crafts; Cards; Games; Reading groups; Prayer groups; Movies; Social/Cultural gatherings.

Elms Convalescent Hospital
212 W Chevy Chase Dr, Glendale, CA, 91204-2399
(213) 240-6720
Admin William L Knell. *Medical Dir/Dir of Nursing* Carmen Garcia RN DON.
Licensure Skilled care. *Beds* SNF 52.
Owner Proprietary Corp.
Admissions Requirements Physician's request.

Staff RNs 1 (ft), 1 (pt); LPNs 4 (ft), 5 (pt); Nurses aides 14 (ft), 11 (pt); Physical therapists 1 (pt); Occupational therapists 1 (pt); Speech therapists 1 (pt); Activities coordinators 1 (ft), 2 (pt).
Languages Spanish, Tagalog
Facilities Dining room; Activities room; Laundry room; Barber/Beauty shop; Library.
Activities Arts & crafts; Games; Reading groups; Prayer groups; Movies; Picnic outings.

Glenoaks Convalescent Hospital*
409 W Glenoaks Blvd, Glendale, CA, 91202
(818) 240-4300
Admin Pamela Hamilton. *Medical Dir/Dir of Nursing* O W Janes MD.
Licensure Skilled care. *Beds* 94. *Certified* Medicare; Medi-Cal.
Owner Proprietary Corp.
Admissions Requirements Medical examination; Physician's request.
Staff RNs 3 (ft), 2 (pt); LPNs 7 (ft), 3 (pt); Nurses aides 40 (ft), 2 (pt); Reality therapists 1 (ft); Recreational therapists 1 (pt); Activities coordinators 1 (ft); Dietitians 1 (ft).
Facilities Dining room; Physical therapy room; Activities room; Crafts room; Laundry room; Barber/Beauty shop; Library.
Activities Arts & crafts; Cards; Games; Reading groups; Prayer groups; Movies; Shopping trips; Social/Cultural gatherings.

Glenridge Center*
611 S Central, Glendale, CA, 91203
(213) 246-6591
Admin Rodney Meacham. *Medical Dir/Dir of Nursing* R Cabnenn MD.
Licensure Skilled care. *Beds* ICF 116. *Certified* Medicare.
Owner Proprietary Corp (Beverly Enterprises).
Admissions Requirements Minimum age 3.
Staff Physicians 2 (pt); RNs 10 (ft), 5 (pt); LPNs 10 (ft), 5 (pt); Orderlies 25 (ft); Nurses aides 35 (ft); Physical therapists 1 (ft); Recreational therapists 1 (ft); Occupational therapists 1 (pt); Speech therapists 1 (pt); Activities coordinators 1 (ft); Dietitians 1 (ft); Dentists 1 (pt); Ophthalmologists 1 (pt); Podiatrists 1 (pt); Audiologists 1 (pt).
Facilities Dining room; Physical therapy room; Activities room; Crafts room; Laundry room; Barber/Beauty shop.
Activities Arts & crafts; Games; Movies; Shopping trips; Social/Cultural gatherings.

Long-Term Care Inc*
1505 Colby Dr, Glendale, CA, 91205
(213) 247-4476
Admin Carroll Gillespie.
Licensure Skilled care. *Beds* 94. *Certified* Medicare; Medi-Cal.
Owner Proprietary Corp.
Staff RNs 1 (ft), 4 (pt); LPNs 13 (ft), 4 (pt); Orderlies 6 (ft), 1 (pt); Nurses aides 38 (ft), 6 (pt); Physical therapists 1 (pt); Recreational therapists 2 (pt); Occupational therapists 1 (pt); Speech therapists 1 (pt); Dietitians 1 (pt).
Facilities Dining room; Activities room; Crafts room; Barber/Beauty shop.
Activities Arts & crafts; Cards; Games; Prayer groups; Movies.

Royale Oaks Convalescent Hospital
0 Verdugo Rd, Glendale, CA, 91206
(818) 244-1133
Admin Kamra Dideban.
Licensure Skilled care. *Beds* SNF 136. *Certified* Medicare; Medi-Cal.
Owner Proprietary Corp (Beverly Enterprises).
Admissions Requirements Physician's request.
Facilities Dining room; Physical therapy room; Activities room; Laundry room; Barber/Beauty shop; Library.

Activities Arts & crafts; Cards; Games; Reading groups; Prayer groups; Movies; Shopping trips; Social/Cultural gatherings.

Tropico Convalescent Hospital*
130 W Los Feliz Rd, Glendale, CA, 91204
(213) 245-3978
Admin Roberta Gayor.
Licensure Skilled care. *Beds* 56. *Certified* Medicare; Medi-Cal.
Owner Proprietary Corp (ARA Living Centers).

Windsor Manor*
1230 E Windsor Rd, Glendale, CA, 91205
(213) 245-1623
Admin John K Hughes.
Licensure Skilled care. *Beds* 28. *Certified* Medi-Cal.
Owner Nonprofit Corp.

GLENDORA

Adventist Convalescent Hospital
435 E Gladstone, Glendora, CA, 91740
(818) 963-5955
Admin Peter Peabody. *Medical Dir/Dir of Nursing* Timothy Fergeson MD; Annette Munson RN DON.
Licensure Skilled care. *Beds* SNF 118. *Certified* Medicare; Medi-Cal.
Owner Nonprofit Corp (Adventist Health Sys-USA).
Admissions Requirements Minimum age 18; Medical examination; Physician's request.
Staff RNs 6 (ft), 2 (pt); LPNs 9 (ft), 1 (pt); Nurses aides 40 (ft), 4 (pt); Activities coordinators 1 (ft).
Languages Spanish
Affiliation Seventh-Day Adventist
Facilities Dining room; Physical therapy room; Activities room; Chapel; Laundry room; Barber/Beauty shop.
Activities Arts & crafts; Games; Reading groups; Prayer groups; Movies; Social/Cultural gatherings.

Community Convalescent Hospital of Glendora
638 E Colorado Ave, Glendora, CA, 91740
(818) 963-6091
Admin G Slapper. *Medical Dir/Dir of Nursing* Onn T Chan MD; R Wittenbraker RN DON.
Licensure Skilled care. *Beds* SNF 96. *Certified* Medicare; Medi-Cal.
Owner Privately owned.
Admissions Requirements Physician's request.
Staff Physicians 1 (pt); RNs 1 (ft), 2 (pt); LPNs 7 (ft), 6 (pt); Orderlies 4 (ft), 1 (pt); Nurses aides 26 (ft), 5 (pt); Physical therapists 1 (pt); Speech therapists 1 (pt); Activities coordinators 1 (ft); Dietitians 1 (ft); Dentists 1 (pt); Ophthalmologists 1 (pt); Podiatrists 1 (pt).
Languages Spanish, Russian, German, Hungarian, Chinese
Facilities Dining room; Physical therapy room; Activities room; Barber/Beauty shop.
Activities Arts & crafts; Cards; Games; Reading groups; Prayer groups; Movies; Shopping trips.

Oakview Convalescent Hospital
805 W Arrow Hwy, Glendora, CA, 91740
(818) 331-0781
Admin Barbara Dube. *Medical Dir/Dir of Nursing* George Magallon MD; Cynthia Perez RN DON.
Licensure Skilled care. *Beds* SNF 292. *Certified* Medicare; Medi-Cal.
Owner Proprietary Corp.
Staff RNs 9 (ft); LPNs 35 (ft); Orderlies 10 (ft); Nurses aides 120 (ft); Physical therapists 2 (ft); Occupational therapists 1 (pt); Speech therapists 1 (pt); Activities coordinators 5 (ft); Dietitians 1 (ft); Dentists 1 (pt).

Facilities Dining room; Physical therapy room; Activities room; Crafts room; Laundry room; Barber/Beauty shop.
Activities Arts & crafts; Games; Reading groups; Movies; Shopping trips; Social/Cultural gatherings.

San Dimas Golden Age Convalescent Home*
1033 E Arrow Hwy, Glendora, CA, 91740
(213) 963-7531
Admin Herbert G Thompson.
Licensure Skilled care. *Beds* 98. *Certified* Medicare; Medi-Cal.
Owner Proprietary Corp (National Heritage).

GRANADA HILLS

Casitas Care Center
10626 Balboa Blvd, Granada Hills, CA, 91344
(818) 368-2802
Admin Evelyn N Dold. *Medical Dir/Dir of Nursing* A Beckerman.
Licensure Skilled care. *Beds* SNF 99. *Certified* Medicare; Medi-Cal.
Owner Proprietary Corp.
Admissions Requirements Minimum age 35.
Staff RNs 3 (ft), 2 (pt); LPNs 8 (ft), 2 (pt); Orderlies 8 (ft), 2 (pt); Nurses aides 30 (ft), 4 (pt); Reality therapists 1 (pt); Recreational therapists 1 (ft), 1 (pt); Activities coordinators 1 (ft).
Languages Spanish, Russian, Polish, Hebrew, Yiddish, Tagalog, Korean
Facilities Dining room; Physical therapy room; Activities room; Chapel; Crafts room; Laundry room; Barber/Beauty shop; Library.
Activities Arts & crafts; Cards; Games; Reading groups; Prayer groups; Movies; Shopping trips; Social/Cultural gatherings.

Granada Hills Convalescent Hospital*
16123 Chatsworth, Granada Hills, CA, 91344
(213) 365-5645
Admin Abraham Birnbaum.
Licensure Skilled care. *Beds* 48. *Certified* Medicare; Medi-Cal.
Owner Proprietary Corp (Coastal Care Centers Inc).

Magnolia Gardens Convalescent Hospital
17922 San Fernando Mission Blvd, Granada Hills, CA, 91344
(818) 360-1864
Admin Betty Schaper. *Medical Dir/Dir of Nursing* Baker; Alma Jastia RN.
Licensure Skilled care. *Beds* SNF 99. *Certified* Medicare; Medi-Cal.
Owner Proprietary Corp.
Admissions Requirements Minimum age 18; Medical examination; Physician's request.
Staff RNs 1 (ft), 2 (pt); LPNs 10 (ft), 2 (pt); Nurses aides 28 (ft), 10 (pt); Activities coordinators 3 (pt); Social Service 1 (pt).
Languages Spanish, Korean, Tagalog
Facilities Dining room; Physical therapy room; Activities room; Chapel; Crafts room; Laundry room; Barber/Beauty shop; Library; TV room; Smoking room; Reading room.
Activities Arts & crafts; Cards; Games; Reading groups; Prayer groups; Movies; Shopping trips; Social/Cultural gatherings; Music; Cookouts; Country breakfast; Candlelight dinner.

Rinaldi Convalescent Hospital*
16553 Rinaldi St, Granada Hills, CA, 91344
(213) 360-1003
Admin David L Hibarger.
Licensure Skilled care. *Beds* 99. *Certified* Medicare; Medi-Cal.
Owner Proprietary Corp.

GRASS VALLEY

Golden Empire Convalescent Hospital*
121 Dorsey Dr, Grass Valley, CA, 95945
(916) 273-1316

Admin Cleolue White.
Licensure Skilled care. *Beds* 150. *Certified* Medicare; Medi-Cal.
Owner Proprietary Corp.

Grass Valley Convalescent Hospital*
107 Catherine Ln, Grass Valley, CA, 95945
(916) 273-4447
Admin Betty Rhodes. *Medical Dir/Dir of Nursing* Jerome Frey MD.
Licensure Skilled care. *Beds* 59. *Certified* Medicare; Medi-Cal.
Owner Proprietary Corp.
Admissions Requirements Physician's request.
Staff RNs 3 (ft); LPNs 3 (ft), 4 (pt); Orderlies 1 (ft); Nurses aides 18 (ft), 7 (pt); Activities coordinators 1 (ft); Dietitians 1 (ft).
Facilities Dining room; Activities room; Crafts room; Laundry room; Barber/Beauty shop; Library; TV room.
Activities Arts & crafts; Games; Reading groups; Prayer groups; Movies; Shopping trips; Social/Cultural gatherings.

Oak Park Nursing Center Inc*
10716 Cedar Ave, Grass Valley, CA, 95945
(916) 273-2470
Admin Iva Jean Harmon.
Licensure Skilled care. *Beds* 27. *Certified* Medi-Cal.
Owner Proprietary Corp.

Spring Hill Manor Convalescent Hospital*
10355 Joerschke Dr, Grass Valley, CA, 95945
(916) 273-7247
Admin Anne Peterson. *Medical Dir/Dir of Nursing* Jerome F Frey MD.
Licensure Skilled care. *Beds* 49. *Certified* Medicare; Medi-Cal.
Owner Proprietary Corp.
Admissions Requirements Physician's request.
Staff RNs 1 (ft), 2 (pt); LPNs 4 (ft); Nurses aides 36 (ft), 4 (pt).
Facilities Dining room.
Activities Arts & crafts; Prayer groups.

GREENBRAE

Greenbrae Convalescent Hospital Inc
1220 S Eliseo Dr, Greenbrae, CA, 94904
(415) 461-9700
Admin Sue Huttlinger. *Medical Dir/Dir of Nursing* Janet Bodle MD; Catherine Kelly RN.
Licensure Skilled care. *Beds* 72. *Certified* Medicare.
Owner Nonprofit Corp (Guardian Fdn Inc).
Admissions Requirements Medical examination; Physician's request.
Staff RNs 5 (ft), 8 (pt); LPNs 1 (pt); Orderlies 1 (ft); Nurses aides; Activities coordinators 1 (ft), 1 (pt).
Facilities Dining room; Physical therapy room; Activities room; Crafts room; Laundry room; Barber/Beauty shop.
Activities Arts & crafts; Cards; Games; Reading groups; Prayer groups; Movies; Shopping trips; Social/Cultural gatherings.

HACIENDA HEIGHTS

Helen Evans Home for Retarded Children*
15125 Gale Ave, Hacienda Heights, CA, 91745
(213) 330-4048
Admin Thomas Evans. *Medical Dir/Dir of Nursing* Rolando Atiga MD.
Licensure Intermediate care for mentally retarded. *Beds* 59. *Certified* Medi-Cal.
Owner Proprietary Corp.
Staff RNs 3 (ft), 7 (pt); Nurses aides 27 (ft), 13 (pt); Activities coordinators 1 (ft).
Facilities Dining room; Activities room.
Activities Arts & crafts; Outings.

HANFORD

Hanford Convalescent Hospital
361 E Grangeville Blvd, Hanford, CA, 93230
(209) 582-9221
Admin Robert A Barker. *Medical Dir/Dir of Nursing* George Guerwsey MD; Delores Wheeler RN.
Licensure Skilled care. *Beds* SNF 133. *Certified* Medicare; Medi-Cal.
Owner Proprietary Corp.
Admissions Requirements Physician's request.
Languages Spanish, Portuguese
Facilities Dining room; Physical therapy room; Activities room; Laundry room; Barber/Beauty shop.
Activities Arts & crafts; Cards; Games; Reading groups; Prayer groups; Movies; Shopping trips; Social/Cultural gatherings.

Hillhaven Convalescent Hospital*
1007 W Lacey Blvd, Hanford, CA, 93230
(209) 582-2871
Admin Floyd E Hull.
Licensure Skilled care. *Beds* 124. *Certified* Medicare; Medi-Cal.
Owner Proprietary Corp.

Kings Convalescent Center
851 Leslie Ln, Hanford, CA, 93230
(209) 582-4414
Admin Sheila Ockey. *Medical Dir/Dir of Nursing* Dr George Guernsey.
Licensure Skilled care. *Beds* SNF 59. *Certified* Medi-Cal.
Owner Nonprofit Corp (Wilshire Foundation).
Admissions Requirements Physician's request.
Staff Physicians 22 (pt); RNs 1 (ft), 3 (pt); LPNs 4 (ft), 7 (pt); Nurses aides 22 (ft), 11 (pt); Physical therapists 1 (pt); Occupational therapists 1 (pt); Speech therapists 1 (pt); Activities coordinators 1 (ft); Dietitians 1 (pt); Ophthalmologists 1 (pt).
Languages Spanish, Japanese, Portuguese, Tagalog
Facilities Dining room; Activities room; Laundry room; Barber/Beauty shop; Library.
Activities Arts & crafts; Cards; Games; Reading groups; Prayer groups; Movies; Shopping trips; Social/Cultural gatherings; Oral history; Homecoming; County fair; Baby pageant.

HAWTHORNE

Golden West Convalescent Hospital
11834 Inglewood Ave, Hawthorne, CA, 90250
(213) 679-1461
Admin Lydia P Milligan. *Medical Dir/Dir of Nursing* Marvin H Stein MD; Pastora Lagmay RN.
Licensure Skilled care. *Beds* SNF 105. *Certified* Medicare; Medi-Cal.
Owner Privately owned.
Staff RNs; LPNs; Orderlies; Nurses aides; Activities coordinators; Dietitians.
Languages Spanish
Facilities Dining room; Physical therapy room; Activities room; Laundry room; Barber/Beauty shop.
Activities Arts & crafts; Cards; Games; Reading groups; Prayer groups; Movies; Shopping trips; Social/Cultural gatherings; Church trips.

Hawthorne Convalescent Center*
11630 S Grevillea Ave, Hawthorne, CA, 90250
(213) 679-9732
Admin Esther Williams. *Medical Dir/Dir of Nursing* Daryl Hutchinson.
Licensure Skilled care. *Beds* 88. *Certified* Medicare; Medi-Cal.
Owner Nonprofit Corp (Wilshire Foundation).

South Bay Child Care Center*
13812 Cordary Ave, Hawthorne, CA, 90250
(213) 679-9223

Admin Ethel Holtzclaw.
Licensure Skilled care; Intermediate care for
mentally retarded. *Beds* 90. *Certified*
Medicare; Medi-Cal.
Owner Proprietary Corp.

Southwest Convalescent Center*
13922 Cerise Ave, Hawthorne, CA, 90250
(213) 675-3304
Admin Margaret Westerfield. *Medical Dir/Dir
of Nursing* Michael Platt MD.
Licensure Skilled care. *Beds* 99. *Certified*
Medicare; Medi-Cal.
Owner Nonprofit Corp (Everhealth Fdn).
Staff RNs 2 (ft), 2 (pt); LPNs 6 (ft), 3 (pt);
Orderlies 2 (ft), 1 (pt); Nurses aides 30 (ft),
15 (pt); Recreational therapists 1 (ft), 1 (pt);
Dietitians 1 (pt).
Facilities Dining room; Physical therapy
room; Activities room; Crafts room; Laundry
room; Barber/Beauty shop; Classroom.
Activities Arts & crafts; Cards; Games;
Reading groups; Prayer groups; Movies;
Shopping trips.

HAYWARD

Barrett Convalescent Hospital Inc*
1625 Denton Ave, Hayward, CA, 94545
(415) 352-0210
Admin Margie R Melone. *Medical Dir/Dir of
Nursing* Dr Andrew May Jr.
Licensure Skilled care. *Beds* 74. *Certified*
Medicare; Medi-Cal.
Owner Proprietary Corp.
Staff Physicians 7 (pt); RNs 3 (ft); LPNs 7
(ft); Orderlies 1 (pt); Nurses aides 44 (ft);
Physical therapists 1 (pt); Recreational
therapists 1 (ft); Speech therapists 1 (pt);
Activities coordinators 1 (ft); Dietitians 1
(ft); Dentists 1 (pt); Podiatrists 1 (pt).
Facilities Dining room; Physical therapy
room; Activities room; Chapel; Crafts room;
Laundry room.
Activities Arts & crafts; Games; Reading
groups; Prayer groups; Social/Cultural
gatherings.

Bartlett Convalescent Hospital*
718 Bartlett Ave, Hayward, CA, 94541
(415) 785-3630
Admin Marvin D Carrigan.
Licensure Skilled care. *Beds* 48. *Certified*
Medicare; Medi-Cal.
Owner Proprietary Corp.

Bassard Convalescent Hospital Inc
3269 D St, Hayward, CA, 94541
(415) 537-6700
Admin Yvonne Bassard. *Medical Dir/Dir of
Nursing* Fred Meltz MD; Sara L Cita DON.
Licensure Skilled care. *Beds* SNF 71. *Certified*
Medicare; Medi-Cal.
Owner Proprietary Corp.
Staff Physicians 3 (pt); RNs 2 (ft), 2 (pt);
LPNs 4 (ft), 4 (pt); Nurses aides 29 (ft);
Activities coordinators 1 (ft); Dietitians 1
(pt).
Facilities Dining room; Activities room;
Chapel; Crafts room; Laundry room; Barber/
Beauty shop.
Activities Arts & crafts; Cards; Games;
Reading groups; Prayer groups; Movies;
Social/Cultural gatherings.

Bethesda Home
22427 Montgomery St, Hayward, CA, 94541
(415) 538-8300
Admin Donald G Williams. *Medical Dir/Dir
of Nursing* William Arthur MD.
Licensure Skilled care. *Beds* 40. *Certified*
Medicare; Medi-Cal.
Owner Nonprofit Corp (Bethesda Care
Centers).
Staff RNs 1 (ft), 3 (pt); Nurses aides 16 (ft);
Physical therapists 1 (pt); Activities
coordinators 1 (ft); Dietitians 1 (pt);
Ophthalmologists 1 (pt); Dentist 1 (pt).

Facilities Dining room; Activities room;
Chapel; Crafts room; Laundry room; Barber/
Beauty shop.
Activities Prayer groups; Movies; Shopping
trips.

CareWest-Gateway Nursing Center
26660 Patrick Ave, Hayward, 94544
(415) 782-1845
Admin Helen D Anderson. *Medical Dir/Dir of
Nursing* Fred Meltz MD; Helen Jones RN.
Licensure Skilled care. *Beds* 99. *Certified*
Medicaid; Medicare; Medi-Cal.
Owner Proprietary Corp.
Admissions Requirements Medical
examination; Physician's request.
Staff RNs 2 (ft), 2 (pt); LPNs 10 (ft), 2 (pt);
Nurses aides 35 (ft), 5 (pt); Physical
therapists 1 (ft); Occupational therapists 1
(ft); Speech therapists 1 (ft); Activities
coordinators 1 (ft); Dietitians 1 (ft), 15 (ft).
Languages Spanish
Facilities Dining room; Physical therapy
room; Activities room; Laundry room;
Barber/Beauty shop; Library.
Activities Arts & crafts; Games; Reading
groups; Prayer groups; Movies; Shopping
trips; Social/Cultural gatherings; Cooking;
Exercise.

**Creekside Terrace Intermediate Care Facility
Inc**
629 Hampton Rd, Hayward, CA, 94541
(415) 276-5403
Admin Bradley M Besaw. *Medical Dir/Dir of
Nursing* Gary Miller MD; Kathryn Fujii
LVN.
Licensure Intermediate care. *Beds* 25.
Certified Medi-Cal.
Owner Proprietary Corp.
Admissions Requirements Medical
examination; Physician's request.
Staff Physicians 4 (pt); RNs 1 (pt); LPNs 1
(ft), 2 (pt); Nurses aides 4 (ft), 1 (pt);
Occupational therapists 1 (pt); Activities
coordinators 2 (pt); Dietitians 1 (pt).
Languages Spanish
Facilities Dining room; Laundry room.
Activities Arts & crafts; Cards; Games;
Reading groups; Prayer groups; Movies;
Shopping trips; Social/Cultural gatherings.

Driftwood Manor*
19700 Hesperian Blvd, Hayward, CA, 94541
(415) 785-2880
Admin Candis Lompe.
Licensure Skilled care. *Beds* 85. *Certified*
Medicare; Medi-Cal.
Owner Proprietary Corp (ARA Living
Centers).

Eden West Rehabilitation Hospital
1805 West St, Hayward, CA, 94545
(415) 783-4811
Admin Margaret Westerfield. *Medical Dir/Dir
of Nursing* Dr Sharp; Gloria Scott RN.
Licensure Skilled care. *Beds* 99. *Certified*
Medicare; Medi-Cal.
Owner Proprietary Corp.
Admissions Requirements Minimum age 18.
Staff RNs 2 (ft), 2 (pt); LPNs 12 (ft), 4 (pt);
Orderlies 3 (ft); Nurses aides 30 (ft), 6 (pt);
Physical therapists 1 (ft); Recreational
therapists 1 (ft); Occupational therapists 1
(pt); Speech therapists 1 (pt); Activities
coordinators 1 (ft); Dietitians 1 (pt);
Podiatrists 1 (pt).
Facilities Dining room; Physical therapy
room; Activities room; Laundry room;
Barber/Beauty shop; Library.
Activities Arts & crafts; Cards; Games;
Reading groups; Prayer groups; Movies;
Shopping trips; Social/Cultural gatherings.

Glen Ellen Convalescent Hospital*
21568 Banyan St, Hayward, CA, 94541
(415) 538-2348
Admin Oleta Dillard.

Licensure Intermediate care. *Beds* 26.
Certified Medi-Cal.
Owner Proprietary Corp.

Hayward Convalescent Hospital
1832 B St, Hayward, CA, 94541
(415) 538-3866
Admin Mark Tornga. *Medical Dir/Dir of
Nursing* Fred Meltz MD; Myra Leeper RN
DON.
Licensure Skilled care. *Beds* SNF 145.
Certified Medicaid; Medicare; Medi-Cal.
Owner Proprietary Corp.
Admissions Requirements Physician's request.
Staff RNs 5 (ft), 6 (pt); LPNs 8 (ft), 7 (pt);
Orderlies 2 (ft), 1 (pt); Nurses aides 49 (ft),
5 (pt); Physical therapists 1 (pt);
Recreational therapists 1 (ft); Occupational
therapists 1 (pt); Speech therapists 1 (pt);
Activities coordinators 1 (ft); Dietitians 1
(pt); Ophthalmologists 1 (pt); Social worker.
Languages Spanish
Facilities Dining room; Physical therapy
room; Activities room; Crafts room; Laundry
room; Barber/Beauty shop; Library.
Activities Arts & crafts; Cards; Games;
Reading groups; Prayer groups; Movies;
Shopping trips; As baseball games; Picnics;
BBQs.

Hayward Hills Convalescent Hospital
1768 B St, Hayward, CA, 94541
(415) 538-4424
Admin Jeanne Brennan. *Medical Dir/Dir of
Nursing* Ernest Williamson MD; Helen
Gustauson RN DON.
Licensure Skilled care. *Beds* SNF 72. *Certified*
Medicare.
Owner Proprietary Corp (ARA Living
Centers).
Admissions Requirements Medical
examination; Physician's request.
Staff Physicians 4 (pt); RNs 1 (ft), 2 (pt);
LPNs 8 (pt); Physical therapists 1 (pt);
Recreational therapists 1 (pt); Occupational
therapists 1 (pt); Speech therapists 1 (pt);
Activities coordinators 1 (ft); Dietitians 1
(pt); Dentists 1 (pt); Ophthalmologists 1 (pt);
Podiatrists 1 (pt); Dentist 1 (pt).
Facilities Dining room; Physical therapy
room; Crafts room; Laundry room.
Activities Arts & crafts; Cards; Games;
Reading groups; Prayer groups; Movies;
Shopping trips; Social/Cultural gatherings.

Holly Tree Convalescent Hospital
553 Smalley Ave, Hayward, CA, 94541
(415) 537-2755
Admin Shirley A Ernest. *Medical Dir/Dir of
Nursing* William Arthur MD; Mildred
Pickett DON.
Licensure Skilled care. *Beds* SNF 30. *Certified*
Medicare; Medi-Cal.
Owner Privately owned.
Admissions Requirements Medical
examination; Physician's request.
Staff RNs 1 (ft), 2 (pt); LPNs 2 (ft), 2 (pt);
Nurses aides 6 (ft), 6 (pt); Physical therapists
1 (pt); Occupational therapists 1 (pt); Speech
therapists 1 (pt); Activities coordinators 1
(ft); Dietitians 1 (pt).
Facilities Dining room; Activities room;
Crafts room; Laundry room; TV room.
Activities Arts & crafts; Cards; Games;
Reading groups; Prayer groups; Movies;
Social/Cultural gatherings; Journalism;
Exercise; Music.

Majestic Pines Convalescent Hospital*
1628 B St, Hayward, CA, 94541
(415) 582-4639
Admin Valerie Capone. *Medical Dir/Dir of
Nursing* William Arthur.
Licensure Skilled care. *Beds* 75. *Certified*
Medicare; Medi-Cal.
Owner Proprietary Corp.
Admissions Requirements Medical
examination; Physician's request.

Staff RNs 3 (ft), 3 (pt); LPNs 7 (ft), 1 (pt); Orderlies 2 (ft); Nurses aides 23 (ft), 6 (pt); Recreational therapists 1 (ft); Activities coordinators 1 (ft).
Facilities Dining room; Physical therapy room; Activities room; Crafts room; Laundry room; Barber/Beauty shop.
Activities Arts & crafts; Cards; Games; Reading groups; Prayer groups; Movies; Shopping trips; Social/Cultural gatherings.

Parkview Convalescent Hospital
27350 Tampa Ave, Hayward, CA, 94544
(415) 783-8150
Admin Annamarie R Magna. *Medical Dir/Dir of Nursing* Geraldine Fulks.
Licensure Skilled care. *Beds* SNF 121. *Certified* Medicare; Medi-Cal.
Owner Proprietary Corp (ARA Living Centers).
Staff RNs; LPNs; Nurses aides; Physical therapists 1 (pt); Occupational therapists 1 (pt); Speech therapists 1 (pt); Activities coordinators 1 (ft), 1 (pt); Dietitians 1 (ft).
Facilities Dining room; Physical therapy room; Activities room; Chapel; Crafts room; Laundry room; Barber/Beauty shop; Library.
Activities Arts & crafts; Cards; Games; Reading groups; Prayer groups; Movies; Shopping trips; Social/Cultural gatherings.

St Christopher Convalescent Hospital
22822 Myrtle St, Hayward, CA, 94541
(415) 537-4844
Admin Lawrence Eckman. *Medical Dir/Dir of Nursing* Andrew May MD; Doll Coleman DON.
Licensure Skilled care. *Beds* SNF 36. *Certified* Medi-Cal.
Owner Proprietary Corp.
Admissions Requirements Physician's request.
Staff RNs 1 (ft), 2 (pt); LPNs 3 (ft), 3 (pt); Nurses aides 10 (ft); Activities coordinators 1 (ft).
Languages Spanish, Tagalog
Facilities Dining room; Activities room; Laundry room.
Activities Arts & crafts; Games; Movies; Shopping trips.

St Michael Convalescent Hospital*
25919 Gading Rd, Hayward, CA, 94544
(415) 782-8424
Admin Elizabeth Christian.
Licensure Skilled care. *Beds* 99. *Certified* Medicare; Medi-Cal.
Owner Proprietary Corp.

Stonehaven Convalescent Hospital Inc*
1782 B St, Hayward, CA, 94541
(415) 581-3766
Admin Bradley Besaw. *Medical Dir/Dir of Nursing* Andrew May MD.
Licensure Skilled care. *Beds* 25. *Certified* Medi-Cal.
Owner Proprietary Corp.
Admissions Requirements Physician's request.
Facilities Dining room; Activities room; Crafts room; Laundry room.
Activities Arts & crafts; Cards; Games; Reading groups; Prayer groups; Movies; Social/Cultural gatherings.

Sunset Boulevard Convalescent Hospital*
442 Sunset Blvd, Hayward, CA, 94541
(415) 582-8311
Admin Charles W Drake.
Licensure Skilled care. *Beds* 99. *Certified* Medicare; Medi-Cal.
Owner Proprietary Corp.

Sunset Boulevard Convalescent Hospital 1*
458 Sunset Blvd, Hayward, CA, 94541
(415) 582-8311
Admin Charles W Drake.
Licensure Intermediate care. *Beds* 26. *Certified* Medi-Cal.
Owner Proprietary Corp.

HEALDSBURG

Berryman Health Healdsburg Convalescent Hospital
14745 Grove St, Healdsburg, CA, 95448
(707) 433-4813
Admin Evan D Keeney. *Medical Dir/Dir of Nursing* Dr Martin Rubinger; Elsie Keller.
Licensure Skilled care. *Beds* 46. *Certified* Medicaid; Medicare; Medi-Cal.
Owner Proprietary Corp (Redwood Empire Enterprises).
Admissions Requirements Medical examination; Physician's request.
Staff Physicians 10 (pt); RNs 1 (ft), 1 (pt); LPNs 7 (ft), 2 (pt); Orderlies 1 (ft); Nurses aides 22 (ft), 4 (pt); Physical therapists 3 (pt); Recreational therapists 1 (pt); Occupational therapists 1 (pt); Speech therapists 1 (pt); Activities coordinators 1 (ft); Dietitians 1 (pt); Dentists 1 (pt); Ophthalmologists 1 (pt); Podiatrists 1 (pt); Social service 1 (pt).
Languages Spanish
Facilities Dining room; Activities room; Crafts room; Laundry room; Barber/Beauty shop; Library.
Activities Arts & crafts; Games; Reading groups; Prayer groups; Movies; Shopping trips; Social/Cultural gatherings.

HEMET

Hemet Convalescent Center
40300 E Devonshire Ave, Hemet, CA, 92344
(714) 925-2571
Admin Charles E Sinclair. *Medical Dir/Dir of Nursing* Joseph Karcher MD; Cindi Feuestein RN.
Licensure Skilled care. *Beds* SNF 99. *Certified* Medicare; Medi-Cal.
Owner Proprietary Corp (Summit Health Ltd).
Staff RNs 4 (ft); LPNs 4 (ft); Nurses aides 27 (ft); Physical therapists 1 (ft); Occupational therapists 1 (pt); Speech therapists 1 (pt); Activities coordinators 1 (ft), 1 (pt).

Hillhaven Convalescent Center*
275 N San Jacinto St, Hemet, CA, 92343
(714) 658-9441
Admin Linda F Williams.
Licensure Skilled care. *Beds* 99. *Certified* Medicare; Medi-Cal.
Owner Proprietary Corp (Hillhaven Corp).

Meadowbrook Convalescent Hospital Inc*
461 E Johnston, Hemet, CA, 92343
(714) 658-2293
Admin Arthur L Brook. *Medical Dir/Dir of Nursing* Dr D Michael Crile.
Licensure Skilled care. *Beds* 64. *Certified* Medicare; Medi-Cal.
Owner Proprietary Corp.
Staff RNs 1 (ft), 2 (pt); LPNs 3 (ft), 3 (pt); Orderlies 1 (ft), 2 (pt); Nurses aides 20 (ft), 15 (pt); Activities coordinators 1 (ft), 1 (pt).
Facilities Dining room; Activities room; Laundry room; Barber/Beauty shop.
Activities Arts & crafts; Games; Prayer groups; Movies; Shopping trips; Social/Cultural gatherings; Music entertainment.

Ramona Manor Convalescent Hospital
485 W Johnston Ave, Hemet, CA, 92343
(714) 652-0011
Admin Cynthia Tipton. *Medical Dir/Dir of Nursing* Michael Crile MD; Francine Grant.
Licensure Skilled care. *Beds* SNF 104. *Certified* Medicare; Medi-Cal.
Owner Privately owned.
Admissions Requirements Medical examination; Physician's request.
Staff Physicians 1 (pt); RNs 6 (ft), 3 (pt); LPNs 5 (ft), 4 (pt); Orderlies 1 (ft), 1 (pt); Nurses aides 30 (ft), 6 (pt); Physical therapists 1 (ft); Occupational therapists 1 (pt); Speech therapists 1 (pt); Activities

coordinators 1 (ft), 2 (pt); Dietitians 1 (ft); Dentists 1 (pt); Ophthalmologists 1 (pt);; Dentist 1 (pt).
Languages Spanish
Facilities Dining room; Physical therapy room; Activities room; Laundry room; Barber/Beauty shop; Library; Speech therapy room.
Activities Arts & crafts; Cards; Games; Reading groups; Prayer groups; Movies; Shopping trips; Social/Cultural gatherings; Various parties & entertainment by community groups.

HERMOSA BEACH

Bay Shore Sanitarium*
160 Manhattan Ave, Hermosa Beach, CA, 90254
(213) 372-2090
Admin Bernard G Wayne.
Licensure Skilled care. *Beds* 49. *Certified* Medicare; Medi-Cal.
Owner Proprietary Corp.

HIGHLAND

Hillhaven Highland House
7534 Palm Ave, Highland, CA, 92346
(714) 862-0611
Admin Tom Lee. *Medical Dir/Dir of Nursing* Dr Frank Randolph.
Licensure Skilled care. *Beds* 99. *Certified* Medicare; Medi-Cal.
Owner Proprietary Corp (Hillhaven Corp).
Admissions Requirements Physician's request.
Staff RNs; LPNs; Nurses aides; Physical therapists; Activities coordinators.
Facilities Dining room; Physical therapy room; Activities room; Crafts room; Laundry room; Barber/Beauty shop.
Activities Arts & crafts; Cards; Games; Movies.

Sierra Vista
3455 E Highland Ave, Highland, CA, 92346
(714) 862-6454
Admin $8 Janet Seawell.
Licensure Skilled care. *Beds* 116. *Certified* Medi-Cal.
Owner Proprietary Corp.

HOLLISTER

Hazel Hawkins Convalescent Hospital
3110 Southside Rd, Hollister, CA, 95023
(408) 637-5711
Admin Thomas J Harn. *Medical Dir/Dir of Nursing* Dixie DeMaggio Rn DON.
Licensure Skilled care. *Beds* 52. *Certified* Medicare; Medi-Cal.
Owner Publicly owned.
Admissions Requirements Physician's request.
Staff Physicians 12 (pt); RNs 2 (ft), 4 (pt); LPNs 1 (ft), 1 (pt); Nurses aides 16 (ft), 14 (pt); Physical therapists 1 (pt); Recreational therapists 1 (pt); Occupational therapists 1 (pt); Speech therapists 1 (pt); Activities coordinators 1 (ft); Dietitians 1 (pt).
Facilities Dining room; Physical therapy room; Activities room; Barber/Beauty shop.
Activities Arts & crafts; Cards; Games; Reading groups; Prayer groups; Movies; Shopping trips; Social/Cultural gatherings.

Hollister Convalescent Hospital*
900 Sunset Dr, Hollister, CA, 95023
(408) 637-5772
Medical Dir/Dir of Nursing Robert D Quinn MD.
Licensure Skilled care. *Beds* 70. *Certified* Medicare; Medi-Cal.
Owner Proprietary Corp (Care Enterprises).

Staff RNs 3 (ft); LPNs 2 (pt); Orderlies 2 (ft); Nurses aides 25 (ft); Physical therapists 1 (ft); Occupational therapists 1 (ft); Speech therapists 1 (ft); Activities coordinators 1 (ft); Dietitians 1 (ft).
Facilities Dining room; Physical therapy room; Activities room; Chapel; Laundry room; Barber/Beauty shop; Library.
Activities Arts & crafts; Cards; Games; Reading groups; Prayer groups; Movies; Shopping trips; Social/Cultural gatherings; Group discussions with staff.

HOLLYWOOD

Orchard Gables*
1277 N Wilcox Ave, Hollywood, CA, 90038
(213) 469-7231
Admin Rita Rohkar.
Licensure Skilled care. *Beds* 59. *Certified* Medicare; Medi-Cal.
Owner Proprietary Corp.

HUNTINGTON BEACH

CareWest Huntington Valley Nursing Center
8382 Newman Ave, Huntington Beach, CA, 92647
(714) 842-5551
Admin Candy Bennett. *Medical Dir/Dir of Nursing* Gary Anderson MD; Judy Revell RN.
Licensure Skilled care. *Beds* SNF 144. *Certified* Medicaid; Medicare; Medi-Cal.
Owner Proprietary Corp (Care Enterprises).
Admissions Requirements Physician's request.
Staff Physicians; RNs; LPNs; Orderlies; Nurses aides; Physical therapists; Occupational therapists; Speech therapists; Activities coordinators 2 (ft); Dietitians 1 (ft); Dentists; Ophthalmologists.
Languages Spanish
Facilities Dining room; Physical therapy room; Activities room; Crafts room; Laundry room; Barber/Beauty shop; Library; Lovely patio areas; Formal private dining room available on request.
Activities Arts & crafts; Cards; Games; Reading groups; Prayer groups; Movies; Shopping trips; Social/Cultural gatherings; Special interest clubs; Functional living skills classes.

Garfield Care Convalescent Hospital*
7781 Garfield Ave, Huntington Beach, CA, 92648
(714) 847-9671
Admin Bill Mohr.
Licensure Skilled care. *Beds* 59. *Certified* Medicare; Medi-Cal.
Owner Proprietary Corp (Care Enterprises).

Huntington Beach Convalescent Hospital*
18811 Florida St, Huntington Beach, CA, 92648
(714) 847-3515
Admin Wayne D Kyckelhahn. *Medical Dir/Dir of Nursing* Victor Siew MD.
Licensure Skilled care; Intermediate care. *Beds* SNF 123; ICF 59. *Certified* Medicare; Medi-Cal.
Owner Proprietary Corp.
Admissions Requirements Minimum age 60.
Staff RNs 15 (ft), 6 (pt); LPNs 15 (ft), 8 (pt); Nurses aides 35 (ft), 14 (pt); Physical therapists 1 (pt); Reality therapists 3 (ft); Recreational therapists 1 (pt); Occupational therapists 1 (pt); Speech therapists 1 (pt); Activities coordinators 1 (ft); Dietitians 1 (ft); Dentists 1 (pt); Ophthalmologists 1 (pt); Podiatrists 1 (pt); Audiologists 1 (pt).
Facilities Dining room; Physical therapy room; Activities room; Chapel; Crafts room; Laundry room; Barber/Beauty shop; Library.
Activities Arts & crafts; Cards; Games; Reading groups; Prayer groups; Movies; Shopping trips; Social/Cultural gatherings.

HUNTINGTON PARK

Huntington Park Convalescent Center*
6419-29 Miles Ave, Huntington Park, CA, 90255
(213) 589-5941
Admin Ted Stulz. *Medical Dir/Dir of Nursing* Edward Panzer MD.
Licensure Skilled care. *Beds* 99. *Certified* Medicare; Medi-Cal.
Owner Nonprofit Corp (Everhealth Fdn).
Admissions Requirements Physician's request.
Facilities Dining room; Physical therapy room; Activities room; Chapel; Crafts room; Laundry room; Barber/Beauty shop; Library.
Activities Arts & crafts; Cards; Games; Reading groups; Prayer groups; Movies; Shopping trips.

IMPERIAL

Imperial Manor Inc
100 E 2nd St, Imperial, CA, 92251
(619) 355-2858
Admin William W Alexander Jr. *Medical Dir/Dir of Nursing* Dr Keith MacGaffey; Flora Buzo RN DON.
Licensure Skilled care. *Beds* SNF 25. *Certified* Medi-Cal.
Owner Nonprofit Corp (Volunteers of America).
Admissions Requirements Minimum age 21.
Staff RNs 1 (ft), 3 (pt); Nurses aides 6 (ft), 2 (pt); Activities coordinators 1 (pt); Dietitians 1 (ft); LVNs 2 (ft), 3 (pt).
Languages Spanish
Affiliation Volunteers of America
Facilities Dining room; Laundry room; Day room.
Activities Arts & crafts; Cards; Games; Prayer groups; Movies; Shopping trips; Walks.

INDIO

Desert Palms Convalescent Hospital
82-262 Valencia St, Indio, CA, 92201
(619) 347-7779
Admin John W Ryan. *Medical Dir/Dir of Nursing* David Christensen; Joyce Walton.
Licensure Skilled care. *Beds* SNF 68. *Certified* Medicare; Medi-Cal.
Owner Privately owned.

Mul-Care Desert Convalescent Hospital*
45-500 Aladdin St, Indio, CA, 92201
(714) 347-0876
Admin G Mulcahy & E S Mulcahy.
Licensure Skilled care. *Beds* 64. *Certified* Medicare; Medi-Cal.
Owner Proprietary Corp (National Heritage).

INGLEWOOD

Angelus Convalescent Center East
1001 S Osage Ave, Inglewood, CA, 90301
(213) 674-3216
Admin Jerry Eisinger. *Medical Dir/Dir of Nursing* Alan Allen MD.
Licensure Skilled care. *Beds* SNF 55. *Certified* Medicare; Medi-Cal.
Owner Proprietary Corp.
Admissions Requirements Minimum age 21.
Staff LPNs 4 (ft), 3 (pt); Orderlies 1 (ft); Nurses aides 20 (ft), 4 (pt) 13F 1 (ft); Reality therapists 1 (ft); Recreational therapists 1 (ft); Occupational therapists 1 (ft); Speech therapists 1 (ft); Activities coordinators 1 (ft); Dietitians 1 (ft); Dentists 1 (ft); Ophthalmologists 1 (ft); Podiatrists 1 (ft).
Facilities Dining room; Activities room; Chapel; Crafts room; Laundry room; Barber/Beauty shop.
Activities Arts & crafts; Cards; Games; Reading groups; Prayer groups; Movies; Shopping trips; Social/Cultural gatherings.

Angelus Convalescent Center—West
950 S Flower Ave, Inglewood, CA, 90308
(213) 674-3216
Admin Jerry Eisinger.
Licensure Skilled care. *Beds* 59. *Certified* Medicare; Medi-Cal.
Owner Proprietary Corp.

Centinela Park Convalescent Hospital*
515 Centinela Blvd, Inglewood, CA, 90302
(213) 674-4500
Admin Thomas Erdosi. *Medical Dir/Dir of Nursing* Richard Heath MD.
Licensure Skilled care. *Beds* 69. *Certified* Medicare; Medi-Cal.
Owner Proprietary Corp.
Staff RNs 1 (ft), 3 (pt); LPNs 6 (ft), 3 (pt); Nurses aides 20 (ft), 14 (pt).
Facilities Dining room; Activities room; Laundry room; Barber/Beauty shop.
Activities Arts & crafts; Cards; Games; Reading groups; Prayer groups; Movies.

Inglewood Convalarium*
100 S Hillcrest Blvd, Inglewood, CA, 90301
(213) 677-9114
Admin Pearl E Williams.
Licensure Skilled care. *Beds* 99. *Certified* Medicare; Medi-Cal.
Owner Proprietary Corp (CV American).

Palomar Convalescent Hospital*
301 N Centinela, Inglewood, CA, 90302
(213) 674-2660
Admin Nelson T Roberts.
Licensure Intermediate care. *Beds* 99. *Certified* Medicare.
Owner Proprietary Corp (Care Enterprises).

St Erne Sanitarium*
527 W Regent St, Inglewood, CA, 90301
(213) 674-7851
Admin Maurice P Playford. *Medical Dir/Dir of Nursing* Frederick Krieger MD.
Licensure Skilled care. *Beds* 276. *Certified* Medicare; Medi-Cal.
Owner Proprietary Corp.
Admissions Requirements Minimum age 21; Medical examination; Physician's request.
Staff RNs; LPNs; Orderlies; Nurses aides; Physical therapists; Reality therapists; Recreational therapists; Occupational therapists; Speech therapists; Activities coordinators; Dietitians; Dentists; Ophthalmologists; Podiatrists; Audiologists.
Facilities Dining room; Activities room; Laundry room; Barber/Beauty shop.
Activities Arts & crafts; Cards; Games; Reading groups; Prayer groups; Movies; Shopping trips; Social/Cultural gatherings.

JACKSON

Kit Carson Convalescent Hospital*
811 Court St, Jackson, CA, 95642
(209) 223-2231
Admin Meredith J Miller.
Licensure Skilled care. *Beds* 84. *Certified* Medicare; Medi-Cal.
Owner Proprietary Corp.

KENTFIELD

CareWest Bayside Nursing & Rehabilitation Center
1251 S Eliseo Dr, Kentfield, CA, 94904
(415) 461-1900
Admin Catherine J Mohline. *Medical Dir/Dir of Nursing* Mary Kay Carroll DON.
Licensure Skilled care. *Beds* 99. *Certified* Medicare; Medi-Cal.
Owner Proprietary Corp.
Staff RNs; Nurses aides; Physical therapists; Occupational therapists; Speech therapists; Activities coordinators; Dietitians; Podiatrists.

Facilities Dining room; Physical therapy room; Activities room; Crafts room; Laundry room; Barber/Beauty shop.
Activities Arts & crafts; Cards; Games; Reading groups; Prayer groups; Movies; Shopping trips; Social/Cultural gatherings.

KINGSBURG

CareWest-Kingsburg
1101 Stroud Ave, Kingsburg, CA, 93631
(209) 897-5881
Admin Beverly Harper. *Medical Dir/Dir of Nursing* Mary Rosenthal RN DON.
Licensure Skilled care. *Beds* SNF 86. *Certified* Medicaid; Medicare; Medi-Cal.
Owner Proprietary Corp (Care Enterprises).
Admissions Requirements Physician's request.
Staff RNs 4 (ft); LPNs 8 (ft), 6 (pt); Nurses aides 38 (ft), 12 (pt); Physical therapists 2 (ft); Reality therapists 1 (ft); Recreational therapists 1 (ft); Occupational therapists 1 (pt); Speech therapists 1 (pt); Activities coordinators 1 (ft); Dietitians 1 (ft); Ophthalmologists 1 (pt); Volunteer social worker; Social services 1 (ft); Community services representative.
Languages Japanese, Spanish
Facilities Dining room; Physical therapy room; Activities room; Crafts room; Laundry room; Barber/Beauty shop; Lounge.
Activities Arts & crafts; Cards; Games; Reading groups; Prayer groups; Movies; Shopping trips; Social/Cultural gatherings; Shuffleboard; Field trips.

LA CRESCENTA

Verdugo Vista Convalescent Hospital*
3050 Montrose Ave, La Crescenta, CA, 91214
(213) 248-0322
Admin Elaine Silverman.
Licensure Skilled care. *Beds* 92. *Certified* Medicare; Medi-Cal.
Owner Proprietary Corp (ARA Living Centers).

LA HABRA

La Habra Convalescent Hospital
1233 W La Habra Blvd, La Habra, CA, 90631
(213) 691-0781
Admin Roberta I Gayer. *Medical Dir/Dir of Nursing* Jorge Soffici MD.
Licensure Skilled care. *Beds* SNF 86. *Certified* Medicare; Medi-Cal.
Owner Proprietary Corp (Columbia Corp).
Admissions Requirements Minimum age 18; Medical examination; Physician's request.
Staff RNs 3 (ft); LPNs 8 (ft); Orderlies 4 (ft); Nurses aides 25 (ft); Activities coordinators 1 (ft); Dietitians 1 (ft).
Languages Spanish, Tagalog
Facilities Dining room; Physical therapy room; Activities room; Crafts room; Barber/Beauty shop; Library.
Activities Arts & crafts; Cards; Games; Reading groups; Prayer groups; Movies; Shopping trips; Social/Cultural gatherings; Visits outside Sr Citizens.

LA JOLLA

Cloisters of La Jolla Convalescent Hospital*
7160 Fay Ave, La Jolla, CA, 92037
(714) 459-4361
Admin Paul N Ellingsen. *Medical Dir/Dir of Nursing* Arthur Edwards MD.
Licensure Skilled care. *Beds* 59.
Owner Proprietary Corp.
Staff RNs 4 (ft), 5 (pt); LPNs 3 (ft), 2 (pt); Nurses aides 16 (ft), 6 (pt); Activities coordinators 1 (ft).

Facilities Dining room; Barber/Beauty shop.
Activities Arts & crafts; Cards; Games; Reading groups; Prayer groups; Movies; Shopping trips; Social/Cultural gatherings.

La Jolla Convalescent Hospital
6211 La Jolla Hermosa Ave, La Jolla, CA, 92037
(619) 454-0739
Admin Cynthia Harker Johnson. *Medical Dir/Dir of Nursing* Dr Leonard H Lazarus; Grace Roldan DON.
Licensure Skilled care. *Beds* SNF 41. *Certified* Medicare.
Owner Proprietary Corp (Pacific Homes).
Admissions Requirements Minimum age 62; Physician's request.
Staff RNs 1 (ft), 3 (pt); LPNs 3 (ft), 4 (pt); Orderlies 10 (ft), 6 (pt); Activities coordinators 1 (ft), 1 (pt); PT aide 1 (ft).
Facilities Dining room; Physical therapy room; Activities room; Crafts room; Laundry room; Barber/Beauty shop.
Activities Arts & crafts; Cards; Games; Reading groups; Prayer groups; Movies; Van trips; Exercise; Music; Entertainment.

Torrey Pines Convalescent Hospital*
2552 Torrey Pines Rd, La Jolla, CA, 92037
(714) 453-5810
Admin Donald Veverka.
Licensure Skilled care. *Beds* 161. *Certified* Medicare; Medi-Cal.
Owner Proprietary Corp.

White Sands of La Jolla*
7450 Olivetas Ave, La Jolla, CA, 92037
(714) 454-4201
Admin David C Goodin. *Medical Dir/Dir of Nursing* L J Schwartz MD.
Licensure Skilled care. *Beds* 50.
Owner Nonprofit Corp.
Admissions Requirements Minimum age 62; Medical examination; Physician's request.
Staff Physicians 4 (pt); RNs 2 (ft), 3 (pt); LPNs 2 (ft), 5 (pt); Nurses aides 20 (ft), 4 (pt); Physical therapists 1 (pt); Occupational therapists 1 (pt); Speech therapists 1 (pt); Activities coordinators 1 (ft); Dietitians 1 (pt); Dentists 1 (pt); Podiatrists 1 (pt); Audiologists 1 (pt).
Affiliation Presbyterian
Facilities Dining room; Physical therapy room; Activities room; Chapel; Crafts room; Laundry room; Barber/Beauty shop; Library.
Activities Arts & crafts; Cards; Games; Reading groups; Prayer groups; Movies; Shopping trips; Social/Cultural gatherings.

LA MESA

Beverly Manor Convalescent Hospital
5696 Lake Murray Blvd, La Mesa, CA, 92042
(619) 460-7871
Admin Jerry C Strand. *Medical Dir/Dir of Nursing* Frank B Flint MD; Barbara Kerstetter RN.
Licensure Skilled care. *Beds* SNF 99. *Certified* Medicare; Medi-Cal.
Owner Proprietary Corp (Beverly Enterprises).
Admissions Requirements Minimum age 18; Medical examination; Physician's request.
Staff Physicians; RNs 5 (ft), 1 (pt); LPNs 9 (ft), 3 (pt); Orderlies 4 (ft); Nurses aides 37 (ft), 4 (pt); Physical therapists 1 (pt); Recreational therapists 1 (ft), 2 (pt); Occupational therapists 1 (pt); Speech therapists 1 (pt); Activities coordinators 1 (ft); Dietitians 1 (pt); Dentists 1 (pt); Ophthalmologists 1 (pt); Podiatrists 1 (pt); Dentist 1 (pt).
Facilities Dining room; Physical therapy room; Activities room; Crafts room; Laundry room; Barber/Beauty shop; Spacious living room.

Activities Arts & crafts; Cards; Games; Reading groups; Prayer groups; Movies; Shopping trips; Social/Cultural gatherings; BBQ's; Special outings.

California Convalescent Hospital of La Mesa*
8787 Center Dr, La Mesa, CA, 92041
(714) 460-4444
Admin Judith Cox. *Medical Dir/Dir of Nursing* Robert Pullman MD.
Licensure Skilled care. *Beds* 90. *Certified* Medicare; Medi-Cal.
Owner Proprietary Corp.
Staff Physicians 1 (pt); RNs 3 (ft); LPNs 20 (ft); Nurses aides 35 (ft); Physical therapists 1 (ft), 1 (pt); Recreational therapists 1 (ft); Occupational therapists 1 (pt); Speech therapists 1 (pt); Activities coordinators 1 (pt); Dietitians 1 (pt); Dentists 1 (pt); Podiatrists 1 (pt); Psychologists 1 (ft).

Community Convalescent Hospital of La Mesa*
8665 La Mesa Blvd, La Mesa, CA, 92041
(714) 465-0702
Admin Kenneth M Steele.
Licensure Skilled care. *Beds* 122. *Certified* Medicare; Medi-Cal.
Owner Proprietary Corp.

Hacienda de la Mesa Convalescent Hospital*
7760 Parkway Dr, La Mesa, CA, 92041
(714) 469-0124
Admin Siegmund Diener.
Licensure Skilled care. *Beds* 51. *Certified* Medicare; Medi-Cal.
Owner Proprietary Corp.

Hilldale Convalescent Center
7979 La Mesa Blvd, La Mesa, CA, 92041
(619) 465-8010
Admin Kathryn E Mumford. *Medical Dir/Dir of Nursing* Daria Gaynes.
Licensure Intermediate care for mentally retarded. *Beds* ICF 57. *Certified* Medi-Cal.
Owner Proprietary Corp (Care Enterprises).
Staff RNs; Nurses aides; Activities coordinators; Dietitians.
Languages Spanish
Facilities Dining room; Activities room; Laundry room.
Activities Arts & crafts; Movies; Shopping trips.

La Mesa Convalescent Hospital*
7800 Parkway Dr, La Mesa, CA, 92041
(714) 460-2330
Admin Arthur E Brandt.
Licensure Skilled care. *Beds* 110. *Certified* Medicare; Medi-Cal.
Owner Proprietary Corp.

San Diego Convalescent Hospital
3780 Massachusetts Ave, La Mesa, CA, 92041
(619) 465-1313
Admin Janice E Robertson. *Medical Dir/Dir of Nursing* Lee Schner.
Licensure Skilled care. *Beds* SNF 94. *Certified* Medicare; Medi-Cal.
Owner Privately owned.
Admissions Requirements Medical examination.
Facilities Dining room; Physical therapy room; Activities room; Chapel; Crafts room; Laundry room; Barber/Beauty shop; Library.
Activities Arts & crafts; Cards; Games; Reading groups; Prayer groups; Movies; Shopping trips; Social/Cultural gatherings.

LA MIRADA

Imperial Convalescent Center
11926 La Mirada Blvd, La Mirada, CA, 90638
(213) 943-7156
Admin Gail A Pearce. *Medical Dir/Dir of Nursing* Marion Jalil MD.
Licensure Skilled care. *Beds* SNF 99. *Certified* Medicare; Medi-Cal.
Owner Proprietary Corp (Columbia Corp).

Admissions Requirements Medical examination; Physician's request.
Staff RNs 3 (ft), 4 (pt); LPNs 5 (ft), 4 (pt); Nurses aides 25 (ft), 7 (pt).
Languages Spanish, Korean, Indian, Tagalog
Facilities Dining room; Activities room; Barber/Beauty shop.
Activities Arts & crafts; Cards; Games; Reading groups; Prayer groups; Movies; Shopping trips; Social/Cultural gatherings; Adult education classes.

Mirada Hills Rehabilitation & Convalescent Hospital*
12200 S La Mirada Blvd, La Mirada, CA, 90638
(213) 947-8691
Admin Donna Aten. *Medical Dir/Dir of Nursing* William Welsh DO.
Licensure Skilled care. *Beds* 158. *Certified* Medicare; Medi-Cal.
Owner Nonprofit Corp.
Admissions Requirements Medical examination; Physician's request.
Staff Physicians 2 (pt); RNs 6 (ft), 4 (pt); LPNs 13 (ft), 8 (pt); Orderlies 4 (ft), 1 (pt); Nurses aides 60 (ft), 15 (pt); Activities coordinators 3 (ft).
Facilities Dining room; Physical therapy room; Activities room; Crafts room; Laundry room; Barber/Beauty shop; Library; Occupational therapy room; Speech therapy room.
Activities Arts & crafts; Cards; Games; Reading groups; Prayer groups; Movies; Shopping trips; Social/Cultural gatherings.

LA VERNE

Woods Memorial Convalescent Hospital*
2600 A St, La Verne, CA, 91750
(714) 593-4917
Admin Jack Hansen. *Medical Dir/Dir of Nursing* Eugene St Clair MD.
Licensure Skilled care. *Beds* 75. *Certified* Medicare; Medi-Cal.
Owner Nonprofit Corp.
Admissions Requirements Minimum age 65.
Facilities Dining room; Activities room; Chapel; Crafts room; Laundry room; Barber/Beauty shop; Library.
Activities Arts & crafts; Cards; Games; Reading groups; Prayer groups; Movies; Shopping trips; Social/Cultural gatherings.

LAFAYETTE

Lafayette Convalescent Hospital*
1010 1st St, Lafayette, CA, 94549
(415) 284-1420
Admin Ruby D Brown.
Licensure Skilled care. *Beds* 52. *Certified* Medicare; Medi-Cal.
Owner Proprietary Corp.

Woodland Lafayette
3721 Mt Diablo Blvd, Lafayette, CA, 94549
(415) 284-5544
Admin Bob Lauderdale. *Medical Dir/Dir of Nursing* Dennis Stone MD.
Licensure Skilled care. *Beds* SNF 30. *Certified* Medicare.
Owner Proprietary Corp.
Admissions Requirements Medical examination; Physician's request.
Staff RNs 3 (ft), 5 (pt); LPNs 2 (ft), 2 (pt); Nurses aides 13 (ft), 4 (pt); Occupational therapists 1 (pt); Speech therapists 1 (pt); Activities coordinators 1 (ft), 2 (pt); Dietitians 1 (ft).
Facilities Dining room; Activities room; Laundry room.
Activities Arts & crafts; Cards; Games; Reading groups; Movies; Social/Cultural gatherings; Pets; Outside music.

LAGUNA BEACH

The Gardens
450 Glenneyre, Laguna Beach, CA, 92651
(714) 494-8075
Admin Alice Riddell. *Medical Dir/Dir of Nursing* Dzarius Vallis MD; Tonia Flaff DON.
Licensure Skilled care. *Beds* 47.
Owner Proprietary Corp (Columbia Corp).
Admissions Requirements Physician's request.
Staff Activities coordinators 1 (ft); Dietitians 1 (pt).
Languages Spanish, German, Hungarian
Facilities Laundry room; Barber/Beauty shop.
Activities Arts & crafts; Cards; Games; Reading groups; Prayer groups; Movies; Shopping trips; Social/Cultural gatherings.

LAGUNA HILLS

Beverly Manor Convalescent Hospital*
24452 Via Estrada, Laguna Hills, CA, 92653
(714) 837-8000
Admin Stanley F Main.
Licensure Skilled care. *Beds* 218. *Certified* Medicare; Medi-Cal.
Owner Proprietary Corp (Beverly Enterprises).

LAKEPORT

Lakeport Skilled Nursing Center Inc
625 16th St, Lakeport, CA, 95453
(707) 263-6101
Admin Patricia A Treppa. *Medical Dir/Dir of Nursing* Donald L Browning MD; Barbara Medina RN DNS.
Licensure Skilled care. *Beds* 90. *Certified* Medicare; Medi-Cal.
Owner Proprietary Corp.
Admissions Requirements Medical examination; Physician's request.
Staff Physicians 10 (pt); RNs 5 (ft); LPNs 8 (ft); Physical therapists 2 (pt); Occupational therapists 1 (pt); Speech therapists 1 (pt); Activities coordinators 1 (ft); Dietitians 1 (ft); Dentists 1 (pt); Ophthalmologists 1 (pt); Podiatrists 1 (pt).
Facilities Dining room; Physical therapy room; Activities room; Crafts room; Laundry room; Barber/Beauty shop.
Activities Arts & crafts; Cards; Games; Reading groups; Prayer groups; Movies; Shopping trips; Social/Cultural gatherings.

LAKESIDE

Friendship Manor Lakeside
11962 Woodside Ave, Lakeside, CA, 92040
(619) 561-1222
Admin Abel D Santiago. *Medical Dir/Dir of Nursing* Dr Maloney; Del Julian RN DON.
Licensure Skilled care. *Beds* SNF 94. *Certified* Medi-Cal.
Owner Proprietary Corp.
Admissions Requirements Minimum age 60; Medical examination; Physician's request.
Staff RNs 3 (ft); Activities coordinators 1 (ft), 1 (pt); Dietitians 1 (ft).
Languages Spanish, Tagalog
Facilities Dining room; Activities room; Chapel; Crafts room; Laundry room; Barber/Beauty shop; Courtyards.
Activities Arts & crafts; Games; Reading groups; Prayer groups; Movies; Shopping trips; Social/Cultural gatherings; Cooking classes.

LAKEVIEW TERRACE

Good Shepherd Convalescent Center
11505 Kagel Canyon St, Lakeview Terrace, CA, 91342
(818) 896-5391

Admin Nathaniel R Chivi. *Medical Dir/Dir of Nursing* H M Cohen MD; L Skelton RN DON.
Licensure Skilled care. *Beds* SNF 126.
Owner Proprietary Corp.
Admissions Requirements Medical examination.
Staff RNs.
Languages Spanish, Tagalog, Korean, Indian, Pakistani
Facilities Dining room; Physical therapy room; Activities room; Crafts room; Laundry room; Barber/Beauty shop; Sunroom; Reception area.
Activities Arts & crafts; Cards; Games; Reading groups; Prayer groups; Movies; Shopping trips; Social/Cultural gatherings; Outings.

LANCASTER

Antelope Valley Convalescent Hospital & Nursing Home*
44445 N 15th St W, Lancaster, CA, 93534
(805) 948-7501
Admin Maurice H Potkin.
Licensure Skilled care. *Beds* 193.
Owner Proprietary Corp.

Lancaster Convalescent Hospital
1642 W Ave J, Lancaster, CA, 93534
(805) 942-8463
Admin Genevieve L Skidmore. *Medical Dir/Dir of Nursing* B K Sudhir MD Med Dir; L M Fils RN DON.
Licensure Skilled care. *Beds* SNF 99. *Certified* Medicare; Medi-Cal.
Owner Proprietary Corp (American Med Services Inc).
Admissions Requirements Minimum age 18; Physician's request.
Staff Physicians 1 (ft); RNs 5 (ft), 1 (pt); LPNs 14 (ft); Nurses aides 51 (pt); Physical therapists 1 (pt); Reality therapists 1 (pt); Recreational therapists 2 (ft); Occupational therapists 1 (pt); Speech therapists 1 (pt); Activities coordinators 1 (ft); Dietitians 1 (ft); Ophthalmologists 1 (pt).
Languages Spanish, German, French
Facilities Dining room; Physical therapy room; Activities room; Crafts room; Barber/Beauty shop; Library; Enclosed patio; Indoor garden.
Activities Arts & crafts; Cards; Games; Reading groups; Prayer groups; Movies; Shopping trips; Social/Cultural gatherings; Annual ice cream social.

Mayflower Gardens Convalescent Hospital
6705 W Ave M, Lancaster, CA, 93534
(805) 943-3212
Admin Paul G Dumin. *Medical Dir/Dir of Nursing* C Pathmarajah MD; C Fletcher RN GNP.
Licensure Skilled care. *Beds* SNF 48. *Certified* Medicare; Medi-Cal.
Owner Nonprofit Corp.
Admissions Requirements Physician's request.
Staff Physicians 1 (ft), 3 (pt); RNs 1 (ft), 1 (pt); LPNs 5 (ft), 1 (pt); Nurses aides 14 (ft), 2 (pt); Physical therapists 1 (pt); Recreational therapists 1 (ft); Speech therapists 1 (pt); Activities coordinators 1 (ft); Dietitians 1 (ft); Ophthalmologists 1 (pt); GNP 1 (ft).
Facilities Dining room; Physical therapy room; Activities room; Crafts room; Barber/Beauty shop; Library.
Activities Arts & crafts; Games; Reading groups; Prayer groups; Movies; Shopping trips; Social/Cultural gatherings.

LARKSPUR

Tamalpais*
501 Via Casitas, Larkspur, CA, 94904
(415) 461-2300

Admin Robert E Vidaurri.
Licensure Skilled care; Intermediate care. *Beds* SNF 25; ICF 27.
Owner Nonprofit Corp.

LAWNDALE

Park Imperial Lodge*
15100 S Prairie Blvd, Lawndale, CA, 90250
(213) 679-3344
Admin Katy Link. *Medical Dir/Dir of Nursing* Darryl Hutchison.
Licensure Skilled care. *Beds* 59. *Certified* Medicare; Medi-Cal.
Owner Proprietary Corp.
Admissions Requirements Physician's request.
Staff Physicians 11 (pt); RNs 1 (ft), 2 (pt); LPNs 5 (ft), 2 (pt); Nurses aides 18 (ft), 4 (pt); Physical therapists 1 (pt); Recreational therapists 1 (pt); Speech therapists 1 (pt); Activities coordinators 1 (ft); Dietitians 1 (pt); Dentists 1 (pt); Ophthalmologists 1 (pt); Podiatrists 1 (pt).
Facilities Dining room; Activities room; Laundry room; Barber/Beauty shop.
Activities Arts & crafts; Cards; Games; Reading groups; Prayer groups; Shopping trips; Social/Cultural gatherings.

LEMON GROVE

Cresta Loma Convalescent & Guest Home
7922 Palm St, Lemon Grove, CA, 92045
(714) 464-3488
Admin Phillip O Jordan. *Medical Dir/Dir of Nursing* Simon Brumbaugh.
Licensure Skilled care. *Beds* SNF 99. *Certified* Medicare; Medi-Cal.
Owner Proprietary Corp.
Admissions Requirements Medical examination; Physician's request.
Staff RNs 3 (ft), 1 (pt); LPNs 7 (ft), 4 (pt); Orderlies 3 (ft); Nurses aides 30 (ft), 4 (pt); Physical therapists 2 (pt); Activities coordinators 2 (pt); Dietitians 1 (pt).
Languages Spanish, Tagalog
Facilities Dining room; Physical therapy room; Activities room; Chapel; Crafts room; Laundry room; Barber/Beauty shop; Patios.
Activities Arts & crafts; Cards; Games; Reading groups; Prayer groups; Movies; Shopping trips; Social/Cultural gatherings; Music concerts.

Lemon Grove Convalescent Center*
8351 Broadway, Lemon Grove, CA, 92045
(714) 463-0294
Admin Alma E Howe.
Licensure Skilled care. *Beds* 165. *Certified* Medicare; Medi-Cal.
Owner Proprietary Corp (Care Enterprises).

Monte Vista Lodge
2211 Massachusetts Ave, Lemon Grove, CA, 92045
(619) 465-1331
Admin Violet M Hertzberg. *Medical Dir/Dir of Nursing* Eunice Simmons MD.
Licensure Skilled care. *Beds* 21.
Owner Proprietary Corp.
Facilities Dining room; Activities room; Chapel; Crafts room; Laundry room; Barber/Beauty shop; Library.
Activities Arts & crafts; Cards; Games; Prayer groups; Shopping trips; Social/Cultural gatherings.

LIVERMORE

Hacienda Convalescent Hospitals Inc*
76 Fenton St, Livermore, CA, 94550
(415) 443-1800
Admin Marjorie Stout. *Medical Dir/Dir of Nursing* Lionel Pfefer MD.
Licensure Skilled care. *Beds* 83. *Certified* Medicare; Medi-Cal.
Owner Proprietary Corp (Hillhaven Corp).

Admissions Requirements Physician's request.
Staff Physicians 1 (pt); RNs 4 (ft), 1 (pt); LPNs 4 (ft), 4 (pt); Physical therapists 1 (pt); Speech therapists 1 (pt); Activities coordinators 2 (pt); Dietitians 1 (ft), 1 (pt); Dentists 1 (pt); Podiatrists 1 (pt).
Facilities Dining room; Physical therapy room; Activities room; Barber/Beauty shop; Library.
Activities Arts & crafts; Cards; Games; Prayer groups; Shopping trips; Social/Cultural gatherings.

Livermore Manor Convalescent Hospital
788 Holmes St, Livermore, CA, 94550
(415) 447-2280
Admin Ruth Murphy. *Medical Dir/Dir of Nursing* L M Pfefer MD; Judy Johnson RN DON.
Licensure Skilled care. *Beds* SNF 37. *Certified* Medicare.
Owner Privately owned.
Admissions Requirements Medical examination; Physician's request.
Staff Physicians 1 (pt); RNs 1 (ft), 2 (pt); LPNs 3 (ft), 2 (pt); Nurses aides; Activities coordinators 1 (pt); Dietitians 1 (pt); Ophthalmologists 1 (pt).
Languages Spanish
Facilities Dining room; Laundry room.
Activities Arts & crafts; Games; Reading groups; Prayer groups; Movies; Shopping trips; Social/Cultural gatherings.

LIVINGSTON

Grace Nursing Home
13435 W Peach Ave, Livingston, CA, 95334
(209) 394-2440
Admin Wilmont Koehn. *Medical Dir/Dir of Nursing* Donald F Harrington MD; Joy Nightengale RN DON.
Licensure Skilled care. *Beds* SNF 33. *Certified* Medi-Cal.
Owner Nonprofit Corp.
Admissions Requirements Medical examination; Physician's request.
Staff Physicians 9 (pt); RNs 2 (ft), 3 (pt); LPNs 1 (ft), 3 (pt); Physical therapists 8 (ft), 10 (pt); Activities coordinators 1 (ft); Dietitians 1 (pt); Ophthalmologists 1 (pt).
Languages Spanish, Dutch
Affiliation Church of God
Facilities Dining room; Activities room; Chapel; Crafts room; Laundry room.
Activities Arts & crafts; Games; Reading groups; Prayer groups; Bible study.

LODI

Bechthold Convalescent Hospital*
610 S Fairmout Ave, Lodi, CA, 95240
(209) 368-1374
Admin Greg Christensen.
Licensure Skilled care; Intermediate care. *Beds* SNF 25; ICF 3. *Certified* Medicare; Medi-Cal.
Owner Proprietary Corp.
Staff RNs 1 (ft), 1 (pt); LPNs 20 (ft), 4 (pt); Nurses aides 12 (ft), 6 (pt); Activities coordinators 1 (pt).
Facilities Dining room; Physical therapy room; Activities room; Laundry room.
Activities Arts & crafts; Games; Reading groups; Prayer groups; Movies.

Delta Convalescent Hospital
1334 S Ham Ln, Lodi, CA, 95242
(209) 334-3825
Admin Albert C Cross. *Medical Dir/Dir of Nursing* Paul M Inae MD; Cheryl Novak RN.
Licensure Skilled care. *Beds* SNF 74. *Certified* Medicare; Medi-Cal.
Owner Privately owned.
Admissions Requirements Physician's request.

Staff Physicians 1 (pt); RNs 3 (ft), 2 (pt); LPNs 5 (ft), 4 (pt); Nurses aides 28 (ft), 10 (pt); Physical therapists 2 (pt); Activities coordinators 2 (ft); Dietitians 1 (pt).
Languages Tagalog, Spanish
Facilities Dining room; Physical therapy room; Activities room; Crafts room; Laundry room; Barber/Beauty shop; Library.
Activities Arts & crafts; Games; Reading groups; Prayer groups; Movies; Shopping trips; Social/Cultural gatherings.

Fairmont Rehabilitation Hospital*
950 S Fairmont Ave, Lodi, CA, 95240
(209) 368-0693
Admin L Samuelson. *Medical Dir/Dir of Nursing* Dr Williams.
Licensure Skilled care. *Beds* 59. *Certified* Medicare; Medi-Cal.
Owner Proprietary Corp (Beverly Enterprises).

Gross Convalescent Hospital
321 W Turner Rd, Lodi, CA, 95240
(209) 334-3760
Admin Paul G Gross MA. *Medical Dir/Dir of Nursing* Dr Ming.
Licensure Skilled care. *Beds* 90. *Certified* Medicare; Medi-Cal.
Owner Proprietary Corp.
Admissions Requirements Females only; Medical examination.
Staff RNs 3 (ft); LPNs 8 (ft); Nurses aides 38 (ft).
Languages Spanish, German, Japanese, Tagalog
Facilities Dining room; Physical therapy room; Activities room; Chapel; Crafts room; Laundry room; Barber/Beauty shop; Library.
Activities Arts & crafts; Cards; Games; Reading groups; Prayer groups; Movies; Shopping trips; Social/Cultural gatherings.

Vienna Golden State Convalescent Hospital*
800 S Ham Ln, Lodi, CA, 95240
(209) 368-7141
Admin Kenneth D Heffel.
Licensure Skilled care. *Beds* 134. *Certified* Medicare; Medi-Cal.
Owner Proprietary Corp.

Vista Ray Convalescent Hospital*
1120 Sylvia Dr, Lodi, CA, 95240
(209) 368-6641
Admin Alfred Johnson.
Licensure Skilled care. *Beds* 72. *Certified* Medicare; Medi-Cal.
Owner Proprietary Corp.

Vista Ray Convalescent Hospital 2*
1108 Sylvia Dr, Lodi, CA, 95240
(209) 368-0677
Admin Alfred Johnson.
Licensure Skilled care. *Beds* 42. *Certified* Medicare; Medi-Cal.
Owner Proprietary Corp.

LOMA LINDA

Heritage Gardens*
25271 Barton Rd, Loma Linda, CA, 92354
(714) 796-0216
Admin J William Westphal. *Medical Dir/Dir of Nursing* Raymond West MD.
Licensure Skilled care. *Beds* 103. *Certified* Medicare; Medi-Cal.
Owner Proprietary Corp.
Facilities Dining room; Physical therapy room; Activities room; Crafts room; Laundry room; Barber/Beauty shop; Library.
Activities Arts & crafts; Games; Prayer groups; Shopping trips.

Linda Valley Convalescent Hospital*
25383 Cole St, Loma Linda, CA, 92354
(714) 796-0235
Admin Dinning R Clifford.

Licensure Skilled care. *Beds* 83. *Certified* Medicare; Medi-Cal.
Owner Proprietary Corp.

Mt View Child Care Center Inc*
10132 Mount View Ave, Loma Linda, CA, 92354
(714) 796-0030
Admin Gail Horrigan. *Medical Dir/Dir of Nursing* Dr Robert McCormick.
Licensure Intermediate care for mentally retarded. *Beds* 59. *Certified* Medi-Cal.
Owner Proprietary Corp.
Admissions Requirements Minimum age Birth.
Staff Physicians; RNs; Orderlies; Nurses aides; Physical therapists; Recreational therapists; Occupational therapists; Speech therapists; Activities coordinators; Dietitians; Dentists; Ophthalmologists; Audiologists.
Facilities Dining room; Activities room; Laundry room.
Activities Arts & crafts; Games; Movies; Shopping trips.

LOMITA

Lomita Golden Age Convalescent Home*
1955 W Lomita Blvd, Lomita, CA, 90717
(213) 325-1970
Admin Iris Doiron. *Medical Dir/Dir of Nursing* Stephen Russell MD.
Licensure Skilled care. *Beds* 71. *Certified* Medicare; Medi-Cal.
Owner Proprietary Corp (National Heritage).

Peninsula Rehabilitation Center*
26303 S Western Ave, Lomita, CA, 90717
(213) 325-3202
Admin Jerry Sass.
Licensure Skilled care. *Beds* 48. *Certified* Medicare; Medi-Cal.
Owner Proprietary Corp.

LOMPOC

Lompoc Hospital District Convalescent Care Center*
3rd & Walnut Sts, Lompoc, CA, 93436
(805) 736-3466
Admin William E Diebner.
Licensure Skilled care; Intermediate care. *Beds* SNF 50; ICF 24. *Certified* Medicare; Medi-Cal.
Owner Publicly owned.

LONE PINE

Southern Inyo County Sanatorium*
103 Pangborn, Lone Pine, CA, 93545
(714) 876-5537
Admin Michael Cosenza.
Licensure Skilled care. *Beds* 51. *Certified* Medicare; Medi-Cal.
Owner Publicly owned.

LONG BEACH

Akin's Convalescent Hospital*
2750 Atlantic Ave, Long Beach, CA, 90806
(213) 424-8101
Admin Ronald M Akin.
Licensure Skilled care. *Beds* 109. *Certified* Medicare; Medi-Cal.
Owner Proprietary Corp.

Alamitos Belmont Rehabilitation Hospital
3901 E 4th St, Long Beach, CA, 90814
(213) 434-8421
Admin Alan H Anderson. *Medical Dir/Dir of Nursing* Robert Pinder MD; Helen Scalera RN.
Licensure Skilled care. *Beds* 97. *Certified* Medicare; Medi-Cal.
Owner Proprietary Corp.
Admissions Requirements Physician's request.

Staff Physicians 6 (pt); RNs 10 (ft), 8 (pt); LPNs 10 (ft), 6 (pt); Nurses aides 36 (ft), 28 (pt); Physical therapists 8 (ft); Recreational therapists 1 (ft), 2 (pt); Occupational therapists 4 (ft), 1 (pt); Speech therapists 1 (ft), 2 (pt); Dietitians 1 (ft); Dentists 1 (pt); Podiatrists 1 (pt).
Facilities Dining room; Physical therapy room; Activities room; Crafts room; Laundry room; Barber/Beauty shop; Occupational therapy; Conference rooms.
Activities Arts & crafts; Cards; Games; Reading groups; Prayer groups; Movies; Shopping trips; Social/Cultural gatherings; Special dinners & luncheons.

Bay Convalescent Hospital
5901 Downey Ave, Long Beach, CA, 90805
(213) 636-1961, 634-4693
Admin Eli Berkovits. *Medical Dir/Dir of Nursing* Frank A James MD; June Carnes RN.
Licensure Skilled care. *Beds* SNF 70. *Certified* Medicaid; Medicare; Medi-Cal.
Owner Proprietary Corp.
Admissions Requirements Minimum age 18; Medical examination; Physician's request.
Staff RNs 1 (ft), 1 (pt); LPNs 5 (ft), 2 (pt); Nurses aides 20 (ft), 7 (pt); Activities coordinators 1 (ft); Dietitians 3 (ft).
Languages Spanish
Facilities Dining room; Physical therapy room; Activities room; Crafts room; Laundry room; Barber/Beauty shop.
Activities Arts & crafts; Cards; Games; Reading groups; Prayer groups; Movies; Social/Cultural gatherings.

Bel Vista Convalescent Hospital Inc*
5001 E Anaheim St, Long Beach, CA, 90804
(213) 494-5001
Admin Hilary Pomatto & Irene Pomatto.
Licensure Skilled care. *Beds* 46. *Certified* Medicare; Medi-Cal.
Owner Proprietary Corp.
Admissions Requirements Medical examination; Physician's request.
Staff RNs 3 (ft); LPNs 4 (ft); Nurses aides 24 (ft); Physical therapists 1 (pt); Reality therapists 1 (pt); Recreational therapists 1 (pt); Activities coordinators 1 (ft).
Activities Arts & crafts; Games; Prayer groups.

Bixby Knolls Towers Nursing Home
3747 Atlantic Ave, Long Beach, CA, 90807
(213) 426-6123
Licensure Skilled care. *Beds* 99. *Certified* Medicare; Medi-Cal.
Owner Nonprofit Corp.

California Convalescent Hospital*
3850 E Esther St, Long Beach, CA, 90804
(213) 498-3368
Admin Sharon Kurtz. *Medical Dir/Dir of Nursing* Thomas Hendon MD.
Licensure Skilled care. *Beds* 99. *Certified* Medicare; Medi-Cal.
Owner Proprietary Corp.
Facilities Dining room; Barber/Beauty shop.
Activities Arts & crafts; Cards; Games; Reading groups; Prayer groups; Movies; Social/Cultural gatherings.

Catered Manor
4010 Virginia Rd, Long Beach, CA, 90807
(213) 426-0394
Admin Sara Thomas. *Medical Dir/Dir of Nursing* Marvin Zamost MD.
Licensure Skilled care. *Beds* SNF 83. *Certified* Medicare; Medi-Cal.
Owner Proprietary Corp (Beverly Enterprises).
Admissions Requirements Minimum age 18; Physician's request.
Staff RNs 2 (ft); LPNs 6 (ft), 2 (pt); Nurses aides 35 (ft); Activities coordinators 1 (ft); Dietitians 1 (ft).
Languages Spanish, Tagalog

Facilities Dining room; Activities room; Crafts room; Laundry room; Barber/Beauty shop.
Activities Arts & crafts; Cards; Games; Reading groups; Prayer groups; Movies; Shopping trips; Social/Cultural gatherings.

Centralia Convalescent Center Inc*
5401 E Centralia St, Long Beach, CA, 90808
(213) 421-4717
Admin Leonard Einhorn. *Medical Dir/Dir of Nursing* Francis James MD.
Licensure Skilled care. *Beds* 109. *Certified* Medicare; Medi-Cal.
Owner Proprietary Corp (Health Care Grp).
Staff RNs; LPNs; Orderlies; Nurses aides; Physical therapists; Recreational therapists; Speech therapists; Activities coordinators; Dietitians; Dentists; Ophthalmologists; Podiatrists; Audiologists.
Facilities Dining room; Physical therapy room; Activities room; Crafts room; Laundry room; Barber/Beauty shop; Library.
Activities Arts & crafts; Cards; Games; Reading groups; Prayer groups; Movies; Shopping trips.

Coastview Convalescent Hospital*
455 Columbia St, Long Beach, CA, 90806
(213) 426-0537
Admin Charles Bird.
Licensure Skilled care. *Beds* 150. *Certified* Medicare; Medi-Cal.
Owner Proprietary Corp.

Colonial Manor Convalescent Hospital—Extended Care Facility*
1913 E 5th St, Long Beach, CA, 90812
(213) 432-5751
Admin John B Hornung.
Licensure Skilled care. *Beds* 181. *Certified* Medicare; Medi-Cal.
Owner Proprietary Corp.

Columbia Convalescent Home
521 E Columbia St, Long Beach, CA, 90806
(213) 426-2557
Admin Zoltan Schwartz. *Medical Dir/Dir of Nursing* David Bockoff; Mara Lyn Miller Rn.
Licensure Skilled care. *Beds* 48. *Certified* Medicaid; Medicare; Medi-Cal.
Owner Privately owned.
Admissions Requirements Minimum age 40; Medical examination; Physician's request.
Staff RNs 1 (ft), 1 (pt); Nurses aides 15 (ft), 5 (pt); Activities coordinators 1 (ft);; LVN 3 (ft), 2 (pt).
Languages Spanish, Tagalog
Facilities Dining room; Activities room; Laundry room; Barber/Beauty shop.
Activities Arts & crafts; Cards; Games; Reading groups; Prayer groups; Movies; Social/Cultural gatherings.

Crest Knoll Convalescent Hospital*
260 E Market St, Long Beach, CA, 90805
(213) 774-2872
Admin Karlin Reich Schultz. *Medical Dir/Dir of Nursing* Dr Platt.
Licensure Skilled care. *Beds* 112. *Certified* Medicare; Medi-Cal.
Owner Proprietary Corp.
Admissions Requirements Medical examination; Physician's request.
Staff RNs 5 (ft), 5 (pt); LPNs 8 (ft), 10 (pt); Orderlies 5 (ft), 2 (pt); Nurses aides 35 (ft), 3 (pt); Activities coordinators 1 (ft).

Eastwood Convalescent Hospital*
4029 E Anaheim St, Long Beach, CA, 90804
(213) 434-4421
Admin Ronald M Akin. *Medical Dir/Dir of Nursing* David E Jewell MD.
Licensure Skilled care. *Beds* 75. *Certified* Medicare; Medi-Cal.
Owner Proprietary Corp.
Admissions Requirements Minimum age 18; Medical examination; Physician's request.

Staff RNs 2 (ft), 1 (pt); LPNs 6 (ft), 1 (pt); Orderlies 1 (ft); Nurses aides 27 (ft), 3 (pt); Activities coordinators; Dietitians.
Facilities Dining room; Activities room; Laundry room; Barber/Beauty shop.
Activities Arts & crafts; Cards; Games; Reading groups; Prayer groups; Movies; Shopping trips; Social/Cultural gatherings.

Edgewater Convalescent Hospital*
2625 E 4th St, Long Beach, CA, 90814
(213) 434-0974
Admin Debbie Ketland Krevel. *Medical Dir/ Dir of Nursing* Dr Paul Lorhan.
Licensure Skilled care. *Beds* 81. *Certified* Medicare; Medi-Cal.
Owner Proprietary Corp.
Admissions Requirements Minimum age 21; Physician's request.
Facilities Dining room; Physical therapy room; Activities room; Crafts room; Laundry room; Barber/Beauty shop; Library.
Activities Arts & crafts; Cards; Games; Reading groups; Prayer groups; Movies; Shopping trips; Social/Cultural gatherings.

Empress Convalescent Center
1020 Termino Ave, Long Beach, CA, 90804
(213) 433-6791
Admin James A & Dorothy Pine.
Licensure Skilled care. *Beds* SNF 133. *Certified* Medicare; Medi-Cal.
Owner Proprietary Corp.
Admissions Requirements Physician's request.

Ennoble Center of Long Beach*
2666 Grand Ave, Long Beach, CA, 90815
(213) 426-8187
Admin Tom Williams.
Licensure Intermediate care; Intermediate care for mentally retarded. *Beds* 99.
Owner Nonprofit Corp.

Extended Care Hospital of Long Beach*
3232 E Artesia Blvd, Long Beach, CA, 90805
(213) 423-6401
Admin Norman Miller. *Medical Dir/Dir of Nursing* Dr Platt.
Licensure Skilled care. *Beds* 240. *Certified* Medicare; Medi-Cal.
Owner Proprietary Corp.
Admissions Requirements Minimum age 18.
Staff RNs 5 (ft), 4 (pt); LPNs 14 (ft), 7 (pt); Orderlies 8 (ft), 2 (pt); Nurses aides 33 (ft), 14 (pt); Activities coordinators 1 (ft); Dietitians 1 (ft).
Facilities Dining room; Physical therapy room; Activities room; Laundry room; Barber/Beauty shop.
Activities Arts & crafts; Cards; Games; Reading groups; Prayer groups; Movies.

Grand Avenue Convalescent Hospital
1730 Grand Ave, Long Beach, CA, 80804
(213) 597-8817
Admin Ben C Jakobovits. *Medical Dir/Dir of Nursing* Marvelle Harris Pruitt.
Licensure Skilled care. *Beds* SNF 117. *Certified* Medicare; Medi-Cal.
Owner Proprietary Corp.
Admissions Requirements Medical examination; Physician's request.
Staff Physicians; RNs; LPNs; Orderlies; Nurses aides; Physical therapists; Occupational therapists; Speech therapists; Activities coordinators; Dietitians; Ophthalmologists.
Facilities Dining room; Physical therapy room; Activities room; Crafts room; Laundry room; Barber/Beauty shop.
Activities Arts & crafts; Cards; Games; Reading groups; Prayer groups; Movies.

Hacienda Convalescent Hospital
2725 E Broadway, Long Beach, CA, 90803
(213) 434-4494
Admin Iris J Doiron. *Medical Dir/Dir of Nursing* Edward R Woerz MD; Shirley McDougal RN DON.

Licensure Skilled care. *Beds* SNF 98. *Certified* Medicare; Medi-Cal.
Owner Proprietary Corp.
Admissions Requirements Physician's request.
Staff Physicians 3 (pt); RNs 3 (ft); LPNs 9 (ft), 3 (pt); Orderlies 6 (ft); Nurses aides 30 (ft); Physical therapists 3 (pt); Recreational therapists 1 (pt); Occupational therapists 2 (pt); Speech therapists 1 (pt); Activities coordinators 1 (ft); Dietitians 1 (pt); Dentists 1 (pt); Ophthalmologists 1 (pt); Podiatrists 1 (pt); Dentist 1 (pt).
Languages Spanish
Facilities Dining room; Physical therapy room; Activities room; Barber/Beauty shop.
Activities Arts & crafts; Cards; Games; Reading groups; Prayer groups; Movies; Monthly outings.

Hillcrest Convalescent Hospital Inc
3401 Cedar Ave, Long Beach, CA, 90807
(213) 426-4461
Admin Teresita Valdez. *Medical Dir/Dir of Nursing* Robert Clough MD; P Tana.
Licensure Skilled care. *Beds* SNF 154. *Certified* Medicare; Medi-Cal.
Owner Proprietary Corp.
Admissions Requirements Minimum age 18; Medical examination; Physician's request.
Staff RNs 4 (ft), 3 (pt); LPNs 12 (ft), 7 (pt); Orderlies 6 (ft); Nurses aides 50 (ft), 3 (pt); Activities coordinators 1 (ft), 1 (pt).
Languages Spanish, Tagalog, Russian, Romanian, Hebrew, Yiddish, French, German, Thai
Facilities Dining room; Physical therapy room; Activities room; Crafts room; Laundry room; Barber/Beauty shop; Educational room.
Activities Arts & crafts; Cards; Games; Reading groups; Prayer groups; Movies; Shopping trips; Social/Cultural gatherings; Reality orientation; Group sessions; Current events; Entertainment by special groups; Music; Rhythm band; Cartoon shows; Cocktails; Music.

Intercommunity Sanitarium*
2626 Grand Ave, Long Beach, CA, 90815
(213) 427-8915
Admin Robert L Pruitt.
Licensure Skilled care. *Beds* 147. *Certified* Medi-Cal.
Owner Nonprofit Corp.

Marlora Manor Convalescent Hospital*
3801 E Anaheim St, Long Beach, CA, 90804
(213) 494-3311
Admin Marilyn Hauser.
Licensure Skilled care. *Beds* 99. *Certified* Medicare; Medi-Cal.
Owner Proprietary Corp.

Palmcrest Medallion Convalescent Hospital*
3355 Pacific Pl, Long Beach, CA, 90806
(213) 595-4336
Admin Shirley H Feingold. *Medical Dir/Dir of Nursing* George Bryant MD.
Licensure Skilled care. *Beds* 99. *Certified* Medicare; Medi-Cal.
Owner Proprietary Corp.
Admissions Requirements Minimum age 55; Medical examination; Physician's request.
Staff Physicians 1 (pt); RNs 2 (ft), 1 (pt); LPNs 7 (ft), 1 (pt); Nurses aides 35 (ft), 6 (pt); Physical therapists 1 (ft), 1 (pt); Reality therapists 1 (pt); Recreational therapists 1 (ft); Occupational therapists 1 (ft); Speech therapists 1 (pt); Dietitians 1 (pt); Dentists 1 (pt); Podiatrists 1 (pt).
Facilities Dining room; Physical therapy room; Activities room; Chapel; Laundry room; Barber/Beauty shop.
Activities Arts & crafts; Games; Reading groups; Prayer groups; Movies; Social/ Cultural gatherings.

Palmcrest North Convalescent Hospital*
3501 Cedar Ave, Long Beach, CA, 90807
(213) 595-1731
Admin Richard Feingold. *Medical Dir/Dir of Nursing* David B Bockoff MD.
Licensure Skilled care. *Beds* 99. *Certified* Medicare; Medi-Cal.
Owner Proprietary Corp.
Admissions Requirements Minimum age 40; Medical examination; Physician's request.
Staff RNs 2 (ft), 1 (pt); LPNs 8 (ft), 1 (pt); Orderlies 5 (ft); Nurses aides 55 (ft); Recreational therapists 1 (ft); Activities coordinators 1 (ft); Dietitians 1 (ft); Podiatrists 1 (pt).
Facilities Dining room; Physical therapy room; Activities room; Crafts room; Laundry room; Barber/Beauty shop; Library; Theater; Art Gallery; Greenhouse.
Activities Arts & crafts; Cards; Games; Reading groups; Prayer groups; Movies; Shopping trips; Social/Cultural gatherings; Art show openings; Special entertainment.

Royal Care Skilled Nursing Facility*
2725 Pacific Ave, Long Beach, CA, 90806
(213) 427-7493
Admin Gerald Price.
Licensure Skilled care. *Beds* 98. *Certified* Medicare; Medi-Cal.
Owner Proprietary Corp.

Santa Fe Convalescent Hospital*
3294 Santa Fe Ave, Long Beach, CA, 90810
(213) 424-0757
Admin Michael Kremer.
Licensure Skilled care. *Beds* 87. *Certified* Medicare; Medi-Cal.
Owner Proprietary Corp.

Walnut Convalescent Hospital
1201 Walnut Ave, Long Beach, CA, 90813
(213) 434-4224
Admin John Mryze. *Medical Dir/Dir of Nursing* Alan Greenburg MD; Linda Bince RN DON.
Licensure Skilled care. *Beds* SNF 78. *Certified* Medicaid; Medicare; Medi-Cal.
Owner Proprietary Corp.
Admissions Requirements Minimum age 40; Medical examination; Physician's request.
Staff RNs 2 (ft); LPNs 11 (ft); Orderlies 3 (ft); Nurses aides 40 (ft); Activities coordinators 1 (ft); Dietitians 1 (ft).
Languages Spanish
Facilities Dining room; Physical therapy room; Activities room; Crafts room; Laundry room; Barber/Beauty shop; Library.
Activities Arts & crafts; Cards; Games; Reading groups; Prayer groups; Shopping trips; Social/Cultural gatherings; Movie videos.

Willow Lake Convalescent Hospital*
2615 Grand Ave, Long Beach, CA, 90815
(213) 426-6141
Admin Margaret F Emery.
Licensure Skilled care. *Beds* 160. *Certified* Medicare; Medi-Cal.
Owner Nonprofit Corp.

LOS ALAMITOS

Alamitos West Convalescent Hospital
3902 Katella Ave, Los Alamitos, CA, 90720
(213) 596-5561 or (714) 821-8580
Admin Nita Lindsey. *Medical Dir/Dir of Nursing* John Cowles MD.
Licensure Skilled care. *Beds* 199. *Certified* Medicare; Medi-Cal.
Owner Privately owned.
Admissions Requirements Minimum age 50; Physician's request.
Staff RNs 8 (ft), 3 (pt); LPNs 24 (ft), 8 (pt); Orderlies 10 (ft); Nurses aides 42 (ft); Activities coordinators 3 (ft), 1 (pt).
Languages Spanish, Asian

Facilities Dining room; Physical therapy room; Activities room; Crafts room; Laundry room; Barber/Beauty shop; Library.
Activities Arts & crafts; Cards; Games; Reading groups; Prayer groups; Movies.

LOS ALTOS

Beverly Manor Convalescent Hospital*
809 Fremont Ave, Los Altos, CA, 94022
(415) 941-5255
Admin Karen Faria.
Licensure Skilled care. *Beds* 152. *Certified* Medicare; Medi-Cal.
Owner Proprietary Corp (Beverly Enterprises).

Pilgrim Haven Home
373 Pine Ln, Los Altos, CA, 94022
(415) 948-8291
Admin William G Maxwell. *Medical Dir/Dir of Nursing* Harold Cramer MD; Edith Azevedo RN DON.
Licensure Skilled care; Retirement home. *Beds* SNF 66; Retirement home 127. *Certified* Medicare; Medi-Cal.
Owner Nonprofit Corp (American Baptist Homes W).
Admissions Requirements Minimum age 62; Medical examination.
Staff RNs 11 (pt); LPNs 2 (pt); Nurses aides 18 (ft), 8 (pt); Activities coordinators 1 (ft), 1 (pt); Dietitians 1 (ft).
Affiliation Baptist
Facilities Dining room; Activities room; Chapel; Crafts room; Laundry room; Barber/Beauty shop; Library.
Activities Arts & crafts; Cards; Games; Shopping trips; Social/Cultural gatherings.

LOS ANGELES

Alcott Rehabilitation Hospital*
3551 W Olympic Blvd, Los Angeles, CA, 90019
(213) 737-2000
Admin Belle Yarmish. *Medical Dir/Dir of Nursing* Stephnie DeClouette.
Licensure Skilled care. *Beds* SNF 121. *Certified* Medicare; Medi-Cal.
Owner Proprietary Corp.
Admissions Requirements Medical examination; Physician's request.
Staff Physicians 1 (pt); RNs 8 (ft); LPNs 10 (ft); Orderlies 10 (ft); Nurses aides 50 (ft); Physical therapists 5 (ft).
Languages Korean, Spanish
Facilities Dining room; Physical therapy room; Activities room; Chapel; Crafts room; Laundry room; Barber/Beauty shop; Library.
Activities Arts & crafts; Cards; Games; Reading groups; Prayer groups; Movies; Shopping trips; Social/Cultural gatherings.

Alden Terrace Convalescent Hospital
1241 S Lake St, Los Angeles, CA, 90006
(213) 382-8461
Admin Vivian Chianello. *Medical Dir/Dir of Nursing* Dr F Evans Powell.
Licensure Skilled care. *Beds* 121. *Certified* Medicare; Medi-Cal.
Owner Proprietary Corp.
Admissions Requirements Physician's request.
Facilities Dining room; Physical therapy room; Activities room; Crafts room; Laundry room; Barber/Beauty shop.
Activities Arts & crafts; Cards; Games; Reading groups; Prayer groups; Movies.

Alexandria Convalescent Hospital*
1515 N Alexandria, Los Angeles, CA, 90027
(213) 660-1800
Admin Salamon Mandel.
Licensure Skilled care. *Beds* 150. *Certified* Medicare; Medi-Cal.
Owner Proprietary Corp.

Alpha-Wilshire Convalescent Hospital*
915 S Crenshaw Blvd, Los Angeles, CA, 90019
(213) 937-5466
Admin David Elliott.
Licensure Skilled care. *Beds* 98. *Certified* Medicare; Medi-Cal.
Owner Proprietary Corp.

Amberwood Convalescent Hospital*
6071 York Blvd, Los Angeles, CA, 90042
(213) 254-3407
Admin Jacqueline R O'Connor. *Medical Dir/Dir of Nursing* Julita Phillips MD.
Licensure Skilled care. *Beds* 107. *Certified* Medicare; Medi-Cal.
Owner Proprietary Corp.
Admissions Requirements Minimum age 18.
Facilities Dining room; Physical therapy room; Activities room; Laundry room; Barber/Beauty shop.
Activities Arts & crafts; Cards; Games; Reading groups; Prayer groups; Movies; Social/Cultural gatherings.

Angels Nursing Center
415 S Union Ave, Los Angeles, CA, 90017
(213) 484-0784
Admin Michele Nichols. *Medical Dir/Dir of Nursing* M Salant MD; Lois Young RN DON.
Licensure Skilled care. *Beds* SNF 49. *Certified* Medicare; Medi-Cal.
Owner Privately owned.
Admissions Requirements Minimum age 30; Physician's request.
Staff RNs; Orderlies; Nurses aides; Physical therapists; Recreational therapists; Occupational therapists; Speech therapists; Activities coordinators; Dietitians; Ophthalmologists; Occupational therapists Dentist.
Facilities Dining room; Activities room; Laundry room.
Activities Arts & crafts; Cards; Games; Reading groups; Prayer groups; Shopping trips; Social/Cultural gatherings.

Ararat Convalescent Hospital
2373 Colorado Blvd, Los Angeles, CA, 90041
(213) 257-8012
Admin Lorraine M Thomas. *Medical Dir/Dir of Nursing* E H Janbazian RN.
Licensure Skilled care. *Beds* SNF 42. *Certified* Medicare; Medi-Cal.
Owner Nonprofit Corp.
Admissions Requirements Minimum age 65; Physician's request.
Staff Physicians 1 (pt); RNs 3 (ft); Nurses aides 13 (ft).
Languages Armenian, Arabic, Spanish, Turkish, Farsi, Russian, Italian
Facilities Dining room; Activities room.
Activities Arts & crafts; Cards; Games; Reading groups; Movies; Social/Cultural gatherings.

Beverly Manor of Los Angeles
3002 Rowena Ave, Los Angeles, CA, 90039
(213) 666-1544
Admin Marcia S Weldon. *Medical Dir/Dir of Nursing* Barbara Williams RN.
Licensure Skilled care. *Beds* SNF 131. *Certified* Medicare; Medi-Cal.
Owner Proprietary Corp (Beverly Enterprises).
Staff RNs 4 (ft), 2 (pt); LPNs 12 (ft), 4 (pt); Orderlies; Nurses aides; Recreational therapists; Activities coordinators.

Beverly Palms Rehabilitation Hospital
8000 Beverly Blvd, Los Angeles, CA, 90048
(213) 651-3200
Admin Salvador Atendido. *Medical Dir/Dir of Nursing* Lita Boter RN.
Licensure Skilled care; Short-term Rehab only. *Beds* SNF 41. *Certified* Medicare.
Owner Privately owned.

Staff RNs 4 (ft), 3 (pt); LPNs 8 (ft), 4 (pt); Orderlies 3 (ft); Nurses aides 15 (ft), 4 (pt); Physical therapists 4 (ft); Occupational therapists 2 (ft); Speech therapists 2 (ft); Activities coordinators 1 (ft); Dietitians 2 (ft); Ophthalmologists 1 (ft);; Physical therapy aides 4 (ft); Restorative nursing 1 (ft).
Languages Spanish, Yiddish
Affiliation Jewish
Facilities Dining room; Physical therapy room; Activities room; Crafts room; Library.
Activities Arts & crafts; Cards; Games; Reading groups; Prayer groups; Movies; Social/Cultural gatherings.

Bonnie Brae Manor Convalescent Hospital*
420 S Bonnie Brae, Los Angeles, CA, 90057
(213) 483-8144
Admin Leslie Grant.
Licensure Skilled care. *Beds* 59. *Certified* Medicare; Medi-Cal.
Owner Proprietary Corp.

Brier Oak Terrace Convalescent Center*
5154 Sunset Blvd, Los Angeles, CA, 90027
(213) 663-3951
Admin Frank J Garcia Jr. *Medical Dir/Dir of Nursing* Steven Jacobs MD.
Licensure Skilled care. *Beds* 159. *Certified* Medicare; Medi-Cal.
Owner Proprietary Corp.
Staff Physicians 22 (pt); RNs 5 (ft); LPNs 10 (ft); Orderlies 9 (ft); Nurses aides 22 (ft); Physical therapists 2 (pt); Reality therapists 1 (pt); Occupational therapists 1 (pt); Speech therapists 1 (pt); Activities coordinators 1 (ft); Dietitians 1 (pt); Dentists 1 (pt); Ophthalmologists 1 (pt); Podiatrists 1 (pt); Audiologists 1 (pt).
Facilities Dining room; Physical therapy room; Activities room; Crafts room; Laundry room; Barber/Beauty shop.
Activities Arts & crafts; Cards; Games; Reading groups; Prayer groups; Movies; Shopping trips; Social/Cultural gatherings.

Buena Ventura Convalescent Hospital
1016 S Record St, Los Angeles, CA, 90023
(213) 268-0106
Admin Wayne H Beck. *Medical Dir/Dir of Nursing* Louis T Bascoy MD.
Licensure Skilled care. *Beds* 99. *Certified* Medicare; Medi-Cal.
Owner Proprietary Corp.
Admissions Requirements Medical examination; Physician's request.
Staff RNs 2 (ft), 1 (pt); LPNs 6 (ft), 6 (pt); Orderlies 3 (ft), 1 (pt); Nurses aides 25 (ft), 8 (pt); Physical therapists 1 (pt); Occupational therapists 1 (pt); Speech therapists 1 (pt); Activities coordinators 1 (ft); Dietitians 1 (ft); Dentists 1 (pt); Ophthalmologists 1 (pt); Podiatrists 1 (pt).
Languages Korean, Tagalog, Spanish
Facilities Dining room; Physical therapy room; Activities room; Crafts room; Laundry room; Barber/Beauty shop.
Activities Arts & crafts; Cards; Games; Reading groups; Prayer groups; Movies; Shopping trips; Social/Cultural gatherings.

Burlington Convalescent Hospital*
845 S Burlington, Los Angeles, CA, 90048
(213) 381-5585
Admin Robert Jones.
Licensure Skilled care. *Beds* 124. *Certified* Medicare; Medi-Cal.
Owner Proprietary Corp.

California Convalescent Center 1*
909 S Lake St, Los Angeles, CA, 90006
(213) 385-7301
Admin James W Whitney.
Licensure Skilled care. *Beds* 66. *Certified* Medicare; Medi-Cal.
Owner Proprietary Corp.

California Convalescent Center 2
1154 S Alvarado St, Los Angeles, CA, 90006
(213) 385-1715
Admin L Domingo. *Medical Dir/Dir of
Nursing* Dr James L Meltzer MD; Annette F
Ordonia DON.
Licensure Skilled care. *Beds* 72. *Certified*
Medicaid; Medicare; Medi-Cal.
Owner Privately owned.
Admissions Requirements Minimum age 20.
Staff RNs 2 (ft), 1 (pt); LPNs 6 (ft); Orderlies
6 (ft); Nurses aides 19 (ft); Physical
therapists 1 (pt); Recreational therapists 1
(pt); Occupational therapists 1 (pt); Speech
therapists 1 (pt); Activities coordinators 1
(ft); Dietitians 1 (ft); Ophthalmologists 1
(pt); Podiatrists 1 (pt).
Languages Spanish, Tagalog
Facilities Dining room; Physical therapy
room; Activities room; Crafts room; Laundry
room; Barber/Beauty shop.
Activities Arts & crafts; Cards; Games;
Reading groups; Prayer groups; Movies;
Shopping trips; Social/Cultural gatherings.

Chandler Care Center—Fairfax*
1020 S Fairfax Ave, Los Angeles, CA, 90019
(213) 938-2451
Admin Charlotte Ulrich.
Licensure Skilled care. *Beds* 120. *Certified*
Medicare; Medi-Cal.
Owner Proprietary Corp.

Cheviot Garden Convalescent Hospital*
3533 Motor Ave, Los Angeles, CA, 90034
(213) 836-8900
Admin Rita Rohkar.
Licensure Skilled care. *Beds* 99. *Certified*
Medicare; Medi-Cal.
Owner Proprietary Corp.

College Vista Convalescent Hospital
4681 Eagle Rock Blvd, Los Angeles, CA,
90041
(213) 257-8151
Admin Lois M Pinkham. *Medical Dir/Dir of
Nursing* Albert Killian MD; V Gold RN.
Licensure Skilled care. *Beds* 49. *Certified*
Medicare; Medi-Cal.
Owner Proprietary Corp.
Admissions Requirements Minimum age 35;
Physician's request.
Staff Physicians; RNs; LPNs; Orderlies;
Nurses aides; Physical therapists;
Recreational therapists; Occupational
therapists; Speech therapists; Activities
coordinators; Dietitians; Dentists;
Ophthalmologists; Podiatrists.
Languages Spanish, German, Italian
Facilities Dining room; Activities room;
Laundry room; Barber/Beauty shop.
Activities Arts & crafts; Games; Reading
groups; Prayer groups; Movies; Shopping
trips.

Convalescent Care Center*
230 E Adams Blvd, Los Angeles, CA, 90011
(213) 748-0491
Admin Charles V Adams. *Medical Dir/Dir of
Nursing* William Cottles MD.
Licensure Skilled care. *Beds* 88. *Certified*
Medicare; Medi-Cal.
Owner Proprietary Corp.
Admissions Requirements Minimum age 18;
Physician's request.
Staff RNs 1 (ft), 4 (pt); LPNs 7 (ft), 6 (pt);
Orderlies 1 (pt); Nurses aides 21 (ft), 4 (pt);
Physical therapists 1 (pt); Activities
coordinators 1 (ft); Dietitians 1 (ft).

Convalescent Hospital Casa Descanso
4515 Huntington Dr S, Los Angeles, CA,
90032
(213) 225-5991
Admin Georgianna Tucci. *Medical Dir/Dir of
Nursing* Dr Marvin Salant; Margaret
Vickerson.

Licensure Skilled care. *Beds* SNF 104.
Certified Medi-Cal.
Owner Proprietary Corp.
Admissions Requirements Minimum age 55;
Medical examination; Physician's request.
Staff Physicians 7 (pt); RNs 4 (ft); LPNs 6
(ft); Orderlies 15 (ft); Nurses aides 33 (ft);
Physical therapists 1 (pt); Reality therapists
1 (pt); Recreational therapists 1 (pt);
Occupational therapists 1 (pt) 413J 1 (pt);
Activities coordinators 2 (ft); Dietitians 1
(ft), 1 (pt); Ophthalmologists 1 (pt);
Podiatrists 1 (pt).
Languages Spanish
Facilities Dining room; Activities room;
Crafts room; Laundry room; Barber/Beauty
shop.
Activities Arts & crafts; Cards; Games;
Reading groups; Prayer groups; Movies;
Shopping trips; Social/Cultural gatherings.

Coronado Sanitarium*
2534 Beverly Blvd, Los Angeles, CA, 90057
(213) 380-3186
Admin Lilly Binnbaum. *Medical Dir/Dir of
Nursing* Dr Ferdinand Kunze.
Licensure Skilled care. *Beds* 22. *Certified*
Medicare.
Owner Proprietary Corp.
Admissions Requirements Physician's request.
Facilities Dining room; Activities room;
Crafts room; Laundry room.
Activities Arts & crafts; Cards; Games;
Reading groups; Prayer groups.

Country Villa South Convalescent Center*
3515 Overland Ave, Los Angeles, CA, 90034
(213) 839-5201
Admin Stephen Reissman.
Licensure Skilled care. *Beds* 87. *Certified*
Medicare; Medi-Cal.
Owner Proprietary Corp (Country Villa Svc
Corp).

Country Villa Westwood
12121 Santa Monica Blvd, Los Angeles, CA,
90025
(213) 826-0821
Admin Carol De Petris. *Medical Dir/Dir of
Nursing* Alan Greenberg MD.
Licensure Skilled care. *Beds* SNF 93. *Certified*
Medicaid; Medicare; Medi-Cal.
Owner Proprietary Corp (Country Villa Svc
Corp).
Admissions Requirements Minimum age 18;
Physician's request.
Staff RNs 1 (ft), 4 (pt); LPNs 6 (ft), 2 (pt);
Orderlies 6 (ft); Nurses aides 32 (ft);
Physical therapists 1 (pt); Occupational
therapists 1 (pt); Speech therapists 1 (pt);
Activities coordinators 2 (ft); Dietitians 1
(pt); Dentists 1 (pt); Ophthalmologists 1 (pt);
Podiatrists 1 (pt).
Languages Spanish, Arabic
Facilities Dining room; Activities room;
Laundry room; Barber/Beauty shop.
Activities Arts & crafts; Cards; Games;
Reading groups; Prayer groups; Movies;
Shopping trips; Social/Cultural gatherings;
Beach trips.

Country Villa Wilshire*
855 N Fairfax Ave, Los Angeles, CA, 90046
(213) 870-8781
Admin T M Henry.
Licensure Skilled care. *Beds* 81. *Certified*
Medicare; Medi-Cal.
Owner Proprietary Corp (Country Villa Svc
Corp).

Crenshaw Nursing Home*
1900 S Longwood Ave, Los Angeles, CA,
90016
(213) 935-1158
Admin Brian Gaffney. *Medical Dir/Dir of
Nursing* Dr Powell.
Licensure Skilled care. *Beds* 55. *Certified*
Medicare; Medi-Cal.

Owner Proprietary Corp.
Admissions Requirements Minimum age 18.
Staff Physicians 9 (pt); RNs 3 (pt); LPNs 6
(ft); Orderlies 7 (ft); Nurses aides 45 (ft), 6
(pt); Physical therapists 1 (pt); Reality
therapists 1 (pt); Recreational therapists 1
(ft); Occupational therapists 1 (pt); Speech
therapists 1 (pt); Activities coordinators 1
(ft); Dietitians 1 (pt); Dentists 1 (pt);
Ophthalmologists 1 (pt); Podiatrists 1 (pt);
Audiologists 1 (pt).
Facilities Dining room; Physical therapy
room; Activities room; Crafts room; Laundry
room; Barber/Beauty shop.
Activities Arts & crafts; Cards; Games;
Reading groups; Prayer groups; Movies;
Social/Cultural gatherings; Monthly outings
to points of interest.

Culver West Convalescent Hospital
4035 Grandview Blvd, Los Angeles, CA,
90066
(213) 390-9506
Admin Florence Patton. *Medical Dir/Dir of
Nursing* Paul O Meyer MD.
Licensure Skilled care. *Beds* SNF 91. *Certified*
Medicare; Medi-Cal.
Owner Privately owned.
Admissions Requirements Physician's request.
Staff Physical therapists 1 (ft), 1 (pt);
Occupational therapists 1 (ft); Speech
therapists 1 (ft); Activities coordinators 1
(ft), 2 (pt); Dietitians 1 (pt);; Social Service 1
(ft).
Languages Korean, Japanese, Chinese,
Spanish
Facilities Dining room; Physical therapy
room; Activities room; Barber/Beauty shop;
Library; TV room.
Activities Arts & crafts; Games; Reading
groups; Prayer groups; Movies; Shopping
trips; Social/Cultural gatherings; Adopt-a-
grandparent.

Dunlap Sanitarium
6011 West Blvd, Los Angeles, CA, 90043
(213) 292-0748
Admin Mary F Jackson. *Medical Dir/Dir of
Nursing* R Cole MD; Edna Clements DON.
Licensure Skilled care. *Beds* SNF 40. *Certified*
Medicare; Medi-Cal.
Owner Privately owned.
Admissions Requirements Minimum age 50.
Staff Physicians; RNs; LPNs; Orderlies;
Nurses aides; Physical therapists; Reality
therapists; Recreational therapists; Speech
therapists; Activities coordinators; Dietitians;
Dentists; Ophthalmologists.
Facilities Dining room; Physical therapy
room; Activities room; Crafts room; Laundry
room; Barber/Beauty shop.
Activities Arts & crafts; Cards; Games;
Reading groups; Prayer groups; Shopping
trips; Social/Cultural gatherings.

East Los Angeles Convalescent Hospital
101 S Fickett St, Los Angeles, CA, 90033
(213) 261-8108
Admin Luzviminda Mondonedo. *Medical Dir/
Dir of Nursing* Louis T Bascoy; Candida
Cardones.
Licensure Skilled care. *Beds* SNF 99. *Certified*
Medicare; Medi-Cal.
Owner Proprietary Corp.
Admissions Requirements Physician's request.
Staff RNs 1 (ft); Orderlies; Nurses aides 24
(ft); Activities coordinators 1 (ft); LVNs 6
(ft).
Languages Spanish
Facilities Dining room; Activities room;
Crafts room; Laundry room.
Activities Arts & crafts; Cards; Games; Prayer
groups; Movies; Social/Cultural gatherings;
Trip to park.

Eastern Star Home*
11725 Sunset Blvd, Los Angeles, CA, 90049
(213) 472-1251

Admin Mary Lou McElroy.
Licensure Skilled care. *Beds* 38.
Owner Nonprofit Corp.
Affiliation Order of Eastern Star

Eaton Care Nursing Center*
3737 Don Felipe Dr, Los Angeles, CA, 90008
(213) 295-7737
Admin Larry J Will.
Licensure Skilled care. *Beds* 99. *Certified*
   Medicare; Medi-Cal.
Owner Proprietary Corp.

Echo Park Skilled Nursing Facility Hospital Inc
1633 E Echo Park Ave, Los Angeles, CA, 90026
(213) 628-4115
Admin Carolyn Madison.
Licensure Skilled care. *Beds* 59. *Certified*
   Medicare; Medi-Cal.
Owner Proprietary Corp.

Elizabeth Manor
340 S Alvarado, Los Angeles, CA, 90057
(213) 484-9730
Admin Varina Newcomb. *Medical Dir/Dir of Nursing* Robert Palmer MD.
Licensure Skilled care. *Beds* SNF 180.
   Certified Medi-Cal.
Owner Proprietary Corp (Medicrest of California).
Admissions Requirements Minimum age 65.
Staff RNs; LPNs; Orderlies; Nurses aides;
   Activities coordinators.
Facilities Dining room; Activities room;
   Laundry room; Barber/Beauty shop.
Activities Arts & crafts; Cards; Games;
   Reading groups; Prayer groups; Movies;
   Social/Cultural gatherings.

Extended Care Hospital of Los Angeles*
340 S Alvarado St, Los Angeles, CA, 90057
(213) 483-6520
Admin Raymond Marks.
Licensure Skilled care. *Beds* 180. *Certified*
   Medicare; Medi-Cal.
Owner Proprietary Corp.

Flora Terrace Convalescent Hospital Inc*
5916 W Pico Blvd, Los Angeles, CA, 90035
(213) 939-3184
Admin Flora Rosman.
Licensure Skilled care. *Beds* 66. *Certified*
   Medicare; Medi-Cal.
Owner Proprietary Corp.

Flora Terrace West Convalescent & Rehabilitation Hospital
6070 W Pico Blvd, Los Angeles, CA, 90035
(213) 653-3980
Admin Romy Rosman.
Licensure Skilled care. *Beds* 49. *Certified*
   Medicare; Medi-Cal.
Owner Proprietary Corp.

Fountain Gardens Convalescent Hospital*
2222 Santa Ana Blvd, Los Angeles, CA, 90059
(213) 564-4461
Admin Celia Markovitz.
Licensure Skilled care. *Beds* 99. *Certified*
   Medicare; Medi-Cal.
Owner Proprietary Corp.

Fountain View Convalescent Hospital
5310 Fountain Ave, Los Angeles, CA, 90029
(213) 461-9961
Admin Scott M Harmon.
Licensure Skilled care. *Beds* 99. *Certified*
   Medicare; Medi-Cal.
Owner Proprietary Corp.

Garden Crest Convalescent Hospital Inc*
909 N Lucile Ave, Los Angeles, CA, 90026
(213) 663-8281
Admin Lester Barron.
Licensure Skilled care. *Beds* 72. *Certified*
   Medicare; Medi-Cal.
Owner Proprietary Corp.

Garden Plaza Convalescent Hospital*
12029 S Avalon Blvd, Los Angeles, CA, 90061
(213) 756-8191
Admin William H Johnson.
Licensure Skilled care. *Beds* 99. *Certified*
   Medicare; Medi-Cal.
Owner Proprietary Corp.

Good Hope Convalescent Hospital*
2000 W Washington Blvd, Los Angeles, CA, 90018
(213) 735-5146
Admin Robert Smith.
Licensure Skilled care. *Beds* 93. *Certified*
   Medicare; Medi-Cal.
Owner Proprietary Corp.

Good Shepherd Nursing Home Inc
9705 Holmes Ave, Los Angeles, CA, 90002
(213) 564-7851
Admin Robert L Williams. *Medical Dir/Dir of Nursing* Rayfield Lewis MD; Althea Grady RN.
Licensure Skilled care. *Beds* SNF 32. *Certified* Medi-Cal.
Owner Proprietary Corp.
Admissions Requirements Physician's request.
Staff RNs 1 (ft), 1 (pt); LPNs 2 (ft), 3 (pt);
   Orderlies 1 (pt); Activities coordinators 1 (ft).
Facilities Dining room; Activities room;
   Crafts room; Laundry room.
Activities Arts & crafts; Cards; Games;
   Reading groups; Prayer groups; Social/
   Cultural gatherings; Exercise class.

Grand Park Convalescent Hospital*
2312 W 8th St, Los Angeles, CA, 90057
(213) 382-7315
Admin Jeanne Willard.
Licensure Skilled care. *Beds* 151. *Certified*
   Medicare; Medi-Cal.
Owner Proprietary Corp.

Guardian Rehabilitation Hospital
533 S Fairfax Ave, Los Angeles, CA, 90036
(213) 931-1061
Admin Sigmund Gest. *Medical Dir/Dir of Nursing* William J Zack MD; Virginia Tingzon RN DON.
Licensure Skilled care. *Beds* SNF 93. *Certified*
   Medicare; Medi-Cal.
Owner Proprietary Corp.
Admissions Requirements Minimum age 50;
   Medical examination; Physician's request.
Staff RNs; LPNs; Orderlies; Nurses aides;
   Physical therapists; Reality therapists;
   Recreational therapists; Occupational
   therapists; Speech therapists; Activities
   coordinators; Dietitians.
Languages Spanish, Tagalog, German
Facilities Dining room; Physical therapy
   room; Activities room; Crafts room; Laundry
   room; Barber/Beauty shop.
Activities Arts & crafts; Cards; Games;
   Reading groups; Movies; Shopping trips;
   Social/Cultural gatherings.

Hancock Park Convalescent Hospital & Rehabilitation Center
505 N La Brea Ave, Los Angeles, CA, 90036
(213) 937-4860
Admin Claire Padama. *Medical Dir/Dir of Nursing* William Wanamaker MD; Cyril Lazado DON.
Licensure Skilled care. *Beds* SNF 141.
   Certified Medicare; Medi-Cal.
Owner Proprietary Corp.
Admissions Requirements Medical
   examination; Physician's request.
Staff RNs 10 (ft); LPNs 16 (ft); Nurses aides
   54 (ft); Physical therapists 1 (ft);
   Occupational therapists 1 (ft); Speech
   therapists 1 (ft); Activities coordinators 2
   (ft); Dietitians 1 (pt); Dentists 1 (pt);
   Ophthalmologists 1 (pt); Podiatrists 1 (pt);
   Physical therapist aide 1 (ft); Social service 1
   (ft).

Languages Spanish, Yiddish
Facilities Dining room; Physical therapy
   room; Activities room; Laundry room;
   Barber/Beauty shop; Speech & Occupational
   therapy room.
Activities Arts & crafts; Cards; Games;
   Movies; Field trips; Bingo; Birthday parties.

The Hollenbeck Home for Gracious Retirement Living
573 S Boyle Ave, Los Angeles, CA, 90033
(213) 263-6195
Admin William G Heideman. *Medical Dir/Dir of Nursing* John D Walters MD; Dora Peterson RN.
Licensure Intermediate care; Retirement
   home. *Beds* SNF 84; ICF 28. *Certified*
   Medicaid; Medicare; Medi-Cal.
Owner Nonprofit organization/foundation.
Admissions Requirements Minimum age 65;
   Medical examination.
Staff Physicians 3 (pt); RNs 2 (ft), 2 (pt);
   LPNs 8 (ft), 2 (pt); Nurses aides 37 (ft), 5
   (pt); Physical therapists 1 (pt); Occupational
   therapists 1 (pt); Speech therapists 1 (pt);
   Activities coordinators 2 (ft); Dietitians 1
   (pt); Dentists 1 (pt); Ophthalmologists 1 (pt);
   Podiatrists 1 (pt).
Facilities Dining room; Physical therapy
   room; Activities room; Chapel; Crafts room;
   Laundry room; Barber/Beauty shop; Library;
   Ice cream parlor; Whirlpool.
Activities Arts & crafts; Cards; Games;
   Reading groups; Prayer groups; Movies;
   Shopping trips; Social/Cultural gatherings.

Hyde Park Convalescent Hospital
6520 W Blvd, Los Angeles, CA, 90043
(213) 753-1354
Admin Elaine M Wiesel.
Licensure Skilled care. *Beds* 72. *Certified*
   Medicare; Medi-Cal.
Owner Proprietary Corp.
Admissions Requirements Minimum age 21.
Staff Physicians; RNs; LPNs; Orderlies;
   Nurses aides; Physical therapists; Reality
   therapists; Recreational therapists;
   Occupational therapists; Speech therapists;
   Activities coordinators; Dietitians; Dentists;
   Ophthalmologists; Podiatrists; Dentist.
Languages Spanish, Hungarian, German,
   Hebrew, Yiddish
Facilities Dining room; Activities room;
   Crafts room; Laundry room; Barber/Beauty
   shop.
Activities Arts & crafts; Cards; Games;
   Reading groups; Prayer groups; Movies.

Japanese Retirement Home-Intermediate Care Facility
325 S Boyle Ave, Los Angeles, CA, 90033
(213) 263-9651
Admin Edwin C Hiroto. *Medical Dir/Dir of Nursing* Dr Sakaye Shigekawa; Sachiko Ward RN.
Licensure Intermediate care; Residential care.
   Beds ICF 96; Residential 112. *Certified*
   Medi-Cal.
Owner Nonprofit Corp.
Admissions Requirements Minimum age 60.
Staff RNs 1 (ft); LPNs 3 (ft), 3 (pt); Nurses
   aides 19 (ft), 5 (pt); Activities coordinators 1
   (ft), 1 (pt); Dietitians 1 (pt).
Languages Japanese, Chinese, Korean
Facilities Dining room; Activities room;
   Crafts room; Laundry room; Barber/Beauty
   shop; Auditorium.
Activities Arts & crafts; Games; Prayer groups;
   Movies; Shopping trips; Social/Cultural
   gatherings; Music group.

Keiro Nursing Home*
2221 Lincoln Park Ave, Los Angeles, CA, 90031
(213) 225-1393
Admin Margaret Hiroto.
Licensure Skilled care. *Beds* 87. *Certified*
   Medicare; Medi-Cal.

Owner Nonprofit Corp.
Languages Japanese

Kennedy Convalescent Hospital*
619 N Fairfax Ave, Los Angeles, CA, 90036
(213) 651-5331
Admin Solomon Gruer.
Licensure Skilled care. *Beds* 97. *Certified*
Medicare; Medi-Cal.
Owner Proprietary Corp.

Kingsley Manor Convalescent Hospital
1055 N Kingsley Dr, Los Angeles, CA, 90029
(213) 661-1128
Admin June McKee. *Medical Dir/Dir of
Nursing* Dolores Guiy.
Licensure Skilled care. *Beds* 51. *Certified*
Medicare; Medi-Cal.
Owner Proprietary Corp (Pacific Homes).
Admissions Requirements Medical
examination; Physician's request.
Staff RNs 1 (ft), 8 (pt); LPNs 7 (ft), 4 (pt);
Nurses aides 22 (ft), 2 (pt); Physical
therapists 1 (pt); Occupational therapists 1
(pt); Speech therapists 1 (pt); Activities
coordinators 1 (ft); Dietitians 1 (pt); Dentists
1 (pt); Ophthalmologists 1 (pt); Podiatrists 1
(pt).
Languages Spanish, Italian
Facilities Dining room; Activities room;
Chapel; Crafts room; Laundry room; Barber/
Beauty shop; Library.
Activities Arts & crafts; Cards; Games;
Reading groups; Prayer groups; Movies;
Shopping trips; Social/Cultural gatherings.

Lakewood Manor North*
831 S Lake St, Los Angeles, CA, 90057
(213) 380-9175
Admin Arthur F Elliott. *Medical Dir/Dir of
Nursing* Dr Marvin Salant.
Licensure Skilled care. *Beds* 99. *Certified*
Medicare; Medi-Cal.
Owner Proprietary Corp.
Admissions Requirements Physician's request.
Staff Physicians 8 (pt); RNs 1 (ft), 3 (pt);
LPNs 22 (ft), 6 (pt); Orderlies 16 (ft), 5 (pt);
Nurses aides 30 (ft), 15 (pt); Physical
therapists 4 (pt); Reality therapists 1 (pt);
Recreational therapists 1 (pt); Occupational
therapists 2 (pt); Speech therapists 2 (pt);
Activities coordinators 2 (pt); Dietitians 3
(pt); Dentists 2 (pt); Ophthalmologists 1 (pt);
Podiatrists 1 (pt); Audiologists 1 (pt).
Facilities Dining room; Physical therapy
room; Activities room; Barber/Beauty shop.
Activities Arts & crafts; Cards; Games;
Reading groups; Prayer groups; Movies;
Social/Cultural gatherings.

Longwood Manor Sanitarium*
4853 W Washington, Los Angeles, CA, 90016
(213) 935-1157
Admin Jon Fletcher.
Licensure Skilled care. *Beds* 123. *Certified*
Medicare; Medi-Cal.
Owner Proprietary Corp.

Manchester Manor Convalescent Hospital*
837 W Manchester, Los Angeles, CA, 90044
(213) 753-1789
Admin Mabel Crockett.
Licensure Skilled care. *Beds* 49. *Certified*
Medi-Cal.
Owner Proprietary Corp.

Maple Convalescent Hospital*
2625 S Maple Ave, Los Angeles, CA, 90011
(213) 747-6371
Admin Andre Pollak. *Medical Dir/Dir of
Nursing* Dr Edward J Panzer.
Licensure Skilled care. *Beds* 56. *Certified*
Medicare; Medi-Cal.
Owner Proprietary Corp.
Facilities Dining room; Activities room;
Laundry room.
Activities Arts & crafts; Cards; Games; Prayer
groups; Movies.

Mar Vista Sanitarium*
3966 Marcasel Ave, Los Angeles, CA, 90066
(213) 870-3716
Admin Ruth Von Buskirk. *Medical Dir/Dir of
Nursing* Dr Daniel Weston.
Licensure Skilled care. *Beds* 68.
Owner Proprietary Corp.
Admissions Requirements Minimum age 50;
Females only.
Staff RNs 2 (ft), 1 (pt); LPNs 3 (ft), 3 (pt);
Nurses aides 30 (ft), 15 (pt); Activities
coordinators 1 (ft), 1 (pt); Dietitians 1 (ft).
Facilities Dining room; Activities room;
Laundry room; Barber/Beauty shop.
Activities Arts & crafts; Cards; Games;
Reading groups; Movies.

Meadowbrook Manor Sanitarium*
3951 East Blvd, Los Angeles, CA,
(213) 870-0380
Admin J Krider. *Medical Dir/Dir of Nursing*
Paul Berns MD.
Licensure Skilled care. *Beds* 77. *Certified*
Medicare.
Owner Proprietary Corp.
Admissions Requirements Minimum age 18;
Medical examination; Physician's request.
Facilities Dining room; Activities room;
Laundry room.
Activities Arts & crafts; Games; Reading
groups; Prayer groups; Movies; Shopping
trips; Social/Cultural gatherings.

Mid-Wilshire Extended Care Facility
676 S Bonnie Brae, Los Angeles, CA, 90057
(213) 483-9921
Admin William Kite. *Medical Dir/Dir of
Nursing* Richard Weiss MD; Ann Clark
DON.
Licensure Skilled care; Intermediate care. *Beds*
SNF 80; ICF. *Certified* Medicaid; Medicare;
Medi-Cal; VA.
Owner Proprietary Corp (Medicrest of
California).
Admissions Requirements Minimum age 18;
Medical examination; Physician's request.
Staff Physicians 2 (pt); RNs 1 (ft), 1 (pt);
LPNs 6 (ft), 3 (pt); Orderlies 5 (ft), 2 (pt);
Nurses aides 20 (ft), 5 (pt); Activities
coordinators 8 (ft).
Languages Thai, Spanish
Facilities Dining room; Physical therapy
room; Activities room; Crafts room; Laundry
room; Barber/Beauty shop; Library.
Activities Arts & crafts; Cards; Games;
Reading groups; Prayer groups; Movies;
Shopping trips; Social/Cultural gatherings;
Walks.

Minami Keiro Nursing Home*
3619 N Mission Rd, Los Angeles, CA, 90031
(213) 225-1393
Admin Margaret Hiroto.
Licensure Skilled care. *Beds* 97. *Certified*
Medicare; Medi-Cal.
Owner Nonprofit Corp.
Languages Japanese

Nazareth House
3333 Manning Ave, Los Angeles, CA, 90064
(213) 839-2361
Admin Sr Teresa Grant.
Licensure Skilled care. *Beds* 20. *Certified*
Medi-Cal.
Owner Nonprofit Corp.
Admissions Requirements Minimum age 65;
Medical examination; Physician's request.
Affiliation Roman Catholic
Facilities Dining room; Activities room;
Chapel; Crafts room; Laundry room; Barber/
Beauty shop; Library.

Olympia Convalescent Hospital
1100 S Alvarado St, Los Angeles, CA, 90006
(213) 487-3000
Admin Otto Schwartz. *Medical Dir/Dir of
Nursing* Marvin Salant MD; Zenaida
Medina RN.

Licensure Skilled care; Intermediate care. *Beds*
SNF 135; ICF. *Certified* Medicare; Medi-
Cal.
Owner Proprietary Corp (Golden State Health
Centers).
Staff Physicians; RNs; LPNs; Orderlies;
Nurses aides; Physical therapists; Reality
therapists; Recreational therapists;
Occupational therapists; Speech therapists;
Activities coordinators; Dietitians; Dentists;
Ophthalmologists; Podiatrists.
Languages Spanish, Tagalog, Hungarian,
Korean, Yiddish, Hebrew
Facilities Dining room; Physical therapy
room; Activities room; Laundry room;
Barber/Beauty shop; Library; TV room.
Activities Arts & crafts; Cards; Games;
Reading groups; Prayer groups; Movies;
Shopping trips; Social/Cultural gatherings.

Paradise Convalescent Hospital*
2415 S Western Ave, Los Angeles, CA, 90018
(213) 734-1101
Admin J Sinay.
Licensure Skilled care. *Beds* 99. *Certified*
Medicare; Medi-Cal.
Owner Proprietary Corp.

Park Vista Convalescent Hospital*
5125 Monte Vista St, Los Angeles, CA, 90042
(213) 254-6125
Admin Gordon Dagg.
Licensure Skilled care. *Beds* 59. *Certified*
Medicare; Medi-Cal.
Owner Proprietary Corp.

RGR Sanitarium*
12001 Santa Monica Blvd, Los Angeles, CA,
90025
(213) 478-0273
Admin Ida H Rios. *Medical Dir/Dir of
Nursing* Harry J Silver MD.
Licensure Skilled care. *Beds* 59. *Certified*
Medicare; Medi-Cal.
Owner Proprietary Corp.
Facilities Dining room; Physical therapy
room; Activities room; Crafts room; Laundry
room; Barber/Beauty shop.
Activities Arts & crafts; Cards; Games;
Movies; Shopping trips.

Rubins Brierwood Terrace
1480 S La Cienega Blvd, Los Angeles, CA,
90035
(213) 655-8390
Admin Eva Ury. *Medical Dir/Dir of Nursing*
Dr Morris Feder; Polly Hernandez DON.
Licensure Skilled care. *Beds* SNF 41. *Certified*
Medicare; Medi-Cal.
Owner Privately owned.
Admissions Requirements Minimum age 55;
Medical examination; Physician's request.
Staff Physicians 1 (pt); RNs 1 (ft), 2 (pt);
LPNs 3 (ft), 2 (pt); Orderlies 3 (pt); Nurses
aides 25 (ft), 5 (pt); Physical therapists 1
(pt); Reality therapists 1 (pt); Recreational
therapists 1 (ft); Occupational therapists 1
(pt); Speech therapists 1 (pt); Activities
coordinators 1 (ft); Dietitians 1 (pt); Dentists
1 (pt); Ophthalmologists 1 (pt); Podiatrists 1
(pt).
Languages Hebrew, Yiddish, Spanish,
Russian, German, French
Facilities Dining room; Activities room;
Crafts room; Laundry room.
Activities Arts & crafts; Cards; Games;
Reading groups; Prayer groups; Social/
Cultural gatherings.

**St John of God Nursing Hospital & Residence
Inc**
2035 W Adams Blvd, Los Angeles, CA, 90018
(213) 731-0641
Admin Thomas Kruze. *Medical Dir/Dir of
Nursing* Harry J Silver MD; JoAnne
Deisinger RN.

Licensure Skilled care; Intermediate care; RCF; Independent living. *Beds* SNF 78; ICF 26; RCF 40; Independent living 5. *Certified* Medicare; Medi-Cal.
Owner Nonprofit Corp.
Admissions Requirements Minimum age 50; Medical examination; Physician's request.
Staff RNs 5 (ft); LPNs 9 (ft), 6 (pt); Orderlies 2 (ft); Nurses aides 45 (ft), 5 (pt); Activities coordinators 2 (ft); 73 (ft).
Languages Spanish, Korean
Affiliation Roman Catholic
Facilities Dining room; Physical therapy room; Activities room; Chapel; Crafts room; Laundry room; Barber/Beauty shop; Library.
Activities Arts & crafts; Cards; Games; Reading groups; Prayer groups; Movies; Shopping trips; Social/Cultural gatherings.

Serrano Convalescent Hospital
5401 Fountain Ave, Los Angeles, CA, 90029
(213) 465-2106
Admin Lydia F Cruz. *Medical Dir/Dir of Nursing* Dr Felipi Chu MD; Audrey Dunnigan DON.
Licensure Skilled care. *Beds* 99. *Certified* Medicare; Medi-Cal.
Owner Proprietary Corp.
Admissions Requirements Minimum age 65.
Staff Physicians 1 (pt); RNs 2 (ft); LPNs 5 (ft), 5 (pt); Orderlies 5 (ft), 1 (pt); Nurses aides 24 (ft); Occupational therapists 1 (pt); Speech therapists 1 (pt); Activities coordinators 1 (pt); Dietitians 1 (ft); Dentists 1 (pt); Ophthalmologists 1 (pt); Podiatrists 1 (pt).
Facilities Dining room; Physical therapy room; Activities room; Laundry room; Barber/Beauty shop.
Activities Arts & crafts; Cards; Games; Reading groups; Prayer groups; Movies; Social/Cultural gatherings; Field trips.

Serrano Convalescent Hospital—South*
5400 Fountain Ave, Los Angeles, CA, 90029
(213) 461-4301
Admin Trudi Weimer.
Licensure Skilled care. *Beds* 99. *Certified* Medicare; Medi-Cal.
Owner Proprietary Corp.

Sharon Care Center
8167 W 3rd St, Los Angeles, CA, 91423
(213) 655-2023
Admin Jean B Salkind. *Medical Dir/Dir of Nursing* James Meltzer MD; Mabel Kiester RN DON.
Licensure Skilled care. *Beds* SNF 86. *Certified* Medicare; Medi-Cal.
Owner Proprietary Corp (Summit Health Ltd).
Admissions Requirements Minimum age 65; Physician's request.
Staff RNs 1 (ft), 1 (pt); LPNs; Orderlies 6 (ft); Nurses aides 35 (ft); Physical therapists 2 (pt); Recreational therapists 1 (pt); Occupational therapists 1 (pt); Speech therapists 1 (pt); Activities coordinators 1 (ft); Dietitians 1 (ft), 1 (pt).
Languages Spanish, Hebrew, Yiddish, German
Facilities Dining room; Physical therapy room; Activities room; Laundry room; Barber/Beauty shop.
Activities Arts & crafts; Cards; Games; Reading groups; Prayer groups; Movies; Shopping trips; Social/Cultural gatherings.

Skyline Convalescent Hospital
3032 Rowena Ave, Los Angeles, CA, 90039
(213) 665-1185
Admin Kim G Simmons. *Medical Dir/Dir of Nursing* Dr Salant; Mrs Sheler DON.
Licensure Skilled care. *Beds* SNF 99. *Certified* Medicaid; Medicare; Medi-Cal.
Owner Proprietary Corp (ARA Living Centers).

Admissions Requirements Minimum age Geriatrics; Medical examination; Physician's request.
Staff Physicians; RNs; LPNs; Orderlies; Nurses aides; Activities coordinators; Dietitians.
Facilities Dining room; Physical therapy room; Activities room; Crafts room; Laundry room; Barber/Beauty shop; Library; TV room; Living room.
Activities Arts & crafts; Cards; Games; Prayer groups; Movies; Shopping trips; Social/Cultural gatherings; Field trips; Los Angeles Zoo; Chinatown; Glendale Galleria; Verdugo park picnic; Beach; Lake Cascade.

Solheim Lutheran Home for the Aged
2236 Merton Ave, Los Angeles, CA, 90041
(213) 257-7518
Admin Elizabeth C Batchelder. *Medical Dir/ Dir of Nursing* Dr Ralph Boyd; Mary Ellen Lieber RN DON.
Licensure Skilled care; Residential facility for elderly. *Beds* SNF 19; Residential 98. *Certified* Medicaid; Medi-Cal.
Owner Nonprofit Corp.
Admissions Requirements Minimum age 62.
Staff RNs; LPNs; Nurses aides; Recreational therapists.
Languages Spanish, Chinese, German
Affiliation Lutheran
Facilities Dining room; Activities room; Chapel; Crafts room; Laundry room; Barber/ Beauty shop; Library.
Activities Arts & crafts; Cards; Games; Reading groups; Prayer groups; Movies; Shopping trips; Social/Cultural gatherings.

Sparr Convalescent Hospital
2367 W Pico Blvd, Los Angeles, CA, 90006
(213) 388-1481
Admin Carmen Zuno. *Medical Dir/Dir of Nursing* F Evans Powell MD; DeBorah Jackson RN.
Licensure Skilled care. *Beds* SNF 59. *Certified* Medicare; Medi-Cal.
Owner Privately owned.
Admissions Requirements Physician's request.
Staff Physicians 10 (pt); RNs 1 (ft), 3 (pt); LPNs 5 (ft), 4 (pt); Orderlies 4 (ft); Nurses aides 17 (ft), 6 (pt); Physical therapists 1 (pt); Recreational therapists 1 (pt); Occupational therapists 1 (pt); Speech therapists 1 (pt); Activities coordinators 1 (ft), 1 (pt); Dietitians 1 (pt); Dentists 1 (pt); Ophthalmologists 1 (pt).
Languages Spanish
Facilities Dining room; Activities room; Laundry room; Barber/Beauty shop; Library; 2 Patios.
Activities Arts & crafts; Cards; Games; Reading groups; Prayer groups; Movies; Shopping trips; Social/Cultural gatherings; Resident council.

Sunray East Convalescent Hospital*
3210 W Pico Blvd, Los Angeles, CA, 90019
(213) 734-2173
Admin Mildred Garcia.
Licensure Skilled care. *Beds* 99. *Certified* Medicare; Medi-Cal.
Owner Proprietary Corp.

Sunray North Convalescent Hospital*
3233 W Pico Blvd, Los Angeles, CA, 90019
(213) 734-9122
Admin Jordan Fishman.
Licensure Skilled care. *Beds* 95. *Certified* Medicare; Medi-Cal.
Owner Proprietary Corp.

Sunshine Terrace Convalescent Hospital Inc*
7951 Beverly Blvd, Los Angeles, CA, 90048
(213) 655-1500
Admin A Goldstein.
Licensure Skilled care. *Beds* 50.
Owner Proprietary Corp.

Sycamore Park Convalescent Hospital
4585 N Figueroa St, Los Angeles, CA, 90065
(213) 223-3441
Admin Scott M Harmon. *Medical Dir/Dir of Nursing* Stanley Kahan MD; Cyril Lazado RN DON.
Licensure Skilled care. *Beds* 90. *Certified* Medicare; Medi-Cal.
Owner Proprietary Corp.
Staff Physicians 1 (pt); RNs 2 (ft); LPNs 11 (ft), 2 (pt); Orderlies 4 (ft); Nurses aides 25 (ft); Physical therapists 1 (ft); Recreational therapists 1 (pt); Occupational therapists 1 (pt); Speech therapists 1 (pt); Activities coordinators 1 (ft); Dietitians 1 (pt); Dentists 1 (pt); Ophthalmologists 1 (pt); Podiatrists 1 (pt).
Languages Spanish, Tagalog, Thai
Facilities Dining room; Activities room; Chapel; Crafts room; Laundry room; Barber/ Beauty shop; TV room.
Activities Arts & crafts; Cards; Games; Reading groups; Prayer groups; Movies; Shopping trips; Social/Cultural gatherings; Exercise groups; Adopt-a-grandparent program; Trips to local attractions.

Temple Park Convalescent Hospital
2411 W Temple St, Los Angeles, CA, 90026
(213) 380-3210
Admin Barry Kohn. *Medical Dir/Dir of Nursing* Marilyn Constantino.
Licensure Skilled care. *Beds* SNF 99. *Certified* Medicaid; Medicare; Medi-Cal.
Owner Proprietary Corp.
Staff RNs; LPNs; Orderlies; Nurses aides; Physical therapists; Recreational therapists; Occupational therapists; Speech therapists; Dietitians; Ophthalmologists.
Languages Spanish, Tai, Tagalog
Facilities Dining room; Physical therapy room; Activities room; Laundry room; Barber/Beauty shop.
Activities Arts & crafts; Cards; Games; Reading groups; Prayer groups; Movies; Shopping trips; Social/Cultural gatherings.

United Cerebral Palsy/Spastic Childrens Foundation
1307 W 105th St, Los Angeles, CA, 90044
(213) 757-9361
Admin Daniel J Kingma. *Medical Dir/Dir of Nursing* Vivien Hatcher RN DON.
Licensure ICF-DD. *Beds* ICF-DD 91. *Certified* Medicaid.
Owner Nonprofit Corp.
Admissions Requirements Minimum age 3.
Staff Physicians 1 (pt); RNs 1 (ft); LPNs 6 (ft), 6 (pt); Nurses aides 45 (ft); Physical therapists 1 (pt); Recreational therapists 1 (ft); Occupational therapists 1 (pt); Speech therapists 1 (pt); Activities coordinators 1 (ft); Dietitians 1 (pt); Dentists 1 (pt); Ophthalmologists 1 (pt).
Facilities Dining room; Physical therapy room; Activities room; Crafts room; Laundry room; Barber/Beauty shop; Communications lab; Pool.
Activities Arts & crafts; Games; Prayer groups; Movies; Shopping trips; Social/Cultural gatherings.

Vermont Knolls Convalescent Hospital*
11234 S Vermont Ave, Los Angeles, CA, 90044
(213) 754-3173
Admin Victor Rodgers.
Licensure Skilled care. *Beds* 99. *Certified* Medicare; Medi-Cal.
Owner Proprietary Corp.

Vernon Convalescent Hospital*
1037 W Vernon, Los Angeles, CA, 90037
(213) 232-4895
Admin Edward Markovitz.
Licensure Skilled care. *Beds* 99. *Certified* Medicare; Medi-Cal.
Owner Proprietary Corp.

View Heights Convalescent Hospital*
12619 S Avalon Blvd, Los Angeles, CA, 90061
(213) 757-1881
Admin Monica A Fenton.
Licensure Skilled care. *Beds* 163. *Certified*
Medicare; Medi-Cal.
Owner Proprietary Corp.

Virgil Sanitarium & Convalescent Hospital
975 N Virgil Ave, Los Angeles, CA, 90029
(213) 665-5793
Admin Nancy S Chow. *Medical Dir/Dir of*
Nursing Max Davidson MD; Madeline
Rulon RN DON.
Licensure Skilled care. *Beds* SNF 119.
Certified Medicare; Medi-Cal.
Owner Proprietary Corp (Golden State Health
Centers).
Admissions Requirements Minimum age 21.
Staff RNs 6 (ft), 4 (pt); LPNs 8 (ft), 4 (pt);
Orderlies 8 (ft), 2 (pt); Nurses aides 29 (ft),
12 (pt); Activities coordinators 2 (ft), 1 (pt).
Languages Russian, Armenian, Chinese,
French, Egyptian, Hebrew, Yiddish
Facilities Dining room; Activities room;
Laundry room; Outdoor patio.
Activities Arts & crafts; Cards; Games;
Reading groups; Prayer groups; Movies;
Shopping trips; Field trips.

Vista Del Sol Care Center
11620 W Washington Blvd, Los Angeles, CA,
90066
(213) 390-9045
Admin Terry M Henry. *Medical Dir/Dir of*
Nursing Max Davidson MD; Stella Mora-
Henry RN DON.
Licensure Skilled care; Board & care. *Beds*
SNF 50; Board & care 25. *Certified*
Medicare.
Owner Proprietary Corp.
Admissions Requirements Minimum age 65;
Physician's request.
Staff RNs; LPNs; Orderlies; Nurses aides;
Recreational therapists; Activities
coordinators.
Languages Spanish
Facilities Dining room; Physical therapy
room; Activities room; Crafts room; Laundry
room; Barber/Beauty shop.
Activities Arts & crafts; Cards; Games;
Reading groups; Prayer groups; Movies;
Shopping trips; Social/Cultural gatherings.

Washington Nursing & Convalescent*
2300 W Washington, Los Angeles, CA, 90018
(213) 731-0861
Admin Henry Pagkalinawan. *Medical Dir/Dir*
of Nursing Leroy Ewell MD.
Licensure Skilled care. *Beds* 59. *Certified*
Medicare.
Owner Proprietary Corp.
Admissions Requirements Medical
examination; Physician's request.
Staff Physicians 8 (pt); RNs 1 (ft), 2 (pt);
LPNs 3 (ft), 3 (pt); Orderlies 2 (ft); Nurses
aides 16 (ft), 8 (pt); Physical therapists 1
(pt); Occupational therapists 1 (pt); Speech
therapists 1 (pt); Activities coordinators 1
(ft); Dietitians 1 (pt); Dentists 1 (pt);
Ophthalmologists 1 (pt); Podiatrists 1 (pt).
Facilities Dining room; Activities room;
Crafts room; Laundry room; Barber/Beauty
shop.
Activities Arts & crafts; Cards; Games;
Reading groups; Prayer groups; Social/
Cultural gatherings.

WCTU Home for Women
2235 Norwalk Ave, Los Angeles, CA, 90041
(213) 255-7108
Admin Edna Young.
Licensure Residential care. *Beds* 140.
Owner Nonprofit organization/foundation.
Admissions Requirements Minimum age 62;
Females only; Medical examination;
Physician's request.

Staff Nurses aides 5 (ft), 2 (pt); Recreational
therapists 1 (ft); Activities coordinators 1
(ft)O; Dietitians 1 (pt); Ophthalmologists 1
(pt).
Facilities Dining room; Activities room;
Chapel; Crafts room; Laundry room; Barber/
Beauty shop; Library; Auditorium.
Activities Arts & crafts; Cards; Games;
Reading groups; Prayer groups; Movies;
Social/Cultural gatherings; Teas; Sales;
Grandmothers program.

Western Convalescent Hospital*
2190 W Adams Blvd, Los Angeles, CA, 90018
(213) 737-7778
Admin Frank Garcia.
Licensure Skilled care. *Beds* 129. *Certified*
Medicare; Medi-Cal.
Owner Proprietary Corp.

Westlake Convalescent Hospital
316 S Westlake Ave, Los Angeles, CA, 90057
(213) 484-0510
Admin Neng F Chen-Campos. *Medical Dir/*
Dir of Nursing Dr Max Davidson; Estelita
Nacion RN.
Licensure Skilled care. *Beds* 114. *Certified*
Medicare; Medi-Cal.
Owner Proprietary Corp.
Admissions Requirements Minimum age 65;
Physician's request.
Staff Physicians 1 (pt); RNs 3 (ft), 4 (pt);
LPNs 8 (ft), 3 (pt); Orderlies 13 (ft), 2 (pt);
Nurses aides 25 (ft), 1 (pt); Physical
therapists 1 (pt); Occupational therapists 1
(pt); Speech therapists 1 (pt); Activities
coordinators 1 (ft); Dietitians 1 (pt).
Languages Spanish, Hebrew, Yiddish,
Tagalog, Chinese
Facilities Dining room; Activities room;
Crafts room; Laundry room; Barber/Beauty
shop; Library.
Activities Arts & crafts; Cards; Games;
Reading groups; Prayer groups; Movies;
Social/Cultural gatherings; Outdoor trips.

LOS BANOS

Los Banos Convalescent Hospital
931 Idaho Ave, Los Banos, CA, 93635
(209) 826-0790
Admin John Williams. *Medical Dir/Dir of*
Nursing Oscar Ansaldo MD; Glenn Eslinger
DON.
Licensure Skilled care. *Beds* SNF 59. *Certified*
Medicare; Medi-Cal.
Owner Privately owned.
Admissions Requirements Medical
examination; Physician's request.
Staff Physicians 1 (pt); RNs 1 (ft), 1 (pt);
LPNs 4 (ft), 1 (pt); Nurses aides 26 (ft), 9
(pt); Physical therapists 1 (pt); Speech
therapists 1 (pt); Activities coordinators 1
(ft), 1 (pt); Dietitians 1 (pt);
Ophthalmologists 1 (pt).
Languages Spanish, Portuguese
Facilities Dining room; Activities room.
Activities Arts & crafts; Cards; Games; Prayer
groups; Movies.

LOS GATOS

Bethesda Manor & Convalescent Center
371 Los Gatos Blvd, Los Gatos, CA, 95030
(408) 356-3116
Admin Martin S Neham. *Medical Dir/Dir of*
Nursing James Guetzkow MD.
Licensure Skilled care. *Beds* 124. *Certified*
Medicare; Medi-Cal.
Owner Proprietary Corp (Natl Bnvlnt Assn of
Chrstn Homes).
Staff Physicians 1 (pt); RNs 6 (ft), 2 (pt);
Orderlies 5 (ft), 2 (pt); Nurses aides 40 (ft),
20 (pt); Physical therapists 2 (pt); Reality
therapists 1 (pt); Recreational therapists 1
(pt); Occupational therapists 1 (pt); Speech
therapists 1 (pt); Activities coordinators 2

(ft); Dietitians 1 (ft); Dentists 1 (pt);
Ophthalmologists 1 (pt); Podiatrists 1 (pt);
Dentist 1 (pt).
Affiliation Disciples of Christ
Facilities Dining room; Physical therapy
room; Activities room; Crafts room; Laundry
room; Barber/Beauty shop; Library.
Activities Arts & crafts; Cards; Games;
Reading groups; Prayer groups; Movies;
Shopping trips; Social/Cultural gatherings.

Beverly Manor Convalescent Hospital*
350 De Soto Dr, Los Gatos, CA, 95030
(408) 356-9151
Admin Susan E Bazsuly.
Licensure Skilled care. *Beds* 73. *Certified*
Medicare; Medi-Cal.
Owner Proprietary Corp (Beverly Enterprises).

Beverly Manor Convalescent Hospital
14966 Terreno De Flores Ln, Los Gatos, CA,
95030
(408) 356-8136
Admin Kelly Wiest. *Medical Dir/Dir of*
Nursing Dr Stephen Tilles.
Licensure Skilled care. *Beds* 65. *Certified*
Medicare; Medi-Cal.
Owner Proprietary Corp (Beverly Enterprises).
Staff Physical therapists; Occupational
therapists; Speech therapists; Activities
coordinators 1 (ft); Dietitians;
Ophthalmologists; Dentist.
Facilities Dining room; Activities room;
Crafts room; Laundry room; Barber/Beauty
shop; Large patio area.
Activities Arts & crafts; Cards; Games;
Reading groups; Prayer groups; Movies;
Shopping trips; Social/Cultural gatherings;
Bingo.

Gem Convalescent Hospital
15245 National Ave, Los Gatos, CA, 95032
(408) 356-2151
Admin Michael A Straub. *Medical Dir/Dir of*
Nursing Elaine Cassey.
Licensure Skilled care. *Beds* SNF 66. *Certified*
Medicaid; Medicare; Medi-Cal.
Owner Proprietary Corp.
Admissions Requirements Medical
examination; Physician's request.
Staff RNs 3 (ft); LPNs 10 (ft); Orderlies 3 (ft);
Nurses aides 18 (ft), 14 (pt); Physical
therapists 1 (ft); Activities coordinators 1
(ft); Dietitians 1 (ft).
Languages Spanish
Facilities Dining room; Activities room;
Laundry room.
Activities Arts & crafts; Games; Prayer groups;
Movies; Social/Cultural gatherings.

Lark Manor Convalescent Hospital
16605 Lark Ave, Los Gatos, CA, 95030
(408) 356-9146
Admin Wm Carroll Parks. *Medical Dir/Dir of*
Nursing Jean Lyonn DON.
Licensure Skilled care. *Beds* SNF 30. *Certified*
Medicaid; Medicare; Medi-Cal.
Owner Proprietary Corp.
Admissions Requirements Minimum age 25;
Medical examination.
Staff Physicians 1 (pt); RNs 1 (ft); LPNs 2
(ft); Nurses aides 7 (ft), 4 (pt); Activities
coordinators 1 (ft); Dietitians 1 (pt).
Languages Spanish, German
Facilities Dining room; Physical therapy
room; Activities room.
Activities Cards; Games; Reading groups;
Movies; Shopping trips.

Los Gatos Convalescent Hospital
16412 Los Gatos Blvd, Los Gatos, CA, 95030
(408) 356-2191
Admin Marjorie Thomas. *Medical Dir/Dir of*
Nursing Donna Bruns.
Licensure Skilled care. *Beds* 50. *Certified*
Medicare; Medi-Cal.
Owner Proprietary Corp.

Los Gatos Meadows
110 Wood Rd, Los Gatos, CA, 95030
(408) 354-0211
Admin James P Hempler. *Medical Dir/Dir of Nursing* Donald Conlon MD.
Licensure Skilled care. *Beds* 39. *Certified* Medicare.
Owner Nonprofit Corp (Episcopal Homes Fdn).
Admissions Requirements Minimum age 65; Medical examination.
Affiliation Episcopal
Facilities Dining room; Physical therapy room; Activities room; Chapel; Crafts room; Laundry room; Barber/Beauty shop; Library.
Activities Arts & crafts; Cards; Games; Reading groups; Prayer groups; Movies; Shopping trips; Social/Cultural gatherings.

LYNWOOD

Community Convalescent Hospital
3611 Imperial Hwy, Lynwood, CA, 90262
(213) 537-2500
Admin Ron Dodgen.
Licensure Skilled care. *Beds* 99. *Certified* Medicare; Medi-Cal.
Owner Proprietary Corp (Beverly Enterprises).

Lynwood Care Center*
3598 E Century Blvd, Lynwood, CA, 90262
(213) 639-5220
Admin Ronald Morgan. *Medical Dir/Dir of Nursing* Ramon Cabrera MD.
Licensure Skilled care. *Beds* 128. *Certified* Medicare; Medi-Cal.
Owner Proprietary Corp (Beverly Enterprises).
Admissions Requirements Minimum age 3; Medical examination; Physician's request.
Staff Physicians 1 (pt); RNs 4 (ft), 2 (pt); LPNs 6 (ft), 2 (pt); Orderlies 8 (ft), 1 (pt); Nurses aides 35 (ft), 6 (pt); Physical therapists 1 (pt); Occupational therapists 1 (pt); Speech therapists 1 (pt); Activities coordinators 1 (ft); Dietitians 1 (pt); Dentists 1 (pt); Ophthalmologists 1 (pt); Podiatrists 1 (pt); Audiologists 1 (pt).
Facilities Dining room; Physical therapy room; Activities room; Crafts room; Laundry room; Barber/Beauty shop.
Activities Arts & crafts; Cards; Games; Movies; Shopping trips.

Majestic Convalescent Center
3565 E Imperial Hwy, Lynwood, CA, 90262
(213) 638-9377
Admin Ralph J Bak. *Medical Dir/Dir of Nursing* Robert Tsai MD; Carolyn Marry RN.
Licensure Skilled care; Intermediate care. *Beds* SNF 98; ICF 6. *Certified* Medicare; Medi-Cal.
Owner Proprietary Corp.
Admissions Requirements Minimum age 30; Medical examination; Physician's request.
Staff Physicians 6 (pt); RNs 2 (ft), 1 (pt); LPNs 8 (ft), 2 (pt); Orderlies 4 (ft); Nurses aides 32 (ft), 4 (pt); Physical therapists 1 (pt); Recreational therapists 1 (pt); Occupational therapists 1 (pt); Speech therapists 1 (pt); Activities coordinators 2 (ft); Dietitians 1 (pt); Dentists 1 (pt); Ophthalmologists 1 (pt); Podiatrists 1 (pt); Medical records 1 (pt); Pharmacy 1 (pt); Dietary staff 6 (ft), 2 (pt); Housekeeping, Laundry, Maintenance 8 (ft).
Languages Spanish
Facilities Dining room; Physical therapy room; Activities room; Crafts room; Laundry room; Barber/Beauty shop.
Activities Arts & crafts; Cards; Games; Reading groups; Prayer groups; Movies; Shopping trips; Social/Cultural gatherings.

Marlinda Nursing Home
3615 Imperial Hwy, Lynwood, CA, 90262
(213) 639-4623

Admin Martha E Lang. *Medical Dir/Dir of Nursing* Dr Robert S Tsai.
Licensure Skilled care. *Beds* SNF 130. *Certified* Medicare; Medi-Cal.
Owner Proprietary Corp.
Staff RNs 5 (ft), 4 (pt); LPNs 11 (ft); Nurses aides 50 (ft); Physical therapists 1 (pt); Recreational therapists 1 (ft); Occupational therapists 1 (pt); Speech therapists 1 (pt); Activities coordinators 1 (ft); Dietitians 1 (ft); Ophthalmologists 1 (pt).
Facilities Dining room; Physical therapy room; Activities room; Crafts room; Laundry room; Barber/Beauty shop; Library.
Activities Arts & crafts; Cards; Games; Reading groups; Prayer groups; Movies; Sing-along.

Marlinda West Nursing Home
3333 E Imperial Hwy, Lynwood, CA, 90262
(213) 631-6122
Admin Katherine Lance.
Licensure Skilled care; Intermediate care for mentally retarded. *Beds* ICF/MR 90. *Certified* Medi-Cal.
Owner Privately owned.
Staff Physicians 2 (pt); RNs 1 (ft), 2 (pt); LPNs 10 (ft); Orderlies 10 (ft); Nurses aides 50 (ft); Physical therapists 1 (pt); Recreational therapists 1 (pt); Occupational therapists 1 (pt); Speech therapists 1 (pt); Activities coordinators 1 (ft); Dietitians 1 (pt); Dentists 1 (pt); Ophthalmologists 1 (pt); Podiatrists 1 (pt).
Facilities Dining room; Physical therapy room; Activities room; Crafts room.
Activities Arts & crafts; Games; Movies; Shopping trips; Social/Cultural gatherings.

MADERA

Madera Rehabilitation & Convalescent Center
517 S "A" St, Madera, CA, 93638
(209) 673-9228
Admin George Eslinger. *Medical Dir/Dir of Nursing* Crystal Eggleston RN DON.
Licensure Skilled care. *Beds* 176. *Certified* Medicare; Medi-Cal.
Owner Proprietary Corp (Health Care Management).
Admissions Requirements Physician's request.
Staff RNs 6 (ft); LPNs 12 (ft); Orderlies 5 (ft); Nurses aides 44 (ft); Physical therapists 1 (ft); Recreational therapists 1 (ft), 1 (pt); Occupational therapists 1 (pt); Speech therapists 1 (pt); Activities coordinators 1 (ft); Dietitians 1 (pt); Ophthalmologists 1 (pt); Podiatrists 1 (pt).
Languages Spanish
Facilities Dining room; Physical therapy room; Activities room; Crafts room; Laundry room; Barber/Beauty shop; Library.
Activities Arts & crafts; Cards; Games; Prayer groups; Movies; Shopping trips; Mens club.

Westgate Manor Convalescent Hospital
1700 Howard Rd, Madera, CA, 93637
(209) 673-9278
Admin Margaret A Tynan. *Medical Dir/Dir of Nursing* Mary Hyde RN DON.
Licensure Skilled care. *Beds* SNF 64. *Certified* Medicare; Medi-Cal.
Owner Proprietary Corp (Beverly Enterprises).

MANTECA

CareWest-Manteca Nursing & Rehabilitation Center
PO Box 766, 410 Eastwood Ave, Manteca, CA, 95336
(209) 239-1222
Admin Geraldine M Grimshaw RN. *Medical Dir/Dir of Nursing* Russell Carter MD; Shirley Sadler RN DON.
Licensure Skilled care. *Beds* SNF 99. *Certified* Medicaid; Medicare; Medi-Cal.
Owner Proprietary Corp (Care Enterprises).

Admissions Requirements Physician's request.
Staff RNs 5 (ft), 5 (pt); LPNs 4 (ft), 3 (pt); Orderlies 1 (ft); Nurses aides 41 (ft), 17 (pt); Physical therapists 1 (ft); Activities coordinators 1 (ft).
Facilities Dining room; Physical therapy room; Activities room; Crafts room; Laundry room; Barber/Beauty shop.
Activities Arts & crafts; Games; Prayer groups; Movies; Shopping trips; Social/Cultural gatherings.

MARIPOSA

Mariposa Manor
5201 Crystal Aire Dr, Mariposa, CA, 95338
(209) 966-2244
Admin JoAnn J Weston. *Medical Dir/Dir of Nursing* Arthur Dahlem MD; Kay Martella RN DON.
Licensure Skilled care. *Beds* SNF 23. *Certified* Medi-Cal.
Owner Proprietary Corp.
Admissions Requirements Physician's request.
Staff Physicians; RNs; LPNs; Orderlies; Nurses aides; Activities coordinators.
Facilities Dining room; Activities room; Laundry room.
Activities Arts & crafts; Cards; Games; Reading groups; Prayer groups; Movies.

MARTINEZ

Alhambra Convalescent Hospital
331 Ilene St, Martinez, CA, 94553
(415) 228-2020
Admin Lowell Callaway. *Medical Dir/Dir of Nursing* Dr Voelker; Karen Jarvis DON.
Licensure Skilled care. *Beds* SNF 42.
Owner Proprietary Corp.
Admissions Requirements Physician's request.
Staff Physicians 1 (pt); RNs 1 (ft), 1 (pt); LPNs 3 (ft), 3 (pt); Nurses aides 12 (ft), 6 (pt); Physical therapists 1 (pt); Occupational therapists 1 (pt); Speech therapists 1 (pt); Activities coordinators 1 (ft); Dietitians 1 (pt); Ophthalmologists 1 (pt).
Facilities Dining room; Laundry room.
Activities Arts & crafts; Cards; Games; Reading groups; Prayer groups; Movies; Shopping trips.

Martinez Convalescent Hospital*
4110 Alhambra Way, Martinez, CA, 94553
(415) 228-4260
Admin Michael W Hart.
Licensure Skilled care. *Beds* 36. *Certified* Medi-Cal.
Owner Proprietary Corp.

Mt Diablo Nursing Center*
1790 Muir Rd, Martinez, CA, 94553
(415) 228-8383
Admin Melinda L Hutchings. *Medical Dir/Dir of Nursing* Dr Carlos Anderson.
Licensure Skilled care. *Beds* 99. *Certified* Medicare; Medi-Cal.
Owner Proprietary Corp.
Staff Physicians 1 (pt); RNs 2 (ft), 2 (pt); Nurses aides 18 (ft), 6 (pt); Physical therapists 1 (pt); Recreational therapists 1 (pt); Occupational therapists 1 (pt); Speech therapists 1 (pt); Activities coordinators 1 (ft), 1 (pt); Dietitians 1 (pt); Dentists 1 (pt); Ophthalmologists 1 (pt); Podiatrists 1 (pt); Audiologists 1 (pt); LVNs 5 (ft), 3 (pt).
Facilities Dining room; Physical therapy room; Activities room; Laundry room; Barber/Beauty shop; Living room; Lounge.
Activities Arts & crafts; Cards; Games; Reading groups; Prayer groups; Movies; Shopping trips; Social/Cultural gatherings; Sightseeing tours; Visits to senior center; Adult education classes.

MARYSVILLE

Marysville Care Center
1617 Ramirez St, Marysville, CA, 95901
(916) 742-7311
Admin Shirley E Delamere. *Medical Dir/Dir of Nursing* W Hoffman MD; Mary Hathaway RN DON.
Licensure Skilled care. *Beds* SNF 86. *Certified* Medicare; Medi-Cal.
Owner Proprietary Corp (Chartham Management).
Admissions Requirements Physician's request.
Staff RNs 1 (ft), 1 (pt); LPNs 8 (ft), 1 (pt); Nurses aides 1 (pt); Occupational therapists 1 (pt); Speech therapists 1 (pt); Activities coordinators 2 (ft); Dietitians 1 (pt); Ophthalmologists 1 (pt).
Languages Tagalog, Spanish, German
Facilities Dining room; Physical therapy room; Activities room; Crafts room; Laundry room; Barber/Beauty shop.
Activities Arts & crafts; Cards; Games; Reading groups; Prayer groups; Movies; Shopping trips; Social/Cultural gatherings.

MAYWOOD

Pine Crest Convalescent Hospital*
6025 Pine Ave, Maywood, CA, 90270
(213) 560-0720
Admin Kathy Keil. *Medical Dir/Dir of Nursing* Edward Panzer MD.
Licensure Skilled care. *Beds* 133. *Certified* Medicare; Medi-Cal.
Owner Proprietary Corp (ARA Living Centers).
Staff RNs; LPNs; Orderlies; Nurses aides; Physical therapists; Reality therapists; Recreational therapists; Occupational therapists; Speech therapists; Activities coordinators; Dietitians; Dentists; Ophthalmologists; Podiatrists; Audiologists.
Facilities Dining room; Physical therapy room; Activities room; Laundry room; Barber/Beauty shop.
Activities Arts & crafts; Cards; Games; Reading groups; Prayer groups; Movies; Shopping trips; Social/Cultural gatherings.

MENLO PARK

College Park Convalescent Hospital*
1275 Crane St, Menlo Park, CA, 94025
(415) 322-7261
Admin William Collins.
Licensure Skilled care. *Beds* 160. *Certified* Medicare; Medi-Cal.
Owner Proprietary Corp (ARA Living Centers).

Convalescent Hospital University Branch*
2122 Santa Cruz Ave, Menlo Park, CA, 94025
(415) 854-4020
Admin Basil A Hogan.
Licensure Skilled care. *Beds* 80. *Certified* Medicare; Medi-Cal.
Owner Proprietary Corp (Hillhaven Corp).

Hillhaven Convalescent Hospital
16 Coleman Pl, Menlo Park, CA, 94025
(415) 326-0802
Admin Carl Baeuerlen. *Medical Dir/Dir of Nursing* Leo Harkavy; Dottie Heaney.
Licensure Skilled care. *Beds* 53. *Certified* Medicare; Medi-Cal.
Owner Proprietary Corp (Hillhaven Corp).
Admissions Requirements Medical examination; Physician's request.
Staff RNs 4 (ft), 3 (pt); LPNs 4 (ft), 3 (pt); Nurses aides 14 (ft), 6 (pt); Recreational therapists 1 (ft); Dietitians 1 (ft).
Languages Spanish, Tagalog

Facilities Dining room 19C; Laundry room; Barber/Beauty shop.
Activities Arts & crafts; Games; Reading groups; Prayer groups; Shopping trips; Social/Cultural gatherings.

Le Havre Convalescent Hospital
800 Roble Ave, Menlo Park, CA, 94025
(415) 323-6189
Admin Suzanne Heisler.
Licensure Skilled care. *Beds* 50. *Certified* Medicaid; Medicare.
Owner Proprietary Corp.
Admissions Requirements Minimum age 68; Medical examination.
Staff RNs; LPNs; Nurses aides; Physical therapists; Recreational therapists; Occupational therapists; Activities coordinators; Dietitians.
Languages French, Spanish
Facilities Dining room; Physical therapy room; Activities room; Laundry room; Barber/Beauty shop; Library.
Activities Arts & crafts; Cards; Games; Reading groups; Movies; Shopping trips; Singing group Le Havre Seniorettes.

Sharon Heights Convalescent Hospital
1185 Monte Rosa Dr, Menlo Park, CA, 94025
(415) 854-4230
Admin Leslee J Fennell. *Medical Dir/Dir of Nursing* Morris Gutterman MD.
Licensure Skilled care. *Beds* SNF 96. *Certified* Medicare.
Owner Proprietary Corp.
Admissions Requirements Physician's request.
Staff RNs 8 (ft), 5 (pt); LPNs 3 (ft), 2 (pt); Orderlies 3 (ft), 1 (pt); Nurses aides 20 (ft), 15 (pt); Physical therapists 1 (ft); Recreational therapists 1 (ft), 1 (pt); Dietitians 1 (ft);; Social worker 1 (ft) Dentist 1 (pt).
Languages Tagalogue, Spanish, Italian
Facilities Dining room; Physical therapy room; Activities room; Chapel; Barber/Beauty shop.
Activities Arts & crafts; Cards; Games; Reading groups; Prayer groups; Movies; Outings to museums; Gardens; Sports events.

MENTONE

Braswell's Ivy Retreat
2278 Nice Ave, Mentone, CA, 92359
(714) 794-1189
Admin Caroline J Braswell. *Medical Dir/Dir of Nursing* H J Cozzolino; Joan Byard DON.
Licensure Skilled care. *Beds* SNF 50. *Certified* Medicare; Medi-Cal.
Owner Proprietary Corp.
Admissions Requirements Physician's request.
Staff RNs 1 (ft), 3 (pt); LPNs 3 (ft), 2 (pt); Orderlies 2 (ft); Nurses aides 20 (ft), 1 (pt); Activities coordinators 1 (ft); Dietitians 1 (ft).
Languages Spanish, German
Facilities Dining room; Activities room; Laundry room; Barber/Beauty shop.
Activities Arts & crafts; Cards; Games; Reading groups; Prayer groups; Movies; Social/Cultural gatherings.

MERCED

Franciscan Convalescent Hospital*
3169 M St, Merced, CA, 95340
(209) 722-6231
Admin John Sears.
Licensure Skilled care. *Beds* 71. *Certified* Medicare; Medi-Cal.
Owner Proprietary Corp (Beverly Enterprises).
Affiliation Roman Catholic

Hy-Lond Convalescent Hospital
3170 M St, Merced, CA, 95340
(209) 723-1056

Admin Carmela Williams. *Medical Dir/Dir of Nursing* Joyce Russo DON.
Licensure Skilled care. *Beds* SNF 121. *Certified* Medicare; Medi-Cal.
Owner Proprietary Corp (Beverly Enterprises).
Admissions Requirements Medical examination; Physician's request.
Staff RNs; LPNs; Orderlies; Nurses aides; Physical therapists; Occupational therapists; Speech therapists; Activities coordinators.
Languages Spanish, Italian, Portuguese, Tagalog
Facilities Dining room; Physical therapy room; Activities room; Crafts room; Laundry room; Barber/Beauty shop; Library.
Activities Arts & crafts; Cards; Games; Reading groups; Prayer groups; Movies; Shopping trips; Social/Cultural gatherings; Field trips; Cooking groups.

La Sierra Convalescent Hospital*
2424 M St, Merced, CA, 95340
(209) 723-4224
Admin Charles Roy Wagner. *Medical Dir/Dir of Nursing* Dr Arthur Dahlem.
Licensure Skilled care. *Beds* 68. *Certified* Medicare; Medi-Cal.
Owner Proprietary Corp.
Admissions Requirements Medical examination; Physician's request.
Staff Physicians 1 (pt); RNs 1 (ft), 1 (pt); LPNs 5 (ft), 1 (pt); Orderlies 2 (ft), 1 (pt); Nurses aides 38 (ft), 6 (pt); Physical therapists 1 (pt); Occupational therapists 1 (pt); Speech therapists 1 (pt); Activities coordinators 1 (ft); Dietitians 1 (pt); Dentists 1 (pt); Podiatrists 1 (pt); Audiologists 1 (pt).

Merced Convalescent Hospital*
510 W 26th St, Merced, CA, 95340
(209) 723-2911
Admin Charles Roy Wagner. *Medical Dir/Dir of Nursing* Dr Arthur Dahlem.
Licensure Skilled care. *Beds* 79. *Certified* Medicare; Medi-Cal.
Owner Proprietary Corp.
Admissions Requirements Medical examination; Physician's request.
Staff Physicians 1 (pt); RNs 1 (ft), 1 (pt); LPNs 5 (ft), 2 (pt); Orderlies 3 (ft); Nurses aides 28 (ft), 12 (pt); Physical therapists 1 (pt); Occupational therapists 1 (pt); Speech therapists 1 (pt); Activities coordinators 1 (ft); Dietitians 1 (pt); Dentists 1 (pt); Podiatrists 1 (pt); Audiologists 1 (pt).

Merced Manor
1255 B St, Merced, CA, 95340
(209) 723-8814
Admin Linda S WahlBaker. *Medical Dir/Dir of Nursing* Arthur Harris MD; Ruth Bonath RN.
Licensure Skilled care for mentally disordered. *Beds* 96. *Certified* Medi-Cal.
Owner Proprietary Corp.
Admissions Requirements Minimum age 18; Physician's request.
Staff RNs 2 (ft), 1 (pt); LPNs 8 (ft); Nurses aides 25 (ft); Activities coordinators 1 (ft); Counselors 9 (ft), 4 (pt).
Facilities Dining room; Activities room; Laundry room; Barber/Beauty shop.
Activities Arts & crafts; Cards; Games; Reading groups; Movies; Shopping trips; Social/Cultural gatherings.

MILL VALLEY

Hillhaven Convalescent Hospital*
505 Miller Ave, Mill Valley, CA, 94941
(415) 388-8244
Admin Jay Roberts.
Licensure Skilled care. *Beds* 120. *Certified* Medicare; Medi-Cal.
Owner Proprietary Corp (Hillhaven Corp).

The Redwoods*
40 Camino Alto, Mill Valley, CA, 94941
(415) 383-3141
Admin Jean Naquin.
Licensure Skilled care. *Beds* 58. *Certified*
Medicare; Medi-Cal.
Owner Nonprofit Corp.

MILLBRAE

Millbrae Serra Convalescent Hospital
150 Serra Ave, Millbrae, CA, 94030
(415) 697-8386
Admin Michael Vano. *Medical Dir/Dir of
Nursing* Richard Avlwurm MD; Mrs Shiek
RN DON.
Licensure Skilled care. *Beds* SNF 125.
Certified Medi-Cal.
Owner Proprietary Corp.
Admissions Requirements Physician's request.
Staff Physicians 1 (pt); RNs 10 (ft), 1 (pt);
LPNs 4 (ft); Nurses aides 60 (ft);
Recreational therapists 3 (ft); Dietitians 1
(pt).
Languages Italian, Spanish
Facilities Dining room; Activities room;
Laundry room.
Activities Arts & crafts; Cards; Games;
Reading groups; Prayer groups; Movies;
Social/Cultural gatherings; Outings.

Sheltering Pine Convalescent Hospital
33 Mateo Ave, Millbrae, CA, 94030
(415) 583-8937
Admin G S Karki. *Medical Dir/Dir of Nursing*
Irving Stern MD.
Licensure Skilled care; Retirement center.
Beds SNF 140; Retirement center 50.
Certified Medicaid; Medicare; Medi-Cal.
Owner Proprietary Corp (Golden State Health
Centers).
Admissions Requirements Minimum age 18;
Medical examination; Physician's request.
Staff Physicians 1 (pt); RNs 8 (ft), 8 (pt);
LPNs 4 (ft), 4 (pt); Nurses aides 60 (ft);
Physical therapists 1 (pt); Reality therapists
1 (pt); Recreational therapists 1 (pt);
Occupational therapists 1 (pt); Speech
therapists 1 (pt); Activities coordinators 1
(ft); Dietitians 1 (pt); Ophthalmologists 1
(pt).
Languages Spanish
Facilities Dining room; Physical therapy
room; Activities room; Crafts room; Laundry
room; Barber/Beauty shop; Library.
Activities Arts & crafts; Cards; Games;
Reading groups; Prayer groups; Movies;
Social/Cultural gatherings; Tours.

MILPITAS

Rosscare Convalescent Hospital
120 Corning Ave, Milpitas, CA, 95035
(408) 262-0217
Admin Michael L Skaggs. *Medical Dir/Dir of
Nursing* Norman Woods MD; Julie Quiba
DON.
Licensure Skilled care. *Beds* SNF 35. *Certified*
Medicare; Medi-Cal.
Owner Proprietary Corp.
Admissions Requirements Minimum age 60;
Females only.
Staff Physicians 1 (ft), 1 (pt); RNs 2 (ft), 2
(pt); LPNs 2 (ft), 4 (pt); Nurses aides 7 (ft),
4 (pt); Physical therapists 1 (pt); Reality
therapists 1 (pt); Recreational therapists 1
(pt); Occupational therapists 1 (pt); Speech
therapists 1 (pt); Activities coordinators 1
(ft); Dietitians 1 (ft), 3 (pt); Dentists 1 (pt);
Ophthalmologists 1 (pt); Podiatrists 1 (pt);;
Dentist 1 (pt).
Languages Tagalog Spanish
Facilities Dining room; Activities room;
Crafts room; Laundry room; Barber/Beauty
shop; Living room.

Activities Arts & crafts; Cards; Games;
Reading groups; Prayer groups; Movies;
Shopping trips; Social/Cultural gatherings.

MODESTO

Casa De Modesto*
1745 Eldena Way, Modesto, CA, 95350
(209) 529-4950
Admin Felton Daniels.
Licensure Skilled care. *Beds* 59. *Certified*
Medi-Cal.
Owner Nonprofit Corp.

Colony Park Care Center
159 E Orangeburg Ave, Modesto, CA, 95350
(209) 526-2811
Admin Debra Campbell. *Medical Dir/Dir of
Nursing* Dr M Harris.
Licensure Skilled care. *Beds* 99. *Certified*
Medicaid; Medicare; Medi-Cal.
Owner Proprietary Corp (Health Care
Management).
Admissions Requirements Physician's request.
Staff RNs 1 (ft), 3 (pt); LPNs 7 (ft), 3 (pt);
Orderlies 3 (ft), 2 (pt); Nurses aides 35 (ft),
6 (pt); Physical therapists 2 (pt);
Recreational therapists 1 (ft), 1 (pt);
Occupational therapists 1 (pt); Activities
coordinators 1 (pt); Activities coordinators 1
(ft); Dietitians 2 (pt); Ophthalmologists 1
(pt).
Languages Spanish, Cambodian, Hindi,
Portuguese
Facilities Dining room; Physical therapy
room; Activities room; Crafts room; Laundry
room; Barber/Beauty shop; Coffee shop;
Family style dining.
Activities Arts & crafts; Cards; Games;
Reading groups; Prayer groups; Movies;
Shopping trips; Social/Cultural gatherings;
Exercises; Coffee social.

Crestwood Manor*
1400 Celeste Dr, Modesto, CA, 95355
(209) 526-8050
Admin George Lytal.
Licensure Skilled care. *Beds* 192. *Certified*
Medi-Cal.
Owner Proprietary Corp (Crestwood Hosp).

Driftwood Convalescent Hospital*
1611 Scenic Dr, Modesto, CA, 95350
(209) 523-5667
Admin Catherine Haley.
Licensure Skilled care. *Beds* 99. *Certified*
Medicare; Medi-Cal.
Owner Proprietary Corp (ARA Living
Centers).

Edson Convalescent Hospital*
3456 McHenry Ave, Modesto, CA, 95350
(209) 577-3200
Admin David G Howell.
Licensure Skilled care. *Beds* 25. *Certified*
Medicare; Medi-Cal.
Owner Proprietary Corp.

English Oaks Convalescent Hospital
2633 W Rumble Rd, Modesto, CA, 95350
(209) 577-1001
Admin Terry L Mundy. *Medical Dir/Dir of
Nursing* Michael Wray RN DON.
Licensure Skilled care. *Beds* SNF. *Certified*
Medicare.
Owner Proprietary Corp.
Admissions Requirements Minimum age 16;
Medical examination; Physician's request.
Staff RNs; LPNs; Nurses aides; Physical
therapists; Occupational therapists; Speech
therapists; Activities coordinators; Dietitians.
Languages Spanish, Vietnamese
Facilities Dining room; Physical therapy
room; Activities room; Chapel; Crafts room;
Laundry room; Barber/Beauty shop; Library;
TV lounge; Outside courts.

Activities Arts & crafts; Cards; Games;
Reading groups; Prayer groups; Movies;
Shopping trips; Social/Cultural gatherings.

Evergreen Convalescent Hospital Inc*
2030 Evergreen Ave, Modesto, CA, 95350
(209) 577-1055
Admin B V Cipponeri.
Licensure Skilled care. *Beds* 70. *Certified*
Medicare; Medi-Cal.
Owner Proprietary Corp.

Hillhaven Convalescent Hospital*
1310 W Granger Ave, Modesto, CA, 95350
(209) 524-4817
Admin Terry L Mundy. *Medical Dir/Dir of
Nursing* Marvin Montgomery MD.
Licensure Skilled care. *Beds* 104. *Certified*
Medicare; Medi-Cal.
Owner Proprietary Corp (Hillhaven Corp).
Staff RNs 7 (ft); LPNs 11 (ft); Orderlies 4 (ft);
Nurses aides 42 (ft); Physical therapists 1
(pt); Occupational therapists 1 (pt); Speech
therapists 1 (pt); Activities coordinators 1
(ft), 1 (pt); Dietitians 1 (pt); Podiatrists 1
(pt).
Facilities Dining room; Physical therapy
room; Activities room; Crafts room; Laundry
room; Barber/Beauty shop.
Activities Arts & crafts; Cards; Games;
Reading groups; Prayer groups; Movies;
Shopping trips; Social/Cultural gatherings.

Hy-Lond Convalescent Hospital*
1900 Coffee Rd, Modesto, CA, 95350
(209) 526-1775
Admin Fernando Rodriquez. *Medical Dir/Dir
of Nursing* Mattice Harris MD.
Licensure Skilled care. *Beds* 120. *Certified*
Medicare; Medi-Cal.
Owner Proprietary Corp (Beverly Enterprises).
Admissions Requirements Medical
examination.
Staff RNs 4 (ft), 2 (pt); LPNs 12 (ft), 3 (pt);
Physical therapists 1 (ft); Reality therapists 1
(pt); Recreational therapists 1 (pt); Speech
therapists 1 (pt); Activities coordinators 1
(ft), 1 (pt); Dietitians 1 (ft), 1 (pt); Dentists 1
(pt); Ophthalmologists 1 (pt); Podiatrists 1
(pt); Audiologists 1 (pt).
Facilities Dining room; Physical therapy
room; Activities room; Crafts room; Laundry
room; Barber/Beauty shop; Library.
Activities Arts & crafts; Cards; Games;
Reading groups; Prayer groups; Movies;
Shopping trips; Social/Cultural gatherings.

Modesto Convalescent Hospital*
515 E Orangeburg Ave, Modesto, CA, 95350
(209) 529-0516
Admin Loretta Smith.
Licensure Skilled care. *Beds* 70. *Certified*
Medicare; Medi-Cal.
Owner Proprietary Corp.

Orangeburg Convalescent Hospital*
823 E Orangeburg Ave, Modesto, CA, 95350
(209) 524-4641
Admin Rebecca Jane Collins.
Licensure Skilled care. *Beds* 40. *Certified*
Medicare; Medi-Cal.
Owner Proprietary Corp.

Reno Convalescent Hospital
1028 Reno Ave, Modesto, CA, 95351
(209) 524-1146
Admin Helayne Hendrickson. *Medical Dir/Dir
of Nursing* Dr Grant Bare; Vera Jennings
RN DON.
Licensure Skilled care. *Beds* SNF 25. *Certified*
Medi-Cal.
Owner Proprietary Corp.
Admissions Requirements Minimum age 65;
Medical examination; Physician's request.
Staff RNs 2 (ft), 1 (pt); LPNs 1 (ft), 2 (pt);
Nurses aides 9 (ft), 1 (pt); Activities
coordinators 1 (ft).
Languages Spanish, Hindi, Chinese

Facilities Dining room; Activities room; Crafts room; Laundry room.
Activities Arts & crafts; Cards; Games; Reading groups; Prayer groups; Movies; Shopping trips; Social/Cultural gatherings.

MONROVIA

Beverly Manor Convalescent Hospital*
615 W Duarte Rd, Monrovia, CA, 91016
(213) 358-4547
Admin Floy Wulk.
Licensure Skilled care. *Beds* 99. *Certified* Medicare; Medi-Cal.
Owner Proprietary Corp (Beverly Enterprises).

MONTCLAIR

Montclair Manor Convalescent Hospital
5119 Bandera St, Montclair, CA, 91763
(714) 626-1294
Admin Rosalie Mitchell. *Medical Dir/Dir of Nursing* Robert Bom MD; Aloise Withorne DON.
Licensure Skilled care. *Beds* 59. *Certified* Medicare; Medi-Cal.
Owner Proprietary Corp (Medicrest of California).
Admissions Requirements Medical examination.
Staff RNs 1 (ft), 4 (pt); LPNs 4 (ft), 1 (pt); Orderlies 2 (ft); Nurses aides 20 (ft); Activities coordinators 1 (ft).
Facilities Dining room; Activities room; Crafts room; Laundry room; Barber/Beauty shop; Library.
Activities Arts & crafts; Games; Movies; Social/Cultural gatherings.

Monte Vista Child Care Center*
9140 Monte Vista, Montclair, CA, 91763
(714) 624-2774
Admin Barbara Risinger.
Licensure Intermediate care for mentally retarded. *Beds* 58. *Certified* Medi-Cal.
Owner Proprietary Corp.
Admissions Requirements Minimum age 8; Medical examination; Physician's request.
Staff RNs; LPNs; Orderlies; Nurses aides; Activities coordinators.
Facilities Dining room; Crafts room; Laundry room; Program rooms.
Activities Arts & crafts; Movies; Shopping trips.

Suntown at Montclair Convalescent Hospital*
9620 Fremont Ave, Montclair, CA, 91763
(714) 621-4751
Admin Benjamin F Davis. *Medical Dir/Dir of Nursing* Herman Mirkin MD.
Licensure Skilled care. *Beds* 140. *Certified* Medicare; Medi-Cal.
Owner Proprietary Corp.
Staff RNs 5 (ft), 4 (pt); LPNs 9 (ft), 8 (pt); Orderlies 1 (ft), 1 (pt); Nurses aides 52 (ft), 10 (pt); Physical therapists 1 (pt); Reality therapists 1 (pt); Recreational therapists 1 (pt); Occupational therapists 1 (pt); Speech therapists 1 (pt); Activities coordinators 2 (ft); Dietitians 1 (pt); Dentists 1 (pt); Ophthalmologists 1 (pt); Podiatrists 1 (pt).
Facilities Dining room; Physical therapy room; Activities room; Crafts room; Laundry room; Barber/Beauty shop; Library; Coffee room.
Activities Arts & crafts; Cards; Games; Reading groups; Prayer groups; Movies; Social/Cultural gatherings; Parties.

MONTEBELLO

Montebello Convalescent Hospital*
1035 W Beverly Blvd, Montebello, CA, 90640
(213) 724-1315
Admin Mary B Ringen.

Licensure Skilled care. *Beds* 99. *Certified* Medicare; Medi-Cal.
Owner Proprietary Corp (Care Enterprises).

Rio Hondo CareWest Nursing Center
273 E Beverly Blvd, Montebello, CA, 90640
(213) 724-5100
Admin Ann S Walshe. *Medical Dir/Dir of Nursing* Dr L Pollock.
Licensure Skilled care. *Beds* 200. *Certified* Medicare; Medi-Cal.
Owner Proprietary Corp (Care Enterprises).
Admissions Requirements Minimum age 18; Medical examination; Physician's request.
Staff Physicians 30 (ft); RNs 15 (ft); LPNs 20 (ft); Orderlies 10 (ft); Nurses aides 80 (ft); Physical therapists 1 (ft); Occupational therapists; Speech therapists; Activities coordinators 3 (ft); Dietitians 1 (ft); Dentists; Ophthalmologists; Podiatrists; Physical therapy aide 1 (ft); Asst 1 (ft); Restorative CNA 3 (ft); Dentist.
Facilities Dining room; Physical therapy room; Activities room; Crafts room; Laundry room; Barber/Beauty shop.
Activities Arts & crafts; Cards; Games; Reading groups; Prayer groups; Movies; Shopping trips.

MONTECITO

Casa Dorinda*
300 Hot Springs Rd, Montecito, CA, 93108
(805) 969-8026
Admin William Ducharme. *Medical Dir/Dir of Nursing* Dr Robert Hartzman.
Licensure Skilled care. *Beds* 47. *Certified* Medicare; Medi-Cal.
Owner Proprietary Corp.
Admissions Requirements Medical examination.
Staff Physicians 1 (pt); RNs 8 (ft), 3 (pt); LPNs 4 (ft), 1 (pt); Nurses aides 13 (ft); Physical therapists 2 (ft); Occupational therapists 1 (pt); Speech therapists 1 (pt); Activities coordinators 1 (ft), 1 (pt); Dietitians 1 (pt); Dentists 1 (pt); Podiatrists 1 (pt).
Facilities Dining room; Physical therapy room; Activities room; Crafts room; Laundry room; Barber/Beauty shop; Library.
Activities Arts & crafts; Cards; Games; Reading groups; Prayer groups; Movies; Shopping trips; Social/Cultural gatherings; Picnics; Rides; BBQs.

MONTEREY

Ave Maria Convalescent Hospital
1249 Josselyn Canyon Rd, Monterey, CA, 93940
(408) 373-1216
Admin Sr M Constance. *Medical Dir/Dir of Nursing* Olga Titus.
Licensure Skilled care. *Beds* SNF 30.
Owner Nonprofit Corp.
Admissions Requirements Physician's request.
Staff RNs 2 (ft); LPNs 3 (ft); Nurses aides 18 (ft); Activities coordinators 2 (ft).
Affiliation Roman Catholic
Facilities Dining room; Activities room; Chapel; Crafts room; Laundry room; Barber/Beauty shop; Library; TV room.
Activities Arts & crafts; Cards; Games; Reading groups; Prayer groups; Movies; Shopping trips; Social/Cultural gatherings; Music; Trips to fairs, horse shows & seashore.

Beverly Manor Convalescent Hospital*
23795 W R Holman Hwy, Monterey, CA, 93940
(408) 624-1875
Admin Susan E Bazsuly. *Medical Dir/Dir of Nursing* Donald M Dubrasich MD.
Licensure Skilled care. *Beds* 99. *Certified* Medicare; Medi-Cal.

Owner Proprietary Corp (Beverly Enterprises).
Admissions Requirements Physician's request.
Facilities Dining room; Physical therapy room; Activities room; Crafts room; Laundry room; Barber/Beauty shop; Library.
Activities Arts & crafts; Cards; Games; Reading groups; Prayer groups; Movies; Shopping trips; Social/Cultural gatherings.

Driftwood Convalescent Hospital
1575 Skyline Dr, Monterey, CA, 93940
(408) 373-2731
Admin Dorothy Filson.
Licensure Skilled care. *Beds* SNF 77. *Certified* Medicare; Medi-Cal.
Owner Proprietary Corp (ARA Living Centers).
Staff RNs 4 (ft), 2 (pt); LPNs 3 (ft), 3 (pt); Nurses aides 20 (ft), 8 (pt); Activities coordinators 1 (ft); Dietitians 1 (ft).
Facilities Dining room; Physical therapy room; Laundry room; Barber/Beauty shop.
Activities Arts & crafts; Cards; Games; Reading groups; Prayer groups; Movies.

Monterey Convalescent Hospital*
735 Pacific St, Monterey, CA, 93940
(408) 373-1323
Admin Charlene Henion.
Licensure Skilled care. *Beds* 52. *Certified* Medicare; Medi-Cal.
Owner Proprietary Corp (ARA Living Centers).

Monterey Pines Skilled Nursing Facility
1501 Skyline Dr, Monterey, CA, 93940
(408) 373-3716
Admin Linda Curtis. *Medical Dir/Dir of Nursing* Harry Nervino MD.
Licensure Skilled care. *Beds* SNF 99. *Certified* Medicare; Medi-Cal.
Owner Nonprofit Corp.
Admissions Requirements Medical examination; Physician's request.
Staff RNs 3 (ft), 1 (pt); Nurses aides 33 (ft), 5 (pt); Physical therapists 1 (pt); Occupational therapists 1 (pt); Speech therapists 1 (pt); Activities coordinators 1 (ft); Dietitians 1 (pt); Dentists 1 (pt); Ophthalmologists 1 (pt); Podiatrists 1 (pt); LVNs 8 (ft), 5 (pt).
Languages Spanish, Russian, German, Tagalog, Korean, Japanese
Facilities Dining room; Physical therapy room; Activities room; Crafts room; Laundry room; Barber/Beauty shop.
Activities Arts & crafts; Cards; Games; Reading groups; Prayer groups; Movies; Shopping trips; Social/Cultural gatherings.

MONTEREY PARK

Hillhaven Health Care*
610 N Garfield Ave, Monterey Park, CA, 91754
(213) 573-3141
Admin Ferri Fathi. *Medical Dir/Dir of Nursing* Sander Peck.
Licensure Skilled care. *Beds* 99. *Certified* Medicare; Medi-Cal.
Owner Proprietary Corp (Hillhaven Corp).
Staff RNs 3 (ft); LPNs 8 (ft); Orderlies 4 (ft); Nurses aides 42 (ft); Physical therapists 1 (pt); Reality therapists 1 (pt); Recreational therapists 1 (ft); Occupational therapists 1 (pt); Speech therapists 1 (pt); Activities coordinators 1 (ft); Dietitians 1 (pt); Dentists 1 (pt); Ophthalmologists 1 (pt); Podiatrists 1 (pt); Audiologists 1 (pt).
Facilities Dining room; Physical therapy room; Activities room; Crafts room; Laundry room; Barber/Beauty shop.
Activities Arts & crafts; Cards; Games; Reading groups; Prayer groups; Movies; Shopping trips; Social/Cultural gatherings.

Monterey Park Convalescent Hospital*
416 N Garfield Ave, Monterey Park, CA,
91754
(213) 280-0280
Admin Alan John.
Licensure Skilled care. *Beds* 89. *Certified*
Medicare; Medi-Cal.
Owner Proprietary Corp.

MONTROSE

Montrose Convalescent Hospital
2123 Verdugo Blvd, Montrose, CA, 91020
(818) 249-3925
Admin Suzanne W Trotter. *Medical Dir/Dir of
Nursing* Albert Killian MD; Patricia Alfonso
DON.
Licensure Skilled care. *Beds* SNF 59. *Certified*
Medicare; Medi-Cal.
Owner Proprietary Corp (Beverly Enterprises).
Admissions Requirements Minimum age 21;
Medical examination; Physician's request.
Staff RNs 2 (ft), 3 (pt); LPNs 5 (ft), 3 (pt);
Nurses aides 15 (ft), 9 (pt).
Languages Spanish
Facilities Dining room; Activities room;
Barber/Beauty shop.
Activities Prayer groups; Social/Cultural
gatherings; Entertainment; Musicals;
Exercise; Religious gatherings; Special dinner
groups.

Verdugo Valley Convalescent Hospital*
2635 Honolulu Ave, Montrose, CA, 91020
(213) 248-6856
Admin Khatchadurian.
Licensure Skilled care. *Beds* 138. *Certified*
Medicare; Medi-Cal.
Owner Proprietary Corp (Health Care Grp).

MORGAN HILL

Eldercare Convalescent Hospital*
370 Noble St, Morgan Hill, CA, 95037-4134
(408) 779-7346
Admin L Armstrong.
Licensure Skilled care. *Beds* 25. *Certified*
Medicare; Medi-Cal.
Owner Proprietary Corp.

Hillview Convalescent Hospital
530 W Dunne Ave, Morgan Hill, CA, 95037
(408) 779-3633
Admin James C Ross. *Medical Dir/Dir of
Nursing* Dr B Joyce; Elena Dunton DON.
Licensure Skilled care. *Beds* SNF 40; ICF 12.
Certified Medi-Cal.
Owner Privately owned.
Admissions Requirements Minimum age
Geriatrics only; Medical examination.
Staff RNs 1 (ft), 2 (pt); LPNs 3 (ft), 2 (pt);
Nurses aides 16 (ft), 5 (pt); Activities
coordinators 1 (ft), 1 (pt).
Languages Spanish, Tagalog, French
Facilities Dining room; Activities room;
Laundry room.
Activities Arts & crafts; Cards; Games; Prayer
groups; Movies; Social/Cultural gatherings.

Pleasant Acres Convalescent Hospital*
17090 Peak Ave, Morgan Hill, CA, 95037
(408) 779-2252
Admin Ralph N Tisdial.
Licensure Skilled care. *Beds* 29. *Certified*
Medicare; Medi-Cal.
Owner Proprietary Corp.

MORRO BAY

Morro Bay Convalescent Center*
Hwy 1 at S Bay Blvd, Morro Bay, CA, 93442
(805) 772-2237
Admin Pauline I Elders.
Licensure Skilled care. *Beds* 74. *Certified*
Medicare; Medi-Cal.
Owner Proprietary Corp.

MOUNTAIN VIEW

Grant Cuesta Convalescent Hospital
1949 Grant Rd, Mountain View, CA, 94040
(415) 986-2990
Admin Betsy Dickinson. *Medical Dir/Dir of
Nursing* Patricia Guilfoy.
Licensure Skilled care. *Beds* 104. *Certified*
Medicare; Medi-Cal.
Owner Proprietary Corp.
Admissions Requirements Physician's request.
Staff Physicians 1 (pt); RNs 3 (ft), 4 (pt);
LPNs 6 (ft), 4 (pt); Nurses aides 32 (ft), 11
(pt); Physical therapists 4 (pt); Reality
therapists 1 (ft), 1 (pt); Occupational
therapists 1 (pt); Speech therapists 1 (pt);
Activities coordinators 1 (ft), 1 (pt);
Dietitians 1 (ft), 1 (pt); Ophthalmologists 1
(pt).
Facilities Dining room; Physical therapy
room; Activities room; Crafts room; Laundry
room; Barber/Beauty shop; Library services;
Patio; BBQ.
Activities Arts & crafts; Games; Reading
groups; Prayer groups; Movies; Musical
entertainment; Animal visits.

Julia Convalescent Hospital
276 Sierra Vista Ave, Mountain View, CA,
94042
(415) 967-5714
Admin Yvonne Wood. *Medical Dir/Dir of
Nursing* Dr Inocencio.
Licensure Skilled care. *Beds* 99. *Certified*
Medicare; Medi-Cal.
Owner Proprietary Corp (Beverly Enterprises).
Staff Physicians; RNs; LPNs; Orderlies;
Nurses aides; Physical therapists; Reality
therapists; Recreational therapists;
Occupational therapists; Speech therapists;
Activities coordinators; Dietitians; Dentists;
Ophthalmologists; Dentist.
Facilities Dining room; Physical therapy
room; Activities room; Crafts room; Barber/
Beauty shop; TV rooms.
Activities Arts & crafts; Cards; Games; Prayer
groups; Movies; Social/Cultural gatherings;
Adult education classes.

Mountain View Convalescent Hospital
2530 Solace Pl, Mountain View, CA, 94040
(415) 961-6161
Admin Elayne Groton. *Medical Dir/Dir of
Nursing* Harry Wong; Sylvie Deschenes.
Licensure Skilled care. *Beds* SNF 138.
Certified Medicare; Medi-Cal.
Owner Proprietary Corp.
Admissions Requirements Physician's request.
Staff Physicians 2 (pt); RNs 8 (ft), 5 (pt);
LPNs 7 (ft), 1 (pt); Orderlies 5 (ft), 1 (pt);
Nurses aides 50 (ft), 8 (pt); Physical
therapists 2 (pt); Occupational therapists 1
(pt); Speech therapists 1 (pt); Activities
coordinators 1 (ft), 7 (pt); Dietitians 1 (pt);
Ophthalmologists 1 (pt); Psychologist 1 (pt).
Languages Chinese, French, Spanish, Tagalog
Facilities Dining room; Physical therapy
room; Activities room; Laundry room;
Barber/Beauty shop; Library.
Activities Arts & crafts; Cards; Games;
Reading groups; Prayer groups; Movies;
Shopping trips; Social/Cultural gatherings.

Villa Siena
1855 Miramonte Ave, Mountain View, CA,
94040
(415) 961-6484
Admin Carl Braginsky. *Medical Dir/Dir of
Nursing* Mary McCue DON.
Licensure Skilled care. *Beds* SNF 20. *Certified*
Medi-Cal.
Owner Nonprofit Corp.
Admissions Requirements Minimum age 62;
Medical examination.
Staff RNs 2 (ft); LPNs 6 (ft); Orderlies 12 (ft).
Languages Spanish

Facilities Dining room; Activities room;
Chapel; Barber/Beauty shop.
Activities Arts & crafts; Games; Prayer groups;
Movies.

NAPA

Crystal Care Center
2300 Brown St, Napa, CA, 94558
(707) 226-1821
Admin W Chip Atkin Jr.
Licensure Skilled care. *Beds* 84. *Certified*
Medicare; Medi-Cal.
Owner Proprietary Corp.

Hy-Lond Convalescent Hospital*
705 Trancas St, Napa, CA, 94558
(707) 255-6060
Admin Robert W Bates.
Licensure Skilled care. *Beds* 120. *Certified*
Medicare; Medi-Cal.
Owner Proprietary Corp.

Piners Convalescent Hospital Inc
1800 Pueblo Ave, Napa, CA, 94558
(707) 224-7925
Admin Gary Piner. *Medical Dir/Dir of
Nursing* Robert Gaither.
Licensure Skilled care. *Beds* SNF 49. *Certified*
Medicare.
Owner Proprietary Corp.
Admissions Requirements Medical
examination; Physician's request.
Staff RNs; LPNs; Nurses aides; Physical
therapists; Recreational therapists;
Occupational therapists; Speech therapists;
Activities coordinators; Dietitians.
Facilities Dining room; Activities room;
Crafts room; Laundry room; Barber/Beauty
shop.
Activities Arts & crafts; Cards; Games;
Reading groups; Movies.

Redwood Christian Convalescent Hospital
2465 Redwood Rd, Napa, CA, 94558
(707) 255-3012
Admin Clement J Doran Jr. *Medical Dir/Dir
of Nursing* Dr Ronald Julis; Geraldine
Furth.
Licensure Skilled care. *Beds* 59. *Certified*
Medicare; Medi-Cal.
Owner Proprietary Corp.
Admissions Requirements Physician's request.
Staff RNs; LPNs; Nurses aides; Activities
coordinators; Dietitians.
Languages Spanish
Facilities Dining room; Activities room;
Barber/Beauty shop; Library.
Activities Arts & crafts; Games; Reading
groups; Prayer groups; Movies; Shopping
trips.

Roberts Nursing Home
3415 Browns Valley Rd, Napa, CA, 94558
(707) 257-3515
Admin Edythe Cambra. *Medical Dir/Dir of
Nursing* Pamela Kinsey RN.
Licensure Skilled care. *Beds* SNF 35. *Certified*
Medi-Cal.
Owner Privately owned.
Admissions Requirements Medical
examination; Physician's request.
Staff RNs; Orderlies; Nurses aides; Activities
coordinators; LVNs.
Activities Arts & crafts; Games; Reading
groups; Prayer groups; Movies.

NATIONAL CITY

Continana Convalescent Hospital*
220 E 24th St, National City, CA, 92050
(714) 474-6741
Admin Walter N Ross.
Licensure Skilled care. *Beds* 99. *Certified*
Medicare; Medi-Cal.
Owner Proprietary Corp.

Friendship Homes
2300 E 7th St, National City, CA, 92050
(619) 267-8400
Admin Charles I Cheneweth. *Medical Dir/Dir of Nursing* Leon Kelley MD.
Licensure Skilled care; Intermediate care for mentally retarded. *Beds* SNF 27; ICF/MR 59. *Certified* Medi-Cal.
Owner Proprietary Corp.
Admissions Requirements Minimum age 3 months.
Staff Physicians 1 (pt); RNs 6 (ft); LPNs 10 (ft), 1 (pt); Orderlies 4 (ft), 1 (pt); Nurses aides 63 (ft), 12 (pt); Physical therapists 1 (pt); Recreational therapists 1 (pt); Occupational therapists 1 (pt); Speech therapists 1 (pt); Activities coordinators 1 (pt); Dietitians 1 (pt); Podiatrists 1 (pt).
Facilities Dining room; Physical therapy room; Activities room; Laundry room.

Friendship Manor Convalescent Center*
902 Euclid Ave, National City, CA, 92050
(619) 267-9220
Admin J Edwin Cheneweth. *Medical Dir/Dir of Nursing* C G Maloney MD.
Licensure Skilled care. *Beds* 104. *Certified* Medicare; Medi-Cal.
Owner Proprietary Corp.
Admissions Requirements Medical examination; Physician's request.
Staff RNs 7 (ft), 2 (pt); LPNs 5 (ft), 2 (pt); Nurses aides 40 (ft), 7 (pt); Physical therapists 1 (ft); Recreational therapists 1 (ft); Activities coordinators 1 (ft).
Facilities Dining room; Physical therapy room; Activities room; Laundry room; Barber/Beauty shop; Conference room; TV lounge.
Activities Arts & crafts; Cards; Games; Prayer groups; Movies; Shopping trips; Social/Cultural gatherings; Picnics; Outings.

Hillcrest Manor Sanitarium*
1889 National City Blvd, National City, CA, 92050
(619) 477-1176
Admin Gary R Byrnes. *Medical Dir/Dir of Nursing* M Brent Campbell MD.
Licensure Skilled care. *Beds* 85. *Certified* Medicare; Medi-Cal.
Owner Proprietary Corp.
Admissions Requirements Minimum age 35; Medical examination; Physician's request.
Staff RNs 4 (ft), 2 (pt); LPNs 5 (ft); Nurses aides 38 (ft), 2 (pt); Activities coordinators 2 (ft).
Facilities Dining room; Physical therapy room; Activities room; Enclosed patio.
Activities Arts & crafts; Cards; Games; Reading groups; Prayer groups; Movies; Shopping trips; Social/Cultural gatherings.

Paradise Valley Health Care Center
2575 E 8th St, National City, CA, 92050
(714) 470-6700
Admin James C Allen. *Medical Dir/Dir of Nursing* Patsy Villarin.
Licensure Skilled care; Residential care. *Beds* SNF 86; Residential 76. *Certified* Medicare; Medi-Cal.
Owner Proprietary Corp.
Admissions Requirements Medical examination; Physician's request.
Staff RNs 4 (ft), 2 (pt); LPNs 8 (ft), 2 (pt); Nurses aides 59 (ft), 14 (pt); Activities coordinators 1 (ft).
Languages Spanish, Tagalog
Facilities Dining room; Activities room; Chapel; Laundry room; Barber/Beauty shop; Library.
Activities Arts & crafts; Games; Reading groups; Prayer groups; Movies; Shopping trips; Social/Cultural gatherings.

NEWBURY PARK

Mary Health of Sick Convalescent & Nursing Hospital*
2929 Theresa Dr, Newbury Park, CA, 91320
(805) 498-3644
Admin Charles F Comley.
Licensure Skilled care. *Beds* 61. *Certified* Medicare; Medi-Cal.
Owner Nonprofit Corp.

Ventura Estates Health Manor
915 Estates Dr, Newbury Park, CA, 91320
(805) 498-3691
Admin Elwood Sherrard. *Medical Dir/Dir of Nursing* Arthur C Fingerle MD; Dorothy Kuester RN.
Licensure Intermediate care. *Beds* ICF 18. *Certified* Medi-Cal.
Owner Nonprofit Corp.
Admissions Requirements Females only; Medical examination; Physician's request.
Staff RNs 1 (ft), 3 (pt); Nurses aides 1 (ft), 2 (pt).
Languages Spanish, Korean
Affiliation Seventh-Day Adventist
Facilities Dining room; Activities room; Chapel; Crafts room; Laundry room; Barber/Beauty shop; Library.
Activities Arts & crafts; Games; Reading groups; Movies; Shopping trips; Exercises; Individual activities.

Ventura Estates Health Manor
915 Estates Dr, Newbury Park, CA, 91320
(805) 498-3691
Admin Elwood Sherrard. *Medical Dir/Dir of Nursing* Arthur C Fingerle MD; Dorothy Kuester, RN DON.
Licensure Skilled care. *Beds* SNF 48. *Certified* Medicare; Medi-Cal.
Owner Nonprofit Corp.
Admissions Requirements Medical examination; Physician's request.
Staff RNs 2 (ft), 6 (pt); LPNs 3 (ft), 2 (pt); Nurses aides 18 (ft), 6 (pt).
Languages Korean, Spanish, Tagalog
Affiliation Seventh-Day Adventist
Facilities Dining room; Activities room; Chapel; Crafts room; Laundry room; Barber/Beauty shop; Library.
Activities Arts & crafts; Games; Reading groups; Prayer groups; Exercises.

NEWMAN

San Luis Convalescent Hospital*
709 N St, Newman, CA, 95360
(209) 862-2862
Admin Avenal Miller. *Medical Dir/Dir of Nursing* Dr La Torre.
Licensure Skilled care. *Beds* 71. *Certified* Medicare; Medi-Cal.
Owner Proprietary Corp (Beverly Enterprises).
Staff Nurses aides 19 (ft).
Facilities Dining room; Activities room; Laundry room; Barber/Beauty shop.
Activities Arts & crafts; Cards; Games; Reading groups; Prayer groups; Movies.

NEWPORT BEACH

Flagship Convalescent Center*
466 Flagship Rd, Newport Beach, CA, 92663
(714) 642-8044
Admin Allen J June.
Licensure Skilled care. *Beds* 99. *Certified* Medicare; Medi-Cal.
Owner Proprietary Corp (American Medical Services Inc).

Newport Convalescent Center*
1555 Superior Ave, Newport Beach, CA, 92660
(714) 646-7764
Admin Ruthe Hamilton.

Licensure Skilled care. *Beds* 74. *Certified* Medicare; Medi-Cal.
Owner Proprietary Corp.

Park Superior Healthcare*
1445 Superior Ave, Newport Beach, CA, 92660
(714) 642-2410
Admin Alice Riddell.
Licensure Skilled care. *Beds* 96. *Certified* Medicare; Medi-Cal.
Owner Proprietary Corp (American Medical Services Inc).

NORTH HOLLYWOOD

All Saints Convalescent Center*
11810 Saticoy St, North Hollywood, CA, 91605
(213) 982-4600
Admin Hale J Scott.
Licensure Skilled care. *Beds* 128. *Certified* Medicare.
Owner Proprietary Corp.

Chandler Convalescent Hospital Inc
5335 Laurel Canyon Blvd, North Hollywood, CA, 91607
(213) 985-1814
Admin Arthur E Goldfarb. *Medical Dir/Dir of Nursing* Sandor Zuckerman MD; Emma Parica RN DON.
Licensure Skilled care; Intermediate care. *Beds* 201. *Certified* Medicare; Medi-Cal.
Owner Proprietary Corp.
Admissions Requirements Minimum age 45; Physician's request.
Staff RNs 4 (ft), 3 (pt); LPNs 14 (ft), 3 (pt); Orderlies 7 (ft); Nurses aides 54 (ft); Activities coordinators 3 (ft); Dietitians 18 (ft).
Languages Spanish, French, Korean, Hungarian, Czech, Hindi
Facilities Dining room; Physical therapy room; Activities room; Chapel; Crafts room; Laundry room; Barber/Beauty shop; Library.
Activities Arts & crafts; Games; Reading groups; Movies; Social/Cultural gatherings.

Golden State Colonial Convalescent Hospital
10830 Oxnard St, North Hollywood, CA, 91606
(818) 763-8247
Admin Bette Zimmer. *Medical Dir/Dir of Nursing* Dr David Antrobus; Mavis Poulson RN DON.
Licensure Skilled care. *Beds* SNF 49. *Certified* Medicare; Medi-Cal.
Owner Proprietary Corp (Golden State Health Centers).
Admissions Requirements Minimum age 65; Physician's request.
Staff Physicians 3 (pt); RNs 1 (ft), 1 (pt); LPNs 3 (ft), 2 (pt); Orderlies; Nurses aides; Physical therapists; Occupational therapists; Speech therapists; Activities coordinators; Dietitians; Dentists; Ophthalmologists; Podiatrists.
Languages Spanish, German
Facilities Dining room; Activities room; Crafts room; Laundry room; Barber/Beauty shop; Library.
Activities Arts & crafts; Cards; Games; Reading groups; Prayer groups; Movies; Shopping trips; Social/Cultural gatherings; Trips to park.

Laurelwood Convalescent Center*
13000 Victory Blvd, North Hollywood, CA, 91606
(213) 985-5990
Admin Lynn Lewarton.
Licensure Skilled care. *Beds* 99. *Certified* Medicare; Medi-Cal.
Owner Proprietary Corp (ARA Living Centers).

North Hollywood Extended Care*
6120 Vineland, North Hollywood, CA, 91606
(213) 763-6275
Admin Deborah Collins.
Licensure Skilled care. *Beds* 72. *Certified*
Medicare; Medi-Cal.
Owner Proprietary Corp.
Admissions Requirements Physician's request.
Staff RNs 1 (ft), 1 (pt); LPNs 6 (ft); Nurses
aides 25 (ft); Physical therapists 1 (ft);
Reality therapists 1 (ft); Recreational
therapists 1 (ft); Speech therapists 1 (pt);
Activities coordinators 1 (ft); Dietitians 1
(pt); Dentists 1 (pt); Ophthalmologists 1 (pt);
Podiatrists 1 (pt); Audiologists 1 (pt).
Facilities Dining room; Physical therapy
room; Activities room; Laundry room;
Barber/Beauty shop.
Activities Arts & crafts; Games; Reading
groups; Prayer groups; Shopping trips.

Riverside Convalescent Hospital
12750 Riverside Dr, North Hollywood, CA,
91607
(213) 766-6105
Admin Joellen Zayer. *Medical Dir/Dir of
Nursing* Saeed Humayun MD.
Licensure Skilled care. *Beds* SNF 108.
Certified Medicare; Medi-Cal.
Owner Proprietary Corp.
Admissions Requirements Minimum age 65;
Medical examination; Physician's request.
Staff RNs; LPNs; Orderlies; Nurses aides;
Physical therapists; Occupational therapists;
Speech therapists; Activities coordinators;
Dietitians; Dentists; Ophthalmologists;
Podiatrists.
Languages Spanish
Facilities Dining room; Physical therapy
room; Activities room; Laundry room;
Barber/Beauty shop.
Activities Arts & crafts; Cards; Games;
Reading groups; Prayer groups; Movies;
Shopping trips; Social/Cultural gatherings;
Resident & family candle-light dinners held
monthly.

**St Elizabeth Toluca Lake Convalescent
Hospital**
10425 Magnolia Blvd, North Hollywood, CA,
91601
(818) 984-2918
Admin Janice Delano. *Medical Dir/Dir of
Nursing* Lewis Trostler MD; Judy Farabaugh
RN DON.
Licensure Skilled care. *Beds* SNF 52. *Certified*
Medicare; Medi-Cal.
Owner Nonprofit Corp.
Admissions Requirements Minimum age 65;
Medical examination; Physician's request.
Staff RNs 1 (ft), 2 (pt); LPNs 2 (ft), 3 (pt);
Nurses aides 19 (ft), 2 (pt); Activities
coordinators 1 (ft).
Languages Spanish, German
Facilities Dining room; Physical therapy
room; Activities room; Crafts room; Laundry
room; Barber/Beauty shop.
Activities Arts & crafts; Cards; Games;
Reading groups; Prayer groups; Movies;
Shopping trips; Bingo; Exercise;
Entertainment.

Valley Palms Care Center
13400 Sherman Way, North Hollywood, CA,
91344
(818) 983-0103
Admin Brenda Manke. *Medical Dir/Dir of
Nursing* Luz Villena.
Licensure Skilled care. *Beds* SNF 99. *Certified*
Medicare; Medi-Cal.
Owner Proprietary Corp (Summit Health Ltd).
Admissions Requirements Physician's request.
Staff RNs 3 (ft); LPNs 12 (ft); Orderlies;
Nurses aides 50 (ft); Activities coordinators
1 (ft); Dietitians 1 (ft).
Languages Spanish

Facilities Dining room; Physical therapy
room; Activities room; Crafts room; Barber/
Beauty shop.
Activities Arts & crafts; Cards; Games;
Reading groups; Prayer groups; Movies;
Shopping trips; Social/Cultural gatherings.

NORWALK

Bird Haven Christian Convalescent Hospital*
12350 Rosecrans, Norwalk, CA, 90650
(213) 921-6624
Admin Andrea Fostvedt.
Licensure Skilled care. *Beds* 59. *Certified*
Medicare; Medi-Cal.
Owner Proprietary Corp.

Glen Terrace Convalescent Center
11510 E Imperial Hwy, Norwalk, CA, 90650
(213) 868-6791
Admin Jeri-Anne Ickstadt-Shelton. *Medical
Dir/Dir of Nursing* Dr Lawrence Pollock.
Licensure Skilled care. *Beds* SNF 99. *Certified*
Medicare; Medi-Cal.
Owner Proprietary Corp (ARA Living
Centers).
Admissions Requirements Minimum age 65;
Physician's request.
Staff RNs 2 (ft), 1 (pt); LPNs 8 (ft); Orderlies
12 (ft); Nurses aides 46 (ft); Physical
therapists 1 (pt); Recreational therapists 1
(pt); Occupational therapists 1 (pt); Speech
therapists 1 (pt); Activities coordinators 1
(ft); Dietitians 1 (ft); Dentists 1 (pt);
Ophthalmologists 1 (pt); Podiatrists 1 (pt).
Languages Tagalog, Spanish
Facilities Dining room; Physical therapy
room; Activities room; Laundry room;
Barber/Beauty shop.
Activities Arts & crafts; Cards; Games; Prayer
groups; Movies; Shopping trips; Social/
Cultural gatherings; Reality orientation.

Intercommunity Convalescent Hospital*
12627 Studebaker Rd, Norwalk, CA, 90650
(213) 868-4767
Admin Michael Spence.
Licensure Skilled care. *Beds* 86. *Certified*
Medicare; Medi-Cal.
Owner Proprietary Corp (Care Enterprises).

Rancho Los Padres Convalescent Hospital
10625 Leffingwell Rd, Norwalk, CA, 90650
(213) 864-2541
Admin Sharon Kearney RN MA. *Medical Dir/
Dir of Nursing* Dr M Jalil; Barbara Gormley.
Licensure Skilled care. *Beds* SNF 99. *Certified*
Medicare; Medi-Cal.
Owner Proprietary Corp.
Admissions Requirements Physician's request.
Staff Physicians; RNs; LPNs; Orderlies;
Nurses aides; Physical therapists; Reality
therapists; Recreational therapists;
Occupational therapists; Speech therapists;
Activities coordinators; Dietitians; Dentists;
Ophthalmologists; Podiatrists.
Facilities Dining room; Physical therapy
room; Activities room; Crafts room; Laundry
room; Barber/Beauty shop.
Activities Arts & crafts; Cards; Games;
Reading groups; Prayer groups; Movies;
Shopping trips; Social/Cultural gatherings.

Southland Geriatric Center
11701 Studebaker Rd, Norwalk, CA, 90650
(213) 868-9761
Admin Gilbert C Moore. *Medical Dir/Dir of
Nursing* James H Holman MD; D J Busch
RN.
Licensure Skilled care; Intermediate care. *Beds*
SNF 80; ICF 40. *Certified* Medicare; Medi-
Cal.
Owner Nonprofit Corp.
Admissions Requirements Minimum age 55.
Staff RNs 3 (ft), 5 (pt); LPNs 8 (ft), 6 (pt);
Orderlies 4 (ft); Nurses aides 49 (ft), 14 (pt);
Physical therapists 1 (pt); Occupational
therapists 1 (pt); Speech therapists 2 (pt);

Activities coordinators 1 (ft), 2 (pt);
Dietitians 1 (pt); Dentists 1 (pt);
Ophthalmologists 1 (pt); Podiatrists 1 (pt);
Restorative aide 1 (ft).
Affiliation Lutheran
Facilities Dining room; Physical therapy
room; Activities room; Chapel; Crafts room;
Laundry room; Barber/Beauty shop; Library;
Class room.
Activities Arts & crafts; Cards; Games;
Reading groups; Prayer groups; Movies;
Shopping trips; Social/Cultural gatherings.

Villa Elena Convalescent Hospital
13226 Studebaker Rd, Norwalk, CA, 90650
(213) 868-0591
Admin James A Hall. *Medical Dir/Dir of
Nursing* James Jetlon MD; Dora Craft RN.
Licensure Skilled care. *Beds* SNF 98. *Certified*
Medicaid; Medicare; Medi-Cal.
Owner Proprietary Corp.
Admissions Requirements Medical
examination; Physician's request.
Staff RNs 3 (ft), 2 (pt); LPNs 7 (ft), 3 (pt);
Orderlies 4 (ft), 2 (pt); Nurses aides 30 (ft),
10 (pt); Recreational therapists 2 (ft);
Activities coordinators 1 (ft); Dietitians 1
(ft).
Languages Spanish
Facilities Dining room; Physical therapy
room; Activities room; Laundry room;
Barber/Beauty shop.
Activities Arts & crafts; Cards; Games;
Reading groups; Prayer groups; Movies;
Shopping trips; Social/Cultural gatherings.

NOVATO

Canyon Manor*
655 Canyon Rd, Novato, CA, 94947
(415) 892-1628
Admin Richard Evatz. *Medical Dir/Dir of
Nursing* Jeffrey Berlant MD.
Licensure Skilled care. *Beds* 89. *Certified*
Medicare; Medi-Cal.
Owner Proprietary Corp.
Admissions Requirements Minimum age 18.
Facilities Dining room; Activities room;
Crafts room; Library.
Activities Arts & crafts; Cards; Games;
Reading groups; Shopping trips; Social/
Cultural gatherings.

Hill Road Convalescent Hospital*
1565 Hill Rd, Novato, CA, 94947
(415) 897-6161
Admin Carolyn Hankinson.
Licensure Skilled care. *Beds* 187. *Certified*
Medicare; Medi-Cal.
Owner Proprietary Corp (Beverly Enterprises).

OAKDALE

Oakdale Convalescent Hospital*
275 S Oak St, Oakdale, CA, 95361
(209) 847-0367
Admin Buren Boone.
Licensure Skilled care. *Beds* 78. *Certified*
Medicare; Medi-Cal.
Owner Proprietary Corp (Beverly Enterprises).

OAKHURST

Sierra Meadows Convalescent Hospital
40131 Hwy 49, Oakhurst, CA, 93644
(209) 683-2992
Admin A M Richards. *Medical Dir/Dir of
Nursing* C Mitchell MD.
Licensure Skilled care. *Beds* 59. *Certified*
Medicare; Medi-Cal.
Owner Nonprofit Corp.
Admissions Requirements Physician's request.
Staff RNs 1 (ft), 4 (pt); LPNs 2 (ft), 5 (pt);
Orderlies 4 (pt); Nurses aides 12 (ft), 16 (pt);
Speech therapists 1 (pt); Activities
coordinators 1 (ft).

Facilities Dining room; Laundry room;
  Barber/Beauty shop; Library; Adjacent
  emergicenter; lab & x-ray.
Activities Arts & crafts; Cards; Games;
  Reading groups; Prayer groups; Movies;
  Shopping trips; Social/Cultural gatherings.

OAKLAND

Alpha Convalescent Hospital*
3550 Foothill Blvd, Oakland, CA, 94601
(415) 534-5026
Admin Clarence Schlenker. *Medical Dir/Dir of
Nursing* Dr Karl Konstantin.
Licensure Skilled care. *Beds* 30. *Certified*
  Medicare; Medi-Cal.
Owner Proprietary Corp.
Admissions Requirements Minimum age 45;
  Medical examination; Physician's request.
Staff Physicians 4 (pt); RNs 1 (ft), 1 (pt);
  LPNs 2 (ft), 2 (pt); Orderlies 1 (ft); Nurses
  aides 10 (ft); Recreational therapists 1 (pt);
  Activities coordinators 1 (pt); Dietitians 1
  (pt); Dentists 1 (pt); Ophthalmologists 1 (pt);
  Podiatrists 1 (pt).
Facilities Dining room; Activities room;
  Laundry room.
Activities Arts & crafts; Cards; Games;
  Reading groups; Prayer groups; Movies;
  Shopping trips.

Altenheim Inc
1720 MacArthur Blvd, Oakland, CA, 94602
(415) 530-4013
Admin Helen P Cathey. *Medical Dir/Dir of
Nursing* Jean Sharp MD.
Licensure Skilled care; Residential care. *Beds*
  SNF 16; Residential 210.
Owner Nonprofit Corp.
Admissions Requirements Minimum age 60;
  Medical examination; Physician's request.
Staff Physicians 1 (pt); RNs 1 (ft), 2 (pt);
  LPNs 2 (ft), 1 (pt); Orderlies 1 (ft); Nurses
  aides 7 (ft), 3 (pt); Activities coordinators 1
  (ft), 1 (pt); Dietitians 1 (pt).
Languages German, Greek, Spanish, Tagalog
Affiliation Altenheim Society
Facilities Dining room; Activities room;
  Laundry room; Barber/Beauty shop; Library.
Activities Arts & crafts; Games; Reading
  groups; Prayer groups; Movies; Shopping
  trips; Social/Cultural gatherings.

Beulah Home Inc*
4690 Tompkins Ave, Oakland, CA, 94619
(415) 531-4830
Admin James P Roth.
Licensure Skilled care. *Beds* 17. *Certified*
  Medi-Cal.
Owner Nonprofit Corp.

Clinton Village Convalescent Hospital*
1833 10th Ave, Oakland, CA, 94606
(415) 536-6512
Admin Tom C Duarte. *Medical Dir/Dir of
Nursing* John Chokatos MD.
Licensure Skilled care. *Beds* 99. *Certified*
  Medicare; Medi-Cal.
Owner Proprietary Corp.
Admissions Requirements Minimum age 65;
  Medical examination; Physician's request.
Facilities Dining room; Physical therapy
  room; Activities room; Chapel; Crafts room;
  Laundry room; Barber/Beauty shop; Library.
Activities Arts & crafts; Cards; Games;
  Reading groups; Prayer groups; Movies;
  Shopping trips; Social/Cultural gatherings;
  Social work.

Coberly Green Intermediate Care Facility*
2420 Fruitvale Ave, Oakland, CA, 94601
(415) 532-5090
Admin Jeannie Griffin. *Medical Dir/Dir of
Nursing* W H Arthur.
Licensure Intermediate care. *Beds* 21.
  Certified Medi-Cal.
Owner Proprietary Corp.

Staff RNs 1 (ft); LPNs 1 (pt); Nurses aides 3
  (ft); Activities coordinators 1 (pt).
Facilities Dining room; Activities room;
  Crafts room; Laundry room.
Activities Arts & crafts; Cards; Games;
  Reading groups; Prayer groups; Movies;
  Shopping trips; Social/Cultural gatherings.

Dowling Convalescent Hospital
451 28th St, Oakland, CA, 94609-4066
(415) 893-4066
Admin Harry H Appeldorn MD; Pauline
  Pojorlie.
Licensure Skilled care. *Beds* 30. *Certified*
  Medi-Cal.
Owner Proprietary Corp.
Staff RNs; Nurses aides; Activities
  coordinators.
Languages Spanish, Chinese
Activities Arts & crafts; Games; Prayer groups.

Fruitvale Care Convalescent Hospital
3020 E 15th St, Oakland, CA, 94601
(415) 261-5613
Admin Tanny Lansang. *Medical Dir/Dir of
Nursing* Dr Robert Tuff; Ms V Byrdette
DON.
Licensure Skilled care; Semi-acute. *Beds* SNF
  113; Semi-acute 27. *Certified* Medicare;
  Medi-Cal.
Owner Privately owned.
Admissions Requirements Medical
  examination; Physician's request.
Staff Physicians; RNs; Nurses aides;
  Physical therapists; Reality therapists;
  Recreational therapists; Occupational
  therapists; Speech therapists; Activities
  coordinators; Dietitians; Dentists;
  Ophthalmologists; Podiatrists.
Facilities Dining room; Physical therapy
  room; Activities room; Crafts room; Laundry
  room; Barber/Beauty shop.
Activities Arts & crafts; Cards; Games;
  Reading groups; Prayer groups; Movies;
  Shopping trips; Social/Cultural gatherings.

Garfield Geropsychiatric Hospital
1451 28th Ave, Oakland, CA, 94601
(415) 532-0820
Admin Jeffrey P Lambkin. *Medical Dir/Dir of
Nursing* Martin Held MD; Patricia A
Goehner RN MS.
Licensure Skilled care; Geropsychiatric. *Beds*
  SNF; Geropsychiatric 96. *Certified* Medi-
  Cal.
Owner Proprietary Corp.
Admissions Requirements Minimum age 57.
Staff Physicians 1 (ft); RNs 7 (ft); LPNs 13
  (ft); Nurses aides 24 (ft), 7 (pt); Recreational
  therapists 1 (ft); Occupational therapists 2
  (ft); Activities coordinators 3 (ft).
Languages Spanish
Facilities Dining room; Physical therapy
  room; Activities room; Crafts room; Laundry
  room; Barber/Beauty shop.
Activities Arts & crafts; Cards; Games;
  Reading groups; Prayer groups; Movies;
  Shopping trips; Social/Cultural gatherings;
  Individual & group therapy.

High Street Convalescent Hospital*
3145 High St, Oakland, CA, 94619
(415) 533-9970
Admin Joe Vance. *Medical Dir/Dir of Nursing*
Dr Richmond.
Licensure Skilled care. *Beds* 44. *Certified*
  Medicare; Medi-Cal.
Owner Proprietary Corp.
Admissions Requirements Medical
  examination; Physician's request.
Staff RNs 2 (ft), 4 (pt); LPNs 2 (ft), 6 (pt);
  Nurses aides 15 (ft), 11 (pt); Physical
  therapists 1 (pt); Occupational therapists 1
  (pt); Speech therapists 1 (pt); Activities
  coordinators 1 (ft); Dentists 1 (pt);
  Podiatrists 1 (pt).

Facilities Dining room; Activities room;
  Barber/Beauty shop.
Activities Arts & crafts; Cards; Games;
  Reading groups; Prayer groups; Movies;
  Shopping trips; Social/Cultural gatherings;
  Animals visits.

Hillhaven Convalescent Hospital*
3030 Webster St, Oakland, CA, 94609
(415) 451-3856
Admin Margaret M Boyd.
Licensure Skilled care. *Beds* 98. *Certified*
  Medicare; Medi-Cal.
Owner Proprietary Corp (Hillhaven Corp).

Home for Jewish Parents
2780 26th Ave, Oakland, CA, 94601
(415) 536-4604
Admin Ben Laub. *Medical Dir/Dir of Nursing*
Herbert Lints; Kelly Gaglione.
Licensure Skilled care; Residential. *Beds* SNF
  57; Residential 58. *Certified* Medicare;
  Medi-Cal.
Owner Nonprofit organization/foundation.
Admissions Requirements Minimum age 65;
  Medical examination.
Staff RNs 6 (ft); LPNs 6 (ft); Orderlies 1 (ft);
  Nurses aides 24 (ft); Physical therapists 3
  (pt); Reality therapists 1 (pt); Occupational
  therapists 1 (pt); Speech therapists 1 (pt);
  Activities coordinators 1 (ft); Dietitians 1
  (ft); Dentists 1 (pt); Ophthalmologists 1 (pt);
  Podiatrists 1 (pt).
Languages Yiddish
Affiliation Jewish
Facilities Dining room; Physical therapy
  room; Activities room; Chapel; Crafts room;
  Laundry room; Barber/Beauty shop; Library.
Activities Arts & crafts; Cards; Games;
  Reading groups; Prayer groups; Movies;
  Shopping trips; Social/Cultural gatherings.

Lake Park Retirement Residence
1850 Alice St, Oakland, CA, 94612
(415) 835-5511
Admin Dudley Thompson. *Medical Dir/Dir of
Nursing* Dr Thomas Richmond; Shirley
Graham DON.
Licensure Skilled care. *Beds* SNF 271.
  Certified Medicare.
Owner Nonprofit Corp.
Admissions Requirements Minimum age 62;
  Medical examination; Physician's request.
Staff RNs 3 (ft); LPNs 5 (ft), 5 (pt); Nurses
  aides 8 (ft), 2 (pt); Recreational therapists 1
  (ft); Activities coordinators 1 (pt).
Affiliation Methodist
Facilities Dining room; Physical therapy
  room; Activities room; Chapel; Crafts room;
  Laundry room; Barber/Beauty shop; Library.
Activities Arts & crafts; Cards; Games;
  Reading groups; Prayer groups; Movies;
  Shopping trips; Social/Cultural gatherings.

Lakeshore Convalescent
1901 3rd Ave, Oakland, CA, 94606
(415) 834-9880
Admin Carol Wooster. *Medical Dir/Dir of
Nursing* Robert Tufft MD; Anita M Brass
DON.
Licensure Skilled care. *Beds* SNF 38. *Certified*
  Medicare; Medi-Cal.
Owner Privately owned.
Admissions Requirements Medical
  examination; Physician's request.
Staff Physicians; RNs 2 (ft); LPNs 3 (ft), 2
  (pt); Nurses aides 12 (ft); Physical therapists
  1 (pt); Occupational therapists 1 (pt); Speech
  therapists 1 (pt); Activities coordinators 1
  (ft); Dietitians 1 (pt); Dentists 1 (pt);
  Ophthalmologists 1 (pt); Podiatrists 1 (pt).
Facilities Dining room; Activities room;
  Crafts room; Laundry room.
Activities Arts & crafts; Cards; Games;
  Reading groups; Prayer groups; Movies;
  Shopping trips; Social/Cultural gatherings.

MacArthur Convalescent Hospital*
309 MacArthur Blvd, Oakland, CA, 94610
(415) 836-3777
Admin Richard Traylor.
Licensure Skilled care. *Beds* 53. *Certified*
Medicare; Medi-Cal.
Owner Proprietary Corp (Health Enter of
America).

McClure Convalescent Hospital*
2910 McClure St, Oakland, CA, 94609
(415) 836-3677
Admin Daniel W Alger. *Medical Dir/Dir of
Nursing* Dr F Bongiorno.
Licensure Skilled care. *Beds* 59. *Certified*
Medicare; Medi-Cal.
Owner Proprietary Corp.
Staff RNs 1 (ft), 3 (pt); LPNs 5 (ft), 4 (pt);
Nurses aides 17 (ft), 10 (pt); Physical
therapists 1 (pt); Recreational therapists 1
(pt); Occupational therapists 1 (pt); Speech
therapists 1 (pt); Activities coordinators 1
(ft); Dietitians 1 (pt); Dentists 1 (pt);
Podiatrists 1 (pt).
Facilities Dining room; Activities room;
Chapel; Crafts room; Laundry room; Barber/
Beauty shop.
Activities Arts & crafts; Cards; Games;
Movies; Shopping trips; Social/Cultural
gatherings; Monthly outings.

Mercy Manor
3121 Fruitvale Ave, Oakland, CA, 94602
(415) 534-5169
Admin Sue Huttlinger. *Medical Dir/Dir of
Nursing* Herbert Lints MD; Kitti Gordon
RN DON.
Licensure Skilled care. *Beds* SNF 122.
Certified Medicare; Medi-Cal.
Owner Nonprofit Corp.
Admissions Requirements Medical
examination; Physician's request.
Staff RNs 3 (ft), 3 (pt); LPNs 15 (ft), 6 (pt);
Nurses aides 25 (ft), 4 (pt); Recreational
therapists 1 (ft); Activities coordinators 1
(ft), 1 (pt); Chaplain.
Languages Spanish, Indonesian
Facilities Dining room; Physical therapy
room; Activities room; Crafts room; Laundry
room; Barber/Beauty shop.
Activities Arts & crafts; Cards; Games;
Reading groups; Prayer groups; Social/
Cultural gatherings; Outside community
visits; Ballgames; Fishermans Wharf.

Oak Tree Convalescent Hospital*
2777 Foothill Blvd, Oakland, CA, 94601
(415) 261-3172
Admin Bernadine Walker.
Licensure Skilled care. *Beds* 49. *Certified*
Medicare; Medi-Cal.
Owner Proprietary Corp.

Oakridge Convalescent Hospital
2919 Fruitvale Ave, Oakland, CA, 94602
(415) 261-8564
Admin Gary D Vernon. *Medical Dir/Dir of
Nursing* Herbert Lints MD; Annie Dela
Cuesta RN.
Licensure Skilled care. *Beds* 99. *Certified*
Medicare; Medi-Cal.
Owner Proprietary Corp (Hillhaven Corp).
Admissions Requirements Medical
examination; Physician's request.
Staff RNs 3 (ft), 2 (pt); LPNs 10 (ft), 5 (pt);
Nurses aides 35 (ft), 20 (pt); Physical
therapists 1 (pt); Occupational therapists 1
(pt); Speech therapists 1 (pt); Activities
coordinators 4 (pt); Dietitians 1 (pt).
Languages Spanish, Tagalog, Chinese
Facilities Dining room; Physical therapy
room; Activities room; Chapel; Crafts room;
Laundry room; Barber/Beauty shop; Library.
Activities Arts & crafts; Cards; Games;
Reading groups; Prayer groups; Movies;
Shopping trips; Social/Cultural gatherings;
Intergenerational program; Adopt-a-resident;
Art with elders.

Pacific Care Convalescent Hospital*
3025 High St, Oakland, CA, 94619
(415) 261-5200
Admin Frankie Ingram.
Licensure Skilled care. *Beds* 99. *Certified*
Medicare; Medi-Cal.
Owner Proprietary Corp (Care Enterprises).

Park Merritt Intermediate Care*
525 E 18th St, Oakland, CA, 94606
(415) 834-8491
Admin Helen L Arbogast.
Licensure Intermediate care. *Beds* 24.
Certified Medi-Cal.
Owner Proprietary Corp.
Facilities Dining room; Activities room;
Laundry room.
Activities Arts & crafts; Cards; Games;
Reading groups; Prayer groups; Movies;
Shopping trips; Social/Cultural gatherings.

Piedmont Gardens Health Facility
110 41st St, Oakland, CA, 94611
(415) 654-7172
Admin Linda L Garland. *Medical Dir/Dir of
Nursing* Dr William Weeden.
Licensure Skilled care; Intermediate care. *Beds*
SNF 47; ICF 47. *Certified* Medicare; Medi-
Cal.
Owner Nonprofit Corp (American Baptist
Homes W).
Admissions Requirements Medical
examination; Physician's request.
Staff RNs 3 (ft), 7 (pt); LPNs 6 (ft), 4 (pt);
Nurses aides 21 (ft), 7 (pt); Physical
therapists 1 (pt); Occupational therapists 1
(pt); Speech therapists 1 (pt); Activities
coordinators 2 (ft), 2 (pt).
Affiliation Baptist
Facilities Dining room; Physical therapy
room; Activities room; Chapel; Crafts room;
Laundry room; Barber/Beauty shop; Library.
Activities Arts & crafts; Games; Prayer groups;
Movies; Shopping trips; Social/Cultural
gatherings.

St Paul's Towers
100 Bay Pl, Oakland, CA, 94610
(415) 891-8524
Admin Delores Crist. *Medical Dir/Dir of
Nursing* Dr Thomas Richmond; Vona da
Silva RN DON.
Licensure Skilled care. *Beds* SNF 43. *Certified*
Medicare.
Owner Nonprofit Corp (Episcopal Homes
Fdn).
Admissions Requirements Minimum age 65;
Medical examination; Physician's request.
Staff Physicians 6 (pt); RNs 3 (ft), 4 (pt);
LPNs 5 (pt); Nurses aides 17 (ft), 4 (pt);
Physical therapists 1 (pt); Recreational
therapists 1 (pt); Occupational therapists 1
(pt); Speech therapists 1 (pt); Activities
coordinators 1 (pt); Dietitians 1 (pt);
Ophthalmologists 1 (pt); Podiatrists 1 (pt).
Facilities Dining room; Physical therapy
room; Activities room; Crafts room; Barber/
Beauty shop.
Activities Arts & crafts; Cards; Games;
Reading groups; Prayer groups; Movies;
Social/Cultural gatherings; Outings; Picnics.

Salem Lutheran Home Skilled Nursing Facility
3003 Fruitvale Ave, Oakland, CA, 94602
(415) 534-3219
Admin Paul Basting. *Medical Dir/Dir of
Nursing* Robert W Tufft MD.
Licensure Skilled care. *Beds* 35. *Certified*
Medicare; Medi-Cal.
Owner Nonprofit Corp.
Admissions Requirements Minimum age 62;
Medical examination; Physician's request.
Staff RNs 5 (pt); LPNs 3 (pt); Nurses aides 15
(pt); Activities coordinators 1 (ft); Dietitians
1 (ft).
Affiliation Lutheran

Facilities Dining room; Activities room;
Laundry room; Barber/Beauty shop.
Activities Cards; Games; Prayer groups;
Movies; Shopping trips; Social/Cultural
gatherings.

**Wayne Rounseville Memorial Convalescent
Hospital***
210 40th Street Way, Oakland, CA, 94611
(415) 658-2041
Admin J Ralph Holder. *Medical Dir/Dir of
Nursing* Thomas Richmond MD.
Licensure Skilled care. *Beds* 70. *Certified*
Medicare; Medi-Cal.
Owner Proprietary Corp.
Staff RNs 6 (ft); LPNs 10 (ft); Nurses aides 32
(ft); Physical therapists 1 (pt); Reality
therapists 1 (pt); Recreational therapists 1
(pt); Occupational therapists 1 (pt); Speech
therapists 1 (pt); Activities coordinators 1
(ft), 1 (pt); Dietitians 1 (pt).
Facilities Dining room; Physical therapy
room; Activities room; Crafts room; Laundry
room; Barber/Beauty shop; Library.
Activities Arts & crafts; Cards; Games;
Reading groups; Prayer groups; Movies;
Shopping trips; Social/Cultural gatherings.

Willow Tree Convalescent Hospital Ltd*
2124 57th Ave, Oakland, CA, 94621
(415) 261-2628
Admin Luealisyrine Cannon. *Medical Dir/Dir
of Nursing* Dr Karl Konstantin.
Licensure Skilled care. *Beds* 82. *Certified*
Medicare; Medi-Cal.
Owner Proprietary Corp.
Staff Physicians 7 (ft); RNs 1 (ft), 3 (pt);
LPNs 7 (ft); Orderlies 3 (ft); Nurses aides 20
(ft); Physical therapists 1 (ft); Reality
therapists 1 (ft); Occupational therapists 1
(pt); Speech therapists 1 (ft); Activities
coordinators 1 (ft); Dietitians 1 (pt); Dentists
1 (pt); Ophthalmologists 1 (pt); Podiatrists 1
(pt).
Facilities Dining room; Physical therapy
room; Activities room; Crafts room; Laundry
room; Barber/Beauty shop; Library.
Activities Arts & crafts; Cards; Games;
Reading groups; Prayer groups; Social/
Cultural gatherings; Project Outreach.

OCEANSIDE

Tri-City Convalescent Center
3232 Thunder Dr, Oceanside, CA, 92054
(714) 724-2193
Admin R Wayne Grigsby. *Medical Dir/Dir of
Nursing* Dr Robert Nelson; Terri Jucenas
DON.
Licensure Skilled care. *Beds* SNF 93. *Certified*
Medicare; Medi-Cal.
Owner Proprietary Corp (Care Enterprises).
Admissions Requirements Medical
examination; Physician's request.
Staff RNs 4 (ft); LPNs 6 (ft); Nurses aides 50
(ft), 15 (pt); Physical therapists 1 (ft);
Occupational therapists 1 (ft); Speech
therapists 1 (pt); Activities coordinators 1
(ft); Dietitians 1 (ft); Ophthalmologists 1
(pt).
Languages Spanish, French
Facilities Dining room; Physical therapy
room; Activities room; Laundry room;
Barber/Beauty shop; Garden & patio area.
Activities Arts & crafts; Games; Prayer groups;
Movies; Social/Cultural gatherings; Exercise
groups; Family & resident council.

OJAI

Acacias NRTA & AARP Nursing Home*
601 N Montgomery Ave, Ojai, CA, 93023
(805) 646-8124
Admin Dolores Diehl. *Medical Dir/Dir of
Nursing* Dr King.
Licensure Skilled care. *Beds* 50. *Certified*
Medicare; Medi-Cal.

Owner Nonprofit Corp.
Admissions Requirements Minimum age 62.
Facilities Dining room; Activities room;
  Laundry room; Barber/Beauty shop; Library.
Activities Arts & crafts; Games; Reading
  groups; Prayer groups; Movies; Shopping
  trips; Social/Cultural gatherings.

Ojai Valley Community Hospital—Skilled Nursing Unit
1306 Maricopa Hwy, Ojai, CA, 93023
(805) 646-5586
Admin Scott Kroell. *Medical Dir/Dir of Nursing* Richard S Gould MD; Mary Wells RN.
Licensure Skilled care. *Beds* 45. *Certified* Medicare; Medi-Cal.
Owner Proprietary Corp.
Admissions Requirements Medical examination.
Staff Physicians 8 (pt); RNs 2 (ft), 2 (pt); LPNs 2 (ft), 4 (pt); Physical therapists 2 (pt); Occupational therapists 1 (pt); Activities coordinators 1 (ft); Dietitians 1 (pt); Ophthalmologists 1 (pt); CNA's 10 (ft), 11 (pt).
Facilities Dining room; Activities room; Crafts room; Laundry room; Barber/Beauty shop.
Activities Arts & crafts; Cards; Games; Reading groups; Prayer groups; Movies; Shopping trips; Social/Cultural gatherings; SNF adjustment group.

St Josephs Convalescent Hospital
PO Box 760, 2464 E Ojai Ave, Ojai, CA, 93023
(805) 646-1466
Admin Brother Michael Bassemier. *Medical Dir/Dir of Nursing* Dr Raymond Sims; Sandy Mangan RN.
Licensure Skilled care. *Beds* SNF 28; 18. *Certified* Medicare; Medi-Cal.
Owner Nonprofit Corp.
Admissions Requirements Minimum age 16; Medical examination; Physician's request.
Staff RNs 4 (ft); LPNs 7 (ft); Nurses aides 20 (ft); Activities coordinators 1 (ft).
Languages Spanish
Affiliation Roman Catholic
Facilities Dining room; Activities room; Chapel; Crafts room; Laundry room; Barber/ Beauty shop; Library.
Activities Arts & crafts; Cards; Games; Reading groups; Prayer groups; Movies; Shopping trips; Social/Cultural gatherings.

ONTARIO

Bella Vista Convalescent Hospital Inc
933 E Deodar St, Ontario, CA, 91764
(714) 985-2731
Admin W J Cloonan. *Medical Dir/Dir of Nursing* Joanna Lund MD; Perdeia Bilka DON.
Licensure Skilled care. *Beds* SNF 59. *Certified* Medicare; Medi-Cal.
Owner Privately owned.
Admissions Requirements Medical examination; Physician's request.
Staff RNs 1 (ft), 1 (pt); LPNs 4 (ft), 3 (pt); Nurses aides 19 (ft), 6 (pt).
Facilities Dining room; Activities room; Crafts room; Laundry room; Barber/Beauty shop.
Activities Arts & crafts; Cards; Games; Reading groups; Prayer groups; Movies; Shopping trips.

Home of Angels
540 W Maple St, Ontario, CA, 91761
(714) 986-5668
Admin Mavis Moretta. *Medical Dir/Dir of Nursing* Olosola Oyemade; Barbara McCord RN DON.
Licensure Skilled care. *Beds* SNF 59. *Certified* Medi-Cal.
Owner Privately owned.

Admissions Requirements Medical examination.
Staff Physicians 1 (ft); RNs 1 (ft), 3 (pt); LPNs ʿ (ft), 1 (pt); Nurses aides 16 (ft); Physical therapists 1 (pt); Occupational therapists 1 (pt); Activities coordinators 1 (ft); Dietitians 1 (pt).
Languages Spanish
Facilities Dining room; Activities room; Laundry room.
Activities Movies; Limited to each child's ability & medical condition.

Inland Christian Home Inc
1950 S Mountain Ave, Ontario, CA, 91761
(714) 983-0084
Admin Peter Edwin Hoekstra. *Medical Dir/Dir of Nursing* Dr Ron Davis; Shelia Norris RN DON.
Licensure Skilled care. *Beds* SNF 59. *Certified* Medicaid; Medicare; Medi-Cal.
Owner Nonprofit Corp.
Admissions Requirements Medical examination; Physician's request.
Staff RNs 3 (ft); LPNs 6 (ft); Nurses aides 22 (ft); Activities coordinators 1 (ft).
Affiliation Christian Reformed
Facilities Dining room; Physical therapy room; Activities room; Crafts room; Laundry room; Barber/Beauty shop; Library; Recreational hall.
Activities Arts & crafts; Cards; Games; Reading groups; Prayer groups; Movies; Shopping trips; Social/Cultural gatherings; Bus trips.

Ontario Nursing Home Inc
1661 S Euclid Ave, Ontario, CA, 91761
(714) 984-6713
Admin W J Cloonan. *Medical Dir/Dir of Nursing* Joanna Lund MD; Ruth Clark DON.
Licensure Skilled care. *Beds* SNF 59. *Certified* Medicare; Medi-Cal.
Owner Proprietary Corp.
Admissions Requirements Medical examination; Physician's request.
Staff RNs 1 (ft), 1 (pt); LPNs 3 (ft), 4 (pt) 13E 20 (ft); Activities coordinators 1 (ft); Dietitians 1 (ft).
Facilities Dining room; Activities room; Laundry room; Barber/Beauty shop.
Activities Arts & crafts; Cards; Games; Reading groups; Prayer groups; Movies; Shopping trips; Social/Cultural gatherings.

Plott Nursing Home*
800 E 5th St, Ontario, CA, 91764
(714) 984-8629
Admin Thomas Plott. *Medical Dir/Dir of Nursing* Robert Bom MD.
Licensure Skilled care. *Beds* 57. *Certified* Medicare; Medi-Cal.
Owner Proprietary Corp.
Admissions Requirements Physician's request.
Staff RNs 1 (ft), 1 (pt); LPNs 3 (ft), 3 (pt); Nurses aides 15 (ft), 5 (pt); Activities coordinators 1 (ft); Dietitians 1 (ft); Dentists 1 (pt); Podiatrists 1 (pt).
Facilities Dining room; Activities room; Laundry room; Barber/Beauty shop.
Activities Arts & crafts; Cards; Games; Reading groups; Prayer groups; Movies; Shopping trips; Social/Cultural gatherings.

ORANGE

Fountain Care Center
1835 W La Veta Ave, Orange, CA, 92668
(714) 978-6800
Admin Claire D Crocker. *Medical Dir/Dir of Nursing* Bruce Muttey MD.
Licensure Skilled care. *Beds* SNF 285. *Certified* Medicare; Medi-Cal.
Owner Proprietary Corp (Summit Health Ltd).
Admissions Requirements Minimum age 55; Medical examination; Physician's request.

Staff Physicians 30 (pt); RNs 6 (ft); LPNs 20 (ft); Orderlies 10 (ft); Nurses aides 50 (ft); Physical therapists 1 (ft); Occupational therapists 1 (pt); Speech therapists 1 (pt); Activities coordinators 1 (ft); Dietitians 1 (pt); Dentists 1 (pt); Ophthalmologists 1 (pt); Podiatrists 1 (pt).
Languages Spanish
Facilities Dining room; Physical therapy room; Activities room; Crafts room; Laundry room; Barber/Beauty shop; Library; Garden patios.
Activities Arts & crafts; Cards; Games; Reading groups; Prayer groups; Movies; Shopping trips; Social/Cultural gatherings; Ball games; Picnics.

Hillhaven Convalescent Hospital*
920 W La Veta St, Orange, CA, 92668
(714) 633-3568
Admin Robert E Karnatz.
Licensure Skilled care. *Beds* 110. *Certified* Medicare; Medi-Cal.
Owner Proprietary Corp (Hillhaven Corp).

Royal Grove Convalescent Hospital
PO Box 4398, 238 S Flower St, Orange, CA, 92613-4398
(714) 978-6261
Admin Mary Corrine Bart.
Licensure Skilled care. *Beds* 43. *Certified* Medicare; Medi-Cal.
Owner Proprietary Corp.

ORANGEVALE

Orangevale Convalescent Hospital*
9260 Loma Ln, Orangevale, CA, 95662
(916) 988-1935
Admin J E Carper.
Licensure Skilled care. *Beds* 25. *Certified* Medicare; Medi-Cal.
Owner Proprietary Corp.

ORINDA

Orinda Rehabilitation & Convalescent Hospital*
11 Altarinda Rd, Orinda, CA, 94563
(415) 254-6500
Admin Selma R Cronin. *Medical Dir/Dir of Nursing* Richard Homrighausen MD.
Licensure Skilled care. *Beds* 49. *Certified* Medicare.
Owner Proprietary Corp.
Admissions Requirements Medical examination; Physician's request.
Staff RNs 3 (ft), 6 (pt); LPNs 1 (ft); Orderlies 4 (ft); Nurses aides 20 (ft), 7 (pt); Activities coordinators 1 (ft); Dietitians 1 (pt).
Facilities Dining room; Physical therapy room; Activities room; Laundry room; Barber/Beauty shop; Sundeck.
Activities Arts & crafts; Cards; Games; Reading groups; Prayer groups; Movies.

OROVILLE

Gilmore Lane Convalescent Hospital*
1 Gilmore Ln, Oroville, CA, 95965
(916) 534-1353
Admin Harold L Cook. *Medical Dir/Dir of Nursing* Dr Olson.
Licensure Skilled care. *Beds* 50. *Certified* Medicare; Medi-Cal.
Owner Proprietary Corp.
Admissions Requirements Physician's request.
Staff Physicians 12 (ft); RNs 2 (ft), 2 (pt); LPNs 4 (ft), 2 (pt); Orderlies 1 (ft); Nurses aides 16 (ft), 3 (pt); Physical therapists 1 (ft); Reality therapists 1 (pt); Recreational therapists 1 (ft); Occupational therapists 1 (pt); Speech therapists 1 (pt); Activities coordinators 1 (ft); Dietitians 1 (pt); Dentists 1 (pt); Ophthalmologists 1 (pt); Podiatrists 2 (pt).

Facilities Dining room; Physical therapy room; Activities room; Crafts room; Laundry room; Barber/Beauty room.
Activities Arts & crafts; Cards; Games; Reading groups; Prayer groups; Movies; Social/Cultural gatherings.

Lakeview Nursing Home Inc*
1912 20th St, Oroville, CA, 95965
(916) 533-1874
Admin Nellie K Walker. *Medical Dir/Dir of Nursing* W R Olson MD.
Licensure Skilled care. *Beds* 28. *Certified* Medicare.
Owner Proprietary Corp.
Admissions Requirements Physician's request.
Staff RNs 1 (ft); LPNs 3 (ft), 1 (pt); Nurses aides 11 (ft); Physical therapists 1 (pt); Reality therapists 1 (pt); Recreational therapists 1 (ft); Occupational therapists 1 (pt); Speech therapists 1 (pt); Activities coordinators 1 (ft); Dietitians 1 (pt); Dentists 1 (pt); Podiatrists 1 (pt).
Facilities Dining room; Activities room; Laundry room.
Activities Arts & crafts; Cards; Games; Reading groups; Prayer groups; Movies; Social/Cultural gatherings.

Oroville Community Convalescent Hospital*
1511 Robinson St, Oroville, CA, 95965
(916) 534-5701
Admin A Perreras & P Beltran.
Licensure Skilled care. *Beds* 41.
Owner Proprietary Corp.

OXNARD

Glenwood Convalescent Hospital
1300 N "C" St, Oxnard, CA, 93030
(805) 983-0305
Admin Jerry Wells. *Medical Dir/Dir of Nursing* E Falcon MD; Maricela Santana RN DON.
Licensure Skilled care. *Beds* SNF 99.
Owner Proprietary Corp.
Admissions Requirements Minimum age 18; Medical examination; Physician's request.
Staff RNs 4 (ft); LPNs 11 (ft); Nurses aides 40 (ft); Physical therapists 1 (ft); Reality therapists 1 (ft); Recreational therapists 1 (ft); Occupational therapists 1 (ft); Speech therapists 1 (ft); Activities coordinators 1 (ft); Dietitians 1 (ft); Dentists 1 (ft); Ophthalmologists 1 (ft); Podiatrists 1 (ft).
Languages Spanish, Japanese, Tagalog
Facilities Dining room; Physical therapy room; Activities room; Crafts room; Laundry room; Barber/Beauty shop; Library.
Activities Arts & crafts; Cards; Games; Reading groups; Prayer groups; Movies; Shopping trips; Social/Cultural gatherings.

Maywood Acres Healthcare*
2641 S 'C' St, Oxnard, CA, 93030
(805) 487-7840
Admin Nancy J Moore.
Licensure Skilled care. *Beds* 98. *Certified* Medicare; Medi-Cal.
Owner Proprietary Corp (Hillhaven Corp).

Oxnard Manor Convalescent Hospital*
1400 W Gonzlaes Rd, Oxnard, CA, 93030
(805) 983-0324
Admin Frank Donovan. *Medical Dir/Dir of Nursing* Dr Loder.
Licensure Skilled care. *Beds* 82. *Certified* Medicare; Medi-Cal.
Owner Proprietary Corp.
Admissions Requirements Medical examination; Physician's request.
Facilities Dining room; Laundry room.
Activities Arts & crafts; Cards; Games; Reading groups; Shopping trips; Social/ Cultural gatherings.

Pleasant Valley Intermediate Care Facility*
5235 S "J" St, Oxnard, CA, 93030
(805) 488-3696
Admin John P Devine.
Licensure Intermediate care. *Beds* 73. *Certified* Medi-Cal.
Owner Proprietary Corp.

Pleasant Valley Rehabilitation & Convalescent Hospital*
5225 S "J" St, Oxnard, CA, 93030
(805) 488-3696
Admin John P Devine. *Medical Dir/Dir of Nursing* Joseph McGuire MD.
Licensure Skilled care. *Beds* 193. *Certified* Medicare; Medi-Cal.
Owner Proprietary Corp.
Admissions Requirements Medical examination; Physician's request.
Staff RNs 8 (ft), 6 (pt); LPNs 13 (ft), 3 (pt); Nurses aides 58 (ft), 16 (pt); Recreational therapists 1 (ft); Activities coordinators 2 (ft).
Facilities Dining room; Activities room; Laundry room; Barber/Beauty shop.
Activities Arts & crafts; Cards; Games; Reading groups; Prayer groups; Movies; Shopping trips; Social/Cultural gatherings.

PACIFIC GROVE

Canterbury Woods
651 Sinex Ave, Pacific Grove, CA, 93950
(408) 373-3111
Admin Robert B Butterfield. *Medical Dir/Dir of Nursing* Dr James Lee; Constance Golden DON.
Licensure Skilled care; Personal care; Apartments. *Beds* SNF 24; Personal 10; Apts 153. *Certified* Medicare.
Owner Nonprofit Corp (Episcopal Homes Fdn).
Admissions Requirements Minimum age 65; Medical examination.
Staff Physicians 1 (pt); RNs 3 (ft), 3 (pt); Nurses aides 10 (ft), 6 (pt); Physical therapists 1 (pt); Occupational therapists 1 (pt); Speech therapists 1 (pt); Activities coordinators 1 (ft); Dietitians 1 (pt); Ophthalmologists 1 (pt).
Affiliation Episcopal
Facilities Dining room; Physical therapy room; Activities room; Chapel; Crafts room; Laundry room; Barber/Beauty shop; Library.
Activities Arts & crafts; Cards; Games; Reading groups; Prayer groups; Movies; Shopping trips; Social/Cultural gatherings.

Pacific Grove Convalescent Hospital
200 Lighthouse Ave, Pacific Grove, CA, 93950
(408) 375-2695
Admin Eileen Daly. *Medical Dir/Dir of Nursing* Dr John Lord.
Licensure Skilled care. *Beds* SNF 51. *Certified* Medicare; Medi-Cal.
Owner Nonprofit Corp.
Admissions Requirements Medical examination; Physician's request.
Staff RNs; LPNs; Nurses aides; Activities coordinators 1 (ft), 1 (pt).
Affiliation Methodist
Facilities Dining room; Activities room; Crafts room; Laundry room; Barber/Beauty shop.
Activities Arts & crafts; Cards; Games; Reading groups; Prayer groups; Movies; Shopping trips; Social/Cultural gatherings; Special outings.

PACIFICA

Linda Mar Convalescent Hospital
751 San Pedro Rd, Pacifica, CA, 94044
(415) 359-4800

Admin Rosalyn R Isaac. *Medical Dir/Dir of Nursing* Herbert Fisher MD; Mary Jo Sands RN DON.
Licensure Skilled care. *Beds* SNF 59. *Certified* Medicare; Medi-Cal.
Owner Proprietary Corp (American Health Care Inc).
Admissions Requirements Minimum age 18; Medical examination; Physician's request.
Staff Physicians; RNs 3 (ft); LPNs 4 (ft); Orderlies; Nurses aides 22 (ft), 5 (pt); Physical therapists; Occupational therapists; Speech therapists; Activities coordinators 1 (ft); Dietitians; Pharmacist; Food service supervisor.
Facilities Dining room; Physical therapy room; Activities room; Laundry room; Barber/Beauty shop; Library.
Activities Arts & crafts; Games; Reading groups; Prayer groups; Movies; Social/ Cultural gatherings; Outings; Adopt-a-grandparent; Pioneer Scouts; Ceramics.

Pacifica Convalescent Hospital*
385 Esplanade Ave, Pacifica, CA, 94044
(415) 993-5576
Admin Betty J Ellis. *Medical Dir/Dir of Nursing* C Allen Wall MD.
Licensure Skilled care. *Beds* 68. *Certified* Medicare; Medi-Cal.
Owner Proprietary Corp.
Admissions Requirements Medical examination; Physician's request.
Staff Physicians 2 (ft); RNs 3 (ft), 5 (pt); LPNs 2 (ft), 4 (pt); Orderlies 1 (pt); Nurses aides 9 (ft), 14 (pt); Physical therapists 2 (ft), 1 (pt); Recreational therapists 1 (ft), 2 (pt); Occupational therapists 1 (pt); Speech therapists 1 (pt); Activities coordinators 1 (pt); Dietitians 1 (pt); Dentists 1 (pt); Ophthalmologists 1 (pt); Podiatrists 1 (pt); Audiologists 1 (pt).
Facilities Dining room; Physical therapy room; Laundry room; Barber/Beauty shop.
Activities Arts & crafts; Cards; Games; Reading groups; Prayer groups; Movies; Shopping trips; Social/Cultural gatherings.

PALM SPRINGS

California Nursing & Rehabilitation Center of Palm Springs
2299 N Indian Ave, Palm Springs, CA, 92262
(619) 325-2937
Admin Carol Van Horst. *Medical Dir/Dir of Nursing* Charles Supple MD.
Licensure Skilled care. *Beds* 80. *Certified* Medicare.
Owner Proprietary Corp.
Admissions Requirements Medical examination; Physician's request.
Staff Physicians 1 (pt); RNs 4 (ft), 2 (pt); LPNs 4 (ft), 5 (pt); Orderlies 2 (ft); Nurses aides 20 (ft), 3 (pt); Physical therapists 1 (pt); Occupational therapists 1 (pt); Speech therapists 1 (pt); Activities coordinators 1 (ft); Dietitians 1 (pt); Dentists 1 (pt); Ophthalmologists 1 (pt); Podiatrists 1 (pt);; Dentist 1 (pt).
Facilities Dining room; Physical therapy room; Activities room; Crafts room; Laundry room; Barber/Beauty shop.
Activities Arts & crafts; Cards; Games; Reading groups; Prayer groups; Movies; Shopping trips; Social/Cultural gatherings.

Coachella House Inc*
2990 E Ramon Rd, Palm Springs, CA, 92262
(714) 323-2638
Admin Marilyn D Dodd.
Licensure Skilled care. *Beds* 99. *Certified* Medicare; Medi-Cal.
Owner Proprietary Corp.

Palm Springs Healthcare
277 S Sunrise Way, Palm Springs, CA, 92262
(619) 327-8541

Admin Jacqueline Arcara. *Medical Dir/Dir of Nursing* Irving Hershleifer; Debra Bona.
Licensure Skilled care. *Beds* SNF 99. *Certified* Medicare; Medi-Cal.
Owner Proprietary Corp (American Medical Services Inc).
Admissions Requirements Medical examination; Physician's request.
Staff RNs 2 (ft), 1 (pt); LPNs 7 (ft), 2 (pt); Orderlies 1 (ft); Nurses aides 30 (ft), 2 (pt); Physical therapists 1 (pt); Recreational therapists 1 (ft); Occupational therapists 1 (pt); Speech therapists 1 (pt); Activities coordinators 1 (ft); Dietitians 1 (pt); Dentists 1 (pt); Ophthalmologists 1 (pt); Podiatrists 1 (pt);; Staff Developer.
Languages Spanish, Tagalog
Facilities Dining room; Physical therapy room; Activities room; Laundry room; Barber/Beauty shop.
Activities Arts & crafts; Cards; Games; Reading groups; Prayer groups; Movies; Shopping trips; Social/Cultural gatherings; Overnight camping; Desert drives.

PALO ALTO

Bay Health Care—Palo Alto
4277 Miranda Ave, Palo Alto, CA, 94306
(415) 948-5041
Admin John C Bird. *Medical Dir/Dir of Nursing* Dr William McKenna; Mr Tony Zapata.
Licensure Skilled care; Geropsychiatric. *Beds* 50. *Certified* Medi-Cal.
Owner Proprietary Corp.
Admissions Requirements Minimum age 55.
Staff RNs 2 (ft), 2 (pt); LPNs 6 (ft), 2 (pt); Orderlies 5 (ft); Nurses aides 12 (ft), 4 (pt); Occupational therapists 1 (ft), 1 (pt);; 1 (ft) Clinical psychologist.
Facilities Dining room; Activities room; Crafts room; Laundry room; Library; Occupational kitchen.
Activities Arts & crafts; Cards; Games; Reading groups; Prayer groups; Movies; Shopping trips; Social/Cultural gatherings; Bowling; "Outside" trips.

Casa Olga Intermediate Health Care Facility*
180 Hamilton Ave, Palo Alto, CA, 94306
(415) 325-7821
Admin Robert Waldsmith.
Licensure Intermediate care. *Beds* 144. *Certified* Medi-Cal.
Owner Proprietary Corp.

Channing House
850 Webster St, Palo Alto, CA, 94301
(415) 327-0950
Admin Fred H Seal. *Medical Dir/Dir of Nursing* Karen Fry.
Licensure Skilled care.
Owner Nonprofit Corp.
Admissions Requirements Minimum age 62; Medical examination.
Staff RNs 5 (ft), 6 (pt); Nurses aides 12 (ft), 6 (pt); Activities coordinators 1 (ft); Dietitians 1 (ft).
Facilities Dining room; Physical therapy room; Activities room; Laundry room; Barber/Beauty shop; Library.
Activities Arts & crafts; Cards; Games; Reading groups; Movies.

Hillhaven Convalescent Hospital*
911 Bryant St, Palo Alto, CA, 94301
(415) 327-0511
Admin Irmke Schoebel.
Licensure Skilled care. *Beds* 66. *Certified* Medicare; Medi-Cal.
Owner Proprietary Corp.

Lytton Gardens Care Center
437 Webster, Palo Alto, CA, 94301
(415) 328-3300
Admin Charles Fieist. *Medical Dir/Dir of Nursing* W Bortz MD; Linda Harrop RN.

Licensure Skilled care. *Beds* SNF 128. *Certified* Medicaid; Medicare; Medi-Cal.
Owner Nonprofit organization/foundation.
Admissions Requirements Physician's request.
Staff RNs 5 (ft), 7 (pt); LPNs 10 (ft), 5 (pt); Orderlies 6 (ft), 2 (pt); Nurses aides 24 (ft), 12 (pt); Physical therapists 2 (ft); Recreational therapists 1 (ft); Occupational therapists 1 (ft); Activities coordinators 1 (ft).
Languages Spanish, Tagalog
Facilities Dining room; Physical therapy room; Activities room; Chapel; Crafts room; Laundry room; Barber/Beauty shop.
Activities Arts & crafts; Cards; Games; Reading groups; Prayer groups; Movies; Shopping trips; Social/Cultural gatherings.

PANORAMA CITY

Beverly Manor Convalescent Hospital
9541 Van Nuys Blvd, Panorama City, CA, 91402
(818) 893-6385
Admin Marcia S Weldon. *Medical Dir/Dir of Nursing* Melvin Kirschner MD; Elizabeth Soriano DON.
Licensure Skilled care. *Beds* SNF 151. *Certified* Medicare; Medi-Cal.
Owner Proprietary Corp (Beverly Enterprises).
Admissions Requirements Physician's request.
Staff Physicians; RNs; LPNs; Orderlies; Nurses aides; Physical therapists; Recreational therapists; Occupational therapists; Speech therapists; Activities coordinators; Dietitians; Dentists; Ophthalmologists; Podiatrists.
Languages Spanish
Facilities Dining room; Physical therapy room; Activities room; Laundry room; Barber/Beauty shop.
Activities Arts & crafts; Cards; Games; Reading groups; Prayer groups; Movies; Shopping trips; Social/Cultural gatherings.

Sun Air Convalescent Hospital
14857 Roscoe Blvd, Panorama City, CA, 91402
(818) 894-5707
Admin David Schleidt. *Medical Dir/Dir of Nursing* Freda Fahid RN.
Licensure Skilled care. *Beds* SNF 98. *Certified* Medicare; Medi-Cal.
Owner Proprietary Corp.
Staff Physicians; RNs 2 (ft), 4 (pt); LPNs 4 (ft), 4 (pt); Orderlies 5 (ft), 3 (pt); Nurses aides 30 (ft), 3 (pt); Activities coordinators 1 (ft), 1 (pt); Dietitians 1 (pt).
Languages Spanish, Farsi, Tagalog
Facilities Dining room; Physical therapy room; Activities room; Chapel; Crafts room; Laundry room; Barber/Beauty shop; Library.
Activities Arts & crafts; Cards; Games; Prayer groups; Movies; Shopping trips; Social/Cultural gatherings.

PARADISE

Cypress Acres Convalescent Hospital
1633 Cypress Ln, Paradise, CA, 95969
(916) 877-9316
Admin Jean K Filer. *Medical Dir/Dir of Nursing* M Wesley Farr MD; Linda Livesay RN DON.
Licensure Skilled care. *Beds* SNF 108. *Certified* Medicare; Medi-Cal.
Owner Proprietary Corp.
Admissions Requirements Medical examination; Physician's request.
Staff RNs 8 (ft), 3 (pt); LPNs 6 (ft), 1 (pt); Nurses aides 26 (ft), 21 (pt); Physical therapists 2 (ft); Recreational therapists 1 (pt); Occupational therapists 1 (pt); Speech therapists 1 (pt); Activities coordinators 1 (ft), 2 (pt); Dietitians 1 (ft); Dentists 1 (pt); Ophthalmologists 1 (pt).

Facilities Dining room; Physical therapy room; Activities room; Chapel; Crafts room; Laundry room; Barber/Beauty shop; Library.
Activities Arts & crafts; Cards; Games; Reading groups; Prayer groups; Movies; Shopping trips; Social/Cultural gatherings.

Cypress Acres Intermediate Care Facility
6900 Clark Rd, Paradise, CA, 95969
(916) 872-4055
Admin Jean K Filer. *Medical Dir/Dir of Nursing* M Wesley Farr MD.
Licensure Intermediate care. *Beds* ICF 29. *Certified* Medi-Cal.
Owner Proprietary Corp.
Admissions Requirements Medical examination; Physician's request.
Staff RNs 2 (ft); LPNs 1 (ft); Nurses aides 7 (ft); Physical therapists 1 (pt); Recreational therapists 1 (pt); Occupational therapists 1 (pt); Speech therapists 1 (pt); Activities coordinators 1 (ft); Dietitians 1 (ft); Dentists 1 (pt); Ophthalmologists 1 (pt); Social Service 1 (ft).
Facilities Dining room; Physical therapy room; Activities room; Crafts room; Laundry room; Library.
Activities Arts & crafts; Cards; Games; Reading groups; Prayer groups; Movies; Shopping trips; Social/Cultural gatherings.

Paradise Convalescent Hospital
7419 Skyway, Paradise, CA, 95969
(916) 877-7676
Admin Dixie Anderson.
Licensure Skilled care. *Beds* 44. *Certified* Medi-Cal.
Owner Proprietary Corp.

PARAMOUNT

Bird Haven Christian Convalescent Hospital*
7039 Alondra Blvd, Paramount, CA, 90723
(213) 531-0990
Admin Mary L Muir.
Licensure Skilled care. *Beds* 99. *Certified* Medicare; Medi-Cal.
Owner Proprietary Corp.

Paramount Convalescent Hospital*
8558 E Rosecrans Ave, Paramount, CA, 90723
(213) 634-6877
Admin June McKee.
Licensure Skilled care. *Beds* 59. *Certified* Medicare.
Owner Proprietary Corp.

Terrace Gardens Convalescent Center
8835 Vans Ave, Paramount, CA, 90723
(213) 634-9805
Admin William Kite. *Medical Dir/Dir of Nursing* Dr Y Lee; Ms P Edmenson.
Licensure Skilled care; Intermediate care. *Beds* SNF 173. *Certified* Medicaid; Medicare; Medi-Cal.
Owner Proprietary Corp.
Admissions Requirements Minimum age 20; Medical examination.
Staff Physicians 10 (pt); RNs 6 (ft); LPNs 10 (ft); Orderlies 3 (ft), 2 (pt); Nurses aides 50 (ft); Physical therapists 1 (ft); Recreational therapists 1 (ft), 1 (pt); Speech therapists 1 (pt); Dietitians 1 (pt); Ophthalmologists 1 (pt).
Languages Spanish
Facilities Dining room; Physical therapy room; Activities room; Chapel; Crafts room; Laundry room; Barber/Beauty shop; Library.
Activities Arts & crafts; Cards; Games; Reading groups; Prayer groups; Movies; Shopping trips; Social/Cultural gatherings.

PASADENA

The Californian—Pasadena Convalescent Hospital
120 Bellefontaine, Pasadena, CA, 91105
(818) 793-5114
Admin A Rose Bower. *Medical Dir/Dir of Nursing* Jean Snell RN.
Licensure Skilled care. *Beds* SNF 82. *Certified* Medicare.
Owner Proprietary Corp.
Admissions Requirements Medical examination; Physician's request.
Staff RNs 6 (ft), 4 (pt); Physical therapists 1 (ft); Occupational therapists 1 (pt); Speech therapists 1 (pt); Activities coordinators 1 (ft); Dietitians 1 (pt); Ophthalmologists 1 (pt).
Facilities Dining room; Physical therapy room; Barber/Beauty shop.
Activities Arts & crafts; Cards; Games; Reading groups; Movies.

Congress Convalescent Hospital*
716 S Fair Oaks Ave, Pasadena, CA, 91105
(213) 793-6127
Admin Ann Walshe.
Licensure Skilled care. *Beds* 75. *Certified* Medicare; Medi-Cal.
Owner Proprietary Corp (Beverly Enterprises).

Crestwood Convalescent Hospital
1836 N Fair Oaks Ave, Pasadena, CA, 91103
(818) 798-9125
Admin Berna-Dean Darms RN. *Medical Dir/Dir of Nursing* T Hee MD; Jim Parker RN.
Licensure Skilled care. *Beds* SNF 99. *Certified* Medicare; Medi-Cal.
Owner Proprietary Corp (Crestwood Hosp).
Admissions Requirements Minimum age 30; Medical examination; Physician's request.
Staff RNs 2 (ft), 3 (pt); LPNs 9 (ft), 4 (pt); Orderlies 7 (ft), 1 (pt); Nurses aides 42 (ft), 4 (pt); Physical therapists; Occupational therapists; Speech therapists; Activities coordinators 1 (ft); Dietitians; Dentists; Ophthalmologists; Podiatrists; SS Cord 1 (ft).
Languages Armenian, Spanish
Facilities Dining room; Physical therapy room; Activities room; Barber/Beauty shop.
Activities Arts & crafts; Cards; Games; Reading groups; Prayer groups; Movies; Shopping trips; Social/Cultural gatherings; Candlelight dinner; Country breakfast; Special events every month.

Eisenhower Nursing & Convalescent Hospital
1470 N Fair Oaks, Pasadena, CA, 91103
(213) 798-9133
Admin Marcella Brown. *Medical Dir/Dir of Nursing* Stanley Cuba MD; Virginia Estorninos RN DON.
Licensure Skilled care. *Beds* 71. *Certified* Medicare; Medi-Cal.
Owner Proprietary Corp (Medstar Mgmt Sys).
Admissions Requirements Physician's request.
Staff RNs 1 (ft); LPNs 5 (ft); Nurses aides 20 (ft); Activities coordinators 1 (ft); Dietitians 1 (ft).
Facilities Dining room; Activities room; Laundry room; Barber/Beauty shop.
Activities Arts & crafts; Cards; Games; Reading groups; Prayer groups; Movies; Shopping trips; Social/Cultural gatherings; Country breakfast; Candlelight dinner; Wine/cheese social.

Hacienda Convalescent Hospital—South*
1899 N Raymond Ave, Pasadena, CA, 91103
(213) 798-6777
Admin Sheryl Hancock.
Licensure Skilled care. *Beds* 99. *Certified* Medicare; Medi-Cal.
Owner Proprietary Corp (Hillhaven Corp).

Hillhaven Care Center
1920 N Fair Oaks Ave, Pasadena, CA, 91103
(818) 798-6777
Admin Helen Cox. *Medical Dir/Dir of Nursing* William Putnam MD; Dorothy Montgomery RN DON.
Licensure Skilled care. *Beds* SNF 80. *Certified* Medicare; Medi-Cal.
Owner Proprietary Corp (Hillhaven Corp).
Admissions Requirements Minimum age 20; Medical examination; Physician's request.
Staff Physicians 40 (pt); RNs 3 (ft), 3 (pt); LPNs 6 (ft), 5 (pt); Orderlies 2 (ft); Nurses aides 22 (ft), 4 (pt); Physical therapists 2 (ft); Reality therapists 1 (ft); Occupational therapists 1 (pt); Speech therapists 1 (pt); Activities coordinators 1 (ft); Dietitians 1 (ft); Dentists 1 (pt); Ophthalmologists 1 (pt); Podiatrists 1 (pt).
Facilities Dining room; Physical therapy room; Activities room; Crafts room; Laundry room; Barber/Beauty shop Sun room; Lounge.
Activities Arts & crafts; Cards; Games; Reading groups; Prayer groups; Movies; Shopping trips; Social/Cultural gatherings.

Kent Convalescent Hospital
1640 N Fair Oaks Ave, Pasadena, CA, 91103
(818) 798-1175
Admin Victor M Marefka. *Medical Dir/Dir of Nursing* Peter Dunn MD; Nadine Ford RN.
Licensure Skilled care; Intermediate care. *Beds* SNF 88; ICF 11. *Certified* Medicare; Medi-Cal.
Owner Proprietary Corp.
Admissions Requirements Minimum age 65; Medical examination; Physician's request.
Staff RNs 1 (ft); LPNs 9 (ft); Nurses aides 32 (ft); Activities coordinators 1 (ft).
Languages Spanish
Facilities Dining room; Physical therapy room; Activities room; Barber/Beauty shop.
Activities Arts & crafts; Cards; Games; Movies; Shopping trips.

Sophia Lyn Convalescent Hospital
1570 N Fair Oaks Ave, Pasadena, CA, 91103
(213) 798-0558
Admin Marcella A Brown.
Licensure Skilled care. *Beds* 54. *Certified* Medicare; Medi-Cal.
Owner Proprietary Corp.

Marlinda Convalescent Hospital
2637 E Washington Blvd, Pasadena, CA, 91107
(213) 798-8991
Admin Mrs Demchuk. *Medical Dir/Dir of Nursing* Dr Moritz; Mrs Rohde.
Licensure Skilled care. *Beds* SNF 50. *Certified* Medicare; Medi-Cal.
Owner Privately owned.
Admissions Requirements Physician's request.
Staff Physicians; RNs; LPNs; Orderlies; Nurses aides; Physical therapists; Reality therapists; Recreational therapists; Occupational therapists; Speech therapists; Activities coordinators; Dietitians; Dentists; Ophthalmologists; Podiatrists.
Languages Spanish, Tagalog
Facilities Dining room; Activities room; Chapel; Crafts room; Laundry room; Barber/Beauty shop; Library; Patio; TV room.
Activities Arts & crafts; Cards; Games; Reading groups; Prayer groups; Movies; Shopping trips.

Marlinda-Imperial Convalescent Hospital
150 Bellefontaine, Pasadena, CA, 91105
(213) 796-1103
Admin Marthann Demchuk. *Medical Dir/Dir of Nursing* Ray George MD; Lorene Wohlgemuth RN DON.
Licensure Skilled care. *Beds* SNF 130. *Certified* Medicare; Medi-Cal.
Owner Privately owned.

Admissions Requirements Medical examination; Physician's request.
Staff Physicians 1 (pt); RNs 5 (ft), 4 (pt); LPNs 7 (ft), 2 (pt); Orderlies 5 (ft), 1 (pt); Nurses aides 20 (ft), 5 (pt); Physical therapists 1 (ft); Occupational therapists 1 (ft); Speech therapists 1 (pt); Activities coordinators 2 (ft); Dietitians 1 (pt); Dentists 1 (pt); Ophthalmologists 1 (pt); Podiatrists 1 (pt);; Respiratory aide 1 (ft); Physical therapy aides 2 (ft), 1 (pt); Hairdresser 1 (ft).
Languages Spanish, Tagalog, Polish, Lebanese
Facilities Dining room; Physical therapy room; Activities room; Crafts room; Laundry room; Barber/Beauty shop; Outside patios.
Activities Arts & crafts; Cards; Games; Reading groups; Prayer groups; Movies; Shopping trips; Social/Cultural gatherings; Birthday parties; Exercise class.

Monte Vista Grove Homes
2889 San Pasqual St, Pasadena, CA, 91107
(818) 796-6135
Admin Sandra K Atkins. *Medical Dir/Dir of Nursing* Ray George MD; Helen Baatz RN DON.
Licensure Skilled care. *Beds* SNF 40.
Owner Nonprofit Corp.
Staff Physicians 1 (pt); RNs 6 (ft), 2 (pt); LPNs 1 (ft), 3 (pt); Nurses aides 23 (ft); Activities coordinators 1 (ft).
Languages Spanish
Affiliation Presbyterian
Facilities Dining room; Laundry room; Barber/Beauty shop; Library.
Activities Arts & crafts; Cards; Games; Reading groups; Prayer groups; Movies; Shopping trips; Social/Cultural gatherings.

Park Marino Convalescent Center*
2585 E Washington, Pasadena, CA, 91107
(213) 798-6753
Admin Kitty Batho.
Licensure Skilled care. *Beds* 99.
Owner Proprietary Corp.

Robinson Home*
275 Robincroft Dr, Pasadena, CA, 91104
(213) 794-7144
Admin Herbert G Thompson. *Medical Dir/Dir of Nursing* Peter Dunn MD.
Licensure Skilled care. *Beds* 30. *Certified* Medicare; Medi-Cal.
Owner Proprietary Corp.
Admissions Requirements Minimum age 18.
Staff RNs 1 (ft); LPNs 4 (ft), 2 (pt); Orderlies 3 (ft); Nurses aides 4 (ft); Physical therapists 1 (pt); Reality therapists 1 (pt); Recreational therapists 1 (ft); Occupational therapists 1 (pt); Speech therapists 1 (pt); Activities coordinators 1 (ft); Dietitians 1 (pt); Dentists 1 (pt); Ophthalmologists 1 (pt); Podiatrists 1 (pt); Audiologists 1 (pt).
Facilities Dining room; Physical therapy room; Activities room; Chapel; Crafts room; Laundry room; Barber/Beauty shop; Library.
Activities Arts & crafts; Cards; Games; Reading groups; Prayer groups; Movies; Shopping trips; Social/Cultural gatherings.

Sacred Heart Culture Hospital
1810 N Fair Oaks Ave, Pasadena, CA, 91103
(818) 797-1352
Admin Norma L Abenoja. *Medical Dir/Dir of Nursing* Dr Jose Mutia; Thelma Grafil.
Licensure Skilled care. *Beds* SNF 78. *Certified* Medi-Cal.
Owner Proprietary Corp.
Staff Physicians; RNs; LPNs; Orderlies; Nurses aides; Physical therapists; Recreational therapists; Occupational therapists; Speech therapists; Activities coordinators; Dietitians; Dentists; Ophthalmologists; Podiatrists.
Facilities Dining room; Activities room; Crafts room; Laundry room; Barber/Beauty shop; Library.

Activities Arts & crafts; Cards; Games;
Reading groups; Prayer groups; Movies;
Shopping trips; Social/Cultural gatherings.

Villa Gardens Health Care Unit*
842 E Villa St, Pasadena, CA, 91101
(213) 681-8704
Admin Jean Brophy. *Medical Dir/Dir of
Nursing* Dr Stanley Cuba.
Licensure Skilled care. *Beds* 31. *Certified*
Medicare; Medi-Cal.
Owner Nonprofit Corp.
Admissions Requirements Minimum age 62;
Medical examination.
Staff RNs 1 (ft); LPNs 2 (ft), 3 (pt); Nurses
aides 12 (ft), 5 (pt); Physical therapists;
Occupational therapists; Speech therapists;
Activities coordinators 1 (ft); Dietitians;
Dentists; Podiatrists.
Facilities Dining room; Chapel; Laundry
room; Barber/Beauty shop; Library.
Activities Arts & crafts; Reading groups;
Prayer groups; Movies; Shopping trips;
Social/Cultural gatherings.

Villa Oaks Convalescent Hospital
1515 N Fair Oaks Ave, Pasadena, CA, 91103
(818) 798-1111
Admin James M Lewis Jr. *Medical Dir/Dir of
Nursing* Z Malcom RN.
Licensure Skilled care. *Beds* SNF 49. *Certified*
Medicare; Medi-Cal.
Owner Proprietary Corp (Medstar Mgmt Sys).
Admissions Requirements Minimum age 40;
Physician's request.
Staff Physicians; RNs; LPNs; Orderlies;
Nurses aides; Physical therapists; Reality
therapists; Occupational therapists; Speech
therapists; Activities coordinators; Dietitians;
Dentists; Ophthalmologists; Podiatrists.
Languages Spanish, Tagalog
Facilities Dining room; Activities room;
Laundry room; Barber/Beauty shop.
Activities Arts & crafts; Cards; Games;
Reading groups; Prayer groups; Shopping
trips; Social/Cultural gatherings.

PASO ROBLES

Paso Robles Convalescent Hospital
321 12th St, Paso Robles, CA, 93446
(805) 238-4637, 238-4646
Admin Doug Wamsley. *Medical Dir/Dir of
Nursing* Dr Tom Harper; Carlene Powell
DON.
Licensure Skilled care. *Beds* SNF 42. *Certified*
Medicare; Medi-Cal.
Owner Proprietary Corp (American Health
Care Inc).
Admissions Requirements Physician's request.
Staff Physicians 7 (pt); RNs 1 (ft), 3 (pt);
LPNs 3 (ft), 3 (pt); Nurses aides 13 (ft), 4
(pt); Physical therapists 1 (pt); Reality
therapists 1 (pt); Recreational therapists 1
(pt); Occupational therapists 1 (pt); Speech
therapists 1 (pt); Activities coordinators 1
(ft), 1 (pt); Dietitians 1 (pt); Dentists 1 (pt);
Ophthalmologists 1 (pt); Podiatrists 1 (pt).
Facilities Dining room; Activities room;
Crafts room; Laundry room; Barber/Beauty
shop.
Activities Arts & crafts; Cards; Games;
Reading groups; Prayer groups; Movies;
Shopping trips; Social/Cultural gatherings.

PERRIS

Medical Arts Convalescent Hospital*
2225 N Perris Blvd, Perris, CA, 92370
(714) 657-2135
Admin Lilly M Swegles. *Medical Dir/Dir of
Nursing* Harry Fandrich MD.
Licensure Skilled care. *Beds* 99. *Certified*
Medicare; Medi-Cal.
Owner Proprietary Corp.

Staff RNs 2 (ft), 2 (pt); Orderlies 2 (ft);
Nurses aides 27 (ft), 14 (pt); Activities
coordinators 1 (ft).
Facilities Dining room; Physical therapy
room; Laundry room; Barber/Beauty shop;
Library.
Activities Arts & crafts; Cards; Games;
Reading groups; Prayer groups; Movies;
Shopping trips; Social/Cultural gatherings.

PETALUMA

Beverly Manor of Petaluma
101 Monroe St, Petaluma, CA, 94952
(707) 763-4109
Admin Arlene Garietz. *Medical Dir/Dir of
Nursing* Rex Harner MD; Wanda Elliott RN
DON.
Licensure Skilled care. *Beds* SNF 99. *Certified*
Medicare; Medi-Cal.
Owner Proprietary Corp (Beverly Enterprises).
Admissions Requirements Medical
examination; Physician's request.
Staff RNs; LPNs; Nurses aides; Physical
therapists; Occupational therapists; Speech
therapists; Activities coordinators; Dietitians;
Dentists; Ophthalmologists.
Languages Spanish, French
Facilities Dining room; Physical therapy
room; Activities room; Barber/Beauty shop.
Activities Arts & crafts; Cards; Games;
Reading groups; Prayer groups; Movies;
Shopping trips; Social/Cultural gatherings.

Crestview Convalescent Hospital*
523 Hayes Ave, Petaluma, CA, 94952
(707) 763-2457
Admin Donald Bais. *Medical Dir/Dir of
Nursing* Dean O'Neil MD.
Licensure Skilled care. *Beds* 90. *Certified*
Medicare; Medi-Cal.
Owner Proprietary Corp.
Admissions Requirements Minimum age 60;
Medical examination; Physician's request.
Staff RNs 4 (ft); LPNs 6 (ft); Orderlies 4 (ft);
Nurses aides 30 (ft); Physical therapists 1
(pt); Occupational therapists 1 (pt); Speech
therapists 1 (pt); Activities coordinators 1
(ft); Dietitians 1 (pt); Dentists 1 (pt);
Ophthalmologists 1 (pt); Podiatrists 1 (pt);
Audiologists 1 (pt).
Facilities Dining room; Physical therapy
room; Activities room; Barber/Beauty shop.
Activities Arts & crafts; Cards; Games;
Movies.

The Oaks*
450 Hayes Ln, Petaluma, CA, 94952
(707) 778-8686
Admin Betty L Green. *Medical Dir/Dir of
Nursing* John Rodnick MD.
Licensure Skilled care. *Beds* 59. *Certified*
Medicare; Medi-Cal.
Owner Proprietary Corp.
Staff Physicians 4 (pt); RNs 4 (ft), 3 (pt);
LPNs 3 (ft), 4 (pt); Orderlies 3 (ft); Nurses
aides 34 (ft); Physical therapists 2 (pt);
Recreational therapists 1 (pt); Occupational
therapists 1 (pt); Speech therapists 1 (pt);
Activities coordinators 1 (ft); Dietitians 1
(pt); Dentists 1 (pt); Ophthalmologists 1 (pt);
Podiatrists 1 (pt); Audiologists 1 (pt).
Facilities Dining room; Physical therapy
room; Activities room; Chapel; Crafts room;
Laundry room; Barber/Beauty shop; Library.
Activities Arts & crafts; Cards; Games;
Reading groups; Prayer groups; Movies;
Shopping trips; Social/Cultural gatherings;
Outside entertainment.

Petaluma Convalescent Hospital*
1115 B St, Petaluma, CA, 94952
(707) 763-6871
Admin Barbara Spiro-Garner. *Medical Dir/Dir
of Nursing* Dean O'Neil MD.
Licensure Skilled care. *Beds* 90. *Certified*
Medicare; Medi-Cal.
Owner Proprietary Corp (Care Enterprises).

Staff Physicians; RNs; LPNs; Orderlies;
Nurses aides; Physical therapists;
Recreational therapists; Occupational
therapists; Speech therapists; Activities
coordinators; Dietitians; Dentists;
Ophthalmologists; Podiatrists; Audiologists.
Facilities Dining room; Physical therapy
room; Activities room; Crafts room; Laundry
room; Barber/Beauty shop.
Activities Arts & crafts; Cards; Games;
Reading groups; Prayer groups; Movies;
Social/Cultural gatherings.

PICO RIVERA

Colonial Gardens Nursing Home
7246 S Rosemead Blvd, Pico Rivera, CA,
90660
(213) 949-2591
Admin David H Lewis. *Medical Dir/Dir of
Nursing* Rolando Atiga MD; Christine
Chung RN.
Licensure Skilled care. *Beds* SNF 99. *Certified*
Medi-Cal.
Owner Proprietary Corp.
Admissions Requirements Minimum age 45;
Medical examination.
Staff Physicians; RNs; LPNs; Orderlies;
Nurses aides; Physical therapists; Reality
therapists; Recreational therapists;
Occupational therapists; Speech therapists;
Activities coordinators; Dietitians; Dentists;
Ophthalmologists; Podiatrists; Social service.
Languages Spanish, Korean, Tagalog
Facilities Dining room; Activities room;
Crafts room; Laundry room; Barber/Beauty
shop; Library.
Activities Arts & crafts; Cards; Games;
Reading groups; Prayer groups; Movies;
Shopping trips; Social/Cultural gatherings;
Outside trips for meals.

El Rancho Vista Convalescent Center
8925 Mines Ave, Pico Rivera, CA, 90660
(213) 942-7019
Admin Ronda Evans. *Medical Dir/Dir of
Nursing* Kathy Blanco DON.
Licensure Skilled care. *Beds* SNF 86. *Certified*
Medicare; Medicare; Medi-Cal.
Owner Proprietary Corp (ARA Living
Centers).
Admissions Requirements Minimum age 62;
Medical examination; Physician's request.
Staff RNs 1 (ft), 1 (pt); LPNs 5 (ft); Orderlies
5 (ft); Nurses aides 17 (ft); Physical
therapists 1 (pt); Recreational therapists 1
(pt); Occupational therapists 1 (pt); Speech
therapists 1 (pt); Activities coordinators 1
(ft); Dietitians 1 (pt); Dentists 1 (pt);
Ophthalmologists 1 (pt); Podiatrists 1 (pt).
Languages Spanish
Facilities Dining room; Physical therapy
room; Activities room; Crafts room; Laundry
room; Barber/Beauty shop; Library.
Activities Arts & crafts; Cards; Games;
Reading groups; Prayer groups; Movies;
Shopping trips; Social/Cultural gatherings.

Riviera Nursing & Convalescent Home Inc
8203 Telegraph Rd, Pico Rivera, CA, 90660
(213) 806-2576
Admin James H Fenton. *Medical Dir/Dir of
Nursing* Lawrence Pollock MD; Nelcy
Knutson DON.
Licensure Skilled care. *Beds* SNF 154.
Certified Medicare; Medi-Cal.
Owner Proprietary Corp.
Staff Physicians 36 (pt); RNs 5 (ft), 3 (pt);
Orderlies 8 (ft), 2 (pt); Nurses aides 50 (ft),
5 (pt); Activities coordinators 2 (pt), 1 (pt);
Dentists 2 (pt); Ophthalmologists 2 (pt);
Podiatrists 1 (pt); Psychiatrist 1 (pt).
Facilities Dining room; Physical therapy
room; Activities room; Laundry room;
Barber/Beauty shop; Living room; Enclosed
private patio.

Activities Arts & crafts; Games; Prayer groups; Social/Cultural gatherings; Bingo; Tours; Outings.

St Theresa Convalescent Hospital*
9140 Verner St, Pico Rivera, CA, 90660
(213) 948-1961
Admin Charles V Williams. *Medical Dir/Dir of Nursing* J E Altamirano MD.
Licensure Skilled care. *Beds* 99. *Certified* Medicare; Medi-Cal.
Owner Proprietary Corp (Care Enterprises).
Admissions Requirements Physician's request.
Staff RNs 3 (ft), 2 (pt); LPNs 6 (ft), 3 (pt); Nurses aides 20 (ft), 4 (pt); Physical therapists 1 (pt); Reality therapists 1 (pt); Recreational therapists 1 (pt); Occupational therapists 1 (pt); Speech therapists 1 (pt); Activities coordinators 1 (ft); Dietitians 1 (pt); Dentists 1 (pt); Ophthalmologists 1 (pt); Podiatrists 1 (pt); Audiologists 1 (pt).
Facilities Dining room; Physical therapy room; Activities room; Crafts room; Laundry room; Barber/Beauty shop; Large outdoor patio & side yard.
Activities Arts & crafts; Cards; Games; Reading groups; Prayer groups; Movies; Gardening club; Kite flying.

PITTSBURG

Pittsburg Manor Convalescent Hospital
535 School St, Pittsburg, CA, 94565
(415) 432-3831
Admin Max B O'Melia. *Medical Dir/Dir of Nursing* Edwin Boysen.
Licensure Skilled care. *Beds* 49. *Certified* Medicare; Medi-Cal.
Owner Proprietary Corp.
Admissions Requirements Physician's request.
Staff Physicians 6 (pt); RNs 3 (pt); LPNs 3 (ft), 3 (pt); Nurses aides 10 (ft), 7 (pt); Physical therapists 1 (pt); Occupational therapists 1 (pt); Speech therapists 1 (pt); Activities coordinators 1 (pt); Dietitians 1 (pt); Ophthalmologists 1 (pt); Dentist 1 (pt).
Facilities Dining room; Physical therapy room; Activities room; Crafts room; Laundry room.
Activities Arts & crafts; Cards; Games; Reading groups; Movies.

PLACERVILLE

El Dorado Convalescent Hospital
3280 Washington St, Placerville, CA, 95667
(916) 622-6842
Admin Darlene C Maddox. *Medical Dir/Dir of Nursing* Ted Christy MD; Vicki Fry RN DON.
Licensure Skilled care. *Beds* SNF 99. *Certified* Medicare; Medi-Cal.
Owner Proprietary Corp.
Staff RNs 3 (ft), 5 (pt); LPNs 2 (ft), 2 (pt); Nurses aides 25 (ft), 5 (pt); Physical therapists; Occupational therapists; Speech therapists; Activities coordinators.
Facilities Dining room; Physical therapy room; Activities room; Crafts room; Laundry room; Barber/Beauty shop; Library.
Activities Arts & crafts; Cards; Games; Reading groups; Prayer groups; Movies; Shopping trips; Social/Cultural gatherings.

Placerville Pines Convalescent Hospital*
1040 Marshall Way, Placerville, CA, 95667
(916) 622-3400
Admin Louis J Yost.
Licensure Skilled care. *Beds* 99. *Certified* Medicare; Medi-Cal.
Owner Proprietary Corp.
Facilities Dining room; Physical therapy room; Activities room; Chapel; Crafts room; Laundry room; Barber/Beauty shop; Library.
Activities Arts & crafts; Cards; Games; Reading groups; Prayer groups; Movies; Shopping trips.

PLEASANT HILL

Baywood Convalescent Hospital*
550 Patterson Blvd, Pleasant Hill, CA, 94523
(415) 939-5400
Admin Charlene May.
Licensure Skilled care. *Beds* 166. *Certified* Medicare; Medi-Cal.
Owner Proprietary Corp (ARA Living Centers).

Oak Park Convalescent Hospital*
1625 Oak Park Blvd, Pleasant Hill, CA, 94523
(415) 935-5222
Admin John Milford.
Licensure Skilled care. *Beds* 51. *Certified* Medicare; Medi-Cal.
Owner Proprietary Corp.

Rosewood Convalescent Hospital
1911 Oak Park Blvd, Pleasant Hill, CA, 94523
(415) 935-6630
Admin Lisa E Churches. *Medical Dir/Dir of Nursing* Dr D K Fisher; Phyllis O'Leary RN.
Licensure Skilled care; Intermediate care. *Beds* 117. *Certified* Medicare; Medi-Cal.
Owner Proprietary Corp (ARA Living Centers).
Admissions Requirements Screen patients.
Staff Physicians 17 (pt); Orderlies 3 (ft), 1 (pt); Nurses aides 24 (ft), 2 (pt).
Languages Spanish, Arabic, Finnish, German, Italian, Yiddish, Russian, Chinese
Facilities Dining room; Physical therapy room; Activities room; Laundry room; Barber/Beauty shop; Library.
Activities Arts & crafts; Cards; Games; Reading groups; Prayer groups; Movies; Shopping trips; Social/Cultural gatherings; Exercise.

Sun Valley Manor Convalescent Hospital
540 Patterson Blvd, Pleasant Hill, CA, 94523
(415) 932-3850
Admin Charles E Sutton. *Medical Dir/Dir of Nursing* Barbara S Gagne RN DON.
Licensure Skilled care. *Beds* SNF 105. *Certified* Medicare.
Owner Proprietary Corp (ARA Living Centers).
Staff RNs; LPNs; Orderlies; Nurses aides; Physical therapists; Recreational therapists; Occupational therapists; Speech therapists; Activities coordinators; Dietitians; Ophthalmologists.
Facilities Dining room; Physical therapy room; Activities room; Barber/Beauty shop.
Activities Arts & crafts; Cards; Games; Reading groups; Movies.

POMONA

CareWest-Pomona Vista Nursing Center
651 N Main St, Pomona, CA, 91768
(714) 623-2481
Admin Laurel Anderson MBA.
Licensure Skilled care. *Beds* SNF 66. *Certified* Medicaid 416B 416C.
Owner Proprietary Corp (Care Enterprises).
Staff Physicians; RNs; LPNs; Orderlies; Nurses aides; Physical therapists; Occupational therapists; Speech therapists; Activities coordinators; Dietitians; Dentists; Ophthalmologists; Podiatrists.
Facilities Dining room; Activities room; Barber/Beauty shop.
Activities Arts & crafts; Cards; Games; Reading groups; Prayer groups; Movies; Shopping trips.

Country House*
1041 S White Ave, Pomona, CA, 91766
(213) 623-0581
Admin Dorothy Broadway.
Licensure Skilled care; Intermediate care for mentally retarded. *Beds* 91. *Certified* Medi-Cal.

Owner Proprietary Corp (Beverly Enterprises).

Foothill Convalescent Hospital*
219 E Foothill Blvd, Pomona, CA, 91767
(714) 593-1391
Admin George Curtis.
Licensure Skilled care. *Beds* 99. *Certified* Medicare.
Owner Proprietary Corp (Care Enterprises).

Landmark Medical Center
2030 N Garey Ave, Pomona, CA, 91767
(714) 593-2585
Admin Karen L Trahan. *Medical Dir/Dir of Nursing* Indran Selvaratnum.
Licensure Skilled care. *Beds* 95. *Certified* Medi-Cal.
Owner Proprietary Corp.
Admissions Requirements Minimum age 18.
Staff Physicians 2 (pt); RNs 3 (ft), 2 (pt); Nurses aides 23 (ft), 6 (pt); Activities coordinators 1 (ft); Dietitians 1 (pt); STPs Staff 10 (ft); LPTs 5 (ft), 10 (pt).
Languages Spanish
Facilities Dining room; Activities room; Crafts room; Laundry room; Barber/Beauty shop; Day room.
Activities Arts & crafts; Cards; Games; Movies; Shopping trips; Social/Cultural gatherings; Birthday & holiday parties.

Lanterman Developmental Center
3530 W Pomona Blvd, Pomona, CA, 91768
(714) 595-1221
Admin Rowena J Taylor. *Medical Dir/Dir of Nursing* Lorenda Vergara, Celia Rios.
Licensure Skilled care; Intermediate care for mentally retarded. *Beds* 1286. *Certified* Medicare; Medi-Cal.
Owner Publicly owned.
Staff Physicians 20 (ft), 1 (pt); RNs 61 (ft), 2 (pt); Physical therapists 10 (ft); Recreational therapists 30 (ft), 3 (pt); Occupational therapists 6 (ft); Speech therapists 3 (ft); Dietitians 9 (ft); Ophthalmologists 1 (ft); Podiatrists 3 (ft).
Facilities Dining room; Physical therapy room; Activities room; Chapel; Crafts room; Laundry room; Barber/Beauty shop; Library; Camp; Swimming pool.
Activities Arts & crafts; Cards; Games; Reading groups; Prayer groups; Movies; Shopping trips; Social/Cultural gatherings; Swimming pool; Camping.

Laurel Park—A Center for Effective Living
1425 Laurel Ave, Pomona, CA, 92670
(714) 622-1069
Admin Kathleen Millett. *Medical Dir/Dir of Nursing* Harry Steinberg MD.
Licensure Skilled care; IMD-Special treatment program. *Beds* SNF 43. *Certified* Medi-Cal.
Owner Proprietary Corp.
Admissions Requirements Minimum age 18; Medical examination; Physician's request.
Staff Physicians 1 (pt); RNs 1 (ft), 2 (pt); LPNs 6 (ft); Nurses aides; Activities coordinators; Psychologist; Counselors.
Facilities Dining room; Activities room; Laundry room; Group rooms.
Activities Arts & crafts; Cards; Games; Reading groups; Prayer groups; Movies; Shopping trips; Social/Cultural gatherings; Vocational training; Psycho-social skills training.

Mount San Antonio Gardens/Congregational Homes
900 E Harrison Ave, Pomona, CA, 91767
(714) 624-5061
Admin Theodore Radamaker. *Medical Dir/Dir of Nursing* Stephen Rothbun MD; Cathy Lightner RN.
Licensure Skilled care. *Beds* SNF 55. *Certified* Medicare.
Owner Nonprofit Corp.

Admissions Requirements Minimum age 62;
Physician's request.
Affiliation Church of Christ

Olive Vista—A Center for Problems of Living
2350 Culver Ct, Pomona, CA, 91766
(714) 628-6024
Admin Cheryl Jumonville. *Medical Dir/Dir of
Nursing* Louise F Iacueo MD; Judy
Arterburn RN.
Licensure Skilled care. *Beds* 120. *Certified*
Medi-Cal.
Owner Proprietary Corp.
Staff RNs; Orderlies; Nurses aides; Activities
coordinators.

Palomares Center*
250 W Artesia, Pomona, CA, 91768
(213) 623-3564
Admin Robert Foster. *Medical Dir/Dir of
Nursing* Valentine G Birds MD.
Licensure Skilled care. *Beds* 175. *Certified*
Medicare; Medi-Cal.
Owner Proprietary Corp (Beverly Enterprises).
Admissions Requirements Minimum age 20;
Physician's request.
Staff Physicians 1 (pt); RNs 5 (ft), 4 (pt);
LPNs 13 (ft), 5 (pt); Orderlies 7 (ft), 3 (pt);
Nurses aides 49 (ft), 19 (pt); Physical
therapists 2 (ft); Occupational therapists 1
(pt); Speech therapists 1 (pt); Activities
coordinators 1 (ft), 2 (pt); Dietitians 1 (pt);
Dentists 1 (pt); Ophthalmologists 1 (pt);
Podiatrists 1 (pt); Audiologists 1 (pt).
Facilities Dining room; Physical therapy
room; Activities room; Chapel; Crafts room;
Laundry room; Barber/Beauty shop; Library.
Activities Arts & crafts; Cards; Games;
Reading groups; Prayer groups; Movies;
Shopping trips; Social/Cultural gatherings.

Park Place Convalescent Hospital*
1550 N Park Ave, Pomona, CA, 91768
(213) 623-0791
Admin Harold Moser.
Licensure Skilled care. *Beds* 231. *Certified*
Medi-Cal.
Owner Proprietary Corp (Care Enterprises).

**Pomona Golden Age Convalescent Hospital &
Nursing Home***
215 W Pearl St, Pomona, CA, 91768
(714) 622-1067
Admin Ron Millett. *Medical Dir/Dir of
Nursing* Felimon Soria.
Licensure Skilled care. *Beds* 81. *Certified*
Medicare; Medi-Cal.
Owner Proprietary Corp (National Heritage).
Staff RNs 1 (ft), 1 (pt); LPNs 8 (ft), 4 (pt);
Orderlies 8 (ft), 3 (pt); Nurses aides 30 (ft),
6 (pt); Physical therapists 1 (pt); Reality
therapists 1 (pt); Recreational therapists 1
(ft), 2 (pt); Occupational therapists 1 (pt);
Speech therapists 1 (pt); Activities
coordinators 1 (pt); Dietitians 1 (ft), 1 (pt);
Dentists 1 (pt); Ophthalmologists 1 (pt);
Podiatrists 1 (pt); Audiologists 1 (pt).
Facilities Dining room; Activities room;
Laundry room; Barber/Beauty shop.
Activities Arts & crafts; Cards; Games;
Reading groups; Prayer groups; Movies;
Shopping trips; Social/Cultural gatherings.

Towne Avenue Convalescent Hospital
2351 S Towne Ave, Pomona, CA, 91766
(714) 628-1245
Admin Glen A Crume.
Licensure Skilled care. *Beds* SNF 94. *Certified*
Medicare; Medi-Cal.
Owner Proprietary Corp.
Admissions Requirements Minimum age 18.
Staff Physicians; RNs; LPNs; Orderlies;
Nurses aides; Physical therapists;
Occupational therapists; Speech therapists;
Activities coordinators; Dietitians.
Languages Spanish

Facilities Dining room; Physical therapy
room; Activities room; Crafts room; Laundry
room; Barber/Beauty shop.
Activities Arts & crafts; Cards; Games;
Reading groups; Prayer groups; Movies;
Social/Cultural gatherings.

PORTERVILLE

Hacienda Convalescent Hospital
301 W Putnam Ave, Porterville, CA, 93257
(209) 784-7375, 784-5760
Admin Hernando E Guzman. *Medical Dir/Dir
of Nursing* Dr Robert A Dexter MD; Beverly
G Brandt RN.
Licensure Skilled care. *Beds* SNF 139.
Certified Medicare; Medi-Cal.
Owner Proprietary Corp.
Admissions Requirements Medical
examination; Physician's request.
Staff RNs 4 (ft), 3 (pt); LPNs 9 (ft), 6 (pt);
Orderlies 4 (ft), 1 (pt); Nurses aides 39 (ft),
13 (pt); Activities coordinators 2 (ft), 1 (pt).
Facilities Dining room; Physical therapy
room; Activities room; Laundry room;
Barber/Beauty shop; Family room; Outside
patio.
Activities Arts & crafts; Cards; Games;
Reading groups; Prayer groups; Movies;
Shopping trips; Social/Cultural gatherings.

Valley Care Center
661 W Poplar Ave, Porterville, CA, 93257
(209) 784-8371
Admin Donald C Smith. *Medical Dir/Dir of
Nursing* Robert Dexter MD; Douglas Smith
RN.
Licensure Skilled care. *Beds* SNF 55. *Certified*
Medicare; Medi-Cal.
Owner Proprietary Corp.
Admissions Requirements Medical
examination; Physician's request.
Staff Physicians 1 (pt); RNs 2 (ft); LPNs 6
(ft); Orderlies 1 (ft); Nurses aides 20 (ft), 4
(pt); Physical therapists 1 (pt); Activities
coordinators 1 (ft); Dietitians 1 (pt);
Ophthalmologists 1 (pt); Dentist 1 (pt).
Languages Spanish
Facilities Dining room; Activities room;
Crafts room; Laundry room; Barber/Beauty
shop.
Activities Arts & crafts; Cards; Games;
Reading groups; Prayer groups; Movies;
Shopping trips; Social/Cultural gatherings;
Green house gardening.

Villa Manor Care Center Inc*
350 N Villa, Porterville, CA, 93257
(209) 784-6644
Admin R Wesley Jordan. *Medical Dir/Dir of
Nursing* Robert Dexter MD.
Licensure Skilled care. *Beds* 89. *Certified*
Medicare; Medi-Cal.
Owner Proprietary Corp.
Staff Physicians 1 (pt); RNs 2 (ft), 2 (pt);
LPNs 10 (ft), 3 (pt); Nurses aides 35 (ft), 10
(pt); Physical therapists 1 (pt); Recreational
therapists 1 (pt); Occupational therapists 1
(pt); Speech therapists 1 (pt); Activities
coordinators 1 (ft); Dietitians 1 (pt); Dentists
1 (pt); Podiatrists 1 (pt).
Facilities Dining room; Activities room;
Laundry room; Barber/Beauty shop.
Activities Arts & crafts; Cards; Games;
Reading groups; Prayer groups; Movies;
Shopping trips; Social/Cultural gatherings.

PORTOLA VALLEY

The Sequoias
501 Portola Rd, Portola Valley, CA, 94025
(415) 851-1501
Admin Richard L Wiens.
Licensure Skilled care. *Beds* 48.
Owner Nonprofit Corp.

QUINCY

Quincy Convalescent Hospital*
PO Box L, Quincy, CA, 95971
(916) 283-2110
Admin Merry Nickerson. *Medical Dir/Dir of
Nursing* Dr Price.
Licensure Skilled care. *Beds* 57. *Certified*
Medicare; Medi-Cal.
Owner Proprietary Corp (Care Enterprises).
Staff Physicians; RNs; LPNs; Orderlies;
Nurses aides; Physical therapists;
Recreational therapists; Speech therapists;
Activities coordinators; Dietitians; Dentists;
Podiatrists; Audiologists.
Facilities Dining room; Physical therapy
room; Activities room; Laundry room;
Barber/Beauty shop; Library.
Activities Arts & crafts; Cards; Games;
Reading groups; Prayer groups; Movies;
Social/Cultural gatherings; Exercise program
at local college.

RANCHO CORDOVA

Casa Coloma Health Care Center*
10410 Coloma Rd, Rancho Cordova, CA,
95670
(916) 363-4843
Admin Arden Millermon.
Licensure Skilled care. *Beds* 99. *Certified*
Medicare; Medi-Cal.
Owner Proprietary Corp.

RANCHO PALOS VERDES

The Canterbury
5801 W Crestridge Rd, Rancho Palos Verdes,
CA, 90274
(213) 541-2410
Admin Alvin P Lafon. *Medical Dir/Dir of
Nursing* Dr Christopher J Traughber; Joan
Roth RN.
Licensure Skilled care; Retirement
Community. *Beds* SNF 28; apts 127.
Certified Medicare.
Owner Nonprofit Corp.
Admissions Requirements Minimum age 62;
Medical examination Retirement
Apartments; Physician's request SNF.
Staff Physicians; RNs; LPNs; Orderlies;
Nurses aides; Physical therapists;
Recreational therapists; Activities
coordinators; Dietitians; Masseuse.
Affiliation Episcopal
Facilities Dining room; Physical therapy
room; Activities room; Crafts room; Laundry
room; Barber/Beauty shop; Library.
Activities Arts & crafts; Cards; Games;
Reading groups; Prayer groups; Movies;
Shopping trips; Social/Cultural gatherings.

RED BLUFF

Brentwood Convalescent Hospital*
1795 Walnut St, Red Bluff, CA, 96080
(916) 527-2046
Admin Joseph Fernandez.
Licensure Skilled care. *Beds* 55. *Certified*
Medicare; Medi-Cal.
Owner Proprietary Corp.

Cedars Convalescent Hospital*
555 Luther Rd, Red Bluff, CA, 96080
(916) 527-6232
Admin Maxine Niel.
Licensure Skilled care. *Beds* 56. *Certified*
Medicare; Medi-Cal.
Owner Proprietary Corp (Care Enterprises).

Tehema County Health Center*
1850 Walnut St, Red Bluff, CA, 96080
(916) 527-0350
Admin Nora M Roberson. *Medical Dir/Dir of
Nursing* Eva Jalkotzy.

Licensure Skilled care. *Beds* 40. *Certified*
Medicare; Medi-Cal.
Owner Publicly owned.
Staff Physicians; RNs; LPNs; Orderlies;
Nurses aides; Physical therapists; Reality
therapists; Recreational therapists;
Occupational therapists; Speech therapists;
Activities coordinators; Dietitians; Dentists;
Ophthalmologists; Podiatrists; Audiologists.
Facilities Dining room; Physical therapy
room; Activities room; Crafts room; Laundry
room.
Activities Arts & crafts; Cards; Games;
Reading groups; Prayer groups; Movies.

REDDING

Beverly Manor Convalescent Hospital
1836 Gold St, Redding, CA, 96001
(916) 241-6756
Admin Betty L Groton. *Medical Dir/Dir of
Nursing* Paul Freeman MD; E Evans RN
DON.
Licensure Skilled care. *Beds* SNF 89. *Certified*
Medicare; Medi-Cal.
Owner Proprietary Corp (Beverly Enterprises).
Admissions Requirements Medical
examination; Physician's request.
Staff RNs 6 (ft), 3 (pt); LPNs 8 (ft); Orderlies;
Nurses aides 44 (ft); Activities coordinators
1 (ft);; Social services 1 (ft).
Languages Spanish, Thai
Facilities Dining room; Physical therapy
room; Activities room; Crafts room; Laundry
room; Barber/Beauty shop; Library.
Activities Arts & crafts; Cards; Games;
Reading groups; Prayer groups; Movies;
Shopping trips; Social/Cultural gatherings;
Exercise; Facility van.

Crestwood Convalescent Hospital*
2490 Court St, Redding, CA, 96001
(916) 246-0600
Admin Linda Rink.
Licensure Skilled care. *Beds* 113. *Certified*
Medicare; Medi-Cal.
Owner Proprietary Corp (Crestwood Hosp).

Shasta Convalescent Hospital
3550 Churn Creek Rd, Redding, CA, 96002
(916) 222-3630
Admin Harold Becker. *Medical Dir/Dir of
Nursing* Norman Arai MD; Helen Pfilf
DON.
Licensure Skilled care. *Beds* SNF 165.
Certified Medicaid; Medicare; Medi-Cal.
Owner Proprietary Corp.
Staff Physicians; RNs; LPNs; Orderlies;
Nurses aides; Physical therapists;
Recreational therapists; Occupational
therapists; Speech therapists; Activities
coordinators; Dietitians.
Facilities Dining room; Physical therapy
room; Activities room; Chapel; Crafts room;
Laundry room; Barber/Beauty shop.
Activities Arts & crafts; Cards; Games;
Reading groups; Prayer groups; Movies;
Shopping trips; Social/Cultural gatherings.

REDLANDS

Beverly Manor Convalescent Hospital
700 E Highland Ave, Redlands, CA, 92373
(714) 793-2678
Admin Sandra Haskins. *Medical Dir/Dir of
Nursing* Tim O'Neal MD; Lenore Acosta
DON.
Licensure Skilled care. *Beds* SNF 82. *Certified*
Medicaid; Medicare; Medi-Cal.
Owner Proprietary Corp (Beverly Enterprises).
Admissions Requirements Medical
examination; Physician's request.
Staff RNs 2 (ft), 2 (pt); LPNs 8 (ft), 2 (pt);
Nurses aides 40 (ft), 10 (pt); Activities
coordinators 1 (ft); Dietitians 1 (ft).

Facilities Dining room; Physical therapy
room; Activities room; Laundry room;
Barber/Beauty shop.
Activities Arts & crafts; Cards; Games;
Reading groups; Prayer groups; Movies;
Shopping trips.

CareWest Redlands Nursing Center
105 Terracina Blvd, Redlands, CA, 92373
(714) 793-2271
Admin William Meert. *Medical Dir/Dir of
Nursing* William Thompson MD; Celine
Moddie.
Licensure Skilled care. *Beds* SNF 97. *Certified*
Medicare; Medi-Cal.
Owner Proprietary Corp (Care Enterprises).
Staff Physicians; RNs; LPNs; Orderlies;
Nurses aides; Physical therapists;
Occupational therapists; Speech therapists;
Activities coordinators; Dietitians; Dentists;
Ophthalmologists; Podiatrists; Dentist.
Facilities Dining room; Physical therapy
room; Activities room; Laundry room;
Barber/Beauty shop.
Activities Arts & crafts; Cards; Games;
Reading groups; Prayer groups; Movies;
Shopping trips; Social/Cultural gatherings.

**Plymouth Village Redlands Convalescent
Hospital**
819 Salem Dr, Redlands, CA, 92373
(714) 793-1233
Admin Robert L Balsley. *Medical Dir/Dir of
Nursing* Dr Jon Tueten; Joan Cox RN.
Licensure Skilled care. *Beds* 48. *Certified*
Medicaid; Medicare; Medi-Cal.
Owner Nonprofit Corp (American Baptist
Homes W).
Admissions Requirements Medical
examination; Physician's request.
Staff RNs 5 (pt); LPNs 5 (ft); Nurses aides 17
(ft), 10 (pt); Occupational therapists 1 (pt);
Speech therapists 1 (pt); Activities
coordinators 2 (ft); Dietitians 1 (pt).
Affiliation Baptist
Facilities Dining room; Physical therapy
room; Activities room; Chapel; Crafts room;
Barber/Beauty shop.
Activities Arts & crafts; Games; Prayer groups;
Movies; Shopping trips; Social/Cultural
gatherings; Exercise classes; Physical
activities.

Terracina Convalescent Hospital*
1620 Fern Ave, Redlands, CA, 92373
(714) 793-2609
Admin Ritchie Wetherwax. *Medical Dir/Dir of
Nursing* Bernard E Telton MD.
Licensure Skilled care. *Beds* 78. *Certified*
Medicare; Medi-Cal.
Owner Proprietary Corp (Beverly Enterprises).
Admissions Requirements Minimum age 18.
Staff Physicians 1 (pt); RNs 1 (ft), 2 (pt);
LPNs 6 (ft), 5 (pt); Orderlies 2 (ft), 3 (pt);
Nurses aides 24 (ft), 11 (pt); Physical
therapists 1 (pt); Occupational therapists 1
(pt); Speech therapists 1 (pt); Activities
coordinators 1 (ft); Dietitians 1 (pt); Dentists
1 (pt); Ophthalmologists 1 (pt); Podiatrists 1
(pt); Audiologists 1 (pt).
Facilities Dining room; Physical therapy
room; Activities room; Laundry room;
Barber/Beauty shop.
Activities Arts & crafts; Games; Reading
groups; Prayer groups; Movies; Shopping
trips; Social/Cultural gatherings.

REDWOOD CITY

Cordelleras Center*
200 Edmonds Rd, Redwood City, CA, 94062
(415) 397-1890
Admin Henry Lewis.
Licensure Skilled care. *Beds* 120. *Certified*
Medi-Cal.
Owner Proprietary Corp.

Devonshire Oaks
3635 Jefferson Ave, Redwood City, CA,
94062
(415) 366-9503
Admin Rod Darner. *Medical Dir/Dir of
Nursing* Henry Mayer MD; Ebba Rosager
RN.
Licensure Skilled care. *Beds* SNF 39.
Owner Privately owned.
Admissions Requirements Physician's request.
Staff RNs 3 (ft), 2 (pt); LPNs 2 (ft), 2 (pt);
Nurses aides 14 (ft), 3 (pt); Activities
coordinators 1 (ft); Dietitians 1 (pt).
Languages Spanish, Italian, Native American,
Danish, German
Facilities Dining room; Activities room;
Laundry room; Barber/Beauty shop; Library.
Activities Arts & crafts; Cards; Games;
Reading groups; Movies; Hug-A-Pet; Art
study; California history.

Laurel Glen Convalescent Hospital*
885 Woodside Rd, Redwood City, CA, 94061
(415) 368-4174
Admin Daniel Sheehan.
Licensure Skilled care. *Beds* 45. *Certified*
Medicare; Medi-Cal.
Owner Proprietary Corp.

REEDLEY

Pleasant View Manor
856 S Reed Ave, Reedley, CA, 93654
(209) 638-3615
Admin Howard Fast. *Medical Dir/Dir of
Nursing* Dr John Hayward.
Licensure Skilled care. *Beds* 99. *Certified*
Medi-Cal.
Owner Proprietary Corp (Mennonite Brethren
Homes).
Admissions Requirements Medical
examination; Physician's request.
Staff RNs 5 (ft), 5 (pt); LPNs 6 (ft), 3 (pt);
Orderlies 1 (ft); Nurses aides 39 (ft), 11 (pt);
Activities coordinators 2 (ft); Dietitians 10
(ft), 5 (pt).
Languages German, Spanish
Affiliation Mennonite
Facilities Dining room; Activities room;
Crafts room; Laundry room; Barber/Beauty
shop; Library.
Activities Arts & crafts; Games; Prayer groups;
Movies; Social/Cultural gatherings.

Reedley Convalescent Hospital*
1090 E Dinuba Ave, Reedley, CA, 93654
(209) 638-3577
Admin Marjory Norris.
Licensure Skilled care. *Beds* 56. *Certified*
Medicare; Medi-Cal.
Owner Proprietary Corp (Beverly Enterprises).

Sierra View Homes Inc
1155 E Springfield Ave, Reedley, CA, 93654
(209) 638-9226
Admin Mr Clayton Auernheimer. *Medical
Dir/Dir of Nursing* Marden C Habegger MD;
Gloria Jones RN DON.
Licensure Skilled care. *Beds* SNF 59. *Certified*
Medicare; Medi-Cal.
Owner Nonprofit Corp.
Admissions Requirements Medical
examination; Physician's request.
Staff Physicians 1 (ft); RNs 6 (ft); LPNs 1 (ft),
1 (pt); Nurses aides 24 (ft), 3 (pt); Activities
coordinators 1 (ft), 1 (pt).
Languages Spanish
Affiliation Mennonite
Facilities Dining room; Activities room;
Laundry room; Barber/Beauty shop; Library.
Activities Arts & crafts; Cards; Games;
Reading groups; Prayer groups; Movies;
Social/Cultural gatherings; Guest entertainers
& speakers.

RESEDA

Convalescent Center of Reseda*
6740 Wilbur Ave, Reseda, CA, 91335
(213) 881-2302
Admin Ronald D O'Haver.
Licensure Skilled care. *Beds* 99. *Certified* Medicare; Medi-Cal.
Owner Proprietary Corp.
Languages Spanish, Polish

Corbin Convalescent Hospital*
7120 Corbin Ave, Reseda, CA, 91335
(213) 881-4540
Admin Gita Wheelis.
Licensure Skilled care. *Beds* 157. *Certified* Medicare; Medi-Cal.
Owner Proprietary Corp.

Menorah Village*
7150 Tampa Ave, Reseda, CA, 91335
(213) 345-1746
Admin Ray Shapero.
Licensure Skilled care; Intermediate care. *Beds* SNF 66; ICF 33. *Certified* Medi-Cal.
Owner Nonprofit Corp.

Reseda Arms Convalescent Hospital*
7836 Reseda Blvd, Reseda, CA, 91335
(213) 881-7414
Admin Robert Garrick.
Licensure Skilled care. *Beds* 97. *Certified* Medicare; Medi-Cal.
Owner Proprietary Corp (Care Enterprises).

RHEEM

Rheem Valley Convalescent Hospital*
332 Park St, Rheem, CA, 94570
(415) 376-5995
Admin Elizabeth Schmidt. *Medical Dir/Dir of Nursing* Gary Miller DO.
Licensure Skilled care. *Beds* 49. *Certified* Medicare; Medi-Cal.
Owner Proprietary Corp.
Admissions Requirements Minimum age 55; Medical examination; Physician's request.
Staff Physicians 4 (pt); RNs 3 (ft), 5 (pt); LPNs 2 (ft); Nurses aides 10 (ft), 25 (pt); Physical therapists 1 (pt); Speech therapists 1 (pt); Activities coordinators 1 (pt); Dietitians 1 (pt); Dentists 1 (pt); Podiatrists 1 (pt).
Facilities Dining room; Physical therapy room; Activities room; Crafts room; Barber/Beauty shop; Sitting rooms.
Activities Arts & crafts; Games; Reading groups; Prayer groups; Movies; Social/Cultural gatherings; Volunteers groups and/or individual.

RIALTO

Crestview Convalescent Hospital
1471 S Riverside Ave, Rialto, CA, 92376
(714) 877-0783
Admin Louise Start. *Medical Dir/Dir of Nursing* Roy V Berglund MD.
Licensure Skilled care. *Beds* SNF 201. *Certified* Medicare; Medi-Cal.
Owner Privately owned.
Staff RNs 4 (ft), 2 (pt); LPNs 20 (ft), 8 (pt); Orderlies; Nurses aides 95 (ft), 2 (pt); Occupational therapists 1 (pt); Speech therapists 1 (pt); Activities coordinators 2 (ft); Dietitians 1 (pt); Dentists 1 (pt); Ophthalmologists 1 (pt); Podiatrists 1 (pt).
Facilities Dining room; Physical therapy room; Activities room; Crafts room; Laundry room; Barber/Beauty shop.
Activities Arts & crafts; Cards; Games; Prayer groups; Movies; Shopping trips; Social/Cultural gatherings.

RICHMOND

Ellen S Memorial Convalescent Hospital*
2716 Ohio Ave, Richmond, CA, 94804
(415) 233-6720
Admin E B Griffin Jr.
Licensure Skilled care. *Beds* 43.
Owner Proprietary Corp.

Greenridge Heights Convalescent Hospital*
2150 Pyramid Dr, Richmond, CA, 94803
(415) 222-1242
Admin Ronald K Martin.
Licensure Skilled care. *Beds* 59. *Certified* Medicare; Medi-Cal.
Owner Proprietary Corp.

Shields & Terrell Convalescent Hospital*
1919 Cutting Blvd, Richmond, CA, 94804
(415) 233-8513
Admin William M Shields.
Licensure Skilled care. *Beds* 84. *Certified* Medicare; Medi-Cal.
Owner Proprietary Corp.

Walker Convalescent Hospital Inc*
955 23rd St, Richmond, CA, 94804
(415) 235-6550
Admin Johnnie M Walker.
Licensure Intermediate care. *Beds* 25. *Certified* Medicare.
Owner Proprietary Corp.

RIPON

Bethany Home Society San Joaquin County*
930 W Main St, Ripon, CA, 95366
(209) 599-4221
Admin Kenneth M Hekman.
Licensure Skilled care. *Beds* 74. *Certified* Medicare; Medi-Cal.
Owner Nonprofit Corp.
Admissions Requirements Minimum age 21; Medical examination; Physician's request.
Staff RNs 2 (ft), 4 (pt); LPNs 4 (ft), 6 (pt); Nurses aides 20 (ft), 10 (pt); Physical therapists 2 (pt); Activities coordinators 1 (ft); Dietitians 1 (pt); Podiatrists 1 (pt).
Facilities Dining room; Physical therapy room; Activities room; Crafts room; Laundry room; Barber/Beauty shop; Library.
Activities Arts & crafts; Games; Prayer groups; Movies; Shopping trips.

RIVERBANK

River Bluff Convalescent Hospital
2649 W Topeka St, Riverbank, CA, 95367
(209) 869-2569
Admin Donna Ferguson. *Medical Dir/Dir of Nursing* Joann Messinger RN.
Licensure Skilled care. *Beds* 99. *Certified* Medicare; Medi-Cal.
Owner Proprietary Corp (Chartham Management).
Staff RNs 2 (ft); LPNs 5 (ft); Nurses aides 24 (ft); Physical therapists 1 (pt); Occupational therapists 1 (pt); Speech therapists 1 (pt); Activities coordinators 1 (pt); Dentists 1 (pt); Ophthalmologists 1 (pt); Podiatrists 1 (pt).
Languages Spanish, German
Facilities Dining room; Physical therapy room; Activities room; Crafts room; Laundry room; Barber/Beauty shop.
Activities Arts & crafts; Cards; Games; Reading groups; Prayer groups; Movies; Shopping trips; Social/Cultural gatherings; Candlelight dinners.

RIVERSIDE

Arlington Gardens Convalescent Hospital*
3766 Nye Ave, Riverside, CA, 92505
(714) 689-2340
Admin Eileen McPherson. *Medical Dir/Dir of Nursing* Stanley Chartier MD.
Licensure Skilled care. *Beds* 27. *Certified* Medicare; Medi-Cal.
Owner Proprietary Corp.
Staff RNs 1 (ft), 1 (pt); LPNs 2 (ft), 2 (pt); Nurses aides 6 (ft), 4 (pt); Physical therapists 1 (pt); Reality therapists 1 (pt); Recreational therapists 1 (pt); Occupational therapists 1 (pt); Speech therapists 1 (pt); Activities coordinators 1 (ft); Dietitians 1 (pt); Dentists 1 (pt); Ophthalmologists 1 (pt); Podiatrists 1 (pt); Audiologists 1 (pt).
Facilities Dining room; Activities room; Crafts room; Laundry room; Barber/Beauty shop.
Activities Arts & crafts; Cards; Games; Reading groups; Prayer groups; Shopping trips; Social/Cultural gatherings.

Beverly Manor Convalescent Hospital
4768 Palm Ave, Riverside, CA, 92501-4070
(714) 686-9000
Admin J Gregory Bordenkircher. *Medical Dir/Dir of Nursing* V Prabhy Dhalla MD; Edna Ormsby RN DON.
Licensure Skilled care. *Beds* SNF 51. *Certified* Medicare; Medi-Cal.
Owner Proprietary Corp (Beverly Enterprises).
Admissions Requirements Minimum age 18; Medical examination; Physician's request.
Staff Physicians; RNs; LPNs; Orderlies; Nurses aides; Physical therapists; Recreational therapists; Occupational therapists; Speech therapists; Activities coordinators; Dietitians; Ophthalmologists; Podiatrists.
Languages Spanish
Facilities Dining room; Physical therapy room; Activities room; Crafts room; Laundry room; Barber/Beauty shop.
Activities Arts & crafts; Cards; Games; Reading groups; Prayer groups; Movies; Shopping trips; Social/Cultural gatherings.

Beverly Manor Sanitarium*
4580 Palm Ave, Riverside, CA, 92501
(714) 684-7701
Admin Charles Eggleston. *Medical Dir/Dir of Nursing* Dr L Murad.
Licensure Skilled care. *Beds* 120. *Certified* Medi-Cal.
Owner Proprietary Corp (Beverly Enterprises).
Admissions Requirements Minimum age 18; Medical examination; Physician's request.
Staff Physicians; RNs; LPNs; Orderlies; Nurses aides; Occupational therapists; Speech therapists; Activities coordinators; Dietitians; Dentists; Ophthalmologists; Podiatrists; Audiologists.

Chapman Convalescent Hospital*
4301 Caroline Ct, Riverside, CA, 92506
(714) 683-7111
Admin Betty Lou Beeman.
Licensure Skilled care. *Beds* 33. *Certified* Medi-Cal.
Owner Proprietary Corp.

Community Convalescent Center*
4070 Jurupa Ave, Riverside, CA, 92506
(714) 682-2522
Admin Bruce W Bennett. *Medical Dir/Dir of Nursing* H H Stone MD.
Licensure Skilled care. *Beds* 158. *Certified* Medicare; Medi-Cal.
Owner Proprietary Corp.
Staff Physicians 1 (pt); RNs 7 (ft), 7 (pt); LPNs 10 (ft), 7 (pt); Orderlies 5 (ft), 2 (pt); Nurses aides 66 (ft), 28 (pt); Physical therapists 3 (ft); Reality therapists 1 (ft); Occupational therapists 1 (pt); Speech therapists 1 (pt); Activities coordinators 3 (ft), 1 (pt); Dietitians 1 (pt); Dentists 1 (pt); Podiatrists 1 (pt).
Facilities Dining room; Physical therapy room; Activities room; Crafts room; Barber/Beauty shop; Library.

Activities Arts & crafts; Cards; Games;
Reading groups; Prayer groups; Movies;
Shopping trips; Social/Cultural gatherings.

Cypress Gardens Convalescent Hospital
9025 Colorado Ave, Riverside, CA, 92503
(714) 688-3643
Admin Gretchen Reynolds. *Medical Dir/Dir of
Nursing* Rodney Soholt MD; Mary Ann
Crowley DON.
Licensure Skilled care. *Beds* SNF 120.
Certified Medicare; Medi-Cal.
Owner Proprietary Corp.
Admissions Requirements Minimum age 18;
Medical examination; Physician's request.
Staff Physicians 1 (pt); RNs 6 (ft), 4 (pt);
LPNs 8 (ft), 2 (pt); Nurses aides 45 (ft), 4
(pt); Physical therapists 1 (pt); Recreational
therapists 2 (ft); Occupational therapists 1
(pt); Speech therapists 1 (pt); Activities
coordinators 2 (ft); Dietitians 1 (ft); Dentists
1 (pt); Ophthalmologists 1 (pt); Podiatrists 1
(pt).
Languages Spanish
Facilities Dining room; Physical therapy
room; Activities room; Crafts room; Laundry
room; Barber/Beauty shop.
Activities Arts & crafts; Cards; Games;
Reading groups; Prayer groups; Movies;
Shopping trips; Social/Cultural gatherings;
Outings.

Extended Care Hospital of Riverside
8171 Magnolia Ave, Riverside, CA, 92504
(714) 687-3842
Admin Shirley Y Leedy.
Licensure Skilled care. *Beds* 99. *Certified*
Medicare; Medi-Cal.
Owner Proprietary Corp.

La Sierra Convalescent Hospital*
11162 Palm Terrace Ln, Riverside, CA, 92505
(714) 687-7330
Admin Onie L Denson.
Licensure Skilled care. *Beds* 75. *Certified*
Medicare; Medi-Cal.
Owner Proprietary Corp.

Lakeview Developmental Disability Center*
8781 Lakeview Ave, Riverside, CA, 92509
(714) 685-1531
Admin Violet Livingston.
Licensure Skilled care; Intermediate care for
mentally retarded. *Beds* 188. *Certified*
Medicare; Medi-Cal.
Owner Proprietary Corp.

Magnolia Convalescent Hospital*
8133 Magnolia Ave, Riverside, CA, 92504
(714) 688-4321
Admin Raymond N Beeman.
Licensure Skilled care. *Beds* 94. *Certified*
Medicare; Medi-Cal.
Owner Proprietary Corp.

Millers Progressive Care
8951 Granite Hill Dr, Riverside, CA, 92509
(714) 685-7474
Admin W W Miller. *Medical Dir/Dir of
Nursing* B Tilton MD; Alida Arnold DON.
Licensure Skilled care. *Beds* SNF 70. *Certified*
Medi-Cal.
Owner Proprietary Corp.
Staff Physicians; RNs; LPNs; Orderlies;
Nurses aides; Activities coordinators;
Dietitians; Ophthalmologists; Podiatrists.
Facilities Dining room; Activities room;
Crafts room; Laundry room; Barber/Beauty
shop.
Activities Arts & crafts; Cards; Games;
Reading groups; Prayer groups; Movies;
Shopping trips; Social/Cultural gatherings;
Adult education from local school district.

Mission Convalescent Hospital*
8487 Magnolia Ave, Riverside, CA, 92504
(714) 688-2222
Admin Jack E Easterday.

Licensure Skilled care. *Beds* 40. *Certified*
Medicare; Medi-Cal.
Owner Proprietary Corp (Care Enterprises).

Orangetree Convalescent Hospital*
4000 Harrison St, Riverside, CA, 92503
(714) 785-6060
Admin A M Richards.
Licensure Skilled care. *Beds* 140. *Certified*
Medicare; Medi-Cal.
Owner Proprietary Corp.

Plymouth Tower
3401 Lemon St, Riverside, CA, 92501
(714) 686-8202
Admin Barbara A Emert. *Medical Dir/Dir of
Nursing* Dr Herman Stone MD; J
McMichael RN DON.
Licensure Skilled care; Community care. *Beds*
36; Community care 110. *Certified* Medi-
Cal.
Owner Nonprofit organization/foundation.
Admissions Requirements Minimum age 65;
Medical examination; Physician's request.
Staff RNs 1 (ft), 3 (pt); LPNs 3 (ft), 3 (pt);
Nurses aides 11 (ft), 3 (pt); Physical
therapists 1 (pt); Speech therapists 1 (pt);
Activities coordinators 2 (ft); Dietitians 1
(ft); Ophthalmologists 1 (pt).
Affiliation Church of Christ
Facilities Dining room; Activities room;
Laundry room; Barber/Beauty shop; Multi-
purpose room; Lounges.
Activities Arts & crafts; Cards; Games;
Reading groups; Prayer groups; Movies;
Shopping trips; Social/Cultural gatherings;
Outings in van.

Villa Convalescent Hospital
8965 Magnolia Ave, Riverside, CA, 92503-
4493
(714) 689-5788
Admin Larry J Mays. *Medical Dir/Dir of
Nursing* Kathleen McConnel RN.
Licensure Skilled care. *Beds* SNF 59. *Certified*
Medi-Cal.
Owner Proprietary Corp.
Admissions Requirements Physician's request.
Facilities Dining room; Activities room;
Laundry room; Barber/Beauty shop.
Activities Arts & crafts; Cards; Games;
Reading groups; Prayer groups; Movies;
Shopping trips; Social/Cultural gatherings.

Vista Pacifica Convalescent Home
3662 Pacific Ave, Riverside, CA, 92509
(714) 682-4833
Admin Thomas A Prchal. *Medical Dir/Dir of
Nursing* Peter Paul MD; Peggy Kane.
Licensure Skilled care. *Beds* 49.
Owner Proprietary Corp.
Admissions Requirements Minimum age 18;
Medical examination; Physician's request.
Staff Physicians 4 (ft); RNs 1 (ft), 1 (pt);
LPNs 3 (ft), 2 (pt); Nurses aides 15 (ft), 4
(pt); Physical therapists 1 (ft); Activities
coordinators 1 (ft); Dietitians 1 (ft);
Ophthalmologists 1 (ft).
Languages Spanish
Facilities Dining room; Activities room;
Chapel; Crafts room; Laundry room; Barber/
Beauty shop; Library.
Activities Arts & crafts; Cards; Games;
Reading groups; Prayer groups; Movies;
Shopping trips; Social/Cultural gatherings.

**Vista Pacifica—A Center for Rehabilitation &
Growth**
3674 Pacific Ave, Riverside, CA, 92509
(714) 682-4833
Admin Thomas A Prchal. *Medical Dir/Dir of
Nursing* Paul DeSilva MD; Mary Duron.
Licensure Skilled care. *Beds* 108. *Certified*
Medi-Cal.
Owner Proprietary Corp.
Admissions Requirements Minimum age 18;
Medical examination; Physician's request.

Staff Physicians 6 (ft); RNs 3 (ft), 4 (pt);
LPNs 6 (ft), 2 (pt); Orderlies 8 (ft); Nurses
aides 19 (ft), 1 (pt); Reality therapists 1 (ft);
Recreational therapists 2 (ft); Activities
coordinators 1 (ft), 1 (pt); Dietitians 1 (ft).
Languages Spanish
Facilities Dining room; Activities room;
Chapel; Crafts room; Laundry room; Barber/
Beauty shop; Library; Classroom.
Activities Arts & crafts; Cards; Games;
Reading groups; Prayer groups; Movies;
Shopping trips; Social/Cultural gatherings;
Pet therapy; Monthly family day picnics;
Yearly talent show.

ROSEMEAD

California Christian Home
8417 E Mission Dr, Rosemead, CA, 91770
(818) 287-0438
Admin James R Stricker. *Medical Dir/Dir of
Nursing* Dr Francesco Vetri; Anne Keogh
DON.
Licensure Skilled care. *Beds* SNF 59. *Certified*
Medi-Cal.
Owner Nonprofit Corp (Natl Bnvlnt Assn of
Chrstn Homes).
Admissions Requirements Minimum age 62;
Medical examination.
Staff Physicians 10 (pt); RNs 2 (ft); LPNs 7
(ft); Nurses aides 20 (ft); Activities
coordinators 1 (ft); Dietitians 1 (pt).
Affiliation Disciples of Christ
Facilities Dining room; Activities room;
Barber/Beauty shop.
Activities Arts & crafts; Games; Reading
groups; Movies; Shopping trips; Social/
Cultural gatherings.

Del Mar Convalescent Hospital*
3136 N Del Mar Ave, Rosemead, CA, 91770
(213) 288-8353
Admin Charles P Leggett.
Licensure Skilled care. *Beds* 59. *Certified*
Medicare; Medi-Cal.
Owner Proprietary Corp.

Green Acres Lodge*
8101 E Hill Dr, Rosemead, CA, 91770
(213) 280-5682
Admin Baird D Wayne.
Licensure Skilled care. *Beds* 85. *Certified*
Medicare; Medi-Cal.
Owner Proprietary Corp (CV American).

Monterey Care Center
1267 San Gabriel Blvd, Rosemead, CA, 91770
(818) 280-3220
Admin Darlene Freeman. *Medical Dir/Dir of
Nursing* William Beard; Lydia Pamintuan.
Licensure Skilled care; Locked facility. *Beds*
SNF 103. *Certified* Medi-Cal.
Owner Proprietary Corp (Care Enterprises).
Admissions Requirements Minimum age 45;
Physician's request.
Staff Physicians; RNs 4 (ft); LPNs 4 (ft);
Orderlies 7 (ft); Nurses aides 20 (ft);
Physical therapists; Recreational therapists;
Occupational therapists; Speech therapists;
Activities coordinators 1 (ft); Dietitians 1
(ft); Dentists; Ophthalmologists; Podiatrists.
Languages Spanish, Tagalog
Facilities Dining room; Activities room;
Crafts room; Laundry room; Barber/Beauty
shop.
Activities Arts & crafts; Cards; Games;
Reading groups; Prayer groups; Movies;
Shopping trips; Social/Cultural gatherings.

San Gabriel Convalescent Center
8035 E Hill Dr, Rosemead, CA, 91770
(213) 280-4820
Admin Jan Stine. *Medical Dir/Dir of Nursing*
Samuel Zia MD; Mary Savage RN DON.
Licensure Skilled care. *Beds* SNF 151.
Certified Medicare; Medi-Cal.
Owner Proprietary Corp (CV American).

Admissions Requirements Minimum age 55;
Medical examination; Physician's request.
Staff RNs 3 (ft), 3 (pt); LPNs 6 (ft), 4 (pt);
Nurses aides; Physical therapists;
Occupational therapists; Speech therapists;
Activities coordinators 1 (ft); Dietitians;
Dentists; Ophthalmologists; Podiatrists.
Languages Spanish, Chinese, Korean, Tagalog
Facilities Dining room; Physical therapy
room; Activities room; Crafts room; Laundry
room; Barber/Beauty shop; Library.
Activities Arts & crafts; Cards; Games;
Reading groups; Prayer groups; Movies;
Shopping trips; Social/Cultural gatherings.

ROSEVILLE

CareWest-Sierra Nursing Center
310 Oak Ridge Dr, Roseville, CA, 95678
(916) 782-3188
Admin Gail Anderson. *Medical Dir/Dir of
Nursing* Isidro Cardeno MD; Lois Maguire
RN DON.
Licensure Skilled care. *Beds* SNF 67. *Certified*
Medicare; Medi-Cal.
Owner Proprietary Corp (Care Enterprises).
Admissions Requirements Minimum age 45;
Medical examination; Physician's request.
Staff RNs 4 (ft), 1 (pt); LPNs 5 (ft), 4 (pt);
Nurses aides 27 (ft), 16 (pt); Activities
coordinators 1 (ft); Dietitians 1 (ft).
Languages Spanish
Facilities Dining room; Physical therapy
room; Activities room; Crafts room; Laundry
room; Barber/Beauty shop; Library.
Activities Arts & crafts; Cards; Games;
Reading groups; Prayer groups; Movies;
Shopping trips; Social/Cultural gatherings;
BBQs; Outings.

Hacienda Convalescent Hospital*
600 Sunrise Ave, Roseville, CA, 95678
(916) 782-3131
Admin Donald D Williams.
Licensure Skilled care. *Beds* 98. *Certified*
Medicare; Medi-Cal.
Owner Proprietary Corp (Hillhaven Corp).

Roseville Convalescent Hospital*
1161 Cirby St, Roseville, CA, 95678
(916) 782-1238
Admin Bernice Schrabeck. *Medical Dir/Dir of
Nursing* Richard Chun MD.
Licensure Skilled care. *Beds* 210. *Certified*
Medicare; Medi-Cal.
Owner Proprietary Corp.
Admissions Requirements Medical
examination; Physician's request.
Staff RNs 7 (ft), 4 (pt); LPNs 12 (ft), 5 (pt);
Orderlies 2 (ft); Nurses aides 56 (ft), 24 (pt);
Physical therapists 1 (pt); Occupational
therapists 1 (pt); Speech therapists 1 (pt);
Activities coordinators 2 (ft); Dietitians 1
(ft); Dentists 1 (pt); Ophthalmologists 1 (pt);
Podiatrists 1 (pt); Audiologists 1 (pt).
Facilities Dining room; Physical therapy
room; Activities room; Chapel; Crafts room;
Laundry room; Barber/Beauty shop; Library.
Activities Arts & crafts; Cards; Games;
Reading groups; Prayer groups; Movies;
Shopping trips; Social/Cultural gatherings.

RUBIDOUX

Mt Rubidoux Convalescent Hospital*
6401 33rd St, Rubidoux, CA, 92509
(714) 681-2200
Admin Bertha Campos. *Medical Dir/Dir of
Nursing* Dr Robert Bom.
Licensure Skilled care; Intermediate care. *Beds*
99. *Certified* Medicare; Medi-Cal.
Owner Proprietary Corp.
Admissions Requirements Physician's request.
Staff RNs 2 (ft), 2 (pt); LPNs 7 (ft), 3 (pt);
Orderlies 4 (ft); Nurses aides 26 (ft), 5 (pt);
Physical therapists 1 (pt); Activities
coordinators 4 (ft).

Facilities Dining room; Activities room;
Laundry room; Barber/Beauty shop; TV
room; Enclosed outdoor patios.
Activities Arts & crafts; Cards; Games;
Reading groups; Prayer groups; Movies;
Shopping trips; Social/Cultural gatherings;
Cooking classes.

SACRAMENTO

Arden Memorial Convalescent Hospital*
3400 Alta Arden Expwy, Sacramento, CA,
95825
(916) 481-5500
Admin Harold D Mays. *Medical Dir/Dir of
Nursing* B G Wagner MD.
Licensure Skilled care. *Beds* 190. *Certified*
Medicare; Medi-Cal.
Owner Proprietary Corp.
Staff RNs 6 (ft), 6 (pt); LPNs 11 (ft), 5 (pt);
Nurses aides 63 (ft), 13 (pt); Activities
coordinators 1 (ft).
Facilities Dining room; Physical therapy
room; Activities room; Crafts room; Laundry
room; Barber/Beauty shop.
Activities Arts & crafts; Cards; Games;
Reading groups; Prayer groups; Movies;
Social/Cultural gatherings.

Ashland Manor*
500 Jessie Ave, Sacramento, CA, 95838
(916) 922-7177
Admin Dorris Ash.
Licensure Skilled care. *Beds* 162. *Certified*
Medicare; Medi-Cal.
Owner Proprietary Corp.

Center Skilled Nursing Facility
2257 Fair Oaks Blvd, Sacramento, CA, 95825
(916) 927-4763
Admin Darrell Zimmerman. *Medical Dir/Dir
of Nursing* William T Kelley MD; Marie
Dibble RN DON.
Licensure Skilled care. *Beds* 139. *Certified*
Medicare; Medi-Cal.
Owner Proprietary Corp.
Admissions Requirements Physician's request.
Staff RNs 8 (ft), 2 (pt); LPNs 9 (ft), 2 (pt);
Orderlies 3 (ft); Nurses aides 45 (ft), 8 (pt);
Activities coordinators 2 (ft); Dietitians 1
(ft).
Facilities Dining room; Physical therapy
room; Activities room; Crafts room; Laundry
room; Barber/Beauty shop.
Activities Arts & crafts; Cards; Games;
Reading groups; Prayer groups; Movies;
Shopping trips; Social/Cultural gatherings;
Outside expeditions to railroad museum,
zoo, etc.

Cottage Park Place
Parkwood and La Mesa, Sacramento, CA,
95825
(916) 391-7891
Admin Linda Gordon.
Licensure Skilled care; Assisted living. *Beds*
SNF 120; Assisted living 55. *Certified*
Medicare; Medi-Cal.
Owner Privately owned.
Admissions Requirements Minimum age 18.
Staff Physicians 1 (pt); RNs 15 (ft); LPNs 15
(ft); Orderlies 3 (ft); Nurses aides 60 (ft);
Physical therapists 2 (ft); Reality therapists 1
(ft); Recreational therapists 1 (ft);
Occupational therapists 1 (pt); Speech
therapists 1 (pt); Activities coordinators 1
(ft); Dietitians 1 (ft).
Facilities Dining room; Physical therapy
room; Activities room; Chapel; Crafts room;
Laundry room; Barber/Beauty shop; Library;
Day care.
Activities Arts & crafts; Cards; Games;
Reading groups; Prayer groups; Movies;
Shopping trips; Social/Cultural gatherings.

Crestwood Manor
2600 Stockton Blvd, Sacramento, CA, 95817
(916) 452-1431

Admin Rufus L (Skip) McDonald PhD.
Medical Dir/Dir of Nursing Donald N
ReVille MD; Judy Thomas RN.
Licensure Skilled care; Specialized mental
health care. *Beds* SNF 130. *Certified* Medi-
Cal.
Owner Proprietary Corp (Crestwood Hosp).
Admissions Requirements Minimum age 18;
Medical examination; Physician's request.
Staff Physicians 5 (pt); RNs 7 (ft); LPNs 13
(ft); Orderlies 30 (ft); Nurses aides 40 (ft);
Activities coordinators 2 (ft), 1 (pt);
Dietitians 1 (pt).
Languages Spanish, Tagalog, Vietnamese
Facilities Dining room; Activities room;
Library; Rehabilitation Center.
Activities Arts & crafts; Reading groups;
Prayer groups; Movies; Shopping trips;
Social/Cultural gatherings.

Elizabeth Manor Convalescent Hospital*
5000 Folsom Blvd, Sacramento, CA, 95819
(916) 452-4191
Admin Janice A McDonald.
Licensure Skilled care. *Beds* 121.
Owner Proprietary Corp.

Eskaton Glenwood Manor*
501 Jessie Ave, Sacramento, CA, 95838
(916) 922-8855
Admin Fred Stacey. *Medical Dir/Dir of
Nursing* Justin English MD.
Licensure Intermediate care. *Beds* 128.
Certified Medi-Cal.
Owner Nonprofit Corp.
Admissions Requirements Minimum age 65;
Medical examination; Physician's request.
Staff RNs 4 (ft); LPNs 4 (ft); Nurses aides 17
(ft); Activities coordinators 2 (ft).
Facilities Dining room; Physical therapy
room; Activities room; Crafts room; Laundry
room; Barber/Beauty shop; Library.
Activities Arts & crafts; Cards; Games;
Reading groups; Prayer groups; Movies;
Shopping trips; Social/Cultural gatherings.

Florin Convalescent Hospital
7400 24th St, Sacramento, CA, 95822
(916) 422-4825
Admin Catherine Haley RN. *Medical Dir/Dir
of Nursing* Margaret Pintea RN DON.
Licensure Skilled care. *Beds* SNF 122.
Certified Medicare; Medi-Cal.
Owner Proprietary Corp (ARA Living
Centers).
Admissions Requirements Physician's request.
Staff RNs; LPNs; Orderlies; Nurses aides;
Physical therapists; Recreational therapists;
Occupational therapists; Speech therapists;
Activities coordinators; Dietitians.
Facilities Dining room; Physical therapy
room; Activities room; Crafts room; Laundry
room; Barber/Beauty shop.
Activities Arts & crafts; Cards; Games;
Reading groups; Prayer groups; Movies;
Shopping trips; Social/Cultural gatherings.

Garden Court Convalescent Hospital*
2291 Fair Oaks Blvd, Sacramento, CA, 95825
(916) 927-2741
Admin Michael A Hideiros. *Medical Dir/Dir
of Nursing* W Dugdale MD.
Licensure Skilled care. *Beds* 63. *Certified*
Medicare; Medi-Cal.
Owner Proprietary Corp.
Admissions Requirements Minimum age 40;
Medical examination; Physician's request.
Staff Physicians 1 (pt); RNs 1 (ft), 1 (pt);
LPNs 7 (ft), 2 (pt); Orderlies 4 (ft), 1 (pt);
Nurses aides 28 (ft), 8 (pt); Physical
therapists 1 (pt); Occupational therapists 1
(pt); Speech therapists 1 (pt); Activities
coordinators 1 (ft); Dietitians 1 (pt); Dentists
1 (pt); Ophthalmologists 1 (pt); Podiatrists 1
(pt); Audiologists 1 (pt).
Facilities Dining room; Physical therapy
room; Activities room; Laundry room;
Barber/Beauty shop.

Activities Arts & crafts; Cards; Games; Reading groups; Prayer groups; Shopping trips; Social/Cultural gatherings.

Gardens Skilled Nursing Facility
2221 Fair Oaks Blvd, Sacramento, CA, 95825
(916) 927-1802
Admin Darrell Zimmerman. *Medical Dir/Dir of Nursing* Kenneth Hodge MD; Betty Lumbert RN DON.
Licensure Intermediate care for mentally retarded. *Beds* ICF/MR 56. *Certified* Medi-Cal.
Owner Proprietary Corp.
Admissions Requirements Minimum age 16.
Staff Physicians 2 (ft); RNs 3 (ft); LPNs 4 (ft); Orderlies 25 (ft); Activities coordinators 1 (ft); Psychiatrist; Psychologist; Social workers.
Facilities Dining room; Physical therapy room; Activities room; Laundry room.
Activities Arts & crafts; Cards; Games; Reading groups; Prayer groups; Movies; Shopping trips; Social/Cultural gatherings.

Heritage Convalescent Hospital*
5255 Hemlock St, Sacramento, CA, 95841
(916) 331-4590
Admin Sheila Waddell. *Medical Dir/Dir of Nursing* William Hedges MD.
Licensure Skilled care. *Beds* 99. *Certified* Medicare; Medi-Cal.
Owner Proprietary Corp.
Staff Physicians 1 (pt); RNs 3 (ft), 1 (pt); LPNs 12 (ft), 2 (pt); Orderlies 2 (ft), 1 (pt); Nurses aides 45 (ft), 6 (pt); Physical therapists 2 (pt); Reality therapists 1 (pt); Recreational therapists 2 (pt); Occupational therapists 1 (pt); Speech therapists 1 (pt); Activities coordinators 2 (ft); Dietitians 1 (pt); Dentists 1 (pt); Ophthalmologists 1 (pt); Podiatrists 1 (pt); Audiologists 1 (pt).
Facilities Dining room; Physical therapy room; Activities room; Crafts room; Laundry room; Barber/Beauty shop.
Activities Arts & crafts; Cards; Games; Reading groups; Prayer groups; Movies; Shopping trips; Social/Cultural gatherings.

Hillhaven—Sherwood Convalescent Hospital
4700 Elvas Ave, Sacramento, CA, 95819
(916) 452-5752
Admin Mary Tommolilo.
Licensure Skilled care. *Beds* SNF 62. *Certified* Medicare; Medi-Cal.
Owner Proprietary Corp (Hillhaven Corp).
Staff Physicians 1 (pt); RNs 1 (ft); LPNs 1 (ft); Orderlies 1 (ft); Nurses aides 1 (ft); Physical therapists 1 (pt); Reality therapists 1 (pt); Recreational therapists 1 (pt); Occupational therapists 1 (pt); Speech therapists 1 (pt); Activities coordinators 1 (ft); Dietitians 1 (pt); Dentists 1 (pt); Ophthalmologists 1 (pt); Podiatrists 1 (pt).

Hy-Lond Convalescent Hospital*
4635 College Oak Dr, Sacramento, CA, 95841
(916) 481-7434
Admin Sylvia A Hatfield.
Licensure Skilled care. *Beds* 120. *Certified* Medicare; Medi-Cal.
Owner Proprietary Corp (Beverly Enterprises).

Mt Olivette Meadows Convalescent Hospital*
2240 Northrop Ave, Sacramento, CA, 95825
(916) 927-1337
Admin Ronald T Vanderbeek.
Licensure Skilled care; Intermediate care for mentally retarded. *Beds* 58. *Certified* Medi-Cal.
Owner Proprietary Corp.

Park Sutter Convalescent Hospital
2600 L St, Sacramento, CA, 95816
(916) 444-7290
Admin Bill Davis. *Medical Dir/Dir of Nursing* Dr David Dachler; Carol Loftin RN.
Licensure Skilled care. *Beds* SNF 132. *Certified* Medicare; Medi-Cal.

Owner Nonprofit organization/foundation.
Admissions Requirements Physician's request.
Staff RNs 9 (ft), 3 (pt); LPNs 13 (ft), 4 (pt); Orderlies 8 (ft); Nurses aides 63 (ft); Physical therapists 1 (ft); Occupational therapists 1 (ft); Speech therapists 1 (ft); Activities coordinators 3 (ft); Dietitians 1 (ft).
Languages Spanish
Facilities Dining room; Physical therapy room; Activities room.
Activities Arts & crafts; Cards; Games; Prayer groups; Movies; Social/Cultural gatherings.

Pioneer House
415 P St, Sacramento, CA, 95814
(916) 442-4906
Admin Philip S Richardson. *Medical Dir/Dir of Nursing* J English MD; Pearl Lamont DON.
Licensure Skilled care; Residential care; Independent living. *Beds* 50. *Certified* Medicaid; Medi-Cal.
Owner Nonprofit Corp.
Admissions Requirements Minimum age 62; Medical examination.
Staff RNs 3 (ft); LPNs 8 (ft); Nurses aides 15 (ft); Physical therapists 1 (pt); Reality therapists 1 (pt); Recreational therapists 1 (pt); Occupational therapists 1 (pt); Speech therapists 1 (pt); Activities coordinators 1 (ft); Dietitians 1 (pt); Dentists 1 (pt); Ophthalmologists 1 (pt); Podiatrists 1 (pt).
Languages Spanish, Thai, Chinese, Tagalog
Facilities Dining room; Activities room; Crafts room; Laundry room; Barber/Beauty shop; Library.
Activities Arts & crafts; Cards; Games; Reading groups; Prayer groups; Movies; Shopping trips; Social/Cultural gatherings.

Quinlan Manor*
PO Box 13188, 919 8th Ave, Sacramento, CA, 95813-3188
(916) 922-7177
Admin Ann Pelzman.
Licensure Intermediate care. *Beds* 22. *Certified* Medi-Cal.
Owner Proprietary Corp.

Riverside Convalescent Hospital
1090 Rio Ln, Sacramento, CA, 95822
(916) 446-2506
Admin Ann Garren. *Medical Dir/Dir of Nursing* G W O'Brien MD; Donna Albertson.
Licensure Skilled care. *Beds* 51. *Certified* Medicare; Medi-Cal.
Owner Proprietary Corp.
Admissions Requirements Medical examination; Physician's request.
Staff RNs 1 (ft), 1 (pt); LPNs 3 (ft), 2 (pt); Physical therapists 2 (pt); Reality therapists 1 (pt); Recreational therapists 1 (ft); Occupational therapists 1 (pt); Speech therapists 1 (pt); Activities coordinators 1 (ft), 1 (pt); Dietitians 1 (pt); Dentists 1 (pt); Ophthalmologists 1 (pt); Podiatrists 1 (pt).
Facilities Dining room; Activities room; Crafts room; Laundry room; Barber/Beauty shop.
Activities Arts & crafts; Games; Reading groups; Prayer groups; Movies.

Royal Manor Health Care Inc
5901 Lemon Hill Ave, Sacramento, CA, 95824
(916) 383-2741
Admin Ann Garren. *Medical Dir/Dir of Nursing* Anna Vaughn MD; Hester Tober RN DON.
Licensure Skilled care. *Beds* SNF 49. *Certified* Medicare; Medi-Cal.
Owner Proprietary Corp.
Admissions Requirements Physician's request.
Staff RNs 2 (ft); LPNs 5 (ft), 2 (pt); Nurses aides 21 (ft), 8 (pt).

Facilities Dining room; Physical therapy room; Activities room; Crafts room; Laundry room; Barber/Beauty shop.
Activities Arts & crafts; Cards; Games; Reading groups; Prayer groups; Movies; Shopping trips; Social/Cultural gatherings.

Sacramento Convalescent Hospital
3700 H St, Sacramento, CA, 95816
(916) 452-3592
Admin David H Dixon. *Medical Dir/Dir of Nursing* Claire Rabidou.
Licensure Skilled care. *Beds* SNF 86. *Certified* Medicare; Medi-Cal.
Owner Proprietary Corp (Medicrest of California).
Admissions Requirements Medical examination; Physician's request.
Staff Physicians 1 (pt); RNs 2 (ft); LPNs 5 (ft); Nurses aides 21 (ft); Physical therapists 1 (pt); Occupational therapists 1 (pt); Speech therapists 1 (pt); Activities coordinators 1 (ft); Dietitians 1 (pt); Dentists 1 (pt); Ophthalmologists 1 (pt); Podiatrists 1 (pt).
Facilities Dining room; Physical therapy room; Activities room; Crafts room; Laundry room; Barber/Beauty shop.
Activities Arts & crafts; Cards; Games; Reading groups; Prayer groups; Movies; Shopping trips; Social/Cultural gatherings.

Saylor Lane Convalescent Hospital
3500 Folsom Blvd, Sacramento, CA, 95816
(916) 457-6521
Admin Louise U Muller. *Medical Dir/Dir of Nursing* Dr James Coyle; Violet Underwood RN DON.
Licensure Skilled care. *Beds* 42. *Certified* Medicare; Medi-Cal.
Owner Proprietary Corp (Hillhaven Corp).
Admissions Requirements Medical examination; Physician's request.
Staff RNs 3 (ft), 3 (pt); LPNs 2 (ft); Nurses aides 16 (ft), 4 (pt); Activities coordinators 1 (ft).
Facilities Dining room; Physical therapy room; Activities room; Crafts room; Laundry room; Library.
Activities Arts & crafts; Cards; Games; Prayer groups; Movies; Social/Cultural gatherings; Van trips.

Trinity House
2701 Capitol Ave, Sacramento, CA, 95816
(916) 446-4806
Admin Philip S Richardson. *Medical Dir/Dir of Nursing* Dr Justin English.
Licensure Skilled care. *Beds* 29. *Certified* Medi-Cal.
Owner Nonprofit Corp.
Admissions Requirements Minimum age 62; Medical examination.
Staff Physicians 1 (pt); RNs 1 (ft), 1 (pt); LPNs 4 (ft); Orderlies 1 (ft), 1 (pt); Nurses aides 8 (ft), 2 (pt); Physical therapists 1 (pt); Speech therapists 1 (pt); Activities coordinators 1 (ft); Dietitians 1 (pt); Dentists 1 (pt); Ophthalmologists 1 (pt); Podiatrists 1 (pt).
Facilities Dining room; Activities room; Laundry room; Barber/Beauty shop; Library.
Activities Arts & crafts; Cards; Games; Reading groups; Prayer groups; Movies; Shopping trips; Social/Cultural gatherings.

Valley Skilled Nursing Facility
2120 Stockton Blvd, Sacramento, CA, 95817
(916) 452-6631
Admin Lita Milke.
Licensure Skilled care. *Beds* 59. *Certified* Medicaid; Medicare; Medi-Cal.
Owner Proprietary Corp.
Admissions Requirements Medical examination.
Staff Physicians 5 (pt); RNs 3 (ft); LPNs 6 (ft); Orderlies 4 (ft); Nurses aides 25 (ft); Activities coordinators 1 (ft), 1 (pt); Dietitians 1 (pt).

Facilities Dining room; Physical therapy room; Activities room; Crafts room; Laundry room; Barber/Beauty shop.
Activities Arts & crafts; Cards; Games; Reading groups; Prayer groups; Movies; Shopping trips; Social/Cultural gatherings.

SAINT HELENA

Vintage Convalescent Hospital*
830 Pratt Ave, Saint Helena, CA, 94574
(707) 963-2791
Admin Michael Giardullo.
Licensure Skilled care. *Beds* 70. *Certified* Medicare; Medi-Cal.
Owner Proprietary Corp (Care Enterprises).

SALINAS

Casa Serena de Salinas
720 E Romie Ln, Salinas, CA, 93901
(408) 424-8072
Admin Ronald L Walton. *Medical Dir/Dir of Nursing* Dr Engerhorn.
Licensure Skilled care. *Beds* 96. *Certified* Medicare; Medi-Cal.
Owner Proprietary Corp.
Staff RNs 5 (ft); LPNs 6 (ft), 4 (pt); Orderlies 4 (ft); Nurses aides 40 (ft), 5 (pt); Physical therapists 1 (pt); Occupational therapists 1 (pt); Speech therapists 1 (pt); Activities coordinators 2 (ft); Dietitians 1 (pt).
Facilities Dining room; Physical therapy room; Activities room; Crafts room; Laundry room; Barber/Beauty shop; Living room; Speech therapy room; Occupational therapy room.
Activities Arts & crafts; Games; Reading groups; Prayer groups; Movies; Shopping trips; Social/Cultural gatherings; Candlelight dinners; BBQs.

Driftwood Convalescent Hospital
350 Iris Dr, Salinas, CA, 93906
(408) 449-1515
Admin Rosemarie S Williams. *Medical Dir/Dir of Nursing* Raymond L Hack MD; Michele Noriega RN DON.
Licensure Skilled care. *Beds* SNF 10; ICF 89. *Certified* Medicare; Medi-Cal.
Owner Proprietary Corp (ARA Living Centers).
Staff Physicians; RNs; LPNs; Orderlies; Nurses aides; Recreational therapists; Occupational therapists; Speech therapists; Activities coordinators; Dietitians; Dentists; Ophthalmologists; Podiatrists.
Languages Spanish, Tagalog
Facilities Dining room; Physical therapy room; Activities room; Crafts room; Laundry room; Barber/Beauty shop; Library.
Activities Arts & crafts; Cards; Games; Reading groups; Prayer groups; Movies; Shopping trips; Social/Cultural gatherings.

Katherine Convalescent Hospital
315 Alameda St, Salinas, CA, 93901
(408) 424-1878
Admin Julia Ann Alsop. *Medical Dir/Dir of Nursing* A L Wessels MD; Margaret Adams RN DON.
Licensure Skilled care. *Beds* SNF 51. *Certified* Medicare; Medi-Cal.
Owner Privately owned.
Admissions Requirements Minimum age 21; Physician's request.
Staff RNs; LPNs; Orderlies; Nurses aides; Activities coordinators.
Facilities Dining room; Physical therapy room; Activities room; Chapel; Crafts room; Laundry room; Barber/Beauty shop.
Activities Arts & crafts; Cards; Games; Movies; Shopping trips.

Romie Lane Convalescent Hospital*
637 E Romie Lane, Salinas, CA, 93901
(408) 424-0687

Admin Frank J Balestrieri. *Medical Dir/Dir of Nursing* Dr A L Wessels.
Licensure Skilled care. *Beds* 99. *Certified* Medicare; Medi-Cal.
Owner Proprietary Corp.
Admissions Requirements Medical examination; Physician's request.
Staff Physicians; RNs; LPNs; Orderlies; Nurses aides; Physical therapists; Reality therapists; Recreational therapists; Occupational therapists; Speech therapists; Activities coordinators; Dietitians; Dentists; Podiatrists.
Facilities Dining room; Physical therapy room; Activities room; Laundry room; Barber/Beauty shop; TV room with pool table.
Activities Arts & crafts; Cards; Games; Reading groups; Prayer groups; Movies; Shopping trips; Social/Cultural gatherings; Field trips.

Skyline Convalescent Hospital
348 Iris Dr, Salinas, CA, 93901
(408) 449-5496
Admin Laurie Behrend. *Medical Dir/Dir of Nursing* Raymond Hack MD; Dorothy Turnbill DON.
Licensure Skilled care. *Beds* SNF 80. *Certified* Medicare; Medi-Cal.
Owner Proprietary Corp (ARA Living Centers).
Staff Physicians; RNs 2 (ft); LPNs 4 (ft), 3 (pt); Nurses aides 30 (ft), 7 (pt); Physical therapists 1 (pt); Recreational therapists 1 (pt); Occupational therapists 1 (pt); Speech therapists 1 (pt); Activities coordinators 1 (ft); Dietitians 1 (ft), 1 (pt); Dentists 1 (pt); Ophthalmologists 1 (pt); Podiatrists 1 (pt).
Languages Tagalog, Spanish
Facilities Dining room; Physical therapy room; Activities room; Laundry room; Barber/Beauty shop.
Activities Arts & crafts; Cards; Games; Reading groups; Prayer groups; Movies; Social/Cultural gatherings.

SAN ANDREAS

Mark Twain Convalescent Hospital*
900 Mountain Ranch Rd, San Andreas, CA, 95249
(209) 754-3823
Admin Elaine Hoff.
Licensure Skilled care. *Beds* 99. *Certified* Medicare; Medi-Cal.
Owner Proprietary Corp (Beverly Enterprises).

San Andreas Convalescent Hospital*
556 Toyon Rd, San Andreas, CA, 95249
(209) 754-4213
Admin Elaine Hoff.
Licensure Skilled care. *Beds* 30. *Certified* Medicare; Medi-Cal.
Owner Proprietary Corp (Beverly Enterprises).

SAN BERNARDINO

Arrowhead Home*
4343 Sierra Way, San Bernardino, CA, 92404
(714) 886-4731
Admin Donald N Popovich.
Licensure Intermediate care. *Beds* 58. *Certified* Medi-Cal.
Owner Proprietary Corp.

Del Rosa Convalescent Hospital*
1311 Date St, San Bernardino, CA, 92404
(714) 882-3316
Admin Dan L Murray. *Medical Dir/Dir of Nursing* Dr Leslie Musad.
Licensure Skilled care. *Beds* 99. *Certified* Medicare; Medi-Cal.
Owner Proprietary Corp (Hillhaven Corp).
Admissions Requirements Minimum age 16; Medical examination; Physician's request.

Staff Physicians 46 (pt); RNs 4 (ft), 4 (pt); LPNs 7 (ft), 4 (pt); Nurses aides 33 (ft), 9 (pt); Physical therapists 1 (ft), 1 (pt); Occupational therapists 1 (pt); Speech therapists 1 (pt); Activities coordinators 1 (ft); Dietitians 1 (pt); Dentists 1 (pt); Podiatrists 1 (pt); Audiologists 1 (pt).
Facilities Dining room; Physical therapy room; Activities room; Barber/Beauty shop; Library.
Activities Arts & crafts; Cards; Games; Reading groups; Prayer groups; Movies; Shopping trips; Social/Cultural gatherings.

Hillcrest Nursing Home*
4280 Cypress Dr, San Bernardino, CA, 92407
(714) 882-2965
Admin C David Benfield.
Licensure Skilled care. *Beds* 59. *Certified* Medi-Cal.
Owner Proprietary Corp.

Medical Center Convalescent Hospital*
467 E Gilbert St, San Bernardino, CA, 92404
(714) 884-4781
Admin Ann Ethridge.
Licensure Skilled care. *Beds* 99. *Certified* Medicare; Medi-Cal.
Owner Proprietary Corp (Medicrest of California).

Pacific Park Convalescent Hospital
1676 Medical Center Dr, San Bernardino, CA, 92411
(714) 887-6481
Admin Linda K Jackson. *Medical Dir/Dir of Nursing* Frank Randolph MD; Lois Kirschner RN.
Licensure Skilled care. *Beds* SNF 99. *Certified* Medicare; Medi-Cal.
Owner Nonprofit Corp.
Admissions Requirements Medical examination; Physician's request.
Staff Physicians 1 (pt); RNs 2 (ft); LPNs 7 (ft); Orderlies 1 (ft); Nurses aides 25 (ft); Physical therapists 4 (pt); Occupational therapists 1 (pt); Speech therapists 1 (pt); Activities coordinators 1 (ft); Dietitians 1 (pt); Ophthalmologists 1 (pt); Podiatrists 1 (pt); Dentist 1 (pt).
Languages Spanish
Facilities Dining room; Physical therapy room; Activities room; Crafts room; Laundry room; Barber/Beauty shop.
Activities Arts & crafts; Cards; Games; Reading groups; Prayer groups; Movies; Shopping trips; Social/Cultural gatherings.

Shandin Hills Behavior Therapy Center
4164 N 4th Ave, San Bernardino, CA, 92407
(714) 886-6786
Admin Janet L Seawell.
Licensure Skilled care. *Beds* 78. *Certified* Medi-Cal.
Owner Proprietary Corp.

Shandin Hills Convalescent Hospital*
4160 4th Ave, San Bernardino, CA, 92407
(714) 886-6786
Admin Patrick Clisham.
Licensure Skilled care. *Beds* 29. *Certified* Medi-Cal.
Owner Proprietary Corp.

Shea Convalescent Hospital
1335 N Waterman Ave, San Bernardino, CA, 92404
(714) 885-0268
Admin Jocey Hallman. *Medical Dir/Dir of Nursing* William P Thompson MD; Carol Wagner.
Licensure Skilled care. *Beds* SNF 120. *Certified* Medicare; Medi-Cal.
Owner Proprietary Corp.
Admissions Requirements Medical examination; Physician's request.
Staff Physicians 1 (pt); RNs 1 (ft); LPNs 1 (ft); Orderlies 1 (ft); Nurses aides 1 (ft); Physical therapists 1 (pt); Reality therapists

1 (ft); Recreational therapists 1 (ft); Occupational therapists 1 (pt); Speech therapists 1 (pt); Activities coordinators 1 (ft); Dietitians 1 (pt); Dentists 1 (pt); Ophthalmologists 1 (pt); Podiatrists 1 (pt).
Languages Spanish
Facilities Dining room; Physical therapy room; Activities room; Crafts room; Laundry room; Barber/Beauty shop.
Activities Arts & crafts; Cards; Games; Reading groups; Prayer groups; Movies; Shopping trips; Social/Cultural gatherings.

Valley Convalescent Hospital
1680 N Waterman Ave, San Bernardino, CA, 92404
(714) 886-5291
Admin Stanley R Smith. *Medical Dir/Dir of Nursing* Lois Freeman RN.
Licensure Skilled care. *Beds* SNF 122. *Certified* Medicare; Medi-Cal.
Owner Proprietary Corp.
Admissions Requirements Medical examination; Physician's request.
Staff Physicians; RNs; LPNs; Orderlies; Nurses aides; Physical therapists; Recreational therapists; Occupational therapists; Speech therapists; Activities coordinators; Dietitians; Dentists; Ophthalmologists; Podiatrists; Dentist.
Languages Spanish
Facilities Dining room; Physical therapy room; Activities room; Chapel; Crafts room; Laundry room; Barber/Beauty shop; Patient lounge.
Activities Arts & crafts; Cards; Games; Reading groups; Prayer groups; Movies; Shopping trips.

Waterman Convalescent Hospital*
1850 N Waterman Ave, San Bernardino, CA, 92404
(714) 882-1215
Admin Elizabeth Plott.
Licensure Skilled care. *Beds* 166. *Certified* Medicare; Medi-Cal.
Owner Proprietary Corp.

SAN BRUNO

San Bruno Convalescent Hospital*
890 El Camino Real, San Bruno, CA, 94066
(415) 583-7768
Admin Kenneth J Hargraves.
Licensure Skilled care. *Beds* 45. *Certified* Medi-Cal.
Owner Publicly owned.

SAN DIEGO

Alvarado Convalescent & Rehabilitation Hospital
6599 Alvarado Rd, San Diego, CA, 92120
(619) 286-7421
Admin Franxis X Rodgers. *Medical Dir/Dir of Nursing* Dr Nicholas Lind; Paula Scheurs DON.
Licensure Skilled care. *Beds* SNF 301.
Owner Proprietary Corp (Hillhaven Corp).
Staff RNs; LPNs; Orderlies; Nurses aides; Recreational therapists 1 (ft); Dietitians 1 (ft).
Facilities Dining room; Physical therapy room; Activities room; Chapel; Crafts room; Laundry room; Barber/Beauty shop; Library.
Activities Arts & crafts; Cards; Games; Reading groups; Prayer groups; Movies; Shopping trips; Social/Cultural gatherings.

Arroyo Vista Convalescent Center*
3022 45th St, San Diego, CA, 92105
(714) 283-5855
Admin Gilbert Fimbres. *Medical Dir/Dir of Nursing* Dr A K Williams.
Licensure Skilled care. *Beds* 53. *Certified* Medicare; Medi-Cal.
Owner Proprietary Corp (Care Enterprises).

Staff RNs 4 (ft), 1 (pt); LPNs 3 (ft), 1 (pt); Orderlies 3 (ft); Nurses aides 15 (ft), 5 (pt); Physical therapists 1 (ft); Recreational therapists 1 (ft); Occupational therapists 1 (pt); Speech therapists 1 (pt); Activities coordinators 1 (ft); Dietitians 1 (ft); Dentists 1 (pt).
Facilities Dining room; Physical therapy room; Activities room; Laundry room; Barber/Beauty shop; Library.
Activities Arts & crafts; Cards; Games; Reading groups; Movies; Social/Cultural gatherings.

Childrens Convalescent Hospital
8022 Birmingham Dr, San Diego, CA, 92123
(714) 292-3455
Admin Joyce M Turner. *Medical Dir/Dir of Nursing* Marilyn Jones MD.
Licensure Skilled care; Intermediate care for mentally retarded. *Beds* SNF 6; ICF/MR 49. *Certified* Medi-Cal.
Owner Nonprofit Corp.
Admissions Requirements Medical examination.
Staff Physicians 6 (pt); RNs 4 (ft), 3 (pt); LPNs 2 (ft); Nurses aides 20 (ft), 35 (pt); Physical therapists 2 (pt); Recreational therapists 1 (ft); Occupational therapists 2 (pt); Activities coordinators 1 (ft); Dietitians 1 (pt); Dentists 2 (pt); Ophthalmologists 2 (pt).
Facilities Dining room; Physical therapy room; Activities room; Crafts room; Laundry room; Activity rooms.
Activities Arts & crafts; Games; Prayer groups; Movies; Shopping trips; Social/Cultural gatherings; Sensori motor program.

Cloisters of Mission Hills Convalescent Hospital
3680 Reynard Way, San Diego, CA, 92103
(714) 297-4484
Admin L M Gray.
Licensure Skilled care. *Beds* 70. *Certified* Medicare; Medi-Cal.
Owner Nonprofit Corp.

Del Capri Terrace Convalescent Hospital*
5602 University Ave, San Diego, CA, 92105
(714) 583-1993
Admin Ellena R Church.
Licensure Skilled care. *Beds* 87. *Certified* Medicare; Medi-Cal.
Owner Proprietary Corp (Care Enterprises).

Euclid Convalescent Center
1350 N Euclid Ave, San Diego, CA, 92105
(714) 253-2166
Admin Berry T Crow. *Medical Dir/Dir of Nursing* Daisy Reyes RN.
Licensure Skilled care. *Beds* SNF 99. *Certified* Medicare; Medi-Cal.
Owner Proprietary Corp.
Staff Physicians; RNs; LPNs; Nurses aides; Physical therapists; Recreational therapists; Occupational therapists; Speech therapists; Activities coordinators; Dietitians; Dentists; Ophthalmologists; Podiatrists.

Fraser Intermediate Care Facility
726 Torrance St, San Diego, CA, 92103
(619) 296-2175
Admin Barbara C Carter. *Medical Dir/Dir of Nursing* Dr Sam C Hsieh; Esperanza Olarte LVN DON.
Licensure Intermediate care. *Beds* ICF 36. *Certified* Medi-Cal.
Owner Privately owned.
Admissions Requirements Medical examination; Physician's request.
Staff Physicians; RNs; LPNs 4 (ft), 3 (pt); Nurses aides 5 (ft), 3 (pt); Recreational therapists; Occupational therapists; Speech therapists; Activities coordinators 1 (pt); Dietitians; Dentists; Ophthalmologists.
Languages Spanish

Facilities Dining room; Activities room; Chapel; Crafts room; Laundry room.
Activities Arts & crafts; Cards; Games; Movies; Shopping trips; Social/Cultural gatherings; Baseball games.

Frost Street Convalescent Hospital*
8060 Frost St, San Diego, CA, 92123
(714) 278-4750
Admin Gary D Devoir. *Medical Dir/Dir of Nursing* Arthur G Edwards.
Licensure Skilled care. *Beds* 99. *Certified* Medicare; Medi-Cal.
Owner Proprietary Corp.
Facilities Dining room; Physical therapy room; Barber/Beauty shop.
Activities Arts & crafts; Cards; Games; Reading groups; Prayer groups.

Georgian Court Nursing & Rehabilitation Center
2828 Meadowlark Dr, San Diego, CA, 92123
(619) 277-6460
Admin Charles Bloom. *Medical Dir/Dir of Nursing* Harry Brookler; Jan Torbit.
Licensure Skilled care. *Beds* SNF 305. *Certified* Medicaid; Medicare; Medi-Cal.
Owner Proprietary Corp (Care Enterprises).
Admissions Requirements Physician's request.
Staff Physicians; RNs; LPNs; Orderlies; Nurses aides; Physical therapists; Recreational therapists; Occupational therapists; Speech therapists; Activities coordinators; Dietitians.
Facilities Dining room; Physical therapy room; Activities room; Crafts room; Laundry room; Barber/Beauty shop; O T & speech therapy rooms.
Activities Arts & crafts; Cards; Games; Reading groups; Prayer groups; Movies; Shopping trips; Social/Cultural gatherings.

Golden Hill Healthcare Center
1201 34th St, San Diego, CA, 92102
(619) 232-2946
Admin Donald W Chance. *Medical Dir/Dir of Nursing* A K Williams; Alberta Caneda RN.
Licensure Skilled care. *Beds* SNF 99. *Certified* Medicare; Medi-Cal.
Owner Proprietary Corp (American Medical Services Inc).
Admissions Requirements Minimum age 40; Medical examination; Physician's request.
Staff RNs; LPNs; Orderlies; Nurses aides; Physical therapists; Reality therapists; Recreational therapists; Occupational therapists; Speech therapists; Activities coordinators; Dietitians; Dentists; Ophthalmologists; Podiatrists.
Facilities Dining room; Physical therapy room; Activities room; Crafts room; Laundry room; Barber/Beauty shop; Library; Outside recreation area.
Activities Arts & crafts; Cards; Games; Reading groups; Prayer groups; Movies; Shopping trips; Social/Cultural gatherings.

Hillcrest Rehabilitation & Convalescent Center
3520 4th Ave, San Diego, CA, 92103
(619) 291-5270
Admin Kenneth Thompson. *Medical Dir/Dir of Nursing* A K Williams MD; Terry Pumphrey RN DON.
Licensure Skilled care. *Beds* SNF 194. *Certified* Medicare; Medi-Cal.
Owner Proprietary Corp (Care Enterprises).
Admissions Requirements Physician's request.
Staff Physicians 1 (pt); RNs 8 (ft); LPNs 12 (ft); Nurses aides 53 (ft), 5 (pt); Physical therapists 2 (ft), 2 (pt); Activities coordinators 1 (ft); Dietitians 1 (ft).
Languages Spanish
Facilities Dining room; Physical therapy room; Activities room; Crafts room; Laundry room; Barber/Beauty shop; Library.

Activities Arts & crafts; Cards; Games;
Reading groups; Prayer groups; Movies;
Shopping trips; Social/Cultural gatherings;
Physical fitness; Music.

Kearny Mesa Convalescent & Nursing Home*
7675 Family Circle Dr, San Diego, CA, 92111
(714) 278-8121
Admin Richard J Hebbel.
Licensure Skilled care. *Beds* 98. *Certified*
Medicare; Medi-Cal.
Owner Proprietary Corp.

Meadowlark Convalescent Hospital*
8001 Birmingham Dr, San Diego, CA, 92123
(619) 279-7701
Admin Mary M Doherty. *Medical Dir/Dir of
Nursing* Renato Masilungan MD.
Licensure Skilled care. *Beds* 92. *Certified*
Medicare; Medi-Cal.
Owner Proprietary Corp.
Admissions Requirements Minimum age 18.
Staff RNs 4 (ft), 2 (pt); LPNs 6 (ft), 3 (pt);
Physical therapists 1 (ft), 2 (pt); Activities
coordinators 1 (ft).
Facilities Dining room; Physical therapy
room; Activities room; Laundry room.
Activities Arts & crafts; Cards; Games;
Reading groups; Prayer groups; Movies;
Family dinners.

Mission Convalescent Hospital*
4033 6th Ave Extension, San Diego, CA,
92103
(714) 297-4086
Admin Gary Novack.
Licensure Skilled care. *Beds* 97. *Certified*
Medicare; Medi-Cal.
Owner Proprietary Corp.

Nazareth House
6333 Rancho Mission Rd, San Diego, CA,
92108
(714) 563-0480
Admin Mother Malachy. *Medical Dir/Dir of
Nursing* Dr M Kielty; V McDonnell RN,
BSN DON.
Licensure Skilled care; Intermediate care;
Residential. *Beds* SNF 30; ICF 8;
Residential 88. *Certified* Medi-Cal.
Owner Nonprofit organization/foundation.
Staff RNs 11 (ft), 2 (pt); LPNs 3 (ft), 1 (pt);
Nurses aides 22 (ft), 3 (pt); Activities
coordinators 1 (ft); Dietitians 1 (ft).
Affiliation Roman Catholic
Facilities Dining room; Activities room;
Chapel; Crafts room; Laundry room; Barber/
Beauty shop.
Activities Arts & crafts; Cards; Games;
Reading groups; Prayer groups; Movies;
Shopping trips.

Paradise Hills Convalescent Center
6061 Banbury St, San Diego, CA, 92139
(714) 475-2211
Admin Roger L Caddell. *Medical Dir/Dir of
Nursing* Max Nelson MD; Patricia Youmans
DON.
Licensure Skilled care. *Beds* SNF 162.
Certified Medicare; Medi-Cal.
Owner Proprietary Corp.
Admissions Requirements Minimum age 18.
Staff Physicians 1 (pt); RNs 15 (ft), 2 (pt);
LPNs 17 (ft), 6 (pt); Orderlies 5 (ft), 2 (pt);
Nurses aides 62 (ft), 10 (pt); Physical
therapists 2 (ft); Occupational therapists 1
(ft); Speech therapists 1 (ft); Activities
coordinators 3 (ft), 1 (pt); Dietitians 1 (ft), 1
(pt); Dentists 1 (pt); Ophthalmologists 1 (pt);
Podiatrists 1 (pt).
Languages Spanish, Tagalog, French
Facilities Dining room; Physical therapy
room; Activities room; Crafts room; Laundry
room; Barber/Beauty shop; Library.
Activities Arts & crafts; Cards; Games;
Reading groups; Prayer groups; Movies;
Shopping trips; Social/Cultural gatherings;
Trips to restaurants; Olympiatrics.

Point Loma Convalescent Hospital*
3202 Duke St, San Diego, CA, 92110
(714) 224-4141
Admin Vivian E Herrmann. *Medical Dir/Dir
of Nursing* Kenneth Taylor MD.
Licensure Skilled care. *Beds* 120. *Certified*
Medicare; Medi-Cal.
Owner Proprietary Corp.
Admissions Requirements Minimum age 18;
Medical examination; Physician's request.
Staff RNs 5 (ft), 3 (pt); LPNs 4 (ft), 3 (pt);
Nurses aides 29 (ft), 15 (pt); Physical
therapists; Activities coordinators; Dietitians.
Facilities Dining room; Physical therapy
room; Laundry room; Barber/Beauty shop;
Living room.
Activities Arts & crafts; Cards; Games;
Reading groups; Prayer groups; Movies;
Shopping trips; Outside activities.

St Paul's Health Care Center
2635 2nd Ave, San Diego, CA, 92103
(619) 239-2097
Admin David P Steele. *Medical Dir/Dir of
Nursing* Mary Ellen Dellefield.
Licensure Skilled care. *Beds* SNF 59. *Certified*
Medicare; Medi-Cal.
Owner Nonprofit Corp.
Admissions Requirements Minimum age 62;
Physician's request.
Staff Physicians; RNs; Nurses aides; Physical
therapists; Recreational therapists;
Occupational therapists; Speech therapists;
Activities coordinators; Dietitians; CNAs;
Social Services Director.
Languages Spanish
Affiliation Episcopal
Facilities Dining room; Physical therapy
room; Activities room; Chapel; Crafts room;
Laundry room; Barber/Beauty shop.
Activities Arts & crafts; Games; Reading
groups; Prayer groups Church Services;
Movies; Social/Cultural gatherings; Special
events; Birthdays; Family parties.

San Diego Hebrew Home for the Aged*
4075 54th St, San Diego, CA, 92105
(714) 582-5168
Admin Michael J Ellentuck.
Licensure Skilled care. *Beds* 71. *Certified*
Medicare; Medi-Cal.
Owner Nonprofit Corp.
Affiliation Jewish

San Diego Intermediate Care Center*
1119 28th St, San Diego, CA, 92102
(714) 233-0505
Admin Marietta Vaughn. *Medical Dir/Dir of
Nursing* Dr J P De Luca.
Licensure Intermediate care. *Beds* 37.
Certified Medi-Cal.
Owner Proprietary Corp.
Admissions Requirements Minimum age 18;
Medical examination.
Staff Physicians 1 (ft), 1 (pt); RNs 1 (pt);
LPNs 3 (ft), 4 (pt); Nurses aides 5 (ft), 3
(pt); Recreational therapists 1 (ft), 1 (pt).
Facilities Dining room; Activities room;
Laundry room; Library.
Activities Arts & crafts; Games; Reading
groups; Prayer groups; Movies; Social/
Cultural gatherings; Outdoor activities/
picnics.

Sharp Knollwood Convalescent Hospital
7944 Birmingham Dr, San Diego, CA, 92123
(619) 278-8810
Admin Linda Pinney MHA. *Medical Dir/Dir
of Nursing* Thomas Spethmann MD; Janine
Kruger BSN RN.
Licensure Skilled care. *Beds* 166. *Certified*
Medicare; Medi-Cal.
Owner Nonprofit Corp.
Staff Physicians; RNs 15 (ft); LPNs 17 (ft);
Nurses aides 70 (ft); Physical therapists 1
(ft); Occupational therapists 1 (ft); Activities
coordinators 1 (ft); Dietitians 1 (ft);
Psychologist, Social worker.

Facilities Dining room; Physical therapy
room; Activities room; Laundry room;
Barber/Beauty shop.
Activities Arts & crafts; Cards; Games;
Reading groups; Prayer groups; Movies;
Shopping trips; Social/Cultural gatherings.

SAN DIMAS

Casa Bonita Convalescent Hospital
535 E Bonita Ave, San Dimas, CA, 91773
(714) 599-1248
Admin Deborah Collins. *Medical Dir/Dir of
Nursing* Dr George McGallon; Kim Butrum
RN.
Licensure Skilled care. *Beds* 106. *Certified*
Medicare; Medi-Cal.
Owner Proprietary Corp.
Admissions Requirements Physician's request.
Facilities Dining room; Physical therapy
room; Activities room; Crafts room; Laundry
room; Barber/Beauty shop.
Activities Arts & crafts; Cards; Games;
Reading groups; Prayer groups; Movies;
Shopping trips.

SAN FERNANDO

Country Manor Convalescent Hospital*
11723 Fenton Ave, San Fernando, CA, 91342
(213) 899-0251
Admin Vernon B Monson.
Licensure Skilled care. *Beds* 99.
Owner Proprietary Corp.

Forester Haven*
12249 N Lopez Canyon Rd, San Fernando,
CA, 91342
(213) 899-7422
Admin Mary Wiggins.
Licensure Skilled care. *Beds* 49. *Certified*
Medi-Cal.
Owner Nonprofit Corp.

SAN FRANCISCO

Beverly Manor Convalescent Hospital*
1477 Grove St, San Francisco, CA, 94117
(415) 563-0565
Admin Frank Garrison.
Licensure Skilled care. *Beds* 168. *Certified*
Medicare; Medi-Cal.
Owner Proprietary Corp (Beverly Enterprises).

Bowman-Harrison Convalescent Hospital*
1020 Haight St, San Francisco, CA, 94117
(415) 552-3198
Admin Paul M Levesque.
Licensure Skilled care. *Beds* 21.
Owner Proprietary Corp.

Broderick Convalescent Hospital
1421 Broderick St, San Francisco, CA, 94115-
3398
(415) 922-3244
Admin Grant N Edelstone. *Medical Dir/Dir of
Nursing* Joseph Muscat MD; Elsie Loh RN.
Licensure Skilled care. *Beds* SNF 48. *Certified*
Medicare; Medi-Cal.
Owner Privately owned.
Admissions Requirements Physician's request.
Staff RNs 2 (ft), 1 (pt); LPNs 4 (ft), 3 (pt);
Nurses aides 13 (ft), 13 (pt); Physical
therapists; Occupational therapists; Speech
therapists; Activities coordinators 1 (ft);
Dietitians; Ophthalmologists; Podiatrists;
Dentist; X-Ray.
Languages Mandarin, Cantonese, Tagalog,
Burmese
Facilities Dining room; Physical therapy
room; Activities room; Chapel; Crafts room;
Laundry room; Barber/Beauty shop; Library.
Activities Arts & crafts; Games; Reading
groups; Prayer groups; Social/Cultural
gatherings; Field trips; Bingo; Workshops;
Spelling bee; Story hour.

California Convalescent Hospital*
2704 California St, San Francisco, CA, 94115
(415) 931-7846
Admin Mary Ellen Forrest.
Licensure Skilled care. *Beds* 29.
Owner Proprietary Corp.

Central Gardens
1355 Ellis St, San Francisco, CA, 94115
(415) 567-2967
Admin Marc R Toro. *Medical Dir/Dir of Nursing* Arthur Z Cerf MD.
Licensure Skilled care. *Beds* 92. *Certified* Medicare; Medi-Cal.
Owner Proprietary Corp.
Staff RNs 3 (ft), 5 (pt); LPNs 7 (ft), 3 (pt); Nurses aides 26 (ft), 13 (pt); Activities coordinators 1 (ft).
Facilities Dining room; Physical therapy room; Laundry room.
Activities Arts & crafts; Cards; Reading groups; Prayer groups; Movies; Shopping trips.

Convalescent Center Mission Street Inc*
5767 Mission St, San Francisco, CA, 94112
(415) 584-3294
Admin Cheryl Weiss.
Licensure Skilled care. *Beds* 53. *Certified* Medicare; Medi-Cal.
Owner Proprietary Corp.

Hayes Convalescent Hospital*
1250 Hayes St, San Francisco, CA, 94117
(415) 931-8806
Admin Eli Chalich.
Licensure Skilled care. *Beds* 34. *Certified* Medicare; Medi-Cal.
Owner Proprietary Corp.

Hebrew Home for Aged Disabled*
302 Silver Ave, San Francisco, CA, 94112
(415) 334-2500
Admin Jerry Levine. *Medical Dir/Dir of Nursing* Dr Bernard Blumberg.
Licensure Skilled care. *Beds* 345. *Certified* Medicare; Medi-Cal.
Owner Nonprofit Corp.
Admissions Requirements Minimum age 65; Medical examination; Physician's request.
Staff Physicians 4 (pt); RNs 29 (ft), 4 (pt); LPNs 5 (ft), 1 (pt); Orderlies 12 (ft); Nurses aides 97 (ft), 13 (pt); Physical therapists 1 (ft); Recreational therapists 1 (ft); Occupational therapists 1 (pt); Speech therapists 1 (pt); Activities coordinators 1 (ft); Dietitians 1 (ft), 1 (pt); Dentists 2 (pt); Ophthalmologists 1 (pt); Podiatrists 3 (pt).
Affiliation Jewish
Facilities Dining room; Physical therapy room; Activities room; Chapel; Crafts room; Laundry room; Barber/Beauty shop; Library.
Activities Arts & crafts; Cards; Games; Reading groups; Prayer groups; Movies; Shopping trips; Social/Cultural gatherings.

The Heritage
3400 Laguna St, San Francisco, CA, 94123
(415) 567-6900
Admin Edward J Bednedict. *Medical Dir/Dir of Nursing* John Henderson MD; Roberta Helms RN DON.
Licensure Skilled care; Life care. *Beds* SNF 32; Life care 98.
Owner Nonprofit Corp.
Admissions Requirements Minimum age 65; Medical examination.
Staff Physicians 1 (pt); RNs 3 (ft), 1 (pt); LPNs 2 (ft), 2 (pt); Nurses aides 9 (ft), 4 (pt); Dietitians 1 (pt).
Facilities Dining room; Activities room; Chapel; Crafts room; Laundry room; Barber/Beauty shop; Library.
Activities Arts & crafts; Cards; Games; Reading groups; Prayer groups; Movies; Shopping trips; Social/Cultural gatherings.

Hillhaven Convalescent Center*
2043 19th Ave, San Francisco, CA, 94116
(415) 661-8787
Admin Nancy L Hopp.
Licensure Skilled care. *Beds* 140. *Certified* Medicare; Medi-Cal.
Owner Proprietary Corp (Hillhaven Corp).

Laurel Heights Convalescent Hospital*
2740 California St, San Francisco, CA, 94115
(415) 567-3133
Admin Jill Lee.
Licensure Intermediate care. *Beds* 32.
Owner Proprietary Corp.

Mission Bay Convalescent Hospital
331 Pennsylvania Ave, San Francisco, CA, 94107
(415) 647-3587
Admin May Wong. *Medical Dir/Dir of Nursing* Catalina Madrid RN DON.
Licensure Skilled care. *Beds* SNF 50. *Certified* Medicare; Medi-Cal.
Owner Privately owned.
Staff RNs; LPNs; Orderlies; Nurses aides.
Languages Chinese, Tagalog, Spanish
Facilities Dining room; Physical therapy room; Activities room; Laundry room; Outdoor patio.
Activities Arts & crafts; Cards; Games; Prayer groups; Movies; Shopping trips; Social/Cultural gatherings.

Mission Villa Convalescent Hospital
1420 Hampshire St, San Francisco, CA, 94110
(415) 285-7660
Admin Barbara L Springer. *Medical Dir/Dir of Nursing* Richard Munter MD; Rita B Brown RN.
Licensure Skilled care. *Beds* 51. *Certified* Medicare; Medi-Cal.
Owner Proprietary Corp.
Admissions Requirements Medical examination.
Staff Physicians 1 (pt); RNs 3 (ft), 2 (pt); LPNs 4 (ft), 1 (pt); Orderlies 4 (ft); Nurses aides 11 (ft), 3 (pt); Physical therapists 1 (pt); Recreational therapists 1 (pt); Occupational therapists 1 (pt); Speech therapists 1 (pt); Activities coordinators 1 (ft), 1 (pt); Dietitians 1 (pt); Ophthalmologists 1 (pt).
Languages Spanish, Mandarin, Tagalog
Facilities Dining room; Activities room; Crafts room; Laundry room; Barber/Beauty shop.
Activities Arts & crafts; Cards; Games; Prayer groups; Movies; Social/Cultural gatherings; Monthly outings.

Pine Towers Convalescent Hospital Inc*
2707 Pine St, San Francisco, CA, 94115
(415) 563-7600
Admin Janis M Jones. *Medical Dir/Dir of Nursing* Robert V Brody.
Licensure Skilled care. *Beds* 120. *Certified* Medicare; Medi-Cal.
Owner Proprietary Corp (Hillhaven Corp).
Admissions Requirements Physician's request.
Staff RNs 7 (ft), 2 (pt); LPNs 12 (ft), 3 (pt); Orderlies 4 (ft), 2 (pt); Nurses aides 33 (ft), 12 (pt); Physical therapists 1 (pt); Recreational therapists 1 (ft); Occupational therapists 1 (pt); Speech therapists 1 (pt); Activities coordinators 1 (ft); Dietitians 1 (pt); Dentists 1 (pt).
Facilities Dining room; Physical therapy room; Activities room; Laundry room; Barber/Beauty shop; 5 Day rooms.
Activities Arts & crafts; Cards; Games; Reading groups; Prayer groups; Movies; Shopping trips; Social/Cultural gatherings; Social outings; Singing group trips.

St Annes Home
300 Lake St, San Francisco, CA, 94118
(415) 751-6510

Admin Marie Anne Reagan. *Medical Dir/Dir of Nursing* Dr Quock Fong; Sr Clotilde Jardim.
Licensure Skilled care; Intermediate care. *Beds* SNF 48; ICF 48. *Certified* Medi-Cal.
Owner Nonprofit Corp.
Admissions Requirements Minimum age 60; Medical examination.
Staff Physicians 3 (ft), 9 (pt); RNs 4 (ft); LPNs 6 (ft); Orderlies 1 (ft); Nurses aides 20 (ft), 8 (pt); Physical therapists 1 (pt); Recreational therapists 2 (ft); Activities coordinators 1 (ft); Dietitians 6 (ft), 2 (pt); Dentists 2 (pt); Podiatrists 2 (pt).
Affiliation Roman Catholic
Facilities Dining room; Physical therapy room; Activities room; Chapel; Crafts room; Laundry room; Barber/Beauty shop; Library; Ice cream shop; Country store.
Activities Arts & crafts; Cards; Games; Reading groups; Prayer groups; Movies; Shopping trips; Social/Cultural gatherings; Resident council.

San Francisco Community Convalescent Hospital*
2655 Bush St, San Francisco, CA, 94115
(415) 922-4141
Admin Jocelyn S Carter. *Medical Dir/Dir of Nursing* Ricahrd Lanzerotti MD.
Licensure Skilled care. *Beds* 116. *Certified* Medicare; Medi-Cal.
Owner Proprietary Corp.
Staff Physicians 3 (pt); RNs 13 (ft), 3 (pt); LPNs 10 (ft), 6 (pt); Nurses aides 40 (ft), 20 (pt); Physical therapists 2 (ft); Recreational therapists 3 (ft); Occupational therapists 1 (pt); Speech therapists 1 (pt); Activities coordinators 1 (ft); Dietitians 1 (ft); Dentists 1 (pt); Podiatrists 1 (pt).
Facilities Dining room; Physical therapy room; Activities room; Crafts room; Laundry room; Barber/Beauty shop.
Activities Arts & crafts; Cards; Games; Reading groups; Prayer groups; Movies; Social/Cultural gatherings.

San Francisco Convalescent Center*
1359 Pine St, San Francisco, CA, 94109
(415) 673-8405
Admin Gary Collins. *Medical Dir/Dir of Nursing* Dr Richard Lanzerlti.
Licensure Skilled care. *Beds* 172. *Certified* Medicare; Medi-Cal.
Owner Proprietary Corp (Hillhaven Corp).
Admissions Requirements Medical examination.
Staff RNs 7 (ft), 4 (pt); LPNs 20 (ft), 15 (pt); Nurses aides 50 (ft), 20 (pt); Physical therapists 2 (ft), 1 (pt); Recreational therapists 1 (ft); Occupational therapists 1 (ft); Speech therapists 1 (ft); Activities coordinators 2 (ft); Dietitians 1 (pt); Dentists 1 (pt); Podiatrists 1 (pt).
Facilities Dining room; Physical therapy room; Activities room; Chapel; Crafts room; Laundry room; Barber/Beauty shop; Library; Parking garage.
Activities Arts & crafts; Cards; Games; Reading groups; Prayer groups; Movies; Shopping trips; Social/Cultural gatherings; Field trips.

Sequoias San Francisco Convalescent Hospital
1400 Geary Blvd, San Francisco, CA, 94109
(415) 922-9700
Admin Scot Sinclair. *Medical Dir/Dir of Nursing* Wade Aubry MD; Elizabeth Weidenbach RN.
Licensure Skilled care. *Beds* SNF 49. *Certified* Medicare.
Owner Nonprofit Corp.
Admissions Requirements Minimum age 62; Medical examination; Physician's request.
Staff Physicians 4 (pt); RNs 4 (ft), 5 (pt); LPNs 2 (ft), 2 (pt); Nurses aides 16 (ft), 4 (pt); Physical therapists 2 (pt); Occupational therapists 1 (pt); Speech therapists 1 (pt);

Activities coordinators 1 (ft), 2 (pt);
Dietitians 1 (ft); Ophthalmologists 2 (pt);
Podiatrists 1 (pt).
Facilities Dining room; Physical therapy
room; Activities room; Barber/Beauty shop.
Activities Arts & crafts; Cards; Games;
Reading groups; Movies; Social/Cultural
gatherings; Restaurant outings;
Intergenerational programs.

Sheffield Convalescent Hospital*
1133 S Van Ness Ave, San Francisco, CA,
94110
(415) 647-3117
Admin Mary Ellen Forrest.
Licensure Skilled care. *Beds* 34.
Owner Proprietary Corp.

Sunnyside Van Ness Convalescent Hospital
1218 S Van Ness Ave, San Francisco, CA,
94110
(415) 647-6365
Admin Aaron Straus. *Medical Dir/Dir of
Nursing* Dr Robert Durand; Jesusa Straus
RN DON.
Licensure Skilled care. *Beds* SNF 36; RFE 24.
Certified Medicaid.
Owner Proprietary Corp.
Admissions Requirements Physician's request.
Staff RNs 2 (ft), 1 (pt); LPNs 3 (ft), 1 (pt);
Nurses aides 8 (ft), 1 (pt); Physical therapists
1 (pt); Reality therapists 1 (pt); Occupational
therapists 1 (pt); Speech therapists 1 (pt);
Activities coordinators 1 (ft); Dietitians 1
(pt); Ophthalmologists 1 (pt).
Languages Spanish, Tagalog
Facilities Dining room; Physical therapy
room; Activities room; Laundry room;
Library.
Activities Arts & crafts; Cards; Games;
Reading groups; Prayer groups; Movies;
Shopping trips; Outside trips & shows.

Victorian Convalescent Hospital Inc*
2121 Pine St, San Francisco, CA, 94115
(415) 922-5085
Medical Dir/Dir of Nursing Robert
Minkowsky.
Licensure Skilled care. *Beds* 90. *Certified*
Medicare; Medi-Cal.
Owner Proprietary Corp (Hillhaven Corp).
Staff Physicians 1 (pt); RNs 4 (ft); Physical
therapists 1 (pt); Reality therapists 1 (pt);
Occupational therapists 1 (pt); Speech
therapists 1 (pt); Activities coordinators 1
(ft), 1 (pt); Dentists 1 (pt).
Facilities Dining room; Physical therapy
room; Activities room; Laundry room;
Barber/Beauty shop.
Activities Arts & crafts; Cards; Games;
Reading groups; Prayer groups; Movies;
Shopping trips; Social/Cultural gatherings.

SAN GABRIEL

Alderwood Manor Convalescent Hospital*
115 Bridge St, San Gabriel, CA, 91775
(213) 289-4439
Admin Carolyn L Zera.
Licensure Skilled care. *Beds* 98. *Certified*
Medicare.
Owner Proprietary Corp.

Broadway Convalescent Hospital*
112 E Broadway, San Gabriel, CA, 91776
(818) 285-2165
Admin Dale Mueller. *Medical Dir/Dir of
Nursing* F Kunze MD.
Licensure Skilled care. *Beds* 59. *Certified*
Medicare; Medi-Cal.
Owner Proprietary Corp (Beverly Enterprises).
Staff RNs 2 (ft); LPNs 6 (ft); Physical
therapists 1 (pt); Occupational therapists 1
(pt); Speech therapists 1 (pt); Activities
coordinators 1 (ft); Dietitians 1 (pt); Dentists
1 (pt); Ophthalmologists 1 (pt); Podiatrists 1
(pt).

Facilities Dining room; Physical therapy
room; Activities room; Crafts room; Laundry
room; Barber/Beauty shop; Library.
Activities Arts & crafts; Cards; Games;
Reading groups; Prayer groups; Movies;
Shopping trips; Social/Cultural gatherings;
Adopt-a-grandparent program.

**Community Convalescent Hospital of San
Gabriel***
537 W Live Oak, San Gabriel, CA, 91776
(213) 289-3763
Admin Anthony Riggio. *Medical Dir/Dir of
Nursing* James Femino MD.
Licensure Skilled care. *Beds* 99. *Certified*
Medicare; Medi-Cal.
Owner Nonprofit Corp.
Admissions Requirements Physician's request.
Staff RNs 4 (ft), 1 (pt); LPNs 10 (ft), 2 (pt);
Orderlies 1 (ft); Nurses aides 35 (ft).
Facilities Dining room; Physical therapy
room; Activities room; Laundry room;
Barber/Beauty shop.
Activities Arts & crafts; Cards; Games;
Reading groups; Prayer groups; Movies.

Fernview Convalescent Hospital*
126 N San Gabriel Blvd, San Gabriel, CA,
91775
(213) 285-3131
Admin Homer Sommerville.
Licensure Skilled care. *Beds* 75. *Certified*
Medicare; Medi-Cal.
Owner Proprietary Corp.

Mission Convalescent Hospital
909 W Santa Anita St, San Gabriel, CA,
91776
(818) 289-5365
Admin Diane L Conway. *Medical Dir/Dir of
Nursing* Juanita Philipps MD; Yongi Kim
RN DON.
Licensure Skilled care. *Beds* SNF 99. *Certified*
Medicare; Medi-Cal.
Owner Proprietary Corp (Beverly Enterprises).
Admissions Requirements Physician's request.
Staff RNs 1 (ft), 1 (pt); LPNs 8 (ft), 6 (pt);
Orderlies 8 (ft), 2 (pt); Nurses aides 30 (ft),
10 (pt); Physical therapists 1 (pt);
Occupational therapists 1 (pt); Speech
therapists 1 (pt); Activities coordinators 2
(ft); Dietitians 1 (pt); Dentists 1 (pt);
Ophthalmologists 1 (pt); Podiatrists 1 (pt);
Social service 1 (ft).
Languages Spanish, Korean, Chinese, Tagalog,
Italian, Sicilian, French
Facilities Dining room; Physical therapy
room; Activities room; Crafts room; Laundry
room; Barber/Beauty shop; Social services.
Activities Arts & crafts; Cards; Games;
Reading groups; Prayer groups; Movies;
Shopping trips; Social/Cultural gatherings;
Music; Gardening; Educational programs;
Personal grooming.

Mission Lodge Sanitarium
824 S Gladys Ave, San Gabriel, CA, 91776
(818) 287-0753
Admin Norman E Gagliardi. *Medical Dir/Dir
of Nursing* Douglas Copley MD; Linda Scott
RN DON.
Licensure Skilled care; Intermediate care. *Beds*
SNF 133; ICF 20. *Certified* Medi-Cal.
Owner Privately owned.
Staff RNs 5 (ft), 5 (pt); LPNs 8 (ft), 3 (pt);
Nurses aides 63 (ft), 14 (pt); Activities
coordinators 2 (ft).
Facilities Dining room; Activities room;
Crafts room; Laundry room; Barber/Beauty
shop.
Activities Arts & crafts; Cards; Games;
Reading groups; Prayer groups; Movies;
Shopping trips; Social/Cultural gatherings;
Adult education; Special sports programs;
Mini-socials.

San Marino Manor
6812 N Oak Ave, San Gabriel, CA, 91775
(818) 446-5263
Admin B Silberberg. *Medical Dir/Dir of
Nursing* Gary Schlecter MD.
Licensure Skilled care. *Beds* SNF 59. *Certified*
Medicaid.
Owner Proprietary Corp.
Admissions Requirements Minimum age 40.
Facilities Dining room; Activities room;
Laundry room; Barber/Beauty shop.
Activities Arts & crafts; Prayer groups.

SAN JACINTO

Colonial Convalescent Hospital Inc
980 W 7th, San Jacinto, CA, 92383
(714) 654-9347
Admin Jean E Reed. *Medical Dir/Dir of
Nursing* H E Kicenski MD; Joy Mason RN
DON.
Licensure Skilled care. *Beds* SNF 44. *Certified*
Medicare; Medi-Cal.
Owner Proprietary Corp.
Staff RNs; LPNs; Nurses aides; Activities
coordinators; Dietitians.
Facilities Dining room; Activities room;
Crafts room; Laundry room; Barber/Beauty
shop.
Activities Arts & crafts; Cards; Games;
Reading groups; Prayer groups; Movies;
Social/Cultural gatherings.

SAN JOSE

Bellerose Convalescent Hospital
160 Bellerose Dr, San Jose, CA, 95128
(408) 286-4161
Admin Francisco Cerezo. *Medical Dir/Dir of
Nursing* Dr Howard Michael.
Licensure Skilled care. *Beds* 39.
Owner Proprietary Corp.
Staff RNs 1 (ft), 2 (pt); LPNs 3 (ft), 2 (pt);
Orderlies 1 (ft); Nurses aides 9 (ft), 3 (pt);
Activities coordinators 1 (ft); Dietitians 1
(pt); Podiatrists 1 (pt).
Facilities Dining room; Activities room;
Laundry room; Barber/Beauty shop.
Activities Arts & crafts; Cards; Games;
Reading groups; Prayer groups; Movies;
Social/Cultural gatherings; Outings.

Bethany Convalescent Hospital
180 N Jackson Ave, San Jose, CA, 95116
(408) 259-8700
Admin Doug Pannabecker. *Medical Dir/Dir of
Nursing* James Guetzkow MD; Sharon
Green DON.
Licensure Skilled care; Intermediate care. *Beds*
SNF 157; ICF 42. *Certified* Medicare; Medi-
Cal.
Owner Nonprofit Corp (Natl Bnvlnt Assn of
Chrstn Homes).
Admissions Requirements Minimum age 18.
Staff RNs 10 (ft), 2 (pt); LPNs 18 (ft), 10 (pt);
Orderlies 5 (ft), 2 (pt); Nurses aides 44 (ft),
26 (pt); Physical therapists 1 (pt);
Occupational therapists 1 (pt); Activities
coordinators 3 (ft); Dietitians 1 (pt);
Ophthalmologists 1 (pt).
Languages Spanish, Tagalog
Affiliation Disciples of Christ
Facilities Dining room; Physical therapy
room; Activities room; Chapel; Crafts room;
Laundry room; Barber/Beauty shop; Library.
Activities Arts & crafts; Cards; Games;
Reading groups; Prayer groups; Movies;
Shopping trips.

Blossom Convalescent Hospital
4060 MoorPark Ave, San Jose, CA, 95117-
1848
(415) 538-2060
Medical Dir/Dir of Nursing Thomas E
Richmond MD.
Licensure Skilled care. *Beds* 99. *Certified*
Medicare; Medi-Cal.

Owner Proprietary Corp.
Facilities Dining room; Physical therapy room; Activities room; Chapel; Crafts room; Laundry room; Barber/Beauty shop; Library.
Activities Arts & crafts; Cards; Games; Reading groups; Prayer groups; Movies; Shopping trips; Social/Cultural gatherings.

California PEO Home—San Jose Unit*
5203 Alum Rock Ave, San Jose, CA, 95127
(408) 251-9030
Admin Evelyn Niederbrach.
Licensure Skilled care. *Beds* 22. *Certified* Medicare.
Owner Nonprofit Corp.

Casa Serena*
1990 Fruitdale Ave, San Jose, CA, 95128
(408) 998-8447
Admin George Vickerman. *Medical Dir/Dir of Nursing* Dr William Weller.
Licensure Skilled care. *Beds* 129. *Certified* Medicare; Medi-Cal.
Owner Proprietary Corp.
Admissions Requirements Medical examination; Physician's request.
Staff Physicians 1 (pt); RNs 10 (ft), 2 (pt); LPNs 13 (ft), 2 (pt); Nurses aides 57 (ft), 6 (pt); Physical therapists 1 (ft); Activities coordinators 2 (ft); Dietitians 1 (ft).
Facilities Dining room; Physical therapy room; Activities room; Chapel; Crafts room; Laundry room; Barber/Beauty shop; Library.
Activities Arts & crafts; Cards; Games; Reading groups; Prayer groups; Movies; Shopping trips; Social/Cultural gatherings.

Crestwood Manor*
1425 Fruitdale Ave, San Jose, CA, 95128
(408) 275-1010
Admin John Suggs.
Licensure Skilled care. *Beds* 174. *Certified* Medicare; Medi-Cal.
Owner Proprietary Corp (Crestwood Hosp).

Driftwood Convalescent Hospital
2065 Los Gatos-Almaden Rd, San Jose, CA, 95124
(408) 377-9275
Admin David N Hutchinson. *Medical Dir/Dir of Nursing* Robert Reid MD; Sandra Mueller RN DON.
Licensure Skilled care. *Beds* SNF 77. *Certified* Medicare.
Owner Proprietary Corp (ARA Living Centers).
Admissions Requirements Medical examination; Physician's request.
Staff RNs 2 (ft), 1 (pt); LPNs 8 (ft), 4 (pt); Orderlies 1 (pt); Nurses aides 31 (ft), 5 (pt); Physical therapists 1 (pt); Occupational therapists 1 (pt); Speech therapists 1 (pt); Activities coordinators 1 (ft); Podiatrists 1 (pt).
Languages Spanish
Facilities Dining room; Physical therapy room; Activities room; Chapel; Crafts room; Laundry room; Barber/Beauty shop; Library.
Activities Arts & crafts; Cards; Games; Reading groups; Prayer groups; Movies; Shopping trips; Social/Cultural gatherings.

Empress Convalescent Hospital
1299 S Bascom Ave, San Jose, CA, 95128
(408) 287-0616
Admin S M Lambrecht. *Medical Dir/Dir of Nursing* William Garcia MD; M Anderson RN DON.
Licensure Skilled care. *Beds* SNF 67. *Certified* Medicare; Medi-Cal.
Owner Proprietary Corp.
Admissions Requirements Physician's request.
Staff RNs; LPNs; Nurses aides; Activities coordinators.

Facilities Dining room; Physical therapy room; Activities room; Barber/Beauty shop.
Activities Arts & crafts; Games; Reading groups; Prayer groups; Movies; Shopping trips.

The Herman Sanitarium*
2295 Plummer Ave, San Jose, CA, 95125
(408) 269-0701
Admin Robert Sollis.
Licensure Skilled care. *Beds* 99. *Certified* Medi-Cal.
Owner Proprietary Corp.

Homewood Convalescent Hospital Inc*
75 N 13th St, San Jose, CA, 95112
(408) 295-2665
Admin Anne Morgan. *Medical Dir/Dir of Nursing* Dr William Ness.
Licensure Skilled care. *Beds* 58. *Certified* Medicare; Medi-Cal.
Owner Nonprofit Corp (Guardian Fdn Inc).
Admissions Requirements Medical examination; Physician's request.
Facilities Dining room; Activities room; Laundry room; Barber/Beauty shop.
Activities Arts & crafts; Cards; Games; Movies.

Lincoln Glen Intermediate Care*
2671 Plummer Ave, San Jose, CA, 95125
(408) 265-3222
Admin Dan Wiebe.
Licensure Intermediate care. *Beds* 59. *Certified* Medi-Cal.
Owner Nonprofit Corp.

Marcus Manor Convalescent Hospital
264 N Morrison Ave, San Jose, CA, 95126
(408) 297-4420
Admin Steve R Marcus. *Medical Dir/Dir of Nursing* Karin Goodman MD.
Licensure Skilled care; Nursing care. *Beds* 32. *Certified* Medi-Cal.
Owner Proprietary Corp.
Admissions Requirements Minimum age 18; Medical examination; Physician's request.
Staff RNs 1 (ft), 4 (pt); LPNs 2 (ft), 6 (pt); Nurses aides 10 (ft), 5 (pt); Activities coordinators 1 (ft).
Facilities Dining room; Activities room; Laundry room.
Activities Arts & crafts; Cards; Games; Prayer groups; Movies.

Mt Pleasant Convalescent Hospital Inc
1355 Clayton Rd, San Jose, CA, 95127
(408) 251-3070
Admin Judi Woodby. *Medical Dir/Dir of Nursing* Dr Albert Currlin.
Licensure Skilled care. *Beds* SNF 56. *Certified* Medi-Cal.
Owner Proprietary Corp.
Staff RNs 1 (ft), 1 (pt); LPNs 2 (ft), 2 (pt); Nurses aides 20 (ft), 2 (pt); Activities coordinators 1 (ft); Restorative aide 1 (ft).
Facilities Dining room; Physical therapy room; Activities room; Chapel; Barber/Beauty shop.
Activities Arts & crafts; Games; Reading groups; Movies.

Park View Nursing Center*
120 Jose Figueres Ave, San Jose, CA, 95116
(408) 272-1400
Admin Larry Mobley.
Licensure Skilled care. *Beds* 99. *Certified* Medicare; Medi-Cal.
Owner Proprietary Corp.

Plum Tree Convalescent Hospital*
2580 Samaritan Dr, San Jose, CA, 95124
(408) 356-8181
Admin Margaret A Hauer. *Medical Dir/Dir of Nursing* David Morgan MD.
Licensure Skilled care. *Beds* 76. *Certified* Medicare; Medi-Cal.
Owner Nonprofit Corp (Guardian Fdn Inc).

Staff RNs 3 (ft), 7 (pt); LPNs 3 (ft); Nurses aides 27 (ft), 3 (pt); Physical therapists; Reality therapists; Recreational therapists; Occupational therapists; Activities coordinators 1 (ft), 1 (pt); Dietitians; Dentists; Ophthalmologists; Podiatrists; Audiologists.
Facilities Dining room; Physical therapy room; Activities room; Crafts room; Laundry room; Barber/Beauty shop.
Activities Arts & crafts; Cards; Games; Reading groups; Prayer groups; Movies; Shopping trips; Social/Cultural gatherings.

San Jose Care & Guidance Center*
401 Ridge Vista Ave, San Jose, CA, 95127
(408) 923-7232
Admin Yvonne Molanan. *Medical Dir/Dir of Nursing* Dr Mayerle.
Licensure Skilled care; Special Treatment Program. *Beds* 116. *Certified* Medi-Cal.
Owner Proprietary Corp (Beverly Enterprises).
Admissions Requirements Minimum age 21.
Staff Physicians 2 (ft); RNs 6 (ft), 2 (pt); LPNs 8 (ft), 4 (pt).
Facilities Dining room; Activities room; Crafts room.
Activities Arts & crafts; Cards; Games; Prayer groups; Movies; Shopping trips; Social/Cultural gatherings.

San Tomas Convalescent Hospital*
3580 Payne Ave, San Jose, CA, 95117
(408) 248-7100
Admin Alice K Mau.
Licensure Skilled care. *Beds* 70. *Certified* Medicare; Medi-Cal.
Owner Proprietary Corp.

Skyline Convalescent Hospital*
2065 Forest Ave, San Jose, CA, 95128
(408) 298-3950
Admin Mary MacPherson.
Licensure Skilled care. *Beds* 277. *Certified* Medicare; Medi-Cal.
Owner Proprietary Corp (ARA Living Centers).

Westgate Convalescent Center
1601 Petersen Ave, San Jose, CA, 95129-4898
(408) 253-7502
Admin Ron McKaigg. *Medical Dir/Dir of Nursing* Steven Tilles MD; Gracia Barerra RN DON.
Licensure Skilled care. *Beds* SNF 268. *Certified* Medicare; Medi-Cal.
Owner Proprietary Corp (Beverly Enterprises).
Admissions Requirements Minimum age 18; Medical examination; Physician's request.
Staff Physicians 1 (pt); RNs 13 (ft), 7 (pt); LPNs 17 (ft), 7 (pt); Nurses aides 66 (ft), 18 (pt); Physical therapists 1 (pt); Recreational therapists 1 (ft); Occupational therapists 1 (pt); Speech therapists 1 (pt); Dietitians 1 (ft); Dentists 1 (pt); Ophthalmologists 1 (pt); Podiatrists 1 (pt).
Languages Spanish, Russian, Polish
Facilities Dining room; Physical therapy room; Activities room; Crafts room; Barber/Beauty shop; Library.
Activities Arts & crafts; Cards; Games; Reading groups; Prayer groups; Movies; Shopping trips; Social/Cultural gatherings.

Willow Glen Convalescent Hospital Rest Care Center*
1267 Meridian Ave, San Jose, CA, 95125
(408) 265-4211
Admin Helen K Kim.
Licensure Skilled care. *Beds* 152. *Certified* Medicare; Medi-Cal.
Owner Proprietary Corp.

Winchester Living Center
1250 S Winchester Blvd, San Jose, CA, 95128
(408) 241-8666
Admin Chuck Reed. *Medical Dir/Dir of Nursing* Mark Campbell MD; Patricia Fitzgerald RN DON.

Licensure Skilled care. *Beds* SNF 166.
Certified Medicare; Medi-Cal.
Owner Proprietary Corp (ARA Living Centers).
Staff Physicians 1 (pt); RNs 4 (ft), 6 (pt); LPNs 12 (ft); Nurses aides 61 (ft); Physical therapists 1 (ft); Occupational therapists 1 (ft), 1 (pt); Speech therapists 1 (ft), 1 (pt); Activities coordinators 1 (ft); Dietitians 1 (pt); Ophthalmologists 1 (pt); Dentist 1 (pt).
Facilities Dining room; Physical therapy room; Activities room; Laundry room; Barber/Beauty shop; Protected patios.
Activities Arts & crafts; Cards; Games; Reading groups; Prayer groups; Movies; Shopping trips; Social/Cultural gatherings; Live Oak community & core groups; In-room activities; BBQs.

SAN LEANDRO

Bancroft Convalescent Hospital*
1475 Bancroft Ave, San Leandro, CA, 94577
(415) 483-1680
Admin Edith E Parrott.
Licensure Skilled care. *Beds* 39. *Certified* Medicare; Medi-Cal.
Owner Proprietary Corp.

Jones Rest Home & Convalescent Hospital
524 Callan Ave, San Leandro, CA, 94577
(415) 483-6200
Admin C Charles Monedero. *Medical Dir/Dir of Nursing* Steven Rosenthal MD; Santiago Hayo RN.
Licensure Skilled care; Residential care. *Beds* SNF 25; Residential 23.
Owner Proprietary Corp.
Admissions Requirements Medical examination; Physician's request.
Staff RNs 1 (ft), 3 (pt); LPNs 2 (ft), 2 (pt); Nurses aides 6 (ft), 4 (pt); Activities coordinators 1 (ft); Dietitians 1 (pt).
Facilities Dining room; Activities room; Crafts room; Laundry room; Barber/Beauty shop.
Activities Arts & crafts; Cards; Games; Prayer groups; Movies; Social/Cultural gatherings; Musical programs; Exercise classes; Bingo.

Parkland Convalescent Hospital Inc
1440 168th Ave, San Leandro, CA, 94578
(415) 278-4323
Admin Jennifer Okamoto. *Medical Dir/Dir of Nursing* Esther LaPorte.
Licensure Skilled care. *Beds* SNF 176. *Certified* Medicaid; Medicare; Medi-Cal.
Owner Proprietary Corp (ARA Living Centers).
Admissions Requirements Physician's request.
Staff RNs; LPNs; Orderlies; Nurses aides; Activities coordinators.
Facilities Dining room; Physical therapy room; Activities room; Crafts room; Laundry room; Barber/Beauty shop.
Activities Arts & crafts; Cards; Games; Reading groups; Prayer groups; Movies; Shopping trips; Social/Cultural gatherings; Baseball game trips.

St Luke's Extended Care Hospital & Nursing Centre
1652 Mono Ave, San Leandro, CA, 94578
(413) 357-5351
Admin Guy R Seaton. *Medical Dir/Dir of Nursing* Andrew May MD; Jacqueline L Seaton DON.
Licensure Skilled care. *Beds* SNF 72. *Certified* Medicare; Medi-Cal.
Owner Privately owned.
Admissions Requirements Physician's request.
Staff Physicians 20 (pt); RNs 10 (ft), 10 (pt); LPNs 12 (ft), 10 (pt); Nurses aides 40 (ft), 10 (pt); Physical therapists 1 (pt); Recreational therapists 2 (ft); Occupational therapists 1 (pt); Speech therapists 1 (pt);

Activities coordinators 1 (ft); Dietitians 1 (ft); Dentists 1 (pt); Ophthalmologists 1 (pt); Podiatrists 1 (pt); 5 (ft), 5 (pt).
Facilities Dining room; Physical therapy room; Activities room; Laundry room; Library.
Activities Arts & crafts; Cards; Games; Reading groups; Prayer groups; Movies; Shopping trips; Social/Cultural gatherings.

San Leandro Convalescent Hospital*
368 Juana Ave, San Leandro, CA, 94577
(415) 357-4015
Admin Emery E Reuss.
Licensure Skilled care. *Beds* 59. *Certified* Medicare; Medi-Cal.
Owner Proprietary Corp (Hillhaven Corp).

Washington Convalescent Hospital*
2274 Washington Ave, San Leandro, CA, 94577
(415) 483-7671
Admin Juanita V Norman.
Licensure Skilled care. *Beds* 25. *Certified* Medicare.
Owner Proprietary Corp.

Washington Manor Convalescent Hospital*
14766 Washington, San Leandro, CA, 94578
(415) 352-2211
Admin Hugh B Herring.
Licensure Skilled care. *Beds* 99. *Certified* Medicare; Medi-Cal.
Owner Proprietary Corp (Care Enterprises).

SAN LUIS OBISPO

Cabrillo Extended Care Hospital*
3033 Augusta St, San Luis Obispo, CA, 93401
(805) 544-5100
Admin Wayne A Evans.
Licensure Intermediate care. *Beds* 162. *Certified* Medicare; Medi-Cal.
Owner Proprietary Corp.

Casa De Vida
879 Meinecke St, San Luis Obispo, CA, 93401
(805) 544-5332
Admin George Brudney. *Medical Dir/Dir of Nursing* Barbara Wisehart DON.
Licensure Intermediate care for mentally retarded. *Beds* ICF/MR 99. *Certified* Medi-Cal.
Owner Proprietary Corp.
Admissions Requirements Minimum age 18; Medical examination.
Staff Physicians 1 (pt); RNs 3 (ft); LPNs 5 (ft); Nurses aides 30 (ft); Physical therapists 1 (pt); Recreational therapists 1 (pt); Occupational therapists 1 (pt); Speech therapists 1 (pt); Dietitians 1 (ft), 1 (pt).
Languages Spanish
Facilities Dining room; Physical therapy room; Activities room; Crafts room; Laundry room; Barber/Beauty shop; Clothing-work shop; Garden.
Activities Arts & crafts; Games; Reading groups; Movies; Shopping trips; Social/Cultural gatherings; Camping; Swimming; Boating.

Hillhaven Care Center
1425 Woodside Dr, San Luis Obispo, CA, 93401
(805) 543-0210
Admin Brian Johnson. *Medical Dir/Dir of Nursing* Roger Steele MD; Norma Jean Kelly RN.
Licensure Skilled care. *Beds* SNF 162. *Certified* Medicare; Medi-Cal.
Owner Proprietary Corp (Hillhaven Corp).
Admissions Requirements Medical examination; Physician's request.
Facilities Dining room; Physical therapy room; Activities room; Crafts room; Barber/Beauty shop.

Activities Arts & crafts; Cards; Games; Reading groups; Movies; Social/Cultural gatherings.

SAN MATEO

Brookside Convalescent Hospital
2620 Flores St, San Mateo, CA, 94033
(415) 349-2161
Admin Valerie Capone RN. *Medical Dir/Dir of Nursing* Dr Donald Jaffe; Mary Rollins RN.
Licensure Skilled care. *Beds* 100. *Certified* Medicare; Medi-Cal.
Owner Nonprofit Corp.
Admissions Requirements Physician's request.
Staff RNs 6 (ft), 10 (pt); LPNs 1 (ft), 1 (pt); Orderlies 1 (ft); Nurses aides 30 (ft), 7 (pt); Activities coordinators 2 (ft).
Languages German, Spanish, Russian, Polish, Tagalog, Yugoslavian.
Facilities Dining room; Physical therapy room; Activities room; Crafts room; Laundry room; Barber/Beauty shop.
Activities Arts & crafts; Cards; Games; Reading groups; Prayer groups; Movies; Shopping trips; Social/Cultural gatherings; Flower arranging; Gardening.

Hillsdale Manor Convalescent Hospital*
2883 S Norfolk St, San Mateo, CA, 94403
(415) 341-8781
Admin Leona Kuhl. *Medical Dir/Dir of Nursing* Dr Donald Jaffe.
Licensure Skilled care. *Beds* 59. *Certified* Medicare; Medi-Cal.
Owner Proprietary Corp.
Admissions Requirements Medical examination; Physician's request.
Staff Physicians 1 (pt); RNs 4 (ft), 1 (pt); LPNs 2 (ft), 3 (pt); Nurses aides 17 (ft), 6 (pt); Physical therapists 1 (pt); Activities coordinators 1 (ft); Dietitians 1 (pt); Dentists 1 (pt); Podiatrists 1 (pt).
Facilities Dining room; Physical therapy room; Activities room; Crafts room; Laundry room; Barber/Beauty shop; Library; Enclosed patio.
Activities Arts & crafts; Cards; Games; Reading groups; Prayer groups; Movies; Shopping trips; Social/Cultural gatherings.

San Mateo Convalescent Hospital
453 N San Mateo Dr, San Mateo, CA, 94401
(415) 342-6255
Admin Betty J Frint. *Medical Dir/Dir of Nursing* Robert George Spencer MD; Irene Breining RN DON.
Licensure Skilled care. *Beds* SNF 34. *Certified* Medicare.
Owner Privately owned.
Admissions Requirements Physician's request.
Staff RNs 3 (ft), 3 (pt); LPNs 2 (ft), 1 (pt); Nurses aides 14 (ft), 3 (pt); Activities coordinators 1 (ft), 2 (pt); 1 (ft) Food supervisor; Housekeeping supervisor.
Facilities Multipurpose room.
Activities Arts & crafts; Cards; Games; Reading groups; Prayer groups; Movies; Social/Cultural gatherings.

SAN PABLO

Church Lane Convalescent Hospital
1900 Church Ln, San Pablo, CA, 94806
(415) 235-5514
Admin Sandra D Cassidy. *Medical Dir/Dir of Nursing* V T Archibald MD; Karenlouise Johnson RN DON.
Licensure Skilled care. *Beds* SNF 80. *Certified* Medicare; Private.
Owner Proprietary Corp.
Admissions Requirements Medical examination; Physician's request.
Languages Spanish, Tagalog

Facilities Dining room; Activities room; Crafts room; Laundry room; Barber/Beauty shop.
Activities Arts & crafts; Cards; Games; Reading groups; Movies; Shopping trips; Social/Cultural gatherings.

Greenvale Convalescent Hospital*
2140 Vale Rd, San Pablo, CA, 94806
(415) 235-1052
Admin Eric Mawson.
Licensure Skilled care. *Beds* 57. *Certified* Medicare; Medi-Cal.
Owner Proprietary Corp.

Hillhaven-Brookvue Convalescent Hospital
13328 San Pablo Ave, San Pablo, CA, 94806
(415) 235-3720
Admin William Kruse. *Medical Dir/Dir of Nursing* Marilyn White.
Licensure Skilled care. *Beds* SNF 108. *Certified* Medicare; Medi-Cal.
Owner Proprietary Corp (Hillhaven Corp).
Staff Physicians 1 (pt); RNs 3 (ft), 3 (pt); LPNs 8 (ft), 5 (pt); Orderlies 2 (pt); Nurses aides 24 (ft), 20 (pt); Physical therapists 1 (ft), 1 (pt); Reality therapists 1 (pt); Recreational therapists 1 (ft); Occupational therapists 1 (ft); Speech therapists 1 (ft); Activities coordinators 1 (ft); Dietitians 1 (pt); Dentists 1 (pt); Ophthalmologists 1 (pt); Podiatrists 1 (pt);; Chaplain 1 (pt).
Languages Spanish, German
Facilities Dining room; Physical therapy room; Activities room; Laundry room; Barber/Beauty shop; Library.
Activities Arts & crafts; Cards; Games; Reading groups; Prayer groups; Movies; Shopping trips; Social/Cultural gatherings.

Monterey Care Center*
13484 San Pablo Ave, San Pablo, CA, 94806
(415) 237-5711
Admin Paul D Tunnell.
Licensure Skilled care. *Beds* 202.
Owner Proprietary Corp.

SAN PEDRO

Harbor View House*
921 S Beacon St, San Pedro, CA, 90731
(213) 547-2402
Admin James Crumpler.
Licensure Intermediate care. *Beds* 83. *Certified* Medi-Cal.
Owner Nonprofit Corp.

Little Sisters of the Poor
2100 S Western Ave, San Pedro, CA, 90732
(213) 548-0625
Admin Sr Kathleen Bartz. *Medical Dir/Dir of Nursing* Asa Hubbard MD.
Licensure Skilled care; Intermediate care. *Beds* SNF 48; ICF 48. *Certified* Medi-Cal.
Owner Nonprofit Corp.
Admissions Requirements Minimum age 60; Medical examination.
Affiliation Roman Catholic
Facilities Dining room; Physical therapy room; Activities room; Chapel; Crafts room; Laundry room; Barber/Beauty shop; Library; Medical offices; Country store; Ice cream parlor.
Activities Arts & crafts; Cards; Games; Reading groups; Prayer groups; Movies; Shopping trips; Social/Cultural gatherings.

Los Palos Convalescent Hospital
1430 W 6th St, San Pedro, CA, 90732
(213) 832-6431
Admin J S Valdomar. *Medical Dir/Dir of Nursing* Robert Lewis MD; Ric DeGuia DON.
Licensure Skilled care. *Beds* SNF 99. *Certified* Medicare; Medi-Cal.
Owner Proprietary Corp.
Admissions Requirements Medical examination; Physician's request.

Staff RNs 5 (ft); LPNs 6 (ft); Orderlies 6 (ft); Nurses aides 35 (ft); Physical therapists 1 (ft); Recreational therapists 1 (ft); Occupational therapists 1 (ft); Speech therapists 1 (ft); Activities coordinators 1 (ft); Dietitians 1 (ft); Ophthalmologists 1 (ft).
Facilities Dining room; Physical therapy room; Activities room; Laundry room; Barber/Beauty shop.
Activities Arts & crafts; Cards; Games; Reading groups; Prayer groups; Movies; Social/Cultural gatherings.

San Pedro Peninsula Hospital Pavilion
1322 W 6th St, San Pedro, CA, 90732
(213) 514-5270
Admin Rodney Aymond. *Medical Dir/Dir of Nursing* Dr S Stock, Dr F Workman, Dr H Webb; Rose Forbish RN DON.
Licensure Skilled care; Sub-acute. *Beds* SNF 128. *Certified* Medicare; Medi-Cal.
Owner Nonprofit Corp.
Staff Physicians 3 (pt); RNs 2 (ft), 1 (pt); LPNs 9 (ft); Nurses aides 36 (ft); Physical therapists 1 (ft); Activities coordinators 2 (ft); Dietitians 1 (pt).
Facilities Dining room; Physical therapy room; Activities room; Laundry room; Barber/Beauty shop.
Activities Arts & crafts; Cards; Games; Reading groups; Movies; Shopping trips; Social/Cultural gatherings.

Seacrest Convalescent Hospital
1416 W 6th St, San Pedro, CA, 90732
(213) 833-3526
Admin Jose S Valdomar. *Medical Dir/Dir of Nursing* James Schmidt; Eli Nacconales.
Licensure Skilled care. *Beds* SNF 80. *Certified* Medicaid; Medicare; Medi-Cal.
Owner Proprietary Corp.
Admissions Requirements Physician's request.
Staff RNs; LPNs; Orderlies; Nurses aides; Activities coordinators; Social worker.
Facilities Dining room; Activities room; Laundry room; Barber/Beauty shop.
Activities Arts & crafts; Games; Reading groups; Prayer groups.

SAN RAFAEL

Aldersly Inc—Danish Home Senior Citizens
326 Mission Ave, San Rafael, CA, 94901
(415) 453-7425
Admin Stephanie Sutton. *Medical Dir/Dir of Nursing* Dr Fred Yates; Charlene Sharp DON.
Licensure Skilled care; Residential retirement. *Beds* SNF 13; Residential retirement 120.
Owner Nonprofit Corp.
Admissions Requirements Minimum age 62.
Staff Physicians 1 (pt); RNs 1 (ft), 3 (pt); LPNs 2 (ft), 2 (pt); Nurses aides 5 (ft), 2 (pt); Activities coordinators 2 (pt).
Languages Danish
Facilities Dining room; Activities room; Chapel; Crafts room; Laundry room; Barber/Beauty shop; Library; Lounges; Kitchen; Clinic.
Activities Arts & crafts; Cards; Games; Reading groups; Movies; Shopping trips; Social/Cultural gatherings; Educational programs; Health lectures.

Fifth Avenue Convalescent Hospital Inc
1601 5th Ave, San Rafael, CA, 94901
(415) 456-7170
Admin Rocio Rubio. *Medical Dir/Dir of Nursing* Dr Carol Numelstein; Ann Smyth DON.
Licensure Skilled care. *Beds* 57. *Certified* Medicaid; Medicare; Medi-Cal.
Owner Proprietary Corp (Hillhaven Corp).
Admissions Requirements Physician's request.
Staff RNs 1 (ft); LPNs 3 (ft); Nurses aides 13 (ft); Physical therapists 1 (ft); Activities coordinators 1 (ft).
Languages Spanish, French

Facilities Dining room; Physical therapy room; Activities room; Laundry room; Barber/Beauty shop.
Activities Arts & crafts; Cards; Games; Reading groups; Prayer groups; Movies; Shopping trips; Social/Cultural gatherings; Adopt-a-resident.

Hillside Manor Convalescent Hospital*
81 Professional Center Pkwy, San Rafael, CA, 94903
(415) 479-5161
Admin Paul Levesque.
Licensure Skilled care. *Beds* 99.
Owner Proprietary Corp (Hillhaven Corp).

Linda Terra Convalescent Hospital*
45 Professional Center Pkwy, San Rafael, CA, 94903
(415) 479-3610
Admin James McAndrew.
Licensure Skilled care. *Beds* 99. *Certified* Medicare; Medi-Cal.
Owner Proprietary Corp (Beverly Enterprises).

Nazareth House*
245 Nova Albion Way, San Rafael, CA, 94903
(415) 479-8282
Admin Sr Teresa Grant.
Licensure Skilled care. *Beds* 21. *Certified* Medi-Cal.
Owner Nonprofit Corp.

Northgate Convalescent Hospital
40 Professional Pkwy, San Rafael, CA, 94903
(415) 479-1230
Admin Rene Sommer.
Licensure Skilled care. *Beds* SNF 52. *Certified* Medicare; Medi-Cal.
Owner Proprietary Corp.
Admissions Requirements Medical examination; Physician's request.
Staff Physicians 1 (pt); Speech therapists 1 (pt); Activities coordinators 1 (ft); Dietitians 1 (pt); Ophthalmologists 1 (pt).
Facilities Dining room; Physical therapy room; Activities room; Crafts room; Laundry room; Barber/Beauty shop; Library.
Activities Arts & crafts; Cards; Games; Reading groups; Prayer groups; Movies; Social/Cultural gatherings.

Rafael Convalescent Hospital*
234 N San Pedro Rd, San Rafael, CA, 94903
(415) 479-3450
Admin Timothy Egan.
Licensure Skilled care. *Beds* 168. *Certified* Medicare; Medi-Cal.
Owner Proprietary Corp.

SANGER

Maple Grove Intermediate Care Home*
1808 5th St, Sanger, CA, 93657
(209) 875-6110
Admin Donald J Botts Jr.
Licensure Intermediate care. *Beds* 18. *Certified* Medi-Cal.
Owner Proprietary Corp.

Sanger Convalescent Hospital
2550 9th St, Sanger, CA, 93657
(209) 875-6501
Admin Samuel A Macomber.
Licensure Skilled care. *Beds* SNF 99. *Certified* Medicare; Medi-Cal.
Owner Proprietary Corp (Beverly Enterprises).
Staff RNs 3 (ft); LPNs 10 (ft); Orderlies 6 (ft); Nurses aides 46 (ft); Recreational therapists 1 (ft).
Languages Spanish, Chinese
Facilities Dining room; Crafts room; Laundry room; Barber/Beauty shop.
Activities Arts & crafts; Cards; Games; Reading groups; Prayer groups; Movies; Shopping trips; Social/Cultural gatherings.

SANTA ANA

Carehouse Convalescent Center
1800 Old Tustin Rd, Santa Ana, CA, 92701
(714) 835-4900
Admin Ann S Bates. *Medical Dir/Dir of Nursing* Gordon Glasgow MD.
Licensure Skilled care. *Beds* 150. *Certified* Medicare; Medi-Cal.
Owner Proprietary Corp.
Admissions Requirements Medical examination.
Staff RNs 8 (ft), 3 (pt); LPNs 8 (ft), 1 (pt); Orderlies 4 (ft); Nurses aides 57 (ft), 4 (pt); Physical therapists 1 (pt); Activities coordinators 2 (ft); Dietitians 1 (ft).
Facilities Dining room; Physical therapy room; Activities room; Crafts room; Laundry room; Barber/Beauty shop; Library; Transportation van.
Activities Arts & crafts; Cards; Games; Prayer groups; Movies; Shopping trips; Social/ Cultural gatherings; Swimming; Bowling; Tennis; Picnics; Outings; Adopt-a-grandparent.

Chandler Care Center—Bristol*
1209 W Hemlock Way, Santa Ana, CA, 92707
(714) 546-1966
Admin Geertruida Strano.
Licensure Skilled care. *Beds* 146. *Certified* Medicare; Medi-Cal.
Owner Proprietary Corp.

Country Club Convalescent Hospital Inc*
20362 SW Santa Ana Ave, Santa Ana, CA, 92707
(714) 549-3061
Admin Isabel C Hernandez.
Licensure Skilled care. *Beds* 41.
Owner Proprietary Corp.

Hillhaven Convalescent Hospital
2210 E 1st St, Santa Ana, CA, 92705
(714) 547-7091
Admin Jacqueline Lanter. *Medical Dir/Dir of Nursing* Edgar Stewart MD.
Licensure Skilled care. *Beds* 99. *Certified* Medicare; Medi-Cal.
Owner Proprietary Corp (Hillhaven Corp).
Admissions Requirements Physician's request.
Staff RNs 3 (ft), 4 (pt); LPNs 6 (ft), 4 (pt); Orderlies 3 (ft); Nurses aides 28 (ft), 3 (pt); Occupational therapists 1 (ft); Speech therapists 1 (ft); Activities coordinators 1 (ft); Dietitians 1 (ft).
Facilities Dining room; Physical therapy room; Activities room; Laundry room; Barber/Beauty shop; Library.
Activities Arts & crafts; Cards; Games; Prayer groups; Movies; Shopping trips; Social/ Cultural gatherings.

Royale Convalescent Hospital*
1030 W Warner Ave, Santa Ana, CA, 92707
(714) 546-6450
Admin Marshall N Horsman. *Medical Dir/Dir of Nursing* H M Sung MD.
Licensure Skilled care. *Beds* 261. *Certified* Medicare; Medi-Cal.
Owner Proprietary Corp.
Admissions Requirements Minimum age 21; Medical examination; Physician's request.
Staff RNs 10 (ft); LPNs 20 (ft); Orderlies 20 (ft); Nurses aides 60 (ft); Physical therapists 1 (pt); Recreational therapists 2 (ft); Occupational therapists 1 (pt); Speech therapists 1 (ft); Activities coordinators 1 (ft); Dietitians 1 (pt); Dentists 1 (pt); Ophthalmologists 1 (pt); Podiatrists 1 (pt); Audiologists 1 (pt).
Facilities Dining room; Physical therapy room; Activities room; Crafts room; Laundry room; Barber/Beauty shop; Library.

Activities Arts & crafts; Cards; Games; Reading groups; Prayer groups; Movies; Shopping trips; Social/Cultural gatherings; Music therapy; World affairs; Current events; Resident & family councils.

St Edna Convalescent Center
1929 N Fairview St, Santa Ana, CA, 92706
(714) 554-9700
Admin Kathryn T Creeth. *Medical Dir/Dir of Nursing* Gordon A Glasgow MD; Barbara Pirc DON.
Licensure Skilled care. *Beds* SNF 144. *Certified* Medicare; Medi-Cal.
Owner Privately owned.
Admissions Requirements Medical examination; Physician's request.
Staff Physicians 3 (pt); RNs 9 (ft), 1 (pt); LPNs 10 (ft), 2 (pt); Nurses aides 54 (ft), 4 (pt); Physical therapists 2 (pt); Recreational therapists 1 (pt); Occupational therapists 2 (pt); Speech therapists 2 (pt); Activities coordinators 2 (ft); Dietitians 1 (pt); Dentists 1 (pt); Ophthalmologists 1 (pt); Podiatrists 1 (pt);; Social service 1 (ft), 1 (pt).
Facilities Dining room; Physical therapy room; Activities room; Crafts room; Laundry room; Barber/Beauty shop.
Activities Arts & crafts; Cards; Games; Reading groups; Prayer groups; Movies; Shopping trips; Social/Cultural gatherings.

Town & Country Manor Health Care Center*
555 E Memory Ln, Santa Ana, CA, 92706
(714) 547-7581
Admin Gail A Conser. *Medical Dir/Dir of Nursing* S A Kerkhoff MD.
Licensure Skilled care; Intermediate care. *Beds* 122. *Certified* Medicare; Medi-Cal.
Owner Nonprofit Corp.
Admissions Requirements Physician's request.
Staff Physicians 1 (pt); RNs 3 (ft), 5 (pt); LPNs 5 (ft), 3 (pt); Nurses aides 22 (ft), 6 (pt); Activities coordinators 2 (ft); Dietitians 1 (ft).
Facilities Dining room; Physical therapy room; Activities room; Chapel; Crafts room; Laundry room; Barber/Beauty shop; Library.
Activities Arts & crafts; Games; Reading groups; Prayer groups; Movies; Shopping trips.

SANTA BARBARA

Beverly La Cumbre Convalescent Hospital
3880 Via Lucero, Santa Barbara, CA, 93110
(805) 687-6651
Admin Philip Coldwell.
Licensure Skilled care. *Beds* 189.
Owner Proprietary Corp (Beverly Enterprises).

Beverly Manor Convalescent Hospital
2225 de la Vina St, Santa Barbara, CA, 93105
(805) 963-1861
Licensure Skilled care. *Beds* 68. *Certified* Medicare; Medi-Cal.
Owner Proprietary Corp (Beverly Enterprises).

CareWest Santa Barbara
623 W Junipero St, Santa Barbara, CA, 93105
(805) 682-7443
Admin Richard Tovar. *Medical Dir/Dir of Nursing* Paul Aijian; Julie McManus DON.
Licensure Skilled care. *Beds* SNF 137. *Certified* Medicare; Medi-Cal.
Owner Publicly owned.
Staff RNs 9 (ft), 1 (pt); LPNs 5 (ft); Nurses aides 47 (ft); Physical therapists 1 (ft); Occupational therapists 1 (ft); Speech therapists 2 (pt); Activities coordinators 1 (ft); Dietitians 1 (ft).
Languages Spanish
Facilities Dining room; Physical therapy room; Activities room; Laundry room; Barber/Beauty shop.
Activities Arts & crafts; Reading groups; Movies.

Extended Care Hospital of Santa Barbara*
160 S Patterson Ave, Santa Barbara, CA, 93111
(805) 964-4871
Admin W Howard Wortman. *Medical Dir/Dir of Nursing* Paul Aijian MD.
Licensure Skilled care. *Beds* 150. *Certified* Medicare; Medi-Cal.
Owner Proprietary Corp.
Admissions Requirements Medical examination; Physician's request.
Staff RNs 10 (ft), 1 (pt); LPNs 12 (ft); Orderlies 10 (ft); Nurses aides 42 (ft); Physical therapists 1 (ft); Recreational therapists 2 (ft); Occupational therapists 1 (pt); Speech therapists 1 (pt); Activities coordinators 1 (ft); Dietitians 1 (pt); Dentists 1 (pt); Ophthalmologists 1 (pt); Podiatrists 1 (pt); Audiologists 1 (pt).
Facilities Dining room; Physical therapy room; Activities room; Crafts room; Laundry room; Barber/Beauty shop.
Activities Arts & crafts; Cards; Games; Reading groups; Prayer groups; Movies; Shopping trips; Social/Cultural gatherings.

Hillside House Inc*
1235 Veronica Springs Rd, Santa Barbara, CA, 93105
(805) 687-0788
Admin Cecil C Cooprider.
Licensure Skilled care. *Beds* 59. *Certified* Medi-Cal.
Owner Nonprofit Corp.

Samarkand Health Center
2566 Treasure Dr, Santa Barbara, CA, 93105
(805) 687-0701
Admin Wendell Rempel. *Medical Dir/Dir of Nursing* Robert Hartzman MD; Jean Robertson DON.
Licensure Skilled care. *Beds* SNF 59. *Certified* Medicare; Medi-Cal.
Owner Nonprofit Corp.
Admissions Requirements Minimum age 62; Medical examination; Physician's request.
Staff RNs 8 (ft), 2 (pt); LPNs 2 (ft), 1 (pt); Nurses aides 15 (ft), 10 (pt); Activities coordinators 1 (ft); Dietitians 1 (ft).
Languages Spanish, Danish, German
Affiliation Evangelical Covenant Church
Facilities Dining room; Physical therapy room; Activities room; Chapel; Barber/ Beauty shop.
Activities Arts & crafts; Cards; Games; Reading groups; Prayer groups; Movies; Shopping trips; Social/Cultural gatherings.

Santa Barbara Convalescent Hospital*
540 W Pueblo St, Santa Barbara, CA, 93105
(805) 682-7174
Admin Kehar S Johl.
Licensure Skilled care. *Beds* 62. *Certified* Medicare; Medi-Cal.

Valle Verde Health Facility
900 Calle De Los Amigos, Santa Barbara, CA, 93105
(805) 687-1566
Admin Catherine Lee. *Medical Dir/Dir of Nursing* Henry L Holderman MD.
Licensure Skilled care. *Beds* 80. *Certified* Medicare; Medi-Cal.
Owner Nonprofit Corp.
Staff Physicians 4 (pt); RNs 6 (ft), 6 (pt); LPNs 3 (ft), 3 (pt); Nurses aides 18 (ft), 8 (pt); Physical therapists 1 (pt); Activities coordinators 3 (pt); Dietitians 1 (pt); Podiatrists 1 (pt).
Affiliation Baptist
Facilities Dining room; Physical therapy room; Activities room; Chapel; Crafts room; Laundry room; Barber/Beauty shop; Library; Dental clinic; Grocery & variety store.
Activities Arts & crafts; Cards; Games; Reading groups; Prayer groups; Movies; Shopping trips; Social/Cultural gatherings; Resident string quartet; Trips; Putting green.

Vista Del Monte
3775 Modoc Rd, Santa Barbara, CA, 93105
(805) 687-0793
Admin Charles E Frazier. *Medical Dir/Dir of Nursing* Dr James N Fisher MD; Evelyn Bertanyi RN DON.
Licensure Skilled care; Intermediate care. *Beds* SNF 16; ICF 14. *Certified* Medicare; Medi-Cal.
Owner Nonprofit organization/foundation.
Admissions Requirements Minimum age 62; Medical examination.
Staff Physicians 1 (pt); RNs 1 (ft), 7 (pt); LPNs 4 (pt); Nurses aides 8 (ft), 4 (pt); Recreational therapists 1 (ft); Activities coordinators 1 (ft); Gerontologist 1 (pt).
Facilities Dining room; Activities room; Barber/Beauty shop; Lounges for personal "get-togethers"; Large meeting room & main lounge adjacent to dining room.
Activities Arts & crafts; Cards; Games; Reading groups; Movies; Social/Cultural gatherings; Reminiscence groups; Exercise; Motoring; Adaptive education; Cooking & baking.

SANTA CLARA

Hy-Lond Convalescent Hospital*
991 Clyde Ave, Santa Clara, CA, 95050
(408) 988-7666
Admin Bruce Strayer. *Medical Dir/Dir of Nursing* Harry Wong MD.
Licensure Skilled care. *Beds* 200. *Certified* Medicare; Medi-Cal.
Owner Proprietary Corp (Beverly Enterprises).
Admissions Requirements Minimum age 18; Medical examination; Physician's request.
Staff RNs 9 (ft), 2 (pt); LPNs 14 (ft), 6 (pt); Orderlies 21 (ft), 3 (pt); Nurses aides 67 (ft), 8 (pt); Activities coordinators 2 (ft); Dietitians 1 (ft).
Facilities Dining room; Physical therapy room; Activities room; Crafts room; Barber/Beauty shop.
Activities Arts & crafts; Cards; Games; Reading groups; Prayer groups; Movies; Shopping trips; Social/Cultural gatherings.

Mission Skilled Nursing Facility*
410 N Winchester Blvd, Santa Clara, CA, 95050
(408) 248-3736
Admin Larry Blitz.
Licensure Skilled care. *Beds* 111. *Certified* Medicare; Medi-Cal.
Owner Proprietary Corp.

SANTA CLARITA

Santa Clarita Convalescent Hospital
23801 San Fernando Rd, Santa Clarita, CA, 91321
(818) 365-9138
Admin Jean Priestman. *Medical Dir/Dir of Nursing* Karen Ansell RN.
Licensure Skilled care. *Beds* 99. *Certified* Medicare; Medi-Cal.
Owner Proprietary Corp.
Admissions Requirements Physician's request.
Staff Physicians; RNs; LPNs; Orderlies; Nurses aides; Physical therapists; Reality therapists; Recreational therapists; Occupational therapists; Speech therapists; Activities coordinators; Dietitians; Dentists; Ophthalmologists; Podiatrists; Social services.
Languages Spanish, German, Czech
Facilities Dining room; Physical therapy room; Activities room; Crafts room; Laundry room; Barber/Beauty shop.
Activities Arts & crafts; Cards; Games; Reading groups; Prayer groups; Movies; Shopping trips; Social/Cultural gatherings.

SANTA CRUZ

Batterson Convalescent Hospital
2555 Mattison Ln, Santa Cruz, CA, 95062
(408) 475-4065
Admin Ruth B Findlay. *Medical Dir/Dir of Nursing* Francis M Jacks MD; Patricia Battels RN DON.
Licensure Skilled care. *Beds* 40. *Certified* Medicare.
Owner Privately owned.
Admissions Requirements Minimum age 18; Medical examination; Physician's request.
Staff RNs 3 (ft), 3 (pt); LPNs 2 (pt); Nurses aides 15 (ft), 2 (pt); Activities coordinators 1 (ft).
Languages Spanish
Facilities Dining room; Activities room; Crafts room; Library.
Activities Arts & crafts; Cards; Games; Reading groups; Prayer groups; Movies; Social/Cultural gatherings.

Brommer Manor*
2000 Brommer St, Santa Cruz, CA, 95060
(408) 476-5500
Admin Norma K Colby.
Licensure Skilled care. *Beds* 38. *Certified* Medicare; Medi-Cal.
Owner Proprietary Corp.
Activities Arts & crafts; Cards; Games; Reading groups; Movies; Shopping trips; Social/Cultural gatherings.

Cresthaven Inc
740 17th Ave, Santa Cruz, CA, 95062
(408) 475-3812
Admin Romeo Hernandez. *Medical Dir/Dir of Nursing* Dr John Catlin; Ruth Hernandez.
Licensure Skilled care. *Beds* 20. *Certified* Medi-Cal.
Owner Proprietary Corp.
Admissions Requirements Minimum age 60; Medical examination.
Staff Physicians 1 (pt); RNs 2 (ft), 2 (pt); LPNs 2 (ft), 1 (pt); Nurses aides 5 (ft), 2 (pt); Recreational therapists 1 (pt); Activities coordinators 1 (ft), 1 (pt); Dietitians 1 (ft), 1 (pt); Dentists 1 (pt); Ophthalmologists 1 (pt); Podiatrists 1 (pt).
Facilities Dining room; Activities room; Chapel; Crafts room; Laundry room; Barber/Beauty shop.
Activities Arts & crafts; Cards; Games; Reading groups; Prayer groups; Movies; Shopping trips; Social/Cultural gatherings.

Cypress Care Center of Santa Cruz
1098 38th Ave, Santa Cruz, CA, 95060
(408) 475-6900
Admin Nancy L Hopp. *Medical Dir/Dir of Nursing* Dr Martin.
Licensure Skilled care. *Beds* 99. *Certified* Medicare.
Owner Proprietary Corp.
Staff RNs 3 (ft), 3 (pt); LPNs 6 (ft), 4 (pt); Orderlies 4 (ft); Nurses aides 35 (ft), 15 (pt); Recreational therapists 1 (ft), 1 (pt); Activities coordinators.
Facilities Dining room; Physical therapy room; Activities room; Crafts room; Laundry room; Barber/Beauty shop.
Activities Arts & crafts; Cards; Games; Reading groups; Prayer groups; Movies; Shopping trips.

Driftwood Convalescent Hospital*
675 24th Ave, Santa Cruz, CA, 95060
(408) 475-6323
Admin Elizabeth P Byrne. *Medical Dir/Dir of Nursing* Dr Allan Martin.
Licensure Skilled care. *Beds* 92. *Certified* Medicare; Medi-Cal.
Owner Proprietary Corp (ARA Living Centers).
Admissions Requirements Minimum age 18.

Staff RNs 5 (ft); LPNs 4 (ft); Orderlies 4 (ft); Nurses aides 35 (ft); Occupational therapists 1 (pt); Speech therapists 1 (pt); Activities coordinators 1 (ft); Dietitians 1 (ft); Dentists 1 (pt); Ophthalmologists 1 (pt); Podiatrists 1 (pt); Audiologists 1 (pt).
Facilities Dining room; Physical therapy room; Activities room; Crafts room; Laundry room; Barber/Beauty shop.
Activities Arts & crafts; Cards; Games; Reading groups; Prayer groups; Movies.

Garden Nursing Home & Convalescent Hospital*
1410 Ocean St, Santa Cruz, CA, 95062
(408) 423-6045
Admin Cheryl A Mitchum.
Licensure Skilled care. *Beds* 55. *Certified* Medicare; Medi-Cal.
Owner Proprietary Corp.

Harbor Hills*
1171 7th Ave, Santa Cruz, CA, 95062
(408) 476-1700
Admin Joyce Bahnsen. *Medical Dir/Dir of Nursing* Ron Krasner MD.
Licensure Skilled care. *Beds* 99. *Certified* Medi-Cal.
Owner Proprietary Corp.
Admissions Requirements Minimum age 18; Physician's request.
Staff Physicians 5 (pt); RNs 3 (ft), 1 (pt); LPNs 5 (ft), 5 (pt); Nurses aides 32 (ft), 12 (pt); Activities coordinators 1 (ft); Dietitians 1 (ft); Dentists 1 (pt).
Facilities Dining room; Activities room; Crafts room; Laundry room; Barber/Beauty shop; Library; TV room.
Activities Arts & crafts; Cards; Games; Movies; Shopping trips; Social/Cultural gatherings.

Hillhaven Extended Care Hospital
1115 Capitola Rd, Santa Cruz, CA, 95060
(408) 475-4055
Admin Marise Goetzl. *Medical Dir/Dir of Nursing* Dr Anthony Tyler; Candace Eiseman RN.
Licensure Skilled care. *Beds* 149. *Certified* Medicare; Medi-Cal.
Owner Proprietary Corp (Hillhaven Corp).
Admissions Requirements Medical examination; Physician's request.
Staff RNs 3 (ft); LPNs 6 (ft); Nurses aides 32 (ft); Physical therapists 1 (ft); Occupational therapists 1 (ft); Speech therapists 1 (ft); Activities coordinators 2 (ft); Dietitians 1 (ft); Dentists 1 (ft); Ophthalmologists 1 (ft); Podiatrists 1 (ft); Dentist 1 (ft).
Facilities Dining room; Physical therapy room; Activities room; Crafts room; Laundry room; Barber/Beauty shop; Library.
Activities Arts & crafts; Cards; Games; Reading groups; Prayer groups; Movies; Social/Cultural gatherings.

Live Oak Skilled Nursing & Manor
2990 Soquel Ave, Santa Cruz, CA, 95060
(408) 475-8832
Admin Charlene Henion. *Medical Dir/Dir of Nursing* Allen Martin MD.
Licensure Skilled care; Intermediate care. *Beds* SNF 121; ICF 93. *Certified* Medicare.
Owner Proprietary Corp.
Staff Physicians 35 (pt); RNs 6 (ft), 4 (pt); LPNs 13 (ft), 6 (pt); Orderlies 11 (ft), 4 (pt); Nurses aides 28 (ft), 14 (pt); Physical therapists 2 (pt); Reality therapists 1 (ft); Recreational therapists 5 (ft), 2 (pt); Occupational therapists 1 (pt); Speech therapists 1 (pt); Activities coordinators 1 (ft); Dietitians 1 (pt); Dentists 1 (pt); Ophthalmologists 1 (pt); Podiatrists 1 (pt); Dentist 1 (pt).
Facilities Dining room; Physical therapy room; Activities room; Chapel; Crafts room; Laundry room; Barber/Beauty shop; Library.

Activities Arts & crafts; Cards; Games; Reading groups; Movies; Social/Cultural gatherings.

Rose Crest Nursing Home
PO Box 2128, 941 El Dorado Ave, Santa Cruz, CA, 95063-2128
(408) 475-7544
Admin Beverly Lowland. *Medical Dir/Dir of Nursing* Dr Allen Martin.
Beds 28. *Certified* Medi-Cal.
Owner Proprietary Corp.
Admissions Requirements Minimum age 50.
Staff RNs 1 (ft), 3 (pt); LPNs 2 (ft), 5 (pt); Nurses aides 5 (ft), 10 (pt); Activities coordinators 1 (pt); Dietitians 1 (ft), 3 (pt).
Facilities Dining room; Activities room; Laundry room.
Activities Arts & crafts; Cards; Games; Reading groups; Movies; Shopping trips; Social/Cultural gatherings.

SANTA MARIA

Continana Convalescent Hospital
830 E Chapel, Santa Maria, CA, 93454
(805) 922-6657
Admin James G Golden. *Medical Dir/Dir of Nursing* Victoria Collatz MD; Joan Hankin RN DON.
Licensure Skilled care. *Beds* 59. *Certified* Medicare; Medi-Cal.
Admissions Requirements Minimum age 16; Medical examination; Physician's request.
Staff Physicians 1 (pt); RNs 5 (ft), 4 (pt); Orderlies 3 (ft); Nurses aides 20 (ft), 3 (pt); Physical therapists 1 (pt); Reality therapists 1 (pt); Recreational therapists 1 (pt); Occupational therapists 1 (pt); Speech therapists 1 (pt); Activities coordinators 1 (ft); Dietitians 1 (pt); Dentists 1 (pt); Ophthalmologists 1 (pt); Podiatrists 1 (pt); Dentist 1 (pt); LVNs 3 (ft), 3 (pt).
Facilities Dining room; Physical therapy room; Activities room; Crafts room; Laundry room; Barber/Beauty shop.
Activities Arts & crafts; Cards; Games; Reading groups; Prayer groups; Movies; Shopping trips; Social/Cultural gatherings.

Kimberly Convalescent Hospital*
820 W Cook St, Santa Maria, CA, 93454
(805) 925-8877
Admin Carroll Silvera.
Licensure Skilled care. *Beds* 55. *Certified* Medicare; Medi-Cal.
Owner Proprietary Corp.

Villa Maria Convalescent Hospital*
425 E Barcellus, Santa Maria, CA, 93454
(805) 922-3558
Admin Laurie Osborn-Smith. *Medical Dir/Dir of Nursing* Joseph Cohan MD.
Licensure Skilled care. *Beds* 88. *Certified* Medicare; Medi-Cal.
Owner Proprietary Corp.
Staff Physicians 1 (ft); RNs 7 (ft), 2 (pt); Orderlies 6 (ft); Nurses aides 37 (ft); Physical therapists 1 (pt); Reality therapists 1 (pt); Recreational therapists 1 (pt); Occupational therapists 1 (pt); Speech therapists 1 (pt); Activities coordinators 1 (ft); Dietitians 1 (pt); Dentists 1 (pt); Ophthalmologists 1 (pt); Podiatrists 1 (pt); Audiologists 1 (pt); LVNs 6 (ft), 3 (pt).
Facilities Dining room; Physical therapy room; Activities room; Crafts room; Laundry room; Barber/Beauty shop; Library.
Activities Arts & crafts; Cards; Games; Reading groups; Prayer groups; Movies; Shopping trips; Social/Cultural gatherings; Monthly luncheons; Holiday programs.

SANTA MONICA

Bay Vista Convalescent Hospital*
1338 20th St, Santa Monica, CA, 90404
(213) 870-9761
Admin Piraro Donnell.
Licensure Skilled care. *Beds* 154. *Certified* Medicare; Medi-Cal.
Owner Proprietary Corp (ARA Living Centers).

Berkley East Convalescent Hospital
2021 Arizona Ave, Santa Monica, CA, 90404
(213) 451-4748
Admin Paul Bartolucci.
Licensure Skilled care. *Beds* 235. *Certified* Medicare.
Owner Proprietary Corp.

Berkley West Convalescent Hospital
1623 Arizona Ave, Santa Monica, CA, 90404
(213) 829-4565
Admin Steven Galper. *Medical Dir/Dir of Nursing* Kathryn J Ghavamian RN.
Licensure Skilled care. *Beds* SNF 54. *Certified* Medicare.
Owner Proprietary Corp.
Admissions Requirements Minimum age 21; Physician's request.
Staff RNs 2 (ft); LPNs 4 (ft), 3 (pt); Orderlies 3 (ft); Nurses aides 25 (ft); Physical therapists 2 (pt); Reality therapists 1 (pt); Recreational therapists 11 (pt); Occupational therapists 1 (pt); Speech therapists 1 (pt); Activities coordinators 1 (ft); Dietitians 1 (ft); Ophthalmologists 1 (pt); Podiatrists 1 (pt).
Languages Spanish
Facilities Dining room; Activities room; Crafts room; Laundry room; Barber/Beauty shop; Patio with fish pond.
Activities Arts & crafts; Cards; Games; Reading groups; Prayer groups; Movies; Paid entertainers; Birthday parties for patients & staff.

Berkshire, A Skilled Nursing Facility*
2602 Broadway, Santa Monica, CA, 90404
(213) 453-8816
Admin William K Kolodin. *Medical Dir/Dir of Nursing* James H Shumaker MD.
Licensure Skilled care. *Beds* 33.
Owner Proprietary Corp.
Admissions Requirements Minimum age 62.
Staff RNs 1 (ft), 2 (pt); LPNs 2 (ft), 2 (pt); Nurses aides 12 (ft), 3 (pt); Physical therapists 1 (pt); Recreational therapists 1 (pt); Occupational therapists 1 (pt); Speech therapists 1 (pt); Activities coordinators 1 (ft), 1 (pt); Dietitians 1 (pt); Dentists 1 (pt); Ophthalmologists 1 (pt); Podiatrists 1 (pt); Audiologists Dentist 1 (pt).
Facilities Dining room; Activities room; Laundry room; Barber/Beauty shop.
Activities Arts & crafts; Cards; Games; Prayer groups; Movies; Social/Cultural gatherings; BBQs; Emeritus college classes.

Beverly Manor Convalescent Hospital*
1340 15th St, Santa Monica, CA, 90404
(213) 451-9706
Admin James Scadlock.
Licensure Skilled care. *Beds* 227. *Certified* Medicare; Medi-Cal.
Owner Proprietary Corp (Beverly Enterprises).

CareWest Arizona Nursing Center
1330 17th St, Santa Monica, CA, 90404
(213) 829-5411
Admin Jane Anderson. *Medical Dir/Dir of Nursing* Betty Henry.
Licensure Skilled care. *Beds* 72. *Certified* Medicare; Medi-Cal.
Owner Proprietary Corp (Care Enterprises).
Admissions Requirements Minimum age 60.

Staff RNs 1 (ft), 3 (pt); LPNs 9 (ft), 3 (pt); Orderlies 3 (ft); Nurses aides 30 (ft), 5 (pt); Physical therapists 1 (ft); Occupational therapists 1 (pt); Speech therapists 1 (pt); Activities coordinators 1 (ft).
Languages Spanish
Facilities Dining room; Physical therapy room; Activities room; Laundry room; Barber/Beauty shop.
Activities Arts & crafts; Cards; Games; Reading groups; Prayer groups; Movies; Social/Cultural gatherings.

Crescent Bay Convalescent Hospital*
1437 14th St, Santa Monica, CA, 90404
(213) 394-3726
Admin Sherman Miller.
Licensure Skilled care. *Beds* 69. *Certified* Medicare; Medi-Cal.
Owner Proprietary Corp.

Fireside Convalescent Hospital*
947 3rd St, Santa Monica, CA, 90403
(213) 393-0475
Admin N R Chivi.
Licensure Skilled care. *Beds* 66. *Certified* Medicare; Medi-Cal.
Owner Proprietary Corp.

Good Shepherd Convalescent Hospital*
1131 Arizona Ave, Santa Monica, CA, 90404
(213) 451-4809
Admin Paul W Cosgrove.
Licensure Skilled care. *Beds* 48. *Certified* Medicare; Medi-Cal.
Owner Proprietary Corp.

Santa Monica Care Convalescent Hospital*
1321 Franklin, Santa Monica, CA, 90404
(213) 828-5597
Admin Stephen Fitch. *Medical Dir/Dir of Nursing* Victor Wylie MD.
Licensure Skilled care. *Beds* 59. *Certified* Medicare; Medi-Cal.
Owner Proprietary Corp (Care Enterprises).
Staff RNs 1 (ft), 4 (pt); Orderlies 2 (ft), 1 (pt); Nurses aides 9 (ft), 4 (pt); Physical therapists 1 (ft); Occupational therapists 1 (pt); Speech therapists 1 (pt); Activities coordinators 1 (ft); Dentists 1 (pt); Podiatrists 1 (pt); Audiologists 1 (pt).
Facilities Dining room; Physical therapy room; Activities room; Barber/Beauty shop.
Activities Arts & crafts; Cards; Games; Prayer groups; Movies.

Santa Monica Convalarium
1320 20th St, Santa Monica, CA, 90404
(213) 829-4301
Admin Carol Wagner. *Medical Dir/Dir of Nursing* Phillip Rossman MD; Julanne Rias RN DON.
Licensure Skilled care. *Beds* SNF 59. *Certified* Medicare.
Owner Proprietary Corp (American Medical Services Inc).
Admissions Requirements Physician's request.
Staff Physicians 50 (pt); RNs 4 (ft), 4 (pt); LPNs 4 (pt); Orderlies 1 (ft), 1 (pt); Nurses aides 18 (ft), 10 (pt); Physical therapists 1 (pt); Reality therapists 1 (pt); Recreational therapists 1 (pt); Occupational therapists 1 (pt); Speech therapists 1 (pt); Activities coordinators 1 (ft), 1 (pt); Dietitians 1 (ft), 1 (pt); Dentists 1 (pt); Ophthalmologists 1 (pt); Podiatrists 1 (pt); Dentist 1 (pt).
Languages Spanish, German
Facilities Dining room; Activities room; Crafts room; Barber/Beauty shop; Library; Patio area.
Activities Arts & crafts; Cards; Games; Movies; Shopping trips; Social/Cultural gatherings; Non-denomination meetings; Adult education.

Santa Monica Lodge*
2250 29th St, Santa Monica, CA, 90405
(213) 450-7694 & 450-7695

Admin Ruth Gelford. *Medical Dir/Dir of Nursing* Paul A Berns MD.
Licensure Skilled care. *Beds* 44. *Certified* Medicare.
Owner Proprietary Corp (Beverly Enterprises).
Admissions Requirements Physician's request.
Staff Physicians 17 (ft); RNs 1 (ft), 3 (pt); LPNs 3 (ft), 5 (pt); Orderlies 1 (ft), 2 (pt); Nurses aides 12 (ft), 1 (pt); Physical therapists 1 (pt); Recreational therapists 1 (pt); Speech therapists 1 (pt); Activities coordinators 1 (pt); Dietitians 1 (pt); Dentists 1 (pt); Ophthalmologists 1 (pt); Podiatrists 1 (pt).
Facilities Dining room; Laundry room; Barber/Beauty shop.
Activities Arts & crafts; Cards; Games; Reading groups; Prayer groups; Movies; Shopping trips; Social/Cultural gatherings.

SANTA PAULA

Santa Paula Healthcare
220 W Main St, Santa Paula, CA, 93060
(805) 525-6621
Admin Marieta Moore. *Medical Dir/Dir of Nursing* Sam Edwards MD; G Paja RN DON.
Licensure Skilled care. *Beds* SNF 49. *Certified* Medicaid; Medicare; Medi-Cal.
Owner Proprietary Corp (Hillhaven Corp).
Admissions Requirements Medical examination; Physician's request.
Staff RNs; LPNs; Nurses aides; Activities coordinators; Dietitians.
Languages Spanish
Facilities Dining room; Activities room; Barber/Beauty shop.
Activities Arts & crafts; Cards; Games; Reading groups; Prayer groups; Movies; Shopping trips; Social/Cultural gatherings.

Twin Pines Healthcare
250 March St, Santa Paula, CA, 93060
(805) 525-7134
Admin Marieta Moore. *Medical Dir/Dir of Nursing* Samuel Edwards MD; Shirley Ebert RN DON.
Licensure Skilled care. *Beds* SNF 99. *Certified* Medicare; Medi-Cal.
Owner Proprietary Corp (Hillhaven Corp).
Admissions Requirements Medical examination; Physician's request.
Staff RNs; LPNs; Nurses aides; Activities coordinators; Dietitians.
Facilities Dining room; Activities room; Crafts room; Laundry room; Barber/Beauty shop.
Activities Arts & crafts; Games; Reading groups; Prayer groups; Movies; Social/Cultural gatherings.

SANTA ROSA

Creekside Convalescent Hospital
850 Sonoma Ave, Santa Rosa, CA, 95404
(707) 544-7750
Admin Robert Bates. *Medical Dir/Dir of Nursing* Dr DeVore; Jackie Englestadt DON.
Licensure Skilled care. *Beds* SNF 181. *Certified* Medicaid; Medicare; Medi-Cal.
Owner Proprietary Corp.
Admissions Requirements Physician's request.
Staff RNs; LPNs; Orderlies; Nurses aides; Recreational therapists; Activities coordinators.
Languages Korean, German, Spanish, Italian
Facilities Dining room; Physical therapy room; Activities room; Crafts room; Laundry room; Barber/Beauty shop; Library.
Activities Arts & crafts; Cards; Games; Reading groups; Prayer groups; Movies; Social/Cultural gatherings.

London House Convalescent Hospital*
4650 Hoen Ave, Santa Rosa, CA, 95405
(707) 546-0471

Admin Jay Underwood. *Medical Dir/Dir of Nursing* Gertrude Van Steyn MD.
Licensure Skilled care. *Beds* 99. *Certified* Medicare; Medi-Cal.
Owner Proprietary Corp (Beverly Enterprises).
Admissions Requirements Medical examination; Physician's request.
Staff RNs 9 (ft); LPNs 6 (ft); Nurses aides 65 (ft); Physical therapists 1 (ft); Recreational therapists 1 (ft); Occupational therapists 1 (pt); Speech therapists 1 (pt); Activities coordinators 1 (ft); Dietitians 1 (ft); Dentists 1 (pt); Ophthalmologists 1 (pt); Podiatrists 1 (pt); Audiologists 1 (pt).
Facilities Dining room; Physical therapy room; Activities room; Chapel; Crafts room; Laundry room; Barber/Beauty shop; Library; TV lounge.
Activities Arts & crafts; Cards; Games; Reading groups; Prayer groups; Movies; Shopping trips; Social/Cultural gatherings.

Maralie Convalescent Hospital
2080 Guerneville Rd, Santa Rosa, CA, 95401
(707) 542-1510
Admin Donald H Bais. *Medical Dir/Dir of Nursing* Dr William Hopper MD.
Licensure Skilled care. *Beds* SNF 52. *Certified* Medicaid; Medicare; Medi-Cal.
Owner Proprietary Corp.
Admissions Requirements Minimum age 18; Physician's request.
Staff RNs 3 (ft), 2 (pt); LPNs 4 (ft), 2 (pt); Orderlies 2 (ft); Nurses aides 15 (ft), 4 (pt); Physical therapists 1 (ft); Activities coordinators 1 (ft), 1 (pt).
Facilities Dining room; Physical therapy room; Activities room; Crafts room; Barber/Beauty shop.
Activities Arts & crafts; Games; Reading groups; Prayer groups; Movies; Social/Cultural gatherings.

Montgomery Manor*
3751 Montgomery Dr, Santa Rosa, CA, 95405
(707) 525-1250
Admin Dorothy J Bennett.
Licensure Skilled care. *Beds* 122. *Certified* Medicare; Medi-Cal.
Owner Proprietary Corp.

Santa Rosa Convalescent Hospital
446 Arrowood Dr, Santa Rosa, CA, 95407
(707) 528-2100
Admin Henry Weiland. *Medical Dir/Dir of Nursing* Kent Beams MD.
Licensure Skilled care. *Beds* SNF 59. *Certified* Medicare; Medi-Cal.
Owner Privately owned.
Admissions Requirements Medical examination; Physician's request.
Staff Physicians; RNs; LPNs; Nurses aides; Activities coordinators.
Languages Spanish
Facilities Dining room; Physical therapy room; Activities room; Chapel; Laundry room.
Activities Arts & crafts; Cards; Games; Reading groups; Prayer groups; Movies; Social/Cultural gatherings.

Summerfield Convalescent Hospital*
1280 Summerfield Rd, Santa Rosa, CA, 95405
(707) 539-1515
Admin Arlene Garietz. *Medical Dir/Dir of Nursing* Michael MacLean MD.
Licensure Skilled care. *Beds* 70. *Certified* Medicare; Medi-Cal.
Owner Proprietary Corp (Redwood Empire Enterprises).
Facilities Dining room; Activities room; Crafts room; Laundry room.
Activities Arts & crafts; Cards; Games; Reading groups; Prayer groups; Movies; Social/Cultural gatherings.

SANTEE

Edgemoor Geriatric Hospital*
9065 Edgemoor Dr, Santee, CA, 92071
(714) 448-2411
Admin Francoise R Euliss. *Medical Dir/Dir of Nursing* William Bailey MD.
Licensure Skilled care. *Beds* 342. *Certified* Medicare; Medi-Cal.
Owner Publicly owned.
Admissions Requirements Minimum age 18; Medical examination.
Staff Physicians 2 (ft), 2 (pt); RNs 21 (ft), 10 (pt); LPNs 8 (ft); Nurses aides 90 (ft), 15 (pt); Physical therapists 3 (ft); Reality therapists 2 (ft); Recreational therapists 2 (ft); Occupational therapists 1 (ft), 1 (pt); Speech therapists 1 (pt); Activities coordinators 1 (ft); Dietitians 2 (pt); Dentists 1 (pt); Ophthalmologists 1 (pt); Podiatrists 1 (pt).
Facilities Dining room; Physical therapy room; Activities room; Chapel; Crafts room; Laundry room; Barber/Beauty shop; Library.
Activities Arts & crafts; Games; Reading groups; Prayer groups; Movies; Shopping trips; Field trips.

SARATOGA

Odd Fellows Home of California
14500 Fruitvale Ave, Saratoga, CA, 95070
(408) 867-3891
Admin Lawrence F Wilkinson. *Medical Dir/Dir of Nursing* John Henion; Violet Segura DON.
Licensure Skilled care; Intermediate care; Residential. *Beds* SNF 62; ICF 6; Residential 174. *Certified* Medicaid; Medicare; Medi-Cal.
Owner Nonprofit organization/foundation.
Admissions Requirements Minimum age 65; Medical examination.
Staff Physicians 1 (pt); RNs 3 (ft); LPNs 4 (ft); Nurses aides 25 (ft); Physical therapists 1 (pt); Reality therapists 1 (pt); Recreational therapists 1 (pt); Activities coordinators 2 (ft); Dietitians 1 (ft); Ophthalmologists 1 (pt).
Languages Spanish, Asian dialects
Facilities Dining room; Physical therapy room; Activities room; Chapel; Laundry room; Barber/Beauty shop; Library.
Activities Arts & crafts; Cards; Games; Reading groups; Prayer groups; Movies; Shopping trips; Social/Cultural gatherings.

Our Lady of Fatima Villa
20400 Saratoga-Los Gatos Rd, Saratoga, CA, 95070
(408) 741-5100
Admin Louise A Pahl. *Medical Dir/Dir of Nursing* J Wortley MD; Mary Ellen Barber DON.
Licensure Skilled care. *Beds* SNF 85. *Certified* Medicare; Medi-Cal.
Owner Nonprofit Corp.
Admissions Requirements Females only; Medical examination; Physician's request.
Staff RNs 6 (ft), 6 (pt); LPNs 3 (ft), 2 (pt); Nurses aides 41 (ft), 8 (pt); Activities coordinators 1 (ft), 1 (pt).
Languages Spanish
Affiliation Roman Catholic
Facilities Dining room; Physical therapy room; Activities room; Chapel; Crafts room; Barber/Beauty shop.
Activities Arts & crafts; Cards; Games; Reading groups; Prayer groups; Movies; Social/Cultural gatherings.

Saratoga Place Skilled Nursing Facility*
18611 Sousa Ln, Saratoga, CA, 95070
(408) 378-8875
Admin Opal Schlesinger.

Licensure Skilled care. *Beds* 38. *Certified* Medi-Cal.
Owner Proprietary Corp.

SEAL BEACH

Beverly Manor Convalescent Hospital
3000 Beverly Manor Rd, Seal Beach, CA, 90740
(213) 598-2477
Admin Robert C Brozowski. *Medical Dir/Dir of Nursing* Dr Alan Greenberg; Joyce Ritz RNC DON.
Licensure Skilled care. *Beds* SNF 198. *Certified* Medicare; Medi-Cal.
Owner Proprietary Corp (Beverly Enterprises).
Admissions Requirements Medical examination; Physician's request.
Staff Physicians 1 (pt); RNs 10 (ft); LPNs 30 (ft); Nurses aides 60 (ft); Activities coordinators 1 (ft).
Facilities Dining room; Physical therapy room; Activities room; Crafts room; Laundry room; Barber/Beauty shop; Library; Fireside room; TV room; Patios.
Activities Arts & crafts; Cards; Games; Reading groups; Prayer groups; Movies; Shopping trips; Social/Cultural gatherings; Bowling; Stroke group.

SEBASTOPOL

Fircrest Convalescent Hospital
7025 Corline Ct, Sebastopol, CA, 95472
(707) 823-7444
Admin Carol J Grundstrom. *Medical Dir/Dir of Nursing* Jane Walters RN DON.
Licensure Skilled care. *Beds* SNF 49. *Certified* Medicare; Medi-Cal.
Owner Privately owned.
Admissions Requirements Minimum age 18.
Staff Physicians 1 (pt); RNs 2 (ft), 4 (pt) 13C 5 (ft), 1 (pt); Nurses aides 18 (ft); Activities coordinators 1 (ft); Dietitians 1 (ft), 1 (pt).
Facilities Dining room; Activities room; Laundry room; Barber/Beauty shop; Library.
Activities Arts & crafts; Cards; Games; Reading groups; Prayer groups; Movies.

Gravenstein Convalescent Hospital*
1035 Gravenstein Ave, Sebastopol, CA, 95472
(707) 823-7675
Admin Richard A Clark.
Licensure Skilled care. *Beds* 95. *Certified* Medicare; Medi-Cal.
Owner Proprietary Corp.

Sebastopol Convalescent Hospital*
477 Petaluma Ave, Sebastopol, CA, 95472
(707) 823-7855
Admin Fred Lenschmidt.
Licensure Skilled care. *Beds* 35. *Certified* Medicare; Medi-Cal.
Owner Proprietary Corp.

SELMA

Bethel Lutheran Home Inc*
2280 Dockery Ave, Selma, CA, 93662
(209) 896-4900
Admin Ken Truckenbrod.
Licensure Skilled care. *Beds* 30. *Certified* Medi-Cal.
Owner Nonprofit Corp.

Selma Convalescent Hospital*
2108 Stillman St, Selma, CA, 93662
(209) 896-4990
Admin Ida Lee.
Licensure Skilled care. *Beds* 34. *Certified* Medi-Cal.
Owner Proprietary Corp (Beverly Enterprises).

SEPULVEDA

Sheraton Convalescent Center
9655 Sepulveda Blvd, Sepulveda, CA, 91343
(818) 892-8665
Admin Lander S Warren. *Medical Dir/Dir of Nursing* Melvin Kirschner MD; Romy Brubaker RN DON.
Licensure Skilled care. *Beds* SNF 138. *Certified* Medicare; Medi-Cal.
Owner Nonprofit Corp (Wilshire Foundation).
Admissions Requirements Minimum age 35; Physician's request.
Staff Physicians; RNs; LPNs; Orderlies; Nurses aides; Activities coordinators; Dietitians.
Facilities Dining room; Physical therapy room; Activities room; Crafts room; Laundry room; Barber/Beauty shop.
Activities Arts & crafts; Cards; Games; Reading groups; Prayer groups; Movies; Shopping trips; Social/Cultural gatherings; Entertainment provided.

SHAFTER

Shafter Convalescent Hospital*
140 E Tulare Ave, Shafter, CA, 93263
(805) 746-3912
Admin T Wayne Smith.
Licensure Skilled care. *Beds* 99. *Certified* Medicare; Medi-Cal.
Owner Proprietary Corp (Beverly Enterprises).

SHERMAN OAKS

Sherman Oaks Convalescent Hospital
14401 Huston St, Sherman Oaks, CA, 91403
(213) 986-7242
Admin Christine S Godoy. *Medical Dir/Dir of Nursing* Glenn Randall MD; Catherine Barabas RN DON.
Licensure Skilled care. *Beds* SNF 120. *Certified* Medicare; Medi-Cal.
Owner Proprietary Corp (Beverly Enterprises).
Staff RNs 3 (ft), 3 (pt); LPNs 7 (ft), 3 (pt); Orderlies 6 (ft); Nurses aides 28 (ft), 6 (pt); Activities coordinators 1 (ft), 2 (pt).
Languages Spanish, Tagalog
Facilities Dining room; Physical therapy room; Activities room; Chapel; Laundry room; Barber/Beauty shop; Library.
Activities Arts & crafts; Cards; Games; Reading groups; Prayer groups; Movies; Social/Cultural gatherings; Scenic rides.

SIERRA MADRE

Sierra Madre Skilled Nursing Facility
225 W Sierra Madre Blvd, Sierra Madre, CA, 91024
(818) 355-7181
Admin Beth A Freedman. *Medical Dir/Dir of Nursing* Ivan Reeve MD: Dorothy Lacour RN DON.
Licensure Skilled care. *Beds* SNF 56. *Certified* Medicare; Medi-Cal.
Owner Nonprofit organization/foundation.
Staff RNs 5 (ft), 5 (pt); LPNs 2 (ft), 1 (pt); Nurses aides 30 (ft), 6 (pt); Physical therapists 2 (pt); Occupational therapists 1 (pt); Speech therapists 1 (pt); Activities coordinators 1 (ft), 1 (pt); Dietitians 1 (pt).
Languages Spanish, German, Tagalog
Facilities Dining room; Physical therapy room; Activities room; Barber/Beauty shop.
Activities Arts & crafts; Cards; Games; Prayer groups; Movies; Social/Cultural gatherings.

SIGNAL HILL

St Christopher Convalescent Hospital & Sanitarium*
1880 Dawson St, Signal Hill, CA, 90806
(213) 433-0408

Admin Dorothy K Oleson.
Licensure Skilled care. *Beds* 59. *Certified* Medicare; Medi-Cal.
Owner Proprietary Corp.

SOLVANG

Santa Ynez Valley Recovery Residence*
636 Atterdag Rd, Solvang, CA, 93463
(805) 688-3263
Admin F Massingill.
Licensure Skilled care; Intermediate care. *Beds* SNF 40; ICF 10. *Certified* Medicare; Medi-Cal.
Owner Nonprofit Corp.

SONOMA

London House Convalescent Hospital*
678 2nd St W, Sonoma, CA, 95476
(707) 938-1096
Admin Donald H Bais. *Medical Dir/Dir of Nursing* Richard F H Kirk MD.
Licensure Skilled care. *Beds* 83. *Certified* Medicare; Medi-Cal.
Owner Proprietary Corp (Beverly Enterprises).
Admissions Requirements Minimum age 20; Medical examination; Physician's request.
Staff Physicians 1 (pt); RNs 4 (ft); LPNs 5 (ft); Orderlies 3 (ft); Nurses aides 60 (ft); Physical therapists 1 (pt); Reality therapists 1 (pt); Occupational therapists 1 (pt); Speech therapists 1 (pt); Activities coordinators 1 (ft); Dietitians 1 (ft); Dentists 1 (pt); Ophthalmologists 1 (pt); Podiatrists 1 (pt); Audiologists 1 (pt).
Facilities Dining room; Physical therapy room; Activities room; Crafts room; Laundry room; Barber/Beauty shop.
Activities Arts & crafts; Cards; Games; Reading groups; Prayer groups; Movies; Shopping trips.

Mission Convalescent Hospital*
1250 Broadway, Sonoma, CA, 95476
(707) 938-8406
Admin James S O'Hare.
Licensure Skilled care. *Beds* 144. *Certified* Medicare; Medi-Cal.
Owner Proprietary Corp.

Sonoma Acres*
765 Donald Ave, Sonoma, CA, 95476
(707) 996-2161
Admin Clyde Bailey.
Licensure Skilled care. *Beds* 32.
Owner Proprietary Corp.

SONORA

Sonora Convalescent Hospital Inc*
538 Ponderosa Dr, Sonora, CA, 95370
(209) 532-3668
Admin E G Wilson.
Licensure Skilled care. *Beds* 36. *Certified* Medicare; Medi-Cal.
Owner Proprietary Corp.

SOUTH GATE

State Convalescent Hospital
8455 State St, South Gate, CA, 90280
(213) 564-7761
Admin Aleene Brown. *Medical Dir/Dir of Nursing* Yvonne Jones.
Licensure Skilled care. *Beds* 99. *Certified* Medicare; Medi-Cal.
Owner Proprietary Corp.
Staff RNs 1 (ft), 2 (pt); LPNs 8 (ft), 1 (pt); Orderlies 4 (ft); Nurses aides 34 (ft); Activities coordinators 1 (ft).
Languages Spanish
Facilities Dining room; Physical therapy room; Activities room; Crafts room; Laundry room; Barber/Beauty shop.

Activities Arts & crafts; Cards; Games;
Reading groups; Prayer groups; Movies.

SOUTH PASADENA

Braewood Convalescent Center*
1625 Meridian Ave, South Pasadena, CA,
91030
(213) 255-1585
Admin Donald G Laws.
Licensure Skilled care. *Beds* 90.
Owner Proprietary Corp (Care Enterprises).

**The South Pasadena Convalescent Hospital &
Sanitarium**
904 Mission St, South Pasadena, CA, 91030
(213) 799-9571
Admin Miriam Harrison. *Medical Dir/Dir of
Nursing* Dr Barry Blum; Beverly Fineman
RN DON.
Licensure Skilled care. *Beds* SNF 156.
Certified Medicaid; Medicare; Medi-Cal.
Owner Privately owned.
Admissions Requirements Minimum age 55;
Medical examination; Physician's request.
Staff Physicians; RNs; LPNs; Orderlies;
Nurses aides; Physical therapists; Reality
therapists; Recreational therapists;
Occupational therapists; Activities
coordinators; Dietitians; Dentists;
Ophthalmologists; Podiatrists.
Languages Spanish, Japanese, Hebrew,
Yiddish, Romanian, Hungarian, German,
French, Italian, Chinese
Facilities Dining room; Physical therapy
room; Activities room; Chapel; Crafts room;
Laundry room; Barber/Beauty shop; Library.
Activities Arts & crafts; Cards; Games;
Reading groups; Prayer groups; Movies;
Shopping trips; Social/Cultural gatherings.

SPRING VALLEY

Mt Miguel Covenant Village
325 Kempton St, Spring Valley, CA, 92077
(619) 479-4790
Admin Bruce Erickson. *Medical Dir/Dir of
Nursing* Andrew Alongi.
Licensure Skilled care; Intermediate care. *Beds*
SNF 83; ICF 16. *Certified* Medicare; Medi-
Cal.
Owner Nonprofit Corp (Cov Benevolent Inst).
Admissions Requirements Minimum age 62;
Physician's request.
Staff RNs 3 (ft), 4 (pt); LPNs 7 (ft), 6 (pt);
Nurses aides 25 (ft), 25 (pt); Physical
therapists 1 (pt); Occupational therapists 1
(pt); Speech therapists 1 (pt); Activities
coordinators 1 (ft), 3 (pt); Dietitians 1 (pt);
Dentists 1 (pt); Ophthalmologists 1 (pt);
Podiatrists 1 (pt).
Affiliation Evangelical Covenant Church
Facilities Dining room; Physical therapy
room; Activities room; Chapel; Crafts room;
Laundry room; Barber/Beauty shop; Library;
Patios; Nature trails.
Activities Arts & crafts; Cards; Games;
Reading groups; Prayer groups; Movies;
Social/Cultural gatherings; Current events
class.

Spring Valley Convalescent Hospital
9009 Campo Rd, Spring Valley, CA, 92077
(619) 460-2711
Admin Violet K Mathews. *Medical Dir/Dir of
Nursing* Dr Berger; Dorothy Morse.
Licensure Skilled care. *Beds* SNF 75. *Certified*
Medicare; Medi-Cal.
Owner Proprietary Corp.
Admissions Requirements Minimum age 38;
Medical examination; Physician's request.
Staff RNs 2 (ft), 1 (pt); LPNs 8 (ft), 2 (pt);
Orderlies 1 (ft); Nurses aides 40 (ft), 4 (pt);
Activities coordinators 1 (ft).
Facilities Dining room; Physical therapy
room; Activities room; Crafts room; Laundry
room; Barber/Beauty shop; Library.

Activities Arts & crafts; Games; Reading
groups; Prayer groups; Movies; Shopping
trips; Social/Cultural gatherings; Dining out;
BBQs; Adapt-a-grandparent.

Wilson Manor Convalescent Hospital Inc
8625 La Mar St, Spring Valley, CA, 92077
(619) 461-3222
Admin Violet K Mathews. *Medical Dir/Dir of
Nursing* Dr Berger; Ann Amalfitano.
Licensure Skilled care. *Beds* SNF 75. *Certified*
Medicare; Medi-Cal.
Owner Proprietary Corp.
Admissions Requirements Minimum age 34.
Staff RNs 2 (ft); LPNs 7 (ft), 1 (pt); Orderlies
1 (ft); Nurses aides 20 (ft), 4 (pt); Activities
coordinators 1 (ft).
Facilities Dining room; Physical therapy
room; Activities room; Crafts room; Laundry
room; Barber/Beauty shop; Library.
Activities Arts & crafts; Cards; Games;
Reading groups; Prayer groups; Movies;
Shopping trips; Social/Cultural gatherings;
Candelight dinners; BBQs; Outside
entertainment; Adopt-a-grandparent.

STANTON

Quaker Gardens
12151 Dale St, Stanton, CA, 90680
(714) 530-9100
Admin Charles Hise. *Medical Dir/Dir of
Nursing* Dr Michael Fine; Bonnie Lanz RN.
Licensure Skilled care. *Beds* SNF 58.
Owner Nonprofit organization/foundation.
Admissions Requirements Minimum age 62;
Physician's request.
Staff Physicians; RNs; LPNs; Nurses aides.
Affiliation Society of Friends
Facilities Dining room; Activities room;
Chapel; Crafts room; Laundry room; Barber/
Beauty shop; Library.
Activities Arts & crafts; Cards; Games;
Reading groups; Prayer groups; Shopping
trips; Social/Cultural gatherings.

STOCKTON

Chateau Convalescent Hospital
1221 Rose Marie Ln, Stockton, CA, 95207
(209) 477-2664
Admin Beverly Cortner. *Medical Dir/Dir of
Nursing* George Schilling MD; Claudia
Styles DON.
Licensure Skilled care. *Beds* SNF 106.
Certified Medicaid; Medicare; Medi-Cal.
Owner Proprietary Corp (Beverly Enterprises).
Staff RNs 5 (ft), 8 (pt); LPNs 5 (ft), 3 (pt);
Nurses aides 36 (ft), 8 (pt); Dietitians 1 (pt);
Social service 1 (ft).
Languages Spanish, Tagalog
Facilities Dining room; Physical therapy
room; Activities room; Crafts room; Laundry
room; Barber/Beauty shop.
Activities Arts & crafts; Cards; Games;
Reading groups; Prayer groups; Movies;
Shopping trips; Social/Cultural gatherings.

Crestwood Convalescent Hospital*
442 Hampton St, Stockton, CA, 95204
(209) 466-0456
Admin Janet Eisenbeis.
Licensure Skilled care. *Beds* 100.
Owner Proprietary Corp (Crestwood Hosp).

Crestwood Manor
1130 Monaco Ct, Stockton, CA, 95207
(209) 478-2060
Admin John L Blaufus. *Medical Dir/Dir of
Nursing* John Larson MD; Candy Hayashi
DON.
Licensure Skilled care. *Beds* SNF 190.
Certified Medicare; Medi-Cal.
Owner Proprietary Corp (Crestwood Hosp).
Staff Physicians 1 (ft), 6 (pt); RNs 4 (ft), 7
(pt); LPNs 13 (ft), 12 (pt); Nurses aides 61
(ft), 14 (pt); Recreational therapists 1 (ft);

Activities coordinators 3 (ft), 1 (pt);
Dietitians 1 (ft); Ophthalmologists 1 (pt);
Dentist 1 (pt).
Facilities Dining room; Activities room;
Crafts room; Barber/Beauty shop.
Activities Arts & crafts; Cards; Games;
Reading groups; Prayer groups; Movies;
Shopping trips; Social/Cultural gatherings.

Delta Valley Convalescent Hospital
1032 N Lincoln St, Stockton, CA, 95203
(209) 466-5341
Admin Alfred Johnson. *Medical Dir/Dir of
Nursing* Thomas Werner MD; Elizabeth
Wright RN DON.
Licensure Skilled care. *Beds* SNF 68. *Certified*
Medicare; Medi-Cal.
Owner Privately owned.
Staff Physicians 30 (pt); RNs 1 (ft), 1 (pt);
LPNs 5 (ft), 6 (pt); Nurses aides 29 (ft), 4
(pt); Physical therapists 1 (pt); Occupational
therapists 1 (pt); Activities coordinators 1
(ft); Dietitians 1 (pt); Ophthalmologists 1
(pt).
Facilities Dining room; Physical therapy
room; Activities room; Crafts room; Laundry
room; Barber/Beauty shop; Library.
Activities Arts & crafts; Cards; Games;
Reading groups; Movies; Shopping trips;
Social/Cultural gatherings; Church groups.

Elmhaven Convalescent Hospital Inc*
6940 Pacific Ave, Stockton, CA, 95207
(209) 477-4817
Admin Bernice Wahler.
Licensure Skilled care. *Beds* 128. *Certified*
Medicare; Medi-Cal.
Owner Proprietary Corp (Crestwood Hosp).

Glen Convalescent Hospital*
5964 Glen St, Stockton, CA, 95207
(209) 477-1816
Admin Joseph Castagna Jr.
Licensure Skilled care. *Beds* 18. *Certified*
Medicare; Medi-Cal.
Owner Proprietary Corp.

Hy-Pana House Convalescent Hospital*
4520 N El Dorado, Stockton, CA, 95207
(209) 477-0271
Admin Phil Sullivan.
Licensure Skilled care. *Beds* 117. *Certified*
Medicare; Medi-Cal.
Owner Proprietary Corp (Beverly Enterprises).

**La Salette Rehabilitation & Convalescent
Hospital**
537 E Fulton St, Stockton, CA, 95204
(209) 466-2066
Admin Ruth Hillenbrand. *Medical Dir/Dir of
Nursing* Dr A Wu MD; Susan Hillenberand
RNC BSN PhN DON.
Licensure Skilled care; Out-patient physical
therapy. *Beds* SNF 122. *Certified* Medicaid;
Medicare; Medi-Cal.
Owner Proprietary Corp.
Admissions Requirements Medical
examination; Physician's request.
Staff Physicians 1 (pt); RNs 5 (ft), 2 (pt);
LPNs 10 (ft); Orderlies 1 (ft); Nurses aides
58 (ft), 20 (pt); Physical therapists 1 (ft);
Speech therapists 1 (pt); Activities
coordinators 3 (ft); Dietitians 1 (ft);
Ophthalmologists 1 (pt);; Social service 1
(ft).
Facilities Dining room; Physical therapy
room; Activities room; Crafts room; Laundry
room; Barber/Beauty shop; Library.
Activities Arts & crafts; Cards; Games;
Reading groups; Prayer groups; Movies;
Shopping trips; Social/Cultural gatherings;
Animal shows; Adopt-a-grandparent; Night-
time activities.

Plymouth Square
1319 N Madison St, Stockton, CA, 95202
(209) 466-4341

Admin Don Williams. *Medical Dir/Dir of Nursing* Dr Anthony Wu MD; Barbara Thomson DON.
Licensure Skilled care; Personal care; Apartments. *Beds* SNF 38; Personal 21; Apts 68. *Certified* Medi-Cal.
Owner Nonprofit organization/foundation.
Admissions Requirements Minimum age 62; Physician's request.
Staff Physicians 1 (pt); RNs 2 (ft), 4 (pt); LPNs 3 (ft), 7 (pt); Nurses aides 19 (ft), 11 (pt); Physical therapists 1 (pt); Recreational therapists 1 (ft), 1 (pt); Occupational therapists 1 (pt); Speech therapists 1 (pt); Activities coordinators 1 (ft), 1 (pt); Dietitians 1 (pt); Ophthalmologists 1 (pt).
Affiliation Congregational
Facilities Dining room; Activities room; Chapel; Crafts room; Laundry room; Barber/Beauty shop; Library.
Activities Arts & crafts; Cards; Games; Reading groups; Prayer groups; Movies; Shopping trips; Social/Cultural gatherings.

Stockton Convalescent Hospital*
2740 N California St, Stockton, CA, 95204
(209) 466-3522
Admin Margherita Fagan. *Medical Dir/Dir of Nursing* George Shilling.
Licensure Skilled care. *Beds* 99. *Certified* Medicare; Medi-Cal.
Owner Proprietary Corp (Beverly Enterprises).
Admissions Requirements Physician's request.
Staff RNs 10 (ft); LPNs 10 (ft); Orderlies 5 (ft); Nurses aides 50 (ft); Recreational therapists 1 (ft); Activities coordinators 1 (ft); Dietitians 1 (ft).
Facilities Dining room; Physical therapy room; Activities room; Crafts room; Laundry room; Barber/Beauty shop; Library.
Activities Arts & crafts; Cards; Games; Reading groups; Prayer groups; Movies; Shopping trips; Social/Cultural gatherings.

Villa Rehabilitation Center
1630 N Edison St, Stockton, CA, 95204
(209) 948-8762
Admin A Z Lopez. *Medical Dir/Dir of Nursing* M Z Robertson RN DON.
Licensure Skilled care; Rehabilitation. *Beds* 98. *Certified* Medicare; Medi-Cal.
Owner Proprietary Corp.
Admissions Requirements Medical examination.
Staff Physicians 1 (pt); RNs 5 (ft), 2 (pt); LPNs 12 (ft), 2 (pt); Nurses aides 50 (ft); Physical therapists 2 (pt); Occupational therapists 1 (pt); Speech therapists 1 (pt); Activities coordinators 1 (pt); Dietitians 1 (pt); Podiatrists 1 (pt).
Languages Spanish, Tagalog
Facilities Dining room; Physical therapy room; Activities room; Crafts room; Laundry room; Barber/Beauty shop.
Activities Arts & crafts; Cards; Games; Reading groups; Prayer groups; Movies; Shopping trips; Social/Cultural gatherings; Parties.

STUDIO CITY

Imperial Convalescent Hospital*
11441 Ventura Blvd, Studio City, CA, 91604
(213) 980-8200
Admin Catherine Mason.
Licensure Skilled care. *Beds* 130. *Certified* Medi-Cal.
Owner Proprietary Corp.

Studio City Convalescent Hospital*
11429 Ventura Blvd, Studio City, CA, 91604
(213) 766-9551
Admin Eunice Fletcher. *Medical Dir/Dir of Nursing* Dr D W Donahue.
Licensure Skilled care. *Beds* 99. *Certified* Medicare; Medi-Cal.
Owner Proprietary Corp.

Admissions Requirements Minimum age 75; Medical examination; Physician's request.
Staff Physicians 12 (pt); RNs 3 (ft), 2 (pt); LPNs 5 (ft); Orderlies 3 (ft); Nurses aides 37 (ft); Physical therapists 1 (pt); Recreational therapists 1 (ft); Occupational therapists 1 (pt); Speech therapists 1 (pt); Activities coordinators 1 (ft); Dietitians 1 (ft); Dentists 1 (pt); Ophthalmologists 1 (pt); Podiatrists 1 (pt); Audiologists 1 (pt).
Facilities Dining room; Activities room; Crafts room; Laundry room; Barber/Beauty shop; Library; Patios.
Activities Arts & crafts; Cards; Games; Reading groups; Movies; Social/Cultural gatherings; Religious services.

SUN CITY

Sun City Convalescent Center*
27600 Encanto Dr, Sun City, CA, 92381
(714) 679-6858
Admin Roy Nee. *Medical Dir/Dir of Nursing* Dr Rex LaGrange.
Licensure Skilled care. *Beds* 99. *Certified* Medicare; Medi-Cal.
Owner Proprietary Corp.
Admissions Requirements Minimum age 50; Physician's request.
Staff RNs 1 (ft), 2 (pt); LPNs 7 (ft), 5 (pt); Nurses aides 29 (ft), 7 (pt); Physical therapists 1 (pt); Activities coordinators 1 (ft).
Facilities Dining room; Physical therapy room; Activities room; Crafts room; Laundry room; Barber/Beauty shop.
Activities Arts & crafts; Reading groups; Prayer groups; Movies; Social/Cultural gatherings.

SUNLAND

Diana Lynn Lodge*
8647 Fenwick St, Sunland, CA, 91040
(213) 352-1421
Admin Marc R Toro.
Licensure Skilled care. *Beds* 59. *Certified* Medicare; Medi-Cal.
Owner Proprietary Corp.

High Valley Lodge
7912 Topley Ln, Sunland, CA, 91040
(818) 352-3158
Admin Sandra N Spear. *Medical Dir/Dir of Nursing* F Morada MD.
Licensure Skilled care; Intermediate care. *Beds* SNF 45; ICF 5. *Certified* Medicare; Medi-Cal.
Owner Proprietary Corp.
Admissions Requirements Minimum age 65.
Staff RNs 1 (ft), 2 (pt); LPNs 3 (ft), 1 (pt); Orderlies 3 (ft); Nurses aides 12 (ft), 3 (pt); Physical therapists 1 (pt); Occupational therapists 1 (pt); Speech therapists 1 (pt); Activities coordinators 1 (ft); Dietitians 1 (pt); Dentists 1 (pt); Podiatrists 1 (pt).
Languages Spanish, Korean, Farsi
Facilities Dining room; Activities room; Barber/Beauty shop; Library.
Activities Arts & crafts; Cards; Games; Reading groups; Prayer groups; Movies; Shopping trips; Social/Cultural gatherings.

Lakeview Terrace Sanitarium*
PO Box 399, Sunland, CA, 91040
(213) 896-7452
Admin Beatryce Moyle. *Medical Dir/Dir of Nursing* James C Johnson.
Licensure Skilled care. *Beds* 87. *Certified* Medicare.
Owner Proprietary Corp.
Staff Physicians 1 (pt); RNs 1 (ft), 1 (pt); LPNs 6 (ft), 4 (pt); Orderlies 8 (ft); Nurses aides 19 (ft); Physical therapists 1 (pt); Recreational therapists 1 (pt); Occupational therapists 1 (pt); Speech therapists 1 (pt);

Activities coordinators 1 (ft); Dietitians 1 (pt); Dentists 1 (pt); Ophthalmologists 1 (pt); Podiatrists 1 (pt); Audiologists 1 (pt).
Facilities Dining room; Activities room; Crafts room; Laundry room; Barber/Beauty shop; Library.
Activities Arts & crafts; Cards; Games; Reading groups; Prayer groups; Movies; Shopping trips; Social/Cultural gatherings.

Shadow Hill Convalescent Hospital
10158 Sunland Blvd, Sunland, CA, 91040
(213) 353-7800
Admin Orlando Clarizio. *Medical Dir/Dir of Nursing* Dr James Johnson.
Licensure Skilled care. *Beds* SNF 67. *Certified* Medicare; Medi-Cal.
Owner Privately owned.
Staff Physicians 12 (pt); RNs 1 (ft), 1 (pt); LPNs 6 (ft); Orderlies 2 (ft); Nurses aides 22 (ft); Physical therapists 1 (ft); Reality therapists 1 (ft); Recreational therapists 1 (ft), 1 (pt); Occupational therapists 1 (pt); Speech therapists 1 (ft); Activities coordinators 1 (ft); Dietitians 1 (ft); Dentists 1 (pt); Ophthalmologists 1 (pt); Podiatrists 1 (pt).
Languages Spanish, Tagalog
Facilities Dining room; Physical therapy room; Activities room; Crafts room; Laundry room; Barber/Beauty shop.
Activities Arts & crafts; Cards; Games; Movies; Shopping trips; Social/Cultural gatherings.

SUNNYVALE

Hy-Lond Convalescent Hospital*
797 E Fremont Ave, Sunnyvale, CA, 94087
(408) 738-4880
Admin Sharon Gately.
Licensure Skilled care. *Beds* 99. *Certified* Medicare; Medi-Cal.
Owner Proprietary Corp (Beverly Enterprises).

Idylwood Acres Convalescent Hospital*
1002 Fremont Ave, Sunnyvale, CA, 94087
(408) 739-2383
Admin Richard B Hart.
Licensure Skilled care. *Beds* 185. *Certified* Medicare; Medi-Cal.
Owner Proprietary Corp.

Sunnyvale Convalescent Hospital*
1291 S Bernardo Ave, Sunnyvale, CA, 94087
(408) 245-8070
Admin William J Kennedy.
Licensure Skilled care. *Beds* 99. *Certified* Medicare; Medi-Cal.
Owner Proprietary Corp.

SUSANVILLE

Susanville Convalescent Hospital*
2005 River St, Susanville, CA, 96130
(916) 257-5341
Admin George Eslinger. *Medical Dir/Dir of Nursing* Dr Kenneth Korver.
Licensure Skilled care. *Beds* 96. *Certified* Medicare; Medi-Cal.
Owner Proprietary Corp (Care Enterprises).
Admissions Requirements Physician's request.
Staff RNs 4 (ft), 1 (pt); LPNs 10 (ft), 1 (pt); Orderlies 3 (ft); Nurses aides 46 (ft); Physical therapists 1 (pt); Speech therapists 1 (pt); Activities coordinators 1 (ft); Dietitians 1 (pt); Dentists 1 (pt); Podiatrists 1 (pt); Audiologists 1 (pt).
Facilities Dining room; Physical therapy room; Activities room; Laundry room; Barber/Beauty shop; Library.
Activities Arts & crafts; Cards; Games; Movies; Shopping trips.

SYLMAR

Astoria Conv/Waldorf Astoria ICF
14040 Astoria St, Sylmar, CA, 91342
(818) 367-5881
Admin Jo Ellen Zayer. *Medical Dir/Dir of Nursing* Gary Prophet; D Jeanne Phinney.
Licensure Skilled care; Intermediate care. *Beds* SNF 139; ICF 80. *Certified* Medicare; Medi-Cal.
Owner Proprietary Corp.
Admissions Requirements Minimum age 65; Medical examination; Physician's request.
Staff Physicians 40 (pt); RNs 6 (ft), 2 (pt); LPNs 12 (ft), 4 (pt); Nurses aides 60 (ft), 5 (pt); Physical therapists 3 (pt); Reality therapists 1 (ft); Recreational therapists 1 (ft); Occupational therapists 2 (pt); Speech therapists 1 (pt); Activities coordinators 2 (ft); Dietitians 1 (pt); Dentists 1 (pt); Ophthalmologists 2 (pt); Podiatrists 2 (pt).
Languages Spanish
Facilities Dining room; Physical therapy room; Activities room; Crafts room; Barber/Beauty shop; Library.
Activities Arts & crafts; Cards; Games; Reading groups; Prayer groups; Movies; Shopping trips; Social/Cultural gatherings; Theater group.

Crestwood Convalescent Hospital—Sylmar
14122 Hubbard St, Sylmar, CA, 91342
(213) 361-0191
Admin Kent Berkey. *Medical Dir/Dir of Nursing* Harold Cohen MD.
Licensure Skilled care. *Beds* 75. *Certified* Medicare; Medi-Cal.
Owner Proprietary Corp.
Staff RNs 3 (ft); LPNs 8 (ft), 4 (pt); Orderlies 5 (ft); Nurses aides 16 (ft), 1 (pt); Activities coordinators 1 (ft); Dietitians 1 (pt).
Facilities Dining room; Physical therapy room; Activities room; Laundry room; Barber/Beauty shop; Library.
Activities Arts & crafts; Cards; Games; Movies; Shopping trips; Social/Cultural gatherings.

Foothill Health & Rehabilitation Center*
12260 Foothill Blvd, Sylmar, CA, 91342
(213) 899-9545
Admin C W Hunter. *Medical Dir/Dir of Nursing* J Clarfield MD.
Licensure Skilled care. *Beds* 150. *Certified* Medicare; Medi-Cal.
Owner Proprietary Corp.
Facilities Dining room; Activities room; Crafts room; Laundry room; Barber/Beauty shop; Library.
Activities Arts & crafts; Cards; Games; Reading groups; Prayer groups; Movies; Shopping trips; Social/Cultural gatherings.

Mountain View Sanitarium
13333 Fenton Ave, Sylmar, CA, 91342
(818) 367-1033
Admin Norman A Zecca. *Medical Dir/Dir of Nursing* Robert Skelton MD; Ethel Riggs RN DON.
Licensure Skilled care. *Beds* SNF 114. *Certified* Medicare; Medi-Cal.
Owner Privately owned.
Admissions Requirements Minimum age 50; Medical examination.
Staff Physicians 8 (pt); RNs 5 (ft), 3 (pt); LPNs 5 (ft); Orderlies 4 (ft); Nurses aides 40 (ft), 5 (pt); Physical therapists 1 (pt); Recreational therapists 1 (pt); Occupational therapists 1 (pt); Speech therapists 1 (pt); Activities coordinators 2 (ft); Dietitians 1 (pt); Dentists 1 (pt); Ophthalmologists 1 (pt); Podiatrists 1 (pt).
Facilities Dining room; Physical therapy room; Activities room; Barber/Beauty shop.
Activities Arts & crafts; Cards; Games; Reading groups; Prayer groups; Movies; Social/Cultural gatherings; Outings; Trips to ocean and parks; Luncheons; Picnics.

United Cerebral Palsy/Spastic Children's Foundation
12831 Maclay St, Sylmar, CA, 91342
(818) 365-8081
Admin A Mae Stephenson. *Medical Dir/Dir of Nursing* Charles Parker.
Licensure Skilled care; Intermediate care. *Beds* 141. *Certified* Medi-Cal.
Owner Nonprofit Corp.
Admissions Requirements Minimum age 16.
Staff Physicians 4 (pt); RNs 7 (ft); LPNs 7 (ft); Nurses aides 70 (ft); Physical therapists 1 (pt); Recreational therapists 1 (pt); Occupational therapists 1 (pt); Speech therapists 1 (pt); Activities coordinators 1 (ft); Dietitians 1 (pt); Dentists 2 (pt); Ophthalmologists 2 (pt); Podiatrists 1 (pt).
Facilities Dining room; Physical therapy room; Activities room; Crafts room; Laundry room; Barber/Beauty shop; Library; Educational classrooms.
Activities Arts & crafts; Cards; Games; Reading groups; Prayer groups; Movies; Shopping trips; Non-verbal communication training.

TAFT

Pacific Regency/Taft
111 W Ash St, Taft, CA, 93268
(805) 763-3333
Admin Vera Traffanstedt. *Medical Dir/Dir of Nursing* T Hasadsri MD; Mona Vekas RN DON.
Licensure Skilled care. *Beds* SNF 34. *Certified* Medicare; Medi-Cal.
Owner Proprietary Corp.
Admissions Requirements Medical examination; Physician's request.
Staff RNs 3 (ft); LPNs 3 (ft), 4 (pt); Nurses aides 15 (ft), 10 (pt); Activities coordinators 1 (ft).
Facilities Dining room; Laundry room; Barber/Beauty shop.
Activities Arts & crafts; Cards; Games; Reading groups; Prayer groups; Movies; Shopping trips; Social/Cultural gatherings.

TARZANA

Tarzana Health Care Center
5650 Reseda Blvd, Tarzana, CA, 91356
(818) 881-4261
Admin Mary M (Molly) Forrest. *Medical Dir/Dir of Nursing* Edwin Marcus MD; Amada Hernandez RN BSN.
Licensure Skilled care. *Beds* SNF 192. *Certified* Medicaid; Medicare; Medi-Cal.
Owner Proprietary Corp (American Medical Services Inc).
Admissions Requirements Physician's request.
Staff RNs 8 (ft), 2 (pt); LPNs 18 (ft), 2 (pt); Nurses aides 68 (ft); Physical therapists 2 (pt); Occupational therapists 1 (pt); Speech therapists 1 (pt); Activities coordinators 4 (ft); Dietitians 1 (pt).
Languages Spanish, Tagalog
Facilities Dining room; Physical therapy room; Activities room; Crafts room; Laundry room; Barber/Beauty shop; Library; Gift shop; Two indoor patios.
Activities Arts & crafts; Cards; Games; Reading groups; Prayer groups; Movies; Shopping trips; Social/Cultural gatherings; Birthday parties; Community schools; Educational programs.

TEMPLE CITY

Evergreen Convalescent Center Inc
10786 Live Oak Ave, Temple City, CA, 91780
(818) 447-3553
Admin La Wanda Olson. *Medical Dir/Dir of Nursing* Jack Baker MD; John Hudson RN.
Licensure Skilled care. *Beds* SNF 59. *Certified* Medicare; Medi-Cal.

Owner Proprietary Corp (American Health Care Inc).
Admissions Requirements Physician's request.
Staff Physicians 1 (pt); RNs 1 (ft), 1 (pt); Physical therapists 1 (pt); Occupational therapists 1 (pt); Speech therapists 1 (pt); Activities coordinators 1 (ft); Dietitians 1 (pt); Dentists 1 (pt); Ophthalmologists 1 (pt); Podiatrists 1 (pt); LVNs 3 (ft), 3 (pt); CNAS 21 (ft).
Languages Spanish, Tagalog, Chinese
Facilities Dining room; Physical therapy room; Activities room; Laundry room; Barber/Beauty shop; Patio.
Activities Arts & crafts; Cards; Games; Reading groups; Prayer groups; Movies; Shopping trips; Social/Cultural gatherings.

Santa Anita Convalescent Hospital & Retirement Center Inc
5522 Gracewood Ave, Temple City, CA, 91780
(213) 579-0310
Admin Israel Bastomski. *Medical Dir/Dir of Nursing* Dr Marianne Scarborough; Gail Azain RN DON.
Licensure Skilled care. *Beds* SNF 391. *Certified* Medicare; Medi-Cal.
Owner Proprietary Corp.
Admissions Requirements Minimum age Adult; Medical examination; Physician's request.
Staff Physicians 1 (ft); RNs 6 (ft), 7 (pt); LPNs 30 (ft), 10 (pt); Orderlies 39 (ft), 3 (pt); Nurses aides 101 (ft), 5 (pt); Physical therapists 1 (ft); Recreational therapists 1 (ft), 1 (pt); Occupational therapists 1 (pt); Speech therapists 1 (pt); Activities coordinators 7 (ft); Dietitians 1 (pt); Dentists 1 (pt); Ophthalmologists 1 (pt); Dentist 1 (pt).
Languages Italian, Spanish, French, Japanese, Chinese
Facilities Dining room; Physical therapy room; Activities room; Chapel; Crafts room; Laundry room; Barber/Beauty shop; Library.
Activities Arts & crafts; Cards; Games; Reading groups; Prayer groups; Movies; Shopping trips; Social/Cultural gatherings.

Temple City Convalescent Hospital*
5101 Tyler Ave, Temple City, CA, 91780
(213) 443-3028
Admin Brian Elliot.
Licensure Skilled care. *Beds* 59. *Certified* Medicare; Medi-Cal.
Owner Proprietary Corp.

THOUSAND OAKS

Thousand Oaks Healthcare Center
93 W Avenida de los Arboles, Thousand Oaks, CA, 91360
(805) 492-2444
Admin Jolana K Borlaug. *Medical Dir/Dir of Nursing* Sharon Fischer DON.
Licensure Skilled care. *Beds* SNF 124. *Certified* Medicaid; Medicare; Medi-Cal.
Owner Proprietary Corp.
Admissions Requirements Physician's request.
Staff Physicians; RNs 10 (ft); LPNs 20 (ft); Orderlies 10 (ft), 5 (pt); Nurses aides 30 (ft), 25 (pt); Physical therapists 3 (pt); Reality therapists 1 (pt); Recreational therapists 1 (pt); Occupational therapists 1 (pt); Speech therapists 1 (pt); Activities coordinators 1 (ft), 1 (pt); Dietitians; Ophthalmologists.
Facilities Dining room; Physical therapy room; Activities room; Laundry room; Barber/Beauty shop.
Activities Arts & crafts; Cards; Games; Reading groups; Prayer groups; Movies; Shopping trips; Social/Cultural gatherings; BBQs; Cooking class; Pet therapy.

TIBURON

Marin Convalescent & Rehabilitation Hospital
30 Hacienda Dr, Tiburon, CA, 94920
(415) 435-4554
Admin Mary E Kelly. *Medical Dir/Dir of Nursing* Dr Thomas Stone; Lillian Lee DON.
Licensure Skilled care. *Beds* SNF 56. *Certified* Private Title 22 only.
Owner Proprietary Corp.
Admissions Requirements Medical examination; Physician's request.
Staff Physicians 1 (pt); RNs 6 (ft), 7 (pt); LPNs 1 (ft), 1 (pt); Orderlies 2 (ft); Nurses aides 14 (ft), 16 (pt); Physical therapists 2 (pt); Occupational therapists 2 (pt); Speech therapists 1 (pt); Activities coordinators 4 (pt); Dietitians 1 (pt); Ophthalmologists 1 (pt).
Facilities Dining room; Physical therapy room; Activities room; Chapel; Crafts room; Laundry room; Barber/Beauty shop; Library.
Activities Arts & crafts; Cards; Games; Reading groups; Prayer groups; Movies; Shopping trips; Social/Cultural gatherings.

TORRANCE

Bay Crest Convalescent Hospital*
3750 Garnet Ave, Torrance, CA, 90503
(213) 371-2431
Admin Steven P Hass. *Medical Dir/Dir of Nursing* Dr Harold C Dorin.
Licensure Skilled care. *Beds* 79. *Certified* Medicare; Medi-Cal.
Owner Proprietary Corp.
Admissions Requirements Minimum age 40; Physician's request.
Staff RNs 1 (ft), 2 (pt); LPNs 7 (ft), 1 (pt); Orderlies 2 (ft); Nurses aides 27 (ft), 3 (pt); Activities coordinators 1 (ft).
Facilities Dining room; Activities room; Laundry room; Barber/Beauty shop.
Activities Arts & crafts; Cards; Games; Prayer groups; Movies; Shopping trips; Social/Cultural gatherings; Adult education.

Bay Harbor Rehabilitation Center
3620 Lomita Blvd, Torrance, CA, 90505
(213) 378-8587
Admin Angel Ramos. *Medical Dir/Dir of Nursing* Stephen Russell MD; Carleen Minckler RN DON.
Licensure Skilled care. *Beds* SNF 212. *Certified* Medicare; Medi-Cal.
Owner Nonprofit Corp.
Staff Physicians; RNs; LPNs; Nurses aides; Physical therapists; Reality therapists; Recreational therapists; Occupational therapists; Speech therapists; Dietitians.
Facilities Dining room; Physical therapy room; Activities room; Crafts room; Laundry room; Barber/Beauty shop; Library.
Activities Arts & crafts; Cards; Games; Reading groups; Prayer groups; Movies; Shopping trips; Social/Cultural gatherings.

Best Care Convalescent Hospital Corp*
22035 S Vermont Ave, Torrance, CA, 90502
(213) 775-6427
Admin Rody Tamparong.
Licensure Skilled care. *Beds* 200. *Certified* Medicare; Medi-Cal.
Owner Proprietary Corp.

Driftwood Convalescent Center
4109 Emerald Ave, Torrance, CA, 90503
(213) 371-4628
Admin Fred Frank. *Medical Dir/Dir of Nursing* Brice T Martin MD; Betty J Riker DON.
Licensure Skilled care. *Beds* SNF 99. *Certified* Medicare; Medi-Cal.
Owner Proprietary Corp (ARA Living Centers).
Admissions Requirements Minimum age 18.

Staff RNs 1 (ft), 1 (pt); LPNs 8 (ft), 2 (pt); Orderlies 2 (ft); Nurses aides 32 (ft); Recreational therapists 1 (ft); Dietitians 1 (pt).
Languages Spanish, Tagalog
Facilities Dining room; Physical therapy room; Activities room; Crafts room; Laundry room; Barber/Beauty shop.
Activities Arts & crafts; Cards; Games; Reading groups; Prayer groups; Movies; Shopping trips; Social/Cultural gatherings; Picnics; Olympiatrics; BBQs; Music & singing; Zoo animals.

Earlwood Convalescent Hospital*
20820 Early St, Torrance, CA, 90503
(213) 371-1228
Admin Claire D Crocker. *Medical Dir/Dir of Nursing* Dale Vanderbrink MD.
Licensure Skilled care. *Beds* 87. *Certified* Medicare; Medi-Cal.
Owner Proprietary Corp.
Admissions Requirements Medical examination; Physician's request.
Staff RNs 1 (ft), 1 (pt); LPNs 9 (ft), 2 (pt); Physical therapists 2 (pt); Speech therapists 1 (pt); Activities coordinators 1 (ft); Dietitians 1 (pt); Podiatrists 1 (pt).
Facilities Dining room; Activities room; Laundry room; Barber/Beauty shop; Library.
Activities Arts & crafts; Cards; Games; Reading groups; Prayer groups; Movies; Shopping trips.

Harbor Convalescent Hospital*
21521 S Vermont Ave, Torrance, CA, 90502
(213) 320-0961
Admin Ofelia T David.
Licensure Skilled care. *Beds* 118. *Certified* Medicare; Medi-Cal.
Owner Proprietary Corp.

Heritage Convalescent Center of Torrance
21414 S Vermont Ave, Torrance, CA, 90502
(213) 320-8714
Admin Samuel G Bergstrom. *Medical Dir/Dir of Nursing* Wing Mar MD; Angela Tang RN DON.
Licensure Skilled care. *Beds* SNF 166. *Certified* Medicaid; Medicare; Medi-Cal.
Owner Proprietary Corp.
Admissions Requirements Minimum age 45.
Staff RNs 14 (ft), 3 (pt); LPNs 20 (ft); Nurses aides 80 (ft), 10 (pt); Occupational therapists 1 (ft); Speech therapists 1 (ft); Activities coordinators 2 (ft); Dietitians 1 (ft); Ophthalmologists 1 (ft); Podiatrists 1 (ft).
Languages French, Chinese, Tagalog, Spanish
Facilities Dining room; Physical therapy room; Activities room; Chapel; Crafts room; Laundry room; Barber/Beauty shop; Library; Coffee shop.
Activities Arts & crafts; Cards; Games; Reading groups; Prayer groups; Movies; Shopping trips; Social/Cultural gatherings.

Mira Costa Convalescent Hospital*
4320 Miracopa St, Torrance, CA, 90503
(213) 542-5555
Admin Warren R Bratland.
Licensure Skilled care. *Beds* 124. *Certified* Medi-Cal.
Owner Proprietary Corp (Care Enterprises).

Royalwood Convalescent Hospital*
22520 Maple Ave, Torrance, CA, 90505
(213) 326-9131
Admin Dawn Didion. *Medical Dir/Dir of Nursing* Dr Harry Silver.
Licensure Skilled care. *Beds* 110. *Certified* Medicare; Medi-Cal.
Owner Proprietary Corp.
Staff Physicians 1 (pt); RNs 13 (ft); LPNs 21 (ft); Orderlies 43 (ft); Physical therapists 1 (pt); Reality therapists 1 (pt); Recreational therapists 1 (ft); Occupational therapists 1 (pt); Speech therapists 1 (pt); Activities

coordinators 1 (ft); Dietitians 1 (ft); Dentists 1 (pt); Ophthalmologists 1 (pt); Podiatrists 1 (pt); Audiologists 1 (pt).
Facilities Dining room; Physical therapy room; Activities room; Crafts room; Laundry room; Barber/Beauty shop.
Activities Arts & crafts; Cards; Games; Reading groups; Prayer groups; Movies.

Sunnyside Nursing Center*
22617 S Vermont Ave, Torrance, CA, 90502
(213) 320-4130
Admin Mark Deutsch. *Medical Dir/Dir of Nursing* Dr Allan Greenberg.
Licensure Skilled care. *Beds* 263. *Certified* Medicare; Medi-Cal.
Owner Proprietary Corp.
Staff Physicians 15 (pt); RNs 7 (ft), 4 (pt); LPNs 18 (ft), 5 (pt); Nurses aides 100 (ft), 25 (pt); Physical therapists 1 (ft), 3 (pt); Recreational therapists 6 (ft); Occupational therapists 1 (pt); Speech therapists 1 (pt); Dietitians 1 (pt); Dentists 1 (pt); Ophthalmologists 1 (pt); Podiatrists 1 (pt).
Facilities Dining room; Physical therapy room; Activities room; Crafts room; Laundry room; Barber/Beauty shop; Library.
Activities Arts & crafts; Cards; Games; Reading groups; Prayer groups; Movies; Social/Cultural gatherings; Outings.

Torrance Convalescent Hospital
4315 Torrance Blvd, Torrance, CA, 90503
(213) 772-5782
Admin Martin Kahan. *Medical Dir/Dir of Nursing* Dr George Csengeri.
Licensure Skilled care. *Beds* 99. *Certified* Medicare; Medi-Cal.
Owner Proprietary Corp.
Admissions Requirements Minimum age 18; Physician's request.
Staff Physicians 1 (pt); RNs 3 (ft), 3 (pt); LPNs 7 (ft); Nurses aides 25 (ft), 10 (pt); Physical therapists 2 (pt); Occupational therapists 1 (pt); Speech therapists 1 (pt); Activities coordinators 1 (ft); Dietitians 1 (pt); Dentists 1 (pt); Ophthalmologists 1 (pt); Podiatrists 1 (pt); Dentist 2 (pt).
Facilities Dining room; Physical therapy room; Activities room; Chapel; Crafts room; Laundry room; Barber/Beauty shop; Library.
Activities Arts & crafts; Cards; Games; Reading groups; Prayer groups; Movies.

West Torrance Convalescent Hospital*
4333 Torrance Blvd, Torrance, CA, 90503
(213) 772-4021
Admin Frank Oehlbaum.
Licensure Skilled care. *Beds* 96. *Certified* Medicare; Medi-Cal.
Owner Proprietary Corp.

TRACY

Tracy Convalescent Hospital
545 W Beverly Pl, Tracy, CA, 95376
(209) 835-6034
Admin G G Ramirez. *Medical Dir/Dir of Nursing* H L McClelland MD; Mary McReynalds.
Licensure Skilled care. *Beds* SNF 59. *Certified* Medicare; Medi-Cal.
Owner Proprietary Corp.
Admissions Requirements Medical examination; Physician's request.
Staff Physicians; RNs 2 (ft), 1 (pt); LPNs 3 (ft); Orderlies 2 (ft); Nurses aides 18 (ft); Physical therapists; Recreational therapists; Occupational therapists; Speech therapists; Activities coordinators 1 (ft); Dietitians; Dentists; Ophthalmologists; Podiatrists.
Languages Spanish, Japanese, German, Portuguese
Facilities Dining room; Physical therapy room; Activities room; Chapel; Crafts room; Laundry room; Barber/Beauty shop; Library.

Activities Arts & crafts; Cards; Games;
Reading groups; Prayer groups; Movies;
Shopping trips.

TUJUNGA

Community Convalescent Center of Sunland Tujunga*
7660 Wyngate St, Tujunga, CA, 91042
(213) 352-1454
Admin C T McDonald.
Licensure Skilled care. *Beds* 92. *Certified*
Medicare; Medi-Cal.
Owner Proprietary Corp.

Oakview Convalescent Hospital*
9166 Tujunga Canyon, Tujunga, CA, 91042
(213) 352-4426
Admin Homer Summerville.
Licensure Skilled care. *Beds* 49. *Certified*
Medicare; Medi-Cal.
Owner Proprietary Corp.

TULARE

Merritt Manor Convalescent Hospital
604 E Merritt Ave, Tulare, CA, 93274
(209) 686-1601
Admin D Marlene Luiz. *Medical Dir/Dir of
Nursing* Erwood G Edgar MD; Lisa DiSieno
RN DON.
Licensure Skilled care; Intermediate care. *Beds*
SNF 78; ICF 20. *Certified* Medicare; Medi-Cal.
Owner Proprietary Corp.
Admissions Requirements Medical
examination; Physician's request.
Staff RNs 1 (ft), 3 (pt); LPNs 10 (ft), 2 (pt);
Nurses aides 36 (ft), 6 (pt); Activities
coordinators 2 (ft).
Languages Spanish, Portuguese
Facilities Dining room; Activities room;
Laundry room; Barber/Beauty shop.
Activities Arts & crafts; Cards; Games;
Reading groups; Prayer groups; Movies;
Shopping trips; Social/Cultural gatherings.

Terrace Park Convalescent Hospital
680 E Merritt St, Tulare, CA, 93274
(209) 686-8581
Admin D Marlene Luiz. *Medical Dir/Dir of
Nursing* Erwood G Edgar MD; Jean DiSieno
RN DON.
Licensure Skilled care. *Beds* SNF 97. *Certified*
Medicare; Medi-Cal.
Owner Proprietary Corp.
Admissions Requirements Medical
examination; Physician's request.
Staff RNs 1 (ft), 2 (pt); LPNs 11 (ft), 3 (pt);
Orderlies 2 (ft), 2 (pt); Nurses aides 38 (ft),
4 (pt); Activities coordinators 2 (ft).
Languages Spanish, Portuguese
Facilities Dining room; Activities room;
Laundry room; Barber/Beauty shop.
Activities Arts & crafts; Cards; Games;
Reading groups; Prayer groups; Movies;
Shopping trips; Social/Cultural gatherings;
Pet therapy.

TURLOCK

Bel-Air Lodge Convalescent Hospital*
180 Starr Ave, Turlock, CA, 95380
(209) 632-1075
Admin Mary E Baker.
Licensure Skilled care. *Beds* 31. *Certified*
Medi-Cal.
Owner Proprietary Corp.

Brandel Manor*
1801 N Olive Ave, Turlock, CA, 95380
(209) 632-3141
Admin Jeanne Daniel. *Medical Dir/Dir of
Nursing* Robert Clark MD.
Licensure Skilled care. *Beds* 145. *Certified*
Medicare; Medi-Cal.
Owner Nonprofit Corp.

Admissions Requirements Medical
examination; Physician's request.
Staff RNs 6 (ft), 6 (pt); LPNs 8 (ft), 4 (pt);
Orderlies 2 (ft), 1 (pt); Nurses aides 31 (ft),
30 (pt).
Affiliation Evangelical Covenant Church
Facilities Dining room; Physical therapy
room; Activities room; Chapel; Crafts room;
Barber/Beauty shop; Smoking room.
Activities Arts & crafts; Games; Reading
groups; Prayer groups; Movies; Shopping
trips; Social/Cultural gatherings.

Elness Convalescent Hospital*
812 W Main St, Turlock, CA, 95380
(209) 632-3973
Admin Mary E Baker.
Licensure Skilled care. *Beds* 99. *Certified*
Medicare; Medi-Cal.
Owner Proprietary Corp.

TUSTIN

Tustin Convalescent Hospital*
165 N Myrtle St, Tustin, CA, 92680
(714) 832-9200
Admin Loretta Myers.
Licensure Skilled care. *Beds* 59. *Certified*
Medicare; Medi-Cal.
Owner Proprietary Corp.

Tustin Manor*
1051 Bryan St, Tustin, CA, 92680
(714) 832-6780
Admin Donald J Beld.
Licensure Intermediate care. *Beds* 99.
Certified Medi-Cal.
Owner Proprietary Corp.

UKIAH

Hacienda Convalescent Hospital*
131 Whitmore Ln, Ukiah, CA, 95482
(707) 462-6636
Admin Charles T Byerly.
Licensure Skilled care; Intermediate care for
mentally retarded. *Beds* 113. *Certified*
Medicare; Medi-Cal.
Owner Proprietary Corp.

Ukiah Convalescent Hospital
PO Box 630, 1349 S Dora St, Ukiah, CA,
95482
(707) 462-8864
Admin J S Pritchard.
Licensure Skilled care. *Beds* 58. *Certified*
Medicare; Medi-Cal.
Owner Proprietary Corp.

Valley View Skilled Nursing Center
1162 S Dora St, Ukiah, CA, 95482
(707) 462-1436
Admin James Brende. *Medical Dir/Dir of
Nursing* Bernard Lemke MD; Lorraine
Vanoven RN DON.
Licensure Skilled care. *Beds* SNF 59. *Certified*
Medicare; Medi-Cal.
Owner Proprietary Corp.
Admissions Requirements Physician's request.
Staff Physicians; RNs; LPNs; Orderlies;
Nurses aides; Physical therapists;
Occupational therapists; Speech therapists;
Activities coordinators; Dietitians;
Ophthalmologists; Dentist.
Facilities Dining room; Physical therapy
room; Activities room; Crafts room; Laundry
room; Barber/Beauty shop.
Activities Arts & crafts; Cards; Games;
Reading groups; Prayer groups; Shopping
trips.

UPLAND

Shea Convalescent & California Villa
867 E 11th St, Upland, CA, 91786
(714) 985-1981

Admin Leona M Porcelli. *Medical Dir/Dir of
Nursing* Sue Corey.
Licensure Skilled care. *Beds* 99. *Certified*
Medicare; Medi-Cal.
Owner Proprietary Corp.
Admissions Requirements Minimum age 55.
Staff RNs; LPNs; Orderlies; Nurses aides;
Physical therapists; Recreational therapists;
Occupational therapists; Speech therapists;
Activities coordinators; Dietitians;
Ophthalmologists.
Facilities Dining room; Physical therapy
room; Activities room; Crafts room; Laundry
room; Barber/Beauty shop.
Activities Arts & crafts; Cards; Games;
Reading groups; Prayer groups; Movies.

Upland Convalescent Hospital*
1221 E Arrow Hwy, Upland, CA, 91786
(714) 985-1903
Admin William C Milton. *Medical Dir/Dir of
Nursing* C Sanborn Jr MD.
Licensure Skilled care. *Beds* 208. *Certified*
Medicare; Medi-Cal.
Owner Proprietary Corp (Medicrest of
California).
Admissions Requirements Minimum age 18.
Staff Physicians; RNs; LPNs; Nurses aides;
Physical therapists; Recreational therapists;
Occupational therapists; Speech therapists;
Dietitians; Dentists; Ophthalmologists;
Podiatrists; Audiologists; Gerontological
nurse practitioner.
Facilities Dining room; Physical therapy
room; Activities room; Laundry room;
Barber/Beauty shop.
Activities Arts & crafts; Cards; Games;
Reading groups; Prayer groups; Movies.

VACAVILLE

Windsor House Convalescent Hospital*
101 S Orchard St, Vacaville, CA, 95688
(707) 448-6458
Admin Richard Schacten.
Licensure Skilled care. *Beds* 86. *Certified*
Medicare; Medi-Cal.
Owner Proprietary Corp.

VALLEJO

Crestwood Manor*
2201 Tuolumne, Vallejo, CA, 94590
(707) 552-0215
Admin June Gaylord. *Medical Dir/Dir of
Nursing* Matthew Gibbons MD.
Licensure Skilled care. *Beds* 102. *Certified*
Medicare.
Owner Proprietary Corp (Crestwood Hosp).
Admissions Requirements Minimum age 18;
Medical examination; Physician's request.
Staff Physicians 2 (pt); RNs 6 (ft), 2 (pt);
LPNs 2 (ft); Nurses aides 20 (ft);
Occupational therapists 1 (ft); Activities
coordinators 1 (ft); Dietitians 1 (pt); Dentists
1 (pt); Ophthalmologists 1 (pt); Podiatrists 1
(pt).
Facilities Dining room; Activities room;
Crafts room; Laundry room; Barber/Beauty
shop.
Activities Arts & crafts; Cards; Games;
Reading groups; Prayer groups; Movies;
Shopping trips; Social/Cultural gatherings.

Heartwood Avenue Living Center*
1044 Heartwood Ave, Vallejo, CA, 94590
(707) 643-2793
Admin Elliott Silver. *Medical Dir/Dir of
Nursing* Alan Plutchok MD.
Licensure Skilled care. *Beds* 57. *Certified*
Medi-Cal.
Owner Proprietary Corp.
Admissions Requirements Minimum age 18;
Medical examination; Physician's request.

Staff Physicians 1 (pt); RNs 2 (ft), 3 (pt);
LPNs 3 (ft), 3 (pt); Nurses aides 19 (ft), 5
(pt); Occupational therapists 1 (pt);
Activities coordinators 1 (ft); Dietitians 1
(pt); Dentists 1 (pt); Podiatrists 1 (pt).
Facilities Dining room; Activities room;
Crafts room; Barber/Beauty shop; Library.
Activities Arts & crafts; Cards; Games;
Reading groups; Prayer groups; Movies;
Shopping trips; Social/Cultural gatherings.

Louisiana Living Center*
1101 Louisiana St, Vallejo, CA, 94590
(707) 643-2793
Admin Elliott Silver. *Medical Dir/Dir of
Nursing* Alan Plutchok MD.
Licensure Skilled care. *Beds* 37. *Certified*
Medicare; Medi-Cal.
Owner Proprietary Corp.
Admissions Requirements Minimum age 18;
Medical examination; Physician's request.
Staff Physicians 1 (pt); RNs 3 (ft), 3 (pt);
LPNs 1 (ft), 2 (pt); Nurses aides 10 (ft), 4
(pt); Occupational therapists 1 (pt);
Activities coordinators 1 (ft); Dietitians 1
(pt); Dentists 1 (pt); Podiatrists 1 (pt).
Facilities Dining room; Activities room;
Crafts room; Barber/Beauty shop; Library.
Activities Arts & crafts; Cards; Games;
Reading groups; Prayer groups; Movies;
Shopping trips; Social/Cultural gatherings.

Maxicare Convalescent Hospital*
2200 Tuolumne, Vallejo, CA, 94590
(707) 644-7401
Admin Frank L Smith.
Licensure Skilled care. *Beds* 166. *Certified*
Medicare; Medi-Cal.
Owner Proprietary Corp.

Springs Road Living Center*
1527 Springs Rd, Vallejo, CA, 94590
(707) 643-2793
Admin Elliott Silver. *Medical Dir/Dir of
Nursing* Alan Plutchok MD.
Licensure Skilled care. *Beds* 62. *Certified*
Medicare; Medi-Cal.
Owner Proprietary Corp.
Admissions Requirements Minimum age 18;
Medical examination; Physician's request.
Staff RNs 1 (ft), 5 (pt); LPNs 4 (ft), 1 (pt);
Nurses aides 20 (ft), 8 (pt); Occupational
therapists 1 (pt); Activities coordinators 1
(ft); Dietitians 1 (pt); Dentists 1 (pt);
Podiatrists 1 (pt).
Facilities Dining room; Activities room;
Crafts room; Barber/Beauty shop; Library.
Activities Arts & crafts; Cards; Games;
Reading groups; Prayer groups; Movies;
Shopping trips; Social/Cultural gatherings.

Vallejo Convalescent Hospital
900 Sereno Dr, Vallejo, CA, 94589
(707) 643-8453
Admin June Gaylord. *Medical Dir/Dir of
Nursing* Dr Rubin Velesquez; Alice
Bettencourt DON.
Licensure Skilled care. *Beds* 99. *Certified*
Medicare; Medi-Cal.
Owner Proprietary Corp.
Staff RNs; LPNs; Nurses aides; Physical
therapists; Occupational therapists; Speech
therapists; Activities coordinators; Dietitians;
Dentists; Ophthalmologists; Podiatrists.
Languages Spanish, Tagalog, Chinese
Facilities Dining room; Physical therapy
room; Activities room; Laundry room;
Barber/Beauty shop.
Activities Arts & crafts; Cards; Games;
Reading groups; Prayer groups; Movies;
Social/Cultural gatherings.

VAN NUYS

Balowen Convalescent Hospital*
16955 Van Owens St, Van Nuys, CA, 91406
(213) 987-3606
Admin Delva W Larson.

Licensure Skilled care. *Beds* 50. *Certified*
Medicare; Medi-Cal.
Owner Proprietary Corp.

Beverly Manor Convalescent Hospital
6700 Sepulveda Blvd, Van Nuys, CA, 91411
(818) 988-2501
Admin Marc Herrera. *Medical Dir/Dir of
Nursing* R Panchanathan MD; Margaret
White RN DON.
Licensure Skilled care. *Beds* SNF 201.
Certified Medicare; Medi-Cal.
Owner Proprietary Corp (Beverly Enterprises).
Admissions Requirements Minimum age 18;
Medical examination; Physician's request.
Staff RNs; LPNs; Orderlies; Nurses aides.
Facilities Dining room; Physical therapy
room; Activities room; Crafts room; Laundry
room; Barber/Beauty shop; Library.
Activities Arts & crafts; Cards; Games;
Reading groups; Prayer groups; Movies;
Shopping trips; Social/Cultural gatherings.

Sepulveda Convalescent Hospital Inc
5510 Sepulveda Blvd, Van Nuys, CA, 91411
(818) 782-6800
Admin Ray Wark.
Licensure Skilled care. *Beds* SNF 115.
Certified Medicare; Medi-Cal.
Owner Proprietary Corp.
Admissions Requirements Physician's request.
Staff RNs 4 (ft), 3 (pt); LPNs 8 (ft), 4 (pt);
Orderlies 5 (ft), 2 (pt); Nurses aides 26 (ft),
7 (pt); Activities coordinators 1 (ft), 1 (pt).
Languages Spanish, Tagalog, Greek, Turkish,
Chinese, Korean
Facilities Dining room; Physical therapy
room; Activities room; Crafts room; Laundry
room; Barber/Beauty shop; Library.
Activities Arts & crafts; Cards; Games; Prayer
groups; Movies; Social/Cultural gatherings.

Sherwood Convalescent Hospital
13524 Sherman Way, Van Nuys, CA, 91405
(818) 786-3470
Admin Robert Ives. *Medical Dir/Dir of
Nursing* Dr Edwin Marcus; Laura Rogenson
RN.
Licensure Skilled care; Intermediate care. *Beds*
SNF 91; ICF 8. *Certified* Medicare; Medi-
Cal.
Owner Proprietary Corp.
Staff RNs 4 (ft); LPNs 13 (ft); Orderlies 10
(ft); Nurses aides 28 (ft); Physical therapists
1 (ft); Recreational therapists 1 (ft); Speech
therapists 1 (ft); Activities coordinators 1
(ft); Dietitians 1 (ft); Dentists 1 (ft);
Ophthalmologists 1 (ft).
Languages Spanish, Hebrew, Yiddish
Facilities Dining room; Physical therapy
room; Activities room; Crafts room; Laundry
room; Barber/Beauty shop; Library.
Activities Arts & crafts; Cards; Games;
Reading groups; Prayer groups; Movies;
Shopping trips.

Sunair Home for Asthmatic Children
5817 Nagle Ave, Van Nuys, CA, 91401-4026
(818) 352-1461
Admin Damon DeCrow.
Licensure Intermediate care. *Beds* 39.
Certified Medi-Cal.
Owner Nonprofit Corp.
Admissions Requirements Minimum age 5;
Medical examination.
Staff Physicians 1 (pt); RNs 4 (ft), 1 (pt);
LPNs 2 (ft), 1 (pt); Recreational therapists 1
(pt); Speech therapists 1 (pt); Activities
coordinators 1 (pt); Dietitians 1 (pt).
Facilities Dining room; Activities room;
Crafts room; Laundry room; Library.
Activities Arts & crafts; Games; Reading
groups; Movies; Shopping trips; Social/
Cultural gatherings.

VENTURA

The California-Ventura Convalescent Hospital*
4020 Loma Vista Rd, Ventura, CA, 93003
(805) 642-4196
Admin Norman R Hanson.
Licensure Skilled care. *Beds* 67. *Certified*
Medicare; Medi-Cal.
Owner Proprietary Corp.

The Venturan Convalescent Center*
4904 Telegraph Rd, Ventura, CA, 93003
(805) 642-4101
Admin Charles A McClain.
Licensure Skilled care. *Beds* 89. *Certified*
Medicare; Medi-Cal.
Owner Proprietary Corp.

VERDUGO CITY

Rockhaven Sanitarium*
2713 Honolulu Ave, Verdugo City, CA, 91046
(213) 249-2838
Admin Patricia Traviss.
Licensure Skilled care. *Beds* 80.
Owner Proprietary Corp.

VICTORVILLE

Desert Knolls Convalescent Hospital*
14973 Hesperia Rd, Victorville, CA, 92392
(714) 245-1558
Admin Gary L Bechtold.
Licensure Skilled care. *Beds* 126. *Certified*
Medicare; Medi-Cal.
Owner Proprietary Corp.

VISALIA

Delta Convalescent Hospital*
514 N Bridge St, Visalia, CA, 93277
(209) 732-8614
Admin Harold Miller.
Licensure Skilled care. *Beds* 39. *Certified*
Medi-Cal.
Owner Proprietary Corp.

Kaweah Manor Convalescent Hospital*
3710 W Tulare, Visalia, CA, 93277
(209) 732-2244
Admin Amelia Drew.
Licensure Skilled care. *Beds* 99. *Certified*
Medicare; Medi-Cal.
Owner Proprietary Corp.

Linwood Gardens Convalescent Center
4444 W Meadow Ln, Visalia, CA, 93277
(209) 627-1241
Admin Mary L Marchbanks. *Medical Dir/Dir
of Nursing* E P Brauner MD.
Licensure Skilled care. *Beds* 98. *Certified*
Medicare; Medi-Cal.
Owner Proprietary Corp (Medicrest of
California).
Admissions Requirements Medical
examination; Physician's request.
Staff RNs 1 (ft), 3 (pt); LPNs 8 (ft); Orderlies
4 (ft); Nurses aides 45 (ft), 10 (pt); Physical
therapists 1 (ft); Speech therapists 1 (pt);
Activities coordinators 1 (ft); Dietitians 1
(ft), 1 (pt).
Facilities Dining room; Physical therapy
room; Activities room; Crafts room; Laundry
room; Barber/Beauty shop.
Activities Arts & crafts; Cards; Games;
Reading groups; Prayer groups; Movies;
Shopping trips; Social/Cultural gatherings.

Visalia Convalescent Hospital
1925 E Houston St, Visalia, CA, 93278
(209) 732-6661
Admin Delores L Helberg. *Medical Dir/Dir of
Nursing* L D Farrelly MD; Wanda Madden
DON.
Licensure Skilled care; Intermediate care. *Beds*
SNF 149; ICF 23. *Certified* Medicare; Medi-
Cal.

Owner Proprietary Corp.
Admissions Requirements Physician's request.
Staff Physicians 40 (pt); RNs 4 (ft), 1 (pt);
LPNs 13 (ft), 4 (pt); Orderlies 4 (ft), 2 (pt);
Nurses aides 58 (ft), 16 (pt); Recreational
therapists 1 (ft); Occupational therapists 1
(pt); Speech therapists 1 (pt); Activities
coordinators 1 (ft); Dietitians 1 (ft);
Ophthalmologists 1 (pt).
Languages Spanish
Facilities Dining room; Physical therapy
room; Activities room; Crafts room; Laundry
room; Barber/Beauty shop; Covered patio.
Activities Arts & crafts; Cards; Games;
Reading groups; Prayer groups; Movies;
Shopping trips; Social/Cultural gatherings.

VISTA

Vista Golden Age Convalescent Home*
304 N Melrose Dr, Vista, CA, 92083
(714) 724-8222
Admin Jack Hermes.
Licensure Skilled care. *Beds* 35. *Certified*
Medi-Cal.
Owner Nonprofit Corp.

WALNUT CREEK

Arroyo-Creekside Convalescent Hospital*
1310 Creekside Dr, Walnut Creek, CA, 94596
(415) 939-1090
Admin Shirley B Begovich. *Medical Dir/Dir of
Nursing* Dr Carlos Anderson.
Licensure Skilled care. *Beds* 42. *Certified*
Medicare; Medi-Cal.
Owner Proprietary Corp.
Admissions Requirements Physician's request.
Staff RNs 1 (ft), 2 (pt); LPNs 3 (ft), 5 (pt);
Nurses aides 12 (ft), 4 (pt).
Facilities Dining room; Physical therapy
room; Activities room; Laundry room;
Barber/Beauty shop.
Activities Arts & crafts; Cards; Games;
Reading groups; Prayer groups; Movies;
Social/Cultural gatherings.

Rossmoor Manor
1224 Rossmoor Pkwy, Walnut Creek, CA,
94595
(415) 937-7450
Admin Eva Hecker. *Medical Dir/Dir of
Nursing* Roland Schoen MD; Dorothy
Almquist RN DON.
Licensure Skilled care. *Beds* SNF 180.
Certified Medicare; Medi-Cal.
Owner Nonprofit Corp (Guardian Fdn Inc).
Admissions Requirements Physician's request.
Staff RNs 13 (ft), 3 (pt); Orderlies 6 (ft);
Nurses aides 75 (ft); Physical therapists 1
(ft); Activities coordinators 1 (ft); LVNs 11
(ft).
Languages German, Spanish, French, Tagalog
Facilities Dining room; Physical therapy
room; Activities room; Crafts room; Laundry
room; Barber/Beauty shop; Library; Lounges;
Sundeck.
Activities Arts & crafts; Cards; Games;
Reading groups; Prayer groups; Movies;
Social/Cultural gatherings; Live
entertainment.

San Marco Convalescent Hospital*
130 Tampico St, Walnut Creek, CA, 94598
(415) 933-7970
Admin Lee S Murillo.
Licensure Skilled care. *Beds* 128. *Certified*
Medicare; Medi-Cal.
Owner Proprietary Corp (Care Enterprises).

Walnut Creek Convalescent Hospital Inc
2015 Mount Diablo Blvd, Walnut Creek, CA,
94596
(415) 935-2222
Admin Anne Morgan. *Medical Dir/Dir of
Nursing* Jan Saale RN DON.

Licensure Skilled care. *Beds* 93. *Certified*
Medicare.
Owner Nonprofit organization/foundation.
Admissions Requirements Medical
examination; Physician's request.
Staff RNs 2 (ft), 4 (pt); LPNs; Nurses aides.
Facilities Dining room; Barber/Beauty shop.
Activities Arts & crafts; Cards; Games; Prayer
groups; Movies; Shopping trips.

Ygnacio Convalescent Hospital
1449 Ygnacio Valley Rd, Walnut Creek, CA,
94598
(415) 939-5820
Admin Zona Kalustian.
Licensure Skilled care. *Beds* 99. *Certified*
Medicare.
Owner Nonprofit Corp (Guardian Fdn Inc).

WATSONVILLE

Pajaro Convalescent Hospital*
421 Arthur Rd, Watsonville, CA, 95076
(408) 724-7505
Admin Bonnie Reese.
Licensure Skilled care. *Beds* 87. *Certified*
Medicare; Medi-Cal.
Owner Proprietary Corp.

Pajaro West Convalescent Hospital*
425 Arthur Rd, Watsonville, CA, 95076
(408) 724-7505
Admin Bonnie Reese.
Licensure Skilled care. *Beds* 95. *Certified*
Medicare; Medi-Cal.
Owner Proprietary Corp.

Valley Convalescent Hospital*
919 Freedom Blvd, Watsonville, CA, 95076
(408) 722-3581
Admin Richard Murphy.
Licensure Skilled care. *Beds* 59. *Certified*
Medicare; Medi-Cal.
Owner Proprietary Corp.

WEED

CareWest Weed Nursing Center
445 Park St, Weed, CA, 96094
(916) 938-4429
Admin Gary Ralston. *Medical Dir/Dir of
Nursing* W S Williams MD; Annemetta
Olsen RN DON.
Licensure Skilled care. *Beds* SNF 59. *Certified*
Medicaid; Medicare; Medi-Cal.
Owner Proprietary Corp (Care Enterprises).
Admissions Requirements Physician's request.
Staff RNs 1 (ft), 1 (pt); LPNs 4 (ft), 2 (pt);
Orderlies 2 (ft); Nurses aides 10 (ft), 6 (pt);
Recreational therapists 1 (ft).
Languages Italian
Facilities Dining room; Physical therapy
room; Activities room; Crafts room; Laundry
room; Barber/Beauty shop.
Activities Arts & crafts; Cards; Games;
Reading groups; Prayer groups; Movies;
Shopping trips; Social/Cultural gatherings.

WEST COVINA

Ambassador Convalescent Hospital
1495 W Cameron Ave, West Covina, CA,
91790
(818) 962-4461
Admin Jim Scanlon. *Medical Dir/Dir of
Nursing* P F Lagrosa MD; Janet Herrera
DON.
Licensure Skilled care. *Beds* SNF 99. *Certified*
Medicare; Medi-Cal.
Owner Proprietary Corp (ARA Living
Centers).
Admissions Requirements Minimum age 45.
Staff Physicians 15 (pt); RNs 4 (ft); LPNs 2
(ft); Orderlies 3 (ft); Nurses aides 36 (ft);
Physical therapists 3 (pt); Reality therapists
2 (pt); Occupational therapists 1 (pt); Speech

therapists 1 (pt); Activities coordinators 1
(ft); Dietitians 1 (ft); Ophthalmologists 1
(pt); Podiatrists 1 (pt).
Languages Spanish
Facilities Dining room; Physical therapy
room; Activities room; Crafts room; Laundry
room; Barber/Beauty shop.
Activities Arts & crafts; Cards; Games;
Reading groups; Prayer groups; Shopping
trips.

Beverly Manor Convalescent Hospital
850 S Sunkist Ave, West Covina, CA, 91790
(818) 962-3368
Admin Dorothy Pratt. *Medical Dir/Dir of
Nursing* Forrest Tennant MD; Lorraine
Magner RN DON.
Licensure Skilled care. *Beds* SNF 97. *Certified*
Medicare; Medi-Cal.
Owner Proprietary Corp (Beverly Enterprises).
Admissions Requirements Minimum age 40;
Physician's request.
Staff RNs 2 (ft), 1 (pt); LPNs 5 (ft), 3 (pt);
Orderlies 2 (ft); Nurses aides 25 (ft), 10 (pt);
Activities coordinators 1 (ft).
Languages Spanish
Facilities Dining room; Physical therapy
room; Activities room; Crafts room; Laundry
room; Barber/Beauty shop.
Activities Arts & crafts; Cards; Games;
Reading groups; Prayer groups; Movies;
Shopping trips; Social/Cultural gatherings.

Clara Baldwin Stocker Home for Women
527 S Valinda Ave, West Covina, CA, 91790
(818) 962-7151
Admin Robert P Mullender. *Medical Dir/Dir
of Nursing* Dr Bradley; Lorraine Salter RN.
Licensure Skilled care. *Beds* 48.
Owner Nonprofit organization/foundation.
Admissions Requirements Minimum age 60;
Medical examination; Physician's request.
Staff Physicians 1 (pt); RNs 3 (ft), 3 (pt);
LPNs 3 (ft); Nurses aides 23 (ft), 9 (pt);
Activities coordinators 2 (ft); Dietitians 1
(pt); Ophthalmologists 1 (pt).
Languages Spanish, Japanese, French
Facilities Dining room; Physical therapy
room; Activities room; Crafts room; Laundry
room; Barber/Beauty shop; Library.
Activities Arts & crafts; Cards; Games;
Reading groups; Prayer groups; Movies.

Colonial Manor Convalescent Hospital*
919 N Sunset, West Covina, CA, 91790
(213) 962-4489
Admin David T Perry.
Licensure Skilled care. *Beds* 54. *Certified*
Medicare; Medi-Cal.
Owner Proprietary Corp.

Lark Ellen Towers Skilled Nursing Facility
1350 San Bernardino Rd, West Covina, CA,
91790
(818) 966-7558
Admin Samuel Mintz MD. *Medical Dir/Dir of
Nursing* S Dhand MD; Pat Jorgensen RN
DON.
Licensure Skilled care; Retirement. *Beds* SNF
40; Retirement 110. *Certified* Medicare.
Owner Proprietary Corp.
Admissions Requirements Minimum age 65;
Medical examination; Physician's request.
Staff Physicians 1 (ft), 2 (pt); RNs 1 (ft), 2
(pt); LPNs 3 (ft), 3 (pt); Orderlies 1 (ft);
Nurses aides 10 (ft), 3 (pt).
Facilities Dining room; Activities room;
Laundry room; Barber/Beauty shop; Library;
Independence Hall for movies; parties.
Activities Arts & crafts; Cards; Games;
Reading groups; Movies; Shopping trips;
Social/Cultural gatherings.

WEST SACRAMENTO

Somerset Golden State Convalescent Hospital
2215 Oakmont Way, West Sacramento, CA, 95691
(916) 371-1890
Admin Donald J Hunter. *Medical Dir/Dir of Nursing* Shu Chen MD; Elsebeth Bryant RN DON.
Licensure Skilled care. *Beds* SNF 99. *Certified* Medicaid; Medicare; Medi-Cal.
Owner Proprietary Corp.
Staff Physicians 1 (pt); RNs 5 (ft), 4 (pt); LPNs 4 (ft), 2 (pt); Nurses aides 40 (ft), 6 (pt); Activities coordinators 1 (ft), 1 (pt); Dietitians 1 (ft).
Facilities Dining room; Physical therapy room; Activities room; Crafts room; Laundry room; Barber/Beauty shop.
Activities Arts & crafts; Cards; Games; Reading groups; Prayer groups; Movies; Shopping trips; Social/Cultural gatherings; Outings; Special dinners; Music.

WESTMINSTER

Hy-Lond Convalescent Hospital
240 Hospital Circle, Westminster, CA, 92683
(714) 892-6686
Admin Bill Jumonville. *Medical Dir/Dir of Nursing* Dr Rifat; Beverly Heberden DON.
Licensure Skilled care. *Beds* SNF 99. *Certified* Medicare; Medi-Cal.
Owner Proprietary Corp (Beverly Enterprises).
Admissions Requirements Physician's request.
Staff RNs 5 (ft), 4 (pt); LPNs 7 (ft), 3 (pt); Orderlies 2 (ft); Nurses aides 23 (ft), 19 (pt); Activities coordinators 1 (ft); Social Services 1 (pt).
Languages German, Swedish, Spanish
Facilities Dining room; Physical therapy room; Activities room; Crafts room; Laundry room; Barber/Beauty shop.
Activities Arts & crafts; Cards; Games; Reading groups; Prayer groups; Movies; Shopping trips; Social/Cultural gatherings; Self help & improvement skills.

Stanley Convalescent Hospital
14102 Springdale St, Westminster, CA, 92683
(714) 893-0026
Admin Richard Christensen. *Medical Dir/Dir of Nursing* John D Cowles MD; Susanne Kellogg RN DON.
Licensure Skilled care. *Beds* SNF 30. *Certified* Medicare.
Owner Privately owned.
Staff Physicians 3 (pt); RNs 5 (pt); LPNs 2 (pt); Nurses aides 8 (ft); Activities coordinators 1 (ft).
Languages Spanish, Polish, Arabic, German
Facilities Dining room; Activities room; Crafts room; Laundry room; Barber/Beauty shop.
Activities Arts & crafts; Games; Reading groups; Movies.

WHITTIER

Beemans Sanitarium*
14015 E Telegraph Rd, Whittier, CA, 90604
(213) 944-3292 & 941-0116
Admin Ann Whitefoot. *Medical Dir/Dir of Nursing* Donn D Beeman MD.
Licensure Skilled care. *Beds* 74. *Certified* Medicare; Medi-Cal.
Owner Proprietary Corp.
Admissions Requirements Minimum age 45.
Staff Physicians 1 (ft); RNs 1 (ft), 1 (pt); LPNs 8 (ft); Nurses aides 30 (ft); Activities coordinators 1 (ft); Dietitians 1 (ft).
Facilities Dining room; Activities room; Chapel; Crafts room; Laundry room; Barber/ Beauty shop.

Activities Arts & crafts; Cards; Games; Movies; Church services; Exercise program; Yoga; Birthday parties once monthly; Ice cream social once monthly; Money management for country store.

Berryman Health West Whittier
12385 E Washington Blvd, Whittier, CA, 90606
(213) 693-7701
Admin Ann E Koeckritz. *Medical Dir/Dir of Nursing* Randolf Holmes MD; Renee Bedard RN.
Licensure Skilled care. *Beds* SNF 162. *Certified* Medicare; Medi-Cal.
Owner Proprietary Corp.
Admissions Requirements Medical examination; Physician's request.
Staff RNs 15 (ft); LPNs 5 (ft), 10 (pt); Orderlies 5 (ft); Nurses aides 35 (ft), 15 (pt); Physical therapists 1 (pt); Occupational therapists 1 (pt); Speech therapists 1 (pt); Activities coordinators 2 (ft); Dietitians 1 (pt); Dentists 1 (pt); Ophthalmologists 1 (pt); Podiatrists 1 (pt); Social service 1 (ft), 1 (pt).
Facilities Dining room; Physical therapy room; Activities room; Crafts room; Laundry room; Barber/Beauty shop; Library.
Activities Arts & crafts; Cards; Games; Reading groups; Prayer groups; Movies; Social/Cultural gatherings; Exercise; Outings; In room activities.

Doctor's Convalescent Hospital*
7926 S Painter Ave, Whittier, CA, 90602
(213) 693-5618
Admin H L Boulenaz & K M Boulenaz. *Medical Dir/Dir of Nursing* Lawrence Pollock.
Licensure Skilled care. *Beds* 36. *Certified* Medi-Cal.
Owner Proprietary Corp.
Admissions Requirements Minimum age 21; Medical examination; Physician's request.
Staff Physicians 1 (pt); RNs 1 (ft), 2 (pt); LPNs 2 (ft), 3 (pt); Nurses aides 13 (ft), 1 (pt); Physical therapists 1 (pt); Recreational therapists 1 (pt); Occupational therapists 1 (pt); Speech therapists 1 (pt); Activities coordinators 1 (ft); Dietitians 1 (pt); Dentists 1 (pt); Ophthalmologists 1 (pt); Podiatrists 2 (pt); Audiologists 1 (pt).

Shea Convalescent Hospital*
7716 S Pickering Ave, Whittier, CA, 90602
(213) 693-9229
Admin Helen W Saunderson.
Licensure Skilled care. *Beds* 54. *Certified* Medicare; Medi-Cal.
Owner Proprietary Corp.

Sorenson Convalescent Hospital*
7931 Sorenson Ave, Whittier, CA, 90606
(213) 698-0451
Admin Doris M Ruff.
Licensure Skilled care. *Beds* 59. *Certified* Medicare; Medi-Cal.
Owner Proprietary Corp.

Whittier Care Center
10426 Bogardus Ave, Whittier, CA, 90603
(213) 647-7817, (714) 871-5980
Admin Diane Herschberg. *Medical Dir/Dir of Nursing* Sheryle Williams RN.
Licensure Skilled care. *Beds* SNF 160. *Certified* Medicaid; Medicare; Medi-Cal.
Owner Proprietary Corp (Beverly Enterprises).
Admissions Requirements Medical examination.
Staff Physicians; RNs; LPNs; Orderlies; Nurses aides; Physical therapists; Reality therapists; Recreational therapists; Occupational therapists; Speech therapists; Activities coordinators; Dietitians; Dentists; Ophthalmologists; Podiatrists.
Facilities Dining room; Physical therapy room; Activities room; Crafts room; Laundry room; Barber/Beauty shop; Library.

Activities Arts & crafts; Cards; Games; Reading groups; Prayer groups; Movies; Shopping trips; Social/Cultural gatherings.

WILLIAMS

Valley West Convalescent Hospital*
1224 E St, Williams, CA, 95987
(916) 473-5321
Admin Duane S Reed. *Medical Dir/Dir of Nursing* Charles McCarl MD.
Licensure Skilled care. *Beds* 59. *Certified* Medi-Cal.
Owner Proprietary Corp.
Admissions Requirements Medical examination; Physician's request.
Staff Physicians 8 (ft); RNs 8 (ft); LPNs 7 (ft); Nurses aides 20 (ft); Physical therapists 1 (ft); Speech therapists 1 (pt); Activities coordinators 1 (ft); Dietitians 1 (pt); Dentists 1 (pt); Podiatrists 1 (pt).
Facilities Dining room; Activities room; Crafts room; Laundry room; Barber/Beauty shop.
Activities Arts & crafts; Cards; Games; Reading groups; Prayer groups; Movies; Social/Cultural gatherings.

WILLITS

CareWest—Northbrook Nursing Center
64 Northbrook Way, Willits, CA, 95490
(707) 459-5592
Admin Duane S Reed. *Medical Dir/Dir of Nursing* John Glyer MD; Mae Williams RN DON.
Licensure Skilled care. *Beds* SNF 70. *Certified* Medicare; Medi-Cal.
Owner Proprietary Corp (Care Enterprises).
Admissions Requirements Medical examination; Physician's request.
Staff RNs 1 (ft), 3 (pt); LPNs 6 (ft), 7 (pt); Nurses aides 21 (ft), 10 (pt); Physical therapists 1 (pt); Speech therapists 1 (pt); Activities coordinators 1 (ft); Dietitians 1 (pt).
Facilities Dining room; Physical therapy room; Activities room; Barber/Beauty shop.
Activities Arts & crafts; Cards; Games; Reading groups; Movies; Shopping trips; Social/Cultural gatherings.

WILLOW

Willow View Manor*
320 N Crawford, Willow, CA, 95988
(916) 934-2834
Admin Ruthe Hamilton. *Medical Dir/Dir of Nursing* Joseph Duba MD.
Licensure Skilled care. *Beds* 79. *Certified* Medicare.
Owner Proprietary Corp.
Staff Physicians 5 (pt); RNs 2 (ft), 2 (pt); LPNs 6 (ft), 6 (pt); Orderlies 3 (ft); Nurses aides 28 (ft), 2 (pt); Physical therapists 1 (pt); Recreational therapists 1 (ft); Occupational therapists 1 (pt); Speech therapists 1 (pt); Activities coordinators 1 (ft); Dietitians 1 (pt); Dentists 2 (pt); Ophthalmologists 1 (pt); Podiatrists 1 (pt); Audiologists 1 (pt).
Facilities Dining room; Physical therapy room; Activities room; Laundry room; Barber/Beauty shop.
Activities Arts & crafts; Cards; Games; Reading groups; Prayer groups; Movies; Shopping trips; Social/Cultural gatherings.

WOODLAND

Alderson Convalescent Hospital*
124 Walnut St, Woodland, CA, 95695
(916) 662-9161
Admin Thomas E Mullen.

Licensure Skilled care; Intermediate care. *Beds* SNF 98; ICF 57. *Certified* Medicare; Medi-Cal.
Owner Proprietary Corp.

Countryside Intermediate Care Facility*
435 Aspen St, Woodland, CA, 95695
(916) 662-3128
Admin Santi Miguel.
Licensure Intermediate care. *Beds* 30. *Certified* Medi-Cal.
Owner Proprietary Corp.

Hillhaven
625 Cottonwood St, Woodland, CA, 95695
(916) 662-9193
Admin Jim Bursey. *Medical Dir/Dir of Nursing* J T Barrett MD.
Licensure Skilled care. *Beds* SNF 98. *Certified* Medicare; Medi-Cal.
Owner Proprietary Corp (Hillhaven Corp).
Admissions Requirements Minimum age 18.
Staff RNs 4 (ft), 2 (pt); LPNs 6 (ft), 3 (pt); Orderlies 30 (ft), 4 (pt); Physical therapists 1 (ft); Recreational therapists 1 (ft); Occupational therapists 1 (pt); Speech therapists 1 (pt); Activities coordinators 1 (ft); Dietitians 1 (pt).
Facilities Dining room; Physical therapy room; Activities room; Crafts room; Laundry room; Barber/Beauty shop.
Activities Arts & crafts; Cards; Games; Reading groups; Prayer groups; Social/Cultural gatherings.

Stollwood Convalescent Hospital
135 Woodland Ave, Woodland, CA, 95695
(916) 662-9674
Admin Carol Dahnke. *Medical Dir/Dir of Nursing* Dr Ronald Harper; Bernice Blickle DON.
Licensure Skilled care. *Beds* SNF 48. *Certified* Medicare; Medi-Cal.
Owner Nonprofit Corp.
Admissions Requirements Minimum age 65; Physician's request.
Staff RNs 4 (ft), 2 (pt); LPNs 4 (ft), 4 (pt); Nurses aides 20 (ft), 5 (pt); Activities coordinators 1 (ft); Dietitians 1 (ft).
Languages Spanish
Facilities Dining room; Physical therapy room; Activities room; Chapel; Crafts room; Laundry room; Barber/Beauty shop; Library.
Activities Arts & crafts; Cards; Games; Reading groups; Prayer groups; Movies; Shopping trips; Social/Cultural gatherings.

Woodland Skilled Nursing Facility
678 3rd St, Woodland, CA, 95695
(916) 662-9643
Admin David J Tarpin. *Medical Dir/Dir of Nursing* Dr Stansell; Margie Stapleton DON.
Licensure Skilled care. *Beds* SNF 55; 41. *Certified* Medicare; Medi-Cal.
Owner Proprietary Corp.

Admissions Requirements Physician's request.
Staff RNs 2 (ft); LPNs 7 (ft); Nurses aides 42 (ft), 6 (pt).
Facilities Dining room; Physical therapy room; Activities room; Laundry room; Barber/Beauty shop.
Activities Cards; Games; Reading groups; Movies; Social/Cultural gatherings.

YREKA

Beverly Manor of Yreka
1515 S Oregon St, Yreka, CA, 96097
(916) 842-4361
Admin Jerry Pearl. *Medical Dir/Dir of Nursing* Nancy Smith DON.
Licensure Skilled care. *Beds* SNF 99. *Certified* Medicaid; Medicare; Medi-Cal.
Owner Proprietary Corp (Beverly Enterprises).
Staff Physicians 12 (pt); RNs 5 (ft); LPNs 9 (ft); Nurses aides 70 (ft); Physical therapists 1 (ft); Recreational therapists 1 (ft); Speech therapists 1 (ft); Activities coordinators 2 (ft); Dietitians 1 (ft).
Facilities Dining room; Physical therapy room; Activities room; Crafts room; Laundry room; Barber/Beauty shop; Library.
Activities Arts & crafts; Cards; Games; Reading groups; Prayer groups; Movies; Shopping trips; Social/Cultural gatherings.

YUBA CITY

Driftwood Care Center
1220 Plumas St, Yuba City, CA, 95991
(916) 671-0550
Admin Shirley S Ma. *Medical Dir/Dir of Nursing* William Hoffman MD; Virginia Frizzell MD DON.
Licensure Skilled care. *Beds* SNF 59. *Certified* Medicare; Medi-Cal.
Owner Proprietary Corp (Chartham Management).
Admissions Requirements Physician's request.
Staff Physicians 1 (pt); RNs 1 (ft); LPNs 2 (ft); Nurses aides 7 (ft); Physical therapists 1 (pt); Reality therapists 1 (pt); Recreational therapists 1 (pt); Occupational therapists 1 (pt); Speech therapists 1 (pt); Activities coordinators 1 (ft); Dietitians 1 (pt); Dentists 1 (pt); Ophthalmologists 1 (pt); Podiatrists 1 (pt).
Languages Spanish, Chinese, Hawaiian, Portuguese, Hindi, Tagalog
Facilities Dining room; Physical therapy room; Activities room; Crafts room; Laundry room; Barber/Beauty shop.
Activities Arts & crafts; Cards; Games; Reading groups; Prayer groups; Movies; Shopping trips; Social/Cultural gatherings.

Hillhaven Convalescent Hospital*
521 Lorel Way, Yuba City, CA, 95991
(916) 674-9140

Admin Clarence Shackelford. *Medical Dir/Dir of Nursing* Charles Cotham MD.
Licensure Skilled care. *Beds* 151. *Certified* Medicare; Medi-Cal.
Owner Proprietary Corp.
Facilities Dining room; Physical therapy room; Activities room; Crafts room; Laundry room; Barber/Beauty shop.
Activities Arts & crafts; Cards; Games; Reading groups; Movies; Shopping trips; Social/Cultural gatherings.

YUCAIPA

Braswells Yucaipa Valley Convalescent Hospital
35253 Ave H, Yucaipa, CA, 92399
(714) 795-2476
Admin James H Braswell. *Medical Dir/Dir of Nursing* H J Cozzolino MD; Gladys Emmerson DON.
Licensure Skilled care. *Beds* SNF 59. *Certified* Medicaid; Medicare; Medi-Cal.
Owner Proprietary Corp.
Admissions Requirements Physician's request.
Staff RNs; LPNs; Orderlies; Nurses aides; Physical therapists; Activities coordinators.
Facilities Dining room; Physical therapy room; Activities room; Laundry room; Barber/Beauty shop.
Activities Arts & crafts; Cards; Games; Reading groups; Prayer groups; Movies; Shopping trips; Social/Cultural gatherings; Bus rides.

Community Convalescent Center of Yucaipa/Calimesa*
13542 2nd St, Yucaipa, CA, 92399
(714) 795-2421
Admin William C Fehr.
Licensure Skilled care. *Beds* 82. *Certified* Medicare; Medi-Cal.
Owner Proprietary Corp.

YUCCA VALLEY

Hi-Desert Convalescent Hospital
55475 Santa Fe Trail, Yucca Valley, CA, 92284
(619) 365-7635
Admin Mark R Miller.
Licensure Skilled care. *Beds* 99. *Certified* Medicare; Medi-Cal.
Owner Proprietary Corp.

Moyle Manor
8515 Cholla Ave, Yucca Valley, CA, 92284
(619) 365-0717
Admin Patricia Hacklitch.
Licensure Skilled care. *Beds* 56. *Certified* Medicare; Medi-Cal.
Owner Proprietary Corp.

COLORADO

AGUILAR

Simpsons Foster Care
212 W Main, Aguilar, CO, 81082
(303) 941-4100
Admin Dorothy Simpson.
Licensure Developmentally disabled. *Beds* 4.
Owner Proprietary Corp.

AKRON

Washington County Public Nursing Home
465 Main St, Akron, CO, 80720
(303) 345-2211
Admin Terry L Hoffart. *Medical Dir/Dir of Nursing* Dr Clark Brittain; Gary Peterson RN.
Licensure Skilled care. *Beds* SNF 29. *Certified* Medicaid.
Owner Nonprofit Corp (Luth Hosp & Homes Socty).
Admissions Requirements Physician's request.
Staff Physicians 1 (ft), 7 (pt); RNs 4 (ft), 3 (pt); LPNs 4 (ft), 3 (pt); Nurses aides 6 (ft), 7 (pt); Physical therapists 1 (pt); Speech therapists 1 (pt); Activities coordinators 1 (pt); Dietitians 1 (pt).
Languages Spanish
Facilities Dining room; Physical therapy room; Activities room; Crafts room; Laundry room; Barber/Beauty shop; Library.
Activities Arts & crafts; Cards; Games; Reading groups; Prayer groups; Movies; Shopping trips; Social/Cultural gatherings.

ALAMOSA

Evergreen Nursing Home
PO Box 1149, 1991 Carroll St, Alamosa, CO, 81101
(303) 589-4951
Admin Cathy A Cooling. *Medical Dir/Dir of Nursing* Mabel Cotton DON.
Licensure Skilled care. *Beds* SNF 60. *Certified* Medicaid; Medicare.
Owner Proprietary Corp.
Admissions Requirements Medical examination; Physician's request.
Staff RNs 4 (ft), 5 (pt); LPNs 2 (ft); Orderlies 3 (ft); Nurses aides 17 (ft), 3 (pt); Physical therapists 1 (pt); Activities coordinators 1 (ft); Dietitians 1 (ft).
Languages Spanish
Facilities Dining room; Activities room; Laundry room; Barber/Beauty shop.
Activities Arts & crafts; Games; Reading groups; Prayer groups; Movies; Shopping trips; Social/Cultural gatherings.

La Posada*
522 Alamosa, Alamosa, CO, 81101
(303) 589-3673
Admin Luis B Medina.
Licensure Intermediate care. *Beds* 5.
Owner Nonprofit Corp.

Stephens House*
78 Monterey, Alamosa, CO, 81101
(303) 589-5135
Admin Elaine C Marrangoni.
Licensure Developmentally disabled. *Beds* 7.
Owner Nonprofit Corp.

ARVADA

Ames Way House*
8130 Ames Way, Arvada, CO, 80005
(303) 424-2713
Admin Mike Hannon.
Licensure Intermediate care for mentally retarded. *Beds* 8.
Owner Nonprofit Corp.

Arvada Health Center
6121 W 60th Ave, Arvada, CO, 80003
(303) 420-4550
Admin Sonia Gale Morgan. *Medical Dir/Dir of Nursing* Dr F Burdick; Jan Steinberg DON.
Licensure Skilled care; Intermediate care. *Beds* SNF 23; ICF 31. *Certified* Medicaid.
Owner Privately owned.
Admissions Requirements Medical examination.
Staff Physicians; RNs; LPNs; Orderlies; Nurses aides; Activities coordinators; Dietitians.
Activities Arts & crafts; Cards; Games; Reading groups; Prayer groups; Movies; Shopping trips; Social/Cultural gatherings; Outings to zoo, circus; Exercise.

Cochran Family Care Home*
7552 Pierce, Arvada, CO, 80003
(303) 420-0967
Admin Elwood Cochran.
Licensure Intermediate care. *Beds* SNF.
Owner Proprietary Corp.

Colorado Lutheran Health Care Center*
7991 W 71 Ave, Arvada, CO, 80005
(303) 422-5088
Admin Donald C Colander.
Licensure Skilled care. *Beds* 120. *Certified* Medicaid.
Owner Nonprofit Corp.

58th Avenue*
19825 W 58th Ave, Arvada, CO, 80005
(303) 424-6824
Admin Mike Hannon.
Licensure Residential MR care. *Beds* 8. *Certified* Medicaid.
Owner Nonprofit Corp.

King Family Care Home*
8640 Calvin Dr, Arvada, CO, 80002
(303) 425-6141
Admin Jeanette King.
Licensure Intermediate care. *Beds* 2.
Owner Proprietary Corp.

Lake View*
11059 W 82nd Pl, Arvada, CO, 80003
(303) 425-1327
Admin Ruth Stallings.

Licensure Intermediate care for mentally retarded. *Beds* 8.
Owner Proprietary Corp.

Lee Street*
6039 Lee St, Arvada, CO, 80004
(303) 423-7158
Admin Mike Hannon.
Licensure Intermediate care for mentally retarded. *Beds* 7.
Owner Nonprofit Corp.

Spring Valley*
5900 Nelson Court, Arvada, CO, 80005
(303) 423-7158
Admin Mike Hannon.
Licensure Residential MR care. *Beds* 8. *Certified* Medicaid.
Owner Nonprofit Corp.

AURORA

Aurora Care Center
10201 E 3rd Ave, Aurora, CO, 80010
(303) 364-3364
Admin Anne E Chapman. *Medical Dir/Dir of Nursing* Dr A Heaton; Donna McCormack.
Licensure Skilled care; Intermediate care. *Beds* 118. *Certified* Medicaid; Medicare.
Owner Proprietary Corp (Hillhaven Corp).
Admissions Requirements Minimum age 21.
Staff RNs; LPNs; Orderlies; Nurses aides; Physical therapists; Recreational therapists; Activities coordinators.
Facilities Dining room; Physical therapy room; Activities room; Chapel; Crafts room; Laundry room; Barber/Beauty shop; Library.
Activities Arts & crafts; Cards; Games; Reading groups; Prayer groups; Movies; Shopping trips; Social/Cultural gatherings.

Camellia Care Center
500 Geneva St, Aurora, CO, 80010
(303) 364-9311
Admin Claudia Kay Hunter. *Medical Dir/Dir of Nursing* Dr Alexander Jacobs; Linda Burniston RN.
Licensure Skilled care; Intermediate care. *Beds* SNF 113; ICF 59. *Certified* Medicaid; Medicare.
Owner Proprietary Corp (American Medical Services Inc).
Admissions Requirements Minimum age 45; Medical examination; Physician's request.
Staff RNs 8 (ft), 4 (pt); LPNs 20 (ft), 10 (pt); Orderlies 10 (ft); Nurses aides 45 (ft), 15 (pt); Physical therapists 1 (pt); Recreational therapists 2 (ft), 1 (pt); Speech therapists 1 (ft); Dietitians 1 (pt).
Languages German, Spanish, Tagalog
Facilities Dining room; Physical therapy room; Activities room; Crafts room; Laundry room; Barber/Beauty shop; Library.
Activities Arts & crafts; Cards; Games; Reading groups; Prayer groups; Shopping trips; Social/Cultural gatherings.

Cherry Creek Nursing Center Inc
14699 E Hampden Ave, Aurora, CO, 80014
(303) 693-0111
Admin Bernard C Heese. *Medical Dir/Dir of
Nursing* Dr Thomas McCloskey; Marleen
Carlson DON.
Licensure Skilled care; Intermediate care. *Beds*
SNF 180; ICF 47. *Certified* Medicare.
Owner Proprietary Corp (Life Care Centers of
America).
Admissions Requirements Minimum age 50;
Physician's request.
Staff RNs 6 (ft), 11 (pt); LPNs 4 (ft), 2 (pt);
Orderlies 3 (ft), 1 (pt); Nurses aides 28 (ft),
7 (pt); Physical therapists 2 (ft); Reality
therapists 1 (ft), 1 (pt); Recreational
therapists 2 (ft); Occupational therapists;
Speech therapists; Activities coordinators 3
(ft), 2 (pt); Dietitians 1 (pt);
Ophthalmologists; Dentist; Social services.
Facilities Dining room; Physical therapy
room; Activities room; Chapel; Crafts room;
Laundry room; Barber/Beauty shop; Library.
Activities Arts & crafts; Cards; Games;
Reading groups; Prayer groups; Movies;
Shopping trips; Social/Cultural gatherings;
Dog races; Horse races; Tours; Mountain
trips.

Delmar House
10801 Delmar Pkwy, Aurora, CO, 80010
(303) 696-7002
Admin Margaret Lowe.
Licensure Residential MR care. *Beds* 8.
Certified Medicaid.
Owner Nonprofit Corp.
Admissions Requirements Minimum age 18;
Medical examination; Physician's request.
Staff RNs 1 (pt); Recreational therapists 1
(pt).
Facilities Dining room; Laundry room.
Activities Movies; Shopping trips; Social/
Cultural gatherings; Community integration.

Mountain View House*
1125 Dayton St, Aurora, CO, 80010
(303) 341-2086
Admin John Meeker.
Licensure Intermediate care for mentally
retarded. *Beds* 8.
Owner Nonprofit Corp.

Ponderosa*
11204 E Colorado Dr, Aurora, CO, 80012
(303) 752-1920
Admin Margaret Lowe.
Licensure Residential MR care. *Beds* 8.
Certified Medicaid.
Owner Nonprofit Corp.

Sable Care Center Inc*
656 Dillon Way, Aurora, CO, 80011
(303) 344-0636
Admin Lorraine Gill. *Medical Dir/Dir of
Nursing* Frances Burdrik.
Licensure Skilled care. *Beds* SNF 120.
Certified Medicaid; Medicare.
Owner Proprietary Corp.
Facilities Dining room; Physical therapy
room; Activities room; Barber/Beauty shop;
Library.
Activities Arts & crafts; Games; Reading
groups; Prayer groups; Movies; Shopping
trips; Social/Cultural gatherings.

Therapeutic Intervention Model Dev Disability*
1455 Beeler St, Aurora, CO, 80010
(303) 696-7002
Admin Margaret Lowe. *Medical Dir/Dir of
Nursing* Mr Stephen Gilson.
Licensure Intermediate care for mentally
retarded. *Beds* 15.
Owner Nonprofit Corp.
Admissions Requirements Minimum age 18;
Medical examination; Physician's request.
Staff Physicians 2 (pt); RNs 1 (ft), 1 (pt);
Recreational therapists 1 (pt); Dietitians 1
(pt).

Village East*
1505 S Ironton, Aurora, CO, 80012
(303) 696-7002
Admin Margaret Lowe.
Licensure Residential MR care. *Beds* 8.
Certified Medicaid.
Owner Nonprofit Corp.

BAYFIELD

Valley View Residential Care Home*
RT 1, Bayfield, CO, 81122
(303) 884-2200
Admin Arline M Beaver.
Licensure Intermediate care. *Beds* 8.
Owner Proprietary Corp.

BERTHOUD

Grandview Manor
PO Box 70, 855 Franklin Ave, Berthoud, CO,
80513
(303) 532-2683
Admin Martin F Kuhn. *Medical Dir/Dir of
Nursing* David McCarty MD; Mrs Edwards
DON.
Licensure Skilled care; Intermediate care. *Beds*
54. *Certified* Medicaid.
Owner Proprietary Corp (ARA Living
Centers).
Admissions Requirements Minimum age 18;
Physician's request.
Staff RNs 4 (ft), 4 (pt); LPNs 1 (ft); Nurses
aides 13 (ft), 6 (pt); Activities coordinators.
Languages Spanish, German
Facilities Dining room; Activities room;
Laundry room; Barber/Beauty shop.
Activities Cards; Games; Reading groups;
Prayer groups; Movies; Social/Cultural
gatherings.

BOONE

Boone Guest Home*
526 Main St, Boone, CO, 81025
(303) 947-3045
Admin Ed Jordan & Louise Jordan.
Licensure Developmentally disabled. *Beds* 17.
Owner Proprietary Corp.

BOULDER

Boulder Good Samaritan Health Care Center*
2525 Taft Dr, Boulder, CO, 80302
(303) 449-6157
Admin Dwight J Boe. *Medical Dir/Dir of
Nursing* Darvin Smith MD.
Licensure Skilled care. *Beds* 60. *Certified*
Medicaid.
Owner Nonprofit Corp (Evangelical Lutheran/
Good Samaritan).
Admissions Requirements Minimum age 55;
Medical examination; Physician's request.
Staff RNs 3 (ft), 8 (pt); LPNs 1 (pt); Nurses
aides 14 (ft), 7 (pt); Physical therapists 1
(pt); Recreational therapists 1 (ft), 1 (pt);
Dietitians 1 (pt).
Affiliation Lutheran
Facilities Dining room; Physical therapy
room; Activities room; Chapel; Crafts room;
Laundry room; Barber/Beauty shop; Library;
Indoor heated swimming pool.
Activities Arts & crafts; Cards; Games;
Reading groups; Prayer groups; Movies;
Shopping trips; Social/Cultural gatherings.

Boulder Manor
4685 Baseline Rd, Boulder, CO, 80302
(303) 494-0535
Admin Norma Harrison. *Medical Dir/Dir of
Nursing* William Blanchet MD; Ellen
Bradford RN.
Licensure Skilled care; Intermediate care. *Beds*
SNF 120; ICF 60. *Certified* Medicaid;
Medicare.

Owner Proprietary Corp (ARA Living
Centers).
Admissions Requirements Minimum age 40;
Medical examination; Physician's request.
Staff RNs 12 (ft), 2 (pt); LPNs 13 (ft), 2 (pt);
Orderlies 5 (ft), 5 (pt); Nurses aides 43 (ft),
9 (pt); Physical therapists 1 (ft), 1 (pt);
Occupational therapists 1 (ft); Speech
therapists 1 (ft); Activities coordinators 2
(ft); Dietitians 2 (ft).
Facilities Dining room; Physical therapy
room; Chapel; Barber/Beauty shop; 3
lounges.
Activities Arts & crafts; Cards; Games;
Reading groups; Prayer groups; Movies;
Shopping trips; Social/Cultural gatherings;
Adopt-a-grandparent; Oral history; Exercise;
Music therapy.

Carmel Ltd*
1005 12th St, Boulder, CO, 80302
(303) 444-0573
Admin James Graves. *Medical Dir/Dir of
Nursing* Marvin Dunaway MD.
Licensure Intermediate care for mentally
retarded. *Beds* 75. *Certified* Medicaid;
Medicare.
Owner Proprietary Corp.
Admissions Requirements Minimum age 18;
Medical examination.
Staff Physicians 5 (pt); RNs 1 (pt); LPNs 5
(ft)O; Orderlies 9 (pt); Nurses aides 8 (ft);
Physical therapists 1 (pt); Recreational
therapists 1 (pt); Activities coordinators 1
(pt); Dietitians 1 (pt); Podiatrists 1 (pt).
Facilities Dining room; Activities room;
Crafts room; Laundry room; Library.
Activities Arts & crafts; Games; Movies;
Shopping trips; Social/Cultural gatherings.

Chestor House*
3786 Eldorado Springs Drive, Boulder, CO,
80303
(303) 444-0573
Admin Daniel H Fairchild.
Licensure Residential MR care. *Beds* 8.
Certified Medicaid.
Owner Proprietary Corp.

Frasier Meadows Manor Health Care Center
350 Ponca Pl, Boulder, CO, 80303
(303) 499-8412
Admin Deanna Carter. *Medical Dir/Dir of
Nursing* James T Murphy MD; Virjean
Bulter RN DON.
Licensure Skilled care; Residential/Personal
care. *Beds* SNF 90; Residential/Personal 10.
Certified Medicaid.
Owner Nonprofit Corp.
Admissions Requirements Minimum age 60;
Medical examination; Physician's request.
Staff Physicians 1 (pt); RNs 3 (ft), 6 (pt);
LPNs 10 (ft), 7 (pt); Orderlies 4 (ft), 1 (pt);
Nurses aides 25 (ft), 14 (pt); Physical
therapists 2 (pt); Activities coordinators 2
(ft); Dietitians 1 (pt);; Social service 1 (ft).
Languages Spanish
Affiliation Methodist
Facilities Dining room; Physical therapy
room; Activities room; Chapel; Crafts room;
Laundry room; Barber/Beauty shop; Library.
Activities Arts & crafts; Cards; Games;
Reading groups; Prayer groups; Movies;
Shopping trips; Social/Cultural gatherings;
Dinning out.

Johnson House*
1478 Meadowlark Dr, Boulder, CO, 80303
(303) 494-6249
Admin Timothy O'Neill.
Licensure Residential MR care. *Beds* 8.
Certified Medicaid.
Owner Nonprofit Corp.

Terrace Heights Care Center
2121 Mesa Dr, Boulder, CO, 80302
(303) 442-4037

Admin M Kirby Ambler Jr. *Medical Dir/Dir of Nursing* Frank Bolles MD.
Licensure Skilled care; Intermediate care. *Beds* SNF 138; ICF 24. *Certified* Medicaid; Medicare.
Owner Proprietary Corp (Waverly Group).
Admissions Requirements Medical examination; Physician's request.
Staff RNs 12 (ft), 2 (pt); LPNs 20 (ft), 2 (pt); Orderlies 12 (ft), 5 (pt); Nurses aides 30 (ft), 5 (pt); Physical therapists 1 (ft); Recreational therapists; Occupational therapists 1 (pt); Speech therapists 1 (pt); Activities coordinators 2 (ft); Dietitians 1 (pt); Dentists 1 (pt); Ophthalmologists 1 (pt); Podiatrists 1 (pt).
Languages Spanish
Facilities Dining room; Physical therapy room; Activities room; Crafts room; Laundry room; Barber/Beauty shop; Library; Patio; Garden spaces.
Activities Arts & crafts; Cards; Games; Reading groups; Prayer groups; Movies; Shopping trips; Social/Cultural gatherings; Gardening; Horticultural therapy; Family barbeques.

BRIGHTON

Beverly Manor of Brighton
2311 E Bridge St, Brighton, CO, 80601
(303) 659-2253
Admin Darlene Inman.
Licensure Intermediate care. *Beds* 112. *Certified* Medicaid.
Owner Proprietary Corp (Beverly Enterprises).

Brighton Care Center
2025 Egbert St, Brighton, CO, 80601
(303) 659-4580
Admin Juli A Ludwig.
Licensure Skilled care. *Beds* 120. *Certified* Medicaid.
Owner Proprietary Corp (Hillhaven Corp).

7th Street*
441 S 7th St, Brighton, CO, 80609
(303) 429-9714
Admin Jo Vincelli.
Licensure Intermediate care for mentally retarded. *Beds* 9. *Certified* Medicaid.
Owner Nonprofit Corp.

Wilson's Family Care Services*
2620 E 165th Ave, Rte 2, Brighton, CO, 80601
(303) 451-9105
Admin Eileen Wilson.
Licensure Developmentally disabled. *Beds* 5.
Owner Proprietary Corp.

BRUSH

Eben Ezer Lutheran Care Center*
PO Box 344, Brush, CO, 80723
(303) 842-2861
Admin Rev Robert A Herrboldt. *Medical Dir/Dir of Nursing* Dr Robert Kulp.
Licensure Skilled care; Intermediate care. *Beds* SNF 88; ICF 42. *Certified* Medicaid; Medicare.
Owner Nonprofit Corp.
Admissions Requirements Medical examination; Physician's request.
Staff Physicians 9 (pt); RNs 6 (ft), 5 (pt); LPNs 9 (ft), 3 (pt); Orderlies 1 (pt); Nurses aides 33 (ft), 30 (pt); Physical therapists 1 (pt); Recreational therapists 1 (ft); Occupational therapists 1 (pt); Speech therapists 1 (pt); Activities coordinators 2 (ft), 2 (pt); Dietitians 1 (ft), 1 (pt); Dentists 1 (pt); Ophthalmologists 1 (pt); Podiatrists 1 (pt); Audiologists 1 (pt).
Affiliation Lutheran
Facilities Dining room; Activities room; Chapel; Crafts room; Laundry room; Barber/Beauty shop; Library; Hubbard tub.

Activities Arts & crafts; Cards; Games; Reading groups; Prayer groups; Movies; Shopping trips; Social/Cultural gatherings.

Sunset Manor*
2200 Edison St, Brush, CO, 80723
(303) 842-2825
Admin Linda Sue Barley.
Licensure Skilled care; Intermediate care. *Beds* SNF 48; ICF 36. *Certified* Medicaid; Medicare.
Owner Proprietary Corp (ARA Living Centers).

BURLINGTON

Grace Manor Care Center
PO Box 98, 210 Madison, Burlington, CO, 80807
(303) 346-7512
Admin Lottie Whitmer. *Medical Dir/Dir of Nursing* R C Beethe MD; Gerrie K Evans DON.
Licensure Skilled care; Intermediate care. *Beds* SNF 20; ICF 30. *Certified* Medicaid.
Owner Proprietary Corp.
Staff RNs; LPNs; Orderlies; Nurses aides; Activities coordinators.
Facilities Dining room; Laundry room; Barber/Beauty shop.
Activities Arts & crafts; Cards; Games; Prayer groups; Movies; Shopping trips; Social/Cultural gatherings.

Martin House*
1776 Martin, Burlington, CO, 80807
(303) 346-8550
Admin ZuAnn Hogan.
Licensure Intermediate care for mentally retarded. *Beds* 8.
Owner Nonprofit Corp.
Admissions Requirements Minimum age 16; Females only; Medical examination.
Facilities Dining room; Activities room; Crafts room; Laundry room.
Activities Arts & crafts; Cards; Games; Reading groups; Movies; Shopping trips; Social/Cultural gatherings.

CANON

Barr House*
1115 Barr, Canon, CO, 81212
(303) 275-0017
Admin Roger Jensen.
Licensure Intermediate care for mentally retarded. *Beds* 8. *Certified* Medicaid.
Owner Nonprofit Corp.

CANON CITY

Bethesda Care Center
515 Fairview St, Canon City, CO, 81212
(303) 275-0665
Admin Joseph E Stock. *Medical Dir/Dir of Nursing* Dr Jack Vincent MD; Carolyn Beitler RN.
Licensure Skilled care. *Beds* SNF 110. *Certified* Medicaid; VA.
Owner Nonprofit Corp (Bethesda Care Centers).
Admissions Requirements Physician's request.
Staff Physicians 1 (pt); RNs 5 (ft), 4 (pt); LPNs 6 (ft), 5 (pt); Orderlies 1 (ft), 2 (pt); Nurses aides 30 (ft), 20 (pt); Physical therapists 1 (pt); Reality therapists 1 (pt); Recreational therapists 1 (pt); Occupational therapists 1 (pt); Speech therapists 1 (pt); Activities coordinators 1 (ft), 1 (pt); Dietitians 1 (pt); Dentists 1 (pt); Ophthalmologists 1 (pt); Podiatrists 1 (pt).
Facilities Dining room; Activities room; Chapel; Crafts room; Laundry room; Barber/Beauty shop.
Activities Arts & crafts; Cards; Games; Reading groups; Prayer groups; Movies; Shopping trips; Social/Cultural gatherings.

Canon Lodge
905 Harding Ave, Canon City, CO, 81212
(303) 275-4106
Admin Judith P Cloyd. *Medical Dir/Dir of Nursing* Dr J F Vincent; Margaret Paul.
Licensure Skilled care. *Beds* 60. *Certified* Medicaid; Medicare.
Owner Proprietary Corp (Life Care Centers of America).
Admissions Requirements Medical examination; Physician's request.
Staff RNs 1 (ft), 3 (pt); LPNs 3 (ft), 2 (pt); Nurses aides 15 (ft), 6 (pt); Recreational therapists 1 (ft); Activities coordinators 1 (ft); Dietitians 1 (pt).
Facilities Dining room; Activities room; Crafts room; Barber/Beauty shop.
Activities Arts & crafts; Cards; Games; Reading groups; Prayer groups; Movies; Shopping trips; Social/Cultural gatherings.

Field House*
612 Fields, Canon City, CO, 81212
(303) 275-0031
Admin Roger Jensen.
Licensure Intermediate care for mentally retarded. *Beds* 8. *Certified* Medicaid.
Owner Nonprofit Corp.

Hildebrand Care Center*
1401 Phay St, Canon City, CO, 81212
(303) 275-8656
Admin Joyce L Stapleton. *Medical Dir/Dir of Nursing* Dr Jack Vincent.
Licensure Skilled care. *Beds* 120. *Certified* Medicaid; Medicare.
Owner Proprietary Corp.
Admissions Requirements Medical examination.
Staff RNs 9 (ft), 2 (pt); LPNs 10 (ft); Orderlies 6 (ft); Nurses aides 35 (ft), 5 (pt); Reality therapists 1 (pt); Activities coordinators 1 (ft), 1 (pt); Dietitians 1 (pt).
Affiliation Independent Order of Odd Fellows & Rebekahs
Facilities Dining room; Physical therapy room; Activities room; Chapel; Crafts room; Laundry room; Barber/Beauty shop; Library; Picnics; Fishing trips.
Activities Arts & crafts; Cards; Games; Reading groups; Prayer groups; Movies; Shopping trips; Social/Cultural gatherings.

St Thomas More Progressive Care Center
1019 Sheridan, Canon City, CO, 81212
(303) 275-3381
Admin Sr M Judith Kuhn. *Medical Dir/Dir of Nursing* Gary Mohr MD; Charlotte Herman RN DON.
Licensure Skilled care. *Beds* SNF 105. *Certified* Medicaid; Medicare.
Owner Nonprofit Corp.
Admissions Requirements Physician's request.
Staff RNs 4 (ft), 3 (pt); LPNs 8 (ft), 4 (pt); Orderlies 3 (ft); Nurses aides 10 (ft), 2 (pt); Physical therapists 3 (ft); Occupational therapists 2 (ft); Speech therapists 1 (pt); Activities coordinators 1 (ft); Dietitians 1 (ft).
Affiliation Roman Catholic
Facilities Dining room; Physical therapy room; Activities room; Chapel; Crafts room; Laundry room; Barber/Beauty shop.
Activities Arts & crafts; Cards; Games; Reading groups; Prayer groups; Movies; Shopping trips.

Valley View Health Care Center*
2120 N 10 St, Canon City, CO, 81212
(303) 275-7569
Admin Shirley Smylie.
Licensure Skilled care. *Beds* 60. *Certified* Medicaid.
Owner Proprietary Corp.

Westridge Apartments*
329 Rudd, Canon City, CO, 80212
(303) 275-1616

Admin Roger G Jensen.
Licensure Intermediate care for mentally retarded. *Beds* 8. *Certified* Medicaid.
Owner Nonprofit Corp.

CASTLE ROCK

Castle Rock Care Center*
4001 Home St, Castle Rock, CO, 80104
(303) 688-3174
Admin Doug Spies.
Licensure Skilled care; Intermediate care. *Beds* SNF 59; ICF 21. *Certified* Medicaid.
Owner Proprietary Corp (LTC).

CHEYENNE WELLS

Cheyenne Manor
561 W 1st North, Cheyenne Wells, CO, 80810
(303) 767-5602
Admin Wayne Bute. *Medical Dir/Dir of Nursing* Dr Keefe.
Licensure Intermediate care. *Beds* 40. *Certified* Medicaid.
Owner Nonprofit Corp.
Admissions Requirements Medical examination; Physician's request.
Staff RNs 1 (ft), 1 (pt); LPNs 4 (ft), 1 (pt); Nurses aides 16 (ft), 8 (pt); Recreational therapists 1 (pt); Activities coordinators 1 (pt); Dietitians 1 (pt).
Facilities Dining room; Activities room; Chapel; Laundry room; Barber/Beauty shop.
Activities Arts & crafts; Cards; Games; Reading groups; Prayer groups; Movies; Shopping trips; Social/Cultural gatherings; Van outings.

CLIFTON

Laurel Lane*
3301 Laural Ln, Clifton, CO, 81520
(303) 243-3702
Admin Laura Schumacher.
Licensure Residential MR care. *Beds* 8. *Certified* Medicaid.
Owner Nonprofit Corp.

COLLBRAN

Plateau Valley Hospital District Nursing Home
PO Box 88, 5812 Hwy 330, Collbran, CO, 81624
(303) 245-3565, 245-3981
Admin Sharon Hill. *Medical Dir/Dir of Nursing* Charles F King MD; Marvin Ivy LPN, Doris Walck RN.
Licensure Intermediate care. *Beds* ICF 26. *Certified* Medicaid.
Owner Nonprofit Corp.
Admissions Requirements Medical examination; Physician's request.
Staff Physicians 1 (ft); RNs 5 (ft), 1 (pt); LPNs 1 (ft); Nurses aides 6 (ft), 7 (pt); Physical therapists 1 (pt); Activities coordinators 1 (ft); Dietitians 1 (pt).
Facilities Dining room; Activities room; Crafts room; Library.
Activities Arts & crafts; Cards; Games; Reading groups; Prayer groups; Movies; Social/Cultural gatherings.

COLORADO SPRINGS

Aspen Living Center
1795 Monterey Rd, Colorado Springs, CO, 80910
(303) 471-7850
Admin Richard C Bonneville. *Medical Dir/Dir of Nursing* Dr Lester Williams.
Licensure Skilled care; Intermediate care. *Beds* SNF 60; ICF 60. *Certified* Medicaid; Medicare.
Owner Proprietary Corp (ARA Living Centers).

Bethesda Care Center
3625 Parkmoor Village Dr, Colorado Springs, CO, 80917
(303) 550-0200
Admin James D Smith. *Medical Dir/Dir of Nursing* Penny Spika RN BSN.
Licensure Skilled care; Intermediate care; Alternate care facility. *Beds* SNF; ICF; Alternate care facility-apts 167. *Certified* Medicaid.
Owner Nonprofit Corp (Bethesda Care Centers).
Admissions Requirements Minimum age 18; Medical examination.
Staff Physicians 1 (pt); RNs 4 (ft), 4 (pt); LPNs 6 (ft), 5 (pt); Nurses aides 23 (ft), 7 (pt); Physical therapists 1 (ft); Occupational therapists 1 (pt); Activities coordinators 1 (ft), 1 (pt); Dietitians 1 (pt).
Languages Spanish, German
Facilities Dining room; Physical therapy room; Activities room; Chapel; Crafts room; Laundry room; Barber/Beauty shop; Library; Physician exam room; Family day rooms; Outdoor patio.
Activities Arts & crafts; Cards; Games; Reading groups; Prayer groups; Movies; Shopping trips; Social/Cultural gatherings; Oil painting; Cooking; Exercise class; Van rides; Green thumbs; Sewing circle; Newsletter.

Cedarwood Health Care Center Inc
924 W Kiowa St, Colorado Springs, CO, 80905
(303) 636-5221
Admin Marilyn Myers. *Medical Dir/Dir of Nursing* Dr Lester Williams; Barbara Azbill.
Licensure Skilled care; Intermediate care. *Beds* SNF 60; ICF 40. *Certified* Medicaid; Medicare.
Owner Proprietary Corp (ARA Living Centers).
Admissions Requirements Physician's request.
Staff RNs 5 (ft), 3 (pt); LPNs 5 (ft), 3 (pt); Orderlies 2 (ft); Nurses aides 16 (ft), 2 (pt); Physical therapists 1 (pt); Recreational therapists 1 (ft); Occupational therapists 1 (pt); Speech therapists 1 (pt); Activities coordinators 1 (ft); Dietitians 1 (pt).
Languages Spanish
Facilities Dining room; Activities room; Crafts room; Laundry room; Barber/Beauty shop; Library.
Activities Arts & crafts; Cards; Games; Reading groups; Prayer groups; Movies; Shopping trips; Social/Cultural gatherings.

Cheyenne Mountain Nursing Center
835 Tenderfoot Hill Rd, Colorado Springs, CO, 80906
(719) 576-8380
Admin Berna M Smith RN NHA. *Medical Dir/Dir of Nursing* Dr John Hays Medical Director; Cathleen Kelly RN DON.
Licensure Skilled care. *Beds* SNF 180.
Owner Proprietary Corp (Life Care Centers of America).

Admissions Requirements Physician's request.
Staff RNs 12 (ft); LPNs 12 (ft); Orderlies 3 (ft); Nurses aides 35 (ft), 20 (pt); Physical therapists; Recreational therapists 1 (ft); Occupational therapists 1 (ft); Speech therapists 1 (pt); Activities coordinators 3 (pt); Dietitians 1 (ft).
Facilities Dining room; Physical therapy room; Activities room; Chapel; Crafts room; Laundry room; Barber/Beauty shop; Library.
Activities Arts & crafts; Cards; Games; Reading groups; Prayer groups; Movies; Shopping trips; Social/Cultural gatherings.

Colonial Columns Health Care Center
1340 E Fillmore St, Colorado Springs, CO, 80907
(303) 473-1105
Admin Karl Schmidt.
Licensure Skilled care; Intermediate care. *Beds* SNF 46; ICF 47. *Certified* Medicaid; Medicare.
Owner Proprietary Corp (ARA Living Centers).
Admissions Requirements Medical examination; Physician's request.
Staff RNs; LPNs; Orderlies; Nurses aides; Recreational therapists.
Languages Spanish
Facilities Dining room; Physical therapy room; Laundry room; Barber/Beauty shop; Library.
Activities Arts & crafts; Cards; Games; Reading groups; Prayer groups; Movies; Shopping trips; Social/Cultural gatherings.

Fairview Care Center*
PO Box 15317, 825 S Hancock Ave, Colorado Springs, CO, 80933
(303) 635-2532
Admin Paul Whisler.
Licensure Skilled care. *Beds* 60. *Certified* Medicaid.
Owner Proprietary Corp.

Garden of the Gods Care Center
PO Box 6129, 104 Lois Ln, Colorado Springs, CO, 80934
(303) 635-2569
Admin Pamela J Marques. *Medical Dir/Dir of Nursing* Lester Williams MD; Charlene Stillmunks RN.
Licensure Skilled care. *Beds* SNF 52. *Certified* Medicaid; Medicare.
Owner Proprietary Corp (LTC).
Admissions Requirements Minimum age 50; Physician's request.
Staff RNs 3 (ft), 4 (pt); LPNs 2 (ft), 2 (pt); Orderlies 2 (ft); Nurses aides 10 (ft), 10 (pt); Activities coordinators 2 (pt).
Languages Japanese, Spanish, Greek
Facilities Dining room; Laundry room.
Activities Arts & crafts; Cards; Games; Reading groups; Prayer groups; Movies; Shopping trips; Social/Cultural gatherings.

Hampton Drive Home*
6736 Hampton Dr, Colorado Springs, CO, 80918
Admin Sandra S Volker.
Licensure Residential DD care. *Beds* 8.
Owner Nonprofit Corp.
Affiliation Lutheran

Laurel Manor Care Center
920 S Chelton Rd, Colorado Springs, CO, 80910
(303) 473-7780

Admin Connie J Miller. *Medical Dir/Dir of Nursing* Dr Lester Williams; Ann Clasby RN DON.
Licensure Skilled care; Intermediate care. *Beds* SNF 100; ICF 8. *Certified* Medicaid.
Owner Nonprofit Corp (Volunteers of America Care).
Admissions Requirements Medical examination; Physician's request.
Staff Physicians; RNs; LPNs; Orderlies 413E; Physical therapists; Speech therapists; Activities coordinators; Dietitians; Ophthalmologists.
Affiliation Volunteers of America
Facilities Dining room; Activities room; Laundry room; Barber/Beauty shop.
Activities Arts & crafts; Cards; Games; Reading groups; Prayer groups; Movies; Social/Cultural gatherings; Exercises.

Medalion Health Center*
1719 E Bijou, Colorado Springs, CO, 80909
(303) 471-4800
Admin William D McMullen. *Medical Dir/Dir of Nursing* Lyle Graham DO.
Licensure Skilled care. *Beds* 32. *Certified* Medicare.
Owner Nonprofit Corp.
Admissions Requirements Minimum age 14; Physician's request.
Staff RNs 6 (ft), 1 (pt); Nurses aides 15 (ft), 2 (pt); Physical therapists 1 (pt); Activities coordinators 1 (ft); Dietitians 1 (pt); Dentists 1 (pt); Podiatrists 1 (pt).
Facilities Dining room; Chapel; Laundry room; Barber/Beauty shop; Library; Swimming pool & deck.
Activities Arts & crafts; Games; Reading groups; Prayer groups; Movies; Shopping trips; Social/Cultural gatherings.

Mountain View Care Center
2612 W Cucharras St, Colorado Springs, CO, 80904
(303) 632-7474
Admin Jean Bauermeister. *Medical Dir/Dir of Nursing* Dana Olson.
Licensure Skilled care; Intermediate care; Residential care. *Beds* SNF 60; ICF 30; Residential care 35. *Certified* Medicaid; Medicare.
Owner Proprietary Corp.
Admissions Requirements Females only; Medical examination.
Staff RNs; LPNs; Orderlies; Nurses aides; Activities coordinators.
Facilities Dining room; Activities room; Crafts room; Laundry room; Barber/Beauty shop.
Activities Arts & crafts; Cards; Games; Reading groups; Prayer groups; Movies; Shopping trips; Social/Cultural gatherings.

Pikes Peak Manor*
2719 N Union Blvd, Colorado Springs, CO, 80909
(303) 636-1676
Admin James M Sanner. *Medical Dir/Dir of Nursing* John McWilliams MD.
Licensure Skilled care; Intermediate care. *Beds* SNF 146; ICF 94. *Certified* Medicaid; Medicare.
Owner Proprietary Corp (National Heritage).
Staff RNs 11 (ft), 5 (pt); LPNs 9 (ft), 10 (pt); Orderlies 1 (ft), 1 (pt); Nurses aides 44 (ft), 16 (pt); Physical therapists 3 (pt); Recreational therapists 1 (ft), 2 (pt); Occupational therapists 1 (pt); Speech therapists 1 (pt); Activities coordinators 2 (pt); Dietitians 1 (ft).
Facilities Dining room; Activities room; Crafts room; Laundry room; Barber/Beauty shop.
Activities Arts & crafts; Cards; Games; Reading groups; Prayer groups; Movies; Shopping trips; Social/Cultural gatherings.

Prospect Lake Health Care Center
1420 E Fountain Blvd, Colorado Springs, CO, 80910
(303) 632-7604
Admin Barbara G Strombeck. *Medical Dir/Dir of Nursing* Lester Williams MD; Elsie Keith RN DON.
Licensure Skilled care. *Beds* SNF 49. *Certified* Medicaid; Medicare.
Owner Proprietary Corp.
Admissions Requirements Medical examination; Physician's request.
Staff RNs 3 (ft), 3 (pt); Orderlies 1 (pt); Nurses aides 9 (ft), 6 (pt); Recreational therapists 1 (ft); Activities coordinators 1 (pt).
Languages Spanish
Facilities Dining room; Activities room; Chapel; Crafts room; Laundry room.
Activities Arts & crafts; Cards; Games; Reading groups; Prayer groups; Movies; Shopping trips; Social/Cultural gatherings; Swimming; Bowling; Exercise group.

St Clare Convent
1440 E Fountain Blvd, Colorado Springs, CO, 80910
(303) 632-3752
Admin Sr M Carmelia Lohaus. *Medical Dir/Dir of Nursing* G J Joshi MD; Sr M Francesca Hausladen.
Licensure Skilled care. *Beds* SNF 40.
Owner Privately owned.
Admissions Requirements Physician's request.
Staff Physicians 1 (pt); RNs 1 (ft), 2 (pt); LPNs 1 (ft), 2 (pt); Nurses aides 20 (pt); Occupational therapists 1 (pt).
Facilities Dining room; Activities room; Chapel; Crafts room; Reading area.
Activities Arts & crafts; Cards; Movies.

Springs Village Recovery Center*
PO Box 7690, 110 W Van Buren, Colorado Springs, CO, 80909
(303) 475-8686
Admin Larry W Smith.
Licensure Skilled care; Intermediate care; Residential care. *Beds* SNF 60; ICF 60; Residential 17. *Certified* Medicaid; Medicare.
Owner Nonprofit Corp (Bethesda Care Centers).

Stroh Resident Home*
2129 N Nevada Ave, Colorado Springs, CO, 80907
(303) 473-7374
Admin Wayne D Stroh & Marjorie M Stroh.
Licensure Developmentally disabled. *Beds* 10.
Owner Proprietary Corp.

Sunnyrest Sanatorium*
2400 E Cache La Poudre St, Colorado Springs, CO, 80909
(303) 471-8700
Admin Cynthia J Cordle. *Medical Dir/Dir of Nursing* Dr H H Rodman.
Licensure Skilled care. *Beds* 107. *Certified* Medicaid.
Owner Nonprofit Corp.
Admissions Requirements Medical examination; Physician's request.
Staff RNs 6 (ft), 6 (pt); LPNs 2 (ft), 6 (pt); Nurses aides 56 (ft), 4 (pt); Activities coordinators 1 (ft), 1 (pt).
Facilities Dining room; Physical therapy room; Activities room; Laundry room; Barber/Beauty shop.
Activities Arts & crafts; Cards; Games; Reading groups; Prayer groups; Movies; Shopping trips; Social/Cultural gatherings.

Terrace Gardens Health Care Center
2438 Fountain Blvd, Colorado Springs, CO, 80910
(303) 473-8000

Admin Delores L Heidenreich. *Medical Dir/Dir of Nursing* Lester Williams MD; Helen Hedemark RN DON.
Licensure Skilled care; Intermediate care. *Beds* SNF 60; ICF 60. *Certified* Medicaid; Medicare; VA.
Owner Proprietary Corp (ARA Living Centers).
Admissions Requirements Physician's request.
Staff RNs; LPNs; Nurses aides; Recreational therapists; Activities coordinators; Dietitians.
Facilities Dining room; Activities room; Laundry room; Barber/Beauty shop.
Activities Arts & crafts; Cards; Games; Reading groups; Prayer groups; Movies; Shopping trips; Social/Cultural gatherings.

Union Printers Home & Hospital*
PO Box 817, Pikes Peak & Union Blvd, Colorado Springs, CO, 80901
(303) 634-3711
Admin Donald M Fifield.
Licensure Skilled care; Intermediate care. *Beds* SNF 65; ICF 32.
Owner Nonprofit Corp.

Whoolery's Residential Care Facility
607 Lansing Dr, Colorado Springs, CO, 80909
(303) 596-2621
Admin Angeline Whoolery.
Licensure Intermediate care for mentally retarded. *Beds* 5.
Owner Proprietary Corp.
Admissions Requirements Minimum age 18; Females only; Medical examination.
Facilities Dining room; Laundry room.
Activities Arts & crafts; Cards; Games; Reading groups; Prayer groups; Movies; Shopping trips; Social/Cultural gatherings.

COMMERCE CITY

Bentley Gardens Health Care Center Inc
5230 E 66th Way, Commerce City, CO, 80022
(303) 289-5541
Admin Jacqueline Dassler. *Medical Dir/Dir of Nursing* Ruby Torkilson RN.
Licensure Skilled care; Intermediate care. *Beds* SNF 60; ICF 50. *Certified* Medicaid.
Owner Proprietary Corp.
Admissions Requirements Physician's request.
Staff RNs 5 (ft); LPNs 4 (ft), 2 (pt); Orderlies 6 (ft); Nurses aides 16 (ft); Activities coordinators 2 (ft); Dietitians 1 (ft).
Languages Spanish
Facilities Dining room; Physical therapy room; Activities room; Laundry room; Barber/Beauty shop; Library.
Activities Arts & crafts; Games; Reading groups; Prayer groups; Movies; Shopping trips; Social/Cultural gatherings.

Crocker Family Care Home*
6050 Ivanhoe, Commerce City, CO, 80022
(303) 287-7604
Admin Shirley Crocker.
Licensure Intermediate care. *Beds* 4.
Owner Proprietary Corp.

Giles Family Care Home*
6391 Quebec St, Commerce City, CO, 80222
(303) 287-0673
Admin Mildred Giles.
Licensure Intermediate care. *Beds* 4.
Owner Proprietary Corp.

The Ruth Owen Family Care Home*
6801 E 64th Ave, Commerce City, CO, 80022
(303) 287-7984
Admin Ruth Owen.
Licensure Intermediate care. *Beds* 2.
Owner Proprietary Corp.

Sunshine Health Care Center Inc*
7150 Poplar St, Commerce City, CO, 80022
(303) 289-7110
Admin Jim Chappell.

Licensure Skilled care; Intermediate care. *Beds* SNF 84; ICF 32. *Certified* Medicaid; Medicare.
Owner Proprietary Corp.

CORTEZ

Vista Grande Nursing Home
1311 N Mildred Rd, Cortez, CO, 81321
(303) 565-6666
Admin Tyler M Erickson. *Medical Dir/Dir of Nursing* Edward Merritt MD; Marti Bills MD.
Licensure Skilled care; Intermediate care. *Beds* 76. *Certified* Medicaid; Medicare.
Owner Publicly owned.
Admissions Requirements Medical examination; Physician's request.
Staff Physicians 18 (ft); RNs 4 (ft), 2 (pt); LPNs 9 (ft), 3 (pt); Nurses aides 31 (ft), 7 (pt); Physical therapists 1 (ft); Occupational therapists 1 (ft); Speech therapists 1 (pt); Activities coordinators 1 (ft); Dietitians 1 (ft).
Languages Spanish, Navajo
Facilities Dining room; Physical therapy room; Activities room; Crafts room; Laundry room; Barber/Beauty shop; Library.
Activities Arts & crafts; Cards; Games; Reading groups; Prayer groups; Movies; Shopping trips; Social/Cultural gatherings; Picnics; Exercises.

CORY

Horizons Health Care & Retirement Community
1141 Hy 65, Cory, CO, 81414-0116
(303) 835-3113
Admin A Lucille Beals. *Medical Dir/Dir of Nursing* Charles T Frey MD; Mary E Simin DON.
Licensure Skilled care. *Beds* SNF 68. *Certified* Medicaid.
Owner Nonprofit Corp (Volunteers of America).
Admissions Requirements Minimum age 16; Physician's request.
Staff RNs 4 (ft), 4 (pt); LPNs 4 (ft), 4 (pt); Orderlies 3 (ft); Nurses aides 15 (ft), 4 (pt); Recreational therapists 1 (ft).
Facilities Dining room; Physical therapy room; Activities room; Chapel; Crafts room; Laundry room; Barber/Beauty shop; Library.
Activities Arts & crafts; Cards; Games; Reading groups; Prayer groups; Movies; Shopping trips; Social/Cultural gatherings; Church groups come in on Sunday.

CRAIG

Valley View Manor*
943 W 8th Dr, Craig, CO, 81625
(303) 824-4432
Admin John Filkoski.
Licensure Skilled care; Intermediate care. *Beds* SNF 54; ICF 6. *Certified* Medicaid.
Owner Proprietary Corp (ARA Living Centers).

Victory Way House*
1243 E Victoria Way, Craig, CO, 80477
(303) 879-4466
Admin Christine K Collins.
Licensure Residential MR care. *Beds* 8.
Owner Nonprofit Corp.

CRIPPLE CREEK

Hilltop Nursing Home
PO Box 397, "A" St at Hettig Ave, Cripple Creek, CO, 80813
(303) 689-2931
Admin Mary Milne. *Medical Dir/Dir of Nursing* Dr John J Zajac.

Licensure Intermediate care. *Beds* ICF 60. *Certified* Medicaid.
Owner Nonprofit organization/foundation.
Staff Physicians 1 (ft); RNs 2 (ft); LPNs 5 (ft); Nurses aides 15 (ft); Physical therapists 1 (pt); Occupational therapists 1 (pt); Speech therapists 1 (pt); Activities coordinators 1 (ft); Dietitians 1 (pt); Ophthalmologists 1 (pt).
Affiliation Lutheran
Facilities Dining room; Activities room; Laundry room; Barber/Beauty shop.
Activities Arts & crafts; Cards; Games; Prayer groups; Movies; Shopping trips; Social/Cultural gatherings; Activities on volunteer basis.

DEL NORTE

St Joseph's Hospital & Nursing Home of Del Norte Inc*
1280 Grande, Del Norte, CO, 81132
(303) 657-3311
Admin E L Medford. *Medical Dir/Dir of Nursing* Norman Haug MD.
Licensure Skilled care. *Beds* 30. *Certified* Medicaid.
Owner Nonprofit Corp.
Admissions Requirements Medical examination.
Staff RNs 1 (ft), 2 (pt); LPNs 2 (ft), 3 (pt); Physical therapists 1 (pt); Occupational therapists 1 (ft); Activities coordinators 1 (ft); Dietitians 1 (pt).
Affiliation Roman Catholic
Facilities Dining room; Physical therapy room; Activities room; Chapel; Crafts room; Laundry room; Barber/Beauty shop; Library.
Activities Arts & crafts; Cards; Games; Reading groups; Prayer groups; Movies; Shopping trips; Social/Cultural gatherings.

DELTA

Bethesda Care Center
2050 S Main St, Delta, CO, 81416
(303) 874-9773
Admin Larry DeBuhr.
Licensure Skilled care. *Beds* 100. *Certified* Medicaid.
Owner Nonprofit Corp (Bethesda Care Centers).

Delta Care Center*
1102 Grand Ave, Delta, CO, 81416
(303) 874-5773
Admin LaVerne Sharpe.
Licensure Intermediate care. *Beds* 40. *Certified* Medicaid.
Owner Proprietary Corp.
Admissions Requirements Physician's request.
Staff RNs 1 (ft); LPNs 4 (ft), 2 (pt); Nurses aides 6 (ft), 4 (pt); Physical therapists 1 (pt); Recreational therapists 1 (ft); Activities coordinators 1 (ft); Dietitians 1 (pt); Dentists 1 (pt); Podiatrists 1 (pt).
Facilities Dining room; Activities room; Crafts room; Laundry room.
Activities Arts & crafts; Cards; Games; Reading groups; Prayer groups; Movies; Shopping trips; Social/Cultural gatherings.

DENVER

Argyle Park Square
4115 W 38th Ave, Denver, CO, 80212
(303) 455-9513
Admin Ann R Brown.
Licensure Intermediate care; Assisted living. *Beds* ICF 60; Assisted living 100.
Owner Nonprofit organization/foundation.
Admissions Requirements Minimum age 65.
Staff RNs 1 (ft); LPNs 7 (ft), 3 (pt); Nurses aides 12 (ft), 3 (pt); Recreational therapists 1 (ft); Activities coordinators 1 (ft); Dietitians 1 (pt).

Facilities Dining room; Physical therapy room; Activities room; Crafts room; Laundry room; Barber/Beauty shop; Library.
Activities Arts & crafts; Cards; Games; Prayer groups; Movies; Shopping trips; General entertainment.

Arkansas Manor Nursing Home Inc*
3185 W Arkansas, Denver, CO, 80219
(303) 922-1169
Admin Betty McDonald. *Medical Dir/Dir of Nursing* Frank I Dubin MD.
Licensure Skilled care; Intermediate care. *Beds* SNF 110; ICF 10. *Certified* Medicaid.
Owner Proprietary Corp.
Admissions Requirements Minimum age 65.
Facilities Dining room; Laundry room; Barber/Beauty shop; Library.
Activities Arts & crafts; Games; Reading groups; Prayer groups; Movies; Shopping trips; Social/Cultural gatherings.

Asbury Circle Living Center
4660 E Asbury Cr, Denver, CO, 80222
(303) 756-1546
Admin Lavern O Huenergardt. *Medical Dir/Dir of Nursing* Pauline Williams DON.
Licensure Skilled care; Intermediate care. *Beds* SNF 60; ICF 22. *Certified* Medicaid.
Owner Nonprofit Corp (Adventist Health Sys-USA).
Affiliation Seventh-Day Adventist
Facilities Dining room; Activities room; Crafts room; Laundry room; Barber/Beauty shop.
Activities Arts & crafts; Cards; Games; Reading groups; Prayer groups; Movies; Social/Cultural gatherings.

Ashley Nursing Center*
1825 S Federal Blvd, Denver, CO, 80219
(303) 935-4609
Admin Donald Burt.
Licensure Skilled care; Intermediate care. *Beds* SNF 75; ICF 8. *Certified* Medicaid.
Owner Proprietary Corp.

The Aspen Siesta
5353 E Yale Ave, Denver, CO, 80222
(303) 757-1209
Admin Paul Stabel. *Medical Dir/Dir of Nursing* Nancy Stabel RN.
Licensure Skilled care. *Beds* 70.
Owner Privately owned.
Admissions Requirements Physician's request.
Facilities Dining room; Physical therapy room; Activities room; Crafts room; Laundry room; Barber/Beauty shop; Library.
Activities Arts & crafts; Cards; Games; Reading groups; Movies; Social/Cultural gatherings.

Autumn Heights Health Care Center
3131 S Federal Blvd, Denver, CO, 80236
(303) 761-0260
Admin Marvin Bishop. *Medical Dir/Dir of Nursing* William Hines MD; Arloa Johnson RN.
Licensure Skilled care; Intermediate care. *Beds* SNF 89; ICF 89. *Certified* Medicaid; Medicare.
Owner Proprietary Corp (Waverly Group).
Admissions Requirements Medical examination; Physician's request.
Staff RNs 6 (ft), 1 (pt); LPNs 25 (ft); Orderlies 69 (ft); Physical therapists 1 (ft); Reality therapists 1 (ft); Recreational therapists 1 (ft); Speech therapists 1 (pt); Activities coordinators 1 (ft); Dietitians 1 (ft); Dentists 1 (pt); Ophthalmologists 1 (pt); Podiatrists 1 (pt); Dentist 1 (pt).
Facilities Dining room; Physical therapy room; Activities room; Chapel; Crafts room; Laundry room; Barber/Beauty shop; Library.
Activities Arts & crafts; Cards; Games; Reading groups; Prayer groups; Movies; Social/Cultural gatherings; Rehab activities for sensory stimulation.

Bella Vita Towers
4450 E Jewell Ave, Denver, CO, 80222
(303) 757-7438
Admin Carl T Zarlengo. *Medical Dir/Dir of Nursing* Francis Burdick MD; Lori Elliott RN.
Licensure Skilled care. *Beds* SNF 136. *Certified* Medicaid; Medicare.
Owner Privately owned.
Admissions Requirements Minimum age 50.
Staff RNs 9 (ft), 1 (pt); LPNs 9 (ft), 1 (pt); Orderlies 3 (ft); Nurses aides 36 (ft), 1 (pt); Physical therapists 1 (ft); Activities coordinators 1 (ft); Dietitians 1 (ft).
Facilities Dining room; Physical therapy room; Activities room; Chapel; Crafts room; Laundry room; Barber/Beauty shop.
Activities Arts & crafts; Cards; Games; Reading groups; Prayer groups; Movies; Shopping trips; Social/Cultural gatherings.

Berkley Manor Care Center*
735 S Locust, Denver, CO, 80224
(303) 320-4377
Admin Dick Devers. *Medical Dir/Dir of Nursing* Francis Burdick MD.
Licensure Skilled care; Intermediate care. *Beds* 60. *Certified* Medicaid.
Owner Proprietary Corp (Life Care Centers of America).
Admissions Requirements Minimum age 50; Medical examination; Physician's request.
Facilities Dining room; Activities room; Laundry room; Barber/Beauty shop.
Activities Arts & crafts; Cards; Games; Reading groups; Prayer groups; Movies; Shopping trips; Social/Cultural gatherings.

Beth Israel Hospital & Geriatric Center*
1601 Lowell Blvd, Denver, CO, 80204
(303) 825-2190
Admin Harry Yaffe. *Medical Dir/Dir of Nursing* Dr Sydney Foster.
Licensure Skilled care; Intermediate care. *Beds* SNF 82; ICF 65. *Certified* Medicaid; Medicare.
Owner Nonprofit Corp.
Admissions Requirements Minimum age 15; Physician's request.
Staff Physicians 1 (ft); RNs 5 (ft), 3 (pt); LPNs 18 (ft); Orderlies 2 (ft); Nurses aides 32 (ft), 2 (pt); Physical therapists 1 (pt); Occupational therapists 1 (pt); Speech therapists 1 (pt); Activities coordinators 3 (ft); Dietitians 1 (pt); Dentists 1 (pt); Podiatrists 1 (pt); Audiologists 1 (pt).
Affiliation Jewish
Facilities Dining room; Activities room; Chapel; Crafts room; Laundry room; Barber/Beauty shop; Library.
Activities Arts & crafts; Cards; Games; Reading groups; Movies; Shopping trips; Social/Cultural gatherings.

Bragg Residential Care Home Inc*
1461 Cook St, Denver, CO, 80206
(303) 355-0035
Admin Ellen M Bragg.
Licensure Developmentally disabled. *Beds* 6.
Owner Proprietary Corp.

Burton Family Care Home*
3553 Hudson, Denver, CO, 80207
(303) 321-3693
Admin Oleria P Burton.
Licensure Intermediate care for mentally retarded. *Beds* 4.
Owner Proprietary Corp.

Costigan Family Care Home*
600 S Quitman, Denver, CO, 80219
(303) 934-4906
Admin Arabella M Costigan.
Licensure Intermediate care. *Beds* 4.
Owner Proprietary Corp.

Davis Nursing Home Inc
1440 Vine St, Denver, CO, 80206
(303) 399-0350

Admin H Virgil Davis. *Medical Dir/Dir of Nursing* Robert L McKenna MD; Bethany A Davis RN.
Licensure Skilled care; Intermediate care. *Beds* SNF 120; ICF 117.
Owner Proprietary Corp.
Admissions Requirements Minimum age 18.
Staff RNs 10 (ft); LPNs 9 (ft); Orderlies 4 (ft); Nurses aides 45 (ft); Physical therapists 1 (pt); Occupational therapists 1 (pt); Speech therapists 1 (pt); Activities coordinators 1 (ft); Dietitians 1 (pt); Ophthalmologists 1 (pt); Podiatrists 1 (pt).
Facilities Dining room; Physical therapy room; Activities room; Chapel; Crafts room; Laundry room; Barber/Beauty shop; Library.
Activities Arts & crafts; Cards; Games; Reading groups; Prayer groups; Movies; Social/Cultural gatherings; Bingo, pool;, and bowling.

Frickell Family Care Home*
4988 Stuart St, Denver, CO, 80212
(303) 455-9398
Admin Mary Frickell.
Licensure Intermediate care. *Beds* 4.
Owner Proprietary Corp.

David Gottesfeld House*
8160 Linsvale Ave, Denver, CO, 80211
(303) 458-8242
Admin Timothy O'Neil.
Licensure Residential MR care. *Beds* 8.
Owner Nonprofit Corp.

Highland Park Care Center
2741 Federal Blvd, Denver, CO, 80211
(303) 455-3693
Admin Robert C High, FACHA. *Medical Dir/Dir of Nursing* Francis Burdick MD; Michelle LeChevalier-Pfoht.
Licensure Skilled care; Intermediate care. *Beds* SNF 30; ICF 30. *Certified* Medicaid.
Owner Proprietary Corp (Regency Health Care Centers).
Staff RNs 4 (ft); LPNs 4 (ft); Orderlies 2 (ft); Nurses aides 8 (ft); Recreational therapists 1 (ft); Activities coordinators 1 (ft); Dietitians 1 (ft).
Languages Spanish
Facilities Dining room; Activities room; Crafts room; Laundry room; Barber/Beauty shop.
Activities Arts & crafts; Cards; Games; Reading groups; Prayer groups; Movies; Shopping trips; Social/Cultural gatherings.

Highlands Center Hospital*
1920 High St, Denver, CO, 80218
(303) 320-5871
Admin Jeffrey Hausler.
Licensure Intermediate care. *Beds* 52. *Certified* Medicaid.
Owner Proprietary Corp.

Holly Heights Nursing Home Inc
6000 E Iliff, Denver, CO, 80222
(303) 757-5441
Admin Janet L Snipes. *Medical Dir/Dir of Nursing* Stanley Kerstein MD; Jeanne Hurlburt RN DON.
Licensure Skilled care; Intermediate care. *Beds* SNF 60; ICF 91. *Certified* Medicaid; Medicare.
Owner Proprietary Corp.
Admissions Requirements Minimum age 65.
Staff RNs 10 (ft); LPNs 10 (ft); Orderlies 4 (ft); Nurses aides 20 (ft); Activities coordinators 2 (ft), 2 (pt); Dietitians 1 (pt); Ophthalmologists 1 (pt).
Facilities Dining room; Activities room; Laundry room; Barber/Beauty shop.
Activities Arts & crafts; Cards; Games; Reading groups; Prayer groups; Movies; Shopping trips; Social/Cultural gatherings.

Iliff Care Center
6060 E Iliff Ave, Denver, CO, 80222
(303) 759-4221

Admin Donna Rayer. *Medical Dir/Dir of Nursing* Dr Karl Shipman; Clarence Acklam DON.
Licensure Skilled care; Intermediate care. *Beds* SNF 120; ICF 60. *Certified* Medicaid.
Owner Proprietary Corp (Hillhaven Corp).
Admissions Requirements Physician's request.
Staff RNs 11 (ft); LPNs 15 (ft); Orderlies 3 (ft); Nurses aides 43 (ft); Activities coordinators 3 (ft); Dietitians 1 (ft).
Languages French, Spanish
Facilities Dining room; Physical therapy room; Activities room; Crafts room; Barber/Beauty shop; Library; Country store.
Activities Arts & crafts; Cards; Games; Reading groups; Prayer groups; Movies; Shopping trips; Social/Cultural gatherings; RO classes, 2 levels; Exercise & cooking classes; Music appreciation.

Ivy Nursing Home
2205 W 29th Ave, Denver, CO, 80211
(303) 458-1112
Admin Tracy Newman. *Medical Dir/Dir of Nursing* Dr Jardine.
Licensure Skilled care; Intermediate care. *Beds* SNF 102; ICF 60. *Certified* Medicaid.
Owner Proprietary Corp (Beverly Enterprises).
Admissions Requirements Minimum age 18.
Staff RNs 2 (ft); LPNs 12 (ft); Nurses aides 39 (ft), 1 (pt); Activities coordinators 1 (ft); Dietitians 1 (ft).
Languages Spanish, German
Affiliation Roman Catholic
Facilities Dining room; Physical therapy room; Activities room; Chapel; Crafts room; Laundry room; Barber/Beauty shop; Library; Kitchen.
Activities Arts & crafts; Cards; Games; Reading groups; Prayer groups; Movies; Shopping trips; Social/Cultural gatherings; AA group; Entertainment; Exercises.

Lena Crews Family Care Home*
838 S Vallejo, Denver, CO, 80223
(303) 936-1414
Admin Lena Crews.
Licensure Intermediate care. *Beds* 2.
Owner Proprietary Corp.

Leslie Family Care Home*
5231 Lowell Blvd, Denver, CO, 80221
(303) 455-2289
Admin C M Leslie.
Licensure Intermediate care. *Beds* 4.
Owner Proprietary Corp.

Martin Family Care Home*
1996 S Newton, Denver, CO, 80219
(303) 935-7528
Admin Mary E Martin.
Licensure Intermediate care. *Beds* 3.
Owner Proprietary Corp.

Mazotti Family Care Home*
2767 W 38th Ave, Denver, CO, 80211
(303) 433-5933
Admin Jeannie Mazotti.
Licensure Intermediate care. *Beds* 4.
Owner Proprietary Corp.

McCallum Family Care Center*
2536 Downing, Denver, CO, 80205
(303) 355-6524
Admin Willie H McCallum.
Licensure Intermediate care. *Beds* 4.
Owner Proprietary Corp.

McCovy Goldon Age Home Inc*
2858 California St, Denver, CO, 80205
(303) 623-3428
Admin Gertrude McCovy.
Licensure Developmentally disabled. *Beds* 8.
Owner Nonprofit Corp.

Montclair Health Care Center
5775 E 8th Ave, Denver, CO, 80220
(303) 320-4600

Admin Carolyn A Williams. *Medical Dir/Dir of Nursing* Dr S Ferguson; Marva Bruner RN.
Licensure Skilled care; Intermediate care; RIL. *Beds* SNF 275; ICF. *Certified* Medicaid; Medicare.
Owner Nonprofit Corp (Good Shepherd Health Fac).
Admissions Requirements Minimum age 45.
Staff Physicians 2 (pt); RNs 8 (ft), 3 (pt); LPNs 31 (ft), 11 (pt); Orderlies 140 (ft), 22 (pt); Nurses aides; Physical therapists 1 (ft); Recreational therapists 1 (ft); Occupational therapists 1 (pt); Speech therapists; Activities coordinators 4 (ft); Dietitians 1 (ft);; Licensed social worker 1 (ft).
Facilities Dining room; Physical therapy room; Activities room; Chapel; Crafts room; Laundry room; Barber/Beauty shop; Library; Large accessible lobby.
Activities Arts & crafts; Cards; Games; Reading groups; Prayer groups; Movies; Shopping trips; Social/Cultural gatherings.

Mullen Home for the Elderly*
3629 29th Ave, Denver, CO, 80211
(303) 433-7221
Admin Sr Mary John Cain.
Licensure Skilled care; Intermediate care. *Beds* SNF 42; ICF 76. *Certified* Medicaid; Medicare.
Owner Nonprofit Corp.

Nikkel Family Care Home*
5030 W Park Pl, Denver, CO, 80219
(303) 936-6430
Admin Mildred I Nikkel.
Licensure Intermediate care. *Beds* 6.
Owner Proprietary Corp.

Park Avenue Baptist Home
1535 Park Ave, Denver, CO, 80218
(303) 832-9323
Admin Clarence R Hoton. *Medical Dir of Nursing* Mary Grace Smigiel.
Licensure Skilled care; Intermediate care; Residential care. *Beds* SNF 56; ICF 56; Residential 10. *Certified* Medicaid; Medicare.
Owner Nonprofit Corp (Baptist Home Associates).
Admissions Requirements Minimum age 50.
Staff RNs 7 (ft); LPNs 10 (ft); Orderlies 10 (ft); Nurses aides 25 (ft); Physical therapists 2 (ft); Recreational therapists 2 (ft); Activities coordinators 1 (ft); Dietitians 1 (pt).
Affiliation Baptist
Facilities Dining room; Physical therapy room; Activities room; Chapel; Crafts room; Laundry room; Barber/Beauty shop; Library.
Activities Arts & crafts; Cards; Games; Reading groups; Prayer groups; Movies; Shopping trips; Social/Cultural gatherings.

Parkview Manor Nursing Home Inc*
3105 W Arkansas Ave, Denver, CO, 80219
(303) 936-3497
Admin Ruth E Thomann.
Licensure Skilled care; Intermediate care. *Beds* SNF 88; ICF 2. *Certified* Medicaid.
Owner Proprietary Corp.

Presbyterian Medical Center*
1719 E 19th Ave, Denver, CO, 80218
(303) 839-6000
Admin Errol Biggs.
Licensure Intermediate care. *Beds* 24.
Owner Nonprofit Corp.

Regency Rehabilitation Center*
1500 Hooker, Denver, CO, 80204
(303) 534-5968
Admin Marion A Allen.
Licensure Skilled care; Rehabilitation. *Beds* SNF 56; Rehabilitaiton 96. *Certified* Medicaid; Medicare.
Owner Proprietary Corp (Regency Health Care Centers).

Rocky Mountain Health Care Center
2201 Downing St, Denver, CO, 80205
(303) 861-4825
Admin Linda Lovato. *Medical Dir/Dir of Nursing* Werner Prenzlau MD; Shirley William DON.
Licensure Skilled care; Intermediate care. *Beds* 120. *Certified* Medicaid.
Owner Proprietary Corp (National Heritage).
Admissions Requirements Minimum age 18; Physician's request.
Staff Physicians 5 (ft); RNs 8 (ft), 2 (pt); LPNs 8 (ft), 2 (pt); Orderlies 4 (ft); Nurses aides 25 (ft); Recreational therapists 1 (ft); Activities coordinators 1 (ft); Dietitians 1 (ft).
Facilities Dining room; Physical therapy room; Activities room; Crafts room; Laundry room.
Activities Arts & crafts; Cards; Games; Reading groups; Prayer groups; Movies; Shopping trips; Social/Cultural gatherings.

Rose Mary's Home*
7939 Pecos St, Denver, CO, 80221
(303) 429-1857
Admin Rose Mary Hoff.
Licensure Intermediate care. *Beds* 4.
Owner Proprietary Corp.

St Paul Health Center*
1667 Saint Paul St, Denver, CO, 80206
(303) 399-2040
Admin Mina Hull Stolz.
Licensure Skilled care; Intermediate care. *Beds* SNF 104; ICF 156. *Certified* Medicaid; Medicare.
Owner Proprietary Corp.

Sherrelwood Residential Care Facility
1780 Sherrelwood Dr, Denver, CO, 80221
(303) 429-6534
Admin Anita M Sherman.
Licensure Skilled care. *Beds* SNF 10. *Certified* Medicaid; Medicare.
Owner Privately owned.
Admissions Requirements Minimum age 65; Medical examination; Physician's request.
Staff RNs; Nurses aides; Recreational therapists; Activities coordinators.
Languages Spanish, Sign
Facilities Dining room; Activities room; Crafts room; Laundry room; Library; Patios.
Activities Arts & crafts; Cards; Games; Reading groups; Movies; Shopping trips; Social/Cultural gatherings; BBQs; Picnics; Sing-alongs; Cooking classes.

South Monaco Care Center*
895 S Monaco, Denver, CO, 80222
(303) 321-3110
Admin Palma Chambers.
Licensure Skilled care. *Beds* 60.
Owner Proprietary Corp (Convalescent Services).
Admissions Requirements Minimum age 65; Medical examination.
Staff RNs 6 (ft); LPNs 2 (ft); Orderlies 2 (ft); Nurses aides 14 (ft); Recreational therapists 1 (ft).
Facilities Dining room; Physical therapy room; Activities room; Laundry room; Barber/Beauty shop.
Activities Arts & crafts; Cards; Games; Reading groups.

Stovall Care Center
3345 Forest St, Denver, CO, 80207
(303) 355-1666
Admin Viola B Garlington. *Medical Dir/Dir of Nursing* Jitze DeJong MD; Mary E Russell RN.
Licensure Skilled care. *Beds* 60. *Certified* Medicaid; Medicare.
Owner Nonprofit Corp.
Admissions Requirements Minimum age 27; Medical examination; Physician's request.

Staff RNs 4 (ft), 3 (pt); LPNs 2 (ft), 2 (pt); Orderlies 3 (ft), 1 (pt); Nurses aides 14 (ft), 1 (pt); Activities coordinators 1 (ft); Social workers 1 (ft).
Affiliation Baptist
Facilities Activities room; Crafts room; Laundry room; Barber/Beauty shop; Library.
Activities Arts & crafts; Cards; Games; Prayer groups; Movies; Social/Cultural gatherings.

Sunny Acres Villa
2501 E 104th Ave, Denver, CO, 80233
(303) 452-4181
Admin Cheryl Long. *Medical Dir/Dir of Nursing* Dr Robert Jardine; Nancy Hokanson RN DON.
Licensure Skilled care; Intermediate care; Life care retirement community. *Beds* SNF 118; ICF. *Certified* Medicaid; Medicare.
Owner Nonprofit Corp.
Admissions Requirements Minimum age 55; Medical examination.
Staff RNs 7 (ft), 8 (pt); LPNs 8 (ft), 6 (pt); Nurses aides 28 (ft), 13 (pt); Physical therapists 1 (ft); Activities coordinators 1 (ft), 1 (pt); Dietitians 1 (ft); GNP 1 (ft).
Facilities Dining room; Physical therapy room; Activities room; Chapel; Crafts room; Laundry room; Barber/Beauty shop; Library; Stocked lake; Outdoor covered patio.
Activities Arts & crafts; Cards; Games; Reading groups; Prayer groups; Movies; Shopping trips; Social/Cultural gatherings; Community service projects.

Sunny Hill*
3400 E 34th Ave, Denver, CO, 80205
(303) 333-3439
Admin Lillian Duran.
Licensure Intermediate care for mentally retarded. *Beds* 10.
Owner Proprietary Corp.

Tiger Residential Programs (Fairview House)*
6000 E Evans, Bldg 3, Suite 205, Denver, CO, 80222
Admin Gary Davidson.
Licensure Intermediate care for mentally retarded. *Beds* 14. *Certified* Medicaid; Medicare.
Owner Nonprofit Corp.
Admissions Requirements Minimum age 18.
Staff RNs 1 (ft); Recreational therapists 1 (pt); Dietitians 1 (pt); Counselors 14 (ft).
Facilities Dining room; Activities room; Laundry room.
Activities Arts & crafts; Games; Movies; Shopping trips; Social/Cultural gatherings; Camping.

University Hills Christian Nursing Home
2480 S Clermont, Denver, CO, 80222
(303) 758-4528
Admin John Spoelstra. *Medical Dir/Dir of Nursing* William Hines MD; Barbara Cotts RN.
Licensure Skilled care; Intermediate care; Assisted/Independent living. *Beds* SNF 50; ICF 44; 30 Assisted living units 124 Independent apts. *Certified* Medicaid.
Owner Nonprofit Corp.
Admissions Requirements Minimum age 62; Medical examination.
Staff RNs 7 (ft), 8 (pt); LPNs 3 (ft), 4 (pt); Orderlies 4 (ft); Nurses aides 25 (ft), 4 (pt); Activities coordinators 4 (ft); Dietitians; Chaplain.
Facilities Dining room; Physical therapy room; Activities room; Chapel; Crafts room; Laundry room; Barber/Beauty shop; Library; Overnight guest room.
Activities Arts & crafts; Cards; Games; Reading groups; Prayer groups; Movies; Shopping trips; Bowling.

Valley Hi Nursing Home Inc
4686 E Asbury Circle, Denver, CO, 80222
(303) 756-1566

Admin Jo Anne Freeman. *Medical Dir/Dir of Nursing* Francis Burdick MD; Rosemary Jaques.
Licensure Skilled care; Intermediate care. *Beds* 100. *Certified* Medicaid; Medicare.
Owner Proprietary Corp.
Admissions Requirements Minimum age 50.
Staff RNs 9 (ft), 3 (pt); LPNs 2 (ft), 2 (pt); Nurses aides 26 (ft), 5 (pt); Physical therapists 1 (pt); Recreational therapists 1 (pt); Occupational therapists 1 (pt); Speech therapists 1 (pt); Activities coordinators 1 (ft); Dietitians 1 (pt); Dentists 1 (pt); Ophthalmologists 1 (pt); Podiatrists 1 (pt).
Facilities Dining room; Physical therapy room; Activities room; Chapel; Crafts room; Laundry room; Barber/Beauty shop.
Activities Arts & crafts; Cards; Games; Reading groups; Movies; Shopping trips; Social/Cultural gatherings.

Valley Manor*
4601 E Asbury Circle, Denver, CO, 80222
(303) 757-1228
Admin Sieglinde Mazula. *Medical Dir/Dir of Nursing* Francis Burdick MD.
Licensure Skilled care; Intermediate care. *Beds* SNF 45; ICF 39. *Certified* Medicaid; Medicare.
Owner Proprietary Corp (American Medical Services Inc).
Admissions Requirements Minimum age 55; Physician's request.
Staff Physicians 32 (pt); RNs 5 (ft), 5 (pt); LPNs 2 (ft), 2 (pt); Orderlies 3 (ft); Nurses aides 18 (ft), 3 (pt); Physical therapists 1 (pt); Recreational therapists 1 (ft); Occupational therapists; Speech therapists; Activities coordinators 1 (ft); Dietitians; Dentists; Ophthalmologists; Podiatrists; Audiologists.
Facilities Dining room; Activities room; Crafts room; Laundry room; Barber/Beauty shop; Library.
Activities Arts & crafts; Cards; Games; Reading groups; Prayer groups; Movies; Shopping trips; Social/Cultural gatherings; Bus trips; Picnics; Fishing trips; Circus outings; Chamber music concerts.

Wheatridge Manor Nursing Home Inc
2920 Fenton St, Denver, CO, 80214
(303) 238-0481
Admin Sylvia Sara Ruda. *Medical Dir/Dir of Nursing* Paul Fishman MD; Darlene Gaskin DON.
Licensure Skilled care; Intermediate care. *Beds* 84. *Certified* Medicaid.
Owner Proprietary Corp.
Staff RNs 12 (ft); LPNs 4 (ft); Orderlies 4 (ft); Nurses aides 22 (ft); Physical therapists 1 (ft); Reality therapists 1 (pt); Recreational therapists 1 (pt); Occupational therapists 1 (pt); Speech therapists 1 (pt); Activities coordinators 1 (ft), 1 (pt); Dietitians 1 (pt); Dentists 1 (pt); Ophthalmologists 1 (pt); Podiatrists 1 (pt).
Languages French, German, Polish, Yiddish, Hebrew, Spanish, Russian
Facilities Dining room; Physical therapy room; Activities room; Chapel; Crafts room; Laundry room; Barber/Beauty shop; Library.
Activities Arts & crafts; Cards; Games; Reading groups; Prayer groups; Movies; Shopping trips; Social/Cultural gatherings.

Yellow House*
3445 W Mansfield, Denver, CO, 80236
(303) 789-2463
Admin Sally Neuville.
Licensure Developmentally disabled. *Beds* 17.
Owner Proprietary Corp.

DURANGO

Browning House*
205 W Park Ave, Durango, CO, 81301
(303) 259-2887

Admin David Trautman.
Licensure Intermediate care for mentally retarded. *Beds* 8.
Owner Nonprofit Corp.

Four Corners Health Care Center*
2911 Junction St, Durango, CO, 81301
(303) 247-2215
Admin Lillian Marlau.
Licensure Skilled care; Intermediate care. *Beds* SNF 60; ICF 58. *Certified* Medicaid.
Owner Proprietary Corp (ARA Living Centers).

EADS

Weisbrod Hospital & Nursing Home
PO Box 817, Eads, CO, 81036
(303) 438-5401
Admin Andrew Wills. *Medical Dir/Dir of Nursing* John Hadley DO; Connie Richardson RN.
Licensure Intermediate care. *Beds* ICF 34. *Certified* Medicaid.
Owner Publicly owned.
Admissions Requirements Medical examination.
Staff Physicians 1 (ft); RNs 6 (ft); LPNs 4 (ft), 2 (pt); Nurses aides 6 (ft), 8 (pt); Activities coordinators 1 (ft), 1 (pt); Dietitians 1 (pt).
Facilities Dining room; Activities room; Crafts room.
Activities Arts & crafts; Cards; Games; Prayer groups; Movies; Shopping trips; Social/Cultural gatherings; Picnics; Adopt-a-grandparent program.

ENGLEWOOD

Cherry Hills Nursing Home*
3575 S Washington St, Englewood, CO, 80110
(303) 789-2265
Admin June Richard. *Medical Dir/Dir of Nursing* Dr Angela Heaton.
Licensure Skilled care; Intermediate care. *Beds* SNF 89; ICF 6. *Certified* Medicaid; Medicare.
Owner Proprietary Corp (Hillhaven Corp).
Admissions Requirements Medical examination; Physician's request.
Staff RNs 5 (ft), 4 (pt); LPNs 3 (ft), 4 (pt); Orderlies 2 (ft); Nurses aides 38 (ft), 10 (pt); Physical therapists 1 (pt); Recreational therapists 1 (pt); Occupational therapists 1 (ft); Speech therapists 1 (pt); Activities coordinators 1 (ft); Dietitians 1 (ft); Dentists 1 (pt); Podiatrists 1 (pt).
Facilities Dining room; Physical therapy room; Activities room; Laundry room; Barber/Beauty shop; Library.
Activities Arts & crafts; Cards; Games; Reading groups; Prayer groups; Movies; Shopping trips; Social/Cultural gatherings.

Cherry Park Health Care Facility*
3636 S Pearl St, Englewood, CO, 80110
(303) 761-1640
Admin Fred Kilfoy.
Licensure Skilled care; Intermediate care. *Beds* SNF 52; ICF 44. *Certified* Medicaid.
Owner Proprietary Corp (ARA Living Centers).

Englewood House*
5001 S Hooker, Englewood, CO, 80110
(303) 696-7002
Admin Margaret Lowe.
Licensure Developmentally disabled. *Beds* 8.
Owner Nonprofit Corp.

Julia Temple Center
3401 S Lafayette St, Englewood, CO, 80110
(303) 761-0075
Admin Marcia Pilgrim. *Medical Dir/Dir of Nursing* A Lee Anneberg MD; Mary Kramer RN.

Licensure Skilled care; Residential care. *Beds* SNF 59; ICF 77; Residential 44. *Certified* Medicaid.
Owner Proprietary Corp.
Admissions Requirements Minimum age 50; Medical examination; Physician's request.
Staff RNs; LPNs; Orderlies; Nurses aides; Recreational therapists; Activities coordinators; Dietitians.
Languages Spanish
Facilities Dining room; Activities room; Crafts room; Laundry room; Barber/Beauty shop; Outside secured courtyard.
Activities Arts & crafts; Cards; Games; Prayer groups; Movies; Shopping trips; Social/Cultural gatherings.

ERIE

Bland Residential Care Home*
RR 1 Box 5050, Erie, CO, 80516
(303) 447-9196
Admin Marie Bland.
Licensure Intermediate care. *Beds* 6.
Owner Proprietary Corp.

ESTES PARK

Prospect Park Living Center
PO Box 2740, 555 Prospect Ave, Estes Park, CO, 80517
(303) 586-8103
Admin Andy Wills CEO. *Medical Dir/Dir of Nursing* Shelly Units DON.
Licensure Skilled care. *Beds* SNF 60. *Certified* Medicaid; Medicare.
Owner Publicly owned.
Admissions Requirements Medical examination; Physician's request.
Staff Physicians 6 (ft); RNs 5 (ft), 3 (pt); LPNs 6 (ft), 4 (pt); Orderlies 2 (ft); Nurses aides 10 (ft), 2 (pt); Physical therapists 1 (ft), 1 (pt); Recreational therapists 1 (pt); Occupational therapists 1 (pt); Speech therapists 1 (pt); Activities coordinators 1 (ft), 2 (pt); Dietitians 1 (ft).
Facilities Dining room; Physical therapy room; Activities room; Chapel; Crafts room; Laundry room; Barber/Beauty shop; Library.
Activities Arts & crafts; Cards; Games; Reading groups; Prayer groups; Movies; Shopping trips; Social/Cultural gatherings; Scenic tours.

FAIRPLAY

McNamara Mercy Hospital & Nursing Home*
525 Costello, Fairplay, CO, 80440
(303) 836-2701
Admin William D Phipps.
Licensure Skilled care. *Beds* 14. *Certified* Medicaid; Medicare.
Owner Publicly owned.

FLORENCE

Colorado State Veterans Nursing Home
Moore Dr, Florence, CO, 81226
(303) 784-6331
Admin Roger Nelson. *Medical Dir/Dir of Nursing* Dr John Buglewicz.
Licensure Skilled care. *Beds* 120. *Certified* Medicaid.
Owner Publicly owned.
Admissions Requirements Medical examination; Physician's request.
Staff RNs 10 (ft); LPNs 8 (ft); Orderlies 4 (ft); Nurses aides 29 (ft); Activities coordinators 1 (ft).
Facilities Dining room; Physical therapy room; Activities room; Chapel; Crafts room; Laundry room; Barber/Beauty shop.
Activities Arts & crafts; Cards; Games; Reading groups; Prayer groups; Movies; Shopping trips; Social/Cultural gatherings; Pet therapy; Music therapy.

St Joseph Manor
3rd & Washington Ave, Florence, CO, 81226
(303) 784-4891
Admin Betty Lewis. *Medical Dir/Dir of Nursing* Peter J Gamache MD; Jill Psaty RN DON.
Licensure Skilled care. *Beds* SNF 43. *Certified* Medicaid.
Owner Nonprofit Corp.
Admissions Requirements Minimum age 50; Medical examination; Physician's request.
Staff Physicians 4 (pt); RNs 2 (ft); LPNs 6 (ft); Orderlies 1 (ft); Nurses aides 26 (ft); Physical therapists 1 (pt); Reality therapists 1 (pt); Recreational therapists 1 (pt); Occupational therapists 1 (pt); Activities coordinators 1 (ft); Dietitians 1 (pt); Ophthalmologists 1 (pt).
Affiliation Roman Catholic
Facilities Dining room; Physical therapy room; Activities room; Chapel; Crafts room; Laundry room; Barber/Beauty shop.
Activities Arts & crafts; Cards; Games; Reading groups; Prayer groups; Movies; Shopping trips; Social/Cultural gatherings.

FORT COLLINS

Columbine Care Center
421 Parker St, Fort Collins, CO, 80525
(303) 482-1584
Admin Jean Niedringhaus. *Medical Dir/Dir of Nursing* L A Merkel MD; Marlene Sinclair RN DON.
Licensure Skilled care; Intermediate care; Residential care. *Beds* SNF 65; ICF 55; Residential care 5. *Certified* Medicaid; Medicare.
Owner Proprietary Corp.
Admissions Requirements Medical examination; Physician's request.
Staff RNs 5 (ft), 6 (pt); LPNs 8 (ft), 2 (pt); Orderlies 3 (ft); Nurses aides 33 (ft), 17 (pt); Physical therapists 1 (ft); Activities coordinators 2 (ft).
Languages Spanish
Facilities Dining room; Physical therapy room; Activities room; Barber/Beauty shop.
Activities Arts & crafts; Cards; Games; Reading groups; Prayer groups; Movies; Shopping trips; Social/Cultural gatherings.

Fort Collins Good Samaritan Retirement Village
508 W Trilby Rd, Fort Collins, CO, 80525
(303) 226-4909
Admin Eugene N Fox. *Medical Dir/Dir of Nursing* Dr James Bush.
Licensure Skilled care. *Beds* SNF 50. *Certified* Medicaid; Medicare.
Owner Nonprofit Corp (Evangelical Lutheran/ Good Samaritan).
Admissions Requirements Minimum age 60; Medical examination.
Staff RNs; LPNs; Orderlies; Nurses aides; Activities coordinators.
Affiliation Lutheran
Facilities Dining room; Activities room; Chapel; Crafts room; Barber/Beauty shop; Library.
Activities Arts & crafts; Games; Reading groups; Movies; Shopping trips; Social/ Cultural gatherings; Exercise group; Daily devotions; Weekly Bible study; Monthly Communion; Monthly memorial service; Sunday school; Sunday worship.

Fort Collins Health Care Center*
1000 Lemay Ave, Fort Collins, CO, 80524
(303) 482-7925
Admin Rae Rose. *Medical Dir/Dir of Nursing* Dr Harold Dupper.
Licensure Skilled care; Intermediate care. *Beds* SNF 50; ICF 50. *Certified* Medicaid; Medicare.
Owner Proprietary Corp (ARA Living Centers).

Admissions Requirements Physician's request.
Staff RNs 2 (ft), 5 (pt); LPNs 2 (ft), 5 (pt); Orderlies 1 (ft), 2 (pt); Nurses aides 8 (ft), 27 (pt); Activities coordinators 1 (pt).
Facilities Dining room; Physical therapy room; Activities room; Crafts room; Laundry room; Barber/Beauty shop.
Activities Arts & crafts; Games; Movies; Shopping trips; Social/Cultural gatherings.

Four Seasons Health Care Center
1020 Patton St, Fort Collins, CO, 80524
(303) 484-6133
Admin Kathryn L Butler. *Medical Dir/Dir of Nursing* Steven Tippin MD; Marilyn Garrity RN DON.
Licensure Skilled care. *Beds* SNF 106. *Certified* Medicaid; Medicare.
Owner Proprietary Corp (ARA Living Centers).
Admissions Requirements Physician's request.
Staff RNs; LPNs; Orderlies; Nurses aides; Activities coordinators; Dietitians.
Languages Spanish, German
Facilities Dining room; Laundry room; Barber/Beauty shop; Library; Private courtyard.
Activities Arts & crafts; Cards; Games; Reading groups; Prayer groups; Movies; Shopping trips; Social/Cultural gatherings; Men's group; Exercise group; Reality orientation group.

Golden West Nursing Home Inc*
1005 E Elizabeth St, Fort Collins, CO, 80521
(303) 482-2525
Admin Scott Nelson. *Medical Dir/Dir of Nursing* Dr William Abbey.
Licensure Intermediate care; Residential care. *Beds* ICF 50; Residential 10.
Owner Proprietary Corp (Hillhaven Corp).
Admissions Requirements Physician's request.
Staff RNs 3 (pt); LPNs 2 (ft), 4 (pt); Nurses aides 5 (ft), 11 (pt); Activities coordinators 1 (ft); Dietitians 1 (pt).
Facilities Dining room; Activities room; Laundry room; Barber/Beauty shop; Library.
Activities Arts & crafts; Cards; Games; Reading groups; Prayer groups; Movies; Shopping trips.

Mountain Duplex*
820 W Mountain, Fort Collins, CO, 80524
(303) 484-1609
Admin Sharon Jacksi.
Licensure Residential MR care. *Beds* 8.
Owner Proprietary Corp.

Pioneer Home*
811 E Myrtle St, Fort Collins, CO, 80521
(303) 482-5035
Admin J Klein.
Licensure Intermediate care for mentally retarded. *Beds* 34. *Certified* Medicaid.
Owner Proprietary Corp.

Spring Creek Health Care Center*
1000 Stuart St, Fort Collins, CO, 80521
(303) 482-5712
Admin Donna Harding. *Medical Dir/Dir of Nursing* David K Allen MD.
Licensure Skilled care; Intermediate care; Residential care. *Beds* SNF 120; ICF 60; Residential 50. *Certified* Medicaid; Medicare.
Owner Proprietary Corp (ARA Living Centers).
Admissions Requirements Minimum age 6 months; Medical examination; Physician's request.
Staff Physicians 30 (pt); RNs 8 (ft), 6 (pt); LPNs 15 (ft), 5 (pt); Orderlies 2 (ft); Nurses aides 40 (ft), 10 (pt); Physical therapists 1 (pt); Reality therapists 1 (ft); Recreational therapists 1 (ft); Occupational therapists 1 (pt); Speech therapists 1 (pt); Activities

coordinators 1 (ft); Dietitians 1 (pt); Dentists 1 (pt); Ophthalmologists 1 (pt); Podiatrists 1 (pt); Audiologists 1 (pt).
Facilities Dining room; Physical therapy room; Activities room; Crafts room; Laundry room; Barber/Beauty shop; Library.
Activities Arts & crafts; Cards; Games; Reading groups; Prayer groups; Movies; Shopping trips; Social/Cultural gatherings.

FORT MORGAN

Gayle Street Residential Center*
425 Gayle St, Fort Morgan, CO, 80701
(303) 867-5365
Admin William E Duffield.
Licensure Developmentally disabled. *Beds* 9.
Owner Nonprofit Corp.

Valley View Villa Nursing Home*
815 Fremont, Fort Morgan, CO, 80701
(303) 867-8261
Admin Fred Nuss.
Licensure Skilled care. *Beds* 120. *Certified* Medicaid.
Owner Proprietary Corp (Life Care Centers of America).

FOWLER

Fowler Health Care Center
2nd & Florence St, Fowler, CO, 81039
(303) 263-4234
Admin Harry N Harrison. *Medical Dir/Dir of Nursing* Mary Jean Berg MD; Beverly Harrison DON.
Licensure Skilled care; Residential care. *Beds* SNF; Residential 63. *Certified* Medicaid; Medicare.
Owner Proprietary Corp.
Admissions Requirements Medical examination; Physician's request.
Staff RNs 5 (ft), 3 (pt); LPNs 2 (ft), 1 (pt); Orderlies 1 (ft); Nurses aides 14 (ft), 5 (pt); Recreational therapists 1 (ft); Activities coordinators 1 (ft); Dietitians 1 (ft).
Languages Spanish
Facilities Dining room; Activities room; Crafts room; Laundry room; Barber/Beauty shop.
Activities Arts & crafts; Cards; Games; Reading groups; Prayer groups; Movies; Shopping trips; Social/Cultural gatherings.

FRUITA

Family Health West
PO Box 668, Fruita, CO, 81521
(303) 858-9871
Admin Carroll E Rushold. *Medical Dir/Dir of Nursing* Jean Rose RN.
Licensure Skilled care; Intermediate care; Secure Alzheimer's unit; Low Income Elderly Housing. *Beds* SNF 95; ICF 25; Housing 75. *Certified* Medicaid.
Owner Nonprofit Corp.
Admissions Requirements Physician's request.
Staff RNs 10 (ft), 4 (pt); LPNs 8 (ft), 4 (pt); Physical therapists 2 (pt); Occupational therapists 1 (pt); Speech therapists 1 (pt); Activities coordinators 2 (ft), 1 (pt); Dietitians 1 (ft), 1 (pt).
Facilities Dining room; Physical therapy room; Activities room; Crafts room; Barber/ Beauty shop; Library.
Activities Arts & crafts; Cards; Games; Reading groups; Prayer groups; Movies; Shopping trips; Social/Cultural gatherings.

GLENWOOD SPRINGS

Glen Valley Nursing Home*
PO Box 1179, 2305 Blake Ave, Glenwood Springs, CO, 81601
(303) 945-5476
Admin Alice Applegate Letang.

Licensure Intermediate care. *Beds* 60.
Certified Medicaid.
Owner Proprietary Corp.

GRAND JUNCTION

Bethesda Care Center
2961 Hermosa Ct, Grand Junction, CO,
81506
(303) 243-9824
Admin Betty Stephenson. *Medical Dir/Dir of
Nursing* Eileen Gooch DON.
Licensure Intermediate care. *Beds* ICF 60.
Certified Medicaid.
Owner Nonprofit Corp (Bethesda Care
Centers).
Admissions Requirements Medical
examination; Physician's request.
Staff RNs 1 (ft); LPNs 4 (ft), 3 (pt); Orderlies
2 (pt); Nurses aides 12 (ft), 9 (pt); Activities
coordinators 1 (ft).
Facilities Dining room; Activities room;
Chapel; Crafts room; Laundry room; Barber/
Beauty shop; Library.
Activities Arts & crafts; Cards; Games;
Reading groups; Prayer groups; Movies;
Shopping trips; Social/Cultural gatherings;
Community trips; Picnics.

Grand Junction Care Center
2425 Teller Ave, Grand Junction, CO, 81501
(303) 243-3381
Admin M June McCoy. *Medical Dir/Dir of
Nursing* Roy E Kearns DO; Melissa Gentry
RN DON.
Licensure Skilled care. *Beds* 108. *Certified*
Medicaid; Medicare.
Owner Proprietary Corp (Beverly Enterprises).
Admissions Requirements Physician's request.
Staff Physicians; RNs; LPNs; Orderlies;
Nurses aides; Physical therapists; Reality
therapists; Recreational therapists;
Occupational therapists; Speech therapists;
Activities coordinators; Dietitians; Dentists;
Podiatrists.
Languages Spanish
Facilities Dining room; Physical therapy
room; Activities room; Laundry room;
Barber/Beauty shop.
Activities Arts & crafts; Cards; Games;
Reading groups; Prayer groups; Movies;
Shopping trips; Social/Cultural gatherings.

Grand Junction Regional Center
2800 D Rd, Grand Junction, CO, 81501
(303) 245-2100
Admin William H Jackson.
Licensure Skilled care for Developmentally
disabled; Intermediate care for
Developmentally disabled. *Beds* 340.
Certified Medicaid.
Owner Publicly owned.
Staff Physicians 4 (pt); RNs 19 (ft); LPNs 3
(pt); Physical therapists 3 (ft); Recreational
therapists 4 (ft); Occupational therapists 6
(ft); Speech therapists 4 (ft); Dietitians 3 (ft);
Podiatrists 1 (ft).

Hilltop Rehabilitation Center*
1100 Patterson Rd, Grand Junction, CO,
81501
(303) 242-8980
Admin Ronald W Cronk.
Licensure Skilled care. *Beds* 58. *Certified*
Medicare.
Owner Nonprofit Corp.

Lavilla Grande Care CTR*
2501 Little Bookcliff Dr, Grand Junction, CO,
81501
(303) 245-1211
Admin Terry Stephenson. *Medical Dir/Dir of
Nursing* Dr Douglas C Shenk.
Licensure Skilled care. *Beds* 119. *Certified*
Medicaid.
Owner Nonprofit Corp (Bethesda Care
Centers).

Admissions Requirements Medical
examination.
Staff RNs 6 (ft), 3 (pt); LPNs 5 (ft), 2 (pt);
Nurses aides 26 (ft), 12 (pt); Physical
therapists 1 (ft); Activities coordinators 1
(ft).
Facilities Dining room; Physical therapy
room; Activities room; Chapel; Crafts room;
Barber/Beauty shop; Kitchen.
Activities Arts & crafts; Cards; Games;
Reading groups; Prayer groups; Movies;
Shopping trips; Social/Cultural gatherings;
Pet therapy.

Mesa Manor Nursing Center
2901 N 12th St, Grand Junction, CO, 81506
(303) 243-7211
Admin Eugene H Knight. *Medical Dir/Dir of
Nursing* Jacobo A Ruybac MD; Vickie L
Newman RN.
Licensure Skilled care. *Beds* SNF 108.
Certified Medicaid; Medicare.
Owner Proprietary Corp (National Heritage).
Admissions Requirements Medical
examination; Physician's request.
Staff RNs; LPNs; Orderlies; Nurses aides;
Activities coordinators; Dietitians.
Languages Spanish
Facilities Dining room; Activities room;
Chapel; Crafts room; Laundry room; Barber/
Beauty shop.
Activities Arts & crafts; Cards; Games;
Reading groups; Prayer groups; Movies;
Shopping trips; Social/Cultural gatherings.

GREELEY

Bonell Good Samaritan Center*
708 22nd St, Greeley, CO, 80631
(303) 352-6082
Admin Mark Turk.
Licensure Skilled care; Intermediate care. *Beds*
SNF 173; ICF 106. *Certified* Medicaid;
Medicare.
Owner Nonprofit Corp (Evangelical Lutheran/
Good Samaritan).

Centennial Health Care Center
1637 29th Ave Pl, Greeley, CO, 80631
(303) 356-8181
Admin Sharon Pebley. *Medical Dir/Dir of
Nursing* Dr Baldwin; Jane Rumrill.
Licensure Skilled care; Intermediate care. *Beds*
SNF 120; ICF. *Certified* Medicaid;
Medicare.
Owner Proprietary Corp (ARA Living
Centers).
Staff RNs 6 (ft), 5 (pt); LPNs 7 (ft), 3 (pt);
Orderlies 2 (ft); Nurses aides 29 (ft), 10 (pt);
Physical therapists 1 (pt); Recreational
therapists 1 (ft); Occupational therapists 1
(pt); Speech therapists 1 (pt).
Languages German, Spanish
Facilities Dining room; Activities room;
Laundry room; Barber/Beauty shop.
Activities Arts & crafts; Cards; Games;
Reading groups; Prayer groups; Movies;
Shopping trips; Social/Cultural gatherings;
Men's group.

Fairacres Manor Inc
1700 18th Ave, Greeley, CO, 80631
(303) 353-3370
Admin LaVern Weber. *Medical Dir/Dir of
Nursing* Dr David Bagley; Phyllis Coyle RN.
Licensure Skilled care. *Beds* SNF 112.
Certified Medicaid; Medicare.
Owner Privately owned.
Admissions Requirements Minimum age
Prefer geriatric; Medical examination;
Physician's request.
Facilities Dining room; Activities room;
Chapel; Barber/Beauty shop.
Activities Arts & crafts; Cards; Games;
Reading groups; Prayer groups; Movies;
Social/Cultural gatherings.

Kenton Manor
850 27th Ave, Greeley, CO, 80631
(303) 353-1018
Admin Linda McClatchey.
Licensure Skilled care; Intermediate care. *Beds*
SNF 60; ICF 60; Apts 11. *Certified*
Medicaid; Medicare.
Owner Proprietary Corp (ARA Living
Centers).

New Life Center
1819 Birch Ave, Greeley, CO, 80631
(303) 353-0535
Admin Rita M Schilling. *Medical Dir/Dir of
Nursing* Barbara Crespin.
Licensure Intermediate care for mentally
retarded. *Beds* 56. *Certified* Medicaid.
Owner Proprietary Corp (ARA Living
Centers).
Admissions Requirements Minimum age 18.
Staff RNs 1 (ft); LPNs 4 (ft), 2 (pt); Physical
therapists 1 (pt); Recreational therapists 1
(ft); Occupational therapists 1 (ft); Speech
therapists 1 (pt); Activities coordinators 1
(ft).
Facilities Dining room; Activities room;
Crafts room; Laundry room.
Activities Arts & crafts; Cards; Games;
Reading groups; Prayer groups; Movies;
Shopping trips; Social/Cultural gatherings.

Wareheime Residential Care*
1429 12th Ave, Greeley, CO, 80631
(303) 352-2949
Admin Zella Mae Wareheime.
Licensure Intermediate care for mentally
retarded. *Beds* 8.
Owner Proprietary Corp.

Weld County Community Center Group Home*
1618 11th Ave, Greeley, CO, 80631
(303) 339-5360
Admin John H Wooster.
Licensure Intermediate care for mentally
retarded. *Beds* 6.
Owner Nonprofit Corp.

GUNNISON

Gunnison Health Care Center
1500 W Tomichi Ave, Gunnison, CO, 81230
(303) 641-0704
Admin Clair Krehbiel. *Medical Dir/Dir of
Nursing* Dr Ron Meyer.
Licensure Skilled care; Intermediate care. *Beds*
SNF 51. *Certified* Medicaid; Medicare.
Owner Nonprofit Corp.
Admissions Requirements Medical
examination; Physician's request.
Staff RNs 4 (ft), 3 (pt); LPNs 1 (ft), 2 (pt);
Nurses aides 6 (ft), 18 (pt); Recreational
therapists 1 (ft); Activities coordinators 1
(ft).
Facilities Dining room; Physical therapy
room; Activities room; Crafts room; Barber/
Beauty shop.
Activities Arts & crafts; Cards; Games;
Reading groups; Prayer groups; Movies;
Shopping trips; Social/Cultural gatherings.

HAXTUN

Haxtun Hospital District
PO Box 308, 253 W Fletcher St, Haxtun, CO,
80731
(303) 774-6123
Admin Douglas A McMillan. *Medical Dir/Dir
of Nursing* James Ley MD; Caroline Newth
RN DON.
Licensure Intermediate care. *Beds* ICF 17.
Certified Medicaid; Medicare.
Owner Nonprofit organization/foundation.
Staff Physicians 1 (ft); RNs 6 (ft); LPNs 1 (ft),
1 (pt); Nurses aides 9 (ft), 5 (pt).

Facilities Dining room; Chapel; Barber/Beauty shop.
Activities Arts & crafts; Cards; Games; Reading groups; Prayer groups; Social/Cultural gatherings.

HOLLY

Holly Nursing Care Center
320 N 8th, Holly, CO, 81047
(303) 537-6555
Admin Etha Martinson. *Medical Dir/Dir of Nursing* R G Ward DO.
Licensure Intermediate care. *Beds* 60. *Certified* Medicaid.
Owner Proprietary Corp.

HOLYOKE

Prarie Vista Care Center
816 S Interocean, Holyoke, CO, 80734
854-2251
Admin Dolores M McGinnis. *Medical Dir/Dir of Nursing* Myrlen Chesnut DO.
Licensure Intermediate care. *Beds* ICF 55. *Certified* Medicaid.
Owner Proprietary Corp.
Admissions Requirements Medical examination; Physician's request.
Staff Physicians 1 (pt); LPNs 5 (ft), 2 (pt); Nurses aides 18 (ft), 3 (pt); Physical therapists 1 (ft), 1 (pt); Recreational therapists 1 (ft); Dietitians 1 (ft).
Facilities Dining room; Physical therapy room; Activities room; Chapel; Laundry room.
Activities Arts & crafts; Cards; Games; Reading groups; Prayer groups; Movies; Shopping trips; Social/Cultural gatherings; Monthly newspaper.

HOMELAKE

Colorado State Veterans Center—Homelake
PO Box 97, Homelake, CO, 81135
(303) 852-5118
Admin Dennis Karnowski. *Medical Dir/Dir of Nursing* Eugene Gonzales MD; Yvonne Olme RN DON.
Licensure Skilled care; Domicilary unit. *Beds* SNF 60; Domiciliary unit 120. *Certified* Medicaid; VA.
Owner Publicly owned.
Admissions Requirements Medical examination.
Staff Physicians 3 (pt); RNs 7 (ft); LPNs 3 (ft); Orderlies 2 (ft); Nurses aides 5 (ft); Physical therapists 1 (pt); Reality therapists 1 (pt); Recreational therapists 1 (ft); Occupational therapists 1 (pt); Speech therapists 1 (pt); Activities coordinators 1 (ft); Dietitians 1 (pt); Dentists 1 (pt); Ophthalmologists 1 (pt); Podiatrists 1 (pt).
Languages Spanish
Facilities Dining room; Physical therapy room; Activities room; Chapel; Crafts room; Laundry room; Barber/Beauty shop; Library.
Activities Arts & crafts; Cards; Games; Reading groups; Prayer groups; Movies; Shopping trips; Social/Cultural gatherings.

HUGO

Lincoln Community Hospital & Nursing Home
PO Box 248, 111 6th St, Hugo, CO, 80821
(303) 743-2421
Admin Delores Nance. *Medical Dir/Dir of Nursing* Mark Olsen MD; Debbie Parrish RN.
Licensure Skilled care; Adult daycare; Respite care. *Beds* SNF 35. *Certified* Medicaid; Medicare.
Owner Publicly owned.
Admissions Requirements Medical examination; Physician's request.

Staff Physicians 2 (ft); RNs 5 (ft), 5 (pt); LPNs 4 (ft); Nurses aides 16 (ft), 4 (pt); Physical therapists 1 (pt); Activities coordinators 1 (ft); Dietitians 1 (pt); Dentists 1 (pt); Dental Hygienist 1 (pt).
Facilities Dining room; Physical therapy room; Activities room; Chapel; Crafts room; Barber/Beauty shop; Library.
Activities Arts & crafts; Cards; Games; Reading groups; Prayer groups; Movies; Shopping trips; Social/Cultural gatherings.

JULESBURG

Al Mar Residence*
823 W 9th St, Julesburg, CO, 80737
(303) 522-7121
Admin William Duffield.
Beds 8. *Certified* Medicare.
Owner Nonprofit Corp.

Sedgwick County Hospital & Nursing Home
900 Cedar St, Julesburg, CO, 80737
(303) 474-3323
Admin Mike Bildner. *Medical Dir/Dir of Nursing* Kevin Shafer DO; Patricia Farmer DON.
Licensure Intermediate care. *Beds* ICF 32. *Certified* Medicaid.
Owner Publicly owned.
Admissions Requirements Physician's request.
Staff RNs 1 (ft); LPNs 6 (ft); Orderlies 1 (ft); Nurses aides 3 (ft), 11 (pt); Physical therapists 1 (pt); Activities coordinators 1 (pt); Dietitians 1 (pt).
Facilities Dining room; Physical therapy room; Activities room; Chapel; Crafts room; Laundry room; Barber/Beauty shop; Library; Covered patio.
Activities Arts & crafts; Cards; Games; Reading groups; Prayer groups; Shopping trips.

LA JUNTA

Arkansas Valley Regional Medical Center Nursing Care Center
514 W 10th, La Junta, CO, 81050
(303) 384-5412
Admin Dana Froelich. *Medical Dir/Dir of Nursing* Dr C C Weber; Janice R Wilson RN DON.
Licensure Skilled care; Intermediate care. *Beds* SNF 43; ICF 107. *Certified* Medicaid.
Owner Nonprofit organization/foundation.
Admissions Requirements Minimum age 15; Physician's request.
Staff Physicians 10 (pt); RNs 5 (ft), 3 (pt); LPNs 11 (ft), 2 (pt); Orderlies 2 (ft), 2 (pt); Nurses aides 36 (ft), 4 (pt); Activities coordinators 3 (ft); Dietitians 1 (ft).
Affiliation Mennonite
Facilities Dining room; Physical therapy room; Activities room; Chapel; Crafts room; Laundry room; Barber/Beauty shop.
Activities Arts & crafts; Cards; Games; Reading groups; Prayer groups; Movies; Shopping trips; Social/Cultural gatherings.

Lovato Residential Care Facility*
302 Carson, La Junta, CO, 81050
(303) 384-7687
Admin Josie Lovato.
Licensure Intermediate care. *Beds* 10.
Owner Proprietary Corp.

Matthews Care Home*
821 San Juan, La Junta, CO, 81050
(303) 384-2246
Admin Orley W Matthews.
Licensure Intermediate care. *Beds* 10.
Owner Proprietary Corp.

LAKEWOOD

Allison Health Care Center
1660 Allison St, Lakewood, CO, 80215
(303) 232-7177
Admin McNair Ezzard. *Medical Dir/Dir of Nursing* F Burdick MD; Patricia Jenkins DON.
Licensure Skilled care; Intermediate care; Respite. *Beds* SNF 60; ICF 60. *Certified* Medicaid.
Owner Proprietary Corp (National Heritage).
Admissions Requirements Medical examination.
Staff Physicians; RNs; LPNs; Nurses aides; Physical therapists; Reality therapists; Recreational therapists; Occupational therapists; Speech therapists; Activities coordinators; Dietitians.
Facilities Dining room; Physical therapy room; Activities room; Chapel; Crafts room; Laundry room; Barber/Beauty shop.
Activities Arts & crafts; Cards; Games; Reading groups; Movies; Shopping trips; Social/Cultural gatherings; Current events; Mens club; Church.

Applewood Hills Care Center Inc*
1625 Simms St, Lakewood, CO, 80215
(303) 238-8161
Admin David Guinlivan. *Medical Dir/Dir of Nursing* Jitze DeJong MD.
Licensure Skilled care. *Beds* 60. *Certified* Medicaid; Medicare.
Owner Proprietary Corp.
Staff RNs 5 (ft), 2 (pt); LPNs 2 (ft), 2 (pt); Orderlies 2 (ft), 1 (pt); Nurses aides 12 (ft), 5 (pt); Recreational therapists 1 (ft); Occupational therapists 1 (ft).
Facilities Dining room; Activities room; Laundry room; Barber/Beauty shop.
Activities Arts & crafts; Cards; Games; Reading groups; Prayer groups; Movies; Shopping trips; Social/Cultural gatherings; Exercises.

Bethany Care Center
5301 W 1st Ave, Lakewood, CO, 80226
(303) 238-8333
Admin Dale R Turner. *Medical Dir/Dir of Nursing* Frances Burdick; Ann Romaglia DON.
Licensure Skilled care; Intermediate care. *Beds* SNF 110; ICF 100. *Certified* Medicaid.
Owner Nonprofit Corp (Bethesda Care Centers).
Staff RNs 7 (ft), 2 (pt); LPNs 29 (ft), 3 (pt); Orderlies 15 (ft); Nurses aides 50 (ft); Recreational therapists 2 (ft), 1 (pt); Chaplain 1 (pt).
Facilities Dining room; Physical therapy room; Activities room; Chapel; Crafts room; Barber/Beauty shop; Patio.
Activities Arts & crafts; Cards; Games; Reading groups; Prayer groups; Movies; Shopping trips; Social/Cultural gatherings; Outings; Fishing; Picnics; Special events; Ceramics; Cooking.

The Briarwood Way
11503 W Briarwood Dr, Lakewood, CO, 80226
(303) 988-7776
Admin SeaJaye Sillasen.
Licensure Intermediate care for mentally retarded. *Beds* ICF/MR 6. *Certified* Medicaid; Medicare.
Owner Privately owned.
Admissions Requirements Minimum age 18; Females only; Medical examination; Physician's request.
Facilities Dining room; Activities room; Crafts room; Laundry room.
Activities Arts & crafts; Cards; Games; Reading groups; Movies; Shopping trips; Social/Cultural gatherings.

Cedars Health Care Center
1599 Ingalls, Lakewood, CO, 80214
(303) 232-3551
Admin James Levstek. *Medical Dir/Dir of Nursing* Francis Burdick MD; Paula Walker.
Licensure Skilled care; Intermediate care. *Beds* 200. *Certified* Medicaid; Medicare.
Owner Proprietary Corp (American Medical Services Inc).
Admissions Requirements Minimum age 55; Medical examination; Physician's request.
Staff Physicians 40 (pt); Activities coordinators 1 (ft), 2 (pt); Dietitians 1 (ft); Dentists 1 (pt); Ophthalmologists 1 (pt).
Languages Spanish
Facilities Dining room; Physical therapy room; Activities room; Chapel; Laundry room; Barber/Beauty shop; Library.
Activities Arts & crafts; Cards; Games; Reading groups; Prayer groups; Movies; Shopping trips; Social/Cultural gatherings; Bus trips; Camping.

Desserich House*
9150 Morrison Rd, Lakewood, CO, 80227
(303) 987-4396
Admin Richard Mason.
Licensure Developmentally disabled. *Beds* 7.
Owner Nonprofit Corp.

Everett Court Community*
1325 Everett Ct, Lakewood, CO, 80215
(303) 238-0501
Admin Melanie Tem.
Licensure Intermediate care. *Beds* 74. *Certified* Medicaid.
Owner Proprietary Corp.

Garden Manor Nursing Home Inc
115 Ingalls St, Lakewood, CO, 80226
(303) 237-1325
Admin Russell Lancaster. *Medical Dir/Dir of Nursing* Dr Robert Starr.
Licensure Skilled care; Intermediate care. *Beds* SNF 60; ICF 60. *Certified* Medicaid; Medicare.
Owner Proprietary Corp (Arvada Management).
Admissions Requirements Minimum age 65; Medical examination; Physician's request.
Staff RNs 5 (ft); LPNs 3 (ft); Orderlies 4 (ft); Nurses aides 15 (ft), 8 (pt); Physical therapists 1 (pt); Reality therapists 2 (ft); Occupational therapists 1 (pt); Activities coordinators 1 (ft); Dietitians 1 (pt); Dentists 1 (pt); Podiatrists 1 (pt).
Languages Spanish
Facilities Dining room; Physical therapy room; Activities room; Crafts room; Laundry room; Barber/Beauty shop.
Activities Arts & crafts; Cards; Games; Reading groups; Prayer groups; Movies; Shopping trips; Social/Cultural gatherings; Current events; Resident council; Remotivation cart; Reality orientation.

Glen Ayr Health Center
1655 Eaton St, Lakewood, CO, 80214
(303) 238-5363
Admin Bonny Conrad. *Medical Dir/Dir of Nursing* Karen Schutt.
Licensure Skilled care; Intermediate care. *Beds* SNF 59; ICF 60. *Certified* Medicaid; Medicare.
Owner Proprietary Corp.
Admissions Requirements Minimum age 60.
Staff RNs 6 (ft), 2 (pt); LPNs 4 (ft), 3 (pt); Orderlies 10 (ft), 3 (pt); Nurses aides 10 (ft), 4 (pt); Speech therapists 1 (ft); Activities coordinators 1 (ft), 1 (pt); Dietitians 1 (ft); Dentists 1 (pt); Podiatrists 1 (pt).
Languages Spanish
Facilities Dining room; Physical therapy room; Activities room; Laundry room; Barber/Beauty shop; Library.

Activities Arts & crafts; Cards; Games; Reading groups; Prayer groups; Movies; Shopping trips; Social/Cultural gatherings; Exercise groups.

Grand Place*
10365 W Grand Pl, Lakewood, CO, 80123
(303) 978-0951
Admin Mike Hannon.
Licensure Residential MR care. *Beds* 7. *Certified* Medicaid.
Owner Nonprofit Corp.

Lakeridge Village Health Care Center
1650 Allison St, Lakewood, CO, 80215
(303) 238-1275
Admin Linda Tatum. *Medical Dir/Dir of Nursing* Dr Eccles; Joey Wall DON.
Licensure Skilled care; Intermediate care. *Beds* SNF 143; ICF 37. *Certified* Medicaid; Medicare.
Owner Proprietary Corp (National Heritage).
Admissions Requirements Medical examination; Physician's request.
Staff RNs; LPNs; Orderlies; Nurses aides; Recreational therapists 2 (ft).
Languages Spanish
Facilities Dining room; Physical therapy room; Activities room; Crafts room; Laundry room; Barber/Beauty shop; Library.
Activities Arts & crafts; Cards; Games; Reading groups; Prayer groups; Movies; Shopping trips; Social/Cultural gatherings.

Lakewood Nursing Home
1432 Depew St, Lakewood, CO, 80214
(303) 238-1375
Admin Riva Weissbrot. *Medical Dir/Dir of Nursing* Dr Leonard Levisohn; Karen Steele RN.
Licensure Skilled care; Intermediate care. *Beds* SNF 93; ICF 60. *Certified* Medicaid.
Owner Proprietary Corp.
Admissions Requirements Medical examination; Physician's request.
Staff Physicians; RNs; LPNs; Orderlies; Nurses aides; Physical therapists; Reality therapists; Recreational therapists; Occupational therapists; Speech therapists; Activities coordinators; Dietitians; Dentists; Ophthalmologists; Podiatrists.
Facilities Dining room; Activities room; Laundry room; Barber/Beauty shop; Library.
Activities Arts & crafts; Cards; Games; Prayer groups; Movies.

Parkside House*
8355 W 19th Ave, Lakewood, CO, 80215
(303) 238-5447
Admin Richard Mason.
Licensure Intermediate care for mentally retarded. *Beds* 7.
Owner Nonprofit Corp.

Regency Health Care Center—Eaton Street*
1685 Eaton St, Lakewood, CO, 80215
(303) 232-4405
Admin Rhonda Buck. *Medical Dir/Dir of Nursing* Werner Prenzlau MD.
Licensure Skilled care; Intermediate care. *Beds* SNF 60; ICF 85. *Certified* Medicaid; Medicare.
Owner Proprietary Corp.
Admissions Requirements Minimum age 21.
Staff RNs; LPNs; Orderlies; Nurses aides; Physical therapists; Recreational therapists; Speech therapists; Activities coordinators; Dietitians; Dentists; Podiatrists.
Facilities Dining room; Physical therapy room; Activities room; Crafts room; Laundry room; Barber/Beauty shop; Library.
Activities Arts & crafts; Cards; Games; Reading groups; Prayer groups; Movies; Shopping trips; Social/Cultural gatherings.

Villa Manor Nursing Home*
7950 W Mississippi Ave, Lakewood, CO, 80226
(303) 986-4511

Admin Sara Jones.
Licensure Skilled care; Intermediate care. *Beds* SNF 120; ICF 120. *Certified* Medicaid; Medicare.
Owner Proprietary Corp (Life Care Centers of America).

Western Hills Health Care Center
1625 Carr St, Lakewood, CO, 80215
(303) 238-6881
Admin Terrylea Entsminger. *Medical Dir/Dir of Nursing* Jean Schwartz RN BSN.
Licensure Skilled care; Intermediate care. *Beds* SNF; ICF 150. *Certified* Medicaid; Medicare.
Owner Proprietary Corp.
Admissions Requirements Medical examination.
Staff RNs; LPNs; Orderlies; Nurses aides; Physical therapists; Occupational therapists; Speech therapists; Activities coordinators; Dietitians.
Languages Spanish
Facilities Dining room; Physical therapy room; Activities room; Crafts room; Laundry room; Barber/Beauty shop; Library; Ice cream parlor; Outdoor patio; Private formal dining room; Gift shop; Popcorn shop.
Activities Arts & crafts; Cards; Games; Reading groups; Prayer groups; Movies; Shopping trips; Social/Cultural gatherings; Restaurant outings.

Westland Manor Nursing Center
1150 Oak St, Lakewood, CO, 80215
(303) 238-7505
Admin Judith A Dimon. *Medical Dir/Dir of Nursing* Dr Robert Starr; Maureen Christensen-Oster RN.
Licensure Skilled care; Intermediate care. *Beds* SNF 53; ICF 94. *Certified* Medicaid; Medicare.
Owner Proprietary Corp (Arvada Management).
Admissions Requirements Minimum age 50; Medical examination.
Staff Physicians 3 (pt); RNs 3 (ft), 7 (pt); LPNs 4 (ft), 10 (pt); Orderlies 5 (ft); Nurses aides 20 (ft), 5 (pt); Physical therapists 1 (pt); Occupational therapists 1 (pt); Speech therapists 1 (pt); Activities coordinators 1 (ft), 1 (pt); Dietitians 1 (ft).
Languages Spanish
Facilities Dining room; Physical therapy room; Activities room; Laundry room; Barber/Beauty shop.
Activities Arts & crafts; Cards; Games; Reading groups; Prayer groups; Movies; Shopping trips; Social/Cultural gatherings.

LAMAR

Sandhaven Nursing Home*
205 S 10th, Lamar, CO, 81052
(303) 336-3434
Admin Mary Eldonna Mosier. *Medical Dir/Dir of Nursing* Eldonna Mosier.
Licensure Intermediate care. *Beds* 60. *Certified* Medicaid.
Owner Proprietary Corp.
Admissions Requirements Physician's request.
Staff RNs 2 (ft); LPNs 3 (ft), 1 (pt); Nurses aides 20 (ft), 3 (pt); Activities coordinators 2 (ft); Dietitians 1 (ft).
Facilities Dining room; Activities room; Crafts room; Laundry room; Barber/Beauty shop.
Activities Arts & crafts; Cards; Games; Reading groups; Prayer groups; Movies; Shopping trips; Social/Cultural gatherings.

LAS ANIMAS

Bent County Memorial Nursing Home
810 3rd St, Las Animas, CO, 81054
(303) 456-1340

Admin Donna Delatorre. *Medical Dir/Dir of Nursing* Dr W R Wight; P Snyder RN.
Licensure Skilled care. *Beds* SNF 58. *Certified* Medicaid.
Owner Publicly owned.
Admissions Requirements Physician's request.
Staff Physicians 3 (ft); RNs 13 (ft); LPNs 2 (ft); Orderlies 5 (ft), 3 (pt); Nurses aides 15 (ft), 4 (pt); Physical therapists 1 (pt); Activities coordinators 2 (ft), 1 (pt); Dietitians 1 (pt).
Languages Spanish
Facilities Dining room; Physical therapy room; Activities room; Chapel; Crafts room; Barber/Beauty shop; Library; Emergency clinic; Fenced park.
Activities Arts & crafts; Cards; Games; Reading groups; Prayer groups; Movies; Shopping trips; Social/Cultural gatherings; Sensory stimulation; Memory sharing.

Bueno's Group Home*
PO Box 385, 903 Vine, Las Animas, CO, 81054
(303) 456-1125
Admin Elizabeth Bueno.
Licensure Developmentally disabled. *Beds* 9.
Owner Proprietary Corp.

Jordan & Cole Residential Care Facility*
1108 4th St, Las Animas, CO, 81054
(303) 456-1764
Admin Mary E Cole.
Licensure Skilled care. *Beds* 10.
Owner Proprietary Corp.

Lela Wilson's Residential Care Facility*
403 Vigil, Las Animas, CO, 81054
(303) 456-1764
Admin Lela Wilson.
Licensure Intermediate care. *Beds* 6.
Owner Proprietary Corp.

Lucero Residential Care Facility*
920 Vine, Las Animas, CO, 81054
(303) 456-0643
Admin Maria Lucero.
Licensure Intermediate care. *Beds* 10.
Owner Proprietary Corp.

Seal Residential Care Home*
401 Elm, Las Animas, CO, 81054
(303) 456-1181
Admin Margaret Seal.
Licensure Intermediate care. *Beds* 2.
Owner Proprietary Corp.

LIMON

Prairie View Nursing Home*
1720-1750 Circle Ln, Limon, CO, 80828
(303) 775-9583
Admin Sr Mary Jean Tenhaeff.
Licensure Intermediate care. *Beds* 60. *Certified* Medicaid.
Owner Proprietary Corp.

LITTLETON

Cherrelyn Manor Health Care Center
5555 S Elati St, Littleton, CO, 80120
(303) 798-8686
Admin Richard C Bonneville. *Medical Dir/Dir of Nursing* Dr John Van Buskirk.
Licensure Skilled care; Intermediate care. *Beds* SNF 186; ICF 75. *Certified* Medicaid; Medicare.
Owner Proprietary Corp (American Medical Services Inc).
Admissions Requirements Minimum age 16; Medical examination; Physician's request.
Staff Physicians; RNs; LPNs; Orderlies; Nurses aides; Physical therapists; Recreational therapists; Occupational therapists; Speech therapists; Activities coordinators; Dietitians; Dentists; Ophthalmologists; Podiatrists.
Languages Spanish, French, German

Facilities Dining room; Physical therapy room; Activities room; Chapel; Crafts room; Laundry room; Barber/Beauty shop; Library.
Activities Arts & crafts; Cards; Games; Reading groups; Prayer groups; Movies; Shopping trips; Social/Cultural gatherings.

Good Shepard Lutheran Home of the West
445 West Berry Ave, Littleton, CO, 80120
(303) 795-2061
Admin Cynthia Warren.
Licensure Intermediate care for mentally retarded. *Beds* 40. *Certified* Medicaid.
Owner Nonprofit Corp.
Admissions Requirements Minimum age 18.
Affiliation Lutheran
Facilities Dining room; Physical therapy room; Activities room; Crafts room; Laundry room.
Activities Arts & crafts; Games; Prayer groups; Movies; Shopping trips; Social/Cultural gatherings.

Littleton House*
6680 S Downing, Littleton, CO, 80120
(303) 794-0641
Admin Bruce Anderson.
Licensure Intermediate care for mentally retarded. *Beds* 7.
Owner Nonprofit Corp.

Littleton Manor Nursing Home
5822 S Lowell Way, Littleton, CO, 80123
(303) 798-2497
Admin M Margaret Norton. *Medical Dir/Dir of Nursing* Dr Thomas Pulk; Nancy Fox RN DON.
Licensure Skilled care; Intermediate care. *Beds* SNF 45. *Certified* Private.
Owner Proprietary Corp.
Admissions Requirements Physician's request.
Staff Physicians 1 (pt); RNs 2 (ft), 5 (pt); LPNs 2 (ft); Nurses aides 14 (ft), 5 (pt); Physical therapists 1 (pt); Reality therapists 1 (pt); Recreational therapists 1 (ft), 1 (pt); Occupational therapists 1 (pt); Speech therapists 1 (pt); Activities coordinators 1 (ft); Dietitians 1 (pt); Ophthalmologists 1 (pt); Social workers 1 (pt).
Facilities Dining room; Physical therapy room; Activities room; Crafts room; Laundry room; Barber/Beauty shop.
Activities Arts & crafts; Cards; Games; Reading groups; Prayer groups; Movies; Shopping trips; Social/Cultural gatherings.

LONGMONT

Applewood Living Center*
1800 Stroh Pl, Longmont, CO, 80501
(303) 776-6081
Admin Bonnie Sue Larson. *Medical Dir/Dir of Nursing* David McCarty Sr MD.
Licensure Skilled care; Intermediate care. *Beds* SNF 60; ICF 60. *Certified* Medicaid.
Owner Proprietary Corp (ARA Living Centers).
Admissions Requirements Medical examination; Physician's request.
Staff RNs 10 (ft); LPNs 4 (pt); Nurses aides 40 (ft); Recreational therapists 1 (ft); Activities coordinators 1 (ft); Dietitians 1 (ft).
Facilities Dining room; Physical therapy room; Activities room; Chapel; Crafts room; Laundry room; Barber/Beauty shop.
Activities Arts & crafts; Cards; Games; Reading groups; Prayer groups; Movies; Social/Cultural gatherings.

Country View Care Center
5425 Weld County Road 32, Longmont, CO, 80501
(303) 535-4491
Admin Randy P May. *Medical Dir/Dir of Nursing* Erin Bee Prog Dir.

Licensure Intermediate care for mentally retarded. *Beds* ICF/MR 87. *Certified* Medicaid.
Owner Proprietary Corp (ARA Living Centers).
Admissions Requirements Minimum age 18; Medical examination; Physician's request.
Staff RNs 1 (ft); LPNs 8 (ft); Nurses aides 40 (ft); Physical therapists 1 (pt); Occupational therapists 1 (pt); Speech therapists 1 (pt); Activities coordinators 1 (ft); Dietitians 1 (pt); Psychologist 1 (ft); Recreation assistants 10 (ft).
Facilities Dining room; Physical therapy room; Activities room; Crafts room; Laundry room; Library.
Activities Arts & crafts; Cards; Games; Reading groups; Prayer groups; Movies; Shopping trips; Social/Cultural gatherings; Classes on socialization, self-help, recreation, & vocational.

Foothills Care Center Inc
1440 Coffman St, Longmont, CO, 80501
(303) 776-2814
Admin Fred Kilfoy. *Medical Dir/Dir of Nursing* Dr D W McCarty Sr; Jeanette Morrell BSN.
Licensure Skilled care; Intermediate care. *Beds* SNF 120; ICF 60. *Certified* Medicaid; Medicare.
Owner Proprietary Corp (ARA Living Centers).
Staff RNs 10 (ft), 1 (pt); LPNs 14 (ft); Orderlies 5 (ft), 2 (pt); Nurses aides 38 (ft), 7 (pt); Physical therapists 1 (pt); Recreational therapists 1 (ft); Occupational therapists 1 (pt); Speech therapists 1 (pt); Activities coordinators 1 (ft); Dietitians 1 (pt); Podiatrists 1 (pt).
Facilities Dining room; Physical therapy room; Activities room; Laundry room; Barber/Beauty shop.
Activities Arts & crafts; Cards; Games; Reading groups; Prayer groups; Movies; Shopping trips; Social/Cultural gatherings.

LOVELAND

Eden Valley Nursing Home
6263 N County Rd Number 29, Loveland, CO, 80537
(303) 667-6911
Admin J LaMon Furr. *Medical Dir/Dir of Nursing* Dr R Grosboll; Minnie Bird.
Licensure Skilled care; Intermediate care. *Beds* SNF 12; ICF 11. *Certified* Medicaid.
Owner Nonprofit Corp.
Admissions Requirements Medical examination; Physician's request.
Staff Physicians 1 (pt); RNs 5 (ft), 3 (pt); Orderlies 1 (ft), 2 (pt); Nurses aides 5 (ft), 2 (pt); Physical therapists 1 (pt); Reality therapists 1 (pt); Recreational therapists 1 (pt); Occupational therapists 1 (pt); Speech therapists 1 (pt); Activities coordinators 1 (pt); Dietitians 1 (pt); Dentists 1 (pt); Ophthalmologists 1 (pt); Podiatrists 1 (pt).
Languages Korean
Affiliation Seventh-Day Adventist
Facilities Dining room; Physical therapy room; Activities room; Chapel; Barber/Beauty shop; Library.
Activities Arts & crafts; Games; Reading groups; Prayer groups; Movies; Shopping trips; Social/Cultural gatherings.

Loveland Good Samaritan Village*
2101 S Garfield, Loveland, CO, 80537
(303) 669-3100
Admin Leland Johnson.
Licensure Skilled care. *Beds* 60. *Certified* Medicaid; Medicare.
Owner Nonprofit Corp (Evangelical Lutheran/ Good Samaritan).
Admissions Requirements Medical examination; Physician's request.

Staff RNs; LPNs; Orderlies; Nurses aides; Occupational therapists; Activities coordinators.
Affiliation Lutheran
Facilities Dining room; Activities room; Chapel; Crafts room; Laundry room; Barber/Beauty shop; Library.
Activities Arts & crafts; Games; Reading groups; Shopping trips; Social/Cultural gatherings.

North Shore Manor Inc*
1365 W 29th St, Loveland, CO, 80537
(303) 667-6111
Admin Barry Fancher.
Licensure Skilled care; Intermediate care. *Beds* SNF 120; ICF 32. *Certified* Medicaid; Medicare.
Owner Proprietary Corp.

Sierra Vista Health Care Center
821 Duffield Ct, Loveland, CO, 80537
(303) 669-0345
Admin Sue Keohane. *Medical Dir/Dir of Nursing* Dr Thomas Kasenberg; Audry Bopp RN BSN.
Licensure Skilled care; Intermediate care; Residential apts. *Beds* SNF 60; ICF 60; Residential apts 7. *Certified* Medicaid; Medicare; VA.
Owner Proprietary Corp (ARA Living Centers).
Admissions Requirements Medical examination; Physician's request.
Staff RNs; LPNs; Orderlies; Nurses aides; Physical therapists; Reality therapists; Recreational therapists; Occupational therapists; Speech therapists; Activities coordinators; Dietitians.
Facilities Dining room; Physical therapy room; Activities room; Laundry room; Barber/Beauty shop; Private visiting areas; Patio; Courtyard area.
Activities Arts & crafts; Cards; Games; Reading groups; Prayer groups; Movies; Shopping trips; Social/Cultural gatherings; Library cart; Bingo.

MANITOU SPRINGS

Cheyenne Village Inc
441 Manitou Ave, Manitou Springs, CO, 80829
(303) 685-1801
Admin Linda Bloom. *Medical Dir/Dir of Nursing* Mary Gannon.
Licensure Intermediate care for mentally retarded. *Beds* ICF/MR 40; Group homes 8. *Certified* Medicaid; Medicare.
Owner Nonprofit Corp.
Admissions Requirements Minimum age 18.
Staff RNs 1 (ft); LPNs 1 (pt); Nurses aides 35 (ft); Recreational therapists 1 (ft); Dietitians 1 (ft).
Activities Arts & crafts; Cards; Games; Reading groups; Prayer groups; Movies; Shopping trips; Social/Cultural gatherings.

MANZANOLA

Horne Home*
521 N Canal, Manzanola, CO, 81085
(303) 465-5795
Admin Rozanna R Horn.
Licensure Intermediate care. *Beds* 10.
Owner Proprietary Corp.

MEEKER

Walbridge Memorial Conv Wing
345 Cleveland, Meeker, CO, 81641
(303) 878-3232
Admin Hugh M Sargent. *Medical Dir/Dir of Nursing* Beka Anderson DON.
Licensure Skilled care. *Beds* SNF 25. *Certified* Medicaid.

Admissions Requirements Medical examination; Physician's request.
Staff RNs 11 (ft), 2 (pt); LPNs 2 (pt); Dietitians 1 (ft).
Languages Greek, German, Spanish
Facilities Dining room; Activities room; Chapel; Crafts room; Laundry room; Barber/Beauty shop.
Activities Arts & crafts; Games; Reading groups; Prayer groups; Movies; Shopping trips; Social/Cultural gatherings.

MONTE VISTA

Mountain Meadows
2277 E Drive, Monte Vista, CO, 81144
(303) 852-5138
Admin Cathy Howard. *Medical Dir/Dir of Nursing* Jack Jordan; MD; Becky Hardaway RN.
Licensure Intermediate care. *Beds* 60. *Certified* Medicaid.
Owner Proprietary Corp.
Admissions Requirements Minimum age 50; Medical examination.
Staff RNs 1 (ft), 1 (pt); LPNs 7 (ft); Nurses aides 25 (ft); Physical therapists 1 (pt); Activities coordinators 1 (ft).
Languages Spanish
Facilities Dining room; Activities room; Chapel; Laundry room; Barber/Beauty shop.
Activities Arts & crafts; Cards; Games; Reading groups; Movies; Shopping trips; Social/Cultural gatherings.

MONTROSE

Chipeta Drive
16357 Chipeta Dr, Montrose, CO, 81401
(303) 249-1133
Admin Mary Kalina.
Licensure Intermediate care for mentally retarded. *Beds* 8. *Certified* Medicaid; Medicare.
Owner Nonprofit Corp.
Admissions Requirements Minimum age 18.
Staff RNs; LPNs; Dietitians.
Facilities Dining room; Laundry room; Living room; Private bedrooms; Resident cooking facilities; Private sitting room; Resident garden & yard.
Activities Arts & crafts; Cards; Games; Movies; Shopping trips; Bowling; Picnics; Walks; Camping; Individualized vacations; Gardening; Pets allowed.

Evergreen Care Center
300 N Cascade Ave, Montrose, CO, 81401
(303) 249-7764
Admin John Fitzmaurice. *Medical Dir/Dir of Nursing* Dr Reginald Guy; Mary Rossiter RN.
Licensure Skilled care; Intermediate care. *Beds* SNF 20; ICF 40. *Certified* Medicaid; Medicare.
Owner Proprietary Corp.
Admissions Requirements Minimum age 18; Physician's request.
Staff RNs 4 (ft); LPNs 2 (ft), 1 (pt); Orderlies 3 (ft); Nurses aides 12 (ft); Recreational therapists 1 (pt); Activities coordinators 1 (pt); Dietitians 1 (pt); Social worker 1 (pt).
Languages Spanish
Facilities Dining room; Physical therapy room; Activities room; Crafts room; Laundry room; Barber/Beauty shop.
Activities Arts & crafts; Cards; Games; Reading groups; Prayer groups; Movies; Shopping trips; Social/Cultural gatherings.

San Juan Living Center
1043 Ridge St, Montrose, CO, 81401
(303) 249-9683
Admin William F Morgan. *Medical Dir/Dir of Nursing* Anna K Ruggles DON.

Licensure Skilled care; Intermediate care for mentally retarded. *Beds* SNF 56; ICF/MR 48. *Certified* Medicaid; Medicare.
Owner Proprietary Corp (ARA Living Centers).
Admissions Requirements Minimum age 21; Mentally retarded; Physician's request.
Staff RNs 4 (ft); LPNs 5 (ft); Orderlies 2 (ft); Nurses aides 12 (ft), 4 (pt); Activities coordinators 2 (ft); Psychologist 1 (pt).
Languages Spanish
Facilities Dining room; Physical therapy room; Activities room; Chapel; Crafts room; Laundry room; Barber/Beauty shop.
Activities Arts & crafts; Cards; Games; Movies; Shopping trips; Social/Cultural gatherings.

South 4th Street*
447 S 4th St, Montrose, CO, 81401
(303) 249-2972
Admin Charles Allison.
Licensure Intermediate care for mentally retarded. *Beds* 8. *Certified* Medicaid.
Owner Nonprofit Corp.

Valley Manor Care Center
1401 S Cascade Ave, Montrose, CO, 81401
(303) 249-9634
Admin Craig J Kalina. *Medical Dir/Dir of Nursing* Dr Robert Van Gemert.
Licensure Skilled care; Intermediate care. *Beds* SNF 120. *Certified* Medicaid; Medicare.
Owner Nonprofit Corp (Volunteers of America Care).
Admissions Requirements Medical examination.
Staff RNs 6 (ft), 3 (pt); LPNs 4 (ft), 2 (pt); Nurses aides 31 (ft), 30 (pt); Physical therapists 2 (pt); Recreational therapists 2 (pt); Activities coordinators 1 (ft); Dietitians 1 (pt); Dentists 1 (pt); Dentist 1 (pt).
Facilities Dining room; Physical therapy room; Activities room; Chapel; Crafts room; Laundry room; Barber/Beauty shop.
Activities Arts & crafts; Cards; Games; Reading groups; Prayer groups; Movies; Shopping trips; Social/Cultural gatherings.

MORRISON

Bear Creek Nursing Center
150 Spring St, Morrison, CO, 80465
(303) 697-8181
Admin Margaret Stander. *Medical Dir/Dir of Nursing* Dr Lee Anneberg; Gisella Kagy RN DON.
Licensure Skilled care; Intermediate care. *Beds* 180. *Certified* Medicaid; Medicare.
Owner Proprietary Corp (Hillhaven Corp).
Admissions Requirements Minimum age 50; Medical examination.
Staff RNs 15 (ft), 1 (pt); LPNs 14 (ft); Nurses aides 71 (ft); Physical therapists 1 (pt); Activities coordinators 3 (ft), 1 (pt); Dietitians 1 (ft).
Languages Spanish
Facilities Dining room; Physical therapy room; Activities room; Chapel; Crafts room; Laundry room; Barber/Beauty shop; Library; Special dining room for oriented, sociable resident.
Activities Arts & crafts; Cards; Games; Reading groups; Prayer groups; Movies; Shopping trips; Social/Cultural gatherings.

NORTHGLENN

Castle Gardens Nursing Home
401 Malley Dr, Northglenn, CO, 80233
(303) 452-4700
Admin Gregory A Drapes. *Medical Dir/Dir of Nursing* Dr Robert Jardine; Dawn Utzman.
Licensure Skilled care. *Beds* 180. *Certified* Medicaid; Medicare.
Owner Proprietary Corp (Hillhaven Corp).
Admissions Requirements Physician's order.

Staff RNs; LPNs; Orderlies; Nurses aides;
Physical therapists; Occupational therapists;
Activities coordinators; Dietitians.
Facilities Dining room; Physical therapy
room; Activities room; Chapel; Crafts room;
Laundry room; Barber/Beauty shop; Library.
Activities Arts & crafts; Cards; Games;
Reading groups; Prayer groups; Movies;
Shopping trips; Social/Cultural gatherings.

OLATHE

Colorow Care Center*
750 8th St, PO Box 710, Olathe, CO, 81425
(303) 323-5504
Admin Mary Pfalzgraff. Medical Dir/Dir of
Nursing Dr Simon.
Licensure Intermediate care. Beds 60.
Certified Medicaid.
Owner Proprietary Corp.
Admissions Requirements Physician's request.
Staff RNs 2 (ft); LPNs 6 (ft), 2 (pt); Nurses
aides 18 (ft), 3 (pt); Physical therapists 1
(pt); Activities coordinators 1 (ft), 1 (pt);
Dietitians 1 (ft), 1 (pt).
Facilities Dining room; Physical therapy
room; Activities room; Crafts room; Laundry
room; Barber/Beauty shop; Library.
Activities Arts & crafts; Cards; Games;
Reading groups; Prayer groups; Movies;
Shopping trips.

Harold Group Home*
418 Hersum, Olathe, CO, 81425
(303) 323-5831
Admin John Harold.
Licensure Residential MR care. Beds 18.
Owner Proprietary Corp.

ORDWAY

Crowley County Nursing Center*
401 Idaho PO Box 488, Ordway, CO, 81063
(303) 267-3561
Admin A Habib Khaliqi.
Licensure Intermediate care. Beds 59.
Certified Medicaid; Medicare.
Owner Nonprofit Corp.
Staff RNs 2 (ft); LPNs 4 (ft); Orderlies 1 (ft);
Nurses aides 15 (ft), 5 (pt); Physical
therapists 1 (pt); Dietitians 1 (pt).
Facilities Dining room; Activities room;
Chapel; Laundry room; Barber/Beauty shop.
Activities Cards; Games; Prayer groups;
Movies; Shopping trips; Social/Cultural
gatherings.

PALISADE

Palisades Nursing Home
PO Box 190, 151 E 3rd St, Palisade, CO,
81526
(303) 464-7500
Admin Ardath Hunt. Medical Dir/Dir of
Nursing Michaelene Kent RN DON.
Licensure Skilled care; Intermediate care. Beds
96. Certified Medicaid; Medicare.
Owner Proprietary Corp (ARA Living
Centers).
Admissions Requirements Minimum age 16.
Staff RNs; LPNs; Orderlies; Nurses aides;
Activities coordinators.
Facilities Dining room; Activities room;
Crafts room; Laundry room; Barber/Beauty
shop; Rehabilitation room.
Activities Arts & crafts; Cards; Games;
Reading groups; Prayer groups; Movies;
Shopping trips; Social/Cultural gatherings;
Van rides.

PAONIA

Bethesda Care Center
PO Box 1048, 1625 Meadowbrook, Paonia,
CO, 81428
(303) 527-4837

Admin Beatrice Reece. Medical Dir/Dir of
Nursing Dr Don Ridgway; Mary Ellen
Cranor DON.
Licensure Skilled care; Intermediate care. Beds
60. Certified Medicaid.
Owner Nonprofit Corp (Bethesda Care
Centers).
Admissions Requirements Physician's request.
Staff RNs 1 (ft); LPNs 4 (ft); Nurses aides 18
(ft); Activities coordinators 1 (ft); Dietitians
1 (ft).
Facilities Dining room; Physical therapy
room; Activities room; Barber/Beauty shop.
Activities Arts & crafts; Reading groups;
Prayer groups; Movies; Social/Cultural
gatherings.

PUEBLO

Belmont Lodge Inc
1601 Constitution Rd, Pueblo, CO, 81001
(719) 584-2400
Admin James Wisehart. Medical Dir/Dir of
Nursing Judy Warren.
Licensure Skilled care. Beds SNF 120.
Certified Medicaid; Medicare.
Owner Proprietary Corp (ARA Living
Centers).
Staff RNs 7 (ft), 5 (pt); LPNs 8 (ft), 2 (pt);
Orderlies 2 (ft), 1 (pt); Nurses aides 34 (ft),
8 (pt); Activities coordinators 2 (ft);
Dietitians 1 (ft).
Facilities Dining room; Activities room;
Chapel; Crafts room; Laundry room; Barber/
Beauty shop.
Activities Arts & crafts; Cards; Games;
Reading groups; Prayer groups; Movies;
Shopping trips; Social/Cultural gatherings.

Citadel Health Care & Day Health Care
431 Quincy, Pueblo, CO, 81004
(719) 545-0112
Admin Paula J Cicerelli. Medical Dir/Dir of
Nursing L J Farabaugh MD; Carol
Pannunzio DON.
Licensure Intermediate care; Residential care.
Beds ICF 38; Residential. Certified
Medicaid.
Owner Privately owned.
Admissions Requirements Physician's request.
Staff Physicians; RNs; LPNs; Nurses aides;
Activities coordinators; Dietitians.
Languages Spanish
Facilities Dining room; Activities room;
Chapel; Crafts room; Laundry room; Barber/
Beauty shop; Library.
Activities Arts & crafts; Cards; Games;
Reading groups; Prayer groups; Movies;
Shopping trips; Social/Cultural gatherings.

Cordova Residential Care*
2108 E 12th, Pueblo, CO, 81001
(719) 546-1475
Admin Donna Cordova.
Licensure Intermediate care. Beds 8.
Owner Proprietary Corp.

J & C Residential Care Facility*
328 Colorado, Pueblo, CO, 81004
(719) 546-1875
Admin Lydia Jordan.
Licensure Intermediate care. Beds 10.
Owner Proprietary Corp.

Jordan Residential Services Inc
2202 E 6th St, Pueblo, CO, 81001
(719) 545-3905
Admin Mike & Dolores Jordan.
Licensure Intermediate care for mentally
retarded. Beds ICF/MR 16. Certified
Medicaid.
Owner Privately owned.
Admissions Requirements Minimum age 16;
Medical examination.
Staff Podiatrists; Psychiatric techs 4 (ft); MR
techs 2 (pt).

Facilities Dining room; Activities room;
Crafts room; Laundry room.
Activities Arts & crafts; Cards; Games;
Reading groups; Movies; Shopping trips;
Social/Cultural gatherings; Camping;
Boating; Fishing.

Pueblo Manor
2611 Jones Ave, Pueblo, CO, 81004
(719) 564-1735
Admin Brooke Groff. Medical Dir/Dir of
Nursing Harold Smith MD; Pat Vigil RN
DON.
Licensure Skilled care; Intermediate care. Beds
SNF 160; ICF. Certified Medicaid;
Medicare.
Owner Proprietary Corp (National Heritage).
Admissions Requirements Medical
examination.
Staff RNs 8 (ft), 1 (pt); LPNs 12 (ft), 4 (pt);
Orderlies 3 (ft), 5 (pt); Nurses aides 45 (ft),
20 (pt); Physical therapists 2 (pt); Reality
therapists 1 (pt); Recreational therapists 1
(pt); Activities coordinators 1 (ft), 1 (pt);
Dietitians 1 (ft).
Languages Spanish
Facilities Dining room; Physical therapy
room; Activities room; Chapel; Crafts room;
Laundry room; Barber/Beauty shop; Library;
Large patio areas.
Activities Arts & crafts; Cards; Games;
Reading groups; Prayer groups; Movies;
Shopping trips; Social/Cultural gatherings.

Sharmar Nursing Center*
1201 W Abriendo Ave, Pueblo, CO, 81005
(719) 544-1173
Admin Donald J Prose. Medical Dir/Dir of
Nursing Harvey W Phelp.
Licensure Intermediate care; Intermediate care
for mentally retarded. Beds ICF 42; ICF/MR
15. Certified Medicaid.
Owner Proprietary Corp.
Admissions Requirements Physician's request.
Staff RNs 2 (ft); LPNs 3 (ft); Orderlies 5 (ft);
Nurses aides 10 (ft); Physical therapists 1
(pt); Recreational therapists 2 (pt);
Occupational therapists 1 (pt); Speech
therapists 1 (pt); Activities coordinators 1
(pt); Dietitians 1 (pt); Dentists 1 (pt);
Ophthalmologists 1 (pt); Podiatrists 1 (pt);
Audiologists 1 (pt).
Facilities Dining room; Physical therapy
room; Activities room; Chapel; Crafts room;
Laundry room; Barber/Beauty shop; Library.
Activities Arts & crafts; Cards; Games;
Reading groups; Prayer groups; Movies;
Shopping trips; Social/Cultural gatherings.

Spanish Peaks Mental Health Center*
29145 Hwy 50 E, Pueblo, CO, 81001
(719) 948-3346
Admin Gilbert A Sanchez.
Licensure Intermediate care. Beds 10.
Owner Nonprofit Corp.

State Home & Training School—Eleventh St*
2206 E 11th St, Pueblo, CO, 81001
(719) 534-1170
Admin Larry I Dalton.
Licensure Intermediate care for mentally
retarded. Beds 10.
Owner Publicly owned.

2201 East 10th Street Home
2201 E 10th St, Pueblo, CO, 81001
(719) 546-0572
Admin Lawrence Velasco.
Licensure Intermediate care for mentally
retarded. Beds 8.
Owner Nonprofit Corp.

Villa Pueblo Towers*
1111 Bonforte Blvd, Pueblo, CO, 81001
(719) 545-5911
Admin Ann Genova. Medical Dir/Dir of
Nursing D Manolis MD.
Licensure Skilled care. Beds 32. Certified
Medicare.

Owner Nonprofit Corp.
Admissions Requirements Minimum age 62; Medical examination.
Facilities Dining room; Activities room; Chapel; Laundry room; Library.
Activities Cards; Games; Prayer groups; Movies; Shopping trips; Social/Cultural gatherings.

RIFLE

E Dene Moore Memorial Home
707 E 5th, Rifle, CO, 81650
(303) 625-1510
Admin Edwin A Gast.
Licensure Skilled care. *Beds* 57. *Certified* Medicaid.
Owner Publicly owned.
Admissions Requirements Medical examination.
Staff RNs 4 (ft), 3 (pt); LPNs 3 (ft), 1 (pt); Orderlies 1 (pt); Nurses aides 11 (ft), 15 (pt); Physical therapists 1 (pt); Occupational therapists 1 (pt); Speech therapists 1 (pt); Activities coordinators 1 (ft); Dietitians 1 (ft); Dentists 1 (pt); Podiatrists 1 (pt).
Facilities Dining room; Physical therapy room; Crafts room; Barber/Beauty shop; Library.
Activities Arts & crafts; Cards; Games; Prayer groups; Movies; Shopping trips; Social/Cultural gatherings.

ROCKY FORD

Bauer-Home Residential Care*
803 Maple Ave, Rocky Ford, CO, 81067
(303) 254-7638
Admin CLara M Bauer.
Licensure Intermediate care. *Beds* 10.
Owner Proprietary Corp.

Malouff Manor*
28111 Rd 20, Rocky Ford, CO, 81067
(303) 384-8741
Admin Sam Maxwell.
Licensure Intermediate care for mentally retarded. *Beds* 8.
Owner Nonprofit Corp.

Pioneers Memorial Hospital & Nursing Home*
12th St & Washington Ave, Rocky Ford, CO, 81067
(303) 254-3314
Admin Marcia Joyce Hughey.
Licensure Intermediate care. *Beds* 65. *Certified* Medicaid; Medicare.
Owner Nonprofit Corp.
Staff RNs 1 (ft), 1 (pt); LPNs 7 (ft), 1 (pt); Nurses aides 20 (ft), 1 (pt).
Affiliation Mennonite
Facilities Dining room; Physical therapy room; Activities room; Chapel; Crafts room; Laundry room; Barber/Beauty shop; Library.
Activities Arts & crafts; Cards; Games; Reading groups; Prayer groups; Movies.

SALIDA

Columbine Manor*
530 W 16th St, Salida, CO, 81201
(303) 539-6112
Admin David Haneke.
Licensure Skilled care; Intermediate care. *Beds* SNF 50; ICF 10. *Certified* Medicaid.
Owner Proprietary Corp (Life Care Centers of America).

I Street House*
1110 I St, Salida, CO, 81201
(303) 539-3423
Admin Roger Jensen.
Licensure Intermediate care for mentally retarded. *Beds* 8.
Owner Proprietary Corp.
Admissions Requirements Minimum age 18; Medical examination.

Staff RNs 1 (pt); Physical therapists 1 (pt); Occupational therapists 1 (pt); Speech therapists 1 (pt); Activities coordinators 1 (ft).
Facilities Dining room; Activities room; Laundry room.
Activities Arts & crafts; Cards; Games; Movies; Shopping trips; Social/Cultural gatherings.

SIMLA

Simla Good Samaritan Center
PO Box 38, 320 Pueblo Ave, Simla, CO, 80835
(303) 541-2269
Admin Helen Enger. *Medical Dir/Dir of Nursing* Marion J Anderson.
Licensure Intermediate care. *Beds* ICF 32. *Certified* Medicaid.
Owner Nonprofit Corp (Evangelical Lutheran/ Good Samaritan).
Admissions Requirements Physician's request.
Staff RNs 1 (ft), 1 (pt); LPNs 2 (ft), 4 (pt); Orderlies 1 (pt); Nurses aides 4 (ft); Physical therapists 5 (pt); Activities coordinators 1 (ft).
Affiliation Lutheran
Facilities Dining room; Activities room; Laundry room; Barber/Beauty shop; Library.
Activities Arts & crafts; Cards; Games; Prayer groups; Movies; Social/Cultural gatherings.

SPRINGFIELD

Southeast Colorado Hospital & LTC
373 E 10th Ave, Springfield, CO, 81073
(303) 523-4501
Admin Robert L Shaffer RN. *Medical Dir/Dir of Nursing* Laverne Westphall RN.
Licensure Intermediate care. *Beds* ICF 40; Hospital 25. *Certified* Medicaid; Medicare.
Owner Publicly owned.
Admissions Requirements Physician's request.
Staff Physicians 2 (ft); RNs 5 (ft), 3 (pt); LPNs 3 (ft), 2 (pt); Orderlies 4 (ft), 1 (pt); Nurses aides 38 (ft), 5 (pt); Physical therapists 1 (pt); Activities coordinators 1 (ft); Dietitians 1 (pt); Ophthalmologists 1 (pt).
Facilities Dining room; Physical therapy room; Activities room; Chapel; Crafts room; Laundry room; Barber/Beauty shop.
Activities Arts & crafts; Cards; Games; Reading groups; Prayer groups; Movies; Shopping trips; Social/Cultural gatherings.

STEAMBOAT SPRINGS

Routt Memorial Extended Care Center
80 W Park Ave, Steamboat Springs, CO, 80487
(303) 879-1322
Admin John Richawagen. *Medical Dir/Dir of Nursing* Dr Mark McCaulley; Jane Powers DON.
Licensure Skilled care; Intermediate care. *Beds* SNF 50; ICF. *Certified* Medicaid.
Owner Nonprofit organization/foundation.
Staff RNs 7 (ft), 4 (pt); LPNs 2 (pt); Nurses aides 3 (ft), 7 (pt); Physical therapists 1 (pt); Activities coordinators 1 (ft); Dietitians 1 (pt).
Facilities Dining room; Physical therapy room; Activities room; Barber/Beauty shop; 2 Television Rooms.
Activities Arts & crafts; Cards; Games; Reading groups; Prayer groups; Movies; Shopping trips; Social/Cultural gatherings; Children's day care—Intergenerational Program; Wellness program.

STERLING

Clark Residential Care Facility*
117 Clark St, Sterling, CO, 80751
(303) 522-2656
Admin William Duffield.
Licensure Developmentally disabled. *Beds* 12.
Owner Nonprofit Corp.

Devonshire Acres Ltd
PO Box 392, 1330 N Sidney Ave, Sterling, CO, 80751
(303) 522-4888
Admin Gloria Kaiser. *Medical Dir/Dir of Nursing* Dr Robert Fillion; Elizabeth Beer RN.
Licensure Skilled care; Intermediate care. *Beds* SNF 58; ICF 20. *Certified* Medicaid; Medicare.
Owner Proprietary Corp.
Admissions Requirements Medical examination; Physician's request.
Staff RNs 5 (ft), 1 (pt); LPNs 13 (ft); Nurses aides 30 (ft), 20 (pt); Recreational therapists 1 (ft), 1 (pt); Activities coordinators 1 (ft), 1 (pt); Dietitians 1 (pt).
Facilities Dining room; Physical therapy room; Activities room; Chapel; Crafts room; Laundry room; Barber/Beauty shop; Library.
Activities Arts & crafts; Cards; Games; Reading groups; Prayer groups; Movies; Shopping trips; Social/Cultural gatherings.

North Division Residential Center*
223 N Division, Sterling, CO, 80751
(303) 522-2430
Admin William E Duffield.
Licensure Intermediate care for mentally retarded. *Beds* 6. *Certified* Medicaid.
Owner Nonprofit Corp.
Admissions Requirements Minimum age 16.
Activities Arts & crafts; Cards; Games; Reading groups; Movies; Shopping trips; Social/Cultural gatherings.

Rose Arbor Nursing Home*
1420 S 3rd Ave, Sterling, CO, 80751
(303) 522-2933
Admin Linda McClatchey. *Medical Dir/Dir of Nursing* M J Ollhoff DO.
Licensure Skilled care; Intermediate care. *Beds* SNF 60; ICF 60. *Certified* Medicaid; Medicare.
Owner Proprietary Corp (ARA Living Centers).
Admissions Requirements Medical examination; Physician's request.
Facilities Dining room; Physical therapy room; Activities room; Laundry room; Barber/Beauty shop; Van.
Activities Arts & crafts; Games; Reading groups; Prayer groups; Shopping trips; Social/Cultural gatherings.

THORNTON

Alpine Manor*
501 Thornton Parkway, Thornton, CO, 80229
(303) 452-6101
Admin Terrylea Entsminger. *Medical Dir/Dir of Nursing* Robert Jardine MD.
Licensure Skilled care; Intermediate care. *Beds* SNF 60; ICF 60. *Certified* Medicaid.
Owner Proprietary Corp (ARA Living Centers).
Admissions Requirements Medical examination.
Staff RNs 9 (ft), 4 (pt); LPNs 6 (ft), 2 (pt); Orderlies 1 (ft); Nurses aides 33 (ft), 7 (pt); Activities coordinators 1 (ft).

TRINIDAD

Alta Vista Group Home*
301 E Second, Trinidad, CO, 81082
(303) 846-4409
Admin Rae Bulson.

Licensure Developmentally disabled. *Beds* 8.
Owner Nonprofit Corp.

Trinidad State Nursing Home
409 Benedicta Ave, Trinidad, CO, 81082
(303) 846-9291
Admin Ralph L Fausone. *Medical Dir/Dir of
Nursing* G E Jimenez MD; Daria Gyurman
RN DON.
Licensure Skilled care; Intermediate care. *Beds*
SNF 135; ICF 91. *Certified* Medicaid.
Owner Publicly owned.
Admissions Requirements Physician's request.
Staff RNs 6 (ft); LPNs 21 (ft); Orderlies 6 (ft);
Nurses aides 40 (ft); Activities coordinators
2 (ft); Dietitians 1 (ft);; Social workers 2 (ft).
Languages Spanish, Italian
Facilities Dining room; Physical therapy
room; Activities room; Chapel; Barber/
Beauty shop; Library.
Activities Cards; Games; Prayer groups;
Movies.

WALSENBURG

Walsenburg Care Center Inc*
135 W 7th St, Walsenburg, CO, 81089
(303) 738-2750
Admin Fern B Sandoval. *Medical Dir/Dir of
Nursing* Arthur Vialpando MD.
Licensure Skilled care; Intermediate care. *Beds*
50. *Certified* Medicaid.
Owner Proprietary Corp (LTC).
Admissions Requirements Physician's request.
Staff Physicians 1 (pt); RNs 3 (ft), 1 (pt);
LPNs 2 (ft), 1 (pt); Orderlies 1 (ft); Nurses
aides 15 (ft), 5 (pt); Physical therapists 1
(pt); Occupational therapists 1 (pt); Speech
therapists 1 (pt); Activities coordinators 1
(ft); Dietitians 1 (pt); Dentists 1 (pt);
Podiatrists 1 (pt).
Facilities Dining room; Activities room;
Crafts room; Laundry room; Barber/Beauty
shop; Library; Living room.
Activities Arts & crafts; Cards; Games;
Reading groups; Prayer groups; Movies;
Shopping trips; Social/Cultural gatherings.

WELD COUNTY

Country View Care Center*
5425 Weld County Rd 32, Weld County, CO,
80501
(303) 444-0489, 535-4491
Admin Thomas Paul Malik.
Licensure Intermediate care for mentally
retarded. *Beds* 87. *Certified* Medicaid.
Owner Proprietary Corp.

WESTMINSTER

Adams Group Home*
7666 Stuart St, Westminster, CO, 80030
(303) 427-2779
Admin Jo Vincelli.
Licensure Intermediate care for mentally
retarded. *Beds* 8. *Certified* Medicaid.
Owner Nonprofit Corp.

Aspen Care Center—West*
7490 Lowell Blvd, Westminster, CO, 80030
(303) 428-7481
Admin Carolyn S Westin. *Medical Dir/Dir of
Nursing* Dr Foster Cline.
Licensure Skilled care; Intermediate care. *Beds*
SNF 163; ICF 31. *Certified* Medicaid;
Medicare.
Owner Proprietary Corp.
Admissions Requirements Medical
examination.
Staff RNs 8 (ft), 3 (pt); LPNs 14 (ft), 3 (pt);
Orderlies 1 (ft); Nurses aides 50 (ft), 7 (pt);
Activities coordinators 1 (ft).

Facilities Dining room; Activities room;
Laundry room; Barber/Beauty shop; Library.
Activities Arts & crafts; Cards; Games;
Reading groups; Prayer groups; Movies;
Shopping trips; Social/Cultural gatherings.

Aspen Care East
7481 Knox Pl, Westminster, CO, 80030
(303) 427-7101
Admin Donald R Bergen. *Medical Dir/Dir of
Nursing* Foster Cline MD; Donna Huber
DON.
Licensure Skilled care; Intermediate care. *Beds*
SNF 60; ICF 60. *Certified* Medicaid;
Medicare.
Owner Proprietary Corp.
Admissions Requirements Medical
examination; Physician's request.
Staff RNs 12 (ft), 1 (pt); LPNs 10 (ft), 2 (pt);
Orderlies 3 (ft); Nurses aides 30 (ft), 5 (pt);
Activities coordinators 1 (ft).
Languages Spanish
Facilities Dining room; Activities room;
Crafts room; Barber/Beauty shop; Library.
Activities Arts & crafts; Cards; Games;
Reading groups; Prayer groups; Movies;
Shopping trips; Social/Cultural gatherings.

Johnson Home
4354 Apex Ln, Westminster, CO, 80030
(303) 427-2779
Admin Marlene J Johnson.
Licensure Intermediate care. *Beds* 7.
Owner Proprietary Corp.
Facilities Dining room; Activities room;
Laundry room.

Plaza Care Center Inc
7045 Stuart St, Westminster, CO, 80030
(303) 427-7045
Admin Jeanne Johnson. *Medical Dir/Dir of
Nursing* Larry Plunkett MD; Marti Jewell
DON.
Licensure Intermediate care. *Beds* ICF 103.
Certified Medicaid.
Owner Proprietary Corp.
Admissions Requirements Minimum age 21;
Medical examination; Physician's request.
Staff RNs 2 (ft); LPNs 5 (ft), 2 (pt); Orderlies
2 (ft); Nurses aides 14 (ft); Recreational
therapists 1 (ft); Activities coordinators 1
(ft).
Languages Spanish
Facilities Dining room; Activities room;
Laundry room.
Activities Arts & crafts; Cards; Games;
Reading groups; Prayer groups; Movies;
Shopping trips; Social/Cultural gatherings.

WHEAT RIDGE

Christopher House Nursing Home
6270 W 38th Ave, Wheat Ridge, CO, 80033
(303) 421-2272
Admin Louis C Lilly.
Licensure Skilled care. *Beds* 90.
Owner Proprietary Corp.
Staff Physicians; RNs; LPNs; Nurses aides;
Physical therapists; Recreational therapists;
Speech therapists; Activities coordinators;
Dietitians; Ophthalmologists.
Facilities Dining room; Physical therapy
room; Activities room; Crafts room; Laundry
room; Barber/Beauty shop.
Activities Arts & crafts; Cards; Games;
Reading groups; Prayer groups; Movies;
Shopping trips; Social/Cultural gatherings.

Columbine Manor Inc
3835 Harlan St, Wheat Ridge, CO, 80033
(303) 422-2338
Admin Jennifer D Golden. *Medical Dir/Dir of
Nursing* Robert Starr MD.
Licensure Skilled care; Intermediate care. *Beds*
SNF 44; ICF 107. *Certified* Medicaid;
Medicare.
Owner Proprietary Corp (Arvada
Management).

Admissions Requirements Minimum age 65;
Medical examination.
Staff Physicians 1 (pt); RNs 4 (ft), 9 (pt);
LPNs 5 (ft), 8 (pt); Nurses aides 31 (ft), 16
(pt); Physical therapists 1 (pt); Occupational
therapists 1 (pt); Speech therapists 1 (pt);
Activities coordinators 2 (ft); Dietitians 1
(pt); Dentists 1 (pt); Podiatrists 1 (pt).
Facilities Dining room; Physical therapy
room; Activities room; Crafts room; Laundry
room; Barber/Beauty shop.
Activities Arts & crafts; Cards; Games;
Reading groups; Prayer groups; Movies;
Shopping trips; Social/Cultural gatherings;
Swimming; Overnight camping; Culinary
arts.

Independence House*
3900 Independence Court, Wheat Ridge, CO,
80030
(303) 433-2801
Admin Timothy O'Neil.
Licensure Intermediate care for mentally
retarded. *Beds* 8.
Owner Nonprofit Corp.

Johnstone Developmental Center
5361 W 26th Ave, Wheat Ridge, CO, 80214
(303) 233-8518
Admin Richard K Mason NHA. *Medical Dir/
Dir of Nursing* Dr Emerson Harvey; Kay
Hainlen LPN DON.
Licensure Intermediate care for mentally
retarded. *Beds* ICF/MR 40. *Certified*
Medicaid.
Owner Nonprofit Corp.
Admissions Requirements Minimum age 18;
Medical examination.
Staff LPNs 3 (ft), 2 (pt); Nurses aides 15 (ft),
3 (pt); Recreational therapists 1 (ft).
Facilities Dining room; Activities room;
Crafts room; Laundry room; Outdoor sports
equipment.
Activities Arts & crafts; Cards; Games;
Movies; Shopping trips; Social/Cultural
gatherings; Special Olympics; Resident
council meetings.

Mountain Vista Nursing Home
4800 Tabor St, Wheat Ridge, CO, 80033
(303) 421-4161
Admin L Maxine Wendt. *Medical Dir/Dir of
Nursing* Katherine Mason RN.
Licensure Skilled care; Intermediate care. *Beds*
90. *Certified* Medicaid; Medicare.
Owner Nonprofit Corp (Baptist Home
Associates).
Admissions Requirements Minimum age 50.
Staff RNs 13 (ft); LPNs 4 (ft); Nurses aides 16
(ft); Dietitians 1 (pt).
Affiliation Baptist
Facilities Dining room; Physical therapy
room; Activities room; Chapel; Crafts room;
Laundry room; Barber/Beauty shop; Library.
Activities Arts & crafts; Cards; Games;
Reading groups; Prayer groups; Movies;
Shopping trips; Social/Cultural gatherings.

Temenos House Inc
3113 Teller St, Wheat Ridge, CO, 80215
(303) 233-2808
Admin Marian Gibson. *Medical Dir/Dir of
Nursing* Judy Ohs DON.
Licensure Intermediate care. *Beds* ICF 8.
Owner Proprietary Corp.
Admissions Requirements Minimum age 55.
Staff RNs; Nurses aides; Activities
coordinators; Ophthalmologists.
Facilities Dining room; Activities room;
Chapel; Crafts room; Laundry room;
Library.
Activities Arts & crafts; Cards; Games;
Reading groups; Prayer groups; Movies;
Shopping trips; Social/Cultural gatherings.

Wheat Ridge Regional Center*
10285 Ridge Rd, Wheat Ridge, CO, 80033
(303) 424-7791

Admin Vicky Jeanene Campbell. *Medical Dir/ Dir of Nursing* Gabriel Bonnet MD.
Licensure Intermediate care for mentally retarded; Skilled care for mentally retarded. *Beds* ICF/MR 492; Skilled care for mentally retarded 76. *Certified* Medicaid.
Owner Publicly owned.
Admissions Requirements Medical examination; Physician's request.
Staff Physicians 2 (ft), 2 (pt); RNs 36 (ft); Nurses aides 381 (ft); Physical therapists 5 (ft); Recreational therapists 8 (ft), 1 (pt); Occupational therapists 4 (ft); Speech therapists 1 (ft), 2 (pt); Activities coordinators 1 (ft); Dietitians 1 (ft).
Facilities Dining room; Physical therapy room; Activities room; Chapel; Crafts room; Barber/Beauty shop; Library.
Activities Arts & crafts; Games; Movies; Shopping trips; Social/Cultural gatherings.

Wide Horizons Inc*
8900 W 38th Ave, Wheat Ridge, CO, 80033
(303) 424-4445
Admin Joe Wechsler.
Licensure Skilled care. *Beds* 30.
Owner Nonprofit Corp.

Willow Brook Care Center
3315 Sheridan Blvd, Wheat Ridge, CO, 80212
(303) 237-9521
Admin Morey N Melnick.
Licensure Skilled care. *Beds* 56. *Certified* Medicaid; Medicare.
Owner Proprietary Corp.

WINDSOR

Windsor Health Care Center
PO Box 999, 710 3rd St, Windsor, CO, 80550
(303) 686-7474

Admin Dennis H Ziefel. *Medical Dir/Dir of Nursing* E D Kadlub MD; Betsy Weiss.
Licensure Skilled care; Intermediate care; Special Mental Health; Alzheimer's units. *Beds* 120. *Certified* Medicaid; VA.
Owner Proprietary Corp (ARA Living Centers).
Admissions Requirements Minimum age 18; Medical examination.
Staff Physicians 6 (pt); RNs 7 (ft); LPNs 9 (ft); Orderlies 32 (ft); Nurses aides; Physical therapists 1 (pt); Recreational therapists 4 (ft); Speech therapists 1 (pt); Dietitians 1 (pt); Dentists 1 (pt); Ophthalmologists 1 (pt); Podiatrists 1 (pt).
Languages Spanish, German
Facilities Dining room; Activities room; Crafts room; Laundry room; Barber/Beauty shop.
Activities Arts & crafts; Cards; Games; Reading groups; Prayer groups; Movies; Shopping trips; Social/Cultural gatherings.

WRAY

Cedardale Health Care Facility
PO Box 97, 720 Clay St, Wray, CO, 80758
(303) 332-5375
Admin Mr Clair Morrison. *Medical Dir/Dir of Nursing* Sue Spraque DON.
Licensure Intermediate care. *Beds* ICF 33. *Certified* Medicaid.
Owner Privately owned.
Admissions Requirements Physician's request.
Staff RNs 1 (ft); LPNs 5 (ft); Nurses aides 6 (ft), 4 (pt); Physical therapists 1 (pt); Activities coordinators 1 (ft).
Facilities Dining room; Activities room; Chapel; Crafts room; Laundry room; Barber/ Beauty shop.

Activities Arts & crafts; Cards; Games; Reading groups; Prayer groups; Movies; Shopping trips; County fairs; Circus; Plays.

Renotta Nursing Home*
815 Franklin St, Wray, CO, 80758
(303) 332-4856
Admin Stanley C Fisher.
Licensure Intermediate care. *Beds* 38. *Certified* Medicaid.
Owner Proprietary Corp.
Staff Physicians 2 (ft); RNs 2 (ft); LPNs 1 (ft), 6 (pt); Orderlies 1 (ft); Nurses aides 6 (ft), 15 (pt); Activities coordinators 1 (pt); Dietitians 1 (ft).
Facilities Dining room; Activities room; Crafts room; Laundry room; Barber/Beauty shop.
Activities Arts & crafts; Cards; Games; Movies; Shopping trips.

YUMA

Yuma Life Care Center
323 W 9th Ave, Yuma, CO, 80759
(303) 848-2403
Admin Robert W Allen. *Medical Dir/Dir of Nursing* Jack Pearse MD; Barbara Sweet RN.
Licensure Skilled care. *Beds* 60. *Certified* Medicaid.
Owner Proprietary Corp (ARA Living Centers).
Admissions Requirements Physician's request.
Staff RNs 1 (ft), 3 (pt); LPNs; Nurses aides; Activities coordinators 1 (pt).
Facilities Dining room; Laundry room; Barber/Beauty shop.
Activities Arts & crafts; Games; Reading groups; Prayer groups; Movies; Shopping trips.

CONNECTICUT

ASHFORD

Evangelical Baptist Home
PO Box 131, RFD 1, Ashford, CT, 06278
(203) 429-2743
Licensure Intermediate care. *Beds* 30.
Owner Nonprofit Corp.
Languages Spanish, French, German, Russian, Polish
Affiliation Baptist

AVON

Avon Convalescent Home Inc
652 W Avon Rd, Avon, CT, 06001
(203) 673-2521
Beds 120. *Certified* Medicaid; Medicare.
Owner Proprietary Corp.

Brightview Nursing & Retirement Center Ltd
220 Scoville Rd, Avon, CT, 06001
(203) 673-3265
Admin Gregory J Hamley. *Medical Dir/Dir of Nursing* Dr Wm Williams; Sally Smith DON.
Licensure Skilled care. *Beds* SNF 56.
Owner Proprietary Corp (Health Care Associates Inc).
Admissions Requirements Physician's request.
Staff RNs 8 (ft); LPNs 1 (ft); Nurses aides 23 (ft); Physical therapists 1 (ft); Recreational therapists 1 (ft); Activities coordinators 1 (ft); Dietitians 1 (pt).
Languages Italian, Polish
Facilities Dining room; Physical therapy room; Activities room; Crafts room; Barber/Beauty shop; Library.
Activities Arts & crafts; Games; Prayer groups; Movies; Social/Cultural gatherings.

BLOOMFIELD

Canterbury Villa of Bloomfield*
160 Coventry St, Bloomfield, CT, 06002
(203) 243-2995
Licensure Intermediate care. *Beds* 113. *Certified* Medicaid.
Owner Proprietary Corp (Health Enter of America).
Staff RNs 3 (ft); LPNs 3 (ft); Nurses aides 4 (ft); Dietitians.
Languages Spanish, Farsi, Malayasain, Tagalog
Activities Arts & crafts; Shopping trips; Social/Cultural gatherings; Exercise groups.

Caleb Hitchcock Health Center—Duncaster
40 Loeffler Rd, Bloomfield, CT,
726-2000
Admin Mary Fiorello. *Medical Dir/Dir of Nursing* Dr Joel Miller; Patricia Logee.
Licensure Skilled care; Intermediate care. *Beds* SNF 30; ICF 30.

Owner Nonprofit Corp.
Staff Physicians 1 (ft); RNs 9 (ft); Nurses aides 19 (ft); Physical therapists 2 (ft); Recreational therapists 2 (ft); Occupational therapists 1 (ft); Speech therapists 1 (ft); Dietitians 1 (ft).

Oak Ridge Conv Center*
55 Tunxis Ave, Bloomfield, CT, 06002
(203) 242-0703
Medical Dir/Dir of Nursing Dr Daniel Marshall.
Licensure Skilled care. *Beds* 120. *Certified* Medicaid; Medicare.
Owner Proprietary Corp.
Admissions Requirements Minimum age 14; Medical examination; Physician's request.
Staff RNs 6 (ft), 2 (pt); LPNs 4 (ft); Nurses aides 38 (ft), 1 (pt); Physical therapists 1 (pt); Recreational therapists 2 (ft); Dietitians 1 (pt); Dentists 1 (pt); Ophthalmologists 1 (pt); Podiatrists 1 (pt); Audiologists 1 (pt).
Facilities Dining room; Physical therapy room; Activities room; Crafts room; Laundry room; Barber/Beauty shop.
Activities Arts & crafts; Cards; Games; Reading groups; Prayer groups; Movies; Shopping trips; Social/Cultural gatherings.

Wintonbury Continuing Care Center
140 Park Ave, Bloomfield, CT, 06002
(203) 243-9591
Admin Ray Talamona. *Medical Dir/Dir of Nursing* Joseph O'Keefe MD; Pat Fiocchetta RN DON.
Licensure Skilled care; Intermediate care. *Beds* SNF 120; ICF 30. *Certified* Medicaid; Medicare.
Owner Proprietary Corp.
Admissions Requirements Minimum age 18.
Staff RNs 11 (ft), 13 (pt); LPNs 8 (ft), 4 (pt); Nurses aides 42 (ft), 16 (pt); Physical therapists 1 (ft), 3 (pt); Recreational therapists 2 (ft), 1 (pt); Speech therapists 1 (pt); Dietitians 1 (pt); Resident needs coordinator.
Languages Italian, Spanish
Facilities Dining room; Physical therapy room; Activities room; Chapel; Crafts room; Laundry room; Barber/Beauty shop; Library.
Activities Arts & crafts; Cards; Games; Reading groups; Prayer groups; Movies; Shopping trips; Social/Cultural gatherings; Ceramics; Gardening.

BRANFORD

Branford Hills Health Care Center*
Alps Rd, Branford, CT, 06405
(203) 481-6221
Licensure Skilled care. *Beds* 120. *Certified* Medicaid; Medicare.
Owner Proprietary Corp.
Staff LPNs 28 (ft); Nurses aides 72 (ft); Physical therapists 2 (ft); Activities coordinators 5 (ft); Dietitians; Social workers 2 (ft).

Languages Polish, Italian
Activities Arts & crafts; Games; Social/Cultural gatherings; Cooking; Gardening; Resident newspaper & council; Exercises.

BRIDGEPORT

Burroughs Home Inc
2470 Fairfield Ave, Bridgeport, CT, 06605
(203) 334-0293
Admin Sr Rita DuBois DW.
Licensure Home for aged. *Beds* 25.
Owner Nonprofit organization/foundation.
Admissions Requirements Minimum age 60; Females only.
Facilities Dining room; Activities room; Laundry room.
Activities Cards; Movies; Shopping trips; Social/Cultural gatherings; Bingo.

Dinan Memorial Center
600 Bond St, Bridgeport, CT, 06497
(203) 384-6400
Admin Marie Squattrito. *Medical Dir/Dir of Nursing* Joseph Connally MD; Judith Marin RN DON.
Licensure Skilled care; Intermediate care. *Beds* SNF 480; ICF 30. *Certified* Medicaid; Medicare.
Owner Publicly owned.
Admissions Requirements Minimum age 14; Medical examination; Physician's request.
Staff RNs 50 (ft); LPNs 50 (ft); Nurses aides 203 (ft), 1 (pt); Physical therapists 5 (ft); Recreational therapists 12 (ft); Occupational therapists 1 (ft); Speech therapists 1 (ft); Activities coordinators 3 (ft); Dietitians 3 (ft); Occupational therapists Social workers 4 (ft).
Languages Portuguese, Spanish, Italian
Facilities Dining room; Physical therapy room; Activities room; Chapel; Crafts room; Laundry room; Barber/Beauty shop; Library.
Activities Arts & crafts; Cards; Games; Reading groups; Prayer groups; Movies; Shopping trips; Social/Cultural gatherings.

Golden Heights Health Care Center Inc*
62 Coleman St, Bridgeport, CT, 06604
(203) 367-8444
Licensure Skilled care; Intermediate care. *Beds* 140. *Certified* Medicaid; Medicare.
Owner Proprietary Corp.
Staff RNs 11 (ft); LPNs 14 (ft); Nurses aides 42 (ft); Activities coordinators 1 (ft).
Languages Italian, Portuguese, Spanish, Polish
Activities Arts & crafts; Prayer groups; Movies; Shopping trips; Resident council.

Laurel Avenue Rest Home Inc*
217 Laurel Ave, Bridgeport, CT, 06605
(203) 367-0945
Licensure Intermediate care. *Beds* 12.
Owner Proprietary Corp.

Park Avenue Health Care Center
725 Park Ave, Bridgeport, CT, 06604
(203) 366-3653

Admin Donald L Franco. *Medical Dir/Dir of Nursing* Wayne S Levin MD; Diane G MacSweeney RN DON.
Licensure Skilled care. *Beds* SNF 132. *Certified* Medicaid; Medicare.
Owner Proprietary Corp.
Admissions Requirements Minimum age 16; Medical examination; Physician's request.
Staff RNs 10 (ft), 4 (pt); LPNs 11 (ft); Nurses aides 50 (ft); Physical therapists 1 (ft), 1 (pt); Recreational therapists 3 (ft), 1 (pt); Speech therapists 1 (pt); Activities coordinators 3 (ft), 1 (pt); Dietitians 1 (pt); Dentists 1 (pt); Ophthalmologists 1 (pt); Podiatrists 1 (pt); Social workers 1 (ft), 1 (pt).
Languages Spanish, French, Italian, German, Russian, Lithuanian.
Facilities Dining room; Physical therapy room; Activities room; Barber/Beauty shop.
Activities Arts & crafts; Cards; Games; Reading groups; Prayer groups; Movies; Shopping trips; Social/Cultural gatherings; Culinary groups; Special interest groups; Sensory integration.

Roncalli Health Center Inc*
425 Grant St, Bridgeport, CT, 06610
(203) 366-5255
Licensure Skilled care; Intermediate care. *Beds* 150. *Certified* Medicaid; Medicare.
Owner Nonprofit Corp.
Staff RNs 9 (ft); LPNs 14 (ft); Nurses aides 58 (ft); Physical therapists 1 (ft); Activities coordinators 2 (ft).
Languages Russian, Italian, Spanish, Polish, French, German

Sterling Home of Bridgeport
354 Prospect St, Bridgeport, CT, 06604
(203) 334-2310
Admin Marie C Franck.
Licensure Independent living. *Beds* 25. *Certified* Medicaid.
Owner Nonprofit organization/foundation.
Admissions Requirements Minimum age 65; Females only; Medical examination; Physician's request.
Staff Dietitians; Ophthalmologists.
Languages Italian, Spanish, French
Facilities Dining room; Activities room; Chapel; Laundry room; Barber/Beauty shop; Library; Plant room; Sewing room.
Activities Arts & crafts; Cards; Games; Prayer groups; Movies; Shopping trips; Social/Cultural gatherings.

Sylvan Manor Inc
1037 Sylvan Ave, Bridgeport, CT, 06606
(203) 372-3508
Admin Kenneth S Kopchik. *Medical Dir/Dir of Nursing* Dr Robert Yasner; Janice Caserta RN DON.
Licensure Skilled care. *Beds* SNF 40. *Certified* Medicaid; Medicare.
Owner Proprietary Corp.
Admissions Requirements Medical examination; Physician's request.
Staff Physicians 3 (pt); RNs 2 (ft), 5 (pt); LPNs 1 (pt); Orderlies 1 (ft); Nurses aides 8 (ft), 9 (pt); Physical therapists 1 (pt) 9; Recreational therapists 1 (pt); Occupational therapists 1 (pt); Speech therapists 1 (pt); Dietitians 1 (pt); Dentists 1 (pt); Ophthalmologists 1 (pt); Podiatrists 1 (pt);; Social worker 1 (pt).
Languages Slavic
Facilities Dining room; Physical therapy room; Activities room; Crafts room; Laundry room; Barber/Beauty shop; Patio.
Activities Arts & crafts; Cards; Games; Reading groups; Prayer groups; Movies; Garden.

BRISTOL

Bristol Extended Care*
456 King St, Bristol, CT, 06010
(203) 583-1827

Medical Dir/Dir of Nursing Dr Steven Isaacs.
Licensure Skilled care. *Beds* 160. *Certified* Medicaid; Medicare.
Owner Proprietary Corp.
Admissions Requirements Minimum age 14; Medical examination; Physician's request.
Staff Physicians 10 (pt); RNs 6 (ft), 4 (pt); LPNs 14 (ft), 9 (pt); Orderlies 8 (ft), 2 (pt); Nurses aides 37 (ft), 26 (pt); Physical therapists 1 (ft); Recreational therapists 3 (ft); Occupational therapists 1 (pt); Speech therapists 1 (pt); Dietitians 1 (pt); Dentists 1 (pt); Ophthalmologists 1 (pt); Podiatrists 1 (pt).
Languages Italian, French, Polish
Facilities Dining room; Physical therapy room; Activities room; Crafts room; Barber/Beauty shop.
Activities Arts & crafts; Cards; Games; Reading groups; Prayer groups; Movies; Shopping trips; Social/Cultural gatherings.

Countryside Manor*
1660 Stafford Ave, Bristol, CT, 06010
(203) 583-8483
Admin Dorothy Hultman.
Licensure Intermediate care. *Beds* 59. *Certified* Medicaid.
Owner Proprietary Corp.
Staff RNs 5 (ft); LPNs 4 (ft); Physical therapists 1 (ft); Recreational therapists 1 (ft); Dietitians 1 (ft); Social workers 1 (ft).
Languages Polish, Italian, German, Swedish
Activities Prayer groups; Arts & crafts; Shopping trips; Bus trips; Special education.

Nursing Care Center of Bristol*
61 Bellevue Ave, Bristol, CT, 06010
(203) 589-1682
Licensure Skilled care. *Beds* 132. *Certified* Medicaid; Medicare.
Owner Proprietary Corp.
Staff RNs 22 (ft); LPNs 20 (ft); Nurses aides 68 (ft); Recreational therapists; Social workers.
Languages French, Polish, Japanese

BROOKLYN

Brooklyn Rest Home
8 Wolf Den Rd, Brooklyn, CT, 06234
(203) 774-2260
Admin Thomas Reese. *Medical Dir/Dir of Nursing* Dr Howe; Virginia Scriven RN.
Licensure Intermediate care. *Beds* 30. *Certified* Medicaid.
Owner Proprietary Corp.
Admissions Requirements Minimum age 14; Medical examination.
Staff Physicians 1 (pt); RNs 4 (ft), 4 (pt); Nurses aides 7 (ft), 6 (pt); Physical therapists 1 (pt); Recreational therapists 1 (ft), 1 (pt); Dietitians 1 (pt).
Languages French
Facilities Activities room; Laundry room.
Activities Arts & crafts; Cards; Games; Reading groups; Prayer groups; Movies; Shopping trips; Social/Cultural gatherings.

Norcliffe Rest Home*
Canterbury Rd, Brooklyn, CT, 06234
(203) 774-3296
Licensure Intermediate care. *Beds* 60. *Certified* Medicaid.
Owner Proprietary Corp.
Staff RNs 7 (ft); Nurses aides 8 (ft); Activities coordinators 1 (ft); Dietitians 1 (ft).
Languages French, Polish, Italian

Pierce Memorial Baptist Home Inc
Rte 169, Brooklyn, CT, 06234
(203) 774-9050
Admin Rev John H Zendzian Jr. *Medical Dir/ Dir of Nursing* Lavius Robinson.
Licensure Home for aged. *Beds* 10. *Certified* Medicaid; Medicare.
Owner Nonprofit Corp.

Admissions Requirements Minimum age 65; Medical examination.
Staff Physicians 6 (pt); RNs 3 (ft), 8 (pt); LPNs 1 (ft), 7 (pt); Nurses aides 19 (ft), 6 (pt); Physical therapists 1 (pt); Recreational therapists 1 (ft), 1 (pt); Speech therapists 1 (pt); Dietitians 1 (pt); Dentists 1 (pt); Ophthalmologists 2 (pt); Podiatrists 1 (pt).
Languages German, Spanish, Finnish, French
Affiliation Baptist
Facilities Dining room; Physical therapy room; Activities room; Chapel; Crafts room; Laundry room; Library.
Activities Arts & crafts; Games; Reading groups; Prayer groups; Movies; Shopping trips; Social/Cultural gatherings; Swimming; Dining out.

CANAAN

Geer Memorial Health Center
PO Box 819, S Canaan Rd, Canaan, CT, 06018
(203) 824-5137
Admin Mariellyn F Hill. *Medical Dir/Dir of Nursing* Malcolm M Brown MD; Dorothy Shelton RN DON.
Licensure Skilled care. *Beds* SNF 120. *Certified* Medicaid; Medicare.
Owner Nonprofit Corp (Adventist Health Sys-USA).
Admissions Requirements Minimum age 16; Medical examination; Physician's request.
Staff Physicians 10 (pt); RNs 13 (ft), 4 (pt); LPNs 3 (ft), 4 (pt); Orderlies 4 (ft); Nurses aides 43 (ft), 5 (pt); Physical therapists 1 (pt); Recreational therapists 3 (ft); Occupational therapists 2 (pt); Speech therapists 1 (pt); Dietitians 1 (pt); Ophthalmologists 1 (pt); Podiatrists 1 (pt).
Affiliation Seventh-Day Adventist
Facilities Dining room; Physical therapy room; Activities room; Chapel; Crafts room; Laundry room; Barber/Beauty shop; Library; Dental; Horticulture.
Activities Arts & crafts; Cards; Games; Reading groups; Prayer groups; Movies; Shopping trips; Social/Cultural gatherings.

CHESHIRE

Cheshire Convalescent Center
745 Highland Ave, Cheshire, CT, 06410
(203) 272-7285
Admin Mary P Fehr. *Medical Dir/Dir of Nursing* Edward Oxnard MD.
Licensure Skilled care; Intermediate care. *Beds* SNF 80; ICF 40. *Certified* Medicaid; Medicare.
Owner Proprietary Corp (Mediplex).
Admissions Requirements Minimum age 15; Medical examination.
Staff Physicians 4 (pt); RNs 14 (ft), 6 (pt); LPNs 7 (ft), 2 (pt); Nurses aides 32 (ft), 12 (pt); Physical therapists 1 (ft); Recreational therapists 2 (ft), 1 (pt); Occupational therapists 1 (pt); Speech therapists 1 (pt); Dietitians 1 (pt); Dentists 1 (pt); Ophthalmologists 1 (pt); Podiatrists 1 (pt).
Languages Spanish, French
Facilities Dining room; Physical therapy room; Activities room; Chapel; Laundry room; Barber/Beauty shop.
Activities Arts & crafts; Cards; Games; Reading groups; Prayer groups; Movies; Shopping trips; Social/Cultural gatherings.

The Elim Park Baptist Home Inc
140 Cook Hill Rd, Cheshire, CT, 06410
(203) 272-3547
Medical Dir/Dir of Nursing Gerhard T Mack MD.
Licensure Skilled care; Intermediate care; Home for aged. *Beds* SNF 60; ICF 30; Home for aged 52. *Certified* Medicaid; Medicare.
Owner Nonprofit Corp.

Admissions Requirements Minimum age 60;
Medical examination.
Staff RNs 6 (ft), 13 (pt); LPNs 1 (ft), 4 (pt);
Nurses aides 17 (ft), 29 (pt); Activities
coordinators 2 (ft).
Affiliation Baptist
Facilities Dining room; Physical therapy
room; Activities room; Chapel; Crafts room;
Laundry room; Barber/Beauty shop; Library.
Activities Arts & crafts; Games; Reading
groups; Prayer groups; Movies; Shopping
trips; Social/Cultural gatherings.

New Lakeview Convalescent Home*
50 Hazel Dr, Cheshire, CT, 06410
(203) 272-7204
Licensure Skilled care; Intermediate care. *Beds*
210. *Certified* Medicaid; Medicare.
Owner Proprietary Corp (Greenery Rehab
Grp).
Staff RNs 14 (ft); LPNs 20 (ft); Nurses aides
61 (ft); Activities coordinators 3 (ft), 1 (pt);
Social workers 2 (ft).
Languages Italian, Spanish, Japanese, Korean,
German, Portuguese

CHESTER

Aaron Manor Health Care Facility*
Rte 148, Chester, CT, 06412
(203) 526-5316
Licensure Intermediate care. *Beds* 60.
Certified Medicaid.
Owner Proprietary Corp.
Staff LPNs 4 (ft), 1 (pt); Nurses aides 8 (ft), 1
(pt); Activities coordinators 1 (ft).
Activities Arts & crafts; Games; Movies;
Social/Cultural gatherings.

**Chesterfields Chronic & Convalescent
Hospital***
132 Main St, Chester, CT, 06412
(203) 526-5363
Licensure Skilled care. *Beds* 60. *Certified*
Medicaid; Medicare.
Owner Proprietary Corp.
Staff RNs 5 (ft), 1 (pt); LPNs 5 (ft), 1 (pt);
Nurses aides 25 (ft), 1 (pt).
Languages Greek, Italian
Activities Arts & crafts; Games; Movies; Bus
trips; Music.

CLINTON

Clinton Health Care Center*
5 Harbor Pkwy, Clinton, CT, 06413
(203) 669-5717
Medical Dir/Dir of Nursing Arnold C Winokur
MD.
Licensure Intermediate care. *Beds* 40.
Certified Medicaid.
Owner Proprietary Corp.
Admissions Requirements Minimum age 16;
Medical examination; Physician's request.
Staff Physicians 6 (pt); RNs 3 (ft), 2 (pt);
LPNs 1 (ft), 2 (pt); Orderlies 1 (ft); Nurses
aides 6 (ft), 10 (pt); Physical therapists 1
(pt); Reality therapists 1 (ft); Recreational
therapists 1 (ft); Occupational therapists 1
(pt); Speech therapists 2 (pt); Activities
coordinators 1 (pt); Dietitians 1 (pt);
Dentists 1 (pt); Ophthalmologists 1 (pt);
Podiatrists 1 (pt); Audiologists 1 (pt).
Languages Spanish, German

COLCHESTER

Colchester Conv Home*
18 Harrington Ct, Colchester, CT, 06415
(203) 537-2339
Medical Dir/Dir of Nursing Dr Carl Conrad.
Licensure Skilled care. *Beds* 120. *Certified*
Medicaid; Medicare.
Owner Proprietary Corp (Multicare
Management).
Admissions Requirements Medical
examination; Physician's request.

Staff Physicians; Dietitians; Nurses aides.
Languages Polish, French, Japanese, Spanish,
Russian
Facilities Dining room; Physical therapy
room; Activities room; Chapel; Laundry
room.
Activities Arts & crafts; Cards; Games;
Reading groups; Prayer groups; Movies;
Shopping trips; Social/Cultural gatherings.

Liberty Hall Nursing Center
10 Broadway, Colchester, CT, 06415
(203) 537-4606
Admin Stuart T Fisher. *Medical Dir/Dir of
Nursing* Dr David Boxwell MD; Rosemarie
Hanover RN DNS.
Licensure Skilled care; Intermediate care. *Beds*
SNF 60; ICF 20. *Certified* Medicaid;
Medicare.
Owner Privately owned.
Staff RNs; LPNs; Nurses aides; Physical
therapists; Recreational therapists.
Languages Polish, French
Facilities Dining room; Physical therapy
room; Activities room; Laundry room;
Barber/Beauty shop; Library.
Activities Arts & crafts; Cards; Games;
Reading groups; Prayer groups; Movies;
Social/Cultural gatherings; Cooking; Sing-
alongs; Picnics.

CROMWELL

Cromwell Crest Convalescent Home Inc*
385 Main St, Cromwell, CT, 06416
(203) 635-5613
Licensure Skilled care; Intermediate care. *Beds*
90. *Certified* Medicaid; Medicare.
Owner Proprietary Corp.
Staff RNs 8 (ft), 1 (pt); LPNs 4 (ft); Nurses
aides 23 (ft); Physical therapists 1 (ft).
Languages Spanish, Italian
Activities Arts & crafts; Cards; Games;
Reading groups; Prayer groups; Movies;
Shopping trips; Social/Cultural gatherings;
Exercises; Current events.

Pilgrim Manor
52 Missionary Rd, Cromwell, CT, 06416
(203) 635-5511
Admin Robert Johnson.
Licensure Skilled care; Intermediate care;
Home for aged. *Beds* SNF 30; ICF 30;
Home for aged 52. *Certified* Medicaid;
Medicare.
Owner Nonprofit Corp (Covenant Benevolent
Inst).
Admissions Requirements Minimum age 62;
Medical examination.
Staff Physicians; RNs; Nurses aides; Activities
coordinators.
Languages Swedish
Affiliation Evangelical Covenant Church
Facilities Dining room; Physical therapy
room; Activities room; Crafts room; Laundry
room; Barber/Beauty shop; Library.
Activities Arts & crafts; Games; Reading
groups; Prayer groups; Movies; Shopping
trips; Social/Cultural gatherings.

Ridgeview Rest Home Inc
156 Berlin Rd, Cromwell, CT, 06416
(203) 828-6381, 635-1010
Admin Mrs Adel Coccomo. *Medical Dir/Dir of
Nursing* Dr Richard Alberti; Barbara Baron.
Licensure Intermediate care. *Beds* ICF 60.
Certified Medicaid.
Owner Proprietary Corp.
Admissions Requirements Minimum age 55.
Staff RNs 3 (ft), 5 (pt); LPNs 1 (ft); Nurses
aides 4 (ft), 5 (pt); Activities coordinators 1
(ft); Dietitians 1 (pt); Ophthalmologists 1
(pt).
Languages Italian, French, Polish
Facilities Dining room; Activities room;
Crafts room; Laundry room; Barber/Beauty
shop.

Activities Arts & crafts; Cards; Games;
Reading groups; Prayer groups; Movies;
Shopping trips; Social/Cultural gatherings.

DANBURY

Danbury Pavilion Healthcare
22 Hospital Ave, Danbury, CT, 06810
(203) 744-3700
Medical Dir/Dir of Nursing Dr Alan Shafto
MD.
Licensure Skilled care. *Beds* 150. *Certified*
Medicaid; Medicare.
Owner Proprietary Corp (Beverly Enterprises).
Admissions Requirements Medical
examination.
Staff Physicians 4 (ft); RNs 18 (ft); LPNs 7
(ft); Nurses aides 84 (ft); Physical therapists
2 (ft); Recreational therapists 2 (ft), 1 (pt);
Speech therapists 1 (pt); Dietitians 1 (pt);
Dentists 1 (pt); Ophthalmologists 1 (pt);
Podiatrists 2 (pt).
Languages Spanish
Facilities Dining room; Physical therapy
room; Activities room; Chapel; Crafts room;
Laundry room; Barber/Beauty shop; Library;
Outdoor patio.
Activities Arts & crafts; Cards; Games;
Reading groups; Prayer groups; Movies;
Shopping trips; Social/Cultural gatherings.

Filosa Convalescent Home Inc*
13 Hakim St, Danbury, CT, 06810
(203) 744-3366
Licensure Skilled care. *Certified* Medicaid;
Medicare.
Owner Proprietary Corp.
Staff RNs 16 (ft); LPNs 5 (ft); Nurses aides 23
(ft); Physical therapists 1 (ft); Activities
coordinators 1 (ft), 1 (pt); Social workers 2
(ft).
Languages Spanish, Polish, Arabic, German,
Swedish

Glen Hill Conv Center
Glen Hill Rd, Danbury, CT, 06811
(203) 744-2840
Admin James K Malloy. *Medical Dir/Dir of
Nursing* W Alan Schafto MD; Patricia Roth
RN.
Licensure Skilled care. *Beds* SNF 90. *Certified*
Medicaid; Medicare.
Owner Proprietary Corp.
Staff Physicians 5 (pt); RNs 10 (ft), 15 (pt);
LPNs 6 (ft), 2 (pt); Nurses aides 25 (ft), 21
(pt); Physical therapists 1 (ft); Recreational
therapists 2 (ft); Occupational therapists 1
(pt); Speech therapists 1 (pt); Dietitians 1
(ft); Dentists 1 (pt); Ophthalmologists 1 (pt).
Languages Spanish, French, Portuguese
Facilities Dining room; Physical therapy
room; Activities room; Crafts room; Laundry
room; Barber/Beauty shop; Library.
Activities Arts & crafts; Cards; Games;
Reading groups; Prayer groups; Movies;
Shopping trips; Social/Cultural gatherings.

Mediplex of Danbury*
107 Osborne St, Danbury, CT, 06810
(203) 792-8102
Licensure Skilled care; Intermediate care. *Beds*
120. *Certified* Medicaid; Medicare.
Owner Proprietary Corp (Mediplex).
Staff LPNs 28 (ft); Nurses aides 52 (ft);
Physical therapists 2 (ft); Activities
coordinators 2 (ft), 1 (pt); Social workers 1
(ft).
Languages Spanish, Hungarian, German,
French
Activities Arts & crafts; Games; Social/
Cultural gatherings; Outings; Music.

DANIELSON

Canterbury Villa of Danielson Inc
65 Westcott Rd, Danielson, CT, 06239
(203) 774-9540

Admin Leo Attella Jr. *Medical Dir/Dir of Nursing* Phillip Goyette MD; Shelly Spencer RN.
Licensure Skilled care. *Beds* SNF 180. *Certified* Medicaid; Medicare.
Owner Proprietary Corp (Health Enter of America).
Admissions Requirements Physician's request.
Staff Physicians; RNs; LPNs; Orderlies; Nurses aides; Physical therapists; Reality therapists; Recreational therapists; Occupational therapists; Speech therapists; Activities coordinators; Dietitians; Dentists; Ophthalmologists; Podiatrists.
Languages Spanish, Italian, French
Facilities Dining room; Physical therapy room; Activities room; Chapel; Crafts room; Barber/Beauty shop; Library.
Activities Arts & crafts; Cards; Games; Reading groups; Prayer groups; Movies; Shopping trips; Social/Cultural gatherings.

DARIEN

Darien Convalescent Center*
599 Boston Post Rd, Darien, CT, 06820
(203) 655-7727
Licensure Skilled care; Intermediate care. *Beds* 90. *Certified* Medicare.
Owner Proprietary Corp (New Medico Assoc).
Staff RNs 11 (ft), 1 (pt); LPNs 4 (ft), 1 (pt); Nurses aides 36 (ft), 1 (pt); Physical therapists 1 (ft), 1 (pt); Activities coordinators 5 (ft), 1 (pt); Social workers 2 (ft), 1 (pt).
Languages Spanish, Portuguese, French, Yiddish

DAYVILLE

Westview Conv Center Inc*
RFD 1, Ware Rd, Dayville, CT, 06241
(203) 774-8574
Admin Eileen Panteleakes. *Medical Dir/Dir of Nursing* Dr R Philip Goyette.
Licensure Skilled care. *Beds* 90. *Certified* Medicaid; Medicare.
Owner Proprietary Corp.
Admissions Requirements Minimum age 14; Medical examination.
Staff Physicians 2 (pt); RNs 8 (ft); LPNs 15 (ft); Nurses aides 32 (ft); Physical therapists 1 (ft); Reality therapists 1 (pt); Recreational therapists 2 (ft); Speech therapists 1 (pt); Activities coordinators 1 (ft); Dietitians 1 (ft); Dentists 1 (pt); Ophthalmologists 1 (pt); Podiatrists 1 (pt); Audiologists 1 (pt).
Languages French, Polish, Swedish, Spanish, Finnish
Facilities Dining room; Physical therapy room; Activities room; Crafts room; Laundry room; Barber/Beauty shop; Library.
Activities Arts & crafts; Cards; Games; Reading groups; Prayer groups; Movies; Shopping trips; Social/Cultural gatherings.

DEEP RIVER

Deep River Conv Home Inc*
59 Elm St, Deep River, CT, 06417-0393
(203) 526-5902
Licensure Skilled care. *Beds* 30. *Certified* Medicaid.
Owner Proprietary Corp.
Staff RNs 3 (ft); Nurses aides 18 (ft); Activities coordinators 1 (ft); Social workers 1 (ft).
Languages Greek, French, Russian
Activities Outings; Therapeutic recreation.

DERBY

Derby Nursing Center
210 Chatfield St, Derby, CT, 06418
(203) 735-7401

Admin Albert E Saunders. *Medical Dir/Dir of Nursing* Donald Roach MD; Nancy Gambone RN DON.
Licensure Skilled care. *Beds* SNF 121. *Certified* Medicaid; Medicare.
Owner Proprietary Corp (National Healthcare Affilates).
Admissions Requirements Medical examination; Physician's request.
Staff Physicians 1 (pt); RNs 6 (ft), 8 (pt); LPNs 5 (ft), 6 (pt); Nurses aides 30 (ft), 16 (pt); Physical therapists 1 (pt); Recreational therapists 2 (ft); Speech therapists 1 (pt); Dietitians 1 (pt); Ophthalmologists 1 (pt); Dentist 1 (pt).
Languages Italian, Polish
Facilities Dining room; Physical therapy room; Activities room; Crafts room; Laundry room; Barber/Beauty shop; TV rooms.
Activities Arts & crafts; Games; Reading groups; Prayer groups; Movies; Social/Cultural gatherings.

Marshall Lane Manor
101 Marshall Ln, Derby, CT, 06418
(203) 734-3393
Medical Dir/Dir of Nursing John J Narowski MD.
Licensure Intermediate care. *Beds* 120. *Certified* Medicaid.
Owner Proprietary Corp.
Admissions Requirements Medical examination.
Staff RNs 15 (ft); LPNs 3 (ft); Nurses aides 21 (ft); Activities coordinators 2 (ft); Dietitians 1 (ft).
Languages Italian, Polish, Spanish
Facilities Dining room; Physical therapy room; Activities room; Chapel; Crafts room; Laundry room; Barber/Beauty shop; Library; TV room.
Activities Arts & crafts; Cards; Games; Reading groups; Prayer groups; Movies; Shopping trips; Social/Cultural gatherings.

DURHAM

Dogwood Acres ICF
PO Box 301-F, RR 1, Brick Ln, Durham, CT, 06422
(203) 349-8000
Admin Thomas Reese. *Medical Dir/Dir of Nursing* Matthew Raider MD.
Licensure Intermediate care. *Beds* ICF 29. *Certified* Medicaid.
Owner Proprietary Corp.
Admissions Requirements Minimum age 14; Physician's request.
Staff Physicians 1 (pt); RNs 2 (ft), 8 (pt); LPNs 1 (ft), 2 (pt); Orderlies 1 (ft); Nurses aides 4 (ft), 7 (pt); Physical therapists 1 (pt); Recreational therapists 1 (ft); Dietitians 1 (pt); Ophthalmologists 1 (pt).
Facilities Dining room; Activities room.
Activities Arts & crafts; Cards; Games; Reading groups; Prayer groups; Movies; Shopping trips; Social/Cultural gatherings.

Twin Maples Home Inc*
New Haven Rd, Durham, CT, 06422
(203) 349-1041
Licensure Intermediate care. *Beds* 44. *Certified* Medicaid.
Owner Proprietary Corp.
Staff RNs 5 (ft); Nurses aides 5 (ft); Activities coordinators 1 (ft).
Languages Polish, Italian
Activities Therapeutic recreation; Sheltered workshops.

EAST HAMPTON

Cobalt Lodge Convalescent Home*
Rte 151, PO Box 246, East Hampton, CT, 06414
(203) 267-9034

Licensure Skilled care. *Beds* 60. *Certified* Medicaid; Medicare.
Owner Proprietary Corp.
Staff RNs 4 (ft); LPNs 5 (ft); Nurses aides 20 (ft); Activities coordinators; Dietitians.
Languages Polish, Italian
Activities Arts & crafts; Games; Prayer groups; Movies.

Lakeside Residential Care Facility*
PO Box 279, 9 W High St, East Hampton, CT, 06424
(203) 267-4401
Licensure Intermediate care. *Beds* 41.
Owner Proprietary Corp.
Activities Arts & crafts; Games; Mental health programs.

EAST HARTFORD

Burnside Convalescent Home Inc
870 Burnside Ave, East Hartford, CT, 06108
(203) 289-9571
Admin Jean O'Connor. *Medical Dir/Dir of Nursing* Rhea Palczynski.
Licensure Skilled care. *Beds* SNF 90. *Certified* Medicaid; Medicare.
Owner Proprietary Corp.
Admissions Requirements Minimum age 80; Medical examination; Physician's request.
Staff Physicians 4 (pt); RNs 10 (ft); LPNs 12 (ft); Orderlies 2 (ft); Nurses aides 18 (ft); Physical therapists 1 (ft); Recreational therapists 2 (ft); Dietitians 1 (ft); Dentists 1 (pt); Ophthalmologists 1 (pt); Podiatrists 1 (pt).
Languages Polish, Spanish
Facilities Dining room; Physical therapy room; Activities room; Chapel; Crafts room; Laundry room; Barber/Beauty shop; Library; TV rooms.
Activities Arts & crafts; Cards; Games; Reading groups; Prayer groups; Movies; Shopping trips; Social/Cultural gatherings; Bingo.

Riverside Health Care Center
745 Main St, East Hartford, CT, 06108
(203) 289-2791
Licensure Skilled care; Intermediate care. *Beds* 360. *Certified* Medicaid; Medicare.
Owner Proprietary Corp.
Staff Physicians; RNs 219 (ft); Physical therapists; Activities coordinators 7 (ft); Dietitians; Social workers.
Languages Lithuanian, Estonian, Yiddish, Hebrew, Spanish, Portuguese, Italian
Activities Arts & crafts; Games; Reading groups; Prayer groups; Movies; Shopping trips; Social/Cultural gatherings; AA group; Cooking.

St Elizabeth Health Center
51 Applegate Ln, East Hartford, CT, 06118
(203) 568-7520
Admin Jonathan A Neagle. *Medical Dir/Dir of Nursing* Michael Jacuch MD; Kay B LaForge RN DON.
Licensure Skilled care. *Beds* 180. *Certified* Medicaid; Medicare.
Owner Nonprofit organization/foundation.
Admissions Requirements Minimum age 14; Medical examination; Physician's request.
Staff Physicians 5 (pt); RNs 5 (ft), 19 (pt); LPNs 7 (ft), 12 (pt); Orderlies 2 (ft); Nurses aides 58 (ft), 14 (pt); Physical therapists 1 (pt); Recreational therapists 3 (ft).
Languages Spanish, Italian, French, German, Polish, Dutch
Affiliation Roman Catholic
Facilities Dining room; Physical therapy room; Activities room; Chapel; Crafts room; Laundry room; Barber/Beauty shop; Library; Lounges.
Activities Arts & crafts; Cards; Games; Prayer groups; Movies; Shopping trips; Social/Cultural gatherings.

EAST HAVEN

East Haven Rest Home*
83 Main St, East Haven, CT, 06512
(203) 467-5828
Licensure Intermediate care. *Beds* 20.
Staff RNs 4 (ft), 1 (pt); LPNs 1 (ft), 1 (pt).
Languages Italian

Talmadge Park Health Care
Talmadge Ave, East Haven, CT, 06512
(203) 469-2316
Admin Lorraine A Franco. *Medical Dir/Dir of Nursing* Dr E Leach; Pearl Mattie.
Licensure Skilled care; Intermediate care. *Beds* SNF 30; ICF 30. *Certified* Medicaid; Medicare.
Owner Privately owned.
Staff Physicians 1 (pt); RNs 11 (ft); LPNs 4 (pt); Nurses aides 26 (ft); Physical therapists 1 (pt); Speech therapists 1 (pt); Activities coordinators 2 (ft), 2 (pt); Dietitians 1 (pt); Ophthalmologists 1 (pt); Podiatrists 1 (pt).
Languages Italian
Activities Arts & crafts; Games; Movies; Social/Cultural gatherings; Picnics; Current events; Cooking; Exercises; Sensory intergration.

Teresa Rest Home Inc
PO Box 313, 57 Main St, East Haven, CT, 06512
(203) 467-0836
Admin Josephine Santino. *Medical Dir/Dir of Nursing* Dr Edward Scherr.
Licensure Rest Home. *Beds* Rest home 21.
Owner Proprietary Corp.
Admissions Requirements Minimum age 50; Medical examination.
Staff Nurses aides; Recreational therapists; Activities coordinators; Ophthalmologists.

EAST WINDSOR

D'Amore Rest Haven Inc*
171 Main St, East Windsor, CT, 06088
(203) 623-3174
Licensure Intermediate care. *Beds* 90. *Certified* Medicaid.
Owner Proprietary Corp.
Staff RNs 3 (ft).
Languages Polish, French, Spanish, Italian

Prospect Hill Rehabilitation Center*
96 Prospect Hill Rd, East Windsor, CT, 06088
(203) 623-9846
Licensure Skilled care; Intermediate care. *Beds* 120. *Certified* Medicaid.
Owner Proprietary Corp.
Staff LPNs 39 (ft); Nurses aides 75 (ft); Physical therapists 1 (ft); Activities coordinators 2 (ft); Social workers 1 (ft).
Languages French, Italian, Polish
Activities Games; Movies; Social/Cultural gatherings; Music; Discussion groups; Resident council.

ENFIELD

Enfield Nursing Center*
PO Box 2241, 612 Hazard Ave, Enfield, CT, 06082
(203) 749-8388
Licensure Skilled care; Intermediate care. *Beds* 130. *Certified* Medicaid; Medicare.
Owner Proprietary Corp (Unicare).
Staff RNs 3 (ft); LPNs 3 (ft); Social workers 1 (ft).
Languages Italian
Activities Arts & crafts; Shopping trips; Social/Cultural gatherings; Church; Disscusions; Resident council.

Parkway Pavilion Healthcare
1157 Enfield St, Enfield, CT, 06082
(203) 745-1641
Medical Dir/Dir of Nursing Dr George Donahue.
Licensure Skilled care. *Beds* 140. *Certified* Medicaid; Medicare.
Owner Proprietary Corp (Hillhaven Corp).
Admissions Requirements Minimum age 14; Medical examination; Physician's request.
Staff Physicians 8 (pt); RNs 4 (ft), 18 (pt); LPNs 4 (ft), 12 (pt); Orderlies 3 (pt); Nurses aides 15 (ft), 36 (pt); Physical therapists 1 (pt); Reality therapists 1 (pt); Speech therapists 1 (pt); Activities coordinators 2 (ft), 1 (pt); Dietitians 1 (pt); Dentists 1 (pt); Ophthalmologists 1 (pt); Podiatrists 1 (pt).
Languages Polish, Italian
Facilities Dining room; Physical therapy room; Activities room; Chapel; Crafts room; Laundry room; Barber/Beauty shop; Library.
Activities Arts & crafts; Cards; Games; Reading groups; Prayer groups; Movies; Shopping trips; Social/Cultural gatherings.

St Joseph's Residence*
1365 Enfield St, Enfield, CT, 06082
(203) 741-0791
Medical Dir/Dir of Nursing Brendan Maganran MD.
Licensure Skilled care; Intermediate care. *Beds* 94. *Certified* Medicaid; Medicare.
Owner Nonprofit Corp.
Languages French, Spanish, Italian, Polish, German, Lithuanian
Affiliation Roman Catholic
Facilities Dining room; Physical therapy room; Activities room; Chapel; Crafts room; Laundry room; Barber/Beauty shop; Library.
Activities Arts & crafts; Cards; Games; Prayer groups; Movies; Shopping trips; Social/Cultural gatherings.

ESSEX

Highland Hall Manor
16 Prospect St, Essex, CT, 06426
(203) 767-8244
Admin Amelia Cart. *Medical Dir/Dir of Nursing* Dr John Stanford.
Licensure Boarding-Rest home. *Beds* 33. *Certified* Medicaid.
Owner Proprietary Corp.
Admissions Requirements Minimum age 21.
Languages Spanish, Italian
Facilities Dining room; Activities room; Laundry room.
Activities Arts & crafts; Cards; Games; Prayer groups; Movies; Shopping trips; Day trips.

Pettipaug Manor
63 S Main St, Essex, CT, 06426
(203) 767-8422
Admin Betty Jane Cosenza RN. *Medical Dir/Dir of Nursing* John Stanford MD; Michele Cosenza RN BS DNS.
Licensure Intermediate care. *Beds* ICF 49. *Certified* Medicaid.
Owner Proprietary Corp.
Admissions Requirements Minimum age 21; Medical examination; Physician's request.
Staff RNs 5 (ft); LPNs 1 (ft); Nurses aides 7 (ft); Recreational therapists 1 (ft).
Facilities Dining room; Activities room; Library; 2 lounges for smokers; 1 lounge for non-smokers.
Activities Arts & crafts; Cards; Games; Reading groups; Prayer groups; Movies; Shopping trips; Social/Cultural gatherings; Swimming; Pet therapy; Bingo.

FAIRFIELD

Carolton Chronic & Convalescent Hospital Inc
400 Mill Plain Rd, Fairfield, CT, 06430
(203) 255-3573
Medical Dir/Dir of Nursing Dr Richard Van de Berghe; Angara Lombard.
Licensure Skilled care. *Beds* 219. *Certified* Medicaid; Medicare.
Owner Proprietary Corp.
Staff RNs 31 (ft), 26 (pt); LPNs 9 (ft), 13 (pt); Nurses aides 120 (ft), 22 (pt); Physical therapists 4 (ft); Recreational therapists 4 (ft); Occupational therapists 3 (pt); Speech therapists 3 (pt); Dietitians 1 (ft).
Languages Spanish, Dutch, Italian, Russian, Yiddish, Hebrew
Facilities Dining room; Physical therapy room; Activities room; Laundry room; Barber/Beauty shop; Library; Physical therapy swimming pool.
Activities Arts & crafts; Cards; Games; Reading groups; Prayer groups; Movies.

Jewish Home for the Elderly
175 Jefferson St, Fairfield, CT, 06432
(203) 374-9461
Admin Dennis J Magid. *Medical Dir/Dir of Nursing* Marvinb Garrell MD; Donna Joyce DON.
Licensure Skilled care; Intermediate care. *Beds* SNF 120; ICF 120. *Certified* Medicaid; Medicare.
Owner Nonprofit Corp.
Staff Physicians 9 (pt); RNs 150 (ft); LPNs 12 (ft); Nurses aides 101 (ft); Activities coordinators 4 (ft); Social workers 2 (ft).
Languages Hebrew, French, Spanish, Portuguese
Affiliation Jewish
Activities Arts & crafts; Reading groups; Movies; Shopping trips; Social/Cultural gatherings; Music; Current events; Picnics; Sheltered workshops.

North Fairfield Geriatric Center Inc
118 Jefferson St, Fairfield, CT, 06432
(203) 372-4501
Admin Lois E Perrini. *Medical Dir/Dir of Nursing* John A Simpson MD; Florence Kavulish RN DON.
Licensure Skilled care. *Beds* SNF 112. *Certified* Medicaid; Medicare.
Owner Proprietary Corp.
Staff Physicians 1 (ft), 3 (pt); RNs 15 (ft); LPNs 10 (ft); Nurses aides 58 (ft); Physical therapists 1 (ft), 1 (pt); Reality therapists 1 (pt); Recreational therapists 1 (pt); Occupational therapists 1 (pt); Speech therapists 1 (pt); Activities coordinators 2 (ft), 3 (pt); Dietitians 1 (ft); Dentists 1 (pt); Ophthalmologists 1 (pt); Podiatrists 1 (pt); Dentist 1 (pt); Social workers 1 (ft).
Languages French, Polish, German, Italian, Hebrew, Yiddish, Spanish
Facilities Dining room; Physical therapy room; Activities room; Chapel; Crafts room; Laundry room; Barber/Beauty shop.
Activities Arts & crafts; Cards; Games; Reading groups; Prayer groups; Movies; Shopping trips.

FARMINGTON

Care Manor of Farmington
Scott Swamp Rd, Farmington, CT, 06032
(203) 677-7707
Admin Francis Q Meyer. *Medical Dir/Dir of Nursing* Murray Wellner MD; Rebecca Pope RN DON.
Licensure Skilled care. *Beds* SNF 120. *Certified* Medicaid; Medicare.
Owner Proprietary Corp (Health Care & Retirement Corp).
Admissions Requirements Minimum age 14.
Staff RNs 6 (ft), 8 (pt); LPNs 6 (ft), 8 (pt); Nurses aides 25 (ft), 20 (pt); Physical therapists 1 (pt); Recreational therapists 2 (ft); Speech therapists 1 (pt); Dietitians 1 (ft); Dentists 1 (pt); Ophthalmologists 1 (pt); Podiatrists 1 (pt).
Languages Spanish, French, Polish
Facilities Dining room; Physical therapy room; Activities room; Crafts room; Laundry room; Barber/Beauty shop.

Activities Arts & crafts; Cards; Games; Reading groups; Prayer groups; Movies; Shopping trips; Social/Cultural gatherings.

Farmington Convalescent Home*
Rte 6, Colt Hwy, Farmington, CT, 06032
(203) 677-1671
Licensure Skilled care; Intermediate care. *Beds* 70. *Certified* Medicaid; Medicare.
Owner Proprietary Corp.
Staff RNs 6 (ft), 1 (pt); LPNs 5 (ft), 1 (pt); Nurses aides 25 (ft), 1 (pt); Dietitians; Activities coordinators 1 (ft), 1 (pt).
Languages French, Polish
Activities Arts & crafts; Games; Movies; Social/Cultural gatherings; Reality orientation; Holiday celebrations.

FORESTVILLE

Forestville Nursing Center*
23 Fair St, Forestville, CT, 06010
(203) 589-2923
Medical Dir/Dir of Nursing Dr Moschello.
Licensure Skilled care. *Beds* 120. *Certified* Medicaid; Medicare.
Owner Proprietary Corp.
Admissions Requirements Minimum age 14; Medical examination.
Staff Physicians 6 (pt); RNs 14 (ft), 3 (pt); LPNs 7 (ft), 5 (pt); Orderlies 2 (ft), 2 (pt); Nurses aides 50 (ft), 22 (pt); Physical therapists 1 (ft), 2 (pt); Recreational therapists 4 (ft), 1 (pt); Occupational therapists 1 (ft); Speech therapists 2 (ft); Activities coordinators 1 (ft); Dietitians 1 (pt).
Languages Greek, Polish, Italian, French, Spanish
Facilities Dining room; Physical therapy room; Activities room; Crafts room; Laundry room; Barber/Beauty shop.
Activities Arts & crafts; Cards; Games; Reading groups; Prayer groups; Movies; Shopping trips; Social/Cultural gatherings.

GLASTONBURY

Salmon Brook Convalescent Home*
72 Salmon Brook Dr, Glastonbury, CT, 06033
(203) 633-5244
Licensure Skilled care; Intermediate care. *Beds* 120. *Certified* Medicaid; Medicare.
Owner Proprietary Corp.
Staff RNs 14 (ft), 1 (pt); LPNs 44 (ft), 1 (pt); Nurses aides 2 (ft); Activities coordinators 2 (ft); Dietitians 13 (pt).
Languages Italian, Spanish
Activities Arts & crafts; Prayer groups; Movies; Shopping trips; Musicals.

GREENWICH

Greenwich Laurelton Nursing & Convalescent Home
PO Box 11029, 1188 King St, Greenwich, CT, 06831
(203) 531-8300
Admin Louise Caputo. *Medical Dir/Dir of Nursing* James Orphenos MD; Jeanne Miller RN.
Licensure Skilled care. *Beds* SNF 75. *Certified* Medicaid; Medicare.
Owner Proprietary Corp.
Admissions Requirements Minimum age 14; Medical examination; Physician's request.
Staff Physicians 15 (pt); RNs 5 (ft), 15 (pt); LPNs 2 (ft), 3 (pt); Nurses aides 29 (ft); Physical therapists 1 (pt); Recreational therapists 1 (ft), 1 (pt); Speech therapists 1 (pt); Dietitians 1 (ft), 1 (pt); Dentists 1 (pt); Ophthalmologists 1 (pt); Podiatrists 1 (pt).
Languages Italian, Polish, Spanish
Facilities Dining room; Physical therapy room; Activities room; Crafts room; Laundry room; Barber/Beauty shop; Library.

Activities Arts & crafts; Cards; Games; Reading groups; Prayer groups; Movies; Shopping trips; Social/Cultural gatherings; Support groups; Stroke group; Parkinsons group; Resident council.

The Nathaniel Witherell
70 Parsonage Rd, Greenwich, CT, 06830
(203) 869-4130
Admin Peter J Engelmann. *Medical Dir/Dir of Nursing* Michael Whitcomb MD; Judith M Sheehan DON.
Licensure Skilled care. *Beds* SNF 200. *Certified* Medicaid; Medicare.
Owner Publicly owned.
Admissions Requirements Minimum age 14; Medical examination; Physician's request.
Staff Physicians 6 (ft); RNs 24 (ft), 16 (pt); LPNs 10 (ft), 3 (pt); Orderlies 2 (pt); Nurses aides 61 (ft), 39 (pt); Physical therapists 2 (ft); Recreational therapists 3 (ft), 3 (pt); Occupational therapists 1 (ft); Speech therapists 1 (pt); Activities coordinators 1 (ft); Dietitians 1 (ft); Dentists 1 (pt); Ophthalmologists 4 (pt); Podiatrists 1 (pt).
Languages Spanish, German, Italian, French
Facilities Dining room; Physical therapy room; Activities room; Chapel; Crafts room; Laundry room; Barber/Beauty shop; Library; Auditorium.
Activities Arts & crafts; Cards; Games; Reading groups; Prayer groups; Movies; Bell choir; Cooking/Baking clubs; Picnics; BBQs; Out trips; Boat rides; Current events.

GROTON

Fairview
Starr Hill Rd, Groton, CT, 06340
(203) 445-7478
Medical Dir/Dir of Nursing Richard Brent.
Licensure Skilled care; Intermediate care. *Beds* 120. *Certified* Medicaid; Medicare.
Owner Nonprofit Corp.
Admissions Requirements Minimum age 14; Medical examination; Physician's request.
Staff Physicians 2 (pt); RNs 10 (ft), 7 (pt); LPNs 5 (pt); Orderlies 1 (pt); Nurses aides 12 (ft), 24 (pt); Physical therapists 1 (ft); Recreational therapists 2 (ft); Speech therapists 1 (pt); Activities coordinators 1 (ft); Dietitians 1 (pt); Dentists 1 (pt); Dentist.
Languages Tagalog
Affiliation Independent Order of Odd Fellows & Rebekahs
Facilities Dining room; Physical therapy room; Activities room; Chapel; Crafts room; Laundry room; Barber/Beauty shop; Auditorium.
Activities Arts & crafts; Cards; Games; Reading groups; Prayer groups; Movies; Shopping trips; Social/Cultural gatherings; Outside scenic trips; Dine out club.

Groton Regency Retirement & Nursing Center
1145 Poquonnock Rd, Groton, CT, 06340
(203) 446-9960
Admin Arthur P Panteleakos. *Medical Dir of Nursing* Dr Richard Benton; Claire Brennan RN DON.
Licensure Skilled care; Intermediate care; Home for aged. *Beds* SNF 120; ICF 60; Home for aged 120. *Certified* Medicaid; Medicare.
Owner Proprietary Corp.
Staff Physicians 3 (pt); RNs 15 (ft), 2 (pt); LPNs 11 (ft), 4 (pt); Nurses aides 56 (ft), 16 (pt); Physical therapists 1 (ft); Recreational therapists 5 (ft), 1 (pt); Speech therapists 1 (pt); Dietitians 1 (ft); Ophthalmologists 1 (pt).
Languages French, Greek, Italian
Facilities Dining room; Physical therapy room; Activities room; Chapel; Crafts room; Laundry room; Barber/Beauty shop; Library.

Activities Arts & crafts; Cards; Games; Reading groups; Prayer groups; Movies; Shopping trips; Social/Cultural gatherings.

GUILFORD

Fowler Nursing Center Inc*
10 Boston Post Rd, Guilford, CT, 06437
(203) 453-3725
Medical Dir/Dir of Nursing Martin E Fink.
Licensure Skilled care. *Beds* 90. *Certified* Medicaid; Medicare.
Owner Proprietary Corp.
Admissions Requirements Minimum age 14; Medical examination; Physician's request.
Staff Physicians 1 (pt); RNs 8 (ft), 12 (pt); LPNs 3 (ft), 1 (pt); Orderlies 1 (ft); Nurses aides 20 (ft), 22 (pt); Physical therapists 1 (pt); Recreational therapists 1 (ft), 1 (pt); Speech therapists 1 (pt); Dietitians 4 (ft), 1 (pt).
Facilities Dining room; Physical therapy room; Activities room; Crafts room; Laundry room; Barber/Beauty shop.
Activities Arts & crafts; Cards; Games; Reading groups; Prayer groups; Movies; Shopping trips; Social/Cultural gatherings.

West Lake Lodge Nursing Home
109 West Lake Ave, Guilford, CT, 06437
(203) 488-9142
Admin Mary D Carpenella. *Medical Dir/Dir of Nursing* John Schiavone MD.
Licensure Skilled care. *Beds* SNF 60. *Certified* Medicaid; Medicare.
Owner Proprietary Corp.
Admissions Requirements Medical examination.
Staff RNs 7 (ft), 6 (pt); LPNs 1 (ft), 2 (pt); Orderlies 6 (ft); Nurses aides 27 (ft), 6 (pt); Physical therapists 1 (pt); Recreational therapists 1 (ft); Speech therapists 1 (pt); Dietitians 1 (pt).
Languages Italian, French, Polish
Facilities Dining room; Physical therapy room; Activities room; Crafts room; Laundry room; Barber/Beauty shop.
Activities Arts & crafts; Cards; Games; Reading groups; Prayer groups; Movies.

HAMDEN

Arden House Inc*
850 Mix Ave, Hamden, CT, 06514
(203) 281-3500
Licensure Skilled care; Intermediate care. *Beds* 360. *Certified* Medicaid; Medicare.
Owner Proprietary Corp.
Staff RNs 32 (ft); LPNs 14 (ft); Nurses aides 98 (ft); Activities coordinators 7 (ft).
Languages Italian
Activities Arts & crafts; Games; Reading groups; Movies; Shopping trips; Social/Cultural gatherings; Resident volunteers; Discussion groups; Sheltered workshops; Resident council; Cooking; Newspaper.

Hamden Health Care Facility
1270 Sherman Ln, Hamden, CT, 06514
(203) 281-7555
Licensure Skilled care; Intermediate care. *Beds* SNF 90; ICF 30. *Certified* Medicaid; Medicare.
Owner Proprietary Corp.
Admissions Requirements Minimum age 18; Medical examination.
Staff Physicians 3 (ft); RNs 30 (ft); LPNs 10 (ft); Nurses aides 60 (ft); Physical therapists 1 (ft); Recreational therapists 2 (ft); Occupational therapists 1 (ft); Speech therapists 1 (ft); Dietitians 1 (ft); Dentists 1 (ft); Ophthalmologists 1 (ft); Podiatrists 1 (ft); Art therapist 1 (ft).
Languages Spanish, Italian
Facilities Dining room; Physical therapy room; Activities room; Chapel; Crafts room; Laundry room; Barber/Beauty shop; Library.

Activities Arts & crafts; Cards; Games; Reading groups; Prayer groups; Movies; Shopping trips; Social/Cultural gatherings.

Hyde Park Convalescent Home Inc*
1840 State St, Hamden, CT, 06511
(203) 624-1558
Licensure Skilled care. *Beds* 26. *Certified* Medicaid; Medicare.
Owner Proprietary Corp.
Staff RNs 3 (ft); Nurses aides 4 (ft).
Languages Italian
Activities Arts & crafts; Games; Reading groups; Prayer groups; Movies; Social/ Cultural gatherings; Current events; Discussion groups.

Whitney Center Medical Unit
200 Leeder Hill Dr, Hamden, CT, 06517
(203) 281-6745
Admin Keith Johannessen. *Medical Dir/Dir of Nursing* Albert Dolinsky MD; Rose Stockman.
Licensure Skilled care. *Beds* SNF 59. *Certified* Medicaid; Medicare.
Owner Nonprofit Corp (Life Care Services Corp).
Admissions Requirements Medical examination; Physician's request.
Staff RNs 2 (ft), 7 (pt); LPNs 7 (pt); Nurses aides 11 (ft), 19 (pt); Physical therapists 1 (pt); Recreational therapists 1 (ft), 1 (pt); Speech therapists 1 (pt); Dietitians 1 (pt).
Languages Italian, German
Facilities Dining room; Physical therapy room; Activities room; Barber/Beauty shop.
Activities Arts & crafts; Games; Reading groups; Prayer groups; Movies; Social/ Cultural gatherings.

Whitney Manor Convalescent Center Inc
2800 Whitney Ave, Hamden, CT, 06518
(203) 288-6230
Admin Lawrence Amkraut. *Medical Dir/Dir of Nursing* Ronald E Coe MD; Shirley M Lee RN.
Licensure Skilled care. *Beds* 150. *Certified* Medicaid; Medicare.
Owner Proprietary Corp.
Admissions Requirements Minimum age 14; Medical examination; Physician's request.
Staff Physicians 15 (pt); RNs 15 (ft), 5 (pt); LPNs 7 (ft), 4 (pt); Orderlies 5 (ft); Nurses aides 60 (ft), 20 (pt); Physical therapists 1 (pt); Recreational therapists 3 (ft), 1 (pt); Occupational therapists 1 (pt); Speech therapists 1 (pt); Activities coordinators 1 (ft); Dietitians 1 (pt); Dentists 2 (pt); Ophthalmologists 1 (pt); Podiatrists 1 (pt).
Languages Italian, Spanish, French
Facilities Dining room; Physical therapy room; Activities room; Crafts room; Laundry room; Barber/Beauty shop.
Activities Arts & crafts; Cards; Games; Reading groups; Prayer groups; Movies; Shopping trips; Social/Cultural gatherings.

HARTFORD

Avery Nursing Home*
705 New Britain Ave, Hartford, CT, 06106
(203) 527-9126
Medical Dir/Dir of Nursing Dr John T Beebe.
Licensure Skilled care. *Beds* 90. *Certified* Medicaid; Medicare.
Owner Nonprofit Corp.
Staff Physicians; Nurses aides.
Languages Spanish, Polish, Russian, French
Activities Prayer groups.

Buckley Convalescent Home
210 George St, Hartford, CT, 06114
(203) 249-9166
Admin Walter L Talarski. *Medical Dir/Dir of Nursing* Zbigniew Woznica MD; Rita Bonesio RN DNS.
Licensure Skilled care. *Beds* 120. *Certified* Medicaid; Medicare.

Owner Proprietary Corp.
Admissions Requirements Minimum age 18; Medical examination; Physician's request.
Staff Physicians 31 (pt); RNs 9 (ft), 1 (pt); LPNs 4 (ft), 4 (pt); Orderlies 2 (ft); Nurses aides 34 (ft), 2 (pt); Physical therapists 1 (ft); Recreational therapists 2 (ft); Speech therapists 1 (pt); Dietitians 1 (ft), 1 (pt); Ophthalmologists 1 (pt); Podiatrists 1 (pt).
Languages Polish, French, Italian, Spanish, Japanese
Facilities Dining room; Physical therapy room; Activities room; Crafts room; Laundry room; Barber/Beauty shop.
Activities Arts & crafts; Cards; Games; Reading groups; Prayer groups; Movies; Shopping trips; Social/Cultural gatherings.

The Gables Inc
276 Washington St, Hartford, CT, 06106
(203) 522-8209
Admin Collin M Tierney. *Medical Dir/Dir of Nursing* Paul West MD; Judith Carboni RN MSN.
Licensure Skilled care; Intermediate care. *Beds* 73. *Certified* Medicaid; Medicare.
Owner Proprietary Corp.
Admissions Requirements Medical examination; Physician's request.
Staff Physicians 3 (pt); RNs 5 (ft), 4 (pt); LPNs 5 (ft), 2 (pt); Nurses aides 25 (ft), 5 (pt); Physical therapists 1 (pt); Recreational therapists 2 (ft), 1 (pt); Speech therapists 1 (pt); Activities coordinators 1 (ft); Dietitians 1 (ft); Dentists 1 (pt); Ophthalmologists 1 (pt); Podiatrists 1 (pt).
Languages Spanish, French
Facilities Dining room; Physical therapy room; Activities room; Barber/Beauty shop; Library.
Activities Arts & crafts; Games; Prayer groups; Music; Psychogeriatric group; Reality orientation; Remotivation.

Greenwood Health Center
5 Greenwood St, Hartford, CT, 06106
(203) 236-2901
Admin Terri Golec. *Medical Dir/Dir of Nursing* Dr Giarnella; Mary Brazel DON.
Licensure Skilled care. *Beds* SNF 240. *Certified* Medicaid; Medicare.
Owner Proprietary Corp (Beverly Enterprises).
Admissions Requirements Minimum age 18; Medical examination.
Staff Physicians 3 (pt); RNs 19 (ft), 16 (pt); LPNs 17 (ft), 19 (pt); Nurses aides 64 (ft), 46 (pt); Physical therapists 1 (ft); Recreational therapists 4 (ft), 1 (pt); Occupational therapists 1 (pt); Speech therapists 1 (ft); Dietitians 1 (ft); Ophthalmologists 1 (pt); Podiatrists 1 (pt);; Diet tech 1 (ft); Dentist 1 (pt).
Languages Portuguese, French, Armenian, Italian, Spanish, Polish
Facilities Dining room; Physical therapy room; Activities room; Laundry room; Barber/Beauty shop; Patio; Courtyard; Wheelchair garden; TV room.
Activities Arts & crafts; Cards; Games; Reading groups; Prayer groups; Movies; Shopping trips; Social/Cultural gatherings; Discussion groups; Dinner club; Cooking groups; Exercise; Resident council; Sensory groups; Pet therapy; Newspapers.

Hebrew Home & Hospital
615 Tower Ave, Hartford, CT, 06112
(203) 242-6207
Admin Irving Kronenberg. *Medical Dir/Dir of Nursing* J L Brandt MD; Dorothy Varholak RN DON.
Licensure Skilled care; Intermediate care; Chronic disease. *Beds* SNF 262; ICF 8; Chronic Disease 45. *Certified* Medicaid; Medicare.
Owner Nonprofit Corp.
Admissions Requirements Medical examination.

Staff Physicians 2 (ft), 4 (pt); RNs 26 (ft), 9 (pt); LPNs 19 (ft), 4 (pt); Nurses aides 93 (ft), 29 (pt); Physical therapists 2 (ft); Recreational therapists 3 (ft); Occupational therapists 2 (ft); Speech therapists 1 (pt); Activities coordinators 1 (ft); Dietitians 3 (ft).
Languages Yiddish, Hebrew
Affiliation Jewish
Facilities Dining room; Physical therapy room; Activities room; Chapel; Crafts room; Laundry room; Barber/Beauty shop; Library.
Activities Arts & crafts; Games; Reading groups; Prayer groups; Movies; Shopping trips; Social/Cultural gatherings; Dinner theater; Outings.

Hillside Manor Nursing Home
151 Hillside Ave, Hartford, CT, 06106
(203) 278-1060
Licensure Skilled care. *Beds* 180. *Certified* Medicaid; Medicare.
Owner Proprietary Corp (Gen'l Health Management Inc).
Staff RNs 10 (ft); LPNs 10 (ft); Nurses aides 70 (ft); Physical therapists 1 (ft); Occupational therapists 1 (ft); Activities coordinators 3 (ft); COTA 2 (ft); Social workers 2 (ft).
Languages Spanish, Portuguese, French, Polish, Yiddish, Hebrew
Activities Theraputic recreation.

Hughes Convalescent Inc
29 Highland St, Hartford, CT, 06111
(203) 236-5623
Admin Burton J Mitchell RN. *Medical Dir/Dir of Nursing* Joseph J Lucas MD; Iris Zaricor RN DON.
Licensure Skilled care. *Beds* SNF 180. *Certified* Medicaid; Medicare.
Owner Proprietary Corp.
Staff RNs 15 (ft), 5 (pt); LPNs 12 (ft), 4 (pt); Orderlies 3 (ft); Nurses aides 80 (ft); Physical therapists 2 (ft), 1 (pt); Recreational therapists 3 (ft), 1 (pt); Speech therapists 1 (pt); Dietitians 1 (ft), 1 (pt).
Languages Spanish, Portuguese, Korean, Italian
Facilities Physical therapy room; Activities room; Chapel; Crafts room; Laundry room; Barber/Beauty shop; Library.
Activities Arts & crafts; Cards; Games; Reading groups; Prayer groups; Movies.

Lorraine Manor*
25 Lorraine St, Hartford, CT, 06105
(203) 233-8241
Licensure Skilled care; Intermediate care. *Beds* 270. *Certified* Medicaid.
Owner Proprietary Corp (Gen'l Health Management Inc).
Staff Physicians; RNs 1 (ft), 10 (pt); LPNs 14 (ft); Nurses aides 95 (ft); Physical therapists 3 (ft); Occupational therapists 1 (ft); Activities coordinators 6 (ft); Social workers 2 (ft); Special educator 1 (ft).
Languages Polish, Spanish, French
Activities Arts & crafts; Shopping trips; Social/ Cultural gatherings; Pet therapy; Music therapy.

Noble Building*
705 New Britain Ave, Hartford, CT, 06106
(203) 527-9126
Licensure Intermediate care. *Beds* 57. *Certified* Medicaid.
Owner Nonprofit Corp.
Staff LPNs 9 (ft), 1 (pt); Activities coordinators 1 (ft), 1 (pt); Social workers 1 (pt).
Languages Spanish, Polish, Russian, French
Affiliation Congregational

JEWETT CITY

Summit Conv Home Inc*
15 Preston Rd, Jewett City, CT, 06351
(203) 376-4438
Licensure Skilled care. *Beds* 90. *Certified*
Medicaid; Medicare.
Owner Proprietary Corp.
Staff Physicians; Dietitians; Nurses aides.
Languages French, Polish, Italian, Greek,
Finnish
Activities Prayer groups; Social/Cultural
gatherings.

KENSINGTON

Ledgecrest Conv Home*
154 Kensington Rd, Kensington, CT, 06037
(203) 828-8690
Licensure Skilled care. *Beds* 60. *Certified*
Medicaid; Medicare.
Owner Proprietary Corp.
Staff Physicians; RNs 14 (ft), 1 (pt); LPNs 6
(ft), 1 (pt); Nurses aides 44 (ft), 1 (pt);
Activities coordinators; Dietitians; Social
workers 1 (ft).
Languages Polish, Italian, Spanish
Activities Arts & crafts; Games; Movies;
Social/Cultural gatherings; Church services.

LITCHFIELD

Rose-Haven Ltd*
North St, Litchfield, CT, 06759
(203) 567-9475
Licensure Skilled care. *Beds* 25.
Owner Proprietary Corp.
Staff RNs 3 (ft), 1 (pt); LPNs 2 (ft), 1 (pt);
Nurses aides 8 (ft), 1 (pt); Activities
coordinators 1 (pt); Dietitians 1 (pt).
Languages Italian, French

MADISON

Watrous Nursing Center
9 Neck Rd, Madison, CT, 06443
(203) 245-9483
Admin Carol Ernandez. *Medical Dir/Dir of
Nursing* Arnold Winokur MD; Barbara
Vigneau RN DON.
Licensure Skilled care. *Beds* SNF 45. *Certified*
Medicaid.
Owner Proprietary Corp.
Admissions Requirements Minimum age 15;
Medical examination; Physician's request.
Staff Physicians 4 (pt); RNs 14 (ft); Nurses
aides 10 (ft), 20 (pt); Physical therapists 1
(pt); Recreational therapists 1 (ft), 1 (pt);
Speech therapists 1 (pt); Dietitians 1 (pt);
Dentists 1 (pt); Ophthalmologists 1 (pt);
Podiatrists 1 (pt).
Facilities Dining room; Physical therapy
room; Activities room; Crafts room; Laundry
room; Barber/Beauty shop.
Activities Arts & crafts; Cards; Games;
Reading groups; Prayer groups; Movies;
Shopping trips; Social/Cultural gatherings;
Outdoor garden club.

MANCHESTER

Crestfield Convalescent Home*
565 Vernon St, Manchester, CT, 06040
(203) 643-5151
Licensure Skilled care. *Beds* 95. *Certified*
Medicaid; Medicare.
Owner Proprietary Corp.
Staff Physicians; Dietitians; Nurses aides.
Languages Italian, Polish, French, Spanish
Facilities Dining room; Physical therapy
room; Activities room; Barber/Beauty shop.
Activities Arts & crafts; Cards; Games;
Reading groups; Prayer groups; Movies;
Shopping trips; Social/Cultural gatherings.

Fenwood Manor Inc*
565 Vernon Rd, Manchester, CT, 06040
(203) 643-5151
Licensure Intermediate care. *Beds* 60.
Owner Proprietary Corp.
Staff Physicians; Dietitians; Nurses aides.
Languages Polish, Italian, French, Spanish
Facilities Dining room; Physical therapy
room; Activities room; Barber/Beauty shop.
Activities Arts & crafts; Cards; Games;
Reading groups; Prayer groups; Movies;
Shopping trips; Social/Cultural gatherings.

Holiday House
29 Cottage St, Manchester, CT, 06040
(203) 649-2358
Admin Katherine M Giblin.
Licensure Home for aged. *Beds* 27. *Certified*
Medicaid; Medicare.
Owner Proprietary Corp.
Staff RNs 2 (ft); LPNs 1 (ft), 1 (pt); Nurses
aides 4 (ft); Social workers.
Languages French, German, Polish, Italian
Activities Sing-along; Picnics.

Laurel Living Center Inc*
91 Chestnut St, Manchester, CT, 06040
(203) 649-4519
Licensure Home for aged. *Beds* 43.
Owner Proprietary Corp.
Languages Italian, Spanish, French
Activities Arts & crafts; Games; Movies;
Social/Cultural gatherings; Field trips.

Manchester Manor Nursing Home*
385 W Center St, Manchester, CT, 06040
(203) 646-0129
Licensure Skilled care; Intermediate care. *Beds*
45.
Owner Proprietary Corp.
Staff RNs 8 (ft); Nurses aides 20 (ft), 1 (pt);
Activities coordinators 1 (ft); Dietitians 1
(ft); Social workers 1 (ft).
Languages French, Italian, German
Activities Arts & crafts; Cards; Games;
Reading groups; Movies.

Manchester Manor Rest Home*
385 W Center St, Manchester, CT, 06040
(203) 646-0129
Licensure Intermediate care. *Beds* 71.
Certified Medicaid.
Owner Proprietary Corp.
Staff RNs 5 (ft); LPNs 2 (ft); Nurses aides 12
(ft); Activities coordinators 1 (ft); Dietitians
1 (ft); Social workers 1 (ft).
Languages French, Italian, German
Activities Arts & crafts; Games; Movies.

Meadows Manor*
333 Bidwell St, Manchester, CT, 06040
(203) 647-9191
Admin Philip S Viner. *Medical Dir/Dir of
Nursing* Robert K Butterfield MD.
Licensure Skilled care; Intermediate care. *Beds*
518. *Certified* Medicaid; Medicare.
Owner Proprietary Corp (Health Care &
Retirement Corp).
Admissions Requirements Minimum age 14;
Medical examination.
Staff Physicians 5 (pt); RNs 38 (ft); LPNs 32
(ft); Nurses aides 132 (ft); Physical therapists
1 (ft), 2 (pt); Speech therapists 1 (pt);
Activities coordinators 9 (ft); Dietitians 1
(ft); Dentists 1 (pt); Ophthalmologists 1 (pt);
Podiatrists 2 (pt); Audiologists 1 (pt).
Languages French, Italian, Spanish
Facilities Dining room; Physical therapy
room; Activities room; Chapel; Crafts room;
Laundry room; Barber/Beauty shop; Library.
Activities Arts & crafts; Cards; Games;
Reading groups; Prayer groups; Movies;
Shopping trips; Social/Cultural gatherings.

MARLBOROUGH

Marlborough Health Care Center Inc*
85 Stage Harbor Rd, Marlborough, CT, 06447
(203) 295-9531
Medical Dir/Dir of Nursing Dr Donald
Timmerman.
Licensure Intermediate care. *Beds* 120.
Certified Medicaid.
Owner Proprietary Corp.
Admissions Requirements Minimum age 16;
Medical examination.
Staff RNs 7 (ft); LPNs 2 (ft); Nurses aides 13
(ft); Recreational therapists 2 (ft).
Languages Polish, Italian, Dutch, German,
French
Facilities Dining room; Activities room;
Chapel; Laundry room; Barber/Beauty shop;
Library.
Activities Arts & crafts; Cards; Games;
Reading groups; Prayer groups; Movies;
Shopping trips; Social/Cultural gatherings.

MERIDEN

The Bradley Home Infirmary*
PO Box 886, 320 Colony St, Meriden, CT,
06450
(203) 235-5716
Licensure Skilled care. *Beds* 30.
Owner Nonprofit Corp.
Staff RNs 7 (ft); Nurses aides 14 (ft).
Languages Spanish, German, Polish, French
Activities Arts & crafts; Games; Movies;
Shopping trips; Social/Cultural gatherings;
Cooking; Exercises; Picnics; Discussion
groups; Resident council.

Thomas A Coccomo Memorial
33 Cone Ave, Meriden, CT, 06450
(203) 238-1606
Admin Carol A Ernandez. *Medical Dir/Dir of
Nursing* Dr Jay Kaplan; Janet Robinson.
Licensure Intermediate care. *Beds* 90.
Certified Medicaid.
Owner Proprietary Corp (Health Care
Associates Inc).
Admissions Requirements Medical
examination; Physician's request.
Staff RNs 9 (ft); LPNs 2 (ft); Nurses aides 17
(ft); Recreational therapists 2 (ft), 1 (pt);
Activities coordinators 1 (ft); Dietary,
Housekeeping, Laundry, Social Services,
Maintenance 25 (ft), 1 (pt).
Languages German, Polish, Italian
Facilities Dining room; Activities room;
Chapel; Crafts room; Laundry room; Barber/
Beauty shop; Library; Den; Three lounges.
Activities Arts & crafts; Cards; Games; Prayer
groups; Movies; Shopping trips; Social/
Cultural gatherings.

Corner House Nursing Inc*
1 Griswold St, Meriden, CT, 06450
(203) 237-2257
Licensure Intermediate care. *Beds* 30.
Certified Medicaid.
Owner Proprietary Corp.
Staff RNs 8 (ft); LPNs 2 (ft); Nurses aides 7
(ft); Activities coordinators 1 (ft); Dietitians
2 (ft).
Languages French, Polish
Activities Arts & crafts; Games; Social/
Cultural gatherings.

The Curtis Home—St Elizabeth Center
380 Crown St, Meriden, CT, 06450
(203) 237-4338
Admin Walter A Stroly. *Medical Dir/Dir of
Nursing* Dr C Martell; Patricia Bishop RN
DON.
Licensure Skilled care; Intermediate care;
Home for aging; Independent elderly
housing; Adult day health care. *Beds* 118.
Certified Medicaid; Medicare.
Owner Nonprofit Corp.
Admissions Requirements Females only.

Staff Nurses aides 8 (ft).
Languages Polish, Italian, Spanish, German, French
Facilities Dining room; Physical therapy room; Activities room; Chapel; Crafts room; Laundry room; Barber/Beauty shop; Library.
Activities Arts & crafts; Cards; Games; Reading groups; Prayer groups; Movies; Shopping trips; Social/Cultural gatherings; Sing-alongs; Excursions.

Independence Manor*
33 Roy St, Meriden, CT, 06450
(203) 237-8457
Licensure Skilled care; Intermediate care. *Beds* SNF 120; ICF 59. *Certified* Medicaid; Medicare.
Owner Proprietary Corp (Health Care & Retirement Corp).
Staff RNs 3 (ft); LPNs 15 (ft).
Languages Spanish, Polish
Activities Arts & crafts; Shopping trips; Social/Cultural gatherings; Workshops; Music; Current events.

Meriden Nursing Home
845 Paddock Ave, Meriden, CT, 06450
(203) 238-2645
Admin Michele Carney. *Medical Dir/Dir of Nursing* Dr Zimerman.
Licensure Skilled care. *Beds* SNF 120. *Certified* Medicaid; Medicare.
Owner Proprietary Corp (Multicare Management).
Staff Physicians; RNs 7 (ft), 2 (pt); LPNs 6 (ft); Nurses aides 40 (ft), 2 (pt); Physical therapists 1 (ft); Recreational therapists 2 (ft); Activities coordinators; Dietitians.
Languages Spanish
Facilities Dining room; Physical therapy room; Activities room; Chapel; Crafts room; Laundry room; Barber/Beauty shop.
Activities Arts & crafts; Cards; Games; Reading groups; Prayer groups; Movies; Shopping trips; Social/Cultural gatherings; Van; Pet therapy.

Miller Memorial Community
360 Broad St, Meriden, CT, 06450
(203) 237-8815
Admin Sr Ann Noonan. *Medical Dir/Dir of Nursing* Dr John Flynn; Dolores Gambino RNC.
Licensure Skilled care; Intermediate care. *Beds* SNF 30; ICF 60; Independent cottages; Efficiency apartments. *Certified* Medicaid; Medicare.
Owner Nonprofit organization/foundation.
Admissions Requirements Minimum age 62; Medical examination.
Staff RNs 2 (ft), 8 (pt); LPNs 7 (pt); Nurses aides 13 (ft), 16 (pt); Physical therapists 1 (pt); Recreational therapists 3 (ft); Dietitians 1 (pt).
Languages Polish, French, Spanish
Facilities Dining room; Physical therapy room; Activities room; Crafts room; Laundry room; Barber/Beauty shop; Library; Lounges; Snack nooks.
Activities Arts & crafts; Cards; Games; Reading groups; Prayer groups; Movies; Shopping trips; Social/Cultural gatherings.

Mills Manor*
292 Thorpe Ave, Meriden, CT, 06450
(203) 237-1206
Licensure Skilled care. *Beds* 30. *Certified* Medicaid; Medicare.
Owner Proprietary Corp.
Staff RNs 3 (ft), 1 (pt); LPNs 1 (ft); Nurses aides 9 (ft), 1 (pt); Activities coordinators 1 (pt).
Activities Arts & crafts; Games; Movies; Shopping trips; Social/Cultural gatherings; Music.

Westfield Manor Health Care Center*
65 Westfield Rd, Meriden, CT, 06450
(203) 238-1291
Licensure Skilled care; Intermediate care. *Beds* 120. *Certified* Medicaid; Medicare.
Owner Proprietary Corp.
Staff RNs 15 (ft); LPNs 10 (ft); Nurses aides 45 (ft).
Languages Italian, Polish, French, Spanish
Activities Arts & crafts; Games.

MIDDLEBURY

Middlebury Convalescent Home Inc
778 Middlebury Rd, Middlebury, CT, 06762
(203) 758-2471
Admin Genevieve Buckmiller. *Medical Dir/Dir of Nursing* Dr William P Arnold Jr; Norma Rossiter RN DNS.
Licensure Skilled care. *Beds* SNF 58. *Certified* Medicaid; Medicare.
Owner Proprietary Corp.
Staff Physicians 1 (pt); RNs 5 (ft), 10 (pt); LPNs 1 (ft); Nurses aides 17 (ft), 8 (pt); Physical therapists 1 (pt); Recreational therapists 1 (ft); Dietitians 1 (pt).
Languages Italian, German, Lebanese, Lithuanian
Facilities Dining room; Physical therapy room; Activities room; Laundry room; Barber/Beauty shop.
Activities Arts & crafts; Cards; Games; Reading groups; Prayer groups; Movies.

MIDDLETOWN

Lutheran Home of Middletown Inc
Ridgewood Rd, Middletown, CT, 06457
(203) 347-7479
Admin Arnold R Eggert. *Medical Dir/Dir of Nursing* Dr Matthew Raider; Caroline Guilty RN DON.
Licensure Skilled care. *Beds* 28. *Certified* Medicaid.
Owner Nonprofit Corp.
Admissions Requirements Minimum age 65; Medical examination.
Staff Physicians 5 (pt); RNs 3 (ft), 4 (pt); Nurses aides 6 (ft), 9 (pt); Physical therapists 1 (pt); Activities coordinators 1 (ft), 1 (pt); Dietitians 1 (pt); Ophthalmologists 1 (pt); Dentist 1 (pt).
Languages Spanish, German, Polish, Swedish, Italian
Affiliation Lutheran
Facilities Dining room; Physical therapy room; Activities room; Crafts room; Laundry room; Barber/Beauty shop; Library; Solariums.
Activities Arts & crafts; Cards; Games; Reading groups; Prayer groups; Movies; Shopping trips; Social/Cultural gatherings; Bingo; Excursions.

Middlesex Convalescent Center Inc
100 Randolph Rd, Middletown, CT, 06457
(203) 344-0353
Medical Dir/Dir of Nursing A Wazed Mahmud MD.
Licensure Skilled care; Intermediate care. *Beds* 150. *Certified* Medicaid; Medicare.
Owner Proprietary Corp.
Admissions Requirements Minimum age 18; Medical examination.
Staff RNs 10 (ft), 8 (pt); LPNs 9 (ft), 8 (pt); Nurses aides 37 (ft), 28 (pt); Physical therapists 1 (ft); Recreational therapists 2 (ft), 1 (pt); Occupational therapists 1 (pt); Speech therapists 1 (pt); Dietitians 1 (pt).
Languages Spanish, Italian, Polish
Facilities Dining room; Physical therapy room; Activities room; Chapel; Crafts room; Barber/Beauty shop; TV rooms.
Activities Arts & crafts; Cards; Games; Reading groups; Prayer groups; Movies; Shopping trips; Social/Cultural gatherings.

Middletown Healthcare Center Inc*
111 Church St, Middletown, CT, 06457
(203) 347-7286
Licensure Intermediate care. *Beds* 180.
Owner Proprietary Corp.
Staff RNs 12 (ft), 1 (pt); LPNs 15 (ft), 1 (pt); Nurses aides 32 (ft); Activities coordinators 5 (ft), 1 (pt); Social workers 4 (ft).
Languages Italian, Polish, Spanish

Queen's Convalescent Inc*
600 Highland Ave, PO Box 1056, Middletown, CT, 06457
(203) 347-3315
Medical Dir/Dir of Nursing Felix G Sheehan MD.
Licensure Skilled care. *Beds* 90. *Certified* Medicaid; Medicare.
Owner Proprietary Corp.
Admissions Requirements Minimum age 21; Medical examination.
Staff Physicians 4 (pt); RNs 6 (ft), 4 (pt); LPNs 3 (ft), 4 (pt); Orderlies 3 (ft), 2 (pt); Nurses aides 28 (ft), 13 (pt); Physical therapists 1 (pt); Recreational therapists 1 (ft), 1 (pt).
Languages Italian, German
Facilities Dining room; Physical therapy room; Activities room; Chapel; Crafts room; Laundry room; Barber/Beauty shop; Library.
Activities Arts & crafts; Cards; Games; Reading groups; Prayer groups; Movies; Shopping trips; Entertainment.

Ridgewood Central Inc—Health Care Facility
955 Washington St Ext, Middletown, CT, 06457
(203) 347-5604
Admin Frank C Biello. *Medical Dir/Dir of Nursing* Donald Timmerman MD; Patricia S Gorman RN DON.
Licensure Skilled care. *Beds* 90. *Certified* Medicaid; Medicare.
Owner Proprietary Corp.
Admissions Requirements Physician's request.
Staff Physicians; RNs; LPNs; Nurses aides; Physical therapists; Recreational therapists; Speech therapists; Dietitians; Dentists; Ophthalmologists.
Facilities Dining room; Physical therapy room; Activities room; Chapel; Crafts room; Laundry room; Barber/Beauty shop; Solariums; TV.
Activities Arts & crafts; Cards; Games; Reading groups; Prayer groups; Movies; Shopping trips; Sing-alongs.

Sanibel Convalescent Home*
S Main St, Middletown, CT, 06457
(203) 347-1696
Licensure Skilled care. *Beds* 60. *Certified* Medicaid.
Owner Proprietary Corp.
Staff Physicians; Dietitians; Nurses aides.
Languages Polish, Italian, German
Activities Prayer groups; Arts & crafts; Shopping trips.

MILFORD

Golden Hill Health Care Center
PO Box 109, 2028 Bridgeport Ave, Milford, CT, 06460
(203) 877-0371
Admin Barbara L Brown. *Medical Dir/Dir of Nursing* Dr Thelma Batiancila; Bettie Smith RN DON.
Licensure Skilled care. *Beds* SNF 120. *Certified* Medicaid; Medicare.
Owner Proprietary Corp (New Medico Assoc).
Admissions Requirements Minimum age 14; Medical examination; Physician's request.
Staff RNs 11 (ft), 8 (pt); LPNs 4 (ft), 8 (pt); Nurses aides 38 (ft), 22 (pt); Physical therapists 1 (ft), 1 (pt); Recreational therapists 2 (ft), 3 (pt); Occupational therapists 1 (ft); Speech therapists 1 (ft);

Activities coordinators 1 (ft), 3 (pt);
Dietitians 1 (ft); Dentists 1 (ft); Podiatrists 1
(ft).
Languages Italian, Hungarian, Spanish,
Swedish, Tagalog
Facilities Dining room; Physical therapy
room; Activities room; Chapel; Barber/
Beauty shop.
Activities Arts & crafts; Cards; Games;
Reading groups; Prayer groups; Movies;
Shopping trips; Social/Cultural gatherings.

Milford Health Care Center Inc
195 Platt St, Milford, CT, 06460
(203) 878-5958
Admin Donna C Stango. *Medical Dir/Dir of
Nursing* Mildred Locke RN DON.
Licensure Skilled care. *Beds* SNF 120.
Certified Medicaid; Medicare.
Owner Proprietary Corp.
Admissions Requirements Physician's request.
Staff RNs; LPNs 12 (ft); Nurses aides 35 (ft);
Physical therapists; Recreational therapists 3
(ft); Activities coordinators 2 (ft); Dietitians
1 (ft); Social workers 1 (ft).
Languages Polish, Spanish, Italian, Ukranian
Facilities Dining room; Physical therapy
room; Activities room; Laundry room;
Barber/Beauty shop.
Activities Arts & crafts; Games; Reading
groups; Prayer groups; Movies; Shopping
trips; Social/Cultural gatherings; Outside
entertainment; Excursions.

Pond Point Health Care Center Inc
60 Platt St, Milford, CT, 06460
(203) 878-5786
Licensure Skilled care; Intermediate care. *Beds*
142. *Certified* Medicaid; Medicare.
Owner Proprietary Corp (Beverly Enterprises).
Staff RNs 24 (ft); LPNs 9 (ft); Nurses aides 41
(ft); Activities coordinators 3 (ft); Dietitians
1 (ft).
Languages Polish, Italian, Spanish
Facilities Waterfront.

MOODUS

Chestelm Conv Home*
534 Town St, Moodus, CT, 06469
(203) 873-1455
Medical Dir/Dir of Nursing Dr Phillip
Berwick.
Licensure Skilled care; Intermediate care. *Beds*
SNF 50; ICF 13. *Certified* Medicaid.
Owner Proprietary Corp.
Staff Physicians 5 (pt); RNs 7 (ft), 4 (pt);
LPNs 3 (ft), 5 (pt); Nurses aides 18 (ft), 9
(pt); Physical therapists 1 (pt); Recreational
therapists 2 (pt); Occupational therapists 1
(pt); Speech therapists 1 (pt); Activities
coordinators 1 (pt); Dietitians 1 (pt);
Dentists 1 (pt); Podiatrists 1 (pt);
Audiologists 1 (pt).
Languages Czech, French, Italian, Polish
Facilities Dining room; Physical therapy
room; Activities room; Crafts room; Laundry
room; Library.
Activities Arts & crafts; Cards; Games;
Reading groups; Movies; Shopping trips;
Social/Cultural gatherings.

MYSTIC

Mary Elizabeth Nursing Center Inc
PO Box 98, 28 Broadway, Mystic, CT, 06355
(203) 536-9655
Admin Judith Hilburger. *Medical Dir/Dir of
Nursing* Dr Howard Brensilver; Sharon
Kaylor RN.
Licensure Skilled care. *Beds* 50. *Certified*
Medicaid; Medicare.
Owner Proprietary Corp (Health Care
Associates Inc).

Staff Physicians 11 (ft); RNs 9 (ft); LPNs 4
(ft); Nurses aides 21 (ft); Recreational
therapists 1 (ft); Activities coordinators 1
(ft).
Facilities Dining room; Physical therapy
room; Activities room; Laundry room;
Barber/Beauty shop.
Activities Arts & crafts; Cards; Games; Prayer
groups; Movies; Social/Cultural gatherings.

Mystic Manor Inc*
475 High St, Mystic, CT, 06355
(203) 536-2167 & 536-6070
Admin Samuel Whipple. *Medical Dir/Dir of
Nursing* L Edwin Sproul MD.
Licensure Skilled care. *Beds* 60. *Certified*
Medicaid; Medicare.
Owner Proprietary Corp.
Admissions Requirements Minimum age 14;
Medical examination.
Staff Physicians 5 (pt); RNs 2 (ft), 16 (pt);
LPNs 3 (ft), 1 (pt); Nurses aides 16 (ft), 21
(pt); Physical therapists 1 (pt); Recreational
therapists 2 (pt); Speech therapists 1 (pt);
Dietitians 1 (ft); Dentists 1 (pt); Podiatrists
1 (pt); Audiologists 1 (pt).
Languages Korean
Facilities Dining room; Physical therapy
room; Activities room; Chapel; Laundry
room; Library; Dental care unit; Medical
examination & treatment room.
Activities Arts & crafts; Cards; Games;
Reading groups; Prayer groups; Movies;
Social/Cultural gatherings; Excursions.

Rita's Rest Home
14 Godfrey St, Mystic, CT, 06355
(203) 536-8854
Admin Frank Nocera. *Medical Dir/Dir of
Nursing* Dr Weiss.
Licensure Boarding Home. *Beds* 25. *Certified*
Medicaid; Aid to disabled.
Owner Proprietary Corp.
Admissions Requirements Minimum age 21.
Staff Nurses aides 10 (ft), 4 (pt).
Facilities Dining room; Activities room;
Laundry room.
Activities Arts & crafts; Cards; Games;
Movies; Shopping trips; Social/Cultural
gatherings; Day trips.

NAUGATUCK

Glendale Health Care Center Inc
4 Hazel Ave, Naugatuck, CT, 06770
(203) 723-1456
Admin Frank Salvatore.
Licensure Skilled care; Intermediate care. *Beds*
120. *Certified* Medicaid; Medicare.
Owner Proprietary Corp.
Staff RNs 16 (ft); LPNs 5 (ft); Nurses aides 66
(ft); Physical therapists 1 (ft); Activities
coordinators 2 (ft); Social workers 1 (ft).
Languages German, Italian, French, Swedish,
Polish

NEW BRITAIN

Andrew House Healthcare
66 Clinic Dr, New Britain, CT, 06051
(203) 225-8608
Admin Doris H Leitgeb. *Medical Dir/Dir of
Nursing* Dr Edward Martin.
Licensure Skilled care. *Beds* SNF 90. *Certified*
Medicaid; Medicare.
Owner Proprietary Corp (Hillhaven Corp).
Admissions Requirements Physician's request.
Staff Physicians; RNs; LPNs; Nurses aides;
Physical therapists; Reality therapists;
Recreational therapists; Activities
coordinators; Dietitians.
Languages Polish, Spanish, French
Facilities Dining room; Physical therapy
room; Activities room; Laundry room;
Barber/Beauty shop.

Activities Arts & crafts; Cards; Games;
Reading groups; Prayer groups; Movies;
Shopping trips; Social/Cultural gatherings.

Brittany Farms Health Center
400 Brittany Farms Rd, New Britain, CT,
06053
(203) 224-3111
Admin Thomas V Tolisano. *Medical Dir/Dir
of Nursing* Dr D Balazs & Dr Giarnella.
Licensure Skilled care; Intermediate care. *Beds*
SNF 120; ICF 180. *Certified* Medicaid;
Medicare.
Owner Proprietary Corp.
Admissions Requirements Minimum age 55;
Medical examination; Physician's request.
Staff Physicians 10 (pt); RNs 45 (ft); LPNs 10
(ft); Orderlies 2 (ft); Nurses aides 95 (ft);
Physical therapists 4 (ft); Recreational
therapists 6 (ft); Occupational therapists 2
(ft); Speech therapists 1 (ft); Activities
coordinators 1 (ft); Dietitians 2 (ft); Dentists
1 (ft); Ophthalmologists 1 (ft); Podiatrists 1
(ft); Dentist 1 (ft).
Languages Polish, Spanish, Italian
Facilities Dining room; Physical therapy
room; Activities room; Crafts room; Laundry
room; Barber/Beauty shop; Library.
Activities Arts & crafts; Cards; Games;
Reading groups; Prayer groups; Movies;
Shopping trips; Social/Cultural gatherings.

Jerome Home*
975 Corbin Ave, New Britain, CT, 06052
(203) 299-3707
Licensure Intermediate care. *Beds* 60.
Certified Medicaid.
Owner Nonprofit Corp.
Staff RNs 4 (ft); LPNs 5 (ft); Nurses aides 12
(ft); Recreational therapists; Activities
coordinators 1 (ft); Dietitians 3 (ft).
Languages French, Polish
Activities Arts & crafts; Games; Social/
Cultural gatherings; Exercises; Musicals;
Outings; Outside entertainment.

Lexington Convalescent Home Inc*
32 Lexington St, New Britain, CT, 06052
(203) 225-6397
Medical Dir/Dir of Nursing Abraham
Bernstein.
Licensure Skilled care. *Beds* 65. *Certified*
Medicaid; Medicare.
Owner Proprietary Corp.
Admissions Requirements Minimum age 18;
Medical examination; Physician's request.
Staff RNs 4 (ft), 1 (pt); LPNs 5 (ft); Orderlies
1 (ft), 1 (pt); Nurses aides 18 (ft), 9 (pt);
Physical therapists 1 (pt); Reality therapists
1 (ft), 1 (pt); Recreational therapists 1 (ft), 1
(pt).
Languages French, Italian, Polish, Spanish
Facilities Dining room; Physical therapy
room; Activities room; Crafts room; Laundry
room.
Activities Arts & crafts; Cards; Games;
Reading groups; Prayer groups; Movies;
Shopping trips; Entertainment; Pet therapy.

Monsignor Bojnowski Manor Inc
50 Pulaski St, New Britain, CT, 06053
(203) 229-0336
Admin Sr Mary Honorata. *Medical Dir/Dir of
Nursing* L B Slysz MD.
Licensure Skilled care. *Beds* 60. *Certified*
Medicaid; Medicare.
Owner Nonprofit Corp.
Admissions Requirements Minimum age 14;
Medical examination.
Staff Physicians 1 (pt); RNs 7 (ft), 4 (pt);
LPNs 5 (ft), 4 (pt); Nurses aides 27 (ft), 4
(pt); Physical therapists 1 (ft); Recreational
therapists 1 (ft); Dietitians 1 (pt); Dentists 1
(pt); Ophthalmologists 1 (pt).
Languages Polish, Spanish, German, French
Affiliation Roman Catholic

Facilities Dining room; Physical therapy room; Activities room; Chapel; Crafts room; Laundry room; Barber/Beauty shop; Library.
Activities Arts & crafts; Cards; Games; Reading groups; Prayer groups; Movies; Shopping trips; Picnics; Birthday parties.

Walnut Hill Convalescent Home*
55 Grand St, New Britain, CT, 06052
(203) 223-3617
Medical Dir/Dir of Nursing Stephen Greenberg MD.
Licensure Skilled care. *Beds* 180. *Certified* Medicaid; Medicare.
Owner Proprietary Corp.
Admissions Requirements Minimum age 14; Physician's request.
Staff RNs 11 (ft), 4 (pt); LPNs 8 (ft), 14 (pt); Orderlies 7 (ft); Nurses aides 55 (ft), 6 (pt); Physical therapists 1 (ft); Recreational therapists 2 (ft); Activities coordinators 1 (ft); Dietitians 1 (ft), 1 (pt).
Languages Polish, Spanish, Italian
Facilities Dining room; Physical therapy room; Activities room; Chapel; Crafts room; Barber/Beauty shop.
Activities Arts & crafts; Cards; Games; Reading groups; Prayer groups; Movies.

NEW CANAAN

Waveny Care Center
3 Farm Rd, New Canaan, CT, 06840
(203) 966-8725
Admin Mr Charles E Otto. *Medical Dir/Dir of Nursing* Dr Basil Papaharis; Mrs Rachel Orstad RN.
Licensure Skilled care. *Beds* SNF 67. *Certified* Medicaid; Medicare.
Owner Nonprofit Corp.
Admissions Requirements Minimum age 16.
Staff Physicians 1 (pt); RNs 12 (ft), 13 (pt); LPNs 2 (ft), 2 (pt); Nurses aides 21 (ft), 11 (pt); Reality therapists 2 (ft); Recreational therapists 3 (ft); Occupational therapists 1 (pt); Speech therapists 1 (pt); Dietitians 2 (pt).
Languages Spanish, French, German, Italian, Danish, Swedish, Hungarian
Facilities Dining room; Physical therapy room; Activities room; Crafts room; Laundry room; Barber/Beauty shop; Library.
Activities Arts & crafts; Cards; Games; Reading groups; Prayer groups; Movies; Shopping trips; Social/Cultural gatherings.

NEW HAVEN

Carewell Rest Home*
260 Dwight St, New Haven, CT, 06511
(203) 562-8596
Licensure Intermediate care. *Beds* 45. *Certified* Medicaid.
Owner Proprietary Corp.
Staff RNs 4 (ft); LPNs 5 (ft); Nurses aides 12 (ft); Activities coordinators 1 (ft).
Languages Italian, Spanish, French
Activities Therapeutic recreation.

Cove Manor Conv Center Inc
36 Morris Cove Rd, New Haven, CT, 06512
(203) 467-6357
Admin Anne D Ryder. *Medical Dir/Dir of Nursing* Luca E Celentano MD; Lois Forgione RN.
Licensure Skilled care. *Beds* 70. *Certified* Medicaid; Medicare.
Owner Proprietary Corp.
Admissions Requirements Minimum age 21.
Staff RNs 4 (ft), 7 (pt); LPNs 5 (ft), 6 (pt); Nurses aides 22 (ft), 8 (pt); Physical therapists 1 (ft), 2 (pt); Speech therapists 1 (pt); Dietitians 1 (pt).
Languages Italian, Polish, Russian, Spanish

Facilities Dining room; Physical therapy room; Activities room; Crafts room; Laundry room; Barber/Beauty shop.
Activities Arts & crafts; Cards; Games; Reading groups; Prayer groups; Movies; Shopping trips; Social/Cultural gatherings.

Jewish Home for the Aged
167-169 Davenport Ave, New Haven, CT, 06519
(203) 789-1650
Admin Bryan R Mesh. *Medical Dir/Dir of Nursing* Dr Jacqueline Kutcher-Henchel; K Robison RN.
Licensure Skilled care; Intermediate care; Adult day care. *Beds* SNF 150; ICF 60. *Certified* Medicaid; Medicare.
Owner Nonprofit Corp.
Admissions Requirements Minimum age 65; Medical examination.
Staff Physicians 1 (ft), 1 (pt); RNs 50; LPNs; Orderlies 100; Nurses aides; Physical therapists 4 (ft); Recreational therapists 5 (ft), 2 (pt); Occupational therapists 1 (pt); Activities coordinators; Dietitians 2 (ft).
Affiliation Jewish
Facilities Dining room; Physical therapy room; Activities room; Chapel; Crafts room; Barber/Beauty shop; Library.
Activities Arts & crafts; Cards; Games; Reading groups; Prayer groups; Movies; Shopping trips; Social/Cultural gatherings.

New Fairview Health Care Facility
181 Clifton St, New Haven, CT, 06513
(203) 467-1666
Admin Helen Craig. *Medical Dir/Dir of Nursing* A Dolinsky MD & A Mancini MD; M Sullivan DON.
Licensure Skilled care. *Beds* SNF 195. *Certified* Medicaid; Medicare.
Owner Proprietary Corp.
Admissions Requirements Minimum age; Medical examination; Physician's request.
Staff Physicians 3 (pt); RNs 11 (ft), 6 (pt); LPNs 11 (ft), 6 (pt); Orderlies 3 (ft); Nurses aides 73 (ft); Physical therapists 1 (ft), 1 (pt); Reality therapists 1 (ft); Recreational therapists 4 (ft), 1 (pt); Occupational therapists 1 (pt); Activities coordinators 1 (ft); Dietitians 1 (ft).
Languages Italian, German, Polish, Greek, French, Spanish
Facilities Dining room; Physical therapy room; Activities room; Chapel; Crafts room; Laundry room; Barber/Beauty shop; Library.
Activities Arts & crafts; Cards; Games; Reading groups; Prayer groups; Movies; Shopping trips; Social/Cultural gatherings.

New Haven Convalescent Center*
50 Mead St, New Haven, CT, 06511
(203) 777-3491
Medical Dir/Dir of Nursing Dr Michael Devbaty.
Licensure Skilled care. *Beds* 89. *Certified* Medicaid; Medicare.
Owner Proprietary Corp.
Staff RNs 11 (ft), 9 (pt); LPNs 3 (ft), 5 (pt); Nurses aides 30 (ft), 17 (pt); Dietitians 1 (pt).
Languages Italian, Slavic
Facilities Dining room; Activities room; Crafts room; Barber/Beauty shop.
Activities Arts & crafts; Cards; Games; Reading groups; Prayer groups; Movies; Social/Cultural gatherings.

Parkview Medical Recovery Center Inc
915 Boulevard, New Haven, CT, 06511
(203) 865-5155
Medical Dir/Dir of Nursing Quiyam Merjtaba MD.
Licensure Skilled care. *Beds* 120. *Certified* Medicaid; Medicare.
Owner Proprietary Corp.
Admissions Requirements Minimum age 16; Medical examination; Physician's request.

Staff Physicians 4 (pt); RNs 7 (ft); LPNs 10 (ft); Nurses aides 47 (ft); Physical therapists 1 (pt); Recreational therapists 2 (ft); Speech therapists 1 (pt); Dietitians 1 (pt); Dentists 1 (pt); Ophthalmologists 1 (pt); Podiatrists 1 (pt); Dentist 1 (pt).
Languages Polish, Spanish, Italian
Facilities Dining room; Physical therapy room; Activities room; Chapel; Crafts room; Laundry room; Barber/Beauty shop; Library.
Activities Arts & crafts; Cards; Games; Reading groups; Prayer groups; Movies; Shopping trips; Social/Cultural gatherings.

Regis Multi-Health Center*
1354 Chapel St, New Haven, CT, 06511
(203) 865-0505
Licensure Skilled care; Intermediate care. *Beds* 125. *Certified* Medicaid; Medicare.
Owner Proprietary Corp.
Staff LPNs 18 (ft); Nurses aides 46 (ft); Physical therapists 1 (pt); Activities coordinators 2 (ft), 1 (pt); Social workers 1 (ft).
Languages Ukrainain, Polish, Spanish, Italian

Riverview Rest Home*
92-94 Lexington Ave, New Haven, CT, 06513
(203) 468-7325
Admin Natalie Iovieno.
Licensure Residential care. *Certified* Medicaid; Medicare.
Owner Proprietary Corp.
Staff Dietitians.
Facilities Dining room; Laundry room; Smoking room.
Activities Games; Prayer groups; Movies.

St Johns Extended Care*
54 E Ramsdell St, New Haven, CT, 06515
(203) 389-9558
Licensure Skilled care; Intermediate care. *Beds* 90. *Certified* Medicaid; Medicare.
Owner Nonprofit Corp.
Staff RNs 9 (ft); LPNs 6 (ft); Nurses aides 38 (ft); Activities coordinators 1 (ft), 1 (pt); Social workers 1 (pt).
Languages Spanish

West Rock Health Care
34 Level St, New Haven, CT, 06515
(203) 389-9744
Admin Luisa Franco Russo. *Medical Dir/Dir of Nursing* Andrew Weinberg MD; Joanna Panzo RN DNS.
Licensure Intermediate care. *Beds* ICF 90. *Certified* Medicaid.
Owner Proprietary Corp.
Admissions Requirements Minimum age 16; Medical examination; Physician's request.
Staff Physicians 3 (ft), 1 (pt); RNs 9 (ft), 2 (pt); LPNs 4 (ft), 1 (pt); Recreational therapists 2 (ft), 1 (pt); Dietitians 1 (pt); Dentists 1 (pt); Ophthalmologists 1 (pt); Podiatrists 1 (pt).
Languages Spanish
Facilities Dining room; Activities room; Laundry room; Barber/Beauty shop; Library.
Activities Arts & crafts; Cards; Games; Reading groups; Prayer groups; Movies; Shopping trips; Social/Cultural gatherings.

Winthrop Health Care Center Inc
240 Winthrop Ave, New Haven, CT, 06511
(203) 789-0500
Admin Joan McSherry. *Medical Dir/Dir of Nursing* Brett Gerstenhaber MD; Martha Crowther RN.
Licensure Skilled care; Intermediate care. *Beds* SNF 180; ICF 60. *Certified* Medicaid; Medicare.
Owner Proprietary Corp.
Admissions Requirements Minimum age SNF 21; ICF 45; Medical examination; Physician's request.
Staff Physicians 6 (pt); RNs 9 (ft), 12 (pt); LPNs 23 (ft), 19 (pt); Orderlies 4 (ft); Nurses aides 71 (ft), 21 (pt); Physical therapists 1

(ft); Recreational therapists 3 (ft), 2 (pt); Occupational therapists 1 (pt); Speech therapists 1 (pt); Dietitians 1 (ft); Dentists 1 (pt); Ophthalmologists 1 (pt); Podiatrists 1 (pt); Rehabilitation consultant 1 (pt).
Languages Spanish, Italian, Hebrew, Yiddish
Facilities Dining room; Physical therapy room; Activities room; Laundry room; Barber/Beauty shop.
Activities Arts & crafts; Cards; Games; Reading groups; Prayer groups; Movies; Shopping trips; Social/Cultural gatherings; Reality orientation.

NEW LONDON

Beechwood Manor Inc*
31 Vauxhall St, New London, CT, 06320
(203) 442-4363
Medical Dir/Dir of Nursing Clemens E Prokesch MD.
Licensure Skilled care. *Beds* 45. *Certified* Medicaid; Medicare.
Owner Proprietary Corp.
Staff RNs 6 (ft), 2 (pt); LPNs 2 (ft), 1 (pt); Orderlies 1 (ft); Nurses aides 12 (ft), 7 (pt); Physical therapists 1 (pt); Recreational therapists 1 (ft); Dietitians 1 (pt); Dentists 1 (pt); Podiatrists 1 (pt).
Facilities Dining room; Physical therapy room; Activities room; Laundry room; Barber/Beauty shop.
Activities Arts & crafts; Games; Reading groups; Prayer groups; Movies; Shopping trips.

Briarcliff Manor
179 Colman St, New London, CT, 06320
(203) 443-5376
Admin Amelia W Cart.
Licensure Home for aged. *Beds* 25.
Owner Proprietary Corp.
Admissions Requirements Minimum age 21.
Languages Italian, Spanish
Facilities Dining room; Activities room; Laundry room.
Activities Arts & crafts; Cards; Games; Reading groups; Prayer groups; Movies; Shopping trips.

Camelot Nursing Home*
89 Viets St, New London, CT, 06320
(203) 447-1471
Admin David J Friedler. *Medical Dir/Dir of Nursing* Melvin A Yoselevsky MD Medical Director; Joal Patterson RN Director of Nurses.
Licensure Skilled care. *Beds* 60. *Certified* Medicaid; Medicare.
Owner Proprietary Corp (Hillhaven Corp).
Staff Physicians 18 (pt); RNs 2 (ft), 8 (pt); LPNs 3 (pt); Nurses aides 9 (ft), 19 (pt); Physical therapists 1 (pt); Reality therapists 1 (ft); Recreational therapists 1 (ft); Speech therapists 1 (pt); Dietitians 1 (pt); Dentists 1 (pt); Podiatrists 1 (pt); Audiologists 1 (pt).
Languages Spanish, Italian, German
Facilities Dining room; Physical therapy room; Activities room; Crafts room; Laundry room; Barber/Beauty shop.
Activities Arts & crafts; Games; Reading groups; Prayer groups; Movies; Shopping trips.

Nutmeg Pavilion Healthcare
78 Viets St Extension, New London, CT, 06320
(203) 447-1416
Licensure Skilled care; Intermediate care. *Beds* 140. *Certified* Medicaid; Medicare.
Owner Proprietary Corp (Hillhaven Corp).
Staff RNs 18 (ft); Nurses aides 25 (ft); Physical therapists 2 (ft); Social workers 1 (ft).
Languages Spanish, Italian
Activities Arts & crafts; Games; Reading groups; Social/Cultural gatherings; Reality orientation; Music.

NEW MILFORD

Candlewood Valley Care Center
30 Park I n E, New Milford, CT, 06776
(203) 355-0971
Admin Elianm B Baird. *Medical Dir/Dir of Nursing* Robert L McDonald MD.
Licensure Skilled care; Intermediate care; Residential care; Day care. *Beds* SNF 60; ICF 44; Residential 44. *Certified* Medicaid; Medicare.
Owner Proprietary Corp.
Admissions Requirements Minimum age 14.
Staff Physicians 12 (pt); RNs 14 (ft), 8 (pt); LPNs 10 (ft), 4 (pt); Nurses aides 42 (ft), 22 (pt); Physical therapists 1 (ft); Reality therapists 1 (pt); Recreational therapists 4 (ft); Occupational therapists 1 (ft); Speech therapists 1 (pt); Activities coordinators 1 (ft); Dietitians 1 (ft); Dentists 2 (pt); Ophthalmologists 2 (pt); Podiatrists 1 (pt); Dentist 4 (pt); Medical Social worker 1 (ft); 21 (ft), 10 (pt).
Languages French, Italian, Spanish, German, Polish
Facilities Dining room; Physical therapy room; Activities room; Crafts room; Laundry room; Barber/Beauty shop; Library.
Activities Arts & crafts; Cards; Games; Reading groups; Prayer groups; Movies; Shopping trips; Social/Cultural gatherings; Community projects.

New Milford Nursing Home*
19 Poplar St, New Milford, CT, 06776
(203) 354-9365
Licensure Skilled care; Intermediate care. *Beds* 99. *Certified* Medicaid; Medicare.
Owner Proprietary Corp.
Staff RNs 15 (ft); LPNs 14 (ft); Nurses aides 53 (ft); Physical therapists 1 (ft); Activities coordinators 1 (ft); Social workers 1 (ft).
Languages Polish, German, Hebrew, Yiddish, Italian

NEWINGTON

Bel-Air Manor
256 New Britain Ave, Newington, CT, 06111
(203) 666-5689
Admin Gene Yacovone. *Medical Dir/Dir of Nursing* John E Pulaski; Phyllis I Condon RN DNS.
Licensure Intermediate care. *Beds* ICF 71. *Certified* Medicaid.
Owner Proprietary Corp.
Admissions Requirements Medical examination; Physician's request.
Staff Physicians 1 (ft), 4 (pt); RNs 3 (ft), 9 (pt); LPNs 2 (ft), 3 (pt); Nurses aides 11 (ft), 6 (pt); Recreational therapists 1 (ft), 1 (pt).
Languages Polish, French, Italian
Facilities Dining room; Activities room; Chapel; Crafts room; Laundry room; Barber/Beauty shop; Library.
Activities Arts & crafts; Cards; Games; Reading groups; Prayer groups; Movies; Shopping trips; Social/Cultural gatherings; Exercises; Baking; Lunches out.

Jefferson House*
1 John H Stewart Dr, Newington, CT, 06111
(203) 667-4453
Medical Dir/Dir of Nursing Dr Arthur Wolf.
Licensure Intermediate care. *Beds* SNF 60; ICF 30. *Certified* Medicaid; Medicare.
Owner Nonprofit Corp.
Staff RNs 13 (ft); LPNs 10 (ft); Nurses aides 40 (ft); Physical therapists 5 (ft), 1 (pt); Recreational therapists 3 (ft), 1 (pt); Dietitians 2 (ft).
Languages Spanish, Polish, French
Facilities Dining room; Physical therapy room; Activities room; Crafts room; Laundry room; Barber/Beauty shop; Library.

Activities Arts & crafts; Cards; Games; Reading groups; Prayer groups; Movies; Shopping trips; Social/Cultural gatherings.

Mediplex of Newington*
240 Church St, Newington, CT, 06111
(203) 667-2256
Licensure Skilled care; Intermediate care. *Beds* 120. *Certified* Medicaid; Medicare.
Owner Proprietary Corp (Mediplex).
Staff Physicians; RNs 8 (ft); LPNs 4 (ft); Nurses aides 27 (ft); Physical therapists 2 (ft); Activities coordinators 2 (ft); Social workers 1 (ft).
Languages Portuguese, Spanish, Polish, French
Activities Arts & crafts; Reading groups; Shopping trips; Social/Cultural gatherings; Music; Current events.

NEWTOWN

Ashlar of Newtown*
Toddy Hill Rd, Newtown, CT, 06470
(203) 426-5847
Licensure Skilled care; Intermediate care. *Beds* 156. *Certified* Medicaid; Medicare.
Owner Proprietary Corp.
Staff RNs 22 (ft), 1 (pt); LPNs 10 (ft), 1 (pt); Nurses aides 64 (ft), 1 (pt); Physical therapists 1 (ft), 1 (pt); Activities coordinators 3 (ft), 1 (pt); Social workers 1 (ft), 1 (pt).
Languages Spanish, German, Italian, French
Affiliation Masons

NORTH HAVEN

Montowese Health Care Center
163 Quinnipiac Ave, North Haven, CT, 06473
(203) 624-3303
Admin Eileen M Ichan RN. *Medical Dir/Dir of Nursing* Bjorn Ringstad MD; Gena Tannoia RN DNS.
Licensure Skilled care. *Beds* SNF 60. *Certified* Medicaid; Medicare.
Owner Proprietary Corp.
Admissions Requirements Physician's request.
Staff RNs 12 (ft); LPNs 6 (ft); Nurses aides 27 (ft); Physical therapists; Recreational therapists; Occupational therapists; Speech therapists; Activities coordinators 2 (ft); Dietitians; Dentists; Ophthalmologists.
Languages Italian, Spanish, Portuguese, Polish
Facilities Dining room; Physical therapy room; Activities room; Laundry room; Barber/Beauty shop.
Activities Arts & crafts; Cards; Games; Reading groups; Prayer groups; Movies; Social/Cultural gatherings.

NORWALK

Fairfield Manor Health Care Center Inc*
23 Prospect Ave, Norwalk, CT, 06850
(203) 853-0010
Medical Dir/Dir of Nursing Robert Yazmer MD.
Licensure Skilled care; Intermediate care. *Beds* 210. *Certified* Medicaid; Medicare.
Owner Proprietary Corp (Beverly Enterprises).
Admissions Requirements Minimum age 17.
Staff RNs 11 (ft), 11 (pt); LPNs 10 (ft), 10 (pt); Orderlies 3 (ft); Nurses aides 65 (ft), 25 (pt); Physical therapists 1 (ft), 1 (pt); Recreational therapists 1 (ft); Occupational therapists 1 (ft), 1 (pt); Speech therapists 1 (ft); Activities coordinators 2 (ft); Dietitians 1 (ft), 1 (pt).
Languages Haitian, French, Spanish, Italian, Polish
Facilities Dining room; Physical therapy room; Activities room; Chapel; Crafts room; Laundry room; Barber/Beauty shop; Library.

Activities Arts & crafts; Cards; Games;
Reading groups; Prayer groups; Movies;
Shopping trips; Social/Cultural gatherings.

Lea Manor Health Care Center
73 Strawberry Hill Ave, Norwalk, CT, 06855
(203) 852-8833
Admin Margaret A Kalsched. *Medical Dir/Dir
of Nursing* Dr A Joel Papowitz; Gail S
Favano.
Licensure Skilled care; Intermediate care. *Beds*
SNF 60; ICF 60. *Certified* Medicaid;
Medicare.
Owner Proprietary Corp (Multicare
Management).
Admissions Requirements Minimum age 18;
Medical examination; Physician's request.
Staff Physicians; Dietitians; Nurses aides.
Languages French, Polish
Facilities Dining room; Physical therapy
room; Activities room; Chapel; Crafts room;
Laundry room; Barber/Beauty shop; Library.
Activities Arts & crafts; Cards; Games;
Reading groups; Prayer groups; Movies;
Shopping trips; Social/Cultural gatherings.

Notre Dame Convalescent Home Inc
76 W Rocks Rd, Norwalk, CT, 06851
(203) 847-5893
Medical Dir/Dir of Nursing Dr James Griffith.
Licensure Skilled care. *Beds* 60. *Certified*
Medicaid.
Owner Nonprofit Corp.
Admissions Requirements Minimum age 14;
Medical examination; Physician's request.
Staff Physicians 12 (pt); RNs 4 (ft), 12 (pt);
LPNs 3 (ft); Nurses aides 26 (ft), 6 (pt);
Physical therapists 1 (pt); Recreational
therapists 1 (ft); Speech therapists 1 (pt);
Activities coordinators 1 (ft); Dietitians 1
(pt); Dentists 1 (pt); Podiatrists 1 (pt);
Audiologists 1 (pt); Optometrists 1 (pt).
Languages French
Affiliation Roman Catholic
Facilities Dining room; Physical therapy
room; Activities room; Chapel; Laundry
room; Barber/Beauty shop; Library; Lounge.
Activities Arts & crafts; Cards; Games;
Reading groups; Prayer groups; Movies;
Shopping trips.

NORWICH

Convalescent Center of Norwich Inc
60 Crouch Ave, Norwich, CT, 06360
(203) 889-2631
Admin Raymond J LeBlanc. *Medical Dir/Dir
of Nursing* Dr Torres.
Licensure Skilled care. *Beds* 119. *Certified*
Medicaid; Medicare.
Owner Proprietary Corp.
Admissions Requirements Minimum age 14;
Medical examination; Physician's request.
Staff Physicians 6 (pt); RNs 8 (ft), 14 (pt);
LPNs 6 (ft), 10 (pt); Orderlies 3 (pt); Nurses
aides 27 (ft), 41 (pt); Physical therapists 2
(pt); Reality therapists 1 (pt); Recreational
therapists 2 (ft); Speech therapists 1 (pt);
Activities coordinators 2 (pt); Dietitians 2
(pt); Dentists 1 (pt); Ophthalmologists 1 (pt);
Podiatrists 1 (pt); Dentist 1 (pt).
Languages Polish, French
Facilities Dining room; Physical therapy
room; Activities room; Chapel; Laundry
room; Barber/Beauty shop; Library; TV
lounges; Patio; Sunroom.
Activities Arts & crafts; Cards; Games;
Reading groups; Prayer groups; Movies;
Shopping trips; Social/Cultural gatherings.

Elmachri Convalescent Home*
251 Washington St, Norwich, CT, 06360
(203) 889-1721
Medical Dir/Dir of Nursing David G Rousseau
MD.
Licensure Skilled care. *Beds* SNF 20; ICF 10.
Certified Medicaid; Medicare.
Owner Proprietary Corp.

Staff RNs 1 (ft), 9 (pt); LPNs 3 (pt); Nurses
aides 8 (ft), 12 (pt); Recreational therapists 1
(ft), 2 (pt); Dietitians 2 (ft), 2 (pt).
Languages Spanish, French, Italian, Polish
Facilities Activities room.
Activities Arts & crafts; Cards; Games;
Movies; Shopping trips; Social/Cultural
gatherings.

Fairlawn Convalescent Home*
5 Rockwell Terrace, Norwich, CT, 06360
(203) 887-7690
Licensure Skilled care. *Beds* 45. *Certified*
Medicaid.
Owner Proprietary Corp.
Staff RNs 9 (ft); LPNs 3 (ft); Nurses aides 17
(ft); Activities coordinators 1 (ft).
Languages Polish, French, Russian
Activities Therapeutic recreation.

Hamilton Pavilion Healthcare*
50 Palmer St, Norwich, CT, 06360
(203) 889-8358
Licensure Skilled care; Intermediate care. *Beds*
160. *Certified* Medicaid; Medicare.
Owner Proprietary Corp (Hillhaven Corp).
Staff RNs 21 (ft); LPNs 11 (ft); Nurses aides
38 (ft); Activities coordinators 4 (ft); Social
workers 1 (ft).
Languages French, Polish, Italian

Norwichtown Convalescent Inc
93 W Town St, Norwich, CT, 06360
(203) 889-2614
Admin Alan DeBlasio. *Medical Dir/Dir of
Nursing* Dr David Rousseau; Catherine
McMahon.
Licensure Skilled care. *Beds* SNF 120.
Certified Medicaid; Medicare.
Owner Proprietary Corp.
Admissions Requirements Minimum age 14.
Staff Physicians 17 (pt); RNs 5 (ft), 9 (pt);
LPNs 1 (ft), 13 (pt); Nurses aides 14 (ft), 53
(pt); Physical therapists 1 (pt); Recreational
therapists 2 (ft); Speech therapists 1 (pt);
Dietitians 1 (pt); Dentists 1 (pt);
Ophthalmologists 1 (pt); Podiatrists 1 (pt).
Languages Italian
Facilities Dining room; Physical therapy
room; Activities room; Crafts room; Barber/
Beauty shop.
Activities Arts & crafts; Cards; Games;
Reading groups; Prayer groups; Movies;
Shopping trips; Social/Cultural gatherings;
Bus trips; Cocktail lounge; Dinner & theater;
State park outings; Restaurant outings.

OLD SAYBROOK

Ferry Point—SNCF*
PO Box F, 175 Ferry Rd, Old Saybrook, CT,
06475
(203) 388-4677
Licensure Skilled care. *Beds* 120. *Certified*
Medicaid; Medicare.
Owner Proprietary Corp.
Staff RNs 9 (ft); LPNs 10 (ft); Physical
therapists 1 (ft); Activities coordinators 1
(ft); Social workers 1 (ft).
Languages Italian, French

Saybrook Convalescent Hospital
1775 Boston Post Rd, Old Saybrook, CT,
06457
(203) 399-6216
Admin James H Sbrolla. *Medical Dir/Dir of
Nursing* Donald Cook MD; Therese
Firgelewski DON.
Licensure Skilled care. *Beds* SNF 120.
Certified Medicaid; Medicare.
Owner Proprietary Corp.
Admissions Requirements Minimum age 21.
Staff RNs 22 (ft); LPNs 7 (ft); Nurses aides 50
(ft); Physical therapists 2 (ft); Activities
coordinators 2 (ft).
Languages Spanish, French, Italian

Facilities Dining room; Physical therapy
room; Activities room; Laundry room;
Barber/Beauty shop.
Activities Arts & crafts; Cards; Games;
Reading groups; Prayer groups; Movies;
Shopping trips; Social/Cultural gatherings.

ORANGE

The Lydian Corporation
PO Box 945, 324 Grassy Hill Rd, Orange, CT,
06477
(203) 878-0613
Admin Jean M Mario. *Medical Dir/Dir of
Nursing* Vincent E Kerr; Mary D Nigro
DON.
Licensure Intermediate care. *Beds* ICF 27.
Certified Medicaid.
Owner Proprietary Corp.
Admissions Requirements Minimum age 15.
Staff Physicians 2 (pt); RNs 2 (ft), 8 (pt);
Nurses aides 4 (ft), 4 (pt); Physical therapists
1 (pt); Recreational therapists 1 (ft);
Activities coordinators 1 (ft); Dietitians 1
(pt); Dentists 1 (pt); Ophthalmologists 1 (pt);
Podiatrists 1 (pt).
Languages Italian, Spanish
Facilities Dining room; Activities room;
Laundry room.
Activities Arts & crafts; Cards; Games;
Reading groups; Prayer groups; Shopping
trips; Social/Cultural gatherings.

Orange Health Care Center
225 Boston Post Rd, Orange, CT, 06477
(203) 795-0835
Medical Dir/Dir of Nursing Evan M Ginsberg
MD.
Licensure Intermediate care. *Beds* ICF 60.
Certified Medicaid.
Owner Proprietary Corp.
Admissions Requirements Minimum age 14.
Staff Physicians 3 (pt); RNs 7 (ft), 5 (pt);
LPNs 5 (pt); Nurses aides 6 (ft), 15 (pt);
Recreational therapists 1 (ft); Speech
therapists 1 (pt); Dietitians 1 (pt); Dentists 1
(pt); Ophthalmologists 3 (pt); Podiatrists 1
(pt); Dentist 1 (pt).
Languages Italian, German, Spanish
Facilities Dining room; Physical therapy
room; Activities room; Crafts room; Laundry
room; Barber/Beauty shop.
Activities Arts & crafts; Cards; Games;
Reading groups; Prayer groups; Movies;
Shopping trips; Social/Cultural gatherings.

PLAINFIELD

Crest Haven Rest Home*
34 Pleasant St, Plainfield, CT, 06374
(203) 564-8414
Licensure Intermediate care. *Beds* 30.
Certified Medicaid.
Owner Proprietary Corp.
Staff RNs 1 (ft), 1 (pt); LPNs 3 (ft); Nurses
aides 4 (ft); Activities coordinators 1 (pt);
Dietitians 1 (pt).
Activities Arts & crafts; Games; Prayer groups;
Shopping trips; Social/Cultural gatherings;
Picnics; Sing-alongs.

Villa Maria Conv Home Inc*
20 Babcock Ave, Plainfield, CT, 06374
(203) 564-3387
Admin Daniel E Disco & Natalie D Disco.
Medical Dir/Dir of Nursing Philip Goyette.
Licensure Skilled care. *Beds* 52. *Certified*
Medicaid; Medicare.
Owner Proprietary Corp.
Admissions Requirements Medical
examination; Physician's request.
Staff Physicians 1 (pt); RNs 5 (ft), 5 (pt);
LPNs 3 (ft), 3 (pt); Nurses aides 17 (ft), 7
(pt); Physical therapists 1 (pt); Recreational
therapists 1 (ft); Activities coordinators 1

(ft); Dietitians 1 (pt); Dentists 1 (pt);
Ophthalmologists 1 (pt); Podiatrists 1 (pt);
Audiologists 1 (pt).
Languages French
Facilities Dining room; Physical therapy
room; Activities room; Chapel; Crafts room;
Laundry room; Barber/Beauty shop; Library.
Activities Arts & crafts; Cards; Games;
Reading groups; Prayer groups; Movies;
Shopping trips; Social/Cultural gatherings.

PLAINVILLE

Plainville Health Care Center Inc
269 Farmington Ave, Plainville, CT, 06062
(203) 747-1637
Admin Raymond E Hackley. *Medical Dir/Dir
of Nursing* John P Iannotti MD; Sandra P
Young RN.
Licensure Skilled care; Intermediate care. *Beds*
SNF 120; ICF 60. *Certified* Medicaid;
Medicare.
Owner Proprietary Corp (Health Care
Associates Inc).
Admissions Requirements Minimum age 14;
Medical examination; Physician's request.
Staff RNs 31 (ft); LPNs 8 (ft); Nurses aides 74
(ft); Recreational therapists 3 (ft).
Languages French, Italian, Polish, Vietnamese
Facilities Dining room; Physical therapy
room; Activities room; Crafts room; Laundry
room; Barber/Beauty shop.
Activities Arts & crafts; Cards; Games;
Reading groups; Prayer groups; Movies;
Shopping trips; Social/Cultural gatherings.

PLATTEVILLE

Woodmere Health Care Center*
261 Summit St, Platteville, CT, 06479
(203) 628-0364
Licensure Skilled care; Intermediate care. *Beds*
120. *Certified* Medicare.
Owner Proprietary Corp.
Staff RNs 11 (ft); LPNs 11 (ft); Physical
therapists 1 (ft); Activities coordinators 4
(ft).
Languages French, Italian, Spanish
Activities Arts & crafts; Games; Prayer groups;
Shopping trips; Social/Cultural gatherings;
Discussion groups; Baking; Music;
Newsletter.

PLYMOUTH

Cook-Willow Conv Hospital Inc*
41 Hillside Ave, Plymouth, CT, 06782
(203) 283-8208
Admin Susan C Armstrong.
Licensure Skilled care. *Beds* 30. *Certified*
Medicaid.
Owner Proprietary Corp.
Staff RNs 5 (ft); LPNs 1 (ft); Activities
coordinators 1 (ft).
Activities Therapeutic recreation.

PORTLAND

Portland Convalescent Center Inc*
333 Main St, Portland, CT, 06480
(203) 342-0370
Licensure Skilled care. *Beds* 89. *Certified*
Medicaid; Medicare.
Owner Proprietary Corp.
Staff LPNs 13 (ft), 1 (pt); Nurses aides 37 (ft),
1 (pt); Physical therapists 1 (ft); Activities
coordinators 1 (ft), 1 (pt).
Languages Polish, German, Italian, French
Activities Arts & crafts; Games; Movies;
Social/Cultural gatherings; Newspaper.

PROSPECT

Country Manor Health Care Center*
64 Summit Rd, Prospect, CT, 06712
(203) 758-4431
Licensure Skilled care; Intermediate care. *Beds*
150. *Certified* Medicaid; Medicare.
Owner Proprietary Corp (Beverly Enterprises).
Staff LPNs 27 (ft); Nurses aides 55 (ft);
Activities coordinators 2 (ft), 1 (pt).
Languages Italian, German
Activities Games; Prayer groups; Singing
group.

Eastview Manor Inc
170 Scott Rd, Prospect, CT, 06712
(203) 758-5491
Admin Loretta J D'Alessio. *Medical Dir/Dir of
Nursing* Evan J Whalley MD; Marion
Stevenson RN DON.
Licensure Skilled care. *Beds* SNF 30. *Certified*
Medicaid; Medicare.
Owner Proprietary Corp.
Admissions Requirements Minimum age 18;
Medical examination.
Staff Physicians 6 (pt); RNs 3 (ft), 4 (pt);
Nurses aides 5 (ft), 6 (pt); Physical therapists
1 (pt); Recreational therapists 1 (pt);
Dietitians 1 (pt); Dentists 1 (pt);
Ophthalmologists 1 (pt).
Languages French, Portuguese, Lithuanian,
German, Spanish
Facilities Dining room; Physical therapy
room; Crafts room; Barber/Beauty shop.
Activities Arts & crafts; Cards; Games;
Reading groups; Prayer groups; Movies;
Shopping trips; Social/Cultural gatherings.

PUTNAM

Matulaitis Nursing Home*
Thurber Rd, Putnam, CT, 06260
(203) 928-7976
Licensure Skilled care; Intermediate care. *Beds*
SNF 60; ICF 59. *Certified* Medicaid.
Owner Nonprofit Corp.
Admissions Requirements Medical
examination.
Staff Physicians 7 (pt); RNs 12 (ft), 2 (pt);
LPNs 1 (ft), 2 (pt); Nurses aides 36 (ft), 6
(pt); Physical therapists 1 (pt); Recreational
therapists 2 (ft); Speech therapists 1 (pt);
Dietitians 1 (ft); Dentists 1 (pt);
Ophthalmologists 1 (pt); Podiatrists 1 (pt);
Audiologists 1 (pt).
Languages Lithuanian, French, Polish,
Spanish, Swedish, German, Italian
Affiliation Roman Catholic
Facilities Dining room; Physical therapy
room; Activities room; Chapel; Crafts room;
Laundry room; Barber/Beauty shop; Library.
Activities Arts & crafts; Cards; Games;
Reading groups; Prayer groups; Movies;
Shopping trips; Social/Cultural gatherings.

ROCKVILLE

Rockville Memorial Nursing Home*
22 South St, Rockville, CT, 06066
(203) 875-0771
Licensure Skilled care; Intermediate care. *Beds*
150. *Certified* Medicaid; Medicare.
Owner Proprietary Corp.
Staff RNs 22 (ft), 1 (pt); LPNs 44 (ft), 1 (pt);
Nurses aides 13 (ft), 1 (pt); Activities
coordinators; Dietitians 2 (ft), 1 (pt).
Languages French, Polish, Italian, Russian,
Spanish, Lithuanian, Hawaiian

ROCKY HILL

Elm Hill Nursing Center
45 Elm St, Rocky Hill, CT, 06067
(203) 529-8661

Admin Melvin C Smith. *Medical Dir/Dir of
Nursing* Dr Jacque Mendelsohn; Barbara
McCarthy RN.
Licensure Skilled care; Intermediate care. *Beds*
SNF 120; ICF 30. *Certified* Medicaid;
Medicare.
Owner Proprietary Corp.
Admissions Requirements Minimum age 14;
Physician's request.
Staff Physicians 1 (pt); RNs 12 (ft); LPNs 16
(ft); Orderlies 1 (ft); Nurses aides 20 (ft), 5
(pt); Physical therapists 1 (pt); Reality
therapists 1 (pt); Recreational therapists 3
(ft), 2 (pt); Speech therapists 1 (pt);
Dietitians 2 (pt); Dentists 1 (pt);
Ophthalmologists 1 (pt); Podiatrists 1 (pt).
Languages Polish, Italian, Spanish
Facilities Dining room; Physical therapy
room; Activities room; Chapel; Crafts room;
Laundry room; Barber/Beauty shop; Library.
Activities Arts & crafts; Cards; Games;
Reading groups; Prayer groups; Movies;
Shopping trips; Social/Cultural gatherings;
Musical events.

Maple View Manor Inc*
856 Maple St, Rocky Hill, CT, 06067
(203) 563-2861
Licensure Skilled care. *Beds* 120. *Certified*
Medicaid; Medicare.
Owner Nonprofit Corp.
Staff RNs 8 (ft); LPNs 7 (ft); Nurses aides 22
(ft); Activities coordinators 1 (ft); Dietitians
1 (ft).
Languages Spanish, French

West Hill Convalescent Home*
60 West St, Rocky Hill, CT, 06067
(203) 529-2521
Admin Malcolm Glazer.
Licensure Skilled care. *Beds* 120. *Certified*
Medicaid; Medicare.
Owner Proprietary Corp.
Staff RNs 11 (ft), 1 (pt); LPNs 7 (ft), 1 (pt);
Nurses aides 43 (ft), 1 (pt); Physical
therapists 1 (ft), 1 (pt); Activities
coordinators 2 (ft), 1 (pt); Dietitians 1 (ft), 1
(pt).
Languages French, Polish, German, Italian
Activities Arts & crafts; Games; Shopping
trips.

SALISBURY

Whitridge Nursing Wing*
Lower Cobble Rd, Salisbury, CT, 06068
(203) 435-9851
Licensure Skilled care. *Beds* 30. *Certified*
Medicaid; Medicare.
Owner Proprietary Corp.
Staff RNs 7 (ft), 1 (pt); Nurses aides 12 (ft);
Dietitians 1 (ft).
Languages Spanish, Italian, Chinese, German,
French
Activities Arts & crafts; Movies; Social/
Cultural gatherings; Musical programs;
Greenhouse.

SHELTON

Gardner Heights Convalescent Center Inc
172 Rocky Rest Rd, Shelton, CT, 06484
(203) 929-1481
Admin Michael P Connor. *Medical Dir/Dir of
Nursing* Dr Joel Zaretzky; Lucille Wdowiak.
Licensure Skilled care; Intermediate care. *Beds*
179. *Certified* Medicaid.
Owner Nonprofit organization/foundation.
Admissions Requirements Minimum age 16;
Physician's request.
Staff RNs; LPNs; Nurses aides; Recreational
therapists; Activities coordinators; Dietitians.
Languages Polish, Italian
Facilities Dining room; Physical therapy
room; Activities room; Chapel; Crafts room;
Laundry room; Barber/Beauty shop.

Activities Arts & crafts; Prayer groups; Cooking; Happy hour; Reality orientation.

The Flora & Mary Hewitt Memorial Hospital Inc*
230 Coram Ave, Shelton, CT, 06484
(203) 735-4671
Medical Dir/Dir of Nursing Murugesapillai Koneswaran MD SNF & Donald P Roach MD ICF.
Licensure Skilled care; Intermediate care. *Beds* 210. *Certified* Medicaid; Medicare.
Owner Nonprofit Corp.
Admissions Requirements Minimum age 16; Medical examination; Physician's request.
Staff RNs 8 (ft), 16 (pt); LPNs 11 (ft), 6 (pt); Nurses aides 34 (ft), 62 (pt); Physical therapists 1 (ft), 2 (pt); Recreational therapists 3 (ft), 1 (pt); Speech therapists 1 (pt); Dietitians 1 (ft), 1 (pt); Dentists 1 (pt); Podiatrists 4 (pt).
Languages Italian, Polish, Spanish
Facilities Dining room; Physical therapy room; Activities room; Chapel; Crafts room; Laundry room; Barber/Beauty shop; Library.
Activities Arts & crafts; Cards; Games; Reading groups; Prayer groups; Movies; Shopping trips; Social/Cultural gatherings.

Shelton Lakes Residence & Health Care*
5 Lake Rd, Shelton, CT, 06484
(203) 736-2635
Beds 59.
Owner Nonprofit Corp.
Languages Spanish, Polish Italian, German, Portuguese

United Methodist Conv Home of Connecticut Inc
584 Long Hill Ave, Shelton, CT, 06484
(203) 929-5321
Admin Shapleigh M Drisko. *Medical Dir/Dir of Nursing* M Koneswaraw MD; Corrine Conroy RN DON.
Licensure Skilled care. *Beds* SNF 120. *Certified* Medicaid; Medicare.
Owner Nonprofit Corp.
Admissions Requirements Minimum age 16; Medical examination; Physician's request.
Staff Physicians 2 (pt); RNs 12 (ft), 2 (pt); LPNs 4 (ft), 7 (pt); Orderlies 1 (pt); Nurses aides 60 (ft), 2 (pt); Physical therapists 2 (pt); Recreational therapists 2 (ft); Dietitians 1 (ft), 1 (pt); Dentists 3 (pt); Dentist 1 (pt).
Affiliation Methodist
Facilities Dining room; Physical therapy room; Activities room; Chapel; Laundry room; Barber/Beauty shop; Library.
Activities Arts & crafts; Cards; Games; Reading groups; Prayer groups; Movies; Shopping trips; Social/Cultural gatherings.

SIMSBURY

Holly Hill Health Care
40 Firetown Rd, Simsbury, CT, 06070
(203) 658-4407
Admin James E Wrinn. *Medical Dir/Dir of Nursing* Dr Ronald Josephson; Eleanor Clark RN DNS.
Licensure Skilled care. *Beds* SNF 60. *Certified* Medicaid.
Owner Proprietary Corp.
Admissions Requirements Minimum age 14.
Staff RNs 3 (ft), 10 (pt); LPNs 3 (ft), 2 (pt); Nurses aides 17 (ft), 6 (pt); Physical therapists 1 (ft); Recreational therapists 1 (ft); Dietitians 1 (pt).
Languages French, Lithuanian
Facilities Dining room; Physical therapy room; Activities room; Laundry room.
Activities Arts & crafts; Cards; Games; Reading groups; Prayer groups; Movies; Shopping trips; Social/Cultural gatherings; Twilight dinners.

McLean Home*
75 Great Pond Rd, Simsbury, CT, 06070
(203) 658-2254
Licensure Skilled care; Intermediate care. *Beds* 58. *Certified* Medicaid; Medicare.
Owner Nonprofit Corp.
Staff Physicians 1 (pt); LPNs 36 (ft), 1 (pt); Physical therapists 1 (pt); Dietitians 1 (pt); Dentists 1 (pt); Social workers 1 (ft), 1 (pt).
Languages French, German, Polish, Ukrainian, Laotion

SOUTH WINDSOR

South Windsor Convalescent Home Inc*
1060 Main St, South Windsor, CT, 06074
(203) 289-7771
Licensure Skilled care. *Beds* 120. *Certified* Medicaid; Medicare.
Owner Proprietary Corp.
Staff RNs 12 (ft), 1 (pt); LPNs 4 (ft), 1 (pt); Nurses aides 33 (ft); Physical therapists 1 (ft); Activities coordinators 2 (ft); Social workers 1 (ft).
Languages French, Polish
Activities Arts & crafts; Games; Movies; Shopping trips; Social/Cultural gatherings.

SOUTHBURY

Lutheran Home of Southbury
990 Main St N, Southbury, CT, 06488
(203) 264-9135
Admin David D Boyd. *Medical Dir/Dir of Nursing* Daniel G Goodman MD.
Licensure Skilled care; Intermediate care; Home for aged. *Beds* SNF 60; ICF 60; Home for aged 31. *Certified* Medicaid.
Owner Nonprofit Corp.
Admissions Requirements Minimum age 65; Medical examination; Physician's request.
Staff Physicians 7 (pt); RNs 3 (ft), 9 (pt); LPNs 4 (pt); Nurses aides 11 (ft), 14 (pt); Physical therapists 1 (pt); Speech therapists 1 (pt); Activities coordinators 3 (ft); Dietitians 1 (pt); Dentists 1 (pt); Ophthalmologists 1 (pt); Podiatrists 1 (pt).
Affiliation Lutheran
Facilities Dining room; Physical therapy room; Activities room; Chapel; Crafts room; Laundry room; Barber/Beauty shop; Library.
Activities Arts & crafts; Cards; Games; Reading groups; Prayer groups; Movies; Shopping trips; Social/Cultural gatherings.

River Glen Continuing Care Center*
S Britain Rd, Southbury, CT, 06488
(203) 264-9600
Licensure Skilled care; Intermediate care. *Beds* 60. *Certified* Medicaid; Medicare.
Owner Proprietary Corp (New Medico Assoc).
Staff LPNs 18 (ft); Nurses aides 33 (ft); Physical therapists 1 (ft); Occupational therapists 1 (ft); Activities coordinators 1 (ft); Social workers 1 (ft).
Languages Italian, Spanish, Lithuanian
Activities Therapeutic recreation.

SOUTHINGTON

Ridgewood Health Care Facility Inc*
582 Meriden Ave, Southington, CT, 06489
(203) 628-0388
Licensure Skilled care. *Beds* 38. *Certified* Medicaid.
Owner Proprietary Corp.
Staff RNs 9 (ft); Nurses aides 10 (ft), 1 (pt); Activities coordinators 1 (ft).
Languages Polish, Italian, French, German
Activities Therapeutic recreation.

SOUTHPORT

Southport Manor Convalescent Center
930 Mill Hill Terrace, Southport, CT, 06490
(203) 259-7894

Medical Dir/Dir of Nursing Dr Kenneth Higgins.
Licensure Skilled care. *Beds* 140. *Certified* Medicaid; Medicare.
Owner Proprietary Corp.
Admissions Requirements Minimum age 18; Medical examination; Physician's request.
Staff Physicians 2 (pt); RNs 13 (ft), 22 (pt); LPNs 2 (ft), 7 (pt); Nurses aides 61 (ft), 6 (pt); Physical therapists 1 (ft); Recreational therapists 3 (ft); Occupational therapists 1 (pt); Speech therapists 1 (pt); Dietitians 1 (pt); Dentists 1 (pt); Ophthalmologists 1 (pt); Dentist 1 (pt).
Languages Spanish
Facilities Dining room; Physical therapy room; Activities room; Laundry room; Barber/Beauty shop.
Activities Arts & crafts; Cards; Games; Reading groups; Prayer groups; Movies.

STAMFORD

Courtland Gardens Health Care*
59 Courtland Ave, Stamford, CT, 06902
(203) 359-2000
Licensure Skilled care; Intermediate care. *Beds* 180. *Certified* Medicare.
Owner Proprietary Corp.
Staff RNs 24 (ft); LPNs 22 (ft); Nurses aides 110 (ft); Activities coordinators; Dietitians.
Languages French, Spanish, Polish

Homestead Health Center
160 Glenbrook Rd, Stamford, CT, 06902
(203) 359-2000
Licensure Skilled care. *Beds* 87. *Certified* Medicaid; Medicare.
Owner Proprietary Corp.
Staff RNs 15 (ft); LPNs 9 (ft); Nurses aides 49 (ft); Activities coordinators 2 (ft).
Languages French, Spanish, Polish

Smith House Skilled Nursing Facility
88 Rockrimmon Rd, Stamford, CT, 06903
(203) 322-3428
Admin Margaret Joyce. *Medical Dir/Dir of Nursing* Bernard O Nemoitin MD; Kathryn M Dolan RN DON.
Licensure Skilled care. *Beds* SNF 128. *Certified* Medicaid; Medicare.
Owner Publicly owned.
Admissions Requirements Minimum age 14; Medical examination.
Staff RNs 8 (ft), 11 (pt); LPNs 7 (ft), 8 (pt); Nurses aides 54 (ft), 16 (pt); Physical therapists 1 (ft); Recreational therapists 2 (ft), 1 (pt); Social workers 1 (ft), 2 (pt).
Languages Spanish, Italian, French, German, Hebrew, Yiddish, Polish
Facilities Dining room; Physical therapy room; Activities room; Laundry room; Barber/Beauty shop.
Activities Arts & crafts; Cards; Games; Reading groups; Prayer groups; Movies; Social/Cultural gatherings; Trips; Theater; Beach; Pet shows.

STRATFORD

Lord Chamberlain
7003 Main St, Stratford, CT, 06497
(203) 375-5894
Admin Martin Sbrilie. *Medical Dir/Dir of Nursing* Dr Saul Feldman.
Licensure Skilled care. *Beds* 240. *Certified* Medicaid; Medicare.
Owner Proprietary Corp.
Admissions Requirements Physician's request.
Staff Physicians; RNs; LPNs; Orderlies; Nurses aides; Physical therapists; Reality therapists; Recreational therapists; Occupational therapists; Speech therapists; Activities coordinators; Dietitians; Dentists; Ophthalmologists; Podiatrists; Audiologists.
Languages Spanish, Polish, Hebrew, Yiddish, French, Italian, Greek, German

Facilities Dining room; Physical therapy room; Activities room; Chapel; Crafts room; Laundry room; Barber/Beauty shop; Library; Greenhouse.
Activities Arts & crafts; Cards; Games; Reading groups; Prayer groups; Movies; Shopping trips; Social/Cultural gatherings; Picnics; Horticulture in greenhouse.

TORRINGTON

Adams House Health Care*
80 Fern Dr, Torrington, CT, 06790
(203) 482-7668
Medical Dir/Dir of Nursing Dr Frank Vanoni.
Licensure Skilled care. *Beds* 90. *Certified* Medicaid; Medicare.
Owner Proprietary Corp (Hillhaven Corp).
Staff RNs 8 (ft), 5 (pt); LPNs 3 (ft), 4 (pt); Nurses aides 14 (ft), 29 (pt); Physical therapists 1 (pt); Recreational therapists 1 (ft), 1 (pt).
Languages Polish, Italian, Lebanese, French, German, Hungarian
Facilities Dining room; Physical therapy room; Laundry room; Barber/Beauty shop.
Activities Arts & crafts; Cards; Games; Reading groups; Prayer groups; Movies; Shopping trips; Social/Cultural gatherings.

Torrington Extend-A-Care Centre
225 Wyoming Ave, Torrington, CT, 06790
(203) 482-8563
Admin Christopher S Smith. *Medical Dir/Dir of Nursing* David P Hebert MD; Linda Koski RNBS.
Licensure Skilled care. *Beds* SNF 120. *Certified* Medicaid; Medicare.
Owner Proprietary Corp (Beverly Enterprises).
Admissions Requirements Medical examination; Physician's request.
Staff Physicians 6 (pt); RNs 8 (ft), 7 (pt); LPNs 6 (ft), 2 (pt); Nurses aides 33 (ft), 20 (pt); Physical therapists 1 (pt); Recreational therapists 2 (ft); Speech therapists 1 (pt); Activities coordinators 1 (ft), 1 (pt); Dietitians 1 (pt); Ophthalmologists 1 (pt).
Languages Italian, Spanish
Facilities Dining room; Physical therapy room; Activities room; Chapel; Crafts room; Laundry room; Barber/Beauty shop; TV lounge.
Activities Arts & crafts; Cards; Games; Reading groups; Prayer groups; Movies; Social/Cultural gatherings.

Wolcott Hall Nursing Center
215 Forest St, Torrington, CT, 06790
(203) 482-8554
Admin Peter J Belual. *Medical Dir/Dir of Nursing* Dr Alfred J Finn; Dorothy Preston RN DNS.
Licensure Skilled care. *Beds* SNF 90. *Certified* Medicaid; Medicare.
Owner Proprietary Corp (Health Care Associates Inc).
Admissions Requirements Minimum age 14.
Staff Physicians 25 (pt); RNs 10 (ft); LPNs 6 (ft), 3 (pt); Nurses aides 32 (ft), 7 (pt); Physical therapists 1 (pt); Recreational therapists 1 (ft), 1 (pt); Dietitians 1 (pt).
Languages Polish, Italian, French, Spanish
Facilities Dining room; Physical therapy room; Activities room; Laundry room; Barber/Beauty shop; Patient lounges.
Activities Arts & crafts; Cards; Games; Reading groups; Prayer groups; Movies; Shopping trips; Social/Cultural gatherings; Formal dinners; Exercise groups; Pet therapy; Resident council; Cocktail parties.

TRUMBULL

St Joseph's Manor
6448 Main St, Trumbull, CT, 06611
(203) 268-6204
Admin Sr Mary Ann Davis. *Medical Dir/Dir of Nursing* Everitt P Dolan MD; Kathleen Banville RN.
Licensure Skilled care; Intermediate care; Home for aged (Residential); Outpatient clinic. *Beds* SNF 201; ICF 72; Home for aged 21. *Certified* Medicaid; Medicare.
Owner Nonprofit Corp.
Admissions Requirements Minimum age 60; Medical examination; Physician's request.
Staff Physicians 6 (pt); RNs 16 (ft), 26 (pt); LPNs 6 (ft), 9 (pt); Nurses aides 103 (ft), 30 (pt); Physical therapists 1 (ft); Recreational therapists 5 (ft); Occupational therapists 1 (ft); Speech therapists 1 (pt); Activities coordinators 1 (ft); Dietitians 1 (ft); Dentists 2 (pt); Ophthalmologists 2 (pt); Podiatrists 1 (pt); Dentist 2 (pt).
Affiliation Roman Catholic
Facilities Dining room; Physical therapy room; Activities room; Chapel; Crafts room; Laundry room; Barber/Beauty shop; Library; Store; Coffee shop/Lounge; Giftshop; Clinic wing; Pharmacy.
Activities Arts & crafts; Cards; Games; Prayer groups; Movies; Shopping trips; Social/ Cultural gatherings; Resident council; Therapeutic groups; Dramatics; Swimming.

Trumbull St Mary's Convalescent Home & Rest Home*
401 Unity Rd, Trumbull, CT, 06611
(203) 372-6879
Medical Dir/Dir of Nursing Dr James D Garrity.
Licensure Skilled care 10B. *Beds* SNF 23; ICF 6. *Certified* Medicaid.
Owner Proprietary Corp.
Admissions Requirements Minimum age 15; Medical examination; Physician's request.
Staff Physicians 1 (pt); RNs 8 (ft); LPNs 1 (pt); Nurses aides 10 (ft); Recreational therapists 1 (ft); Dietitians 1 (pt); Dentists 1 (pt); Podiatrists 1 (pt).
Languages Italian, French, German, Yiddish, Hebrew
Activities Prayer groups; Arts & crafts; Shopping trips.

VERNON

Vernon Manor Health Care Facility
180 Regan Rd, Vernon, CT, 06066
(203) 871-0385
Admin David F Graves, A Jean Henry RN. *Medical Dir/Dir of Nursing* Neil H Brooks MD; Dolores P Rady RN.
Licensure Skilled care. *Beds* SNF 120.
Owner Privately owned.
Admissions Requirements Minimum age 50; Medical examination; Physician's request.
Staff Physicians 18 (pt); RNs 13 (ft), 11 (pt); LPNs 7 (ft), 7 (pt); Nurses aides 45 (ft), 28 (pt); Physical therapists 1 (ft), 2 (pt); Reality therapists 1 (ft); Recreational therapists 2 (ft), 1 (pt); Speech therapists 1 (pt); Activities coordinators 1 (ft); Dietitians 1 (pt); Dentists 1 (pt); Ophthalmologists 1 (pt); Podiatrists 1 (pt).
Languages Italian, Polish, French
Facilities Dining room; Physical therapy room; Activities room; Chapel; Crafts room; Laundry room; Barber/Beauty shop; Library; Private dining room; Dental & examination room; Greenhouse; Garden.
Activities Arts & crafts; Cards; Games; Reading groups; Prayer groups; Movies; Shopping trips; Social/Cultural gatherings; Sports; Resident council; Welcome committee; Sensory stimulation; Wine & cheese parties; Baking; Gardening; Leathercrafts; Ceramics.

WALLINGFORD

Brook Hollow Health Care Center
55 Kondracki Ln, Wallingford, CT, 06492
(203) 265-6771
Admin J Kevin Prisco. *Medical Dir/Dir of Nursing* Dr Richard Wein; Sharon Hermonat RN.
Licensure Skilled care. *Beds* SNF 180. *Certified* Medicaid; Medicare.
Owner Proprietary Corp (New Medico Assoc).
Staff Physicians 6 (pt); RNs 10 (ft), 17 (pt); LPNs 6 (ft), 13 (pt); Nurses aides 75 (ft), 25 (pt); Physical therapists 1 (ft), 1 (pt); Recreational therapists 4 (ft); Speech therapists 2 (ft); Dietitians 1 (ft).
Facilities Dining room; Physical therapy room; Activities room; Crafts room; Laundry room; Barber/Beauty shop; Large lobby/ sitting area; 4 large lounges w/entertainment units.
Activities Arts & crafts; Cards; Games; Reading groups; Prayer groups; Movies; Shopping trips; Social/Cultural gatherings.

Masonic Home & Hospital
PO Box 70, 22 Masonic Ave, Wallingford, CT, 06492
(203) 265-0931
Admin Edgar G Kilby. *Medical Dir/Dir of Nursing* Dr Urlinda Rauch; JoAnn PreFontaine RN DON.
Licensure Skilled care; Intermediate care; Home for aged; Chronic disease hospital. *Beds* SNF 148; ICF 234; Home for aged 86; Chronic disease hospital 100. *Certified* Medicaid; Medicare.
Owner Nonprofit organization/foundation.
Staff Physicians 4 (ft), 1 (pt); RNs 59 (ft); LPNs 42 (ft); Orderlies; Nurses aides 243 (ft), 10 (pt); Physical therapists 4 (ft); Recreational therapists 7 (ft); Occupational therapists 2 (ft); Speech therapists 1 (ft); Dietitians 2 (ft); Dentists 1 (pt); Ophthalmologists 1 (pt); Podiatrists 1 (ft).
Languages German, French, Spanish, Polish, Italian, Hungarian, Portuguese
Affiliation Masons
Facilities Dining room; Physical therapy room; Activities room; Chapel; Crafts room; Laundry room; Barber/Beauty shop; Library.
Activities Arts & crafts; Cards; Games; Reading groups; Prayer groups; Movies; Shopping trips; Social/Cultural gatherings.

New Brook Hollow Health Care Center Inc*
55 Kondracki Ln, Wallingford, CT, 06492
(203) 265-6771
Licensure Skilled care; Intermediate care. *Beds* 180. *Certified* Medicare.
Owner Proprietary Corp.
Staff RNs 20 (ft), 1 (pt); LPNs 11 (ft), 13 (pt); Physical therapists 1 (pt); Activities coordinators 4 (ft); Dietitians 1 (ft); Social workers 2 (ft).
Languages Italian, French, Polish
Activities Arts & crafts; Games; Prayer groups; Movies; Shopping trips; Social/Cultural gatherings; Music; Cooking; Resident council.

Skyview Convalescent Hospital Inc*
Marc Dr, Wallingford, CT, 06492
(202) 265-0981
Licensure Skilled care; Intermediate care. *Beds* 60. *Certified* Medicaid; Medicare.
Owner Proprietary Corp.
Staff LPNs 8 (ft), 1 (pt); Nurses aides 24 (ft), 1 (pt); Activities coordinators 1 (ft); Social workers 1 (ft).
Languages Italian, Polish

Wallingford Convalescent Home Inc
181 E Main St, Wallingford, CT, 06492
(203) 265-1661
Admin Michele Wills. *Medical Dir/Dir of Nursing* Dr Breck.

Licensure Skilled care. *Beds* SNF 130.
 Certified Medicaid; Medicare.
Owner Proprietary Corp.
Admissions Requirements Medical
 examination; Physician's request.
Staff RNs 14 (ft); LPNs 17 (ft); Nurses aides
 63 (ft); Physical therapists 1 (pt);
 Recreational therapists 2 (ft), 1 (pt);
 Occupational therapists 1 (pt); Dietitians 1
 (ft).
Languages Spanish, Italian, Polish
Facilities Dining room; Physical therapy
 room; Activities room; Laundry room;
 Barber/Beauty shop.
Activities Arts & crafts; Cards; Games; Prayer
 groups; Movies.

WATERBURY

Birchwood Cluter Manor Inc*
140 Willow St, Waterbury, CT, 06710
(203) 754-6536
Licensure Intermediate care. *Beds* 23.
 Certified Medicaid.
Owner Proprietary Corp.
Staff RNs 4 (ft); LPNs 6 (ft); Nurses aides 6
 (ft); Activities coordinators 1 (ft); Dietitians
 1 (ft).
Languages Lithuanian, Russian, Italian

**Cedar Lane Rehabilitation & Health Care
Center**
128 Cedar Ave, Waterbury, CT, 06705
(203) 757-9271
Admin Ira M Schoenberger. *Medical Dir/Dir
 of Nursing* Louis Olore MD.
Licensure Skilled care. *Beds* 180. *Certified*
 Medicaid; Medicare.
Owner Proprietary Corp (New Medico Assoc).
Admissions Requirements Minimum age 14;
 Medical examination; Physician's request.
Staff RNs 15 (ft), 20 (pt); LPNs 20 (ft), 12
 (pt); Nurses aides 60 (ft), 20 (pt); Physical
 therapists 2 (ft), 2 (pt); Recreational
 therapists 3 (ft), 1 (pt); Occupational
 therapists 2 (ft); Speech therapists; Activities
 coordinators; Dietitians 1 (pt).
Languages Italian, Spanish
Facilities Dining room; Physical therapy
 room; Activities room; Chapel; Crafts room;
 Laundry room; Barber/Beauty shop; Library.
Activities Arts & crafts; Cards; Games;
 Reading groups; Prayer groups; Movies;
 Shopping trips; Social/Cultural gatherings.

Cliff Health Care Facility Inc*
21 Cliff St, Waterbury, CT, 06710
(203) 753-0344
Licensure Skilled care. *Beds* 52. *Certified*
 Medicaid.
Owner Proprietary Corp.
Staff RNs 5 (ft); LPNs 4 (ft); Social workers 1
 (ft).
Languages Polish, Spanish, German, French,
 Italian

East End Conv Home Inc
3396 E Main St, Waterbury, CT, 06705
(203) 754-2161
Admin Pauline DiChiara. *Medical Dir/Dir of
 Nursing* Louis Olore MD; Joann Calabro
 RN DON.
Licensure Skilled care. *Beds* SNF 60. *Certified*
 Medicaid.
Owner Proprietary Corp.
Admissions Requirements Minimum age 14;
 Medical examination; Physician's request.
Staff Physicians 2 (pt); RNs 4 (ft), 8 (pt);
 LPNs 4 (ft), 2 (pt); Nurses aides 11 (ft), 5
 (pt); Physical therapists 1 (pt); Recreational
 therapists 1 (ft); Activities coordinators 1
 (ft); Dietitians 1 (pt).
Languages Italian, Spanish, French
Facilities Dining room; Physical therapy
 room; Activities room; Chapel; Crafts room;
 Laundry room; Barber/Beauty shop.

Activities Arts & crafts; Cards; Games;
 Reading groups; Prayer groups; Movies;
 Shopping trips; Social/Cultural gatherings.

Fleetcrest Manor Inc*
62 Fleet St, PO Box 4147, Waterbury, CT,
06704
(203) 755-3383
Licensure Intermediate care. *Beds* 18.
 Certified Medicaid.
Owner Proprietary Corp.
Staff Physicians 1 (pt); RNs 3 (ft); Nurses
 aides 5 (ft); Recreational therapists 1 (pt).
Languages Italian
Facilities Dining room.
Activities Arts & crafts; Cards; Games; Prayer
 groups; Movies; Shopping trips; Social/
 Cultural gatherings.

Grove Manor Nursing Home Inc*
145 Grove St, Waterbury, CT, 06710
(203) 753-7205
Licensure Skilled care. *Beds* 60. *Certified*
 Medicaid; Medicare.
Owner Proprietary Corp.
Staff RNs 5 (ft), 1 (pt); LPNs 4 (ft), 1 (pt);
 Nurses aides 17 (ft), 1 (pt); Activities
 coordinators 1 (ft); Dietitians 1 (ft); Social
 workers 1 (pt).
Languages Italian, French, Spanish, Tagalog

Hillside Manor Retirement Home
157 Hillside Ave, Waterbury, CT, 06710
(203) 755-2216
Admin Richard F Astyk. *Medical Dir/Dir of
 Nursing* H Crane Huber MD.
Licensure Intermediate care. *Beds* ICF 23.
Owner Proprietary Corp.
Admissions Requirements Minimum age 50;
 Medical examination.
Staff RNs 6 (ft), 23 (pt); LPNs 1 (ft), 23 (pt);
 Nurses aides 10 (ft), 23 (pt); Physical
 therapists 1 (ft), 23 (pt); Recreational
 therapists 1 (ft), 23 (pt); Occupational
 therapists 1 (ft), 23 (pt); Speech therapists 1
 (ft), 23 (pt); Activities coordinators 1 (ft), 23
 (pt); Dietitians 1 (ft), 23 (pt).
Languages French, Polish, Italian, German
Facilities Dining room; Activities room;
 Library.
Activities Arts & crafts; Cards; Games;
 Reading groups; Prayer groups; Movies;
 Shopping trips; Social/Cultural gatherings.

Hope Hall Convalescent Home Inc
355 Piedmont St, Waterbury, CT, 06706
(203) 756-3617
Licensure Skilled care. *Beds* SNF 34.
Owner Proprietary Corp.
Staff RNs 2 (ft); LPNs 1 (ft); Nurses aides 5
 (ft); Activities coordinators 1 (ft); Social
 worker 1 (ft).
Languages French, Polish, Lithuanian
Activities Arts & crafts; Prayer groups;
 Exercise; Music.

Mattatuck Health Care Facility Inc*
9 Cliff St, Waterbury, CT, 06710
(203) 573-9924
Medical Dir/Dir of Nursing Joseph A
 Vincitonio MD.
Licensure Intermediate care. *Beds* 43.
 Certified Medicaid; Medicare.
Owner Proprietary Corp.
Admissions Requirements Minimum age 14;
 Medical examination; Physician's request.
Staff Physicians 1 (pt); RNs 3 (ft), 2 (pt);
 LPNs 1 (pt); Nurses aides 4 (ft), 3 (pt);
 Recreational therapists 1 (ft); Dietitians 1
 (pt); Dentists 1 (pt); Podiatrists 1 (pt).
Languages Italian
Activities Prayer groups; Arts & crafts;
 Shopping trips.

Medicare Pavilion Corp*
1132 Meriden Rd, Waterbury, CT, 06705
(203) 757-1228
Licensure Skilled care; Intermediate care. *Beds*
 94. *Certified* Medicaid; Medicare.

Owner Proprietary Corp.
Staff RNs 6 (ft); LPNs 10 (ft); Nurses aides 36
 (ft); Physical therapists 1 (ft); Activities
 coordinators 2 (ft); Social workers 1 (ft).
Languages Italian, Lithuanian, Spanish,
 French, German
Activities Arts & crafts; Games; Social/
 Cultural gatherings; Exercises; Current
 events; Sing-alongs.

Oakcliff Convalescent Home Inc
71 Plaza Ave, Waterbury, CT, 06710
(203) 754-6015
Medical Dir/Dir of Nursing Arthur Sullivan
 MD.
Licensure Skilled care. *Beds* 75. *Certified*
 Medicaid; Medicare.
Owner Proprietary Corp.
Admissions Requirements Minimum age 18;
 Medical examination.
Staff RNs 8 (ft), 1 (pt); LPNs 3 (ft), 3 (pt);
 Nurses aides 21 (ft), 5 (pt); Physical
 therapists 1 (pt); Recreational therapists 1
 (ft), 1 (pt); Speech therapists 1 (pt);
 Activities coordinators 1 (ft); Dietitians 1
 (pt); Dentists 1 (pt); Ophthalmologists 1 (pt);
 Dentist 1 (pt).
Languages French, Lithuanian, Spanish
Facilities Dining room; Physical therapy
 room; Activities room; Crafts room; Laundry
 room.
Activities Arts & crafts; Cards; Games;
 Reading groups; Prayer groups; Movies;
 Shopping trips; Social/Cultural gatherings.

Park Manor*
1312 W Main St, Waterbury, CT, 06708
(203) 757-9464
Medical Dir/Dir of Nursing Arthur Sullivan
 MD.
Licensure Skilled care. *Beds* 148. *Certified*
 Medicaid; Medicare.
Owner Proprietary Corp (Health Care &
 Retirement Corp).
Staff RNs 3 (ft), 13 (pt); LPNs 6 (ft), 18 (pt);
 Nurses aides 20 (ft), 42 (pt); Recreational
 therapists 2 (ft), 1 (pt); Dietitians 1 (ft).
Languages Spanish, Turkish, French, Italian,
 Lithuanian, Polish
Facilities Dining room; Physical therapy
 room; Activities room; Crafts room; Laundry
 room; Barber/Beauty shop; TV lounges.
Activities Arts & crafts; Cards; Games;
 Reading groups; Prayer groups; Movies;
 Shopping trips; Social/Cultural gatherings.

Roncalli Woodland Inc
3584 E Main St, Waterbury, CT, 06705
(203) 754-4181
Admin Michael L Santoro. *Medical Dir/Dir of
 Nursing* Virginia Allen RN DNS.
Licensure Intermediate care. *Beds* 90.
 Certified Medicaid.
Owner Proprietary Corp.
Admissions Requirements Physician's request.
Staff Physicians 1 (ft), 2 (pt); RNs; LPNs;
 Nurses aides; Recreational therapists 2 (ft);
 Dietitians 1 (pt).
Languages Portuguese, Italian, Spanish,
 French
Facilities Dining room; Activities room;
 Crafts room; Laundry room; Barber/Beauty
 shop.
Activities Arts & crafts; Cards; Games;
 Reading groups; Prayer groups; Movies;
 Shopping trips; Social/Cultural gatherings.

Rose Manor*
107 S View St, Waterbury, CT, 06706
(203) 754-0786
Licensure Intermediate care. *Beds* 22.
 Certified Medicaid.
Owner Proprietary Corp.
Staff RNs 5 (ft), 1 (pt); Nurses aides 7 (ft), 1
 (pt).
Languages Italian, Greek, Spanish

Affiliation Roman Catholic
Activities Arts & crafts; Games; Shopping trips; Social/Cultural gatherings; Picnics.

Waterbury Convalescent Center Inc*
2817 N Main St, Waterbury, CT, 06704
(203) 757-0731
Licensure Skilled care; Intermediate care. *Beds* 120. *Certified* Medicaid; Medicare.
Owner Proprietary Corp.
Staff RNs 7 (ft), 1 (pt); LPNs 12 (ft); Nurses aides 35 (ft); Activities coordinators 2 (ft); Social workers 1 (ft).
Languages Spanish, Italian, Polish
Activities Arts & crafts; Cards; Games; Reading groups; Prayer groups; Movies; Shopping trips; Social/Cultural gatherings.

Waterbury Nursing Center
1243 W Main St, Waterbury, CT, 06708
(203) 757-0561
Admin Terrence Brennan. *Medical Dir/Dir of Nursing* Joseph Vincitorio MD; Arlene Grossman-Potpinka RN.
Licensure Skilled care; Intermediate care. *Beds* SNF 100; ICF 29. *Certified* Medicaid; Medicare.
Owner Proprietary Corp (Unicare).
Staff Physicians 40 (pt); RNs 3 (ft), 18 (pt); LPNs 6 (ft), 1 (pt); Nurses aides 21 (ft), 25 (pt); Physical therapists 1 (pt); Recreational therapists 1 (ft), 1 (pt); Speech therapists 1 (pt); Activities coordinators 1 (ft); Dietitians 1 (pt); Ophthalmologists 1 (pt); Dentist 1 (pt); Psychiatrist 1 (pt).
Languages German, Lithuanian, Polish, Italian, Spanish, French
Facilities Dining room; Physical therapy room; Activities room; Crafts room; Laundry room; Barber/Beauty shop; Library on wheels; 3rd floor dining room is used for religious purposes.
Activities Arts & crafts; Cards; Games; Reading groups; Prayer groups; Movies; Shopping trips; Social/Cultural gatherings.

Whitewood Rehabilitation Center*
177 Whitewood Rd, Waterbury, CT, 06708
(203) 757-9491
Licensure Skilled care; Intermediate care. *Beds* 180. *Certified* Medicare.
Owner Proprietary Corp (New Medico Assoc).
Staff RNs 32 (ft); LPNs 15 (ft); Nurses aides 68 (ft); Activities coordinators; Dietitians; Social workers.
Languages Portuguese, Yiddish, Italian, French, German

Willow Rest Home*
94 Willow St, Waterbury, CT, 06710
(203) 753-5442
Licensure Intermediate care. *Beds* 17. *Certified* Medicaid.
Owner Proprietary Corp.
Staff RNs 4 (ft); Nurses aides 3 (ft); Activities coordinators 1 (ft).
Languages French
Activities Arts & crafts; Movies; Shopping trips; Therapeutic recreation; Dining out.

WATERFORD

Canterbury Villa of Waterford Inc
171 Rope Ferry Rd, Waterford, CT, 06385
(203) 443-8357
Admin Jean F McAneery. *Medical Dir/Dir of Nursing* Dr R Brent.
Licensure Skilled care. *Beds* 150. *Certified* Medicaid; Medicare.
Owner Proprietary Corp (Horizon Healthcare Corp).
Admissions Requirements Minimum age 15.
Staff Physicians 1 (pt); RNs 6 (ft), 13 (pt); LPNs 7 (ft), 10 (pt); Nurses aides 34 (ft), 30 (pt); Physical therapists 1 (pt); Recreational therapists 2 (ft), 2 (pt); Occupational

therapists 1 (pt); Speech therapists 1 (pt); Dietitians 1 (ft); Dentists 1 (pt); Ophthalmologists 1 (pt); Podiatrists 1 (pt).
Languages Spanish, Italian, Portuguese
Facilities Dining room; Physical therapy room; Activities room; Laundry room; Barber/Beauty shop.
Activities Arts & crafts; Cards; Games; Reading groups; Prayer groups; Movies; Shopping trips; Social/Cultural gatherings.

Greentree Manor Convalescent Home*
4 Greentree Dr, Waterford, CT, 06385
(203) 442-0647
Licensure Skilled care. *Beds* 90. *Certified* Medicaid; Medicare.
Owner Proprietary Corp.
Staff RNs 14 (ft); LPNs 7 (ft); Nurses aides 36 (ft); Activities coordinators 2 (ft); Social workers 1 (ft).
Languages Greek, Korean, Tagalog, Spanish, German, Polish, Italian
Activities Arts & crafts; Games; Reading groups; Social/Cultural gatherings; Music.

New London Convalescent Home*
88 Clark Ln, Waterford, CT, 06385
(203) 442-0471
Licensure Skilled care. *Beds* 120. *Certified* Medicaid; Medicare.
Owner Proprietary Corp.
Staff RNs 14 (ft); LPNs 12 (ft); Nurses aides 46 (ft); Physical therapists.
Languages French
Activities Arts & crafts; Games; Prayer groups; Movies; Social/Cultural gatherings.

WATERTOWN

Pleasant View Manor
225 Bunker Hill Rd, Watertown, CT, 06795
(203) 756-3557
Admin Antoinette Toule. *Medical Dir/Dir of Nursing* Dr Caporado.
Licensure Home for aged. *Beds* 19. *Certified* Medicaid; Medicare.
Owner Proprietary Corp.
Admissions Requirements Minimum age 45.
Staff RNs 1 (ft); Nurses aides 6 (ft); Dietitians 1 (ft); Ophthalmologists 1 (ft).
Facilities Dining room; Activities room; Crafts room; Laundry room.
Activities Arts & crafts; Cards; Games; Reading groups; Prayer groups; Movies; Shopping trips; Social/Cultural gatherings.

Waterbury Extended Care Facility Inc
35 Bunker Hill Rd, Watertown, CT, 06795
(203) 274-5428
Admin Timothy L Curran Jr. *Medical Dir/Dir of Nursing* Dr William Bassford; Judith A Griesbach RN.
Licensure Skilled care. *Beds* SNF 60. *Certified* Medicaid; Medicare.
Owner Proprietary Corp (Health Care Associates Inc).
Admissions Requirements Physician's request.
Staff Physicians; RNs; LPNs; Nurses aides; Physical therapists; Recreational therapists; Speech therapists; Activities coordinators; Dietitians; Ophthalmologists.
Languages Italian, French
Affiliation Roman Catholic
Facilities Dining room; Physical therapy room; Activities room; Laundry room; Barber/Beauty shop; Television rooms; Patio.
Activities Arts & crafts; Cards; Games; Reading groups; Prayer groups; Movies; Entertainment; Family functions; Garden club.

Watertown Convalarium*
560 Woodbury Rd, Watertown, CT, 06795
(203) 274-6748
Licensure Skilled care. *Beds* 36. *Certified* Medicaid.
Owner Nonprofit Corp.

Staff Physicians; Dietitians; Nurses aides.
Languages Italian, French
Activities Prayer groups; Arts & crafts; Shopping trips.

WEST HARTFORD

Brookview Health Care Facility
130 Loomis Dr, West Hartford, CT, 06107
(203) 521-8700
Admin Patricia Fried. *Medical Dir/Dir of Nursing* Robert Safer MD.
Licensure Skilled care; Intermediate care. *Beds* SNF 88; ICF 90. *Certified* Medicaid; Medicare.
Owner Proprietary Corp.
Admissions Requirements Medical examination; Physician's request.
Staff RNs 10 (ft), 34 (pt); LPNs 2 (ft), 9 (pt); Nurses aides 14 (ft), 74 (pt); Physical therapists 1 (pt); Recreational therapists 2 (ft), 1 (pt); Activities coordinators 1 (ft).
Facilities Dining room; Physical therapy room; Activities room; Crafts room; Laundry room; Barber/Beauty shop.
Activities Arts & crafts; Cards; Games; Reading groups; Prayer groups; Movies; Shopping trips; Social/Cultural gatherings; Garden club; Jewish community group; Overnight trips; Family dinners; Racquetball.

Mercyknoll Inc
243 Steele Rd, West Hartford, CT, 06117
(203) 236-3503
Admin Sr Irene Holowesko. *Medical Dir/Dir of Nursing* Sr Margaret Ann Mathis.
Licensure Skilled care; Intermediate care. *Beds* 38.
Owner Nonprofit organization/foundation.
Admissions Requirements Females only; Medical examination.
Staff RNs 8 (ft), 4 (pt); LPNs 1 (pt); Nurses aides 12 (ft), 9 (pt); Physical therapists 2 (pt); Recreational therapists 1 (ft); Speech therapists 1 (pt); Activities coordinators 1 (ft); Dietitians 1 (pt); Podiatrists 1 (pt).
Affiliation Roman Catholic
Facilities Dining room; Physical therapy room; Activities room; Chapel; Crafts room; Laundry room; Barber/Beauty shop; Library.
Activities Arts & crafts; Games; Prayer groups; Movies; Shopping trips.

St Mary Home*
291 Steele Rd, West Hartford, CT, 06117
(203) 236-1924
Licensure Intermediate care; Home for aged. *Beds* 167. *Certified* Medicaid.
Owner Nonprofit Corp.
Staff Physicians 1 (pt); RNs 2 (ft), 1 (pt); LPNs 1 (pt); Nurses aides 5 (ft), 1 (pt); Physical therapists; Occupational therapists; Speech therapists; Dietitians; Social workers 1 (ft).
Languages Spanish, French, German
Affiliation Roman Catholic
Activities Arts & crafts; Games; Prayer groups; Social/Cultural gatherings; Outings.

West Hartford Manor*
2432 Albany Ave, West Hartford, CT, 06117
(203) 236-3557
Licensure Skilled care. *Beds* 120. *Certified* Medicaid; Medicare.
Owner Proprietary Corp.
Staff RNs 12 (ft); LPNs 3 (ft); Nurses aides 43 (ft); Physical therapists 1 (ft); Activities coordinators 2 (ft); Social workers 1 (ft).
Languages Spanish
Activities Reading groups; Prayer groups; Social/Cultural gatherings; Current events.

WEST HAVEN

Arterburn Home Inc
267 Union Ave, West Haven, CT, 06516
(203) 934-5256
Medical Dir/Dir of Nursing Dominic B
Schioppo MD; Donna Masto RN DON.
Licensure Intermediate care. *Beds* 40.
Certified Medicaid.
Owner Proprietary Corp.
Admissions Requirements Minimum age 18;
Medical examination; Physician's request.
Staff LPNs 2 (ft); Nurses aides 10 (ft), 2 (pt).
Languages Italian, Spanish, Polish
Facilities Dining room; Activities room;
Crafts room; Laundry room; Barber/Beauty
shop.
Activities Arts & crafts; Cards; Games; Prayer
groups; Movies; Shopping trips.

Bentley Gardens Health Care Center
310 Terrace Ave, West Haven, CT, 06516
(203) 932-2247
Admin Carole Bergeron RN. *Medical Dir/Dir
of Nursing* Dr John Milici.
Licensure Skilled care. *Beds* SNF 97. *Certified*
Medicaid; Medicare.
Owner Proprietary Corp (Beverly Enterprises).
Admissions Requirements Minimum age 21;
Medical examination.
Staff RNs 9 (ft), 10 (pt); LPNs 5 (ft), 5 (pt);
Nurses aides 32 (ft), 21 (pt); Physical
therapists 1 (ft); Recreational therapists 4
(ft); Occupational therapists 1 (pt); Speech
therapists 1 (pt); Activities coordinators 1
(pt).
Languages Italian, Spanish
Facilities Dining room; Physical therapy
room; Activities room; Crafts room; Laundry
room; Barber/Beauty shop; Library; Garden
& patio.
Activities Arts & crafts; Cards; Games;
Reading groups; Prayer groups; Movies;
Shopping trips; Social/Cultural gatherings.

Breakers Convalescent Home*
307 Beech St, West Haven, CT, 06516
(203) 934-7943
Licensure Skilled care. *Beds* 39. *Certified*
Medicaid; Medicare.
Owner Proprietary Corp.
Staff Physicians; Dietitians; Nurses aides.
Languages Italian
Activities Prayer groups; Arts & crafts;
Shopping trips.

Harbor View Manor*
308 Savin Ave, West Haven, CT, 06516
(203) 932-6411
Licensure Intermediate care. *Beds* 120.
Certified Medicaid.
Owner Proprietary Corp.
Staff RNs 4 (ft), 1 (pt); LPNs 7 (ft); Nurses
aides 14 (ft); Activities coordinators 2 (ft), 1
(pt); Social workers 1 (ft).
Languages Spanish, French
Activities Arts & crafts; Movies; Shopping
trips; Social/Cultural gatherings; Picnics;
Discussion groups.

Seacrest Nursing & Retire Center*
588 Ocean Ave, West Haven, CT, 06516
(203) 934-2676
Medical Dir/Dir of Nursing Dr John Milici.
Licensure Intermediate care. *Beds* 39.
Certified Medicaid.
Owner Proprietary Corp.
Admissions Requirements Minimum age 21;
Medical examination; Physician's request.
Staff Physicians 2 (pt); RNs 3 (ft), 4 (pt);
LPNs 1 (ft); Nurses aides 6 (ft), 4 (pt);
Physical therapists 1 (pt); Activities
coordinators 1 (ft); Dietitians 1 (pt); Dentists
1 (pt); Podiatrists 1 (pt); Audiologists 1 (pt).
Languages German, Spanish

Facilities Dining room; Activities room;
Crafts room; Laundry room.
Activities Arts & crafts; Cards; Games;
Reading groups; Prayer groups; Movies;
Shopping trips; Social/Cultural gatherings.

Sound View Nursing Center
Care Ln, West Haven, CT, 06516
(203) 934-7955
Admin Lucinda Hart. *Medical Dir/Dir of
Nursing* Leo Cooney MD; Catherine Ahern
RN DON.
Licensure Skilled care. *Beds* SNF 100.
Certified Medicaid; Medicare.
Owner Proprietary Corp (Health Care
Associates Inc).
Admissions Requirements Minimum age 14.
Staff Physicians 1 (pt); RNs 10 (ft), 9 (pt);
LPNs 7 (ft), 2 (pt); Nurses aides 28 (ft), 22
(pt); Physical therapists 2 (ft); Recreational
therapists 2 (ft), 1 (pt); Occupational
therapists 1 (pt); Speech therapists 1 (pt);
Dietitians 1 (pt); Ophthalmologists 1 (pt);
Podiatrists 1 (pt).
Languages Italian, Slavic, Spanish
Facilities Dining room; Physical therapy
room; Activities room; Laundry room;
Barber/Beauty shop.
Activities Arts & crafts; Cards; Games;
Reading groups; Prayer groups; Movies;
Social/Cultural gatherings.

West Haven Nursing Facility
555 Saw Mill Rd, West Haven, CT, 06516
(203) 934-8326
Admin Mary Crowley. *Medical Dir/Dir of
Nursing* Dominic B Schioppo MD; Evelyn
Glass.
Licensure Skilled care. *Beds* SNF 120.
Certified Medicaid; Medicare.
Owner Proprietary Corp (Beverly Enterprises).
Admissions Requirements Medical
examination; Physician's request.
Staff Physicians 4 (pt); RNs 7 (ft); LPNs 6
(ft); Nurses aides 42 (ft); Physical therapists
1 (pt); Reality therapists 1 (pt); Recreational
therapists 3 (ft); Occupational therapists 1
(pt); Speech therapists 1 (pt); Activities
coordinators 1 (ft); Dietitians 1 (pt); Dentists
1 (pt); Ophthalmologists 1 (pt); Podiatrists 1
(pt).
Languages Spanish, Italian, Portuguese
Facilities Dining room; Physical therapy
room; Activities room; Laundry room;
Barber/Beauty shop.
Activities Arts & crafts; Cards; Games;
Reading groups; Prayer groups; Movies;
Shopping trips; Social/Cultural gatherings.

WESTPORT

Mediplex of Westport*
1 Burr Rd, Westport, CT, 06880
(203) 226-4201
Licensure Skilled care; Intermediate care. *Beds*
SNF 30; ICF 90. *Certified* Medicaid;
Medicare.
Owner Proprietary Corp (Mediplex).
Staff RNs 25 (ft); LPNs 4 (ft); Nurses aides 42
(ft); Physical therapists 4 (ft); Activities
coordinators 3 (ft); Social workers 1 (ft), 1
(pt).
Languages Spanish, French, Italian, Polish,
Hungarian, Norwegian
Activities Arts & crafts; Movies; Shopping
trips; Social/Cultural gatherings; Gardening.

WETHERSFIELD

Mediplex of Wethersfield*
341 Jordan Ln, Wethersfield, CT, 06109
(203) 563-0101
Licensure Intermediate care. *Beds* 60.
Certified Medicaid; Medicare.
Owner Proprietary Corp (Mediplex).

Staff Nurses aides 5 (ft); Physical therapists 1
(ft), 10 (pt); Activities coordinators 1 (ft);
Dietitians.
Languages Italian, Portuguese, Polish, French,
German, Spanish, Hebrew
Activities Arts & crafts; Games; Shopping
trips; Social/Cultural gatherings.

WILLIMANTIC

Canterbury Villa of Willimantic
595 Valley St, Willimantic, CT, 06226
(203) 423-2597
Licensure Skilled care; Intermediate care. *Beds*
SNF 120. *Certified* Medicaid; Medicare.
Owner Proprietary Corp (Horizon Healthcare
Corp).
Admissions Requirements Minimum age 14;
Medical examination; Physician's request.
Staff RNs 6 (ft); LPNs 7 (ft); Orderlies 30 (ft);
Nurses aides; Physical therapists 1 (ft);
Recreational therapists; Activities
coordinators 1 (ft); Dietitians.
Languages French, Polish, Spanish
Facilities Dining room; Physical therapy
room; Activities room; Barber/Beauty shop.
Activities Arts & crafts; Cards; Games;
Reading groups; Prayer groups; Movies;
Shopping trips; Social/Cultural gatherings;
Community involvement; Exercises; Current
events.

WINDHAM

Abbey Manor Inc
103 North Rd, Rte 14, Windham, CT, 06280
(203) 423-4636
Admin Michael S Lawless. *Medical Dir/Dir of
Nursing* Mary E Barry MD; Jean A Cole
RN.
Licensure Skilled care. *Beds* 60. *Certified*
Medicaid; Medicare.
Owner Proprietary Corp.
Staff RNs 8 (ft); LPNs 3 (ft); Nurses aides 21
(ft); Recreational therapists 1 (ft); Dentist;
Pharmacists.
Facilities Physical therapy room; Activities
room; Crafts room; Laundry room; Barber/
Beauty shop.
Activities Arts & crafts; Cards; Games; Prayer
groups; Movies; Shopping trips; Social/
Cultural gatherings; Religious services; Pet
therapy; Ceramics.

WINDSOR

Kimberly Hall Nursing Home—North
1 Kimberly Dr, Windsor, CT, 06095
(203) 688-6443
Admin Mary Ellen Gaudette. *Medical Dir/Dir
of Nursing* Sally Ardolino MD.
Licensure Skilled care. *Beds* SNF 150.
Certified Medicaid; Medicare.
Owner Proprietary Corp (Genesis Health
Ventures).
Admissions Requirements Minimum age
Adult; Medical examination; Physician's
request.
Staff Physicians 1 (pt); RNs; LPNs; Nurses
aides; Physical therapists; Recreational
therapists; Occupational therapists; Speech
therapists; Activities coordinators; Dietitians;
Dentists; Ophthalmologists; Podiatrists.
Facilities Dining room; Physical therapy
room; Activities room; Chapel; Crafts room;
Laundry room; Barber/Beauty shop; Library;
TV lounges; Inner courtyards.
Activities Arts & crafts; Cards; Games;
Reading groups; Prayer groups; Movies;
Social/Cultural gatherings; Oil painting;
Intergenerational learning.

Kimberly Hall Nursing Home—South*
1 Kimberly Dr, Windsor, CT, 06095
(203) 688-6443

Licensure Intermediate care. *Beds* 180.
Certified Medicaid; Medicare.
Owner Proprietary Corp.
Staff RNs 16 (ft); LPNs 7 (ft); Nurses aides 78
(ft); Activities coordinators 3 (ft).
Languages Spanish, Italian, Portuguese,
Laotian

Mountain View Healthcare*
581 Poquonock Ave, Windsor, CT, 06095
(203) 688-7211
Medical Dir/Dir of Nursing Joseph Misiak
MD.
Licensure Skilled care. *Beds* 120. *Certified*
Medicaid; Medicare.
Owner Proprietary Corp (Hillhaven Corp).
Admissions Requirements Medical
examination; Physician's request.
Staff Physicians; RNs; LPNs; Nurses aides;
Physical therapists 1 (ft), 1 (pt); Recreational
therapists 2 (ft); Speech therapists;
Dietitians; Dentists; Podiatrists.
Languages Italian, Polish
Facilities Dining room; Physical therapy
room; Laundry room; Library.
Activities Arts & crafts; Cards; Games;
Reading groups; Reading groups; Prayer
groups; Movies; Social/Cultural gatherings.

Windsor Hall Retirement Center
519 Palisado Ave, Windsor, CT, 06095
(203) 688-4918
Admin E Leo Attella Jr. *Medical Dir/Dir of
Nursing* Dr George Donahue; Lilla Bruyette
RN DON.
Licensure Intermediate care. *Beds* ICF 170.
Certified Medicaid.
Owner Proprietary Corp (Genesis Health
Ventures).
Admissions Requirements Minimum age 14;
Medical examination; Physician's request.
Staff RNs 10 (ft), 5 (pt); LPNs 10 (ft), 6 (pt);
Orderlies 3 (ft), 3 (pt); Nurses aides 19 (ft),
13 (pt); Physical therapists 1 (pt); Reality
therapists; Recreational therapists 3 (ft);

Occupational therapists; Speech therapists 1
(pt); Activities coordinators; Dietitians 1 (ft),
1 (pt); Ophthalmologists 1 (pt); Podiatrists 1
(pt); Dentist 1 (pt).
Languages Polish, French, German, Sign
Language
Facilities Dining room; Physical therapy
room; Activities room; Chapel; Crafts room;
Laundry room; Barber/Beauty shop; Library.
Activities Arts & crafts; Cards; Games;
Reading groups; Prayer groups; Movies;
Shopping trips; Social/Cultural gatherings;
Bowling; Fishing trips; Baseball games.

WINDSOR LOCKS

Bickford Convalescent and Rest Home
14 Main St, Windsor Locks, CT, 06096
(203) 623-4351
Admin Laura L Nelson. *Medical Dir/Dir of
Nursing* John J Kennedy MD; LaVerne M
Shary RN DNS.
Licensure Skilled care; Intermediate care. *Beds*
59. *Certified* Medicaid.
Owner Proprietary Corp.
Admissions Requirements Minimum age 65;
Medical examination; Physician's request.
Staff Physicians 1 (ft), 7 (pt); RNs 6 (ft), 4
(pt); LPNs 3 (ft), 2 (pt); Nurses aides 20 (ft),
15 (pt); Physical therapists 1 (pt); Reality
therapists 1 (pt); Recreational therapists 1
(ft); Speech therapists 1 (pt); Activities
coordinators 1 (ft), 1 (pt); Dietitians 1 (pt);
Dentists 1 (pt); Ophthalmologists 1 (pt);
Podiatrists 1 (pt).
Languages Polish, Italian, French
Facilities Dining room; Physical therapy
room; Activities room; Crafts room; Laundry
room; Barber/Beauty shop; Screened in
porch; Solarium.
Activities Arts & crafts; Cards; Games;
Reading groups; Prayer groups; Movies;
Shopping trips; Social/Cultural gatherings;
Poetry club; Cooking.

WINSTED

Highland Acres Extend-A-Care Center*
108 E Lake St, Winsted, CT, 06098
(203) 379-8591
Medical Dir/Dir of Nursing Dr David Hebert.
Licensure Skilled care; Intermediate care. *Beds*
75. *Certified* Medicaid; Medicare.
Owner Proprietary Corp (Multicare
Management).
Admissions Requirements Minimum age 14.
Staff RNs 5 (ft), 10 (pt); LPNs 1 (ft), 1 (pt);
Nurses aides 9 (ft), 15 (pt); Physical
therapists 1 (pt); Recreational therapists 1
(ft), 1 (pt); Dietitians 1 (pt).
Languages French, Italian, German
Facilities Dining room; Physical therapy
room; Activities room; Chapel; Laundry
room; Barber/Beauty shop; Library.
Activities Arts & crafts; Cards; Games;
Reading groups; Prayer groups; Movies;
Shopping trips; Social/Cultural gatherings.

WOLCOTT

Wolcott Rest Home*
55 Beach Rd, Wolcott, CT, 06716
(203) 879-0600
Licensure Intermediate care. *Beds* 20.
Owner Proprietary Corp.
Languages French, Italian

Wolcott View Manor*
50 Beach Rd, Wolcott, CT, 06716
(203) 879-1479
Licensure Intermediate care. *Beds* 59.
Certified Medicaid.
Owner Proprietary Corp.
Staff RNs 3 (ft); Nurses aides 4 (ft); Activities
coordinators 3 (ft); Dietitians 1 (ft); Social
workers 1 (ft).
Languages French, Italian

DELAWARE

BRIDGEVILLE

Catherine V Reynolds
Rte 1, Box 290, Bridgeville, DE, 19933
(302) 337-7716, 337-7406, 337-8886
Admin Catherine Reynolds.
Licensure Intermediate care for mentally retarded. *Beds* 6.
Owner Privately owned.
Facilities Dining room; Activities room; Laundry room.
Activities Arts & crafts; Cards; Games; Reading groups; Prayer groups; Movies; Shopping trips; Social/Cultural gatherings.

CLAYMONT

Rosewood Rest Home Inc
PO Box 10, 3 Wistar St, Claymont, DE, 19703
(302) 798-9620
Admin Nancy Olsen. *Medical Dir/Dir of Nursing* Barbara McCann RN.
Licensure Intermediate care. *Beds* ICF 13.
Owner Privately owned.
Admissions Requirements Medical examination.
Staff RNs 1 (ft), 3 (pt); LPNs 1 (pt); Nurses aides 4 (ft), 3 (pt).
Activities Games; Prayer groups.

DELAWARE CITY

Governor Bacon Health Center*
Tilton Bldg, Delaware City, DE, 19706
(302) 834-9201
Admin C Ronald McGinnis.
Licensure Intermediate care. *Beds* 122.
Certified Medicaid.

DELMAR

Shangri-La Nursing Home*
Delaware Ave, Delmar, DE, 19940
(302) 846-3031
Admin Margaret Barnes.
Licensure Skilled care; Intermediate care. *Beds* 120. *Certified* Medicaid; Medicare.

DOVER

Courtland Manor Nursing & Conv Home*
889 S Little Creek Rd, Dover, DE, 19901
(302) 674-0566
Admin Irma M Schurman.
Licensure Skilled care; Intermediate care. *Beds* 100. *Certified* Medicaid; Medicare.

Crescent Farm Nursing & Conv Home
PO Box 635, Dover, DE, 19903
(302) 734-5953
Admin Louzena Melvin.
Licensure Intermediate care. *Beds* 80. *Certified* Medicaid.

Palmer Home Inc
PO Box 1751, 115 American Ave, Dover, DE, 19901-1751
(302) 734-5591
Admin Iva Arnold.
Licensure Residential care. *Beds* 4.

Silver Lake Nursing & Rehabilitation Center
1080 Silver Lake Blvd, Dover, DE, 19901
(302) 734-5990
Admin Judy Grieco.
Beds 120.
Owner Proprietary Corp (Genesis Health Ventures).

FELTON

Felton Convalescent Home
PO Box C, Church & High St, Felton, DE, 19943
(302) 284-4667
Admin Courtney Marshall. *Medical Dir/Dir of Nursing* Lillian C Dodd LPN DON.
Licensure Intermediate care. *Beds* ICF 12.
Owner Privately owned.
Admissions Requirements Medical examination.
Staff Physicians 1 (ft); RNs 1 (ft); LPNs 2 (ft); Nurses aides 6 (ft); Pharmacist 1 (ft).
Facilities Dining room; Activities room; Laundry room.
Activities Prayer groups; TV.

Golden Years Manor
Drawer S, Church & Sewell Sts, Felton, DE, 19943
(302) 284-4510, 284-3510
Admin Rosemary Sluter. *Medical Dir/Dir of Nursing* F B Lane Haines MD; Arlieen Gloscoch DON.
Licensure Intermediate care. *Beds* ICF 12. *Certified* Medicaid.
Owner Privately owned.
Staff Physicians 1 (pt); RNs 1 (ft); LPNs 2 (pt); Nurses aides 16 (ft), 4 (pt); Activities coordinators 1 (pt); Dietitians 1 (pt).
Facilities Dining room; Activities room; Laundry room; Barber/Beauty shop.
Activities Arts & crafts; Games; Reading groups; Prayer groups.

GEORGETOWN

Harrison House of Georgetown
110 W North St, Georgetown, DE, 19947
(302) 856-4574
Admin Daniel J Wooley. *Medical Dir/Dir of Nursing* Fred T Kahn MD; Carolyn Hoffacker RN DON.
Licensure Skilled care. *Beds* SNF 101. *Certified* Medicaid; Medicare.
Owner Proprietary Corp.
Admissions Requirements Medical examination.
Staff Physicians 1 (pt); Physical therapists 2 (pt); Activities coordinators 1 (ft); Dietitians 1 (pt).

Facilities Dining room; Physical therapy room; Activities room; Laundry room; Barber/Beauty shop.
Activities Arts & crafts; Cards; Games; Reading groups; Movies; Social/Cultural gatherings.

GREENWOOD

Country Rest Home*
Greenwood, DE, 19950
(302) 349-4114
Admin Mark Yoder.
Licensure Intermediate care. *Beds* 32. *Certified* Medicaid.
Admissions Requirements Medical examination; Physician's request.
Staff Physicians 1 (pt); RNs 1 (pt); LPNs 2 (ft), 3 (pt); Orderlies 1 (pt); Nurses aides 25 (pt); Activities coordinators 1 (ft).
Affiliation Mennonite
Facilities Dining room; Lobby.
Activities Arts & crafts; Cards; Games; Reading groups; Movies; Shopping trips; Trips.

Mast Boarding Home*
Rte 1, Box 201, Greenwood, DE, 19950
(302) 349-4179
Admin Sally Mast.
Licensure Residential care. *Beds* 4.

HARRINGTON

Haven Hill Residential Home*
Rte 2, Box 215, Harrington, DE, 19952
(302) 398-8854
Admin Mrs Norman Rust.
Licensure Residential care. *Beds* 6.

HOCKESSIN

Cokesbury Village
Lancaster Pike & Loveville Rd, Hockessin, DE, 19707
(302) 239-2371
Admin Dianne Moran. *Medical Dir/Dir of Nursing* William L Jaffee MD; June Valentine RN.
Licensure Skilled care; Residential care. *Beds* 80; Residential 36. *Certified* Medicare.
Owner Nonprofit Corp (PA United Meth Homes).
Admissions Requirements Minimum age 60; Medical examination.
Staff Physicians 2 (pt); RNs 7 (ft), 21 (pt); LPNs 3 (ft), 4 (pt); Nurses aides 32 (ft), 15 (pt); Physical therapists 2 (pt); Reality therapists 3 (pt); Occupational therapists 1 (pt); Speech therapists 1 (pt); Activities coordinators 1 (ft); Podiatrists 2 (pt).
Affiliation Methodist
Facilities Dining room; Physical therapy room; Activities room; Chapel; Crafts room; Laundry room; Barber/Beauty shop; Library; Store; Woodshop.

Activities Arts & crafts; Cards; Games;
Reading groups; Prayer groups; Movies;
Shopping trips; Social/Cultural gatherings.

Episcopal Church Home
Rte 3 Box 233, Hockessin, DE, 19707
(302) 998-0181
Admin Davie Anna Alleman. *Medical Dir/Dir
of Nursing* Tae Sup Song.
Licensure Skilled care; Intermediate care. *Beds*
122. *Certified* Medicaid; Medicare.
Admissions Requirements Minimum age 14;
Medical examination; Physician's request.
Staff RNs 8 (ft), 7 (pt); LPNs 8 (ft), 8 (pt);
Nurses aides 35 (ft), 45 (pt); Physical
therapists 1 (pt); Activities coordinators 1
(ft); Dietitians 1 (pt).
Affiliation Episcopal
Facilities Dining room; Physical therapy
room; Activities room; Chapel; Crafts room;
Laundry room; Barber/Beauty shop; Library.
Activities Arts & crafts; Cards; Games;
Reading groups; Prayer groups; Movies;
Shopping trips.

LEWES

Lewes Convalescent Center*
440 Market St, Lewes, DE, 19958
(302) 645-6606
Admin Christine Evans.
Licensure Skilled care; Intermediate care. *Beds*
SNF 50; ICF 40. *Certified* Medicaid;
Medicare.
Owner Proprietary Corp (Forum Grp).

MILFORD

Delaware Care Center
PO Box 119, Rte 1, Milford, DE, 19963
(302) 422-4351
Admin Mario Schreiber. *Medical Dir/Dir of
Nursing* Dr W F Chen; Lois Cooper RN
DON.
Licensure Intermediate care. *Beds* ICF 14.
Owner Privately owned.
Staff Physicians 1 (pt); RNs 1 (ft); Nurses
aides 3 (ft), 3 (pt); Dietitians 1 (ft).
Facilities Dining room.
Activities Cards; Reading groups.

Ingram's Rest Home*
Rte 1, Rehoboth Hwy, Milford, DE, 19963
(302) 422-4351
Admin Virginia Ingram.
Licensure Intermediate care. *Beds* 14.
Certified Medicare.

Milford Manor*
700 Marvel Rd, Milford, DE, 19963
(302) 422-3303
Admin Juanita J Roberts. *Medical Dir/Dir of
Nursing* Harvey Mast MD.
Licensure Skilled care; Intermediate care;
Residential care. *Beds* SNF 24; ICF 88;
Residential 14. *Certified* Medicaid;
Medicare.
Owner Proprietary Corp (Forum Grp).
Admissions Requirements Minimum age 50;
Medical examination.
Staff RNs 2 (ft), 4 (pt); LPNs 8 (ft), 4 (pt);
Nurses aides 24 (ft), 28 (pt); Physical
therapists 1 (pt); Activities coordinators 1
(ft), 1 (pt); Dietitians 1 (pt).
Facilities Dining room; Physical therapy
room; Activities room; Crafts room; Laundry
room; Barber/Beauty shop.
Activities Arts & crafts; Cards; Games;
Reading groups; Prayer groups; Movies;
Shopping trips; Social/Cultural gatherings.

MILLSBORO

Millsboro Nursing Home Inc
231 Washington St, Millsboro, DE, 19966
(302) 934-9281; 934-7300

Admin Mario Schreiber. *Medical Dir/Dir of
Nursing* Dr Wm Zeit.
Licensure Skilled care; Intermediate care. *Beds*
SNF 96; ICF. *Certified* Medicaid; Medicare.
Owner Proprietary Corp.
Admissions Requirements Minimum age 14;
Medical examination; Physician's request.
Staff Physicians 3 (pt); RNs 2 (ft), 1 (pt);
LPNs 4 (ft), 3 (pt); Orderlies 2 (ft), 2 (pt);
Nurses aides 20 (ft), 30 (pt); Physical
therapists 1 (pt); Activities coordinators 1
(ft); Dietitians 1 (pt).
Facilities Dining room; Physical therapy
room; Activities room; Chapel; Crafts room;
Laundry room; Barber/Beauty shop; Library.
Activities Arts & crafts; Cards; Games;
Reading groups; Prayer groups; Movies;
Shopping trips; Social/Cultural gatherings.

NEWARK

Churchman Village
4949 Ogletown-Stanton Rd, Newark, DE,
19713
(302) 998-6900
Admin Courtney Marshall. *Medical Dir/Dir of
Nursing* Dr E C Hewlett; Naomi Pinkerton
DON.
Licensure Skilled care; Intermediate care;
Retirement apartments. *Beds* SNF 50; ICF
49; Retirement apts 59. *Certified* Medicaid;
Medicare.
Owner Proprietary Corp (Beverly Enterprises).
Admissions Requirements Medical
examination.
Staff Physicians; RNs; LPNs; Orderlies;
Nurses aides; Physical therapists;
Recreational therapists; Occupational
therapists; Speech therapists; Activities
coordinators; Dietitians; Dentists;
Ophthalmologists; Podiatrists.
Facilities Dining room; Physical therapy
room; Activities room; Chapel; Crafts room;
Laundry room; Barber/Beauty shop.
Activities Arts & crafts; Cards; Games;
Reading groups; Prayer groups; Movies;
Shopping trips; Social/Cultural gatherings.

Jeanne Jugan Residence*
185 Salem Church Rd, Newark, DE, 19713
(302) 368-5886
Admin Sr Patricia Friel. *Medical Dir/Dir of
Nursing* S W Bartoshesky MD.
Licensure Skilled care; Intermediate care;
Residential care. *Beds* SNF 22; ICF 60;
Residential 36. *Certified* Medicaid.
Admissions Requirements Minimum age 60;
Medical examination.
Staff Physicians 3 (pt); RNs 5 (ft), 2 (pt);
LPNs 4 (ft), 6 (pt); Nurses aides 24 (ft), 12
(pt); Physical therapists 1 (pt); Reality
therapists 1 (pt); Recreational therapists 1
(pt); Occupational therapists 1 (pt); Speech
therapists 1 (pt); Activities coordinators 1
(ft); Dietitians 1 (pt); Dentists 1 (pt);
Podiatrists 1 (pt); Audiologists 1 (pt).
Affiliation Roman Catholic
Facilities Dining room; Physical therapy
room; Activities room; Chapel; Crafts room;
Laundry room; Barber/Beauty shop; Library.
Activities Arts & crafts; Cards; Games;
Reading groups; Prayer groups; Movies;
Shopping trips; Social/Cultural gatherings.

Millcroft
255 Possum Park Rd, Newark, DE, 19711
(302) 366-0160
Admin Richard L Weimann. *Medical Dir/Dir
of Nursing* Dr Thomas Maxwell; Martha
Galbo DON.
Licensure Skilled care; Intermediate care;
Retirement. *Beds* SNF 52; ICF 47;
Retirement 61. *Certified* Medicaid;
Medicare.
Owner Proprietary Corp (Forum Grp).
Staff RNs; LPNs; Nurses aides; Physical
therapists; Activities coordinators; Dietitians.

Facilities Dining room; Physical therapy
room; Activities room; Crafts room; Laundry
room; Barber/Beauty shop; Library; Living-
day room; Porches; Courtyards.
Activities Arts & crafts; Cards; Games;
Reading groups; Prayer groups; Movies;
Shopping trips; Social/Cultural gatherings.

Newark Manor Nursing Home*
254 W Main St, Newark, DE, 19711
(302) 731-5576
Admin Russell L Ellis. *Medical Dir/Dir of
Nursing* David Messinger.
Licensure Intermediate care. *Beds* 53.
Staff Physicians 1 (pt); RNs 8 (pt); LPNs 2
(pt); Nurses aides 11 (ft), 22 (pt); Reality
therapists 1 (pt); Recreational therapists 1
(pt); Activities coordinators 1 (ft).
Facilities Dining room; Physical therapy
room; Activities room; Crafts room; Laundry
room; Barber/Beauty shop; Library.
Activities Arts & crafts; Cards; Games;
Reading groups; Movies; Shopping trips;
Social/Cultural gatherings; Remotivation
therapy.

SEAFORD

Fair Holme Convalescent Center*
117 Willey St, Seaford, DE, 19973
(302) 629-9440
Admin Dolores F McDaniel.
Licensure Intermediate care. *Beds* 7. *Certified*
Medicaid.

Methodist Manor House*
1001 Middleford Rd, Seaford, DE, 19973
(302) 629-4593
Admin Rev Olin Shockley Jr.
Licensure Skilled care. *Beds* 50. *Certified*
Medicaid; Medicare.
Owner Nonprofit Corp (PA United Meth
Homes).
Affiliation Methodist

Seaford Retirement & Rehabilitation Center
1100 Norman Eskridge Hwy, Seaford, DE,
19973
(302) 629-3575
Admin John A Shuford. *Medical Dir/Dir of
Nursing* Nancy S Smith DON.
Licensure Skilled care; Intermediate care;
Retirement. *Beds* SNF 66; ICF 58;
Retirement 11. *Certified* Medicaid;
Medicare.
Owner Proprietary Corp (Forum Grp).
Admissions Requirements Medical
examination; Physician's request.
Staff RNs 2 (ft), 6 (pt); LPNs 5 (ft), 10 (pt);
Nurses aides 29 (ft), 27 (pt); Physical
therapists 1 (pt); Occupational therapists 1
(pt); Speech therapists 1 (pt); Activities
coordinators 1 (ft); Dietitians 1 (pt); Dentists
1 (pt); Ophthalmologists 1 (pt); Podiatrists 1
(pt).
Facilities Dining room; Physical therapy
room; Activities room; Crafts room; Laundry
room; Barber/Beauty shop.
Activities Arts & crafts; Cards; Games;
Reading groups; Prayer groups; Movies;
Shopping trips; Social/Cultural gatherings.

SMYRNA

Delaware Hospital for the Chronically Ill
Sunnyside Rd, Smyrna, DE, 19977
(302) 653-8556
Admin Robert N Davidson Jr. *Medical Dir/
Dir of Nursing* Harold J Laggner MD;
Cheryl J Moore.
Licensure Skilled care; Intermediate care. *Beds*
SNF 42; ICF 494. *Certified* Medicaid.
Owner Publicly owned.
Admissions Requirements Medical
examination.

Staff Physicians 4 (ft); RNs 58 (ft), 10 (pt); LPNs 21 (ft), 1 (pt); Orderlies 292 (ft), 18 (pt); Nurses aides; Physical therapists 1 (ft); Activities coordinators 2 (ft); Admissions Social workers 3 (ft); In-house Social workers 2 (ft).
Facilities Physical therapy room; Activities room; Chapel; Crafts room; Barber/Beauty shop; Library; Ancillary Services-PT; X-Ray; Laboratory; Dental lab.
Activities Arts & crafts; Cards; Games; Reading groups; Prayer groups; Movies; Shopping trips; Social/Cultural gatherings; Remotivation/Sensory training; Discussion groups.

Kent Convalescent Center
1455 S DuPont Hwy, Smyrna, DE, 19901
(302) 674-2959
Admin E Ray Quillen. *Medical Dir/Dir of Nursing* William Rogers MD; Diane Townsend RN.
Licensure Skilled care; Intermediate care. *Beds* SNF 36; Protected Retirement 103. *Certified* Medicaid; Medicare.
Owner Proprietary Corp (Forum Grp).
Admissions Requirements Medical examination; Physician's request.
Staff Physicians 1 (pt); RNs 2 (ft), 8 (pt); LPNs 7 (ft), 16 (pt); Orderlies 1 (ft); Nurses aides 35 (ft), 20 (pt); Activities coordinators 2 (ft), 1 (pt); Dietitians 1 (pt).
Facilities Dining room; Physical therapy room; Activities room; Crafts room; Laundry room; Barber/Beauty shop.
Activities Arts & crafts; Cards; Games; Reading groups; Prayer groups; Movies; Shopping trips; Social/Cultural gatherings; Ceramics; Gardening.

Scott Nursing Home inc
Main & Mount Vernon St, Smyrna, DE, 19977
(302) 653-8554
Admin Maryjane Copes. *Medical Dir/Dir of Nursing* Dr Ciriaco G Bongalos Jr; Ann Ackles DON.
Licensure Intermediate care. *Beds* ICF 33. *Certified* Medicaid.
Owner Privately owned.
Staff Physicians; RNs; LPNs; Nurses aides; Physical therapists 413K; Ophthalmologists.
Facilities Dining room; Activities room; Chapel; Crafts room; Laundry room.
Activities Arts & crafts; Cards; Games; Reading groups; Prayer groups; Movies; Shopping trips; Music therapy; Horticulture.

TOWNSEND

Mundey Manor*
Rte 1, Box 65A, Townsend, DE, 19734
(302) 378-2860
Admin Kathryn E Mundey.
Licensure Residential care. *Beds* 6.
Admissions Requirements Minimum age 60; Males only.

WILMINGTON

Brandywine Convalescent Home*
505 Greenbank Rd, Wilmington, DE, 19808
(302) 998-0101
Admin Mary Woodstock. *Medical Dir/Dir of Nursing* James Harkness DO.
Licensure Skilled care; Intermediate care. *Beds* 106. *Certified* Medicaid; Medicare.
Staff Physicians 1 (ft); RNs 1 (ft), 11 (pt); LPNs 3 (ft), 3 (pt); Nurses aides 17 (ft), 22 (pt); Physical therapists 1 (ft); Speech therapists 1 (ft); Activities coordinators 1 (ft); Dietitians 1 (ft); Dentists 1 (ft); Podiatrists 1 (ft); Technicians 2 (ft), 4 (pt).
Facilities Dining room; Physical therapy room; Activities room; Crafts room; Laundry room; Barber/Beauty shop; Library.

Activities Arts & crafts; Cards; Games; Reading groups; Prayer groups; Movies; Social/Cultural gatherings.

Mary Campbell Center Inc
4641 Weldin Rd, Wilmington, DE, 19803
(302) 762-6025
Admin Jerrold P. Spilecki. *Medical Dir/Dir of Nursing* Edward J McConnell III MD; Susan Keegan-France RN.
Licensure Intermediate care. *Beds* 56. *Certified* Medicaid.
Owner Nonprofit Corp.
Admissions Requirements Minimum age Young; Medical examination.
Staff RNs 4 (ft), 4 (pt); LPNs 2 (ft), 3 (pt); Nurses aides 14 (ft), 9 (pt); Recreational therapists 2 (ft); Activities coordinators 1 (ft).
Languages Sign
Facilities Dining room; Physical therapy room; Activities room; Crafts room; Laundry room; Barber/Beauty shop; Library; Hydrotherapy center; Patios; Wooded grounds; Computer room; Learning center.
Activities Arts & crafts; Cards; Games; Reading groups; Prayer groups; Movies; Shopping trips; Social/Cultural gatherings; Adaptive aquatics; Computer education; Adult basic education; Extensive social & recreational programming.

Chariot Nursing & Convalescent Home*
2735 W 6th St, Wilmington, DE, 19807
(302) 654-7616
Admin Paul A Paradise Jr.
Licensure Intermediate care. *Beds* 30. *Certified* Medicaid.

Foulk Manor—North
1212 Foulk Rd, Wilmington, DE, 19803
(302) 478-4296
Admin Russell A DiGilio. *Medical Dir/Dir of Nursing* D W MacKelcan MD.
Licensure Skilled care; Intermediate care. *Beds* SNF 26; ICF 18.
Owner Proprietary Corp (Forum Grp).
Admissions Requirements Minimum age 65; Medical examination; Physician's request.
Staff Physicians 1 (pt); RNs 6 (ft), 14 (pt); Nurses aides 9 (ft), 17 (pt); Physical therapists 1 (pt); Activities coordinators 1 (ft), 2 (pt); Dietitians 1 (ft); Podiatrists 1 (pt).
Facilities Dining room; Physical therapy room; Activities room; Crafts room; Laundry room; Barber/Beauty shop; Library.
Activities Arts & crafts; Cards; Games; Reading groups; Prayer groups; Movies; Shopping trips; Social/Cultural gatherings.

Foulk Manor South
407 Foulk Rd, Wilmington, DE, 19803
(302) 655-6249
Admin Vivian C Heinbaugh. *Medical Dir/Dir of Nursing* Linda Davis.
Licensure Skilled care; Intermediate care; Retirement. *Beds* SNF 25; ICF 17; Retirement 65.
Owner Proprietary Corp (Forum Grp).
Admissions Requirements Minimum age 18; Medical examination.
Staff RNs 4 (ft), 5 (pt); LPNs 2 (ft), 1 (pt); Orderlies 1 (pt); Nurses aides 40 (ft), 10 (pt); Physical therapists 1 (pt); Speech therapists 1 (pt); Activities coordinators 1 (ft), 1 (pt); Dietitians 1 (pt); Ophthalmologists 1 (pt).
Facilities Dining room; Physical therapy room; Laundry room; Barber/Beauty shop; Living room.
Activities Cards; Games; Reading groups; Prayer groups; Movies; Shopping trips; Social/Cultural gatherings; Paid entertainment.

Gibbs Boarding Home*
177 Bunche Blvd, Wilmington, DE, 19801
(302) 658-4739

Admin Mary Gibbs.
Licensure Residential care. *Beds* 5.

Hillside House*
810 S Broom St, Wilmington, DE, 19805
(302) 652-1181
Admin Vivian Heinbaugh. *Medical Dir/Dir of Nursing* D W MacKelcan MD.
Licensure Skilled care; Intermediate care. *Beds* SNF 68; ICF 36. *Certified* Medicaid; Medicare.
Owner Proprietary Corp (Forum Grp).
Admissions Requirements Medical examination.
Staff Physicians 1 (pt); RNs 4 (ft), 6 (pt); LPNs 6 (ft), 7 (pt); Nurses aides 30 (ft), 17 (pt); Physical therapists 1 (pt); Occupational therapists; Speech therapists; Activities coordinators 1 (ft), 1 (pt); Dietitians.
Facilities Dining room; Physical therapy room; Activities room; Barber/Beauty shop.
Activities Arts & crafts; Games; Shopping trips; Social/Cultural gatherings; Sightseeing trips.

Home for Aged Women—Minquadale*
1109 Gilpin Ave, Wilmington, DE, 19806
(302) 655-6411
Admin Mrs E C Reese. *Medical Dir/Dir of Nursing* Frederick A Bowdle MD.
Licensure Intermediate care; Residential care. *Beds* ICF 43; Residential 5. *Certified* Medicaid.
Admissions Requirements Minimum age 65; Medical examination.
Staff Physicians 1 (pt); RNs 2 (ft), 1 (pt); LPNs 3 (ft), 1 (pt); Nurses aides 10 (ft), 3 (pt); Physical therapists 1 (pt); Activities coordinators 1 (ft), 2 (pt); Dietitians 1 (pt).
Facilities Dining room; Physical therapy room; Activities room; Crafts room; Laundry room; Barber/Beauty shop; Library.
Activities Arts & crafts; Cards; Games; Reading groups; Prayer groups; Movies; Shopping trips.

Kentmere—The Home of Merciful Rest Society Inc
1900 Lovering Ave, Wilmington, DE, 19806
(302) 652-3311
Admin Frieda E Enss. *Medical Dir/Dir of Nursing* Stephen Bartoshesky.
Licensure Skilled care; Intermediate care. *Beds* SNF 49; ICF 57. *Certified* Medicaid; Medicare.
Owner Nonprofit organization/foundation.
Admissions Requirements Minimum age 18; Medical examination.
Staff RNs; LPNs; Nurses aides; Physical therapists 1 (pt); Activities coordinators 1 (ft), 2 (pt); Dietitians 1 (pt); Ophthalmologists 1 (pt); Podiatrists 1 (pt).
Facilities Dining room; Physical therapy room; Activities room; Chapel; Crafts room; Laundry room; Barber/Beauty shop; Gift shop; Volunteer office.
Activities Arts & crafts; Cards; Games; Reading groups; Prayer groups; Movies; Shopping trips; Social/Cultural gatherings; Poetry group; Current events club; Garden club; Armchair travel club; Residents council.

Milton & Hattie Kutz Home Inc
704 River Rd, Wilmington, DE, 19809
(302) 764-7000
Admin Daniel G Thurman. *Medical Dir/Dir of Nursing* M Javed Gilani MD; Jane B Kelly RN.
Licensure Skilled care; Intermediate care. *Beds* 82. *Certified* Medicaid.
Owner Nonprofit Corp.
Admissions Requirements Minimum age 65; Physician's request.
Staff Physicians 1 (pt); RNs 5 (ft), 8 (pt); LPNs 1 (ft), 2 (pt); Nurses aides 9 (ft), 6 (pt); Physical therapists 1 (pt); Recreational

therapists 1 (ft); Occupational therapists 1
(pt); Activities coordinators 1 (ft); Dietitians
1 (ft); Ophthalmologists 1 (pt).
Languages Yiddish
Affiliation Jewish
Facilities Dining room; Physical therapy
room; Activities room; Chapel; Crafts room;
Laundry room; Barber/Beauty shop; Library.
Activities Arts & crafts; Cards; Games;
Reading groups; Games; Movies; Shopping trips;
Social/Cultural gatherings.

The Layton Home for Aged Person
300 E 8th St, Wilmington, DE, 19801
(302) 656-6413
Admin Kenneth C Snow Jr. *Medical Dir/Dir
of Nursing* Kr James A Thomas MD;
Dorothy B Hutt DON.
Licensure Skilled care; Intermediate care. *Beds*
SNF 108; ICF. *Certified* Medicaid;
Medicare.
Owner Nonprofit Corp.
Admissions Requirements Medical
examination; Physician's request.
Staff Physicians 2 (pt); RNs 2 (ft), 2 (pt);
LPNs 7 (ft), 6 (pt); Nurses aides 22 (ft), 18
(pt); Physical therapists 1 (pt); Occupational
therapists 1 (pt); Speech therapists 1 (pt);
Activities coordinators 1 (ft);
Ophthalmologists 1 (pt); Podiatrists 1 (pt).
Facilities Dining room; Physical therapy
room; Activities room; Chapel; Laundry
room; Barber/Beauty shop.
Activities Arts & crafts; Cards; Games;
Reading groups; Prayer groups; Movies;
Shopping trips; Social/Cultural gatherings.

Masonic Home
4800 Lancaster Pike, Wilmington, DE, 19807
(302) 994-4434
Admin Claude Husted. *Medical Dir/Dir of
Nursing* Dr LeRoy Kimble.
Licensure Intermediate care; Residential care.
Beds ICF 8; Residential 32.
Admissions Requirements Medical
examination.

Staff Physicians 2 (pt); RNs 3 (ft), 2 (pt);
LPNs 2 (ft); Nurses aides 17 (ft); Dietitians
1 (pt).
Affiliation Masons
Facilities Dining room; Activities room;
Chapel; Crafts room; Laundry room; Barber/
Beauty shop; Library; Smoking lounge; TV
room.
Activities Arts & crafts; Movies; Shopping
trips; Social/Cultural gatherings.

Methodist Country House
4830 Kennett Pike, Wilmington, DE, 19807
(302) 654-5101
Admin Leona Brown.
Licensure Skilled care; Intermediate care. *Beds*
72. *Certified* Medicare.
Owner Nonprofit Corp (PA United Meth
Homes).
Affiliation Methodist

Orsini Boarding Home*
702 Greenbank Rd, Wilmington, DE, 19808
(302) 999-0409
Admin Gloria Orsini.
Licensure Residential care. *Beds* 6.

Parkview Nursing Center
2801 W 6th St, Wilmington, DE, 19805
(302) 655-6135
Admin Stephen S Silver. *Medical Dir/Dir of
Nursing* L Kimble MD.
Licensure Skilled care. *Beds* SNF 150.
Certified Medicaid; Medicare.
Owner Privately owned.
Facilities Dining room; Physical therapy
room; Activities room; Chapel; Crafts room;
Laundry room; Barber/Beauty shop; Library.
Activities Arts & crafts; Cards; Games;
Reading groups; Prayer groups; Movies;
Shopping trips; Social/Cultural gatherings.

Shipley Manor Health Center
2723 Shipley Rd, Wilmington, DE, 19810
(302) 479-0111
Admin Dina Hughes. *Medical Dir/Dir of
Nursing* Virginia Marzoula RN.

Licensure Skilled care; Intermediate care. *Beds*
SNF 80; ICF. *Certified* Medicaid; Medicare.
Owner Proprietary Corp (Forum Grp).
Admissions Requirements Medical
examination.
Staff Physicians 22 (pt); RNs 5 (ft), 3 (pt);
LPNs 5 (ft), 5 (pt); Orderlies 1 (ft), 1 (pt);
Nurses aides 18 (ft), 12 (pt); Nurses aides 1
(pt); Activities coordinators 1 (ft), 2 (pt);
Dietitians 1 (pt); Ophthalmologists 1 (pt);
Podiatrists 1 (pt).
Facilities Dining room; Physical therapy
room; Activities room; Crafts room; Laundry
room; Barber/Beauty shop; Outside patio;
TV with VCR.
Activities Arts & crafts; Cards; Games;
Reading groups; Prayer groups; Movies;
Shopping trips; Social/Cultural gatherings;
Picnics; Trips to park; Longwood gardens;
Live muisical entertainment.

Tilton Terrace
801 N Broom St, Wilmington, DE, 19806
(302) 652-3861
Admin Ruth G Murphy. *Medical Dir/Dir of
Nursing* Dr Marvin H Dorph; Rita L
Archangelo.
Licensure Skilled care; Intermediate care. *Beds*
SNF 100; ICF. *Certified* Medicaid;
Medicare.
Owner Privately owned.
Staff Physicians 1 (pt); RNs 8 (ft), 7 (pt);
LPNs 6 (ft), 2 (pt); Nurses aides 24 (ft), 27
(pt); Physical therapists 1 (pt); Reality
therapists 1 (ft); Occupational therapists 1
(pt); Speech therapists 1 (pt); Activities
coordinators 2 (ft); Dietitians 1 (ft); Dentists
1 (pt); Ophthalmologists 1 (pt); Podiatrists 1
(pt).
Facilities Dining room; Physical therapy
room; Activities room; Chapel; Crafts room;
Laundry room; Barber/Beauty shop; Library.
Activities Arts & crafts; Cards; Games;
Reading groups; Prayer groups; Movies;
Shopping trips; Social/Cultural gatherings;
Ceramics; Gardening.

DISTRICT OF COLUMBIA

WASHINGTON

Army Distaff Hall—Health Services Center
6200 Oregon Ave NW, Washington, DC, 20015
(202) 541-0150
Admin Tom Jenkins Jr. *Medical Dir/Dir of Nursing* Kay Kaye RN.
Licensure Skilled care; Intermediate care. *Beds* SNF 12; ICF 36.
Owner Nonprofit Corp.
Admissions Requirements Females only; Medical examination.
Staff RNs 5 (ft), 2 (pt); LPNs 2 (ft), 2 (pt); Orderlies 1 (ft); Nurses aides 18 (ft), 15 (pt).
Facilities Dining room; Activities room; Laundry room.

Capitol Health Care Center Inc*
900 3rd St NE, Washington, DC, 20005
(202) 546-4513
Admin Barbara Savory.
Licensure Intermediate care. *Certified* Medicaid.

DC Village*
2 DC Village Ln SW, Washington, DC, 20032
(202) 767-7740
Admin Donald Brooks.
Licensure Skilled care; Intermediate care. *Beds* SNF 51; ICF 488. *Certified* Medicaid; Medicare.

Grant Park Care Center
5000 Nannie Helen Burroughs Ave NE, Washington, DC, 20019
(202) 399-7504
Admin Barbara Ann Nash. *Medical Dir/Dir of Nursing* Barry Smith MD; Maxine Faison RN.
Licensure Skilled care; Intermediate care. *Beds* SNF; ICF. *Certified* Medicaid; Medicare.
Owner Proprietary Corp.
Admissions Requirements Minimum age 21; Medical examination; Physician's request.
Staff RNs 27 (ft); LPNs 39 (ft); Nurses aides 131 (ft); Physical therapists 1 (ft); Recreational therapists 2 (ft); Activities coordinators 1 (ft); Dietitians 2 (ft).
Facilities Dining room; Physical therapy room; Activities room; Laundry room; Barber/Beauty shop.
Activities Arts & crafts; Cards; Games; Reading groups; Prayer groups; Movies; Shopping trips; Social/Cultural gatherings.

Health Care Institute
1380 Southern Ave SE, Washington, DC, 20032
(202) 563-8100
Admin Craig Lakin. *Medical Dir/Dir of Nursing* Dr Yvonne Treakle; Sheila Warren.
Licensure Skilled care; Intermediate care. *Beds* 180. *Certified* Medicaid; Medicare.
Owner Nonprofit Corp.

Staff RNs 16 (ft), 4 (pt); LPNs 16 (ft), 4 (pt); Nurses aides 60 (ft), 5 (pt); Physical therapists 1 (ft); Recreational therapists 1 (ft); Activities coordinators 1 (ft); Dietitians 1 (pt).
Languages Spanish
Facilities Dining room; Physical therapy room; Activities room; Crafts room; Laundry room; Barber/Beauty shop; Library.
Activities Arts & crafts; Cards; Games; Reading groups; Prayer groups; Movies; Shopping trips; Social/Cultural gatherings; Pet therapy; Support groups; Young residents stroke club; Discharge group.

Jeanne Jugan Residence*
4200 Harewood Rd NE, Washington, DC, 20032
(202) 269-1831
Admin Sr Monique Gallagher.
Licensure Skilled care; Intermediate care. *Beds* SNF 25; ICF 75.
Owner Nonprofit Corp (Little Sisters of the Poor).

J B Johnson Nursing Center*
901 1st St NW, Washington, DC, 20015
(202) 289-7715
Admin Margarie Cornor.
Licensure Intermediate care. *Beds* 244. *Certified* Medicaid.

Lisner-Louise Home Inc
5425 Western Ave NW, Washington, DC, 20015
(202) 966-6667
Admin Ward Orem. *Medical Dir/Dir of Nursing* James Brodsky MD.
Licensure Intermediate care; Community residential facility. *Beds* ICF 25; Community residential facility 56. *Certified* Medicaid.
Owner Nonprofit Corp.
Admissions Requirements Medical examination.
Staff RNs; LPNs; Nurses aides; Physical therapists; Reality therapists; Recreational therapists; Activities coordinators; Dietitians.
Facilities Dining room; Activities room; Crafts room; Laundry room; Barber/Beauty shop; Library.
Activities Arts & crafts; Cards; Games; Reading groups; Prayer groups; Movies; Social/Cultural gatherings.

Medlantic Manor at Lamond—Riggs
6000 New Hampshire Ave NE, Washington, DC, 20011
(202) 882-9300
Admin Lauren Rock. *Medical Dir/Dir of Nursing* Dr J Kelman; Cathy Shine RN.
Licensure Intermediate care. *Beds* ICF 63; CRF 17. *Certified* Medicaid.
Owner Nonprofit Corp.
Staff RNs 7 (ft), 2 (pt); LPNs 4 (ft), 2 (pt); Orderlies 1 (ft); Nurses aides 20 (ft), 6 (pt); Physical therapists 5 (pt); Occupational therapists; Speech therapists; Activities coordinators 1 (ft); Dietitians 1 (pt).
Affiliation Masons

Methodist Home of DC*
4901 Connecticut Ave NW, Washington, DC, 20008
(202) 966-7623
Admin Elsie D Lesko.
Licensure Intermediate care. *Beds* 97. *Certified* Medicaid.
Affiliation Methodist

Presbyterian Home of DC*
3050 Military Rd NW, Washington, DC, 20015
(202) 363-8310
Admin Robert Bell.
Licensure Intermediate care; Residential care. *Beds* SNF 32; Residential 132. *Certified* Medicaid.
Affiliation Presbyterian

Rock Creek Manor
2131 O St NW, Washington, DC, 20037
(202) 785-2577
Admin Elizabeth Muchnick. *Medical Dir/Dir of Nursing* Valery Portnoi MD; Maureen Gallager RN DON.
Licensure Intermediate care. *Beds* ICF 180. *Certified* Medicaid.
Owner Proprietary Corp.
Admissions Requirements Minimum age 18; Medical examination.
Staff Physicians 1 (pt); RNs 10 (ft), 3 (pt); LPNs 11 (ft), 2 (pt); Orderlies 2 (ft); Nurses aides 58 (ft), 8 (pt); Recreational therapists 3 (ft); Occupational therapists 1 (pt); Speech therapists 1 (pt); Activities coordinators 1 (ft); Dietitians 1 (ft); Ophthalmologists 1 (pt); Social workers 2 (ft).
Facilities Dining room; Physical therapy room; Activities room; Barber/Beauty shop.
Activities Arts & crafts; Cards; Games; Reading groups; Prayer groups; Movies; Social/Cultural gatherings; Picnics; Exercise; Cooking.

Thomas House
1330 Massachusettes Ave NW, Washington, DC, 20005
(202) 628-2092
Admin David Zwald. *Medical Dir/Dir of Nursing* Dr Barbara Carroll.
Licensure Intermediate care. *Beds* 53. *Certified* Medicaid.
Admissions Requirements Minimum age 62; Medical examination.
Affiliation Baptist
Facilities Dining room; Physical therapy room; Activities room; Chapel; Crafts room; Laundry room; Barber/Beauty shop; Library.
Activities Arts & crafts; Cards; Games; Reading groups; Prayer groups; Movies; Shopping trips; Social/Cultural gatherings.

Washington Center for Aging Services
2601 18th St NE, Washington, DC, 20018
(202) 269-1530
Admin Solanges Vivens. *Medical Dir/Dir of Nursing* Vinod Mody MD; Marilyn Kohler RN DON.

Licensure Skilled care; Intermediate care. *Beds* SNF 37; ICF 225. *Certified* Medicaid; Medicare.
Owner Publicly owned.
Admissions Requirements Minimum age 60; Medical examination.
Staff RNs 18 (ft), 10 (pt); LPNs 32 (ft), 7 (pt); Orderlies 3 (ft); Nurses aides 119 (ft), 27 (pt); Recreational therapists 5 (ft), 1 (pt).
Facilities Physical therapy room; Activities room; Chapel; Barber/Beauty shop; Library.
Activities Arts & crafts; Cards; Games; Reading groups; Prayer groups; Movies; Shopping trips; Social/Cultural gatherings; Resident council; Bingo; Music therapy; Current events groups; Chorus.

Washington Home
3720 Upton St NW, Washington, DC, 20016
(202) 966-3720
Admin Jared I Falek. *Medical Dir/Dir of Nursing* Dr Joanne Lynn.
Licensure Skilled care; Intermediate care. *Beds* 178. *Certified* Medicaid; Medicare.
Owner Proprietary Corp.

Admissions Requirements Minimum age 16.
Staff Physicians 7 (pt); RNs 17 (ft); LPNs 17 (ft); Orderlies 4 (ft); Nurses aides 93 (ft); Physical therapists 1 (ft); Reality therapists 1 (ft); Recreational therapists 2 (ft); Occupational therapists 1 (ft); Speech therapists 1 (pt); Activities coordinators 1 (pt); Dietitians 1 (ft); Dentists 1 (pt); Podiatrists 1 (pt); Psychologists 1 (pt); Neurologists 1 (pt); Clinical social worker 3 (ft).
Facilities Dining room; Physical therapy room; Activities room; Chapel; Crafts room; Laundry room; Barber/Beauty shop; Library; Dental clinic; Adult day health care center.
Activities Arts & crafts; Cards; Games; Reading groups; Prayer groups; Movies; Shopping trips; Social/Cultural gatherings; Music therapy; Special event luncheons.

Wisconsin Avenue Nursing Home
3333 Wisconsin Ave NW, Washington, DC, 20016
(202) 362-5500

Admin Sybil Hunter. *Medical Dir/Dir of Nursing* Jerry Earle MD; Andrea Brown RN DON.
Licensure Skilled care; Intermediate care. *Beds* SNF 50; ICF 305. *Certified* Medicaid; Medicare.
Owner Proprietary Corp (Beverly Enterprises).
Admissions Requirements Minimum age 60; Medical examination; Physician's request.
Staff RNs 10 (ft), 10 (pt); LPNs 15 (ft), 10 (pt); Orderlies 20 (ft); Nurses aides 125 (ft), 26 (pt); Physical therapists 1 (ft); Recreational therapists 5 (ft); Activities coordinators 1 (ft); Dietitians 1 (ft).
Facilities Dining room; Physical therapy room; Activities room; Crafts room; Laundry room; Barber/Beauty shop.
Activities Arts & crafts; Cards; Games; Reading groups; Prayer groups; Movies; Shopping trips; Social/Cultural gatherings.

FLORIDA

ALTAMONTE SPRINGS

Life Care Center of Altamonte Springs*
989 Orienta Ave, Altamonte Springs, FL,
32701
(305) 831-3446
Medical Dir/Dir of Nursing Charles A Morgan
MD.
Licensure Skilled care. *Beds* 240. *Certified*
Medicaid; Medicare.
Owner Proprietary Corp (Life Care Centers of
America).
Admissions Requirements Medical
examination.
Staff Physicians 1 (pt); RNs 12 (ft); LPNs 23
(ft); Orderlies 4 (ft); Nurses aides 73 (ft);
Physical therapists 3 (ft); Speech therapists 1
(pt); Activities coordinators 1 (ft); Dietitians
1 (ft), 1 (pt).
Facilities Dining room; Physical therapy
room; Activities room; Laundry room;
Barber/Beauty shop.
Activities Arts & crafts; Cards; Games; Prayer
groups; Movies; Shopping trips.

ALTOONA

**Lakeview Terrace Christian Retirement
Community**
PO Drawer 100, 331 Raintree Drive, Altoona,
FL, 32702
(904) 669-2133
Admin Linda Rowe. *Medical Dir/Dir of
Nursing* Glenn E Miles MD; Karen Atwell
RN DON.
Licensure Skilled care; Intermediate care;
Adult Congregate living facility. *Beds* SNF
20; Adult congregate living 400. *Certified*
Medicaid.
Owner Privately owned.
Admissions Requirements Minimum age 65;
Medical examination.
Staff Physicians 1 (pt); RNs 4 (ft); LPNs 8
(ft), 2 (pt); Nurses aides 21 (ft), 4 (pt);
Physical therapists 1 (pt); Occupational
therapists 1 (pt); Speech therapists 1 (pt);
Activities coordinators 2 (ft); Dietitians 1
(pt).
Facilities Dining room; Physical therapy
room; Activities room; Chapel; Crafts room;
Laundry room; Barber/Beauty shop; Library;
Lawn bowling; Swimming; Pool;
Shuffleboard; Transportation.
Activities Arts & crafts; Cards; Games;
Reading groups; Prayer groups; Movies;
Shopping trips; Social/Cultural gatherings.

Lakeview Terrace Medical Care Facility*
PO Drawer 100, Altoona, FL, 32702
Admin Linda Rowe. *Medical Dir/Dir of
Nursing* Glenn Miles MD.
Licensure Skilled care. *Beds* 20.
Owner Proprietary Corp.
Admissions Requirements Minimum age 65;
Medical examination; Physician's request.

Staff Physicians 1 (pt); RNs 4 (ft), 4 (pt);
LPNs 4 (ft), 5 (pt); Nurses aides 16 (ft), 11
(pt); Activities coordinators 1 (ft); Dietitians
1 (pt); Gerontologists 1 (ft); Physician
assistants 1 (pt).
Facilities Dining room; Activities room;
Crafts room; Barber/Beauty shop; Library.
Activities Arts & crafts; Cards; Games; Prayer
groups; Movies; Shopping trips; Social/
Cultural gatherings.

APALACHICOLA

Apalachicola Health Care Center Inc
150 10th St, Apalachicola, FL, 32320
(904) 653-8844
Admin James Blue Darby. *Medical Dir/Dir of
Nursing* Dr Photis Nichols; Faye Deskins
RN DON.
Licensure Skilled care. *Beds* SNF 60. *Certified*
Medicaid.
Owner Proprietary Corp.
Admissions Requirements Minimum age 16;
Medical examination; Physician's request.
Staff Physicians 3 (pt); RNs 2 (ft), 1 (pt);
LPNs 5 (ft), 4 (pt); Orderlies 2 (ft); Nurses
aides 17 (ft), 8 (pt); Physical therapists 1
(pt); Recreational therapists 1 (pt); Speech
therapists 1 (pt); Activities coordinators 1
(ft); Dietitians 1 (ft), 1 (pt);
Ophthalmologists 1 (pt).
Languages Spanish
Facilities Dining room; Physical therapy
room; Activities room; Crafts room; Laundry
room; Barber/Beauty shop.
Activities Arts & crafts; Cards; Games;
Reading groups; Prayer groups; Movies;
Shopping trips; Social/Cultural gatherings.

ARCADIA

DeSoto Manor Nursing Home
1002 N Brevard, Arcadia, FL, 33821
(813) 494-5766
Admin Richard Kjelland. *Medical Dir/Dir of
Nursing* R C Gammad MD.
Licensure Skilled care; Intermediate care. *Beds*
SNF; ICF 63. *Certified* Medicaid; Medicare.
Owner Proprietary Corp (Diversicare Corp).
Admissions Requirements Minimum age 16.
Staff RNs 2 (ft), 1 (pt); LPNs 7 (ft), 2 (pt);
Nurses aides 18 (ft), 3 (pt); Recreational
therapists 1 (pt); Activities coordinators 1
(ft); Dietitians 1 (ft).
Languages Spanish, Italian
Facilities Dining room; Physical therapy
room; Activities room; Crafts room; Laundry
room; Barber/Beauty shop; Library.
Activities Arts & crafts; Cards; Games;
Reading groups; Prayer groups; Movies.

AUBURNDALE

Central Park Lodge Nursing Center
919 Old Winter Haven Rd, Auburndale, FL,
33833
(813) 967-4125

Admin Beverly Gelvin. *Medical Dir/Dir of
Nursing* Harold Mines MD; Julia Pryer RN
DON.
Licensure Skilled care; Intermediate care. *Beds*
SNF 120; ICF. *Certified* Medicaid;
Medicare.
Owner Proprietary Corp.
Admissions Requirements Minimum age 21;
Medical examination; Physician's request.
Staff Physicians 12 (ft); RNs 4 (ft), 1 (pt);
LPNs 16 (ft), 4 (pt); Orderlies 2 (ft); Nurses
aides 4 (pt); Physical therapists 1 (pt);
Recreational therapists 1 (ft), 1 (pt);
Occupational therapists 1 (pt); Speech
therapists 1 (pt); Activities coordinators 1
(ft), 1 (pt); Dietitians 1 (ft);
Ophthalmologists 1 (pt); Podiatrists 1 (pt);
Dentist 1 (pt).
Facilities Dining room; Physical therapy
room; Activities room; Crafts room; Barber/
Beauty shop; Landscaped courtyard.
Activities Arts & crafts; Cards; Games;
Reading groups; Prayer groups; Movies;
Shopping trips; Social/Cultural gatherings;
Individualized recreational therapy.

AVON PARK

Hillcrest Nursing Home*
80 Stratford Rd, Avon Park, FL, 33825
(813) 453-6675
Medical Dir/Dir of Nursing Donald B Geldart
MD.
Licensure Skilled care. *Beds* 90. *Certified*
Medicaid.
Owner Proprietary Corp.
Staff Physicians 8 (pt); RNs 3 (ft), 4 (pt);
LPNs 7 (ft), 6 (pt); Nurses aides 22 (ft);
Physical therapists 1 (pt); Speech therapists
1 (pt); Activities coordinators 1 (pt);
Dietitians 1 (pt); Dentists 1 (pt); Podiatrists
1 (pt).
Languages French, Spanish, German, Walon,
Kituba, Ishiluba
Facilities Dining room; Physical therapy
room; Activities room; Barber/Beauty shop;
Library.
Activities Arts & crafts; Cards; Games;
Reading groups; Prayer groups; Movies;
Shopping trips; Social/Cultural gatherings.

BARTOW

Bartow Convalescent Center*
2055 E Georgia St, Bartow, FL, 33830
(813) 533-0578
Admin Richard J Kuhlmeyer. *Medical Dir/Dir
of Nursing* Harold K Mines MD.
Licensure Skilled care. *Beds* 120. *Certified*
Medicaid; Medicare.
Owner Proprietary Corp.
Admissions Requirements Medical
examination; Physician's request.
Staff RNs 4 (ft), 1 (pt); LPNs 7 (ft); Nurses
aides 40 (ft); Physical therapists 1 (pt);
Reality therapists 1 (pt); Recreational
therapists 1 (pt); Occupational therapists 1

(pt); Speech therapists 1 (pt); Activities
coordinators 1 (ft); Dietitians 1 (pt); Dentists
1 (pt); Ophthalmologists 1 (pt); Podiatrists 1
(pt); Audiologists 1 (pt).
Languages Spanish
Facilities Dining room; Physical therapy
room; Activities room; Crafts room; Laundry
room; Barber/Beauty shop; Library.
Activities Arts & crafts; Cards; Games;
Reading groups; Prayer groups; Movies;
Shopping trips; Social/Cultural gatherings.

The Rohr Home
2010 E Georgia St, Bartow, FL, 33830
(813) 533-1111, 533-1806
Admin Sr M Constance Pellicer. *Medical Dir/*
Dir of Nursing Robert McMillan MD;
Louise Gravel RN.
Licensure Skilled care; Intermediate care. *Beds*
SNF 60; ICF. *Certified* Medicaid.
Owner Publicly owned.
Admissions Requirements Minimum age 21;
Medical examination; Physician's request.
Staff Physicians 5 (pt); RNs 4 (ft), 2 (pt);
LPNs 5 (ft), 1 (pt); Orderlies 3 (ft); Nurses
aides 24 (ft); Physical therapists 1 (pt);
Activities coordinators 1 (ft); Dietitians 1
(pt).
Languages Spanish
Facilities Dining room; Laundry room;
Barber/Beauty shop; Library; Screened porch
& patio area.
Activities Arts & crafts; Cards; Games;
Reading groups; Prayer groups; Movies;
Social/Cultural gatherings; Educational
program; Library program; Exercise groups;
School classes.

BELLE GLADE

Sunset Heights Nursing Home
841 SW Ave B, Belle Glade, FL, 33430
(305) 996-9176
Licensure Skilled care. *Beds* 25. *Certified*
Medicaid.
Owner Nonprofit Corp.
Staff Physicians; Dietitians; Nurses aides.
Languages Spanish, Italian
Activities Prayer groups; Arts & crafts;
Shopping trips.

BLOUNSTOWN

Apalachicola Valley Nursing Center*
1510 Crozier St, Blounstown, FL, 32424
(904) 674-5464
Licensure Skilled care; Intermediate care. *Beds*
80. *Certified* Medicaid.
Owner Proprietary Corp.
Staff RNs 4 (ft); LPNs 9 (ft); Nurses aides 24
(ft).

BOCA RATON

Boca Raton Convalescent Center
755 Meadows Rd, Boca Raton, FL, 33432
(305) 391-5200
Admin Tom Glass. *Medical Dir/Dir of Nursing*
George Dullghan MD; Doreen DeRoberts
DON.
Licensure Skilled care. *Beds* SNF 120.
Certified Medicaid; Medicare.
Owner Proprietary Corp (Hillhaven Corp).
Admissions Requirements Medical
examination.
Staff Physicians 1 (pt); RNs 7 (ft), 5 (pt);
LPNs 9 (ft), 3 (pt); Orderlies 1 (ft); Nurses
aides 35 (ft), 6 (pt); Physical therapists 1
(pt); Reality therapists 1 (pt); Recreational
therapists 1 (pt); Occupational therapists 1
(pt); Speech therapists 1 (pt); Activities
coordinators 1 (ft); Dietitians 1 (pt); Dentists
1 (pt); Ophthalmologists 1 (pt); Podiatrists 1
(pt).
Languages Spanish

Facilities Dining room; Physical therapy
room; Activities room; Crafts room; Laundry
room; Barber/Beauty shop; Library; Outdoor
screened patio.
Activities Arts & crafts; Cards; Games;
Reading groups; Prayer groups; Movies;
Shopping trips; Social/Cultural gatherings;
Happy hour.

Fountains Nursing Home
3800 N Federal Hwy, Boca Raton, FL, 33432
(305) 395-7510
Admin Mary Schoborg. *Medical Dir/Dir of*
Nursing Alvern Friedman.
Licensure Skilled care. *Beds* SNF 51. *Certified*
Medicaid; Medicare.
Owner Proprietary Corp (Vari-Care Inc).
Staff RNs 4 (ft); Nurses aides 17 (ft).

Manor Care Nursing Center
375 NW 51st St, Boca Raton, FL, 33487
(305) 997-8111
Admin David E Wodehouse. *Medical Dir/Dir*
of Nursing Fred J Schilling MD; Gilda
Osborn RN DON.
Licensure Skilled care. *Beds* SNF 120.
Certified Medicaid; Medicare.
Owner Proprietary Corp (Manor Care).
Admissions Requirements Medical
examination; Physician's request.
Staff RNs 6 (ft); LPNs 10 (ft); Orderlies 5 (ft);
Nurses aides 50 (ft); Physical therapists 1
(ft); Speech therapists 1 (pt); Activities
coordinators 1 (ft), 2 (pt); Dietitians 1 (ft).
Facilities Dining room; Physical therapy
room; Activities room; Crafts room; Laundry
room; Barber/Beauty shop.
Activities Arts & crafts; Cards; Games;
Reading groups; Prayer groups; Movies;
Shopping trips; Social/Cultural gatherings.

St Andrews Estates Medical Center
6152 N Verde Trail, Boca Raton, FL, 33433
(305) 487-5200
Admin Maureen J Obrien. *Medical Dir/Dir of*
Nursing Dr George Dullaghan; Margareth
Gordon RN.
Licensure Skilled care. *Beds* SNF 120.
Certified Medicare.
Owner Nonprofit organization/foundation.
Admissions Requirements Life Care
Community Resident.
Staff RNs 4 (ft), 4 (pt); LPNs 6 (ft), 5 (pt);
Nurses aides 28 (ft), 10 (pt); Recreational
therapists 1 (ft), 1 (pt); Social Services 1 (ft).
Facilities Dining room; Physical therapy
room; Activities room; Barber/Beauty shop;
Courtyard; Patio.
Activities Arts & crafts; Cards; Games;
Reading groups; Prayer groups; Movies;
Shopping trips; Social/Cultural gatherings;
Pet therapy.

BONIFAY

Bonifay Nursing Home*
108 Wagner Rd, Bonifay, FL, 32425
(904) 547-2418
Medical Dir/Dir of Nursing H E Brooks MD.
Licensure Skilled care. *Beds* 60. *Certified*
Medicaid.
Owner Proprietary Corp.
Admissions Requirements Minimum age 16;
Medical examination.
Staff RNs 3 (ft), 2 (pt); LPNs 3 (ft), 3 (pt);
Nurses aides 21 (ft), 3 (pt); Activities
coordinators 1 (ft), 1 (pt).
Facilities Dining room; Physical therapy
room; Activities room; Laundry room;
Barber/Beauty shop; Library.
Activities Arts & crafts; Cards; Games;
Reading groups; Prayer groups; Movies;
Social/Cultural gatherings.

BOYNTON BEACH

Boulevard Manor Nursing Center*
2839 S Seacrest Blvd, Boynton Beach, FL,
33435
(305) 732-2467
Medical Dir/Dir of Nursing Dr Nayer.
Licensure Skilled care. *Beds* 110. *Certified*
Medicaid; Medicare.
Owner Proprietary Corp (Vari-Care Inc).
Admissions Requirements Minimum age 16;
Medical examination; Physician's request.
Staff Physicians 1 (ft); RNs 10 (ft); LPNs 7
(ft); Orderlies 2 (ft); Nurses aides 37 (ft);
Physical therapists 2 (ft); Reality therapists 1
(ft); Recreational therapists 2 (ft);
Occupational therapists 1 (ft), 1 (pt); Speech
therapists 1 (pt); Activities coordinators 1
(ft); Dietitians 1 (pt); Dentists 1 (pt);
Ophthalmologists 1 (pt); Podiatrists 1 (pt);
Audiologists 1 (pt).
Languages French, Spanish, Norwegian,
German
Facilities Dining room; Physical therapy
room; Activities room; Crafts room; Laundry
room; Barber/Beauty shop; Library.
Activities Arts & crafts; Cards; Games;
Reading groups; Prayer groups; Movies;
Shopping trips; Social/Cultural gatherings.

BRADENTON

Asbury Towers
1533 4th Ave W, Bradenton, FL, 33505
(813) 747-1881
Admin Austin R Pickering. *Medical Dir/Dir of*
Nursing W Wentzel MD; Susie Liebe.
Licensure Skilled care. *Beds* SNF 34.
Owner Nonprofit Corp.
Admissions Requirements Minimum age 15;
Medical examination.
Staff RNs 3 (ft), 3 (pt); LPNs 5 (ft), 6 (pt);
Nurses aides 7 (ft), 6 (pt); Activities
coordinators 1 (ft).
Affiliation Methodist
Facilities Dining room; Activities room;
Chapel; Crafts room; Laundry room; Barber/
Beauty shop; Library.
Activities Arts & crafts; Cards; Games;
Reading groups; Prayer groups; Movies;
Shopping trips; Social/Cultural gatherings.

Bradenton Convalescent Center*
105 15th St E, Bradenton, FL, 33505
(813) 748-4031
Licensure Skilled care. *Beds* 110. *Certified*
Medicaid.
Owner Proprietary Corp (Hillhaven Corp).

Bradenton Manor*
1700 21st Ave W, Bradenton, FL, 33505
(813) 748-4161
Licensure Skilled care. *Beds* 59.
Owner Nonprofit Corp.
Admissions Requirements Medical
examination; Physician's request.
Staff RNs 4 (ft), 3 (pt); LPNs 5 (ft), 5 (pt);
Nurses aides 21 (ft), 4 (pt); Activities
coordinators 1 (ft); Dietitians 1 (pt).
Affiliation Presbyterian

Greenbriar Nursing Center
210 21st Ave W, Bradenton, FL, 33505
(813) 747-3786
Admin Joyce A Coleman. *Medical Dir/Dir of*
Nursing Dr Gawey Jr; Dolores Green RN.
Licensure Skilled care. *Beds* 60. *Certified*
Medicaid; Medicare; VA.
Owner Proprietary Corp (Unicare).
Admissions Requirements Minimum age 16;
Physician's request.
Staff RNs 5 (ft); LPNs 2 (ft), 3 (pt); Nurses
aides 13 (ft), 5 (pt); Physical therapists 2
(pt); Reality therapists 1 (pt); Recreational
therapists 1 (ft); Occupational therapists 1
(pt); Speech therapists 1 (pt); Activities

coordinators 1 (ft); Dietitians 2 (pt); Dentists 1 (pt); Ophthalmologists 1 (pt); Podiatrists 1 (pt); Dentist 1 (pt).
Facilities Dining room; Physical therapy room; Activities room; Laundry room; Barber/Beauty shop; Covered patio; BBQ area.
Activities Arts & crafts; Cards; Games; Reading groups; Prayer groups; Movies; Shopping trips; Social/Cultural gatherings.

Manatee Convalescent Center Inc*
302 Manatee Ave E, Bradenton, FL, 33508
(813) 746-6131
Admin Joanne Proffitt.
Licensure Skilled care. *Beds* 147. *Certified* Medicaid; Medicare.
Owner Proprietary Corp (Beverly Enterprises).
Admissions Requirements Medical examination.
Staff RNs 6 (ft), 3 (pt); LPNs 11 (ft); Nurses aides 46 (ft), 10 (pt); Recreational therapists; Occupational therapists; Speech therapists; Activities coordinators 2 (ft); Dietitians; Dentists; Ophthalmologists; Podiatrists; Audiologists.
Languages Spanish
Facilities Dining room; Physical therapy room; Activities room; Chapel; Crafts room; Laundry room; Barber/Beauty shop.
Activities Arts & crafts; Cards; Games; Reading groups; Prayer groups; Movies; Shopping trips; Social/Cultural gatherings.

Carol Lou Mora Care Center*
2010 59th St W, Bradenton, FL, 33506
(813) 792-1515
Licensure Skilled care. *Beds* 120. *Certified* Medicaid; Medicare.
Owner Proprietary Corp.
Staff RNs 5 (ft); LPNs 13 (ft); Nurses aides 29 (ft).

Shores Health Center
1700 3rd Ave W, Bradenton, FL, 33205
(813) 748-1700
Admin Lucretia L Hess NHA. *Medical Dir/Dir of Nursing* Joseph Dimino MD.
Licensure Skilled care. *Beds* SNF 21.
Owner Proprietary Corp.
Admissions Requirements Minimum age 64; Medical examination; Physician's request.
Staff RNs 2 (ft), 3 (pt); LPNs 3 (ft); Nurses aides 6 (ft), 1 (pt).
Facilities Dining room; Activities room; Chapel; Crafts room; Laundry room; Barber/Beauty shop; Library.
Activities Arts & crafts; Cards; Games; Reading groups; Prayer groups; Movies; Shopping trips; Social/Cultural gatherings.

SunCoast Manor Nursing Home
2010 Manatee Ave E, Bradenton, FL, 33505
(813) 747-3706
Admin Douglas E Webb. *Medical Dir/Dir of Nursing* Dr Frederick Allen MD; Mrs Grace Hansen RN.
Licensure Skilled care; Intermediate care. *Beds* SNF 55; ICF 153. *Certified* Medicaid; Medicare.
Owner Proprietary Corp (Life Care Centers of America).
Admissions Requirements Minimum age 16; Medical examination.
Staff RNs 11 (ft); LPNs 23 (ft), 3 (pt); Nurses aides 70 (ft), 5 (pt); Physical therapists 2 (pt); Recreational therapists 1 (ft); Occupational therapists 1 (pt); Speech therapists 1 (pt); Activities coordinators 2 (ft); Dietitians 2 (ft), 1 (pt).
Facilities Dining room; Physical therapy room; Activities room; Chapel; Crafts room; Laundry room; Barber/Beauty shop; Library; TV/day room; Restor; Dining room.
Activities Arts & crafts; Cards; Games; Reading groups; Prayer groups; Movies; Shopping trips; Social/Cultural gatherings; Special dinners; Exercise groups.

BRISTOL

Liberty Intermediate Care—Bristol*
PO Box 66, Bristol, FL, 32321
(904) 643-2256
Licensure Intermediate care for mentally retarded. *Beds* 80. *Certified* Medicaid; Medicare.
Owner Proprietary Corp.
Staff RNs 2 (ft); LPNs 3 (ft); Nurses aides 31 (ft).

BROOKSVILLE

Brooksville Nursing Manor
1114 Chatman Blvd, Brooksville, FL, 34601
(904) 796-6701
Admin Karen L Cross. *Medical Dir/Dir of Nursing* James M Marlowe MD; Kathryn Schneider RN.
Licensure Skilled care. *Beds* 180. *Certified* Medicaid; Medicare; VA.
Owner Nonprofit organization/foundation.
Admissions Requirements Minimum age 18.
Staff RNs 6 (ft), 5 (pt); LPNs 19 (ft), 2 (pt); Nurses aides 69 (ft), 3 (pt); Activities coordinators 1 (ft), 3 (pt); Dietitians 1 (ft).
Facilities Dining room; Physical therapy room; Activities room; Chapel; Crafts room; Laundry room; Barber/Beauty shop.
Activities Arts & crafts; Cards; Games; Reading groups; Prayer groups; Movies; Shopping trips; Social/Cultural gatherings.

Eastbrooke Health Care Center
10295 N Howell Ave, Brooksville, FL, 34601
(904) 799-1451
Admin Nancy E Hall. *Medical Dir/Dir of Nursing* Richard Henry MD; Susan Snyder RN DON.
Licensure Skilled care. *Beds* 120. *Certified* Medicaid; Medicare.
Owner Proprietary Corp (Beverly Enterprises).
Admissions Requirements Minimum age 16; Medical examination; Physician's request.
Staff RNs 4 (ft), 1 (pt); LPNs 7 (ft), 2 (pt); Orderlies 4 (ft); Nurses aides 30 (ft), 15 (pt); Activities coordinators 1 (ft).
Facilities Dining room; Physical therapy room; Activities room; Chapel; Laundry room; Barber/Beauty shop.
Activities Arts & crafts; Cards; Games; Reading groups; Prayer groups; Movies; Shopping trips; Social/Cultural gatherings.

CAPE CORAL

Cape Coral Nursing Pavilion*
2629 Del Prado Blvd, Cape Coral, FL, 33904
(813) 574-4434
Medical Dir/Dir of Nursing Lawrence D Hughes.
Licensure Skilled care. *Beds* 120. *Certified* Medicaid; Medicare.
Owner Proprietary Corp.
Admissions Requirements Minimum age 16; Medical examination; Physician's request.
Staff RNs 11 (ft); LPNs 12 (ft); Orderlies 4 (ft); Nurses aides 40 (ft); Physical therapists 2 (ft); Occupational therapists 1 (ft); Speech therapists 1 (ft); Activities coordinators 1 (ft); Dietitians 1 (ft); Podiatrists 1 (pt).
Languages Spanish
Facilities Dining room; Physical therapy room; Activities room; Chapel; Crafts room; Laundry room; Barber/Beauty shop; Library.
Activities Arts & crafts; Cards; Games; Reading groups; Prayer groups; Movies; Social/Cultural gatherings; Birthday parties; Sing-alongs; Wine & cheese parties.

CHIPLEY

Washington County Convalescent Center*
805 Usery Rd, Chipley, FL, 32428
(904) 638-4654

Beds 120.
Owner Proprietary Corp.

CLEARWATER

Belleair East Health Care Center
1150 Ponce de Leon Blvd, Clearwater, FL, 33616
(813) 585-5491
Admin Brian A Rougeux. *Medical Dir/Dir of Nursing* Jeffrey Sourbee.
Licensure Skilled care; Intermediate care. *Beds* 120. *Certified* Medicaid; Medicare.
Owner Proprietary Corp (Convalescent Services).
Admissions Requirements Minimum age 18; Medical examination; Physician's request.
Staff Physicians 1 (pt); RNs 15 (ft), 11 (pt); LPNs 10 (ft), 9 (pt); Orderlies 4 (ft), 2 (pt); Nurses aides 52 (ft), 29 (pt); Physical therapists 2 (pt); Reality therapists 1 (pt); Recreational therapists 1 (pt); Occupational therapists 1 (pt); Speech therapists 1 (pt); Activities coordinators 2 (ft), 1 (pt); Dietitians 2 (pt); Ophthalmologists 1 (pt); Podiatrists 1 (pt).
Languages Spanish
Facilities Dining room; Physical therapy room; Activities room; Laundry room; Barber/Beauty shop; Library.
Activities Arts & crafts; Cards; Games; Reading groups; Prayer groups; Movies; Shopping trips; Social/Cultural gatherings; Cooking class; Picnics; Painting class.

Bruce Manor Nursing Home
1100 Pine St, Clearwater, FL, 34516
(813) 422-7106
Admin Norman Rosewarne. *Medical Dir/Dir of Nursing* Joseph Baird MD; Maria Miller RN DON.
Licensure Skilled care. *Beds* SNF 76.
Owner Proprietary Corp.
Admissions Requirements Medical examination; Physician's request.
Staff RNs 3 (ft), 3 (pt); LPNs 5 (ft), 2 (pt); Nurses aides 15 (ft); Activities coordinators 1 (ft); Dietitians 1 (ft).
Facilities Dining room; Physical therapy room; Activities room; Crafts room; Barber/Beauty shop; Library.
Activities Arts & crafts; Cards; Games; Reading groups; Prayer groups; Movies; Shopping trips; Social/Cultural gatherings.

Clearwater Convalescent Center*
1270 Turner St, Clearwater, FL, 33516
(813) 443-7639
Licensure Skilled care. *Beds* 120. *Certified* Medicaid; Medicare.
Owner Proprietary Corp.
Staff RNs 4 (ft); LPNs 7 (ft); Nurses aides 26 (ft).

Drew Village Nursing Center
401 Fairwood Ave, Clearwater, FL,
(813) 797-6313
Admin Jane Knight. *Medical Dir/Dir of Nursing* Dr Charles Becker; Donna Curran DON.
Licensure Skilled care. *Beds* SNF 120. *Certified* Medicaid; Medicare.
Owner Proprietary Corp (Continental Medical Systems).
Admissions Requirements Minimum age 16; Medical examination.
Facilities Dining room; Physical therapy room; Activities room; Crafts room; Laundry room; Barber/Beauty shop; Library.
Activities Arts & crafts; Cards; Games; Reading groups; Prayer groups; Movies; Shopping trips; Social/Cultural gatherings.

Druid Hills Nursing Home
905 S Highland Ave, Clearwater, FL, 33516
(813) 442-9606
Admin Robynn J Kirkkwood. *Medical Dir/Dir of Nursing* Marsha Leonhardt.

Licensure Skilled care. *Beds* SNF 103. *Certified* Medicaid.
Owner Proprietary Corp.
Admissions Requirements Medical examination; Physician's request.
Staff RNs 15 (ft); LPNs 10 (ft); Nurses aides 30 (ft).
Languages Spanish, French, German, Belgian
Facilities Dining room; Physical therapy room; Laundry room; Barber/Beauty shop.
Activities Arts & crafts; Cards; Games; Reading groups; Prayer groups; Movies; Shopping trips; Social/Cultural gatherings.

Highland Pines Nursing Manor
1111 S Highland Ave, Clearwater, FL, 33516
(813) 446-0581
Medical Dir/Dir of Nursing Mark S Franklin DO.
Licensure Skilled care. *Beds* 120. *Certified* Medicaid.
Owner Proprietary Corp (Southern Management Services).
Admissions Requirements Minimum age 18; Medical examination; Physician's request.
Staff Nurses aides 14 (ft); Dietitians 15 (pt).
Languages Latin, Greek, German, Italian
Facilities Dining room; Activities room; Chapel; Crafts room; Laundry room; Barber/Beauty shop; Private lounge; Dining room.
Activities Arts & crafts; Cards; Games; Reading groups; Prayer groups; Movies; Shopping trips; Social/Cultural gatherings.

Morton F Plant Rehabilitation & Nursing Center
1250 S Fort Harrison Ave, Clearwater, FL, 33516
(813) 734-4419
Admin Linda A Kirk. *Medical Dir/Dir of Nursing* James E Lett II MD; Sharon Schaefer RN.
Licensure Skilled care. *Beds* SNF 126. *Certified* Medicaid; Medicare.
Owner Nonprofit Corp.
Admissions Requirements Minimum age 18; Medical examination.
Staff RNs 15 (ft), 4 (pt); LPNs 7 (ft), 4 (pt); Nurses aides 43 (ft); Physical therapists 7 (ft); Recreational therapists 2 (ft); Occupational therapists 1 (ft); Speech therapists 1 (ft); Dietitians 1 (ft).
Languages Spanish, German, Greek, French
Facilities Dining room; Activities room; Laundry room; Barber/Beauty shop.
Activities Arts & crafts; Cards; Games; Prayer groups; Movies; Shopping trips; Social/Cultural gatherings; Restaurant outings; Baking.

Oak Bluffs Nursing Center*
420 Bay Ave, Clearwater, FL, 33516
(813) 461-4466
Medical Dir/Dir of Nursing Dr Charles Becker.
Licensure Skilled care. *Beds* 60.
Owner Nonprofit Corp.
Staff RNs 4 (ft), 2 (pt); LPNs 4 (ft); Orderlies 1 (pt); Nurses aides 22 (ft), 4 (pt); Activities coordinators 1 (ft); Dietitians 1 (ft).
Facilities Dining room; Physical therapy room; Activities room; Chapel; Crafts room; Laundry room; Barber/Beauty shop; Library.
Activities Arts & crafts; Cards; Games; Reading groups; Prayer groups; Shopping trips; Social/Cultural gatherings.

Oak Cove Retirement & Health Center
210 S Osceola Ave, Clearwater, FL, 33516
(813) 441-3763
Admin R Eugene Fleming. *Medical Dir/Dir of Nursing* Julie Jackson.
Licensure Skilled care. *Beds* SNF 56. *Certified* Medicare.
Owner Nonprofit Corp.
Admissions Requirements Medical examination.

Staff Physicians; RNs; LPNs; Orderlies; Nurses aides; Physical therapists; Recreational therapists; Occupational therapists; Speech therapists; Activities coordinators; Dietitians; Ophthalmologists; Podiatrists; Social Service Director.
Facilities Dining room; Activities room; Crafts room; Laundry room; Barber/Beauty shop; Library.
Activities Arts & crafts; Cards; Games; Reading groups; Prayer groups; Movies; Shopping trips; Social/Cultural gatherings; Exercise.

Osceola Inn*
221 N Osceola, Clearwater, FL, 33515
(813) 461-3321
Medical Dir/Dir of Nursing Gaylord Church MD.
Licensure Skilled care. *Beds* 13.
Owner Nonprofit Corp.
Admissions Requirements Minimum age 65; Medical examination.
Staff RNs 2 (ft), 3 (pt); LPNs 1 (ft), 3 (pt); Nurses aides 6 (ft), 3 (pt); Activities coordinators 1 (pt); Dietitians 1 (pt).
Languages French
Affiliation Presbyterian
Facilities Dining room; Activities room; Chapel; Laundry room; Barber/Beauty shop; Library.
Activities Arts & crafts; Cards; Games; Reading groups; Prayer groups; Social/Cultural gatherings.

Sunset Point Nursing Center*
1980 Sunset Point Rd, Clearwater, FL, 33515
(813) 443-1588
Medical Dir/Dir of Nursing Dr Raymond Zimmerman.
Licensure Skilled care; Intermediate care. *Beds* SNF 72; ICF 48. *Certified* Medicaid; Medicare.
Owner Proprietary Corp (Shive Nursing Centers).
Staff Physicians 1 (pt); RNs 4 (ft), 3 (pt); LPNs 8 (ft), 2 (pt); Physical therapists 1 (pt); Recreational therapists 1 (pt); Occupational therapists 1 (pt); Speech therapists 1 (pt); Activities coordinators 1 (ft); Dietitians 1 (pt); Dentists 1 (pt); Ophthalmologists 1 (pt); Podiatrists 1 (pt); Audiologists 1 (pt).
Facilities Dining room; Physical therapy room; Activities room; Crafts room; Barber/Beauty shop; Library.
Activities Arts & crafts; Cards; Games; Reading groups; Prayer groups; Movies; Shopping trips; Social/Cultural gatherings.

CLERMONT

Lake Highlands Nursing Home
151 E Minnehaha Ave, Clermont, FL, 32711
(904) 394-2188
Admin Herbert Rogers. *Medical Dir/Dir of Nursing* Melvin Thomas MD.
Licensure Skilled care; Intermediate care. *Beds* 142. *Certified* Medicaid; Medicare; VA.
Owner Privately owned.
Admissions Requirements Medical examination.
Staff Physicians 1 (pt); RNs 6 (ft); LPNs 21 (ft); Nurses aides 63 (ft), 8 (pt); Activities coordinators 1 (ft); Dietitians 1 (pt).
Languages Spanish, French, Swedish
Facilities Dining room; Physical therapy room; Activities room; Chapel; Crafts room; Laundry room; Barber/Beauty shop.
Activities Arts & crafts; Cards; Games; Reading groups; Prayer groups; Movies; Shopping trips; Social/Cultural gatherings.

CLEWISTON

Clewiston Health Care Center*
300 Gloria St, Clewiston, FL, 33440
(813) 983-5123

Licensure Skilled care. *Beds* 120. *Certified* Medicaid.
Owner Proprietary Corp (Beverly Enterprises).
Staff Nurses aides 19 (ft).

CORAL GABLES

New Riviera Health Resort
6901 Yumuri St, Coral Gables, FL, 33146
(305) 661-0078
Admin Shirley H St Clair JD. *Medical Dir/Dir of Nursing* Norman Spitzer MD; Beryl Rogers DON.
Licensure Skilled care. *Beds* 52. *Certified* Medicaid; Medicare.
Owner Proprietary Corp.
Admissions Requirements Physician's request.
Staff RNs 3 (ft), 1 (pt); LPNs 3 (ft); Nurses aides 20 (ft); Physical therapists 1 (pt); Dietitians 1 (pt).
Languages Spanish
Facilities Dining room; Activities room; Laundry room; Barber/Beauty shop.
Activities Arts & crafts; Cards; Games; Reading groups; Prayer groups; Movies; Social/Cultural gatherings.

CRAWFORDVILLE

Wakulla Manor
PO Box 549, Crawfordville, FL, 32433
(904) 926-7181
Licensure Skilled care. *Beds* 120. *Certified* Medicaid; Medicare.
Owner Proprietary Corp (Health Care & Retirement Corp).
Staff RNs 8 (ft); LPNs 8 (ft); Nurses aides 25 (ft).

CRESCENT CITY

Lakeshore Nursing Home
100 Lake St, Crescent City, FL, 32012
(904) 698-2222
Admin Martha Jean Brown. *Medical Dir/Dir of Nursing* Bernard Prudencio; Caroline Kellerman DON.
Licensure Skilled care; Intermediate care. *Beds* SNF 92; ICF. *Certified* Medicaid.
Owner Proprietary Corp (Beverly Enterprises).
Admissions Requirements Physician's request.
Staff Physicians 1 (pt); RNs 7 (ft); LPNs 7 (ft); Nurses aides 37 (ft); Physical therapists 1 (ft); Speech therapists 1 (ft); Activities coordinators 2 (ft); Dietitians 1 (ft).
Facilities Dining room; Physical therapy room; Activities room; Crafts room; Laundry room; Barber/Beauty shop; Library.
Activities Arts & crafts; Cards; Games; Reading groups; Prayer groups; Movies; Shopping trips; Social/Cultural gatherings.

CRESTVIEW

Crestview Nursing & Convalescent Home
1849 E 1st St, Crestview, FL, 32536
(904) 682-5322
Admin Cynthia K Ledford. *Medical Dir/Dir of Nursing* Kenneth E Carroll MD; Patricia M Dingess RNC.
Licensure Skilled care. *Beds* SNF 120. *Certified* Medicaid; Medicare.
Owner Proprietary Corp.
Staff RNs 5 (ft); LPNs 7 (ft); Nurses aides 20 (ft).
Activities Arts & crafts; Cards; Games; Reading groups; Prayer groups; Shopping trips; Social/Cultural gatherings.

CRYSTAL RIVER

Crystal River Geriatric Center*
136 NE 12th Ave, Crystal River, FL, 32629
(904) 795-5044

Medical Dir/Dir of Nursing Dr Carlos
Gonzalez.
Licensure Skilled care; Intermediate care. *Beds*
150. *Certified* Medicaid; Medicare.
Owner Proprietary Corp (Waverly Group).
Admissions Requirements Minimum age 16.
Staff Physical therapists 1 (pt); Occupational
therapists 1 (pt); Speech therapists 1 (pt);
Activities coordinators 1 (ft); Dietitians 1
(pt); Dentists 1 (pt); Podiatrists 1 (pt).
Languages Spanish, German
Facilities Dining room; Physical therapy
room; Activities room; Laundry room;
Barber/Beauty shop.
Activities Arts & crafts; Cards; Games;
Reading groups; Prayer groups; Movies;
Social/Cultural gatherings.

Cypress Cove Care Center
700 SE 8th Ave, Crystal River, FL, 32629
(904) 795-8832
Admin Ted Hagey NHA. *Medical Dir/Dir of
Nursing* James Marlowe MD; Betty Klein
RNC DON.
Licensure Skilled care. *Beds* SNF 120.
Certified Medicaid; Medicare.
Owner Proprietary Corp.
Admissions Requirements Minimum age 16;
Medical examination; Physician's request.
Staff Physicians 15 (pt); RNs 3 (ft), 4 (pt);
LPNs 13 (ft), 5 (pt); Orderlies 1 (ft); Nurses
aides 41 (ft), 3 (pt); Activities coordinators 1
(ft); Dietitians 1 (ft); Ophthalmologists 2
(pt).
Languages Swedish
Facilities Dining room; Physical therapy
room; Activities room; Chapel; Laundry
room; Barber/Beauty shop.
Activities Arts & crafts; Cards; Games;
Reading groups; Prayer groups; Movies;
Shopping trips; Social/Cultural gatherings.

DADE CITY

Dade City Geriatric Center*
805 W Coleman Ave, Dade City, FL, 33525
(904) 567-8615
Medical Dir/Dir of Nursing Dr McBath.
Licensure Skilled care. *Beds* 120. *Certified*
Medicaid; Medicare.
Owner Proprietary Corp (Beverly Enterprises).
Admissions Requirements Minimum age 16;
Medical examination; Physician's request.
Staff Physicians 12 (pt); RNs 5 (pt); LPNs 14
(pt); Nurses aides 36 (pt); Physical therapists
1 (pt); Recreational therapists 1 (pt);
Occupational therapists 1 (pt); Speech
therapists 1 (pt); Activities coordinators 1
(pt); Dietitians 1 (pt); Dentists 1 (pt);
Podiatrists 1 (pt); Audiologists 1 (pt).
Languages Spanish
Facilities Dining room; Physical therapy
room; Activities room; Laundry room;
Barber/Beauty shop.
Activities Arts & crafts; Cards; Games;
Reading groups; Prayer groups; Movies;
Shopping trips; Social/Cultural gatherings.

Pasco Nursing Center
PO Box 1197, 447 N 5th St, Dade City, FL,
34297-1197
(904) 567-1978
Medical Dir/Dir of Nursing Donald McBath
DO; Pat Brown RN.
Licensure Skilled care; Intermediate care. *Beds*
SNF 40; ICF. *Certified* Medicaid.
Owner Proprietary Corp.
Admissions Requirements Minimum age 16;
Medical examination; Physician's request.
Staff RNs 1 (ft), 1 (pt); LPNs 3 (ft), 3 (pt);
Orderlies 2 (ft); Nurses aides 12 (ft), 2 (pt);
Activities coordinators 1 (ft); Dietitians 1
(pt).
Languages Spanish, German

Facilities Dining room; Activities room;
Chapel; Laundry room.
Activities Arts & crafts; Cards; Games;
Reading groups; Prayer groups; Movies;
Shopping trips; Social/Cultural gatherings;
Current events; Ride in country.

Royal Oak Nursing Resort
700 Royal Oak Ln, Dade City, FL, 33525
(904) 567-3122
Admin David W Cross. *Medical Dir/Dir of
Nursing* James Marlowe; James D Murphy.
Licensure Skilled care. *Beds* 120. *Certified*
Medicaid; Medicare; VA.
Owner Nonprofit Corp.
Admissions Requirements Minimum age 18;
Medical examination; Physician's request.
Staff RNs 4 (ft); LPNs 10 (ft), 5 (pt); Nurses
aides 55 (ft), 20 (pt); Recreational therapists
1 (pt); Activities coordinators 2 (pt).
Languages Spanish
Facilities Dining room; Physical therapy
room; Activities room; Chapel; Crafts room;
Laundry room; Barber/Beauty shop; Park.
Activities Arts & crafts; Cards; Games;
Reading groups; Prayer groups; Movies;
Shopping trips; Social/Cultural gatherings.

DANIA

Dania Nursing Home*
440 Phippen Rd, Dania, FL, 33004
(305) 927-0508
Licensure Skilled care. *Beds* 88. *Certified*
Medicaid; Medicare.
Owner Proprietary Corp.
Staff RNs 3 (ft); LPNs 10 (ft); Nurses aides 30
(ft).
Languages French, Hebrew, Yiddish

DAVENPORT

William L Hargrave Health Center
206 W Orange St, Davenport, FL, 33827
(813) 422-4961
Medical Dir/Dir of Nursing Edward Jukes.
Licensure Skilled care. *Beds* 60. *Certified*
Medicaid.
Owner Nonprofit Corp.
Admissions Requirements Minimum age 70;
Medical examination.
Staff Physicians 2 (ft); RNs 4 (ft), 1 (pt);
LPNs 7 (ft), 2 (pt); Nurses aides 28 (ft), 1
(pt); Occupational therapists 1 (pt); Speech
therapists 1 (pt); Activities coordinators 3
(ft), 1 (pt); Dietitians 1 (ft); Dentists 3 (pt);
Ophthalmologists 1 (pt); Podiatrists 1 (pt).
Affiliation Episcopal
Facilities Dining room; Activities room;
Chapel; Crafts room; Laundry room; Barber/
Beauty shop; Library.
Activities Arts & crafts; Cards; Games;
Reading groups; Prayer groups; Movies;
Shopping trips; Social/Cultural gatherings;
Church activities.

DAVIE

BARC Housing Inc
2750 SW 75th Ave, Davie, FL, 33314
(305) 474-5277
Admin Carol Eger. *Medical Dir/Dir of Nursing*
Irving Bratt MD.
Licensure Intermediate care for mentally
retarded. *Beds* 36. *Certified* Medicaid.
Owner Nonprofit Corp.
Admissions Requirements Minimum age 18;
Medical examination; ICF MR eligibility.
Staff Physicians 1 (pt); RNs 1 (pt); LPNs 4
(ft); Physical therapists 1 (pt); Recreational
therapists 1 (ft); Occupational therapists 1
(pt); Speech therapists 2 (pt); Dietitians 1
(pt); Ophthalmologists 1 (pt); Podiatrists 1
(pt); Social worker 1 (ft); Instructors 19 (ft),
18 (pt); Psychologists 1 (pt).

Facilities Homelike environment; Dining
room; Recreation area; Living room; Family
room; Kitchen; Bedrooms.
Activities Arts & crafts; Cards; Games;
Movies; Shopping trips; Social/Cultural
gatherings; Wide variety of normalized
recreational & leisure activities.

DAYTONA BEACH

Clyatt Memorial Center*
1001 S Beach St, Daytona Beach, FL, 32014
(904) 258-3334
Licensure Skilled care. *Beds* 99. *Certified*
Medicaid; Medicare.
Owner Nonprofit Corp.
Staff RNs 3 (ft); LPNs 7 (ft); Nurses aides 31
(ft).

Daytona Beach Geriatric Center*
1055 3rd St, Daytona Beach, FL, 32017
(904) 252-3686
Medical Dir/Dir of Nursing Dr Ronald
Cabreza.
Licensure Skilled care. *Beds* 180. *Certified*
Medicaid; Medicare.
Owner Proprietary Corp.
Admissions Requirements Minimum age 18;
Medical examination; Physician's request.
Staff Orderlies 2 (ft); Physical therapists;
Recreational therapists; Occupational
therapists; Speech therapists; Activities
coordinators 1 (ft); Dietitians 1 (ft).
Facilities Dining room; Physical therapy
room; Activities room; Laundry room;
Barber/Beauty shop; Conference room;
Treatment room.
Activities Arts & crafts; Cards; Games;
Reading groups; Prayer groups; Movies;
Social/Cultural gatherings.

**Daytona Beach Olds Hall Good Samaritan
Nursing Center**
325 S Segrave St, Daytona Beach, FL, 32014
(904) 253-6791
Admin Bruce W Markkula. *Medical Dir/Dir of
Nursing* Ernest Cook Jr MD; Fran Jones
DON.
Licensure Skilled care; Intermediate care. *Beds*
120; Apts 67. *Certified* Medicaid.
Owner Nonprofit Corp (Evangelical Lutheran/
Good Samaritan).
Admissions Requirements Minimum age 16;
Medical examination.
Staff RNs 5 (ft), 1 (pt); LPNs 15 (ft), 13 (pt);
Nurses aides 39 (ft), 18 (pt); Recreational
therapists 5 (ft), 1 (pt); Activities
coordinators 1 (ft); Dietitians 1 (pt);
Ophthalmologists 1 (pt); Chaplain 1 (ft)
Educator 1 (ft) Staff development 1 (ft)
Dentist 1 (pt).
Affiliation Lutheran
Facilities Dining room; Activities room;
Chapel; Crafts room; Laundry room; Barber/
Beauty shop; Library.
Activities Arts & crafts; Cards; Games;
Reading groups; Prayer groups; Movies;
Shopping trips; Social/Cultural gatherings;
Adopt-a-grandparent program; Farmer's
market; Picnics at state park.

Golden Age Health Care
324 Wilder Blvd, Daytona Beach, FL, 32014
(904) 252-2600
Admin James L Adkins. *Medical Dir/Dir of
Nursing* Dr James Carratt; Adrianna
Patterson.
Licensure Skilled care. *Beds* SNF 192.
Certified Medicaid; Medicare.
Owner Proprietary Corp (Southwood Health
Care).
Admissions Requirements Minimum age 16;
Medical examination; Physician's request.
Staff RNs 14 (ft); LPNs 14 (ft); Orderlies 7
(ft); Nurses aides 60 (ft); Speech therapists 1
(ft); Activities coordinators 1 (ft); Dietitians
1 (ft).
Languages Dutch, Spanish, Russian

Facilities Dining room; Physical therapy room; Laundry room; Barber/Beauty shop.
Activities Arts & crafts; Games; Movies; Social/Cultural gatherings.

Holiday Care Center
1031 S Beach St, Daytona Beach, FL, 32014
(904) 255-2453
Medical Dir/Dir of Nursing C M Crouch MD.
Licensure Skilled care. *Beds* 48. *Certified* Medicaid.
Owner Proprietary Corp.
Admissions Requirements Minimum age 18; Medical examination; Physician's request.
Staff RNs 1 (ft), 2 (pt); LPNs 3 (ft), 1 (pt); Nurses aides 11 (ft), 8 (pt); Activities coordinators 1 (ft).
Facilities Dining room; Activities room; Crafts room; Laundry room; Barber/Beauty shop; Library.
Activities Arts & crafts; Cards; Games; Prayer groups; Movies; Social/Cultural gatherings.

DEBARY

DeBary Manor
60 N Hwy 17-92, DeBary, FL, 32713
(305) 668-4426
Admin Patrick Lane. *Medical Dir/Dir of Nursing* Dr Miltonberger.
Licensure Skilled care; Intermediate care. *Beds* 93. *Certified* Medicaid; Medicare; VA.
Owner Privately owned.
Staff RNs 5 (ft), 2 (pt); LPNs 9 (ft), 2 (pt); Orderlies 2 (ft), 1 (pt); Nurses aides 20 (ft), 5 (pt); Activities coordinators 1 (ft).
Languages Spanish,
Facilities Dining room; Crafts room; Laundry room; Barber/Beauty shop; Library.
Activities Arts & crafts; Cards; Games; Reading groups; Prayer groups; Movies; Shopping trips.

DEFUNIAK SPRINGS

Walton County Convalescent Center*
PO Box 745, Rte 6, DeFuniak Springs, FL, 32433
(904) 892-2176
Licensure Skilled care. *Beds* 107. *Certified* Medicaid.
Owner Proprietary Corp (Beverly Enterprises).
Staff RNs 4 (ft); LPNs 5 (ft); Nurses aides 22 (ft).

DELAND

Alliance Nursing Center*
151 Winnemissett W, Deland, FL, 32720
(904) 734-6401
Licensure Skilled care. *Beds* 60. *Certified* Medicaid; Medicare.
Owner Nonprofit Corp.
Staff RNs 4 (ft); LPNs 8 (ft); Nurses aides 15 (ft).
Languages Spanish
Affiliation Christian & Missionary Alliance Foundation

Deland Convalescent Center
451 S Amelia Ave, Deland, FL, 32724
(904) 734-8614
Admin Patricia S Lane. *Medical Dir/Dir of Nursing* Carol Price.
Licensure Skilled care; Intermediate care. *Beds* 122. *Certified* Medicaid; Medicare.
Owner Proprietary Corp.
Admissions Requirements Minimum age 16; Medical examination.
Staff RNs 5 (ft), 4 (pt); LPNs 4 (ft), 3 (pt); Orderlies 4 (ft); Nurses aides 32 (ft), 17 (pt); Activities coordinators 1 (ft).
Languages Spanish, German
Facilities Dining room; Barber/Beauty shop.
Activities Arts & crafts; Cards; Games; Reading groups; Prayer groups; Movies; Shopping trips.

Ridgecrest Manor
1200 N Stone St, Deland, FL, 32721
(904) 734-6200
Admin Ginger Smith. *Medical Dir/Dir of Nursing* Curt N Rausch MD; Karen Dickenson DON.
Licensure Skilled care. *Beds* 134. *Certified* Medicaid; Medicare; VA.
Owner Nonprofit Corp.
Admissions Requirements Medical examination.
Staff Physicians 17 (pt); RNs 10 (ft), 2 (pt); LPNs 6 (ft), 2 (pt); Nurses aides 45 (ft), 6 (pt); Activities coordinators 2 (ft); Dietitians 1 (pt); Ophthalmologists 1 (pt); Podiatrists 1 (pt).
Languages Spanish
Facilities Dining room; Physical therapy room; Activities room; Barber/Beauty shop.
Activities Arts & crafts; Cards; Games; Reading groups; Prayer groups; Movies; Shopping trips; Social/Cultural gatherings.

University Convalescent Center East Inc
919 E New York Ave, Deland, FL, 32720
(904) 734-9083
Admin Carol J McGauvran. *Medical Dir/Dir of Nursing* D S Rauschenberger MD; Leyon E Frierson RN DON.
Licensure Skilled care. *Beds* SNF 60. *Certified* Medicaid; Medicare.
Owner Proprietary Corp.
Admissions Requirements Physician's request.
Staff Physicians; RNs 6 (ft); LPNs 7 (ft); Orderlies 1 (ft); Nurses aides 18 (ft); Physical therapists; Speech therapists; Activities coordinators; Dietitians; Ophthalmologists.
Languages Spanish
Facilities Dining room; Activities room; Laundry room; Barber/Beauty shop.
Activities Arts & crafts; Cards; Games; Prayer groups; Movies; Shopping trips; Social/Cultural gatherings.

University Convalescent Center West
545 W Euclid Ave, Deland, FL, 32720
(904) 734-9085
Admin Barbara Hodges. *Medical Dir/Dir of Nursing* D Rauschenberger MD; Carol Mee RN DON.
Licensure Skilled care; Intermediate care. *Beds* 60. *Certified* Medicaid; Medicare; VA.
Owner Proprietary Corp.
Admissions Requirements Minimum age 18; Medical examination; Physician's request.
Staff RNs 3 (ft), 1 (pt); Orderlies 3 (ft); Nurses aides 17 (ft), 3 (pt).
Facilities Dining room; Activities room; Crafts room; Laundry room; Barber/Beauty shop; Library; Outside activities space.
Activities Arts & crafts; Cards; Games; Reading groups; Prayer groups; Movies; Shopping trips; Social/Cultural gatherings; Reality orientation; Mental health group sessions.

DELEON SPRINGS

Van Hook School of Fla Inc
PO Box 607, DeLeon Springs, FL, 32028
(904) 985-5031
Admin Linda Burgess. *Medical Dir/Dir of Nursing* Andrew Randolph MD; JoAnn Brown.
Licensure Residential habilitation center for mentally retarded. *Beds* 84.
Owner Proprietary Corp.
Admissions Requirements Minimum age 6; Medical examination.
Staff Physicians 1 (pt); LPNs 3 (ft); Nurses aides 45 (ft), 7 (pt); Activities coordinators 1 (ft); Dietitians 1 (pt); Behavior Specialists 1 (ft).

Facilities Dining room; Activities room; Crafts room; Laundry room.
Activities Arts & crafts; Cards; Games; Reading groups; Movies; Shopping trips; Social/Cultural gatherings; Outdoor games; Special Olympics training; Competitive games.

DELRAY BEACH

Health Center at Abbey Delray
2000 Lowson Blvd, Delray Beach, FL, 33445
(305) 278-3249
Admin Gary J Vasquez. *Medical Dir/Dir of Nursing* Donald Bebout; Betty Ann Abe.
Licensure Skilled care. *Beds* SNF 100. *Certified* Medicaid; Medicare.
Owner Nonprofit Corp (Life Care Services Corp).
Admissions Requirements Medical examination; Physician's request.
Staff RNs; LPNs; Nurses aides; Physical therapists; Recreational therapists; Occupational therapists; Speech therapists; Activities coordinators; Dietitians.
Facilities Dining room; Physical therapy room; Activities room; Chapel; Crafts room; Laundry room; Barber/Beauty shop; Library.
Activities Arts & crafts; Cards; Games; Reading groups; Prayer groups; Movies; Shopping trips; Social/Cultural gatherings; Patients' council; Monthly field trips.

DELTONA

Deltona Health Care Center
1851 Elkcam Blvd, Deltona, FL, 32725
(904) 789-3769
Admin Helen H Smith. *Medical Dir/Dir of Nursing* Dr Clyde Meade; Patricia Tuten DON.
Licensure Skilled care. *Beds* 120. *Certified* Medicaid; Medicare.
Owner Proprietary Corp (Beverly Enterprises).
Admissions Requirements Minimum age 16; Medical examination; Physician's request.
Languages Spanish
Facilities Dining room; Physical therapy room; Activities room; Chapel; Crafts room; Laundry room; Barber/Beauty shop.
Activities Arts & crafts; Cards; Games; Reading groups; Prayer groups; Movies; Shopping trips; Social/Cultural gatherings.

DUNEDIN

Dunedin Care Center
Drawer 937, 1351 San Christopher Dr, Dunedin, FL, 34698
(813) 736-1421
Admin Patricia McCormack. *Medical Dir/Dir of Nursing* Joy Pike RN DON.
Licensure Skilled care. *Beds* 104. *Certified* Medicaid; Medicare.
Owner Proprietary Corp (National Heritage).
Admissions Requirements Medical examination; Physician's request.
Staff Physicians 1 (ft); RNs 4 (ft), 3 (pt); LPNs 4 (ft), 2 (pt); Nurses aides 30 (ft); Activities coordinators 1 (ft); Dietitians 1 (pt); Social Services 1 (ft).
Languages German, French, Spanish, Swedish
Facilities Dining room; Physical therapy room; Activities room; Crafts room; Laundry room; Barber/Beauty shop; Library; Patio.
Activities Arts & crafts; Cards; Games; Reading groups; Prayer groups; Movies; Shopping trips; Social/Cultural gatherings; Rehab groups for restorative therapies.

Spanish Gardens Nursing Center
1061 Virginia St, Dunedin, FL, 33528
(813) 733-4189
Admin Richard P Ninis. *Medical Dir/Dir of Nursing* Javier Bleichner MD; Bernadette Darcangelo DON.

Licensure Skilled care. Beds SNF 93. Certified
Medicaid; Medicare.
Owner Proprietary Corp (Beverly Enterprises).
Admissions Requirements Minimum age 16;
Medical examination.
Staff RNs 5 (ft); Orderlies 3 (ft); Activities
coordinators 1 (ft).
Languages Spanish, German
Facilities Dining room; Physical therapy
room; Activities room; Laundry room;
Barber/Beauty shop; Library; Covered patio.
Activities Arts & crafts; Cards; Games;
Reading groups; Prayer groups; Movies;
Shopping trips; Social/Cultural gatherings.

EUSTIS

Eustis Manor Inc*
2810 Ruleme St, Eustis, FL, 32726
Admin Danny K Prince. Medical Dir/Dir of
Nursing Dr B W Price.
Licensure Skilled care. Beds 120. Certified
Medicaid.
Owner Proprietary Corp.
Admissions Requirements Medical
examination.
Staff Physicians 13 (pt); RNs 6 (ft), 1 (pt);
LPNs 8 (ft), 2 (pt); Nurses aides 38 (ft);
Physical therapists 3 (pt); Reality therapists
1 (pt); Speech therapists 2 (pt); Activities
coordinators 1 (ft); Dietitians 1 (ft); Dentists;
Ophthalmologists; Podiatrists; Audiologists.
Facilities Dining room; Laundry room;
Barber/Beauty shop.
Activities Arts & crafts; Cards; Games;
Reading groups; Prayer groups; Movies;
Shopping trips; Social/Cultural gatherings.

Lake Eustis Care Center
411 W Woodward Ave, Eustis, FL, 32726
(904) 357-3565
Licensure Skilled care. Beds SNF 60. Certified
Medicaid; Medicare.
Owner Proprietary Corp.
Staff RNs 3 (ft), 1 (pt); LPNs 6 (ft), 2 (pt);
Orderlies 2 (ft); Nurses aides 15 (ft), 4 (pt);
Activities coordinators 1 (ft); Dietitians 1
(ft).
Facilities Dining room; Activities room;
Chapel; Laundry room; Barber/Beauty shop;
TV Room.
Activities Arts & crafts; Cards; Games;
Reading groups; Prayer groups; Shopping
trips; Social/Cultural gatherings; Church;
Exercise Classes; Music; Fishing; Bowling.

Oakwood Nursing Center
301 S Bay St, Eustis, FL, 32726
(904) 357-8105
Admin Darrel L Hager. Medical Dir/Dir of
Nursing Dr Robert Crow; Ann Lewis DON.
Licensure Skilled care; Intermediate care. Beds
120. Certified Medicaid; Medicare.
Owner Proprietary Corp (National Healthcare
Affiliates).
Admissions Requirements Minimum age 16;
Medical examination; Physician's request.
Staff Physicians 21 (pt); RNs 4 (ft), 2 (pt);
LPNs 8 (ft), 5 (pt); Orderlies 3 (ft), 1 (pt);
Nurses aides 39 (ft), 5 (pt); Occupational
therapists 1 (pt); Speech therapists 1 (pt);
Activities coordinators 1 (ft); Dietitians 1
(pt); Ophthalmologists 1 (pt).
Facilities Dining room; Physical therapy
room; Laundry room; Barber/Beauty shop.
Activities Arts & crafts; Cards; Games;
Reading groups; Prayer groups; Movies;
Social/Cultural gatherings; Bingo; Bowling.

FERNANDINA BEACH

Amelia Island Care Center
2700 Atlantic Ave, Fernandina Beach, FL,
32034
(904) 261-5518

Admin Thelma L Phillips. Medical Dir/Dir of
Nursing Dr Edward Tribuzio; Demetris
Smith RN DON.
Licensure Intermediate care for mentally
retarded. Beds ICF/MR 90. Certified
Medicaid.
Owner Proprietary Corp (Unicare).
Admissions Requirements Minimum age 18;
Medical examination.
Staff Physicians 1 (ft); RNs 2 (ft); LPNs 6 (ft);
Nurses aides 58 (ft), 12 (pt); Physical
therapists 1 (ft); Occupational therapists 1
(ft); Speech therapists 1 (ft); Activities
coordinators 1 (ft); Dietitians 1 (ft); Resident
living aides 45 (ft).
Languages Spanish
Facilities Dining room; Physical therapy
room; Activities room; Crafts room; Laundry
room; Barber/Beauty shop.
Activities Arts & crafts; Cards; Games;
Reading groups; Prayer groups; Movies;
Shopping trips; Social/Cultural gatherings.

FOREST CITY

Florida Living Nursing Center*
PO Box 3186, Forest City, FL, 32751
(305) 862-6263
Medical Dir/Dir of Nursing Michael Gebauer
MD.
Licensure Skilled care. Beds 104. Certified
Medicaid; Medicare.
Owner Nonprofit Corp (Adventist Health Sys-
USA).
Admissions Requirements Minimum age 16;
Medical examination; Physician's request.
Staff Physicians 1 (pt); RNs 3 (ft), 3 (pt);
LPNs 10 (ft), 7 (pt); Orderlies 5 (ft), 2 (pt);
Nurses aides 33 (ft), 10 (pt); Physical
therapists; Speech therapists; Activities
coordinators 2 (ft), 1 (pt); Podiatrists.
Languages Spanish
Affiliation Seventh-Day Adventist
Facilities Dining room; Physical therapy
room; Activities room; Chapel; Crafts room;
Laundry room; Barber/Beauty shop; Library.
Activities Arts & crafts; Games; Reading
groups; Prayer groups; Movies; Shopping
trips; Social/Cultural gatherings.

FORT LAUDERDALE

Alden House*
1800 E Oakland Park Blvd, Fort Lauderdale,
FL, 33307
(305) 565-7785
Licensure Skilled care. Beds 84. Certified
Medicaid; Medicare.
Owner Proprietary Corp.
Staff Physicians; Dietitians; Nurses aides.

Ann Stock Center*
1790 SW 43rd Way, Fort Lauderdale, FL,
3317
(305) 584-8000
Licensure Intermediate care for mentally
retarded. Beds 16. Certified Medicaid.
Owner Proprietary Corp.

Broward Convalescent Home
1330 S Andrews Ave, Fort Lauderdale, FL,
33316
(305) 524-5587
Admin Keith V Kroeger. Medical Dir/Dir of
Nursing Barbara Gill RN.
Licensure Skilled care. Beds SNF 198.
Certified Medicaid; Medicare.
Owner Proprietary Corp (HBA Management
Inc).
Admissions Requirements Minimum age 16.
Staff RNs 15 (ft), 2 (pt); LPNs 14 (ft), 5 (pt);
Nurses aides 55 (ft), 20 (pt); Physical
therapists 1 (pt); Speech therapists 1 (pt);
Activities coordinators 2 (ft), 1 (pt);
Dietitians 1 (pt).
Languages Spanish

Facilities Dining room; Physical therapy
room; Activities room; Chapel; Crafts room;
Laundry room; Barber/Beauty shop.
Activities Arts & crafts; Cards; Games;
Reading groups; Prayer groups; Movies;
Shopping trips; Social/Cultural gatherings.

Daystar Inc
3800 Flamingo Rd, Fort Lauderdale, FL,
33330
(305) 473-0167
Admin Neal Frank. Medical Dir/Dir of
Nursing Ruby O Morris DON.
Licensure Skilled care. Beds 44. Certified
Medicare.
Owner Nonprofit Corp.
Staff RNs 6 (ft); LPNs 8 (ft); Orderlies 1 (ft);
Nurses aides 2 (ft); Activities coordinators 1
(ft); Dietitians 1 (ft).
Languages Spanish, German, Japanese,
Portuguese
Affiliation Christian Science
Activities Arts & crafts; Cards; Games;
Reading groups; Prayer groups; Movies;
Shopping trips; Social/Cultural gatherings.

Harbor Beach Convalescent Home
1615 S Miami Rd, Fort Lauderdale, FL,
33316
(305) 523-5673
Admin Cindy Newman. Medical Dir/Dir of
Nursing Guillermo Rodriquez MD; JoAnn
Adlerman DON.
Licensure Skilled care. Beds 59.
Owner Proprietary Corp (Beverly Enterprises).
Admissions Requirements Minimum age 16.
Staff Physicians 1 (ft); RNs 3 (ft), 1 (pt);
LPNs 4 (ft), 2 (pt); Nurses aides 15 (ft), 2
(pt); Recreational therapists; Activities
coordinators 1 (ft).
Facilities Dining room; Activities room;
Crafts room; Laundry room; Barber/Beauty
shop; Library; 3 Outdoor patios.
Activities Arts & crafts; Cards; Games;
Reading groups; Prayer groups; Movies;
Shopping trips; Social/Cultural gatherings;
Culture months; Adopt-a-grandparent
program.

Manor Pines Convalescent Center*
1701 NE 26th St, Fort Lauderdale, FL, 33305
(305) 566-8353
Licensure Skilled care. Beds 206. Certified
Medicaid.
Owner Proprietary Corp.
Staff RNs 18 (ft); LPNs 15 (ft); Nurses aides
62 (ft).

Monticello Manor*
1701 N Federal Hwy, Fort Lauderdale, FL,
33308
(305) 564-3237
Licensure Skilled care. Beds 34.
Owner Proprietary Corp.
Admissions Requirements Minimum age 16;
Medical examination; Physician's request.
Staff RNs 4 (ft); LPNs 2 (ft); Nurses aides 8
(ft), 1 (pt); Physical therapists 1 (pt); Reality
therapists 1 (pt); Recreational therapists 1
(pt); Occupational therapists 1 (pt); Speech
therapists 1 (pt); Activities coordinators 1
(pt); Dietitians 1 (pt); Dentists 1 (pt);
Podiatrists 1 (pt).
Facilities Dining room; Physical therapy
room; Activities room; Crafts room; Laundry
room; Barber/Beauty shop.
Activities Arts & crafts; Cards; Games;
Reading groups; Prayer groups; Movies.

Mt Vernon Manor*
2331 NE 53rd St, Fort Lauderdale, FL, 33308
(305) 771-0739
Licensure Skilled care. Beds 29.
Owner Proprietary Corp.
Staff RNs 3 (ft); LPNs 2 (ft); Nurses aides 11
(ft).
Languages Spanish, German

National Health Care Center
2000 E Commercial Blvd, Fort Lauderdale, FL, 33308
(305) 771-2300
Admin J W Dunwoody. *Medical Dir/Dir of Nursing* Dr Lawrence Katzell; Delores Thompson RN.
Licensure Skilled care; Intermediate care. *Beds* SNF 209; ICF 44. *Certified* Medicaid; Medicare.
Owner Proprietary Corp.
Admissions Requirements Minimum age 16; Physician's request.
Staff Physicians 1 (pt); RNs 18 (ft); LPNs 26 (ft); Orderlies 4 (ft); Nurses aides 87 (ft); Physical therapists 1 (ft); Recreational therapists 1 (ft); Occupational therapists 1 (pt); Speech therapists 1 (pt); Activities coordinators 3 (ft); Dietitians 1 (ft); Ophthalmologists 1 (pt); Social worker 1 (ft); Medical records admin 1 (ft).
Languages German, Spanish, Italian, Yiddish
Facilities Dining room; Physical therapy room; Activities room; Laundry room; Barber/Beauty shop; Library.
Activities Arts & crafts; Cards; Games; Reading groups; Prayer groups; Movies; Social/Cultural gatherings.

Palm Court Nursing & Rehabilitation Center
2675 N Andrews Ave, Fort Lauderdale, FL, 33311
(305) 563-5711
Admin Bruce Atlas. *Medical Dir/Dir of Nursing* Dr Mark Copen; Nancy Moore.
Licensure Skilled care. *Beds* SNF 118. *Certified* Medicaid; Medicare.
Owner Proprietary Corp (Unicare).
Admissions Requirements Medical examination; Physician's request.
Staff RNs 6 (ft), 3 (pt); LPNs 8 (ft), 8 (pt); Orderlies 3 (ft), 1 (pt); Nurses aides 27 (ft), 7 (pt); Physical therapists 3 (ft); Occupational therapists 1 (ft); Speech therapists 2 (ft); Activities coordinators 2 (ft); Dietitians 2 (ft); Social service director 1 (ft); Admissions Coordinator 1 (ft).
Languages Spanish
Facilities Dining room; Physical therapy room; Activities room; Crafts room; Laundry room; Barber/Beauty shop; Library.
Activities Arts & crafts; Cards; Games; Reading groups; Prayer groups; Movies; Shopping trips; Social/Cultural gatherings; Exercise class; Continuing education; Reality orientation; Pet therapy; Resident council.

FORT MYERS

Beacon-Donegan Manor
8400 Beacon Blvd, Fort Myers, FL, 33907
(813) 936-1300
Admin Johnnie D Gonzalez. *Medical Dir/Dir of Nursing* Washington Baquero MD; Armida Seckler DON.
Licensure Skilled care; Intermediate care. *Beds* SNF 98; ICF 52. *Certified* Medicaid; Medicare.
Owner Proprietary Corp (Beverly Enterprises).
Admissions Requirements Medical examination; Physician's request.
Staff Physicians; RNs; LPNs; Orderlies; Nurses aides; Physical therapists; Reality therapists; Recreational therapists; Occupational therapists; Speech therapists; Activities coordinators; Dietitians; Ophthalmologists; Podiatrists.
Languages Spanish
Facilities Dining room; Physical therapy room; Activities room; Chapel; Crafts room; Laundry room; Barber/Beauty shop.
Activities Arts & crafts; Cards; Games; Reading groups; Prayer groups; Movies; Shopping trips; Social/Cultural gatherings.

Cypress Manor
7173 Cypress Dr SW, Fort Myers, FL, 33907
(813) 936-0203
Admin Dennis X Stress. *Medical Dir/Dir of Nursing* Edward Gonzales MD; Billie M Sorter RN DON.
Licensure Skilled care. *Beds* SNF 120.
Owner Proprietary Corp (Beverly Enterprises).
Staff Physicians 1 (pt); RNs 8 (ft), 1 (pt); LPNs 4 (ft), 5 (pt); Orderlies 4 (ft); Nurses aides 54 (ft), 3 (pt); Physical therapists 1 (pt); Occupational therapists 1 (pt); Speech therapists 1 (pt); Activities coordinators 1 (ft), 1 (pt); Dietitians 1 (pt).

Fort Myers Care Center
13755 Golf Club Pkwy, Fort Myers, FL, 33906
(813) 482-2848
Beds 107.
Owner Proprietary Corp (FL Living Care Inc).

Gulf Coast Center/Sunland
RR 1, PO Box 506, Fort Myers, FL, 33902
(813) 692-2151 *Certified* Medicaid.
Owner Publicly owned.

Lee Convalescent Center
2826 Cleveland Ave, Fort Myers, FL, 33901
(813) 334-1091
Admin Michael Ellis. *Medical Dir/Dir of Nursing* Rolando Jamilla MD; Linda Strommen RN.
Licensure Skilled care. *Beds* SNF 146. *Certified* Medicaid; Medicare; VA.
Owner Proprietary Corp (Beverly Enterprises).
Admissions Requirements Minimum age 16; Medical examination.
Staff Physicians 7 (pt); RNs 5 (ft), 3 (pt); LPNs 15 (ft), 3 (pt); Orderlies 2 (ft); Nurses aides 52 (ft), 7 (pt); Physical therapists 1 (pt); Recreational therapists 1 (pt); Occupational therapists 1 (pt); Speech therapists 1 (pt); Activities coordinators 2 (ft); Dietitians 1 (pt); Dentists 1 (pt); Ophthalmologists 1 (pt); Podiatrists 1 (pt).
Languages German
Activities Arts & crafts; Cards; Games; Reading groups; Prayer groups; Movies; Shopping trips; Social/Cultural gatherings; Community entertainment.

Shady Rest Nursing Home
Fort Myers, FL, 33907
(813) 936-2357
Admin Roger J Soricelli. *Medical Dir/Dir of Nursing* Lanette Cummings DON.
Licensure Skilled care. *Beds* SNF 105. *Certified* Medicaid.
Owner Publicly owned.
Admissions Requirements Medical examination.
Staff RNs 8 (ft); LPNs 12 (ft); Nurses aides 46 (ft); Activities coordinators 1 (ft); Dietitians 1 (ft).
Languages Spanish
Facilities Dining room; Activities room; Chapel; Laundry room; Barber/Beauty shop.
Activities Arts & crafts; Cards; Games; Reading groups; Prayer groups; Movies; Social/Cultural gatherings.

Shell Point Village Nursing Pavilion
Rte 12, Shell Point Blvd, Fort Myers, FL, 33901
(813) 466-1111
Admin Mary Lou Coleman. *Medical Dir/Dir of Nursing* Dr David Nesselroade; Susan Diggs RN DON.
Licensure Skilled care. *Beds* SNF 180. *Certified* Medicare.
Owner Nonprofit organization/foundation.
Admissions Requirements Medical examination; Physician's request.
Staff Physicians 3 (pt); RNs 6 (ft), 4 (pt); LPNs 17 (ft), 4 (pt); Orderlies 5 (ft), 1 (pt); Nurses aides 53 (ft), 2 (pt); Physical therapists 1 (ft); Occupational therapists 1

(pt); Speech therapists 1 (pt); Activities coordinators 1 (ft); Dietitians 1 (pt); Ophthalmologists 1 (pt); Podiatrists 1 (pt); Dentist 1 (pt).
Languages Spanish
Affiliation Christian & Missionary Alliance Foundation
Facilities Dining room; Physical therapy room; Activities room; Chapel; Crafts room; Barber/Beauty shop; Screened patio; Waterfront picnic area.
Activities Arts & crafts; Cards; Games; Reading groups; Prayer groups; Movies; Shopping trips; Social/Cultural gatherings; Music groups; Exercise club; Current events; Pet program; Birthday celebrations.

FORT PIERCE

Fort Pierce Care Center*
703 S 29th St, Fort Pierce, FL, 33450
(305) 466-3322
Medical Dir/Dir of Nursing Carmen Ebalo MD.
Licensure Skilled care. *Beds* 102.
Owner Proprietary Corp (FL Living Care Inc).
Admissions Requirements Minimum age 16; Medical examination.
Staff RNs 5 (ft), 6 (pt); LPNs 4 (ft), 7 (pt); Orderlies 1 (ft); Nurses aides 30 (ft), 7 (pt); Activities coordinators 1 (ft); Dietitians 1 (ft).
Facilities Dining room; Physical therapy room; Activities room; Laundry room; Barber/Beauty shop.

Abbiejean Russell Care Center
700 S 29th St, Fort Pierce, FL, 33456
(305) 465-7560
Admin R C Schriever. *Medical Dir/Dir of Nursing* Richard F Kaine MD.
Licensure Skilled care. *Beds* 79. *Certified* Medicaid.
Owner Nonprofit Corp.
Admissions Requirements Minimum age 21; Medical examination; Physician's request.
Staff Physicians 3 (pt); RNs 3 (ft), 2 (pt); LPNs 8 (ft), 3 (pt); Orderlies 2 (ft); Nurses aides 26 (ft), 1 (pt); Physical therapists 4 (pt); Occupational therapists 2 (pt); Speech therapists 2 (pt); Activities coordinators 2 (ft); Dietitians 1 (pt); Dentists 1 (pt); Podiatrists 1 (pt); Audiologists 1 (pt); Psychologist 1 (pt).
Languages Spanish, German, Polish
Facilities Dining room; Physical therapy room; Activities room; Laundry room; Barber/Beauty shop; Library; Large screened patio; Large fenced yeard; Shuffleboard court; Outdoor barbecue.
Activities Arts & crafts; Cards; Games; Reading groups; Prayer groups; Movies; Shopping trips; Social/Cultural gatherings; Morning fitness class; Weekly cooking class.

Sunrise Manor Nursing Home
611 S 13th St, Fort Pierce, FL, 33454
(305) 464-5262
Licensure Skilled care. *Beds* 171. *Certified* Medicaid; Medicare.
Owner Proprietary Corp.
Staff RNs 8 (ft); LPNs 16 (ft); Nurses aides 50 (ft).
Languages Spanish, French, Tagalog

FORT WALTON BEACH

Fort Walton Developmental Center
113 Barks Dr, Fort Walton Beach, FL, 32548
(904) 862-0108
Admin Robert Bowman PhD. *Medical Dir/Dir of Nursing* Mary Harper RN HSD.
Licensure Intermediate care for mentally retarded. *Beds* 63.

Gulf Convalescent Center
114 3rd St SE, Fort Walton Beach, FL, 32548
(904) 243-6135
Medical Dir/Dir of Nursing T L Louisville.
Licensure Skilled care. *Beds* 120. *Certified*
Medicaid; Medicare.
Owner Proprietary Corp.
Admissions Requirements Medical
examination; Physician's request.
Staff RNs 3 (ft), 3 (pt); LPNs 9 (ft), 3 (pt);
Nurses aides 39 (ft), 20 (pt); Physical
therapists 1 (pt); Occupational therapists;
Speech therapists; Activities coordinators 1
(pt); Dietitians 1 (pt); Ophthalmologists 1
(pt); Dentist 1 (pt).
Languages Spanish, French, Japanese
Facilities Dining room; Physical therapy
room; Activities room; Laundry room;
Barber/Beauty shop; Library.
Activities Arts & crafts; Cards; Games;
Reading groups; Prayer groups; Shopping
trips; Social/Cultural gatherings.

Westwood Retirement Center*
1001 Mar-Walt Dr, Fort Walton Beach, FL,
32548
(904) 863-5471
Beds 60. *Certified* Medicaid; Medicare.
Owner Proprietary Corp.

GAINESVILLE

Community Convalescent Center*
100 SW 16th Ave, Gainesville, FL, 32601
(904) 376-2461
Licensure Skilled care. *Beds* 120. *Certified*
Medicaid; Medicare.
Owner Proprietary Corp (Beverly Enterprises).
Staff RNs 8 (ft); LPNs 7 (ft); Nurses aides 26
(ft).

Gainesville Nursing Center
4000 SW 20th Ave, Gainesville, FL, 32608
(904) 377-1981
Admin R B Lockeby. *Medical Dir/Dir of
Nursing* Dr David Black; Betty J Owens RN.
Licensure Skilled care. *Beds* 93. *Certified*
Medicaid; VA.
Owner Proprietary Corp.
Admissions Requirements Minimum age 16;
Medical examination; Physician's request.
Staff Physicians 3 (pt); RNs 4 (ft), 1 (pt);
LPNs 6 (ft), 2 (pt); Orderlies 2 (ft), 1 (pt);
Nurses aides 40 (ft), 10 (pt); Physical
therapists 2 (pt); Reality therapists 1 (ft);
Recreational therapists 1 (ft); Speech
therapists 1 (pt); Activities coordinators 1
(ft), 1 (pt); Dietitians 1 (pt); Podiatrists 1
(pt).
Languages Spanish, German,
Facilities Dining room; Physical therapy
room; Activities room; Crafts room; Laundry
room; Barber/Beauty shop; Library.
Activities Arts & crafts; Cards; Games;
Reading groups; Prayer groups; Movies.

Regency Oaks*
3250 SW 41st Pl, Gainesville, FL, 32601
(904) 378-1558
Medical Dir/Dir of Nursing William Warrick
III MD.
Licensure Skilled care. *Beds* 119. *Certified*
Medicaid; Medicare.
Owner Proprietary Corp.
Admissions Requirements Minimum age 16;
Medical examination; Physician's request.
Staff Physicians 1 (ft), 1 (pt); RNs 8 (ft), 2
(pt); LPNs 12 (ft), 4 (pt); Orderlies 4 (ft);
Nurses aides 31 (ft), 10 (pt); Physical
therapists 1 (ft); Reality therapists 1 (ft);
Recreational therapists 1 (ft); Occupational
therapists 1 (ft); Speech therapists 1 (ft);
Activities coordinators 1 (ft); Dietitians 1
(ft); Dentists 1 (pt); Ophthalmologists 1 (pt);
Podiatrists 1 (pt); Audiologists 1 (pt).
Facilities Dining room; Physical therapy
room; Activities room; Laundry room;
Barber/Beauty shop.

Activities Arts & crafts; Cards; Games;
Reading groups; Prayer groups; Movies;
Shopping trips; Social/Cultural gatherings.

Sunland Center—Gainesville Facility I
PO Box 1150, Gainesville, FL, 32602
(904) 395-1455
Admin David English & Max Jackson.
Medical Dir/Dir of Nursing Dr Charles
Williams; Carolyn Steadham.
Licensure Intermediate care for mentally
retarded. *Beds* ICF/MR 120. *Certified*
Medicaid.
Owner Publicly owned.
Admissions Requirements Medical
examination.
Staff Physicians 1 (ft); RNs 7 (ft); LPNs 4 (ft);
Physical therapists 4 (ft); Recreational
therapists 10 (ft); Occupational therapists 2
(ft); Speech therapists 2 (ft); Dietitians 1 (ft);
Podiatrists 1 (ft); Dentist 4 (ft).
Facilities Dining room; Physical therapy
room; Activities room; Chapel; Crafts room;
Laundry room; Barber/Beauty shop; Library;
Gymnasium; Theater; Weight room; On-site
24 hr Clinic; Dentist office; Hospital.
Activities Arts & crafts; Games; Movies;
Shopping trips; Social/Cultural gatherings.

Sunland Center—Gainesville Facility II*
PO Box 1150, Gainesville, FL, 32602
(904) 376-5381
Licensure Intermediate care for mentally
retarded. *Beds* 120.
Owner Publicly owned.

Sunland Center—Gainesville Facility III*
PO Box 1150, Gainesville, FL, 32602
(904) 376-5381
Licensure Intermediate care for mentally
retarded. *Beds* 60.
Owner Publicly owned.

University Nursing Care Center
1311 SW 16th St, Gainesville, FL, 32608
Admin S L Keach. *Medical Dir/Dir of Nursing*
Dr J Cerda; L Hawley DON.
Licensure Skilled care; Intermediate care. *Beds*
180. *Certified* Medicaid; Medicare.
Owner Privately owned.
Admissions Requirements Medical
examination; Physician's request.
Staff RNs 8 (ft), 7 (pt); LPNs 5 (ft), 3 (pt);
Nurses aides 25 (ft), 6 (pt); Physical
therapists 2 (ft); Speech therapists 1 (pt);
Activities coordinators 1 (ft); Dietitians 1
(pt).
Facilities Dining room; Physical therapy
room; Activities room; Chapel; Laundry
room; Barber/Beauty shop.
Activities Arts & crafts; Cards; Games;
Reading groups; Prayer groups; Movies;
Shopping trips; Social/Cultural gatherings.

GLENWOOD

Duvall Home for Retarded Children
PO Box 36, 3395 Grand Ave, Glenwood, FL,
32722
(904) 734-2874
Admin W Blake Davis. *Medical Dir/Dir of
Nursing* Carolyn Righter.
Licensure Home for special services. *Beds*
250.
Owner Nonprofit Corp.
Staff RNs 1 (ft), 1 (pt); LPNs 11 (ft);
Orderlies 121 (ft), 3 (pt); Physical therapists
1 (ft); Recreational therapists 5 (ft);
Activities coordinators 1 (ft); Dietitians 1
(ft).
Languages Spanish
Facilities Dining room; Physical therapy
room; Activities room; Chapel; Crafts room;
Laundry room; Barber/Beauty shop; Junior
size Olympic swimming pool.
Activities Arts & crafts; Games; Movies;
Shopping trips; Social/Cultural gatherings.

GOULDS

Lincoln Memorial Nursing Home*
11295 SW 216th St, Goulds, FL, 33170
(305) 235-7461
Medical Dir/Dir of Nursing Manuel E Abella
MD.
Licensure Skilled care. *Beds* 32. *Certified*
Medicaid; Medicare.
Owner Nonprofit Corp.
Admissions Requirements Minimum age 16;
Medical examination; Physician's request.
Staff Physicians 2 (pt); RNs 1 (ft), 1 (pt);
LPNs 3 (ft), 4 (pt); Nurses aides 9 (ft), 3
(pt); Physical therapists 1 (pt); Recreational
therapists 1 (pt); Occupational therapists 1
(pt); Speech therapists 1 (pt); Activities
coordinators 1 (ft); Dietitians 1 (pt); Dentists
1 (pt).
Languages Spanish, French
Facilities Dining room; Activities room;
Crafts room; Laundry room.
Activities Arts & crafts; Cards; Games; Prayer
groups; Social/Cultural gatherings.

Sunrise Community-Miami
22300 SW 162 Ave, Goulds, FL, 33170
(305) 245-6150
Admin Henry C Sterner DPA. *Medical Dir/
Dir of Nursing* Eliza Perry RN DON.
Licensure Intermediate care for mentally
retarded. *Beds* ICF/MR 120. *Certified*
Medicaid.
Owner Proprietary Corp.
Admissions Requirements Minimum age 3;
Medical examination.
Staff Physicians 1 (ft); RNs 9 (ft); LPNs 12
(ft), 5 (pt); Nurses aides 4 (ft); Physical
therapists 2 (ft); Recreational therapists 4
(ft); Occupational therapists 2 (ft); Speech
therapists 2 (ft), 1 (pt); Activities
coordinators 1 (pt); Dietitians 1 (ft).
Facilities Dining room; Physical therapy
room; Activities room; Crafts room; Laundry
room; Bedroom; Medical clinic; Auditorium;
Transportation.
Activities Arts & crafts; Cards; Games; Prayer
groups; Movies; Shopping trips; Social/
Cultural gatherings.

Sunrise Group Home 1—Goulds*
1600 SW 216th St, Goulds, FL, 33170
(305) 248-3701
Licensure Intermediate care for mentally
retarded. *Beds* 15. *Certified* Medicaid.
Owner Proprietary Corp.

GRACEVILLE

Jackson County Convalescent Center*
1002 Sanders Ave, Graceville, FL, 32440
(904) 263-4447
Licensure Skilled care. *Beds* 99. *Certified*
Medicaid.
Owner Proprietary Corp (Beverly Enterprises).

GREEN COVE SPRINGS

Green Cove Springs Geriatric Center*
803 Oak St, Green Cove Springs, FL, 32043
(904) 284-5606
Licensure Skilled care. *Beds* 120. *Certified*
Medicaid; Medicare.
Owner Proprietary Corp (Beverly Enterprises).
Staff RNs 5 (ft); LPNs 12 (ft); Nurses aides 37
(ft).
Languages Spanish, German

GREENVILLE

Pine Lake Nursing Home
Hwy 90 E, Greenville, FL, 32331
(904) 948-4601
Admin Susan Michael. *Medical Dir/Dir of
Nursing* J M Durant MD.

Licensure Skilled care. *Beds* 58. *Certified* Medicaid.
Owner Proprietary Corp.
Admissions Requirements Medical examination; Physician's request.
Staff Physicians 3 (pt); RNs 2 (ft); LPNs 4 (ft), 6 (pt); Nurses aides 19 (ft), 5 (pt); Physical therapists 1 (pt); Activities coordinators 1 (ft); Dietitians 1 (pt); Dentists 1 (pt); Ophthalmologists 1 (pt); Dentist 1 (pt).
Facilities Dining room; Activities room; Laundry room; Barber/Beauty shop.
Activities Arts & crafts; Cards; Games; Reading groups; Prayer groups; Movies; Shopping trips; Social/Cultural gatherings.

GULFPORT

Gulfport Convalescent Center*
1414 59th St S, Gulfport, FL, 33707
(813) 344-4608
Medical Dir/Dir of Nursing Robert Jenkins MD.
Licensure Skilled care. *Beds* 120. *Certified* Medicaid; Medicare.
Owner Proprietary Corp.
Staff Physicians; RNs; LPNs; Orderlies; Nurses aides; Physical therapists; Speech therapists; Activities coordinators; Dietitians; Dentists.
Languages Spanish
Facilities Dining room; Activities room; Barber/Beauty shop; Library.
Activities Arts & crafts; Cards; Games; Prayer groups; Movies; Shopping trips; Social/Cultural gatherings.

HALLANDALE

Hallandale Rehabilitation Center
2400 E Hallandale Beach Blvd, Hallandale, FL, 33009
(305) 457-9717
Licensure Skilled care. *Beds* 149. *Certified* Medicaid; Medicare.
Owner Proprietary Corp.
Staff RNs 6 (ft); LPNs 19 (ft); Nurses aides 55 (ft).
Languages Spanish

HIALEAH

Hialeah Convalescent Home
190 W 28th St, Hialeah, FL, 33010
(305) 885-2437
Admin Kathryn Saretsky. *Medical Dir/Dir of Nursing* Manuel Abella MD; Madeline Sawin RN.
Licensure Skilled care. *Beds* SNF 276. *Certified* Medicaid; Medicare.
Owner Proprietary Corp (Angell Group).
Admissions Requirements Minimum age 16; Medical examination; Physician's request.
Staff Physicians 1 (pt); RNs 28 (ft); LPNs 5 (ft); Nurses aides 98 (ft); Occupational therapists 1 (pt); Speech therapists 1 (pt); Activities coordinators 1 (ft); Dietitians 1 (pt); Dentists 1 (pt); Ophthalmologists 1 (pt); Podiatrists 1 (pt).
Languages Spanish
Facilities Dining room; Physical therapy room; Activities room; Crafts room; Laundry room; Barber/Beauty shop.
Activities Arts & crafts; Cards; Games; Reading groups; Prayer groups; Movies; Shopping trips; Social/Cultural gatherings.

HOBE SOUND

Hobe Sound Geriatric Village
9555 SE Federal Hwy, Hobe Sound, FL, 33455
(305) 546-5800

Admin Milly Barry. *Medical Dir/Dir of Nursing* Maghraj Thanvi MD; Rita Brexel RN.
Licensure Skilled care. *Beds* SNF 120. *Certified* Medicaid; Medicare.
Owner Proprietary Corp (Eden Park Management).
Admissions Requirements Minimum age 16; Medical examination; Physician's request.
Staff Physicians 1 (pt); RNs 6 (pt); LPNs 8 (ft), 2 (pt); Orderlies 1 (ft); Nurses aides 35 (ft), 7 (pt); Physical therapists 2 (pt); Activities coordinators 1 (ft); Dietitians 1 (pt); Ophthalmologists 1 (pt).
Languages Spanish
Facilities Dining room; Physical therapy room; Activities room; Chapel; Crafts room; Laundry room; Barber/Beauty shop; Library.
Activities Arts & crafts; Cards; Games; Reading groups; Prayer groups; Movies; Shopping trips; Social/Cultural gatherings.

HOLLYWOOD

Golfcrest Nursing Home
600 N 17th Ave, Hollywood, FL, 33020
(305) 927-2531
Admin Van K Isler. *Medical Dir/Dir of Nursing* Samuel Colton MD; Colleen Sturgis DON.
Licensure Skilled care. *Beds* 67. *Certified* Medicaid; Medicare.
Owner Proprietary Corp (Americare Corp).
Admissions Requirements Minimum age 16; Medical examination; Physician's request.
Staff RNs 6 (ft), 3 (pt); LPNs 6 (ft), 3 (pt); Nurses aides 30 (ft), 8 (pt); Physical therapists 1 (pt); Speech therapists 1 (pt); Activities coordinators 1 (ft); Dietitians 1 (ft); Ophthalmologists 1 (pt); Podiatrists 1 (pt).
Languages Spanish
Facilities Dining room; Physical therapy room; Activities room; Laundry room; Barber/Beauty shop.
Activities Arts & crafts; Games; Reading groups; Movies; Social/Cultural gatherings.

Hollywood Hills Nursing Home
1200 N 35th Ave, Hollywood, FL, 33023
(305) 981-5511
Admin Karen Kallen. *Medical Dir/Dir of Nursing* Keith Custer MD; Caryl B Custer RN DON.
Licensure Skilled care; Intermediate care. *Beds* 152. *Certified* Medicaid; Medicare.
Owner Proprietary Corp.
Admissions Requirements Medical examination.
Staff Physicians; RNs; LPNs; Orderlies; Nurses aides; Physical therapists; Recreational therapists; Occupational therapists; Speech therapists; Activities coordinators; Dietitians; Dentists; Ophthalmologists; Podiatrists.
Languages German, Hindi, Spanish
Facilities Dining room; Physical therapy room; Activities room; Chapel; Crafts room; Laundry room; Barber/Beauty shop; Library.
Activities Arts & crafts; Cards; Games; Reading groups; Prayer groups; Movies; Shopping trips; Social/Cultural gatherings; Language; Class video; BBQs.

Washington Manor Nursing & Rehabilitation Center
4200 Washington St, Hollywood, FL, 33021
(305) 981-6300
Medical Dir/Dir of Nursing Dr Richard Reines.
Licensure Skilled care; Intermediate care. *Beds* 240. *Certified* Medicare.
Owner Proprietary Corp (Beverly Enterprises).
Admissions Requirements Minimum age 18; Medical examination.

Staff RNs 6 (ft), 2 (pt); LPNs 17 (ft), 6 (pt); Nurses aides 50 (ft), 15 (pt); Physical therapists 1 (ft), 1 (pt); Reality therapists 1 (pt); Recreational therapists 1 (pt); Occupational therapists 1 (pt); Speech therapists 1 (pt); Activities coordinators 3 (ft); Dietitians 1 (ft); Ophthalmologists 1 (pt); Social worker 1 (ft), 1 (pt).
Languages Spanish
Facilities Dining room; Physical therapy room; Activities room; Chapel; Laundry room; Barber/Beauty shop; Library; 2 Outdoor garden patios.
Activities Arts & crafts; Cards; Games; Reading groups; Prayer groups; Movies; Shopping trips; Social/Cultural gatherings; Pet therapy; BBQs.

HOMESTEAD

Homestead Manor Nursing Home*
1330 NW 1st Ave, Homestead, FL, 33030
(305) 248-0271
Medical Dir/Dir of Nursing Dr Bankett & Dr Crump.
Licensure Skilled care. *Beds* 54. *Certified* Medicaid; Medicare.
Owner Proprietary Corp.
Staff Physicians; Dietitians; Nurses aides.
Languages Spanish, Italian, German, French
Facilities Dining room; Activities room; Crafts room; Laundry room; Barber/Beauty shop.
Activities Arts & crafts; Games; Movies; Shopping trips; Social/Cultural gatherings.

HUDSON

Bear Creek Nursing Center
8041 SR 52, Hudson, FL, 34667
(813) 863-5488
Admin Van S McGlawn. *Medical Dir/Dir of Nursing* Louise Maben.
Licensure Skilled care; Intermediate care. *Beds* SNF 120; ICF. *Certified* Medicaid; Medicare.
Owner Proprietary Corp.
Admissions Requirements Minimum age 16.
Staff RNs 6 (ft); LPNs 12 (ft); Orderlies 4 (ft); Nurses aides 40 (ft); Activities coordinators 2 (ft).
Activities Arts & crafts; Cards; Games; Prayer groups; Movies; Shopping trips; Social/Cultural gatherings.

INVERNESS

Inverness Health Care Facility
304 S Citrus Ave, Inverness, FL, 32650
(904) 726-3141
Admin Kirk A Copley. *Medical Dir/Dir of Nursing* Dr William Du.
Licensure Skilled care. *Beds* SNF; ICF 104. *Certified* Medicaid; Medicare.
Owner Publicly owned.
Admissions Requirements Minimum age 17; Medical examination; Physician's request.
Staff Physicians 8 (pt); RNs 10 (ft); LPNs 12 (ft); Orderlies 3 (ft); Nurses aides 3 (ft); Physical therapists 2 (ft); Recreational therapists 1 (ft); Occupational therapists 1 (ft); Speech therapists 1 (ft); Activities coordinators 1 (ft); Dietitians 2 (ft); Dentists 1 (ft); Ophthalmologists 1 (ft); Podiatrists 1 (ft).
Facilities Dining room; Physical therapy room; Activities room; Laundry room; Barber/Beauty shop.
Activities Arts & crafts; Cards; Games; Reading groups; Prayer groups; Movies; Shopping trips; Social/Cultural gatherings.

JACKSONVILLE

The Adams Plaza
33 W Adams St, Jacksonville, FL, 32202
(904) 358-1832
Admin James Lundy. *Medical Dir/Dir of Nursing* Dr Groover; Patti Kink.
Licensure Skilled care. *Beds* SNF 35. *Certified* Medicaid.
Owner Privately owned.
Staff Physicians 1 (ft); RNs 1 (ft), 1 (pt); LPNs 3 (ft), 2 (pt); Physical therapists 21 (ft); Activities coordinators 1 (pt); Dietitians 1 (pt).
Facilities Dining room; Physical therapy room; Activities room; Crafts room; Barber/Beauty shop.
Activities Arts & crafts; Cards; Games; Reading groups; Prayer groups; Movies.

All Saints Catholic Nursing Home*
2040 Riverside Ave, Jacksonville, FL, 32204
(904) 389-4671
Licensure Skilled care. *Beds* 57. *Certified* Medicaid.
Owner Nonprofit Corp.
Staff RNs 2 (ft); LPNs 6 (ft); Nurses aides 25 (ft).
Languages Spanish, French, Italian, Tagalog
Affiliation Roman Catholic

Americana Healthcare Center
3648 University Blvd S, Jacksonville, FL, 32216
(904) 733-7440
Admin Brian C Pollett. *Medical Dir/Dir of Nursing* Thomas E Michelsen DO.
Licensure Skilled care. *Beds* SNF 89. *Certified* Medicaid; Medicare.
Owner Proprietary Corp (Manor Care).
Admissions Requirements Medical examination; Physician's request.
Staff RNs 3 (ft), 3 (pt); LPNs 7 (ft), 6 (pt); Orderlies 2 (ft); Nurses aides 32 (ft), 10 (pt); Recreational therapists 1 (pt); Activities coordinators 1 (ft); Dietitians 1 (ft).
Languages Spanish, Tagalog
Facilities Dining room; Physical therapy room; Activities room; Chapel; Crafts room; Laundry room; Barber/Beauty shop; Lounge; Outdoor patio.
Activities Arts & crafts; Cards; Games; Reading groups; Prayer groups; Movies; Shopping trips.

Arlington Manor Care Center
7723 Jasper Ave, Jacksonville, FL, 32211
(904) 725-8044
Admin Deborah L Simmons. *Medical Dir/Dir of Nursing* Dr John C Hackenberg; Jean Staley RN.
Licensure Skilled care; Intermediate care. *Beds* 100. *Certified* Medicaid; Medicare.
Owner Proprietary Corp (Unicare).
Admissions Requirements Minimum age 21; Females only.
Staff Physicians 1 (pt); RNs 3 (ft); LPNs 7 (ft); Nurses aides 22 (ft); Physical therapists 1 (pt); Speech therapists 1 (pt); Activities coordinators 1 (pt); Dietitians 1 (ft); Podiatrists 1 (pt).
Languages Spanish
Facilities Dining room; Activities room; Laundry room.
Activities Arts & crafts; Cards; Games; Reading groups; Prayer groups; Movies; Shopping trips; Social/Cultural gatherings.

Cathedral Health & Rehabilitation Center*
333 E Ashley St, Jacksonville, FL, 32202
(904) 355-1761
Licensure Skilled care. *Beds* 32. *Certified* Medicaid; Medicare.
Owner Nonprofit Corp.
Languages Spanish, Tagalog
Activities Prayer groups.

Cedar Hills Nursing Center
2061 Hyde Park Rd, Jacksonville, FL, 32210
(904) 786-7331
Admin Billy F Miles. *Medical Dir/Dir of Nursing* Thomas Thommi MD; Elaine H Drury RN DON.
Licensure Skilled care. *Beds* SNF 180. *Certified* Medicaid; Medicare.
Owner Proprietary Corp (Americare Corp).
Admissions Requirements Medical examination.
Staff Physicians 1 (ft); Physical therapists 4 (pt); Speech therapists 1 (pt); Activities coordinators 3 (ft); Dietitians 1 (ft), 1 (pt); Dentists 1 (pt); Ophthalmologists 1 (pt); Podiatrists 1 (pt).
Languages French, German, Spanish
Facilities Dining room; Physical therapy room; Activities room; Chapel; Laundry room; Barber/Beauty shop.
Activities Arts & crafts; Cards; Games; Reading groups; Prayer groups; Movies; Shopping trips.

Florida Christian Health Center
1827 Stockton St, Jacksonville, FL, 32204
(904) 384-3457
Admin W C Wheatley Jr. *Medical Dir/Dir of Nursing* H June King RN.
Licensure Skilled care; Intermediate care. *Beds* 128. *Certified* Medicaid; Medicare.
Owner Nonprofit Corp (Natl Bnvlnt Assn of Chrstn Homes).
Admissions Requirements Minimum age 17; Medical examination; Physician's request.
Staff Physicians 2 (pt); RNs 3 (ft), 2 (pt); LPNs 14 (ft), 2 (pt); Nurses aides 46 (ft), 5 (pt); Physical therapists 1 (pt); Activities coordinators 1 (ft); Dietitians 1 (pt); Ophthalmologists 1 (pt).
Languages Spanish, German
Affiliation Disciples of Christ
Facilities Dining room; Physical therapy room; Activities room; Crafts room; Barber/Beauty shop.
Activities Arts & crafts; Movies; Shopping trips; Social/Cultural gatherings; Discussion groups; Sightseeing trips; Worship services.

Hodges Boulevard Cluster Homes*
3615 Hodges Blvd, RR 1, Jacksonville, FL, 32224
(904) 241-4173
Licensure Intermediate care for mentally retarded. *Beds* 24.
Owner Publicly owned.

Hospitality Care Center*
1504 Seabreeze Ave, Jacksonville, FL, 32250
(904) 249-7421
Licensure Skilled care. *Beds* 120. *Certified* Medicaid.
Owner Proprietary Corp (Beverly Enterprises).
Staff RNs 7 (ft); LPNs 13 (ft); Nurses aides 26 (ft).
Languages Spanish

Jacksonville Convalescent Center
730 College St, Jacksonville, FL, 32204
(904) 354-5589
Licensure Skilled care; Intermediate care. *Beds* 104. *Certified* Medicaid.
Owner Proprietary Corp (Beverly Enterprises).
Admissions Requirements Medical examination; Physician's request.
Staff Physicians; RNs; LPNs; Orderlies; Nurses aides; Physical therapists; Recreational therapists; Occupational therapists; Speech therapists; Activities coordinators; Dietitians; Ophthalmologists.
Facilities Dining room; Physical therapy room; Activities room; Chapel; Laundry room; Barber/Beauty shop.
Activities Arts & crafts; Cards; Games; Prayer groups; Movies; Shopping trips; Social/Cultural gatherings.

Mandarin Manor
10680 Old Saint Augustine Rd, Jacksonville, FL, 32223
(904) 268-4953
Admin W Joseph Ganzenhuber. *Medical Dir/Dir of Nursing* Jack E Giddings MD; Norma Williams.
Licensure Skilled care; Intermediate care. *Beds* 120. *Certified* Medicaid; Medicare.
Owner Proprietary Corp.
Admissions Requirements Medical examination; Physician's request.
Staff Physicians 4 (pt); RNs 4 (ft), 2 (pt); LPNs 12 (ft), 2 (pt); Orderlies 3 (ft), 1 (pt); Nurses aides 35 (ft), 2 (pt); Physical therapists 1 (pt); Activities coordinators 2 (ft); Dietitians 1 (ft); Ophthalmologists 1 (ft).
Facilities Dining room; Physical therapy room; Activities room; Crafts room; Barber/Beauty shop; Library.
Activities Arts & crafts; Cards; Games; Prayer groups; Movies; Shopping trips; Social/Cultural gatherings.

River Garden Hebrew Home for the Aged*
1800 Stockton St, Jacksonville, FL, 32204
(904) 389-3665
Admin Elliott Palevsky. *Medical Dir/Dir of Nursing* Lawrence E Geeslin MD.
Licensure Skilled care; Intermediate care. *Beds* SNF 182; ICF 10. *Certified* Medicaid; Medicare.
Owner Nonprofit Corp.
Admissions Requirements Medical examination; Physician's request.
Staff Physicians 1 (ft), 2 (pt); RNs 10 (ft), 2 (pt); LPNs 24 (ft); Nurses aides 87 (ft); Physical therapists 2 (ft), 2 (pt); Reality therapists 1 (ft); Recreational therapists 5 (ft); Occupational therapists 1 (pt); Speech therapists 2 (pt); Activities coordinators 1 (ft); Dietitians 1 (pt); Dentists 6 (pt); Ophthalmologists 4 (pt); Audiologists 2 (pt); Social workers 3 (ft).
Languages Spanish, German, Hebrew, Yiddish
Affiliation Jewish
Facilities Dining room; Physical therapy room; Activities room; Chapel; Crafts room; Laundry room; Barber/Beauty shop; Library; Landscaped river front garden with walks; Medical clinic.
Activities Arts & crafts; Cards; Games; Reading groups; Prayer groups; Movies; Shopping trips; Social/Cultural gatherings.

Rosewood Nursing Home
12739 Dunns Creek Rd, Jacksonville, FL, 32218
(904) 757-0600
Admin Pat Scanlin. *Medical Dir/Dir of Nursing* Annie Reese.
Licensure Skilled care; Intermediate care. *Beds* SNF 5; ICF 50. *Certified* Medicaid; Medicare.
Owner Privately owned.
Admissions Requirements Physician's request.
Facilities Dining room; Activities room.
Activities Arts & crafts; Cards; Games; Prayer groups; Shopping trips.

St Catherine Laboure Manor
1717 Barrs St, Jacksonville, FL, 32204
(904) 387-0587
Admin E Jack Huben. *Medical Dir/Dir of Nursing* Gerald Gillrato MD; Emily Edmondson RN DON.
Licensure Skilled care; Intermediate care. *Beds* 232. *Certified* Medicaid; Medicare.
Owner Nonprofit Corp.
Admissions Requirements Females only; Medical examination.
Staff RNs 10 (ft); LPNs 31 (ft); Nurses aides 87 (ft); Recreational therapists 3 (ft); Activities coordinators 1 (ft).
Languages Spanish, Vietnamese, Farsi
Affiliation Roman Catholic

Facilities Dining room; Physical therapy room; Activities room; Chapel; Barber/ Beauty shop.
Activities Arts & crafts; Cards; Games; Reading groups; Prayer groups; Movies; Shopping trips; Social/Cultural gatherings; Fishing.

St Jude Manor Nursing Home*
2802 Parental Home Rd, Jacksonville, FL, 32216
(904) 721-0088
Licensure Skilled care. *Beds* 238. *Certified* Medicaid; Medicare.
Owner Proprietary Corp (National Healthcare Affiliates).
Staff RNs 12 (ft); LPNs 17 (ft); Nurses aides 48 (ft).
Affiliation Roman Catholic

Southside Nursing Center Inc
40 Acme St, Jacksonville, FL, 32211
(904) 724-5933
Admin Raymond R Savage. *Medical Dir/Dir of Nursing* Guy T Selander MD.
Licensure Skilled care. *Beds* 118.
Staff Physicians 2 (pt); RNs 4 (ft); LPNs 8 (ft), 4 (pt); Nurses aides 28 (ft), 10 (pt); Activities coordinators 1 (ft); Dietitians 1 (pt); Dentists 1 (pt); Ophthalmologists 1 (pt); Podiatrists 1 (pt).
Facilities Dining room; Activities room; Laundry room; Barber/Beauty shop; Library.

Fannie E Taylor Home for the Aged*
3937 Spring Park Rd, Jacksonville, FL, 32207
(904) 737-6777
Licensure Intermediate care. *Beds* 24. *Certified* Medicaid.
Owner Nonprofit Corp.
Staff Physicians; Dietitians; Nurses aides.
Activities Arts & crafts; Shopping trips.

Turtle Creek Health Care Center
11565 Harts Rd, Jacksonville, FL, 32218
(904) 751-1834
Admin Joseph DeBelder. *Medical Dir/Dir of Nursing* Dr Samara; Sandra Hudson RN DON.
Licensure Skilled care. *Beds* 180. *Certified* Medicaid.
Owner Proprietary Corp (Beverly Enterprises).
Admissions Requirements Minimum age 18; Medical examination.
Staff RNs 6 (ft); LPNs 24 (ft); Nurses aides 60 (ft).
Facilities Dining room; Physical therapy room; Activities room; Laundry room; Barber/Beauty shop.
Activities Arts & crafts; Cards; Games; Reading groups; Prayer groups; Movies; Shopping trips.

Wesley Manor Retirement Village
State Rd 13 at Julington Creek Rd, Jacksonville, FL, 32223
(904) 262-7300
Medical Dir/Dir of Nursing Virginia Johnson RN.
Licensure Skilled care. *Beds* 57.
Owner Nonprofit Corp.
Admissions Requirements Minimum age 62; Medical examination.
Staff Physicians 3 (pt); Physical therapists 1 (pt); Recreational therapists 1 (pt); Occupational therapists 1 (pt); Speech therapists 1 (pt); Activities coordinators 1 (ft); Dietitians 1 (ft); Podiatrists 1 (pt).
Languages Italian
Affiliation Methodist
Facilities Dining room; Physical therapy room; Activities room; Chapel; Crafts room; Laundry room; Barber/Beauty shop; Library.
Activities Arts & crafts; Cards; Games; Reading groups; Prayer groups; Movies; Shopping trips; Social/Cultural gatherings.

Eartha M M White Nursing Home*
5377 Moncrief Rd, Jacksonville, FL, 32209
(904) 768-1506
Admin S L Patterson.
Licensure Skilled care. *Beds* 120. *Certified* Medicaid; Medicare.
Owner Nonprofit Corp.
Admissions Requirements Minimum age 18; Medical examination.
Staff Physicians 4 (pt); RNs 3 (ft), 4 (pt); LPNs 10 (ft), 7 (pt); Orderlies 2 (ft); Nurses aides 40 (ft), 1 (pt); Physical therapists 1 (ft); Reality therapists 1 (pt); Recreational therapists 1 (pt); Occupational therapists 1 (pt); Speech therapists 1 (pt); Activities coordinators 1 (ft); Dietitians 1 (pt); Dentists 1 (pt); Ophthalmologists 1 (pt); Podiatrists 1 (pt); Audiologists 1 (pt).
Languages Tagalog
Facilities Dining room; Physical therapy room; Activities room; Chapel; Crafts room; Laundry room; Barber/Beauty shop; Library.
Activities Arts & crafts; Cards; Games; Reading groups; Prayer groups; Movies; Shopping trips; Social/Cultural gatherings; Birthday parties.

JASPER

Suwannee Valley Nursing Center*
PO Drawer 1058, Jasper, FL, 32502
(904) 792-1868
Licensure Skilled care. *Beds* 60. *Certified* Medicaid.
Owner Proprietary Corp.
Staff RNs 5 (ft), 5 (pt); LPNs 2 (ft), 3 (pt); Nurses aides 10 (ft), 10 (pt); Activities coordinators 1 (ft); Dietitians 1 (ft).

JUNO BEACH

The Waterford Health Center
601 S US Hwy 1, Juno Beach, FL, 33408
(305) 627-3800
Admin Becky Brown. *Medical Dir/Dir of Nursing* Cathy Hazen DON.
Licensure Skilled care. *Beds* SNF 60. *Certified* Medicaid; Medicare.
Owner Nonprofit Corp (Life Care Services Corp).
Admissions Requirements Medical examination.
Staff RNs 4 (ft), 1 (pt); LPNs 8 (ft), 1 (pt); Nurses aides 18 (ft), 3 (pt); Physical therapists 1 (ft); Occupational therapists; Speech therapists; Activities coordinators 1 (ft); Dietitians 1 (ft).
Facilities Dining room; Physical therapy room; Activities room; Crafts room; Barber/ Beauty shop; Library.
Activities Arts & crafts; Cards; Games; Reading groups; Prayer groups; Movies; Shopping trips; Social/Cultural gatherings.

JUPITER

Jupiter Convalescence Pavilion
1230 S Old Dixie Hwy, Jupiter, FL, 33458
(305) 744-4444
Medical Dir/Dir of Nursing Andres Svarez MD; Doris M Ferriol RN.
Licensure Skilled care. *Beds* 120. *Certified* Medicaid; Medicare.
Owner Nonprofit Corp.
Admissions Requirements Minimum age 21; Medical examination; Physician's request.
Staff Physicians 3 (pt); RNs 9 (ft), 6 (pt); LPNs 9 (ft), 3 (pt); Orderlies 1 (ft); Nurses aides 45 (ft), 5 (pt); Physical therapists 1 (ft); Activities coordinators 1 (ft); Dietitians 1 (ft).
Facilities Dining room; Physical therapy room; Activities room; Chapel; Crafts room; Laundry room; Barber/Beauty shop; Library.

Activities Arts & crafts; Cards; Games; Reading groups; Prayer groups; Movies; Shopping trips; Social/Cultural gatherings.

KEY WEST

Key West Convalescent Center
5860 W Jr College Rd, Key West, FL, 33040
(305) 296-2459
Admin Raymond Wasil. *Medical Dir/Dir of Nursing* Herman K Moore MD; Carol Stubbs RN DON.
Licensure Skilled care. *Beds* SNF 120. *Certified* Medicaid; Medicare.
Owner Proprietary Corp.
Admissions Requirements Minimum age 18; Medical examination; Physician's request.
Staff RNs; LPNs; Orderlies; Nurses aides; Physical therapists 1 (ft); Occupational therapists 1 (pt); Speech therapists 1 (pt); Activities coordinators 1 (ft), 1 (pt); Dietitians 1 (pt); Dentists 1 (pt); Ophthalmologists 1 (pt).
Languages Spanish
Facilities Dining room; Physical therapy room; Activities room; Crafts room; Laundry room; Barber/Beauty shop.
Activities Arts & crafts; Cards; Games; Reading groups; Prayer groups; Movies; Shopping trips.

KISSIMMEE

Kissimmee Good Samaritan Nursing Center*
1500 Southgate Dr, Kissimmee, FL, 32741
(305) 846-7201
Medical Dir/Dir of Nursing Pedro Gonzales.
Licensure Skilled care; Intermediate care. *Beds* SNF 142; ICF 28. *Certified* Medicaid.
Owner Nonprofit Corp (Evangelical Lutheran/ Good Samaritan).
Admissions Requirements Minimum age 21; Medical examination; Physician's request.
Staff RNs 3 (ft), 6 (pt); LPNs 11 (ft), 3 (pt); Orderlies 2 (ft); Nurses aides 66 (ft), 2 (pt); Activities coordinators 3 (ft).
Languages Spanish, French, German
Affiliation Lutheran
Facilities Dining room; Physical therapy room; Activities room; Crafts room; Laundry room.
Activities Arts & crafts; Cards; Games; Reading groups; Prayer groups; Movies; Shopping trips; Social/Cultural gatherings.

Kissimmee Health Care Center*
320 N Mitchell St, Kissimmee, FL, 32741
(305) 847-7200
Licensure Skilled care. *Beds* 59. *Certified* Medicare.
Owner Proprietary Corp (US Care Corp).
Staff Nurses aides 17 (ft).

John Milton Nursing Home*
1120 W Donegan Ave, Kissimmee, FL, 32741
(305) 847-2854
Licensure Skilled care. *Beds* 149. *Certified* Medicaid.
Owner Proprietary Corp (Beverly Enterprises).
Staff RNs 4 (ft); LPNs 10 (ft).
Languages Spanish

LAKE ALFRED

Lake Alfred Restorium & ACLF
PO Box 1427, 350 W Haines Blvd, Lake Alfred, FL, 33850
(813) 956-1700
Admin Lavon R Childers. *Medical Dir/Dir of Nursing* Ernest DiLorenzo MD; Flora Connelly RN.
Licensure Skilled care; ACLF. *Beds* SNF 31; ACLF 25. *Certified* Medicaid.
Owner Proprietary Corp (Sunbelt Healthcare Center).
Admissions Requirements Minimum age 19; Medical examination; Physician's request.

Staff RNs 1 (ft), 1 (pt); LPNs 3 (ft), 3 (pt); Nurses aides 17 (ft), 2 (pt); Activities coordinators 1 (ft), 1 (pt).
Languages Spanish
Affiliation Seventh-Day Adventist
Facilities Dining room; Activities room; Laundry room; Barber/Beauty shop.
Activities Arts & crafts; Cards; Games; Reading groups; Prayer groups; Movies; Shopping trips; Social/Cultural gatherings; Ceramics.

LAKE CITY

Tanglewood Convalescent Center
2400 S 1st St, Lake City, FL, 32055
(904) 752-7900
Admin Nancy L Pryor. *Medical Dir/Dir of Nursing* Sarian Vunk.
Licensure Skilled care; Intermediate care. *Beds* 95. *Certified* Medicaid; Medicare.
Owner Nonprofit Corp (Volunteers of America Care).
Admissions Requirements Minimum age 18; Medical examination.
Staff RNs 12 (pt); RNs 4 (ft), 2 (pt); LPNs 7 (ft), 4 (pt); Nurses aides 31 (ft), 7 (pt); Physical therapists 1 (pt); Recreational therapists 1 (pt); Speech therapists 1 (pt); Activities coordinators 1 (ft), 1 (pt); Dietitians 1 (ft), 1 (pt); Ophthalmologists 1 (pt).
Languages German, Spanish, Polish
Facilities Dining room; Physical therapy room; Activities room; Crafts room; Laundry room; Barber/Beauty shop; Library.
Activities Arts & crafts; Cards; Games; Reading groups; Prayer groups; Movies; Shopping trips; Social/Cultural gatherings; Garden club; Travel club; Sunshine club.

LAKE PARK

Helen Wilkes Residence
750 Bayberry Dr, Lake Park, FL, 33403
(305) 844-4396
Medical Dir/Dir of Nursing Ramona Russell.
Licensure Skilled care. *Beds* SNF 85. *Certified* Medicaid.
Owner Proprietary Corp (Continental Medical Systems).
Admissions Requirements Minimum age 18.
Staff RNs; LPNs; Nurses aides; Activities coordinators.
Facilities Dining room; Activities room; Laundry room; Barber/Beauty shop.
Activities Arts & crafts; Cards; Games; Reading groups; Prayer groups; Movies; Shopping trips; Social/Cultural gatherings.

LAKE WALES

Lake Wales Convalescent Center
730 W Scenic Hwy, Lake Wales, FL, 33853
(813) 676-1512, 5751
Admin Stephen C Brown. *Medical Dir/Dir of Nursing* Fredrick M Rawlings MD; Virginia Cranfill RN.
Licensure Skilled care; Intermediate care. *Beds* SNF 100; ICF. *Certified* Medicaid.
Owner Proprietary Corp (Sunbelt Healthcare Centers).
Admissions Requirements Minimum age 18; Medical examination; Physician's request.
Staff Physicians 9 (pt); RNs 6 (ft), 2 (pt); LPNs 5 (ft), 5 (pt); Nurses aides 26 (ft), 8 (pt); Physical therapists 1 (pt); Recreational therapists 2 (ft); Occupational therapists 1 (pt); Speech therapists 1 (pt); Activities coordinators 2 (ft); Dietitians 1 (pt); Ophthalmologists 1 (pt).
Affiliation Seventh-Day Adventist
Facilities Dining room; Activities room; Crafts room; Laundry room; Barber/Beauty shop; Library.

Activities Arts & crafts; Cards; Games; Reading groups; Prayer groups; Movies; Shopping trips; Social/Cultural gatherings.

Ridge Convalescent Center
512 S 11th St, Lake Wales, FL, 33853
(813) 676-8502
Admin David A Crosby. *Medical Dir/Dir of Nursing* Dr Joseph A Wiltshire; Josephine Meeks.
Licensure Skilled care. *Beds* 120. *Certified* Medicaid; Medicare.
Owner Proprietary Corp.
Admissions Requirements Medical examination.
Staff Physicians 4 (ft), 3 (pt); RNs 3 (ft), 1 (pt); LPNs 10 (ft), 3 (pt); Nurses aides 40 (ft); Physical therapists 1 (ft); Speech therapists 1 (ft); Activities coordinators 1 (ft); Dietitians 1 (ft); Dentists 2 (pt); Ophthalmologists 1 (pt); Podiatrists 1 (pt).
Facilities Dining room; Activities room; Crafts room; Laundry room; Barber/Beauty shop.
Activities Arts & crafts; Cards; Games; Reading groups; Prayer groups.

LAKE WORTH

American Finnish Nursing Home, Finnish-American Rest Home, Inc
1800 South Dr, Lake Worth, FL, 33461
(305) 588-4333
Admin Sara B Reid.
Licensure Skilled care; ACLF. *Beds* 60; ACLF 198. *Certified* Medicaid.
Owner Nonprofit Corp.
Admissions Requirements Minimum age 55; Medical examination; Physician's request.
Staff RNs 5 (ft), 1 (pt); LPNs 8 (ft); Orderlies 2 (ft), 1 (pt); Nurses aides 21 (ft), 3 (pt); Physical therapists 1 (ft); Recreational therapists 2 (ft); Speech therapists 1 (ft); Activities coordinators 2 (ft); Dietitians 1 (pt).
Languages Finnish, Swedish, Spanish
Facilities Dining room; Physical therapy room; Activities room; Chapel; Crafts room; Laundry room; Barber/Beauty shop; Library; Recreation hall.
Activities Arts & crafts; Cards; Games; Reading groups; Prayer groups; Movies; Shopping trips; Social/Cultural gatherings; Spontaneous & planned parties.

Crest Manor Nursing Center
504 Third Ave S, Lake Worth, FL, 33460
(305) 585-4695
Admin Arthur J Maguire. *Medical Dir/Dir of Nursing* David Kiner DO; Jacqueline Rubins RN.
Licensure Skilled care. *Beds* SNF 71. *Certified* Medicaid; Medicare.
Owner Proprietary Corp.
Admissions Requirements Minimum age 16.
Staff RNs 2 (ft), 3 (pt); LPNs 5 (ft), 1 (pt); Nurses aides 19 (ft), 3 (pt); Physical therapists 1 (pt); Speech therapists 1 (pt); Activities coordinators 1 (ft); Dietitians 1 (pt); Ophthalmologists 1 (pt).
Languages Spanish, German
Facilities Dining room; Physical therapy room; Activities room.
Activities Arts & crafts; Cards; Games; Reading groups; Prayer groups; Movies; Shopping trips; Social/Cultural gatherings.

Eason Nursing Home*
1711 6th Ave S, Lake Worth, FL, 33460
(305) 582-1472
Admin T C Gervais. *Medical Dir/Dir of Nursing* Robert J Miquel MD.
Licensure Skilled care. *Beds* 99. *Certified* Medicaid; Medicare.
Owner Proprietary Corp.
Admissions Requirements Minimum age 65; Medical examination; Physician's request.

Staff RNs 6 (ft), 1 (pt); LPNs 5 (ft), 1 (pt); Nurses aides 30 (ft), 5 (pt); Activities coordinators 1 (ft), 1 (pt); Dietitians 1 (ft); Social workers 1 (ft).
Languages French, Spanish, Finnish
Facilities Dining room; Activities room; Crafts room; Laundry room; Barber/Beauty shop.
Activities Arts & crafts; Cards; Games; Prayer groups; Movies; Shopping trips; Social/Cultural gatherings; Picnics; Park outings.

Lake Worth Health Care Center
2501 N "A" St, Lake Worth, FL, 33460
(305) 585-9301
Admin Linda L Casale. *Medical Dir/Dir of Nursing* Gregory Aslanian MD; Michele A Daley DON.
Licensure Skilled care. *Beds* 162. *Certified* Medicaid; Medicare.
Owner Proprietary Corp (Beverly Enterprises).
Admissions Requirements Minimum age 16; Medical examination; Physician's request.
Staff Physicians 1 (ft), 10 (pt); RNs 25 (ft), 3 (pt); LPNs 10 (ft), 2 (pt); Orderlies 1 (ft); Nurses aides 55 (ft), 5 (pt); Physical therapists 1 (pt); Occupational therapists 1 (pt); Activities coordinators 1 (ft), 1 (pt); Dietitians 1 (pt); Ophthalmologists 1 (pt).
Languages Spanish
Facilities Dining room; Physical therapy room; Activities room; Laundry room; Barber/Beauty shop; Private dining room.
Activities Arts & crafts; Games; Movies; Shopping trips; Social/Cultural gatherings.

Mason's Nursing Home*
3185 Boutwell Rd, Lake Worth, FL, 33461
(305) 585-6437
Admin Steven I Silverstein. *Medical Dir/Dir of Nursing* Allan Marcus.
Licensure Skilled care; Intermediate care. *Beds* 44.
Owner Proprietary Corp.
Admissions Requirements Minimum age 16; Medical examination; Physician's request.
Staff RNs; LPNs; Orderlies; Nurses aides; Activities coordinators; Dietitians.
Languages Spanish
Facilities Dining room; Physical therapy room; Activities room; Chapel; Crafts room; Laundry room; Barber/Beauty shop; Library.
Activities Arts & crafts; Cards; Games; Reading groups; Prayer groups; Movies; Shopping trips; Social/Cultural gatherings.

Medicana Nursing Center
1710 Lucerne Ave, Lake Worth, FL, 33460
(305) 582-5331
Admin Jeanne Trudell. *Medical Dir/Dir of Nursing* Benedicto San Pedro MD; Ruth Fairbanks DON.
Licensure Skilled care. *Beds* 117. *Certified* Medicaid; Medicare; VA.
Owner Proprietary Corp (Vari-Care Inc).
Admissions Requirements Minimum age 16.
Staff RNs 3 (ft), 2 (pt); LPNs 17 (ft), 2 (pt); Orderlies 1 (ft); Nurses aides 35 (ft), 10 (pt); Physical therapists 2 (ft); Recreational therapists 1 (ft); Occupational therapists 2 (ft); Speech therapists 2 (ft); Activities coordinators 1 (pt); Dietitians 1 (pt); Dentists 1 (pt); Ophthalmologists 1 (pt); Podiatrists 1 (pt).
Languages French, Creole, Spanish, Finnish
Facilities Dining room; Physical therapy room; Activities room; Chapel; Crafts room; Laundry room; Barber/Beauty shop; Library; Resident vehicle; Patio; TV lounge.
Activities Arts & crafts; Cards; Games; Reading groups; Prayer groups; Movies; Shopping trips; Social/Cultural gatherings; Adopt-a-grandparent; Resident council; Music therapy.

Regency Health Care Center
3599 S Congress Ave, Lake Worth, FL, 33460
(305) 965-8876

Admin Mrs Lois G Collins. *Medical Dir/Dir of Nursing* Dr Randolph Romano; Miss Ester D Calalo.
Licensure Skilled care; Intermediate care. *Beds* SNF 108; ICF 58. *Certified* Medicaid.
Owner Proprietary Corp (Regency Health Care Centers).
Staff RNs 6 (ft); LPNs 11 (ft); Orderlies; Nurses aides 32 (ft); Activities coordinators.
Languages Spanish, Japanese

LAKELAND

Lakeland Convalescent Center*
610 E Bella Vista Dr, Lakeland, FL, 33805
(813) 688-8591
Licensure Skilled care. *Beds* 120. *Certified* Medicaid; Medicare.
Owner Proprietary Corp.
Staff RNs 6 (ft); LPNs 10 (ft); Nurses aides 26 (ft).

Lakeland Health Care Center
1530 Kennedy Blvd, Lakeland, FL, 33809
(813) 858-4402
Admin John Case. *Medical Dir/Dir of Nursing* Dr Sergio Vallejo; Ruth Williams DON.
Licensure Skilled care; Intermediate care. *Beds* 300. *Certified* Medicaid; Medicare.
Owner Proprietary Corp.
Staff RNs 12 (ft); LPNs 10 (ft); Nurses aides 53 (ft).

Presbyterian Nursing Center—Florida Presbyterian Homes Inc
1919 Lakeland Hills Blvd, Lakeland, FL, 33805
(813) 688-5612
Admin E Max Hauth. *Medical Dir/Dir of Nursing* Sergio Valleljo MD; Rebecca Johnson RN.
Licensure Skilled care; Intermediate care. *Beds* 120. *Certified* Medicaid; Medicare.
Owner Nonprofit Corp (United Presbyterian Homes).
Admissions Requirements Medical examination; Physician's request.
Staff RNs 9 (ft), 1 (pt); LPNs 10 (ft), 1 (pt); Orderlies 1 (ft); Nurses aides 58 (ft); Activities coordinators 2 (ft); Dietitians 1 (ft).
Languages Indonesian, Haitian
Affiliation Presbyterian
Facilities Dining room; Physical therapy room; Activities room; Chapel; Laundry room; Barber/Beauty shop; Library.
Activities Arts & crafts; Cards; Games; Reading groups; Prayer groups; Movies; Shopping trips.

LANTANA

Atlantis Convalescent Center*
6026 Old Congress Rd, Lantana, FL, 33462
(305) 964-4430
Admin Barry Cohen. *Medical Dir/Dir of Nursing* Richard Sulman DO.
Licensure Skilled care. *Beds* 120. *Certified* Medicaid; Medicare.
Owner Proprietary Corp (National Healthcare Affiliates).
Admissions Requirements Minimum age 55; Medical examination; Physician's request.
Staff RNs 5 (ft); LPNs 20 (ft); Orderlies 3 (ft); Nurses aides 36 (ft); Physical therapists 3 (ft); Speech therapists 1 (ft); Activities coordinators 2 (ft); Dietitians 1 (ft); Dentists 1 (ft); Podiatrists 2 (ft); Audiologists 1 (ft).
Languages Spanish, German, French
Facilities Dining room; Physical therapy room; Activities room; Crafts room; Laundry room; Barber/Beauty shop; Library; Outdoor patios & enclosed patio; Pharmacy services.

Activities Arts & crafts; Cards; Games; Reading groups; Prayer groups; Movies; Shopping trips; Social/Cultural gatherings; Wheelchair exercises; Bingo; Music therapy; Reality orientation.

LARGO

Oak Manor Nursing Center*
3500 Oak Manor Ln, Largo, FL, 33540
(813) 581-9427
Medical Dir/Dir of Nursing Paul Straub MD.
Licensure Skilled care. *Beds* 180. *Certified* Medicare.
Owner Proprietary Corp.
Admissions Requirements Physician's request.
Staff RNs 18 (ft), 3 (pt); LPNs 10 (ft), 4 (pt); Nurses aides 70 (ft), 13 (pt); Physical therapists 1 (ft), 1 (pt); Recreational therapists 1 (ft), 1 (pt); Occupational therapists 1 (ft); Speech therapists 1 (ft); Dietitians 1 (ft).
Facilities Dining room; Physical therapy room; Activities room; Crafts room; Laundry room; Barber/Beauty shop; Library.
Activities Arts & crafts; Cards; Games; Reading groups; Prayer groups; Movies; Shopping trips; Social/Cultural gatherings.

Tierra Pines Convalescent Center*
7625 Ulmerton Rd, Largo, FL, 33540
Admin John P Williams.
Licensure Skilled care. *Beds* 120. *Certified* Medicaid; Medicare.
Owner Proprietary Corp.
Admissions Requirements Minimum age 16; Medical examination; Physician's request.
Staff Physicians 2 (pt); RNs 6 (ft); LPNs 12 (ft); Nurses aides 43 (ft); Physical therapists; Reality therapists; Recreational therapists 2 (ft); Occupational therapists; Speech therapists; Activities coordinators 1 (ft); Dietitians; Dentists; Ophthalmologists; Podiatrists; Audiologists.
Facilities Dining room; Physical therapy room; Activities room; Crafts room; Laundry room; Barber/Beauty shop; Library.
Activities Arts & crafts; Cards; Games; Reading groups; Prayer groups; Movies; Social/Cultural gatherings.

Wrights Nursing Home*
11300 110th Ave N, Largo, FL, 33540
(813) 896-3651
Admin Darlene Kreuger. *Medical Dir/Dir of Nursing* Fred Leslie DO.
Licensure Skilled care. *Beds* 60.
Owner Proprietary Corp.
Admissions Requirements Physician's request.
Staff RNs 5 (ft), 9 (pt); LPNs 2 (pt); Nurses aides 16 (ft), 9 (pt); Activities coordinators 1 (ft); Dietitians 1 (pt); Dentists 1 (pt); Podiatrists 1 (pt).
Languages Spanish
Facilities Dining room; Physical therapy room; Activities room; Chapel; Crafts room; Laundry room; Library.
Activities Arts & crafts; Cards; Games; Reading groups; Shopping trips.

LAUDERDALE LAKES

Aviva Manor*
3370 NW 47th Terrace, Lauderdale Lakes, FL, 33319
(305) 733-0655
Medical Dir/Dir of Nursing Arturo Blanco MD.
Licensure Skilled care. *Beds* 120. *Certified* Medicare.
Owner Proprietary Corp.
Staff Physicians 4 (pt); RNs 3 (ft), 5 (pt); LPNs 6 (ft), 6 (pt); Nurses aides 43 (ft), 3 (pt); Reality therapists 1 (pt); Recreational therapists 2 (ft); Occupational therapists 1

(pt); Activities coordinators 1 (ft); Dietitians 1 (ft), 1 (pt); Dentists 1 (pt); Podiatrists 1 (pt).
Affiliation Jewish
Facilities Dining room; Physical therapy room; Activities room; Chapel; Crafts room; Laundry room; Barber/Beauty shop; Library; TV lounge.
Activities Arts & crafts; Cards; Games; Reading groups; Prayer groups; Movies; Shopping trips; Social/Cultural gatherings; Bread baking; Yiddish classes.

St Johns Nursing & Rehabilitation Hospital/St John's Health Care Center
3075 NW 35th Ave, Lauderdale Lakes, FL, 33311
(305) 739-6233
Admin Gloria Hansen. *Medical Dir/Dir of Nursing* Mark Reiner MD; Carol Hamaway RN.
Licensure Skilled care; Speciality rehab hospital. *Beds* SNF 160; Rehab hospital 20. *Certified* Medicaid; Medicare.
Owner Nonprofit Corp.
Admissions Requirements Minimum age 18.
Staff RNs; LPNs; Orderlies; Nurses aides; Recreational therapists; Activities coordinators 1 (ft); Dietitians 1 (ft); Pastoral Care 1 (ft).
Affiliation Roman Catholic
Facilities Dining room; Physical therapy room; Activities room; Chapel; Crafts room; Laundry room; Barber/Beauty shop; Library.
Activities Arts & crafts; Cards; Games; Reading groups; Prayer groups; Movies; Social/Cultural gatherings.

LECANTO

Key Pine Village
1275 N Rainbow Loop, Lecanto, FL, 32661-9759
(904) 746-3262
Admin Chester V Cole.
Licensure Intermediate care for mentally retarded. *Beds* ICF/MR 48. *Certified* Medicaid.
Owner Nonprofit Corp.
Admissions Requirements Minimum age 18; Medical examination.
Staff RNs 1 (ft); LPNs 3 (ft), 1 (pt); Nurses aides 1 (pt); Recreational therapists 1 (ft).
Facilities Dining room; Physical therapy room; Activities room; Laundry room.
Activities Arts & crafts; Games; Movies; Shopping trips; Social/Cultural gatherings.

LEESBURG

Lake Memorial Nursing Home*
400 E Dixie Ave, Leesburg, FL, 32748
(904) 787-2412
Licensure Skilled care. *Beds* 36. *Certified* Medicaid.
Owner Publicly owned.
Staff RNs 2 (ft); LPNs 3 (ft); Nurses aides 12 (ft).

Leesburg Healthcare Center*
2000 Edgewood Ave, Leesburg, FL, 32748
(904) 787-3545
Medical Dir/Dir of Nursing Dr George Engelhard.
Licensure Skilled care. *Beds* 116. *Certified* Medicaid; Medicare.
Owner Proprietary Corp (Beverly Enterprises).
Staff RNs; LPNs; Orderlies; Nurses aides; Physical therapists; Recreational therapists; Speech therapists; Activities coordinators.
Facilities Dining room; Physical therapy room; Activities room; Laundry room; Barber/Beauty shop; Library.
Activities Arts & crafts; Cards; Games; Reading groups; Prayer groups; Movies; Social/Cultural gatherings.

Leesburg Nursing Center
715 E Dixie Ave, Leesburg, FL, 32748
(904) 728-3020
Admin Tom Robeson. *Medical Dir/Dir of Nursing* Dr J Holland; Laura Fain DON.
Licensure Skilled care. *Beds* SNF 120. *Certified* Medicaid; Medicare.
Owner Proprietary Corp (Diversicare Corp).
Admissions Requirements Minimum age 18; Medical examination; Physician's request.
Staff RNs 3 (ft), 3 (pt); LPNs 9 (ft), 7 (pt); Orderlies 2 (ft), 1 (pt); Nurses aides 30 (ft), 22 (pt); Physical therapists 1 (ft); Occupational therapists 1 (ft); Speech therapists 1 (ft); Activities coordinators 1 (ft); Dietitians 1 (ft); Ophthalmologists 1 (ft).
Languages Spanish
Facilities Dining room; Physical therapy room; Activities room; Chapel; Crafts room; Laundry room; Barber/Beauty shop.
Activities Arts & crafts; Cards; Games; Reading groups; Prayer groups; Movies.

LIVE OAK

Suwannee Health Care Center
PO Box 1360, 1620 E Helvenston St, Live Oak, FL, 32060
(904) 362-7860
Admin James T Lutes. *Medical Dir/Dir of Nursing* Dr Andrew C Bass; Kathleen Carter RN DON.
Licensure Skilled care. *Beds* SNF 120. *Certified* Medicaid.
Owner Proprietary Corp (Beverly Enterprises).

LONGWOOD

Longwood Health Care Center*
1512 Grant St, Longwood, FL, 32750
(305) 339-9200
Medical Dir/Dir of Nursing David Parsons MD.
Licensure Skilled care. *Beds* 120. *Certified* Medicaid; Medicare.
Owner Proprietary Corp (Beverly Enterprises).
Admissions Requirements Minimum age 18; Medical examination; Physician's request.
Staff Physicians 20 (ft); RNs 6 (ft); LPNs 9 (ft), 4 (pt); Nurses aides 33 (ft); Physical therapists 1 (ft); Speech therapists 1 (ft); Activities coordinators 1 (ft); Dentists 1 (ft); Ophthalmologists 1 (ft); Podiatrists 1 (ft); Audiologists 1 (ft).
Facilities Dining room; Physical therapy room; Activities room; Crafts room; Laundry room; Barber/Beauty shop.
Activities Arts & crafts; Games; Reading groups; Prayer groups; Movies; Shopping trips.

MACCLENNY

W Frank Wells Nursing Home
159 N 3rd St, MacClenny, FL, 32063
(904) 259-3151
Admin Melba J Beaty. *Medical Dir/Dir of Nursing* Robert A Manley DO; Frances Kay Dowling RN DON.
Licensure Skilled care; Intermediate care. *Beds* SNF 68; ICF. *Certified* Medicaid; Medicare.
Admissions Requirements Minimum age 17; Physician's request.
Staff Physicians 4 (pt); RNs 3 (ft), 1 (pt); LPNs 7 (ft), 3 (pt); Orderlies 1 (ft), 3 (pt); Nurses aides 20 (ft), 12 (pt); Activities coordinators 2 (ft); Dietitians 1 (pt).
Languages Spanish
Facilities Dining room; Activities room; Crafts room.
Activities Arts & crafts; Cards; Games; Reading groups; Prayer groups; Movies; Shopping trips; Social/Cultural gatherings.

MADISON

Madison Nursing Center
PO Box 2310, Rte 3, Madison, FL, 32340
(904) 973-4880
Admin Frank Eckert. *Medical Dir/Dir of Nursing* Dr A Dulay; Joyce Harrison DON.
Licensure Skilled care. *Beds* SNF 60. *Certified* Medicaid.
Owner Privately owned.
Admissions Requirements Medical examination.
Staff RNs 2 (ft); LPNs 7 (ft), 3 (pt); Nurses aides 22 (ft), 4 (pt); Activities coordinators 1 (ft); Dietitians 1 (pt).
Facilities Dining room; Physical therapy room; Activities room; Barber/Beauty shop; OT room.
Activities Arts & crafts; Games; Prayer groups; Movies; Shopping trips.

MARIANNA

Intermediate Care Facility for Mentally Retarded—Facility I
PO Box 852, Hwy 71, Sunland Center, Marianna, FL, 32446
(904) 526-2123
Admin Doris L Culver. *Medical Dir/Dir of Nursing* Mary Schwenche RN.
Licensure Intermediate care for mentally retarded. *Beds* ICF/MR 115.
Owner Publicly owned.
Staff Physicians; RNs; LPNs; Physical therapists; Recreational therapists; Occupational therapists; Speech therapists; Activities coordinators; Dietitians.

Marianna Convalescent Center
PO Drawer L, Marianna, FL, 32446
(904) 482-8091
Admin Jonnie Cloud. *Medical Dir/Dir of Nursing* Carol Morris RN DON.
Licensure Skilled care; Intermediate care; Veterans Administration. *Beds* 180. *Certified* Medicaid.
Owner Publicly owned.
Admissions Requirements Minimum age 16 (unless prior approval from department); Medical examination; Physician's request.
Staff RNs 4 (ft), 6 (pt); LPNs 16 (ft), 14 (pt); Orderlies 5 (ft), 2 (pt); Nurses aides 50 (ft), 24 (pt); Activities coordinators 1 (ft).
Facilities Dining room; Physical therapy room; Activities room; Crafts room; Laundry room; Barber/Beauty shop; Library; Family room; Privacy room.
Activities Arts & crafts; Games; Prayer groups; Movies; Shopping trips; Social/Cultural gatherings.

Sunland—Marianna Facility II*
PO Box 852, Marianna, FL, 32446
(904) 526-2123
Licensure Intermediate care for mentally retarded. *Beds* 60. *Certified* Medicaid.
Owner Publicly owned.
Staff RNs 3 (ft); LPNs 7 (ft); Nurses aides 32 (ft).

MELBOURNE

Carnegie Gardens Nursing Center
1415 S Hickory St, Melbourne, FL, 32901
(305) 723-1321
Admin Maureen Laverty. *Medical Dir/Dir of Nursing* John Potomski DO; Mary Frances Crown.
Licensure Skilled care. *Beds* SNF; ICF; VA 138. *Certified* Medicaid; Medicare.
Owner Proprietary Corp.
Admissions Requirements Minimum age 18; Medical examination.
Staff RNs 8 (ft); LPNs 15 (ft); Orderlies 2 (ft); Nurses aides 46 (ft); Activities coordinators 2 (ft); Dietitians 1 (ft).
Languages Spanish

Facilities Dining room; Physical therapy room; Activities room; Chapel; Crafts room; Barber/Beauty shop; Library.
Activities Arts & crafts; Cards; Games; Reading groups; Prayer groups; Movies; Shopping trips; Social/Cultural gatherings; Luncheon outings; Picnics; Fishing trips; Sightseeing trips.

Holmes Regional Convalescent Home
516 E Sheridan Rd, Melbourne, FL, 32901
(305) 727-0984
Admin John H Patrick Jr. *Medical Dir/Dir of Nursing* Timothy Poirier MD; Barbara Duncklee RN DON.
Licensure Skilled care. *Beds* 60. *Certified* Medicaid; Medicare.
Owner Nonprofit Corp.
Admissions Requirements Minimum age 18; Medical examination.
Staff RNs 4 (ft), 2 (pt); LPNs 3 (ft), 2 (pt); Nurses aides 18 (ft), 7 (pt); Activities coordinators 1 (ft); Dietitians 1 (ft); Social service 1 (ft).
Facilities Dining room; Activities room.
Activities Arts & crafts; Cards; Games; Prayer groups; Movies.

Medic Home Health Center
1420 S Oak St, Melbourne, FL, 32901
(305) 723-3215
Admin Patricia Collins. *Medical Dir/Dir of Nursing* W S Lanford MD; Catherine Baldwin DON.
Licensure Skilled care; Intermediate care. *Beds* SNF; ICF 110. *Certified* Medicaid.
Owner Proprietary Corp (Beverly Enterprises).
Staff RNs; LPNs; Nurses aides; Activities coordinators; Dietitians.
Facilities Dining room; Activities room; Crafts room; Laundry room; Barber/Beauty shop.
Activities Arts & crafts; Cards; Games; Reading groups; Prayer groups; Movies; Shopping trips; Social/Cultural gatherings.

MERRITT ISLAND

Merritt Manor Nursing Home
125 Alma Blvd, Merritt Island, FL, 32953
(305) 453-0202
Admin Ed Hawkins. *Medical Dir/Dir of Nursing* Dr Jack Hatfield; Aileen Mueller RN.
Licensure Skilled care. *Beds* 120. *Certified* Medicaid; Medicare.
Owner Proprietary Corp (Beverly Enterprises).
Admissions Requirements Medical examination.
Staff RNs 4 (ft), 1 (pt); LPNs 11 (ft), 1 (pt); Nurses aides 42 (ft), 4 (pt); Physical therapists 1 (ft); Occupational therapists 1 (ft); Speech therapists 1 (ft); Activities coordinators 1 (ft); Dietitians 1 (ft).
Facilities Dining room; Physical therapy room; Activities room; Laundry room; Barber/Beauty shop.
Activities Arts & crafts; Cards; Games; Reading groups; Prayer groups; Movies.

MIAMI

Arch Creek Nursing Home
12505 NE 16th Ave, Miami, FL, 33161
(305) 891-1710
Licensure Skilled care; Intermediate care. *Beds* 118. *Certified* Medicaid; Medicare.
Owner Proprietary Corp.
Staff RNs 5 (ft); LPNs 13 (ft); Nurses aides 26 (ft).
Languages Spanish, Russian, Yiddish, Hebrew, French

Ashley Manor Care Center*
8785 NW 32nd Ave, Miami, FL, 33147
(305) 691-5711

Admin E Renee1 Gibson. *Medical Dir/Dir of Nursing* Ramon Alvarez MD.
Licensure Skilled care. *Beds* 120. *Certified* Medicaid.
Owner Proprietary Corp.
Admissions Requirements Medical examination.
Staff RNs 5 (ft); LPNs 5 (ft), 8 (pt); Orderlies 1 (ft); Nurses aides 39 (ft), 3 (pt); Physical therapists 1 (pt); Reality therapists 1 (pt); Recreational therapists 1 (ft); Speech therapists 1 (pt); Activities coordinators 1 (ft); Dietitians 1 (pt); Dentists 1 (pt); Ophthalmologists 1 (pt); Podiatrists 1 (pt).
Languages French, Yiddish, Hebrew, Spanish, Creole
Facilities Dining room; Activities room; Crafts room; Laundry room; Barber/Beauty shop.
Activities Arts & crafts; Cards; Games; Reading groups; Prayer groups; Movies; Shopping trips; Social/Cultural gatherings.

Coral Gables Convalescent Home*
7060 SW 8th St, Miami, FL, 33144
(305) 261-1363
Licensure Skilled care. *Beds* 87. *Certified* Medicare.
Owner Proprietary Corp.
Staff RNs 7 (ft), 4 (pt); LPNs 3 (ft), 3 (pt); Nurses aides 31 (ft), 3 (pt); Physical therapists 1 (pt); Reality therapists 1 (pt); Recreational therapists 4 (pt); Speech therapists 1 (pt); Activities coordinators 1 (ft); Dietitians 1 (pt).
Languages Spanish, German, Yiddish, Hebrew
Facilities Dining room; Physical therapy room; Activities room; Crafts room; Laundry room; Barber/Beauty shop; Library.
Activities Arts & crafts; Cards; Games; Reading groups; Prayer groups; Movies.

East Ridge Retirement Village Health Center
19301 SW 87th Ave, Miami, FL, 33157-8999
(305) 238-2623
Admin David A Perry. *Medical Dir/Dir of Nursing* Chauncey Stone MD.
Licensure Skilled care. *Beds* SNF 60.
Owner Nonprofit Corp.
Admissions Requirements Minimum age 62; Medical examination.
Staff Physicians 2 (pt); RNs 3 (ft), 1 (pt); LPNs 8 (ft), 1 (pt); Nurses aides 15 (ft), 7 (pt); Physical therapists 1 (pt); Activities coordinators 1 (ft); Dermatologist 1 (pt).
Languages Polish, Spanish
Facilities Dining room; Physical therapy room; Activities room; Chapel; Crafts room; Laundry room; Barber/Beauty shop; Library.
Activities Arts & crafts; Cards; Games; Reading groups; Prayer groups; Movies; Social/Cultural gatherings.

El Ponce De Leon Convalescent Center
335 SW 12th Ave, Miami, FL, 33130
(305) 545-5417
Admin Gail Lasris. *Medical Dir/Dir of Nursing* Dr Edward Gottler; Pusa Bouza RN DON.
Licensure Skilled care; Intermediate care. *Beds* 147. *Certified* Medicaid; Medicare.
Owner Proprietary Corp.
Staff RNs 21 (ft), 3 (pt); LPNs 4 (ft); Orderlies 5 (ft); Nurses aides 74 (ft); Physical therapists 2 (ft); Recreational therapists 2 (ft); Occupational therapists 1 (ft); Speech therapists 1 (ft); Activities coordinators 1 (ft); Dietitians 1 (ft); Dentists 1 (ft); Ophthalmologists 1 (ft).
Languages Spanish, French
Facilities Dining room; Physical therapy room; Activities room; Chapel; Crafts room; Laundry room; Barber/Beauty shop; Library.
Activities Arts & crafts; Cards; Games; Reading groups; Prayer groups; Movies; Shopping trips; Social/Cultural gatherings.

Fair Havens Center
201 Curtiss Pkwy, Miami, FL, 33166-5291
(305) 887-1565
Admin William D Cole. *Medical Dir/Dir of Nursing* James Hutson MD; Georgiana Wagner RN DON.
Licensure Skilled care; Intermediate care; Adult congregate living. *Beds* SNF 221; ICF 45; Adult congregate living 45. *Certified* Medicaid; Medicare.
Owner Nonprofit Corp.
Admissions Requirements Minimum age 18; Medical examination.
Staff Physicians 23 (pt); RNs 15 (ft); LPNs 15 (ft), 3 (pt); Orderlies 2 (ft); Nurses aides 110 (ft); Physical therapists 4 (pt); Recreational therapists 3 (ft); Occupational therapists 1 (pt); Speech therapists 1 (pt); Activities coordinators 4 (ft); Dietitians 2 (ft); Dentists 1 (pt); Ophthalmologists 3 (pt); Chaplain 1 (ft); Volunteer coordinator 1 (ft).
Languages Spanish, German, French, Creole, Estonian, Italian
Affiliation Lutheran
Facilities Dining room; Physical therapy room; Activities room; Chapel; Crafts room; Laundry room; Barber/Beauty shop; Library; Gardens.
Activities Arts & crafts; Cards; Games; Reading groups; Prayer groups; Movies; Shopping trips; Social/Cultural gatherings; Classes.

Floridean Nursing Home Inc
47 NW 32nd Pl, Miami, FL, 33125
(305) 649-2911
Admin Julia Rice. *Medical Dir/Dir of Nursing* J J Hutson MD; Esther Quinoa RN DON.
Licensure Skilled care. *Beds* 52. *Certified* Medicaid.
Owner Proprietary Corp.
Admissions Requirements Medical examination.
Staff Physicians; RNs 3 (ft); LPNs 8 (ft); Nurses aides 19 (ft); Physical therapists; Recreational therapists; Occupational therapists; Speech therapists; Activities coordinators; Dietitians; Dentists; Ophthalmologists; Podiatrists.
Facilities Dining room; Laundry room.
Activities Arts & crafts; Cards; Games; Sewing class; Cooking class; Current events; Church service; Bithday & holiday parties.

Gramercy Park Nursing Center
17475 S Dixie Hwy, Miami, FL, 33157
(305) 255-1045
Admin Mary-Annice Heinle. *Medical Dir/Dir of Nursing* Marianne Martin DON.
Licensure Skilled care; Intermediate care. *Beds* SNF 60; ICF 120. *Certified* Medicaid; Medicare.
Owner Proprietary Corp.
Admissions Requirements Minimum age 18; Physician's request.
Staff RNs 5 (ft); LPNs 9 (ft), 3 (pt); Nurses aides 42 (ft), 8 (pt); Physical therapists 2 (pt); Occupational therapists 1 (pt); Speech therapists 1 (pt); Activities coordinators 2 (ft), 1 (pt); Dietitians 1 (ft); Ophthalmologists 1 (pt); Podiatrists 1 (pt).
Languages French, Spanish
Facilities Dining room; Physical therapy room; Activities room; Crafts room; Laundry room; Barber/Beauty shop.
Activities Arts & crafts; Cards; Games; Reading groups; Prayer groups; Movies; Shopping trips; Social/Cultural gatherings; Adult basic education.

Green Briar Nursing Center*
9820 N Kendall Dr, Miami, FL, 33176
(305) 271-6311
Licensure Skilled care. *Beds* 203. *Certified* Medicare.
Owner Proprietary Corp.
Staff Physicians; Dietitians; Nurses aides.

Languages Spanish, French, Yiddish
Activities Prayer groups; Arts & crafts; Shopping trips.

Human Resources Health Center
2500 NW 22nd Ave, Miami, FL, 33142
(305) 638-6661
Admin Lou DiDomenico. *Medical Dir/Dir of Nursing* John Cleveland; Maxine Austin.
Licensure Skilled care; Intermediate care. *Beds* SNF 150; ICF. *Certified* Medicaid; Medicare.
Owner Publicly owned.
Admissions Requirements Minimum age 18; Medical examination; Physician's request.
Staff Physicians 3 (pt); RNs 11 (ft); LPNs 23 (ft); Orderlies 8 (ft); Nurses aides 67 (ft); Physical therapists 1 (ft); Recreational therapists 1 (ft); Occupational therapists 1 (pt); Speech therapists 1 (pt); Activities coordinators 1 (ft); Dietitians 1 (ft), 1 (pt); Dentists 1 (pt); Ophthalmologists 1 (pt).
Languages Spanish, French, Yiddish, Hebrew, Creole
Facilities Dining room; Physical therapy room; Activities room; Chapel; Crafts room; Laundry room; Barber/Beauty shop.
Activities Arts & crafts; Cards; Games; Reading groups; Prayer groups; Movies; Shopping trips; Social/Cultural gatherings; Adopt-a-grandparent.

Jackson Heights Nursing Home*
1404 NW 22nd St, Miami, FL, 33142
(305) 325-1050
Licensure Skilled care. *Beds* 298. *Certified* Medicaid; Medicare.
Owner Proprietary Corp (Unicare).
Staff RNs 12 (ft); LPNs 14 (ft); Nurses aides 14 (ft); Nurses aides 107 (ft).
Languages Spanish, French, Tagalog

Jackson Manor Nursing Home Inc
1861 NW 8th Ave, Miami, FL, 33136
(305) 324-0280
Admin Isaac Mizrahi. *Medical Dir/Dir of Nursing* Ed H Cottler MD; Beverly Pelersen DON.
Licensure Skilled care. *Beds* SNF 174. *Certified* Medicaid; Medicare.
Owner Proprietary Corp.
Admissions Requirements Minimum age 16; Medical examination.
Staff RNs 5 (ft); LPNs 20 (ft), 3 (pt); Nurses aides 60 (ft); Physical therapists 4 (pt); Recreational therapists 2 (ft); Occupational therapists 3 (pt); Speech therapists 3 (pt); Activities coordinators 1 (ft); Dietitians 1 (ft); Dentists 1 (pt); Ophthalmologists 1 (pt).
Languages Creole, Arabic, Russian, Spanish, French
Facilities Dining room; Physical therapy room; Chapel; Barber/Beauty shop; Library.
Activities Arts & crafts; Cards; Games; Reading groups; Prayer groups; Movies; Shopping trips; Social/Cultural gatherings.

La Posada Convalescent Home*
5271 SW 8th St, Miami, FL, 33134
(305) 448-4963
Licensure Skilled care. *Beds* 54. *Certified* Medicaid.
Owner Proprietary Corp.
Admissions Requirements Minimum age 65.
Staff Nurses aides 8 (ft); Dietitians 4 (ft).
Languages Spanish
Facilities Dining room; Activities room.
Activities Arts & crafts; Cards; Games; Reading groups; Prayer groups; Movies; Shopping trips; Social/Cultural gatherings.

MACtown Inc
127 NE 62nd St, Miami, FL, 33138
(305) 758-4485
Admin Gordon B Scott Jr. *Medical Dir/Dir of Nursing* Dr Gilbert White.
Licensure Intermediate care for mentally retarded. *Beds* 56. *Certified* Medicaid.

Owner Nonprofit Corp.
Admissions Requirements Minimum age 18;
Medical examination; Physician's request.
Staff Physicians 1 (pt); RNs 1 (pt); LPNs 3
(ft), 1 (pt); Physical therapists 1 (pt);
Recreational therapists 2 (ft), 1 (pt);
Occupational therapists 1 (pt); Speech
therapists 1 (ft); Dietitians 1 (ft);
Ophthalmologists 1 (pt).
Facilities Dining room; Physical therapy
room; Activities room; Laundry room;
Workshop.
Activities Arts & crafts; Cards; Games;
Movies; Shopping trips; Social/Cultural
gatherings; Special Olympics.

Miami Jewish Home for the Aged at Douglas Gardens
151 NE 52nd St, Miami, FL, 33137
(305) 751-8626
Admin Marc Lichtman. *Medical Dir/Dir of
Nursing* Dr Charles Beber; Joan Bilingsley.
Licensure Skilled care; Intermediate care. *Beds*
454. *Certified* Medicaid; Medicare.
Owner Nonprofit Corp.
Admissions Requirements Minimum age 65;
Medical examination.
Staff Physicians 3 (ft); RNs 32 (ft); LPNs 52
(ft); Nurses aides 237 (ft); Physical therapists
2 (ft); Recreational therapists 6 (ft);
Occupational therapists 1 (pt); Speech
therapists 1 (pt); Activities coordinators 1
(ft).
Languages Spanish, German, Yiddish,
Russian, French, Polish
Affiliation Jewish
Facilities Dining room; Physical therapy
room; Activities room; Chapel; Crafts room;
Laundry room; Barber/Beauty shop; Library;
Convenience store in lobby of congregate
living facility.
Activities Arts & crafts; Cards; Games;
Reading groups; Prayer groups; Movies;
Shopping trips; Social/Cultural gatherings.

North Shore Nursing Home*
9380 NW 7th Ave, Miami, FL, 33150
(305) 759-8711
Medical Dir/Dir of Nursing Stanley Roth MD.
Licensure Skilled care. *Beds* 101. *Certified*
Medicare.
Owner Proprietary Corp.
Staff RNs 2 (ft), 2 (pt); LPNs 12 (ft), 4 (pt);
Nurses aides 26 (ft); Recreational therapists
1 (ft); Activities coordinators 1 (ft); Social
workers 1 (ft).
Languages Spanish
Facilities Dining room; Physical therapy
room; Barber/Beauty shop.
Activities Arts & crafts; Cards; Games;
Reading groups; Prayer groups; Movies;
Shopping trips; Social/Cultural gatherings;
Picnics.

Palmetto Extended Care Facility*
7600 SW 8th St, Miami, FL, 33144
(305) 261-2525
Licensure Skilled care; Intermediate care. *Beds*
85. *Certified* Medicaid; Medicare.
Owner Proprietary Corp.
Staff RNs 3 (ft); LPNs 8 (ft); Nurses aides 21
(ft).
Languages Spanish, Tagalog, Italian, Japanese

Palms Convalescent Home*
14601 NE 16th Ave, Miami, FL, 33161
(305) 945-7631
Licensure Skilled care. *Beds* 85. *Certified*
Medicaid.
Owner Proprietary Corp.
Staff RNs 3 (ft); LPNs 15 (ft); Nurses aides 18
(ft).
Languages Spanish, Hungarian, German,
Yiddish, Hebrew, Polish

Perdue Medical Center*
2001 E Ridge Village Dr, Miami, FL, 33157
(305) 233-8931

Licensure Skilled care. *Beds* 197. *Certified*
Medicaid; Medicare.
Owner Publicly owned.
Staff RNs 12 (ft); LPNs 10 (ft); Nurses aides
55 (ft).
Languages Spanish

Pines Nursing Home
301 NE 141st St, Miami, FL, 33161
(305) 893-1102
Medical Dir/Dir of Nursing Dr Walter
DeMaio.
Licensure Skilled care. *Beds* 46. *Certified*
Medicaid; Medicare.
Owner Proprietary Corp.
Staff Physicians 5 (pt); RNs 2 (ft); LPNs 5
(ft), 3 (pt); Nurses aides 42 (ft), 4 (pt);
Physical therapists 1 (pt); Recreational
therapists 1 (pt); Occupational therapists 1
(pt); Speech therapists 1 (pt); Activities
coordinators 1 (ft); Dietitians 1 (ft); Dentists
1 (pt); Ophthalmologists 1 (pt); Podiatrists 1
(pt).
Languages French, Hatian, Hungarian,
German, Russian, Polish, Spanish, Yiddish,
Hebrew
Facilities Dining room; Activities room;
Crafts room; Laundry room; Library.
Activities Arts & crafts; Cards; Games;
Reading groups; Prayer groups; Movies.

Riverside Care Center*
899 NW 4th St, Miami, FL, 33128
(305) 326-1236
Medical Dir/Dir of Nursing Water J Demaio
MD.
Licensure Skilled care. *Beds* 80. *Certified*
Medicaid; Medicare.
Owner Proprietary Corp.
Admissions Requirements Minimum age 21.
Staff RNs 2 (ft); LPNs 6 (ft), 6 (pt); Orderlies
1 (ft); Recreational therapists 1 (ft), 1 (pt);
Activities coordinators 1 (ft), 1 (pt);
Dietitians 1 (pt); Dentists 1 (pt); Podiatrists
1 (pt).
Languages Spanish
Facilities Dining room; Activities room;
Crafts room; Laundry room; Barber/Beauty
shop.
Activities Arts & crafts; Cards; Games;
Reading groups; Prayer groups; Movies;
Shopping trips; Social/Cultural gatherings;
Special holiday dinners.

Snapper Creek Nursing Home Inc
9200 SW 87th Ave, Miami, FL, 33176
(305) 271-1313
Admin Virginia Anders. *Medical Dir/Dir of
Nursing* Ed H Cottler MD; Janet Hicks RN
DON.
Licensure Skilled care. *Beds* SNF 115.
Certified Medicare.
Owner Proprietary Corp.
Admissions Requirements Minimum age 16.
Staff RNs 10 (ft); LPNs 7 (ft); Orderlies 30
(ft); Physical therapists 1 (pt); Recreational
therapists 2 (ft); Occupational therapists 1
(pt); Speech therapists 1 (pt); Activities
coordinators 1 (ft); Dietitians 1 (ft); Dentists
1 (pt); Ophthalmologists 1 (pt).
Languages Spanish, Italian
Facilities Dining room; Physical therapy
room; Activities room; Chapel; Crafts room;
Barber/Beauty shop; Library; Large day
room; Enclosed patios.
Activities Arts & crafts; Cards; Games;
Reading groups; Prayer groups; Movies;
Shopping trips; Social/Cultural gatherings.

MIAMI BEACH

Gem Care Center
550 9th St, Miami Beach, FL, 33139
(305) 531-3321
Admin Josefina Lardizabal. *Medical Dir/Dir of
Nursing* Dr Leo Whitman MD; Belinda
Shover.

Licensure Skilled care. *Beds* 196. *Certified*
Medicaid; Medicare.
Owner Proprietary Corp.
Admissions Requirements Minimum age 18.
Staff RNs 9 (ft), 10 (pt); LPNs 9 (ft);
Orderlies 1 (ft), 1 (pt); Nurses aides 58 (ft),
5 (pt); Physical therapists 2 (pt); Activities
coordinators 2 (ft); Dietitians 1 (ft).
Languages French, Spanish, Tagalog, Creole,
Polish, Hungarian, Russian
Facilities Dining room; Physical therapy
room; Activities room; Laundry room;
Barber/Beauty shop; Library.
Activities Arts & crafts; Cards; Games; Prayer
groups; Movies; Social/Cultural gatherings;
Adult education classes & discussion groups.

Miami Beach Hebrew Home for the Aged*
320 Collins Ave, Miami Beach, FL, 33139
(305) 672-6464
Licensure Skilled care. *Beds* 104. *Certified*
Medicaid; Medicare.
Owner Nonprofit Corp.
Staff RNs 8 (ft); LPNs 4 (ft); Nurses aides 53
(ft).
Languages Yiddish, Hebrew, Spanish, French
Affiliation Jewish

Southpoint Manor
42 Collins Ave, Miami Beach, FL, 33139
(305) 672-1771
Admin Jesse Dunwoody. *Medical Dir/Dir of
Nursing* Dr Charles R Beber MD; Jackie
Carter RN DON.
Licensure Skilled care. *Beds* 230. *Certified*
Medicaid; Medicare.
Owner Proprietary Corp.
Admissions Requirements Minimum age 16;
Medical examination; Physician's request.
Staff RNs 7 (ft), 6 (pt); LPNs 26 (ft), 4 (pt);
Nurses aides 95 (ft); Physical therapists 1
(pt); Reality therapists 1 (pt); Recreational
therapists 1 (pt); Occupational therapists 1
(pt); Speech therapists 1 (pt); Activities
coordinators 3 (ft); Dietitians 1 (pt); Dentists
1 (pt); Ophthalmologists 2 (pt); Podiatrists 1
(pt).
Languages Spanish, French, Italian, Yiddish,
Hebrew, Tagalog, Russian
Facilities Dining room; Physical therapy
room; Activities room; Chapel; Crafts room;
Laundry room; Barber/Beauty shop; Library;
Secure outdoor patio.
Activities Arts & crafts; Cards; Games;
Reading groups; Prayer groups; Movies;
Shopping trips; Social/Cultural gatherings.

MILTON

Santa Rosa Convalescent Center*
500 Broad St, Milton, FL, 32570
(904) 623-4661
Medical Dir/Dir of Nursing Rufus Thames.
Licensure Skilled care. *Beds* 120. *Certified*
Medicaid; Medicare.
Owner Proprietary Corp.
Admissions Requirements Minimum age 50;
Medical examination; Physician's request.
Staff Physicians 6 (pt); RNs 4 (ft), 1 (pt);
LPNs 8 (ft), 5 (pt); Nurses aides 36 (ft), 15
(pt); Physical therapists 1 (pt); Speech
therapists 1 (pt); Activities coordinators 1
(ft); Dietitians 1 (pt); Dentists 1 (pt);
Podiatrists 1 (pt).
Languages French
Facilities Dining room; Physical therapy
room; Activities room; Chapel; Laundry
room; Barber/Beauty shop; Library.
Activities Arts & crafts; Games; Reading
groups; Prayer groups; Social/Cultural
gatherings.

MONTICELLO

Jefferson Nursing Center*
PO Box 477, Monticello, FL, 32344
(904) 997-2313

Licensure Skilled care. *Beds* 60. *Certified* Medicaid.
Owner Proprietary Corp.
Staff RNs 1 (ft), 1 (pt); LPNs 3 (ft), 2 (pt); Nurses aides 15 (ft), 5 (pt); Recreational therapists 1 (ft), 1 (pt); Activities coordinators 1 (ft); Dietitians 1 (pt).
Facilities Dining room; Activities room; Crafts room; Laundry room; Barber/Beauty shop.
Activities Arts & crafts; Games; Reading groups; Prayer groups; Movies; Shopping trips.

MOUNT DORA

Mt Dora Healthcare Center
1550 Brown St, Mount Dora, FL, 32757
(904) 383-4161
Admin Joseph A Borho NHA. *Medical Dir/ Dir of Nursing* C Robert Crow MD; Joyce Saladin RN DON.
Licensure Skilled care. *Beds* SNF 116. *Certified* Medicaid; Medicare.
Owner Proprietary Corp (Beverly Enterprises).
Admissions Requirements Minimum age 16; Medical examination; Physician's request.
Staff RNs 4 (ft), 1 (pt); LPNs 14 (ft), 2 (pt); Nurses aides 37 (ft); Physical therapists 1 (pt); Speech therapists 1 (pt); Activities coordinators 1 (ft); Ophthalmologists 1 (pt); Podiatrists 1 (pt); Social Svcs Coord 1 (ft).
Languages Spanish
Facilities Dining room; Physical therapy room; Activities room; Chapel; Crafts room; Laundry room; Barber/Beauty shop; Library.
Activities Arts & crafts; Cards; Games; Reading groups; Prayer groups; Movies; Shopping trips; Social/Cultural gatherings; Picnics; Candlelight dinners.

NAPLES

Americana Health Care Center
3601 Lakewood Blvd, Naples, FL, 33962
(813) 775-7757
Admin Cindy Mehalshick. *Medical Dir/Dir of Nursing* Terrance A Johnson MD; Anna Moore RN.
Licensure Skilled care. *Beds* 120. *Certified* Medicaid; Medicare.
Owner Proprietary Corp (Manor Care).
Admissions Requirements Minimum age 18; Medical examination; Physician's request.
Staff Physicians; RNs 7 (ft); LPNs 7 (ft); Nurses aides 20 (ft); Physical therapists 1 (pt); Occupational therapists 1 (pt); Speech therapists 1 (pt); Activities coordinators 4 (ft); Dietitians 1 (pt); Ophthalmologists 1 (pt).
Languages Spanish, Haitian
Facilities Dining room; Physical therapy room; Activities room; Laundry room; Barber/Beauty shop.
Activities Arts & crafts; Cards; Games; Reading groups; Prayer groups; Movies; Shopping trips; Social/Cultural gatherings; Daily cocktail hour; Pet therapy; Holiday events.

Heritage Healthcare Center
777 9th St N, Naples, FL, 33940
(813) 261-8126
Admin Lorna M Mamelson. *Medical Dir/Dir of Nursing* Roberta B Harris DON.
Licensure Skilled care; Intermediate care. *Beds* 97. *Certified* Medicaid; Medicare.
Owner Proprietary Corp (Beverly Enterprises).
Admissions Requirements Medical examination.
Staff RNs 6 (ft), 3 (pt); LPNs 11 (ft), 1 (pt); Orderlies 1 (ft); Speech therapists 1 (pt); Activities coordinators 1 (ft), 1 (pt).
Languages Spanish, French

Facilities Dining room; Physical therapy room; Activities room; Crafts room; Laundry room; Barber/Beauty shop; Screened porches.
Activities Arts & crafts; Cards; Games; Reading groups; Prayer groups; Movies; Shopping trips; Social/Cultural gatherings.

Heritage Healthcare Center
777 9th St N, Naples, FL, 33940
(813) 261-8126
Admin Lorna Mamelson. *Medical Dir/Dir of Nursing* Louis Moore MD; Roberta Harris DON.
Licensure Skilled care; Intermediate care. *Beds* 97. *Certified* Medicaid; Medicare.
Owner Proprietary Corp.
Admissions Requirements Medical examination.
Staff RNs 6 (ft), 3 (pt); LPNs 11 (ft), 1 (pt); Nurses aides 25 (ft), 6 (pt); Physical therapists 1 (pt); Occupational therapists 1 (pt); Speech therapists 1 (pt); Activities coordinators 1 (ft), 1 (pt); Dietitians 1 (pt); Podiatrists 1 (pt).
Languages Spanish, French
Facilities Dining room; Physical therapy room; Activities room; Crafts room; Laundry room; Barber/Beauty shop; Screened patios.
Activities Arts & crafts; Cards; Games; Reading groups; Prayer groups; Movies; Shopping trips; Social/Cultural gatherings.

Lakeside Plantation
2900 12th St N, Naples, FL, 33940
(813) 261-2554
Admin Pamela M Cox. *Medical Dir/Dir of Nursing* Rasik Mehta MD; Joyce Brokopp RN DON.
Licensure Skilled care; Intermediate care. *Beds* 99. *Certified* Medicaid; Medicare.
Owner Proprietary Corp (Convalescent Services).
Admissions Requirements Medical examination; Physician's request.
Staff Physicians 1 (pt); RNs 4 (ft), 3 (pt); LPNs 8 (ft), 3 (pt); Nurses aides 30 (ft), 5 (pt); Physical therapists 1 (pt); Occupational therapists 1 (pt); Speech therapists 1 (pt); Activities coordinators 1 (ft); Dietitians 1 (pt).
Languages Spanish
Facilities Dining room; Physical therapy room; Activities room; Laundry room; Barber/Beauty shop; TV rooms; Sun porch; Covered dock on lake.
Activities Arts & crafts; Cards; Games; Reading groups; Movies; Shopping trips; Social/Cultural gatherings.

Moorings Park Health Center
111 Moorings Park Dr, Naples, FL, 33942
(813) 261-1616
Admin Jerry Jaques. *Medical Dir/Dir of Nursing* Dr Rasik Mehta; Lily L'Esperance.
Licensure Skilled care. *Beds* SNF 60. *Certified* Medicare.
Owner Nonprofit Corp (Life Care Services Corp).
Admissions Requirements Physician's request.
Staff Physicians 10 (pt); RNs 3 (ft), 4 (pt); LPNs 5 (ft), 1 (pt); Nurses aides 23 (ft), 2 (pt); Physical therapists 1 (pt); Recreational therapists 1 (pt); Occupational therapists 1 (pt); Speech therapists 1 (pt); Activities coordinators 1 (ft); Dietitians 2 (pt); Ophthalmologists 1 (pt); Podiatrists 1 (pt).
Languages Spanish, Tagalog
Facilities Dining room; Physical therapy room; Activities room; Crafts room; Laundry room; Barber/Beauty shop.
Activities Arts & crafts; Cards; Games; Reading groups; Prayer groups; Movies; Shopping trips; Social/Cultural gatherings.

NEW PORT RICHEY

Heather Hill Nursing Home*
1151 E Kentucky Ave, New Port Richey, FL, 33552
(813) 849-6939
Licensure Skilled care. *Beds* 120. *Certified* Medicaid; Medicare.
Owner Proprietary Corp.
Staff RNs 7 (ft); LPNs 11 (ft); Nurses aides 36 (ft).
Languages German, Greek, Spanish

Richey Manor Nursing Home
505 Indiana Ave, New Port Richey, FL, 34653
(813) 849-7555
Admin Edward E Alderson. *Medical Dir/Dir of Nursing* Francis K S Oey MD; Patricia Hoppert RN DON.
Licensure Skilled care. *Beds* SNF 119. *Certified* Medicaid; Medicare.
Owner Proprietary Corp (Unicare).
Admissions Requirements Minimum age 16; Medical examination; Physician's request.
Staff RNs 3 (ft), 2 (pt); LPNs 12 (ft), 2 (pt); Nurses aides 38 (ft), 1 (pt); Recreational therapists 1 (ft); Activities coordinators 1 (ft); Dietitians 1 (pt).
Facilities Dining room; Physical therapy room; Activities room; Laundry room; Barber/Beauty shop.
Activities Arts & crafts; Cards; Games; Reading groups; Prayer groups; Movies; Shopping trips; Social/Cultural gatherings.

Southern Pines Nursing Center
312 S Congress St, New Port Richey, FL, 34653
(813) 842-8402
Admin Vern V Charbonneau. *Medical Dir/Dir of Nursing* Lorraine Sedlock RN DON.
Licensure Skilled care. *Beds* 120. *Certified* Medicaid; Medicare.
Owner Proprietary Corp (Americare Corp).
Admissions Requirements Minimum age 18; Medical examination.
Staff RNs 6 (ft); LPNs 10 (ft); Nurses aides 30 (ft); Reality therapists 1 (ft); Activities coordinators 1 (ft); Dietitians 1 (ft).
Languages Spanish
Facilities Dining room; Physical therapy room; Activities room; Crafts room; Barber/Beauty shop.
Activities Arts & crafts; Cards; Games; Reading groups; Prayer groups; Movies; Social/Cultural gatherings.

NEW SMYRNA BEACH

Ocean-View Nursing Home
2810 S Atlantic Ave, New Smyrna Beach, FL, 32069
(904) 428-6424
Admin Dennis W O'Leary NHA. *Medical Dir/Dir of Nursing* Durrand Wallar MD; Margaret Varano RN DNS.
Licensure Skilled care. *Beds* SNF 179. *Certified* Medicaid; Medicare.
Owner Proprietary Corp (HBA Management Inc).
Admissions Requirements Minimum age 21; Medical examination; Physician's request.
Staff Physicians 1 (pt); RNs 8 (ft), 4 (pt); LPNs 11 (ft), 4 (pt); Nurses aides 75 (ft), 20 (pt); Physical therapists 1 (ft); Speech therapists 1 (pt); Activities coordinators 2 (ft); Dietitians 1 (ft); Ophthalmologists 1 (pt); Podiatrists 1 (pt).
Languages Spanish, Italian, German
Facilities Dining room; Physical therapy room; Activities room; Crafts room; Laundry room; Barber/Beauty shop.
Activities Arts & crafts; Cards; Games; Reading groups; Prayer groups; Movies; Shopping trips; Social/Cultural gatherings; Cookouts; Picnics.

NORTH BAY VILLAGE

Treasure Isle Care Center
1735 N Treasure Dr, North Bay Village, FL, 33141
(305) 865-2383
Admin Donald Policastro. *Medical Dir/Dir of Nursing* Dr Richard Jacobs; Janet Moritt.
Licensure Skilled care; Intermediate care. *Beds* 176. *Certified* Medicaid; Medicare.
Owner Proprietary Corp (Unicare).
Admissions Requirements Minimum age 18.
Staff Physicians 7 (pt); RNs 8 (ft), 15 (pt); LPNs 8 (ft), 4 (pt); Nurses aides 53 (ft), 13 (pt); Physical therapists 4 (pt); Reality therapists 2 (pt); Recreational therapists 1 (pt); Occupational therapists 1 (pt); Speech therapists 1 (ft); Activities coordinators 1 (ft); Dietitians 1 (ft); Dentists 1 (pt); Ophthalmologists 1 (pt); Podiatrists 1 (pt).
Languages Spanish, Creole, Tagalog
Facilities Dining room; Physical therapy room; Activities room; Chapel; Crafts room; Laundry room; Barber/Beauty shop; Outside patio; Prayer area.
Activities Arts & crafts; Cards; Games; Reading groups; Prayer groups; Movies; Shopping trips; Social/Cultural gatherings; Language classes.

NORTH FORT MYERS

Pines Village Care Center
991 Pondella Rd, North Fort Myers, FL, 33903
(813) 995-8809
Admin J William McIntyre. *Medical Dir/Dir of Nursing* Victoria Mullins RN DON.
Licensure Skilled care. *Beds* SNF 120. *Certified* Medicaid; Medicare.
Admissions Requirements Medical examination; Physician's request.
Staff RNs 4 (ft), 3 (pt); LPNs 3 (ft), 4 (pt); Nurses aides 18 (ft), 5 (pt); Activities coordinators 1 (ft), 1 (pt); Dietitians 1 (pt).
Languages German, Slavic
Facilities Dining room; Physical therapy room; Activities room; Crafts room; Laundry room; Barber/Beauty shop.
Activities Arts & crafts; Cards; Games; Reading groups; Prayer groups; Movies; Social/Cultural gatherings.

NORTH MIAMI

Bon Secours Hospital/Villa Maria Nursing Center*
1050 NE 125th St, North Miami, FL, 33161
(305) 891-8850
Medical Dir/Dir of Nursing Dr Harold Weiner & Dr David Lipkin.
Licensure Rehabilitation; Nursing Center. *Beds* Rehabilitation 60; Nursing Center 212. *Certified* Medicaid; Medicare.
Owner Proprietary Corp.
Admissions Requirements Medical examination; Physician's request.
Staff Physicians 2 (ft); RNs 17 (ft), 6 (pt); LPNs 18 (ft), 7 (pt); Nurses aides 78 (ft), 12 (pt); Physical therapists 13 (ft); Recreational therapists 2 (ft); Occupational therapists 12 (ft); Speech therapists 2 (ft); Activities coordinators 1 (ft); Dietitians 1 (ft).
Languages Spanish, Hebrew, Yiddish, French, German, Greek, Polish, Tagalog, Yomba
Affiliation Roman Catholic
Facilities Dining room; Physical therapy room; Activities room; Chapel; Crafts room; Laundry room; Barber/Beauty shop; Library.
Activities Arts & crafts; Cards; Games; Reading groups; Prayer groups; Movies; Shopping trips; Social/Cultural gatherings.

Claridge House Nursing & Rehabilitation Center
13900 NE 3rd Ct, North Miami, FL, 33161
(305) 893-2288
Admin Larry Mankoff. *Medical Dir/Dir of Nursing* Janet Morrit.
Licensure Skilled care; Alzheimer unit. *Beds* 240. *Certified* Medicaid; Medicare.
Owner Proprietary Corp.
Admissions Requirements Minimum age 16; Medical examination.
Staff RNs 24 (ft); LPNs 18 (ft); Orderlies 3 (ft); Nurses aides 60 (ft); Recreational therapists 2 (ft); Dietitians 1 (pt).
Languages Spanish, Yiddish, Hebrew, German, Polish
Facilities Dining room; Physical therapy room; Activities room; Chapel; Crafts room; Barber/Beauty shop; Day lounges; Shaded outdoor patio.
Activities Arts & crafts; Cards; Games; Reading groups; Prayer groups; Movies; Shopping trips; Social/Cultural gatherings; Resident council; Newsletter.

Fountainhead Nursing & Convalescent Home*
390 NE 135th St, North Miami, FL, 33161
(305) 893-0660
Licensure Skilled care. *Beds* 146. *Certified* Medicaid.
Owner Proprietary Corp (Angell Group).
Staff RNs 6 (ft); LPNs 10 (ft); Nurses aides 34 (ft).
Languages Spanish, French

Meadow Brook Manor of North Miami
1255 NE 135th St, North Miami, FL, 33161
(305) 891-6850
Admin Jon H Steinmeyer. *Medical Dir/Dir of Nursing* Barbara Cowart RN DON; Dr Stanford Cooke Med Dir.
Licensure Skilled care. *Beds* SNF; ICF 245. *Certified* Medicaid; Medicare.
Owner Proprietary Corp (Angell Group).
Admissions Requirements Minimum age 18.
Staff Physicians 1 (pt); RNs 6 (ft), 2 (pt); LPNs 17 (ft); Orderlies 5 (ft); Nurses aides 80 (ft); Physical therapists 2 (ft), 2 (pt); Recreational therapists 2 (pt); Occupational therapists 1 (pt); Speech therapists 1 (pt); Activities coordinators 1 (ft); Dietitians 1 (pt); Dentists 1 (pt); Ophthalmologists 1 (pt); Podiatrists 1 (pt).
Languages Spanish, French, Creole
Facilities Dining room; Physical therapy room; Activities room; Crafts room; Barber/Beauty shop; Outdoor patio with patio furniture.
Activities Arts & crafts; Cards; Games; Reading groups; Prayer groups; Movies; Shopping trips; Social/Cultural gatherings; Hispanic cultural activities; Parties & foods.

Pinecrest Convalescent Center
13650 NE 3rd Ct, North Miami, FL, 33161
(305) 893-1170
Admin James Reiss. *Medical Dir/Dir of Nursing* Joel Pershkow; Virginia Carpenter.
Licensure Skilled care. *Beds* SNF 100. *Certified* Medicaid; Medicare.
Owner Privately owned.
Admissions Requirements Minimum age 16.
Staff Physicians 2 (pt); RNs 4 (ft); LPNs 10 (ft); Nurses aides 33 (ft); Physical therapists 2 (pt); Recreational therapists 2 (ft); Occupational therapists 1 (pt); Speech therapists 1 (pt); Activities coordinators 2 (ft); Dietitians 1 (pt); Dentists 1 (pt); Ophthalmologists 1 (pt).
Languages German, Spanish
Facilities Dining room; Physical therapy room; Activities room; Crafts room; Laundry room; Barber/Beauty shop; Library.
Activities Arts & crafts; Cards; Games; Reading groups; Prayer groups; Movies; Shopping trips; Social/Cultural gatherings.

NORTH MIAMI BEACH

Greynolds Park Manor Rehabilitation Center
17400 W Dixie Hwy, North Miami Beach, FL, 33160
(305) 944-2361
Admin George N Leader; Martin E Casper Executive Director. *Medical Dir/Dir of Nursing* Sheldon Staller MD; Francis Komara DO Co-MD; Londa Ilhardt RN DON.
Licensure Skilled care. *Beds* SNF 324. *Certified* Medicaid; Medicare.
Owner Proprietary Corp.
Admissions Requirements Medical examination.
Staff Physicians 2 (pt); RNs 28 (ft); LPNs 22 (ft); Nurses aides 109 (ft); Physical therapists 2 (ft); Occupational therapists 2 (ft); Speech therapists 1 (pt); Activities coordinators 1 (ft), 3 (pt); Dietitians 1 (pt); Ophthalmologists 1 (pt); Dentist 1 (pt).
Languages Spanish, French, Creole, Yiddish, Hebrew
Facilities Dining room; Physical therapy room; Activities room; Chapel; Crafts room; Laundry room; Barber/Beauty shop; Library; Park adjacent to facility for patient picnics.
Activities Arts & crafts; Cards; Games; Reading groups; Prayer groups; Movies; Shopping trips; Social/Cultural gatherings; Picnics.

Hebrew Home for the Aged—North Dade*
1800 NE 168th St, North Miami Beach, FL, 33162
(305) 947-3445
Medical Dir/Dir of Nursing Dr Salvatore Certo.
Licensure Skilled care. *Beds* 50. *Certified* Medicaid; Medicare.
Owner Nonprofit Corp.
Admissions Requirements Minimum age 40; Medical examination.
Staff Physicians 1 (pt); RNs 4 (ft); LPNs 3 (ft); Nurses aides 38 (ft); Physical therapists 1 (pt); Recreational therapists 1 (pt); Occupational therapists 1 (pt); Speech therapists 1 (pt); Activities coordinators 1 (ft); Dietitians 1 (pt); Dentists 1 (pt); Podiatrists 1 (pt); Audiologists 1 (pt).
Languages Spanish, Yiddish, Hebrew
Affiliation Jewish
Facilities Dining room; Activities room; Laundry room.
Activities Arts & crafts; Cards; Games; Reading groups; Movies; Shopping trips.

Heritage Nursing & Rehabilitation Center
2201 NE 170th St, North Miami Beach, FL, 33160
(305) 945-1401
Admin Deborah L Simmons. *Medical Dir/Dir of Nursing* Dr Sheldon Staller; Cora Rich RN DON.
Licensure Skilled care; Intermediate care. *Beds* 99. *Certified* Medicaid; Medicare.
Owner Proprietary Corp (Unicare).
Admissions Requirements Medical examination; Physician's request.
Staff Physicians 3 (ft); RNs 5 (ft); LPNs 7 (ft), 4 (pt); Orderlies 2 (ft); Nurses aides 31 (ft), 5 (pt); Physical therapists 1 (ft), 1 (pt); Recreational therapists 1 (ft); Occupational therapists 1 (ft); Speech therapists 1 (ft); Activities coordinators 1 (ft); Dietitians 1 (ft); Dentists 1 (ft); Ophthalmologists 1 (ft); Podiatrists 1 (ft).
Facilities Dining room; Physical therapy room; Activities room; Barber/Beauty shop; Outdoor patio.
Activities Arts & crafts; Cards; Games; Reading groups; Prayer groups; Movies; Shopping trips; Social/Cultural gatherings.

Kraver Institute*
1800 NE 168th St, North Miami Beach, FL,
33162
(305) 947-3445
Licensure Intermediate care for mentally
retarded. *Beds* 20.
Owner Nonprofit Corp.
Staff Physicians; Dietitians; Nurses aides.
Languages Spanish
Activities Arts & crafts; Shopping trips.

Royal Glades Convalescent Home*
16650 W Dixie Hwy, North Miami Beach, FL,
33160
(305) 945-7447
Licensure Skilled care. *Beds* 150. *Certified*
Medicaid; Medicare.
Owner Proprietary Corp.
Staff RNs 6 (ft); LPNs 14 (ft); Nurses aides 36
(ft).
Languages Spanish, French, Hebrew, Yiddish

OCALA

New Horizon Rehabilitationilitative Center
635 SE 17th St, Ocala, FL, 32670
(904) 629-7921
Licensure Skilled care; Intermediate care. *Beds*
89. *Certified* Medicaid; Medicare; VA.
Owner Proprietary Corp (Unicare).
Staff RNs 6 (ft); LPNs 9 (ft); Nurses aides 28
(ft).
Languages German, French, Greek, Polish,
Spanish
Facilities Dining room; Physical therapy
room; Activities room; Crafts room; Laundry
room; Barber/Beauty shop; Enclosed patio
area.
Activities Arts & crafts; Cards; Games;
Reading groups; Prayer groups; Movies;
Shopping trips; Social/Cultural gatherings.

Oakhurst Manor
1501 SE 24th Rd, Ocala, FL, 32671
(904) 629-8900
Admin Steve Watson. *Medical Dir/Dir of
Nursing* Dr McLaughlin; Joan Whittenham
DON.
Licensure Skilled care. *Beds* SNF 120.
Owner Proprietary Corp (Shive Nursing
Centers).
Staff Physicians 1 (pt); RNs 5 (ft), 4 (pt);
LPNs 6 (ft), 5 (pt); Nurses aides 46 (ft), 4
(pt); Physical therapists 2 (pt); Occupational
therapists 1 (pt); Speech therapists 1 (pt);
Activities coordinators 1 (ft); Dietitians 1
(pt); Ophthalmologists 1 (pt).

Ocala Geriatric Center Inc
1201 SE 24th & 2nd, Ocala, FL, 32671
(904) 732-2449
Admin William I Riddle. *Medical Dir/Dir of
Nursing* Carl S Lytle MD; Ellen Cain RN.
Licensure Skilled care; Intermediate care. *Beds*
180. *Certified* Medicaid; Medicare.
Owner Proprietary Corp (Waverly Group).
Admissions Requirements Minimum age 16;
Medical examination; Physician's request.
Staff Physicians 1 (pt); RNs 12 (ft), 2 (pt);
LPNs 10 (ft), 4 (pt); Nurses aides 55 (ft), 20
(pt); Physical therapists 1 (pt); Reality
therapists 1 (ft); Recreational therapists 1
(ft); Occupational therapists 1 (pt); Speech
therapists 1 (pt); Activities coordinators 1
(ft); Dietitians 1 (pt); Ophthalmologists 1
(pt); Podiatrists 1 (pt).
Languages Spanish
Facilities Dining room; Physical therapy
room; Activities room; Chapel; Crafts room;
Laundry room; Barber/Beauty shop; Library;
Day room; picnic area.
Activities Arts & crafts; Cards; Games;
Reading groups; Prayer groups; Movies;
Shopping trips; Social/Cultural gatherings.

Ocala Health Care Center*
2021 SW 1st Ave, Ocala, FL, 32670
(904) 629-0063

Licensure Skilled care. *Beds* 133. *Certified*
Medicaid; Medicare.
Owner Proprietary Corp (Beverly Enterprises).
Staff RNs 9 (ft); LPNs 11 (ft); Nurses aides 29
(ft).

OLDSMAR

West Bay Nursing Center
400 State Rd 584 W, Oldsmar, FL, 33557
(813) 855-4661
Admin Staci Harrison. *Medical Dir/Dir of
Nursing* Don DeHaven MD; Elizabeth
Mould RN DON.
Licensure Skilled care; Intermediate care. *Beds*
120. *Certified* Medicaid; Medicare.
Owner Proprietary Corp (Shive Nursing
Centers).
Admissions Requirements Medical
examination; Physician's request.
Staff RNs 4 (ft), 3 (pt); LPNs 5 (ft); Orderlies
3 (ft); Nurses aides 31 (ft), 4 (pt); Physical
therapists 1 (ft); Occupational therapists 1
(pt); Speech therapists 1 (pt); Activities
coordinators 1 (ft); Dietitians 1 (pt);
Ophthalmologists 1 (pt).
Languages Spanish
Facilities Dining room; Physical therapy
room; Activities room; Laundry room;
Barber/Beauty shop.
Activities Arts & crafts; Cards; Games; Prayer
groups; Movies; Shopping trips; Social/
Cultural gatherings.

OPA LOCKA

Landmark Learning Center—Facility I*
PO Box 1898, Opa Locka, FL, 33055
(305) 624-9671
Licensure Intermediate care for mentally
retarded. *Beds* 120. *Certified* Medicaid.
Owner Publicly owned.
Staff RNs 4 (ft); LPNs 7 (ft); Nurses aides 71
(ft).

**Landmark Learning Center—Miami Facility
II***
PO Box 1898, Opa Locka, FL, 33055
(305) 624-9671
Licensure Intermediate care for mentally
retarded. *Beds* 60.
Owner Publicly owned.

Sunland Center—Miami Facility III*
PO Box 1898, Opa Locka, FL, 33055
(305) 624-9671
Licensure Intermediate care for mentally
retarded. *Beds* 60.
Owner Publicly owned.

ORANGE CITY

John Knox Village Medical Center*
101 N Lake Dr, Orange City, FL, 32763
(904) 775-3840
Beds 60.
Owner Nonprofit Corp.

ORANGE PARK

Moosehaven Health Center*
Hwy 17, PO Box 102, Orange Park, FL,
32073
(904) 264-9551
Medical Dir/Dir of Nursing H L Stephens
MD.
Licensure Skilled care; Intermediate care. *Beds*
SNF 20; ICF 180.
Owner Nonprofit Corp.
Admissions Requirements Minimum age 65.
Staff Physicians 1 (ft), 3 (pt); Physical
therapists 2 (ft); Activities coordinators 1
(ft); Dietitians 1 (ft); Dentists 1 (ft);
Podiatrists 1 (ft); Audiologists 1 (ft).
Languages Spanish, Tagalog
Affiliation Royal Order of Moose

Facilities Dining room; Physical therapy
room; Chapel; Crafts room; Laundry room;
Barber/Beauty shop; Library.
Activities Arts & crafts; Cards; Games; Prayer
groups; Shopping trips; Social/Cultural
gatherings; Aerobic exercises.

Orange Park Care Center
2029 Professional Center Dr, Orange Park,
FL, 32073
(904) 272-6194
Admin Robert E Green. *Medical Dir/Dir of
Nursing* George Wilson MD; Christine
Martin.
Licensure Skilled care; Intermediate care. *Beds*
105. *Certified* Medicaid; Medicare.
Owner Proprietary Corp (National Heritage).
Admissions Requirements Medical
examination; Physician's request.
Staff RNs 5 (ft), 2 (pt); LPNs 7 (ft); Orderlies
2 (ft); Nurses aides 35 (ft); Physical
therapists 2 (pt); Occupational therapists 2
(pt); Speech therapists 2 (pt); Activities
coordinators 1 (ft); Dietitians 2 (pt);
Ophthalmologists 1 (pt); Podiatrists 1 (pt).
Facilities Dining room; Physical therapy
room; Activities room; Crafts room; Laundry
room; Barber/Beauty shop; Library.
Activities Arts & crafts; Cards; Games; Prayer
groups; Movies; Shopping trips; Social/
Cultural gatherings.

ORLANDO

Americana Health Care Center of Orlando*
2414 Bedford Rd, Orlando, FL, 32803
(305) 898-5051
Licensure Skilled care. *Beds* 102. *Certified*
Medicare.
Owner Proprietary Corp (Manor Care).
Staff RNs 7 (ft); LPNs 10 (ft), 1 (pt); Nurses
aides 23 (ft).
Languages German, Spanish, Italian

Barrington Terrace Nursing Home*
215 Annie St, Orlando, FL, 32806
(305) 841-4371
Medical Dir/Dir of Nursing Dr Louis C
Murry.
Licensure Skilled care. *Beds* 60.
Owner Proprietary Corp.
Staff Physicians; Dietitians; Nurses aides.
Languages Spanish, Italian
Facilities Dining room; Activities room;
Crafts room; Laundry room; Barber/Beauty
shop.
Activities Arts & crafts; Cards; Games; Prayer
groups; Movies; Shopping trips.

Florida Manor Nursing Home
830 W 29th St, Orlando, FL, 32805
(305) 843-3230
Admin Arthur H Harris. *Medical Dir/Dir of
Nursing* John Royer MD; Joyce L Niec RN
DON.
Licensure Skilled care; Intermediate care. *Beds*
SNF 300; ICF 120. *Certified* Medicaid.
Owner Nonprofit Corp.
Admissions Requirements Minimum age 16;
Medical examination; Physician's request.
Staff RNs 20 (ft), 4 (pt); LPNs 26 (ft), 2 (pt);
Orderlies 2 (ft); Nurses aides 128 (ft), 1 (pt);
Physical therapists 1 (ft); Reality therapists 1
(ft); Recreational therapists 6 (ft), 2 (pt);
Occupational therapists 1 (ft); Speech
therapists 1 (ft); Activities coordinators 1
(ft); Dietitians 2 (ft); Dentist 2 (pt); Director
of social service & one assistant 2 (ft).
Languages Spanish
Affiliation Roman Catholic
Facilities Dining room; Physical therapy
room; Activities room; Chapel; Crafts room;
Laundry room; Barber/Beauty shop; Library.
Activities Arts & crafts; Cards; Games;
Reading groups; Prayer groups; Movies;
Shopping trips; Social/Cultural gatherings.

Guardian Care Convalescent Center
2500 W Church St, Orlando, FL, 32805
(305) 295-5371
Admin Noel W Bridgett. *Medical Dir/Dir of Nursing* A L Bookhardt MD; Rose Williams.
Licensure Skilled care; Intermediate care. *Beds* 120. *Certified* Medicaid.
Owner Nonprofit Corp.
Admissions Requirements Minimum age 16; Medical examination; Physician's request.
Staff Physicians 2 (pt); RNs 6 (ft), 6 (pt); LPNs 12 (ft), 2 (pt); Orderlies 2 (ft); Nurses aides 36 (ft), 5 (pt); Physical therapists 1 (ft), 1 (pt); Reality therapists 1 (pt); Recreational therapists 2 (ft); Occupational therapists 1 (ft), 1 (pt); Speech therapists 1 (pt); Activities coordinators 1 (ft); Dietitians 1 (ft); Dentists 1 (pt); Ophthalmologists 1 (pt); Podiatrists 1 (pt); Dentist 1 (pt).
Languages Spanish, Arabic
Facilities Dining room; Physical therapy room; Activities room; Chapel; Crafts room; Laundry room; Barber/Beauty shop.
Activities Arts & crafts; Cards; Games; Reading groups; Movies; Shopping trips; Social/Cultural gatherings.

Loch Haven Lodge*
2250 Bedford Rd, Orlando, FL, 32803
(305) 898-4721
Licensure Skilled care. *Beds* 50. *Certified* Medicaid.
Owner Proprietary Corp (Beverly Enterprises).
Staff RNs 3 (ft); LPNs 5 (ft); Nurses aides 15 (ft).

Orlando Health Care Center
2000 N Semorian Blvd, Orlando, FL, 32870
(305) 671-5400
Admin Bob Borders. *Medical Dir/Dir of Nursing* Shirley Piceolmini DON.
Licensure Skilled care; Intermediate care. *Beds* 118. *Certified* Medicaid; Medicare.
Owner Proprietary Corp (Beverly Enterprises).
Admissions Requirements Medical examination.
Staff RNs 4 (ft); LPNs 13 (ft); Nurses aides 26 (ft); Occupational therapists 1 (pt); Speech therapists 1 (pt); Activities coordinators 5 (ft).
Facilities Dining room; Physical therapy room; Activities room; Crafts room; Laundry room; Barber/Beauty shop.
Activities Arts & crafts; Cards; Games; Reading groups; Prayer groups; Movies; Shopping trips; Social/Cultural gatherings.

Orlando Lutheran Towers
300 E Church St, Orlando, FL, 32801
(305) 425-1033
Admin Darrell Jensen. *Medical Dir/Dir of Nursing* Dr Edwin O'Neal; Rosemary Hogan RN.
Licensure Skilled care; Intermediate care. *Beds* SNF 30; ICF 30. *Certified* Medicaid.
Owner Nonprofit Corp.
Admissions Requirements Minimum age 65.
Staff RNs 4 (ft), 1 (pt); LPNs 3 (ft); Orderlies 1 (ft); Nurses aides 12 (ft), 1 (pt); Physical therapists 1 (pt); Activities coordinators 1 (ft), 1 (pt); Dietitians 1 (pt).
Languages German
Affiliation Lutheran
Facilities Dining room; Physical therapy room; Activities room; Chapel; Crafts room; Laundry room; Barber/Beauty shop; Library.
Activities Arts & crafts; Cards; Games; Reading groups; Prayer groups; Movies; Shopping trips; Social/Cultural gatherings.

Orlando Memorial Convalescent Center*
1730 Lucerne Terrace, Orlando, FL, 32806
(305) 423-1612
Licensure Skilled care. *Beds* 115. *Certified* Medicaid.
Owner Proprietary Corp (Hillhaven Corp).
Admissions Requirements Minimum age 21; Medical examination; Physician's request.

Staff Physicians 15 (pt); RNs 4 (ft), 1 (pt); LPNs 8 (ft), 3 (pt); Orderlies 3 (ft), 2 (pt); Nurses aides 28 (ft), 17 (pt); Physical therapists 1 (pt); Reality therapists 1 (pt); Recreational therapists 1 (pt); Occupational therapists 1 (pt); Speech therapists 1 (pt); Activities coordinators 2 (ft); Dietitians 1 (pt); Podiatrists 1 (pt); Audiologists 1 (pt).
Facilities Dining room; Physical therapy room; Activities room; Crafts room; Laundry room; Barber/Beauty shop.
Activities Arts & crafts; Cards; Games; Reading groups; Prayer groups; Movies; Shopping trips.

Westminster Towers
70 Lucerne Circle, Orlando, FL, 32801
(305) 841-1310
Admin Blaine Henry.
Licensure Skilled care; Congregate living; Retirement home. *Beds* SNF 120; Congregate living 49; Retirement home 248.
Owner Nonprofit Corp.
Admissions Requirements Medical examination.
Staff RNs; LPNs; Orderlies; Nurses aides; Physical therapists; Activities coordinators; Dietitians.
Affiliation Presbyterian
Facilities Dining room; Physical therapy room; Activities room; Chapel; Crafts room; Laundry room; Barber/Beauty shop; Library.
Activities Arts & crafts; Cards; Games; Reading groups; Prayer groups; Movies; Social/Cultural gatherings.

ORMOND BEACH

Bowman's Nursing Center
350 S Ridgewood Ave, Ormond Beach, FL, 32074
(904) 677-4545
Admin Robert E Green. *Medical Dir/Dir of Nursing* James Shoemaker; Pauline Ouellette RN DON.
Licensure Skilled care. *Beds* SNF 143. *Certified* Medicaid; Medicare.
Owner Proprietary Corp (National Healthcare Affiliates).
Admissions Requirements Medical examination; Physician's request.
Staff Physicians 1 (ft); RNs 4 (ft), 1 (pt); LPNs 9 (ft), 1 (pt); Nurses aides 33 (ft), 3 (pt); Physical therapists 1 (ft); Occupational therapists 1 (pt); Speech therapists 1 (ft); Activities coordinators 1 (ft); Dietitians 1 (ft); Ophthalmologists 1 (ft).
Facilities Dining room; Physical therapy room; Activities room; Crafts room; Laundry room; Barber/Beauty shop; Library.
Activities Arts & crafts; Cards; Games; Reading groups; Prayer groups; Movies; Shopping trips; Social/Cultural gatherings.

Ormond Beach Health Care Center
170 N Kings Rd, Ormond Beach, FL, 32074
(904) 677-7955
Medical Dir/Dir of Nursing Roman Hendrickson MD; Marlene Thomson RN.
Licensure Skilled care. *Beds* 133. *Certified* Medicaid; Medicare.
Owner Proprietary Corp (Beverly Enterprises).
Admissions Requirements Minimum age 25; Physician's request.
Staff Physicians 30 (ft); RNs 10 (ft), 4 (pt); LPNs 7 (ft), 2 (pt); Nurses aides 38 (ft), 9 (pt); Physical therapists 3 (ft); Recreational therapists 2 (ft); Activities coordinators 1 (ft); Dietitians 1 (pt); Ophthalmologists 1 (ft); Dentist 1 (ft); Social Service 1 (ft).
Languages French, Spanish, German
Facilities Dining room; Activities room; Chapel; Crafts room; Laundry room; Barber/Beauty shop.
Activities Arts & crafts; Cards; Games; Reading groups; Prayer groups; Movies; Shopping trips; Social/Cultural gatherings.

OVIEDO

Lutheran Haven*
Rte 3, Box 300, Hwy 426, Oviedo, FL, 32765
(305) 365-5676
Licensure Skilled care. *Beds* 42.
Owner Nonprofit Corp.
Staff RNs 4 (ft); LPNs 7 (ft); Nurses aides 11 (ft).
Affiliation Lutheran

PAHOKEE

Glades Health Care Center
230 S Barfield Hwy, Pahokee, FL, 33476
(305) 924-5561
Admin June L Doherty. *Medical Dir/Dir of Nursing* Dr Richard Sulman; Darrold Gooley RN DON.
Licensure Skilled care. *Beds* SNF 120. *Certified* Medicaid; Medicare.
Owner Proprietary Corp.
Admissions Requirements Minimum age 18; Medical examination.
Staff Physicians 1 (pt); RNs 6 (ft); LPNs 12 (ft); Orderlies 1 (ft); Nurses aides 45 (ft); Activities coordinators 1 (ft).
Languages Haitian, Spanish
Facilities Dining room; Physical therapy room; Activities room; Crafts room; Laundry room; Barber/Beauty shop; Dining room for large group activities.
Activities Arts & crafts; Cards; Games; Reading groups; Prayer groups; Movies; Church services; Birthday parties; Family night; Musicals.

PALATKA

Putnam Memorial Nursing Home*
501 S Palm Ave, Palatka, FL, 32077
(904) 328-1472
Licensure Skilled care. *Beds* 65. *Certified* Medicaid; Medicare.
Owner Proprietary Corp (Beverly Enterprises).
Staff RNs 4 (ft); LPNs 11 (ft); Nurses aides 14 (ft).

PALM HARBOR

Baytree Nursing Center
2600 Highlands Blvd N, Palm Harbor, FL, 34684
(813) 785-5671
Admin Mary F Byrne. *Medical Dir/Dir of Nursing* Arthur Polin MD; Susan Fuller RN.
Licensure Skilled care. *Beds* 120. *Certified* Medicaid; Medicare.
Owner Proprietary Corp (Shive Nursing Centers).
Admissions Requirements Medical examination; Physician's request.
Staff Physicians; RNs; LPNs; Orderlies; Nurses aides; Physical therapists; Occupational therapists; Speech therapists; Activities coordinators; Dietitians; Ophthalmologists; Podiatrists.
Languages Spanish, German
Facilities Dining room; Physical therapy room; Activities room; Crafts room; Laundry room; Barber/Beauty shop.
Activities Arts & crafts; Cards; Games; Prayer groups; Movies; Social/Cultural gatherings.

St Mark Village
2655 Nebraska Ave, Palm Harbor, FL, 34684
(813) 785-2576
Admin Jackson Pierce. *Medical Dir/Dir of Nursing* Dr James R Kinney DO; Rosalie Earley RN DON.
Licensure Skilled care. *Beds* SNF 60. *Certified* Medicare.
Owner Nonprofit Corp.
Admissions Requirements Medical examination; Physician's request.

Staff RNs 3 (ft), 3 (pt); LPNs 1 (ft), 4 (pt); Nurses aides 17 (ft), 7 (pt); Physical therapists 1 (pt); Recreational therapists 1 (ft); Occupational therapists 1 (pt); Speech therapists 1 (pt); Activities coordinators 1 (ft); Dietitians 1 (pt); Ophthalmologists 1 (pt); Podiatrists 1 (pt).
Affiliation Lutheran
Facilities Dining room; Physical therapy room; Activities room; Chapel; Crafts room; Barber/Beauty shop.
Activities Arts & crafts; Cards; Games; Reading groups; Prayer groups; Movies; Social/Cultural gatherings.

PANAMA CITY

Bay Convalescent Center*
1336 Saint Andrews Blvd, Panama City, FL, 32401
(904) 763-3911
Licensure Skilled care; Intermediate care. *Beds* 160. *Certified* Medicaid; Medicare.
Owner Proprietary Corp.
Staff RNs 3 (ft); LPNs 15 (ft); Nurses aides 37 (ft).
Languages Spanish

Gulf Coast Convalescent Center
1937 Jenks Ave, Panama City, FL, 32405
(914) 769-7686
Admin Paul D Gomia. *Medical Dir/Dir of Nursing* Rebecca Harmon.
Licensure Skilled care; Intermediate care. *Beds* 120. *Certified* Medicaid; Medicare.
Owner Proprietary Corp (Beverly Enterprises).
Admissions Requirements Minimum age 14; Medical examination; Physician's request.
Languages Spanish
Facilities Dining room; Physical therapy room; Activities room; Crafts room; Laundry room; Barber/Beauty shop.
Activities Arts & crafts; Cards; Games; Reading groups; Prayer groups; Movies; Shopping trips; Social/Cultural gatherings.

Lelah G Wagner Nursing Home*
3409 W 19th St, Panama City, FL, 32401
(904) 763-3401
Licensure Skilled care. *Beds* 66. *Certified* Medicaid; Medicare.
Owner Proprietary Corp (Vantage Healthcare).
Staff RNs 3 (ft); LPNs 7 (ft); Nurses aides 23 (ft).
Languages Spanish

Panama City Developmental Center
1407 Lincoln Dr, Panama City, FL, 32401
Admin Larry E Weishaar. *Medical Dir/Dir of Nursing* Freddie Williams FAFP.
Licensure Intermediate care for mentally retarded. *Beds* 64. *Certified* Medicaid.
Owner Nonprofit Corp.
Staff Physicians 1 (pt); RNs 2 (ft); LPNs 3 (ft), 3 (pt); Nurses aides 54 (ft); Physical therapists 1 (pt); Recreational therapists 1 (ft); Occupational therapists 1 (pt); Speech therapists 1 (pt); Dietitians 1 (ft); Dentists 1 (pt); Psychologists 2 (pt); Recreational aides 1 (ft); Dentist 1 (pt).
Facilities Dining room; Physical therapy room; Activities room; Crafts room; Laundry room.
Activities Arts & crafts; Cards; Games; Prayer groups; Movies; Shopping trips; Social/Cultural gatherings; Training.

Panama City Nursing Center
924 W 13th St, Panama City, FL, 32401
(904) 763-8463
Admin Joy Raponi. *Medical Dir/Dir of Nursing* Thomas G Merrill DO; Charlotte Spears RN.
Licensure Skilled care. *Beds* SNF 120. *Certified* Medicaid; Medicare; VA.
Owner Proprietary Corp.
Admissions Requirements Minimum age 18; Medical examination; Physician's request.

Staff Physicians 18 (pt); RNs 5 (ft); LPNs 12 (ft); Orderlies 3 (ft); Nurses aides 41 (ft); Physical therapists 2 (ft); Occupational therapists 1 (pt); Speech therapists 1 (pt); Activities coordinators 2 (ft); Dietitians 1 (pt); Dentists 1 (pt); Ophthalmologists 1 (pt); Podiatrists 1 (pt).
Languages Chinese, German
Facilities Dining room; Physical therapy room; Activities room; Chapel; Crafts room; Laundry room; Barber/Beauty shop; Library.
Activities Arts & crafts; Cards; Games; Reading groups; Prayer groups; Shopping trips; Social/Cultural gatherings.

PENNY FARMS

Mary M Olin Clinic
PO Box 483, Penny Farms, FL, 32079
(904) 529-9403
Licensure Skilled care. *Beds* SNF 40.
Owner Nonprofit Corp.
Admissions Requirements Minimum age 60; Females only; Medical examination.
Staff Physicians 3 (pt); RNs 1 (ft), 5 (pt); LPNs 3 (pt); Nurses aides 13 (ft), 7 (pt); Activities coordinators; Dietitians 1 (pt); Ophthalmologists 1 (pt); Podiatrists 1 (pt).
Facilities Physical therapy room; Activities room; Chapel; Barber/Beauty shop.
Activities Arts & crafts; Games; Reading groups; Prayer groups; Shopping trips; Social/Cultural gatherings; Afternoon tour bus.

PENSACOLA

Azalea Trace
10100 Hillview Rd, Pensacola, FL, 32514
(904) 474-0880
Admin William J Nuelle. *Medical Dir/Dir of Nursing* Dr Finley Holmes; Ruth Ann Haller RN.
Licensure Skilled care. *Beds* 90. *Certified* Medicare.
Owner Nonprofit Corp.
Admissions Requirements Minimum age 17.
Staff Physicians 1 (pt); RNs 4 (ft), 5 (pt); LPNs 9 (ft), 2 (pt); Orderlies; Nurses aides 22 (ft), 8 (pt); Physical therapists 1 (pt); Occupational therapists 1 (pt); Speech therapists 1 (pt); Activities coordinators 1 (ft); Dietitians 1 (pt); Dentists 1 (pt); Ophthalmologists 1 (pt); Social services 1 (ft).
Languages Spanish, French
Facilities Dining room; Physical therapy room; Activities room; Chapel; Crafts room; Barber/Beauty shop; Library; Store.
Activities Arts & crafts; Cards; Games; Reading groups; Prayer groups; Movies; Shopping trips; Social/Cultural gatherings; Handbell choir; Tea parties.

The Bluffs Care Center*
4343 Langley Ave, Pensacola, FL, 32504
(904) 477-4550
Licensure Skilled care. *Beds* 120. *Certified* Medicaid; Medicare.
Owner Proprietary Corp (Advocare Inc).
Staff RNs 3 (ft); LPNs 13 (ft); Nurses aides 27 (ft).

Escambia County Nursing Home
3107 N "H" St, Pensacola, FL, 32501
(904) 436-9300
Admin Shirley L Hoggard. *Medical Dir/Dir of Nursing* Thomas L Hoyt MD; Mary A Cook RN DON.
Licensure Skilled care. *Beds* SNF 155. *Certified* Medicaid.
Owner Publicly owned.
Admissions Requirements Females only; Medical examination.

Staff Physicians 2 (pt); RNs 6 (ft), 4 (pt); LPNs 17 (ft), 2 (pt); Orderlies 8 (ft); Nurses aides 45 (ft), 3 (pt); Activities coordinators 1 (ft); Dietitians 1 (ft); Dentists 1 (pt); Podiatrists 1 (pt).
Facilities Dining room; Physical therapy room; Activities room; Crafts room; Laundry room; Barber/Beauty shop; Library; Permanent outdoor stage; Covered patios.
Activities Arts & crafts; Cards; Games; Reading groups; Prayer groups; Movies; Shopping trips; Social/Cultural gatherings; Fishing trips; Picnics; Annual circus.

Haven of Our Lady of Peace
5203 N 9th Ave, Pensacola, FL, 32504
(904) 477-0531
Admin Olin D Tisdale. *Medical Dir/Dir of Nursing* Finley C Holmes MD.
Licensure Skilled care; Intermediate care. *Beds* SNF 47; ICF 42. *Certified* Medicaid; Medicare.
Owner Nonprofit Corp.
Admissions Requirements Minimum age 16; Medical examination.
Staff Physicians 1 (pt); RNs 2 (ft), 1 (pt); LPNs 10 (ft), 6 (pt); Nurses aides 29 (ft), 3 (pt); Activities coordinators 2 (pt).
Languages Spanish
Affiliation Roman Catholic
Facilities Dining room; Activities room; Chapel; Crafts room; Laundry room; Barber/Beauty shop; Library; Porches; Transportation.
Activities Arts & crafts; Cards; Games; Reading groups; Prayer groups; Movies; Shopping trips; Social/Cultural gatherings; Picnics.

Magnolias Nursing & Convalescent Center
600 W Gregory St, Pensacola, FL, 32501
(904) 438-2000
Admin Douglas R Eitel. *Medical Dir/Dir of Nursing* William Balk MD.
Licensure Skilled care. *Beds* 210. *Certified* Medicaid; Medicare.
Owner Proprietary Corp.
Admissions Requirements Minimum age 16; Medical examination; Physician's request.
Staff Physicians 12 (pt); RNs 7 (ft), 8 (pt); LPNs 15 (ft), 14 (pt); Orderlies 4 (ft), 1 (pt); Nurses aides 59 (ft), 21 (pt); Physical therapists 1 (ft); Recreational therapists 1 (ft); Speech therapists 1 (pt); Activities coordinators 1 (ft); Dietitians 1 (pt); Social workers 1 (ft); Physical therapy assistants; Dentist.
Facilities Dining room; Physical therapy room; Activities room; Crafts room; Laundry room; Barber/Beauty shop.
Activities Arts & crafts; Cards; Games; Reading groups; Prayer groups; Movies; Shopping trips; Social/Cultural gatherings.

Northview Community
10050 Hillview Rd, Pensacola, FL, 32533
(904) 476-2261
Admin Ruthie Andrews. *Medical Dir/Dir of Nursing* Dr Keegan; Delores Morgan RN DON.
Licensure Intermediate care for mentally retarded. *Beds* ICF/MR 30. *Certified* Medicaid.
Owner Nonprofit organization/foundation.
Admissions Requirements Minimum age 0-21; Medical examination.
Staff RNs 1 (ft), 1 (pt); LPNs 3 (ft), 6 (pt); Physical therapists 1 (pt); Recreational therapists 1 (ft); Occupational therapists 1 (pt); Speech therapists 1 (pt); Dietitians 1 (pt).
Languages Sign
Facilities Dining room; Activities room; Laundry room.
Activities Arts & crafts; Games; Movies; Shopping trips; Social/Cultural gatherings.

Pensacola Health Care Facility
1717 W Avery St, Pensacola, FL, 32501
(904) 434-2355
Admin John F McCullen. *Medical Dir/Dir of Nursing* Linda B Seeley DON.
Licensure Skilled care. *Beds* 118. *Certified* Medicaid.
Owner Proprietary Corp (Beverly Enterprises).
Admissions Requirements Minimum age 18; Medical examination; Physician's request.
Staff Physicians 2 (pt); RNs 4 (ft); LPNs 12 (ft); Orderlies 2 (ft); Nurses aides 25 (ft); Physical therapists 1 (pt); Speech therapists 1 (pt); Activities coordinators 1 (ft); Dietitians 1 (ft); Dentists 1 (pt); Ophthalmologists 1 (pt).
Languages Spanish
Facilities Dining room; Physical therapy room; Activities room; Chapel; Laundry room; Barber/Beauty shop; Library.
Activities Arts & crafts; Cards; Games; Reading groups; Prayer groups; Movies; Shopping trips; Social/Cultural gatherings.

PERRY

Perry Health Facility
207 Forest Dr, Perry, FL, 32347
(904) 584-6334
Admin Debra O Delgado. *Medical Dir/Dir of Nursing* Susan Lore.
Licensure Skilled care. *Beds* SNF 120. *Certified* Medicaid.
Owner Proprietary Corp (Beverly Enterprises).
Admissions Requirements Minimum age 18; Medical examination.
Staff RNs 4 (ft); LPNs 20 (ft); Nurses aides 40 (ft); Physical therapists 1 (pt); Recreational therapists 1 (ft); Occupational therapists 1 (pt); Speech therapists 1 (ft); Dietitians 1 (ft); Ophthalmologists 1 (pt).
Facilities Dining room; Physical therapy room; Activities room; Barber/Beauty shop; Protected garden/gazebo area.
Activities Arts & crafts; Cards; Games; Reading groups; Prayer groups; Movies; Shopping trips; Social/Cultural gatherings; Pet therapy.

PINELLAS PARK

Morningside Inc
6770 102nd Ave N, Pinellas Park, FL, 34666
(813) 541-3561
Admin Shirley E Bennison. *Medical Dir/Dir of Nursing* Dorothy Barnacle.
Licensure Skilled care; Intermediate care; Sheltered care. *Beds* SNF 19; ICF; Sheltered care 40. *Certified* Medicare.
Owner Nonprofit Corp.
Admissions Requirements Minimum age 18; Must be practicing Christian Scientist.
Staff RNs 10 (ft), 1 (pt); LPNs 4 (ft); Nurses aides 6 (ft), 2 (pt); Activities coordinators 1 (ft); Dietitians 1 (pt).
Languages German
Affiliation Christian Science
Facilities Dining room; Activities room; Chapel; Crafts room; Laundry room; Barber/Beauty shop; Library.
Activities Arts & crafts; Cards; Games; Reading groups; Prayer groups; Movies; Shopping trips; Social/Cultural gatherings.

Parkway Nursing Home*
7575 65th Way N, Pinellas Park, FL, 33565
(813) 544-6673
Licensure Skilled care. *Beds* 55. *Certified* Medicaid; Medicare.
Owner Proprietary Corp.
Staff RNs 6 (ft); LPNs 7 (ft); Nurses aides 23 (ft).

PLANT CITY

Community Convalescent Center
2202 W Oak Ave, Plant City, FL, 33566
(813) 754-3761
Admin D Lee Griffis. *Medical Dir/Dir of Nursing* Rees Morgan MD; Shelby Flanary RN DON.
Licensure Skilled care; Intermediate care. *Beds* SNF 120; ICF. *Certified* Medicaid; Medicare.
Owner Proprietary Corp (Health Care & Retirement Corp).
Staff RNs 5 (ft), 1 (pt); LPNs 11 (ft), 1 (pt); Nurses aides 37 (ft), 4 (pt); Reality therapists 1 (ft); Recreational therapists 1 (ft); Activities coordinators 1 (ft); Dietitians 1 (ft).
Languages Spanish
Facilities Dining room; Physical therapy room; Activities room; Laundry room; Barber/Beauty shop.
Activities Arts & crafts; Cards; Games; Reading groups; Prayer groups; Movies; Shopping trips; Social/Cultural gatherings; Restaurant day; Adopted grandparents day; Grooming class.

Forest Park Nursing Center
1702 W Oak Ave, Plant City, FL, 33566
(813) 752-4129
Admin Patricia C Jordan. *Medical Dir/Dir of Nursing* Edgar Sapp MD; Kathy Schiavinato RN.
Licensure Skilled care. *Beds* 97. *Certified* Medicaid; Medicare.
Owner Proprietary Corp (Beverly Enterprises).
Admissions Requirements Medical examination.
Staff Physicians 1 (pt); RNs 4 (ft); LPNs 7 (ft), 1 (pt); Orderlies 35 (ft), 3 (pt); Physical therapists 1 (pt); Recreational therapists 1 (pt); Speech therapists 1 (pt); Activities coordinators 1 (ft); Dietitians 1 (pt); Ophthalmologists 1 (pt).
Facilities Dining room; Activities room; Laundry room; Barber/Beauty shop.
Activities Arts & crafts; Cards; Games; Reading groups; Prayer groups; Movies; Shopping trips; Social/Cultural gatherings.

PLANTATION

Manor Care—Plantation
6931 W Sunrise Blvd, Plantation, FL, 33313
(305) 583-6200
Admin Garland Cline. *Medical Dir/Dir of Nursing* Dr Greiff; Robin Neville.
Licensure Skilled care. *Beds* SNF 120. *Certified* Medicaid; Medicare.
Owner Proprietary Corp (Manor Care).
Admissions Requirements Minimum age 16; Medical examination.
Staff Physicians; RNs; LPNs; Orderlies; Physical therapists; Recreational therapists; Occupational therapists; Speech therapists; Activities coordinators; Dietitians.
Languages Spanish
Facilities Dining room; Physical therapy room; Activities room; Crafts room; Laundry room; Barber/Beauty shop.
Activities Arts & crafts; Cards; Games; Reading groups; Prayer groups; Movies; Shopping trips; Social/Cultural gatherings.

Meridian Nursing Center—Plantation
7751 W Broward Blvd, Plantation, FL, 33324
(305) 473-8040
Admin Paul D Bach. *Medical Dir/Dir of Nursing* Michael C Cunningham MD; Carol U Campbell RN.
Licensure Skilled care; Intermediate care. *Beds* SNF 60; ICF 60. *Certified* Medicaid; Medicare.
Owner Proprietary Corp (Meridan Healthcare).
Admissions Requirements Physician's request.

Staff Physicians 1 (pt); RNs 7 (ft), 3 (pt); LPNs 10 (ft), 5 (pt); Nurses aides 38 (ft), 8 (pt); Activities coordinators 2 (ft).
Facilities Dining room; Physical therapy room; Activities room; Chapel; Crafts room; Laundry room; Barber/Beauty shop; Library.
Activities Arts & crafts; Cards; Games; Reading groups; Prayer groups; Movies; Shopping trips; Social/Cultural gatherings.

Plantation Nursing Home*
4250 NW 5th St, Plantation, FL, 33317
(305) 587-3296
Licensure Skilled care. *Beds* 152. *Certified* Medicaid; Medicare.
Owner Proprietary Corp (HBA Management Inc).
Staff RNs 12 (ft); LPNs 14 (ft); Nurses aides 33 (ft).
Languages Spanish

POMPANO BEACH

Colonial Palms*
51 W Sample Rd, Pompano Beach, FL, 33064
(305) 942-5530
Medical Dir/Dir of Nursing Mike Solnik MD & Dr Richman.
Licensure Skilled care. *Beds* 81.
Owner Proprietary Corp.
Admissions Requirements Minimum age 16; Medical examination.
Staff RNs 6 (ft); LPNs 9 (ft); Nurses aides 36 (ft), 9 (pt); Physical therapists 1 (pt); Recreational therapists 1 (pt); Occupational therapists 1 (pt); Speech therapists 1 (pt); Activities coordinators 4 (ft); Dietitians 1 (pt); Dentists 1 (pt); Podiatrists 1 (pt).
Languages Spanish
Facilities Dining room; Physical therapy room; Activities room; Chapel; Crafts room; Barber/Beauty shop; Library.
Activities Arts & crafts; Cards; Games; Reading groups; Prayer groups; Movies; Social/Cultural gatherings.

Colonial Palms East Nursing Home*
3670 NE 3rd St, Pompano Beach, FL, 33064
(305) 941-4100
Medical Dir/Dir of Nursing Mike Solnik MD.
Licensure Skilled care. *Beds* 120.
Owner Proprietary Corp.
Admissions Requirements Minimum age 16; Medical examination.
Staff RNs 9 (ft); LPNs 13 (ft); Orderlies 1 (ft); Nurses aides 44 (ft); Physical therapists; Occupational therapists; Speech therapists; Activities coordinators 7 (ft); Dietitians 1 (ft); Dentists; Ophthalmologists; Podiatrists; Audiologists.
Facilities Dining room; Physical therapy room; Activities room; Chapel; Crafts room; Laundry room; Barber/Beauty shop; Library.
Activities Arts & crafts; Cards; Games; Reading groups; Prayer groups; Movies; Shopping trips; Social/Cultural gatherings.

John Knox Village Medical Center
631 SW 6th St, Pompano Beach, FL, 33060
(305) 782-1300
Admin Mel Causey. *Medical Dir/Dir of Nursing* Jerome Froelich MD; James Lafier RN.
Licensure Skilled care. *Beds* SNF 120. *Certified* Medicaid; Medicare.
Owner Nonprofit Corp.
Admissions Requirements Minimum age 65.
Staff Physicians 1 (pt); RNs 5 (ft); LPNs 14 (ft); Nurses aides 44 (ft); Physical therapists 1 (pt); Recreational therapists 2 (ft); Occupational therapists 1 (pt); Speech therapists 1 (pt); Activities coordinators 2 (ft); Dietitians 1 (ft); Social service director 1 (ft).
Facilities Dining room; Physical therapy room; Activities room; Chapel; Crafts room; Laundry room; Barber/Beauty shop; Library.

Activities Arts & crafts; Cards; Games; Reading groups; Prayer groups; Movies; Shopping trips; Social/Cultural gatherings.

Pinehurst Convalescent Facility
2401 NE 2nd St, Pompano Beach, FL, 33062
(305) 943-5100
Admin Fred Austin. *Medical Dir/Dir of Nursing* Jean-C E Bourgue MD; Susan Yerkes RN DON.
Licensure Skilled care. *Beds* 83. *Certified* Medicaid; Medicare.
Owner Proprietary Corp (Beverly Enterprises).
Admissions Requirements Medical examination; Physician's request.
Staff RNs 3 (ft), 2 (pt); LPNs 9 (ft), 1 (pt); Orderlies 1 (ft); Nurses aides 32 (ft), 1 (pt); Speech therapists 1 (pt); Activities coordinators 1 (ft); Dietitians 1 (pt); Dentists 1 (pt); Ophthalmologists 1 (pt); Podiatrists 1 (pt).
Languages Spanish, Italian
Facilities Dining room; Physical therapy room; Activities room; Laundry room; Barber/Beauty shop; Courtyard; conference room.
Activities Arts & crafts; Cards; Games; Reading groups; Prayer groups; Movies; Shopping trips; Social/Cultural gatherings.

PORT CHARLOTTE

Port Charlotte Care Center
4033 Beaver Ln, Port Charlotte, FL, 33952
(813) 625-3200
Licensure Skilled care. *Beds* 103.
Owner Proprietary Corp (FL Living Care Inc).
Staff Nurses aides 5 (ft).

PORT SAINT JOE

Bay St Joseph Care Center
220 9th St, Port Saint Joe, FL, 32456
(904) 229-8244
Medical Dir/Dir of Nursing Dr Jorge San Pedro; Judith Howell DON.
Licensure Skilled care; Intermediate care. *Beds* 120. *Certified* Medicaid; Medicare.
Owner Proprietary Corp (Horizon Healthcare Corp).
Admissions Requirements Physician's request.
Staff Physical therapists 1 (pt); Speech therapists 1 (pt); Activities coordinators 1 (ft).
Facilities Dining room; Physical therapy room; Activities room; Chapel; Laundry room; Barber/Beauty shop.
Activities Arts & crafts; Cards; Games; Reading groups; Prayer groups; Movies; Shopping trips; Social/Cultural gatherings.

PORT SAINT LUCIE

Port St Lucie Convalescent Center*
7300 Oleander Ave, Port Saint Lucie, FL, 33452
(305) 466-4100
Beds 60.
Owner Proprietary Corp (Eden Park Management).

QUINCY

Gadsden Nursing Home*
1621 Experiment Station Rd, Quincy, FL, 32351
(904) 627-9276
Licensure Skilled care. *Beds* 60. *Certified* Medicaid.
Owner Nonprofit Corp.
Staff RNs 5 (ft); LPNs 11 (ft); Nurses aides 14 (ft).

ROCKLEDGE

Adare Medical Center
1770 S Huntington Ln, Rockledge, FL, 32955
(305) 632-7341
Licensure Skilled care. *Beds* SNF 100. *Certified* Medicaid; Medicare.
Owner Proprietary Corp.
Admissions Requirements Minimum age 21; Medical examination.
Staff Physicians 54 (pt); RNs 7 (ft), 2 (pt); LPNs 9 (ft), 3 (pt); Nurses aides 35 (ft), 3 (pt); Physical therapists 4 (pt); Speech therapists 1 (pt); Activities coordinators 1 (ft); Dietitians 1 (pt); Dentists 1 (pt); Ophthalmologists 1 (pt).
Languages Spanish
Facilities Dining room; Physical therapy room; Activities room; Laundry room; Barber/Beauty shop; Library; Privacy room.
Activities Arts & crafts; Cards; Games; Reading groups; Prayer groups; Movies; Social/Cultural gatherings; Pet therapy; Garden club.

Sunnypines Convalescent Center*
587 Barton Blvd, Rockledge, FL, 32955
(305) 632-6300
Licensure Skilled care. *Beds* 75. *Certified* Medicaid; Medicare.
Owner Proprietary Corp (Unicare).
Languages Spanish

SAINT AUGUSTINE

Buckingham-Smith Memorial Home*
169 Central Ave, Saint Augustine, FL, 32084
(904) 824-3638
Admin Lillian Gatlin. *Medical Dir/Dir of Nursing* Dr Julietta Alcontara.
Licensure Skilled care. *Beds* 51. *Certified* Medicaid.
Owner Nonprofit Corp.
Staff RNs 4 (ft), 2 (pt); LPNs 2 (ft), 4 (pt); Orderlies 6 (ft); Nurses aides 15 (ft), 2 (pt); Recreational therapists 1 (ft); Activities coordinators.
Facilities Dining room; Activities room; Laundry room.
Activities Arts & crafts; Cards; Games; Prayer groups; Shopping trips.

Gilmer Nursing Home
189 San Marco Ave, Saint Augustine, FL, 32084
(904) 824-3326
Admin Barbara M Hunter. *Medical Dir/Dir of Nursing* Dr Tessler; Deborah Ferquson RN DON.
Licensure Skilled care. *Beds* 68. *Certified* Medicaid.
Owner Proprietary Corp (Beverly Enterprises).
Admissions Requirements Minimum age 18; Medical examination; Physician's request.
Staff RNs 3 (ft); LPNs 7 (ft) 33; Orderlies 1 (ft); Nurses aides 20 (ft); Physical therapists 1 (ft); Recreational therapists 1 (ft); Occupational therapists 1 (ft); Speech therapists 1 (ft); Activities coordinators 1 (ft); Dietitians 1 (pt); Ophthalmologists 1 (pt); Podiatrists 1 (pt)ee.
Facilities Dining room; Activities room; Laundry room; Barber/Beauty shop.
Activities Arts & crafts; Cards; Games; Reading groups; Prayer groups; Movies; Shopping trips; Social/Cultural gatherings.

Ponce de Leon Care Center
404 Old Moultrie Rd, Saint Augustine, FL, 32086
(904) 824-3311
Admin Roxann Longworth. *Medical Dir/Dir of Nursing* Dr Terry Hayes MD; Connie Doane RN DON.
Licensure Skilled care. *Beds* SNF 120. *Certified* Medicaid; Medicare.
Owner Proprietary Corp.

Admissions Requirements Minimum age 18.
Staff RNs; LPNs; Nurses aides; Activities coordinators 2 (ft); Dietitians 1 (ft).
Facilities Dining room; Physical therapy room; Activities room; Crafts room; Laundry room; Barber/Beauty shop.
Activities Arts & crafts; Cards; Games; Reading groups; Prayer groups; Movies; Shopping trips.

St Augustine Center for Living
5155 US 1 South, Saint Augustine, FL, 32086
(904) 797-5027
Admin Craig Greiner. *Medical Dir/Dir of Nursing* Bonnie Hopper.
Licensure Intermediate care for mentally retarded. *Beds* ICF/MR 60. *Certified* Medicaid.
Owner Proprietary Corp.
Admissions Requirements Minimum age 18.
Staff Physicians 1 (pt); RNs 1 (ft); LPNs 1 (ft), 2 (pt); Recreational therapists 1 (ft); Occupational therapists 1 (pt); Speech therapists 1 (pt); Dietitians 1 (pt).
Facilities Dining room; Activities room; Crafts room.
Activities Arts & crafts; Games; Movies; Shopping trips; Social/Cultural gatherings.

St Augustine Geriatric Center*
51 Sunrise Blvd, Saint Augustine, FL, 32084
(904) 824-4479
Medical Dir/Dir of Nursing Dr Micheal P Tessler.
Licensure Skilled care. *Beds* 120. *Certified* Medicaid; Medicare.
Owner Proprietary Corp (Waverly Group).
Admissions Requirements Medical examination; Physician's request.
Staff Physicians 21 (ft); RNs 3 (ft), 1 (pt); LPNs 15 (ft), 3 (pt); Nurses aides 48 (ft), 4 (pt); Physical therapists 2 (ft), 1 (pt); Speech therapists 1 (pt); Activities coordinators 1 (ft); Dietitians 1 (ft), 1 (pt); Dentists 1 (pt); Ophthalmologists 1 (pt); Podiatrists 2 (pt); Audiologists 1 (pt); Psychologist 1 (pt).
Facilities Dining room; Physical therapy room; Activities room; Crafts room; Laundry room; Barber/Beauty shop; 2 Covered; paved; fenced outdoor patios.
Activities Arts & crafts; Cards; Games; Reading groups; Prayer groups; Movies; Shopping trips; Social/Cultural gatherings; Sports events; Mass & Rosary; Pet therapy; Adopt-a-grandchild.

St Johns County Senior Citizens Home*
169 Marine St, Saint Augustine, FL, 32084
(904) 824-1755
Licensure Skilled care. *Beds* 51. *Certified* Medicaid.
Owner Publicly owned.
Staff RNs 8 (ft); LPNs 6 (ft); Nurses aides 15 (ft).

SAINT CLOUD

St Cloud Health Care Center*
1301 Kansas Ave, Saint Cloud, FL, 32769
(305) 892-5121
Licensure Skilled care. *Beds* 131. *Certified* Medicaid.
Owner Proprietary Corp (Beverly Enterprises).
Staff RNs 4 (ft); LPNs 11 (ft); Nurses aides 26 (ft).
Languages Spanish, French, German

SAINT PETERSBURG

Abbey Nursing Home
7101 9th St N, Saint Petersburg, FL, 33702
(813) 527-7231
Medical Dir/Dir of Nursing Dr Ernest Frierson.
Licensure Skilled care. *Beds* 152. *Certified* Medicaid.

Owner Proprietary Corp (Southern
Management Services).
Admissions Requirements Minimum age 21;
Medical examination; Physician's request.
Staff RNs 11 (ft), 3 (pt); LPNs 8 (ft), 3 (pt);
Orderlies 7 (ft); Nurses aides 54 (ft), 9 (pt);
Activities coordinators 2 (ft); Dietitians 1
(ft).
Languages Italian, Hungarian, German,
Spanish
Facilities Dining room; Activities room;
Crafts room; Laundry room; Barber/Beauty
shop.
Activities Arts & crafts; Cards; Games;
Reading groups; Movies.

The Alhambra Nursing Home Inc
7501 38th Ave N, Saint Petersburg, FL, 33710
(813) 345-9307
Admin Larry Growney. *Medical Dir/Dir of
Nursing* Roger Laughlin MD; Carol
Baumann DON.
Licensure Skilled care. *Beds* 60. *Certified*
Private pay.
Owner Proprietary Corp.
Admissions Requirements Minimum age 20;
Medical examination; Physician's request.
Staff Physicians 10 (pt); RNs 3 (ft), 3 (pt);
LPNs 4 (ft), 3 (pt); Nurses aides 28 (ft), 3
(pt); Physical therapists 2 (pt); Recreational
therapists 2 (pt); Occupational therapists 2
(pt); Speech therapists 1 (pt); Activities
coordinators 1 (ft), 1 (pt); Dietitians 1 (ft);
Ophthalmologists 1 (pt); Podiatrists 1 (pt).
Facilities Dining room; Activities room;
Crafts room; Laundry room; Barber/Beauty
shop.
Activities Arts & crafts; Cards; Games;
Reading groups; Prayer groups; Movies;
Shopping trips; Social/Cultural gatherings.

Alpine Nursing Center
3456 21st Ave S, Saint Petersburg, FL, 33711
(813) 327-1988
Admin Doris Maxwell. *Medical Dir/Dir of
Nursing* Dr David Hobbs; Julia Price.
Licensure Intermediate care. *Beds* ICF 57.
Certified Medicaid.
Owner Proprietary Corp (Unicare).
Admissions Requirements Medical
examination; Physician's request.
Staff Physicians 1 (ft); RNs 1 (ft), 4 (pt);
LPNs 2 (ft), 2 (pt); Nurses aides 13 (ft), 4
(pt); Physical therapists 1 (pt); Reality
therapists 1 (ft); Speech therapists 1 (pt);
Activities coordinators 1 (ft); Dietitians 2
(ft); Ophthalmologists 1 (ft); Social services
1 (ft).
Facilities Dining room; Activities room;
Crafts room; Barber/Beauty shop.
Activities Arts & crafts; Cards; Games;
Reading groups; Prayer groups; Movies;
Social/Cultural gatherings.

Bayou Manor Health Care Center
435 42nd Ave S, Saint Petersburg, FL, 33705
(813) 822-1871
Admin Thomas J Scudiero. *Medical Dir/Dir of
Nursing* Robert Dawson MD; Earnestine
Davis RN DON.
Licensure Skilled care. *Beds* 159. *Certified*
Medicaid.
Owner Proprietary Corp (National Health
Corp).
Admissions Requirements Minimum age 16;
Medical examination; Physician's request.
Staff RNs 6 (ft); LPNs 12 (ft); Nurses aides 48
(ft); Activities coordinators 4 (ft); Dietitians
1 (ft).
Languages Spanish
Facilities Dining room; Physical therapy
room; Activities room; Chapel; Crafts room;
Laundry room; Barber/Beauty shop; Library.
Activities Arts & crafts; Cards; Games;
Reading groups; Prayer groups; Movies;
Shopping trips; Social/Cultural gatherings;
Cooking; Bowling.

Beverly Manor Convalescent Center*
550 9th Ave S, Saint Petersburg, FL, 33701
(813) 898-4105
Licensure Skilled care; Intermediate care. *Beds*
SNF 158; ICF 104. *Certified* Medicaid;
Medicare.
Owner Proprietary Corp (Beverly Enterprises).
Staff RNs 8 (ft); LPNs 18 (ft); Nurses aides 79
(ft).

Colonial Care Center
6300 46th Ave N, Saint Petersburg, FL, 33709
(813) 544-1444
Admin Carol Sweetland. *Medical Dir/Dir of
Nursing* Dr George Camarinos; Diane
Mackey.
Licensure Skilled care; Intermediate care. *Beds*
102. *Certified* Medicaid; Medicare.
Owner Proprietary Corp (Unicare).
Admissions Requirements Minimum age 16;
Medical examination; Physician's request.
Staff Physicians 7 (pt); RNs 4 (ft), 4 (pt);
LPNs 7 (ft), 6 (pt); Orderlies 2 (ft); Nurses
aides 32 (ft), 6 (pt); Occupational therapists
1 (pt); Speech therapists 1 (pt); Activities
coordinators 1 (ft), 1 (pt); Dietitians 1 (pt);
Ophthalmologists 1 (pt); Podiatrists 1 (pt).
Languages Italian, Spanish
Facilities Dining room; Activities room;
Crafts room; Barber/Beauty shop.
Activities Arts & crafts; Cards; Games;
Reading groups; Prayer groups; Movies;
Shopping trips.

Concordia Manor*
321 13th Ave N, Saint Petersburg, FL, 33701
(813) 822-3030
Licensure Skilled care. *Beds* 39. *Certified*
Medicaid.
Owner Proprietary Corp (Unicare).
Staff RNs 2 (ft); LPNs 4 (ft); Nurses aides 9
(ft).

Convalescent Care Center*
550 62nd St S, Saint Petersburg, FL, 33707
(813) 347-6151
Licensure Skilled care. *Beds* 120. *Certified*
Medicaid; Medicare.
Owner Proprietary Corp.
Staff RNs 8 (ft); LPNs 8 (ft); Nurses aides 25
(ft).

Golfview Nursing Home
3636 10th Ave N, Saint Petersburg, FL, 33713
(813) 323-3611
Admin Flora B Morrison. *Medical Dir/Dir of
Nursing* Dr Nanda; Cynthia Osgood DON.
Licensure Skilled care. *Beds* SNF 56. *Certified*
Medicaid; Medicare.
Owner Proprietary Corp.
Admissions Requirements Minimum age 18;
Medical examination.
Staff RNs 3 (ft), 4 (pt); LPNs 4 (ft), 3 (pt);
Nurses aides 22 (ft), 1 (pt); Activities
coordinators 1 (ft), 1 (pt).
Facilities Dining room; Activities room;
Laundry room; Barber/Beauty shop.
Activities Arts & crafts; Cards; Games;
Reading groups; Movies; Shopping trips;
Social/Cultural gatherings.

Good Samaritan Nursing Home*
3127 57th Ave N, Saint Petersburg, FL, 33714
(813) 527-2171
Licensure Skilled care. *Beds* 60. *Certified*
Medicaid; Medicare.
Owner Proprietary Corp.
Staff RNs 5 (ft); LPNs 5 (ft); Nurses aides 14
(ft).
Languages German

Greenbrook Nursing Center
1000 24th St N, Saint Petersburg, FL, 33713
(813) 323-4711
Admin Scott W Clark. *Medical Dir/Dir of
Nursing* Dr Joel Prawer; Gayle Jones DON.
Licensure Skilled care. *Beds* SNF 120.
Certified Medicaid; Medicare.
Owner Proprietary Corp (Unicare).

Admissions Requirements Minimum age 17.
Staff Physicians 1 (pt); RNs 5 (ft); LPNs 9
(ft), 4 (pt); Orderlies 3 (ft); Nurses aides 26
(ft), 10 (pt); Physical therapists 1 (pt);
Reality therapists 1 (pt); Recreational
therapists 1 (pt); Activities coordinators 1
(ft); Dietitians 1 (pt); Ophthalmologists 1
(pt); Podiatrists 1 (pt).
Languages Spanish, French
Facilities Dining room; Physical therapy
room; Activities room; Crafts room; Barber/
Beauty shop.
Activities Arts & crafts; Cards; Games;
Reading groups; Prayer groups; Movies;
Shopping trips; Social/Cultural gatherings.

Heartland of St Petersburg
1001 9th Street North, Saint Petersburg, FL,
33701
(813) 896-8619
Admin Tonja D Pittman. *Medical Dir/Dir of
Nursing* Malcolm Fraser; Geraldine White.
Licensure Skilled care. *Beds* 108. *Certified*
Medicaid; Medicare.
Owner Proprietary Corp (Health Care &
Retirement Corp).
Admissions Requirements Minimum age 18;
Medical examination; Physician's request.
Staff RNs 5 (ft), 2 (pt); LPNs 8 (ft), 1 (pt);
Orderlies 1 (ft); Nurses aides 25 (ft);
Physical therapists 1 (pt); Occupational
therapists 1 (pt); Speech therapists 1 (pt);
Activities coordinators 1 (ft), 1 (pt);
Dietitians 1 (pt); Dentists 1 (pt);
Ophthalmologists 1 (pt); Podiatrists 1 (pt).
Languages Spanish
Facilities Dining room; Physical therapy
room; Activities room; Crafts room; Laundry
room; Barber/Beauty shop; Library; Family
dining room.
Activities Arts & crafts; Cards; Games;
Reading groups; Prayer groups; Movies;
Shopping trips; Social/Cultural gatherings.

The Huber Restorium
521 69th Ave N, Saint Petersburg, FL, 33702
(813) 526-7000
Admin Walter M Huber. *Medical Dir/Dir of
Nursing* Henry E Newman MD; Betty
Thompson RN DON.
Licensure Skilled care. *Beds* SNF 96. *Certified*
Medicare.
Owner Proprietary Corp.
Admissions Requirements Minimum age 21;
Medical examination; Physician's request.
Staff Physicians 45 (pt); RNs 10 (ft), 2 (pt);
LPNs 7 (ft), 4 (pt); Nurses aides 35 (ft), 35
(pt); Physical therapists 2 (pt); Reality
therapists 1 (pt); Recreational therapists 1
(ft); Occupational therapists 1 (pt); Speech
therapists 1 (pt); Activities coordinators 1
(ft); Dietitians 1 (ft); Dentists 1 (pt);
Ophthalmologists 1 (pt); Podiatrists 1 (pt).
Languages German, Italian, Spanish, French
Facilities Dining room; Physical therapy
room; Activities room; Chapel; Crafts room;
Laundry room; Barber/Beauty shop; Library.
Activities Arts & crafts; Cards; Games;
Reading groups; Prayer groups; Movies;
Shopping trips; Social/Cultural gatherings.

Jacaranda Manor*
4250 66th St N, Saint Petersburg, FL, 33709
(813) 546-2405
Licensure Skilled care. *Beds* 299. *Certified*
Medicare.
Owner Proprietary Corp (Health Care &
Retirement Corp).
Staff RNs 9 (ft); LPNs 12 (ft); Nurses aides 68
(ft).
Languages Hebrew, Yiddish, Spanish, French,
Tagalog

Jaylene Manor Nursing Home*
896 73rd Ave N, Saint Petersburg, FL, 33702
Licensure Skilled care. *Beds* 63. *Certified*
Medicaid.
Owner Proprietary Corp.

Staff RNs 4 (ft); LPNs 6 (ft); Nurses aides 20 (ft).
Languages Italian, Spanish

Leisure Manor*
336 4th Ave N, Saint Petersburg, FL, 33701
(813) 896-4171
Licensure Skilled care. *Beds* 24.
Owner Proprietary Corp.
Staff RNs 7 (ft); LPNs 4 (ft); Nurses aides 10 (ft).
Affiliation Presbyterian

Majestic Towers*
1255 Pasadena Ave S, Saint Petersburg, FL, 33707
(813) 347-2160
Admin Virginia Dressler. *Medical Dir/Dir of Nursing* Gilbert Pena MD.
Licensure Skilled care. *Beds* 97.
Owner Proprietary Corp.
Staff RNs 5 (ft), 3 (pt); LPNs 9 (ft), 2 (pt); Orderlies 6 (ft); Nurses aides 27 (ft), 1 (pt); Physical therapists; Recreational therapists; Occupational therapists; Activities coordinators 2 (ft); Dietitians 1 (ft), 1 (pt); Dentists; Podiatrists; Audiologists; Social workers 1 (ft).
Facilities Dining room; Physical therapy room; Activities room; Chapel; Crafts room; Laundry room; Barber/Beauty shop; Library.
Activities Arts & crafts; Cards; Games; Reading groups; Prayer groups; Movies; Shopping trips; Social/Cultural gatherings.

Maria Manor Health Care
10300 4th St N, Saint Petersburg, FL, 33716
(813) 576-1025
Admin Margaret R McDonald. *Medical Dir/Dir of Nursing* Julio Valdes MD; P Liles RN.
Licensure Skilled care. *Beds* SNF 274. *Certified* Medicaid.
Owner Nonprofit organization/foundation.
Admissions Requirements Medical examination; Physician's request.
Staff Physicians 3 (pt); RNs 12 (ft); LPNs 22 (pt); Nurses aides 68 (ft), 10 (pt); Physical therapists 2 (pt); Activities coordinators 1 (ft); Dietitians 1 (ft); Ophthalmologists 2 (pt); Social services 2 (pt).
Languages Spanish, Italian, Polish, Yugoslavian
Affiliation Roman Catholic
Facilities Dining room; Physical therapy room; Activities room; Chapel; Crafts room; Laundry room; Barber/Beauty shop; Library.
Activities Arts & crafts; Cards; Games; Reading groups; Prayer groups; Movies; Shopping trips; Social/Cultural gatherings.

Masonic Home of Florida*
125 32nd Ave NE, Saint Petersburg, FL, 33704
(813) 822-3499
Medical Dir/Dir of Nursing Dr E Young.
Licensure Skilled care. *Beds* 85.
Owner Nonprofit Corp.
Staff Physicians 2 (ft); RNs 12 (ft), 2 (pt); LPNs 9 (ft); Orderlies 1 (ft); Nurses aides 36 (ft), 4 (pt); Physical therapists 1 (pt); Reality therapists 1 (pt); Recreational therapists 1 (pt); Speech therapists 1 (pt); Activities coordinators 1 (ft); Dietitians 1 (ft); Dentists 2 (ft); Ophthalmologists 1 (ft); Podiatrists 1 (ft); Audiologists 1 (pt).
Affiliation Masons
Facilities Dining room; Physical therapy room; Activities room; Chapel; Crafts room; Laundry room; Barber/Beauty shop; Library.
Activities Arts & crafts; Cards; Games; Prayer groups; Shopping trips; Social/Cultural gatherings.

Menorah Manor
255 59th St N, Saint Petersburg, FL, 33710
(813) 345-2775

Admin Edward W Vinown. *Medical Dir/Dir of Nursing* H James Brownlee MD; David J Pagano RN DON.
Licensure Skilled care; Intermediate care. *Beds* SNF 120; ICF.
Owner Nonprofit Corp.
Staff Physicians 1 (pt); RNs 6 (ft); LPNs 20 (ft); Nurses aides 37 (ft); Physical therapists 2 (ft); Recreational therapists 2 (ft); Occupational therapists 1 (pt); Speech therapists 1 (pt); Activities coordinators 1 (ft); Dietitians 1 (pt); Ophthalmologists 1 (pt); Podiatrists 1 (pt).

North Horizon Health Care Center
1301 16th St N, Saint Petersburg, FL, 33705
(813) 898-5119
Admin Patricia M Lycett. *Medical Dir/Dir of Nursing* Joel S Prauler MC; Laurie A Miller.
Licensure Skilled care. *Beds* 49. *Certified* Medicaid; Medicare.
Owner Proprietary Corp (Unicare).
Staff RNs; LPNs; Orderlies; Nurses aides; Activities coordinators; Ophthalmologists.
Activities Arts & crafts; Cards; Games; Reading groups; Prayer groups; Movies; Shopping trips; Social/Cultural gatherings.

North Shores Health Center
939 Beach Dr NE, Saint Petersburg, FL, 33701
(813) 823-1571
Admin Beverly J Baxter. *Medical Dir/Dir of Nursing* Susan Betzer MD; Julia Price RN.
Licensure Skilled care; Intermediate care. *Beds* 26.
Owner Proprietary Corp.
Admissions Requirements Minimum age; Medical examination; Physician's request.
Staff RNs 2 (ft); LPNs 2 (ft), 1 (pt); Nurses aides 10 (ft), 1 (pt); Activities coordinators 1 (ft); Food Services Director 1 (ft); Medical Records 1 (pt).
Languages Spanish
Facilities Dining room; Activities room; Barber/Beauty shop; Library.
Activities Arts & crafts; Cards; Games; Prayer groups; Movies; Shopping trips; Social/Cultural gatherings; Circus; Ice Show.

Palm Shores Retirement Center
830 N Shore Dr, Saint Petersburg, FL, 33701
(813) 894-2102
Licensure Skilled care. *Beds* 42.
Owner Nonprofit Corp.
Staff RNs 4 (ft); LPNs 3 (ft); Nurses aides 8 (ft).
Languages Spanish
Affiliation Baptist

Parc Center Apartments*
3190 75th St N, Saint Petersburg, FL, 33710
(813) 384-0607
Licensure Intermediate care for mentally retarded. *Beds* 48.
Owner Nonprofit Corp.

PARC Cottage
3100 75th St N, Saint Petersburg, FL, 33710
(813) 345-4508
Admin Faith Young Bedford. *Medical Dir/Dir of Nursing* Jane Ott RN.
Licensure Intermediate care for mentally retarded. *Beds* ICF/MR 16. *Certified* Medicaid.
Owner Nonprofit organization/foundation.
Admissions Requirements Minimum age 3.
Staff Physicians; RNs; LPNs; Physical therapists; Recreational therapists; Occupational therapists; Speech therapists; Activities coordinators; Dietitians; Dentists.
Facilities Dining room; Activities room; Laundry room.
Activities Arts & crafts; Games; Movies; Shopping trips.

Rosedale Restorium*
3479 54th Ave N, Saint Petersburg, FL, 33714
(813) 527-7315

Licensure Skilled care. *Beds* 192. *Certified* Medicaid.
Owner Proprietary Corp (Health Care & Retirement Corp).
Staff RNs 8 (ft); LPNs 18 (ft); Nurses aides 40 (ft).

St Petersburg Cluster*
1101 102nd Ave N, Saint Petersburg, FL, 33702
(813) 536-5911
Licensure Intermediate care for mentally retarded. *Beds* 8.

Shore Acres Nursing & Convalescent Home
4500 Indianapolis St NE, Saint Petersburg, FL, 33703
(813) 527-5801
Admin Eugene R Keeton. *Medical Dir/Dir of Nursing* Harold Vick.
Licensure Skilled care. *Beds* SNF 109. *Certified* Medicaid; Medicare.
Owner Proprietary Corp (Continental Medical Systems).
Admissions Requirements Medical examination.
Staff Physicians 1 (pt); RNs 3 (ft); LPNs 10 (ft), 2 (pt); Orderlies 5 (ft); Nurses aides 38 (ft); Physical therapists 1 (pt); Recreational therapists 1 (pt); Occupational therapists 1 (pt); Speech therapists 1 (pt); Activities coordinators 1 (ft); Dietitians 1 (pt); Ophthalmologists 1 (pt).
Languages Spanish, German
Facilities Dining room; Physical therapy room; Activities room; Crafts room; Laundry room; Barber/Beauty shop; Library.
Activities Arts & crafts; Games; Reading groups; Prayer groups; Movies; Shopping trips; Social/Cultural gatherings.

South Heritage Health Care Center*
718 Lakeview Ave S, Saint Petersburg, FL, 33705
(813) 894-5125
Medical Dir/Dir of Nursing Dr Malcolm Fraser.
Licensure Skilled care. *Beds* 75. *Certified* Medicaid; Medicare.
Owner Proprietary Corp (Unicare).
Staff Physicians 1 (pt); RNs 3 (ft); LPNs 12 (ft); Nurses aides 27 (ft), 4 (pt); Physical therapists 1 (pt); Speech therapists 1 (pt); Activities coordinators 1 (ft); Dietitians 1 (pt); Dentists 1 (pt); Podiatrists 1 (pt); Audiologists 1 (pt).
Facilities Dining room; Activities room; Barber/Beauty shop.
Activities Arts & crafts; Cards; Games; Reading groups; Prayer groups; Movies; Shopping trips; Social/Cultural gatherings.

Suncoast Manor
6909 9th St S, Saint Petersburg, FL, 33705
(813) 867-1131
Admin Pat Shoemaker. *Medical Dir/Dir of Nursing* David L Jones MD; Maris Bledsoe RN DON.
Licensure Skilled care. *Beds* 161.
Owner Nonprofit Corp.
Admissions Requirements Minimum age 62; Females only; Medical examination.
Staff Physicians 3 (pt); RNs 6 (ft), 2 (pt); LPNs 10 (ft), 3 (pt); Nurses aides 34 (ft), 5 (pt); Physical therapists 1 (pt); Occupational therapists 1 (pt); Speech therapists 1 (pt); Activities coordinators 1 (ft); Dietitians 1 (pt); Podiatrists 2 (pt); Audiologists 1 (pt); Private duty aides 13 (ft), 3 (pt).
Languages Spanish
Affiliation Episcopal
Facilities Dining room; Physical therapy room; Activities room; Chapel; Crafts room; Barber/Beauty shop; Library.
Activities Arts & crafts; Cards; Games; Prayer groups; Movies; Shopping trips; Social/Cultural gatherings.

Suncoast Nursing Home*
2000 17th Ave S, Saint Petersburg, FL, 33712
(813) 823-1861
Licensure Skilled care. *Beds* 59. *Certified*
Medicaid.
Owner Proprietary Corp.
Staff RNs 2 (ft); LPNs 5 (ft); Nurses aides 9
(ft).

Sunny Shores Villas Health Center
125-56th Ave S, Saint Petersburg, FL, 33705
(813) 867-2131 ext 548
Admin Sarah S McGlathery. *Medical Dir/Dir
of Nursing* Claude V Murr MD; Florence R
Wilde RN DON.
Licensure Skilled care. *Beds* SNF 120.
Owner Nonprofit Corp.
Admissions Requirements Minimum age 65;
Medical examination; Physician's request.
Staff Physicians 2 (pt); RNs 13 (ft); LPNs 11
(ft); Orderlies 1 (ft); Nurses aides 54 (ft);
Physical therapists 1 (pt); Reality therapists
1 (pt); Recreational therapists 1 (pt);
Occupational therapists 1 (pt); Speech
therapists 1 (pt); Activities coordinators 1
(ft); Dietitians 1 (pt); Dentists 1 (pt);
Ophthalmologists 1 (pt); Podiatrists 1 (pt);
Social worker 1 (ft).
Affiliation Methodist
Facilities Dining room; Activities room;
Crafts room; Laundry room; Barber/Beauty
shop; Library.
Activities Arts & crafts; Cards; Games;
Reading groups; Prayer groups; Movies;
Shopping trips; Social/Cultural gatherings.

Swanholm Nursing & Rehabilitation Center
6200 Central Ave, Saint Petersburg, FL,
33707
(813) 347-5196
Admin Harold E Bahlow. *Medical Dir/Dir of
Nursing* Robert L Dawson MD; Barbara
Quehl RN DON.
Licensure Skilled care. *Beds* SNF 273.
Certified Medicaid; Medicare.
Owner Nonprofit Corp.
Admissions Requirements Minimum age 17;
Medical examination; Physician's request.
Staff RNs; LPNs; Orderlies; Nurses aides;
Physical therapists 2 (ft), Aides 5 (ft);
Activities coordinators 1 (ft).
Languages Spanish, Polish, French, Italian,
Sign
Affiliation Lutheran
Facilities Dining room; Physical therapy
room; Activities room; Chapel; Crafts room;
Laundry room; Barber/Beauty shop; Library.
Activities Arts & crafts; Cards; Games;
Reading groups; Prayer groups; Movies;
Shopping trips; Social/Cultural gatherings;
Bowling; Reality orientation; Exercise
groups; Music therapy; Bingo; Happy hour.

Tyrone Medical Inn*
1100 66th St N, Saint Petersburg, FL, 33710
(813) 345-9331
Medical Dir/Dir of Nursing Douglas W Hood
MD.
Licensure Skilled care. *Beds* 59. *Certified*
Medicare.
Owner Proprietary Corp.
Staff RNs 2 (ft); LPNs 7 (ft); Nurses aides 22
(ft).
Facilities Dining room; Activities room;
Barber/Beauty shop.
Activities Arts & crafts; Games; Movies.

Victoria Martin Nursing Home*
555 31st St S, Saint Petersburg, FL, 33712
(813) 821-0995
Medical Dir/Dir of Nursing Dr Orion T Ayer.
Licensure Skilled care. *Beds* 38. *Certified*
Medicaid.
Owner Proprietary Corp.
Admissions Requirements Medical
examination; Physician's request.

Staff RNs 3 (ft), 5 (pt); LPNs 4 (pt); Nurses
aides 12 (ft), 2 (pt); Physical therapists;
Activities coordinators 1 (ft).
Facilities Dining room; Activities room;
Laundry room.
Activities Arts & crafts; Cards; Games;
Reading groups; Prayer groups; Movies;
Social/Cultural gatherings.

Wedgewood Health Care*
1735 9th St S, Saint Petersburg, FL, 33705
(813) 821-8866
Licensure Skilled care; Intermediate care. *Beds*
SNF 109; ICF 163. *Certified* Medicaid;
Medicare.
Owner Proprietary Corp.
Staff RNs 10 (ft); LPNs 21 (ft); Nurses aides
56 (ft).
Languages French, German

Whitehall Nursing Home
5601 31st St S, Saint Petersburg, FL, 33712
(813) 867-6955
Admin Sandra L Bollenback. *Medical Dir/Dir
of Nursing* Betty Barbieri.
Licensure Skilled care. *Beds* SNF 58.
Owner Privately owned.
Admissions Requirements Minimum age 21;
Medical examination.
Staff RNs 4 (ft); LPNs 5 (ft); Nurses aides 18
(ft).
Languages French, Hindi, Spanish, Arabic
Facilities Dining room; Activities room;
Chapel; Crafts room; Barber/Beauty shop.
Activities Arts & crafts; Cards; Games;
Reading groups; Prayer groups; Movies;
Shopping trips; Social/Cultural gatherings.

William & Mary Nursing Home
811 Jackson St N, Saint Petersburg, FL, 33705
(813) 896-3651
Admin Susan Poirier. *Medical Dir/Dir of
Nursing* Patricia Vesey RN DON.
Licensure Skilled care; Intermediate care. *Beds*
65. *Certified* Medicaid; Medicare; VA.
Owner Proprietary Corp (Integrated Health
Services Inc).
Admissions Requirements Minimum age 17;
Medical examination; Physician's request.
Staff RNs 5 (ft); LPNs 7 (ft); Nurses aides 21
(ft).
Languages Spanish
Facilities Dining room; Physical therapy
room; Activities room; Crafts room; Laundry
room; Barber/Beauty shop.
Activities Arts & crafts; Cards; Games;
Reading groups; Prayer groups; Movies;
Shopping trips; Social/Cultural gatherings.

SAINT PETERSBURG BEACH

Beach Convalescent Nursing Home
8008 Blind Pass Rd, Saint Petersburg Beach,
FL, 33706
(813) 367-7651
Admin Joan H Bayley. *Medical Dir/Dir of
Nursing* Malcolm Fraser MD; Catherine
Sprunger RN DON.
Licensure Intermediate care; ACLF. *Beds* ICF
38; ACLF 16. *Certified* Medicaid.
Owner Proprietary Corp (Vantage Healthcare).
Admissions Requirements Minimum age 21;
Medical examination; Physician's request.
Staff RNs 1 (ft), 3 (pt); LPNs 2 (ft), 1 (pt);
Orderlies 1 (ft); Nurses aides 9 (ft), 2 (pt);
Physical therapists 1 (pt); Activities
coordinators 1 (ft), 1 (pt); Dietitians 1 (pt);
Ophthalmologists 1 (pt); Podiatrists 1 (pt).
Languages Greek
Facilities Dining room; Laundry room;
Barber/Beauty shop.
Activities Cards; Games; Prayer groups;
Movies; Social/Cultural gatherings.

Crown Nursing Home
5351 Gulf Blvd, Saint Petersburg Beach, FL,
33706
(813) 360-5548

Admin Flora Morrison. *Medical Dir/Dir of
Nursing* Malcolm Fraser MD; Mary Wheeler
RN.
Licensure Skilled care. *Beds* SNF 53. *Certified*
Medicaid; Medicare.
Owner Proprietary Corp.
Admissions Requirements Medical
examination; Physician's request.
Staff Physicians 1 (pt); RNs 2 (ft), 1 (pt);
LPNs 4 (ft), 3 (pt); Physical therapists 1 (pt);
Activities coordinators 1 (ft); Dietitians 1
(pt); Ophthalmologists 1 (pt).
Languages Polish, German
Facilities Dining room; Activities room;
Laundry room; Barber/Beauty shop.
Activities Arts & crafts; Cards; Games;
Reading groups; Prayer groups; Movies;
Shopping trips; Social/Cultural gatherings;
Dietary committee; Nursing committee;
Activity committee.

SANFORD

Hillhaven Healthcare Center
950 Mellonville Ave, Sanford, FL, 32771
(305) 322-8566
Admin Barbara LaWall. *Medical Dir/Dir of
Nursing* Anup Lahiry MD; Marietta Fenton
DON.
Licensure Skilled care. *Beds* SNF 114.
Certified Medicaid; Medicare.
Owner Proprietary Corp (Hillhaven Corp).
Staff RNs 5 (ft); LPNs 5 (ft); Orderlies;
Nurses aides 24 (ft); Physical therapists;
Recreational therapists; Activities
coordinators; Dietitians.
Facilities Dining room; Physical therapy
room; Activities room; Chapel; Crafts room;
Laundry room; Barber/Beauty shop; Library.
Activities Arts & crafts; Cards; Games;
Reading groups; Prayer groups; Movies;
Shopping trips; Social/Cultural gatherings.

Lakeview Nursing Center*
919 E 2nd St, Sanford, FL, 32771
(305) 322-6707
Licensure Skilled care. *Beds* 105.
Owner Proprietary Corp.
Staff RNs 3 (ft); LPNs 8 (ft); Nurses aides 29
(ft).
Languages Spanish, German

SARASOTA

Bay Village of Sarasota
8400 Vamo Rd, Sarasota, FL, 34231-7899
(813) 966-5611
Licensure Skilled care. *Beds* SNF 107.
Owner Nonprofit Corp.
Admissions Requirements Minimum age 65;
Medical examination.
Staff RNs 8 (ft), 14 (pt); LPNs 4 (ft), 1 (pt);
Orderlies 1 (ft); Nurses aides 39 (ft), 8 (pt);
Physical therapists 1 (pt); Occupational
therapists 1 (pt); Speech therapists 1 (pt);
Dietitians 1 (ft); Ophthalmologists 1 (pt).
Affiliation Presbyterian
Facilities Dining room; Physical therapy
room; Activities room; Chapel; Crafts room;
Laundry room; Barber/Beauty shop; Library.
Activities Arts & crafts; Cards; Games;
Reading groups; Prayer groups; Movies;
Social/Cultural gatherings.

Beneva Nursing Pavilion*
741 S Beneva Rd, Sarasota, FL, 35582
(813) 857-0310
Beds 120.
Owner Proprietary Corp.

Burzenski Nursing Home*
4450 8th St, Sarasota, FL, 33582
(813) 371-6430
Licensure Skilled care. *Beds* 60.
Owner Proprietary Corp (Glenmark Assocs).

East Manor Medical Care Center
1524 East Ave S, Sarasota, FL, 34239
(813) 365-2422
Admin Richard N Thrower. *Medical Dir/Dir of Nursing* Randy Powell MD; Leonore Ruggles RN DON.
Licensure Skilled care. *Beds* SNF 169. *Certified* Medicaid; Medicare.
Owner Proprietary Corp (Hillhaven Corp).
Admissions Requirements Medical examination; Physician's request.
Staff RNs 11 (ft); LPNs 13 (ft); Nurses aides 49 (ft); Physical therapists 1 (pt); Occupational therapists 1 (pt); Speech therapists 1 (pt); Activities coordinators 2 (ft); Dietitians 1 (pt); Podiatrists 1 (pt).
Facilities Dining room; Physical therapy room; Activities room; Laundry room; Barber/Beauty shop.
Activities Arts & crafts; Cards; Games; Reading groups; Prayer groups; Movies; Shopping trips; Social/Cultural gatherings.

J H Floyd Sunshine Manor*
1755 18th St, Sarasota, FL, 33578
(813) 955-4915
Licensure Skilled care. *Beds* 70. *Certified* Medicaid.
Owner Nonprofit Corp.
Staff RNs 4 (ft); LPNs 5 (ft); Nurses aides 24 (ft).

Hillhaven Convalescent Center*
1625 S Osprey Ave, Sarasota, FL, 33579
(813) 955-5741
Licensure Skilled care. *Beds* 77. *Certified* Medicaid; Medicare.
Owner Proprietary Corp.
Staff RNs 13 (ft); LPNs 6 (ft); Nurses aides 17 (ft).

Kensington Manor Inc
3250 12th St, Sarasota, FL, 34237
(813) 365-4185
Admin Al J Robbins. *Medical Dir/Dir of Nursing* Dr John Steel; Carol Davies RN DON.
Licensure Skilled care; Intermediate care. *Beds* 147. *Certified* Medicaid; Medicare.
Owner Proprietary Corp (Health Care & Retire Corp).
Admissions Requirements Medical examination; Physician's request.
Staff Physicians 1 (ft); RNs 8 (ft), 2 (pt); LPNs 8 (ft), 3 (pt); Nurses aides 45 (ft), 4 (pt); Physical therapists 2 (pt); Occupational therapists 1 (pt); Speech therapists 1 (pt); Activities coordinators 2 (ft); Dietitians 1 (pt); Ophthalmologists 1 (pt).
Languages Spanish, Italian
Facilities Dining room; Activities room; Crafts room; Laundry room; Barber/Beauty shop; Library.
Activities Arts & crafts; Cards; Games; Reading groups; Prayer groups; Movies; Shopping trips.

Plymouth Harbor Inc
700 John Ringling Blvd, Sarasota, FL, 34236
(813) 365-2600
Admin J Mark Vanderbeck. *Medical Dir/Dir of Nursing* Scott Elsbree MD; Dorothy Barichak DON.
Licensure Skilled care. *Beds* SNF 43.
Owner Nonprofit Corp.
Admissions Requirements Minimum age 65; Medical examination.
Staff Physicians 1 (pt); RNs 7 (ft), 2 (pt); LPNs 5 (ft), 1 (pt); Nurses aides 22 (ft), 6 (pt); Physical therapists 1 (ft), 1 (pt); Recreational therapists 1 (pt); Occupational therapists 1 (pt); Speech therapists 1 (pt); Activities coordinators 1 (pt); Dietitians 1 (pt); Ophthalmologists 1 (pt).
Affiliation Church of Christ
Facilities Dining room; Activities room; Chapel; Crafts room; Laundry room; Barber/Beauty shop; Library.
Activities Arts & crafts; Cards; Games; Reading groups; Prayer groups; Movies; Shopping trips; Social/Cultural gatherings.

Sarasota Nursing Pavilion
2600 Courtland St, Sarasota, FL, 33577
(813) 365-2926
Admin Claire Fellema. *Medical Dir/Dir of Nursing* Ernest W Chapman MD; Esther Gatto RN DON.
Licensure Skilled care. *Beds* 180. *Certified* Medicaid; Medicare.
Owner Proprietary Corp.
Admissions Requirements Minimum age 16; Medical examination; Physician's request.
Staff RNs 25 (ft), 5 (pt); LPNs; Orderlies 3 (ft); Nurses aides 35 (ft), 20 (pt); Physical therapists 2 (ft); Recreational therapists 1 (ft); Occupational therapists 2 (ft), 2 (pt); Speech therapists 1 (pt); Activities coordinators 1 (ft); Dietitians 1 (ft).
Languages Spanish
Facilities Dining room; Physical therapy room; Activities room; Crafts room; Laundry room; Barber/Beauty shop; Library.
Activities Arts & crafts; Cards; Games; Reading groups; Prayer groups; Movies; Shopping trips; Social/Cultural gatherings.

Sarasota Welfare Home Inc
1501 N Orange Ave, Sarasota, FL, 34236
(813) 365-0250
Licensure Skilled care; Intermediate care. *Beds* 204. *Certified* Medicaid; Medicare.
Owner Nonprofit Corp.
Admissions Requirements Minimum age 65; Medical examination; 5 year county residency.
Staff Physicians; Nurses aides; Dietitians.
Languages Spanish
Facilities Dining room; Activities room; Chapel; Crafts room; Laundry room; Barber/Beauty shop; Library.
Activities Arts & crafts; Cards; Games; Reading groups; Prayer groups; Movies; Shopping trips; Social/Cultural gatherings.

Springwood Nursing Center Ltd*
4602 Northgate Court, Sarasota, FL, 33580
(813) 355-2913
Beds 120.
Owner Proprietary Corp (Shive Nursing Centers).

Sunnyside Nursing Home
5201 Bahia Vista, Sarasota, FL, 34232
(813) 371-2729 or 371-2750
Admin Ben E Eberly. *Medical Dir/Dir of Nursing* Dr Loren Zehr.
Licensure Skilled care. *Beds* SNF 60. *Certified* Medicaid.
Owner Nonprofit Corp.
Admissions Requirements Minimum age 16; Medical examination.
Staff RNs 3 (ft), 2 (pt); LPNs 5 (ft), 2 (pt); Orderlies 2 (ft); Nurses aides 17 (ft), 4 (pt); Activities coordinators 2 (ft).
Languages German, Spanish
Affiliation Mennonite
Facilities Dining room; Activities room; Laundry room; Barber/Beauty shop.
Activities Arts & crafts; Cards; Games; Reading groups; Prayer groups; Movies; Social/Cultural gatherings.

Wilhelms Nursing Home*
1507 S Tuttle Ave, Sarasota, FL, 33580
(813) 365-2737
Licensure Skilled care. *Beds* 123. *Certified* Medicaid.
Owner Proprietary Corp (Beverly Enterprises).
Staff RNs 5 (ft); LPNs 11 (ft); Nurses aides 22 (ft).
Languages Spanish

SEBRING

Palms Health Care Center
725 S Pine St, Sebring, FL, 33870
(813) 385-0161
Admin Benjamin A Brooks. *Medical Dir/Dir of Nursing* Vinod Thakker MD; Jean Fishburn RN DON.
Licensure Skilled care; Retirement Community. *Beds* SNF 104. *Certified* Medicaid; Medicare.
Owner Nonprofit Corp.
Admissions Requirements Minimum age 62; Females only; Medical examination.
Staff Physicians 1 (pt); RNs 4 (ft); LPNs 11 (ft); Nurses aides 40 (ft); Physical therapists 1 (pt); Reality therapists 1 (pt); Recreational therapists 1 (pt); Occupational therapists 1 (pt); Speech therapists 1 (pt); Activities coordinators 1 (ft), 2 (pt); Dietitians 1 (ft); Ophthalmologists 1 (pt); Podiatrists 1 (pt).
Affiliation Church of the Brethren
Facilities Dining room; Physical therapy room; Activities room; Chapel; Crafts room; Laundry room; Barber/Beauty shop; Library; Lobby; Social space.
Activities Arts & crafts; Cards; Games; Reading groups; Prayer groups; Movies; Shopping trips; Social/Cultural gatherings; Ceramics; Basket weaving.

Sebring Care Center
3011 Kenilworth Blvd, Sebring, FL, 33870
(813) 382-2153
Admin Carolyn Jacobs RN. *Medical Dir/Dir of Nursing* Dr Hanford Brace; Margaret Wilke RN.
Licensure Skilled care. *Beds* SNF 104. *Certified* Medicaid; Medicare.
Owner Proprietary Corp (National Heritage).
Admissions Requirements Medical examination; Physician's request.
Staff Physicians 1 (pt); RNs 6 (ft); LPNs 8 (ft), 2 (pt); Orderlies 2 (ft); Nurses aides 36 (ft); Physical therapists 2 (ft), 2 (pt); Occupational therapists 1 (ft), 1 (pt); Speech therapists 2 (ft), 2 (pt); Activities coordinators 1 (ft); Dietitians 1 (pt); Dentists 1 (pt); Ophthalmologists 1 (pt); Podiatrists 1 (pt).
Languages Spanish
Facilities Dining room; Physical therapy room; Activities room; Laundry room; Barber/Beauty shop.
Activities Arts & crafts; Cards; Games; Reading groups; Prayer groups; Movies; Shopping trips; Social/Cultural gatherings.

SEMINOLE

Seminole Nursing Pavilion
10800 Temple Terrace, Seminole, FL, 34642
(813) 398-0123
Admin Jerry Harden. *Medical Dir/Dir of Nursing* Mark F Franklin DO; Patricia J Steffenhagen RN DON.
Licensure Skilled care; Intermediate care. *Beds* 120. *Certified* Medicaid; Medicare; VA.
Owner Proprietary Corp (Southern Management Services).
Admissions Requirements Medical examination; Physician's request.
Staff Physicians 1 (ft), 15 (pt); RNs 8 (ft), 3 (pt); LPNs 13 (ft), 2 (pt); Orderlies 5 (ft), 1 (pt); Nurses aides 40 (ft), 4 (pt); Physical therapists 1 (ft), 3 (pt); Occupational therapists 1 (pt); Speech therapists 1 (ft); Activities coordinators 1 (ft), 2 (pt); Dietitians 1 (ft); Ophthalmologists 1 (pt); Podiatrists 1 (pt).
Facilities Dining room; Physical therapy room; Activities room; Crafts room; Laundry room; Barber/Beauty shop; Library.
Activities Arts & crafts; Games; Reading groups; Prayer groups; Movies; Shopping trips.

SOUTH DAYTONA

Daytona Manor Nursing Home
650 Reed Canal St, South Daytona, FL, 32019
(904) 767-4831
Admin Ginger Smith. *Medical Dir/Dir of Nursing* George B Powell DO.
Licensure Skilled care. *Beds* 65. *Certified* Medicaid.
Owner Proprietary Corp (Waverly Group).
Admissions Requirements Minimum age 16; Medical examination; Physician's request.
Staff Physicians; RNs; LPNs; Orderlies; Nurses aides; Physical therapists; Speech therapists; Activities coordinators; Dietitians; Ophthalmologists; Podiatrists; Dentist.
Languages German, French, Spanish, Greek, Slavic
Facilities Dining room; Activities room; Barber/Beauty shop.
Activities Arts & crafts; Cards; Games; Prayer groups; Movies.

SOUTH PASADENA

Deluxe Care Inn*
1820 Shore Dr S, South Pasadena, FL, 33707
(813) 384-9300
Licensure Skilled care. *Beds* 58. *Certified* Medicare.
Owner Proprietary Corp.
Staff RNs 4 (ft); LPNs 9 (ft); Nurses aides 13 (ft).
Languages Spanish

Pasadena Manor*
1430 Pasadena Ave S, South Pasadena, FL, 33707
(813) 347-1257
Licensure Skilled care. *Beds* 126. *Certified* Medicaid; Medicare.
Owner Proprietary Corp.
Staff RNs 6 (ft); LPNs 6 (ft); Nurses aides 28 (ft).
Languages Spanish, Tagalog

SPRING HILL

Evergreen Woods*
PO Box 3091, Spring Hill, FL, 33526
(904) 596-2055
Beds 60. *Certified* Medicaid; Medicare.
Owner Nonprofit Corp.

STARKE

Whispering Pines Care Center
808 S Colley Rd, Starke, FL, 32091
(904) 964-6220
Admin Frederick H Cline. *Medical Dir/Dir of Nursing* Pete G Felos MD; Elaine Slocum DON.
Licensure Skilled care. *Beds* SNF 120. *Certified* Medicaid; Medicare; VA.
Owner Proprietary Corp.
Admissions Requirements Physician's request.
Staff RNs 4 (ft); LPNs 4 (ft); Nurses aides 20 (ft), 8 (pt); Activities coordinators 1 (ft), 1 (pt); Dietitians 1 (pt).
Facilities Dining room; Physical therapy room; Activities room; Laundry room; Barber/Beauty shop; 2 day rooms; Screened front patio; Wheelchair park/picnic area; Meditation room.
Activities Arts & crafts; Cards; Games; Reading groups; Prayer groups; Movies; Social/Cultural gatherings; Outings to restaurants; County fair; Musicals; Plays; Parades.

STUART

Stuart Convalescent Center*
1500 Palm Beach Rd, Stuart, FL, 33494
(305) 283-5887

Licensure Skilled care. *Beds* 182. *Certified* Medicaid; Medicare.
Owner Proprietary Corp (Eden Park Management).
Staff RNs 5 (ft); LPNs 7 (ft); Nurses aides 32 (ft).

SUN CITY CENTER

Lake Towers Health Center*
101 Trinity Lakes Dr, Sun City Center, FL, 33570
(813) 634-3347
Medical Dir/Dir of Nursing Gaspar Salvador MD.
Licensure Skilled care. *Beds* 60. *Certified* Medicare.
Owner Proprietary Corp.
Staff RNs 2 (ft), 3 (pt); LPNs 7 (ft), 11 (pt); Nurses aides 13 (ft), 9 (pt); Activities coordinators 1 (ft).
Languages Spanish, French, Italian
Facilities Dining room; Physical therapy room; Activities room; Crafts room; Barber/ Beauty shop; Library.
Activities Arts & crafts; Cards; Games; Reading groups; Prayer groups; Movies; Shopping trips; Social/Cultural gatherings.

Sun Terrace Health Care Center
105 Trinity Lakes Dr, Sun City Center, FL, 33570
(813) 634-3324
Admin Christine LaCourse. *Medical Dir/Dir of Nursing* Gaspar Salvador MD.
Licensure Skilled care; Intermediate care. *Beds* 120. *Certified* Medicaid; Medicare.
Owner Proprietary Corp (Convalescent Services).
Staff Physicians 3 (pt); RNs 4 (ft), 2 (pt); LPNs 8 (ft), 4 (pt); Nurses aides 22 (ft); Activities coordinators 1 (ft).
Languages Spanish, French, Italian
Facilities Dining room; Physical therapy room; Activities room; Crafts room; Barber/ Beauty shop.
Activities Arts & crafts; Cards; Games; Reading groups; Prayer groups; Movies; Shopping trips; Social/Cultural gatherings.

TALLAHASSEE

Capital Health Care Center
3333 Capital Medical Blvd, Tallahassee, FL, 32308
(904) 877-4115
Licensure Skilled care. *Beds* 120. *Certified* Medicaid; Medicare.
Owner Proprietary Corp (Vantage Healthcare).
Admissions Requirements Minimum age 16; Medical examination; Physician's request.
Staff Dietitians; Nurses aides.
Facilities Dining room; Physical therapy room; Activities room; Crafts room; Laundry room; Barber/Beauty shop; Library.
Activities Arts & crafts; Cards; Games; Reading groups; Prayer groups; Movies; Shopping trips; Social/Cultural gatherings.

McCauley Cluster*
1385 McCauley Rd, Tallahassee, FL, 32308
(904) 487-1724
Licensure Intermediate care for mentally retarded. *Beds* 24.
Owner Proprietary Corp.

Miracle Hill Nursing & Convalescent Home*
1329 Abraham St, Tallahassee, FL, 32304
(904) 224-8486
Medical Dir/Dir of Nursing Dr Earl Britt & Dr Charlie Richardson.
Licensure Skilled care. *Beds* 60. *Certified* Medicaid.
Owner Nonprofit Corp.
Admissions Requirements Minimum age 18; Medical examination.

Staff Physicians 3 (pt); RNs 2 (ft), 3 (pt); LPNs 5 (ft), 2 (pt); Orderlies 1 (ft); Nurses aides 24 (ft), 4 (pt); Physical therapists 1 (pt); Reality therapists 1 (pt); Recreational therapists 1 (pt); Speech therapists 1 (pt); Activities coordinators 1 (ft); Dietitians 1 (pt); Dentists 1 (pt); Podiatrists 1 (pt).
Facilities Dining room; Activities room; Crafts room; Laundry room; Barber/Beauty shop.
Activities Arts & crafts; Games; Reading groups; Prayer groups; Movies; Shopping trips; Social/Cultural gatherings.

Tallahassee Convalescent Home*
2510 Miccosukee Rd, Tallahassee, FL, 32303
(904) 877-3131
Medical Dir/Dir of Nursing William T Kepper MD.
Licensure Skilled care. *Beds* 72. *Certified* Medicaid.
Owner Proprietary Corp.
Admissions Requirements Medical examination.
Staff Physicians 1 (pt); RNs 4 (ft), 3 (pt); LPNs 4 (ft), 3 (pt); Nurses aides 22 (ft), 5 (pt); Reality therapists; Recreational therapists; Occupational therapists; Speech therapists; Activities coordinators; Dietitians; Podiatrists.
Languages French, Spanish
Facilities Dining room; Laundry room; Barber/Beauty shop; 2 Large TV rooms.
Activities Arts & crafts; Cards; Games; Reading groups; Prayer groups; Movies; Shopping trips; Social/Cultural gatherings.

Tallahassee Developmental Center
455 Appleyard Dr, Tallahassee, FL, 32304
(904) 575-0619
Admin Steven Taylor. *Medical Dir/Dir of Nursing* Javonna McEnchin.
Licensure Intermediate care for mentally retarded. *Beds* ICF/MR 63. *Certified* Medicaid.
Owner Nonprofit organization/foundation.
Staff RNs 2 (ft); LPNs 6 (ft); Nurses aides 70 (ft), 10 (pt); Recreational therapists 2 (ft); Dietitians 1 (ft).
Facilities Dining room.
Activities Arts & crafts; Cards; Games; Movies; Shopping trips; Social/Cultural gatherings.

Westminister Oaks Nursing Home*
4449 Meandering Way, Tallahassee, FL, 32308
Admin Robert F Wernet Jr. *Medical Dir/Dir of Nursing* Leslie S Emhof.
Licensure Skilled care. *Beds* 60.
Owner Nonprofit Corp.
Admissions Requirements Minimum age 62; Medical examination; Physician's request.
Staff Physicians 1 (pt); RNs 5 (ft); LPNs 4 (ft); Orderlies 2 (ft); Nurses aides 15 (ft); Physical therapists 1 (pt); Reality therapists 1 (pt); Recreational therapists 1 (ft); Speech therapists 1 (pt); Activities coordinators 1 (ft); Dietitians 1 (ft); Dentists 1 (pt); Podiatrists 1 (pt); Audiologists 1 (pt).
Affiliation Presbyterian
Facilities Dining room; Physical therapy room; Activities room; Chapel; Crafts room; Laundry room; Barber/Beauty shop; Library.
Activities Arts & crafts; Cards; Games; Reading groups; Prayer groups; Movies; Shopping trips; Social/Cultural gatherings.

TAMARAC

Tamarac Convalescent Center
7901 NW 88th Ave, Tamarac, FL, 33321
(305) 722-9330
Admin Paul H Hladick. *Medical Dir/Dir of Nursing* Juan Lopez.
Licensure Skilled care; Intermediate care. *Beds* SNF 60; ICF 60; VA. *Certified* Medicaid; Medicare.

Owner Proprietary Corp (HBA Management Inc).
Admissions Requirements Physician's request.
Staff Physicians 6 (pt); RNs 2 (ft), 9 (pt); LPNs 7 (ft), 4 (pt); Orderlies 1 (ft); Nurses aides 40 (ft); Physical therapists 2 (ft); Reality therapists 1 (ft); Recreational therapists 1 (ft); Occupational therapists 1 (pt); Speech therapists 1 (pt); Activities coordinators 1 (ft); Dietitians 1 (pt); Dentists 1 (pt); Ophthalmologists 1 (pt); Podiatrists 1 (pt); Dentist 1 (pt).
Languages German, Spanish, Italian, Hebrew, Yiddish
Facilities Dining room; Physical therapy room; Activities room; Crafts room; Laundry room; Barber/Beauty shop; Library.
Activities Arts & crafts; Cards; Games; Reading groups; Prayer groups; Movies; Shopping trips; Social/Cultural gatherings; Musical entertainment.

TAMPA

Ambrosia Home Inc
1709 Taliaferro Ave, Tampa, FL, 33602
(813) 223-4623
Admin Albert Shepard. *Medical Dir/Dir of Nursing* Frederick Taylor DO; Alice Miller RN BSN.
Licensure Skilled care. *Beds* SNF 80. *Certified* Medicaid; VA.
Owner Proprietary Corp.
Admissions Requirements Minimum age 16; Medical examination; Physician's request.
Staff RNs 4 (ft); LPNs 8 (ft); Orderlies 6 (ft); Nurses aides 20 (ft); Activities coordinators 2 (ft); Social Services 1 (ft).
Languages Spanish, Italian
Facilities Dining room; Activities room; Laundry room; Barber/Beauty shop; Patios; Porches.
Activities Arts & crafts; Cards; Games; Reading groups; Prayer groups; Movies; Shopping trips; Social/Cultural gatherings; Small group programs.

Bay to Bay Nursing Center*
3405 Bay to Bay Blvd, Tampa, FL, 33609
(813) 839-5325
Licensure Skilled care. *Beds* 75. *Certified* Medicaid.
Owner Proprietary Corp.
Staff RNs 7 (ft); LPNs 6 (ft); Nurses aides 18 (ft).

Cambridge Convalescent Center
9709 N Nebraska Ave, Tampa, FL, 33612
(813) 935-2101
Admin James B Hereford. *Medical Dir/Dir of Nursing* Henry Gomez MD; Suzanne Litton RN.
Licensure Skilled care. *Beds* SNF 70. *Certified* Medicaid.
Owner Proprietary Corp (Vantage Healthcare).
Admissions Requirements Minimum age 21; Medical examination; Physician's request.
Staff Physicians 1 (ft); RNs 2 (ft), 1 (pt); LPNs 4 (ft), 3 (pt); Nurses aides 17 (ft), 6 (pt); Physical therapists 1 (pt); Reality therapists 1 (pt); Speech therapists 1 (pt); Activities coordinators 1 (ft); Dietitians 1 (pt); Ophthalmologists 1 (pt).
Languages Spanish
Facilities Dining room; Physical therapy room; Activities room; Crafts room; Laundry room; Barber/Beauty shop; Library.
Activities Arts & crafts; Cards; Games; Reading groups; Prayer groups; Movies; Social/Cultural gatherings; Picnics.

Canterbury Towers*
3501 Bayshore Blvd, Tampa, FL, 33609
(813) 837-1083
Licensure Skilled care. *Beds* 40. *Certified* Medicaid; Medicare.
Owner Nonprofit Corp.

Staff RNs 4 (ft); LPNs 5 (ft); Nurses aides 12 (ft).
Languages French, Spanish, German

The Home Association Inc
1203 22nd Ave, Tampa, FL, 33605
(813) 229-6901
Admin Ralph G Clutton. *Medical Dir/Dir of Nursing* R Maurice Bonilla MD.
Licensure Skilled care; Intermediate care. *Beds* SNF 41; ICF 56. *Certified* Medicaid.
Owner Nonprofit Corp.
Admissions Requirements Minimum age 65; Medical examination.
Staff Physicians 3 (pt); RNs 3 (ft); LPNs 9 (ft); Nurses aides 33 (ft); Activities coordinators 1 (ft); Dietitians 1 (ft); Ophthalmologists 1 (ft).
Facilities Dining room; Activities room; Chapel; Crafts room; Laundry room; Barber/ Beauty shop.
Activities Arts & crafts; Cards; Games; Prayer groups; Shopping trips; Social/Cultural gatherings; Dinner theater.

John Knox Village Medical Center
4100 E Fletcher Ave, Tampa, FL, 33613
(813) 971-7038
Admin John T Holcombe. *Medical Dir/Dir of Nursing* J R Warren MD; Carolyn H Boylan RN DON.
Licensure Skilled care. *Beds* SNF 110. *Certified* Medicare.
Owner Nonprofit Corp.
Admissions Requirements Minimum age 16; Medical examination; Physician's request.
Staff RNs 5 (ft), 1 (pt); LPNs 11 (ft), 1 (pt); Orderlies 1 (ft); Nurses aides 36 (ft); Physical therapists 1 (ft); Activities coordinators 2 (ft); Dietitians 1 (ft);; Social service 1 (ft).
Languages Spanish
Facilities Dining room; Physical therapy room; Activities room; Crafts room; Laundry room; Barber/Beauty shop; Library.
Activities Arts & crafts; Cards; Games; Reading groups; Prayer groups; Movies; Shopping trips; Social/Cultural gatherings.

Manhattan Convalescent Center*
4610 S Manhattan Ave, Tampa, FL, 33611
(813) 839-5311
Licensure Skilled care. *Beds* 179. *Certified* Medicaid.
Owner Proprietary Corp (Beverly Enterprises).
Staff RNs 7 (ft); LPNs 19 (ft); Nurses aides 36 (ft).
Languages Spanish, French

Medicenter of Tampa
4411 N Habana Ave, Tampa, FL, 33614
(813) 872-2771
Admin Charles Hines. *Medical Dir/Dir of Nursing* Juan Valdez MD; Chris Cosgrove.
Licensure Skilled care; Intermediate care. *Beds* SNF 116; ICF 58. *Certified* Medicaid; Medicare.
Owner Proprietary Corp (Hillhaven Corp).
Admissions Requirements Medical examination; Physician's request.
Staff RNs 12 (ft); LPNs 11 (ft); Orderlies; Nurses aides; Physical therapists; Occupational therapists; Activities coordinators.
Languages Spanish
Facilities Dining room; Physical therapy room; Activities room; Crafts room; Laundry room; Barber/Beauty shop.
Activities Arts & crafts; Cards; Games; Prayer groups; Movies; Social/Cultural gatherings.

Oakwood Park Su Casa*
1514 E Chelsea, Tampa, FL, 33610
(813) 238-6406
Licensure Skilled care. *Beds* 240. *Certified* Medicaid; Medicare.
Owner Proprietary Corp.

Staff RNs 9 (ft); LPNs 23 (ft); Nurses aides 52 (ft).
Languages Spanish, Italian

Padgett Nursing Home
5010 40th St, Tampa, FL, 33610
(813) 626-7109
Admin Rubin E Padgett.
Licensure Skilled care; Intermediate care. *Beds* 100. *Certified* Medicaid; Medicare.
Owner Proprietary Corp.
Staff Physicians 1 (ft); RNs 3 (ft); LPNs 8 (ft), 3 (pt); Nurses aides 32 (ft), 1 (pt); Activities coordinators 2 (ft), 1 (pt); Dietitians 1 (pt); Podiatrists 1 (ft).
Languages Spanish
Facilities Dining room; Physical therapy room; Activities room; Laundry room.
Activities Arts & crafts; Cards; Games; Reading groups; Prayer groups; Movies; Shopping trips; Social/Cultural gatherings.

River Heights Nursing Home*
2730 Ridgewood Ave, Tampa, FL, 33602
(813) 223-1303
Medical Dir/Dir of Nursing Dr Luis Crespo.
Licensure Skilled care. *Beds* 42. *Certified* Medicaid.
Owner Proprietary Corp.
Admissions Requirements Minimum age 18; Medical examination; Physician's request.
Staff Physicians 1 (pt); RNs 4 (pt); LPNs 6 (pt); Orderlies 2 (pt); Nurses aides 10 (pt); Activities coordinators 1 (pt); Dietitians 1 (pt).
Languages Italian, Spanish, Czech
Facilities Dining room; Physical therapy room; Activities room; Crafts room; Laundry room; Barber/Beauty shop.
Activities Arts & crafts; Cards; Games; Reading groups; Prayer groups; Movies; Shopping trips; Social/Cultural gatherings.

Tampa Health Care Center
2916 Habana Way, Tampa, FL, 33614
(813) 876-5141
Admin Mary Estlow. *Medical Dir/Dir of Nursing* E A Perez MD; Cheryl Seronick RN DON.
Licensure Skilled care. *Beds* SNF 116; ICF; Certified Medicare 34. *Certified* Medicaid; Medicare.
Owner Proprietary Corp (Beverly Enterprises).
Staff Physicians 1 (pt); RNs 6 (ft), 4 (pt); LPNs 14 (ft), 2 (pt); Orderlies 4 (ft); Nurses aides 50 (ft), 4 (pt); Physical therapists 1 (pt); Reality therapists 1 (ft); Recreational therapists 1 (ft); Occupational therapists 1 (pt); Speech therapists 1 (pt); Activities coordinators 1 (ft); Dietitians 1 (ft); Ophthalmologists 1 (pt); Dentist 1 (pt).
Languages Spanish
Facilities Dining room; Physical therapy room; Activities room; Crafts room; Laundry room; Barber/Beauty shop; Library.
Activities Arts & crafts; Cards; Games; Reading groups; Prayer groups; Movies; Shopping trips; Social/Cultural gatherings.

Town N County Convalescent Center
8720 Jackson Springs Rd, Tampa, FL, 33615
(813) 885-6053
Admin David E Wilson. *Medical Dir/Dir of Nursing* Louis Azan MD; Nancy Matherson DON.
Licensure Skilled care. *Beds* SNF 120. *Certified* Medicaid; Medicare.
Owner Proprietary Corp (Hillhaven Corp).
Admissions Requirements Minimum age 18; Medical examination; Physician's request.
Staff Physicians; RNs; LPNs; Orderlies; Nurses aides; Physical therapists; Reality therapists; Recreational therapists; Occupational therapists; Speech therapists; Activities coordinators; Dietitians; Dentists; Ophthalmologists; Podiatrists.
Languages Spanish

Facilities Dining room; Physical therapy room; Activities room; Crafts room; Laundry room; Barber/Beauty shop; Library.
Activities Arts & crafts; Cards; Games; Reading groups; Prayer groups; Movies; Shopping trips; Social/Cultural gatherings; Cookouts; Happy hour; Ice cream parties.

University Park Convalescent Center*
1818 E Fletcher Ave, Tampa, FL, 33612
(813) 977-2383
Medical Dir/Dir of Nursing Aldo J Almaguer MD.
Licensure Skilled care. *Beds* 266. *Certified* Medicaid; Medicare.
Owner Proprietary Corp (Brian Center Management Corp).
Admissions Requirements Minimum age 17; Medical examination; Physician's request.
Staff RNs 12 (ft), 3 (pt); LPNs 23 (ft), 2 (pt); Orderlies 9 (ft); Nurses aides 95 (ft); Physical therapists 1 (pt); Occupational therapists 1 (pt); Speech therapists 1 (pt); Activities coordinators 2 (ft); Dietitians 1 (pt); Dentists 1 (pt); Podiatrists 1 (pt); Audiologists 1 (pt).
Facilities Dining room; Physical therapy room; Activities room; Chapel; Barber/Beauty shop; Library.
Activities Arts & crafts; Cards; Games; Reading groups; Prayer groups; Movies; Shopping trips; Social/Cultural gatherings.

Wellington Manor*
10049 N Florida Ave, Tampa, FL, 33612
(813) 935-3185
Licensure Skilled care. *Beds* 180. *Certified* Medicaid.
Owner Proprietary Corp (Beverly Enterprises).
Staff RNs 4 (ft); LPNs 17 (ft); Nurses aides 35 (ft).

TARPON SPRINGS

Central Park Lodge-Tarpon Springs
900 Beckett Way, Tarpon Springs, FL, 34689
(813) 934-0876, 937-6141
Admin Dennis Norton. *Medical Dir/Dir of Nursing* Dr David Lindberg MD; June Mansour RNC DON.
Licensure Skilled care; Intermediate care. *Beds* SNF 120; ICF. *Certified* Medicaid; Medicare.
Owner Proprietary Corp.
Admissions Requirements Minimum age 16.
Staff Physicians; RNs; LPNs; Orderlies; Nurses aides; Physical therapists; Recreational therapists; Occupational therapists; Speech therapists; Activities coordinators; Dietitians; Dentists; Ophthalmologists; Podiatrists.
Languages French
Facilities Dining room; Physical therapy room; Activities room; Crafts room; Laundry room; Barber/Beauty shop.
Activities Arts & crafts; Cards; Games; Reading groups; Prayer groups; Movies; Shopping trips; Social/Cultural gatherings.

Tarpon Health Care Center*
501 S Walton Ave, Tarpon Springs, FL, 33589
(813) 938-2814
Licensure Skilled care. *Beds* 120. *Certified* Medicaid.
Owner Proprietary Corp (Beverly Enterprises).
Staff RNs 2 (ft); LPNs 2 (ft); Nurses aides 26 (ft).

Tarpon Springs Convalescent Center
515 Chesapeake Dr, Tarpon Springs, FL, 33589
(813) 934-4629
Admin Barbara Johnson. *Medical Dir/Dir of Nursing* Dr Sanchez.
Licensure Skilled care. *Beds* 120. *Certified* Medicaid; Medicare.
Owner Proprietary Corp.

Admissions Requirements Minimum age 18; Medical examination; Physician's request.
Staff RNs 2 (ft), 4 (pt); LPNs 7 (ft), 5 (pt); Nurses aides 40 (ft), 1 (pt); Physical therapists 1 (pt); Occupational therapists 1 (pt); Speech therapists 1 (pt); Activities coordinators 1 (ft); Dietitians 1 (pt); Dentists 1 (pt); Ophthalmologists 1 (pt); Podiatrists 1 (pt).
Languages Greek
Facilities Dining room; Physical therapy room; Activities room; Chapel; Crafts room; Laundry room; Barber/Beauty shop; Library.
Activities Arts & crafts; Cards; Games; Reading groups; Prayer groups; Movies; Shopping trips; Social/Cultural gatherings.

THONOTOSASSA

Lowe's Nursing & Convalescent Home
PO Box 187, McIntosh Rd, Thonotosassa, FL, 33592
(813) 986-4848
Admin Ed Vail. *Medical Dir/Dir of Nursing* E A Perez MD; M Haffner DON.
Licensure Skilled care; Intermediate care. *Beds* SNF; ICF 180. *Certified* Medicaid; Medicare.
Owner Proprietary Corp.
Admissions Requirements Medical examination.
Staff RNs 8 (ft); LPNs 22 (ft); Nurses aides 50 (ft); Activities coordinators 2 (ft); Dietitians 1 (pt).
Languages Spanish
Facilities Dining room; Physical therapy room; Activities room; Laundry room; Barber/Beauty shop.
Activities Arts & crafts; Cards; Games; Reading groups; Prayer groups; Movies; Shopping trips; Social/Cultural gatherings.

TITUSVILLE

Titusville Nursing & Convalescent Center
1705 Jess Parrish Ct, Titusville, FL, 32796
(305) 269-5720
Admin Diane Kendrick. *Medical Dir/Dir of Nursing* Victor Boodhoo MD; Pearlie Jackson.
Licensure Skilled care. *Beds* SNF 157. *Certified* Medicaid; Medicare.
Owner Proprietary Corp (Hillhaven Corp).
Admissions Requirements Minimum age 21; Medical examination.
Staff Physicians 11 (pt); RNs 2 (pt); LPNs 16 (pt); Orderlies 5 (pt); Nurses aides 35 (pt); Physical therapists 1 (pt); Occupational therapists 1 (pt); Speech therapists 1 (pt); Activities coordinators 2 (pt); Dietitians 1 (pt); Ophthalmologists 2 (pt); Podiatrists 1 (pt).
Languages French, Spanish
Facilities Dining room; Physical therapy room; Activities room; Chapel; Crafts room; Laundry room; Barber/Beauty shop.
Activities Arts & crafts; Cards; Games; Reading groups; Prayer groups; Movies; Shopping trips; Social/Cultural gatherings.

TRENTON

Medic-Ayers Nursing Home*
RT 2, Box 32693, NE 7th St, Trenton, FL, 32693
Beds 60.
Owner Proprietary Corp.

VENICE

Pinebrook Place Healthcare Center
1240 Pinebrook Rd, Venice, FL, 33595
(813) 488-6733
Admin Joyce Coleman. *Medical Dir/Dir of Nursing* Dr Thomas McNaughton; Jimmie Coffey RN BSN DON.

Licensure Skilled care; Intermediate care. *Beds* SNF 20; ICF 100. *Certified* Medicaid; Medicare.
Owner Proprietary Corp (Convalescent Services).
Admissions Requirements Medical examination; Physician's request.
Staff Physicians; RNs; LPNs; Orderlies; Nurses aides; Physical therapists; Reality therapists; Recreational therapists; Occupational therapists; Speech therapists; Activities coordinators; Dietitians; Dentists; Ophthalmologists; Podiatrists.
Languages German, French, Polish
Facilities Dining room; Physical therapy room; Activities room; Chapel; Crafts room; Laundry room; Barber/Beauty shop; Library; Private dining room; Family room; Enclosed courtyards.
Activities Arts & crafts; Cards; Games; Reading groups; Prayer groups; Movies; Shopping trips; Social/Cultural gatherings.

Venice Nursing Pavilion—North
437 S Nokomis Ave, Venice, FL, 34285
(813) 488-9696
Admin Jack C Rutenberg. *Medical Dir/Dir of Nursing* Samuel E Kaplan MD; Evelyn Sembrot RN DON.
Licensure Skilled care. *Beds* SNF 180. *Certified* Medicaid; Medicare.
Owner Proprietary Corp (FL Living Care Inc).
Staff RNs 10 (ft), 2 (pt); LPNs 10 (ft), 6 (pt); Orderlies 4 (ft), 1 (pt); Nurses aides 34 (ft), 6 (pt); Activities coordinators 2 (ft); Dietitians 1 (ft).
Languages Italian, Spanish, Polish, French, German
Activities Arts & crafts; Cards; Games; Reading groups; Prayer groups; Movies; Shopping trips; Social/Cultural gatherings; Wine & cheese; Ice cream socials; Talent shows.

Venice Nursing Pavilion—South
200 Field Ave E, Venice, FL, 33595
(813) 484-2477
Admin Yolanda Brewer. *Medical Dir/Dir of Nursing* Dr Kaplan; Ruth Perelli.
Licensure Skilled care. *Beds* SNF 120. *Certified* Medicaid; Medicare.
Owner Proprietary Corp (FL Living Care Inc).
Staff RNs 12 (ft); LPNs 6 (ft); Nurses aides 26 (ft).
Languages Spanish

VERO BEACH

Florida Baptist Retirement Center
1006 33rd St, Vero Beach, FL, 32960
(305) 567-5248
Admin William H Lord. *Medical Dir/Dir of Nursing* Carol Burdette.
Licensure Skilled care; ACLF 34. *Beds* SNF 24; ACLF 34.
Owner Nonprofit Corp.
Staff RNs 5 (ft), 24 (pt); LPNs 2 (ft), 24 (pt); Nurses aides 9 (ft), 24 (pt); Activities coordinators 1 (ft), 24 (pt).
Affiliation Baptist
Facilities Dining room; Activities room; Crafts room; Laundry room; Barber/Beauty shop.
Activities Arts & crafts; Prayer groups; Movies; Social/Cultural gatherings; Tapes.

Royal Palm Convalescent Center
2180 10th Ave, Vero Beach, FL, 32960
(305) 567-5166
Medical Dir/Dir of Nursing Dr Donald Gold.
Licensure Skilled care. *Beds* 72. *Certified* Medicare.
Owner Proprietary Corp.
Admissions Requirements Minimum age 16.
Staff Nurses aides 32 (ft); Dietitians 9 (ft).
Languages German

Facilities Dining room; Physical therapy
room; Activities room; Crafts room; Laundry
room; Barber/Beauty shop; Library.
Activities Arts & crafts; Cards; Games;
Reading groups; Prayer groups; Movies;
Shopping trips; Social/Cultural gatherings.

Vero Beach Care Center Inc
3663 15th Ave, Vero Beach, FL, 32960
(305) 567-2552
Admin Vincent Cacciatore. *Medical Dir/Dir of
Nursing* Edith Rodes RN DON.
Licensure Skilled care. *Beds* SNF 110.
Certified Medicaid; Medicare.
Owner Proprietary Corp (FL Living Care Inc).
Admissions Requirements Medical
examination; Physician's request.
Staff RNs; LPNs; Nurses aides; Activities
coordinators; Dietitians.
Facilities Dining room; Physical therapy
room; Activities room; Barber/Beauty shop.
Activities Arts & crafts; Games; Prayer groups;
Movies; Outings; Bingo; Current events.

WACHULA

Hardee Manor Nursing Home*
401 Orange Pl, Wachula, FL, 33873
(813) 773-3231
Admin Ruth A Lewis. *Medical Dir/Dir of
Nursing* Felix E Perez MD.
Licensure Skilled care. *Beds* 60. *Certified*
Medicaid; Medicare.
Owner Proprietary Corp.
Staff RNs 3 (ft); LPNs 6 (ft), 1 (pt); Orderlies
3 (ft), 1 (pt); Nurses aides 15 (ft), 6 (pt);
Physical therapists; Speech therapists;
Activities coordinators 1 (ft).
Languages Spanish
Facilities Dining room; Physical therapy
room; Activities room; Chapel; Laundry
room; Barber/Beauty shop.
Activities Arts & crafts; Games; Prayer groups;
Movies; Social/Cultural gatherings.

WEST MELBOURNE

West Melbourne Health Care Center
2125 W New Haven Ave, West Melbourne,
FL, 32904
(305) 725-7360
Admin Lynette Reichner. *Medical Dir/Dir of
Nursing* Dr Hugo Dujovne; Susan Burch RN
DON.
Licensure Skilled care; Intermediate care. *Beds*
SNF 120; ICF. *Certified* Medicaid;
Medicare.
Owner Proprietary Corp (Waverly Group).
Admissions Requirements Minimum age 18;
Medical examination; Physician's request.
Staff RNs 9 (ft), 1 (pt); LPNs 8 (ft), 3 (pt);
Nurses aides 57 (ft), 5 (pt); Activities
coordinators 1 (ft), 1 (pt); Dietitians 1 (ft).
Facilities Dining room; Physical therapy
room; Activities room; Laundry room;
Barber/Beauty shop; Library.
Activities Arts & crafts; Cards; Games;
Reading groups; Prayer groups; Movies;
Shopping trips; Social/Cultural gatherings.

WEST PALM BEACH

Convalescent Center of the Palm Beaches
300 15th St, West Palm Beach, FL, 33401
(305) 832-6409
Medical Dir/Dir of Nursing Dr Wm Adkins.
Licensure Skilled care. *Beds* 99. *Certified*
Medicaid; Medicare; VA Contract.
Owner Proprietary Corp (Hillhaven Corp).
Admissions Requirements Medical
examination.
Staff RNs 4 (ft), 1 (pt); LPNs 11 (ft), 1 (pt);
Nurses aides 29 (ft), 6 (pt); Physical
therapists 1 (ft); Occupational therapists 1
(pt); Speech therapists 1 (pt); Activities

coordinators 1 (ft); Dietitians 1 (pt); Dentists
1 (pt); Ophthalmologists 1 (pt); Podiatrists 1
(pt); Dentist 1 (pt).
Facilities Dining room; Physical therapy
room; Activities room; Crafts room; Laundry
room; Barber/Beauty shop.
Activities Arts & crafts; Cards; Games;
Reading groups; Prayer groups; Movies.

Darcy Hall Nursing Home*
2170 Palm Beach Lakes Blvd, West Palm
Beach, FL, 33409
(305) 683-3333
Licensure Skilled care. *Beds* 220. *Certified*
Medicaid.
Owner Proprietary Corp (Life Care Centers of
America).
Staff RNs 6 (ft); LPNs 20 (ft); Nurses aides 66
(ft).
Languages French, Spanish, Italian, German,
Tagalog

King David Center at Palm Beach
1101 45th St, West Palm Beach, FL, 33407
(305) 844-4343
Admin Eugene Kruger. *Medical Dir/Dir of
Nursing* Steven L Kanner DO; Jocelyn
Cameau RN DON.
Licensure Skilled care. *Beds* 191. *Certified*
Medicaid; Medicare.
Owner Proprietary Corp.
Admissions Requirements Medical
examination; Physician's request.
Staff RNs 9 (ft); LPNs 18 (ft); Nurses aides 65
(ft); Physical therapists 1 (ft); Occupational
therapists 1 (ft); Speech therapists 1 (ft);
Activities coordinators 1 (ft), 2 (pt).
Languages Italian, Spanish
Affiliation Jewish
Facilities Dining room; Physical therapy
room; Activities room; Laundry room;
Barber/Beauty shop.
Activities Arts & crafts; Cards; Games;
Reading groups; Prayer groups; Movies;
Social/Cultural gatherings.

Lakeside Health Center*
2501 Australian Ave, West Palm Beach, FL,
33407
(305) 655-7780
Medical Dir/Dir of Nursing Dr Purcell.
Licensure Skilled care. *Beds* 97. *Certified*
Medicaid; Medicare.
Owner Proprietary Corp (Life Care Centers of
America).
Staff RNs 5 (ft); LPNs 6 (ft); Nurses aides 32
(ft); Physical therapists 2 (pt); Occupational
therapists 1 (pt); Speech therapists 1 (pt);
Activities coordinators 1 (ft); Dietitians 1
(pt); Dentists 1 (pt); Ophthalmologists 1 (pt);
Podiatrists 1 (pt); Audiologists 1 (pt).
Facilities Dining room; Physical therapy
room; Activities room; Laundry room;
Barber/Beauty shop.
Activities Arts & crafts; Cards; Games;
Reading groups; Prayer groups; Movies;
Shopping trips; Social/Cultural gatherings.

Lakeview Manor Nursing Home*
208 Lake View Ave, West Palm Beach, FL,
33401
(305) 655-8322
Medical Dir/Dir of Nursing Dr Romano.
Licensure Skilled care. *Beds* 102. *Certified*
Medicaid.
Owner Proprietary Corp.
Admissions Requirements Minimum age 21;
Medical examination; Physician's request.
Staff RNs 5 (ft); LPNs 11 (ft); Orderlies 1 (ft);
Nurses aides 37 (ft); Physical therapists;
Reality therapists; Speech therapists;
Activities coordinators 1 (ft); Dietitians 1
(ft); Dentists; Podiatrists; Pharmacists.
Languages Spanish, French, Yiddish

Facilities Dining room; Activities room;
Crafts room; Barber/Beauty shop.
Activities Arts & crafts; Cards; Games;
Reading groups; Prayer groups; Movies;
Shopping trips; Social/Cultural gatherings.

Lourdes-Noreen McKeen Residence for Geriatric Care Inc
315 S Flagler Dr, West Palm Beach, FL,
33401
(305) 655-8544
Admin Sr M Fidelis. *Medical Dir/Dir of
Nursing* Dr Thomas E Murphy; Florence
Ondich RN DON.
Licensure Skilled care. *Beds* SNF 120.
Certified Medicaid; Medicare.
Owner Nonprofit Corp.
Admissions Requirements Minimum age 65;
Medical examination; Physician's request.
Staff Physicians 3 (pt); RNs 9 (ft), 10 (pt);
LPNs 4 (ft), 3 (pt); Nurses aides 44 (ft);
Physical therapists 1 (ft); Recreational
therapists 1 (ft); Occupational therapists 1
(ft); Speech therapists 1 (ft); Activities
coordinators 2 (ft); Dietitians 1 (pt);
Ophthalmologists 3 (pt); Social workers 2
(ft).
Affiliation Roman Catholic
Facilities Dining room; Physical therapy
room; Activities room; Chapel; Crafts room;
Laundry room; Barber/Beauty shop; Library.
Activities Arts & crafts; Cards; Games;
Reading groups; Prayer groups; Movies;
Shopping trips; Social/Cultural gatherings;
Current events; Exercises.

Palm Beach County Home & General Care Facility
1200 45th St, West Palm Beach, FL, 33407
(305) 842-6111
Medical Dir/Dir of Nursing Dr Adil
Sokmensuer; Salle Stepongzi.
Licensure Skilled care; Intermediate care. *Beds*
SNF 210. *Certified* Medicaid.
Owner Nonprofit organization/foundation.
Admissions Requirements Physician's request.
Staff Physicians 1 (pt); RNs 12 (ft); LPNs 16
(ft); Nurses aides 101 (ft); Physical therapists
1 (pt); Occupational therapists 1 (pt); Speech
therapists 1 (pt); Activities coordinators 1
(ft); Dietitians 1 (pt); Podiatrists 1 (pt).
Languages English, Spanish, French
Facilities Dining room; Physical therapy
room; Activities room; Laundry room;
Barber/Beauty shop; Occupational Therapy
room; Xray room; AIDS wing; TV lounges.
Activities Arts & crafts; Cards; Games;
Reading groups; Prayer groups; Movies;
Shopping trips; Social/Cultural gatherings;
Fishing trips; Live entertainment/shows;
Bingo; Birthday parties.

WILDWOOD

We Care Wildwood Healthcare Inc
490 S Old Wire Rd, Wildwood, FL, 32785
(904) 748-3322
Admin Cathy Bowlin. *Medical Dir/Dir of
Nursing* Richard Wiley MD; Cindy Griffin
DON.
Licensure Skilled care. *Beds* SNF 180.
Certified Medicaid.
Owner Proprietary Corp.
Admissions Requirements Minimum age 18;
Medical examination; Physician's request.
Staff RNs 9 (ft), 2 (pt); LPNs 10 (ft), 5 (pt);
Orderlies 4 (ft), 2 (pt); Nurses aides 44 (ft),
5 (pt); Physical therapists 1 (pt); Speech
therapists 1 (pt); Activities coordinators 1
(ft); Dietitians 1 (pt); Ophthalmologists 1
(pt); Podiatrists 1 (pt); Dentist 1 (pt).
Languages Spanish
Facilities Dining room; Physical therapy
room; Activities room; Chapel; Crafts room;
Laundry room; Barber/Beauty shop; Library.

Activities Arts & crafts; Cards; Games;
Reading groups; Prayer groups; Movies;
Shopping trips; Social/Cultural gatherings.

WILLISTON

Oak View Care Center
300 NW 1st Ave, Williston, FL, 32696
(904) 528-3561
Admin Harvey J Cox. *Medical Dir/Dir of
Nursing* James O Dailey MD; Helen Meeks
DON.
Licensure Skilled care; Intermediate care. *Beds*
180. *Certified* Medicaid; Medicare; VA.
Owner Proprietary Corp (Comprehen Health
Care Assn).
Admissions Requirements Medical
examination; Physician's request.
Staff RNs 6 (ft); LPNs 23 (ft); Nurses aides 65
(ft); Activities coordinators 1 (ft); Dietitians
1 (ft).
Languages German, Spanish, Vietnamese
Facilities Dining room; Activities room;
Crafts room; Barber/Beauty shop; Library.
Activities Arts & crafts; Cards; Games;
Reading groups; Prayer groups; Movies;
Social/Cultural gatherings.

WINTER GARDEN

Quality Health Care Center
941 E Hwy 50, Winter Garden, FL, 32787
(305) 877-6636
Admin Richard E Morrison. *Medical Dir/Dir
of Nursing* Terry Harbilas RN.
Licensure Skilled care; Intermediate care. *Beds*
SNF 120; ICF. *Certified* Medicaid;
Medicare.
Owner Proprietary Corp.
Admissions Requirements Medical
examination; Physician's request.
Staff Physicians 7 (pt); RNs 5 (ft), 2 (pt);
LPNs 7 (ft), 2 (pt); Nurses aides 35 (ft), 3
(pt); Physical therapists 4 (pt); Reality
therapists 1 (pt); Recreational therapists 1
(pt); Occupational therapists 1 (pt); Speech
therapists 1 (pt); Activities coordinators 2
(ft); Dietitians 1 (ft); Dentists 1 (pt);
Ophthalmologists 1 (pt); Podiatrists 1 (pt).
Languages Spanish
Facilities Dining room; Physical therapy
room; Activities room; Crafts room; Laundry
room; Barber/Beauty shop.
Activities Arts & crafts; Cards; Games;
Reading groups; Shopping trips.

West Orange Manor*
122 E Division St, Winter Garden, FL, 32787
(305) 656-3810
Licensure Skilled care. *Beds* 118. *Certified*
Medicaid.

Owner Publicly owned.
Staff RNs 5 (ft); LPNs 10 (ft); Nurses aides 37
(ft).

WINTER HAVEN

Grovemont Nursing & Rehabilitation Center
2201 Ave "O" NE, Winter Haven, FL, 33881
(813) 293-3103
Admin Jerry Pyle. *Medical Dir/Dir of Nursing*
Michael Carey MD; Patricia Andrews DON.
Licensure Skilled care. *Beds* SNF 144.
Certified Medicaid; Medicare.
Owner Proprietary Corp (Unicare).
Admissions Requirements Minimum age 18;
Medical examination; Physician's request.
Staff RNs 4 (ft), 3 (pt); LPNs 5 (ft), 3 (pt);
Nurses aides 43 (ft), 2 (pt); Physical
therapists 1 (ft); Occupational therapists 1
(pt); Speech therapists 1 (ft); Activities
coordinators 2 (ft); Dietitians 1 (ft);
Ophthalmologists 2 (pt); Podiatrists 1 (pt);
Dentist 1 (pt).
Facilities Dining room; Physical therapy
room; Activities room; Chapel; Crafts room;
Laundry room; Barber/Beauty shop.
Activities Arts & crafts; Cards; Games;
Reading groups; Prayer groups; Movies;
Shopping trips; Social/Cultural gatherings.

WINTER PARK

Americana Healthcare Center
2075 Loch Lomond Dr, Winter Park, FL,
32792
(305) 628-5418
Admin Frank S Bellinger. *Medical Dir/Dir of
Nursing* Dr E Forrester; Jill Miller RN
DON.
Licensure Skilled care. *Beds* SNF 135.
Certified Medicaid; Medicare.
Owner Proprietary Corp (Manor Care).
Admissions Requirements Minimum age 16;
Medical examination; Physician's request.
Staff RNs 10 (ft), 2 (pt); LPNs 11 (ft), 2 (pt);
Nurses aides 41 (ft), 5 (pt); Physical
therapists; Occupational therapists; Speech
therapists; Activities coordinators; Dietitians.
Languages German, Spanish
Facilities Dining room; Physical therapy
room; Activities room; Laundry room;
Barber/Beauty shop; Occupational therapy
room.
Activities Arts & crafts; Cards; Games;
Reading groups; Prayer groups; Movies;
Shopping trips; Social/Cultural gatherings.

Mary Lee Depugh Nursing Home*
550 W Morse Blvd, Winter Park, FL, 32789
(305) 644-6634

Medical Dir/Dir of Nursing Dr Kenneth
Richards.
Licensure Skilled care. *Beds* 40. *Certified*
Medicaid.
Owner Nonprofit Corp.
Admissions Requirements Minimum age 18;
Medical examination; Physician's request.
Staff RNs 2 (ft); LPNs 5 (ft), 1 (pt); Nurses
aides 12 (ft), 2 (pt); Activities coordinators 1
(ft); Dietitians 1 (pt).
Facilities Dining room; Activities room;
Crafts room; Laundry room.
Activities Arts & crafts; Cards; Games; Prayer
groups; Movies; Shopping trips.

Winter Park Care Center*
2970 Scarlet Rd, Winter Park, FL, 32793
(305) 671-8030
Licensure Skilled care. *Beds* 106. *Certified*
Medicaid; Medicare.
Owner Proprietary Corp (FL Living Care Inc)
Staff RNs 7 (ft); LPNs 9 (ft); Nurses aides 22
(ft).
Languages Spanish, Italian, Vietnamese

Winter Park Towers*
1111 S Lakemont Ave, Winter Park, FL,
32789
(305) 647-4083
Licensure Skilled care. *Beds* 106.
Owner Nonprofit Corp.
Staff RNs 19 (ft); LPNs 2 (ft); Nurses aides 30
(ft).
Languages Polish, German, Italian, Russian,
Hebrew, Yiddish, Spanish, French
Affiliation Presbyterian

ZEPHYRHILLS

Zephyr Haven Nursing Home
310 Ave A, Zephyrhills, FL, 33599
(813) 782-5508
Admin Patricia E Whitfield NHA. *Medical
Dir/Dir of Nursing* W C Chandler MD;
Judith Regan DON.
Licensure Skilled care. *Beds* SNF 60.
Owner Publicly owned.
Admissions Requirements Minimum age 16;
Medical examination; Physician's request.
Staff RNs 5 (ft); LPNs 6 (ft), 2 (pt); Nurses
aides 25 (ft), 6 (pt); Physical therapists 1
(pt); Speech therapists 1 (pt); Activities
coordinators 2 (ft); Dietitians 1 (pt);
Ophthalmologists 1 (pt).
Facilities Dining room; Physical therapy
room; Activities room; Chapel; Crafts room;
Laundry room; Barber/Beauty shop; Library.
Activities Arts & crafts; Cards; Games;
Reading groups; Prayer groups; Movies;
Shopping trips; Social/Cultural gatherings.

GEORGIA

ABBEVILLE

Abbeville Nursing Home Intermediate Care Facility*
PO Box 445, Abbeville, GA, 31001
(912) 467-2515
Admin Homer S Fowler. *Medical Dir/Dir of Nursing* Dr William Hammond.
Licensure Intermediate care. *Beds* 101. *Certified* Medicaid.
Admissions Requirements Medical examination; Physician's request.
Staff Physicians 1 (pt); RNs 1 (pt); LPNs 7 (ft); Orderlies 3 (ft); Nurses aides 18 (ft), 2 (pt); Physical therapists 1 (pt); Activities coordinators 2 (ft); Dietitians 1 (ft), 1 (pt); Dentists 1 (pt); Ophthalmologists 1 (pt).
Facilities Dining room; Physical therapy room; Activities room; Laundry room; Barber/Beauty shop.
Activities Games; Reading groups; Prayer groups; Movies; Shopping trips; Social/Cultural gatherings.

ADEL

Memorial Convalescent Center*
PO Box 677, Adel, GA, 31620
(912) 896-3182
Admin James E Cunningham.
Licensure Skilled care; Intermediate care. *Beds* 80. *Certified* Medicaid; Medicare.

ADRIAN

Johnson County Intermediate Care Home*
PO Box 207, Adrian, GA, 31002
(912) 668-3225
Admin Steve C Taylor.
Licensure Intermediate care. *Beds* 59. *Certified* Medicaid.

ALBANY

Albany Health Care
PO Box 2003, 233 3rd Ave, Albany, GA, 31701
(912) 435-0741
Admin Pat Doss. *Medical Dir/Dir of Nursing* Luellen Tucker.
Licensure Skilled care; Intermediate care. *Beds* 168. *Certified* Medicaid.
Owner Proprietary Corp.
Admissions Requirements Medical examination.
Facilities Dining room; Physical therapy room; Activities room; Crafts room; Laundry room; Barber/Beauty shop; Library.
Activities Arts & crafts; Games; Reading groups; Prayer groups; Movies; Shopping trips; Social/Cultural gatherings.

Palmyra Nursing Home Inc
1904 Palmyra Rd, Albany, GA, 31701
(912) 883-0500

Admin Davis W King. *Medical Dir/Dir of Nursing* Dr Chapel Collins; Edith Williams DON.
Licensure Skilled care; Intermediate care. *Beds* SNF 250; ICF. *Certified* Medicaid.
Owner Proprietary Corp.
Admissions Requirements Medical examination; Physician's request.
Staff Physicians 90 (ft); RNs 8 (ft); LPNs 30 (ft); Orderlies 12 (ft); Nurses aides 125 (ft); Physical therapists 2 (ft); Recreational therapists 1 (ft); Occupational therapists 1 (ft); Speech therapists 1 (ft); Activities coordinators 3 (ft); Dietitians 1 (ft).
Facilities Dining room; Physical therapy room; Activities room; Chapel; Crafts room; Laundry room; Barber/Beauty shop; Library.
Activities Arts & crafts; Cards; Games; Reading groups; Prayer groups; Movies; Shopping trips; Social/Cultural gatherings.

ALMA

Twin Oaks Convalescent Center*
Worth St, Alma, GA, 31510
(912) 632-7293
Admin Betty Ann Stroud.
Licensure Skilled care; Intermediate care. *Beds* 88. *Certified* Medicaid.

AMERICUS

Ideal Health Care Center
PO Box 120, Americus, GA, 31041
(912) 949-2270
Admin William G Sampson. *Medical Dir/Dir of Nursing* Richard Chase DO; Donald L Smith DON.
Licensure Skilled care; Intermediate care. *Beds* 100. *Certified* Medicaid; Medicare.
Owner Proprietary Corp.
Admissions Requirements Medical examination; Physician's request.
Staff Physicians 1 (ft); RNs 2 (ft); LPNs 6 (ft), 2 (pt); Orderlies 5 (ft); Nurses aides 24 (ft), 4 (pt); Physical therapists 2 (ft); Recreational therapists 1 (ft); Activities coordinators 1 (ft); Dietitians 1 (ft); Dentists 1 (pt); Ophthalmologists 1 (pt).
Facilities Dining room; Physical therapy room; Activities room; Crafts room; Laundry room; Barber/Beauty shop.
Activities Arts & crafts; Cards; Games; Reading groups; Prayer groups; Movies; Shopping trips; Social/Cultural gatherings.

Magnolia Manor Methodist Nursing Home
Box 346, S Lee St, Americus, GA, 31709
(912) 924-9352
Admin John Sims. *Medical Dir/Dir of Nursing* John H Robinson III.
Licensure Skilled care; Intermediate care. *Beds* 238. *Certified* Medicaid; Medicare.
Admissions Requirements Medical examination.

Staff Physicians 2 (pt); RNs 13 (ft), 3 (pt); LPNs 25 (ft); Orderlies 5 (ft), 1 (pt); Nurses aides 68 (ft), 5 (pt); Physical therapists 1 (ft), 1 (pt); Speech therapists 1 (pt); Activities coordinators 3 (ft); Dietitians 1 (pt);; Dentist 2 (pt).
Affiliation Methodist
Facilities Dining room; Physical therapy room; Activities room; Chapel; Crafts room; Laundry room; Barber/Beauty shop; Library.
Activities Arts & crafts; Cards; Games; Reading groups; Prayer groups; Movies; Shopping trips; Social/Cultural gatherings.

ASHBURN

Ashburn Conver-Care Inc*
Industrial Blvd, Box 629, Ashburn, GA, 31714
(912) 567-3473
Admin Brenda H Campbell. *Medical Dir/Dir of Nursing* Woodrow Gass MD.
Licensure Skilled care. *Beds* 76. *Certified* Medicaid.
Admissions Requirements Medical examination; Physician's request.
Staff Physicians 2 (ft); RNs 2 (ft); LPNs 7 (ft); Orderlies 5 (ft); Nurses aides 30 (ft); Activities coordinators 1 (ft); Dietitians 1 (ft).
Facilities Dining room; Activities room; Chapel; Crafts room; Laundry room; Barber/Beauty shop.
Activities Arts & crafts; Games; Prayer groups; Movies.

ATHENS

Athens Health Care Center Inc*
139 Alps Rd, Athens, GA, 30610
(404) 549-8020
Admin Mary Barnhart.
Licensure Skilled care; Intermediate care. *Beds* 120. *Certified* Medicaid; Medicare.

Athens Heritage Home Inc*
960 Hawthorne Ave, Athens, GA, 30610
(404) 549-1613
Admin Garnelle T Armour.
Licensure Skilled care. *Beds* 104.
Admissions Requirements Minimum age 50; Medical examination; Physician's request.
Staff Physicians 8 (pt); RNs 2 (ft), 1 (pt); LPNs 8 (ft), 2 (pt); Physical therapists 1 (ft), 1 (pt); Activities coordinators 2 (ft); Dietitians 1 (pt); Dentists 1 (pt).
Facilities Dining room; Physical therapy room; Activities room; Chapel; Laundry room; Barber/Beauty shop; Library.
Activities Arts & crafts; Cards; Games; Reading groups; Prayer groups; Movies; Shopping trips; Social/Cultural gatherings.

Cedar Hill Nursing Home
PO Box 5676, Epps Bridge Rd, Athens, GA, 30601
(404) 549-5382
Admin Nancy A Seagraves. *Medical Dir/Dir of Nursing* Dr A P Brooks; Labretta Farr.

Licensure Skilled care; Intermediate care. *Beds* SNF 40; ICF 82. *Certified* Medicaid. *Owner* Proprietary Corp (Angell Group). *Admissions Requirements* Medical examination.
Staff Physicians 6 (pt); RNs 2 (ft), 1 (pt); LPNs 10 (ft), 2 (pt); Orderlies 5 (ft); Nurses aides 34 (ft), 5 (pt); Physical therapists 1 (pt); Recreational therapists 1 (ft); Dietitians 1 (pt); Dentists 1 (pt); Podiatrists 1 (pt).
Facilities Dining room; Physical therapy room; Activities room; Laundry room; Barber/Beauty shop.
Activities Arts & crafts; Games; Reading groups; Prayer groups; Movies; Shopping trips; Social/Cultural gatherings.

Georgia Retardation Center—Athens
850 College Station Rd, Athens, GA, 30610
(404) 542-8970
Admin Dr Sally Carter. *Medical Dir/Dir of Nursing* Victor Payton MD.
Licensure Intermediate care for mentally retarded. *Beds* 40. *Certified* Medicaid.
Owner Publicly owned.
Admissions Requirements Minimum age 3-18.
Staff Physicians 1 (pt); RNs 3 (ft); LPNs 5 (ft); Nurses aides 55 (ft); Physical therapists 1 (pt); Recreational therapists 2 (ft); Occupational therapists 1 (pt); Speech therapists 1 (pt); Dietitians 1 (ft).
Facilities Dining room; Physical therapy room; Activities room; Crafts room; Laundry room; Library.
Activities Arts & crafts; Games; Movies; Shopping trips; Social/Cultural gatherings.

Grandview Care Center, Inc
PO Box 146, Athens, GA, 30603
(404) 549-6013
Admin B Brown Williamson. *Medical Dir/Dir of Nursing* Dr W Morris; Mrs Pam Smith RN DON.
Licensure Skilled care; Intermediate care. *Beds* SNF 100; ICF. *Certified* Medicaid.
Owner Proprietary Corp.
Admissions Requirements Medical examination; Physician's request.
Staff Physicians 1 (pt); RNs 1 (ft), 2 (pt); LPNs 12 (ft), 2 (pt); Orderlies 8 (ft), 1 (pt); Nurses aides 30 (ft), 4 (pt); Reality therapists 1 (ft); Orderlies 1 (ft).
Facilities Dining room; Physical therapy room; Activities room; Crafts room; Laundry room; Barber/Beauty shop; Library; Sitting rooms.
Activities Arts & crafts; Games; Reading groups; Prayer groups; Shopping trips; Social/Cultural gatherings; Picnics.

ATLANTA

Ansley Pavilion*
560 St Charles Ave, Atlanta, GA, 30308
(404) 874-2233
Admin Aaron Baranan.
Licensure Intermediate care. *Beds* 90. *Certified* Medicaid.

Ashton Woods Convalescent Center
3535 Ashton Woods Dr, Atlanta, GA, 30319
(404) 451-0236
Admin Ken O Stuck. *Medical Dir/Dir of Nursing* Gretchen Evans RN DON.
Licensure Skilled care. *Beds* 157. *Certified* Medicare.
Owner Proprietary Corp (National Heritage).
Admissions Requirements Medical examination.
Staff Physicians; RNs; LPNs; Orderlies; Nurses aides; Physical therapists; Recreational therapists; Occupational therapists; Speech therapists; Activities coordinators; Dietitians; Dentists; Ophthalmologists; Podiatrists.
Facilities Dining room; Physical therapy room; Activities room; Crafts room; Laundry room; Barber/Beauty shop; Library.

Briarcliff Haven
1000 Briarcliff Rd NE, Atlanta, GA, 30306
(404) 875-6456
Admin James I Kaufmann. *Medical Dir/Dir of Nursing* Agnes Church RN DON.
Licensure Skilled care; Intermediate care. *Beds* SNF 103; ICF 53. *Certified* Medicaid.
Owner Proprietary Corp.
Admissions Requirements Physician's request.
Facilities Dining room; Physical therapy room; Activities room; Chapel; Crafts room; Laundry room; Barber/Beauty shop; Library.
Activities Arts & crafts; Cards; Games; Reading groups; Prayer groups; Movies; Shopping trips; Social/Cultural gatherings.

Budd Terrace Intermediate Care Home
1833 Clifton Rd NE, Atlanta, GA, 30029
(404) 728-6506
Admin Elaine R Burge. *Medical Dir/Dir of Nursing* Herbert Karp MD; Jean Copeland RN DON.
Licensure Intermediate care. *Beds* ICF 270.
Owner Nonprofit Corp.
Admissions Requirements Minimum age 62; Medical examination; Physician's request.
Staff RNs 3 (ft), 8 (pt); LPNs 18 (ft), 10 (pt); Nurses aides 40 (ft); Physical therapists 5 (ft); Recreational therapists 3 (ft); Occupational therapists; Speech therapists; Activities coordinators 1 (ft); Dietitians 1 (ft).
Affiliation Methodist
Facilities Dining room; Physical therapy room; Activities room; Chapel; Crafts room; Laundry room; Barber/Beauty shop; TV lounges on each unit.
Activities Arts & crafts; Cards; Games; Reading groups; Prayer groups; Movies; Shopping trips; Social/Cultural gatherings.

Camilla Street Intermediate Care Home
1011 Camilla St SW, Atlanta, GA, 30314
(404) 753-8839
Admin Arthur E Simpson. *Medical Dir/Dir of Nursing* J B Ellison MD; Lula Mae Jackson DON.
Licensure Intermediate care. *Beds* ICF 14. *Certified* Medicaid.
Owner Proprietary Corp.
Admissions Requirements Medical examination; Physician's request.
Staff Physicians 1 (ft); RNs 1 (ft); LPNs 4 (ft), 2 (pt); Orderlies 1 (ft), 3 (pt); Nurses aides 6 (ft), 1 (pt); Physical therapists 1 (pt); Recreational therapists 1 (ft); Speech therapists 1 (pt); Activities coordinators 1 (pt); Dietitians 1 (pt); Ophthalmologists 1 (pt); Podiatrists 1 (pt).
Facilities Dining room; Activities room; Crafts room; Laundry room.
Activities Arts & crafts; Cards; Games; Reading groups; Prayer groups; Movies; Shopping trips; Social/Cultural gatherings.

Canterbury Court Intermediate Care Unit*
3750 Peachtree Rd NE, Atlanta, GA, 30319
(404) 261-6611
Admin R A Lawrence.
Licensure Intermediate care. *Beds* 16.

Christian City Convalescent Center
7300 Lester Rd, Atlanta, GA, 30349
(404) 964-3301
Admin Fred A Watson. *Medical Dir/Dir of Nursing* Robert Webster MD.
Licensure Skilled care; Intermediate care. *Beds* 200. *Certified* Medicaid.
Admissions Requirements Minimum age 16; Medical examination.
Staff Physicians 5 (pt); RNs 13 (ft), 3 (pt); LPNs 5 (ft), 1 (pt); Nurses aides 80 (ft), 20 (pt); Physical therapists 1 (pt); Reality therapists 1

(ft); Occupational therapists 1 (pt); Speech therapists 1 (pt); Activities coordinators 1 (ft); Dietitians 1 (ft); Dentists 1 (pt); Ophthalmologists 1 (pt); Podiatrists 1 (pt).
Facilities Dining room; Physical therapy room; Activities room; Chapel; Laundry room; Barber/Beauty shop; Library.
Activities Arts & crafts; Cards; Games; Reading groups; Prayer groups; Movies; Shopping trips; Social/Cultural gatherings.

Kathy Crawford Nursing Center*
460 Auburn Ave NE, Atlanta, GA, 30312
(404) 523-1613
Admin James E Kinsey. *Medical Dir/Dir of Nursing* Dr Joseph Williams.
Licensure Intermediate care. *Beds* 186. *Certified* Medicaid.
Staff Physicians 2 (pt); RNs 2 (ft); LPNs 11 (ft); Orderlies 11 (ft); Nurses aides 37 (ft); Reality therapists 2 (ft); Recreational therapists 2 (ft); Occupational therapists 1 (ft); Activities coordinators 1 (ft).
Facilities Dining room; Physical therapy room; Activities room; Chapel; Laundry room; Barber/Beauty shop.
Activities Arts & crafts; Games; Reading groups; Prayer groups; Movies; Shopping trips; Social/Cultural gatherings.

Crestview Nursing Home
2800 Springdale Rd, Atlanta, GA, 30315
(404) 767-7406
Admin Linda Brooks. *Medical Dir/Dir of Nursing* Dr Phillip Benton.
Licensure Skilled care; Intermediate care. *Beds* SNF 388; ICF. *Certified* Medicaid; Medicare.
Owner Proprietary Corp.
Admissions Requirements Medical examination; Physician's request.
Staff Physicians 7 (pt); RNs 4 (ft), 3 (pt); LPNs 38 (ft), 11 (pt); Orderlies 42 (ft), 6 (pt); Nurses aides 96 (ft), 17 (pt); Physical therapists 1 (ft); Recreational therapists 5 (ft); Speech therapists 1 (pt); Activities coordinators 1 (ft); Dietitians 1 (ft); Dentists 1 (pt); Ophthalmologists 1 (pt); Podiatrists 1 (pt).
Facilities Dining room; Physical therapy room; Activities room; Chapel; Crafts room; Laundry room; Barber/Beauty shop.
Activities Arts & crafts; Cards; Games; Reading groups; Prayer groups; Movies; Shopping trips; Social/Cultural gatherings.

Emory Convalescent Home
1466 Oxford Rd NE, Atlanta, GA, 30307
(404) 378-7339 or 378-7106
Admin Mary Alta Goodspeed. *Medical Dir/Dir of Nursing* Tim Harden MD; Rose Johnson DON.
Licensure Intermediate care. *Beds* SNF 41. *Certified* Medicaid; VA; Private Pay.
Admissions Requirements Medical examination; Physician's request.
Staff Physicians 5 (pt); RNs 1 (ft), 3 (pt); LPNs 3 (ft), 1 (pt); Orderlies 1 (ft), 1 (pt); Nurses aides 12 (ft), 4 (pt).
Facilities Dining room; Laundry room.
Activities Arts & crafts; Games; Reading groups; Prayer groups; Movies; Shopping trips; Social/Cultural gatherings.

Fountainview Convalescent Center*
1400 Briarcliff Rd, Atlanta, GA, 30306
(404) 378-2303
Admin Ms Taber B King.
Licensure Skilled care. *Beds* 65.

A G Rhodes Home Inc
350 Boulevard SE, Atlanta, GA, 30312
(404) 688-6731
Admin Pat McMurry. *Medical Dir/Dir of Nursing* Libby Herman.
Licensure Skilled care; Intermediate care. *Beds* 158. *Certified* Medicaid; Medicare.
Owner Nonprofit Corp.

Admissions Requirements Minimum age 21.
Staff Physicians; RNs 6 (ft), 2 (pt); LPNs 15 (ft), 5 (pt); Orderlies 3 (ft), 2 (pt); Nurses aides 65 (ft), 10 (pt); Physical therapists 1 (ft), 1 (pt); Activities coordinators 1 (ft), 1 (pt); Dietitians 1 (pt); Ophthalmologists 1 (pt).
Facilities Dining room; Physical therapy room; Activities room; Chapel; Crafts room; Laundry room; Barber/Beauty shop; Library.
Activities Arts & crafts; Cards; Games; Reading groups; Movies; Shopping trips; Social/Cultural gatherings.

Georgia Retardation Center*
4770 N Peachtree Rd, Atlanta, GA, 30341
(404) 393-7157
Admin Bernard R Wagner. *Medical Dir/Dir of Nursing* Wiliam S Talley MD.
Licensure Skilled care; Intermediate care for mentally retarded. *Beds* SNF 94; ICF/MR 286. *Certified* Medicare.
Owner Publicly owned.
Staff Physicians 6 (ft); RNs 40 (ft); LPNs 10 (ft); Nurses aides 480 (ft); Physical therapists 6 (ft); Recreational therapists 12 (ft); Occupational therapists 8 (ft); Speech therapists 6 (ft); Activities coordinators 21 (ft); Dietitians 6 (ft); Dentists 5 (ft); Ophthalmologists 1 (pt); Podiatrists 1 (pt); Audiologists 2 (ft), 1 (pt).
Facilities Dining room; Physical therapy room; Activities room; Chapel; Crafts room; Laundry room; Barber/Beauty shop; Library; Adaptive swimming pool.
Activities Arts & crafts; Cards; Games; Reading groups; Prayer groups; Movies; Shopping trips; Social/Cultural gatherings.

Heritage Convalescent Center*
54 Peachtree Park Dr, Atlanta, GA, 30309
(404) 351-6041
Admin Rose Marie Moore. *Medical Dir/Dir of Nursing* Dr Roy A Wiggins Jr.
Licensure Skilled care; Intermediate care. *Beds* 180. *Certified* Medicaid; Medicare.
Admissions Requirements Medical examination; Physician's request.
Staff RNs 2 (ft), 2 (pt); LPNs 10 (ft); Orderlies 4 (ft); Nurses aides 53 (ft); Physical therapists 1 (pt); Activities coordinators 1 (ft); Dietitians 1 (ft).
Facilities Dining room; Physical therapy room; Activities room; Chapel; Crafts room; Laundry room; Barber/Beauty shop; Library.
Activities Arts & crafts; Cards; Games; Reading groups; Prayer groups; Movies; Shopping trips; Social/Cultural gatherings.

Imperial Health Care Center
2645 Whiting St NW, Atlanta, GA, 30318
(404) 799-9268, 799-9278
Admin Coy C Williamson Jr. *Medical Dir/Dir of Nursing* Joann Stevens RN.
Licensure Skilled care; Intermediate care; Intermediate care for mentally retarded. *Beds* SNF 120; ICF. *Certified* Medicaid; Medicare.
Owner Privately owned.
Staff RNs; LPNs; Orderlies; Nurses aides; Physical therapists; Recreational therapists; Activities coordinators.

The Jewish Home for the Aged
3150 Howell Mill Rd NW, Atlanta, GA, 30327
(404) 351-8410
Admin Deborah Beards. *Medical Dir/Dir of Nursing* Sanford Shmerling MD; Patrick Shipley RN.
Licensure Skilled care; Intermediate care. *Beds* 120. *Certified* Medicaid; Medicare.
Owner Nonprofit Corp.
Admissions Requirements Minimum age 62; Females only.

Staff Physicians 1 (pt); RNs 7 (ft); LPNs 17 (ft); Nurses aides 50 (ft); Physical therapists 1 (ft); Recreational therapists 2 (ft); Occupational therapists 1 (pt); Dietitians 1 (pt).
Languages Yiddish, Hebrew
Affiliation Jewish
Facilities Dining room; Physical therapy room; Activities room; Chapel; Crafts room; Laundry room; Barber/Beauty shop; Library.
Activities Arts & crafts; Cards; Games; Movies; Social/Cultural gatherings.

Sadie G Mays Memorial Nursing Home
1821 W Anderson Ave SW, Atlanta, GA, 30314
(404) 794-2477
Admin Charles Robinson Jr. *Medical Dir/Dir of Nursing* A M Davis MD; Eva Price RN DON.
Licensure Skilled care; Intermediate care. *Beds* 206. *Certified* Medicaid.
Owner Nonprofit Corp.
Admissions Requirements Medical examination; Physician's request.
Staff Physicians 2 (pt); RNs 4 (ft); LPNs 20 (ft), 5 (pt); Orderlies 8 (ft); Nurses aides 55 (ft); Physical therapists 1 (ft); Speech therapists 1 (pt); Activities coordinators 1 (ft); Dietitians 1 (ft); Ophthalmologists 1 (pt); Dentist 1 (pt).
Facilities Dining room; Physical therapy room; Activities room; Chapel; Laundry room; Barber/Beauty shop.
Activities Arts & crafts; Cards; Games; Prayer groups; Movies; Shopping trips; Social/Cultural gatherings; Exercise.

Northside Convalescent Center*
993-E Johnson Ferry, Atlanta, GA, 30342
(404) 256-5131
Admin James R Fanger. *Medical Dir/Dir of Nursing* John McCoy MD.
Licensure Skilled care. *Beds* 180. *Certified* Medicare.
Owner Proprietary Corp (Beverly Enterprises).
Admissions Requirements Medical examination; Physician's request.
Staff Physicians 112 (pt); RNs 19 (ft), 4 (pt); LPNs 16 (ft), 7 (pt); Orderlies 9 (ft), 1 (pt); Nurses aides 90 (ft), 10 (pt); Physical therapists 3 (ft), 1 (pt); Reality therapists 4 (ft); Recreational therapists 2 (ft); Occupational therapists 1 (pt); Speech therapists 1 (pt); Dietitians 1 (ft); Dentists 1 (ft); Ophthalmologists 1 (ft); Podiatrists 2 (ft); Respiratory therapists 3 (ft), 2 (pt).
Facilities Dining room; Physical therapy room; Activities room; Crafts room; Laundry room; Barber/Beauty shop; Library; Bus & limo services.
Activities Arts & crafts; Cards; Games; Reading groups; Prayer groups; Movies; Shopping trips; Social/Cultural gatherings; Happy hour.

Nursecare of Atlanta
2920 S Pharr Court NW, Atlanta, GA, 30363
(404) 261-9043
Admin La Venia R Miller. *Medical Dir/Dir of Nursing* Charles Johnson MD; Kit Giles RN DON.
Licensure Skilled care; Intermediate care. *Beds* 220. *Certified* Medicaid; Medicare.
Owner Proprietary Corp.
Admissions Requirements Minimum age 16; Medical examination.
Staff Physicians 3 (ft); RNs 6 (ft); LPNs 20 (ft), 6 (pt); Orderlies 6 (ft), 2 (pt); Nurses aides 60 (ft), 16 (pt); Physical therapists 1 (ft); Recreational therapists 1 (ft); Activities coordinators 2 (ft); Dietitians 1 (ft), 1 (pt); Social worker 2 (ft).
Languages Spanish
Facilities Dining room; Physical therapy room; Activities room; Chapel; Crafts room; Barber/Beauty shop; Library; Garden area.

Activities Arts & crafts; Cards; Games; Reading groups; Prayer groups; Movies; Shopping trips; Social/Cultural gatherings.

Our Lady of Perpetual Help Home
760 Washington St SW, Atlanta, GA, 30315
(404) 688-9515
Admin Sr Mary Peter. *Medical Dir/Dir of Nursing* Dr Thomas F Lowry; Sr Mary de Paul RN.
Licensure Skilled care. *Beds* 48.
Owner Nonprofit Corp.
Admissions Requirements Medical examination; Physician's request.
Staff Physicians 1 (pt); RNs 2 (ft); LPNs 11 (ft); Orderlies 3 (ft); Nurses aides 2 (ft), 1 (pt) 13K 2 (pt); Dietitians 1 (pt); Ophthalmologists 1 (pt).
Affiliation Roman Catholic
Facilities Chapel; Crafts room; Laundry room; Barber/Beauty shop; Library.
Activities Arts & crafts; Cards; Games; Prayer groups; Movies.

Piedmont Hospital Extended Care Unit
1968 Peachtree Rd NW, Atlanta, GA, 30309
(404) 350-2222
Admin Shirley M Thomas RN. *Medical Dir/Dir of Nursing* Dan Ferguson MD; JoAnn Akers RN DON.
Licensure Skilled care. *Beds* SNF 42. *Certified* Medicare.
Owner Nonprofit organization/foundation.
Staff Physicians; RNs; LPNs; Orderlies; Nurses aides; Physical therapists; Occupational therapists 1 (pt); Activities coordinators 1 (pt); Dietitians 1 (ft).
Facilities Physical therapy room; Activities room; Chapel; Barber/Beauty shop; Library.
Activities Arts & crafts; Cards.

Sky Ranch Nursing Home
3700 Cascade-Palmetto Rd, Atlanta, GA, 30331
(404) 964-6950
Admin Anita Dempsey. *Medical Dir/Dir of Nursing* Joe Cruise MD; Brenda Giles LPN.
Licensure Intermediate care. *Beds* 60. *Certified* Medicaid.
Owner Proprietary Corp.
Admissions Requirements Medical examination; Physician's request.
Staff Physicians 2 (pt); RNs 1 (ft); LPNs 4 (ft), 2 (pt); Nurses aides 12 (ft), 6 (pt); Physical therapists 1 (pt); Recreational therapists 1 (ft); Occupational therapists 1 (ft); Activities coordinators 1 (pt); Dietitians 1 (pt); Ophthalmologists 1 (pt).
Facilities Dining room; Physical therapy room; Activities room; Crafts room; Laundry room; Barber/Beauty shop.
Activities Arts & crafts; Cards; Games; Reading groups; Prayer groups; Movies; Shopping trips; Social/Cultural gatherings.

Springdale Convalescent Center
2850 Springdale Rd SW, Atlanta, GA, 30315
(404) 762-8672
Admin Cheri S Underwood. *Medical Dir/Dir of Nursing* Dr Jimmie Williams; Carolyn H Boyd DON.
Licensure Skilled care; Intermediate care. *Beds* 109. *Certified* Medicaid.
Owner Proprietary Corp.
Admissions Requirements Medical examination; Physician's request.
Staff Physicians; RNs; LPNs; Nurses aides; Physical therapists; Recreational therapists; Speech therapists; Activities coordinators; Dietitians.
Facilities Dining room; Physical therapy room; Activities room; Laundry room; Barber/Beauty shop.
Activities Arts & crafts; Cards; Games; Reading groups; Prayer groups; Movies; Shopping trips; Social/Cultural gatherings.

Wesley Woods Health Center
1841 Clifton Rd NE, Atlanta, GA, 30029
(404) 728-6407
Admin Pamela C. Deaton. *Medical Dir/Dir of Nursing* Dr Herbert Karp; Jean Copeland DON.
Licensure Skilled care. *Beds* SNF 171.
Certified Medicaid; Medicare.
Owner Proprietary Corp (Wesley Homes).
Admissions Requirements Medical examination.
Staff RNs 98 (ft), 57 (pt); Physical therapists 2 (ft); Recreational therapists 2 (ft); Occupational therapists 1 (pt); Speech therapists 1 (pt); Activities coordinators 1 (ft); Dietitians 1 (ft); Social worker 2 (ft).
Languages Spanish
Affiliation Methodist
Facilities Dining room; Physical therapy room; Activities room; Crafts room; Barber/Beauty shop.
Activities Arts & crafts; Games; Reading groups; Prayer groups; Movies; Shopping trips; Social/Cultural gatherings; Pet therapy.

AUGUSTA

Augusta Health Care Facility*
PO Box 5778, Augusta, GA, 30906
(404) 793-1057
Admin Paul Phillips. *Medical Dir/Dir of Nursing* Louis Scharff III MD.
Licensure Skilled care. *Beds* 31. *Certified* Medicaid; Medicare.
Owner Proprietary Corp (Wessex Corp).
Admissions Requirements Medical examination; Physician's request.
Staff Physicians 5 (pt); RNs 2 (ft), 1 (pt); LPNs 17 (ft), 7 (pt); Orderlies 5 (ft); Nurses aides 62 (ft), 4 (pt); Physical therapists 1 (ft), 1 (pt); Recreational therapists 2 (ft); Speech therapists 1 (pt); Activities coordinators 1 (ft); Dietitians 1 (ft), 1 (pt).
Facilities Dining room; Physical therapy room; Activities room; Chapel; Crafts room; Laundry room; Barber/Beauty shop; Library.
Activities Arts & crafts; Cards; Games; Reading groups; Prayer groups; Movies; Shopping trips; Social/Cultural gatherings.

Beverly Manor Convalescent Center*
1600 Anthony Rd, Augusta, GA, 30904
(404) 738-3301
Admin Larry Swicegood. *Medical Dir/Dir of Nursing* Dr Nathan Reeves.
Licensure Skilled care; Intermediate care. *Beds* 99. *Certified* Medicaid; Medicare.
Owner Proprietary Corp (Beverly Enterprises).
Admissions Requirements Medical examination; Physician's request.
Staff RNs 5 (ft); LPNs 15 (ft), 10 (pt); Orderlies 3 (ft), 1 (pt); Nurses aides 27 (ft), 15 (pt); Physical therapists 1 (pt); Occupational therapists 1 (pt); Speech therapists 1 (pt); Activities coordinators 1 (ft); Dietitians 1 (ft); Dentists 1 (pt); Podiatrists 1 (pt).
Facilities Dining room; Physical therapy room; Activities room; Chapel; Crafts room; Laundry room; Barber/Beauty shop.
Activities Arts & crafts; Games; Prayer groups; Movies; Shopping trips.

Blair House
2541 Milledgville Rd, Augusta, GA, 30904
(404) 738-2581
Admin Frank Feltham. *Medical Dir/Dir of Nursing* Luther M Thomas Jr; Marie Rollins.
Licensure Skilled care; Intermediate care. *Beds* 100. *Certified* Medicaid; Medicare.
Owner Proprietary Corp.
Staff Physicians 5 (pt); RNs 1 (ft), 2 (pt); LPNs 6 (ft), 10 (pt); Nurses aides 16 (ft), 22 (pt); Activities coordinators 1 (ft); Dietitians 1 (ft).

Facilities Dining room; Physical therapy room; Activities room; Chapel; Laundry room; Barber/Beauty shop.
Activities Arts & crafts; Games; Reading groups; Prayer groups; Shopping trips; Social/Cultural gatherings.

Bon Air Life Care Center
PO Box 3409, 873 Hickman Rd, Augusta, GA, 30904-1409
(404) 737-8258
Admin Wanda J Hinton.
Beds 128.

Georgia War Veterans Nursing Home
1101 15th St, Augusta, GA, 30910
(404) 828-2531
Admin Charles Esposito. *Medical Dir/Dir of Nursing* Arthur O Gelbart MD; Leah Hunter DON.
Licensure Skilled care. *Beds* SNF 192.
Owner Nonprofit organization/foundation.
Staff Physicians 1 (ft), 1 (pt); RNs 16 (ft), 4 (pt); LPNs 24 (ft); Nurses aides 83 (ft); Physical therapists 1 (ft), 1 (pt); Recreational therapists 1 (ft); Occupational therapists 2 (ft); Speech therapists 1 (pt); Activities coordinators 1 (ft); Dietitians 1 (ft); Ophthalmologists 1 (pt).
Facilities Dining room; Physical therapy room; Activities room; Chapel; Crafts room; Laundry room; Barber/Beauty shop; Library.
Activities Arts & crafts; Cards; Games; Reading groups; Prayer groups; Movies; Shopping trips; Birthday parties.

Jennings Healthcare Inc*
3235 Deans Bridge Rd, Augusta, GA, 30906
(404) 798-1430
Admin Kathleen Mixon. *Medical Dir/Dir of Nursing* O L Gray.
Licensure Skilled care; Intermediate care. *Beds* 76. *Certified* Medicaid; Medicare.
Admissions Requirements Medical examination; Physician's request.
Facilities Dining room; Physical therapy room; Activities room; Laundry room; Barber/Beauty shop; Library.
Activities Arts & crafts; Cards; Games; Reading groups; Prayer groups; Movies; Shopping trips; Social/Cultural gatherings.

University Hospital—Extended Care Facility
1355 Nelson St, Augusta, GA, 30910
(404) 724-4038
Admin Kathy Lesnevich. *Medical Dir/Dir of Nursing* Joseph D Lee MD.
Licensure Skilled care. *Beds* 60. *Certified* Medicaid; Medicare.
Admissions Requirements Physician's request.
Staff Physicians 1 (pt); RNs 9 (ft), 4 (pt); LPNs 15 (ft), 3 (pt); Nurses aides 11 (ft), 1 (pt); Physical therapists 2 (ft); Recreational therapists 1 (ft); Occupational therapists 1 (ft); Speech therapists 1 (pt); Dietitians 1 (ft), 1 (pt).
Facilities Dining room; Physical therapy room; Activities room; Crafts room; Laundry room; Barber/Beauty shop.

West Lake Manor Health Care Center*
820 Stevens Creek Rd, Augusta, GA, 30907
(404) 860-6622
Medical Dir/Dir of Nursing Richard E Melcher MD.
Licensure Skilled care; Intermediate care. *Beds* 100. *Certified* Medicaid; Medicare.
Staff RNs 4 (ft), 1 (pt); LPNs 7 (ft), 4 (pt); Nurses aides 27 (ft), 10 (pt); Physical therapists 1 (pt); Recreational therapists 1 (ft); Speech therapists 1 (pt); Activities coordinators 1 (ft); Dietitians 1 (ft); Social workers 1 (ft).
Facilities Dining room; Physical therapy room; Activities room; Chapel; Crafts room; Laundry room; Barber/Beauty shop.

Activities Arts & crafts; Cards; Games; Reading groups; Prayer groups; Movies; Social/Cultural gatherings.

Windermere*
2618 J Dewey Gray Circle, Augusta, GA, 30909
(404) 860-7572
Admin Charles Esposito.
Beds 120.
Owner Proprietary Corp (Beverly Enterprises).

AUSTELL

Atlanta Health Care Center*
1700 Mulkey Rd, Austell, GA, 30001
(404) 941-5750
Admin Lloyd Schlegel.
Licensure Skilled care; Intermediate care. *Beds* 62. *Certified* Medicaid; Medicare.
Owner Proprietary Corp (Wessex Corp).

Brian Center of Nursing Care
2130 Anderson Mill Rd, Austell, GA, 30001
(404) 941-8813
Admin Frances Horton. *Medical Dir/Dir of Nursing* Ellis Malone MD; Diane Brown RN.
Licensure Skilled care; Intermediate care. *Beds* 170. *Certified* Medicaid; Medicare.
Owner Proprietary Corp (Brian Center Management Corp).
Staff Physicians 12 (pt); RNs 4 (ft); LPNs 15 (ft), 4 (pt); Orderlies 4 (ft), 2 (pt); Nurses aides 50 (ft), 10 (pt); Physical therapists 1 (ft); Occupational therapists 1 (pt); Speech therapists 1 (pt); Activities coordinators 1 (ft); Dietitians 1 (pt); Dentists 1 (pt); Podiatrists 1 (pt); Ophthalmologists 1 (pt).
Facilities Dining room; Physical therapy room; Activities room; Crafts room; Laundry room; Barber/Beauty shop; Inner enclosed courtyard.
Activities Arts & crafts; Cards; Games; Reading groups; Prayer groups; Social/Cultural gatherings.

BAINBRIDGE

Bainbridge Health Care Inc*
Rte 2, 1155 W College St, Box 20, Bainbridge, GA, 31717
(404) 243-0931
Admin Doris Grant.
Beds 100.
Owner Proprietary Corp (Stuckey Health Care).

Memorial Manor Nursing Home*
1500 E Shotwell St, Bainbridge, GA, 31717
(912) 246-3500
Admin Raymond W Wright.
Licensure Skilled care; Intermediate care. *Beds* 107. *Certified* Medicaid; Medicare.

Southwestern Developmental Center
PO Box 935, Bainbridge, GA, 31717
(912) 246-6750
Admin Sharon Haire. *Medical Dir/Dir of Nursing* Dr Martin Bailey.
Licensure Intermediate care for mentally retarded. *Beds* 216. *Certified* Medicare.
Staff Physicians 2 (ft), 1 (pt); RNs 12 (ft); LPNs 15 (ft); Physical therapists 2 (ft); Recreational therapists 6 (ft); Occupational therapists 2 (ft); Speech therapists 2 (ft); Activities coordinators 1 (ft); Dietitians 2 (ft); Dentists 1 (ft), 1 (pt).
Facilities Dining room; Physical therapy room; Activities room; Chapel; Crafts room; Laundry room; Barber/Beauty shop; Library.
Activities Arts & crafts; Cards; Games; Reading groups; Prayer groups; Movies; Shopping trips; Social/Cultural gatherings.

BALDWIN

Scenic View Health Care Center*
PO Box 288, Baldwin, GA, 30511
(404) 778-8377
Admin Sallie Y Powell.
Licensure Skilled care; Intermediate care. *Beds* 112. *Certified* Medicaid.

BARNESVILLE

Heritage Inn—Barnesville
Box 380, 148 Ft Valley Rd, Barnesville, GA, 30204
(404) 358-2485
Admin Jim Pritchett. *Medical Dir/Dir of Nursing* George Henry MD; Mary Lou Harris RN.
Licensure Skilled care; Intermediate care. *Beds* 117. *Certified* Medicaid.
Owner Privately owned.
Staff Physicians 2 (ft); RNs 3 (ft), 1 (pt); LPNs 12 (ft), 3 (pt); Orderlies 3 (ft); Nurses aides 60 (ft), 4 (pt); Physical therapists 1 (ft); Occupational therapists 1 (ft); Activities coordinators 1 (ft); Dietitians 1 (ft).
Facilities Dining room; Physical therapy room; Activities room; Crafts room; Laundry room; Barber/Beauty shop.
Activities Arts & crafts; Cards; Games; Reading groups; Movies; Shopping trips.

BAXLEY

Appling County Nursing Home*
E Walnut St, Baxley, GA, 31513
(912) 367-4645
Admin Stanley Crews.
Licensure Skilled care. *Beds* 31. *Certified* Medicaid; Medicare.

Baxley Manor Inc—Intermediate Care Facility*
Rt 3 Box 18, Donnie Ln, Baxley, GA, 31513
(912) 367-4663
Admin Mary L Price. *Medical Dir/Dir of Nursing* A E Suarez MD.
Licensure Intermediate care. *Beds* 70. *Certified* Medicaid; Medicare.
Owner Proprietary Corp (Stuckey Health Care).
Admissions Requirements Physician's request.
Staff RNs 1 (ft), 1 (pt); LPNs 6 (ft), 2 (pt); Orderlies 7 (ft), 2 (pt); Nurses aides 13 (ft); Physical therapists 1 (pt); Activities coordinators 1 (ft); Dietitians 1 (pt); Podiatrists 1 (pt); Pharmacist 1 (pt).
Facilities Dining room; Physical therapy room; Activities room; Chapel; Crafts room; Laundry room; Barber/Beauty shop; Solarium.
Activities Arts & crafts; Cards; Games; Reading groups; Prayer groups; Movies; Shopping trips; Social/Cultural gatherings.

BLACKSHEAR

Pierce County Nursing Home
PO Box 32, 221 Carter Ave, Blackshear, GA, 31516
(912) 449-6631
Admin Warnell Wolkowski. *Medical Dir/Dir of Nursing* Don Waters MD; Emily Aguirre DON.
Licensure Skilled care. *Beds* SNF 29. *Certified* Medicaid; Medicare.
Owner Publicly owned.
Admissions Requirements Medical examination; Physician's request.
Staff RNs 2 (ft), 1 (pt); LPNs 3 (ft), 1 (pt); Nurses aides 11 (ft).
Facilities Dining room; Physical therapy room; Laundry room; Barber/Beauty shop.
Activities Arts & crafts; Cards; Games; Prayer groups; Movies.

BLAIRSVILLE

Union County Nursing Home
Rte 7, Box 7650, Blairsville, GA, 30512
(404) 745-2111
Admin Rebecca T Dyer. *Medical Dir/Dir of Nursing* George D Gowder Jr MD.
Licensure Skilled care; Intermediate care. *Beds* 96. *Certified* Medicaid; Medicare.
Admissions Requirements Medical examination; Physician's request.
Staff Physicians 6 (pt); RNs 2 (ft), 1 (pt); LPNs 9 (ft), 2 (pt); Orderlies 6 (ft); Nurses aides 25 (ft); Recreational therapists 1 (ft); Dietitians 1 (pt).
Facilities Dining room; Physical therapy room; Chapel; Laundry room; Barber/Beauty shop.
Activities Arts & crafts; Prayer groups; Movies.

BLAKLEY

Early Memorial Nursing Home*
630 Columbia Rd, Blakley, GA, 31723
(912) 723-3794
Admin Robert E Tiner.
Licensure Skilled care; Intermediate care. *Beds* 127. *Certified* Medicaid; Medicare.

BLUE RIDGE

Fannin County Nursing Home
PO Box 1227, Blue Ridge, GA, 30513
(404) 632-2271
Admin Mike Coultas. *Medical Dir/Dir of Nursing* Jack B Roof MD.
Licensure Skilled care; Intermediate care. *Beds* 101. *Certified* Medicaid.
Admissions Requirements Minimum age 18; Medical examination; Physician's request.
Staff RNs 1 (ft), 1 (pt); LPNs 7 (ft), 1 (pt); Nurses aides 16 (ft), 6 (pt); Physical therapists 1 (pt); Recreational therapists 1 (ft); Activities coordinators 1 (ft); Dietitians 1 (pt); Podiatrists 1 (pt).
Facilities Dining room; Physical therapy room; Activities room; Chapel; Crafts room; Laundry room; Barber/Beauty shop.
Activities Arts & crafts; Cards; Games; Reading groups; Prayer groups; Movies; Shopping trips; Social/Cultural gatherings.

BREMEN

Haralson County Nursing Home*
Box 724, 315 Field St, Bremen, GA, 30110
(404) 537-4482
Admin Lettie D Wilson.
Licensure Skilled care; Intermediate care. *Beds* 120. *Certified* Medicaid; Medicare.

BRUNSWICK

Goodwill Intermediate Care Home*
2708 Lee St, Brunswick, GA, 31520
(912) 267-6771
Admin F B McKenzie. *Medical Dir/Dir of Nursing* Dr Mark T Pierce.
Licensure Intermediate care. *Beds* 60. *Certified* Medicaid.
Staff Physicians 1 (ft); RNs 2 (ft); LPNs 3 (ft), 1 (pt); Nurses aides 9 (ft), 3 (pt); Physical therapists 1 (pt); Recreational therapists 1 (ft); Activities coordinators 1 (ft); Dietitians 1 (pt).
Facilities Dining room; Laundry room; Barber/Beauty shop.
Activities Arts & crafts; Games; Reading groups; Prayer groups; Movies; Social/Cultural gatherings.

Medical Arts Center—Coastal Georgia*
2611 Wildwood Dr, Brunswick, GA, 31520
(912) 264-1434
Admin Thelma W Davis.

Licensure Skilled care; Intermediate care. *Beds* 158. *Certified* Medicaid; Medicare.

Sears Manor*
3311 Lee St, Brunswick, GA, 31530
(912) 264-1826
Admin Claude G Sears.
Licensure Intermediate care. *Beds* 60. *Certified* Medicaid.

BUCHANAN

Countryside Health Center
PO Box 750, 303 Carrollton St, Buchanan, GA, 30113
(404) 646-3861
Admin Mary Ann Wood. *Medical Dir/Dir of Nursing* Dr I S Kim; Margaret Davis DON.
Licensure Intermediate care. *Beds* ICF 62. *Certified* Medicaid.
Owner Proprietary Corp.
Staff RNs; LPNs; Orderlies; Nurses aides; Recreational therapists; Activities coordinators; Dietitians.

Resthaven Intermediate Care Home
PO Box 409, Buchanan, GA, 30113
(404) 646-5512
Admin Mary B Tucker. *Medical Dir/Dir of Nursing* Dr P J Kim; Emily Briscoe DON.
Licensure Intermediate care. *Beds* ICF 60. *Certified* Medicaid.
Owner Proprietary Corp.
Admissions Requirements Medical examination; Physician's request.
Staff RNs 1 (ft); LPNs 4 (ft), 1 (pt); Nurses aides 12 (ft), 3 (pt); Dietitians 4 (ft), 2 (pt).
Facilities Dining room; Activities room; Chapel; Crafts room; Laundry room; Barber/Beauty shop.
Activities Arts & crafts; Games; Reading groups; Prayer groups; Movies; Shopping trips; Social/Cultural gatherings.

BUENA VISTA

Marion Memorial Nursing Home
PO Box 197, Buena Vista, GA, 31803
(912) 649-7100
Admin Faye B Lane. *Medical Dir/Dir of Nursing* Frank Catrett MD; Deborah Harbuck DON.
Licensure Skilled care; Intermediate care. *Beds* 50. *Certified* Medicaid.
Owner Proprietary Corp (Healthcare Management).
Admissions Requirements Physician's request.
Staff Physicians 4 (ft); RNs 1 (ft), 2 (pt); LPNs 7 (ft); Orderlies 6 (ft); Nurses aides 15 (ft); Activities coordinators 1 (ft); Dietitians 1 (pt); Ophthalmologists 1 (pt).
Facilities Dining room; Physical therapy room; Activities room; Chapel; Crafts room; Laundry room; Barber/Beauty shop; Library.
Activities Arts & crafts; Cards; Games; Reading groups; Prayer groups; Movies; Shopping trips; Social/Cultural gatherings.

BUFORD

Buford Manor Nursing Home*
2451 Peachtree Industrial Blvd, Buford, GA, 30518
(404) 945-6778
Admin Dana L Yon.
Licensure Skilled care; Intermediate care. *Beds* 117. *Certified* Medicaid; Medicare.

BYROMVILLE

Rosewood Medical Nursing Center*
PO Box 24, Byromville, GA, 31007
(912) 433-5711
Admin Nancy Herndon.
Licensure Skilled care. *Beds* 102. *Certified* Medicaid.

CALHOUN

Cherokee Nursing Home
PO Box 937, 1387 US Hwy 41 N, Calhoun,
GA, 30701
(404) 629-1289
Admin Joyce L Crawford. *Medical Dir/Dir of
Nursing* G W Brown MD.
Licensure Skilled care. *Beds* 100. *Certified*
Medicaid.
Admissions Requirements Medical
examination; Physician's request.
Staff Physicians 1 (pt); RNs 2 (ft), 1 (pt);
LPNs 7 (ft), 5 (pt); Nurses aides 20 (ft), 10
(pt); Activities coordinators 1 (ft), 1 (pt);
Dietitians 1 (pt).
Facilities Dining room; Physical therapy
room; Activities room; Crafts room; Laundry
room; Barber/Beauty shop.
Activities Arts & crafts; Cards; Games;
Reading groups; Prayer groups; Movies;
Shopping trips; Social/Cultural gatherings.

Gordon Health Care Inc*
PO Box 789, Calhoun, GA, 30701
(404) 625-0044
Admin Ben E Crawford.
Licensure Skilled care; Intermediate care. *Beds*
117. *Certified* Medicaid; Medicare.

CAMILLA

Mitchell Convalescent Center
37 S Ellis St, Camilla, GA, 31730
(912) 336-8377
Admin Cheryl H Coleman. *Medical Dir/Dir of
Nursing* A A McNeill Jr MD; Tammy
Gurley RN DON.
Licensure Skilled care; Intermediate care. *Beds*
SNF 35; ICF. *Certified* Medicaid; Medicare.
Owner Nonprofit organization/foundation.
Admissions Requirements Medical
examination; Physician's request.
Staff Physicians 4 (pt); RNs 1 (ft), 4 (pt);
LPNs 4 (ft), 2 (pt); Orderlies 2 (ft), 1 (pt);
Nurses aides 6 (ft), 8 (pt); Physical therapists
1 (ft), 1 (pt); Activities coordinators 1 (ft);
Dietitians 1 (pt); Ophthalmologists 1 (pt);
Dentist 1 (pt).
Facilities Dining room; Physical therapy
room; Chapel; Laundry room; Barber/Beauty
shop; Courtyard.
Activities Arts & crafts; Cards; Games;
Reading groups; Prayer groups; Movies;
Shopping trips; Social/Cultural gatherings;
Special theme events.

CANTON

Canton Nursing Center
Rte 6, Box 18, Hwy 5, Canton, GA, 30114
(404) 479-8791
Admin Betty Soriano. *Medical Dir/Dir of
Nursing* Dr David Field.
Licensure Intermediate care. *Beds* ICF 36.
Certified Medicaid.
Owner Proprietary Corp.
Admissions Requirements Medical
examination; Physician's request.
Staff RNs 1 (pt); LPNs 4 (ft), 3 (pt); Nurses
aides 5 (ft), 4 (pt); Speech therapists 1 (pt);
Activities coordinators 1 (ft); Dietitians 1
(pt); Dentist 1 (pt).
Facilities Dining room; Activities room;
Crafts room; Laundry room; Barber/Beauty
shop.
Activities Arts & crafts; Games; Reading
groups; Prayer groups; Movies; Shopping
trips; Social/Cultural gatherings.

Coker Intermediate Care Home
150 Hospital Circle, Canton, GA, 30114
(404) 479-5649
Admin Melba G Coker. *Medical Dir/Dir of
Nursing* William Early MD.
Licensure Intermediate care. *Beds* 81.
Certified Medicaid.

Admissions Requirements Medical
examination.
Staff RNs 1 (ft); LPNs 3 (ft), 2 (pt); Nurses
aides 15 (ft), 4 (pt); Activities coordinators 1
(ft); Dietitians 6 (ft), 5 (pt).
Facilities Dining room; Activities room;
Chapel; Crafts room; Laundry room; Barber/
Beauty shop; Library.
Activities Arts & crafts; Cards; Games; Prayer
groups; Movies; Shopping trips; Social/
Cultural gatherings; Exercise groups; Adaopt-
a-grandparent program; Bible study groups;
Sunday school; Rhythm band & music
related activities.

CARROLLTON

Bagwell Nursing Home Inc*
443 Bagwell Rd, Carrollton, GA, 30117
(404) 834-3501
Admin Mrs Bill Bagwell. *Medical Dir/Dir of
Nursing* Dr E C Bass Jr.
Licensure Skilled care; Intermediate care. *Beds*
42. *Certified* Medicaid.
Admissions Requirements Medical
examination; Physician's request.
Staff Physicians 1 (pt); RNs 1 (ft), 1 (pt);
LPNs 3 (ft), 1 (pt); Nurses aides 10 (ft), 5
(pt); Activities coordinators 2 (ft); Dietitians
2 (ft), 4 (pt).
Facilities Dining room; Activities room;
Laundry room; Barber/Beauty shop.
Activities Arts & crafts; Games; Reading
groups; Prayer groups; Shopping trips.

Carroll Convalescent Center*
Rte 5, PO Box 292, 2327 N Hwy 27,
Carrollton, GA, 30117
(404) 834-4404
Admin Edwin E Harman Jr. *Medical Dir/Dir
of Nursing* Dr Dean B Talley.
Licensure Skilled care; Intermediate care. *Beds*
159. *Certified* Medicaid.
Admissions Requirements Medical
examination; Physician's request.
Staff RNs 3 (ft), 1 (pt); LPNs 18 (ft), 6 (pt);
Orderlies 8 (ft), 4 (pt); Nurses aides 65 (ft),
15 (pt); Physical therapists 1 (ft), 1 (pt);
Recreational therapists 1 (ft), 1 (pt); Speech
therapists 1 (pt); Activities coordinators 1
(ft), 1 (pt).
Facilities Dining room; Physical therapy
room; Activities room; Laundry room;
Barber/Beauty shop; Library.
Activities Arts & crafts; Cards; Games;
Reading groups; Prayer groups; Shopping
trips.

Pine Knoll Nursing Home*
PO Box 430, Carrollton, GA, 30117
(404) 832-8243
Admin Shirley Green.
Licensure Skilled care; Intermediate care. *Beds*
122. *Certified* Medicaid.

James C Polk Rest Home*
PO Box 1216, Carrollton, GA, 30117
(404) 832-6333
Admin Evelyn T Polk.
Licensure Intermediate care. *Beds* 27.
Certified Medicaid.

CARTERSVILLE

Springdale Convalescent Center*
78 Opal St, Cartersville, GA, 30120
(404) 382-6120
Admin Elizabeth Russell.
Licensure Skilled care; Intermediate care. *Beds*
118. *Certified* Medicaid.

CEDARTOWN

Cedartown Nursing Home
148 Cason Rd, Cedartown, GA, 30125
(404) 748-3622

Admin Marvin Johns. *Medical Dir/Dir of
Nursing* Marc Well.
Licensure Intermediate care. *Beds* ICF 116.
Certified Medicaid.
Owner Proprietary Corp.
Admissions Requirements Medical
examination; Physician's request.
Activities Arts & crafts; Cards; Games;
Reading groups; Prayer groups; Movies;
Shopping trips; Social/Cultural gatherings.

Polk County Nursing Home*
225 Philpot St, Cedartown, GA, 30125
(404) 748-4116
Admin Joan J Sanders.
Licensure Skilled care; Intermediate care. *Beds*
100. *Certified* Medicaid.

CHATSWORTH

Chatsworth Health Care Center*
PO Box 1126, Chatsworth, GA, 30705
(404) 695-8313
Admin Patricia W Haynes. *Medical Dir/Dir of
Nursing* Dr Glenn Boyd.
Licensure Skilled care; Intermediate care. *Beds*
120. *Certified* Medicaid; Medicare.
Admissions Requirements Medical
examination; Physician's request.
Staff Physicians 9 (pt); RNs 3 (ft); LPNs 12
(ft), 4 (pt); Nurses aides 36 (ft), 8 (pt);
Physical therapists 1 (ft); Reality therapists 1
(pt); Speech therapists 1 (pt); Activities
coordinators 1 (ft); Dietitians 1 (pt); Dentists
1 (pt); Ophthalmologists 2 (pt); Podiatrists 1
(pt).
Facilities Dining room; Physical therapy
room; Activities room; Chapel; Crafts room;
Laundry room; Barber/Beauty shop; Library.
Activities Arts & crafts; Cards; Games;
Reading groups; Prayer groups; Movies;
Shopping trips; Social/Cultural gatherings.

CLAXTON

Claxton Nursing Home*
PO Box 712, Claxton, GA, 30417
(912) 739-2245
Admin Judy Tippins.
Licensure Skilled care; Intermediate care. *Beds*
87. *Certified* Medicaid; Medicare.

CLAYTON

Mountain View Convalescent Center*
Box 865, Warwoman Rd, Clayton, GA, 30525
(404) 782-4276
Admin R P Carothers. *Medical Dir/Dir of
Nursing* Gene Westmoreland.
Licensure Skilled care; Intermediate care. *Beds*
117. *Certified* Medicaid.
Staff RNs 2 (ft); LPNs 6 (ft), 2 (pt); Orderlies
8 (ft), 1 (pt); Nurses aides 30 (ft), 8 (pt);
Physical therapists 1 (ft); Activities
coordinators 1 (ft); Dietitians 1 (ft); Dentists
1 (pt); Podiatrists 1 (pt).
Facilities Dining room; Physical therapy
room; Activities room; Chapel; Crafts room;
Laundry room; Barber/Beauty shop.
Activities Arts & crafts; Cards; Games;
Reading groups; Prayer groups; Movies;
Shopping trips; Social/Cultural gatherings.

CLEVELAND

Cross Roads Intermediate Care Facility*
Rte 2, Cleveland, GA, 30528
(404) 865-3131
Admin Ed L Stephens.
Licensure Intermediate care. *Beds* 60.
Certified Medicaid.

Huntington Convalescent Home Inc*
Rte 2, Cleveland, GA, 30528
(404) 865-3131
Admin Ed L Stephens.

Licensure Skilled care; Intermediate care. *Beds* 89. *Certified* Medicaid; Medicare.

COCHRAN

Bryant Nursing Center
PO Box 476, 6th St, Cochran, GA, 31014
(912) 934-7682
Admin Johnson Henson. *Medical Dir/Dir of Nursing* Grace Smith.
Licensure Skilled care; Intermediate care. *Beds* 75. *Certified* Medicaid.
Owner Proprietary Corp (Beverly Enterprises).
Admissions Requirements Medical examination; Physician's request.
Staff Physicians 5 (ft); RNs 3 (ft), 1 (pt); LPNs 8 (ft), 3 (pt); Orderlies 3 (ft), 3 (pt); Nurses aides 16 (ft), 8 (pt); Physical therapists 1 (pt); Speech therapists 1 (pt); Activities coordinators 1 (pt); Dietitians 1 (pt).
Facilities Dining room; Physical therapy room; Activities room; Chapel; Crafts room; Laundry room; Barber/Beauty shop.
Activities Arts & crafts; Cards; Games; Reading groups; Prayer groups; Movies; Shopping trips; Social/Cultural gatherings.

COLLEGE PARK

College Park Convalescent Home*
1765 Temple Ave, College Park, GA, 30337
(404) 767-8600
Admin JoAnne Floyd. *Medical Dir/Dir of Nursing* Dr Reginald Smith.
Licensure Intermediate care. *Beds* 100. *Certified* Medicaid.
Admissions Requirements Medical examination; Physician's request.
Staff Physicians 1 (ft); RNs 1 (pt); LPNs 6 (ft); Nurses aides 56 (ft); Physical therapists 1 (pt); Speech therapists 1 (pt); Activities coordinators 1 (ft); Dietitians 1 (ft); Dentists 1 (ft); Ophthalmologists 1 (pt); Podiatrists 1 (ft).
Facilities Dining room; Physical therapy room; Activities room; Laundry room; Barber/Beauty shop.
Activities Arts & crafts; Cards; Games; Reading groups; Prayer groups; Movies; Shopping trips; Social/Cultural gatherings.

Oak Hill Intermediate Care Home*
4550 Janice Dr, College Park, GA, 30337
(404) 761-3817
Admin Annell Smith.
Licensure Intermediate care. *Beds* 20.

COLQUITT

Miller Nursing Home*
209 N Cuthbert St, Colquitt, GA, 31737
(912) 758-2500
Admin Don Miller.
Licensure Skilled care; Intermediate care. *Beds* 83. *Certified* Medicaid; Medicare.

COLUMBUS

Columbus Intermediate Care Home*
5131 Warm Springs Rd, Columbus, GA, 31904
(404) 561-1371
Admin William Levinsohn.
Licensure Intermediate care. *Beds* 210. *Certified* Medicaid.

Hamilton House
1911 Hamilton Rd, Columbus, GA, 31904
(404) 324-5194
Admin Mark Vanarsdale.
Licensure Skilled care. *Beds* 128. *Certified* Medicaid; Medicare.

Med Arts Health Facility*
910 Talbotton Rd, Columbus, GA, 31904
(404) 323-9513
Admin Pat Gray.
Licensure Skilled care; Intermediate care. *Beds* 110. *Certified* Medicaid; Medicare.

Muscogee Manor
7150 Manor Rd, Columbus, GA, 31995
(404) 561-3218
Admin Joseph F Cobis. *Medical Dir/Dir of Nursing* Walker Rivers MD.
Licensure Skilled care; Intermediate care. *Beds* 242. *Certified* Medicaid; Medicare.
Admissions Requirements Medical examination; Physician's request.
Staff Physicians 1 (pt); RNs 8 (ft); LPNs 15 (ft); Orderlies 3 (ft); Nurses aides 135 (ft); Physical therapists 1 (pt); Reality therapists 1 (pt); Recreational therapists 3 (ft); Occupational therapists 1 (pt); Speech therapists 1 (pt); Activities coordinators 1 (ft); Dietitians 1 (pt); Dentists 1 (pt); Ophthalmologists 1 (pt); Podiatrists 1 (pt).
Facilities Dining room; Physical therapy room; Activities room; Chapel; Crafts room; Laundry room; Barber/Beauty shop; Library; Dental office.
Activities Arts & crafts; Cards; Games; Reading groups; Prayer groups; Movies; Shopping trips; Social/Cultural gatherings.

Oak Manor Inc
2010 Warm Springs Rd, Columbus, GA, 31995
(404) 324-0387
Admin Clara K Brown. *Medical Dir/Dir of Nursing* Dr Jack W Hirsch; Carol Nahley RN.
Licensure Skilled care. *Beds* SNF 210. *Certified* Medicaid; Medicare.
Owner Proprietary Corp.
Admissions Requirements Medical examination; Physician's request.
Staff RNs 4 (ft), 1 (pt); LPNs 17 (ft), 4 (pt); Nurses aides 70 (ft), 11 (pt); Physical therapists 1 (ft), 2 (pt); Occupational therapists 1 (pt); Speech therapists 1 (pt); Activities coordinators 2 (ft), 1 (pt); Dietitians 1 (ft).
Languages German, Spanish
Facilities Dining room; Physical therapy room; Activities room; Chapel; Barber/Beauty shop; Library.
Activities Arts & crafts; Games; Reading groups; Prayer groups; Movies.

Pine Manor Inc
2000 Warm Springs Rd, Columbus, GA, 31995
(404) 324-2251
Admin Clara K Brown. *Medical Dir/Dir of Nursing* Dr Jack W Hirsch; Carol Nahley RN.
Licensure Intermingled. *Beds* Intermingled 166. *Certified* Medicaid; Medicare.
Owner Proprietary Corp.
Admissions Requirements Medical examination; Physician's request.
Staff RNs 3 (ft), 2 (pt); LPNs 11 (ft), 2 (pt); Nurses aides 60 (ft), 14 (pt); Physical therapists 1 (ft), 2 (pt); Occupational therapists 1 (pt); Speech therapists 1 (pt); Activities coordinators 2 (ft), 1 (pt); Dietitians 1 (ft).
Languages German, Spanish
Facilities Dining room; Physical therapy room; Activities room; Chapel; Barber/Beauty shop; Library.
Activities Arts & crafts; Games; Reading groups; Prayer groups; Movies.

COMER

Comer Health Care Inc
200 Paoli Rd, Comer, GA, 30629
(404) 783-5116
Admin Evelyn Bevers.

Beds 100.
Owner Proprietary Corp (Stuckey Health Care).

COMMERCE

Banks-Jackson-Commerce Nursing Home
655 Hospital Rd, Commerce, GA, 30529
(404) 335-5175
Admin David Lawrence. *Medical Dir/Dir of Nursing* Dr Joe L Griffeth; Sharon Hix RN DON.
Licensure Skilled care; Intermediate care. *Beds* Intermingled 72. *Certified* Medicaid; Medicare.
Owner Nonprofit organization/foundation.
Admissions Requirements Medical examination; Physician's request.
Staff Physicians 5 (ft); RNs 2 (ft); LPNs 8 (ft); Orderlies 2 (ft); Nurses aides 22 (ft), 6 (pt); Physical therapists 2 (ft); Activities coordinators 1 (ft); Dietitians 1 (ft); Professional social worker 1 (ft).
Affiliation Baptist
Facilities Dining room; Physical therapy room; Activities room; Laundry room; Barber/Beauty shop; Library.
Activities Arts & crafts; Cards; Games; Reading groups; Prayer groups; Movies; Shopping trips; Social/Cultural gatherings; Cooking; Arranging flowers; Garden club.

Barrett Convalescent Home Inc*
Ridgeway Rd, Commerce, GA, 30529
(404) 335-5118
Admin Johnny L Barrett.
Licensure Intermediate care. *Beds* 50.
Staff Physicians 1 (pt); RNs 1 (ft); LPNs 6 (ft); Nurses aides 11 (ft); Physical therapists 1 (pt); Recreational therapists 1 (pt); Activities coordinators 2 (ft); Dietitians 1 (pt); Podiatrists 1 (pt).
Facilities Dining room; Physical therapy room; Activities room; Laundry room; Barber/Beauty shop.
Activities Games; Reading groups; Prayer groups; Movies; Social/Cultural gatherings.

COMMING

Lanier Nursing Home*
125 Samaritan Dr, Comming, GA, 30130
Medical Dir/Dir of Nursing Fred Boling MD.
Admissions Requirements Medical examination; Physician's request.
Staff RNs 3 (ft); LPNs 9 (ft), 1 (pt); Orderlies 1 (ft), 1 (pt); Nurses aides 40 (ft), 10 (pt); Physical therapists; Occupational therapists; Speech therapists; Activities coordinators 1 (ft); Dietitians; Podiatrists.
Facilities Dining room; Physical therapy room; Activities room; Laundry room; Barber/Beauty shop.
Activities Cards; Games; Prayer groups; Movies; Shopping trips; Social/Cultural gatherings.

CONYERS

Starcrest Home of Conyers*
PO Box 438, Conyers, GA, 30207
(404) 483-3902
Admin Rachel B Athon.
Licensure Skilled care; Intermediate care. *Beds* 164. *Certified* Medicaid.

CORDELE

Crane Retirement Home Inc*
902 Blackshear Rd, Cordele, GA, 31015
(912) 273-1481
Admin W B Crane.
Licensure Skilled care; Intermediate care. *Beds* 143. *Certified* Medicaid; Medicare.

Crisp County Medical Nursing Center
1106 N 4th St, Cordele, GA, 31015
(912) 273-1227
Admin Carolyn Kidd. *Medical Dir/Dir of Nursing* Dr J T Christmas; Carolyn Howard.
Licensure Intermingled. *Beds* 100. *Certified* Medicaid; VA.
Owner Proprietary Corp (Beverly Enterprises).
Admissions Requirements Medical examination.
Staff RNs; LPNs; Orderlies; Nurses aides; Activities coordinators.
Facilities Dining room; Physical therapy room; Activities room; Laundry room; Barber/Beauty shop.
Activities Arts & crafts; Games; Reading groups; Prayer groups; Movies; Shopping trips; Social/Cultural gatherings.

COVINGTON

Covington Manor Intermediate Care Home*
4148 Carroll St, Ex-C, Covington, GA, 30209
(404) 786-0428
Admin Joyce Bohanan.
Licensure Intermediate care. *Beds* 71.
Certified Medicaid.

Riverside Medical of Covington
5100 West St, Covington, GA, 30209
(404) 787-0211
Admin C L Johnson. *Medical Dir/Dir of Nursing* Timmothy Park MD; Jane Jones RN.
Licensure Skilled care; Intermediate care. *Beds* SNF 128; ICF. *Certified* Medicaid.
Owner Proprietary Corp.
Admissions Requirements Medical examination.
Staff Physicians; RNs 2 (ft), 2 (pt); LPNs 10 (ft), 5 (pt); Orderlies 2 (ft); Nurses aides 48 (ft), 18 (pt); Physical therapists 2 (ft), 1 (pt); Speech therapists 1 (pt); Activities coordinators 1 (ft); Dietitians 1 (ft), 1 (pt).
Facilities Dining room; Physical therapy room; Activities room; Chapel; Laundry room; Barber/Beauty shop; Library.
Activities Games; Movies; Shopping trips; Social/Cultural gatherings; Exercise; Sing-alongs; Worship services; Luncheons.

CUMMING

Cumming Convalescent Home*
PO Box 24, Cumming, GA, 30130
(404) 887-2308
Admin Irwin William Winter.
Licensure Intermediate care. *Beds* 53.
Certified Medicaid.

CUTHBERT

Joe-Anne Burgin Nursing Home
203 Randolph St, Cuthbert, GA, 31740
(912) 732-2181
Admin Patricia R Prescott. *Medical Dir/Dir of Nursing* Carl E Sills MD; Christina Scribner RN DON.
Licensure Skilled care; Intermediate care. *Beds* 80. *Certified* Medicaid; Medicare.
Owner Publicly owned.
Admissions Requirements Physician's request.
Staff RNs 2 (ft), 2 (pt); LPNs 6 (ft), 3 (pt); Orderlies 4 (ft), 3 (pt); Nurses aides 20 (ft), 12 (pt); Physical therapists 1 (pt); Recreational therapists 1 (pt); Activities coordinators 1 (pt); Dietitians 1 (pt).
Facilities Dining room; Physical therapy room; Activities room; Chapel; Crafts room; Laundry room; Barber/Beauty shop.
Activities Arts & crafts; Cards; Games; Prayer groups; Movies; Shopping trips; Social/Cultural gatherings; Outings.

DAHLONEGA

Gold City Convalescent Center
PO Box 96, Dahlonega, GA, 30533
(404) 864-3045
Admin Mark Aladean McBurnett. *Medical Dir/Dir of Nursing* Eugene Westmoreland MD.
Licensure Skilled care; Intermediate care. *Beds* SNF 102; ICF. *Certified* Medicaid.
Owner Proprietary Corp.
Admissions Requirements Medical examination; Physician's request.
Staff Physicians 1 (pt); RNs 4 (ft), 1 (pt); LPNs 5 (ft), 2 (pt); Physical therapists 1 (ft), 1 (pt); Recreational therapists 1 (ft); Activities coordinators 1 (ft); Dietitians 1 (ft); Podiatrists 1 (pt).
Facilities Dining room; Physical therapy room; Activities room; Chapel; Crafts room; Laundry room; Barber/Beauty shop.
Activities Arts & crafts; Games; Reading groups; Prayer groups; Shopping trips.

DALLAS

Paulding Medical Nursing
600 W Memorial Dr, Dallas, GA, 30132
(404) 445-4411
Admin Ray C Brees. *Medical Dir/Dir of Nursing* J Henry Bunter MD; Pauline Merris DON.
Licensure Skilled care; Intermediate care. *Beds* 136. *Certified* Medicaid.
Owner Nonprofit organization/foundation.
Admissions Requirements Medical examination; Physician's request.
Staff RNs 3 (ft); LPNs 12 (ft); Nurses aides 39 (ft); Activities coordinators 1 (ft); Dietitians 1 (ft).
Facilities Dining room; Physical therapy room; Activities room; Crafts room; Barber/ Beauty shop; Library.
Activities Arts & crafts; Games; Reading groups; Prayer groups; Movies; Shopping trips; Social/Cultural gatherings.

DALTON

Quinton Memorial Health Center*
1114 Burleyson Dr, Dalton, GA, 30720
(404) 226-4642
Admin Wayne Benson. *Medical Dir/Dir of Nursing* Neil Boggess MD.
Licensure Skilled care; Intermediate care. *Beds* 120. *Certified* Medicaid.
Admissions Requirements Medical examination.
Staff RNs 3 (ft); LPNs 9 (ft), 4 (pt); Orderlies 1 (ft), 1 (pt); Nurses aides 34 (ft), 4 (pt); Physical therapists 1 (ft), 1 (pt); Activities coordinators 1 (ft); Dietitians 1 (pt).
Facilities Dining room; Physical therapy room; Activities room; Chapel; Crafts room; Laundry room; Barber/Beauty shop.
Activities Arts & crafts; Cards; Games; Prayer groups; Movies; Shopping trips; Birthday parties; Devotionals by multi-denominational leaders.

Ridgewood Manor
1110 Burleyson Dr, Dalton, GA, 30720
(404) 226-1021
Admin John S Driggers. *Medical Dir/Dir of Nursing* Dr Earl McGhee; Karen Ismail.
Licensure Skilled care; Intermediate care. *Beds* 102. *Certified* Medicaid; Medicare.
Owner Proprietary Corp.
Admissions Requirements Medical examination; Physician's request.
Staff RNs 3 (ft); LPNs 10 (ft), 2 (pt); Nurses aides 22 (ft), 10 (pt); Physical therapists 1 (pt); Activities coordinators 1 (ft); Dietitians 1 (pt).
Facilities Dining room; Physical therapy room; Activities room; Chapel; Laundry room; Barber/Beauty shop.

Activities Arts & crafts; Cards; Games; Prayer groups; Shopping trips; Social/Cultural gatherings.

Wood Dale Health Care Center*
1102 Burleyson Dr, Dalton, GA, 30720
(404) 226-1285
Admin Eugene P Harrison. *Medical Dir/Dir of Nursing* Robert L Raitz MD.
Licensure Skilled care; Intermediate care. *Beds* 108. *Certified* Medicaid.
Admissions Requirements Medical examination; Physician's request.
Staff Physicians 15 (pt); RNs 2 (ft), 1 (pt); LPNs 13 (ft), 6 (pt); Nurses aides 28 (ft), 12 (pt); Physical therapists 1 (pt); Speech therapists 1 (pt); Activities coordinators 1 (ft); Dietitians 1 (pt); Dentists 1 (pt).
Facilities Dining room; Physical therapy room; Activities room; Chapel; Crafts room; Laundry room; Barber/Beauty shop.
Activities Arts & crafts; Cards.

DAWSON

Dawson Manor*
Box 607, 507 E Georgia Ave, Dawson, GA, 31742
(912) 995-5016
Admin Jimmy C Johns.
Licensure Skilled care; Intermediate care. *Beds* 74. *Certified* Medicaid.

DECATUR

Americana Health Care Center*
2722 N Decatur Rd, Decatur, GA, 30033
(404) 296-5440
Admin Patricia Sheppard. *Medical Dir/Dir of Nursing* Dr Philip Jardina.
Licensure Skilled care; Intermediate care. *Beds* 141. *Certified* Medicare.
Owner Proprietary Corp (Manor Care).
Admissions Requirements Minimum age 21; Medical examination.
Staff Physicians 3 (pt); RNs 7 (ft), 4 (pt); LPNs 10 (ft), 7 (pt); Nurses aides 47 (ft), 4 (pt); Physical therapists 2 (ft), 1 (pt); Reality therapists 2 (ft); Recreational therapists 2 (ft); Occupational therapists 1 (ft); Speech therapists 1 (pt); Activities coordinators 1 (ft); Dietitians 1 (ft); Dentists 1 (pt); Podiatrists 1 (pt); Audiologists 1 (pt).
Facilities Dining room; Physical therapy room; Activities room; Barber/Beauty shop; Occupational therapy room.
Activities Arts & crafts; Cards; Games; Reading groups; Prayer groups; Movies; Shopping trips; Social/Cultural gatherings.

Atlantacare Convalescent Center*
304 5th Ave, Decatur, GA, 30030
(404) 373-6231
Admin Roy Carter.
Licensure Intermediate care. *Beds* 103.
Certified Medicaid.

Beverly Manor Convalescent Center
2787 N Decatur Rd, Decatur, GA, 30033
(404) 292-0626
Admin Donna W Huffstutler. *Medical Dir/Dir of Nursing* Dr J Tabatabai; Regina Ford.
Licensure Skilled care. *Beds* SNF 73. *Certified* Medicaid; Medicare.
Owner Proprietary Corp (Beverly Enterprises).
Admissions Requirements Medical examination.
Staff Physicians; RNs; LPNs; Orderlies; Nurses aides; Physical therapists; Occupational therapists; Speech therapists; Activities coordinators; Dietitians; Ophthalmologists.
Facilities Dining room; Physical therapy room; Activities room; Crafts room; Laundry room; Barber/Beauty shop.

Activities Arts & crafts; Cards; Games; Reading groups; Prayer groups; Movies; Shopping trips; Social/Cultural gatherings.

DeKalb General Skilled Nursing Unit
2701 N Decatur Rd, Decatur, GA, 30033
(404) 297-5458
Admin Naomi Harman. *Medical Dir/Dir of Nursing* John A Harrel MD; Pamela Koen.
Licensure Skilled care. *Beds* 50. *Certified* Medicaid; Medicare.
Owner Nonprofit organization/foundation.
Admissions Requirements Medical examination; Physician's request.
Staff RNs 7 (ft), 7 (pt); LPNs 1 (ft), 1 (pt); Nurses aides 12 (ft), 11 (pt); Physical therapists 1 (ft); Recreational therapists 1 (ft); Occupational therapists 1 (ft); Speech therapists 1 (ft); Activities coordinators 1 (ft); Dietitians 1 (ft); Ophthalmologists 1 (pt); Podiatrists 1 (ft).
Facilities Dining room; Physical therapy room; Activities room; Chapel; Crafts room; Barber/Beauty shop.
Activities Arts & crafts; Cards; Games; Reading groups; Prayer groups; Movies; Shopping trips; Social/Cultural gatherings.

Georgia Regional Development Learning Center*
PO Box 32407, Decatur, GA, 30032
(404) 243-2160
Admin Stephen L Watson. *Medical Dir/Dir of Nursing* Tomas Naura MD.
Licensure Intermediate care for mentally retarded. *Beds* 67. *Certified* Medicare.
Admissions Requirements Minimum age 1-17; Medical examination; Physician's request.
Staff Physicians 1 (ft); RNs 3 (ft); LPNs 14 (ft); Orderlies 52 (ft); Physical therapists 1 (ft); Recreational therapists 1 (ft); Occupational therapists 1 (ft); Speech therapists 1 (ft); Activities coordinators 1 (ft); Dietitians 1 (ft); Dentists 1 (ft).
Facilities Dining room; Physical therapy room; Activities room; Chapel; Crafts room; Laundry room; Barber/Beauty shop; Library.
Activities Arts & crafts; Cards; Games; Reading groups; Movies; Shopping trips; Social/Cultural gatherings.

Glenwood Manor*
4115 Glenwood Rd, Decatur, GA, 30032
(404) 284-6414
Admin Lewis Brewer.
Licensure Skilled care. *Beds* 185. *Certified* Medicaid.
Owner Proprietary Corp (Beverly Enterprises).

Harvest Heights Baptist Home Center
3200 Panthersville Rd, Decatur, GA, 30034
(404) 243-8460
Admin Joyce Byars. *Medical Dir/Dir of Nursing* Darlene Greenhill DON.
Licensure Skilled care; Intermediate care. *Certified* Medicaid; Medicare.
Owner Nonprofit Corp (GA Bapt Med Center).
Admissions Requirements Minimum age 18; Medical examination.
Staff Physicians 10 (ft); RNs 5 (ft), 6 (pt); LPNs 7 (ft), 5 (pt); Nurses aides 45 (ft), 12 (pt); Physical therapists 1 (pt); Reality therapists 1 (pt); Recreational therapists 1 (pt); Occupational therapists 1 (pt); Speech therapists 1 (pt); Activities coordinators 2 (ft); Dietitians 2 (ft); Dentists 2 (pt); Ophthalmologists 1 (pt); Podiatrists 2 (pt); Dentist 1 (pt); Social workers 1 (ft).
Affiliation Baptist
Facilities Dining room; Physical therapy room; Activities room; Chapel; Crafts room; Laundry room; Barber/Beauty shop; Library; Patios.
Activities Arts & crafts; Cards; Games; Prayer groups; Movies; Shopping trips; Social/Cultural gatherings.

DEMOREST

Habersham Home*
PO Box 37, Demorest, GA, 30535
(404) 754-2134
Admin John H Bridges Sr.
Licensure Skilled care; Intermediate care. *Beds* 84. *Certified* Medicaid; Medicare.

DONALSONVILLE

Seminole Manor*
PO Box 1006, Donalsonville, GA, 31745
(912) 524-2062
Admin Linda Abbott. *Medical Dir/Dir of Nursing* Dr Jacob Holley.
Licensure Intermediate care. *Beds* 62. *Certified* Medicaid.
Admissions Requirements Medical examination; Physician's request.
Staff RNs 1 (ft); LPNs 5 (ft); Nurses aides 12 (ft); Activities coordinators 1 (ft); Dietitians 1 (ft).
Facilities Dining room; Activities room; Laundry room; Barber/Beauty shop.
Activities Arts & crafts; Cards; Games; Reading groups; Prayer groups; Movies; Shopping trips; Social/Cultural gatherings.

DOUGLAS

Fair Haven Convalescent Home Inc
Box 270, 210 S Coffee Ave, Douglas, GA, 31533
(912) 384-1330
Admin Myrtle A Vickers. *Medical Dir/Dir of Nursing* Calvin Meeks MD; Paula Jewell DON.
Licensure Skilled care; Intermediate care. *Beds* SNF 57; ICF. *Certified* Medicaid.
Owner Proprietary Corp.
Admissions Requirements Medical examination; Physician's request.
Staff Physicians 10 (pt); RNs 3 (ft); LPNs 3 (ft), 2 (pt); Nurses aides 15 (ft), 6 (pt); Physical therapists 1 (pt); Recreational therapists 1 (ft); Speech therapists 1 (pt); Activities coordinators 1 (pt); Dietitians 1 (pt); Ophthalmologists 1 (pt).
Facilities Dining room; Physical therapy room; Activities room; Laundry room; Barber/Beauty shop.
Activities Arts & crafts; Cards; Games; Reading groups; Prayer groups; Movies; Shopping trips.

Shady Acres Convalescent Center
PO Box 1059, Douglas, GA, 31533
(912) 384-7811
Admin Joyce S Suttler. *Medical Dir/Dir of Nursing* Dr Calvin Meeks; Judy O Brigmood RN.
Licensure Skilled care. *Beds* SNF 91. *Certified* Medicaid.
Owner Privately owned.
Admissions Requirements Medical examination; Physician's request.
Facilities Dining room; Physical therapy room; Activities room; Crafts room; Laundry room; Barber/Beauty shop.
Activities Arts & crafts; Cards; Games; Reading groups; Prayer groups; Movies; Shopping trips; Social/Cultural gatherings.

DOUGLASVILLE

Garden Terrace Nursing Center
PO Box 86, Hwy 5, Douglasville, GA, 30134
(912) 942-7111
Admin Cynthia Hendry. *Medical Dir/Dir of Nursing* George Artress.
Licensure Skilled care; Intermediate care. *Beds* 160. *Certified* Medicaid; Medicare.
Owner Proprietary Corp (Beverly Enterprises).
Admissions Requirements Medical examination; Physician's request.

Staff Physicians 5 (pt); RNs 4 (ft), 3 (pt); LPNs 19 (ft), 6 (pt); Nurses aides 64 (ft), 18 (pt); Physical therapists 1 (ft); Speech therapists 1 (pt); Activities coordinators 2 (ft); Dietitians 1 (ft); Dentists 1 (pt); Ophthalmologists 1 (pt); Podiatrists 1 (pt).
Facilities Dining room; Physical therapy room; Activities room; Chapel; Laundry room; Barber/Beauty shop; Library; County book mobile.
Activities Arts & crafts; Cards; Games; Reading groups; Prayer groups; Movies; Shopping trips.

DUBLIN

Dublinaire Nursing Home*
Rte 4, Box 147, Dublin, GA, 31021
(912) 272-7437
Admin Kaye Bracewell.
Licensure Skilled care; Intermediate care. *Beds* 149. *Certified* Medicaid; Medicare.

Laurens County Convalescent Center*
PO Box 549, Dublin, GA, 31041
(912) 272-1666
Admin Mrs Freddie M Webb. *Medical Dir/Dir of Nursing* John A Bell MD.
Licensure Skilled care; Intermediate care. *Beds* 130. *Certified* Medicaid.
Admissions Requirements Physician's request.
Staff Physicians 1 (ft), 10 (pt); RNs 1 (ft), 1 (pt); LPNs 9 (ft), 4 (pt); Orderlies 6 (ft), 4 (pt); Nurses aides 19 (ft), 10 (pt); Physical therapists 1 (pt); Activities coordinators 1 (ft); Dietitians 1 (pt); Dentists 1 (pt); Podiatrists 1 (pt).
Facilities Dining room; Physical therapy room; Activities room; Crafts room; Laundry room; Barber/Beauty shop.
Activities Arts & crafts; Cards; Games; Reading groups; Prayer groups; Shopping trips; Social/Cultural gatherings.

Southern Medical of Dublin Inc*
1634 Telfair St, Dublin, GA, 31021
(912) 272-3220
Admin Larry L Shriver.
Licensure Skilled care; Intermediate care. *Beds* 108. *Certified* Medicaid; Medicare.

EAST POINT

Bonterra Nursing Center
2801 Felton Dr, East Point, GA, 30344
(404) 767-7591
Admin Julie F H Booth. *Medical Dir/Dir of Nursing* Rebecca Langdon DON.
Licensure Skilled care; Intermediate care. *Beds* SNF 118; ICF. *Certified* Medicaid; Medicare.
Owner Proprietary Corp (Southeastern Health Care Inc).
Admissions Requirements Medical examination.
Staff RNs 3 (ft); LPNs 13 (ft), 3 (pt); Nurses aides 45 (ft), 2 (pt); Activities coordinators 2 (ft); Dietitians 1 (pt).
Facilities Dining room; Physical therapy room; Activities room; Laundry room; Barber/Beauty shop; Private dining room.
Activities Arts & crafts; Cards; Games; Reading groups; Prayer groups; Social/Cultural gatherings.

South Fulton Hospital—Extended Care Facility*
1170 Cleveland Ave, East Point, GA, 30044
(404) 763-5000
Admin Frank Conort.
Licensure Skilled care. *Beds* 36. *Certified* Medicare.
Admissions Requirements Medical examination; Physician's request.

Staff RNs 5 (ft), 1 (pt); LPNs 3 (ft), 2 (pt); Nurses aides 11 (ft), 1 (pt); Physical therapists 4 (ft); Speech therapists 1 (ft); Activities coordinators 1 (pt); Dietitians 3 (ft).
Facilities Dining room; Physical therapy room; Activities room; Chapel; Barber/Beauty shop.
Activities Cards; Games; Birthday parties monthly; Parties special holidays.

Ware Avenue Personal Care Home
1662 Ware Ave, East Point, GA, 30344
(404) 767-5874
Admin E L Smith. *Medical Dir/Dir of Nursing* Robert Webster MD; Debbie Bohan DON.
Licensure Personal care home. *Beds* 24. *Certified* Private pay.
Owner Privately owned.
Admissions Requirements Minimum age 30; Medical examination; Physician's request.
Staff Orderlies 2 (ft); Nurses aides 8 (ft); Physical therapists 1 (ft).
Facilities Dining room; Activities room; Laundry room.
Activities Cards; Games; Prayer groups.

EASTMAN

Heart of Georgia Nursing Home
PO Box 816, Eastman, GA, 31023
(912) 374-5571
Admin Clifford Durden. *Medical Dir/Dir of Nursing* Dr D H Conner; Julianne Dunn DON.
Licensure Skilled care; Intermediate care. *Beds* 100. *Certified* Medicaid.
Owner Proprietary Corp.
Admissions Requirements Medical examination; Physician's request.
Staff RNs 2 (ft), 2 (pt); LPNs 8 (ft), 4 (pt); Orderlies 6 (ft), 4 (pt); Nurses aides 26 (ft), 12 (pt); Activities coordinators 1 (ft); Dietitians 1 (ft).
Facilities Dining room; Physical therapy room; Activities room; Crafts room; Laundry room; Barber/Beauty shop.
Activities Arts & crafts; Games; Reading groups; Prayer groups; Movies; Shopping trips.

Middle Georgia Nursing Home
PO Box 159, Eastman, GA, 31023
(912) 374-4733
Admin Willene Dykes. *Medical Dir/Dir of Nursing* Dr David H Conner.
Licensure Skilled care; Intermediate care. *Beds* 100. *Certified* Medicare.
Admissions Requirements Medical examination; Physician's request.
Staff RNs 1 (ft), 1 (pt); LPNs 9 (ft), 3 (pt); Orderlies 5 (ft), 2 (pt); Nurses aides 14 (ft), 4 (pt); Physical therapists 1 (ft); Activities coordinators 1 (ft); Dietitians 1 (ft); Podiatrists 1 (ft).
Facilities Dining room; Physical therapy room; Activities room; Chapel; Crafts room; Laundry room; Barber/Beauty shop.
Activities Arts & crafts; Cards; Games; Reading groups; Prayer groups; Movies; Shopping trips; Social/Cultural gatherings.

EATONTON

Regency Health Care Center*
PO Box 541, Eatonton, GA, 31024
(404) 485-8573
Admin Robert Hudson.
Licensure Skilled care; Intermediate care. *Beds* 92. *Certified* Medicaid; Medicare.
Owner Proprietary Corp (Regency Health Care Centers).

EDISON

Calhoun Nursing Home
PO Box 387, Edison, GA, 31746
(912) 835-2251
Admin Newana C Williams.
Licensure Skilled care; Intermediate care. *Beds* 60. *Certified* Medicaid; Medicare.
Owner Publicly owned.
Admissions Requirements Medical examination; Physician's request.
Facilities Dining room; Physical therapy room; Activities room; Crafts room; Laundry room; Barber/Beauty shop; Library.
Activities Arts & crafts; Cards; Games; Reading groups; Prayer groups; Movies; Shopping trips; Social/Cultural gatherings.

ELBERTON

Nancy Hart Intermediate Care Facility
PO Box 753, Elberton, GA, 30635
(404) 283-3335
Admin Lynn H Blackmon. *Medical Dir/Dir of Nursing* J Daniel McAvoy MD; Judy Albertson.
Licensure Intermediate care. *Beds* ICF 67. *Certified* Medicaid.
Owner Proprietary Corp.
Admissions Requirements Medical examination; Physician's request.
Staff Physicians 1 (ft), 1 (pt); RNs 1 (pt); LPNs 3 (ft), 3 (pt); Orderlies 2 (ft), 1 (pt); Nurses aides 9 (ft), 3 (pt); Physical therapists 1 (ft); Speech therapists 1 (pt); Activities coordinators 1 (ft); Dietitians 5 (ft), 2 (pt); Ophthalmologists 1 (pt); Social services director 1 (ft).
Facilities Dining room; Activities room; Laundry room; Barber/Beauty shop.
Activities Arts & crafts; Games; Reading groups; Prayer groups; Movies; Picnics; Outings.

Heardmont Health Care Center*
Route 6, Box 249, Elberton, GA, 30635
(404) 283-5429
Admin Aubrey T Fleming.
Licensure Skilled care; Intermediate care. *Beds* 60. *Certified* Medicaid; Medicare.
Owner Proprietary Corp (Stuckey Health Care).

Spring Valley Health Care Center
651 Rhodes Dr, Elberton, GA, 30635
(404) 283-3880
Admin Wilma Castellaw. *Medical Dir/Dir of Nursing* Dr M H Arnold; LaVerne Bowdoin RN DON.
Licensure Skilled care; Intermediate care. *Beds* SNF 60; ICF. *Certified* Medicaid.
Owner Privately owned.
Admissions Requirements Medical examination; Physician's request.
Staff Physicians 1 (pt); RNs 1 (ft), 1 (pt); LPNs 4 (ft), 2 (pt); Nurses aides 19 (ft), 5 (pt); Physical therapists 2 (pt); Activities coordinators 1 (ft), 1 (pt); Dietitians 1 (pt); Ophthalmologists 1 (pt); Podiatrists 1 (pt).
Facilities Dining room; Physical therapy room; Activities room; Laundry room; Barber/Beauty shop.
Activities Arts & crafts; Reading groups; Prayer groups; Movies; Shopping trips.

ELLIJAY

Gilmer Nursing Home
PO Box 346, Ellijay, GA, 30540
(404) 276-4741
Admin John Downs. *Medical Dir/Dir of Nursing* Robert K Bond MD; Joanne Ferguson RN.
Licensure Skilled care. *Beds* SNF 50. *Certified* Medicaid; Medicare.
Owner Nonprofit Corp (GA Bapt Med Center).

Admissions Requirements Medical examination; Physician's request.
Staff Physicians 4 (ft); RNs 1 (ft), 1 (pt); LPNs 6 (ft), 5 (pt); Nurses aides 12 (ft), 7 (pt); Physical therapists 1 (pt); Speech therapists 1 (pt); Activities coordinators 1 (ft); Dietitians 1 (pt).
Languages Spanish (translation available)
Facilities Dining room; Physical therapy room; Activities room; Chapel; Crafts room; Laundry room; Barber/Beauty shop; Solarium; Large veranda; Fenced 1/2 acre lawn.
Activities Arts & crafts; Cards; Games; Reading groups; Prayer groups; Movies; Shopping trips; Social/Cultural gatherings; Bingo; Aerobics; Gardening; Music.

EVANS

Evans Health Care*
PO Box 338, N Belair Rd, Evans, GA, 30809
(404) 863-7514
Admin John Pulliam.
Beds 120.
Owner Proprietary Corp (Stuckey Health Care).

FAIRBURN

Fairburn Health Care Center
178 W Campbellton St, Fairburn, GA, 30213
(404) 964-1320
Admin Patricia Doss. *Medical Dir/Dir of Nursing* Stanley Gregoroff MD; Pamela Howell DON.
Licensure Skilled care; Intermediate care. *Beds* SNF 120; ICF. *Certified* Medicaid; Medicare.
Admissions Requirements Medical examination; Physician's request.
Staff Physicians 3 (ft); RNs 3 (ft); LPNs 10 (ft), 2 (pt); Orderlies 3 (ft); Nurses aides 40 (ft); Physical therapists 1 (ft); Speech therapists 1 (pt); Activities coordinators 1 (ft); Dietitians 1 (ft).
Facilities Dining room; Physical therapy room; Activities room; Laundry room; Barber/Beauty shop.
Activities Arts & crafts; Games; Reading groups; Prayer groups; Movies.

FITZGERALD

Fitzgerald Nursing Home*
Rte 1, Box 22, Fitzgerald, GA, 31750
(912) 423-4361
Admin Michael A Norkus.
Licensure Skilled care; Intermediate care. *Beds* 150. *Certified* Medicaid; Medicare.

Life Care Center Inc*
PO Box 1289, Fitzgerald, GA, 31750
(912) 423-4353
Admin Edward M Coop. *Medical Dir/Dir of Nursing* Dr Roy Johnson.
Licensure Skilled care; Intermediate care. *Beds* 167. *Certified* Medicaid; Medicare.
Owner Proprietary Corp (Stuckey Health Care).
Staff RNs 1 (ft), 5 (pt); LPNs 20 (ft), 10 (pt); Orderlies 3 (ft), 3 (pt); Nurses aides 40 (ft), 10 (pt); Physical therapists 2 (pt); Occupational therapists 1 (pt); Speech therapists 1 (pt); Activities coordinators 2 (ft); Dietitians 1 (ft); Dentists 1 (pt); Ophthalmologists 1 (pt); Podiatrists 1 (pt).
Facilities Dining room; Physical therapy room; Activities room; Crafts room; Laundry room; Barber/Beauty shop.
Activities Arts & crafts; Games; Reading groups; Prayer groups; Movies; Shopping trips; Social/Cultural gatherings.

FOLKSTON

Mullis Manor II
401 N Okefenokee, Folkston, GA, 31534
(912) 496-7396
Admin Barbara Aldridge. *Medical Dir/Dir of Nursing* Dr Addison; Mary Davis.
Licensure Intermediate care. *Beds* 92.
Certified Medicaid.
Owner Privately owned.
Staff Physicians 1 (ft); RNs 1 (ft), 1 (pt); LPNs 7 (ft), 2 (pt); Orderlies 3 (ft); Nurses aides 28 (ft), 2 (pt); Physical therapists 1 (ft); Activities coordinators 1 (ft); Dietitians 1 (ft); Ophthalmologists 1 (pt).
Facilities Dining room; Physical therapy room; Activities room; Laundry room; Barber/Beauty shop.
Activities Arts & crafts; Games; Reading groups; Shopping trips; Church groups.

FORSYTH

Forsyth Nursing Home*
PO Box 1067, Forsyth, GA, 31029
(912) 994-5671
Admin Kate Cotton. *Medical Dir/Dir of Nursing* Dr A W Bramblett.
Licensure Skilled care; Intermediate care. *Beds* 72. *Certified* Medicaid.
Admissions Requirements Medical examination; Physician's request.
Staff Physicians 7 (pt); RNs 1 (ft), 1 (pt); LPNs 6 (ft), 2 (pt); Nurses aides 17 (ft), 3 (pt); Physical therapists 1 (ft), 1 (pt); Recreational therapists 1 (ft); Activities coordinators 1 (ft).
Facilities Dining room; Physical therapy room; Activities room; Chapel; Crafts room; Laundry room; Barber/Beauty shop; Library.
Activities Arts & crafts; Cards; Games; Reading groups; Prayer groups; Movies; Shopping trips; Social/Cultural gatherings.

Hilltop Nursing Home
Rte 2, Box 619, Forsyth, GA, 31029
(912) 994-5662
Admin Rosalyn M Harbuck. *Medical Dir/Dir of Nursing* Rachel Garrison DON.
Licensure Skilled care; Intermediate care. *Beds* SNF 83; ICF. *Certified* Medicaid.
Owner Proprietary Corp.
Admissions Requirements Medical examination; Physician's request.
Staff Physicians 6 (pt); RNs 1 (ft), 2 (pt); LPNs 6 (ft), 6 (pt); Orderlies 5 (ft), 2 (pt); Nurses aides 25 (ft), 2 (pt); Physical therapists 1 (pt); Activities coordinators 2 (ft); Dietitians 1 (pt); Dentists 1 (pt); Ophthalmologists 1 (pt).
Facilities Dining room; Physical therapy room; Activities room; Crafts room; Laundry room; Barber/Beauty shop.
Activities Arts & crafts; Cards; Games; Prayer groups; Movies; Shopping trips; Social/Cultural gatherings.

FORT GAINES

Fort Gaines Nursing Home
PO Box 160, Fort Gaines, GA, 31751
(912) 768-2521
Admin Gayle Calhoun NHA. *Medical Dir/Dir of Nursing* Homer P Wood MD; Bob Espy RN DON.
Licensure Skilled care; Intermediate care. *Beds* SNF 21; ICF 28. *Certified* Medicaid; Medicare.
Owner Proprietary Corp (Healthcare Management).
Admissions Requirements Minimum age 16; Medical examination; Physician's request.
Staff Physicians; RNs; LPNs; Orderlies; Nurses aides; Physical therapists; Recreational therapists; Speech therapists; Activities coordinators; Dietitians; Dentists; Ophthalmologists; Podiatrists.

Facilities Dining room; Physical therapy room; Activities room; Barber/Beauty shop.
Activities Arts & crafts; Cards; Games; Reading groups; Prayer groups; Movies; Shopping trips; Social/Cultural gatherings.

FORT OGLETHORPE

Fort Oglethorpe Nursing Center*
528 Battlefield Pkwy, Fort Oglethorpe, GA, 30742
(404) 861-5154
Admin Martha Q Dunn.
Licensure Intermediate care. *Beds* 120.

Hutcheson Medical Center Extended Care Unit
200 Gross Crescent, Fort Oglethorpe, GA, 30742
(404) 866-2121
Admin Pamela C Richards. *Medical Dir/Dir of Nursing* Dr Leroy Serrill.
Licensure Skilled care. *Beds* SNF 25. *Certified* Medicaid; Medicare.
Admissions Requirements Medical examination; Physician's request.
Staff RNs 3 (ft); LPNs 4 (ft), 1 (pt); Nurses aides 9 (ft); Physical therapists 1 (ft); Activities coordinators 1 (ft); Dietitians 1 (ft); Dentist 1 (ft).
Facilities Dining room; Physical therapy room; Activities room; Chapel; Crafts room.
Activities Arts & crafts; Cards; Games; Reading groups; Prayer groups.

FORT VALLEY

Fort Valley Health Care Center
PO Box 1237, Fort Valley, GA, 31030
(912) 825-2031
Admin Carolyn J Wilson. *Medical Dir/Dir of Nursing* Dr Daniel E Nathan; Martha Martin RN DON.
Licensure Skilled care; Intermediate care. *Beds* 75. *Certified* Medicaid.
Owner Proprietary Corp (Stuckey Health Care).
Admissions Requirements Medical examination; Physician's request.
Staff RNs 2 (ft), 3 (pt); LPNs 7 (ft), 4 (pt); Orderlies 6 (ft), 3 (pt); Nurses aides 15 (ft), 9 (pt); Activities coordinators 1 (ft).
Facilities Dining room; Physical therapy room; Activities room; Laundry room; Barber/Beauty shop.
Activities Reading groups; Prayer groups; Movies; Entertainment groups; Religious programs.

FRANKLIN

Franklin Health Care Center
PO Box 472, Franklin, GA, 30217
(404) 675-6674
Admin Jeanette Hammond. *Medical Dir/Dir of Nursing* J L Robinson MD; Reita Pope RN.
Licensure Skilled care; Intermediate care. *Beds* 78. *Certified* Medicaid.
Owner Proprietary Corp.
Admissions Requirements Medical examination; Physician's request.
Staff Physicians 10 (pt); RNs 3 (ft), 1 (pt); LPNs 7 (ft), 5 (pt); Nurses aides 22 (ft), 3 (pt); Physical therapists 1 (ft), 1 (pt); Occupational therapists 1 (pt); Speech therapists 1 (pt); Activities coordinators 2 (ft); Dietitians 1 (ft), 1 (pt); Dentists 1 (pt); Ophthalmologists 1 (pt); Podiatrists 1 (pt).
Facilities Dining room; Physical therapy room; Activities room; Laundry room; Barber/Beauty shop; Library.
Activities Arts & crafts; Cards; Games; Reading groups; Prayer groups; Movies; Shopping trips; Social/Cultural gatherings.

GAINESVILLE

Bell-Minor Home Inc*
447 Bradford St NW, Gainesville, GA, 30505
(404) 532-2066
Admin Doris G Bell.
Licensure Skilled care; Intermediate care. *Beds* 92. *Certified* Medicaid; Medicare.

Camelot Care Intermediate Care Facility
Rte 6, Box 471, Gainesville, GA, 30506
(404) 983-3771
Admin Jo Stephens. *Medical Dir/Dir of Nursing* David N Westfall MD.
Licensure Intermediate care. *Beds* ICF 60. *Certified* Medicaid.
Owner Privately owned.
Admissions Requirements Medical examination.
Staff Physicians 1 (pt); RNs 1 (ft); LPNs 3 (ft), 2 (pt); Nurses aides 16 (ft); Activities coordinators 1 (ft); Dietitians 1 (pt).
Facilities Dining room; Activities room; Crafts room; Laundry room; Barber/Beauty shop.
Activities Arts & crafts; Games; Movies; Shopping trips.

Gainesville Health Care Center*
Box JJ, Dawsonville Hwy, Gainesville, GA, 30501
(404) 536-9835
Admin Jonathan Hitt. *Medical Dir/Dir of Nursing* Terry Jones MD.
Licensure Intermediate care. *Beds* 100. *Certified* Medicaid.
Staff RNs 2 (ft), 1 (pt); LPNs 8 (ft), 1 (pt); Orderlies 1 (ft); Nurses aides 36 (ft); Physical therapists 1 (ft); Recreational therapists 1 (ft); Activities coordinators 1 (ft); Dietitians 1 (ft).
Facilities Dining room; Physical therapy room; Activities room; Chapel; Crafts room; Laundry room; Barber/Beauty shop; Library.
Activities Arts & crafts; Cards; Games; Reading groups; Movies; Shopping trips; Social/Cultural gatherings; Church groups.

Lakeshore Heights Nursing Care Center
PO Box D, Gainesville, GA, 30501
(404) 536-3391
Admin Brenda C Newhart.
Licensure Skilled care; Intermediate care. *Beds* 104. *Certified* Medicaid.
Owner Proprietary Corp.
Admissions Requirements Females only; Medical examination.
Staff Physicians 1 (pt); RNs 3 (ft); LPNs 11 (ft); Nurses aides 34 (ft), 2 (pt); Activities coordinators 1 (ft).
Facilities Dining room; Physical therapy room; Activities room; Laundry room; Barber/Beauty shop.
Activities Games; Reading groups; Prayer groups.

Lanier North Intermediate Care Facility*
103 Clarks Branch Rd, Gainesville, GA, 30501
(404) 534-3565
Admin Jack Head.
Licensure Intermediate care. *Beds* 46. *Certified* Medicaid.

GIBSON

Gibson Rest & Convalescent Home*
Beall Springs Rd, Gibson, GA, 30810
(404) 598-3201
Admin J Dwight Todd.
Licensure Skilled care; Intermediate care. *Beds* 104. *Certified* Medicaid; Medicare.

GLENVILLE

Glenvue Nursing Home
721 N Main St, Glenville, GA, 30427
(912) 654-2138
Admin Dale P Dutton. *Medical Dir/Dir of Nursing* Charles H Drake MD; Betty Durrence RN DON.
Licensure Skilled care; Intermediate care. *Beds* SNF; ICF 160. *Certified* Medicaid; Medicare.
Owner Proprietary Corp.
Admissions Requirements Medical examination; Physician's request.
Staff Physicians 1 (pt); RNs 3 (ft), 1 (pt); LPNs 14 (ft), 3 (pt); Orderlies 10 (ft), 4 (pt); Nurses aides 28 (ft), 8 (pt); Physical therapists 1 (ft), 2 (pt); Reality therapists 1 (pt); Activities coordinators 1 (ft); Dietitians 1 (ft), 1 (pt); Ophthalmologists 1 (pt).
Facilities Dining room; Physical therapy room; Activities room; Chapel; Laundry room; Barber/Beauty shop; Library.
Activities Arts & crafts; Cards; Games; Reading groups; Prayer groups; Movies; Shopping trips; Social/Cultural gatherings.

GLENWOOD

Conner Nursing Home
PO Box 618, Glenwood, GA, 30428-0618
(912) 523-5597
Admin Peggy Yarborough.
Licensure Skilled care; Intermediate care. *Beds* 62. *Certified* Medicaid; Medicare.

GRACEWOOD

Gracewood Developmental Center*
Gracewood State Hospital, Division B, Gracewood, GA, 30812
(404) 790-2254
Admin W Martin Peterson.
Beds 596.

Gracewood Nursing Home*
Unit 9, Bldg 76, Ward 1-2, Gracewood, GA, 30812
(404) 30812
Admin Martin Peterson.
Beds 84.

Gracewood State School & Hospital
Gracewood State Hospital, Division A, Gracewood, GA, 30812
(404) 790-2030
Admin Joanne P Miklas PhD. *Medical Dir/Dir of Nursing* Donald Dunagan MD; Sharon Anthonis RN DON.
Licensure Skilled care; Intermediate care for mentally retarded. *Beds* SNF 56; ICF/MR 600. *Certified* Medicaid.
Owner Publicly owned.
Admissions Requirements Mentally retarded & residents of east region of Georgia.
Staff Physicians 8 (ft); RNs 26 (ft); LPNs 79 (ft); Nurses aides 611 (ft); Physical therapists 3 (ft); Recreational therapists 18 (ft); Occupational therapists 9 (ft); Speech therapists 11 (ft); Dietitians 6 (ft); Podiatrists 1 (ft).
Facilities Dining room; Physical therapy room; Activities room; Chapel; Crafts room; Laundry room; Barber/Beauty shop.
Activities Arts & crafts; Movies; Shopping trips; Social/Cultural gatherings; Individualized developmental training programs.

GRAY

Gray Nursing Home*
Dolly St, PO Box 175, Gray, GA, 31032
(912) 986-3151
Admin Mildred J Jiles. *Medical Dir/Dir of Nursing* H B Jones Jr MD.

Licensure Skilled care; Intermediate care. *Beds* 58. *Certified* Medicaid.
Staff Physicians 2 (pt); RNs 1 (ft), 1 (pt); LPNs 4 (ft), 1 (pt); Orderlies 2 (ft); Nurses aides 12 (ft), 2 (pt); Physical therapists 1 (pt); Activities coordinators 1 (ft); Dietitians 1 (ft); Dentists 1 (pt); Podiatrists 1 (pt).
Facilities Dining room; Physical therapy room; Activities room; Laundry room.
Activities Arts & crafts; Cards; Games; Reading groups; Prayer groups; Movies; Shopping trips; Social/Cultural gatherings.

Lynn Haven Nursing Home*
PO Box 356, Rte 1, Box 62, Gray, GA, 31032
(912) 986-3196
Admin William Repzynski.
Licensure Skilled care; Intermediate care. *Beds* 104. *Certified* Medicaid; Medicare.

GREENVILLE

Alvista Care Home Inc
PO Box 129, Greenville, GA, 30222
(404) 672-4241
Admin Aubrey P Green. *Medical Dir/Dir of Nursing* James W Smith Jr MD; Laura Edwards RN DON.
Licensure Intermediate care. *Beds* ICF 113. *Certified* Medicaid.
Owner Privately owned.
Admissions Requirements Medical examination; Physician's request.
Staff Physicians 1 (ft); RNs 2 (ft); LPNs 6 (ft), 1 (pt); Nurses aides 21 (ft), 4 (pt); Activities coordinators 1 (ft); Dietitians 1 (pt).
Facilities Dining room; Physical therapy room; Activities room; Chapel; Crafts room; Laundry room; Barber/Beauty shop.
Activities Arts & crafts; Cards; Games; Reading groups; Prayer groups; Movies; Shopping trips.

GRIFFIN

Brightmoor Medical Care Home*
Rte 3, Box 119M, Griffin, GA, 30223
(404) 228-8599
Admin R H Monkus.
Licensure Skilled care; Intermediate care. *Beds* 133. *Certified* Medicaid; Medicare.

Living Center of Griffin*
415 Airport Rd, Griffin, GA, 30223
(404) 227-8636
Admin Larry W Lawrence. *Medical Dir/Dir of Nursing* Kenneth Reynolds MD.
Licensure Skilled care; Intermediate care. *Beds* 146. *Certified* Medicaid; Medicare.
Staff Physicians 1 (pt); RNs 2 (ft), 1 (pt); LPNs 12 (ft), 2 (pt); Nurses aides 43 (ft), 4 (pt); Physical therapists 1 (pt); Reality therapists 1 (pt); Activities coordinators 1 (ft); Dietitians 1 (pt); Dentists 1 (pt); Ophthalmologists 1 (pt); Podiatrists 1 (pt).
Facilities Dining room; Physical therapy room; Activities room; Chapel; Crafts room; Laundry room; Barber/Beauty shop.
Activities Arts & crafts; Games; Reading groups; Prayer groups; Movies; Shopping trips.

Spalding Convalescent Center
619 Northside Dr, Griffin, GA, 30223
(404) 228-4517
Admin Ronda S Sumner. *Medical Dir/Dir of Nursing* Dr C C Releford; Marie Cody RN.
Licensure Skilled care; Intermediate care. *Beds* 69. *Certified* Medicaid.
Owner Proprietary Corp.
Admissions Requirements Medical examination.
Staff Physicians 1 (ft); RNs 2 (ft); LPNs 5 (ft), 2 (pt); Orderlies 1 (ft); Nurses aides 26 (ft), 2 (pt); Physical therapists 1 (pt); Activities coordinators 1 (ft); Dietitians 1 (ft).

Facilities Dining room; Physical therapy room; Activities room; Laundry room; Barber/Beauty shop.
Activities Arts & crafts; Games; Reading groups; Prayer groups; Movies.

HARTWELL

Hart Care Center
PO Box 766, 127 Fairview Ave, Hartwell, GA, 30643
(404) 376-7121
Admin Theresa Boteler. *Medical Dir/Dir of Nursing* L G Cacchioli; Susan Sanders DON.
Licensure Skilled care. *Beds* SNF 117. *Certified* Medicaid.
Owner Proprietary Corp.
Admissions Requirements Medical examination; Physician's request.
Staff Physicians 1 (pt); RNs 2 (ft), 1 (pt); LPNs 5 (ft), 3 (pt); Orderlies 4 (ft), 2 (pt); Nurses aides 30 (ft), 10 (pt); Physical therapists 1 (pt); Speech therapists 1 (pt); Activities coordinators 1 (ft); Dietitians 1 (pt).
Facilities Dining room; Physical therapy room; Activities room; Crafts room; Laundry room; Barber/Beauty shop.
Activities Arts & crafts; Cards; Games; Reading groups; Prayer groups; Movies; Social/Cultural gatherings.

Heritage Inn of Hartwell*
108 Cade St, Hartwell, GA, 30643
(404) 376-3185
Admin Susan Walters. *Medical Dir/Dir of Nursing* L C Cauhioli.
Licensure Skilled care; Intermediate care. *Beds* 92. *Certified* Medicaid; Medicare.
Admissions Requirements Physician's request.
Staff Physicians 5 (pt); RNs 1 (ft), 2 (pt); LPNs 8 (ft), 1 (pt); Orderlies 5 (ft), 3 (pt); Nurses aides 15 (ft), 12 (pt); Physical therapists 1 (pt); Activities coordinators 1 (ft); Dietitians 1 (pt); Dentists 1 (pt).
Facilities Dining room; Activities room; Crafts room; Laundry room; Barber/Beauty shop.
Activities Arts & crafts; Cards; Games; Movies; Shopping trips; Social/Cultural gatherings.

HAWKINSVILLE

Pinewood Manor Inc*
PO Box 587, Hawkinsville, GA, 31036
(912) 892-7171
Admin Earl Ray Tripp.
Licensure Intermediate care. *Beds* 102. *Certified* Medicaid.

HAZELHURST

Chapman Convalescent Home*
PO Box 754, Hazelhurst, GA, 31539
(912) 375-2539
Admin Phil Chapman.
Licensure Skilled care; Intermediate care. *Beds* 73. *Certified* Medicaid; Medicare.

HIAWASSEE

Towns County Nursing Home
PO Box 509, Main Street, Hiawassee, GA, 30546
(404) 896-2231
Admin Donald C Novak. *Medical Dir/Dir of Nursing* Robert F Stahlkuppe MD; June Gifford RN.
Licensure Skilled care; Intermediate care. *Beds* SNF 30; ICF. *Certified* Medicaid; Medicare.
Owner Publicly owned.
Admissions Requirements Medical examination; Physician's request.

Staff Physicians 4 (ft); RNs 1 (ft), 2 (pt); LPNs 3 (ft), 2 (pt); Orderlies 3 (ft), 2 (pt); Nurses aides 6 (ft), 6 (pt); Physical therapists 2 (pt); Activities coordinators 1 (pt); Dietitians 1 (pt); Social services 2 (pt).
Facilities Dining room; Physical therapy room; Activities room; Chapel; Crafts room; Laundry room; Barber/Beauty shop; Library.
Activities Arts & crafts; Cards; Games; Prayer groups; Movies; Shopping trips; Social/Cultural gatherings.

HIGH SHOALS

Family Life Enrichment*
Highshoals Rd, Biox 37A, High Shoals, GA, 30645
(404) 769-7738
Admin Magda D Bennett.
Beds 100.

HOMERVILLE

Mullis Manor Inc*
410 Sweat St, Homerville, GA, 31634
(912) 487-5328
Admin Barbara Mullis.
Licensure Intermediate care. *Beds* 92. *Certified* Medicaid.

JASPER

Grandview Health Care Center*
208 S Main St, Jasper, GA, 30143
(404) 692-5123
Admin Patton W Childers.
Licensure Intermediate care. *Beds* 45. *Certified* Medicare.

Pickens General Nursing Center
1319 Church St, Jasper, GA, 30143
(404) 692-2441
Admin Jerry Jummel. *Medical Dir/Dir of Nursing* Dr G H Perrow.
Licensure Skilled care. *Beds* SNF 60; ICF. *Certified* Medicaid.
Owner Nonprofit organization/foundation.
Staff Physicians 5 (pt); RNs 1 (ft); LPNs 8 (ft) 2 (pt); Orderlies 2 (ft), 1 (pt); Nurses aides 26 (ft), 6 (pt); Nurses aides 1 (pt); Ophthalmologists 1 (pt).
Facilities Dining room; Physical therapy room; Chapel; Laundry room; Barber/Beauty shop.

JEFFERSONVILLE

Spring Valley Intermediate Care Facility*
PO Box 308, Jeffersonville, GA, 31044
(912) 945-3255
Admin Marcelle Hiatt.
Licensure Intermediate care. *Beds* 131. *Certified* Medicaid.
Owner Proprietary Corp (Brian Center Management Corp).

JENKINSBURG

Westbury Nursing Home*
PO Box 38, Jenkinsburg, GA, 30234
(404) 775-7832
Admin James R Westbury.
Licensure Skilled care; Intermediate care. *Beds* 197. *Certified* Medicaid.

JESUP

Altamaha Convalescent Center Inc
PO Box 807, 1311 W Cherry St, Jesup, GA, 31545
(912) 427-7792
Admin Bobbye Richardson. *Medical Dir/Dir of Nursing* Lorene Howard; Grace McCullough.

Licensure Intermediate care. *Beds* 62. *Certified* Medicaid.
Admissions Requirements Medical examination; Physician's request.
Staff RNs; LPNs; Orderlies; Nurses aides; Physical therapists; Recreational therapists; Activities coordinators; Dietitians; Ophthalmologists.
Facilities Dining room; Physical therapy room; Activities room; Crafts room; Laundry room; Barber/Beauty shop.
Activities Arts & crafts; Cards; Games; Reading groups; Prayer groups; Movies; Shopping trips; Social/Cultural gatherings.

Jesup Manor Nursing Center
PO Box 917, 1090 W Orange St, Jesup, GA, 31545
(912) 427-6858
Admin Sabra Priester RN. *Medical Dir/Dir of Nursing* Charlotte Heirs RN.
Licensure Skilled care; Intermediate care. *Beds* 90. *Certified* Medicaid.
Staff RNs 1 (ft), 2 (pt); LPNs 10 (ft), 3 (pt); Orderlies 1 (ft); Nurses aides 22 (ft), 5 (pt); Physical therapists 1 (pt); Recreational therapists 1 (ft); Speech therapists 1 (pt); Activities coordinators 1 (ft); Dietitians 1 (ft).
Facilities Dining room; Physical therapy room; Activities room; Crafts room; Laundry room; Barber/Beauty shop.
Activities Arts & crafts; Cards; Games; Reading groups; Prayer groups; Movies; Shopping trips; Social/Cultural gatherings.

Jesup Rest-A-While Nursing Home*
PO Box 827, Jesup, GA, 31545
(912) 427-6873
Admin Madeline Houston. *Medical Dir/Dir of Nursing* Dr R A Pumpelly Jr.
Licensure Skilled care; Intermediate care. *Beds* 72. *Certified* Medicaid.
Admissions Requirements Medical examination.
Staff Physicians 1 (ft); RNs 1 (ft), 1 (pt); LPNs 8 (ft), 1 (pt); Orderlies 1 (pt); Nurses aides 16 (ft), 4 (pt); Physical therapists 1 (ft); Activities coordinators 1 (ft); Dietitians 1 (pt); Dentists 1 (pt).
Facilities Dining room; Physical therapy room; Activities room; Crafts room; Laundry room; Barber/Beauty shop.
Activities Arts & crafts; Games; Reading groups; Prayer groups; Movies; Shopping trips.

JONESBORO

Styrons Arrowhead Nursing Center*
239 Arrowhead Blvd, Jonesboro, GA, 30236
(404) 478-3013
Admin Marian Styron.
Licensure Skilled care; Intermediate care. *Beds* 116. *Certified* Medicaid.

KENNESAW

Shady Grove Rest Home
1790 Hwy 41 NW, Kennesaw, GA, 30144
(404) 427-7256
Admin James A Ross. *Medical Dir/Dir of Nursing* Robert Townsend.
Licensure Intermediate care. *Beds* 32. *Certified* Medicaid.
Owner Proprietary Corp.
Admissions Requirements Physician's request.
Staff LPNs; Nurses aides; Activities coordinators; Dietitians.
Facilities Dining room; Activities room; Laundry room; Barber/Beauty shop.
Activities Arts & crafts; Cards; Games; Reading groups; Prayer groups; Movies.

KEYSVILLE

Keysville Convalescent & Nursing Center Inc
PO Box 277, Hwy 88, Keysville, GA, 30816
(404) 547-2591
Admin William C Harmon. *Medical Dir/Dir of Nursing* Dr Richard N Moss; Elvie J Harmon.
Licensure Skilled care; Intermediate care. *Beds* 64. *Certified* Medicaid; Medicare.
Owner Proprietary Corp.
Staff Physicians 2 (pt); RNs 2 (ft), 3 (pt); LPNs 4 (ft), 2 (pt); Orderlies 1 (pt); Nurses aides 23 (ft), 2 (pt); Physical therapists 1 (pt); Activities coordinators 1 (ft); Dietitians 1 (pt); Ophthalmologists 1 (pt).

LAFAYETTE

LaFayette Health Care Inc
PO Box 4, Rte 4, LaFayette, GA, 30728
(404) 638-4662
Admin David Currie. *Medical Dir/Dir of Nursing* Paul Shaw; Annie R Ledlow.
Licensure Skilled care; Intermediate care. *Beds* 100. *Certified* Medicaid; Medicare.
Owner Proprietary Corp (Stuckey Health Care).
Admissions Requirements Physician's request.
Staff RNs 2 (ft), 1 (pt); LPNs 7 (ft), 2 (pt); Nurses aides 32 (ft), 7 (pt); Physical therapists 1 (pt); Occupational therapists 1 (pt); Speech therapists 1 (pt); Activities coordinators 1 (ft); Dietitians 1 (pt); Ophthalmologists 1 (pt).
Facilities Dining room; Physical therapy room; Activities room; Laundry room; Barber/Beauty shop.
Activities Arts & crafts; Games; Reading groups; Prayer groups; Movies; Shopping trips.

Shepherd Hills Health Care
Box 647, Lafayette, GA, 30728
(404) 638-4112
Admin Michelle Coker. *Medical Dir/Dir of Nursing* H C Derrick Jr MD; Sonda Plemmons RN.
Licensure Skilled care. *Beds* SNF 106. *Certified* Medicaid.
Owner Proprietary Corp.
Staff RNs 2 (ft); LPNs 10 (ft); Orderlies 5 (ft); Nurses aides 18 (ft); Physical therapists 1 (ft); Recreational therapists 1 (ft); Activities coordinators 1 (ft); Dietitians 1 (ft); Dentists; Ophthalmologists; Podiatrists.
Facilities Dining room; Physical therapy room; Activities room; Chapel; Crafts room; Laundry room; Barber/Beauty shop; Library; Living room; Outside sitting areas.
Activities Arts & crafts; Cards; Games; Reading groups; Prayer groups; Movies; Shopping trips; Social/Cultural gatherings.

LAGRANGE

Florence Hand Home—Skilled Nursing Facility
200 Medical Dr, LaGrange, GA, 30240
(404) 882-1411 ext 5256
Admin Charles L Foster Jr. *Medical Dir/Dir of Nursing* Mark Adams MD; Katie McAlister RN.
Licensure Skilled care; Intermediate care. *Beds* SNF 150; ICF. *Certified* Medicaid; Medicare.
Owner Nonprofit Corp.
Admissions Requirements Medical examination; Physician's request.
Staff RNs 7 (ft); LPNs 21 (ft); Orderlies 2 (ft); Nurses aides 46 (ft); Physical therapists; Recreational therapists 1 (ft); Speech therapists 1 (pt); Activities coordinators 1 (ft); Dietitians; Dentists; Ophthalmologists; Podiatrists 1 (pt).
Facilities Dining room; Physical therapy room; Activities room; Chapel; Crafts room; Laundry room; Barber/Beauty shop; Library.

Activities Arts & crafts; Cards; Games;
Reading groups; Movies; Shopping trips;
Social/Cultural gatherings; Picnics; Patio
luncheons.

LaGrange Medcraft Nursing Home*
PO Box 280, LaGrange, GA, 30241
(404) 882-1405
Admin James L Ambrose.
Licensure Skilled care; Intermediate care. *Beds*
138. *Certified* Medicaid; Medicare.

Negro Old Folks Home Inc*
609 Union St, LaGrange, GA, 30240
(404) 884-9466
Admin Mina B Wood.
Licensure Intermediate care. *Beds* 12.
Certified Medicaid.

Royal Elaine Intermediate Care Facility*
Box 1346, Hogansville Rd, LaGrange, GA,
30241
(404) 882-0121
Admin Eleanor S Neely.
Licensure Intermediate care. *Beds* 116.
Certified Medicaid.

LAKELAND

Lakeland Villa Convalescent Center
W Thigpen Rd, PO Box 86, Lakeland, GA,
31635
(912) 482-2229
Admin John A Nosworthy. *Medical Dir/Dir of
Nursing* Guy Mann MD.
Licensure Skilled care; Intermediate care. *Beds*
62. *Certified* Medicaid; Medicare.
Owner Proprietary Corp (Sunbelt Healthcare
Centers).
Staff Physicians 5 (pt); RNs 1 (ft), 2 (pt);
LPNs 5 (ft), 2 (pt); Orderlies 2 (ft); Nurses
aides 17 (ft), 8 (pt); Physical therapists 1
(pt); Activities coordinators 1 (ft); Dietitians
1 (pt); Podiatrists 1 (pt).
Affiliation Seventh-Day Adventist
Facilities Dining room; Physical therapy
room; Activities room; Laundry room;
Barber/Beauty shop.
Activities Cards; Games; Reading groups;
Prayer groups; Movies.

LAWRENCEVILLE

Medical Arts Health Facility*
213 Scenic Hwy, Lawrenceville, GA, 30245
(404) 963-5275
Admin Pat Tanner. *Medical Dir/Dir of
Nursing* Dr Michael Lipsitt.
Licensure Skilled care; Intermediate care. *Beds*
124. *Certified* Medicaid; Medicare.
Owner Proprietary Corp (Beverly Enterprises).
Admissions Requirements Medical
examination.
Staff Physicians 9 (pt); RNs 3 (ft), 4 (pt);
LPNs 6 (ft), 2 (pt); Nurses aides 29 (ft), 30
(pt); Speech therapists 1 (pt); Activities
coordinators 1 (ft).
Facilities Dining room; Physical therapy
room; Activities room; Chapel; Crafts room;
Laundry room; Barber/Beauty shop.
Activities Arts & crafts; Cards; Games;
Reading groups; Prayer groups; Movies;
Social/Cultural gatherings.

LILBURN

Lilburn Health Care Center
PO Box 848, 788 Indian Trail, Lilburn, GA,
30247
(404) 923-2020
Admin Janice Russell.
Licensure Skilled care; Intermediate care. *Beds*
120. *Certified* Medicaid; Medicare.

LITHONIA

Starcrest of Lithonia*
PO Box 855, Lithonia, GA, 30058
(404) 482-2961
Admin Larry H Athon.
Licensure Skilled care; Intermediate care. *Beds*
117. *Certified* Medicaid.

LOUISVILLE

**Old Capital Inn Convalescent & Nursing
Home***
PO Box 32, Louisville, GA, 30434
(912) 625-3742
Admin Diane Rhodes. *Medical Dir/Dir of
Nursing* W J Revell Sr MD.
Licensure Skilled care; Intermediate care. *Beds*
143. *Certified* Medicaid.
Admissions Requirements Minimum age 16;
Medical examination; Physician's request.
Staff Physicians 6 (pt); RNs 2 (ft); LPNs 8
(ft), 3 (pt); Orderlies 4 (ft); Nurses aides 32
(ft); Physical therapists 1 (pt); Activities
coordinators 2 (ft); Dietitians 1 (ft).
Facilities Dining room; Physical therapy
room; Activities room; Chapel; Crafts room;
Laundry room; Barber/Beauty shop.
Activities Arts & crafts; Cards; Games;
Reading groups; Prayer groups; Movies;
Shopping trips; Social/Cultural gatherings.

LUMBER CITY

Lumber City Healthcare Center
PO Box 188, Lumber City, GA, 31549
(912) 363-4356
Admin Jill Bowen. *Medical Dir/Dir of Nursing*
B Macalalad MD; Sarah Quinn DON.
Licensure Skilled care; Intermediate care. *Beds*
86. *Certified* Medicaid.
Owner Proprietary Corp (Brian Center
Management Corp).
Staff Physicians; RNs; LPNs; Orderlies;
Nurses aides; Physical therapists;
Recreational therapists; Speech therapists;
Activities coordinators; Dietitians;
Ophthalmologists.
Facilities Dining room; Physical therapy
room; Activities room; Crafts room; Laundry
room; Barber/Beauty shop.
Activities Arts & crafts; Cards; Games;
Reading groups; Prayer groups; Movies;
Shopping trips; Social/Cultural gatherings.

LYONS

Toombs Nursing & Intermediate Care Home*
100 Oxley Dr, Lyons, GA, 30436
(912) 526-6336
Admin Herbert Conner.
Licensure Intermediate care. *Beds* 104.
Certified Medicaid.

MACON

Bel Arbor Health Care Facility
3468 Napier Ave, Macon, GA, 31204
(912) 474-4464
Admin Martha J Hampton. *Medical Dir/Dir of
Nursing* John P Atkinson MD; Faye Ryle
DON.
Licensure Skilled care; Intermediate care. *Beds*
130. *Certified* Medicaid; Medicare.
Owner Proprietary Corp.
Admissions Requirements Medical
examination.
Staff Physicians 1 (ft), 1 (pt); RNs 2 (ft), 1
(pt); LPNs 9 (ft), 2 (pt); Orderlies 5 (ft), 1
(pt); Nurses aides 84 (ft), 6 (pt); Physical
therapists 1 (ft); Activities coordinators 2
(ft); Dietitians 2 (ft); Ophthalmologists 1
(pt).
Facilities Dining room; Physical therapy
room; Activities room; Crafts room; Laundry
room; Barber/Beauty shop.

Activities Arts & crafts; Cards; Games;
Reading groups; Prayer groups; Movies;
Shopping trips; Social/Cultural gatherings.

Bloomfield Nursing Home
3520 Kenneth Dr, Macon, GA, 31206
(912) 784-1574
Admin Mildred Hollingshed. *Medical Dir/Dir
of Nursing* Robert Nelson MD; Diane
Noble.
Licensure Intermediate care. *Beds* ICF 90.
Certified Medicaid.
Owner Privately owned.
Admissions Requirements Medical
examination.
Staff Physicians 2 (ft), 2 (pt); RNs 1 (ft), 1
(pt); LPNs 4 (ft), 2 (pt); Orderlies 3 (ft), 4
(pt); Nurses aides 17 (ft); Physical therapists
1 (ft), 1 (pt); Recreational therapists 2 (ft);
Occupational therapists 2 (ft); Activities
coordinators 1 (ft); Dietitians 1 (ft), 1 (pt);
Dentists 1 (ft); Ophthalmologists 1 (ft);
Podiatrists 1 (ft); Psychologist 1 (pt); Dentist
1 (pt).
Facilities Dining room; Physical therapy
room; Activities room; Crafts room; Laundry
room; Barber/Beauty shop.
Activities Arts & crafts; Cards; Games;
Reading groups; Prayer groups; Movies;
Shopping trips; Social/Cultural gatherings.

Eastview Nursing Home
3020 Jeffersonville Rd, Macon, GA, 31298
(912) 746-3547
Admin Beverly F Hardison. *Medical Dir/Dir
of Nursing* Robert Buckley MD; Ann Smith
DON.
Licensure Skilled care; Intermediate care. *Beds*
92. *Certified* Medicaid.
Admissions Requirements Minimum age 18.
Staff Physicians 5 (pt); RNs 2 (ft), 2 (pt);
LPNs 12 (ft), 4 (pt); Orderlies 8 (ft), 2 (pt);
Nurses aides 40 (ft), 8 (pt); Physical
therapists 2 (ft), 1 (pt); Recreational
therapists 2 (ft); Occupational therapists 1
(pt); Speech therapists 1 (pt); Activities
coordinators 1 (ft); Dietitians 1 (pt); Dentists
1 (pt); Ophthalmologists 1 (pt); Podiatrists 1
(pt).
Facilities Dining room; Physical therapy
room; Activities room; Crafts room; Laundry
room; Barber/Beauty shop.
Activities Arts & crafts; Cards; Games;
Reading groups; Prayer groups; Movies;
Shopping trips; Social/Cultural gatherings.

Goodwill Nursing Home
4373 Houston Ave, Macon, GA, 31206
(912) 784-1500
Admin Linda G Peachey. *Medical Dir/Dir of
Nursing* William Pound; Diana Harden.
Licensure Intermingled. *Beds* 172. *Certified*
Medicaid.
Owner Proprietary Corp.
Admissions Requirements Medical
examination; Physician's request.
Staff Physicians 1 (pt); RNs 4 (ft), 1 (pt);
LPNs 19 (ft), 8 (pt); Orderlies 3 (ft), 1 (pt);
Nurses aides 51 (ft), 8 (pt); Physical
therapists 1 (pt); Activities coordinators 2
(ft); Dietitians 1 (ft); Ophthalmologists 1
(pt).
Facilities Dining room; Physical therapy
room; Activities room; Chapel; Crafts room;
Laundry room; Barber/Beauty shop.
Activities Arts & crafts; Cards; Games;
Reading groups; Prayer groups; Movies;
Shopping trips; Social/Cultural gatherings.

Hospitality Care Center of Macon*
505 Coliseum Dr, Macon, GA, 31201
(912) 743-8687
Admin Wesley Vincent.
Licensure Skilled care; Intermediate care. *Beds*
100. *Certified* Medicaid; Medicare.

Macon Health Care Center
3051 Whiteside Rd, Macon, GA, 31206
(912) 788-1421
Admin Michael R Little. *Medical Dir/Dir of Nursing* Dr William Brooks; Pat Hall Tucker DON.
Licensure Skilled care. *Beds* SNF 144. *Certified* Medicaid.
Owner Proprietary Corp.
Staff RNs 3 (ft), 1 (pt); LPNs 13 (ft), 4 (pt); Orderlies 9 (ft); Nurses aides 39 (ft), 5 (pt); Physical therapists 1 (ft); Activities coordinators 2 (ft); Dietitians 1 (ft).
Facilities Dining room; Physical therapy room; Activities room; Barber/Beauty shop; Outdoor recreation area.
Activities Arts & crafts; Cards; Games; Prayer groups; Shopping trips; Social/Cultural gatherings; Fishing; Pet therapy; Morning exercise; Sing-along; Cooking groups.

Memorial Intermediate Care Home*
1509 Cedar Ave, Macon, GA, 31208
(912) 743-4678
Admin Georgia Evans. *Medical Dir/Dir of Nursing* Dr C W James.
Licensure Intermediate care. *Beds* 68. *Certified* Medicaid.
Staff RNs 1 (pt); LPNs 4 (ft), 3 (pt); Orderlies 3 (ft); Nurses aides 9 (ft), 9 (pt); Physical therapists 1 (pt); Reality therapists 1 (pt); Recreational therapists 1 (ft); Occupational therapists 1 (pt); Speech therapists 1 (pt); Activities coordinators 1 (ft); Dietitians 1 (pt).
Facilities Dining room; Physical therapy room; Activities room; Crafts room; Laundry room; Barber/Beauty shop.
Activities Arts & crafts; Cards; Games; Reading groups; Prayer groups; Shopping trips; Social/Cultural gatherings.

North Macon Health Care
2255 Anthony Rd, Macon, GA, 31204
(912) 743-9347
Admin Susan Doreen Hansard. *Medical Dir/Dir of Nursing* Clyatt W James; Mary Dunwody.
Licensure Skilled care. *Beds* SNF 228. *Certified* Medicaid; Medicare.
Owner Proprietary Corp.
Admissions Requirements Physician's request.
Staff Physicians 1 (ft); RNs 4 (ft); LPNs 25 (ft), 2 (pt); Orderlies 10 (ft), 2 (pt); Nurses aides 100 (ft), 7 (pt); Physical therapists 1 (ft); Recreational therapists 3 (ft); Speech therapists 1 (ft); Dietitians 1 (ft); Ophthalmologists 1 (pt).
Languages Sign
Facilities Dining room; Physical therapy room; Activities room; Chapel; Laundry room; Barber/Beauty shop.
Activities Arts & crafts; Cards; Games; Reading groups; Prayer groups; Movies; Shopping trips; Social/Cultural gatherings.

Oak Valley Nursing Home*
2795 Finney Circle, Macon, GA, 31201
(912) 745-4231
Admin Theo Fountain.
Licensure Skilled care; Intermediate care. *Beds* 130. *Certified* Medicaid; Medicare.

Riverside of Macon*
Rte 1, Pate Rd, Macon, GA, 31210
(912) 477-1720
Admin Joseph W Butler. *Medical Dir/Dir of Nursing* Dr J R Fountain.
Licensure Skilled care; Intermediate care. *Beds* 121. *Certified* Medicaid.
Owner Proprietary Corp (Riverside Med Services).
Staff Physicians 2 (pt); RNs 1 (ft), 2 (pt); LPNs 6 (ft), 2 (pt); Orderlies 8 (ft); Nurses aides 40 (ft), 6 (pt); Physical therapists 1 (pt); Activities coordinators 1 (ft); Dietitians 1 (ft), 1 (pt); Dentists 1 (pt); Ophthalmologists 1 (pt); Podiatrists 1 (pt).

Facilities Dining room; Physical therapy room; Activities room; Chapel; Laundry room; Barber/Beauty shop.
Activities Arts & crafts; Games; Prayer groups; Movies; Shopping trips.

Southern Medical of East Macon*
1060 Old Clinton Rd, Macon, GA, 31201
(912) 746-0266
Admin Paul R Noblitt.
Licensure Skilled care; Intermediate care. *Beds* 122. *Certified* Medicaid.

Three Oaks Intermediate Care Home*
PO Box 7531, Macon, GA, 31204
(912) 986-6245
Admin Kenneth A Goings.
Licensure Intermediate care. *Beds* 34. *Certified* Medicaid.

MADISON

Hospitality Care Center
Box 228, Hwy 278, Madison, GA, 30650
(404) 342-3200
Admin Donna W Huffstutler. *Medical Dir/Dir of Nursing* Sheilah Harrison.
Licensure Skilled care. *Beds* SNF 67. *Certified* Medicaid.

MARIETTA

Americana Healthcare Center
4360 Johnson Ferry Pl, Marietta, GA, 30068
(404) 971-5870
Admin Richard St Martin. *Medical Dir/Dir of Nursing* Dr Mannan; Julie Blan DON.
Licensure Skilled care. *Beds* SNF 120. *Certified* Medicare.
Owner Proprietary Corp (Manor Care).
Admissions Requirements Medical examination; Physician's request.
Staff RNs; LPNs; Orderlies; Nurses aides; Physical therapists; Reality therapists; Recreational therapists; Occupational therapists; Speech therapists; Activities coordinators; Dietitians; Podiatrists.
Facilities Dining room; Physical therapy room; Activities room; Chapel; Crafts room; Laundry room; Barber/Beauty shop; Library; Rehabilitative dining area.
Activities Arts & crafts; Cards; Games; Reading groups; Prayer groups; Movies; Shopping trips; Social/Cultural gatherings.

Autumn Breeze Nursing Home*
1480 Sandtown, Box 310, Marietta, GA, 30060
(404) 422-1755
Admin David Morgan. *Medical Dir/Dir of Nursing* George Artress MD.
Licensure Skilled care; Intermediate care. *Beds* 127.
Admissions Requirements Medical examination; Physician's request.
Staff Physicians 13 (ft); RNs 4 (ft), 2 (pt); LPNs 8 (ft), 3 (pt); Orderlies 3 (ft); Nurses aides 45 (ft), 3 (pt); Physical therapists 1 (ft); Recreational therapists 1 (ft); Speech therapists 1 (pt); Activities coordinators 1 (ft); Dietitians 1 (ft).
Facilities Dining room; Physical therapy room; Activities room; Crafts room; Laundry room; Barber/Beauty shop.
Activities Arts & crafts; Cards; Games; Reading groups; Prayer groups; Movies; Shopping trips; Social/Cultural gatherings.

Hillhaven Rehabilitation Convalescent Center
26 Tower Rd, Marietta, GA, 30060
(404) 422-8913
Admin James H Derick.
Licensure Skilled care. *Beds* 146. *Certified* Medicaid; Medicare.
Owner Proprietary Corp (Hillhaven Corp).

Marietta Health Care Center*
85 Saine Rd Southwest, Marietta, GA, 30060
(404) 429-8600
Admin Helen M Besal. *Medical Dir/Dir of Nursing* Gary Cowan MD.
Licensure Skilled care; Intermediate care. *Beds* 119. *Certified* Medicaid; Medicare.
Owner Proprietary Corp (Beverly Enterprises).
Admissions Requirements Medical examination; Physician's request.
Staff RNs 6 (ft), 1 (pt); LPNs 12 (ft), 4 (pt); Orderlies 2 (ft); Nurses aides 35 (ft), 8 (pt); Physical therapists 1 (ft); Speech therapists 1 (pt); Activities coordinators 1 (ft); Dietitians 1 (ft); Dentists 1 (pt); Social workers 1 (ft).
Facilities Dining room; Physical therapy room; Activities room; Crafts room; Barber/Beauty shop; Library.
Activities Arts & crafts; Cards; Games; Reading groups; Prayer groups; Movies; Shopping trips; Social/Cultural gatherings.

Shoreham Convalescent Center*
811 Kennesaw Ave, Marietta, GA, 30060
(404) 422-2451
Admin Beulah Holmberg.
Licensure Skilled care; Intermediate care. *Beds* 118. *Certified* Medicaid; Medicare.

MARSHALLVILLE

The Oaks Nursing Home Inc*
Rte 1, Marshallville, GA, 31057
(912) 967-2223
Admin N Jule Windham.
Licensure Skilled care. *Beds* 48.

MARTINEZ

Forrest Lake Manor Inc
PO Box 11529, 409 Pleasant Home Rd, Martinez, GA, 30907-0529
(404) 863-6030
Admin Thema R Allgood.
Licensure Skilled care; Intermediate care. *Beds* 92. *Certified* Medicaid; Medicare.

MCDONOUGH

Westbury Home*
PO Box 796, McDonough, GA, 30253
(404) 957-9081
Admin Phillip J Westbury.
Licensure Skilled care; Intermediate care. *Beds* 180. *Certified* Medicaid.

MCRAE

McRae Manor Inc*
1104 S 1st Ave, McRae, GA, 31055
(912) 868-6473
Admin Buford T Cook.
Licensure Skilled care; Intermediate care. *Beds* 133. *Certified* Medicaid; Medicare.

METTER

Metter Nursing Home*
PO Box 356, Metter, GA, 30439
(912) 685-5734
Admin William J Byrd.
Licensure Skilled care; Intermediate care. *Beds* 89. *Certified* Medicaid; Medicare.

Pleasant View Nursing Home*
303 Anderson, Box 576, Metter, GA, 30439
(912) 685-2168
Admin Cother Lee Hodges. *Medical Dir/Dir of Nursing* Dr J D Smith.
Licensure Skilled care; Intermediate care. *Beds* SNF 58; ICF 62. *Certified* Medicaid.
Admissions Requirements Medical examination; Physician's request.
Staff Physicians 4 (ft); RNs 1 (ft), 2 (pt); LPNs 9 (ft), 1 (pt); Orderlies 7 (ft); Nurses aides 15 (ft), 7 (pt); Physical therapists 1 (ft);

Activities coordinators 1 (ft); Dietitians 1 (ft); Dentists 1 (ft); Ophthalmologists 1 (ft); Podiatrists 1 (ft).
Facilities Dining room; Physical therapy room; Activities room; Chapel; Crafts room; Laundry room; Barber/Beauty shop.
Activities Arts & crafts; Cards; Games; Reading groups; Prayer groups; Movies; Shopping trips; Social/Cultural gatherings; Class programs; Community affairs.

MIDWAY

Liberty Manor*
PO Box 270, Midway, GA, 31320
(912) 884-3361
Admin Barbara Streetman. *Medical Dir/Dir of Nursing* Whitman Fraser.
Licensure Skilled care; Intermediate care. *Beds* 169. *Certified* Medicaid.
Admissions Requirements Medical examination; Physician's request.
Staff Physicians 3 (ft), 2 (pt); RNs 3 (ft), 1 (pt); LPNs 11 (ft), 3 (pt); Orderlies 6 (ft); Nurses aides 24 (ft), 4 (pt); Physical therapists 1 (ft); Recreational therapists 1 (ft); Activities coordinators 1 (ft); Dietitians 1 (ft); Dentists 1 (ft); Ophthalmologists 1 (ft); Podiatrists 1 (ft).
Facilities Dining room; Physical therapy room; Activities room; Crafts room; Laundry room; Barber/Beauty shop; Library; Mental retardation room for skills teaching.
Activities Arts & crafts; Games; Reading groups; Prayer groups; Movies; Shopping trips; Social/Cultural gatherings.

MILLEDGEVILLE

Allen Hall*
Central State Hospital, Milledgeville, GA, 31062
(912) 453-4145
Admin Lynne F Wright.
Licensure Intermediate care. *Beds* 270. *Certified* Medicare.

Central State Hospital
Milledgeville, GA, 31062
(912) 453-4219
Admin Alice K Paschal. *Medical Dir/Dir of Nursing* James Umberhandt MD.
Licensure Skilled care. *Beds* 236.
Owner Publicly owned.
Admissions Requirements Applicants to this facility must be veterans of a war & disabled by age or physical disability as described on a special physician's certificate.
Staff Physicians 4 (ft); RNs 19 (ft), 2 (pt); LPNs 27 (ft); Nurses aides 130 (ft).
Facilities Dining room; Activities room; Crafts room; Laundry room; Barber/Beauty shop; Library.
Activities Arts & crafts; Cards; Games; Reading groups; Prayer groups; Movies; Shopping trips; Social/Cultural gatherings.

Chaplinwood Nursing Home*
Allen Memorial Dr, Milledgeville, GA, 31061
(912) 452-4596
Admin Troy Anthon.
Licensure Skilled care; Intermediate care. *Beds* 100. *Certified* Medicaid; Medicare.

Green Acres Intermediate Care Facility*
Allen Dr, Milledgeville, GA, 31061
(912) 452-4596
Admin Edward C Nelson.
Licensure Intermediate care. *Beds* 95. *Certified* Medicaid.

Nursing Home Center*
Central State Hospital, Boone Bldg, Milledgeville, GA, 31062
(404) 453-4311
Admin Marion K Garland.
Beds 94.

Pecan Manor 1*
Central State Hospital, Milledgeville, GA, 31062
(912) 452-3511
Admin Byron O Merritt III.
Licensure Intermediate care for mentally retarded. *Beds* 30. *Certified* Medicare.

Pecan Manor 3*
Central State Hospital, Milledgeville, GA, 31061
(912) 452-5558
Admin Jerry T Bush.
Licensure Intermediate care. *Beds* 134. *Certified* Medicare.

Piedmont Hall*
Central State Hospital, Milledgeville, GA, 31061
(912) 453-5776
Admin John Gates.
Licensure Intermediate care for mentally retarded. *Beds* 149. *Certified* Medicare.

Riverside Nursing Center*
Central State Hospital, Milledgeville, GA, 31062
(404) 453-4455
Admin Paul Mitchell.
Beds 75.

Carl Vinson Skilled Nursing Home*
Vinson Hwy, Milledgeville, GA, 31062
(912) 453-4547
Admin Alice K Paschal. *Medical Dir/Dir of Nursing* Ernesto Coligado MD.
Licensure Skilled care. *Beds* 100.
Admissions Requirements Medical examination; Physician's request.
Staff Physicians 2 (ft); RNs 8 (ft); LPNs 12 (ft); Nurses aides 24 (ft); Physical therapists 1 (ft); Recreational therapists 1 (ft); Occupational therapists 1 (ft); Activities coordinators 1 (ft); Dietitians 1 (ft).
Facilities Dining room; Physical therapy room; Activities room; Chapel; Crafts room; Laundry room; Barber/Beauty shop; Library; Music; Vending machine room; Visiting room; Occupational therapy room.
Activities Arts & crafts; Cards; Games; Reading groups; Prayer groups; Movies; Shopping trips; Social/Cultural gatherings; Monthly birthday party; Overnight trips; Special event trips to baseball games & holiday events.

MILLEN

Bethany Home for Men
PO Box 600, Gray St Exten, Millen, GA, 30442
(912) 982-2531
Admin Raymond Vaughn. *Medical Dir/Dir of Nursing* M L Campo MD; Sarah B Brinson RN DON.
Licensure Skilled care; Intermediate care. *Beds* SNF 100; ICF. *Certified* Medicaid.
Owner Nonprofit Corp.
Admissions Requirements Minimum age 16; Males only; Medical examination; Physician's request.
Staff Physicians 1 (ft); RNs 1 (ft), 1 (pt); LPNs 6 (ft); Orderlies 5 (ft), 2 (pt); Nurses aides 20 (ft), 3 (pt); Physical therapists 1 (ft), 1 (pt); Reality therapists 1 (ft); Recreational therapists 1 (ft); Occupational therapists 1 (pt); Speech therapists 1 (pt); Activities coordinators 1 (ft); Dietitians 1 (ft); Dentists 1 (pt); Ophthalmologists 1 (pt); Podiatrists 1 (pt).
Affiliation Baptist
Facilities Dining room; Physical therapy room; Activities room; Chapel; Crafts room; Laundry room; Barber/Beauty shop; Library.
Activities Arts & crafts; Cards; Games; Reading groups; Prayer groups; Movies; Shopping trips; Farm; Coffee groups; Fishing trips; Picnics.

MOLENA

Molena Care Home
PO Box 397, Molena, GA, 30258
(404) 495-5138
Admin Michael S Greene. *Medical Dir/Dir of Nursing* Isabelle Bradsher.
Licensure Intermediate care. *Beds* ICF 62. *Certified* Medicaid.
Owner Proprietary Corp.
Admissions Requirements Medical examination.
Staff Physicians 1 (pt); RNs 1 (ft); LPNs 5 (ft); Nurses aides 18 (ft); Physical therapists 1 (pt); Reality therapists 1 (pt); Recreational therapists 1 (pt); Occupational therapists 1 (pt); Speech therapists 1 (pt); Activities coordinators 1 (ft); Dietitians 1 (ft); Ophthalmologists 1 (pt).
Facilities Dining room; Physical therapy room; Laundry room; Barber/Beauty shop.
Activities Arts & crafts; Cards; Games; Reading groups; Prayer groups; Shopping trips; Social/Cultural gatherings; Van trips.

MONROE

Monroe Intermediate Care Facility*
Rte 3, Monroe, GA, 30655
(404) 267-7541
Admin E Kenneth Murray. *Medical Dir/Dir of Nursing* Dr Phillip Enslen.
Licensure Intermediate care. *Beds* 112. *Certified* Medicaid.
Admissions Requirements Minimum age 21; Medical examination; Physician's request.
Staff Physicians 5 (pt); RNs 1 (pt); LPNs 7 (ft), 1 (pt); Orderlies 1 (ft), 3 (pt); Physical therapists 1 (pt); Reality therapists 1 (pt); Recreational therapists 1 (ft), 1 (pt); Occupational therapists 1 (pt); Speech therapists 1 (pt); Activities coordinators 1 (ft); Dietitians 1 (ft), 1 (pt); Dentists 1 (pt); Ophthalmologists 1 (pt); Podiatrists 1 (pt); Audiologists 1 (pt).
Facilities Dining room; Physical therapy room; Activities room; Chapel; Crafts room; Laundry room.
Activities Arts & crafts; Cards; Games; Reading groups; Prayer groups; Shopping trips; Social/Cultural gatherings.

Walton County Hospital Convalescent Unit
PO Box 1346, 330 Alcova St, Monroe, GA, 30655
(404) 267-8461
Admin Raymond McCulloch Jr. *Medical Dir/Dir of Nursing* C C Moreland MD; Rita Michael RN.
Licensure Skilled care. *Beds* SNF 58. *Certified* Medicaid; Medicare.
Owner Nonprofit Corp.
Admissions Requirements Medical examination; Physician's request.
Staff RNs 1 (ft), 1 (pt); LPNs 7 (ft), 1 (pt); Orderlies 13 (ft), 1 (pt); Nurses aides; Recreational therapists 1 (ft).
Facilities Dining room; Physical therapy room; Activities room; Crafts room; Barber/Beauty shop.
Activities Arts & crafts; Cards; Games; Reading groups; Prayer groups; Movies; Shopping trips; Social/Cultural gatherings; Outside programs by groups.

MONTEZUMA

Montezuma Health Care Center*
521 Sumter St, Box 639, Montezuma, GA, 31063
(912) 472-8168
Admin Lillian M Baggett.
Licensure Skilled care; Intermediate care. *Beds* 100. *Certified* Medicaid; Medicare.

MONTICELLO

Jasper Memorial Hospital & Nursing Home
898 College St, Monticello, GA, 31064
(404) 468-6411
Admin W Phillip Jordan Jr. *Medical Dir/Dir of Nursing* J Corbitt Kelly MD; Kay Huff RN DON.
Licensure Skilled care; Intermediate care; Hospital; Ambulance service. *Beds* SNF 56; ICF; Hospital 16. *Certified* Medicaid; Medicare.
Owner Publicly owned.
Admissions Requirements Medical examination; Physician's request.
Staff Physicians 2 (ft), 5 (pt); RNs 6 (ft), 3 (pt); LPNs 5 (ft), 2 (pt); Orderlies 2 (ft), 1 (pt); Nurses aides 20 (ft), 3 (pt); Physical therapists 1 (pt); Activities coordinators 1 (ft), 1 (pt); Dietitians 1 (pt).
Facilities Dining room; Activities room; Laundry room.
Activities Cards; Games; Prayer groups; Movies; Shopping trips; Social/Cultural gatherings.

MORROW

Lake City Health Care Center*
2055 Rex Rd, Box 728, Morrow, GA, 30252
(404) 361-5114
Admin Margaret Griffin. *Medical Dir/Dir of Nursing* J Nam Lee MD.
Licensure Skilled care; Intermediate care. *Beds* 118. *Certified* Medicaid.
Admissions Requirements Medical examination; Physician's request.
Staff Physicians 3 (pt); RNs 1 (ft), 1 (pt); LPNs 7 (ft), 1 (pt); Nurses aides 41 (ft); Physical therapists 2 (ft); Recreational therapists 1 (ft); Activities coordinators 1 (ft); Dietitians 1 (ft).
Facilities Dining room; Physical therapy room; Activities room; Crafts room; Laundry room; Barber/Beauty shop; Library.
Activities Arts & crafts; Cards; Games; Reading groups; Prayer groups; Movies; Shopping trips; Social/Cultural gatherings.

MOULTRIE

Brownwood Nursing Home
PO Box 2010, 233 Sunset Cr, Moultrie, GA, 31776
(912) 985-3422
Admin Jeffrey Jursik. *Medical Dir/Dir of Nursing* Seth Berl/Gwen Bonner.
Licensure Skilled care; Intermediate care. *Beds* 100. *Certified* Medicaid; Medicare.
Owner Proprietary Corp (National Heritage).
Admissions Requirements Medical examination; Physician's request.
Staff Physicians 10 (pt); RNs 2 (ft), 1 (pt); LPNs 8 (ft), 2 (pt); Orderlies 7 (ft); Nurses aides 34 (ft), 4 (pt); Physical therapists 1 (ft), 1 (pt); Speech therapists 1 (pt); Activities coordinators 1 (ft), 1 (pt); Dietitians 1 (pt); Ophthalmologists 1 (pt).
Facilities Dining room; Physical therapy room; Activities room; Crafts room; Laundry room; Barber/Beauty shop.
Activities Arts & crafts; Cards; Games; Reading groups; Prayer groups; Movies; Shopping trips; Social/Cultural gatherings.

Moultrie Rest-A-While Nursing Home*
PO Box 666, 2015 1st Ave, Moultrie, GA, 31768
(912) 985-4319
Admin Joann Turner.
Licensure Skilled care; Intermediate care. *Beds* 68. *Certified* Medicaid; Medicare.

Rest Awhile Nursing Home*
422 5th Ave SE, Moultrie, GA, 31768
(912) 985-3637
Admin Eugene E Reid Jr.

Licensure Skilled care; Intermediate care. *Beds* 59. *Certified* Medicaid.

Sunrise Nursing Home of Georgia Inc
2709 S Main St, Moultrie, GA, 31768
(912) 985-7173
Admin P Z Clark Sr. *Medical Dir/Dir of Nursing* Lisa Trimble RN DON.
Licensure Skilled care; Intermediate care. *Beds* 50. *Certified* Medicaid.
Owner Proprietary Corp.
Admissions Requirements Medical examination; Physician's request.
Staff RNs 2 (ft); LPNs 7 (ft); Nurses aides 20 (ft); Activities coordinators 1 (ft); Dietitians 1 (pt).
Facilities Dining room; Physical therapy room; Activities room; Chapel; Crafts room; Laundry room; Barber/Beauty shop.
Activities Arts & crafts; Cards; Games; Reading groups; Prayer groups; Movies; Shopping trips; Social/Cultural gatherings.

NASHVILLE

Berrien Nursing Center Inc*
704 N Davis St, Nashville, GA, 31639
(912) 686-2034
Admin DeMaris P Hughes. *Medical Dir/Dir of Nursing* Dr James R Wilhoite.
Licensure Skilled care; Intermediate care. *Beds* 54. *Certified* Medicaid; Medicare.
Owner Proprietary Corp (National Healthcare).
Admissions Requirements Medical examination; Physician's request.
Staff Physicians 5 (pt); RNs 1 (ft), 2 (pt); LPNs 4 (ft), 3 (pt); Orderlies 1 (ft); Nurses aides 11 (ft), 5 (pt); Physical therapists 1 (pt); Activities coordinators 1 (ft); Dietitians 1 (pt); Dentists 1 (pt); Podiatrists 1 (pt).
Facilities Dining room; Activities room; Crafts room; Laundry room; Barber/Beauty shop.
Activities Arts & crafts; Cards; Games; Reading groups; Prayer groups; Movies; Shopping trips; Social/Cultural gatherings.

NEWNAN

Beaulieu Nursing Home*
Box 40, E Broad St, Newnan, GA, 30264
(404) 253-7160
Admin Kathleen Adams.
Licensure Skilled care. *Beds* 66. *Certified* Medicaid; Medicare.

Newnan Healthcare Center
120 Spring St, Newnan, GA, 30263
(404) 253-1475
Admin Carolyn Stenger. *Medical Dir/Dir of Nursing* John Wells MD.
Licensure Intermediate care. *Beds* ICF 70. *Certified* Medicaid.
Owner Proprietary Corp.
Staff Physicians 10 (pt); RNs 2 (ft); LPNs 10 (ft); Orderlies 4 (ft); Nurses aides 3 (ft); Physical therapists 1 (pt); Activities coordinators 1 (ft); Dietitians 1 (pt); Dentists 1 (pt); Ophthalmologists 1 (ft).

OCILLA

Osceola Nursing Home*
8th & Alder, PO Box 505, Ocilla, GA, 31774
(912) 468-9431
Admin George Christopher Cook. *Medical Dir/Dir of Nursing* Dr W C Sams.
Licensure Skilled care; Intermediate care. *Beds* 83. *Certified* Medicaid; Medicare.
Admissions Requirements Minimum age 35; Medical examination; Physician's request.
Staff Physicians 3 (ft); RNs 1 (ft), 2 (pt); LPNs 10 (ft), 4 (pt); Orderlies 6 (ft), 1 (pt); Nurses aides 14 (ft), 8 (pt); Physical therapists 1 (ft); Reality therapists 1 (ft); Recreational therapists 1 (ft); Speech

---

therapists 1 (pt); Activities coordinators 1 (pt); Dietitians 1 (pt); Dentists 1 (pt); Ophthalmologists 1 (pt).
Facilities Dining room; Physical therapy room; Activities room; Crafts room; Laundry room; Barber/Beauty shop.
Activities Arts & crafts; Cards; Games; Reading groups; Prayer groups; Movies; Shopping trips; Social/Cultural gatherings.

Palemon Gaskin Memorial Nursing Home
201 W Dismuke Ave, Ocilla, GA, 31774
(912) 468-7456
Admin Nellie Jo Spicer. *Medical Dir/Dir of Nursing* W C Sams MD; Shirlene Royal RN.
Licensure Skilled care; Intermediate care. *Beds* SNF 30; ICF. *Certified* Medicaid; Medicare.
Owner Publicly owned.
Staff Physicians 2 (ft), 1 (pt); RNs 1 (ft), 4 (pt); LPNs 4 (ft), 2 (pt); Orderlies 1 (ft), 2 (pt); Nurses aides 8 (ft), 5 (pt); Physical therapists 1 (pt); Recreational therapists 1 (pt); Activities coordinators 1 (ft); Dietitians 1 (pt).
Facilities Dining room; Chapel; Laundry room; Barber/Beauty shop.
Activities Arts & crafts; Cards; Games; Reading groups; Prayer groups; Movies; Shopping trips; Social/Cultural gatherings.

OCONEE

Oconee Health Care Center*
PO Box 130, Oconee, GA, 31067
(912) 552-7381
Admin Laverne Bloodworth.
Licensure Intermediate care. *Beds* 52. *Certified* Medicaid.

PELHAM

Pelham Parkway Nursing Home
608 Dogwood Dr NE, Pelham, GA, 31779
(912) 294-8602
Admin Voncille H Rumble. *Medical Dir/Dir of Nursing* W C Arwood Jr MD.
Licensure Skilled care; Intermediate care. *Beds* SNF 108; ICF. *Certified* Medicaid; Medicare.
Owner Publicly owned.
Admissions Requirements Medical examination; Physician's request.
Staff Physicians 4 (ft); RNs 2 (ft), 2 (pt); LPNs 7 (ft), 2 (pt); Orderlies 8 (ft), 4 (pt); Nurses aides 18 (ft), 10 (pt); Physical therapists 1 (ft); Speech therapists 1 (pt); Activities coordinators 1 (ft); Dietitians 1 (pt); Ophthalmologists 1 (pt); Dentist 1 (pt).
Languages Spanish
Facilities Dining room; Physical therapy room; Activities room; Laundry room; Barber/Beauty shop; Library.
Activities Arts & crafts; Cards; Games; Reading groups; Prayer groups; Movies; Social/Cultural gatherings.

PERRY

Church Home for the Aged
PO Box 1376, Perry, GA, 31069
(912) 987-1239
Admin Mariola Cosby. *Medical Dir/Dir of Nursing* Gregory Harold MD; Deborah Warner DON.
Licensure Skilled care; Intermediate care. *Beds* 31. *Certified* Medicaid.
Owner Nonprofit organization/foundation.
Admissions Requirements Physician's request.
Staff Physicians 6 (pt); RNs 2 (ft), 1 (pt); LPNs 1 (ft), 3 (pt); Physical therapists 1 (pt); Recreational therapists 1 (pt); Activities coordinators 1 (ft); Dietitians 1 (ft); Ophthalmologists 1 (pt).

Facilities Dining room; Laundry room; Barber/Beauty shop.
Activities Arts & crafts; Prayer groups; Movies; Shopping trips; Social/Cultural gatherings.

New Perry Nursing Home*
PO Drawer P, Perry, GA, 31068
(912) 987-3251
Admin William C Davis Jr. *Medical Dir/Dir of Nursing* Dr J L Gallemore.
Licensure Skilled care; Intermediate care. *Beds* 73. *Certified* Medicaid.
Staff Physicians 4 (pt); RNs 3 (ft); LPNs 3 (ft), 2 (pt); Orderlies 2 (ft), 1 (pt); Nurses aides 27 (ft); Physical therapists 1 (pt); Recreational therapists 1 (ft); Activities coordinators 1 (ft); Dietitians 1 (pt); Podiatrists 1 (pt).
Facilities Dining room; Activities room; Chapel; Crafts room; Laundry room; Barber/Beauty shop; Library.
Activities Arts & crafts; Cards; Games; Movies; Social/Cultural gatherings.

PINEVIEW

Pineview Health Care Center
PO Box 148, Bay St, Pineview, GA, 31071
(912) 624-2432
Admin Jaye M Stewart Jr. *Medical Dir/Dir of Nursing* Elise Wells.
Licensure Skilled care; Intermediate care. *Beds* 102. *Certified* Medicaid.
Owner Proprietary Corp.
Staff Physicians; RNs; LPNs; Orderlies; Nurses aides; Physical therapists; Reality therapists; Recreational therapists; Speech therapists; Activities coordinators; Dietitians; Dentists; Ophthalmologists.
Facilities Dining room; Physical therapy room; Activities room; Chapel; Crafts room; Laundry room; Barber/Beauty shop; Library.
Activities Arts & crafts; Cards; Games; Reading groups; Prayer groups; Movies; Shopping trips; Social/Cultural gatherings.

PLAINS

Plains Nursing Center Inc
PO Box 366, 225 Hospital St, Plains, GA, 31780
(912) 824-7796
Admin Glenn Godwin. *Medical Dir/Dir of Nursing* H L Simpson Jr MD; Susie E Potter RN DON.
Licensure Skilled care. *Beds* SNF 100. *Certified* Medicaid.
Owner Proprietary Corp.
Admissions Requirements Medical examination; Physician's request.
Staff Physicians 2 (pt); RNs 4 (ft), 1 (pt); LPNs 8 (ft), 4 (pt); Orderlies 1 (ft); Nurses aides 45 (ft), 8 (pt); Physical therapists 1 (ft), 2 (pt); Reality therapists 1 (ft); Recreational therapists 1 (ft); Speech therapist 1 (pt); Activities coordinators 1 (ft), 1 (pt); Dietitians 1 (ft), 1 (pt); Ophthalmologists 1 (pt).
Languages Spanish
Facilities Dining room; Physical therapy room; Activities room; Laundry room; Barber/Beauty shop.
Activities Arts & crafts; Cards; Games; Reading groups; Prayer groups; Movies; Shopping trips.

POOLER

Moss Oaks Health Care
508 S Rogers St, Pooler, GA, 31322
(912) 748-6840
Admin Virginia B Hinely. *Medical Dir/Dir of Nursing* William S Medart; Laura Chan.
Licensure Skilled care; Intermediate care. *Beds* 122. *Certified* Medicaid; Medicare.

Owner Proprietary Corp.
Admissions Requirements Medical examination; Physician's request.
Staff Physicians 4 (ft); RNs 3 (ft), 2 (pt); LPNs 10 (ft), 4 (pt); Orderlies 3 (ft); Nurses aides 41 (ft); Physical therapists 1 (ft); Recreational therapists 1 (ft); Speech therapists 1 (ft); Dietitians 1 (ft); Ophthalmologists 2 (pt).
Facilities Dining room; Physical therapy room; Activities room; Crafts room; Laundry room; Barber/Beauty shop.
Activities Arts & crafts; Cards; Games; Reading groups; Prayer groups; Movies; Shopping trips; Social/Cultural gatherings.

PORT WENTWORTH

Westview Medical Care Home
PO Box 4134, Port Wentworth, GA, 31407
(912) 964-1515
Admin Cleveland J Fountain.
Licensure Skilled care; Intermediate care. *Beds* 101. *Certified* Medicaid.

PULASKI

Pulaski Nursing Home*
PO Box 118, Pulaski, GA, 30451
(912) 685-5072
Admin Kay Hendricks. *Medical Dir/Dir of Nursing* Dorsey Smith MD.
Licensure Intermediate care. *Beds* 89. *Certified* Medicaid.
Staff Physicians 4 (ft); RNs 1 (ft), 1 (pt); LPNs 7 (ft), 5 (pt); Orderlies 4 (ft), 2 (pt); Nurses aides 16 (ft), 6 (pt); Physical therapists 1 (pt); Activities coordinators 1 (ft); Dietitians 1 (pt); Dentists 1 (pt); Podiatrists 1 (pt).
Facilities Dining room; Physical therapy room; Activities room; Laundry room; Barber/Beauty shop.
Activities Arts & crafts; Cards; Games; Reading groups; Prayer groups; Movies; Shopping trips; Social/Cultural gatherings.

QUITMAN

The Presbyterian Home Inc
1850 W Screven St, Quitman, GA, 31643
(912) 263-4183
Admin Carol F New. *Medical Dir/Dir of Nursing* Robert T Cain MD; Sara Webb RN.
Licensure Skilled care; Intermediate care; Personal care; Retirement living. *Beds* SNF 188; ICF; Personal 31; Retirement living 50. *Certified* Medicaid.
Owner Nonprofit Corp.
Admissions Requirements Medical examination; Physician's request.
Staff Physicians 3 (ft); RNs 5 (ft), 1 (pt); LPNs 21 (ft), 7 (pt); Orderlies 4 (ft), 1 (pt); Nurses aides 85 (ft), 10 (pt); Physical therapists 1 (ft); Occupational therapists 1 (pt); Speech therapists 1 (pt); Activities coordinators 1 (pt); Dietitians 1 (ft); Ophthalmologists 1 (pt).
Affiliation Presbyterian
Facilities Dining room; Physical therapy room; Activities room; Chapel; Crafts room; Laundry room; Barber/Beauty shop; Library; Swimming pool; Lake.
Activities Arts & crafts; Cards; Games; Reading groups; Prayer groups; Movies; Shopping trips; Social/Cultural gatherings; Pond for fishing; Paddle boating; Miniature golf; Shuffle board; Swimming.

REIDSVILLE

Tattnall Nursing Care
PO Box 860, Memorial Drive, Reidsville, GA, 30453
(912) 557-4345

Admin Linda Ray. *Medical Dir/Dir of Nursing* H J Kim MD; Jewel Clifton RN.
Licensure Skilled care; Intermediate care. *Beds* SNF 92; ICF. *Certified* Medicaid.
Owner Nonprofit Corp.
Admissions Requirements Medical examination; Physician's request.
Staff Physicians 1 (ft); RNs 2 (ft); LPNs 5 (ft), 4 (pt); Nurses aides 25 (ft), 8 (pt); Physical therapists 1 (ft), 1 (pt); Reality therapists 1 (ft); Recreational therapists 1 (ft); Activities coordinators 1 (ft); Dietitians 1 (ft); Ophthalmologists 1 (pt).
Facilities Dining room; Physical therapy room; Activities room; Laundry room; Barber/Beauty shop.
Activities Arts & crafts; Cards; Games; Reading groups; Prayer groups; Movies; Shopping trips; Social/Cultural gatherings; 4-H; Adopt-a-grandparent.

RIVERDALE

Hospitality Care Center of Clayton*
PO Box 917, Riverdale, GA, 30274
(404) 478-1144
Admin Ken Carithers.
Licensure Skilled care. *Beds* 100. *Certified* Medicaid; Medicare.

ROBERTA

Roberta Intermediate Care Home*
PO Box 146, Roberta, GA, 31078
(912) 836-3101
Admin Sally Aderhold.
Licensure Intermediate care. *Beds* 100. *Certified* Medicaid.

ROCKMART

Rockmart Intermediate Care Center
528 Hunter St, Rockmart, GA, 30153
(404) 684-5491
Admin Ann Gober. *Medical Dir/Dir of Nursing* Umpon Sangmalee MD.
Licensure Intermediate care. *Beds* 73. *Certified* Medicaid.
Admissions Requirements Medical examination; Physician's request.
Staff Physicians 1 (ft); RNs 1 (ft); LPNs 3 (ft), 2 (pt); Nurses aides 20 (ft), 4 (pt); Physical therapists 1 (pt); Activities coordinators 1 (ft); Dietitians 1 (pt); Ophthalmologists 1 (pt).
Facilities Dining room; Physical therapy room; Activities room; Chapel; Crafts room; Laundry room; Barber/Beauty shop.
Activities Arts & crafts; Cards; Games; Reading groups; Prayer groups; Movies; Shopping trips; Social/Cultural gatherings.

ROME

Brentwood Park/Three Rivers Health Care Co
PO Box 1441, Moran Lake Rd, Rome, GA, 30161
(404) 291-8212
Admin David Kniffen. *Medical Dir/Dir of Nursing* Dr R Cook; Sharon Vaughan RN DON.
Licensure Skilled care; Intermediate care. *Beds* 100. *Certified* Medicaid; Medicare.
Owner Proprietary Corp.
Admissions Requirements Minimum age 12; Medical examination; Physician's request.
Staff RNs 3 (ft), 3 (pt); LPNs 6 (ft), 3 (pt); Orderlies 3 (ft); Nurses aides 36 (ft), 4 (pt); Physical therapists 1 (ft); Recreational therapists 1 (pt); Speech therapists 1 (pt); Activities coordinators 1 (ft); Dietitians 1 (pt); Ophthalmologists 1 (pt).
Facilities Dining room; Physical therapy room; Activities room; Chapel; Crafts room; Laundry room; Barber/Beauty shop.

Activities Arts & crafts; Cards; Games; Prayer groups; Movies; Shopping trips; Social/Cultural gatherings; Resident council; Community activities participation; Videos.

Creswell Convalescent Center*
1345 Redmond Rd, Rome, GA, 30161
(404) 234-8281
Admin Michael Coultas. *Medical Dir/Dir of Nursing* Grant Lewis.
Licensure Skilled care; Intermediate care. *Beds* 100. *Certified* Medicaid; Medicare.
Admissions Requirements Physician's request.
Staff RNs 2 (ft); LPNs 15 (ft); Orderlies 1 (ft); Nurses aides 40 (ft), 26 (pt); Physical therapists 1 (pt); Reality therapists 1 (ft); Recreational therapists 1 (ft); Occupational therapists 1 (pt); Speech therapists 1 (pt); Activities coordinators 1 (ft); Dietitians 1 (pt); Dentists 1 (pt); Podiatrists 1 (pt).
Facilities Dining room; Physical therapy room; Activities room; Crafts room; Laundry room; Barber/Beauty shop; Library; Gift shop.
Activities Arts & crafts; Cards; Games; Reading groups; Prayer groups; Movies; Shopping trips; Social/Cultural gatherings.

Fifth Avenue Health Care Center
505 N 5th Ave, Rome, GA, 30161
(404) 291-0521
Admin Clark H Peek. *Medical Dir/Dir of Nursing* Dr Ingrid Sturgis.
Licensure Skilled care; Intermediate care. *Beds* SNF 100; ICF. *Certified* Medicaid; Medicare.
Owner Proprietary Corp.
Admissions Requirements Medical examination; Physician's request.
Staff RNs 3 (ft); LPNs 6 (ft), 5 (pt); Orderlies 1 (ft); Nurses aides 27 (ft), 9 (pt); Activities coordinators 1 (ft).
Facilities Dining room; Physical therapy room; Activities room; Laundry room; Barber/Beauty shop; Library.
Activities Arts & crafts; Cards; Games; Reading groups; Prayer groups; Movies; Social/Cultural gatherings.

Northwest Regional Intermediate Care Home
400 Redmond Rd, Rome, GA, 30161
(404) 295-6018
Admin Susan J Gooch. *Medical Dir/Dir of Nursing* Georgette Wright DON.
Licensure Intermediate care for mentally retarded. *Beds* ICF/MR 98. *Certified* Medicaid.
Owner Publicly owned.
Admissions Requirements Medical examination.
Staff Physicians 1 (ft); RNs 11 (ft); LPNs 13 (ft); Recreational therapists 3 (ft); Activities coordinators 1 (ft); Dietitians 1 (ft); 20 (ft) Social workers 4 (ft); Special education teacher 1 (ft); Behavioral staff 7 (ft); Psychologist 1 (ft); Health service technicians 55 (ft); Shift Supv 6 (ft).
Activities Arts & crafts; Cards; Games; Movies; Shopping trips; Social/Cultural gatherings.

Riverview Nursing Home*
809 S Broad St, Rome, GA, 30161
(404) 235-1337
Admin Annie Mae Langham.
Licensure Skilled care; Intermediate care. *Beds* 100. *Certified* Medicaid.
Owner Proprietary Corp (Riverside Med Services).

Springwood Nursing Home*
109 Hemlock St, Rome, GA, 30161
(404) 235-8121
Admin Bruce Behner.
Licensure Skilled care; Intermediate care. *Beds* 95. *Certified* Medicaid.

Sun Mountain Nursing Center
PO Box 1664, 3 Mile Rd, Rome, GA, 30162
(404) 291-4606
Admin David L Kniffen. *Medical Dir/Dir of Nursing* Micheal Carter.
Licensure Skilled care. *Beds* SNF 100; ICF. *Certified* Medicaid; Medicare.
Owner Proprietary Corp.
Admissions Requirements Medical examination; Physician's request.
Staff RNs 3 (ft), 3 (pt); LPNs 10 (ft), 6 (pt); Orderlies 3 (ft), 4 (pt); Nurses aides 16 (ft), 18 (pt); Activities coordinators 1 (ft); Dietitians 1 (ft); Ophthalmologists 1 (pt); Podiatrists 1 (pt).
Languages Spanish
Facilities Dining room; Physical therapy room; Activities room; Crafts room; Laundry room; Barber/Beauty shop; Library.
Activities Arts & crafts; Cards; Games; Reading groups; Prayer groups; Movies; Shopping trips; Social/Cultural gatherings.

Valley View Health Care
1166 Chulio Rd, Rome, GA, 30161
(404) 235-1132
Admin Linda Stewart. *Medical Dir/Dir of Nursing* Dr Robert Smith.
Licensure Skilled care; Intermediate care. *Beds* SNF; ICF 77. *Certified* Medicaid.
Owner Proprietary Corp.
Admissions Requirements Medical examination; Physician's request.
Staff Physicians 1 (ft); RNs 2 (ft); LPNs 4 (ft), 5 (pt); Orderlies 2 (ft), 1 (pt); Nurses aides 12 (ft), 22 (pt); Physical therapists 1 (pt); Speech therapists 1 (pt); Activities coordinators 1 (ft); Dietitians 1 (pt); Ophthalmologists 1 (pt).
Facilities Dining room; Activities room; Chapel; Crafts room; Laundry room; Barber/Beauty shop.
Activities Arts & crafts; Cards; Games; Reading groups; Prayer groups; Movies; Shopping trips; Social/Cultural gatherings.

ROSSVILLE

Rossville Convalescent Center Inc
1425 McFarland Ave, Rossville, GA, 30741
(404) 861-0863
Admin Doug Anderson. *Medical Dir/Dir of Nursing* Dr Sahin S Kocacitak; Wilma Walden RN.
Licensure Skilled care; Intermediate care. *Beds* SNF 32; ICF 80. *Certified* Medicaid; Medicare.
Owner Proprietary Corp (National Health Corp).
Admissions Requirements Medical examination; Physician's request.
Staff Physicians 1 (pt); RNs 2 (ft), 1 (pt); LPNs 10 (ft), 3 (pt); Orderlies 3 (ft); Nurses aides 32 (ft), 10 (pt); Physical therapists 1 (pt); Speech therapists 1 (pt); Activities coordinators 1 (ft); Dietitians 1 (pt); Dentists 1 (pt); Ophthalmologists 1 (pt).
Facilities Dining room; Physical therapy room; Activities room; Crafts room; Laundry room; Barber/Beauty shop; Library.
Activities Arts & crafts; Cards; Games; Reading groups; Prayer groups; Movies; Bingo; Church.

ROSWELL

Great Oaks Nursing Home*
Box 397, 1109 Green St, Roswell, GA, 30075
(404) 998-1802
Admin Doris A Jones.
Licensure Skilled care; Intermediate care. *Beds* 269. *Certified* Medicaid; Medicare.

ROYSTON

Brown Memorial Convalescent Center
PO Box 8, Royston, GA, 30662
(404) 245-5034
Admin Mrs Johnnie Escoe. *Medical Dir/Dir of Nursing* William Ford MD; Frances Osborne RN DON.
Licensure Skilled care; Intermediate care. *Beds* SNF; ICF 144. *Certified* Medicaid; Medicare.
Owner Nonprofit Corp.
Admissions Requirements Medical examination; Physician's request.
Staff RNs 2 (ft), 2 (pt); LPNs 10 (ft), 6 (pt); Orderlies; Nurses aides 37 (ft), 34 (pt); Physical therapists 1 (pt); Activities coordinators 2 (ft); Dietitians 1 (pt); Social worker 1 (ft).
Facilities Dining room; Physical therapy room; Activities room; Chapel; Crafts room; Laundry room; Barber/Beauty shop; In house pharmacy.
Activities Arts & crafts; Games; Reading groups; Prayer groups; Movies; Shopping trips; Social/Cultural gatherings.

SAINT MARYS

St Mary's Convalescent Center*
805 Dilworth St, Saint Mary's, GA, 31558
(912) 882-4281
Admin Lois Cooper.
Licensure Skilled care; Intermediate care. *Beds* 69. *Certified* Medicaid.

SAINT SIMONS ISLAND

Heritage Inn
2255 Fredrica Rd, Saint Simons Island, GA, 31522
(912) 638-9988
Admin Wade Barr.
Licensure Skilled care; Intermediate care. *Beds* 125. *Certified* Medicaid.

SANDERSVILLE

Rawlings Nursing Home
111 Brookins St, Sandersville, GA, 31082
(912) 552-3015
Admin Ronald G Warnock. *Medical Dir/Dir of Nursing* Dr Chandler McDavid; Nancy Robinson RN DON.
Licensure Skilled care; Intermediate care. *Beds* SNF; ICF 56. *Certified* Medicaid.
Owner Proprietary Corp.
Admissions Requirements Medical examination; Physician's request.
Staff Physicians 7 (pt); RNs 1 (ft), 4 (pt); LPNs 6 (ft), 5 (pt); Orderlies 1 (ft), 1 (pt); Nurses aides 20 (ft), 1 (pt); Physical therapists 1 (pt); Reality therapists 1 (ft); Activities coordinators 1 (ft).
Facilities Dining room; Activities room; Crafts room; Laundry room; Barber/Beauty shop.
Activities Arts & crafts; Games; Prayer groups; Movies.

Smith Medical Nursing Care Center*
501 E McCarty St, Sandersville, GA, 31082
(912) 552-5155
Admin Katie Smith Poole. *Medical Dir/Dir of Nursing* Dr William E Taylor.
Licensure Skilled care; Intermediate care. *Beds* 56.
Admissions Requirements Medical examination; Physician's request.
Staff Physicians 1 (pt); RNs 1 (ft), 2 (pt); LPNs 6 (ft), 1 (pt); Orderlies 5 (ft); Nurses aides 8 (ft), 1 (pt); Physical therapists 1 (pt), 1 (pt); Activities coordinators 1 (pt), 2 (pt); Dietitians 1 (ft).

Facilities Dining room; Physical therapy room; Activities room; Crafts room; Laundry room; Barber/Beauty shop.
Activities Arts & crafts; Cards; Games; Reading groups; Prayer groups; Movies; Shopping trips; Social/Cultural gatherings.

Washington County Extended Care Facility
PO Box 636, Sandersville, GA, 31082
(912) 552-3901
Admin Larry W Anderson. *Medical Dir/Dir of Nursing* Dr William Helton; Wylene Lewis RN.
Licensure Skilled care; Intermediate care. *Beds* SNF 40; ICF 10. *Certified* Medicaid.
Owner Nonprofit organization/foundation.
Admissions Requirements Physician's request.
Staff Physicians 8 (pt); RNs 1 (ft), 1 (pt); LPNs 8 (ft), 1 (pt); Orderlies 1 (ft), 1 (pt); Nurses aides 12 (ft), 4 (pt); Physical therapists 2 (pt); Speech therapists 1 (pt); Activities coordinators 1 (ft); Dietitians 1 (pt); Podiatrists 1 (pt).
Facilities Dining room; Physical therapy room; Activities room; Chapel; Barber/Beauty shop.
Activities Arts & crafts; Games; Reading groups; Prayer groups; Movies; Shopping trips; Social/Cultural gatherings.

SAVANNAH

Azalealand Nursing Home Inc*
2040 Colonial Dr, Savannah, GA, 31406
(912) 354-2752
Admin Chas L Von Waldner. *Medical Dir/Dir of Nursing* Jules Victor Jr.
Licensure Skilled care; Intermediate care. *Beds* 107.
Admissions Requirements Minimum age 65; Medical examination; Physician's request.
Staff RNs 3 (ft), 2 (pt); LPNs 7 (ft), 2 (pt); Nurses aides 20 (ft), 8 (pt); Physical therapists 1 (pt); Reality therapists 2 (pt); Recreational therapists 1 (ft), 1 (pt); Activities coordinators 1 (ft).
Facilities Dining room; Physical therapy room; Activities room; Chapel; Laundry room; Barber/Beauty shop; Library.
Activities Cards; Games; Movies; Shopping trips.

Chatham Nursing Home I*
6711 La Roche Ave, Savannah, GA, 31406
(912) 354-8225
Admin Harold C Sims II.
Licensure Skilled care; Intermediate care. *Beds* 284. *Certified* Medicaid; Medicare.

Chatham Nursing Home II
6711 La Roche Ave, Savannah, GA, 31406
(912) 354-8225
Admin Harold C Sims II.
Licensure Skilled care; Intermediate care. *Beds* 100. *Certified* Medicaid; Medicare.

Cohen's Retreat
5715 Skidaway Rd, Savannah, GA, 31406
(912) 355-2843
Admin T'Lene H Wilson. *Medical Dir/Dir of Nursing* Lawrence J Lynch Jr MD; Darlene Keith DON.
Licensure Skilled care; Intermediate care; Intermingled. *Beds* Intermingled 31. *Certified* Medicaid.
Owner Nonprofit Corp.
Admissions Requirements Males only; Medical examination; Physician's request.
Staff Physicians 1 (pt); RNs 1 (ft), 1 (pt); LPNs 3 (ft), 2 (pt); Orderlies 3 (ft), 1 (pt); Nurses aides 2 (ft), 2 (pt); Physical therapists 1 (pt); Dietitians 1 (pt); Ophthalmologists 1 (pt); Social worker 1 (ft); Dentist 1 (pt).
Affiliation King's Daughters & Sons
Facilities Dining room; Laundry room; Barber/Beauty shop; Library.
Activities Arts & crafts; Games; Movies; Social/Cultural gatherings.

Hillhaven Convalescent Center*
11800 Abercorn St, Savannah, GA, 31406
(912) 925-4402
Admin Betty J Hargrett.
Licensure Skilled care. *Beds* 104. *Certified* Medicaid; Medicare.
Owner Proprietary Corp (Hillhaven Corp).

Savannah Convalescent Center
815 E 63rd St, Savannah, GA, 31405
(912) 352-8615
Admin Mary Burroughs. *Medical Dir/Dir of Nursing* John Fillingim MD; Rose Robbins RN DON.
Licensure Skilled care. *Beds* SNF 120. *Certified* Medicaid; Medicare.
Owner Proprietary Corp (Hillhaven Corp).
Admissions Requirements Medical examination.
Staff Physicians 40 (ft); RNs 6 (ft), 2 (pt); LPNs 13 (ft), 6 (pt); Orderlies 6 (ft), 2 (pt); Nurses aides 40 (ft), 13 (pt); Physical therapists 1 (ft), 1 (pt); Reality therapists 1 (pt); Recreational therapists 1 (pt); Occupational therapists 1 (pt); Speech therapists 1 (pt); Activities coordinators 1 (ft); Dietitians 1 (pt); Dentists 1 (pt); Ophthalmologists 1 (pt); Podiatrists 1 (pt).
Facilities Dining room; Physical therapy room; Activities room; Crafts room; Laundry room; Barber/Beauty shop.
Activities Arts & crafts; Cards; Games; Prayer groups; Movies; Social/Cultural gatherings; Religious services.

Savannah Health Care*
12825 White Bluff Rd, Savannah, GA, 31406
(404) 925-5157
Admin Joe Hunt.
Beds 120.

SNELLVILLE

Snellville Nursing & Rehabilitation Center
3000 Lenora Church Rd, Snellville, GA, 30278
(404) 972-2040
Admin M E Hill III. *Medical Dir/Dir of Nursing* Bill Martin MD; Dolly DeProspero RN.
Licensure Skilled care; Intermediate care. *Beds* SNF 118; ICF. *Certified* Medicaid.
Owner Proprietary Corp.
Admissions Requirements Medical examination; Physician's request.
Staff Physicians 1 (ft); RNs 4 (ft), 2 (pt); LPNs 11 (ft), 1 (pt); Nurses aides 31 (ft), 12 (pt); Physical therapists 1 (pt); Speech therapists 1 (pt); Activities coordinators 1 (ft); Dietitians 1 (ft); Dentists 1 (pt); Ophthalmologists 1 (pt); Dentist 1 (pt).
Facilities Dining room; Physical therapy room; Activities room; Crafts room; Laundry room; Barber/Beauty shop; Library.
Activities Arts & crafts; Cards; Games; Reading groups; Prayer groups; Movies; Shopping trips; Social/Cultural gatherings; Bowling.

SOCIAL CIRCLE

Social Circle Intermediate Care Facility*
671 N Cherokee Rd, Social Circle, GA, 30279
(404) 464-2019
Admin Mary Ann Wood.
Licensure Intermediate care. *Beds* 65. *Certified* Medicare.

SOPERTON

Treutlen County Nursing Home*
PO Box 646, Soperton, GA, 30457
(912) 529-4418
Admin Aubrey Fleming.
Licensure Skilled care; Intermediate care. *Beds* 50. *Certified* Medicaid.

SPARTA

Providence Health Care*
Box 86, Providence St, Sparta, GA, 31087
(404) 444-5153
Admin Joy A Hill.
Licensure Skilled care; Intermediate care. *Beds* 71. *Certified* Medicaid.
Owner Proprietary Corp (Vantage Healthcare).

Sparta Intermediate Care Center*
Rte 22, Sparta, GA, 31087
(404) 444-6057
Admin Carolyn Lovitz.
Licensure Intermediate care. *Beds* 81. *Certified* Medicaid.

SPRINGFIELD

Effingham County Hospital—E C F
PO Box 386, Springfield, GA, 31329
(912) 754-6451
Admin Norma J Morgan. *Medical Dir/Dir of Nursing* Jack D Heneisen MD.
Licensure Skilled care; Intermediate care. *Beds* SNF 56; ICF. *Certified* Medicaid; Medicare.
Owner Nonprofit organization/foundation.
Admissions Requirements Minimum age 18; Medical examination; Physician's request.
Staff Physicians 5 (ft); RNs 1 (ft), 1 (pt); LPNs 4 (ft), 5 (pt); Orderlies 3 (ft), 3 (pt); Nurses aides 11 (ft), 14 (pt); Recreational therapists 1 (ft); Activities coordinators 1 (ft); Dietitians 1 (ft).
Facilities Dining room; Physical therapy room; Activities room; Chapel; Crafts room; Laundry room; Barber/Beauty shop; Library.
Activities Arts & crafts; Cards; Games; Reading groups; Prayer groups; Movies; Shopping trips; Social/Cultural gatherings; Fishing.

STATESBORO

Browns Nursing Home*
226 College St, Statesboro, GA, 30458
(912) 764-9631
Admin Harold H Brown.
Licensure Skilled care; Intermediate care. *Beds* 63. *Certified* Medicaid; Medicare.

Georgia Grace Memorial Home Inc*
PO Box 421, Statesboro, GA, 30458
(912) 764-6903
Admin Beatrice Riggs.
Licensure Skilled care; Intermediate care. *Beds* 60. *Certified* Medicaid.

Nightingale Home Inc
307 Jones Mill Rd, Statesboro, GA, 30458
(912) 764-9011
Admin Martha A Firges. *Medical Dir/Dir of Nursing* Dr R H Smith; Pansy Bird RN DON.
Licensure Skilled care; Intermediate care. *Beds* 92. *Certified* Medicaid.
Owner Privately owned.
Admissions Requirements Medical examination; Physician's request.
Staff Physicians 1 (pt); RNs 2 (ft), 2 (pt); LPNs 5 (ft), 7 (pt); Orderlies 6 (ft), 3 (pt); Recreational therapists 1 (pt); Activities coordinators 1 (ft); Dietitians 1 (pt).
Facilities Dining room; Physical therapy room; Activities room; Laundry room; Barber/Beauty shop.
Activities Arts & crafts; Games; Reading groups; Prayer groups; Movies.

Statesboro Nursing Home*
PO Box 746, Statesboro, GA, 30458
(912) 764-6108
Admin Roger W Popham. *Medical Dir/Dir of Nursing* Dr D Scarborough & Dr R Smith.
Licensure Skilled care; Intermediate care. *Beds* 99. *Certified* Medicaid.

Admissions Requirements Medical
examination; Physician's request.
Staff Physicians 5 (pt); RNs 2 (ft), 1 (pt);
LPNs 9 (ft), 2 (pt); Orderlies 3 (ft), 4 (pt);
Nurses aides 24 (ft), 6 (pt); Physical
therapists 1 (pt); Speech therapists 1 (pt);
Activities coordinators 1 (ft); Dietitians 1
(pt); Dentists 1 (pt); Podiatrists 1 (pt).
Facilities Dining room; Physical therapy
room; Activities room; Laundry room;
Barber/Beauty shop.
Activities Arts & crafts; Games; Movies;
Shopping trips; Social/Cultural gatherings.

SUMMERVILLE

Oak View Nursing Home*
PO Box 449, Summerville, GA, 30747
(404) 857-3419
Admin Randall Smith.
Licensure Skilled care; Intermediate care. *Beds*
90. *Certified* Medicaid; Medicare.

SWAINSBORO

Emanuel County Nursing Home*
PO Box 7, Swainsboro, GA, 30401
(912) 237-9911
Admin Joe Tucker.
Licensure Skilled care. *Beds* 47. *Certified*
Medicaid; Medicare.

Swainsboro Nursing Home Inc*
Rte 4, Box 184, Swainsboro, GA, 30401
(912) 237-7022
Admin Dorothy Schrader.
Licensure Skilled care; Intermediate care. *Beds*
103. *Certified* Medicaid.

SYLVANIA

Syl-View Health Care Center*
Box 199, 411 Pine St, Sylvania, GA, 30467
(912) 564-2015
Admin Karen Zeigler.
Licensure Skilled care; Intermediate care. *Beds*
128. *Certified* Medicaid.

SYLVESTER

Sylvester Health Care Inc
PO Box 406, Sylvester, GA, 31791
(912) 776-5541
Admin Donna M King. *Medical Dir/Dir of
Nursing* Faye Davidson.
Licensure Skilled care; Intermediate care. *Beds*
SNF; ICF 59. *Certified* Medicaid.
Owner Proprietary Corp.
Admissions Requirements Medical
examination.
Staff RNs; LPNs; Orderlies; Nurses aides;
Physical therapists; Activities coordinators;
Dietitians.
Facilities Dining room; Physical therapy
room; Activities room; Laundry room;
Barber/Beauty shop; Library.
Activities Cards; Games; Reading groups;
Prayer groups; Movies; Shopping trips.

TALKING ROCK

Wildwood Intermediate Care Home*
Rte 2, Talking Rock, GA, 30175
(404) 692-6014
Admin Dee F Wilbanks.
Licensure Intermediate care. *Beds* 44.
Certified Medicaid.

THOMASTON

Clear View Nursing Care Center*
Box 1162, 310 Ave F, Thomaston, GA, 30286
(404) 647-6676
Admin Charles E Aspinwall.

Licensure Skilled care; Intermediate care. *Beds*
119. *Certified* Medicaid; Medicare.

Riverside Medical of Thomaston
101 Old Talbotton Rd, Thomaston, GA,
30286
(404) 647-8161
Admin Sue G Estes. *Medical Dir/Dir of
Nursing* H D Tyler MD; Brenda Spillers
DON.
Licensure Skilled care; Intermediate care. *Beds*
73. *Certified* Medicaid; VA.
Owner Proprietary Corp (Riverside Med
Services).
Admissions Requirements Medical
examination; Physician's request.
Staff Physicians 16 (ft); RNs 3 (ft); LPNs 9
(ft); Orderlies 5 (ft), 2 (pt); Speech therapists
1 (pt); Activities coordinators 1 (ft);
Dietitians 1 (ft), 1 (pt); Ophthalmologists 1
(pt); Physical therapist aides 1 (ft), 3 (pt).
Facilities Dining room; Physical therapy
room; Activities room; Chapel; Crafts room;
Laundry room; Barber/Beauty shop.
Activities Arts & crafts; Cards; Games;
Reading groups; Prayer groups; Movies;
Shopping trips; Social/Cultural gatherings.

THOMASVILLE

Camellia Garden of Life Care
PO Box 1959, Thomasville, GA, 31792
(912) 226-0076
Admin Michael D Denney. *Medical Dir/Dir of
Nursing* Dr J Rawlings.
Licensure Intermediate care. *Beds* 83.
Owner Proprietary Corp (Life Care Centers of
America).
Admissions Requirements Medical
examination; Physician's request.
Staff RNs 1 (ft), 1 (pt); LPNs 7 (ft), 8 (pt);
Orderlies 2 (pt); Nurses aides 16 (ft), 13 (pt);
Activities coordinators 1 (ft); Dietitians 1
(ft).
Facilities Dining room; Activities room;
Crafts room; Laundry room; Barber/Beauty
shop.
Activities Arts & crafts; Cards; Games;
Reading groups; Prayer groups; Movies;
Shopping trips; Social/Cultural gatherings.

Glenn-Mor Home*
Rte 1, PO Box 464, Thomasville, GA, 31792
(912) 226-8942
Admin Mary A Goodspeed. *Medical Dir/Dir
of Nursing* Dr John Brinson.
Licensure Skilled care; Intermediate care. *Beds*
64. *Certified* Medicaid; Medicare.
Admissions Requirements Medical
examination.
Staff Physicians 7 (pt); RNs 1 (ft), 2 (pt);
LPNs 4 (ft), 7 (pt); Orderlies 4 (ft); Nurses
aides 15 (ft), 4 (pt); Physical therapists 1
(pt); Activities coordinators 1 (ft); Dietitians
1 (ft).
Facilities Dining room; Physical therapy
room; Activities room; Crafts room; Laundry
room; Barber/Beauty shop.
Activities Arts & crafts; Games; Reading
groups; Prayer groups; Movies; Shopping
trips; Social/Cultural gatherings; Rhythm
band; Sing-alongs; Music & motions;
Painting/sketching classes.

Hospitality Care of Thomasville*
930 S Broad St, Thomasville, GA, 31792
(912) 226-9322
Admin James R Kallevig.
Licensure Skilled care; Intermediate care. *Beds*
68. *Certified* Medicaid; Medicare.
Owner Proprietary Corp (Vantage Healthcare).

**Rose Haven ICF/MR & Skilled Nursing
Facility**
PO Box 1378, Thomasville, GA, 31799
(912) 228-2271
Admin Andre' Marria. *Medical Dir/Dir of
Nursing* Antonio Santos MD.

Licensure Skilled care; Intermediate care for
mentally retarded. *Beds* SNF 21; ICF/MR
91. *Certified* Medicaid.
Owner Publicly owned.
Admissions Requirements Medical
examination; Physician's request.
Staff Physicians 1 (ft); RNs 9 (ft); LPNs 22
(ft); Nurses aides 81 (ft); Physical therapists
1 (pt); Reality therapists 4 (ft), 2 (pt);
Recreational therapists 1 (ft); Occupational
therapists 2 (pt); Speech therapists 1 (ft);
Activities coordinators 1 (ft); Dietitians 1
(ft); Podiatrists 1 (ft); 30 (ft).
Facilities Dining room; Physical therapy
room; Activities room; Chapel; Crafts room;
Laundry room; Barber/Beauty shop.
Activities Arts & crafts; Games; Movies;
Shopping trips; Social/Cultural gatherings.

Thomasville Health Care Center*
4 Skyline Dr, Thomasville, GA, 31792
(912) 226-4101
Admin Pat Reagan. *Medical Dir/Dir of
Nursing* Dr Joe Rawlings.
Licensure Skilled care; Intermediate care. *Beds*
52. *Certified* Medicaid.
Admissions Requirements Medical
examination.
Facilities Dining room; Physical therapy
room; Activities room; Laundry room;
Barber/Beauty shop.
Activities Arts & crafts; Cards; Games; Prayer
groups; Movies; Shopping trips; Social/
Cultural gatherings.

THOMSON

Thomson Manor Nursing Home Inc*
PO Drawer 1080, Thomson, GA, 30824
(404) 595-5574
Admin William C McConnell.
Licensure Skilled care; Intermediate care. *Beds*
150. *Certified* Medicaid.
Owner Proprietary Corp (Stuckey Health
Care).

TIFTON

Tift Health Care Inc*
PO Box 1668, 215 20th St, Tifton, GA,
31793-1668
(912) 382-7342
Admin Frances D Moody.
Licensure Skilled care; Intermediate care. *Beds*
86. *Certified* Medicaid.

Tifton Nursing Home*
1451 Newton Dr, Tifton, GA, 31794
(912) 382-1665
Admin R Vernon Bankston. *Medical Dir/Dir
of Nursing* Morris Davis MD.
Licensure Intermingled. *Beds* 100. *Certified*
Medicaid.
Admissions Requirements Medical
examination; Physician's request.
Staff Physicians 6 (pt); RNs 1 (ft), 1 (pt);
LPNs 6 (ft), 6 (pt); Orderlies 5 (ft), 3 (pt);
Nurses aides 16 (ft), 16 (pt); Physical
therapists 1 (ft); Activities coordinators 1
(ft); Dietitians 1 (ft); Dentists 1 (pt);
Ophthalmologists 1 (pt); Podiatrists 1 (pt);
Audiologists 1 (pt).
Facilities Dining room; Physical therapy
room; Activities room; Crafts room; Laundry
room; Barber/Beauty shop; Library.
Activities Arts & crafts; Cards; Games;
Reading groups; Prayer groups; Shopping
trips; Social/Cultural gatherings.

TOCCOA

Toccoa Nursing Center*
PO Box 1129, Toccoa, GA, 30577
(404) 886-8491
Admin Frieda Weeks. *Medical Dir/Dir of
Nursing* Arthur Singer MD.

Licensure Skilled care; Intermediate care. *Beds* 181. *Certified* Medicaid.
Admissions Requirements Medical examination.
Staff RNs 2 (ft), 3 (pt); LPNs 8 (ft), 8 (pt); Orderlies 3 (ft), 2 (pt); Nurses aides 63 (ft), 19 (pt); Activities coordinators 1 (ft), 1 (pt).
Facilities Dining room; Physical therapy room; Laundry room; Barber/Beauty shop.
Activities Arts & crafts; Cards; Games; Reading groups; Prayer groups; Movies; Shopping trips; Social/Cultural gatherings.

TRENTON

Sandmont Gala Nursing Home
PO Box 45, Rte 2, Trenton, GA, 30752
(404) 657-4171
Admin Kathy Fitzpatrick. *Medical Dir/Dir of Nursing* Dr Alan Mangan; Jill Shrader RN.
Licensure Skilled care; Intermediate care. *Beds* 65. *Certified* Medicaid.
Owner Privately owned.
Admissions Requirements Medical examination; Physician's request.
Staff Physicians 1 (ft); RNs 3 (ft), 2 (pt); LPNs 4 (ft), 1 (pt); Nurses aides 30 (ft), 2 (pt); Physical therapists 1 (ft); Activities coordinators 1 (ft); Dietitians 1 (pt).
Facilities Dining room; Physical therapy room; Activities room; Crafts room; Laundry room; Barber/Beauty shop.
Activities Arts & crafts; Games; Reading groups; Prayer groups; Movies; Social/Cultural gatherings.

TUCKER

Briarwood Nursing Center Inc*
3888 LaVista Rd, Tucker, GA, 30084
(404) 938-5740
Admin Coralee Long.
Licensure Skilled care. *Beds* 100.
Owner Proprietary Corp (Beverly Enterprises).

Meadowbrook Nursing Home Inc
4608 Lawrenceville Hwy, Tucker, GA, 30084
(404) 491-9444
Admin Robert L Greene. *Medical Dir/Dir of Nursing* Debra Lanter.
Licensure Skilled care; Intermediate care. *Beds* 42. *Certified* Medicaid.
Owner Privately owned.
Admissions Requirements Females only; Medical examination.
Staff Physicians 1 (ft); RNs 1 (ft), 3 (pt); LPNs 3 (ft), 1 (pt); Nurses aides 14 (ft), 3 (pt); Physical therapists 1 (pt); Activities coordinators 1 (ft); Dietitians 4 (ft), 1 (pt).
Facilities Dining room; Physical therapy room; Activities room; Laundry room; Barber/Beauty shop.
Activities Arts & crafts; Games; Reading groups; Prayer groups; Movies; Shopping trips; Social/Cultural gatherings; Cooking classes; Picnics; Outlings.

Tucker Nursing Center*
2165 Idlewood Rd, Tucker, GA, 30084
(404) 934-3172
Admin Michelle DesCarpenter. *Medical Dir/Dir of Nursing* Michael Lipsitt MD.
Licensure Skilled care. *Beds* 120. *Certified* Medicaid.
Staff Physicians 3 (pt); RNs 6 (ft), 3 (pt); LPNs 4 (ft), 5 (pt); Nurses aides 28 (ft), 11 (pt); Physical therapists 1 (pt); Activities coordinators 2 (ft).
Facilities Dining room; Activities room; Crafts room; Laundry room; Barber/Beauty shop; Library.
Activities Arts & crafts; Cards; Games; Movies; Social/Cultural gatherings; Atlanta Braves games; Bus trips.

TWIN CITY

Twin View Nursing Home*
Box 128, Twin City, GA, 30471
(912) 763-2141
Admin Theo H Fountain.
Licensure Skilled care; Intermediate care. *Beds* 110. *Certified* Medicaid.

TYBEE ISLAND

Oceanside Nursing Home*
77 Van Horn, Box 870, Tybee Island, GA, 31328
(912) 786-4511
Admin Jewell S Towns. *Medical Dir/Dir of Nursing* Carmen Gannon MD.
Licensure Skilled care; Intermediate care. *Beds* 85. *Certified* Medicaid; Medicare.
Admissions Requirements Medical examination; Physician's request.
Staff Physicians 3 (pt); RNs 4 (ft), 1 (pt); LPNs 8 (ft), 2 (pt); Orderlies 2 (ft); Nurses aides 22 (ft); Recreational therapists 1 (ft); Activities coordinators 1 (ft); Dietitians 1 (pt); Podiatrists 1 (pt).
Facilities Dining room; Physical therapy room; Activities room; Crafts room; Laundry room; Barber/Beauty shop.
Activities Arts & crafts; Cards; Games; Reading groups; Prayer groups; Movies; Shopping trips; Social/Cultural gatherings.

Savannah Beach Nursing Home Inc*
PO Box 870, Tybee Island, GA, 31328
(912) 786-5711
Admin Teresa Jackson. *Medical Dir/Dir of Nursing* A P Phillips.
Licensure Skilled care; Intermediate care. *Beds* 50. *Certified* Medicaid; Medicare.
Admissions Requirements Minimum age 18; Medical examination; Physician's request.
Staff Physicians 3 (pt); RNs 2 (ft); LPNs 3 (ft), 1 (pt); Nurses aides 17 (ft), 1 (pt); Physical therapists 1 (pt); Activities coordinators 1 (ft); Dietitians 1 (ft); Dentists; Podiatrists; Music therapist 1 (pt).
Facilities Dining room; Physical therapy room; Activities room; Chapel; Crafts room; Laundry room; Barber/Beauty shop; Library.
Activities Arts & crafts; Cards; Games; Reading groups; Prayer groups; Movies; Shopping trips; Social/Cultural gatherings; Ceramics.

UNION POINT

Greene Point Health Care*
PO Box 312, Union Point, GA, 30669
(404) 486-2167
Admin Teresa Dyar.
Licensure Skilled care; Intermediate care. *Beds* 71. *Certified* Medicaid; Medicare.
Owner Proprietary Corp (Beverly Enterprises).

VALDOSTA

Crestwood Nursing Home
PO Box 2999, Valdosta, GA, 31602
(912) 242-6868
Admin Charles O Templeton Jr. *Medical Dir/Dir of Nursing* Dr Joe C Stubbs; Nancy Harnage RN DON.
Licensure Skilled care. *Beds* SNF 79. *Certified* Medicaid.
Owner Proprietary Corp.
Staff RNs 2 (ft), 1 (pt); LPNs 8 (ft), 1 (pt); Orderlies 1 (ft); Nurses aides 30 (ft), 8 (pt); Physical therapists 1 (pt); Speech therapists 1 (pt); Activities coordinators 1 (ft); Dietitians 1 (pt); Dentists 1 (pt); Ophthalmologists 1 (pt).

Heritage House Nursing Home
PO Box 2999, 2501 N Ashley, Valdosta, GA, 31604
(912) 244-7368
Admin Olleta T Baggett. *Medical Dir/Dir of Nursing* Joe C Stubb Jr MD, Susan Blevins RN.
Licensure Intermingled care. *Beds* 98. *Certified* Medicaid.
Owner Proprietary Corp.
Admissions Requirements Minimum age 21; Medical examination; Physician's request.
Staff RNs 3 (pt); LPNs 9 (ft), 3 (pt); Orderlies 1 (pt); Nurses aides; Physical therapists 1 (pt); Recreational therapists 1 (ft); Speech therapists 1 (pt); Activities coordinators 1 (ft).
Facilities Dining room; Physical therapy room; Activities room; Chapel; Crafts room; Laundry room; Barber/Beauty shop; Library.
Activities Arts & crafts; Cards; Games; Reading groups; Prayer groups; Movies; Shopping trips; Social/Cultural gatherings; Reminiscence groups.

Holly Hill Intermediate Care Facility
PO Box 2999, Valdosta, GA, 31601
(912) 244-6968
Admin Charles O Templeton Jr. *Medical Dir/Dir of Nursing* Dr Joe C Stubbs; Betty Council LPN.
Licensure Intermediate care. *Beds* ICF 100. *Certified* Medicaid.
Owner Proprietary Corp.
Staff RNs 1 (pt); LPNs 9 (ft), 1 (pt); Orderlies 1 (ft); Nurses aides 35 (ft), 4 (pt); Physical therapists 1 (pt); Speech therapists 1 (pt); Activities coordinators 1 (ft); Dietitians 1 (pt); Ophthalmologists 1 (pt).

Lakehaven Nursing Home
PO Box 2999, Valdosta, GA, 31604-2999
(912) 242-7368
Admin John H Eades. *Medical Dir/Dir of Nursing* Joe C Stubbs MD; Mattie Roundtree RN DON.
Licensure Skilled care; Intermediate care. *Beds* SNF 50; ICF 40. *Certified* Medicaid.
Owner Proprietary Corp.
Admissions Requirements Minimum age 21; Medical examination; Physician's request.
Staff RNs 1 (ft), 1 (pt); LPNs 9 (ft); Nurses aides 23 (ft), 12 (pt); Activities coordinators 1 (ft).
Facilities Dining room; Physical therapy room; Activities room; Chapel; Barber/Beauty shop; Library.
Activities Arts & crafts; Cards; Games; Reading groups; Prayer groups; Movies; Shopping trips; Social/Cultural gatherings; Yard sales; Rock-a-thons; Bible study; Sunday school.

Parkwood Development Center*
1501 N Lee St, Valdosta, GA, 31601
(912) 242-6268
Admin Ruth T Adkins. *Medical Dir/Dir of Nursing* Joseph C Stubbs MD.
Licensure Intermediate care for mentally retarded. *Beds* 110. *Certified* Medicaid.
Owner Proprietary Corp.
Admissions Requirements Minimum age 6; Medical examination.
Staff Physicians 6 (ft); RNs 5 (ft); Nurses aides 95- 110 (ft); Physical therapists 1 (ft); Recreational therapists 1 (ft); Occupational therapists 1 (pt); Speech therapists 1 (ft); Activities coordinators 1 (ft); Dietitians 1 (ft); Dentists 3 (pt); Ophthalmologists 2 (pt); Podiatrists 1 (pt); Audiologists 1 (pt); Pharmacist 1 (ft); Psychologist 1 (pt); Psychiatrist 1 (ft); Social workers 1 (ft); Social work technicians 2 (ft); Teachers 4 (ft); QMRPs 2 (ft); Programming specialists 4 (ft).

Facilities Dining room; Physical therapy
room; Chapel; Crafts room; Laundry room;
Barber/Beauty shop; Library; Classrooms;
Speech therapy; Activities center.
Activities Arts & crafts; Cards; Games;
Reading groups; Prayer groups; Movies;
Shopping trips; Social/Cultural gatherings.

VIDALIA

Bethany Home for Ladies*
PO Box 668, Vidalia, GA, 30474
(912) 537-7922
Admin Lonnie C Vaughn.
Licensure Skilled care; Intermediate care. *Beds*
168. *Certified* Medicaid; Medicare.
Admissions Requirements Females only.

Precious Intermediate Care Home*
309 Mosley St, Box 89, Vidalia, GA, 30474
(912) 537-7532
Admin George H Yarbrough.
Licensure Intermediate care. *Beds* 40.
Certified Medicaid.

WADLEY

Glendale Nursing Home Inc*
PO Box 326, Wadley, GA, 30477
(912) 252-5254
Admin George T Harrison.
Licensure Skilled care; Intermediate care. *Beds*
98. *Certified* Medicaid.

WARM SPRINGS

**Meriwether Memorial Hospital & Nursing
Home**
PO Box 8, Warm Springs, GA, 31830
(404) 655-3331
Admin George T Hudson. *Medical Dir/Dir of
Nursing* Betty Mailey RN DON.
Licensure Skilled care; Intermediate care. *Beds*
58. *Certified* Medicaid.
Owner Nonprofit organization/foundation.
Staff RNs 1 (ft), 1 (pt); LPNs 6 (ft), 2 (pt);
Orderlies 4 (ft); Nurses aides 23 (ft), 3 (pt);
Physical therapists 1 (pt); Activities
coordinators 1 (ft); Dietitians 1 (ft).
Facilities Dining room; Physical therapy
room; Activities room; Crafts room; Laundry
room; Barber/Beauty shop; Library.
Activities Arts & crafts; Games; Movies;
Shopping trips; Social/Cultural gatherings;
Family group activities; Fishing.

WARNER ROBINS

Elberta Convalescent Home
PO Box 1483, Warner Robins, GA, 31099
(912) 923-5922
Admin Gertrude F Hooley. *Medical Dir/Dir of
Nursing* Ellen Muegge LPN.
Licensure Intermediate care. *Beds* 66.
Certified Medicaid.
Owner Proprietary Corp.
Admissions Requirements Medical
examination; Physician's request.
Staff RNs 1 (pt); LPNs 4 (ft), 3 (pt); Orderlies
4 (ft), 1 (pt); Nurses aides 10 (ft), 3 (pt);
Recreational therapists 1 (ft); Activities
coordinators 1 (ft); Dietitians 1 (ft).
Facilities Dining room; Physical therapy
room; Crafts room; Laundry room; Barber/
Beauty shop.
Activities Arts & crafts; Games; Reading
groups; Prayer groups; Movies; Shopping
trips; Social/Cultural gatherings.

Hallmark Nursing Home
1601 Elberta Rd, Warner Robins, GA, 31093
(912) 922-2241
Admin Leah Swinford. *Medical Dir/Dir of
Nursing* Dr C Crawford; June Walker RN.
Licensure Skilled care; Intermediate care. *Beds*
126. *Certified* Medicaid.

Owner Proprietary Corp (Southeastern Health
Care Inc).
Admissions Requirements Minimum age
Adult; Medical examination; Physician's
request.
Staff Physicians 1 (ft); RNs 2 (ft), 1 (pt);
LPNs 7 (ft), 7 (pt); Orderlies 7 (ft), 1 (pt);
Nurses aides 41 (ft), 3 (pt); Physical
therapists 1 (ft); Activities coordinators 1
(ft); Dietitians 1 (ft).
Facilities Dining room; Physical therapy
room; Laundry room; Barber/Beauty shop.
Activities Games; Reading groups; Prayer
groups; Social/Cultural gatherings.

Peach Belt Nursing Home
801 Elberta Rd, Warner Robins, GA, 31056
(912) 923-3156
Admin Irene Reynolds. *Medical Dir/Dir of
Nursing* Perry Melvin; Susan Ables DON.
Licensure Skilled care; Intermediate care. *Beds*
106. *Certified* Medicaid.
Owner Privately owned.
Admissions Requirements Medical
examination.
Staff Physicians; RNs; LPNs; Orderlies;
Nurses aides; Physical therapists;
Recreational therapists; Activities
coordinators; Dietitians.
Facilities Dining room; Physical therapy
room; Activities room; Crafts room; Laundry
room; Barber/Beauty shop.
Activities Arts & crafts; Cards; Games;
Reading groups; Prayer groups; Movies;
Shopping trips; Social/Cultural gatherings.

WARRENTON

Providence Health Care*
PO Box 69, Warrenton, GA, 30828
(404) 465-3328
Admin Marsha D Todd. *Medical Dir/Dir of
Nursing* Dr John Lemley.
Licensure Skilled care. *Beds* 110. *Certified*
Medicaid; Medicare.
Owner Proprietary Corp (Beverly Enterprises).
Admissions Requirements Medical
examination; Physician's request.
Staff RNs 2 (ft), 1 (pt) 13C 8 (ft), 3 (pt);
Orderlies 1 (ft); Nurses aides 30 (ft), 6 (pt);
Physical therapists 1 (pt); Recreational
therapists 1 (pt); Activities coordinators 1
(ft); Dietitians 1 (pt); Dentists 1 (pt);
Podiatrists 1 (pt).
Facilities Dining room; Physical therapy
room; Activities room; Chapel; Crafts room;
Laundry room; Barber/Beauty shop.
Activities Arts & crafts; Cards; Games;
Reading groups; Prayer groups; Movies;
Shopping trips; Social/Cultural gatherings.

WASHINGTON

Wilkes Health Care
PO Box 578, 112 Hospital Dr, Washington,
GA, 30673
(404) 678-7804 or 678-7807
Admin Joyce B Barden. *Medical Dir/Dir of
Nursing* C E Pollock MD; Joan Wigton
DON.
Licensure Skilled care; Intermediate care. *Beds*
47. *Certified* Medicaid; Medicare.
Owner Proprietary Corp (National Heritage).
Admissions Requirements Medical
examination.
Staff RNs 1 (ft), 2 (pt); LPNs 3 (ft), 2 (pt);
Nurses aides 13 (ft), 7 (pt); Physical
therapists 1 (pt); Speech therapists 1 (pt);
Activities coordinators 1 (pt); Dietitians 1
(ft); Ophthalmologists 1 (pt); Dentist 1 (pt).
Facilities Dining room; Physical therapy
room; Activities room; Laundry room;
Barber/Beauty shop.
Activities Arts & crafts; Cards; Games; Prayer
groups; Movies; Shopping trips; Social/
Cultural gatherings.

WAVERLY HALL

Oak View Home Inc
PO Box 468, 2 Oak View St, Waverly Hall,
GA, 31906
(404) 582-2117
Admin Theodore C Bowen. *Medical Dir/Dir of
Nursing* Dr Thomas Blake; Kathy Layfield.
Licensure Intermediate care. *Beds* ICF 100.
Certified Medicaid.
Owner Proprietary Corp.
Admissions Requirements Medical
examination.
Staff Physicians 1 (pt); RNs 1 (ft); LPNs 6
(ft); Orderlies 3 (ft), 1 (pt); Nurses aides 11
(ft), 1 (pt); Physical therapists 1 (pt); Speech
therapists 1 (pt); Activities coordinators 2
(ft); Dietitians 1 (pt); Ophthalmologists 1
(pt); Social worker 1 (ft).
Facilities Dining room; Physical therapy
room; Activities room; Chapel; Crafts room;
Laundry room; Barber/Beauty shop.
Activities Arts & crafts; Cards; Games;
Reading groups; Prayer groups; Movies;
Shopping trips; Social/Cultural gatherings.

WAYCROSS

Baptist Village Inc
PO Box 179, Waycross, GA, 31502
(912) 283-7050
Admin J Olan Jones. *Medical Dir/Dir of
Nursing* W B Bates MD.
Licensure Skilled care; Intermediate care;
Retirement. *Beds* SNF 148; ICF 106;
Retirement 84. *Certified* Medicaid.
Admissions Requirements Minimum age 65;
Medical examination; Physician's request.
Staff RNs 8 (ft), 4 (pt); LPNs 29 (ft), 3 (pt);
Nurses aides 87 (ft), 7 (pt); Activities
coordinators 1 (ft); Social services 4 (ft), 3
(pt); Admissions director 1 (ft);
Housekeeping & maintenance 28 (ft), 6 (pt);
Dietary 31 (ft), 9 (pt).
Affiliation Baptist
Facilities Dining room; Physical therapy
room; Activities room; Chapel; Crafts room;
Laundry room; Barber/Beauty shop; Library.
Activities Arts & crafts; Games; Reading
groups; Prayer groups; Movies; Shopping
trips.

Riverside Nursing Home
1600 Riverside Ave, Waycross, GA, 31501
(912) 283-1185, 283-1182
Admin Alpha W Davis. *Medical Dir/Dir of
Nursing* Dr D Richard Lynch; Rebecca A
Hester.
Licensure Skilled care; Intermingled. *Beds*
SNF 96. *Certified* Medicaid; Medicare.
Owner Nonprofit Corp.
Admissions Requirements Medical
examination; Physician's request.
Staff RNs 3 (ft), 1 (pt); LPNs 14 (ft), 2 (pt);
Orderlies 3 (ft), 2 (pt); Nurses aides 23 (ft),
4 (pt); Physical therapists 2 (pt);
Recreational therapists 2 (pt); Occupational
therapists 1 (pt); Speech therapists 1 (pt);
Activities coordinators 1 (ft); Dietitians 1
(ft); Ophthalmologists 1 (pt); Podiatrists 1
(pt).
Facilities Dining room; Physical therapy
room; Activities room; Crafts room; Laundry
room; Barber/Beauty shop; Day rooms.
Activities Cards; Games; Prayer groups;
Movies; Social/Cultural gatherings.

Ware Manor Nursing Home
2210 Dorothy St, Waycross, GA, 31501
(912) 285-4721
Admin James A Goodman. *Medical Dir/Dir of
Nursing* Wiley B Lewis MD; Cynthia Greene
RN BSN.
Licensure Skilled care; Intermediate care. *Beds*
SNF; ICF 92. *Certified* Medicaid.
Owner Proprietary Corp.

Admissions Requirements Medical examination; Physician's request.
Staff Physicians 1 (ft); RNs 3 (ft), 2 (pt); LPNs 8 (ft), 2 (pt); Orderlies 4 (ft); Nurses aides 30 (ft), 15 (pt); Physical therapists 1 (ft); Recreational therapists 1 (ft); Speech therapists 1 (ft); Activities coordinators 1 (ft); Dietitians 1 (ft).
Facilities Dining room; Physical therapy room; Activities room; Chapel; Crafts room; Laundry room; Barber/Beauty shop; Library.
Activities Arts & crafts; Cards; Games; Reading groups; Prayer groups; Movies; Shopping trips; Social/Cultural gatherings.

WAYNESBORO

Brentwood Terrace Health Center
PO Box 907, Waynesboro, GA, 30830
(404) 554-4425
Admin Shelia N Weddon. *Medical Dir/Dir of Nursing* Dr Joseph L Jackson.
Licensure Skilled care; Intermediate care. *Beds* SNF 103; ICF. *Certified* Medicaid.
Owner Proprietary Corp (Beverly Enterprises).
Admissions Requirements Minimum age 18; Medical examination; Physician's request.
Staff Physicians 8 (pt); RNs 5 (ft), 3 (pt); LPNs 8 (ft), 6 (pt); Orderlies 6 (ft), 3 (pt); Nurses aides 24 (ft), 4 (pt); Physical therapists 1 (pt); Recreational therapists 1 (pt); Speech therapists 1 (pt); Activities coordinators 1 (ft); Dietitians 1 (pt).
Languages Spanish (Interpreter available)
Facilities Dining room; Physical therapy room; Activities room; Chapel; Crafts room; Laundry room; Barber/Beauty shop; Library.
Activities Arts & crafts; Cards; Games; Reading groups; Prayer groups; Movies; Shopping trips; Social/Cultural gatherings.

WHIGHAM

Heritage Inn of Whigham*
PO Box 46, Whigham, GA, 31797
(912) 762-4121
Admin Edd W Johnson. *Medical Dir/Dir of Nursing* William J Morton MD.
Licensure Skilled care; Intermediate care. *Beds* 108. *Certified* Medicaid; Medicare.
Staff RNs 1 (ft), 2 (pt); LPNs 10 (ft), 3 (pt); Nurses aides 25 (ft), 7 (pt); Physical therapists 1 (pt); Activities coordinators 1 (ft); Dietitians 1 (pt).
Facilities Dining room; Physical therapy room; Activities room; Crafts room; Laundry room; Barber/Beauty shop.
Activities Arts & crafts; Cards; Games; Reading groups; Prayer groups; Movies; Shopping trips; Social/Cultural gatherings.

WINDER

Russell Nursing Home
PO Box 588, Winder, GA, 30680
(404) 867-2108
Admin Sue Lane. *Medical Dir/Dir of Nursing* John House MD; Jane McDaniel DON.
Licensure Skilled care; Intermediate care. *Beds* SNF 137; ICF 19. *Certified* Medicaid.
Owner Proprietary Corp.
Admissions Requirements Medical examination; Physician's request.
Staff RNs 5 (ft), 1 (pt); LPNs 17 (ft), 4 (pt); Orderlies 6 (ft), 1 (pt); Nurses aides 52 (ft), 7 (pt); Recreational therapists 3 (ft); Activities coordinators 1 (ft), 1 (pt).
Facilities Dining room; Physical therapy room; Activities room; Chapel; Crafts room; Laundry room; Barber/Beauty shop.

Activities Arts & crafts; Games; Reading groups; Movies.

WOODSTOCK

Boddy Nursing Center*
Drawer M, Arnold Mill, Woodstock, GA, 30188
(404) 926-0016
Admin Linda Morris.
Licensure Skilled care; Intermediate care. *Beds* 117. *Certified* Medicaid; Medicare.

WRIGHTSVILLE

Wrightsville Manor Nursing Home
PO Box 209, Wrightsville, GA, 31096
(912) 864-2286
Admin Shirley A Hall. *Medical Dir/Dir of Nursing* William A Dodd MD; Peggy Crooms RN DON.
Licensure Skilled care; Intermediate care. *Beds* SNF; ICF 94. *Certified* Medicaid.
Owner Privately owned.
Admissions Requirements Medical examination; Physician's request.
Staff RNs 1 (ft), 2 (pt); LPNs 9 (ft), 1 (pt); Orderlies 5 (ft), 2 (pt); Nurses aides 18 (ft), 18 (pt); Physical therapists 1 (ft); Recreational therapists 1 (ft); Activities coordinators 1 (ft); Dietitians 1 (ft); Dentist 1 (pt).
Facilities Dining room; Physical therapy room; Activities room; Laundry room; Barber/Beauty shop.
Activities Arts & crafts; Cards; Games; Reading groups; Prayer groups; Movies; Shopping trips; Social/Cultural gatherings.

HAWAII

HALEIWA

Crawford's Convalescent Home*
58-130 Kamehameha Hwy, Haleiwa, HI, 96712
(808) 638-8514
Admin Alice Lew.
Licensure Intermediate care. *Beds* 68. *Certified* Medicaid.
Admissions Requirements Medical examination.
Staff RNs 3 (ft), 2 (pt); LPNs 1 (ft); Nurses aides 28 (ft); Physical therapists 1 (pt); Recreational therapists 1 (ft); Occupational therapists 1 (pt); Activities coordinators 1 (ft); Dietitians 1 (pt).
Facilities Dining room; Physical therapy room; Activities room; Crafts room; Laundry room.
Activities Arts & crafts; Cards; Games; Prayer groups; Movies; Shopping trips; Social/Cultural gatherings.

HILO

Hilo Hospital (DP)
1190 Waianuenue Ave, Hilo, HI, 96720
(808) 969-4152
Admin Jerry Merrill. *Medical Dir/Dir of Nursing* Dr G Matsuda; Ms P Lambeth.
Licensure Skilled care; Intermediate care. *Beds* SNF 36; ICF 72. *Certified* Medicaid; Medicare.
Owner Publicly owned.
Admissions Requirements Physician's request.
Staff RNs 7 (ft); LPNs 26 (ft); Nurses aides 32 (ft); Physical therapists 1 (ft); Occupational therapists 3 (ft); Dietitians 1 (ft).
Languages Japanese, Chinese, Tagalog, Portuguese
Facilities Dining room; Physical therapy room; Activities room; Laundry room; Barber/Beauty shop; Library.
Activities Arts & crafts; Games; Prayer groups; Movies; Shopping trips; Social/Cultural gatherings; Outings.

Life Care Center of Hilo
944 W Kawailani St, Hilo, HI, 96720
(808) 959-9151
Admin Marcus Kaya. *Medical Dir/Dir of Nursing* Ernest Bape; Liz Holt.
Licensure Intermediate care. *Beds* ICF 240. *Certified* Medicaid.
Owner Proprietary Corp (Life Care Centers of America).
Admissions Requirements Medical examination; Physician's request.
Staff RNs 3 (ft), 3 (pt); LPNs 8 (ft), 8 (pt); Nurses aides 45 (ft), 20 (pt); Activities coordinators 1 (ft); Dietitians 1 (ft).
Languages Tagalog, Japanese
Facilities Dining room; Activities room; Crafts room; Laundry room; Barber/Beauty shop; Library.
Activities Arts & crafts; Cards; Games; Reading groups; Prayer groups; Movies; Shopping trips; Social/Cultural gatherings.

HONOKAA

Honokaa Hospital*
Box 37, Honokaa, HI, 96727
(808) 775-7211
Admin Yoshito Iwamoto.
Licensure Skilled care. *Beds* 8. *Certified* Medicaid; Medicare.

HONOLULU

Arcadia Retirement Residence
1434 Punahou St, Honolulu, HI, 96822
(808) 941-0941
Admin Helen E Meredith. *Medical Dir/Dir of Nursing* Patricia Vierw DON.
Licensure Skilled care; Life care residence. *Beds* SNF 58. *Certified* Medicare.
Owner Nonprofit Corp.
Admissions Requirements Minimum age 60; Medical examination; Physician's request.
Staff RNs; LPNs; Nurses aides; Geriatric nurse practitioner 1 (ft).
Affiliation Church of Christ
Facilities Dining room; Physical therapy room; Activities room; Chapel; Crafts room; Laundry room; Barber/Beauty shop.
Activities Arts & crafts; Cards; Games; Reading groups; Prayer groups; Movies; Shopping trips; Social/Cultural gatherings.

Beverly Manor Convalescent Center*
1930 Kamehameha IV Rd, Honolulu, HI, 96819
(808) 847-4834
Admin Virginia Hueftle.
Licensure Skilled care; Intermediate care. *Beds* 108. *Certified* Medicaid; Medicare.
Owner Proprietary Corp (Beverly Enterprises).

Convalescent Center of Honolulu
1900 Bachelot St, Honolulu, HI, 96817
(808) 531-5302
Admin Abe Sakai. *Medical Dir/Dir of Nursing* Dr Walter W Y Chang; Sai Chantary RN DON.
Licensure Skilled care. *Beds* 182. *Certified* Medicaid; Medicare.
Admissions Requirements Medical examination; Physician's request.
Staff Physicians 1 (pt); RNs 16 (pt); LPNs 13 (pt); Nurses aides 80 (pt); Physical therapists 1 (pt); Reality therapists 1 (pt); Recreational therapists 2 (pt); Occupational therapists 1 (ft); Activities coordinators 1 (ft); Dietitians 1 (ft).
Facilities Dining room; Physical therapy room; Activities room; Laundry room; Library.
Activities Arts & crafts; Cards; Games; Prayer groups; Movies; Shopping trips; Social/Cultural gatherings.

Hale Ho Aloha ICF
2630 Pacific Heights Rd, Honolulu, HI, 96813
(808) 524-1955
Admin Lorraine Manayan.
Licensure Intermediate care. *Beds* 85.

Owner Proprietary Corp.
Admissions Requirements Medical examination.
Staff Physicians 3 (pt); RNs 3 (ft), 5 (pt); LPNs 3 (ft), 3 (pt); Nurses aides 42 (ft), 6 (pt); Physical therapists 1 (pt); Recreational therapists 1 (ft); Occupational therapists 1 (pt); Activities coordinators 1 (ft); Dietitians 1 (pt).
Facilities Dining room; Physical therapy room; Activities room; Crafts room; Laundry room; Barber/Beauty shop.
Activities Arts & crafts; Cards; Games; Reading groups; Prayer groups; Movies; Social/Cultural gatherings.

Hale Malamalama*
6163 Summer St, Honolulu, HI, 96821
(808) 396-0537
Admin Agnes Uyehara. *Medical Dir/Dir of Nursing* Dr George Seberg.
Licensure Intermediate care. *Beds* 31. *Certified* Medicaid.
Admissions Requirements Minimum age 21; Medical examination; Physician's request.
Staff RNs 2 (ft), 1 (pt); LPNs 1 (ft); Nurses aides 13 (ft); Physical therapists 1 (pt); Recreational therapists 1 (pt); Occupational therapists 1 (pt).
Facilities Dining room; Physical therapy room; Activities room; Crafts room; Laundry room.
Activities Arts & crafts; Cards; Games; Movies; Entertainment by clubs & groups.

Hale Nani Health Center*
1677 Pensacola St, Honolulu, HI, 96822
(808) 537-3371
Admin Jerry Minson. *Medical Dir/Dir of Nursing* Dr Gladys Fryer.
Licensure Skilled care; Intermediate care. *Beds* 232. *Certified* Medicaid; Medicare.
Admissions Requirements Medical examination; Physician's request.
Staff Physicians 1 (pt); RNs 10 (ft), 5 (pt); LPNs 10 (ft), 6 (pt); Physical therapists 1 (ft); Recreational therapists 2 (ft), 4 (pt); Occupational therapists 1 (ft); Speech therapists 1 (pt); Activities coordinators 1 (ft); Dietitians 2 (pt).
Facilities Dining room; Physical therapy room; Activities room; Chapel; Crafts room; Laundry room; Barber/Beauty shop; Library.
Activities Arts & crafts; Cards; Games; Reading groups; Prayer groups; Movies.

Hawaii Select Care Inc
1814 Liliha St, Honolulu, HI, 96817
(808) 523-5402
Admin Francis M Okita. *Medical Dir/Dir of Nursing* Dr Gerald Soon; Dorothy Moon.
Licensure Intermediate care. *Beds* ICF 92. *Certified* Medicaid.
Owner Proprietary Corp.
Admissions Requirements Medical examination.
Staff RNs 3 (ft); LPNs 3 (ft), 1 (pt); Nurses aides 13 (ft), 21 (pt); Activities coordinators 1 (ft); Social worker 1 (ft).

Facilities Dining room; Activities room; Laundry room; Recreation areas; Office.
Activities Arts & crafts; Cards; Games; Reading groups; Prayer groups; Movies; Shopping trips; Social/Cultural gatherings.

Island Nursing Home
1205 Alexander St, Honolulu, HI, 96826
(808) 946-5027
Admin Leland Yagi. *Medical Dir/Dir of Nursing* Jean Sudduth RN DON.
Licensure SNF/ICF Swing beds. *Beds* SNF/ICF Swing beds 42. *Certified* Medicaid; Medicare.
Owner Privately owned.
Admissions Requirements Physician's request.
Staff RNs 5 (ft), 3 (pt); LPNs 1 (ft); Nurses aides 21 (ft), 6 (pt); Occupational therapists 1 (pt); Activities coordinators 1 (ft), 1 (pt).
Languages Japanese
Facilities Dining room; Activities room.
Activities Arts & crafts; Cards; Games; Reading groups; Prayer groups; Movies; Shopping trips; Social/Cultural gatherings; Beach; Zoo; Restaurants.

Kuakini Geriatric Care Inc
347 N Kuakini St, Honolulu, HI, 96817
(808) 547-9231
Admin Satoru Izutsu. *Medical Dir/Dir of Nursing* Isaac Kawasaki MD; Natsumi Hodson DON.
Licensure Skilled care; Intermediate care; Care home; Day health; Day care. *Beds* SNF 50; ICF 150; care home 50. *Certified* Medicaid; Medicare.
Owner Nonprofit organization/foundation.
Admissions Requirements Medical examination; Physician's request.
Staff RNs; LPNs; Nurses aides; Physical therapists; Recreational therapists; Occupational therapists; Speech therapists; Activities coordinators; Dietitians.
Facilities Dining room; Activities room; Chapel; Crafts room; Laundry room; Barber/Beauty shop; Library.
Activities Arts & crafts; Cards; Games; Reading groups; Prayer groups; Movies; Shopping trips; Social/Cultural gatherings.

Leahi Hospital (DP)
3675 Kilauea Ave, Honolulu, HI, 96816
(808) 734-0221
Admin Abraham L Choy. *Medical Dir/Dir of Nursing* Verne C Waite MD; Ellen F Sherman.
Licensure Skilled care; Intermediate care. *Beds* 166. *Certified* Medicaid; Medicare.
Owner Publicly owned.
Admissions Requirements Medical examination; Physician's request.
Staff Physicians 1 (ft); RNs 26 (ft); LPNs 32 (ft); Nurses aides 56 (ft); Physical therapists 1 (ft); Recreational therapists 2 (ft); Occupational therapists 3 (ft); Dietitians 3 (ft).
Languages Japanese, Chinese, Tagalog
Facilities Dining room; Physical therapy room; Activities room; Crafts room; Laundry room; Library.
Activities Arts & crafts; Games; Reading groups; Prayer groups; Movies; Social/Cultural gatherings.

Maluhia (A Long-Term Care Health Center)
1027 Hala Dr, Honolulu, HI, 96817
(808) 845-2951
Admin Gilbert A Gima. *Medical Dir/Dir of Nursing* Dr Yoshie Takagi; June Nakashima RN.
Licensure Skilled care; Intermediate care. *Beds* 158. *Certified* Medicaid; Medicare.
Owner Publicly owned.
Admissions Requirements Minimum age 18; Physician's request.

Staff Physicians 1 (ft), 1 (pt); RNs 20 (ft); LPNs 14 (ft); Nurses aides 74 (ft); Physical therapists 1 (pt); Recreational therapists 1 (ft); Occupational therapists 2 (ft); Activities coordinators 1 (ft); Dietitians 2 (ft).
Languages Japanese, Tagalog Hawaiian, Chinese, Vietnamese
Facilities Dining room; Physical therapy room; Activities room; Chapel; Crafts room; Laundry room; Barber/Beauty shop; Library.
Activities Arts & crafts; Cards; Games; Reading groups; Prayer groups; Movies; Shopping trips; Social/Cultural gatherings; Exercise; Rides; Picnics.

Maunalani Hospital*
5113 Maunalani Circle, Honolulu, HI, 96816
(808) 732-0771
Admin Kenneth Halpenny. *Medical Dir/Dir of Nursing* Dr George Mills.
Licensure Skilled care. *Beds* 101. *Certified* Medicaid; Medicare.
Staff Physicians 1 (ft); RNs 9 (ft); LPNs 8 (ft); Nurses aides 43 (ft); Physical therapists 1 (ft); Recreational therapists 1 (ft); Occupational therapists 1 (ft); Speech therapists 1 (ft); Activities coordinators 1 (ft); Dietitians 1 (ft).
Facilities Dining room; Physical therapy room; Activities room; Crafts room; Laundry room.
Activities Arts & crafts; Cards; Games; Reading groups; Movies; Shopping trips.

Nuuanu Hale Hospital*
2900 Pali Hwy, Honolulu, HI, 96817
(808) 595-6311
Admin Sallie Y Miyawaki. *Medical Dir/Dir of Nursing* Dr Dennis S Murakami.
Licensure Skilled care. *Beds* 75. *Certified* Medicaid; Medicare.
Admissions Requirements Medical examination; Physician's request.
Staff Physicians 1 (pt); RNs 6 (ft), 5 (pt); LPNs 6 (pt); Nurses aides 32 (ft), 7 (pt); Physical therapists 1 (pt); Occupational therapists 1 (pt); Speech therapists 1 (pt); Activities coordinators 1 (ft); Dietitians 1 (pt); Dentists 1 (pt); Ophthalmologists 1 (pt); Podiatrists 1 (pt); Audiologists 1 (pt).
Facilities Dining room; Physical therapy room; Activities room; Crafts room.
Activities Arts & crafts; Cards; Games; Reading groups; Prayer groups; Movies; Shopping trips; Social/Cultural gatherings; Outings.

St Francis Hospital (DP)*
2230 Liliha St, Honolulu, HI, 96817
(808) 547-6011
Admin Michael Matsuura. *Medical Dir/Dir of Nursing* Robert Ballard MD.
Licensure Skilled care. *Beds* 52. *Certified* Medicaid; Medicare.
Admissions Requirements Medical examination; Physician's request.
Staff RNs 3 (ft), 2 (pt); LPNs 10 (ft); Nurses aides 19 (ft), 2 (pt); Physical therapists 1 (ft); Recreational therapists 1 (ft); Occupational therapists 1 (ft); Speech therapists 1 (pt); Activities coordinators 1 (ft), 1 (pt); Dietitians 1 (ft); Dentists 3 (ft); Podiatrists 1 (ft).
Affiliation Roman Catholic
Facilities Dining room; Physical therapy room; Activities room; Chapel; Crafts room; Laundry room; Library; Occupational therapy room.
Activities Arts & crafts; Cards; Games; Prayer groups; Movies; Shopping trips; Social/Cultural gatherings; Monthly luncheons.

KAHUKU

Kahuku Hospital
Box 218, Kahuku, HI, 96731
(808) 293-9221

Admin Rikio Tanji. *Medical Dir/Dir of Nursing* Judith Correa DON.
Licensure Skilled care. *Beds* 11. *Certified* Medicaid; Medicare.
Owner Nonprofit organization/foundation.
Admissions Requirements Physician's request.
Staff Physicians 7 (ft); RNs 16 (ft); LPNs 8 (ft); Nurses aides 8 (ft), 1 (pt); Physical therapists 1 (ft); Dietitians 1 (pt).
Languages Tagalog
Facilities Physical therapy room; Activities room.
Activities Games; Prayer groups.

KANEOHE

Ann Pearl Intermediate Care Facility*
45-181 Waikalua Rd, Kaneohe, HI, 96744
(808) 247-8558
Admin Clifford Miller Jr.
Licensure Intermediate care. *Beds* 86. *Certified* Medicaid.

Pohai Nani Care Center
45-090 Namoku St, Kaneohe, HI, 96744
(808) 246-1670
Admin Dean Joel Mertz. *Medical Dir/Dir of Nursing* Glenn Stahl MD; Carolyn Morrison RN.
Licensure Skilled care; Intermediate care. *Beds* SNF 42; ICF. *Certified* Medicaid; Medicare.
Owner Nonprofit Corp (Evangelical Lutheran/Good Samaritan).
Admissions Requirements Medical examination; Physician's request.
Staff Physicians 1 (pt); RNs 4 (ft), 4 (pt); LPNs 1 (ft); Nurses aides 13 (ft), 5 (pt); Activities coordinators 1 (ft).
Languages Hawaiian
Affiliation Lutheran
Facilities Dining room; Physical therapy room; Activities room; Laundry room; Barber/Beauty shop; Lanai & garden area.
Activities Arts & crafts; Cards; Games; Reading groups; Prayer groups; Movies; Shopping trips; Social/Cultural gatherings; Entertainment by community groups.

KAPAA

Samuel Mahelona Memorial Hospital (DP)
4800 Kawaihau Rd, Kapaa, HI, 96746
(808) 822-4961
Admin John M English. *Medical Dir/Dir of Nursing* Sasha E Myers MD; Sheila Ventura DON.
Licensure Skilled care; Intermediate care. *Beds* 61. *Certified* Medicaid; Medicare.
Admissions Requirements Medical examination; Physician's request.
Staff Physicians 1 (ft), 11 (pt); RNs 17 (ft); LPNs 28 (ft); Nurses aides 20 (ft); Physical therapists 1 (ft); Occupational therapists 2 (ft); Activities coordinators 1 (ft); Dietitians 1 (ft);; Social worker 2 (ft).
Facilities Dining room; Physical therapy room; Activities room; Crafts room; Laundry room; Barber/Beauty shop; Library.
Activities Arts & crafts; Cards; Games; Prayer groups; Movies; Shopping trips; Social/Cultural gatherings.

KAPAAU

Kohala Hospital (DP)
Box 10, Kapaau, HI, 96755
(808) 889-6211
Admin Jack O Halstead. *Medical Dir/Dir of Nursing* Patrick Siu MD; Tom Knott RN.
Licensure Skilled care; Intermediate care; Hospital acute; Outpatient; Ambulance. *Beds* SNF 18; SNF/Acute 4; Acute 4. *Certified* Medicaid; Medicare.
Owner Publicly owned.
Admissions Requirements Medical examination; Physician's request.

Staff Physicians 5 (ft), 1 (pt); RNs 6 (ft); LPNs 5 (ft); Orderlies 6 (ft); Nurses aides 2 (ft); Occupational therapists 1 (ft); Activities coordinators 1 (ft); Dietitians 1 (pt).
Languages Japanese, Tagalog, Chinese, Hawaiian
Facilities Activities room; Laundry room.
Activities Arts & crafts; Games; Prayer groups; Movies; Mystery excursions.

KAUNAKAKAI

Molokai General Hospital (DP)
PO Box 408, Kaunakakai, HI, 96748
(808) 553-5331
Admin Herbert K Yim. *Medical Dir/Dir of Nursing* Jo Ann Ennis.
Licensure Skilled care; Intermediate care; Acute. *Beds* 30. *Certified* Medicaid; Medicare.
Owner Nonprofit Corp.
Staff RNs; LPNs; Nurses aides; Physical therapists; Occupational therapists; Dietitians; Activities Aide.
Languages Japanese, Tagalog
Facilities Dining room; Physical therapy room; Activities room; Crafts room; Laundry room.
Activities Arts & crafts; Cards; Games; Movies; Social/Cultural gatherings; Sightseeing.

KEALAKEKUA

Kona Hospital (DP)
PO Box 69, Kealakekua, HI, 96750
(808) 322-9311
Admin Jennie Wung RN. *Medical Dir/Dir of Nursing* Robert DeMello.
Licensure Skilled care; Intermediate care; Acute care. *Beds* SNF 14; ICF 8; Acute 53. *Certified* Medicaid; Medicare.
Owner Publicly owned.
Admissions Requirements Physician's request.
Staff RNs 5 (ft); LPNs 4 (ft); Nurses aides 6 (ft); Physical therapists 1 (ft); Occupational therapists 1 (ft); Speech therapists 1 (pt); Activities coordinators 1 (ft); Dietitians 2 (ft).
Facilities Physical therapy room; Activities room.
Activities Arts & crafts; Cards; Games.

KULA

Kula Hospital
204 Kula Hwy, Kula, HI, 96790
(808) 878-1221
Admin Romel Dela Cruz. *Medical Dir/Dir of Nursing* Richard M Gordon MD; Shirley K Takahashi RN DON.
Licensure Skilled care; Intermediate care; Intermediate care for mentally retarded. *Beds* SNF; ICF 94; ICF/MR 8. *Certified* Medicaid; Medicare.
Owner Publicly owned.
Admissions Requirements Medical examination.
Staff Physicians 2 (ft); RNs 18 (ft); LPNs 7 (ft); Nurses aides 43 (ft); Occupational therapists 1 (ft); Dietitians 1 (ft).
Languages Japanese, Hawaiian
Facilities Dining room; Physical therapy room; Activities room; Crafts room; Laundry room; Barber/Beauty shop; Library; A van for patient outings.
Activities Arts & crafts; Cards; Games; Reading groups; Prayer groups; Movies; Shopping trips; Social/Cultural gatherings.

LANAI

Lanai Community Hospital (DP)
Box 797, Lanai, HI, 96763
(808) 565-6411

Admin Monica L Borges. *Medical Dir/Dir of Nursing* Robert Cary MD; D Fabrao DON.
Licensure Skilled care; Intermediate care; Acute. *Beds* SNF 8; ICF; Acute 6. *Certified* Medicaid; Medicare.
Owner Publicly owned.
Admissions Requirements Physician's request.
Staff Physicians 1 (ft); RNs 6 (ft); Nurses aides 5 (ft); Physical therapists 1 (pt); Occupational therapists 1 (pt); Dietitians 1 (pt); Ophthalmologists 1 (pt).
Facilities Dining room; Physical therapy room; Activities room; Laundry room; Library; Whirlpool.
Activities Arts & crafts; Cards; Games; Shopping trips; Parties for birthdays; Senior Citizen dining groups.

LIHUE

G N Wilcox Memorial Hospital
3420 Kuhio Hwy, Lihue, HI, 96766
(808) 245-1100
Admin Phillip Palmer. *Medical Dir/Dir of Nursing* William A Renti Cruz MD; Patricia Palmer RN.
Licensure Skilled care; Intermediate care. *Beds* SNF 80; ICF. *Certified* Medicaid; Medicare.
Owner Nonprofit Corp.
Admissions Requirements Physician's request.
Staff Physicians 1 (pt); RNs 6 (ft); LPNs 8 (ft), 2 (pt); Nurses aides 21 (ft), 3 (pt); Physical therapists 1 (ft); Recreational therapists 3 (pt); Occupational therapists 1 (ft); Speech therapists 1 (pt); Activities coordinators 1 (ft); Dietitians 1 (ft).
Languages Tagalog, Japanese
Facilities Dining room; Physical therapy room; Activities room; Chapel; Crafts room.
Activities Arts & crafts; Games; Prayer groups; Movies; Shopping trips.

PAHALA

Kau Hospital
PO Box 40, Pahala, HI, 96777
(808) 928-8331
Admin Kenji Nagao. *Medical Dir/Dir of Nursing* Debra M Javar.
Licensure Skilled care; Acute; Day hospital program. *Beds* SNF 8; Acute 5; Day hospital 2. *Certified* Medicaid; Medicare.
Admissions Requirements Medical examination; Physician's request.
Staff Physicians 2 (ft), 1 (pt); RNs 7 (ft); LPNs 6 (ft); Nurses aides 5 (ft); Physical therapists 1 (pt); Occupational therapists 1 (pt); Activities coordinators 1 (ft); Dietitians 1 (pt).
Facilities Dining room; Physical therapy room; Activities room.
Activities Arts & crafts; Cards; Games; Reading groups; Prayer groups; Movies; Shopping trips; Social/Cultural gatherings.

PEARL CITY

Waimano Training School & Hospital*
Pearl City, HI, 96782
(808) 456-6211
Admin Lois Suenishi. *Medical Dir/Dir of Nursing* Louise Iwaishi MD.
Licensure Intermediate care for mentally retarded. *Beds* 575. *Certified* Medicaid.
Admissions Requirements Medical examination; Physician's request.
Staff Physicians 3 (ft); RNs 74 (ft); LPNs 61 (ft); Nurses aides 174 (ft); Physical therapists 2 (ft); Recreational therapists 21 (ft); Occupational therapists 5 (ft); Speech therapists 3 (ft); Dietitians 2 (ft); Audiologists 1 (ft).
Facilities Dining room; Physical therapy room; Laundry room.
Activities Arts & crafts; Games; Movies; Shopping trips; Social/Cultural gatherings.

WAHIAWA

Wahiawa General Hospital
PO Box 580, Wahiawa, HI, 96786
(808) 621-8411
Admin Kenam Kim. *Medical Dir/Dir of Nursing* Robert Mookini MD.
Licensure Skilled care; Intermediate care. *Beds* 93. *Certified* Medicaid; Medicare.
Owner Nonprofit Corp.
Admissions Requirements Medical examination; Physician's request.
Staff RNs 13 (ft), 1 (pt); LPNs 12 (ft), 1 (pt); Nurses aides 37 (ft), 1 (pt); Physical therapists 2 (ft); Occupational therapists 1 (ft); Activities coordinators 1 (ft); Dietitians 1 (pt); Podiatrists Clerk 1 (ft).
Languages Japanese, Korean, Tagalog, Samoan, Spanish, Portuguese, Chinese
Facilities Dining room; Physical therapy room; Activities room; Crafts room; Barber/Beauty shop.
Activities Arts & crafts; Cards; Games; Reading groups; Prayer groups; Movies; Social/Cultural gatherings.

WAIANAE

Leeward Nursing Home Inc
84-390 Jade St, Waianae, HI, 69792
(808) 695-9508
Admin Jean Dyer BSN. *Medical Dir/Dir of Nursing* Linda Carr RN DON.
Licensure Intermediate care. *Beds* ICF 50. *Certified* Medicaid.
Owner Proprietary Corp.
Admissions Requirements Medical examination; Physician's request.
Staff RNs 3 (ft); LPNs 1 (ft), 1 (pt); Nurses aides 17 (ft), 1 (pt); Activities coordinators 1 (pt); Dietitians 1 (pt).
Languages Tagalog, Japanese, Chinese
Facilities Dining room; Activities room; Chapel; Crafts room; Library; Laundry room; Barber/Beauty shop.
Activities Arts & crafts; Cards; Games; Reading groups; Prayer groups; Movies; Shopping trips; Social/Cultural gatherings; Reality orientation; Music; Picnics; Beauty class; Exercise; Sunshine therapy; Gardening; Birthday parties.

WAILUKU

Hale Makua
1540 E Main St, Wailuku, HI, 96732
(808) 877-2761
Admin Lillian Higa BSN. *Medical Dir/Dir of Nursing* Alice M Broadhurst MD.
Licensure Intermediate care. *Beds* ICF 124. *Certified* Medicaid.
Owner Nonprofit organization/foundation.
Admissions Requirements Medical examination; Physician's request.
Staff RNs 8 (ft), 3 (pt); LPNs 6 (ft), 1 (pt); Nurses aides 40 (ft), 2 (pt); Activities coordinators 1 (ft); Dietitians; Ophthalmologists.
Languages Japanese
Facilities Dining room; Activities room; Crafts room; Laundry room; Barber/Beauty shop; Library; Gardens.
Activities Arts & crafts; Cards; Games; Reading groups; Prayer groups; Movies; Shopping trips; Social/Cultural gatherings; Picnics; Social groups & schools present programs.

WAILUKU MAUI

Hale Makua Home Health Care Agency
Saburo Bldg, 771 Alua St, Wailuku, Maui, HI, 96793
(808) 242-4790
Admin Martha Turner. *Medical Dir/Dir of Nursing* Alice M Broardhurst MD.

Beds 120. *Certified* Medicaid; Medicare.
Owner Nonprofit organization/foundation.
Admissions Requirements Physician's request.
Staff RNs 6 (ft), 3 (pt); Nurses aides 23 (ft), 3
(pt); Physical therapists 2 (ft), 2 (pt);
Occupational therapists 1 (pt); Speech
therapists 1 (pt); Dietitians 1 (pt).

WAIMEA

Kauai Veterans Memorial Hospital (DP)
PO Box 337, Waimea, HI, 96796
(808) 338-9431
Admin Keith Horinouchi. *Medical Dir/Dir of
Nursing* Dr Yonemichi Miyashiro; Janet
Kawamura RN DON.
Licensure Skilled care. *Beds* SNF 6. *Certified*
Medicaid; Medicare.
Owner Publicly owned.

Admissions Requirements Medical
examination; Physician's request.
Staff RNs 1 (ft); LPNs 5 (ft); Nurses aides 3
(ft); Physical therapists 1 (ft); Occupational
therapists 1 (ft); Dietitians 1 (ft).
Languages Tagalog, Japanese, Hawaiian
Facilities Physical therapy room; Activities
room; Crafts room; Library.
Activities Arts & crafts; Games; Movies;
Shopping trips; Monthly & holiday parties.

IDAHO

AMERICAN FALLS

Power County Nursing Home
Gifford at Roosevelt, American Falls, ID, 83211
(208) 226-2327
Admin Francis X McNamara. *Medical Dir/Dir of Nursing* Jerry Knouf MD; Susan Fletcher RN DON.
Licensure Skilled care; Intermediate care. *Beds* 31. *Certified* Medicaid; Medicare.
Owner Publicly owned.
Admissions Requirements Medical examination; Physician's request.
Staff Activities coordinators 1 (pt); Dietitians 1 (pt); Ophthalmologists 1 (pt).
Facilities Dining room; Physical therapy room; Activities room; Chapel; Crafts room; Laundry room; Barber/Beauty shop; Library.
Activities Arts & crafts; Cards; Games; Reading groups; Prayer groups; Movies; Shopping trips; Social/Cultural gatherings; Bingo; Volleyball; Quilting.

ARCO

Lost Rivers District Hospital & Nursing Home
PO Box 145, 551 Highland Dr, Arco, ID, 83213
(208) 527-8206
Admin Martha Danz. *Medical Dir/Dir of Nursing* R F Barter MD; Jessie Bell RN DON.
Licensure Skilled care; Intermediate care; Sheltered care. *Beds* 10. *Certified* Medicaid; Medicare.
Owner Publicly owned.
Admissions Requirements Minimum age 21; Medical examination; Physician's request.
Staff Physicians 1 (ft); RNs 3 (ft), 4 (pt); LPNs 3 (ft), 2 (pt); Orderlies 1 (ft); Physical therapists 1 (pt); Activities coordinators 1 (pt); Dietitians 1 (pt).
Facilities Dining room; Physical therapy room; Activities room; Crafts room; Laundry room; Barber/Beauty shop.
Activities Arts & crafts; Cards; Games; Reading groups; Prayer groups; Movies; Shopping trips; Social/Cultural gatherings.

ASHTON

Ashton Nursing Home*
Box 378, 801 Main St, Ashton, ID, 83420
(208) 652-7461
Admin Howard D Bergman.
Licensure Intermediate care. *Beds* 12. *Certified* Medicaid.

BLACKFOOT

Bingham County Nursing Home
98 Poplar St, Blackfoot, ID, 83221
(208) 785-4100
Admin Carl Staley. *Medical Dir/Dir of Nursing* W G Hoge MD; Ada Mae Exeter RN.

Licensure Skilled care; Intermediate care. *Beds* 56. *Certified* Medicaid; Medicare.
Owner Nonprofit organization/foundation.
Admissions Requirements Medical examination; Physician's request.
Staff Physicians 7 (pt); RNs 1 (ft), 1 (pt); LPNs 4 (ft), 1 (pt); Nurses aides 30 (ft), 2 (pt); Physical therapists 1 (pt); Occupational therapists 1 (pt); Speech therapists 1 (pt); Activities coordinators 1 (ft); Dietitians 1 (pt); Dentists 1 (pt); Ophthalmologists 1 (pt); Podiatrists 1 (pt).
Languages Spanish
Facilities Dining room; Activities room; Crafts room; Laundry room; Barber/Beauty shop.
Activities Arts & crafts; Cards; Games; Reading groups; Prayer groups; Movies; Shopping trips.

Syrings Chalet*
Box 390, State Hospital South, Blackfoot, ID, 83221
(208) 785-1200
Admin Dwight J Petersen.
Licensure Intermediate care. *Beds* 45. *Certified* Medicaid.

BOISE

Boise Group Home 1*
1736 N Five Mile Rd, Boise, ID, 83704
(208) 376-1861
Admin Richard Davis.
Licensure Intermediate care for mentally retarded. *Beds* 12. *Certified* Medicaid.

Boise Group Home 2
10528 Milclay St, Boise, ID, 83704
(208) 376-1861
Admin H Michael Day PhD.
Licensure Intermediate care for mentally retarded. *Beds* ICF/MR 6. *Certified* Medicaid.
Owner Nonprofit Corp.
Admissions Requirements Minimum age 6; Medical examination.
Staff Physicians 1 (pt); RNs 1 (pt); LPNs 1 (pt); Orderlies 5 (ft); Physical therapists 1 (pt); Recreational therapists 1 (pt); Occupational therapists 1 (pt); Speech therapists 1 (pt); Dietitians 1 (pt); Podiatrists 1 (pt).
Facilities Home setting.

Boise Group Home 3*
10349 Summerwind Dr, Boise, ID, 83704
(208) 376-1861
Admin Richard Davis.
Licensure Skilled care; Intermediate care. *Certified* Medicaid.

Boise Samaritan Village
3115 Sycamore Dr, Boise, ID, 83703
(208) 343-7726
Admin Dwight Wuenschel. *Medical Dir/Dir of Nursing* Ward Dickey MD; Audry Smith DON.

Licensure Skilled care. *Beds* 215. *Certified* Medicaid; Medicare.
Owner Nonprofit Corp (Evangelical Lutheran/Good Samaritan).
Admissions Requirements Medical examination.
Staff Physicians; RNs; LPNs; Orderlies; Nurses aides; Recreational therapists; Speech therapists; Activities coordinators; Dietitians; Podiatrists.
Languages Sign
Affiliation Lutheran
Facilities Dining room; Physical therapy room; Activities room; Chapel; Crafts room; Laundry room; Barber/Beauty shop; Library; Snack bar.
Activities Arts & crafts; Cards; Games; Reading groups; Prayer groups; Movies; Shopping trips; Social/Cultural gatherings.

Capital Care Center
8211 Ustick Rd, Boise, ID, 83704
(208) 375-3700
Admin Brent P Barraclough. *Medical Dir/Dir of Nursing* Edward H Newcombe MD; Leann Patterson RN DNS.
Licensure Skilled care; Intermediate care; Sheltered care. *Beds* SNF 164; ICF; Sheltered care 54. *Certified* Medicaid; Medicare.
Owner Proprietary Corp (National Heritage).
Staff Physicians 1 (pt); RNs 9 (ft), 3 (pt); LPNs 13 (ft), 2 (pt); Nurses aides 52 (ft), 8 (pt); Physical therapists 1 (ft); Occupational therapists 1 (pt); Speech therapists 1 (pt); Activities coordinators 1 (ft); Dietitians 1 (ft); Ophthalmologists 1 (pt); Podiatrists 1 (pt); Dentist 1 (pt).
Facilities Dining room; Physical therapy room; Activities room; Chapel; Barber/Beauty shop.
Activities Arts & crafts; Cards; Games; Reading groups; Prayer groups; Movies; Shopping trips; Social/Cultural gatherings; Singing programs; Exercise groups.

CommuniCare
2650 S Pond, Boise, ID, 83705
(208) 344-6683
Admin Tom Whittemore.
Licensure Intermediate care for mentally retarded. *Beds* 8. *Certified* Medicaid.
Admissions Requirements Minimum age 18.
Staff Physicians 2 (pt); RNs 1 (pt); LPNs 1 (pt); Physical therapists 1 (pt); Recreational therapists 1 (pt); Speech therapists 1 (pt); Activities coordinators 1 (pt); Dietitians 1 (pt); Dentists 1 (pt); Ophthalmologists 1 (pt); Podiatrists 1 (pt).
Facilities Dining room; Activities room; Crafts room.
Activities Arts & crafts; Cards; Games; Movies; Shopping trips; Social/Cultural gatherings.

Emerald Care Center
808 N Curtis, Boise, ID, 83706
376-5273

Admin Mel Everett. *Medical Dir/Dir of Nursing* Edward Newcombe MD; Diana Logan DON.
Licensure Skilled care. *Beds* SNF 164. *Certified* Medicaid; Medicare.
Owner Proprietary Corp.
Admissions Requirements Medical examination; Physician's request.
Staff Physicians; RNs; LPNs; Orderlies; Nurses aides; Physical therapists; Reality therapists; Recreational therapists; Occupational therapists; Speech therapists; Activities coordinators; Dietitians; Dentists; Ophthalmologists.
Facilities Dining room; Physical therapy room; Activities room; Crafts room; Laundry room; Barber/Beauty shop; Library.
Activities Arts & crafts; Cards; Games; Reading groups; Prayer groups; Movies; Shopping trips; Social/Cultural gatherings; Field trips; Birthday parties; Anniversaries; Monthly resident newspaper.

Gem State Homes Inc 4*
4150 Leland Way, Boise, ID, 83709
(208) 362-3003
Admin Jerry R Fowler.
Licensure Intermediate care for mentally retarded. *Beds* 8. *Certified* Medicaid.
Admissions Requirements Minimum age; Medical examination; Physician's request.
Staff Physicians 1 (pt); RNs 1 (pt); LPNs 1 (pt); Physical therapists 1 (pt); Recreational therapists 1 (pt); Speech therapists 1 (pt); Dietitians 1 (pt); Dentists 1 (pt); Audiologists 1 (pt).
Facilities Dining room; Activities room.
Activities Arts & crafts; Games; Movies; Shopping trips; Social/Cultural gatherings.

Grand Oaks Healthcare*
316 W Washington, Boise, ID, 83702
(208) 343-7755
Admin William J Scifres.
Licensure Skilled care. *Beds* 88. *Certified* Medicaid; Medicare.

Hillcrest Care Center*
1001 S Hilton St, Boise, ID, 83705
(208) 345-4464
Admin Steven H Schreiber. *Medical Dir/Dir of Nursing* Dr David Weeks.
Licensure Skilled care. *Beds* 123. *Certified* Medicaid; Medicare.
Owner Proprietary Corp (Hillhaven Corp).
Admissions Requirements Minimum age 16.
Staff Physicians 1 (pt); RNs 6 (ft), 5 (pt); LPNs 5 (ft), 4 (pt); Orderlies 2 (ft), 2 (pt); Nurses aides 27 (ft), 25 (pt); Physical therapists 1 (ft); Occupational therapists 1 (pt); Speech therapists 1 (pt); Activities coordinators 1 (ft); Dietitians 1 (pt).
Facilities Dining room; Physical therapy room; Activities room; Crafts room; Barber/Beauty shop; Greenhouse.
Activities Arts & crafts; Cards; Games; Reading groups; Prayer groups; Movies; Shopping trips; Social/Cultural gatherings.

Idaho State Veterans Home
PO Box 7765, 320 Collins Rd, Boise, ID, 83707
(208) 334-5000
Admin Gary Bermeosolo. *Medical Dir/Dir of Nursing* James Branahl; Sally Johnson.
Licensure Skilled care; Domiciliary care; Sheltered care. *Beds* SNF 80; Domiciliary care 124; Sheltered care 10.
Owner Publicly owned.
Admissions Requirements Medical examination; Physician's request.
Staff Physicians 12 (pt); RNs 7 (ft), 7 (pt); LPNs 6 (pt), 5 (pt); Nurses aides 25 (ft), 12 (pt); Physical therapists 1 (pt); Recreational therapists 1 (pt); Occupational therapists 1 (pt); Activities coordinators 1 (ft); Dietitians 1 (pt).

Facilities Dining room; Physical therapy room; Activities room; Chapel; Crafts room; Laundry room; Barber/Beauty shop; Library.
Activities Arts & crafts; Cards; Games; Reading groups; Prayer groups; Movies; Shopping trips; Social/Cultural gatherings.

Treasure Valley Manor
909 Reserve St, Boise, ID, 83712
(208) 343-7717
Admin Jean Heazle. *Medical Dir/Dir of Nursing* Theodore Walters MD; Cynthia Mintun RN.
Licensure Skilled care; Intermediate care. *Beds* SNF 165; ICF. *Certified* Medicaid; Medicare.
Owner Proprietary Corp.
Admissions Requirements Minimum age 18; Medical examination.
Staff RNs; LPNs; Orderlies; Nurses aides; Activities coordinators; Dietitians.
Facilities Dining room; Physical therapy room; Activities room; Crafts room; Laundry room; Barber/Beauty shop; Library.
Activities Arts & crafts; Cards; Games; Reading groups; Prayer groups; Movies; Shopping trips; Social/Cultural gatherings.

BONNERS FERRY

Boundary County Nursing Home*
551 Kaniksu, Box 448, Bonners Ferry, ID, 83805
(208) 267-3141
Admin Donald M Johnstone.
Licensure Skilled care. *Beds* 26. *Certified* Medicaid; Medicare.
Admissions Requirements Medical examination; Physician's request.
Staff Physicians 5 (ft), 1 (pt); RNs 2 (ft); LPNs 3 (ft), 2 (pt); Nurses aides 8 (ft), 6 (pt); Physical therapists 1 (pt); Activities coordinators 1 (ft); Dietitians 1 (pt).
Facilities Dining room; Physical therapy room; Activities room.
Activities Arts & crafts; Games; Reading groups.

BUHL

Harral's Nursing Home
820 Sprague Ave, Buhl, ID, 83316
(208) 543-6401
Admin Joyce Ellis. *Medical Dir/Dir of Nursing* Nancy Montgomery DON.
Licensure Skilled care; Intermediate care. *Beds* SNF 64; ICF. *Certified* Medicaid; Medicare.
Owner Proprietary Corp (Beverly Enterprises).
Admissions Requirements Medical examination; Physician's request.
Staff RNs 3 (ft), 2 (pt); LPNs 5 (ft), 2 (pt); Orderlies 1 (ft); Nurses aides 20 (ft), 8 (pt); Activities coordinators 1 (ft).
Facilities Dining room; Activities room; Crafts room; Laundry room; Barber/Beauty shop.
Activities Arts & crafts; Cards; Games; Reading groups; Prayer groups; Movies; Social/Cultural gatherings.

BURLEY

Burley Care Center*
1729 Miller St, Burley, ID, 83318
(208) 678-9474
Admin Phil Dieter. *Medical Dir/Dir of Nursing* H W Crawford MD.
Licensure Skilled care. *Beds* 59. *Certified* Medicaid; Medicare.
Admissions Requirements Minimum age 21; Medical examination; Physician's request.
Staff RNs 3 (ft); LPNs 4 (ft), 5 (pt); Orderlies 1 (ft), 1 (pt); Nurses aides 12 (ft); Physical therapists 1 (pt); Speech therapists 1 (pt); Activities coordinators 1 (ft); Dietitians 1 (pt).

Facilities Dining room; Activities room; Crafts room; Barber/Beauty shop.
Activities Arts & crafts; Games; Reading groups; Prayer groups; Movies; Shopping trips.

Cassia Memorial Hospital & Medical Center
PO Box 489, 2303 Park Ave, Burley, ID, 83318
(208) 678-4444
Admin Richard Packer. *Medical Dir/Dir of Nursing* James Kircher MD; Mary Ovitt RN DON.
Licensure Skilled care; Intermediate care. *Beds* SNF 34; ICF. *Certified* Medicaid; Medicare.
Owner Nonprofit Corp.
Admissions Requirements Medical examination; Physician's request.
Staff Physicians 19 (ft); RNs 3 (ft); LPNs 2 (ft), 2 (pt); Nurses aides 12 (ft), 6 (pt); Physical therapists 2 (ft), 1 (pt); Reality therapists 1 (ft); Recreational therapists 1 (ft); Occupational therapists 1 (ft); Speech therapists 1 (ft); Activities coordinators 1 (ft); Dietitians 1 (ft); Dentists 2 (ft); Ophthalmologists 1 (ft).
Facilities Dining room; Physical therapy room; Activities room; Crafts room; Laundry room; Barber/Beauty shop.
Activities Arts & crafts; Cards; Games; Reading groups; Prayer groups; Movies; Shopping trips; Social/Cultural gatherings.

CALDWELL

Caldwell Care Center*
210 Cleveland, Caldwell, ID, 83605
(208) 459-1522
Admin Claire Whitney.
Licensure Skilled care. *Beds* 75. *Certified* Medicaid; Medicare.
Owner Proprietary Corp (Hillhaven Corp).

Cascade Care Center*
2814 S Indiana Ave, Caldwell, ID, 83605
(208) 459-0808
Admin Cheryl Killian.
Licensure Skilled care. *Beds* 112. *Certified* Medicaid; Medicare.
Owner Proprietary Corp (Hillhaven Corp).

COEUR D'ALENE

Coeur d'Alene Convalescent Center*
2200 Ironwood Pl, Coeur d'Alene, ID, 83814
(208) 667-6486
Admin Keith Eitemiller.
Licensure Skilled care. *Beds* 125. *Certified* Medicaid; Medicare.
Owner Proprietary Corp (Unicare).

Pinewood Care Center
2514 N 7th St, Coeur d'Alene, ID, 83814
(208) 664-8128
Admin Taylor "Vic" Wallner. *Medical Dir/Dir of Nursing* William T Wood MD; Sarah Luster RN DON.
Licensure Intermediate care for mentally retarded. *Beds* SNF 89. *Certified* Medicaid; Medicare.
Owner Proprietary Corp (National Heritage).
Admissions Requirements Medical examination; Physician's request.
Staff RNs 3 (ft), 1 (pt); LPNs 6 (ft), 2 (pt); Nurses aides 27 (ft), 6 (pt); Recreational therapists 1 (ft), 1 (pt); Social service 1 (pt).
Facilities Dining room; Physical therapy room; Activities room; Crafts room; Laundry room; Barber/Beauty shop.
Activities Arts & crafts; Cards; Games; Reading groups; Prayer groups; Movies; Shopping trips; Social/Cultural gatherings; Cooking.

Sunset Terrace Convalescent Center*
210 LaCrosse St, Coeur d'Alene, ID, 83814
(208) 664-2185

Admin Brian Morris.
Licensure Skilled care. *Beds* 89. *Certified* Medicaid; Medicare.

EMMETT

Emmett Care Center
714 N Butte, Emmett, ID, 83617
(208) 365-4425
Admin Gary Obenauer. *Medical Dir/Dir of Nursing* Harmon Holverson MD; Alice Ennis RN DON.
Licensure Skilled care. *Beds* SNF 95. *Certified* Medicaid; Medicare; VA.
Owner Proprietary Corp (Hillhaven Corp).
Admissions Requirements Physician's request.
Staff RNs 6 (ft); LPNs 8 (ft); Orderlies 2 (ft); Nurses aides 28 (ft); Physical therapists 1 (ft); Activities coordinators 1 (ft).
Languages Spanish, German
Facilities Dining room; Physical therapy room; Activities room; Crafts room; Laundry room; Barber/Beauty shop; Library.
Activities Arts & crafts; Cards; Games; Reading groups; Prayer groups; Movies; Shopping trips; Social/Cultural gatherings.

Holly Hills Care Center*
501 W Idaho Blvd, Emmett, ID, 83617
(208) 365-3597
Admin Don Kinnaman. *Medical Dir/Dir of Nursing* Dr Harmon Holverson.
Licensure Intermediate care. *Beds* 32. *Certified* Medicaid.
Owner Proprietary Corp (National Heritage).
Admissions Requirements Physician's request.
Staff RNs 1 (ft), 2 (pt); LPNs 2 (ft), 4 (pt); Nurses aides 5 (ft), 3 (pt); Activities coordinators 1 (ft); Audiologists 1 (ft).
Facilities Dining room; Physical therapy room; Activities room; Crafts room; Laundry room; Barber/Beauty shop.
Activities Arts & crafts; Cards; Games; Reading groups; Prayer groups; Shopping trips.

GOODING

Green Acres Care Center*
1220 Montana St, Gooding, ID, 83330
(208) 934-5601
Admin David D Farnes.
Licensure Skilled care. *Beds* 76. *Certified* Medicaid; Medicare.

GRANGEVILLE

Grangeville Convalescent & Shelter Care Center, Inc
410 E N 2nd St, Grangeville, ID, 83530
(208) 983-1131
Admin Ron Deeney; Arden Higgs. *Medical Dir/Dir of Nursing* Dr William Greenwood; Lorene Halsted RN.
Licensure Skilled care; Intermediate care; Shelter & retirement wing. *Beds* SNF; ICF 46; Shelter & retirement 16. *Certified* Medicaid; Medicare.
Owner Proprietary Corp.
Admissions Requirements Minimum age 18; Medical examination; Physician's request.
Staff RNs 4 (ft), 1 (pt); LPNs 2 (ft); Nurses aides 21 (ft); Physical therapists 1 (pt); Recreational therapists 1 (ft); Occupational therapists; Speech therapists; Activities coordinators 1 (ft); Dietitians 1 (pt).
Facilities Dining room; Activities room; Chapel; Crafts room; Laundry room; Barber/Beauty shop.
Activities Arts & crafts; Cards; Games; Reading groups; Prayer groups; Movies; Shopping trips; Social/Cultural gatherings.

Idaho County Nursing Home
W 722 North St, Grangeville, ID, 83530
(208) 983-1470

Admin Douglas A Winter. *Medical Dir/Dir of Nursing* D J Soltman MD; Carol Hackney DON.
Licensure Skilled care; Intermediate care. *Beds* SNF 35; ICF. *Certified* Medicaid; Medicare.
Owner Nonprofit organization/foundation.
Admissions Requirements Minimum age 18; Medical examination; Physician's request.
Staff Physicians; RNs; LPNs; Orderlies; Nurses aides; Physical therapists; Speech therapists; Activities coordinators; Dietitians; Dentists.
Facilities Dining room; Activities room; Crafts room; Laundry room; Barber/Beauty shop.
Activities Arts & crafts; Cards; Games; Reading groups; Prayer groups; Movies; Shopping trips; Social/Cultural gatherings.

HOMEDALE

Homedale Nursing Home Inc
Box 96, 108 W Owyhee, Homedale, ID, 83628
(208) 337-3168
Admin Sid E Tucker; David Hoewing.
Licensure Skilled care. *Beds* 38. *Certified* Medicaid; Medicare.

IDAHO FALLS

Good Samaritan Center*
640 E Elva, Idaho Falls, ID, 83401
(208) 523-4795
Admin Kent Burgess.
Licensure Skilled care. *Beds* 103. *Certified* Medicaid; Medicare.
Owner Nonprofit Corp (Evangelical Lutheran/ Good Samaritan).
Affiliation Lutheran

Idaho Falls Nursing Home
900 Riverside Dr, Idaho Falls, ID, 83401
(208) 525-6600
Admin Kenneth K Lancaster. *Medical Dir/Dir of Nursing* Dr D O Smith MD; Karen Williams RN.
Licensure Skilled care. *Beds* 92. *Certified* Medicaid; Medicare.
Owner Proprietary Corp (Beverly Enterprises).
Admissions Requirements Minimum age 20.
Staff RNs; LPNs; Orderlies; Nurses aides; Activities coordinators.
Facilities Dining room; Physical therapy room; Activities room; Chapel; Crafts room; Laundry room; Barber/Beauty shop.
Activities Arts & crafts; Cards; Games; Reading groups; Prayer groups; Movies; Social/Cultural gatherings.

Valley Care Center
2725 E 17th, Idaho Falls, ID, 83401
(208) 529-4567
Admin Doug Christensen. *Medical Dir/Dir of Nursing* Coy Lou Stephens.
Licensure Skilled care; Intermediate care. *Beds* SNF; ICF 110. *Certified* Medicaid; Medicare.
Owner Proprietary Corp (National Heritage).
Admissions Requirements Minimum age 16; Medical examination; Physician's request.
Staff RNs; LPNs; Nurses aides; Activities coordinators.
Languages Spanish
Facilities Dining room; Physical therapy room; Activities room; Chapel; Barber/ Beauty shop.
Activities Arts & crafts; Cards; Games; Reading groups; Movies; Social/Cultural gatherings.

Yellowstone Care Center*
2460 S Yellowstone, Idaho Falls, ID, 83401
(208) 523-9839
Admin Douglas B Christensen.
Licensure Intermediate care for mentally retarded. *Beds* 30. *Certified* Medicaid.

JEROME

St Benedict's Long-Term Care Unit*
709 N Lincoln, Jerome, ID, 83338
(208) 324-4301
Admin Robert Campbell. *Medical Dir/Dir of Nursing* James Sloat MD.
Licensure Skilled care. *Beds* 40. *Certified* Medicaid; Medicare.
Admissions Requirements Medical examination; Physician's request.
Staff RNs 2 (ft), 1 (pt); LPNs 3 (ft), 2 (pt); Nurses aides 17 (ft), 9 (pt); Physical therapists 1 (ft); Occupational therapists 1 (pt); Speech therapists 1 (pt); Activities coordinators 1 (ft); Dietitians 1 (pt).
Affiliation Roman Catholic
Facilities Dining room; Physical therapy room; Activities room; Chapel; Barber/ Beauty shop.
Activities Arts & crafts; Cards; Games; Reading groups; Prayer groups; Movies; Social/Cultural gatherings.

KELLOGG

Shoshone Living Center
Box 689, 601 W Cameron, Kellogg, ID, 83837
(208) 784-1283
Admin Patsy Walker. *Medical Dir/Dir of Nursing* Frederick Haller MD; Rita Armor DNS.
Licensure Skilled care; Intermediate care. *Beds* SNF 68; ICF. *Certified* Medicaid; Medicare.
Owner Proprietary Corp (Hillhaven Corp).
Admissions Requirements Physician's request.
Staff RNs 3 (ft), 1 (pt); LPNs 6 (ft); Orderlies 3 (ft); Nurses aides 28 (ft); Physical therapists 1 (pt); Occupational therapists 1 (pt); Activities coordinators 1 (ft); Dietitians 1 (pt); Dentist 1 (pt).
Facilities Dining room; Physical therapy room; Activities room; Chapel; Crafts room; Laundry room; Barber/Beauty shop.
Activities Arts & crafts; Cards; Games; Reading groups; Prayer groups; Movies; Shopping trips; Social/Cultural gatherings.

KIMBERLY

Mountain View Care Center*
Rte 1, Box X, Polk St E, Kimberly, ID, 83341
(208) 423-5591
Admin Gary Morgan.
Licensure Skilled care. *Beds* 64. *Certified* Medicaid; Medicare.
Owner Proprietary Corp (National Heritage).

LEWISTON

Lewiston Care Center
3315 8th St, Lewiston, ID, 83501
(208) 743-9543
Admin Turid K Reichert. *Medical Dir/Dir of Nursing* Richard M Alford MD; Mary L Bodden RNC.
Licensure Skilled care; Intermediate care. *Beds* SNF 96. *Certified* Medicaid; Medicare.
Owner Proprietary Corp (Hillhaven Corp).
Admissions Requirements Minimum age 16; Medical examination; Physician's request.
Staff RNs 5 (ft), 6 (pt); LPNs 7 (ft), 2 (pt); Orderlies 3 (ft); Nurses aides 25 (ft), 11 (pt); Physical therapists 1 (pt); Reality therapists 1 (pt); Activities coordinators 1 (ft), 2 (pt); Dietitians 1 (pt); Ophthalmologists 1 (pt).
Languages Norweigian, Swedish, Danish, German
Facilities Dining room; Physical therapy room; Activities room; Laundry room; Barber/Beauty shop.
Activities Arts & crafts; Cards; Games; Reading groups; Prayer groups; Movies; Shopping trips; Social/Cultural gatherings; Bingo; Music; Restorative exercise.

Orchards Villa Nursing Center*
1014 Burrell Ave, Lewiston, ID, 83501
(208) 743-4558
Admin Ron Preston.
Licensure Skilled care. *Beds* 140. *Certified*
Medicaid; Medicare.

MALAD

Oneida County Nursing Home
PO Box 126, 150 N 200 W, Malad, ID, 83252
(208) 766-2231
Admin D Mahender Nath. *Medical Dir/Dir of
Nursing* Stephen C Johnson DO; Myrna
Tovey RN.
Licensure Skilled care. *Beds* SNF 24. *Certified*
Medicaid; Medicare.
Owner Publicly owned.
Admissions Requirements Medical
examination; Physician's request.
Staff Physicians 1 (pt); RNs 3 (ft), 3 (pt);
LPNs 5 (ft), 2 (pt); Nurses aides 9 (ft), 1
(pt); Physical therapists 1 (ft); Recreational
therapists 1 (pt); Activities coordinators 1
(pt); Dietitians 1 (pt).
Facilities Dining room; Physical therapy
room; Activities room.
Activities Arts & crafts; Cards; Games; Prayer
groups; Movies.

MCCALL

Payette Lakes Care Center*
PO Box P, 201 Floyd St, McCall, ID, 83638
(208) 634-2112
Admin Ronald D Nelson.
Licensure Skilled care. *Beds* 64. *Certified*
Medicaid; Medicare.
Owner Proprietary Corp (Beverly Enterprises).

MERIDIAN

Gem State Homes Inc 2*
40 W Franklin, Unit F, Meridian, ID, 83642
(208) 888-1155
Admin Martin Landholm. *Medical Dir/Dir of
Nursing* Leslie Madsen RN.
Licensure Intermediate care for mentally
retarded. *Beds* 16. *Certified* Medicaid.
Admissions Requirements Minimum age 6;
Medical examination.
Staff Physicians 1 (pt); RNs 1 (pt); LPNs 1
(pt); Physical therapists 1 (pt); Recreational
therapists 1 (pt); Speech therapists 1 (pt);
Dietitians 1 (pt); Dentists 1 (pt);
Ophthalmologists 1 (pt); Podiatrists 1 (pt);
Audiologists 1 (pt).
Activities Arts & crafts; Games; Movies;
Shopping trips; Social/Cultural gatherings.

Tomorrows Hope Inc
4782 Armga Rd, Meridian, ID, 83642
(208) 322-6550 or 322-6570
Admin Deborah A Pond.
Licensure Intermediate care for mentally
retarded. *Beds* ICF/MR 8. *Certified*
Medicaid.
Owner Nonprofit Corp.
Admissions Requirements Minimum age 5;
Medical examination; Physician's request.
Staff Physicians 1 (pt); RNs 1 (pt); Nurses
aides 9 (ft), 1 (pt); Recreational therapists 1
(pt); Occupational therapists 1 (pt); Speech
therapists 1 (pt); Activities coordinators 1
(pt); Dietitians 1 (pt); Dentists 1 (pt);
Ophthalmologists 1 (pt); Podiatrists 1 (pt).
Facilities Dining room; Activities room;
Crafts room; Laundry room.
Activities Arts & crafts; Cards; Games;
Movies; Shopping trips; Social/Cultural
gatherings; Concerts; Bowling; Swimming;
Library.

MONTPELIER

Bear Lake Memorial Nursing Home*
164 S 5th, Montpelier, ID, 83254
(208) 847-1630
Admin D Mahender Nath. *Medical Dir/Dir of
Nursing* R V Bjarnason DO.
Licensure Skilled care. *Beds* 37. *Certified*
Medicaid; Medicare.
Admissions Requirements Medical
examination; Physician's request.
Staff Physicians 4 (ft); RNs 2 (ft), 1 (pt);
LPNs 2 (ft), 2 (pt); Nurses aides 13 (ft), 2
(pt); Physical therapists 1 (ft); Activities
coordinators 1 (ft); Dietitians 1 (pt); Dentists
3 (pt).
Facilities Dining room; Physical therapy
room; Activities room; Crafts room; Laundry
room; Barber/Beauty shop.
Activities Arts & crafts; Cards; Games;
Reading groups; Movies.

MOSCOW

Good Samaritan Village*
640 N Eisenhower St, Moscow, ID, 83843
(208) 882-6560
Admin Allan Tramel.
Licensure Skilled care. *Beds* 60. *Certified*
Medicaid; Medicare.
Owner Nonprofit Corp (Evangelical Lutheran/
Good Samaritan).
Affiliation Lutheran

Latah Care Center
W 510 Palouse River Dr, Moscow, ID, 83843
(208) 882-7586
Admin Verla Olson. *Medical Dir/Dir of
Nursing* Frances Spain MD; Sandy Cameron
DON.
Licensure Skilled care. *Beds* 76. *Certified*
Medicaid; Medicare.
Owner Nonprofit Corp.
Admissions Requirements Minimum age 18;
Medical examination; Physician's request.
Staff RNs 10 (ft); LPNs 3 (ft); Orderlies 10
(ft); Nurses aides 40 (ft); Physical therapists
7 (ft); Recreational therapists 2 (ft);
Dietitians 1 (pt).
Facilities Dining room; Activities room;
Crafts room; Laundry room; Barber/Beauty
shop; Library.
Activities Arts & crafts; Cards; Games;
Reading groups; Movies; Shopping trips;
Social/Cultural gatherings.

Paradise Villa Convalescent Center*
420 Rowe St, Moscow, ID, 83843
(208) 882-4576
Admin George Wiemerslage.
Licensure Skilled care. *Beds* 94. *Certified*
Medicaid; Medicare.

Stepping Stones Inc
408 S Main, Moscow, ID, 83843
(208) 883-0523
Admin Larry D Clott. *Medical Dir/Dir of
Nursing* Lynda Peterson.
Licensure Intermediate care for mentally
retarded. *Beds* ICF/MR 16. *Certified*
Medicaid; Private pay.
Owner Nonprofit Corp.
Admissions Requirements Minimum age 21.
Staff Physicians; RNs; LPNs 1 (ft); Physical
therapists; Recreational therapists 1 (ft);
Occupational therapists; Speech therapists;
Activities coordinators 1 (pt); Dietitians;
Dentists; Ophthalmologists; Podiatrists;
Special education teachers aides; Personal
care; Service workers 25 (ft).
Facilities Family style homes.
Activities Individual programs.

MOUNTAIN HOME

Elmore Memorial Nursing Home*
PO Drawer H, Mountain Home, ID, 83647
(208) 587-8406
Admin John Kee.
Licensure Skilled care. *Beds* 55. *Certified*
Medicaid; Medicare.

NAMPA

Gem State Homes Inc 1*
512 Gem St, Nampa, ID, 83651
(208) 467-7589
Admin Martin Landholm.
Licensure Intermediate care for mentally
retarded. *Beds* 8. *Certified* Medicaid.

Holly Care Center*
472 Nampa-Caldwell Blvd, Nampa, ID, 83651
(208) 467-5721
Admin Rosemary Helms.
Licensure Skilled care. *Beds* 49. *Certified*
Medicaid; Medicare.
Owner Proprietary Corp (National Heritage).

**Idaho State School & Hospital—Intermediate
Care Facility**
3100 11th Ave N, Nampa, ID, 83651
(208) 466-9255
Admin Dan Fazzini Ph D.
Licensure Intermediate care for mentally
retarded. *Beds* 320. *Certified* Medicaid.

Midland Manor Nursing Home
436 Midland Blvd, Nampa, ID, 83651
(208) 466-7803
Admin Velma Green. *Medical Dir/Dir of
Nursing* Dr Harold Brown.
Licensure Skilled care. *Beds* 111. *Certified*
Medicaid; Medicare.
Owner Proprietary Corp (National Heritage).
Admissions Requirements Physician's request.
Staff RNs 5 (ft), 3 (pt); LPNs 4 (ft), 5 (pt);
Orderlies 2 (ft); Nurses aides 38 (ft), 4 (pt);
Activities coordinators 3 (ft); Dietitians 1
(pt).
Facilities Dining room; Activities room;
Crafts room; Laundry room; Barber/Beauty
shop; Library; Patio areas; Large backyard
area.
Activities Arts & crafts; Cards; Games;
Reading groups; Prayer groups; Movies;
Shopping trips; Social/Cultural gatherings;
Parties for staffs' children; Coffee hours.

Nampa Care Center
404 Horton, Nampa, ID, 83651
(208) 466-9292
Admin Donna Lant. *Medical Dir/Dir of
Nursing* Dr Michael Crim; Millie Holmes.
Licensure Skilled care. *Beds* SNF 97;
Medicare 10; Alzheimer's unit 25. *Certified*
Medicaid; Medicare.
Owner Proprietary Corp (Hillhaven Corp).
Admissions Requirements Females only;
Medical examination.
Staff Physicians; RNs; LPNs; Orderlies;
Nurses aides; Physical therapists;
Occupational therapists; Activities
coordinators.
Languages Spanish
Facilities Dining room; Physical therapy
room; Activities room; Laundry room;
Barber/Beauty shop.
Activities Arts & crafts; Cards; Games; Prayer
groups; Movies.

Sunny Ridge Manor
2609 Sunnybrook Dr, Nampa, ID, 83651
(208) 467-7298
Admin Dorwin E Smith. *Medical Dir/Dir of
Nursing* Linda Vail DON.
Licensure Skilled care. *Beds* SNF 30. *Certified*
Medicaid; Medicare.
Owner Privately owned.
Admissions Requirements Minimum age 55.

Staff RNs 3 (ft); LPNs 4 (ft), 1 (pt); Nurses aides 19 (ft); Activities coordinators 1 (ft); Dietitians 1 (pt).
Languages Spanish
Facilities Dining room; Crafts room; Laundry room; Barber/Beauty shop; Library.
Activities Arts & crafts; Games; Prayer groups; Movies; Social/Cultural gatherings; Exercise group.

OROFINO

Orofino Care Center Inc
Box 2607, Ahsahka Rd, Orofino, ID, 83544
(208) 476-4568
Admin James Griffin.
Licensure Skilled care. *Beds* 59. *Certified* Medicaid; Medicare.
Owner Proprietary Corp (National Heritage).

PAYETTE

Casa Loma Convalescent Center*
1019 3rd Ave S, Payette, ID, 83661
(208) 642-4455
Admin Carol Ronk.
Licensure Skilled care. *Beds* 103. *Certified* Medicaid; Medicare.

POCATELLO

Bannock County Nursing Home
527 Memorial Dr, Pocatello, ID, 83201
(208) 232-8956
Admin Alan Stevenson. *Medical Dir/Dir of Nursing* Evelyn Richmond DON.
Licensure Skilled care; Intermediate care. *Beds* SNF 56; ICF 56. *Certified* Medicaid; Medicare.
Owner Publicly owned.
Admissions Requirements Physician's request.
Staff RNs 1 (ft), 3 (pt); LPNs 1 (ft), 6 (pt); Nurses aides 8 (ft), 21 (pt); Activities coordinators 1 (ft); Dietitians 1 (pt).
Facilities Dining room; Physical therapy room; Activities room; Crafts room; Laundry room; Barber/Beauty shop.
Activities Arts & crafts; Cards; Games; Social/Cultural gatherings.

Eastgate Healthcare Associates Inc*
2200 E Terry, Pocatello, ID, 83201
(208) 232-2570
Admin Jim Zeim. *Medical Dir/Dir of Nursing* Dr E F Hyde.
Licensure Skilled care; Intermediate care. *Beds* 121. *Certified* Medicaid; Medicare.
Owner Proprietary Corp (Beverly Enterprises).
Admissions Requirements Medical examination; Physician's request.
Staff RNs 6 (ft), 4 (pt); LPNs 4 (ft), 6 (pt); Orderlies 1 (ft), 2 (pt); Nurses aides 42 (ft), 9 (pt); Physical therapists 1 (ft), 2 (pt); Recreational therapists 1 (ft), 1 (pt); Activities coordinators 1 (ft); Dietitians 1 (ft).
Facilities Dining room; Physical therapy room; Activities room; Laundry room; Barber/Beauty shop; Conference room.
Activities Arts & crafts; Cards; Games; Reading groups; Prayer groups; Movies; Shopping trips.

Hillcrest Haven Convalescent Center*
1071 Renee Ave, Pocatello, ID, 83201
(208) 233-1411
Admin Gary Beasley.
Licensure Skilled care. *Beds* 110. *Certified* Medicaid; Medicare.

Rucon House
2369 Rucon, Pocatello, ID, 83201
(208) 237-5538
Admin Frances Roberts.
Licensure Intermediate care for mentally retarded. *Beds* ICF/MR 8. *Certified* Medicaid.

Owner Nonprofit Corp.
Admissions Requirements Minimum age 18.
Staff LPNs 1 (pt).
Languages Spanish
Activities Arts & crafts; Cards; Games; Movies; Shopping trips.

South Park Group Home
3625 Vaughn St, Pocatello, ID, 83204
(208) 233-6833
Admin Frances L Roberts.
Licensure Intermediate care for mentally retarded. *Beds* ICF/MR 15. *Certified* Medicaid.
Owner Nonprofit Corp.
Admissions Requirements Minimum age 18.
Staff LPNs 2 (ft).
Facilities Dining room; Physical therapy room; Training room.
Activities Arts & crafts; Games; Reading groups; Movies; Shopping trips; Social/Cultural gatherings.

PRESTON

Franklin County Nursing Home
44 N 1st St E, Preston, ID, 83263
(208) 852-0137
Admin Michael G Andrus. *Medical Dir/Dir of Nursing* Rodney Grover DO; Maurene Hodges RN DON.
Licensure Skilled care; Intermediate care. *Beds* 45. *Certified* Medicaid; Medicare.
Owner Publicly owned.
Admissions Requirements Medical examination; Physician's request.
Staff Physicians 3 (ft); RNs 1 (ft), 1 (pt); LPNs 5 (ft), 3 (pt); Orderlies 1 (pt); Nurses aides 20 (ft), 11 (pt); Physical therapists 1 (pt); Activities coordinators 1 (ft); Dietitians 1 (pt); Social worker 1 (pt).
Facilities Dining room; Physical therapy room; Activities room; Crafts room; Laundry room; Barber/Beauty shop; Library.
Activities Arts & crafts; Games; Reading groups; Prayer groups; Movies; Social/Cultural gatherings.

RUPERT

Minidoka Memorial Hospital & Extended Care Unit
1224 8th St, Rupert, ID, 83350
(208) 436-0481
Admin Ed Richardson. *Medical Dir/Dir of Nursing* Howard Crawford MD; Mary Kamp RN DON.
Licensure Skilled care. *Beds* SNF 78. *Certified* Medicaid; Medicare.
Owner Publicly owned.
Admissions Requirements Medical examination; Physician's request.
Staff Physicians; RNs 1 (ft), 6 (pt); LPNs 10 (ft), 4 (pt); Nurses aides 17 (ft), 27 (pt); Physical therapists 1 (ft); Occupational therapists 1 (pt); Speech therapists 1 (pt); Activities coordinators 1 (ft); Dietitians 1 (pt).
Languages Spanish, Basque, French
Facilities Dining room; Physical therapy room; Activities room; Crafts room; Laundry room; Barber/Beauty shop; Library; Solariums; Television room; Patios Fireplace room.
Activities Arts & crafts; Cards; Games; Reading groups; Prayer groups; Movies; Shopping trips; Social/Cultural gatherings.

SAINT MARIES

Bethesda Care Center
820 Elm St, Saint Maries, ID, 83861
(208) 245-4576
Admin Scott Burpee. *Medical Dir/Dir of Nursing* Dr Katovich; Shirley White DON.

Licensure Skilled care; Intermediate care. *Beds* SNF; ICF 59. *Certified* Medicaid; Medicare.
Owner Nonprofit Corp (Bethesda Care Centers).
Admissions Requirements Medical examination; Physician's request.
Staff RNs 2 (ft), 2 (pt); LPNs 4 (ft), 3 (pt); Nurses aides 18 (ft), 5 (pt); Activities coordinators 1 (ft), 1 (pt).
Facilities Dining room; Physical therapy room; Activities room; Chapel; Crafts room; Laundry room; Barber/Beauty shop.
Activities Arts & crafts; Cards; Games; Reading groups; Prayer groups; Movies; Shopping trips; Social/Cultural gatherings; Pet therapy program.

SALMON

Casabello Estate Intermediate Care Facility*
PO Box 1319, Salmon, ID, 83467
(208) 756-3543
Admin Joyce Hammond.
Licensure Intermediate care. *Beds* 39. *Certified* Medicaid.
Admissions Requirements Physician's request.
Staff RNs 2 (ft), 1 (pt); LPNs 3 (ft); Nurses aides 6 (ft), 2 (pt); Activities coordinators 1 (pt).
Facilities Dining room; Activities room; Chapel; Crafts room; Laundry room; Barber/Beauty shop; Library; Garden room.
Activities Arts & crafts; Cards; Games; Reading groups; Prayer groups; Movies; Shopping trips; Social/Cultural gatherings.

SANDPOINT

Sandpoint Manor*
220 S Division, Sandpoint, ID, 83864
(208) 263-3933
Admin Craig A Johnson. *Medical Dir/Dir of Nursing* Dr H Leedy.
Licensure Skilled care; Intermediate care. *Beds* 89. *Certified* Medicaid; Medicare.
Staff RNs 5 (ft), 4 (pt); LPNs 2 (ft), 2 (pt); Nurses aides 25 (ft), 18 (pt); Physical therapists 1 (ft), 1 (pt); Occupational therapists 1 (pt); Speech therapists 1 (pt); Activities coordinators 1 (ft); Dietitians 1 (ft); Dentists 1 (pt).
Facilities Dining room; Physical therapy room; Activities room; Chapel; Crafts room; Laundry room; Barber/Beauty shop.
Activities Arts & crafts; Cards; Games; Movies; Shopping trips; Social/Cultural gatherings.

SHOSHONE

Wood River Convalescent Center
511 E 4th St, Shoshone, ID, 83352
(208) 324-5190
Admin Helen Shewmaker. *Medical Dir/Dir of Nursing* Keith Davis MD; Chris Arrate RN DON.
Licensure Skilled care. *Beds* SNF 40. *Certified* Medicaid; Medicare; VA.
Owner Publicly owned.
Admissions Requirements Medical examination; Physician's request.
Staff Physicians 1 (pt); RNs 2 (ft), 1 (pt); LPNs 2 (ft), 3 (pt); Orderlies 1 (ft); Nurses aides 10 (ft), 3 (pt); Physical therapists 1 (pt); Activities coordinators 1 (ft); Restorative therapist 2 (ft).
Facilities Dining room; Activities room; Laundry room.
Activities Arts & crafts; Cards; Games; Reading groups; Prayer groups; Movies; Shopping trips.

SILVERTON

Silver Wood Good Samaritan Center
Box 358, Silverton, ID, 83867
(208) 556-1147
Admin Gary Bokelman. *Medical Dir/Dir of Nursing* Thomas Prenger MD; Louise A West RN DON.
Licensure Skilled care; Intermediate care; apartments. *Beds* 89. *Certified* Medicaid; Medicare.
Owner Nonprofit Corp (Evangelical Lutheran/ Good Samaritan).
Admissions Requirements Medical examination; Physician's request.
Staff RNs 1 (ft), 2 (pt); LPNs 4 (ft), 4 (pt); Nurses aides 10 (ft), 15 (pt); Physical therapists 1 (pt); Activities coordinators 1 (ft).
Affiliation Lutheran
Facilities Dining room; Physical therapy room; Activities room; Chapel; Crafts room; Laundry room; Barber/Beauty shop; Library; Resident use kitchenette.
Activities Arts & crafts; Cards; Games; Reading groups; Prayer groups; Movies; Shopping trips; Social/Cultural gatherings; Fishing trips; Picnics; Bowling trips.

SODA SPRINGS

Caribou Memorial Nursing Home*
300 S Third W, Soda Springs, ID, 83276
(208) 547-3341
Admin Pearl S Fryar.

Licensure Skilled care. *Beds* 37. *Certified* Medicaid; Medicare.

TWIN FALLS

Skyview—Hazeldel*
640 Filer Ave W, Twin Falls, ID, 83301
(208) 734-8645
Admin Richard Drake. *Medical Dir/Dir of Nursing* A C Emery MD.
Licensure Skilled care. *Beds* 185. *Certified* Medicaid.
Admissions Requirements Medical examination; Physician's request.
Staff RNs 8 (ft), 4 (pt); LPNs 10 (ft), 5 (pt); Orderlies 3 (ft); Nurses aides 80 (ft), 10 (pt); Physical therapists 1 (ft); Activities coordinators 2 (ft), 2 (pt); Dietitians 1 (pt).
Facilities Dining room; Physical therapy room; Activities room; Crafts room.
Activities Arts & crafts; Cards; Games; Reading groups; Movies; Social/Cultural gatherings.

WEISER

Weiser Care Center
331 E Park St, Weiser, ID, 83672
(208) 549-2416
Admin Almeta Ingram. *Medical Dir/Dir of Nursing* Dr Richard Giever; Janice Allen RN.
Licensure Skilled care. *Beds* SNF 89. *Certified* Medicaid; Medicare.
Owner Proprietary Corp (Hillhaven Corp).

Admissions Requirements Minimum age 18.
Staff RNs 4 (ft), 3 (pt); LPNs 5 (ft), 1 (pt); Nurses aides 25 (ft), 9 (pt); Physical therapists 1 (ft); Activities coordinators 1 (ft), 1 (pt).
Facilities Dining room; Physical therapy room; Activities room; Laundry room; Barber/Beauty shop.
Activities Arts & crafts; Games; Reading groups; Prayer groups; Movies; Shopping trips.

WENDELL

Magic Valley Manor*
PO Box 306, N Idaho St, Wendell, ID, 83355
(208) 536-5571
Admin Kerry Arbuckle. *Medical Dir/Dir of Nursing* Mark Spencer MD.
Licensure Skilled care. *Beds* 40. *Certified* Medicaid.
Owner Proprietary Corp (Beverly Enterprises).
Staff Physicians 1 (pt); RNs 1 (ft), 2 (pt); LPNs 1 (ft), 2 (pt); Nurses aides 6 (ft), 5 (pt); Physical therapists 1 (pt); Occupational therapists 1 (pt); Speech therapists 1 (pt); Activities coordinators 1 (ft); Dietitians 1 (pt); Dentists 1 (pt).
Facilities Dining room; Activities room; Laundry room.
Activities Arts & crafts; Cards; Games; Prayer groups; Movies; Shopping trips; Social/ Cultural gatherings.

ILLINOIS

ABINGDON

Care Center of Abingdon*
2000 W Martin St, Abingdon, IL, 61410
(309) 462-2356
Admin Debbie A Owen.
Licensure Skilled care. *Beds* 74. *Certified*
Medicaid.
Owner Proprietary Corp.

ADDISON

Iona Glos Specialized Living Center
50 S Fairbank St, Addison, IL, 60101
(312) 543-2440
Admin Laura Abernathy. *Medical Dir/Dir of*
Nursing Gail Ing.
Licensure Intermediate care for mentally
retarded. *Beds* ICF/MR 100. *Certified*
Medicaid.
Owner Nonprofit organization/foundation.
Admissions Requirements Minimum age 18.
Staff RNs 1 (ft); LPNs 4 (ft), 1 (pt); Nurses
aides 56 (ft), 48 (pt); Occupational therapists
1 (ft); Speech therapists 1 (ft); Activities
coordinators 1 (ft); Dietitians 1 (pt); Social
workers 1 (ft).
Facilities Dining room; Activities room;
Crafts room; Laundry room; 6 Individual
homes.
Activities Arts & crafts; Games; Reading
groups; Movies; Shopping trips; Social/
Cultural gatherings; Special Olympics; Social
clubs; Community outings.

ALBION

Rest Haven Manor Inc*
120 W Main, Albion, IL, 62806
(618) 445-2815
Admin Bernetta Daubs.
Licensure Intermediate care. *Beds* 49.
Certified Medicaid.
Owner Proprietary Corp.

ALEDO

Georgetown Manor
3rd Ave at 12th St SW, Aledo, IL, 61231
(309) 582-5376
Admin Diane Marquis.
Licensure Intermediate care. *Beds* SNF 100.
Certified Medicaid; Medicare.
Owner Proprietary Corp.

Mercer County Nursing Home*
NW 9th Ave & NW 3rd St, Aledo, IL, 61231
(309) 582-5361
Admin Frederick J Ehrenhart.
Licensure Intermediate care. *Beds* 95.
Certified Medicaid.
Owner Publicly owned.

ALHAMBRA

Hampton Nursing Care Inc
PO Box 237, Main & Warsaw Sts, Alhambra,
IL, 62001
(618) 488-3565
Admin Carol Gibbons. *Medical Dir/Dir of*
Nursing Betty Zweck.
Licensure Intermediate care. *Beds* ICF 87.
Certified Medicaid.
Owner Proprietary Corp.
Staff RNs 1 (ft); LPNs 6 (ft), 2 (pt); Nurses
aides 23 (ft).
Facilities Dining room; Activities room;
Crafts room; Laundry room; Barber/Beauty
shop.
Activities Arts & crafts; Cards; Games;
Reading groups; Prayer groups; Movies;
Shopping trips; Social/Cultural gatherings.

Hitz Memorial Home
Belle St, Alhambra, IL, 62001
(618) 488-2355
Admin Jon R Lyerla. *Medical Dir/Dir of*
Nursing Dr Edward Hediger; Ida M
Nuernberger RN.
Licensure Intermediate care. *Beds* ICF 67.
Certified Medicaid.
Owner Nonprofit Corp.
Admissions Requirements Minimum age 55;
Medical examination; Physician's request.
Staff RNs 2 (ft), 2 (pt); LPNs 4 (ft), 1 (pt);
Nurses aides 18 (ft), 7 (pt); Physical
therapists 1 (pt); Speech therapists 1 (pt);
Activities coordinators 1 (ft), 1 (pt);
Dietitians 1 (pt); Podiatrists 1 (pt); Dentist 1
(pt).
Affiliation Church of Christ
Facilities Dining room; Physical therapy
room; Activities room; Crafts room; Laundry
room; Barber/Beauty shop; Library.
Activities Arts & crafts; Cards; Games;
Movies; Shopping trips; Social/Cultural
gatherings.

ALTAMONT

Lutheran Care Center*
US Hwy 40 W, Altamont, IL, 62411
(618) 483-6136
Admin Barbara Hamann. *Medical Dir/Dir of*
Nursing Dr Delbert G Huelskoetter.
Licensure Skilled care. *Beds* 97.
Owner Nonprofit Corp.
Admissions Requirements Minimum age 20;
Medical examination; Physician's request.
Staff Physicians 1 (ft); RNs 4 (ft), 2 (pt);
LPNs 8 (ft), 2 (pt); Orderlies 1 (ft), 1 (pt);
Nurses aides 42 (ft), 5 (pt); Physical
therapists 1 (pt); Recreational therapists 1
(ft); Dietitians 1 (ft).
Affiliation Lutheran
Facilities Dining room; Physical therapy
room; Activities room; Chapel; Crafts room;
Laundry room; Barber/Beauty shop; Library.
Activities Arts & crafts; Cards; Games;
Reading groups; Prayer groups; Movies;
Shopping trips; Social/Cultural gatherings.

ALTON

Burt Sheltered Care Home*
1414 Milton Rd, Alton, IL, 62002
(618) 465-1351
Admin Mary Jo Swengrosh.
Licensure Sheltered care. *Beds* 29.
Owner Nonprofit Corp.

Eldercare of Alton*
3523 Wickenhauser, Alton, IL, 62002
(618) 465-8887
Admin Joyce A Wild.
Licensure Skilled care; Intermediate care. *Beds*
SNF 147; ICF 49. *Certified* Medicaid;
Medicare.
Owner Proprietary Corp.

Lifecare Center of Alton
2349 Virden Dr, Alton, IL, 62002
(618) 466-5331
Admin Denise E St Peters. *Medical Dir/Dir of*
Nursing Jean Strager.
Licensure Intermediate care. *Beds* ICF 43.
Certified Medicaid.
Owner Proprietary Corp (Community Lifecare
Enterprises).
Admissions Requirements Minimum age 18;
Medical examination.
Staff LPNs 5 (ft); Nurses aides 15 (ft), 1 (pt);
Physical therapists 1 (pt); Activities
coordinators 1 (ft); Dietitians 1 (pt).
Facilities Dining room; Activities room;
Crafts room; Laundry room.
Activities Arts & crafts; Cards; Games;
Reading groups; Movies; Shopping trips;
Social/Cultural gatherings.

Eunice C Smith Nursing Home*
1251 College Ave, Alton, IL, 62002
(618) 462-7330
Admin Ron McMullen.
Licensure Skilled care. *Beds* 64. *Certified*
Medicaid; Medicare.
Owner Proprietary Corp.

AMBOY

Mapleside Manor
15 W Wasson Rd, Amboy, IL, 61310
(815) 858-2550
Admin Morris F Forman. *Medical Dir/Dir of*
Nursing Pervez A Khan MD; Margaret L
Otto RN.
Licensure Skilled care. *Beds* SNF 97. *Certified*
Medicaid; Medicare.
Owner Proprietary Corp.
Admissions Requirements Minimum age 18.
Staff RNs 2 (ft), 2 (pt); LPNs 3 (ft), 5 (pt);
Orderlies 2 (ft), 2 (pt); Nurses aides 20 (ft),
15 (pt); Recreational therapists 3 (ft).
Facilities Dining room; Physical therapy
room; Activities room; Crafts room; Laundry
room; Barber/Beauty shop; Library.
Activities Arts & crafts; Cards; Games;
Reading groups; Prayer groups; Movies;
Shopping trips; Social/Cultural gatherings.

ANNA

City Care Center
Rte 1, Brady Mill Rd, Anna, IL, 62906
(618) 833-6343
Admin Patricia L Chamness. *Medical Dir/Dir of Nursing* Margaret Ury DON.
Licensure Skilled care. *Beds* SNF 70. *Certified* Medicaid.
Owner Privately owned.
Staff RNs 2 (ft); LPNs 4 (ft); Orderlies 2 (ft), 1 (pt); Nurses aides 25 (ft), 3 (pt); Activities coordinators 1 (ft); Dietitians 1 (ft); Housekeeping 6 (ft); Laundry 2 (ft); Cooks 6 (ft).
Facilities Dining room; Activities room; Crafts room; Laundry room; Barber/Beauty shop; Family lounge.
Activities Arts & crafts; Cards; Games; Reading groups; Prayer groups; Movies; Shopping trips; Social/Cultural gatherings.

Holly Hill
203 Lafayette St, Anna, IL, 62906
(618) 833-3322
Admin Jimmy Keller. *Medical Dir/Dir of Nursing* Diana Alley RN.
Licensure Intermediate care for mentally retarded. *Beds* ICF/MR 15. *Certified* Medicaid.
Owner Privately owned.
Admissions Requirements Minimum age 18; Physician's request.
Staff RNs 1 (pt); Nurses aides 3 (ft), 1 (pt).
Facilities Dining room; Activities room; Crafts room; Laundry room.
Activities Arts & crafts; Cards; Games; Reading groups; Prayer groups; Movies; Shopping trips; Social/Cultural gatherings.

Mulberry Manor Inc
612 E Davie St, Anna, IL, 62906
(618) 833-6012
Admin Joann A Keller. *Medical Dir/Dir of Nursing* William H Whiting MD.
Licensure Intermediate care for mentally retarded. *Beds* 80. *Certified* Medicaid.
Owner Proprietary Corp.
Admissions Requirements Minimum age 18; Medical examination; Physician's request.
Staff RNs; LPNs; Orderlies; Nurses aides; Activities coordinators.
Facilities Dining room; Physical therapy room; Activities room; Laundry room; Barber/Beauty shop; Lounge; Living room.
Activities Arts & crafts; Cards; Games; Reading groups; Prayer groups; Movies; Shopping trips; Social/Cultural gatherings.

Spanish Oaks Center*
223 W Vienna, Anna, IL, 62906
(618) 833-8013
Admin Connie L Ury.
Licensure Sheltered care. *Beds* 37.
Owner Proprietary Corp.

Union County Skilled Nursing Home
517 N Main St, Anna, IL, 62906
(618) 833-4511
Admin Eugene A Helfrich. *Medical Dir/Dir of Nursing* Carol L Goodman DON.
Licensure Skilled care. *Beds* SNF 60. *Certified* Medicaid.
Owner Publicly owned.
Admissions Requirements Medical examination; Physician's request.
Staff Physicians; RNs; LPNs; Orderlies; Nurses aides; Physical therapists; Activities coordinators; Dietitians.
Facilities Dining room; Physical therapy room; Activities room; Barber/Beauty shop.
Activities Arts & crafts; Cards; Games; Reading groups; Prayer groups; Movies; Shopping trips; Social/Cultural gatherings.

ARCOLA

We Care Nursing Facilities Inc
422 E South 4th St, Arcola, IL, 61910
(217) 268-3555
Admin Patricia M Hackler. *Medical Dir/Dir of Nursing* Dr Mondul; Peggy Swartz RN.
Licensure Skilled care. *Beds* SNF 109. *Certified* Medicaid.
Owner Proprietary Corp.
Admissions Requirements Minimum age 18; Medical examination; Physician's request.
Staff Physicians; RNs; LPNs; Orderlies; Nurses aides; Physical therapists; Recreational therapists; Occupational therapists; Speech therapists; Activities coordinators; Dietitians.
Facilities Dining room; Activities room; Crafts room; Laundry room; Barber/Beauty shop; Library.
Activities Arts & crafts; Cards; Games; Reading groups; Prayer groups; Movies; Shopping trips; Social/Cultural gatherings.

ARLINGTON HEIGHTS

Americana Healthcare Center of Arlington Heights
715 W Central Rd, Arlington Heights, IL, 60005
(312) 392-2020
Admin Jeffrey M Floyd. *Medical Dir/Dir of Nursing* Dr Cameron Thomson; Mary Schalow.
Licensure Skilled care. *Beds* 151. *Certified* Medicare.
Owner Proprietary Corp (Manor Care).
Admissions Requirements Minimum age 18.
Staff Physicians 12 (pt); RNs 12 (ft), 7 (pt); LPNs 3 (ft); Orderlies 2 (ft), 1 (pt); Nurses aides 26 (ft), 20 (pt); Physical therapists 1 (ft); Recreational therapists 3 (ft), 1 (pt); Activities coordinators 1 (ft); Dietitians 1 (ft); Ophthalmologists 1 (pt).
Facilities Dining room; Physical therapy room; Activities room; Crafts room; Laundry room; Barber/Beauty shop.
Activities Arts & crafts; Cards; Games; Reading groups; Prayer groups; Movies; Shopping trips; Social/Cultural gatherings.

Lutheran Home & Services for Aged
800 W Oakton St, Arlington Heights, IL, 60004
(312) 253-3710
Admin Paul A Hauer Pres. *Medical Dir/Dir of Nursing* T M Homa MD.
Licensure Skilled care; Intermediate care; Sheltered care. *Beds* SNF 252; ICF/MR 60; Sheltered care 167. *Certified* Medicaid.
Owner Nonprofit Corp.
Admissions Requirements Minimum age 60; Medical examination.
Staff Physicians 3 (pt); RNs 15 (ft), 16 (pt); LPNs 5 (ft), 9 (pt); Orderlies 2 (ft); Nurses aides 52 (ft), 69 (pt); Physical therapists 1 (ft); Reality therapists 2 (ft); Recreational therapists 4 (ft); Occupational therapists 1 (pt); Speech therapists 1 (pt); Activities coordinators 2 (ft); Dietitians 2 (ft); Dentists 1 (pt); Ophthalmologists 1 (pt); Podiatrists 1 (pt); 1 (pt) Chaplain 1 (ft).
Affiliation Lutheran
Facilities Dining room; Physical therapy room; Activities room; Chapel; Crafts room; Laundry room; Barber/Beauty shop; Library.
Activities Arts & crafts; Cards; Games; Reading groups; Prayer groups; Movies; Shopping trips; Social/Cultural gatherings.

Magnus Farm Nursing Home
600 W Rand Rd, Arlington Heights, IL, 60004
(312) 439-0018
Admin A B Magnus. *Medical Dir/Dir of Nursing* Anna Marie Moran RN DON.
Licensure Intermediate care; Sheltered care. *Beds* ICF 25; Sheltered care 96.

Owner Nonprofit Corp (Adventist Health Sys-USA).
Admissions Requirements Minimum age 60; Medical examination; Physician's request.
Staff RNs 2 (ft), 2 (pt); LPNs 5 (ft), 3 (pt); Nurses aides 4 (ft).
Languages Polish
Facilities Dining room; Activities room; Chapel; Crafts room; Barber/Beauty shop; Library.
Activities Arts & crafts; Cards; Games; Reading groups; Prayer groups; Movies; Shopping trips; Bus trips.

Northwest Community Continuing Care Center
901 W Kirchoff Rd, Arlington Heights, IL, 60005
(312) 259-5850
Admin Celeste J Little. *Medical Dir/Dir of Nursing* Dr R Treanor; Carol Klein DON.
Licensure Skilled care; Intermediate care; Alzheimer unit. *Beds* SNF; ICF; Alzheimer unit 200. *Certified* Medicare.
Owner Nonprofit organization/foundation.
Admissions Requirements Medical examination; Physician's request.
Staff RNs; LPNs; Nurses aides; Physical therapists; Recreational therapists; Occupational therapists; Speech therapists; Activities coordinators; Dietitians; Dentists; Ophthalmologists.
Facilities Dining room; Physical therapy room; Activities room; Chapel; Crafts room; Laundry room; Barber/Beauty shop.
Activities Arts & crafts; Cards; Games; Reading groups; Prayer groups; Movies; Shopping trips; Social/Cultural gatherings.

AROMA PARK

Park View Manor
103 W 4th St, Aroma Park, IL, 60910
(815) 932-4332
Admin Audrey Cook. *Medical Dir/Dir of Nursing* Marie Williams.
Licensure Sheltered care. *Beds* 27. *Certified* Medicaid.
Owner Privately owned.
Admissions Requirements Minimum age 18.
Staff RNs; LPNs; Nurses aides; Activities coordinators.
Facilities Dining room; Activities room; Laundry room; 3 Living rooms.
Activities Arts & crafts; Cards; Games; Reading groups; Prayer groups; Movies; Shopping trips; Social/Cultural gatherings.

ARTHUR

The Arthur Home*
423 Eberhardt Dr, Arthur, IL, 61911
(217) 543-2103
Admin Leona M Hughes.
Licensure Skilled care. *Beds* 69. *Certified* Medicaid; Medicare.
Owner Nonprofit Corp.

ASHMORE

Ashmore Estates*
RFD Box 400, Ashmore, IL, 61912
(217) 349-8328
Admin Araceli M Henson. *Medical Dir/Dir of Nursing* Dr Carl Johnson.
Licensure Intermediate care for mentally retarded.
Admissions Requirements Minimum age 18.
Staff Physicians 2 (pt); RNs 1 (ft), 1 (pt); LPNs 3 (ft); Nurses aides 15 (ft); Activities coordinators 1 (ft).
Facilities Dining room; Activities room; Crafts room; Laundry room; Lounges; Multipurpose & motor development building.

Activities Arts & crafts; Cards; Games; Movies; Shopping trips; Social/Cultural gatherings; Special Olympics; Family nights; Church services; Softball games; Pizza nights.

ASTORIA

Astoria Health Care Center
1008 E Broadway, Astoria, IL, 61501
(309) 329-2136
Admin Caroline Stine. *Medical Dir/Dir of Nursing* Melanine Beans DON.
Licensure Intermediate care. *Beds* ICF 69. *Certified* Medicaid.
Owner Proprietary Corp.
Staff RNs 1 (pt); LPNs 7 (pt); Nurses aides 24 (ft); Activities coordinators 1 (ft); Dietitians 1 (pt).
Facilities Dining room; Activities room; Crafts room; Laundry room; Barber/Beauty shop.
Activities Arts & crafts; Cards; Games; Reading groups; Prayer groups; Movies; Shopping trips; Social/Cultural gatherings.

ATLANTA

Bartmann Nursing & Home Sheltered Care Facility*
RR 1, Box 145, Atlanta, IL, 61723
(217) 642-5231
Admin Thomas W Booth.
Licensure Intermediate care. *Beds* 64.
Owner Proprietary Corp.

AUBURN

Park's Memorial Home*
304 Maple Ave, Auburn, IL, 62615
(217) 438-6125
Admin Dave Lambert. *Medical Dir/Dir of Nursing* Kenneth Malmberg MD.
Licensure Skilled care. *Beds* 70. *Certified* Medicaid; Medicare.
Owner Proprietary Corp.
Staff RNs 2 (ft), 1 (pt); LPNs 6 (ft), 2 (pt); Nurses aides 18 (ft), 6 (pt); Physical therapists 1 (ft); Recreational therapists 1 (ft); Occupational therapists 1 (pt); Speech therapists 1 (pt); Activities coordinators 1 (ft); Dietitians 1 (ft); Dentists 1 (pt); Ophthalmologists 1 (pt); Podiatrists 1 (pt); Audiologists 1 (pt); 1 (pt).
Facilities Dining room; Physical therapy room; Activities room; Laundry room; Barber/Beauty shop.
Activities Arts & crafts; Cards; Games; Reading groups; Prayer groups; Movies.

AUGUSTA

Hancock County Shelter Care
W Main St, Augusta, IL, 62311
(217) 392-2116
Admin Vicki S Carriger. *Medical Dir/Dir of Nursing* Olive Maizie Mecum.
Licensure Sheltered care. *Beds* Shelter care 45.
Owner Publicly owned.
Admissions Requirements Minimum age 18; Medical examination.
Staff RNs 1 (ft), 1 (pt); LPNs 2 (ft); Nurses aides 8 (pt); Activities coordinators 1 (ft); Dietitians 1 (pt).
Facilities Dining room; Activities room; Laundry room; Barber.
Activities Arts & crafts; Cards; Games; Reading groups; Prayer groups; Movies; Shopping trips; Social/Cultural gatherings.

AURORA

Aurora Community Living Facility*
2080 Best Pl, Aurora, IL, 60506
(312) 896-5200
Admin Linda Dider.
Licensure Intermediate care. *Beds* 20.
Owner Nonprofit Corp.

Aurora Manor*
1601 N Farnsworth, Aurora, IL, 60505
(312) 898-1180
Admin Diana E Kramer.
Licensure Skilled care; Intermediate care. *Beds* SNF 112; ICF 96. *Certified* Medicaid; Medicare.
Owner Proprietary Corp.

Countryside Healthcare Center*
2330 W Galena Blvd, Aurora, IL, 60506
(312) 896-4686
Admin Kim Kohls. *Medical Dir/Dir of Nursing* Marc Schlesinger MD.
Licensure Skilled care; Intermediate care. *Beds* SNF 107; ICF 104. *Certified* Medicaid; Medicare.
Owner Proprietary Corp.
Admissions Requirements Medical examination.
Staff Physical therapists 1 (pt); Reality therapists 1 (pt); Recreational therapists 1 (pt); Occupational therapists 1 (pt); Speech therapists 1 (pt); Activities coordinators 1 (ft); Dietitians 1 (pt); Dentists 1 (pt); Ophthalmologists 1 (pt); Podiatrists 1 (pt).
Facilities Dining room; Physical therapy room; Activities room; Barber/Beauty shop.
Activities Arts & crafts; Cards; Games; Reading groups; Prayer groups; Movies; Shopping trips; Social/Cultural gatherings; Church services.

Elmwood Living Center
1017 W Galena Blvd, Aurora, IL, 60506
(312) 897-3100
Admin Peggy Snow. *Medical Dir/Dir of Nursing* Patrick McNellis MD; Marilyn Swan RN DON.
Licensure Skilled care. *Beds* SNF 64.
Owner Nonprofit Corp.
Admissions Requirements Minimum age 18; Medical examination; Physician's request.
Staff RNs 4 (ft); LPNs 5 (ft); Nurses aides 20 (ft); Activities coordinators; Dietitians.
Languages Greek, Spanish
Affiliation Seventh-Day Adventist
Facilities Dining room; Physical therapy room; Activities room; Chapel; Barber/Beauty shop.
Activities Arts & crafts; Cards; Games; Reading groups; Prayer groups; Movies; Shopping trips; Social/Cultural gatherings.

Jennings Terrace*
275 S LaSalle, Aurora, IL, 60505
(312) 897-6946
Admin Martin J Scarpetta.
Licensure Sheltered care. *Beds* 104.
Owner Nonprofit Corp.

Parkview East Nursing & Conv Center*
400 E New York, Aurora, IL, 60505
(312) 897-8714
Admin Rebecca L Lind. *Medical Dir/Dir of Nursing* William Weigel MD.
Licensure Skilled care; Intermediate care. *Beds* SNF 80; ICF 41.
Owner Proprietary Corp (Signature Corp).
Admissions Requirements Minimum age 22.
Staff Physicians 2 (pt); RNs 3 (ft), 2 (pt); LPNs 2 (ft), 3 (pt); Orderlies 2 (pt); Nurses aides 17 (ft), 8 (pt); Physical therapists 1 (pt); Occupational therapists 1 (pt); Speech therapists 1 (pt); Activities coordinators 1 (pt); Dietitians 1 (pt); Dentists 1 (pt); Ophthalmologists 1 (pt); Podiatrists 1 (pt).
Facilities Dining room; Physical therapy room; Activities room; Chapel; Crafts room; Laundry room; Barber/Beauty shop; Library; Ice cream parlour/snack shop.
Activities Arts & crafts; Games; Reading groups; Movies; Social/Cultural gatherings; Baking.

Sunnymere Inc
925 6th Ave, Aurora, IL, 60505
(312) 898-7844
Admin Edith W Anderson.
Licensure Sheltered care. *Beds* 49.
Owner Nonprofit Corp.

AVON

Avon Nursing Home Inc
PO Box S, Avon, IL, 61415
(309) 465-3102
Admin Nancy Stenger RN. *Medical Dir/Dir of Nursing* Fay Slife RN.
Licensure Intermediate care. *Beds* ICF 48. *Certified* Medicaid.
Owner Proprietary Corp.
Admissions Requirements Medical examination.
Staff Physicians; RNs; LPNs; Nurses aides; Physical therapists; Activities coordinators; Dietitians.
Facilities Dining room; Physical therapy room; Activities room; Laundry room; Barber/Beauty shop.
Activities Arts & crafts; Cards; Games; Reading groups; Prayer groups; Movies; Shopping trips; Social/Cultural gatherings.

BARRINGTON

Governors Park of Barrington
1420 S Barrington Rd, Barrington, IL, 60010
(312) 382-6664
Admin Dale C Hagen. *Medical Dir/Dir of Nursing* Dee Coulson.
Licensure Skilled care; Intermediate care. *Beds* SNF 75; ICF 75. *Certified* Medicare.
Owner Proprietary Corp.
Admissions Requirements Minimum age 18; Medical examination; Physician's request.
Staff RNs 12 (ft), 14 (pt); LPNs 2 (ft); Nurses aides 32 (ft), 18 (pt); Physical therapists 1 (ft); Occupational therapists 1 (pt); Speech therapists 1 (pt); Activities coordinators 1 (ft); Dietitians 1 (pt); Ophthalmologists 1 (pt).
Languages Spanish
Facilities Dining room; Physical therapy room; Activities room; Chapel; Crafts room; Barber/Beauty shop; Library.
Activities Arts & crafts; Cards; Games; Reading groups; Movies; Shopping trips; Social/Cultural gatherings.

BARRY

Barry Community Care Center*
1313 Pratt St, Barry, IL, 62312
(217) 335-2326
Admin Mark W Hubbard.
Licensure Skilled care. *Beds* 76. *Certified* Medicaid; Medicare.
Owner Proprietary Corp.

BATAVIA

Covenant Health Care Center Inc
831 N Batavia Ave, Batavia, IL, 60510
(312) 879-4300
Admin Richard K Waltmire. *Medical Dir/Dir of Nursing* Dr John O'Dwyer; Alice Voruz DON.
Licensure Skilled care; Intermediate care. *Beds* SNF 128; ICF. *Certified* Medicaid; Medicare.
Owner Nonprofit Corp (Covenant Benevolent Inst).
Admissions Requirements Minimum age 18; Medical examination; Physician's request.
Staff Physicians; RNs; LPNs; Orderlies; Nurses aides; Physical therapists; Recreational therapists; Occupational therapists; Speech therapists; Activities coordinators; Dietitians.
Affiliation Evangelical Covenant Church

Facilities Dining room; Physical therapy
room; Activities room; Chapel; Crafts room;
Laundry room; Barber/Beauty shop.
Activities Arts & crafts; Cards; Games;
Reading groups; Prayer groups; Movies;
Shopping trips; Social/Cultural gatherings.

Roosevelt Square Nursing Center
520 Fabyan Pkwy, Batavia, IL, 60510
(312) 879-5266
Admin Sharon Kuhlman. *Medical Dir/Dir of
Nursing* Dr Robert Reeder; Deanna Schulz
RN.
Licensure Intermediate care. *Beds* ICF 63.
Certified Medicaid.
Owner Proprietary Corp (Beverly Enterprises).
Admissions Requirements Minimum age 60;
Medical examination; Physician's request.
Staff Physicians; RNs 5 (ft); LPNs 3 (pt);
Nurses aides 10 (ft), 8 (pt); Recreational
therapists 1 (ft); Activities coordinators 1
(ft); Dietitians; Ophthalmologists.
Facilities Dining room; Physical therapy
room; Activities room; Chapel; Crafts room;
Laundry room; Barber/Beauty shop; Library.
Activities Arts & crafts; Cards; Games;
Reading groups; Prayer groups; Movies;
Shopping trips; Social/Cultural gatherings;
Van rides; Family potluck dinners.

BEARDSTOWN

Elmwood Manor Inc*
13th Grand Ave, Beardstown, IL, 62618
(217) 323-4055
Admin Eugene Pontius.
Licensure Intermediate care. *Beds* 49.
Certified Medicaid.
Owner Proprietary Corp.

Myers Nursing Home*
1501 Canal St, Beardstown, IL, 62618
(217) 323-1900
Admin John W Myers. *Medical Dir/Dir of
Nursing* H C Zingher MD.
Licensure Skilled care; Intermediate care. *Beds*
83. *Certified* Medicaid; Medicare.
Owner Proprietary Corp.
Admissions Requirements Minimum age 18;
Medical examination; Physician's request.
Staff Physicians 1 (pt); RNs 2 (ft), 3 (pt);
LPNs 9 (ft), 1 (pt); Nurses aides 19 (ft), 13
(pt); Physical therapists 2 (pt); Recreational
therapists 1 (pt); Speech therapists 1 (pt);
Activities coordinators 1 (ft); Dietitians 1
(pt); Dentists 1 (pt); Podiatrists 1 (pt);
Audiologists 1 (pt).
Facilities Dining room; Activities room;
Crafts room; Barber/Beauty shop.
Activities Arts & crafts; Cards; Games;
Reading groups; Prayer groups; Movies;
Shopping trips.

BELLEVILLE

Belleville Nursing Center*
900 Royal Heights Rd, Belleville, IL, 62223
(618) 235-6133
Admin Susan M Franklin. *Medical Dir/Dir of
Nursing* Dr Paul Biedenharn.
Licensure Skilled care. *Beds* 234. *Certified*
Medicaid; Medicare.
Owner Proprietary Corp (Beverly Enterprises).
Admissions Requirements Medical
examination.
Staff RNs 3 (ft); LPNs 14 (ft); Nurses aides 80
(ft), 20 (pt); Physical therapists 1 (pt);
Recreational therapists 1 (pt); Speech
therapists 1 (pt); Activities coordinators 1
(ft); Dietitians 1 (pt); Dentists 1 (pt).
Facilities Dining room; Physical therapy
room; Activities room; Crafts room; Laundry
room; Barber/Beauty shop.
Activities Arts & crafts; Cards; Games;
Reading groups; Prayer groups; Movies;
Shopping trips; Social/Cultural gatherings.

Castlehaven Nursing Center
225 Castellano Dr, Belleville, IL, 62221
(618) 235-1300
Admin Julie Savage. *Medical Dir/Dir of
Nursing* H P Dexheimer MD; Barbara
LePere DON.
Licensure Skilled care; Intermediate care. *Beds*
SNF 144; ICF 97. *Certified* Medicaid;
Medicare.
Owner Proprietary Corp.
Admissions Requirements Minimum age 18.
Staff Physicians 1 (pt); RNs 7 (ft); LPNs 15
(ft); Orderlies 1 (ft); Nurses aides 66 (ft);
Physical therapists 1 (ft); Reality therapists 1
(ft); Occupational therapists 1 (pt); Speech
therapists 1 (pt); Activities coordinators 4
(ft); Dietitians 1 (pt); Podiatrists 1 (pt);
Dentist 1 (pt).
Facilities Dining room; Physical therapy
room; Activities room; Crafts room; Laundry
room; Barber/Beauty shop; Library; 5 living
rooms.
Activities Arts & crafts; Cards; Games;
Reading groups; Prayer groups; Movies;
Shopping trips; Social/Cultural gatherings;
Excursions to ballgames; Fishing; Botanical
gardens; Zoo; Interfacility olympics.

Dammert Geriatric Center
Rte 15, 9500 W Illinois, Belleville, IL, 62223
(618) 397-6700
Admin D Robert McCardle. *Medical Dir/Dir
of Nursing* Charlotte Perillo.
Licensure Skilled care; Life care. *Beds* SNF
56. *Certified* Medicare.
Owner Nonprofit Corp (Missionary Oblates of
Mary Imm).
Admissions Requirements Minimum age 62;
Medical examination; Physician's request.
Staff RNs 3 (ft), 4 (pt); LPNs 3 (ft), 3 (pt);
Nurses aides 17 (ft), 8 (pt); Activities
coordinators 1 (ft).
Affiliation Roman Catholic
Facilities Dining room; Physical therapy
room; Activities room; Chapel; Crafts room;
Laundry room; Barber/Beauty shop; Library.
Activities Arts & crafts; Cards; Games;
Reading groups; Prayer groups; Movies;
Shopping trips; Social/Cultural gatherings.

Four Fountains Convalescent Center
101 S Belt West, Belleville, IL, 62220
(618) 277-7700
Admin Steven D Brant.
Licensure Skilled care; Intermediate care. *Beds*
156. *Certified* Medicaid; Medicare.
Owner Privately owned.
Staff Physicians 1 (pt); RNs 12 (ft); LPNs 10
(ft); Nurses aides 60 (ft), 10 (pt); Physical
therapists 3 (ft), 2 (pt); Occupational
therapists 1 (pt); Speech therapists 1 (pt);
Activities coordinators 2 (ft); Dietitians 2
(pt); Dentists 1 (pt); Podiatrists 1 (pt).
Facilities Dining room; Physical therapy
room; Activities room; Crafts room; Laundry
room; Barber/Beauty shop; Library.
Activities Arts & crafts; Cards; Games; Prayer
groups; Movies; Shopping trips; Social/
Cultural gatherings.

Calvin D Johnson Nursing Home
727 N 17th St, Belleville, IL, 62223
(618) 234-3323
Admin Michael L Brady. *Medical Dir/Dir of
Nursing* J Paul Newell MD.
Licensure Skilled care; Intermediate care. *Beds*
SNF 196; ICF 51. *Certified* Medicaid;
Medicare.
Owner Proprietary Corp.
Admissions Requirements Medical
examination; Physician's request.
Staff Physicians 4 (pt); RNs 3 (ft), 3 (pt);
LPNs 13 (ft), 9 (pt); Orderlies 4 (pt); Nurses
aides 50 (ft), 16 (pt); Physical therapists 1
(ft); Recreational therapists 4 (pt);
Occupational therapists 1 (ft); Speech
therapists 1 (pt); Activities coordinators 1

(ft); Dietitians 1 (pt); Dentists 1 (pt);
Ophthalmologists 1 (pt); Podiatrists 1 (pt);
Dentist 1 (pt).
Facilities Dining room; Physical therapy
room; Activities room; Chapel; Crafts room;
Laundry room; Barber/Beauty shop.
Activities Arts & crafts; Cards; Games;
Reading groups; Prayer groups; Movies;
Shopping trips; Social/Cultural gatherings;
Elderbuggy bus.

The Lincoln Home
150 N 27th St, Belleville, IL, 62223
(618) 235-6600
Admin Wilma D Seppi. *Medical Dir/Dir of
Nursing* Dr Paul Biedenharn.
Licensure Intermediate care. *Beds* 152.
Owner Proprietary Corp.
Admissions Requirements Medical
examination.
Staff RNs 1 (ft); LPNs 16 (pt); Nurses aides
20 (ft), 6 (pt); Reality therapists 1 (pt);
Activities coordinators 1 (ft); Dietitians 1
(pt).
Facilities Dining room; Activities room;
Chapel; Crafts room; Laundry room; Barber/
Beauty shop; Library.
Activities Arts & crafts; Cards; Games;
Reading groups; Prayer groups; Movies;
Shopping trips; Social/Cultural gatherings.

Memorial Conv Center*
4315 Memorial Dr, Belleville, IL, 62223
(618) 233-7750
Admin Patricia Adams. *Medical Dir/Dir of
Nursing* Mathew Erscle.
Licensure Skilled care. *Beds* 108. *Certified*
Medicaid; Medicare.
Owner Nonprofit Corp.
Admissions Requirements Minimum age 18;
Medical examination; Physician's request.
Staff Physicians 1 (pt); RNs 7 (ft), 11 (pt);
LPNs 3 (ft), 2 (pt); Orderlies 1 (ft), 2 (pt);
Nurses aides 26 (ft), 29 (pt); Physical
therapists 1 (pt); Recreational therapists 2
(ft).
Facilities Dining room; Physical therapy
room; Activities room; Chapel; Crafts room;
Barber/Beauty shop; Library.
Activities Arts & crafts; Cards; Games;
Reading groups; Prayer groups; Movies;
Shopping trips; Social/Cultural gatherings.

Notre Dame Hills Living Center
6401 W Main St, Belleville, IL, 62223
(618) 397-8400
Admin Lois J Snyder. *Medical Dir/Dir of
Nursing* William Lesko MD; Dorothy Miller
DON.
Licensure Skilled care; Intermediate care. *Beds*
SNF 61; ICF 61. *Certified* Medicaid;
Medicare.
Owner Nonprofit Corp (Adventist Health Sys-
USA).
Admissions Requirements Minimum age 21;
Medical examination; Physician's request.
Staff RNs 3 (ft), 4 (pt); LPNs 4 (ft), 4 (pt);
Orderlies 1 (pt); Nurses aides 24 (ft), 18 (pt);
Physical therapists 1 (pt); Recreational
therapists 1 (ft), 2 (pt); Occupational
therapists 1 (pt); Dietitians 1 (pt);
Ophthalmologists 1 (pt); Dentist 1 (pt).
Affiliation Seventh-Day Adventist
Facilities Dining room; Physical therapy
room; Activities room; Laundry room;
Barber/Beauty shop; TV rooms; Patio; 3
lounge areas.
Activities Arts & crafts; Cards; Games;
Reading groups; Prayer groups; Movies;
Shopping trips; Social/Cultural gatherings;
Restaurant outings; Cooking; Reality
orientation classes; Pet therapy.

St Pauls Home*
1021 W "E" St, Belleville, IL, 62220
(618) 233-2095
Admin Warren W Peters.

Licensure Intermediate care; Sheltered care. *Beds* ICF 113; Sheltered care 62. *Certified* Medicaid.
Owner Nonprofit Corp.

Weier Retirement Nursing Home*
5 Gundlach Pl, Belleville, IL, 62221
(618) 233-6625
Admin Roger W Hotson.
Licensure Intermediate care. *Beds* 94. *Certified* Medicaid.
Owner Proprietary Corp.

BELLWOOD

Dale Johnson Center*
2614 Saint Charles Rd, Bellwood, IL, 60104
(312) 547-3550
Admin Cathie J Kniebe.
Licensure Intermediate care. *Beds* 20.
Owner Nonprofit Corp.

PARC Home*
105 Eastern Ave, Bellwood, IL, 60104
(312) 547-3580
Admin Elaine P Bernabe. *Medical Dir/Dir of Nursing* Raymond McDonald MD.
Licensure Intermediate care; ICF/ Developmentally disabled. *Beds* 95.
Owner Nonprofit Corp.
Admissions Requirements Minimum age 18; Medical examination.
Staff Physicians 1 (pt); RNs 1 (pt); LPNs 4 (ft), 3 (pt); Nurses aides 20 (ft), 20 (pt); Reality therapists 3 (ft); Recreational therapists 1 (ft); Occupational therapists 1 (ft), 1 (pt); Speech therapists 1 (ft); Activities coordinators 1 (ft); Dietitians 1 (pt); Dentists 1 (pt); Ophthalmologists 1 (pt); Podiatrists 1 (pt); Audiologists 1 (pt).
Facilities Dining room; Activities room; Laundry room; Barber/Beauty shop.
Activities Arts & crafts; Games; Prayer groups; Movies; Shopping trips; Social/Cultural gatherings.

BELVIDERE

Fairview Manor*
1701 W 5th Ave, Belvidere, IL, 61008
(815) 547-5451
Admin Norman John Gross. *Medical Dir/Dir of Nursing* Kent Hess MD.
Licensure Intermediate care. *Beds* 79. *Certified* Medicaid.
Owner Proprietary Corp.
Admissions Requirements Medical examination; Physician's request.
Staff RNs 1 (ft); LPNs 4 (ft), 2 (pt); Nurses aides 16 (ft), 4 (pt); Physical therapists 1 (pt); Activities coordinators 1 (ft), 1 (pt); Dietitians 1 (ft).
Facilities Dining room; Physical therapy room; Activities room; Laundry room; Barber/Beauty shop; Library.
Activities Arts & crafts; Cards; Games; Reading groups; Prayer groups; Movies; Shopping trips; Social/Cultural gatherings.

Maple Crest-Boone County Nursing Home*
4452 Squaw Prairie Rd, Belvidere, IL, 61008
(815) 547-6377
Admin Gregory A Olson.
Licensure Skilled care. *Beds* 78. *Certified* Medicaid.
Owner Publicly owned.

Northwoods Healthcare Center*
2250 S Pearl Street Rd, Belvidere, IL, 61008
(815) 544-0358
Admin Susan Mead.
Licensure Skilled care. *Beds* 120. *Certified* Medicaid; Medicare.
Owner Proprietary Corp.

BEMENT

Bement Manor
601 N Morgan, Bement, IL, 61813
(217) 678-2191
Admin Diane Jones. *Medical Dir/Dir of Nursing* Dr Rohidas Patil; Janet Adamson DON.
Licensure Intermediate care. *Beds* ICF 63. *Certified* Medicaid; Medicare.
Owner Proprietary Corp.
Admissions Requirements Minimum age 18.
Staff RNs 2 (ft), 2 (pt); LPNs 3 (ft), 2 (pt); Nurses aides 12 (ft), 3 (pt); Physical therapists 1 (pt); Recreational therapists 1 (pt); Occupational therapists 1 (pt); Speech therapists 1 (pt); Activities coordinators 1 (ft); Dietitians 1 (pt); Dentists 1 (pt); Ophthalmologists 1 (pt); Podiatrists 1 (pt).
Facilities Dining room; Activities room; Chapel; Laundry room; Barber/Beauty shop; Occupational therapy room.
Activities Arts & crafts; Cards; Games; Reading groups; Prayer groups; Movies; Shopping trips; Social/Cultural gatherings.

BENSENVILLE

The Anchorage Bensenville Home
111 E Washington, Bensenville, IL, 60106
(312) 766-5800
Admin Jane M Muller. *Medical Dir/Dir of Nursing* Dr P Kini; Ada Bowen.
Licensure Skilled care; Intermediate care. *Beds* SNF 90; ICF 142. *Certified* Medicaid; Medicare.
Owner Nonprofit Corp.
Admissions Requirements Minimum age 65; Medical examination.
Staff Physicians 3 (pt); RNs 7 (ft), 19 (pt); LPNs 8 (ft), 2 (pt); Orderlies 3 (ft); Nurses aides 50 (ft), 24 (pt); Physical therapists 1 (pt); Reality therapists 1 (pt); Recreational therapists 6 (ft), 38 (pt); Occupational therapists 1 (pt); Speech therapists 1 (pt); Activities coordinators 2 (ft); Dietitians 1 (ft); Dentists 1 (pt); Ophthalmologists 1 (pt); Dentist 1 (pt).
Affiliation Church of Christ
Facilities Dining room; Physical therapy room; Activities room; Chapel; Crafts room; Laundry room; Barber/Beauty shop; Library; Clinic area.
Activities Arts & crafts; Cards; Games; Reading groups; Prayer groups; Movies; Shopping trips; Social/Cultural gatherings; Bus rides; Outings; Ceramics; Psychosocial groups; Music therapy; Pet therapy.

BENTON

Lifecare Center of Benton
PO Box 480, 1409 N Main St, Benton, IL, 62812
(618) 435-2712
Admin H Jeanne Michael.
Licensure Intermediate care. *Beds* ICF 71. *Certified* Medicaid.
Owner Proprietary Corp (Community Lifecare Enterprises).
Admissions Requirements Medical examination.
Staff LPNs 4 (ft), 1 (ft); Nurses aides 26 (ft); Physical therapists 1 (pt); Activities coordinators 1 (ft); Dietitians 1 (pt).
Facilities Dining room; Physical therapy room; Activities room; Laundry room; Barber/Beauty shop.
Activities Arts & crafts; Cards; Games; Reading groups; Prayer groups; Movies; Shopping trips; Social/Cultural gatherings.

Severin Intermediate Care Facility*
902 S McLeansboro St, Benton, IL, 62812
(618) 435-2442
Admin Paul D Leffler.

Licensure Intermediate care. *Beds* 96. *Certified* Medicaid.
Owner Proprietary Corp.

BERWYN

Fairfax Health Care Center
3601 S Harlem Ave, Berwyn, IL, 60402
(312) 749-4160
Admin Frances W Schweig. *Medical Dir/Dir of Nursing* Dr Alberto Saltiel.
Licensure Skilled care. *Beds* SNF 160. *Certified* Medicaid; Medicare.
Owner Proprietary Corp.
Admissions Requirements Minimum age 19; Medical examination; Physician's request.
Staff Physicians 3 (pt); RNs 11 (ft), 4 (pt); LPNs 7 (ft), 4 (pt); Orderlies 1 (ft); Nurses aides 50 (ft), 4 (pt); Physical therapists 1 (pt); Recreational therapists 4 (ft), 1 (pt); Occupational therapists 1 (pt); Speech therapists 1 (pt); Dietitians 1 (pt); Dentists; Ophthalmologists; Podiatrists; Respiratory Therapists; Dentist.
Facilities Dining room; Physical therapy room; Activities room; Laundry room; Barber/Beauty shop; Sunrooms.
Activities Arts & crafts; Cards; Games; Reading groups; Prayer groups; Movies; Shopping trips; Social/Cultural gatherings.

BETHALTO

Bethalto Care Center Inc*
815 S Prairie St, Bethalto, IL, 62010
(618) 377-2144
Admin Linda M Daniels.
Licensure Intermediate care. *Beds* 98. *Certified* Medicaid.
Owner Proprietary Corp.

BLOOMINGDALE

Applewood Manor Convalescent Center*
275 Army Trail Rd, Bloomingdale, IL, 60108
(312) 893-9616
Admin Judith Silverstein.
Licensure Skilled care. *Beds* 207. *Certified* Medicaid; Medicare.
Owner Proprietary Corp.

Bloomingdale Pavilion*
311 Edgewater Dr, Bloomingdale, IL, 60108
(312) 894-7400
Admin Linda L Cecconi.
Licensure Skilled care. *Beds* 215. *Certified* Medicaid; Medicare.
Owner Proprietary Corp.

Elaine Boyd Creche Childrens Home
267 E Lake St, Bloomingdale, IL, 60108
(312) 529-3350
Admin Chermaine Gorski Bell. *Medical Dir/ Dir of Nursing* Oscar Novick MD.
Licensure Skilled care; Children. *Beds* SNF 109. *Certified* Medicaid.
Owner Privately owned.
Admissions Requirements Minimum age Birth to 21; Medical examination; Physician's request; AIDS testing.
Staff Physicians 1 (ft); RNs 9 (ft), 2 (pt); LPNs 4 (ft), 2 (pt); Nurses aides 64 (ft), 21 (pt); Physical therapists 1 (ft); Recreational therapists 1 (ft); Occupational therapists 1 (ft); Speech therapists 1 (ft); Activities coordinators 1 (ft); Dietitians 1 (ft); Podiatrists 1 (ft);; Music therapist 1 (ft); Certified teachers 4 (ft).
Languages Spanish
Facilities Physical therapy room; Activities room; Laundry room; Special education classrooms.
Activities Arts & crafts; Games; Movies; Shopping trips; Special Olympics; Musical groups; Music aerobics.

Marklund Home
164 S Prairie Ave, Bloomingdale, IL, 60108
(312) 529-2871
Admin Patricia Pearce. *Medical Dir/Dir of Nursing* Val Moller.
Licensure Skilled care. *Beds* 98. *Certified* Medicaid; Medicare.
Owner Nonprofit Corp.
Admissions Requirements Medical examination; Physician's request.
Staff Physicians 1 (ft); RNs 4 (ft), 10 (pt); LPNs 1 (ft), 3 (pt); Orderlies 1 (ft); Nurses aides 30 (ft), 34 (pt); Physical therapists 1 (ft); Recreational therapists 1 (ft); Occupational therapists 1 (ft); Speech therapists 1 (ft); Activities coordinators 1 (pt); Dietitians 1 (pt); Dentists 2 (pt).
Facilities Dining room; Physical therapy room; Activities room; Crafts room; Laundry room; Library.
Activities Arts & crafts; Games; Prayer groups; Movies; Shopping trips.

BLOOMINGTON

Bloomington Manor*
1925 S Main, Bloomington, IL, 61701
(309) 829-4348
Admin Mary Whiteford Leung. *Medical Dir/Dir of Nursing* Dr Ravi Kottoor.
Licensure Intermediate care. *Beds* 77. *Certified* Medicaid.
Owner Proprietary Corp (Beverly Enterprises).
Admissions Requirements Medical examination.
Staff RNs 1 (ft); LPNs 3 (ft), 3 (pt); Orderlies 1 (pt); Nurses aides 6 (ft), 5 (pt); Physical therapists 1 (pt); Reality therapists 1 (ft), 1 (pt); Recreational therapists 1 (ft); Activities coordinators 1 (ft); Dietitians 1 (pt).
Facilities Dining room; Physical therapy room; Activities room; Crafts room; Laundry room; Barber/Beauty shop; Library.
Activities Arts & crafts; Cards; Games; Reading groups; Prayer groups; Movies; Shopping trips; Social/Cultural gatherings.

Bloomington Nursing & Rehabilitation Center*
1509 N Calhoun St, Bloomington, IL, 61701
(309) 827-6046
Admin Thelma Wesle. *Medical Dir/Dir of Nursing* Dr Virgil Short.
Licensure Skilled care. *Beds* 123.
Owner Proprietary Corp.
Admissions Requirements Minimum age 50; Medical examination.
Staff RNs 4 (ft), 1 (pt); LPNs 6 (ft), 3 (pt); Orderlies 6 (ft), 2 (pt); Nurses aides 30 (ft), 10 (pt); Physical therapists 1 (pt); Recreational therapists 1 (ft), 2 (pt); Speech therapists 1 (pt); Activities coordinators 1 (ft); Dietitians 1 (pt); Dentists 1 (pt); Ophthalmologists 1 (pt); Podiatrists 1 (pt); Audiologists 1 (pt).
Facilities Dining room; Physical therapy room; Activities room; Crafts room; Laundry room; Barber/Beauty shop.
Activities Arts & crafts; Cards; Games; Reading groups; Prayer groups; Movies; Shopping trips; Social/Cultural gatherings.

Hage House
806 Four Seasons Rd, Bloomington, IL, 61701
(309) 827-6272
Admin Diane Boeck.
Licensure Intermediate care for mentally retarded. *Beds* ICF/MR 15. *Certified* Medicaid; Medicare.
Owner Nonprofit organization/foundation.
Admissions Requirements Minimum age 18; Medical examination.
Staff RNs 1 (pt); Activities coordinators 1 (ft).
Facilities Dining room; Activities room; Laundry room.
Activities Arts & crafts; Cards; Games; Social/Cultural gatherings; SOAR.

Heritage Manor
700 E Walnut St, Bloomington, IL, 61701
(309) 827-8004
Admin Jean Dulin. *Medical Dir/Dir of Nursing* Seymour R Goldberg MD; Jane DeBlois RN DON.
Licensure Skilled care. *Beds* SNF 110. *Certified* Medicaid; Medicare.
Owner Proprietary Corp (Heritage Enterprises).
Admissions Requirements Medical examination; Physician's request.
Staff Physicians 1 (pt); RNs 7 (ft), 2 (pt); LPNs 5 (ft), 7 (pt); Orderlies 2 (ft); Nurses aides 56 (ft); Physical therapists 2 (pt); Reality therapists 1 (pt); Recreational therapists 1 (pt); Occupational therapists 1 (pt); Speech therapists 1 (pt); Activities coordinators 1 (ft); Dietitians 1 (pt); Dentists 1 (pt); Ophthalmologists 1 (pt); Podiatrists 1 (pt).
Facilities Dining room; Physical therapy room; Activities room; Chapel; Crafts room; Laundry room; Barber/Beauty shop; Library.
Activities Arts & crafts; Cards; Games; Reading groups; Prayer groups; Movies; Shopping trips; Social/Cultural gatherings.

Westminster Village Inc
2025 E Lincoln St, Bloomington, IL, 61701
(309) 663-6474
Admin Martha K Butler. *Medical Dir/Dir of Nursing* James E Swanson MD; Carol DeVore DON.
Licensure Skilled care; Intermediate care. *Beds* SNF 39; ICF 39. *Certified* Medicare.
Owner Nonprofit Corp.
Admissions Requirements Minimum age 18; Medical examination; Physician's request.
Staff RNs 3 (ft), 4 (pt); LPNs 5 (ft), 5 (pt); Orderlies 4 (ft); Nurses aides 16 (ft), 4 (pt); Recreational therapists 1 (ft); Activities coordinators 1 (ft); Dietitians 1 (ft); Social services 1 (ft).
Facilities Dining room; Physical therapy room; Activities room; Crafts room; Barber/Beauty shop; Library.
Activities Arts & crafts; Cards; Games; Reading groups; Prayer groups; Movies; Shopping trips; Social/Cultural gatherings; Exercise; Cooking class; Men's club; Sing-along.

BLUE ISLAND

Blue Island Nursing Home*
2427 W 127th St, Blue Island, IL, 60406
(312) 389-7799
Admin John A Heuser.
Licensure Intermediate care. *Beds* 30. *Certified* Medicaid.
Owner Proprietary Corp.

BOURBONNAIS

Bourbonnais Terrace*
133 Mohawk Dr, Bourbonnais, IL, 60914
(815) 937-4790
Admin Carolyn Brinkman. *Medical Dir/Dir of Nursing* Samuel DeGuzman.
Licensure Skilled care; Intermediate care. *Beds* SNF 100; ICF 97. *Certified* Medicaid.
Owner Proprietary Corp.
Admissions Requirements Minimum age 21.
Staff RNs 6 (ft); LPNs 7 (ft).
Facilities Dining room; Physical therapy room; Activities room; Laundry room; Barber/Beauty shop.
Activities Games; Prayer groups; Movies; Social/Cultural gatherings; Community programs.

Kankakee Terrace*
100 Belle Aire, Bourbonnais, IL, 60914
(815) 939-0910
Admin Barbara H Daum. *Medical Dir/Dir of Nursing* Dr Samuel DeGuzman.

Licensure Intermediate care. *Beds* 126.
Owner Proprietary Corp.
Staff RNs 4 (pt); LPNs 2 (ft), 2 (pt); Nurses aides 13 (ft), 9 (pt); Activities coordinators 3 (ft), 1 (pt); Dietitians 1 (ft).
Facilities Dining room; Activities room; Laundry room; Barber/Beauty shop.
Activities Arts & crafts; Cards; Games; Movies; Shopping trips; Social/Cultural gatherings.

Our Lady of Victory Nursing Home*
20 Briarcliff Ln, Bourbonnais, IL, 60914
(815) 937-2022
Admin Henrietta Chamnens. *Medical Dir/Dir of Nursing* Dr J M Dave.
Licensure Intermediate care. *Beds* 81. *Certified* Medicaid.
Owner Proprietary Corp.
Admissions Requirements Medical examination; Physician's request.
Staff RNs 1 (ft), 3 (pt); LPNs 5 (ft), 3 (pt); Orderlies 1 (ft); Nurses aides 19 (ft), 8 (pt); Physical therapists 2 (ft), 1 (pt); Activities coordinators 1 (ft).
Affiliation Roman Catholic
Facilities Dining room; Physical therapy room; Activities room; Chapel; Crafts room; Laundry room; Library.
Activities Arts & crafts; Cards; Games; Reading groups; Prayer groups; Movies; Shopping trips; Social/Cultural gatherings.

BRADLEY

Bradley Royale Inc*
650 N Kinzie, Bradley, IL, 60915
(815) 933-1666
Admin Sherry L Crews.
Licensure Skilled care; Intermediate care. *Beds* SNF 48; ICF 50.
Owner Proprietary Corp.

BREESE

Breese Nursing Home*
1155 N 1st, Breese, IL, 62230
(618) 526-4521
Admin Joyce Haege. *Medical Dir/Dir of Nursing* Dr R J Sosa.
Licensure Skilled care. *Beds* 123. *Certified* Medicaid; Medicare.
Owner Proprietary Corp.
Admissions Requirements Minimum age 18; Medical examination; Physician's request.
Staff Physicians 10 (pt); RNs 3 (ft), 2 (pt); LPNs 4 (ft), 3 (pt); Orderlies 1 (ft); Nurses aides 21 (ft), 20 (pt); Physical therapists 1 (pt); Speech therapists 1 (pt); Activities coordinators 1 (pt); Dietitians 1 (pt); Dentists 2 (pt); Ophthalmologists 1 (pt); Audiologists 1 (pt).
Facilities Dining room; Physical therapy room; Activities room; Chapel; Crafts room; Laundry room; Barber/Beauty shop; Social services.
Activities Arts & crafts; Cards; Games; Reading groups; Prayer groups; Movies; Shopping trips; Social/Cultural gatherings.

BRIDGEPORT

Bridgeport Terrace
900 E Corporation St, Bridgeport, IL, 62417
(618) 945-2091
Admin Kathryn A Blackwell. *Medical Dir/Dir of Nursing* Dr Gary D Carr; Patricia Leib DON.
Licensure Intermediate care. *Beds* ICF 99. *Certified* Medicaid.
Owner Proprietary Corp.
Admissions Requirements Minimum age 21; Medical examination; Physician's request.
Staff Physicians 1 (pt); RNs 1 (ft); LPNs 4 (ft), 5 (pt); Orderlies 2 (ft); Nurses aides 14 (ft), 4 (pt); Physical therapists 1 (ft), 1 (pt);

Recreational therapists 1 (pt); Occupational therapists 1 (pt); Activities coordinators 2 (ft), 1 (pt); Dietitians 1 (pt); Dentists; Ophthalmologists; Podiatrists.
Facilities Dining room; Physical therapy room; Activities room; Laundry room; Barber/Beauty shop; Library; Sunroom; TV room.
Activities Arts & crafts; Cards; Games; Reading groups; Prayer groups; Movies; Shopping trips; Social/Cultural gatherings; Van trips; Community outreach; ADL programs; Special Olympics; Picnics; Special holiday activities.

BRIDGEVIEW

Bridgeview Convalescent Center
8100 S Harlem Ave, Bridgeview, IL, 60455
(312) 594-5440
Admin Paul J Dudek. *Medical Dir/Dir of Nursing* Dr P Punjabi.
Licensure Skilled care; Intermediate care. *Beds* SNF 101; ICF 51. *Certified* Medicaid; Medicare.
Owner Proprietary Corp.
Staff Physicians 6 (pt); RNs 8 (ft), 4 (pt); LPNs 6 (ft), 10 (pt); Orderlies 6 (ft); Nurses aides 77 (ft); Physical therapists 2 (pt); Reality therapists 1 (pt); Recreational therapists 1 (pt); Occupational therapists 1 (pt); Speech therapists 1 (pt); Activities coordinators 1 (ft); Dietitians 1 (pt); Dentists 1 (pt); Ophthalmologists 1 (pt); Podiatrists 1 (pt); Dentist 1 (pt).
Facilities Dining room; Physical therapy room; Activities room; Crafts room; Laundry room; Barber/Beauty shop.
Activities Arts & crafts; Cards; Games; Reading groups; Prayer groups; Movies; Shopping trips; Social/Cultural gatherings.

BRIGHTON

Robings Manor Nursing Home*
502 N Main, Brighton, IL, 62012
(618) 372-3232
Admin Catherine D Hale.
Licensure Skilled care. *Beds* 68. *Certified* Medicare.
Owner Proprietary Corp.

BROOKFIELD

The British Home
31st St & McCormick, Brookfield, IL, 60513
(312) 485-0135
Admin Robert C Lytle. *Medical Dir/Dir of Nursing* Dr Richard Dirkes.
Licensure Intermediate care; Sheltered care; Independent living. *Beds* ICF 26; Sheltered care 64; Independent living 66.
Owner Nonprofit Corp.
Admissions Requirements Minimum age 60.
Staff RNs 6 (ft); LPNs 2 (pt); Nurses aides 8 (ft), 5 (pt); Activities coordinators 2 (ft); Dietitians 1 (ft).
Facilities Dining room; Activities room; Crafts room; Barber/Beauty shop; Library.
Activities Arts & crafts; Cards; Games; Reading groups; Prayer groups; Movies; Shopping trips.

BUNKER HILL

South Lawn Sheltered Care
PO Box H, 512 S Franklin, Bunker Hill, IL, 62014
(618) 585-4875
Admin Gary G Rull.
Licensure Sheltered care. *Beds* 50. *Certified* Medicaid.
Owner Privately owned.
Admissions Requirements Minimum age 18; Medical examination.

Staff LPNs; Nurses aides; Activities coordinators.
Facilities Dining room; Laundry room; Barber/Beauty shop.
Activities Arts & crafts; Cards; Games; Reading groups; Prayer groups; Movies; Shopping trips; Social/Cultural gatherings.

BURBANK

Brentwood Nursing & Rehabilitation Center
5400 W 87th St, Burbank, IL, 60459
(312) 423-1200
Admin Janet Hanson-Kirby. *Medical Dir/Dir of Nursing* Timothy Knox MD; Mary Beth Desmond RN.
Licensure Skilled care. *Beds* SNF 165. *Certified* Medicare.
Owner Proprietary Corp (Integrated Health Services Inc).
Admissions Requirements Medical examination.
Staff RNs; LPNs; Nurses aides; Physical therapists; Recreational therapists; Occupational therapists; Speech therapists; Activities coordinators; Dietitians; Ophthalmologists; Podiatrists.
Languages Spanish
Facilities Dining room; Physical therapy room; Activities room; Crafts room; Laundry room; Barber/Beauty shop.
Activities Arts & crafts; Cards; Games; Prayer groups; Movies.

Parkside Gardens*
5701 W 79th St, Burbank, IL, 60459
(312) 636-3850
Admin Frances E Merz.
Licensure Intermediate care. *Beds* 78. *Certified* Medicaid.
Owner Proprietary Corp.
Facilities Dining room; Physical therapy room; Activities room; Laundry room; Barber/Beauty shop.
Activities Arts & crafts; Cards; Games; Reading groups; Prayer groups; Movies.

BYRON

The Neighbors*
PO Box 585, Byron, IL, 61010
(815) 234-2511
Admin Grant Bullock. *Medical Dir/Dir of Nursing* P John Seward MD.
Licensure Skilled care. *Beds* SNF 99. *Certified* Medicaid; Medicare.
Owner Proprietary Corp.
Admissions Requirements Medical examination.
Staff RNs 5 (ft), 2 (pt); LPNs 3 (ft), 4 (pt); Nurses aides 33 (ft), 6 (pt); Speech therapists 1 (pt); Activities coordinators 1 (ft), 1 (pt).
Facilities Dining room; Physical therapy room; Activities room; Laundry room; Barber/Beauty shop.
Activities Arts & crafts; Cards; Games; Reading groups; Prayer groups; Movies; Shopping trips; Social/Cultural gatherings.

CAHOKIA

River Bluffs of Cahokia
3354 Jerome Ln, Cahokia, IL, 62206
(618) 337-9824
Admin Martha Barron. *Medical Dir/Dir of Nursing* Theodore Bryan MD.
Licensure Skilled care; Intermediate care. *Beds* SNF 140; ICF. *Certified* Medicaid.
Owner Proprietary Corp.
Admissions Requirements Minimum age 21; Medical examination; Physician's request.
Staff Physicians 4 (pt); RNs 2 (ft), 1 (pt); LPNs 8 (ft), 2 (pt); Orderlies 3 (ft); Nurses aides 38 (ft), 1 (pt); Physical therapists 2 (ft); Recreational therapists 3 (ft); Speech

therapists 1 (pt); Activities coordinators 1 (ft); Dietitians 1 (ft), 1 (pt); Dentists 1 (pt); Ophthalmologists 1 (pt); Podiatrists 1 (pt).
Facilities Dining room; Physical therapy room; Activities room; Crafts room; Laundry room; Barber/Beauty shop; Library.
Activities Arts & crafts; Cards; Games; Reading groups; Prayer groups; Movies; Shopping trips; Social/Cultural gatherings; Cooking class.

CAIRO

Greenbriar Manor
1101 Cedar St, Cairo, IL, 62914
(618) 734-1816
Admin Angela Oliver. *Medical Dir/Dir of Nursing* Gemo Wong MD; Bea Becton RN.
Licensure Intermediate care. *Beds* ICF 64. *Certified* Medicare.
Owner Proprietary Corp.
Admissions Requirements Minimum age 18; Medical examination.
Staff RNs 1 (ft); LPNs 5 (ft), 2 (pt); Orderlies 2 (pt); Nurses aides 19 (ft); Physical therapists; Occupational therapists; Speech therapists; Activities coordinators 1 (ft); Dietitians; Medical Social worker 1 (ft).
Facilities Dining room; Physical therapy room; Activities room; Laundry room; Barber/Beauty shop.
Activities Arts & crafts; Cards; Games; Reading groups; Prayer groups; Movies; Shopping trips; Social/Cultural gatherings; Resident Council.

CAMP POINT

Grandview Manor*
205 E Spring, Camp Point, IL, 62320
(217) 593-7734
Admin Mary Louise Owens. *Medical Dir/Dir of Nursing* Dr Frank Chamberlin.
Licensure Skilled care; Intermediate care. *Beds* 124. *Certified* Medicaid.
Owner Proprietary Corp.
Admissions Requirements Minimum age 21; Medical examination; Physician's request.
Staff RNs 3 (ft); LPNs 4 (ft), 5 (pt); Nurses aides 25 (ft), 4 (pt); Activities coordinators 2 (ft).
Facilities Dining room; Physical therapy room; Activities room; Laundry room; Barber/Beauty shop.
Activities Arts & crafts; Cards; Games; Reading groups; Prayer groups; Movies; Shopping trips.

CANTON

Nursing Center of Canton
1675 E Ash St, Canton, IL, 61520
(309) 647-5631
Admin Kathryn S Demler. *Medical Dir/Dir of Nursing* Frantz Straub MD.
Licensure Skilled care; Intermediate care; Pediatric care. *Beds* 190. *Certified* Medicaid; Medicare.
Owner Proprietary Corp (Signature Corp).
Admissions Requirements Medical examination; Physician's request.
Staff RNs 10 (ft); LPNs 13 (ft); Orderlies 3 (ft); Nurses aides 90 (ft); Physical therapists 1 (pt); Speech therapists 1 (pt); Activities coordinators 3 (ft); Dietitians 1 (pt); Dentists 2 (pt); Ophthalmologists 1 (pt); Podiatrists 1 (pt).
Facilities Dining room; Physical therapy room; Activities room; Chapel; Crafts room; Laundry room; Barber/Beauty shop.
Activities Arts & crafts; Cards; Games; Reading groups; Prayer groups; Movies; Shopping trips; Social/Cultural gatherings.

Sunset Healthcare Center
129 S First Ave, Canton, IL, 61520
(309) 647-4327
Admin Deborah Huggins. *Medical Dir/Dir of Nursing* Dr Linda Forrestier.
Licensure Intermediate care. *Beds* 98.
Certified Medicaid.
Owner Proprietary Corp (National Heritage).
Admissions Requirements Minimum age 18; Medical examination.
Staff RNs 3 (ft), 2 (pt); LPNs 5 (ft), 2 (pt); Orderlies 2 (ft); Nurses aides 21 (ft), 15 (pt); Physical therapists 1 (ft), 1 (pt); Occupational therapists 1 (ft), 1 (pt); Activities coordinators 1 (ft), 1 (pt); Dietitians 5 (ft), 3 (pt).
Facilities Dining room; Physical therapy room; Activities room; Laundry room; Barber/Beauty shop.
Activities Arts & crafts; Cards; Games; Reading groups; Prayer groups; Movies; Shopping trips; Social/Cultural gatherings.

CARBONDALE

Carbondale Manor*
500 Lewis Ln, Carbondale, IL, 62901
(618) 529-5355
Admin Virginia M Roberts.
Licensure Skilled care; Intermediate care. *Beds* SNF 90; ICF 119.
Owner Proprietary Corp (Angell Group).

Styrest Nursing Home*
120 N Tower Rd, Carbondale, IL, 62901
(618) 549-3355
Admin Betty S Vick.
Licensure Skilled care; Sheltered care. *Beds* SNF 132; Sheltered care 130. *Certified* Medicaid; Medicare.
Owner Proprietary Corp.

CARLINVILLE

Barry Care Center of Carlinville*
1200 University Ave, Carlinville, IL, 62626
(217) 854-4433
Admin Jamie Barry Verticchio.
Licensure Skilled care. *Beds* 91.
Owner Proprietary Corp.

Doral Country Manor*
RR 3, Carlinville, IL, 62626
(217) 854-4491
Admin Elaine M Ottersburg.
Licensure Intermediate care. *Beds* 71.
Certified Medicaid.
Admissions Requirements Minimum age 18; Medical examination.
Staff Physicians 2 (pt); RNs 1 (ft); LPNs 3 (ft), 3 (pt); Orderlies 1 (ft), 2 (pt); Nurses aides 11 (ft), 9 (pt); Physical therapists 1 (pt); Recreational therapists 1 (pt); Occupational therapists 1 (pt); Speech therapists 1 (pt); Activities coordinators 1 (pt); Dietitians 1 (pt); Dentists 1 (pt); Podiatrists 1 (pt); Audiologists 1 (pt).
Facilities Dining room; Physical therapy room; Activities room; Chapel; Crafts room; Laundry room; Barber/Beauty shop.
Activities Arts & crafts; Games; Reading groups; Prayer groups; Movies; Shopping trips; Social/Cultural gatherings; Orientation.

Friendship Home*
826 N High St, Carlinville, IL, 62626
(217) 854-9606
Admin Lyle Kay Stinnett.
Licensure Intermediate care. *Beds* 49.
Certified Medicaid.
Owner Proprietary Corp.

Sunshine Manor Nursing Center
751 N Oak St, Carlinville, IL, 62626
(217) 854-2511

Admin Eunice Adcock. *Medical Dir/Dir of Nursing* Mary Raffety DON.
Licensure Skilled care. *Beds* SNF 98. *Certified* Medicaid; Medicare.
Owner Nonprofit Corp (First Humanics).
Admissions Requirements Minimum age 18; Medical examination.
Staff RNs; LPNs; Orderlies; Nurses aides; Physical therapists; Recreational therapists; Occupational therapists; Activities coordinators.
Facilities Dining room; Physical therapy room; Activities room; Crafts room; Barber/Beauty shop; Library.
Activities Arts & crafts; Games; Reading groups; Prayer groups; Movies; Shopping trips; Social/Cultural gatherings.

CARLYLE

Carlyle Healthcare Center Inc
501 Clinton St, Carlyle, IL, 62231
(618) 594-3112
Admin Joann L Brave.
Licensure Intermediate care. *Beds* 127. *Certified* Medicaid.
Owner Proprietary Corp.

CARMI

Wabash Christian Retirement Center
College Blvd, Carmi, IL, 62821
(618) 382-4644
Admin Troy Hart. *Medical Dir/Dir of Nursing* Carol Bell.
Licensure Skilled care; Intermediate care. *Beds* 160. *Certified* Medicaid.
Owner Nonprofit Corp (Christian Homes).
Staff RNs 8 (ft), 2 (pt); LPNs 10 (ft), 4 (pt); Orderlies 2 (ft); Nurses aides 25 (ft), 15 (pt); Activities coordinators 2 (ft), 2 (pt).
Facilities Dining room; Physical therapy room; Activities room; Chapel; Crafts room; Laundry room; Barber/Beauty shop.
Activities Arts & crafts; Cards; Games; Reading groups; Prayer groups; Movies; Shopping trips; Social/Cultural gatherings.

White County Nursing Home
PO Box 339, Rte 3, Carmi, IL, 62821
(618) 382-7116
Admin Faye Frashie R Driggers.
Licensure Intermediate care. *Beds* 72. *Certified* Medicaid.
Owner Publicly owned.

CARRIER MILLS

Carrier Mills Nursing Home Inc
US Rte 45 E, Carrier Mills, IL, 62917
(618) 994-2232
Admin George L Storms. *Medical Dir/Dir of Nursing* Larry Jones MD; Mary Barler.
Licensure Skilled care. *Beds* SNF 68. *Certified* Medicaid; Medicare.
Owner Proprietary Corp.
Admissions Requirements Minimum age 22; Medical examination; Physician's request.
Staff Physicians 8 (pt); RNs 2 (ft), 1 (pt); LPNs 7 (ft), 4 (pt); Orderlies 4 (ft); Nurses aides 17 (ft), 4 (pt); Physical therapists 1 (ft), 2 (pt); Recreational therapists 1 (pt); Occupational therapists 1 (pt); Speech therapists 1 (pt); Activities coordinators 2 (ft), 1 (pt); Dietitians 1 (ft), 1 (pt); Dentists 1 (pt); Ophthalmologists 1 (pt); Podiatrists 1 (pt).
Facilities Dining room; Physical therapy room; Activities room; Crafts room; Laundry room; Barber/Beauty shop.
Activities Arts & crafts; Cards; Games; Reading groups; Prayer groups; Movies; Social/Cultural gatherings.

CARROLLTON

Mt Gilead Shelter Care Home*
Rte 3, Box 53, Carrollton, IL, 62016
(217) 942-5362
Admin Alfreda Steinacher.
Licensure Sheltered care. *Beds* 28.
Owner Proprietary Corp.
Admissions Requirements Minimum age 19; Medical examination; Physician's request.
Facilities Dining room; Activities room.
Activities Arts & crafts; Cards; Games; Prayer groups; Movies; Shopping trips; Social/Cultural gatherings.

Reisch Memorial Nursing Home*
800 School St, Carrollton, IL, 62016
(217) 942-6946
Admin Thomas J McKula.
Licensure Skilled care. *Beds* 40. *Certified* Medicaid.
Owner Nonprofit Corp.

CARTHAGE

Hancock County Nursing Home*
S Adams St, Carthage, IL, 62321
(217) 357-3131
Admin Steven T Moburg.
Licensure Skilled care; Intermediate care. *Beds* SNF 14; ICF 36. *Certified* Medicaid.
Owner Nonprofit Corp.
Admissions Requirements Physician's request.
Staff RNs 1 (ft), 2 (pt); LPNs 2 (ft), 2 (pt); Nurses aides 18 (ft), 4 (pt); Physical therapists 1 (pt); Speech therapists 1 (pt); Activities coordinators 1 (ft), 1 (pt); Dietitians 1 (pt).
Facilities Dining room; Physical therapy room; Activities room; Chapel; Crafts room; Laundry room; Barber/Beauty shop.
Activities Arts & crafts; Cards; Games; Reading groups; Prayer groups; Movies; Social/Cultural gatherings.

CASEY

Birchwood
100 NE 15th St, Casey, IL, 62420
(217) 932-5217
Admin Patricia J Bellinger. *Medical Dir/Dir of Nursing* Nancy A Collins RN DON.
Licensure Intermediate care. *Beds* ICF 72. *Certified* Medicaid.
Owner Proprietary Corp.
Admissions Requirements Minimum age; Medical examination.
Staff RNs 3 (pt); LPNs 1 (ft), 9 (pt); Nurses aides 2 (ft), 15 (pt); Activities coordinators 1 (ft), 1 (pt).
Facilities Dining room; Activities room; Crafts room; Laundry room; Barber/Beauty shop; Library.
Activities Arts & crafts; Cards; Games; Reading groups; Prayer groups; Movies; Shopping trips; Social/Cultural gatherings.

Heartland Manor Inc Nursing Center
410 NW 3rd, Casey, IL, 62420
(217) 932-4081
Admin David J Sauer.
Licensure Skilled care. *Beds* 92. *Certified* Medicaid; Medicare.
Owner Nonprofit Corp.
Admissions Requirements Medical examination; Physician's request.
Staff Physicians 3 (pt); RNs 3 (ft), 4 (pt); LPNs 4 (ft), 3 (pt); Orderlies 3 (ft); Nurses aides 24 (ft), 16 (pt); Physical therapists 1 (pt); Reality therapists 1 (pt); Recreational therapists 1 (pt); Occupational therapists 1 (pt); Speech therapists 1 (pt); Activities coordinators 1 (ft); Dietitians 1 (pt); Dentists 1 (pt).
Facilities Dining room; Activities room; Chapel; Crafts room; Laundry room; Barber/Beauty shop.

Activities Arts & crafts; Games; Reading groups; Prayer groups; Movies; Shopping trips; Van rides; Bingo; Traveling for other nursing homes.

CENTRALIA

Brookside Manor Inc
Hwy 161 W, Centralia, IL, 62801
(618) 532-2428
Admin Genevieve Diekemper. *Medical Dir/Dir of Nursing* Dr M A Junidi.
Licensure Intermediate care. *Beds* ICF 49. *Certified* Medicaid.
Owner Proprietary Corp (Community Lifecare Enterprises).
Admissions Requirements Medical examination.
Staff LPNs 4 (ft); Nurses aides 18 (ft); Activities coordinators 1 (ft); Dietitians 1 (pt).
Facilities Dining room; Physical therapy room; Activities room; Crafts room; Laundry room; Barber/Beauty shop.
Activities Arts & crafts; Cards; Games; Reading groups; Prayer groups; Movies; Shopping trips; Social/Cultural gatherings.

Centralia Care Center
1411 E Frazier, Centralia, IL, 62801
(618) 533-1369
Admin Barbara Babb.
Licensure Skilled care; Intermediate care. *Beds* SNF 43; ICF 16. *Certified* Medicaid; Medicare.
Owner Proprietary Corp (Community Lifecare Enterprises).
Admissions Requirements Medical examination.
Staff RNs 1 (ft); LPNs 3 (ft); Nurses aides 24 (ft); Physical therapists 1 (ft), 1 (pt); Activities coordinators 1 (ft); Dietitians 1 (pt).
Facilities Dining room; Physical therapy room; Activities room; Crafts room; Laundry room; Barber/Beauty shop.
Activities Arts & crafts; Cards; Games; Reading groups; Prayer groups; Movies; Shopping trips; Social/Cultural gatherings.

Centralia Fireside House
1030 E McCord St, Centralia, IL, 62801
(618) 532-1833
Admin Geralyn Isenberg.
Licensure Skilled care; Intermediate care. *Beds* SNF 51; ICF 47. *Certified* Medicaid.
Owner Proprietary Corp.

Centralia Friendship House
PO Box 454, 1000 E McCord, Centralia, IL, 62801
(618) 532-3642, 532-3326
Admin Kyle C Moore. *Medical Dir/Dir of Nursing* Dr Aziz Rahman, Deb Ziegler.
Licensure Intermediate care. *Beds* ICF 94. *Certified* Medicaid.
Owner Proprietary Corp.
Admissions Requirements Minimum age 18; Medical examination; Physician's request.
Staff RNs 2 (ft), 1 (pt); LPNs 5 (ft), 5 (pt); Nurses aides 10 (ft), 14 (pt); Physical therapists 1 (ft); Activities coordinators 2 (ft); Dietitians 3 (ft), 5 (pt).
Facilities Dining room; Physical therapy room; Activities room; Laundry room; Barber/Beauty shop.
Activities Arts & crafts; Games; Reading groups; Prayer groups; Movies; Shopping trips; Bus trips; Picnics.

CHAMPAIGN

Americana Healthcare Center of Champaign
309 E Springfield Ave, Champaign, IL, 61820
(217) 352-5135
Admin Dorothy Mikuck. *Medical Dir/Dir of Nursing* Dr Robert Bosler.
Licensure Skilled care. *Beds* 102. *Certified* Medicaid; Medicare.
Owner Proprietary Corp (Manor Care).
Admissions Requirements Medical examination; Physician's request.
Staff RNs 8 (ft), 2 (pt); LPNs 9 (ft); Orderlies 4 (ft); Nurses aides 27 (ft), 4 (pt); Physical therapists 1 (ft); Reality therapists 1 (pt); Recreational therapists 1 (ft); Occupational therapists 1 (pt); Speech therapists 1 (pt); Activities coordinators 1 (ft); Dietitians 1 (ft).
Facilities Dining room; Physical therapy room; Activities room; Barber/Beauty shop; Outdoor patio - enclosed.
Activities Arts & crafts; Cards; Games; Reading groups; Prayer groups; Movies; Shopping trips; Social/Cultural gatherings.

Champaign Childrens Home
109 Kenwood Rd, Champaign, IL, 61821
(217) 356-5164
Admin Ellen R Morris. *Medical Dir/Dir of Nursing* William Farris MD; Eve Peterson DON.
Licensure Pediatrics. *Beds* Pediatrics 87. *Certified* Medicaid.
Owner Proprietary Corp.
Admissions Requirements Minimum age 0-22; Medical examination.
Staff Physicians 1 (pt); RNs 6 (ft); LPNs; Orderlies 6 (ft); Nurses aides 60 (ft); Physical therapists 1 (pt); Recreational therapists 1 (pt); Occupational therapists 2 (pt); Speech therapists 1 (pt); Activities coordinators 1 (pt); Dietitians 1 (pt); Special education teachers 18 (ft); Activity aides 8 (pt).
Languages Children are non-verbal
Facilities Dining room; Physical therapy room; Activities room; Laundry room; Handicapped playground; Classrooms.
Activities Arts & crafts; Games; Movies; Shopping trips; Education program; Pet-a-pet.

The Garwood Home
1515 N Market St, Champaign, IL, 61820
(217) 352-1412
Admin Carol Ann Edwards. *Medical Dir/Dir of Nursing* Robert Atkins MD; Jean Bagaasen DON.
Licensure Sheltered care. *Beds* 34.
Owner Nonprofit Corp.
Admissions Requirements Minimum age 60; Medical examination; Physician's request.
Staff RNs 1 (ft); LPNs 4 (pt); Nurses aides 4 (pt); Recreational therapists 1 (ft).
Facilities Dining room; Activities room; Crafts room; Laundry room; Barber/Beauty shop.
Activities Arts & crafts; Cards; Games; Reading groups; Prayer groups; Movies; Shopping trips; Social/Cultural gatherings.

The Greenbrier Nursing Center Inc
1915 S Mattis Ave, Champaign, IL, 61821
(217) 352-0516
Admin Edward J Haas. *Medical Dir/Dir of Nursing* Charles R Shepardson MD; Nancy Richardson RN DON.
Licensure Skilled care. *Beds* SNF 118. *Certified* Medicaid; Medicare.
Owner Proprietary Corp.
Admissions Requirements Minimum age 21; Medical examination; Physician's request.
Staff Physicians 2 (pt); RNs 3 (ft), 2 (pt); LPNs 6 (ft); Orderlies 3 (ft), 2 (pt); Nurses aides 28 (ft), 2 (pt); Reality therapists 1 (pt); Recreational therapists 1 (pt); Occupational therapists 1 (pt); Speech therapists 1 (pt); Activities coordinators 1 (ft), 1 (pt); Dietitians 1 (pt); Ophthalmologists 1 (pt).
Facilities Dining room; Activities room; Crafts room; Laundry room; Barber/Beauty shop; Library; Smoking room.

Activities Arts & crafts; Games; Reading groups; Prayer groups; Movies; Shopping trips; Social/Cultural gatherings Church services.

Heritage House of Champaign
1315 Curt Dr, Champaign, IL, 61821
(217) 352-5707
Admin Candy J Carroll. *Medical Dir/Dir of Nursing* Dr W Gonzalez; Natalie Alagna RN.
Licensure Intermediate care. *Beds* 60. *Certified* Medicaid.
Owner Proprietary Corp (National Heritage).
Admissions Requirements Minimum age 18; Medical examination; Physician's request.
Staff RNs 2 (ft); LPNs 4 (ft), 2 (pt); Orderlies 1 (ft), 1 (pt); Nurses aides 9 (ft), 5 (pt); Physical therapists 1 (pt); Reality therapists 1 (pt); Recreational therapists 1 (pt); Occupational therapists 1 (pt); Speech therapists 1 (pt); Activities coordinators 1 (ft), 1 (pt); Dietitians 1 (pt); Ophthalmologists 1 (pt).
Facilities Dining room; Physical therapy room; Activities room; Laundry room; Barber/Beauty shop.
Activities Arts & crafts; Cards; Games; Reading groups; Prayer groups; Movies; Shopping trips; Social/Cultural gatherings; Pet therapy.

Opportunity House
1315-A Curt Dr, Champaign, IL, 61821
(217) 351-3590
Admin Kathy M Baird. *Medical Dir/Dir of Nursing* Dr Na Nagawa MD; B Hutcherson DON.
Licensure Intermediate care for mentally retarded. *Beds* 60. *Certified* Medicaid.
Owner Proprietary Corp.
Admissions Requirements Minimum age 21; Medical examination; Physician's request.
Staff LPNs 5 (ft), 1 (pt); Nurses aides 21 (ft), 4 (pt); Activities coordinators; Physical therapy aide; 1 (ft) Occupational therapy aide 1 (ft); Speech therapy aide 1 (ft); FSS 1 (ft); QMRP 2 (ft).
Facilities Dining room; Physical therapy room; Activities room; Crafts room; Laundry room.
Activities Arts & crafts; Cards; Games; Reading groups; Prayer groups; Movies; Shopping trips; Social/Cultural gatherings.

CHARLESTON

Cambridge Court Manor Inc*
716 18th St, Charleston, IL, 61920
(217) 345-7054
Admin Barb Clark.
Licensure Skilled care; Intermediate care. *Beds* SNF 45; ICF 94. *Certified* Medicaid.
Owner Proprietary Corp.

Charleston Manor*
415 18th St, Charleston, IL, 61920
(217) 345-7048
Admin Helen Eckhoff.
Licensure Intermediate care. *Beds* 62. *Certified* Medicaid.
Owner Proprietary Corp.
Admissions Requirements Medical examination.
Staff Physicians 1 (pt); RNs 1 (pt); LPNs 7 (ft); Nurses aides 16 (ft); Physical therapists 1 (pt); Dietitians 1 (pt).
Facilities Dining room; Activities room; Crafts room; Laundry room; Barber/Beauty shop.
Activities Arts & crafts; Cards; Games; Reading groups; Prayer groups; Movies; Shopping trips; Social/Cultural gatherings.

Heritage House of Charleston*
738 18th St, Charleston, IL, 61920
(217) 345-2220
Admin Robert K Zabka.

Licensure Intermediate care for mentally retarded. *Beds* 89. *Certified* Medicaid.
Owner Proprietary Corp.
Admissions Requirements Minimum age 18.
Facilities Dining room; Physical therapy room; Activities room; Chapel; Crafts room; Laundry room.
Activities Arts & crafts; Cards; Games; Reading groups; Prayer groups; Movies; Shopping trips; Social/Cultural gatherings.

Hilltop Conv Center*
910 W Polk St, Charleston, IL, 61920
(217) 345-7066
Admin Robert Mattox.
Licensure Skilled care; Intermediate care. *Beds* SNF 36; ICF 72. *Certified* Medicaid; Medicare.
Owner Proprietary Corp.

CHENOA

Meadows Mennonite Home
RR 1, Chenoa, IL, 61726
(309) 747-2702
Admin Catherine A Beery. *Medical Dir/Dir of Nursing* Hazel Yoder.
Licensure Intermediate care; Sheltered care. *Beds* ICF 130; Sheltered care. *Certified* Medicaid.
Owner Nonprofit organization/foundation.
Admissions Requirements Minimum age 60; Medical examination.
Staff Physicians; RNs; LPNs; Orderlies; Nurses aides; Physical therapists; Activities coordinators; Dietitians; Ophthalmologists.
Affiliation Mennonite
Facilities Dining room; Physical therapy room; Activities room; Chapel; Laundry room; Barber/Beauty shop; Library.
Activities Arts & crafts; Cards; Games; Reading groups; Prayer groups; Movies; Shopping trips; Social/Cultural gatherings; Fitness program.

CHESTER

St Anns Healthcare Center Inc
770 State St, Chester, IL, 62233
(618) 826-2314
Admin J Michael Greer. *Medical Dir/Dir of Nursing* John R Beck MD; Sr Angela Heimann RN DON.
Licensure Skilled care; Intermediate care. *Beds* SNF 27; ICF 87. *Certified* Medicaid; Medicare; VA.
Owner Proprietary Corp.
Admissions Requirements Minimum age 21; Medical examination.
Staff Physicians 1 (pt); RNs 2 (ft), 5 (pt); LPNs 1 (ft), 6 (pt); Orderlies 1 (pt); Nurses aides 21 (ft), 12 (pt); Physical therapists 1 (pt); Reality therapists 1 (ft); Recreational therapists 1 (pt); Occupational therapists 1 (pt); Speech therapists 1 (pt); Activities coordinators 1 (ft); Dietitians 1 (ft), 1 (pt); Ophthalmologists 1 (pt).
Facilities Dining room; Activities room; Chapel; Crafts room; Laundry room; Barber/Beauty shop.
Activities Arts & crafts; Cards; Games; Reading groups; Prayer groups; Movies; Shopping trips; Social/Cultural gatherings.

Three Springs Lodge Nursing Home Inc*
Rte 1, Box 324, Chester, IL, 62233
(618) 826-3210
Admin Kenneth Rowold.
Licensure Intermediate care. *Beds* 85. *Certified* Medicaid.
Owner Proprietary Corp.

CHICAGO

All American Nursing Home*
5448 N Broadway St, Chicago, IL, 60640
(312) 334-2244

Admin Howard L Wengrow. *Medical Dir/Dir of Nursing* Riccardo Benvenuto MD.
Licensure Skilled care; Intermediate care. *Beds* SNF 48; ICF 96. *Certified* Medicaid.
Owner Proprietary Corp.
Admissions Requirements Minimum age 23.
Staff Physicians 4 (pt); RNs 5 (ft); LPNs 12 (ft); Nurses aides 38 (ft); Physical therapists 1 (pt); Reality therapists 1 (pt); Recreational therapists 1 (pt); Occupational therapists 1 (pt); Speech therapists 1 (pt); Activities coordinators 1 (ft); Dietitians 1 (pt); Dentists 1 (pt); Podiatrists 1 (pt).
Facilities Physical therapy room; Activities room; Chapel; Crafts room; Laundry room; Barber/Beauty shop; Library.
Activities Arts & crafts; Cards; Games; Reading groups; Prayer groups; Movies; Shopping trips; Social/Cultural gatherings.

Alshore House*
2840 W Foster Ave, Chicago, IL, 60625
(312) 561-2040
Admin Pamela Solomon.
Licensure Intermediate care. *Beds* 48. *Certified* Medicaid.
Owner Proprietary Corp.

Ambassador Nursing Center Inc
4900 N Bernard, Chicago, IL, 60625
(312) 583-7130
Admin Fred Cantz. *Medical Dir/Dir of Nursing* Thomas Duffy.
Licensure Skilled care. *Beds* SNF 190. *Certified* Medicaid.
Owner Proprietary Corp.
Admissions Requirements Minimum age 65; Medical examination; Physician's request.
Staff Physicians 22 (pt); RNs 15 (ft), 6 (pt); LPNs 2 (ft); Nurses aides 45 (ft); Physical therapists 1 (pt); Reality therapists 2 (ft); Recreational therapists 1 (ft); Occupational therapists 1 (ft); Speech therapists 1 (pt); Activities coordinators 5 (ft); Dietitians 2 (pt); Dentists 1 (pt); Ophthalmologists 1 (pt); Podiatrists 1 (ft).
Languages Korean, Spanish, Russian, Polish, Yiddish, Hebrew
Facilities Dining room; Physical therapy room; Activities room; Chapel; Crafts room; Laundry room; Barber/Beauty shop; Library.
Activities Arts & crafts; Cards; Games; Reading groups; Prayer groups; Movies; Shopping trips; Social/Cultural gatherings.

Approved Home Inc
909 W Wilson Ave, Chicago, IL, 60640
(312) 275-2422
Admin Barbara Farkas. *Medical Dir/Dir of Nursing* Roberta Phillips.
Licensure Intermediate care for mentally retarded. *Beds* ICF/MR 150. *Certified* Medicaid.
Owner Proprietary Corp.
Admissions Requirements Minimum age 18; Medical examination; Physician's request.
Staff Physicians; RNs; LPNs; Recreational therapists; Occupational therapists; Speech therapists; Activities coordinators; Dietitians; Dentists; Ophthalmologists; Podiatrists.
Facilities Dining room; Activities room; Crafts room; Laundry room.
Activities Arts & crafts; Cards; Games; Reading groups; Prayer groups; Movies; Shopping trips; Social/Cultural gatherings.

Auburn Park Club
7748 S Emerald, Chicago, IL, 60640
(312) 874-0012
Admin Fred D Jones.
Licensure Intermediate care for mentally retarded; Community living facility. *Beds* 32. *Certified* Medicaid; Medicare.
Owner Nonprofit organization/foundation.
Admissions Requirements Males only.
Staff Activities coordinators 1 (ft).

Facilities Dining room; Activities room; Crafts room; Laundry room.
Activities Arts & crafts; Cards; Games; Reading groups; Movies; Shopping trips; Social/Cultural gatherings.

Augustana Center for Developmentally Disabled Children
7464 N Sheridan Rd, Chicago, IL, 60626
(312) 973-5200
Admin Judith Buchner. *Medical Dir/Dir of Nursing* Herman B Lander MD; Dorthy Schwartz RN.
Licensure Skilled care; Skilled pediatric; developmentally disabled. *Beds* SNF 150. *Certified* Medicaid.
Owner Nonprofit Corp.
Admissions Requirements Minimum age Birth; Medical examination.
Staff Physicians 5 (pt); RNs 21 (ft), 7 (pt); LPNs 2 (ft), 3 (pt); Nurses aides 82 (ft), 8 (pt); Physical therapists 1 (ft); Recreational therapists 1 (ft); Occupational therapists 1 (pt); Speech therapists 1 (pt); Dietitians 1 (pt); Teachers 22 (ft).
Languages Spanish
Affiliation Lutheran
Facilities Dining room; Physical therapy room; Activities room; Chapel.
Activities Games.

Balmoral Nursing Centre Inc*
2055 W Balmoral Ave, Chicago, IL, 60625
(312) 561-8661
Admin Herman Katz.
Licensure Skilled care. *Beds* 213. *Certified* Medicaid.
Owner Proprietary Corp.

Warren N Barr Pavilion
66 W Oak St, Chicago, IL, 60610
(312) 337-5400
Admin Wetzel McCormick. *Medical Dir/Dir of Nursing* Cara L Culmer MD; Karen Kraker Urso DON.
Licensure Skilled care. *Beds* SNF 330. *Certified* Medicaid; Medicare.
Owner Nonprofit Corp.
Admissions Requirements Minimum age 18; Medical examination; Physician's request.
Staff Physicians 3 (pt); RNs 34 (ft); LPNs 27 (ft); Orderlies 1 (ft); Nurses aides 140 (ft); Physical therapists 2 (ft); Recreational therapists 6 (ft), 1 (pt); Occupational therapists 2 (ft); Speech therapists 2 (pt); Activities coordinators 1 (ft); Dietitians 2 (ft); Dentists 2 (pt); Ophthalmologists 1 (pt); Podiatrists 1 (pt).
Languages Polish, Spanish
Affiliation Masons
Facilities Dining room; Physical therapy room; Activities room; Chapel; Crafts room; Laundry room; Barber/Beauty shop; Library; Solarium; Gift shop; Ice cream & soda fountain.
Activities Arts & crafts; Cards; Games; Reading groups; Prayer groups; Movies; Shopping trips; Social/Cultural gatherings; Out trips; College classes; Pet therapy; Gardening.

Belmont Nursing Home Inc*
1936 W Belmont Ave, Chicago, IL, 60657
(312) 252-7176
Admin Eileen Conway.
Licensure Intermediate care. *Beds* 61. *Certified* Medicaid.
Owner Proprietary Corp.

Bethany Methodist Home
4950 N Ashland, Chicago, IL, 60640
(312) 271-9040
Admin Eric Northard. *Medical Dir/Dir of Nursing* Dr Joseph Martin.
Licensure Retirement home. *Beds* Sheltered care 269.
Owner Nonprofit Corp.

Admissions Requirements Minimum age 65; Medical examination.
Staff LPNs 6 (ft); Activities coordinators 3 (ft); Dietitians 1 (ft); Ophthalmologists 1 (pt).
Affiliation Methodist
Facilities Dining room; Activities room; Chapel; Crafts room; Laundry room; Barber/ Beauty shop; Library; Cafe; Game room; Enclosed park & garden; Rooftop garden.
Activities Arts & crafts; Cards; Games; Prayer groups; Movies; Shopping trips; Social/ Cultural gatherings; Bus trips; Restaurant visits; Exercise/walking groups.

Bethesda Home & Retirement Center
2833 N Nordica Ave, Chicago, IL, 60634
(312) 622-6144
Admin Carol Page Beecher. *Medical Dir/Dir of Nursing* Harold S Sarran MD; Lorraine Deneen RN DON.
Licensure Intermediate care; Assisted living; Individual living. *Beds* ICF 65; Assisted living 55; Individual living 19. *Certified* Medicaid.
Owner Nonprofit organization/foundation.
Admissions Requirements Minimum age 65; Medical examination.
Staff Physicians 2 (pt); RNs 4 (ft), 2 (pt); LPNs 4 (ft), 4 (pt); Nurses aides 30 (ft), 8 (pt); Activities coordinators 1 (ft); Dietitians 1 (ft).
Affiliation Lutheran
Facilities Dining room; Physical therapy room; Activities room; Chapel; Crafts room; Barber/Beauty shop; Library.
Activities Arts & crafts; Cards; Games; Reading groups; Prayer groups; Movies; Shopping trips; Social/Cultural gatherings.

Bethune Plaza Inc*
4537 S Drexel, Chicago, IL, 60653
(312) 268-8950
Admin Jerome E Morgan Jr.
Licensure Intermediate care. *Beds* 276.
Owner Proprietary Corp.

Beverly Nursing Home*
8001 S Western Ave, Chicago, IL, 60620
(312) 436-6600
Admin Frank Kleinerman.
Licensure Skilled care. *Beds* 328. *Certified* Medicaid.
Owner Proprietary Corp.

Birchwood Plaza Inc*
1426 W Birchwood Ave, Chicago, IL, 60626
(312) 274-4405
Admin Abraham Schiffman.
Licensure Skilled care. *Beds* 192. *Certified* Medicaid.
Owner Proprietary Corp.

Bohemian Home for the Aged
5061 N Pulaski Rd, Chicago, IL, 60630
(312) 588-1220
Admin Z Peter Brandler. *Medical Dir/Dir of Nursing* Stephen Dubala MD.
Licensure Skilled care; Intermediate care. *Beds* SNF 30; ICF 188. *Certified* Medicaid.
Owner Nonprofit Corp.
Admissions Requirements Minimum age 75; Medical examination.
Staff Physicians 1 (pt); RNs 14 (ft), 7 (pt); LPNs 11 (ft); Nurses aides 50 (ft); Activities coordinators 1 (ft); Dietitians 1 (ft).
Languages Czech, Polish
Facilities Dining room; Physical therapy room; Activities room; Crafts room; Laundry room; Barber/Beauty shop; Library.
Activities Arts & crafts; Games; Reading groups; Prayer groups; Movies; Shopping trips; Social/Cultural gatherings.

Brightview Care Center Inc
4538 N Beacon, Chicago, IL, 60640
(312) 275-7200
Admin Mary L Grondin. *Medical Dir/Dir of Nursing* Dr A Rezvan; Linda Houston.

Licensure Skilled care. *Beds* 143. *Certified* Medicaid.
Owner Proprietary Corp.
Admissions Requirements Minimum age 21; Medical examination; Physician's request.
Staff Physicians; RNs; LPNs; Orderlies; Nurses aides; Physical therapists; Recreational therapists; Occupational therapists; Activities coordinators; Dietitians.
Facilities Dining room; Physical therapy room; Activities room; Crafts room; Laundry room; Barber/Beauty shop; Library; Day room.
Activities Arts & crafts; Cards; Games; Reading groups; Prayer groups; Movies; Shopping trips; Social/Cultural gatherings.

Buckingham Pavilion*
2625 W Touhy Ave, Chicago, IL, 60645
(312) 764-6850
Admin Margaret Stern. *Medical Dir/Dir of Nursing* Dr H Kurz.
Licensure Skilled care; Intermediate care. *Beds* 247. *Certified* Medicaid; Medicare.
Owner Proprietary Corp.
Admissions Requirements Minimum age 18.
Staff Physicians; RNs; Orderlies; Nurses aides; Physical therapists; Reality therapists; Recreational therapists; Occupational therapists; Speech therapists; Activities coordinators; Dietitians; Dentists; Ophthalmologists; Podiatrists; Audiologists.
Affiliation Jewish
Facilities Dining room; Physical therapy room; Activities room; Chapel; Crafts room; Laundry room; Barber/Beauty shop; Library.
Activities Arts & crafts; Cards; Games; Reading groups; Prayer groups; Movies; Social/Cultural gatherings.

Burnham Terrace Care Center*
14500 S Manistee, Chicago, IL, 60633
(312) 862-1260
Admin Herman W Frey.
Licensure Skilled care; Intermediate care. *Beds* SNF 103; ICF 206.
Owner Proprietary Corp.

California Gardens Nursing Center
2829 S California Blvd, Chicago, IL, 60608
(312) 847-8061
Admin Brian J Cloch. *Medical Dir/Dir of Nursing* Bart Mayron MD; Wanda Bowling RN.
Licensure Skilled care. *Beds* SNF 306. *Certified* Medicaid.
Owner Proprietary Corp.
Admissions Requirements Minimum age 21.
Staff RNs; LPNs; Nurses aides; Activities coordinators.
Languages Spanish, Lithuanian
Facilities Dining room; Physical therapy room; Activities room; Crafts room; Laundry room; Barber/Beauty shop.
Activities Arts & crafts; Cards; Games; Reading groups; Prayer groups; Movies; Shopping trips; Social/Cultural gatherings.

Carci Hall*
11321 S Wentworth, Chicago, IL, 60612
(312) 995-1127
Admin Janet Conner.
Licensure Intermediate care for mentally retarded. *Beds* 35.
Owner Nonprofit Corp.

Carlton House Nursing Center
725 W Montrose Ave, Chicago, IL, 60613
(312) 929-1700
Admin Rose Marie Betz RN. *Medical Dir/Dir of Nursing* Dr David Edelberg MD; Esther Jenkins RN DON.
Licensure Skilled care. *Beds* 244. *Certified* Medicaid.
Owner Proprietary Corp.
Staff Physicians; RNs 34 (ft); LPNs 5 (ft); Orderlies 2 (ft); Nurses aides 54 (ft); Physical therapists 2 (pt); Recreational

therapists 2 (ft); Occupational therapists; Activities coordinators 1 (ft); Dietitians 1 (ft); Dentists; Ophthalmologists; Podiatrists.
Facilities Dining room; Physical therapy room; Activities room; Crafts room; Laundry room; Barber/Beauty shop; Library.
Activities Arts & crafts; Cards; Games; Reading groups; Prayer groups; Movies; Shopping trips; Social/Cultural gatherings; Cooking classes.

Carmen Manor*
1470 W Carmen, Chicago, IL, 60640
(312) 878-7000
Admin Moises Mareovich.
Licensure Intermediate care. *Beds* 113. *Certified* Medicaid.
Owner Proprietary Corp.

Casa Central Center*
1401 N California Ave, Chicago, IL, 60622
(312) 278-1902
Admin Rev Edgar I Morales.
Licensure Skilled care; Intermediate care. *Beds* SNF 47; ICF 49. *Certified* Medicaid.
Owner Nonprofit Corp.

Central Nursing
2450 N Central Ave, Chicago, IL, 60639
(312) 889-1333
Admin Henry Mermelstein.
Licensure Skilled care. *Beds* 245. *Certified* Medicaid.
Owner Proprietary Corp.

Central Plaza Residential Home*
321-27 N Central, Chicago, IL, 60644
(312) 626-2300
Admin Gwendolyn Washington. *Medical Dir/ Dir of Nursing* David Edelberg.
Licensure Intermediate care. *Beds* 290. *Certified* Medicaid.
Owner Proprietary Corp.
Admissions Requirements Minimum age 18.
Staff Physicians; RNs; LPNs; Nurses aides; Physical therapists; Recreational therapists; Occupational therapists; Activities coordinators; Dietitians; Dentists; Ophthalmologists; Podiatrists; Audiologists.
Facilities Dining room; Physical therapy room; Activities room; Crafts room; Laundry room; Library.
Activities Arts & crafts; Cards; Games; Reading groups; Movies; Shopping trips; Social/Cultural gatherings.

Chevy Chase Nursing Center
3400 S Indiana Ave, Chicago, IL, 60616
(312) 842-5000
Admin Edward A Eddy. *Medical Dir/Dir of Nursing* Abolmajid Rezvan MD; Linda Howard RN.
Licensure Skilled care; Intermediate care. *Beds* SNF 322; ICF. *Certified* Medicaid; Medicare.
Owner Proprietary Corp.
Admissions Requirements Minimum age 60; Medical examination.
Staff Physicians 5 (pt); RNs 5 (ft); LPNs 20 (ft); Orderlies 10 (ft); Nurses aides 80 (ft); Physical therapists 1 (pt); Recreational therapists 1 (pt); Occupational therapists 1 (pt); Speech therapists 1 (pt); Activities coordinators 1 (ft); Dietitians 1 (pt); Dentists 1 (pt); Ophthalmologists 1 (pt); Podiatrists 1 (pt).
Facilities Dining room; Physical therapy room; Activities room; Chapel; Crafts room; Laundry room; Barber/Beauty shop; Recreation room.
Activities Arts & crafts; Cards; Games; Prayer groups; Movies; Shopping trips; Social/ Cultural gatherings.

Clark Manor
7433 N Clark St, Chicago, IL, 60626
(312) 338-8778
Admin Mark Schlichting. *Medical Dir/Dir of Nursing* Melvina McClendon DON.

Licensure Skilled care. *Beds* 273. *Certified*
Medicaid; Medicare.
Owner Privately owned.
Admissions Requirements Minimum age 55.
Staff Physicians 14 (pt); RNs 20 (ft); LPNs 3
(pt); Nurses aides 50 (ft); Physical therapists
1 (pt); Recreational therapists 1 (ft);
Occupational therapists 1 (pt); Speech
therapists 1 (pt); Activities coordinators 1
(ft); Dietitians 1 (pt); Dentists 1 (pt);
Ophthalmologists 1 (pt); Podiatrists 1 (pt).
Facilities Dining room; Physical therapy
room; Activities room; Crafts room; Laundry
room; Barber/Beauty shop; Library.
Activities Arts & crafts; Cards; Games;
Reading groups; Prayer groups; Movies;
Shopping trips; Social/Cultural gatherings.

Clayton Residential Home*
2026 N Clark St, Chicago, IL, 60614
(312) 549-1840
Admin Robert B Baily. *Medical Dir/Dir of
Nursing* Lester Baranov MD.
Licensure Intermediate care. *Beds* 252.
Certified Medicaid.
Owner Proprietary Corp.
Admissions Requirements Minimum age 18;
Medical examination.
Staff Physicians 3 (pt); LPNs 9 (ft); Nurses
aides 20 (ft); Physical therapists 1 (ft), 1 (pt);
Reality therapists 2 (ft); Recreational
therapists 1 (ft); Occupational therapists 1
(ft); Activities coordinators 1 (ft); Dietitians
1 (ft); Podiatrists 1 (pt).
Facilities Dining room; Physical therapy
room; Activities room; Crafts room; Laundry
room.
Activities Arts & crafts; Games; Reading
groups; Movies; Shopping trips; Social/
Cultural gatherings.

Cojeunaze Nursing Center
3311 S Michigan Ave, Chicago, IL, 60640
(312) 326-5700
Admin Faye H Nazon. *Medical Dir/Dir of
Nursing* Pancho Degand MD.
Licensure Skilled care; Intermediate care. *Beds*
SNF; ICF 200. *Certified* Medicaid.
Owner Proprietary Corp.
Admissions Requirements Minimum age 60;
Medical examination; Physician's request.
Staff Physicians 4 (pt); RNs 2 (ft), 5 (pt);
LPNs 9 (ft), 4 (pt); Orderlies 1 (ft); Nurses
aides 45 (ft), 3 (pt); Physical therapists;
Reality therapists; Recreational therapists 1
(pt); Occupational therapists 1 (pt);
Activities coordinators 1 (ft), 2 (pt);
Dietitians 1 (pt); Dentists 1 (pt);
Ophthalmologists 1 (pt).
Languages French
Facilities Dining room; Activities room;
Crafts room; Laundry room; Barber/Beauty
shop; Library.
Activities Arts & crafts; Cards; Games;
Reading groups; Prayer groups; Movies;
Shopping trips; Social/Cultural gatherings.

Columbus Manor Residential Care Home
5107 W Jackson Blvd, Chicago, IL, 60644
(312) 378-5490
Admin Daniel J O'Brien, Patrick J O'Brien.
Medical Dir/Dir of Nursing Philomina Philip
RN.
Licensure Intermediate care. *Beds* 189.
Certified Medicaid.
Owner Proprietary Corp.
Admissions Requirements Minimum age 35;
Medical examination.
Staff Physicians; RNs; LPNs; Orderlies;
Nurses aides; Recreational therapists;
Activities coordinators; Dietitians.
Languages Spanish, Polish
Facilities Dining room; Activities room;
Crafts room; Laundry room; Library.
Activities Arts & crafts; Cards; Games;
Reading groups; Prayer groups; Movies;
Shopping trips; Social/Cultural gatherings;
Field trips.

Commodore Inn Inc*
5547 N Kenmore, Chicago, IL, 60640
(312) 561-7040
Admin Jay Einhorn.
Licensure Intermediate care. *Beds* 174.
Certified Medicaid.
Owner Proprietary Corp.

Community Care Center Inc*
4314 S Wabash Ave, Chicago, IL, 60653
(312) 538-8300
Admin Eva L Davis. *Medical Dir/Dir of
Nursing* Carroll E Smith MD.
Licensure Skilled care; Intermediate care. *Beds*
SNF 143; ICF 56. *Certified* Medicaid.
Owner Nonprofit Corp.
Admissions Requirements Minimum age 21.
Staff Physicians 5 (pt); RNs 2 (ft); LPNs 16
(ft), 6 (pt); Orderlies 6 (ft), 2 (pt); Nurses
aides 50 (ft), 3 (pt); Reality therapists 1 (pt);
Activities coordinators 2 (ft); Dietitians 1
(ft), 1 (pt); Dentists 1 (pt); Ophthalmologists
1 (pt); Podiatrists 1 (pt).
Facilities Dining room; Physical therapy
room; Activities room; Chapel; Crafts room;
Laundry room; Barber/Beauty shop; Library.
Activities Arts & crafts; Cards; Games;
Reading groups; Prayer groups; Movies;
Shopping trips; Social/Cultural gatherings.

Congress Care Center
901 S Austin Ave, Chicago, IL, 60644
(312) 287-5959
Admin Susan M Lippert. *Medical Dir/Dir of
Nursing* Salomon Dayan MD.
Licensure Skilled care; Intermediate care. *Beds*
SNF 70; ICF 70. *Certified* Medicaid.
Owner Proprietary Corp.
Admissions Requirements Minimum age 21;
Medical examination.
Staff Physicians 4 (pt); RNs 3 (ft), 20 (pt);
LPNs 5 (ft); Orderlies 2 (ft); Nurses aides 32
(ft); Physical therapists 1 (pt); Reality
therapists 3 (ft); Recreational therapists 3
(ft); Occupational therapists 1 (pt); Speech
therapists 1 (pt); Activities coordinators 1
(ft); Dietitians 1 (pt); Dentists 1 (pt);
Ophthalmologists 1 (pt); Podiatrists 1 (pt).
Facilities Dining room; Physical therapy
room; Activities room; Crafts room; Laundry
room; Library.
Activities Arts & crafts; Cards; Games;
Reading groups; Prayer groups; Movies;
Shopping trips; Social/Cultural gatherings.

Continental Care Center Inc
5336 N Western Ave, Chicago, IL, 60634
(312) 271-5600
Admin E Joseph Steinfeld. *Medical Dir/Dir of
Nursing* Dr Abdul Sattar.
Licensure Skilled care. *Beds* 208. *Certified*
Medicaid.
Owner Proprietary Corp.
Admissions Requirements Minimum age 65.
Staff Physicians 38 (pt); RNs 6 (ft), 1 (pt);
LPNs 11 (ft), 2 (pt); Nurses aides 66 (ft);
Activities coordinators 1 (ft).
Facilities Dining room; Physical therapy
room; Activities room; Crafts room; Barber/
Beauty shop; Library.
Activities Arts & crafts; Cards; Games;
Movies; Shopping trips; Social/Cultural
gatherings; Church services; Fitness trail.

Covenant Home
2725 W Foster Ave, Chicago, IL, 60625
(312) 878-8200 ext 5013
Admin Dwayne D Gabrielson. *Medical Dir/
Dir of Nursing* Philip D Anderson MD;
Doris Johnson DON.
Licensure Intermediate care; Sheltered care.
Beds ICF 52; Sheltered care 105. *Certified*
Medicaid; Medicare.
Owner Nonprofit Corp (Covenant Benevolent
Inst).
Admissions Requirements Minimum age 62;
Medical examination.

Staff RNs; LPNs; Nurses aides; Activities
coordinators.
Affiliation Evangelical Covenant Church
Facilities Dining room; Activities room;
Chapel; Crafts room; Laundry room; Barber/
Beauty shop; Library.
Activities Arts & crafts; Games; Reading
groups; Prayer groups; Movies; Shopping
trips; Social/Cultural gatherings.

William L Dawson Nursing Home*
3500 S Giles Ave, Chicago, IL, 60653
(312) 326-2000
Admin Pamela M Orr.
Licensure Skilled care. *Beds* 245. *Certified*
Medicaid.
Owner Proprietary Corp.

Deauville Healthcare Center*
7445 N Sheridan Rd, Chicago, IL, 60626
(312) 338-3300
Admin Daniel B Shabat. *Medical Dir/Dir of
Nursing* Dr Paul Vega.
Licensure Intermediate care. *Beds* 149.
Certified Medicaid.
Owner Proprietary Corp.
Admissions Requirements Minimum age 35;
Medical examination; Physician's request.
Staff Physicians 4 (ft); RNs 3 (ft); LPNs 5 (ft);
Orderlies 2 (ft); Nurses aides 25 (ft), 5 (pt);
Physical therapists 1 (ft); Recreational
therapists 1 (ft); Occupational therapists 1
(ft); Speech therapists 1 (ft); Activities
coordinators 1 (ft); Dietitians 1 (ft); Dentists
1 (pt); Ophthalmologists 1 (pt); Podiatrists 1
(pt); Audiologists 1 (pt).
Facilities Dining room; Physical therapy
room; Activities room; Crafts room; Laundry
room; Barber/Beauty shop.
Activities Arts & crafts; Cards; Games;
Reading groups; Prayer groups; Movies;
Shopping trips; Social/Cultural gatherings.

Deborah House*
7428 N Rogers, Chicago, IL, 60626
(312) 761-0395
Admin Rav'l Nadal Jr.
Licensure Intermediate care. *Beds* 18.
Owner Nonprofit Corp.

DLA Senn Park Nursing Center*
5888 N Ridge Ave, Chicago, IL, 60660
(312) 769-2626
Admin Marilyn Doyle.
Licensure Intermediate care. *Beds* 128.
Certified Medicaid.
Owner Proprietary Corp.
Staff RNs; LPNs; Orderlies; Nurses aides;
Physical therapists; Reality therapists;
Occupational therapists; Speech therapists;
Activities coordinators; Dietitians; Dentists;
Ophthalmologists; Podiatrists.
Facilities Dining room; Activities room;
Crafts room; Laundry room.
Activities Arts & crafts; Cards; Games; Prayer
groups; Movies; Shopping trips; Social/
Cultural gatherings.

Edgewater Nursing & Geriatric Center
5838 N Sheridan Rd, Chicago, IL, 60660
(312) 769-2230
Admin Charles A Trocchio. *Medical Dir/Dir
of Nursing* Solomon Dayan MD; Lorraine
Compton RN.
Licensure Skilled care; Intermediate care. *Beds*
SNF 127; ICF 61. *Certified* Medicaid;
Medicare.
Owner Proprietary Corp.
Admissions Requirements Minimum age 35;
Medical examination; Physician's request.
Staff RNs 14 (ft); LPNs 3 (ft); Nurses aides 28
(ft); Reality therapists 3 (ft); Recreational
therapists 4 (ft); Activities coordinators 2
(ft).
Facilities Dining room; Physical therapy
room; Activities room; Crafts room; Laundry
room; Barber/Beauty shop.

Activities Arts & crafts; Cards; Games;
Reading groups; Prayer groups; Movies;
Shopping trips; Social/Cultural gatherings.

Elston Nursing Center
4340 N Keystone, Chicago, IL, 60641
(312) 545-8700
Admin Steven Schayer. *Medical Dir/Dir of
Nursing* Dr Paul Vega.
Licensure Skilled care; Intermediate care. *Beds*
116. *Certified* Medicaid; Medicare.
Owner Proprietary Corp.
Admissions Requirements Minimum age 18;
Medical examination; Physician's request.
Staff Physicians 10 (ft); RNs 6 (ft), 2 (pt);
LPNs 7 (ft), 1 (pt); Nurses aides 33 (ft), 3
(pt); Physical therapists 1 (ft); Reality
therapists 4 (ft); Recreational therapists 3
(ft); Occupational therapists 1 (ft); Activities
coordinators F 1 (ft) 413L 1 (ft); Dentists 1
(ft); Ophthalmologists 1 (ft);; Occupational
aide 1 (ft); Superintendent 1 (ft).
Languages Polish, German, Tagalog
Facilities Dining room; Physical therapy
room; Activities room; Crafts room; Laundry
room; Barber/Beauty shop.
Activities Arts & crafts; Cards; Games;
Reading groups; Prayer groups; Movies;
Shopping trips; Intergenerational stamp
collecting.

Garden View Home Inc*
6450 N Ridge Ave, Chicago, IL, 60626
(312) 743-8700
Admin Howard D Geller. *Medical Dir/Dir of
Nursing* A Sattar.
Licensure Skilled care; Intermediate care. *Beds*
SNF 110; ICF 26. *Certified* Medicaid.
Owner Proprietary Corp.
Staff Physicians; RNs; LPNs; Orderlies;
Nurses aides; Physical therapists; Reality
therapists; Recreational therapists;
Occupational therapists; Speech therapists;
Activities coordinators; Dietitians; Dentists;
Ophthalmologists; Podiatrists; Audiologists.
Facilities Dining room; Physical therapy
room; Activities room; Crafts room; Laundry
room; Barber/Beauty shop; Library.
Activities Arts & crafts; Cards; Games;
Reading groups; Prayer groups; Movies;
Shopping trips; Social/Cultural gatherings.

Glencrest Nursing Rehabilitation Center Ltd
2451 W Touhy Ave, Chicago, IL, 60645
(312) 338-6800
Admin Nancy Crutcher. *Medical Dir/Dir of
Nursing* Dr Paul Vega.
Licensure Skilled care; Intermediate care. *Beds*
SNF 312. *Certified* Medicaid; Medicare; VA.
Owner Proprietary Corp.
Admissions Requirements Minimum age 50.
Staff Physical therapists; Activities
coordinators; Dietitians; Speech therapists;
Occupational therapists; Respiratory
therapists; Social worker; Geriatric
therapists.
Facilities Dining room (Restaurant style);
Physical therapy room; Activities room;
Crafts room; Laundry room; Barber/Beauty
shop; Library; Private sitting rooms.
Activities Arts & crafts; Cards; Games;
Reading groups; Prayer groups; Movies;
Shopping trips; Social/Cultural gatherings;
Intergenerational programs; Speakers;
Resident educational programs; Courtesy
van.

Gracell Terrace Inc*
6410 S Kenwood Ave, Chicago, IL, 60637
(312) 752-8600
Admin Ida Smith.
Licensure Sheltered care. *Beds* 150.
Owner Proprietary Corp.

Grasmere Resident Home Inc
4621 N Sheridan Rd, Chicago, IL, 60640
(312) 334-6601

Admin Susan Morse. *Medical Dir/Dir of
Nursing* Dr David Edelberg.
Licensure Intermediate care. *Beds* 216.
Certified Medicaid.
Owner Proprietary Corp.
Admissions Requirements Minimum age 18.
Staff Physicians 6 (pt); RNs 2 (ft); LPNs 6
(ft), 3 (pt); Nurses aides 37 (ft), 1 (pt);
Occupational therapists 1 (pt); Activities
coordinators 4 (ft); Dietitians 1 (pt).
Facilities Dining room; Activities room;
Crafts room; Laundry room; Barber/Beauty
shop; Library; Gym; Park.
Activities Arts & crafts; Cards; Games;
Reading groups; Movies; Shopping trips;
Social/Cultural gatherings; Sensory
integration; Reality orientation; Yoga.

Greenview Pavilion*
1425 W Estes, Chicago, IL, 60626
(312) 973-4780
Admin Ronald B Silver.
Licensure Skilled care; Intermediate care. *Beds*
160. *Certified* Medicaid.
Owner Proprietary Corp.
Staff Physicians 8 (pt); RNs 16 (pt); Orderlies
6 (pt); Nurses aides 24 (pt); Physical
therapists 2 (pt); Reality therapists 1 (pt);
Recreational therapists 1 (pt); Occupational
therapists 1 (pt); Speech therapists 1 (pt);
Activities coordinators 1 (pt); Dietitians 1
(pt); Dentists 1 (pt); Ophthalmologists 1 (pt);
Podiatrists 1 (pt); Audiologists 1 (pt).
Facilities Dining room; Physical therapy
room; Activities room; Crafts room; Barber/
Beauty shop.
Activities Arts & crafts; Cards; Games;
Reading groups; Prayer groups; Movies;
Shopping trips.

Halsted Terrace Nursing Center
10935 S Halsted St, Chicago, IL, 60628
(312) 928-2000
Admin Annie R Sutton. *Medical Dir/Dir of
Nursing* William London; Nira West.
Licensure Skilled care. *Beds* SNF 300.
Certified Medicaid.
Owner Proprietary Corp.
Admissions Requirements Physician's request.
Staff Physicians 6 (pt); RNs 6 (ft), 2 (pt);
LPNs 20 (ft), 5 (pt); Orderlies 2 (ft); Nurses
aides 76 (ft), 3 (pt); Physical therapists 1
(pt); Occupational therapists 1 (pt); Speech
therapists 1 (pt); Activities coordinators;
Dietitians 1 (pt).
Facilities Dining room; Physical therapy
room; Activities room; Crafts room; Laundry
room; Barber/Beauty shop.
Activities Arts & crafts; Cards; Games;
Movies; Shopping trips; Social/Cultural
gatherings.

Hearthside Nursing Home Inc*
1223 W 87th St, Chicago, IL, 60625
(312) 238-2019
Admin Michael Neikrug. *Medical Dir/Dir of
Nursing* Dr Cornelius Bolton.
Licensure Skilled care; Intermediate care. *Beds*
SNF 33; ICF 42. *Certified* Medicaid.
Owner Proprietary Corp.
Admissions Requirements Minimum age 18;
Medical examination.
Staff Physicians 2 (pt); RNs 1 (ft), 1 (pt);
LPNs 3 (ft), 4 (pt); Orderlies 1 (ft); Nurses
aides 13 (ft), 7 (pt); Physical therapists 1
(pt); Reality therapists 1 (ft); Recreational
therapists 1 (ft); Occupational therapists 1
(pt); Speech therapists 1 (pt); Activities
coordinators 2 (ft); Dietitians 1 (pt); Dentists
1 (pt); Ophthalmologists 1 (pt); Podiatrists 1
(pt).
Facilities Dining room; Activities room;
Crafts room; Laundry room; Barber/Beauty
shop.
Activities Arts & crafts; Cards; Games;
Reading groups; Prayer groups; Movies;
Shopping trips; Social/Cultural gatherings.

Home Association Jewish Blind*
3525 W Foster Ave, Chicago, IL, 60625
(312) 478-7040
Admin Fred I Oskin. *Medical Dir/Dir of
Nursing* Dr Jerome Dalinka.
Licensure Sheltered care. *Beds* 53.
Owner Nonprofit Corp.
Admissions Requirements Minimum age 17;
Medical examination.
Staff Physicians 1 (pt); RNs 4 (pt); Nurses
aides 9 (ft); Occupational therapists 1 (pt);
Activities coordinators 1 (pt);
Ophthalmologists 1 (pt); Podiatrists 1 (pt).
Affiliation Jewish
Facilities Dining room; Activities room;
Chapel; Crafts room; Laundry room; Barber/
Beauty shop.
Activities Arts & crafts; Games; Prayer groups;
Social/Cultural gatherings.

Hyde Park Nursing Center Inc*
4505 S Drexel, Chicago, IL, 60653
(312) 285-0550
Admin Lester E Okun.
Licensure Skilled care. *Beds* 155. *Certified*
Medicaid.
Owner Proprietary Corp.

Jewish Peoples Convalescent Home
6512 N California Ave, Chicago, IL, 60645
(312) 743-8077
Admin Mike Applebaum. *Medical Dir/Dir of
Nursing* Dr Dan Stockhammer.
Licensure Sheltered care. *Beds* 35.
Owner Nonprofit Corp.
Admissions Requirements Minimum age 60;
Medical examination.
Staff Physicians 1 (pt); RNs 1 (pt); LPNs 2
(ft), 2 (pt); Nurses aides 4 (ft), 3 (pt);
Recreational therapists 1 (pt); Occupational
therapists 1 (pt); Activities coordinators 1
(pt); Dietitians 1 (pt).
Affiliation Jewish
Facilities Dining room; Activities room;
Crafts room; Barber/Beauty shop.
Activities Arts & crafts; Cards; Games.

Johnson Rehabilitation Nursing Home*
3456 W Franklin Blvd, Chicago, IL, 60624
(312) 533-3033
Admin H Shirley Sneed. *Medical Dir/Dir of
Nursing* Dorval R Carter MD.
Licensure Skilled care; Intermediate care. *Beds*
76. *Certified* Medicaid; Medicare.
Owner Proprietary Corp.
Admissions Requirements Minimum age 18;
Medical examination; Physician's request.
Staff Physicians 4 (pt); RNs 2 (ft); LPNs 8
(ft); Nurses aides 17 (ft); Physical therapists
1 (pt); Recreational therapists 1 (ft);
Dietitians 1 (pt); Dentists 1 (pt); Podiatrists
1 (pt).
Facilities Dining room; Physical therapy
room; Activities room; Laundry room.
Activities Arts & crafts; Cards; Games;
Reading groups; Prayer groups; Movies;
Shopping trips; Social/Cultural gatherings.

Kenwood Terrace*
6125 S Kenwood Ave, Chicago, IL, 60632
(312) 752-6000
Admin Ronald Glen Weiss.
Licensure Skilled care; Intermediate care. *Beds*
SNF 128; ICF 190. *Certified* Medicare.
Owner Proprietary Corp.

Kraus Home Inc*
1620 W Chase, Chicago, IL, 60626
(312) 973-2100
Admin Lawrence Kraus.
Licensure Sheltered care. *Beds* 60.
Owner Proprietary Corp.
Admissions Requirements Medical
examination.

Staff Physicians 1 (pt); RNs 1 (ft); LPNs 5 (ft); Nurses aides 5 (ft); Recreational therapists 1 (ft); Occupational therapists 1 (ft); Activities coordinators 1 (ft); Dietitians 1 (pt).
Facilities Dining room; Activities room; Crafts room; Laundry room; Barber/Beauty shop; Library.
Activities Arts & crafts; Cards; Games; Reading groups; Movies; Shopping trips; Social/Cultural gatherings.

Lake Front Healthcare Center Inc*
7618 N Sheridan Rd, Chicago, IL, 60626
(312) 743-7711
Admin Malka Mermelstein.
Licensure Skilled care. *Beds* 99. *Certified* Medicaid; Medicare.
Owner Proprietary Corp.

Lake Shore Nursing Centre Inc
7200 N Sheridan Rd, Chicago, IL, 60626
(312) 973-7200
Admin Isadore Goldberg. *Medical Dir/Dir of Nursing* Lester Baranov MD; Janet Q Hawkins DON.
Licensure Skilled care; Intermediate care. *Beds* 328. *Certified* Medicaid; Medicare.
Owner Proprietary Corp.
Admissions Requirements Minimum age 21.
Staff RNs 36 (ft), 8 (pt); LPNs 2 (ft); Nurses aides 89 (ft), 12 (pt); Physical therapists 4 (pt); Reality therapists 1 (ft); Recreational therapists 3 (ft); Occupational therapists 2 (ft), 1 (pt); Speech therapists 1 (pt); Activities coordinators 1 (ft); Dietitians 1 (ft), 1 (pt); Dentists 1 (pt); Ophthalmologists 1 (pt); Podiatrists 1 (pt).
Facilities Dining room; Physical therapy room; Activities room; Crafts room; Laundry room; Barber/Beauty shop; Library.
Activities Arts & crafts; Cards; Games; Reading groups; Prayer groups; Movies; Shopping trips; Social/Cultural gatherings.

Lakeland Manor*
820 W Lawrence, Chicago, IL, 60640
(312) 769-2570
Admin Annette Cota-Salem.
Licensure Skilled care. *Beds* 310. *Certified* Medicaid; Medicare.
Owner Proprietary Corp (Alden Management Services).

Lakeside Boarding Home
6330 N Sheridan Rd, Chicago, IL, 60660
(312) 338-2811
Admin Dinesh Gandhi. *Medical Dir/Dir of Nursing* Pareshkumar Jani MD; Dorothy Metthews.
Licensure Sheltered care. *Beds* 34. *Certified* Medicaid; Medicare.
Owner Proprietary Corp.
Admissions Requirements Minimum age 21; Males only; Medical examination; Physician's request.
Staff LPNs; Nurses aides; Activities coordinators; Dietitians.
Facilities Dining room; Activities room; Crafts room; Laundry room.
Activities Arts & crafts; Cards; Games; Reading groups; Prayer groups; Movies; Shopping trips; Social/Cultural gatherings.

Lakeview Nursing & Geriatric Center Inc*
735 W Diversey, Chicago, IL, 60614
(312) 348-4055
Admin Karen Petersen. *Medical Dir/Dir of Nursing* Dr T Kioutas.
Licensure Skilled care; Intermediate care. *Beds* SNF 63; ICF 117. *Certified* Medicaid.
Owner Proprietary Corp.
Admissions Requirements Minimum age 60.
Staff Physicians; RNs 12 (ft); LPNs 8 (ft); Orderlies 2 (ft); Nurses aides 52 (ft); Physical therapists 2 (ft); Recreational therapists 3 (ft); Occupational therapists;

Speech therapists; Activities coordinators 1 (ft); Dietitians; Dentists; Ophthalmologists; Podiatrists; Audiologists.
Facilities Dining room; Physical therapy room; Activities room; Crafts room; Laundry room; Barber/Beauty shop; Library.
Activities Arts & crafts; Cards; Games; Reading groups; Prayer groups; Movies; Shopping trips; Social/Cultural gatherings.

Lincoln Park Terrace Inc*
2732 N Hampden Ct, Chicago, IL, 60614
(312) 248-6000
Admin Dov Solomon. *Medical Dir/Dir of Nursing* Solomon Dayan.
Licensure Skilled care. *Beds* 109.
Owner Proprietary Corp.
Admissions Requirements Minimum age 21.
Staff Physicians 6 (pt); RNs 5 (ft), 4 (pt); LPNs 8 (ft), 3 (pt); Nurses aides 25 (ft), 3 (pt); Physical therapists 1 (pt); Occupational therapists 1 (pt); Speech therapists 1 (pt); Activities coordinators 2 (ft); Dietitians 1 (pt); Dentists 1 (pt); Ophthalmologists 1 (pt); Podiatrists 1 (pt); Audiologists 1 (pt).
Facilities Dining room; Physical therapy room; Activities room; Crafts room; Laundry room; Barber/Beauty shop; Library.
Activities Arts & crafts; Cards; Games; Reading groups; Movies; Shopping trips; Social/Cultural gatherings.

Little Sisters of the Poor
2325 N Lakewood Ave, Chicago, IL, 60614
(312) 973-9600
Admin Sr Catherine M Cavanaugh. *Medical Dir/Dir of Nursing* Dr Dayan; Sr Loraine.
Licensure Skilled care; Intermediate care. *Beds* SNF 25; ICF 83. *Certified* Medicaid.
Owner Nonprofit Corp.
Admissions Requirements Minimum age 60.
Staff RNs 7 (ft), 5 (pt); LPNs 3 (ft), 3 (pt); Nurses aides 18 (ft), 15 (pt); Physical therapists 1 (ft); Occupational therapists 1 (ft); Activities coordinators 1 (ft).
Affiliation Roman Catholic
Facilities Dining room; Physical therapy room; Activities room; Chapel; Crafts room; Laundry room; Barber/Beauty shop; Library; Outdoor park.
Activities Arts & crafts; Cards; Games; Reading groups; Prayer groups; Movies; Shopping trips; Social/Cultural gatherings.

Maple Terrace Shelter Care Home*
4743 W Washington, Chicago, IL, 60644
(312) 626-1439
Admin Pearl J Brooks.
Licensure Sheltered care. *Beds* 12.
Owner Proprietary Corp.

Margaret Manor
1121 N Orleans, Chicago, IL, 60610
(312) 943-4300
Admin Cynthia Halgard.
Licensure Intermediate care. *Beds* 135. *Certified* Medicaid.
Owner Proprietary Corp.
Admissions Requirements Medical examination.
Staff RNs 1 (ft); LPNs 4 (ft); Nurses aides 16 (ft); Activities coordinators 1 (ft).
Languages Polish, Spanish
Facilities Dining room; Activities room; Chapel; Crafts room; Laundry room.
Activities Arts & crafts; Cards; Games; Reading groups; Prayer groups; Movies; Shopping trips; Social/Cultural gatherings.

Margaret Manor North Branch
940 W Cullom Ave, Chicago, IL, 60613
(312) 525-9000
Admin Felisa B Talavera. *Medical Dir/Dir of Nursing* S Day a4n MD; Adelina Lagadan DON.
Licensure Intermediate care. *Beds* ICF 99. *Certified* Medicaid.
Owner Proprietary Corp.

Admissions Requirements Minimum age 21-60; Medical examination; Physician's request.
Staff Physicians 4 (pt); RNs 3 (ft), 3 (pt); LPNs 1 (pt); Orderlies 1 (ft); Nurses aides 11 (ft), 4 (pt); Occupational therapists 1 (pt); Activities coordinators 1 (ft); Dietitians 1 (pt); Ophthalmologists 1 (pt); Laboratory technician 1 (pt).
Languages Spanish, German
Facilities Dining room; Physical therapy room; Activities room; Crafts room; Laundry room; Library.
Activities Arts & crafts; Cards; Games; Reading groups; Prayer groups; Movies; Shopping trips; Social/Cultural gatherings.

Mayfield Care Center*
5905 W Washington, Chicago, IL, 60644
(312) 261-7074
Admin Moises Marcovich. *Medical Dir/Dir of Nursing* Dr Dayan.
Licensure Skilled care; Intermediate care. *Beds* 150. *Certified* Medicaid.
Owner Proprietary Corp.
Admissions Requirements Minimum age 21; Medical examination.
Staff Physicians 3 (pt); RNs 4 (ft); LPNs 18 (ft); Orderlies 7 (ft); Nurses aides 40 (ft); Physical therapists 3 (ft); Reality therapists 3 (ft); Recreational therapists 3 (ft); Occupational therapists 1 (pt); Speech therapists 1 (pt); Activities coordinators 1 (ft); Dietitians 1 (pt); Dentists 3 (pt); Ophthalmologists 3 (pt); Podiatrists 3 (pt); Audiologists 1 (pt).
Facilities Dining room; Physical therapy room; Activities room; Chapel; Crafts room; Laundry room; Barber/Beauty shop.
Activities Arts & crafts; Cards; Games; Reading groups; Prayer groups; Movies; Shopping trips; Social/Cultural gatherings.

The Methodist Home
1415 W Foster Ave, Chicago, IL, 60640
(312) 769-5500
Admin Annie D Mark. *Medical Dir/Dir of Nursing* Dr Noel De Backer; Karen Brors RN MSN.
Licensure Skilled care; Intermediate care; Sheltered care. *Beds* SNF 23; ICF 83; Sheltered care 23. *Certified* Medicaid.
Owner Nonprofit Corp.
Admissions Requirements Minimum age 62; Medical examination.
Staff Physicians 2 (pt); RNs 6 (ft), 4 (pt); LPNs 5 (ft), 5 (pt); Nurses aides 30 (ft), 5 (pt); Physical therapists 1 (pt); Occupational therapists 1 (pt); Activities coordinators 2 (ft), 1 (pt); Dietitians 1 (pt); Dentists 1 (pt); Ophthalmologists 1 (pt); Podiatrists 1 (pt).
Affiliation Methodist
Facilities Dining room; Physical therapy room; Activities room; Chapel; Crafts room; Laundry room; Barber/Beauty shop; Library; Parlors.
Activities Arts & crafts; Cards; Games; Reading groups; Prayer groups; Movies; Shopping trips; Social/Cultural gatherings.

Michigan Terrace Nursing Center Inc*
3405 S Michigan, Chicago, IL, 60616
(312) 791-0035
Admin Mark L Steinberg. *Medical Dir/Dir of Nursing* Dr Sheldon Levine.
Licensure Skilled care; Intermediate care. *Beds* 155. *Certified* Medicaid.
Owner Proprietary Corp.
Admissions Requirements Medical examination; Physician's request.
Staff Physicians 3 (pt); RNs 2 (ft), 2 (pt); LPNs 10 (ft), 4 (pt); Orderlies 5 (ft); Nurses aides 30 (ft), 5 (pt); Physical therapists 1 (pt); Recreational therapists 2 (ft); Occupational therapists 1 (pt); Speech therapists 1 (pt); Activities coordinators 1 (ft); Dietitians 1 (pt); Dentists 1 (pt); Ophthalmologists 1 (pt); Podiatrists 1 (pt).

Facilities Dining room; Physical therapy room; Activities room; Chapel; Crafts room; Laundry room; Barber/Beauty shop.
Activities Arts & crafts; Cards; Games; Reading groups; Prayer groups; Social/Cultural gatherings.

Mid-America Convalescent Centers Inc*
4920 N Kenmore, Chicago, IL, 60640
(312) 769-2700
Admin Paul Horvath.
Licensure Skilled care. *Beds* 310. *Certified* Medicaid.
Owner Proprietary Corp.

Misericordia Home*
2916 W 47th St, Chicago, IL, 60632
(312) 254-9595
Admin Elizabeth Flynn RN. *Medical Dir/Dir of Nursing* Roseanne V Proteau MD.
Licensure Skilled care. *Beds* 122. *Certified* Medicaid.
Owner Nonprofit Corp.
Admissions Requirements Minimum age Birth; Medical examination.
Staff Physicians 2 (ft); RNs 8 (ft), 6 (pt); LPNs 5 (ft), 3 (pt); Occupational therapists 1 (ft).
Affiliation Roman Catholic
Facilities Dining room; Physical therapy room; Activities room; Chapel; Crafts room; Laundry room; Library.
Activities Arts & crafts; Reading groups; Prayer groups; Movies; Shopping trips.

Monroe Pavilion Health Center Inc
7001 S Yale Ave, Chicago, IL, 60607
(312) 666-4090
Admin Wayne J Hanik. *Medical Dir/Dir of Nursing* A Rezvan MD; Tom Carroll RN DON.
Licensure Intermediate care. *Beds* ICF 136. *Certified* Medicaid.
Owner Proprietary Corp.
Admissions Requirements Minimum age 18; Medical examination; Physician's request.
Staff Physicians 3 (pt); RNs 1 (ft); LPNs 10 (ft), 1 (pt); Orderlies 8 (ft); Nurses aides 23 (ft); Physical therapists 1 (ft), 2 (pt); Reality therapists 1 (pt); Recreational therapists 1 (pt); Occupational therapists 1 (pt); Speech therapists 1 (pt); Activities coordinators 1 (ft); Dietitians 1 (ft); Dentists 1 (pt); Ophthalmologists 1 (pt); Podiatrists 1 (pt); Psychiatrist 2 (pt).
Facilities Dining room; Physical therapy room; Activities room; Crafts room; Laundry room; Barber/Beauty shop; Library.
Activities Arts & crafts; Cards; Games; Reading groups; Prayer groups; Movies; Shopping trips; Social/Cultural gatherings.

Ora G Morrow Nursing Home
5001 S Michigan, Chicago, IL, 60615
(312) 924-9292
Admin Williams Dorothy. *Medical Dir/Dir of Nursing* Yrech Pardo MD.
Licensure Skilled care; Intermediate care. *Beds* 192.
Owner Proprietary Corp (Alden Management Services).
Admissions Requirements Minimum age 21.
Staff Physicians 12 (pt); RNs 6 (ft), 3 (pt); LPNs 13 (ft), 6 (pt); Orderlies 7 (ft); Nurses aides 43 (ft), 4 (pt); Physical therapists 1 (pt); Recreational therapists 4 (ft), 1 (pt); Occupational therapists 2 (pt); Speech therapists 2 (pt); Activities coordinators 1 (ft); Dietitians 1 (pt); Dentists 1 (pt); Ophthalmologists 2 (pt); Podiatrists 1 (pt).
Facilities Dining room; Physical therapy room; Activities room; Crafts room; Laundry room; Barber/Beauty shop.
Activities Arts & crafts; Cards; Games; Prayer groups; Movies; Social/Cultural gatherings.

Norridge Nursing Centre Inc
7001 W Cullom, Chicago, IL, 60634
(312) 457-0700
Admin Barbara I Lyons. *Medical Dir/Dir of Nursing* Samuel Kruger MD; Evelyn Troike.
Licensure Skilled care; Intermediate care. *Beds* SNF 210; ICF 105. *Certified* Medicaid; Medicare.
Owner Privately owned.
Admissions Requirements Minimum age 18; Medical examination; Physician's request.
Staff Physicians 5 (pt); RNs 21 (ft), 5 (pt); LPNs 35 (ft), 3 (pt); Orderlies 5 (ft); Nurses aides 120 (ft); Physical therapists 2 (pt); Recreational therapists 1 (pt); Occupational therapists 1 (pt); Speech therapists 1 (pt); Activities coordinators 2 (ft); Dietitians 1 (pt); Dentists 1 (pt); Ophthalmologists 1 (pt).
Facilities Dining room; Physical therapy room; Activities room; Crafts room; Laundry room; Barber/Beauty shop; Library.
Activities Arts & crafts; Cards; Games; Reading groups; Prayer groups; Movies; Shopping trips; Social/Cultural gatherings; Luncheon trips; Cooking; Exercise classes.

Northwest Home for the Aged
6300 N California Ave, Chicago, IL, 60659
(312) 973-1900
Admin Haim Perlstein. *Medical Dir/Dir of Nursing* Michael Preodor MD; Everlyn Liberson RN DON.
Licensure Skilled care; Intermediate care. *Beds* SNF 108; ICF 52. *Certified* Medicaid.
Owner Nonprofit Corp.
Admissions Requirements Minimum age 65; Medical examination.
Staff Physicians 2 (pt); RNs 15 (ft), 10 (pt); LPNs 8 (ft); Orderlies 1 (ft); Nurses aides 59 (ft), 1 (pt); Physical therapists 1 (pt); Recreational therapists 5 (ft); Occupational therapists 1 (pt); Speech therapists 1 (pt); Activities coordinators 1 (ft); Dietitians 1 (pt); Dentists 1 (pt); Ophthalmologists 1 (pt); Podiatrists 1 (pt).
Languages Yiddish, Hebrew
Facilities Dining room; Physical therapy room; Activities room; Chapel; Crafts room; Laundry room; Barber/Beauty shop; Library.
Activities Arts & crafts; Cards; Games; Reading groups; Prayer groups; Movies; Social/Cultural gatherings.

Norwood Park Home
6016 N Nina Ave, Chicago, IL, 60631
(312) 631-4856
Admin James E Herbon. *Medical Dir/Dir of Nursing* Thomas Pawlowski MD; Nancy Lucarini RN DON.
Licensure Intermediate care; Sheltered care & Adult day care. *Beds* ICF 131; Sheltered care 140. *Certified* Medicaid.
Owner Nonprofit Corp.
Admissions Requirements Minimum age 65; Medical examination.
Staff Physicians 1 (pt); RNs 5 (ft), 5 (pt); LPNs 6 (ft), 3 (pt); Orderlies 1 (ft); Nurses aides 38 (ft), 10 (pt); Physical therapists 1 (pt); Recreational therapists 4 (ft), 1 (pt); Activities coordinators 1 (ft); Dietitians 1 (pt); Ophthalmologists 1 (pt).
Facilities Dining room; Physical therapy room; Activities room; Chapel; Crafts room; Laundry room; Barber/Beauty shop; Library.
Activities Arts & crafts; Cards; Games; Reading groups; Movies; Shopping trips; Social/Cultural gatherings; Scrabble tournaments.

Palmer Terrace Nursing Center
2242 N Kedzie Ave, Chicago, IL, 60647
(312) 486-7700
Admin Sidney K Goldstein. *Medical Dir/Dir of Nursing* Dr A Rezvan MD; Virginia Kurz RN DON.
Licensure Skilled care; Intermediate care. *Beds* 222. *Certified* Medicaid.
Owner Proprietary Corp.

Staff Physicians 8 (pt); RNs 9 (ft); LPNs 14 (ft); Nurses aides 44 (ft); Physical therapists 2 (ft), 1 (pt); Reality therapists 1 (pt); Occupational therapists 1 (ft), 1 (pt); Speech therapists 1 (ft), 1 (pt); Activities coordinators 5 (ft); Dietitians 1 (pt); Dentists 1 (pt); Ophthalmologists 1 (pt); Podiatrists 2 (pt).
Languages Spanish
Facilities Dining room; Physical therapy room; Activities room; Crafts room; Laundry room; Barber/Beauty shop.
Activities Arts & crafts; Cards; Games; Reading groups; Prayer groups; Movies; Shopping trips; Social/Cultural gatherings; Outings to zoos; Bingo.

Park Nursing Home Inc*
2320 S Lawndale, Chicago, IL, 60623
(312) 522-0400
Admin Beni Held. *Medical Dir/Dir of Nursing* Ralph De Jesus.
Licensure Intermediate care. *Beds* 105. *Certified* Medicaid.
Owner Proprietary Corp.
Admissions Requirements Minimum age 18; Medical examination.
Staff RNs 1 (ft); LPNs 6 (ft); Nurses aides 24 (ft); Activities coordinators 1 (ft).
Facilities Dining room; Physical therapy room; Activities room; Crafts room; Laundry room.
Activities Arts & crafts; Cards; Games; Reading groups; Prayer groups; Movies; Shopping trips; Social/Cultural gatherings.

Peterson Park Health Care Center
6141 N Pulaski Rd, Chicago, IL, 60646
(312) 478-2000
Admin Sheila Bogen. *Medical Dir/Dir of Nursing* Dr A Riazi; E MacPherson RN.
Licensure Skilled care; Intermediate care. *Beds* SNF 93; ICF 95. *Certified* Medicaid.
Owner Privately owned.
Admissions Requirements Minimum age 55.
Staff Physicians 15 (pt); RNs 12 (ft), 10 (pt); LPNs 8 (ft), 4 (pt); Nurses aides 33 (ft); Physical therapists 3 (ft); Reality therapists 2 (ft); Recreational therapists 4 (ft); Occupational therapists 3 (ft); Speech therapists 1 (ft); Activities coordinators 1 (ft); Dietitians 1 (ft); Dentists 1 (ft); Ophthalmologists 1 (ft); Podiatrists 1 (ft).
Languages Korean, Tagalog, Polish, Spanish
Facilities Dining room; Physical therapy room; Activities room; Laundry room; Barber/Beauty shop.
Activities Arts & crafts; Cards; Games; Reading groups; Prayer groups; Movies; Shopping trips; Social/Cultural gatherings.

Renaissance House*
6050 N California Ave, Chicago, IL, 60659
(312) 761-4651
Admin Kathleen McClory.
Licensure Intermediate care. *Beds* 20.
Owner Nonprofit Corp.

Rogers Park Manor Nursing Home
1512 W Fargo, Chicago, IL, 60626
(312) 465-7751
Admin Bradley Alter. *Medical Dir/Dir of Nursing* Dr Aboul Sattar;j Joyce Mixon DON.
Licensure Skilled care; Intermediate care. *Beds* SNF 70; ICF 29. *Certified* Medicaid.
Owner Proprietary Corp.
Admissions Requirements Minimum age 60; Medical examination; Physician's request.
Staff RNs; LPNs; Orderlies; Nurses aides; Physical therapists; Reality therapists; Recreational therapists; Occupational therapists; Activities coordinators; Dietitians.
Facilities Dining room; Physical therapy room; Activities room; Crafts room; Barber/Beauty shop; Library.

Activities Arts & crafts; Cards; Games; Reading groups; Prayer groups; Movies; Shopping trips; Social/Cultural gatherings.

Rosewood-Damen Nursing Home Inc*
6700-10 N Damen Ave, Chicago, IL, 60645
(312) 465-5000
Admin W E Lamz.
Licensure Skilled care; Intermediate care. *Beds* SNF 51; ICF 76. *Certified* Medicaid.
Owner Proprietary Corp.

Sacred Heart Home*
1550 S Albany, Chicago, IL, 60623
(312) 277-6868
Admin Virginia E Barry.
Licensure Intermediate care. *Beds* 172. *Certified* Medicaid.
Owner Proprietary Corp.

St Agnes Health Care Center*
60 E 18th St, Chicago, IL, 60610
(312) 922-2777
Admin Eugene Caldwell.
Licensure Skilled care. *Beds* 107.
Owner Proprietary Corp.

St Joseph Home of Chicago Inc
2650 N Ridgeway Ave, Chicago, IL, 606471199
(312) 235-8600
Admin Joseph A Bonnan. *Medical Dir/Dir of Nursing* Salomon Dayan MD; Henly Delcarpio RN.
Licensure Skilled care. *Beds* SNF 173. *Certified* Medicaid.
Owner Nonprofit Corp (Franciscan Sisters).
Admissions Requirements Minimum age 65; Medical examination; Physician's request.
Staff Physicians 3 (pt); RNs 15 (ft), 29 (pt); LPNs 5 (ft); Orderlies 1 (ft); Nurses aides 51 (ft), 6 (pt); Physical therapists 1 (pt); Recreational therapists 1 (pt); Occupational therapists 1 (pt); Speech therapists 1 (pt); Activities coordinators 1 (ft); Dietitians 1 (pt); Dentists 1 (pt); Ophthalmologists 1 (pt); Podiatrists 1 (pt); Rehabilitation Aides 4 (ft).
Languages Polish
Affiliation Roman Catholic
Facilities Dining room; Physical therapy room; Activities room; Chapel; Crafts room; Laundry room; Barber/Beauty shop; Library; Lounges; Porches; Large garden area.
Activities Arts & crafts; Cards; Games; Reading groups; Prayer groups; Movies; Shopping trips; Social/Cultural gatherings; Pastoral services; Reminiscence therapy; Walking groups; Picnics; Exercises; Health orientation.

St Martha Manor*
4621 N Racine Ave, Chicago, IL, 60640
(312) 784-2300
Admin Kathleen Stumpf. *Medical Dir/Dir of Nursing* Arsenio Agngarayngay.
Licensure Skilled care. *Beds* 132. *Certified* Medicaid.
Owner Nonprofit Corp.
Admissions Requirements Minimum age 18.
Staff Physicians 5 (pt); RNs 17 (ft); LPNs 4 (ft); Orderlies 6 (ft); Nurses aides 20 (ft); Physical therapists 3 (pt); Reality therapists 1 (ft); Recreational therapists 1 (ft); Occupational therapists 1 (ft); Speech therapists 1 (ft), 1 (pt); Activities coordinators 5 (ft); Dietitians 1 (pt); Dentists 1 (pt); Podiatrists 1 (pt).
Facilities Dining room; Physical therapy room; Activities room; Crafts room; Laundry room; Barber/Beauty shop.
Activities Arts & crafts; Cards; Games; Reading groups; Prayer groups; Movies; Shopping trips; Social/Cultural gatherings.

St Mary Square Living Center of Chicago
7270 S Shore Dr, Chicago, IL, 60649
(312) 721-7700
Admin Dale Mitchell.

Licensure Intermediate care; Developmentally disabled. *Beds* ICF 55; Developmentally disabled 100.
Owner Nonprofit Corp.

St Pauls House/Grace Convalescent Home
Chicago, IL, 60618
(312) 478-4222
Admin Dorothy Pipenhagen; Carol Zeck. *Medical Dir/Dir of Nursing* Virginia deLeon RN.
Licensure Skilled care; Intermediate care; Sheltered care. *Beds* SNF 141; Sheltered 74. *Certified* Medicaid.
Owner Nonprofit Corp.
Admissions Requirements Minimum age 65 for St Pauls; Minimum age 18 for Grace Home.
Staff Physicians 2 (pt); RNs 17 (ft), 7 (pt); LPNs 3 (ft), 3 (pt); Orderlies 1 (ft); Nurses aides 52 (ft); Physical therapists 2 (pt); Reality therapists 1 (pt); Occupational therapists 1 (ft); Speech therapists 1 (pt); Activities coordinators 1 (ft); Dietitians 2 (ft); Dentists 2 (pt); Ophthalmologists 2 (pt); Podiatrists 1 (pt);; Activity aides 3 (ft); Social worker 1 (pt).
Affiliation Church of Christ
Facilities Dining room; Physical therapy room; Activities room; Chapel; Crafts room; Laundry room; Barber/Beauty shop; Library.
Activities Arts & crafts; Cards; Games; Reading groups; Prayer groups; Movies; Shopping trips; Social/Cultural gatherings; Adult education classes.

Selfhelp Home for the Aged
908 W Argyle St, Chicago, IL, 60640
(312) 271-0300
Admin Dorothy W Becker. *Medical Dir/Dir of Nursing* Hyman Mackler MD; Evelyn Dagovitz.
Licensure Intermediate care. *Beds* 65. *Certified* Medicaid.
Owner Nonprofit Corp.
Admissions Requirements Minimum age 65; Medical examination; Physician's request.
Staff RNs 1 (ft); LPNs 2 (ft), 5 (pt); Nurses aides 17 (ft), 6 (pt); Physical therapists 1 (pt); Recreational therapists 1 (pt); Occupational therapists 1 (pt).
Languages German
Affiliation Jewish
Facilities Dining room; Physical therapy room; Activities room; Chapel; Crafts room; Laundry room; Barber/Beauty shop; Library.
Activities Arts & crafts; Cards; Games; Reading groups; Prayer groups; Movies; Social/Cultural gatherings; Parties.

Sherwin Manor Nursing Center*
7350 N Sheridan Rd, Chicago, IL, 60626
(312) 274-1000
Admin Joseph Osina.
Licensure Skilled care. *Beds* 219. *Certified* Medicaid.
Owner Proprietary Corp.

Society for the Danish Home
5656 N Newcastle Ave, Chicago, IL, 60631
(312) 775-7383
Admin Leif Nielsen. *Medical Dir/Dir of Nursing* Dr Philip Anderson; Lina Robinson.
Licensure Intermediate care; Sheltered care. *Beds* ICF 15; Sheltered care 57.
Owner Nonprofit organization/foundation.
Admissions Requirements Minimum age 62; Medical examination.
Languages Danish
Facilities Dining room; Activities room; Laundry room; Barber/Beauty shop; Library.
Activities Arts & crafts; Cards; Games; Movies; Shopping trips; Social/Cultural gatherings.

Somerset House
5009 N Sheridan, Chicago, IL, 60640
(312) 561-0700
Admin Edward Farmilant. *Medical Dir/Dir of Nursing* Dr David Edelberg.
Licensure Intermediate care. *Beds* 450. *Certified* Medicaid.
Owner Proprietary Corp.
Admissions Requirements Minimum age 18.
Staff Physicians 7 (pt); RNs 5 (ft); LPNs 20 (ft), 2 (pt); Nurses aides 56 (ft); Recreational therapists 7 (ft); Occupational therapists 1 (ft), 2 (pt); Speech therapists 1 (pt); Activities coordinators 9 (ft); Dietitians 1 (pt); Dentists 2 (pt); Ophthalmologists 1 (pt); Dentist 1 (pt).
Facilities Dining room; Activities room; Crafts room; Laundry room; Barber/Beauty shop; Library.
Activities Arts & crafts; Cards; Games; Reading groups; Prayer groups; Movies; Shopping trips; Social/Cultural gatherings; Softball team; Bus w/chair lift.

South Shore Kosher Rest Home Inc
7325 S Exchange Ave, Chicago, IL, 60649
(312) 731-7300
Admin Andrew Phillps.
Licensure Intermediate care. *Beds* 111. *Certified* Medicaid; Medicare.
Owner Proprietary Corp.

The Sovereign Home*
6159 N Kenmore Ave, Chicago, IL, 60660
(312) 761-9050
Admin David Stren.
Licensure Intermediate care. *Beds* 55. *Certified* Medicaid.
Owner Proprietary Corp.

Squire's Sheltered Care Home
2601 N California, Chicago, IL, 60647
(312) 278-5300
Admin Eitan Squire.
Licensure Sheltered care. *Beds* 37.
Owner Proprietary Corp.
Admissions Requirements Minimum age 18; Medical examination.
Staff Activities coordinators; Housemothers.
Facilities Dining room; Activities room; Laundry room; TV room.
Activities Arts & crafts; Cards; Games; Shopping trips; Social/Cultural gatherings; Classes; Music therapy; Cooking; Gymnastics; Grooming.

Uptown Shelter Care Home
4646 N Beacon St, Chicago, IL, 60640
(312) 561-7707
Admin Dinesh Gandhi. *Medical Dir/Dir of Nursing* Dr Paresh Jani; Ms Anderson.
Licensure Sheltered care. *Beds* 52. *Certified* Medicaid.
Owner Proprietary Corp.
Admissions Requirements Minimum age 18.
Staff Physicians 1 (pt); RNs 1 (pt); LPNs 2 (ft), 1 (pt); Nurses aides 4 (ft), 3 (pt); Activities coordinators 1 (ft); Dietitians 1 (pt); Dentists 1 (pt); Ophthalmologists 1 (pt).
Facilities Dining room; Activities room; Crafts room; Laundry room; Library.
Activities Arts & crafts; Cards; Games; Reading groups; Prayer groups; Movies; Shopping trips; Social/Cultural gatherings; Outside activities; Visits to zoo.

Vista Laguna Aftercare Facility Inc*
449 W Winnecona Pkwy, Chicago, IL, 60620
(312) 224-3900
Admin Myrtle Martin.
Licensure Intermediate care. *Beds* 164. *Certified* Medicaid.
Owner Proprietary Corp.

Washington & Jane Smith Home*
2340 W 113th Pl, Chicago, IL, 60643
(312) 238-8305
Admin Gary T Johanson.

Licensure Skilled care; Sheltered care. *Beds*
SNF 44; Sheltered care 201.
Owner Nonprofit Corp.

Waterfront Terrace
7750 S Shore Dr, Chicago, IL, 60649
(312) 731-4200
Admin Fred L Aaron. *Medical Dir/Dir of
Nursing* Anne Wizawoty DON.
Licensure Intermediate care. *Beds* 118.
Certified Medicaid; Medicare.
Owner Proprietary Corp.
Admissions Requirements Minimum age 35;
Medical examination; Physician's request.
Staff Physicians 3 (pt); LPNs 12 (ft); Nurses
aides 30 (ft); Physical therapists 1 (ft);
Occupational therapists 1 (ft); Activities
coordinators 3 (ft); Dietitians 1 (pt); Dentists
1 (pt); Ophthalmologists 1 (pt).
Facilities Dining room; Activities room;
Laundry room; Barber/Beauty shop.
Activities Arts & crafts; Cards; Games;
Reading groups; Prayer groups; Movies;
Shopping trips; Social/Cultural gatherings.

Wellington Plaza Therapy & Nursing Center
504 W Wellington Ave, Chicago, IL, 60657
(312) 281-6200
Admin Maila Tiffany. *Medical Dir/Dir of
Nursing* Martin Ross MD.
Licensure Skilled care; Intermediate care. *Beds*
SNF 34; ICF 62. *Certified* Medicare.
Owner Proprietary Corp.
Admissions Requirements Minimum age 50;
Medical examination; Physician's request.
Staff Physicians 4 (pt); RNs 7 (ft), 14 (pt);
LPNs 3 (ft), 4 (pt); Orderlies 2 (ft); Nurses
aides 30 (ft), 5 (pt); Physical therapists 1 (ft);
Reality therapists 3 (ft); Recreational
therapists 1 (ft); Occupational therapists 1
(pt); Speech therapists 1 (pt); Activities
coordinators 1 (ft); Dietitians 1 (ft); Dentists
1 (pt); Ophthalmologists 1 (pt); Podiatrists 1
(pt); Social worker 1 (pt).
Languages Hebrew, Yiddish, Spanish,
Tagalog, Portuguese, German, Estonian
Facilities Dining room; Physical therapy
room; Activities room; Chapel; Crafts room;
Laundry room; Barber/Beauty shop; Library.
Activities Arts & crafts; Cards; Games;
Reading groups; Prayer groups; Movies;
Shopping trips; Social/Cultural gatherings;
Visiting pets.

Wentworth Nursing Center
201 W 69th St, Chicago, IL, 60621
(312) 487-1200
Admin Ruben Garza. *Medical Dir/Dir of
Nursing* Pancho Degand MD; Ann Garrett
RN.
Licensure Skilled care. *Beds* SNF 300.
Certified Medicaid; Medicare.
Owner Proprietary Corp (Alden Management
Services).
Staff Physicians; RNs; LPNs; Orderlies;
Nurses aides; Physical therapists; Reality
therapists; Recreational therapists;
Occupational therapists; Speech therapists;
Activities coordinators; Dietitians; Dentists;
Ophthalmologists; Podiatrists.
Activities Arts & crafts; Cards; Games;
Reading groups; Prayer groups; Movies;
Shopping trips; Social/Cultural gatherings;
Bingo; Outings to zoo; Ball games; Social
events; Theater; Picnics.

The Westwood Manor Inc*
2444 W Touhy Ave, Chicago, IL, 60645
(312) 274-7705
Admin Chaya Liberman. *Medical Dir/Dir of
Nursing* Dr Lawrence Mazur.
Licensure Skilled care; Intermediate care. *Beds*
SNF 9; ICF 106. *Certified* Medicaid.
Owner Proprietary Corp.
Admissions Requirements Minimum age 18.

Facilities Dining room; Physical therapy
room; Activities room; Crafts room.
Activities Arts & crafts; Cards; Games; Prayer
groups; Movies; Shopping trips; Social/
Cultural gatherings.

Whitehall Convalescent & Nursing Home Inc
1901 Lincoln Park W, Chicago, IL, 60614
(312) 943-2846
Admin Dorothy L Kleinhenz RN. *Medical
Dir/Dir of Nursing* Raja Khuri MD; Diane
Fabro RN DON.
Licensure Skilled care. *Beds* SNF 91.
Owner Proprietary Corp.
Admissions Requirements Minimum age 18;
Medical examination; Physician's request.
Staff Physicians; RNs; LPNs; Nurses aides;
Physical therapists; Reality therapists;
Recreational therapists; Speech therapists;
Activities coordinators; Dietitians; Dentists;
Ophthalmologists.
Facilities Dining room; Physical therapy
room; Activities room; Barber/Beauty shop;
Solarium; Sun Deck; Patio.
Activities Arts & crafts; Games; Reading
groups; Movies; Social/Cultural gatherings;
Reality classes; Remotivation.

Wilson Care Inc
4544 N Hazel, Chicago, IL, 60640
(312) 561-7241
Admin Bryan G Barrish. *Medical Dir/Dir of
Nursing* Mitchell Sokoloff.
Licensure Intermediate care. *Beds* 188.
Certified Medicaid.
Owner Proprietary Corp.
Admissions Requirements Minimum age 21.
Staff Physicians 2 (pt); RNs 1 (ft); Orderlies 5
(ft); Nurses aides 21 (ft); Occupational
therapists 2 (pt); Dietitians 1 (pt); Dentists 1
(pt); Podiatrists 1 (pt).

Wincrest Nursing Center
6326 N Winthrop Ave, Chicago, IL, 60660
(312) 338-7800
Admin Georgene Mogyorssy. *Medical Dir/Dir
of Nursing* Sidney Fieldman.
Licensure Intermediate care. *Beds* ICF 82.
Certified Medicaid.
Owner Proprietary Corp.
Admissions Requirements Minimum age 50;
Medical examination; Physician's request.
Staff Physicians; RNs; LPNs; Orderlies;
Nurses aides; Physical therapists;
Recreational therapists; Occupational
therapists; Activities coordinators; Dietitians;
Dentists; Ophthalmologists.
Facilities Dining room; Activities room;
Laundry room; Barber/Beauty shop.
Activities Arts & crafts; Cards; Games; Prayer
groups; Movies; Shopping trips; Social/
Cultural gatherings.

Winston Manor Conv & Nursing Home*
2155 W Pierce Ave, Chicago, IL, 60622
(312) 252-2066
Admin Loren B Levin.
Licensure Intermediate care. *Beds* 180.
Certified Medicaid.
Owner Proprietary Corp.

CHICAGO HEIGHTS

Meridian Nursing Center—Suburban*
120 W 26th St, Chicago Heights, IL, 60411
(312) 756-5200
Admin Patrick L Saunders.
Licensure Skilled care; Intermediate care. *Beds*
SNF 63; ICF 48.
Owner Proprietary Corp.

Riviera Manor Inc*
490 W 16th Pl, Chicago Heights, IL, 60411
(312) 481-4444
Admin Gus G Potekin.
Licensure Skilled care; Intermediate care. *Beds*
SNF 150; ICF 50. *Certified* Medicaid;
Medicare.

Owner Proprietary Corp.

Thornton Heights Terrace Ltd*
160 W 10th St, Chicago Heights, IL, 60411
(312) 754-2220
Admin Elvira L Cull.
Licensure Intermediate care. *Beds* 222.
Certified Medicaid.
Owner Proprietary Corp.
Admissions Requirements Minimum age 18.
Facilities Dining room; Activities room;
Crafts room; Laundry room; Barber/Beauty
shop; Library.
Activities Arts & crafts; Cards; Games;
Reading groups; Prayer groups; Movies;
Shopping trips; Social/Cultural gatherings.

CHICAGO RIDGE

Chicago Ridge Nursing Center
10602 Southwest Hwy, Chicago Ridge, IL,
60415
(312) 448-1540
Admin Barry R Taerbaum. *Medical Dir/Dir of
Nursing* Solomon Payan.
Licensure Skilled care; Intermediate care. *Beds*
231. *Certified* Medicaid; Medicare.
Owner Proprietary Corp.
Admissions Requirements Minimum age 21.
Staff Physicians 4 (pt); RNs 12 (ft); LPNs 11
(ft); Orderlies 2 (ft); Nurses aides 43 (ft);
Physical therapists 2 (pt); Reality therapists
4 (ft), 2 (pt); Recreational therapists 4 (ft), 2
(pt); Occupational therapists 1 (pt); Speech
therapists 1 (pt); Activities coordinators 4
(ft), 2 (pt); Dietitians 1 (pt); Dentists 1 (pt);
Ophthalmologists 1 (pt); Podiatrists 1 (pt).
Facilities Dining room; Physical therapy
room; Activities room; Chapel; Crafts room;
Laundry room; Barber/Beauty shop; Library.
Activities Arts & crafts; Cards; Games;
Reading groups; Prayer groups; Movies;
Shopping trips; Social/Cultural gatherings;
Outings; Baseball games; Circus.

CHILLICOTHE

Parkhill Skilled Nursing Facility
PO Box 319, 1028 Hillcrest Dr, Chillicothe,
IL, 61523
(309) 274-2194
Admin John L Wachtel. *Medical Dir/Dir of
Nursing* Marilyn K Rennolett RN DON.
Licensure Skilled care. *Beds* 113. *Certified*
Medicaid; Medicare; VA.
Owner Nonprofit Corp.
Admissions Requirements Medical
examination.
Staff Physicians 1 (pt); RNs 3 (ft), 7 (pt);
LPNs 5 (ft), 5 (pt); Nurses aides 27 (ft), 7
(pt); Physical therapists 1 (pt); Recreational
therapists 1 (pt); Speech therapists 1 (pt);
Activities coordinators 1 (pt); Dietitians 1
(pt).
Facilities Dining room; Physical therapy
room; Activities room; Laundry room;
Barber/Beauty shop.
Activities Arts & crafts; Cards; Games;
Reading groups; Prayer groups; Movies;
Shopping trips; Social/Cultural gatherings;
Exercise groups.

CHRISMAN

Pleasant Meadows Christian Village*
PO Box 375, 400 W Washington, Chrisman,
IL, 61924
(217) 269-2396
Admin Robert Vincent.
Licensure Skilled care. *Beds* 99. *Certified*
Medicaid.
Owner Nonprofit Corp (Christian Homes).

CICERO

Westshire Retirement & Healthcare Center*
5825 W Cermak Rd, Cicero, IL, 60650
(312) 656-9120
Admin Morton J Gelberd. *Medical Dir/Dir of
Nursing* Dr S Slodki.
Licensure Skilled care; Intermediate care. *Beds*
SNF 152; ICF 388. *Certified* Medicaid.
Owner Proprietary Corp.
Staff RNs 13 (ft), 3 (pt); LPNs 24 (ft), 1 (pt);
Orderlies 14 (ft); Nurses aides 82 (ft);
Physical therapists; Recreational therapists 1
(ft); Occupational therapists; Speech
therapists; Dentists 1 (pt); Podiatrists 1 (pt).
Facilities Dining room; Physical therapy
room; Activities room; Crafts room; Laundry
room; Barber/Beauty shop; Library.
Activities Arts & crafts; Cards; Games; Prayer
groups; Shopping trips; Social/Cultural
gatherings; Cooking; Gardening.

CISNE

Cisne Manor Inc
PO Box 370, Cisne, IL, 62823
(618) 673-2177
Admin Carol A Lawler. *Medical Dir/Dir of
Nursing* Dr Michael Blood; Sharolene
Knight RN DON.
Licensure Intermediate care. *Beds* ICF 35.
Certified Medicaid.
Owner Privately owned.
Admissions Requirements Minimum age 18.
Staff RNs 2 (ft); LPNs 2 (ft), 2 (pt); Nurses
aides 6 (ft), 4 (pt); Activities coordinators 1
(ft).
Facilities Dining room; Activities room;
Laundry room; Barber/Beauty shop.
Activities Arts & crafts; Cards; Games;
Reading groups; Prayer groups; Movies;
Shopping trips.

CLIFTON

A Merkle-C Knipprath Nursing Home*
RR 1, Clifton, IL, 60927
(815) 694-2306
Admin Stephen A Debraikeleer.
Licensure Long-Term care. *Beds* 99.
Owner Nonprofit Corp.
Admissions Requirements Medical
examination; Physician's request.
Affiliation Roman Catholic
Facilities Dining room; Physical therapy
room; Activities room; Chapel; Crafts room;
Laundry room; Barber/Beauty shop; Library.
Activities Arts & crafts; Cards; Games;
Reading groups; Prayer groups; Movies;
Shopping trips; Social/Cultural gatherings.

CLINTON

Crestview Nursing Center
RR 3, US Hwy 51 N, Clinton, IL, 61727
(217) 935-3826
Admin Wm A Johnston. *Medical Dir/Dir of
Nursing* Robert Myers MD.
Licensure Intermediate care. *Beds* 103.
Certified Medicaid.
Owner Proprietary Corp.
Admissions Requirements Minimum age 18;
Medical examination.
Staff RNs 1 (pt); LPNs 6 (ft), 3 (pt); Nurses
aides 24 (ft), 9 (pt); Recreational therapists 1
(pt); Occupational therapists 1 (pt);
Activities coordinators 2 (ft); Dietitians 1
(pt).
Facilities Dining room; Physical therapy
room; Activities room; Chapel; Crafts room;
Laundry room; Barber/Beauty shop; Library.
Activities Arts & crafts; Cards; Games;
Reading groups; Prayer groups; Movies;
Shopping trips; Social/Cultural gatherings.

Dewitt County Nursing Home*
RFD 1, Box 336, Clinton, IL, 61727
(217) 935-9418
Admin Rhonda L Komnick. *Medical Dir/Dir
of Nursing* Selah Obasi MD.
Licensure Skilled care; Intermediate care;
Sheltered care. *Beds* SNF 30; ICF 60;
Sheltered care 25.
Owner Publicly owned.
Admissions Requirements Minimum age 18;
Medical examination; Physician's request.
Staff Physicians 7 (ft); RNs 2 (ft); LPNs 6 (ft),
1 (pt); Orderlies 1 (ft); Nurses aides 37 (ft);
Physical therapists 1 (pt); Occupational
therapists 1 (pt); Speech therapists 1 (pt);
Activities coordinators 1 (ft); Dietitians 1
(pt); Dentists 1 (pt).
Facilities Dining room; Physical therapy
room; Activities room; Crafts room; Laundry
room; Barber/Beauty shop; Library.
Activities Arts & crafts; Games; Reading
groups; Prayer groups; Movies; Shopping
trips; Social/Cultural gatherings.

COAL VALLEY

Oak Glen Home*
11210 95th St, Coal Valley, IL, 61240
(309) 799-3161
Admin David L Cray. *Medical Dir/Dir of
Nursing* Alex J Pareigis MD.
Licensure Skilled care; Intermediate care. *Beds*
285. *Certified* Medicaid; Medicare.
Owner Publicly owned.
Admissions Requirements Minimum age 18;
Medical examination; Physician's request.
Staff Physicians 1 (pt); RNs 12 (ft); LPNs 20
(ft), 3 (pt); Orderlies 6 (ft); Nurses aides 47
(ft), 12 (pt); Activities coordinators 1 (ft);
Dietitians 1 (pt).

COBDEN

**Hillside Terrace Skilled & Intermediate
Nursing Facility**
PO Box 22038, Cobden, IL, 62920
(618) 893-4214
Admin Gloria G DeWitt. *Medical Dir/Dir of
Nursing* Dr William H Whiting.
Licensure Skilled care; Intermediate care. *Beds*
SNF 16; ICF 58. *Certified* Medicaid.
Owner Proprietary Corp.
Admissions Requirements Minimum age 18;
Females only; Medical examination.
Staff Physicians 5 (pt); RNs 1 (ft), 3 (pt);
LPNs 1 (ft), 6 (pt); Nurses aides 19 (ft);
Physical therapists 1 (pt); Recreational
therapists 1 (ft); Speech therapists 1 (pt);
Activities coordinators 1 (ft); Dietitians 1
(pt).
Facilities Dining room; Physical therapy
room; Activities room; Crafts room; Laundry
room; Barber/Beauty shop.
Activities Arts & crafts; Cards; Games;
Reading groups; Prayer groups; Movies;
Shopping trips; Social/Cultural gatherings.

Tripp Shelter Care Home
Box 336, Cobden, IL, 62920
(618) 893-2291
Admin Sylvia M Tripp.
Licensure Sheltered care. *Beds* 28.
Owner Proprietary Corp.

Village Sheltered Care Home*
114 Ash St, Cobden, IL, 62920
(618) 893-4222
Admin Henrietta Smith.
Licensure Sheltered care. *Beds* 22.
Owner Proprietary Corp.

COLCHESTER

Colchester Nursing Center
222 N Hun St, Colchester, IL, 62326
(309) 776-3236, 833-5866

Admin Deborah R Finch. *Medical Dir/Dir of
Nursing* Stephen Roth MD; Ramona Reed
LPN.
Licensure Intermediate care. *Beds* ICF 54.
Certified Medicaid.
Owner Proprietary Corp.
Admissions Requirements Minimum age
Geriatric; Medical examination.
Staff LPNs 5 (ft), 1 (pt); Orderlies 1 (ft);
Nurses aides 10 (ft), 6 (pt); Physical
therapists 1 (ft), 1 (pt); Reality therapists 1
(pt); Recreational therapists 1 (pt); Speech
therapists 1 (pt); Activities coordinators 1
(ft), 1 (pt); Dietitians 1 (pt).
Facilities Dining room; Physical therapy
room; Activities room; Laundry room;
Barber/Beauty shop; Family room.
Activities Arts & crafts; Cards; Games;
Reading groups; Prayer groups; Movies;
Shopping trips; Social/Cultural gatherings;
Gardening; Bingo.

COLFAX

Octavia Manor Inc
402 S Harrison, Colfax, IL, 61728
(309) 723-2591
Admin Shirley J Geske. *Medical Dir/Dir of
Nursing* Dr Marcus Que.
Licensure Intermediate care. *Beds* 60.
Certified Medicaid.
Owner Proprietary Corp.
Admissions Requirements Minimum age 60;
Medical examination; Physician's request.
Staff Physicians 1 (pt); RNs 1 (ft), 1 (pt);
LPNs 4 (ft), 4 (pt); Nurses aides 20 (ft), 15
(pt); Activities coordinators 1 (ft); Dietitians
1 (pt).
Facilities Dining room; Physical therapy
room; Activities room; Crafts room; Laundry
room; Barber/Beauty shop.
Activities Arts & crafts; Cards; Games;
Reading groups; Prayer groups; Movies;
Shopping trips; Social/Cultural gatherings.

COLLINSVILLE

Pleasant Rest Nursing Home
614 N Summit Ave, Collinsville, IL, 62234
(618) 344-8476
Admin Michael R Myler. *Medical Dir/Dir of
Nursing* Shirley Hunsinger RN.
Licensure Skilled care. *Beds* SNF 122.
Certified Medicaid; Medicare.
Owner Proprietary Corp.
Admissions Requirements Minimum age 21;
Medical examination.
Staff Physicians; RNs; LPNs; Orderlies;
Nurses aides; Physical therapists; Speech
therapists; Activities coordinators; Dietitians;
Dentists; Ophthalmologists.
Facilities Dining room; Physical therapy
room; Activities room; Crafts room; Laundry
room; Barber/Beauty shop.
Activities Arts & crafts; Cards; Games;
Reading groups; Prayer groups; Movies;
Shopping trips; Social/Cultural gatherings.

CREAL SPRINGS

Creal Springs Nursing Home*
S Line St, Creal Springs, IL, 62922
(618) 996-2313
Admin James F Avery. *Medical Dir/Dir of
Nursing* Dr A Z Goldstein.
Licensure Skilled care; Intermediate care. *Beds*
80. *Certified* Medicaid.
Owner Proprietary Corp.
Admissions Requirements Minimum age 21;
Medical examination; Physician's request.
Staff Physicians 3 (pt); RNs 1 (ft), 2 (pt);
LPNs 7 (ft), 2 (pt); Orderlies 1 (ft); Nurses
aides 19 (ft); Physical therapists 1 (pt);
Reality therapists 1 (pt); Recreational
therapists 1 (pt); Occupational therapists 1

(pt); Speech therapists 1 (pt); Activities
coordinators 1 (ft); Dietitians 1 (pt); Dentists
1 (pt).
Facilities Dining room; Physical therapy
room; Activities room; Crafts room; Laundry
room; Barber/Beauty shop.
Activities Arts & crafts; Cards; Games;
Reading groups; Prayer groups; Movies;
Shopping trips; Social/Cultural gatherings.

CRESTWOOD

**Crestwood Terrace Intermediate Care Nursing
Home**
13301 S Central, Crestwood, IL, 60445
(312) 597-5251
Admin Maureen M Skopick. *Medical Dir/Dir
of Nursing* Antonio Noreiga MD; Judy
Majchrowicz DON.
Licensure Intermediate care. *Beds* ICF 126.
Certified Medicaid.
Owner Proprietary Corp.
Admissions Requirements Minimum age 50;
Medical examination.
Staff Physicians 1 (ft), 10 (pt); RNs 3 (ft), 2
(pt); LPNs 3 (ft), 2 (pt); Nurses aides 18 (ft),
10 (pt); Physical therapists 1 (pt); Reality
therapists 1 (ft), 1 (pt); Recreational
therapists 2 (ft), 1 (pt); Occupational therapists 1
(ft), 1 (pt); Speech therapists 1 (pt);
Activities coordinators 1 (ft); Dietitians 1
(pt); Dentists 1 (pt); Ophthalmologists 1 (pt);
Podiatrists 1 (pt); Dentist 1 (pt).
Languages Polish
Facilities Dining room; Physical therapy
room; Activities room; Crafts room; Laundry
room; Barber/Beauty shop; Library; Van.
Activities Arts & crafts; Cards; Games;
Reading groups; Prayer groups; Movies;
Shopping trips; Social/Cultural gatherings.

CRYSTAL LAKE

Crystal Pines Health Care Center
335 N Illinois St, Crystal Lake, IL, 60014
(815) 459-7791
Admin Joan P Swekosky. *Medical Dir/Dir of
Nursing* Z Ted Lorenc; Jan Lavin DON.
Licensure Skilled care. *Beds* SNF 83. *Certified*
Medicare.
Owner Nonprofit Corp (First Humanics).
Admissions Requirements Physician's request.
Staff RNs; LPNs; Nurses aides; Activities
coordinators.
Facilities Dining room; Physical therapy
room; Activities room; Laundry room;
Barber/Beauty shop.
Activities Arts & crafts; Cards; Games; Prayer
groups; Movies; Shopping trips; Social/
Cultural gatherings.

Fair Oaks Nursing Home*
471 W Terra Cotta, Crystal Lake, IL, 60014
(815) 455-0550
Admin Susan A Cheek.
Licensure Skilled care. *Beds* 46.
Owner Proprietary Corp.

CUBA

The Clayberg*
E Monroe St, Cuba, IL, 61427
(309) 785-5012
Admin Vicki Sue Hoke. *Medical Dir/Dir of
Nursing* Dr Bruce Long.
Licensure Intermediate care. *Beds* 49.
Certified Medicaid.
Owner Publicly owned.
Admissions Requirements Minimum age 62.
Facilities Dining room; Activities room;
Crafts room; Laundry room; Barber/Beauty
shop.
Activities Arts & crafts; Cards; Games;
Reading groups; Prayer groups; Movies;
Social/Cultural gatherings.

DANFORTH

Prairieview Lutheran Home*
PO Box 4, Danforth, IL, 60930
(815) 269-2970
Admin Michael Royer.
Licensure Skilled care; Intermediate care. *Beds*
60. *Certified* Medicaid.
Owner Nonprofit Corp.
Staff RNs 3 (ft), 2 (pt); LPNs 3 (ft), 3 (pt);
Orderlies 3 (ft); Nurses aides 15 (ft), 20 (pt);
Physical therapists 1 (pt); Speech therapists
1 (pt); Activities coordinators 2 (ft);
Dietitians 1 (pt); Dentists 1 (pt); Podiatrists
1 (pt).
Affiliation Lutheran
Facilities Dining room; Physical therapy
room; Activities room; Chapel; Crafts room;
Laundry room; Barber/Beauty shop.
Activities Arts & crafts; Cards; Games;
Reading groups; Prayer groups; Movies;
Shopping trips; Social/Cultural gatherings;
Community college continuing education
classes.

DANVILLE

Americana Healthcare Center
801 N Logan Ave, Danville, IL, 61832
(217) 443-3106
Admin Mary Alice Falconio. *Medical Dir/Dir
of Nursing* Mary Nagle RN.
Licensure Skilled care. *Beds* SNF 108.
Certified Medicaid; Medicare.
Owner Proprietary Corp (Manor Care).
Admissions Requirements Minimum age 18;
Medical examination.
Staff RNs; LPNs; Nurses aides; Physical
therapists; Occupational therapists; Speech
therapists; Activities coordinators; Dietitians.
Facilities Dining room; Physical therapy
room; Activities room; Barber/Beauty shop.
Activities Arts & crafts; Cards; Games; Prayer
groups; Movies; Shopping trips; Social/
Cultural gatherings.

Colonial Manor Inc*
620 Warrington, Danville, IL, 61832
(217) 446-0660
Admin Richard W Black.
Licensure Skilled care; Intermediate care. *Beds*
55. *Certified* Medicaid; Medicare.
Owner Proprietary Corp.
Staff RNs 3 (ft), 2 (pt); LPNs 2 (ft), 3 (pt);
Nurses aides 18 (ft), 2 (pt); Activities
coordinators 1 (ft); Dietitians 1 (pt).
Facilities Dining room; Laundry room;
Barber/Beauty shop.
Activities Arts & crafts; Cards; Games;
Reading groups; Prayer groups; Movies;
Shopping trips.

Danville Care Center*
1701 N Bowman, Danville, IL, 61832
(217) 443-2955
Admin Barbara Snapp.
Licensure Skilled care; Intermediate care. *Beds*
SNF 101; ICF 82. *Certified* Medicaid.
Owner Proprietary Corp.

Danville Manor
1215 Holiday Dr, Danville, IL, 61832
(217) 443-4123
Admin Terry Ellis. *Medical Dir/Dir of Nursing*
Marcia Landers.
Licensure Intermediate care; Intermediate care
for mentally retarded. *Beds* ICF 40; ICF/MR
43. *Certified* Medicaid.
Owner Proprietary Corp (Beverly Enterprises).
Admissions Requirements Minimum age 21;
Medical examination; Physician's request.
Staff RNs 2 (pt); LPNs 6 (ft), 2 (pt); Nurses
aides 30 (ft), 2 (pt); Activities coordinators 1
(ft).
Facilities Dining room; Physical therapy
room; Activities room; Crafts room; Laundry
room.

Activities Arts & crafts; Cards; Games;
Reading groups; Movies; Shopping trips;
Social/Cultural gatherings.

International Nursing Home
207 S Buchanan St, Danville, IL, 61832
(217) 446-1433
Admin Debra L Porter. *Medical Dir/Dir of
Nursing* Cheryl Hernandez RN.
Licensure Intermediate care. *Beds* ICF 48.
Certified Medicaid.
Owner Proprietary Corp (Beverly Enterprises).
Admissions Requirements Medical
examination; Physician's request.
Staff RNs; LPNs; Nurses aides; Physical
therapists; Activities coordinators; Dietitians;
Ophthalmologists.
Facilities Dining room; Activities room;
Crafts room; Laundry room.
Activities Arts & crafts; Cards; Games;
Reading groups; Prayer groups; Movies;
Shopping trips; Social/Cultural gatherings;
Holiday & birthday parties.

Vermillion Manor Nursing Home
Rte 1, Box 13, Danville, IL, 61832
(217) 443-6430
Admin D Joanne Livengood. *Medical Dir/Dir
of Nursing* Joseph Karinattu MD: Marsha
Lock RN DON.
Licensure Intermediate care. *Beds* SNF 249.
Certified Medicaid.
Owner Publicly owned.
Admissions Requirements Minimum age 18;
Medical examination; Physician's request.
Staff Physicians 1 (pt); RNs 4 (ft), 2 (pt);
LPNs 11 (ft), 4 (pt); Nurses aides 100 (ft);
Physical therapists Aides 4 (ft), 1 (pt);
Occupational therapists 1 (pt); Speech
therapists 1 (pt); Activities coordinators 5
(ft), 1 (pt); Dietitians 1 (pt).
Languages Spanish, Sign
Facilities Dining room; Physical therapy
room; Activities room; Chapel; Crafts room;
Laundry room; Barber/Beauty shop.
Activities Arts & crafts; Cards; Games;
Reading groups; Prayer groups; Movies;
Shopping trips; Social/Cultural gatherings.

DE KALB

Community Center*
360 E Grand Ave, De Kalb, IL, 62526
(217) 428-6350
Admin Daniel Keefe.
Licensure Intermediate care. *Beds* 58.
Owner Proprietary Corp.

De Kalb County Nursing Home*
2331 Sycamore Rd, De Kalb, IL, 60115
(815) 758-2477
Admin David A Coble.
Licensure Skilled care. *Beds* 194. *Certified*
Medicaid.
Owner Publicly owned.

Pine Acres Retirement Center
1212 S 2nd St, De Kalb, IL, 60115
(815) 758-8151
Admin Carol Sue Meeks. *Medical Dir/Dir of
Nursing* Janet Warren.
Licensure Skilled care. *Beds* SNF 110.
Certified Medicaid; Medicare.
Owner Nonprofit Corp.
Staff Physicians 1 (pt); RNs 6 (ft), 5 (pt);
LPNs 3 (ft), 1 (pt); Nurses aides 20 (ft), 17
(pt); Physical therapists 2 (pt); Recreational
therapists 1 (ft), 2 (pt); Occupational
therapists 1 (pt); Speech therapists 1 (pt);
Activities coordinators 1 (ft); Dietitians 1
(pt); Ophthalmologists 1 (pt).

DECATUR

Americana Healthcare Center of Decatur
444 W Harrison St, Decatur, IL, 62526
(217) 877-7333

Admin Laura Kuber. *Medical Dir/Dir of Nursing* Mary Roberts.
Licensure Skilled care; Intermediate care. *Beds* 96. *Certified* Medicaid; Medicare.
Owner Proprietary Corp (Manor Care).

Fair Havens Christian Home
1790 S Fairview Ave, Decatur, IL, 62521
(217) 429-2551
Admin Brian K Hodges. *Medical Dir/Dir of Nursing* Dr Dale Sunderland.
Licensure Skilled care. *Beds* 161. *Certified* Medicaid; Medicare.
Owner Nonprofit Corp (Christian Homes).
Admissions Requirements Minimum age 18; Medical examination.
Staff RNs 5 (ft), 5 (pt); LPNs 9 (ft), 9 (pt); Orderlies 1 (ft); Nurses aides 35 (ft), 35 (pt); Physical therapists 1 (pt); Activities coordinators 1 (ft); Ophthalmologists 1 (pt).
Affiliation Church of Christ
Facilities Dining room; Physical therapy room; Activities room; Chapel; Crafts room; Laundry room; Barber/Beauty shop; Library; Large day room; 5 duplex apt.
Activities Arts & crafts; Cards; Games; Reading groups; Prayer groups; Movies; Shopping trips; Social/Cultural gatherings.

Fairview Nursing Care Center
136 S Dipper Ln, Decatur, IL, 62522-1898
(217) 428-7767
Admin Candy J Carroll. *Medical Dir/Dir of Nursing* Dr N L Still; Betty P Estes RN.
Licensure Intermediate care. *Beds* ICF 48.
Owner Proprietary Corp (Beverly Enterprises).
Admissions Requirements Minimum age 18; Medical examination; Physician's request.
Staff RNs 1 (ft); LPNs 3 (ft), 4 (pt); Nurses aides 6 (ft), 7 (pt).
Facilities Dining room; Physical therapy room; Activities room; Laundry room; Barber/Beauty shop; Library; Solarium.
Activities Arts & crafts; Games; Prayer groups; Movies; Social/Cultural gatherings; Adopt-a-grandparent group; Gardening club.

Lakeshore Manor Nursing Home*
1293 S 34th St, Decatur, IL, 62521
(217) 429-2313
Admin Shelby Warner.
Licensure Skilled care. *Beds* 131. *Certified* Medicaid; Medicare.
Owner Proprietary Corp.

Lincoln Manor North Inc
2650 N Monroe St, Decatur, IL, 62526
(217) 875-1973
Admin Shelba J Donoho.
Licensure Intermediate care. *Beds* 121. *Certified* Medicaid.
Owner Proprietary Corp.

McKinley Court
500 W McKinley Ave, Decatur, IL, 62526
(217) 875-0020
Admin Carol S Johnson. *Medical Dir/Dir of Nursing* Dr Rohidas Patil; Sandra Guest.
Licensure Intermediate care. *Beds* ICF 150. *Certified* Medicaid.
Owner Proprietary Corp.
Admissions Requirements Minimum age 18.
Staff Activities coordinators 1 (ft); Dietitians 1 (pt).
Facilities Dining room; Activities room; Barber/Beauty shop; Several sitting areas; 2 lounges.
Activities Arts & crafts; Cards; Games; Reading groups; Prayer groups; Movies; Shopping trips; Social/Cultural gatherings.

Monroe House*
2530 N Monroe St, Decatur, IL, 62526
(217) 875-0920
Admin H Douglas Henry.
Licensure Skilled care; Intermediate care. *Beds* SNF 153; ICF 51.
Owner Proprietary Corp.

Oak Manor Health Care Center
438 W North St, Decatur, IL, 62522
(217) 429-7265
Admin Robert McDonald. *Medical Dir/Dir of Nursing* Marcy Butts.
Licensure Intermediate care. *Beds* ICF 126; Sheltered 5. *Certified* Medicaid.
Owner Nonprofit Corp (First Humanics).
Admissions Requirements Minimum age 65; Physician's request.
Staff RNs 1 (ft), 1 (pt); LPNs 11 (ft), 1 (pt); Orderlies 2 (ft); Nurses aides 27 (ft); Physical therapists 1 (pt); Occupational therapists 1 (pt); Activities coordinators 1 (ft); Dietitians 1 (pt); Ophthalmologists 1 (pt); Social workers 1 (ft), 2 (pt).
Languages Spanish
Facilities Dining room; Physical therapy room; Activities room; Crafts room; Laundry room; Barber/Beauty shop.
Activities Arts & crafts; Cards; Games; Reading groups; Prayer groups; Movies; Shopping trips; Social/Cultural gatherings; Cooking clubs; Men's groups.

Pershing Estates
Decatur, IL, 62526
(217) 875-0833
Admin Sheila Herndon. *Medical Dir/Dir of Nursing* Dr Patil; Bonnie Truxell DON.
Licensure Intermediate care. *Beds* ICF 127. *Certified* Medicaid.
Owner Proprietary Corp.
Admissions Requirements Minimum age 18; Medical examination; Physician's request.
Staff LPNs 6 (ft), 4 (pt); Nurses aides 24 (ft), 7 (pt); Recreational therapists 1 (ft); Occupational therapists 1 (ft); Activities coordinators 1 (pt); Dietitians 1 (ft).
Facilities Dining room; Activities room; Laundry room; Barber/Beauty shop.
Activities Arts & crafts; Cards; Games; Reading groups; Prayer groups; Movies; Shopping trips; Social/Cultural gatherings.

South Side Manor
729 S Webster, Decatur, IL, 62521
(217) 422-5478
Admin Angela Barr-Connell.
Licensure Intermediate care for mentally retarded. *Beds* ICF/MR 15. *Certified* Medicaid.
Owner Proprietary Corp.
Admissions Requirements Minimum age 18.
Staff Activities coordinators 1 (pt); Rehab aids 1 (ft), 7 (pt); Cook 1 (ft); Housekeeper 1 (pt).
Facilities Dining room; Activities room; Laundry room.
Activities Arts & crafts; Cards; Games; Reading groups; Prayer groups; Movies; Shopping trips; Social/Cultural gatherings.

DEERFIELD

The Whitehall North
300 Waukegan Rd, Deerfield, IL, 60015
(312) 945-4600
Admin Barbara K Harms. *Medical Dir/Dir of Nursing* Dr David Littman; Judy Hattendorf RN.
Licensure Skilled care. *Beds* SNF 170.
Owner Privately owned.
Admissions Requirements Medical examination.
Staff Physicians 2 (pt); RNs 40 (ft); LPNs 2 (ft); Orderlies 2 (ft); Nurses aides 80 (ft); Physical therapists 1 (ft); Occupational therapists 1 (ft); Speech therapists 1 (pt); Activities coordinators 2 (ft), 3 (pt); Dietitians 1 (ft); Ophthalmologists 1 (pt); Rehabilitation Specialist 1 (ft).
Facilities Dining room; Physical therapy room; Activities room; Chapel; Crafts room; Laundry room; Barber/Beauty shop; Library; Soda shop; Solariums; Dental Suite; Patio.

Activities Arts & crafts; Cards; Games; Reading groups; Prayer groups; Movies; Social/Cultural gatherings.

DEKALB

Oak Crest
2944 Greenwood Acres Dr, DeKalb, IL, 60115
(815) 756-8461
Admin Stephen P Cichy. *Medical Dir/Dir of Nursing* Mary A Burnell RN.
Licensure Intermediate care. *Beds* ICF 30.
Owner Nonprofit Corp.
Admissions Requirements Minimum age 62; Medical examination.
Staff RNs 1 (ft), 8 (pt); Nurses aides 13 (ft), 13 (pt); Recreational therapists 2 (ft); Activities coordinators 1 (ft).
Affiliation Methodist
Facilities Dining room; Physical therapy room; Activities room; Chapel; Crafts room; Laundry room; Barber/Beauty shop; Library.
Activities Arts & crafts; Cards; Games; Reading groups; Prayer groups; Movies; Shopping trips; Social/Cultural gatherings.

DES PLAINES

Ballard Nursing Center Inc*
9300 Ballard Rd, Des Plaines, IL, 60016
(312) 299-0182
Admin Eli Pick. *Medical Dir/Dir of Nursing* Dr Mazur.
Licensure Skilled care; Intermediate care. *Beds* 231. *Certified* Medicaid; Medicare.
Owner Proprietary Corp.
Admissions Requirements Minimum age 60; Medical examination.
Staff RNs 12 (ft), 4 (pt); LPNs 6 (ft), 1 (pt); Orderlies 13 (ft); Nurses aides 39 (pt); Physical therapists 1 (ft); Reality therapists 1 (pt); Recreational therapists 1 (pt); Occupational therapists 1 (pt); Speech therapists 1 (pt); Activities coordinators 1 (ft); Dietitians 1 (pt); Dentists 1 (pt); Ophthalmologists 1 (pt); Podiatrists 1 (pt); Audiologists 1 (pt).
Facilities Dining room; Physical therapy room; Activities room; Crafts room; Laundry room; Barber/Beauty shop.
Activities Arts & crafts; Cards; Games; Reading groups; Prayer groups; Movies; Social/Cultural gatherings; Foster grandparents program; Pet therapy program.

Golfview Developmental Center Inc
9555 W Golf Rd, Des Plaines, IL, 60016
(312) 827-6628
Admin Anthony R Miner. *Medical Dir/Dir of Nursing* Edith O Stockey RN DON.
Licensure Intermediate care for mentally retarded. *Beds* ICF/MR 118. *Certified* Medicaid.
Owner Proprietary Corp.
Admissions Requirements Minimum age 18; Medical examination; Physician's request.
Staff RNs 3 (ft), 1 (pt); LPNs 2 (ft), 1 (pt); Nurses aides 38 (ft); Activities coordinators 1 (ft).
Facilities Dining room; Activities room; Crafts room; Laundry room; Classrooms.
Activities Arts & crafts; Cards; Games; Reading groups; Prayer groups; Movies; Shopping trips; Social/Cultural gatherings.

Holy Family Health Center
2380 E Dempster St, Des Plaines, IL, 60016
(312) 296-3335
Admin Sr M Elizabeth Trembczynski. *Medical Dir/Dir of Nursing* William Bagnuolo MD; Christine Busse DON.
Licensure Skilled care; Intermediate care. *Beds* 362. *Certified* Medicaid; Medicare.
Owner Nonprofit Corp.
Admissions Requirements Minimum age 18; Medical examination.

Staff Physicians 1 (pt); RNs 33 (ft), 21 (pt); LPNs 5 (ft), 3 (pt); Orderlies 10 (ft), 5 (pt); Nurses aides 99 (ft), 18 (pt); Physical therapists 3 (ft); Recreational therapists 3 (ft), 2 (pt); Activities coordinators 1 (ft).
Affiliation Roman Catholic
Facilities Dining room; Physical therapy room; Activities room; Chapel; Crafts room; Laundry room; Barber/Beauty shop; Library.
Activities Arts & crafts; Cards; Games; Reading groups; Prayer groups; Movies; Shopping trips; Social/Cultural gatherings.

Lee Manor
1301 Lee St, Des Plaines, IL, 60018
(312) 827-9450
Admin Donald G Plodzien. *Medical Dir/Dir of Nursing* Dr K Beckman; Barbara Rex RN.
Licensure Skilled care. *Beds* SNF 282. *Certified* Medicaid; Medicare.
Owner Proprietary Corp.
Staff RNs; LPNs; Orderlies; Nurses aides; Physical therapists 1 (pt); Recreational therapists 1 (pt); Occupational therapists 1 (pt); Speech therapists 1 (pt); Activities coordinators 1 (ft); Dietitians 1 (pt); Dentists 1 (pt); Ophthalmologists 1 (pt).

Nazarethville
300 N River Rd, Des Plaines, IL, 60016
(312) 297-5900
Admin Sr RoseMarie Machalski. *Medical Dir/Dir of Nursing* John Meyenberg MD; Marcia O'Connor RN DON.
Licensure Intermediate care; Sheltered care. *Beds* ICF 68; Sheltered care 15. *Certified* Medicaid.
Owner Nonprofit Corp.
Admissions Requirements Minimum age 60; Medical examination.
Staff RNs 2 (ft), 10 (pt); LPNs 3 (pt); Nurses aides 20 (ft), 9 (pt); Activities coordinators 1 (ft), 2 (pt); Dietitians 1 (ft).
Affiliation Roman Catholic
Facilities Dining room; Physical therapy room; Activities room; Chapel; Crafts room; Laundry room; Barber/Beauty shop; Library.
Activities Arts & crafts; Cards; Games; Reading groups; Prayer groups; Movies; Shopping trips; Social/Cultural gatherings.

Oakton Pavillion Inc
1660 Oakton Pl, Des Plaines, IL, 60018
(312) 299-5588
Admin Jay Lewkowitz. *Medical Dir/Dir of Nursing* R Levitan MD.
Licensure Skilled care. *Beds* SNF 294. *Certified* Medicaid; Medicare.
Owner Proprietary Corp.
Admissions Requirements Minimum age 18; Medical examination; Physician's request.
Staff Physicians 4 (ft), 35 (pt); RNs 37 (ft), 3 (pt); LPNs 6 (ft); Orderlies 35 (ft); Nurses aides 110 (ft); Activities coordinators 1 (ft).
Languages German, Polish
Facilities Dining room; Physical therapy room; Activities room; Chapel; Crafts room; Laundry room; Barber/Beauty shop; Library.
Activities Arts & crafts; Cards; Games; Reading groups; Prayer groups; Movies; Shopping trips; Social/Cultural gatherings; Intergenerational programs.

DIXON

Dixon Health Care Center*
141 N Court St, Dixon, IL, 61021
(815) 288-1477
Admin Eileen Wilson. *Medical Dir/Dir of Nursing* Dr Howard Edwards Jr.
Licensure Skilled care; Intermediate care. *Beds* SNF 110; ICF 17. *Certified* Medicaid.
Owner Proprietary Corp.
Admissions Requirements Minimum age 18; Medical examination; Physician's request.
Staff Physicians 6 (pt); RNs 6 (ft), 3 (pt); LPNs 2 (ft), 1 (pt); Orderlies 1 (pt); Nurses aides 14 (ft), 7 (pt); Physical therapists 1 (ft);

Reality therapists 1 (pt); Recreational therapists 1 (pt); Occupational therapists 1 (pt); Speech therapists 1 (pt); Activities coordinators 1 (ft); Dietitians 1 (ft); Dentists 1 (pt); Podiatrists 1 (pt).
Facilities Dining room; Physical therapy room; Activities room; Crafts room; Laundry room; Barber/Beauty shop; Library.
Activities Arts & crafts; Cards; Games; Reading groups; Prayer groups; Movies; Shopping trips; Social/Cultural gatherings.

Dixon Village Inn
135 N Court St, Dixon, IL, 61021
(815) 284-2253
Admin Marge Cornejo. *Medical Dir/Dir of Nursing* Sheila McCarty RN DON.
Licensure Intermediate care for mentally retarded. *Beds* ICF/MR 134. *Certified* Medicaid.
Owner Proprietary Corp (National Heritage).
Admissions Requirements Minimum age 18; Medical examination.
Staff Physicians 1 (pt); RNs 1 (ft); LPNs 5 (ft), 2 (pt); Nurses aides 52 (ft); Physical therapists 1 (pt); Occupational therapists 1 (pt); Activities coordinators 1 (ft); Dietitians 1 (pt); Dentists 1 (pt); Ophthalmologists 1 (pt); Podiatrists 1 (pt).
Facilities Dining room; Physical therapy room; Activities room; Laundry room; Library.
Activities Arts & crafts; Cards; Games; Reading groups; Prayer groups; Movies; Shopping trips; Social/Cultural gatherings; Sheltered Workshop.

Heritage Square Retirement Home
620 N Ottawa Ave, Dixon, IL, 61021
(815) 288-2251
Admin Sylvia Montavon. *Medical Dir/Dir of Nursing* Joseph Welty MD; Trudie Matznick RN DON.
Licensure Skilled care; Sheltered care. *Beds* SNF 19; Sheltered care 94. *Certified* Medicaid.
Owner Nonprofit organization/foundation.
Admissions Requirements Minimum age 60; Medical examination; Physician's request.
Staff Physicians 6 (pt); RNs 3 (ft), 6 (pt); LPNs 2 (ft), 5 (pt); Nurses aides 9 (ft), 11 (pt); Physical therapists 1 (pt); Activities coordinators 4 (pt).
Facilities Dining room; Physical therapy room; Activities room; Crafts room; Laundry room; Barber/Beauty shop; Library; TV Lounges.
Activities Arts & crafts; Cards; Games; Reading groups; Prayer groups; Movies; Shopping trips; Social/Cultural gatherings; Seasonal teas; Receptions.

Lee County Nursing Home
800 Division St, Dixon, IL, 61021
(815) 284-3393
Admin John M Edmunds. *Medical Dir/Dir of Nursing* Thomas Welty MD; L Jeanne O'Connor RN DON.
Licensure Skilled care; Intermediate care. *Beds* 92.
Owner Publicly owned.
Admissions Requirements Minimum age 18; Medical examination; Physician's request.
Staff RNs 4 (ft), 2 (pt); LPNs 6 (ft), 3 (pt); Orderlies 2 (ft); Nurses aides 33 (ft), 10 (pt); Activities coordinators 3 (ft), 5 (pt); Dietitians 7 (ft), 7 (pt).
Facilities Dining room; Physical therapy room; Activities room; Chapel; Crafts room; Laundry room; Barber/Beauty shop; Library.
Activities Arts & crafts; Cards; Games; Reading groups; Prayer groups; Movies; Shopping trips; Social/Cultural gatherings.

DOLTON

Countryside Plaza
1635 E 154th St, Dolton, IL, 60419
(312) 841-9550
Admin Joanne De Pergola.
Licensure Skilled care; Intermediate care. *Beds* 192. *Certified* Medicaid.
Owner Proprietary Corp.

Dolton Healthcare Center
14325 S Blackstone, Dolton, IL, 60411
(312) 849-5000
Admin Roxane Goad. *Medical Dir/Dir of Nursing* Judith Lovato.
Licensure Skilled care; Intermediate care. *Beds* SNF 25; ICF 42. *Certified* Medicaid.
Owner Proprietary Corp.
Admissions Requirements Medical examination.
Staff Physicians 8 (pt); RNs 3 (ft), 4 (pt); LPNs 2 (ft), 1 (pt); Nurses aides 12 (ft), 9 (pt); Physical therapists 1 (ft), 1 (pt); Reality therapists 1 (ft), 1 (pt); Recreational therapists 1 (ft), 1 (pt); Occupational therapists 1 (ft), 1 (pt); Activities coordinators 1 (ft), 1 (pt); Dietitians 1 (pt); Dentists 1 (pt); Ophthalmologists 1 (pt).
Facilities Dining room; Physical therapy room; Activities room; Laundry room; Barber/Beauty shop.
Activities Arts & crafts; Cards; Games; Reading groups; Prayer groups; Movies; Shopping trips; Social/Cultural gatherings.

DONGOLA

Keller Sheltered Care Home 1*
201 Cross St, Dongola, IL, 62926
(618) 827-4402
Admin Dorothy Henard.
Licensure Sheltered care. *Beds* 26.
Owner Proprietary Corp.

DOWNERS GROVE

Fairview Baptist Home
7 S 241 Fairview Ave, Downers Grove, IL, 60516
(312) 852-4350
Admin Wesley P Ringdahl. *Medical Dir/Dir of Nursing* Farouk F Girgis MD; Barbara Coleman RN.
Licensure Skilled care; Intermediate care; Sheltered care. *Beds* ICF 14; ICF 60; Sheltered care 119.
Owner Nonprofit Corp.
Admissions Requirements Minimum age 60; Medical examination.
Staff RNs 6 (ft), 10 (pt); LPNs 3 (ft), 5 (pt); Orderlies 1 (ft); Nurses aides 23 (ft), 10 (pt); Activities coordinators 1 (ft); Dietitians 1 (ft); Dietary aides 11 (ft), 22 (pt).
Affiliation Baptist
Facilities Dining room; Physical therapy room; Activities room; Chapel; Crafts room; Laundry room; Barber/Beauty shop; Library.
Activities Arts & crafts; Cards; Games; Reading groups; Prayer groups; Movies; Shopping trips; Social/Cultural gatherings.

Rest Haven West Christian Nursing Center
3450 Saratoga Dr, Downers Grove, IL, 60515
(312) 963-2900
Admin Mary E Busch. *Medical Dir/Dir of Nursing* Anthony Kotin; Mary Barton.
Licensure Skilled care. *Beds* SNF 145.
Owner Nonprofit Corp.
Admissions Requirements Minimum age 18.
Staff Physicians 6 (pt); RNs; LPNs; Orderlies; Nurses aides; Physical therapists 1 (pt); Reality therapists 1 (pt); Recreational therapists 1 (pt); Occupational therapists 1 (pt); Speech therapists 1 (pt); Activities coordinators 1 (ft); Dietitians 1 (pt); Dentists 1 (pt); Ophthalmologists 1 (pt); Podiatrists 1 (pt).

Affiliation Christian Reformed
Facilities Dining room; Physical therapy room; Activities room; Crafts room; Laundry room; Barber/Beauty shop; Garden room.
Activities Arts & crafts; Cards; Games; Reading groups; Prayer groups; Movies; Shopping trips.

DU QUOIN

Fair Acres Nursing Home Inc*
514 E Jackson, Du Quoin, IL, 62832
(618) 542-4731
Admin Randee Slover.
Licensure Skilled care; Intermediate care. *Beds* SNF 29; ICF 45. *Certified* Medicaid; Medicare.
Owner Proprietary Corp.

Fairview Nursing Center
602 E Jackson St, Du Quoin, IL, 62832
(618) 542-3441
Admin Sue Robinson. *Medical Dir/Dir of Nursing* Joann Eickelman.
Licensure Intermediate care. *Beds* ICF 77. *Certified* Medicaid.
Owner Proprietary Corp.
Admissions Requirements Minimum age None; Medical examination; Physician's request.
Staff RNs; LPNs; Nurses aides; Physical therapists; Activities coordinators; Dietitians; Physical therapists.
Facilities Dining room; Physical therapy room; Activities room; Laundry room; Barber/Beauty shop.
Activities Arts & crafts; Cards; Games; Reading groups; Prayer groups; Movies; Shopping trips; Social/Cultural gatherings.

DURAND

Medina Nursing Center
PO Box 538, Durand, IL, 61024
(815) 248-2151
Admin Holgeir J Oksnevad. *Medical Dir/Dir of Nursing* Lou Hill DON.
Licensure Skilled care. *Beds* SNF 89. *Certified* Medicaid; Medicare.
Owner Proprietary Corp.
Admissions Requirements Physician's request.
Staff RNs 3 (ft), 2 (pt); LPNs 4 (ft), 4 (pt); Nurses aides 20 (ft), 20 (pt); Physical therapists 1 (pt); Speech therapists 1 (pt); Activities coordinators 1 (ft); Dietitians 1 (pt); Ophthalmologists 1 (pt).
Facilities Dining room; Physical therapy room; Activities room; Crafts room; Laundry room; Barber/Beauty shop.
Activities Arts & crafts; Cards; Games; Reading groups; Prayer groups; Movies; Shopping trips; Social/Cultural gatherings; Cooking.

DWIGHT

Continental Manor of Dwight
300 E Mazon Ave, Dwight, IL, 60420-1197
(815) 584-1240
Admin William R Provence. *Medical Dir of Nursing* Lynn Terry.
Licensure Skilled care. *Beds* SNF 92. *Certified* Medicaid; Medicare.
Owner Proprietary Corp (Beverly Enterprises).
Admissions Requirements Medical examination.
Staff RNs 2 (ft), 1 (pt); LPNs 6 (ft), 1 (pt); Nurses aides 15 (ft), 8 (pt); Physical therapists 1 (pt); Occupational therapists 1 (pt); Activities coordinators 1 (ft).
Facilities Dining room; Physical therapy room; Activities room; Chapel; Crafts room; Laundry room; Barber/Beauty shop.
Activities Arts & crafts; Cards; Games; Reading groups; Prayer groups; Movies; Shopping trips; Social/Cultural gatherings.

EAST MOLINE

East Moline Care Center*
4747 11th St, East Moline, IL, 61244
(309) 796-0922
Admin Alberta Smith. *Medical Dir/Dir of Nursing* John M Peterson MD.
Licensure Intermediate care. *Beds* 97. *Certified* Medicaid.
Owner Proprietary Corp.
Admissions Requirements Minimum age 65; Medical examination; Physician's request.
Staff RNs 4 (ft); LPNs 6 (ft); Orderlies 1 (ft); Nurses aides 35 (ft); Physical therapists 1 (pt); Recreational therapists 1 (pt); Occupational therapists 1 (pt); Speech therapists 1 (pt); Activities coordinators 1 (ft); Dietitians 1 (pt); Dentists 1 (pt).
Facilities Dining room; Physical therapy room; Activities room; Crafts room; Barber/Beauty shop.
Activities Arts & crafts; Cards; Games; Reading groups; Movies; Shopping trips; Social/Cultural gatherings.

East Moline Garden Plaza
430 30th Ave, East Moline, IL, 61244
(309) 755-3466
Admin Lester Okun. *Medical Dir/Dir of Nursing* Helen Kapinas DON.
Licensure Intermediate care. *Beds* 120. *Certified* Medicaid.
Owner Proprietary Corp.
Admissions Requirements Minimum age 21; Medical examination; Physician's request.
Staff Physicians 2 (pt); RNs 1 (ft), 1 (pt); LPNs 5 (ft), 3 (pt); Orderlies 1 (ft); Nurses aides 15 (ft), 8 (pt); Physical therapists 1 (pt); Recreational therapists 1 (pt); Occupational therapists 1 (pt); Activities coordinators 1 (ft); Dietitians 1 (pt); Dentists 1 (pt); Ophthalmologists 1 (pt); Podiatrists 1 (pt).
Facilities Dining room; Physical therapy room; Activities room; Crafts room; Laundry room; Barber/Beauty shop; Library.
Activities Arts & crafts; Cards; Games; Reading groups; Prayer groups; Movies; Shopping trips; Social/Cultural gatherings.

EAST PEORIA

Fondulac Nursing Home*
901 Illini Dr, East Peoria, IL, 61611
(309) 694-6446
Admin Marsha Reardon. *Medical Dir/Dir of Nursing* Romona Brooks RN.
Licensure Skilled care; Intermediate care. *Beds* 98. *Certified* Medicaid.
Owner Proprietary Corp.
Staff RNs 3 (ft); LPNs 5 (ft); Orderlies 2 (ft); Nurses aides 18 (ft); Physical therapists 1 (ft), 1 (pt); Speech therapists 1 (pt); Activities coordinators 1 (ft), 2 (pt); Dietitians 1 (ft).
Facilities Dining room; Physical therapy room; Activities room; Laundry room; Barber/Beauty shop; Library.
Activities Arts & crafts; Cards; Games; Reading groups; Prayer groups; Movies; Social/Cultural gatherings.

Good Samaritan Healthcare Center
1910 Springfield Rd, East Peoria, IL, 61611
(309) 694-1435
Admin David L Ennis. *Medical Dir/Dir of Nursing* Linda Krueger.
Licensure Intermediate care. *Beds* ICF 120. *Certified* Medicaid.
Owner Proprietary Corp (National Heritage).
Admissions Requirements Minimum age 50; Medical examination; Physician's request.
Staff RNs 1 (ft); LPNs 8 (ft); Orderlies 14 (ft), 2 (pt); Nurses aides 20 (ft), 10 (pt); Physical therapists 2 (ft); Occupational therapists 2 (ft); Activities coordinators 2 (ft); Dietitians 1 (ft); Ophthalmologists 1 (pt).

Facilities Dining room; Physical therapy room; Activities room; Laundry room; Barber/Beauty shop; Library.
Activities Arts & crafts; Cards; Games; Reading groups; Prayer groups; Movies; Shopping trips; Social/Cultural gatherings.

EDWARDSVILLE

Anna-Henry Nursing Home*
637 Hillsboro Ave, Edwardsville, IL, 62025
(618) 656-1136
Admin Mary Joann Newell.
Licensure Skilled care; Intermediate care. *Beds* SNF 64; ICF 61. *Certified* Medicaid.
Owner Proprietary Corp.

Eden Retirement Center Inc
400 S Station Rd, Edwardsville, IL, 62025
(618) 288-5016
Admin Wesley D Barber. *Medical Dir/Dir of Nursing* Max Eakin MD; Juline Lambert DON.
Licensure Skilled care; Intermediate care. *Beds* SNF 120. *Certified* Medicaid; Medicare.
Owner Nonprofit Corp.
Admissions Requirements Minimum age 18; Medical examination; Physician's request.
Staff RNs 7 (ft); LPNs 9 (ft), 2 (pt); Nurses aides 40 (ft), 12 (ft); Physical therapists 1 (ft), 1 (pt); Occupational therapists 3 (pt); Activities coordinators 1 (ft); Dietitians.
Affiliation Church of Christ
Facilities Dining room; Physical therapy room; Activities room; Crafts room; Laundry room; Barber/Beauty shop; Library.
Activities Arts & crafts; Cards; Games; Reading groups; Prayer groups; Movies.

Edwardsville Care Center*
1095 University Dr, Edwardsville, IL, 62025
(618) 656-1081
Admin Vincent A Aiello. *Medical Dir/Dir of Nursing* Robert Ayres.
Licensure Skilled care; Intermediate care. *Beds* SNF 92; ICF 28. *Certified* Medicaid; Medicare.
Owner Proprietary Corp.
Admissions Requirements Minimum age 21.
Staff RNs 3 (ft), 2 (pt); LPNs 8 (ft), 2 (pt); Nurses aides 30 (ft), 3 (pt); Physical therapists 1 (ft); Recreational therapists 1 (ft); Occupational therapists 1 (pt); Speech therapists 1 (pt); Activities coordinators 1 (ft); Dietitians 1 (pt); Dentists 1 (pt); Podiatrists 1 (pt); Audiologists 1 (pt).
Facilities Dining room; Physical therapy room; Activities room; Crafts room; Laundry room; Barber/Beauty shop.
Activities Arts & crafts; Cards; Games; Reading groups; Prayer groups; Movies; Shopping trips; Social/Cultural gatherings.

Madison County Nursing Home*
2121 Troy Rd, Edwardsville, IL, 62025
(618) 692-4556
Admin Billy L Rainwater.
Licensure Intermediate care. *Beds* 100. *Certified* Medicaid.
Owner Publicly owned.

Madison County Sheltered Care
S Main St, Box 441, Edwardsville, IL, 62025
(618) 692-6003
Admin Elizabeth M Agles. *Medical Dir/Dir of Nursing* Laura Blotevogel LPN.
Licensure Sheltered care. *Beds* 65.
Owner Publicly owned.
Admissions Requirements Minimum age 18; Medical examination.
Staff LPNs 1 (ft); Nurses aides 15 (ft); Activities coordinators 1 (ft).
Facilities Dining room; Laundry room; Library.
Activities Arts & crafts; Cards; Games; Reading groups; Prayer groups; Movies; Shopping trips; Social/Cultural gatherings; Greenhouse; Vegetable garden for residents.

EFFINGHAM

Country Care Manor Inc
1115 N Wenthe Ave, Effingham, IL, 62401
(217) 347-7121
Admin Florence Glenn RN. *Medical Dir/Dir of Nursing* Alma Byrd RN.
Licensure Skilled care. *Beds* 120. *Certified* Medicaid.
Owner Proprietary Corp.
Admissions Requirements Minimum age 18; Medical examination; Physician's request.
Staff RNs 3 (ft), 2 (pt); LPNs 6 (ft), 1 (pt); Orderlies 1 (ft), 1 (pt); Nurses aides 24 (ft), 3 (pt); Speech therapists 1 (pt).
Facilities Dining room; Physical therapy room; Activities room; Laundry room; Barber/Beauty shop.
Activities Arts & crafts; Cards; Games; Reading groups; Prayer groups; Movies; Shopping trips; Social/Cultural gatherings; Van rides.

Lakeland Healthcare Center
800 W Temple St, Effingham, IL, 62401
(217) 342-2171
Admin Karen Sue Wendt.
Licensure Skilled care; Intermediate care. *Beds* SNF 53; ICF 141. *Certified* Medicaid; Medicare.
Owner Nonprofit Corp (First Humanics).
Admissions Requirements Physician's request.
Facilities Dining room; Physical therapy room; Activities room; Chapel; Crafts room; Laundry room; Barber/Beauty shop.
Activities Arts & crafts; Cards; Games; Reading groups; Prayer groups; Movies; Shopping trips; Social/Cultural gatherings.

Van Dyke Care Center-Effingham
1600 W Lakewood, Effingham, IL, 62401
(217) 347-7781
Admin Marilyn E Meyer.
Licensure Intermediate care. *Beds* 93.
Owner Proprietary Corp (Van Dyke Health Services).

EL PASO

El Paso Hawthorne Lodge*
850 E 2nd St, El Paso, IL, 61738
(309) 527-2700
Admin Becky Hall.
Licensure Skilled care. *Beds* 123. *Certified* Medicaid; Medicare.
Owner Proprietary Corp.

McDaniel Nursing Home*
555 E Clay St, El Paso, IL, 61738
(309) 527-6240
Admin Mary McDaniel.
Licensure Skilled care. *Beds* 49. *Certified* Medicaid; Medicare.
Owner Proprietary Corp.

ELDORADO

Eldorado Nursing Home Inc*
3rd & Railroad Sts, Eldorado, IL, 62930
(618) 273-3318
Admin George W Baker.
Licensure Intermediate care. *Beds* 74. *Certified* Medicaid.
Owner Proprietary Corp.

Fountain View Inc
Rte 45, S Jefferson, Eldorado, IL, 62930
(618) 273-3353
Admin Billy L Jones. *Medical Dir/Dir of Nursing* Sandra Dixon DON.
Licensure Intermediate care. *Beds* ICF 135. *Certified* Medicaid.
Owner Proprietary Corp.
Admissions Requirements Minimum age 18; Medical examination.

Staff RNs 1 (ft); LPNs 10 (ft), 2 (pt); Nurses aides; Physical therapists 1 (pt); Reality therapists 1 (ft); Activities coordinators 1 (ft), 2 (pt); Dietitians 1 (pt).
Facilities Dining room; Physical therapy room; Activities room; Crafts room; Laundry room; Barber/Beauty shop.
Activities Arts & crafts; Cards; Games; Reading groups; Prayer groups; Movies; Shopping trips; Social/Cultural gatherings.

Lifecare Center of Eldorado I
1700 Jasper St, Eldorado, IL, 62930
(618) 273-2161
Admin Keith Hufsey.
Licensure Intermediate care. *Beds* ICF 79. *Certified* Medicaid.
Owner Proprietary Corp (Community Lifecare Enterprises).
Admissions Requirements Medical examination.
Staff RNs 1 (ft); LPNs 5 (ft); Nurses aides 16 (ft), 1 (pt); Physical therapists 1 (ft), 1 (pt); Activities coordinators 1 (ft); Dietitians 1 (ft), 1 (pt).
Facilities Dining room; Physical therapy room; Activities room; Crafts room; Laundry room; Barber/Beauty shop.
Activities Arts & crafts; Cards; Games; Reading groups; Prayer groups; Movies; Shopping trips; Social/Cultural gatherings.

Magnolia Manor*
1100 Grant St, Eldorado, IL, 62930
(618) 273-5261
Admin Charles Huston.
Licensure Sheltered care. *Beds* 44.
Owner Proprietary Corp.

ELGIN

Americana Healthcare Center of Elgin
180 S State St, Elgin, IL, 60123
(312) 742-3310
Admin Carolyn J Stahl. *Medical Dir/Dir of Nursing* Vikram Shah MD.
Licensure Skilled care; Intermediate care. *Beds* SNF 43; ICF 30. *Certified* Medicare.
Owner Proprietary Corp (Manor Care).
Admissions Requirements Minimum age 18; Medical examination; Physician's request.
Staff Physicians 3 (pt); RNs 11 (ft); LPNs 2 (ft); Orderlies 1 (ft); Nurses aides 20 (ft), 3 (pt); Physical therapists 1 (ft); Occupational therapists 1 (pt); Speech therapists 1 (pt); Activities coordinators 1 (ft); Dietitians 1 (ft); Dentists 1 (pt); Ophthalmologists 1 (pt); Podiatrists 1 (pt).
Facilities Dining room; Physical therapy room; Activities room; Crafts room; Laundry room; Barber/Beauty shop; Living rooms.
Activities Arts & crafts; Cards; Games; Reading groups; Prayer groups; Movies; Shopping trips; Social/Cultural gatherings; Country store.

Apostolic Christian Resthaven
2750 W Highland Ave, Elgin, IL, 60123
(312) 741-4543
Admin Rick Schmidgall. *Medical Dir/Dir of Nursing* Dr Walter Gasser MD; Jean Mogler DON.
Licensure Skilled care; Independent living. *Beds* SNF 37; Independent living 12. *Certified* Medicaid.
Owner Nonprofit Corp.
Admissions Requirements Minimum age 18; Medical examination.
Staff RNs 3 (ft), 5 (pt); LPNs 1 (ft); Orderlies 1 (pt); Nurses aides 10 (ft), 15 (pt); Activities coordinators 1 (ft).
Languages Spanish
Affiliation Apostolic Christian Church
Facilities Dining room; Physical therapy room; Activities room; Crafts room; Laundry room; Barber/Beauty shop.

Activities Arts & crafts; Games; Reading groups; Prayer groups; Movies; Shopping trips; Outings.

Countryside Manor
971 Bode Rd, Elgin, IL, 60120
(312) 695-9600
Admin William R Strackany. *Medical Dir/Dir of Nursing* Kathy Darrow RN.
Licensure Sheltered care. *Beds* 39.
Owner Privately owned.
Staff RNs 1 (ft); LPNs 2 (pt); Nurses aides 2 (ft), 8 (pt); Activities coordinators 1 (ft), 1 (pt).

Elgin Community Living Facility*
1640 Mark Ave, Elgin, IL, 60120
(312) 741-9175
Admin James W McNeil.
Licensure Intermediate care. *Beds* 20.
Owner Nonprofit Corp.

Ray Graham Elmhurst Conv Living Facility*
188-192 E Park Ave, Elgin, IL, 60126
(312) 543-2440
Admin Ivan Browne.
Licensure Intermediate care. *Beds* 21.
Owner Nonprofit Corp.

Imperial Nursing Center of Elgin*
50 N Jane Dr, Elgin, IL, 60120
(312) 697-3750
Admin Richard J Payne.
Licensure Skilled care. *Beds* 203. *Certified* Medicaid; Medicare.
Owner Proprietary Corp.

Little Angels Nursing Home Inc
Box 304, Rte 4, Elgin, IL, 60120
(312) 741-1609
Admin Shelley C Wasmind. *Medical Dir/Dir of Nursing* Eric Zurbrugg MD; Susan Bagherpour DON.
Licensure Skilled care; For persons under 22 years of age. *Beds* SNF 50. *Certified* Medicaid.
Owner Proprietary Corp.
Admissions Requirements Minimum age Birth to 22 yrs; Medical examination; Physician's request.
Staff Physicians 1 (pt); RNs 7 (ft), 4 (pt); LPNs 1 (ft); Nurses aides 22 (ft), 25 (pt); Physical therapists 1 (pt); Occupational therapists 1 (pt); Speech therapists 1 (pt); Activities coordinators 1 (pt); Dietitians 1 (pt).
Facilities Dining room; Physical therapy room; Activities room.
Activities Games; Movies; Shopping trips; Social/Cultural gatherings; Activities appropriate for mentally retarded children.

Mary Margaret Manor
134 N McLean Blvd, Elgin, IL, 60123
(312) 742-8822
Admin Wanda Paulin. *Medical Dir/Dir of Nursing* Fred Slager MD; Patricia Stephens DON.
Licensure Skilled care; Intermediate care. *Beds* SNF 25; ICF 81.
Owner Proprietary Corp (Beverly Enterprises).
Admissions Requirements Minimum age 55; Medical examination; Physician's request.
Staff RNs; LPNs; Orderlies; Nurses aides; Occupational therapists; Speech therapists; Activities coordinators; Dietitians; Dentists; Ophthalmologists.
Facilities Dining room; Physical therapy room; Activities room; Crafts room; Barber/Beauty shop.
Activities Arts & crafts; Cards; Games; Reading groups; Prayer groups; Movies; Shopping trips; Social/Cultural gatherings.

Oak Crest Residence*
204 S State St, Elgin, IL, 60120
(312) 742-2255
Admin Susan Cincinelli.

Licensure Sheltered care. *Beds* 42.
Owner Nonprofit Corp.

Olivette Nursing Home*
355 Raymond St, Elgin, IL, 60120
(312) 695-4300
Admin Beth Schaumburg. *Medical Dir/Dir of Nursing* Dr V Shah.
Licensure Skilled care; Intermediate care. *Beds* SNF 72; ICF 18.
Owner Nonprofit Corp (Good Shepherd Health Fac).
Facilities Dining room; Physical therapy room; Activities room; Laundry room; Barber/Beauty shop.
Activities Arts & crafts; Cards; Games; Prayer groups; Movies; Social/Cultural gatherings.

ELIZABETH

Elizabeth Nursing Home Inc
540 Pleasant St, Elizabeth, IL, 61028
(815) 858-2275
Admin Nelson E Marks. *Medical Dir/Dir of Nursing* Helen Reid.
Licensure Intermediate care. *Beds* ICF 49. *Certified* Medicaid.
Owner Proprietary Corp.
Admissions Requirements Minimum age 65.
Staff RNs; LPNs; Nurses aides; Physical therapists; Reality therapists; Recreational therapists; Occupational therapists; Activities coordinators; Dietitians; Dentist.
Facilities Dining room; Physical therapy room; Activities room; Chapel; Crafts room; Laundry room; Barber/Beauty shop.
Activities Arts & crafts; Cards; Games; Reading groups; Prayer groups; Movies; Shopping trips; Social/Cultural gatherings; Pet shows; Picnics; Van rides; Active nursing home auxiliary.

ELMHURST

Elmhurst Extended Care Center Inc
200 E Lake St, Elmhurst, IL, 60126
(312) 834-4337
Admin John Massard. *Medical Dir/Dir of Nursing* Paul J Concepcion MD.
Licensure Skilled care. *Beds* SNF 112. *Certified* Medicare.
Owner Proprietary Corp.
Admissions Requirements Minimum age 18.
Staff Physicians 4 (pt); RNs 9 (ft), 4 (pt); LPNs 5 (ft), 4 (pt); Orderlies 1 (ft); Nurses aides 28 (ft), 29 (pt); Physical therapists 1 (pt); Recreational therapists 1 (ft); Occupational therapists 1 (pt); Speech therapists 1 (pt); Activities coordinators 2 (pt); Dietitians 1 (ft); Dentists 1 (pt); Ophthalmologists 1 (pt); Podiatrists 1 (pt).
Facilities Dining room; Physical therapy room; Activities room; Chapel; Crafts room; Laundry room; Barber/Beauty shop; Library.
Activities Arts & crafts; Cards; Games; Reading groups; Prayer groups; Movies; Shopping trips; Social/Cultural gatherings; Resident council.

York Convalescent Center
127 W Diversey, Elmhurst, IL, 60126
(312) 530-5225
Admin Shirley Holt. *Medical Dir/Dir of Nursing* Dr Norton Fishman; Ginger Kloskowski.
Licensure Skilled care; Intermediate care. *Beds* SNF 125; ICF 63. *Certified* Medicaid; Medicare.
Owner Privately owned.
Admissions Requirements Minimum age 25.
Staff RNs; LPNs; Orderlies; Nurses aides; Physical therapists 1 (pt); Reality therapists 1 (ft); Recreational therapists 1 (ft); Activities coordinators 1 (ft); Dietitians 1 (ft); Dentists 1 (pt); Ophthalmologists 1 (pt); Podiatrists 1 (pt).

Facilities Dining room; Physical therapy room; Activities room; Laundry room; Barber/Beauty shop; Library.
Activities Arts & crafts; Cards; Games; Reading groups; Prayer groups; Movies; Shopping trips.

ELMWOOD PARK

Royal Elm Inc
7733 Grand Ave, Elmwood Park, IL, 60635
(312) 452-9200
Admin Don J Bonet.
Licensure Skilled care. *Beds* 245. *Certified* Medicaid.
Owner Proprietary Corp.

ENERGY

Mattingly Health Care Center
207 E College St, Energy, IL, 62933
(618) 942-7014
Admin Brenda J Loyd. *Medical Dir/Dir of Nursing* Roger C Hendricks MD; Dorie Covey DON.
Licensure Intermediate care; Intermediate care for mentally retarded. *Beds* ICF 86; ICF/MR 73. *Certified* Medicaid.
Owner Proprietary Corp.
Admissions Requirements Minimum age 18; Medical examination; Physician's request.
Staff RNs 1 (ft); LPNs 14 (ft), 2 (pt); Orderlies 4 (ft); Nurses aides 37 (ft); Activities coordinators 1 (ft); Physical therapists aides 2 (ft); Occupational therapists aides 2 (ft).
Facilities Dining room; Physical therapy room; Activities room; Laundry room; Barber/Beauty shop.
Activities Arts & crafts; Cards; Games; Reading groups; Prayer groups; Movies; Shopping trips; Social/Cultural gatherings.

ENFIELD

Lifecare Center of Enfield
PO Box 285, N Wilson St, Enfield, IL, 62835
(618) 963-2713
Admin Marcia Baxley.
Licensure Intermediate care. *Beds* ICF 49. *Certified* Medicaid.
Owner Proprietary Corp.
Admissions Requirements Medical examination.
Staff LPNs 3 (ft); Nurses aides 18 (ft); Physical therapists 1 (pt); Activities coordinators 1 (ft); Dietitians 1 (pt).
Facilities Dining room; Physical therapy room; Activities room; Crafts room; Laundry room; Barber/Beauty shop.
Activities Arts & crafts; Cards; Games; Reading groups; Prayer groups; Movies; Shopping trips; Social/Cultural gatherings.

EUREKA

Eureka Apostolic Christian Home
610 Cruger, Eureka, IL, 61530
(309) 467-2311
Admin Joel E Banwart. *Medical Dir/Dir of Nursing* Dr Robert Easton Jr.
Licensure Intermediate care; Sheltered care. *Beds* ICF 46; Sheltered care 54. *Certified* Medicaid.
Owner Nonprofit Corp.
Admissions Requirements Minimum age 55; Medical examination; Physician's request.
Staff Physicians 5 (pt); RNs 4 (ft), 5 (pt); LPNs 5 (ft), 6 (pt); Orderlies 3 (pt); Nurses aides 18 (ft), 25 (pt); Physical therapists 1 (pt); Reality therapists 1 (ft); Recreational therapists 1 (pt); Activities coordinators 1 (ft); Dietitians 1 (pt).
Affiliation Apostolic Christian

Facilities Dining room; Physical therapy room; Activities room; Crafts room; Laundry room; Barber/Beauty shop; Library; Large community room.
Activities Arts & crafts; Games; Movies; Shopping trips; Song worship; Church services.

Maple Lawn Health Center
700 N Main, Eureka, IL, 61530
(309) 467-2337
Admin Clifford E King. *Medical Dir/Dir of Nursing* Ronald Meyer MD; Pauline Sohn RN DON.
Licensure Skilled care; Intermediate care. *Beds* SNF 90; Shelter care 29. *Certified* Medicaid; Medicare.
Owner Nonprofit Corp.
Admissions Requirements Physician's request.
Staff Physicians 1 (pt); RNs 3 (ft); LPNs 9 (pt); Nurses aides 42 (pt); Physical therapists 1 (ft), 1 (pt); Reality therapists 1 (pt); Recreational therapists 1 (pt); Occupational therapists 1 (pt); Speech therapists 1 (pt); Activities coordinators 1 (ft); Dietitians 1 (pt); Dentists 1 (pt); Ophthalmologists 1 (pt); Podiatrists 1 (pt).
Affiliation Mennonite
Facilities Dining room; Physical therapy room; Activities room; Chapel; Crafts room; Laundry room; Barber/Beauty shop; Library.
Activities Arts & crafts; Cards; Games; Reading groups; Prayer groups; Movies; Shopping trips; Social/Cultural gatherings.

EVANSTON

American Plaza Nursing Center*
1406 N Chicago Ave, Evanston, IL, 60201
(312) 328-6503
Admin Jeffrey Joe Webster.
Licensure Intermediate care. *Beds* 145. *Certified* Medicaid.
Owner Proprietary Corp.

Dobson Plaza Nursing Home
120 Dodge Ave, Evanston, IL, 60202
(312) 869-7744
Admin Charlotte Kohn. *Medical Dir/Dir of Nursing* Edwin Funk MD; Edith Pandagian.
Licensure Skilled care. *Beds* SNF 60; ICF 31. *Certified* Medicaid; Medicare.
Owner Proprietary Corp.
Staff Physicians; RNs; LPNs; Orderlies; Nurses aides; Physical therapists; Recreational therapists; Occupational therapists; Speech therapists; Activities coordinators; Dietitians; Dentists; Ophthalmologists; Podiatrists.
Facilities Dining room; Physical therapy room; Activities room; Crafts room; Laundry room; Barber/Beauty shop.
Activities Arts & crafts; Cards; Games; Reading groups; Prayer groups; Movies; Social/Cultural gatherings; Truman College educational programming.

The Georgian Home
422 Davis St, Evanston, IL, 60201
(312) 475-4100
Admin Robert R Porter.
Licensure Skilled care; Sheltered care. *Beds* SNF 22; Sheltered care 223.
Owner Nonprofit Corp.

James C King Home
1555 Oak Ave, Evanston, IL, 60201
(312) 864-5460
Admin David Benni. *Medical Dir/Dir of Nursing* Dr W Swisher; Mary Helen O'Conner.
Licensure Intermediate care; Sheltered care. *Beds* ICF 20; Sheltered care 90. *Certified* Medicaid.
Owner Nonprofit Corp.
Admissions Requirements Minimum age 60; Males only; Medical examination.

Staff Physicians 3 (pt); Occupational therapists 1 (pt); Activities coordinators 1 (ft), 2 (pt); Dietitians 1 (pt); Dentists 1 (pt); Ophthalmologists 1 (pt).
Facilities Dining room; Physical therapy room; Activities room; Crafts room; Barber/ Beauty shop Barber; Library; Barber shop.
Activities Arts & crafts; Cards; Games; Reading groups; Movies.

Lake Crest Villa*
2601 Central St, Evanston, IL, 60201
(312) 328-8700
Admin Blanche H Dunbar.
Licensure Sheltered care. *Beds* Sheltered Care 25.
Owner Nonprofit Corp.

Oakwood Terrace Inc
1300 Oak Ave, Evanston, IL, 60201
(312) 869-1300
Admin Ross S Brown. *Medical Dir/Dir of Nursing* Peter Jaggard MD; Linda Richards DON.
Licensure Skilled care; Intermediate care. *Beds* SNF 4; ICF 53. *Certified* Medicaid.
Owner Proprietary Corp.
Staff Physicians 1 (ft), 12 (pt); RNs 15 (ft), 6 (pt); LPNs 1 (ft); Nurses aides 22 (ft), 9 (pt); Physical therapists 1 (ft); Reality therapists 1 (ft); Recreational therapists 2 (ft), 1 (pt); Occupational therapists 2 (ft), 1 (pt); Speech therapists 1 (ft); Activities coordinators 1 (ft); Dietitians 1 (ft); Dentists 1 (ft); Ophthalmologists 1 (ft); Podiatrists 1 (ft).
Facilities Dining room; Physical therapy room; Activities room; Chapel; Crafts room; Laundry room; Barber/Beauty shop; Library.
Activities Arts & crafts; Cards; Games; Reading groups; Prayer groups; Movies; Shopping trips; Social/Cultural gatherings.

Pioneer Place Swedish Retirement Assn
2320 Pioneer Pl, Evanston, IL, 60201
(312) 328-8700
Admin Clare N Boehm.
Licensure Intermediate care; Sheltered care. *Beds* ICF 50; Sheltered care 99.
Owner Nonprofit Corp.
Admissions Requirements Minimum age 60; Medical examination.
Staff Physicians; RNs; LPNs; Nurses aides; Physical therapists; Recreational therapists; Occupational therapists; Activities coordinators; Dietitians; Dentists; Ophthalmologists; Podiatrists.
Facilities Dining room; Physical therapy room; Activities room; Chapel; Crafts room; Laundry room; Barber/Beauty shop; Library.
Activities Arts & crafts; Cards; Games; Reading groups; Prayer groups; Movies; Shopping trips.

The Presbyterian Home
3200 Grant St, Evanston, IL, 60201
(312) 492-4800
Admin Peter S Mulvey. *Medical Dir/Dir of Nursing* Monte J Levinson MD; Kathryn Roberts RN DON.
Licensure Skilled care; Intermediate care; Sheltered care. *Beds* SNF 111; ICF 81; Sheltered care 51. *Certified* Medicare.
Owner Nonprofit Corp.
Admissions Requirements Minimum age 65; Medical examination; Physician's request.
Staff Physicians 3 (pt); RNs 26 (ft), 13 (pt); LPNs 7 (ft), 4 (pt); Nurses aides 67 (ft), 3 (pt); Physical therapists 1 (ft), 1 (pt); Recreational therapists 4 (ft), 2 (pt); Occupational therapists 1 (ft); Speech therapists 1 (pt); Activities coordinators 1 (ft); Dietitians 2 (ft); Dentists 1 (pt); Ophthalmologists 1 (pt); Podiatrists 1 (pt).
Languages Spanish
Affiliation Presbyterian
Facilities Dining room; Physical therapy room; Activities room; Chapel; Crafts room; Laundry room; Barber/Beauty shop; Library.

Activities Arts & crafts; Cards; Games; Reading groups; Prayer groups; Movies; Shopping trips; Social/Cultural gatherings.

Ridgeview House Inc*
901 Maple Ave, Evanston, IL, 60202
(312) 475-4000
Admin Corrine L Lerman.
Licensure Intermediate care. *Beds* 437.
Certified Medicaid.
Owner Proprietary Corp.
Activities Arts & crafts; Cards; Games; Reading groups; Prayer groups; Movies; Shopping trips; Social/Cultural gatherings.

Ridgeview Pavilion*
820 Foster St, Evanston, IL, 60201
(312) 869-0142
Admin Bryan G Barrish.
Licensure Skilled care. *Beds* 300. *Certified* Medicaid.
Owner Proprietary Corp.

St Francis Extended Care Center
500 Asbury St, Evanston, IL, 60202
(312) 492-3320
Admin Mary Brown. *Medical Dir/Dir of Nursing* Julio C Mora MD; Donna Lundahl RN DON.
Licensure Skilled care; Intermediate care. *Beds* SNF 39; ICF 85. *Certified* Medicaid; Medicare.
Owner Nonprofit Corp.
Admissions Requirements Minimum age 18; Medical examination; Physician's request.
Staff Physicians 4 (ft), 10 (pt); RNs 14 (ft), 1 (pt); LPNs 6 (ft), 1 (pt); Nurses aides 40 (ft); Physical therapists 1 (ft); Recreational therapists 2 (ft); Occupational therapists 1 (ft); Speech therapists 1 (ft); Activities coordinators 1 (ft); Dietitians 1 (ft); Dentists 1 (pt); Ophthalmologists 1 (pt); Podiatrists 1 (pt).
Facilities Dining room; Physical therapy room; Activities room; Chapel; Laundry room; Barber/Beauty shop.
Activities Arts & crafts; Cards; Games; Reading groups; Prayer groups; Movies; Shopping trips; Bus tours.

EVERGREEN PARK

Evergreen Manor Nursing Home*
3327 W 95th St, Evergreen Park, IL, 60642
(312) 423-8020
Admin Ieman Helal.
Licensure Intermediate care. *Beds* 21.
Owner Proprietary Corp.
Admissions Requirements Minimum age 18.
Staff Physicians 1 (ft), 1 (pt); RNs 1 (ft); LPNs 4 (ft); Nurses aides 3 (ft), 2 (pt); Activities coordinators 1 (ft), 1 (pt); Dietitians 1 (pt).
Facilities Dining room; Activities room; Laundry room.
Activities Arts & crafts; Games; Prayer groups.

Gunderson's Retirement Home*
2701 W 95th St, Evergreen Park, IL, 60642
(312) 422-5995
Admin Jerold E Gunderson. *Medical Dir of Nursing* Dr Carballo.
Licensure Retirement home. *Beds* Retirement home 12.
Owner Proprietary Corp.
Admissions Requirements Minimum age 35; Medical examination; Physician's request.
Staff Nurses aides 1 (ft), 1 (pt); Activities coordinators.
Facilities Dining room; Activities room; Laundry room.
Activities Arts & crafts; Cards; Games; Movies.

Park Lane Nursing Center
9125 S Pulaski Ave, Evergreen Park, IL, 60642
(312) 425-3400

Admin Paula Malpeli. *Medical Dir/Dir of Nursing* Thomas Klein MD; Kim Peters RN.
Licensure Skilled care. *Beds* SNF 249.
Certified Medicaid.
Owner Proprietary Corp.
Admissions Requirements Minimum age 45.
Staff RNs; LPNs; Orderlies; Nurses aides; Physical therapists; Reality therapists; Activities coordinators 1 (ft).
Facilities Dining room; Physical therapy room; Activities room; Barber/Beauty shop.
Activities Arts & crafts; Cards; Games; Reading groups; Prayer groups; Movies; Shopping trips; Social/Cultural gatherings.

Peace Memorial Home
10124 S Kedzie Ave, Evergreen Park, IL, 60642
(312) 636-9200
Admin Harold M Schoup. *Medical Dir/Dir of Nursing* Dr John O'Brien.
Licensure Skilled care. *Beds* SNF 242.
Certified Medicaid.
Owner Nonprofit organization/foundation.
Admissions Requirements Minimum age 18; Medical examination; Physician's request.
Staff Physicians 1 (pt); RNs 15 (ft); LPNs 14 (ft); Nurses aides 102 (ft); Physical therapists 1 (pt); Reality therapists 1 (pt); Recreational therapists 1 (pt); Occupational therapists 1 (pt); Speech therapists 1 (pt); Activities coordinators 1 (pt); Dietitians 1 (pt); Dentists 1 (pt); Podiatrists 1 (pt).
Affiliation Church of Christ
Facilities Dining room; Physical therapy room; Activities room; Chapel; Crafts room; Barber/Beauty shop.
Activities Arts & crafts; Cards; Games; Prayer groups; Movies; Social/Cultural gatherings.

FAIRBURY

Fairview Haven Inc
605-609 N 4th St, Fairbury, IL, 61739
(815) 692-2572
Admin Wayne Drayer. *Medical Dir/Dir of Nursing* Dr Kothari; Dr Oreshkov; Marilyn Dennis.
Licensure Intermediate care. *Beds* ICF 54.
Certified Medicaid.
Owner Nonprofit Corp.
Admissions Requirements Minimum age 60; Medical examination.
Staff RNs 1 (pt); LPNs 4 (ft), 2 (pt); Nurses aides 16 (ft), 8 (pt); Activities coordinators 1 (ft), 1 (pt).
Affiliation Apostolic Christian
Facilities Dining room; Activities room; Chapel; Crafts room; Laundry room; Barber/ Beauty shop.
Activities Arts & crafts; Games; Reading groups; Movies; Shopping trips; Social/ Cultural gatherings; Bible Study.

Helen Lewis Smith Pavilion
519 S Fifth St, Fairbury, IL, 61739
(815) 692-2346
Admin Dr John Tummons. *Medical Dir/Dir of Nursing* Vesselin Oreshkov MD; Sandra Schlager DON.
Licensure Skilled care; Intermediate care. *Beds* SNF 19; ICF 49. *Certified* Medicaid; Medicare.
Owner Nonprofit organization/foundation.
Admissions Requirements Minimum age 21; Medical examination.
Staff Physicians 7 (ft), 1 (pt); RNs 1 (ft), 2 (pt); LPNs 5 (ft), 4 (pt); Nurses aides 17 (ft), 3 (pt); Physical therapists 1 (ft); Speech therapists 1 (pt); Activities coordinators 2 (ft); Dietitians 1 (ft), 1 (pt).
Facilities Dining room; Physical therapy room; Activities room; Chapel; Barber/ Beauty shop.

Activities Arts & crafts; Cards; Games;
Reading groups; Prayer groups; Movies;
Social/Cultural gatherings.

FAIRFIELD

Way Fair Restorium*
11th & Harding Sts, Fairfield, IL, 62837
(618) 842-2723
Admin Chalmers F Kerchner.
Licensure Skilled care. *Beds* 104. *Certified*
Medicaid; Medicare.
Owner Nonprofit Corp.

FARMER CITY

Jackson Heights Nursing Home
10 Brookview Dr, Farmer City, IL, 61842
(309) 928-2118
Admin Mary K Hirsbrunner. *Medical Dir/Dir
of Nursing* D J Lash MD; Kayla Porter
DON.
Licensure Intermediate care. *Beds* ICF 51.
Certified Medicaid.
Owner Nonprofit organization/foundation.
Admissions Requirements Minimum age 60.
Staff Physicians 6 (pt); RNs 1 (ft), 6 (pt);
LPNs 1 (ft), 1 (pt); Nurses aides 14 (ft), 10
(pt); Physical therapists; Reality therapists;
Activities coordinators 1 (ft); Dietitians;
Ophthalmologists.
Facilities Dining room; Activities room;
Chapel; Crafts room; Laundry room; Barber/
Beauty shop.
Activities Arts & crafts; Cards; Games;
Reading groups; Prayer groups; Movies;
Shopping trips; Social/Cultural gatherings.

FARMINGTON

Farmington Nursing Home
S Main St, Farmington, IL, 61531
(309) 245-2408
Admin Cindy Norton. *Medical Dir/Dir of
Nursing* Mary Lou Record.
Licensure Skilled care. *Beds* 84. *Certified*
Medicaid; Medicare.
Owner Proprietary Corp (American Health
Care Inc).
Admissions Requirements Medical
examination.
Staff Physicians 8 (pt); RNs 3 (ft), 3 (pt);
LPNs 5 (ft), 5 (pt); Orderlies 2 (ft); Nurses
aides 20 (ft), 15 (pt); Physical therapists 2
(pt); Reality therapists 1 (pt); Recreational
therapists 1 (pt); Occupational therapists 1
(pt); Speech therapists 1 (pt); Activities
coordinators 2 (ft); Dietitians 1 (ft).
Facilities Dining room; Physical therapy
room; Activities room; Crafts room; Laundry
room; Barber/Beauty shop; Courtyard; 3
Lounges.
Activities Arts & crafts; Cards; Games;
Reading groups; Prayer groups; Movies;
Shopping trips; Social/Cultural gatherings.

FLANAGAN

Beulah Land Christian Home
PO Box C, Rte 116, Flanagan, IL, 61740
(815) 796-2267
Admin Thomas A Novy. *Medical Dir/Dir of
Nursing* Margaret Jackson DON.
Licensure Skilled care; Intermediate care;
Independent living. *Beds* SNF 15; ICF 28;
Shelter care 30. *Certified* Medicaid.
Owner Nonprofit Corp (Christian Homes).
Admissions Requirements Minimum age 18;
Medical examination.
Affiliation Church of Christ
Facilities Dining room; Physical therapy
room; Activities room; Chapel; Crafts room;
Laundry room; Barber/Beauty shop; Library.
Activities Arts & crafts; Cards; Games;
Reading groups; Prayer groups; Movies;
Shopping trips.

Good Samaritan Home of Flanagan
Box 199A, RR 1, Flanagan, IL, 61740
(815) 796-2288
Admin Mark Hovren. *Medical Dir/Dir of
Nursing* Dr John Purnell; Carolyn
Ringenberg DON.
Licensure Skilled care; Intermediate care. *Beds*
SNF; ICF 60. *Certified* Medicaid.
Owner Nonprofit Corp.
Admissions Requirements Minimum age 60;
Medical examination.
Staff RNs 2 (ft), 6 (pt); LPNs 2 (ft), 3 (pt);
Nurses aides 14 (ft), 35 (pt); Recreational
therapists 2 (pt); Activities coordinators 1
(ft).
Affiliation Lutheran
Facilities Dining room; Physical therapy
room; Activities room; Chapel; Laundry
room; Barber/Beauty shop; Library.
Activities Arts & crafts; Cards; Games; Prayer
groups; Shopping trips; Social/Cultural
gatherings.

FLORA

Flora Care Center Inc*
Frontage Rd W, Flora, IL, 62839
(618) 662-8381
Admin Philip E Pennington. *Medical Dir/Dir
of Nursing* Dr Eugene Foss MD.
Licensure Skilled care; Intermediate care. *Beds*
98. *Certified* Medicaid.
Owner Proprietary Corp.
Staff RNs 3 (ft), 5 (pt); LPNs 2 (ft), 3 (pt);
Orderlies 2 (ft); Nurses aides 26 (ft), 4 (pt);
Activities coordinators 1 (ft), 1 (pt).
Facilities Dining room; Physical therapy
room; Activities room; Crafts room; Laundry
room; Barber/Beauty shop; Library.
Activities Arts & crafts; Cards; Games;
Reading groups; Prayer groups; Movies;
Shopping trips.

Flora Manor*
E 12th St, Flora, IL, 62839
(618) 622-8494
Admin Dennis W Armbrust.
Licensure Intermediate care. *Beds* 59.
Owner Nonprofit Corp.

Flora Nursing Center
701 Shadwell, Flora, IL, 62839
(618) 662-8361
Admin Georgianna Feagans. *Medical Dir/Dir
of Nursing* Dr Eugene Foss.
Licensure Skilled care; Intermediate care. *Beds*
SNF 56; ICF 54. *Certified* Medicaid.
Owner Proprietary Corp (Signature Corp).
Admissions Requirements Medical
examination; Physician's request.
Staff RNs 5 (ft), 2 (pt); LPNs 3 (ft), 2 (pt);
Nurses aides 25 (ft), 6 (pt); Physical
therapists 1 (pt); Speech therapists 1 (pt);
Activities coordinators 1 (ft); Dietitians 1
(pt); Podiatrists 1 (pt); Dentist 1 (pt).
Facilities Dining room; Physical therapy
room; Activities room; Laundry room;
Barber/Beauty shop; Library.
Activities Arts & crafts; Cards; Games;
Reading groups; Movies; Shopping trips;
Social/Cultural gatherings.

FOREST PARK

Altenheim German Home
7824 W Madison St, Forest Park, IL, 60130
(312) 366-2206
Admin Richard Ludwigson. *Medical Dir/Dir
of Nursing* Donald Pochyly MD.
Licensure Skilled care; Intermediate care;
Sheltered care. *Beds* SNF 52; ICF 99.
Certified Medicaid.
Owner Nonprofit Corp.
Admissions Requirements Minimum age 65;
Medical examination.

Staff Physicians 3 (pt); RNs 2 (ft), 8 (pt);
LPNs 4 (ft), 2 (pt); Orderlies 2 (ft), 1 (pt);
Nurses aides 32 (ft), 8 (pt); Physical
therapists 1 (pt); Occupational therapists 1
(pt); Speech therapists 1 (pt); Activities
coordinators 1 (ft); Dietitians 1 (pt); Dentists
1 (pt); Ophthalmologists 1 (pt); Podiatrists 1
(pt); Dentist 1 (pt).
Facilities Dining room; Activities room;
Chapel; Crafts room; Laundry room; Barber/
Beauty shop; TV room.
Activities Arts & crafts; Cards; Games;
Reading groups; Prayer groups; Movies;
Shopping trips; Social/Cultural gatherings;
Educational programs.

FRANKFORT

Frankfort Terrace
PO Box 460, 40 N Smith, Frankfort, IL,
60423
(815) 469-3156
Admin Louise M Coburn.
Licensure Intermediate care. *Beds* 118.
Certified Medicaid.
Owner Proprietary Corp.

FRANKLIN GROVE

Franklin Grove Health Care Center
N State St, Franklin Grove, IL, 61031
(815) 456-2374
Admin Pamela Sue Farley. *Medical Dir/Dir of
Nursing* Dr Wm Johanson; Grace Rumph
RN.
Licensure Skilled care; Intermediate care. *Beds*
SNF 70; ICF 51. *Certified* Medicaid;
Medicare.
Owner Nonprofit Corp (First Humanics).
Staff Physicians 1 (pt); RNs 5 (ft); LPNs 10
(ft), 6 (pt); Orderlies 2 (ft), 1 (pt); Nurses
aides 20 (ft), 20 (pt); Physical therapists 1
(pt); Occupational therapists 1 (pt); Speech
therapists 1 (pt); Activities coordinators 2
(ft), 1 (pt); Dietitians 1 (pt);
Ophthalmologists 1 (pt); Podiatrists 1 (pt).

FRANKLIN PARK

Westlake Pavillion
10500 W Grand Ave, Franklin Park, IL,
60131
(312) 451-1520
Admin Elizabeth Polcar. *Medical Dir/Dir of
Nursing* Dr Glenn Kushner.
Licensure Skilled care; Intermediate care;
Alzheimer's Program; Respite care. *Beds*
154. *Certified* Medicaid; Medicare.
Owner Nonprofit Corp.
Staff Physicians; RNs; LPNs; Nurses aides;
Physical therapists; Recreational therapists;
Occupational therapists; Speech therapists;
Activities coordinators; Dietitians; Dentists;
Ophthalmologists.

FREEBURG

Freeburg Care Center Inc
Rte 2, Box 180M, Hwy 15E, Freeburg, IL,
62243
(618) 539-5856
Admin Robin Bozsa. *Medical Dir/Dir of
Nursing* Pam Woodward DON.
Licensure Skilled care; Intermediate care. *Beds*
SNF 66; ICF 42. *Certified* Medicaid;
Medicare.
Owner Proprietary Corp.
Admissions Requirements Minimum age 18;
Medical examination; Physician's request.
Staff Physicians; RNs; LPNs; Orderlies;
Nurses aides; Physical therapists;
Recreational therapists; Speech therapists;
Activities coordinators; Dietitians; Dentists;
Ophthalmologists; Podiatrists.

Facilities Dining room; Physical therapy
room; Activities room; Crafts room; Laundry
room; Barber/Beauty shop; Library.
Activities Arts & crafts; Cards; Games;
Reading groups; Prayer groups; Movies;
Shopping trips; Social/Cultural gatherings.

FREEPORT

Freeport Manor Nursing Center
900 S Kiwanis Dr, Freeport, IL, 61032
(815) 235-6196
Admin Dolores Currier. *Medical Dir/Dir of
Nursing* Dr Frank Descourovez; Nancy
Lassiter DON.
Licensure Skilled care; Intermediate care. *Beds*
SNF 116; ICF. *Certified* Medicaid;
Medicare.
Owner Nonprofit Corp (First Humanics).
Admissions Requirements Minimum age 18;
Medical examination; Physician's request.
Staff RNs 5 (ft), 3 (pt); LPNs 4 (ft), 3 (pt);
Nurses aides 29 (ft), 21 (pt); Physical
therapists 1 (pt); Dietitians 1 (pt).
Facilities Dining room; Physical therapy
room; Activities room; Crafts room; Laundry
room; Barber/Beauty shop.
Activities Arts & crafts; Cards; Games;
Reading groups; Prayer groups; Movies;
Shopping trips; Social/Cultural gatherings.

Parkview Home of Freeport IL Inc
1234 S Park Blvd, Freeport, IL, 61032
(815) 232-8612
Admin Dr M Gerald Robey. *Medical Dir/Dir
of Nursing* Allen W Workman MD; Lois
Wachlin RN.
Licensure Intermediate care; Sheltered care;
Independent living. *Beds* ICF 16; Sheltered
care 49; Independent living 28.
Owner Nonprofit Corp.
Admissions Requirements Minimum age 60;
Medical examination.
Staff Physicians 1 (pt); RNs 5 (ft), 1 (pt);
LPNs 3 (ft); Nurses aides 12 (ft), 8 (pt);
Physical therapists 1 (pt); Recreational
therapists 1 (pt); Occupational therapists 1
(pt); Speech therapists 1 (pt); Activities
coordinators 1 (ft), 2 (pt); Dietitians 1 (pt);
Dentists 1 (pt); Ophthalmologists 1 (pt);
Podiatrists 1 (pt).
Facilities Dining room; Physical therapy
room; Activities room; Chapel; Crafts room;
Laundry room; Barber/Beauty shop; Library;
Multi-purpose room; Game room; Lounge
areas.
Activities Arts & crafts; Cards; Games;
Reading groups; Prayer groups; Movies;
Shopping trips; Social/Cultural gatherings;
Exercise groups; Bowling; Singing groups;
Field trips & tours.

St Joseph Home for the Aged
649 E Jefferson St, Freeport, IL, 61032
(815) 232-6181
Admin Peter J Witynski. *Medical Dir/Dir of
Nursing* Robert Geller MD; Belle Dose
DON.
Licensure Intermediate care. *Beds* ICF 108.
Certified Medicaid.
Owner Nonprofit Corp.
Admissions Requirements Medical
examination.
Staff Physicians 1 (pt); RNs 4 (ft), 2 (pt);
LPNs 4 (ft), 5 (pt); Orderlies 1 (ft); Nurses
aides 29 (ft), 16 (pt); Occupational therapists
1 (pt); Activities coordinators 1 (ft), 2 (pt);
Dietitians 1 (pt); Dentist 1 (pt).
Facilities Dining room; Physical therapy
room; Activities room; Chapel; Crafts room;
Laundry room; Barber/Beauty shop; Library.
Activities Arts & crafts; Cards; Games;
Reading groups; Prayer groups; Movies;
Shopping trips; Social/Cultural gatherings.

St Mary Square Living Center Inc*
239 S Cherry, Freeport, IL, 61401
(309) 343-4101

Admin Bobby Dillard.
Licensure Intermediate care. *Beds* 257.
Owner Nonprofit Corp.

St Vincent Community Living Facility*
659 E Jefferson, Freeport, IL, 61032
(815) 232-6181
Admin Alria J Cole.
Licensure Intermediate care. *Beds* 20.
Owner Nonprofit Corp.

Stephenson Nursing Home*
2946 S Walnut Rd, Freeport, IL, 61032
(815) 235-6173
Admin R Douglas McCollum. *Medical Dir/Dir
of Nursing* Dr William Metcalf.
Licensure Skilled care; Intermediate care. *Beds*
SNF 98; ICF 51. *Certified* Medicaid;
Medicare.
Owner Publicly owned.
Admissions Requirements Minimum age 18;
Medical examination; Physician's request.
Staff RNs 7 (ft), 15 (pt); LPNs 2 (ft), 10 (pt);
Orderlies 1 (ft), 3 (pt); Nurses aides 30 (ft),
20 (pt); Activities coordinators 1 (ft).
Facilities Dining room; Physical therapy
room; Activities room; Laundry room;
Barber/Beauty shop.
Activities Arts & crafts; Cards; Games;
Reading groups; Prayer groups; Movies;
Shopping trips; Social/Cultural gatherings.

FULTON

Harbor Crest Home Inc*
810 E 17th St, Fulton, IL, 61252
(815) 589-3411
Admin James A Huber.
Licensure Intermediate care. *Beds* 84.
Certified Medicaid.
Owner Nonprofit Corp.

GALATIA

Finnie Good Shepherd Nursing Home Inc
Cross & Legion Sts, Galatia, IL, 62935
(618) 268-4631
Admin Bobby Joe Finnie.
Licensure Intermediate care. *Beds* 73.
Certified Medicaid.
Owner Proprietary Corp.

GALENA

**Galena Stauss Hospital & Nursing Care
Facility**
215 Summit St, Galena, IL, 61036
(815) 777-1340
Admin Roger D Hervey.
Licensure Skilled care; Intermediate care. *Beds*
34. *Certified* Medicaid.
Owner Publicly owned.

GALESBURG

Applegate East Nursing Home
1145 Frank St, Galesburg, IL, 61401
(309) 342-3203
Admin Carol Neal McCrery. *Medical Dir/Dir
of Nursing* Jerry Ramunis MD; Kathleen
Highee DON.
Licensure Intermediate care; Sheltered care.
Beds ICF 89; Sheltered care 16. *Certified*
Medicaid.
Owner Proprietary Corp (Beverly Enterprises).
Admissions Requirements Minimum age 60;
Medical examination.
Staff RNs 1 (ft); LPNs 9 (ft); Nurses aides 37
(ft); Activities coordinators 2 (ft).
Facilities Dining room; Activities room;
Laundry room; Barber/Beauty shop.
Activities Arts & crafts; Cards; Games;
Reading groups; Prayer groups; Movies;
Shopping trips; Social/Cultural gatherings.

Galesburg Nursing & Rehabilitation Center
280 E Losey St, Galesburg, IL, 61401
(309) 343-2166
Admin Karen L Utterback. *Medical Dir/Dir of
Nursing* Jeffery Hill MD; Joyce E Simms
DON.
Licensure Skilled care; Intermediate care. *Beds*
SNF 69; ICF. *Certified* Medicaid; Medicare.
Owner Proprietary Corp (Health Care &
Retirement Corp).
Admissions Requirements Minimum age 18;
Medical examination; Physician's request.
Staff Physicians; RNs; LPNs; Nurses aides;
Physical therapists; Occupational therapists;
Speech therapists; Activities coordinators;
Dietitians; Ophthalmologists.
Facilities Dining room; Physical therapy
room; Laundry room; Barber/Beauty shop.
Activities Arts & crafts; Cards; Games;
Reading groups; Prayer groups; Movies;
Shopping trips; Social/Cultural gatherings.

Knox Manor*
820 E 5th St, Galesburg, IL, 61401
(309) 342-5135
Admin Marjorie Mahnesmith. *Medical Dir/Dir
of Nursing* Dr Jerry Ramunis.
Licensure Intermediate care. *Beds* 101.
Certified Medicaid.
Owner Proprietary Corp.
Admissions Requirements Minimum age 18;
Medical examination; Physician's request.
Staff Physicians 1 (pt); RNs 1 (ft); LPNs 5
(ft), 4 (pt); Orderlies 3 (ft), 2 (pt); Nurses
aides 14 (ft), 7 (pt); Activities coordinators 2
(ft), 1 (pt).
Facilities Dining room; Physical therapy
room; Activities room; Crafts room; Laundry
room; Barber/Beauty shop.
Activities Arts & crafts; Cards; Games;
Reading groups; Movies; Shopping trips;
Social/Cultural gatherings; Worship service.

Marigold Health Care Center
275 E Carl Sandburg Dr, Galesburg, IL, 61401
(309) 344-1151
Admin Marilyn M Burke. *Medical Dir/Dir of
Nursing* Dr Robert Currie; Elaine Carr RN.
Licensure Skilled care. *Beds* SNF 182.
Certified Medicaid; Medicare.
Owner Nonprofit Corp (First Humanics).
Staff RNs; LPNs; Nurses aides; Activities
coordinators.
Facilities Dining room; Physical therapy
room; Activities room; Crafts room; Laundry
room; Barber/Beauty shop; Library.
Activities Arts & crafts; Cards; Games;
Reading groups; Prayer groups; Movies;
Shopping trips; Social/Cultural gatherings.

GENESEO

Geneseo Good Samaritan*
704 S Illinois St, Geneseo, IL, 61254
(309) 944-6424
Admin Barbara Mask. *Medical Dir/Dir of
Nursing* Marilyn Klundt.
Licensure Intermediate care. *Beds* 72.
Certified Medicaid.
Owner Nonprofit Corp (Evangelical Lutheran/
Good Samaritan).
Admissions Requirements Minimum age 21;
Medical examination.
Staff RNs 5 (pt); LPNs 2 (pt); Nurses aides 15
(ft), 19 (pt); Activities coordinators 1 (ft), 1
(pt).
Facilities Dining room; Physical therapy
room; Activities room; Chapel; Crafts room;
Laundry room; Barber/Beauty shop.
Activities Arts & crafts; Cards; Games;
Reading groups; Prayer groups; Movies.

Hillcrest Home*
Rte 4, Geneseo, IL, 61254
(309) 944-6407
Admin Robert J Ruskin.

Licensure Skilled care; Intermediate care. *Beds* SNF 106; ICF 102. *Certified* Medicaid.
Owner Publicly owned.

GENEVA

Geneva Retirement Center
1101 E State St, Geneva, IL, 60134
(312) 232-7544
Admin Nora Connors. *Medical Dir/Dir of Nursing* Dr Peter Cladis; Peggy Faught RN DON.
Licensure Skilled care. *Beds* 107.
Owner Proprietary Corp.
Admissions Requirements Medical examination.
Staff RNs 2 (ft), 3 (pt); LPNs 3 (ft), 3 (pt); Nurses aides 7 (ft), 4 (pt); Activities coordinators 1 (ft), 2 (pt); Dietitians 1 (ft).
Facilities Dining room; Activities room; Chapel; Crafts room; Laundry room; Barber/Beauty shop; Library.
Activities Arts & crafts; Cards; Games; Reading groups; Prayer groups; Shopping trips; Social/Cultural gatherings.

GENOA

Genesis House
Hwy 23 S, Genoa, IL, 60135
(815) 784-5146
Admin Heidi Kluga. *Medical Dir/Dir of Nursing* Ellen Taylor DON.
Licensure Intermediate care for mentally retarded. *Beds* ICF/MR 94. *Certified* Medicaid.
Owner Proprietary Corp.
Admissions Requirements Minimum age 18; Medical examination.
Staff RNs; LPNs; Activities coordinators.
Facilities Dining room; Activities room; Laundry room.
Activities Arts & crafts; Cards; Games; Reading groups; Prayer groups; Movies; Shopping trips; Social/Cultural gatherings.

GIBSON CITY

Gibson Community Hospital Annex
430 E 19th St, Gibson City, IL, 60936
(217) 784-4251
Admin Terry Thompson. *Medical Dir/Dir of Nursing* Ross N Hutchison MD; James Dick Cates RN DON.
Licensure Skilled care. *Beds* SNF 43.
Owner Nonprofit organization/foundation.
Admissions Requirements Medical examination; Physician's request.
Staff Physicians 7 (ft), 1 (pt); RNs 1 (ft), 3 (pt); LPNs 5 (ft), 3 (pt); Nurses aides 16 (ft), 7 (pt); Physical therapists 1 (ft); Activities coordinators 3 (ft); Dietitians 1 (ft).
Facilities Dining room; Physical therapy room; Activities room; Chapel; Crafts room; Barber/Beauty shop.
Activities Arts & crafts; Cards; Games; Reading groups; Prayer groups; Movies; Shopping trips; Social/Cultural gatherings.

Gibson Manor
525 Hazel Dr, Gibson City, IL, 60936
(217) 784-4257
Admin Charlotte Roth. *Medical Dir/Dir of Nursing* Kelly Christ.
Licensure Intermediate care. *Beds* ICF 71. *Certified* Medicaid.
Owner Proprietary Corp (Heritage Enterprises).
Admissions Requirements Minimum age 18; Medical examination.
Staff RNs 3 (ft); LPNs 5 (ft); Nurses aides 24 (ft).
Facilities Dining room; Activities room; Crafts room; Laundry room; Barber/Beauty shop.

Activities Arts & crafts; Cards; Games; Reading groups; Prayer groups; Social/Cultural gatherings.

GIFFORD

Country Health Inc
Rte 1, Box 14, Gifford, IL, 61847
(217) 568-7362
Admin Lavon A Heubrock. *Medical Dir/Dir of Nursing* Dr Tamara Mitchell.
Licensure Skilled care; Intermediate care. *Beds* 89. *Certified* Medicaid.
Owner Nonprofit Corp (Evangelical Lutheran/ Good Samaritan).
Staff RNs 3 (ft), 3 (pt); LPNs 4 (ft), 3 (pt); Nurses aides 14 (ft), 24 (pt); Physical therapists 1 (pt); Activities coordinators 2 (ft); Dietitians 1 (pt).
Affiliation Lutheran
Facilities Dining room; Physical therapy room; Activities room; Chapel; Crafts room; Laundry room; Barber/Beauty shop.
Activities Arts & crafts; Cards; Games; Reading groups; Prayer groups; Movies; Shopping trips; Social/Cultural gatherings.

GILLESPIE

Barry Care Center of Gillespie*
RR 3, Gillespie, IL, 62033
(217) 839-2171
Admin Sandra L Clay.
Licensure Skilled care. *Beds* 51.
Owner Proprietary Corp.

GILMAN

Gilman Nursing Center*
Box 307, Rte 45 S, Gilman, IL, 60938
(217) 265-7207
Admin Judy Pree. *Medical Dir/Dir of Nursing* Dr Harry Barnett.
Licensure Skilled care; Intermediate care. *Beds* 51. *Certified* Medicaid; Medicare.
Owner Proprietary Corp.
Admissions Requirements Minimum age 19.
Staff RNs 3 (ft), 2 (pt); LPNs 1 (ft), 1 (pt); Nurses aides 12 (ft), 10 (pt); Physical therapists 1 (pt); Recreational therapists 1 (ft); Occupational therapists 1 (pt); Speech therapists 1 (pt); Dietitians 1 (pt); Dentists 1 (pt); Ophthalmologists 1 (pt); Podiatrists 1 (pt); Audiologists 1 (pt).

GIRARD

Pleasant Hill Village*
1010 W North St, Girard, IL, 62640
(217) 627-2181
Admin Philip E Flory. *Medical Dir/Dir of Nursing* David E Stevard MD.
Licensure Intermediate care. *Beds* 92. *Certified* Medicaid.
Owner Nonprofit Corp.
Staff RNs 2 (ft); LPNs 8 (ft), 2 (pt); Nurses aides 30 (ft), 10 (pt); Activities coordinators 1 (ft).
Affiliation Church of the Brethren
Facilities Dining room; Physical therapy room; Activities room; Chapel; Crafts room; Laundry room; Barber/Beauty shop.
Activities Arts & crafts; Cards; Games; Reading groups; Prayer groups; Movies; Shopping trips.

GLENVIEW

Glenview Terrace Nursing Center
1511 Greenwood Rd, Glenview, IL, 60025
(312) 729-9090
Admin Dolores C Schroder. *Medical Dir/Dir of Nursing* Floraine Jansen DON.
Licensure Skilled care. *Beds* SNF 253. *Certified* Medicaid; Medicare.

Owner Proprietary Corp.
Admissions Requirements Minimum age 18.
Staff Physicians; RNs; LPNs; Orderlies; Nurses aides; Physical therapists; Recreational therapists; Occupational therapists; Speech therapists; Activities coordinators; Dietitians; Dentists; Ophthalmologists; Podiatrists.
Languages Spanish, Polish, Indian, Tagalog
Facilities Dining room; Physical therapy room; Activities room; Crafts room; Barber/ Beauty shop; Library.
Activities Arts & crafts; Cards; Games; Reading groups; Prayer groups; Movies; Shopping trips; Social/Cultural gatherings.

Maryhaven Inc*
1700 E Lake Ave, Glenview, IL, 60025
(312) 729-1300
Admin Dennis G Lackie.
Licensure Skilled care; Intermediate care. *Beds* SNF 42; ICF 105. *Certified* Medicaid.
Owner Nonprofit Corp.

GLENWOOD

Glenwood Terrace Nursing Center
19330 S Cottage Grove, Glenwood, IL, 60425
(312) 758-6200
Admin Irene Glass. *Medical Dir/Dir of Nursing* Dr Kruger.
Licensure Skilled care; Intermediate care. *Beds* 184. *Certified* Medicaid.
Admissions Requirements Medical examination.
Facilities Dining room; Physical therapy room; Activities room; Crafts room; Laundry room; Barber/Beauty shop.
Activities Arts & crafts; Cards; Games; Reading groups; Prayer groups; Movies; Shopping trips; Social/Cultural gatherings.

GODFREY

Alby Residence
110 N Alby Ct, Godfrey, IL, 62035
(618) 466-8848
Admin Earleen Cashill.
Licensure Intermediate care for mentally retarded. *Beds* ICF/MR 15. *Certified* Medicaid.
Owner Proprietary Corp.
Admissions Requirements Minimum age 18; Medical examination.
Staff Nurses aides 9 (pt); Speech therapists 1 (pt); Activities coordinators 1 (ft).
Facilities Dining room; Activities room; Laundry room.
Activities Arts & crafts; Games; Prayer groups; Movies; Shopping trips; Social/Cultural gatherings.

Beverly Farm Foundation
6301 Humbert Rd, Godfrey, IL, 62035
(618) 466-0367
Admin Monte E Welker. *Medical Dir/Dir of Nursing* Elvera Davis DON.
Licensure Skilled care; Intermediate care; Intermediate care for mentally retarded. *Beds* 431. *Certified* Medicaid; Medicare.
Owner Nonprofit organization/foundation.
Admissions Requirements Minimum age 5; Medical examination.
Staff Physicians 3 (pt); RNs 5 (ft); Nurses aides 230 (ft), 4 (pt); Physical therapists 1 (pt); Recreational therapists 1 (ft); Occupational therapists 1 (pt); Speech therapists 1 (ft); Activities coordinators 5 (ft); Dietitians 1 (ft), 1 (pt); Podiatrists 1 (ft).
Facilities Dining room; Physical therapy room; Activities room; Chapel; Crafts room; Laundry room; Barber/Beauty shop.
Activities Arts & crafts; Cards; Games; Reading groups; Prayer groups; Movies; Shopping trips; Social/Cultural gatherings.

Blu-Fountain Manor
1623-29 W Delmar, Godfrey, IL, 62035
(618) 466-0443
Admin Arbedella A Carrico.
Licensure Skilled care; Intermediate care. *Beds*
SNF 29; ICF 46. *Certified* Medicaid.
Owner Proprietary Corp.
Admissions Requirements Minimum age 16;
Medical examination; Physician's request.
Facilities Dining room; Activities room;
Crafts room; Laundry room; Barber/Beauty
shop; Library.
Activities Arts & crafts; Cards; Games;
Reading groups; Prayer groups; Movies;
Shopping trips; Social/Cultural gatherings.

D'Adrian Convalescent Center*
1318 W Delmar, Godfrey, IL, 62035
(618) 466-0153
Admin Ray Vern Taylor.
Licensure Skilled care; Intermediate care. *Beds*
SNF 81; ICF 38. *Certified* Medicaid;
Medicare.
Owner Proprietary Corp.

GOLCONDA

Pope County Care Center Inc*
Rosalie St, Box 69, Golconda, IL, 62938
(618) 683-7711
Admin Alan L Robbs.
Licensure Intermediate care. *Beds* 53.
Certified Medicaid.
Owner Proprietary Corp.

GOLDEN

Golden Good Shepherd Home Inc*
Golden, IL, 62339
(217) 696-4421
Admin Lois B Albers. *Medical Dir/Dir of
Nursing* Frank E Adrian MD.
Licensure Intermediate care. *Beds* 42.
Certified Medicaid.
Owner Nonprofit Corp.
Admissions Requirements Minimum age 65;
Medical examination.
Staff RNs 1 (ft), 2 (pt); LPNs 2 (ft), 3 (pt);
Nurses aides 22 (pt); Activities coordinators
2 (pt).
Facilities Dining room; Physical therapy
room; Activities room; Chapel; Crafts room;
Barber/Beauty shop.
Activities Arts & crafts; Cards; Games; Prayer
groups; Movies.

GRANITE CITY

Colonial Haven Nursing Home Inc*
3900 Stearns Ave, Granite City, IL, 62040
(618) 931-3900
Admin Clarence Repp. *Medical Dir/Dir of
Nursing* Dr Felicia Koch.
Licensure Skilled care; Intermediate care. *Beds*
SNF 61; ICF 61. *Certified* Medicaid;
Medicare.
Owner Proprietary Corp.
Admissions Requirements Medical
examination; Physician's request.
Staff RNs 2 (ft), 1 (pt); LPNs 7 (ft), 4 (pt);
Nurses aides 26 (ft), 19 (pt); Reality
therapists 1 (ft); Recreational therapists 2
(pt); Activities coordinators 1 (ft).
Facilities Dining room; Physical therapy
room; Activities room; Laundry room;
Barber/Beauty shop.
Activities Arts & crafts; Games; Reading
groups; Prayer groups; Movies.

The Colonnades*
1 Colonial Dr, Granite City, IL, 62040
(618) 877-2700
Admin Roger M Martin.
Licensure Intermediate care. *Beds* 90.
Certified Medicaid.
Owner Proprietary Corp.

GRAYVILLE

Meadowood
2nd & Commerce, Grayville, IL, 62844
(618) 375-2171
Admin Rebecca S Alcorn.
Licensure Skilled care. *Beds* 104. *Certified*
Medicaid.
Owner Proprietary Corp.

GREENUP

Cumberland Nursing Center
PO Box 86, Rte 1, Greenup, IL, 62428
(217) 923-3186
Admin Lee Markwell. *Medical Dir/Dir of
Nursing* Joan Ettelbrick RN.
Licensure Intermediate care. *Beds* 60.
Certified Medicaid.
Owner Proprietary Corp.
Staff RNs 1 (ft); LPNs 5 (ft), 1 (pt); Nurses
aides 19 (ft), 3 (pt); Activities coordinators 1
(ft); Dietitians 1 (pt).
Facilities Dining room; Activities room;
Crafts room; Laundry room; Barber/Beauty
shop.
Activities Arts & crafts; Games; Reading
groups; Prayer groups; Movies.

GREENVILLE

Hillview Retirement Center
S 4th St, Greenville, IL, 62246
(618) 664-1622
Admin Lois J Palmer. *Medical Dir/Dir of
Nursing* James Goggin MD; Debarah
Deavare RN.
Licensure Skilled care; Intermediate care. *Beds*
SNF 33; ICF 65. *Certified* Medicaid.
Owner Proprietary Corp.
Admissions Requirements Minimum age 21;
Medical examination; Physician's request.
Staff Physicians 1 (pt); RNs 1 (ft), 3 (pt);
LPNs 4 (ft), 3 (pt); Orderlies 1 (ft), 3 (pt);
Nurses aides 10 (ft), 10 (pt); Physical
therapists 1 (ft); Occupational therapists 1
(pt); Speech therapists 1 (pt); Activities
coordinators 2 (ft); Dietitians 1 (ft); Dentists
1 (pt); Ophthalmologists 1 (pt); Podiatrists 1
(pt).
Facilities Dining room; Physical therapy
room; Activities room; Crafts room; Laundry
room; Barber/Beauty shop; Library.
Activities Arts & crafts; Cards; Games;
Movies; Shopping trips; Social/Cultural
gatherings.

HAMILTON

Montebello Nursing Home*
16th St & Keokuk, Hamilton, IL, 62341
(217) 847-3931
Admin Theodore M DeBonis. *Medical Dir/Dir
of Nursing* B C Kappmeyer MD.
Licensure Skilled care; Intermediate care. *Beds*
149. *Certified* Medicaid.
Owner Proprietary Corp.
Admissions Requirements Minimum age 18;
Medical examination.
Staff Physicians 7 (pt); RNs 2 (ft), 4 (pt);
LPNs 2 (ft), 4 (pt); Orderlies 1 (ft), 3 (pt);
Nurses aides 17 (ft), 22 (pt); Physical
therapists 2 (ft), 2 (pt); Reality therapists 2
(pt); Activities coordinators 2 (ft); Dietitians
1 (ft); Dentists 1 (pt); Podiatrists 1 (pt).
Facilities Dining room; Physical therapy
room; Activities room; Laundry room;
Barber/Beauty shop.
Activities Arts & crafts; Cards; Games;
Reading groups; Prayer groups; Movies;
Shopping trips; Social/Cultural gatherings.

HARDIN

Calhoun Care Center
908 S Park, Hardin, IL, 62047
(618) 576-9021
Admin Karen J Porter. *Medical Dir/Dir of
Nursing* Bernard Baalman MD; Vickie
Longnecker RN DON.
Licensure Skilled care. *Beds* SNF 90. *Certified*
Medicaid; Medicare.
Owner Proprietary Corp (Beverly Enterprises).
Admissions Requirements Minimum age 21.
Staff Physicians 3 (pt); RNs 3 (pt); LPNs 3
(ft), 2 (pt); Nurses aides 15 (ft), 8 (pt);
Activities coordinators 1 (ft), 1 (pt);
Dietitians 1 (ft).
Facilities Dining room; Physical therapy
room; Activities room; Crafts room; Laundry
room; Barber/Beauty shop.
Activities Arts & crafts; Cards; Games;
Reading groups; Prayer groups; Movies;
Shopping trips; Social/Cultural gatherings.

HARRISBURG

Bacon Nursing Home Inc*
PO Box 296, N Land St, Harrisburg, IL,
62946
(618) 252-6341
Admin Loretta W Turner. *Medical Dir/Dir of
Nursing* Dr H Andrew Cserny.
Licensure Intermediate care. *Beds* 50.
Certified Medicaid.
Owner Proprietary Corp.
Admissions Requirements Minimum age 18;
Medical examination; Physician's request.
Staff Physicians 1 (pt); RNs 1 (pt); LPNs 5
(ft), 1 (pt); Nurses aides 23 (ft), 3 (pt);
Reality therapists 1 (ft); Occupational
therapists 1 (pt); Speech therapists 1 (pt);
Activities coordinators 1 (ft); Dietitians 1
(pt); Dentists 1 (pt); Ophthalmologists 1 (pt);
Podiatrists 1 (pt); Audiologists 1 (pt).
Facilities Dining room; Physical therapy
room; Activities room; Crafts room; Laundry
room; Barber/Beauty shop.
Activities Arts & crafts; Cards; Games;
Reading groups; Prayer groups; Movies;
Shopping trips; Social/Cultural gatherings.

Harrisburg Manor Inc*
1000 W Sloan St, Harrisburg, IL, 62946
(618) 253-7807
Admin Patsy J Colson.
Licensure Intermediate care. *Beds* 68.
Certified Medicaid.
Owner Proprietary Corp.

Little Egypt Manor*
901 N Webster, Harrisburg, IL, 62946
(618) 252-0576
Admin Theresa S Walker. *Medical Dir/Dir of
Nursing* Dr Carl Hauptmann.
Licensure Intermediate care. *Beds* 48.
Certified Medicaid.
Owner Proprietary Corp.
Admissions Requirements Minimum age 18;
Medical examination; Physician's request.
Staff RNs 1 (pt); LPNs 3 (ft), 2 (pt); Nurses
aides 9 (ft); Speech therapists 1 (pt);
Activities coordinators 1 (ft); Dietitians 3
(ft), 3 (pt); Dentists 1 (pt).
Facilities Dining room; Activities room;
Crafts room; Laundry room; Barber/Beauty
shop.
Activities Arts & crafts; Cards; Games;
Reading groups; Prayer groups; Movies;
Shopping trips; Social/Cultural gatherings.

Saline Care Center
120 S Land St, Harrisburg, IL, 62946
(618) 252-7405
Admin Alice A Stallings.
Licensure Intermediate care. *Beds* 127.
Certified Medicaid.
Owner Proprietary Corp.

HARVEY

Children's Habilitation Center
121 W 154th St, Harvey, IL, 60426
(312) 596-2220
Admin Barbara J Thomas. *Medical Dir/Dir of Nursing* Lowell M Zoms MD; Helga Wostl RN.
Licensure Skilled Pediatric long-term care. *Beds* Skilled Pediatric 128. *Certified* Medicaid.
Owner Proprietary Corp.
Admissions Requirements Minimum age 0-22; Medical examination.
Staff Physicians 6 (ft); RNs 6 (ft), 1 (pt); LPNs 7 (ft), 2 (pt); Nurses aides 42 (ft), 24 (pt); Physical therapists 1 (pt); Occupational therapists 1 (pt); Speech therapists 1 (ft); Activities coordinators 3 (ft); Dietitians 1 (ft), 1 (pt); Dentists 1 (pt).
Facilities Physical therapy room; Laundry room.
Activities Arts & crafts; Games; Movies; Shopping trips; Social/Cultural gatherings; Cookouts; Beach; Zoo; Horseback riding.

Dixie Manor Sheltered Care*
15535 Dixie Hwy, Harvey, IL, 60426
(312) 339-6438
Admin Leona Thompson.
Licensure Sheltered care. *Beds* 23.
Owner Proprietary Corp.

Halsted Manor*
16048 S Halsted St, Harvey, IL, 60426
(312) 339-5311
Admin Vondell L Kennibrew.
Licensure Sheltered care. *Beds* 42.
Owner Proprietary Corp.

Heather Manor Nursing Center*
15600 S Honore St, Harvey, IL, 60426
(312) 333-9550
Admin Mary Stanley. *Medical Dir/Dir of Nursing* Sheldon Levine DO.
Licensure Skilled care; Intermediate care. *Beds* 172. *Certified* Medicaid; Medicare.
Owner Proprietary Corp (Alden Management Services).
Admissions Requirements Minimum age 18; Medical examination; Physician's request.
Staff Physicians 5 (pt); RNs 3 (ft); LPNs 12 (ft), 4 (pt); Orderlies 3 (ft), 1 (pt); Nurses aides 42 (ft), 3 (pt); Physical therapists 1 (ft); Recreational therapists 2 (ft); Occupational therapists 1 (pt); Speech therapists 1 (pt); Activities coordinators 1 (ft); Dietitians 1 (pt); Dentists 1 (pt); Ophthalmologists 1 (pt); Podiatrists 1 (pt); Audiologists 1 (pt).
Facilities Dining room; Physical therapy room; Activities room; Chapel; Crafts room; Laundry room; Barber/Beauty shop.
Activities Arts & crafts; Cards; Games; Reading groups; Prayer groups; Movies; Shopping trips; Social/Cultural gatherings; Field trips.

Kenniebrew Home*
14812 S Marshfield, Harvey, IL, 60426
(312) 339-9345
Admin Erma Johnson.
Licensure Sheltered care. *Beds* 23.
Owner Proprietary Corp.

Starnes Nursing Home Inc*
14434 S Hoyne, Harvey, IL, 60426
(312) 3892730
Admin Shirley Q White.
Licensure Intermediate care. *Beds* 39. *Certified* Medicaid.
Owner Proprietary Corp.

HAVANA

Havana Healthcare Center
609 N Harpham St, Havana, IL, 62644
(309) 543-6121

Admin Vincent M Marquess. *Medical Dir/Dir of Nursing* Albert Maurer MD; Sally Strode RN.
Licensure Skilled care; Intermediate care. *Beds* SNF 49; ICF 49. *Certified* Medicaid.
Owner Proprietary Corp (H S Healthcare).
Admissions Requirements Minimum age 21; Medical examination; Physician's request.
Staff Physicians 2 (pt); RNs 5 (ft), 1 (pt); LPNs 4 (ft), 3 (pt); Orderlies 3 (ft); Nurses aides 20 (ft), 6 (pt); Physical therapists 1 (pt); Recreational therapists 1 (ft), 1 (pt); Activities coordinators 1 (ft), 1 (pt); Dietitians 1 (ft); Ophthalmologists 2 (pt).
Facilities Dining room; Physical therapy room; Activities room; Chapel; Crafts room; Laundry room; Barber/Beauty shop.
Activities Arts & crafts; Cards; Games; Reading groups; Prayer groups; Movies; Shopping trips; Social/Cultural gatherings.

HAZEL CREST

Imperial Nursing Center of Hazel Crest*
3300 W 175th St, Hazel Crest, IL, 60429
(312) 935-7474
Admin Barbara J Schubert.
Licensure Skilled care; Intermediate care. *Beds* 204. *Certified* Medicaid; Medicare.
Owner Proprietary Corp.
Admissions Requirements Medical examination; Physician's request.
Staff Physicians 3 (ft); RNs 11 (ft), 4 (pt); LPNs 5 (ft), 3 (pt); Nurses aides 45 (ft), 10 (pt); Physical therapists 1 (ft); Recreational therapists 1 (ft); Occupational therapists 1 (pt); Speech therapists 1 (pt); Activities coordinators 1 (ft); Dietitians 1 (pt); Dentists 1 (pt); Ophthalmologists 1 (pt); Podiatrists 1 (pt); Audiologists 1 (pt).
Facilities Dining room; Physical therapy room; Activities room; Crafts room; Laundry room; Barber/Beauty shop.
Activities Arts & crafts; Cards; Games; Reading groups; Prayer groups; Movies; Shopping trips; Social/Cultural gatherings.

HERRIN

Friendship Care Center—Herrin*
1900 N Park St, Herrin, IL, 62948
(618) 942-2525
Admin Pamela Garris.
Licensure Intermediate care. *Beds* 49. *Certified* Medicaid.
Owner Proprietary Corp.

Park Avenue Health Care Home*
PO Box 68, Herrin, IL, 62948
(618) 942-3928
Admin Connie Dodson.
Licensure Intermediate care. *Beds* 69. *Certified* Medicaid.
Owner Proprietary Corp.

Shawnee Christian Nursing Center
1900 13th St, Herrin, IL, 62948
(618) 942-7391
Admin Scott Payne.
Licensure Skilled care. *Beds* 151. *Certified* Medicaid; Medicare.
Owner Nonprofit Corp (Christian Homes).

HICKORY HILLS

Hickory Nursing Pavilion Inc
9246 S Roberts Rd, Hickory Hills, IL, 60457
(312) 598-4040
Admin Howard L Wengrow. *Medical Dir/Dir of Nursing* Lourdene Johnson RN DON.
Licensure Intermediate care. *Beds* 74. *Certified* Medicaid.
Owner Proprietary Corp.
Staff RNs 2 (ft); LPNs 3 (ft), 3 (pt); Nurses aides 16 (ft).

Facilities Dining room; Physical therapy room; Activities room; Laundry room; Barber/Beauty shop.
Activities Arts & crafts; Cards; Games; Reading groups; Prayer groups; Movies; Shopping trips; Social/Cultural gatherings.

HIGHLAND

Chastains of Highland
2510 Lemon Street Rd, Highland, IL, 62249
(618) 654-2368
Admin Brian Blink. *Medical Dir/Dir of Nursing* Norbert Belz MD; Barbara Brown DON.
Licensure Skilled care; Intermediate care. *Beds* SNF 28; ICF 100. *Certified* Medicaid; Medicare.
Owner Proprietary Corp (Hillhaven Corp).
Staff RNs 7 (ft), 1 (pt); LPNs 14 (ft), 1 (pt); Orderlies 4 (ft); Nurses aides 34 (ft), 2 (pt); Physical therapists 1 (ft); Speech therapists 1 (pt); Activities coordinators 1 (ft); Dietitians 1 (ft).
Facilities Dining room; Physical therapy room; Activities room; Chapel; Laundry room; Barber/Beauty shop.
Activities Arts & crafts; Cards; Games; Reading groups; Prayer groups; Movies; Shopping trips; Social/Cultural gatherings.

Faith Countryside Homes Nursing Center
PO Box 220, 1216 27th St, Highland, IL, 62249
(618) 654-2393
Admin Gerald D Brown. *Medical Dir/Dir of Nursing* Donald Chaney MD; Lelynna Langdoc RN DON.
Licensure Intermediate care. *Beds* ICF 65. *Certified* Medicaid.
Owner Nonprofit Corp.
Admissions Requirements Minimum age 55; Medical examination.
Staff Physicians 1 (pt); RNs 1 (ft), 1 (pt); LPNs 6 (ft), 2 (pt); Orderlies 3 (ft); Nurses aides 14 (ft), 7 (pt); Activities coordinators 1 (ft), 1 (pt); Dietitians 1 (pt); Ophthalmologists 1 (pt).
Affiliation Church of Christ
Facilities Dining room; Physical therapy room; Activities room; Barber/Beauty shop.
Activities Arts & crafts; Cards; Games; Reading groups; Prayer groups; Movies; Shopping trips; Social/Cultural gatherings.

HIGHLAND PARK

Abbott House
405 Central Ave, Highland Park, IL, 60035
(312) 432-6080
Admin Joanne Minorini. *Medical Dir/Dir of Nursing* Sam Kruger MD; Maria Martinez RN DON.
Licensure Intermediate care. *Beds* 106. *Certified* Medicaid.
Owner Privately owned.
Admissions Requirements Minimum age 18; Medical examination; Physician's request.
Staff Physicians; RNs 4 (ft), 2 (pt); LPNs 2 (ft), 2 (pt); Orderlies 2 (ft); Nurses aides 20 (ft), 1 (pt); Activities coordinators; Ophthalmologists; FSS; Psychosocial coordinator; Activity assistants; Social worker.
Facilities Dining room; Activities room; Laundry room; Barber/Beauty shop; Occupational therapy room.
Activities Arts & crafts; Cards; Games; Prayer groups; Movies; Shopping trips; Social/Cultural gatherings.

Villa St Cyril*
1111 Saint Johns Ave, Highland Park, IL, 60035
(312) 432-9104
Admin Sr M Milada Sukany. *Medical Dir/Dir of Nursing* Jules H Last MD.

Licensure Intermediate care. *Beds* 82.
Certified Medicaid.
Owner Nonprofit Corp.
Admissions Requirements Minimum age 65;
Medical examination.
Staff Physicians 2 (pt); RNs 7 (ft), 2 (pt);
LPNs 1 (ft); Orderlies 3 (ft); Nurses aides 12
(ft), 4 (pt); Reality therapists 1 (ft);
Recreational therapists 3 (ft), 1 (pt);
Occupational therapists 1 (pt); Activities
coordinators 1 (ft); Dietitians 1 (ft); Dentists
1 (pt); Podiatrists 1 (pt).
Affiliation Roman Catholic
Facilities Dining room; Activities room;
Chapel; Crafts room; Laundry room; Barber/
Beauty shop; Library.
Activities Arts & crafts; Cards; Games;
Reading groups; Prayer groups; Movies;
Shopping trips; Social/Cultural gatherings;
Luncheons; Concert outings; Children's
outreach program.

HIGHWOOD

Highland Park Health Care Center Inv
50 Pleasant Avenue, Highwood, IL, 60040
(312) 432-9142
Admin Mary C Niederhauser. *Medical Dir/Dir
of Nursing* Dr Solomon Dayan.
Licensure Skilled care; Intermediate care. *Beds*
SNF 82; ICF 13. *Certified* Medicaid.
Owner Proprietary Corp.
Admissions Requirements Medical
examination.
Staff RNs 5 (ft), 6 (pt); LPNs 1 (ft); Orderlies
2 (ft); Nurses aides 20 (ft), 5 (pt); Activities
coordinators 1 (ft); Dietitians 1 (ft).
Facilities Dining room; Physical therapy
room; Activities room; Chapel; Laundry
room; Barber/Beauty shop; Gift shop.
Activities Arts & crafts; Cards; Games;
Reading groups; Prayer groups; Movies;
Shopping trips; Social/Cultural gatherings.

HILLSBORO

Hillsboro Health Care Center
1300 E Tremont St, Hillsboro, IL, 62049
(217) 532-6191
Admin Gayle Buel RN NHA. *Medical Dir/Dir
of Nursing* Dr Douglas Byers; Maureen
Folkerts RN DON.
Licensure Skilled care. *Beds* SNF 123;
Medicare 4. *Certified* Medicare.
Owner Nonprofit Corp (First Humanics).
Admissions Requirements Minimum age 18;
Medical examination; Physician's request.
Staff Physicians; RNs 3 (ft), 2 (pt); LPNs 6
(ft), 2 (pt); Orderlies 1 (ft); Nurses aides 35
(ft), 10 (pt); Physical therapists; Recreational
therapists 1 (ft), 1 (pt); Occupational
therapists; Speech therapists; Activities
coordinators 1 (ft), 1 (pt); Dietitians;
Dentists; Ophthalmologists; Podiatrists;
Social service consultant.
Facilities Dining room; Physical therapy
room; Activities room; Crafts room; Laundry
room; Barber/Beauty shop.
Activities Arts & crafts; Cards; Games;
Reading groups; Prayer groups; Movies;
Shopping trips; Social/Cultural gatherings;
Quilting class; Cooking class.

Hillsboro Nursing Home
S Route 127, Hillsboro, IL, 62049
(217) 532-6126
Admin Faye Hamrock. *Medical Dir/Dir of
Nursing* Dr R McFarlin MD; Connie
Zumwalt RN DON.
Licensure Skilled care; Intermediate care. *Beds*
SNF 21; ICF 99. *Certified* Medicaid;
Medicare.
Owner Proprietary Corp (Beverly Enterprises).
Admissions Requirements Minimum age 18;
Medical examination.
Staff RNs 3 (ft); LPNs 5 (ft), 2 (pt); Nurses
aides; Activities coordinators 1 (ft), 1 (pt).

Facilities Dining room; Physical therapy
room; Barber/Beauty shop.
Activities Arts & crafts; Cards; Games;
Reading groups; Prayer groups; Movies;
Shopping trips.

HILLSIDE

Oakridge Conv Home Inc*
323 Oakridge Ave, Hillside, IL, 60162
(312) 547-6595
Admin Lynn L Acerra.
Licensure Skilled care. *Beds* 73.
Owner Proprietary Corp.

HINSDALE

King Bruwaert House
6101 S County Line Rd, Hinsdale, IL, 60521
(312) 323-2250
Admin Carl Baker. *Medical Dir/Dir of Nursing*
Kathleen Hessler DON.
Licensure Intermediate care; Sheltered care;
Independent living units. *Beds* ICF 18;
Sheltered care 79.
Owner Nonprofit organization/foundation.
Admissions Requirements Minimum age 65;
Medical examination.
Staff Physicians; RNs; LPNs; Orderlies;
Nurses aides; Activities coordinators;
Dietitians.
Facilities Dining room; Activities room;
Crafts room; Laundry room; Barber/Beauty
shop; Library; Pool table room.
Activities Arts & crafts; Cards; Games;
Reading groups; Prayer groups; Movies;
Shopping trips; Social/Cultural gatherings.

Monticello Convalescent Center
600 W Ogden Ave, Hinsdale, IL, 60521
(312) 325-9630
Admin Jeanne M Chiligiris. *Medical Dir/Dir
of Nursing* Dr Gary A Moore; Ms Dorothy
Pustelnikas RN.
Licensure Skilled care. *Beds* SNF 200.
Certified Medicare.
Owner Proprietary Corp (Manor Care).
Admissions Requirements Minimum age 18;
Medical examination.
Staff Physicians; RNs; LPNs; Nurses aides;
Physical therapists; Occupational therapists 1
(ft); Activities coordinators; Dietitians 1 (ft);
Ophthalmologists 1 (pt).
Facilities Dining room; Physical therapy
room; Activities room; Crafts room; Laundry
room; Barber/Beauty shop; Library; Ice
cream palor.
Activities Arts & crafts; Cards; Games;
Reading groups; Prayer groups; Movies;
Shopping trips; Social/Cultural gatherings;
Gardening; Baseball.

West Suburban Shelter Care Center*
Rte 83 & 91st, Hinsdale, IL, 60521
(312) 323-0198
Admin Suresh R Mehta.
Licensure Sheltered care. *Beds* 48.
Owner Proprietary Corp.

HOFFMAN ESTATE

Cambridge Poplar Creek
1545 Barrington Rd, Hoffman Estate, IL,
60194
(312) 884-0011
Admin Daniel Barrett.
Licensure Skilled care; Intermediate care. *Beds*
SNF 154; ICF 63. *Certified* Medicaid;
Medicare.
Owner Proprietary Corp (Cambridge Grp Inc).

HOMEWOOD

Mercy Health Care Rehabilitation Center*
19000 Halsted St, Homewood, IL, 60430
(312) 957-9200

Admin Joanne T Jurkovic.
Licensure Skilled care. *Beds* 256. *Certified*
Medicaid; Medicare.
Owner Nonprofit Corp.

HOOPESTON

Hoopeston Regional Nursing Home
701 E Orange St, Hoopeston, IL, 60942
(217) 283-5531
Admin Bradley V Solberg. *Medical Dir/Dir of
Nursing* Dr T C Lee; Margaret Feller.
Licensure Skilled care; Intermediate care. *Beds*
50. *Certified* Medicaid; Medicare.
Owner Nonprofit Corp.
Staff RNs 1 (ft); LPNs 2 (ft), 2 (pt); Nurses
aides 12 (ft), 8 (pt); Physical therapists 1 (ft);
Activities coordinators 1 (ft), 1 (pt).
Affiliation Lutheran
Facilities Dining room; Physical therapy
room; Activities room; Crafts room; Laundry
room; Barber/Beauty shop.
Activities Arts & crafts; Cards; Games;
Reading groups; Prayer groups; Social/
Cultural gatherings.

HOPEDALE

Hopedale House*
2nd St, Hopedale, IL, 61747
(309) 449-3321
Admin William L Marshall.
Licensure Sheltered care. *Beds* 50.
Owner Nonprofit Corp.

Hopedale Nursing Home*
2nd St, Hopedale, IL, 61747
(309) 449-3321
Admin Barbara S Wirtjes.
Licensure Skilled care. *Beds* 96. *Certified*
Medicaid; Medicare.
Owner Nonprofit Corp.

HUTSONVILLE

Heritage Sheltered Care Home
207 Wood Ln, Hutsonville, IL, 62433
(618) 563-4806
Admin Rena A Smith.
Licensure Sheltered care. *Beds* 48.
Owner Proprietary Corp.
Admissions Requirements Minimum age 18;
Medical examination.
Facilities Dining room; Activities room;
Crafts room; Laundry room; Barber/Beauty
shop.
Activities Arts & crafts; Cards; Games;
Shopping trips; Social/Cultural gatherings;
Vacations.

INDIAN HEAD PARK

Briar Place Nursing Center
6800 W Joliet Rd, Indian Head Park, IL,
60425
(312) 246-8500
Admin Joan Milkent.
Licensure Skilled care; Intermediate care. *Beds*
SNF 88; ICF 157.
Owner Proprietary Corp.

IRVINGTON

St Mary's Square Living Center of Irvington*
PO Box 189, Hwy 177 W, Irvington, IL,
62848
(618) 249-6216
Admin Mark L Leafgreen.
Licensure Intermediate care. *Beds* 72.
Owner Nonprofit Corp.

ISLAND LAKE

Sheltering Oak*
PO Box 367, Island Lake, IL, 60042
(312) 526-3636
Admin Robert A Bundy.
Licensure Intermediate care. *Beds* 70.
  Certified Medicaid.
Owner Proprietary Corp.

ITASCA

Arbor of Itasca Inc
535 S Elm St, Itasca, IL, 60143
(312) 773-9416
Admin John C Florina Jr. *Medical Dir/Dir of
  Nursing* Jane Geske.
Licensure Intermediate care. *Beds* ICF 80.
  Certified Medicaid.
Owner Proprietary Corp.
Admissions Requirements Medical
  examination.
Staff Physicians; RNs; LPNs; Nurses aides;
  Recreational therapists; Activities
  coordinators; Dietitians; Ophthalmologists.
Facilities Dining room; Activities room;
  Crafts room; Laundry room; Barber/Beauty
  shop; Library; Courtyard; Bounded by forest
  preserve.
Activities Arts & crafts; Cards; Games; Prayer
  groups; Movies; Shopping trips; Social/
  Cultural gatherings; Bowling; Library visits;
  Lunch outings.

JACKSONVILLE

Barton W Stone Christian Home*
873 Grove St, Jacksonville, IL, 62650
(217) 243-3376
Admin Loren T Cline.
Licensure Intermediate care; Sheltered care.
  Beds ICF 99; Sheltered care 24. *Certified*
  Medicaid.
Owner Nonprofit Corp.

Ivanhoe Manor Health Care Center Inc*
1316 Tendick, Jacksonville, IL, 62650
(217) 243-6405
Admin Mary Shields.
Licensure Intermediate care. *Beds* 93.
  Certified Medicaid.
Owner Proprietary Corp.
Admissions Requirements Minimum age 18;
  Medical examination.
Facilities Dining room; Physical therapy
  room; Activities room; Chapel; Crafts room;
  Laundry room; Barber/Beauty shop.
Activities Arts & crafts; Games; Reading
  groups; Prayer groups; Movies; Shopping
  trips; Social/Cultural gatherings; Orientation.

Ivanhoe Manor Nursing Center*
1313 Tendick, Jacksonville, IL, 62650
(217) 243-6405
Admin Mary W Shields.
Licensure Intermediate care. *Beds* 93.
  Certified Medicaid.
Owner Proprietary Corp.

Jacksonville Conv Center*
1517 W Walnut St, Jacksonville, IL, 62650
(217) 243-6451
Admin Wesley Trendle.
Licensure Skilled care; Intermediate care. *Beds*
  SNF 61; ICF 27. *Certified* Medicaid;
  Medicare.
Owner Proprietary Corp.

Meline Manor Inc
1024 W Walnut St, Jacksonville, IL, 62650
(217) 245-5175
Admin Paul Harper.
Licensure Skilled care. *Beds* 138. *Certified*
  Medicaid; Medicare.
Owner Proprietary Corp.
Admissions Requirements Minimum age 18.

Staff RNs 2 (ft), 3 (pt); LPNs 7 (ft), 1 (pt);
  Nurses aides 25 (ft).
Facilities Dining room; Physical therapy
  room; Laundry room; Barber/Beauty shop.
Activities Arts & crafts; Cards; Games;
  Movies; Social/Cultural gatherings.

Modern Care Convalescent & Nursing Home
1500 W Walnut St, Jacksonville, IL, 62650
(217) 245-4183
Admin Marian E Chalcraft. *Medical Dir/Dir of
  Nursing* John Peterson MD; Gerry Coyle
  RN DON.
Licensure Skilled care. *Beds* SNF 68. *Certified*
  Medicaid; Medicare.
Owner Proprietary Corp.
Admissions Requirements Minimum age 18;
  Physician's request.
Staff RNs 3 (ft), 2 (pt); LPNs 6 (ft), 2 (pt);
  Nurses aides 26 (ft), 1 (pt); Activities
  coordinators 1 (ft), 1 (pt); Dietitians 1 (pt).
Facilities Dining room; Physical therapy
  room; Activities room; Laundry room;
  Barber/Beauty shop.
Activities Arts & crafts; Cards; Games;
  Reading groups; Prayer groups; Movies;
  Shopping trips; Social/Cultural gatherings.

Skyview Nursing Manor
1021 N Church St, Jacksonville, IL, 62650
(217) 245-4174
Admin Ann Newingham. *Medical Dir/Dir of
  Nursing* James A Bohan MD; Barbara Hart
  RN DON.
Licensure Intermediate care. *Beds* ICF 113.
  Certified Medicaid.
Owner Proprietary Corp (National Heritage).
Admissions Requirements Minimum age 18.
Staff RNs 2 (ft); LPNs 7 (ft); Orderlies 5 (ft);
  Nurses aides 20 (ft); Physical therapists 1
  (ft); Occupational therapists 1 (ft); Activities
  coordinators 2 (ft).
Facilities Dining room; Physical therapy
  room; Activities room; Laundry room;
  Barber/Beauty shop.
Activities Arts & crafts; Cards; Games; Prayer
  groups; Movies; Shopping trips; Social/
  Cultural gatherings.

JERSEYVILLE

Garnets Chateau*
608 W Pearl St, Jerseyville, IL, 62052
(618) 498-4312
Admin Dolly Liles.
Licensure Intermediate care. *Beds* 48.
  Certified Medicaid.
Owner Proprietary Corp.

Greenwood Manor Nursing Home*
410 Fletcher, Jerseyville, IL, 62052
(618) 498-6427
Admin Barbara Molloy.
Licensure Skilled care. *Beds* 98. *Certified*
  Medicaid.
Owner Proprietary Corp.

Jerseyville Care Center
923 S State St, Jerseyville, IL, 62052
(618) 498-6496
Admin Earnest Williams. *Medical Dir/Dir of
  Nursing* Janeth Zota MD; Betty Warte RN.
Licensure Skilled care; Intermediate care.
  Certified Medicaid; Medicare.
Owner Proprietary Corp (Beverly Enterprises).
Admissions Requirements Minimum age 21.
Staff RNs; LPNs; Orderlies; Nurses aides;
  Activities coordinators.
Facilities Dining room; Physical therapy
  room; Activities room; Laundry room;
  Barber/Beauty shop; TV room.
Activities Arts & crafts; Cards; Games;
  Movies; Shopping trips.

JOHNSTON CITY

Heartland Care Center
205 E 3rd, Johnston City, IL, 62951
(618) 983-5731
Admin Nancy Whitson. *Medical Dir/Dir of
  Nursing* Dr Javed; Pat Wood.
Licensure Sheltered care. *Beds* 23. *Certified*
  Medicaid; Medicare.
Owner Proprietary Corp.
Admissions Requirements Minimum age 18;
  Medical examination; Physician's request.
Staff Physicians 1 (pt); RNs 1 (pt); Nurses
  aides 3 (ft), 2 (pt); Activities coordinators 1
  (ft); Dietitians 1 (pt); Dentists 1 (pt).
Facilities Dining room; Activities room;
  Crafts room; Laundry room.
Activities Arts & crafts; Cards; Games;
  Reading groups; Prayer groups; Movies;
  Shopping trips; Social/Cultural gatherings.

JOLIET

Broadway Nursing Home Inc
216 N Broadway, Joliet, IL, 60435
(815) 727-7672
Admin Alice J Connor. *Medical Dir/Dir of
  Nursing* Dr Bruce Corwin; Perlita Shipp.
Licensure Intermediate care. *Beds* ICF 60.
Owner Proprietary Corp.
Admissions Requirements Minimum age 45;
  Medical examination.
Staff RNs 1 (ft), 2 (pt); LPNs 3 (ft), 2 (pt);
  Nurses aides 7 (ft), 7 (pt); Activities
  coordinators 2 (ft), 1 (pt); Dietitians 1 (pt).
Languages Polish, Tagalog, Hindi
Facilities Dining room; Activities room;
  Laundry room; Fenced & shaded patio near
  bandshell.
Activities Arts & crafts; Cards; Games; Prayer
  groups; Movies; Cookouts; Picnics on patio;
  Summer concerts weekly in bandshell.

Cornerstone Services Inc CLF
611 E Cass St, Joliet, IL, 60432
(815) 723-3411
Admin Bette J Reed.
Licensure Community living facility. *Beds*
  Community living facility 58.
Owner Nonprofit Corp.
Admissions Requirements Minimum age 18;
  Medical examination.
Staff RNs 1 (pt); Dietitians 1 (pt).
Facilities Dining room; Laundry room; Living
  rooms; Recreation areas.
Activities Games; Reading groups; Movies;
  Shopping trips; Social/Cultural gatherings;
  Vocational training; Daily living skills
  training.

Deerbrook Nursing Centre*
306 N Larkin Ave, Joliet, IL, 60435
(815) 744-5560
Admin Margaret Sullivan.
Licensure Skilled care. *Beds* 224. *Certified*
  Medicaid; Medicare.
Owner Proprietary Corp.

Draper Plaza*
777 Draper Ave, Joliet, IL, 60432
(815) 727-4794
Admin Theresa Okun.
Licensure Skilled care; Intermediate care. *Beds*
  168. *Certified* Medicaid; Medicare.
Owner Nonprofit Corp.

Franciscan Nursing Home
300 N Madison St, Joliet, IL, 60435
(815) 725-3400
Admin Diane M Mikes. *Medical Dir/Dir of
  Nursing* Anthony Razma MD; Carole
  Parrish DON.
Licensure Skilled care. *Beds* 129. *Certified*
  Medicaid; Medicare.
Owner Nonprofit Corp.
Admissions Requirements Medical
  examination; Physician's request.

Staff RNs 1 (ft), 3 (pt); LPNs 10 (ft), 8 (pt); Nurses aides 27 (ft), 9 (pt); Activities coordinators 2 (ft), 3 (pt).
Languages Spanish
Affiliation Roman Catholic
Facilities Dining room; Physical therapy room; Activities room; Chapel; Laundry room; Barber/Beauty shop.
Activities Arts & crafts; Cards; Games; Reading groups; Prayer groups; Movies; Shopping trips; Social/Cultural gatherings.

Imperial Nursing Center of Joliet*
222 N Hammes, Joliet, IL, 60435
(815) 725-0443
Admin Martha Reid. *Medical Dir/Dir of Nursing* Louis Minella.
Licensure Skilled care; Intermediate care. *Beds* 203. *Certified* Medicaid; Medicare.
Owner Proprietary Corp.
Staff Physicians 3 (pt); RNs 10 (ft), 7 (pt); LPNs 10 (ft), 12 (pt); Orderlies 3 (ft), 1 (pt); Nurses aides 20 (ft), 8 (pt); Physical therapists 1 (ft); Reality therapists 3 (ft); Recreational therapists 4 (ft); Occupational therapists 2 (ft), 1 (pt); Speech therapists 1 (ft); Activities coordinators 1 (ft); Dietitians 1 (ft), 1 (pt); Dentists 3 (pt); Ophthalmologists 2 (pt); Podiatrists 1 (pt); Audiologists 1 (pt).

Joliet Terrace
2230 McDonough, Joliet, IL, 60436
(815) 729-3801
Admin Marilyn Ferbend.
Licensure Intermediate care. *Beds* 120. *Certified* Medicaid.
Owner Proprietary Corp.

Our Lady of Angels Retirement
1201 Wyoming Ave, Joliet, IL, 60435
(815) 725-6631
Admin Albert M Papesh.
Licensure Intermediate care; Sheltered care. *Beds* ICF 50; Sheltered care 50. *Certified* Medicaid.
Owner Nonprofit Corp.
Admissions Requirements Minimum age 65; Medical examination.
Staff RNs 1 (ft), 5 (pt); LPNs 2 (pt); Nurses aides 21 (ft), 12 (pt); Physical therapists 1 (pt); Activities coordinators 1 (pt); Dietitians 1 (ft).
Affiliation Roman Catholic
Facilities Dining room; Physical therapy room; Activities room; Chapel; Crafts room; Laundry room; Barber/Beauty shop; Library.
Activities Arts & crafts; Cards; Games; Reading groups; Prayer groups; Movies; Shopping trips; Social/Cultural gatherings.

St Patrick's Residence
22 E Clinton St, Joliet, IL, 60431-1172
(815) 727-5291
Admin Sr M Jacqueline Wagner. *Medical Dir/Dir of Nursing* Roy Alcala MD; Sr M Josa RN DON.
Licensure Skilled care; Intermediate care; Sheltered care. *Beds* SNF 10; ICF 97; Sheltered care 73. *Certified* Medicaid.
Owner Nonprofit organization/foundation.
Admissions Requirements Minimum age 65; Females only.
Staff Physicians 1 (pt); RNs 7 (ft), 2 (pt); LPNs 7 (ft), 7 (pt); Nurses aides 55 (ft); Occupational therapists ; Activities coordinators 1 (ft); Dietitians 1 (ft).
Affiliation Roman Catholic
Facilities Dining room; Physical therapy room; Activities room; Chapel; Crafts room; Laundry room; Barber/Beauty shop; Library; Coffee shop.
Activities Arts & crafts; Cards; Games; Reading groups; Prayer groups; Movies; Shopping trips; Social/Cultural gatherings.

Salem Village
1314 Rowell Ave, Joliet, IL, 60433
(815) 727-5451
Admin Ray W Hemphill. *Medical Dir/Dir of Nursing* Bruce C Corwin MD; Mary Naughton-Walsh DON.
Licensure Skilled care; Intermediate care; Sheltered care; Independent living units. *Beds* ICF 36; ICF/MR 246; Sheltered care 59. *Certified* Medicaid.
Owner Nonprofit organization/foundation.
Admissions Requirements Minimum age 62; Medical examination.
Staff Physicians 1 (pt); RNs 6 (ft), 5 (pt); LPNs 20 (ft), 8 (pt); Orderlies 1 (ft); Nurses aides 55 (ft), 39 (pt); Physical therapists 1 (pt); Reality therapists 1 (pt); Recreational therapists 1 (pt); Occupational therapists 1 (pt); Activities coordinators 1 (ft), 6 (pt); Dietitians 1 (ft).
Affiliation Lutheran
Facilities Dining room; Physical therapy room; Activities room; Chapel; Crafts room; Laundry room; Barber/Beauty shop; Library; Retirement apartments; Townhouses; Resale shop.
Activities Arts & crafts; Cards; Games; Reading groups; Prayer groups; Movies; Shopping trips; Social/Cultural gatherings; Resident journal; Physical fitness.

Sunny Hill Nursing Home
Doris & Neal Sts, Joliet, IL, 60433
(815) 727-8710
Admin Vicki Lynn Tomer. *Medical Dir/Dir of Nursing* Dr Kishor Ajmere; Annette Etheridge.
Licensure Skilled care; Intermediate care. *Beds* SNF 50; ICF 250. *Certified* Medicaid.
Owner Publicly owned.
Admissions Requirements Minimum age 18; Medical examination.
Staff RNs 10 (ft), 2 (pt); LPNs 25 (ft), 10 (pt); Nurses aides 85 (ft), 21 (pt); Recreational therapists 6 (ft); Activities coordinators 1 (ft); Dietitians 2 (ft).
Facilities Dining room; Physical therapy room; Activities room; Chapel; Crafts room; Laundry room; Barber/Beauty shop; Library.
Activities Arts & crafts; Cards; Games; Reading groups; Prayer groups; Movies; Shopping trips; Social/Cultural gatherings; Resident council; Reality orientation; Exercises; Service projects; Resident newsletter; Van trips.

JONESBORO

Gibbs & McRaven Sheltered Care Home*
204 S Pecan, Jonesboro, IL, 62952
(618) 833-5740
Admin Howard H McRaven. *Medical Dir/Dir of Nursing* Burton E Rogby MD.
Licensure Sheltered care. *Beds* 25.
Owner Proprietary Corp.
Admissions Requirements Minimum age 18; Medical examination.
Staff Physicians 1 (pt); RNs 1 (pt); Orderlies 2 (ft); Nurses aides 4 (ft); Occupational therapists 1 (pt); Activities coordinators 1 (ft), 1 (pt); Dietitians 1 (pt); Dentists 1 (pt).
Facilities Dining room; Activities room; Crafts room; Laundry room; Library; Large sitting & visitors room.
Activities Arts & crafts; Cards; Games; Reading groups; Prayer groups; Movies; Shopping trips; Social/Cultural gatherings; Community outings to local restaurants & parks; Yearly trip to wild animal park.

Henard Sheltered Care Home*
204 S Main, Jonesboro, IL, 62952
(618) 833-6134
Admin Joyce Harrington.
Licensure Sheltered care. *Beds* 16.
Owner Proprietary Corp.

Lifecare Center of Jonesboro
PO Box B, Rte 127 S, Jonesboro, IL, 62952
(618) 833-7093
Admin Lonnie D Harvel. *Medical Dir/Dir of Nursing* Dr William H Whiting.
Licensure Intermediate care. *Beds* ICF 81. *Certified* Medicaid.
Owner Proprietary Corp (Community Lifecare Enterprises).
Admissions Requirements Medical examination.
Staff RNs 1 (ft); LPNs 7 (ft); Nurses aides 21 (ft); Physical therapists 1 (ft); Recreational therapists 2 (ft); Activities coordinators 2 (ft); Dietitians 1 (pt).
Facilities Dining room; Physical therapy room; Activities room; Crafts room; Laundry room; Barber/Beauty shop.
Activities Arts & crafts; Cards; Games; Reading groups; Prayer groups; Movies; Shopping trips; Social/Cultural gatherings.

JUSTICE

Rosary Hill Home
9000 Rosary Hill Dr, Justice, IL, 60458
(312) 458-3040
Admin Sr Catherine M Lasiewicki. *Medical Dir/Dir of Nursing* Frank J Wall Jr MD.
Licensure Intermediate care; Sheltered care. *Beds* ICF 18; Sheltered care 32.
Owner Nonprofit Corp.
Admissions Requirements Minimum age 65; Females only.
Staff RNs 1 (ft); LPNs 1 (ft); Nurses aides 8 (ft); Activities coordinators 1 (pt); Dietitians 1 (pt); Ophthalmologists 1 (pt).
Affiliation Roman Catholic
Facilities Dining room; Activities room; Chapel; Laundry room; Barber/Beauty shop; Library.
Activities Arts & crafts; Cards; Games; Prayer groups; Movies.

KANKAKEE

Americana Healthcare Center
900 W River Pl, Kankakee, IL, 60901
(815) 933-1711
Admin Susan Lucas. *Medical Dir/Dir of Nursing* Reinhold Schuller MD; Sharon Leydens RN DON.
Licensure Skilled care. *Beds* SNF 96. *Certified* Medicaid; Medicare.
Owner Proprietary Corp (Manor Care).
Staff RNs 5 (ft), 3 (pt); LPNs 6 (ft), 4 (pt); Nurses aides 20 (ft), 10 (pt); Activities coordinators 1 (ft); Dietitians 1 (ft).
Facilities Dining room; Physical therapy room; Activities room; Crafts room; Laundry room; Barber/Beauty shop; 2 resident lounges.
Activities Arts & crafts; Cards; Games; Reading groups; Prayer groups; Movies; Shopping trips; Social/Cultural gatherings.

The Heritage House
901 N Entrance, Kankakee, IL, 60901
(815) 939-4500
Admin Carol D Kehoe.
Licensure Skilled care; Sheltered care. *Beds* SNF 31; Sheltered care 99.
Owner Nonprofit organization/foundation.
Admissions Requirements Minimum age 60; Medical examination.
Staff RNs 4 (ft), 2 (pt); LPNs 1 (ft), 4 (pt); Nurses aides 23 (ft), 5 (pt); Physical therapists; Speech therapists; Activities coordinators 1 (ft), 1 (pt); Dietitians 1 (ft).
Facilities Dining room; Activities room; Chapel; Crafts room; Laundry room; Barber/Beauty shop; Library.
Activities Arts & crafts; Cards; Games; Prayer groups; Movies; Social/Cultural gatherings.

Stratford Square Ltd*
1050 N Jeffrey St, Kankakee, IL, 60901
(815) 933-1660
Admin Philip Mendelson.
Licensure Skilled care; Intermediate care. *Beds* SNF 90; ICF 110. *Certified* Medicaid.
Owner Proprietary Corp.

KEWANEE

Kewanee Care Home
144 Junior Ave S, Kewanee, IL, 61443
(309) 853-4429
Admin Robert L Petersen. *Medical Dir/Dir of Nursing* Glenn Miller MD; Helen L Park LPN DON.
Licensure Intermediate care. *Beds* ICF 65. *Certified* Medicaid.
Owner Proprietary Corp.
Admissions Requirements Minimum age 18; Medical examination; Physician's request.
Staff Physicians 1 (ft); RNs 3 (pt); LPNs 4 (ft), 1 (pt); Nurses aides 3 (ft), 18 (pt); Physical therapists 1 (ft); Recreational therapists 1 (ft); Activities coordinators 1 (pt); Dietitians 1 (pt); Dentists 1 (pt); Ophthalmologists 1 (pt); Podiatrists 1 (pt).
Facilities Dining room; Activities room; Laundry room; Barber/Beauty shop.
Activities Arts & crafts; Cards; Games; Reading groups; Prayer groups; Movies; Shopping trips.

Kewanee Convalescent Center
605 E Church St, Kewanee, IL, 61443
(309) 852-3389
Admin Vicky L Debord. *Medical Dir/Dir of Nursing* Glenn Miller; Debra Hurley.
Licensure Skilled care. *Beds* 200. *Certified* Medicaid; Medicare.
Owner Proprietary Corp (Beverly Enterprises).
Admissions Requirements Medical examination; Physician's request.
Staff RNs 6 (ft), 2 (pt); LPNs 11 (ft), 4 (pt); Orderlies 4 (ft); Nurses aides 49 (ft), 36 (pt); Physical therapists 1 (pt); Occupational therapists 1 (pt); Activities coordinators 2 (ft), 1 (pt).
Facilities Dining room; Physical therapy room; Activities room; Crafts room; Laundry room; Barber/Beauty shop.
Activities Arts & crafts; Cards; Games; Reading groups; Prayer groups; Movies; Shopping trips; Pet therapy; Church services; Intergenerational visits; Music appreciation.

KNOXVILLE

Good Samaritan Nursing Home
407 N Hebard St, Knoxville, IL, 61448
(309) 289-2614
Admin Anna Wang. *Medical Dir/Dir of Nursing* Robert G Hickerson Jr MD; Sharlene Morris LPN.
Licensure Intermediate care. *Beds* ICF 49. *Certified* Medi-Cal.
Owner Nonprofit Corp.
Admissions Requirements Minimum age 18; Medical examination; Physician's request.
Staff RNs 1 (ft), 1 (pt); LPNs 4 (ft), 1 (pt); Nurses aides 26 (ft), 10 (pt); Physical therapists 1 (ft); Reality therapists 1 (ft); Recreational therapists 2 (ft), 1 (pt); Occupational therapists 1 (ft); Activities coordinators 1 (ft), 1 (pt); Dietitians 1 (ft).
Facilities Dining room; Physical therapy room; Activities room; Chapel; Crafts room; Laundry room; Library; Garden; Social hall.
Activities Arts & crafts; Cards; Games; Reading groups; Prayer groups; Movies; Shopping trips; Social/Cultural gatherings; Music band; Sunshine Singers.

Knox County Nursing Home
N Market St, Knoxville, IL, 61448
(309) 289-2338

Admin Mary E Peterson. *Medical Dir/Dir of Nursing* Beverly Asbury DON.
Licensure Skilled care. *Beds* SNF 204. *Certified* Medicaid.
Owner Nonprofit organization/foundation.
Admissions Requirements Medical examination; Physician's request.
Staff RNs 7 (ft), 2 (pt); LPNs 10 (ft), 10 (pt); Nurses aides 54 (ft), 37 (pt).
Facilities Dining room; Physical therapy room; Activities room; Chapel; Crafts room; Laundry room; Barber/Beauty shop; Library.
Activities Arts & crafts; Cards; Games; Prayer groups; Movies; Social/Cultural gatherings.

LA GRANGE

Colonial Manor Living Center
339 S 9th Ave, La Grange, IL, 60525
(312) 354-4660
Admin Leland R Schultz. *Medical Dir/Dir of Nursing* Russell Zitek MD; Koren Hart RN.
Licensure Skilled care; Intermediate care. *Beds* SNF 96; ICF 107. *Certified* Medicaid; Medicare.
Owner Nonprofit Corp (Adventist Health Sys-USA).
Admissions Requirements Medical examination; Physician's request.
Staff Physicians; RNs; LPNs; Orderlies; Nurses aides; Physical therapists; Reality therapists; Recreational therapists; Occupational therapists; Speech therapists; Activities coordinators; Dietitians.
Facilities Dining room; Physical therapy room; Activities room; Chapel; Crafts room; Laundry room; Barber/Beauty shop; Library.
Activities Arts & crafts; Cards; Games; Reading groups; Prayer groups; Movies; Shopping trips; Social/Cultural gatherings.

LA GRANGE PARK

Fairview Health Care Center
701 N La Grange Rd, La Grange Park, IL, 60525
(312) 354-7300
Admin Phyllis Lavenau. *Medical Dir/Dir of Nursing* Dr Alberto Saltiel; Sue Bruzan.
Licensure Skilled care. *Beds* SNF 131. *Certified* Medicare.
Owner Proprietary Corp.
Admissions Requirements Minimum age 19; Medical examination.
Staff RNs; LPNs; Nurses aides; Physical therapists; Reality therapists; Recreational therapists; Occupational therapists; Speech therapists; Activities coordinators; Dietitians.
Facilities Dining room; Physical therapy room; Activities room; Chapel; Crafts room; Laundry room; Barber/Beauty shop.
Activities Arts & crafts; Cards; Games; Reading groups; Prayer groups; Movies; Shopping trips; Social/Cultural gatherings; Field trips; Picnics.

Plymouth Place Inc
315 N La Grange Rd, La Grange Park, IL, 60525
(312) 354-0340
Admin Donald E Clawson. *Medical Dir/Dir of Nursing* Dr Aubrey Moore; Ann Schultz.
Licensure Skilled care; Intermediate care; Assisted living; Independent living. *Beds* SNF 10; ICF 70; Assisted living 132; Independent living 176; Apts 88.
Owner Nonprofit Corp.
Admissions Requirements Minimum age 60; Medical examination; Physician's request; Church report; Social history.
Staff Physicians; RNs; LPNs; Nurses aides; Physical therapists; Reality therapists; Recreational therapists; Occupational therapists; Speech therapists; Activities coordinators; Dietitians; Dentists; Ophthalmologists; Podiatrists; Social worker.
Affiliation Church of Christ

Facilities Dining room; Physical therapy room; Activities room; Chapel; Crafts room; Laundry room; Barber/Beauty shop; Library; Woodworking shop; Health center.
Activities Arts & crafts; Cards; Games; Reading groups; Prayer groups; Movies; Shopping trips; Social/Cultural gatherings; Exercises; Baseball team sponsorship; National & international travel.

LA ROSE

The Evergreens*
102 Locust St, La Rose, IL, 61541
(309) 399-7181
Admin Anna Stoens.
Licensure Sheltered care. *Beds* 26.
Owner Proprietary Corp.
Admissions Requirements Minimum age 18.
Staff Physicians 1 (ft); RNs 1 (ft); Nurses aides 5 (ft); Activities coordinators 1 (ft); Dietitians 1 (ft), 1 (pt).
Facilities Dining room; Activities room; Laundry room.
Activities Games; Reading groups; Prayer groups; Social/Cultural gatherings.

LA SALLE

Care Inn Convalescent Center of LaSalle
1445 Chartres St, La Salle, IL, 61301
(815) 223-4700
Admin Alice M Ghilino. *Medical Dir/Dir of Nursing* Dr J B Aplington; Mary Pelka RN.
Licensure Skilled care; Intermediate care. *Beds* SNF 50; ICF 51. *Certified* Medicaid; Medicare.
Owner Proprietary Corp (ARA Living Centers).
Admissions Requirements Minimum age 21; Medical examination; Physician's request.
Staff RNs 5 (ft), 3 (pt); LPNs 4 (ft), 3 (pt); Orderlies 1 (ft), 1 (pt); Physical therapists 1 (pt); Activities coordinators 2 (ft); Dietitians 1 (ft); Dentists 2 (pt); Ophthalmologists 2 (pt).
Facilities Dining room; Physical therapy room; Laundry room; Barber/Beauty shop; Library.
Activities Arts & crafts; Cards; Games; Reading groups; Prayer groups; Movies; Shopping trips; Social/Cultural gatherings.

LACON

St Joseph Nursing Home*
401 9th St, Lacon, IL, 61540
(309) 246-2175
Admin Sr Catherine Platte.
Licensure Intermediate care. *Beds* 104. *Certified* Medicaid.
Owner Nonprofit Corp.

LAKE BLUFF

Hill Top
502 Waukegan Rd, Lake Bluff, IL, 60044
(312) 295-1550
Admin Marion W Tarbutton.
Licensure Skilled care. *Beds* 26.
Owner Nonprofit Corp.
Affiliation Christian Science
Facilities Dining room; Activities room; Chapel; Crafts room; Laundry room; Barber/Beauty shop; Library.
Activities Arts & crafts; Reading groups; Prayer groups; Movies.

Lake Bluff Health Care Center
700 Jenkisson Ave, Lake Bluff, IL, 60044
(312) 295-3900
Admin James D Bowden. *Medical Dir/Dir of Nursing* David Schimel MD; Pat Miller RN DON.
Licensure Skilled care; Intermediate care. *Beds* 231. *Certified* Medicaid; Medicare.

Owner Proprietary Corp.
Admissions Requirements Minimum age 21; Medical examination; Physician's request.
Staff Physicians 8 (pt); RNs 19 (ft); LPNs 26 (ft); Orderlies 18 (ft); Nurses aides 90 (ft); Physical therapists 1 (ft); Reality therapists 1 (ft); Recreational therapists 1 (ft); Occupational therapists 1 (pt); Speech therapists 1 (pt); Activities coordinators 1 (ft); Dietitians 1 (ft); Dentists 1 (pt); Ophthalmologists 1 (pt); Podiatrists 1 (pt).
Facilities Dining room; Physical therapy room; Activities room; Crafts room; Laundry room; Barber/Beauty shop; Library.
Activities Arts & crafts; Cards; Games; Reading groups; Prayer groups; Movies; Shopping trips; Social/Cultural gatherings.

LAKE FOREST

Grove School Comm Liv Center*
40 E Old Mill Rd, Lake Forest, IL, 60045
(312) 234-5540
Admin Robert E Matson. *Medical Dir/Dir of Nursing* Dr Shaku Chhabria.
Licensure Skilled care; Intermediate care. *Beds* SNF 48; ICF 18. *Certified* Medicaid.
Owner Nonprofit Corp.
Admissions Requirements Minimum age 10; Medical examination; Physician's request.
Staff Physicians 1 (ft), 3 (pt); RNs 3 (ft), 1 (pt); LPNs 1 (ft), 2 (pt); Nurses aides 22 (ft); Physical therapists 1 (pt); Occupational therapists 1 (pt); Speech therapists 1 (ft); Activities coordinators 1 (ft); Dietitians 1 (pt).
Facilities Dining room; Physical therapy room; Activities room; Crafts room; Laundry room.
Activities Arts & crafts; Games; Movies; Shopping trips.

Latham Estates*
Box 6, Lake Forest, IL, 62543
(217) 674-3738
Admin Donna M Britton.
Licensure Intermediate care. *Beds* 139.
Owner Proprietary Corp.

LAKE ZURICH

Mt St Joseph
24955 N Hwy 12, Lake Zurich, IL, 60047
(312) 438-5050
Admin Sr Linda M Willette. *Medical Dir/Dir of Nursing* Dr Sanjoy Majumdar; Sr Mary Walker.
Licensure Intermediate care for mentally retarded. *Beds* ICF/MR 162. *Certified* Medicaid.
Owner Nonprofit Corp.
Admissions Requirements Minimum age 21; Females only.
Staff Physicians 1 (pt); RNs 6 (ft); LPNs 3 (ft); Nurses aides 40 (ft), 20 (pt); Recreational therapists; Occupational therapists; Speech therapists 2 (ft); Activities coordinators 8 (ft); Dietitians 1 (pt); Dentists 1 (pt); Ophthalmologists 1 (pt).
Affiliation Roman Catholic
Facilities Dining room; Physical therapy room; Activities room; Chapel; Crafts room; Laundry room; Library.
Activities Arts & crafts; Cards; Games; Reading groups; Prayer groups; Movies; Shopping trips; Social/Cultural gatherings; Music therapy; Recreational therapy.

LANSING

Tri State Manor Nursing Home*
2500 E 175th St, Lansing, IL, 60438
(312) 474-7330
Admin Olive J Horeshimer.
Licensure Intermediate care. *Beds* 56.
Owner Proprietary Corp.

LAWRENCEVILLE

The United Methodist Village Inc
1616 Cedar St, Lawrenceville, IL, 62439-2199
(618) 943-3347
Admin Dale C Swenson. *Medical Dir/Dir of Nursing* Dr R T Kirkwood; Pat Smith RN DON.
Licensure Skilled care; Intermediate care; Sheltered care; Independent living units. *Beds* SNF 161; ICF 40; Shelter care; 80 Independent living units 42. *Certified* Medicaid; Medicare.
Owner Nonprofit Corp.
Admissions Requirements Minimum age 18.
Staff Physicians 6 (pt); RNs 6 (ft), 11 (pt); LPNs 9 (ft), 7 (pt); Orderlies 3 (ft); Nurses aides 50 (ft), 26 (pt); Physical therapists 1 (ft), 1 (pt); Activities coordinators 1 (ft); Dietitians 1 (ft).
Affiliation Methodist
Facilities Dining room; Physical therapy room; Activities room; Chapel; Crafts room; Laundry room; Barber/Beauty shop; Library.
Activities Arts & crafts; Cards; Games; Reading groups; Prayer groups; Movies; Shopping trips; Social/Cultural gatherings; Support groups; Walking groups; Adult day care; Home care.

LEBANON

Bohannon Nursing Home Inc*
1201 N Alton, Lebanon, IL, 62254
(618) 537-4401
Admin Diana Bohannon.
Licensure Intermediate care. *Beds* 51. *Certified* Medicaid.
Owner Proprietary Corp.

LEMONT

Alvernia Manor Retirement Home
1598 Main St, Lemont, IL, 60439
(312) 257-7721
Admin Sr M Clement Korenic. *Medical Dir/Dir of Nursing* Sr M Josephine Tominac.
Licensure Sheltered care. *Beds* 56.
Owner Privately owned.
Admissions Requirements Minimum age 65; Medical examination.
Staff RNs 2 (pt); LPNs 1 (ft), 1 (pt); Activities coordinators 1 (ft); Dietitians 1 (pt).
Languages Polish, Slovic, Spanish, German
Affiliation Roman Catholic
Facilities Dining room; Activities room; Chapel; Crafts room; Laundry room; Barber/Beauty shop; Library.
Activities Arts & crafts; Cards; Games; Reading groups; Prayer groups; Movies; Shopping trips; Social/Cultural gatherings.

Holy Family Villa
123rd St, Lemont, IL, 60439
(312) 257-2291
Admin Sr Genevieve Kripas.
Licensure Intermediate care. *Beds* 99. *Certified* Medicaid.
Owner Nonprofit Corp.
Affiliation Roman Catholic

Mother Theresa Home Inc
1270 Main St, Lemont, IL, 60439
(312) 257-5801
Admin Sr M Dorothea Micek. *Medical Dir/Dir of Nursing* Maureen Derkacz RN.
Licensure Intermediate care; Sheltered care. *Beds* ICF 46; Sheltered care 11. *Certified* Medicaid.
Owner Nonprofit Corp (Franciscan Sisters).
Admissions Requirements Minimum age 65; Medical examination.
Staff RNs 3 (ft), 4 (pt); LPNs 2 (ft), 2 (pt); Nurses aides 15 (ft), 6 (pt); Recreational therapists 1 (ft); Activities coordinators 1 (ft).
Affiliation Roman Catholic

Facilities Dining room; Activities room; Chapel; Crafts room; Barber/Beauty shop; Library.
Activities Arts & crafts; Games; Reading groups; Prayer groups; Movies; Shopping trips; Social/Cultural gatherings.

LENA

Lena Continental Manor Nursing Home Inc
1010 S Logan St, Lena, IL, 61048
(815) 369-4561
Admin Lynn M Lyvers. *Medical Dir/Dir of Nursing* Norma Streeb.
Licensure Intermediate care. *Beds* ICF 92. *Certified* Medicaid.
Owner Proprietary Corp.
Admissions Requirements Medical examination.
Staff RNs 3 (ft), 3 (pt); LPNs 3 (ft), 4 (pt); Nurses aides 17 (ft), 15 (pt); Activities coordinators 1 (ft), 1 (pt); Dietitians 1 (ft).
Facilities Dining room; Physical therapy room; Activities room; Crafts room; Laundry room; Barber/Beauty shop.
Activities Arts & crafts; Cards; Games; Reading groups; Prayer groups; Movies; Social/Cultural gatherings.

LEWISTOWN

Broadway Arms Community Living Center*
1003 N Broadway, Lewistown, IL, 61542
(309) 686-3310
Admin Gail Leiby.
Licensure Intermediate care. *Beds* 12.
Owner Nonprofit Corp.

Clarytona Manor*
175 E Sycamore Dr, Lewistown, IL, 61542
(309) 547-2267
Admin Annabel Gray.
Licensure Intermediate care. *Beds* 99. *Certified* Medicaid.
Owner Proprietary Corp (Signature Corp).

LEXINGTON

Lexington House Healthcare Center
301 S Vine St, Lexington, IL, 61753
(309) 365-2541
Admin Sandra Wood. *Medical Dir/Dir of Nursing* Jacqueline French.
Licensure Intermediate care. *Beds* 51. *Certified* Medicaid.
Owner Proprietary Corp (National Heritage).
Admissions Requirements Physician's request.
Staff Physicians 1 (pt); RNs 1 (pt); LPNs 3 (ft), 3 (pt); Nurses aides 9 (ft), 4 (pt); Physical therapists 1 (ft), 1 (pt); Occupational therapists 1 (ft), 1 (pt); Activities coordinators 1 (ft); Dietitians 1 (pt); Dentists 1 (pt); Ophthalmologists 1 (pt); Podiatrists 1 (pt).
Facilities Dining room; Activities room; Laundry room; Barber/Beauty shop.
Activities Arts & crafts; Games; Movies; Shopping trips.

LIBERTYVILLE

The Lambs Inc*
PO Box 520, Libertyville, IL, 60048
(312) 362-4636
Admin Jacqueline M Cohen.
Licensure Intermediate care for mentally retarded. *Beds* 37.
Owner Nonprofit Corp.

Libertyville Manor Extended Care*
610 Peterson Rd, Libertyville, IL, 60048
(312) 367-6100
Admin Slavko Stokovich. *Medical Dir/Dir of Nursing* Brenda Dahl.
Licensure Skilled care; Intermediate care. *Beds* 129. *Certified* Medicaid; Medicare.

Owner Proprietary Corp.
Staff Physicians 6 (pt); RNs 8 (ft), 4 (pt);
LPNs 1 (ft), 2 (pt); Orderlies 3 (ft); Nurses
aides 28 (ft), 8 (pt); Physical therapists 1
(pt); Recreational therapists 3 (ft);
Occupational therapists 1 (pt); Speech
therapists 1 (pt); Dietitians 1 (pt); Dentists 1
(pt); Podiatrists 1 (pt).
Facilities Dining room; Physical therapy
room; Activities room; Laundry room;
Barber/Beauty shop; Library.
Activities Arts & crafts; Cards; Games;
Reading groups; Prayer groups; Movies;
Shopping trips; Social/Cultural gatherings.

Winchester House
1125 N Milwaukee Ave, Libertyville, IL,
60048
(312) 362-4340
Admin Robert H Roiland.
Licensure Skilled care; Intermediate care. *Beds*
359. *Certified* Medicaid; Medicare.
Owner Publicly owned.
Admissions Requirements Minimum age 18.
Staff RNs 30 (ft); LPNs 13 (ft); Nurses aides
146 (ft); Physical therapists 1 (pt);
Recreational therapists 1 (ft); Occupational
therapists 1 (ft); Speech therapists 1 (pt);
Activities coordinators 1 (ft); Dietitians 2
(ft).
Facilities Dining room; Physical therapy
room; Activities room; Chapel; Crafts room;
Laundry room; Barber/Beauty shop; Library.
Activities Arts & crafts; Cards; Games;
Reading groups; Prayer groups; Movies;
Shopping trips; Social/Cultural gatherings.

LINCOLN

Christian Nursing Home Inc*
1507 7th St, Lincoln, IL, 62656
(217) 732-2189
Admin Timothy E Searby.
Licensure Skilled care. *Beds* 99. *Certified*
Medicaid.
Owner Nonprofit Corp (Christian Homes).

Lincoln Land Nursing Home*
2202 N Kickapoo St, Lincoln, IL, 62656
(217) 735-1538
Admin Mabel M Worth.
Licensure Skilled care; Intermediate care. *Beds*
SNF 59; ICF 25. *Certified* Medicaid.
Owner Proprietary Corp.

St Claras Manor
200 5th St, Lincoln, IL, 62656
(217) 735-1507
Admin George E Davis. *Medical Dir/Dir of
Nursing* Dean A Hauter; Mary Jane
O'Donnell.
Licensure Skilled care; Intermediate care. *Beds*
SNF 70; ICF 70. *Certified* Medicaid.
Owner Nonprofit Corp.
Admissions Requirements Minimum age 65;
Physician's request.
Staff RNs; LPNs; Orderlies; Nurses aides;
Physical therapists; Recreational therapists;
Activities coordinators.
Facilities Dining room; Physical therapy
room; Activities room; Chapel; Crafts room;
Barber/Beauty shop.
Activities Arts & crafts; Cards; Games; Prayer
groups; Movies; Shopping trips; Social/
Cultural gatherings.

Sunshine Meadow Care Center
1800 5th St, Lincoln, IL, 62656
(217) 735-5436
Admin Linda Simmons.
Licensure Skilled care. *Beds* SNF 61. *Certified*
Medicaid.
Owner Privately owned.
Staff RNs 2 (ft), 2 (pt); LPNs 5 (ft); Nurses
aides 1 (pt); Physical therapists 1 (pt);
Occupational therapists 1 (pt); Speech
therapists 1 (pt); Activities coordinators 1
(ft); Dietitians 1 (ft).

LISLE

Snow Valley Nursing Home*
5000 Lincoln, Lisle, IL, 60532
(312) 852-5100
Admin Mary Anne Coburn. *Medical Dir/Dir
of Nursing* Dr Timothy Brandt.
Licensure Skilled care. *Beds* 49.
Owner Proprietary Corp.
Staff RNs 5 (ft), 4 (pt); Orderlies 1 (ft);
Nurses aides 14 (ft), 8 (pt); Recreational
therapists 1 (ft), 1 (pt); Dietitians 1 (pt).
Facilities Dining room; Activities room;
Chapel; Crafts room; Laundry room; Barber/
Beauty shop.
Activities Arts & crafts; Cards; Games;
Reading groups; Prayer groups; Movies;
Shopping trips; Social/Cultural gatherings.

LITCHFIELD

Allison Manor Healthcare Center Inc*
Tyler & McKinley Sts, Litchfield, IL, 62056
(217) 324-3842
Admin Florence Russell. *Medical Dir/Dir of
Nursing* Dr R Somner.
Licensure Intermediate care. *Beds* 65.
Certified Medicaid.
Owner Proprietary Corp.
Admissions Requirements Minimum age 18.
Staff RNs 1 (pt); LPNs 6 (ft); Orderlies 3 (ft),
1 (pt); Nurses aides 20 (ft), 2 (pt); Physical
therapists 1 (ft); Reality therapists 1 (ft);
Recreational therapists 1 (ft); Speech
therapists 1 (pt); Activities coordinators 1
(ft); Dietitians 1 (pt); Dentists 1 (pt);
Ophthalmologists 1 (pt); Podiatrists 1 (pt);
Audiologists 1 (pt).
Facilities Dining room; Physical therapy
room; Activities room; Chapel; Crafts room;
Laundry room; Barber/Beauty shop.
Activities Arts & crafts; Cards; Games;
Reading groups; Prayer groups; Movies;
Shopping trips; Social/Cultural gatherings.

Barry Care Center of Litchfield
628 S Illinois St, Litchfield, IL, 62056
(217) 324-2153
Admin Connie Hartman. *Medical Dir/Dir of
Nursing* Dr Rudolph Sommers.
Licensure Skilled care. *Beds* SNF 102.
Certified Medicaid; Medicare.
Owner Privately owned.
Admissions Requirements Medical
examination.
Staff RNs; LPNs; Nurses aides; Physical
therapists; Recreational therapists;
Occupational therapists; Speech therapists;
Activities coordinators; Dietitians;
Podiatrists.
Affiliation Baptist
Facilities Dining room; Physical therapy
room; Activities room; Chapel; Crafts room;
Laundry room; Barber/Beauty shop; Library.
Activities Arts & crafts; Cards; Games;
Reading groups; Prayer groups; Movies;
Shopping trips; Social/Cultural gatherings.

Care Inn Convalescent Center of Litchfield*
1285 E Union St, Litchfield, IL, 62056
(217) 324-3996
Admin Mary Coss. *Medical Dir/Dir of Nursing*
J J Epplin MD.
Licensure Skilled care; Intermediate care. *Beds*
SNF 26; ICF 97. *Certified* Medicaid;
Medicare.
Owner Proprietary Corp (ARA Living
Centers).
Admissions Requirements Minimum age 18;
Physician's request.
Staff RNs 4 (ft); LPNs 8 (ft); Nurses aides 31
(ft); Physical therapists 1 (ft); Recreational
therapists 1 (ft); Occupational therapists 1
(ft); Speech therapists 1 (pt); Activities
coordinators 1 (ft); Dietitians 1 (ft); Dentists
1 (pt).

Facilities Dining room; Physical therapy
room; Activities room; Chapel; Crafts room;
Laundry room; Barber/Beauty shop; Library.
Activities Arts & crafts; Cards; Games;
Reading groups; Prayer groups; Movies;
Shopping trips; Social/Cultural gatherings.

LOMBARD

Beacon Hill
2400 S Finley Rd, Lombard, IL, 60148
620-5850
Admin Dale Lilburn.
Licensure Skilled care. *Beds* SNF 45. *Certified*
Medicare.
Owner Nonprofit organization/foundation.
Admissions Requirements Physician's request.
Staff RNs 3 (ft), 2 (pt); LPNs 5 (ft), 2 (pt);
Orderlies 1 (pt); Nurses aides 14 (ft);
Recreational therapists 1 (ft); Activities
coordinators 1 (ft); Dietitians 1 (ft).
Facilities Dining room; Physical therapy
room; Activities room; Crafts room; Barber/
Beauty shop; Library.
Activities Arts & crafts; Cards; Games;
Reading groups; Prayer groups; Movies;
Shopping trips; Social/Cultural gatherings;
Travelogs.

Ray Graham Lombard Comm Living Center*
143 E Grove, Lombard, IL, 60148
(312) 543-2440
Admin Ivan Browne.
Licensure Intermediate care. *Beds* 18.
Owner Nonprofit Corp.

LONG GROVE

Maple Hill Nursing Home Ltd*
RFD, Box 2308, Hicks Rd, Long Grove, IL,
60047
(312) 438-8275
Admin Lucille Devaux. *Medical Dir/Dir of
Nursing* Bijan Farah MD.
Licensure Intermediate care. *Beds* 154.
Certified Medicaid.
Owner Proprietary Corp.
Staff Physicians 8 (pt); RNs 7 (ft), 4 (pt);
LPNs 1 (ft), 3 (pt); Orderlies 25 (ft); Nurses
aides 3 (ft); Physical therapists 1 (pt);
Recreational therapists 4 (ft); Occupational
therapists 1 (pt); Dietitians 1 (ft), 1 (pt);
Dentists 1 (pt); Podiatrists 1 (pt).
Facilities Dining room; Physical therapy
room; Activities room; Chapel; Crafts room;
Laundry room; Barber/Beauty shop; Library.
Activities Arts & crafts; Cards; Games;
Reading groups; Prayer groups; Movies;
Shopping trips; Social/Cultural gatherings.

LOUISVILLE

Chestnut Corner Sheltered Care*
905 W Chestnut St, Louisville, IL, 62858
(618) 665-3332
Admin Linda Kincaid.
Licensure Sheltered care. *Beds* 36.
Owner Proprietary Corp.

Country Manor*
RR 4, Box 119, Louisville, IL, 62858
(618) 686-4542
Admin Janice I Webb.
Licensure Sheltered care. *Beds* 23.
Owner Proprietary Corp.

Twilight Haven Sheltered Care Home*
Rte 45 S, Box 307, Louisville, IL, 62858
(618) 665-3153
Admin Peggy L Pidgeon.
Licensure Sheltered care. *Beds* 22.
Owner Proprietary Corp.

LOVINGTON

Moultrie County Community Center
PO Box 135, 240 E State, Lovington, IL, 61937
(217) 873-5266
Admin Kim Jacobus.
Licensure Intermediate care for mentally retarded. *Beds* ICF/MR 15. *Certified* Medicaid.
Owner Proprietary Corp.
Admissions Requirements Minimum age 18; Physician's request.
Staff Physicians 1 (pt); RNs 1 (pt); Nurses aides 2 (ft), 10 (pt); Occupational therapists 1 (pt); Speech therapists 1 (pt); Podiatrists 1 (pt).
Facilities Dining room; Activities room; Crafts room; Laundry room.
Activities Arts & crafts; Cards; Games; Prayer groups; Movies; Shopping trips; Social/Cultural gatherings; Family visits; Exercise programs.

MACOMB

Elms Nursing Home
1212 Madelyn Ave, Macomb, IL, 61455
(309) 837-5482
Admin Cherles Kneedy. *Medical Dir/Dir of Nursing* David Reem MD; Jean Huff RN.
Licensure Skilled care; Intermediate care. *Beds* 98. *Certified* Medicaid; Medicare.
Owner Publicly owned.
Admissions Requirements Minimum age 18; Medical examination; Physician's request.
Facilities Dining room; Physical therapy room; Activities room; Crafts room; Laundry room; Barber/Beauty shop; Library.
Activities Arts & crafts; Cards; Games; Reading groups; Prayer groups; Movies; Social/Cultural gatherings.

Macomb Manor
S Johnson & W Grant, Macomb, IL, 61455
(309) 837-2387
Admin Dorothy D Pape.
Licensure Intermediate care. *Beds* 65. *Certified* Medicaid.
Owner Proprietary Corp.

Macomb Nursing & Rehabilitation Center
PO Box 789, 8 Doctors' Ln, Macomb, IL, 61455-0789
(309) 833-5555
Admin Julie Schwere.
Licensure Skilled care. *Beds* 58. *Certified* Medicaid; Medicare.
Owner Proprietary Corp.

Wesley Village U M C Health Care Center
1200 E Grant St, Macomb, IL, 61455
(309) 833-2123
Admin David Pease.
Licensure Intermediate care; Sheltered care. *Beds* ICF/MR 42; Sheltered care 16.
Owner Nonprofit Corp.
Affiliation Methodist

MACON

Eastern Star Home*
PO Box 516, Macon, IL, 62544
(217) 764-3348
Admin Mardell K Taft. *Medical Dir/Dir of Nursing* Dr Robert Atz.
Licensure Intermediate care; Sheltered care. *Beds* ICF 49; Sheltered care 39.
Owner Nonprofit Corp.
Admissions Requirements Minimum age 62; Medical examination.
Staff Physicians 1 (pt); RNs 1 (ft); LPNs 6 (ft); Nurses aides 22 (ft); Physical therapists 1 (pt); Reality therapists 1 (pt); Recreational therapists 1 (pt); Occupational therapists 1 (pt); Activities coordinators 2 (ft); Dietitians 1 (pt).

Affiliation Order of Eastern Star
Facilities Dining room; Physical therapy room; Activities room; Chapel; Crafts room; Laundry room; Barber/Beauty shop.
Activities Arts & crafts; Cards; Games; Reading groups; Prayer groups; Movies; Shopping trips; Social/Cultural gatherings.

MARENGO

Florence Nursing Home
546 E Grant Hwy, Marengo, IL, 60152
(815) 568-8322
Admin Alice L Aumiller. *Medical Dir/Dir of Nursing* Charles J Lockwood MD; Jo Ann Wilde RN.
Licensure Intermediate care. *Beds* ICF 49.
Owner Privately owned.
Admissions Requirements Minimum age 22; Medical examination.
Facilities Dining room; Activities room; Laundry room; Barber/Beauty shop.
Activities Arts & crafts; Cards; Games; Reading groups; Prayer groups; Movies; Shopping trips; Social/Cultural gatherings; Exercise program; Pet visits.

MARION

Fountains Nursing Home
1301 E DeYoung St, Marion, IL, 62959
(618) 997-1365
Admin Joan W Baugher. *Medical Dir/Dir of Nursing* Elizabeth Brymer LPM.
Licensure Intermediate care. *Beds* ICF 68. *Certified* Medicaid.
Owner Proprietary Corp.
Admissions Requirements Medical examination; Physician's request.
Staff Physicians 1 (pt); RNs 1 (pt); LPNs 4 (ft), 1 (pt); Nurses aides 19 (ft), 2 (pt); Recreational therapists 1 (pt); Occupational therapists 1 (pt); Speech therapists 1 (pt); Activities coordinators 1 (pt); Dietitians 1 (pt).
Facilities Dining room; Activities room; Laundry room; Barber/Beauty shop.
Activities Arts & crafts; Cards; Games; Reading groups; Prayer groups; Movies; Shopping trips; Social/Cultural gatherings.

Friendship Care Center
1101 N Madison St, Marion, IL, 62959
(618) 993-8650
Admin Eileene C Norman. *Medical Dir/Dir of Nursing* Geneva Bloodworth.
Licensure Intermediate care. *Beds* 57. *Certified* Medicaid.
Owner Proprietary Corp.
Admissions Requirements Medical examination; Physician's request.
Staff Physicians; RNs; LPNs; Nurses aides; Physical therapists; Recreational therapists; Speech therapists; Dietitians.
Facilities Dining room; Laundry room; Barber/Beauty shop.
Activities Arts & crafts; Cards; Games; Reading groups; Prayer groups; Movies; Shopping trips.

MARSEILLES

Rivershores Living Center
578 W Commercial St, Marseilles, IL, 61351
(815) 795-5121
Admin Eric J Wrangell. *Medical Dir/Dir of Nursing* Don E Morehead MD; Susan N Norsen RN DON.
Licensure Skilled care. *Beds* SNF 96. *Certified* Medicaid; Medicare.
Owner Nonprofit Corp (Adventist Health Sys-USA).
Admissions Requirements Minimum age 18; Medical examination; Physician's request.

Staff Physicians 2 (pt); RNs 5 (ft), 3 (pt); LPNs 1 (ft), 4 (pt); Nurses aides 24 (ft), 13 (pt); Physical therapists 1 (pt); Recreational therapists 1 (pt); Occupational therapists 1 (pt); Speech therapists 1 (pt); Activities coordinators 1 (ft); Dietitians 1 (pt); Ophthalmologists 1 (pt).
Languages Sign
Affiliation Seventh-Day Adventist
Facilities Dining room; Physical therapy room; Activities room; Chapel; Laundry room; Barber/Beauty shop; Lift van; TV room; Patient lounge.
Activities Arts & crafts; Cards; Games; Reading groups; Prayer groups; Movies; Shopping trips; Social/Cultural gatherings; Outside entertainers; Demonstrations; Music therapy; Sing-alongs; Guessing games.

MARSHALL

Burnside Nursing Home Inc*
410 N Second St, Marshall, IL, 62441
(217) 826-2358
Admin Elizabeth M Clark.
Licensure Skilled care; Intermediate care. *Beds* SNF 50; ICF 64. *Certified* Medicaid.
Owner Nonprofit Corp.

MARYVILLE

Meadow View Care Center
Rte 159, Interstate 70, Maryville, IL, 62062
(618) 344-7750
Admin Nancy G Clark. *Medical Dir/Dir of Nursing* Dr Biedenharn; Sandra Krug.
Licensure Intermediate care. *Beds* ICF 104. *Certified* Medicaid.
Owner Proprietary Corp (Beverly Enterprises).
Admissions Requirements Minimum age 21; Medical examination; Physician's request.
Staff RNs 1 (ft); LPNs 7 (ft), 2 (pt); Orderlies 1 (ft); Nurses aides 20 (ft), 2 (pt); Physical therapists 1 (pt); Occupational therapists 1 (pt); Speech therapists 1 (pt); Activities coordinators 1 (ft); Dietitians 1 (pt).
Facilities Dining room; Activities room; Chapel; Laundry room; Barber/Beauty shop.
Activities Arts & crafts; Cards; Games; Reading groups; Prayer groups; Movies; Shopping trips; Social/Cultural gatherings.

MASCOUTAH

The Grange Nursing Home*
901 N 10th St, Mascoutah, IL, 62258
(618) 566-2183
Admin Sundra L Comer. *Medical Dir/Dir of Nursing* Paul Biedenharn MD.
Licensure Intermediate care. *Beds* 54. *Certified* Medicaid.
Owner Nonprofit Corp.
Admissions Requirements Minimum age 18.
Staff RNs 1 (ft), 1 (pt); LPNs 3 (ft), 2 (pt); Orderlies 1 (ft), 1 (pt); Nurses aides 12 (ft), 3 (pt); Activities coordinators 1 (ft).
Facilities Dining room; Physical therapy room; Laundry room.
Activities Arts & crafts; Cards; Games; Movies; Social/Cultural gatherings.

Marka Nursing Home
201 S 10th St, Mascoutah, IL, 62258
(618) 566-8000
Admin Jayne Haege. *Medical Dir/Dir of Nursing* Larry Leone MD; Gail Kimmle DON.
Licensure Skilled care; Intermediate care. *Beds* SNF 23; ICF 52. *Certified* Medicaid; Medicare.
Owner Proprietary Corp (Community Care Centers).
Admissions Requirements Minimum age 18.

Staff Physicians; RNs 2 (ft); LPNs 6 (pt); Nurses aides 8 (ft), 10 (pt); Physical therapists; Speech therapists; Activities coordinators 1 (ft); Dietitians 1 (pt); Ophthalmologists.
Facilities Dining room; Physical therapy room; Activities room; Chapel; Crafts room; Laundry room; Barber/Beauty shop.
Activities Arts & crafts; Cards; Games; Reading groups; Prayer groups; Movies; Shopping trips; Social/Cultural gatherings.

West Main Nursing Home
1244 W Main St, Mascoutah, IL, 62258
(618) 566-7327
Admin Mary Keenan. *Medical Dir/Dir of Nursing* Dr Galloway MD; Theresa Poole DON.
Licensure Intermediate care. *Beds* 34. *Certified* Medicare.
Owner Proprietary Corp (Community Care Centers).
Admissions Requirements Minimum age 18; Medical examination.
Staff Physicians 1 (pt); RNs 2 (ft); LPNs 4 (ft), 1 (pt); Orderlies 1 (ft); Nurses aides 5 (ft), 2 (pt); Physical therapists 1 (pt); Recreational therapists 1 (ft), 1 (pt); Occupational therapists 1 (pt); Dietitians 1 (pt).
Facilities Dining room; Activities room; Crafts room; Laundry room; Barber/Beauty shop.
Activities Arts & crafts; Cards; Games; Reading groups; Prayer groups; Movies; Shopping trips; Social/Cultural gatherings.

MATTESON

Applewood Living Center
21020 S Kostner Ave, Matteson, IL, 60443
(312) 747-1300
Admin Steven Bakken. *Medical Dir/Dir of Nursing* E G Wygant MD; Louise Biltgen RN DON.
Licensure Skilled care. *Beds* SNF 105.
Owner Nonprofit Corp (Adventist Health Sys-USA).
Admissions Requirements Medical examination.
Staff RNs; LPNs; Nurses aides; Activities coordinators.
Affiliation Seventh-Day Adventist
Facilities Dining room; Physical therapy room; Activities room; Crafts room; Laundry room; Barber/Beauty shop.
Activities Arts & crafts; Cards; Games; Reading groups; Prayer groups; Movies; Shopping trips; Social/Cultural gatherings.

MATTOON

Convalescent Care Center of Mattoon*
1000 Palm, Mattoon, IL, 61938
(217) 234-7403
Admin William J Heise. *Medical Dir/Dir of Nursing* Wilfred Brunswick MD.
Licensure Skilled care; Intermediate care. *Beds* SNF 162; ICF 92. *Certified* Medicaid.
Owner Proprietary Corp.
Staff RNs 2 (ft), 2 (pt); LPNs 11 (ft); Nurses aides 46 (ft); Occupational therapists 1 (ft), 2 (pt); Speech therapists 2 (pt); Activities coordinators 1 (ft); Dentists 1 (ft); Physical therapist aides 2 (ft); Recreational therapist aides 3 (ft).
Facilities Dining room; Physical therapy room; Activities room; Chapel; Crafts room; Laundry room; Barber/Beauty shop; Library.
Activities Arts & crafts; Cards; Games; Reading groups; Prayer groups; Movies; Shopping trips; Social/Cultural gatherings.

Douglas Living Center
W Rte 121, Mattoon, IL, 61938
(217) 234-6401

Admin Rick Harding. *Medical Dir/Dir of Nursing* Wilfred Brunsloick MD; Roxanne Osborne RN DON.
Licensure Skilled care. *Beds* 75. *Certified* Medicaid; Medicare.
Owner Nonprofit Corp (Adventist Health Sys-USA).
Admissions Requirements Minimum age 18; Medical examination; Physician's request.
Staff RNs 3 (ft); LPNs 4 (ft), 5 (pt); Orderlies 1 (pt); Nurses aides 22 (ft), 4 (pt); Physical therapists 1 (ft); Activities coordinators 1 (ft); Dietitians 1 (ft).
Affiliation Seventh-Day Adventist
Facilities Dining room; Physical therapy room; Activities room; Chapel; Crafts room; Laundry room; Barber/Beauty shop.
Activities Arts & crafts; Cards; Games; Reading groups; Prayer groups; Movies; Shopping trips.

Mattoon Health Care Center Inc
2121 S 9th St, Mattoon, IL, 61938
(217) 235-7138
Admin Carl D Taniges. *Medical Dir/Dir of Nursing* Dr L E McNiell MD; Elizabeth Howard RN DON.
Licensure Skilled care; Intermediate care. *Beds* SNF 148. *Certified* Medicaid; Medicare.
Owner Proprietary Corp.
Admissions Requirements Medical examination; Physician's request.
Staff RNs 3 (ft); LPNs 10 (ft), 3 (pt); Nurses aides 30 (ft); Physical therapists 1 (pt); Occupational therapists 1 (pt); Speech therapists 1 (pt); Activities coordinators 2 (ft), 1 (pt); Dietitians 1 (pt); Ophthalmologists 1 (pt); Podiatrists 1 (pt); 1 (ft), 1 (pt).
Facilities Dining room; Physical therapy room; Activities room; Crafts room; Laundry room; Barber/Beauty shop.
Activities Arts & crafts; Cards; Games; Reading groups; Prayer groups; Movies; Shopping trips; Social/Cultural gatherings.

Odd Fellow-Rebekah Home
201 E Lafayette Ave, Mattoon, IL, 61938
(217) 235-5449
Admin Lualyce C Brown. *Medical Dir/Dir of Nursing* Dr Robert F Swengel; Mary Jane Taylor RN DON.
Licensure Skilled care; Intermediate care. *Beds* 120. *Certified* Medicaid.
Owner Nonprofit Corp.
Admissions Requirements Minimum age 65; Medical examination; Physician's request.
Staff RNs 5 (ft), 2 (pt); LPNs 9 (ft), 2 (pt); Orderlies 3 (ft); Nurses aides 40 (ft), 8 (pt); Physical therapists 3 (ft); Occupational therapists 1 (ft); Speech therapists 1 (pt); Activities coordinators 2 (ft), 1 (pt); Dietitians 1 (ft); Social services 2 (ft), 1 (pt).
Affiliation Independent Order of Odd Fellows & Rebekahs
Facilities Dining room; Physical therapy room; Activities room; Chapel; Crafts room; Laundry room; Barber/Beauty shop; Library.
Activities Arts & crafts; Cards; Games; Reading groups; Prayer groups; Movies; Shopping trips; Social/Cultural gatherings.

MAYWOOD

Baptist Retirement Home
316 Randolph, Maywood, IL, 60153
(312) 344-1541
Admin Rev T Arthur Guscott. *Medical Dir/Dir of Nursing* Raymond J MacDonald MD; Beverly Duryea RN DON.
Licensure Intermediate care; Independent living. *Beds* ICF 69; Independent living 109. *Certified* Medicaid.
Owner Nonprofit organization/foundation.
Admissions Requirements Medical examination.

Staff Physicians 2 (ft); RNs 3 (ft); LPNs 5 (ft); Nurses aides 24 (ft); Physical therapists 1 (pt); Recreational therapists 2 (ft); Occupational therapists 1 (pt); Speech therapists 1 (pt); Activities coordinators 2 (ft); Dietitians 1 (ft); Dentists 1 (pt); Ophthalmologists 1 (pt); Podiatrists 1 (pt).
Affiliation Baptist
Facilities Dining room; Physical therapy room; Activities room; Chapel; Crafts room; Laundry room; Barber/Beauty shop; Library.
Activities Arts & crafts; Cards; Games; Reading groups; Prayer groups; Movies; Shopping trips; Social/Cultural gatherings.

MCHENRY

Royal Terrace Inc
803 Royal Dr, McHenry, IL, 60050
(815) 344-2600
Admin Corrine Lerman. *Medical Dir/Dir of Nursing* James Skopec MD; Mary Randolph RN DON.
Licensure Skilled care. *Beds* SNF 316. *Certified* Medicaid; Medicare.
Owner Proprietary Corp.
Admissions Requirements Minimum age 18; Medical examination; Physician's request.
Staff Physicians 20 (pt); RNs 30 (ft), 8 (pt); LPNs 15 (ft), 4 (pt); Orderlies 10 (ft); Nurses aides 110 (ft), 10 (pt); Physical therapists 3 (ft); Recreational therapists 1 (ft); Occupational therapists 1 (pt); Speech therapists 1 (pt); Activities coordinators 1 (ft); Dietitians 1 (pt); Dentists 1 (pt); Ophthalmologists 1 (pt); Dentist 2 (pt).
Languages Spanish, Polish
Facilities Dining room; Physical therapy room; Activities room; Chapel; Crafts room; Laundry room; Barber/Beauty shop; Library; Greenhouse; Fitness trails both outside & inside.
Activities Arts & crafts; Cards; Games; Reading groups; Prayer groups; Movies; Shopping trips; Social/Cultural gatherings; Concerts; Psychosocial groups; Exercise groups; Cooking groups.

MCLEANSBORO

Lifecare Center of McLeansboro Inc
405 E Carpenter St, McLeansboro, IL, 62859
(618) 643-3728
Admin Marsha Depoister. *Medical Dir/Dir of Nursing* D I Tomaneng.
Licensure Intermediate care. *Beds* ICF 43. *Certified* Medicaid.
Owner Proprietary Corp (Community Lifecare Enterprises).
Admissions Requirements Medical examination.
Staff LPNs 3 (ft); Nurses aides 15 (ft), 1 (pt); Physical therapists 1 (pt); Activities coordinators 1 (ft); Dietitians 1 (ft).
Facilities Dining room; Physical therapy room; Activities room; Laundry room; Barber/Beauty shop.
Activities Arts & crafts; Cards; Games; Reading groups; Prayer groups; Movies; Shopping trips; Social/Cultural gatherings.

MENDON

North Adams Home Inc
Rte 2, Box 100, Mendon, IL, 62351
(217) 936-2137
Admin John D Bainum. *Medical Dir/Dir of Nursing* Donna R Smith RN DON.
Licensure Intermediate care. *Beds* SNF 98. *Certified* Medicaid.
Owner Nonprofit Corp.
Admissions Requirements Minimum age Adult; Medical examination.
Staff RNs 1 (ft), 1 (pt); LPNs 5 (ft), 9 (pt); Nurses aides 14 (ft), 22 (pt); Activities coordinators 1 (ft).

Facilities Dining room; Physical therapy room; Activities room; Chapel; Crafts room; Laundry room; Barber/Beauty shop; Library; Lounge.
Activities Arts & crafts; Cards; Games; Prayer groups; Movies; Social/Cultural gatherings.

MENDOTA

Heritage Manor & Nursing Conv Home
1201 1st Ave, Mendota, IL, 61342
(815) 539-6745
Admin Marilee T Holzner RN. *Medical Dir/Dir of Nursing* R H Musick MD; Marianne Etzbach RN DON.
Licensure Skilled care; Intermediate care. *Beds* SNF 50; ICF 49. *Certified* Medicaid; Medicare.
Owner Proprietary Corp (Heritage Enterprises).
Admissions Requirements Minimum age 19; Medical examination.
Staff RNs 5 (ft), 4 (pt); LPNs 3 (ft), 2 (pt); Orderlies 1 (ft); Nurses aides 20 (ft), 10 (pt); Physical therapists 1 (pt); Activities coordinators 1 (ft).
Facilities Dining room; Physical therapy room; Activities room; Crafts room; Laundry room; Barber/Beauty shop; Library.
Activities Arts & crafts; Cards; Games; Reading groups; Prayer groups; Movies; Shopping trips; Social/Cultural gatherings.

Mendota Lutheran Home
500 6th St, Mendota, IL, 61342
(815) 539-7439
Admin Earnest L Serr. *Medical Dir/Dir of Nursing* William Schuler MD.
Licensure Intermediate care; Sheltered care. *Beds* ICF 80; Sheltered care 21.
Owner Nonprofit Corp.
Admissions Requirements Minimum age 65.
Staff Physicians 1 (pt); RNs 2 (ft), 3 (pt); LPNs 3 (ft), 4 (pt); Nurses aides 23 (ft), 19 (pt); Activities coordinators 1 (ft).
Affiliation Lutheran
Facilities Dining room; Activities room; Chapel; Laundry room; Barber/Beauty shop; Library.
Activities Arts & crafts; Cards; Games; Reading groups; Prayer groups; Movies; Social/Cultural gatherings.

METROPOLIS

Magnolia Manor—SNF
2101 Metropolis St, Metropolis, IL, 62960
(618) 524-5677
Admin Michelle Cavitt. *Medical Dir/Dir of Nursing* Dr E T Yap; Marilyn Carlock.
Licensure Skilled care. *Beds* SNF 63. *Certified* Medicaid.
Owner Proprietary Corp.
Admissions Requirements Minimum age 18.
Staff RNs 1 (ft), 2 (pt); LPNs 4 (ft), 1 (pt); Nurses aides 15 (ft), 3 (pt); Physical therapists 1 (pt); Recreational therapists 1 (ft), 1 (pt); Speech therapists 1 (pt); Activities coordinators 1 (ft); Dietitians 4 (ft), 2 (pt); Ophthalmologists 1 (pt).
Facilities Dining room; Physical therapy room; Activities room; Laundry room; Barber/Beauty shop.
Activities Arts & crafts; Cards; Games; Reading groups; Prayer groups; Shopping trips; Social/Cultural gatherings.

Metropolis Good Samaritan Home
2299 Metropolis St, Metropolis, IL, 62960
(618) 524-2634
Admin Ronald D Philips. *Medical Dir/Dir of Nursing* Dr Benito Bajuyo; Zena Wells.
Licensure Skilled care. *Beds* 85. *Certified* Medicaid.
Owner Nonprofit Corp (Evangelical Lutheran/ Good Samaritan).

Admissions Requirements Medical examination.
Staff RNs 2 (ft), 2 (pt); LPNs 6 (ft), 3 (pt); Orderlies 3 (ft), 1 (pt); Nurses aides 17 (ft), 5 (pt); Activities coordinators 1 (ft).
Affiliation Lutheran
Facilities Dining room; Physical therapy room; Activities room; Laundry room; Barber/Beauty shop.
Activities Arts & crafts; Cards; Games; Reading groups; Prayer groups; Movies; Shopping trips; Social/Cultural gatherings.

Southgate Health Care Center
900 E 9th St, Metropolis, IL, 62960
(618) 524-2683
Admin Jane Ann Parker. *Medical Dir/Dir of Nursing* Helen Bowman.
Licensure Skilled care; Intermediate care. *Beds* SNF 125; ICF. *Certified* Medicaid; Medicare.
Owner Proprietary Corp.
Admissions Requirements Minimum age 21.
Staff Physicians 6 (pt); RNs 2 (ft), 1 (pt); LPNs 9 (ft); Nurses aides 32 (ft); Physical therapists 1 (pt); Activities coordinators 1 (ft); Dietitians 1 (pt); Ophthalmologists 2 (pt).
Facilities Dining room; Physical therapy room; Activities room; Crafts room; Laundry room; Barber/Beauty shop.
Activities Arts & crafts; Games; Prayer groups; Movies; Shopping trips; Social/Cultural gatherings; Trips to zoo; Train rides; Educational trips.

MIDLOTHIAN

Bowman Nursing Home
3249 W 147th St, Midlothian, IL, 60445
(312) 389-3141
Admin Loretta T Ebers; Francine J Petrarca. *Medical Dir/Dir of Nursing* Sheldon Levine MD; Barbara Miller DON.
Licensure Intermediate care. *Beds* ICF 92. *Certified* Medicaid.
Owner Privately owned.
Admissions Requirements Minimum age 18.
Staff RNs 1 (ft), 2 (pt); LPNs 6 (ft), 6 (pt); Nurses aides 16 (ft), 12 (pt); Activities coordinators 1 (ft), 1 (pt).
Facilities Dining room; Activities room; Crafts room; Laundry room; Barber/Beauty shop.
Activities Arts & crafts; Cards; Games; Reading groups; Prayer groups; Movies; Shopping trips; Social/Cultural gatherings.

Crestwood Terrace
13301 S Central Ave, Midlothian, IL, 60445
(312) 597-5251
Admin Maureen M Skopick. *Medical Dir/Dir of Nursing* Dr A Noreiga.
Licensure Intermediate care. *Beds* 126. *Certified* Medicaid.
Owner Proprietary Corp.
Admissions Requirements Medical examination.
Staff Physicians 1 (ft), 10 (pt); RNs 2 (ft), 2 (pt); LPNs 3 (ft), 6 (pt); Nurses aides 14 (ft), 10 (pt); Reality therapists 3 (ft); Recreational therapists 3 (ft); Occupational therapists 1 (pt); Speech therapists 1 (pt); Activities coordinators 1 (ft); Dietitians 1 (pt); Dentists 2 (pt); Ophthalmologists 1 (pt); Podiatrists 1 (pt).
Facilities Dining room; Physical therapy room; Activities room; Chapel; Crafts room; Laundry room; Barber/Beauty shop; Library; Van for outings.
Activities Arts & crafts; Cards; Games; Reading groups; Prayer groups; Movies; Shopping trips; Social/Cultural gatherings.

MILAN

Comfort Harbor Home*
114 W 2nd St, Milan, IL, 61264
(309) 787-2066
Admin J Michael Lavery.
Licensure Sheltered care. *Beds* 38.
Owner Proprietary Corp.

MILLSTADT

Mill Haven Care Center*
415 Veterans Dr, Millstadt, IL, 62260
(618) 476-3575
Admin Dorothy Davis.
Licensure Intermediate care. *Beds* 101. *Certified* Medicaid.
Owner Proprietary Corp.

MINONK

Lida Home Nursing Home*
201 Locust, Minonk, IL, 61760
(309) 432-2557
Admin John C Kirkton.
Licensure Intermediate care. *Beds* 49. *Certified* Medicaid.
Owner Nonprofit Corp.

MOLINE

Heritage 53*
4601 53rd St, Moline, IL, 61265
(309) 757-9540
Admin Kyle R Rick.
Licensure Intermediate care. *Beds* 64.
Owner Nonprofit Corp.

Moline Nursing & Rehabilitation Center
833 16th Ave, Moline, IL, 61265
(309) 764-6744
Admin James Huber. *Medical Dir/Dir of Nursing* Dr Bruce Vesole; Marvis Hafner DON.
Licensure Skilled care; Intermediate care. *Beds* 117. *Certified* Medicaid; Medicare.
Owner Proprietary Corp (Health Care & Retirement Corp).
Admissions Requirements Medical examination.
Staff RNs 6 (ft); LPNs 8 (ft), 5 (pt); Orderlies 2 (ft); Nurses aides 38 (ft), 10 (pt); Physical therapists 2 (ft), 1 (pt); Speech therapists 1 (pt); Dietitians 1 (pt); Dentists 1 (pt); Ophthalmologists 1 (pt); Podiatrists 1 (pt); Occupational therapists aides 2 (ft), 1 (pt).
Facilities Dining room; Physical therapy room; Activities room; Crafts room; Laundry room; Barber/Beauty shop.
Activities Arts & crafts; Cards; Games; Reading groups; Prayer groups; Movies; Shopping trips; Social/Cultural gatherings.

MOMENCE

Good Shepherd Manor
PO Box 260, IL Hwy 1, Momence, IL, 60954
(815) 472-6492
Admin Doris Williamson RN. *Medical Dir/Dir of Nursing* Paul Wolfe MD; Susan Fox RN.
Licensure Sheltered care MR. *Beds* 120.
Owner Nonprofit organization/foundation.
Admissions Requirements Minimum age 18; Males only.
Staff Physicians 1 (pt); RNs 1 (ft); LPNs 1 (ft); Orderlies 9 (ft); Recreational therapists 1 (pt); Speech therapists 1 (pt); Activities coordinators 1 (pt); Dietitians 1 (pt); Dentists 1 (pt).
Affiliation Roman Catholic
Facilities Dining room; Activities room; Chapel; Crafts room; Laundry room; Barber/ Beauty shop.
Activities Arts & crafts; Movies; Shopping trips.

Momence Meadows Nursing Center Inc*
500 S Walnut, Momence, IL, 60954
(815) 472-2423
Admin Teresa Thompson RN. *Medical Dir/ Dir of Nursing* Dr Verapaneni.
Licensure Skilled care; Intermediate care. *Beds* SNF 34; ICF 40. *Certified* Medicaid.
Owner Proprietary Corp.
Admissions Requirements Minimum age 21; Medical examination; Physician's request.
Staff Physicians 5 (pt); RNs 3 (ft), 2 (pt); LPNs 2 (ft), 4 (pt); Orderlies 1 (ft); Nurses aides 12 (ft), 7 (pt); Physical therapists 1 (pt); Reality therapists 1 (pt); Recreational therapists 1 (pt); Occupational therapists 1 (pt); Speech therapists 1 (pt); Activities coordinators 1 (ft), 1 (pt); Dietitians 1 (pt); Dentists 1 (pt); Ophthalmologists 1 (pt); Podiatrists 1 (pt).
Facilities Dining room; Physical therapy room; Activities room; Chapel; Crafts room; Laundry room; Barber/Beauty shop; Library.
Activities Arts & crafts; Cards; Games; Reading groups; Prayer groups; Movies; Shopping trips; Social/Cultural gatherings.

MONMOUTH

Applegate Manor Inc*
515 E Euclid Ave, Monmouth, IL, 61462
(309) 734-5163
Admin Richard Green.
Licensure Skilled care; Intermediate care; Sheltered care. *Beds* SNF 30; ICF 58; Sheltered care 30.
Owner Proprietary Corp.

Monmouth Nursing Home
116 S "H" St, Monmouth, IL, 61462
(309) 734-3811
Admin Suzann Pieper. *Medical Dir/Dir of Nursing* Madhav Ratnakar MD; Donna Twomey RN DON.
Licensure Intermediate care. *Beds* ICF 35.
Owner Privately owned.
Admissions Requirements Medical examination; Physician's request.
Staff RNs 1 (ft); LPNs 3 (ft), 3 (pt); Nurses aides 6 (ft), 6 (pt); Activities coordinators 1 (ft), 1 (pt).
Facilities Dining room; Laundry room; Barber/Beauty shop.
Activities Arts & crafts; Games; Reading groups; Prayer groups; Movies; Shopping trips; Social/Cultural gatherings.

MONTICELLO

Piatt County Nursing Home*
PO Box 449, 1111 N State St, Monticello, IL, 61856
(217) 762-2506
Admin Marilyn Benedino.
Licensure Skilled care; Intermediate care. *Beds* 99. *Certified* Medicaid.
Owner Publicly owned.
Admissions Requirements Minimum age 55.
Facilities Dining room; Activities room; Crafts room; Laundry room; Barber/Beauty shop.
Activities Arts & crafts; Cards; Games; Reading groups; Prayer groups; Movies; Shopping trips; Social/Cultural gatherings.

MORRIS

Grundy County Home
Clay & Quarry Sts, PO Box 669, Morris, IL, 60450
(815) 942-3255
Admin S Morse.
Licensure Intermediate care. *Beds* 143. *Certified* Medicaid.
Owner Publicly owned.
Admissions Requirements Minimum age 18; Medical examination; Physician's request.

Morris Lincoln Nursing Home
PO Box 689, 916 Fremont Ave, Morris, IL, 60450
(815) 942-1202
Admin Marjorie D Johnson. *Medical Dir/Dir of Nursing* Sandra Johnson RN.
Licensure Intermediate care; Sheltered care. *Beds* ICF 47; Sheltered care 34. *Certified* Medicaid.
Owner Proprietary Corp.
Admissions Requirements Minimum age 45; Medical examination.
Staff RNs 2 (ft); LPNs 3 (ft), 2 (pt); Nurses aides 14 (ft), 10 (pt); Physical therapists 1 (ft); Recreational therapists 1 (pt); Speech therapists 1 (pt); Activities coordinators 1 (ft); Dietitians 1 (ft); Rehab aides 2 (ft).
Facilities Dining room; Physical therapy room; Activities room.
Activities Arts & crafts.

MORRISON

Morrison Community Hospital
303 N Jackson St, Morrison, IL, 61270
(815) 772-4003
Admin Kent L Brown. *Medical Dir/Dir of Nursing* David Fell MD.
Licensure Skilled care; Intermediate care. *Beds* SNF 24; ICF 14. *Certified* Medicaid; Medicare.
Owner Publicly owned.
Admissions Requirements Physician's request.
Staff Physicians 6 (ft); RNs 6 (ft), 3 (pt); LPNs 1 (ft), 1 (pt); Nurses aides 11 (ft), 5 (pt); Physical therapists 1 (ft); Occupational therapists 1 (ft); Speech therapists 1 (ft); Activities coordinators 1 (ft); Dietitians 1 (ft).
Facilities Dining room; Physical therapy room; Activities room; Chapel; Crafts room; Laundry room; Barber/Beauty shop; Library.
Activities Arts & crafts; Cards; Games; Reading groups; Prayer groups; Movies; Social/Cultural gatherings; Shopping trips.

Pleasant View Home*
N Jackson St, Morrison, IL, 61270
(815) 772-7288
Admin Mary K McKnight.
Licensure Intermediate care. *Beds* 74. *Certified* Medicaid.
Owner Publicly owned.

Resthave Home of Whiteside County
408 Maple Ave, Morrison, IL, 61270
(815) 772-4021
Admin Ronald L Garwick. *Medical Dir/Dir of Nursing* Dr R Londo.
Licensure Intermediate care; Sheltered care. *Beds* ICF 49; Sheltered care 27. *Certified* Medicare.
Owner Nonprofit Corp.
Admissions Requirements Medical examination.
Staff RNs 2 (ft), 2 (pt); LPNs 1 (ft), 3 (pt); Nurses aides 15 (ft), 10 (pt); Activities coordinators 1 (ft); Dietitians 1 (pt).
Facilities Dining room; Activities room; Crafts room; Laundry room; Barber/Beauty shop.
Activities Arts & crafts; Cards; Games; Reading groups; Prayer groups; Movies.

MORTON

Apostolic Christian Home for the Handicapped
Rte 3, Veterans Rd, Morton, IL, 61550
(309) 266-9781
Admin Robert Knobloch. *Medical Dir/Dir of Nursing* Maureen Collette DON.
Licensure Intermediate care for developmentally disabled. *Beds* ICF/DD 104. *Certified* Medicaid.
Owner Nonprofit organization/foundation.
Admissions Requirements Minimum age 18; Medical examination.

Staff RNs; LPNs; Nurses aides; Physical therapists; Recreational therapists; Occupational therapists; Activities coordinators.
Affiliation Apostolic Christian
Facilities Dining room; Physical therapy room; Activities room; Chapel; Crafts room; Laundry room; Barber/Beauty shop.
Activities Arts & crafts; Cards; Games; Reading groups; Prayer groups; Movies; Shopping trips; Social/Cultural gatherings.

Apostolic Christian Restmor I*
935 E Jefferson St, Morton, IL, 61550
(309) 266-7141
Admin James L Metzger. *Medical Dir/Dir of Nursing* Dr James Early.
Licensure Skilled care; Sheltered care. *Beds* SNF 115; Sheltered care 27.
Owner Nonprofit Corp.
Admissions Requirements Minimum age 18; Medical examination.
Staff Physicians; RNs 5 (ft), 9 (pt); LPNs 4 (ft), 7 (pt); Orderlies 2 (ft); Nurses aides 42 (ft), 13 (pt); Physical therapists; Occupational therapists; Speech therapists; Activities coordinators 1 (ft); Dietitians; Dentists; Pharmacists 1 (ft), 2 (pt); Social workers 1 (ft).
Affiliation Apostolic Christian
Facilities Dining room; Physical therapy room; Activities room; Chapel; Crafts room; Laundry room; Barber/Beauty shop.
Activities Arts & crafts; Cards; Games; Reading groups; Prayer groups; Movies; Shopping trips; Social/Cultural gatherings.

Morton Healthcare Center*
190 E Queenwood, Morton, IL, 61550
(309) 266-9741
Admin Irene Johnson. *Medical Dir/Dir of Nursing* Dr Phillip A Immesoete.
Licensure Skilled care; Intermediate care. *Beds* 106. *Certified* Medicaid; Medicare.
Owner Proprietary Corp.
Admissions Requirements Minimum age 18.
Staff Physicians 1 (ft), 2 (pt); RNs 3 (ft), 2 (pt); LPNs 2 (ft), 3 (pt); Orderlies 1 (pt); Nurses aides 22 (ft), 1 (pt); Physical therapists 1 (pt); Occupational therapists 1 (ft); Speech therapists 1 (pt); Activities coordinators 1 (pt); Dietitians 1 (pt); Dentists 1 (pt); Ophthalmologists 1 (pt); Podiatrists 1 (pt).
Facilities Dining room; Physical therapy room; Activities room; Crafts room; Laundry room; Barber/Beauty shop; Library.
Activities Arts & crafts; Cards; Games; Reading groups; Prayer groups; Movies; Social/Cultural gatherings.

Morton Terrace Ltd
191 E Queenwood Rd, Morton, IL, 61550
(309) 266-5331
Admin Patricia Chism. *Medical Dir/Dir of Nursing* Dr Stan Koch; Judith Tidaback RN DON.
Licensure Intermediate care. *Beds* 144. *Certified* Medicaid.
Owner Proprietary Corp.
Admissions Requirements Minimum age 18; Medical examination; Physician's request.
Staff RNs 1 (ft); LPNs 9 (ft); Nurses aides 25 (ft).
Facilities Dining room; Physical therapy room; Activities room; Laundry room; Barber/Beauty shop.
Activities Arts & crafts; Cards; Games; Reading groups; Prayer groups; Movies; Shopping trips; Social/Cultural gatherings.

MORTON GROVE

Bethany Terrace Retirement & Nursing Home
8425 Waukegan Rd, Morton Grove, IL, 60053
(312) 965-8100
Admin Bonnie K Lindgren. *Medical Dir/Dir of Nursing* Paul Vega MD; Trudee Gast RN.

Licensure Skilled care; Intermediate care; Sheltered care. *Beds* SNF 103; ICF 150; Sheltered care 12. *Certified* Medicaid; Medicare.
Owner Nonprofit Corp.
Admissions Requirements Minimum age 18; Medical examination; Physician's request.
Staff Physicians 3 (pt); RNs 15 (ft), 25 (pt); LPNs 8 (ft), 1 (pt); Orderlies 5 (ft), 2 (pt); Nurses aides 81 (ft), 26 (pt); Physical therapists 3 (ft); Reality therapists 4 (ft), 3 (pt); Occupational therapists 1 (pt); Activities coordinators 1 (ft); Dietitians 1 (ft).
Affiliation Methodist
Facilities Dining room; Physical therapy room; Activities room; Chapel; Crafts room; Laundry room; Barber/Beauty shop; Library; Occupational Therapy room; Rehab room; Enclosed patios.
Activities Arts & crafts; Cards; Games; Reading groups; Prayer groups; Movies; Shopping trips; Social/Cultural gatherings; Luncheons; Baseball; Community activities; Church; Botanical gardens; Tropical fish; Parrakeets; Rabbits; Baking; Resident council; Gardening; Mens' club; Parkinsons' group; Choral club; Community service projects.

MOUNDS

Meridian Manor
420 S Blanche St, Mounds, IL, 62964
(618) 745-6537
Admin Jane Connell Flournoy. *Medical Dir/Dir of Nursing* Ann Nottage LPN.
Licensure Intermediate care. *Beds* ICF 64. *Certified* Medicaid.
Owner Proprietary Corp.
Admissions Requirements Minimum age 18; Medical examination.
Staff LPNs 4 (ft), 2 (pt); Nurses aides 10 (ft), 5 (pt); Activities coordinators 1 (ft), 1 (pt).
Facilities Dining room; Activities room; Laundry room; Barber/Beauty shop.
Activities Arts & crafts; Games; Prayer groups; Movies; Shopping trips.

MOUNT CARMEL

General Baptist Nursing Home
RR 4, Mount Carmel, IL, 62863
(618) 263-4337
Admin Jack R Cole. *Medical Dir/Dir of Nursing* R L Fuller MD; Yvonne Pohl DON.
Licensure Skilled care. *Beds* 160. *Certified* Medicaid; Medicare.
Owner Nonprofit Corp.
Admissions Requirements Minimum age 18; Medical examination.
Staff RNs 2 (ft), 5 (pt); LPNs 9 (ft), 5 (pt); Orderlies 6 (ft); Nurses aides 45 (ft); Physical therapists 1 (pt); Speech therapists 1 (pt); Activities coordinators 2 (ft), 1 (pt); Dietitians 10 (ft), 5 (pt); Ophthalmologists 2 (pt).
Facilities Dining room; Physical therapy room; Activities room; Chapel; Crafts room; Laundry room; Barber/Beauty shop; Library.
Activities Arts & crafts; Cards; Games; Reading groups; Prayer groups; Movies; Shopping trips; Social/Cultural gatherings.

Shurtleff Manor Residential*
1527 N College Dr, Mount Carmel, IL, 62863
(618) 263-3511
Admin Helen R Lewis. *Medical Dir/Dir of Nursing* Dr C L Johns.
Licensure Intermediate care. *Beds* 84. *Certified* Medicaid.
Owner Proprietary Corp.
Staff Physicians 7 (ft); RNs 1 (ft); LPNs 5 (ft); Nurses aides 15 (ft); Physical therapists 1 (ft); Reality therapists 1 (ft); Recreational therapists 2 (ft); Speech therapists 1 (ft);

Activities coordinators 2 (ft); Dietitians 1 (ft); Dentists 2 (ft); Ophthalmologists 2 (ft); Podiatrists 1 (ft); Audiologists 1 (ft).
Facilities Dining room; Activities room; Crafts room; Laundry room; Barber/Beauty shop; Smoking & drinking lounge.
Activities Arts & crafts; Cards; Games; Reading groups; Prayer groups; Movies; Shopping trips; Social/Cultural gatherings.

MOUNT CARROLL

Carroll County Good Samaritan Center
Box 111, N Washington St, Mount Carroll, IL, 61053
(815) 244-7715
Admin Margaret D Charlton. *Medical Dir/Dir of Nursing* Dr Rachuy; Bonnie Johns DON.
Licensure Intermediate care. *Beds* ICF 68. *Certified* Medicaid.
Owner Nonprofit Corp (Evangelical Lutheran/Good Samaritan).
Admissions Requirements Minimum age 22; Medical examination; Physician's request.
Staff RNs 6 (pt); LPNs 4 (pt); Nurses aides 11 (ft), 13 (pt); Physical therapists 2 (ft), 1 (pt); Activities coordinators 2 (ft), 1 (pt); Dietitians 1 (ft); Social services 1 (ft).
Affiliation Lutheran
Facilities Dining room; Physical therapy room; Activities room; Chapel; Laundry room; Barber/Beauty shop.
Activities Arts & crafts; Cards; Games; Reading groups; Prayer groups; Movies; Shopping trips; Social/Cultural gatherings; Outings in facility bus.

MOUNT MORRIS

Pinecrest Manor
414 S Wesley, Mount Morris, IL, 61054
(815) 734-4103
Admin Gary E Montel. *Medical Dir/Dir of Nursing* C L Edwards MD; Jackie Bacon DON.
Licensure Skilled care; Intermediate care; Congregate living; Independent living. *Beds* SNF 54; ICF 65; Congregate living 48; Independent living 9. *Certified* Medicaid; Medicare.
Owner Nonprofit Corp.
Admissions Requirements Minimum age 62; Medical examination.
Staff Physicians 3 (pt); RNs 8 (ft), 6 (pt); LPNs 4 (ft), 4 (pt); Orderlies 2 (ft), 1 (pt); Nurses aides 42 (ft), 24 (pt); Physical therapists 1 (pt); Activities coordinators 3 (ft); Dietitians 1 (ft).
Facilities Dining room; Physical therapy room; Activities room; Chapel; Crafts room; Barber/Beauty shop; Library.
Activities Arts & crafts; Cards; Games; Reading groups; Prayer groups; Movies.

MOUNT PULASKI

The Henry & Jane Vonderlieth Living Center Inc
Rte 121 & Elkhart Rd, Mount Pulaski, IL, 62548
(217) 792-3218
Admin Steven E Evans. *Medical Dir/Dir of Nursing* James B Borgerson MD; Mary L Brown RN DON.
Licensure Skilled care. *Beds* SNF 90. *Certified* Medicaid.
Owner Nonprofit Corp.
Admissions Requirements Minimum age 18; Medical examination; Physician's request.
Staff RNs 3 (ft); LPNs 9 (ft), 4 (pt); Nurses aides 31 (ft), 7 (pt); Physical therapists 1 (pt); Recreational therapists 1 (pt); Speech therapists 1 (pt); Activities coordinators 2 (ft), 2 (pt); Dietitians 1 (pt); Ophthalmologists 1 (pt).

Facilities Dining room; Physical therapy room; Activities room; Crafts room; Laundry room; Barber/Beauty shop; Library; Lounges.
Activities Arts & crafts; Cards; Games; Reading groups; Prayer groups; Movies; Shopping trips; Social/Cultural gatherings.

MOUNT STERLING

Modern Manor Inc*
Camden Rd, Mount Sterling, IL, 62353
(217) 773-3377
Admin Marianna Pontius. *Medical Dir/Dir of Nursing* Russell R Dohner MD.
Licensure Skilled care; Intermediate care. *Beds* 87. *Certified* Medicaid; Medicare.
Owner Proprietary Corp.
Admissions Requirements Medical examination.
Staff RNs 4 (ft); LPNs 4 (ft), 1 (pt); Nurses aides 13 (ft), 16 (pt); Activities coordinators 1 (ft).
Facilities Dining room; Physical therapy room; Activities room; Chapel; Laundry room; Barber/Beauty shop.
Activities Arts & crafts; Cards; Games; Prayer groups; Movies; Shopping trips; Social/Cultural gatherings.

MOUNT VERNON

Casey Manor Health Facility I*
5 Doctors' Park Rd, Mount Vernon, IL, 62864
(618) 242-1064
Admin Patricia Ray Forsythe.
Licensure Intermediate care. *Beds* 113. *Certified* Medicaid.
Owner Proprietary Corp.

The Jeffersonian
1700 White St, Mount Vernon, IL, 62864
(618) 242-4075
Admin Margaret Setzekorn. *Medical Dir/Dir of Nursing* Goff Thompson; Ann Bargaresser RN.
Licensure Skilled care. *Beds* 64. *Certified* Medicaid.
Owner Privately owned.
Admissions Requirements Minimum age 16; Medical examination; Physician's request.
Staff Physicians; RNs; LPNs; Nurses aides; Physical therapists; Recreational therapists; Dietitians.
Facilities Dining room; Physical therapy room; Chapel; Laundry room; Barber/Beauty shop.
Activities Arts & crafts; Cards; Games; Reading groups; Prayer groups; Movies; Shopping trips; Social/Cultural gatherings.

Mt Vernon Care Facility Inc*
1717 Jefferson St, Mount Vernon, IL, 62864
(618) 224-2861
Admin Darleen E Dycus.
Licensure Intermediate care. *Beds* 64. *Certified* Medicaid.
Owner Proprietary Corp.
Admissions Requirements Minimum age 20; Medical examination; Physician's request.
Staff RNs 1 (pt); LPNs 6 (ft); Orderlies 4 (ft); Nurses aides 18 (ft); Dietitians 1 (pt).
Facilities Dining room; Activities room; Laundry room; Barber/Beauty shop.
Activities Arts & crafts; Cards; Games; Reading groups; Prayer groups; Shopping trips; Social/Cultural gatherings.

Nature Trail Home Inc
1001 S 34th St, Mount Vernon, IL, 62864
(618) 242-5700
Admin Doris Brickey. *Medical Dir/Dir of Nursing* Marge Frakes DON.
Licensure Intermediate care. *Beds* ICF 74. *Certified* Medicaid.
Owner Proprietary Corp.
Admissions Requirements Minimum age 55; Medical examination.

Staff RNs 1 (ft), 1 (pt); LPNs 4 (ft), 1 (pt);
Nurses aides 17 (ft); Physical therapists 1
(pt); Activities coordinators 3 (ft).
Facilities Dining room; Physical therapy
room; Activities room; Crafts room; Laundry
room; Barber/Beauty shop.
Activities Arts & crafts; Cards; Games;
Reading groups; Prayer groups; Movies;
Shopping trips.

MOUNT ZION

Woodland Nursing Center
1225 Woodland Dr, Mount Zion, IL, 62549
(217) 864-2356
Admin W H Silver. *Medical Dir/Dir of
Nursing* E J Boros MD; Millie Gromoll RN
DON.
Licensure Skilled care. *Beds* SNF 73. *Certified*
Medicaid; Medicare.
Owner Proprietary Corp (Columbia Corp).
Staff Physicians 2 (pt); RNs 2 (ft), 1 (pt);
LPNs 6 (ft), 4 (pt); Orderlies 1 (pt); Nurses
aides 22 (ft), 17 (pt); Activities coordinators
1 (ft), 1 (pt).
Facilities Dining room; Physical therapy
room; Activities room; Crafts room; Laundry
room; Barber/Beauty shop; Library; Family
visiting room.
Activities Arts & crafts; Cards; Games;
Reading groups; Prayer groups; Movies.

MUNDELEIN

Glenkirk Circle
27219 N Owens Rd, Mundelein, IL, 60060
(312) 526-1333
Admin Lisa K Dworkin. *Medical Dir/Dir of
Nursing* Theresa Holmes.
Licensure Intermediate care for mentally
retarded. *Beds* ICF/MR 15. *Certified*
Medicaid.
Owner Nonprofit Corp.
Admissions Requirements Minimum age 18;
Medical examination.
Staff Physicians 1 (pt); RNs 1 (ft), 1 (pt);
LPNs 2 (pt); Occupational therapists 1 (pt);
Speech therapists 1 (pt); Activities
coordinators 1 (pt).
Facilities Dining room; Activities room; Den.
Activities Arts & crafts; Movies; Shopping
trips; Social/Cultural gatherings.

Riverside Foundation*
14588 W Hwy 22, Mundelein, IL, 60060
(312) 634-3973
Admin Patricia T Weisser.
Licensure Intermediate care. *Beds* 99.
Certified Medicaid.
Owner Nonprofit Corp.

MURPHYSBORO

Jackson County Nursing Home
1441 N 14th St, Murphysboro, IL, 62966
(618) 684-2136
Admin Richard A Ligon. *Medical Dir/Dir of
Nursing* Andrew R Esposito MD; Marge
Eisenhauer RN.
Licensure Skilled care. *Beds* SNF 260.
Certified Medicaid; Medicare.
Owner Nonprofit organization/foundation.
Admissions Requirements Minimum age 18;
Medical examination; Physician's request.
Staff Physicians; RNs; LPNs; Nurses aides;
Physical therapists; Recreational therapists;
Occupational therapists; Speech therapists;
Activities coordinators; Dietitians;
Ophthalmologists.
Facilities Dining room; Physical therapy
room; Activities room; Chapel; Crafts room;
Barber/Beauty shop; Library.
Activities Arts & crafts; Cards; Games;
Reading groups; Prayer groups; Movies;
Shopping trips; Social/Cultural gatherings;
Library study; Cooking class; Weekly bingo.

Roosevelt Square—Murphysboro
PO Box 707, 1501 Shomaker Dr,
Murphysboro, IL, 62966
(618) 684-2693
Admin Irwin L Faulkner.
Licensure Intermediate care for mentally
retarded. *Beds* 81.
Owner Proprietary Corp.

NAPERVILLE

Alden Nursing Center of Naperville
1525 S Oxford Ln, Naperville, IL, 60565
(312) 983-0300
Admin F Holly Striska. *Medical Dir/Dir of
Nursing* Manvinder Singh; Kathy
Brockmann.
Licensure Skilled care. *Beds* SNF 206.
Certified Medicaid; Medicare.
Owner Proprietary Corp.
Admissions Requirements Minimum age 18;
Medical examination.
Staff Physicians 9 (pt); RNs 7 (ft); LPNs 14
(ft); Orderlies 10 (ft); Nurses aides 45 (ft);
Physical therapists 1 (pt); Reality therapists
2 (ft); Recreational therapists 1 (pt);
Occupational therapists 1 (ft), 1 (pt); Speech
therapists 1 (pt); Activities coordinators 1
(ft), 8 (pt); Dietitians 1 (ft), 1 (pt); Dentists 1
(pt); Ophthalmologists 1 (pt); Podiatrists 1
(pt).
Languages Spanish, Tagalog
Facilities Dining room; Physical therapy
room; Activities room; Chapel; Crafts room;
Laundry room; Barber/Beauty shop; Library;
Occupational therapy room; Lounge; Patio.
Activities Arts & crafts; Cards; Games;
Reading groups; Prayer groups; Movies;
Shopping trips; Social/Cultural gatherings.

Americana Nursing Center
200 W Martin Ave, Naperville, IL, 60540
(312) 355-4111
Admin Sheiley R Leverso. *Medical Dir/Dir of
Nursing* Dr Farouk Girgis; Linda Morris
RN.
Licensure Skilled care. *Beds* SNF 92. *Certified*
Medicaid; Medicare.
Owner Proprietary Corp (Manor Care).
Admissions Requirements Minimum age 18;
Physician's request.
Staff RNs 8 (ft), 6 (pt); LPNs 2 (ft), 2 (pt);
Orderlies 2 (ft), 1 (pt); Nurses aides 20 (ft),
10 (pt); Physical therapists 1 (ft), 1 (pt);
Recreational therapists 1 (ft), 1 (pt);
Occupational therapists 1 (ft); Speech
therapists 1 (pt); Activities coordinators 1
(ft).
Facilities Dining room; Physical therapy
room; Activities room; Crafts room; Laundry
room; Barber/Beauty shop.
Activities Arts & crafts; Cards; Games;
Reading groups; Prayer groups; Movies;
Social/Cultural gatherings.

Mill Street Conv Center*
1136 Mill St, Naperville, IL, 60540
(312) 355-3300
Admin Alan J Litwiller. *Medical Dir/Dir of
Nursing* Dr William Perkins.
Licensure Skilled care; Intermediate care. *Beds*
SNF 129; ICF 26. *Certified* Medicare.
Owner Proprietary Corp.
Admissions Requirements Minimum age 18;
Medical examination; Physician's request.
Staff Physicians 4 (pt); RNs 10 (ft), 10 (pt);
LPNs 5 (ft), 5 (pt); Orderlies 30 (ft), 20 (pt);
Physical therapists 1 (ft); Occupational
therapists 1 (pt); Speech therapists 1 (pt);
Activities coordinators 1 (ft); Dietitians 1
(pt); Dentists 2 (pt); Ophthalmologists 1 (pt);
Podiatrists 1 (pt).
Facilities Dining room; Physical therapy
room; Activities room; Crafts room; Laundry
room; Barber/Beauty shop; Library.

Activities Arts & crafts; Cards; Games;
Reading groups; Prayer groups; Movies;
Shopping trips; Social/Cultural gatherings.

NASHVILLE

Friendship Manor Inc*
305 Friendship Dr, Nashville, IL, 62263
(618) 327-3041
Admin Floyed Wreath.
Licensure Skilled care; Intermediate care. *Beds*
SNF 90; ICF 140. *Certified* Medicaid;
Medicare.
Owner Proprietary Corp.

NEW ATHENS

New Athens Home*
203 S Johnson St, New Athens, IL, 62264
(618) 475-2550
Admin Richard Sutter.
Licensure Intermediate care. *Beds* 64.
Certified Medicaid.
Owner Nonprofit Corp.

NEW BADEN

Clinton Manor
111 E Illinois St, New Baden, IL, 62265
(618) 588-4924
Admin Dolores J Krebs. *Medical Dir/Dir of
Nursing* Dr Paul Biedenharn; Lynn
Timmermann.
Licensure Intermediate care; Intermediate care
for mentally retarded. *Beds* ICF 27; ICF/MR
42. *Certified* Medicaid.
Owner Proprietary Corp.
Admissions Requirements Minimum age 18;
Medical examination.
Staff RNs 1 (ft); LPNs 2 (ft), 4 (pt); Orderlies
4 (ft); Nurses aides 16 (ft), 6 (pt);
Recreational therapists 2 (ft); Activities
coordinators 1 (ft).
Facilities Dining room; Activities room;
Laundry room; Barber/Beauty shop.
Activities Arts & crafts; Cards; Games;
Reading groups; Prayer groups; Movies;
Shopping trips; Social/Cultural gatherings;
Bingo.

NEWMAN

Continental Manor of Newman*
PO Box 335, Newman, IL, 61942
(217) 837-2421
Admin Benjamina A Prince. *Medical Dir/Dir
of Nursing* Dr Guinto.
Licensure Skilled care; Intermediate care. *Beds*
60. *Certified* Medicaid.
Owner Proprietary Corp.
Admissions Requirements Medical
examination.
Staff Physicians 1 (pt); Physical therapists 1
(pt); Activities coordinators 1 (ft); Dietitians
1 (pt).
Facilities Dining room; Physical therapy
room; Activities room; Crafts room; Laundry
room; Barber/Beauty shop.
Activities Arts & crafts; Games; Reading
groups; Prayer groups; Movies; Shopping
trips.

NEWTON

Newton Rest Haven Inc
PO Box 360, 300 S Scott St, Newton, IL,
62448
(618) 783-2309
Admin Karen Eyman Kinder. *Medical Dir/Dir
of Nursing* JoAnn Miller.
Licensure Skilled care. *Beds* SNF 92. *Certified*
Medicaid.
Owner Proprietary Corp.

NILES

Forest Villa Nursing Center
6840 W Touhy Ave, Niles, IL, 60648
(312) 647-8994
Admin William A Ladra. *Medical Dir/Dir of Nursing* Todd Grendon MD.
Licensure Skilled care; Intermediate care. *Beds* SNF 55; ICF 151. *Certified* Medicaid.
Owner Proprietary Corp.
Admissions Requirements Minimum age 62; Medical examination.
Staff Physicians 4 (pt); RNs 7 (ft), 3 (pt); LPNs 8 (ft); Orderlies 8 (ft); Nurses aides 34 (ft); Physical therapists 1 (pt); Recreational therapists 1 (pt); Occupational therapists 1 (pt); Activities coordinators 1 (ft); Dietitians 1 (pt); Dentists 1 (pt); Ophthalmologists 1 (pt); Podiatrists 1 (pt).
Facilities Dining room; Physical therapy room; Activities room; Crafts room; Laundry room; Barber/Beauty shop.
Activities Arts & crafts; Cards; Games; Reading groups; Prayer groups; Movies; Shopping trips; Social/Cultural gatherings.

George J Goldman Memorial Home for the Aged
6601 W Touhy Ave, Niles, IL, 60648
(312) 647-9875
Admin Daniel E Novick.
Licensure Skilled care. *Beds* 99. *Certified* Medicaid.
Owner Proprietary Corp.

Golf Mill Plaza I*
9777 Greenwood, Niles, IL, 60648
(312) 967-7000
Admin Lester M Edelson. *Medical Dir/Dir of Nursing* Jerome Podgers MD.
Licensure Skilled care; Intermediate care. *Beds* SNF 99; ICF 88. *Certified* Medicaid.
Owner Proprietary Corp.
Admissions Requirements Minimum age 18.
Staff Physicians; RNs; LPNs; Orderlies; Nurses aides; Physical therapists; Reality therapists; Recreational therapists; Occupational therapists; Speech therapists; Activities coordinators; Dietitians; Dentists; Ophthalmologists; Podiatrists; Audiologists.
Facilities Dining room; Physical therapy room; Activities room; Crafts room; Laundry room; Barber/Beauty shop; Library.
Activities Arts & crafts; Cards; Games; Reading groups; Prayer groups; Movies; Shopping trips; Social/Cultural gatherings.

Miranda Manor Ltd*
8333 W Golf Rd, Niles, IL, 60648
(312) 966-9190
Admin Nancy L Ashenbrenner.
Licensure Skilled care; Intermediate care. *Beds* SNF 148; ICF 148. *Certified* Medicaid.
Owner Proprietary Corp.

Regency Nursing Centre Inc*
6631 Milwaukee Ave, Niles, IL, 60648
(312) 647-7444
Admin Barbara Hecht.
Licensure Skilled care. *Beds* 300. *Certified* Medicaid; Medicare.
Owner Proprietary Corp.

St Andrew Home for the Aged
7000 N Newark, Niles, IL, 60648
(312) 647-8332
Admin Sr M Rasalita Wojtykunas. *Medical Dir/Dir of Nursing* Conrad Wiet MD.
Licensure Intermediate care; Sheltered care. *Beds* ICF 33; Sheltered care. *Certified* Medicaid.
Owner Nonprofit Corp.
Admissions Requirements Minimum age 65; Medical examination.
Staff Physicians 1 (pt); RNs 3 (ft), 4 (pt).
Facilities Dining room; Physical therapy room; Activities room; Chapel; Crafts room; Laundry room; Barber/Beauty shop.

Activities Arts & crafts; Cards; Games; Prayer groups; Movies; Shopping trips; Social/Cultural gatherings.

St Benedict Home for Aged
6930 W Touhy Ave, Niles, IL, 60648
(312) 774-1440
Admin Sr Irene I Sebo. *Medical Dir/Dir of Nursing* Donald Quinlan MD.
Licensure Intermediate care. *Beds* 52.
Owner Nonprofit Corp.
Admissions Requirements Minimum age 70; Medical examination.
Staff Physicians; RNs; LPNs 3 (ft), 2 (pt); Nurses aides 3 (ft), 2 (pt); Reality therapists 1 (pt); Occupational therapists 1 (pt); Dietitians 1 (ft); Dentists 1 (pt); Ophthalmologists 1 (pt); Dentist 1 (pt).
Affiliation Roman Catholic
Facilities Dining room; Activities room; Chapel; Laundry room; Barber/Beauty shop.
Activities Arts & crafts; Cards; Games; Reading groups; Prayer groups; Movies; Shopping trips; Social/Cultural gatherings; Gardening; Trips.

Sterling Manor
8555 Maynard Rd, Niles, IL, 60648
(312) 967-7000
Admin Mark S Segal. *Medical Dir/Dir of Nursing* Jerome Podgers; Mariamma Pillai DON.
Licensure Skilled care; Intermediate care. *Beds* SNF 112; ICF 188. *Certified* Medicaid; Medicare.
Owner Proprietary Corp.
Staff RNs 16 (ft), 2 (pt); LPNs 3 (ft); Nurses aides 60 (ft), 10 (pt); Physical therapists 2 (ft); Recreational therapists 5 (ft), 1 (pt); Occupational therapists 2 (ft); Speech therapists 1 (pt); Activities coordinators 1 (ft); Dietitians 1 (pt); Dentists 1 (pt); Ophthalmologists 1 (pt); Podiatrists 1 (pt).
Languages German, Polish
Facilities Dining room; Physical therapy room; Activities room; Crafts room; Laundry room; Barber/Beauty shop.
Activities Arts & crafts; Cards; Games; Reading groups; Prayer groups; Movies; Shopping trips; Social/Cultural gatherings.

NOKOMIS

Nokomis Golden Manor
505 Stevens St, Nokomis, IL, 62075
(217) 563-7513
Admin Joyce A Pauley. *Medical Dir/Dir of Nursing* Dr D Quizon; Kathleen Culberson RN DON.
Licensure Skilled care; Intermediate care. *Beds* SNF; ICF 94. *Certified* Medicaid; Medicare.
Owner Proprietary Corp.
Admissions Requirements Minimum age 18; Medical examination; Physician's request.
Staff RNs 2 (ft), 1 (pt); LPNs 3 (ft), 3 (pt); Nurses aides 20 (ft), 20 (pt); Physical therapists 1 (pt); Recreational therapists 1 (pt); Occupational therapists 1 (pt); Speech therapists 1 (pt); Activities coordinators 1 (ft); Dietitians 1 (pt); Ophthalmologists 1 (pt); 15 (ft), 10 (pt); Dentist 1 (pt).
Facilities Dining room; Physical therapy room; Activities room; Chapel; Laundry room; Barber/Beauty shop; Library.
Activities Arts & crafts; Games; Prayer groups; Movies; Shopping trips; Social/Cultural gatherings.

NORMAL

Americana Healthcare Center of Normal*
510 Broadway, Normal, IL, 61761
(309) 452-4406
Admin Linda L Morrison.
Licensure Skilled care. *Beds* 90. *Certified* Medicaid; Medicare.
Owner Proprietary Corp (Manor Care).

Heritage Manor of Normal
509 N Adelaide St, Normal, IL, 61761
(309) 452-7468
Admin Rose M Stadel. *Medical Dir/Dir of Nursing* Pramern Sriratana MD; Diane Schraufnagel DON.
Licensure Skilled care; Intermediate care. *Beds* SNF 44; ICF 130. *Certified* Medicaid.
Owner Proprietary Corp (Heritage Enterprises).
Admissions Requirements Medical examination.
Staff RNs 3 (ft), 2 (pt); LPNs 11 (ft), 5 (pt); Orderlies 13 (ft), 1 (ft); Nurses aides 27 (ft), 4 (pt); Activities coordinators 1 (ft); Dietitians 1 (ft).
Facilities Dining room; Physical therapy room; Activities room; Chapel; Crafts room; Laundry room; Barber/Beauty shop; Library.
Activities Arts & crafts; Cards; Games; Reading groups; Prayer groups; Movies; Shopping trips; Social/Cultural gatherings.

McLean County Nursing Home*
901 N Main, Normal, IL, 61761
(309) 452-8337
Admin Donald W Lee.
Licensure Skilled care. *Beds* 150. *Certified* Medicaid.
Owner Publicly owned.

NORRIDGE

Central Baptist Home for the Aged
4750 N Orange Ave, Norridge, IL, 60656
(312) 452-3700
Admin Alan Kegel. *Medical Dir/Dir of Nursing* Dorothy Rittmueller.
Licensure Intermediate care; Sheltered care; Retirement care. *Beds* ICF 38; Sheltered care 23; Retirement care 52. *Certified* Medicaid.
Owner Nonprofit Corp.
Admissions Requirements Minimum age 62; Medical examination.
Staff RNs; LPNs; Orderlies; Nurses aides; Recreational therapists 7 (ft); Activities coordinators 1 (ft); Dietitians 1 (ft).
Affiliation Baptist
Facilities Dining room; Physical therapy room; Activities room; Chapel; Crafts room; Laundry room; Barber/Beauty shop; Library.
Activities Arts & crafts; Cards; Games; Reading groups; Prayer groups; Movies; Shopping trips; Social/Cultural gatherings.

NORTH AURORA

North Aurora Manor
PO Box E, 310 Banbury Rd, North Aurora, IL, 60542
(312) 892-7627
Admin Cathy Spiller. *Medical Dir/Dir of Nursing* H Kim MD.
Licensure Intermediate care. *Beds* ICF 129. *Certified* Medicaid.
Owner Proprietary Corp (Beverly Enterprises).
Admissions Requirements Minimum age 55; Medical examination; Physician's request.
Staff Physicians; RNs; LPNs; Nurses aides; Physical therapists; Occupational therapists; Speech therapists; Activities coordinators; Dietitians.
Facilities Dining room; Physical therapy room; Activities room; Chapel; Barber/Beauty shop; Solarium.
Activities Arts & crafts; Cards; Games; Reading groups; Prayer groups; Movies; Shopping trips; Social/Cultural gatherings.

NORTH RIVERSIDE

The Scottish Home
28th St & Des Plaines Ave, North Riverside, IL, 60546
(312) 447-5092

Admin Wayne Rethford. *Medical Dir/Dir of Nursing* Edwin Nebblett MD; Doris Burt DON.
Licensure Intermediate care; Sheltered care. *Beds* ICF 14; Sheltered care 49.
Owner Nonprofit organization/foundation.
Admissions Requirements Minimum age 60; Medical examination.
Staff Physicians 13 (pt); RNs 1 (ft), 2 (pt); LPNs 4 (ft); Nurses aides 9 (ft), 5 (pt); Physical therapists 1 (pt); Activities coordinators 2 (ft), 1 (pt); Dietitians 1 (ft); Dentists 1 (pt); Ophthalmologists 1 (pt); Podiatrists 1 (pt).
Facilities Dining room; Physical therapy room; Activities room; Crafts room; Laundry room; Barber/Beauty shop; Library; Living room.
Activities Arts & crafts; Cards; Games; Reading groups; Prayer groups; Movies; Shopping trips; Social/Cultural gatherings; Theatre trips; Musical entertainment; Parties; Residents council; Restaurant dining.

NORTHBROOK

Brandel Care Center
2155 Pfingston Rd, Northbrook, IL, 60062
(312) 480-6350
Admin Beverly Z Smith. *Medical Dir/Dir of Nursing* Dr Russell Elmer; Geraldine Wesner DON.
Licensure Skilled care. *Beds* SNF 104. *Certified* Medicaid; Medicare.
Owner Nonprofit Corp (Covenant Benevolent Inst).
Admissions Requirements Minimum age 18; Medical examination; Physician's request.
Staff Physicians 20 (pt); RNs 8 (ft), 12 (pt); LPNs 2 (ft), 1 (pt); Orderlies 5 (ft); Nurses aides 30 (ft), 30 (pt); Physical therapists 1 (pt); Activities coordinators 1 (ft), 2 (pt); Dietitians 1 (ft).
Affiliation Evangelical Covenant Church
Facilities Dining room; Physical therapy room; Activities room; Chapel; Laundry room; Barber/Beauty shop; Library.
Activities Arts & crafts; Cards; Games; Reading groups; Prayer groups; Movies; Shopping trips.

G A F Lake Cook Terrace
222 Dennis Dr, Northbrook, IL, 60062
(312) 564-0505
Admin Flavia Ambrogi. *Medical Dir/Dir of Nursing* Scott Braunlich MD; Marla Yanes RN DON.
Licensure Skilled care; Intermediate care. *Beds* SNF 90; ICF 50. *Certified* Medicaid.
Owner Proprietary Corp.
Admissions Requirements Minimum age 50.
Staff Physicians 1 (ft), 3 (pt); RNs 6 (ft), 3 (pt); LPNs 4 (ft), 1 (pt); Orderlies 10 (ft); Nurses aides 31 (ft), 3 (pt); Reality therapists 1 (pt); Occupational therapists 2 (pt); Activities coordinators 1 (ft); Dietitians 1 (pt).
Facilities Dining room; Physical therapy room; Activities room; Crafts room; Laundry room; Barber/Beauty shop; Library; Patio.
Activities Arts & crafts; Cards; Games; Reading groups; Prayer groups; Movies; Shopping trips; Social/Cultural gatherings; Writing groups; Breakfast club; Lunch groups; In-house luncheons.

Glen Oaks Nursing Home Inc
270 Skokie Hwy, Northbrook, IL, 60062
(312) 498-9320
Admin Rita Steinback. *Medical Dir/Dir of Nursing* Dr Edward Sutoris.
Licensure Skilled care; Intermediate care. *Beds* SNF 164; ICF 130. *Certified* Medicaid; Medicare.
Owner Proprietary Corp.

Staff Physicians 7 (pt); RNs 38 (ft); LPNs 14 (ft); Orderlies 14 (ft); Nurses aides 64 (ft), 3 (pt); Physical therapists 5 (ft), 2 (pt); Reality therapists 2 (ft); Recreational therapists 7 (ft); Occupational therapists 1 (ft); Speech therapists 1 (pt); Activities coordinators 1 (ft); Dietitians 1 (pt); Dentists 1 (pt); Ophthalmologists 1 (pt); Podiatrists 2 (pt); Art therapist 1 (ft).
Facilities Dining room; Physical therapy room; Activities room; Crafts room; Laundry room; Barber/Beauty shop; Library.
Activities Arts & crafts; Cards; Games; Reading groups; Prayer groups; Movies; Shopping trips; Social/Cultural gatherings.

NORTHLAKE

Villa Scalabrini
480 N Wolf Rd, Northlake, IL, 60164
(312) 526-0040
Admin Lawrence Cozzi.
Licensure Skilled care; Intermediate care; Sheltered care. *Beds* SNF 98; ICF 62; Sheltered care 89. *Certified* Medicaid.
Owner Proprietary Corp.

OAK BROOK

Oak Brook Nursing Center
2013 W Midwest Rd, Oak Brook, IL, 60521
(312) 495-0220
Admin Richard Darling BSN. *Medical Dir/Dir of Nursing* Norton Fishman MD; Sheila Nelson RN.
Licensure Skilled care; Intermediate care. *Beds* SNF 110; ICF 28. *Certified* Medicaid; Medicare.
Owner Proprietary Corp.
Admissions Requirements Minimum age 65; Medical examination.
Staff RNs 4 (ft), 4 (pt); LPNs 8 (ft), 5 (pt); Nurses aides 27 (ft), 10 (pt); Physical therapists 1 (ft), 1 (pt); Recreational therapists 1 (pt); Occupational therapists 2 (ft), 1 (pt); Speech therapists 1 (pt); Activities coordinators 3 (ft); Dietitians 1 (pt); Ophthalmologists 1 (pt).
Facilities Dining room; Physical therapy room; Activities room; Chapel; Crafts room; Laundry room; Barber/Beauty shop; Gift shop; Patio; TV room; Day rooms.
Activities Arts & crafts; Cards; Games; Reading groups; Prayer groups; Shopping trips; Social/Cultural gatherings; Bingo; Trips to parks; Zoo.

OAK FOREST

Kosary Home*
6660 W 147th St, Box E, Oak Forest, IL, 60452
(312) 687-4300
Admin Julius Kosary.
Licensure Sheltered care. *Beds* 66.
Owner Proprietary Corp.

OAK LAWN

Americana Healthcare Center
9401 S Kostner Ave, Oak Lawn, IL, 60453
(312) 423-7882
Admin Leslie G Ohm. *Medical Dir/Dir of Nursing* Dr A Ricker; Diana Fidler DON.
Licensure Skilled care. *Beds* SNF 157. *Certified* Medicare.
Owner Proprietary Corp (Manor Care).
Admissions Requirements Minimum age 18.
Staff Physicians 3 (pt); RNs 8 (ft), 8 (pt); LPNs 12 (ft), 10 (pt); Nurses aides 46 (ft), 7 (pt); Physical therapists 1 (ft), 1 (pt); Recreational therapists 3 (pt); Occupational therapists 2 (pt); Speech therapists 1 (ft); Activities coordinators 1 (ft); Dietitians 1 (pt); Ophthalmologists 1 (pt).

Facilities Dining room; Physical therapy room; Activities room; Crafts room; Laundry room; Barber/Beauty shop; Speech therapy room; Occupational therapy room; 4 lounge areas.
Activities Arts & crafts; Cards; Games; Prayer groups; Movies; Social/Cultural gatherings; Happy hour; Exercise groups; Reality orientation classes; Baking classes; Social cart; "Green Thumb" plant club; Ceramics classes.

Americana-Monticello Convalescent Center*
6300 W 95th St, Oak Lawn, IL, 60453
(312) 735-5454
Admin Lise P Miller. *Medical Dir/Dir of Nursing* Dr Stanley Ruzich.
Licensure Skilled care; Intermediate care. *Beds* 175. *Certified* Medicare.
Owner Proprietary Corp (Manor Care).
Facilities Dining room; Physical therapy room; Activities room; Laundry room; Barber/Beauty shop.
Activities Arts & crafts; Cards; Games; Reading groups; Prayer groups; Movies; Shopping trips; Social/Cultural gatherings.

Concord Extended Care
9401 S Ridgeland Ave, Oak Lawn, IL, 60453
(312) 599-6700
Admin Elsie Hoover. *Medical Dir/Dir of Nursing* B G Shreenivan; Barbara Ryan RN DON.
Licensure Skilled care. *Beds* SNF 99; 35. *Certified* Medicaid; Medicare.
Owner Proprietary Corp.
Admissions Requirements Minimum age 45; Medical examination; Physician's request.
Staff Physicians 1 (pt); RNs 4 (ft), 4 (pt); LPNs 3 (ft), 5 (pt); Nurses aides 25 (ft), 19 (pt); Physical therapists 1 (pt); Recreational therapists 1 (ft), 3 (pt); Occupational therapists 1 (pt); Activities coordinators 1 (ft); Dietitians 1 (pt); Ophthalmologists 1 (pt).
Facilities Dining room; Physical therapy room; Activities room; Laundry room; Barber/Beauty shop.
Activities Arts & crafts; Cards; Games; Prayer groups; Movies; Shopping trips; Social/Cultural gatherings; Field trips.

Greentree Nursing Center*
8540 S Harlem Ave, Oak Lawn, IL, 60455
(312) 598-2605
Admin Marshall A Mauer.
Licensure Skilled care. *Beds* 404. *Certified* Medicaid.
Owner Proprietary Corp.

Oak Lawn Convalescent Home
9525 S Mayfield, Oak Lawn, IL, 60453
(312) 636-7000
Admin William Krukar. *Medical Dir/Dir of Nursing* Judith Oftedahl.
Licensure Skilled care; Intermediate care. *Beds* SNF 71; ICF 66. *Certified* Medicaid.
Owner Proprietary Corp.
Admissions Requirements Medical examination.
Staff Physicians; RNs; LPNs; Orderlies; Nurses aides; Physical therapists; Occupational therapists; Activities coordinators; Dietitians; Dentists; Ophthalmologists.
Facilities Dining room; Physical therapy room; Activities room; Laundry room; Barber/Beauty shop.
Activities Arts & crafts; Cards; Games; Prayer groups; Movies; Shopping trips; Social/Cultural gatherings.

OAK PARK

Oak Park Convalescent & Geriatric Center
625 N Harlem Ave, Oak Park, IL, 60302
(312) 848-5966

Admin Robert J Molitor. *Medical Dir/Dir of Nursing* Dr Wallace Turkland; Dorothy Sweet.
Licensure Skilled care; Intermediate care. *Beds* SNF 176; ICF 28. *Certified* Medicaid; Medicare.
Owner Proprietary Corp.
Admissions Requirements Medical examination.
Staff RNs; LPNs; Nurses aides; Physical therapists; Occupational therapists; Speech therapists; Activities coordinators; Dietitians; Ophthalmologists; Podiatrists.
Facilities Dining room; Physical therapy room; Activities room; Crafts room; Laundry room; Barber/Beauty shop.
Activities Arts & crafts; Cards; Games; Reading groups; Prayer groups; Movies; Shopping trips.

Renaissance Manor Ltd
637 S Maple Ave, Oak Park, IL, 60304
(312) 848-4400
Admin Mary Kay Cabay RN.
Licensure Sheltered care. *Beds* Shelter care 26. *Certified* Medicaid.
Owner Proprietary Corp.
Staff RNs 1 (ft); LPNs 6 (pt); Nurses aides 15 (pt); Ophthalmologists 1 (pt).
Facilities Dining room; Activities room; Crafts room; Laundry room; Library.
Activities Arts & crafts; Cards; Games; Reading groups; Prayer groups; Movies; Shopping trips; Social/Cultural gatherings; Church services.

The Woodbine
6909 W North Ave, Oak Park, IL, 60302
(312) 386-1112
Admin Helen Soyer Smith RN. *Medical Dir/Dir of Nursing* Fred Barber MD.
Licensure Skilled care; Intermediate care. *Beds* SNF 66.
Owner Proprietary Corp.
Admissions Requirements Minimum age 21; Medical examination; Physician's request.
Staff Physicians 3 (pt); RNs 7 (ft), 5 (pt); LPNs 2 (ft), 4 (pt); Nurses aides 30 (ft); Physical therapists 2 (pt); Reality therapists 1 (pt); Recreational therapists 1 (pt); Occupational therapists 1 (pt); Speech therapists 1 (pt); Activities coordinators 1 (pt); Dietitians 1 (pt); Dentists 1 (pt); Ophthalmologists 1 (pt); Podiatrists 1 (pt); Dentist 1 (pt).
Facilities Dining room; Physical therapy room; Activities room; Crafts room; Laundry room; Barber/Beauty shop; Library.
Activities Arts & crafts; Cards; Games; Reading groups; Prayer groups; Movies; Social/Cultural gatherings.

OBLONG

Ridgeview Care Center*
1 Ridgeview Ln, Oblong, IL, 62449
Admin Eileen W Cunningham.
Licensure Skilled care. *Beds* 49. *Certified* Medicaid.
Owner Proprietary Corp.

ODIN

Odin Care Center*
Green St, Odin, IL, 62870
(618) 775-6444
Admin Philip E Pennington. *Medical Dir/Dir of Nursing* P T Durion MD.
Licensure Skilled care; Intermediate care. *Beds* 98. *Certified* Medicaid; Medicare.
Owner Proprietary Corp.
Admissions Requirements Minimum age 18; Medical examination; Physician's request.
Staff Physicians 11 (pt); RNs 3 (ft); LPNs 6 (ft); Orderlies 5 (ft); Nurses aides 30 (ft); Physical therapists 1 (pt); Occupational therapists 1 (ft); Speech therapists 1 (ft);

Activities coordinators 2 (ft); Dietitians 1 (pt); Dentists 1 (pt); Ophthalmologists 1 (pt); Podiatrists 1 (pt); Audiologists 1 (pt).
Facilities Dining room; Physical therapy room; Activities room; Crafts room; Laundry room; Barber/Beauty shop; Library; Living room; Patio.
Activities Arts & crafts; Cards; Games; Reading groups; Prayer groups; Movies; Shopping trips; Social/Cultural gatherings; Remotivation group; Community affairs; Bingo.

OFALLON

Parkview Colonial Manor
300 Weber Rd, O'Fallon, IL, 62269
(618) 632-3511
Admin Judy R Mincher. *Medical Dir/Dir of Nursing* Dr Bradley Sakrin; Karen Ernst RN DON.
Licensure Skilled care; Intermediate care. *Beds* SNF 108; ICF 41. *Certified* Medicaid; Medicare.
Owner Proprietary Corp.
Admissions Requirements Minimum age 21; Medical examination.
Staff Physicians 17 (pt); RNs 3 (ft), 2 (pt); LPNs 5 (ft), 4 (pt); Nurses aides 35 (ft), 25 (pt); Physical therapists 1 (pt); Recreational therapists 1 (pt); Occupational therapists 1 (pt); Speech therapists 1 (pt); Activities coordinators 1 (ft); Dietitians 1 (pt); Dentists 1 (pt); Ophthalmologists 1 (pt); Podiatrists 1 (pt).
Facilities Dining room; Physical therapy room; Activities room; Laundry room; Barber/Beauty shop.
Activities Arts & crafts; Cards; Games; Reading groups; Prayer groups; Movies; Shopping trips; Social/Cultural gatherings.

OGLESBY

Horizon South Living Center*
Pool Dr & Lehigh Ave, Oglesby, IL, 61348
(815) 883-3317
Admin Gerlyn J Koehler. *Medical Dir/Dir of Nursing* Dr W Y Kim.
Licensure Intermediate care for mentally retarded. *Beds* 16.
Admissions Requirements Minimum age 18; Medical examination; Physician's request.
Staff RNs 3 (ft); LPNs 3 (ft); Recreational therapists 1 (ft); Activities coordinators 1 (ft); Training staff 15 (ft), 18 (pt).
Facilities Dining room; Activities room; Crafts room; Laundry room.
Activities Arts & crafts; Cards; Games; Reading groups; Prayer groups; Movies; Shopping trips; Social/Cultural gatherings.

OLNEY

Burgin Manor
900-928 E Scott St, Olney, IL, 62450
(618) 393-2914
Admin Sue Burgin. *Medical Dir/Dir of Nursing* Dr Arcot Suresh; Donna Brant RN.
Licensure Skilled care. *Beds* SNF 150. *Certified* Medicaid; Medicare.
Owner Proprietary Corp.
Admissions Requirements Medical examination.
Staff RNs 6 (ft), 2 (pt); LPNs 8 (ft), 2 (pt); Orderlies 4 (ft); Nurses aides 35 (ft), 20 (pt); Physical therapists 1 (ft), 1 (pt); Reality therapists 1 (ft); Recreational therapists 3 (ft); Occupational therapists 1 (ft), 1 (pt); Speech therapists 1 (ft), 1 (pt); Activities coordinators 1 (ft); Dietitians 1 (ft), 1 (pt).
Facilities Dining room; Physical therapy room; Activities room; Chapel; Crafts room; Laundry room; Barber/Beauty shop.

Activities Arts & crafts; Cards; Games; Reading groups; Prayer groups; Movies; Shopping trips; Social/Cultural gatherings; Bus tours; Fishing trips.

Marks Sunset Manor
1044 Whittle Ave, Olney, IL, 62450
(618) 392-0846
Admin Glen E Marks. *Medical Dir/Dir of Nursing* Jane Shaw.
Licensure Sheltered care. *Beds* 49. *Certified* Medicaid.
Owner Proprietary Corp.
Admissions Requirements Minimum age 18.
Staff Physicians 1 (pt); RNs 1 (pt); Orderlies 12 (ft); Reality therapists 1 (ft); Activities coordinators 1 (ft); Dietitians 1 (pt).
Facilities Dining room; Activities room; Crafts room; Laundry room; Library.
Activities Arts & crafts; Cards; Games; Reading groups; Prayer groups; Movies; Shopping trips; Social/Cultural gatherings.

Olney Care Center*
410 E Mack Ave, Olney, IL, 62450
(618) 395-7421
Admin Alice Berger.
Licensure Skilled care. *Beds* 98. *Certified* Medicaid; Medicare.
Owner Proprietary Corp.

OREGON

White Pines Manor Inc*
811 S 10th St, Oregon, IL, 61061
(815) 732-7994
Admin Thomas E Sutton. *Medical Dir/Dir of Nursing* Dr Swan.
Licensure Skilled care. *Beds* 63. *Certified* Medicaid; Medicare.
Staff RNs 2 (ft), 2 (pt); LPNs 2 (ft), 3 (pt); Nurses aides 20 (ft), 10 (pt); Physical therapists 1 (pt); Speech therapists 1 (pt); Activities coordinators 1 (ft); Dietitians 1 (pt).
Facilities Dining room; Physical therapy room; Activities room; Crafts room; Laundry room; Barber/Beauty shop; Library.
Activities Arts & crafts; Cards; Games; Reading groups; Prayer groups; Movies; Shopping trips; Social/Cultural gatherings.

OSWEGO

The Tillers Nursing Home Inc
PO Box 950, Rte 71, Oswego, IL, 60543
(312) 554-1001
Admin Robert M Saxon. *Medical Dir/Dir of Nursing* Dr Bjorn Fersell; Sue Woods DON.
Licensure Skilled care; Intermediate care. *Beds* SNF 90; ICF 9.
Owner Proprietary Corp.
Admissions Requirements Minimum age 18; Medical examination; Physician's request.
Staff Physicians 1 (pt); RNs 4 (ft), 10 (pt); Nurses aides 16 (ft), 20 (pt); Physical therapists 1 (ft); Recreational therapists 2 (ft); Occupational therapists 1 (pt); Speech therapists 1 (pt); Activities coordinators 2 (ft); Dietitians 1 (pt); Dentists 1 (pt); Ophthalmologists 1 (pt); Podiatrists 1 (pt).
Facilities Dining room; Physical therapy room; Activities room; Crafts room; Laundry room; Barber/Beauty shop; Library; TV room; Lounges; Patios; Screened porch.
Activities Arts & crafts; Cards; Games; Reading groups; Prayer groups; Movies; Shopping trips; Social/Cultural gatherings; Creative-type drama & poetry; Current events; Picnics; Mini-antique shows; Quilt shows; Style shows.

OTTAWA

La Salle County Nursing Home
Rte 1, Ottawa, IL, 61350
(815) 433-0476

Admin Franz C Devantier. *Medical Dir/Dir of Nursing* German Gonzalo MD; Kathleen Brown RN DON.
Licensure Intermediate care. *Beds* ICF 104. *Certified* Medicaid.
Owner Publicly owned.
Admissions Requirements Minimum age 18; Medical examination; Physician's request.
Staff RNs 1 (ft), 5 (pt); LPNs 4 (ft), 3 (pt); Nurses aides 29 (ft), 5 (pt); Activities coordinators 2 (ft).
Facilities Dining room; Activities room; Chapel; Laundry room; Barber/Beauty shop; Library.
Activities Arts & crafts; Cards; Games; Reading groups; Prayer groups; Movies; Social/Cultural gatherings.

Ottawa Care Center
800 E Center St, Ottawa, IL, 61350
(815) 434-7144
Admin Lois M Kallestad. *Medical Dir/Dir of Nursing* Dr G Andrews; Cindy Myer RN DON.
Licensure Skilled care. *Beds* SNF 93. *Certified* Medicaid; Medicare.
Owner Proprietary Corp.
Admissions Requirements Medical examination; Physician's request.
Staff Physicians 1 (pt); RNs 8 (ft); LPNs 4 (ft); Orderlies; Nurses aides 35 (ft); Physical therapists 1 (pt); Occupational therapists 1 (pt); Speech therapists 1 (pt); Activities coordinators 1 (ft); Dietitians 1 (pt); Ophthalmologists 1 (pt).
Facilities Dining room; Physical therapy room; Activities room; Chapel; Crafts room; Laundry room; Barber/Beauty shop; Library; Hospice for family.
Activities Arts & crafts; Cards; Games; Reading groups; Prayer groups; Movies; Shopping trips; Social/Cultural gatherings.

Pleasant View Luther Home
505 College Ave, Ottawa, IL, 61350
(815) 434-1130
Admin Karl O Norem. *Medical Dir/Dir of Nursing* Dr A G Giger; Dora Seth RN DON.
Licensure Intermediate care. *Beds* ICF 235. *Certified* Medicare.
Owner Nonprofit Corp.
Admissions Requirements Minimum age 60.
Staff Physicians 1 (pt); RNs 6 (ft), 6 (pt); LPNs 7 (ft), 6 (pt); Nurses aides 55 (ft), 24 (pt); Physical therapists 1 (pt); Recreational therapists 1 (pt); Occupational therapists 1 (pt); Speech therapists 1 (pt); Activities coordinators 1 (ft); Dietitians 1 (pt); Ophthalmologists 1 (pt); Podiatrists 1 (pt).
Affiliation Lutheran
Facilities Dining room; Physical therapy room; Activities room; Chapel; Crafts room; Laundry room; Barber/Beauty shop; Library.
Activities Arts & crafts; Cards; Games; Reading groups; Prayer groups; Movies; Shopping trips; Social/Cultural gatherings.

PALANTINE

Plum Grove Nursing Home
24 S Plum Grove Rd, Palantine, IL, 60067
(312) 358-0311
Admin G Paine. *Medical Dir/Dir of Nursing* Dr Daniel Schnuda; Anita Nie DON.
Licensure Skilled care. *Beds* SNF 35; ICF 34.
Owner Proprietary Corp (Convalescent Services).
Admissions Requirements Minimum age 18; Medical examination; Physician's request.
Staff Physicians; RNs 3 (ft), 4 (pt); LPNs 2 (ft), 2 (pt); Nurses aides 12 (ft), 2 (pt); Physical therapists; Recreational therapists; Occupational therapists; Activities coordinators; Dietitians; Dentists; Ophthalmologists; Podiatrists; Dentist.
Languages Spanish, German

Facilities Dining room; Activities room; Crafts room; Laundry room; Barber/Beauty shop; Library.
Activities Arts & crafts; Cards; Games; Reading groups; Prayer groups; Movies; Shopping trips; Social/Cultural gatherings.

PALATINE

Little City Foundation*
1706 W Algonquin Rd, Palatine, IL, 60067
(312) 358-5510
Admin D R Becker.
Licensure Intermediate care. *Beds* 80.
Owner Nonprofit Corp.

St Joseph's Home for the Elderly
80 W Northwest Hwy, Palatine, IL, 60067
(312) 358-5700
Admin Sr Gertrude Mary. *Medical Dir/Dir of Nursing* Dr Andrew Cornejo; Sr Martha DON.
Licensure Skilled care; Intermediate care; Residential. *Beds* SNF 50; ICF 54; Residential 33. *Certified* Medicaid.
Owner Nonprofit Corp.
Admissions Requirements Minimum age 65.
Staff Physicians 4 (pt); RNs 20 (ft); LPNs 2 (pt); Orderlies 2 (pt); Nurses aides 40 (ft); Physical therapists 1 (pt); Occupational therapists 1 (pt); Activities coordinators 1 (ft); Dietitians 1 (pt); Dentists 1 (pt); Ophthalmologists 1 (pt); Podiatrists 2 (pt).
Affiliation Roman Catholic
Facilities Dining room; Physical therapy room; Activities room; Chapel; Crafts room; Laundry room; Barber/Beauty shop; Library.
Activities Arts & crafts; Cards; Games; Reading groups; Prayer groups; Movies; Shopping trips; Social/Cultural gatherings.

PALOS HEIGHTS

Rest Haven Central Christian Nursing Home
13259 S Central Ave, Palos Heights, IL, 60463
(312) 597-1000
Admin Edwin T Mulder. *Medical Dir/Dir of Nursing* Marian Kickert.
Licensure Skilled care; Intermediate care. *Beds* SNF 96; ICF 99. *Certified* Medicaid.
Owner Nonprofit Corp.
Admissions Requirements Medical examination.
Staff Physicians 20 (pt); RNs 3 (ft), 20 (pt); LPNs 1 (ft), 11 (pt); Nurses aides 27 (ft), 94 (pt); Physical therapists 1 (pt); Occupational therapists 1 (ft); Speech therapists 1 (pt); Activities coordinators 3 (ft); Ophthalmologists 1 (pt).
Facilities Dining room; Physical therapy room; Activities room; Chapel; Crafts room; Laundry room; Barber/Beauty shop; Library.
Activities Arts & crafts; Cards; Games; Prayer groups; Movies; Shopping trips.

PALOS HILLS

Windsor Manor Nursing & Rehabilitation Center
10426 S Roberts Rd, Palos Hills, IL, 60465
(312) 598-3460
Admin Jacqueline Grant. *Medical Dir/Dir of Nursing* Ronald Walsh MD; Connie Elerbie RN DON.
Licensure Skilled care; Intermediate care. *Beds* SNF 120; ICF 83. *Certified* Medicaid.
Owner Proprietary Corp.
Admissions Requirements Minimum age 40; Medical examination.
Staff Physicians 5 (pt); RNs 7 (ft); LPNs 16 (ft), 2 (pt); Orderlies 3 (ft); Nurses aides 56 (ft), 8 (pt); Physical therapists 2 (ft); Reality therapists; Recreational therapists; Occupational therapists; Speech therapists 1

(pt); Activities coordinators 3 (ft), 1 (pt); Dietitians 1 (ft); Dentists 1 (pt); Ophthalmologists 1 (pt).
Languages Polish
Facilities Dining room; Physical therapy room; Activities room; Crafts room; Laundry room; Barber/Beauty shop.
Activities Arts & crafts; Cards; Games; Reading groups; Prayer groups; Movies; Shopping trips; Social/Cultural gatherings.

PANA

Barry Care Center of Pana*
1000 E 6th Street Rd, Pana, IL, 62557
(217) 562-2174
Admin Michael A Van Meter.
Licensure Skilled care. *Beds* 166. *Certified* Medicaid; Medicare.
Owner Proprietary Corp.

Pana Health Care Center
900 S Chestnut St, Pana, IL, 62557
(217) 562-3996
Admin Kathy Epley. *Medical Dir/Dir of Nursing* Virgilio Pycoco MD; Mary Schneider RN DON.
Licensure Skilled care. *Beds* 123. *Certified* Medicaid; Medicare.
Owner Nonprofit Corp (First Humanics).
Admissions Requirements Minimum age 18; Medical examination; Physician's request.
Staff RNs 2 (ft), 1 (pt); LPNs 9 (ft), 1 (pt); Orderlies 2 (ft); Nurses aides 19 (ft), 8 (pt); Physical therapists 1 (pt); Recreational therapists 1 (pt); Speech therapists 1 (pt); Activities coordinators 2 (ft); Dietitians 1 (pt).
Facilities Dining room; Physical therapy room; Activities room; Crafts room; Laundry room; Barber/Beauty shop; Kitchen; Quiet room.
Activities Arts & crafts; Cards; Games; Reading groups; Prayer groups; Movies; Social/Cultural gatherings.

PARIS

Heritage Conv Center
310 S Eads Ave, Paris, IL, 61944
(217) 465-5395
Admin Patricia Revell. *Medical Dir/Dir of Nursing* Dr Reid Sutton; Linda Stanfield.
Licensure Skilled care. *Beds* 62. *Certified* Medicaid.
Owner Proprietary Corp.
Admissions Requirements Medical examination.
Staff Physicians; RNs 5 (ft); LPNs 3 (ft), 2 (pt); Orderlies 1 (ft); Nurses aides 40 (ft); Physical therapists 1 (pt); Occupational therapists 1 (pt); Speech therapists 1 (pt); Activities coordinators 1 (ft); Dietitians 1 (pt); Dentists; Ophthalmologists.
Facilities Dining room; Laundry room; Barber/Beauty shop.
Activities Arts & crafts; Cards; Games; Reading groups; Prayer groups; Movies; Shopping trips; Social/Cultural gatherings; Van rides; Dining out; Groups; Exercise programs; Fitness trail.

Paris Healthcare Center
1011 N Main St, Paris, IL, 61944
(217) 465-5376
Admin Nancy D Davis.
Licensure Skilled care. *Beds* SNF 98. *Certified* Medicaid; Medicare.
Owner Proprietary Corp.
Admissions Requirements Minimum age 18; Medical examination.
Staff RNs; LPNs; Nurses aides; Physical therapists; Speech therapists; Activities coordinators; Dietitians.
Facilities Dining room; Physical therapy room; Activities room; Crafts room; Laundry room; Barber/Beauty shop; 3 Living Rooms.

Activities Arts & crafts; Cards; Games; Reading groups; Prayer groups; Movies; Shopping trips; Social/Cultural gatherings; Birthday parties.

PARK RIDGE

Park Ridge Healthcare Center
665 Busse Hwy, Park Ridge, IL, 60068
(312) 825-5517
Admin Joy P Rathe. *Medical Dir/Dir of Nursing* Dr E Forkos; Pat Mikes RN.
Licensure Intermediate care. *Beds* ICF 49.
Owner Proprietary Corp (H S Healthcare).
Admissions Requirements Minimum age 21; Medical examination.
Staff Physicians 8 (pt); RNs 1 (ft), 1 (pt); LPNs 3 (ft), 2 (pt); Nurses aides 10 (ft), 5 (pt); Physical therapists 1 (pt); Recreational therapists 1 (ft); Occupational therapists 1 (pt); Speech therapists 1 (pt); Activities coordinators 1 (ft); Dietitians 1 (pt); Ophthalmologists 1 (pt); Social services 1 (pt).
Facilities Dining room; Activities room; Laundry room; Sunroom; Outdoor terrace.
Activities Arts & crafts; Cards; Games; Reading groups; Prayer groups; Movies; Social/Cultural gatherings; Musical entertainment; Parties; Reality orientation; Picnics; Celebrations of all kinds.

Resurrection Nursing Pavilion*
1001 Greenwood Ave, Park Ridge, IL, 60068
(312) 692-5600
Admin Paul Crevis.
Licensure Skilled care. *Beds* 298. *Certified* Medicaid; Medicare.
Owner Nonprofit Corp.

St Matthew Lutheran Home
1601 N Western Ave, Park Ridge, IL, 60068
(312) 825-5531
Admin Will C Rasmussen. *Medical Dir/Dir of Nursing* Dr S Shastri; Karen Carter DON.
Licensure Skilled care; Intermediate care; Sheltered care. *Beds* SNF 130; ICF 14; Sheltered care 32. *Certified* Medicaid.
Owner Nonprofit Corp.
Admissions Requirements Minimum age 62; Medical examination.
Staff RNs 15 (ft), 15 (pt); LPNs 3 (pt); Orderlies 20 (ft); Nurses aides 60 (ft); Physical therapists 1 (ft); Occupational therapists 1 (pt); Activities coordinators 1 (ft); Dietitians 1 (ft).
Affiliation Lutheran
Facilities Dining room; Physical therapy room; Activities room; Chapel; Crafts room; Laundry room; Barber/Beauty shop.
Activities Arts & crafts; Cards; Games; Reading groups; Prayer groups; Movies; Shopping trips; Social/Cultural gatherings.

PAXTON

Ford County Nursing Home
Box 300, RR 2, Paxton, IL, 60957
(217) 379-4896
Admin Judith L Ondercho. *Medical Dir/Dir of Nursing* Dr Richard Fuellner; Patricia Glessner.
Licensure Skilled care. *Beds* ICF 69. *Certified* Medicaid.
Owner Publicly owned.
Admissions Requirements Minimum age 18; Medical examination; Physician's request.
Staff Physicians 4 (ft); RNs 4 (ft), 3 (pt); LPNs 5 (ft); Nurses aides 25 (ft), 3 (pt); Recreational therapists 1 (ft), 1 (pt); Activities coordinators 1 (ft); Dietitians 1 (ft), 1 (pt).
Facilities Dining room; Physical therapy room; Activities room; Laundry room; Barber/Beauty shop; Outside screened shelter.

Activities Arts & crafts; Cards; Games; Reading groups; Prayer groups; Movies; Shopping trips; Social/Cultural gatherings; Commu ity projects; Interhome outings; Special dinners; Baking/cooking sessions.

Illinois Knights Templar Home
450 Fulton St, Paxton, IL, 60957
(217) 379-2116
Admin John W Becker. *Medical Dir/Dir of Nursing* Robert C Basler MD.
Licensure Skilled care; Intermediate care. *Beds* 50. *Certified* Medicaid; Medicare.
Owner Nonprofit Corp.
Admissions Requirements Minimum age 60; Medical examination.
Staff RNs 5 (ft); LPNs 4 (ft); Nurses aides 13 (ft), 10 (pt); Activities coordinators 1 (ft), 1 (pt); Dietitians 1 (ft); Social service 1 (ft).
Affiliation Masons
Facilities Dining room; Physical therapy room; Activities room; Laundry room; Barber/Beauty shop; Library; Day room.
Activities Arts & crafts; Cards; Games; Reading groups; Prayer groups; Movies; Shopping trips; Social/Cultural gatherings; Monthly banquets.

PEKIN

Hallmark House Nursing Home*
2501 Allentown Rd, Pekin, IL, 61554
(309) 347-3121
Admin William E Hurd Jr.
Licensure Intermediate care. *Beds* 71. *Certified* Medicaid.
Owner Proprietary Corp.

Pekin Conv Center*
2220 State Rd, Pekin, IL, 61554
(309) 347-1110
Admin Melvin L Zimmerman.
Licensure Skilled care. *Beds* 202. *Certified* Medicaid; Medicare.
Owner Proprietary Corp.

B J Perino Nursing Home Inc*
601-603 Prince St, Pekin, IL, 61554
(309) 346l-1118
Admin Tommy E Wittekiend. *Medical Dir of Nursing* R Urban MD.
Licensure Intermediate care. *Beds* 84. *Certified* Medicaid.
Owner Proprietary Corp.
Admissions Requirements Medical examination.
Staff Physicians 16 (pt); RNs 1 (ft); LPNs 8 (ft), 3 (pt); Orderlies 2 (ft); Nurses aides 15 (ft); Physical therapists 1 (ft), 1 (pt); Occupational therapists 1 (pt); Activities coordinators 1 (ft); Dietitians 1 (ft), 1 (pt); Dentists 1 (ft), 1 (pt); Podiatrists 1 (pt).
Facilities Dining room; Physical therapy room; Activities room; Crafts room; Laundry room; Barber/Beauty shop; Library.
Activities Arts & crafts; Cards; Games; Reading groups; Prayer groups; Movies; Shopping trips; Social/Cultural gatherings; Reality orientation; Remotivation.

Twin Oaks Community Living Facility*
2421 S 14th St, Pekin, IL, 61554
(309) 686-3310
Admin Joseph Budde.
Licensure Intermediate care. *Beds* 12.
Owner Nonprofit Corp.

PEORIA

Americana Healthcare Center of Peoria*
5600 Glen Elm Dr, Peoria, IL, 61614
(309) 688-8777
Admin Mark Comerford.
Licensure Skilled care. *Beds* 104. *Certified* Medicaid; Medicare.
Owner Proprietary Corp (Manor Care).

Apostolic Christian Home
7023 NE Skyline Dr, Peoria, IL, 61614
(309) 691-8091
Admin Roger D Herman. *Medical Dir/Dir of Nursing* Glenna M Coats.
Licensure Intermediate care; Sheltered care. *Beds* ICF 37; Sheltered care 32.
Owner Nonprofit Corp.
Staff RNs 1 (ft); LPNs 5 (ft), 2 (pt); Nurses aides 16 (ft), 14 (pt); Activities coordinators 1 (ft).
Affiliation Apostolic Christian Church

Bel-Wood Nursing Home*
6701 W Plank Rd, Peoria, IL, 61604
(309) 697-4541
Admin Stella Marie Lewis. *Medical Dir/Dir of Nursing* William R Nace MD.
Licensure Intermediate care. *Beds* 300. *Certified* Medicaid.
Owner Publicly owned.
Admissions Requirements Minimum age 18; Medical examination.
Staff RNs 16 (ft); LPNs 15 (ft); Nurses aides 72 (ft); Activities coordinators 1 (ft); Dietitians 1 (ft); Dentists 1 (pt); Podiatrists 1 (pt).
Facilities Dining room; Physical therapy room; Activities room; Chapel; Crafts room; Laundry room; Barber/Beauty shop; Library.
Activities Arts & crafts; Cards; Games; Reading groups; Prayer groups; Movies; Shopping trips; Swimming; Bowling.

Christian Buehler Memorial Home
3415 N Sheridan Rd, Peoria, IL, 61604
(309) 685-6236
Admin Louis E Amberg.
Licensure Skilled care. *Beds* 71.
Owner Nonprofit Corp.

Galena Park Home*
5533 N Galena Rd, Peoria, IL, 61614
(309) 682-5428
Admin Julia K King.
Licensure Skilled care; Sheltered Home. *Beds* SNF 60; Sheltered care 4. *Certified* Medicaid.
Owner Nonprofit Corp.

High View Nursing Center Inc
2308 W Nebraska, Peoria, IL, 61604
(309) 673-8251
Admin Ramona Brooks. *Medical Dir/Dir of Nursing* Benito Camacho MD; Sally Webster RN DON.
Licensure Skilled care; Intermediate care. *Beds* SNF 105. *Certified* Medicaid; Medicare.
Owner Proprietary Corp (Beverly Enterprises).
Admissions Requirements Minimum age 18; Medical examination.
Staff Physicians 1 (pt); RNs 3 (ft), 2 (pt); LPNs 9 (ft), 5 (pt); Orderlies 3 (ft), 2 (pt); Nurses aides 28 (ft), 11 (pt); Physical therapists 1 (pt); Occupational therapists 1 (pt); Speech therapists 1 (pt); Activities coordinators 1 (ft); Dietitians 1 (pt); Ophthalmologists 1 (pt).
Facilities Dining room; Physical therapy room; Activities room; Crafts room; Laundry room; Barber/Beauty shop; Library; 3 courtyards.
Activities Arts & crafts; Cards; Games; Reading groups; Prayer groups; Movies; Shopping trips; Social/Cultural gatherings.

The Lutheran Home
7019 N Galena Rd, Peoria, IL, 61614-2294
(309) 692-4494
Admin G H Vander Schaaf. *Medical Dir/Dir of Nursing* Dr Robert Brandes; Mary Helen Erdman.
Licensure Skilled care; Intermediate care; Retirement center. *Beds* SNF 72; ICF 8; Retirement center 50. *Certified* Medicaid.
Owner Nonprofit Corp.
Admissions Requirements Minimum age 62; Medical examination.

Staff RNs 9 (ft); LPNs 12 (ft); Nurses aides 39
(ft); Physical therapists 1 (pt); Recreational
therapists 1 (pt); Occupational therapists 1
(pt); Speech therapists 1 (pt); Activities
coordinators 1 (ft); Dietitians 1 (pt); Dentists
1 (pt); Ophthalmologists 1 (pt); Podiatrists 1
(pt).
Affiliation Lutheran
Facilities Dining room; Physical therapy
room; Activities room; Chapel; Crafts room;
Laundry room; Barber/Beauty shop; Library.
Activities Arts & crafts; Cards; Games;
Reading groups; Prayer groups; Movies;
Shopping trips; Social/Cultural gatherings.

Pavilion Healthcare South
3614 N Rochelle Ln, Peoria, IL, 61604
(309) 688-0350
Admin Patricia Sheridan. *Medical Dir/Dir of
Nursing* Dr Phillip Immesoete MD; Cherrill
Vanlandingham DON.
Licensure Intermediate care. *Beds* 120.
Certified Medicaid.
Owner Proprietary Corp.
Admissions Requirements Medical
examination; Physician's request.
Staff RNs 1 (pt); LPNs 7 (ft), 3 (pt); Orderlies
1 (ft), 1 (pt); Nurses aides 20 (ft), 9 (pt);
Physical therapists 1 (ft); Occupational
therapists 2 (pt); Speech therapists 1 (pt);
Activities coordinators 2 (ft).
Facilities Dining room; Physical therapy
room; Activities room; Barber/Beauty shop.
Activities Arts & crafts; Games; Shopping
trips; Social/Cultural gatherings; Exercises.

Pavilion North Healthcare Inc
3111 Richwoods Blvd, Peoria, IL, 61614
(309) 688-2457
Admin Joyce Conrady. *Medical Dir/Dir of
Nursing* Dr A Maurer; Louise Mosher DON.
Licensure Intermediate care. *Beds* 120.
Certified Medicaid.
Owner Proprietary Corp.
Admissions Requirements Medical
examination; Physician's request.
Staff RNs 1 (ft), 1 (pt); LPNs 4 (ft), 4 (pt);
Nurses aides 13 (ft), 5 (pt); Physical
therapists 1 (pt); Occupational therapists 1
(pt); Speech therapists 1 (pt); Activities
coordinators 1 (ft); Dietitians 1 (pt).
Facilities Dining room; Physical therapy
room; Activities room; Crafts room; Laundry
room; Barber/Beauty shop; Library.
Activities Arts & crafts; Cards; Games;
Reading groups; Prayer groups; Movies;
Shopping trips; Social/Cultural gatherings.

Pavilion Oaks
3520 N Rochelle, Peoria, IL, 61604
(309) 688-0451
Admin Louise M Wilson. *Medical Dir/Dir of
Nursing* Dr Phillip Immesoete; Louise M
Wilson DON.
Licensure Skilled care. *Beds* SNF 99. *Certified*
Medicaid; Medicare.
Owner Proprietary Corp (Pavillion Health
Care Centers).
Admissions Requirements Minimum age 18;
Medical examination; Physician's request.
Staff Physicians 1 (ft); RNs 3 (ft), 2 (pt);
LPNs 10 (ft), 4 (pt); Orderlies 3 (ft); Nurses
aides 30 (ft), 5 (pt); Physical therapists 1 (ft),
1 (pt); Reality therapists 1 (pt); Recreational
therapists 1 (pt); Occupational therapists 1
(pt); Speech therapists 1 (ft); Activities
coordinators 1 (ft); Dietitians 1 (pt); Dentists
1 (pt); Ophthalmologists 1 (pt); Podiatrists 1
(pt).
Facilities Dining room; Physical therapy
room; Activities room; Chapel; Crafts room;
Laundry room; Barber/Beauty shop; Library.
Activities Arts & crafts; Cards; Games;
Reading groups; Prayer groups; Movies;
Shopping trips; Social/Cultural gatherings.

Pavilion West Health Care Center
3611 N Rochelle, Peoria, IL, 61614
(309) 688-4412
Medical Dir/Dir of Nursing Dr Phillip
Immesoete; Joanne Schuely DON.
Licensure Intermediate care. *Beds* ICF 99.
Certified Medicaid.
Owner Proprietary Corp (Pavillion Care
Centers).
Admissions Requirements Minimum age 50;
Medical examination; Physician's request.
Staff Physicians; RNs; LPNs; Orderlies;
Nurses aides; Physical therapists;
Recreational therapists; Occupational
therapists; Speech therapists; Activities
coordinators; Dietitians; Dentists;
Ophthalmologists; Podiatrists.
Languages Sign
Facilities Dining room; Physical therapy
room; Activities room; Crafts room; Laundry
room; Barber/Beauty shop; Library; Patio &
park setting.
Activities Arts & crafts; Cards; Games;
Reading groups; Prayer groups; Movies;
Shopping trips; Social/Cultural gatherings.

Proctor J C Endowment Home*
2724 W Reservior, Peoria, IL, 61615
(309) 685-6580
Admin Robert Ziegenhagen.
Licensure Skilled care. *Beds* 59.
Owner Nonprofit Corp.

Richwoods Terrace*
3301 W Richwoods Blvd, Peoria, IL, 61604
(309) 685-5241
Admin Nancy J Smith.
Licensure Intermediate care. *Beds* 152.
Certified Medicaid.
Owner Proprietary Corp.
Admissions Requirements Minimum age 19.
Facilities Dining room; Physical therapy
room; Activities room; Crafts room; Laundry
room; Barber/Beauty shop; Gymnasium-
auditorium.
Activities Arts & crafts; Cards; Games;
Reading groups; Prayer groups; Movies;
Shopping trips; Social/Cultural gatherings.

St Josephs Home of Peoria
2223 W Heading Ave, Peoria, IL, 61604
(309) 673-7425
Admin Sr Mary Paul Mazzorana & Sr Mary
Dries. *Medical Dir/Dir of Nursing* Ann
Steiner DON.
Licensure Intermediate care; Sheltered care.
Beds ICF 43; Sheltered care 145. *Certified*
Medicaid.
Owner Nonprofit Corp.
Admissions Requirements Minimum age 65;
Medical examination.
Staff RNs 1 (ft), 3 (pt); LPNs 9 (ft), 8 (pt);
Nurses aides 19 (ft), 7 (pt); Activities
coordinators 1 (ft), 3 (pt).
Affiliation Roman Catholic
Facilities Dining room; Physical therapy
room; Activities room; Chapel; Crafts room;
Laundry room; Barber/Beauty shop; Library.
Activities Arts & crafts; Cards; Games;
Reading groups; Prayer groups; Movies;
Social/Cultural gatherings.

Stuttle Community Living Facility*
201 Columbia Terrace, Peoria, IL, 61606
(309) 686-3300
Admin Joseph L Budde.
Licensure Intermediate care. *Beds* 20.
Owner Nonprofit Corp.

PEORIA HEIGHTS

Heights Colonial Manor
1629 Gardner Ln, Peoria Heights, IL, 61614
(309) 688-8758
Admin Ella Allbritton. *Medical Dir/Dir of
Nursing* Debbie Davison.
Licensure Skilled care; Intermediate care. *Beds*
SNF 110; ICF. *Certified* Medicaid.

Owner Proprietary Corp.
Admissions Requirements Minimum age 18;
Medical examination; Physician's request.
Staff Physicians; RNs; LPNs; Orderlies;
Nurses aides; Physical therapists; Speech
therapists; Activities coordinators; Dietitians;
Dentists; Ophthalmologists; Podiatrists;
Social services.
Facilities Dining room; Physical therapy
room; Activities room; Crafts room; Laundry
room; Barber/Beauty shop; Library.
Activities Arts & crafts; Cards; Games;
Reading groups; Prayer groups; Movies;
Shopping trips; Social/Cultural gatherings.

PEOTONE

Peotone Bensenville Home
PO Box 669, 104 S West St, Peotone, IL,
60468
(312) 258-6879
Admin Laura J Stone. *Medical Dir/Dir of
Nursing* Dr Scott Lowry; Marjorie Eberle.
Licensure Intermediate care. *Beds* ICF 34.
Certified Medicaid.
Owner Nonprofit Corp.
Admissions Requirements Medical
examination.
Staff RNs 1 (ft), 6 (pt); LPNs 2 (ft); Nurses
aides 4 (ft), 7 (pt); Activities coordinators 1
(pt).
Affiliation Church of Christ
Facilities Dining room; Activities room;
Crafts room; Laundry room; Barber/Beauty
shop.
Activities Arts & crafts; Games; Reading
groups; Prayer groups; Movies.

PERU

Heritage Manor of Peru
22nd & Rock St, Peru, IL, 61354
(815) 223-4901
Admin Rose Zimmer. *Medical Dir/Dir of
Nursing* Dr Jerome F Sickley; Judy Wright
RN DON.
Licensure Skilled care. *Beds* SNF 129.
Certified Medicaid; Medicare.
Owner Proprietary Corp (Heritage
Enterprises).
Admissions Requirements Minimum age 18;
Medical examination.
Staff RNs 10 (ft), 2 (pt); LPNs 4 (ft), 1 (pt);
Nurses aides 27 (ft), 8 (pt); Physical
therapists 1 (pt); Recreational therapists 2
(ft), 2 (pt); Activities coordinators 1 (ft).
Facilities Dining room; Physical therapy
room; Activities room; Crafts room; Laundry
room; Barber/Beauty shop.
Activities Arts & crafts; Cards; Games; Prayer
groups; Movies; Shopping trips.

PETERSBURG

Menard Conv Center*
120 Antle St, Petersburg, IL, 62675
(217) 632-2249
Admin Robert D McDonald. *Medical Dir/Dir
of Nursing* Dr Barry Free.
Licensure Skilled care; Intermediate care. *Beds*
SNF 59; ICF 27. *Certified* Medicaid;
Medicare.
Owner Proprietary Corp.
Staff Physicians 3 (pt); RNs 2 (ft), 1 (pt);
LPNs 10 (ft); Nurses aides 50 (ft); Physical
therapists 1 (pt); Activities coordinators 1
(ft); Dietitians 1 (pt); Dentists 1 (pt).
Facilities Dining room; Physical therapy
room; Barber/Beauty shop.
Activities Arts & crafts; Cards; Games; Prayer
groups; Movies; Shopping trips.

Petersburg Manor*
Rte 3, Petersburg, IL, 62675
(217) 632-7442
Admin David L Pizzo.

Licensure Sheltered care. *Beds* 59.
Owner Proprietary Corp.

Sunny Acres Nursing Home*
RR 3, Petersburg, IL, 62675
(217) 632-2334
Admin Dick R Warren.
Licensure Intermediate care. *Beds* 96.
  Certified Medicaid.
Owner Publicly owned.

PINCKNEYVILLE

Perry Manor
PO Box 407, 708 Virginia Ct, Pinckneyville,
IL, 62274
(618) 357-2493
Admin Hildred Secrease.
Licensure Intermediate care. *Beds* ICF 60.
  Certified Medicaid.
Owner Proprietary Corp (Community Lifecare
  Enterprises).
Admissions Requirements Medical
  examination.
Staff RNs 1 (ft); LPNs 3 (ft); Nurses aides 23
  (ft); Physical therapists 1 (pt); Activities
  coordinators 1 (ft); Dietitians 1 (pt).
Facilities Dining room; Physical therapy
  room; Activities room; Crafts room; Laundry
  room; Barber/Beauty shop.
Activities Arts & crafts; Cards; Games;
  Reading groups; Prayer groups; Movies;
  Shopping trips; Social/Cultural gatherings.

PIPER CITY

Greenbrier Lodge
600 Maple St, Piper City, IL, 60959
(815) 686-2277
Admin Harland L Bicking. *Medical Dir/Dir of
  Nursing* Dr A G Baxter.
Licensure Intermediate care. *Beds* 60.
  Certified Medicaid.
Owner Proprietary Corp.
Admissions Requirements Minimum age 18.
Staff RNs 3 (ft), 1 (pt); LPNs 1 (ft), 3 (pt);
  Nurses aides 17 (ft), 10 (pt); Physical
  therapists 1 (pt); Activities coordinators 1
  (ft); Dietitians 1 (ft); Podiatrists 1 (pt).
Facilities Dining room; Physical therapy
  room; Activities room; Crafts room; Laundry
  room; Barber/Beauty shop.
Activities Arts & crafts; Cards; Games;
  Reading groups; Prayer groups; Movies;
  Shopping trips; Social/Cultural gatherings.

PITTSFIELD

Owen Care Center—Pittsfield
Rte 36, Pittsfield, IL, 62363
(217) 285-4491
Admin Ann Smith. *Medical Dir/Dir of Nursing*
  Julie Eddinger.
Licensure Intermediate care. *Beds* ICF 99.
  Certified Medicaid.
Owner Privately owned.
Admissions Requirements Minimum age 18;
  Medical examination; Physician's request.
Staff RNs 1 (ft); LPNs 8 (ft), 1 (pt); Nurses
  aides 17 (ft), 9 (pt); Physical therapists 2
  (pt); Activities coordinators 1 (pt); Dietitians
  1 (pt); Ophthalmologists 1 (pt).
Facilities Dining room; Physical therapy
  room; Activities room; Laundry room;
  Barber/Beauty shop.
Activities Arts & crafts; Games; Prayer groups;
  Movies; Shopping trips; Social/Cultural
  gatherings.

PLAINFIELD

Lakewood Living Center
1112 N Eastern Ave, Plainfield, IL, 60544
(815) 436-3400

Admin Gary D Hixon. *Medical Dir/Dir of
  Nursing* Frank Bender MD; Bonnie
  McDavitt DON.
Licensure Skilled care. *Beds* SNF 50.
Owner Nonprofit Corp (Adventist Health Sys-
  USA).
Admissions Requirements Minimum age 18;
  Medical examination; Physician's request.
Staff Physicians 1 (pt); RNs 2 (ft), 10 (pt);
  LPNs 2 (pt); Nurses aides 5 (ft), 21 (pt);
  Activities coordinators 1 (ft), 2 (pt);
  Dietitians 1 (pt).
Affiliation Seventh-Day Adventist
Facilities Dining room; Activities room;
  Chapel; Crafts room; Barber/Beauty shop.
Activities Arts & crafts; Cards; Games;
  Reading groups; Prayer groups; Movies;
  Shopping trips; Social/Cultural gatherings.

POLO

Polo Continental Manor
703 E Buffalo, Polo, IL, 61064
(815) 946-2203
Admin Kathleen J Boehme. *Medical Dir/Dir
  of Nursing* Dr Franklin Swan.
Licensure Intermediate care. *Beds* 81.
  Certified Medicaid; Medicare.
Owner Nonprofit Corp (First Humanics).
Admissions Requirements Medical
  examination.
Staff RNs 3 (ft), 2 (pt); LPNs 3 (ft), 4 (pt);
  Nurses aides 12 (ft), 6 (pt); Physical
  therapists 1 (ft); Activities coordinators 1
  (ft), 2 (pt); Dietitians 1 (pt); Dentists 1 (pt);
  Ophthalmologists 1 (pt).

PONTIAC

Evenglow Lodge
215 E Washington, Pontiac, IL, 61764
(815) 844-6131
Admin Frank Deninger. *Medical Dir/Dir of
  Nursing* Elizabeth Jane Wold.
Licensure Intermediate care; Sheltered care.
  Beds ICF 70; Sheltered care 141. *Certified*
  Medicaid.
Owner Nonprofit Corp.
Admissions Requirements Minimum age 65;
  Medical examination.
Staff RNs 2 (ft), 3 (pt); LPNs 5 (ft), 8 (pt);
  Nurses aides 22 (ft), 6 (pt); Activities
  coordinators 2 (ft).
Affiliation Methodist
Facilities Dining room; Physical therapy
  room; Activities room; Chapel; Crafts room;
  Laundry room; Barber/Beauty shop; Library.
Activities Arts & crafts; Games; Reading
  groups; Prayer groups; Movies; Shopping
  trips.

Humiston Haven
300 W Lowell Ave, Pontiac, IL, 61764
(815) 842-1181
Admin Phylis A Brown. *Medical Dir/Dir of
  Nursing* John Purnell MD; Mary Ann Dehm
  RN DON.
Licensure Intermediate care. *Beds* ICF 88.
  Certified Medicaid.
Owner Nonprofit Corp.
Admissions Requirements Minimum age 21;
  Medical examination.
Staff RNs 3 (ft), 4 (pt); LPNs 6 (ft), 2 (pt);
  Orderlies 1 (ft), 1 (pt); Nurses aides 31 (ft),
  10 (pt); Physical therapists 1 (pt);
  Occupational therapists 1 (pt); Activities
  coordinators 3 (ft); Dietitians 1 (pt).
Facilities Dining room; Physical therapy
  room; Chapel; Crafts room; Laundry room;
  Barber/Beauty shop; Library.
Activities Arts & crafts; Cards; Games;
  Movies.

Livingston Manor
RR 1, Pontiac, IL, 61764
(815) 844-5121

Admin Ann L Klien, RN. *Medical Dir/Dir of
  Nursing* L S Lowenthal MD; Kathy Duffy
  DON.
Licensure Intermediate care. *Beds* 125.
  Certified Medicaid.
Owner Publicly owned.
Admissions Requirements Minimum age 18;
  Medical examination.
Staff Physicians 1 (pt); RNs 2 (ft); LPNs 8
  (ft), 3 (pt); Orderlies 2 (ft); Nurses aides 42
  (ft), 10 (pt); Physical therapists 1 (pt);
  Recreational therapists 2 (ft), 2 (pt); 1 (ft), 1
  (pt) Social Service.
Facilities Dining room; Physical therapy
  room; Activities room; Chapel; Crafts room;
  Laundry room; Barber/Beauty shop.
Activities Arts & crafts; Cards; Games;
  Reading groups; Prayer groups; Movies;
  Shopping trips; Social/Cultural gatherings.

PRAIRIE CITY

Prairie City Nursing Center
RR 2, Prairie City, IL, 61470
(309) 775-3313
Admin Jeanette A Rutherford. *Medical Dir/
  Dir of Nursing* Joan Sinnett DON.
Licensure Intermediate care. *Beds* ICF 48.
  Certified Medicaid.
Owner Proprietary Corp.
Admissions Requirements Minimum age 21;
  Medical examination; Physician's request.
Staff RNs 1 (pt); LPNs 6 (ft), 2 (pt); Nurses
  aides 14 (ft), 10 (pt); Activities coordinators
  1 (ft), 1 (pt).
Facilities Dining room; Activities room;
  Crafts room; Barber/Beauty shop; Library.
Activities Arts & crafts; Cards; Games;
  Reading groups; Prayer groups; Movies;
  Shopping trips; Social/Cultural gatherings.

PRINCETON

Colonial Hall Nursing Home
515 S 6th St, Princeton, IL, 61356
(815) 875-3347
Admin Francis S Philbin. *Medical Dir/Dir of
  Nursing* Renee Denault DNS.
Licensure Skilled care. *Beds* SNF 80. *Certified*
  Medicaid; Medicare.
Owner Nonprofit Corp (Adventist Health Sys-
  USA).
Admissions Requirements Minimum age 18;
  Medical examination.
Staff RNs 8 (ft); LPNs 4 (ft); Nurses aides 14
  (ft), 10 (pt); Physical therapists 1 (pt);
  Occupational therapists 1 (pt); Speech
  therapists 1 (pt); Activities coordinators 1
  (ft); Dietitians 1 (pt); Dentists 1 (pt);
  Ophthalmologists 1 (pt); Podiatrists 1 (pt).
Affiliation Seventh-Day Adventist
Facilities Dining room; Physical therapy
  room; Activities room; Chapel; Crafts room;
  Laundry room; Barber/Beauty shop.
Activities Arts & crafts; Cards; Games;
  Reading groups; Prayer groups; Movies;
  Shopping trips; Social/Cultural gatherings.

Greenfield Home
508 Park Ave E, Princeton, IL, 61356
(815) 872-2261
Admin Barbara M Mueller. *Medical Dir/Dir of
  Nursing* Dr Greg Davis; Betty Redmond RN
  DON.
Licensure Sheltered care. *Beds* 40.
Owner Nonprofit organization/foundation.
Admissions Requirements Minimum age 55;
  Medical examination.
Staff RNs 2 (ft), 3 (pt); LPNs 2 (pt); Nurses
  aides 5 (ft), 3 (pt); Activities coordinators 1
  (ft).
Facilities Dining room; Activities room.
Activities Arts & crafts; Cards; Games;
  Reading groups; Prayer groups; Movies;
  Shopping trips; Social/Cultural gatherings.

Prairie View Home
RR 5, Princeton, IL, 61356
(815) 875-1196
Admin George E Maupin. *Medical Dir/Dir of Nursing* Dr Paul Buller; Lana Pogliano RN.
Licensure Skilled care; Intermediate care; Sheltered care. *Beds* SNF 160; ICF; Shelter care. *Certified* Medicare.
Owner Publicly owned.
Admissions Requirements Minimum age 18; Medical examination; Physician's request.
Staff Physicians 1 (pt); RNs 11 (ft), 3 (pt); LPNs 5 (ft), 1 (pt); Orderlies 4 (ft), 1 (pt); Nurses aides 52 (ft), 9 (pt); Physical therapists 1 (pt); Recreational therapists 3 (ft); Occupational therapists 1 (pt); Activities coordinators 1 (pt); Dietitians 1 (pt); Ophthalmologists 1 (pt).
Facilities Dining room; Physical therapy room; Activities room; Chapel; Crafts room; Laundry room; Barber/Beauty shop; Library.
Activities Arts & crafts; Cards; Games; Reading groups; Prayer groups; Movies; Shopping trips; Social/Cultural gatherings.

Roosevelt Square Nursing Center
1015 Park Ave E, Princeton, IL, 61356
(815) 875-1144
Admin Diane R Baccheschi. *Medical Dir/Dir of Nursing* Edwin L Johnson MD; Anna Jean Bell.
Licensure Intermediate care. *Beds* ICF 63. *Certified* Medicaid.
Owner Proprietary Corp (Beverly Enterprises).
Admissions Requirements Minimum age 18; Medical examination; Physician's request.
Staff RNs 2 (ft); LPNs 5 (ft); Orderlies 1 (ft); Nurses aides 20 (ft).
Facilities Dining room; Physical therapy room; Chapel; Laundry room; Barber/Beauty shop.
Activities Arts & crafts; Cards; Games; Reading groups; Prayer groups; Movies; Shopping trips; Social/Cultural gatherings.

PROPHETSTOWN

Prophets Riverview Good Samaritan Center
310 Mosher Dr, Prophetstown, IL, 61277
(815) 537-5175
Admin Shirley J Lintner. *Medical Dir/Dir of Nursing* Delores Iben.
Licensure Intermediate care; Sheltered care. *Beds* ICF 69; Sheltered care 5. *Certified* Medicaid.
Owner Nonprofit Corp (Evangelical Lutheran/ Good Samaritan).
Admissions Requirements Minimum age 16; Medical examination; Physician's request.
Staff RNs 1 (ft), 5 (pt); LPNs 4 (pt); Nurses aides 4 (ft), 27 (pt); Activities coordinators 1 (ft).
Affiliation Lutheran
Facilities Dining room; Physical therapy room; Activities room; Chapel; Crafts room; Laundry room; Barber/Beauty shop; Library; Patios; Lounges; Conference/family room.
Activities Arts & crafts; Cards; Games; Reading groups; Prayer groups; Movies; Shopping trips; Social/Cultural gatherings; Specialized care; Busette rides; Art therapy/ Music therapy; Occupational therapy.

Winning Wheels Inc
PO Box 12A, RR 3, Prophetstown, IL, 61277
(815) 537-5168
Admin Alan J Gapinski. *Medical Dir/Dir of Nursing* Dr Bradley Meek; Mary Burgess.
Licensure Skilled care. *Beds* SNF 80. *Certified* Medicaid.
Owner Nonprofit Corp.
Admissions Requirements Minimum age 18; Medical examination.
Staff Physicians 2 (pt); RNs 3 (ft), 3 (pt); LPNs 6 (ft), 2 (pt); Nurses aides 30 (ft), 4 (pt); Physical therapists 1 (pt); Recreational therapists 1 (ft); Occupational therapists 1 (pt); Speech therapists 1 (pt); Dietitians 1 (pt); Ophthalmologists 1 (pt).
Facilities Dining room; Physical therapy room; Activities room; Chapel; Crafts room; Laundry room; Barber/Beauty shop; Library; Occupational therapy room.
Activities Arts & crafts; Cards; Games; Prayer groups; Movies; Shopping trips; Social/ Cultural gatherings.

QUINCY

Christian Shelticenter
1340 N 10th St, Quincy, IL, 62301
(217) 222-0083
Admin Ruth A Lefoe. *Medical Dir/Dir of Nursing* Janis Brink.
Licensure Sheltered care. *Beds* 212. *Certified* Medicaid.
Owner Proprietary Corp.
Admissions Requirements Minimum age 14; Physician's request.
Staff LPNs 6 (ft); Orderlies 1 (ft); Nurses aides 7 (ft); Activities coordinators 1 (ft).
Facilities Dining room; Activities room; Chapel; Laundry room; Barber/Beauty shop.
Activities Arts & crafts; Cards; Games; Reading groups; Prayer groups; Movies; Shopping trips; Social/Cultural gatherings.

Good Samaritan Home of Quincy
2130 Harrison St, Quincy, IL, 62301
(217) 223-8717
Admin Dr Larry M Watson. *Medical Dir/Dir of Nursing* Sally Lehner.
Licensure Skilled care; Intermediate care; Sheltered care; Retirement living. *Beds* SNF 36; ICF 174; Sheltered care 101; Cottages 90. *Certified* Medicaid.
Owner Nonprofit Corp.
Admissions Requirements Medical examination.
Staff RNs 4 (ft), 1 (pt); LPNs 20 (ft), 15 (pt); Nurses aides 80 (ft), 20 (pt).
Affiliation Church of Christ
Facilities Dining room; Physical therapy room; Activities room; Chapel; Crafts room; Laundry room; Barber/Beauty shop; Library.
Activities Arts & crafts; Cards; Games; Reading groups; Prayer groups; Movies; Shopping trips; Social/Cultural gatherings.

Lincoln Hill Nursing Center
1440 N 10th St, Quincy, IL, 62301
(217) 224-3780
Admin Diane Peter. *Medical Dir/Dir of Nursing* Dr Karl Laping; Cassie Rocke RN DON.
Licensure Skilled care; Intermediate care. *Beds* SNF 99. *Certified* Medicaid; Medicare.
Owner Proprietary Corp.
Admissions Requirements Minimum age 18; Medical examination.
Staff RNs 2 (ft), 1 (pt); LPNs 10 (ft), 4 (pt); Nurses aides 26 (ft), 15 (pt); Activities coordinators 1 (ft).
Facilities Dining room; Physical therapy room; Activities room; Laundry room; Barber/Beauty shop.
Activities Arts & crafts; Cards; Games; Reading groups; Prayer groups; Movies; Social/Cultural gatherings; Cooking classes.

Quinsippi LTC Facility Inc
720 Sycamore St, Quincy, IL, 62301
(217) 222-1480
Admin Penny L Griffin. *Medical Dir/Dir of Nursing* David Lockhart MD; Joye Anderson RN.
Licensure Skilled care; Intermediate care. *Beds* SNF 94; ICF 120. *Certified* Medicaid; Medicare.
Owner Proprietary Corp.
Admissions Requirements Minimum age 18.

Staff Physicians 2 (pt); RNs 5 (ft), 3 (pt); LPNs 13 (ft), 9 (pt); Orderlies 2 (ft); Nurses aides 49 (ft), 16 (pt); Activities coordinators 3 (ft).
Facilities Dining room; Physical therapy room; Activities room; Chapel; Crafts room; Laundry room; Barber/Beauty shop; Alzheimers unit.
Activities Arts & crafts; Cards; Games; Reading groups; Prayer groups; Movies; Shopping trips; Social/Cultural gatherings.

Sunset Home of the United Methodist Church
418 Washington St, Quincy, IL, 62301
(217) 223-2636
Admin Herbert A Crede. *Medical Dir/Dir of Nursing* Dr Terry Arnold; Dorothy Mortimore RN.
Licensure Skilled care; Intermediate care; Sheltered care. *Beds* SNF 19; ICF 138; Sheltered care 96.
Owner Nonprofit organization/foundation.
Admissions Requirements Minimum age 65; Medical examination.
Staff RNs 7 (ft); LPNs 24 (ft), 6 (pt); Orderlies 1 (ft); Nurses aides 50 (ft), 14 (pt); Physical therapists 1 (pt); Occupational therapists 1 (pt); Speech therapists 1 (pt); Activities coordinators 1 (ft), 4 (pt); Dietitians 1 (pt).
Affiliation Methodist
Facilities Dining room; Physical therapy room; Activities room; Chapel; Crafts room; Laundry room; Barber/Beauty shop; Library; Lounges.
Activities Arts & crafts; Cards; Games; Movies; Shopping trips; Social/Cultural gatherings.

RED BUD

Red Bud Care Center*
350 W South 1st St, Red Bud, IL, 62278
(618) 282-3891
Admin Brenda Hughes.
Licensure Skilled care. *Beds* 112. *Certified* Medicaid.

RICHTON PARK

Richton Crossing Convalescent Center
PO Box B345, Imperial Dr & Cicero Ave, Richton Park, IL, 60471
(312) 747-6120
Admin Roberta Magurany. *Medical Dir/Dir of Nursing* Dr Sheldon Levine; Rita Piepenbrink.
Licensure Skilled care. *Beds* 294. *Certified* Medicaid; Medicare.
Owner Privately owned.
Admissions Requirements Medical examination.
Staff Physicians 16 (pt); RNs 9 (ft), 6 (pt); LPNs 14 (ft), 10 (pt); Nurses aides 54 (ft), 13 (pt); Physical therapists 2 (ft), 1 (pt); Reality therapists 2 (ft); Recreational therapists 2 (ft); Occupational therapists 1 (pt); Speech therapists 1 (ft); Activities coordinators 8 (ft); Dietitians 1 (pt); Dentists 1 (pt); Ophthalmologists 1 (pt); Podiatrists 1 (pt).
Facilities Dining room; Physical therapy room; Activities room; Barber/Beauty shop; Library.
Activities Arts & crafts; Cards; Games; Reading groups; Movies; Shopping trips; Social/Cultural gatherings; In-house talent shows & entertainers.

RIDGWAY

Ridgway Manor Inc*
RR 1, Box 181A, Ridgway, IL, 62979
(618) 272-8831
Admin Gennia S Canimore.

Licensure Intermediate care. *Beds* 71.
Certified Medicaid.
Owner Proprietary Corp.

RIVERWOODS

Brentwood North Nursing & Rehabilitation Center Inc
3705 Deerfield Rd, Riverwoods, IL, 60015
(312) 459-1200
Admin Sheldon M Novoselsky. *Medical Dir/
Dir of Nursing* Rohit Shah MD; Sharon
Roberts RN.
Licensure Skilled care. *Beds* 248. *Certified*
Medicare.
Owner Proprietary Corp.
Admissions Requirements Minimum age 21;
Medical examination; Physician's request.
Staff RNs 38 (ft), 27 (pt); LPNs 3 (ft), 3 (pt);
Orderlies 2 (ft), 2 (pt); Nurses aides 44 (ft),
13 (pt); Physical therapists 5 (ft), 2 (pt);
Recreational therapists 7 (ft), 5 (pt);
Occupational therapists 2 (ft), 1 (pt);
Activities coordinators 1 (ft); Dietitians 3
(ft).
Facilities Dining room; Physical therapy
room; Activities room; Chapel; Crafts room;
Laundry room; Barber/Beauty shop; Library.
Activities Arts & crafts; Cards; Games;
Reading groups; Prayer groups; Movies;
Shopping trips; Social/Cultural gatherings.

ROANOKE

Apostolic Christian Home
1102 W Randolph, Roanoke, IL, 61561
(309) 923-5541
Admin Joseph A Aeschleman. *Medical Dir/Dir
of Nursing* Marj Moritz.
Licensure Intermediate care. *Beds* ICF 75.
Certified Medicaid.
Owner Nonprofit Corp.
Admissions Requirements Medical
examination.
Affiliation Apostolic Christian
Facilities Dining room; Physical therapy
room; Activities room; Crafts room; Laundry
room; Barber/Beauty shop.
Activities Arts & crafts; Cards; Games;
Reading groups; Prayer groups; Movies;
Social/Cultural gatherings.

ROBBINS

Esma A Wright Pavilion*
13901 Lydia Ave, Robbins, IL, 60472
(312) 385-8700
Admin Allen L Wright III.
Licensure Intermediate care. *Beds* ICF 225.
Certified Medicaid.
Owner Proprietary Corp.
Admissions Requirements Minimum age 18;
Medical examination.
Staff Physicians 1 (ft), 6 (pt); RNs 2 (ft), 2
(pt); LPNs 18 (ft); Orderlies 8 (ft); Nurses
aides 31 (ft); Physical therapists 1 (pt);
Reality therapists 1 (pt); Recreational
therapists 1 (ft); Occupational therapists 1
(pt); Activities coordinators 1 (ft); Dietitians
1 (ft); Dentists 1 (pt); Ophthalmologists 1
(pt); Podiatrists 1 (pt).
Facilities Dining room; Physical therapy
room; Activities room; Chapel; Crafts room;
Laundry room; Barber/Beauty shop; Library;
Gift shop; Coffee shop; Boutique (free
clothes); Pool hall.
Activities Arts & crafts; Cards; Games;
Reading groups; Prayer groups; Movies;
Shopping trips; Social/Cultural gatherings;
Fashion shows; Private bus service.

ROBINSON

Cotillion Ridge Nursing Center*
Rte 3, Robinson, IL, 62454
(618) 544-3192

Admin Gerald J Opiela.
Licensure Intermediate care. *Beds* 69.
Certified Medicaid.
Owner Proprietary Corp.
Admissions Requirements Minimum age 28;
Medical examination.
Staff RNs 3 (ft), 1 (pt); LPNs 1 (ft), 2 (pt);
Activities coordinators 1 (ft), 1 (pt).
Facilities Dining room; Physical therapy
room; Laundry room; Barber/Beauty shop.
Activities Arts & crafts; Cards; Games;
Movies; Shopping trips.

Crawford County Conv Center
902 W Mefford St, Robinson, IL, 62454
(618) 546-5638
Admin Dwight L Miller. *Medical Dir/Dir of
Nursing* D J Pelley MD; Barbara Hancock.
Licensure Intermediate care. *Beds* 54.
Certified Medicaid.
Owner Proprietary Corp.
Staff Physicians 5 (pt); RNs 4 (ft); LPNs 1
(ft); Orderlies 1 (ft); Nurses aides 25 (ft);
Physical therapists 1 (pt); Recreational
therapists 1 (pt); Speech therapists 1 (pt);
Activities coordinators 1 (ft); Dietitians 1
(pt); Ophthalmologists 1 (pt).
Facilities Dining room 21.
Activities Arts & crafts; Cards; Games;
Reading groups; Prayer groups; Shopping
trips; Social/Cultural gatherings.

ROCHELLE

Rochelle Healthcare Center East
Box 29, Caron Rd, Rochelle, IL, 61068
(815) 562-4047
Admin Susan Fitzgerald. *Medical Dir/Dir of
Nursing* Don Hinderliter; Linda Good.
Licensure Intermediate care. *Beds* ICF 74.
Certified Medicaid.
Owner Proprietary Corp (H S Healthcare).
Admissions Requirements Minimum age 18;
Medical examination; Physician's request.
Staff RNs; LPNs; Nurses aides; Activities
coordinators.
Facilities Dining room; Activities room;
Barber/Beauty shop.
Activities Arts & crafts; Cards; Games;
Reading groups; Prayer groups; Movies;
Shopping trips; Social/Cultural gatherings.

Rochelle Nursing & Rehabilitation Center*
900 N 3rd St, Rochelle, IL, 61068
(815) 562-4111
Admin Dina Lee Cline. *Medical Dir/Dir of
Nursing* L T Koritz MD.
Licensure Skilled care; Intermediate care. *Beds*
50. *Certified* Medicaid; Medicare.
Owner Proprietary Corp.
Admissions Requirements Minimum age 19.
Staff RNs 2 (ft), 4 (pt); LPNs 3 (pt); Nurses
aides 10 (ft), 10 (pt); Recreational therapists
1 (ft); Activities coordinators 1 (ft).
Facilities Dining room; Physical therapy
room; Activities room; Laundry room;
Barber/Beauty shop.
Activities Arts & crafts; Cards; Games;
Reading groups; Prayer groups; Movies;
Shopping trips; Social/Cultural gatherings.

ROCK FALLS

Colonial Acres*
1000 Dixon Ave, Rock Falls, IL, 61071
(815) 625-8510
Admin Donna M Lattimer.
Licensure Skilled care. *Beds* 55. *Certified*
Medicaid; Medicare.
Owner Proprietary Corp.

Rock Falls Manor*
430 Martin Rd, Rock Falls, IL, 61071
(815) 626-4575
Admin Jerome F Callahan.

Licensure Intermediate care. *Beds* 57.
Certified Medicaid.
Owner Proprietary Corp (Beverly Enterprises).

ROCK ISLAND

Friendship Manor
1209 21st Ave, Rock Island, IL, 61201
(309) 786-9667
Admin Marie Brobston. *Medical Dir/Dir of
Nursing* John M Peterson MD; Gleyn Ann
Unde RN.
Licensure Skilled care; Sheltered care;
Independent living. *Beds* SNF 63; Sheltered
care 34.
Owner Nonprofit Corp.
Admissions Requirements Minimum age 65;
Medical examination.
Staff Physicians 1 (pt); RNs 8 (ft); LPNs 8
(ft); Nurses aides 30 (ft); Physical therapists
1 (pt); Recreational therapists 3 (ft);
Occupational therapists 1 (pt); Speech
therapists 1 (pt); Activities coordinators 2
(ft); Dietitians 1 (pt); Ophthalmologists 1
(pt); Podiatrists 1 (pt).
Affiliation King's Daughters & Sons
Facilities Dining room; Physical therapy
room; Activities room; Chapel; Crafts room;
Laundry room; Barber/Beauty shop; Library;
Wood working.
Activities Arts & crafts; Cards; Games;
Reading groups; Prayer groups; Movies;
Shopping trips; Social/Cultural gatherings.

Rock Island Conv Center*
2545 24th St, Rock Island, IL, 61201
(309) 788-0458
Admin Margaret L Trousil.
Licensure Skilled care. *Beds* 117. *Certified*
Medicaid; Medicare.
Owner Proprietary Corp.

Rock Island County Health Care Center
2122 25th Ave, Rock Island, IL, 61201
(309) 786-4429
Admin Carolyn K Matson. *Medical Dir/Dir of
Nursing* Mark J Valliere MD; Kathleen
Crawford RN.
Licensure Skilled care. *Beds* SNF 83. *Certified*
Medicaid.
Owner Nonprofit organization/foundation.
Admissions Requirements Minimum age 21;
Medical examination; Physician's request.
Staff Physicians 1 (pt); RNs 6 (ft), 3 (pt);
LPNs 9 (ft), 3 (pt); Nurses aides 24 (ft), 14
(pt); Physical therapists 1 (pt); Occupational
therapists 1 (pt); Speech therapists 1 (pt);
Dietitians 1 (pt); Dentists 2 (pt);
Ophthalmologists 1 (pt); Social worker 1
(pt); Dentist.
Languages Spanish, German
Facilities Dining room; Physical therapy
room; Activities room; Crafts room; Laundry
room; Barber/Beauty shop.
Activities Arts & crafts; Cards; Games;
Reading groups; Prayer groups; Movies;
Shopping trips; Social/Cultural gatherings.

St Anthonys Continuing Care Center*
767 30th St, Rock Island, IL, 61201
(309) 788-7631
Admin Mother Mary Anthony OSF.
Licensure Skilled care; Intermediate care. *Beds*
SNF 143; ICF 46. *Certified* Medicaid;
Medicare.
Owner Nonprofit Corp.
Affiliation Roman Catholic

ROCKFORD

Alma Nelson Manor
550 S Mulford Rd, Rockford, IL, 61108
(815) 399-4914
Admin Barbara A Peterson. *Medical Dir/Dir
of Nursing* John Schoenwald MD; Carol
Liedberg Rn.

Licensure Skilled care. *Beds* 174. *Certified* Medicaid; Medicare.
Owner Proprietary Corp.
Admissions Requirements Minimum age 18; Medical examination; Physician's request.
Staff RNs 9 (ft), 1 (pt); LPNs 13 (ft), 1 (pt); Nurses aides 35 (ft), 1 (pt); Physical therapists 3 (ft); Recreational therapists 1 (ft); Occupational therapists 1 (ft); Speech therapists 1 (pt); Activities coordinators 1 (ft); Dietitians 1 (ft).
Languages Swedish
Facilities Dining room; Physical therapy room; Activities room; Crafts room; Laundry room; Barber/Beauty shop.
Activities Arts & crafts; Cards; Games; Reading groups; Prayer groups; Movies; Shopping trips; Social/Cultural gatherings.

Alpine Fireside Health Center*
3650 N Alpine Rd, Rockford, IL, 61111
(815) 877-7408
Admin Kenneth E Alberts.
Licensure Intermediate care; Sheltered care. *Beds* ICF 47; Sheltered care 80.
Owner Proprietary Corp.

Briar Glen Healthcare Centre*
321 Arnold, Rockford, IL, 61108
(815) 397-5531
Admin Thomas A Drog.
Licensure Skilled care; Intermediate care. *Beds* SNF 74; ICF 129. *Certified* Medicaid; Medicare.
Owner Proprietary Corp.

Burgess Square Health Care Centre
2313 N Rockton Ave, Rockford, IL, 61103
(815) 964-4611
Admin Monty L Miller. *Medical Dir/Dir of Nursing* Harry Darland MD.
Licensure Skilled care. *Beds* 160. *Certified* Medicaid; Medicare.
Owner Privately owned.
Admissions Requirements Minimum age 21; Medical examination; Physician's request.
Staff RNs 4 (ft); LPNs 5 (ft), 2 (pt); Nurses aides 49 (ft), 11 (pt); Activities coordinators 1 (ft); Dietitians 1 (ft).
Facilities Dining room; Physical therapy room; Activities room; Laundry room; Barber/Beauty shop; 2 courtyards.
Activities Arts & crafts; Cards; Games; Reading groups; Prayer groups; Movies; Shopping trips; Social/Cultural gatherings; Trips to zoo, Metro Centre.

Deacon Home Ltd*
611 N Court St, Rockford, IL, 61103
(815) 964-0234
Admin Ivan Gibbs.
Licensure Sheltered care. *Beds* 16.
Owner Proprietary Corp.

Fairhaven Christian Home
3470 N Alpine Rd, Rockford, IL, 61111
(815) 877-1441
Admin Marvin E Johnson. *Medical Dir/Dir of Nursing* Michael Werckle MD; Lucille Brundine RN.
Licensure Intermediate care; Sheltered care. *Beds* ICF 96; Sheltered care 158. *Certified* Medicaid.
Owner Nonprofit Corp.
Admissions Requirements Minimum age 65; Physician's request.
Staff Physicians 2 (pt); RNs 10 (ft); LPNs 8 (ft); Nurses aides 60 (ft); Physical therapists 1 (pt); Recreational therapists 1 (ft); Activities coordinators 1 (ft); Dietitians 1 (pt); Ophthalmologists 1 (pt).
Affiliation Evangelical Free Church
Facilities Dining room; Physical therapy room; Activities room; Chapel; Crafts room; Laundry room; Barber/Beauty shop; Library.
Activities Arts & crafts; Games; Reading groups; Prayer groups; Movies; Shopping trips.

Fountain Terrace*
6131 Park Ridge Rd, Rockford, IL, 61111
(815) 633-6810
Admin Kathleen A Demler.
Licensure Skilled care. *Beds* 54.
Owner Proprietary Corp.

Highview Retirement Home
4149 Safford Rd, Rockford, IL, 61103
(815) 964-3368
Admin Myrta Jean Smith. *Medical Dir/Dir of Nursing* Helen Minnick RN.
Licensure Intermediate care; Sheltered care. *Beds* ICF 16; Sheltered care 33.
Owner Nonprofit Corp.
Admissions Requirements Medical examination.
Staff RNs; LPNs; Nurses aides; Reality therapists; Recreational therapists; Occupational therapists; Activities coordinators; Dietitians.
Facilities Dining room; Activities room; Crafts room; Laundry room; Barber/Beauty shop; Library.
Activities Arts & crafts; Cards; Games; Reading groups; Prayer groups; Movies; Shopping trips; Social/Cultural gatherings.

Walter J Lawson Memorial Home for Children
1820 Walter Lawson Dr, Rockford, IL, 61111
(815) 633-6636
Admin Theo A Brandel.
Licensure Skilled care. *Beds* SNF 93.

Maria Linden
5330 Maria Linden Dr, Rockford, IL, 61111
(815) 877-7416
Admin Sr Rose Marie Bushman. *Medical Dir/Dir of Nursing* Robin Spencer MD; Jean Johnson RN DON.
Licensure Intermediate care; Sheltered care. *Beds* ICF 43; Sheltered care 65.
Owner Nonprofit Corp (School Sisters of St Francis).
Admissions Requirements Females only.
Staff RNs 4 (ft); LPNs 2 (ft), 5 (pt); Nurses aides 21 (ft), 5 (pt); Program Director 1 (ft).
Languages German
Affiliation Roman Catholic
Facilities Dining room; Physical therapy room; Activities room; Chapel; Crafts room; Laundry room; Barber/Beauty shop; Library; Lounges for reading; TV & VCR viewing area.
Activities Arts & crafts; Cards; Games; Reading groups; Prayer groups; Movies; Shopping trips; Social/Cultural gatherings.

North Rockford Convalescent Home
1920 N Main St, Rockford, IL, 61103
(815) 964-6834
Admin Scott L Swanson. *Medical Dir/Dir of Nursing* Dr Michael Werckle; Myrna Pullin RN.
Licensure Intermediate care. *Beds* ICF 97. *Certified* Medicaid.
Owner Nonprofit Corp.
Admissions Requirements Medical examination.
Staff Physicians 1 (pt); RNs 7 (ft), 1 (pt); LPNs 8 (ft); Nurses aides 36 (ft), 3 (pt); Physical therapists 1 (pt); Occupational therapists 1 (pt); Speech therapists 1 (pt); Activities coordinators 1 (ft); Dietitians 1 (ft); Ophthalmologists 1 (pt); Podiatrists 1 (pt); Dentist 1 (pt).
Affiliation Methodist
Facilities Dining room; Physical therapy room; Activities room; Crafts room; Laundry room; Barber/Beauty shop.
Activities Arts & crafts; Cards; Games; Reading groups; Prayer groups; Movies; Shopping trips; Social/Cultural gatherings.

Park Strathmoor
5668 Strathmoor Dr, Rockford, IL, 61107
(815) 229-5200

Admin Donald L Dalicandro. *Medical Dir/Dir of Nursing* Dr Ralph Valezquez; Dixie Costanza RN.
Licensure Skilled care. *Beds* 189. *Certified* Medicaid; Medicare.
Owner Proprietary Corp.
Admissions Requirements Minimum age 18.
Staff RNs 6 (ft), 5 (pt); LPNs 20 (ft), 6 (pt); Nurses aides 30 (ft), 18 (pt); Physical therapists 1 (pt); Recreational therapists 1 (pt); Activities coordinators 1 (ft).
Facilities Dining room; Physical therapy room; Activities room; Barber/Beauty shop.
Activities Arts & crafts; Cards; Games; Reading groups; Prayer groups; Movies; Shopping trips; Social/Cultural gatherings.

P A Peterson Home for the Aging
1311 Parkview Ave, Rockford, IL, 61107
(815) 399-8832
Admin Elmer W Johnson. *Medical Dir/Dir of Nursing* William Gorski MD.
Licensure Intermediate care; Sheltered care. *Beds* ICF 101; Sheltered care 77. *Certified* Medicaid.
Owner Nonprofit Corp.
Admissions Requirements Minimum age 62; Medical examination.
Staff RNs 5 (ft), 3 (pt); LPNs 7 (ft), 3 (pt); Nurses aides 25 (ft), 23 (pt); Activities coordinators 4 (ft); Dietitians 1 (ft).
Affiliation Lutheran
Facilities Dining room; Physical therapy room; Activities room; Chapel; Crafts room; Laundry room; Barber/Beauty shop; Library; Wood shop.
Activities Arts & crafts; Cards; Games; Reading groups; Prayer groups; Movies; Shopping trips; Social/Cultural gatherings.

River Bluff Nursing Home
4401 N Main St, Rockford, IL, 61103
(815) 877-8061
Admin John M Ross. *Medical Dir/Dir of Nursing* Warren C Lewis MD; Mary Wilson RN DON.
Licensure Skilled care. *Beds* SNF 304. *Certified* Medicaid.
Owner Publicly owned.
Admissions Requirements Minimum age 18; Medical examination; Physician's request.
Staff Physicians 2 (pt); RNs 18 (ft), 2 (pt); LPNs 18 (ft), 2 (pt); Nurses aides 109 (ft), 47 (pt); Physical therapists 1 (pt); Activities coordinators 1 (ft); Dentists 1 (pt); Ophthalmologists 1 (pt).
Facilities Dining room; Physical therapy room; Activities room; Chapel; Crafts room; Laundry room; Barber/Beauty shop; X-ray; Dental unit.
Activities Arts & crafts; Cards; Games; Reading groups; Prayer groups; Movies; Shopping trips; Social/Cultural gatherings.

Riverside Terrace Nursing Home*
707 W Riverside Blvd, Rockford, IL, 61103
(815) 877-5752
Admin Marilyn Elliott. *Medical Dir/Dir of Nursing* Dr Mrizek.
Licensure Skilled care; Intermediate care. *Beds* 135. *Certified* Medicaid; Medicare.
Owner Proprietary Corp.
Facilities Dining room; Physical therapy room; Activities room; Chapel; Crafts room; Laundry room; Barber/Beauty shop; Lounge areas; Pool table.
Activities Arts & crafts; Cards; Games; Reading groups; Prayer groups; Movies; Shopping trips; Social/Cultural gatherings.

Rockford Manor Inc
310 Arnold Ave, Rockford, IL, 61108
(815) 398-7954
Admin Vi Turenne. *Medical Dir/Dir of Nursing* Merrikay Armour.
Licensure Intermediate care. *Beds* 81. *Certified* Medicaid.
Owner Proprietary Corp (H S Healthcare).

Admissions Requirements Minimum age 55; Medical examination; Physician's request.
Staff RNs 1 (pt); LPNs 4 (ft), 2 (pt); Orderlies 1 (ft); Nurses aides 7 (ft), 12 (pt); Physical therapists 1 (pt); Activities coordinators 2 (ft); Dietitians 1 (pt); Dentists 1 (pt); Podiatrists 1 (pt).
Facilities Dining room; Activities room; Crafts room; Laundry room; Barber/Beauty shop.
Activities Arts & crafts; Cards; Games; Reading groups; Prayer groups; Movies; Shopping trips; Social/Cultural gatherings.

Roosevelt Square—Rockford
3520 School St, Rockford, IL, 61103
(815) 968-4280
Admin Marilyn M Gibson. *Medical Dir/Dir of Nursing* Dr Warren Lewis; Roberta Bonsall.
Licensure Intermediate care. *Beds* ICF 63. *Certified* Medicaid.
Owner Proprietary Corp (Beverly Enterprises).
Admissions Requirements Medical examination; Physician's request.
Staff RNs 1 (ft); LPNs 5 (ft); Nurses aides 25 (ft), 5 (pt); Physical therapists 1 (pt); Recreational therapists 1 (pt); Activities coordinators 1 (pt); Dietitians 1 (pt); Ophthalmologists 1 (pt); Podiatrists 1 (pt); Dietary Supervisor 1 (ft).
Facilities Dining room; Physical therapy room; Activities room; Crafts room; Laundry room; Barber/Beauty shop; Library.
Activities Arts & crafts; Cards; Games; Reading groups; Prayer groups; Movies; Shopping trips; Social/Cultural gatherings; Daily exercises; Intellectual activities; Community involvement; Remotivation therapy; Reality orientation; Music therapy; Adopt-a-grandparent; Pets; Contacts w/ children.

Wesley Willcourt Willows Health Center
4141 N Rockton Ave, Rockford, IL, 61103
(815) 654-2534
Admin Robert E Ash. *Medical Dir/Dir of Nursing* Dr Craig Rogers.
Licensure Skilled care; Sheltered care. *Beds* SNF 83; Sheltered care 206; Independent living unit 20.
Owner Nonprofit Corp.
Admissions Requirements Minimum age 62; Medical examination.
Staff Physicians 1 (pt); RNs 12 (ft); LPNs 11 (ft); Nurses aides 51 (ft); Physical therapists 3 (ft); Recreational therapists 3 (ft); Occupational therapists 3 (ft); Speech therapists 1 (pt); Activities coordinators 7 (ft); Dietitians 1 (pt); Dentists 1 (pt); Podiatrists 1 (pt).
Affiliation Methodist
Facilities Dining room; Physical therapy room; Activities room; Chapel; Crafts room; Laundry room; Barber/Beauty shop; Library.
Activities Arts & crafts; Cards; Games; Reading groups; Prayer groups; Movies; Shopping trips; Social/Cultural gatherings.

ROLLING MEADOWS

Americana Healthcare Center of Rolling Meadows*
4225 Kirchoff Rd, Rolling Meadows, IL, 60008
(312) 397-2400
Admin Joy P Rathe.
Licensure Skilled care; Intermediate care. *Beds* 155. *Certified* Medicaid; Medicare.
Owner Proprietary Corp (Manor Care).
Admissions Requirements Medical examination.
Staff Physicians 2 (pt); RNs; LPNs; Orderlies; Nurses aides; Physical therapists 1 (ft), 2 (pt); Recreational therapists 1 (ft); Occupational therapists 1 (pt); Speech

therapists 1 (pt); Activities coordinators 1 (ft); Dietitians 1 (pt); Dentists 1 (pt); Podiatrists 1 (pt).
Facilities Dining room; Physical therapy room; Activities room; Crafts room; Laundry room; Barber/Beauty shop.
Activities Arts & crafts; Cards; Games; Reading groups; Prayer groups; Movies; Shopping trips; Social/Cultural gatherings.

Meadows*
3250 S Plum Grove Rd, Rolling Meadows, IL, 60008
(312) 397-0055
Admin Byrn T Witt. *Medical Dir/Dir of Nursing* Dr Petel.
Licensure Intermediate care for mentally retarded. *Certified* Medicaid.
Owner Proprietary Corp.
Admissions Requirements Minimum age 18; Medical examination.
Staff Physicians 1 (pt); RNs 2 (ft), 2 (pt); LPNs 3 (ft), 4 (pt); Nurses aides 5 (ft); Physical therapists 1 (pt); Recreational therapists 1 (pt); Occupational therapists 1 (pt); Speech therapists 1 (pt); Activities coordinators 1 (ft); Dietitians 1 (pt); Dentists 1 (pt); Ophthalmologists 1 (pt); Podiatrists 1 (pt); Audiologists 1 (pt); Acting aides 8 (ft); Rehabilitation aides 10 (ft).
Facilities Dining room; Physical therapy room; Activities room; Crafts room; Laundry room; Barber/Beauty shop.
Activities Arts & crafts; Games; Reading groups; Movies; Shopping trips; Social/ Cultural gatherings.

ROSELLE

Abbington House Inc
31 W Central, Roselle, IL, 60172
(312) 894-5058
Admin Marvin M Struck. *Medical Dir/Dir of Nursing* Dr Robert Dick; Phyllis Struck RN DON.
Licensure Intermediate care. *Beds* ICF 82. *Certified* Medicaid.
Owner Privately owned.
Admissions Requirements Minimum age 65; Medical examination.
Staff Physicians 5 (pt); RNs 3 (ft); LPNs 3 (pt); Orderlies 2 (ft), 3 (pt); Nurses aides 6 (ft), 5 (pt); Physical therapists 1 (pt); Activities coordinators 1 (ft); Dietitians 1 (pt); Dentists 1 (pt); Ophthalmologists 1 (pt).
Facilities Dining room; Activities room; Crafts room; Laundry room; Barber/Beauty shop; Library.
Activities Arts & crafts; Cards; Games; Reading groups; Prayer groups; Movies; Shopping trips; Social/Cultural gatherings.

Sunrise Courts*
439 Lawrence, Roselle, IL, 60172
(312) 543-2440
Admin Ivan Browne.
Licensure Intermediate care. *Beds* 20.
Owner Nonprofit Corp.

ROSEVILLE

La Moine Christian Nursing Home
PO Box 347, 145 S Chamberlain St, Roseville, IL, 61473-0747
(309) 426-2134
Admin James M Oliver. *Medical Dir/Dir of Nursing* Dr Ronald Leonard; G David Welty RN DON.
Licensure Skilled care. *Beds* SNF 99. *Certified* Medicaid.
Owner Nonprofit Corp (Christian Homes).
Admissions Requirements Minimum age 18; Physician's request.
Staff RNs 6 (ft), 4 (pt); LPNs 4 (ft), 3 (pt); Orderlies 1 (ft), 2 (pt); Nurses aides 26 (ft), 17 (pt); Physical therapists 1 (ft), 1 (pt);

Recreational therapists 1 (pt); Activities coordinators 2 (ft); Dietitians 5 (ft), 7 (pt); Ophthalmologists 1 (pt); Podiatrists 1 (pt).
Facilities Dining room; Physical therapy room; Activities room; Chapel; Crafts room; Laundry room; Barber/Beauty shop; Library.
Activities Arts & crafts; Games; Reading groups; Prayer groups; Movies; Shopping trips; Social/Cultural gatherings.

ROSICLARE

Fairview House Nursing Home
Rte 1 Box 56B, Fairview Rd, Rosiclare, IL, 62982
(618) 285-6613 or 285-6614
Admin James C Stunson. *Medical Dir/Dir of Nursing* Rogelio Arevino; Rhonda Belford DON.
Licensure Intermediate care. *Beds* ICF 60. *Certified* Medicaid.
Owner Proprietary Corp.
Admissions Requirements Medical examination.
Staff Physicians; RNs; LPNs; Nurses aides; Activities coordinators; Dietitians; Social services.
Facilities Dining room; Physical therapy room; Activities room; Chapel; Laundry room; Barber/Beauty shop.
Activities Arts & crafts; Cards; Games; Reading groups; Prayer groups; Movies; Shopping trips; Social/Cultural gatherings.

ROUND LAKE BEACH

Hillcrest Retirement Village Ltd
1740 N Circuit Dr, Round Lake Beach, IL, 60073
(312) 546-5301
Admin Ruth C Lange. *Medical Dir/Dir of Nursing* Mark J Round MD; Mary Ann Gedvilas RN DON.
Licensure Intermediate care. *Beds* ICF 93. *Certified* Medicaid.
Owner Proprietary Corp.
Admissions Requirements Minimum age 40; Medical examination; Physician's request.
Staff RNs; LPNs; Orderlies; Nurses aides; Activities coordinators.
Facilities Dining room; Activities room; Chapel; Laundry room; Barber/Beauty shop; Library.
Activities Arts & crafts; Cards; Games; Reading groups; Prayer groups; Movies; Shopping trips; Social/Cultural gatherings.

RUSHVILLE

Snyder's Vaughn-Haven Inc
135 S Morgan St, Rushville, IL, 62681
(217) 322-3420
Admin Dianne Snyder. *Medical Dir/Dir of Nursing* Dr Russel Dohner.
Licensure Skilled care. *Beds* SNF 99. *Certified* Medicaid; Medicare.
Owner Proprietary Corp.
Admissions Requirements Minimum age 18.
Staff RNs 4 (ft), 2 (pt); LPNs 8 (ft), 1 (pt); Nurses aides 32 (ft); Recreational therapists 1 (ft); Activities coordinators 2 (ft); Dietitians 1 (ft).
Facilities Dining room; Physical therapy room; Activities room; Crafts room; Laundry room; Barber/Beauty shop.
Activities Arts & crafts; Cards; Games; Reading groups; Prayer groups; Movies; Shopping trips; Social/Cultural gatherings.

SAINT CHARLES

Pine View Care Center
611 Allen Ln, Saint Charles, IL, 60174
(312) 377-2211
Admin Patricia F Patrick. *Medical Dir/Dir of Nursing* Dr Robert Reeder.

Licensure Skilled care. *Beds* SNF 120.
Certified Medicare.
Owner Nonprofit Corp.
Admissions Requirements Minimum age 22;
Medical examination.
Staff Physicians 3 (pt); RNs 8 (ft); LPNs 12
(ft); Nurses aides 25 (ft); Physical therapists
4 (pt); Occupational therapists 1 (pt); Speech
therapists (pt); Activities coordinators 1
(ft); Dietitians 1 (pt); Ophthalmologists 1
(pt); Podiatrists 1 (pt); Dentist 1 (pt).
Languages Spanish
Affiliation Church of Christ
Facilities Dining room; Physical therapy
room; Activities room; Crafts room; Barber/
Beauty shop; Library; Library cart (use of all
audio/visual & reading material from public
library).
Activities Arts & crafts; Cards; Games;
Reading groups; Prayer groups; Movies;
Shopping trips; Social/Cultural gatherings;
Lunch outings; Holiday & special events
monthly.

SAINT ELMO

Heritage Home Care Center
PO Box 126, Rte 40 East, Saint Elmo, IL,
62458
(618) 829-5551
Admin Tammy B Woolsey. *Medical Dir/Dir of
Nursing* Dr Lawrence Oder.
Licensure Intermediate care. *Beds* ICF 49.
Certified Medicaid.
Owner Proprietary Corp (Community Lifecare
Enterprises).
Admissions Requirements Minimum age 18;
Medical examination.
Staff Physicians 1 (pt); RNs 110; LPNs 5 (ft);
Nurses aides 10 (ft), 8 (pt); Physical
therapists 1 (pt); Reality therapists 1 (pt);
Speech therapists 1 (pt); Activities
coordinators 1 (ft); Dietitians 1 (ft); Dentists
1 (pt); Ophthalmologists 2 (pt); Podiatrists 1
(pt); Dentist 1 (pt).
Facilities Dining room; Activities room;
Laundry room; Barber/Beauty shop.
Activities Arts & crafts; Cards; Games;
Reading groups; Prayer groups; Movies;
Shopping trips.

SALEM

Bryan Manor*
PO Box 687, Rte 37 N, Salem, IL, 62881
(618) 548-4561
Admin Linda Horton.
Licensure Intermediate care. *Beds* 82.
Owner Nonprofit Corp.

Doctors Nursing Home
1201 Hawthorn Rd, Salem, IL, 62881
(618) 548-4884
Admin Catherine E Bailey. *Medical Dir/Dir of
Nursing* Virginia Milam RN DON.
Licensure Skilled care; Intermediate care. *Beds*
SNF 122; ICF. *Certified* Medicaid;
Medicare.
Owner Proprietary Corp (Columbia Corp).
Staff RNs; LPNs; Orderlies; Nurses aides;
Physical therapists; Occupational therapists;
Speech therapists; Activities coordinators;
Dietitians.

Twin Willow Nursing Center*
Rte 37 N, Salem, IL, 62881
(618) 548-0542
Admin Todd C Woodruff.
Licensure Intermediate care. *Beds* 76.
Certified Medicaid.
Owner Proprietary Corp.

SANDWICH

Roosevelt Square—Sandwich
902 E Arnold, Sandwich, IL, 60548
(815) 786-8409

Admin Carol C Price. *Medical Dir/Dir of
Nursing* Dr O H Fischer.
Licensure Intermediate care. *Beds* 63.
Certified Medicaid.
Owner Proprietary Corp (Beverly Enterprises).
Admissions Requirements Minimum age 60;
Medical examination.
Staff RNs; LPNs; Nurses aides; Recreational
therapists; Activities coordinators; Dietitians.
Facilities Dining room; Physical therapy
room; Activities room; Crafts room; Laundry
room; Barber/Beauty shop; Living room.
Activities Arts & crafts; Cards; Games;
Reading groups; Prayer groups; Movies;
Shopping trips; Social/Cultural gatherings;
Exercises; Current events; Interest groups.

Sandhaven Conv Center*
515 N Main, Sandwich, IL, 60548
(815) 786-8426
Admin Carole A Whalen.
Licensure Skilled care; Intermediate care. *Beds*
SNF 58; ICF 58. *Certified* Medicaid;
Medicare.
Owner Proprietary Corp (Signature Corp).

SAVANNA

Big Meadows Inc
1000 Longmoor Ave, Savanna, IL, 61074
(815) 273-2238
Admin Julienne Lund. *Medical Dir/Dir of
Nursing* Dr L B Hussey; K Carroll RN.
Licensure Intermediate care. *Beds* ICF 122.
Certified Medicaid.
Owner Proprietary Corp.
Admissions Requirements Physician's request.
Staff Physicians 4 (pt); RNs 3 (ft), 2 (pt);
LPNs 4 (ft), 1 (pt); Nurses aides 31 (ft), 5
(pt); Activities coordinators 1 (pt); Dietitians
1 (pt); Social worker 1 (ft).
Facilities Dining room; Physical therapy
room; Activities room; Chapel; Crafts room;
Laundry room; Barber/Beauty shop; Library.
Activities Arts & crafts; Cards; Games;
Reading groups; Prayer groups; Movies;
Shopping trips; Social/Cultural gatherings.

SAVOY

The Carle Arbours*
203 W Burwash Ave, Savoy, IL, 61874
(217) 337-3090
Admin Ruth Shankin.
Licensure Skilled care. *Beds* 240. *Certified*
Medicaid; Medicare.
Owner Proprietary Corp.

SCHAUMBURG

Friendship Village Health Care Center
350 W Schaumburg Rd, Schaumburg, IL,
60194
(312) 884-5005
Admin Frank Miezio. *Medical Dir/Dir of
Nursing* Gregory Ostrom MD; Mardi
Wiedlman DON.
Licensure Skilled care. *Beds* SNF 188.
Certified Medicaid; Medicare.
Owner Nonprofit Corp.
Admissions Requirements Medical
examination; Physician's request.
Staff RNs 12 (ft), 16 (pt); LPNs 1 (ft), 1 (pt);
Nurses aides 46 (ft), 36 (pt); Physical
therapists 1 (ft), 3 (pt); Recreational
therapists 2 (ft), 2 (pt); Occupational
therapists 1 (pt); Speech therapists 1 (pt);
Activities coordinators 1 (ft); Dietitians 1
(ft); Dentists 1 (pt); Ophthalmologists 1 (pt);
Podiatrists 1 (pt).
Facilities Dining room; Physical therapy
room; Activities room; Chapel; Crafts room;
Laundry room; Barber/Beauty shop; Library.
Activities Arts & crafts; Cards; Games;
Reading groups; Prayer groups; Movies;
Shopping trips; Social/Cultural gatherings.

SESSER

Redwood Manor
W Franklin St, Sesser, IL, 62884
(618) 625-5261
Admin Gloria Pasko. *Medical Dir/Dir of
Nursing* Dr Joseph Campanella; Linda
Brodley DON.
Licensure Intermediate care. *Beds* ICF 58.
Certified Medicaid.
Owner Proprietary Corp.
Admissions Requirements Minimum age 18;
Medical examination; Physician's request.
Staff Physicians 1 (ft); RNs 2 (pt); LPNs 4
(ft), 2 (pt); Orderlies 2 (ft); Nurses aides 10
(ft), 2 (pt); Activities coordinators 3 (ft).
Facilities Dining room; Activities room;
Laundry room; Barber/Beauty shop.
Activities Arts & crafts; Cards; Games;
Reading groups; Prayer groups; Movies;
Shopping trips; Social/Cultural gatherings;
Camping; Swimming; Fishing; Boating;
Picnics.

SHABBONA

Shabbona Nursing Home Inc*
W Comanche St, Shabbona, IL, 60550
(815) 824-2194
Admin Jackie Goken. *Medical Dir/Dir of
Nursing* Dr Robert Purdy.
Licensure Skilled care; Intermediate care. *Beds*
91. *Certified* Medicaid.
Owner Proprietary Corp.
Admissions Requirements Minimum age 21;
Medical examination; Physician's request.
Staff Physicians 6 (pt); RNs 6 (ft), 3 (pt);
LPNs 1 (ft), 2 (pt); Orderlies 2 (ft); Nurses
aides 19 (ft), 20 (pt); Physical therapists 1
(pt); Reality therapists 1 (pt); Recreational
therapists 1 (pt); Occupational therapists 1
(pt); Speech therapists 1 (pt); Activities
coordinators 1 (pt); Dietitians 1 (pt);
Dentists 1 (pt); Ophthalmologists 1 (pt);
Podiatrists 1 (pt); Audiologists 1 (pt).
Facilities Dining room; Physical therapy
room; Activities room; Chapel; Crafts room;
Laundry room; Barber/Beauty shop; Library.
Activities Arts & crafts; Cards; Games;
Reading groups; Prayer groups; Movies;
Shopping trips; Social/Cultural gatherings.

SHANNON

Villas of Shannon Nursing Home*
418 S Ridge St, Shannon, IL, 61078
(815) 864-2425
Admin Blaine Fox.
Licensure Intermediate care. *Beds* 73.
Certified Medicaid.
Owner Proprietary Corp.

SHAWNEETOWN

Loretta Nursing Home
Logan & Lincoln Sts, Shawneetown, IL, 62984
(618) 269-3109
Admin Delbert H York. *Medical Dir/Dir of
Nursing* Andrew Cserny MD.
Licensure Skilled care; Intermediate care. *Beds*
107. *Certified* Medicaid.
Owner Proprietary Corp.
Admissions Requirements Minimum age 18;
Medical examination; Physician's request.
Staff RNs 2 (ft), 2 (pt); LPNs 5 (ft), 4 (pt);
Nurses aides 27 (ft), 7 (pt); Activities
coordinators 1 (ft); Dietitians 1 (pt).

SHELBYVILLE

Reservoir Manor
PO Box 467, 419 E Main St, Shelbyville, IL,
62565
(217) 774-9544
Admin Rita Armbrust. *Medical Dir/Dir of
Nursing* Karen Forcum RN.

Licensure Intermediate care for mentally retarded. *Beds* ICF/MR 15. *Certified* Medicaid.
Owner Proprietary Corp (Health Care Management).
Admissions Requirements Minimum age 18; Medical examination.
Staff RNs 1 (ft); Nurses aides 5 (ft), 3 (pt); Activities coordinators 1 (ft).
Facilities Dining room; Activities room; Laundry room.
Activities Arts & crafts; Cards; Games; Reading groups; Movies; Shopping trips; Social/Cultural gatherings; Many community activities.

Shelby Manor
Dacey & SW 3rd St, Shelbyville, IL, 62565
(217) 774-2128
Admin Lula M Robertson. *Medical Dir/Dir of Nursing* Dr Edwin Sirov.
Licensure Intermediate care. *Beds* 80. *Certified* Medicaid.
Owner Proprietary Corp (Beverly Enterprises).
Admissions Requirements Minimum age 21; Medical examination.
Staff Physicians 6 (ft); RNs 1 (pt); LPNs 5 (ft), 1 (pt); Nurses aides 9 (ft), 9 (pt); Occupational therapists 1 (pt); Activities coordinators 1 (ft), 1 (pt); Dietitians 1 (pt); Dentists 1 (pt); Podiatrists 1 (pt).
Facilities Dining room; Activities room; Crafts room; Laundry room; Barber/Beauty shop.
Activities Arts & crafts; Games; Reading groups; Prayer groups; Movies; Shopping trips; Social/Cultural gatherings.

Shelby Memorial Home*
Rte 128 N, Shelbyville, IL, 62565
(217) 774-2111
Admin Albert E Wimer.
Licensure Skilled care. *Beds* 99. *Certified* Medicaid.
Owner Proprietary Corp.

Shelby Memorial Hospital Nursing Home
200 S Cedar St, Shelbyville, IL, 62565
(217) 774-3961
Admin W Garland Strohl. *Medical Dir/Dir of Nursing* Lilliam Yates RN.
Licensure Skilled care. *Beds* SNF 19.
Owner Nonprofit Corp.
Admissions Requirements Physician's request.
Staff RNs 1 (ft); LPNs 10 (ft); Nurses aides 5 (ft).
Facilities Dining room; Activities room; Barber/Beauty shop.
Activities Arts & crafts; Games; Social/Cultural gatherings.

SHELDON

Sheldon Healthcare Inc
PO Box 456, 170 W Concord St, Sheldon, IL, 60966
(815) 429-3522
Admin Janice K Conrad. *Medical Dir/Dir of Nursing* N D Hungness MD; Myrna Steiner RN DON.
Licensure Intermediate care. *Beds* ICF 31. *Certified* Medicaid.
Owner Proprietary Corp.
Admissions Requirements Minimum age 70; Medical examination; Physician's request.
Staff Physicians 9 (pt); RNs 2 (ft), 5 (pt); Nurses aides 10 (ft), 4 (pt); Recreational therapists 1 (pt); Activities coordinators 1 (ft), 1 (pt); Dietitians 2 (ft), 1 (pt).
Facilities Dining room; Activities room; Crafts room; Laundry room; Barber/Beauty shop.
Activities Arts & crafts; Cards; Games; Reading groups; Prayer groups; Movies; Social/Cultural gatherings.

SILVIS

Roosevelt Square—Silvis
1403 E 9th Ave, Silvis, IL, 61282
(309) 796-2600
Admin Deborah A Rutter. *Medical Dir/Dir of Nursing* Shirley J Schroeder.
Licensure Intermediate care. *Beds* 63. *Certified* Medicaid.
Owner Proprietary Corp (Beverly Enterprises).
Staff RNs; LPNs; Orderlies; Nurses aides; Activities coordinators; Dietitians.
Activities Arts & crafts; Cards; Games; Reading groups; Prayer groups; Movies; Shopping trips; Social/Cultural gatherings.

SIMPSON

Shawnee Shelter Care*
Rte 1, Simpson, IL, 62985
(618) 695-3321
Admin Georgia L Brown.
Licensure Sheltered care. *Beds* 13.
Owner Proprietary Corp.

SKOKIE

Lieberman Geriatric Health Centre
9700 Gross Point Rd, Skokie, IL, 60076
(312) 674-7200
Admin Mary Ellen Lavery. *Medical Dir/Dir of Nursing* Dr David Staats.
Licensure Skilled care. *Beds* SNF 240. *Certified* Medicaid.
Owner Nonprofit organization/foundation.
Admissions Requirements Medical examination.
Staff Physicians 1 (ft), 1 (pt); RNs 31 (ft); LPNs 7 (ft); Nurses aides 94 (ft); Recreational therapists 6 (ft); Speech therapists 1 (pt); Activities coordinators 1 (ft); Dietitians 2 (ft); Social workers 5 (ft), 1 (pt); Nurse practitioner 1 (ft).
Languages Yiddish, Hebrew, Russian
Affiliation Jewish
Facilities Dining room; Physical therapy room; Activities room; Chapel Synagogue; Crafts room; Laundry room; Barber/Beauty shop; Social hall; Doctor's office; Park.
Activities Arts & crafts; Cards; Games; Reading groups; Prayer groups; Movies; Shopping trips; Social/Cultural gatherings.

Old Orchard Manor
4660 Old Orchard Rd, Skokie, IL, 60076
(312) 676-4800
Admin Jane Judsen Ionescu. *Medical Dir/Dir of Nursing* Arthur R Peterson MD; Sharon Eager RN DON.
Licensure Skilled care. *Beds* SNF 61.
Owner Proprietary Corp.
Admissions Requirements Minimum age 18; Medical examination; Physician's request.
Staff RNs 8 (ft), 7 (pt); Nurses aides 20 (ft); Physical therapists 3 (pt); Recreational therapists 3 (pt); Activities coordinators 1 (ft).
Facilities Dining room; Physical therapy room; Activities room; Crafts room; Laundry room; Barber/Beauty shop.
Activities Arts & crafts; Cards; Games; Reading groups; Prayer groups; Movies; Shopping trips; Social/Cultural gatherings; Lectures.

Orchard Village*
7670 Marmora Manor, Skokie, IL, 60077
(312) 967-1800
Admin Jack Dohr.
Licensure Intermediate care. *Beds* 55.
Owner Nonprofit Corp.

Skokie Meadows Nursing Center No I*
9615 N Knox Ave, Skokie, IL, 60076
(312) 679-4161
Admin Doris E Teschner RN. *Medical Dir/Dir of Nursing* Dr Edward Sutoris.

Licensure Skilled care; Intermediate care. *Beds* SNF 55; ICF 58. *Certified* Medicaid; Medicare.
Owner Proprietary Corp.
Admissions Requirements Minimum age 20; Medical examination; Physician's request.
Staff RNs; Orderlies; Nurses aides; Physical therapists; Reality therapists; Recreational therapists; Occupational therapists; Speech therapists; Activities coordinators; Dietitians; Dentists; Ophthalmologists; Podiatrists; Audiologists.
Facilities Dining room; Physical therapy room; Activities room; Crafts room; Laundry room; Barber/Beauty shop.
Activities Arts & crafts; Cards; Games; Reading groups; Prayer groups; Movies; Shopping trips; Social/Cultural gatherings.

Skokie Meadows Nursing Center No II*
4600 W Golf Dr, Skokie, IL, 60076
(312) 679-1157
Admin Jacob M Graff.
Licensure Intermediate care. *Beds* 111. *Certified* Medicaid.
Owner Proprietary Corp.

Village Nursing Home Inc*
9000 La Vergne Ave, Skokie, IL, 60077
(312) 679-2322
Admin Samuel Brandman.
Licensure Skilled care; Intermediate care. *Beds* SNF 98; ICF 51. *Certified* Medicaid; Medicare.
Owner Proprietary Corp.

SMITHTON

Park Haven Care Center*
107 S Lincoln, Smithton, IL, 62285
(618) 235-4600
Admin Jacqueline Hern.
Licensure Intermediate care. *Beds* 101. *Certified* Medicaid.
Owner Proprietary Corp.

SOUTH BELOIT

Fair Oaks Nursing Health Care Center
1515 Blackhawk Blvd, South Beloit, IL, 61080
(815) 389-3911
Admin Mary Lou Healy. *Medical Dir/Dir of Nursing* T P Long MD; Betty Thurner RN.
Licensure Skilled care. *Beds* SNF 42.
Owner Nonprofit Corp.
Admissions Requirements Minimum age 19; Medical examination; Physician's request.
Staff RNs 2 (ft), 3 (pt); LPNs 4 (pt); Nurses aides 10 (ft), 10 (pt); Activities coordinators 1 (ft), 1 (pt).
Facilities Dining room; Physical therapy room; Activities room; Laundry room; Barber/Beauty shop.
Activities Arts & crafts; Cards; Games; Reading groups; Prayer groups; Movies; Shopping trips; Social/Cultural gatherings.

SOUTH ELGIN

Fox Valley Nursing Center Inc
759 Kane St, South Elgin, IL, 60177
(312) 697-3310
Admin Jerry L Rhoads. *Medical Dir/Dir of Nursing* Barbara Blust.
Licensure Skilled care; Intermediate care. *Beds* SNF 107; ICF 99. *Certified* Medicaid; Medicare.
Owner Privately owned.
Admissions Requirements Minimum age 18.
Staff RNs 10 (ft); LPNs 2 (ft); Nurses aides 30 (ft); Physical therapists 1 (ft); Occupational therapists 1 (pt); Speech therapists 1 (pt); Activities coordinators 1 (ft).
Languages French, Italian, Polish
Facilities Dining room; Physical therapy room; Activities room; Chapel; Crafts room; Laundry room; Barber/Beauty shop.

Activities Arts & crafts; Cards; Games;
Reading groups; Prayer groups; Movies;
Shopping trips; Social/Cultural gatherings.

South Elgin Manor*
746 Spring St, South Elgin, IL, 60177
(312) 697-0565
Admin Alice J Clough.
Licensure Intermediate care. *Beds* 96.
Certified Medicaid.
Owner Proprietary Corp (Beverly Enterprises).

SOUTH HOLLAND

Holland Home for the Aged*
16300 S Louis Ave, South Holland, IL, 60473
(312) 596-3050
Admin Rev Paul deVries.
Licensure Intermediate care. *Beds* 326.
Certified Medicaid.
Owner Nonprofit Corp.

Rest Haven South
16300 Wausau Ave, South Holland, IL, 60473
(312) 596-5500
Admin Timothy J Abbring. *Medical Dir/Dir of Nursing* G Gnade MD; Judith McDonald RN DON.
Licensure Skilled care; Intermediate care. *Beds* 166.
Owner Nonprofit Corp.
Admissions Requirements Minimum age 60;
Medical examination.
Staff Physicians 2 (pt); RNs 5 (ft), 17 (pt);
LPNs 1 (ft), 4 (pt); Orderlies 2 (pt); Nurses
aides 35 (ft), 65 (pt); Activities coordinators
1 (ft).
Languages Dutch
Affiliation Christian Reformed
Facilities Dining room; Physical therapy
room; Activities room; Crafts room; Laundry
room; Barber/Beauty shop.
Activities Arts & crafts; Cards; Games;
Reading groups; Prayer groups; Movies;
Shopping trips.

Windmill Nursing Pavilion LTD
16000 S Wabash Ave, South Holland, IL, 60473
(312) 339-0600
Admin Maurice Aaron. *Medical Dir/Dir of Nursing* Dr S Levine.
Licensure Skilled care; Intermediate care. *Beds* SNF 50; ICF 100. *Certified* Medicaid.
Owner Proprietary Corp.
Admissions Requirements Minimum age 21;
Physician's request.
Staff Physicians; RNs; LPNs; Orderlies;
Nurses aides; Physical therapists;
Occupational therapists; Speech therapists;
Activities coordinators; Dietitians; Dentists;
Ophthalmologists; Podiatrists.
Facilities Dining room; Physical therapy
room; Activities room; Chapel; Crafts room;
Laundry room; Barber/Beauty shop; Library.
Activities Arts & crafts; Cards; Games;
Reading groups; Prayer groups; Movies;
Shopping trips; Social/Cultural gatherings;
Outings.

SPARTA

Randolph County Nursing Home
310 W Belmont, Sparta, IL, 62286
(618) 443-4351
Admin Paulette A Buch. *Medical Dir/Dir of Nursing* Edith Besher DON.
Licensure Skilled care; Intermediate care;
Medicare. *Beds* SNF 136; ICF. *Certified*
Medicaid; Medicare.
Owner Nonprofit Corp.
Admissions Requirements Minimum age 18;
Medical examination.
Staff RNs 3 (ft), 3 (pt); LPNs 5 (ft), 5 (pt);
Nurses aides 30 (ft), 18 (pt).

Facilities Dining room; Physical therapy
room; Activities room; Chapel; Crafts room;
Barber/Beauty shop.
Activities Arts & crafts; Cards; Games;
Reading groups; Prayer groups; Movies;
Shopping trips.

Senior Manor Nursing Center Inc
223 E 4th St, Sparta, IL, 62286
(618) 443-4411
Admin Ruth Jung. *Medical Dir/Dir of Nursing*
Penny Jetter DON.
Licensure Intermediate care. *Beds* 59.
Certified Medicaid.
Owner Proprietary Corp.
Admissions Requirements Medical
examination.
Staff RNs 1 (ft), 1 (pt); LPNs 3 (ft), 3 (pt);
Nurses aides 5 (ft), 10 (pt); Physical
therapists 1 (pt); Recreational therapists 1
(pt); Occupational therapists 1 (pt); Speech
therapists 1 (pt); Activities coordinators 1
(ft); Dietitians 1 (pt).
Facilities Dining room; Physical therapy
room; Activities room; Chapel; Crafts room;
Laundry room; Barber/Beauty shop; Library;
Visitors lounge.
Activities Arts & crafts; Cards; Games;
Reading groups; Prayer groups; Movies;
Shopping trips; Social/Cultural gatherings.

SPRING VALLEY

Argyle House
534 W Miller, Spring Valley, IL, 62702
(217) 786-2560
Admin Mark Miller.
Licensure Community living facility. *Beds* 20.
Owner Nonprofit organization/foundation.

Spring Valley Nursing Center
1300 N Greenwood St, Spring Valley, IL, 61362
(815) 664-4708
Admin Shirley M Michalski. *Medical Dir/Dir of Nursing* Donald Gallagher MD; Barbara J Lansing RN DON.
Licensure Skilled care. *Beds* SNF 98. *Certified*
Medicaid; Medicare.
Owner Proprietary Corp.
Admissions Requirements Minimum age 18;
Medical examination; Physician's request.
Staff RNs 1 (ft), 9 (pt); LPNs 2 (ft), 2 (pt);
Nurses aides 23 (ft), 18 (pt); Activities
coordinators 1 (ft), 2 (pt).
Facilities Dining room; Physical therapy
room; Activities room; Laundry room;
Barber/Beauty shop; Library.
Activities Arts & crafts; Cards; Games;
Movies.

SPRINGFIELD

Brother James Court
RR 1, Sangamon Ave Rd E, Springfield, IL, 62707
(217) 544-4876
Admin David Sarnecki. *Medical Dir/Dir of Nursing* H B Henkel MD; Michael Groesch.
Licensure Intermediate care for mentally retarded. *Beds* 96. *Certified* Medicaid.
Owner Nonprofit Corp.
Admissions Requirements Minimum age 18;
Males only; Medical examination;
Physician's request.
Staff RNs 2 (ft); LPNs 2 (ft), 2 (pt); Orderlies
6 (ft), 2 (pt); Nurses aides 14 (ft), 2 (pt);
Recreational therapists 5 (pt); Occupational
therapists 1 (pt); Speech therapists 1 (pt);
Activities coordinators 1 (ft); Dietitians 1
(pt).
Affiliation Roman Catholic
Facilities Dining room; Activities room;
Chapel; Crafts room; Laundry room;
Library.

Activities Arts & crafts; Games; Prayer groups;
Movies; Shopping trips; Social/Cultural
gatherings.

Mary Bryant Home for the Visually Impaired
2960 Stanton St, Springfield, IL, 62703
(217) 529-1611
Admin Frances Trees. *Medical Dir/Dir of Nursing* Mark Hansen MD.
Licensure Sheltered care. *Beds* 46.
Owner Nonprofit Corp.
Admissions Requirements Minimum age 18
(Visually Impaired); Medical examination.
Staff RNs; LPNs.
Facilities Dining room; Activities room;
Crafts room; Laundry room; Barber/Beauty
shop; Library; Family room.
Activities Arts & crafts; Cards; Games;
Reading groups; Prayer groups; Shopping
trips; Social/Cultural gatherings; Exercise
equipment.

Dirksen House Healthcare
555 W Carpenter St, Springfield, IL, 62702
(217) 525-1880
Admin Bruce L Vaca.
Licensure Skilled care; Intermediate care. *Beds*
SNF 65; ICF 198. *Certified* Medicaid;
Medicare.
Owner Proprietary Corp (Hillhaven Corp).

Eastgate Manor*
525 S 18th St, Springfield, IL, 62703
(217) 789-1680
Admin Jill Spurgeon.
Licensure Intermediate care. *Beds* 65.
Certified Medicaid.
Owner Proprietary Corp.
Admissions Requirements Minimum age 18;
Medical examination.
Facilities Dining room; Physical therapy
room; Activities room; Chapel; Crafts room;
Laundry room; Barber/Beauty shop.
Activities Arts & crafts; Games; Reading
groups; Prayer groups; Movies; Shopping
trips; Social/Cultural gatherings; Orientation.

Haven Retirement Center*
2301 W Monroe, Springfield, IL, 62704
(217) 546-0272
Admin Glen L Ferguson.
Licensure Skilled care; Intermediate care. *Beds*
SNF 61; ICF 133. *Certified* Medicaid.
Owner Proprietary Corp.

Heritage Manor Nursing & Conv Home*
900 N Rutledge, Springfield, IL, 62702
(217) 789-0930
Admin Kathleen Peters.
Licensure Skilled care; Intermediate care. *Beds*
SNF 127; ICF 26. *Certified* Medicaid;
Medicare.
Owner Proprietary Corp.

Illinois Presbyterian Home
2005 W Lawrence, Springfield, IL, 62704
(217) 546-5622
Admin Thomas P O'Fallon.
Licensure Intermediate care; Sheltered care.
Beds ICF 15; Sheltered care 68. *Certified*
Medicaid.
Owner Nonprofit Corp.
Admissions Requirements Minimum age 65;
Medical examination.
Staff RNs 2 (ft), 2 (pt); LPNs 2 (ft), 3 (pt);
Nurses aides 7 (ft), 3 (pt); Activities
coordinators 1 (ft); Dietitians 1 (pt).
Affiliation Presbyterian
Facilities Dining room; Activities room;
Crafts room; Laundry room; Library.
Activities Arts & crafts; Cards; Games;
Reading groups; Prayer groups; Movies;
Shopping trips; Social/Cultural gatherings.

Lewis Memorial Christian Village
3400 W Washington, Springfield, IL, 62702
(217) 787-9600
Admin Robert Florence. *Medical Dir/Dir of Nursing* Dr John Meyer.

Licensure Skilled care; Intermediate care. *Beds* SNF 76; ICF 79. *Certified* Medicaid.
Owner Nonprofit Corp (Christian Homes).
Admissions Requirements Minimum age 18; Medical examination; Physician's request.
Staff RNs 4 (ft), 6 (pt); LPNs 12 (ft), 8 (pt); Orderlies 3 (ft), 2 (pt); Nurses aides 48 (ft), 8 (pt); Physical therapists 1 (pt); Recreational therapists 1 (pt); Occupational therapists 1 (pt); Speech therapists 1 (pt); Activities coordinators 1 (ft); Dietitians 1 (ft).
Affiliation Church of Christ
Facilities Dining room; Physical therapy room; Activities room; Chapel; Crafts room; Laundry room; Barber/Beauty shop; Library.
Activities Arts & crafts; Cards; Games; Reading groups; Prayer groups; Movies; Shopping trips.

Oak Terrace Retirement*
1750 W Washington, Springfield, IL, 62702
(217) 787-6466
Admin Anasue L Haines. *Medical Dir/Dir of Nursing* Norman Scheibling.
Licensure Intermediate care; Sheltered care. *Beds* ICF 58; Sheltered care 40.
Owner Proprietary Corp.
Admissions Requirements Minimum age 18; Medical examination.
Staff RNs 1 (ft), 2 (pt); LPNs 4 (ft), 2 (pt); Orderlies 1 (pt); Nurses aides 4 (ft), 10 (pt); Activities coordinators 1 (ft), 1 (pt); Dietitians 1 (pt).
Facilities Dining room; Activities room; Crafts room; Laundry room; Barber/Beauty shop; Library.
Activities Arts & crafts; Cards; Games; Reading groups; Prayer groups; Movies; Shopping trips.

Roosevelt Square Nursing Home
2120 W Washington Ave, Springfield, IL, 62702
(217) 546-1325
Admin Jean Marie Boggs. *Medical Dir/Dir of Nursing* Marge Thompson.
Licensure Intermediate care. *Beds* ICF 77. *Certified* Medicaid.
Owner Proprietary Corp.
Admissions Requirements Minimum age 18; Medical examination.
Staff LPNs 4 (ft), 2 (pt); Nurses aides 10 (ft), 8 (pt); Physical therapists 1 (ft); Recreational therapists 2 (ft); Occupational therapists 2 (ft); Dietitians 1 (ft).
Facilities Dining room; Laundry room.
Activities Arts & crafts; Games; Reading groups; Prayer groups; Movies; Shopping trips; Social/Cultural gatherings.

Rutledge Manor Care Home Inc*
913 N Rutledge St, Springfield, IL, 62702
(217) 525-1722
Admin Betty Hickman.
Licensure Intermediate care; Sheltered care. *Beds* ICF 155; Sheltered care 12.
Owner Proprietary Corp.

St Joseph's Home of Springfield
3306 S 6th St Rd, Springfield, IL, 62703
(217) 529-5596
Admin Sr Ann Regina Hughes & Sr Mary Barbara Buckley. *Medical Dir/Dir of Nursing* Dr Richard H Suhs; Lora Suter RN.
Licensure Intermediate care; Sheltered care. *Beds* ICF 72; Sheltered care 48.
Owner Proprietary Corp.
Admissions Requirements Minimum age 65; Medical examination.
Staff RNs 1 (ft), 1 (pt); LPNs 12 (ft), 7 (pt); Nurses aides 29 (ft), 8 (pt); Activities coordinators 2 (ft).
Affiliation Roman Catholic
Facilities Dining room; Activities room; Chapel; Barber/Beauty shop; Snack bar; Gift shop.

Activities Arts & crafts; Cards; Games; Movies; Shopping trips; Religious services.

Springfield Manor
2800 W Lawrence Ave, Springfield, IL, 62703
(217) 787-1955
Admin Margaret A Patton.
Licensure Intermediate care. *Beds* 170. *Certified* Medicaid.
Owner Proprietary Corp.

STAUNTON

Barry Care Center of Staunton*
215 W Pennsylvania Ave, Staunton, IL, 62088
(618) 635-5577
Admin Judith Ann Ragland.
Licensure Skilled care. *Beds* 99. *Certified* Medicaid; Medicare.
Owner Proprietary Corp.

STERLING

Exceptional Care & Training Center
2601 Woodlawn Rd, Sterling, IL, 61081
(815) 626-5820
Admin Jerry B Fyhrlund.
Licensure Skilled care. *Beds* SNF 64. *Certified* Medicaid.
Owner Proprietary Corp.

Sterling Care Center*
105 E 23rd St, Sterling, IL, 61081
(815) 626-4264
Admin Jeanne E Radunz.
Licensure Skilled care. *Beds* 102. *Certified* Medicaid; Medicare.
Owner Proprietary Corp.

STICKNEY

Pershing Convalescent Home Inc
3900 S Oak Park Ave, Stickney, IL, 60402
(312) 484-7543
Admin Lucille R Engelsman. *Medical Dir/Dir of Nursing* Donna Ott.
Licensure Skilled care; Intermediate care. *Beds* SNF 3; ICF 48. *Certified* Medicaid.
Owner Proprietary Corp.
Staff Physicians; RNs; LPNs; Nurses aides; Activities coordinators.
Facilities Dining room; Physical therapy room; Activities room; Laundry room.
Activities Arts & crafts; Cards; Games; Reading groups; Prayer groups; Movies; Shopping trips; Social/Cultural gatherings.

STOCKTON

Morgan Memorial Home
501 E Front Ave, Stockton, IL, 61085
(815) 947-2215
Admin Genevieve Parker. *Medical Dir/Dir of Nursing* Ruth Chumbler.
Licensure Intermediate care. *Beds* ICF 37. *Certified* Medicaid.
Owner Proprietary Corp.
Admissions Requirements Minimum age 18; Medical examination.
Staff RNs 3 (ft); LPNs 6 (ft); Nurses aides 6 (ft), 13 (pt); Activities coordinators 1 (ft); Dietitians 2 (ft); Social Consultant; Social service designer 2 (ft).
Facilities Dining room; Activities room; Crafts room; Laundry room; Barber/Beauty shop; Living room.
Activities Arts & crafts; Cards; Games; Reading groups; Prayer groups; Movies; Shopping trips; Social/Cultural gatherings; Pet show yearly; Flea market involving entire area; Bingo; Music.

STREATOR

Camelot Manor*
516 W Frech St, Streator, IL, 61364
(815) 672-9390
Admin R S Gomes.
Licensure Intermediate care. *Beds* 100. *Certified* Medicaid.
Owner Proprietary Corp.
Admissions Requirements Minimum age 18; Medical examination.
Staff RNs 1 (ft), 2 (pt); LPNs 3 (ft), 4 (pt); Orderlies 2 (ft); Nurses aides 13 (ft), 3 (pt); Recreational therapists 1 (ft), 2 (pt); Activities coordinators 1 (ft); Podiatrists 1 (pt).
Facilities Dining room; Physical therapy room; Activities room; Laundry room; Barber/Beauty shop.
Activities Arts & crafts; Cards; Games; Reading groups; Prayer groups; Movies; Shopping trips; Social/Cultural gatherings; Bowling league.

Heritage Manor
1525 E Main St, Streator, IL, 61364
(815) 672-4516
Admin Mary Colson. *Medical Dir/Dir of Nursing* Dr Bacayo; Vela Hogue RN.
Licensure Skilled care. *Beds* 110. *Certified* Medicaid; Medicare.
Owner Proprietary Corp (Heritage Enterprises).
Admissions Requirements Physician's request.
Staff RNs 8 (ft), 4 (pt); LPNs 10 (ft), 4 (pt); Nurses aides 16 (ft), 6 (pt); Physical therapists 1 (pt); Reality therapists 1 (pt); Recreational therapists 1 (pt); Occupational therapists 1 (pt); Activities coordinators 1 (ft), 2 (pt); Dietitians 1 (pt).
Facilities Dining room; Physical therapy room; Activities room; Crafts room; Laundry room; Barber/Beauty shop.
Activities Arts & crafts; Cards; Games; Reading groups; Prayer groups; Movies; Shopping trips; Social/Cultural gatherings; Restaurant trips; Boat trip to Ottawa.

Knox Estates Living Center
PO Box 706, Streator, IL, 61364
(815) 672-7611
Admin Cynthia J Dear.
Licensure Intermediate care for mentally retarded. *Beds* ICF/MR 15. *Certified* Medicaid.
Owner Nonprofit Corp.
Admissions Requirements Minimum age 18; Medical examination; Physician's request.
Staff Physicians 1 (pt); RNs 1 (pt); Recreational therapists 1 (pt); Speech therapists 1 (pt); Activities coordinators 1 (pt); Dietitians 1 (pt).
Facilities Dining room; Laundry room.
Activities Arts & crafts; Cards; Games; Movies; Shopping trips; Social/Cultural gatherings.

SULLIVAN

Illinois Masonic Home*
Rte 121 E, Sullivan, IL, 61951
(217) 728-4394
Admin James E Hart.
Licensure Skilled care; Intermediate care; Sheltered care. *Beds* SNF 10; ICF 183; Sheltered care 101.
Owner Nonprofit Corp.
Affiliation Masons

Sullivan Health Care Center
11 Hawthorne Ln, Sullivan, IL, 61951
(217) 728-4327
Admin David Standerfer. *Medical Dir/Dir of Nursing* Dr Dean McLaughin; Dolores Ryherd RN.

Licensure Skilled care; Intermediate care. *Beds* SNF 123; ICF. *Certified* Medicaid; Medicare.
Owner Nonprofit Corp (First Humanics).
Staff RNs 3 (ft), 2 (pt); LPNs 6 (ft), 3 (pt); Orderlies 4 (ft); Nurses aides 18 (ft), 10 (pt); Activities coordinators 2 (ft).
Facilities Dining room; Physical therapy room; Activities room; Crafts room; Laundry room; Barber/Beauty shop.
Activities Arts & crafts; Cards; Games; Reading groups; Prayer groups; Movies; Shopping trips; Social/Cultural gatherings.

Sullivan Living Center*
E View Pl, Sullivan, IL, 61951
(217) 728-7367
Admin John M Brinkoetter.
Licensure Intermediate care. *Beds* 55. *Certified* Medicaid.
Owner Proprietary Corp.
Staff Physicians 1 (pt); RNs 1 (pt); LPNs 4 (ft); Orderlies 2 (ft); Nurses aides 17 (ft), 6 (pt); Physical therapists 1 (pt); Reality therapists 1 (pt); Recreational therapists 1 (pt); Occupational therapists 1 (pt); Speech therapists 1 (pt); Activities coordinators 1 (ft), 1 (pt); Dietitians 1 (pt); Dentists 1 (pt); Ophthalmologists 1 (pt); Podiatrists 1 (pt); Audiologists 1 (pt).
Facilities Dining room; Activities room; Chapel; Crafts room; Laundry room; Barber/Beauty shop; Library.
Activities Arts & crafts; Cards; Games; Reading groups; Prayer groups; Movies; Shopping trips; Social/Cultural gatherings.

Titus Memorial Presbyterian Home*
513 N Worth St, Sullivan, IL, 61951
(217) 728-4725
Admin Peggy Auten.
Licensure Sheltered care. *Beds* 14.
Owner Nonprofit Corp.
Affiliation Presbyterian

SUMNER

Pine Lawn Manor Care Center
PO Box 166, Poplar & Maple Sts, Sumner, IL, 62466
(618) 936-2703
Admin Peter B Narish. *Medical Dir/Dir of Nursing* Nancy Wells.
Licensure Intermediate care; Intermediate care for mentally retarded. *Beds* ICF 58; ICF/MR 48. *Certified* Medicaid.
Owner Proprietary Corp.
Staff Physicians 1 (pt); RNs 1 (pt); LPNs 7 (ft); Orderlies 4 (ft); Nurses aides 20 (ft); Physical therapists 1 (ft); Reality therapists 4 (ft); Recreational therapists 4 (ft); Speech therapists 1 (ft); Activities coordinators 1 (ft); Dietitians 1 (pt).
Facilities Dining room; Physical therapy room; Activities room; Chapel; Crafts room; Laundry room; Barber/Beauty shop; Library.
Activities Arts & crafts; Cards; Games; Reading groups; Prayer groups; Movies; Shopping trips; Social/Cultural gatherings.

Red Hills Rest Haven
1 Poplar Dr, Sumner, IL, 62466
(618) 936-2522
Admin Gwenda J Zellars. *Medical Dir/Dir of Nursing* Dr Gary Carr; Edna Couch.
Licensure Skilled care; Intermediate care. *Beds* 96. *Certified* Medicaid; Medicare; VA.
Owner Proprietary Corp.
Admissions Requirements Minimum age 18.
Staff Physicians 7 (pt); RNs 4 (pt); LPNs 6 (pt); Orderlies 4 (pt); Nurses aides 29 (pt); Physical therapists 2 (pt); Reality therapists 1 (pt); Speech therapists 1 (pt); Activities coordinators 2 (pt); Dietitians 1 (pt); Ophthalmologists 1 (pt); Podiatrists 1 (pt).
Facilities Dining room; Physical therapy room; Activities room; Crafts room; Laundry room; Barber/Beauty shop.

Activities Arts & crafts; Cards; Games; Reading groups; Prayer groups; Movies; Shopping trips; Social/Cultural gatherings; Van rides.

SWANSEA

St Clair County Specialized Living Center
1450 Caseyville Ave, Swansea, IL, 62220
(618) 277-7730, 397-6877
Admin Agnes Schloemann. *Medical Dir/Dir of Nursing* Dr Khalid MD; Betty Daubauch RN.
Licensure Intermediate care for mentally retarded. *Beds* ICF/MR 108. *Certified* Medicaid.
Owner Nonprofit organization/foundation.
Admissions Requirements Minimum age 18; Medical examination; Certified MR.
Staff Physicians 1 (pt); RNs 1 (pt); LPNs 9 (ft); Nurses aides Certified Habilitation Technicians; Recreational therapists 2 (ft); Occupational therapists 1 (pt); Speech therapists 1 (pt); Activities coordinators 7 (ft); Dietitians 1 (ft); Ophthalmologists 1 (pt); Podiatrists 1 (pt); Social Services 1 (ft), 1 (pt).
Facilities Dining room; Physical therapy room; Activities room; Crafts room; Laundry room; Barber/Beauty shop; Library.
Activities Arts & crafts; Cards; Games; Reading groups; Prayer groups; Movies; Shopping trips; Social/Cultural gatherings.

SYCAMORE

Opportunity House Inc*
PO Box 301, 202 Lucas St, Sycamore, IL, 60178
(815) 895-5108
Admin John Kroos.
Licensure Intermediate care. *Beds* 17.
Owner Nonprofit Corp.

TAMMS

H & S Care Center*
PO Box 367, 3rd St Near Carpenter, Tamms, IL, 62988
(618) 747-2613
Admin Carolyn L Harvel.
Licensure Sheltered care. *Beds* 26.
Owner Proprietary Corp.
Admissions Requirements Minimum age 18; Medical examination; Physician's request.
Staff Physicians 1 (pt); RNs 1 (pt); Nurses aides 3 (ft), 4 (pt); Activities coordinators 1 (pt).
Facilities Dining room; Activities room; Laundry room.
Activities Arts & crafts; Cards; Games; Reading groups; Prayer groups; Shopping trips.

TAYLORVILLE

Meadow Manor Inc
Rte 48 N, Taylorville, IL, 62568
(217) 824-2277
Admin Billy G Morgan. *Medical Dir/Dir of Nursing* I DelValle; Carol Harden.
Licensure Skilled care; Intermediate care. *Beds* SNF 23; ICF 127. *Certified* Medicaid; Medicare.
Owner Proprietary Corp.
Admissions Requirements Minimum age 18.
Staff Physicians; RNs; LPNs; Orderlies; Nurses aides; Physical therapists; Speech therapists; Activities coordinators; Dietitians; Ophthalmologists.
Facilities Dining room; Physical therapy room; Activities room; Laundry room; Barber/Beauty shop.
Activities Arts & crafts; Cards; Games; Reading groups; Prayer groups; Movies; Shopping trips; Social/Cultural gatherings.

Taylorville Care Center Inc
600 S Houston, Taylorville, IL, 62568
(217) 824-9636
Admin Constance J Le Vault. *Medical Dir/Dir of Nursing* Dr T E Brewer; J Griffith RN.
Licensure Skilled care. *Beds* 98. *Certified* Medicaid; Medicare.
Owner Proprietary Corp.
Admissions Requirements Medical examination; Physician's request.
Staff RNs 1 (ft), 2 (pt); LPNs 5 (ft), 5 (pt); Nurses aides 20 (ft), 9 (pt).
Facilities Dining room; Physical therapy room; Activities room; Crafts room; Laundry room; Barber/Beauty shop.
Activities Arts & crafts; Games; Reading groups; Prayer groups; Movies; Shopping trips; Social/Cultural gatherings.

TINLEY PARK

The Mc Allister Nursing Home Inc*
18300 S La Vergne Ave, Tinley Park, IL, 60477
(312) 798-2272
Admin Theresa M Russo. *Medical Dir/Dir of Nursing* Bakul K Pankya MD.
Licensure Skilled care; Intermediate care. *Beds* SNF 59; ICF 42. *Certified* Medicaid; Medicare.
Owner Proprietary Corp.
Admissions Requirements Minimum age 18; Medical examination; Physician's request.
Staff Physicians 2 (pt); RNs 6 (ft), 2 (pt); LPNs 5 (ft), 2 (pt); Orderlies 28 (ft), 4 (pt); Physical therapists 1 (ft), 1 (pt); Reality therapists 1 (pt); Recreational therapists 2 (ft); Occupational therapists 1 (ft), 1 (pt); Speech therapists 1 (pt); Activities coordinators 1 (pt); Dietitians 1 (ft), 1 (pt); Dentists 1 (pt); Ophthalmologists 1 (pt); Audiologists 1 (pt).
Facilities Dining room; Physical therapy room; Activities room; Chapel; Crafts room; Laundry room; Barber/Beauty shop; Library.
Activities Arts & crafts; Cards; Games; Reading groups; Prayer groups; Movies; Shopping trips; Social/Cultural gatherings.

TOLUCA

Monte Cassino Healthcare Center*
101 E Via Ghiglieri, Toluca, IL, 61369
(815) 452-2321
Admin Betty Adolphson.
Licensure Skilled care; Intermediate care. *Beds* SNF 71; ICF 33. *Certified* Medicaid.
Owner Proprietary Corp.

TOULON

Stark County Health Center*
E Main St, Box 14, Toulon, IL, 61483
(309) 286-2631
Admin Irwin F Malone. *Medical Dir/Dir of Nursing* Josef Unhold MD.
Licensure Skilled care; Intermediate care. *Beds* SNF 82; ICF 54. *Certified* Medicaid; Medicare.
Owner Proprietary Corp.
Admissions Requirements Medical examination; Physician's request.
Facilities Dining room; Physical therapy room; Activities room; Chapel; Crafts room; Laundry room; Barber/Beauty shop; Library; TV rooms; Greenhouse.
Activities Arts & crafts; Cards; Games; Reading groups; Prayer groups; Movies; Social/Cultural gatherings; Nail care; Cooking.

TROY

Professional Care Inc
200 E Taylor, Troy, IL, 62294
(618) 667-6691

Admin Charles H Gerstenecker.
Licensure Intermediate care for mentally retarded. *Beds* 149. *Certified* Medicaid; Medicare.
Owner Proprietary Corp.
Admissions Requirements Minimum age 18; Medical examination; Physician's request.
Staff Physicians 11 (pt); RNs 1 (pt); LPNs 12 (ft); Orderlies 4 (ft); Nurses aides 34 (ft); Physical therapists 2 (ft); Reality therapists 3 (ft); Recreational therapists 5 (ft); Occupational therapists 1 (pt); Speech therapists 1 (pt); Activities coordinators 1 (ft); Dietitians 1 (ft); Dentists 1 (pt); Ophthalmologists 1 (pt); Podiatrists 1 (pt).
Facilities Dining room; Physical therapy room; Activities room; Crafts room; Laundry room; Barber/Beauty shop; Library; Day room.
Activities Arts & crafts; Cards; Games; Reading groups; Prayer groups; Movies; Shopping trips; Social/Cultural gatherings; Dining trips; Trips to big league baseball games & museums.

TUSCOLA

Douglas Manor Nursing Complex*
RR 2, Tuscola, IL, 61953
(217) 253-2337
Admin George S Barnett.
Licensure Skilled care; Intermediate care. *Beds* SNF 30; ICF 123. *Certified* Medicaid.
Owner Proprietary Corp.

URBANA

Americana Healthcare Center of Urbana*
600 N Coler Ave, Urbana, IL, 61801
(217) 367-1191
Admin Cathy A Moses. *Medical Dir/Dir of Nursing* Dr Phillip Johnson.
Licensure Skilled care; Intermediate care. *Beds* 100. *Certified* Medicaid; Medicare.
Owner Proprietary Corp (Manor Care).
Admissions Requirements Medical examination.
Staff Physicians; RNs; LPNs; Orderlies; Nurses aides; Physical therapists; Reality therapists; Recreational therapists; Occupational therapists; Speech therapists; Activities coordinators; Dietitians; Dentists; Ophthalmologists; Podiatrists; Audiologists.
Facilities Dining room; Physical therapy room; Activities room; Crafts room; Laundry room; Barber/Beauty shop.
Activities Arts & crafts; Cards; Games; Reading groups; Prayer groups; Movies; Shopping trips; Social/Cultural gatherings.

Champaign County Nursing Home
1701 E Main, Urbana, IL, 61801
(217) 384-3784
Admin Joyce Ettensohn. *Medical Dir/Dir of Nursing* Dr Kathleen O'Hare; Marjorie Letot.
Licensure Skilled care; Intermediate care; Sheltered care. *Beds* SNF 153; ICF 56; Sheltered care 79. *Certified* Medicaid; Medicare.
Owner Publicly owned.
Admissions Requirements Minimum age 45; Medical examination; Physician's request.
Staff RNs 15 (ft), 5 (pt); LPNs 9 (ft), 5 (pt); Orderlies; Nurses aides 78 (ft), 4 (pt); Physical therapists 1 (pt); Reality therapists 1 (ft); Recreational therapists 3 (ft); Occupational therapists 1 (pt); Activities coordinators 1 (ft); Dietitians 1 (pt); Dentists 1 (pt); Dental Hygienist 1 (pt); MSW 1 (ft).
Facilities Dining room; Physical therapy room; Activities room; Chapel; Crafts room; Barber/Beauty shop; Library; Dental Clinic.

Activities Arts & crafts; Cards; Games; Reading groups; Prayer groups; Movies; Shopping trips; Social/Cultural gatherings; Adult education classes; Pet-a-pet program; Ceramics.

Clark-Lindsey Village Inc
101 W Windsor Rd, Urbana, IL, 61801
(217) 344-2144
Admin Clifford E Ingersoll. *Medical Dir/Dir of Nursing* Margaret Hoffman.
Licensure Skilled care; Intermediate care; Sheltered care. *Beds* SNF 40; ICF 12; Sheltered care 28. *Certified* Medicaid; Medicare.
Owner Nonprofit Corp.
Admissions Requirements Minimum age 62; Medical examination; Physician's request.
Staff RNs 4 (ft), 4 (pt); LPNs 5 (ft), 8 (pt); Nurses aides 16 (ft), 16 (pt); Physical therapists 1 (pt); Occupational therapists 1 (pt); Speech therapists 1 (pt); Activities coordinators 2 (ft); Dietitians 2 (ft).
Facilities Dining room; Physical therapy room; Activities room; Chapel; Crafts room; Laundry room; Barber/Beauty shop; Library.
Activities Arts & crafts; Cards; Games; Reading groups; Movies; Shopping trips; Social/Cultural gatherings.

Royal Fontana Nursing Center Inc*
907 N Lincoln, Urbana, IL, 61801
(217) 367-8421
Admin Leighton Collins.
Licensure Skilled care. *Beds* 99. *Certified* Medicaid; Medicare.
Owner Proprietary Corp.

Urbana Nursing Home
2006 S Philo Rd, Urbana, IL, 61801
(217) 344-0777
Admin William Mooman. *Medical Dir/Dir of Nursing* Roxie Sage DON.
Licensure Intermediate care. *Beds* ICF 48. *Certified* Medicaid.
Owner Proprietary Corp.
Admissions Requirements Physician's request.
Staff RNs; LPNs; Orderlies; Nurses aides; Physical therapists; Activities coordinators; Dietitians.
Facilities Dining room; Activities room; Laundry room; Barber/Beauty shop.
Activities Arts & crafts; Cards; Games; Reading groups; Prayer groups; Movies; Shopping trips; Social/Cultural gatherings.

VANDALIA

Heritage House of Vandalia
1610 Hillsboro Rd, Vandalia, IL, 62471
(618) 283-1434
Admin Charles Hutson. *Medical Dir/Dir of Nursing* Hans Rollinger MD.
Licensure Intermediate care. *Beds* ICF 79. *Certified* Medicaid.
Owner Proprietary Corp (National Heritage).
Admissions Requirements Minimum age 18; Medical examination.
Staff RNs 1 (ft), 2 (pt); LPNs 5 (ft), 2 (pt); Nurses aides 20 (ft), 10 (pt); Physical therapists 1 (pt); Occupational therapists; Speech therapists 1 (pt); Activities coordinators 1 (ft); Dietitians 1 (pt); Dentists 1 (pt); Ophthalmologists 1 (pt); Podiatrists 1 (pt).
Facilities Dining room; Physical therapy room; Activities room; Laundry room; Barber/Beauty shop.
Activities Cards; Games; Prayer groups; Movies; Shopping trips; Social/Cultural gatherings.

Sunnydale Acres*
1500 W Saint Louis Ave, Vandalia, IL, 62471
(618) 283-4262
Admin Donna L Hannagan.

Licensure Intermediate care. *Beds* 116. *Certified* Medicaid.
Owner Proprietary Corp (Beverly Enterprises).

VIENNA

Hillview Healthcare Center*
11th St, Vienna, IL, 62995
(618) 658-2951
Admin Janice F Miller.
Licensure Skilled care; Intermediate care. *Beds* SNF 25; ICF 47. *Certified* Medicaid.
Owner Proprietary Corp.

Mt Shelter Care Home*
PO Box 215, Vienna, IL, 62995
(618) 695-2494
Admin Phyllis M Taylor.
Licensure Sheltered care. *Beds* 29.
Owner Proprietary Corp.

VIRDEN

Sunrise Manor of Virden Inc
333 S Wrightsam St, Virden, IL, 62690
(217) 965-4821
Admin Patricia J Barnes. *Medical Dir/Dir of Nursing* Dr Kenneth Malmberg.
Licensure Skilled care; Intermediate care. *Beds* SNF 53; ICF 46. *Certified* Medicaid; Medicare.
Owner Proprietary Corp.
Admissions Requirements Physician's request.
Staff RNs 2 (ft); LPNs 7 (ft), 5 (pt); Orderlies 2 (ft); Nurses aides 20 (ft), 25 (pt); Activities coordinators 2 (ft).
Facilities Dining room; Physical therapy room; Activities room; Chapel; Crafts room; Laundry room; Barber/Beauty shop; TV room with fire place.
Activities Arts & crafts; Cards; Games; Reading groups; Prayer groups; Movies; Shopping trips; Social/Cultural gatherings.

Virden Nursing Center
402 W Loud, Virden, IL, 62690
(217) 965-4336
Admin Mary Ellen Wade. *Medical Dir/Dir of Nursing* Dr Malmberg.
Licensure Intermediate care. *Beds* ICF 51. *Certified* Medicaid.
Owner Privately owned.
Admissions Requirements Minimum age 18; Physician's request.
Staff LPNs 5 (ft); Orderlies 3 (ft); Nurses aides 23 (ft), 23 (pt); Activities coordinators 1 (ft); Dietitians 1 (ft).
Facilities Dining room; Physical therapy room; Activities room; Laundry room; Barber/Beauty shop.
Activities Arts & crafts; Cards; Games; Reading groups; Prayer groups; Movies; Shopping trips; Social/Cultural gatherings.

VIRGINIA

Walker Nursing Home Inc*
530 E Beardstown St, Virginia, IL, 62691
(217) 452-3218
Admin George W White.
Licensure Intermediate care. *Beds* 55. *Certified* Medicaid.
Owner Proprietary Corp.

WALNUT

Walnut Manor
308 S 2nd St, Walnut, IL, 61376
(815) 379-2131
Admin Robert D Yearian. *Medical Dir/Dir of Nursing* Nancy Christensen RN.
Licensure Intermediate care. *Beds* ICF 62. *Certified* Medicaid.

Owner Proprietary Corp.
Staff RNs 1 (ft), 4 (pt); LPNs 1 (ft), 3 (pt); Nurses aides 10 (ft), 20 (pt); Physical therapists 1 (pt); Activities coordinators 1 (ft), 2 (pt); Dietitians 1 (pt).

WASHINGTON

Washington Christian Village
1110 New Castle Rd, Washington, IL, 61571
(309) 444-3161
Admin Andrew T Felix. *Medical Dir/Dir of Nursing* Dr Philip Immesoete; Jaqueline Henderson.
Licensure Skilled care. *Beds* SNF 122. *Certified* Medicaid; Medicare.
Owner Nonprofit Corp (Christian Homes).
Admissions Requirements Minimum age 18.
Staff RNs 6 (ft), 4 (pt); LPNs 6 (ft), 5 (pt); Orderlies 1 (pt); Nurses aides 30 (ft), 33 (pt); Physical therapists 1 (pt); Speech therapists 1 (pt); Activities coordinators 1 (ft); Dietitians 1 (ft).
Affiliation Church of Christ
Facilities Dining room; Physical therapy room; Activities room; Chapel; Crafts room; Laundry room; Barber/Beauty shop.
Activities Arts & crafts; Games; Movies; Shopping trips; Church services; Community service activities.

WATERLOO

Canterbury Manor Nursing Center Inc
718 N Market, Waterloo, IL, 62298
(618) 939-8565
Admin Mary G Wood. *Medical Dir/Dir of Nursing* Bernice Phelps RN DON.
Licensure Intermediate care. *Beds* ICF 74. *Certified* Medicaid.
Owner Proprietary Corp.
Admissions Requirements Minimum age 19.
Staff Physicians 6 (pt); RNs 1 (ft); LPNs 6 (pt); Nurses aides 20 (ft), 10 (pt); Physical therapists 1 (pt); Recreational therapists 1 (pt); Occupational therapists 1 (pt); Speech therapists 1 (pt); Activities coordinators 1 (pt); Dietitians 1 (pt); Ophthalmologists 1 (pt); Podiatrists 1 (pt).
Facilities Dining room; Physical therapy room; Activities room; Chapel; Crafts room; Laundry room; Barber/Beauty shop; Library; Lounges.
Activities Arts & crafts; Cards; Games; Reading groups; Prayer groups; Movies; Shopping trips; Social/Cultural gatherings; Outings/picnics; Tours.

Monroe County Nursing Home*
500 Illinois Ave, Waterloo, IL, 62298
(618) 939-3488
Admin Collette Rau. *Medical Dir/Dir of Nursing* Russell W Jost MD.
Licensure Skilled care; Intermediate care. *Beds* SNF 143; ICF 82. *Certified* Medicaid; Medicare.
Owner Publicly owned.
Admissions Requirements Minimum age 16; Medical examination; Physician's request.
Staff Physicians 7 (pt); RNs 4 (ft), 8 (pt); LPNs 7 (ft), 11 (pt); Orderlies 2 (pt); Nurses aides 47 (ft), 60 (pt); Physical therapists 1 (pt); Reality therapists 1 (pt); Recreational therapists 1 (pt); Activities coordinators 1 (ft); Dietitians 1 (pt); Dentists 1 (pt); Podiatrists 1 (pt).
Facilities Dining room; Physical therapy room; Activities room; Chapel; Crafts room; Laundry room; Barber/Beauty shop.
Activities Arts & crafts; Cards; Games; Reading groups; Prayer groups; Movies; Shopping trips; Social/Cultural gatherings.

WATSEKA

The Iroquois Resident Home
200 Fairman St, Watseka, IL, 60970
(815) 432-5201
Admin Paul F Wenz. *Medical Dir/Dir of Nursing* J R Schlereth MD N D Hungness MD; Gloria R Hassen RN DON.
Licensure Skilled care; Intermediate care. *Beds* 56. *Certified* Medicare.
Owner Nonprofit Corp.
Admissions Requirements Minimum age 22; Medical examination; Physician's request.
Staff Physicians 16 (ft); RNs 2 (ft), 2 (pt); LPNs 8 (ft); Nurses aides 17 (ft), 3 (pt); Physical therapists 1 (ft); Occupational therapists 1 (pt); Speech therapists 1 (pt); Activities coordinators 1 (ft); Dietitians 1 (pt).
Facilities Dining room; Physical therapy room; Activities room; Crafts room; Laundry room; Barber/Beauty shop.
Activities Arts & crafts; Cards; Games; Reading groups; Prayer groups; Movies; Shopping trips; Social/Cultural gatherings.

Watseka Health Care Center
715 E Raymond, Watseka, IL, 60970
(815) 432-5476
Admin Jacqueline S DeLong. *Medical Dir/Dir of Nursing* Dean Hungness MD; Jeanne Kinder RN DON.
Licensure Skilled care. *Beds* SNF 123. *Certified* Medicaid; Medicare; VA.
Owner Nonprofit Corp (First Humanics).
Admissions Requirements Minimum age 18; Physician's request.
Staff Physicians 8 (pt); RNs 5 (ft); LPNs 10 (ft), 2 (pt); Orderlies 1 (ft); Nurses aides 40 (ft), 10 (pt); Physical therapists 1 (pt); Recreational therapists 1 (pt); Occupational therapists 1 (pt); Speech therapists 1 (pt); Activities coordinators 1 (ft); Dietitians 1 (pt); Dentists 1 (pt); Ophthalmologists 1 (pt); Podiatrists 1 (pt).
Facilities Dining room; Physical therapy room; Activities room; Crafts room; Laundry room; Barber/Beauty shop; Reality orientation room; Family social room.
Activities Arts & crafts; Cards; Games; Reading groups; Prayer groups; Movies; Shopping trips; Social/Cultural gatherings.

Watseka Manor
900 N Market St, Watseka, IL, 60970
(815) 432-5261
Admin Donna Carlson. *Medical Dir/Dir of Nursing* Donna Daniels RN DON.
Licensure Skilled care; Intermediate care. *Beds* SNF 13; ICF 63. *Certified* Medicaid; Medicare.
Owner Proprietary Corp.
Admissions Requirements Minimum age 21; Medical examination.
Staff RNs 2 (ft); LPNs 3 (ft), 2 (pt); Nurses aides 20 (ft).
Facilities Dining room; Physical therapy room; Activities room; Crafts room; Laundry room; Barber/Beauty shop.
Activities Arts & crafts; Cards; Games; Reading groups; Prayer groups; Movies; Shopping trips; Social/Cultural gatherings.

WAUCONDA

Town Hall Estates
176 Thomas Ct, Wauconda, IL, 60084
(312) 526-5551
Admin Jerry W Willis.
Licensure Intermediate care. *Beds* 98. *Certified* Medicaid.
Owner Nonprofit Corp.
Staff RNs 6 (ft); LPNs 3 (ft); Nurses aides 30 (ft); Dietitians 1 (pt).

WAUKEGAN

Bayside Terrace
1100 S Lewis Ave, Waukegan, IL, 60087
(312) 244-8196
Admin Betty A Satterfield. *Medical Dir/Dir of Nursing* Norberto J Martinez MD.
Licensure Intermediate care. *Beds* ICF 168. *Certified* Medicaid.
Owner Proprietary Corp.
Admissions Requirements Minimum age 30; Medical examination; Physician's request.
Staff Physicians 2 (ft); RNs 3 (ft), 1 (pt); LPNs 4 (ft), 4 (pt); Orderlies 4 (ft); Nurses aides 16 (ft); Reality therapists 1 (ft); Occupational therapists 1 (ft); Activities coordinators 3 (ft), 1 (pt); Dietitians 1 (pt); Ophthalmologists 1 (pt).
Facilities Dining room; Physical therapy room; Activities room; Crafts room; Laundry room; Barber/Beauty shop; Library; TV rooms; Smoking lounge.
Activities Arts & crafts; Cards; Games; Reading groups; Prayer groups; Movies; Shopping trips; Social/Cultural gatherings; Exercise.

Northshore Terrace*
2222 W 14th St, Waukegan, IL, 60085
(312) 249-2400
Admin Daniel Rexroth. *Medical Dir/Dir of Nursing* Sam Krueger MD.
Licensure Skilled care; Intermediate care. *Beds* SNF 123; ICF 138. *Certified* Medicaid; Medicare.
Owner Proprietary Corp.
Admissions Requirements Minimum age 30; Physician's request.
Staff Physicians 10 (pt); RNs 16 (ft); LPNs 8 (ft); Orderlies 12 (ft); Nurses aides 70 (ft), 8 (pt); Physical therapists 1 (pt); Reality therapists 1 (pt); Recreational therapists 1 (pt); Occupational therapists 1 (pt); Speech therapists 1 (pt); Activities coordinators 1 (ft); Dietitians 1 (ft); Dentists 1 (pt); Ophthalmologists 1 (pt); Podiatrists 1 (pt); Audiologists 1 (pt).
Facilities Dining room; Physical therapy room; Activities room; Chapel; Crafts room; Laundry room; Barber/Beauty shop.
Activities Arts & crafts; Cards; Games; Reading groups; Prayer groups; Movies; Shopping trips; Social/Cultural gatherings.

The Terrace
1615 Sunset Ave, Waukegan, IL, 60087
(312) 244-6700
Admin Wendell Studebaker. *Medical Dir/Dir of Nursing* Bruce Frazer MD; Shirley Hollech RN DON.
Licensure Skilled care; Intermediate care. *Beds* 112. *Certified* Medicaid; Medicare; VA.
Owner Proprietary Corp.
Admissions Requirements Minimum age 18; Medical examination.
Staff Physicians 17 (pt); RNs 12 (ft), 2 (pt); LPNs 4 (ft), 3 (pt); Orderlies 4 (ft), 1 (pt); Nurses aides 38 (ft), 7 (pt); Physical therapists 1 (pt); Reality therapists 2 (ft); Recreational therapists 1 (ft); Occupational therapists 2 (pt); Speech therapists 1 (pt); Activities coordinators 1 (ft); Dietitians 1 (pt); Dentists 1 (pt); Ophthalmologists 1 (pt); Podiatrists 1 (pt).
Languages Spanish
Facilities Dining room; Physical therapy room; Activities room; Crafts room; Laundry room; Barber/Beauty shop; Library; Lounge; Family group room.
Activities Arts & crafts; Cards; Games; Reading groups; Prayer groups; Movies; Shopping trips; Social/Cultural gatherings; Cocktail party.

Waukegan Pavilion*
2217 Washington St, Waukegan, IL, 60085
(312) 244-1400
Admin James E Willcox.

Licensure Skilled care. *Beds* 99. *Certified* Medicaid.
Owner Proprietary Corp.

Waukegan Terrace
919 Washington Park, Waukegan, IL, 60085
(312) 623-9100
Admin Neal R Kjos. *Medical Dir/Dir of Nursing* Sam Krugez; Sandra Hernandez.
Licensure Skilled care; Intermediate care. *Beds* SNF 108; ICF 102. *Certified* Medicaid.
Owner Proprietary Corp.
Admissions Requirements Minimum age 18.
Facilities Dining room; Physical therapy room; Activities room; Laundry room; Barber/Beauty shop.
Activities Arts & crafts; Cards; Games; Reading groups; Movies; Shopping trips; Social/Cultural gatherings.

WEST CHICAGO

Foxcrest Manor
30 W 300 North Ave, West Chicago, IL, 60185
(312) 231-4050
Admin Jon Platakis. *Medical Dir/Dir of Nursing* T Klein; Mary Ann Lupa.
Licensure Skilled care; Intermediate care. *Beds* 300.
Owner Nonprofit Corp.
Admissions Requirements Minimum age 65; Medical examination.
Staff Physicians 6 (pt); RNs 6 (ft), 4 (pt); LPNs 4 (ft), 8 (pt); Nurses aides 25 (ft), 6 (pt); Physical therapists 1 (pt); Reality therapists 1 (pt); Recreational therapists 1 (ft); Occupational therapists 1 (pt); Speech therapists 1 (pt); Activities coordinators 1 (ft); Dietitians 1 (ft); Dentists 1 (pt); Ophthalmologists 2 (pt); Podiatrists 1 (pt).
Languages German, Lithuanian, Spanish, Greek
Facilities Dining room; Physical therapy room; Activities room; Chapel; Crafts room; Barber/Beauty shop; Library.
Activities Arts & crafts; Cards; Games; Reading groups; Prayer groups; Movies; Shopping trips; Social/Cultural gatherings.

West Chicago Terrace
928 Joliet St, West Chicago, IL, 60185
(312) 231-9292
Admin Christine Cherney. *Medical Dir/Dir of Nursing* Norton Fishman; Carol Terrill.
Licensure Intermediate care. *Beds* ICF 120. *Certified* Medicaid.
Owner Privately owned.
Admissions Requirements Medical examination.
Staff Physicians; RNs 2 (ft); LPNs 6 (ft); Orderlies 1 (ft); Nurses aides 16 (ft); Activities coordinators 1 (ft); Dentists 1 (pt); Ophthalmologists 1 (pt); Podiatrists 1 (pt).
Languages Spanish, Polish
Facilities Dining room; Physical therapy room; Activities room; Chapel; Laundry room; Barber/Beauty shop; Library.
Activities Arts & crafts; Cards; Games; Prayer groups; Movies; Shopping trips; Social/Cultural gatherings.

WEST FRANKFORT

American Beauty Nursing Home
6th St & Columbia, West Frankfort, IL, 62896
(618) 932-2109
Admin Lillian Crosland. *Medical Dir/Dir of Nursing* Dr Y Norman Chiou; Jo Schofield.
Licensure Skilled care; Intermediate care. *Beds* SNF 96; ICF. *Certified* Medicaid.
Owner Privately owned.
Admissions Requirements Minimum age 18; Medical examination; Physician's request.

Staff Physicians 6 (pt); RNs 1 (ft), 2 (pt); LPNs 6 (ft), 2 (pt); Orderlies 1 (ft); Nurses aides 6 (pt); Physical therapists 1 (pt); Speech therapists 1 (pt); Activities coordinators 1 (ft), 2 (pt); Dietitians 1 (pt).
Facilities Dining room; Activities room; Laundry room; Barber/Beauty shop.
Activities Arts & crafts; Cards; Games; Reading groups; Prayer groups; Shopping trips; Social/Cultural gatherings.

Frankfort Heights Manor*
2500 E Saint Louis St, West Frankfort, IL, 62896
(618) 932-3236
Admin Rosalie McNan.
Licensure Intermediate care. *Beds* 57. *Certified* Medicaid.
Owner Proprietary Corp.

Parkview Nursing Home
301 E Garland St, West Frankfort, IL, 62896
(618) 937-2428
Admin Jeanetta D Underwood. *Medical Dir/Dir of Nursing* Lois Eubanks DON.
Licensure Intermediate care. *Beds* ICF 56. *Certified* Medicaid.
Owner Proprietary Corp.
Admissions Requirements Minimum age 18.
Staff RNs 1 (pt); LPNs 4 (ft), 2 (pt); Nurses aides 20 (ft); Activities coordinators 1 (ft).
Facilities Dining room; Activities room; Barber/Beauty shop.
Activities Arts & crafts; Cards; Games; Reading groups; Prayer groups; Movies; Shopping trips; Social/Cultural gatherings.

WEST SALEM

West Salem Manor*
RR 1, West Salem, IL, 62476
(618) 456-8405
Admin Carol Bowen.
Licensure Sheltered care. *Beds* 33.
Owner Proprietary Corp.

WESTMONT

Americana Healthcare Center of Westmont*
512 E Ogden Ave, Westmont, IL, 60559
(312) 323-4400
Admin Katherine K Keane. *Medical Dir/Dir of Nursing* Azizar Arain MD.
Licensure Skilled care; Intermediate care. *Beds* 155. *Certified* Medicaid; Medicare.
Owner Proprietary Corp (Manor Care).
Admissions Requirements Medical examination; Physician's request.
Staff Physicians 16 (pt); RNs 12 (ft), 6 (pt); LPNs 10 (ft), 8 (pt); Orderlies 3 (ft), 3 (pt); Nurses aides 50 (ft), 10 (pt); Physical therapists 1 (ft), 2 (pt); Recreational therapists 1 (ft), 3 (pt); Occupational therapists; Speech therapists; Dietitians; Dentists; Ophthalmologists; Podiatrists.
Facilities Dining room; Physical therapy room; Activities room; Crafts room; Laundry room; Barber/Beauty shop.
Activities Arts & crafts; Cards; Games; Reading groups; Prayer groups; Movies; Shopping trips; Social/Cultural gatherings.

Burgess Square Healthcare Centre
5801 S Cass Ave, Westmont, IL, 60559
(312) 971-2645
Admin Jo Anne Fisher. *Medical Dir/Dir of Nursing* Irene Kubina DON.
Licensure Skilled care; Intermediate care. *Beds* SNF 106; ICF 105. *Certified* Medicaid; Medicare.
Owner Proprietary Corp.
Admissions Requirements Minimum age 50; Medical examination; Physician's request.
Staff RNs 3 (ft); LPNs 9 (ft), 4 (pt); Nurses aides 37 (ft), 9 (pt); Activities coordinators 4 (ft), 2 (pt).
Languages Polish, Spanish, German

Facilities Dining room; Physical therapy room; Activities room; Crafts room; Laundry room; Barber/Beauty shop.
Activities Arts & crafts; Cards; Games; Reading groups; Prayer groups; Movies; Shopping trips; Social/Cultural gatherings.

Westmont Convalescent Center
6501 S Cass Ave, Westmont, IL, 60559
(312) 960-2026
Admin Nancy Geraci. *Medical Dir/Dir of Nursing* Lawrence LaPalio.
Licensure Skilled care; Intermediate care. *Beds* 215. *Certified* Medicaid; Medicare.
Owner Proprietary Corp.
Admissions Requirements Minimum age 60.
Staff Physicians; RNs; LPNs; Orderlies; Nurses aides; Physical therapists; Occupational therapists; Speech therapists; Activities coordinators; Dietitians; Dentists; Ophthalmologists; Podiatrists.
Languages Polish, Spanish
Facilities Dining room; Physical therapy room; Activities room; Laundry room; Barber/Beauty shop.
Activities Arts & crafts; Games; Reading groups; Prayer groups; Movies; Shopping trips; Social/Cultural gatherings.

WHEATON

Du Page Convalescent Center
PO Box 708, 400 N County Farm Rd, Wheaton, IL, 60187
(312) 665-6400
Admin Ronald R Reinecke. *Medical Dir/Dir of Nursing* John B Pace MD; Kathryn Wiggins DON.
Licensure Skilled care. *Beds* SNF 408. *Certified* Medicaid.
Owner Publicly owned.
Admissions Requirements Minimum age 18.
Staff Physicians; RNs; LPNs; Orderlies; Nurses aides; Physical therapists; Recreational therapists; Occupational therapists; Speech therapists; Activities coordinators; Dietitians; Ophthalmologists; Podiatrists.
Facilities Dining room; Physical therapy room; Activities room; Crafts room; Laundry room; Barber/Beauty shop; Library.
Activities Arts & crafts; Cards; Games; Reading groups; Prayer groups; Movies; Shopping trips; Social/Cultural gatherings.

Parkway Terrace Nursing Home
219 E Parkway Dr, Wheaton, IL, 60187
(312) 668-4635
Admin Stan J Murdoch. *Medical Dir/Dir of Nursing* Dr Clarance Wyngarden; Pat Duhey.
Licensure Skilled care; Intermediate care. *Beds* 69. *Certified* Medicaid.
Owner Nonprofit Corp.
Admissions Requirements Minimum age 18.
Staff Physicians 1 (pt); RNs 6 (ft); LPNs 6 (ft), 3 (pt); Nurses aides 16 (ft); Physical therapists 1 (pt); Reality therapists 1 (pt); Recreational therapists 1 (pt); Occupational therapists 1 (pt); Speech therapists 1 (pt); Activities coordinators 1 (ft); Dietitians 1 (pt); Dentists 1 (pt); Ophthalmologists 1 (pt); Podiatrists 1 (pt).
Affiliation Assembly of God
Facilities Dining room; Physical therapy room; Activities room; Crafts room; Barber/Beauty shop.
Activities Arts & crafts; Cards; Games; Reading groups; Prayer groups; Movies; Shopping trips; Social/Cultural gatherings; Pet therapy; Plant therapy.

Sandalwood Healthcare Centre
2180 W Manchester Rd, Wheaton, IL, 60187
(312) 665-4330
Admin Nancy E Kasky Fox. *Medical Dir/Dir of Nursing* Lawrence Schouten MD; Jena Villarreal RN.

Licensure Skilled care; Intermediate care. *Beds* SNF 106; ICF 103. *Certified* Medicaid; Medicare.
Owner Proprietary Corp.
Admissions Requirements Minimum age 55; Medical examination.
Staff Physicians 37 (ft); RNs 9 (ft), 3 (pt); LPNs 6 (ft), 3 (pt); Orderlies 8 (ft), 2 (pt); Nurses aides 39 (ft), 6 (pt).
Facilities Dining room; Physical therapy room; Activities room; Laundry room; Barber/Beauty shop.
Activities Arts & crafts; Cards; Games; Reading groups; Prayer groups; Movies; Shopping trips; Social/Cultural gatherings.

Wheaton Convalescent Center
1325 Manchester Rd, Wheaton, IL, 60187
(312) 668-2500
Admin Arnold Kaplan. *Medical Dir/Dir of Nursing* Norton Fishman MD; Nancy Ley RN.
Licensure Skilled care; Intermediate care. *Beds* SNF 40; ICF 77. *Certified* Medicaid.
Owner Proprietary Corp.
Admissions Requirements Medical examination.
Staff Physicians 3 (pt); RNs 7 (ft), 4 (pt); LPNs 2 (ft), 3 (pt); Orderlies 9 (ft), 2 (pt); Nurses aides 16 (ft), 4 (pt); Physical therapists 1 (pt); Reality therapists 1 (pt); Recreational therapists 1 (pt); Occupational therapists 1 (pt); Speech therapists 1 (pt); Activities coordinators 2 (ft), 2 (pt); Dietitians 1 (pt); Dentists 11 (pt); Ophthalmologists 1 (pt).
Languages Polish, Spanish
Facilities Dining room; Physical therapy room; Activities room; Crafts room; Laundry room; Barber/Beauty shop.
Activities Arts & crafts; Cards; Games; Reading groups; Prayer groups; Movies; Shopping trips; Social/Cultural gatherings.

WHEELING

Addolorata Villa
555 McHenry Rd, Wheeling, IL, 60090
(312) 577-2900
Admin Sr Mary Roberta Prince. *Medical Dir/Dir of Nursing* Dr I Smith MD; Sandra Michael RN DON.
Licensure Intermediate care; Sheltered care. *Beds* ICF 42; Sheltered 56. *Certified* Medicaid.
Owner Nonprofit Corp.
Admissions Requirements Minimum age 60; Medical examination.
Staff Physicians 4 (pt); RNs; LPNs; Orderlies; Nurses aides; Physical therapists 1 (pt); Recreational therapists; Activities coordinators 1 (ft); Dietitians 1 (pt); Ophthalmologists 1 (pt); Certified Dietary Mgr 1 (ft).
Languages Polish, Spanish
Facilities Dining room; Physical therapy room; Activities room; Chapel; Crafts room; Laundry room; Barber/Beauty shop; Library.
Activities Arts & crafts; Cards; Games; Reading groups; Prayer groups; Movies; Shopping trips; Social/Cultural gatherings.

WHITE HALL

North American Healthcare Center*
620 W Bridgeport, White Hall, IL, 62092
(217) 374-2144
Admin Lorena S Knight.
Licensure Intermediate care. *Beds* 126. *Certified* Medicaid.
Owner Proprietary Corp.

WILMETTE

Baha'i Home
401 Greenleaf Ave, Wilmette, IL, 60091
(312) 251-7000
Admin George T Walker.
Licensure Sheltered care. *Beds* 22.
Owner Nonprofit Corp.
Admissions Requirements Minimum age 65; Medical examination.
Staff RNs 1 (pt); LPNs 1 (pt); Nurses aides 3 (ft), 3 (pt); Recreational therapists 1 (ft); Occupational therapists 1 (pt); Activities coordinators 1 (ft); Dietitians 1 (pt); Ophthalmologists 1 (pt); Podiatrists 1 (pt).
Affiliation Baha'i Faith
Facilities Dining room; Activities room; Crafts room; Laundry room; Barber/Beauty shop; Library; Large & small lounges.
Activities Arts & crafts; Cards; Games; Reading groups; Prayer groups; Movies; Social/Cultural gatherings; Discussion groups; Exercise groups; Sing-alongs; Field trips.

Normandy House
432 Poplar Dr, Wilmette, IL, 60091
(312) 256-5000
Admin O E Lufkin. *Medical Dir/Dir of Nursing* A R Peterson MD; Missy Ware RN DON.
Licensure Skilled care; Intermediate care. *Beds* SNF 28; ICF 52.
Owner Proprietary Corp.
Admissions Requirements Minimum age 22; Medical examination; Physician's request.
Staff Physicians 34 (pt); RNs 12 (ft), 9 (pt); Nurses aides 21 (ft), 6 (pt); Physical therapists 3 (pt); Speech therapists 1 (pt); Activities coordinators 1 (ft), 3 (pt); Dietitians 1 (pt); Podiatrists 3 (pt).
Facilities Dining room; Physical therapy room; Activities room; Crafts room; Barber/Beauty shop; Library.
Activities Arts & crafts; Cards; Games; Reading groups; Prayer groups; Movies; Social/Cultural gatherings.

WILMINGTON

Royal Willows Nursing Care Center*
555 Kahler Rd, Wilmington, IL, 60481
(815) 476-7931
Admin Jeffrey T Oravec. *Medical Dir/Dir of Nursing* Dr Richards.
Licensure Skilled care; Intermediate care. *Beds* SNF 98; ICF 98. *Certified* Medicaid; Medicare.
Owner Proprietary Corp.
Admissions Requirements Medical examination.
Staff Physicians 6 (pt); RNs 3 (ft), 2 (pt); LPNs 7 (ft), 1 (pt); Orderlies 1 (ft); Nurses aides 28 (ft), 3 (pt); Physical therapists 1 (ft), 1 (pt); Recreational therapists 3 (ft); Occupational therapists 1 (pt); Speech therapists 1 (pt); Activities coordinators 1 (ft); Dietitians 1 (pt); Dentists 1 (pt); Ophthalmologists 1 (pt); Podiatrists 1 (pt); Audiologists 1 (pt).
Facilities Dining room; Physical therapy room; Activities room; Crafts room; Laundry room; Barber/Beauty shop; Library; Residents lounge; TV room.
Activities Arts & crafts; Cards; Games; Reading groups; Prayer groups; Movies; Shopping trips; Social/Cultural gatherings.

WINCHESTER

Scott County Nursing Center
RR 2, Winchester, IL, 62694
(217) 742-3101
Admin Inez M Holderman. *Medical Dir of Nursing* Dr James Bohan MD; Jonna Herring RN DON.

Licensure Intermediate care. *Beds* ICF 64. *Certified* Medicaid.
Owner Nonprofit organization/foundation.
Admissions Requirements Minimum age 18; Medical examination.
Staff RNs 1 (ft), 1 (pt); LPNs 6 (ft), 2 (pt); Orderlies 1 (ft); Nurses aides 20 (ft), 4 (pt); Recreational therapists 1 (pt); Speech therapists 1 (pt); Activities coordinators 1 (ft), 1 (pt); Dietitians 1 (pt); Ophthalmologists 1 (pt); PT Aides 2 (ft).
Facilities Dining room; Physical therapy room; Activities room; Laundry room; Barber/Beauty shop.
Activities Arts & crafts; Cards; Games; Reading groups; Movies; Shopping trips; Social/Cultural gatherings; Family night.

WINFIELD

Liberty Hill Healthcare Center
28 W 141 Liberty Rd, Winfield, IL, 60190
(312) 668-2928
Admin Mary Ryan. *Medical Dir/Dir of Nursing* G A Kushner MD; Kenneth Haugen RN DON.
Licensure Intermediate care. *Beds* ICF 115. *Certified* Medicaid.
Owner Proprietary Corp.
Admissions Requirements Minimum age 55.
Staff Physicians 4 (ft); RNs 8 (ft); LPNs 9 (ft), 2 (pt); Orderlies 8 (ft); Nurses aides 16 (ft); Physical therapists 2 (ft); Reality therapists 2 (ft); Recreational therapists 2 (ft); Occupational therapists 1 (ft); Activities coordinators 2 (ft); Dietitians 1 (pt); Dentists 1 (pt); Ophthalmologists 1 (pt); Podiatrists 1 (pt).
Languages Spanish, Polish
Facilities Dining room; Physical therapy room; Activities room; Chapel; Crafts room; Laundry room; Barber/Beauty shop; Resident fitness.
Activities Arts & crafts; Cards; Games; Reading groups; Prayer groups; Movies; Shopping trips; Social/Cultural gatherings.

WOOD RIVER

VIP Manor*
393 Edwardsville Rd, Wood River, IL, 62095
(618) 259-4111
Admin Linda L McGaughey.
Licensure Skilled care; Intermediate care. *Beds* SNF 38; ICF 68. *Certified* Medicaid; Medicare.
Owner Proprietary Corp.

WOODSTOCK

Pioneer Center for the Exceptional's Community Living Facility
1005 McHenry Ave, Woodstock, IL, 60098
(815) 338-5584
Admin Ann Patla; Sandy Diesel Program Manager. *Medical Dir/Dir of Nursing* Carol Neff RN.
Licensure Community living facility. *Beds* Community living facility 20.
Owner Nonprofit Corp.
Admissions Requirements Minimum age 18; Medical examination.
Staff RNs 1 (pt); Activities coordinators 1 (pt); 1 (pt).
Facilities Dining room; Laundry room.
Activities Arts & crafts; Cards; Games; Reading groups; Movies; Shopping trips; Social/Cultural gatherings; Community & special recreational events/activities.

Sheltered Village—Woodstock
600 Borden, Woodstock, IL, 60098
(815) 338-6440
Admin Vella M Ellis. *Medical Dir/Dir of Nursing* Dr Mitra; Barbara Bliss DON.

Licensure Intermediate care for mentally retarded. *Beds* 94.

Admissions Requirements Minimum age 18; Medical examination; Physician's request.

Staff RNs 4 (ft), 3 (pt); Nurses aides 11 (ft), 2 (pt); Reality therapists 2 (pt); Recreational therapists 2 (ft); Occupational therapists 1 (ft); Speech therapists 1 (ft), 1 (pt); Activities coordinators 1 (ft); Dietitians 1 (pt); Dentists 1 (pt); Ophthalmologists 1 (pt); Dentist 1 (pt).

Facilities Dining room; Activities room; Crafts room; Laundry room; Barber/Beauty shop.

Activities Arts & crafts; Cards; Games; Reading groups; Prayer groups; Movies; Shopping trips; Social/Cultural gatherings.

Sunset Manor
PO Box 508, 920 N Seminary Ave, Woodstock, IL, 60098
(815) 338-1749
Admin R Douglas McGrew. *Medical Dir/Dir of Nursing* Ann Wall.
Licensure Skilled care; Intermediate care; Sheltered care. *Beds* SNF 29; ICF 46; Sheltered care 63. *Certified* Medicaid.
Owner Nonprofit Corp.
Admissions Requirements Minimum age 62; Medical examination.
Staff RNs 6 (ft), 9 (pt); LPNs 4 (ft); Orderlies 1 (ft), 1 (pt); Nurses aides 16 (ft), 15 (pt); Physical therapists 1 (pt); Reality therapists 1 (pt); Recreational therapists 1 (pt); Occupational therapists 1 (pt); Speech therapists 1 (pt); Activities coordinators 2 (ft), 1 (pt); Dietitians 1 (pt).
Affiliation Methodist
Facilities Dining room; Physical therapy room; Activities room; Chapel; Crafts room; Laundry room; Barber/Beauty shop.
Activities Arts & crafts; Cards; Games; Reading groups; Prayer groups; Movies; Shopping trips; Social/Cultural gatherings.

Valley Hi Nursing Home
2406 Hartland Rd, Woodstock, IL, 60098
(815) 338-0312
Admin William M Bersted. *Medical Dir of Nursing* Dr Leo A Reyes.
Licensure Skilled care; Intermediate care. *Beds* SNF 47; ICF 43. *Certified* Medicaid.
Owner Publicly owned.
Admissions Requirements Minimum age 18; Medical examination; Physician's request.
Staff RNs 9 (ft), 5 (pt); LPNs 3 (ft); Orderlies 1 (ft); Nurses aides 28 (ft), 4 (pt); Activities coordinators 1 (ft).
Facilities Dining room; Physical therapy room; Activities room; Chapel; Laundry room; Barber/Beauty shop.
Activities Arts & crafts; Cards; Games; Movies; Shopping trips.

The Woodstock Residence
309 McHenry Ave, Woodstock, IL, 60098
(815) 338-1700
Admin Sally Henslee. *Medical Dir/Dir of Nursing* John C Paul MD.
Licensure Skilled care. *Beds* 114. *Certified* Medicaid; Medicare.
Owner Proprietary Corp.
Admissions Requirements Minimum age 21; Medical examination; Physician's request.
Staff Physicians 1 (ft), 12 (pt); RNs 15 (ft); LPNs 1 (ft); Orderlies 2 (ft); Nurses aides 44 (ft), 4 (pt); Physical therapists 3 (ft), 1 (pt); Reality therapists 2 (ft), 1 (pt); Recreational therapists 2 (ft), 1 (pt); Occupational

therapists 2 (ft); Speech therapists 1 (ft); Activities coordinators 3 (ft); Dietitians 1 (ft); Dentists 1 (pt); Ophthalmologists 1 (pt); Podiatrists 1 (pt); Dentist 1 (pt).
Facilities Dining room; Physical therapy room; Activities room; Chapel; Crafts room; Laundry room; Barber/Beauty shop; Library; Covered patios; Gardens.
Activities Arts & crafts; Cards; Games; Prayer groups; Movies; Shopping trips; Social/Cultural gatherings.

WORTH

Park Lawn Center
5831 W 115th St, Worth, IL, 60482
(312) 396-1117
Admin Marjorie Chwastecki. *Medical Dir/Dir of Nursing* Noreen Payne.
Licensure Intermediate care for mentally retarded. *Beds* ICF/MR 40. *Certified* Medicaid.
Owner Nonprofit Corp.
Staff RNs; LPNs; Physical therapists; Recreational therapists; Occupational therapists; Speech therapists; Activities coordinators; Dietitians.
Facilities Dining room; Activities room; Laundry room.
Activities Arts & crafts; Cards; Games; Movies; Shopping trips; Social/Cultural gatherings.

YORKVILLE

Hillside Nursing & Convalescent Home*
Rte 34 & Game Farm Rd, Yorkville, IL, 60560
(312) 553-5811
Admin Robert J Mahoney.
Licensure Skilled care; Intermediate care; Sheltered care. *Beds* 79.
Owner Proprietary Corp.
Admissions Requirements Minimum age 18; Medical examination.
Staff RNs 8 (ft); LPNs 2 (ft); Orderlies 2 (ft); Nurses aides 19 (ft); Activities coordinators 1 (ft), 1 (pt); Dietitians 1 (ft).
Facilities Dining room; Activities room; Crafts room; Laundry room; Barber/Beauty shop; Library.
Activities Arts & crafts; Cards; Games; Reading groups; Prayer groups; Movies; Shopping trips; Social/Cultural gatherings.

ZEIGLER

Zeigler Colonial Manor Inc
300 Church St, Zeigler, IL, 62999
(618) 596-6635
Admin Terra Potocki.
Licensure Intermediate care; Intermediate care for mentally retarded. *Beds* ICF 27; ICF/MR 22. *Certified* Medicaid.
Owner Proprietary Corp.
Admissions Requirements Minimum age 18; Medical examination; Physician's request.
Staff RNs 1 (ft); LPNs 2 (ft), 3 (pt); Orderlies 1 (pt); Nurses aides 15 (ft); Activities coordinators 1 (ft).
Facilities Dining room; Activities room; Crafts room; Laundry room; Barber/Beauty shop.
Activities Arts & crafts; Cards; Games; Reading groups; Prayer groups; Movies; Shopping trips; Social/Cultural gatherings.

ZION

Crown Manor Living Center
1805 27th St, Zion, IL, 60099
(312) 746-3736
Admin Walter Mankowski. *Medical Dir/Dir of Nursing* Barbara Guthrie.
Licensure Skilled care. *Beds* SNF 113. *Certified* Medicaid; Medicare.
Owner Nonprofit Corp (Adventist Health Sys-USA).
Admissions Requirements Medical examination.
Staff Physicians; RNs; LPNs; Nurses aides; Physical therapists; Occupational therapists; Speech therapists; Activities coordinators; Dietitians; Ophthalmologists; Podiatrists.
Affiliation Seventh-Day Adventist
Facilities Dining room; Physical therapy room; Activities room; Chapel; Crafts room; Laundry room; Barber/Beauty shop.
Activities Arts & crafts; Cards; Games; Reading groups; Prayer groups; Movies; Shopping trips; Social/Cultural gatherings.

Rolling Hills Manor
3615 16th St, Zion, IL, 60099
(312) 746-8422
Admin Katherine C Brown. *Medical Dir/Dir of Nursing* C David Engstrom MD; Debbie Pinto RN DON.
Licensure Skilled care. *Beds* SNF 135. *Certified* Medicaid; Medicare.
Owner Nonprofit Corp.
Admissions Requirements Minimum age 65; Medical examination; Physician's request.
Staff RNs 5 (ft), 3 (pt); LPNs 8 (ft), 6 (pt); Orderlies 3 (ft); Nurses aides 36 (ft), 2 (pt); Physical therapists 1 (pt); Reality therapists 1 (pt); Recreational therapists 2 (ft); Occupational therapists 1 (pt); Speech therapists 1 (pt); Activities coordinators 1 (ft); Dietitians 1 (ft); Dentists 1 (pt); Ophthalmologists 1 (pt); Podiatrists 1 (pt); Dentist 1 (ft).
Affiliation Slovak American Charitable Association
Facilities Dining room; Physical therapy room; Activities room; Crafts room; Laundry room; Barber/Beauty shop.
Activities Arts & crafts; Cards; Games; Reading groups; Prayer groups; Movies; Shopping trips; Social/Cultural gatherings; Trips to local senior citizen's center.

Sheridan Health Care Center
2534 Elim Ave, Zion, IL, 60099
(312) 746-8435
Admin Nanjean Painter. *Medical Dir/Dir of Nursing* Abdul Aziz MD; Patricia Davis RN DON.
Licensure Skilled care; Intermediate care. *Beds* SNF 95; ICF 193. *Certified* Medicaid.
Owner Privately owned.
Admissions Requirements Minimum age 40; Medical examination.
Staff Physicians; RNs; LPNs; Orderlies; Nurses aides; Physical therapists; Recreational therapists; Occupational therapists; Speech therapists; Activities coordinators; Dietitians; Dentists; Ophthalmologists.
Facilities Dining room; Physical therapy room; Activities room; Laundry room; Barber/Beauty shop; Library.
Activities Arts & crafts; Cards; Games; Reading groups; Prayer groups; Movies; Shopping trips; Social/Cultural gatherings.

INDIANA

ALBANY

Albany Nursing Care Inc*
910 W Walnut, Albany, IN, 47320
(317) 789-4423
Admin Nicholas E Lefevre. *Medical Dir/Dir of Nursing* Kay Starr RN.
Licensure Intermediate care. *Beds* 101. *Certified* Medicaid.
Admissions Requirements Medical examination.
Staff RNs 1 (ft); LPNs 4 (ft); Nurses aides 37 (ft); Activities coordinators 2 (ft); Dietitians 1 (ft); Qualified medical assistants 3 (ft), 2 (pt).
Facilities Dining room; Activities room; Laundry room; Barber/Beauty shop; Library.
Activities Games; Reading groups; Prayer groups; Movies; Shopping trips; Social/Cultural gatherings.

ALEXANDRIA

Alexandria Convalescent Center*
PO Box 461, Hwy 9 S, Alexandria, IN, 46001
(317) 724-4479
Admin Bart Bingham.
Licensure Intermediate care. *Beds* 16. *Certified* Medicaid.

The Willows Nursing Home*
Rte 4, Box 220, Alexandria, IN, 46001
(317) 724-4464
Admin Tanya A Dickey RN.
Licensure Intermediate care. *Beds* 48. *Certified* Medicaid.

ANDERSON

Americana-Family Tree
1112 Monticello Dr, Anderson, IN, 46011
(317) 649-0496
Admin Marjorie E Shell. *Medical Dir/Dir of Nursing* Ronald Harmening MD; Rebecca Bergman RN DON.
Licensure Intermediate care. *Beds* ICF 110. *Certified* Medicaid.
Owner Proprietary Corp (Manor Care).
Admissions Requirements Medical examination; Physician's request.
Staff RNs; LPNs; Orderlies; Nurses aides; Activities coordinators.
Facilities Dining room; Activities room; Crafts room; Barber/Beauty shop.
Activities Arts & crafts; Cards; Games; Reading groups; Prayer groups; Movies; Shopping trips; Social/Cultural gatherings.

Americana Healthcare Center
1345 N Madison Ave, Anderson, IN, 46011
(317) 644-2888
Admin Betty A Crum. *Medical Dir/Dir of Nursing* Stephen J Wright MD; Cheryl Thrash RN.
Licensure Skilled care; Intermediate care. *Beds* SNF 81; ICF 45. *Certified* Medicaid; Medicare.

Owner Proprietary Corp (Manor Care).
Admissions Requirements Minimum age 18; Medical examination; Physician's request.
Staff Physicians 1 (pt); RNs 5 (ft), 3 (pt); LPNs 11 (ft), 4 (pt); Orderlies 3 (ft); Nurses aides 37 (ft), 12 (pt); Physical therapists 1 (ft); Occupational therapists 1 (pt); Speech therapists 1 (pt); Activities coordinators 1 (ft), 2 (pt); Dietitians 1 (pt); Ophthalmologists 1 (pt); Podiatrists 1 (pt).
Facilities Dining room; Physical therapy room; Activities room; Chapel; Laundry room; Barber/Beauty shop.
Activities Arts & crafts; Cards; Games; Reading groups; Prayer groups; Movies; Shopping trips; Social/Cultural gatherings.

Anderson Healthcare Center*
1809 N Madison Ave, Anderson, IN, 46012
(317) 644-0903
Admin Loretta G Folsom.
Licensure Skilled care; Intermediate care. *Beds* SNF 83; ICF 92. *Certified* Medicaid; Medicare.

Goble Nursing Home
332 W 11th St, Anderson, IN, 46016
(317) 642-8156
Admin Eva Hoover. *Medical Dir/Dir of Nursing* John Woodall MD; Lynn Henthorn RN DON.
Licensure Intermediate care; Residential. *Beds* ICF 30; Residential 10. *Certified* Medicaid.
Owner Proprietary Corp (Blackeye Fam & Nursing Hm).
Admissions Requirements Minimum age 21; Medical examination; Physician's request.
Staff RNs 2 (ft); LPNs 2 (ft), 3 (pt); Nurses aides 6 (ft), 5 (pt); Activities coordinators 1 (ft); Dietitians 1 (pt).
Facilities Dining room; Activities room; Barber/Beauty shop.
Activities Arts & crafts; Cards; Games; Reading groups; Movies; Shopping trips; Social/Cultural gatherings.

New Haven Nursing Home*
1023 E 8th St, Anderson, IN, 46012
(317) 643-7391
Admin Josephine Wade.
Licensure Intermediate care. *Beds* 14.

Rolling Hills Convalescent Center*
1821 Lindberg Rd, Anderson, IN, 46012
(317) 649-2532
Admin Gerald Seifert. *Medical Dir/Dir of Nursing* Dr Linda Stropes.
Licensure Intermediate care. *Beds* SNF 140; ICF 26. *Certified* Medicaid; Medicare.
Owner Proprietary Corp (Beverly Enterprises).
Admissions Requirements Medical examination; Physician's request.
Staff RNs 5 (ft), 2 (pt); LPNs 15 (ft), 4 (pt); Nurses aides 58 (ft), 5 (pt); Physical therapists 1 (ft); Occupational therapists 1 (ft); Speech therapists 1 (ft); Activities coordinators 1 (ft); Dietitians 1 (ft).

Facilities Dining room; Physical therapy room; Activities room; Crafts room; Laundry room; Barber/Beauty shop.
Activities Arts & crafts; Cards; Games; Reading groups; Prayer groups; Movies; Shopping trips; Social/Cultural gatherings; Family/New admission adjustment workshops.

ANGOLA

Angola Nursing Home
600 N Williams St, Angola, IN, 46703
(219) 665-6313
Admin L Marie Winebrenner. *Medical Dir/Dir of Nursing* Dr George David; Maxine Martin.
Licensure Intermediate care. *Beds* ICF 40. *Certified* Medicaid.
Owner Proprietary Corp (Beverly Enterprises).
Admissions Requirements Minimum age 18; Medical examination; Physician's request.
Staff Physicians 1 (pt); RNs 1 (ft), 2 (pt); LPNs 3 (ft), 2 (pt); Nurses aides 4 (ft), 4 (pt); Speech therapists 1 (pt); Activities coordinators 1 (ft); Dietitians 1 (pt); Ophthalmologists 1 (pt); Podiatrists 1 (pt).
Languages French
Facilities Dining room; Activities room; Crafts room; Laundry room.
Activities Arts & crafts; Cards; Games; Reading groups; Prayer groups; Movies; Shopping trips; Social/Cultural gatherings; Picnics.

Carlin Park Healthcare Center
516 N Williams St, Angola, IN, 46703
(219) 665-9467
Admin John Klein. *Medical Dir/Dir of Nursing* George David MD.
Licensure Intermediate care. *Beds* 99. *Certified* Medicaid.
Admissions Requirements Minimum age 18; Medical examination; Physician's request.
Staff Physicians 1 (pt); RNs 2 (ft), 1 (pt); LPNs 6 (ft), 2 (pt); Nurses aides 35 (ft), 7 (pt); Physical therapists 1 (pt); Recreational therapists 1 (ft); Activities coordinators 1 (ft); Dietitians 1 (pt); Dentists 1 (pt); Ophthalmologists 1 (pt); Dentist 1 (pt).
Facilities Dining room; Physical therapy room; Activities room; Chapel; Crafts room; Laundry room; Barber/Beauty shop.
Activities Arts & crafts; Cards; Games; Reading groups; Prayer groups; Movies; Shopping trips; Social/Cultural gatherings.

Lakeland Nursing Center
500 N Williams St, Angola, IN, 46703
(219) 665-2161
Admin Ron McSorley. *Medical Dir/Dir of Nursing* Dr George David MD; Rosemary Cortez RN DON.
Licensure Intermediate care. *Beds* ICF 60. *Certified* Medicaid.
Owner Proprietary Corp (Shive Nursing Centers).

Admissions Requirements Medical examination; Physician's request.
Staff Physicians 1 (pt); RNs 1 (ft), 2 (pt); LPNs 4 (ft), 1 (pt); Nurses aides 16 (ft), 14 (pt); Activities coordinators 1 (ft); Dietitians 1 (pt).
Facilities Dining room; Physical therapy room; Activities room; Crafts room; Laundry room; Barber/Beauty shop; Library.
Activities Arts & crafts; Cards; Games; Reading groups; Movies.

ARCADIA

Arcadia Children's Home*
303 Franklin Ave, Arcadia, IN, 46030
(317) 984-4528
Admin Leonard A Hall.
Licensure Intermediate care. *Beds* 54. *Certified* Medicaid.

Hamilton Heights Health Center*
706 W Main St, Arcadia, IN, 46030
(317) 984-3555
Admin Phillip E Couch. *Medical Dir/Dir of Nursing* Dr Jerry Royer.
Licensure Intermediate care. *Beds* 154. *Certified* Medicaid.
Owner Proprietary Corp (Community Care Centers).
Admissions Requirements Minimum age 18; Medical examination; Physician's request.
Staff Physicians 3 (pt); RNs 3 (ft); LPNs 9 (ft), 2 (pt); Orderlies 2 (ft); Nurses aides 35 (ft), 6 (pt); Physical therapists 1 (pt); Recreational therapists 1 (ft); Occupational therapists 1 (pt); Speech therapists 1 (pt); Activities coordinators 1 (ft); Dietitians 1 (pt); Dentists 1 (pt); Podiatrists 1 (pt); Audiologists 1 (pt).
Facilities Dining room; Physical therapy room; Activities room; Chapel; Crafts room; Laundry room; Barber/Beauty shop; Library.
Activities Arts & crafts; Cards; Games; Reading groups; Prayer groups; Movies; Shopping trips; Social/Cultural gatherings.

ATTICA

Woodland Manor Nursing Center
PO Box 166, State Rd 28 East, Attica, IN, 47918
(317) 762-6133
Admin Linda Short RN. *Medical Dir/Dir of Nursing* William A Ringer MD; Peggy Evans RN.
Licensure Intermediate care. *Beds* ICF 53. *Certified* Medicaid.
Owner Proprietary Corp.
Admissions Requirements Minimum age 18; Medical examination; Physician's request.
Staff Physicians 3 (pt); RNs 2 (ft), 3 (pt); LPNs 2 (ft), 2 (pt); Nurses aides 10 (ft), 16 (pt); Activities coordinators 1 (ft); Dietitians 1 (pt); Dentists 1 (pt); Ophthalmologists 1 (pt).
Facilities Dining room; Activities room; Chapel; Crafts room; Laundry room; Barber/Beauty shop; Library.
Activities Arts & crafts; Cards; Games; Prayer groups; Movies; Social/Cultural gatherings.

AUBURN

Betz Nursing Home Inc
3009 C R 38, Auburn, IN, 46706
(219) 925-3814
Admin Doris Betz Marshall. *Medical Dir/Dir of Nursing* V Carol Marks RN.
Licensure Intermediate care. *Beds* ICF 144. *Certified* Medicaid.
Owner Privately owned.
Admissions Requirements Medical examination; Physician's request.

Staff RNs 3 (ft), 1 (pt); LPNs 5 (ft); Nurses aides 75 (ft); Activities coordinators 1 (ft), 4 (pt); Dietitians 1 (ft).
Facilities Dining room; Activities room; Crafts room; Laundry room; Barber/Beauty shop.
Activities Arts & crafts; Cards; Games; Reading groups; Prayer groups; Social/Cultural gatherings.

Glen Oaks Nursing Home
PO Box 544, 1313 E 7th St, Auburn, IN, 46706
(219) 925-1111
Admin Pamela DeKoninck. *Medical Dir/Dir of Nursing* Dr Floyd Coleman; Debora Rose RN DON.
Licensure Intermediate care. *Beds* ICF 73. *Certified* Medicaid.
Owner Proprietary Corp (Beverly Enterprises).
Admissions Requirements Minimum age 18; Medical examination.
Staff Physicians 1 (ft); RNs 3 (ft); LPNs 1 (ft); Nurses aides 12 (ft); Activities coordinators 3 (ft); Dietitians 1 (ft).
Facilities Dining room; Activities room; Laundry room; Barber/Beauty shop.
Activities Arts & crafts; Cards; Games; Reading groups; Prayer groups; Movies; Shopping trips; Social/Cultural gatherings; Special olympics.

AVILLA

Sacred Heart Home
State Road 3, RR 2, Avilla, IN, 46710
(219) 897-2841
Admin Sr M Alexine Knotek. *Medical Dir/Dir of Nursing* Dr Max Sneary; Welma Poer RN DON.
Licensure Intermediate care. *Beds* ICF 133. *Certified* Medicaid.
Owner Nonprofit Corp.
Admissions Requirements Medical examination.
Staff Physicians 3 (pt); RNs 6 (ft), 4 (pt); LPNs 5 (ft), 1 (pt); Nurses aides 22 (ft), 29 (pt); Physical therapists 2 (pt); Recreational therapists 3 (pt); Activities coordinators 2 (ft); Dietitians 1 (ft); Podiatrists 1 (pt); Social services; Restorative nursing.
Affiliation Roman Catholic
Facilities Dining room; Physical therapy room; Activities room; Chapel; Laundry room; Barber/Beauty shop; Library; Patios; Lawn areas.
Activities Arts & crafts; Cards; Games; Reading groups; Prayer groups; Movies; Shopping trips; Social/Cultural gatherings; Cooking sessions; Rhythm band; Choir; Discussion groups; Study groups; Videos; Entertainment; Volunteers; Community services.

BATESVILLE

Dreyerhaus
958 E Hwy 46, Batesville, IN, 47006
(812) 934-2436
Admin Marcella L Shaul RN. *Medical Dir/Dir of Nursing* Ivan Lindgren MD; Bonnie Greathouse RN.
Licensure Skilled care; Intermediate care. *Beds* SNF 38; ICF 110. *Certified* Medicaid; Medicare.
Owner Proprietary Corp.
Admissions Requirements Minimum age 18; Medical examination.
Staff Physicians 1 (pt); RNs 4 (ft); LPNs 9 (ft); Orderlies 5 (ft); Nurses aides 40 (ft); Physical therapists 1 (ft); Activities coordinators 1 (ft); Dietitians 1 (pt).
Facilities Dining room; Physical therapy room; Activities room; Chapel; Crafts room; Laundry room; Barber/Beauty shop; Library.

Activities Arts & crafts; Cards; Games; Reading groups; Prayer groups; Movies; Shopping trips; Social/Cultural gatherings.

BEDFORD

Bedford Nursing Home
514 E 16th St, Bedford, IN, 47421
(812) 279-4611
Admin Nellie M Camp. *Medical Dir/Dir of Nursing* Hellie Diehl DON.
Licensure Intermediate care. *Beds* ICF 40. *Certified* Medicaid.
Owner Proprietary Corp (Beverly Enterprises).
Admissions Requirements Minimum age 18.
Staff RNs 1 (pt); LPNs 4 (ft), 2 (pt); Nurses aides 6 (ft), 5 (pt); Recreational therapists 1 (pt); Activities coordinators 1 (ft); Dietitians 1 (pt).
Facilities Dining room; Activities room; Laundry room.
Activities Arts & crafts; Cards; Games; Reading groups; Prayer groups; Movies; Shopping trips; Social/Cultural gatherings.

Hospitality House*
2111 Norton Ln, Bedford, IN, 47421
(812) 279-4437
Admin Steven Sanders. *Medical Dir/Dir of Nursing* Dr Lawrence Benham.
Licensure Skilled care; Intermediate care; Pediatric care. *Beds* SNF 32; ICF 95; Pediatric care 40. *Certified* Medicaid; Medicare.
Admissions Requirements Medical examination; Physician's request.
Staff Physicians 14 (pt); RNs 7 (ft); LPNs 17 (ft); Nurses aides 40 (ft), 7 (pt); Physical therapists 1 (pt); Occupational therapists 2 (pt); Speech therapists 1 (pt); Activities coordinators 1 (ft); Dietitians 1 (ft).
Facilities Dining room; Physical therapy room; Activities room; Laundry room; Barber/Beauty shop; Speech therapy room.

Westview Manor Health Care Center
1510 Clinic Dr, Bedford, IN, 47421
(812) 279-4494
Admin Marilyn Johnson. *Medical Dir/Dir of Nursing* Dr D J Kaderabek; June Styborski RN.
Licensure Skilled care; Intermediate care. *Beds* SNF 58; ICF 60. *Certified* Medicaid.
Owner Proprietary Corp (Hillhaven Corp).
Admissions Requirements Minimum age 18; Medical examination; Physician's request.
Staff Physicians 8 (pt); RNs 7 (ft), 1 (pt); LPNs 11 (ft); Nurses aides 43 (ft), 8 (pt); Physical therapists 1 (ft); Activities coordinators 2 (ft); Dietitians 1 (ft); Ophthalmologists 1 (pt).
Facilities Dining room; Physical therapy room; Activities room; Crafts room; Laundry room; Barber/Beauty shop.
Activities Arts & crafts; Cards; Games; Reading groups; Prayer groups; Movies; Shopping trips; Social/Cultural gatherings.

BEECH GROVE

Beech Grove Healthcare Center*
2002 Albany Ave, Beech Grove, IN, 46107
(317) 783-2911
Admin Joan Foley. *Medical Dir/Dir of Nursing* Dr Thomas Moran.
Licensure Skilled care; Intermediate care. *Beds* SNF 77; ICF 122. *Certified* Medicaid; Medicare.
Owner Proprietary Corp (ARA Living Centers).
Admissions Requirements Medical examination; Physician's request.
Staff RNs 5 (ft), 2 (pt); LPNs 8 (ft), 3 (pt); Nurses aides 46 (ft), 12 (pt); Physical therapists 2 (pt); Occupational therapists 2

(pt); Speech therapists 1 (pt); Activities coordinators 2 (ft); Dietitians 1 (ft); Dentists 2 (pt); Podiatrists 1 (pt).
Facilities Dining room; Physical therapy room; Activities room; Chapel; Laundry room; Barber/Beauty shop.
Activities Arts & crafts; Cards; Games; Reading groups; Prayer groups; Movies; Shopping trips; Social/Cultural gatherings.

St Paul Hermitage
501 N 17th Ave, Beech Grove, IN, 46107
(317) 786-2261
Admin Sr Patricia Dede OSB. *Medical Dir/Dir of Nursing* Dr Frank Fortuna; Sr Mary Frederic.
Licensure Intermediate care; Residential. *Beds* ICF 48; Residential 57. *Certified* Medicaid.
Owner Nonprofit Corp.
Admissions Requirements Medical examination.
Staff Physicians 1 (pt); RNs 1 (ft), 3 (pt); LPNs 4 (ft); Nurses aides 18 (ft), 20 (pt); Physical therapists 1 (ft); Activities coordinators 2 (ft); Dietitians 1 (pt); Ophthalmologists 1 (pt); Resident Catholic Priest Chaplain 1 (ft).
Affiliation Roman Catholic
Facilities Dining room; Physical therapy room; Activities room; Chapel; Laundry room; Barber/Beauty shop; Library.
Activities Arts & crafts; Cards; Games; Reading groups; Prayer groups; Movies; Shopping trips.

BERNE

Berne Nursing Home*
906 W Main St, Berne, IN, 46711
(219) 589-2127
Admin David W Springer.
Licensure Intermediate care; Residential care. *Beds* 25.
Owner Proprietary Corp (US Care Corp).
Admissions Requirements Minimum age 18; Medical examination.
Staff RNs 1 (pt); LPNs 1 (ft); Nurses aides 3 (ft), 15 (pt); Activities coordinators 1 (ft); Dietitians 1 (pt).
Facilities Dining room; Activities room; Laundry room; Barber/Beauty shop.
Activities Arts & crafts; Cards; Games; Reading groups; Movies; Shopping trips; Social/Cultural gatherings.

Swiss Village Inc
W Main St, Berne, IN, 46711
(219) 589-3173
Admin Daryl L Martin, Executive Director; Wayne L Smith, Director of Resident Services. *Medical Dir/Dir of Nursing* Dr Boze; LaDene Lehman DON.
Licensure Intermediate care; Residential; Assisted Residential; Independent living Apartments. *Beds* ICF 108; Residential & Assisted Residential 135; Independent living Apts 84. *Certified* Medicaid.
Owner Nonprofit Corp.
Admissions Requirements Minimum age 62; Medical examination.
Staff RNs 7 (ft), 3 (pt); LPNs 10 (ft), 1 (pt); Nurses aides 37 (ft), 39 (pt); Activities coordinators 3 (ft), 3 (pt); Dietitians 1 (pt).
Affiliation Mennonite
Facilities Dining room; Activities room; Chapel; Crafts room; Laundry room; Barber/ Beauty shop; Library.
Activities Arts & crafts; Cards; Games; Reading groups; Prayer groups; Movies; Shopping trips; Social/Cultural gatherings; Field trips; Exercise classes.

BICKNELL

Bicknell Health Care*
204 W 3rd St, Bicknell, IN, 47512
(812) 735-3021

Admin Mary Alyce Cullop. *Medical Dir/Dir of Nursing* Dr B G O'Dell & Dr R W Rompf.
Licensure Intermediate care. *Beds* 47. *Certified* Medicaid.
Admissions Requirements Medical examination.
Staff Physicians 2 (pt); RNs 1 (ft), 1 (pt); LPNs 3 (ft), 3 (pt); Nurses aides 13 (ft), 4 (pt); Physical therapists 1 (pt); Activities coordinators 1 (ft); Dietitians 1 (ft); Dentists 2 (pt); Ophthalmologists 2 (pt); Podiatrists 1 (pt).
Facilities Dining room; Physical therapy room; Activities room; Crafts room; Laundry room; Barber/Beauty shop; Library; Conference room; Supplementary nutrition room.
Activities Arts & crafts; Cards; Games; Reading groups; Prayer groups; Movies; Shopping trips; Social/Cultural gatherings; Birthday parties.

BLOOMFIELD

Bloomfield Health Care Center
150 N Seminary St, Bloomfield, IN, 47424
(812) 384-4448
Admin Mary Black. *Medical Dir/Dir of Nursing* Owen Batterton MD; Kathy Cunningham RN.
Licensure Intermediate care. *Beds* 60. *Certified* Medicaid.
Owner Proprietary Corp.
Admissions Requirements Minimum age 19; Medical examination.
Staff Physicians 4 (pt); RNs 1 (ft); LPNs 4 (ft), 2 (pt); Orderlies 1 (ft); Nurses aides 14 (ft), 2 (pt); Physical therapists 1 (pt); Activities coordinators 1 (ft), 1 (pt); Dietitians 1 (ft).
Facilities Dining room; Physical therapy room; Activities room; Laundry room; Barber/Beauty shop.
Activities Arts & crafts; Cards; Games; Reading groups; Prayer groups; Movies; Shopping trips; Social/Cultural gatherings.

BLOOMINGTON

Bloomington Convalescent Center
714 S Rogers St, Bloomington, IN, 47401
(812) 336-6893
Admin Rodney McBride. *Medical Dir/Dir of Nursing* George Lewis MD; Chris Johns RN DON.
Licensure Skilled care; Intermediate care. *Beds* SNF 33; ICF 135; Residential 9. *Certified* Medicaid; Medicare.
Owner Nonprofit Corp.
Admissions Requirements Minimum age 18; Medical examination; Physician's request.
Staff Physicians 1 (ft); RNs 5 (ft); LPNs 21 (ft), 7 (pt); Orderlies 8 (ft), 1 (pt); Nurses aides 43 (ft), 10 (pt); Physical therapists 1 (ft); Recreational therapists 2 (ft), 1 (pt); Occupational therapists 1 (pt); Speech therapists 1 (pt); Dietitians 1 (pt); Dentists 1 (pt); Ophthalmologists 1 (pt); Ophthalmologists 1 (pt); Podiatrists 1 (pt).
Facilities Dining room; Physical therapy room; Activities room; Crafts room; Barber/ Beauty shop.
Activities Arts & crafts; Cards; Games; Reading groups; Prayer groups; Movies; Shopping trips; Social/Cultural gatherings.

Bloomington Nursing Home*
120 E Miller Dr, Bloomington, IN, 47401
(812) 336-1055
Admin William Doub.
Licensure Intermediate care. *Beds* 40. *Certified* Medicaid.
Owner Proprietary Corp (Waverly Group).
Admissions Requirements Minimum age 18; Medical examination.

Staff RNs 1 (ft); LPNs 4 (pt); Orderlies 1 (pt); Nurses aides 7 (ft), 6 (pt); Activities coordinators 1 (ft); Dietitians 1 (pt).
Facilities Dining room; Activities room; Crafts room.
Activities Arts & crafts; Games; Reading groups; Prayer groups; Movies; Shopping trips; Social/Cultural gatherings.

Fontanbleu Nursing Center
3305 S Hwy 37, Bloomington, IN, 47401
(812) 332-4437
Admin Douglas V Lynch. *Medical Dir/Dir of Nursing* Steven Lewallen MD; Julia Dutton RN DON.
Licensure Skilled care; Intermediate care; Alzheimer's. *Beds* SNF 69; ICF 132. *Certified* Medicaid; Medicare.
Owner Proprietary Corp (Beverly Enterprises).
Admissions Requirements Minimum age 18.

Hospitality House Inc
1100 S Curry Pike, Bloomington, IN, 47401
(812) 339-1657
Admin Caroline Lin. *Medical Dir/Dir of Nursing* S LeWallen MD; Jean Wagner RN.
Licensure Skilled care; Intermediate care. *Beds* SNF 52; ICF 140. *Certified* Medicaid; Medicare.
Owner Proprietary Corp.
Admissions Requirements Minimum age 18; Medical examination; Physician's request.
Staff Physicians 4 (pt); RNs 3 (ft), 6 (pt); LPNs 12 (ft), 1 (pt); Orderlies 8 (ft); Nurses aides 68 (ft), 7 (pt); Physical therapists 1 (pt); Recreational therapists 1 (pt); Occupational therapists 1 (pt); Speech therapists 1 (pt); Activities coordinators 1 (ft), 4 (pt); Dietitians 1 (pt); Ophthalmologists 3 (pt); Podiatrists 1 (pt); Dentist 1 (pt); Optometrist 1 (pt).
Languages Chinese
Facilities Dining room; Physical therapy room; Activities room; Chapel; Crafts room; Laundry room; Barber/Beauty shop; Family room.
Activities Arts & crafts; Cards; Games; Reading groups; Prayer groups; Movies; Shopping trips; Social/Cultural gatherings; Parties; Spelling bees.

BLUFFTON

Cooper Community Care Center*
1509 Fort Wayne Rd, Bluffton, IN, 46714
(219) 824-2434
Admin Frances Coates.
Licensure Skilled care; Intermediate care. *Beds* SNF 30; ICF 53. *Certified* Medicaid; Medicare.
Owner Proprietary Corp (Community Care Centers).

Meadowvale Care Center
1529 W Lancaster St, Bluffton, IN, 46714
(219) 824-4320
Admin Larry E Watkins. *Medical Dir/Dir of Nursing* Dr Joe Greene; Cindy Haynes.
Licensure Intermediate care. *Beds* ICF 120. *Certified* Medicaid.
Owner Proprietary Corp.
Admissions Requirements Medical examination; Physician's request.
Staff Physicians 1 (pt); RNs 3 (ft); LPNs 10 (ft), 6 (pt); Nurses aides 40 (ft), 16 (pt); Recreational therapists 1 (ft), 1 (pt); Speech therapists 1 (pt); Activities coordinators 1 (ft); Dietitians 1 (ft); Podiatrists 1 (pt); Audiologists 1 (pt).
Facilities Dining room; Activities room; Crafts room; Laundry room; Barber/Beauty shop; Library; TV lounge; Critical care wing.
Activities Arts & crafts; Cards; Games; Reading groups; Prayer groups; Movies; Shopping trips; Social/Cultural gatherings.

West Haven Health Care
1001 S Clark Ave, Bluffton, IN, 46714
(219) 824-0326
Admin Lona S Makay. *Medical Dir/Dir of Nursing* Dr George Merkle.
Licensure Intermediate care. *Beds* ICF 40. *Certified* Medicaid.
Owner Proprietary Corp (Beverly Enterprises).
Admissions Requirements Minimum age 18; Medical examination.
Staff RNs 2 (pt); LPNs 3 (ft), 2 (pt); Nurses aides 4 (ft), 4 (pt); Activities coordinators 1 (ft); Dietitians 1 (pt).
Facilities Dining room; Activities room; Laundry room; Barber/Beauty shop.
Activities Arts & crafts; Games; Reading groups; Prayer groups; Movies; Shopping trips; Social/Cultural gatherings; Weekly bus rides.

BOONVILLE

Baker's Rest Haven
305 E North St, Boonville, IN, 47601
(812) 897-2810
Admin David L Batts. *Medical Dir/Dir of Nursing* Ramona J Betz.
Licensure Intermediate care. *Beds* ICF 60. *Certified* Medicaid.
Owner Proprietary Corp.
Admissions Requirements Minimum age 18; Medical examination; Physician's request.
Staff RNs 2 (ft), 3 (pt); LPNs 5 (ft), 1 (pt); Orderlies 1 (ft); Nurses aides 15 (ft), 5 (pt); Activities coordinators 1 (ft); Dietitians 1 (pt).
Facilities Dining room; Activities room; Chapel; Crafts room; Laundry room; Barber/Beauty shop.
Activities Arts & crafts; Games; Reading groups; Prayer groups; Movies; Shopping trips; Social/Cultural gatherings; Field trips such as circus, plays, & concerts.

Boonville Convalescent Center Inc
725 S 2nd St, Boonville, IN, 47601
(812) 897-1375
Admin Gloria Glore.
Licensure Intermediate care. *Beds* 107. *Certified* Medicaid.

BRAZIL

Clay County Health Center Inc*
1408 E Hendrix St, Brazil, IN, 47834
(812) 433-4111
Admin Wilma I Ellison. *Medical Dir/Dir of Nursing* Rahim Farid.
Licensure Skilled care; Intermediate care. *Beds* SNF 39; ICF 60. *Certified* Medicaid; Medicare.
Owner Proprietary Corp (Forum Grp).
Facilities Dining room; Physical therapy room; Activities room; Crafts room; Laundry room; Barber/Beauty shop.
Activities Arts & crafts; Cards; Games; Reading groups; Prayer groups; Movies.

Holly Hill Health Care Facility
PO Box 130, 110 S Murphy, Brazil, IN, 47834
(812) 446-2636
Admin Judie C Scobee. *Medical Dir/Dir of Nursing* Dr Curt Oehler; Dawn Price DON.
Licensure Intermediate care. *Beds* ICF 71. *Certified* Medicaid.
Owner Proprietary Corp.
Admissions Requirements Medical examination.
Staff RNs 1 (ft); LPNs 4 (ft), 3 (pt); Nurses aides 24 (ft), 3 (pt); Activities coordinators 1 (ft); QMAs 3 (ft).
Facilities Dining room; Activities room; Crafts room; Laundry room; Barber/Beauty shop; Lounges.
Activities Arts & crafts; Cards; Games; Reading groups; Prayer groups; Movies; Social/Cultural gatherings.

BREMEN

R N Nursing Home Inc*
316 Woodies Ln, Bremen, IN, 46506
(219) 546-3494
Admin Jack Mueller. *Medical Dir/Dir of Nursing* Dr James Berndt.
Licensure Intermediate care. *Beds* 82. *Certified* Medicaid.
Owner Proprietary Corp.
Admissions Requirements Medical examination; Physician's request.
Staff Physicians 6 (pt); RNs 4 (ft); LPNs 2 (ft); Nurses aides 27 (ft), 16 (pt); Physical therapists 1 (pt); Recreational therapists 1 (ft); Activities coordinators 1 (ft); Dietitians 2 (ft); Dentists 1 (ft); Podiatrists 1 (pt).
Facilities Dining room; Activities room; Chapel; Crafts room; Laundry room; Barber/Beauty shop; Library.
Activities Arts & crafts; Cards; Games; Prayer groups; Movies; Social/Cultural gatherings.

TLC Nursing Home Inc*
8286 US West, Bremen, IN, 46506
(219) 546-4214
Admin Pauline Studt.
Licensure Intermediate care. *Beds* 24. *Certified* Medicaid.

BROOKSTON

Archibald Memorial Home for Aged Deaf
PO Box 33, RR 2, Brookston, IN, 47923
(317) 563-3582
Admin Bess Spaulding. *Medical Dir/Dir of Nursing* Helen Taylor LPN.
Licensure Residential care. *Beds* 16.
Owner Nonprofit Corp.
Admissions Requirements Minimum age; Medical examination.
Staff Physicians 1 (ft); LPNs 1 (ft); Activities Director 1 (ft).
Languages Sign
Facilities Dining room; Activities room; Laundry room; Nurses station.
Activities Arts & crafts; Cards; Games; Movies; Shopping trips; Social/Cultural gatherings.

BROOKVILLE

Elsie Dryer Nursing Home*
273 Main St, Brookville, IN, 47012
(317) 647-6231
Admin Janet E Stevens. *Medical Dir/Dir of Nursing* Dr William Stitt.
Licensure Intermediate care. *Beds* 49. *Certified* Medicaid.
Admissions Requirements Medical examination; Physician's request.
Staff Physicians 4 (pt); RNs 1 (pt); LPNs 3 (ft), 1 (pt); Orderlies 1 (ft); Nurses aides 7 (ft), 13 (pt); Activities coordinators 1 (ft).
Facilities Dining room.
Activities Arts & crafts; Cards; Reading groups; Prayer groups; Movies.

BROWNSBURG

Autumn Care of Brownsburg*
Hornaday Rd, Brownsburg, IN, 46112
(317) 852-3123
Admin Becky Muse.
Licensure Skilled care; Intermediate care. *Beds* 178. *Certified* Medicaid.

BROWNSTOWN

Hoosier Christian Village*
621 S Sugar, Brownstown, IN, 47220
(812) 358-2504
Admin Charles W McCormick.
Licensure Skilled care; Intermediate care. *Beds* 97. *Certified* Medicaid; Medicare.
Owner Nonprofit Corp (Christian Homes).

BUTLER

Butler Health Care Center
117 S Broadway St, Butler, IN, 46721
(219) 868-2161
Admin Phyllis Tittman. *Medical Dir/Dir of Nursing* William Goudy DO; Vickie Gouchenour RN.
Licensure Intermediate care. *Beds* ICF 41.
Owner Proprietary Corp.
Admissions Requirements Minimum age 18.
Staff Physicians 1 (pt); RNs 1 (ft), 1 (pt); LPNs 1 (ft), 3 (pt); Nurses aides 6 (ft), 2 (pt); Occupational therapists 1 (pt); Activities coordinators 1 (ft); Dietitians 1 (pt); Social service 1 (ft).
Facilities Dining room; Activities room; Crafts room; Laundry room.
Activities Arts & crafts; Cards; Games; Prayer groups; Movies; Shopping trips; Social/Cultural gatherings; Camping trips.

Meadowhaven Healthcare Center
520 W Liberty, Butler, IN, 46721
(219) 868-2164
Admin Connie Pierson-Snyder. *Medical Dir/Dir of Nursing* B Graber MD; Mary Husted DON.
Licensure Skilled care; Intermediate care. *Beds* SNF 24; ICF 77. *Certified* Medicaid; Medicare.
Owner Proprietary Corp.
Admissions Requirements Minimum age 18; Medical examination; Physician's request.
Staff RNs; LPNs; Orderlies; Nurses aides; Physical therapists; Occupational therapists; Speech therapists; Activities coordinators; Dietitians; Podiatrists.
Facilities Dining room; Physical therapy room; Activities room; Chapel; Crafts room; Laundry room; Barber/Beauty shop; Library.
Activities Arts & crafts; Cards; Games; Reading groups; Prayer groups; Movies; Shopping trips; Social/Cultural gatherings.

CARMEL

Lakeview Health Care Center
2907 E 136th St, Carmel, IN, 46032
(317) 846-0265
Admin Steven L Dehne. *Medical Dir/Dir of Nursing* Dr Stephen Pennal; Dr Violet Woods White.
Licensure Intermediate care. *Beds* ICF 39. *Certified* Medicaid.
Owner Privately owned.
Admissions Requirements Minimum age 18; Medical examination; Physician's request.
Staff Physicians 1 (pt); RNs 1 (ft); LPNs 3 (ft), 3 (pt); Nurses aides 12 (ft), 3 (pt); Recreational therapists 1 (pt); Activities coordinators 1 (ft); Dietitians 1 (pt).
Facilities Dining room; Activities room; Crafts room; Laundry room; Barber/Beauty shop.
Activities Arts & crafts; Cards; Games; Reading groups; Prayer groups; Movies; Shopping trips; Social/Cultural gatherings.

The Manor House of Carmel
116 Medical Dr, Carmel, IN, 46032
(317) 844-4211
Admin Greg Starnes. *Medical Dir/Dir of Nursing* Norman Fogle MD; Linda Greene RN.
Licensure Skilled care; Intermediate care. *Beds* SNF 25; ICF 90. *Certified* Medicare.
Owner Privately owned.
Admissions Requirements Minimum age 18; Medical examination.
Staff Physicians 30 (pt); RNs 3 (ft), 3 (pt); LPNs 4 (ft), 6 (pt); Orderlies 2 (ft); Nurses aides 26 (ft), 14 (pt); Physical therapists 1 (pt); Occupational therapists 1 (pt); Speech therapists 1 (pt); Activities coordinators 1 (ft); Dietitians 1 (pt); Ophthalmologists 1 (pt); Podiatrists 1 (pt).

Facilities Dining room; Physical therapy room; Activities room; Crafts room; Laundry room; Barber/Beauty shop; Library.
Activities Arts & crafts; Cards; Games; Reading groups; Movies; Shopping trips; Social/Cultural gatherings.

Summer Trace
12999 N Pennsylvania, Carmel, IN, 46032
(317) 848-2448
Admin Julianne Holichy. *Medical Dir/Dir of Nursing* Dr Mark Richards; Nancy DeVault RN.
Licensure Comprehensive; Residential care. *Beds* Comprehensive 60; Residential 30.
Owner Proprietary Corp (Beverly Enterprises).
Admissions Requirements Minimum age 18.
Staff Physicians; RNs 3 (ft); LPNs 7 (ft), 2 (pt); Nurses aides 10 (ft), 3 (pt); Activities coordinators 1 (ft); Dietitians 1 (ft).
Facilities Dining room; Physical therapy room; Activities room; Chapel; Laundry room; Barber/Beauty shop; Library; Gazebo; Exercise room; Solarium; 2 patios; Bank.
Activities Arts & crafts; Cards; Games; Reading groups; Prayer groups; Movies; Shopping trips; Social/Cultural gatherings; Lunch club; Gardening.

CENTER POINT

Macanell Nursing Home Inc*
Rte 2, Box 139, Center Point, IN, 47840
(812) 835-3041
Admin Hugh W McCann.
Licensure Intermediate care. *Beds* 67.
Certified Medicaid.

CENTERVILLE

Pinehurst Nursing Home*
Box 177, Centerville, IN, 47330
(317) 855-3424
Admin Mary McClure RN.
Licensure Intermediate care. *Beds* 72.
Certified Medicaid.

CHANDLER

Medco Chandler
RR 2 PO Box 39, Chandler, IN, 47610
(812) 925-3381
Admin Barbara Cash. *Medical Dir/Dir of Nursing* Linda Roland.
Licensure Intermediate care. *Beds* ICF 74.
Certified Medicaid.
Owner Proprietary Corp (Unicare).
Admissions Requirements Medical examination; Physician's request.
Facilities Dining room; Physical therapy room; Activities room; Barber/Beauty shop.
Activities Arts & crafts; Cards; Games; Prayer groups; Movies; Shopping trips; Social/Cultural gatherings.

CHARLESTOWN

Kentuckiana Christian Home Inc*
Rte 2, Box 337, Charlestown, IN, 47111
(812) 256-3371
Admin Bonnie J Looney.
Licensure Comprehensive care. *Beds* 65.
Certified Medicaid.
Admissions Requirements Minimum age 18; Medical examination.
Staff RNs 1 (pt); LPNs 2 (ft); Nurses aides 20 (ft), 3 (pt); Activities coordinators 1 (ft); Dietitians 1 (ft); 1 (ft).
Facilities Dining room; Activities room; Chapel; Crafts room; Laundry room; Barber/Beauty shop.
Activities Arts & crafts; Cards; Games; Reading groups; Prayer groups; Movies; Shopping trips; Social/Cultural gatherings.

CICERO

Cicero Children's Center Inc*
69 N Harrison, PO Box 217, Cicero, IN, 46034
(317) 934-4393
Admin Lane Guttman.
Licensure Developmentally disabled. *Beds* 28.
Admissions Requirements Minimum age 0-21; Medical examination.
Staff RNs 1 (pt); LPNs 1 (ft); Orderlies 2 (ft); Nurses aides 18 (pt); Activities coordinators 1 (ft); Dietitians 1 (pt).
Facilities Dining room; Activities room; Laundry room.

CLARKS HILL

Houston Health Care Inc—Clarks Hill*
Box 31, 602 Clark St, Clarks Hill, IN, 47930
(317) 523-2144
Admin Jimmie Mae Hudson.
Licensure Intermediate care. *Beds* 34.
Certified Medicaid.

CLARKSVILLE

Clarksville Healthcare Center*
286 Eastern Blvd, Clarksville, IN, 47130
(812) 282-6663
Admin Dorothy Manns. *Medical Dir/Dir of Nursing* Dr Claude Meyer.
Licensure Skilled care; Intermediate care. *Beds* SNF 87; ICF 108. *Certified* Medicaid; Medicare.
Owner Proprietary Corp (ARA Living Centers).
Admissions Requirements Minimum age 18.
Staff Physicians 1 (pt); RNs 3 (ft); LPNs 12 (ft), 4 (pt); Orderlies 3 (ft); Nurses aides 30 (ft), 15 (pt); Physical therapists 1 (ft); Recreational therapists 1 (ft), 1 (pt); Occupational therapists 1 (ft); Speech therapists 1 (ft); Activities coordinators 1 (ft); Dietitians 1 (ft); Dentists 1 (pt); Audiologists 1 (ft).
Facilities Dining room; Physical therapy room; Activities room; Crafts room; Laundry room; Barber/Beauty shop.
Activities Arts & crafts; Cards; Games; Reading groups; Shopping trips; Social/Cultural gatherings.

Medco Center of Clarksville*
517 N Hallmark Dr, Clarksville, IN, 47130
(812) 282-8406
Admin Sharon Schroder. *Medical Dir/Dir of Nursing* E'Austin B Johnson MD.
Licensure Skilled care; Intermediate care. *Beds* SNF 61; ICF 62. *Certified* Medicaid; Medicare.
Owner Proprietary Corp (Unicare).
Admissions Requirements Medical examination.
Staff RNs 4 (ft), 1 (pt); LPNs 10 (ft), 2 (pt); Nurses aides 31 (ft), 1 (pt); Physical therapists; Occupational therapists; Speech therapists; Activities coordinators 2 (ft); Dietitians; Social workers; Qualified medical assistants 4 (ft), 1 (pt).
Facilities Dining room; Physical therapy room; Laundry room; Barber/Beauty shop; Living room; 2 TV lounges.
Activities Arts & crafts; Cards; Games; Prayer groups; Movies; Shopping trips; Social/Cultural gatherings.

Westminster Village Health Care Center
2200 Greentree N, Clarksville, IN, 47130
(812) 282-9691
Admin Ronald C Hoffman.
Licensure Skilled care; Intermediate care. *Beds* 94. *Certified* Medicare.

CLINTON

Clinton Nursing Home
700 S Main St, Clinton, IN, 47842
(317) 832-8388
Admin Cecil Perkins. *Medical Dir/Dir of Nursing* Richard Bloomer MD; Margit Wilburn LPN.
Licensure Intermediate care. *Beds* 40.
Certified Medicaid.
Owner Proprietary Corp (Beverly Enterprises).
Admissions Requirements Minimum age 18; Medical examination; Physician's request.
Staff Physicians 6 (ft); RNs 1 (ft); LPNs 4 (ft), 3 (pt); Nurses aides 10 (ft), 3 (pt); Activities coordinators 1 (ft); Dietitians 1 (pt).
Facilities Dining room; Activities room; Laundry room; Library.
Activities Arts & crafts; Cards; Games; Reading groups; Prayer groups; Movies; Shopping trips; Social/Cultural gatherings; Live bands.

Vermillion Convalescent Center*
1705 S Main St, Box 1A, Clinton, IN, 47842
(317) 832-3573
Admin David J Olson. *Medical Dir/Dir of Nursing* S F Swaim MD.
Licensure Skilled care; Intermediate care. *Beds* SNF 22; ICF 99. *Certified* Medicaid; Medicare.
Staff Physicians 6 (pt); RNs 5 (ft), 3 (pt); LPNs 13 (ft), 6 (pt); Orderlies 4 (ft); Nurses aides 35 (ft), 10 (pt); Physical therapists 1 (pt); Speech therapists 1 (pt); Activities coordinators 2 (ft); Dietitians 1 (pt); Dentists 1 (pt); Podiatrists 1 (pt); Audiologists 1 (pt).
Facilities Dining room; Physical therapy room; Activities room; Crafts room; Laundry room; Barber/Beauty shop; Library.
Activities Arts & crafts; Cards; Games; Reading groups; Prayer groups; Movies; Shopping trips; Social/Cultural gatherings.

CLOVERDALE

Houston Healthcare Inc—Cloverdale
PO Box 247, 34 S Main, Cloverdale, IN, 46120
(317) 795-4260
Admin Janice M Tribbett. *Medical Dir/Dir of Nursing* Dr Keith Ernst; Joan Tucker RN DON.
Licensure Intermediate care. *Beds* ICF 40.
Certified Medicaid.
Owner Proprietary Corp.
Admissions Requirements Medical examination; Physician's request.
Staff Physicians 1 (pt); RNs 2 (ft), 1 (pt); LPNs 2 (ft); Nurses aides 10 (ft), 4 (pt); Activities coordinators 1 (ft); Ophthalmologists 1 (pt).
Languages German
Facilities Dining room; Activities room; Laundry room; Barber/Beauty shop.
Activities Arts & crafts; Cards; Games; Reading groups; Prayer groups; Movies; Shopping trips; Social/Cultural gatherings; Exercise class.

COLUMBIA CITY

Columbia City Community Care Center
RR 9, Columbia City, IN, 46725
(219) 248-8141
Admin Jerry McClanahan. *Medical Dir/Dir of Nursing* David Hurley MD; Linda Orcutt DON.
Licensure Skilled care; Intermediate care. *Beds* SNF 24; ICF 58. *Certified* Medicaid; Medicare; VA Approved.
Admissions Requirements Medical examination; Physician's request.
Staff RNs 1 (ft), 2 (pt); LPNs 4 (ft), 5 (pt); Orderlies 1 (ft); Nurses aides 15 (ft), 2 (pt); Physical therapists 1 (pt); Activities

coordinators 1 (ft); Dietitians 1 (pt);
Ophthalmologists 1 (pt); Social Service 1 (ft);
Dentist 1 (pt).
Facilities Dining room; Physical therapy
room; Activities room; Laundry room;
Barber/Beauty shop.
Activities Arts & crafts; Cards; Games;
Reading groups; Prayer groups; Movies;
Shopping trips; Social/Cultural gatherings;
Bowling; Church services.

Columbia City Nursing Home*
522 N Line St, Columbia City, IN, 46725
(219) 248-8216
Admin Michael H Heet.
Licensure Intermediate care. *Beds* 40.
Certified Medicaid.
Owner Proprietary Corp (Beverly Enterprises).

Miller's Merry Manor Inc*
710 W Ellsworth St, Columbia City, IN,
46725
(219) 248-8101
Admin William E Voit.
Licensure Skilled care; Intermediate care. *Beds*
114. Certified Medicaid; Medicare.
Owner Proprietary Corp (Millers Merry
Manor).

COLUMBUS

Bartholomew County Home*
2525 Illinois, Columbus, IN, 47201
(812) 372-7370
Admin Diane Burford.
Licensure Residential care. *Beds* 31.

Columbus Convalescent Center*
PO Box 690, 2100 Midway St, Columbus, IN,
47201
(812) 372-8447
Admin Diane L Dodge.
Licensure Skilled care; Intermediate care. *Beds*
235. Certified Medicaid; Medicare.
Owner Proprietary Corp (Hillhaven Corp).

Columbus Nursing Home*
5400 E 25th St, Columbus, IN, 47201
(812) 372-6136
Admin Patricia Sneed.
Licensure Intermediate care. *Beds* 40.
Certified Medicaid.
Owner Proprietary Corp (Beverly Enterprises).

**Four Seasons Retirement & Health Care
Center**
1901 Taylor Rd, Columbus, IN, 47203
(812) 372-8481
Admin Marcia G Life. *Medical Dir/Dir of
Nursing* Charles Hatcher MD; Paulette
Wessel DON.
Licensure Skilled care; Intermediate care. *Beds*
ICF 63; Residential 120. Certified Private
pay.
Owner Nonprofit Corp.
Admissions Requirements Minimum age 62;
Medical examination.
Staff Physicians 1 (pt); RNs 1 (ft), 5 (pt);
LPNs 8 (ft), 3 (pt); Orderlies 2 (ft); Nurses
aides 20 (ft), 1 (pt); Dietitians 1 (ft);
Ophthalmologists 1 (pt); QMA 4 (ft), 1 (pt).
Facilities Dining room; Activities room;
Chapel; Crafts room; Laundry room; Barber/
Beauty shop; Library.
Activities Arts & crafts; Cards; Games;
Reading groups; Prayer groups; Movies;
Shopping trips; Social/Cultural gatherings;
Bible study; Bridge; Euchre.

CONNERSVILLE

Connersville Nursing Home
2600 N Grand Ave, Connersville, IN, 47331
(317) 825-9771
Admin Vanessa R Wilson. *Medical Dir/Dir of
Nursing* George Ellis MD; Clara Monroe
RN DON.

Licensure Intermediate care. *Beds* ICF 40.
Certified Medicaid.
Owner Proprietary Corp (Beverly Enterprises).
Admissions Requirements Medical
examination.
Staff RNs 1 (ft), 1 (pt); LPNs 2 (ft), 5 (pt);
Nurses aides 7 (ft), 4 (pt); Activities
coordinators 1 (ft); Dietitians 1 (pt).
Facilities Dining room; Activities room;
Crafts room; Laundry room.
Activities Arts & crafts; Cards; Games;
Reading groups; Prayer groups; Movies;
Shopping trips; Social/Cultural gatherings;
Outdoor activities.

Heartland of Connersville
2500 Iowa Ave, Connersville, IN, 47331
(317) 825-7514
Admin Madge L Fosdick. *Medical Dir/Dir of
Nursing* Jag Patel MD; Joanna Dearth
DON.
Licensure Intermediate care. *Beds* ICF 50.
Certified Medicaid.
Owner Proprietary Corp (Health Care &
Retirement Corp).
Admissions Requirements Minimum age 18;
Medical examination; Physician's request.
Staff RNs 1 (ft); LPNs 3 (ft), 4 (pt); Nurses
aides 14 (ft), 9 (pt); Activities coordinators 1
(pt); Dietitians 1 (pt).
Facilities Dining room; Activities room;
Crafts room; Laundry room; Barber/Beauty
shop.
Activities Arts & crafts; Cards; Games;
Reading groups; Prayer groups; Movies;
Shopping trips; Social/Cultural gatherings;
Family/resident dinners; Exercise groups.

Lincoln Manor Nursing Center
1029 E 5th St, Connersville, IN, 47331
(317) 825-0543
Admin Robert E Rhea. *Medical Dir/Dir of
Nursing* Usha Patel MD; Carolyn Sears RN
DON.
Licensure Intermediate care. *Beds* 100.
Certified Medicaid.
Owner Proprietary Corp.
Admissions Requirements Minimum age 18;
Medical examination; Physician's request.
Staff Physicians 1 (pt); RNs 2 (ft); LPNs 9
(ft); Nurses aides 33 (ft); Activities
coordinators 1 (ft), 1 (pt); Dietitians 1 (pt).
Facilities Dining room; Activities room;
Crafts room; Laundry room; Barber/Beauty
shop.
Activities Arts & crafts; Cards; Games;
Reading groups; Prayer groups; Movies;
Shopping trips; Social/Cultural gatherings.

CORYDON

Corydon Nursing Home
315 Corydon New Middletown Rd, Corydon,
IN, 47112
(812) 738-2190
Admin Inez M LeSaux. *Medical Dir/Dir of
Nursing* George Estill MD; Bob Fehrenbach
DON.
Licensure Intermediate care. *Beds* 40.
Certified Medicaid.
Owner Proprietary Corp (Beverly Enterprises).
Admissions Requirements Minimum age 18;
Medical examination; Physician's request.
Staff LPNs; Nurses aides; Activities
coordinators.
Facilities Dining room; Activities room;
Crafts room; Laundry room; Barber/Beauty
shop.
Activities Arts & crafts; Cards; Games;
Reading groups; Prayer groups; Movies;
Shopping trips; Social/Cultural gatherings.

Indian Creek Convalescent Center
240 Beechmont Dr, Corydon, IN, 47112
(812) 738-8127
Admin Donald Ingle. *Medical Dir/Dir of
Nursing* Dr Bruce Burton.

Licensure Intermediate care. *Beds* ICF 140.
Certified Medicaid.
Owner Proprietary Corp (Hillhaven Corp).
Admissions Requirements Physician's request.
Staff RNs 3 (ft); LPNs 12 (ft); Activities
coordinators 2 (ft).
Facilities Dining room; Physical therapy
room; Activities room; Crafts room; Laundry
room; Barber/Beauty shop.
Activities Arts & crafts; Cards; Games;
Reading groups; Prayer groups; Movies;
Shopping trips; Social/Cultural gatherings.

COVINGTON

Covington Manor Health Care Center
Box 228, 1600 Liberty St E, Covington, IN,
47932
(317) 793-4818
Admin Edward Grogg. *Medical Dir/Dir of
Nursing* Sarfraz A Mirza MD; Judith Cox.
Licensure Skilled care; Intermediate care. *Beds*
SNF 42; ICF 100. Certified Medicaid;
Medicare.
Owner Privately owned.
Admissions Requirements Minimum age 18;
Medical examination; Physician's request.
Staff Physicians 8 (ft); RNs 8 (ft), 3 (pt);
LPNs 8 (ft), 5 (pt); Nurses aides 45 (ft), 22
(pt); Physical therapists 2 (pt); Occupational
therapists 1 (pt); Speech therapists 1 (pt);
Activities coordinators 1 (ft), 1 (pt);
Dietitians 1 (pt); Ophthalmologists 1 (pt).
Facilities Dining room; Physical therapy
room; Activities room; Crafts room; Laundry
room; Barber/Beauty shop; Library; Fishing
trips; Cookouts.
Activities Arts & crafts; Cards; Games;
Reading groups; Prayer groups; Movies;
Shopping trips; Social/Cultural gatherings.

CRAWFORDSVILLE

Ben Hur Home Inc
1375 S Grant Ave, Crawfordsville, IN, 47933
(317) 362-0905
Admin Kae Gallear. *Medical Dir/Dir of
Nursing* Carl B Howland MD; Rebecca
Pefley RN DON.
Licensure Intermediate care. *Beds* ICF 175.
Certified Medicaid.
Owner Proprietary Corp.
Staff Physicians; RNs; LPNs; Orderlies;
Nurses aides; Activities coordinators;
Dietitians; Ophthalmologists.
Facilities Dining room; Activities room;
Crafts room; Laundry room; Barber/Beauty
shop; Ceramic room with kiln.
Activities Arts & crafts; Cards; Games;
Reading groups; Prayer groups; Movies;
Shopping trips; Social/Cultural gatherings;
Ceramics.

Carmen Nursing Home Inc
817 N Whitlock Ave, Crawfordsville, IN,
47933
(317) 362-8590
Admin Larry E Gray. *Medical Dir/Dir of
Nursing* S R Marri MD; Janet Watson
DON.
Licensure Intermediate care. *Beds* ICF 40.
Certified Medicaid.
Owner Proprietary Corp (Beverly Enterprises).
Admissions Requirements Medical
examination.
Staff Physicians 1 (pt); RNs 1 (ft), 1 (pt);
LPNs 4 (ft); Nurses aides 7 (ft), 3 (pt);
Activities coordinators 1 (ft); Dietitians 1
(pt).
Facilities Dining room; Activities room.
Activities Arts & crafts; Cards; Games; Prayer
groups; Movies; Social/Cultural gatherings.

Houston Health Care Inc*
1371 S Grant Ave, Crawfordsville, IN, 47933
(317) 362-5365
Admin Mary Ruth Houston.

Licensure Intermediate care. *Beds* 61.
Certified Medicaid.

Lane House Inc*
1000 Lane Ave, Crawfordsville, IN, 47933
(317) 362-4815
Admin Judith K Rauch.
Licensure Intermediate care. *Beds* 60.
Certified Medicaid.
Owner Proprietary Corp (Life Care Centers of America).
Admissions Requirements Medical examination; Physician's request.
Staff RNs 2 (ft), 1 (pt); LPNs 2 (ft), 1 (pt); Nurses aides 18 (ft), 5 (pt); Activities coordinators 1 (ft), 1 (pt); Dietitians 1 (pt).
Facilities Dining room; Chapel; Laundry room; Barber/Beauty shop.
Activities Arts & crafts; Cards; Games; Prayer groups; Movies; Shopping trips; Social/Cultural gatherings.

CROWN POINT

Colonial Nursing Home Inc*
119 N Indiana Ave, Crown Point, IN, 46307
(219) 663-2532
Admin Laura M Gumbiner & Barbara A Slosson.
Licensure Intermediate care. *Beds* 40.
Certified Medicaid.

Lake County Convalescent Home
2900 W 93rd Ave, Crown Point, IN, 46307
(219) 769-3537
Admin Lawrence R Parducci. *Medical Dir/Dir of Nursing* J C Espino MD; Pearl Novak RN DON.
Licensure Skilled care; Intermediate care. *Beds* SNF 21; ICF 463. *Certified* Medicaid; Medicare.
Owner Publicly owned.
Admissions Requirements Minimum age 18; Medical examination; Physician's request.
Staff Physicians 1 (ft), 2 (pt); RNs 18 (ft), 14 (pt); LPNs 15 (ft); Orderlies 3 (ft), 2 (pt); Nurses aides 133 (ft), 26 (pt); Physical therapists 1 (pt); Activities coordinators 1 (ft); Dietitians 1 (ft); Pharmacists 1 (ft), 1 (pt); Pharmacy tech 2 (ft); Lab tech 1 (ft); Central supply tech 1 (ft), 1 (pt).
Languages Polish, Yugoslavian, Lithuanian, Italian, Spanish
Facilities Dining room; Physical therapy room; Activities room; Chapel; Crafts room; Barber/Beauty shop; Library.
Activities Arts & crafts; Cards; Games; Reading groups; Prayer groups; Movies; Shopping trips; Social/Cultural gatherings; Pet therapy.

Lutheran Home of Northwest Indiana Inc
1200 E Luther Dr, Crown Point, IN, 46307
(219) 633-3860
Admin Wayne A Hahn. *Medical Dir/Dir of Nursing* David Templin MD; Mildred Lundstrom DON.
Licensure Intermediate care; Residential & Respite care. *Beds* 191. *Certified* Medicaid.
Owner Nonprofit Corp.
Admissions Requirements Minimum age 60; Medical examination.
Staff Physicians 16 (pt); RNs 5 (ft), 7 (pt); LPNs 3 (ft), 1 (pt); Nurses aides 29 (ft), 29 (pt); Physical therapists 1 (pt); Reality therapists 1 (pt); Recreational therapists 1 (ft), 2 (pt); Occupational therapists 1 (pt); Speech therapists 1 (ft); Activities coordinators 1 (ft); Dietitians 1 (pt); Dentists 1 (pt); Ophthalmologists 1 (pt); Podiatrists 1 (pt).
Affiliation Lutheran
Facilities Dining room; Physical therapy room; Activities room; Chapel; Crafts room; Laundry room; Barber/Beauty shop; Library; Enclosed courtyard.

Activities Arts & crafts; Cards; Games; Reading groups; Prayer groups; Movies; Shopping trips; Social/Cultural gatherings; Dog lovers groups; Exercise classes.

St Anthony Home Inc
201 Franciscan Rd, Crown Point, IN, 46307
(219) 633-8120
Admin Edw Kolrner. *Medical Dir/Dir of Nursing* Debra Huber.
Licensure Skilled care; Intermediate care. *Beds* SNF 220; ICF. *Certified* Medicaid.
Owner Nonprofit organization/foundation.
Staff Physicians; RNs; LPNs; Orderlies; Nurses aides; Physical therapists; Recreational therapists; Occupational therapists; Speech therapists; Activities coordinators; Dietitians; Dentists; Ophthalmologists; Podiatrists.
Affiliation Roman Catholic
Facilities Dining room; Activities room; Chapel; Crafts room; Laundry room; Barber/Beauty shop.
Activities Arts & crafts; Cards; Games; Reading groups; Prayer groups; Movies; Shopping trips; Social/Cultural gatherings.

CULVER

Miller's Merry Manor Inc*
730 School St, Culver, IN, 46511
(219) 842-3337
Admin Lynn Reynolds.
Licensure Intermediate care. *Beds* 66.
Certified Medicaid.
Owner Proprietary Corp (Millers Merry Manor).

CYNTHIANA

Loving Care Med Center
PO Box 367, 11121 North St, Cynthiana, IN, 47612
(812) 845-2731
Admin Harrison C Neal II. *Medical Dir/Dir of Nursing* Chester Burkett MD; Janet Walker DON.
Licensure Intermediate care. *Beds* ICF 75.
Certified Medicaid.
Owner Proprietary Corp.
Admissions Requirements Medical examination; Physician's request.
Staff Physicians; RNs; LPNs; Nurses aides; Speech therapists; Activities coordinators; Dietitians; Ophthalmologists.
Facilities Dining room; Activities room; Crafts room; Laundry room.
Activities Arts & crafts; Cards; Games; Reading groups; Movies; Shopping trips; Social/Cultural gatherings.

DALE

Community Care Center of Dale
Box 297, Dale, IN, 47523
(812) 937-4442
Admin Melvin D Hamrick. *Medical Dir/Dir of Nursing* Becky Price.
Licensure Intermediate care. *Beds* ICF 60.
Certified Medicaid.
Owner Proprietary Corp (Community Care Centers).
Staff RNs 2 (ft); LPNs 5 (ft), 1 (pt); Nurses aides 14 (ft), 6 (pt); Activities coordinators 1 (pt); Dietitians 1 (pt).
Languages German
Facilities Dining room; Activities room; Crafts room; Laundry room; Barber/Beauty shop.
Activities Cards; Games; Reading groups; Movies; Shopping trips; Social/Cultural gatherings.

Professional Care Nursing Center Inc*
Rte 2, Box 315, 2000 North Rd, Dale, IN, 47523
(812) 937-4489

Admin Barbara K Miller. *Medical Dir/Dir of Nursing* Mario Leon MD.
Licensure Intermediate care. *Beds* 60.
Certified Medicaid.
Owner Proprietary Corp (Unicare).
Admissions Requirements Minimum age 18; Medical examination.
Staff Physicians 4 (pt); RNs 1 (ft), 2 (pt); Nurses aides 15 (ft), 5 (pt); Physical therapists 1 (pt); Activities coordinators 1 (ft); Dietitians 1 (pt); Dentists 1 (pt); Ophthalmologists 1 (pt); Podiatrists 1 (pt).
Facilities Dining room; Activities room; Chapel; Crafts room; Laundry room; Barber/Beauty shop.
Activities Cards; Games; Reading groups; Prayer groups; Social/Cultural gatherings.

DANVILLE

Community Healthcare of Danville*
Rd 3S, 400 E, Danville, IN, 46122
(317) 745-5184
Admin Suzanne Mervis.
Licensure Intermediate care. *Beds* 100.
Certified Medicaid.

Hendricks County Home*
865 E Main, Danville, IN, 46122
(317) 745-9317
Licensure Residential care. *Beds* 31.
Owner Publicly owned.
Admissions Requirements Minimum age 18; Medical examination; Physician's request.
Staff Nurses aides 3 (ft), 1 (pt).
Facilities Dining room; Laundry room; Barber/Beauty shop.
Activities Arts & crafts; Cards; Games.

Medco Center of Danville*
255 Meadow Dr, Danville, IN, 46122
(317) 745-5451
Admin John Singleton.
Licensure Skilled care; Intermediate care. *Beds* SNF 58; ICF 45. *Certified* Medicaid; Medicare.
Owner Proprietary Corp (Beverly Enterprises).

Primrose Manor
337 W Lincoln St, Danville, IN, 46122
(317) 745-5861
Admin Linda R Vest. *Medical Dir/Dir of Nursing* Larry Lovall MD; Donna Boyer LPN.
Licensure Intermediate care. *Beds* ICF 40.
Certified Medicaid.
Owner Proprietary Corp (Beverly Enterprises).
Admissions Requirements Medical examination; Physician's request.
Staff Physicians 1 (pt); RNs 1 (ft); LPNs 3 (ft), 2 (pt); Nurses aides 7 (ft), 1 (pt); Occupational therapists 1 (pt); Activities coordinators 1 (ft); Dietitians 1 (pt).
Facilities Dining room; Activities room; Laundry room.
Activities Arts & crafts; Cards; Games; Reading groups; Prayer groups; Movies; Shopping trips; Social/Cultural gatherings.

DECATUR

Decatur Community Care Center
PO Box 349, Decatur, IN, 46733
(219) 724-2191
Admin Ron Farmer. *Medical Dir/Dir of Nursing* Dr Zwick.
Licensure Intermediate care. *Beds* 101.
Certified Medicaid.
Owner Proprietary Corp (Community Care Centers).
Admissions Requirements Medical examination; Physician's request.
Staff RNs 1 (ft), 2 (pt); LPNs 5 (ft), 4 (pt); Nurses aides 13 (ft), 24 (pt); Activities coordinators 1 (ft), 1 (pt).

Facilities Dining room; Physical therapy room; Activities room; Laundry room; Barber/Beauty shop.
Activities Arts & crafts; Cards; Games; Reading groups; Movies.

DELPHI

Delphi Nursing Home*
1433 S Washington St, Delphi, IN, 46923
(317) 564-3123
Admin Elisabeth M Kilmer. *Medical Dir/Dir of Nursing* Dr Seese.
Licensure Intermediate care. *Beds* 40. *Certified* Medicaid.
Owner Proprietary Corp (Beverly Enterprises).
Admissions Requirements Medical examination; Physician's request.
Staff RNs 2 (ft); LPNs 1 (ft), 1 (pt); Nurses aides 8 (ft), 8 (pt); Activities coordinators 1 (pt); Dietitians 1 (pt).

St Elizabeth Healthcare Center
701 Armory Rd, Delphi, IN, 46923
(317) 564-6380
Admin Janet E LaPointe. *Medical Dir/Dir of Nursing* T Neal Petry MD, Eldon Baker MD, Brian Doggett MD; Peggy Bryant RN DON.
Licensure Skilled care; Intermediate care. *Beds* SNF 20; ICF 40. *Certified* Medicaid; Medicare.
Owner Nonprofit Corp.
Admissions Requirements Minimum age 18; Medical examination; Physician's request.
Staff RNs 3 (ft); LPNs 8 (ft); Nurses aides 20 (ft); Physical therapists 3 (pt); Recreational therapists 1 (pt); Occupational therapists 1 (pt); Activities coordinators 2 (ft).
Affiliation Roman Catholic
Facilities Dining room; Physical therapy room; Activities room; Chapel; Crafts room; Laundry room; Barber/Beauty shop; Large enclosed patio.
Activities Arts & crafts; Cards; Games; Reading groups; Prayer groups; Movies; Shopping trips; Social/Cultural gatherings; Pet therapy; Plant therapy.

DEMOTTE

Lake Holiday Manor Nursing Home
10325 County Line Rd, DeMotte, IN, 46310
(219) 345-5211
Admin Dorothy M Houston. *Medical Dir/Dir of Nursing* Roy Kingma MD; L Joy Sanders RN.
Licensure Intermediate care; Residential care. *Beds* ICF 95; Residential 16. *Certified* Medicaid.
Owner Privately owned.
Admissions Requirements Minimum age 18; Medical examination; Physician's request.
Staff RNs 1 (ft); LPNs 6 (ft); Orderlies 1 (ft); Nurses aides 30 (ft); Activities coordinators 1 (ft), 1 (pt); Dietitians 1 (pt).
Facilities Dining room; Activities room; Chapel; Crafts room; Laundry room; Barber/Beauty shop.
Activities Arts & crafts; Cards; Games; Reading groups; Prayer groups; Movies; Shopping trips; Social/Cultural gatherings.

DILLSBORO

Dillsboro Manor
Box 37 Lenover St, Dillsboro, IN, 47018
(812) 432-5226
Admin John Race. *Medical Dir/Dir of Nursing* Ivan T Lindgren; Judy Gatzke.
Licensure Intermediate care. *Beds* SNF 36; ICF 77. *Certified* Medicaid; Medicare.
Owner Proprietary Corp.
Admissions Requirements Minimum age 18; Medical examination; Physician's request.

Staff Physicians 1 (pt); RNs 4 (ft); LPNs 4 (ft); Nurses aides 60 (ft); Physical therapists 1 (pt); Activities coordinators 2 (ft); Dietitians 1 (pt); Ophthalmologists 1 (pt).
Facilities Dining room; Physical therapy room; Activities room; Chapel; Crafts room; Laundry room; Barber/Beauty shop; Library.
Activities Arts & crafts; Cards; Games; Reading groups; Prayer groups; Movies; Shopping trips; Social/Cultural gatherings.

DUNKIRK

Miller's Merry Manor Inc
Rt 2 PO Box 265, County Road 130, Dunkirk, IN, 47336
(317) 768-6917
Admin Laura T Mihankhah. *Medical Dir/Dir of Nursing* Dr Frank Bonser; Dr James C Hutchinson; Carol Suro RN DON.
Licensure Intermediate care. *Beds* ICF 62. *Certified* Medicaid.
Owner Proprietary Corp (Millers Merry Manor).
Admissions Requirements Minimum age 21; Medical examination; Physician's request.
Staff RNs 2 (ft), 1 (pt); LPNs 4 (ft), 3 (pt); Nurses aides 10 (ft), 9 (pt); Activities coordinators 1 (ft).
Facilities Dining room; Activities room; Crafts room; Laundry room; Barber/Beauty shop.
Activities Arts & crafts; Cards; Games; Reading groups; Prayer groups; Movies; Shopping trips; Social/Cultural gatherings.

DYER

Regency Place Health Care & Rehabilitation Center
2300 Great Lakes Dr, Dyer, IN, 46311
(219) 322-3555
Admin Jeffrey K Toutant. *Medical Dir/Dir of Nursing* Dr Melvin Hirsch; Katheleen Garton RN DON.
Licensure Skilled care; Intermediate care; Residential care. *Beds* SNF 52; ICF 92; Residential 6.
Owner Proprietary Corp.
Staff RNs; LPNs; Orderlies; Nurses aides.

EARL PARK

Earl Park Nursing Home*
402 Chestnut, Box 7, Earl Park, IN, 47942
(219) 474-6140
Admin Robert E McGinn.
Licensure Intermediate care. *Beds* 14. *Certified* Medicaid.
Staff RNs 1 (pt); LPNs 2 (pt); Orderlies 1 (pt); Nurses aides 4 (ft), 3 (pt); Activities coordinators 1 (ft); Dietitians 1 (pt).

EAST CHICAGO

Lake County Rehabilitation Center
5025 McCook Ave, East Chicago, IN, 46312
(219) 397-0380
Admin Estella Watkins. *Medical Dir/Dir of Nursing* Dr Napoleon Santos; Mary Gilbert.
Licensure Skilled care; Intermediate care. *Beds* 122. *Certified* Medicaid; Medicare.
Owner Publicly owned.
Admissions Requirements Minimum age 18; Medical examination; Physician's request.
Staff Physicians 3 (pt); RNs 2 (ft), 1 (pt); LPNs 11 (ft), 1 (pt); Orderlies 1 (ft); Nurses aides 25 (ft), 2 (pt); Activities coordinators 1 (ft); Dietitians 1 (pt); Ophthalmologists 1 (pt).
Languages Spanish
Facilities Dining room; Activities room; Crafts room; Laundry room; Barber/Beauty shop.

Activities Arts & crafts; Cards; Games; Reading groups; Prayer groups; Movies; Shopping trips; Social/Cultural gatherings; Fancy fingers.

EDINBURG

Faith Nursing Home
30 N Eisenhower Dr, Edinburg, IN, 46124
(812) 526-2626
Admin June Goodwin. *Medical Dir/Dir of Nursing* Dr Bill Province.
Licensure Intermediate care; Intermediate care for mentally retarded. *Beds* ICF 34. *Certified* Medicaid.
Owner Proprietary Corp.
Admissions Requirements Minimum age 80; Females only; Medical examination.
Staff Physicians; RNs; LPNs; Nurses aides; Activities coordinators; Dietitians.
Facilities Dining room; Activities room; Crafts room; Laundry room.
Activities Arts & crafts; Cards; Games; Reading groups; Prayer groups; Movies; Shopping trips; Social/Cultural gatherings.

ELKHART

Americana Healthcare Center—Elkhart*
343 S Nappanee St, Elkhart, IN, 46514
(219) 295-0096
Admin Jean Dovey.
Licensure Skilled care; Intermediate care. *Beds* SNF 46; ICF 53. *Certified* Medicaid; Medicare.
Owner Proprietary Corp (Manor Care).
Facilities Dining room; Physical therapy room; Activities room; Chapel; Crafts room; Laundry room; Barber/Beauty shop; Library.
Activities Arts & crafts; Cards; Games; Reading groups; Prayer groups; Movies; Shopping trips; Social/Cultural gatherings.

Elkhart Healthcare Center
PO Box 1107, 1400 W Franklin St, Elkhart, IN, 46516
(219) 293-0511
Admin Roger L Ringenberg. *Medical Dir/Dir of Nursing* Verlin Houck MD; Gertrude Cutchin RN.
Licensure Skilled care; Intermediate care. *Beds* SNF 34; ICF 131. *Certified* Medicaid.
Owner Proprietary Corp (ARA Living Centers).
Admissions Requirements Minimum age 19; Medical examination.
Staff RNs 2 (ft), 1 (pt); LPNs 5 (ft); Orderlies 1 (ft); Nurses aides 15 (ft), 10 (pt); Activities coordinators; Dietitians; QMRP 1 (ft).
Facilities Dining room; Physical therapy room; Activities room; Crafts room; Barber/Beauty shop; Library; Conference room.
Activities Arts & crafts; Cards; Games; Reading groups; Prayer groups; Movies; Shopping trips; Social/Cultural gatherings; Bowling trips; Field trips.

Fountainview Place
1001 W Hively Ave, Elkhart, IN, 46514
(219) 294-7641
Admin Carol V Simmons. *Medical Dir/Dir of Nursing* R G Harswell.
Licensure Skilled care; Intermediate care. *Beds* SNF 116; ICF 182. *Certified* Medicaid; Medicare.
Owner Proprietary Corp (Beverly Enterprises).
Admissions Requirements Medical examination; Physician's request.
Staff RNs 17 (ft), 8 (pt); LPNs 16 (ft), 10 (pt); Nurses aides 72 (ft), 11 (pt); Physical therapists 1 (ft), 1 (pt); Occupational therapists 1 (ft), 1 (pt); Speech therapists 1 (pt); Activities coordinators 2 (ft), 2 (pt); Dietitians 1 (pt); Dentist 1 (pt).
Facilities Dining room; Physical therapy room; Activities room; Chapel; Crafts room; Laundry room; Barber/Beauty shop; Library.

Activities Arts & crafts; Cards; Games; Reading groups; Prayer groups; Movies; Shopping trips; Social/Cultural gatherings.

Hubbard Hill Estates Inc*
28070 County Rd 24, Elkhart, IN, 46514
(219) 295-6260
Admin Floran Mast. *Medical Dir/Dir of Nursing* Charlene Haines RN.
Licensure Intermediate care. *Beds* 22.
Admissions Requirements Minimum age 62; Medical examination.
Staff RNs 1 (ft); LPNs 2 (ft), 1 (pt); Nurses aides 3 (ft), 6 (pt); Activities coordinators 1 (ft); Dietitians 1 (pt).
Affiliation Missionary Church
Facilities Dining room; Activities room; Chapel; Crafts room; Laundry room; Barber/Beauty shop; Library.
Activities Arts & crafts; Cards; Games; Prayer groups; Movies; Shopping trips; Social/Cultural gatherings.

Medco Center of Elkhart*
2600 Morehouse Ave, Elkhart, IN, 46514
(219) 295-8800
Admin Debra Powell. *Medical Dir/Dir of Nursing* Dr R G Horswell.
Licensure Intermediate care. *Beds* 74. *Certified* Medicaid.
Owner Proprietary Corp (Unicare).

Valley View Health Care Center
333 W Mishawaka Rd, Elkhart, IN, 46517
(219) 293-1550
Admin Eunice A Little. *Medical Dir/Dir of Nursing* T Davis MD; Betty Howard RN DON.
Licensure Intermediate care. *Beds* ICF 100. *Certified* Medicaid.
Owner Proprietary Corp.
Admissions Requirements Minimum age 65; Medical examination.
Staff RNs 3 (ft), 1 (pt); LPNs 7 (ft), 1 (pt); Orderlies 2 (ft); Nurses aides 30 (ft), 10 (pt); Activities coordinators 1 (ft), 1 (pt); Dietitians 1 (pt).
Facilities Dining room; Physical therapy room; Activities room; Crafts room; Laundry room; Barber/Beauty shop; Resident lounge.
Activities Arts & crafts; Cards; Games; Reading groups; Prayer groups; Movies; Shopping trips; Social/Cultural gatherings.

ELWOOD

Dickey Nursing Home Inc
PO Box 28, 1007 N 9th St, Elwood, IN, 46036
(317) 552-7308
Admin Dianne E Blackford. *Medical Dir/Dir of Nursing* Terrance Ihnat MD; Carolyn Cunningham RN DON.
Licensure Skilled care; Intermediate care. *Beds* SNF 30; ICF 70. *Certified* Medicaid; Medicare; VA.
Owner Proprietary Corp.
Admissions Requirements Minimum age 18; Medical examination; Physician's request.
Staff Physicians 2 (pt); RNs 3 (ft), 2 (pt); LPNs 1 (ft), 2 (pt); Orderlies 1 (ft); Nurses aides 33 (ft), 11 (pt); Physical therapists 1 (pt); Speech therapists 1 (pt); Activities coordinators 2 (ft); Dietitians 1 (pt); Dentists 1 (pt); Podiatrists 1 (pt); Audiologists 1 (pt); Optometrists 1 (pt).
Facilities Dining room; Physical therapy room; Activities room; Crafts room; Laundry room; Barber/Beauty shop; Library; Patios.
Activities Arts & crafts; Cards; Games; Reading groups; Prayer groups; Movies; Shopping trips; Social/Cultural gatherings; Exercise class; Inhouse shopping.

Parkview Convalescent Centre*
N 19th St, Elwood, IN, 46036
(317) 552-9884
Admin Rev Max Bingham.

Licensure Intermediate care. *Beds* 92. *Certified* Medicaid.

EVANSVILLE

Bethel Sanitarium Inc*
6015 Kratzville Rd, Evansville, IN, 47710
(812) 425-8182
Admin David R Kast.
Licensure Intermediate care. *Beds* 66. *Certified* Medicaid.
Admissions Requirements Medical examination.
Staff RNs 5 (ft); LPNs 4 (ft); Orderlies 1 (ft), 1 (pt); Nurses aides 21 (ft); Physical therapists 1 (pt); Reality therapists 1 (pt); Recreational therapists 1 (ft); Occupational therapists 1 (pt); Speech therapists 1 (pt); Activities coordinators 1 (ft); Dietitians 1 (ft), 1 (pt).
Affiliation Seventh-Day Adventist
Facilities Dining room; Physical therapy room; Activities room; Chapel; Laundry room; Barber/Beauty shop.
Activities Arts & crafts; Games; Reading groups; Prayer groups; Movies; Shopping trips; Social/Cultural gatherings.

Braun's Nursing Home Inc*
909 1st Ave, Evansville, IN, 47710
(812) 423-6214
Admin Ruth H Braun LPN.
Licensure Intermediate care. *Beds* 54. *Certified* Medicaid.

Christopher East Living Center*
4301 Washington Ave, Evansville, IN, 47715
(812) 477-8971
Admin Dorothy Wolf.
Licensure Skilled care; Intermediate care. *Beds* 199. *Certified* Medicaid; Medicare.

Columbia Health Care Facility*
1100 N Read St, Evansville, IN, 47710
(812) 424-8295
Admin Suzann K Campbell.
Licensure Intermediate care. *Beds* 34. *Certified* Medicaid.

Evansville Protestant Home Inc
3701 Washington Ave, Evansville, IN, 47715
(812) 476-3360
Admin Dorothy L Zehner. *Medical Dir/Dir of Nursing* Randall Stoltz MD; Donna Evans RN DON.
Licensure Intermediate care; Residential care. *Beds* ICF 102; Residential 144.
Owner Nonprofit Corp.
Admissions Requirements Minimum age 65; Medical examination.
Staff RNs 8 (ft), 2 (pt); LPNs 8 (ft), 4 (pt); Nurses aides 30 (ft), 4 (pt); Physical therapists 1 (pt); Activities coordinators 2 (ft), 1 (pt); Dietitians 1 (pt).
Affiliation Church of Christ
Facilities Dining room; Physical therapy room; Activities room; Laundry room; Barber/Beauty shop; Library.
Activities Arts & crafts; Cards; Games; Reading groups; Prayer groups; Movies; Shopping trips; Social/Cultural gatherings.

Gertha's Nursing Center Inc
617 Oakley St, Evansville, IN, 47710
(812) 423-4491
Admin Steve T Gossman. *Medical Dir/Dir of Nursing* Dr Richard Wagner; Julie Schrieber DON.
Licensure Skilled care; Intermediate care. *Beds* SNF 45; ICF 110. *Certified* Medicaid; Medicare.
Owner Proprietary Corp (Hillhaven Corp).
Admissions Requirements Minimum age 16; Medical examination; Physician's request.
Staff RNs 3 (ft), 1 (pt); LPNs 10 (ft), 4 (pt); Nurses aides 54 (ft), 8 (pt); Recreational therapists 3 (ft); Activities coordinators 1 (ft); Dietitians 1 (ft).

Facilities Dining room; Physical therapy room; Activities room; Crafts room; Laundry room; Barber/Beauty shop; Library.
Activities Arts & crafts; Cards; Games; Reading groups; Prayer groups; Movies; Social/Cultural gatherings.

The Good Samaritan Home Inc
PO Box 2788, 601 N Boeke, Evansville, IN, 47715
(812) 476-4912
Admin David H Roberts III. *Medical Dir/Dir of Nursing* Charlotte Weigman DON.
Licensure Intermediate care. *Beds* ICF 138. *Certified* Medicaid.
Owner Nonprofit Corp.
Admissions Requirements Medical examination.
Affiliation Church of Christ
Facilities Dining room; Physical therapy room; Activities room; Crafts room; Laundry room; Barber/Beauty shop.
Activities Arts & crafts; Cards; Games; Reading groups; Prayer groups; Movies; Shopping trips; Social/Cultural gatherings.

Holiday Home of Evansville*
1201 W Buena Vista Rd, Evansville, IN, 47710
(812) 426-2221
Admin Donnie L Hester. *Medical Dir/Dir of Nursing* Dr William Gentry.
Licensure Skilled care; Intermediate care; Residential care. *Beds* SNF 31; ICF 141; Residential 36. *Certified* Medicaid; Medicare.
Admissions Requirements Minimum age 65; Medical examination; Physician's request.
Staff RNs 10 (ft); LPNs 18 (ft); Nurses aides 60 (ft); Physical therapists 4 (ft); Activities coordinators 1 (ft), 1 (pt); Dietitians 1 (ft); Audiologists 1 (pt); Speech pathologists 1 (ft).
Facilities Dining room; Physical therapy room; Activities room; Chapel; Crafts room; Laundry room; Barber/Beauty shop; Library.
Activities Arts & crafts; Cards; Games; Reading groups; Prayer groups; Movies; Shopping trips; Social/Cultural gatherings.

Little Sisters of the Poor
1236 Lincoln Ave, Evansville, IN, 47714-1089
(812) 464-3607
Admin Sr Amedee Maxwell. *Medical Dir/Dir of Nursing* Sr Julie.
Licensure Intermediate care; Independent apartments. *Beds* ICF 90; Independent apts 22. *Certified* Medicaid.
Owner Nonprofit Corp.
Admissions Requirements Minimum age 60; Medical examination; Physician's request.
Staff RNs 2 (ft), 2 (pt); LPNs 6 (ft), 7 (pt); Nurses aides 25 (ft), 17 (pt); Physical therapists 1 (pt); Occupational therapists 1 (pt); Speech therapists 1 (pt); Activities coordinators 1 (ft); Dietitians 1 (pt).
Languages Spanish, French
Affiliation Roman Catholic
Facilities Dining room; Physical therapy room; Activities room; Chapel; Crafts room; Laundry room; Barber/Beauty shop; Library.
Activities Arts & crafts; Cards; Games; Reading groups; Prayer groups; Movies; Shopping trips; Social/Cultural gatherings; Exercise; Music therapy.

McCurdy Residential Center
101 SE 1st St, Evansville, IN, 47708
(812) 425-1041
Admin Dorothy L Zehner. *Medical Dir/Dir of Nursing* Lawrene Judy MD.
Licensure Intermediate care; Residential care. *Beds* 475. *Certified* Medicaid.
Owner Proprietary Corp (Unicare).
Admissions Requirements Minimum age 18; Medical examination.

Staff Physicians 1 (pt); RNs 6 (ft), 1 (pt); LPNs 26 (ft), 10 (pt); Orderlies 3 (ft); Nurses aides 24 (ft), 12 (pt); Activities coordinators 1 (ft); Dietitians 1 (ft); Dentists 1 (pt); Ophthalmologists 1 (pt); Podiatrists 1 (pt).
Facilities Dining room; Activities room; Chapel; Crafts room; Laundry room; Barber/Beauty shop; Library; Men's lounge; Theatre.
Activities Arts & crafts; Cards; Games; Reading groups; Prayer groups; Movies; Shopping trips; Social/Cultural gatherings; Ceramics; Chapel services; Current events.

Medco Center of Evansville—North
650 Fairway Dr, Evansville, IN, 47710
(812) 425-5243
Admin James Allan Scheller. *Medical Dir/Dir of Nursing* Dr Robert Davidson.
Licensure Skilled care; Intermediate care. *Beds* SNF 35; ICF 116. *Certified* Medicaid; Medicare; VA.
Owner Proprietary Corp (Unicare).
Admissions Requirements Medical examination.
Staff Physicians; RNs; LPNs; Orderlies; Nurses aides; Physical therapists; Reality therapists; Recreational therapists; Occupational therapists; Speech therapists; Activities coordinators; Dietitians; Dentists; Ophthalmologists; Podiatrists.
Facilities Dining room; Physical therapy room; Activities room; Crafts room; Laundry room; Barber/Beauty shop; Library; Living room; Quiet rooms.
Activities Arts & crafts; Cards; Games; Reading groups; Prayer groups; Movies; Shopping trips; Social/Cultural gatherings; Baseball; Basketball; Philharmonic tickets.

Parkview Convalescent Center Inc
2819 N Saint Joseph Ave, Evansville, IN, 47712
(812) 424-2941
Admin Linda Dickenson. *Medical Dir/Dir of Nursing* W Ayde; K Schmitt DON.
Licensure Skilled care; Intermediate care. *Beds* SNF 31; ICF 77. *Certified* Medicaid; Medicare.
Owner Proprietary Corp (Life Care Centers of America).
Admissions Requirements Medical examination; Physician's request.
Staff Physicians 1 (ft); RNs 4 (ft), 2 (pt); LPNs 9 (ft), 2 (pt); Nurses aides 27 (ft), 4 (pt); Activities coordinators 1 (ft); Dietitians 1 (pt).
Facilities Dining room; Physical therapy room; Activities room; Crafts room; Laundry room; Barber/Beauty shop; Library.
Activities Arts & crafts; Cards; Games; Reading groups; Prayer groups; Movies; Shopping trips; Social/Cultural gatherings.

Pine Haven Nursing Home
Box 6505, 3400 Stocker Dr, Evansville, IN, 47712
(812) 424-8100
Admin Ruth C Smith RN. *Medical Dir/Dir of Nursing* William Sutton MD; Judy Carr LPN DON.
Licensure Intermediate care. *Beds* ICF 96. *Certified* Medicaid.
Owner Proprietary Corp.
Admissions Requirements Minimum age 50; Medical examination; Physician's request.
Staff RNs; LPNs; Nurses aides; Activities coordinators; Dietitians; Ophthalmologists.
Facilities Dining room; Activities room; Chapel; Crafts room; Laundry room; Barber/Beauty shop.
Activities Arts & crafts; Cards; Games; Reading groups; Prayer groups; Movies; Shopping trips; Social/Cultural gatherings.

The Regina Continuing Care Center*
3900 Washington Ave, Evansville, IN, 47715
(812) 479-4226
Admin Ann M Morrow. *Medical Dir/Dir of Nursing* Julian D Present MD.
Licensure Skilled care; Intermediate care. *Beds* SNF 86; ICF 50. *Certified* Medicaid; Medicare.
Admissions Requirements Minimum age 18; Medical examination.
Staff Physicians 1 (pt); RNs 4 (ft), 5 (pt); LPNs 8 (ft), 5 (pt); Nurses aides 37 (ft), 13 (pt); Physical therapists 1 (pt); Occupational therapists 1 (pt); Speech therapists 1 (pt); Activities coordinators 1 (pt); Dietitians 1 (pt); Dentists 1 (pt); Podiatrists 1 (pt).
Affiliation Roman Catholic
Facilities Dining room; Physical therapy room; Activities room; Chapel; Crafts room; Laundry room; Barber/Beauty shop; Library.
Activities Arts & crafts; Cards; Games; Reading groups; Prayer groups; Movies; Social/Cultural gatherings.

Woodbridge Health Care
816 N 1st Ave, Evansville, IN, 47710
(812) 426-2841
Admin Donald Simmons. *Medical Dir/Dir of Nursing* Randall Oliver MD; Alta Lindall DON.
Licensure Intermediate care. *Beds* ICF 92. *Certified* Medicaid.
Owner Proprietary Corp (Beverly Enterprises).
Admissions Requirements Minimum age 19; Medical examination; Physician's request.
Staff Physicians; RNs 1 (ft); LPNs 4 (ft), 1 (pt); Nurses aides 16 (ft), 2 (pt); Activities coordinators 1 (ft).
Facilities Dining room; Activities room; Laundry room; Barber/Beauty shop; Library.
Activities Arts & crafts; Cards; Games; Reading groups; Prayer groups; Movies; Shopping trips; Fall festival shrine temple; Field trip.

FLORA

Brethren's Home of Indiana Inc
Rte 2, Box 97, Flora, IN, 46929-9745
(219) 967-4571
Admin Gene Geaslen. *Medical Dir/Dir of Nursing* Flora Family MD; Nancy Doud RN.
Licensure Intermediate care; Retirement apts. *Beds* ICF 86; Retirement apts 25. *Certified* Medicaid.
Owner Nonprofit Corp.
Admissions Requirements Minimum age 65; Medical examination; Physician's request.
Staff RNs 3 (ft), 2 (pt); LPNs 3 (ft), 5 (pt); Nurses aides 30 (ft), 10 (pt); Activities coordinators 2 (ft), 1 (pt); Dietitians 1 (pt).
Affiliation Church of the Brethren
Facilities Dining room; Activities room; Chapel; Laundry room; Barber/Beauty shop.
Activities Arts & crafts; Cards; Games; Reading groups; Prayer groups; Movies; Shopping trips; Social/Cultural gatherings.

FORT WAYNE

Byron Health Center
RR 13, 12101 Lima Rd, Fort Wayne, IN, 46818
(219) 637-3166
Admin Thomas Katsanis.
Licensure Intermediate care; Residential care. *Beds* ICF 465; Residential 55. *Certified* Medicaid.
Owner Publicly owned.
Admissions Requirements Minimum age 18; Medical examination; Physician's request.
Staff Physicians 1 (ft), 2 (pt); RNs 10 (ft), 1 (pt); LPNs 40 (ft); Nurses aides 153 (ft), 12 (pt); Physical therapists 1 (ft); Recreational therapists 6 (ft); Occupational therapists 1 (ft); Speech therapists 1 (ft); Activities coordinators 1 (pt); Dietitians 1 (ft), 1 (pt); Ophthalmologists 1 (pt); Podiatrists 2 (pt); Optometrist 1 (pt).

Facilities Dining room; Physical therapy room; Activities room; Chapel; Crafts room; Laundry room; Barber/Beauty shop; Library.
Activities Arts & crafts; Cards; Games; Reading groups; Prayer groups; Movies; Shopping trips; Social/Cultural gatherings.

Covington Manor Nursing Center*
5700 Wilkie Dr, Fort Wayne, IN, 46804
(219) 432-7556
Admin Susan Junk. *Medical Dir/Dir of Nursing* Bruce Hoppen MD.
Licensure Intermediate care. *Beds* 115. *Certified* Medicaid.
Owner Proprietary Corp (Shive Nursing Centers).
Admissions Requirements Physician's request.
Staff Physicians 1 (pt); RNs 14 (ft); LPNs 3 (ft); Orderlies 5 (ft); Nurses aides 60 (ft), 11 (pt); Physical therapists 1 (pt); Reality therapists 1 (ft); Recreational therapists 1 (ft); Occupational therapists 1 (pt); Speech therapists 1 (pt); Activities coordinators 1 (ft); Dietitians 1 (pt); Dentists 1 (pt); Ophthalmologists 1 (pt); Podiatrists 1 (pt); Audiologists 1 (pt).
Facilities Dining room; Physical therapy room; Activities room; Chapel; Crafts room; Laundry room; Barber/Beauty shop; Library; Living rooms.
Activities Arts & crafts; Cards; Games; Reading groups; Prayer groups; Movies; Shopping trips; Social/Cultural gatherings.

The Dove Tree
4430 Elsdale Dr, Fort Wayne, IN, 46815
(219) 485-8157
Admin Keith N Ambrose. *Medical Dir/Dir of Nursing* Pauline Forte RN DON.
Licensure Intermediate care. *Beds* ICF 100. *Certified* Medicaid.
Admissions Requirements Medical examination; Physician's request.
Staff Physicians; RNs; LPNs; Orderlies; Nurses aides; Activities coordinators; Dietitians; Ophthalmologists 1 (pt).
Facilities Dining room; Activities room; Chapel; Crafts room; Laundry room; Barber/Beauty shop; Privacy room for families.
Activities Arts & crafts; Cards; Games; Reading groups; Prayer groups; Movies; Shopping trips; Social/Cultural gatherings; Ceramic classes.

Fort Wayne Nursing Home
2402 N Beacon St, Fort Wayne, IN, 46805
(219) 484-3415
Admin Patricia Shea. *Medical Dir/Dir of Nursing* Robert Lohman MD; Marvin Hormann DON.
Licensure Intermediate care. *Beds* ICF 40. *Certified* Medicaid.
Owner Proprietary Corp (Beverly Enterprises).
Admissions Requirements Minimum age 19; Medical examination; Physician's request.
Staff Physicians; RNs; LPNs; Orderlies; Nurses aides; Activities coordinators; Dietitians.
Facilities Dining room; Activities room; Laundry room; Living room; Therapy room; Fenced-in yard.
Activities Arts & crafts; Cards; Games; Reading groups; Prayer groups; Movies; Shopping trips; Social/Cultural gatherings; Luncheons; Special event programs; Bingo.

Golden Years Homestead Inc
8300 Maysville Rd, Fort Wayne, IN, 46815
(219) 749-9655
Admin Thomas G Garman. *Medical Dir/Dir of Nursing* Dr Philip Schubert; Ginny Turner RN DON.
Licensure Intermediate care. *Beds* ICF 69. *Certified* Medicaid.
Owner Nonprofit Corp.
Admissions Requirements Minimum age 62; Medical examination.

Staff RNs 3 (ft), 5 (pt); LPNs 2 (pt); Nurses aides 12 (ft), 18 (pt); Dietitians 1 (pt).
Affiliation Church of Christ
Facilities Dining room; Physical therapy room; Activities room; Chapel; Crafts room; Laundry room; Barber/Beauty shop; Library.
Activities Arts & crafts; Cards; Games; Reading groups; Prayer groups; Movies; Shopping trips; Social/Cultural gatherings.

Heritage Manor Estates
7515 Winchester Rd, Fort Wayne, IN, 46819
(219) 747-1523
Admin Norman L Savage. *Medical Dir/Dir of Nursing* Katie Ansos DON.
Licensure Licensed retirement center. *Beds* Apts 68. *Certified* Medicaid.
Owner Privately owned.
Admissions Requirements Medical examination.
Staff LPNs 1 (ft); Nurses aides 4 (pt); Dietitians 1 (pt).
Facilities Dining room; Activities room; Chapel; Laundry room; Barber/Beauty shop; Library.
Activities Arts & crafts; Cards; Games; Reading groups; Prayer groups; Movies; Shopping trips; Social/Cultural gatherings.

Heritage Manor Health Care Center
7519 Winchester Rd, Fort Wayne, IN, 46819
(219) 747-7435
Admin Kim Hughes. *Medical Dir/Dir of Nursing* William Aeschlimen MD.
Licensure Intermediate care. *Beds* 80. *Certified* Medicaid.
Owner Proprietary Corp.
Admissions Requirements Minimum age 18; Medical examination; Physician's request.
Staff Physicians 1 (pt); RNs 2 (ft), 1 (pt); LPNs 3 (ft), 3 (pt); Orderlies 3 (ft), 2 (pt); Nurses aides 8 (ft), 14 (pt); Activities coordinators 1 (ft); Dietitians 1 (pt); Dentists 1 (pt); Podiatrists 1 (pt).
Facilities Dining room; Activities room; Laundry room; Barber/Beauty shop.
Activities Arts & crafts; Cards; Games; Reading groups; Movies; Shopping trips.

Heritage Manor-North
1010 W Washington Center Rd, Fort Wayne, IN, 46825
(219) 489-2552
Admin Michael Ianucilli. *Medical Dir/Dir of Nursing* Georgia Toedt RN DON.
Licensure Skilled care; Intermediate care. *Beds* SNF 21; ICF 60. *Certified* Medicaid.
Owner Privately owned.
Admissions Requirements Minimum age 18; Medical examination.
Staff RNs 4 (ft), 4 (pt); LPNs 6 (ft), 6 (pt); Orderlies 2 (ft), 2 (pt); Nurses aides 14 (ft), 16 (pt); Activities coordinators 1 (ft); Dietitians 1 (pt).
Facilities Dining room; Physical therapy room; Activities room; Crafts room; Laundry room; Barber/Beauty shop; Private quiet lounge.
Activities Arts & crafts; Cards; Games; Reading groups; Prayer groups; Movies; Social/Cultural gatherings.

Indian Village Health Center Inc
2237 Engle Rd, Fort Wayne, IN, 46809
(219) 747-2353
Admin Ronda K Rennalls. *Medical Dir/Dir of Nursing* Dr Robert Voorhees; Janice Ridings LPN.
Licensure Intermediate care. *Beds* ICF 37. *Certified* Medicaid.
Owner Proprietary Corp.
Admissions Requirements Medical examination; Physician's request.
Staff Physicians 1 (ft); LPNs 4 (ft), 5 (pt); Nurses aides 12 (ft); Recreational therapists 1 (pt); Activities coordinators 1 (pt).

Facilities Dining room; Activities room; Laundry room; Barber/Beauty shop.
Activities Games; Reading groups; Prayer groups; Movies; Shopping trips; Bowling.

Lawton Nursing Home*
1649 Spy Run Ave, Fort Wayne, IN, 46805
(219) 422-8520
Admin Brad Webber. *Medical Dir/Dir of Nursing* L Bayazit MD.
Licensure Intermediate care. *Beds* 100. *Certified* Medicaid.
Owner Proprietary Corp (Life Care Centers of America).
Admissions Requirements Medical examination; Physician's request.
Staff RNs 5 (ft); LPNs 3 (ft), 3 (pt); Nurses aides 26 (ft), 3 (pt); Activities coordinators 1 (ft), 2 (pt); Dietitians 1 (pt); Dentists 1 (pt); Podiatrists 1 (pt).
Facilities Dining room; Activities room; Laundry room; Barber/Beauty shop.
Activities Arts & crafts; Cards; Games; Reading groups; Prayer groups; Movies; Shopping trips; Social/Cultural gatherings.

Lutheran Homes Inc*
6701 S Anthony Blvd, Fort Wayne, IN, 46806
(219) 447-1591
Admin Robert Scheimann.
Licensure Intermediate care; Residential care. *Beds* ICF 276; Residential 120. *Certified* Medicaid.
Owner Nonprofit Corp (Luth Hosp & Homes Socty).
Admissions Requirements Minimum age 62; Medical examination.
Affiliation Lutheran
Facilities Dining room; Physical therapy room; Activities room; Chapel; Crafts room; Laundry room; Barber/Beauty shop; Library.
Activities Arts & crafts; Cards; Games; Reading groups; Prayer groups; Movies; Shopping trips; Social/Cultural gatherings.

Medco Center of Fort Wayne*
3811 Parnell Ave, Fort Wayne, IN, 46805
(219) 482-4651
Admin Steve Reed.
Licensure Skilled care; Intermediate care. *Beds* SNF 47; ICF 157. *Certified* Medicaid; Medicare.
Owner Proprietary Corp (Unicare).

Riverview Care Center Residential
2827 Northgate Blvd, Fort Wayne, IN, 46835
(219) 485-9691
Admin Joseph E Weingartner. *Medical Dir/Dir of Nursing* Kann Physicians MD; Sheila Benner DON.
Licensure Skilled care; Intermediate care; Residential; Independent living units. *Beds* SNF 30; ICF 27; ICF/MR 3; Comprehensive Non-Certified 60; Residential & Independent 93. *Certified* Medicaid.
Owner Proprietary Corp.
Admissions Requirements Minimum age 18; Medical examination.
Staff Physicians 4 (pt); RNs 3 (ft), 2 (pt); LPNs 12 (ft), 8 (pt); Orderlies 6 (ft), 2 (pt); Nurses aides 35 (ft), 15 (pt); Physical therapists 1 (pt); Recreational therapists 1 (pt); Occupational therapists 1 (pt); Speech therapists 1 (pt); Activities coordinators 1 (ft), 1 (pt); Dietitians 1 (ft); Dentists 1 (pt); Ophthalmologists 1 (pt); Podiatrists 1 (pt); QMRA 1 (pt).
Facilities Dining room; Physical therapy room; Activities room; Chapel; Crafts room; Laundry room; Barber/Beauty shop; Rathskeller.
Activities Arts & crafts; Cards; Games; Reading groups; Prayer groups; Movies; Shopping trips; Social/Cultural gatherings; Outings to plays; Bus trips; Happy hour.

St Anne Home
1900 Randallia Dr, Fort Wayne, IN, 46805
(219) 484-5555
Admin Mary E Haverstick. *Medical Dir/Dir of Nursing* Gerald R Nolan MD; Dolores Helmsing RN.
Licensure Skilled care; Intermediate care. *Beds* SNF 53; ICF 101. *Certified* Medicaid.
Owner Nonprofit organization/foundation.
Admissions Requirements Medical examination.
Staff RNs 6 (ft), 2 (pt); LPNs 11 (ft), 4 (pt); Orderlies 4 (ft); Nurses aides 52 (ft), 5 (pt); Physical therapists 1 (pt); Activities coordinators 1 (ft); Dietitians 1 (pt); Ophthalmologists 1 (pt).
Affiliation Roman Catholic
Facilities Dining room; Physical therapy room; Activities room; Chapel; Crafts room; Laundry room; Barber/Beauty shop; Library.
Activities Arts & crafts; Cards; Games; Reading groups; Prayer groups; Movies; Shopping trips; Social/Cultural gatherings.

The Summit House
2440 Bowser Ave, Fort Wayne, IN, 46803
(219) 745-4508
Admin Mark A Peterson. *Medical Dir/Dir of Nursing* Dr Lohman; Beth Kennedy.
Licensure Intermediate care; Residential. *Beds* ICF 58; Residential 24. *Certified* Medicaid.
Owner Proprietary Corp.
Admissions Requirements Minimum age 18; Medical examination.
Staff RNs 1 (ft); LPNs 3 (ft), 3 (pt); Nurses aides 10 (ft), 5 (pt); Activities coordinators 1 (ft).
Facilities Dining room; Physical therapy room; Activities room; Chapel; Crafts room; Barber/Beauty shop; Library.
Activities Arts & crafts; Cards; Games; Reading groups; Prayer groups; Movies; Shopping trips; Social/Cultural gatherings.

Three Rivers Convalescent Center*
2940 N Clinton St, Fort Wayne, IN, 46805
(219) 484-0602
Admin Lora Thomas. *Medical Dir/Dir of Nursing* Dr Robert Vorhees.
Licensure Skilled care; Intermediate care. *Beds* SNF 77; ICF 67. *Certified* Medicaid; Medicare.
Owner Proprietary Corp (Beverly Enterprises).
Admissions Requirements Medical examination; Physician's request.
Staff Physicians 1 (ft); Physical therapists 1 (ft); Reality therapists 1 (ft); Recreational therapists 1 (ft); Occupational therapists 1 (ft); Speech therapists 1 (ft); Activities coordinators 1 (ft); Dietitians 1 (ft); Dentists 1 (ft); Podiatrists 1 (ft).
Facilities Dining room; Physical therapy room; Activities room; Crafts room; Laundry room; Barber/Beauty shop; Occupational therapy room.
Activities Arts & crafts; Cards; Games; Reading groups; Prayer groups; Movies; Shopping trips; Social/Cultural gatherings.

Towne House Health Center
2209 Saint Joe Center Rd, Fort Wayne, IN, 46825
(219) 483-3116
Admin B Daniel Carr.
Licensure Intermediate care; Residential care. *Beds* ICF 77; Residential 210.

University Park Nursing Center*
1400 Medical Park Dr, Fort Wayne, IN, 46825
(219) 484-1558
Admin Barbara Harrison. *Medical Dir/Dir of Nursing* Dr Jerry Dearth.
Licensure Intermediate care. *Beds* 100.
Owner Proprietary Corp (Shive Nursing Centers).
Admissions Requirements Minimum age 21; Medical examination.

Staff Physicians 1 (pt); RNs 2 (ft), 2 (pt);
LPNs 3 (ft), 3 (pt); Orderlies 1 (ft); Nurses
aides 40 (ft); Physical therapists 1 (pt);
Occupational therapists 1 (pt); Activities
coordinators 1 (ft); Dietitians 1 (pt); Dentists
1 (pt); Ophthalmologists 1 (pt); Podiatrists 1
(pt); Audiologists 1 (pt).
Facilities Dining room; Physical therapy
room; Activities room; Chapel; Crafts room;
Laundry room; Barber/Beauty shop.
Activities Arts & crafts; Cards; Games;
Reading groups; Prayer groups; Movies;
Shopping trips; Social/Cultural gatherings.

Villa of the Woods
5610 Noll Ave, Fort Wayne, IN, 46806
(219) 745-7039
Admin John Martin.
Licensure Residential. *Beds* 27.
Owner Nonprofit organization/foundation.
Admissions Requirements Medical
examination.
Staff Dietitians 1 (pt).
Facilities Dining room; Chapel; Laundry
room.
Activities Arts & crafts.

Anthony Wayne Living Center
2626 Fairfield Ave, Fort Wayne, IN, 46807
(219) 744-4211
Admin Dee Anna Smallman. *Medical Dir/Dir
of Nursing* John Nill; Vary Fischer RN
DON.
Licensure Skilled care; Intermediate care. *Beds*
SNF 63; ICF 63. *Certified* Medicaid;
Medicare.
Owner Proprietary Corp (ARA Living
Centers).
Admissions Requirements Minimum age 19;
Medical examination; Physician's request.
Staff RNs 4 (ft); LPNs 8 (ft), 2 (pt); Nurses
aides 10 (ft), 3 (pt); Physical therapists 1 (ft);
Occupational therapists 1 (ft); Speech
therapists 1 (ft); Activities coordinators 1
(ft); Dietitians 1 (pt); Podiatrists 1 (pt);
Social service 1 (pt).
Facilities Dining room; Physical therapy
room; Activities room; Crafts room; Laundry
room; Barber/Beauty shop.
Activities Arts & crafts; Cards; Games;
Reading groups; Prayer groups; Movies;
Social/Cultural gatherings.

Willow Ridge Living Center*
2001 Hobson Rd, Fort Wayne, IN, 46805
(219) 484-9557
Admin Craig S Schuler. *Medical Dir/Dir of
Nursing* Dr E Bolander.
Licensure Skilled care; Intermediate care. *Beds*
SNF 89; ICF 90. *Certified* Medicaid;
Medicare.
Owner Proprietary Corp (ARA Living
Centers).
Admissions Requirements Minimum age 18;
Medical examination.
Staff Physicians 4 (pt); RNs 8 (ft), 2 (pt);
LPNs 10 (ft), 3 (pt); Nurses aides 34 (ft), 9
(pt); Physical therapists 1 (ft), 1 (pt);
Recreational therapists 1 (ft); Occupational
therapists 1 (pt); Speech therapists 1 (pt);
Activities coordinators 1 (ft); Dietitians 1
(ft); Dentists 1 (pt); Ophthalmologists 1 (pt);
Podiatrists 1 (pt); Audiologists 1 (pt).
Facilities Dining room; Physical therapy
room; Activities room; Chapel; Crafts room;
Laundry room; Barber/Beauty shop; Library.
Activities Arts & crafts; Cards; Games;
Reading groups; Prayer groups; Movies;
Shopping trips; Social/Cultural gatherings.

Woodview Healthcare Inc
3420 E State St, Fort Wayne, IN, 46805
(219) 484-3120
Admin John August.
Licensure Skilled care; Intermediate care. *Beds*
104. *Certified* Medicaid; Medicare.

Facilities Dining room; Physical therapy
room; Activities room; Crafts room; Laundry
room; Barber/Beauty shop.
Activities Arts & crafts; Cards; Games;
Reading groups; Movies; Shopping trips;
Social/Cultural gatherings.

FOWLER

Green-Hill Manor Inc*
501 N Lincoln Ave, Fowler, IN, 47944
(317) 884-1470
Admin Edith Dexter & Connie Brouillette.
Licensure Intermediate care. *Beds* 23.
Certified Medicaid.

FRANCESVILLE

Parkview Haven Retirement Home
PO Box 797, Ada at Brooks St, Francesville,
IN, 47946
(219) 567-9149
Admin Benjamin L Metz. *Medical Dir/Dir of
Nursing* Charles Heinsen; Laurel Widmer.
Licensure Intermediate care; Residential care.
Beds ICF 39; Residential 4. *Certified*
Medicaid.
Owner Nonprofit organization/foundation.
Admissions Requirements Minimum age 65;
Medical examination.
Staff RNs 1 (ft), 3 (pt); LPNs 1 (ft), 2 (pt);
Nurses aides 3 (ft), 14 (pt); Activities
coordinators 1 (pt); Dietitians 1 (pt); Social
service 1 (pt).
Affiliation Apostolic Christian
Facilities Dining room; Physical therapy
room; Activities room; Chapel; Crafts room;
Laundry room; Barber/Beauty shop; Library.
Activities Arts & crafts; Games; Reading
groups; Prayer groups; Movies; Shopping
trips.

FRANKFORT

Clinton House Inc*
809 W Freeman St, Frankfort, IN, 46041
(317) 654-8783
Admin Laura L Peterson.
Licensure Intermediate care. *Beds* 121.
Certified Medicaid.

Frankfort Nursing Home
1234 Rossville Ave, Frankfort, IN, 46041
(317) 654-8118
Admin Evelyn Tidler. *Medical Dir/Dir of
Nursing* Dr Arthur Dannin; Cheryl Moore
RN DON.
Licensure Intermediate care. *Beds* ICF 40.
Certified Medicaid.
Owner Proprietary Corp (Beverly Enterprises).
Admissions Requirements Minimum age 18;
Medical examination; Physician's request.
Staff Physicians 1 (pt); RNs 2 (ft), 1 (pt);
LPNs 3 (ft), 2 (pt); Orderlies 1 (ft); Nurses
aides 6 (ft), 8 (pt); Activities coordinators 1
(ft); Dietitians 1 (ft); Dentists 1 (pt);
Ophthalmologists 1 (pt).
Facilities Dining room; Activities room;
Crafts room; Laundry room.
Activities Arts & crafts; Cards; Games;
Reading groups; Prayer groups; Movies;
Social/Cultural gatherings; Monthly theme
parties; Church services.

Parkview Home*
RR 2, Frankfort, IN, 46041
(317) 659-3803
Admin Dorothy Schriefer, LPN.
Licensure Residential care. *Beds* 40.
Admissions Requirements Medical
examination; Physician's request.
Staff LPNs 1 (ft); Activities coordinators 1
(pt); Dietitians 1 (pt).
Facilities Dining room; Activities room;
Chapel; Laundry room; Barber/Beauty shop;
Library.

Activities Games; Reading groups; Prayer
groups; Movies; Shopping trips.

Wesley Manor Inc
1555 N Main, Frankfort, IN, 46041
(317) 659-1811
Admin Bette J Wommack. *Medical Dir/Dir of
Nursing* Debbie Lineback DON.
Licensure Continuing care retirement. *Beds*
ICF 128.
Owner Nonprofit Corp.
Admissions Requirements Minimum age 60.
Staff Physicians 1 (pt); RNs 4 (ft), 1 (pt);
LPNs 9 (ft), 1 (pt); Orderlies; Nurses aides
13 (ft), 23 (pt); Physical therapists 1 (pt);
Activities coordinators 4 (ft), 1 (pt);
Dietitians 1 (pt); Staff 120 (ft).
Affiliation Methodist
Facilities Dining room; Physical therapy
room; Activities room; Chapel; Crafts room;
Laundry room; Barber/Beauty shop; Library;
Woodshop; Ceramics; Gift shop; Art studio;
Photo studio.
Activities Arts & crafts; Cards; Games;
Reading groups; Prayer groups; Movies;
Shopping trips; Social/Cultural gatherings;
Swimming pool; Bowling alley; Free 18 hole
golf.

FRANKLIN

Franklin Healthcare Center
Rte 1, 1285 W Jefferson St, Franklin, IN,
46131
(317) 736-9113
Admin Ginny Roberts. *Medical Dir/Dir of
Nursing* Dr Wm Province; Vicki Northcot.
Licensure Skilled care; Intermediate care. *Beds*
SNF 63; ICF 60. *Certified* Medicaid;
Medicare.
Staff RNs 4 (ft), 1 (pt); LPNs 10 (ft), 2 (pt);
Nurses aides 26 (ft), 12 (pt); Physical
therapists 1 (pt); Recreational therapists 1
(ft); Occupational therapists 1 (pt); Speech
therapists 1 (pt); Activities coordinators 1
(ft); Dietitians 1 (pt).

Franklin Nursing Home
1130 N Main St, Franklin, IN, 46131
(317) 736-8214
Admin Robert J Brown. *Medical Dir/Dir of
Nursing* Delores Gee RN DON.
Licensure Intermediate care. *Beds* ICF 40.
Certified Medicaid.
Owner Proprietary Corp (Beverly Enterprises).
Staff RNs 2 (ft); LPNs 5 (ft); Nurses aides 10
(ft), 2 (pt); Activities coordinators 1 (ft);
Dietitians 1 (ft).
Activities Arts & crafts; Games; Prayer groups;
Shopping trips.

The Franklin United Methodist Home
1070 W Jefferson, Franklin, IN, 46131
(317) 736-7185
Admin Rev Robert Alred. *Medical Dir/Dir of
Nursing* William Province II; Patricia Deer.
Licensure Comprehensive care. *Beds*
Comprehensive care 560.
Owner Nonprofit Corp.
Admissions Requirements Minimum age 62;
Medical examination.
Staff Physicians 1 (pt); RNs 5 (ft); LPNs 14
(ft); Nurses aides 28 (ft); Physical therapists
1 (pt); Activities coordinators 2 (ft);
Dietitians 1 (ft); Ophthalmologists 1 (pt);
Social workers 2 (ft).
Affiliation Methodist
Facilities Dining room; Physical therapy
room; Activities room; Chapel; Crafts room;
Laundry room; Barber/Beauty shop; Library;
Music room; Meditation room.
Activities Arts & crafts; Cards; Games;
Reading groups; Prayer groups; Movies;
Shopping trips; Social/Cultural gatherings;
Seasonal parties; Sunday school classes;
Shuffleboard.

Homeview Center of Franklin
651 S State St, Franklin, IN, 46131
(317) 736-6414
Admin Timothy H Nix. *Medical Dir/Dir of Nursing* George Small MD; Margaret Kelley RN DON.
Licensure Intermediate care. *Beds* ICF 70. *Certified* Medicaid.
Owner Proprietary Corp.
Admissions Requirements Minimum age 18; Medical examination; Physician's request.
Staff Physicians; RNs; LPNs; Nurses aides; Activities coordinators; Dietitians; Ophthalmologists.
Facilities Dining room; Activities room; Laundry room; Barber/Beauty shop; Lounges.
Activities Arts & crafts; Cards; Games; Reading groups; Prayer groups; Movies; Shopping trips; Social/Cultural gatherings; Exercise.

Indiana Masonic Home
690 State Street, Franklin, IN, 46131
(317) 736-6141
Admin Dean K Arnold.
Licensure Residential care. *Beds* 317.
Affiliation Masons

Welcome Nursing Home
1109 N Main St, Franklin, IN, 46131
(317) 736-7041
Admin Linda R Vest. *Medical Dir/Dir of Nursing* William D Province MD; Katie Lou Morris RN.
Licensure Intermediate care. *Beds* ICF 69. *Certified* Medicaid.
Owner Privately owned.
Admissions Requirements Medical examination.
Staff Physicians 1 (pt); RNs 1 (ft); LPNs 2 (ft), 1 (pt); Nurses aides 18 (ft), 5 (pt); Activities coordinators 1 (pt); Dietitians 1 (pt).
Facilities Dining room; Activities room; Laundry room.
Activities Arts & crafts; Cards; Games; Reading groups; Prayer groups; Movies; Social/Cultural gatherings.

FREELANDVILLE

Freelandville Community Home Inc
Box 288, Hwy 58, Freelandville, IN, 47535
(812) 328-2134
Admin Mary Joyce Buescher. *Medical Dir/Dir of Nursing* Barbara Burke RN DON.
Licensure Intermediate care. *Beds* ICF 50. *Certified* Medicaid.
Owner Nonprofit organization/foundation.
Admissions Requirements Minimum age 50; Medical examination.
Staff Physicians 1 (pt); RNs 2 (ft), 2 (pt); LPNs 2 (ft), 2 (pt); Orderlies 16 (ft), 15 (pt); Activities coordinators 1 (pt); Dietitians 1 (pt); Podiatrists 1 (pt).
Facilities Dining room; Activities room; Chapel; Crafts room; Laundry room.
Activities Arts & crafts; Cards; Games; Reading groups; Prayer groups; Movies; Shopping trips; Social/Cultural gatherings; Outings.

FRENCH LICK

Medco Center of French Lick
RR 2 Box 51, French Lick, IN, 47432
(812) 936-9901
Admin Sheila Watts.
Licensure Skilled care; Intermediate care. *Beds* SNF 42; ICF 42. *Certified* Medicaid; Medicare.
Owner Proprietary Corp (Unicare).

Medco Springs of French Lick*
Hwy 145 & E College, French Lick, IN, 47432
(812) 936-9991

Admin Joe Junod.
Licensure Intermediate care. *Beds* 58. *Certified* Medicaid.
Owner Proprietary Corp (Unicare).

GARRETT

Miller's Merry Manor Inc
1367 S Randolph, Box 149, Garrett, IN, 46738
(219) 357-5174
Admin Ron McSorley. *Medical Dir/Dir of Nursing* Bryce Treadwall MD.
Licensure Intermediate care. *Beds* ICF 63. *Certified* Medicaid.
Owner Proprietary Corp (Millers Merry Manor).
Admissions Requirements Minimum age 18; Medical examination; Physician's request.
Staff Physicians 1 (pt); RNs 2 (ft); LPNs 2 (ft), 1 (pt); Orderlies 1 (pt); Nurses aides 5 (ft), 15 (pt); Physical therapists 1 (pt); Speech therapists 1 (pt); Activities coordinators 1 (ft); Dietitians 1 (ft).
Facilities Dining room; Physical therapy room; Crafts room; Laundry room; Barber/Beauty shop.
Activities Arts & crafts; Cards; Games; Reading groups; Prayer groups; Movies; Shopping trips; Social/Cultural gatherings.

GARY

Greens Geriatric Health Center Inc
2052 Delaware St, Gary, IN, 46407
(219) 886-1511
Admin Horace Brown. *Medical Dir/Dir of Nursing* Dr Bayne Spotwood; Bertha Crowder.
Licensure Intermediate care. *Beds* ICF 35. *Certified* Medicaid.
Owner Proprietary Corp.
Admissions Requirements Medical examination; Physician's request.
Staff Physicians 1 (pt); RNs 1 (pt); LPNs 5 (ft); Orderlies 9 (ft); Nurses aides 9 (ft); Activities coordinators 1 (ft); Dietitians 1 (pt); Dentists 1 (pt); Ophthalmologists 1 (pt); Pharmacist 1 (pt).
Facilities Dining room; Activities room; Laundry room.
Activities Arts & crafts; Cards; Games; Reading groups; Prayer groups; Movies; Shopping trips; Social/Cultural gatherings Outdoor activities.

Meridian Nursing Center—West Side*
353 Tyler St, Gary, IN, 46402
(219) 886-7070
Admin Gerald Rothenberg.
Licensure Intermediate care. *Beds* 214. *Certified* Medicaid.
Owner Proprietary Corp (Meridan Healthcare).

Mills Rest Home*
5011 Maryland St, Gary, IN, 46409
(219) 884-1712
Admin David L Mills & Audrey Mills.
Licensure Intermediate care. *Beds* 34. *Certified* Medicaid.

Simmons Loving Care Health Facility*
PO Box 1675, 700 E 21st Ave, Gary, IN, 46407
(219) 882-2563
Admin Herberta B Miller & Anna L Simmons.
Licensure Intermediate care. *Beds* 46. *Certified* Medicaid.

Wildwood Manor Inc
1964 Clark Rd, Gary, IN, 46404
(219) 949-9640
Admin A Joann Johnson. *Medical Dir/Dir of Nursing* Dr Daniel T Ramker; Lydia M King.

Licensure Skilled care. *Beds* SNF 120. *Certified* Medicaid; Medicare.
Owner Privately owned.
Admissions Requirements Minimum age 21; Medical examination; Physician's request.
Staff Physicians 5 (pt); RNs 3 (ft), 1 (pt); LPNs 12 (ft), 2 (pt); Nurses aides 41 (ft), 10 (pt); Physical therapists 1 (pt); Occupational therapists 2 (pt); Activities coordinators 2 (ft); Dietitians 1 (ft), 2 (pt); Ophthalmologists 1 (pt).
Facilities Dining room; Physical therapy room; Activities room; Chapel; Laundry room; Barber/Beauty shop.
Activities Arts & crafts; Cards; Games; Reading groups; Prayer groups; Movies; Shopping trips; Social/Cultural gatherings.

Wildwood Manor Mt Inc
386 Mount St, Gary, IN, 46406
(219) 949-5600
Admin Paula T Flores. *Medical Dir/Dir of Nursing* Daniel T Ramker MD; May O Gonzalez RN DON.
Licensure Intermediate care. *Beds* ICF 69. *Certified* Medicaid.
Owner Privately owned.
Admissions Requirements Minimum age 18; Medical examination; Physician's request.
Staff Physicians 2 (pt); RNs 1 (ft); LPNs 4 (ft), 3 (pt); Nurses aides 18 (ft), 5 (pt); Physical therapists 1 (pt); Occupational therapists 1 (pt); Speech therapists 1 (pt); Activities coordinators 1 (pt); Dietitians 1 (pt); Dentists 1 (pt); Ophthalmologists 1 (pt); Podiatrists 1 (pt); Dentist 1 (pt).
Languages Spanish
Facilities Dining room; Activities room; Crafts room; Laundry room; Barber/Beauty shop.
Activities Arts & crafts; Cards; Games; Reading groups; Prayer groups; Movies; Shopping trips; Social/Cultural gatherings; Bingo; Shuffle board; Community outings.

GAS CITY

Twin City Nursing Home*
627 East-North H St, Gas City, IN, 46933
(317) 674-8516
Admin Donna Imlay.
Licensure Intermediate care. *Beds* 100. *Certified* Medicaid.

GASTON

Pro Care Development Center
502 N Madison St, Gaston, IN, 47342
(317) 358-3324
Admin Harold K Behm. *Medical Dir/Dir of Nursing* Dr Thaker; JoAnne Johnstone DON.
Licensure Intermediate care for mentally retarded. *Beds* ICF/MR 75. *Certified* Medicaid.
Owner Proprietary Corp.
Admissions Requirements Minimum age 18; Medical examination.
Staff RNs 1 (ft); LPNs 5 (ft); Nurses aides 40 (ft); Recreational therapists 5 (ft); Speech therapists 1 (ft); Dietitians 1 (ft).
Facilities Dining room; Physical therapy room; Laundry room.

GOSHEN

Crystal Valley Care Center*
1101 W Lincoln Ave, Goshen, IN, 46526
(219) 533-8090
Admin Lorraine Kucian. *Medical Dir/Dir of Nursing* William Weybright.
Licensure Intermediate care. *Beds* 40. *Certified* Medicaid.
Owner Proprietary Corp (Waverly Group).
Admissions Requirements Physician's request.

Staff Physicians 1 (pt); RNs 1 (pt); LPNs 1 (ft), 1 (pt); Nurses aides 13 (ft); Activities coordinators 1 (ft); Dietitians 1 (pt); Podiatrists 1 (pt).
Facilities Dining room; Activities room; Laundry room; Barber/Beauty shop.
Activities Arts & crafts; Games; Reading groups; Prayer groups; Movies; Shopping trips; Social/Cultural gatherings.

Fountainview Place
2400 College Ave, Goshen, IN, 46526
(219) 533-0351
Admin James L Norton. *Medical Dir/Dir of Nursing* Donald L Minter MD; Betty Brooks RN.
Licensure Skilled care; Intermediate care; Comprehensive. *Beds* SNF 49; ICF 78; Comprehensive 19. *Certified* Medicaid; Medicare.
Owner Proprietary Corp (Beverly Enterprises).
Admissions Requirements Minimum age 18; Medical examination; Physician's request.
Staff Physicians 1 (pt); RNs 6 (ft), 1 (pt); LPNs 13 (ft), 2 (pt); Orderlies 1 (ft); Nurses aides 27 (ft), 12 (pt); Physical therapists 1 (pt); Occupational therapists 1 (pt); Speech therapists 1 (pt); Activities coordinators 1 (ft), 1 (pt); Dietitians 1 (pt).
Languages Ukranian
Facilities Dining room; Physical therapy room; Activities room; Chapel; Crafts room; Laundry room; Barber/Beauty shop; Library.
Activities Arts & crafts; Cards; Games; Reading groups; Prayer groups; Movies; Shopping trips; Social/Cultural gatherings.

Greencroft Nursing Center
PO Box 240, 1225 Greencroft Dr, Goshen, IN, 46526
(219) 534-1546
Admin Wayne A Badskey. *Medical Dir/Dir of Nursing* Donald L Minter MD; Dee Detweiler RN.
Licensure Skilled care; Intermediate care. *Beds* SNF 50; ICF 130. *Certified* Medicaid; Medicare.
Owner Nonprofit Corp.
Admissions Requirements Minimum age 18; Medical examination.
Staff Physicians 1 (pt); RNs 7 (ft), 5 (pt); LPNs 13 (ft), 7 (pt); Orderlies 3 (ft), 1 (pt); Nurses aides 57 (ft), 33 (pt); Physical therapists 2 (pt); Speech therapists 1 (pt); Activities coordinators 3 (ft); Dietitians 1 (ft), 1 (pt).
Affiliation Mennonite
Facilities Dining room; Physical therapy room; Activities room; Laundry room; Barber/Beauty shop; Library.
Activities Arts & crafts; Games; Reading groups; Prayer groups; Movies; Exercise; Bible study; Hymn singing; Current events.

GOSPORT

Gosport Nursing Home*
27 S 7th St, Gosport, IN, 47433
(812) 879-4242
Admin Fred J Ponton.
Licensure Intermediate care. *Beds* 74. *Certified* Medicaid.

GREENCASTLE

Greencastle Nursing Home
815 E Tacoma Dr, Greencastle, IN, 46135
(317) 653-8280
Admin Kathryn Lemmon. *Medical Dir/Dir of Nursing* Warren Macy MD; Eva Keen RN DON.
Licensure Intermediate care. *Beds* 40. *Certified* Medicaid.
Owner Proprietary Corp (Beverly Enterprises).

Staff RNs 1 (ft); LPNs 2 (ft), 1 (pt); Orderlies 1 (ft), 1 (pt); Nurses aides 8 (ft), 2 (pt); Activities coordinators 1 (ft); Dietitians 1 (pt).
Facilities Dining room; Activities room; Laundry room.
Activities Arts & crafts; Cards; Games; Reading groups; Prayer groups; Movies; Shopping trips; Social/Cultural gatherings.

Heritage House Convalescent Center of Putnam County Inc
PO Box 178, 1601 Hospital Dr, Greencastle, IN, 46135-0178
(317) 653-2602
Admin Douglas V Lynch. *Medical Dir/Dir of Nursing* Dr Kissell & Dr Johnson; Laura Long RN DON.
Licensure Skilled care; Intermediate care. *Beds* SNF 59; ICF 60. *Certified* Medicaid; Medicare.
Owner Proprietary Corp.
Admissions Requirements Medical examination; Physician's request.
Facilities Dining room; Physical therapy room; Activities room; Chapel; Laundry room; Barber/Beauty shop.
Activities Arts & crafts; Cards; Games; Reading groups; Prayer groups; Movies; Shopping trips; Social/Cultural gatherings.

Indiana Asbury Towers United Methodist Home Inc
102 W Poplar St, Greencastle, IN, 46135
(317) 653-5148
Admin James L Ray. *Medical Dir/Dir of Nursing* Bruce Gastinear MD; June Conrad RN DON.
Licensure Intermediate care; Independent living. *Beds* ICF 39; Independent living 77.
Owner Nonprofit Corp.
Admissions Requirements Minimum age 65; Medical examination.
Staff RNs 1 (ft); LPNs 3 (ft); Nurses aides 18 (ft), 5 (pt); Activities coordinators 1 (ft); Dietitians 1 (pt).
Affiliation Methodist
Facilities Dining room; Activities room; Laundry room; Barber/Beauty shop; Library; 8 Lounges.
Activities Arts & crafts; Cards; Games; Reading groups; Prayer groups; Shopping trips; Social/Cultural gatherings.

Shady Creek Health Care Facility
PO Box 524, 1306 S Bloomington St, Greencastle, IN, 46135
(317) 653-2406
Admin Helen P Roe. *Medical Dir/Dir of Nursing* Gregory Larken MD; Kathryn Lawson RN DON.
Licensure Intermediate care. *Beds* ICF 40. *Certified* Medicaid.
Owner Proprietary Corp (Forum Grp).
Admissions Requirements Minimum age 18; Physician's request.
Staff RNs 1 (ft); LPNs 4 (ft), 3 (pt); Orderlies 1 (ft); Nurses aides 10 (ft), 2 (pt); Recreational therapists 1 (ft), 1 (pt); Activities coordinators 1 (ft), 2 (pt); Dietitians 1 (pt).
Facilities Dining room; Activities room; Crafts room; Active programming areas.
Activities Arts & crafts; Cards; Games; Reading groups; Prayer groups; Movies; Shopping trips; Social/Cultural gatherings; Active programming for MR/DD.

Sunset Manor Nursing Home Inc*
1109 S Indiana St, Greencastle, IN, 46135
(317) 653-3143
Admin Brian L Cross.
Licensure Intermediate care. *Beds* 79. *Certified* Medicaid.
Staff RNs 2 (ft).
Facilities Dining room; Activities room; Laundry room.
Activities Cards; Games; Reading groups.

GREENFIELD

Brandywine Manor*
745 N Swope St, Greenfield, IN, 46140
(317) 462-9221
Admin Simon Robinson. *Medical Dir/Dir of Nursing* Hal Rhynearson MD.
Licensure Skilled care; Intermediate care. *Beds* SNF 83; ICF 49. *Certified* Medicaid; Medicare.
Owner Proprietary Corp (Beverly Enterprises).
Admissions Requirements Medical examination; Physician's request.
Staff RNs 7 (ft); LPNs 13 (ft); Nurses aides 40 (ft); Physical therapists 1 (ft); Recreational therapists 1 (ft); Occupational therapists 1 (ft), 1 (pt); Speech therapists 1 (pt); Activities coordinators 1 (ft); Dietitians 1 (pt); Dentists 1 (pt); Ophthalmologists 1 (pt); Podiatrists 1 (pt); Audiologists 1 (pt).
Facilities Dining room; Physical therapy room; Activities room; Chapel; Crafts room; Laundry room; Barber/Beauty shop; Lounge areas.
Activities Arts & crafts; Cards; Games; Reading groups; Prayer groups; Movies; Shopping trips; Social/Cultural gatherings.

Crescent Manor Nursing Home
1310 E Main St, Greenfield, IN, 46140
(317) 462-4344
Admin Nancy Strickland. *Medical Dir/Dir of Nursing* Hal Rhynearson MD; Patricia Furr RN.
Licensure Intermediate care. *Beds* 40. *Certified* Medicaid.
Owner Proprietary Corp (Waverly Group).
Admissions Requirements Minimum age 18; Medical examination; Physician's request.
Staff RNs 1 (ft), 2 (pt); LPNs 3 (ft); Nurses aides 5 (ft), 3 (pt); Activities coordinators 1 (ft); Dietitians 1 (pt).
Facilities Dining room; Activities room; Laundry room.
Activities Arts & crafts; Cards; Games; Prayer groups; Movies; Shopping trips; Social/Cultural gatherings; Make-up lessons.

Regency Place of Greenfield
200 Green Meadows Dr, Greenfield, IN, 46140
(317) 462-3311
Admin Edward L Hastings. *Medical Dir/Dir of Nursing* Gary Sharp MD; Sue Folkenerg DON.
Licensure Skilled care; Intermediate care. *Beds* 230. *Certified* Medicaid; Medicare.
Owner Proprietary Corp.
Admissions Requirements Minimum age 21; Medical examination; Physician's request.
Staff Physicians 1 (pt); RNs 10 (ft), 1 (pt); LPNs 15 (ft), 6 (pt); Orderlies 1 (ft), 1 (pt); Nurses aides 55 (ft), 45 (pt); Physical therapists 1 (ft); Occupational therapists 1 (pt); Speech therapists 1 (pt); Activities coordinators 1 (ft); Dietitians 1 (pt).
Facilities Dining room; Physical therapy room; Activities room; Chapel; Crafts room; Laundry room; Barber/Beauty shop; Library; Courtyard.
Activities Arts & crafts; Cards; Games; Reading groups; Prayer groups; Movies; Shopping trips; Social/Cultural gatherings.

Sugar Creek Convalescent Center Inc*
RR 7, Box 70, Greenfield, IN, 46140
(317) 894-3301
Admin Stanley Springer. *Medical Dir/Dir of Nursing* Joseph P Worley MD.
Licensure Skilled care; Intermediate care. *Beds* SNF 40; ICF 30. *Certified* Medicaid.
Owner Proprietary Corp (Beverly Enterprises).
Admissions Requirements Minimum age 18; Medical examination; Physician's request.
Staff Physicians 2 (pt); RNs 4 (ft), 3 (pt); LPNs 3 (ft), 3 (pt); Nurses aides 14 (ft), 11 (pt); Physical therapists 1 (pt); Reality therapists 1 (pt); Recreational therapists 1

(ft); Occupational therapists 1 (pt); Speech therapists 1 (pt); Activities coordinators 1 (ft); Dietitians 1 (ft); Dentists 1 (pt); Podiatrists 1 (pt); Audiologists 1 (pt).
Facilities Dining room; Physical therapy room; Activities room; Chapel; Crafts room; Laundry room; Barber/Beauty shop; Library; Occupational therapy room.
Activities Arts & crafts; Cards; Games; Reading groups; Prayer groups; Movies; Shopping trips; Social/Cultural gatherings.

GREENSBURG

Greensburg Nursing Home*
1420 Lincoln St, Greensburg, IN, 47240
(812) 663-7503
Admin Linda A Criswell.
Licensure Intermediate care. *Beds* 40.
Certified Medicaid.
Owner Proprietary Corp (Beverly Enterprises).

Heritage House of Greensburg
410 Park Rd, Greensburg, IN, 47240
(812) 663-7543
Admin Martha Waltz. *Medical Dir/Dir of Nursing* Chrystal Pershor DON.
Licensure Skilled care; Intermediate care; Residential. *Beds* SNF 74; ICF 90; 36.
Certified Medicaid; Medicare.
Owner Proprietary Corp.
Admissions Requirements Medical examination; Physician's request.
Staff RNs; LPNs; Nurses aides; Dietitians.
Facilities Dining room; Physical therapy room; Activities room; Crafts room; Laundry room; Barber/Beauty shop; Library.
Activities Arts & crafts; Cards; Games; Reading groups; Prayer groups; Movies; Shopping trips.

Odd Fellows Home
Rte 8, Box 5, Greensburg, IN, 47240
(812) 663-8553
Admin Jon W Kohlmeier. *Medical Dir/Dir of Nursing* Dr James Miller; Theresa Ripperger DON.
Licensure Intermediate care; Residential. *Beds* 111. *Certified* Medicaid.
Owner Nonprofit Corp.
Staff RNs 3 (ft), 1 (pt); LPNs 5 (ft), 3 (pt); Nurses aides 50 (ft), 15 (pt); Physical therapists 1 (pt); Speech therapists 1 (pt); Activities coordinators 1 (ft), 1 (pt); Dietitians 1 (pt); Ophthalmologists 1 (pt); Podiatrists 1 (pt).
Affiliation Independent Order of Odd Fellows & Rebekahs
Activities Arts & crafts; Cards; Games; Reading groups; Prayer groups; Movies; Shopping trips; Social/Cultural gatherings.

GREENWOOD

Greenwood Convalescent Center
PO Box 1317, 937 Fry Rd, Greenwood, IN, 46142
(317) 881-3535
Admin Pat Van Sickel. *Medical Dir/Dir of Nursing* Dr G Small.
Licensure Intermediate care. *Beds* ICF 137.
Certified Medicaid.
Staff RNs 2 (ft); LPNs 5 (ft), 1 (pt); Orderlies 1 (ft); Nurses aides 20 (ft), 10 (pt); Recreational therapists 1 (ft); Activities coordinators 1 (ft); Dietitians 1 (ft).
Facilities Dining room; Activities room; Laundry room; Barber/Beauty shop.
Activities Arts & crafts; Cards; Games; Reading groups; Prayer groups; Movies; Shopping trips; Social/Cultural gatherings.

Greenwood Village Manor
271 Village Ln, Greenwood, IN, 46143
(317) 888-3545

Admin Clare Buckles. *Medical Dir/Dir of Nursing* Joseph Young MD; Judi Miles DON.
Licensure Residential. *Beds* 105.
Owner Nonprofit Corp.
Admissions Requirements Minimum age 65; Medical examination.
Staff LPNs 2 (ft); Nurses aides 11 (ft), 2 (pt); Dietitians 1 (ft).
Facilities Dining room; Physical therapy room; Activities room; Crafts room; Laundry room; Barber/Beauty shop; Library.
Activities Cards; Games; Prayer groups; Movies; Field trips; Bowling; Shuffleboard.

Greenwood Village South
295 Village Ln, Greenwood, IN, 46142
(317) 881-2591
Admin Cynthia Thorland. *Medical Dir/Dir of Nursing* Nancy Eckle DON.
Licensure Skilled care; Intermediate care. *Beds* SNF 43; ICF 48. *Certified* Medicaid; Medicare.
Owner Nonprofit Corp.
Staff Physicians 1 (pt); RNs 7 (ft), 5 (pt); LPNs 5 (ft), 2 (pt); Nurses aides 38 (ft), 9 (pt); Physical therapists 1 (pt); Speech therapists 1 (pt); Activities coordinators 1 (ft), 1 (pt); Dietitians 1 (ft); Ophthalmologists 2 (pt).

Regency Place of Greenwood*
PO Box 469, Greenwood, IN, 46142-0469
(317) 888-4948
Admin Frances Pierce. *Medical Dir/Dir of Nursing* Dr Constance Van Valor.
Licensure Skilled care; Intermediate care. *Beds* SNF 52; ICF 60. *Certified* Medicaid; Medicare.
Admissions Requirements Minimum age 21; Medical examination; Physician's request.
Facilities Dining room; Physical therapy room; Activities room; Chapel; Crafts room; Laundry room; Barber/Beauty shop.
Activities Arts & crafts; Cards; Games; Reading groups; Prayer groups; Movies; Shopping trips; Social/Cultural gatherings.

HAMMOND

Hammond Nursing Home*
1402 E 173rd St, Hammond, IN, 46320
(219) 844-4534
Admin Thelma Zabinski.
Licensure Intermediate care. *Beds* 40.
Certified Medicaid.
Owner Proprietary Corp (Beverly Enterprises).

St Ann's Home*
5927 Columbia Ave, Hammond, IN, 46320
(219) 937-9400
Admin Ernest P Brister.
Licensure Residential care. *Beds* 230.
Affiliation Roman Catholic

HANOVER

Hanover Nursing Center*
RR 2, Hanover, IN, 47243
(812) 866-2625
Admin Barbara J Tumey.
Licensure Intermediate care. *Beds* 151.
Certified Medicaid.
Owner Proprietary Corp (Forum Grp).

HARTFORD CITY

Hartford City Community Care Center
715 N Mill St, Hartford City, IN, 47348
(317) 348-3310
Admin Kenneth W Seiffertt. *Medical Dir/Dir of Nursing* Dr Thomas Lee.
Licensure Intermediate care. *Beds* 52.
Certified Medicaid.
Owner Proprietary Corp (Community Care Centers).

Admissions Requirements Medical examination; Physician's request.
Staff Physicians 1 (pt); RNs 2 (ft), 1 (pt); LPNs 1 (ft), 2 (pt); Nurses aides 7 (ft), 11 (pt); Activities coordinators 1 (ft); Dietitians 1 (ft); Podiatrists 1 (pt).
Facilities Dining room; Activities room; Laundry room.
Activities Arts & crafts; Cards; Games; Reading groups.

Miller's Merry Manor Inc
Rte 2, PO Box 266, Hartford City, IN, 47348
(317) 348-1072
Admin Robert D Lau. *Medical Dir/Dir of Nursing* Roger Frazier DO.
Licensure Intermediate care. *Beds* 86.
Certified Medicaid.
Owner Proprietary Corp (Millers Merry Manor).
Admissions Requirements Minimum age 18; Medical examination; Physician's request.
Staff RNs 3 (ft); LPNs 2 (ft), 2 (pt); Orderlies 1 (ft); Nurses aides 13 (ft), 3 (pt); Activities coordinators 1 (ft); Dietitians 1 (pt).
Facilities Dining room; Activities room; Chapel; Laundry room; Barber/Beauty shop.
Activities Arts & crafts; Games; Reading groups; Prayer groups; Movies; Social/Cultural gatherings.

HIGHLAND

Highland Nursing Home
9630 5th St, Highland, IN, 46322
(219) 924-6953
Admin Richard E Meriwether. *Medical Dir/Dir of Nursing* Mona Stern MD.
Licensure Intermediate care. *Beds* ICF 40.
Certified Medicaid.
Owner Proprietary Corp (Beverly Enterprises).
Admissions Requirements Medical examination; Physician's request.
Staff Physicians 1 (pt); RNs 1 (pt); LPNs 6 (ft); Orderlies 2 (ft); Nurses aides 10 (ft), 6 (pt); Recreational therapists 1 (pt); Activities coordinators 1 (pt); Dietitians 1 (pt).
Facilities Dining room; Activities room; Crafts room; Laundry room.
Activities Arts & crafts; Cards; Games; Reading groups; Prayer groups; Movies; Shopping trips; Social/Cultural gatherings.

HOBART

Miller's Merry Manor
2901 W 37th Ave, Hobart, IN, 46342
(219) 942-2170
Admin Gary A Brubaker. *Medical Dir/Dir of Nursing* R Billena MD; Sandra Jones RN.
Licensure Skilled care; Intermediate care. *Beds* SNF 29; ICF 31. *Certified* Medicaid; Medicare.
Owner Proprietary Corp (Millers Merry Manor).
Admissions Requirements Minimum age 18; Medical examination; Physician's request.
Staff Physicians 1 (pt); RNs 10 (ft), 2 (pt); LPNs 3 (ft), 9 (pt); Nurses aides 29 (ft), 29 (pt); Physical therapists 1 (pt); Occupational therapists 1 (pt); Speech therapists 1 (pt); Activities coordinators 2 (ft), 1 (pt); Dietitians 1 (pt); Dentists 1 (pt); Ophthalmologists 1 (pt); Podiatrists 1 (pt); Medication aides 8 (ft), 3 (pt).
Languages Spanish
Facilities Dining room; Physical therapy room; Activities room; Crafts room; Laundry room; Barber/Beauty shop; 2 resident lounges.
Activities Arts & crafts; Cards; Games; Reading groups; Prayer groups; Movies; Shopping trips; Social/Cultural gatherings; Recreational outings; Holiday celebrations.

Sebo Heritage Manor Nursing Home*
4410 W 49th Ave, Hobart, IN, 46342
(219) 942-1507
Admin Justine Truchan.
Licensure Intermediate care. *Beds* 54.
Certified Medicaid.

HOPE

Ken-Joy Nursing Home
133 Maple St, Hope, IN, 47247
(812) 546-4814
Admin Mary L Johnson Gabbard. *Medical Dir/Dir of Nursing* Mary Lofdell.
Licensure Intermediate care. *Beds* ICF 34.
Certified Medicaid; Medicare.
Owner Proprietary Corp.
Admissions Requirements Medical examination.
Staff RNs 1 (pt); LPNs 1 (ft), 1 (pt); Nurses aides 8 (ft), 6 (pt); Activities coordinators 1 (ft); Dietitians 1 (pt).
Facilities Dining room; Activities room; Laundry room.
Activities Arts & crafts; Cards; Games; Reading groups; Prayer groups; Shopping trips; Social/Cultural gatherings.

Miller's Merry Manor Inc
PO Box 8, Hope, IN, 47246
(812) 546-4416
Admin Martin D Allain, Jr. *Medical Dir/Dir of Nursing* Forest Daugherty MD; Cindy Fields RN.
Licensure Intermediate care. *Beds* ICF 74.
Certified Medicaid.
Owner Proprietary Corp (Millers Merry Manor).
Admissions Requirements Medical examination; Physician's request.
Staff RNs 3 (ft), 1 (pt); LPNs 5 (ft); Nurses aides 22 (ft), 12 (pt); Activities coordinators 1 (ft), 1 (pt); Dietitians 1 (pt).
Facilities Dining room; Activities room; Laundry room; Barber/Beauty shop.
Activities Arts & crafts; Cards; Games; Reading groups; Prayer groups; Movies; Social/Cultural gatherings; Daily rides around the countryside.

HUNTINGBURG

Huntingburg Convalescent Center Inc
1712 Leland Dr, Huntingburg, IN, 47542
(812) 683-4090
Admin Carl Ahrens. *Medical Dir/Dir of Nursing* J G Ellison MD; Margie Bell DON.
Licensure Skilled care; Intermediate care. *Beds* SNF 38; ICF 114. *Certified* Medicaid; Medicare.
Owner Proprietary Corp.
Admissions Requirements Minimum age 18.
Staff Physicians 1 (pt); RNs 4 (ft), 6 (pt); LPNs 2 (ft), 6 (pt); Orderlies 1 (ft), 1 (pt); Nurses aides 32 (pt); Physical therapists 2 (pt); Reality therapists 1 (pt); Recreational therapists 1 (ft); Occupational therapists 1 (pt); Speech therapists 1 (pt); Activities coordinators 2 (ft); Dietitians 1 (pt); Ophthalmologists 1 (pt).
Facilities Dining room; Physical therapy room; Activities room; Chapel; Crafts room; Laundry room; Barber/Beauty shop.
Activities Arts & crafts; Cards; Games; Reading groups; Prayer groups; Movies; Shopping trips; Social/Cultural gatherings.

Medco Center of Huntingburg*
530 4th St, Huntingburg, IN, 47542
(812) 683-2535
Admin Donald Ingle. *Medical Dir/Dir of Nursing* Theodore A Waflart.
Licensure Intermediate care. *Beds* 82.
Certified Medicaid.
Owner Proprietary Corp (Unicare).
Admissions Requirements Minimum age 18; Medical examination; Physician's request.

Staff Physicians 1 (ft), 5 (pt); RNs 3 (ft); LPNs 5 (pt); Nurses aides 9 (ft), 3 (pt); Physical therapists 2 (pt); Occupational therapis.s 2 (pt); Activities coordinators 1 (ft); Dietitians 1 (ft); Dentists 1 (ft); Podiatrists 1 (ft).
Facilities Dining room; Physical therapy room; Activities room; Chapel; Crafts room; Laundry room; Barber/Beauty shop; Library; Meeting rooms.
Activities Arts & crafts; Cards; Games; Reading groups; Prayer groups; Movies; Shopping trips; Social/Cultural gatherings.

HUNTINGTON

Huntington Nursing Home*
1425 Grant St, Huntington, IN, 46750
(219) 356-4867
Admin Sharon Andersen.
Licensure Intermediate care. *Beds* 40.
Certified Medicaid.
Owner Proprietary Corp (Beverly Enterprises).
Admissions Requirements Minimum age 18.
Staff LPNs 2 (ft), 1 (pt); Nurses aides 7 (ft), 8 (pt); Activities coordinators 1 (ft); Dietitians 1 (pt).
Facilities Dining room; Laundry room.
Activities Arts & crafts; Games; Reading groups; Prayer groups; Shopping trips.

Miller's Merry Manor Inc*
1500 Grant St, Huntington, IN, 46750
(219) 356-5713
Admin Greg Spaulding. *Medical Dir/Dir of Nursing* S E Cape MD.
Licensure Skilled care; Intermediate care. *Beds* SNF 37; ICF 132. *Certified* Medicaid; Medicare.
Owner Proprietary Corp (Millers Merry Manor).
Admissions Requirements Minimum age 18.
Staff Physicians 12 (pt); RNs 10 (ft), 4 (pt); LPNs 5 (ft), 4 (pt); Nurses aides 38 (ft), 16 (pt); Occupational therapists 1 (pt); Activities coordinators 2 (ft); Dietitians 1 (ft).
Facilities Dining room; Physical therapy room; Activities room; Crafts room; Laundry room; Barber/Beauty shop.
Activities Arts & crafts; Cards; Games; Reading groups; Prayer groups; Movies; Shopping trips; Social/Cultural gatherings.

Norwood Nursing Center*
3720 N Norwood Rd, Huntington, IN, 46750
(219) 356-1252
Admin Suzanne Whitted. *Medical Dir/Dir of Nursing* Dr Richard Blair.
Licensure Intermediate care. *Beds* 60.
Certified Medicaid.
Owner Proprietary Corp (Shive Nursing Centers).
Staff RNs 2 (ft), 2 (pt); LPNs 3 (ft), 3 (pt); Nurses aides 15 (ft), 23 (pt); Physical therapists 1 (pt); Activities coordinators 1 (ft); Dietitians 1 (pt); Dentists 1 (pt); Podiatrists 1 (pt).
Facilities Dining room; Physical therapy room; Activities room; Laundry room; Barber/Beauty shop.
Activities Arts & crafts; Cards; Games; Reading groups; Prayer groups; Movies; Shopping trips; Social/Cultural gatherings.

INDIANAPOLIS

The Alpha Home*
1910 N Senate Ave, Indianapolis, IN, 46202
(317) 923-1518
Admin Sherlee Butler.
Licensure Intermediate care. *Beds* 44.
Certified Medicaid.

American Village Retirement Community
2026 E 54th St, Indianapolis, IN, 46220
(317) 253-6950

Admin Karl Jacobsen. *Medical Dir/Dir of Nursing* Robert Rudesill MD; Bobby Jo Easter RN.
Licensure Skilled care; Intermediate care. *Beds* SNF 104; ICF. *Certified* Medicaid; Medicare.
Owner Proprietary Corp.
Admissions Requirements Minimum age 18; Medical examination.
Staff RNs; LPNs; Nurses aides; Physical therapists 1 (pt); Reality therapists 1 (ft); Occupational therapists 1 (pt); Speech therapists 1 (pt); Activities coordinators 1 (ft); Dietitians 1 (pt).
Facilities Dining room; Physical therapy room; Activities room; Chapel; Crafts room; Laundry room; Barber/Beauty shop; Library; Assisted living; Respite.
Activities Arts & crafts; Cards; Games; Reading groups; Prayer groups; Movies; Shopping trips; Social/Cultural gatherings.

Americana Healthcare Center—Indianapolis*
5600 E 16th St, Indianapolis, IN, 46218
(317) 356-0911
Admin Jeff A Cooper.
Licensure Skilled care; Intermediate care. *Beds* 98. *Certified* Medicaid; Medicare.
Owner Proprietary Corp (Manor Care).

Americana Healthcare Center—Indianapolis Midtown
2010 N Capitol Ave, Indianapolis, IN, 46202
(317) 924-5821
Admin Christine Martin.
Licensure Skilled care; Intermediate care. *Beds* 153. *Certified* Medicaid; Medicare.
Owner Proprietary Corp (Manor Care).
Admissions Requirements Minimum age 18; Medical examination; Physician's request.
Facilities Dining room; Physical therapy room; Activities room; Barber/Beauty shop; Library.
Activities Arts & crafts; Cards; Games; Reading groups; Prayer groups; Movies; Shopping trips.

Americana Healthcare Center—Indianapolis North*
8350 Naab Rd, Indianapolis, IN, 46260
(317) 872-1110
Admin Arlice M Haris.
Licensure Skilled care; Intermediate care. *Beds* 201. *Certified* Medicaid; Medicare.

The Barton House*
505 N Delaware St, Indianapolis, IN, 46204
(317) 634-9382
Admin Audrey Bonner.
Licensure Intermediate care. *Beds* 120.
Certified Medicaid.

Bethany Village Nursing Home*
3518 Shelby St, Indianapolis, IN, 46227
(317) 788-9114
Admin Stephen Harris.
Licensure Intermediate care. *Beds* 48.
Certified Medicaid.

Broad Ripple Nursing Home
6127 N College Ave, Indianapolis, IN, 46220
(317) 257-8392
Admin John Niemeyer. *Medical Dir/Dir of Nursing* Robert Nation MD; Shirley Christiansen DON.
Licensure Intermediate care. *Beds* ICF 50.
Certified Medicaid.
Owner Proprietary Corp (Beverly Enterprises).
Admissions Requirements Minimum age 21; Medical examination.
Staff RNs 1 (ft); LPNs 3 (ft), 1 (pt); Nurses aides 12 (ft), 1 (pt); Activities coordinators 1 (ft).
Facilities Dining room; Activities room; Laundry room; Barber/Beauty shop.
Activities Arts & crafts; Cards; Games; Reading groups; Prayer groups; Movies; Shopping trips; Social/Cultural gatherings.

Brookview Manor
7145 E 21st St, Indianapolis, IN, 46219
(317) 356-0977
Admin Stanley Springer. *Medical Dir/Dir of Nursing* Dr Fred Hendricks.
Licensure Skilled care; Intermediate care. *Beds* SNF 94; ICF 50. *Certified* Medicaid; Medicare.
Admissions Requirements Minimum age 18; Medical examination.
Staff Physicians 1 (ft); RNs 7 (ft); LPNs 30 (ft); Orderlies 1 (ft); Nurses aides 99 (ft); Physical therapists 1 (ft), 3 (pt); Reality therapists 1 (ft); Recreational therapists 1 (ft); Occupational therapists 2 (ft); Speech therapists 1 (ft); Activities coordinators 2 (ft); Dietitians 1 (ft), 1 (pt); Ophthalmologists 1 (pt); Podiatrists 1 (pt).
Facilities Dining room; Physical therapy room; Activities room; Chapel; Crafts room; Laundry room; Barber/Beauty shop; Library.
Activities Arts & crafts; Cards; Games; Reading groups; Prayer groups; Movies; Shopping trips; Social/Cultural gatherings.

Capital Care Healthcare Facility
2115 N Central Ave, Indianapolis, IN, 46202
(317) 923-8944
Admin Marilyn Dawn Conner LPN. *Medical Dir/Dir of Nursing* Kete Cockerell; Patty Jacks RN.
Licensure Intermediate care. *Beds* 60. *Certified* Medicaid.
Owner Proprietary Corp (Cloverleaf Enterprises).
Admissions Requirements Minimum age 18; Medical examination; Physician's request; PAS.
Staff RNs 1 (ft); LPNs 6 (ft), 2 (pt); Nurses aides 12 (ft), 3 (pt); Activities coordinators 1 (ft).
Facilities Dining room; Activities room; Laundry room; Barber/Beauty shop; Lounges; Courtyards.
Activities Arts & crafts; Cards; Games; Reading groups; Prayer groups; Movies; Shopping trips; Social/Cultural gatherings.

Cedar Crest Health Center East*
1924 Wellesley Blvd, Indianapolis, IN, 46219
(317) 353-6270
Admin David Lennartz. *Medical Dir/Dir of Nursing* Roudolph Rouhana MD.
Licensure Skilled care; Intermediate care. *Beds* SNF 70; ICF 70. *Certified* Medicaid; Medicare.
Admissions Requirements Minimum age 18; Medical examination; Physician's request.
Staff RNs 5 (ft), 1 (pt); LPNs 15 (ft), 5 (pt); Orderlies 2 (ft); Nurses aides 47 (ft), 4 (pt); Physical therapists 1 (ft); Recreational therapists 1 (ft); Occupational therapists 1 (pt); Speech therapists 1 (pt); Activities coordinators 2 (ft); Dietitians 1 (pt); Dentists 1 (pt); Podiatrists 1 (pt); Audiologists 1 (pt).
Facilities Dining room; Physical therapy room; Activities room; Chapel; Crafts room; Barber/Beauty shop; Library.
Activities Arts & crafts; Cards; Games; Reading groups; Prayer groups; Movies; Shopping trips; Social/Cultural gatherings.

Central Healthcare Center
55 W 33rd St, Indianapolis, IN, 46208
(317) 927-2461
Admin Karyn Price.
Licensure Skilled care; Intermediate care. *Beds* 147. *Certified* Medicaid; Medicare.
Owner Proprietary Corp (ARA Living Centers).
Admissions Requirements Minimum age 18; Medical examination.
Facilities Dining room; Physical therapy room; Activities room; Barber/Beauty shop.
Activities Arts & crafts; Cards; Games; Reading groups; Prayer groups; Movies; Shopping trips; Social/Cultural gatherings.

Churchman Manor
2860 Churchman Ave, Indianapolis, IN, 46203
(317) 787-3451
Admin Thomas E Dobbins.
Licensure Skilled care; Intermediate care. *Beds* SNF 78; ICF 40. *Certified* Medicaid; Medicare.
Owner Proprietary Corp (Beverly Enterprises).

Community Healthcare of Indianapolis
PO Box 449264, 2926 N Capitol Ave, Indianapolis, IN, 46202-9264
(317) 926-0254
Admin Kris Turner.
Licensure Intermediate care. *Beds* 40. *Certified* Medicaid.

Continental Convalescent Center*
344 S Ritter Ave, Indianapolis, IN, 46219
(317) 359-5515
Admin Thomas Dobbins.
Licensure Skilled care. *Beds* 54. *Certified* Medicaid.
Owner Proprietary Corp (Beverly Enterprises).

Country Trace Healthcare Center*
2140 W 86th St, Indianapolis, IN, 46260
(317) 844-7211
Admin Richard E Lewis.
Licensure Skilled care; Intermediate care. *Beds* SNF 56; ICF 141. *Certified* Medicaid; Medicare.
Owner Proprietary Corp (ARA Living Centers).

Coventry Village
8400 Clearvista Pl, Indianapolis, IN, 46256
(317) 845-0464
Admin Ruth Hanlon. *Medical Dir/Dir of Nursing* Dr David Pletzer; Marilyn Price RN.
Licensure Skilled care; Intermediate care; Residential assisted living. *Beds* SNF; ICF 132; Residential assisted living 52. *Certified* Medicaid; Medicare.
Owner Proprietary Corp (Millers Merry Manor).
Admissions Requirements Medical examination; Physician's request.
Facilities Dining room; Physical therapy room; Activities room; Chapel; Crafts room; Laundry room; Barber/Beauty shop; Library.
Activities Arts & crafts; Cards; Games; Reading groups; Prayer groups; Movies; Shopping trips; Social/Cultural gatherings; Monthly family nights.

Crestview Health Care Facility*
1118 E 46th St, Indianapolis, IN, 46205
(317) 257-1571
Admin Margaret Cronin.
Licensure Intermediate care. *Beds* 50. *Certified* Medicaid.

Decatur Retirement Park
4851 Timcher Rd, Indianapolis, IN, 46241
(317) 856-4851
Admin Kim Cook. *Medical Dir/Dir of Nursing* Nestor Reyes MD; Jan Davidson RN DON.
Licensure Intermediate care. *Beds* ICF 89. *Certified* Medicaid.
Owner Proprietary Corp.
Admissions Requirements Medical examination; Physician's request.
Staff RNs 1 (ft); LPNs 6 (ft), 9 (pt); Nurses aides 14 (ft), 2 (pt); Physical therapists; Speech therapists; Activities coordinators; Dietitians; Ophthalmologists.
Facilities Dining room; Physical therapy room; Activities room; Chapel; Crafts room; Laundry room; Barber/Beauty shop; Greenhouse.
Activities Arts & crafts; Cards; Games; Reading groups; Prayer groups; Social/Cultural gatherings.

Del Mar Nursing Home
709 S Lynhurst, Indianapolis, IN, 46241
(317) 243-3109
Admin Margaret A Cronin. *Medical Dir/Dir of Nursing* Robert Dwyer.
Licensure Intermediate care. *Beds* ICF 40. *Certified* Medicaid.
Owner Proprietary Corp (Beverly Enterprises).
Admissions Requirements Minimum age 18; Medical examination; Physician's request.
Staff Physicians; RNs; LPNs 5 (ft); Activities coordinators 1 (ft); Dietitians 1 (pt); Dentists 1 (pt); Ophthalmologists 1 (pt); Podiatrists 1 (pt); Dentist.
Facilities Dining room; Activities room; Laundry room; Barber/Beauty shop.
Activities Arts & crafts; Cards; Games; Reading groups; Prayer groups; Movies; Shopping trips; Social/Cultural gatherings.

Delaware Health Care Facility
1910 N Delaware, Indianapolis, IN, 46202
(317) 925-2393
Admin David A Moberg.
Licensure Intermediate care. *Beds* ICF 42. *Certified* Medicaid.
Owner Proprietary Corp.
Admissions Requirements Minimum age 18; Medical examination; Physician's request.
Staff Physicians 3 (pt); RNs 1 (pt); LPNs 3 (ft), 1 (pt); Nurses aides 12 (ft); Activities coordinators 1 (ft); Dietitians 1 (pt).
Facilities Dining room; Activities room; Laundry room.
Activities Arts & crafts; Cards; Games; Reading groups; Prayer groups; Movies; Shopping trips; Social/Cultural gatherings.

Eagle Valley Healthcare Center
3017 Valley Farms Rd, Indianapolis, IN, 46224
(317) 293-2555
Admin Sherry Simons. *Medical Dir/Dir of Nursing* Dr Carl Otten; Pat Cleavenger.
Licensure Skilled care; Intermediate care. *Beds* 120. *Certified* Medicaid; Medicare.
Owner Proprietary Corp (ARA Living Centers).
Admissions Requirements Minimum age 18; Medical examination; Physician's request.
Staff Physicians 1 (ft); RNs 5 (ft); LPNs 7 (ft); Orderlies 2 (ft); Nurses aides 30 (ft); Physical therapists 1 (ft); Occupational therapists 1 (ft); Speech therapists 1 (ft); Activities coordinators 2 (ft); Dietitians 1 (ft); QMRP 1 (ft), 10 (pt).
Facilities Dining room; Physical therapy room; Activities room; Crafts room; Laundry room; Barber/Beauty shop; Smoking lounge; Outside fenced patio; Gazebo.
Activities Arts & crafts; Cards; Games; Reading groups; Prayer groups; Movies; Shopping trips; Social/Cultural gatherings; Cooking.

Eastside Healthcare Center*
1302 N Lesley Ave, Indianapolis, IN, 46219
(317) 353-8061
Admin T Douglas Shuck. *Medical Dir/Dir of Nursing* Linda Stropes MD.
Licensure Skilled care; Intermediate care. *Beds* SNF 89; ICF 90. *Certified* Medicaid; Medicare.
Owner Proprietary Corp (ARA Living Centers).
Admissions Requirements Minimum age 18.
Staff RNs 5 (ft); LPNs 10 (ft); Nurses aides 48 (ft), 10 (pt); Physical therapists 1 (ft); Occupational therapists 1 (ft); Speech therapists 1 (ft); Activities coordinators 2 (ft); Dietitians 1 (ft); Dentists 1 (ft); Podiatrists 1 (ft).
Facilities Dining room; Physical therapy room; Activities room; Crafts room; Laundry room; Barber/Beauty shop; Library.

Activities Arts & crafts; Cards; Games; Reading groups; Prayer groups; Movies; Shopping trips; Social/Cultural gatherings; Reality orientation; Exercises.

Emerson Nursing Home*
3420 N Emerson Ave, Indianapolis, IN, 46218
(317) 546-9567
Admin Raymond E Massengill.
Licensure Intermediate care. *Beds* 40. Certified Medicaid.
Owner Proprietary Corp (Beverly Enterprises).

Fountainview Place of Indianapolis
5353 E Raymond St, Indianapolis, IN, 46203
(317) 353-8015
Admin Brent Waymire. *Medical Dir/Dir of Nursing* Dr John Karedes; Patricia Sanders RN DON.
Licensure Skilled care; Intermediate care; Residential. *Beds* SNF 95; ICF 120; Residential 8. *Certified* Medicaid; Medicare; VA.
Owner Proprietary Corp (Beverly Enterprises).
Admissions Requirements Minimum age 18; Medical examination; Physician's request.
Staff Physicians; RNs; LPNs; Orderlies; Nurses aides; Physical therapists; Reality therapists; Recreational therapists; Occupational therapists; Speech therapists; Activities coordinators; Dietitians; Dentists; Ophthalmologists; Podiatrists.
Facilities Dining room; Physical therapy room; Activities room; Chapel; Crafts room; Laundry room; Barber/Beauty shop; Library; General store; Lounges; Occupational therapy room.
Activities Arts & crafts; Cards; Games; Reading groups; Prayer groups; Movies; Shopping trips; Social/Cultural gatherings; Specialized activities.

Frame House Manor*
1316 N Tibbs, Indianapolis, IN, 46222
(317) 634-8330
Admin David L McCarroll.
Licensure Intermediate care. *Beds* 62. Certified Medicaid.

Frame Nursing Home Inc
373 N Holmes Ave, Indianapolis, IN, 46222
(317) 634-7846
Admin Mark R McCarroll.
Licensure Intermediate care. *Beds* ICF 89. Certified Medicaid.
Owner Proprietary Corp.
Admissions Requirements Medical examination; Physician's request.
Staff Physicians 1 (pt); RNs 1 (ft); LPNs 5 (ft); Nurses aides 45 (ft); Physical therapists 1 (pt); Occupational therapists 1 (pt); Activities coordinators 2 (ft); Dietitians 1 (pt); Ophthalmologists 1 (pt); Podiatrists 1 (pt).
Facilities Dining room; Activities room; Crafts room; Laundry room; Barber/Beauty shop.
Activities Arts & crafts; Cards; Games; Reading groups; Prayer groups; Movies; Shopping trips; Social/Cultural gatherings; Camping trips; Courtesy van.

Garfield Park Health Facility Inc*
2630 S Keystone Ave, Indianapolis, IN, 46227-3540
(317) 787-5364
Admin Thelma B Bryant.
Licensure Intermediate care. *Beds* 55.

Greenbriar Manor*
8181 Harcourt Rd, Indianapolis, IN, 46260
(317) 872-7261
Admin James Rutkrauff.
Licensure Skilled care; Intermediate care. *Beds* SNF 130; ICF 20. *Certified* Medicaid; Medicare.
Owner Proprietary Corp (Beverly Enterprises).

Anthony Hall Nursing Home
2135 N Alabama St, Indianapolis, IN, 46202
(317) 925-7917
Admin Warren Hotte. *Medical Dir/Dir of Nursing* Dan Hurley MD; Carolyn Scalf DON.
Licensure Intermediate care. *Beds* ICF 23. Certified Medicaid.
Owner Proprietary Corp.
Staff RNs 1 (ft); LPNs 1 (ft), 2 (pt); Nurses aides 10 (ft); Occupational therapists 1 (pt); Dietitians 1 (pt); Dentists 1 (pt); Ophthalmologists 1 (pt); Dentist 1 (pt).
Facilities Dining room; Activities room.
Activities Arts & crafts; Cards; Games; Reading groups; Prayer groups; Movies; Shopping trips; Social/Cultural gatherings.

Hallmark Manor Nursing Home*
6851 E 10th St, Indianapolis, IN, 46219
(317) 357-5373
Admin Richard Knight.
Beds 62.
Owner Proprietary Corp (Beverly Enterprises).

The Hoosier Village
5300 W 96th St, Indianapolis, IN, 46268
(317) 873-3349
Admin Hilda Johnson.
Licensure Comprehensive care; Residential care. *Beds* Comprehensive care 70; Residential 90.
Admissions Requirements Medical examination.
Staff RNs 6 (ft), 1 (pt); LPNs 2 (ft), 1 (pt); Nurses aides 30 (ft), 11 (pt); Physical therapists 1 (pt); Speech therapists 1 (pt); Podiatrists 1 (pt).
Facilities Dining room; Activities room; Chapel; Crafts room; Laundry room; Barber/Beauty shop; Library.
Activities Arts & crafts; Cards; Games; Reading groups; Prayer groups; Movies; Shopping trips; Social/Cultural gatherings.

Hooverwood
7001 Hoover Rd, Indianapolis, IN, 46260
(317) 251-2261
Admin Jeffrey F Stern. *Medical Dir/Dir of Nursing* Edward Steinmetz MD; Barbara Horner RN.
Licensure Skilled care; Intermediate care. *Beds* SNF 93; ICF 70. *Certified* Medicaid; Medicare.
Owner Nonprofit Corp.
Admissions Requirements Minimum age 65; Medical examination.
Staff Physicians 1 (pt); RNs 7 (ft), 10 (pt); LPNs 6 (ft), 2 (pt); Nurses aides 30 (ft), 30 (pt); Physical therapists 1 (pt); Recreational therapists 1 (ft); Occupational therapists 1 (pt); Activities coordinators 2 (ft), 1 (pt); Dietitians 1 (ft).
Affiliation Jewish
Facilities Dining room; Physical therapy room; Activities room; Chapel; Crafts room; Laundry room; Barber/Beauty shop; Library.
Activities Arts & crafts; Cards; Games; Reading groups; Prayer groups; Movies; Shopping trips; Social/Cultural gatherings; Sheltered workshop; Adult day care.

Houston Village Inc
PO Box 229043, 5055 W 52nd St, Indianapolis, IN, 46254
(317) 293-8823
Admin Pamela K Westfall. *Medical Dir/Dir of Nursing* Dr Armstrong, Dr Karimi, Dr Bojrab; Sara Habegger DON.
Licensure Intermediate care. *Beds* ICF 39. Certified Medicaid.
Owner Proprietary Corp.
Staff Physicians 3 (pt); LPNs 4 (ft), 2 (pt); Nurses aides 4 (ft), 3 (pt).

Facilities Dining room; Activities room; Barber/Beauty shop.
Activities Arts & crafts; Cards; Games; Reading groups; Prayer groups; Movies; Shopping trips.

Independent Living Club*
6038 W 25th St, Indianapolis, IN, 46224
(317) 291-5228
Admin Jack E Roland.
Licensure Home for aged. *Beds* 31.
Admissions Requirements Medical examination.
Staff Nurses aides 1 (ft), 1 (pt); Activities coordinators 1 (ft); Dietitians 1 (pt); Podiatrists 1 (pt); Audiologists 1 (pt).
Facilities Dining room; Activities room; Crafts room; Laundry room; Barber/Beauty shop; Library.
Activities Cards; Games; Prayer groups; Shopping trips; Social/Cultural gatherings; Church services.

Indianapolis Retirement Home Inc*
1731 N Capitol Ave, Indianapolis, IN, 46202
(317) 924-5839
Admin Betty Sell RN.
Licensure Intermediate care; Residential care. *Beds* ICF 20; Residential 37.

Lakeview Manor Inc
45 Beachway Dr, Indianapolis, IN, 46224
(317) 745-6740
Admin Thomas F Tyson Jr. *Medical Dir/Dir of Nursing* A Alan Fischer MD; Peggy Steinsberger RN DON.
Licensure Skilled care; Intermediate care. *Beds* SNF 43; ICF 144. *Certified* Medicaid; Medicare.
Owner Nonprofit Corp.
Admissions Requirements Minimum age 50; Medical examination.
Staff Physicians 13 (pt); RNs 7 (ft), 7 (pt); LPNs 11 (ft), 1 (pt); Nurses aides 77 (ft), 7 (pt); Physical therapists 1 (ft), 1 (pt); Recreational therapists 1 (ft), 1 (pt); Occupational therapists 1 (pt); Speech therapists 1 (pt); Activities coordinators 1 (ft), 1 (pt); Dietitians 1 (pt); Dentists 1 (pt); Ophthalmologists 1 (pt); Podiatrists 1 (pt).
Facilities Dining room; Physical therapy room; Activities room; Chapel; Crafts room; Laundry room; Barber/Beauty shop; 5 lounges; Outside courtyards.
Activities Arts & crafts; Cards; Games; Reading groups; Prayer groups; Movies; Shopping trips; Social/Cultural gatherings; Cooking; Ceramics; Exercise group; Wood working.

Lawrence Manor Nursing Home*
8935 E 46th St, Indianapolis, IN, 46226
(317) 898-1515
Admin Mark R Feeser. *Medical Dir/Dir of Nursing* Karen Dawes.
Licensure Intermediate care. *Beds* 60. Certified Medicaid.
Staff RNs 1 (ft); LPNs 2 (ft); Nurses aides 18 (ft), 7 (pt); Activities coordinators 1 (ft); Dietitians 1 (pt).
Facilities Dining room; Laundry room; Barber/Beauty shop.
Activities Arts & crafts; Games; Reading groups; Prayer groups; Shopping trips.

Lockerbie Healthcare Center
1629 N College Ave, Indianapolis, IN, 46202
(317) 924-3239
Admin Roy L Anderson. *Medical Dir/Dir of Nursing* Ellen Bidgood RN DON.
Licensure Intermediate care. *Beds* ICF 79. Certified Medicaid.
Owner Proprietary Corp (Cloverleaf Enterprises).
Admissions Requirements Minimum age 21; Medical examination; Physician's request.

Staff Physicians 4 (pt); RNs 1 (ft); LPNs 8 (ft); Orderlies 2 (ft); Nurses aides 30 (ft); Physical therapists 1 (pt); Recreational therapists 1 (pt); Occupational therapists 1 (pt); Speech therapists 1 (pt); Activities coordinators 1 (ft); Dietitians 1 (ft), 1 (pt); Dentists 1 (pt); Ophthalmologists 1 (pt); Podiatrists 1 (pt).
Facilities Dining room; Activities room; Crafts room; Laundry room; Barber/Beauty shop.
Activities Arts & crafts; Cards; Games; Reading groups; Prayer groups; Movies; Shopping trips; Social/Cultural gatherings; Outings.

Lynhurst Healthcare Center
5225 W Morris St, Indianapolis, IN, 46241
(317) 244-3251
Admin Linda Sisson. *Medical Dir/Dir of Nursing* Kete Cockrell MD.
Licensure Intermediate care. *Beds* ICF 41. *Certified* Medicaid.
Owner Proprietary Corp.
Admissions Requirements Minimum age 18; Medical examination; Physician's request.
Facilities Dining room; Activities room; Laundry room; Library.
Activities Arts & crafts; Cards; Games; Reading groups; Prayer groups; Movies; Shopping trips; Social/Cultural gatherings.

Mapleton Health Care Facility Inc*
3650 Central Ave, Indianapolis, IN, 46205
(317) 925-1453
Admin Tena Blakemora. *Medical Dir/Dir of Nursing* Dr Lord, Dr Lebow, & Dr Strapts.
Licensure Intermediate care. *Beds* 52. *Certified* Medicaid.
Admissions Requirements Minimum age 18; Medical examination; Physician's request.
Staff Physicians 3 (ft); RNs 1 (ft); LPNs 3 (ft), 1 (pt); Orderlies 1 (ft); Nurses aides 14 (ft); Activities coordinators 1 (ft); Dietitians 1 (pt); Dentists 1 (pt); Ophthalmologists 1 (pt); Podiatrists 1 (pt).
Facilities Dining room; Activities room; Laundry room; Barber/Beauty shop.
Activities Arts & crafts; Cards; Games; Reading groups; Prayer groups; Movies; Shopping trips; Social/Cultural gatherings.

Marion County Healthcare Center
11850 Brookville Rd, Indianapolis, IN, 46239
(317) 862-6631
Admin Jack Musker. *Medical Dir/Dir of Nursing* Dan Hurley MD; Char Price DON.
Licensure Skilled care; Intermediate care; Residential care. *Beds* SNF 93; ICF 216; Residential 66. *Certified* Medicaid; Medicare.
Owner Publicly owned.
Admissions Requirements Minimum age 18; Medical examination; Physician's request.
Staff Physicians 3 (ft); RNs 5 (ft); LPNs 30 (ft); Nurses aides 80 (ft); Physical therapists 1 (ft); Recreational therapists 1 (ft); Occupational therapists 1 (ft); Speech therapists 1 (ft); Activities coordinators 5 (ft); Dietitians 2 (ft); Ophthalmologists 1 (ft); Podiatrists 1 (ft).
Facilities Dining room; Physical therapy room; Activities room; Chapel; Crafts room; Laundry room; Barber/Beauty shop; Library.
Activities Arts & crafts; Cards; Games; Reading groups; Prayer groups; Movies; Shopping trips; Social/Cultural gatherings.

Marquette Manor
8140 Township Line Rd, Indianapolis, IN, 46260
(317) 875-9700
Admin Donald M Blue. *Medical Dir/Dir of Nursing* Dr Thomas Lord; Gail F Paris RN.
Licensure Skilled care; Comprehensive care. *Beds* SNF 39; Licensed comprehensive 39.
Owner Nonprofit Corp.

Admissions Requirements Minimum age 62 in apartments, 18 in Health Care Centers; Medical examination.
Staff RNs 7 (ft); LPNs 5 (ft); Nurses aides 30 (ft); Activities coordinators 3 (ft).
Facilities Dining room; Physical therapy room; Activities room; Chapel; Crafts room; Laundry room; Barber/Beauty shop; Library; Dark rooms; Potting & planting room.
Activities Arts & crafts; Cards; Games; Reading groups; Prayer groups; Movies; Shopping trips; Social/Cultural gatherings; Travel groups; Exercise groups.

Maryfair Manor
3640 Central Ave, Indianapolis, IN, 46205
(317) 925-2316
Admin Kathleen B Voll. *Medical Dir/Dir of Nursing* Robert Lebow MD; Minnie Leath DON.
Licensure Skilled care; Intermediate care. *Beds* SNF 37; ICF 76. *Certified* Medicaid; Medicare.
Owner Proprietary Corp.
Admissions Requirements Minimum age 18; Medical examination; Physician's request.
Staff Physicians 5 (ft); RNs 1 (ft); LPNs 5 (ft); Orderlies 8 (ft); Nurses aides 12 (ft); Physical therapists 1 (ft), 1 (pt); Recreational therapists 1 (ft), 1 (pt); Activities coordinators 1 (ft); Dietitians 1 (pt); Dentists 1 (pt); Ophthalmologists 1 (pt); Podiatrists.
Facilities Dining room; Physical therapy room; Activities room; Crafts room; Laundry room; Library.
Activities Arts & crafts; Cards; Games; Reading groups; Prayer groups; Movies; Shopping trips; Social/Cultural gatherings.

Meridian Nursing Home*
2102 S Meridian St, Indianapolis, IN, 46225
(317) 786-9426
Admin Julia Nichols.
Licensure Intermediate care. *Beds* 44. *Certified* Medicaid.
Owner Proprietary Corp (Beverly Enterprises).

Miller's Merry Manor Community*
1651 N Campbell St, Indianapolis, IN, 46218
(317) 357-8040
Admin Karen Warner.
Beds 80.
Owner Proprietary Corp (Millers Merry Manor).

Miller's Merry Manor Inc
1700 N Illinois St, Indianapolis, IN, 46202
(317) 924-1325
Admin Sandy Ballenger. *Medical Dir/Dir of Nursing* Hugh Thatcher Jr MD; Betty Charpentier RN DON.
Licensure Skilled care; Intermediate care. *Beds* SNF 102; ICF 51. *Certified* Medicaid; Medicare.
Owner Proprietary Corp (Millers Merry Manor).
Admissions Requirements Minimum age 18; Medical examination; Physician's request.
Staff Physicians 15 (pt); RNs 5 (ft), 2 (pt); LPNs 14 (ft), 5 (pt); Nurses aides 49 (ft), 12 (pt); Physical therapists 1 (pt); Occupational therapists 1 (pt); Speech therapists 1 (pt); Activities coordinators 3 (ft); Dietitians 1 (pt); Dentists 1 (pt); Ophthalmologists 1 (pt); Podiatrists 1 (pt).
Facilities Dining room; Physical therapy room; Activities room; Chapel; Crafts room; Laundry room; Barber/Beauty shop.
Activities Arts & crafts; Cards; Games; Reading groups; Prayer groups; Movies; Shopping trips; Social/Cultural gatherings.

Mt Zion Geriatric Center*
3549 Boulevard Pl, Indianapolis, IN, 46208
(317) 925-9681
Admin Lula Paige-Baxter RN.
Licensure Intermediate care. *Beds* 104. *Certified* Medicaid.

New Hope of Indiana Inc*
8450 N Payne Rd, Indianapolis, IN, 46268
(317) 872-4210
Admin Robert Cannon.
Beds 60.

North Willow Center*
2002 W 86th St, Indianapolis, IN, 46260
(317) 844-8811
Admin Anna Hyden.
Licensure Intermediate care for mentally retarded. *Beds* ICF/MR 208. *Certified* Medicaid; Medicare.
Owner Proprietary Corp (Beverly Enterprises).

Northwest Manor Nursing Home*
6640 W 34th St, Indianapolis, IN, 46224
(317) 293-4930
Admin Jennifer A Knoll RN.
Licensure Skilled care; Intermediate care. *Beds* 138. *Certified* Medicaid; Medicare.

Parkview Manor Nursing Home*
2424 E 46th St, Indianapolis, IN, 46205
(317) 253-3278
Admin Dale Hartman.
Licensure Intermediate care. *Beds* 40. *Certified* Medicaid.
Owner Proprietary Corp (Cloverleaf Enterprises).

Pleasant View Lodge
PO Box 36090C, Rte 12, Indianapolis, IN, 46236
(317) 335-2159
Admin Margaret McCreary. *Medical Dir/Dir of Nursing* H Hensley MD; C Adcock RN DON.
Licensure Intermediate care. *Beds* ICF 48. *Certified* Medicaid.
Owner Proprietary Corp.
Admissions Requirements Minimum age 18; Medical examination; Physician's request.
Staff Physicians; RNs; LPNs; Nurses aides; Activities coordinators; Dietitians.
Facilities Dining room; Physical therapy room; Activities room; Chapel; Laundry room.
Activities Arts & crafts; Cards; Games; Reading groups; Prayer groups; Movies; Shopping trips.

Regency Place of Castleton
5226 E 82nd St, Indianapolis, IN, 46250
(31&) 842-6668
Admin Albert Estes. *Medical Dir/Dir of Nursing* Erin Hattabaugh.
Licensure Skilled care; Intermediate care; Residential care. *Beds* SNF; ICF; Residential 160.
Owner Proprietary Corp.
Staff Physicians 1 (pt); RNs 6 (ft), 6 (pt); LPNs 12 (ft), 6 (pt); Nurses aides 30 (ft); Physical therapists 1 (ft); Recreational therapists 1 (ft); Occupational therapists 1 (ft); Speech therapists 1 (pt); Activities coordinators 1 (ft); Dietitians 1 (pt).

Ritter Healthcare Center*
1301 N Ritter, Indianapolis, IN, 46219
(317) 353-9465
Admin Michael R Butler.
Licensure Skilled care; Intermediate care. *Beds* SNF 33; ICF 198. *Certified* Medicaid; Medicare.
Owner Proprietary Corp (ARA Living Centers).

Rural Health Care Facility*
1747 N Rural St, Indianapolis, IN, 46218
(317) 635-1355
Admin Rohn A McPherson.
Licensure Intermediate care. *Beds* 50. *Certified* Medicaid.
Admissions Requirements Medical examination.

Staff RNs 1 (ft); LPNs 4 (ft), 1 (pt); Orderlies 1 (pt); Activities coordinators 1 (ft); Dietitians 1 (ft); Dentists 1 (pt); Ophthalmologists 1 (pt); Podiatrists 1 (pt); Audiologists 1 (pt).
Facilities Dining room; Activities room; Crafts room; Laundry room; Barber/Beauty shop.
Activities Arts & crafts; Cards; Games; Prayer groups; Movies; Shopping trips; Social/Cultural gatherings.

St Augustine Home for the Aged
2345 W 86th St, Indianapolis, IN, 46260
(317) 872-6420
Admin Sr Regina Loftus. *Medical Dir/Dir of Nursing* Sr Catherine.
Licensure Intermediate care; Home for aged. *Beds* ICF 95; Residential. *Certified* Medicaid.
Owner Nonprofit Corp.
Admissions Requirements Minimum age 60; Medical examination.
Affiliation Roman Catholic
Facilities Dining room; Physical therapy room; Activities room; Chapel; Crafts room; Laundry room; Barber/Beauty shop; Library.
Activities Arts & crafts; Cards; Games; Prayer groups; Movies; Shopping trips.

St Paul Baptist Church Home for the Aged*
1141-45 N Sheffield Ave, Indianapolis, IN, 46222
(317) 637-2429
Admin Anna L Dailey.
Licensure Intermediate care. *Beds* 48. *Certified* Medicaid.
Admissions Requirements Minimum age 18; Medical examination; Physician's request.
Staff Physicians 2 (pt); RNs 1 (ft); LPNs 1 (ft), 2 (pt); Nurses aides 7 (ft), 12 (pt); Activities coordinators 1 (ft); Dietitians 1 (pt); Dentists 1 (pt); Ophthalmologists 1 (pt); Podiatrists 1 (pt).
Affiliation Baptist

Scott Manor Nursing Home Inc
3402 N Schofield, Indianapolis, IN, 46218
(317) 925-6038, 925-1264
Admin Dr Leonard Scott, Donald Golder. *Medical Dir/Dir of Nursing* Dr Linda Stropes, Dr Robert Lebow; Rosella Majors DON.
Licensure Intermediate care. *Beds* ICF 40. *Certified* Medicaid.
Owner Privately owned.
Admissions Requirements Medical examination; Physician's request.
Staff RNs 1 (ft); LPNs 3 (ft), 2 (pt); Orderlies 2 (ft), 1 (pt); Nurses aides 10 (ft), 10 (pt); Activities coordinators 1 (ft); Dietitians 1 (pt).
Facilities Dining room; Activities room; Crafts room; Laundry room; Barber/Beauty shop.
Activities Arts & crafts; Cards; Games; Reading groups; Prayer groups; Movies; Shopping trips.

Sherwood Convalescent Home*
3208 N Sherman Dr, Indianapolis, IN, 46218
(317) 545-6017
Admin Larry E Gray. *Medical Dir/Dir of Nursing* Dr Debra Carter Bluitt.
Licensure Intermediate care. *Beds* 51. *Certified* Medicaid.
Admissions Requirements Minimum age 19; Medical examination.
Staff RNs 2 (ft); LPNs 3 (ft), 2 (pt); Orderlies 1 (ft), 1 (pt); Nurses aides 10 (ft), 2 (pt); Activities coordinators 1 (ft); Dietitians 1 (pt).
Facilities Dining room; Activities room; Laundry room; Barber/Beauty shop.
Activities Arts & crafts; Cards; Games; Prayer groups; Movies; Shopping trips; Social/Cultural gatherings.

Southeastern Nursing Home
4743 Southeastern Ave, Indianapolis, IN, 46203
(317) 356-0901
Admin Daniel J Pittman. *Medical Dir/Dir of Nursing* Dr Linda Stropes; Gloria Spiker DON.
Licensure Intermediate care. *Beds* ICF 40. *Certified* Medicaid.
Owner Proprietary Corp (Beverly Enterprises).
Admissions Requirements Medical examination.
Staff Physicians 3 (pt); LPNs 5 (ft); Nurses aides 13 (ft), 3 (pt).
Languages Italian
Facilities Dining room; Activities room; Crafts room; Laundry room; Barber/Beauty shop.
Activities Arts & crafts; Cards; Games; Reading groups; Movies; Shopping trips; Social/Cultural gatherings; Bingo.

Southside Healthcare Center*
525 E Thompson Rd, Indianapolis, IN, 46227
(317) 787-8253
Admin Steven Still.
Licensure Intermediate care. *Beds* 156. *Certified* Medicaid.
Owner Proprietary Corp (ARA Living Centers).

Stone Manor Convalescent Center
8201 W Washington St, Indianapolis, IN, 46231
(317) 244-6848
Admin Sue Carter. *Medical Dir/Dir of Nursing* Dr Reyes.
Licensure Intermediate care. *Beds* 103. *Certified* Medicaid.
Owner Proprietary Corp.
Admissions Requirements Minimum age 18; Females only.
Staff Physicians; RNs; LPNs; Orderlies; Nurses aides; Physical therapists; Recreational therapists; Occupational therapists; Speech therapists; Activities coordinators; Dietitians; Podiatrists.
Facilities Dining room; Physical therapy room; Activities room; Crafts room; Laundry room; Barber/Beauty shop.
Activities Arts & crafts; Cards; Games; Reading groups; Prayer groups; Movies; Shopping trips; Social/Cultural gatherings.

Three Sisters Nursing Home Inc*
6130 N Michigan Rd, Indianapolis, IN, 46208
(317) 253-3486
Admin Mamie Beamon.
Licensure Intermediate care. *Beds* 100. *Certified* Medicaid.

Warren Park Nursing Home*
6855 E 10th St, Indianapolis, IN, 46219
(317) 353-9666
Admin Glenda Owens. *Medical Dir/Dir of Nursing* Dr Clarence Thomas.
Licensure Intermediate care. *Beds* 40. *Certified* Medicaid.
Owner Proprietary Corp (Beverly Enterprises).
Admissions Requirements Minimum age 18; Medical examination; Physician's request.
Staff RNs 1 (pt); LPNs 3 (ft), 2 (pt); Orderlies 1 (pt); Nurses aides 4 (ft), 8 (pt); Recreational therapists 1 (ft); Activities coordinators 1 (ft); Dietitians 1 (pt).
Facilities Dining room; Activities room; Laundry room.
Activities Arts & crafts; Cards; Games; Reading groups; Prayer groups; Movies; Shopping trips; Social/Cultural gatherings.

Westminster Village North Inc
11050 Presbyterian Dr, Indianapolis, IN, 46236
(317) 823-6841
Admin Gwen A Betor. *Medical Dir/Dir of Nursing* Dr Robert Nation; Joan Gritter.
Licensure Skilled care; Intermediate care. *Beds* 77. *Certified* Medicaid; Medicare.
Admissions Requirements Minimum age 55; Medical examination.
Staff Physicians 1 (ft); RNs 3 (ft), 1 (pt); LPNs 9 (ft); Nurses aides 28 (ft); Physical therapists 1 (ft); Activities coordinators 1 (ft); Dietitians 2 (ft), 1 (pt); Ophthalmologists 1 (pt).
Facilities Dining room; Physical therapy room; Activities room; Crafts room; Laundry room; Barber/Beauty shop.
Activities Arts & crafts; Cards; Games; Reading groups; Prayer groups; Movies; Shopping trips.

Westside Christian Retirement Village Inc
8616 W 10th St, Indianapolis, IN, 46234
(317) 271-1020
Admin Ronald E Davis. *Medical Dir/Dir of Nursing* Dr Joseph C Kirlin; Becky Nash RN BSN.
Licensure Intermediate care; Independent apartments. *Beds* ICF 59; Independent apts 160. *Certified* Medicaid.
Owner Nonprofit Corp.
Admissions Requirements Minimum age 62; Medical examination; Physician's request.
Staff RNs 1 (ft); LPNs 6 (ft); Nurses aides 15 (ft), 2 (pt); Physical therapists 1 (ft); Activities coordinators 1 (ft); Dietitians 1 (ft).
Affiliation Church of the Nazarene
Facilities Dining room; Physical therapy room; Activities room; Chapel; Crafts room; Laundry room; Barber/Beauty shop; Library.
Activities Arts & crafts; Cards; Games; Reading groups; Prayer groups; Movies; Shopping trips; Social/Cultural gatherings.

Westview Nursing Home
5435 W 38th St, Indianapolis, IN, 46254
(317) 293-2266
Admin May Ehresman. *Medical Dir/Dir of Nursing* Dr Fred Brooks; Barb Weddle.
Licensure Intermediate care. *Beds* 44. *Certified* Medicaid.
Owner Proprietary Corp (Beverly Enterprises).
Admissions Requirements Minimum age 18; Medical examination.
Staff RNs; LPNs; Orderlies; Nurses aides; Recreational therapists; Social service.
Facilities Dining room; Laundry room; Barber/Beauty shop.
Activities Arts & crafts; Cards; Games; Prayer groups; Movies; Shopping trips; Social/Cultural gatherings.

JASONVILLE

Shakamak Good Samaritan Center
800 E Ohio St, Jasonville, IN, 47438
(812) 665-2226
Admin Lois I Jensen. *Medical Dir/Dir of Nursing* Dr David Rutman; Ada P Nuckolls.
Licensure Skilled care; Intermediate care. *Beds* SNF 32; ICF 63. *Certified* Medicaid; Medicare.
Owner Nonprofit Corp (Evangelical Lutheran/Good Samaritan).
Admissions Requirements Minimum age 18; Medical examination; Physician's request.
Staff Physicians 4 (pt); RNs 6 (pt); LPNs 20 (pt); Nurses aides 40 (pt); Physical therapists 2 (pt); Speech therapists 1 (pt); Activities coordinators 1 (pt); Dietitians 1 (pt); Ophthalmologists 1 (pt).
Affiliation Lutheran
Facilities Dining room; Physical therapy room; Activities room; Chapel; Crafts room; Laundry room; Barber/Beauty shop; Library.
Activities Arts & crafts; Cards; Games; Reading groups; Prayer groups; Movies; Shopping trips; Social/Cultural gatherings; Camping.

JASPER

Jasper Nursing Center Inc
2909 Howard Dr, Jasper, IN, 47546
(812) 482-6161
Admin Donna Kennedy. *Medical Dir/Dir of Nursing* Frances Goatee MD; Ann Wagner RN DON.
Licensure Intermediate care. *Beds* ICF 138. *Certified* Medicaid.
Owner Proprietary Corp.
Admissions Requirements Minimum age 18.
Staff Physicians 1 (pt); RNs 3 (ft); LPNs 5 (ft), 1 (pt); Orderlies 2 (ft); Nurses aides 25 (ft), 5 (pt); Activities coordinators 1 (ft), 1 (pt); Social workers 1 (ft), 1 (pt).
Facilities Dining room; Physical therapy room; Activities room; Chapel; Crafts room; Laundry room; Barber/Beauty shop.
Activities Arts & crafts; Cards; Games; Reading groups; Prayer groups; Movies; Shopping trips; Social/Cultural gatherings; Garden club.

Northwood Good Samaritan Center
PO Box 459, 2515 Newton St, Jasper, IN, 47546
(812) 482-1722
Admin Kent J Brooks. *Medical Dir/Dir of Nursing* Jeffry Rendel MD; Judy Pund RN DON.
Licensure Skilled care; Intermediate care. *Beds* SNF 7; ICF 100. *Certified* Medicaid; Medicare.
Owner Nonprofit Corp (Evangelical Lutheran/Good Samaritan).
Admissions Requirements Medical examination.
Staff RNs 4 (ft), 1 (pt); LPNs 5 (ft), 3 (pt); Nurses aides 20 (ft), 12 (pt); Activities coordinators 2 (ft).
Languages German
Affiliation Lutheran
Facilities Dining room; Physical therapy room; Activities room; Chapel; Laundry room; Barber/Beauty shop.
Activities Arts & crafts; Cards; Games; Reading groups; Prayer groups; Movies; Shopping trips; Social/Cultural gatherings.

Providence Home
520 W 9th St, Jasper, IN, 47546
(812) 482-6603
Admin Rev Thaddeus Sztuczko. *Medical Dir/Dir of Nursing* Julia Burress.
Licensure Intermediate care. *Beds* ICF 66. *Certified* Medicaid.
Owner Nonprofit Corp.
Admissions Requirements Minimum age 18; Males only.
Staff Physicians 1 (pt); RNs 4 (pt); LPNs 3 (pt); Nurses aides 6 (pt).
Facilities Dining room; Activities room; Chapel; Crafts room; Laundry room; Barber/Beauty shop; Library.
Activities Arts & crafts; Games; Prayer groups; Movies; Shopping trips; Social/Cultural gatherings; Bowling; Picnics; Outings.

JEFFERSONVILLE

Hillcrest Healthcare Center*
203 Sparks Ave, Jeffersonville, IN, 47130
(812) 283-7918
Admin Stuart Reed. *Medical Dir/Dir of Nursing* Leonardo Ramus MD.
Licensure Skilled care; Intermediate care. *Beds* SNF 51; ICF 177. *Certified* Medicaid; Medicare.
Admissions Requirements Minimum age 18; Medical examination; Physician's request.
Staff Physicians 3 (ft); RNs 6 (ft), 6 (pt); LPNs 18 (ft), 10 (pt); Nurses aides 31 (ft), 15 (pt); Physical therapists 2 (ft), 1 (pt); Recreational therapists 1 (ft), 3 (pt); Occupational therapists 1 (pt); Speech therapists 1 (pt); Activities coordinators 1

(ft); Dietitians 1 (ft); Dentists 1 (pt); Ophthalmologists 1 (pt); Podiatrists 1 (pt); Audiologists 1 (pt).
Facilities Dining room; Physical therapy room; Activities room; Chapel; Crafts room; Laundry room; Barber/Beauty shop; Library.
Activities Arts & crafts; Cards; Games; Reading groups; Prayer groups; Movies; Shopping trips; Social/Cultural gatherings.

Jeffersonville Nursing Home
1720 E 8th St, Jeffersonville, IN, 47130
(812) 282-5102
Admin Lynn A Snow. *Medical Dir/Dir of Nursing* Dr Gene Pierce; Gloria Montano RN.
Licensure Intermediate care. *Beds* ICF 40. *Certified* Medicaid.
Owner Proprietary Corp (Beverly Enterprises).
Admissions Requirements Minimum age 18; Medical examination.
Staff RNs 1 (ft); LPNs 3 (ft), 3 (pt); Orderlies 1 (pt); Nurses aides 12 (ft), 4 (pt); Activities coordinators 1 (ft).
Facilities Dining room; Activities room; Laundry room.
Activities Arts & crafts; Cards; Games; Prayer groups; Movies; Social/Cultural gatherings.

Twilight Nursing Home Inc*
418 W Riverside Dr, Jeffersonville, IN, 47130
(812) 283-6401
Admin Delilah J Swaney.
Licensure Intermediate care. *Beds* 11.

KENDALLVILLE

Kendallville Nursing Home*
1433 S Main St, Kendallville, IN, 46755
(219) 347-3612
Admin Pamela DeKoninck. *Medical Dir/Dir of Nursing* Dr C F Stallman.
Licensure Intermediate care. *Beds* 40. *Certified* Medicaid.
Owner Proprietary Corp (Beverly Enterprises).
Admissions Requirements Medical examination; Physician's request.
Staff RNs 1 (ft); LPNs 1 (ft), 1 (pt); Orderlies 1 (pt); Nurses aides 6 (ft), 10 (pt); Activities coordinators 1 (ft); Dietitians 1 (pt); Podiatrists 1 (pt).
Facilities Dining room; Activities room; Laundry room.
Activities Arts & crafts; Cards; Games; Prayer groups; Movies; Field trips; Special outings; Picnics.

Lutheran Homes Inc*
612 E Mitchell St, Kendallville, IN, 46755
(219) 347-2256
Admin Paul Dobler. *Medical Dir/Dir of Nursing* Dr Warrener.
Licensure Intermediate care. *Beds* 80. *Certified* Medicaid.
Admissions Requirements Minimum age 65; Medical examination.
Staff RNs 1 (ft), 2 (pt); LPNs 6 (ft), 4 (pt); Orderlies 2 (ft); Nurses aides 18 (ft), 10 (pt); Activities coordinators 1 (ft); Dietitians 1 (ft).
Affiliation Lutheran
Facilities Dining room; Activities room; Chapel; Crafts room; Laundry room; Barber/Beauty shop; Library.
Activities Arts & crafts; Cards; Games; Reading groups; Prayer groups; Movies; Shopping trips; Social/Cultural gatherings.

KENTLAND

Kentland Nursing Home 2669
620 E Washington St, Kentland, IN, 47951
(219) 474-6741
Admin Marjorie McMillin. *Medical Dir/Dir of Nursing* Basil Datzman MD; Lynette DeWitt LPN DON.

Licensure Intermediate care. *Beds* ICF 40. *Certified* Medicaid.
Owner Proprietary Corp (Beverly Enterprises).
Admissions Requirements Minimum age 18; Medical examination; Physician's request.
Staff RNs 1 (pt); LPNs 3 (ft); Nurses aides 12 (ft), 4 (pt); Recreational therapists 1 (pt); Activities coordinators 1 (pt); Dietitians 1 (pt).
Facilities Dining room; Activities room; Laundry room.
Activities Arts & crafts; Cards; Games; Reading groups; Prayer groups; Movies; Shopping trips; Social/Cultural gatherings.

KNIGHTSVILLE

Harty Nursing Home*
Box 112, Knightsville, IN, 47857
(812) 446-2309
Admin Nita Mayhe.
Licensure Intermediate care. *Beds* 71. *Certified* Medicaid.
Staff RNs 1 (ft); LPNs 3 (ft); Nurses aides 30 (ft); Activities coordinators 1 (ft); Dietitians 1 (pt).
Facilities Dining room; Activities room; Chapel; Crafts room; Laundry room; Barber/Beauty shop.
Activities Arts & crafts; Cards; Games; Reading groups; Prayer groups; Movies; Shopping trips.

KNOX

Countryside Place of Knox*
RR 3, Box 6, 300 Culver Rd, Knox, IN, 46534
(219) 772-6248
Admin Janice A Reed. *Medical Dir/Dir of Nursing* Walter Fritz.
Licensure Skilled care; Intermediate care. *Beds* SNF 39; ICF 39. *Certified* Medicaid; Medicare.
Owner Proprietary Corp (Beverly Enterprises).
Admissions Requirements Minimum age 18; Medical examination; Physician's request.
Staff RNs 4 (ft), 2 (pt); LPNs 3 (ft); Orderlies 1 (pt); Nurses aides 19 (ft), 9 (pt); Physical therapists 1 (pt); Speech therapists 1 (pt); Activities coordinators 2 (pt); Dietitians 1 (ft); Dentists 1 (pt); Podiatrists 1 (pt).
Facilities Dining room; Physical therapy room; Activities room; Crafts room; Laundry room; Barber/Beauty shop.
Activities Arts & crafts; Cards; Games; Reading groups; Prayer groups; Movies; Shopping trips; Social/Cultural gatherings.

KOKOMO

Americana Healthcare Center—Kokomo*
3518 S LaFountain St, Kokomo, IN, 46901
(317) 453-4666
Admin Dorothy Fordyce.
Licensure Skilled care; Intermediate care. *Beds* SNF 36; ICF 69. *Certified* Medicaid; Medicare.
Owner Proprietary Corp (Manor Care).

Forest Park Healthcare Center
2233 W Jefferson St, Kokomo, IN, 46901
(317) 457-9175
Admin Michael D Moore. *Medical Dir/Dir of Nursing* Dr Artis; Doris Marnor RN DON.
Licensure Skilled care; Intermediate care. *Beds* 195. *Certified* Medicaid; Medicare.
Owner Proprietary Corp (ARA Living Centers).
Staff RNs; LPNs; Orderlies; Nurses aides; Physical therapists; Activities coordinators.
Activities Arts & crafts; Cards; Games; Reading groups; Prayer groups; Movies; Shopping trips; Social/Cultural gatherings; Van trips; Pizza parties; Birthday parties.

Kokomo Nursing Home-Greentree Manor
1560 S Plate St, Kokomo, IN, 46902
(317) 452-8934
Admin Linda Crowe. *Medical Dir/Dir of Nursing* Richard Bowling MD; Julie Miller RN DON.
Licensure Intermediate care. *Beds* ICF 40. *Certified* Medicaid.
Owner Proprietary Corp (Waverly Group).
Admissions Requirements Minimum age 18; Medical examination; Physician's request.
Staff RNs 1 (ft); LPNs 1 (ft), 4 (pt); Orderlies 1 (ft); Nurses aides 9 (ft), 4 (pt); Activities coordinators 1 (ft); Dietitians 1 (pt).
Languages Spanish, Sign
Facilities Dining room; Activities room; Laundry room; Barber/Beauty shop.
Activities Arts & crafts; Cards; Games; Reading groups; Prayer groups; Movies; Shopping trips; Social/Cultural gatherings; Birthday parties by McDonalds; Pizza parties by Pizza Hut.

Sycamore Village Health Center*
2905 W Sycamore, Kokomo, IN, 46901
(317) 452-5491
Admin Dan D Wheat.
Licensure Intermediate care. *Beds* 173. *Certified* Medicaid.
Owner Proprietary Corp (Beverly Enterprises).

Windsor Estates of Kokomo*
429 Lincoln Rd W, Kokomo, IN, 46901
(317) 453-5600
Admin Linda Dishon. *Medical Dir/Dir of Nursing* James Whitfield.
Licensure Skilled care; Intermediate care. *Beds* 87. *Certified* Medicaid; Medicare.
Staff RNs 4 (ft), 1 (pt); LPNs 8 (ft), 2 (pt); Nurses aides 22 (ft), 2 (pt); Physical therapists 1 (pt); Speech therapists 1 (pt); Activities coordinators 1 (pt); Dietitians 1 (pt); Dentists 1 (pt); Ophthalmologists 1 (pt); Podiatrists 1 (pt).
Facilities Dining room; Physical therapy room; Activities room; Crafts room; Laundry room; Barber/Beauty shop.
Activities Arts & crafts; Cards; Games; Reading groups; Prayer groups; Movies; Social/Cultural gatherings.

LADOGA

Golden Manor Health Care Center*
1001 E Main St, Ladoga, IN, 47954
(317) 942-2223
Admin David W Vice.
Licensure Intermediate care. *Beds* 95. *Certified* Medicaid.

LAFAYETTE

Americana Healthcare Center—Lafayette*
2201 Cason St, Lafayette, IN, 47901
(317) 447-4102
Admin Betty J Montgomery.
Licensure Skilled care; Intermediate care. *Beds* SNF 19; ICF 38. *Certified* Medicaid; Medicare.
Owner Proprietary Corp (Manor Care).
Admissions Requirements Medical examination; Physician's request.
Staff Physicians 1 (pt); RNs 6 (ft), 4 (pt); LPNs 3 (ft), 4 (pt); Nurses aides 25 (ft), 7 (pt); Physical therapists 1 (ft), 1 (pt); Occupational therapists 1 (ft), 1 (pt); Speech therapists 1 (pt); Activities coordinators 1 (ft); Dietitians 1 (ft).
Facilities Dining room; Physical therapy room; Activities room; Crafts room; Barber/Beauty shop.
Activities Arts & crafts; Cards; Games; Reading groups; Prayer groups; Movies; Social/Cultural gatherings.

Comfort Retirement & Nursing Home Inc*
312 N 8th St, Lafayette, IN, 47901
(317) 742-8455
Admin Richard E Linson.
Licensure Intermediate care. *Beds* 46. *Certified* Medicaid.

Hillcrest Nursing Home*
1123 E South St, Lafayette, IN, 47901
(317) 742-6904
Admin Theresa A Dellwo. *Medical Dir/Dir of Nursing* Dr Mary Ade.
Licensure Intermediate care. *Beds* 40. *Certified* Medicaid.
Owner Proprietary Corp (Beverly Enterprises).
Admissions Requirements Medical examination; Physician's request.
Staff RNs 1 (pt); LPNs 3 (ft); Nurses aides 5 (ft), 8 (pt); Activities coordinators 1 (pt); Dietitians 1 (pt).
Facilities Dining room; Activities room; Laundry room.
Activities Arts & crafts; Cards; Games; Reading groups; Prayer groups; Movies; Shopping trips; Social/Cultural gatherings.

Indiana Pythian Home
1501 S 18th St, Lafayette, IN, 47905
(317) 474-1405
Admin John R Clark. *Medical Dir/Dir of Nursing* Dr Eleanor Filmer; Carol Clark DON.
Licensure Intermediate care; Residential. *Beds* 118. *Certified* Medicaid.
Owner Nonprofit organization/foundation.
Admissions Requirements Medical examination.
Staff RNs 3 (ft); LPNs 5 (ft); Orderlies 1 (ft); Nurses aides 11 (ft); Activities coordinators 1 (ft); Dietitians 1 (ft); Ophthalmologists.
Affiliation Knights of Pythias
Facilities Dining room; Activities room; Chapel; Crafts room; Barber/Beauty shop.
Activities Arts & crafts; Cards; Games; Reading groups; Prayer groups; Movies; Shopping trips; Social/Cultural gatherings.

Lafayette Healthcare Center*
1903 Union St, Lafayette, IN, 47901
(317) 447-9431
Admin Terry Johnson. *Medical Dir/Dir of Nursing* Dr Eleanor Filmer.
Licensure Skilled care; Intermediate care. *Beds* SNF 69; ICF 133. *Certified* Medicaid; Medicare.
Admissions Requirements Medical examination.
Staff Physicians 1 (ft); RNs 2 (ft); LPNs 6 (ft), 3 (pt); Orderlies 4 (ft); Nurses aides 58 (ft), 3 (pt); Physical therapists 1 (ft); Occupational therapists 1 (pt); Speech therapists 1 (pt); Activities coordinators 1 (ft), 1 (pt); Dietitians 1 (ft); Dentists 1 (pt); Podiatrists 1 (pt); Audiologists 1 (pt).
Facilities Dining room; Physical therapy room; Activities room; Chapel; Crafts room; Laundry room; Barber/Beauty shop; Library.
Activities Arts & crafts; Cards; Games; Reading groups; Prayer groups; Movies; Shopping trips; Social/Cultural gatherings.

Regency Place
300 Windy Hill Dr, Lafayette, IN, 47905
(317) 477-7791
Admin David Lennartz. *Medical Dir/Dir of Nursing* Linda Marshall DON.
Licensure Skilled care; Intermediate care; Residential care. *Beds* SNF 51; ICF 102; Residential 6. *Certified* Medicaid; Medicare.
Admissions Requirements Minimum age 18; Medical examination.
Staff RNs 5 (ft), 3 (pt); LPNs 15 (ft), 7 (pt); Nurses aides 38 (ft), 14 (pt); Physical therapists 1 (pt); Activities coordinators 2 (ft); Dietitians 1 (ft).

Facilities Dining room; Physical therapy room; Activities room; Crafts room; Laundry room; Barber/Beauty shop; Library; Resident/family lounges.
Activities Arts & crafts; Cards; Games; Reading groups; Prayer groups; Movies; Shopping trips; Social/Cultural gatherings; Residents lunch club.

St Anthony Health Care Inc
1205 N 14th, Lafayette, IN, 47904
(317) 423-4861
Admin Becky Thompson. *Medical Dir/Dir of Nursing* James Pickerill MD; Heidi Whitus RN DON.
Licensure Intermediate care. *Beds* ICF 80. *Certified* Medicaid.
Owner Privately owned.
Admissions Requirements Medical examination; Physician's request.
Staff Physicians 1 (pt); RNs 5 (ft); LPNs 5 (ft), 3 (pt); Orderlies 1 (ft); Nurses aides 20 (ft), 5 (pt); Physical therapists 1 (pt); Occupational therapists 1 (pt); Speech therapists 1 (pt); Activities coordinators 1 (ft); Dietitians 1 (pt); Ophthalmologists 1 (pt); Podiatrists 1 (pt).
Affiliation Roman Catholic
Facilities Dining room; Physical therapy room; Activities room; Chapel; Crafts room; Laundry room; Barber/Beauty shop.
Activities Arts & crafts; Cards; Games; Reading groups; Prayer groups; Movies; Social/Cultural gatherings; Daily mass.

LAFONTAINE

Shangri-La Health Care Center
604 Rennaker St, LaFontaine, IN, 46940
(317) 981-2081, 662-9350
Admin Paul R Huffman. *Medical Dir/Dir of Nursing* Fred Poehler MD.
Licensure Intermediate care; Residential care. *Beds* ICF 79; Residential 12. *Certified* Medicaid.
Admissions Requirements Medical examination.
Staff Physicians 1 (pt); RNs 1 (ft); LPNs 2 (ft); Orderlies 2 (ft); Nurses aides 30 (ft), 25 (pt); Activities coordinators 1 (ft); Dietitians 1 (pt).
Facilities Dining room; Activities room; Laundry room; Barber/Beauty shop; Lounges.
Activities Arts & crafts; Cards; Games; Reading groups; Prayer groups; Movies; Shopping trips; Social/Cultural gatherings.

LAGRANGE

LaGrange Nursing Home*
Rte 5, Box 74, LaGrange, IN, 46761
(219) 463-7455
Admin Margaret Davis. *Medical Dir/Dir of Nursing* Debra Rose.
Licensure Intermediate care. *Beds* 40. *Certified* Medicaid.
Owner Proprietary Corp (Beverly Enterprises).
Admissions Requirements Medical examination; Physician's request.
Staff Physicians 1 (pt); RNs 1 (ft); LPNs 3 (pt); Nurses aides 7 (ft), 2 (pt); Activities coordinators 1 (ft); Dietitians 1 (pt); Dentists 1 (pt); Ophthalmologists 1 (pt); Podiatrists 1 (pt); Audiologists 1 (pt).
Facilities Dining room; Activities room; Crafts room; Laundry room.
Activities Arts & crafts; Cards; Games; Reading groups; Prayer groups; Movies; Shopping trips; Social/Cultural gatherings.

Miller's Merry Manor Inc
PO Box 89, State Rd 9 N, LaGrange, IN, 46761
(219) 463-2172, (616) 651-4968

Admin Grace M Karst RN. *Medical Dir/Dir of Nursing* M Reed Taylor MD; Karen S Hyska RN DON.
Licensure Skilled care; Intermediate care; Comprehensive. *Beds* SNF 54; ICF 113; Comprehensive 35. *Certified* Medicaid; Medicare.
Owner Proprietary Corp (Millers Merry Manor).
Admissions Requirements Minimum age 18; Medical examination; Physician's request.
Staff RNs 6 (ft), 4 (pt); LPNs 16 (ft), 2 (pt); Orderlies 2 (ft); Nurses aides 28 (ft), 20 (pt); Physical therapists 1 (pt); Activities coordinators 2 (ft); Dietitians 1 (ft); Ophthalmologists 1 (pt).
Facilities Dining room; Physical therapy room; Activities room; Chapel; Crafts room; Laundry room; Barber/Beauty shop.
Activities Arts & crafts; Cards; Games; Reading groups; Prayer groups; Movies; Shopping trips; Social/Cultural gatherings.

LAPORTE

Countryside Place of LaPorte
1700 I St, LaPorte, IN, 46350
(219) 362-6234
Admin Larry Beall. *Medical Dir/Dir of Nursing* Joyce Nicholson DON.
Licensure Skilled care; Intermediate care. *Beds* SNF 39; ICF 60. *Certified* Medicaid; Medicare.
Owner Proprietary Corp (Beverly Enterprises).

Fountainview Terrace
1900 Andrew Ave, LaPorte, IN, 46350
(219) 362-7014
Admin Edward Given. *Medical Dir/Dir of Nursing* Dr Robert Erwin; Pat Barnes DON.
Licensure Skilled care; Intermediate care; Residential. *Beds* SNF 64; ICF 114; Residential 16. *Certified* Medicaid; Medicare.
Owner Proprietary Corp (Beverly Enterprises).
Admissions Requirements Medical examination; Physician's request.
Staff RNs; LPNs; Orderlies; Nurses aides; Physical therapists; Occupational therapists; Speech therapists; Activities coordinators; Dietitians; Dentists; Ophthalmologists; Podiatrists.
Languages Spanish, German, Polish
Facilities Dining room; Physical therapy room; Activities room; Chapel; Crafts room; Laundry room; Barber/Beauty shop; Library.
Activities Arts & crafts; Cards; Games; Reading groups; Prayer groups; Movies; Shopping trips; Social/Cultural gatherings.

LAWRENCEBURG

Shady Nook Care Center*
36 Valley Dr, Lawrenceburg, IN, 47025
(812) 537-0930
Admin Daniel McMullen.
Licensure Intermediate care. *Beds* 39. *Certified* Medicaid.

Terrace View Extended Care Facility*
403 Bielby Rd, Lawrenceburg, IN, 47025
(812) 537-1132
Admin Howard Goodman.
Licensure Skilled care; Intermediate care. *Beds* SNF 41; ICF 82. *Certified* Medicaid; Medicare.

LEAVENWORTH

Todd Dickey Medical Center*
PO Box 134, A & 2nd Sts, Leavenworth, IN, 47137
(812) 739-2292
Admin Jeffery Padgett.
Licensure Intermediate care. *Beds* 78. *Certified* Medicaid; Medicare.
Owner Proprietary Corp (Unicare).

LEBANON

Countryside Healthcare Center
1585 Perryworth Rd, Lebanon, IN, 46052
(317) 482-6391
Admin W David Moffatt. *Medical Dir/Dir of Nursing* Dr Ben Park DON.
Licensure Skilled care; Intermediate care. *Beds* SNF 38; ICF/MR 92. *Certified* Medicaid; Medicare.
Owner Proprietary Corp (Cloverleaf Enterprises).
Admissions Requirements Medical examination.
Staff Physicians 8 (pt); RNs 5 (ft); LPNs 6 (ft), 1 (pt); Orderlies 1 (ft); Nurses aides 24 (ft), 1 (pt); Physical therapists 1 (pt); Occupational therapists 1 (pt); Speech therapists 1 (pt); Activities coordinators 1 (ft); Dietitians 1 (pt); Ophthalmologists 1 (pt); Dentist 1 (pt).
Facilities Dining room; Physical therapy room; Activities room; Laundry room; Barber/Beauty shop; Library.
Activities Arts & crafts; Cards; Games; Reading groups; Prayer groups; Movies; Social/Cultural gatherings; Exercise group.

English Nursing Home
1015 N Lebanon, Lebanon, IN, 46052
(317) 482-5880
Admin Charles W Bellus. *Medical Dir/Dir of Nursing* Kimberly Byrd.
Licensure Intermediate care. *Beds* ICF 36. *Certified* Medicaid.
Owner Proprietary Corp.
Admissions Requirements Minimum age 21.
Staff LPNs; Nurses aides; Activities coordinators; Dietitians.
Facilities Dining room; Activities room; Crafts room; Laundry room; Barber/Beauty shop.
Activities Arts & crafts; Games; Movies; Social/Cultural gatherings.

Lebanon Nursing Home*
301 W Essex St, Lebanon, IN, 46052
(317) 482-1950
Admin Donald M Thompson.
Licensure Intermediate care. *Beds* 40. *Certified* Medicaid.
Owner Proprietary Corp (Beverly Enterprises).
Admissions Requirements Medical examination.
Staff RNs 1 (ft), 1 (pt); LPNs 1 (pt); Nurses aides 8 (ft), 6 (pt); Activities coordinators 2 (pt); Dietitians 1 (pt).
Facilities Dining room; Laundry room.
Activities Cards; Games; Reading groups; Prayer groups; Shopping trips.

Parkwood Health Care Inc*
1001 N Grant St, Lebanon, IN, 46052
(317) 482-6400
Admin Arthur O Dickerson.
Licensure Intermediate care. *Beds* 133. *Certified* Medicaid.
Staff RNs 2 (ft), 3 (pt); LPNs 3 (ft), 2 (pt); Nurses aides 29 (ft), 18 (pt); Physical therapists; Speech therapists; Activities coordinators; Dietitians; Podiatrists; Audiologists; Qualified medical assistants 11 (ft), 6 (pt).
Facilities Dining room; Physical therapy room; Activities room; Laundry room; Barber/Beauty shop.
Activities Arts & crafts; Games; Reading groups; Prayer groups; Movies.

LEWISVILLE

Lewisville Hotel for Senior Citizens*
Box 98, US 40, Lewisville, IN, 47352
(317) 987-7952
Admin Sarah Vollmer.
Licensure Residential care. *Beds* 33.

LEXINGTON

Englishton Park
Highway 203 N, Lexington, IN, 47138
(812) 889-2681
Admin Janet A Heilman. *Medical Dir/Dir of Nursing* Patricia A Mair.
Licensure Residential care. *Beds* Residential 60.
Owner Nonprofit Corp.
Admissions Requirements Minimum age 60; Medical examination; Physician's request.
Staff RNs 1 (ft); Nurses aides 5 (ft); Activities coordinators 1 (ft); Dietitians 1 (pt); Medications Aides 5 (ft).
Affiliation Presbyterian
Facilities Dining room; Activities room; Laundry room; Barber/Beauty shop; Library.
Activities Arts & crafts; Cards; Games; Reading groups; Prayer groups; Movies; Shopping trips; Social/Cultural gatherings; Field trips; Church and community activities.

LIBERTY

Hillcrest Estates
215 W High St, Liberty, IN, 47353
(317) 458-5117
Admin T E Trumbauer. *Medical Dir/Dir of Nursing* Dr J T Hinton; J K Stumbo RN.
Licensure Intermediate care. *Beds* ICF 60. *Certified* Medicaid.
Owner Proprietary Corp.
Admissions Requirements Minimum age 19; Medical examination; Physician's request.
Staff RNs 2 (ft); LPNs 4 (ft), 1 (pt).
Facilities Dining room; Activities room; Laundry room; Barber/Beauty shop.
Activities Arts & crafts; Games; Prayer groups; Movies; Shopping trips; Social/Cultural gatherings.

Park Manor Nursing Home
409 E Union St, Liberty, IN, 47353
(317) 458-6194
Admin Elaine Stubbs RN. *Medical Dir/Dir of Nursing* Dr C G Clarkson; Donna Marling LPN.
Licensure Intermediate care. *Beds* 22. *Certified* Medicaid.
Owner Privately owned.
Admissions Requirements Minimum age 18; Females only.
Staff RNs 1 (pt); LPNs 4 (ft); Nurses aides 12 (ft), 2 (pt); Activities coordinators 1 (ft), 1 (pt); Dietitians 1 (pt).
Facilities Dining room; Activities room; Barber/Beauty shop.
Activities Arts & crafts; Cards; Games; Reading groups; Prayer groups; Movies; Shopping trips; Social/Cultural gatherings.

LIGONIER

Kenney Retirement Community
200 Kenney Cr Dr, Ligonier, IN, 46767
(219) 894-7131
Admin Carol Reed. *Medical Dir/Dir of Nursing* R C Stone MD; Martha Howe RN DON.
Licensure Skilled care; Intermediate care. *Beds* SNF 12; ICF 55. *Certified* Medicaid; Medicare.
Owner Proprietary Corp.
Admissions Requirements Minimum age 19 (Geriatric facility also); Medical examination; Physician's request.
Staff RNs 4 (ft); LPNs 2 (ft), 3 (pt); Nurses aides 13 (ft), 3 (pt); Physical therapists 2 (pt); Occupational therapists 1 (pt); Speech therapists 1 (pt); Activities coordinators 1 (ft); Dietitians 1 (ft); Ophthalmologists 1 (pt); Podiatrists 1 (pt).
Facilities Dining room; Physical therapy room; Activities room; Laundry room; Barber/Beauty shop.

Activities Arts & crafts; Cards; Games; Reading groups; Prayer groups; Movies; Shopping trips; Social/Cultural gatherings.

LINTON

Glenburn Rest Haven Home Inc*
RR 2, Glenburn Rd, Linton, IN, 47441
(812) 847-2221
Admin William T Fisher.
Licensure Intermediate care. *Beds* 154.
Certified Medicaid.

Linton Nursing Home
1501 E "A" St, Linton, IN, 47441
(812) 847-4426
Admin Michael H Leistner. *Medical Dir/Dir of Nursing* William Powers; Peggy Southwood.
Licensure Intermediate care. *Beds* 40.
Certified Medicaid.
Owner Proprietary Corp (Beverly Enterprises).
Admissions Requirements Minimum age 18; Medical examination.
Staff RNs 1 (pt); LPNs 6 (ft); Nurses aides 6 (ft), 4 (pt); Physical therapists 1 (pt); Speech therapists 1 (pt); Activities coordinators 1 (ft); Dietitians 1 (pt); Ophthalmologists 1 (pt).
Facilities Dining room; Activities room; Crafts room; Laundry room.
Activities Arts & crafts; Cards; Games; Reading groups; Prayer groups; Movies; Shopping trips; Social/Cultural gatherings.

LOGANSPORT

Camelot Care Center
1555 Commerce St, Logansport, IN, 46947
(219) 753-0404
Admin Rita Holloway. *Medical Dir/Dir of Nursing* E R Luxenberg MD; Rita Hollingsworth RN DON.
Licensure Intermediate care. *Beds* ICF 75.
Certified Medicaid.
Owner Proprietary Corp.
Admissions Requirements Minimum age 0-2 months (Health care facility for children).
Staff Physicians 1 (pt); RNs 2 (ft); LPNs 2 (ft), 4 (pt); Physical therapists 1 (pt); Occupational therapists 1 (pt); Activities coordinators 1 (ft); Dietitians 1 (pt).
Facilities Dining room; Physical therapy room; Activities room; Crafts room; Laundry room.
Activities Arts & crafts; Games; Reading groups; Movies; Shopping trips; Social/Cultural gatherings; School programs; Sheltered workshop program.

Chase Manor Nursing & Convalescent Center*
2 Chase Park, Logansport, IN, 46947
(219) 753-4137
Admin David J Krizmanich.
Licensure Skilled care; Intermediate care. *Beds* SNF 41; ICF 174. *Certified* Medicaid; Medicare.

Neal Home*
2518 George St, Logansport, IN, 46947
(219) 753-3920
Admin Mary L Strahle.
Licensure Home for aged. *Beds* 20.
Admissions Requirements Females only.

Woodland Acres County Home
Rte 4, Box 121, Logansport, IN, 46947
(219) 753-2791
Admin Mary Jo Jack.
Licensure Residential care. *Beds* 23. *Certified* Medicaid; Medicare.
Owner Publicly owned.
Admissions Requirements Minimum age Adult; Medical examination; Self-sufficient.
Staff Cooks 2 (ft); Housekeeper 1 (ft); Laundry attendant 1 (ft); Vocational attendant 1 (ft), 1 (pt); County Nurse.

Facilities Dining room; Laundry room; Barber/Beauty shop; TV room.
Activities Cards; Games; Prayer groups; Movies; Shopping trips; Social/Cultural gatherings.

LOOGOOTEE

Medco Center of Loogootee
Rte 4, Hwy 550, Loogootee, IN, 47553
(812) 295-3624
Admin Lon R Clark. *Medical Dir/Dir of Nursing* Dr James Poirier; Lana Wells RN.
Licensure Intermediate care. *Beds* ICF 36.
Certified Medicaid.
Owner Proprietary Corp (Unicare).
Admissions Requirements Medical examination; Physician's request.
Staff RNs 3 (ft); LPNs 2 (ft), 1 (pt); Nurses aides 6 (ft), 4 (pt); Activities coordinators 1 (ft).
Facilities Dining room; Activities room; Laundry room; Barber/Beauty shop; Picnic grounds; Garden; Activity Center.
Activities Arts & crafts; Cards; Games; Reading groups; Prayer groups; Movies; Shopping trips; Social/Cultural gatherings; Garden club.

LOWELL

Lowell Healthcare Center
255 Burnham St, Lowell, IN, 46356
(219) 696-7791
Admin Janice A Reed. *Medical Dir/Dir of Nursing* David B Templin MD; Barbara Westerhoff DON.
Licensure Intermediate care. *Beds* ICF 56.
Certified Medicaid.
Owner Proprietary Corp.
Admissions Requirements Medical examination.
Staff Physicians 1 (ft); RNs 1 (pt); LPNs 3 (ft), 3 (pt); Nurses aides 17 (ft), 15 (pt); Activities coordinators 1 (ft); Dietitians 1 (ft), 1 (pt).
Facilities Dining room; Laundry room; Barber/Beauty shop.
Activities Arts & crafts; Cards; Games; Reading groups; Prayer groups; Movies; Shopping trips; Social/Cultural gatherings.

LYNN

Parrott's Home*
304 W Sherman St, PO Box 347, Lynn, IN, 47355
(317) 874-4281
Admin Maxine Parrott.
Licensure Residential care. *Beds* 5.

MADISON

Clifty Falls Convalescent Center
950 Cross Ave, Madison, IN, 47250
(812) 273-4640
Admin Aliene Breitenbach. *Medical Dir/Dir of Nursing* Robert Ellis MD; Cathy Spry DON.
Licensure Skilled care; Intermediate care. *Beds* SNF 52; ICF 64.
Owner Proprietary Corp.
Admissions Requirements Minimum age 18; Medical examination; Physician's request.
Staff RNs 3 (ft), 3 (pt); LPNs 4 (ft), 6 (pt); Nurses aides 35 (ft), 30 (pt); Activities coordinators.
Facilities Dining room; Physical therapy room; Activities room; Laundry room; Barber/Beauty shop.
Activities Arts & crafts; Cards; Games; Reading groups; Prayer groups; Movies; Shopping trips; Social/Cultural gatherings.

Madison Nursing Home*
1945 Cragmont St, Madison, IN, 47250
(812) 273-4696

Admin W R Scott James.
Licensure Intermediate care. *Beds* 40.
Certified Medicaid.
Owner Proprietary Corp (Beverly Enterprises).
Admissions Requirements Minimum age 18.
Staff RNs 1 (pt); LPNs 2 (ft), 1 (pt); Nurses aides 5 (ft), 5 (pt); Activities coordinators 1 (pt); Dietitians 1 (pt).
Facilities Dining room; Activities room; Laundry room.
Activities Arts & crafts; Cards; Games; Movies.

River Valley Living Center
702 Elm St, Madison, IN, 47250
(812) 265-2286
Admin Jean Johnson. *Medical Dir/Dir of Nursing* Robert Johnson MD.
Licensure Intermediate care. *Beds* ICF 32.
Certified Medicaid.
Owner Nonprofit Corp (Adventist Health Sys-USA).
Admissions Requirements Minimum age 18; Medical examination; Physician's request.
Staff Physicians 1 (pt); RNs 1 (ft), 1 (pt); LPNs 3 (ft); Orderlies 1 (ft); Nurses aides 7 (ft), 3 (pt); Activities coordinators 1 (ft); Dietitians 1 (ft), 1 (pt).
Affiliation Seventh-Day Adventist
Facilities Dining room; Activities room; Laundry room; Barber/Beauty shop.
Activities Arts & crafts; Cards; Games; Reading groups; Prayer groups; Movies; Shopping trips; Social/Cultural gatherings; Picnics.

MARION

Bradner Village Health Care Center Inc*
505 Bradner Ave, Marion, IN, 46952
(317) 662-3981
Admin Jim J Walts.
Licensure Skilled care; Intermediate care. *Beds* SNF 48; ICF 153. *Certified* Medicaid.

Colonial Oaks Health Care Center
4725 S Colonial Oaks Dr, Marion, IN, 46953
(317) 674-9791
Admin Penny J Keihn. *Medical Dir/Dir of Nursing* Miles Donaldson MD; Pat Rigsbee RN DON.
Licensure Skilled care; Intermediate care. *Beds* SNF 32; ICF 88. *Certified* Medicaid; Medicare.
Owner Proprietary Corp.
Admissions Requirements Medical examination; Physician's request.
Staff RNs 6 (ft), 4 (pt); LPNs 10 (ft), 8 (pt); Nurses aides 37 (ft), 18 (pt); Physical therapists 1 (ft), 2 (pt); Speech therapists 1 (pt); Activities coordinators 2 (pt); Dietitians 1 (pt); Ophthalmologists 1 (pt); Social services 1 (ft); Dentist 1 (pt).
Facilities Dining room; Physical therapy room; Activities room; Chapel; Crafts room; Laundry room; Barber/Beauty shop.
Activities Arts & crafts; Cards; Games; Reading groups; Prayer groups; Movies; Shopping trips; Social/Cultural gatherings.

Flinn Memorial Home Inc
614 W 14th St, Marion, IN, 46953-2199
(317) 664-0618
Admin John L Andrae. *Medical Dir/Dir of Nursing* Edward A Buhr MD; Barbara Risinger RN DON.
Licensure Intermediate care; Residential. *Beds* ICF 80; Residential 76. *Certified* Medicaid.
Owner Nonprofit Corp.
Admissions Requirements Minimum age 70; Medical examination.
Staff Physicians 1 (pt); RNs 1 (ft); LPNs 5 (ft), 3 (pt); Nurses aides 20 (ft), 12 (pt); Physical therapists 1 (pt); Occupational therapists 1 (pt); Speech therapists 1 (pt); Activities coordinators 3 (ft); Dietitians 1 (pt); Podiatrists 1 (pt).
Affiliation Disciples of Christ

Facilities Dining room; Physical therapy room; Activities room; Chapel; Crafts room; Laundry room; Barber/Beauty shop; Library.
Activities Arts & crafts; Cards; Games; Reading groups; Prayer groups; Movies; Shopping trips.

Golden Age Nursing Home
1800 Kem Rd, Marion, IN, 46952
(317) 664-4573
Admin Amy Lambertson. Medical Dir/Dir of Nursing Dr R Patel; Ruthann Richwine.
Licensure Intermediate care. Beds ICF 80. Certified Medicaid.
Owner Proprietary Corp (Forum Grp).
Admissions Requirements Medical examination; Physician's request.
Staff RNs 2 (ft), 1 (pt); LPNs 2 (ft), 3 (pt); Nurses aides 16 (ft), 9 (pt); Activities coordinators 1 (ft); Dietitians 1 (ft).
Facilities Dining room; Activities room; Crafts room; Laundry room; Barber/Beauty shop.
Activities Arts & crafts; Cards; Games; Reading groups; Prayer groups; Movies; Shopping trips; Social/Cultural gatherings.

Riverview Manor Nursing Home*
221 N Washington St, Marion, IN, 46952
(317) 664-0612
Admin Barbara Winters.
Licensure Intermediate care. Beds 103. Certified Medicaid.
Owner Proprietary Corp (Forum Grp).

Wesleyan Health Care Center
518 W 36th St, Marion, IN, 46953
(317) 674-3371
Admin Dave Clement. Medical Dir/Dir of Nursing Dr Charles Yale; Carol Clark RN DON.
Licensure Skilled care; Intermediate care. Beds SNF 119. Certified Medicaid; Medicare.
Owner Proprietary Corp.
Admissions Requirements Medical examination; Physician's request.
Staff Physicians 20 (pt); RNs 4 (ft), 2 (pt); LPNs 5 (ft), 4 (pt); Orderlies 1 (ft), 1 (pt); Nurses aides 24 (ft), 23 (pt); Physical therapists 1 (pt); Activities coordinators 2 (ft); Dietitians 1 (ft), 1 (pt); Dentists 1 (pt); Ophthalmologists 1 (pt); Podiatrists 1 (pt).
Affiliation First Wesleyan Church
Facilities Dining room; Physical therapy room; Activities room; Chapel; Crafts room; Laundry room; Barber/Beauty shop; Library.
Activities Arts & crafts; Cards; Games; Prayer groups; Movies; Shopping trips; Social/Cultural gatherings.

MARTINSVILLE

Dixon Home Care Center*
60 E Harrison St, Martinsville, IN, 46151
(317) 342-1744
Admin Ruth E Denny.
Licensure Intermediate care. Beds 17.

Grandview Convalescent Center
1959 E Columbus St, Martinsville, IN, 46151
(317) 342-7114
Admin Patricia Walker. Medical Dir/Dir of Nursing Gary Milda DO; Janice Murphy RN DON.
Licensure Intermediate care. Beds ICF 76. Certified Medicaid.
Owner Privately owned.
Admissions Requirements Medical examination; Physician's request.
Staff RNs; LPNs; Nurses aides; Physical therapists; Activities coordinators; Dietitians; Ophthalmologists; Podiatrists.
Facilities Dining room; Activities room; Crafts room; Laundry room; Barber/Beauty shop.
Activities Arts & crafts; Cards; Games; Reading groups; Prayer groups; Movies; Shopping trips; Social/Cultural gatherings.

Heritage House Convalescent Center
2055 Heritage Dr, Martinsville, IN, 46151
(317) 342-3305
Admin Margaret J Dillman. Medical Dir/Dir of Nursing Robert C Beesley MD; Kathy Fetherolf DON.
Licensure Skilled care. Beds SNF 59; ICF 60. Certified Medicaid; Medicare.
Owner Proprietary Corp.
Admissions Requirements Minimum age 18; Medical examination.
Staff RNs 4 (ft), 1 (pt); LPNs 6 (ft), 1 (pt); Nurses aides 41 (ft), 1 (pt); Physical therapists 1 (pt); Speech therapists 1 (pt); Activities coordinators 1 (ft), 1 (pt); Dietitians 1 (pt).
Facilities Dining room; Physical therapy room; Activities room; Crafts room; Laundry room; Barber/Beauty shop; Library.
Activities Arts & crafts; Cards; Games; Reading groups; Prayer groups; Movies; Shopping trips; Social/Cultural gatherings.

Kennedy Memorial Christian Home Inc
310 W Harrison, Martinsville, IN, 46151
(317) 342-6636
Admin Michael W Terhorst. Medical Dir/Dir of Nursing George Ostheimer MD; Carla Weber DON.
Licensure Intermediate care; Residential care. Beds ICF 78; Residential 35.
Owner Nonprofit Corp (Natl Bnvlnt Assn of Chrstn Homes).
Admissions Requirements Minimum age 62; Medical examination.
Staff Physicians 1 (pt); RNs 3 (ft), 1 (pt); LPNs 6 (ft), 1 (pt); Activities coordinators 1 (ft), 2 (pt); Dietitians 1 (pt).
Affiliation Disciples of Christ

MERRILLVILLE

Merrillville Convalescent Center*
601 W 61st Ave, Merrillville, IN, 46410
(219) 980-5950
Admin Thomas Bell.
Licensure Skilled care; Intermediate care. Beds 180. Certified Medicaid; Medicare.

South Lake Care Center*
8800 Virginia Pl, Merrillville, IN, 46410
(219) 736-1310
Admin Lualyce Brown.
Beds 228.

MICHIGAN CITY

Beach Cliff Lodge Nursing Home*
1001 Lake Shore Dr, Michigan City, IN, 46360
(219) 872-0120
Admin Janice Butcher RN. Medical Dir/Dir of Nursing Maurice Miller.
Licensure Intermediate care. Beds 21. Certified Medicaid.
Admissions Requirements Minimum age 21; Medical examination; Physician's request.
Staff RNs 2 (ft), 1 (pt); Nurses aides 4 (ft), 3 (pt); Activities coordinators 1 (pt).
Facilities Dining room; Activities room; Laundry room.
Activities Arts & crafts; Cards; Games; Reading groups; Prayer groups; Shopping trips.

Lakeside Health Center Inc*
802 Hwy 20 E, Michigan City, IN, 46360
(219) 872-7251
Admin Dorothy Snavley.
Licensure Intermediate care. Beds 64. Certified Medicaid.

Meridian Nursing Center—Woodview*
1101 E Coolspring Ave, Michigan City, IN, 46360
(219) 874-5211
Admin Frank Estes.

Licensure Skilled care; Intermediate care. Beds SNF 66; ICF 132. Certified Medicaid; Medicare.

Red Oaks Healthcare Center
910 S Carroll Ave, Michigan City, IN, 46360
(219) 872-0696
Admin Terri Hastings. Medical Dir/Dir of Nursing Amos Arney MD; Claudia Christensen RN.
Licensure Skilled care; Intermediate care. Beds SNF 58; ICF 58. Certified Medicaid; Medicare.
Owner Proprietary Corp (ARA Living Centers).
Admissions Requirements Minimum age 18; Medical examination; Physician's request.
Staff RNs 2 (ft); LPNs 5 (ft), 2 (pt); Nurses aides 29 (ft), 10 (pt); Activities coordinators 1 (ft), 1 (pt).
Facilities Dining room; Physical therapy room; Activities room; Chapel; Crafts room; Laundry room; Barber/Beauty shop.
Activities Arts & crafts; Cards; Games; Prayer groups; Movies; Shopping trips; Social/Cultural gatherings.

Wedow Private Home Care
602 Spring St, Michigan City, IN, 46360
(219) 879-0140
Admin Wilbur E Wedow. Medical Dir/Dir of Nursing Louella Clark RN.
Licensure Residential care. Beds Residential 17.
Owner Privately owned.
Admissions Requirements Females only; Medical examination.
Staff Physicians; RNs; Nurses aides; Activities coordinators; Dietitians.
Languages Polish
Facilities Dining room; Activities room; Laundry room; Barber/Beauty shop.
Activities Arts & crafts; Cards; Games; Movies; Shopping trips.

MIDDLETOWN

Middletown Nursing Center
130 S 10th St, Middletown, IN, 47356
(317) 354-2223
Admin Terry Flannery. Medical Dir/Dir of Nursing Dr F J Woodall; Janet Case DON.
Licensure Intermediate care. Beds ICF 39. Certified Medicaid.
Owner Privately owned.
Admissions Requirements Medical examination; Physician's request.
Staff RNs; LPNs; Nurses aides; Activities coordinators; Dietitians.
Facilities Dining room; Laundry room; Barber/Beauty shop.
Activities Arts & crafts; Cards; Games; Reading groups; Prayer groups; Movies; Shopping trips; Social/Cultural gatherings; Community involvement; Recreation; Van trips.

Miller's Merry Manor Middletown*
Box 135, Middletown, IN, 47356
(317) 354-2278
Admin William K Daugherty.
Licensure Intermediate care. Beds 64. Certified Medicaid.
Owner Proprietary Corp (Millers Merry Manor).
Admissions Requirements Minimum age 21.
Staff RNs 2 (ft); LPNs 3 (ft), 1 (pt); Nurses aides 10 (ft), 10 (pt); Activities coordinators 1 (ft); Dietitians 1 (pt).
Facilities Dining room; Activities room; Chapel; Crafts room; Laundry room; Barber/Beauty shop; Library.
Activities Arts & crafts; Cards; Games; Reading groups; Prayer groups; Shopping trips; Social/Cultural gatherings.

MILAN

Milan Healthcare Center*
Carr St, Milan, IN, 47031
(812) 654-2231
Admin Ted Merrick.
Licensure Intermediate care. *Beds* 65.
Certified Medicaid.
Owner Proprietary Corp (Beverly Enterprises).
Staff RNs; LPNs; Nurses aides; Activities coordinators.
Facilities Dining room; Activities room; Laundry room; Barber/Beauty shop.
Activities Arts & crafts; Cards; Games; Prayer groups; Movies; Shopping trips; Social/Cultural gatherings.

MILFORD

Lakeland Loving Care Center Inc*
PO Box 767, Milford, IN, 46542
(219) 658-9554
Admin Diane K Perry. *Medical Dir/Dir of Nursing* Floyd Rheinheimer.
Licensure Intermediate care. *Beds* 60.
Certified Medicaid.
Staff RNs 2 (ft), 2 (pt); LPNs 1 (ft), 5 (pt); Nurses aides 9 (ft), 20 (pt); Physical therapists 1 (pt); Speech therapists 1 (pt); Activities coordinators 1 (ft); Dietitians 1 (pt); Podiatrists 1 (pt).
Facilities Dining room; Activities room; Crafts room; Laundry room; Barber/Beauty shop.
Activities Arts & crafts; Cards; Games; Reading groups; Prayer groups; Movies; Shopping trips; Social/Cultural gatherings.

MISHAWAKA

Countryside Place of Mishawaka
811 E 12th St, Mishawaka, IN, 46544
(219) 259-1917
Admin Daniel Scott Pyle. *Medical Dir/Dir of Nursing* Dr James Serwatka; Jeannette McKnight.
Licensure Skilled care; Intermediate care. *Beds* SNF 56; ICF 46. *Certified* Medicaid; Medicare.
Owner Proprietary Corp (Beverly Enterprises).
Admissions Requirements Medical examination.
Staff Physicians 4 (ft); RNs 6 (ft); LPNs 6 (ft); Nurses aides 16 (ft); Physical therapists 1 (ft); Occupational therapists 1 (ft); Speech therapists 1 (ft); Activities coordinators 1 (ft); Dietitians 1 (ft); Ophthalmologists 1 (ft).
Facilities Dining room; Physical therapy room; Activities room; Laundry room; Barber/Beauty shop; Fireside lounge; Enclosed outdoor patio.
Activities Arts & crafts; Cards; Games; Prayer groups; Movies; Shopping trips.

Fountainview Place of Mishawaka*
609 W Tanglewood Ln, Mishawaka, IN, 46544
(219) 277-2500
Admin Catherine Gentry. *Medical Dir/Dir of Nursing* David Clayton MD.
Licensure Skilled care; Intermediate care. *Beds* SNF 44; ICF 84. *Certified* Medicaid; Medicare.
Owner Proprietary Corp (Beverly Enterprises).
Staff RNs 1 (ft), 1 (pt); LPNs 10 (ft), 4 (pt); Orderlies 2 (ft); Nurses aides 22 (ft), 19 (pt); Physical therapists 1 (pt); Occupational therapists 1 (pt); Speech therapists 1 (pt); Activities coordinators 1 (ft); Qualified medication aides 3 (ft), 8 (pt).
Facilities Dining room; Physical therapy room; Activities room; Chapel; Crafts room; Barber/Beauty shop.
Activities Arts & crafts; Cards; Games; Reading groups; Prayer groups; Movies; Shopping trips; Social/Cultural gatherings.

St Joseph's Care Center—Melrose*
601 S Russell St, Mishawaka, IN, 46544
(219) 259-5050
Admin Richard Shoupe.
Licensure Intermediate care. *Beds* 38.
Certified Medicaid.
Admissions Requirements Minimum age 18; Medical examination; Physician's request.
Staff RNs 2 (ft); LPNs 2 (ft); Nurses aides 8 (ft), 23 (pt); Recreational therapists 1 (ft), 1 (pt); Activities coordinators 1 (ft).
Facilities Dining room; Activities room; Crafts room.
Activities Arts & crafts; Cards; Games; Reading groups; Prayer groups; Shopping trips.

MITCHELL

Mitchell Manor
PO Box 277, Mitchell, IN, 47446
(812) 849-2221
Admin Larry Carlson. *Medical Dir/Dir of Nursing* Brenda Houchin RN.
Licensure Skilled care; Intermediate care. *Beds* SNF 33; ICF 102. *Certified* Medicaid.
Owner Proprietary Corp (Life Care Centers of America).
Admissions Requirements Minimum age 21; Physician's request.
Facilities Dining room; Physical therapy room; Activities room; Crafts room; Barber/Beauty shop.
Activities Arts & crafts; Cards; Games; Reading groups; Prayer groups; Movies; Shopping trips; Social/Cultural gatherings.

Williams Health Facility*
Hwy 37 S, Mitchell, IN, 47446
(812) 849-2221
Admin Wayne Williams.
Beds 44.

MONTICELLO

Lake View Home*
800 W Norway Rd, Monticello, IN, 47960
(219) 583-3242
Admin Ora Rumple.
Licensure Residential care. *Beds* 28.

Monticello Community Healthcare Center*
RR 6, 1120 N Main St, Monticello, IN, 47960
(219) 583-7073
Admin Jack G Schaeffer.
Licensure Skilled care; Intermediate care. *Beds* SNF 79; ICF 127. *Certified* Medicaid; Medicare.

MOORESVILLE

Miller's Merry Manor*
259 W Harrison, Mooresville, IN, 46158
(317) 831-6272
Admin Ruth Hanlon.
Licensure Intermediate care. *Beds* 99.
Certified Medicaid.
Owner Proprietary Corp (Millers Merry Manor).

MORGANTOWN

Henderson Nursing Home Inc*
140 W Washington St, Morgantown, IN, 46160
(812) 597-4418
Admin Karen Henderson. *Medical Dir/Dir of Nursing* Gary Midla DO.
Licensure Intermediate care. *Beds* 41.
Certified Medicaid.
Admissions Requirements Medical examination.
Staff Physicians 1 (ft); RNs 1 (pt); LPNs 3 (ft), 1 (pt); Orderlies 1 (pt); Nurses aides 15 (ft), 5 (pt); Activities coordinators 1 (ft); Dietitians 1 (pt).

Facilities Dining room; Activities room; Crafts room; Laundry room; Library.
Activities Arts & crafts; Cards; Games; Reading groups; Prayer groups; Movies; Shopping trips; Social/Cultural gatherings.

MORRISTOWN

Morristown Healthcare*
Box 388, Morristown, IN, 46161
(317) 763-6012
Admin Martha Waltz.
Licensure Intermediate care. *Beds* 64.
Certified Medicaid.

MOUNT VERNON

Medco Center of Mt Vernon*
1415 Country Club Rd, Mount Vernon, IN, 47620
(812) 838-6554
Admin William Watson III.
Licensure Intermediate care. *Beds* 123.
Certified Medicaid.
Owner Proprietary Corp (Vantage Healthcare).
Admissions Requirements Minimum age 18; Medical examination.
Facilities Dining room; Physical therapy room; Activities room; Chapel; Crafts room; Laundry room; Barber/Beauty shop.
Activities Arts & crafts; Cards; Games; Reading groups; Prayer groups; Movies; Shopping trips; Social/Cultural gatherings.

MULBERRY

Mulberry Lutheran Home
PO Box 338, Mulberry, IN, 46058-0338
(317) 296-2911
Admin Mark Neubacher. *Medical Dir/Dir of Nursing* Grayson B Davis.
Licensure Intermediate care; Residential care. *Beds* 81. *Certified* Medicaid.
Admissions Requirements Medical examination.
Staff Physicians 1 (pt); RNs 3 (ft), 2 (pt); LPNs 3 (ft), 1 (pt); Orderlies 1 (ft), 1 (pt); Nurses aides 26 (ft), 26 (pt); Physical therapists 1 (pt); Activities coordinators 2 (ft), 1 (pt); Dietitians 1 (ft); Dentists 1 (pt).
Affiliation Lutheran
Facilities Dining room; Physical therapy room; Activities room; Chapel; Crafts room; Laundry room; Barber/Beauty shop; Library; Ceramics room.
Activities Arts & crafts; Cards; Games; Reading groups; Prayer groups; Movies; Shopping trips; Bingo.

MUNCIE

Chateau Convalescent Centre*
2400 Chateau Dr, Muncie, IN, 47303
(317) 747-9044
Admin Betty J Hickey.
Licensure Intermediate care. *Beds* 102.
Certified Medicaid.

Delaware County Health Center
7524 E Jackson, Muncie, IN, 47302
(317) 747-7820
Admin Michael Whitcomb. *Medical Dir/Dir of Nursing* Dr Robert Suer; Barbara King RN DON.
Licensure Intermediate care; Residential. *Beds* ICF 48; Residential 24. *Certified* Medicaid; Medicare.
Owner Publicly owned.
Admissions Requirements Medical examination; Physician's request.
Staff Physicians 2 (ft); RNs 7 (ft), 1 (pt); LPNs 6 (ft), 4 (pt); Nurses aides 18 (ft), 8 (pt); Activities coordinators 2 (ft); Dietitians 1 (pt); Ophthalmologists 1 (pt); Podiatrists 1 (pt); QMA 12 (ft), 3 (pt).

Facilities Dining room; Physical therapy room; Activities room; Crafts room; Laundry room; Barber/Beauty shop; Library.
Activities Arts & crafts; Cards; Games; Reading groups; Prayer groups; Movies; Shopping trips; Social/Cultural gatherings.

Fountainview Place of Muncie*
2701 Lyn-Mar Dr, Muncie, IN, 47302
(317) 286-5979
Admin Donald R Ingle. *Medical Dir/Dir of Nursing* Arnold Carter MD.
Licensure Skilled care; Intermediate care. *Beds* SNF 71; ICF 78. *Certified* Medicaid; Medicare.
Owner Proprietary Corp (Beverly Enterprises).
Admissions Requirements Medical examination.
Staff Physical therapists 1 (ft); Occupational therapists 1 (ft); Speech therapists 1 (pt); Activities coordinators 1 (ft).
Facilities Dining room; Physical therapy room; Activities room; Chapel; Crafts room; Laundry room; Barber/Beauty shop.
Activities Arts & crafts; Cards; Games; Reading groups; Prayer groups; Movies; Shopping trips; Social/Cultural gatherings.

Medco Center of Muncie*
2200 White River Blvd, Muncie, IN, 47303
(317) 289-3341
Admin Rachel Willett. *Medical Dir/Dir of Nursing* Dr Michael Seidle.
Licensure Skilled care; Intermediate care. *Beds* SNF 53; ICF 48. *Certified* Medicaid; Medicare.
Admissions Requirements Minimum age 21; Medical examination; Physician's request.
Staff Physicians 1 (pt); RNs 5 (ft); LPNs 8 (ft); Nurses aides 34 (ft), 8 (pt); Physical therapists; Speech therapists; Activities coordinators 1 (ft); Podiatrists.
Facilities Dining room; Physical therapy room; Activities room; Crafts room; Laundry room; Barber/Beauty shop; Lounge area.
Activities Arts & crafts; Cards; Reading groups; Prayer groups; Movies; Shopping trips; Bi-monthly newspaper; Exercise groups; Chapel twice weekly in lounge area.

Muncie Health Care Center Inc*
PO Box 112, 4301 N Walnut St, Muncie, IN, 47405
(317) 282-0053
Admin David A Davis.
Licensure Intermediate care. *Beds* 100. *Certified* Medicaid.

Northeast Healthcare Center of Muncie
505 N Gavin St, Muncie, IN, 47303
(317) 289-1915
Admin Diana J Peckham. *Medical Dir/Dir of Nursing* Larry Cole MD: Karen Baty RN DON.
Licensure Intermediate care. *Beds* ICF 42. *Certified* Medicaid.
Owner Privately owned.
Admissions Requirements Minimum age 18; Medical examination; Physician's request.
Staff Physicians; RNs; LPNs 13D; Nurses aides; Activities coordinators; Dietitians; Dentists; Ophthalmologists.
Facilities Dining room; Activities room; Laundry room; Barber/Beauty shop.
Activities Arts & crafts; Cards; Games; Reading groups; Prayer groups; Movies; Shopping trips; Social/Cultural gatherings; Fishing trips; Concert trips.

Rosewood Manor I*
RR 2, Box 89, Muncie, IN, 47302
(317) 288-5082
Admin Margaret E Knox.
Licensure Intermediate care. *Beds* 50. *Certified* Medicaid.

Sylvester Nursing Home*
RR 2, Box 79, Muncie, IN, 47302
(317) 284-8283

Admin Kevin S Jeffers. *Medical Dir/Dir of Nursing* Larry G Cole MD.
Licensure Intermediate care. *Beds* 40. *Certified* Medicaid.
Admissions Requirements Medical examination.
Staff RNs 1 (pt); LPNs 2 (ft); Nurses aides 17 (ft), 3 (pt); Activities coordinators 1 (ft); Dietitians 1 (pt).
Facilities Dining room; Activities room; Laundry room; Barber/Beauty shop.
Activities Arts & crafts; Games; Prayer groups; Movies; Shopping trips; Social/Cultural gatherings.

Woodland Nursing Home*
3820 W Jackson St, Muncie, IN, 47304
(317) 289-3451
Admin Anna J Powless.
Licensure Skilled care; Intermediate care. *Beds* SNF 34; ICF 58. *Certified* Medicaid; Medicare.

MUNSTER

Munster Med-Inn
7935 Calumet Ave, Munster, IN, 46321
(219) 836-8300
Admin Jean T Robinson Benavides. *Medical Dir/Dir of Nursing* Dr William H Hehemann; Carol Ploense RN DON.
Licensure Skilled care; Intermediate care; Residential care. *Beds* SNF 210; ICF 48; Residential 30. *Certified* Medicaid; Medicare.
Owner Privately owned.
Admissions Requirements Minimum age 18.
Staff Physicians; RNs 13 (ft), 6 (pt); LPNs 11 (ft), 7 (pt); Orderlies 1 (ft), 1 (pt); Nurses aides 84 (ft), 13 (pt); Physical therapists 1 (ft), 1 (pt); Occupational therapists 2 (pt); Speech therapists 1 (ft), 1 (pt); Activities coordinators 3 (ft), 2 (pt); Dietitians 1 (ft), 1 (pt); Respiratory Therapist 1 (ft), 1 (pt).
Languages Spanish, Polish
Facilities Dining room; Physical therapy room; Activities room; Laundry room; Barber/Beauty shop; Library; Occupational therapy room; Speech therapy room; Lounges on all floors.
Activities Arts & crafts; Cards; Games; Reading groups; Prayer groups; Movies; Shopping trips; Social/Cultural gatherings; Reality orientation; Church services; Exercise groups; Glamour hour; Performing groups from the community.

NAPPANEE

Lu Ann Nursing Home
952 W Walnut St, Nappanee, IN, 46550
(219) 773-4119
Admin John L Mellinger. *Medical Dir/Dir of Nursing* V T Houck MD; Dominica K Beath DON.
Licensure Intermediate care. *Beds* ICF 50. *Certified* Medicaid.
Owner Privately owned.
Staff RNs 3 (ft), 2 (pt); LPNs 2 (ft), 1 (pt); Nurses aides 10 (ft), 3 (pt); Dietitians 1 (ft); Ophthalmologists 1 (pt).
Facilities Dining room; Activities room; Chapel; Crafts room; Laundry room; Barber/Beauty shop; Library.
Activities Arts & crafts; Cards; Games; Reading groups; Prayer groups; Movies; Social/Cultural gatherings.

NASHVILLE

Brown County Community Care Center Inc*
Fred Henderson Dr, PO Box 667, Nashville, IN, 47448
(812) 988-6666
Admin Virginia Burt. *Medical Dir/Dir of Nursing* Tim Alward.

Licensure Intermediate care. *Beds* 70. *Certified* Medicaid.
Owner Proprietary Corp (Community Care Centers).
Staff RNs 1 (ft), 1 (pt); LPNs 3 (ft), 1 (pt); Orderlies 2 (ft); Nurses aides 10 (ft), 9 (pt); Activities coordinators 1 (ft); Dietitians 1 (pt).
Facilities Dining room; Activities room; Laundry room; Barber/Beauty shop.
Activities Arts & crafts; Cards; Games; Reading groups; Prayer groups; Shopping trips; Social/Cultural gatherings.

NEW ALBANY

Green Valley Convalescent Center
3118 Green Valley Rd, New Albany, IN, 47150
(812) 945-2341
Admin Peter Graves. *Medical Dir/Dir of Nursing* Howard Pope MD: JoAnn Ehalt RN DON.
Licensure Skilled care; Intermediate care. *Beds* SNF 120; ICF 120; 8. *Certified* Medicaid; Medicare.
Owner Proprietary Corp (Southmark Heritage).
Admissions Requirements Minimum age 18; Physician's request.
Staff RNs 8 (ft), 3 (pt); LPNs 24 (ft), 4 (pt); Nurses aides 90 (ft), 2 (pt); Physical therapists 1 (ft); Recreational therapists; Occupational therapists; Speech therapists; Activities coordinators; Dietitians.
Facilities Dining room; Physical therapy room; Activities room; Laundry room; Barber/Beauty shop.
Activities Arts & crafts; Cards; Games; Reading groups; Prayer groups; Movies; Shopping trips; Social/Cultural gatherings; Community events.

Robert E Lee Retirement Inn
201 E Elm St, New Albany, IN, 47150
(812) 945-9517
Admin Janet Miller. *Medical Dir/Dir of Nursing* Avona Connell DON.
Licensure Residential care. *Beds* Residential 112. *Certified* Medicaid.
Owner Proprietary Corp.
Admissions Requirements Medical examination; Physician's request.
Staff LPNs 3 (ft), 1 (pt); Nurses aides 1 (ft), 2 (pt); Activities coordinators 1 (ft), 1 (pt).
Facilities Dining room; Activities room; Crafts room; Laundry room; Barber/Beauty shop.
Activities Arts & crafts; Cards; Games; Reading groups; Prayer groups; Movies; Shopping trips; Social/Cultural gatherings; Education; Bingo.

Lincoln Hills of New Albany
PO Box 603, 326 Country Club Dr, New Albany, IN, 47150-0603
(812) 948-1311
Admin Roger Ambrose. *Medical Dir/Dir of Nursing* Dr Kenneth Brown, Dr John Paris; Ila White RN DON.
Licensure Intermediate care. *Beds* ICF 200. *Certified* Medicaid.
Owner Proprietary Corp.
Admissions Requirements Minimum age 18; Medical examination; Physician's request.
Staff Physicians 2 (pt); RNs 2 (ft), 1 (pt); LPNs 13 (ft), 5 (pt); Orderlies 2 (ft); Nurses aides 32 (ft), 16 (pt); Physical therapists 1 (ft); Speech therapists 1 (pt); Activities coordinators 1 (ft); Dietitians 1 (pt); Dentists 1 (pt); Ophthalmologists 1 (pt); Podiatrists 1 (pt); Medication aides 3 (ft), 3 (pt).
Facilities Dining room; Physical therapy room; Activities room; Crafts room; Laundry room; Barber/Beauty shop; Rehab feeding & special care unit.

Activities Arts & crafts; Games; Reading groups; Prayer groups; Movies; Shopping trips; Social/Cultural gatherings.

New Albany Nursing Home*
1919 Bono Rd, New Albany, IN, 47150
(812) 944-4404
Admin Sandra Spencer.
Licensure Intermediate care. *Beds* 40.
 Certified Medicaid.
Owner Proprietary Corp (Beverly Enterprises).

Providence Retirement Home
703 E Spring St, New Albany, IN, 47150
(812) 945-5221
Admin Sr Barbara Ann Zeller. *Medical Dir/ Dir of Nursing* Eli Hallal MD; David Conley RN.
Licensure Retirement home; Residential care. *Beds* Retirement home; Residential 92.
Owner Nonprofit organization/foundation.
Admissions Requirements Minimum age 50; Medical examination.
Staff Physicians; RNs; LPNs; Nurses aides; Activities coordinators; Dietitians.
Affiliation Roman Catholic
Facilities Dining room; Activities room; Chapel; Crafts room; Laundry room; Barber/ Beauty shop; Adult day care center.
Activities Arts & crafts; Cards; Games; Reading groups; Prayer groups; Movies; Shopping trips; Social/Cultural gatherings.

Rolling Hills Health Care Center
3625 St Joseph Rd, New Albany, IN, 47150
(812) 948-0670
Admin Dee Anna Smallman. *Medical Dir/Dir of Nursing* John Paris; Jeanette Kannapel DON.
Licensure Intermediate care. *Beds* ICF 100.
Owner Proprietary Corp.
Admissions Requirements Medical examination; Physician's request.
Staff Physicians 4 (pt); RNs 3 (ft), 1 (pt); LPNs 8 (ft), 5 (pt); Orderlies 4 (ft); Nurses aides 21 (ft), 13 (pt); Physical therapists 1 (pt); Recreational therapists 2 (pt); Occupational therapists 1 (pt); Speech therapists 1 (pt); Activities coordinators 1 (ft), 1 (pt); Dietitians 1 (pt); Dentists 1 (pt); Ophthalmologists 1 (pt); Podiatrists 1 (pt); Social services 1 (ft), 1 (pt).
Facilities Dining room; Physical therapy room; Activities room; Laundry room; Barber/Beauty shop; TV room.
Activities Arts & crafts; Cards; Games; Reading groups; Prayer groups; Movies; Shopping trips; Social/Cultural gatherings.

NEW CARLISLE

Hamilton Grove*
31869 Chicago Trail, New Carlisle, IN, 46552
(219) 654-3118
Admin Joseph S Dzwonar. *Medical Dir/Dir of Nursing* Robert Fenstermacher MD.
Licensure Intermediate care; Residential care. *Beds* 84. *Certified* Medicaid.
Owner Proprietary Corp (Community Care Centers).
Admissions Requirements Minimum age 65.
Staff RNs 4 (ft); LPNs 12 (ft); Nurses aides 30 (ft), 8 (pt); Recreational therapists 2 (ft), 2 (pt); Activities coordinators 1 (ft); Dietitians 1 (pt).
Affiliation Methodist
Facilities Dining room; Physical therapy room; Activities room; Chapel; Crafts room; Laundry room; Barber/Beauty shop; Library; Commisary; Greenhouse.
Activities Arts & crafts; Cards; Games; Reading groups; Prayer groups; Movies; Shopping trips; Social/Cultural gatherings.

Miller's Merry Manor Inc
100 Dunn Rd, New Carlisle, IN, 46552
(219) 654-7244

Admin Jerome H Ouding MSW. *Medical Dir/ Dir of Nursing* Dr Ralph Inabnit.
Licensure Intermediate care. *Beds* ICF 70.
Owner Proprietary Corp (Millers Merry Manor).
Staff Physicians 1 (pt); RNs 2 (ft), 3 (pt); LPNs 5 (ft); Orderlies 1 (ft); Nurses aides 12 (ft), 10 (pt); Physical therapists 1 (ft), 1 (pt); Reality therapists 1 (pt); Recreational therapists 1 (pt); Occupational therapists 1 (pt); Speech therapists 1 (pt); Activities coordinators 1 (ft), 1 (pt); Dietitians 1 (pt); Dentists 1 (pt); Ophthalmologists 1 (pt).

NEW CASTLE

Heritage House of New Castle*
PO Box 546, New Castle, IN, 47362
(317) 529-9694
Admin John Huber.
Licensure Skilled care; Intermediate care. *Beds* SNF 21; ICF 90. *Certified* Medicaid; Medicare.

Holly Hill
901 N 16th St, New Castle, IN, 47362
(317) 529-4695
Admin Karen J Feezor. *Medical Dir/Dir of Nursing* Bruce Ipple MD; Cathy Kunkle RN DON.
Licensure Intermediate care. *Beds* ICF 40. *Certified* Medicaid.
Owner Proprietary Corp (Beverly Enterprises).
Admissions Requirements Physician's request.
Staff RNs 1 (ft); LPNs 4 (ft), 3 (pt); Nurses aides 8 (ft), 5 (pt); Dietitians 1 (ft), 1 (pt).
Facilities Dining room; Laundry room.
Activities Arts & crafts; Cards; Games; Reading groups; Prayer groups; Movies; Shopping trips; Social/Cultural gatherings; Dinner outings.

New Castle Community Care Center*
115 N 10th St, New Castle, IN, 47362
(317) 529-2703
Admin 12.22.86 ar.
Licensure Intermediate care. *Beds* 60. *Certified* Medicaid.
Owner Proprietary Corp (Community Care Centers).

New Castle Healthcare Center*
990 N 16th St, New Castle, IN, 47362
(317) 529-0230
Admin Dale Maryfield.
Licensure Skilled care; Intermediate care. *Beds* SNF 87; ICF 108. *Certified* Medicaid; Medicare.

NEW HARMONY

The Charles Ford Memorial Home
920 S Main St, New Harmony, IN, 47631
(812) 682-4685, 682-4675
Admin Barbara J Tumey RN. *Medical Dir/Dir of Nursing* Dr Chester Burkett; Leigh Ann Gish LPM.
Licensure Residential care. *Beds* 24.
Admissions Requirements Minimum age 62; Females only; Medical examination.
Staff Physicians 1 (ft); LPNs 1 (ft); Activities coordinators 1 (ft); Dietitians 1 (ft).
Facilities Dining room; Activities room; Laundry room; Barber/Beauty shop; Parlor; Sun porches.
Activities Prayer groups; Movies; Shopping trips; Social/Cultural gatherings.

NEW HAVEN

Brighton Hall Nursing Center*
1201 Daly Dr, New Haven, IN, 46774
(219) 749-0413
Admin Robert Shambaugh.
Beds 120.
Owner Proprietary Corp (Shive Nursing Centers).

NEWBURGH

Medco Center of Newburgh*
4255 Medwel Dr, Newburgh, IN, 47630
(812) 853-2993
Admin Rachel Willett.
Licensure Intermediate care. *Beds* 112. *Certified* Medicaid.
Owner Proprietary Corp (Unicare).

Newburgh Health Care & Residential Center
10466 Pollack Ave, Newburgh, IN, 47630
(812) 853-2931
Admin Jerry V Powers.
Licensure Intermediate care. *Beds* 114. *Certified* Medicaid.

NOBLESVILLE

Noblesville Healthcare Center
295 Westfield Rd, Noblesville, IN, 46060
(317) 773-3760
Admin Wayne J Landry. *Medical Dir/Dir of Nursing* Walter Beaver MD; Betty Hall DON.
Licensure Skilled care; Intermediate care; Alzheimer's care center. *Beds* SNF 48; ICF 119; Alzheimer's care center 22. *Certified* Medicaid; Medicare.
Owner Proprietary Corp (ARA Living Centers).
Admissions Requirements Medical examination; Physician's request.
Staff Physicians; RNs; LPNs; Orderlies; Nurses aides; Physical therapists; Reality therapists; Recreational therapists; Occupational therapists; Speech therapists; Activities coordinators; Dietitians; Dentists; Ophthalmologists; Podiatrists.
Languages French
Facilities Dining room; Physical therapy room; Activities room; Crafts room; Laundry room; Barber/Beauty shop; Living rooms; Private rooms for visits.
Activities Arts & crafts; Cards; Games; Reading groups; Prayer groups; Movies; Shopping trips; Social/Cultural gatherings; Sewing; Gardening.

Noblesville Nursing Home
1391 Greenfield Pike, Noblesville, IN, 46060
(317) 773-1264
Admin Richard A Myers.
Licensure Intermediate care. *Beds* 40. *Certified* Medicaid.
Owner Proprietary Corp (Beverly Enterprises).
Staff RNs 1 (ft); LPNs 1 (ft), 1 (pt); Nurses aides 10 (ft), 7 (pt); Activities coordinators 1 (ft); Dietitians 1 (pt); Podiatrists 1 (pt).

NORTH MANCHESTER

Peabody Retirement Community
400 W Seventh St, North Manchester, IN, 46962
(219) 982-8616
Admin Richard M Craig. *Medical Dir/Dir of Nursing* Kathy L Trick RN DON.
Licensure Intermediate care; Residential care; Independent living. *Beds* 235. *Certified* Medicaid.
Owner Nonprofit Corp.
Affiliation Presbyterian

Timbercrest—Church of the Brethren Home Inc
PO Box 501, CR 200E, North Manchester, IN, 46962
(219) 982-2118
Admin David Lawrenz. *Medical Dir/Dir of Nursing* Laverne Mitmoen RN.
Licensure Intermediate care; Residential care. *Beds* ICF 46; Residential 144. *Certified* Medicaid.
Owner Nonprofit Corp.
Admissions Requirements Minimum age 65; Medical examination.

Staff RNs 2 (ft); LPNs 4 (ft), 6 (pt); Nurses aides 12 (ft), 20 (pt); Activities coordinators 1 (ft); Dietitians 1 (ft), 3 (pt).
Affiliation Church of the Brethren
Facilities Dining room; Activities room; Chapel; Crafts room; Laundry room; Barber/Beauty shop; Library.
Activities Arts & crafts; Cards; Games; Reading groups; Prayer groups; Movies; Shopping trips; Social/Cultural gatherings.

NORTH VERNON

Community Care Center of North Vernon*
PO Box 640, 1200 W O & M Ave, North Vernon, IN, 47265
(812) 346-7570
Admin Dawn L Black.
Licensure Intermediate care. *Beds* 64.
Certified Medicaid.

North Vernon Nursing Home
801 N Elm St, North Vernon, IN, 47265
(812) 346-4942
Admin Frances J Cherry RN. *Medical Dir/Dir of Nursing* Dr J B Johuck MD; Betty Piatt LPN DON.
Licensure Intermediate care. *Beds* ICF 40.
Certified Medicaid.
Owner Proprietary Corp (Beverly Enterprises).
Admissions Requirements Minimum age 18; Medical examination; Physician's request.
Staff Physicians 3 (pt); RNs 2 (pt); LPNs 3 (pt); Orderlies 1 (pt); Nurses aides 7 (ft), 6 (pt); Activities coordinators 1 (ft); Dietitians 1 (pt); Dentists 1 (pt).
Facilities Dining room; Activities room; Crafts room; Laundry room; Barber/Beauty shop.
Activities Arts & crafts; Cards; Games; Reading groups; Prayer groups; Shopping trips.

OAKLAND CITY

Good Samaritan Home Inc
210 N Gibson St, Oakland City, IN, 47560
(812) 749-4774
Admin Jeff Padgett. *Medical Dir/Dir of Nursing* Dr Gehlhausen; Jane Rusher DON.
Licensure Intermediate care. *Beds* ICF 114.
Certified Medicaid.
Owner Proprietary Corp.
Admissions Requirements Minimum age 18; Medical examination.
Staff Physicians 5 (pt); RNs 3 (ft); LPNs 9 (ft); Orderlies; Nurses aides 48 (ft); Physical therapists 1 (pt); Activities coordinators 1 (ft); Dietitians 1 (pt); Dentists 1 (pt); Ophthalmologists 1 (pt); Social Service 1 (ft).
Facilities Dining room; Physical therapy room; Activities room; Chapel; Crafts room; Laundry room; Barber/Beauty shop; Library; TV room.
Activities Arts & crafts; Cards; Games; Reading groups; Prayer groups; Movies; Shopping trips; Social/Cultural gatherings.

OAKTOWN

Oak Village Inc
PO Box 270, Oaktown, IN, 47561
(812) 745-2360
Admin Kay Melvin. *Medical Dir/Dir of Nursing* Rita Keyes.
Licensure Intermediate care. *Beds* ICF 50.
Certified Medicaid.
Owner Nonprofit Corp.
Admissions Requirements Medical examination; Physician's request.
Staff RNs 1 (ft), 1 (pt); LPNs 2 (ft), 5 (pt); Nurses aides 5 (ft), 13 (pt); Activities coordinators 1 (ft); Dietitians 1 (ft).
Facilities Dining room; Activities room; Crafts room; Laundry room; Barber/Beauty shop; Library.

Activities Arts & crafts; Cards; Games; Reading groups; Prayer groups; Movies; Shopping trips; Social/Cultural gatherings.

ODON

Bertha D Garten Ketcham Memorial Center Inc
601 E Race St, Odon, IN, 47562
(812) 636-4920
Admin Terri L Shimer. *Medical Dir/Dir of Nursing* Debra Ramsey RN DON.
Licensure Intermediate care. *Beds* ICF 62.
Certified Medicaid.
Owner Nonprofit Corp.
Admissions Requirements Minimum age 18; Medical examination.
Staff RNs 6 (ft); LPNs 5 (ft); Nurses aides 20 (ft), 5 (pt); Activities coordinators 1 (ft); Dietitians 1 (pt).
Facilities Dining room; Activities room; Crafts room; Laundry room; Barber/Beauty shop.
Activities Arts & crafts; Cards; Games; Reading groups; Prayer groups; Movies; Shopping trips; Social/Cultural gatherings.

OSGOOD

Manderley Health Care Center
PO Box 135, Osgood, IN, 47037-0135
(812) 689-4143
Admin Charles F Negangard. *Medical Dir/Dir of Nursing* Dr Thomas Barley; Janet Burdsall LPN DON.
Licensure Intermediate care. *Beds* ICF 71.
Certified Medicaid.
Owner Proprietary Corp.
Admissions Requirements Minimum age 18; Medical examination.
Staff RNs 1 (ft), 1 (pt); LPNs 5 (ft); Orderlies 1 (ft); Nurses aides 30 (ft), 2 (pt); Activities coordinators 1 (ft), 2 (pt); Dietitians 1 (pt).
Facilities Dining room; Activities room; Chapel; Crafts room; Barber/Beauty shop; Library; Living room.
Activities Arts & crafts; Cards; Games; Reading groups; Prayer groups; Movies; Shopping trips; Social/Cultural gatherings.

OWENSVILLE

Owensville Convalescent Center
PO Box 368, Hwy 165 W, Owensville, IN, 47710
(812) 729-7901
Admin Eugene Hall. *Medical Dir/Dir of Nursing* Lisa A Hall RN DON.
Licensure Intermediate care. *Beds* ICF 68.
Certified Medicaid.
Owner Proprietary Corp (Cloverleaf Enterprises).
Admissions Requirements Medical examination.
Staff RNs 2 (ft); LPNs 3 (ft), 5 (pt); Nurses aides 15 (ft), 11 (pt); Physical therapists 1 (pt); Activities coordinators 1 (pt); Dietitians 1 (pt); Ophthalmologists 1 (pt); Medical Director 1 (pt).
Facilities Dining room; Laundry room; Barber/Beauty shop; Lounge.
Activities Arts & crafts; Games; Reading groups; Prayer groups; Movies; Shopping trips; Social/Cultural gatherings.

OXFORD

Edgewood Healthcare
State Rte 55, Oxford, IN, 47971
(317) 385-2291
Admin Robert C Blackford. *Medical Dir/Dir of Nursing* Dorsa Ann Sherman RN.
Licensure Intermediate care. *Beds* ICF 56.
Certified Medicaid.
Owner Proprietary Corp (Health Concepts Corp).

Admissions Requirements Medical examination.
Staff RNs 2 (ft); LPNs 3 (ft); Nurses aides 15 (ft); Activities coordinators 1 (ft).
Facilities Dining room; Activities room; Crafts room; Laundry room; Barber/Beauty shop; Library.
Activities Arts & crafts; Cards; Games; Reading groups; Prayer groups; Movies; Shopping trips; Social/Cultural gatherings.

PAOLI

Paoli Nursing Home
111 W Hospital View Rd, Paoli, IN, 47454
(812) 723-3000
Admin Teresa Kellams. *Medical Dir/Dir of Nursing* Margaret McKnight.
Licensure Intermediate care. *Beds* 40.
Certified Medicaid.
Owner Proprietary Corp (Beverly Enterprises).
Admissions Requirements Minimum age 19; Medical examination; Physician's request.
Staff Physicians 1 (pt); RNs 1 (ft); LPNs 2 (ft); Nurses aides 10 (ft), 5 (pt); Activities coordinators 1 (ft); Dietitians 1 (pt).
Facilities Dining room; Activities room; Chapel; Crafts room; Laundry room.
Activities Arts & crafts; Cards; Games; Reading groups; Prayer groups; Movies; Shopping trips; Social/Cultural gatherings; Exercises; Art & travel clubs.

PARKER CITY

Chrystal's Country Home Inc*
Randolph St, Parker City, IN, 47368
(317) 468-8280
Admin Robert E Steele.
Licensure Intermediate care. *Beds* 99.
Certified Medicaid.

PENDLETON

Rawlins House Inc*
300 J H Walker Dr, PO Box 119, Pendleton, IN, 46064
(317) 778-7501
Admin Cindy L Costerison. *Medical Dir/Dir of Nursing* Robert C Beeson MD.
Licensure Intermediate care. *Beds* 134.
Certified Medicaid.
Owner Proprietary Corp.
Admissions Requirements Physician's request.
Staff Physicians 1 (pt); RNs 2 (ft); LPNs 6 (ft), 5 (pt); Nurses aides 17 (ft), 22 (pt); Activities coordinators 1 (ft), 2 (pt); Dietitians 1 (ft), 1 (pt).
Facilities Dining room; Activities room; Laundry room; Barber/Beauty shop; Sunroom.
Activities Arts & crafts; Cards; Games; Reading groups; Shopping trips; Social/Cultural gatherings.

PERU

Miller's Merry Manor Inc*
317 Blair Pike, Peru, IN, 46970
(317) 473-4426
Admin Roger Gunther.
Licensure Skilled care; Intermediate care. *Beds* SNF 31; ICF 124. *Certified* Medicaid; Medicare.
Owner Proprietary Corp (Millers Merry Manor).

Peru Nursing Home*
390 West Blvd, Peru, IN, 46970
(317) 473-4900
Admin Charlotte LeGere.
Licensure Intermediate care. *Beds* 40.
Certified Medicaid.
Owner Proprietary Corp (Beverly Enterprises).

PETERSBURG

Petersburg Healthcare Center*
Box 100, Pike Ave, Petersburg, IN, 47567
(812) 354-8833
Admin Mike Dailey.
Licensure Skilled care; Intermediate care. *Beds*
SNF 19; ICF 115. *Certified* Medicaid;
Medicare.
Owner Proprietary Corp (Beverly Enterprises).

PLAINFIELD

Autumn Care of Clark's Creek
PO Box 7, 3700 Clark's Creek Rd, Plainfield,
IN, 46168
(317) 839-6577
Admin Dale N Maryfield. *Medical Dir/Dir of
Nursing* David M Hadley MD; Frances
Boone RN DON.
Licensure Skilled care; Intermediate care. *Beds*
SNF 59; ICF 140. *Certified* Medicaid;
Medicare.
Owner Proprietary Corp.
Admissions Requirements Minimum age 18;
Medical examination; Physician's request.
Staff Physicians 1 (ft); RNs 4 (ft), 1 (pt);
LPNs 11 (ft), 3 (pt); Nurses aides 68 (ft), 8
(pt); Physical therapists 1 (ft); Occupational
therapists 1 (pt); Speech therapists 1 (pt);
Activities coordinators 5 (ft), 1 (pt);
Dietitians 1 (pt); Dentists 1 (pt);
Ophthalmologists 1 (pt).
Facilities Dining room; Physical therapy
room; Activities room; Crafts room; Laundry
room; Barber/Beauty shop; Lounges.
Activities Arts & crafts; Cards; Games;
Reading groups; Prayer groups; Movies;
Shopping trips; Social/Cultural gatherings.

Vinewood Nursing Home*
404 N Vine St, Plainfield, IN, 46168
(317) 839-0154
Admin George W Petree.
Licensure Intermediate care. *Beds* 27.
Certified Medicaid.

PLYMOUTH

Mayflower Nursing Home
309 Kingston Dr, Plymouth, IN, 46563
(219) 936-9025
Admin Paul F Duranczyk. *Medical Dir/Dir of
Nursing* James Robertson MD; Geraldine
Kubaszyk.
Licensure Intermediate care. *Beds* 40.
Certified Medicaid.
Owner Proprietary Corp (Beverly Enterprises).
Admissions Requirements Minimum age 18;
Medical examination; Physician's request.
Staff RNs 1 (ft), 1 (pt); LPNs 4 (ft); Nurses
aides 7 (ft), 2 (pt); Activities coordinators 1
(ft).
Facilities Dining room; Activities room;
Laundry room.
Activities Arts & crafts; Cards; Games;
Reading groups; Prayer groups; Movies;
Shopping trips; Social/Cultural gatherings.

Miller's Merry Manor Inc*
PO Box 498, 600 W Oakhill Ave, Plymouth,
IN, 46563
(219) 936-9981
Admin Jane K Miller RN.
Licensure Skilled care; Intermediate care. *Beds*
SNF 33; ICF 106. *Certified* Medicaid;
Medicare.
Owner Proprietary Corp (Millers Merry
Manor).

**Pilgrim Manor Rehabilitation & Convalescent
Center***
222 Parkview St, Plymouth, IN, 46563
(219) 936-9943
Admin G Dean Byers.

Licensure Skilled care; Intermediate care. *Beds*
SNF 37; ICF 53. *Certified* Medicaid;
Medicare.

Shady Rest Home*
10924 Old US 30 Hwy, Plymouth, IN, 46563
(219) 936-2635
Admin Steven Michael Kastner.
Licensure Residential care. *Beds* 40.
Staff RNs 1 (pt); LPNs 1 (ft); Nurses aides 6
(ft); Activities coordinators 1 (ft); Dietitians
1 (pt).
Facilities Dining room; Activities room;
Chapel; Crafts room; Laundry room; Barber/
Beauty shop.
Activities Arts & crafts; Cards; Games;
Movies; Shopping trips; Social/Cultural
gatherings.

PORTAGE

Fountainview Place of Portage
3175 Lancer Dr, Portage, IN, 46368
(219) 762-9571
Admin Glen Wagner.
Licensure Skilled care; Intermediate care;
Residential. *Beds* SNF 48; ICF 95;
Residential 6. *Certified* Medicaid; Medicare.
Owner Proprietary Corp (Beverly Enterprises).
Admissions Requirements Minimum age 18;
Medical examination; Physician's request.
Staff Physicians 1 (pt); RNs 3 (ft); LPNs 10
(ft); Orderlies 5 (ft); Nurses aides 60 (ft), 10
(pt); Physical therapists 1 (pt); Occupational
therapists 1 (pt); Speech therapists 1 (pt);
Activities coordinators 2 (ft); Dietitians 1
(pt); Dentists 1 (pt); Ophthalmologists 1 (pt).
Facilities Dining room; Physical therapy
room; Activities room; Chapel; Crafts room;
Laundry room; Barber/Beauty shop; Library.
Activities Arts & crafts; Cards; Games;
Reading groups; Prayer groups; Movies;
Shopping trips; Social/Cultural gatherings.

PORTLAND

Portland Community Care Center West*
200 N Park St, PO Box 1012, Portland, IN,
47371
(219) 726-9441
Admin Dixie B May. *Medical Dir/Dir of
Nursing* Dr Eugene Gillum.
Licensure Intermediate care. *Beds* 80.
Certified Medicaid.
Owner Proprietary Corp (Community Care
Centers).
Admissions Requirements Minimum age 18;
Medical examination.
Staff RNs; LPNs; Nurses aides; Speech
therapists; Activities coordinators; Dietitians.
Facilities Dining room; Activities room;
Crafts room; Laundry room; Barber/Beauty
shop.
Activities Arts & crafts; Cards; Games;
Reading groups; Prayer groups; Movies.

Portland Community Care Center-East
510 W High St, Portland, IN, 47371
(219) 726-6591
Admin Robert C Blackford. *Medical Dir/Dir
of Nursing* Betty Hisey RN DON.
Licensure Intermediate care. *Beds* ICF 60.
Certified Medicaid.
Owner Proprietary Corp (Community Care
Centers).
Admissions Requirements Medical
examination; Physician's request.
Staff RNs; LPNs; Nurses aides; Activities
coordinators.
Languages Spanish
Facilities Dining room; Activities room;
Crafts room; Laundry room; Barber/Beauty
shop.
Activities Arts & crafts; Cards; Games; Prayer
groups; Movies; Shopping trips; Social/
Cultural gatherings.

POSEYVILLE

Allison Nursing Home Inc
Locust St, Poseyville, IN, 47633
(812) 874-2814
Admin Debra Johnson.
Licensure Intermediate care. *Beds* 39.
Certified Medicaid.

PRINCETON

Forest Del Convalescent Home Inc*
1020 W Vine St, Princeton, IN, 47670
(812) 385-5238
Admin L Phillip Roberts.
Licensure Intermediate care. *Beds* 116.
Certified Medicaid.
Admissions Requirements Minimum age 18;
Medical examination; Physician's request.
Staff Physicians 1 (pt); Reality therapists 1
(pt); Recreational therapists 1 (pt); Activities
coordinators 1 (ft); Dietitians 1 (pt); Dentists
1 (pt); Ophthalmologists 1 (pt); Podiatrists 1
(pt).
Facilities Dining room; Activities room;
Crafts room; Laundry room; Barber/Beauty
shop; TV lounge & entertainment center.
Activities Arts & crafts; Cards; Games;
Reading groups; Prayer groups; Movies;
Shopping trips; Social/Cultural gatherings;
Trips out of facility.

Holiday Manor*
Rte 4, 6th Ave, Princeton, IN, 47670
(812) 385-5288
Admin Robert Lovell.
Licensure Intermediate care. *Beds* 91.
Certified Medicaid.
Admissions Requirements Minimum age 18.
Staff RNs 3 (ft), 1 (pt); LPNs 4 (ft); Orderlies
2 (ft); Nurses aides 20 (ft), 4 (pt); Activities
coordinators 1 (ft); Dietitians 1 (pt); Dentists
1 (pt); Ophthalmologists 1 (pt); Podiatrists 1
(pt).
Facilities Dining room; Activities room;
Laundry room; Barber/Beauty shop.
Activities Arts & crafts; Cards; Games;
Reading groups; Prayer groups; Movies;
Shopping trips; Social/Cultural gatherings.

RENSSELEAR

Rensselaer Care Center*
1109 E Grace, Rensselear, IN, 47978
(219) 866-4181
Admin Larry Vanderwielen.
Licensure Intermediate care. *Beds* 143.
Certified Medicaid.

RICHMOND

Cherish Nursing Center
1811 S 9th St, Richmond, IN, 47374
(317) 962-8175
Admin Bonnie R Newkirk. *Medical Dir/Dir of
Nursing* Dr James R Daggy; Patricia
Sabados DON.
Licensure Intermediate care. *Beds* ICF 59.
Certified Medicaid.
Owner Proprietary Corp.
Admissions Requirements Minimum age 18;
Medical examination; Physician's request.
Staff Physicians 1 (pt); RNs 1 (ft); LPNs 5
(ft), 4 (pt); Nurses aides 10 (ft), 9 (pt);
Activities coordinators 1 (ft); Dietitians 1
(pt).
Facilities Dining room; Activities room;
Laundry room; Library service.
Activities Arts & crafts; Cards; Games;
Reading groups; Prayer groups; Movies;
Shopping trips; Social/Cultural gatherings.

Friends Fellowship Community Inc*
2030 Chester Blvd, Richmond, IN, 47374
(317) 962-6546
Admin Merrill W Baxter.

Licensure Intermediate care; Residential care. *Beds* ICF 38; Residential 218.

Golden Rule Nursing Center*
2001 US 27 S, Richmond, IN, 47374
(317) 966-7681
Admin Rob R James.
Licensure Skilled care; Intermediate care. *Beds* SNF 54; ICF 56. *Certified* Medicaid; Medicare.
Owner Proprietary Corp (Beverly Enterprises).

Heritage House of Richmond Inc*
2070 Chester Blvd, Richmond, IN, 47374
(317) 962-3543
Admin Linda Dotson. *Medical Dir/Dir of Nursing* Dr Glen Ramsdell.
Licensure Skilled care; Intermediate care. *Beds* SNF 59; ICF 60. *Certified* Medicaid; Medicare.
Admissions Requirements Minimum age 19; Medical examination; Physician's request.
Staff RNs 5 (ft), 1 (pt); LPNs 7 (ft), 3 (pt); Nurses aides 49 (ft); Physical therapists 1 (ft); Activities coordinators 1 (ft), 1 (pt).
Facilities Dining room; Physical therapy room; Activities room; Crafts room; Laundry room; Barber/Beauty shop.
Activities Arts & crafts; Cards; Games; Reading groups; Prayer groups; Movies; Social/Cultural gatherings.

Jenkins Hall-Reid Memorial Hospital
1401 Chester Blvd, Richmond, IN, 47374
(317) 983-3200
Admin Shirley W Haley RN. *Medical Dir/Dir of Nursing* James J Johnson MD; Rose Mary Patterson RN DON.
Licensure Intermediate care. *Beds* ICF 58. *Certified* Medicaid.
Owner Nonprofit Corp.
Admissions Requirements Minimum age 19; Medical examination; Physician's request.
Staff RNs 3 (ft), 3 (pt); LPNs 3 (ft), 3 (pt); Nurses aides 6 (ft), 16 (pt); Activities coordinators 1 (ft).
Facilities Dining room; Physical therapy room; Activities room; Chapel; Crafts room; Laundry room; Barber/Beauty shop; Library.
Activities Arts & crafts; Cards; Games; Reading groups; Prayer groups; Movies; Shopping trips; Social/Cultural gatherings.

Oak Ridge Convalescent Center*
1042 Oak Dr, Richmond, IN, 47374
(317) 966-7788
Admin Brent Waymire. *Medical Dir/Dir of Nursing* Francis B Warrick MD.
Licensure Skilled care; Intermediate care. *Beds* SNF 100; ICF 22. *Certified* Medicaid; Medicare.
Owner Proprietary Corp (Beverly Enterprises).
Admissions Requirements Minimum age 18; Medical examination; Physician's request.
Staff RNs 5 (ft); LPNs 11 (ft), 2 (pt); Orderlies 1 (ft); Nurses aides 37 (ft), 11 (pt); Physical therapists 2 (ft); Recreational therapists 1 (ft); Occupational therapists 2 (pt); Speech therapists 1 (pt); Activities coordinators 1 (ft); Dietitians 1 (pt); Dentists 1 (pt); Podiatrists 1 (pt).
Facilities Dining room; Physical therapy room; Activities room; Chapel; Crafts room; Laundry room; Barber/Beauty shop; Library; Occupational therapy room; Speech therapy room.
Activities Arts & crafts; Cards; Games; Reading groups; Prayer groups; Movies; Shopping trips; Social/Cultural gatherings.

Spring Grove Care Center
2302 N Chester Blvd, Richmond, IN, 47374
(317) 962-0043
Admin Sandra K Nicodemus. *Medical Dir/Dir of Nursing* Frances Warrick MD; Joyce A Amos RN.
Licensure Intermediate care. *Beds* ICF 40. *Certified* Medicaid.

Owner Proprietary Corp (Waverly Group).
Admissions Requirements Minimum age 18; Medical examination.
Staff RNs 1 (ft); LPNs 4 (ft); Activities coordinators 1 (ft); Dietitians 1 (pt).
Facilities Dining room; Activities room; Laundry room; Enclosed courtyard.
Activities Arts & crafts; Cards; Games; Reading groups; Prayer groups; Movies; Shopping trips; Social/Cultural gatherings; Remotivation; Reminiscing therapy.

RISING SUN

Rising Sun Care Center
Box 98, Rio Vista Ave, Rising Sun, IN, 47040
(812) 438-2219
Admin Carol A Fleener. *Medical Dir/Dir of Nursing* Ivan Lindgren; Margaret Granatir.
Licensure Intermediate care. *Beds* ICF 58. *Certified* Medicaid.
Owner Proprietary Corp (Southeastern Health Care Inc).
Staff RNs 2 (ft), 1 (pt); LPNs 4 (ft); Nurses aides 21 (ft); Activities coordinators 1 (ft), 1 (pt); Dietitians 1 (pt).
Facilities Dining room; Laundry room; Barber/Beauty shop.
Activities Arts & crafts; Cards; Games; Movies; Shopping trips; Social/Cultural gatherings.

ROCHESTER

Canterbury Manor*
RR 6, Court Rd 50 N, Rochester, IN, 46975
(219) 223-4331
Admin Carl William Miller II.
Licensure Intermediate care. *Beds* 117. *Certified* Medicaid.

Rochester Nursing Home*
240 E 18th St, Rochester, IN, 46975
(219) 223-5100
Admin Michael J Beach.
Licensure Intermediate care. *Beds* 40. *Certified* Medicaid.
Owner Proprietary Corp (Beverly Enterprises).

ROCKPORT

Miller's Merry Manor Inc*
815 Washington St, Rockport, IN, 47635
(812) 649-2276
Admin Marna Ames.
Licensure Intermediate care. *Beds* 92. *Certified* Medicaid.
Owner Proprietary Corp (Millers Merry Manor).

ROCKVILLE

Lee Alan Bryant Health Care Facilities Inc
Box 7, RR 1, Rockville, IN, 47872
(317) 569-6654
Admin Bette A Hein. *Medical Dir/Dir of Nursing* Dr Richard Bloomer; Carole Ladendorf DON.
Licensure Intermediate care; Residential care. *Beds* ICF 80; Residential 156. *Certified* Medicaid.
Owner Proprietary Corp.
Admissions Requirements Medical examination; Physician's request.
Staff Physicians 6 (pt); RNs 1 (ft); LPNs 8 (ft), 8 (pt); Nurses aides 24 (ft), 14 (pt); Physical therapists 1 (pt); Speech therapists 1 (pt); Activities coordinators 2 (ft); Dietitians 1 (pt); Dentists 1 (pt); Ophthalmologists 1 (pt); Podiatrists 1 (pt).
Facilities Dining room; Physical therapy room; Activities room; Chapel; Crafts room; Laundry room; Barber/Beauty shop; Library; 186 acres of grounds; Fishing area.

Activities Arts & crafts; Cards; Games; Reading groups; Prayer groups; Movies; Shopping trips; Social/Cultural gatherings; Field trips; Outings; Bus.

Castle Shannon Nursing Home
Box 251, RR 3, Rockville, IN, 47872
(317) 569-6526
Admin Mary Jane Kirkman. *Medical Dir/Dir of Nursing* Richard Bloomer MD; Nancy Newlin DON.
Licensure Intermediate care. *Beds* ICF 40. *Certified* Medicaid.
Owner Proprietary Corp (Beverly Enterprises).
Admissions Requirements Minimum age 18; Medical examination; Physician's request.
Staff LPNs 4 (ft), 2 (pt); Nurses aides 6 (ft), 9 (pt); Activities coordinators 1 (ft).
Facilities Dining room; Activities room; Laundry room.
Activities Arts & crafts; Cards; Games; Reading groups; Prayer groups; Movies; Shopping trips.

Parke County Nursing Home Inc*
RR 3, Box 260, Rockville, IN, 47872
(317) 569-6700
Admin Gerald Ball.
Licensure Intermediate care. *Beds* 58. *Certified* Medicaid.
Admissions Requirements Minimum age 18; Medical examination.
Staff RNs 2 (pt); LPNs 3 (ft), 3 (pt); Orderlies 1 (ft); Nurses aides 30 (ft); Recreational therapists 1 (ft); Activities coordinators 1 (ft); Dietitians 1 (pt).
Facilities Dining room; Activities room; Crafts room; Laundry room; Barber/Beauty shop.
Activities Arts & crafts; Cards; Games; Reading groups; Prayer groups; Movies; Shopping trips; Social/Cultural gatherings.

ROSSVILLE

Milner Community Health Care Inc
PO Box 15, State Rte 26 E, Rossville, IN, 46065
(317) 379-2112, 296-3099
Admin Ned Kelton Cline. *Medical Dir/Dir of Nursing* Lucy Coghill RN DON.
Licensure Intermediate care. *Beds* 96. *Certified* Medicaid.
Owner Nonprofit Corp (Community Care Centers).
Admissions Requirements Minimum age 18; Medical examination; Physician's request.
Staff RNs 4 (ft), 5 (pt); LPNs 2 (ft), 4 (pt); Activities coordinators 1 (ft), 2 (pt).
Facilities Dining room; Physical therapy room; Activities room; Chapel; Laundry room; Barber/Beauty shop; Library.
Activities Arts & crafts; Cards; Games; Reading groups; Prayer groups; Movies; Shopping trips; Social/Cultural gatherings; Bible study; Religious services; Cooking groups.

RUSHVILLE

Hillside Haven Nursing Home
424 N Perkins St, Rushville, IN, 46173
(317) 932-3024
Admin Catherine Coffman. *Medical Dir/Dir of Nursing* Dr Gilbert Ortiz; Jackie Foist DON.
Licensure Intermediate care. *Beds* ICF 28. *Certified* Medicaid.
Owner Proprietary Corp.
Admissions Requirements Medical examination.
Staff Physicians 1 (pt); RNs 1 (pt); LPNs 2 (ft), 2 (pt); Nurses aides 7 (ft), 5 (pt); Activities coordinators 1 (ft); Dietitians 1 (pt).

Facilities Dining room; Activities room;
Laundry room; Porch.
Activities Arts & crafts; Cards; Games;
Reading groups; Prayer groups; Movies;
Shopping trips; Social/Cultural gatherings;
Exercise class.

Miller's Merry Manor Inc*
612 E 11th St, Rushville, IN, 46173
(317) 932-4127
Admin Michael Forgey.
Licensure Skilled care; Intermediate care. *Beds*
SNF 50; ICF 120. *Certified* Medicaid;
Medicare.
Owner Proprietary Corp (Millers Merry
Manor).

SALEM

Meadow View Health Care Center
Homer & Anson Sts, Salem, IN, 47167
(812) 883-4681
Admin Connie Kellams. *Medical Dir/Dir of
Nursing* Donald Martin MD; Margaret
Kerns DON.
Licensure Skilled care; Intermediate care. *Beds*
SNF 39; ICF 99. *Certified* Medicaid;
Medicare.
Owner Proprietary Corp (Unicare).
Admissions Requirements Minimum age 18.
Staff Physicians; RNs; LPNs; Nurses aides;
Physical therapists; Speech therapists;
Activities coordinators; Dietitians;
Ophthalmologists.
Facilities Dining room; Physical therapy
room; Activities room; Laundry room;
Barber/Beauty shop.
Activities Arts & crafts; Cards; Games; Prayer
groups; Movies; Shopping trips; Social/
Cultural gatherings.

SAN PIERRE

Little Company of Mary Health Facility Inc
Rte 1, Box 22A, San Pierre, IN, 46374
(219) 828-4111
Admin Thomas H Kramer. *Medical Dir/Dir of
Nursing* A N Damodaran MD; Doris
Boisvert RN DON.
Licensure Intermediate care. *Beds* ICF 200.
Certified Medicaid.
Owner Nonprofit Corp.
Admissions Requirements Minimum age 18;
Medical examination.
Staff RNs 3 (ft), 3 (pt); LPNs 2 (ft), 1 (pt);
Nurses aides 60 (ft), 30 (pt); Activities
coordinators 1 (ft).
Languages Polish, Czech
Affiliation Roman Catholic
Facilities Dining room; Activities room;
Chapel; Crafts room; Laundry room; Barber/
Beauty shop; Library; Ceramics room; Social
room; Family dining room.
Activities Arts & crafts; Cards; Games;
Movies; Shopping trips.

SCOTTSBURG

Scott Villa Living Center
RR 1, Box 45, Scottsburg, IN, 47170
(812) 752-3499
Admin Clara E McGinnis. *Medical Dir/Dir of
Nursing* Marvin L McClain MD; Ruth A
Young DON.
Licensure Skilled care; Intermediate care. *Beds*
SNF 20; ICF 50. *Certified* Medicaid;
Medicare.
Owner Nonprofit Corp (Adventist Health Sys-
USA).
Admissions Requirements Minimum age 18;
Medical examination; Physician's request.
Staff RNs 3 (ft); LPNs 10 (ft), 3 (pt); Nurses
aides 20 (ft), 4 (pt); Physical therapists 1
(pt); Ophthalmologists 1 (pt).
Affiliation Seventh-Day Adventist

Facilities Dining room; Physical therapy
room; Activities room; Crafts room; Laundry
room; Barber/Beauty shop.
Activities Arts & crafts; Cards; Games;
Reading groups; Prayer groups; Movies;
Shopping trips; Social/Cultural gatherings.

Scottsburg Nursing Home
1100 N Gardner St, Scottsburg, IN, 47170
(812) 752-5065
Admin JoAnne Kreis. *Medical Dir/Dir of
Nursing* Dr M McClain; Sondra Johnson
RN.
Licensure Intermediate care. *Beds* ICF 40.
Certified Medicaid.
Owner Proprietary Corp (Beverly Enterprises).
Admissions Requirements Medical
examination.
Staff Physicians; LPNs; Orderlies; Nurses
aides; Recreational therapists; Activities
coordinators; Dietitians; Ophthalmologists;
Podiatrists.
Facilities Dining room; Activities room;
Barber/Beauty shop.
Activities Arts & crafts; Cards; Games;
Reading groups; Prayer groups; Movies;
Shopping trips; Social/Cultural gatherings.

Williams Manor*
10 Todd Dr, Scottsburg, IN, 47170
(812) 752-5663
Admin Barbara K Fleener. *Medical Dir/Dir of
Nursing* Dr William Scott.
Licensure Intermediate care. *Beds* 84.
Certified Medicaid.
Admissions Requirements Minimum age 18;
Medical examination; Physician's request.
Staff Physicians 7 (pt); RNs 1 (ft), 1 (pt);
LPNs 4 (ft), 3 (pt); Orderlies 1 (ft), 1 (pt);
Recreational therapists 1 (ft); Activities
coordinators 1 (pt); Dietitians 1 (pt).
Facilities Dining room; Physical therapy
room; Activities room; Laundry room;
Barber/Beauty shop; Conference room.
Activities Arts & crafts; Cards; Games;
Reading groups; Prayer groups; Movies;
Shopping trips; Social/Cultural gatherings;
Picnics.

SELLERSBURG

**Maple Manor Christian Home Inc—Adult
Division**
643 W Utica St, Sellersburg, IN, 47172
(812) 246-4866
Admin Joseph A Blansett. *Medical Dir/Dir of
Nursing* Cindy Shelley DON.
Licensure Self care; Comprehensive nursing.
Beds Self care 22; Comprehensive nursing
17. *Certified* Medi-Cal State.
Owner Nonprofit Corp.
Admissions Requirements Minimum age 21;
Medical examination.
Staff RNs 1 (pt); LPNs 5 (ft), 3 (pt); Nurses
aides 7 (ft), 1 (pt); Activities coordinators 1
(ft).
Affiliation Church of Christ
Facilities Dining room; Activities room;
Laundry room; Barber/Beauty shop; Library;
Lounge.
Activities Arts & crafts; Games; Reading
groups; Prayer groups; Shopping trips.

SEYMOUR

Jackson Park Convalescent Center
707 Jackson Park Dr, Seymour, IN, 47274
(812) 522-2416
Admin Mary C Driver. *Medical Dir/Dir of
Nursing* Dr Paul Page; Vicki Myers RN
DON.
Licensure Skilled care; Intermediate care. *Beds*
SNF 45; ICF 104. *Certified* Medicaid.
Owner Proprietary Corp.
Admissions Requirements Minimum age 18;
Medical examination; Physician's request.

Staff Physicians 1 (pt); RNs 5 (ft), 2 (pt);
LPNs 15 (ft), 7 (pt); Orderlies 1 (ft), 1 (pt);
Orderlies 44 (ft), 16 (pt); Nurses aides 1 (pt);
Recreational therapists 1 (pt); Activities
coordinators 2 (ft); Dietitians 1 (pt); Dentists
1 (pt); Dentist 1 (pt).
Facilities Dining room; Physical therapy
room; Activities room; Chapel; Crafts room;
Laundry room; Barber/Beauty shop; Library.
Activities Arts & crafts; Cards; Games;
Reading groups; Prayer groups; Movies;
Shopping trips; Social/Cultural gatherings.

Jackson Park Convalescent Center Inc*
PO Box 705, 707 Jackson Park Dr, Seymour,
IN, 47274
(812) 522-2416
Admin Mary C Driver RN. *Medical Dir/Dir of
Nursing* Dr Paul E Page.
Licensure Skilled care; Intermediate care. *Beds*
SNF 25; ICF 91. *Certified* Medicaid.
Admissions Requirements Minimum age 18;
Medical examination; Physician's request.
Staff Physicians 1 (pt); RNs 3 (ft), 2 (pt);
LPNs 5 (ft), 3 (pt); Orderlies 1 (pt); Nurses
aides 30 (ft), 15 (pt); Physical therapists 1
(pt); Activities coordinators 2 (ft); Dietitians
2 (pt); Dentists 1 (pt).
Facilities Dining room; Physical therapy
room; Activities room; Chapel; Crafts room;
Laundry room; Barber/Beauty shop.
Activities Arts & crafts; Cards; Games;
Reading groups; Prayer groups; Movies;
Shopping trips; Social/Cultural gatherings.

Lutheran Community Home Inc
111 W Church Ave, Seymour, IN, 47274
(812) 522-5927
Admin Donald Bruce. *Medical Dir/Dir of
Nursing* Dr Kenneth Bobb; Jeanne Corcoran
RN DON.
Licensure Intermediate care; Residential care.
Beds 82; Residential 20. *Certified* Medicaid.
Owner Nonprofit Corp.
Admissions Requirements Minimum age 18;
Females only; Medical examination.
Affiliation Lutheran
Facilities Dining room; Activities room;
Chapel; Crafts room; Laundry room; Barber/
Beauty shop.
Activities Arts & crafts; Cards; Games;
Reading groups; Movies; Shopping trips;
Social/Cultural gatherings.

SHELBYVILLE

Heritage House Children's Center
2325 S Miller St, Shelbyville, IN, 46176
(317) 392-3287
Admin Ava Vogel.
Licensure Skilled care. *Beds* SNF 135.
Certified Medicaid.
Owner Proprietary Corp.

The Heritage House Convalescent Center*
2309 S Miller St, Shelbyville, IN, 46176
(317) 398-9781
Admin Linda S Kuhn.
Licensure Skilled care; Intermediate care. *Beds*
135. *Certified* Medicaid; Medicare.

Heritage Manor Inc
2311 S Miller St, Shelbyville, IN, 46176
(317) 398-9777
Admin Ellave Miles. *Medical Dir/Dir of
Nursing* Dr Douglas Carter; Ruth Garner
DON.
Licensure Intermediate care. *Beds* 95.
Owner Privately owned.
Admissions Requirements Medical
examination; Physician's request.
Staff RNs; LPNs; Nurses aides; Dietitians.
Facilities Dining room; Physical therapy
room; Activities room; Crafts room; Laundry
room; Barber/Beauty shop.
Activities Arts & crafts; Cards; Games;
Reading groups; Prayer groups; Movies;
Shopping trips.

SHERIDAN

Sheridan Special Care Center
903 Sheridan Ave, Sheridan, IN, 46069
(317) 758-5330
Admin Betty Poshusta. *Medical Dir/Dir of Nursing* Mark Ambre MD; Shirley Jeffers DON.
Licensure Intermediate care for mentally retarded. *Beds* ICF/MR 50. *Certified* Medicaid.
Owner Proprietary Corp.
Admissions Requirements Medical examination.
Staff Physicians 1 (pt); RNs 1 (ft); LPNs 4 (ft); Orderlies 2 (ft); Nurses aides 18 (ft); Physical therapists 1 (pt); Occupational therapists 1 (pt); Speech therapists 1 (pt); Activities coordinators 1 (ft); Dietitians 1 (pt).
Facilities Dining room; Physical therapy room; Activities room; Crafts room; Laundry room.
Activities Arts & crafts; Cards; Games; Reading groups; Prayer groups; Movies; Shopping trips; Social/Cultural gatherings.

Sheridan Health Care Center Inc*
803 Hamilton Ave, Sheridan, IN, 46069
(317) 758-4426
Admin Jeanne Roeder.
Licensure Intermediate care. *Beds* 60. *Certified* Medicaid.

SOUTH BEND

Cardinal Manor*
118 S William St, South Bend, IN, 46601
(219) 289-4865
Admin Delores J Polomskey.
Licensure Residential care. *Beds* 59.
Admissions Requirements Minimum age 50; Medical examination.

Carlyle Health Care Corp
5024 W Western Ave, South Bend, IN, 46619
(219) 288-1464
Admin Mary Banky. *Medical Dir/Dir of Nursing* Charles E Myers MD; Janet Hon DON.
Licensure Skilled care; Intermediate care. *Beds* SNF 52; ICF 191. *Certified* Medicaid; Medicare.
Owner Proprietary Corp.
Admissions Requirements Minimum age 18; Medical examination; Physician's request.
Staff Physicians 1 (pt); RNs 7 (ft), 3 (pt); LPNs 15 (ft), 4 (pt); Nurses aides 60 (ft), 5 (pt); Recreational therapists 4 (ft); Activities coordinators 2 (ft); Dietitians 1 (pt).
Facilities Dining room; Physical therapy room; Activities room; Chapel; Crafts room; Laundry room; Barber/Beauty shop.
Activities Arts & crafts; Cards; Games; Reading groups; Prayer groups; Movies; Shopping trips; Social/Cultural gatherings.

Healthwin Hospital*
20531 Darden Rd, South Bend, IN, 46637
(219) 272-0100
Admin Michael J Roman.
Licensure Skilled care; Intermediate care. *Beds* 110. *Certified* Medicaid; Medicare.

Medco Center of South Bend*
1950 E Ridgedale Rd, South Bend, IN, 46614
(219) 291-6722
Admin Lloyd White. *Medical Dir/Dir of Nursing* Dr Zia Chowhan.
Licensure Skilled care; Intermediate care. *Beds* SNF 21; ICF 225. *Certified* Medicaid; Medicare.
Owner Proprietary Corp (Unicare).
Admissions Requirements Medical examination; Physician's request.
Staff RNs 8 (ft), 15 (pt); LPNs 7 (ft), 5 (pt); Physical therapists 1 (pt); Activities coordinators 3 (ft), 1 (pt); Dietitians 1 (ft).

Facilities Dining room; Physical therapy room; Activities room; Laundry room; Barber/Beauty shop.
Activities Arts & crafts; Cards; Games; Reading groups; Prayer groups; Movies; Shopping trips; Social/Cultural gatherings.

Meridian Nursing Center—Cardinal*
1121 E LaSalle, South Bend, IN, 46601
(219) 287-6501
Admin Chris Mueller.
Licensure Skilled care; Intermediate care. *Beds* 291. *Certified* Medicaid; Medicare.

Meridian Nursing Center—River Park
915 S 27th St, South Bend, IN, 46615
(219) 287-1016
Admin William A Beghtel. *Medical Dir/Dir of Nursing* Dr Debra McClain; Jo Ann Dake RN.
Licensure Intermediate care. *Beds* ICF 44. *Certified* Medicaid.
Owner Proprietary Corp (Meridian Healthcare).
Facilities Dining room; Activities room; Barber/Beauty shop.

The Milton Home Inc*
206 E Marion St, South Bend, IN, 46601
(219) 233-0165
Admin Rosemary Ward.
Licensure Intermediate care; Residential care. *Beds* ICF 16; Residential 34.
Owner Proprietary Corp (Meridian Healthcare).

Northwood Nursing Home*
328 N Notre Dame Ave, South Bend, IN, 46617
(219) 232-4486
Admin Emma J Hawk.
Licensure Intermediate care. *Beds* 40. *Certified* Medicaid.
Owner Proprietary Corp (Beverly Enterprises).
Admissions Requirements Physician's request.
Staff Physicians 1 (ft), 1 (pt); RNs 2 (ft); LPNs 2 (ft); Nurses aides 18 (ft), 7 (pt); Activities coordinators 1 (ft); Dietitians 1 (pt); Dentists 1 (pt); Ophthalmologists 1 (pt); Podiatrists 1 (pt).
Facilities Dining room; Laundry room.
Activities Arts & crafts; Cards; Games; Reading groups; Prayer groups; Movies; Shopping trips.

Portage Manor
53308 Portage Rd, South Bend, IN, 46628
(219) 232-9100
Admin Damaris A Smith. *Medical Dir/Dir of Nursing* H O Foley MD.
Licensure Residential care. *Beds* 120.
Owner Publicly owned.
Facilities Dining room; Activities room; Chapel; Crafts room; Laundry room; Barber/Beauty shop.
Activities Arts & crafts; Cards; Games; Reading groups; Prayer groups; Movies; Shopping trips; Social/Cultural gatherings.

Riverside Center Inc*
PO Box 2406, South Bend, IN, 46680
(219) 289-7871
Admin John D Pelzer.
Licensure Intermediate care. *Beds* 81. *Certified* Medicaid.

St Joseph Care Center—Notre Dame
1024 N Notre Dame Ave, South Bend, IN, 46617
(219) 234-3179
Admin Nancy Daniel. *Medical Dir/Dir of Nursing* Dr Logan Dunlap; Mary Fleming.
Licensure Intermediate care. *Beds* ICF 24. *Certified* Medicaid.
Owner Nonprofit organization/foundation.
Admissions Requirements Minimum age 18; Medical examination.

Staff RNs 1 (ft), 1 (pt); LPNs 2 (ft); Nurses aides 6 (ft), 5 (pt); Activities coordinators 1 (ft); Dietitians 1 (pt).
Activities Arts & crafts; Cards; Games; Reading groups; Prayer groups; Shopping trips; Social/Cultural gatherings.

St Josephs Care Center—Lombardy
4600 W Washington Ave, South Bend, IN, 46619
(219) 282-1294
Admin Rae D Leonard. *Medical Dir/Dir of Nursing* Zia Chowhan MD; Evelyn Troub RN DON.
Licensure Intermediate care. *Beds* ICF 180. *Certified* Medicaid.
Owner Nonprofit Corp.
Admissions Requirements Minimum age 18; Medical examination; Physician's request.
Staff Physicians 1 (pt); RNs 4 (ft), 2 (pt); LPNs 4 (ft), 2 (pt); Nurses aides 50 (ft); Occupational therapists 1 (ft); Activities coordinators 3 (ft); Dietitians 1 (pt).
Languages Polish
Affiliation Roman Catholic
Facilities Dining room; Activities room; Chapel; Crafts room; Laundry room; Barber/Beauty shop; Library.
Activities Arts & crafts; Cards; Games; Reading groups; Prayer groups; Movies; Shopping trips; Social/Cultural gatherings.

St Joseph's Care Center—Morningside
18325 Bailey Ave, South Bend, IN, 46637
(219) 272-6410
Admin Rose Ann Antkowiak. *Medical Dir/Dir of Nursing* Dr H Staunton; Karalee Eltzroth RN.
Licensure Intermediate care. *Beds* 40. *Certified* Medicaid.
Owner Nonprofit organization/foundation.
Admissions Requirements Minimum age 18; Medical examination; Physician's request.
Staff RNs 1 (ft), 1 (pt); LPNs 2 (ft), 2 (pt); Nurses aides 8 (ft), 13 (pt); Activities coordinators 1 (pt); Dietitians 1 (pt); Social services 1 (ft).
Affiliation Roman Catholic
Facilities Dining room; Activities room; Laundry room; Barber/Beauty shop.
Activities Arts & crafts; Cards.

St Paul's Retirement Community Inc
3602 S Ironwood Dr, South Bend, IN, 46614
(219) 291-8205
Admin Joseph M Doran. *Medical Dir/Dir of Nursing* Thomas Barbour MD; Lena Weldon RN DON.
Licensure Skilled care; Intermediate care; Retirement Community. *Beds* SNF 39; ICF 39; Apts 254. *Certified* Medicaid; Medicare.
Owner Nonprofit Corp.
Admissions Requirements Minimum age 55; Medical examination; Physician's request.
Staff Physicians 1 (pt); RNs 5 (ft); LPNs 9 (ft); Orderlies 1 (ft); Nurses aides 24 (ft); Physical therapists 1 (pt); Recreational therapists 1 (ft); Occupational therapists 1 (pt); Speech therapists 1 (pt); Activities coordinators 1 (ft); Dietitians 1 (pt); Ophthalmologists 1 (pt); Podiatrists 1 (pt).
Facilities Dining room; Physical therapy room; Activities room; Chapel; Crafts room; Laundry room; Barber/Beauty shop; Library.
Activities Arts & crafts; Cards; Games; Reading groups; Prayer groups; Movies; Shopping trips; Social/Cultural gatherings.

SPENCER

Owen County Home*
RR 3, Box 124, Spencer, IN, 47460
(812) 829-3492
Admin Ruthie Gray.
Beds 31.

Spencer Health Care Center
Box 77, RR 2, Spencer, IN, 47460
(812) 879-4275
Admin Maida Pierson. *Medical Dir/Dir of Nursing* Dr LeBow; Laura Lighter.
Licensure Intermediate care. *Beds* ICF 46. *Certified* Medicaid.
Owner Privately owned.
Admissions Requirements Minimum age 2; Medical examination.
Staff Physicians 5 (pt); RNs 1 (pt); LPNs 2 (ft), 4 (pt); Nurses aides 5 (ft), 1 (pt); Activities coordinators 1 (ft); Dietitians 1 (pt); Dentists 1 (pt); Ophthalmologists 1 (pt); DDS 1 (pt).
Facilities Dining room; Activities room; Chapel; Crafts room; Laundry room; Barber/Beauty shop; Library.
Activities Arts & crafts; Cards; Games; Reading groups; Prayer groups; Movies; Shopping trips; Social/Cultural gatherings.

SULLIVAN

Miller's Merry Manor*
PO Box 525, W Wolfe St, Sullivan, IN, 47882
(812) 268-6361
Admin Donald C Hunt.
Licensure Intermediate care. *Beds* 175. *Certified* Medicaid.
Owner Proprietary Corp (Millers Merry Manor).

Village Nursing Home
975 N Section St, Sullivan, IN, 47882
(812) 268-6810
Admin Richard W Bartnik. *Medical Dir/Dir of Nursing* Betty Dukes MD.
Licensure Intermediate care. *Beds* 40. *Certified* Medicaid.
Owner Proprietary Corp (Beverly Enterprises).
Admissions Requirements Minimum age 18; Medical examination; Physician's request.
Staff Physicians 1 (pt); LPNs 3 (ft), 2 (pt); Nurses aides 6 (ft), 7 (pt); Physical therapists 1 (pt); Reality therapists 1 (pt); Recreational therapists 1 (pt); Speech therapists 1 (pt); Activities coordinators 1 (ft), 1 (pt); Dietitians 1 (pt); Dentists 1 (pt); Ophthalmologists 1 (pt); Podiatrists 1 (pt); Dentist 1 (pt).
Facilities Dining room; Laundry room; Barber/Beauty shop.
Activities Arts & crafts; Cards; Games; Reading groups; Prayer groups; Movies; Shopping trips; Social/Cultural gatherings.

SUMMITVILLE

Summit Convalescent Center Inc
PO Box 398, Rte 1, Summitville, IN, 46070
(317) 536-2261
Admin Diane W Van Ness. *Medical Dir/Dir of Nursing* Wm C Van Ness, II MD; Barbara Hughes RN.
Licensure Intermediate care. *Beds* ICF 34. *Certified* Medicaid.
Owner Privately owned.
Admissions Requirements Minimum age 18; Medical examination; Physician's request.
Staff Physicians 2 (pt); RNs 1 (ft), 1 (pt); LPNs 2 (ft), 3 (pt); Nurses aides 9 (ft), 5 (pt); Activities coordinators 1 (ft), 1 (pt); Dietitians 1 (pt); Ophthalmologists 1 (pt).
Facilities Dining room; Activities room; Crafts room; Laundry room; Barber/Beauty shop.
Activities Arts & crafts; Cards; Games; Reading groups; Prayer groups; Movies; Shopping trips; Social/Cultural gatherings.

TELL CITY

Lincoln Hills Nursing Home
402 19th, Tell City, IN, 47586
(812) 547-3427

Admin William M Scheller. *Medical Dir/Dir of Nursing* Stephen Syler MD.
Licensure Intermediate care. *Beds* 165. *Certified* Medicaid.
Owner Proprietary Corp (Beverly Enterprises).
Admissions Requirements Minimum age 18; Medical examination; Physician's request.
Staff RNs 2 (ft), 1 (pt); LPNs 7 (ft); Nurses aides 40 (ft), 27 (pt); Physical therapists 1 (ft); Activities coordinators 2 (ft); Dietitians 1 (pt).
Facilities Dining room; Physical therapy room; Activities room; Chapel; Crafts room; Laundry room; Barber/Beauty shop.
Activities Arts & crafts; Cards; Games; Reading groups; Prayer groups; Movies; Shopping trips; Social/Cultural gatherings.

TERRE HAUTE

Davis Gardens Health Center
1120 Davis Ave, Terre Haute, IN, 47802
(812) 232-7533
Admin Carl Wilkins. *Medical Dir/Dir of Nursing* Adah Roads.
Licensure Skilled care; Intermediate care. *Beds* 78. *Certified* Medicaid; Medicare.
Owner Nonprofit Corp.
Admissions Requirements Medical examination; Physician's request.
Staff Physicians 1 (pt); RNs 4 (ft); LPNs 10 (ft); Orderlies 2 (ft); Nurses aides 30 (ft), 2 (pt); Activities coordinators 1 (ft).
Facilities Dining room; Physical therapy room; Laundry room; Barber/Beauty shop; Library.
Activities Arts & crafts; Games; Movies; Shopping trips; Social/Cultural gatherings.

Ewing Nursing Home
504 S 15th St, Terre Haute, IN, 47807
(812) 232-3663
Admin Selma Mills RN. *Medical Dir/Dir of Nursing* Selma M Mills RN.
Licensure Intermediate care. *Beds* 18. *Certified* Medicaid.
Staff RNs 1 (ft); LPNs 2 (ft); Orderlies 1 (ft); Nurses aides 4 (ft); Recreational therapists 1 (ft); Activities coordinators 1 (ft).
Facilities Dining room; Activities room; Laundry room.
Activities Arts & crafts; Cards; Games; Reading groups; Shopping trips; Social/Cultural gatherings.

Maplewood Manor*
500 Maple Ave, Terre Haute, IN, 47804
(812) 234-7702
Admin Mike Cahill. *Medical Dir/Dir of Nursing* H G Edwards.
Licensure Skilled care; Intermediate care. *Beds* SNF 124; ICF 93. *Certified* Medicaid; Medicare.
Owner Proprietary Corp (Beverly Enterprises).
Admissions Requirements Minimum age 18.
Staff RNs 7 (ft); LPNs 23 (ft); Nurses aides 110 (ft), 10 (pt); Physical therapists 1 (ft), 1 (pt); Recreational therapists 1 (pt); Occupational therapists 1 (pt); Speech therapists 1 (pt); Activities coordinators 1 (ft); Dietitians 1 (pt); Dentists 1 (pt); Podiatrists 1 (pt); Audiologists 1 (pt).
Facilities Dining room; Physical therapy room; Activities room; Chapel; Crafts room; Laundry room; Barber/Beauty shop.
Activities Arts & crafts; Cards; Games; Reading groups; Prayer groups; Movies; Shopping trips; Social/Cultural gatherings.

Meadows Manor*
3300 Poplar St, Terre Haute, IN, 47803
(812) 235-6281
Admin Jeffrey Stultz.
Licensure Skilled care; Intermediate care. *Beds* 103. *Certified* Medicaid.

Meadows Manor North Inc
3150 N 7th St, Terre Haute, IN, 47804
(812) 466-5217
Admin Nancy F Applegate. *Medical Dir/Dir of Nursing* James Buechler MD; Annette Jenkins RN DON.
Licensure Skilled care. *Beds* SNF 100. *Certified* Medicaid; Medicare.
Owner Proprietary Corp.
Admissions Requirements Minimum age 17; Medical examination.
Staff Physicians 1 (ft), 38 (pt); RNs 6 (ft); LPNs 25 (ft); Orderlies 5 (ft); Nurses aides 40 (ft); Physical therapists 1 (ft); Recreational therapists 1 (ft); Occupational therapists 1 (ft); Speech therapists 1 (ft); Activities coordinators 2 (ft); Dietitians 1 (ft); Dentists; Ophthalmologists; Podiatrists; Social Services 2 (ft); Beauticians 2 (ft); Medical Records 1 (ft).
Languages Italian, German, Sign
Facilities Dining room; Physical therapy room; Activities room; Chapel; Crafts room; Laundry room; Barber/Beauty shop; Library; Lounges.
Activities Arts & crafts; Cards; Games; Reading groups; Prayer groups; Movies; Shopping trips; Social/Cultural gatherings; Pet related activities.

Terre Haute Nursing Home
830 S 6th St, Terre Haute, IN, 47808
(812) 232-7102
Admin Patricia Dunn.
Licensure Intermediate care. *Beds* 40. *Certified* Medicaid.
Owner Proprietary Corp (Waverly Group).

Vigo County Home
3500 Maple Ave, Terre Haute, IN, 47804
(812) 238-8375
Admin Robert D Wallace. *Medical Dir/Dir of Nursing* W L Loewenstein MD.
Licensure Intermediate care. *Beds* 201. *Certified* Medicaid.
Owner Publicly owned.
Admissions Requirements Medical examination; Physician's request.
Staff Physicians 1 (pt); RNs 6 (ft); LPNs 28 (ft); Nurses aides 66 (ft); Physical therapists 1 (pt); Reality therapists 1 (pt); Recreational therapists 3 (ft); Occupational therapists 1 (pt); Speech therapists 1 (pt); Activities coordinators 1 (ft); Dietitians 1 (ft); Dentists 1 (pt); Ophthalmologists 1 (pt); Podiatrists 1 (pt).
Facilities Dining room; Physical therapy room; Activities room; Chapel; Crafts room; Laundry room; Barber/Beauty shop.
Activities Arts & crafts; Cards; Games; Reading groups; Prayer groups; Movies; Shopping trips; Social/Cultural gatherings.

Webster's Rest Home*
513-515 N 14th St, Terre Haute, IN, 47807
(812) 232-4571
Admin Rachel Webster.
Licensure Intermediate care. *Beds* 10. *Certified* Medicaid.

Westridge Health Care Center
120 W Margaret Ave, Terre Haute, IN, 47802
(812) 232-3311
Admin Lowell G Buck. *Medical Dir/Dir of Nursing* W McIntosh MD; Mary Weyls RN.
Licensure Skilled care; Intermediate care. *Beds* SNF 26; ICF 94. *Certified* Medicaid; Medicare.
Owner Nonprofit Corp.
Admissions Requirements Minimum age 18 unless waived by health facilities council.
Staff Physicians 1 (pt); RNs 5 (ft), 1 (pt); LPNs 8 (ft), 6 (pt); Orderlies 4 (ft); Nurses aides 26 (ft), 8 (pt); Physical therapists 1 (pt); Recreational therapists 1 (pt); Speech therapists 3 (pt); Activities coordinators 1 (ft), 2 (pt); Dietitians 1 (ft); Dentists 1 (pt); Ophthalmologists 1 (pt); Podiatrists 1 (pt).

Facilities Dining room; Physical therapy room; Activities room; Chapel; Crafts room; Laundry room; Barber/Beauty shop; Library.
Activities Arts & crafts; Cards; Games; Reading groups; Prayer groups; Movies; Shopping trips; Social/Cultural gatherings; Religious services; Bowling.

TIPTON

Miller's Merry Manor*
4-H Rd, PO Box 418, Tipton, IN, 46072
(317) 675-8791
Admin Rita Fox RN.
Licensure Intermediate care. *Beds* 102. Certified Medicaid.
Owner Proprietary Corp (Millers Merry Manor).
Admissions Requirements Minimum age 19; Medical examination; Physician's request.
Staff RNs 3 (ft); LPNs 3 (ft); Nurses aides 20 (ft), 15 (pt); Physical therapists 1 (pt); Speech therapists 1 (pt); Activities coordinators 1 (ft), 1 (pt); Dietitians 1 (pt); Audiologists 1 (pt).
Facilities Dining room; Physical therapy room; Activities room; Crafts room; Laundry room; Barber/Beauty shop; Library.
Activities Arts & crafts; Cards; Games; Reading groups; Prayer groups; Movies; Social/Cultural gatherings.

Tipton Nursing Home
701 E Jefferson St, Tipton, IN, 46072
(317) 675-4024 or 675-8462
Admin Carolyn Sue Nevin. *Medical Dir/Dir of Nursing* Ruth Jones RN DON.
Licensure Intermediate care. *Beds* ICF 40. Certified Medicaid.
Owner Proprietary Corp (Beverly Enterprises).
Staff Physicians 1 (pt); RNs 2 (ft); LPNs 4 (ft); Nurses aides 4 (ft), 6 (pt); Recreational therapists 1 (pt); Activities coordinators 1 (pt); Dietitians 1 (pt); Social worker 1 (pt).
Facilities Dining room; Activities room; Crafts room; Laundry room; Barber/Beauty shop.
Activities Arts & crafts; Cards; Games; Reading groups; Prayer groups; Movies; Shopping trips; Social/Cultural gatherings; Intergenerational programs.

UPLAND

University Nursing Center
1512 S University Blvd, Upland, IN, 46989-3000
(317) 998-2761
Admin Emily Hayes Garvin. *Medical Dir/Dir of Nursing* Thomas Lee MD; June K Lewis DON.
Licensure Skilled care; Intermediate care. *Beds* SNF 20; ICF 61. Certified Medicaid; Medicare.
Owner Proprietary Corp (Hillhaven Corp).
Admissions Requirements Medical examination; Physician's request.
Staff RNs 2 (pt); LPNs 4 (ft), 4 (pt); Nurses aides 15 (ft), 20 (pt); Physical therapists 1 (pt); Activities coordinators 1 (ft); Dietitians 1 (pt).
Facilities Dining room; Physical therapy room; Activities room; Laundry room; Barber/Beauty shop.
Activities Arts & crafts; Cards; Games; Prayer groups; Movies; Social/Cultural gatherings.

VALPARAISO

Canterbury Place
251 East Dr, Valparaiso, IN, 46383
(219) 462-6158
Admin Eunice Taylor. *Medical Dir/Dir of Nursing* Robert Harvey MD; Tammy Rowe DON.
Licensure Skilled care; Intermediate care. *Beds* SNF 35; ICF 67. Certified Medicaid; Medicare.
Owner Proprietary Corp (Beverly Enterprises).
Admissions Requirements Minimum age 18.
Staff RNs 3 (ft), 2 (pt); LPNs 6 (ft), 4 (pt); Nurses aides 20 (ft), 15 (pt); Recreational therapists 1 (ft); Activities coordinators 1 (ft).
Facilities Dining room; Physical therapy room; Activities room; Laundry room; Barber/Beauty shop.
Activities Arts & crafts; Cards; Games; Reading groups; Prayer groups; Movies; Social/Cultural gatherings.

Pavilion Health Care Center of Valparaiso*
606 Wall St, Valparaiso, IN, 46383
(219) 464-4976
Admin Christopher J Mullaney. *Medical Dir/Dir of Nursing* Joel L Hull MD & Owen H Lucas MD.
Licensure Skilled care; Intermediate care. *Beds* SNF 96; ICF 96. Certified Medicaid; Medicare.
Owner Proprietary Corp.
Admissions Requirements Minimum age 18; Medical examination; Physician's request.
Staff Physicians 1 (pt); RNs 11 (ft), 2 (pt); LPNs 2 (ft), 2 (pt); Nurses aides 61 (ft), 2 (pt); Physical therapists 1 (ft), 1 (pt); Recreational therapists 1 (ft); Occupational therapists 1 (ft); Speech therapists 1 (pt); Activities coordinators 3 (ft); Dietitians 1 (pt); Ophthalmologists 1 (pt); Podiatrists 1 (pt); Audiologists Dentists 1 (pt).
Facilities Dining room; Physical therapy room; Activities room; Crafts room; Laundry room; Barber/Beauty shop.
Activities Arts & crafts; Cards; Games; Reading groups; Prayer groups; Movies; Shopping trips; Social/Cultural gatherings; Cooking club.

Whispering Pines Health Care Center
3301 N Calumet Ave, Valparaiso, IN, 46383
(219) 462-0508
Admin Gregory M Snider. *Medical Dir/Dir of Nursing* Michael Weiss MD; Lillian Barnard RN DON.
Licensure Skilled care; Intermediate care. *Beds* SNF 39; ICF 145. Certified Medicaid; Medicare.
Owner Nonprofit Corp.
Admissions Requirements Minimum age 60; Medical examination.
Staff RNs 5 (ft), 7 (pt); LPNs 6 (ft), 5 (pt); Nurses aides 60 (ft), 45 (pt); Activities coordinators 4 (ft), 1 (pt); Dietitians 1 (ft).
Facilities Dining room; Physical therapy room; Activities room; Chapel; Crafts room; Laundry room; Barber/Beauty shop; Library.
Activities Arts & crafts; Cards; Games; Reading groups; Prayer groups; Movies; Shopping trips; Social/Cultural gatherings; Bible study.

Willows Rehabilitation Center
1000 Elizabeth, Valparaiso, IN, 46383
(219) 464-4858
Admin LuAnn Nebelung. *Medical Dir/Dir of Nursing* Dr James Chia; Marlene Versteeg DON.
Licensure Skilled care; Intermediate care. *Beds* SNF 49; ICF 50. Certified Medicaid; Medicare.
Owner Proprietary Corp (Southmark Heritage Corp).
Admissions Requirements Medical examination; Physician's request.
Staff RNs 3 (ft), 1 (pt); LPNs 4 (ft), 2 (pt); Nurses aides 45 (ft), 25 (pt); Physical therapists 2 (pt); Recreational therapists 1 (ft); Occupational therapists 1 (pt); Speech therapists 2 (pt); Activities coordinators 1 (ft); Dietitians 1 (pt); Ophthalmologists 1 (pt); Podiatrists 1 (pt).

Facilities Dining room; Physical therapy room; Laundry room; Barber/Beauty shop; Library.
Activities Arts & crafts; Cards; Games; Reading groups; Prayer groups; Movies; Shopping trips; Social/Cultural gatherings.

VERSAILLES

Silver Bell Nursing Home
RR 2, Box 106, Versailles, IN, 47402
(812) 689-6222
Admin Phyllis Fields. *Medical Dir/Dir of Nursing* Dr Alan Culbreth; Eula Busteed.
Licensure Intermediate care. *Beds* 21. Certified Medicaid.
Owner Privately owned.
Admissions Requirements Medical examination.
Staff Physicians 1 (ft); RNs 1 (pt); LPNs 3 (ft); Nurses aides 6 (ft); Activities coordinators 3 (ft); Dietitians 1 (pt).
Facilities Dining room; Activities room; Crafts room; Laundry room; Barber/Beauty shop.
Activities Arts & crafts; Cards; Games; Reading groups; Prayer groups; Movies; Shopping trips; Social/Cultural gatherings.

VEVAY

Jackson's Senior Citizens Home*
501 W Pike St, Vevay, IN, 47043
(812) 427-3525
Admin Linda L McDole.
Licensure Residential care. *Beds* 18.
Admissions Requirements Medical examination.
Staff Physicians 1 (pt); RNs 1 (pt); Activities coordinators 1 (ft); Dietitians 1 (pt).
Facilities Dining room; Laundry room.
Activities Arts & crafts; Games; Reading groups; Social/Cultural gatherings.

Swiss Villa Living Center*
Rte 3, Box 169A, Vevay, IN, 47043
(812) 427-2803
Admin Anita Craig. *Medical Dir/Dir of Nursing* Ivan Lindgren MD; Cathy Hart RN.
Licensure Intermediate care. *Beds* ICF 100. Certified Medicaid.
Owner Nonprofit Corp (Adventist Health Sys-USA).
Admissions Requirements Minimum age 18; Medical examination; Physician's request.
Staff RNs 3 (ft); LPNs 6 (ft); Nurses aides; Activities coordinators 1
Affiliation Seventh-Day Adventist
Facilities Dining room; Laundry room; Barber/Beauty shop.
Activities Arts & crafts; Cards; Games; Reading groups; Prayer groups; Movies.

VINCENNES

Crestview Convalescent Center
3801 Old Bruceville Rd, Vincennes, IN, 47591
(812) 882-1783
Admin Douglas H Herrold. *Medical Dir/Dir of Nursing* Daniel J Combs MD; Debra Parish DON.
Licensure Skilled care; Intermediate care. *Beds* SNF 82; ICF 134. Certified Medicaid; Medicare.
Owner Proprietary Corp (Hillhaven Corp).
Admissions Requirements Medical examination; Physician's request.
Staff Physicians; RNs; LPNs; Nurses aides; Physical therapists; Speech therapists; Activities coordinators; Dietitians; Ophthalmologists; Podiatrists.
Facilities Dining room; Physical therapy room; Activities room; Chapel.
Activities Arts & crafts; Cards; Games; Reading groups; Prayer groups; Movies; Shopping trips; Social/Cultural gatherings.

Vincennes Nursing Home*
PO Box 903, 1202 S 16th St, Vincennes, IN, 47591
(812) 882-8292
Admin Frank Harrell.
Licensure Intermediate care. *Beds* 66.
Certified Medicaid.

Willow Manor Convalescent Center Inc*
1321 Willow St, Vincennes, IN, 47591
(812) 882-1136
Admin Judith Ann Drieman.
Licensure Skilled care; Intermediate care. *Beds* SNF 43; ICF 99. *Certified* Medicaid; Medicare.

WABASH

Manor Care, Division of Miller's Merry Manor
RR 2, Mill Creek Pike, Wabash, IN, 46992
(219) 563-4121
Admin Lesley Garrison. *Medical Dir/Dir of Nursing* James Haughn MD.
Licensure Intermediate care. *Beds* 39. *Certified* Medicaid.
Owner Proprietary Corp (Millers Merry Manor).
Admissions Requirements Minimum age 18; Medical examination; Physician's request.
Staff RNs 1 (ft); LPNs 2 (ft), 2 (pt); Nurses aides 5 (ft), 6 (pt); Activities coordinators 1 (ft).
Facilities Dining room; Activities room; Laundry room; Barber/Beauty shop.
Activities Arts & crafts; Games; Movies; Shopping trips; Daily living classes.

Miller's Merry Manor Inc
1035 Manchester Ave, Wabash, IN, 46992
(219) 563-7427
Admin Audrey Hahn. *Medical Dir/Dir of Nursing* Dr James Haughn; Karen Middleton RN.
Licensure Skilled care; Intermediate care. *Beds* SNF 27; ICF 75. *Certified* Medicaid; Medicare.
Owner Proprietary Corp (Millers Merry Manor).
Admissions Requirements Medical examination; Physician's request.
Staff RNs 4 (ft), 8 (pt); LPNs 9 (ft), 3 (pt); Nurses aides 24 (ft), 14 (pt); Activities coordinators 2 (pt).
Facilities Dining room; Physical therapy room; Activities room; Laundry room; Barber/Beauty shop.
Activities Arts & crafts; Cards; Games; Prayer groups; Movies; Shopping trips.

Vernon Manor Children's Home
1955 S Vernon St, Wabash, IN, 46992
(219) 563-8438
Admin Jocelyn Ravenscroft.
Licensure Skilled care. *Beds* 136. *Certified* Medicaid.

Wabash Healthcare Center
600 Washington St, Wabash, IN, 46992
(219) 563-8402
Admin Duane Tripp. *Medical Dir/Dir of Nursing* James McCann MD.
Licensure Skilled care; Intermediate care. *Beds* SNF 54; ICF 54. *Certified* Medicaid; Medicare.
Owner Proprietary Corp.
Admissions Requirements Medical examination; Physician's request.
Staff Physicians 14 (pt); RNs 7 (ft), 3 (pt); LPNs 4 (ft), 3 (pt); Nurses aides 35 (ft), 10 (pt); Physical therapists 2 (pt); Reality therapists 2 (pt); Recreational therapists 2 (pt); Speech therapists 1 (pt); Activities coordinators 1 (ft), 1 (pt); Dietitians 1 (pt); Dentists 1 (pt); Ophthalmologists 1 (pt); Podiatrists 1 (pt).
Facilities Dining room; Physical therapy room; Activities room; Crafts room; Laundry room; Barber/Beauty shop; Library.

Activities Arts & crafts; Cards; Games; Reading groups; Prayer groups; Movies; Shopping trips; Social/Cultural gatherings.

WALDRON

Waldron Health Care Home Inc
PO Box 371, North Main St, Waldron, IN, 46182
(317) 525-4371
Admin Dwain R Kuhn. *Medical Dir/Dir of Nursing* James Peters Med Dir; Carol Shurig DON.
Licensure Intermediate care; Residential. *Beds* ICF; Residential 63/20. *Certified* Medicaid.
Owner Proprietary Corp.
Staff RNs 1 (ft); LPNs 3 (ft), 2 (pt); Nurses aides 15 (ft), 20 (pt); Activities coordinators; Dietitians 1 (ft), 1 (pt).
Facilities Dining room; Activities room; Laundry room; Barber/Beauty shop.
Activities Arts & crafts; Cards; Games; Reading groups; Prayer groups; Movies; Shopping trips.

WALKERTON

Miller's Merry Manor Inc*
Walkerton Trail, Walkerton, IN, 46574
(219) 586-3133
Admin Patrick Boyle.
Licensure Intermediate care. *Beds* 116. *Certified* Medicaid.
Owner Proprietary Corp (Millers Merry Manor).

WARREN

United Methodist Memorial Home
PO Box 326, Warren, IN, 46792
(219) 375-2201
Admin Philip E Souder. *Medical Dir/Dir of Nursing* Gerald Miller MD; Lois Spahr RN DON.
Licensure Residential care; Comprehensive nursing care. *Beds* 655.
Admissions Requirements Minimum age 65; Medical examination; Physician's request.
Staff Physicians 7 (pt); RNs 14 (ft); LPNs 12 (ft); Nurses aides 112 (ft); Physical therapists 2 (ft), 1 (pt); Recreational therapists 2 (ft); Occupational therapists 5 (ft); Activities coordinators 2 (ft), 1 (pt); Dietitians 1 (pt); Ophthalmologists 1 (pt); Podiatrists 1 (pt).
Affiliation Methodist
Facilities Dining room; Physical therapy room; Activities room; Chapel; Crafts room; Laundry room; Barber/Beauty shop; Library; Dentist office; Eye clinic; Post office; Medical clinic on-site.
Activities Arts & crafts; Cards; Games; Reading groups; Prayer groups; Movies; Shopping trips; Social/Cultural gatherings.

WARSAW

Mason Health Care Facility Inc
900 Provident Dr, Warsaw, IN, 46580
(219) 267-6611
Admin Carlyle L Mason. *Medical Dir/Dir of Nursing* Harold Mason MD; Gracie Freeman DON.
Licensure Skilled care; Intermediate care. *Beds* 89. *Certified* Medicaid; Medicare.
Owner Proprietary Corp.
Admissions Requirements Minimum age 18; Medical examination; Physician's request.
Staff RNs 5 (ft), 3 (pt); LPNs 2 (ft), 3 (pt); Nurses aides 24 (ft), 7 (pt); Physical therapists 1 (pt); Recreational therapists 1 (pt); Activities coordinators 1 (ft), 2 (pt); Dietitians 1 (pt); Dentists 1 (pt); Ophthalmologists 1 (pt).
Facilities Dining room; Physical therapy room; Activities room; Crafts room; Laundry room; Barber/Beauty shop.

Activities Arts & crafts; Cards; Games; Reading groups; Shopping trips.

Miller's Merry Manor Inc*
PO Box 377, Country Farm Rd, Warsaw, IN, 46580
(219) 267-8196
Admin Bruce Mehlhop.
Licensure Skilled care; Intermediate care. *Beds* 103. *Certified* Medicaid; Medicare.
Owner Proprietary Corp (Millers Merry Manor).
Admissions Requirements Minimum age 18; Medical examination; Physician's request.

Prairie View Rest Home Inc
300 E Prairie St, Warsaw, IN, 46580
(219) 267-8922
Admin N Charlene Bradbury. *Medical Dir/Dir of Nursing* YuDu Chen MD; Carol Brazo RN DON.
Licensure Intermediate care. *Beds* ICF 126. *Certified* Medicaid.
Owner Proprietary Corp.
Admissions Requirements Minimum age 18; Medical examination; Physician's request.
Staff Physicians 1 (pt); RNs 4 (ft), 4 (pt); LPNs 6 (ft); Orderlies 1 (pt); Nurses aides 25 (ft), 15 (pt); Physical therapists 1 (pt); Activities coordinators 2 (ft); Dietitians 1 (pt).
Facilities Dining room; Physical therapy room; Activities room; Barber/Beauty shop; 2 lounges; Enclosed courtyard; Quiet room; Wheelchair lift van & station wagon.
Activities Arts & crafts; Cards; Games; Prayer groups; Movies; Shopping trips; Social/Cultural gatherings; Trips to zoo; Botanical gardens; Travelogues.

Warsaw Nursing Home
2402 E Center St, Warsaw, IN, 46580
(219) 269-1152
Admin Patricia Beam. *Medical Dir/Dir of Nursing* Yu du Chen MD; Robert Nilsen RN DON.
Licensure Intermediate care. *Beds* ICF 40. *Certified* Medicaid.
Owner Proprietary Corp (Beverly Enterprises).
Admissions Requirements Minimum age 18.
Staff RNs 1 (pt); LPNs 3 (ft); Nurses aides 6 (ft), 3 (pt); Activities coordinators 1 (pt).
Facilities Dining room; Activities room; Laundry room.
Activities Arts & crafts; Cards; Games; Social/Cultural gatherings.

WASHINGTON

Eastgate Manor Nursing & Residential Center Inc*
Hwy 50 E, PO Box 470, Washington, IN, 47501
(812) 254-3301
Admin Jim Ward.
Licensure Intermediate care. *Beds* 82. *Certified* Medicaid.
Owner Proprietary Corp (Unicare).
Admissions Requirements Minimum age 18; Medical examination; Physician's request.
Staff RNs 3 (ft), 2 (pt); LPNs 3 (ft), 6 (pt); Nurses aides 30 (ft), 10 (pt); Physical therapists 1 (pt); Activities coordinators 1 (ft); Dietitians 1 (pt); Dentists 1 (pt); Ophthalmologists 1 (pt).
Facilities Dining room; Physical therapy room; Activities room; Laundry room; Barber/Beauty shop.
Activities Arts & crafts; Cards; Games; Reading groups; Prayer groups; Movies; Shopping trips; Social/Cultural gatherings.

Hillside Manor*
1109 E National Hwy, Washington, IN, 47501
(812) 254-7159
Admin John F Helm. *Medical Dir/Dir of Nursing* Dr T W Davis.

Licensure Intermediate care. *Beds* 27. *Certified* Medicaid.
Admissions Requirements Medical examination; Physician's request.
Staff RNs 1 (ft), 1 (pt); LPNs 1 (ft), 1 (pt); Nurses aides 7 (ft), 5 (pt); Physical therapists 1 (pt); Activities coordinators 1 (ft).
Facilities Dining room; Laundry room.
Activities Arts & crafts; Cards; Games; Reading groups; Shopping trips.

Prairie Village Living Center
1401 Hwy 57 South, Washington, IN, 47501
(812) 254-4516
Admin Stephanie Atwood. *Medical Dir/Dir of Nursing* Donald Hall MD.
Licensure Intermediate care. *Beds* 121. *Certified* Medicaid.
Owner Nonprofit Corp (Adventist Health Sys-USA).
Admissions Requirements Minimum age 18.
Staff Physicians 5 (pt); RNs 3 (ft); LPNs 6 (ft); Orderlies 5 (ft); Nurses aides 40 (ft); Physical therapists 1 (pt); Activities coordinators 2 (ft); Dietitians 1 (pt); Dentists 1 (pt); Ophthalmologists 1 (pt); Podiatrists 1 (pt).
Affiliation Seventh-Day Adventist
Facilities Dining room; Physical therapy room; Activities room; Laundry room; Barber/Beauty shop.
Activities Arts & crafts; Cards; Games; Reading groups; Prayer groups; Shopping trips.

Washington Nursing Center Annex*
209 W Oak St, Washington, IN, 47501
(812) 254-0252
Admin David Snow.
Licensure Intermediate care. *Beds* 17. *Certified* Medicaid.

Washington Nursing Center Inc*
603 E National Hwy, Washington, IN, 47501
(812) 254-5117
Admin Jerome B Walker. *Medical Dir/Dir of Nursing* James P Beck MD.
Licensure Skilled care; Intermediate care. *Beds* 179. *Certified* Medicaid; Medicare.
Admissions Requirements Minimum age 18; Medical examination; Physician's request.
Staff Physicians 7 (pt); RNs 14 (ft); LPNs 6 (ft); Nurses aides 88 (ft); Physical therapists 1 (ft); Speech therapists 1 (pt); Activities coordinators 2 (ft); Dietitians 1 (pt); Dentists 1 (pt); Ophthalmologists 1 (pt); Podiatrists 1 (pt); Audiologists 1 (pt).
Facilities Dining room; Physical therapy room; Activities room; Laundry room; Barber/Beauty shop.
Activities Arts & crafts; Cards; Games; Reading groups; Prayer groups; Movies; Shopping trips; Social/Cultural gatherings.

WEST LAFAYETTE

George Davis Manor
1051 Cumberland Ave, West Lafayette, IN, 47906
(317) 463-2571
Admin Gail A Brown. *Medical Dir/Dir of Nursing* Dr Thomas J Stolz; Jimmie Riddle RN DON.
Licensure Intermediate care; Residential. *Beds* ICF 39; Residential 83. *Certified* Medicaid.
Owner Nonprofit Corp.
Admissions Requirements Minimum age 18; Medical examination.
Staff RNs 2 (ft), 1 (pt); LPNs 7 (ft); Orderlies 2 (ft); Nurses aides 25 (ft), 3 (pt); Activities coordinators 1 (ft); Dietitians 1 (pt).
Facilities Dining room; Physical therapy room; Activities room; Crafts room; Laundry room; Barber/Beauty shop; Library; Lounge.
Activities Arts & crafts; Cards; Games; Reading groups; Prayer groups; Movies; Shopping trips; Social/Cultural gatherings.

Heritage Healthcare Inc
3400 Soldiers Home Rd, West Lafayette, IN, 47906
(317) 463-1541
Admin Linda L Smith RN. *Medical Dir/Dir of Nursing* Dr Tom Stolz.
Licensure Intermediate care. *Beds* 145. *Certified* Medicaid.
Owner Proprietary Corp.
Admissions Requirements Medical examination.
Staff Physicians 1 (pt); RNs 6 (ft), 6 (pt); LPNs 6 (ft), 2 (pt); Orderlies 2 (ft); Nurses aides 65 (ft), 25 (pt); Reality therapists 2 (pt); Recreational therapists 5 (ft); Occupational therapists 1 (pt); Speech therapists 1 (pt); Activities coordinators 1 (ft); Dietitians 1 (ft); Dentists 1 (pt); Ophthalmologists 1 (pt); Podiatrists 1 (pt).
Facilities Dining room; Physical therapy room; Activities room; Crafts room; Laundry room; Barber/Beauty shop; Library; Day care room & activities.
Activities Arts & crafts; Cards; Games; Reading groups; Prayer groups; Movies; Shopping trips; Dinner club.

Indiana Veterans Home
3851 N River Road, West Lafayette, IN, 47906
(317) 463-1502
Admin Col Robert Hinds. *Medical Dir/Dir of Nursing* Ben E Crouse MD; Patricia L Query RN.
Licensure Comprehensive care; Residential care. *Beds* Residential 251; Comprehensive care 549.
Owner Publicly owned.
Admissions Requirements Medical examination; Physician's request.
Staff Physicians 1 (ft), 6 (pt); RNs 38 (ft); LPNs 29 (ft); Nurses aides 168 (ft); Physical therapists 4 (ft); Recreational therapists 12 (ft), 4 (pt); Occupational therapists 4 (ft); Speech therapists 1 (ft), 1 (pt); Activities coordinators 1 (ft); Dietitians 3 (ft); Dentists 1 (pt); Ophthalmologists 1 (pt); Podiatrists 1 (ft), 1 (pt).
Facilities Dining room; Physical therapy room; Activities room; Chapel; Crafts room; Laundry room; Barber/Beauty shop; Library.
Activities Arts & crafts; Cards; Games; Reading groups; Prayer groups; Movies; Shopping trips; Social/Cultural gatherings.

Tippecanoe Villa*
5308 N 50 W, West Lafayette, IN, 47906
(317) 423-9240
Admin C Haan.
Licensure Residential care. *Beds* 121.

Westminster Village West Lafayette
2741 N Salisbury St, West Lafayette, IN, 47906
(317) 463-7546
Admin John J Morrison. *Medical Dir/Dir of Nursing* Eleanor H Filmer MD; Trudy Risemas RN.
Licensure Skilled care. *Beds* SNF 38. *Certified* Medicare.
Owner Nonprofit Corp.
Admissions Requirements Minimum age 62; Medical examination.
Staff Physicians 1 (pt); RNs 4 (ft), 2 (pt); LPNs 1 (ft), 1 (pt); Nurses aides 13 (ft), 8 (pt); Physical therapists 1 (pt); Occupational therapists 1 (pt); Speech therapists 1 (pt); Activities coordinators 1 (ft); Dietitians 1 (pt); Ophthalmologists 1 (pt); Podiatrists 1 (pt); Qualified medication aides 6 (pt); Dentist 1 (pt).
Facilities Dining room; Physical therapy room; Activities room; Chapel; Crafts room; Laundry room; Barber/Beauty shop; Library; Branch bank; General store; Exercise room; Club room.

Activities Arts & crafts; Cards; Games; Reading groups; Prayer groups; Movies; Shopping trips; Social/Cultural gatherings; Trips.

WESTFIELD

Westfield Village*
776 N Union, Westfield, IN, 46074
(317) 896-2515
Admin Deborah Fowler.
Licensure Intermediate care. *Beds* 80. *Certified* Medicaid.

WHITING

Hammond-Whiting Convalescent Center
1000 114th St, Whiting, IN, 46394
(219) 659-2770
Admin Paul Asselin. *Medical Dir/Dir of Nursing* Dr K Pahuja MD.
Licensure Intermediate care. *Beds* 80. *Certified* Medicaid.
Owner Proprietary Corp (Life Care Centers of America).
Admissions Requirements Minimum age 65; Medical examination; Physician's request.
Staff RNs 2 (ft), 6 (pt); LPNs 1 (ft); Orderlies 1 (ft); Nurses aides 20 (ft), 12 (pt); Activities coordinators 1 (ft).
Facilities Dining room; Activities room; Laundry room; Barber/Beauty shop; TV lounge.
Activities Arts & crafts; Cards; Games; Prayer groups; Movies; Social/Cultural gatherings.

WILLIAMSPORT

Meadow Heights Nursing Center Inc
200 Short St, Williamsport, IN, 47993
(317) 762-6111
Admin Joseph P Castro. *Medical Dir/Dir of Nursing* Dr Hugo Brenner; Merridy J Dillman RN DON.
Licensure Skilled care; Intermediate care. *Beds* SNF 95; ICF. *Certified* Medicaid.
Owner Privately owned.
Admissions Requirements Minimum age 16; Medical examination; Physician's request.
Staff RNs 3 (ft); LPNs 4 (ft); Nurses aides 25 (ft); Activities coordinators 1 (ft).
Facilities Dining room; Physical therapy room; Activities room; Crafts room; Laundry room; Barber/Beauty shop.
Activities Arts & crafts; Cards; Games; Reading groups; Prayer groups; Movies; Shopping trips; Social/Cultural gatherings.

WINAMAC

Winamac Nursing Home
515 E 13th St, Winamac, IN, 46996
(219) 946-6143
Admin Jacqueline L Estok. *Medical Dir/Dir of Nursing* Rex Allman MD; Sue DeGroot RN DON.
Licensure Intermediate care. *Beds* ICF 40. *Certified* Medicaid.
Owner Proprietary Corp (Beverly Enterprises).
Staff RNs 2 (ft); LPNs 2 (ft), 1 (pt); Activities coordinators 1 (ft).
Facilities Dining room; Activities room; Laundry room.
Activities Arts & crafts; Cards; Games; Reading groups; Prayer groups; Movies.

WINCHESTER

Randolph Nursing Home Inc*
701 S Oak St, Winchester, IN, 47394
(317) 584-2201
Admin Lorna Kay McAtee.
Licensure Intermediate care. *Beds* 65. *Certified* Medicaid.
Owner Proprietary Corp (Forum Grp).

WINONA LAKE

Grace Village Health Care Facility
PO Box 337, Winona Lake, IN, 46590
(219) 372-6100
Admin Sherwood V Durkee. *Medical Dir/Dir of Nursing* Nancy Derry RN.
Licensure Intermediate care; Residential care. *Beds* ICF 33; Residential 17. *Certified* Medicaid.
Owner Nonprofit Corp.

Admissions Requirements Minimum age 65; Medical examination; Physician's request.
Staff RNs; LPNs; Nurses aides; Activities coordinators; Dietitians.
Affiliation Church of the Brethren
Facilities Dining room; Physical therapy room; Activities room; Chapel; Crafts room; Laundry room; Barber/Beauty shop; Library.
Activities Arts & crafts; Games; Reading groups; Prayer groups; Movies; Shopping trips.

ZIONSVILLE

Indiana Christian Retirement Park*
675 S Ford Rd, Zionsville, IN, 46077
(317) 873-5205
Admin Robert Vincent.
Licensure Intermediate care. *Beds* 43.

IOWA

ACKLEY

Presbyterian Home of Ackley
1020 2nd Ave, Ackley, IA, 50601
(515) 847-3531
Admin Iva Griep. *Medical Dir/Dir of Nursing* Lisa Ubben.
Licensure Intermediate care; Residential care. *Beds* ICF 55; Residential 40. *Certified* Medicaid.
Owner Nonprofit Corp.
Admissions Requirements Medical examination.
Staff RNs 2 (ft); LPNs 5 (pt); Orderlies 1 (ft), 1 (pt); Nurses aides 20 (ft), 26 (pt); Activities coordinators 1 (ft); Dietitians 1 (pt).
Languages German
Affiliation Presbyterian
Facilities Dining room; Activities room; Chapel; Crafts room; Barber/Beauty shop.
Activities Arts & crafts; Cards; Games; Reading groups; Prayer groups; Movies; Shopping trips; Social/Cultural gatherings; Church services; Bible study.

ADAIR

Adair Community Health Center Inc
PO Box 92A, 608 North St, RR 2, Adair, IA, 50002
(515) 742-3205
Admin Linda S Hemminger RN. *Medical Dir/ Dir of Nursing* Judy Schwenneker LPN, Jolene Hinrichs LPN DON.
Licensure Intermediate care. *Beds* ICF 48. *Certified* Medicaid.
Owner Nonprofit Corp.
Admissions Requirements Medical examination; Physician's request.
Staff RNs 3 (pt); LPNs 5 (ft), 2 (pt); Nurses aides 10 (ft), 13 (pt); Activities coordinators 1 (pt).
Facilities Dining room; Activities room; Laundry room; Barber/Beauty shop.
Activities Arts & crafts; Cards; Games; Reading groups; Prayer groups; Movies; Shopping trips; Social/Cultural gatherings; Picnics; Plant flowers; Cooking.

ADEL

Adel Acres Care Center
1919 Greene St, Adel, IA, 50003
(515) 993-4511
Admin Pam Lancial. *Medical Dir/Dir of Nursing* Karen Klisaris DON.
Licensure Intermediate care. *Beds* ICF 59. *Certified* Medicaid.
Owner Privately owned.
Admissions Requirements Medical examination.
Staff RNs 1 (ft), 1 (pt); LPNs 1 (ft), 3 (pt); Nurses aides 10 (ft), 15 (pt); Activities coordinators; Dietitians.

Facilities Dining room; Laundry room; Barber/Beauty shop.
Activities Arts & crafts; Cards; Games; Reading groups; Prayer groups; Movies; Shopping trips; Social/Cultural gatherings.

AFTON

Afton Care Center Inc*
805 W Pearl, Afton, IA, 50830
(515) 347-8416
Admin Mary Cochran.
Licensure Intermediate care. *Beds* 60. *Certified* Medicaid.

AKRON

Akron City Convalescent Care Center
PO Box 847, 276 S St, Akron, IA, 51001
(712) 568-2422
Admin Jerold J Dykstra. *Medical Dir/Dir of Nursing* Dr J Torbert MD; Jan Pritchett DON.
Licensure Skilled care; Intermediate care. *Beds* SNF 15; ICF 45. *Certified* Medicaid; Medicare.
Owner Nonprofit organization/foundation.
Admissions Requirements Medical examination; Physician's request.
Staff Physicians 1 (ft); RNs 4 (ft), 3 (pt); LPNs 4 (ft), 1 (pt); Nurses aides 7 (ft), 9 (pt); Physical therapists 1 (pt); Activities coordinators 1 (ft); Dietitians 1 (ft).
Facilities Dining room; Physical therapy room; Activities room; Chapel; Crafts room; Laundry room; Barber/Beauty shop.
Activities Arts & crafts; Cards; Games; Social/ Cultural gatherings.

ALBERT CITY

Pleasant View Home
410 S 3rd St, Albert City, IA, 50510
(712) 843-2238
Admin Dorothy Nordlund. *Medical Dir/Dir of Nursing* Connie Hansen RN DON.
Licensure Intermediate care. *Beds* ICF 50. *Certified* Medicaid.
Owner Proprietary Corp.
Admissions Requirements Minimum age 18; Medical examination; Physician's request.
Staff RNs 3 (ft), 1 (pt); LPNs 1 (ft), 2 (pt); Nurses aides 12 (ft), 7 (pt); Physical therapists 1 (pt); Activities coordinators 1 (ft); Dietitians 1 (pt); Podiatrists 1 (pt).
Facilities Dining room; Activities room; Laundry room; Barber/Beauty shop.
Activities Arts & crafts; Cards; Games; Reading groups; Prayer groups; Movies; Shopping trips; Social/Cultural gatherings.

ALBIA

Albia Care Center*
116 Benton Ave W, Albia, IA, 52531
Admin Betty James.

Licensure Residential care. *Beds* 50. *Certified* Medicaid.
Owner Proprietary Corp.
Admissions Requirements Medical examination; Physician's request.
Staff LPNs 2 (ft); Orderlies 1 (ft); Nurses aides 12 (ft); Recreational therapists 1 (pt); Activities coordinators 1 (ft); Dietitians.
Facilities Dining room; Activities room; Chapel; Crafts room; Laundry room; Barber/ Beauty shop; Library.
Activities Arts & crafts; Cards; Games; Reading groups; Prayer groups; Movies; Shopping trips; Social/Cultural gatherings.

Albia Manor*
S Florence, Albia, IA, 52531
(515) 932-7105
Admin Connie Byrd.
Licensure Intermediate care. *Beds* 94. *Certified* Medicaid.
Owner Proprietary Corp (Beverly Enterprises).
Admissions Requirements Physician's request.
Staff RNs 3 (ft), 2 (pt); LPNs 5 (ft), 2 (pt); Nurses aides 40 (ft), 15 (pt); Activities coordinators 1 (ft), 1 (pt).
Facilities Dining room; Physical therapy room; Activities room; Laundry room; Barber/Beauty shop.
Activities Arts & crafts; Cards; Games; Reading groups; Prayer groups; Movies; Shopping trips; Social/Cultural gatherings.

ALGONA

Algona Good Samaritan Center
214 W Kennedy St, Algona, IA, 50511
(515) 295-2414
Admin John E Kern. *Medical Dir/Dir of Nursing* Marilyn Stevens DON.
Licensure Intermediate care. *Beds* ICF 121. *Certified* Medicaid.
Owner Nonprofit Corp (Evangelical Lutheran/ Good Samaritan).
Languages German
Affiliation Lutheran
Facilities Dining room; Physical therapy room; Activities room; Crafts room; Laundry room; Barber/Beauty shop.
Activities Arts & crafts; Cards; Games; Reading groups; Prayer groups; Movies; Social/Cultural gatherings.

ALLISON

Allison Care Center
Box 89A, 900 7th St W, Allison, IA, 50602
(319) 267-2791
Admin Ruth Schlitter, Assistant Administrator. *Medical Dir/Dir of Nursing* Barbara Jacobs DON.
Licensure Intermediate care. *Beds* ICF 80. *Certified* Medicaid; Medicare.
Owner Proprietary Corp (ABCM Corp).
Staff RNs; LPNs; Nurses aides; Physical therapists; Activities coordinators; Dietitians.

Facilities Dining room; Physical therapy
room; Activities room; Chapel; Crafts room;
Laundry room; Barber/Beauty shop; Library.
Activities Arts & crafts; Cards; Games;
Reading groups; Prayer groups; Movies;
Shopping trips; Social/Cultural gatherings.

ALTOONA

Altoona Manor Care Center
PO Box 595, 200 7th Ave SW, Altoona, IA,
50009
(515) 967-4267
Admin Norman Hjelmeland.
Licensure Intermediate care. *Beds* 109.
Certified Medicaid.
Owner Proprietary Corp (Life Care Centers of
America).

AMANA

Colonial Manor of Amana Inc
Box 160, Hwy 220 West, Amana, IA, 52203
(319) 622-3131
Admin B H Otte. *Medical Dir/Dir of Nursing*
Dr Stacey Howell.
Licensure Intermediate care. *Beds* ICF 56.
Certified Medicaid.
Owner Proprietary Corp.
Admissions Requirements Minimum age 16.
Staff Physicians 1 (pt); RNs 1 (ft), 1 (pt);
LPNs 6 (ft), 3 (pt); Orderlies 1 (pt); Nurses
aides 25 (ft), 4 (pt); Physical therapists 1
(pt); Recreational therapists 1 (pt);
Occupational therapists 1 (pt); Speech
therapists 1 (pt); Activities coordinators 1
(ft); Dietitians 1 (pt); Ophthalmologists 1
(pt); Podiatrists 1 (pt).
Languages German
Facilities Dining room; Physical therapy
room; Activities room; Chapel; Crafts room;
Laundry room; Barber/Beauty shop.
Activities Arts & crafts; Cards; Games;
Reading groups; Prayer groups; Movies;
Social/Cultural gatherings.

AMES

Center for Personal Development
1008 Burnett, Ames, IA, 50010
(515) 232-8391
Admin Donna J Ruden. *Medical Dir/Dir of
Nursing* Jack Dodd MD.
Licensure Residential care. *Beds* 15.
Owner Nonprofit Corp.
Admissions Requirements Minimum age 18;
Medical examination; Physician's request.
Staff Reality therapists 8 (ft); Recreational
therapists 1 (ft).
Facilities Dining room; Activities room;
Laundry room.
Activities Arts & crafts; Cards; Games;
Reading groups; Movies; Shopping trips;
Social/Cultural gatherings.

North Grand Care Center*
3440 Grand Ave, Ames, IA, 50010
(515) 232-3426
Licensure Intermediate care. *Beds* 100.
Certified Medicaid.
Admissions Requirements Medical
examination.
Staff RNs 5 (ft), 2 (pt); LPNs 3 (ft), 2 (pt);
Orderlies 1 (ft); Nurses aides 25 (ft), 15 (pt);
Physical therapists 1 (ft), 1 (pt); Reality
therapists 1 (pt); Recreational therapists 1
(ft), 1 (pt); Occupational therapists 1 (pt);
Speech therapists 1 (pt); Activities
coordinators 1 (ft); Dietitians 11 (ft);
Podiatrists 1 (pt); Audiologists 1 (pt).
Facilities Dining room; Physical therapy
room; Activities room; Chapel; Crafts room;
Laundry room; Barber/Beauty shop; Library;
TV lounges.

Activities Arts & crafts; Cards; Games;
Reading groups; Prayer groups; Movies;
Shopping trips; Social/Cultural gatherings;
Individualized activities.

Northcrest Health Care Center*
1801 20th St, Ames, IA, 50010
(515) 232-6760
Admin Larry L Allen.
Licensure Intermediate care; Residential care.
Beds ICF 18; Residential 10. *Certified*
Medicaid.

Riverside Manor*
1204 S 4th, Ames, IA, 50010
(515) 233-2903
Admin Lee V Livingston.
Licensure Intermediate care. *Beds* 59.
Certified Medicaid.

ANAMOSA

Anamosa Care Center*
1209 E 3rd St, Anamosa, IA, 52205
(319) 462-4356
Licensure Intermediate care. *Beds* 76.
Certified Medicaid.

ANITA

Colonial Manor*
1000 Hillcrest Dr, Anita, IA, 50020
(712) 762-3219
Admin Brenda Euken.
Licensure Intermediate care. *Beds* 65.
Certified Medicaid.

ANKENY

Sunny View Care Center
410 NW Ash Dr, Ankeny, IA, 50021
(515) 964-1101
Admin Bonnie Ballard. *Medical Dir/Dir of
Nursing* Patricia Naughton DON.
Licensure Intermediate care. *Beds* 75.
Certified Medicaid.
Owner Proprietary Corp.
Admissions Requirements Minimum age 18;
Medical examination; Physician's request.
Staff RNs 2 (ft), 3 (pt); LPNs 2 (ft), 2 (pt);
Nurses aides 18 (ft), 10 (pt); Activities
coordinators 3 (pt).
Facilities Dining room; Activities room;
Crafts room; Laundry room; Barber/Beauty
shop.
Activities Arts & crafts; Games; Reading
groups; Prayer groups; Movies; Shopping
trips; Social/Cultural gatherings; Picnics;
Music.

APLINGTON

Maple Manor Nursing Home*
345 Parrott, Aplington, IA, 50604
(319) 347-2309
Licensure Intermediate care; Residential care.
Beds ICF 38; Residential 20. *Certified*
Medicaid.
Admissions Requirements Medical
examination.
Staff RNs 1 (pt); LPNs 4 (pt); Nurses aides 23
(pt); Physical therapists 1 (pt); Occupational
therapists 1 (pt); Activities coordinators 2
(pt); Dietitians 1 (pt).
Facilities Dining room; Physical therapy
room; Activities room; Laundry room;
Barber/Beauty shop.
Activities Arts & crafts; Cards; Games;
Reading groups; Prayer groups; Movies;
Shopping trips.

ARMSTRONG

Valley Vue Nursing Home*
2nd Ave, Armstrong, IA, 50514
(712) 864-3567

Admin Mary Tirevold.
Licensure Intermediate care. *Beds* 50.
Certified Medicaid.

ATLANTIC

Atlantic Care Center*
1311 Sunnyside Ln, Atlantic, IA, 50022
(712) 243-3952
Medical Dir/Dir of Nursing Dr Keith
Swanson.
Licensure Intermediate care. *Beds* 123.
Certified Medicaid.
Staff RNs 1 (ft); LPNs 8 (ft), 3 (pt); Nurses
aides 18 (ft), 18 (pt); Physical therapists 1
(pt); Speech therapists 1 (pt); Activities
coordinators 1 (ft), 1 (pt); Dietitians 1 (pt);
Dentists 1 (pt); Ophthalmologists 1 (pt);
Podiatrists 1 (pt); Audiologists 1 (pt).

Heritage House Continuing Care Community
1200 Brookridge Circle, Atlantic, IA, 50022
(712) 243-1850
Admin Janet C Marvin NHA RN. *Medical
Dir/Dir of Nursing* Dwain Wilcox MD;
Barbara Fischer RN DON.
Licensure Intermediate care; Residential care;
Independent living; Independent living
assisted. *Beds* ICF 46; Residential 15;
Independent living assisted varies;
Independent living 81. *Certified* Medicaid.
Owner Nonprofit Corp.
Staff Physicians 1 (pt); RNs 2 (ft); LPNs 3
(ft), 5 (pt); Nurses aides 18 (ft), 11 (pt);
Activities coordinators 1 (ft), 1 (pt);
Dietitians 1 (pt); Social worker 1 (ft).
Affiliation Methodist
Facilities Dining room; Physical therapy
room; Activities room; Chapel; Crafts room;
Laundry room; Barber/Beauty shop; Library.
Activities Arts & crafts; Cards; Games;
Reading groups; Prayer groups; Movies;
Shopping trips; Social/Cultural gatherings;
Reminiscence therapy; Remotivation
therapy.

AUDUBON

Friendship Home
714 N Division St, Audubon, IA, 50025
(712) 563-2651
Admin Howard B Benson. *Medical Dir/Dir of
Nursing* Judy Malmberg RN DON.
Licensure Intermediate care; Residential care.
Beds ICF 69; Residential 86. *Certified*
Medicaid.
Owner Nonprofit Corp.
Admissions Requirements Minimum age 62.
Staff Physicians; RNs; LPNs; Nurses aides;
Physical therapists; Activities coordinators;
Dietitians.
Facilities Dining room; Physical therapy
room; Activities room; Chapel; Crafts room;
Laundry room; Barber/Beauty shop; Library.
Activities Arts & crafts; Cards; Games;
Reading groups; Prayer groups; Movies;
Shopping trips; Social/Cultural gatherings.

AURELIA

Sunset Knoll Inc
5th & Spruce, Aurelia, IA, 51005
(712) 434-2294
Admin Orin L Nelson. *Medical Dir/Dir of
Nursing* Richard Berge MD; Carrie Voss
DON.
Licensure Intermediate care; Residential care.
Beds ICF 48; Residential 20. *Certified*
Medicaid.
Owner Proprietary Corp.
Admissions Requirements Minimum age 50;
Medical examination; Physician's request.
Staff RNs 3 (ft), 1 (pt); LPNs 1 (ft), 2 (pt);
Nurses aides 19 (ft), 6 (pt); Physical
therapists 1 (pt); Occupational therapists 1

(pt); Speech therapists 1 (pt); Activities coordinators 2 (pt); Dietitians 1 (pt); Podiatrists 1 (pt).
Facilities Dining room; Physical therapy room; Activities room; Chapel; Laundry room; Barber/Beauty shop.
Activities Arts & crafts; Cards; Games; Reading groups; Prayer groups; Movies; Shopping trips.

AVOCA

Colonial Manor of Avoca
1100 Chestnut St, Avoca, IA, 51521
(712) 343-2665
Admin Suzie Nelson. *Medical Dir/Dir of Nursing* Lois Zobrist.
Licensure Intermediate care. *Beds* ICF 46. *Certified* Medicaid.
Owner Proprietary Corp (Beverly Enterprises).
Staff RNs 2 (ft); LPNs 4 (ft); Nurses aides 18 (ft); Activities coordinators 1 (ft).
Facilities Dining room; Laundry room; Barber/Beauty shop.
Activities Arts & crafts; Cards; Games; Reading groups; Prayer groups; Movies; Shopping trips; Social/Cultural gatherings.

BANCROFT

Heritage Home of Bancroft*
E Ramsey, Bancroft, IA, 50517
(515) 885-2463
Admin Jeanne M Kinney.
Licensure Intermediate care. *Beds* 39. *Certified* Medicaid.

BATTLE CREEK

Willow Dale Care Center
Hwy 175, Battle Creek, IA, 51006
(712) 365-4332
Admin Wilma McClellan. *Medical Dir/Dir of Nursing* Anne Beery RN.
Licensure Intermediate care. *Beds* 61. *Certified* Medicaid.
Owner Proprietary Corp (ABCM Corp).
Admissions Requirements Medical examination; Physician's request.
Staff RNs 1 (ft), 1 (pt); LPNs 3 (ft), 2 (pt); Nurses aides 14 (ft), 10 (pt); Physical therapists 1 (pt); Recreational therapists 1 (pt); Occupational therapists 1 (pt); Speech therapists 1 (pt); Activities coordinators 1 (ft); Dietitians 2 (pt); Ophthalmologists 1 (pt); Podiatrists 1 (pt).
Facilities Dining room; Physical therapy room; Activities room; Crafts room; Laundry room; Barber/Beauty shop.
Activities Arts & crafts; Cards; Games; Reading groups; Prayer groups; Movies; Shopping trips; Social/Cultural gatherings.

BAXTER

Colonial Manor of Jasper Co Inc
PO Box 398, Baxter, IA, 50028
(515) 227-3602
Admin Glen Van Zante. *Medical Dir/Dir of Nursing* Beverley Van Zante.
Licensure Intermediate care. *Beds* ICF 65. *Certified* Medicaid.
Owner Privately owned.
Admissions Requirements Minimum age 20; Medical examination; Physician's request.
Staff Physicians; RNs 2 (ft), 2 (pt); LPNs 1 (ft); Nurses aides 12 (ft), 13 (pt); Activities coordinators 1 (ft); Dietitians 1 (pt).
Languages German
Facilities Dining room; Physical therapy room; Activities room; Chapel; Crafts room; Laundry room; Barber/Beauty shop; Library.
Activities Arts & crafts; Cards; Games; Reading groups; Prayer groups; Movies; Shopping trips; Social/Cultural gatherings.

BAYARD

Bayard Care Center*
2nd Ave, Bayard, IA, 50029
(712) 651-2085
Admin Helen Andersen.
Licensure Intermediate care. *Beds* 50. *Certified* Medicaid.

BEDFORD

Bedford Manor*
1005 W Pearl, Bedford, IA, 50833
(712) 523-2161
Admin Steven Fister.
Licensure Intermediate care. *Beds* 64. *Certified* Medicaid.

BELLE PLAINE

Beverly Manor Convalescent Center
1505 Sunset Dr, Belle Plaine, IA, 52208
(319) 444-2500
Admin Dorie Tammen. *Medical Dir/Dir of Nursing* Linda Meeks.
Licensure Intermediate care. *Beds* ICF 70. *Certified* Medicaid.
Owner Proprietary Corp (Beverly Enterprises).
Admissions Requirements Medical examination.
Staff RNs; LPNs; Nurses aides; Activities coordinators.
Facilities Dining room; Laundry room; Barber/Beauty shop.
Activities Arts & crafts; Cards; Games; Reading groups; Prayer groups; Movies; Shopping trips; Social/Cultural gatherings.

BELLEVUE

Mill Valley Care Center
1201 Park St, Bellevue, IA, 52031
(319) 872-5521
Admin Glinda Ernst. *Medical Dir/Dir of Nursing* Thomas F Garland MD; Auerle Bevan RN DON.
Licensure Intermediate care. *Beds* ICF 68. *Certified* Medicaid.
Owner Proprietary Corp.
Admissions Requirements Minimum age 18; Medical examination; Physician's request.
Staff RNs; LPNs; Nurses aides; Activities coordinators.
Facilities Dining room; Physical therapy room; Activities room; Chapel; Laundry room; Barber/Beauty shop.
Activities Arts & crafts; Cards; Games; Reading groups; Prayer groups; Movies; Shopping trips; Social/Cultural gatherings.

BELMOND

Belmond Nursing Home*
1107 7th St NE, Belmond, IA, 50421
(515) 444-3195
Admin Opal M Ellingston.
Licensure Intermediate care. *Beds* 86. *Certified* Medicaid.

BETTENDORF

Bettendorf Health Care Center*
2730 Crow Creek Rd, Bettendorf, IA, 52722
(319) 359-7463
Admin Steven Dowd.
Licensure Intermediate care. *Beds* 100. *Certified* Medicaid.

Iowa Masonic Nursing Home
26th & State Sts, Bettendorf, IA, 52722
(319) 359-9171
Admin W Ross McCulla.
Licensure Intermediate care. *Beds* 79. *Certified* Medicaid.

Admissions Requirements Minimum age 21; Medical examination; Physician's request.
Staff Physicians 1 (pt); RNs 3 (ft), 3 (pt); LPNs 3 (ft), 3 (pt); Nurses aides 20 (ft), 10 (pt); Physical therapists 1 (pt); Reality therapists 1 (ft), 1 (pt); Occupational therapists 1 (pt); Speech therapists 1 (pt); Activities coordinators 2 (ft), 1 (pt); Dietitians 1 (pt); Dentists 1 (pt); Ophthalmologists 1 (pt); Podiatrists 1 (pt).
Affiliation Masons
Facilities Dining room; Physical therapy room; Activities room; Chapel; Crafts room; Laundry room; Barber/Beauty shop; Library; Game room.
Activities Arts & crafts; Cards; Games; Reading groups; Prayer groups; Movies; Shopping trips; Social/Cultural gatherings.

BLOOMFIELD

ABCM Corporation—Bloomfield Care Center
800 N Davis, State Rte 4, Bloomfield, IA, 52537
(515) 664-2699
Admin Janet Schwieger.
Licensure Intermediate care. *Beds* 104. *Certified* Medicaid.
Owner Proprietary Corp.
Staff RNs 1 (ft); LPNs 10 (ft), 1 (pt); Nurses aides 15 (ft), 19 (pt); Physical therapists 1 (pt); Occupational therapists 1 (pt); Activities coordinators 1 (ft), 1 (pt); Dietitians 1 (pt); Podiatrists.
Facilities Dining room; Physical therapy room; Activities room; Chapel; Crafts room; Barber/Beauty shop; Library; Picnic shelter; TV area.
Activities Arts & crafts; Cards; Games; Reading groups; Prayer groups; Movies; Shopping trips; Social/Cultural gatherings.

BOONE

Eastern Star Masonic Home*
715 Mamie Eisenhower Ave, Boone, IA, 50036
(515) 432-5274
Admin Dennis Bock.
Licensure Intermediate care; Residential care. *Beds* ICF 50; Residential 98. *Certified* Medicaid.
Affiliation Order of Eastern Star

Evangelical Free Church Home*
112 W 4th St, Boone, IA, 50036
(515) 432-1393
Admin Ernest J Vick.
Licensure Intermediate care. *Beds* 120. *Certified* Medicaid.
Affiliation Evangelical Free Church

Ledges Manor Corporation*
1400 22nd St, Boone, IA, 50036
(515) 432-5580
Admin Joe C Johnson.
Licensure Intermediate care. *Beds* 94. *Certified* Medicaid.
Admissions Requirements Minimum age 18.
Staff RNs 2 (ft); LPNs 4 (ft), 3 (pt); Orderlies 1 (ft); Physical therapists 20 (ft), 14 (pt); Activities coordinators 1 (ft), 1 (pt).
Facilities Dining room; Activities room; Crafts room; Laundry room; Barber/Beauty shop.
Activities Arts & crafts; Cards; Games; Reading groups; Prayer groups; Movies; Shopping trips.

BRITT

Westview Manor*
445 8th Ave SW, Britt, IA, 50423
(515) 843-3835
Admin Becky L Smit.
Licensure Intermediate care. *Beds* 59. *Certified* Medicaid.

BROOKLYN

Brookhaven Nursing Home
406 North St, Brooklyn, IA, 52211
(515) 522-9263
Admin Brian Peterson. *Medical Dir/Dir of Nursing* Shirley Mathes RN DON.
Licensure Intermediate care. *Beds* 45. *Certified* Medicaid.
Admissions Requirements Medical examination.
Staff RNs 2 (ft), 1 (pt); LPNs 1 (ft), 1 (pt); Nurses aides 7 (ft), 10 (pt); Physical therapists 1 (pt); Speech therapists 1 (pt); Activities coordinators 1 (ft); Dietitians 1 (pt); Podiatrists 1 (pt).
Facilities Dining room; Laundry room; Barber/Beauty shop.
Activities Arts & crafts; Cards; Games; Reading groups; Prayer groups; Movies.

BUFFALO CENTER

Timely Mission Nursing Home*
109 Mission Dr, Buffalo Center, IA, 50424
(515) 562-2494
Admin Murray D Berggren.
Licensure Intermediate care. *Beds* 51.
Certified Medicaid.

BURLINGTON

Burlington Care Center
2610 S 5th St, Burlington, IA, 52601
(319) 753-2841
Admin Robert Richard. *Medical Dir/Dir of Nursing* Jane Schenk DON.
Licensure Intermediate care. *Beds* ICF 103. *Certified* Medicaid.
Admissions Requirements Minimum age 18; Medical examination; Physician's request.
Staff RNs 3 (ft), 1 (pt); LPNs 5 (ft), 5 (pt); Nurses aides 30 (ft), 18 (pt); Physical therapists 1 (pt); Occupational therapists 1 (pt); Speech therapists 1 (pt); Activities coordinators 1 (ft), 1 (pt); Dietitians 1 (pt); Dentists 1 (pt); Ophthalmologists 1 (pt).
Facilities Dining room; Physical therapy room; Activities room; Chapel; Crafts room; Laundry room; Barber/Beauty shop.
Activities Arts & crafts; Cards; Games; Reading groups; Prayer groups; Movies; Shopping trips; Social/Cultural gatherings.

Burlington Medical Center—Klein Unit
2910 Madison Ave, Burlington, IA, 52601
(319) 752-5461
Admin Richard Miller. *Medical Dir/Dir of Nursing* Burton Stone MD; Carolyn Mackey RN.
Licensure Skilled care; Intermediate care. *Beds* SNF 24; ICF 125. *Certified* Medicaid; Medicare.
Owner Nonprofit Corp.
Admissions Requirements Medical examination; Physician's request.
Staff Physicians; RNs; LPNs; Orderlies; Nurses aides; Physical therapists; Reality therapists; Recreational therapists; Occupational therapists; Speech therapists; Activities coordinators; Dietitians; Dentists; Ophthalmologists; Podiatrists.
Facilities Dining room; Physical therapy room; Activities room; Chapel; Crafts room; Laundry room; Barber/Beauty shop; Library.
Activities Arts & crafts; Cards; Games; Reading groups; Prayer groups; Movies; Shopping trips; Social/Cultural gatherings.

Elm View Care Center
715 Shoquoquon Dr, Burlington, IA, 52601
(319) 752-4525
Admin Patricia M Mumme. *Medical Dir/Dir of Nursing* Linda Gerdner RN.
Licensure Intermediate care. *Beds* ICF 146. *Certified* Medicaid.
Owner Proprietary Corp (Hillhaven Corp).

Admissions Requirements Medical examination; Physician's request.
Staff RNs; LPNs; Orderlies; Nurses aides; Physical therapists 1 (pt); Activities coordinators; Dietitians 1 (pt).
Facilities Dining room; Physical therapy room; Activities room; Chapel; Crafts room; Laundry room; Barber/Beauty shop.
Activities Arts & crafts; Cards; Games; Reading groups; Prayer groups; Movies; Shopping trips; Social/Cultural gatherings.

St Francis Continuing Care & Nursing Home Center
210 S 5th St, Burlington, IA, 52601
(319) 752-4564
Admin Wanda Hale. *Medical Dir/Dir of Nursing* Janice Smith RN DON.
Licensure Skilled care; Intermediate care; Independent living units. *Beds* SNF 29; ICF 59; Independent living units 13. *Certified* Medicaid; Medicare.
Owner Nonprofit Corp.
Admissions Requirements Minimum age 18; Medical examination; Physician's request.
Staff RNs 2 (ft), 7 (pt); LPNs 4 (ft), 2 (pt); Nurses aides 19 (ft), 20 (pt); Physical therapists 1 (ft), 1 (pt); Occupational therapists 1 (pt); Speech therapists 1 (pt); Activities coordinators 1 (ft), 1 (pt); Dietitians 1 (ft), 1 (pt).
Languages Spanish
Affiliation Roman Catholic
Facilities Dining room; Physical therapy room; Activities room; Chapel; Crafts room; Laundry room; Barber/Beauty shop; Library.
Activities Arts & crafts; Cards; Games; Reading groups; Prayer groups; Movies; Shopping trips; Social/Cultural gatherings; Community programs; Festivals; Picnics.

CARLISLE

Carlisle Care Center
Box N-9, 680 Cole St, Carlisle, IA, 50047
(515) 989-0871
Admin Ardis A Dahms. *Medical Dir/Dir of Nursing* Roslie Hunt RN.
Licensure Intermediate care; Residential care. *Beds* ICF 89; Residential 12. *Certified* Medicaid.
Owner Proprietary Corp.
Admissions Requirements Medical examination; Physician's request.
Staff RNs 2 (ft); LPNs 4 (ft), 1 (pt); Orderlies 1 (ft); Nurses aides 18 (ft), 17 (pt); Physical therapists 1 (pt); Speech therapists 1 (pt); Activities coordinators 1 (ft), 1 (pt); Dietitians 1 (pt); Ophthalmologists 1 (pt).
Facilities Dining room; Physical therapy room; Activities room; Laundry room; Barber/Beauty shop; Library.
Activities Arts & crafts; Games; Reading groups; Prayer groups; Movies.

CARROLL

Carroll Health Center*
2241 N West St, Carroll, IA, 51401
(712) 792-9284
Admin Edna Schluter.
Licensure Intermediate care; Residential care. *Beds* ICF 96; Residential 41. *Certified* Medicaid.

Carroll Manor*
500 Valley Dr, Carroll, IA, 51401
(712) 792-9281
Admin Lyle Hight.
Licensure Intermediate care. *Beds* 51. *Certified* Medicaid.
Owner Proprietary Corp (Life Care Centers of America).

New Hope Village Inc*
E 18th St, Carroll, IA, 51401
(712) 792-5500

Admin Frank Hermsen.
Licensure Intermediate care for mentally retarded; Residential MR care. *Beds* ICF/MR 32; Residential MR care 72.

St Anthony Nursing Home*
406 E Anthony St, Carroll, IA, 50058
Admin Robert Blincow.
Licensure Intermediate care. *Beds* 80. *Certified* Medicaid.
Owner Nonprofit Corp.
Staff RNs 2 (ft), 2 (pt); LPNs 3 (ft), 4 (pt); Nurses aides 15 (ft), 12 (pt); Recreational therapists 1 (pt); Speech therapists; Activities coordinators 1 (ft); Dietitians 1 (ft); Dentists; Ophthalmologists; Podiatrists; Audiologists.
Affiliation Roman Catholic
Facilities Dining room; Physical therapy room; Activities room; Chapel; Crafts room; Laundry room; Barber/Beauty shop.
Activities Arts & crafts; Cards; Games; Reading groups; Prayer groups; Movies; Shopping trips; Social/Cultural gatherings.

CASCADE

Shady Rest Care Center
700 N Johnson St, Cascade, IA, 52033
(319) 852-3277
Admin Jean M Lynch. *Medical Dir/Dir of Nursing* William J Mehrl; Lorraine Takes.
Licensure Intermediate care. *Beds* 70. *Certified* Medicaid.
Owner Proprietary Corp.
Admissions Requirements Medical examination; Physician's request.
Staff RNs 3 (ft), 2 (pt); LPNs 2 (ft), 2 (pt); Nurses aides 13 (ft), 17 (pt); Physical therapists; Activities coordinators 1 (ft), 1 (pt); Dietitians 1 (pt).
Facilities Dining room; Physical therapy room; Activities room; Chapel; Crafts room; Laundry room; Barber/Beauty shop.
Activities Arts & crafts; Cards; Games; Prayer groups; Movies; Social/Cultural gatherings.

CEDAR FALLS

Cedar Falls Health Center
1728 W 8th St, Cedar Falls, IA, 50613
(319) 277-2437
Admin John B Studer. *Medical Dir/Dir of Nursing* Linda Mahlis DON.
Licensure Intermediate care. *Beds* ICF 100. *Certified* Medicaid.
Owner Proprietary Corp (Waverly Group).
Admissions Requirements Medical examination.
Staff Physicians; RNs; LPNs; Orderlies; Nurses aides; Physical therapists; Activities coordinators; Dietitians; Ophthalmologists; Podiatrists.
Facilities Dining room; Physical therapy room; Activities room; Crafts room; Laundry room; Barber/Beauty shop.
Activities Arts & crafts; Cards; Games; Reading groups; Prayer groups; Movies; Shopping trips; Social/Cultural gatherings.

Cedar Falls Lutheran Home*
7511 University Ave, Cedar Falls, IA, 50613
(319) 268-0401
Admin Karen Habenicht.
Licensure Intermediate care; Residential care. *Beds* ICF 103; Residential 81. *Certified* Medicaid.
Owner Nonprofit Corp.
Affiliation Lutheran

Sartori Hospital Skilled Nursing Facility
6th & College, Cedar Falls, IA, 50613
(319) 266-3584
Admin Duane Vorseth. *Medical Dir/Dir of Nursing* Verna Klinkenborg.
Licensure Skilled care. *Beds* SNF 18. *Certified* Medicaid; Medicare.
Owner Nonprofit organization/foundation.

Admissions Requirements Physician's request.
Staff Physicians; RNs; LPNs; Nurses aides;
Physical therapists; Recreational therapists;
Occupational therapists; Speech therapists;
Activities coordinators; Dietitians; Dentists;
Ophthalmologists; Podiatrists.
Facilities Dining room; Physical therapy
room; Activities room; Chapel; Crafts room;
Library.
Activities Arts & crafts; Cards; Games;
Reading groups; Movies.

Western Home
420 E 11th St, Cedar Falls, IA, 50613
(319) 277-2141
Admin Dr William Applegate. *Medical Dir/Dir
of Nursing* Dr Richard Frankhauser;
LaVonne Edwards RN DON.
Licensure Intermediate care; Residential care.
Beds ICF 68; Residential 76; Retirement
living 110. *Certified* Medicaid.
Owner Nonprofit organization/foundation.
Admissions Requirements Minimum age 60;
Medical examination.
Staff RNs 4 (ft), 1 (pt); LPNs 5 (ft), 4 (pt);
Orderlies 3 (ft), 1 (pt); Nurses aides 25 (ft),
17 (pt); Activities coordinators 1 (ft);
Dietitians 1 (ft); Social workers; activity
assistants.
Affiliation Methodist
Facilities Dining room; Physical therapy
room; Activities room; Chapel; Crafts room;
Laundry room; Barber/Beauty shop; Library;
Large room with kitchen for family
gatherings.
Activities Arts & crafts; Cards; Games;
Reading groups; Prayer groups; Movies;
Shopping trips; Social/Cultural gatherings;
Special trips.

Windsor Care Center*
2305 Crescent Dr, Cedar Falls, IA, 50613
(319) 268-0489
Licensure Intermediate care. Beds 100.
Certified Medicaid.
Owner Proprietary Corp (Beverly Enterprises).
Admissions Requirements Medical
examination.
Staff RNs 1 (ft), 3 (pt); LPNs 4 (ft), 6 (pt);
Orderlies 1 (ft), 1 (pt); Nurses aides 20 (ft),
15 (pt); Activities coordinators 1 (ft), 1 (pt);
Dietitians 1 (ft).
Facilities Dining room; Physical therapy
room; Activities room; Laundry room;
Barber/Beauty shop.
Activities Arts & crafts; Cards; Games;
Reading groups; Prayer groups; Movies;
Shopping trips; Social/Cultural gatherings.

CEDAR RAPIDS

Americana Healthcare Center*
1940 1st Ave NE, Cedar Rapids, IA, 52402
(319) 364-5151
Admin Jessie Diers.
Licensure Skilled care. Beds 79. *Certified*
Medicaid; Medicare.
Owner Proprietary Corp (Manor Care).

Cedar Rapids Care Center*
1220 5th Ave SE, Cedar Rapids, IA, 52403
(319) 366-8701
Licensure Intermediate care; Intermediate care
for mentally retarded. Beds ICF 92; ICF/MR
26. *Certified* Medicaid.
Staff RNs 3 (ft); LPNs 3 (ft), 5 (pt); Orderlies
4 (ft); Nurses aides 12 (ft), 30 (pt);
Occupational therapists 1 (pt); Speech
therapists 1 (pt); Activities coordinators 1
(ft); Dietitians 1 (pt).
Facilities Dining room; Physical therapy
room; Activities room; Barber/Beauty shop.
Activities Arts & crafts; Cards; Games;
Reading groups; Prayer groups; Movies;
Shopping trips; Social/Cultural gatherings.

Colbert Place
1312 1st Ave NW, Cedar Rapids, IA, 52405

Admin Cherie Clark.
Licensure Residental care for mentally
retarded.
Admissions Requirements Minimum age 18;
Medical examination.
Staff Nurses aides 5 (pt); Activities
coordinators 1 (ft).
Facilities Dining room; Activities room;
Laundry room.
Activities Arts & crafts; Cards; Games;
Movies; Shopping trips; Social/Cultural
gatherings; Community outings.

Hallmar Mercy Hospital
701 10th St SE, Cedar Rapids, IA, 52403
(319) 398-6241, 398-6386
Admin A J Tinker. *Medical Dir/Dir of Nursing*
Julie A May MD.
Licensure Skilled care; Intermediate care. Beds
SNF 29; ICF 47; Respite 15.
Owner Nonprofit organization/foundation.
Admissions Requirements Medical
examination; Physician's request.
Staff RNs 2 (ft); LPNs 8 (ft); Orderlies 1 (ft);
Nurses aides 15 (ft); Recreational therapists
1 (ft); Activities coordinators 1 (pt);
Secretary 2 (ft).
Languages Czech, German
Affiliation Roman Catholic
Facilities Dining room; Physical therapy
room; Activities room; Chapel; Crafts room;
Laundry room; Barber/Beauty shop; Library.
Activities Arts & crafts; Cards; Games;
Reading groups; Prayer groups; Movies;
Shopping trips; Social/Cultural gatherings.

Heritage Acres Care Center*
200 Clive Dr SW, Cedar Rapids, IA, 52404
(319) 396-7171
Licensure Intermediate care. Beds 201.
Certified Medicaid.
Owner Proprietary Corp (Beverly Enterprises).
Admissions Requirements Minimum age 55;
Medical examination; Physician's request.
Staff RNs 3 (ft), 2 (pt); LPNs 10 (ft), 5 (pt);
Orderlies 5 (ft), 2 (pt); Nurses aides 37 (ft),
17 (pt); Physical therapists; Occupational
therapists; Speech therapists; Activities
coordinators 3 (ft), 1 (pt); Dietitians;
Dentists; Ophthalmologists; Podiatrists;
Audiologists.
Facilities Dining room; Physical therapy
room; Activities room; Barber/Beauty shop.
Activities Arts & crafts; Cards; Games;
Reading groups; Prayer groups; Movies;
Shopping trips; Social/Cultural gatherings.

Meth-Wick Manor*
1224 13th St NW, Cedar Rapids, IA, 52405
(319) 365-9171
Medical Dir/Dir of Nursing Dr Joseph Galles.
Licensure Intermediate care; Residential care.
Beds ICF 49; Residential 16. *Certified*
Medicaid.
Admissions Requirements Minimum age 55;
Medical examination.
Staff Physicians 1 (pt); RNs 1 (ft), 5 (pt);
LPNs 6 (pt); Nurses aides 16 (ft), 11 (pt);
Physical therapists 1 (pt); Occupational
therapists 1 (pt); Speech therapists 1 (pt);
Activities coordinators 1 (ft); Dietitians 1
(ft); Dentists 1 (pt); Podiatrists 1 (pt);
Audiologists 1 (pt).
Affiliation Methodist
Facilities Dining room; Physical therapy
room; Activities room; Chapel; Crafts room;
Laundry room; Barber/Beauty shop; Library;
Gift shop; Exercise room; Kitchen; Snack
room; Patio; Garages; Numerous lounges..
Activities Arts & crafts; Games; Prayer groups;
Movies; Shopping trips; Social/Cultural
gatherings; Dining out; Exercise class;
Weight control groups; Resident assemblies;
Bake sales; Bazaars; Garage sales.

Northbrook Manor Care Center*
6420 Council St NE, Cedar Rapids, IA, 52402
(319) 393-1447

Admin Janice M Tague.
Licensure Intermediate care. Beds 102.
Certified Medicaid.

St Luke's Methodist Hospital*
1026 S Ave NE, Cedar Rapids, IA, 52402
(319) 369-7211
Admin Samuel T Wallace.
Licensure Skilled care. Beds 12.
Affiliation Methodist

CENTERVILLE

Centerville Care Center Inc*
Box 447, 1208 Cross, Centerville, IA, 52544
(515) 856-8651
Admin Arthur W Schuttinga.
Licensure Intermediate care. Beds 69.
Certified Medicaid.

Golden Age Manor Inc*
1915 S 18th, Centerville, IA, 52544
(515) 856-2757
Admin Robert E Sacco.
Licensure Intermediate care. Beds 100.
Certified Medicaid.

Profitts Boarding Home*
615 W Washington, Centerville, IA, 52544
(319) 5856-8344
Admin Mary C Profitt.
Licensure Intermediate care for mentally
retarded. Beds 10.

CHARITON

**Chariton Group Home Development
Corporation**
1221 Brookdale Ave, Chariton, IA, 50049
(515) 774-8252
Admin Karen Gorsline.
Licensure Residential care for mentally
retarded. Beds RCF/MR 8. *Certified*
Medicaid.
Owner Nonprofit Corp.
Admissions Requirements Minimum age 18;
Males only; Medical examination;
Physician's request.
Facilities Dining room; Activities room;
Crafts room; Laundry room; Library; Single
private rooms.
Activities Arts & crafts; Cards; Games;
Movies; Shopping trips; Social/Cultural
gatherings; Many other activities, including
bowling, softball, leisure interests.

Chariton Manor*
N 7th St, Chariton, IA, 50049
(515) 774-5921
Admin Stanley Vanderwoude.
Licensure Intermediate care. Beds 130.
Certified Medicaid.
Owner Proprietary Corp (Beverly Enterprises).

Remington Boarding Home*
119 S 8th, Chariton, IA, 50049
Admin Ann L Remington.
Licensure Residential care. Beds 10.
Owner Proprietary Corp.
Admissions Requirements Minimum age 19;
Males only.
Facilities Dining room.
Activities Cards; Games.

CHARLES CITY

Chautauqua Avenue Guest Home 1
120 Chautauqua Ave, Charles City, IA, 50616
(515) 228-6512
Admin David F Ayers. *Medical Dir/Dir of
Nursing* Judy Kelly RN DON.
Licensure Intermediate care. Beds ICF 84.
Certified Medicaid.
Owner Proprietary Corp.
Admissions Requirements Minimum age 16;
Medical examination; Physician's request.

Staff RNs 2 (ft); LPNs 2 (ft), 3 (pt); Nurses aides 11 (ft), 20 (pt); Activities coordinators 1 (ft), 1 (pt).
Facilities Dining room; Activities room; Crafts room; Laundry room; Barber/Beauty shop; Library.
Activities Arts & crafts; Cards; Games; Reading groups; Prayer groups; Movies; Shopping trips; Social/Cultural gatherings.

Chautauqua Guest Home 2
602 11th St, Charles City, IA, 50616
(515) 228-2353
Admin David F Ayers. *Medical Dir/Dir of Nursing* D L Trefz MD; Edward Kielsmeier RN DON.
Licensure Skilled care. *Beds* SNF 75. *Certified* Medicaid; Medicare.
Owner Proprietary Corp.
Admissions Requirements Minimum age 16; Medical examination.
Staff RNs 4 (ft), 1 (pt); LPNs 1 (ft), 1 (pt); Activities coordinators 1 (ft), 1 (pt).
Facilities Dining room; Physical therapy room; Activities room; Barber/Beauty shop.
Activities Arts & crafts; Cards; Games; Reading groups; Prayer groups; Movies; Shopping trips; Social/Cultural gatherings.

Chautauqua Guest Home 3*
302 9th St, Charles City, IA, 50616
(515) 228-5351
Admin Lyle H Koehler.
Licensure Intermediate care. *Beds* 74. *Certified* Medicaid.

Comprehensive Systems Inc
1700 Clark St, Charles City, IA, 50616
(515) 228-6155
Admin Richard Turpin. *Medical Dir/Dir of Nursing* Christine Gohr RN.
Licensure Intermediate care for mentally retarded; Foster care; RCF-MR. *Beds* ICF/MR 12; Foster care 86; RCF-MR 67. *Certified* Medicaid.
Owner Nonprofit organization/foundation.
Admissions Requirements Medical examination.
Staff RNs 2 (ft), 4 (pt); LPNs 4 (ft), 2 (pt); Recreational therapists 2 (ft); Dietitians 2 (ft); Direct care staff 100 (ft), 150 (pt).
Facilities Dining room; Physical therapy room; Activities room; Chapel; Crafts room; Laundry room.
Activities Arts & crafts; Cards; Games; Reading groups; Prayer groups; Movies; Shopping trips; Social/Cultural gatherings; Community activities; Special education in public school system; Vocational training; Sheltered workshop; Employment.

Salsbury Baptist Home
807 5th St, Charles City, IA, 50616
(515) 228-1612
Admin John W Lusk.
Licensure Intermediate care; Residential care. *Beds* ICF 51; Residential 39. *Certified* Medicaid.
Owner Nonprofit Corp (American Baptist Homes).
Admissions Requirements Minimum age 55; Medical examination; Physician's request.
Staff RNs 2 (ft), 2 (pt); LPNs 2 (ft), 2 (pt); Orderlies 1 (ft), 2 (pt); Nurses aides 20 (ft), 15 (pt); Occupational therapists 1 (pt); Activities coordinators 1 (ft), 1 (pt); Dietitians 1 (pt); Podiatrists 1 (pt).
Affiliation Baptist
Facilities Dining room; Physical therapy room; Activities room; Chapel; Crafts room; Laundry room; Barber/Beauty shop; Library.
Activities Arts & crafts; Cards; Games; Reading groups; Prayer groups; Movies; Shopping trips; Reading program for school children.

CHEROKEE

Cherokee Villa*
1011 Roosevelt, Cherokee, IA, 51012
(712) 225-5180
Admin Ailene Shade.
Licensure Intermediate care. *Beds* 72. *Certified* Medicaid.
Admissions Requirements Medical examination; Physician's request.
Staff RNs 1 (ft); LPNs 1 (ft); Nurses aides 1 (ft); Physical therapists 1 (pt); Occupational therapists 1 (pt); Speech therapists 1 (pt); Activities coordinators 1 (ft); Dietitians 1 (pt).
Facilities Dining room; Physical therapy room; Activities room; Chapel; Crafts room; Laundry room; Barber/Beauty shop.
Activities Arts & crafts; Cards; Games; Reading groups; Prayer groups; Movies; Shopping trips.

Country Side Estates
921 Riverview Rd, Cherokee, IA, 51012
(712) 225-5724
Admin Roxanne Smith. *Medical Dir/Dir of Nursing* Karen Riedemann.
Licensure Intermediate care. *Beds* ICF 102. *Certified* Medicaid.
Owner Proprietary Corp.
Admissions Requirements Minimum age 16; Medical examination.
Staff RNs 2 (ft), 1 (pt); LPNs 3 (ft), 2 (pt); Nurses aides 25 (ft), 8 (pt); Physical therapists 1 (pt); Occupational therapists 1 (pt); Speech therapists 1 (pt); Activities coordinators 1 (ft); Dietitians 1 (pt); Ophthalmologists 1 (pt); Podiatrists 1 (pt).
Facilities Dining room; Physical therapy room; Activities room; Chapel; Crafts room; Laundry room; Barber/Beauty shop.
Activities Arts & crafts; Cards; Games; Reading groups; Prayer groups; Movies; Shopping trips; Social/Cultural gatherings; Humanities class.

Hilltop Care Center
725 N 2nd St, Cherokee, IA, 51012
(712) 225-2561
Admin Steven P Wendler. *Medical Dir/Dir of Nursing* Patricia Johansen RN.
Licensure Intermediate care. *Beds* ICF 50. *Certified* Medicaid.
Owner Proprietary Corp (ABCM Corp).
Admissions Requirements Minimum age 18; Medical examination; Physician's request.
Staff RNs 1 (ft), 1 (pt); LPNs 2 (ft), 2 (pt); Orderlies; Nurses aides; Physical therapists; Activities coordinators 1 (ft), 1 (pt); Dietitians; Ophthalmologists.
Languages Sign
Facilities Dining room; Activities room; Laundry room; Barber/Beauty shop; Library.
Activities Arts & crafts; Cards; Games; Reading groups; Prayer groups; Movies; Shopping trips; Social/Cultural gatherings; Daily devotions; Manicures; Current events; Cooking.

CLARENCE

Clarence Nursing Home
2nd & Smith, Clarence, IA, 52216
(319) 452-3262
Admin William Beckley. *Medical Dir/Dir of Nursing* George Utley MD; Karla Ruther DON.
Licensure Intermediate care. *Beds* ICF 46. *Certified* Medicaid.
Owner Nonprofit Corp.
Staff RNs 1 (ft), 1 (pt); LPNs 2 (pt); Nurses aides 12 (ft), 7 (pt); Physical therapists 1 (pt); Recreational therapists 1 (ft); Occupational therapists 1 (pt); Activities coordinators 1 (ft); Dietitians 1 (pt); Podiatrists 1 (pt).

Facilities Dining room; Activities room; Laundry room; Barber/Beauty shop; Library.
Activities Arts & crafts; Cards; Games; Reading groups; Prayer groups; Movies; Social/Cultural gatherings.

CLARINDA

Bethesda Care Center*
600 Manor Dr, Clarinda, IA, 51632
(712) 542-5161
Admin Seth H Grafft.
Licensure Intermediate care. *Beds* 117. *Certified* Medicaid.

Goldenrod Manor Care Center
225 W Laperla Dr, Clarinda, IA, 51632
(712) 542-5621
Admin Marge Spry.
Licensure Intermediate care. *Beds* 51. *Certified* Medicaid.

CLARION

Clarion Care Center
110 13th Ave SW, Clarion, IA, 50525
(515) 532-2893
Admin Cordell Poldberg. *Medical Dir/Dir of Nursing* Cindy Waage.
Licensure Intermediate care; Residential care. *Beds* ICF 89; Residential 3. *Certified* Medicaid.
Owner Proprietary Corp (Quality Health Care Specialists Inc).
Admissions Requirements Minimum age 16; Physician's request.
Staff RNs 5 (ft); LPNs 4 (ft); Nurses aides 25 (ft), 9 (pt); Physical therapists 1 (pt); Reality therapists 1 (pt); Recreational therapists 1 (pt); Occupational therapists 1 (pt); Speech therapists 1 (pt); Activities coordinators 1 (ft), 1 (pt); Dietitians 1 (pt); Dentists 1 (pt); Ophthalmologists 1 (pt); Podiatrists 1 (pt).
Facilities Dining room; Physical therapy room; Activities room; Crafts room; Laundry room; Barber/Beauty shop; Library.
Activities Arts & crafts; Cards; Games; Reading groups; Prayer groups; Movies; Shopping trips; Social/Cultural gatherings.

CLARKSVILLE

Community Nursing Home Inc
115 N Hilton, Clarksville, IA, 50619
(319) 278-4900
Admin Emma DeVries. *Medical Dir/Dir of Nursing* Dr James Rathe; Mary Johnson RN DON.
Licensure Intermediate care; Residential care. *Beds* ICF 53; Retirement apts 28; Residential 13. *Certified* Medicaid.
Owner Proprietary Corp.
Admissions Requirements Minimum age 16; Medical examination; Physician's request.
Staff Physicians 9 (ft); RNs 1 (ft); LPNs 3 (ft), 3 (pt); Nurses aides 12 (ft), 10 (pt); Physical therapists 1 (pt); Activities coordinators 1 (ft), 1 (pt); Dietitians 1 (pt); Social worker 1 (pt).
Facilities Dining room; Physical therapy room; Activities room; Chapel; Crafts room; Laundry room; Barber/Beauty shop; Library.
Activities Arts & crafts; Cards; Games; Reading groups; Prayer groups; Movies; Shopping trips; Social/Cultural gatherings; Library cart.

CLEAR LAKE

Oakwood Manor Corporation*
400 Hwy 18 W, Clear Lake, IA, 50428
(515) 357-5244
Admin Paul G Klus.
Licensure Intermediate care. *Beds* 89. *Certified* Medicaid.

CLEARFIELD

Clearview Home
Box 174, 174 Jefferson, Clearfield, IA, 50840
(515) 336-2333
Admin Joe Routh. *Medical Dir/Dir of Nursing*
Vicky Leonard.
Licensure Intermediate care. *Beds* ICF 36.
Certified Medicaid.
Owner Privately owned.
Staff Physicians; RNs; LPNs; Nurses aides;
Physical therapists; Occupational therapists;
Speech therapists; Activities coordinators;
Dietitians; Pharmacist.
Facilities Dining room; Physical therapy
room; Activities room; Chapel; Laundry
room; Barber/Beauty shop.
Activities Arts & crafts; Cards; Games;
Reading groups; Prayer groups; Movies;
Shopping trips; Social/Cultural gatherings.

CLINTON

Alverno Health Care Facility
849 13th Ave N, Clinton, IA, 52732
(319) 242-1521
Admin Sr Ruth Cox. *Medical Dir/Dir of
Nursing* Pauline Kaufman RN.
Licensure Intermediate care. *Beds* 136.
Certified Medicaid.
Owner Nonprofit Corp.
Admissions Requirements Minimum age 60;
Females only.
Staff RNs 6 (ft), 10 (pt); LPNs 2 (ft), 3 (pt);
Nurses aides 33 (ft), 10 (pt); Physical
therapists 1 (ft); Activities coordinators 1
(ft), 4 (pt); Dietitians 1 (ft).
Affiliation Roman Catholic
Facilities Dining room; Physical therapy
room; Activities room; Chapel; Crafts room;
Laundry room; Barber/Beauty shop; Library.
Activities Arts & crafts; Cards; Games;
Reading groups; Prayer groups; Movies;
Shopping trips; Social/Cultural gatherings;
SDAT support group.

Clinton Retirement Village
2604 N 4th St, Clinton, IA, 52732
(319) 243-6600
Admin Kenneth H Gibson. *Medical Dir/Dir of
Nursing* Diana Van Wychen.
Licensure Intermediate care. *Beds* ICF 150.
Certified Medicaid.
Owner Proprietary Corp (Hillhaven Corp).
Admissions Requirements Medical
examination; Physician's request.
Staff Physicians; RNs 1 (ft), 2 (pt); LPNs 5
(ft), 3 (pt); Orderlies; Nurses aides 19 (ft), 16
(pt); Activities coordinators 1 (ft).
Facilities Dining room; Physical therapy
room; Activities room; Chapel; Crafts room;
Laundry room; Barber/Beauty shop.
Activities Cards; Games; Reading groups;
Prayer groups; Movies; Social/Cultural
gatherings.

Gateway Intermediate Care*
Bluff Terrace, 638 S Bluff Blvd, Clinton, IA,
52732
Admin Douglas Trembath.
Licensure Intermediate care. *Beds* 64.
Certified Medicaid.
Owner Nonprofit Corp.
Admissions Requirements Medical
examination; Physician's request.
Staff RNs 3 (ft), 4 (pt); LPNs 1 (ft), 3 (pt);
Orderlies 1 (pt); Nurses aides 9 (ft), 16 (pt);
Physical therapists 3 (pt); Occupational
therapists 1 (pt); Speech therapists 1 (pt);
Activities coordinators 1 (ft); Dietitians 1
(ft); Audiologists 1 (pt).
Facilities Dining room; Activities room;
Crafts room; Laundry room; Barber/Beauty
shop.
Activities Arts & crafts; Cards; Games;
Reading groups; Prayer groups; Movies;
Shopping trips; Social/Cultural gatherings.

Wyndcrest Nursing Home*
600 14th Ave N, Clinton, IA, 52732
(319) 243-3200
Admin Brian Peterson.
Licensure Intermediate care. *Beds* 95.
Certified Medicaid.

COLUMBUS JUNCTION

Colonial Manor—Columbus Junction
814 Springer Ave, Columbus Junction, IA,
52738
(319) 728-2276
Admin Robert L Solinger. *Medical Dir/Dir of
Nursing* Betty Hamilton.
Licensure Intermediate care. *Beds* ICF 60.
Certified Medicaid.
Owner Proprietary Corp (Beverly Enterprises).
Admissions Requirements Medical
examination; Physician's request.
Staff Physicians 2 (pt); RNs 6 (ft); LPNs 3
(ft); Nurses aides 10 (ft), 15 (pt); Physical
therapists 1 (pt); Speech therapists 1 (pt);
Activities coordinators 1 (ft); Dietitians 1
(ft).
Facilities Dining room; Physical therapy
room; Activities room; Chapel; Crafts room;
Laundry room; Barber/Beauty shop; Library.
Activities Arts & crafts; Cards; Games;
Reading groups; Prayer groups; Movies;
Shopping trips; Social/Cultural gatherings.

CONRAD

Oakview Home*
511 Center St, Conrad, IA, 50621
(515) 366-2212
Admin Bonnie Switzer.
Licensure Intermediate care; Residential care.
Beds ICF 38; Residential 8. *Certified*
Medicaid.

CORALVILLE

Lantern Park Care Center*
915 N 20th Ave, Coralville, IA, 52241
(319) 351-8440
Admin Sydney Vanderwoude.
Licensure Intermediate care. *Beds* 100.
Certified Medicaid.
Owner Proprietary Corp (Beverly Enterprises).

CORNING

Colonial Manor
Northgate Dr, Corning, IA, 50841
(515) 322-4061
Admin Terry Cooper. *Medical Dir/Dir of
Nursing* Norma Camden RN DON.
Licensure Intermediate care. *Beds* ICF 64.
Certified Medicaid.
Owner Proprietary Corp (Beverly Enterprises).
Admissions Requirements Medical
examination; Physician's request.
Staff RNs 1 (ft), 1 (pt); LPNs 4 (ft); Orderlies
1 (ft), 1 (pt); Nurses aides 20 (ft), 2 (pt);
Activities coordinators 1 (ft); Dietitians 1
(pt).
Facilities Dining room; Physical therapy
room; Activities room; Chapel; Barber/
Beauty shop; Family room.
Activities Arts & crafts; Cards; Games;
Reading groups; Prayer groups; Movies;
Social/Cultural gatherings.

Country Haven Corp
PO Box 409, RR 1, Corning, IA, 50841
(515) 322-3291
Admin Lizbeth H Wilkinson. *Medical Dir/Dir
of Nursing* Dixie Lacy LPN.
Licensure Residential care for mentally
retarded. *Beds* 51. *Certified* Medicaid.
Admissions Requirements Minimum age 18;
Medical examination; Physician's request.

Staff LPNs 2 (ft), 1 (pt); Nurses aides 6 (ft), 2
(pt); Activities coordinators 1 (ft); Dietitians
2 (ft), 1 (pt).
Facilities Dining room; Activities room;
Crafts room; Laundry room; Barber/Beauty
shop.
Activities Arts & crafts; Cards; Games;
Reading groups; Prayer groups; Movies;
Shopping trips; Social/Cultural gatherings;
Library; Musical entertainment; Bible school
& pre-school programs; Basic education
programs.

CORRECTIONVILLE

Colonial Manor of Correctionville
PO Box H, 1116 Hwy 20, Correctionville, IA,
51016
(712) 372-4466
Admin John Walz. *Medical Dir/Dir of Nursing*
Nancy Jacobs.
Licensure Intermediate care. *Beds* ICF 65.
Certified Medicaid.
Owner Proprietary Corp (Beverly Enterprises).
Admissions Requirements Medical
examination; Physician's request.
Staff RNs; LPNs; Orderlies; Nurses aides;
Activities coordinators; Dietitians; Social
worker.
Facilities Dining room; Chapel; Laundry
room; Barber/Beauty shop.
Activities Arts & crafts; Cards; Games;
Reading groups; Prayer groups; Movies;
Shopping trips; Social/Cultural gatherings;
Individualized for each patient.

CORYDON

Corydon Care Center
745 E South St, Corydon, IA, 50060
(515) 872-1590
Admin Connie E White. *Medical Dir/Dir of
Nursing* Paula Padavich RN.
Licensure Intermediate care. *Beds* ICF 79.
Certified Medicaid.
Owner Proprietary Corp (Beverly Enterprises).
Admissions Requirements Medical
examination.
Staff RNs 1 (ft); LPNs 2 (ft), 5 (pt); Orderlies
2 (pt); Nurses aides 10 (ft), 19 (pt); Physical
therapists 1 (pt); Recreational therapists 1
(pt); Occupational therapists 1 (pt); Speech
therapists 1 (pt); Activities coordinators 1
(ft), 1 (pt); Dietitians 1 (pt); Podiatrists 1
(pt).
Facilities Dining room; Physical therapy
room; Activities room; Chapel; Crafts room;
Laundry room; Barber/Beauty shop; Library.
Activities Arts & crafts; Cards; Games;
Reading groups; Prayer groups; Movies;
Shopping trips; Social/Cultural gatherings.

COUNCIL BLUFFS

Bethany Lutheran Home Inc
7 Elliott St, Council Bluffs, IA, 51503
(712) 328-9500
Admin M. Sue Mortensen. *Medical Dir/Dir of
Nursing* Joan Burten RN.
Licensure Intermediate care. *Beds* 121.
Certified Medicaid.
Owner Nonprofit Corp.
Admissions Requirements Medical
examination.
Staff RNs 5 (ft), 5 (pt); LPNs 5 (ft), 4 (pt);
Orderlies 2 (ft); Nurses aides 28 (ft), 22 (pt);
Physical therapists 1 (ft), 1 (pt); Recreational
therapists 1 (ft); Occupational therapists 1
(pt); Speech therapists 1 (pt); Activities
coordinators 1 (ft), 1 (pt); Dietitians 1 (pt);
Ophthalmologists 1 (pt); Podiatrists 1 (pt).
Affiliation Lutheran
Facilities Dining room; Physical therapy
room; Activities room; Chapel; Laundry
room; Barber/Beauty shop.

Activities Arts & crafts; Cards; Games; Reading groups; Prayer groups; Movies; Shopping trips; Social/Cultural gatherings.

Council Bluffs Care Center
2452 N Broadway, Council Bluffs, IA, 51501
(712) 323-7135
Admin John L Peterson. *Medical Dir/Dir of Nursing* Saundra Landuall.
Licensure Intermediate care. *Beds* ICF 150.
Certified Medicaid.
Owner Proprietary Corp (Beverly Enterprises).
Admissions Requirements Medical examination; Physician's request.
Staff RNs 3 (ft); LPNs 8 (ft); Nurses aides 65 (ft); Recreational therapists 1 (ft); Activities coordinators 1 (ft); Dietitians 1 (ft).
Facilities Dining room; Physical therapy room; Activities room; Barber/Beauty shop.
Activities Arts & crafts; Cards; Games; Reading groups; Prayer groups; Movies; Shopping trips; Social/Cultural gatherings.

Indian Hills Nursing Center*
1600 McPherson, Council Bluffs, IA, 51501
(712) 322-9285
Admin Lawrence R Cotton.
Licensure Intermediate care. *Beds* 126.
Certified Medicaid.

Northcrest Care Center*
34 Northcrest Dr, Council Bluffs, IA, 51501
(712) 328-2333
Admin Kenneth Opp.
Licensure Intermediate care. *Beds* 102.
Certified Medicaid.
Owner Proprietary Corp (Beverly Enterprises).

CRESCO

Cresco Care Center Inc
Rte 2, Vernon Rd, Cresco, IA, 52136
(319) 547-3580
Admin Dale Weaver.
Licensure Intermediate care. *Beds* 73.
Certified Medicaid.

Evans Memorial Home for the Aged Inc
1010 N Elm, Cresco, IA, 52136
(319) 547-2364
Admin Myron Mikkelms. *Medical Dir/Dir of Nursing* Marlene Ferrie.
Licensure Intermediate care. *Beds* ICF 65.
Certified Medicaid.
Owner Nonprofit Corp.
Admissions Requirements Medical examination; Physician's request.
Staff RNs 1 (ft), 4 (pt); LPNs 4 (pt); Orderlies 1 (pt); Nurses aides 3 (ft), 20 (pt); Physical therapists 1 (pt); Recreational therapists 1 (pt); Occupational therapists 1 (pt); Speech therapists 1 (pt); Activities coordinators 1 (ft), 1 (pt); Dietitians 1 (pt); Podiatrists 1 (pt).
Facilities Dining room; Physical therapy room; Activities room; Chapel; Crafts room; Laundry room; Barber/Beauty shop.
Activities Arts & crafts; Cards; Games; Reading groups; Prayer groups; Movies; Shopping trips; Social/Cultural gatherings; Theatre plays; Cook-outs.

CRESTON

Care Center of Iowa Inc*
1000 E Howard, Creston, IA, 50801
(515) 782-5012
Licensure Intermediate care. *Beds* 71.
Certified Medicaid.
Admissions Requirements Medical examination; Physician's request.
Staff RNs 2 (ft); LPNs 4 (ft); Nurses aides 24 (ft); Occupational therapists 1 (pt); Activities coordinators 1 (ft); Dietitians 1 (pt); Audiologists 1 (pt).

Facilities Dining room; Activities room; Chapel; Crafts room; Laundry room.
Activities Arts & crafts; Cards; Games; Reading groups; Prayer groups; Movies; Shopping trips.

Creston Manor Nursing Home
1001 Cottonwood, Creston, IA, 50801
(515) 782-8511
Admin William Robinson.
Licensure Intermediate care. *Beds* 74.
Certified Medicaid.

DALLAS CENTER

Spurgeon Manor
PO Box 500, 13th & Linden, Dallas Center, IA, 50063
(515) 992-3735
Admin Floyd J Haldeman.
Licensure Intermediate care; Residential care. *Beds* ICF 17; Residential 30. *Certified* Medicaid.

DANVILLE

Danville Care Center*
Birch & Seymour Sts, Danville, IA, 52623
(319) 392-4259
Licensure Intermediate care. *Beds* 40.
Certified Medicaid.

DAVENPORT

Americana Healthcare Center
815 E Locust St, Davenport, IA, 52803
(319) 324-3276
Admin Gretchen M Cluff. *Medical Dir/Dir of Nursing* Monte Skaufle MD.
Licensure Skilled care; Intermediate care. *Beds* SNF 94; ICF 16. *Certified* Medicaid; Medicare.
Owner Proprietary Corp (Manor Care).
Staff Physicians 1 (pt); RNs 6 (ft), 4 (pt); LPNs 4 (ft), 5 (pt); Orderlies 1 (ft), 1 (pt); Nurses aides 15 (ft), 10 (pt); Activities coordinators 1 (ft), 1 (pt).
Facilities Dining room; Physical therapy room; Activities room; Crafts room; Laundry room; Barber/Beauty shop; Library.
Activities Arts & crafts; Cards; Games; Reading groups; Prayer groups; Movies; Shopping trips; Social/Cultural gatherings.

Davenport Good Samaritan*
700 Waverly Rd, Davenport, IA, 52804
(319) 324-1651
Admin Karen Griggs.
Licensure Intermediate care. *Beds* 211.
Certified Medicaid.
Owner Nonprofit Corp (Evangelical Lutheran/Good Samaritan).
Admissions Requirements Minimum age 16; Medical examination; Physician's request.
Staff Physicians 58 (pt); RNs 5 (ft), 6 (pt); LPNs 6 (ft), 5 (pt); Orderlies 4 (ft); Nurses aides 66 (ft), 22 (pt); Physical therapists 2 (pt); Recreational therapists 3 (ft), 2 (pt); Occupational therapists 1 (ft), 1 (pt); Speech therapists 1 (pt); Activities coordinators 1 (ft); Dietitians 1 (ft); Dentists 1 (pt).
Facilities Dining room; Physical therapy room; Activities room; Chapel; Crafts room; Laundry room; Barber/Beauty shop.
Activities Arts & crafts; Cards; Games; Reading groups; Prayer groups; Movies; Shopping trips; Social/Cultural gatherings; Bowling; Horticulture therapy.

Davenport Lutheran Home
1130 W 53rd St, Davenport, IA, 52806
(319) 391-5342
Admin Fern Werning.
Licensure Intermediate care. *Beds* 80.
Certified Medicaid.
Owner Nonprofit Corp.

Admissions Requirements Minimum age 65; Medical examination.
Staff RNs 1 (ft); LPNs 6 (ft), 1 (pt); Nurses aides 18 (ft), 13 (pt); Activities coordinators 1 (ft), 1 (pt); Dietitians 1 (pt).
Affiliation Lutheran
Facilities Dining room; Physical therapy room; Activities room; Chapel; Crafts room; Laundry room; Library.
Activities Arts & crafts; Cards; Games; Reading groups; Prayer groups; Movies; Social/Cultural gatherings.

Davenport Nursing Home
PO Box 2309, Davenport, IA, 52809-2309
(319) 323-8021
Licensure Intermediate care. *Beds* 41.
Certified Medicaid.

Fejervary Health Care Center*
800 E Rusholme, Davenport, IA, 52803
(319) 322-1668
Admin Lawrence Campana.
Licensure Intermediate care. *Beds* 118.
Certified Medicaid.

Hy-Vue*
4117 Eastern Ave, Davenport, IA, 52803
(319) 359-0474
Admin Arlene Jens. *Medical Dir/Dir of Nursing* Charles Andrews DO.
Licensure Intermediate care for mentally retarded; Residential care. *Beds* ICF/MR 51; Residential 14. *Certified* Medicaid.
Admissions Requirements Minimum age 18; Medical examination.
Staff Physicians 3 (pt); RNs 2 (ft); LPNs 5 (pt); Orderlies 10 (ft); Nurses aides 15 (ft), 10 (pt); Physical therapists 3 (pt); Occupational therapists 1 (ft); Speech therapists 1 (pt); Activities coordinators 1 (ft); Dietitians 1 (pt); Dentists 2 (pt); Ophthalmologists 2 (pt); Podiatrists 1 (pt); Audiologists 1 (pt).
Facilities Dining room; Physical therapy room; Activities room.
Activities Arts & crafts; Games; Reading groups; Movies; Shopping trips; Social/Cultural gatherings.

Kahl Home for the Aged
1101 W 9th St, Davenport, IA, 52804
(319) 324-1621
Admin Sr M T Kathleen O Carm. *Medical Dir/Dir of Nursing* Sr M Michael Joseph RN DON.
Licensure Intermediate care. *Beds* ICF 141.
Certified Medicaid.
Owner Nonprofit Corp.
Admissions Requirements Minimum age 64; Medical examination.
Staff RNs 6 (ft), 3 (pt); LPNs 8 (ft), 4 (pt); Nurses aides 46 (ft), 8 (pt); Activities coordinators 2 (ft); Dietitians 1 (ft); Chaplain 1 (ft).
Affiliation Roman Catholic
Facilities Dining room; Physical therapy room; Activities room; Chapel; Crafts room; Laundry room; Barber/Beauty shop; Library.
Activities Arts & crafts; Cards; Games; Prayer groups; Movies; Social/Cultural gatherings; Pet therapy; Bus rides; Daily mass; Video exercise; Music therapy.

Meadow Lawn Nursing Center*
4656 W Kimberly Rd, Davenport, IA, 52806
(319) 391-5150
Admin Elizabeth Finkenhoefer.
Licensure Intermediate care. *Beds* 65.
Certified Medicaid.

Ridgecrest Village
4130 Northwest Blvd, Davenport, IA, 52806
(319) 391-3430
Admin Dr Paul R Ausherman, Executive Director; Sam E Johnson. *Medical Dir/Dir of Nursing* Beverly McLean.

Licensure Skilled care; Intermediate care; Residential care. *Beds* SNF 14; ICF 105; Residential 18. *Certified* Medicaid; Medicare.
Owner Nonprofit Corp.
Admissions Requirements Physician's request.
Staff RNs 6 (ft), 4 (pt); LPNs 11 (ft), 6 (pt); Nurses aides 58 (ft), 16 (pt); Physical therapists 1 (pt); Occupational therapists 1 (pt); Speech therapists 1 (pt); Activities coordinators 2 (ft), 1 (pt); Dietitians 1 (pt); Ophthalmologists 1 (pt).
Facilities Dining room; Physical therapy room; Activities room; Chapel; Crafts room; Barber/Beauty shop.
Activities Arts & crafts; Cards; Games; Reading groups; Prayer groups; Movies; Shopping trips; Social/Cultural gatherings.

Royal Neighbor Home
4760 Rockingham Rd, Davenport, IA, 52802
(319) 322-3591
Admin Evelyn Pealstrom.
Licensure Intermediate care; Residential care. *Beds* ICF 14; Residential 54.

DAYTON

Grandview Care Center
2nd St NE, Dayton, IA, 50530
(515) 547-2288
Admin LaVon G Runkle. *Medical Dir/Dir of Nursing* Dr E DeHaan; Kristi Ott DON.
Licensure Intermediate care. *Beds* ICF 50. *Certified* Medicaid.
Owner Proprietary Corp (Waverly Group).
Admissions Requirements Physician's request.
Staff RNs 2 (ft); LPNs 2 (ft); Nurses aides 15 (ft), 10 (pt); Physical therapists 1 (pt); Recreational therapists 1 (pt); Speech therapists 1 (pt); Activities coordinators 1 (ft); Dietitians 1 (pt); Podiatrists 1 (pt); Dentist 1 (pt).
Facilities Dining room; Physical therapy room; Activities room; Crafts room; Laundry room; Barber/Beauty shop.
Activities Arts & crafts; Cards; Games; Reading groups; Prayer groups; Movies; Shopping trips; Social/Cultural gatherings.

DECORAH

Aase Haugen Homes Inc*
4 Ohio St, Decorah, IA, 52101
(319) 382-3603
Admin Bernadean L Koehler.
Licensure Intermediate care; Residential care. *Beds* ICF 146; Reidential care 13. *Certified* Medicaid.

M A Barthell Order of Eastern Star Home
911 Ridgeway Dr, Decorah, IA, 52101
(319) 382-8787
Admin Gary Gavle. *Medical Dir/Dir of Nursing* Sharon Kidd.
Licensure Intermediate care. *Beds* 46.
Admissions Requirements Physician's request.
Staff RNs 2 (ft), 1 (pt); LPNs 5 (pt); Orderlies 2 (pt); Nurses aides 6 (ft), 10 (pt); Activities coordinators 1 (ft), 1 (pt); Dietitians 1 (pt).
Affiliation Order of Eastern Star
Facilities Dining room; Physical therapy room; Activities room; Chapel; Crafts room; Laundry room; Barber/Beauty shop; Library.
Activities Arts & crafts; Cards; Games; Reading groups; Prayer groups; Movies; Shopping trips; Social/Cultural gatherings.

Winneshiek County Health Care Facility
Box 19, Rte 6, Decorah, IA, 52101
(319) 382-9691
Admin Marlys E Cook. *Medical Dir/Dir of Nursing* Shirley Szabo RN.

Licensure Intermediate care; Residential care; Community living/Social support class. *Beds* ICF 36; Residential 55; Community living/Social support class 8. *Certified* Medicaid; Medicare.
Owner Publicly owned.
Admissions Requirements Minimum age 18.
Staff Physicians 2 (pt); RNs 2 (ft), 1 (pt); LPNs 2 (ft), 3 (pt); Orderlies 2 (ft); Nurses aides 10 (ft), 10 (pt); Physical therapists 1 (ft); Occupational therapists 1 (pt); Speech therapists 1 (pt); Activities coordinators 2 (ft), 2 (pt); Dietitians 1 (pt); Dentists 1 (pt); Ophthalmologists 1 (pt); Podiatrists 1 (pt).
Languages German, Norwegian
Facilities Dining room; Physical therapy room; Activities room; Chapel; Crafts room; Laundry room; Barber/Beauty shop; Library.
Activities Arts & crafts; Cards; Games; Reading groups; Prayer groups; Movies; Shopping trips; Social/Cultural gatherings; Band; Camping.

DENISON

Denison Care Center
Box 188, Ridge Rd, Denison, IA, 51442
(712) 263-5611
Admin Helen Andersen. *Medical Dir/Dir of Nursing* Vera Moeller.
Licensure Intermediate care. *Beds* 50. *Certified* Medicaid.
Owner Proprietary Corp (Beverly Enterprises).
Admissions Requirements Minimum age 16; Medical examination.
Staff RNs 2 (ft), 1 (pt); LPNs 1 (ft), 2 (pt); Nurses aides 9 (ft), 7 (pt).
Facilities Dining room; Physical therapy room; Activities room; Laundry room; Barber/Beauty shop.
Activities Arts & crafts; Cards; Games; Reading groups; Prayer groups; Movies; Social/Cultural gatherings.

Eventide Lutheran Home for the Aged
20th St & 1st Ave S, Denison, IA, 51442
(712) 263-3114
Licensure Intermediate care; Residential care. *Beds* ICF 71; Residential 69. *Certified* Medicaid.
Owner Nonprofit Corp.
Admissions Requirements Minimum age 60; Medical examination.
Staff RNs 1 (ft); LPNs 1 (ft); Orderlies 1 (ft); Nurses aides 1 (ft); Physical therapists 1 (pt); Occupational therapists 1 (pt); Speech therapists 1 (pt); Activities coordinators 1 (ft); Dietitians 1 (pt).
Affiliation Lutheran
Facilities Dining room; Physical therapy room; Activities room; Chapel; Laundry room; Barber/Beauty shop.
Activities Arts & crafts; Cards; Games; Reading groups; Prayer groups; Movies; Shopping trips; Social/Cultural gatherings.

DENVER

Denver Sunset Home
PO Box 383, 235 N Mill St, Denver, IA, 50622
(319) 984-5372
Admin Denise R Willig. *Medical Dir/Dir of Nursing* Judy Gleason.
Licensure Intermediate care. *Beds* ICF 34. *Certified* Medicaid; Medicare.
Owner Nonprofit Corp.
Admissions Requirements Medical examination.
Staff RNs 1 (ft); LPNs 3 (ft), 3 (pt); Nurses aides 8 (ft), 8 (pt); Nurses aides 1 (pt); Activities coordinators 1 (ft); Dietitians 1 (pt).
Facilities Dining room; Activities room; Crafts room; Laundry room.
Activities Arts & crafts; Cards; Games; Reading groups; Prayer groups; Movies.

DES MOINES

Broadlawns West
2501 24th St, Des Moines, IA, 50314
(515) 274-3566
Admin Ed Perry.
Licensure Intermediate care. *Beds* 80. *Certified* Medicaid.

Calvin Manor*
4210 Hickman Rd, Des Moines, IA, 50310
(515) 277-6141
Admin Richard J Shaffer.
Licensure Intermediate care. *Beds* 59. *Certified* Medicaid.

Celebrity Care Center
721 16th St, Des Moines, IA, 50314
(515) 244-8131
Admin Betty Cunningham.
Licensure Intermediate care. *Beds* 48. *Certified* Medicaid.
Owner Proprietary Corp.
Facilities Dining room; Activities room; Crafts room; Laundry room; Barber/Beauty shop.
Activities Arts & crafts; Cards; Games; Reading groups; Prayer groups; Movies; Shopping trips; Social/Cultural gatherings.

Commonwealth Care Center*
5608 SW 9th St, Des Moines, IA, 50315
(515) 285-3070
Admin Barbara Kuhlken.
Licensure Intermediate care. *Beds* 99. *Certified* Medicaid.

Craigmont Care Center*
2348 E 9th St, Des Moines, IA, 50316
(515) 262-9303
Admin Mary J Badgerow.
Licensure Intermediate care. *Beds* 92. *Certified* Medicaid.

Crest Group Home*
1316 22nd St, Des Moines, IA, 50311
Licensure Intermediate care for mentally retarded.
Owner Nonprofit Corp.
Admissions Requirements Minimum age 16; Medical examination.
Staff Nurses aides 1 (pt); Occupational therapists 1 (ft); Activities coordinators 1 (pt); Medication managers 1 (ft); Medical aides 2 (ft).
Affiliation Baptist
Facilities Dining room; Activities room; Laundry room.
Activities Arts & crafts; Cards; Games; Movies; Shopping trips; Social/Cultural gatherings.

Heather Manor*
600 E 5th St, Des Moines, IA, 50316
(515) 243-6195
Admin Dean Schager. *Medical Dir/Dir of Nursing* Lauretta Anderson DON.
Licensure Intermediate care. *Beds* 31.
Owner Nonprofit Corp (Life Care Services Corp).
Admissions Requirements Minimum age 62; Medical examination; Physician's request.
Staff Physicians 1 (pt); RNs 1 (ft), 3 (pt); LPNs 1 (ft), 4 (pt); Nurses aides 6 (ft), 8 (pt); Physical therapists 1 (pt); Occupational therapists 1 (pt); Speech therapists 1 (pt); Activities coordinators 1 (pt); Dietitians 1 (pt); Dentists 1 (pt); Podiatrists 1 (pt).
Facilities Dining room; Activities room; Chapel; Crafts room; Laundry room; Barber/Beauty shop; Library.
Activities Arts & crafts; Cards; Games; Reading groups; Prayer groups; Movies; Shopping trips; Social/Cultural gatherings.

Hillhaven Convalescent Center
233 University, Des Moines, IA, 50314
(515) 284-1280

Admin Brian Farrell. *Medical Dir/Dir of Nursing* Roy W Overton MD; Michael Gross RN.
Licensure Skilled care; Intermediate care. *Beds* SNF 20; ICF 142. *Certified* Medicaid; Medicare.
Owner Proprietary Corp (Hillhaven Corp).
Admissions Requirements Medical examination; Physician's request.
Staff RNs 9 (ft); LPNs 7 (ft), 1 (pt); Orderlies 2 (ft); Nurses aides 54 (ft), 2 (pt); Physical therapists 1 (ft), 1 (pt); Occupational therapists 1 (ft); Speech therapists; Activities coordinators 2 (ft), 1 (pt); Dietitians 1 (pt); Ophthalmologists; Staff development coordinator 1 (ft).
Facilities Dining room; Physical therapy room; Activities room; Crafts room; Laundry room; Barber/Beauty shop.
Activities Arts & crafts; Cards; Games; Reading groups; Prayer groups; Movies; Shopping trips; Social/Cultural gatherings.

Iowa Jewish Home*
1620 Pleasant St, Des Moines, IA, 50314
(515) 288-1001
Admin Michael D Kelner. *Medical Dir/Dir of Nursing* Stanton Danielson MD.
Licensure Skilled care; Intermediate care; Residential care. *Beds* SNF 42; Residential 5. *Certified* Medicaid; Medicare.
Admissions Requirements Minimum age 18; Medical examination.
Staff Physicians 2 (pt); RNs 2 (ft), 8 (pt); LPNs 3 (ft), 1 (pt); Nurses aides 12 (ft), 15 (pt); Physical therapists 1 (pt); Recreational therapists 1 (ft); Occupational therapists 1 (pt); Speech therapists 1 (pt); Activities coordinators 1 (ft); Dietitians 1 (ft), 1 (pt); Podiatrists 2 (pt).
Affiliation Jewish
Facilities Dining room; Chapel; Crafts room; Laundry room; Barber/Beauty shop.
Activities Arts & crafts; Games; Reading groups; Prayer groups; Movies; Shopping trips; Social/Cultural gatherings; Theatre; Restaurants; Bus rides; Pet visitation; Resident council.

Luther Park Health Center
1555 Hull Ave, Des Moines, IA, 50316
(515) 262-5639
Admin Norman Hjelmeland. *Medical Dir/Dir of Nursing* Roy Overton MD; Marcella Drannen RN DON.
Licensure Skilled care; Intermediate care. *Beds* SNF 60; ICF 60. *Certified* Medicaid; Medicare.
Owner Nonprofit organization/foundation.
Admissions Requirements Minimum age 16; Medical examination; Physician's request.
Staff Physicians; RNs 10 (ft), 2 (pt); LPNs 10 (ft); Orderlies 2 (ft); Nurses aides 40 (ft), 10 (pt); Physical therapists 1 (ft); Recreational therapists 2 (ft); Occupational therapists 1 (pt); Speech therapists 1 (pt); Dietitians 1 (pt); Ophthalmologists; Chaplain 2 (pt); Social worker 1 (ft), 1 (pt); Volunteer coord 1 (ft); Admissions coord 1 (ft).
Affiliation Lutheran
Facilities Dining room; Physical therapy room; Activities room; Chapel; Crafts room; Laundry room; Barber/Beauty shop; Library.
Activities Arts & crafts; Cards; Games; Reading groups; Prayer groups; Movies; Shopping trips; Social/Cultural gatherings.

New Oaks Care Center Inc
3806 Easton Blvd, Des Moines, IA, 50317-5799
(515) 265-1474
Admin Craig T Ver Huel. *Medical Dir/Dir of Nursing* Jan Summers.
Licensure Intermediate care. *Beds* ICF 51. *Certified* Medicaid.
Owner Privately owned.
Admissions Requirements Medical examination; Physician's request.

Staff RNs 1 (pt); LPNs 4 (ft), 3 (pt); Nurses aides 12 (ft), 5 (pt); Activities coordinators 1 (ft); Dietitians 1 (ft), 1 (pt); Therapy Aide 1 (ft).
Facilities Dining room; Laundry room; Barber/Beauty shop.
Activities Cards; Games; Reading groups; Prayer groups; Movies; Shopping trips; Ball games.

Park Ridge Manor*
4755 Park Ridge, Des Moines, IA, 50317
(515) 265-5348
Admin Darrell D Hoefling.
Licensure Intermediate care. *Beds* 74. *Certified* Medicaid.
Owner Proprietary Corp (Beverly Enterprises).

Ramsey Home
1611 27th St, Des Moines, IA, 50310
(515) 274-3612
Medical Dir/Dir of Nursing Robert Shires MD.
Licensure Intermediate care; Residential care. *Beds* ICF 54; Residential 78. *Certified* Medicaid.
Owner Nonprofit Corp (Natl Bnvlnt Assn of Chrstn Homes).
Admissions Requirements Minimum age 65; Medical examination.
Staff RNs 2 (ft); LPNs 4 (ft), 5 (pt); Nurses aides 19 (ft), 4 (pt); Physical therapists 1 (pt); Activities coordinators 2 (ft); Dietitians 1 (pt).
Affiliation Disciples of Christ
Facilities Dining room; Activities room; Chapel; Crafts room; Laundry room; Barber/Beauty shop; Library.
Activities Arts & crafts; Cards; Games; Reading groups; Prayer groups; Movies; Shopping trips; Social/Cultural gatherings; Pet therapy program.

Riverview Manor*
701 Riverview, Des Moines, IA, 50316
(515) 266-1106
Admin Daniel R Schwieger.
Licensure Intermediate care. *Beds* 138. *Certified* Medicaid.

Scottish Rite Park Health Care Center
2909 Woodland Ave, Des Moines, IA, 50312
(515) 274-4614
Admin Steve Lockwood. *Medical Dir/Dir of Nursing* Rosemary Fee DON.
Licensure Intermediate care; Residential care. *Beds* ICF 41; Residential 19. *Certified* Medicaid.
Owner Nonprofit Corp.
Admissions Requirements Medical examination.
Staff RNs; LPNs; Nurses aides.
Affiliation Masons
Facilities Dining room; Activities room; Crafts room; Laundry room; Barber/Beauty shop; Library.
Activities Arts & crafts; Cards; Games; Reading groups; Movies; Shopping trips; Social/Cultural gatherings.

Valborg Lutheran Home
1101 Grandview Ave, Des Moines, IA, 50316
265-1629
Admin Betty Nikolaisen. *Medical Dir/Dir of Nursing* Waldine Gookin.
Licensure Residential care. *Beds* Residential 50. *Certified* Medicaid.
Owner Nonprofit organization/foundation.
Admissions Requirements Medical examination; Physician's request.
Staff Nurses aides 4 (ft), 2 (pt); Activities coordinators 1 (ft).
Affiliation Lutheran
Facilities Dining room; Activities room; Chapel; Crafts room; Laundry room; Barber/Beauty shop; Library; Sewing room.

Activities Arts & crafts; Cards; Games; Reading groups; Prayer groups; Movies; Shopping trips; Social/Cultural gatherings.

Valley View Village
2571 Guthrie Ave, Des Moines, IA, 50317
(515) 265-2571
Admin Dennis L Howe. *Medical Dir/Dir of Nursing* Denice Shipley RN DON.
Licensure Intermediate care. *Beds* ICF 79. *Certified* Medicaid.
Admissions Requirements Medical examination; Physician's request.
Staff RNs; LPNs; Nurses aides; Activities coordinators.
Facilities Dining room; Activities room; Chapel; Crafts room; Barber/Beauty shop; Library.
Activities Arts & crafts; Cards; Games; Reading groups; Prayer groups; Movies; Shopping trips; Social/Cultural gatherings.

Villa Inn Home*
1709 10th St, Des Moines, IA, 50314
Medical Dir/Dir of Nursing Cynthia Six.
Admissions Requirements Minimum age 18; Medical examination; Physician's request.
Staff RNs 1 (ft); LPNs 1 (pt); Nurses aides 8 (ft); Activities coordinators 1 (ft).
Facilities Dining room; Activities room; Crafts room; Laundry room; Library.
Activities Arts & crafts; Cards; Games; Reading groups; Prayer groups; Movies; Shopping trips; Social/Cultural gatherings.

Wesley Acres*
3520 Grand, Des Moines, IA, 50312
(515) 274-3417
Medical Dir/Dir of Nursing Dr Robet Knox.
Licensure Intermediate care; Residential care. *Beds* ICF 59; Residential 62. *Certified* Medicaid.
Admissions Requirements Minimum age 60; Medical examination.
Staff Physicians 1 (pt); RNs 2 (ft), 14 (pt); LPNs 3 (pt); Orderlies 1 (ft), 2 (pt); Nurses aides 22 (ft), 16 (pt); Activities coordinators 2 (ft); Dietitians 1 (ft).
Affiliation Methodist
Facilities Dining room; Physical therapy room; Activities room; Chapel; Crafts room; Laundry room; Barber/Beauty shop; Library.
Activities Arts & crafts; Games; Reading groups; Movies; Shopping trips.

DONNELLSON

Donnellson Manor Care Center
901 State St, Donnellson, IA, 52625
(319) 835-5621
Admin Cheryl Walz. *Medical Dir/Dir of Nursing* Nancy Bunnell.
Licensure Intermediate care. *Beds* ICF 73. *Certified* Medicaid.
Facilities Dining room; Activities room; Crafts room; Laundry room; Barber/Beauty shop.
Activities Arts & crafts; Cards; Games; Reading groups; Prayer groups; Movies; Social/Cultural gatherings.

DOWS

Dows Care Center
909 Rowan Rd, Dows, IA, 50071
(515) 852-4147
Admin Cordell Poldberg. *Medical Dir/Dir of Nursing* Charlotte Brim RN.
Licensure Intermediate care. *Beds* ICF 50. *Certified* Medicaid.
Owner Privately owned.
Admissions Requirements Medical examination; Physician's request.
Staff RNs 2 (ft), 1 (pt); LPNs 2 (ft), 1 (pt); Nurses aides; Physical therapists 1 (pt); Occupational therapists 1 (pt); Speech therapists 1 (pt); Activities coordinators 1

(ft), 1 (pt); Dietitians 1 (pt); Ophthalmologists 1 (pt); Podiatrists 1 (pt); Social worker 1 (pt).
Facilities Dining room; Physical therapy room; Activities room; Chapel; Laundry room; Barber/Beauty shop; Library.
Activities Arts & crafts; Cards; Games; Reading groups; Prayer groups; Movies; Shopping trips; Social/Cultural gatherings.

DUBUQUE

Americana Healthcare Center*
901 W 3rd St, Dubuque, IA, 52001
(319) 556-1163
Admin John Jackson.
Licensure Skilled care. *Beds* 92. *Certified* Medicaid; Medicare.
Owner Proprietary Corp (Manor Care).

Bethany Home
1005 Lincoln Ave, Dubuque, IA, 52001
(319) 556-5233
Admin Patricia L Gabrielson. *Medical Dir/Dir of Nursing* Nan Colin.
Licensure Intermediate care; Residential care. *Beds* ICF 56; Residential 32. *Certified* Medicaid.
Owner Nonprofit Corp.
Admissions Requirements Medical examination.
Staff RNs; LPNs; Nurses aides; Activities coordinators; Dietitians.
Affiliation Presbyterian
Facilities Dining room; Activities room; Chapel; Crafts room; Laundry room; Barber/Beauty shop.
Activities Arts & crafts; Cards; Games; Reading groups; Prayer groups; Movies; Shopping trips; Social/Cultural gatherings.

Dubuque Health Care Center*
2935 Kaufman, Dubuque, IA, 52001
(319) 566-0673
Licensure Intermediate care. *Beds* 108. *Certified* Medicaid.
Owner Proprietary Corp (Beverly Enterprises).
Admissions Requirements Minimum age 16; Physician's request.
Staff Recreational therapists 1 (ft); Activities coordinators 3 (pt).
Facilities Dining room; Physical therapy room; Activities room; Crafts room; Barber/Beauty shop.
Activities Arts & crafts; Cards; Games; Reading groups; Prayer groups; Movies; Shopping trips; Social/Cultural gatherings.

Ennoble Manor Care Center*
2000 Pasadena Dr, Dubuque, IA, 52001
(319) 557-1076
Admin Joan Sutherland.
Licensure Intermediate care. *Beds* 102. *Certified* Medicaid.

Heritage Manor
4885 Asbury Rd, Dubuque, IA, 52001
(319) 583-6447
Admin Mary J Bailey. *Medical Dir/Dir of Nursing* John P Vincr MD; Bonnie Fagan.
Licensure Intermediate care. *Beds* ICF 75. *Certified* Medicaid.
Owner Proprietary Corp.
Admissions Requirements Medical examination; Physician's request.
Staff RNs 2 (ft), 3 (pt); LPNs 3 (ft); Nurses aides 19 (ft), 13 (pt); Activities coordinators 1 (ft), 3 (pt); Dietitians 1 (pt).
Facilities Dining room; Physical therapy room; Activities room; Chapel; Crafts room; Laundry room; Barber/Beauty shop; Library; Covered patio; Living room; TV room; Activity van.
Activities Arts & crafts; Cards; Games; Reading groups; Prayer groups; Movies; Shopping trips; Social/Cultural gatherings; Picnics; Sight-seeing trips; Five flag activities.

Luther Manor*
3131 Hillcrest Rd, Dubuque, IA, 52001
(319) 588-1413
Licensure Intermediate care. *Beds* 70. *Certified* Medicaid.
Affiliation Lutheran

Mercy Health Center
Mercy Dr, Dubuque, IA, 52001
(319) 589-8000
Admin Sr Helen Huewe. *Medical Dir/Dir of Nursing* Joan Hentges RN.
Licensure Skilled care; Intermediate care. *Beds* SNF 20; ICF 40. *Certified* Medicaid; Medicare.
Owner Nonprofit Corp.
Staff RNs 7 (ft), 9 (pt); LPNs 3 (ft), 2 (pt); Nurses aides 13 (ft), 17 (pt); Activities coordinators 3 (pt); Nurse Manager 2 (ft).
Affiliation Roman Catholic
Facilities Dining room; Physical therapy room; Activities room; Chapel; Barber/Beauty shop.
Activities Arts & crafts; Cards; Games; Prayer groups; Shopping trips; Social/Cultural gatherings.

Padre Pio Health Care Center
3485 Windsor Ave, Dubuque, IA, 52001
(319) 557-7180
Admin Sr Dolores Ullrich. *Medical Dir/Dir of Nursing* Victoria Anderegg RN.
Licensure Intermediate care; Residential care. *Beds* ICF 168; Residential 82. *Certified* Medicaid.
Owner Nonprofit Corp.
Admissions Requirements Minimum age 60; Medical examination.
Staff RNs 7 (ft), 13 (pt); LPNs 4 (ft), 14 (pt); Nurses aides 35 (ft), 66 (pt); Activities coordinators 2 (ft), 4 (pt); Dietitians 1 (pt).
Affiliation Roman Catholic
Facilities Dining room; Physical therapy room; Activities room; Chapel; Crafts room; Laundry room; Barber/Beauty shop; Library; Green House.
Activities Arts & crafts; Cards; Games; Reading groups; Prayer groups; Movies; Shopping trips; Social/Cultural gatherings; Exercise class; Bible class; Creative writing; Plant therapy.

DUMONT

Dumont Nursing Home*
921 3rd St, Dumont, IA, 50625
(515) 857-3401
Admin Edna Reiners.
Licensure Intermediate care; Residential care. *Beds* ICF 44; Residential 5. *Certified* Medicaid.

DUNLAP

Dunlap Care Center*
1403 Harrison Rd, Dunlap, IA, 51529
(712) 643-2121
Admin Rodney A Hirchert.
Licensure Intermediate care. *Beds* 73. *Certified* Medicaid.

DYSART

Sunnycrest Nursing Center
401 Crisman St, Dysart, IA, 52224
(319) 476-2400
Admin Susan Loeb. *Medical Dir/Dir of Nursing* Dr Pathan; Charlotte Miller RN DON.
Licensure Intermediate care. *Beds* ICF 67. *Certified* Medicaid.
Owner Proprietary Corp (Quality Health Care Specialists Inc).
Admissions Requirements Medical examination.

Staff RNs 2 (ft); LPNs 3 (pt); Orderlies 3 (pt); Nurses aides 15 (ft), 15 (pt); Physical therapists 1 (pt); Occupational therapists 1 (pt); Speech therapists 1 (pt); Activities coordinators 1 (ft); Dietitians 1 (pt).
Facilities Dining room; Physical therapy room; Activities room; Crafts room; Laundry room; Barber/Beauty shop.
Activities Arts & crafts; Cards; Games; Reading groups; Prayer groups; Movies; Shopping trips; Social/Cultural gatherings.

EAGLE GROVE

Rotary Ann Home Inc*
620 SE 5th St, Eagle Grove, IA, 50533
(515) 448-5124
Medical Dir/Dir of Nursing Angelene Kappes RN.
Licensure Intermediate care. *Beds* 51. *Certified* Medicaid.
Admissions Requirements Medical examination.
Staff RNs 2 (ft), 3 (pt); LPNs 2 (ft), 2 (pt); Nurses aides 10 (ft), 12 (pt); Activities coordinators 1 (ft).
Facilities Dining room; Physical therapy room; Activities room; Chapel; Crafts room; Laundry room; Barber/Beauty shop; Library.
Activities Arts & crafts; Cards; Games; Reading groups; Prayer groups; Movies; Shopping trips; Social/Cultural gatherings.

EARLHAM

Earlham Manor Care Center
201 Center St, Earlham, IA, 50072
(515) 758-2244
Admin Karen G Reed. *Medical Dir/Dir of Nursing* Mary O Ralston.
Licensure Intermediate care. *Beds* ICF 29. *Certified* Medicaid; Medicare.
Owner Proprietary Corp (Quality Health Care Specialists Inc).
Admissions Requirements Minimum age 16.
Staff RNs; Orderlies; Nurses aides; Physical therapists; Activities coordinators; Dietitians; Ophthalmologists; Podiatrists.
Facilities Dining room; Laundry room; Barber/Beauty shop.
Activities Arts & crafts; Cards; Games; Reading groups; Prayer groups; Movies; Shopping trips; Social/Cultural gatherings.

EARLING

Little Flower Haven*
Earling, IA, 51530
(712) 747-3301
Admin David Hoffmann.
Licensure Intermediate care. *Beds* 61. *Certified* Medicaid.

EDGEWOOD

Edgewood Convalescent Home*
Edgewood, IA, 52042
(319) 928-6461
Licensure Intermediate care. *Beds* 33. *Certified* Medicaid.
Admissions Requirements Medical examination.
Staff RNs 1 (ft), 1 (pt); LPNs 4 (pt); Nurses aides 4 (ft), 12 (pt); Recreational therapists 1 (pt); Occupational therapists 1 (pt); Speech therapists 1 (pt); Activities coordinators 1 (ft); Dietitians 1 (ft), 1 (pt); Dentists 1 (pt); Ophthalmologists 1 (pt); Podiatrists 1 (pt); Audiologists 1 (pt).
Facilities Dining room; Physical therapy room; Activities room; Chapel; Crafts room; Laundry room; Barber/Beauty shop.
Activities Arts & crafts; Cards; Games; Reading groups; Prayer groups; Movies; Social/Cultural gatherings.

ELDORA

Eldora Manor
1510 22nd St, Eldora, IA, 50627
(515) 858-3491
Admin Deb Hightshoe. *Medical Dir/Dir of Nursing* Sandra Willems.
Licensure Intermediate care. *Beds* ICF 70. *Certified* Medicaid.
Owner Proprietary Corp (Beverly Enterprises).
Admissions Requirements Minimum age 21.
Staff RNs 3 (ft); LPNs 3 (ft), 1 (pt); Orderlies 1 (ft); Nurses aides 20 (ft), 6 (pt); Activities coordinators 1 (ft), 1 (pt); Social worker 1 (pt).
Facilities Dining room; Physical therapy room; Activities room; Crafts room; Laundry room; Barber/Beauty shop.
Activities Arts & crafts; Cards; Games; Reading groups; Prayer groups; Movies; Social/Cultural gatherings.

Valley View Nursing Center*
2313 15th Ave, Eldora, IA, 50627
(515) 858-5422
Admin Dale Moore.
Licensure Intermediate care; Residential care. *Beds* ICF 64; Residential 16. *Certified* Medicaid.

ELK HORN

Salem Lutheran Homes
2024 College St, Elk Horn, IA, 51531
(712) 764-4201
Admin Howard M Hansen. *Medical Dir/Dir of Nursing* Beverly Kleen.
Licensure Intermediate care; Residential care. *Beds* ICF 100; Residential 62. *Certified* Medicaid.
Owner Nonprofit Corp.
Admissions Requirements Minimum age 16; Medical examination; Physician's request.
Staff RNs; LPNs; Orderlies; Nurses aides; Physical therapists; Dietitians.
Affiliation Lutheran
Facilities Dining room; Physical therapy room; Activities room; Chapel; Crafts room; Laundry room; Barber/Beauty shop.
Activities Arts & crafts; Cards; Games; Reading groups; Prayer groups; Movies; Shopping trips; Social/Cultural gatherings.

ELKADER

Elkader Care Center*
116 Reimer St, Elkader, IA, 52043
(319) 245-1620
Admin Jean Westerbeck.
Licensure Intermediate care. *Beds* 51. *Certified* Medicaid.
Admissions Requirements Minimum age 18; Medical examination.
Staff RNs 1 (ft); LPNs 2 (ft), 3 (pt); Nurses aides 4 (ft), 11 (pt); Activities coordinators 1 (ft); Dietitians 1 (pt).
Facilities Dining room; Chapel; Laundry room; Barber/Beauty shop.
Activities Arts & crafts; Cards; Games; Reading groups; Prayer groups; Movies; Shopping trips.

ELMA

Colonial Manor of Elma Inc
9th & Maple, Elma, IA, 50628
(515) 393-2134
Admin Jerome Erdahl. *Medical Dir/Dir of Nursing* Dr Curtis Rainy; Sheila Kobliska RN.
Licensure Intermediate care. *Beds* ICF 62. *Certified* Medicaid.
Owner Proprietary Corp.
Admissions Requirements Minimum age 21; Medical examination; Physician's request.

Staff Physicians 1 (pt); RNs 1 (ft), 1 (pt); LPNs 1 (ft), 3 (pt); Nurses aides 7 (ft), 21 (pt); Physical therapists 1 (pt); Recreational therapists 1 (pt); Occupational therapists 1 (pt); Speech therapists 1 (pt); Activities coordinators 2 (ft); Dietitians 1 (pt); Ophthalmologists 1 (pt); Podiatrists 1 (pt); Social worker 1 (pt); Dentist 1 (pt).
Facilities Dining room; Physical therapy room; Activities room; Chapel; Crafts room; Laundry room; Barber/Beauty shop; Library.
Activities Arts & crafts; Cards; Games; Reading groups; Prayer groups; Movies; Shopping trips; Social/Cultural gatherings.

EMMETSBURG

Emmetsburg Care Center
PO Box 490, 2405 21st St, Emmetsburg, IA, 50536
(712) 852-4266
Admin Lyman D Bailey. *Medical Dir/Dir of Nursing* Nina J Jurries.
Licensure Intermediate care. *Beds* ICF 88. *Certified* Medicaid.
Owner Proprietary Corp.
Admissions Requirements Minimum age 16; Medical examination.
Staff RNs 2 (ft), 1 (pt); LPNs 5 (ft), 5 (pt); Nurses aides 30 (ft), 20 (pt); Physical therapists 1 (pt); Reality therapists 2 (ft); Recreational therapists 2 (ft); Occupational therapists 1 (pt); Speech therapists 1 (pt); Activities coordinators 2 (ft), 1 (pt); Dietitians 1 (pt); Ophthalmologists 1 (pt); Podiatrists 1 (pt).
Facilities Dining room; Physical therapy room; Activities room; Chapel; Crafts room; Laundry room; Barber/Beauty shop; Library.
Activities Arts & crafts; Cards; Games; Reading groups; Prayer groups; Movies; Shopping trips; Social/Cultural gatherings.

Lakeside Lutheran Home*
N Lawler St, Emmetsburg, IA, 50536
(712) 852-4060
Admin Robert Owen.
Licensure Intermediate care. *Beds* 60. *Certified* Medicaid.
Owner Nonprofit Corp.
Affiliation Lutheran

ESTHERVILLE

Good Samaritan Center
1646 5th Ave N, Estherville, IA, 51334
(712) 362-3522
Admin Bruce L Radtke. *Medical Dir/Dir of Nursing* Erla Scherschligt.
Licensure Intermediate care. *Beds* ICF 141. *Certified* Medicaid.
Owner Nonprofit Corp (Evangelical Lutheran/ Good Samaritan).
Admissions Requirements Minimum age 16; Medical examination; Physician's request.
Staff RNs 3 (ft), 3 (pt); LPNs 2 (ft), 6 (pt); Orderlies 2 (ft); Nurses aides 30 (ft), 32 (pt); Physical therapists 1 (pt); Activities coordinators 1 (ft); Dietitians 1 (ft).
Facilities Dining room; Activities room; Chapel; Crafts room; Laundry room; Barber/ Beauty shop.
Activities Arts & crafts; Games; Reading groups; Prayer groups; Movies; Social/ Cultural gatherings.

Rosewood Manor
2001 First Ave N, Estherville, IA, 51334
(712) 362-3594
Admin Jeanne M Hofstader. *Medical Dir/Dir of Nursing* Dianne Howard.
Licensure Intermediate care. *Beds* 55.
Owner Proprietary Corp.
Admissions Requirements Medical examination.

Staff RNs 2 (ft); LPNs 4 (ft), 1 (pt); Nurses aides 10 (ft), 5 (pt); Physical therapists 1 (pt); Recreational therapists 1 (ft); Activities coordinators 1 (ft); Dietitians 1 (pt); Podiatrists 1 (pt).
Facilities Dining room; Physical therapy room; Activities room; Chapel; Crafts room; Laundry room; Barber/Beauty shop.
Activities Arts & crafts; Cards; Games; Reading groups; Prayer groups; Movies.

EXIRA

Exira Care Center*
409 S Carthage, Exira, IA, 50076
(712) 268-5393
Admin Curt B Mardesen.
Licensure Intermediate care; Residential care. *Beds* ICF 46; Residential 16. *Certified* Medicaid.

FAIRFIELD

Nelson Nursing Home*
809 W Taylor, Fairfield, IA, 52556
(515) 472-6126
Admin Arlouine Trent.
Licensure Intermediate care. *Beds* 63. *Certified* Medicaid.

Parkview Care Center
PO Box 193, RR 1, Fairfield, IA, 52556
(515) 472-5022
Admin Christie L Six. *Medical Dir/Dir of Nursing* Connie Ferrell.
Licensure Intermediate care. *Beds* ICF 112. *Certified* Medicaid.
Owner Proprietary Corp.
Staff RNs; LPNs; Orderlies; Nurses aides; Activities coordinators 2 (ft).

FAYETTE

Maple Crest Manor
PO Box 132X, RR 1, Fayette, IA, 52142
(319) 425-3336
Admin Richard L Ford. *Medical Dir/Dir of Nursing* Joyce Dahlquist DON.
Licensure Intermediate care. *Beds* 60. *Certified* Medicaid.
Owner Proprietary Corp.
Admissions Requirements Minimum age 16; Medical examination; Physician's request.
Staff RNs; LPNs; Orderlies; Nurses aides; Physical therapists; Occupational therapists; Speech therapists; Activities coordinators; Dietitians; Podiatrists.
Facilities Dining room; Physical therapy room; Activities room; Crafts room; Laundry room; Barber/Beauty shop.
Activities Arts & crafts; Cards; Games; Reading groups; Prayer groups; Movies; Social/Cultural gatherings.

FONDA

Fonda Care Center*
6th & Queen Ave, Fonda, IA, 50540
(712) 288-4441
Medical Dir/Dir of Nursing Jane Bierstedt RN.
Licensure Intermediate care. *Beds* 49. *Certified* Medicaid.
Admissions Requirements Minimum age 49; Medical examination; Physician's request.
Staff Physicians 1 (pt); RNs 2 (ft); LPNs 1 (ft), 1 (pt); Orderlies 2 (ft), 1 (pt); Nurses aides 10 (ft), 10 (pt); Physical therapists 1 (pt); Occupational therapists 1 (pt); Speech therapists 1 (pt); Activities coordinators 1 (ft); Dietitians 1 (pt); Dentists 1 (pt); Podiatrists 1 (pt); Audiologists 1 (pt).
Facilities Dining room; Physical therapy room; Activities room; Laundry room; Barber/Beauty shop.

Activities Arts & crafts; Cards; Games; Reading groups; Movies; Shopping trips.

FONTANELLE

Fontanelle Good Samaritan Center
PO Box 38, 326 Summerset St, Fontanelle, IA, 50846
(515) 745-4201
Admin Jane Mohror. *Medical Dir/Dir of Nursing* Twilah Tipling RN.
Licensure Intermediate care. *Beds* ICF 63. *Certified* Medicaid.
Owner Nonprofit Corp (Evangelical Lutheran/ Good Samaritan).
Admissions Requirements Medical examination; Physician's request.
Staff RNs; LPNs; Orderlies; Nurses aides; Activities coordinators.
Facilities Dining room; Physical therapy room; Activities room; Laundry room; Barber/Beauty shop.
Activities Cards; Games; Reading groups; Movies; Mental stimulation; Music; Demonstrations.

FOREST CITY

Good Samaritan Center
606 S 7th, Forest City, IA, 50436
(515) 582-2232
Admin Nancy Demmel. *Medical Dir/Dir of Nursing* Dolores Nelson DON.
Licensure Intermediate care. *Beds* ICF 64. *Certified* Medicaid.
Owner Nonprofit Corp (Evangelical Lutheran/ Good Samaritan).
Admissions Requirements Medical examination.
Staff RNs 3 (ft), 6 (pt); LPNs 4 (pt); Orderlies 1 (ft); Nurses aides 12 (ft), 15 (pt); Activities coordinators 1 (pt).
Affiliation Lutheran
Facilities Dining room; Activities room; Chapel; Laundry room; Barber/Beauty shop; Library.
Activities Games; Reading groups; Prayer groups; Movies; Social/Cultural gatherings.

FORT DODGE

Ellens Convalescent Health Center Inc
1305 N 22nd St, Fort Dodge, IA, 50501
(515) 955-4145
Admin James Kratovil. *Medical Dir/Dir of Nursing* Mrs Anderson DON.
Licensure Intermediate care; Residential care. *Beds* ICF 80; Residential 18. *Certified* Medicaid.
Owner Proprietary Corp.
Admissions Requirements Minimum age 13; Medical examination; Physician's request.
Staff RNs 3 (ft), 2 (pt); LPNs 4 (ft), 3 (pt); Nurses aides 20 (ft), 8 (pt); Activities coordinators 2 (ft), 2 (pt); Dietitians 1 (pt).
Facilities Dining room; Physical therapy room; Activities room; Chapel; Crafts room; Laundry room; Barber/Beauty shop; Library.
Activities Arts & crafts; Cards; Games; Reading groups; Prayer groups; Movies; Shopping trips; Social/Cultural gatherings.

Fort Dodge Group Home
525 S 15th St, Fort Dodge, IA, 50501
(515) 965-6578
Admin Michael Wertz.
Licensure Residential care for mentally retarded. *Beds* 12. *Certified* Medicaid; Medicare.
Owner Nonprofit organization/foundation.
Admissions Requirements Minimum age 18; Medical examination.
Facilities Dining room; Laundry room.
Activities Arts & crafts; Cards; Games; Movies; Shopping trips; Social/Cultural gatherings.

Fort Dodge Villa Care Center
2721 10th Ave N, Fort Dodge, IA, 50501
(515) 576-7525
Admin Dori Smith. *Medical Dir/Dir of Nursing* Loretta Tarbox RN DON.
Licensure Intermediate care; Residential care. *Beds* ICF 81; Residential 26. *Certified* Medicaid.
Owner Proprietary Corp (Quality Health Care Specialists Inc).
Admissions Requirements Medical examination; Physician's request.
Staff RNs 4 (ft), 7 (pt); Orderlies 2 (ft), 1 (pt); Nurses aides 20 (ft), 15 (pt); Recreational therapists 1 (ft); Activities coordinators 1 (ft), 1 (pt); Dietitians 1 (ft), 1 (pt).
Facilities Dining room; Physical therapy room; Activities room; Chapel; Crafts room; Laundry room; Barber/Beauty shop; Library.
Activities Arts & crafts; Cards; Games; Reading groups; Prayer groups; Movies; Shopping trips; Social/Cultural gatherings.

Friendship Haven Inc
S Kenyon Rd, Fort Dodge, IA, 50501
(515) 573-2121
Admin Rev Paul G Bousfield. *Medical Dir/Dir of Nursing* James Metzger MD; Sally Young DON.
Licensure Intermediate care; Residential care. *Beds* ICF 241; Residential 352. *Certified* Medicaid.
Owner Nonprofit Corp.
Admissions Requirements Minimum age 65; Medical examination.
Staff Physicians 1 (ft); RNs 21 (ft); LPNs 9 (ft); Nurses aides 130 (ft); Physical therapists 1 (ft); Recreational therapists 1 (ft); Speech therapists 1 (ft); Activities coordinators 1 (ft); Dietitians 1 (ft); Ophthalmologists 1 (ft); Podiatrists 1 (ft).
Affiliation Methodist
Facilities Dining room; Physical therapy room; Activities room; Chapel; Crafts room; Laundry room; Barber/Beauty shop; Library; Kitchen; Coffee shop & small cafeteria; Gift shop & thrift shop; Swimming pool; Jacuzzi.
Activities Arts & crafts; Cards; Games; Reading groups; Prayer groups; Movies; Shopping trips; Social/Cultural gatherings; Outside entertainment; College classes; Exercise; Swimming.

Marian Home
2400 6th Ave N, Fort Dodge, IA, 50501
(515) 576-1138
Admin Gerald J Bruening. *Medical Dir/Dir of Nursing* Mary B Bruening.
Licensure Intermediate care. *Beds* ICF 97. *Certified* Medicaid.
Owner Nonprofit organization/foundation.
Admissions Requirements Physician's request.
Staff RNs 5 (ft), 7 (pt); LPNs 5 (pt); Orderlies 1 (ft), 1 (pt); Nurses aides 15 (ft), 29 (pt); Physical therapists 2 (ft), 1 (pt); Occupational therapists 1 (pt); Speech therapists 1 (pt); Activities coordinators 2 (ft); Dietitians 1 (pt).
Affiliation Roman Catholic
Facilities Dining room; Physical therapy room; Activities room; Chapel; Crafts room; Laundry room; Barber/Beauty shop.
Activities Arts & crafts; Cards; Games; Reading groups; Prayer groups; Movies; Shopping trips; Social/Cultural gatherings.

Villa Park Care Center
728 14th Ave N, Fort Dodge, IA, 50501
(515) 576-7226
Admin Carl E Warrington. *Medical Dir/Dir of Nursing* Paula Horton.
Licensure Intermediate care. *Beds* ICF 100. *Certified* Medicaid.
Owner Proprietary Corp (Quality Health Care Specialists Inc).
Admissions Requirements Minimum age 21.

Staff Physicians; RNs; LPNs; Orderlies; Nurses aides; Physical therapists; Speech therapists; Activities coordinators; Dietitians; Ophthalmologists; Podiatrists.
Facilities Dining room; Physical therapy room; Activities room; Laundry room; Barber/Beauty shop.
Activities Arts & crafts; Cards; Games; Reading groups; Prayer groups; Movies; Shopping trips; Social/Cultural gatherings.

FORT MADISON

Fort Madison Nursing Care Center
1702 41st St, Fort Madison, IA, 52627
(319) 372-8021
Admin Sr Donna Venteicher. *Medical Dir/Dir of Nursing* Betty Lucas.
Licensure Intermediate care. *Beds* ICF 108. *Certified* Medicaid.
Owner Proprietary Corp.
Admissions Requirements Minimum age 16; Medical examination.
Staff RNs 5 (ft), 2 (pt); LPNs 2 (ft), 1 (pt); Nurses aides 18 (ft), 19 (pt); Physical therapists 1 (pt); Occupational therapists 1 (pt); Speech therapists 1 (pt); Activities coordinators; Dietitians 1 (pt); Ophthalmologists 1 (pt); Podiatrists 1 (pt).
Facilities Dining room; Physical therapy room; Activities room; Chapel; Crafts room; Laundry room; Barber/Beauty shop.
Activities Arts & crafts; Cards; Games; Reading groups; Prayer groups; Movies; Shopping trips; Social/Cultural gatherings.

FREDERICKSBURG

Sunrise Guest Home
Lions Rd, Fredericksburg, IA, 50630
(515) 237-5323
Admin Sharon Jan Ploeger.
Licensure Intermediate care. *Beds* ICF 37. *Certified* Medicaid.
Owner Proprietary Corp.
Admissions Requirements Minimum age 16.
Staff RNs 1 (ft); LPNs 3 (ft); Nurses aides 20 (ft); Speech therapists 1 (ft); Activities coordinators 1 (ft); Dietitians 1 (ft).
Facilities Dining room; Physical therapy room; Activities room; Crafts room; Laundry room; Barber/Beauty shop; Library.
Activities Arts & crafts; Cards; Games; Reading groups; Prayer groups; Movies; Social/Cultural gatherings.

GARNER

Concord Care Manor
1375 Division St, Garner, IA, 50438
(515) 923-2677
Admin Debra Roberts. *Medical Dir/Dir of Nursing* Dee Lackore.
Licensure Intermediate care. *Beds* 66. *Certified* Medicaid.
Owner Proprietary Corp.
Admissions Requirements Medical examination.
Staff RNs 1 (ft), 1 (pt); LPNs 4 (ft); Nurses aides 15 (ft), 10 (pt); Physical therapists 1 (pt); Activities coordinators 1 (ft); Dietitians 1 (pt).
Facilities Dining room; Activities room; Chapel; Barber/Beauty shop.
Activities Cards; Games; Reading groups; Prayer groups; Movies; Social/Cultural gatherings.

GEORGE

George Community Good Samaritan Center*
400 N Washington, George, IA, 51237
(712) 475-3391
Admin Eugene R Mathison.

Licensure Intermediate care. *Beds* 48.
Certified Medicaid.
Owner Nonprofit Corp (Evangelical Lutheran/ Good Samaritan).

GLADBROOK

Westbrook Acres*
Hwy 69 W, Gladbrook, IA, 50635
(515) 473-2016
Admin Loretta L Larson.
Licensure Intermediate care. *Beds* 33.
Certified Medicaid.

GLENWOOD

Glen Haven Home*
302 6th St, Glenwood, IA, 51534
(712) 527-3101
Admin Monte L McVey.
Licensure Intermediate care. *Beds* 90.
Certified Medicaid.

Hillside Manor
114 E Green St, Glenwood, IA, 51534
(712) 527-4841
Admin Barbour Pawela. *Medical Dir/Dir of Nursing* Robet K Fryzek MD; Linda Heywood RN DON; Donna Mackey RN DON.
Licensure Intermediate care; Intermediate care for mentally retarded. *Beds* ICF 67; ICF/MR 112. *Certified* Medicaid.
Owner Privately owned.
Admissions Requirements Minimum age 19.
Staff Physicians 1 (pt); RNs 4 (ft), 1 (pt); LPNs 6 (ft); Orderlies 25 (ft); Nurses aides 55 (ft); Physical therapists 1 (pt); Recreational therapists 10 (ft); Occupational therapists 1 (pt); Speech therapists 1 (pt); Activities coordinators 2 (ft); Dietitians 1 (pt).
Facilities Dining room; Physical therapy room; Activities room; Crafts room; Laundry room; Barber/Beauty shop.
Activities Arts & crafts; Cards; Games; Movies; Shopping trips; Social/Cultural gatherings.

GOWRIE

Gowrie Care Center
1808 Main St, Gowrie, IA, 50543
(515) 352-3912
Admin Chris Zunkel. *Medical Dir/Dir of Nursing* Bev Swedlund.
Licensure Intermediate care. *Beds* 51.
Certified Medicaid; Medicare.
Owner Proprietary Corp (ABCM Corp).
Admissions Requirements Medical examination; Physician's request.
Staff RNs 2 (ft); LPNs 5 (ft), 1 (pt); Orderlies 2 (ft); Nurses aides 14 (ft), 3 (pt); Activities coordinators 1 (ft), 1 (pt); Dietitians 1 (pt).
Facilities Dining room; Activities room; Laundry room; Barber/Beauty shop.
Activities Arts & crafts; Cards; Games; Reading groups; Prayer groups; Movies; Social/Cultural gatherings.

GRANGER

Granger Manor Care Center
2001 Kennedy, Granger, IA, 50109
(515) 999-2588
Admin Rex Logan. *Medical Dir/Dir of Nursing* Josephine Kanniainen.
Licensure Intermediate care. *Beds* ICF 67.
Certified Medicaid.
Owner Proprietary Corp (Life Care Centers of America).
Staff RNs 2 (ft); LPNs 4 (ft); Nurses aides 20 (ft); Physical therapists 4 (ft); Recreational therapists 1 (ft); Occupational therapists 1

(ft); Speech therapists 1 (ft); Activities coordinators 1 (ft); Dietitians 1 (ft); Ophthalmologists 1 (ft); Podiatrists 1 (ft).
Facilities Dining room; Physical therapy room; Activities room; Crafts room; Laundry room; Barber/Beauty shop.
Activities Arts & crafts; Cards; Games; Reading groups; Prayer groups; Shopping trips; Social/Cultural gatherings.

GREENE

Mathers Nursing Home
108 S High St, Greene, IA, 50636
(515) 823-4531
Admin Alberta Mathers. *Medical Dir/Dir of Nursing* Linda Schroeder RN DON.
Licensure Intermediate care. *Beds* ICF 25.
Certified Medicaid.
Owner Privately owned.
Admissions Requirements Minimum age 18; Medical examination; Physician's request.
Staff RNs 1 (ft); LPNs 2 (pt); Nurses aides 2 (ft), 12 (pt); Activities coordinators 1 (pt); Dietary 1 (ft), 2 (pt); Housekeeping 2 (pt); Laundry 2 (pt).
Facilities Dining room; Physical therapy room; Activities room; Laundry room; Barber/Beauty shop.
Activities Arts & crafts; Cards; Games; Reading groups; Prayer groups; Movies; Social/Cultural gatherings.

GREENFIELD

Greenfield Manor Inc
RR 2 Box A-1, 615 SE Kent, Greenfield, IA, 50849
(515) 743-6131
Admin Helen L Martin. *Medical Dir/Dir of Nursing* Esther Ramsey DON.
Licensure Intermediate care. *Beds* ICF 57.
Certified Medicaid.
Owner Proprietary Corp.
Admissions Requirements Medical examination; Physician's request.
Staff RNs 1 (ft), 2 (pt); LPNs 3 (ft), 1 (pt); Orderlies 1 (ft), 1 (pt); Nurses aides 16 (ft), 4 (pt); Activities coordinators 2 (pt); Dietitians 1 (pt).
Facilities Dining room; Physical therapy room; Activities room.
Activities Arts & crafts; Cards; Games; Reading groups; Prayer groups; Movies; Social/Cultural gatherings.

GRINNELL

Friendship Manor Inc*
Rte 2, Grinnell, IA, 50112
(515) 236-6511
Admin Gordon Van Donselaar.
Licensure Intermediate care. *Beds* 77.
Certified Medicaid.

Mayflower Home
616 Broad St, Grinnell, IA, 50112
(515) 236-6151
Admin Dennis A Acrea. *Medical Dir/Dir of Nursing* Patricia Avalos RN DON.
Licensure Intermediate care; Residential care. *Beds* ICF 26; Residential 34. *Certified* Medicaid.
Owner Nonprofit Corp.
Admissions Requirements Minimum age 60; Medical examination.
Staff RNs 2 (ft), 2 (pt); LPNs 1 (ft), 1 (pt); Nurses aides 9 (ft), 9 (pt); Physical therapists 1 (pt); Activities coordinators 2 (pt); Dietitians 1 (ft).
Affiliation Church of Christ
Facilities Dining room; Physical therapy room; Activities room; Chapel; Crafts room; Laundry room; Barber/Beauty shop; Library.

Activities Arts & crafts; Cards; Games; Reading groups; Prayer groups; Movies; Shopping trips; Social/Cultural gatherings.

St Francis Manor Inc
2021 4th Ave, Grinnell, IA, 50112
(515) 236-7592
Admin Dion Schrack. *Medical Dir/Dir of Nursing* Toni Mulert RN.
Licensure Intermediate care. *Beds* ICF 59.
Certified Medicaid.
Owner Nonprofit Corp.
Admissions Requirements Physician's request.
Staff RNs 2 (ft); LPNs 8 (ft); Nurses aides 30 (ft); Activities coordinators 1 (ft).
Facilities Dining room; Physical therapy room; Activities room; Crafts room; Laundry room; Barber/Beauty shop.
Activities Arts & crafts; Cards; Games; Reading groups; Prayer groups; Movies; Shopping trips; Social/Cultural gatherings.

GRISWOLD

Griswold Care Center Inc*
106 Harrison St, Griswold, IA, 51535
(712) 778-2534
Admin Joyce Hansen Shultz.
Licensure Intermediate care; Residential care. *Beds* ICF 40; Residential 6. *Certified* Medicaid.

GRUNDY CENTER

Grundy Care Center
1st St & J Ave, Grundy Center, IA, 50638
(319) 824-5436
Admin Lu Ann Modlin. *Medical Dir/Dir of Nursing* Shirley Day.
Licensure Intermediate care. *Beds* ICF 47.
Certified Medicaid.
Owner Proprietary Corp (Waverly Group).
Admissions Requirements Medical examination; Physician's request.
Staff LPNs 2 (ft), 2 (pt); Orderlies 1 (ft); Activities coordinators 1 (ft).
Facilities Dining room; Physical therapy room; Activities room; Laundry room; Barber/Beauty shop.
Activities Arts & crafts; Cards; Games; Reading groups; Prayer groups; Movies; Shopping trips; Social/Cultural gatherings.

Grundy County Memorial Hospital—Nurs Home*
E "J" Ave, Grundy Center, IA, 50638
Admin Ed Whitver.
Licensure Skilled care; Intermediate care. *Beds* 55. *Certified* Medicaid; Medicare.
Owner Publicly owned.
Admissions Requirements Medical examination.
Staff Physicians 3 (ft); RNs 1 (ft), 1 (pt); LPNs 2 (ft), 1 (pt); Nurses aides 12 (ft), 5 (pt); Physical therapists 1 (pt); Occupational therapists 1 (pt); Speech therapists 1 (pt); Activities coordinators 1 (ft); Dietitians 1 (pt); Dentists 1 (pt); Podiatrists 1 (pt); Urologists 1 (pt).
Facilities Dining room; Physical therapy room; Activities room; Laundry room.
Activities Arts & crafts; Games; Reading groups; Prayer groups; Movies; Social/ Cultural gatherings.

GUTHRIE CENTER

The New Homestead
Rte 2 Box 13, Guthrie Center, IA, 50115
(515) 747-2204
Admin Keith A Jennings. *Medical Dir/Dir of Nursing* Gertrude Heise DON.
Licensure Intermediate care. *Beds* ICF 66.
Certified Medicaid.
Owner Nonprofit Corp.
Admissions Requirements Medical examination.

Staff RNs; LPNs; Nurses aides; Physical therapists; Recreational therapists; Occupational therapists; Speech therapists; Activities coordinators; Dietitians.
Facilities Dining room; Physical therapy room; Activities room; Crafts room; Laundry room; Barber/Beauty shop.
Activities Arts & crafts; Cards; Games; Reading groups; Prayer groups; Movies; Social/Cultural gatherings.

GUTTENBERG

Riverview Care Center Inc*
400 Acre St, Guttenberg, IA, 52052
(319) 252-2281
Admin Robert E Wooldridge.
Licensure Intermediate care. *Beds* ICF 93.
Certified Medicaid.

HAMPTON

Franklin General Hospital*
1720 Central Ave E, Hampton, IA, 50441
(515) 456-4721
Admin Gary L Peterson.
Licensure Intermediate care. *Beds* 52.

Franklin Nursing Home*
105 1st Ave SW, Hampton, IA, 50441
(515) 456-4724
Licensure Intermediate care. *Beds* 73.
Certified Medicaid.

Hampton Nursing Home*
700 2nd St SE, Hampton, IA, 50441
(515) 456-4701
Admin Claudia Boeding.
Licensure Intermediate care. *Beds* 97.
Certified Medicaid.

HARLAN

Baptist Memorial Home Elm Crest Apartments
2104 12th St, Harlan, IA, 51537
(712) 755-5174
Admin Warren Rippey. *Medical Dir/Dir of Nursing* Arleatta Bartelson DON.
Licensure Intermediate care; Residential care. *Beds* ICF 71; Residential 54. *Certified* Medicaid.
Owner Nonprofit Corp (American Baptist Homes).
Staff RNs; LPNs; Nurses aides; Physical therapists; Activities coordinators; Dietitians.
Affiliation Baptist

HARTLEY

Community Memorial Hospital*
8th Ave W, Hartley, IA, 51346
(712) 728-2428
Admin Madonna Towne.
Licensure Intermediate care. *Beds* 43.

HAWARDEN

Hass Hillcrest Care Center Inc
2121 Ave L, Hawarden, IA, 51023
(712) 552-1074
Admin Dorinda Martin. *Medical Dir/Dir of Nursing* Marral Sheldon.
Licensure Intermediate care. *Beds* ICF 58. *Certified* Medicaid.
Owner Proprietary Corp.
Admissions Requirements Medical examination; Physician's request.
Staff RNs 1 (ft); LPNs 2 (ft), 4 (pt); Nurses aides 4 (ft), 30 (pt); Recreational therapists 1 (ft); Occupational therapists 1 (pt); Activities coordinators 1 (ft); Dietitians 1 (ft); Ophthalmologists 1 (pt).
Facilities Dining room; Physical therapy room; Activities room; Chapel; Laundry room; Barber/Beauty shop; Quiet room.

Activities Cards; Games; Reading groups; Prayer groups; Movies; Shopping trips; Social/Cultural gatherings.

HILLS

Atrium Village
Brady & 3rd, Hills, IA, 52235
(319) 679-2224
Admin Jessie Diers.
Licensure Intermediate care. *Beds* 20.
Owner Nonprofit Corp.
Admissions Requirements Females only.
Staff RNs 2 (ft), 2 (pt); LPNs 2 (ft); Orderlies 1 (pt); Nurses aides 4 (ft), 4 (pt); Activities coordinators 1 (pt).
Facilities Dining room; Physical therapy room; Activities room; Chapel; Laundry room; Barber/Beauty shop.
Activities Arts & crafts; Cards; Games; Reading groups; Prayer groups; Movies; Shopping trips.

HOLSTEIN

Holstein Good Samaritan Center
505 W 2nd St, Holstein, IA, 51025
(712) 368-4304
Admin John C Ashton. *Medical Dir/Dir of Nursing* Genny Clark DON.
Licensure Intermediate care. *Beds* ICF 60.
Certified Medicaid.
Owner Nonprofit Corp (Evangelical Lutheran/ Good Samaritan).
Staff RNs; LPNs; Orderlies; Nurses aides; Physical therapists; Occupational therapists; Activities coordinators; Dietitians; Ophthalmologists; Podiatrists; Art therapists.

HULL

Pleasant Acres of Hull*
309 Railroad, Hull, IA, 51239
(712) 439-2758
Admin John P Lienemann. *Medical Dir/Dir of Nursing* Helen DeStigter RN.
Licensure Intermediate care. *Beds* 50.
Certified Medicaid.
Owner Proprietary Corp (Beverly Enterprises).
Admissions Requirements Medical examination; Physician's request.
Facilities Dining room; Physical therapy room; Laundry room; Barber/Beauty shop.
Activities Arts & crafts; Cards; Games; Reading groups; Prayer groups; Movies; Shopping trips; Social/Cultural gatherings; Bingo.

HUMBOLDT

Humboldt Care Center—North*
1111 11th Ave N, Humboldt, IA, 50548
(515) 332-2623
Licensure Intermediate care. *Beds* 100.
Certified Medicaid.
Admissions Requirements Medical examination; Physician's request.
Staff RNs 4 (ft), 4 (pt); Orderlies 2 (ft), 3 (pt); Nurses aides 30 (ft), 20 (pt); Activities coordinators 1 (ft), 1 (pt); Dietitians 1 (pt).
Facilities Dining room; Physical therapy room; Activities room; Crafts room; Laundry room; Barber/Beauty shop.
Activities Arts & crafts; Cards; Games; Reading groups; Prayer groups; Movies; Shopping trips; Social/Cultural gatherings.

Humboldt Care Center—South*
Hwy 169 S, Humboldt, IA, 50548
(515) 332-4104
Licensure Intermediate care. *Beds* 50.
Certified Medicaid.
Admissions Requirements Physician's request.
Facilities Dining room; Physical therapy room; Activities room; Crafts room; Laundry room; Barber/Beauty shop.

Activities Arts & crafts; Cards; Games; Reading groups; Prayer groups; Movies; Shopping trips; Social/Cultural gatherings.

IDA GROVE

Morningside Care Center*
600 Morningside Ave, Ida Grove, IA, 51445
(712) 364-3327
Medical Dir/Dir of Nursing Jagne Harter.
Licensure Intermediate care. *Beds* 52.
Certified Medicaid.
Staff RNs 1 (ft); LPNs 3 (ft), 3 (pt); Physical therapists 1 (pt); Activities coordinators 1 (ft); Dietitians 1 (pt); Dentists 1 (pt); Audiologists 1 (pt).
Facilities Dining room; Physical therapy room; Activities room; Laundry room; Barber/Beauty shop.
Activities Arts & crafts; Cards; Games; Reading groups; Prayer groups; Movies; Shopping trips; Social/Cultural gatherings.

INDEPENDENCE

East-Towne Care Center
1700 3rd St NE, Independence, IA, 50644
(319) 334-7015
Admin Peggy Chensvold. *Medical Dir/Dir of Nursing* Mrs Crawford.
Licensure Intermediate care. *Beds* 55.
Certified Medicaid.
Staff RNs 1 (pt); LPNs 4 (ft), 3 (pt); Nurses aides 7 (ft), 20 (pt); Physical therapists 1 (pt); Recreational therapists 1 (pt); Occupational therapists 1 (pt); Speech therapists 1 (pt); Activities coordinators 1 (ft); Dietitians 1 (pt); Dentists 1 (pt); Ophthalmologists 1 (pt); Podiatrists 1 (pt); Dentist 1 (pt).
Facilities Dining room; Physical therapy room; Barber/Beauty shop.
Activities Arts & crafts; Cards; Games; Reading groups; Prayer groups; Movies; Shopping trips; Social/Cultural gatherings.

Independence Care Center*
1600 3rd St NE, Independence, IA, 50644
(319) 334-6039
Admin Lela J Barnes.
Licensure Intermediate care. *Beds* 101.
Certified Medicaid.

People's Memorial Hospital Nursing Care Center*
Hwy 20 E, Independence, IA, 50644
(319) 334-6071
Admin Betty Meehan.
Licensure Intermediate care. *Beds* 59.
Certified Medicaid.

INDIANOLA

Indianola Good Samaritan Center—East
708 S Jefferson, Indianola, IA, 50125
(515) 961-2596
Admin Lanny Ward. *Medical Dir/Dir of Nursing* Doris Decker.
Licensure Intermediate care. *Beds* ICF 101.
Certified Medicaid.
Owner Nonprofit Corp (Evangelical Lutheran/ Good Samaritan).
Staff RNs 4 (ft), 3 (pt); LPNs 3 (ft), 3 (pt); Nurses aides 24 (ft), 20 (pt); Physical therapists 1 (pt); Occupational therapists 1 (pt); Speech therapists 1 (pt); Activities coordinators 1 (ft); Dietitians 1 (pt).
Facilities Dining room; Physical therapy room; Activities room; Chapel; Crafts room; Laundry room; Barber/Beauty shop.
Activities Arts & crafts; Cards; Games; Reading groups; Prayer groups; Movies; Shopping trips; Social/Cultural gatherings.

Indianola Good Samaritan Center—West
709 S Jefferson, Indianola, IA, 50125
(515) 961-2596

Admin Lanny Ward. *Medical Dir/Dir of Nursing* Doris Decker.
Licensure Intermediate care. *Beds* ICF 41. *Certified* Medicaid.
Owner Nonprofit Corp (Evangelical Lutheran/ Good Samaritan).
Staff RNs 2 (ft), 1 (pt); LPNs 2 (ft), 1 (pt); Nurses aides 15 (ft), 12 (pt); Physical therapists 1 (pt); Occupational therapists 1 (pt); Speech therapists 1 (pt); Activities coordinators 1 (ft); Dietitians 1 (ft).
Facilities Dining room; Physical therapy room; Activities room; Chapel; Crafts room; Laundry room; Barber/Beauty shop.
Activities Arts & crafts; Cards; Games; Reading groups; Prayer groups; Movies; Shopping trips; Social/Cultural gatherings.

Salem Manor*
Box 318, Indianola, IA, 50125
Admin Pamela Rogers. *Medical Dir/Dir of Nursing* Ellen Emery.
Licensure Residential care. *Beds* 33. *Certified* Medicaid; Medicare.
Owner Proprietary Corp.
Admissions Requirements Males only; Medical examination; Physician's request.
Staff LPNs 1 (ft); Nurses aides 4 (ft), 2 (pt); Recreational therapists 1 (ft); Activities coordinators 1 (ft).
Facilities Dining room; Activities room; Crafts room; Laundry room.
Activities Arts & crafts; Cards; Games; Prayer groups; Shopping trips.

Westview Care Center Inc*
1900 W 3rd Pl, Indianola, IA, 50125
(515) 961-3189
Admin Maxine L Runyan.
Licensure Intermediate care. *Beds* 74. *Certified* Medicaid.

IOWA CITY

Beverly Manor Convalescent Center*
605 Greenwood Dr, Iowa City, IA, 52240
(319) 338-7912
Licensure Intermediate care. *Beds* 87. *Certified* Medicaid.
Owner Proprietary Corp (Beverly Enterprises).
Admissions Requirements Medical examination.
Staff RNs 5 (ft), 4 (pt); LPNs 2 (ft), 1 (pt); Orderlies 1 (pt); Nurses aides 16 (ft), 16 (pt); Physical therapists 1 (pt); Activities coordinators 1 (ft), 1 (pt); Dietitians 1 (pt).
Facilities Dining room; Physical therapy room; Activities room; Crafts room; Laundry room; Barber/Beauty shop; Library; Outside patio.
Activities Arts & crafts; Cards; Games; Reading groups; Prayer groups; Movies; Shopping trips; Social/Cultural gatherings; Pet days; Visits by school children; Outings to restaurants.

Iowa City Care Center*
Rochester & Scott Rd, Iowa City, IA, 52240
(319) 351-7460
Licensure Intermediate care. *Beds* 89. *Certified* Medicaid.
Admissions Requirements Medical examination; Physician's request.
Staff RNs 4 (ft), 3 (pt); LPNs 3 (ft), 3 (pt); Orderlies 1 (ft); Nurses aides 20 (ft), 11 (pt); Activities coordinators 1 (ft).
Facilities Dining room; Activities room; Crafts room; Laundry room; Barber/Beauty shop.
Activities Arts & crafts; Cards; Games; Reading groups; Prayer groups; Movies; Shopping trips; Social/Cultural gatherings.

Oaknoll Retirement Residence
701 Oaknoll Dr, Iowa City, IA, 52240
(319) 351-1720
Admin Felicia Hope.

Licensure Skilled care; Intermediate care. *Beds* SNF 32; ICF 16. *Certified* Medicare.

IOWA FALLS

Heritage Care Center*
2320 Washington Ave, Iowa Falls, IA, 50126
(515) 648-4250
Licensure Intermediate care. *Beds* 50. *Certified* Medicaid.
Admissions Requirements Minimum age 18; Medical examination; Physician's request.
Staff RNs 1 (ft); LPNs 3 (ft); Nurses aides 11 (ft), 7 (pt); Physical therapists 1 (pt); Recreational therapists 1 (ft); Occupational therapists 1 (pt); Speech therapists 1 (pt); Activities coordinators 1 (ft); Dietitians 1 (pt).
Facilities Dining room; Physical therapy room; Activities room; Laundry room; Barber/Beauty shop; Library.
Activities Arts & crafts; Cards; Games; Reading groups; Prayer groups; Movies; Shopping trips; Social/Cultural gatherings.

Scenic Manor*
Manor Dr & Fremont, Iowa Falls, IA, 50126
(515) 648-4671
Admin Glenn O Doupe.
Licensure Intermediate care. *Beds* 61. *Certified* Medicaid.

JEFFERSON

Greene County Medical Center
1000 W Lincolnway, Jefferson, IA, 50129
(515) 386-2114
Admin Roger W Lenz. *Medical Dir/Dir of Nursing* Lucy Wolterman RN.
Licensure Intermediate care. *Beds* ICF 74. *Certified* Medicaid; Medicare.
Owner Publicly owned.
Admissions Requirements Physician's request.
Staff RNs 1 (ft), 4 (pt); LPNs 2 (ft), 6 (pt); Orderlies 2 (pt); Nurses aides 13 (ft), 14 (pt); Activities coordinators 1 (ft); Dietitians 1 (pt).
Facilities Dining room; Activities room; Chapel; Barber/Beauty shop.
Activities Arts & crafts; Cards; Games; Reading groups; Prayer groups; Movies; Shopping trips; Outings.

Jefferson Manor*
100 E Sunset, Jefferson, IA, 50129
(515) 386-4107
Admin Lyle Hight.
Licensure Intermediate care. *Beds* 93. *Certified* Medicaid.
Owner Proprietary Corp (Life Care Centers of America).

JOHNSTON CITY

Convalescent Home for Children
5900 Pioneer Pkwy, Johnston City, IA, 50131
(515) 270-2205
Medical Dir/Dir of Nursing Sayeed Hussain MD.
Licensure Skilled care; Intermediate care for mentally retarded. *Beds* SNF 19; ICF/MR 44. *Certified* Medicaid.
Admissions Requirements Minimum age Birth.
Staff RNs 9 (ft), 3 (pt); LPNs 8 (ft), 5 (pt); Orderlies 1 (pt); Nurses aides 15 (ft), 22 (pt); Physical therapists 1 (ft); Recreational therapists 1 (ft); Occupational therapists 1 (ft); Speech therapists 1 (pt); Activities coordinators 1 (ft); Dietitians 1 (pt); Dentists 2 (pt).
Facilities Dining room; Physical therapy room; Activities room; Crafts room; Laundry room; Barber/Beauty shop; Library; Game room.

Activities Arts & crafts; Cards; Games; Reading groups; Prayer groups; Movies; Shopping trips; Social/Cultural gatherings; Specific skill training in self-care, prevocational, computers.

Bishop Drumm Care Center
5837 Winwood Dr, Johnston City, IA, 50131
(515) 270-1100
Admin Sr Madeleva Comiskey.
Licensure Intermediate care; Residential care. *Beds* ICF 58; Residential 62. *Certified* Medicaid.
Affiliation Roman Catholic

KALONA

Pleasant View Home
811 3rd St, Kalona, IA, 52247
(319) 656-2421
Admin Ilah L Hebner. *Medical Dir/Dir of Nursing* Phyllis Litwiller DON.
Licensure Intermediate care; Residential; Independent living; Low stimulus unit. *Beds* ICF 60; Resitential 71; Low stimulus unit 11; Independent living 30. *Certified* Medicaid.
Owner Nonprofit Corp.
Admissions Requirements Medical examination.
Staff RNs; LPNs; Orderlies; Nurses aides; Recreational therapists; Activities coordinators; Dietitians.
Affiliation Mennonite
Facilities Dining room; Physical therapy room; Activities room; Barber/Beauty shop; Spacious grounds; Van (wheelchair).
Activities Arts & crafts; Games; Prayer groups; Shopping trips; Bible study; Quilting; Dinner trips.

KANAWHA

Kanawha Community Home
130 W 6th St, Kanawha, IA, 50447
(515) 762-3302
Admin JoAnn Hunt RN. *Medical Dir/Dir of Nursing* Ethelene Hall RN DON.
Licensure Intermediate care. *Beds* ICF 52. *Certified* Medicaid.
Owner Proprietary Corp.
Admissions Requirements Medical examination.
Staff RNs 2 (ft), 2 (pt); LPNs 1 (ft), 1 (pt); Nurses aides 8 (ft), 13 (pt); Activities coordinators 1 (ft); Dietitians 1 (pt); Social worker 1 (pt); Pharmacist 1 (pt).
Facilities Dining room; Physical therapy room; Activities room; Laundry room; Barber/Beauty shop.
Activities Arts & crafts; Games; Reading groups; Prayer groups; Movies; Baking.

KEOKUK

Keokuk Convalescent Center*
500 Mesenger Rd, Keokuk, IA, 52632
(319) 524-5321
Admin Ralph Roberts.
Licensure Skilled care; Intermediate care. *Beds* SNF 21; ICF 105. *Certified* Medicaid; Medicare.

River Hills in Keokuk
3140 Plank Rd, Keokuk, IA, 52632
(319) 524-5772
Admin Lela June Barnes. *Medical Dir/Dir of Nursing* Mary Jo Woods RN.
Licensure Intermediate care. *Beds* 63. *Certified* Medicaid.
Owner Proprietary Corp.
Admissions Requirements Minimum age 18; Medical examination; Physician's request.
Staff RNs 2 (ft); LPNs 2 (ft), 1 (pt); Nurses aides 12 (ft), 14 (pt); Physical therapists 1 (pt); Activities coordinators 1 (ft), 1 (pt); Dietitians 1 (pt).

Facilities Dining room; Chapel; Laundry room; Barber/Beauty shop.
Activities Arts & crafts; Cards; Games; Reading groups; Prayer groups; Movies; Social/Cultural gatherings.

KEOSAUQUA

Van Buren Good Samaritan Center
Dodge & Country Rd, Keosauqua, IA, 52565
(319) 293-3761
Admin Tim A Schneider. *Medical Dir/Dir of Nursing* Dr Kiyoshi Furumoto.
Licensure Intermediate care. *Beds* ICF 75. *Certified* Medicaid.
Owner Nonprofit Corp (Evangelical Lutheran/ Good Samaritan).
Admissions Requirements Minimum age 16; Medical examination; Physician's request.
Staff RNs 3 (ft), 1 (pt); LPNs 4 (ft); Orderlies 2 (ft); Nurses aides 40 (ft), 20 (pt); Activities coordinators 1 (ft), 1 (pt).
Facilities Dining room; Physical therapy room; Activities room; Chapel; Crafts room; Laundry room; Barber/Beauty shop; Library.
Activities Arts & crafts; Cards; Games; Reading groups; Prayer groups; Movies.

KEOTA

Maplewood Manor Inc
County Line Rd, Keota, IA, 52248
(515) 636-3400
Admin Sandra Lehr. *Medical Dir/Dir of Nursing* Jennifer Horras DON.
Licensure Intermediate care. *Beds* ICF 54. *Certified* Medicaid.
Owner Proprietary Corp.
Admissions Requirements Physician's request.
Staff RNs 1 (ft), 7 (pt); LPNs 1 (pt); Nurses aides 4 (ft), 16 (pt); Physical therapists 1 (pt); Occupational therapists 1 (pt); Speech therapists 1 (pt); Activities coordinators 1 (ft); Dietitians 1 (ft), 1 (pt); Podiatrists 1 (pt).
Facilities Dining room; Physical therapy room; Activities room; Crafts room; Laundry room; Barber/Beauty shop; Library.
Activities Arts & crafts; Cards; Games; Reading groups; Prayer groups; Movies; Shopping trips; Social/Cultural gatherings.

KEYSTONE

Keystone Nursing Care Center*
5th St E, Keystone, IA, 52249
(319) 442-3234
Admin Susan Rieck.
Licensure Intermediate care. *Beds* 45.

KINGSLEY

Colonial Manor
305 W 3rd, Kingsley, IA, 51028
(712) 378-2400
Admin Donna L Enderlin. *Medical Dir/Dir of Nursing* Kate Henrich.
Licensure Intermediate care. *Beds* ICF 43. *Certified* Medicaid.
Owner Proprietary Corp (Beverly Enterprises).
Admissions Requirements Minimum age 18; Medical examination; Physician's request.
Staff RNs; LPNs; Nurses aides; Activities coordinators.
Facilities Dining room; Physical therapy room; Activities room; Chapel; Crafts room; Laundry room; Barber/Beauty shop; Library.
Activities Arts & crafts; Cards; Games; Reading groups; Prayer groups; Movies; Shopping trips; Social/Cultural gatherings; Adopt-a-grandparent.

KNOXVILLE

Griffin Nursing Center*
606 N 7th St, Knoxville, IA, 50138
(515) 842-2187
Admin Hazel M Griffin.
Licensure Intermediate care. *Beds* 60. *Certified* Medicaid.

Knoxville Rest Home*
205 N Iowa St, Knoxville, IA, 50138
(515) 842-4618
Licensure Intermediate care. *Beds* 34. *Certified* Medicaid.
Staff RNs 1 (ft), 1 (pt); LPNs 2 (ft); Nurses aides 26 (pt); Physical therapists 1 (pt); Recreational therapists 1 (ft); Occupational therapists 1 (pt); Speech therapists 1 (pt); Activities coordinators 1 (ft); Dietitians 1 (pt); Podiatrists 1 (pt); Audiologists 1 (pt).
Facilities Dining room; Laundry room.
Activities Arts & crafts; Cards; Games; Reading groups; Prayer groups; Movies; Shopping trips; Social/Cultural gatherings.

Marion County Care Facility
Rte 2, Knoxville, IA, 50138
Admin K V Orr.
Licensure Residential care. *Beds* 50.
Owner Nonprofit Corp.
Admissions Requirements Minimum age 18; Medical examination; Physician's request.
Staff LPNs 1 (ft); Nurses aides 5 (ft), 1 (pt); Activities coordinators 1 (ft); Dietitians 1 (ft); Medical aides 5 (ft), 1 (pt).
Facilities Dining room; Activities room; Chapel; Crafts room; Barber/Beauty shop.
Activities Arts & crafts; Cards; Games; Reading groups; Prayer groups; Movies; Shopping trips; Social/Cultural gatherings.

West Ridge Manor*
1201 W Jackson St, Knoxville, IA, 50138
(515) 842-3153
Admin Denna M Ford.
Licensure Intermediate care. *Beds* 78. *Certified* Medicaid.

LAKE CITY

Shady Oaks
Hwy 175 W, Lake City, IA, 51449
(712) 464-3106
Admin Lois Nadine Lindsay. *Medical Dir/Dir of Nursing* Paul Ferguson MD; Michelle Steinkamp RN DON.
Licensure Skilled care; Intermediate care. *Beds* SNF 20; ICF 119. *Certified* Medicaid; Medicare.
Owner Privately owned.
Admissions Requirements Medical examination; Physician's request.
Staff Physicians 7 (pt); RNs 4 (ft), 13 (pt); LPNs 3 (ft), 5 (pt); Orderlies 1 (ft); Nurses aides 14 (ft), 28 (pt); Physical therapists 1 (pt); Occupational therapists 1 (pt); Speech therapists 1 (pt); Activities coordinators 1 (ft), 1 (pt); Dietitians 1 (pt); Ophthalmologists 1 (pt); Pharmacist 1 (pt); Dentist 1 (pt); Social Service 1 (pt).
Facilities Dining room; Physical therapy room; Activities room; Crafts room; Laundry room; Barber/Beauty shop; Game room; Sunroom; Conference room; Courtyard & gazebo; fitness trail.
Activities Arts & crafts; Cards; Games; Reading groups; Prayer groups; Movies; Shopping trips; Exercise.

LAKE MILLS

Lake Mills Nursing Home Inc*
406 S 10th Ave E, Lake Mills, IA, 50450
(515) 592-4900
Admin Robert Helgeson.
Licensure Intermediate care. *Beds* 101. *Certified* Medicaid.

LAKE PARK

Lake Park Care Center*
1304 Market St, Lake Park, IA, 51347
(712) 832-3691
Admin Robert J Hinz.
Licensure Intermediate care. *Beds* 51. *Certified* Medicaid.

LAMONI

Lamoni Manor*
215 S Oak St, Lamoni, IA, 50140
(515) 784-3388
Medical Dir/Dir of Nursing Velma Gleason RN.
Licensure Intermediate care. *Beds* 51. *Certified* Medicaid.
Admissions Requirements Minimum age 16; Medical examination; Physician's request.
Staff RNs 2 (ft), 1 (pt); LPNs 2 (ft); Orderlies 2 (pt); Nurses aides 13 (ft), 9 (pt); Physical therapists 1 (pt); Speech therapists 1 (pt); Activities coordinators 1 (ft); Dietitians 1 (pt); Dentists 1 (pt); Audiologists 1 (pt).
Facilities Dining room; Activities room; Laundry room; Barber/Beauty shop; Library.
Activities Arts & crafts; Cards; Games; Prayer groups; Movies; Shopping trips.

LANSING

Thornton Manor
PO Box 700, 1329 Main Ave, Lansing, IA, 52151
(319) 538-4236
Admin Stephen H Haas. *Medical Dir/Dir of Nursing* G Jane Hawes RN DON.
Licensure Intermediate care. *Beds* ICF 60. *Certified* Medicaid.
Owner Nonprofit organization/foundation.
Admissions Requirements Medical examination.
Staff RNs 4 (ft); LPNs 4 (ft), 1 (pt); Nurses aides 20 (ft), 7 (pt); Activities coordinators 1 (ft), 1 (pt); 10 (ft), 8 (pt) Social worker 1 (ft).
Facilities Dining room; Physical therapy room; Activities room; Chapel; Crafts room; Laundry room; Barber/Beauty shop.
Activities Arts & crafts; Cards; Games; Reading groups; Prayer groups; Movies; Shopping trips; Social/Cultural gatherings.

LAPORTE CITY

Colonial Manor*
Hwy 218 N, LaPorte City, IA, 50651
(319) 342-2125
Licensure Intermediate care. *Beds* 46. *Certified* Medicaid.
Owner Proprietary Corp (Beverly Enterprises).
Admissions Requirements Minimum age 18; Medical examination; Physician's request.
Staff RNs 1 (ft); LPNs 3 (ft); Nurses aides 5 (ft), 5 (pt); Physical therapists 1 (pt); Occupational therapists 1 (pt); Speech therapists 1 (pt); Activities coordinators 1 (ft); Dietitians 1 (pt); Dentists 1 (pt); Podiatrists 1 (pt); Audiologists 1 (pt).
Facilities Dining room; Laundry room; Barber/Beauty shop.
Activities Arts & crafts; Cards; Games; Reading groups; Prayer groups; Movies; Shopping trips; Social/Cultural gatherings; Weekly music therapy.

LAURENS

Hovenden Memorial Good Samaritan Home*
304 E Veterans Rd, Laurens, IA, 50554
(712) 845-4915
Admin Vergene Bailey.
Licensure Intermediate care; Residential care. *Beds* ICF 42; Residential 9. *Certified* Medicaid.

Owner Nonprofit Corp (Evangelical Lutheran/ Good Samaritan).

LEMARS

Brentwood Good Samaritan Center*
Hwy 3 E, Lemars, IA, 51031
(712) 546-4101
Admin Larry D Sieler.
Licensure Intermediate care. *Beds* 65.
   Certified Medicaid.
Owner Nonprofit Corp (Evangelical Lutheran/ Good Samaritan).

Plymouth Manor Care Center*
954 7th Ave SE, Lemars, IA, 51031
(712) 546-7831
Admin Patricia A McDougall.
Licensure Intermediate care. *Beds* 83.
   Certified Medicaid.

LENOX

Lenox Care Center
111 E Van Buren, Lenox, IA, 50851
(515) 333-2226
Admin Virginia Bennett. *Medical Dir/Dir of Nursing* Nancy Bose DON.
Licensure Intermediate care. *Beds* ICF 53.
   Certified Medicaid.
Owner Proprietary Corp (Waverly Group).
Staff Physicians 2 (pt); RNs 1 (ft), 1 (pt); LPNs 5 (ft); Nurses aides 14 (ft), 3 (pt); Physical therapists 1 (pt); Occupational therapists 1 (ft), 1 (pt); Activities coordinators 1 (ft), 1 (pt); Dietitians 4 (ft), 3 (pt); Podiatrists 1 (pt).
Facilities Dining room; Physical therapy room; Activities room; Laundry room; Barber/Beauty shop.
Activities Arts & crafts; Cards; Games; Reading groups; Prayer groups; Movies.

LEON

Leon Care Center
NE 14th at Poplar, Leon, IA, 50144
(515) 446-4833
Admin Gary A Martin. *Medical Dir/Dir of Nursing* Allyson Reynolds LPN DON.
Licensure Intermediate care. *Beds* ICF 61.
   Certified Medicaid.
Owner Proprietary Corp.
Admissions Requirements Medical examination.
Staff RNs 1 (pt); LPNs 3 (ft), 2 (pt); Orderlies 1 (ft); Nurses aides 8 (ft), 11 (pt); Physical therapists 1 (pt); Activities coordinators 2 (pt); Dietitians 1 (pt).
Facilities Dining room; Activities room; Crafts room; Laundry room; Barber/Beauty shop.
Activities Arts & crafts; Cards; Games; Reading groups; Prayer groups; Movies.

Westview Acres*
Jct 2 & 69 W, Leon, IA, 50144
(515) 446-4165
Licensure Intermediate care. *Beds* 91.
   Certified Medicaid.
Admissions Requirements Minimum age 16.
Staff RNs 1 (pt); LPNs 7 (ft); Nurses aides 27 (ft), 5 (pt); Speech therapists 1 (pt); Activities coordinators 2 (ft); Dietitians 1 (pt); Dentists 1 (pt).
Facilities Dining room; Physical therapy room; Activities room; Crafts room; Laundry room; Barber/Beauty shop.
Activities Arts & crafts; Cards; Games; Reading groups; Prayer groups; Movies; Shopping trips; Social/Cultural gatherings.

LOGAN

Westmont Care Center*
314 S Elm, Logan, IA, 51546
(712) 644-2922
Licensure Intermediate care; Residential care. *Beds* ICF 73; Residential 26. *Certified* Medicaid.

LONE TREE

Lone Tree Health Care Center*
Pioneer Rd, Lone Tree, IA, 52755
(319) 629-4255
Admin Dale Van Dewater.
Licensure Intermediate care. *Beds* 46.
   Certified Medicaid.

MADRID

Madrid Home for the Aging
613 W North St, Madrid, IA, 50156
(515) 795-3007
Admin William R Thayer. *Medical Dir/Dir of Nursing* Carol Mallurr RN; Betsy Voga RN.
Licensure Skilled care; Intermediate care; Residential care. *Beds* SNF 40; ICF 99; Residential 34. *Certified* Medicaid; Medicare.
Owner Nonprofit Corp.
Admissions Requirements Minimum age 16; Medical examination.
Staff RNs; LPNs; Orderlies; Nurses aides; Physical therapists; Reality therapists; Recreational therapists; Occupational therapists; Speech therapists; Activities coordinators; Dietitians.
Facilities Dining room; Physical therapy room; Activities room; Chapel; Crafts room; Laundry room; Barber/Beauty shop; Library.
Activities Arts & crafts; Cards; Games; Reading groups; Prayer groups; Movies; Shopping trips; Social/Cultural gatherings.

MALVERN

Nishna Care Center & Nishna Cottage
903 2nd Ave, Malvern, IA, 51551
(712) 624-8300 or 624-8000
Admin Cliff Greedy, Admin. *Medical Dir/Dir of Nursing* Dr Fryek; Rita Maloney DON.
Licensure Intermediate care; RCF. *Beds* ICF 51; RCF 35. *Certified* Medicaid; Medicare.
Owner Privately owned.
Staff Physicians 5 (ft); RNs 1 (ft); LPNs 3 (ft); Orderlies 7 (ft); Nurses aides 12 (ft), 14 (pt); Physical therapists 1 (ft); Reality therapists 1 (ft).
Facilities Dining room; Physical therapy room; Activities room; Chapel; Crafts room; Laundry room; Barber/Beauty shop; Library.
Activities Cards; Games; Reading groups; Prayer groups; Movies; Shopping trips; Social/Cultural gatherings.

MANCHESTER

Delaware County Memorial Hospital
709 W Main, Manchester, IA, 52057
(319) 927-3232
Admin Paul Albright. *Medical Dir/Dir of Nursing* Larry Severidt MD; Betty Reed RN.
Licensure Intermediate care. *Beds* ICF 37.
   Certified Medicaid; Medicare.
Owner Publicly owned.
Admissions Requirements Minimum age 16; Medical examination.
Staff Physicians 11 (ft), 1 (pt); RNs 1 (ft), 1 (pt); LPNs 6 (ft); Nurses aides 6 (ft), 11 (pt); Physical therapists 1 (pt); Activities coordinators 1 (ft); Dietitians 1 (pt).
Facilities Dining room; Activities room; Chapel; Laundry room; Barber/Beauty shop; Library.
Activities Arts & crafts; Cards; Games; Reading groups; Prayer groups; Movies.

Good Neighbor Home
105 McCarren Dr, Manchester, IA, 52057
(319) 927-3907
Admin Joe Klueppel. *Medical Dir/Dir of Nursing* Donaline Mitts RN.
Licensure Intermediate care. *Beds* 106.
   Certified Medicaid.
Owner Nonprofit Corp.
Admissions Requirements Medical examination; Physician's request.
Staff RNs 1 (ft), 6 (pt); LPNs 2 (ft), 3 (pt); Nurses aides 40 (ft), 15 (pt); Activities coordinators 4 (pt); Dietitians 1 (pt).
Affiliation Lutheran
Facilities Dining room; Physical therapy room; Activities room; Chapel; Crafts room; Laundry room; Barber/Beauty shop.

MANILLA

Manilla Manor*
158 N 5th St, Manilla, IA, 51454
(712) 654-6812
Admin Dana Jorgensen.
Licensure Intermediate care. *Beds* 63.
   Certified Medicaid.

MANLY

Manly Care Center*
Hwy 9 E, Manly, IA, 50456
(515) 454-2223
Admin Delores Denney. *Medical Dir/Dir of Nursing* Dr Richard Munns.
Licensure Intermediate care. *Beds* 69.
   Certified Medicaid.
Admissions Requirements Minimum age 21; Medical examination; Physician's request.
Staff RNs 2 (ft), 3 (pt); LPNs 2 (ft), 2 (pt); Orderlies 1 (ft), 1 (pt); Nurses aides 16 (ft), 10 (pt); Activities coordinators 1 (ft); Dietitians 1 (pt).
Facilities Dining room; Physical therapy room; Activities room; Crafts room; Laundry room; Barber/Beauty shop; Library.
Activities Arts & crafts; Cards; Games; Movies; Social/Cultural gatherings.

MANNING

The Manning Plaza
410-412 Main St, Manning, IA, 51455
(712) 653-2072
Admin Greg Hanson. *Medical Dir/Dir of Nursing* Alohn Enenbach.
Licensure Intermediate care. *Beds* 58.
   Certified Medicaid.
Owner Nonprofit Corp.
Admissions Requirements Minimum age 18; Medical examination; Physician's request.
Staff Physicians 4 (ft); RNs 1 (ft), 1 (pt); LPNs 3 (ft), 3 (pt); Nurses aides 12 (ft), 14 (pt); Physical therapists 1 (ft); Recreational therapists 1 (ft); Speech therapists 1 (pt); Activities coordinators 1 (ft), 2 (pt); Dietitians 1 (pt).
Facilities Dining room; Physical therapy room; Activities room; Crafts room; Laundry room; Library.
Activities Arts & crafts; Cards; Games; Reading groups; Prayer groups; Movies; Shopping trips; Social/Cultural gatherings.

MANSON

Manson Good Samaritan Center
1402 Main St, Manson, IA, 50563
(712) 469-3908
Admin Gail Blocker. *Medical Dir/Dir of Nursing* Ella Fistler DON.
Licensure Intermediate care. *Beds* ICF 50.
   Certified Medicaid.
Owner Nonprofit Corp (Evangelical Lutheran/ Good Samaritan).
Admissions Requirements Medical examination; Physician's request.

Staff RNs; LPNs; Nurses aides; Physical
therapists; Activities coordinators; Dietitians.
Facilities Dining room; Physical therapy
room; Activities room; Chapel; Crafts room;
Laundry room; Barber/Beauty shop.
Activities Arts & crafts; Cards; Games;
Reading groups; Prayer groups; Movies;
Social/Cultural gatherings.

MAPLETON

Maple Heights Inc*
Sunrise Ave, Mapleton, IA, 51034
(712) 882-1680
Admin Richard Feauto.
Licensure Intermediate care. *Beds* 64.
Certified Medicaid.

MAQUOKETA

Crestridge Inc
1015 Wesley Dr, Maquoketa, IA, 52060
(319) 652-4967
Admin Holly Myatt. *Medical Dir/Dir of
Nursing* Judy Herkleman.
Licensure Intermediate care. *Beds* ICF 101.
Certified Medicaid.
Owner Proprietary Corp.
Admissions Requirements Medical
examination; Physician's request.
Staff RNs 3 (ft), 2 (pt); LPNs 6 (pt); Nurses
aides 45 (pt); Activities coordinators 2 (ft).
Facilities Dining room; Physical therapy
room; Activities room; Chapel; Crafts room;
Laundry room; Barber/Beauty shop; Library;
Wheelchair heighth soda & liquor bar.
Activities Arts & crafts; Cards; Games;
Reading groups; Prayer groups; Movies;
Shopping trips; Social/Cultural gatherings;
Lots of entertainment type groups.

Jackson County Public Hospital
700 W Grove St, Maquoketa, IA, 52060
(319) 652-2474
Admin Karl C Schroeder. *Medical Dir/Dir of
Nursing* Marcella Bormahl RN.
Licensure Skilled care. *Beds* SNF 16.
Owner Publicly owned.
Staff RNs 2 (ft), 1 (pt); LPNs 3 (ft), 1 (pt);
Nurses aides 4 (ft), 7 (pt); Physical therapists
1 (ft), 1 (pt); Recreational therapists 1 (pt);
Speech therapists 1 (pt); Dietitians 1 (ft).

Manning's Residential Care Center
601 W Summit St, Maquoketa, IA, 52060
(319) 652-3646
Admin Cleo Manning.
Licensure Residential care. *Beds* 15. *Certified*
Medicaid.
Owner Privately owned.
Admissions Requirements Physician's request.
Staff Nurses aides 5 (ft); Activities
coordinators 1 (ft); Dietitians 1 (ft).
Facilities Dining room; Activities room;
Laundry room.
Activities Arts & crafts; Cards; Games; Prayer
groups; Shopping trips.

Maquoketa Care Center
McKinsey Dr, Maquoketa, IA, 52060
(319) 652-5195
Admin Betty L Reed. *Medical Dir/Dir of
Nursing* Edra Clasen.
Licensure Intermediate care. *Beds* ICF 66.
Certified Medicaid.
Owner Proprietary Corp.
Admissions Requirements Minimum age 18;
Medical examination; Physician's request.
Staff RNs 1 (ft), 2 (pt); LPNs 2 (ft), 4 (pt);
Nurses aides 10 (ft), 17 (pt); Activities
coordinators 2 (ft); Dietitians 1 (pt).
Facilities Dining room; Activities room;
Crafts room; Laundry room; Barber/Beauty
shop.
Activities Arts & crafts; Cards; Games;
Reading groups; Prayer groups; Movies;
Shopping trips; Social/Cultural gatherings.

MARENGO

Rose Haven Nursing Home Inc
1500 N Franklin Ave, Marengo, IA, 52301
(319) 642-3221 or 642-5533
Admin David Yearian. *Medical Dir/Dir of
Nursing* Alice Prince.
Licensure Intermediate care. *Beds* ICF 58.
Certified Medicaid.
Owner Privately owned.
Admissions Requirements Minimum age 16;
Medical examination.
Staff RNs 2 (ft), 2 (pt); LPNs 2 (ft); Nurses
aides 17 (ft), 8 (pt); Physical therapists 1
(pt); Activities coordinators 1 (ft); Dietitians
1 (pt).
Facilities Dining room; Activities room;
Chapel; Crafts room; Laundry room; Barber/
Beauty shop.
Activities Arts & crafts; Cards; Games;
Reading groups; Prayer groups; Movies;
Shopping trips; Social/Cultural gatherings.

MARION

Abbe Center for Community Care
1860 County Home Rd, Marion, IA, 52302
(319) 398-3534
Admin Louis Hulseberg. *Medical Dir/Dir of
Nursing* Richard Hodge, James Bell, Steve
Runde; Merry Elliott.
Licensure Intermediate care; Residential care.
Beds ICF 32; Residential 263. *Certified*
Medicaid.
Owner Nonprofit Corp.
Admissions Requirements Minimum age 16;
Medical examination; Physician's request.
Staff Physicians 3 (pt); RNs 6 (ft), 3 (pt);
LPNs 4 (ft), 4 (pt); Nurses aides 30 (ft), 20
(pt); Recreational therapists 4 (ft); Activities
coordinators 3 (ft); Dietitians 1 (pt);
Ophthalmologists 1 (pt); Psychiatrist 1 (pt).
Facilities Dining room; Activities room;
Crafts room; Laundry room; Barber/Beauty
shop; Day room.
Activities Arts & crafts; Cards; Games;
Reading groups; Movies; Shopping trips;
Social/Cultural gatherings; Group therapy.

Crestview Acres
1485 Grand Ave, Marion, IA, 52302
(319) 377-4823
Admin Vivian M DeGreef. *Medical Dir/Dir of
Nursing* Alice M Shea RN DON.
Licensure Intermediate care. *Beds* ICF 129.
Certified Medicaid.
Owner Proprietary Corp (Quality Health Care
Specialists Inc).
Admissions Requirements Medical
examination.
Staff RNs 3 (ft); LPNs 8 (ft), 1 (pt); Orderlies
9 (ft); Nurses aides 41 (ft); Physical
therapists 1 (pt); Occupational therapists 1
(pt); Speech therapists 1 (pt); Activities
coordinators 2 (ft); Dietitians 1 (pt);
Podiatrists 1 (pt).
Facilities Dining room; Physical therapy
room; Activities room; Chapel; Crafts room;
Laundry room; Barber/Beauty shop.
Activities Arts & crafts; Cards; Games;
Reading groups; Prayer groups; Movies;
Social/Cultural gatherings.

Linn Manor*
1140 Elim Dr, Marion, IA, 52302
(319) 377-4611
Admin Grant L Hagen.
Licensure Intermediate care. *Beds* 44.
Certified Medicaid.

Maple Lawn Home
7607 Council St, Marion, IA, 52302
(319) 393-2521
Admin Nadine Trachta.
Licensure Residential care. *Beds* Residential
18. *Certified* Medicaid.
Owner Proprietary Corp.

Admissions Requirements Minimum age 18;
Medical examination; Physician's request.
Staff Nurses aides 6 (ft).
Facilities Dining room; Activities room;
Laundry room; Barber/Beauty shop;
Enclosed patio.
Activities Arts & crafts; Cards; Games;
Reading groups; Prayer groups; Potlucks.

Willow Gardens Care Center
455 31st St, Marion, IA, 52302
(319) 377-7363
Admin Charles Thomas. *Medical Dir/Dir of
Nursing* Terri Hearn.
Licensure Intermediate care. *Beds* ICF 91.
Certified Medicaid.
Owner Proprietary Corp (Pinnacle Care Corp).
Admissions Requirements Medical
examination; Physician's request.
Staff RNs 2 (ft), 2 (pt); LPNs 9 (ft), 8 (pt);
Nurses aides 30 (ft), 10 (pt); Activities
coordinators 1 (ft), 1 (pt); Dietitians 1 (pt).
Facilities Dining room; Physical therapy
room; Activities room; Chapel; Crafts room;
Laundry room; Barber/Beauty shop; Library.
Activities Arts & crafts; Cards; Games;
Reading groups; Prayer groups; Movies;
Social/Cultural gatherings.

Winslow House*
3456 Indian Creek Rd, Marion, IA, 52302
(319) 377-8296
Admin Barry Morrissey.
Licensure Intermediate care. *Beds* 50.
Certified Medicaid.

MARSHALLTOWN

Grandview Heights*
910 E Olive St, Marshalltown, IA, 50158
(515) 752-4581
Admin Charles H Koonce.
Licensure Intermediate care. *Beds* 129.
Certified Medicaid.

Iowa Veterans Home
13th & Summit St, Marshalltown, IA, 50158
(515) 752-1501
Admin Jack J Dack, Commandant.
Licensure Skilled care; Intermediate care;
Domiciliary/Residential care. *Beds* SNF 327;
ICF 391; Domiciliary/Residential 113.
Certified Medicaid; Medicare.
Owner Publicly owned.
Admissions Requirements Medical
examination; Veterans only.
Staff Physicians 5 (ft), 12 (pt); RNs 64 (ft), 9
(pt); LPNs 75 (ft), 4 (pt); Nurses aides 209
(ft), 11 (pt); Physical therapists 2 (ft);
Recreational therapists 12 (ft); Occupational
therapists 1 (pt); Speech therapists 1 (ft), 1
(pt); Activities coordinators 1 (ft); Dietitians
5 (ft); Podiatrists 1 (pt); Chaplain 1 (ft), 1
(pt); Laboratory technician 4 (ft), 2 (pt); X-
ray technician 1 (ft); Occupational therapy
assistant 1 (ft); Physical therapy aides 5 (ft);
Pharmacists 4 (ft), 1 (pt); Pharmacists
assistants 2 (ft), 1 (pt); Drug abuse
counselors 2 (ft); Physicians assistants 2 (ft);
Volunteer director 1 (ft); Social workers 8
(ft), 4 (pt); Respiratory technicians 2 (ft).
Facilities Dining room; Physical therapy
room; Activities room; Chapel; Crafts room;
Laundry room; Barber/Beauty shop; Library;
Speech/audiology; Physical therapy;
Occupatioal therapy; Respiratory therapy;
Dental; Lab; X-ray; Pharmacy; Optometry;
Podiatry.
Activities Arts & crafts; Cards; Games;
Reading groups; Prayer groups; Movies;
Shopping trips; Social/Cultural gatherings;
Off-ground activities.

Marshall County Care Facility
2369 Jessup Ave, Marshalltown, IA, 50158
(515) 752-3694
Admin Marian Malloy. *Medical Dir/Dir of
Nursing* Rose Kelley RN DON.

Licensure Intermediate care; Residential care. *Beds* ICF 80; Residential 64. *Certified* Medicaid.
Owner Nonprofit organization/foundation.
Admissions Requirements Minimum age 16; Medical examination; Physician's request.
Staff RNs 4 (ft); LPNs 5 (ft), 3 (pt); Orderlies 4 (ft); Nurses aides 37 (ft), 12 (pt); Physical therapists 1 (pt); Recreational therapists 3 (pt); Activities coordinators 1 (ft); Dietitians 1 (pt); Pharmacist 1 (pt); Social worker 1 (pt).
Facilities Dining room; Physical therapy room; Activities room; Chapel; Crafts room; Laundry room; Barber/Beauty shop; Library.
Activities Arts & crafts; Cards; Games; Reading groups; Prayer groups; Movies; Shopping trips; Social/Cultural gatherings; Bowling; Flea markets; Fishing; Cooking; Kitchen band; School.

Marshalltown Manor
2206 S Center, Marshalltown, IA, 50158
(515) 752-4553
Admin Niel Froning. *Medical Dir/Dir of Nursing* Brenda Thompson.
Licensure Intermediate care. *Beds* 82. *Certified* Medicaid.
Owner Proprietary Corp (Beverly Enterprises).
Admissions Requirements Minimum age 18; Medical examination.
Staff RNs 5 (ft), 2 (pt); LPNs 2 (ft), 1 (pt); Orderlies 2 (ft); Nurses aides 30 (ft), 5 (pt); Activities coordinators 1 (ft), 1 (pt).
Facilities Dining room; Activities room; Laundry room; Barber/Beauty shop.
Activities Arts & crafts; Cards; Games; Reading groups; Prayer groups; Movies; Shopping trips; Social/Cultural gatherings; Bingo.

Marshalltown Medical Surgical Center Skilled Nursing Facility
3 S 4th Ave, Marshalltown, IA, 50158
754-5368
Admin Omar Varan. *Medical Dir/Dir of Nursing* Dr M Mirovsky; Roberta Brandenberg RN DON.
Licensure Skilled care. *Beds* SNF. *Certified* Medicaid; Medicare.
Owner Nonprofit Corp.
Admissions Requirements Medical examination; Physician's request.
Staff Physicians 40 (ft); RNs 4 (ft), 3 (pt); LPNs 3 (ft), 3 (pt); Orderlies 1 (pt); Nurses aides 4 (ft), 6 (pt); Activities coordinators 1 (pt); Ophthalmologists 6 (ft); Podiatrists 2 (ft); Ward clerk 1 (ft).
Facilities Dining room; Physical therapy room; Activities room; Chapel; Crafts room; Laundry room; Barber/Beauty shop; Library.
Activities Arts & crafts; Cards; Games; Reading groups; Prayer groups; Movies; Social/Cultural gatherings.

Villa del Sol
2401 S 2nd St, Marshalltown, IA, 50158
(515) 752-1553
Admin Janice Plahn. *Medical Dir/Dir of Nursing* Cindy Geater.
Licensure Intermediate care; Residential care. *Beds* ICF 88; Residential 29. *Certified* Medicaid.
Owner Privately owned.
Admissions Requirements Medical examination.
Staff RNs; LPNs; Orderlies; Nurses aides; Activities coordinators.
Facilities Dining room; Activities room; Barber/Beauty shop.
Activities Arts & crafts; Cards; Games; Reading groups; Prayer groups; Movies; Shopping trips; Social/Cultural gatherings.

MASON CITY

Americana Healthcare Center*
222 S Pierce Ave, Mason City, IA, 50401
(515) 423-3355
Licensure Skilled care. *Beds* 77. *Certified* Medicaid; Medicare.
Owner Proprietary Corp (Manor Care).

Good Shepherd Geriatric Center*
302 2nd St NE, Mason City, IA, 50401
(515) 424-1740
Admin Joseph C Kempf.
Licensure Skilled care; Intermediate care; Residential care. *Beds* SNF 20; ICF 236; Residential 10. *Certified* Medicaid; Medicare.

Heritage Care Center
501 S Kentucky, Mason City, IA, 50401
(515) 423-2121
Admin Angela A Klus. *Medical Dir/Dir of Nursing* Jane Papouchis RN.
Licensure Intermediate care. *Beds* ICF 110. *Certified* Medicaid.
Owner Proprietary Corp (ABCM Corp).
Admissions Requirements Minimum age 16; Medical examination; Physician's request.
Staff RNs 2 (ft), 3 (pt); LPNs 1 (ft), 2 (pt); Orderlies 1 (ft); Nurses aides 17 (ft), 18 (pt); Activities coordinators 1 (ft), 1 (pt).
Facilities Dining room; Physical therapy room; Activities room; Laundry room; Barber/Beauty shop.
Activities Arts & crafts; Cards; Games; Reading groups; Prayer groups; Movies; Shopping trips; Social/Cultural gatherings.

Iowa Odd Fellows Home
1037 19th St SW, Mason City, IA, 50401
(515) 432-0428
Admin Beverly S Greathouse. *Medical Dir/Dir of Nursing* Sylvia Lloyd.
Licensure Intermediate care; Residential care. *Beds* ICF 64; Residential 82. *Certified* Medicaid.
Owner Nonprofit Corp.
Admissions Requirements Medical examination; Physician's request.
Staff Physicians 3 (pt); RNs 1 (ft), 1 (pt); LPNs 6 (ft), 5 (pt); Orderlies 1 (ft), 3 (pt); Nurses aides 19 (ft), 19 (pt); Physical therapists 1 (pt); Reality therapists 1 (pt); Occupational therapists 1 (pt); Speech therapists 1 (pt); Activities coordinators 2 (ft), 1 (pt); Dietitians 1 (pt); Dentists 2 (pt); Podiatrists 1 (pt).
Affiliation Independent Order of Odd Fellows & Rebekahs
Facilities Dining room; Physical therapy room; Activities room; Chapel; Crafts room; Barber/Beauty shop; Library.
Activities Arts & crafts; Cards; Games; Reading groups; Prayer groups; Movies; Shopping trips; Social/Cultural gatherings.

MCGREGOR

Great River Care Center
PO Box E, McGregor, IA, 52044
(319) 873-3527
Admin Glen J Oloughlin.
Licensure Intermediate care. *Beds* 51. *Certified* Medicaid.
Admissions Requirements Minimum age 18; Medical examination.
Staff RNs 1 (ft), 2 (pt); LPNs 4 (pt); Nurses aides 3 (ft), 20 (pt); Activities coordinators 1 (ft); Dietitians 1 (pt).
Facilities Dining room; Physical therapy room; Laundry room; Barber/Beauty shop.
Activities Arts & crafts; Cards; Games; Prayer groups; Shopping trips; Social/Cultural gatherings.

MECHANICSVILLE

Mechanicsville Care Center*
206 4th St, Mechanicsville, IA, 52306
(319) 432-7235
Admin Helen B Sheldon.
Licensure Intermediate care. *Beds* 69. *Certified* Medicaid.

MEDIAPOLIS

Bethesda Care Center
608 Prairie St, Mediapolis, IA, 52637
(319) 394-3991
Admin Cheryl M Guild. *Medical Dir/Dir of Nursing* Deborah Stover.
Licensure Intermediate care. *Beds* ICF 61. *Certified* Medicaid.
Owner Nonprofit Corp (Bethesda Care Centers).
Admissions Requirements Medical examination; Physician's request.
Staff RNs 2 (ft), 5 (pt); LPNs 2 (ft), 1 (pt); Nurses aides 11 (ft), 14 (pt); Activities coordinators 1 (ft).
Facilities Dining room; Physical therapy room; Activities room; Crafts room; Laundry room; Barber/Beauty shop; 2 Resident TV lounges.
Activities Arts & crafts; Cards; Games; Reading groups; Prayer groups; Movies; Shopping trips; Social/Cultural gatherings.

MILFORD

Milford Nursing Home
1600 13th St, Milford, IA, 51351
(712) 338-4742
Admin Sandra Bertelson. *Medical Dir/Dir of Nursing* Joni Mitchell DON.
Licensure Intermediate care. *Beds* ICF 50. *Certified* Medicaid.
Owner Privately owned.
Admissions Requirements Medical examination; Physician's request.
Staff Physicians 10 (ft); RNs 2 (ft); LPNs 2 (ft), 2 (pt); Nurses aides 8 (ft), 10 (pt); Physical therapists 1 (pt); Activities coordinators 1 (ft); Dietitians 1 (pt); Ophthalmologists 1 (pt); Podiatrists 1 (pt).
Facilities Dining room; Physical therapy room; Activities room; Chapel; Crafts room; Laundry room; Barber/Beauty shop.
Activities Arts & crafts; Cards; Games; Reading groups; Prayer groups; Movies; Shopping trips; Social/Cultural gatherings.

MISSOURI VALLEY

Longview Home Inc
1010 Longview Rd, Missouri Valley, IA, 51555
(712) 642-2264
Admin John Sherer. *Medical Dir/Dir of Nursing* Diane Nuzum RN.
Licensure Intermediate care. *Beds* ICF 78. *Certified* Medicaid; VA.
Owner Privately owned.
Staff RNs 1 (ft); LPNs 4 (ft), 2 (pt); Orderlies 2 (ft), 1 (pt); Nurses aides 20 (ft), 10 (pt); Activities coordinators 2 (ft).
Facilities Dining room; Physical therapy room; Activities room; Chapel; Crafts room; Laundry room; Barber/Beauty shop.
Activities Arts & crafts; Cards; Games; Reading groups; Prayer groups; Movies; Shopping trips; Social/Cultural gatherings.

MITCHELLVILLE

Mitchell Village Care Center
114 Carter St, Mitchellville, IA, 50169
(515) 967-3726
Admin Roberta Nye. *Medical Dir/Dir of Nursing* Linda Wunn RN.

Licensure Intermediate care. *Beds* ICF 65.
Certified Medicaid.
Owner Proprietary Corp (Quality Health Care
Specialists Inc).
Admissions Requirements Medical
examination.
Staff Physicians 1 (ft); RNs 1 (ft); LPNs 3 (ft),
2 (pt); Orderlies 2 (ft); Nurses aides 12 (ft),
14 (pt); Physical therapists 1 (pt); Reality
therapists; Recreational therapists 1 (ft);
Occupational therapists; Speech therapists;
Activities coordinators; Dietitians; Dentists;
Ophthalmologists; Podiatrists.
Facilities Dining room; Physical therapy
room; Activities room; Crafts room; Laundry
room; Barber/Beauty shop.
Activities Arts & crafts; Cards; Games;
Reading groups; Prayer groups; Movies;
Shopping trips.

MONTEZUMA

Senior Home
Meadowlane Dr, Montezuma, IA, 50171
(515) 623-5497
Admin Ted Powell. *Medical Dir/Dir of
Nursing* Jeri Creswell RN DON.
Licensure Intermediate care. *Beds* ICF 51.
Certified Medicaid.
Owner Proprietary Corp.
Admissions Requirements Medical
examination.
Staff RNs 1 (ft), 3 (pt); LPNs 2 (ft), 3 (pt);
Nurses aides 8 (ft), 10 (pt); Activities
coordinators 1 (ft).
Facilities Dining room; Laundry room;
Barber/Beauty shop.
Activities Arts & crafts; Cards; Games;
Reading groups; Prayer groups; Movies.

MONTICELLO

Senior Home*
500 Pine Haven Dr, Monticello, IA, 52310
(319) 465-5415
Licensure Intermediate care. *Beds* 100.
Certified Medicaid.
Admissions Requirements Medical
examination; Physician's request.
Staff RNs 2 (ft), 3 (pt); LPNs 2 (ft), 4 (pt);
Nurses aides 10 (ft), 24 (pt); Physical
therapists; Occupational therapists; Speech
therapists; Activities coordinators 1 (ft), 1
(pt); Dietitians; Dentists; Audiologists; Social
worker.
Facilities Dining room; Physical therapy
room; Activities room; Chapel; Laundry
room; Barber/Beauty shop; Library.
Activities Arts & crafts; Cards; Games;
Reading groups; Prayer groups; Movies;
Shopping trips; Social/Cultural gatherings.

MONTROSE

Montrose Health Center*
7th St, Montrose, IA, 52639
(319) 463-5438
Admin Donna Venteicher.
Licensure Intermediate care; Residential care.
Beds ICF 60; Residential 20. *Certified*
Medicaid.
Admissions Requirements Minimum age 16;
Medical examination.
Staff RNs 2 (ft), 3 (pt); LPNs 1 (ft), 2 (pt);
Nurses aides 16 (ft), 6 (pt); Activities
coordinators 2 (ft).
Facilities Dining room; Activities room;
Crafts room; Laundry room; Barber/Beauty
shop; Examination room.
Activities Arts & crafts; Cards; Games;
Reading groups; Prayer groups; Movies;
Shopping trips; Social/Cultural gatherings.

MORNING SUN

Morning Sun Care Center
Washington-Manor Rd, Morning Sun, IA,
52640
(319) 868-7751
Admin Barbara Hirt. *Medical Dir/Dir of
Nursing* Nancy Wagner RN.
Licensure Intermediate care. *Beds* ICF 60.
Certified Medicaid.
Owner Proprietary Corp.
Staff RNs 2 (ft), 1 (pt); LPNs 2 (ft); Nurses
aides 10 (ft), 7 (pt); Physical therapists;
Activities coordinators 1 (ft); Dietitians 1
(pt).
Facilities Dining room; Activities room;
Laundry room; Barber/Beauty shop; Library.
Activities Arts & crafts; Games; Reading
groups; Prayer groups; Movies; Social/
Cultural gatherings.

MOUNT AYR

Clearview Home*
406 W Washington St, Mount Ayr, IA, 50854
(515) 464-2240
Admin Richard C Routh.
Licensure Intermediate care. *Beds* 97.
Certified Medicaid.

Mt Ayr Health Care Center*
PO Box 547, Mount Ayr, IA, 50854
(515) 464-3204
Admin L W Gobar.
Licensure Intermediate care. *Beds* 53.
Certified Medicaid.
Admissions Requirements Minimum age 18;
Medical examination; Physician's request.
Staff Physicians; RNs; LPNs; Orderlies;
Nurses aides; Physical therapists; Activities
coordinators; Dietitians; Dentists;
Ophthalmologists; Audiologists.
Facilities Dining room; Physical therapy
room; Activities room; Chapel; Crafts room;
Laundry room; Barber/Beauty shop; Library;
Woodworking shop.
Activities Arts & crafts; Cards; Games;
Reading groups; Prayer groups; Movies;
Shopping trips; Social/Cultural gatherings.

MOUNT PLEASANT

**Henry County Health Center Long-Term Care
Unit**
Saunders Pk, Mount Pleasant, IA, 52641
(319) 385-3141
Admin Robert A Miller. *Medical Dir/Dir of
Nursing* Diane Wickham RN DON.
Licensure Intermediate care. *Beds* ICF 29.
Certified Medicaid; Medicare.
Owner Publicly owned.
Admissions Requirements Medical
examination; Physician's request.
Staff RNs 1 (ft); LPNs 5 (pt); Nurses aides 12
(pt); Physical therapists 1 (ft); Occupational
therapists 1 (pt); Speech therapists 1 (pt);
Activities coordinators 1 (ft); Dietitians 1
(ft); Podiatrists 1 (pt).
Facilities Dining room; Physical therapy
room; Activities room; Laundry room.
Activities Arts & crafts; Cards; Games;
Reading groups; Prayer groups; Movies;
Shopping trips; Social/Cultural gatherings;
Pet therapy.

Mapleleaf Health Care Center*
701 Mapleleaf Dr, Mount Pleasant, IA, 52641
(319) 385-2293
Admin Dale Showalter.
Licensure Intermediate care. *Beds* 63.
Certified Medicaid.
Admissions Requirements Minimum age 16;
Medical examination; Physician's request.
Staff RNs 2 (ft); LPNs 2 (ft), 4 (pt); Nurses
aides 14 (ft), 6 (pt); Physical therapists 1
(pt); Occupational therapists 1 (pt); Speech

therapists 1 (pt); Activities coordinators 1
(ft); Dietitians 1 (pt); Dentists 1 (pt);
Podiatrists 1 (pt); Audiologists 1 (pt).
Facilities Dining room; Physical therapy
room; Activities room; Chapel; Laundry
room; Barber/Beauty shop.
Activities Arts & crafts; Cards; Games;
Reading groups; Movies; Shopping trips;
Social/Cultural gatherings.

Pleasant Manor Care Center
413 Broadway, Mount Pleasant, IA, 52641
(319) 385-8095
Admin Barry Miller.
Licensure Intermediate care. *Beds* ICF 50.
Certified Medicaid.
Owner Proprietary Corp.
Admissions Requirements Minimum age 18;
Medical examination; Physician's request.
Staff RNs 3 (ft); LPNs 1 (ft), 1 (pt); Nurses
aides 8 (ft), 8 (pt); Activities coordinators 1
(ft).
Facilities Dining room; Activities room;
Laundry room; Barber/Beauty shop.
Activities Arts & crafts; Cards; Games;
Reading groups; Prayer groups; Social/
Cultural gatherings.

MOUNT VERNON

Hallmark Care Center
Mount Vernon, IA, 52314
(319) 895-8891
Admin Diane M Sarich. *Medical Dir/Dir of
Nursing* Robert Sautter MD.
Licensure Intermediate care. *Beds* 68.
Certified Medicaid.
Admissions Requirements Minimum age 18;
Medical examination; Physician's request.
Staff Physical therapists; Reality therapists;
Recreational therapists; Occupational
therapists; Speech therapists; Activities
coordinators 1 (ft); Dietitians 1 (ft).
Facilities Dining room; Physical therapy
room; Activities room; Crafts room; Laundry
room; Barber/Beauty shop; Library.
Activities Arts & crafts; Cards; Games;
Reading groups; Prayer groups; Movies;
Social/Cultural gatherings.

MUSCATINE

Bethesda Care Center
3440 Mulberry Ave, Muscatine, IA, 52761
(319) 263-2194
Admin Joseph H Schulte. *Medical Dir/Dir of
Nursing* Arlene Clark.
Licensure Intermediate care. *Beds* ICF 130.
Certified Medicaid.
Owner Nonprofit Corp (Bethesda Care
Centers).
Admissions Requirements Medical
examination; Physician's request.
Staff RNs; LPNs; Nurses aides; Recreational
therapists; Activities coordinators; Dietitians;
Podiatrists.
Facilities Dining room; Physical therapy
room; Activities room; Chapel; Barber/
Beauty shop.
Activities Arts & crafts; Cards; Games; Prayer
groups; Movies; Shopping trips; Social/
Cultural gatherings.

Lutheran Homes Society
Hershey Ave, Muscatine, IA, 52761
(319) 263-1241
Licensure Intermediate care. *Beds* ICF 146.
Certified Medicaid.
Admissions Requirements Medical
examination; Physician's request.
Staff RNs 4 (ft), 2 (pt); LPNs 7 (ft); Nurses
aides 70 (ft), 30 (pt); Occupational therapists
1 (ft); Activities coordinators 1 (ft).
Affiliation Lutheran
Facilities Dining room; Physical therapy
room; Activities room; Chapel; Crafts room;
Laundry room; Barber/Beauty shop; Library.

Activities Arts & crafts; Cards; Games; Reading groups; Movies; Shopping trips; Social/Cultural gatherings; Bible study.

Muscatine Care Center*
2002 Cedar St, Muscatine, IA, 52761
(319) 264-2023
Admin Richard L Mathiot.
Licensure Intermediate care. *Beds* 100. *Certified* Medicaid.

NEVADA

Oak Park Care Center
100 6th St, Nevada, IA, 50201
(515) 382-6556
Admin Paul Livingston. *Medical Dir/Dir of Nursing* Mary Wathen DON.
Licensure Intermediate care. *Beds* ICF 69. *Certified* Medicaid.
Owner Proprietary Corp.
Admissions Requirements Medical examination; Physician's request.
Staff RNs 1 (ft); LPNs 4 (ft), 2 (pt); Nurses aides 16 (ft), 4 (pt); Activities coordinators 1 (ft); Dietitians 1 (pt); Podiatrists 1 (pt).
Languages Spanish
Facilities Dining room; Activities room; Crafts room; Laundry room; Barber/Beauty shop.
Activities Arts & crafts; Cards; Games; Reading groups; Prayer groups; Movies; Shopping trips; Social/Cultural gatherings; Wine & cheese parties; Senior citizens luncheon; Pet therapy.

Story County Hospital & Long-Term Care Facility
630 6th St, Nevada, IA, 50201
(515) 382-2111
Admin John J Kaduce. *Medical Dir/Dir of Nursing* Dr Pandu Bonthala; Nancy Haas RN.
Licensure Skilled care; Intermediate care. *Beds* SNF 28; ICF 80. *Certified* Medicaid; Medicare.
Owner Publicly owned.
Admissions Requirements Medical examination; Physician's request.
Staff RNs 3 (ft); LPNs 8 (ft), 4 (pt); Physical therapists 1 (ft), 1 (pt); Recreational therapists 1 (ft); Occupational therapists 1 (pt); Speech therapists 1 (pt); Activities coordinators 2 (ft); Dietitians 1 (ft); Ophthalmologists 1 (pt); Podiatrists 1 (pt).
Facilities Dining room; Physical therapy room; Activities room; Chapel; Laundry room; Barber/Beauty shop.
Activities Arts & crafts; Cards; Games; Reading groups; Prayer groups; Movies; Shopping trips; Social/Cultural gatherings.

NEW HAMPTON

Health Care Manor*
S 4th St, New Hampton, IA, 50659
(515) 394-4153
Licensure Intermediate care; Residential care. *Beds* ICF 51; Residential 16. *Certified* Medicaid.
Admissions Requirements Medical examination; Physician's request.
Staff RNs 1 (ft), 1 (pt); LPNs 1 (ft), 5 (pt); Nurses aides 15 (ft), 10 (pt); Physical therapists 1 (pt); Occupational therapists 1 (pt); Speech therapists 1 (pt); Activities coordinators 1 (ft), 1 (pt); Dietitians 1 (ft).
Facilities Dining room; Physical therapy room; Activities room; Crafts room; Laundry room; Barber/Beauty shop; Separate lounge area.
Activities Arts & crafts; Cards; Games; Reading groups; Prayer groups; Shopping trips; Social/Cultural gatherings.

New Hampton Care Center Inc*
530 S Linn, New Hampton, IA, 50659
(515) 394-3151
Admin Bonnie L Hubka.
Licensure Intermediate care. *Beds* 50. *Certified* Medicaid.

NEW LONDON

New London Care Center*
Pine St, New London, IA, 52645
(319) 367-5753
Admin Thomas J Wage.
Licensure Intermediate care. *Beds* 51. *Certified* Medicaid.

NEW SHARON

New Sharon Care Center
PO Box 10, Park at Cherry, New Sharon, IA, 50207
(515) 637-4031
Admin Karen Habenicht. *Medical Dir/Dir of Nursing* Linda Williams.
Licensure Intermediate care. *Beds* ICF 63. *Certified* Medicaid.
Owner Proprietary Corp (Beverly Enterprises).
Admissions Requirements Minimum age 18; Medical examination; Physician's request.
Staff RNs 2 (ft); LPNs 2 (ft), 1 (pt); Nurses aides 35 (ft), 15 (pt); Activities coordinators 1 (ft).
Facilities Dining room; Physical therapy room; Activities room; Crafts room; Laundry room; Barber/Beauty shop.
Activities Arts & crafts; Cards; Games; Reading groups; Prayer groups; Movies; Social/Cultural gatherings; Church services.

NEWELL

Newell Good Samaritan Center*
PO Box 395, Newell, IA, 50568
(712) 272-3327
Admin Debra L Jensen.
Licensure Intermediate care. *Beds* 50. *Certified* Medicaid.
Owner Nonprofit Corp (Evangelical Lutheran/ Good Samaritan).

NEWTON

Embassy Manor Care Center*
200 S 8th Ave E, Newton, IA, 50208
(515) 792-7440
Admin Vivian Degreef.
Licensure Intermediate care. *Beds* 101. *Certified* Medicaid.

Heritage Manor Care Center
1743 S 8th Ave E, Newton, IA, 50208
(515) 792-5680
Admin John A Robinson. *Medical Dir/Dir of Nursing* Sue Peterson DON.
Licensure Intermediate care. *Beds* ICF 62. *Certified* Medicaid.
Owner Proprietary Corp.
Admissions Requirements Medical examination; Physician's request.
Staff RNs 1 (ft), 1 (pt); LPNs 3 (ft), 2 (pt); Orderlies 1 (ft); Nurses aides 12 (ft), 9 (pt); Activities coordinators 1 (ft).
Facilities Dining room; Physical therapy room; Activities room; Laundry room; Barber/Beauty shop.
Activities Arts & crafts; Cards; Games; Reading groups; Movies; Shopping trips.

Jasper County Care Facility
Box 68, Rte 4, Newton, IA, 50208
(515) 792-2000
Admin Floyd J Gardner. *Medical Dir/Dir of Nursing* John Ferguson MD; Janet Johnson RN.

Licensure Intermediate care; Intermediate care for mentally retarded; RCF. *Beds* ICF 44; ICF/MR 28; RCF 38. *Certified* Medicaid.
Owner Publicly owned.
Admissions Requirements Minimum age 18; Medical examination; Physician's request.
Staff Physicians 1 (pt); RNs 2 (pt); LPNs 3 (ft), 4 (pt); Orderlies 1 (ft), 4 (pt); Nurses aides 15 (ft), 42 (pt); Physical therapists 1 (pt); Reality therapists 2 (ft); Recreational therapists 2 (ft); Occupational therapists 1 (pt); Speech therapists 1 (pt); Activities coordinators 1 (ft); Dietitians 1 (ft); Dentists 1 (pt); Podiatrists 1 (pt).
Facilities Dining room; Physical therapy room; Activities room; Chapel; Crafts room; Laundry room; Barber/Beauty shop; Library; Occupational therapy room; Gym; Workshop; Living skills.
Activities Arts & crafts; Cards; Games; Reading groups; Movies; Shopping trips; Social/Cultural gatherings; Bell choir; Gardening.

Nelson Manor
1500 1st Ave E, Newton, IA, 50208
(515) 792-1443
Admin Mary Ann Shaw. *Medical Dir/Dir of Nursing* Ann Lutz DON.
Licensure Intermediate care. *Beds* ICF 36. *Certified* Medicaid.
Owner Privately owned.
Admissions Requirements Medical examination.
Staff RNs 2 (ft), 1 (pt); LPNs 1 (ft), 1 (pt); Orderlies 1 (pt); Nurses aides 14 (ft); Physical therapists 1 (pt); Occupational therapists 1 (pt); Speech therapists 1 (pt); Activities coordinators 1 (pt); Dietitians 1 (pt); Ophthalmologists 1 (pt); Podiatrists 1 (pt).
Facilities Laundry room.
Activities Arts & crafts; Cards; Games; Reading groups; Prayer groups; Movies.

NORA SPRINGS

Nora Springs Care Center
Hwy 18 W, Nora Springs, IA, 50458
(515) 749-5331
Admin Kenneth E Davis.
Licensure Intermediate care. *Beds* ICF 60. *Certified* Medicaid.

NORTH ENGLISH

English Valley Nursing Care Center*
Box 156, North English, IA, 52316
(319) 664-3257
Admin Audrey Weldon.
Licensure Intermediate care. *Beds* 67. *Certified* Medicaid.

NORTHWOOD

Lutheran Retirement Home Inc
700 10th St N, Northwood, IA, 50459
(515) 324-1712
Admin James Tweeten. *Medical Dir/Dir of Nursing* Dianne Zaiser RN.
Licensure Intermediate care. *Beds* ICF 81. *Certified* Medicaid.
Owner Nonprofit Corp.
Admissions Requirements Minimum age 16; Medical examination.
Staff RNs 3 (ft), 4 (pt); LPNs 2 (ft), 5 (pt); Nurses aides 10 (ft), 30 (pt); Activities coordinators 1 (ft), 2 (pt).
Affiliation Lutheran
Facilities Dining room; Physical therapy room; Activities room; Chapel; Crafts room; Laundry room; Barber/Beauty shop.

Activities Arts & crafts; Cards; Games; Reading groups; Prayer groups; Movies; Chapel services; One-to-one visits; Reading & writing letters; Reality orientation group; Baking.

NORWALK

Norwalk Manor Care Center
921 Sunset Dr, Norwalk, IA, 50211
(515) 981-0604
Admin Portia K Jackson. *Medical Dir/Dir of Nursing* Edith Manley.
Licensure Intermediate care. *Beds* ICF 51.
Certified Medicaid.
Owner Proprietary Corp (Life Care Centers of America).
Admissions Requirements Medical examination; Physician's request.
Staff LPNs; Orderlies; Nurses aides; Activities coordinators; Dietitians.
Facilities Dining room; Laundry room; Barber/Beauty shop.
Activities Arts & crafts; Cards; Games; Reading groups; Prayer groups; Movies; Shopping trips; Social/Cultural gatherings.

Regency Care Center
815 High Rd, Norwalk, IA, 50211
(515) 981-4269
Admin Robert H Richardson. *Medical Dir/Dir of Nursing* Margaret Beener.
Licensure Intermediate care. *Beds* ICF 101.
Certified Medicare.
Owner Proprietary Corp.
Admissions Requirements Minimum age 65; Medical examination; Physician's request.
Staff RNs; LPNs; Orderlies; Nurses aides; Physical therapists; Occupational therapists; Speech therapists; Activities coordinators; Dietitians; Dentists; Ophthalmologists; Podiatrists.
Facilities Dining room; Physical therapy room; Activities room; Crafts room; Laundry room; Barber/Beauty shop; Fireplace living room.
Activities Arts & crafts; Cards; Games; Reading groups; Prayer groups; Movies; Shopping trips; Social/Cultural gatherings.

OAKLAND

Oakland Manor Nursing Homes
PO Box 487, 737 N Hiway, Oakland, IA, 51560
(712) 482-6403
Admin Carolee Hamblin. *Medical Dir/Dir of Nursing* Gladys Pierce.
Licensure Intermediate care. *Beds* ICF 67.
Certified Medicaid.
Owner Proprietary Corp.
Admissions Requirements Medical examination.
Staff RNs; LPNs; Nurses aides; Activities coordinators.
Facilities Dining room; Physical therapy room; Activities room; Chapel; Crafts room; Laundry room; Barber/Beauty shop.
Activities Arts & crafts; Cards; Games; Reading groups; Prayer groups; Movies; Shopping trips; Social/Cultural gatherings.

ODEBOLT

Colonial Manor of Odebolt*
Hwy 39, Odebolt, IA, 51458
(712) 668-2731
Admin Jack Lavelle.
Licensure Intermediate care. *Beds* 64.
Certified Medicaid.
Owner Proprietary Corp (Beverly Enterprises).

OELWEIN

Grandview Nursing Center*
800 5th St SE, Oelwein, IA, 50662
(319) 283-1908
Admin Randall L Parks.
Licensure Intermediate care. *Beds* 83.
Certified Medicaid.

Oelwein Care Center
600 7th Ave SE, Oelwein, IA, 50662
(319) 283-2794
Admin Betty J Baum. *Medical Dir/Dir of Nursing* Barbara Roberson RN DON.
Licensure Intermediate care. *Beds* ICF 61.
Certified Medicaid.
Owner Proprietary Corp.
Admissions Requirements Minimum age 18; Medical examination.
Staff RNs 1 (ft), 1 (pt); LPNs 3 (ft), 2 (pt); Nurses aides 16 (ft), 12 (pt); Physical therapists 2 (pt); Speech therapists 1 (pt); Activities coordinators 1 (ft), 1 (pt); Dietitians 1 (pt); Ophthalmologists 1 (pt); Podiatrists 1 (pt).
Facilities Dining room; Physical therapy room; Activities room; Chapel; Crafts room; Laundry room; Barber/Beauty shop.
Activities Arts & crafts; Cards; Games; Reading groups; Prayer groups; Movies; Shopping trips; Social/Cultural gatherings.

OGDEN

Ogden Manor
625 E Oak, Ogden, IA, 50212
(515) 275-2481
Admin Charlene Cox. *Medical Dir/Dir of Nursing* Ruth Bryant RN.
Licensure Intermediate care. *Beds* ICF 57.
Certified Medicaid.
Owner Proprietary Corp.
Admissions Requirements Medical examination.
Staff RNs 3 (ft); LPNs 4 (ft); Nurses aides 29 (ft); Activities coordinators 1 (ft).
Facilities Dining room; Activities room; Chapel; Crafts room; Laundry room; Barber/Beauty shop; Library.
Activities Arts & crafts; Cards; Games; Reading groups; Prayer groups; Movies; Shopping trips; Social/Cultural gatherings.

ONAWA

Onawa Home for the Aged Inc*
222 N 15th St, Onawa, IA, 51040
(712) 423-2510
Admin Richard J Feauto.
Licensure Intermediate care. *Beds* 98.
Certified Medicaid.

ORANGE CITY

Heritage House
519 Albany Ave SE, Orange City, IA, 51041
(712) 737-4002
Admin Beth Haarsma. *Medical Dir/Dir of Nursing* Muriel Ravestein.
Licensure Intermediate care. *Beds* ICF 50.
Certified Medicaid.
Owner Proprietary Corp.
Admissions Requirements Minimum age 16.
Staff RNs 2 (ft), 2 (pt); LPNs 3 (ft), 2 (pt); Orderlies 1 (pt); Nurses aides 5 (ft), 17 (pt); Physical therapists 2 (pt); Recreational therapists 2 (pt); Activities coordinators 1 (ft).
Facilities Dining room; Physical therapy room; Activities room; Chapel; Crafts room; Laundry room; Barber/Beauty shop; Library.
Activities Arts & crafts; Cards; Games; Reading groups; Prayer groups; Movies; Shopping trips; Social/Cultural gatherings.

OSAGE

Maple Manor
830 S 5th St, Osage, IA, 50461
(515) 732-5520
Admin Gloria Heathman. *Medical Dir/Dir of Nursing* Shirley Stille DON.
Licensure Intermediate care. *Beds* ICF 77.
Certified Medicaid.
Owner Proprietary Corp (Waverly Group).
Admissions Requirements Medical examination; Physician's request.
Staff RNs 2 (ft); LPNs 3 (ft), 1 (pt); Orderlies 2 (ft); Nurses aides 12 (ft), 10 (pt); Activities coordinators 1 (ft), 1 (pt).
Facilities Dining room; Activities room; Barber/Beauty shop.
Activities Arts & crafts; Games; Prayer groups; Movies.

OSCEOLA

Osceola Leisure Manor*
Hwy 69 N, Osceola, IA, 50213
(515) 342-6061
Admin Ruth Stephens.
Licensure Intermediate care. *Beds* 101.
Certified Medicaid.

OSKALOOSA

Mahaska Manor
914 N 12th St, Oskaloosa, IA, 52577
(515) 673-9408
Admin Linda K Arterburn. *Medical Dir/Dir of Nursing* Gretchen Updegraff.
Licensure Intermediate care. *Beds* 103.
Certified Medicaid.
Owner Proprietary Corp.
Staff RNs; LPNs; Orderlies; Nurses aides; Physical therapists; Recreational therapists; Occupational therapists; Speech therapists; Activities coordinators; Dietitians; Ophthalmologists; Podiatrists; Dentist; Social worker.
Facilities Dining room; Activities room; Laundry room; Barber/Beauty shop; TV lounge.
Activities Arts & crafts; Cards; Games; Reading groups; Prayer groups; Social/Cultural gatherings.

Pleasant Park Manor*
1510 High Ave, Oskaloosa, IA, 52577
(515) 673-7032
Admin Myrna Schutjer.
Licensure Intermediate care. *Beds* 92.
Certified Medicaid.

Siesta Park Manor*
1302 High Ave W, Oskaloosa, IA, 52577
(515) 672-2474
Admin Becky Ruschman.
Licensure Intermediate care. *Beds* 37.

OSSIAN

Ossian Senior Hospice Inc*
PO Box 98, Ossian, IA, 52161
(319) 532-9440
Licensure Intermediate care. *Beds* 38.
Certified Medicaid.
Admissions Requirements Minimum age 21; Medical examination; Physician's request.
Staff Physicians 2 (pt); RNs 2 (ft), 2 (pt); LPNs 3 (pt); Nurses aides 5 (ft), 14 (pt); Physical therapists 1 (pt); Activities coordinators 1 (pt).
Facilities Dining room; Physical therapy room; Activities room; Chapel; Laundry room; Barber/Beauty shop.
Activities Arts & crafts; Cards; Games; Reading groups; Prayer groups; Movies; Social/Cultural gatherings.

OTTUMWA

Crest Group Home
433 N Weller St, Ottumwa, IA, 52501
(515) 682-4624
Admin Chris Zunkel.
Licensure Residential care for mentally
retarded. *Beds* 15. *Certified* Medicaid;
Medicare.
Owner Nonprofit Corp.
Admissions Requirements Minimum age 18;
Medical examination; Physician's request.
Staff Activities coordinators 1 (pt).
Affiliation Baptist
Facilities Dining room; Activities room;
Laundry room; Living room.
Activities Arts & crafts; Cards; Games;
Movies; Shopping trips.

Good Samaritan Center
2035 W Chester Ave, Ottumwa, IA, 52501
(515) 682-8041
Admin Ronald K Moegenburg. *Medical Dir/
Dir of Nursing* Penny Short.
Licensure Intermediate care. *Beds* 126.
Certified Medicaid.
Owner Nonprofit Corp (Evangelical Lutheran/
Good Samaritan).
Staff RNs 2 (pt); LPNs 3 (ft), 8 (pt); Nurses
aides 23 (ft), 32 (pt); Activities coordinators
2 (ft), 1 (pt).
Affiliation Lutheran
Facilities Dining room; Physical therapy
room; Activities room; Chapel; Crafts room;
Laundry room; Barber/Beauty shop.
Activities Arts & crafts; Cards; Games;
Reading groups; Prayer groups; Movies;
Social/Cultural gatherings.

Ottumwa Manor Nursing Home*
927 E Pennsylvania, Ottumwa, IA, 52501
(515) 684-4594
Admin Helen Jo Broerman.
Licensure Intermediate care. *Beds* 101.
Certified Medicaid.

Ridgewood Care Center Inc*
1977 Albia Rd, Ottumwa, IA, 52501
(515) 683-3111
Admin Kay Dudycha.
Licensure Intermediate care; Residential care.
Beds ICF 54; Residential 16. *Certified*
Medicaid.

River Hills Care Center*
606 E Penn Ave, Ottumwa, IA, 52501
(515) 682-8175
Admin Robert Davis.
Licensure Intermediate care. *Beds* 146.
Certified Medicaid.
Staff RNs 4 (pt); LPNs 12 (pt); Orderlies 4
(pt); Nurses aides 51 (pt); Recreational
therapists 3 (pt); Occupational therapists 1
(pt); Speech therapists 1 (pt); Activities
coordinators 1 (ft); Dietitians 1 (pt); Dentists
1 (pt); Ophthalmologists 1 (pt); Podiatrists 1
(pt); Audiologists 1 (pt).
Facilities Dining room; Physical therapy
room; Activities room; Chapel; Laundry
room; Barber/Beauty shop.
Activities Arts & crafts; Cards; Games;
Reading groups; Prayer groups; Movies;
Shopping trips; Social/Cultural gatherings.

Sunnyslope Care Center*
Rte 1, E Steller, Ottumwa, IA, 52501
(515) 684-6523
Admin John J Coler.
Licensure Intermediate care. *Beds* 61.
Certified Medicaid.

PANORA

Craft Care Center
805 E Main St, Panora, IA, 50216
(515) 755-2700
Admin James P Kelly. *Medical Dir/Dir of
Nursing* JoAnn Ostby.

Licensure Intermediate care. *Beds* ICF 108.
Certified Medicaid.
Owner Proprietary Corp (Beverly Enterprises).
Admissions Requirements Medical
examination.
Staff RNs 3 (ft), 2 (pt); LPNs 4 (ft), 3 (pt);
Orderlies 3 (ft), 1 (pt); Nurses aides 30 (ft),
30 (pt); Physical therapists 1 (pt);
Recreational therapists 2 (ft); Occupational
therapists 1 (pt); Speech therapists 1 (pt);
Activities coordinators 1 (ft); Dietitians 1
(pt); Dentists 1 (pt); Ophthalmologists 1 (pt);
Podiatrists 1 (pt).
Facilities Dining room; Activities room;
Crafts room; Laundry room; Barber/Beauty
shop; Library.
Activities Arts & crafts; Cards; Games;
Reading groups; Prayer groups; Movies;
Shopping trips; Social/Cultural gatherings.

PAULLINA

Wide View Rest Home*
423 Willow St, Paullina, IA, 51046
(712) 448-3455
Admin Tom V Nelson.
Licensure Intermediate care. *Beds* 41.
Certified Medicaid.

PELLA

Christian Opportunity Center*
1553 Broadway, Pella, IA, 50219
(515) 628-1162
Medical Dir/Dir of Nursing Jane Klyn RN.
Licensure Intermediate care for mentally
retarded. *Beds* 15. *Certified* Medicaid.
Admissions Requirements Minimum age 18;
Medical examination; Physician's request.
Staff RNs 1 (ft), 1 (pt); Orderlies 5 (ft), 10
(pt); Activities coordinators 1 (pt); Dietitians
1 (pt).
Facilities Dining room; Physical therapy
room; Activities room; Crafts room; Laundry
room.
Activities Arts & crafts; Cards; Games;
Reading groups; Prayer groups; Movies;
Shopping trips; Social/Cultural gatherings.

Pella Community Hospital*
404 Jefferson St, Pella, IA, 50219
(515) 628-3150
Admin John Harmeling.
Licensure Intermediate care. *Beds* 61.

PERRY

Perry Lutheran Home
2323 E Willis Ave, Perry, IA, 50220
(515) 465-5342
Admin Stephen F King. *Medical Dir/Dir of
Nursing* Robin McCauley RN DON.
Licensure Intermediate care. *Beds* ICF 112.
Certified Medicaid.
Owner Nonprofit organization/foundation.
Admissions Requirements Medical
examination; Physician's request.
Affiliation Lutheran
Facilities Dining room; Activities room;
Chapel; Crafts room; Laundry room; Barber/
Beauty shop.
Activities Arts & crafts; Cards; Games;
Reading groups; Prayer groups; Movies;
Shopping trips; Social/Cultural gatherings.

Perry Manor
2625 Iowa St, Perry, IA, 50220
(515) 465-5349
Admin Ruth Owen. *Medical Dir/Dir of
Nursing* Janis Humpal DON.
Licensure Intermediate care. *Beds* ICF 54.
Certified Medicaid.
Owner Proprietary Corp.
Admissions Requirements Medical
examination; Physician's request.
Staff RNs; LPNs; Orderlies; Nurses aides;
Activities coordinators.

Facilities Dining room; Activities room;
Barber/Beauty shop.
Activities Arts & crafts; Cards; Games;
Reading groups; Prayer groups; Movies;
Shopping trips; Social/Cultural gatherings.

Herman L Rowley Memorial Masonic Home
3000 E Willis Ave, Perry, IA, 50220
(515) 465-5316
Admin Louis M Van Sickle. *Medical Dir/Dir
of Nursing* Arvis Gross; LuCinda Friess
DON.
Licensure Intermediate care; Residential care;
Independent living. *Beds* ICF 48;
Residential 28; Independent living 20.
Certified Medicaid.
Owner Nonprofit organization/foundation.
Admissions Requirements Medical
examination.
Staff RNs 2 (ft); LPNs 10 (ft), 2 (pt); Nurses
aides 35 (ft), 7 (pt); Physical therapists 1 (ft);
Recreational therapists 1 (pt); Occupational
therapists 1 (pt); Speech therapists 1 (pt);
Activities coordinators 3 (ft), 1 (pt);
Dietitians 1 (pt).
Affiliation Masons
Facilities Dining room; Physical therapy
room; Activities room; Chapel; Crafts room;
Laundry room; Barber/Beauty shop; Library.
Activities Arts & crafts; Cards; Games;
Reading groups; Prayer groups; Movies;
Shopping trips; Social/Cultural gatherings.

PLEASANT VALLEY

Riverview Manor Nursing Home
Box 50, Pleasant Valley, IA, 52767
(319) 332-4600
Admin Susan Morton RN. *Medical Dir/Dir of
Nursing* Kathleen Grimes LPN.
Licensure Intermediate care. *Beds* ICF 51.
Certified Medicaid.
Owner Proprietary Corp.
Admissions Requirements Minimum age 16;
Medical examination; Physician's request.
Staff RNs 1 (ft); LPNs 3 (ft), 3 (pt); Orderlies
1 (pt); Nurses aides 8 (ft), 7 (pt); Activities
coordinators 1 (ft).
Facilities Dining room; Physical therapy
room; Activities room; Laundry room;
Barber/Beauty shop.
Activities Arts & crafts; Cards; Games;
Reading groups; Prayer groups; Movies;
Shopping trips; Social/Cultural gatherings.

PLEASANTVILLE

Pleasant Care Living Center
909 N State St, Pleasantville, IA, 50225
(515) 848-5718
Admin Randy Kline. *Medical Dir/Dir of
Nursing* Judy Sparks.
Licensure Intermediate care. *Beds* ICF 57.
Certified Medicaid.
Owner Proprietary Corp.
Admissions Requirements Physician's request.
Staff RNs; LPNs; Nurses aides; Activities
coordinators; Dietitians.
Facilities Dining room; Activities room;
Crafts room; Laundry room; Barber/Beauty
shop.
Activities Arts & crafts; Games; Reading
groups; Prayer groups; Movies.

POCAHONTAS

Pocahontas Manor*
700 NW 7th, Pocahontas, IA, 50574
(712) 335-3386
Admin J D Shepard.
Licensure Intermediate care. *Beds* 92.
Certified Medicaid.

POLK CITY

Polk City Manor
1002 NW 114th Ave, Rte 2, Polk City, IA, 50226
(515) 984-6201
Admin Larry R Rodgers. *Medical Dir/Dir of Nursing* Christine Opfer RN.
Licensure Intermediate care. *Beds* 68.
Certified Medicaid.
Owner Proprietary Corp (Life Care Centers of America).
Admissions Requirements Minimum age 18; Medical examination; Physician's request.
Staff RNs 1 (ft); LPNs 3 (ft), 1 (pt); Orderlies 1 (ft); Nurses aides 16 (ft), 7 (pt); Activities coordinators 1 (ft), 1 (pt).
Facilities Dining room; Activities room; Crafts room; Laundry room; Barber/Beauty shop; Library; Wine & cheese.
Activities Arts & crafts; Cards; Games; Reading groups; Prayer groups; Movies; Shopping trips; Social/Cultural gatherings; Van rides.

POMEROY

Pomeroy Care Center*
303 E 7th St, Pomeroy, IA, 50575
(712) 468-2241
Admin Susan Juilfs. *Medical Dir/Dir of Nursing* Lloyd Holm DO.
Licensure Intermediate care. *Beds* 48.
Certified Medicaid.
Admissions Requirements Medical examination; Physician's request.
Staff Physicians 1 (pt); RNs 1 (ft); LPNs 2 (ft), 2 (pt); Nurses aides 2 (ft), 24 (pt); Physical therapists 1 (pt); Activities coordinators 2 (pt); Dietitians 1 (pt); Dentists 1 (pt); Ophthalmologists 1 (pt); Audiologists 1 (pt).
Facilities Dining room; Physical therapy room; Activities room; Laundry room; Barber/Beauty shop; Library.
Activities Arts & crafts; Cards; Games; Reading groups; Prayer groups; Movies; Shopping trips; Social/Cultural gatherings; Bible study.

POSTVILLE

Community Memorial Hospital Long-Term Care Unit
Oak Dr & Hospital Rd, Postville, IA, 52162-0519
(319) 864-7431
Admin John C Meyer. *Medical Dir/Dir of Nursing* Milton F Kiesau MD; Debra Vondersitt RN DON.
Licensure Skilled care; Intermediate care; Acute care. *Beds* ICF 8; Acute care 24 (Used for acute; skilled; or intermediate in the swing bed program). *Certified* Medicaid.
Owner Publicly owned.
Admissions Requirements Medical examination; Physician's request.
Staff RNs 4 (ft), 8 (pt); LPNs 2 (ft), 6 (pt); Nurses aides 2 (ft), 3 (pt); Physical therapists 1 (pt); Occupational therapists 1 (pt); Speech therapists 1 (pt); Activities coordinators 1 (ft); Dietitians 1 (ft).
Facilities Dining room; Activities room; Chapel.
Activities Arts & crafts; Cards; Games; Reading groups.

Good Samaritan Center
PO Box 716, 400 Country Line Rd, Postville, IA, 52162
(319) 864-7425
Admin Fran Gruenhaupt. *Medical Dir/Dir of Nursing* Raletta Thomas RN.
Licensure Intermediate care. *Beds* ICF 60.
Certified Medicaid.
Owner Nonprofit Corp (Evangelical Lutheran/ Good Samaritan).

Admissions Requirements Minimum age 18; Medical examination; Physician's request.
Staff RNs 1 (ft), 2 (pt); LPNs 3 (ft), 3 (pt); Nurses aides 10 (ft), 17 (pt); Activities coordinators 1 (ft), 1 (pt).
Affiliation Lutheran
Facilities Dining room; Activities room; Chapel; Crafts room; Laundry room; Barber/ Beauty shop; Library; Several nice lounges.
Activities Arts & crafts; Cards; Games; Prayer groups; Shopping trips; Social/Cultural gatherings; Conversation hour; Thursday night entertainment; Walking program.

PRAIRIE CITY

Clearview Manor*
501 N Sherman, Prairie City, IA, 50228
(515) 994-2173
Admin Linda Garza.
Licensure Intermediate care. *Beds* 80.
Certified Medicaid.

PRIMGHAR

Primghar Care Center*
980 Cedar St, Primghar, IA, 51245
(712) 757-3655
Admin Robert W Richardson.
Licensure Intermediate care. *Beds* 40.
Certified Medicaid.

RED OAK

Red Oak Good Samaritan Center*
201 Alix Ave, Red Oak, IA, 51566
(712) 623-3170
Admin Stephen Hohbach.
Licensure Intermediate care. *Beds* 75.
Certified Medicaid.
Owner Nonprofit Corp (Evangelical Lutheran/ Good Samaritan).

Vista Gardens Nursing Home*
1600 Summit, Red Oak, IA, 51566
(712) 623-5156
Admin Dale Waldemer. *Medical Dir/Dir of Nursing* Ruth Waldemer RN.
Licensure Intermediate care. *Beds* 68.
Certified Medicaid.
Staff RNs 3 (ft); LPNs 7 (ft), 1 (pt); Nurses aides 14 (ft), 5 (pt); Physical therapists 1 (ft); Activities coordinators 1 (ft); Dietitians 1 (pt).
Facilities Dining room; Physical therapy room; Activities room; Laundry room; Barber/Beauty shop; Sitting area/lounge.
Activities Arts & crafts; Cards; Games; Reading groups; Prayer groups; Movies; Music programs.

REINBECK

Parkview Manor Inc
1009 3rd St, Reinbeck, IA, 50669
(319) 345-2221
Admin Linda R Gould. *Medical Dir/Dir of Nursing* Lois Stephan DON.
Licensure Intermediate care. *Beds* ICF 56.
Certified Medicaid.
Owner Proprietary Corp.
Admissions Requirements Medical examination.
Staff RNs 1 (pt); LPNs 5 (pt); Nurses aides 23 (pt); Activities coordinators 1 (ft), 1 (pt).
Languages German
Facilities Dining room; Activities room; Crafts room; Laundry room; Barber/Beauty shop.
Activities Arts & crafts; Cards; Games; Reading groups; Prayer groups; Movies; Shopping trips; Social/Cultural gatherings.

REMSEN

Happy Siesta Nursing
424 Roosevelt, Remsen, IA, 51050
(712) 786-1117
Admin Sandy Anderson. *Medical Dir/Dir of Nursing* Shirley Stowater.
Licensure Intermediate care. *Beds* ICF 61.
Certified Medicaid.
Owner Proprietary Corp.
Admissions Requirements Physician's request.
Staff RNs 2 (ft), 2 (pt); LPNs 1 (ft), 5 (pt); Nurses aides 6 (ft), 14 (pt); Activities coordinators 3 (pt); Dietitians 1 (pt).
Affiliation Roman Catholic
Facilities Dining room; Activities room; Chapel; Laundry room; Barber/Beauty shop.
Activities Arts & crafts; Cards; Games; Reading groups; Prayer groups; Movies; Shopping trips; Social/Cultural gatherings.

RICEVILLE

Riceville Community Rest Home
Rte 1, Box 40, Riceville, IA, 50466
(515) 985-2606
Admin Lavonne M Mayer. *Medical Dir/Dir of Nursing* Linda Weida.
Licensure Intermediate care. *Beds* ICF 49.
Certified Medicaid.
Owner Nonprofit Corp.
Admissions Requirements Minimum age 18; Medical examination; Physician's request.
Staff RNs 1 (ft), 2 (pt); LPNs 1 (ft), 2 (pt); Nurses aides 3 (ft), 17 (pt); Activities coordinators 1 (ft), 1 (pt); Dietitians 1 (pt).
Activities Arts & crafts; Cards; Games; Reading groups; Prayer groups; Movies; Social/Cultural gatherings.

ROCK RAPIDS

Lyon Manor Care Center*
1010 S Union, Rock Rapids, IA, 51246
(712) 472-3748
Admin Mildred Robinson.
Licensure Intermediate care. *Beds* 50.
Certified Medicaid.
Owner Proprietary Corp (Beverly Enterprises).

Rock Rapids Health Centre*
703 S Union, Rock Rapids, IA, 51246
(712) 472-2585
Admin Daniel Boyle.
Licensure Intermediate care; Residential care. *Beds* ICF 50; Residential 39. *Certified* Medicaid.

ROCK VALLEY

Hegg Memorial Health Center—Valley Manor Division
1300 21st Ave, Rock Valley, IA, 51247
(712) 476-2831
Admin Justin Cassel. *Medical Dir/Dir of Nursing* Sandra Ver Steeg DON.
Licensure Intermediate care. *Beds* ICF 94.
Certified Medicaid.
Owner Nonprofit Corp.
Admissions Requirements Medical examination; Physician's request.
Staff Physicians 3 (ft); RNs 1 (ft), 3 (pt); LPNs 5 (ft), 5 (pt); Nurses aides 13 (ft), 31 (pt); Activities coordinators 3 (pt); Dietitians 1 (pt).
Facilities Dining room; Activities room; Chapel; Barber/Beauty shop.
Activities Arts & crafts; Cards; Games; Reading groups; Prayer groups; Movies; Social/Cultural gatherings.

ROCKWELL

Rockwell Community Nursing Home
707 Elm St, Rockwell, IA, 50469
(515) 822-3203

Admin Richard Blake.
Licensure Intermediate care. *Beds* 52.
Certified Medicaid.

ROCKWELL CITY

Sunny Knoll Care Center Inc*
700 E Lake St, Rockwell City, IA, 50579
(712) 297-8022
Licensure Intermediate care. *Beds* 41.
Certified Medicaid.
Admissions Requirements Minimum age 18;
Medical examination; Physician's request.
Staff RNs 1 (ft), 1 (pt); LPNs 2 (pt); Nurses
aides 4 (ft), 10 (pt); Physical therapists 1
(pt); Activities coordinators 1 (pt).
Facilities Dining room; Physical therapy
room; Activities room; Laundry room;
Barber/Beauty shop.
Activities Arts & crafts; Games; Reading
groups; Prayer groups; Movies; Shopping
trips.

ROLFE

Rolfe Care Center
303 2nd St, Rolfe, IA, 50581
(712) 848-3351
Admin A E Sluiter.
Licensure Intermediate care. *Beds* ICF 33.
Certified Medicaid.
Owner Privately owned.
Admissions Requirements Medical
examination; Physician's request.
Staff RNs 1 (ft); LPNs 1 (ft), 1 (pt); Nurses
aides 4 (ft), 12 (pt); Activities coordinators 1
(pt).
Facilities Dining room; Physical therapy
room; Laundry room; Library.
Activities Arts & crafts; Cards; Games;
Reading groups; Movies.

SAC CITY

Loring Hospital*
Highland Ave, Sac City, IA, 50583
(712) 662-7105
Admin Terry J DeJong.
Licensure Intermediate care. *Beds* 21.

Park View Manor*
Park Ave, Sac City, IA, 50583
(712) 662-7174
Admin Kent Mertens.
Licensure Intermediate care. *Beds* 76.
Certified Medicaid.

SAINT ANSGAR

St Ansgar Good Samaritan Center
701 E 4th St, Saint Ansgar, IA, 50472
(515) 736-4912
Admin Todd L Jacobsen. *Medical Dir/Dir of
Nursing* Mark Johnson MD; Roberta
Howard DON.
Licensure Intermediate care. *Beds* ICF 76.
Certified Medicaid.
Owner Nonprofit Corp (Evangelical Lutheran/
Good Samaritan).
Admissions Requirements Minimum age 16.
Staff Physicians 1 (pt); RNs 2 (ft), 4 (pt);
LPNs 1 (ft), 3 (pt); Nurses aides 8 (ft), 33
(pt); Physical therapists 1 (pt); Occupational
therapists 1 (pt); Activities coordinators 1
(ft); Dietitians 1 (pt); Ophthalmologists 1
(pt); Podiatrists 1 (pt).
Facilities Dining room; Physical therapy
room; Activities room; Chapel; Crafts room;
Laundry room; Barber/Beauty shop; Library.
Activities Arts & crafts; Cards; Games;
Reading groups; Prayer groups; Movies;
Shopping trips; Social/Cultural gatherings.

SANBORN

Prairie View Home
Hwy 18, Sanborn, IA, 51248
(712) 729-3228
Admin Victor E Vogelaar. *Medical Dir/Dir of
Nursing* Mary Tracy RN.
Licensure Intermediate care. *Beds* ICF 73.
Certified Medicaid.
Owner Proprietary Corp.
Admissions Requirements Medical
examination.
Staff RNs 1 (ft); LPNs 5 (ft), 2 (pt); Nurses
aides 19 (ft), 14 (pt); Physical therapists 1
(pt); Recreational therapists 1 (pt); Speech
therapists 1 (pt); Activities coordinators 1
(ft), 2 (pt); Dietitians 1 (pt); Podiatrists 1
(pt).
Facilities Dining room; Activities room;
Chapel; Crafts room; Laundry room; Barber/
Beauty shop; Library.
Activities Arts & crafts; Cards; Games;
Reading groups; Prayer groups; Movies;
Shopping trips; Social/Cultural gatherings;
Church services; Bus rides.

SEYMOUR

Seymour Care Center*
E 4th & Morgan, Seymour, IA, 52590
(515) 898-2294
Admin R Alan Griffith.
Licensure Intermediate care. *Beds* 51.
Certified Medicaid.

SHEFFIELD

Sheffield Care Center Inc
100 Bennett Dr, Sheffield, IA, 50475
(515) 892-4691
Admin Daniel L Kelley. *Medical Dir/Dir of
Nursing* Mary Lahner DON.
Licensure Intermediate care; Residential care.
Beds ICF 56; Residential 4. *Certified*
Medicaid; Medicare.
Owner Nonprofit Corp.
Admissions Requirements Medical
examination.
Staff RNs; LPNs; Orderlies; Nurses aides;
Activities coordinators.
Facilities Dining room; Physical therapy
room; Activities room; Chapel; Crafts room;
Laundry room; Barber/Beauty shop; Library.
Activities Cards; Games; Reading groups;
Prayer groups; Movies; Shopping trips;
Social/Cultural gatherings; Special events.

SHELDON

**Northwest Iowa Health Center & Long-Term
Care Facility**
118 N 7th Ave, Sheldon, IA, 51201
(712) 324-4708
Admin Mark V Dagoberg. *Medical Dir/Dir of
Nursing* Virginia Harson RN.
Licensure Intermediate care. *Beds* ICF 54.
Certified Medicaid.
Owner Nonprofit Corp.
Admissions Requirements Medical
examination; Physician's request.
Staff Physicians 2 (ft); RNs 1 (ft), 2 (pt);
LPNs 2 (ft), 10 (pt); Nurses aides 5 (ft), 30
(pt); Physical therapists 1 (ft); Occupational
therapists 1 (pt); Speech therapists 1 (pt);
Activities coordinators 1 (ft), 1 (pt);
Dietitians 1 (ft); Ophthalmologists 1 (pt);
Podiatrists 1 (pt).
Languages Dutch
Facilities Dining room; Physical therapy
room; Activities room; Laundry room;
Barber/Beauty shop; Library.
Activities Arts & crafts; Cards; Games; Prayer
groups; Movies.

Village Northwest Unlimited
330 Village Circle, Sheldon, IA, 51201
(712) 324-4873
Admin Robert Hoogeveen. *Medical Dir/Dir of
Nursing* Mary Miedema RN.
Licensure Intermediate care for mentally
retarded; Residential MR care. *Beds* ICF/
MR 60; Residential MR care 50. *Certified*
Medicaid.
Owner Nonprofit Corp.
Admissions Requirements Minimum age 18;
Medical examination.
Staff RNs 8 (ft); LPNs 10 (ft); Nurses aides 60
(ft); Physical therapists 1 (ft); Recreational
therapists 3 (ft); Occupational therapists 1
(ft); Speech therapists 1 (ft); Activities
coordinators 5 (ft); Dietitians 1 (pt).
Facilities Dining room; Physical therapy
room; Crafts room; Library.
Activities Arts & crafts; Education programs.

SHELL ROCK

Shell Rock Care Center
Kelly St & Waverly Rd, Shell Rock, IA, 50670
(319) 885-4341
Admin Darrell W Ferry. *Medical Dir/Dir of
Nursing* Marilyn K DeWitt.
Licensure Intermediate care. *Beds* ICF 56.
Certified Medicaid.
Owner Proprietary Corp.
Admissions Requirements Medical
examination; Physician's request.
Staff RNs 1 (pt); LPNs 4 (ft), 3 (pt); Nurses
aides 10 (ft), 22 (pt); Physical therapists 1
(pt); Recreational therapists 1 (pt);
Occupational therapists 1 (pt); Speech
therapists 1 (pt); Activities coordinators 1
(ft); Dietitians 1 (pt); Ophthalmologists 1
(pt); Podiatrists 1 (pt).
Languages Spanish
Facilities Dining room; Physical therapy
room; Activities room; Crafts room; Laundry
room; Barber/Beauty shop.
Activities Arts & crafts; Cards; Games;
Reading groups; Prayer groups; Movies;
Shopping trips; Social/Cultural gatherings;
Boat trips; Picnics; BBQs.

SHENANDOAH

Elm Heights Parkcrest Center
1203 S Elm St, Shenandoah, IA, 51601
(712) 246-4627
Admin Shirley M Teachout. *Medical Dir/Dir
of Nursing* Alison Hutt RN.
Licensure Intermediate care; Residential care.
Beds ICF 61; Residential. *Certified*
Medicaid.
Owner Nonprofit Corp.
Admissions Requirements Medical
examination.
Staff Physicians; RNs; LPNs; Nurses aides;
Physical therapists; Recreational therapists;
Occupational therapists; Speech therapists;
Activities coordinators; Dietitians;
Ophthalmologists.
Facilities Dining room; Activities room;
Barber/Beauty shop.
Activities Arts & crafts; Cards; Games;
Reading groups; Prayer groups; Movies;
Shopping trips; Social/Cultural gatherings.

Garden View Care Center
1200 W Nishna Rd, Shenandoah, IA, 51601
(712) 246-4515
Licensure Intermediate care. *Beds* 101.
Certified Medicaid.
Staff Physicians 8 (pt); RNs 1 (ft); LPNs 12
(ft); Nurses aides 23 (ft), 11 (pt); Physical
therapists 4 (pt); Speech therapists 1 (pt);
Activities coordinators 1 (pt); Dietitians 1
(pt); Dentists 2 (pt); Podiatrists 1 (pt).
Facilities Dining room; Physical therapy
room; Activities room; Laundry room;
Barber/Beauty shop.

Activities Arts & crafts; Cards; Games;
Reading groups; Prayer groups; Movies;
Shopping trips; Social/Cultural gatherings.

SIBLEY

Country View Manor Inc
100 Cedar Ln, Sibley, IA, 51249
(712) 754-2568
Admin Lois J Werdal. Medical Dir/Dir of
Nursing Carol Rice RN DON.
Licensure Intermediate care. Beds ICF 64.
Certified Medicaid.
Owner Proprietary Corp.
Admissions Requirements Medical
examination; Physician's request.
Staff RNs 2 (ft), 3 (pt); LPNs 3 (pt); Nurses
aides 9 (ft), 20 (pt); Activities coordinators 2
(pt).
Facilities Dining room; Activities room;
Chapel; Crafts room; Laundry room; Barber/
Beauty shop; Porch.
Activities Arts & crafts; Cards; Games;
Reading groups; Movies; Shopping trips;
Social/Cultural gatherings; Bingo; Memorial
services; Trips; Exercises; Reality
orientation.

Sibley Care Center
700 9th Ave N, Sibley, IA, 51249
(712) 754-3629
Admin Leann Dohlman RN.
Licensure Intermediate care. Beds 51.
Certified Medicaid.

SIDNEY

Sidney Health Center*
Hwy 275 S, Sidney, IA, 51652
(712) 374-2693
Admin Robert Riggs.
Licensure Intermediate care. Beds 100.
Certified Medicaid.

SIGOURNEY

Manor House*
1212 S Stuart St, Sigourney, IA, 52591
(515) 622-2142
Admin David O Yearian.
Licensure Intermediate care. Beds 80.
Certified Medicaid.

Sigourney Care Center Ltd
900 S Stone, Sigourney, IA, 52591
(515) 622-2971
Admin Mary F Greine. Medical Dir/Dir of
Nursing Marilyn Waechter DON.
Licensure Intermediate care; Residential care.
Beds ICF 53; Residential 8. Certified
Medicaid.
Owner Proprietary Corp.
Admissions Requirements Medical
examination.
Staff RNs 2 (ft), 1 (pt); LPNs 3 (ft), 3 (pt);
Orderlies 1 (pt); Nurses aides 10 (ft), 10 (pt);
Physical therapists 1 (pt); Occupational
therapists 1 (pt); Speech therapists 1 (pt);
Activities coordinators 1 (pt); Dietitians 1
(pt).
Languages German
Facilities Dining room; Physical therapy
room; Activities room; Crafts room; Laundry
room; Barber/Beauty shop.
Activities Arts & crafts; Cards; Games;
Reading groups; Prayer groups; Movies;
Shopping trips; Social/Cultural gatherings.

SIOUX CENTER

Community Hospital & Health Center*
605 S Main, Sioux Center, IA, 51250
(712) 722-1271
Admin Lee P Erikson.
Licensure Intermediate care. Beds 59.

SIOUX CITY

Casa De Paz*
2121 W 19th St, Sioux City, IA, 51103
(712) 233-3127
Admin Jerry Wood.
Licensure Intermediate care. Beds 95.
Certified Medicaid.

Countryside Retirement Home
6120 Morningside Ave, Sioux City, IA, 51106
(712) 276-3000
Admin Karl Luther. Medical Dir/Dir of
Nursing Lorraine Edmunds.
Licensure Intermediate care. Beds ICF 160.
Certified Medicaid.
Owner Nonprofit Corp.
Admissions Requirements Minimum age 55;
Medical examination; Physician's request.
Staff RNs 11 (ft); LPNs 9 (ft), 3 (pt);
Orderlies 6 (ft); Nurses aides 59 (ft), 19 (pt);
Activities coordinators 1 (ft); Dietitians 1
(ft).
Facilities Dining room; Physical therapy
room; Activities room; Crafts room; Laundry
room; Barber/Beauty shop; Library.
Activities Arts & crafts; Cards; Games;
Reading groups; Prayer groups; Movies;
Shopping trips; Social/Cultural gatherings.

Holy Spirit Retirement Home*
1701 W 25th St, Sioux City, IA, 51103
(712) 252-2726
Admin Phyllis J Peters.
Licensure Intermediate care. Beds 94.
Certified Medicaid.

Indian Hills Care Center*
1800 Indian Hills Dr, Sioux City, IA, 51104
(712) 329-4582
Admin R C Caruso.
Licensure Intermediate care. Beds 160.
Certified Medicaid.
Owner Proprietary Corp (Beverly Enterprises).

Julias Valley Manor
3901 Green Ave, Sioux City, IA, 51106
(712) 252-0114
Admin Julia M Tott. Medical Dir/Dir of
Nursing Cynthia J Christiansen BSN RN.
Licensure Intermediate care. Beds 50.
Certified Medicaid.
Owner Privately owned.
Admissions Requirements Minimum age 18;
Medical examination; Physician's request.
Staff RNs 1 (ft), 1 (pt); LPNs 2 (ft), 2 (pt);
Nurses aides 10 (ft), 5 (pt); Activities
coordinators 1 (ft); Dietitians 1 (pt).
Facilities Dining room; Physical therapy
room; Activities room; Chapel; Crafts room;
Laundry room; Barber/Beauty shop; Movie
lounge.
Activities Arts & crafts; Cards; Games; Prayer
groups; Movies; Shopping trips; Social/
Cultural gatherings; Bingo; Auctions;
Exercises; Music.

Matneys Morningside Manor
3420 S Lakeport Rd, Sioux City, IA, 51106
(712) 276-4311
Admin Linda K Holben.
Licensure Intermediate care. Beds 103.
Certified Medicaid.
Admissions Requirements Medical
examination.
Staff RNs 2 (ft), 3 (pt); LPNs 1 (ft), 9 (pt);
Orderlies 1 (ft), 2 (pt); Nurses aides 16 (ft),
16 (pt); Activities coordinators 1 (ft), 1 (pt);
Dietitians 1 (pt).
Facilities Dining room; Physical therapy
room; Activities room; Crafts room; Laundry
room; Barber/Beauty shop.
Activities Arts & crafts; Cards; Games;
Reading groups; Prayer groups; Movies;
Shopping trips; Social/Cultural gatherings.

Matney's Westside Manor
1414 Casselman, Sioux City, IA, 51103
(712) 258-0896

Admin John Buck. Medical Dir/Dir of Nursing
Paula Nelson.
Licensure Intermediate care. Beds ICF 104.
Certified Medicaid.
Owner Proprietary Corp.
Admissions Requirements Minimum age 21;
Medical examination; Physician's request.
Staff RNs 6 (ft), 2 (pt); LPNs 1 (ft), 2 (pt);
Orderlies 3 (ft); Nurses aides 22 (ft), 6 (pt);
Activities coordinators 2 (ft); Dietitians 1
(pt).
Facilities Dining room; Activities room;
Crafts room; Laundry room; Barber/Beauty
shop; Library.
Activities Arts & crafts; Cards; Games;
Reading groups; Prayer groups; Movies;
Shopping trips; Social/Cultural gatherings.

New Horizons Care Center*
3800 Indian Hills, Sioux City, IA, 51104
(712) 239-5025
Admin Lamar Jones.
Licensure Intermediate care. Beds 50.
Certified Medicaid.

Sunrise Retirement Community
5501 Gordon Dr E, Sioux City, IA, 51106
(712) 276-3821
Admin John Gerwulf. Medical Dir/Dir of
Nursing Kathy Gothier.
Licensure Intermediate care; Residential care.
Beds ICF 90; Residential 60. Certified
Medicaid.
Owner Nonprofit Corp.
Admissions Requirements Minimum age 62.
Staff RNs 8 (ft); LPNs 1 (ft); Nurses aides 38
(ft); Recreational therapists 2 (ft).
Facilities Dining room; Physical therapy
room; Activities room; Chapel; Crafts room;
Laundry room; Barber/Beauty shop; Library.
Activities Arts & crafts; Cards; Games;
Reading groups; Prayer groups; Movies;
Shopping trips; Social/Cultural gatherings.

Westwood Convalescent & Rest Home*
3201 Stone Park Blvd, Sioux City, IA, 51104
(712) 258-0135
Admin Steve Lockwood.
Licensure Intermediate care. Beds 85.
Certified Medicaid.
Owner Proprietary Corp (Beverly Enterprises).

Woodbury Country Care Facility*
RFD 2, Box 202, Sioux City, IA, 51103
(712) 943-5093
Admin George J Hemness.
Licensure Intermediate care for mentally
retarded. Beds 120.

SIOUX RAPIDS

Sioux Care Center
702 Blake St, Sioux Rapids, IA, 50585
(712) 283-2302
Admin Sandra Tielbur. Medical Dir/Dir of
Nursing Jacki Bertness.
Licensure Intermediate care. Beds ICF 35.
Certified Medicare.
Owner Proprietary Corp.
Admissions Requirements Physician's request.
Staff RNs 1 (ft), 1 (pt); LPNs 6 (pt); Nurses
aides 13 (pt); Activities coordinators 1 (ft).
Facilities Dining room; Activities room;
Crafts room; Laundry room; Barber/Beauty
shop.
Activities Arts & crafts; Cards; Games;
Reading groups; Prayer groups; Movies;
Shopping trips; Social/Cultural gatherings.

SOLON

Solon Nursing Care Center*
523 E 5th St, Solon, IA, 52333
(319) 644-2752
Admin N Evelyn Edwards.
Licensure Intermediate care. Beds 67.
Certified Medicaid.

SPENCER

Longhouse Residence
711 W 11th St, Spencer, IA, 51301
(712) 262-2344
Admin Jim Manzer. *Medical Dir/Dir of
Nursing* Kathy Pettitt.
Licensure Intermediate care; Residential care.
Beds ICF 93; Residential 60. *Certified*
Medicaid.
Owner Privately owned.
Staff RNs 7 (ft), 2 (pt); LPNs 3 (ft), 3 (pt);
Orderlies 3 (ft); Nurses aides 30 (ft), 10 (pt);
Physical therapists 1 (pt); Recreational
therapists 4 (pt); Activities coordinators 1
(ft).
Facilities Dining room; Activities room;
Laundry room; Barber/Beauty shop.
Activities Arts & crafts; Cards; Games;
Reading groups; Prayer groups; Movies;
Shopping trips; Social/Cultural gatherings.

St Luke Lutheran Home*
Saint Luke Dr, Box 4128, Spencer, IA, 51301
(712) 262-5931
Medical Dir/Dir of Nursing Dr Frink & Dr
Fieselmann.
Licensure Intermediate care. *Beds* 116.
Certified Medicaid.
Staff Physicians 9 (ft); RNs 2 (ft), 7 (pt);
LPNs 3 (ft), 5 (pt); Orderlies 6 (ft); Nurses
aides 30 (ft), 19 (pt); Physical therapists 1
(pt); Recreational therapists 3 (pt); Speech
therapists 1 (pt); Activities coordinators 1
(ft); Dietitians 1 (pt); Dentists 1 (pt);
Audiologists 1 (pt).
Affiliation Lutheran
Facilities Dining room; Physical therapy
room; Activities room; Chapel; Crafts room;
Laundry room; Barber/Beauty shop; Library.
Activities Arts & crafts; Cards; Games;
Reading groups; Prayer groups; Movies;
Shopping trips; Social/Cultural gatherings.

SPIRIT LAKE

Dickinson County Care Facility*
RFD Box 6090, Spirit Lake, IA, 51360
Admin Colleen Van Dee.
Licensure Residential care. *Beds* 38.
Owner Publicly owned.
Admissions Requirements Minimum age 18;
Medical examination.
Staff LPNs 1 (ft); Nurses aides 9 (ft);
Recreational therapists 1 (ft); Activities
coordinators 1 (ft); Dietitians 1 (ft); Social
workers 1 (ft).
Facilities Dining room; Physical therapy
room; Laundry room; Barber/Beauty shop;
Lounges.
Activities Arts & crafts; Cards; Games;
Reading groups; Prayer groups; Movies;
Shopping trips; Social/Cultural gatherings.

Hilltop Care Center*
1901 Zenith Ave, Spirit Lake, IA, 51360
(712) 336-3300
Admin Jon T Neubaum.
Licensure Intermediate care. *Beds* 51.
Certified Medicaid.
Owner Proprietary Corp (ABCM Corp).

STACYVILLE

Stacyville Community Nursing Home*
Rte 1, Box 4C, Stacyville, IA, 50476
(515) 737-2215
Admin Anita Adams.
Licensure Intermediate care. *Beds* 47.
Certified Medicaid.
Owner Nonprofit Corp.
Admissions Requirements Medical
examination.
Staff RNs 1 (ft); LPNs 4 (pt); Nurses aides 10
(ft), 12 (pt); Activities coordinators 1 (ft), 1
(pt).

Facilities Dining room; Physical therapy
room; Activities room; Laundry room;
Barber/Beauty shop.
Activities Arts & crafts; Cards; Games; Prayer
groups; Movies; Social/Cultural gatherings;
Flower gardens.

STANTON

Stanton Care Center*
213 Holland Ave, Stanton, IA, 51573
(712) 829-2727
Medical Dir/Dir of Nursing Allen & Louise
Hart.
Licensure Intermediate care. *Beds* 30.
Certified Medicaid.
Admissions Requirements Minimum age 18;
Medical examination; Physician's request.
Staff Physicians; RNs; LPNs; Nurses aides;
Physical therapists; Recreational therapists;
Speech therapists; Activities coordinators;
Dietitians; Ophthalmologists; Podiatrists;
Audiologists.
Facilities Dining room; Physical therapy
room; Activities room; Chapel; Crafts room;
Laundry room; Barber/Beauty shop; Library.
Activities Arts & crafts; Cards; Games; Prayer
groups; Movies; Social/Cultural gatherings.

STATE CENTER

State Center Manor*
State Center, IA, 50247
(515) 483-2812
Admin Barbara Lawson.
Licensure Intermediate care. *Beds* 51.
Certified Medicaid.

STORM LAKE

Buena Vista Manor
1325 N Lake Ave, Storm Lake, IA, 50588
(712) 732-3254
Admin Patricia J Richard. *Medical Dir/Dir of
Nursing* Sue Redenbaugh.
Licensure Intermediate care. *Beds* ICF 100.
Certified Medicaid.
Owner Proprietary Corp.
Admissions Requirements Medical
examination; Physician's request.
Staff RNs 5 (ft); LPNs 5 (ft), 2 (pt); Nurses
aides 36 (ft), 4 (pt); Physical therapists 1
(pt); Occupational therapists 1 (pt);
Activities coordinators 1 (ft), 1 (pt);
Dietitians 1 (pt).
Facilities Dining room; Activities room;
Chapel; Crafts room; Laundry room; Barber/
Beauty shop.
Activities Arts & crafts; Cards; Games;
Reading groups; Prayer groups; Movies;
Shopping trips; Social/Cultural gatherings.

Methodist Manor*
4th at Larchwood, Storm Lake, IA, 50588
(712) 732-1120
Admin B Donaldson.
Licensure Intermediate care; Residential care.
Beds ICF 93; Residential 88. *Certified*
Medicaid.
Admissions Requirements Minimum age 55;
Medical examination.
Staff Physicians 14 (pt); RNs 4 (ft), 3 (pt);
LPNs 5 (ft), 4 (pt); Nurses aides 19 (ft), 16
(pt); Physical therapists 1 (ft), 1 (pt);
Recreational therapists 1 (ft); Speech
therapists 1 (pt); Activities coordinators 1
(ft); Dietitians 1 (pt); Dentists 2 (pt);
Podiatrists 2 (pt); Audiologists 1 (pt).
Affiliation Methodist
Facilities Dining room; Physical therapy
room; Activities room; Chapel; Crafts room;
Laundry room; Barber/Beauty shop; Library.
Activities Arts & crafts; Cards; Games;
Reading groups; Prayer groups; Movies;
Shopping trips; Social/Cultural gatherings.

STORY CITY

Bethany Manor Inc
212 Lafayette, Story City, IA, 50248
(515) 733-4328
Medical Dir/Dir of Nursing Ruth Gabrielson.
Licensure Intermediate care. *Beds* ICF 167.
Certified Medicaid.
Owner Nonprofit Corp.
Staff RNs 12 (ft), 2 (pt); LPNs 5 (ft), 2 (pt);
Nurses aides 40 (ft), 35 (pt); Physical
therapists 1 (ft); Activities coordinators 1
(ft); Dietitians 1 (pt); Activity aide 2 (ft);
Social worker 1 (ft); Volunteer coordinator 1
(ft); Dietary aides 18 (ft); Cooks 5 (ft).
Affiliation Lutheran
Activities Arts & crafts; Games; Reading
groups; Prayer groups; Movies; Shopping
trips; Social/Cultural gatherings.

STRATFORD

Stratford Care Center*
Hwy 175 E, Stratford, IA, 50249
(515) 838-2795
Licensure Intermediate care. *Beds* 70.
Certified Medicaid.
Admissions Requirements Minimum age 21;
Medical examination.
Staff LPNs 7 (ft); Orderlies 3 (ft); Nurses
aides 16 (ft), 7 (pt); Activities coordinators 1
(ft), 1 (pt); Dietitians 1 (pt).
Facilities Dining room; Physical therapy
room; Activities room; Crafts room; Laundry
room; Barber/Beauty shop.
Activities Arts & crafts; Cards; Games;
Reading groups; Movies; Shopping trips;
Social/Cultural gatherings.

STRAWBERRY POINT

Strawberry Point Lutheran Home
313 Elkader St, Strawberry Point, IA, 52076
(319) 933-6037
Admin Joan Kelley. *Medical Dir/Dir of
Nursing* Craig Thompson MD; Deb Schloss
RN DON.
Licensure Skilled care; Intermediate care;
Independent living. *Beds* SNF 21; ICF 71;
Independent living 40. *Certified* Medicaid;
Medicare.
Owner Nonprofit Corp.
Admissions Requirements Medical
examination; Physician's request.
Staff RNs 10 (ft), 6 (pt); LPNs 3 (ft); Nurses
aides 40 (ft), 23 (pt); Physical therapists 1
(pt); Occupational therapists 1 (pt); Speech
therapists 1 (pt); Activities coordinators 3
(ft); Dietitians 1 (pt); Ophthalmologists 1
(pt); Podiatrists 1 (pt).
Languages Sign
Affiliation Lutheran
Facilities Dining room; Physical therapy
room; Activities room; Chapel; Crafts room;
Laundry room; Barber/Beauty shop; Library.
Activities Arts & crafts; Cards; Games;
Reading groups; Prayer groups; Movies;
Shopping trips; Social/Cultural gatherings.

STUART

Community Care Center Inc
1603 S 7th St, Stuart, IA, 50250
(515) 523-2815
Admin Mary Ellen Gilman. *Medical Dir/Dir of
Nursing* Janet Garrett.
Licensure Intermediate care. *Beds* 60.
Certified Medicaid.
Owner Proprietary Corp (Community Care
Centers).
Admissions Requirements Medical
examination.

Staff Physicians; RNs; LPNs; Orderlies;
Nurses aides; Physical therapists;
Occupational therapists; Speech therapists;
Activities coordinators; Dietitians;
Ophthalmologists; Podiatrists; Dentist.
Facilities Dining room; Physical therapy
room; Activities room; Crafts room; Laundry
room; Barber/Beauty shop; Library; Map
room; Kitchenette.
Activities Arts & crafts; Cards; Games;
Reading groups; Prayer groups; Movies;
Shopping trips; Social/Cultural gatherings;
Spelling bee; Current events; Residents'
council; Field trips; Diner's club.

SUMNER

Hillcrest Rest Home Inc
915 W 1st St, Sumner, IA, 50674
(319) 578-8591
Admin Eunice A Neil.
Licensure Intermediate care. *Beds* 86.
Certified Medicaid.
Admissions Requirements Medical
examination.
Staff Physicians 3 (pt); RNs 2 (ft), 1 (pt);
LPNs 2 (ft), 3 (pt); Nurses aides 15 (ft), 19
(pt); Physical therapists 1 (pt); Reality
therapists 1 (ft), 1 (pt); Activities
coordinators 1 (ft).
Facilities Dining room; Physical therapy
room; Activities room; Chapel; Crafts room;
Laundry room; Barber/Beauty shop.
Activities Arts & crafts; Games; Reading
groups; Prayer groups; Movies; Shopping
trips; Social/Cultural gatherings.

SUTHERLAND

Millie's Rest Home*
506 4th St, Sutherland, IA, 51058
(712) 446-3857
Admin Tom V Nelson.
Licensure Intermediate care. *Beds* 44.
Certified Medicaid.

TABOR

Tabor Manor Care Center
400 Main St, Tabor, IA, 51653
(712) 629-2645
Admin Leonard B Worcester. *Medical Dir/Dir
of Nursing* Shirley Maxwell.
Licensure Intermediate care. *Beds* ICF 63.
Certified Medicaid.
Owner Privately owned.
Admissions Requirements Medical
examination; Physician's request.
Staff RNs; LPNs; Nurses aides; Physical
therapists; Reality therapists; Recreational
therapists; Occupational therapists; Activities
coordinators; Dietitians.
Facilities Dining room; Physical therapy
room; Laundry room; Barber/Beauty shop.
Activities Arts & crafts; Games; Reading
groups; Prayer groups; Movies; Social/
Cultural gatherings.

TAMA

Sunny Hill Care Center
Hwy 63 N, Tama, IA, 52339
(515) 484-4061
Admin Rosemary Schrach. *Medical Dir/Dir of
Nursing* Lucille Morris.
Licensure Intermediate care. *Beds* ICF 51.
Certified Medicaid.
Admissions Requirements Medical
examination.
Staff RNs 2 (ft); LPNs 4 (ft), 2 (pt); Nurses
aides 12 (ft), 6 (pt); Physical therapists 1
(pt); Occupational therapists 1 (pt); Speech
therapists 1 (pt); Activities coordinators 1
(ft); Dietitians 1 (pt); Podiatrists 1 (pt).

Facilities Dining room; Crafts room; Laundry
room; Barber/Beauty shop.
Activities Arts & crafts; Cards; Games;
Reading groups; Prayer groups; Movies;
Shopping trips; Social/Cultural gatherings;
Baking.

TIPTON

Cedar County Care Facility
Rte 2, Box 21, Tipton, IA, 52772
(319) 886-6675
Admin James Ott. *Medical Dir/Dir of Nursing*
Anne Ott.
Licensure Residential care. *Beds* Residential
54. *Certified* Medicare.
Owner Publicly owned.
Admissions Requirements Minimum age 18;
Medical examination.
Staff RNs 1 (ft); LPNs 1 (ft); Nurses aides 6
(ft), 4 (pt); Activities coordinators 2 (pt);
Dietitians 1 (ft).
Languages German
Facilities Dining room; Activities room;
Chapel; Laundry room; Barber/Beauty shop;
Library.
Activities Arts & crafts; Cards; Games;
Reading groups; Prayer groups; Movies;
Shopping trips; Social/Cultural gatherings;
Cooking.

Cedar Manor
1200 Mulberry, Tipton, IA, 52772
(319) 886-2133
Admin Nicki J Aikman. *Medical Dir/Dir of
Nursing* Cathy Ford.
Licensure Intermediate care. *Beds* ICF 55.
Certified Medicaid.
Owner Nonprofit organization/foundation.
Staff RNs 3 (ft); LPNs 1 (ft), 2 (pt); Nurses
aides 17 (ft), 10 (pt); Physical therapists 1
(pt); Activities coordinators 3 (pt); Dietitians
1 (pt); Ophthalmologists 1 (pt).
Facilities Dining room; Physical therapy
room; Activities room; Laundry room;
Barber/Beauty shop; Library.
Activities Arts & crafts; Cards; Games;
Reading groups; Prayer groups; Movies;
Social/Cultural gatherings; Bowling;
Volleyball; Shuffleboard.

TITONKA

Titonka Care Center*
Hwy 226, Titonka, IA, 50480
(515) 928-2600
Admin Murray D Berggren.
Licensure Intermediate care. *Beds* 51.
Certified Medicaid.

TOLEDO

Bethesda Care Center
PO Box 369, Grandview Dr, Toledo, IA,
52342
(515) 484-5080
Admin Paul M Whisler. *Medical Dir/Dir of
Nursing* Marlene Kajer RN DON.
Licensure Intermediate care. *Beds* ICF 99.
Certified Medicaid.
Owner Nonprofit Corp (Bethesda Care
Centers).
Admissions Requirements Minimum age 16;
Medical examination.
Staff RNs 1 (ft), 1 (pt); LPNs 5 (ft); Nurses
aides 25 (ft); Activities coordinators 1 (ft), 1
(pt).
Facilities Dining room; Physical therapy
room; Activities room; Chapel; Crafts room;
Laundry room; Barber/Beauty shop; Library;
Living room.
Activities Arts & crafts; Cards; Games;
Reading groups; Prayer groups; Movies;
Shopping trips; Social/Cultural gatherings.

TRAER

Sunrise Hill Care Center
909 6th St, Traer, IA, 50675
(319) 478-2730
Admin Karen Brezina. *Medical Dir/Dir of
Nursing* Kathy Hark.
Licensure Intermediate care. *Beds* ICF 64.
Certified Medicaid.
Owner Proprietary Corp.
Staff RNs 2 (ft), 2 (pt); LPNs 2 (ft), 2 (pt);
Activities coordinators 1 (ft); Dietitians 1
(pt).
Facilities Dining room; Activities room;
Chapel; Crafts room; Laundry room; Barber/
Beauty shop.
Activities Arts & crafts; Cards; Games;
Reading groups; Movies; Baking.

TRIPOLI

Tripoli Nursing Home*
604 3rd St SW, Tripoli, IA, 50676
(319) 882-4269
Licensure Intermediate care. *Beds* 22.
Certified Medicaid.
Admissions Requirements Physician's request.
Staff Physicians 4 (pt); RNs 3 (pt); LPNs 2
(pt); Nurses aides 4 (ft), 11 (pt); Activities
coordinators 1 (pt); Dietitians 1 (pt).
Facilities Dining room; Activities room;
Crafts room; Laundry room; Main lobby.
Activities Arts & crafts; Cards; Games;
Reading groups; Movies; Shopping trips;
Church groups.

URBANDALE

Karen Acres Nursing Home
3605 Elm Dr, Urbandale, IA, 50322
(515) 276-4969
Admin Betty Cunningham. *Medical Dir/Dir of
Nursing* Cynthia Dabrieo.
Licensure Intermediate care. *Beds* ICF 38.
Certified Medicaid.
Owner Privately owned.
Admissions Requirements Physician's request.
Staff RNs; Nurses aides; Physical therapists;
Reality therapists; Recreational therapists;
Occupational therapists; Speech therapists;
Activities coordinators; Dietitians; Dentists;
Ophthalmologists; Podiatrists.
Facilities Dining room; Laundry room;
Barber/Beauty shop.
Activities Arts & crafts; Cards; Games;
Reading groups; Prayer groups; Movies;
Shopping trips; Social/Cultural gatherings.

Quality Health Care Center
4614 NW 84th St, Urbandale, IA, 50322
(515) 270-6838
Medical Dir/Dir of Nursing Dr Roy Overton.
Licensure Intermediate care. *Beds* 120.
Certified Medicaid.
Admissions Requirements Medical
examination.
Staff RNs 3 (ft), 1 (pt); LPNs 5 (ft), 2 (pt);
Orderlies 4 (ft), 2 (pt); Nurses aides 25 (ft);
Activities coordinators 2 (ft); Dietitians 1
(pt).
Facilities Dining room; Physical therapy
room; Activities room; Chapel; Laundry
room; Barber/Beauty shop.
Activities Arts & crafts; Cards; Games;
Reading groups; Movies.

VILLISCA

Villisca Good Samaritan Center*
Central Ave & Redmond, Villisca, IA, 50864
(712) 826-9591
Admin Loren H Clayton.
Licensure Intermediate care. *Beds* 65.
Certified Medicaid.

VINTON

Benton County Care Facility*
Rte 2, Vinton, IA, 52349
Admin Helen Corcran.
Licensure Residential care. *Beds* 50. *Certified*
Medicaid; Medicare.
Owner Nonprofit Corp.
Admissions Requirements Minimum age 18;
Medical examination; Physician's request.
Staff RNs 1 (ft); LPNs 2 (pt); Orderlies 1 (ft);
Nurses aides 5 (ft), 5 (pt); Activities
coordinators 1 (ft); Dietitians 1 (pt).
Facilities Dining room; Activities room;
Crafts room; Laundry room; Barber/Beauty
shop; Library.
Activities Arts & crafts; Cards; Games;
Reading groups; Prayer groups; Movies;
Shopping trips; Social/Cultural gatherings.

Virginia Gay Hospital*
N 9th Ave, Vinton, IA, 52349
(319) 472-4751
Admin Leon Hodges.
Licensure Intermediate care. *Beds* 58.

Lutheran Home for the Aged
1301 2nd Ave, Vinton, IA, 52349
(319) 472-4751
Admin Rev Leon Hodges. *Medical Dir/Dir of*
Nursing Linda Cole.
Licensure Intermediate care. *Beds* ICF 61.
Certified Medicaid.
Owner Nonprofit Corp.
Admissions Requirements Minimum age 65;
Medical examination.
Staff RNs 1 (ft), 2 (pt); LPNs 3 (ft), 5 (pt);
Nurses aides 13 (ft), 13 (pt); Activities
coordinators 1 (ft); Dietitians 1 (pt).
Affiliation Lutheran
Facilities Dining room; Physical therapy
room; Activities room; Chapel; Laundry
room; Barber/Beauty shop.
Activities Arts & crafts; Cards; Games;
Reading groups; Prayer groups; Movies;
Shopping trips; Social/Cultural gatherings;
Current events; Manicures.

WALL LAKE

Twilight Acres Inc
6th & Melrose Ave, Wall Lake, IA, 51466
(712) 664-2488
Admin Lauretta Skarin. *Medical Dir/Dir of*
Nursing Nadine Peters.
Licensure Intermediate care; Residential care.
Beds ICF 70; Residential 18. *Certified*
Medicaid.
Owner Nonprofit Corp.
Admissions Requirements Medical
examination.
Staff RNs 3 (ft), 3 (pt); LPNs 3 (ft), 2 (pt);
Nurses aides 15 (ft), 13 (pt); Activities
coordinators 2 (ft).
Facilities Dining room; Physical therapy
room; Activities room; Chapel; Crafts room;
Laundry room; Barber/Beauty shop.
Activities Arts & crafts; Cards; Games;
Reading groups; Prayer groups; Movies;
Shopping trips; Social/Cultural gatherings;
Wine party; Dining out; Picnics; Fishing
trips.

WAPELLO

Wapello Nursing Home*
Hwy 61 S, Wapello, IA, 52653
(319) 523-2001
Admin C W Keldgord.
Licensure Intermediate care. *Beds* 40.
Certified Medicaid.

WASHINGTON

Halcyon House
1015 S Iowa Ave, Washington, IA, 52353
(319) 653-3523
Admin Kenneth H Wagner. *Medical Dir/Dir*
of Nursing Sue Knight.
Licensure Intermediate care; Residential care.
Beds ICF 22; Residential 20. *Certified*
Medicaid.
Owner Nonprofit Corp.
Staff RNs; LPNs; Nurses aides; Physical
therapists; Activities coordinators.
Affiliation Methodist
Facilities Dining room; Physical therapy
room; Activities room; Chapel; Crafts room;
Laundry room; Barber/Beauty shop; Library;
Gardening; Potlucks; Programs.
Activities Arts & crafts; Cards; Games;
Reading groups; Movies; Shopping trips;
Social/Cultural gatherings.

United Presbyterian Home
1203 E Washington St, Washington, IA,
52353-2198
(319) 653-5473
Admin Richard R Colby. *Medical Dir/Dir of*
Nursing Janice Yotty RN.
Licensure Intermediate care; Residential care.
Beds ICF 36; Residential 16. *Certified*
Medicaid.
Owner Nonprofit organization/foundation.
Admissions Requirements Minimum age 62;
Medical examination.
Staff RNs 4 (ft), 1 (pt); LPNs 2 (pt); Nurses
aides 16 (ft), 4 (pt); Physical therapists 1
(pt); Occupational therapists 1 (pt); Speech
therapists 1 (pt); Activities coordinators 1
(ft), 1 (pt); Dietitians 1 (pt).
Affiliation Presbyterian
Facilities Dining room; Physical therapy
room; Activities room; Chapel; Crafts room;
Laundry room; Barber/Beauty shop; Library.
Activities Arts & crafts; Cards; Games;
Reading groups; Prayer groups; Movies;
Social/Cultural gatherings.

Washington Care Center
601 E Polk St, Washington, IA, 52353
(319) 653-6526
Admin Jenny Kennedy. *Medical Dir/Dir of*
Nursing Greta Wells DON.
Licensure Intermediate care. *Beds* ICF 125.
Certified Medicaid.
Owner Proprietary Corp.
Admissions Requirements Medical
examination; Physician's request.
Staff RNs 6 (ft); LPNs 3 (ft), 3 (pt); Nurses
aides 26 (ft), 18 (pt); Activities coordinators
2 (ft).
Facilities Dining room; Physical therapy
room; Activities room; Laundry room;
Barber/Beauty shop.
Activities Arts & crafts; Cards; Games;
Reading groups; Prayer groups; Movies;
Social/Cultural gatherings.

WATERLOO

Americana Healthcare Center
201 W Ridgeway Ave, Waterloo, IA, 50701
(319) 234-7777
Admin Stephen Siecin. *Medical Dir/Dir of*
Nursing Dr Ronald Roth; Cheryl Wilson.
Licensure Skilled care; Intermediate care. *Beds*
SNF 67; ICF. *Certified* Medicaid; Medicare.
Owner Proprietary Corp (Manor Care).
Staff RNs 2 (ft), 4 (pt); LPNs 3 (ft), 3 (pt);
Orderlies 5 (ft); Nurses aides 35 (ft), 5 (pt);
Physical therapists 1 (pt); Occupational
therapists 1 (pt); Speech therapists 1 (pt);
Activities coordinators 1 (ft), 1 (pt);
Dietitians 1 (ft).
Facilities Dining room; Physical therapy
room; Activities room; Chapel; Crafts room;
Laundry room; Barber/Beauty shop; Library.
Activities Arts & crafts; Cards; Games;
Reading groups; Prayer groups; Movies;
Shopping trips; Social/Cultural gatherings.

Black Hawk County Health Care*
1407 Independence Ave, Waterloo, IA, 50703
(319) 291-2567
Licensure Intermediate care. *Beds* 120.
Certified Medicaid.
Admissions Requirements Medical
examination; Physician's request.
Staff RNs 2 (ft); LPNs 12 (ft), 2 (pt);
Orderlies 2 (ft); Nurses aides 40 (ft);
Physical therapists 1 (pt); Reality therapists
1 (pt); Recreational therapists 1 (ft);
Occupational therapists 1 (pt); Speech
therapists 1 (pt); Activities coordinators 1
(ft); Dietitians 1 (ft); Dentists 2 (pt);
Podiatrists 1 (pt).
Facilities Dining room; Activities room;
Chapel; Crafts room; Laundry room; Barber/
Beauty shop.
Activities Arts & crafts; Cards; Games;
Reading groups; Prayer groups; Movies;
Shopping trips; Social/Cultural gatherings.

Fairway Group Home*
2221 Fairway Ln, Waterloo, IA, 50702
(319) 236-1033
Admin Bob Bowen.
Licensure Intermediate care for mentally
retarded. *Beds* 12.

Friendship Village Retirement Center
600 Park Ln, Waterloo, IA, 50702
(319) 291-8100
Admin Mary B O'Brien.
Licensure Skilled care; Intermediate care. *Beds*
SNF 17; ICF 33. *Certified* Medicaid;
Medicare.

Harmony House Health Care Center
2950 W Shaulis, Waterloo, IA, 50703
(319) 234-4495
Admin Daniel M Larmore. *Medical Dir/Dir of*
Nursing Ronald Roth MD.
Licensure Intermediate care; Intermediate care
for mentally retarded. *Beds* ICF 46; ICF/MR
68. *Certified* Medicaid.
Admissions Requirements Minimum age 16;
Medical examination; Physician's request.
Staff Physicians 18 (pt); RNs 2 (ft); LPNs 12
(ft), 6 (pt); Orderlies 9 (ft), 3 (pt); Nurses
aides 54 (ft), 16 (pt); Physical therapists 1
(pt); Recreational therapists 3 (ft);
Occupational therapists 1 (ft); Speech
therapists 1 (ft); Activities coordinators 1
(ft); Dietitians 1 (ft); Dentists 1 (pt);
Ophthalmologists 1 (pt); Podiatrists 1 (pt).
Facilities Dining room; Physical therapy
room; Activities room; Crafts room; Laundry
room; Barber/Beauty shop; Living rooms.
Activities Arts & crafts; Cards; Games;
Reading groups; Prayer groups; Movies;
Shopping trips; Social/Cultural gatherings.

Parkview Gardens Care Center*
310 Upland Dr, Waterloo, IA, 50701
(319) 234-4423
Admin Robert F Davis.
Licensure Intermediate care. *Beds* 160.
Certified Medicaid.
Owner Proprietary Corp (Beverly Enterprises).

Ravenwood Health Care Center*
2951 Saint Francis Dr, Waterloo, IA, 50702
(319) 232-6808
Admin Gordon Kline.
Licensure Intermediate care. *Beds* 196.
Certified Medicaid.

WAUKON

Allamakee County Care Center*
RR 2, Waukon, IA, 52172
(319) 568-4251
Admin Harry B Banta.

Licensure Intermediate care for mentally retarded. *Beds* 75.

Northgate Care Center
10th Ave NW, Waukon, IA, 52172
(319) 568-3493
Admin Lou Ann Wikan. *Medical Dir/Dir of Nursing* Maxine Connor RN.
Licensure Intermediate care. *Beds* ICF 51. *Certified* Medicaid.
Owner Proprietary Corp (ABCM Corp).
Admissions Requirements Minimum age 18; Medical examination.
Staff RNs 2 (ft); LPNs 2 (ft), 2 (pt); Orderlies 1 (ft); Nurses aides 10 (ft), 8 (pt); Activities coordinators 1 (ft).
Facilities Dining room; Activities room; Laundry room; Barber/Beauty shop.
Activities Arts & crafts; Cards; Games; Reading groups; Prayer groups; Movies; Social/Cultural gatherings.

Waukon Good Samaritan Center*
21 E Main St, Waukon, IA, 52172
(319) 568-3447
Admin Jay E Johnson.
Licensure Intermediate care; Residential care. *Beds* ICF 100; Residential 11. *Certified* Medicaid.
Owner Nonprofit Corp (Evangelical Lutheran/ Good Samaritan).

WAVERLY

Bartels Lutheran Home Inc*
1922 5th Ave NW, Waverly, IA, 50677
(319) 352-4540
Licensure Intermediate care; Residential care. *Beds* ICF 141; Residential 96. *Certified* Medicaid.
Staff RNs 5 (ft), 1 (pt); LPNs 9 (ft), 11 (pt); Orderlies 2 (pt); Nurses aides 29 (ft), 64 (pt); Activities coordinators 1 (ft); Dietitians 1 (pt).
Affiliation Lutheran
Facilities Dining room; Activities room; Chapel; Crafts room; Laundry room; Barber/ Beauty shop; Library.
Activities Arts & crafts; Cards; Games; Reading groups; Prayer groups; Movies; Shopping trips; Social/Cultural gatherings.

WAYLAND

Parkview Home
102 N Jackson, Wayland, IA, 52654
(319) 256-3525
Admin Duane H Alliman. *Medical Dir/Dir of Nursing* Donna Heisner.
Licensure Intermediate care; Residential apartments. *Beds* ICF 27; Residential apts 22. *Certified* Medicaid.
Owner Nonprofit organization/foundation.
Staff RNs 1 (ft); LPNs 3 (ft); Nurses aides 11 (ft); Recreational therapists 1 (ft); Activities coordinators 1 (ft); Dietitians 1 (pt).
Affiliation Mennonite
Facilities Dining room; Physical therapy room; Activities room; Chapel; Crafts room; Laundry room; Barber/Beauty shop; Library.
Activities Arts & crafts; Cards; Games; Reading groups; Prayer groups; Movies; Shopping trips.

WEBSTER CITY

Crestview Manor Convalescent Center & Apartments
2401 S Des Moines St, Webster City, IA, 50595
(515) 832-2727
Admin Joe H Sherman. *Medical Dir/Dir of Nursing* Lanette Patch.
Licensure Intermediate care; Senior citizen apartments. *Beds* SNF 84; Apts 22. *Certified* Medicaid.
Owner Privately owned.

Admissions Requirements Medical examination.
Staff RNs; LPNs; Orderlies; Nurses aides; Activities coordinators.
Facilities Dining room; Laundry room; Barber/Beauty shop.
Activities Arts & crafts; Games; Reading groups; Prayer groups; Movies.

Southfield Care Center
2416 S Des Moines St, Webster City, IA, 50595
(515) 832-3881
Admin Diana Shefueland. *Medical Dir/Dir of Nursing* Mary Halgrim.
Licensure Intermediate care. *Beds* 52. *Certified* Medicaid.
Owner Privately owned.
Admissions Requirements Minimum age 45; Medical examination.
Staff RNs 1 (ft), 5 (pt); LPNs 1 (ft); Nurses aides 25 (ft), 6 (pt); Activities coordinators 1 (ft).
Facilities Dining room; Activities room; Laundry room; Barber/Beauty shop.
Activities Arts & crafts; Cards; Games; Reading groups; Prayer groups; Movies; Shopping trips; Social/Cultural gatherings.

WELLMAN

Parkview Manor*
516 13th St, Wellman, IA, 52356
(319) 646-2911
Medical Dir/Dir of Nursing Dr Dwight Kauffman.
Licensure Intermediate care. *Beds* 94. *Certified* Medicaid.
Admissions Requirements Medical examination; Physician's request.
Staff RNs 4 (ft), 4 (pt); LPNs 1 (ft), 1 (pt); Orderlies 1 (ft); Nurses aides 21 (ft), 10 (pt); Physical therapists 1 (pt); Activities coordinators 1 (ft), 2 (pt); Dietitians 1 (pt).
Facilities Dining room; Physical therapy room; Activities room; Laundry room; Barber/Beauty shop.
Activities Arts & crafts; Games; Reading groups; Prayer groups; Movies; Shopping trips; Social/Cultural gatherings.

WEST BEND

West Bend Care Center*
203 4th St NW, West Bend, IA, 50597
(515) 887-4071
Admin Phyllis Fandel.
Licensure Intermediate care. *Beds* 40. *Certified* Medicaid.

WEST BRANCH

Crestview Care Center*
Oliphant & Northside Dr, West Branch, IA, 52358
(319) 643-2551
Admin Regina Abel.
Licensure Intermediate care. *Beds* 65. *Certified* Medicaid.
Owner Proprietary Corp (Beverly Enter).

WEST DES MOINES

Fountain West Health Center*
1501 Office Park Rd, West Des Moines, IA, 50265
(515) 223-1223
Admin Gary A Tiemeyer.
Licensure Intermediate care; Residential care. *Beds* ICF 156; Residential 38. *Certified* Medicaid.

Woodbury West Health Care Center
1211 Vine St, West Des Moines, IA, 50265
(515) 223-1251

Admin Darlene Thompson RN. *Medical Dir/ Dir of Nursing* Dr R Overton; Carolyn Tiernan RN.
Licensure Intermediate care. *Beds* ICF 214. *Certified* Medicaid.
Owner Proprietary Corp (Hillhaven Corp).
Admissions Requirements Minimum age 18; Medical examination; Physician's request.
Staff RNs 7 (ft), 2 (pt); LPNs 6 (ft), 3 (pt); Orderlies 10 (ft), 6 (pt); Nurses aides 38 (ft), 21 (pt); Recreational therapists 3 (ft); Activities coordinators 1 (ft); Dietitians 1 (ft).
Facilities Dining room; Physical therapy room; Activities room; Chapel; Crafts room; Laundry room; Barber/Beauty shop; Bits-N-Pieces general store.
Activities Arts & crafts; Cards; Games; Reading groups; Prayer groups; Movies; Shopping trips; Social/Cultural gatherings; 2 Vans; 1 Bus for outdoor events.

WEST LIBERTY

Simpson Memorial Home*
1001 N Miller St, West Liberty, IA, 52776
(319) 627-4775
Admin Jack L McIntosh.
Licensure Intermediate care. *Beds* 63. *Certified* Medicaid.

WEST POINT

West Point Care Center
N 6th & Ave G, West Point, IA, 52656
(319) 837-6117
Admin Barry Miller.
Licensure Intermediate care. *Beds* ICF 51. *Certified* Medicaid.
Owner Proprietary Corp.
Admissions Requirements Minimum age 16; Medical examination; Physician's request.
Staff RNs 2 (ft), 2 (pt); LPNs 2 (ft); Orderlies 1 (pt); Nurses aides 8 (ft), 8 (pt); Activities coordinators 1 (ft), 1 (pt).
Facilities Dining room; Activities room; Chapel; Laundry room; Barber/Beauty shop.
Activities Arts & crafts; Cards; Games; Reading groups; Prayer groups; Movies; Social/Cultural gatherings.

WEST UNION

West Union Good Samaritan Center
201 Hall St, West Union, IA, 52175
(319) 422-3814
Admin Terence M McGinnity. *Medical Dir/ Dir of Nursing* Kathleen Berns RN DON.
Licensure Intermediate care. *Beds* ICF 71. *Certified* Medicaid.
Owner Nonprofit Corp (Evangelical Lutheran/ Good Samaritan).
Admissions Requirements Medical examination; Physician's request.
Staff RNs 2 (ft), 4 (pt); LPNs 1 (ft), 5 (pt); Orderlies 1 (pt); Nurses aides 12 (ft), 18 (pt); Activities coordinators 1 (ft).
Affiliation Lutheran
Facilities Dining room; Activities room; Chapel; Crafts room; Laundry room; Barber/ Beauty shop.
Activities Arts & crafts; Cards; Games; Reading groups; Prayer groups; Movies; Shopping trips; Social/Cultural gatherings.

WHEATLAND

Colonial Manor Nursing & Care Center*
515 E Lincolnway, Wheatland, IA, 52777
(319) 374-2951
Admin Connie Byrd.
Licensure Intermediate care. *Beds* 50. *Certified* Medicaid.

WHITING

Pleasant View Inc*
200 Shannon Dr, Whiting, IA, 51063
(712) 458-2417
Medical Dir/Dir of Nursing Dr John L Garred.
Licensure Intermediate care. *Beds* 106.
Certified Medicaid.
Admissions Requirements Minimum age 16;
Medical examination.
Staff Physicians 6 (pt); RNs 1 (ft), 7 (pt);
LPNs 1 (ft), 3 (pt); Nurses aides 15 (ft), 20
(pt); Physical therapists 1 (pt); Activities
coordinators 1 (ft), 2 (pt); Dietitians 1 (pt).
Facilities Dining room; Physical therapy
room; Activities room; Chapel; Crafts room;
Laundry room; Barber/Beauty shop; Library.
Activities Arts & crafts; Cards; Games;
Reading groups; Prayer groups; Movies;
Shopping trips; Social/Cultural gatherings.

WILLIAMSBURG

Williamsburg Care Center*
104 Court St, Williamsburg, IA, 52361
(319) 668-2311
Admin David O Yearian.
Licensure Intermediate care. *Beds* 44.
Certified Medicaid.

WILTON

Wilton Memorial Home*
415 E Prairie, Wilton, IA, 52778
(319) 732-2086
Admin L R Buroker.
Licensure Intermediate care. *Beds* 34.

WINFIELD

Sunrise Terrace*
W Central Ave, Winfield, IA, 52659
(319) 257-3303
Licensure Intermediate care. *Beds* 62.
Certified Medicaid.
Admissions Requirements Medical
examination.
Staff RNs 2 (ft), 5 (pt); LPNs 1 (ft), 1 (pt);
Nurses aides 12 (ft), 7 (pt); Activities
coordinators 1 (ft).
Facilities Dining room; Physical therapy
room; Activities room; Chapel; Laundry
room; Barber/Beauty shop.

Activities Arts & crafts; Cards; Games;
Reading groups; Prayer groups; Movies;
Shopping trips; Social/Cultural gatherings.

WINTERSET

Bethesda Care Center*
1015 W Summitt, Winterset, IA, 50273
(515) 462-1711
Admin Eva McDonald.
Licensure Intermediate care; Residential care.
Beds ICF 80; Residential 19. *Certified*
Medicaid.
Owner Nonprofit Corp (Bethesda Care
Centers).
Admissions Requirements Minimum age 16;
Medical examination; Physician's request.
Staff RNs 1 (ft), 2 (pt); LPNs 6 (ft), 3 (pt);
Orderlies 2 (pt); Nurses aides 22 (ft), 12 (pt);
Activities coordinators 2 (ft).
Facilities Dining room; Physical therapy
room; Activities room; Chapel; Crafts room;
Laundry room; Barber/Beauty shop; Library.
Activities Arts & crafts; Cards; Games;
Reading groups; Prayer groups; Movies;
Shopping trips; Social/Cultural gatherings;
Baking & cooking classes.

Winterset Care Center—North*
411 E Lane St, Winterset, IA, 50273
(515) 462-1571
Admin Alberta R Little.
Licensure Intermediate care. *Beds* 98.
Certified Medicaid.

Winterset Care Center—South
715 S 2nd Ave, Winterset, IA, 50273
(515) 462-4040
Admin Richard Meyer. *Medical Dir/Dir of
Nursing* Linda Wise.
Licensure Intermediate care. *Beds* ICF 49.
Certified Medicaid.
Owner Privately owned.
Admissions Requirements Medical
examination.
Staff RNs 1 (ft); LPNs 4 (ft), 2 (pt); Orderlies
1 (ft); Nurses aides 8 (ft), 8 (pt); Activities
coordinators 1 (ft).
Facilities Dining room; Physical therapy
room; Laundry room; Barber/Beauty shop.
Activities Arts & crafts; Cards; Games;
Reading groups; Prayer groups; Movies;
Shopping trips; Social/Cultural gatherings.

WOODBINE

Rose Vista Home Inc
1109 Normal St, Woodbine, IA, 51579
(712) 647-2010
Admin Eugene Sherer. *Medical Dir/Dir of
Nursing* Debbie Tiffey.
Licensure Intermediate care. *Beds* ICF 82.
Certified Medicaid.
Owner Proprietary Corp.
Staff RNs 3 (ft); LPNs 3 (ft); Orderlies 2 (ft);
Nurses aides 22 (ft), 10 (pt); Activities
coordinators 2 (ft); Dietitians 1 (pt).
Facilities Dining room; Physical therapy
room; Activities room; Crafts room; Laundry
room; Barber/Beauty shop; Library.
Activities Arts & crafts; Cards; Games;
Reading groups; Prayer groups; Movies;
Shopping trips; Social/Cultural gatherings.

WOODWARD

Parkview Manor Care Center
706 Cedar Ave, Woodward, IA, 50276
(515) 438-2568
Admin Karen Reed. *Medical Dir/Dir of
Nursing* Edith Cerar LPN.
Licensure Intermediate care. *Beds* ICF 39.
Certified Medicaid.
Owner Proprietary Corp (Quality Health Care
Specialists Inc).
Admissions Requirements Minimum age 16;
Medical examination.
Staff LPNs 2 (ft), 1 (pt); Nurses aides 7 (ft), 5
(pt); Activities coordinators 1 (ft).
Facilities Dining room; Laundry room;
Barber/Beauty shop.
Activities Arts & crafts; Cards; Games;
Reading groups; Movies; Shopping trips;
Social/Cultural gatherings.

ZEARING

Colonial Manor of Zearing*
401 E Garfield, Zearing, IA, 50278
(515) 487-7631
Admin Kent Jorgensen.
Licensure Intermediate care. *Beds* 56.
Certified Medicaid.

KANSAS

ABILENE

Abilene Nursing Center
705 N Brady, Abilene, KS, 67410
(913) 263-1431
Admin Sue Jirkovsky. *Medical Dir/Dir of Nursing* J Dennis Biggs MD.
Licensure Intermediate care. *Beds* 108.
  Certified Medicaid.
Owner Proprietary Corp (Beverly Enterprises).
Admissions Requirements Minimum age 16; Medical examination.
Staff RNs 2 (ft), 1 (pt); LPNs 3 (ft), 1 (pt); Nurses aides 25 (ft), 10 (pt); Activities coordinators 1 (ft).
Facilities Dining room; Physical therapy room; Activities room; Chapel; Crafts room; Laundry room; Barber/Beauty shop; Library.
Activities Arts & crafts; Games; Reading groups; Prayer groups; Movies; Social/Cultural gatherings.

Highland Care Home*
1601 W 1st St, Abilene, KS, 67410
(913) 263-2070
Admin Betty Ade. *Medical Dir/Dir of Nursing* Viola Aker.
Licensure Intermediate care. *Beds* 42.
  Certified Medicaid.
Admissions Requirements Minimum age 18; Medical examination.
Staff RNs 1 (ft); LPNs 1 (ft), 1 (pt); Orderlies 1 (ft); Nurses aides 8 (ft), 8 (pt); Physical therapists 1 (pt); Reality therapists 1 (pt); Recreational therapists 1 (pt); Occupational therapists 1 (pt); Speech therapists 1 (pt); Activities coordinators 1 (ft); Dietitians 1 (pt); Audiologists 1 (pt).
Facilities Dining room; Physical therapy room; Activities room; Chapel; Crafts room; Laundry room; Barber/Beauty shop.
Activities Arts & crafts; Cards; Games; Reading groups; Prayer groups; Movies; Shopping trips.

ALMA

Alma Manor Nursing Home
234 Manor Circle, Alma, KS, 66401
(913) 765-3318
Admin Linda Montgomery.
Licensure Intermediate care. *Beds* 76.
  Certified Medicaid.
Owner Proprietary Corp (US Care Corp).
Admissions Requirements Medical examination; Physician's request.
Staff RNs; LPNs; Orderlies; Nurses aides; Activities coordinators; Dietitians.
Facilities Dining room; Physical therapy room; Activities room; Chapel; Crafts room; Laundry room; Barber/Beauty shop; Library.
Activities Arts & crafts; Cards; Games; Reading groups; Prayer groups; Movies; Shopping trips; Social/Cultural gatherings.

ALTAMONT

Retirement Acres*
Rte 1, Box 150, 32nd & 96 Hwy, Altamont, KS, 67330
(316) 784-5346
Admin Judy Roark.
Licensure Intermediate care. *Beds* 46.
  Certified Medicaid.
Owner Proprietary Corp.

ANTHONY

Life Care of Anthony
212 N 5th, Anthony, KS, 67003
(316) 842-5103
Admin Carole Eggert. *Medical Dir/Dir of Nursing* Dr Jeff Bond; Sherry Bahr.
Licensure Intermediate care. *Beds* 50.
  Certified Medicaid.
Admissions Requirements Minimum age 18; Physician's request.
Staff Physicians 1 (pt); RNs 1 (ft); LPNs 4 (ft); Orderlies 1 (ft); Nurses aides 16 (ft); Physical therapists 1 (ft); Recreational therapists 1 (ft); Occupational therapists 1 (ft); Speech therapists 1 (ft); Dietitians 1 (ft); Ophthalmologists 1 (ft); Podiatrists 1 (ft).
Facilities Dining room; Physical therapy room; Activities room; Crafts room; Laundry room; Barber/Beauty shop.
Activities Arts & crafts; Cards; Games; Reading groups; Prayer groups; Movies; Social/Cultural gatherings; Sightseeing trips.

ARKANSAS CITY

Arkansas City Presbyterian Manor
1711 N 4th St, Arkansas City, KS, 67005
(316) 442-8700
Admin Van Wilson. *Medical Dir/Dir of Nursing* Wanda Howard DON.
Licensure Intermediate care. *Beds* ICF 60.
  Certified Medicaid.
Owner Nonprofit Corp.
Admissions Requirements Minimum age 65; Medical examination; Physician's request.
Staff Physicians 6 (pt); RNs 2 (ft), 1 (pt); LPNs 4 (ft), 2 (pt); Nurses aides 20 (ft), 3 (pt); Physical therapists 1 (pt); Occupational therapists 1 (pt); Speech therapists 1 (pt); Activities coordinators 1 (ft); Dietitians 1 (ft); Ophthalmologists 1 (pt).
Affiliation Presbyterian
Facilities Dining room; Physical therapy room; Activities room; Chapel; Laundry room; Barber/Beauty shop; Library.
Activities Arts & crafts; Cards; Games; Reading groups; Prayer groups; Shopping trips.

Medicalodge East of Arkansas City*
203 E Osage, Arkansas City, KS, 67005
(316) 442-9300
Admin Brian Feldhus.

Licensure Intermediate care. *Beds* 91.
  Certified Medicaid.
Owner Proprietary Corp (Medicalodges).

Medicalodge North of Arkansas City
2575 Greenway, Arkansas City, KS, 67005
(316) 442-1120
Admin Linda Wynns. *Medical Dir/Dir of Nursing* Robert Yoachim MD.
Licensure Intermediate care; Specialized care unit for Alzheimer's. *Beds* 82. *Certified* Medicaid.
Owner Proprietary Corp (Medicalodges).
Admissions Requirements Minimum age 16; Medical examination.
Staff Physicians 1 (pt); RNs 1 (ft), 1 (pt); LPNs 2 (ft), 2 (pt); Orderlies 4 (ft); Nurses aides 24 (ft), 2 (pt); Physical therapists 1 (pt); Occupational therapists 1 (pt); Speech therapists 1 (pt); Activities coordinators 1 (ft); Dietitians 1 (pt); Ophthalmologists 1 (pt); Podiatrists 1 (pt).
Facilities Dining room; Physical therapy room; Activities room; Chapel; Crafts room; Laundry room; Barber/Beauty shop; Library; Separate dining for alert residents.
Activities Arts & crafts; Cards; Games; Reading groups; Prayer groups; Movies; Social/Cultural gatherings; Bingo; Rides.

ARMA

Crestview Lodge*
3rd & Melvin Sts, Box 789, Arma, KS, 66712
(316) 347-4103
Admin Karen K Brooks.
Licensure Intermediate care. *Beds* 100.
  Certified Medicaid.
Owner Proprietary Corp.

ASHLAND

Fountain View Villa
528 W 8th St, Ashland, KS, 67831
(316) 635-2311
Admin Sandra Y Butler. *Medical Dir/Dir of Nursing* Marla Williamson RN DON.
Licensure Intermediate care. *Beds* ICF 36.
  Certified Medicaid.
Owner Nonprofit Corp.
Admissions Requirements Minimum age 16; Medical examination; Physician's request.
Staff RNs 2 (ft), 1 (pt); Nurses aides 10 (ft), 3 (pt); Activities coordinators 1 (ft).
Facilities Dining room; Physical therapy room; Activities room; Chapel; Crafts room; Laundry room; Barber/Beauty shop; Living room.
Activities Arts & crafts; Cards; Games; Prayer groups; Movies; Coffee club; Bible study.

ATCHISON

Atchison Senior Village
1419 N 6th St, Atchison, KS, 66002
(913) 367-1905

Admin Mary Mason Clay. *Medical Dir/Dir of Nursing* Janey Lykins.
Licensure Intermediate care. *Beds* ICF 50. *Certified* Medicaid.
Owner Publicly owned.
Admissions Requirements Minimum age 16; Medical examination; Physician's request.
Staff Physicians 1 (pt); RNs 1 (pt); LPNs 6 (ft), 3 (pt); Nurses aides 21 (ft); Physical therapists 1 (pt); Activities coordinators 2 (ft); Dietitians 1 (pt); Pharmacist 1 (pt).
Facilities Dining room; Physical therapy room; Activities room; Chapel; Crafts room; Laundry room; Barber/Beauty shop.
Activities Arts & crafts; Cards; Games; Reading groups; Prayer groups; Movies; Shopping trips; Social/Cultural gatherings; Senior Olympics.

Medicalodge of Atchison
Box A, 1637 Riley, Atchison, KS, 66002
(913) 367-6066
Admin Janieve Ames. *Medical Dir/Dir of Nursing* Virginia Cluck.
Licensure Skilled care; Intermediate care. *Beds* SNF 100; ICF. *Certified* Medicaid; Medicare.
Owner Proprietary Corp (Medicalodges).
Admissions Requirements Medical examination; Physician's request.
Staff Physicians; RNs 3 (ft), 1 (pt); LPNs 5 (ft), 3 (pt); Nurses aides 40 (ft), 15 (pt); Activities coordinators 2 (ft); Social service designee 1 (ft).
Facilities Dining room; Physical therapy room; Activities room; Laundry room; Barber/Beauty shop.
Activities Arts & crafts; Cards; Games; Reading groups; Prayer groups; Movies; Social/Cultural gatherings.

ATWOOD

Good Samaritan Center
Box 216, 650 Lake Rd, Atwood, KS, 67730
(913) 626-3253
Admin Howard R Goehring. *Medical Dir/Dir of Nursing* Janice Busse RN.
Licensure Intermediate care. *Beds* ICF 48. *Certified* Medicaid.
Owner Nonprofit Corp (Evangelical Lutheran/Good Samaritan).
Admissions Requirements Medical examination; Physician's request.
Staff RNs 1 (pt); LPNs 4 (ft); Orderlies 2 (ft); Nurses aides 17 (ft); Occupational therapists 1 (pt); Activities coordinators 2 (ft).
Facilities Dining room; Physical therapy room; Activities room; Laundry room; Barber/Beauty shop.
Activities Arts & crafts; Cards; Games; Reading groups; Prayer groups; Movies; Shopping trips; Social/Cultural gatherings.

AUGUSTA

Walnut Valley Manor
2100 N Ohio, Augusta, KS, 67010
(316) 775-6333
Admin Margarite Dodson. *Medical Dir/Dir of Nursing* Dorothy Leedom.
Licensure Intermediate care. *Beds* ICF 50. *Certified* Medicaid.
Owner Privately owned.
Admissions Requirements Minimum age 18; Medical examination; Physician's request.
Staff Physicians; LPNs; Nurses aides; Activities coordinators; Ophthalmologists.
Facilities Dining room; Physical therapy room; Activities room; Crafts room; Laundry room; Barber/Beauty shop.
Activities Arts & crafts; Cards; Games; Reading groups; Prayer groups; Movies; Shopping trips; Social/Cultural gatherings.

BALDWIN CITY

Orchard Lane Nursing Facility
1223 Orchard Ln, Baldwin City, KS, 66006
(913) 594-6492
Admin Mary Ann Culley.
Licensure Intermediate care. *Beds* ICF 48. *Certified* Medicaid.
Owner Nonprofit organization/foundation.
Admissions Requirements Medical examination; Physician's request.
Staff RNs; LPNs; Nurses aides; Activities coordinators; Dietitians.
Facilities Dining room; Physical therapy room; Activities room; Chapel; Crafts room; Laundry room; Barber/Beauty shop; Library.
Activities Arts & crafts; Cards; Games; Reading groups; Prayer groups; Movies; Shopping trips; Social/Cultural gatherings.

BAXTER SPRINGS

Midwest Nursing Center
217 E 14th St, Baxter Springs, KS, 66713
(316) 856-2662
Admin Mike Mathison. *Medical Dir/Dir of Nursing* C B Smith DO; Linde Myer DON.
Licensure Intermediate care. *Beds* ICF 50. *Certified* Medicaid.
Owner Proprietary Corp (Vetter Health Services).
Admissions Requirements Medical examination; Physician's request.
Staff RNs; LPNs; Orderlies; Nurses aides; Activities coordinators.
Facilities Dining room; Physical therapy room; Activities room; Chapel; Crafts room; Laundry room; Barber/Beauty shop.
Activities Arts & crafts; Cards; Games; Reading groups; Prayer groups; Movies; Shopping trips.

Quaker Hill Manor*
RR 1, Baxter Springs, KS, 66713
(316) 848-3797
Admin James E Galbraith. *Medical Dir/Dir of Nursing* Zina Hopkins.
Licensure Intermediate care. *Beds* 36. *Certified* Medicaid.
Admissions Requirements Minimum age 16; Medical examination.
Staff LPNs 3 (ft); Nurses aides 12 (ft), 1 (pt).
Facilities Dining room; Physical therapy room; Activities room; Laundry room.
Activities Arts & crafts; Reading groups; Prayer groups; Movies; Shopping trips.

BELLE PLAINE

Paradise Valley Living Center
801 N Logan, Belle Plaine, KS, 67013
(316) 488-2228
Admin Martha M Speer. *Medical Dir/Dir of Nursing* Karen Pracht LPN DON.
Licensure Intermediate care. *Beds* ICF 50. *Certified* Medicaid.
Owner Nonprofit Corp (Adventist Health System-USA).
Admissions Requirements Medical examination; Physician's request.
Staff RNs 1 (pt); LPNs 1 (ft), 3 (pt); Orderlies 1 (pt); Nurses aides 8 (ft), 10 (pt); Physical therapists 1 (pt); Recreational therapists 1 (pt); Occupational therapists 1 (pt); Speech therapists 1 (pt); Activities coordinators 1 (ft); Dietitians 1 (pt); Ophthalmologists 1 (pt); Podiatrists 1 (pt).
Affiliation Seventh-Day Adventist
Facilities Dining room; Physical therapy room; Activities room; Chapel; Laundry room; Barber/Beauty shop; Library.
Activities Arts & crafts; Cards; Games; Reading groups; Prayer groups; Movies; Shopping trips; Social/Cultural gatherings.

BELLEVILLE

Belleville Health Care Center
Box 548, 2426 Wesleyan Dr, Belleville, KS, 66935
(913) 527-5636
Admin Sandra Boyles. *Medical Dir/Dir of Nursing* Susan Kesl.
Licensure Intermediate care. *Beds* ICF 87. *Certified* Medicaid.
Owner Proprietary Corp (US Care Corp).
Admissions Requirements Physician's request.
Staff RNs 5 (ft); LPNs 5 (ft); Nurses aides 27 (ft); Activities coordinators 2 (ft).
Facilities Dining room; Physical therapy room; Activities room; Crafts room; Laundry room; Barber/Beauty shop.
Activities Arts & crafts; Cards; Games; Reading groups; Prayer groups; Movies; Shopping trips; Social/Cultural gatherings.

Heartland Care Center—Belleville
500 W 23rd St, Belleville, KS, 66935
(913) 527-2242
Admin Russell W Caswell. *Medical Dir/Dir of Nursing* Vicki Reiter RN DON.
Licensure Intermediate care. *Beds* 88. *Certified* Medicaid.
Owner Proprietary Corp (US Care Corp).

BELOIT

Hilltop Lodge Inc Nursing Home*
815 N Independence, Beloit, KS, 67420
(913) 738-3516
Admin Harold E Heidrick.
Licensure Intermediate care. *Beds* 100. *Certified* Medicaid.
Admissions Requirements Minimum age 18; Medical examination; Physician's request.
Staff Physicians 6 (pt); RNs 5 (pt); LPNs 5 (pt); Orderlies 3 (pt); Nurses aides 20 (ft), 15 (pt); Physical therapists 1 (pt); Recreational therapists 1 (ft); Occupational therapists 1 (pt); Speech therapists 1 (pt); Activities coordinators 1 (pt); Dietitians 1 (pt); Dentists 1 (pt); Ophthalmologists 1 (pt); Podiatrists 1 (pt); Audiologists 1 (pt).
Facilities Dining room; Physical therapy room; Activities room; Chapel; Crafts room; Laundry room; Barber/Beauty shop; Library.
Activities Arts & crafts; Cards; Games; Reading groups; Prayer groups; Movies; Shopping trips; Social/Cultural gatherings.

BLUE RAPIDS

Blue Valley Nursing Home
710 Southwest Ave, Blue Rapids, KS, 66411
(913) 226-7777
Admin Bertha Jane Harden. *Medical Dir/Dir of Nursing* Jean Crane.
Licensure Intermediate care. *Beds* ICF 54. *Certified* Medicaid.
Owner Nonprofit Corp.
Admissions Requirements Medical examination; Physician's request.
Staff RNs 1 (ft); LPNs 4 (ft); Nurses aides 15 (ft); Physical therapists 1 (pt); Recreational therapists 1 (ft), 1 (pt); Occupational therapists 1 (pt); Speech therapists 1 (pt); Activities coordinators 1 (ft); Dietitians 1 (pt); Social service designee 1 (ft).
Facilities Dining room; Physical therapy room; Activities room; Chapel; Laundry room; Barber/Beauty shop.
Activities Arts & crafts; Cards; Games; Prayer groups; Movies; Shopping trips.

BONNER SPRINGS

Bonner Health Center
520 E Morse, Bonner Springs, KS, 66012
(913) 441-2515
Admin Donna B Foster. *Medical Dir/Dir of Nursing* Valorie Jones LPN.

Licensure Intermediate care. *Beds* ICF 50.
Certified Medicaid.
Owner Proprietary Corp (Beverly Enterprises).
Admissions Requirements Minimum age 16;
Physician's request.
Staff LPNs 5 (ft); Orderlies 3 (ft); Nurses
aides 12 (ft); Activities coordinators 1 (ft).
Facilities Dining room; Physical therapy
room; Laundry room; Barber/Beauty shop.
Activities Arts & crafts; Cards; Games;
Reading groups; Prayer groups; Movies;
Shopping trips; Social/Cultural gatherings.

Kaw Valley Manor
510 E Morse Ave, Bonner Springs, KS, 66012
(913) 441-2444
Admin Diana L Jones. *Medical Dir/Dir of
Nursing* Delte Riggs.
Licensure Intermediate care. *Beds* ICF 108.
Certified Medicaid.
Owner Proprietary Corp (Beverly Enterprises).
Admissions Requirements Medical
examination; Physician's request.
Staff Physicians 3 (pt); RNs 1 (ft); LPNs 8
(ft), 1 (pt); Nurses aides 29 (ft), 7 (pt);
Physical therapists 2 (pt); Activities
coordinators 1 (ft); Dietitians 5 (ft), 7 (pt);
Licensed social worker.
Facilities Dining room; Physical therapy
room; Activities room; Crafts room; Laundry
room; Barber/Beauty shop; Library;
Conference room.
Activities Arts & crafts; Cards; Games;
Reading groups; Prayer groups; Movies;
Shopping trips; Social/Cultural gatherings;
Ceramics; Gardening; Happy hour; Exercise
class; Bus trips.

BUCKLIN

Hill Top House*
PO Box 248, 505 W Elm, Bucklin, KS, 67834
(316) 826-3202
Admin Bert L Earls.
Licensure Intermediate care. *Beds* 50.
Certified Medicaid.
Owner Nonprofit Corp.

BUHLER

Buhler Sunshine Home Inc*
412 W "C" Ave, Buhler, KS, 67522
(316) 543-2251
Admin Richard Heim.
Licensure Intermediate care. *Beds* 43.
Certified Medicaid.
Owner Proprietary Corp.

BURLINGAME

Santa Fe Trail Nursing Center
401 Prospect Pl, PO Box 6, Burlingame, KS,
66413
(913) 654-3391
Admin Marion Smith. *Medical Dir/Dir of
Nursing* Carolle May LPN HSS.
Licensure Intermediate care. *Beds* ICF 50.
Certified Medicaid.
Owner Proprietary Corp.
Admissions Requirements Minimum age 17;
Medical examination; Physician's request.
Staff RNs 2 (pt); LPNs 3 (ft); Orderlies 1 (ft);
Nurses aides 14 (ft); Physical therapists 1
(pt); Reality therapists 1 (pt); Recreational
therapists 1 (pt); Occupational therapists 1
(pt); Speech therapists 1 (ft); Activities
coordinators 1 (ft); Dietitians 1 (pt); Dentists
1 (pt); Ophthalmologists 1 (pt); Podiatrists 1
(pt).
Facilities Dining room; Physical therapy
room; Activities room; Chapel; Crafts room;
Laundry room; Barber/Beauty shop.
Activities Arts & crafts; Cards; Games;
Reading groups; Prayer groups; Movies;
Shopping trips; Social/Cultural gatherings;
Field trips in W/C van.

BURLINGTON

Golden Age Lodge of Burlington*
Box 43, Cross & Jarboe, Burlington, KS,
66839
(316) 364-2117
Admin Rosalee Garrett.
Licensure Intermediate care. *Beds* 102.
Certified Medicaid.
Owner Proprietary Corp (Medicalodges).

CALDWELL

Leisure Center
415 S Osage, Caldwell, KS, 67022
(316) 845-6495
Admin Dorothy Robertson. *Medical Dir/Dir of
Nursing* Sherry Stephens RN DON.
Licensure Intermediate care. *Beds* ICF 48.
Certified Medicaid.
Owner Proprietary Corp (Beverly Enterprises).
Admissions Requirements Medical
examination; Physician's request.
Staff RNs; LPNs; Nurses aides; Activities
coordinators.
Languages Czech, Sign
Facilities Dining room; Physical therapy
room; Chapel; Laundry room; Barber/Beauty
shop.
Activities Games; Reading groups; Prayer
groups; Shopping trips; Social/Cultural
gatherings.

CANEY

Caney Nursing Center
615 S High, Caney, KS, 67333
(316) 879-2929
Admin Mildred L Friday. *Medical Dir/Dir of
Nursing* Dr Mike Salrin; Kay Foulk DON.
Licensure Intermediate care. *Beds* ICF 40.
Certified Medicaid.
Owner Proprietary Corp (Beverly Enterprises).
Admissions Requirements Minimum age 16;
Medical examination; Physician's request.
Staff RNs; LPNs; Orderlies; Nurses aides;
Activities coordinators.
Facilities Dining room; Physical therapy
room; Activities room; Crafts room; Laundry
room; Barber/Beauty shop.
Activities Arts & crafts; Cards; Games;
Reading groups; Prayer groups; Movies;
Humanities program through Coffeyville
Community College.

CANTON

Shiloh Manor Nursing Home
PO Box 67, Canton, KS, 67428
(316) 628-4403
Admin Geneva Price. *Medical Dir/Dir of
Nursing* Levonne Minear RN DON.
Licensure Intermediate care. *Beds* ICF 60.
Certified Medicaid.
Owner Nonprofit organization/foundation.
Admissions Requirements Minimum age 16;
Medical examination.
Staff RNs 1 (ft), 1 (pt); LPNs 2 (ft), 2 (pt);
Nurses aides 21 (pt); Activities coordinators
1 (ft); Social worker 1 (ft).
Languages German
Affiliation Lutheran
Facilities Dining room; Physical therapy
room; Chapel; Laundry room; Barber/Beauty
shop.
Activities Arts & crafts; Cards; Games;
Reading groups; Prayer groups; Movies;
Shopping trips; Social/Cultural gatherings.

CEDAR VALE

Cedar Vale Manor*
100 River Rd, Cedar Vale, KS, 67024
(316) 758-2248
Admin Marjorie R Lampson.

Licensure Intermediate care. *Beds* 50.
Certified Medicaid.
Staff LPNs 2 (ft), 1 (pt); Orderlies 3 (ft);
Nurses aides 10 (ft), 2 (pt); Activities
coordinators 1 (ft), 1 (pt).
Facilities Dining room; Physical therapy
room; Activities room; Chapel; Laundry
room; Barber/Beauty shop.
Activities Arts & crafts; Cards; Games;
Reading groups; Prayer groups; Movies;
Shopping trips; Social/Cultural gatherings.

CHANUTE

Applewood Care Center Inc
302 S Denman, Chanute, KS, 66720
(316) 431-7300
Admin Cheryl Borjas. *Medical Dir/Dir of
Nursing* Landa Hughes DON.
Licensure ICF Mentally handicapped. *Beds*
ICF MH 50. *Certified* Medicaid; Medicare.
Owner Proprietary Corp.
Admissions Requirements Minimum age 18;
Medical examination.
Staff RNs 1 (ft), 1 (pt); LPNs 3 (ft), 3 (pt);
Nurses aides 6 (ft), 3 (pt); Activities
coordinators 2 (ft), 1 (pt).
Languages Spanish
Facilities Dining room; Physical therapy
room; Activities room; Crafts room; Laundry
room; Barber/Beauty shop.
Activities Arts & crafts; Games; Reading
groups; Prayer groups; Movies; Shopping
trips; Social/Cultural gatherings.

Arolyn Heights Nursing Home
1709 W 7th, Chanute, KS, 66720
(316) 431-9200
Admin Brenda Corbett. *Medical Dir/Dir of
Nursing* Julie Dickens RN.
Licensure Intermediate care. *Beds* ICF 49.
Certified Medicaid.
Owner Privately owned.
Admissions Requirements Medical
examination.
Staff RNs 1 (ft), 3 (pt); LPNs 2 (ft), 1 (pt);
Nurses aides 12 (ft), 3 (pt); Physical
therapists 1 (ft); Reality therapists 1 (pt);
Recreational therapists 1 (ft); Dietitians 1
(ft); Dentist 1 (pt).
Facilities Dining room; Physical therapy
room; Activities room; Chapel; Crafts room;
Laundry room; Barber/Beauty shop.
Activities Arts & crafts; Cards; Games;
Reading groups; Prayer groups; Movies;
Shopping trips; Social/Cultural gatherings.

Bethesda Nursing Center
530 W 14th St, Chanute, KS, 66720
(316) 431-4940
Admin Gary M Phillips. *Medical Dir/Dir of
Nursing* Albert A Kihm MD; Joan K
Augustine DON.
Licensure Intermediate care. *Beds* ICF 90.
Certified Medicaid.
Owner Proprietary Corp (Hillhaven Corp).
Admissions Requirements Medical
examination; Physician's request.
Staff RNs 2 (ft); LPNs 5 (ft), 2 (pt); Nurses
aides 20 (ft), 5 (pt); Activities coordinators 1
(ft).
Languages Spanish
Facilities Dining room; Physical therapy
room; Activities room; Chapel; Laundry
room; Barber/Beauty shop.
Activities Arts & crafts; Cards; Games; Prayer
groups; Movies; Social/Cultural gatherings.

Heritage Health Care Center
1630 W 2nd, Chanute, KS, 66720
(316) 431-4151
Admin Sonja Ann Emerson. *Medical Dir/Dir
of Nursing* Pamela A Colborn RN.
Licensure Intermediate care; Adult day care.
Beds ICF 105; Adult day care. *Certified*
Medicaid.
Owner Proprietary Corp.

Admissions Requirements Minimum age 16; Medical examination; Physician's request.
Staff RNs 2 (ft), 1 (pt); LPNs 3 (ft), 1 (pt); Nurses aides 20 (ft), 3 (pt); Physical therapists 1 (pt); Occupational therapists 1 (pt); Speech therapists 1 (pt); Activities coordinators 2 (ft); Dietitians 1 (pt); Ophthalmologists 1 (pt); Podiatrists 1 (pt).
Facilities Dining room; Physical therapy room; Activities room; Chapel; Laundry room; Barber/Beauty shop.
Activities Arts & crafts; Cards; Games; Reading groups; Prayer groups; Movies; Shopping trips.

CHAPMAN

Chapman Valley Manor*
1009 N Marshall St, Chapman, KS, 67431
(913) 922-6594
Admin Thomas L Canfield.
Licensure Intermediate care. *Beds* 50.
Certified Medicaid.
Owner Proprietary Corp.

CHENEY

Cheney Golden Age Home Inc
724 N Jefferson, Cheney, KS, 67025
(316) 542-3691
Admin George W Ball Jr. *Medical Dir/Dir of Nursing* Randall Fahrenholtz MD; Kathleen May RN DON.
Licensure Intermediate care. *Beds* ICF 60.
Certified Medicare.
Owner Nonprofit Corp.
Admissions Requirements Minimum age 18; Medical examination.
Staff Physicians 6 (pt); RNs 2 (ft), 1 (pt); LPNs 2 (ft), 1 (pt); Orderlies 1 (pt); Nurses aides 14 (ft), 6 (pt); Physical therapists 1 (ft); Occupational therapists 1 (pt); Speech therapists 1 (pt); Activities coordinators 1 (ft); Dietitians 1 (ft).
Languages German
Facilities Dining room; Physical therapy room; Activities room; Laundry room; Barber/Beauty shop.
Activities Arts & crafts; Cards; Games; Reading groups; Prayer groups; Movies; Shopping trips; Social/Cultural gatherings.

CHERRYVALE

Cherryvale Medi-Lodge*
1001 W Main, Cherryvale, KS, 67335
(316) 336-2102
Admin Sandra Sue Hale.
Licensure Intermediate care. *Beds* 51.
Certified Medicaid.
Admissions Requirements Medical examination; Physician's request.
Staff Physicians 1 (pt); RNs 1 (pt); LPNs 2 (ft); Nurses aides 19 (ft), 1 (pt); Activities coordinators 1 (ft).
Facilities Dining room; Physical therapy room; Activities room; Chapel; Crafts room; Laundry room; Barber/Beauty shop; Library.
Activities Arts & crafts; Cards; Games; Reading groups; Prayer groups; Movies; Shopping trips; Social/Cultural gatherings.

CHETOPA

Chetopa Nursing Home
PO Box 66, 814 Walnut, Chetopa, KS, 67336-0066
(316) 236-7248
Admin Gail Gallo. *Medical Dir/Dir of Nursing* Judy Fromm RN.
Licensure Intermediate care. *Beds* 41.
Certified Medicaid.
Admissions Requirements Minimum age 18; Medical examination; Physician's request.

Staff RNs 1 (ft); LPNs 1 (pt); Nurses aides 12 (ft), 2 (pt); Physical therapists 1 (pt); Reality therapists 1 (pt); Recreational therapists 1 (pt); Occupational therapists 1 (pt); Speech therapists 1 (pt); Activities coordinators 1 (ft); Dietitians 1 (pt); Podiatrists 1 (pt).
Facilities Dining room; Physical therapy room; Activities room; Chapel; Crafts room; Laundry room; Barber/Beauty shop; Library.
Activities Arts & crafts; Cards; Games; Reading groups; Prayer groups; Movies; Shopping trips; Social/Cultural gatherings.

CIMARRON

Heritage of Cimarron*
706 N Main, Cimarron, KS, 67835
(316) 855-3498
Admin Sharon G Fregon.
Licensure Intermediate care. *Beds* 48.
Certified Medicaid.
Owner Nonprofit Corp.

CLAY CENTER

Clay Center Presbyterian Manor
924 8th St, Clay Center, KS, 67432
(913) 632-5646
Admin Mariel Kolle.
Licensure Intermediate care. *Beds* 25.
Certified Medicaid.
Owner Nonprofit Corp.
Affiliation Presbyterian

Medicalodge of Clay Center
Box 517, 715 Liberty, Clay Center, KS, 67432
(913) 632-5696
Admin Rosemary Gonser. *Medical Dir/Dir of Nursing* Eltanis Volen.
Licensure Skilled care; Intermediate care. *Beds* SNF 40; ICF 56. *Certified* Medicaid.
Owner Proprietary Corp (Medicalodges).
Admissions Requirements Minimum age 16; Medical examination; Physician's request.
Staff RNs 1 (ft), 2 (pt); LPNs 4 (ft); Orderlies 2 (ft); Nurses aides 25 (ft), 5 (pt); Physical therapists 2 (ft); Occupational therapists 1 (pt); Activities coordinators 1 (ft); Dietitians 1 (pt).
Facilities Dining room; Physical therapy room; Activities room; Crafts room; Laundry room; Barber/Beauty shop; 2 Quiet rooms which serve many purposes including chapel.
Activities Arts & crafts; Cards; Games; Reading groups; Prayer groups; Movies; Shopping trips; Social/Cultural gatherings; Van trips.

CLEARWATER

Ninnescah Manor Inc
620 Wood St, Clearwater, KS, 67026
(316) 584-2271
Admin Marlis J Felber. *Medical Dir/Dir of Nursing* Roberta Tjaden RN.
Licensure Intermediate care. *Beds* ICF 60.
Certified Medicaid.
Owner Publicly owned.
Admissions Requirements Medical examination; Physician's request.
Staff RNs 1 (ft); LPNs 1 (ft), 1 (pt); Orderlies 2 (ft); Nurses aides 12 (ft), 7 (pt); Activities coordinators 1 (ft); Social Service 1 (ft); Minister 1 (pt).
Facilities Dining room; Physical therapy room; Activities room; Crafts room; Laundry room; Barber/Beauty shop; TV room for smokers; Solarium.
Activities Arts & crafts; Cards; Games; Reading groups; Prayer groups; Movies; Shopping trips; Social/Cultural gatherings; Exercise groups.

CLIFTON

Estelle's Nursing Home
Box 219, RR 1, Clifton, KS, 66937
(913) 455-3522
Admin Carol Saint. *Medical Dir/Dir of Nursing* Judy Chaput LPN.
Licensure Intermediate care. *Beds* ICF 32.
Certified Medicaid.
Owner Privately owned.
Admissions Requirements Minimum age 16; Medical examination; Physician's request.
Staff RNs 1 (pt); LPNs 3 (ft); Nurses aides 10 (ft), 4 (pt); Reality therapists 1 (pt); Recreational therapists 1 (pt); Activities coordinators 1 (pt); Dietitians 5 (ft), 1 (pt).
Facilities Dining room; Physical therapy room; Activities room; Laundry room; Barber/Beauty shop.
Activities Arts & crafts; Cards; Games; Reading groups; Prayer groups; Movies; Shopping trips; Social/Cultural gatherings; Volunteer parties; Bingo.

CLYDE

Park Villa
114 S High, Clyde, KS, 66938
(913) 446-2818
Admin Jane Magaw. *Medical Dir/Dir of Nursing* Marsha Hubert.
Licensure Intermediate care. *Beds* ICF 50.
Certified Medicaid.
Owner Nonprofit Corp.
Admissions Requirements Medical examination; Physician's request.
Staff RNs 1 (pt); LPNs 3 (ft), 2 (pt); Orderlies 1 (ft); Nurses aides 18 (ft), 6 (pt); Activities coordinators 1 (ft).
Facilities Dining room; Physical therapy room; Activities room; Chapel; Crafts room; Laundry room; Barber/Beauty shop.
Activities Arts & crafts; Cards; Games; Reading groups; Prayer groups; Movies; Social/Cultural gatherings.

COFFEYVILLE

Medicalodge East of Coffeyville
720 W 1st, Coffeyville, KS, 67337
(316) 251-3705
Admin Bonita L Schockey. *Medical Dir/Dir of Nursing* Kenneth Parker; Lynn Hatton RN DON.
Licensure Intermediate care. *Beds* 44.
Certified Medicaid.
Owner Proprietary Corp (Medicalodges).
Staff RNs; LPNs; Orderlies; Nurses aides; Activities coordinators.
Facilities Dining room; Physical therapy room; Laundry room; Barber/Beauty shop.
Activities Arts & crafts; Games; Reading groups; Prayer groups; Movies; Shopping trips; Social/Cultural gatherings.

Medicalodge West of Coffeyville
2910 Midland Ave, Coffeyville, KS, 67337
(316) 251-2420
Admin Diane Close. *Medical Dir/Dir of Nursing* Dr Gibbs; Rhonda Craven.
Licensure Skilled care; Intermediate care. *Beds* SNF 44; ICF 136. *Certified* Medicaid.
Owner Proprietary Corp (Medicalodges).
Admissions Requirements Minimum age 16; Medical examination; Physician's request.
Facilities Dining room; Physical therapy room; Activities room; Chapel; Laundry room; Barber/Beauty shop.
Activities Arts & crafts; Cards; Games; Reading groups; Prayer groups; Movies; Shopping trips; Social/Cultural gatherings.

Sunny View Adult Care Home Inc
14th & Roosevelt C, Coffeyville, KS, 67337
(316) 251-4032

Admin Melba Jane Guy. *Medical Dir/Dir of Nursing* James Wilson MD; Fonda Howard RN DON.
Licensure Intermediate care. *Beds* ICF 49. *Certified* Medicaid.
Owner Proprietary Corp.
Admissions Requirements Minimum age 18; Medical examination; Physician's request.
Staff RNs 3 (ft); Nurses aides 15 (ft); Activities coordinators 1 (ft); Certified medication aides 5 (ft).
Languages Spanish
Facilities Dining room; Physical therapy room; Activities room; Laundry room; Barber/Beauty shop.
Activities Arts & crafts; Games; Reading groups; Prayer groups; Movies; Shopping trips; Social/Cultural gatherings; Garden club.

COLBY

Good Samaritan Home*
Rte 1, Box 1, Colby, KS, 67701
(913) 462-7564
Admin Kenneth H Wagner.
Licensure Intermediate care. *Beds* 46. *Certified* Medicaid.

Lantern Park Manor
105 E College Dr, Colby, KS, 67701
(913) 462-6721
Admin Larry L Booth. *Medical Dir/Dir of Nursing* Asher Dahl MD; Carol Steward RN DON.
Licensure Intermediate care. *Beds* ICF 70. *Certified* Medicaid.
Owner Proprietary Corp (Beverly Enterprises).
Admissions Requirements Minimum age 18.
Staff RNs 5 (ft), 1 (pt); LPNs 3 (ft); Orderlies 3 (ft); Nurses aides 25 (ft); Activities coordinators 1 (ft).
Facilities Dining room; Physical therapy room; Activities room; Laundry room; Barber/Beauty shop.
Activities Arts & crafts; Cards; Games; Reading groups; Prayer groups; Movies; Shopping trips; Social/Cultural gatherings; Rhythm band; Gardening.

Thomas County Care Center
PO Box 110, 350 S Range, Colby, KS, 67701
(913) 462-8295
Admin Nancy L Fischer. *Medical Dir/Dir of Nursing* Joan Jamison DON.
Licensure Intermediate care. *Beds* 46. *Certified* Medicaid.
Owner Publicly owned.
Staff Physicians 1 (pt); RNs 1 (ft); LPNs 3 (ft), 3 (pt); Nurses aides 20 (ft); Activities coordinators 1 (ft).

COLDWATER

Pioneer Lodge
3rd & Frisco, Coldwater, KS, 67029
(316) 582-2123
Admin Ernest K Parker. *Medical Dir/Dir of Nursing* Lorena Friend.
Licensure Intermediate care. *Beds* 52. *Certified* Medicaid.
Owner Proprietary Corp.
Staff RNs 2 (pt); LPNs 1 (ft); Nurses aides 15 (ft), 5 (pt); Physical therapists 1 (pt); Occupational therapists 1 (pt); Speech therapists 1 (pt); Activities coordinators 1 (ft); Dietitians 1 (pt); Podiatrists 1 (pt).
Facilities Dining room; Physical therapy room; Activities room; Chapel; Crafts room; Laundry room; Barber/Beauty shop.
Activities Arts & crafts; Cards; Games; Reading groups; Prayer groups; Movies; Shopping trips.

COLUMBUS

Medicalodge of Columbus*
101 N Lee St, Columbus, KS, 66725
(316) 429-2134
Admin Cathy J Bowman.
Licensure Intermediate care. *Beds* 100. *Certified* Medicaid.
Owner Proprietary Corp (Medicalodges).

COLWICH

Colwich Health Center
5th & Colwich, Colwich, KS, 67030
(316) 796-0919
Admin Donald E Schmidt. *Medical Dir/Dir of Nursing* Dr David Hufford; Sharry Turner.
Licensure Intermediate care. *Beds* ICF 60. *Certified* Medicaid.
Owner Proprietary Corp.
Admissions Requirements Medical examination.
Staff RNs 1 (ft), 3 (pt); LPNs 2 (ft), 1 (pt); Nurses aides 12 (ft), 8 (pt); Recreational therapists 1 (ft), 1 (pt); Activities coordinators 1 (ft), 1 (pt).
Facilities Dining room; Physical therapy room; Activities room; Crafts room; Laundry room; Barber/Beauty shop.
Activities Arts & crafts; Cards; Games; Movies; Shopping trips; Social/Cultural gatherings.

CONCORDIA

Concordia Nursing Center*
825 E 7th, Concordia, KS, 66901
(913) 243-3497
Admin Eva L Schwab.
Licensure Intermediate care. *Beds* 48. *Certified* Medicaid.
Owner Proprietary Corp (Beverly Enterprises).
Admissions Requirements Medical examination; Physician's request.
Staff RNs 1 (pt); LPNs 1 (ft); Nurses aides 20 (ft), 2 (pt); Activities coordinators 1 (pt).
Facilities Dining room; Physical therapy room; Activities room; Chapel; Laundry room; Barber/Beauty shop; Library.
Activities Arts & crafts; Cards; Games; Reading groups; Prayer groups; Movies; Shopping trips.

Mt Joseph
Rte 1, Concordia, KS, 66901
(913) 243-1347
Admin Gretchen Storey Barclay. *Medical Dir/Dir of Nursing* Charlotte Wineinger.
Licensure Intermediate care. *Beds* ICF 125. *Certified* Medicaid.
Owner Nonprofit Corp.
Admissions Requirements Physician's request.
Staff RNs 4 (ft), 3 (pt); LPNs 3 (ft), 2 (pt); Nurses aides 40 (ft), 15 (pt); Physical therapists 1 (pt); Recreational therapists 1 (pt); Activities coordinators 2 (ft).
Affiliation Roman Catholic
Facilities Dining room; Physical therapy room; Activities room; Chapel; Crafts room; Barber/Beauty shop; Library.
Activities Arts & crafts; Cards; Games; Prayer groups; Movies.

Sunset Nursing Center
620 Second Ave, Concordia, KS, 66901
(913) 243-2720
Admin Dennis W Knapp.
Licensure Intermediate care. *Beds* ICF 58.
Owner Nonprofit Corp.
Admissions Requirements Minimum age 65; Medical examination.
Staff RNs 3 (ft), 1 (pt); LPNs 2 (pt); Orderlies 1 (ft), 2 (pt); Nurses aides 15 (ft), 11 (pt).
Affiliation Baptist
Facilities Dining room; Physical therapy room; Activities room; Chapel; Crafts room; Laundry room; Barber/Beauty shop; Library.

Activities Arts & crafts; Cards; Games; Reading groups; Prayer groups; Shopping trips; Social/Cultural gatherings.

CONWAY SPRINGS

Spring View Manor Inc
500 S 8th, Conway Springs, KS, 67031
(316) 456-2285
Admin Virginia C Winter. *Medical Dir/Dir of Nursing* Jennella Stitt.
Licensure Intermediate care. *Beds* ICF 47. *Certified* Medicaid.
Owner Privately owned.
Admissions Requirements Medical examination.
Staff Physicians 1 (pt); RNs 1 (pt); LPNs 3 (ft); Orderlies 1 (ft); Nurses aides 12 (ft), 4 (pt); Physical therapists 1 (pt); Reality therapists 1 (pt); Occupational therapists 1 (ft); Speech therapists 1 (pt); Activities coordinators 1 (pt); Dietitians 1 (pt); Dentists 1 (pt); Ophthalmologists 1 (pt); Podiatrists 1 (pt); Dentist 1 (pt).
Facilities Dining room; Physical therapy room; Activities room; Chapel; Laundry room; Barber/Beauty shop.
Activities Cards; Games; Reading groups; Prayer groups; Movies; Social/Cultural gatherings.

COTTONWOOD FALLS

Chase County Nursing Center
PO Box 589, 612 Walnut, Cottonwood Falls, KS, 66845
(316) 273-6360
Admin Earlene Lind. *Medical Dir/Dir of Nursing* Dr Bobby Ellis; Barbara Wente.
Licensure Intermediate care. *Beds* ICF 69. *Certified* Medicaid.
Owner Proprietary Corp (Beverly Enterprises).
Admissions Requirements Medical examination; Physician's request.
Staff RNs 1 (pt); LPNs 5 (ft); Nurses aides 18 (ft), 3 (pt); Physical therapists 1 (pt); Occupational therapists 1 (pt); Speech therapists 1 (pt); Activities coordinators 1 (ft); Dietitians 1 (pt); Social Services 1 (ft).
Languages Spanish
Facilities Dining room; Physical therapy room; Activities room; Chapel; Crafts room; Laundry room; Barber/Beauty shop; Library.
Activities Arts & crafts; Cards; Games; Reading groups; Prayer groups; Movies; Shopping trips; Social/Cultural gatherings.

COUNCIL GROVE

Country Club Home
PO Box 319, 400 Sunset Dr, Council Grove, KS, 66846
(913) 767-5172
Admin Al Germann. *Medical Dir/Dir of Nursing* Carole Downs DON.
Licensure Intermediate care. *Beds* ICF 100. *Certified* Medicaid.
Owner Proprietary Corp (Hillhaven Corp).
Staff RNs 4 (ft); LPNs 1 (ft); Orderlies 1 (ft); Nurses aides 14 (ft), 5 (pt); Recreational therapists 1 (ft); Activities coordinators 1 (ft); Dietitians 1 (ft).
Facilities Dining room; Physical therapy room; Activities room; Crafts room; Laundry room; Barber/Beauty shop.
Activities Arts & crafts; Cards; Games; Reading groups; Prayer groups; Movies; Shopping trips; Social/Cultural gatherings.

CUNNINGHAM

Hilltop Manor Inc
PO Box 8, Saint Leo Rd, Cunningham, KS, 67035
(316) 298-2781

Admin Izena Monk. *Medical Dir/Dir of Nursing* Sonja McGregor DON.
Licensure Intermediate care. *Beds* ICF 76. *Certified* Medicaid.
Owner Proprietary Corp.
Admissions Requirements Medical examination; Physician's request.
Staff RNs 2 (ft), 2 (pt); LPNs 1 (ft); Orderlies; Nurses aides 32 (ft); Physical therapists 1 (pt); Recreational therapists; Occupational therapists 1 (pt); Speech therapists 1 (pt); Activities coordinators; Dietitians 1 (pt); Podiatrists 1 (pt).
Facilities Dining room; Physical therapy room; Activities room; Crafts room; Laundry room; Barber/Beauty shop.
Activities Arts & crafts; Cards; Games; Reading groups; Prayer groups; Movies; Shopping trips; Social/Cultural gatherings.

DELPHOS

Delphos Rest Home Inc
405 N Custer, Delphos, KS, 67436
(913) 523-4234
Admin Carmelita J Berndt. *Medical Dir/Dir of Nursing* Eileen Boatwright.
Licensure Intermediate care. *Beds* ICF 34. *Certified* Medicaid.
Owner Proprietary Corp.
Admissions Requirements Medical examination.
Staff RNs 1 (ft); LPNs 2 (pt); Activities coordinators 1 (ft).
Facilities Dining room; Physical therapy room; Activities room; Laundry room; Barber/Beauty shop.
Activities Arts & crafts; Cards; Games; Reading groups; Prayer groups; Movies; Social/Cultural gatherings.

DERBY

Westview Manor Inc
445 N Westview, Derby, KS, 67037
(316) 788-3739
Admin John A Nicholas. *Medical Dir/Dir of Nursing* Roger L Thomas DO; Pat Mills RN.
Licensure Skilled care; Intermediate care; Residential care. *Beds* SNF 34; ICF 86; Residential 37. *Certified* Medicaid.
Owner Proprietary Corp.
Admissions Requirements Minimum age 21; Medical examination; Physician's request.
Staff Physicians 35 (pt); RNs 4 (ft), 4 (pt); LPNs 4 (ft), 6 (pt); Orderlies 2 (ft), 2 (pt); Nurses aides 35 (ft), 25 (pt); Physical therapists 2 (pt); Reality therapists 1 (pt); Recreational therapists 1 (ft), 1 (pt); Occupational therapists 1 (pt); Speech therapists 1 (pt); Activities coordinators 1 (ft); Dietitians 1 (pt); Dentists 1 (pt); Ophthalmologists 1 (pt); Podiatrists 1 (pt).
Facilities Dining room; Physical therapy room; Activities room; Crafts room; Laundry room; Barber/Beauty shop; Library.
Activities Arts & crafts; Cards; Games; Reading groups; Prayer groups; Movies; Shopping trips; Social/Cultural gatherings; Other outings with N/C transport provided.

DESOTO

Regency Health Care Center
33600 W 85th St, DeSoto, KS, 66018
(913) 422-2060
Admin Serena L Sutton. *Medical Dir/Dir of Nursing* Christopher Murray DO.
Licensure Intermediate care for mental health. *Beds* Intermediate care for mental health 50. *Certified* Medicaid.
Owner Proprietary Corp (Regency Health Care Centers).
Admissions Requirements Minimum age 21; Medical examination; Physician's request.

Staff RNs 1 (pt); LPNs 8 (ft); Nurses aides 7 (ft), 2 (pt); Recreational therapists 1 (ft); Activities coordinators 1 (ft); Art therapist 1 (pt).
Facilities Dining room; Physical therapy room; Activities room; Crafts room; Laundry room; Barber/Beauty shop.
Activities Arts & crafts; Cards; Games; Reading groups; Prayer groups; Movies; Shopping trips; Social/Cultural gatherings; Bingo; Church; Senior citizens; Pets (dog, cats, rabbit); Garden.

DEXTER

Grouse Valley Manor*
PO Box 98, S Main & Grouse, Dexter, KS, 67038
(316) 876-5421
Admin Hazel P Young.
Licensure Intermediate care. *Beds* 50. *Certified* Medicaid.
Owner Proprietary Corp.

DODGE CITY

Good Samaritan Center
501 W Beeson Rd, Dodge City, KS, 67801
(316) 227-7512
Admin William B Bender. *Medical Dir/Dir of Nursing* Lanette Housman.
Licensure Intermediate care; Apartments. *Beds* ICF; Apts 6. *Certified* Medicaid.
Owner Nonprofit Corp (Evangelical Lutheran/ Good Samaritan).
Admissions Requirements Medical examination; Physician's request.
Staff RNs 1 (ft), 1 (pt); LPNs 6 (ft), 3 (pt); Nurses aides 23 (ft), 7 (pt); Activities coordinators 1 (ft), 2 (pt).
Affiliation Lutheran
Facilities Dining room; Physical therapy room; Activities room; Chapel; Crafts room; Laundry room; Barber/Beauty shop.
Activities Arts & crafts; Cards; Games; Reading groups; Prayer groups; Movies; Shopping trips; Social/Cultural gatherings.

Trinity Manor Adult Care Home
510 Frontview, Dodge City, KS, 67801
(316) 227-8551
Admin Barbara R Schroeder. *Medical Dir/Dir of Nursing* Maida Waldman RN.
Licensure Intermediate care. *Beds* ICF 53. *Certified* Medicaid.
Owner Nonprofit Corp.
Admissions Requirements Medical examination.
Staff RNs 2 (ft); LPNs 3 (ft), 1 (pt); Nurses aides 12 (ft), 3 (pt); Physical therapists; Occupational therapists; Speech therapists; Activities coordinators 1 (ft); Dietitians; Podiatrists.
Languages Spanish
Affiliation Methodist
Facilities Dining room; Physical therapy room; Activities room; Crafts room; Laundry room; Barber/Beauty shop.
Activities Arts & crafts; Cards; Games; Reading groups; Prayer groups; Movies; Shopping trips; Social/Cultural gatherings.

DOUGLASS

Medicalodge of Douglass
Box 479, 9541 S Hwy 77, Douglass, KS, 67010
(316) 746-2157
Admin Sandy Nesler. *Medical Dir/Dir of Nursing* Kelly Deeder, LPN.
Licensure Intermediate care. *Beds* ICF 50. *Certified* Medicaid.
Owner Proprietary Corp (Medicalodges).
Admissions Requirements Minimum age 18; Medical examination; Physician's request.

Staff RNs; LPNs; Nurses aides; Activities coordinators; Dietitians.
Facilities Dining room; Physical therapy room; Activities room; Laundry room; Barber/Beauty shop.
Activities Arts & crafts; Cards; Games; Reading groups; Prayer groups; Movies; Shopping trips; Social/Cultural gatherings.

DOWNS

Downs Nursing Center
Rte 2, 1218 Kansas Ave, Downs, KS, 67437
(913) 454-3321
Admin Jacqueline A Williams. *Medical Dir/ Dir of Nursing* Burton Cox DO; Mary Moreland RN DON.
Licensure Skilled care. *Beds* SNF 60. *Certified* Medicaid.
Owner Proprietary Corp (Beverly Enterprises).
Staff RNs 3 (ft); LPNs 3 (ft), 3 (pt); Nurses aides 16 (ft); Activities coordinators 1 (ft).
Facilities Dining room; Physical therapy room; Activities room; Crafts room; Laundry room; Barber/Beauty shop.
Activities Arts & crafts; Cards; Games; Reading groups; Prayer groups; Movies; Shopping trips; Social/Cultural gatherings.

EASTON

Easton Manor
PO Box 277, Hwy 192, Easton, KS, 66020
(913) 773-8254
Admin Martha Hegarty. *Medical Dir/Dir of Nursing* Penny L Wilson.
Licensure Intermediate care. *Beds* ICF 59. *Certified* Medicaid.
Owner Proprietary Corp.
Staff Physicians 4 (pt); RNs 2 (ft), 1 (pt); LPNs 3 (ft); Orderlies 2 (ft); Nurses aides 13 (ft), 1 (pt); Physical therapists 1 (pt); Occupational therapists 1 (pt); Speech therapists 1 (pt); Activities coordinators 1 (ft); Dentists 1 (pt); Ophthalmologists 1 (pt); Podiatrists 1 (pt).
Facilities Dining room; Physical therapy room; Activities room; Crafts room; Laundry room; Barber/Beauty shop.
Activities Arts & crafts; Games; Reading groups; Social/Cultural gatherings.

EDWARDSVILLE

Edwardsville Convalescent Center*
750 Blake St, Edwardsville, KS, 66111
(913) 422-5832
Admin Barbara Grinter.
Licensure Intermediate care. *Beds* 50. *Certified* Medicaid.
Owner Proprietary Corp (Beverly Enterprises).

Edwardsville Manor*
751 Blake St, Edwardsville, KS, 66111
(913) 441-1900
Admin Katherine Littlewood.
Licensure Intermediate care. *Beds* 100. *Certified* Medicaid.
Owner Proprietary Corp (Beverly Enterprises).

Parkway Care Home*
749 Blake St, Edwardsville, KS, 66111
(913) 422-5952
Admin Barbara Taff.
Licensure Intermediate care. *Beds* 50. *Certified* Medicaid.
Owner Proprietary Corp (Beverly Enterprises).

EL DORADO

El Dorado Nursing Center*
900 Country Club Ln, El Dorado, KS, 67042
(316) 321-4444
Admin Larry W Smith.
Licensure Intermediate care. *Beds* 93. *Certified* Medicaid.

Owner Proprietary Corp (Beverly Enterprises).
Admissions Requirements Medical examination; Physician's request.
Staff RNs 2 (ft), 1 (pt); LPNs 3 (ft); Nurses aides 16 (ft), 4 (pt); Activities coordinators 1 (ft).
Facilities Dining room; Physical therapy room; Activities room; Laundry room; Barber/Beauty shop.
Activities Arts & crafts; Cards; Games; Movies; Shopping trips; Social/Cultural gatherings; Adopt-a-grandparent; Resident council; Family council.

Knutson Manor Nursing Center
1313 S High, El Dorado, KS, 67042
(316) 321-4140
Admin Elizabeth L Heinrich. *Medical Dir/Dir of Nursing* Brenda Poe RN DON.
Licensure Skilled care; Intermediate care. *Beds* SNF 117; ICF. *Certified* Medicaid; Medicare.
Owner Privately owned.
Admissions Requirements Medical examination; Physician's request.
Staff RNs 4 (ft); LPNs 4 (ft); Orderlies 1 (ft); Nurses aides 43 (ft); Physical therapists 1 (pt); Occupational therapists 1 (pt); Speech therapists 1 (pt); Activities coordinators; Dietitians 1 (pt); Podiatrists 1 (pt).
Facilities Dining room; Physical therapy room; Activities room; Chapel; Laundry room; Barber/Beauty shop; Library.
Activities Arts & crafts; Cards; Games; Reading groups; Prayer groups; Movies; Shopping trips; Social/Cultural gatherings.

ELLINWOOD

Woodhaven Care Center*
510 W 7th St, Ellinwood, KS, 67526
(316) 564-2337
Admin Della Ann Towse.
Licensure Intermediate care. *Beds* 54. *Certified* Medicaid.
Staff RNs 1 (ft); LPNs 1 (ft); Nurses aides 15 (ft), 5 (pt); Physical therapists 1 (pt); Occupational therapists 1 (pt); Speech therapists 1 (pt); Activities coordinators 1 (ft); Dietitians 1 (pt); Audiologists 1 (pt).
Facilities Dining room; Physical therapy room; Activities room; Crafts room; Laundry room; Barber/Beauty shop; Quiet room.
Activities Arts & crafts; Cards; Games; Reading groups; Prayer groups; Movies; Shopping trips; Social/Cultural gatherings.

ELLIS

Ellis Good Samaritan Center*
1100 Spruce, Ellis, KS, 67637
(913) 726-3101
Admin John R Binder Jr.
Licensure Intermediate care. *Beds* 59. *Certified* Medicaid.
Owner Nonprofit Corp (Evangelical Lutheran/ Good Samaritan).
Affiliation Lutheran

ELLSWORTH

Ellsworth Good Samaritan Center—Villa Grace
Box 47, Hwy 14, Ellsworth, KS, 67439
(913) 472-3167
Admin Virgil Larsen. *Medical Dir/Dir of Nursing* Margaret Long RN.
Licensure Intermediate care. *Beds* ICF 68. *Certified* Medicaid.
Owner Nonprofit Corp (Evangelical Lutheran/ Good Samaritan).
Admissions Requirements Medical examination.
Staff RNs 2 (ft), 1 (pt); LPNs 1 (ft), 1 (pt); Nurses aides 15 (ft), 3 (pt); Physical therapists 1 (pt); Reality therapists 1 (pt); Occupational therapists 1 (pt); Speech

therapists 1 (pt); Activities coordinators 1 (ft); Dietitians 1 (pt); Dentists 1 (pt); Podiatrists 1 (pt); Dentist 1 (pt).
Affiliation Lutheran
Facilities Dining room; Physical therapy room; Activities room; Chapel; Crafts room; Laundry room; Barber/Beauty shop; Library.
Activities Arts & crafts; Cards; Games; Reading groups; Prayer groups; Movies; Shopping trips; Social/Cultural gatherings.

Ellsworth Good Samaritan Center—Villa Hope
PO Box 47, S Hwy 14, Ellsworth, KS, 67439
(913) 472-3146
Admin Janyce J Larsen. *Medical Dir/Dir of Nursing* Mary Lou Pflughoeft RN.
Licensure Intermediate care. *Beds* ICF 48. *Certified* Medicaid.
Owner Nonprofit Corp (Evangelical Lutheran/ Good Samaritan).
Admissions Requirements Minimum age 20; Medical examination.
Staff RNs 2 (ft); LPNs 2 (pt); Nurses aides 10 (ft), 4 (pt); Physical therapists 1 (pt); Reality therapists 1 (pt); Occupational therapists 1 (pt); Speech therapists 1 (pt); Activities coordinators 1 (pt); Dietitians 1 (pt); Dentists 1 (pt); Podiatrists 1 (pt).
Affiliation Lutheran
Facilities Dining room; Physical therapy room; Activities room; Chapel; Crafts room; Laundry room; Barber/Beauty shop; Library.
Activities Arts & crafts; Cards; Games; Reading groups; Prayer groups; Movies; Shopping trips; Social/Cultural gatherings.

EMPORIA

Emporia Presbyterian Manor
2300 Industrial Rd, Emporia, KS, 66801
(316) 343-2613
Admin Floyd Born Exec Dir. *Medical Dir/Dir of Nursing* Beverly Sparks DON.
Licensure Skilled care. *Beds* SNF 60. *Certified* Medicaid.
Owner Nonprofit Corp.
Admissions Requirements Physician's request.
Staff RNs; LPNs; Nurses aides; Activities coordinators; Dietitians.
Affiliation Presbyterian
Facilities Dining room; Physical therapy room; Activities room; Chapel; Crafts room; Laundry room; Barber/Beauty shop; Library.
Activities Arts & crafts; Cards; Games; Reading groups; Prayer groups; Movies; Shopping trips; Social/Cultural gatherings.

Flint Hills Manor*
1620 Wheeler, Emporia, KS, 66801
(316) 342-3280
Admin Roberta Childers.
Licensure Intermediate care. *Beds* 100. *Certified* Medicaid.
Owner Proprietary Corp (Beverly Enterprises).

Heritage Manor of Emporia
217-221 West Logan, Emporia, KS, 66801
(316) 342-4212
Admin Deneice Burk. *Medical Dir/Dir of Nursing* Janet Maltby LPN.
Licensure Intermediate care. *Beds* ICF 105. *Certified* Medicaid.
Owner Proprietary Corp (National Heritage).
Admissions Requirements Minimum age 18.
Facilities Dining room; Physical therapy room; Activities room; Chapel; Crafts room; Barber/Beauty shop.
Activities Arts & crafts; Cards; Games; Reading groups; Prayer groups; Movies; Social/Cultural gatherings.

Shady Lawn Manor Inc*
315 S Commercial, Emporia, KS, 66801
(316) 342-3656
Admin Elizabeth May Grossenbacher.
Licensure Intermediate care. *Beds* 60. *Certified* Medicaid.
Owner Proprietary Corp.

ENTERPRISE

Enterprise Estates Nursing Center
Crestview Dr, Box 395, Enterprise, KS, 67441
(913) 934-2278
Admin Lester E Young. *Medical Dir/Dir of Nursing* Charles Svabada MD; Mary Stroda RN DON.
Licensure Intermediate care. *Beds* ICF 52. *Certified* Medicaid.
Owner Nonprofit Corp.
Admissions Requirements Minimum age 16.
Staff RNs 1 (ft); LPNs 2 (ft); Nurses aides 1 (ft), 3 (pt).
Facilities Dining room; Physical therapy room; Activities room; Crafts room; Laundry room; Barber/Beauty shop.
Activities Cards; Games; Reading groups; Prayer groups; Movies.

ERIE

Arkhaven at Erie
330 N Main, Erie, KS, 66733
(316) 224-5301
Admin Ernestine C Anselmi. *Medical Dir/Dir of Nursing* Carole A Hastong RN.
Licensure Intermediate care. *Beds* ICF 43. *Certified* Medicaid.
Owner Privately owned.
Staff RNs 2 (ft); LPNs 1 (ft), 1 (pt); Nurses aides 10 (ft), 6 (pt); Activities coordinators 1 (ft).
Facilities Dining room; Physical therapy room; Activities room; Chapel; Laundry room; Barber/Beauty shop; Library.
Activities Arts & crafts; Cards; Games; Reading groups; Prayer groups; Movies; Shopping trips.

ESKRIDGE

Heritage Village of Eskridge
505 N Main, Eskridge, KS, 66423
(913) 449-2294
Admin Karen Rockers. *Medical Dir/Dir of Nursing* Dr William Wade.
Licensure Intermediate care. *Beds* 60. *Certified* Medicaid.
Owner Proprietary Corp (Beverly Enterprises).
Admissions Requirements Minimum age 18; Medical examination; Physician's request.
Staff Physicians 1 (pt); RNs 1 (ft); LPNs 4 (ft); Orderlies 2 (ft); Nurses aides 15 (ft), 4 (pt); Physical therapists 1 (pt); Recreational therapists 1 (pt); Occupational therapists Psychiatrist 1 (pt); Speech therapists 1 (pt); Activities coordinators 1 (ft); Dietitians 1 (pt); Dentists 1 (pt); Ophthalmologists 1 (pt); Podiatrists 1 (pt).
Facilities Dining room; Physical therapy room; Activities room; Chapel; Crafts room; Laundry room; Barber/Beauty shop; Library.
Activities Arts & crafts; Cards; Games; Reading groups; Prayer groups; Movies; Shopping trips; Social/Cultural gatherings.

EUDORA

Eudora Nursing Center
PO Box 400, 1415 Maple, Eudora, KS, 66025
(913) 542-2176
Admin Civil Gray. *Medical Dir/Dir of Nursing* Sylvia Neis RN.
Licensure Intermediate care. *Beds* 100. *Certified* Medicaid.
Owner Proprietary Corp.
Admissions Requirements Medical examination.
Staff RNs 3 (ft), 1 (pt); LPNs 2 (ft), 1 (pt); Orderlies 1 (ft); Nurses aides 38 (ft), 2 (pt); Physical therapists 1 (pt); Activities coordinators 1 (ft); Dietitians 1 (pt).
Facilities Dining room; Physical therapy room; Activities room; Chapel; Crafts room; Laundry room; Barber/Beauty shop; Library.

Activities Arts & crafts; Cards; Games; Reading groups; Prayer groups; Movies; Exercise groups.

EUREKA

Medicalodge of Eureka
1020 N School, Eureka, KS, 67045
(316) 583-7418
Admin Jeanne Mertens. *Medical Dir/Dir of Nursing* Vivian Mitchell.
Licensure Intermediate care. *Beds* ICF 120.
Certified Medicaid.
Owner Proprietary Corp (Medicalodges).
Admissions Requirements Minimum age 16; Medical examination; Physician's request.
Staff RNs 1 (ft); LPNs 5 (ft); Activities coordinators 1 (ft), 1 (pt).
Facilities Dining room; Physical therapy room; Activities room; Crafts room; Laundry room; Barber/Beauty shop; Library.
Activities Arts & crafts; Cards; Games; Reading groups; Prayer groups; Movies; Shopping trips; Social/Cultural gatherings.

Regency Health Care Center
1406 N Elm, Eureka, KS, 67045
(316) 583-5630
Admin Rosalie L Garrison. *Medical Dir/Dir of Nursing* Pauline Bone; Karen Stelwell LPN DON.
Licensure Intermediate care. *Beds* ICF 48.
Certified Medicaid.
Owner Proprietary Corp (Regency Health Care Centers).
Admissions Requirements Minimum age 16; Medical examination.
Staff RNs 1 (pt); LPNs 2 (ft), 2 (pt); Nurses aides 20 (ft); Physical therapists 1 (pt); Recreational therapists 1 (ft); Occupational therapists 1 (pt); Speech therapists 1 (pt); Activities coordinators 1 (ft); Dietitians 1 (pt); Dentists 1 (pt); Ophthalmologists 1 (pt).
Facilities Dining room; Physical therapy room; Activities room; Laundry room; Barber/Beauty shop.
Activities Arts & crafts; Cards; Games; Reading groups; Prayer groups; Movies; Shopping trips; Social/Cultural gatherings; Beauty days; Museum visits; Educational groups.

FLORENCE

Regency Health Care Center
9th & Marion, Florence, KS, 66851
(316) 878-4440
Admin Madeline Teufel. *Medical Dir/Dir of Nursing* Larona Loveless.
Licensure Intermediate care. *Beds* ICF 60.
Certified Medicaid.
Owner Proprietary Corp (Regency Health Care Centers).
Admissions Requirements Minimum age 21.
Staff Physicians 1 (pt); RNs 1 (ft); LPNs 3 (ft); Orderlies 2 (ft); Nurses aides 18 (ft); Physical therapists 1 (pt); Recreational therapists 1 (pt); Occupational therapists 2 (ft); Activities coordinators 1 (ft); Dietitians 1 (ft); Ophthalmologists 1 (pt); Podiatrists 1 (pt).
Facilities Dining room; Physical therapy room; Activities room; Chapel; Crafts room; Laundry room; Barber/Beauty shop; Library.
Activities Arts & crafts; Cards; Games; Prayer groups; Movies; Shopping trips; ADL skills training; Living skills training; Outings for fishing; Swimming; Playing pool & Bowling.

FORT SCOTT

Arkhaven at Fort Scott
737 Heylman, Fort Scott, KS, 66701
(316) 223-1620
Admin Cynthia Lipe. *Medical Dir/Dir of Nursing* Jacqueline Vann.

Licensure Intermediate care. *Beds* ICF 60.
Certified Medicaid.
Owner Proprietary Corp.
Admissions Requirements Minimum age 19; Medical examination; Physician's request.
Staff RNs; LPNs; Nurses aides; Physical therapists; Reality therapists; Recreational therapists; Occupational therapists; Speech therapists; Activities coordinators; Dietitians; Ophthalmologists; Podiatrists.
Facilities Dining room; Physical therapy room; Activities room; Crafts room; Laundry room; Barber/Beauty shop.
Activities Arts & crafts; Cards; Games; Prayer groups; Movies; Social/Cultural gatherings; Cooking; Gardening; Self improvement.

Fort Scott Manor
736 Heylman, Fort Scott, KS, 66701
(316) 223-3120
Admin Vicky L Killinger. *Medical Dir/Dir of Nursing* Amy Wiggans.
Licensure Intermediate care. *Beds* 53.
Certified Medicaid.
Owner Proprietary Corp.
Staff RNs 1 (ft); LPNs 2 (ft), 2 (pt); Physical therapists 1 (pt); Occupational therapists 1 (pt); Speech therapists 1 (pt); Activities coordinators 1 (ft); Dietitians 1 (pt); Dentists 1 (pt); Podiatrists 1 (pt).
Facilities Dining room; Physical therapy room; Activities room; Crafts room; Laundry room; Barber/Beauty shop.
Activities Arts & crafts; Cards; Games; Reading groups; Prayer groups; Shopping trips; Social/Cultural gatherings.

Medicalodge of Fort Scott*
PO Box 1135, 915 S Horton, Fort Scott, KS, 66701
(316) 223-0210
Admin Kathleen A Ballbeck RN.
Licensure Intermediate care. *Beds* 132.
Certified Medicaid.
Owner Proprietary Corp (Medicalodges).

FOWLER

Fowler Nursing Home
512 E 5th, Fowler, KS, 67844
(316) 646-5215
Admin Penny Turner. *Medical Dir/Dir of Nursing* Barbara Whitney.
Licensure Intermediate care. *Beds* 38.
Certified Medicaid.
Owner Publicly owned.
Admissions Requirements Minimum age 16; Physician's request.
Staff RNs 3 (ft); LPNs 2 (ft); Nurses aides 20 (ft), 15 (pt); Physical therapists 1 (pt); Occupational therapists 1 (pt); Speech therapists 1 (pt); Activities coordinators 1 (ft), 1 (pt); Podiatrists 1 (pt).
Languages Spanish
Facilities Dining room; Physical therapy room; Activities room; Chapel; Laundry room; Barber/Beauty shop.
Activities Cards; Games; Prayer groups; Movies; Shopping trips; Social/Cultural gatherings.

FRANKFORT

Frankfort Community Care Home Inc
510 Walnut, Frankfort, KS, 66427
(913) 292-4442
Admin Linnea Brandt. *Medical Dir/Dir of Nursing* Shirley Anderson.
Licensure Intermediate care. *Beds* ICF 60.
Certified Medicaid.
Owner Nonprofit Corp.
Admissions Requirements Physician's request.
Staff RNs; LPNs; Nurses aides; Physical therapists; Recreational therapists; Occupational therapists; Speech therapists; Activities coordinators; Dietitians.

Facilities Dining room; Physical therapy room; Activities room; Chapel; Laundry room; Barber/Beauty shop; Storm shelter.
Activities Arts & crafts; Cards; Games; Reading groups; Prayer groups; Movies; Shopping trips; Social/Cultural gatherings; Music; Church services; Picnics; Fishing.

FREDONIA

Hillcrest Manor
240 N 19th St, Fredonia, KS, 66736
(316) 378-4163
Admin Lillian Ghramm. *Medical Dir/Dir of Nursing* Mary E Walker.
Licensure Intermediate care. *Beds* ICF 50.
Certified Medicaid.
Owner Proprietary Corp (Beverly Enterprises).
Admissions Requirements Minimum age 16; Medical examination.
Staff RNs; LPNs; Nurses aides; Activities coordinators; Medication Aide.
Facilities Dining room; Physical therapy room; Activities room; Chapel; Crafts room; Laundry room; Barber/Beauty shop.
Activities Arts & crafts; Cards; Games; Movies.

FRONTENAC

Sunset Manor*
206 S Dittmann, Frontenac, KS, 66762
(316) 231-7340
Admin Raymond R Knaup.
Licensure Intermediate care. *Beds* 116.
Certified Medicaid.
Owner Proprietary Corp.

GALENA

Barker Rest Home*
109 W Empire, Galena, KS, 66739
(316) 783-5048
Admin Barbara Link.
Licensure Intermediate care. *Beds* 50.
Certified Medicaid.
Owner Proprietary Corp.

Galena Manor
8th & Keller, Galena, KS, 66739
(316) 783-1383
Admin Marjorie A Abraham. *Medical Dir/Dir of Nursing* Stephen J Bazzano DO; Raymo Adams LPN DON.
Licensure Intermediate care. *Beds* ICF 60.
Certified Medicaid.
Owner Proprietary Corp (Americare Corp).
Admissions Requirements Minimum age 16; Medical examination; Physician's request.
Staff RNs 1 (pt); LPNs 4 (ft), 2 (pt); Orderlies 1 (ft); Nurses aides 16 (ft), 5 (pt); Occupational therapists 1 (ft); Activities coordinators 1 (ft); Dietitians 1 (ft); Ophthalmologists 1 (pt); Medical records 1 (ft).
Languages Sign
Facilities Dining room; Physical therapy room; Activities room; Crafts room; Laundry room; Barber/Beauty shop; Library; Quiet room; Day room.
Activities Arts & crafts; Cards; Games; Reading groups; Prayer groups; Movies; Shopping trips; Social/Cultural gatherings; Exercises.

GARDEN CITY

Garden Valley Retirement Village
1505 E Spruce St, Garden City, KS, 67846
(316) 275-9651
Admin Al Hill. *Medical Dir/Dir of Nursing* Norma Caldwell.
Licensure Skilled care; Intermediate care; Personal care. *Beds* SNF; ICF; Personal 130.
Certified Medicaid; Medicare.
Owner Nonprofit Corp.

Admissions Requirements Medical examination; Physician's request.
Staff Physicians 3 (pt); RNs 5 (ft), 6 (pt); LPNs 4 (ft), 3 (pt); Nurses aides 16 (ft), 8 (pt); Physical therapists 3 (ft), 1 (pt); Activities coordinators 1 (ft), 1 (pt); Dietitians 1 (pt).
Affiliation Mennonite
Facilities Dining room; Physical therapy room; Activities room; Chapel; Crafts room; Laundry room; Barber/Beauty shop; Library 9; Enclosed privacy patio.
Activities Arts & crafts; Cards; Games; Reading groups; Prayer groups; Movies; Shopping trips; Social/Cultural gatherings.

Terrace Garden Care Center
PO Box 955, 2308 E 3rd St, Garden City, KS, 67846
(316) 276-7643
Admin David J Cerveny.
Licensure Intermediate care. *Beds* 104. *Certified* Medicaid.
Admissions Requirements Minimum age 18; Medical examination; Physician's request.
Facilities Dining room; Physical therapy room; Activities room; Laundry room; Barber/Beauty shop.
Activities Arts & crafts; Cards; Games; Reading groups; Prayer groups; Movies; Shopping trips; Social/Cultural gatherings.

GARDNER

Bedford Nursing Center
223 Bedford St, Gardner, KS, 66030
(913) 884-6520
Admin Ramona Brant Inlow. *Medical Dir/Dir of Nursing* Chris Murray MD; Valorie Jones DON.
Licensure Intermediate care. *Beds* ICF 53. *Certified* Medicaid.
Owner Proprietary Corp (Beverly Enterprises).
Admissions Requirements Minimum age 18; Medical examination; Physician's request.
Staff LPNs 5 (ft); Nurses aides 19 (ft), 4 (pt); Physical therapists 1 (pt); Activities coordinators 1 (ft).
Facilities Dining room; Physical therapy room; Activities room; Crafts room; Laundry room; Barber/Beauty shop.
Activities Arts & crafts; Games; Reading groups; Prayer groups; Movies; Shopping trips; Social/Cultural gatherings.

GARNETT

Arkhaven at Garnett
RR 2, W 7th St, Garnett, KS, 66032
(913) 448-6884
Admin Barbara Watkins. *Medical Dir/Dir of Nursing* Beverly Olson.
Licensure Intermediate care. *Beds* ICF 49. *Certified* Medicaid; Medicare.
Owner Proprietary Corp.
Admissions Requirements Minimum age 16.
Staff RNs 2 (ft), 1 (pt); LPNs 2 (ft); Nurses aides 7 (ft), 6 (pt); Physical therapists 1 (pt); Reality therapists 1 (pt); Occupational therapists 1 (pt); Speech therapists 1 (pt); Activities coordinators 1 (ft); Dietitians 1 (ft).
Facilities Dining room; Physical therapy room; Activities room; Crafts room; Laundry room; Barber/Beauty shop.
Activities Arts & crafts; Cards; Games; Reading groups; Prayer groups; Shopping trips; Social/Cultural gatherings.

Golden Heights Living Center
101 N Pine St, Garnett, KS, 66032
(913) 448-2434
Admin Jon M Covault. *Medical Dir/Dir of Nursing* Debbie Bangs.
Licensure Intermediate care. *Beds* ICF 55. *Certified* Medicaid.
Owner Proprietary Corp.

Admissions Requirements Minimum age 16; Medical examination.
Staff RNs 1 (ft), 1 (pt); LPNs 3 (ft); Nurses aides 15 (ft); Activities coordinators 1 (ft).
Facilities Dining room; Physical therapy room; Activities room; Crafts room; Laundry room; Barber/Beauty shop.
Activities Arts & crafts; Cards; Games; Reading groups; Prayer groups; Movies; Shopping trips; Social/Cultural gatherings.

GIRARD

The Heritage*
PO Box 66, 511 N Western, Girard, KS, 66743
(316) 724-8288
Admin John Twarog.
Licensure Intermediate care. *Beds* 100. *Certified* Medicaid.
Owner Proprietary Corp.

GLASCO

The Nicol Home Inc
PO Box 68, Spear & Buffalo, Glasco, KS, 67445
(913) 568-2251
Admin Sunnie Z Brooks. *Medical Dir/Dir of Nursing* Janice Fief RN DON.
Licensure Intermediate care. *Beds* ICF 32. *Certified* Medicaid.
Owner Nonprofit Corp.
Staff RNs 1 (ft); LPNs 3 (ft); Nurses aides 15 (ft); Occupational therapists 1 (pt); Activities coordinators 1 (ft).
Facilities Dining room; Physical therapy room; Activities room; Laundry room; Barber/Beauty shop; Library.
Activities Arts & crafts; Cards; Games; Reading groups; Movies; Social/Cultural gatherings.

GODDARD

Medicalodge of Goddard*
501 Easy St, Goddard, KS, 67052
(316) 794-8635
Admin Margaret Clapp.
Licensure Intermediate care. *Beds* 50. *Certified* Medicaid.
Owner Proprietary Corp (Medicalodges).

GOODLAND

Golden West Skills Center*
108 Aspen Rd, Goodland, KS, 67735
(913) 899-2322
Admin Glendon L Horn.
Licensure Intermediate care for mentally retarded. *Beds* 53. *Certified* Medicaid.
Owner Proprietary Corp (Beverly Enterprises).

Sherman County Good Samaritan Center
208 W 2nd St, Goodland, KS, 67735
(913) 899-7517
Admin Scott Mutschelknaus. *Medical Dir/Dir of Nursing* Pat Graves DON.
Licensure Intermediate care. *Beds* ICF 60. *Certified* Medicaid.
Owner Nonprofit Corp (Evangelical Lutheran/ Good Samaritan).
Admissions Requirements Medical examination.
Staff RNs 2 (pt); LPNs 5 (ft), 2 (pt); Nurses aides 17 (ft), 5 (pt); Activities coordinators 1 (ft), 1 (pt).
Facilities Dining room; Physical therapy room; Activities room; Chapel; Crafts room; Laundry room; Barber/Beauty shop.
Activities Arts & crafts; Cards; Games; Reading groups; Prayer groups; Movies; Shopping trips; Social/Cultural gatherings.

GREAT BEND

Cherry Village
1401 Cherry Ln, Great Bend, KS, 67530
(316) 792-2165
Admin Clarence M Johansen. *Medical Dir/Dir of Nursing* Pamla S Lewis.
Licensure Skilled care. *Beds* ICF 95. *Certified* Medicaid.
Owner Proprietary Corp.
Admissions Requirements Minimum age 18; Medical examination; Physician's request.
Staff RNs 6 (ft), 2 (pt); LPNs 5 (ft); Orderlies 2 (ft); Nurses aides 24 (ft), 6 (pt); Physical therapists 1 (ft); Recreational therapists 1 (pt).
Facilities Dining room; Physical therapy room; Activities room; Barber/Beauty shop; Crafts room; Laundry room; Barber/Beauty shop.
Activities Arts & crafts; Cards; Games; Prayer groups; Movies.

Great Bend Manor
1560 K-96 Hwy, Great Bend, KS, 67530
(316) 792-2448
Admin Tom A Hermansen.
Licensure Intermediate care. *Beds* 160. *Certified* Medicaid.
Owner Proprietary Corp.

GREENSBURG

Lifecare of Greensburg Kansas
723 S Elm, Greensburg, KS, 67054
(316) 723-2633, 723-2613
Admin Vern Overgaard. *Medical Dir/Dir of Nursing* Irene Monroe LPN DON.
Licensure Intermediate care. *Beds* ICF 50. *Certified* Medicaid; Medicare.
Owner Proprietary Corp (Community Lifecare Enterprises).
Admissions Requirements Minimum age 16.
Staff Physicians 2 (ft); RNs 3 (ft); LPNs 3 (ft); Physical therapists 2 (ft); Activities coordinators 1 (ft).
Facilities Dining room; Physical therapy room; Activities room; Chapel; Crafts room; Laundry room; Barber/Beauty shop.
Activities Arts & crafts; Games; Reading groups; Prayer groups; Movies; Shopping trips; Social/Cultural gatherings.

HALSTEAD

Regency Health Care Center
10th & Walnut Sts, Halstead, KS, 67056
(316) 835-2277
Admin Frank Taylor. *Medical Dir/Dir of Nursing* Andrea Hall RN DON.
Licensure Intermediate care. *Beds* 100. *Certified* Medicaid.
Owner Proprietary Corp (Regency Health Care Centers).
Admissions Requirements Minimum age 18; Medical examination; Physician's request.
Staff Physicians 25 (pt); RNs 3 (ft), 2 (pt); LPNs 5 (ft), 3 (pt); Orderlies 6 (ft); Nurses aides 40 (ft); Physical therapists 1 (pt); Recreational therapists 1 (pt); Occupational therapists 1 (pt); Speech therapists 1 (pt); Activities coordinators 1 (ft); Dietitians 1 (pt); Ophthalmologists 1 (pt).
Facilities Dining room; Physical therapy room; Activities room; Crafts room; Laundry room; Barber/Beauty shop; Library.
Activities Arts & crafts; Cards; Games; Reading groups; Prayer groups; Movies; Shopping trips.

HARDTNER

Achenbach Learning Center*
420 N Cherokee, Box 38, Hardtner, KS, 67057
(316) 296-4421

Admin Bernard Turnbaugh.
Licensure Intermediate care for mentally
retarded. *Beds* 51. *Certified* Medicaid.
Owner Proprietary Corp (Vetter Health
Services).

HARPER

Life Care of Harper
615 W 12th, Harper, KS, 67058
(316) 896-2914
Admin Shirley Smith. *Medical Dir/Dir of
Nursing* Martha Seiwert.
Licensure Intermediate care. *Beds* ICF 57.
Certified Medicaid.
Owner Proprietary Corp.
Staff Physicians; RNs; LPNs; Nurses aides;
Physical therapists; Recreational therapists;
Occupational therapists; Speech therapists;
Activities coordinators; Dietitians;
Ophthalmologists; Podiatrists.
Facilities Dining room; Physical therapy
room; Activities room; Crafts room; Laundry
room; Barber/Beauty shop.
Activities Arts & crafts; Reading groups;
Prayer groups; Movies; Social/Cultural
gatherings.

HARTFORD

Hartford Manor Training Center
413 E Exchange, Hartford, KS, 66854
(316) 392-5524
Admin John Howe. *Medical Dir/Dir of
Nursing* K R Hunter MD; Virginia Sorenson
DON.
Licensure Intermediate care for mentally
retarded. *Beds* ICF/MR 50. *Certified*
Medicaid.
Owner Proprietary Corp.
Admissions Requirements Minimum age 18;
Medical examination.
Staff Physicians 1 (pt); RNs 1 (ft); LPNs 2
(ft); Nurses aides 65 (ft), 7 (pt); Physical
therapists 1 (pt); Occupational therapists 1
(pt); Speech therapists 1 (pt); Activities
coordinators 1 (ft); Dietitians 1 (pt);
Podiatrists 1 (pt); Social worker 1 (ft).
Facilities Dining room; Physical therapy
room; Activities room; Crafts room; Laundry
room; Barber/Beauty shop; Training
facilities.
Activities Arts & crafts; Cards; Games;
Reading groups; Movies; Shopping trips;
Social/Cultural gatherings; Training in all
areas of personal care & independent living.

HAVEN

Cedar Crest Training Center at Haven
PO Box D, 216 N Topeka, Haven, KS, 67543
(316) 465-2249
Admin Mark Davis. *Medical Dir/Dir of
Nursing* Virginia Brawner.
Licensure Intermediate care for mentally
retarded. *Beds* ICF/MR 91. *Certified*
Medicaid.
Owner Proprietary Corp (Cedar Crest Inc).
Admissions Requirements Minimum age 18.
Staff Physicians; RNs; LPNs; Nurses aides;
Physical therapists; Recreational therapists;
Occupational therapists; Speech therapists;
Activities coordinators; Dietitians; Dentists;
Ophthalmologists.
Facilities Dining room; Physical therapy
room; Activities room; Laundry room;
Barber/Beauty shop.
Activities Arts & crafts; Cards; Games;
Reading groups; Prayer groups; Movies;
Shopping trips; Social/Cultural gatherings.

HAVILAND

Lifecare Rehabilitation Center
Box 263, 200 N Main St, Haviland, KS,
67059
(316) 862-5233, 862-5315, 862-5291
Admin John M Van Hook. *Medical Dir/Dir of
Nursing* Bertha M Tuttle RN.
Licensure Intermediate care. *Beds* ICF
Intermediate care for Mental Health 50.
Certified Medicaid.
Owner Proprietary Corp.
Admissions Requirements Minimum age 18;
Medical examination.
Staff Physicians; RNs; LPNs; Nurses aides;
Physical therapists; Occupational therapists;
Speech therapists; Activities coordinators;
Dietitians; Dentists; Ophthalmologists;
Podiatrists.
Facilities Dining room; Physical therapy
room; Activities room; Crafts room; Laundry
room; Barber/Beauty shop; Quiet room.
Activities Arts & crafts; Cards; Games; Prayer
groups; Movies; Shopping trips; Social/
Cultural gatherings.

HAYS

Hays Good Samaritan Center
27th & Canal, Hays, KS, 67601
(913) 625-7331
Admin Elaine Metzger. *Medical Dir/Dir of
Nursing* Linda Hall RN DON.
Licensure Intermediate care. *Beds* ICF 88.
Certified Medicaid.
Owner Nonprofit Corp (Evangelical Lutheran/
Good Samaritan).
Admissions Requirements Medical
examination; Physician's request.
Staff RNs 1 (ft), 1 (pt); LPNs 8 (ft); Nurses
aides 33 (ft); Activities coordinators 1 (ft);
CMAs 5 (ft); Rehabilitation aides 1 (ft), 1
(pt).
Languages German
Affiliation Lutheran
Facilities Dining room; Physical therapy
room; Activities room; Chapel; Laundry
room; Barber/Beauty shop.
Activities Arts & crafts; Cards; Games;
Reading groups; Prayer groups; Movies;
Social/Cultural gatherings.

St John's of Hays
2403 Canterbury Rd, Hays, KS, 67601
(913) 628-3241
Admin Carl L Noyes. *Medical Dir/Dir of
Nursing* Russell Cramm MD; Sr Mary
Martha Karlin DON.
Licensure Skilled care. *Beds* SNF 60. *Certified*
Medicaid; Medicare.
Owner Nonprofit Corp.
Staff Physicians 1 (pt); RNs 3 (ft), 1 (pt);
LPNs 1 (ft), 5 (pt); Nurses aides 5 (ft), 19
(pt); Physical therapists 1 (ft); Speech
therapists 1 (pt); Activities coordinators 1
(ft); Dietitians 1 (ft); Podiatrists 1 (pt).
Languages German
Affiliation Roman Catholic
Facilities Dining room; Physical therapy
room; Activities room; Chapel; Laundry
room; Barber/Beauty shop.
Activities Arts & crafts; Games; Reading
groups; Prayer groups; Movies; Social/
Cultural gatherings.

HAYSVILLE

Green Meadows Nursing Center
215 N Lamar St, Haysville, KS, 67060
(316) 524-3211
Admin Ed Brass. *Medical Dir/Dir of Nursing*
R D Magsalin MD; Donna Malia RN DON.
Licensure Skilled care; Intermediate care. *Beds*
SNF 50; ICF 100. *Certified* Medicaid;
Medicare.
Owner Proprietary Corp (Hillhaven Corp).

Admissions Requirements Minimum age;
Medical examination; Physician's request.
Staff RNs 4 (ft), 2 (pt); LPNs 12 (ft), 3 (pt);
Nurses aides 36 (ft), 10 (pt); Physical
therapists 1 (pt); Recreational therapists 1
(ft); Occupational therapists 1 (pt); Speech
therapists 1 (pt); Activities coordinators 1
(ft); Dietitians 1 (pt); Podiatrists 1 (pt).
Facilities Dining room; Physical therapy
room; Activities room; Laundry room;
Barber/Beauty shop.
Activities Arts & crafts; Cards; Games;
Reading groups; Prayer groups; Movies;
Shopping trips; Social/Cultural gatherings;
Reality orientation; Remotivation groups;
Music therapy.

HERINGTON

Lutheran Home Inc*
2 E Ash St, Herington, KS, 67449
(913) 258-2283
Admin William D Peterson.
Licensure Intermediate care. *Beds* 100.
Certified Medicaid.
Owner Nonprofit Corp.
Affiliation Lutheran

HESSTON

Schowalter Villa
Box 5000, 200 W Cedar, Hesston, KS, 67062
(316) 327-4261
Admin Leo G Schmidt. *Medical Dir/Dir of
Nursing* Paul Fransen MD; Esther Unruh
RN DON.
Licensure Intermediate care. *Beds* ICF 67.
Certified Medicaid.
Owner Nonprofit Corp.
Admissions Requirements Medical
examination; Physician's request.
Staff RNs 3 (ft), 4 (pt); LPNs 2 (pt); Orderlies
1 (ft); Nurses aides 18 (ft), 12 (pt); Activities
coordinators 1 (ft), 1 (pt); Social worker 1
(pt).
Affiliation Mennonite
Facilities Dining room; Physical therapy
room; Activities room; Chapel; Crafts room;
Laundry room; Barber/Beauty shop; Library.
Activities Cards; Games; Reading groups;
Prayer groups; Movies; Shopping trips;
Social/Cultural gatherings.

HIAWATHA

Oak Ridge Acres
200 S Sioux, Hiawatha, KS, 66434
(913) 742-2149
Admin Georgia Loyd. *Medical Dir/Dir of
Nursing* Tracy Britt.
Licensure Intermediate care. *Beds* ICF 49.
Certified Medicaid; Medicare.
Owner Proprietary Corp.
Admissions Requirements Minimum age 16;
Medical examination; Physician's request.
Staff RNs 1 (ft); LPNs 5 (ft); Nurses aides 14
(ft); Physical therapists 1 (pt); Occupational
therapists 1 (pt); Speech therapists 1 (pt);
Activities coordinators 1 (ft); Dietitians 1
(pt); Dentists 1 (pt); Ophthalmologists 1 (pt);
Podiatrists 1 (pt).
Facilities Dining room; Physical therapy
room; Activities room; Laundry room;
Barber/Beauty shop.
Activities Arts & crafts; Cards; Games;
Reading groups; Prayer groups; Movies;
Social/Cultural gatherings; Bible study; One-
to-one individualized activities; Spelling bee;
Bingo; Church service.

Pleasant View Nursing Center*
Rte 4, Hiawatha, KS, 66434
(913) 742-2175
Admin Jerry W Johnson.

Licensure Intermediate care. *Beds* 60.
Certified Medicaid.
Owner Publicly owned.

Regency Health Care Center*
RR 2, Iowa St, Hiawatha, KS, 66434
(913) 742-7465
Admin Myrtle Kindig. *Medical Dir/Dir of Nursing* Dr Larson.
Licensure Skilled care; Intermediate care. *Beds* ICF 100. *Certified* Medicaid; Medicare.
Owner Proprietary Corp (Regency Health Care Centers).
Admissions Requirements Minimum age 16; Physician's request.
Staff RNs 1 (ft), 1 (pt); LPNs 5 (ft); Physical therapists 2 (ft); Activities coordinators 1 (ft).
Facilities Dining room; Physical therapy room; Activities room; Chapel; Crafts room; Laundry room; Barber/Beauty shop; Library.
Activities Arts & crafts; Games; Prayer groups; Movies.

HIGHLAND

Collier Manor*
PO Box 117, South Ave, Highland, KS, 66035
(913) 442-3816
Admin Bette J Fritch.
Licensure Intermediate care. *Beds* 50.
Certified Medicaid.
Owner Proprietary Corp.

HILL CITY

Dawson Place Inc*
208 W Prout, Hill City, KS, 67642
(913) 674-3414
Admin Ladonna Hensley.
Licensure Intermediate care. *Beds* 55.
Certified Medicaid.
Owner Proprietary Corp.

HILLSBORO

Parkside Homes Inc
200 Willow Rd, Hillsboro, KS, 67063
(316) 947-5700, 947-5909
Admin Carlene C Pattie. *Medical Dir/Dir of Nursing* Elva Penner DON.
Licensure Intermediate care. *Beds* 50.
Certified Medicaid.
Owner Nonprofit Corp.
Admissions Requirements Medical examination; Physician's request.
Staff RNs 1 (ft), 2 (pt); LPNs 2 (ft), 1 (pt); Nurses aides 3 (ft), 17 (pt); Activities coordinators 3 (pt).
Languages German, Low German
Affiliation Mennonite
Facilities Dining room; Physical therapy room; Activities room; Chapel; Crafts room; Laundry room; Barber/Beauty shop; Library; Mini store.
Activities Arts & crafts; Games; Reading groups; Prayer groups; Movies; Shopping trips; Social/Cultural gatherings; Tours; Picnics; Quilting; Bible studies; Coffee break.

HOLTON

Jackson County Nursing Home Inc
1121 W 7th, Holton, KS, 66436
(913) 364-3164
Admin Suzanne Misenhelter.
Licensure Intermediate care. *Beds* 64.
Certified Medicaid.

Merry Manor
100 Topeka, Holton, KS, 66436
(913) 364-3840
Admin Mary Ann Kirk. *Medical Dir/Dir of Nursing* Theresa Kirk.

Licensure Intermediate care. *Beds* ICF 47.
Certified Medicaid.
Owner Proprietary Corp.
Admissions Requirements Medical examination.
Staff RNs 1 (pt); LPNs 5 (ft), 1 (pt); Nurses aides 14 (ft); Activities coordinators 1 (ft); Dietitians 1 (ft).
Facilities Dining room; Physical therapy room; Activities room; Laundry room; Barber/Beauty shop.
Activities Arts & crafts; Cards; Games; Reading groups; Prayer groups; Shopping trips; Social/Cultural gatherings.

HORTON

Tri-County Manor Nursing Center*
1890 Euclid, Horton, KS, 66439
(913) 486-2697
Admin Rhonda Parks. *Medical Dir/Dir of Nursing* Dr Edgardo Francisco.
Licensure Intermediate care. *Beds* 110.
Certified Medicaid; Medicare.
Admissions Requirements Minimum age 16; Medical examination; Physician's request.
Staff Physicians 5 (pt); RNs 2 (pt); LPNs 6 (ft), 2 (pt); Orderlies 3 (ft), 1 (pt); Nurses aides 34 (ft), 6 (pt); Physical therapists 1 (pt); Occupational therapists 1 (pt); Speech therapists 1 (pt); Activities coordinators 1 (ft); Dietitians 1 (pt); Dentists 1 (pt); Ophthalmologists 1 (pt); Podiatrists 1 (pt); Audiologists 1 (pt).
Facilities Dining room; Physical therapy room; Activities room; Crafts room; Laundry room; Barber/Beauty shop; Library.
Activities Arts & crafts; Cards; Games; Reading groups; Prayer groups; Shopping trips; Social/Cultural gatherings; Musical programs; Scenic bus rides.

HOWARD

Howard Twilight Manor
PO Box 237, Hwy 99, Howard, KS, 67349
(316) 374-2495
Admin Mary J Smith.
Licensure Intermediate care. *Beds* ICF 50.
Certified Medicaid.
Owner Publicly owned.
Admissions Requirements Minimum age 16; Medical examination; Physician's request.
Staff RNs 1 (pt); LPNs 3 (ft); Nurses aides 20 (ft); Activities coordinators 1 (ft).
Facilities Dining room; Physical therapy room; Activities room; Chapel; Laundry room; Barber/Beauty shop.
Activities Arts & crafts; Cards; Games; Reading groups; Prayer groups; Movies; Shopping trips; Social/Cultural gatherings.

HUGOTON

Pioneer Manor
PO Box 9, 6th & Polk, Hugoton, KS, 67951
(316) 544-2023
Admin Leo L Buss. *Medical Dir/Dir of Nursing* Dr Larry Balzer; Cindy Kuder RN.
Licensure Intermediate care. *Beds* 56.
Certified Medicaid.
Owner Nonprofit Corp (Luth Hosp & Homes Socty).
Admissions Requirements Minimum age 45; Medical examination; Physician's request.
Staff Physicians 1 (pt); RNs 3 (ft); LPNs 2 (ft); Orderlies 1 (pt); Nurses aides 12 (ft), 6 (pt); Speech therapists 1 (pt); Activities coordinators 1 (ft), 1 (pt); Dietitians 7 (ft), 2 (pt); Podiatrists 1 (pt).
Facilities Dining room; Physical therapy room; Activities room; Chapel; Crafts room; Laundry room; Barber/Beauty shop.

Activities Arts & crafts; Games; Reading groups; Prayer groups; Movies; Shopping trips; Social/Cultural gatherings; Make floats for county fair; Make Chamber of Commerce annual banquet decorations.

HUMBOLDT

Pinecrest Care Center*
1020 Pine, Humboldt, KS, 66748
(316) 473-2393
Admin Carolyn J Moore.
Licensure Intermediate care. *Beds* 51.
Certified Medicaid.
Admissions Requirements Medical examination.
Staff RNs 1 (ft); LPNs 4 (ft), 1 (pt); Nurses aides 14 (ft), 2 (pt); Physical therapists 1 (pt); Recreational therapists 1 (ft); Occupational therapists 1 (pt); Speech therapists 1 (pt); Activities coordinators 1 (ft); Dietitians 1 (pt); Dentists 1 (pt); Podiatrists 1 (pt); Audiologists 1 (pt).
Facilities Dining room; Physical therapy room; Activities room; Chapel; Crafts room; Laundry room; Barber/Beauty shop; Library.
Activities Arts & crafts; Cards; Games; Reading groups; Prayer groups; Movies; Shopping trips; Social/Cultural gatherings.

HUTCHINSON

Golden Plains Inc*
1202 E 23rd St, Hutchinson, KS, 67501
(316) 669-9393
Admin Marilyn S Luman. *Medical Dir/Dir of Nursing* W C Goodpasture MD.
Licensure Skilled care. *Beds* 120. *Certified* Medicaid; Medicare.
Admissions Requirements Minimum age 16; Medical examination; Physician's request.
Staff Physicians 1 (ft); RNs 8 (ft), 4 (pt); LPNs 4 (ft), 2 (pt); Nurses aides 45 (ft), 10 (pt); Physical therapists 1 (ft); Speech therapists 1 (ft); Activities coordinators 1 (ft); Dietitians 1 (pt); Dentists 1 (pt); Ophthalmologists 1 (pt); Podiatrists 1 (pt); Audiologists 1 (pt).
Facilities Dining room; Physical therapy room; Activities room; Laundry room; Barber/Beauty shop; Library.
Activities Arts & crafts; Cards; Games; Reading groups; Prayer groups; Movies; Social/Cultural gatherings.

Hutchinson Good Samaritan Center
810 E 30th Ave, Hutchinson, KS, 67501
(316) 663-1189
Admin James A Adix.
Licensure Intermediate care. *Beds* 90.
Certified Medicaid.
Owner Nonprofit Corp (Evangelical Lutheran/Good Samaritan).
Admissions Requirements Minimum age 21.
Staff RNs 3 (ft); LPNs 3 (ft); Nurses aides 30 (ft); Activities coordinators 1 (ft), 1 (pt).
Affiliation Lutheran
Facilities Dining room; Physical therapy room; Activities room; Chapel; Crafts room; Laundry room; Barber/Beauty shop; Library.
Activities Arts & crafts; Cards; Games; Reading groups; Prayer groups; Movies; Shopping trips; Bell choir; Adopt-a-grandparent program.

Hutchinson Heights
PO Box 2123, Hutchinson, KS, 67504
(316) 669-8522
Admin David K Reimer. *Medical Dir/Dir of Nursing* Doris Coats Gray.
Licensure Intermediate care. *Beds* ICF.
Certified Medicaid.
Owner Nonprofit organization/foundation.
Admissions Requirements Minimum age 18; Medical examination; Physician's request.

Staff Physicians 1 (pt); RNs 3 (ft), 2 (pt);
LPNs 1 (pt); Nurses aides 20 (ft), 3 (pt);
Occupational therapists 1 (pt); Speech
therapists 1 (pt); Activities coordinators 2
(pt); Dietitians 1 (pt); Podiatrists 1 (pt).
Affiliation Presbyterian
Facilities Dining room; Physical therapy
room; Activities room; Laundry room.
Activities Arts & crafts; Cards; Games;
Reading groups; Prayer groups; Movies;
Shopping trips; Social/Cultural gatherings.

Oakwood Villa Care Center*
2301 N Severance, Hutchinson, KS, 67501
(316) 662-0597
Admin Dwight D Pflugard. *Medical Dir/Dir of
Nursing* Dr Savage.
Licensure Intermediate care. *Beds* 100.
Certified Medicaid.
Owner Proprietary Corp (Manor Care).
Admissions Requirements Minimum age 18;
Medical examination.
Staff RNs 4 (ft); LPNs 8 (ft); Orderlies 5 (ft);
Nurses aides 30 (ft); Reality therapists 1 (ft);
Recreational therapists 1 (ft); Activities
coordinators 1 (ft); Dietitians 1 (ft).
Facilities Dining room; Physical therapy
room; Activities room; Chapel; Crafts room;
Laundry room; Barber/Beauty shop.
Activities Arts & crafts; Cards; Games;
Reading groups; Prayer groups; Movies;
Shopping trips; Social/Cultural gatherings;
Fishing; BBQs; Shuffleboard; Horseshoes.

Rebekah-Odd Fellow Care Home
PO Box 175, Rte 1, Hutchinson, KS, 67501
(316) 663-3839
Admin Wanda I Carter. *Medical Dir/Dir of
Nursing* David Hanson MD; Regena
McFarland.
Licensure Intermediate care. *Beds* 59.
Certified Medicaid.
Owner Nonprofit organization/foundation.
Admissions Requirements Minimum age 18.
Staff RNs 3 (ft); LPNs 2 (ft), 1 (pt); Physical
therapists 1 (ft); Reality therapists 1 (ft);
Occupational therapists 1 (ft); Speech
therapists 1 (ft); Activities coordinators 1
(ft); Dietitians 1 (ft); Dentist 1 (ft).
Affiliation International Order of Odd Fellows
& Rebekahs
Facilities Dining room; Physical therapy
room; Activities room; Laundry room;
Barber/Beauty shop.
Activities Arts & crafts; Cards; Games;
Reading groups; Prayer groups; Movies;
Shopping trips; Social/Cultural gatherings;
Field trips; Dinning out.

Wesley Towers Inc
700 Monterey Pl, Hutchinson, KS, 67502
(316) 663-9175
Admin Louise Edge. *Medical Dir/Dir of
Nursing* Lorraine Lanzrath RN.
Licensure Intermediate care. *Beds* ICF 130.
Owner Nonprofit organization/foundation.
Admissions Requirements Medical
examination.
Staff RNs 6 (ft), 5 (pt); Nurses aides 22 (ft), 3
(pt); Activities coordinators 1 (ft); Dietitians
1 (ft).
Affiliation Methodist
Facilities Dining room; Physical therapy
room; Activities room; Chapel; Crafts room;
Laundry room; Barber/Beauty shop; Library;
Mens woodwork shop; Weaving room;
Therapy/exercise pool; Home health services;
Dental office; Gardening; Meals on wheels.
Activities Arts & crafts; Cards; Games;
Reading groups; Prayer groups; Movies;
Shopping trips; Social/Cultural gatherings;
Swimming & fishing outings; Golf; Exercise
classes; Weaving; Quilting.

INDEPENDENCE

Colonial Lodge
PO Box 688, 1000 W Mulberry,
Independence, KS, 67301
(316) 331-8420
Admin Bruce Struble. *Medical Dir/Dir of
Nursing* Dr Charles Empson.
Licensure Intermediate care. *Beds* 55.
Certified Medicaid.
Owner Proprietary Corp (Hillhaven Corp).
Staff RNs 2 (ft), 1 (pt); LPNs 1 (ft), 1 (pt);
Nurses aides 19 (ft), 4 (pt).
Facilities Dining room; Physical therapy
room; Activities room; Chapel; Crafts room;
Laundry room; Barber/Beauty shop.
Activities Arts & crafts; Cards; Prayer groups.

Colonial Terrace*
1101 Donald Ave, Independence, KS, 67301
(316) 331-8432
Admin Gary M Phillips.
Licensure Intermediate care. *Beds* 50.
Certified Medicaid.
Owner Proprietary Corp (Hillhaven Corp).

Glenwood Estate*
621 S 2nd, Independence, KS, 67301
(316) 331-2260
Admin Marilyn D Botts.
Licensure Intermediate care. *Beds* 43.
Certified Medicaid.
Admissions Requirements Minimum age 16;
Medical examination; Physician's request.
Staff RNs; LPNs; Nurses aides; Physical
therapists; Recreational therapists;
Occupational therapists; Speech therapists;
Activities coordinators; Dietitians; Dentists;
Ophthalmologists; Podiatrists; Audiologists.
Facilities Dining room; Physical therapy
room; Crafts room; Laundry room; Barber/
Beauty shop.
Activities Arts & crafts; Cards; Games;
Reading groups; Prayer groups; Movies;
Social/Cultural gatherings.

Manor Nursing Home*
614 S 8th, Independence, KS, 67301
(316) 331-0511
Admin James N Riddles.
Licensure Intermediate care. *Beds* 60.
Certified Medicaid.
Owner Nonprofit Corp.
Affiliation Lutheran

INMAN

Pleasant View Home
108 N Walnut, Inman, KS, 67546
(316) 585-6411
Admin Donald G Ratzloff. *Medical Dir/Dir of
Nursing* Dolores Hedrich DON.
Licensure Intermediate care; Personal care.
Beds ICF 67; Personal 20. *Certified*
Medicaid.
Owner Nonprofit Corp.
Admissions Requirements Medical
examination.
Languages German
Facilities Dining room; Physical therapy
room; Activities room; Chapel; Crafts room;
Laundry room; Barber/Beauty shop; Library.
Activities Arts & crafts; Cards; Games;
Reading groups; Prayer groups; Movies;
Social/Cultural gatherings.

IOLA

Arkhaven at Iola*
1336 N Walnut, Iola, KS, 66749
(316) 365-6989
Admin Luella Weems.
Licensure Intermediate care. *Beds* 120.
Certified Medicaid.
Owner Proprietary Corp.

Countryside Estates*
600 E Garfield St, Iola, KS, 66749
(316) 365-5221
Admin Paul H Wilson.
Licensure Intermediate care. *Beds* 100.
Certified Medicaid.
Owner Proprietary Corp (Beverly Enterprises).

Tara Gardens Personal Care Home*
1110 E Carpenter, Iola, KS, 66749
(319) 365-3107
Admin Steart Lallman. *Medical Dir/Dir of
Nursing* Rosemary Davis LPN.
Licensure Intermediate care. *Beds* 45.
Certified Medicaid.
Admissions Requirements Minimum age 16.
Staff RNs 1 (pt); LPNs 2 (ft); Nurses aides 10
(ft); Physical therapists 1 (pt); Reality
therapists 1 (pt); Recreational therapists 1
(pt); Occupational therapists 1 (pt); Speech
therapists 1 (pt); Activities coordinators 1
(pt); Dietitians 1 (pt); Podiatrists 1 (pt);
Audiologists 1 (pt).
Facilities Dining room; Physical therapy
room; Activities room; Chapel; Crafts room;
Laundry room; Barber/Beauty shop.
Activities Arts & crafts; Cards; Games;
Reading groups; Prayer groups; Movies;
Shopping trips.

JAMESTOWN

Cheyenne Lodge Nursing Home
716 Cedar, Jamestown, KS, 66948
(913) 439-6211
Admin Ella Thurston.
Licensure Intermediate care. *Beds* 60.
Certified Medicaid.
Admissions Requirements Minimum age 16;
Medical examination.
Staff RNs 2 (ft), 1 (pt); LPNs 4 (ft); Nurses
aides 12 (ft), 6 (pt); Activities coordinators 1
(ft), 2 (pt).
Facilities Dining room; Physical therapy
room; Chapel; Laundry room; Barber/Beauty
shop.
Activities Arts & crafts; Cards; Games;
Reading groups; Prayer groups; Movies;
Shopping trips; Social/Cultural gatherings.

JUNCTION CITY

Junction City Good Samaritan Center
416 W Spruce, Junction City, KS, 66441
(913) 238-1187
Admin Dorothy Frederick. *Medical Dir/Dir of
Nursing* Deanna Byers RN DON.
Licensure Intermediate care. *Beds* ICF 60.
Certified Medicaid.
Owner Nonprofit Corp (Evangelical Lutheran/
Good Samaritan).
Admissions Requirements Medical
examination; Physician's request.
Staff RNs 1 (ft); LPNs 2 (ft), 4 (pt); Nurses
aides 9 (ft), 9 (pt); Horticulture therapists 1
(ft), 1 (pt); Social worker 1 (ft).
Affiliation Lutheran
Facilities Dining room; Physical therapy
room; Activities room; Chapel; Laundry
room; Barber/Beauty shop; Library.
Activities Arts & crafts; Cards; Games;
Reading groups; Prayer groups; Movies;
Shopping trips; Social/Cultural gatherings;
Pet therapy.

Valley View Professional Care Center
PO Box 107, 1417 W Ash St, Junction City,
KS, 66441
(913) 762-2162
Admin Richard S Jung. *Medical Dir/Dir of
Nursing* Norma J Bush RN.
Licensure Skilled care; Intermediate care. *Beds*
129. *Certified* Medicaid; Medicare.
Owner Proprietary Corp.
Admissions Requirements Minimum age 18;
Medical examination; Physician's request.

Staff Physicians 1 (pt); RNs 6 (ft); LPNs 11 (ft); Nurses aides 46 (ft), 1 (pt); Physical therapists 1 (ft), 1 (pt); Speech therapists 1 (pt); Activities coordinators 1 (ft); Dietitians 1 (pt).
Languages Spanish, German, Korean
Facilities Dining room; Physical therapy room; Activities room; Chapel; Crafts room; Laundry room; Barber/Beauty shop; Library.
Activities Arts & crafts; Cards; Games; Reading groups; Prayer groups; Movies; Shopping trips; Social/Cultural gatherings.

Valley Vista Care Center
1115 W 14th St, Junction City, KS, 66441
(913) 238-2128
Admin Charles V Cobb. *Medical Dir/Dir of Nursing* Alex Scott MD; Joleen Curran RN.
Licensure Intermediate care Intermediate care Mental Health. *Beds* ICF 52. *Certified* Medicaid.
Owner Proprietary Corp.
Admissions Requirements Minimum age 18; Medical examination; Physician's request.
Staff RNs 1 (ft); LPNs 6 (ft); Nurses aides 11 (ft), 3 (pt); Activities coordinators 3 (ft).
Facilities Dining room; Physical therapy room; Activities room; Chapel; Crafts room; Laundry room; Barber/Beauty shop.
Activities Arts & crafts; Cards; Games; Reading groups; Prayer groups; Movies; Shopping trips; Social/Cultural gatherings.

KANSAS CITY

Bryant-Butler-Kitchen Nursing Home*
3500 N 27th St, Kansas City, KS, 66104
(913) 321-7725
Admin John Oliva.
Licensure Intermediate care. *Beds* 100. *Certified* Medicaid.
Owner Nonprofit Corp.

Kansas City Presbyterian Manor
PO Box 9136, 7850 Freeman St, Kansas City, KS, 66112
(913) 334-3666
Admin Roderick Shearer. *Medical Dir/Dir of Nursing* John O Mallory MD.
Licensure Skilled care; Intermediate care; Personal care. *Beds* 194. *Certified* Medicare.
Owner Nonprofit organization/foundation.
Admissions Requirements Minimum age 65; Medical examination.
Staff Physicians 1 (pt); RNs 8 (ft), 2 (pt); LPNs 8 (ft), 3 (pt); Orderlies; Nurses aides 36 (ft); Physical therapists 1 (pt); Recreational therapists 1 (pt); Occupational therapists 1 (pt); Activities coordinators 1 (ft), 1 (pt); Dietitians 1 (ft), 1 (pt); Ophthalmologists 1 (pt); Social worker 1 (ft), 1 (pt).
Affiliation Presbyterian
Facilities Dining room; Physical therapy room; Activities room; Chapel; Crafts room; Laundry room; Barber/Beauty shop; Library; 8 lounges.
Activities Arts & crafts; Cards; Games; Reading groups; Prayer groups; Movies; Shopping trips; News discussion groups; Religious services.

The Manor of Kansas City*
3231 N 61st St, Kansas City, KS, 66104
(913) 299-1770
Admin Joyce Regnier.
Licensure Intermediate care. *Beds* 80. *Certified* Medicaid.
Owner Proprietary Corp (Life Care Centers of America).

Medicalodge East of Kansas City
6261 Leavenworth Rd, Kansas City, KS, 66104
(913) 299-9722
Admin Richard A Shillcutt.
Licensure Intermediate care. *Beds* 75.
Owner Proprietary Corp (Medicalodges).

Medicalodge North of Kansas City
6500 Greeley, Kansas City, KS, 66104
(913) 334-0200
Admin Cindy Frakes. *Medical Dir/Dir of Nursing* Norman Marvin MD.
Licensure Skilled care. *Beds* SNF 50; ICF 50. *Certified* Medicaid; Medicare.
Owner Proprietary Corp (Medicalodges).
Staff RNs 5 (ft), 2 (pt); LPNs 8 (ft), 4 (pt); Orderlies 4 (ft); Nurses aides 40 (ft), 15 (pt); Physical therapists 1 (ft); Occupational therapists 1 (pt); Speech therapists 1 (pt); Activities coordinators 1 (ft); Dietitians 1 (pt); Podiatrists 1 (pt).
Facilities Dining room; Physical therapy room; Activities room; Laundry room; Barber/Beauty shop.
Activities Arts & crafts; Cards; Games; Prayer groups; Movies; Social/Cultural gatherings; Sporting events.

Medicalodge South of Kansas City*
6501 Greeley, Kansas City, KS, 66104
(913) 334-5252
Admin David Gatewood.
Licensure Intermediate care. *Beds* 100. *Certified* Medicaid.
Owner Proprietary Corp (Medicalodges).
Admissions Requirements Medical examination; Physician's request.
Staff Physicians 2 (pt); RNs 1 (ft), 1 (pt); LPNs 5 (ft); Nurses aides 22 (ft), 1 (pt); Physical therapists 1 (pt); Reality therapists 1 (pt); Recreational therapists 1 (pt); Occupational therapists 1 (pt); Speech therapists 1 (pt); Activities coordinators 1 (ft), 1 (pt); Dietitians 1 (pt); Dentists 1 (pt); Podiatrists 1 (pt); Audiologists 1 (pt).
Facilities Dining room; Physical therapy room; Activities room; Chapel; Crafts room; Laundry room; Barber/Beauty shop; Library.
Activities Arts & crafts; Cards; Games; Reading groups; Prayer groups; Movies; Shopping trips.

St Joseph Home
759 Vermont Ave, Kansas City, KS, 66101
(913) 621-6800
Admin William Tevington. *Medical Dir/Dir of Nursing* William Taylor MD; Loretta Cook RN DON.
Licensure Skilled care; Intermediate care; Independent living. *Beds* SNF 20; ICF 181; Independent living 35 units. *Certified* Medicaid; Medicare.
Owner Nonprofit organization/foundation.
Admissions Requirements Minimum age 16; Medical examination; Physician's request.
Staff Physicians 7 (pt); RNs 12 (ft), 5 (pt); LPNs 12 (ft), 2 (pt); Nurses aides 55 (ft), 7 (pt); Physical therapists 1 (pt); Recreational therapists 3 (ft); Occupational therapists 1 (pt); Speech therapists 1 (pt); Activities coordinators 1 (ft); Dietitians 1 (pt).
Languages Croatian, Spanish, Polish, German
Affiliation Roman Catholic
Facilities Dining room; Physical therapy room; Activities room; Chapel; Crafts room; Laundry room; Barber/Beauty shop; Library; Pastoral care.
Activities Arts & crafts; Cards; Games; Reading groups; Prayer groups; Movies; Shopping trips; Social/Cultural gatherings.

KENSINGTON

Prairie Haven Nursing Home*
Box 248, N Hwy 36, Kensington, KS, 66951
(913) 476-2623
Admin Merlyn L Watts.
Licensure Intermediate care. *Beds* 58. *Certified* Medicaid.
Owner Proprietary Corp (Beverly Enterprises).
Admissions Requirements Medical examination; Physician's request.

Staff RNs 2 (ft), 1 (pt); Orderlies 1 (ft); Nurses aides 15 (ft), 1 (pt); Activities coordinators 1 (ft).
Facilities Dining room; Physical therapy room; Activities room; Laundry room; Barber/Beauty shop.
Activities Arts & crafts; Cards; Games; Reading groups; Prayer groups; Shopping trips; Social/Cultural gatherings.

KINGMAN

Lifecare of Kingman
310 W Copeland, Kingman, KS, 67068
(316) 532-2223
Admin Deneice R Burk. *Medical Dir/Dir of Nursing* Doris Simons DON.
Licensure Intermediate care. *Beds* ICF 96. *Certified* Medicaid.
Owner Proprietary Corp.
Admissions Requirements Medical examination.
Facilities Dining room; Physical therapy room; Activities room; Laundry room; Barber/Beauty shop.
Activities Arts & crafts; Cards; Games; Reading groups; Prayer groups; Movies; Shopping trips; Social/Cultural gatherings.

KINSLEY

Medicalodge of Kinsley
Box 65-A, RR 2, W 6th & Winchester, Kinsley, KS, 67547
(316) 659-2156
Admin Carolyn Walker. *Medical Dir/Dir of Nursing* Beth Blackwell DON.
Licensure Intermediate care. *Beds* ICF 94. *Certified* Medicaid.
Owner Proprietary Corp (Medicalodges).
Admissions Requirements Minimum age 45; Medical examination; Physician's request.
Staff RNs 3 (ft); LPNs 4 (ft); Nurses aides 22 (ft), 1 (pt); Activities coordinators 2 (ft).
Facilities Dining room; Physical therapy room; Activities room; Chapel; Laundry room; Barber/Beauty shop; Kitchen.
Activities Arts & crafts; Games; Prayer groups; Shopping trips; Social/Cultural gatherings; Discussion groups; Hygiene groups.

KIOWA

Lifecare of Kiowa
1020 Main, Kiowa, KS, 67070
(316) 825-4732
Admin Jere Schwerdtferger. *Medical Dir/Dir of Nursing* Pat Hockett DON.
Licensure Intermediate care. *Beds* ICF 45. *Certified* Medicaid.
Owner Proprietary Corp (Community Lifecare Enterprises).
Admissions Requirements Medical examination; Physician's request.
Staff RNs 1 (pt); LPNs 2 (ft), 1 (pt); Nurses aides 12 (ft), 2 (pt); Activities coordinators 1 (ft).
Facilities Dining room; Physical therapy room; Activities room; Chapel; Laundry room; Barber/Beauty shop; Exam room.
Activities Arts & crafts; Cards; Games; Reading groups; Prayer groups; Movies; Shopping trips; Social/Cultural gatherings; School & community activities.

LACROSSE

Rush County Nursing Home
701 W 6th St, LaCrosse, KS, 67548
(913) 222-2574
Admin Joanna Wilson RN BSN. *Medical Dir/Dir of Nursing* Diana Torres LPN.
Licensure Intermediate care. *Beds* ICF 60. *Certified* Medicaid.
Owner Nonprofit Corp (Evangelical Lutheran/Good Samaritan).

Admissions Requirements Medical
examination; Physician's request.
Staff RNs 2 (ft), 1 (pt); LPNs 4 (ft), 1 (pt);
Nurses aides 9 (ft), 8 (pt); Activities
coordinators.
Affiliation Lutheran
Facilities Dining room; Physical therapy
room; Activities room; Chapel; Crafts room;
Laundry room; Barber/Beauty shop.
Activities Arts & crafts; Cards; Games;
Reading groups; Prayer groups; Movies;
Shopping trips; Social/Cultural gatherings.

LACYGNE

Swan Manor Inc*
215 N Broadway, Lacygne, KS, 66040
(913) 757-4414
Admin Daniel F Widner. *Medical Dir/Dir of
Nursing* Robert Banks MD.
Licensure Intermediate care. *Beds* 36.
Certified Medicaid.
Staff Physicians 1 (pt); RNs 1 (pt); LPNs 1
(ft), 1 (pt); Physical therapists 1 (pt); Reality
therapists 1 (pt); Recreational therapists 1
(pt); Occupational therapists 1 (pt); Speech
therapists 1 (pt); Activities coordinators 1
(pt); Dietitians 1 (pt); Dentists 1 (pt);
Podiatrists 1 (pt); Audiologists 1 (pt).
Facilities Dining room; Physical therapy
room; Activities room; Crafts room; Laundry
room; Barber/Beauty shop.
Activities Arts & crafts; Cards; Games;
Reading groups; Prayer groups; Movies.

LANSING

Colonial Manor Nursing & Care Center
PO Box 250, Holiday Plaza Ctr, Lansing, KS,
66043
(913) 727-1284
Admin Diana Corpstein. *Medical Dir/Dir of
Nursing* LaRinda McConnaughey LPN.
Licensure Intermediate care. *Beds* 60.
Certified Medicaid.
Owner Proprietary Corp (Beverly Enterprises).
Admissions Requirements Minimum age 16;
Medical examination; Physician's request.
Staff LPNs 5 (ft); Orderlies 5 (ft); Nurses
aides 20 (ft), 5 (pt); Physical therapists;
Activities coordinators 1 (ft).
Facilities Dining room; Physical therapy
room; Activities room; Chapel; Crafts room;
Laundry room; Barber/Beauty shop; Library;
Private conference room.
Activities Cards; Games; Reading groups;
Prayer groups; Movies; Shopping trips;
Social/Cultural gatherings; Bingo.

LARNED

Hammond Holiday Home
1114 W 11th St, Larned, KS, 67550
(316) 285-6914
Admin Mark Bolding. *Medical Dir/Dir of
Nursing* Dr V R Cade; Sherri Burger.
Licensure Intermediate care. *Beds* ICF 100.
Certified Medicaid.
Owner Proprietary Corp (Hillhaven Corp).
Admissions Requirements Minimum age 16;
Medical examination; Physician's request.
Staff Physicians 1 (ft); RNs 8 (ft); LPNs 1 (ft);
Nurses aides 40 (ft); Physical therapists 1
(pt); Occupational therapists 1 (pt); Speech
therapists 1 (pt); Activities coordinators 1
(ft); Dietitians 1 (ft); Podiatrists 1 (pt).
Facilities Dining room; Physical therapy
room; Activities room; Chapel; Crafts room;
Laundry room; Barber/Beauty shop.
Activities Arts & crafts; Cards; Games;
Reading groups; Prayer groups; Movies;
Social/Cultural gatherings.

LAWRENCE

Cedar Wood Care Center*
205 N Michigan, Lawrence, KS, 66044
(913) 843-8934
Admin Mary Lou Shaft. *Medical Dir/Dir of
Nursing* Carl Inzarello MD.
Licensure Intermediate care. *Beds* 50.
Certified Medicaid.
Owner Proprietary Corp (Regency Health
Care Centers).
Admissions Requirements Minimum age 14;
Medical examination.
Staff LPNs; Orderlies; Nurses aides; Reality
therapists; Activities coordinators.
Facilities Dining room; Physical therapy
room; Activities room; Chapel; Crafts room;
Laundry room; Barber/Beauty shop; Library;
Lounge.
Activities Arts & crafts; Cards; Games;
Reading groups; Prayer groups; Movies;
Shopping trips; Social/Cultural gatherings.

Colonial Manor of Lawrence
3015 W 31st St, Lawrence, KS, 66046
(913) 842-7282
Admin Karen J Langlais. *Medical Dir/Dir of
Nursing* Dr John Gravino; Nora Louise
Yarbro RN DON.
Licensure Skilled care. *Beds* SNF 96. *Certified*
Medicaid.
Owner Proprietary Corp (Beverly Enterprises).
Admissions Requirements Medical
examination; Physician's request.
Staff RNs; LPNs; Nurses aides; Physical
therapists; Recreational therapists;
Occupational therapists; Speech therapists;
Dietitians.
Facilities Dining room; Physical therapy
room; Activities room; Laundry room;
Barber/Beauty shop; Library.
Activities Arts & crafts; Cards; Games;
Reading groups; Prayer groups; Movies;
Shopping trips; Social/Cultural gatherings.

Lawrence Presbyterian Manor
1429 Kasold Dr, Lawrence, KS, 66044
(913) 841-4262
Admin Phillip M Levi Jr.
Licensure Skilled care; Intermediate care. *Beds*
60. *Certified* Medicaid.
Admissions Requirements Minimum age 65;
Medical examination.
Staff RNs 2 (ft), 1 (pt); Orderlies 3 (ft);
Nurses aides 24 (pt); Physical therapists 2
(pt); Occupational therapists 2 (pt); Speech
therapists 2 (pt); Activities coordinators 1
(ft); Dietitians 1 (ft); Ophthalmologists 1
(pt); Dentist 1 (pt).
Affiliation Presbyterian
Facilities Dining room; Physical therapy
room; Activities room; Chapel; Crafts room;
Laundry room; Barber/Beauty shop; Library;
Covered parking.

Regency Health Care Center*
1800 W 27th St, Lawrence, KS, 66044
(913) 842-3162
Admin Debra L Jrokoon.
Licensure Intermediate care. *Beds* 100.
Certified Medicaid.
Owner Proprietary Corp (Regency Health
Care Centers).

Valley View Care Home
2518 Ridge Ct, Lawrence, KS, 66046
(913) 842-2610
Medical Dir/Dir of Nursing Judith Harkins
RN.
Licensure Intermediate care. *Beds* ICF 61.
Certified Medicaid.
Owner Publicly owned.
Staff RNs 1 (ft); LPNs 8 (ft); Nurses aides 24
(ft); Activities coordinators 1 (ft).
Facilities Dining room; Physical therapy
room; Activities room; Crafts room; Laundry
room; Barber/Beauty shop.

Activities Arts & crafts; Cards; Games;
Reading groups.

LEAVENWORTH

Leavenworth County Convalescent Infirmary
Broadway and Rees, Leavenworth, KS, 66048
(913) 682-4501
Admin Thomas V McEvoy. *Medical Dir/Dir of
Nursing* Elizabeth J Brown RN.
Licensure Skilled care. *Beds* SNF 47; ICF 34.
Certified Medicaid.
Owner Publicly owned.
Admissions Requirements Minimum age 18;
Medical examination; Physician's request.
Staff Physicians 1 (pt); RNs 4 (ft), 1 (pt);
LPNs 4 (ft), 2 (pt); Orderlies 2 (ft), 1 (pt);
Nurses aides 26 (ft), 4 (pt); Physical
therapists 1 (pt); Recreational therapists 1
(ft); Occupational therapists 1 (pt); Speech
therapists 1 (pt); Dietitians 1 (pt).
Facilities Dining room; Physical therapy
room; Activities room; Laundry room;
Barber/Beauty shop.
Activities Arts & crafts; Cards; Games;
Reading groups; Prayer groups; Shopping
trips; Social/Cultural gatherings.

Medicalodge of Leavenworth
1503 W Ohio, Leavenworth, KS, 66048
(913) 682-1844
Admin Joyce Starling. *Medical Dir/Dir of
Nursing* Nancy Watkins RN.
Licensure Skilled care. *Beds* SNF 36; ICF 84.
Certified Medicaid.
Owner Proprietary Corp (Medicalodges).
Admissions Requirements Medical
examination; Physician's request.
Staff Physicians 1 (ft); RNs 4 (ft), 2 (pt);
LPNs 4 (ft), 5 (pt); Orderlies 2 (ft), 1 (pt);
Nurses aides 43 (ft), 2 (pt); Physical
therapists; Reality therapists; Recreational
therapists; Occupational therapists; Speech
therapists; Activities coordinators 1 (ft);
Dietitians; Ophthalmologists 1 (pt).
Facilities Dining room; Physical therapy
room; Activities room; Chapel; Crafts room;
Laundry room; Barber/Beauty shop; Library.
Activities Arts & crafts; Cards; Games; Prayer
groups; Movies; Shopping trips; Social/
Cultural gatherings; Baseball games; Picnics.

LENEXA

Delmar Gardens of Lenexa
9701 Monrovia, Lenexa, KS, 66215
(913) 492-1130
Admin Richard L Carlson. *Medical Dir/Dir of
Nursing* Norman Marvin MD; Kathleen
Stone RN DON.
Licensure Skilled care. *Beds* SNF 190; ICF
60. *Certified* Medicare.
Owner Proprietary Corp.
Admissions Requirements Medical
examination; Physician's request.
Staff Physicians 2 (pt); RNs 13 (ft), 5 (pt);
LPNs 4 (ft), 3 (pt); Nurses aides 55 (ft), 27
(pt); Physical therapists 3 (ft), 1 (pt);
Occupational therapists 1 (pt); Speech
therapists 1 (pt); Activities coordinators 2
(ft); Dietitians 1 (ft), 1 (pt).
Facilities Dining room; Physical therapy
room; Activities room; Chapel; Crafts room;
Laundry room; Barber/Beauty shop; Library.
Activities Arts & crafts; Cards; Games;
Reading groups; Prayer groups; Movies;
Shopping trips; Social/Cultural gatherings.

Lakeview Village Inc
9100 Park, Lenexa, KS, 66215
(913) 888-1900
Admin Lowell E Strahan.
Licensure Intermediate care. *Beds* 21.
Admissions Requirements Minimum age 62;
Medical examination.

Staff RNs 2 (ft), 1 (pt); LPNs 1 (ft), 2 (pt); Orderlies 1 (ft); Nurses aides 12 (ft); Recreational therapists 1 (ft); Activities coordinators 1 (ft); Dietitians 1 (pt); Dentists 1 (pt); Podiatrists 1 (pt).
Facilities Dining room; Physical therapy room; Activities room; Chapel; Crafts room; Laundry room; Barber/Beauty shop; Library.
Activities Arts & crafts; Cards; Games; Reading groups; Prayer groups; Movies; Shopping trips; Social/Cultural gatherings.

LEONARDVILLE

Leonardville Nursing Home*
Box 148, Hwy 24, Leonardville, KS, 66449
(913) 293-5246
Admin Kathryn Whitley.
Licensure Intermediate care. *Beds* 50.
Certified Medicaid.
Owner Proprietary Corp.

LEOTI

Golden Acres Nursing Home*
Earl & 7th, Leoti, KS, 67861
(316) 375-4600
Admin Jerry Korbe.
Licensure Intermediate care. *Beds* 30.
Certified Medicaid.
Owner Publicly owned.
Admissions Requirements Minimum age 65.
Staff RNs 1 (pt); LPNs 1 (ft), 1 (pt); Nurses aides 13 (ft), 2 (pt); Physical therapists 1 (pt); Activities coordinators 1 (ft).
Facilities Dining room; Physical therapy room; Activities room; Chapel; Barber/Beauty shop.
Activities Arts & crafts; Games; Reading groups; Prayer groups; Movies.

LIBERAL

Liberal Good Samaritan Center
2160 Zinnia Ln, Liberal, KS, 67901
(316) 624-3831
Admin Bonnie L Monnier. *Medical Dir/Dir of Nursing* Donna Culwell.
Licensure Intermediate care. *Beds* ICF 100.
Certified Medicaid.
Owner Nonprofit Corp (Evangelical Lutheran/ Good Samaritan).
Admissions Requirements Medical examination; Physician's request.
Staff RNs 4 (ft); LPNs 3 (ft), 1 (pt); Nurses aides 21 (ft), 20 (pt); Activities coordinators 2 (ft); Ophthalmologists 1 (pt); Dentist 1 (pt).
Affiliation Lutheran
Facilities Dining room; Physical therapy room; Activities room; Chapel; Crafts room; Laundry room; Barber/Beauty shop.
Activities Arts & crafts; Cards; Games; Reading groups; Prayer groups; Movies; Shopping trips; Social/Cultural gatherings.

LINCOLN

Mid America Nursing Center of Lincoln
922 N 5th St, Lincoln, KS, 67455
(913) 524-4428
Admin Jerry J Johnson. *Medical Dir/Dir of Nursing* Colleen Vance.
Licensure Intermediate care. *Beds* ICF 73.
Certified Medicaid.
Owner Proprietary Corp.
Staff RNs 1 (ft), 1 (pt); LPNs 2 (ft), 1 (pt); Nurses aides 10 (ft), 4 (pt); Activities coordinators 1 (ft), 3 (pt).
Facilities Dining room; Physical therapy room; Activities room; Chapel; Crafts room; Laundry room; Barber/Beauty shop; Library.
Activities Arts & crafts; Cards; Games; Reading groups; Prayer groups; Movies; Social/Cultural gatherings.

LINDSBORG

Bethany Home Association of Lindsborg
321 N Chestnut, Lindsborg, KS, 67456
(913) 227-2721
Admin William P Carlson. *Medical Dir/Dir of Nursing* Jeanie Holwenda RN.
Licensure Intermediate care. *Beds* 132.
Certified Medicaid.
Admissions Requirements Minimum age 65.
Staff RNs 1 (ft), 2 (pt); LPNs 5 (ft); Nurses aides 40 (ft), 35 (pt); Physical therapists 1 (ft); Activities coordinators 1 (ft); Dietitians 1 (ft).
Affiliation Lutheran
Facilities Dining room; Physical therapy room; Chapel; Laundry room; Barber/Beauty shop.
Activities Arts & crafts; Cards; Games; Reading groups; Prayer groups; Movies.

LINN

Linn Community Nursing Home Inc
314 W 3rd St, Linn, KS, 66953
(913) 348-5551
Admin Sonia S DeRusseau. *Medical Dir/Dir of Nursing* Carol Rahe.
Licensure Intermediate care; Independent living. *Beds* ICF 69; independent living cottages 8. *Certified* Medicaid.
Owner Nonprofit Corp.
Admissions Requirements Minimum age 55.
Staff RNs 1 (pt); LPNs 4 (ft); Nurses aides 37 (pt); Activities coordinators 2 (pt); Social service coordinator 2 (pt).
Languages German
Affiliation Lutheran
Facilities Dining room; Physical therapy room; Activities room; Crafts room; Laundry room; Barber/Beauty shop; Quiet room.
Activities Arts & crafts; Cards; Games; Prayer groups; Movies; Shopping trips; Social/ Cultural gatherings; Birthday parties; Bingo.

LITTLE RIVER

Sandstone Heights
PO Box 50A, 440 State St, Little River, KS, 67457
(316) 897-6266
Admin Evelyn S Walters.
Licensure Intermediate care. *Beds* ICF 56.
Certified Medicaid.
Owner Publicly owned.
Admissions Requirements Medical examination.
Staff RNs 1 (pt); LPNs 5 (ft); Nurses aides 15 (ft), 5 (pt); Activities coordinators 1 (ft).
Facilities Dining room; Physical therapy room; Activities room; Laundry room; Barber/Beauty shop.
Activities Arts & crafts; Cards; Games; Prayer groups; Movies; Shopping trips; Social/ Cultural gatherings.

LOGAN

Logan Manor Nursing Home*
Main St & 3rd, Logan, KS, 67646
(913) 689-4201
Admin Elizabeth Charlaton.
Licensure Intermediate care. *Beds* 50.
Certified Medicaid.
Owner Publicly owned.

LOUISBURG

Southridge Manor*
PO Box 339, 12th & Broadway, Louisburg, KS, 66053
(913) 837-2916
Admin David J Mercier. *Medical Dir/Dir of Nursing* Barborah Spies MD.
Licensure Intermediate care. *Beds* 55.
Certified Medicaid.

Owner Proprietary Corp (Americare Corp).
Admissions Requirements Physician's request.
Staff RNs 1 (ft); LPNs 2 (ft), 1 (pt); Nurses aides 8 (ft), 5 (pt); Physical therapists 1 (pt); Occupational therapists 1 (pt); Speech therapists 1 (pt); Activities coordinators 1 (ft); Dietitians 1 (pt); Dentists 1 (pt).
Facilities Dining room; Physical therapy room; Activities room; Chapel; Laundry room; Barber/Beauty shop.
Activities Arts & crafts; Cards; Games; Reading groups; Prayer groups; Shopping trips; Social/Cultural gatherings.

LUCAS

Lucas Rest Home*
Johnson & Main, Lucas, KS, 67648
(316) 525-6215
Admin Celia Anschutz.
Licensure Intermediate care. *Beds* 50.
Certified Medicaid.
Owner Proprietary Corp (Beverly Enterprises).

LYNDON

Hilltop Home*
131 W 14th St, Box W, Lyndon, KS, 66451
(913) 828-4842
Admin Robert Harvey.
Licensure Intermediate care. *Beds* 54.
Certified Medicaid.
Owner Proprietary Corp.

LYONS

Lyons Good Samaritan Center
1311 S Douglass, Lyons, KS, 67554
(316) 257-5163
Admin Carlene Phillips. *Medical Dir/Dir of Nursing* Jayne Yates RN.
Licensure Intermediate care. *Beds* ICF 85.
Certified Medicaid.
Owner Nonprofit Corp (Evangelical Lutheran/ Good Samaritan).
Admissions Requirements Medical examination; Physician's request.
Staff RNs 4 (ft), 1 (pt); LPNs 3 (ft), 4 (pt); Nurses aides 23 (ft), 10 (pt); Activities coordinators 1 (ft), 1 (pt).
Languages Spanish
Affiliation Lutheran
Facilities Dining room; Physical therapy room; Activities room; Chapel; Crafts room; Laundry room; Barber/Beauty shop; Library; Day rooms.
Activities Arts & crafts; Games; Reading groups; Prayer groups; Movies; Shopping trips; Social/Cultural gatherings; Outings; Picnics; Church services; Music therapy.

MACKSVILLE

Parkview Manor*
117 N Spickard, Macksville, KS, 67557
(316) 348-3665
Admin Bonita Williams.
Licensure Intermediate care. *Beds* 59.
Certified Medicaid.
Owner Proprietary Corp (Beverly Enterprises).

MADISON

Madison Manor Inc
PO Box 277, Bluestem Dr, Madison, KS, 66860
(316) 437-2470
Admin Mary L Cookson. *Medical Dir/Dir of Nursing* Patti Young LPN.
Licensure Intermediate care. *Beds* ICF 55.
Certified Medicaid.
Owner Nonprofit Corp.
Admissions Requirements Physician's request.

Staff LPNs 6 (ft); Orderlies 1 (ft); Nurses aides 11 (ft), 5 (pt); Activities coordinators 1 (ft); Certified Rest Aides 3 (ft); Medical Records 1 (ft); Medication Aides 3 (pt).
Facilities Dining room; Physical therapy room; Activities room; Chapel; Laundry room; Barber/Beauty shop.
Activities Arts & crafts; Cards; Games; Reading groups; Prayer groups; Movies; Shopping trips.

MANHATTAN

College Hill Skilled Nursing Center
2423 Kimball, Manhattan, KS, 66502
(913) 539-7671
Admin Douglas W Frihart. *Medical Dir/Dir of Nursing* Phil Hostetter MD & Palmer Meed MD; Jan Bennett RN DON.
Licensure Skilled care; Intermediate care. *Beds* SNF 56; ICF 50. *Certified* Medicaid; Medicare.
Owner Privately owned.
Admissions Requirements Medical examination; Physician's request.
Staff Physicians 2 (pt); RNs 3 (ft), 1 (pt); LPNs 8 (ft), 6 (pt); Orderlies 5 (ft), 2 (pt); Nurses aides 23 (ft), 5 (pt); Physical therapists 1 (pt); Occupational therapists 1 (pt); Speech therapists 1 (pt); Activities coordinators 1 (ft); Dietitians 1 (pt); CPTA 1 (ft).
Facilities Dining room; Physical therapy room; Activities room; Crafts room; Laundry room; Barber/Beauty shop; Library; Quiet room; Piano; Flower garden; Court yard.
Activities Arts & crafts; Cards; Games; Reading groups; Prayer groups; Movies; Social/Cultural gatherings; Bus rides; Cooking class; Field trips; Humane society visits; Happy hour.

Meadowlark Hills*
2121 Meadowlark Rd, Manhattan, KS, 66502
(913) 537-4610
Admin Dennis Garland. *Medical Dir/Dir of Nursing* Dr P Meek & Dr W Durkee.
Licensure Skilled care. *Beds* 53. *Certified* Medicaid; Medicare.
Admissions Requirements Minimum age 65; Medical examination; Physician's request.
Staff RNs 1 (ft), 5 (pt); LPNs 2 (ft), 1 (pt); Orderlies 1 (ft); Nurses aides 13 (ft), 6 (pt); Activities coordinators 2 (ft), 1 (pt).
Facilities Dining room; Physical therapy room; Activities room; Crafts room; Laundry room; Barber/Beauty shop; Library.
Activities Arts & crafts; Cards; Games; Reading groups; Prayer groups; Movies; Social/Cultural gatherings.

Wharton Manor
2101 Claflin Rd, Manhattan, KS, 66502
(913) 776-0636
Admin Norman Wallace. *Medical Dir/Dir of Nursing* Betty J Cole.
Licensure Intermediate care. *Beds* ICF 60. *Certified* Medicaid.
Owner Nonprofit Corp.
Admissions Requirements Medical examination; Physician's request.
Staff RNs 1 (ft); LPNs 7 (ft); Nurses aides 23 (ft), 7 (pt); Activities coordinators 1 (ft); Social worker 1 (ft); Restorative aide 1 (ft).
Facilities Dining room; Activities room; Chapel; Laundry room; Barber/Beauty shop; Library.
Activities Arts & crafts; Prayer groups; Movies; Shopping trips.

MARION

Marion Manor*
1500 E Lawrence St, Marion, KS, 66861
(316) 382-2191
Admin Kenneth Vanduska.

Licensure Intermediate care. *Beds* 80. *Certified* Medicaid.
Staff RNs 1 (ft), 3 (pt); LPNs 1 (ft), 1 (pt); Nurses aides 10 (ft), 10 (pt); Physical therapists 1 (pt); Reality therapists 1 (pt); Recreational therapists 1 (pt); Occupational therapists 1 (pt); Speech therapists 1 (pt); Activities coordinators 1 (ft), 1 (pt); Dietitians 1 (pt).
Facilities Dining room; Physical therapy room; Activities room; Crafts room; Laundry room; Barber/Beauty shop.
Activities Arts & crafts; Cards; Games; Reading groups; Prayer groups; Movies; Shopping trips; Social/Cultural gatherings.

MARQUETTE

Riverview Estates Inc
202 S Washington St, Marquette, KS, 67464
(316) 546-2211
Licensure Intermediate care. *Beds* 52. *Certified* Medicaid.
Staff RNs 3 (pt); LPNs 1 (pt); Orderlies 1 (ft), 1 (pt); Nurses aides 10 (ft), 9 (pt); Physical therapists 1 (pt); Occupational therapists 1 (pt); Speech therapists 1 (pt); Activities coordinators 1 (pt); Dietitians 1 (pt); Dentists 1 (pt); Ophthalmologists 1 (pt).
Facilities Dining room; Physical therapy room; Activities room; Chapel; Crafts room; Laundry room; Barber/Beauty shop.
Activities Arts & crafts; Cards; Games; Reading groups; Prayer groups; Movies; Shopping trips; Social/Cultural gatherings; Van for handicapped.

MARYSVILLE

Marshall County Nursing Center
1906 North St, Marysville, KS, 66508
(913) 562-5321
Admin Anne Bradford. *Medical Dir/Dir of Nursing* Carolyn Whitlinger.
Licensure Intermediate care. *Beds* ICF 49. *Certified* Medicaid.
Owner Publicly owned.
Facilities Dining room; Physical therapy room; Activities room; Laundry room.
Activities Arts & crafts; Cards; Games; Reading groups; Prayer groups; Movies; Shopping trips; Social/Cultural gatherings.

Mary Marshall Manor Inc
810 N 18th St, Marysville, KS, 66508
(913) 562-5325
Admin Dorothy L Welch. *Medical Dir/Dir of Nursing* Dr Donald Argo; Donna Anderson RN.
Licensure Intermediate care. *Beds* ICF 92. *Certified* Medicaid.
Owner Proprietary Corp.
Staff RNs; LPNs; Nurses aides; Activities coordinators.
Activities Arts & crafts; Cards; Games; Reading groups; Prayer groups; Movies; Shopping trips; Social/Cultural gatherings.

MCPHERSON

Autumnwood Villa
1601 N Main, McPherson, KS, 67460
(316) 241-5360
Admin Patsy Sutton. *Medical Dir/Dir of Nursing* Jo Colgin.
Licensure Intermediate care. *Beds* 98. *Certified* Medicaid.
Admissions Requirements Minimum age 18; Females only.
Staff RNs 2 (pt); LPNs 8 (ft); Orderlies 6 (ft); Nurses aides 18 (ft); Physical therapists 1 (pt); Occupational therapists 1 (pt); Speech therapists 1 (pt); Activities coordinators 1 (ft); Dietitians 1 (pt).

Facilities Dining room; Physical therapy room; Activities room; Chapel; Crafts room; Laundry room; Barber/Beauty shop.
Activities Arts & crafts; Games; Reading groups; Prayer groups; Movies; Shopping trips.

The Cedars Inc
1021 Cedars Dr, McPherson, KS, 67460
(316) 241-0919
Admin LeRoy C Weddle. *Medical Dir/Dir of Nursing* Kathy Duerkson RN DON.
Licensure Skilled care; Intermediate care. *Beds* SNF 60; ICF 60. *Certified* Medicaid.
Owner Nonprofit Corp.
Admissions Requirements Minimum age 60; Medical examination; Physician's request.
Staff RNs 3 (ft), 1 (pt); LPNs 4 (ft), 3 (pt); Orderlies 2 (ft); Nurses aides 13 (ft), 10 (pt); Activities coordinators 1 (ft), 1 (pt); Dietitians 1 (ft).
Affiliation Church of the Brethren
Facilities Dining room; Physical therapy room; Activities room; Chapel; Crafts room; Laundry room; Barber/Beauty shop; Library; Living room.
Activities Arts & crafts; Cards; Games; Reading groups; Movies; Social/Cultural gatherings; Bible study; Nostalgia groups.

E & M Rainbow Home Inc*
606 E Ave B, McPherson, KS, 67460
(316) 241-3414
Admin Edna R Bruce.
Licensure Personal care. *Beds* 20.

Mac House
225 S Hickory, McPherson, KS, 67460
(316) 241-6780
Admin Larry Elmquist.
Licensure Intermediate care for mentally retarded. *Beds* ICF/MR 15. *Certified* Medicaid.
Owner Nonprofit Corp.
Admissions Requirements Minimum age 18.
Staff RNs 1 (pt); Nurses aides 2 (ft), 2 (pt); Activities coordinators 1 (ft); Medical aides 5 (ft).
Facilities Dining room; Activities room; Laundry room.
Activities Arts & crafts; Cards; Games; Movies; Shopping trips; Social/Cultural gatherings; Work activity; Day program.

MEADE

Lone Tree Lodge
407 E Rainbelt, Meade, KS, 67864
(316) 873-2146
Admin Darrell K Webb. *Medical Dir/Dir of Nursing* Agnes Wiens RN.
Licensure Intermediate care. *Beds* ICF 56. *Certified* Medicaid.
Owner Nonprofit Corp.
Admissions Requirements Minimum age 18; Medical examination; Physician's request.
Staff RNs 1 (ft), 4 (pt); LPNs 3 (ft), 1 (pt); Nurses aides 14 (ft), 4 (pt); Physical therapists 1 (pt); Occupational therapists 1 (pt); Speech therapists 1 (pt); Activities coordinators 1 (ft); Dietitians 1 (pt); Podiatrists 1 (pt).
Facilities Dining room; Physical therapy room; Activities room; Barber/Beauty shop.
Activities Arts & crafts; Cards; Games; Reading groups; Prayer groups; Movies; Shopping trips.

MEDICINE LODGE

Cedar Crest Training Center
106 W Stolp, Medicine Lodge, KS, 67104
(316) 886-3425
Admin Kevin R Reimer. *Medical Dir/Dir of Nursing* Joyce Range.
Licensure Intermediate care for mentally retarded. *Beds* 49. *Certified* Medicaid.

Owner Proprietary Corp (Cedar Crest Inc).
Admissions Requirements Minimum age 21.
Staff RNs 1 (ft), 1 (pt); LPNs 1 (ft); Nurses aides 10 (ft); Dietitians 1 (pt).
Facilities Dining room; Physical therapy room; Activities room; Chapel; Crafts room; Laundry room; Barber/Beauty shop.
Activities Arts & crafts; Cards; Games; Reading groups; Prayer groups; Movies; Shopping trips; Social/Cultural gatherings.

MERRIAM

Trinity Lutheran Manor
9700 W 62nd St, Merriam, KS, 66203
(913) 384-0800
Admin Willa J Hughes. *Medical Dir/Dir of Nursing* Mohan Gollerkeri.
Licensure Skilled care; Intermediate care. *Beds* SNF 60; ICF 60. *Certified* Medicaid; Medicare.
Admissions Requirements Minimum age 18.
Staff RNs; LPNs; Orderlies; Nurses aides; Physical therapists; Recreational therapists; Occupational therapists; Speech therapists; Dietitians; Dentists; Ophthalmologists; Podiatrists.
Languages French, Spanish
Affiliation Lutheran
Facilities Dining room; Physical therapy room; Activities room; Chapel; Crafts room; Laundry room; Barber/Beauty shop; Living rooms; Quiet rooms.
Activities Arts & crafts; Cards; Games; Reading groups; Prayer groups; Movies; Shopping trips; Social/Cultural gatherings; Cooking; Van outings; Happy hour.

MINNEAPOLIS

Minneapolis Good Samaritan Center
816 Argyle, Minneapolis, KS, 67467
(913) 392-2162
Admin Richard Elliott. *Medical Dir/Dir of Nursing* Carolyn Yost.
Licensure Intermediate care. *Beds* ICF 95. *Certified* Medicaid.
Owner Nonprofit Corp (Evangelical Lutheran/ Good Samaritan).
Admissions Requirements Medical examination.
Staff RNs 3 (ft), 2 (pt); LPNs 3 (ft), 5 (pt); Nurses aides 22 (ft), 16 (pt); Occupational therapists 1 (pt); Speech therapists 1 (pt); Activities coordinators 1 (ft), 2 (pt); Dietitians 1 (ft); Podiatrists 1 (pt).
Affiliation Lutheran
Facilities Dining room; Physical therapy room; Activities room; Chapel; Crafts room; Laundry room; Barber/Beauty shop.
Activities Arts & crafts; Cards; Games; Reading groups; Prayer groups; Movies; Shopping trips; Social/Cultural gatherings.

MINNEOLA

Minneola Nursing Home
PO Box 10, 205 Chestnut, Minneola, KS, 67865
(316) 885-4238
Admin Lou A Esplund. *Medical Dir/Dir of Nursing* Lori Skeen.
Licensure Intermediate care. *Beds* ICF 50. *Certified* Medicaid.
Owner Publicly owned.
Admissions Requirements Minimum age 16; Physician's request.
Staff Physicians 1 (pt); RNs 1 (pt); LPNs 6 (ft); Nurses aides 12 (ft), 4 (pt); Physical therapists 1 (pt); Recreational therapists 1 (pt); Occupational therapists 1 (pt); Activities coordinators 1 (pt); Dietitians 1 (pt).
Facilities Dining room; Physical therapy room; Activities room; Chapel; Crafts room; Laundry room; Barber/Beauty shop; Kitchen.

Activities Arts & crafts; Cards; Prayer groups; Movies; Shopping trips; Social/Cultural gatherings.

MOLINE

Elk Manor Home
RR 1, Box 7, Walnut St, Moline, KS, 67353
(316) 647-3336
Admin Bruce R Smith. *Medical Dir/Dir of Nursing* Frances Roper.
Licensure Intermediate care. *Beds* ICF 41. *Certified* Medicaid; Medicare.
Owner Publicly owned.
Admissions Requirements Medical examination; Physician's request.
Staff RNs 1 (pt); LPNs 3 (ft), 1 (pt); Nurses aides 9 (ft), 5 (pt); Physical therapists 1 (ft); Occupational therapists 1 (ft); Activities coordinators 1 (ft); Dietitians 1 (ft).
Facilities Dining room; Physical therapy room; Laundry room; Barber/Beauty shop.
Activities Arts & crafts; Cards; Games; Reading groups; Prayer groups; Movies; Shopping trips; Social/Cultural gatherings; Musical groups (Visiting).

MONTEZUMA

Bethel Home Inc
Rte 1, Aztec St, Montezuma, KS, 67867
(316) 846-2241
Admin Marion D Becker. *Medical Dir/Dir of Nursing* Alma Wiens.
Licensure Intermediate care. *Beds* 48. *Certified* Medicaid.
Admissions Requirements Physician's request.
Staff RNs 1 (ft); LPNs 1 (ft), 5 (pt); Nurses aides 10 (ft), 11 (pt); Physical therapists 2 (pt); Recreational therapists 1 (pt); Activities coordinators 1 (ft), 1 (pt); Dietitians 3 (ft), 4 (pt).
Affiliation Mennonite
Facilities Dining room; Physical therapy room; Activities room; Chapel; Crafts room; Laundry room; Barber/Beauty shop; Library.
Activities Arts & crafts; Games; Reading groups; Prayer groups; Shopping trips; Social/Cultural gatherings.

MORAN

Moran Manor
RR 1, Moran, KS, 66755
(316) 237-4309
Admin Sandra S Northcutt.
Licensure Intermediate care. *Beds* 50. *Certified* Medicaid.
Owner Proprietary Corp (Americare Corp).
Admissions Requirements Minimum age 16; Medical examination.
Staff RNs 1 (ft); LPNs 1 (ft), 2 (pt); Nurses aides 11 (ft), 6 (pt); Physical therapists 1 (ft), 1 (pt); Occupational therapists 1 (pt); Speech therapists 1 (pt); Activities coordinators 1 (ft), 1 (pt); Dietitians 1 (pt); Dentists 1 (pt); Podiatrists 1 (pt).
Facilities Dining room; Physical therapy room; Activities room; Laundry room; Barber/Beauty shop.
Activities Arts & crafts; Cards; Games; Reading groups; Prayer groups; Movies; Shopping trips; Social/Cultural gatherings.

MOUND CITY

Sugar Valley Home Inc
PO Box 130, W Main, Mound City, KS, 66056
(913) 795-2232
Admin Wes W Worthington. *Medical Dir/Dir of Nursing* Sharon Willard RN DON.
Licensure Intermediate care. *Beds* ICF 60. *Certified* Medicaid.
Owner Proprietary Corp.

Admissions Requirements Minimum age 18; Medical examination.
Staff RNs 2 (ft); LPNs 3 (ft); Nurses aides 19 (ft); Activities coordinators 1 (ft).
Facilities Dining room; Physical therapy room; Activities room; Laundry room; Barber/Beauty shop; Library.
Activities Arts & crafts; Cards; Games; Reading groups; Prayer groups; Movies; Shopping trips; Social/Cultural gatherings.

MOUNDRIDGE

Memorial Home for the Aged
Box 29, Moundridge, KS, 67107
(316) 345-2901
Admin Jerry Unruh. *Medical Dir/Dir of Nursing* Dr W E Kaufman; Pat Rupp RN.
Licensure Intermediate care; Assisted self-care. *Beds* ICF 50; assisted self-care 36. *Certified* Medicaid.
Owner Nonprofit Corp.
Admissions Requirements Minimum age 60.
Staff RNs 2 (ft), 2 (pt); LPNs 1 (ft), 3 (pt); Nurses aides 3 (ft), 22 (pt); Activities coordinators 1 (ft).
Affiliation Mennonite
Facilities Dining room; Physical therapy room; Activities room; Chapel; Crafts room; Laundry room; Barber/Beauty shop; Library.
Activities Arts & crafts; Games; Reading groups; Movies; Social/Cultural gatherings.

Moundridge Manor
PO Box 800, 710 N Christian Ave, Moundridge, KS, 67107
(316) 345-6364
Admin Bernard Regehr. *Medical Dir/Dir of Nursing* Dr W Kauffman.
Licensure Intermediate care. *Beds* 66. *Certified* Medicaid.
Owner Nonprofit Corp.
Admissions Requirements Minimum age 16; Medical examination; Physician's request.
Staff RNs 1 (ft), 1 (pt); LPNs 4 (ft), 3 (pt); Nurses aides 23 (ft); Speech therapists 1 (pt); Activities coordinators 1 (ft).
Affiliation Mennonite
Facilities Dining room; Physical therapy room; Activities room; Crafts room; Laundry room; Barber/Beauty shop.
Activities Arts & crafts; Games; Reading groups; Prayer groups.

MOUNT HOPE

Mt Hope Nursing Center
704 E Main, Mount Hope, KS, 67108
(316) 667-2431
Admin Patricia J Elliott RN. *Medical Dir/Dir of Nursing* J M Steck MD.
Licensure Intermediate care. *Beds* ICF 62. *Certified* Medicaid.
Owner Nonprofit organization/foundation.
Admissions Requirements Minimum age 16; Medical examination; Physician's request.
Staff RNs 1 (ft), 1 (pt); LPNs 1 (ft), 1 (pt); Activities coordinators 1 (ft).
Facilities Dining room; Physical therapy room; Activities room; Chapel; Crafts room; Laundry room; Barber/Beauty shop.
Activities Arts & crafts; Cards; Games; Reading groups; Prayer groups; Movies; Shopping trips; Social/Cultural gatherings.

MULVANE

Villa Maria Inc
116 S Central, Mulvane, KS, 67110
(316) 777-1129
Admin Sr M Magdalen Giaretta. *Medical Dir/Dir of Nursing* Leslie H Cobb MD; Sr Justine Busch RN DON.
Licensure Intermediate care. *Beds* ICF 66. *Certified* Medicaid.
Owner Nonprofit Corp.

Admissions Requirements Minimum age 65; Medical examination; Physician's request.
Staff RNs 2 (ft); LPNs 4 (ft), 2 (pt); Nurses aides 18 (ft), 2 (pt); Physical therapists 1 (ft), 1 (pt); Recreational therapists 1 (pt); Occupational therapists 1 (pt); Speech therapists 1 (pt); Activities coordinators 1 (ft); Dietitians 1 (ft); Dietitians 1 (pt); Podiatrists 1 (pt).
Affiliation Roman Catholic
Facilities Dining room; Physical therapy room; Activities room; Chapel; Laundry room; Barber/Beauty shop; Library.
Activities Arts & crafts; Cards; Games; Reading groups; Prayer groups; Movies; Social/Cultural gatherings.

NEODESHA

Golden Keys Nursing Home
221 Mill St, Box 350, Neodesha, KS, 66757
(316) 325-2639
Admin Phyllis C Cunningham. Medical Dir/Dir of Nursing Bert Chronister MD; Toni Barnhart RN DON.
Licensure Intermediate care. Beds ICF 64. Certified Medicaid.
Owner Publicly owned.
Admissions Requirements Minimum age 18; Medical examination; Physician's request.
Staff RNs 1 (ft); LPNs 5 (ft); Nurses aides 22 (ft), 5 (pt); Activities coordinators 1 (ft); Physical therapists aides 2 (ft).
Facilities Dining room; Physical therapy room; Activities room; Crafts room; Laundry room; Barber/Beauty shop; Library.
Activities Arts & crafts; Cards; Games; Reading groups; Prayer groups; Shopping trips; Social/Cultural gatherings.

Neodesha Nursing Home
1626 N 8th, Neodesha, KS, 66757
(316) 325-3088
Admin Sherri R Brown. Medical Dir/Dir of Nursing Jolene Ramey DON.
Licensure Intermediate care. Beds ICF 50. Certified Medicaid.
Owner Proprietary Corp (Beverly Enterprises).
Staff RNs 2 (ft); LPNs 2 (ft); Nurses aides 19 (ft); Activities coordinators 1 (ft).
Facilities Dining room; Physical therapy room; Activities room; Chapel; Crafts room; Laundry room; Barber/Beauty shop.
Activities Arts & crafts; Cards; Games; Reading groups; Prayer groups; Movies; Shopping trips; Bingo.

NEWTON

Friendly Acres Inc
200 SW 14th, Box 648, Newton, KS, 67114
(316) 283-4770
Admin Lu M Janzen. Medical Dir/Dir of Nursing Dr Lee Fent; Linda Luzier DON.
Licensure Intermediate care; Personal care. Beds ICF 144; Personal 46. Certified Medicaid.
Owner Nonprofit Corp.
Admissions Requirements Minimum age 62; Medical examination.
Staff RNs 10 (ft); LPNs 13 (ft); Nurses aides 27 (ft), 14 (pt); Physical therapists 4 (ft); Activities coordinators 1 (ft); Dietitians 1 (ft).
Affiliation Methodist
Facilities Dining room; Physical therapy room; Activities room; Chapel; Crafts room; Laundry room; Barber/Beauty shop; Library.
Activities Arts & crafts; Reading groups; Prayer groups; Shopping trips; Social/Cultural gatherings; Ceramics.

Kansas Christian Home Inc*
PO Box 348, 1035 SE 3rd St, Newton, KS, 67114
(316) 283-6600
Admin Roger Closson.

Licensure Intermediate care. Beds 115. Certified Medicaid.
Owner Nonprofit Corp (Natl Bnvlnt Assn of Chrstn Homes).

Kidron Bethel Retirement Services
222 S Pine, Newton, KS, 67114
(316) 283-4014
Admin Thomas C Wentz. Medical Dir/Dir of Nursing Esther M McDonald RN DON.
Licensure Intermediate care. Beds ICF 67. Certified Medicaid.
Owner Nonprofit Corp.
Admissions Requirements Minimum age 62 or w/special permission; Medical examination.
Staff RNs 3 (ft), 2 (pt); LPNs 2 (ft), 1 (pt); Nurses aides 10 (ft), 8 (pt); Physical therapists 2 (pt); Occupational therapists 1 (pt); Speech therapists 1 (pt); Activities coordinators 1 (ft); Dietitians 1 (pt); Medication Aides 8 (ft), 3 (pt); Social Services 1 (ft).
Languages German
Affiliation Mennonite
Facilities Dining room; Activities room; Chapel; Crafts room; Laundry room; Barber/Beauty shop; Library.
Activities Arts & crafts; Cards; Games; Reading groups; Prayer groups; Movies; Shopping trips; Social/Cultural gatherings; Sing-along; Worship hour; Bible class; Birthday parties.

Newton Presbyterian Manor
1200 E 7th, Box 255, Newton, KS, 67114
(316) 283-5400
Admin Marion Schroeder DON.
Licensure Intermediate care. Beds ICF 60. Certified Medicaid.
Owner Nonprofit Corp.
Admissions Requirements Minimum age 65; Medical examination.
Staff RNs 2 (ft); LPNs 4 (ft); Orderlies; Nurses aides; Occupational therapists; Activities coordinators; Dietitians.
Affiliation Presbyterian
Facilities Dining room; Physical therapy room; Activities room; Chapel; Crafts room; Laundry room; Barber/Beauty shop; Library.
Activities Arts & crafts; Shopping trips; Social/Cultural gatherings; Music therapy; Horticultural therapy; Chapel services.

NORTON

Andbe Home Inc
201 W Crane, Norton, KS, 67654
(913) 877-2601
Admin Wilma Winder RN. Medical Dir/Dir of Nursing Jackie Rutherford RN DON.
Licensure Intermediate care. Beds 100.
Owner Nonprofit Corp.
Admissions Requirements Minimum age 16; Medical examination.
Staff RNs 2 (ft); LPNs 7 (ft), 3 (pt); Orderlies 1 (ft); Nurses aides 40 (ft); Physical therapists 1 (pt); Activities coordinators 1 (ft); Dietitians 1 (pt); CPTA 2 (pt).
Facilities Dining room; Physical therapy room; Activities room; Chapel; Crafts room; Laundry room; Barber/Beauty shop.
Activities Arts & crafts; Cards; Games; Reading groups; Prayer groups; Movies; Shopping trips; Social/Cultural gatherings.

NORTONVILLE

Village Villa Nursing Home
Box 346, Walnut & Taggart, Nortonville, KS, 66060
(913) 886-6400
Admin Linda Ronnebaum. Medical Dir/Dir of Nursing James V Rider DO; Diane Babcock RN.
Licensure Intermediate care. Beds ICF 50. Certified Medicaid.
Owner Proprietary Corp.

Admissions Requirements Minimum age 18; Medical examination; Physician's request.
Staff Physicians 6 (pt); RNs 2 (ft); LPNs 1 (ft), 3 (pt); Nurses aides 5 (ft), 3 (pt); Activities coordinators 1 (ft); Podiatrists 1 (pt); Medication aides 8 (ft); Social worker 1 (pt); Social service 1 (pt).
Facilities Dining room; Physical therapy room; Activities room; Crafts room; Laundry room; Barber/Beauty shop; Sunroom with TV; Quiet room.
Activities Arts & crafts; Cards; Games; Reading groups; Prayer groups; Movies; Bible study by volunteers; Womens support groups; News time & visiting; Music time & singing.

OAKLEY

Oakley Manor*
615 Price, Oakley, KS, 67748
(913) 672-3115
Admin Nancy R Riggs. Medical Dir/Dir of Nursing Rosemary Davis LPN.
Licensure Intermediate care. Beds 45. Certified Medicaid.
Admissions Requirements Minimum age 16.
Staff RNs 1 (pt); LPNs 2 (ft), 1 (pt); Orderlies 1 (ft); Nurses aides 16 (ft), 4 (pt); Physical therapists 1 (ft); Activities coordinators 1 (ft).
Facilities Dining room; Physical therapy room; Laundry room; Barber/Beauty shop.
Activities Arts & crafts; Games; Prayer groups; Movies; Shopping trips; Social/Cultural gatherings.

OBERLIN

Decatur County Good Samaritan Center*
108 E Ash, Oberlin, KS, 67749
(913) 475-2245
Admin Troy Lerseth. Medical Dir/Dir of Nursing Dr Ren Whitacker.
Licensure Intermediate care. Beds 79. Certified Medicaid.
Owner Nonprofit Corp (Evangelical Lutheran/ Good Samaritan).
Admissions Requirements Minimum age 35; Medical examination; Physician's request.
Staff Physicians 4 (pt); RNs 3 (pt); LPNs 4 (pt); Nurses aides 35 (pt); Physical therapists 1 (pt); Activities coordinators 1 (ft), 2 (pt).
Affiliation Lutheran
Facilities Dining room; Physical therapy room; Activities room; Chapel; Laundry room; Barber/Beauty shop.
Activities Arts & crafts; Cards; Games; Reading groups; Prayer groups; Movies; Shopping trips; Social/Cultural gatherings.

OLATHE

Johnson County Nursing Center*
1125 W Spruce, Olathe, KS, 66061
(913) 782-0272
Admin Kenneth F Betterton.
Licensure Intermediate care. Beds 99. Certified Medicaid.
Owner Publicly owned.

Olathe Good Samaritan Center*
572 E Park, Olathe, KS, 66061
(913) 782-1372
Admin Michael Adkins.
Licensure Intermediate care. Beds 162. Certified Medicaid.
Owner Nonprofit Corp (Evangelical Lutheran/ Good Samaritan).
Admissions Requirements Minimum age 18; Medical examination; Physician's request.
Staff RNs 4 (ft); LPNs 10 (ft); Orderlies 1 (ft); Nurses aides 50 (ft), 20 (pt); Activities coordinators 1 (ft).
Affiliation Lutheran

Facilities Dining room; Physical therapy room; Activities room; Chapel; Crafts room; Laundry room; Barber/Beauty shop; Library; Plant room.
Activities Arts & crafts; Cards; Games; Reading groups; Prayer groups; Movies; Shopping trips; Social/Cultural gatherings.

Olathe Nursing Home*
625 N Lincoln, Olathe, KS, 66061
(913) 782-1311
Admin Roxanne M Santoro. *Medical Dir/Dir of Nursing* Ronald LaHue DO.
Licensure Intermediate care. *Beds* 54. *Certified* Medicaid.
Owner Proprietary Corp (Beverly Enterprises).
Admissions Requirements Minimum age 60; Medical examination.
Staff LPNs 2 (ft), 1 (pt); Orderlies 2 (ft); Nurses aides 13 (ft); Physical therapists 1 (ft); Activities coordinators 1 (ft).
Facilities Dining room; Physical therapy room; Activities room; Chapel; Laundry room; Barber/Beauty shop.
Activities Arts & crafts; Cards; Prayer groups; Movies; Shopping trips.

Regency Health Care Center
400 S Rogers Rd, Olathe, KS, 66062
(913) 782-3350
Admin Sally A Gates. *Medical Dir/Dir of Nursing* Robert Nottingham; Carol Browning DON.
Licensure Skilled care; Intermediate care. *Beds* SNF 28; ICF 81. *Certified* Medicaid; Medicare.
Owner Proprietary Corp (Regency Health Care Centers).
Admissions Requirements Minimum age 16; Medical examination.
Staff RNs 5 (ft); LPNs 8 (ft), 6 (pt); Nurses aides 19 (ft), 4 (pt); Physical therapists 1 (pt); Recreational therapists 1 (ft); Occupational therapists 1 (pt); Speech therapists 1 (pt); Activities coordinators 1 (ft); Dietitians 1 (pt); Dentists 1 (pt); Ophthalmologists 1 (pt); Podiatrists 1 (pt).
Facilities Dining room; Physical therapy room; Activities room; Crafts room; Laundry room; Barber/Beauty shop.
Activities Arts & crafts; Cards; Games; Reading groups; Prayer groups; Movies; Shopping trips; Social/Cultural gatherings.

ONAGA

Golden Acres*
500 Western St, Onaga, KS, 66521
(913) 889-4227
Admin Connie Ellis.
Licensure Intermediate care. *Beds* 55. *Certified* Medicaid.
Owner Proprietary Corp.

OSAGE CITY

Osage Manor Inc
10th & Main St, Osage City, KS, 66523
(913) 528-4262, 528-3885
Admin George L Meisner. *Medical Dir/Dir of Nursing* Irene Hasenbank RN.
Licensure Intermediate care. *Beds* ICF 67. *Certified* Medicaid.
Owner Proprietary Corp.
Staff RNs 1 (ft); LPNs 3 (ft); Nurses aides 20 (ft), 4 (pt); Recreational therapists 1 (ft); Occupational therapists 1 (ft); Activities coordinators 1 (ft).
Facilities Dining room; Physical therapy room; Chapel; Crafts room; Laundry room; Barber/Beauty shop.
Activities Arts & crafts; Cards; Games; Reading groups; Prayer groups; Movies; Social/Cultural gatherings; Fishing trips with picnic; Watermelon feeds; Ice cream social; Pot luck suppers; Country/western bands; Balloon lift offs; Movies.

Peterson Nursing Home Inc
Box 246, 630 Holliday, Osage City, KS, 66523-1138
(913) 528-4420, 528-1138
Admin Iris M Peterson. *Medical Dir/Dir of Nursing* Peggy L Lira.
Licensure Intermediate care. *Beds* ICF 60. *Certified* Medicaid.
Owner Proprietary Corp.
Admissions Requirements Medical examination; Physician's request.
Staff RNs; LPNs; Nurses aides; Activities coordinators; Dietitians.
Facilities Dining room; Physical therapy room; Activities room; Chapel; Crafts room; Laundry room; Barber/Beauty shop.
Activities Arts & crafts; Cards; Games; Reading groups; Prayer groups; Movies; Shopping trips; Social/Cultural gatherings; Resident council.

OSAWATOMIE

Osawatomie Rest Home*
PO Box 309, 514 Leroy, Osawatomie, KS, 66064
(913) 755-3519
Admin Martha Frazier.
Licensure Intermediate care. *Beds* 24. *Certified* Medicaid.
Owner Proprietary Corp.

Regency Health Care Center
PO Box 159, 1615 Parker Ave, Osawatomie, KS, 66064
(913) 755-4165
Admin Richard McKinney. *Medical Dir/Dir of Nursing* Robert E Banks MD; Catherine McRoberts RN.
Licensure Skilled care; Intermediate care. *Beds* SNF 28; ICF 118. *Certified* Medicaid; Medicare.
Owner Proprietary Corp (Regency Health Care Centers).
Admissions Requirements Minimum age 16; Medical examination; Physician's request.
Staff Physicians 5 (pt); RNs 4 (ft), 1 (pt); LPNs 8 (ft), 2 (pt); Orderlies 5 (ft); Nurses aides 27 (ft), 8 (pt); Physical therapists 2 (pt); Recreational therapists 2 (ft); Occupational therapists 1 (pt); Speech therapists 1 (pt); Activities coordinators 1 (ft); Dietitians 1 (pt); Dentists 1 (pt); Ophthalmologists 1 (pt).
Facilities Dining room; Physical therapy room; Activities room; Chapel; Crafts room; Laundry room; Barber/Beauty shop; Library.
Activities Arts & crafts; Cards; Games; Reading groups; Prayer groups; Movies; Shopping trips; Social/Cultural gatherings.

OSBORNE

Parkview Manor Care Center
811 N 1st St, Osborne, KS, 67473
(913) 346-2114
Admin Betty Jo Banks. *Medical Dir/Dir of Nursing* Cindy Hyde.
Licensure Intermediate care. *Beds* 104. *Certified* Medicaid.
Owner Proprietary Corp.
Admissions Requirements Physician's request.
Staff RNs 1 (ft), 3 (pt); LPNs 4 (ft); Nurses aides 45 (ft); Activities coordinators 2 (ft), 2 (pt); Dietitians 1 (ft).
Facilities Dining room; Physical therapy room; Activities room; Chapel; Crafts room; Laundry room; Barber/Beauty shop; Library.
Activities Arts & crafts; Cards; Games; Reading groups; Prayer groups; Movies; Shopping trips; Social/Cultural gatherings.

OSKALOOSA

Cherokee Lodge Adult Care*
700 Cherokee, Box 307, Oskaloosa, KS, 66066
(913) 863-2108
Admin James H Tenpenny.
Licensure Intermediate care. *Beds* 100. *Certified* Medicaid.
Owner Proprietary Corp.

OSWEGO

Oswego Guest Home Inc
Box 26 R2, Oswego, KS, 67356
(316) 795-4429, 795-4805
Admin Janice K Schertz. *Medical Dir/Dir of Nursing* Judith Marsh.
Licensure Intermediate care. *Beds* ICF 60. *Certified* Medicaid.
Owner Proprietary Corp.
Admissions Requirements Minimum age 18; Medical examination; Physician's request.
Staff RNs 2 (ft), 1 (pt); LPNs 3 (ft); Nurses aides 20 (ft), 5 (pt); Physical therapists 1 (pt); Occupational therapists 1 (pt); Speech therapists 1 (pt); Activities coordinators 1 (ft); Dietitians 1 (pt); Ophthalmologists 1 (pt); Podiatrists 1 (pt).
Facilities Dining room; Physical therapy room; Activities room; Crafts room; Laundry room; Barber/Beauty shop; Library.
Activities Arts & crafts; Cards; Games; Reading groups; Prayer groups; Movies; Shopping trips; Social/Cultural gatherings.

OTTAWA

Crestview Nursing Home*
1002 W 7th St Terrace, Ottawa, KS, 66067
(913) 242-3454
Admin Cathy Wallace.
Licensure Intermediate care. *Beds* 51. *Certified* Medicaid.
Owner Proprietary Corp.

Ottawa Retirement Village
1100 W 15th St, Ottawa, KS, 66067
(913) 242-5399
Admin Thomas H Keller.
Licensure Intermediate care. *Beds* 113. *Certified* Medicaid.
Staff RNs 2 (ft), 1 (pt); LPNs 3 (ft), 1 (pt); Orderlies 1 (ft); Nurses aides 20 (ft), 3 (pt); Physical therapists 1 (pt); Recreational therapists 1 (ft); Occupational therapists 1 (pt); Speech therapists 1 (pt); Activities coordinators 1 (ft); Dentists 1 (pt).
Facilities Dining room; Physical therapy room; Activities room; Laundry room; Barber/Beauty shop.
Activities Arts & crafts; Cards; Games; Prayer groups; Movies; Social/Cultural gatherings.

OVERBROOK

Brookside Manor
Hwy 56, Box 327, Overbrook, KS, 66524
(913) 665-7124
Admin Clifford E Fischer. *Medical Dir/Dir of Nursing* Judy Bagby.
Licensure Skilled care; Intermediate care. *Beds* SNF 50; ICF 50. *Certified* Medicaid; Medicare.
Owner Proprietary Corp.
Admissions Requirements Medical examination.
Staff Physicians 1 (pt); RNs 4 (ft); LPNs 4 (ft), 2 (pt); Orderlies 5 (ft); Nurses aides 35 (ft), 10 (pt); Physical therapists 1 (pt); Occupational therapists 1 (pt); Speech therapists 1 (pt); Activities coordinators 1 (ft), 1 (pt); Dietitians 1 (pt); Dentists 1 (pt).
Facilities Dining room; Physical therapy room; Activities room; Chapel; Crafts room; Laundry room; Barber/Beauty shop; Visitors lounge.

Activities Arts & crafts; Cards; Games; Reading groups; Prayer groups; Movies; Shopping trips; Social/Cultural gatherings.

OVERLAND PARK

Conser House
7829 Conser, Overland Park, KS, 66204
(913) 381-6623
Admin Michael Strouse.
Licensure Intermediate care for mentally retarded. *Beds* ICF/MR 22. *Certified* Medicaid.
Owner Nonprofit Corp.
Admissions Requirements Minimum age 18; Medical examination; Physician's request.
Staff Physicians 4 (pt); RNs 1 (ft); Nurses aides 25 (ft); Physical therapists 1 (pt); Occupational therapists 1 (pt); Speech therapists 1 (pt); Dietitians 1 (pt).
Facilities Dining room; Activities room; Laundry room.
Activities Arts & crafts; Cards; Games; Prayer groups; Movies; Shopping trips; Social/Cultural gatherings.

Indian Creek Nursing Center
6515 W 103rd St, Overland Park, KS, 66212
(913) 642-5545
Admin John May. *Medical Dir/Dir of Nursing* Dixie Byrnes DON.
Licensure Skilled care. *Beds* SNF 120.
Owner Proprietary Corp (Hillhaven Corp).
Admissions Requirements Minimum age 16; Medical examination; Physician's request.
Staff Physicians; RNs; LPNs; Orderlies; Nurses aides; Physical therapists; Reality therapists; Recreational therapists; Occupational therapists; Speech therapists; Activities coordinators; Dietitians; Dentists; Ophthalmologists; Podiatrists.
Facilities Dining room; Physical therapy room; Activities room; Crafts room; Laundry room; Barber/Beauty shop.
Activities Arts & crafts; Cards; Games; Reading groups; Prayer groups; Movies.

Indian Meadows Nursing Center
6505 W 103rd, Overland Park, KS, 66212
(913) 649-5110
Admin Patricia L Stickler. *Medical Dir/Dir of Nursing* Dr Norman Marvin; Michelle Boudreaux RN DON.
Licensure Skilled care. *Beds* SNF 120.
Owner Proprietary Corp (Hillhaven Corp).
Admissions Requirements Minimum age 16; Medical examination; Physician's request.
Staff Physicians; RNs; LPNs; Orderlies; Nurses aides; Physical therapists; Recreational therapists; Occupational therapists; Speech therapists; Dietitians; Ophthalmologists.
Facilities Dining room; Physical therapy room; Activities room; Crafts room; Laundry room; Barber/Beauty shop.
Activities Arts & crafts; Cards; Games; Reading groups; Prayer groups; Movies; Shopping trips.

Life Care Center of Overland Park*
7541 Switzer Rd, Overland Park, KS, 66214
(913) 631-2273
Admin Russell Hilderbrand. *Medical Dir/Dir of Nursing* Dr Philip Boyer.
Licensure Skilled care; Intermediate care. *Beds* SNF 49; ICF 150. *Certified* Medicaid; Medicare.
Owner Proprietary Corp (Comprehen Health Care Assn).
Admissions Requirements Medical examination.
Staff RNs 4 (ft), 1 (pt); LPNs 8 (ft), 3 (pt); Nurses aides 52 (ft), 3 (pt); Physical therapists 1 (pt); Occupational therapists 1 (pt); Speech therapists 1 (pt); Activities coordinators 1 (ft); Dietitians 1 (ft); Dentists 1 (pt); Podiatrists 1 (pt); Audiologists 1 (pt).

Facilities Dining room; Physical therapy room; Activities room; Crafts room; Laundry room; Barber/Beauty shop; Library.
Activities Arts & crafts; Cards; Games; Reading groups; Movies; Social/Cultural gatherings; Zoo.

OXFORD

Riverview Manor Inc
200 S Ohio, Oxford, KS, 67119
(316) 455-2214
Admin Carol Sue Wilkerson.
Licensure Intermediate care. *Beds* ICF 50. *Certified* Medicaid.
Owner Nonprofit Corp.
Admissions Requirements Medical examination; Physician's request.
Staff RNs; LPNs; Nurses aides.
Facilities Dining room; Physical therapy room; Activities room; Chapel; Laundry room; Barber/Beauty shop.
Activities Arts & crafts; Games; Prayer groups; Movies; Shopping trips.

PAOLA

Country Haven Adult Care Center
908 N Pearl St, Paola, KS, 66071
(913) 294-4308
Admin Karen Rockers. *Medical Dir/Dir of Nursing* Patricia Dunlap DON.
Licensure Intermediate care. *Beds* 80. *Certified* Medicaid.
Owner Proprietary Corp (Americare Corp).
Admissions Requirements Medical examination.
Staff LPNs 6 (ft); Orderlies 5 (ft); Nurses aides 16 (ft); Activities coordinators 1 (ft).
Facilities Dining room; Physical therapy room; Activities room; Chapel; Crafts room; Laundry room; Barber/Beauty shop; Library; Humor room; Adult day care.
Activities Arts & crafts; Cards; Games; Reading groups; Prayer groups; Movies; Shopping trips; Pet therapy; Intergenerational programs.

Medicalodge of Paola*
501 Assembly Ln, Box C, Paola, KS, 66071
(913) 294-3345
Admin Lloyd Grimmet.
Licensure Intermediate care. *Beds* 88. *Certified* Medicaid.
Owner Proprietary Corp (Medicalodges).

Pine Crest Haven*
1004 N Pearl, Paola, KS, 66071
(913) 294-2404
Admin Rufus Turner Jr.
Licensure Intermediate care. *Beds* 50. *Certified* Medicaid.
Owner Proprietary Corp.

PARSONS

ElmHaven
1315 S 15th, Parsons, KS, 67357
(316) 421-1320
Admin Patricia L Woodworth. *Medical Dir/Dir of Nursing* Kim McMunn RN.
Licensure Intermediate care; Licensed day care. *Beds* ICF 60. *Certified* Medicaid.
Owner Privately owned.
Admissions Requirements Minimum age 16; Medical examination.
Staff RNs 4 (ft), 4 (pt); Nurses aides 10 (ft), 1 (pt); Activities coordinators 3 (ft).
Facilities Dining room; Physical therapy room; Activities room; Laundry room; Barber/Beauty shop.
Activities Arts & crafts; Cards; Games; Reading groups; Prayer groups; Movies; Shopping trips; Social/Cultural gatherings; Cooking classes.

The Heritage Home*
1400 S 15th, Parsons, KS, 67357
(316) 421-1430
Admin Jeannie Nichols. *Medical Dir/Dir of Nursing* F N Stephens DO.
Licensure Intermediate care. *Beds* 50. *Certified* Medicaid.
Admissions Requirements Minimum age 18; Medical examination; Physician's request.
Staff RNs 1 (ft), 1 (pt); LPNs 1 (pt); Nurses aides 11 (ft), 2 (pt); Activities coordinators 2 (ft).
Facilities Dining room; Physical therapy room; Activities room; Chapel; Crafts room; Laundry room; Barber/Beauty shop.
Activities Arts & crafts; Cards; Games; Reading groups; Prayer groups; Movies; Shopping trips; Social/Cultural gatherings.

Parsons Good Samaritan Center
709 Leawood Dr, Parsons, KS, 67357
(316) 421-1110
Admin John M Rook. *Medical Dir/Dir of Nursing* Barbara Heady.
Licensure Intermediate care. *Beds* ICF 69. *Certified* Medicaid.
Owner Nonprofit Corp (Evangelical Lutheran/Good Samaritan).
Admissions Requirements Minimum age 21; Physician's request.
Staff RNs 1 (ft); LPNs 3 (ft), 2 (pt); Orderlies 1 (ft); Nurses aides 20 (ft), 8 (pt); Recreational therapists 1 (pt); Activities coordinators 1 (ft).
Affiliation Lutheran
Facilities Dining room; Physical therapy room; Activities room; Chapel; Crafts room; Laundry room; Barber/Beauty shop; Library; Smoke room.
Activities Arts & crafts; Games; Reading groups; Movies; Shopping trips; Social/Cultural gatherings.

Parsons Presbyterian Manor
3501 Dirr, Parsons, KS, 67357
(316) 421-1450
Admin Dana Dugger. *Medical Dir/Dir of Nursing* Dr Dan Pauls; Dennis Riggs DON.
Licensure Intermediate care; Home health-self care. *Beds* ICF 41; Home health-self care 22. *Certified* Medicaid.
Owner Nonprofit Corp.
Admissions Requirements Minimum age 65; Medical examination; Physician's request.
Staff RNs 2 (ft); LPNs 2 (ft), 2 (pt); Nurses aides 18 (ft), 6 (pt); Physical therapists 1 (ft); Recreational therapists 1 (ft), 1 (pt); Activities coordinators 1 (ft), 1 (pt); Dietitians 1 (ft).
Affiliation Presbyterian
Facilities Dining room; Physical therapy room; Activities room; Chapel; Crafts room; Laundry room; Barber/Beauty shop; Library.
Activities Arts & crafts; Games; Prayer groups; Movies; Shopping trips; Social/Cultural gatherings.

Westbrook Manor Nursing Center*
3500 W Broadway, Parsons, KS, 67357
(316) 421-4180
Admin Wade Patton.
Licensure Intermediate care. *Beds* 100. *Certified* Medicaid.
Owner Proprietary Corp.

PEABODY

Peabody Memorial Nursing Home Inc
407 N Locust, Peabody, KS, 66866
(316) 983-2152
Admin Robert G Bethell. *Medical Dir/Dir of Nursing* Dr Ruth Sherman; Jane Voth RN.
Licensure Intermediate care. *Beds* ICF 86. *Certified* Medicare.
Owner Proprietary Corp.
Admissions Requirements Medical examination.

Staff RNs 3 (ft), 2 (pt); LPNs 3 (ft), 1 (pt); Orderlies 25 (ft), 6 (pt); Activities coordinators 1 (ft), 1 (pt).
Facilities Dining room; Physical therapy room; Chapel; Laundry room; Barber/Beauty shop.
Activities Arts & crafts; Games; Reading groups; Prayer groups; Movies; Shopping trips.

Westview Manor*
4th & Peabody, Peabody, KS, 66866
(316) 983-2165
Admin Joleen R Hasker. *Medical Dir/Dir of Nursing* Dorothy Rhodes.
Licensure Intermediate care. *Beds* 52. *Certified* Medicaid.
Owner Proprietary Corp.
Staff RNs 3 (ft); Nurses aides 10 (ft), 3 (pt).
Facilities Dining room; Physical therapy room; Activities room; Laundry room; Barber/Beauty shop.
Activities Arts & crafts; Cards; Games; Reading groups; Prayer groups; Movies; Shopping trips; Social/Cultural gatherings.

PHILLIPSBURG

Evergreen Manor Inc
PO Box 628, E Hwy 36, Phillipsburg, KS, 67661
(913) 543-5209
Admin Shirley Robinson. *Medical Dir/Dir of Nursing* Anne Gower DON.
Licensure Intermediate care. *Beds* ICF 99. *Certified* Medicaid.
Owner Proprietary Corp.
Admissions Requirements Minimum age 18; Medical examination; Physician's request.
Staff RNs 2 (ft); LPNs 3 (ft), 2 (pt); Orderlies 17 (ft); Nurses aides 3 (pt); Activities coordinators.
Facilities Dining room; Physical therapy room; Activities room; Crafts room; Laundry room; Barber/Beauty shop; Quiet Room.
Activities Arts & crafts; Cards; Games; Reading groups; Prayer groups; Movies; Shopping trips; Social/Cultural gatherings.

Phillips County Home*
784 6th St, Phillipsburg, KS, 67661
(913) 543-2131
Admin Sondra K Kester.
Licensure Intermediate care. *Beds* 31. *Certified* Medicaid.
Staff LPNs 1 (ft), 2 (pt); Recreational therapists 1 (pt); Activities coordinators 1 (ft).
Facilities Dining room; Laundry room; Barber/Beauty shop.

PITTSBURG

Beverly Nursing Center
1005 Centennial, Pittsburg, KS, 66762
(316) 231-1120
Admin Wilma Van Houten. *Medical Dir/Dir of Nursing* Robin Nelson.
Licensure Intermediate care. *Beds* ICF 100. *Certified* Medicaid; Medicare.
Owner Proprietary Corp.
Admissions Requirements Minimum age 18; Medical examination; Physician's request.
Staff Physicians 1 (ft); RNs 3 (ft); LPNs 3 (ft); Orderlies 4 (ft); Physical therapists 1 (ft); Reality therapists 1 (ft); Recreational therapists 1 (ft); Occupational therapists 1 (ft); Speech therapists 1 (ft); Activities coordinators 1 (ft); Dietitians 1 (ft); Podiatrists 1 (ft).
Facilities Dining room; Physical therapy room; Activities room; Crafts room; Laundry room; Barber/Beauty shop.
Activities Arts & crafts; Cards; Games; Reading groups; Prayer groups; Movies; Shopping trips; Social/Cultural gatherings; Outings; Shopping; Fishing trips; Picnics.

Medicalodge North of Pittsburg*
2614 N Joplin, Pittsburg, KS, 66762
(316) 231-3970
Admin Pamela Gould.
Licensure Intermediate care. *Beds* 80. *Certified* Medicaid.
Owner Proprietary Corp (Medicalodges).
Admissions Requirements Medical examination.
Staff RNs 2 (ft); LPNs 5 (ft); Orderlies 1 (ft); Nurses aides 25 (ft); Activities coordinators 1 (ft).
Facilities Dining room; Physical therapy room; Activities room; Chapel; Crafts room; Laundry room; Barber/Beauty shop.
Activities Arts & crafts; Cards; Games; Reading groups; Prayer groups; Movies; Shopping trips; Social/Cultural gatherings.

Medicalodge South of Pittsburg
2520 S Rouse, Pittsburg, KS, 66762
(316) 231-0300
Admin Alicia Nicolas. *Medical Dir/Dir of Nursing* Dr G W Pogson.
Licensure Skilled care; Intermediate care. *Beds* SNF 24; ICF 76. *Certified* Medicaid; Medicare.
Owner Proprietary Corp (Medicalodges).
Admissions Requirements Minimum age 16; Medical examination; Physician's request.
Staff Physicians 1 (pt); RNs 7 (ft), 1 (pt); LPNs 8 (ft), 1 (pt); Orderlies 1 (ft); Nurses aides 36 (ft), 4 (pt); Recreational therapists 1 (ft); Activities coordinators 1 (ft), 1 (pt); Dietitians 1 (pt).
Facilities Dining room; Physical therapy room; Activities room; Chapel; Crafts room; Laundry room; Barber/Beauty shop; Library.
Activities Arts & crafts; Cards; Games; Reading groups; Prayer groups; Movies; Social/Cultural gatherings; Shopping trips.

New Horizons of Pittsburg*
2702 N Joplin, Pittsburg, KS, 66762
(316) 231-3910
Admin Jan Blevins.
Licensure Intermediate care for mentally retarded. *Beds* 88. *Certified* Medicaid.
Owner Proprietary Corp (Medicalodges).

Shields Adult Care Home Inc
2420 S Rouse, Pittsburg, KS, 66762
(316) 231-5590
Admin Wilfred C Shields. *Medical Dir/Dir of Nursing* D M Halsinger MD; Gretchen Belfield RN.
Licensure Intermediate care for mentally retarded. *Beds* ICF/MR 50. *Certified* Medicaid.
Owner Proprietary Corp.
Admissions Requirements Minimum age 18 Ambulatory only.
Staff Physicians 1 (pt); RNs 1 (ft); LPNs 2 (ft); Orderlies 5 (ft); Nurses aides 30 (ft); Physical therapists 1 (pt); Occupational therapists 1 (pt); Speech therapists 1 (pt); Activities coordinators 1 (ft); Dietitians 1 (pt); Dentists 1 (pt); Ophthalmologists 1 (pt); Podiatrists 1 (pt); Psychologist 1 (ft); Social worker 1 (ft).
Facilities Dining room; Physical therapy room; Activities room; Chapel; Crafts room; Laundry room; Barber/Beauty shop; Library.
Activities Arts & crafts; Cards; Games; Reading groups; Prayer groups; Movies; Shopping trips; Social/Cultural gatherings.

PLAINVILLE

Rooks County Home*
1000 S Washington, Plainville, KS, 67663
(913) 434-2846
Admin Forrest A Burkholder Jr.
Licensure Intermediate care. *Beds* 52. *Certified* Medicaid.
Owner Publicly owned.

PLEASANTON

Pleasant View Manor Inc*
1005 W 15th, Box 22, Pleasanton, KS, 66075
(913) 352-8455
Admin Kathy Madison. *Medical Dir/Dir of Nursing* Dr Fred Dunlap.
Licensure Intermediate care. *Beds* 50. *Certified* Medicaid.
Admissions Requirements Minimum age 16; Medical examination.
Staff Physicians 1 (pt); RNs 1 (pt); LPNs 2 (ft); Nurses aides 20 (ft); Physical therapists 1 (pt); Occupational therapists 1 (pt); Speech therapists 1 (pt); Activities coordinators 1 (pt); Dietitians 1 (pt); Dentists 1 (pt); Ophthalmologists 1 (pt); Podiatrists 1 (pt); Audiologists 1 (pt).
Facilities Dining room; Physical therapy room; Activities room; Chapel; Crafts room; Laundry room; Barber/Beauty shop; Library.
Activities Arts & crafts; Cards; Games; Reading groups; Prayer groups; Movies; Shopping trips; Social/Cultural gatherings.

PRATT

Lifecare of Pratt
1221 Larimer, Pratt, KS, 67124
(316) 672-6541
Admin Barbara L Frazier. *Medical Dir/Dir of Nursing* Tracy Cavanaugh RN.
Licensure Intermediate care. *Beds* ICF 95. *Certified* Medicaid.
Owner Proprietary Corp.
Admissions Requirements Medical examination.

Siesta Home of Pratt Inc
227 S Howard, Pratt, KS, 67124
(316) 672-5971
Admin Linda M Young. *Medical Dir/Dir of Nursing* Deb Toombs RN DON.
Licensure Intermediate care. *Beds* ICF 57. *Certified* Medicaid.
Owner Proprietary Corp.
Admissions Requirements Medical examination; Physician's request.
Staff RNs 2 (ft); LPNs 1 (ft); Nurses aides 15 (ft); Physical therapists 1 (pt); Occupational therapists 1 (pt); Speech therapists 1 (pt); Activities coordinators 1 (ft); Dietitians 1 (pt); Podiatrists.
Facilities Dining room; Physical therapy room; Activities room; Chapel; Crafts room; Laundry room; Barber/Beauty shop.
Activities Arts & crafts; Cards; Games; Reading groups; Prayer groups; Movies; Shopping trips; Social/Cultural gatherings; Joy rides.

PRESCOTT

Prescott Country View Nursing Home
PO Box 37, Highway 239, Prescott, KS, 66767
(913) 471-4315
Admin Betty S Keiser. *Medical Dir/Dir of Nursing* Mary Smith.
Licensure Intermediate care. *Beds* ICF 50. *Certified* Medicaid.
Owner Nonprofit organization/foundation.
Admissions Requirements Minimum age 20; Medical examination.
Staff Physicians 1 (pt); LPNs 4 (ft), 1 (pt); Orderlies 1 (ft); Nurses aides 16 (ft), 2 (pt); Physical therapists 1 (pt); Speech therapists 1 (pt); Activities coordinators 1 (ft); Dietitians 1 (pt); Ophthalmologists 1 (pt); Podiatrists 1 (pt).
Facilities Dining room; Physical therapy room; Activities room; Chapel; Laundry room; Barber/Beauty shop; Quiet room.
Activities Arts & crafts; Cards; Games; Prayer groups; Movies.

PRETTY PRAIRIE

Prairie Sunset Home*
601 E Main, Pretty Prairie, KS, 67570
(316) 459-6822
Admin Janice Krehbiel.
Licensure Intermediate care. *Beds* 45.
  Certified Medicaid.
Owner Proprietary Corp.

PROTECTION

Protection Valley Manor
PO Box 448, 600 S Broadway, Protection, KS,
  67127
(316) 622-4261
Admin Walter Rex Maris. *Medical Dir/Dir of
  Nursing* Frances Edmonston.
Licensure Intermediate care. *Beds* ICF 25.
  Certified Medicaid.
Owner Nonprofit organization/foundation.
Admissions Requirements Medical
  examination; Physician's request.
Staff LPNs 1 (ft), 1 (pt); Nurses aides 6 (ft), 4
  (pt); Activities coordinators 1 (ft); Dietitians
  1 (ft).
Facilities Dining room; Physical therapy
  room; Activities room; Chapel; Crafts room;
  Laundry room; Barber/Beauty shop.
Activities Arts & crafts; Cards; Games;
  Reading groups; Prayer groups; Movies;
  Shopping trips; Social/Cultural gatherings.

RICHMOND

Oakhaven Nursing Center
340 South St, Richmond, KS, 66080
(913) 835-6135
Admin Mary Sue Cox. *Medical Dir/Dir of
  Nursing* Barbara Neal RN.
Licensure Intermediate care. *Beds* ICF 53.
  Certified Medicaid.
Owner Nonprofit organization/foundation.
Admissions Requirements Minimum age 16;
  Medical examination; Physician's request.
Staff RNs 2 (ft), 1 (pt); LPNs 2 (pt); Nurses
  aides 20 (ft), 10 (pt); Activities coordinators
  1 (ft); Dietitians 1 (pt).
Facilities Dining room; Physical therapy
  room; Activities room; Chapel; Crafts room;
  Laundry room; Barber/Beauty shop; Library;
  Greenhouse.
Activities Arts & crafts; Cards; Games;
  Reading groups; Prayer groups; Movies;
  Shopping trips; Social/Cultural gatherings.

ROSE HILL

Heritage Village of Rose Hill*
601 N Rose Hill Rd, Rose Hill, KS, 67133
(316) 776-2194
Admin James D Knight Jr.
Licensure Intermediate care. *Beds* 60.
  Certified Medicaid.
Owner Proprietary Corp (Beverly Enterprises).

ROSSVILLE

Rossville Valley Manor
Box 328, 600 Perry, Rossville, KS, 66533-
  0787
(913) 584-6104
Admin Aaron D Kelley Jr. *Medical Dir/Dir of
  Nursing* Lisa S Landis RN.
Licensure Intermediate care. *Beds* ICF 91.
  Certified Medicaid.
Owner Proprietary Corp.
Staff Physicians 4 (pt); RNs 2 (ft); LPNs 6
  (ft), 1 (pt); Orderlies 3 (ft), 1 (pt); Nurses
  aides 15 (ft), 3 (pt); Physical therapists 1
  (pt); Occupational therapists 2 (pt); Speech
  therapists 1 (pt); Activities coordinators 2
  (ft); Dietitians 1 (pt); Dentists 1 (pt);
  Ophthalmologists 1 (pt); Ophthalmologists 1
  (pt); Podiatrists 1 (pt); Social worker 1 (ft), 1
  (pt).

Facilities Dining room; Physical therapy
  room; Activities room; Chapel; Crafts room;
  Laundry room; Barber/Beauty shop; Library.
Activities Arts & crafts; Cards; Games;
  Reading groups; Prayer groups; Movies;
  Shopping trips; Social/Cultural gatherings.

RUSSELL

**Ala Fern Intermediate Care Facility for Mental
Health**
PO Box 901, 225 E Jewell, Russell, KS, 67665
(913) 483-2868
Admin Helen E Janes. *Medical Dir/Dir of
  Nursing* Karleen Wolf.
Licensure Intermediate care. *Beds* ICF 46.
  Certified Medicaid.
Owner Proprietary Corp (Americare Corp).
Admissions Requirements Minimum age 18;
  Medical examination; Physician's request.
Staff Physicians 4 (pt); RNs 2 (ft); LPNs 2
  (ft); Nurses aides 10 (ft), 2 (pt); Physical
  therapists 1 (pt); Recreational therapists 1
  (ft); Occupational therapists 1 (pt); Speech
  therapists 1 (pt); Activities coordinators 2
  (ft); Dietitians 1 (pt); Ophthalmologists 1
  (pt); Audiologists 1 (pt); Psychologist 1 (pt)
  Social worker 1 (pt).
Facilities Dining room; Physical therapy
  room; Activities room; Chapel; Laundry
  room; Barber/Beauty shop; Library; TV
  lounge; Quiet room.
Activities Arts & crafts; Cards; Games;
  Reading groups; Prayer groups; Movies;
  Shopping trips; Social/Cultural gatherings;
  Sunday school; Church services; Individual
  & group therapy.

Russell Kare Center
320 S Lincoln, Russell, KS, 67665
(913) 483-2326
Admin H Russell Horton. *Medical Dir/Dir of
  Nursing* Davida Branda.
Licensure Intermediate care. *Beds* ICF 80.
  Certified Medicaid.
Owner Proprietary Corp (Americare Corp).
Admissions Requirements Minimum age 16;
  Medical examination; Physician's request.
Staff LPNs 5 (ft); Nurses aides 30 (ft);
  Activities coordinators 1 (ft); Dietitians 1
  (ft); Ophthalmologists 1 (pt); Social Service 1
  (ft).
Languages German
Facilities Dining room; Physical therapy
  room; Activities room; Crafts room; Laundry
  room; Barber/Beauty shop; Quiet room;
  Living room; Whirlpool.
Activities Arts & crafts; Cards; Games;
  Reading groups; Prayer groups; Movies;
  Shopping trips; Social/Cultural gatherings.

SABETHA

Apostolic Christian Home
511 Paramount St, Sabetha, KS, 66534
(913) 284-3471
Admin John E Lehman. *Medical Dir/Dir of
  Nursing* Ann Kent RN.
Licensure Intermediate care. *Beds* ICF 91.
  Certified Medicaid.
Owner Nonprofit Corp.
Staff RNs 3 (ft), 8 (pt); LPNs 1 (ft), 4 (pt);
  Nurses aides 10 (ft), 24 (pt); Recreational
  therapists 1 (ft).
Affiliation Apostolic Christian
Facilities Dining room; Physical therapy
  room; Activities room; Chapel; Crafts room;
  Laundry room; Barber/Beauty shop; Library;
  Branch bank; Post office branch.
Activities Arts & crafts; Cards; Games;
  Reading groups; Prayer groups; Movies;
  Shopping trips.

Fountain Villa Care Center*
913 Dakota, Sabetha, KS, 66534
(913) 284-3418
Admin Leo Kallenberger.

Licensure Intermediate care. *Beds* 60.
  Certified Medicaid.
Admissions Requirements Medical
  examination.
Staff RNs 1 (ft); LPNs 1 (ft); Nurses aides 19
  (ft), 9 (pt); Physical therapists 2 (pt); Reality
  therapists 1 (ft); Occupational therapists 1
  (pt); Speech therapists 1 (pt); Activities
  coordinators 1 (ft); Dietitians 1 (ft), 1 (pt);
  Dentists 1 (pt).
Facilities Dining room; Physical therapy
  room; Activities room; Crafts room; Laundry
  room; Barber/Beauty shop; Library.
Activities Arts & crafts; Cards; Games;
  Reading groups; Prayer groups; Movies;
  Shopping trips; Social/Cultural gatherings.

Sabetha Manor
1441 Oregon, Sabetha, KS, 66534
(913) 284-3411
Admin Homer K Branham. *Medical Dir/Dir of
  Nursing* Greg Winger MD; Roma Hervey
  RN DON.
Licensure Intermediate care. *Beds* ICF 60.
  Certified Medicaid.
Owner Proprietary Corp (Americare Corp).
Admissions Requirements Minimum age 17;
  Medical examination; Physician's request.
Staff Physicians 1 (pt); RNs 1 (ft), 1 (pt);
  LPNs 3 (ft), 1 (pt); Nurses aides 17 (ft), 4
  (pt); Physical therapists 1 (ft), 1 (pt); Reality
  therapists 1 (ft), 1 (pt); Recreational
  therapists 1 (ft), 1 (pt); Occupational
  therapists 1 (ft), 1 (pt); Speech therapists 1
  (pt); Activities coordinators 1 (ft); Dietitians
  1 (pt); Dentists 1 (pt); Ophthalmologists 1
  (pt); Podiatrists 1 (pt).
Facilities Dining room; Physical therapy
  room; Activities room; Crafts room; Laundry
  room; Barber/Beauty shop.
Activities Arts & crafts; Cards; Games;
  Reading groups; Prayer groups; Movies;
  Shopping trips; Social/Cultural gatherings.

SAINT FRANCIS

Good Samaritan Village*
S Side Hwy 36, Box 747, Saint Francis, KS,
  67756
(913) 332-2531
Admin Michael H Fleming.
Licensure Intermediate care. *Beds* 57.
  Certified Medicaid.
Owner Nonprofit Corp (Evangelical Lutheran/
  Good Samaritan).
Affiliation Lutheran

SAINT JOHN

Hearthstone Nursing Center*
4th & Sante Fe, Saint John, KS, 67576
(316) 549-3541
Admin Phil D England.
Licensure Intermediate care. *Beds* 68.
  Certified Medicaid.
Owner Proprietary Corp (Beverly Enterprises).
Admissions Requirements Medical
  examination; Physician's request.
Staff RNs 1 (ft), 1 (pt); LPNs 2 (ft), 2 (pt);
  Nurses aides 18 (ft), 3 (pt) Activities
  coordinators 1 (ft).
Facilities Dining room; Physical therapy
  room; Activities room; Laundry room;
  Barber/Beauty shop.
Activities Arts & crafts; Cards; Games;
  Reading groups; Prayer groups; Movies;
  Shopping trips; Social/Cultural gatherings;
  Family interaction groups.

SAINT MARYS

St Marys Manor*
206 Grand Ave, Saint Marys, KS, 66536
(913) 437-2286
Admin Michael E McCrite.

Licensure Intermediate care. *Beds* 50.
Certified Medicaid.
Owner Proprietary Corp.

SAINT PAUL

Living Skills Center*
PO Box 278, 5th & Lafayette, Saint Paul, KS, 66771
(316) 449-2277
Admin Calvin J Ennis. *Medical Dir/Dir of Nursing* Asha Verma MD.
Licensure Intermediate care for mentally retarded. *Beds* 63. *Certified* Medicaid.
Owner Proprietary Corp (Beverly Enterprises).
Admissions Requirements Minimum age 18; Medical examination; Physician's request.
Staff Physicians 1 (pt); RNs 1 (ft); LPNs 1 (ft); Nurses aides 25 (ft), 15 (pt); Physical therapists 1 (pt); Recreational therapists 1 (ft); Occupational therapists 1 (pt); Speech therapists 1 (pt); Activities coordinators 1 (ft); Dietitians 1 (pt); Dentists 1 (pt); Ophthalmologists 1 (pt); Podiatrists 1 (pt); Audiologists 1 (pt).
Facilities Dining room; Physical therapy room; Activities room; Crafts room; Laundry room; Barber/Beauty shop.
Activities Arts & crafts; Cards; Games; Reading groups; Prayer groups; Movies; Shopping trips; Social/Cultural gatherings; Special Olympics.

SALINA

Kenwood View Nursing Home*
PO Box 555, 900 Elmhurst Blvd, Salina, KS, 67402-0555
(913) 825-5471
Admin Bob Hodge.
Licensure Skilled care. *Beds* 94. *Certified* Medicaid.
Owner Proprietary Corp (Beverly Enterprises).

Salina Nursing Center
1007 Johnstown, Salina, KS, 67401
(913) 823-7107
Admin Phyllis M Franklin. *Medical Dir/Dir of Nursing* Thomas Taylor MD; Donna Jacobs RN.
Licensure Skilled care; Intermediate care. *Beds* SNF 28; ICF 78. *Certified* Medicaid.
Owner Proprietary Corp (Pinnacle Care Corp).
Staff RNs; LPNs; Orderlies; Nurses aides; Recreational therapists; Activities coordinators.
Activities Arts & crafts; Games; Reading groups; Prayer groups; Shopping trips; Bingo.

Salina Presbyterian Manor
2601 E Crawford, Salina, KS, 67401
(913) 825-1366
Admin James C Moore. *Medical Dir/Dir of Nursing* Betty L Roberts RN DON.
Licensure Intermediate care. *Beds* ICF 60. *Certified* Medicaid.
Owner Nonprofit Corp.
Admissions Requirements Minimum age 65; Medical examination.
Staff RNs 4 (ft), 1 (pt); LPNs 1 (ft), 2 (pt); Nurses aides 17 (ft), 15 (pt); Activities coordinators 1 (ft); Dietitians 1 (ft).
Affiliation Presbyterian
Facilities Dining room; Physical therapy room; Activities room; Chapel; Crafts room; Laundry room; Barber/Beauty shop; Library.
Activities Arts & crafts; Cards; Games; Reading groups; Prayer groups; Movies; Shopping trips; Social/Cultural gatherings.

Shalimar Plaza Nursing Center
2054 Lambertson Ln, Salina, KS, 67401
(913) 827-5589
Admin Alice M Canfield. *Medical Dir/Dir of Nursing* Brenda Ward.

Licensure Intermediate care. *Beds* 46.
Certified Medicaid.
Admissions Requirements Minimum age 21; Medical examination; Physician's request.
Staff RNs 1 (pt); LPNs 3 (ft), 3 (pt); Orderlies 2 (ft), 1 (pt); Nurses aides 12 (ft), 2 (pt); Physical therapists 1 (pt); Recreational therapists 1 (ft); Occupational therapists 1 (pt); Activities coordinators 1 (ft); Dietitians 1 (pt).
Facilities Dining room; Physical therapy room; Activities room; Crafts room; Laundry room; Barber/Beauty shop.
Activities Arts & crafts; Games; Reading groups; Prayer groups; Movies; Social/Cultural gatherings.

Windsor Estates Nursing Home*
623 S 3rd, Salina, KS, 67401
(913) 825-6757
Admin Ann McCall. *Medical Dir/Dir of Nursing* Dr Lou Forster.
Licensure Skilled care. *Beds* 60. *Certified* Medicare.
Facilities Dining room; Physical therapy room; Activities room; Crafts room; Laundry room; Barber/Beauty shop.
Activities Arts & crafts; Cards; Games; Reading groups; Prayer groups; Movies; Shopping trips; Social/Cultural gatherings.

SCOTT CITY

Park Lane Nursing Home*
13th & College, Scott City, KS, 67871
(316) 872-2148
Admin Gregory Uhruh.
Licensure Intermediate care. *Beds* 84. *Certified* Medicaid.
Admissions Requirements Medical examination; Physician's request.
Staff RNs 2 (ft), 1 (pt); LPNs 2 (ft), 1 (pt); Nurses aides 21 (ft), 9 (pt); Physical therapists 1 (pt); Activities coordinators 1 (ft); Dietitians 1 (pt).
Facilities Dining room; Physical therapy room; Activities room; Chapel; Crafts room; Laundry room; Barber/Beauty shop.
Activities Arts & crafts; Cards; Games; Reading groups; Prayer groups; Movies; Shopping trips; Social/Cultural gatherings.

SEDAN

Pleasant Valley Manor
PO Box 40, 623 E Elm St, Sedan, KS, 67361
(316) 725-3153
Admin David L Chrisman. *Medical Dir/Dir of Nursing* Nancy Turner.
Licensure Intermediate care. *Beds* ICF 83. *Certified* Medicaid.
Owner Proprietary Corp (Americare Corp).
Admissions Requirements Medical examination; Physician's request.
Staff RNs 1 (pt); LPNs 4 (ft), 2 (pt); Orderlies 2 (ft); Nurses aides 21 (ft); Physical therapists 1 (pt); Reality therapists 1 (pt); Recreational therapists 1 (pt); Speech therapists 1 (pt); Activities coordinators 1 (ft); Podiatrists 1 (pt); Dentist 1 (pt).
Facilities Dining room; Physical therapy room; Activities room; Chapel; Crafts room; Laundry room; Barber/Beauty shop.
Activities Arts & crafts; Games; Prayer groups; Movies; Bowling; Bus trips.

SEDGWICK

Sedgwick Convalescent Center
Box 49, 712 Monroe, Sedgwick, KS, 67135
(316) 772-5185
Admin Jerry L Korbe. *Medical Dir/Dir of Nursing* Nita King RN.
Licensure Intermediate care. *Beds* ICF 100. *Certified* Medicaid.
Owner Proprietary Corp (Hillhaven Corp).

Admissions Requirements Medical examination; Physician's request.
Staff RNs 2 (ft), 1 (pt); LPNs 4 (ft); Nurses aides 23 (ft); Physical therapists 1 (pt); Occupational therapists 1 (pt); Speech therapists 1 (pt); Activities coordinators 1 (ft).
Facilities Dining room; Physical therapy room; Activities room; Crafts room; Barber/Beauty shop.
Activities Arts & crafts; Cards; Games; Reading groups; Prayer groups; Movies; Social/Cultural gatherings.

SENECA

Country View Estates
512 Community Dr, Seneca, KS, 66538
(913) 336-3528
Admin Edna Jane Werner. *Medical Dir/Dir of Nursing* Janet Hermesch RN DON.
Licensure Intermediate care. *Beds* 75. *Certified* Medicaid.
Owner Proprietary Corp (Life Care Centers of America).
Admissions Requirements Minimum age 16; Medical examination; Physician's request.
Staff RNs 1 (ft), 2 (pt); LPNs 3 (ft), 2 (pt); Nurses aides 11 (ft), 19 (pt); Activities coordinators 3 (pt).
Facilities Dining room; Physical therapy room; Activities room; Laundry room; Barber/Beauty shop; Living room; Quiet room.
Activities Arts & crafts; Cards; Games; Reading groups; Prayer groups; Movies.

Crestview Manor*
808 N 8th, Seneca, KS, 66538
(913) 336-2156
Admin Paul H Bergman.
Licensure Intermediate care. *Beds* 50. *Certified* Medicaid.
Owner Proprietary Corp.

SHARON SPRINGS

Prairie Manor Rest Home
HCI Box 20, 408 E 6th St, Sharon Springs, KS, 67758
(913) 852-4244
Admin Roberta O'Leary. *Medical Dir/Dir of Nursing* Ruby Voth RN DON.
Licensure Intermediate care. *Beds* ICF 28. *Certified* Medicaid.
Owner Publicly owned Wallace County.
Admissions Requirements Medical examination.
Staff RNs 1 (ft); LPNs 2 (ft), 2 (pt); Orderlies 4 (pt); Nurses aides 10 (ft), 2 (pt); Recreational therapists 2 (pt); Activities coordinators 1 (ft), 1 (pt); Dietitians 2 (ft), 2 (pt).
Facilities Dining room; Physical therapy room; Activities room; Laundry room; Barber/Beauty shop; Med room.
Activities Arts & crafts; Cards; Games; Reading groups; Prayer groups; Social/Cultural gatherings; Specials on holidays & birthdays.

SHAWNEE

Sharon Lane Nursing Home
10315 Johnson Dr, Shawnee, KS, 66203
(913) 631-8200
Admin Marjory L Dwight. *Medical Dir/Dir of Nursing* Betty C Price RN DON.
Licensure Intermediate care. *Beds* ICF 66.
Owner Nonprofit Corp (Adventist Health Sys-USA).
Staff RNs 3 (ft), 1 (pt); LPNs 2 (ft); Nurses aides 20 (ft), 2 (pt); Activities coordinators 1 (ft).

Facilities Dining room; Physical therapy room; Activities room; Laundry room; Barber/Beauty shop; Library.
Activities Arts & crafts; Cards; Games; Reading groups; Prayer groups; Movies.

SHAWNEE MISSION

Faith Village
11300 Greenwood, Shawnee Mission, KS, 66215
(913) 469-5566
Admin Richard L Schmitz. *Medical Dir/Dir of Nursing* Judie Gornetzki RN.
Licensure Intermediate care for mentally retarded. *Beds* ICF/MR 45. *Certified* Medicaid; Medicare.
Owner Nonprofit organization/foundation.
Admissions Requirements Minimum age 18.
Staff RNs 1 (pt); LPNs 2 (pt); Nurses aides 25 (ft), 4 (pt); Physical therapists 1 (pt); Speech therapists 1 (pt); Activities coordinators 1 (ft); Dietitians 1 (pt); Recreation aides 6 (pt); Dietary aides 3 (pt); House managers 3 (pt); Social worker 1 (pt).
Facilities Dining room; Activities room; Laundry room.
Activities Arts & crafts; Games; Shopping trips; Special Olympics.

SMITH CENTER

Bethesda Care Center
Box 369, 117 W 1st, Smith Center, KS, 66967
(913) 282-6696
Admin Shirley Steen. *Medical Dir/Dir of Nursing* Dr V W Steinkruger; Leigh Bertholf.
Licensure Intermediate care. *Beds* ICF 66. *Certified* Medicare.
Owner Nonprofit Corp (Bethesda Care Centers).
Admissions Requirements Medical examination.
Staff RNs 1 (ft); LPNs 2 (ft); Nurses aides 40 (ft).
Facilities Dining room; Physical therapy room; Activities room; Chapel; Crafts room; Laundry room; Barber/Beauty shop; Library.
Activities Arts & crafts; Cards; Games; Reading groups; Prayer groups; Movies; Shopping trips.

SMOLAN

White Cross Health Center
9300 S Burma Rd, Smolan, KS, 67479
(913) 668-2251
Admin William Taylor. *Medical Dir/Dir of Nursing* Tammy Wiegert.
Licensure Intermediate care. *Beds* ICF 53. *Certified* Medicaid.
Owner Proprietary Corp.
Staff RNs; LPNs; Nurses aides; Activities coordinators.
Facilities Dining room; Physical therapy room; Laundry room; Barber/Beauty shop.
Activities Arts & crafts; Cards; Reading groups; Movies; Shopping trips; Social/Cultural gatherings.

SOUTH HAVEN

Wheatland Lodge
PO Box 198, South Haven, KS, 67140
(316) 892-5513
Admin Arif Haider. *Medical Dir/Dir of Nursing* Denise Showman.
Licensure Intermediate care. *Beds* ICF 50. *Certified* Medicaid.
Owner Nonprofit organization/foundation.
Admissions Requirements Physician's request.
Staff RNs 1 (ft), 2 (pt); LPNs 2 (ft), 1 (pt); Nurses aides 19 (ft), 7 (pt); Physical therapists 1 (ft); Reality therapists 1 (ft);

Recreational therapists 1 (ft); Occupational therapists 1 (ft); Activities coordinators 1 (ft).
Facilities Dining room; Physical therapy room; Activities room; Chapel; Crafts room; Laundry room; Barber/Beauty shop; Smoking lounge.
Activities Arts & crafts; Cards; Games; Reading groups; Prayer groups; Movies; Shopping trips; Social/Cultural gatherings; Exercise; Picnic trips.

SOUTH HUTCHISON

Mennonite Friendship Manor Inc
600 W Blanchard, South Hutchison, KS, 67505
(316) 663-7175
Admin Allen L Holsopple. *Medical Dir/Dir of Nursing* Bette Hirst RN.
Licensure Intermediate care. *Beds* ICF 120. *Certified* Medicaid.
Owner Nonprofit Corp.
Admissions Requirements Medical examination.
Staff RNs 10 (ft), 4 (pt); LPNs 8 (ft), 4 (pt); Orderlies 2 (ft), 2 (pt); Nurses aides 43 (ft), 10 (pt); Physical therapists 1 (pt); Occupational therapists 1 (pt); Speech therapists 1 (pt); Activities coordinators 2 (ft), 2 (pt); Dietitians 1 (ft).
Languages Spanish, German
Affiliation Mennonite
Facilities Dining room; Physical therapy room; Activities room; Chapel; Crafts room; Laundry room; Barber/Beauty shop; Library; Private lounges; Living room.
Activities Arts & crafts; Cards; Games; Reading groups; Prayer groups; Movies; Shopping trips; Social/Cultural gatherings; Field trips to state fair; Music groups; Walking groups.

SPRING HILL

Spring Hill Manor
251 Wilson Ave, Spring Hill, KS, 66083
(913) 686-3100
Admin Frances Keearns. *Medical Dir/Dir of Nursing* Golda Colles.
Licensure Intermediate care. *Beds* 50. *Certified* Medicaid.
Owner Proprietary Corp (Life Care Centers of America).
Admissions Requirements Medical examination; Physician's request.
Staff LPNs 3 (ft), 1 (pt); Nurses aides 12 (ft), 5 (pt); Physical therapists 1 (pt); Recreational therapists 1 (pt); Occupational therapists 1 (pt); Speech therapists 1 (pt); Activities coordinators 1 (ft); Dietitians 1 (pt).
Facilities Dining room; Physical therapy room; Activities room; Crafts room; Laundry room; Barber/Beauty shop; Library.
Activities Arts & crafts; Cards; Games; Reading groups; Prayer groups; Movies; Shopping trips; Social/Cultural gatherings.

STAFFORD

Leisure Homestead Association
405 E Grand, Stafford, KS, 67578
(316) 234-5208
Admin Jennifer Younie. *Medical Dir/Dir of Nursing* Sharilyn Mead RN.
Licensure Intermediate care. *Beds* ICF 60. *Certified* Medicaid.
Owner Nonprofit Corp.
Admissions Requirements Minimum age 16; Medical examination; Physician's request.
Staff RNs 1 (ft); LPNs 3 (ft); Nurses aides 2 (ft), 3 (pt); Activities coordinators 1 (ft).
Facilities Dining room; Physical therapy room; Activities room; Laundry room; Barber/Beauty shop.

Activities Arts & crafts; Cards; Games; Reading groups; Prayer groups; Movies; Shopping trips; Social/Cultural gatherings.

STERLING

Sterling Presbyterian Manor
204 W Washington, Sterling, KS, 67579
(319) 278-3651
Admin Sadie P Goodwin. *Medical Dir/Dir of Nursing* Dee Fabin RN.
Licensure Intermediate care. *Beds* ICF 60. *Certified* Medicaid.
Owner Proprietary Corp.
Admissions Requirements Minimum age 65; Females only.
Staff RNs 4 (ft); LPNs 3 (ft); Nurses aides 25 (ft), 3 (pt); Activities coordinators 1 (ft).
Affiliation Presbyterian
Facilities Dining room; Physical therapy room; Activities room; Chapel; Crafts room; Laundry room; Barber/Beauty shop; Library.
Activities Arts & crafts; Cards; Games; Reading groups; Prayer groups; Movies; Shopping trips; Social/Cultural gatherings.

STOCKTON

Solomon Valley Manor
315 S Ash, Stockton, KS, 67669
(913) 425-6109
Admin Larry Miller. *Medical Dir/Dir of Nursing* Kris Glendening.
Licensure Intermediate care. *Beds* ICF 50; ICF/MR. *Certified* Medicaid.
Owner Proprietary Corp.
Staff RNs; LPNs; Nurses aides; Physical therapists; Activities coordinators; Dietitians.
Facilities Dining room; Laundry room; Barber/Beauty shop.
Activities Games; Prayer groups; Movies.

SYRACUSE

Hamilton County Rest Home*
E "G" St, Syracuse, KS, 67878
(316) 384-7780
Admin Kathryn D Zimmett. *Medical Dir/Dir of Nursing* Dr C E Petterson.
Licensure Intermediate care. *Beds* 21. *Certified* Medicaid.
Admissions Requirements Minimum age 21; Medical examination; Physician's request.
Staff Physicians 2 (pt); RNs 2 (pt); LPNs 2 (ft); Nurses aides 7 (ft), 8 (pt); Physical therapists 1 (pt); Activities coordinators 1 (ft), 1 (pt); Dietitians 1 (pt); Dentists 1 (pt); Ophthalmologists 1 (pt); Podiatrists 1 (pt).
Facilities Dining room; Physical therapy room; Activities room; Chapel; Crafts room; Laundry room; Barber/Beauty shop.
Activities Arts & crafts; Cards; Games; Reading groups; Prayer groups; Movies; Shopping trips; Social/Cultural gatherings.

TOPEKA

Aldersgate Village Health Unit
3220 Albright Dr, Topeka, KS, 66614
(912) 478-9440
Admin Janice M Jenkins. *Medical Dir/Dir of Nursing* Larry Rumans MD; Pam Lynch.
Licensure Skilled care; Personal care. *Beds* SNF 60; Personal 55.
Owner Nonprofit Corp.
Admissions Requirements Minimum age 16; Medical examination; Physician's request.
Staff Physicians 2 (pt); RNs 4 (ft), 4 (pt); LPNs 7 (ft); Orderlies 4 (ft), 1 (pt); Nurses aides 18 (ft), 8 (pt); Physical therapists 1 (pt); Occupational therapists 1 (pt); Speech therapists 1 (pt); Activities coordinators 3 (ft), 2 (pt); Dietitians 1 (ft), 1 (pt); Dentists 1 (pt); Ophthalmologists 1 (pt); Podiatrists 1 (pt); Massage Therapist 1 (pt).
Affiliation Methodist

Facilities Dining room; Physical therapy room; Activities room; Chapel; Crafts room; Laundry room; Barber/Beauty shop; Library; Outpatient clinic rooms; Dental office; Sundries shop; Wood shop; Spa; Handicap kitchen; Enclosed outdoor patios.
Activities Arts & crafts; Cards; Games; Reading groups; Prayer groups; Movies; Shopping trips; Social/Cultural gatherings; Pet therapy; Music therapy; Men's breakfast; Ladies tea; Creative cooking; Exercise classes; Spelling bee; Quizical quizzes; Play reading; Gardening; Resident council; Van rides.

Brewster Place—The Congregational Home
1205 W 29th, Topeka, KS, 66611
(913) 267-1667
Admin Ronald A Schmoller. *Medical Dir/Dir of Nursing* Dr Mike Atwood; Virginia Tevis.
Licensure Skilled care; Intermediate care. *Beds* SNF 35; ICF 42. *Certified* Medicaid; Medicare.
Owner Nonprofit organization/foundation.
Admissions Requirements Minimum age 62; Medical examination; Physician's request.
Staff Physicians 1 (pt); RNs 5 (ft), 10 (pt); LPNs 1 (ft), 1 (pt); Nurses aides 25 (ft), 14 (pt); Physical therapists 1 (pt); Recreational therapists 1 (ft); Occupational therapists 1 (pt); Speech therapists 1 (pt); Activities coordinators 1 (ft); Dietitians 1 (ft); Dentists 1 (pt); Ophthalmologists 1 (pt); Podiatrists 1 (pt).
Affiliation Congregational
Facilities Dining room; Physical therapy room; Activities room; Chapel; Crafts room; Laundry room; Barber/Beauty shop; Library.
Activities Arts & crafts; Cards; Games; Reading groups; Prayer groups; Movies; Shopping trips; Social/Cultural gatherings.

Briarcliff Manor Inc*
3224 W 29th St, Topeka, KS, 66614
(913) 272-2601
Admin Beverly Hincholiff. *Medical Dir/Dir of Nursing* Dr William Wade.
Licensure Intermediate care. *Beds* 50. *Certified* Medicaid.
Admissions Requirements Medical examination; Physician's request.
Staff RNs 1 (pt); LPNs 4 (ft), 2 (pt); Nurses aides 15 (ft), 4 (pt); Physical therapists 1 (pt); Activities coordinators 1 (ft); Dietitians 1 (pt).
Facilities Dining room; Physical therapy room; Activities room; Crafts room; Laundry room; Barber/Beauty shop; TV room; Quiet room; Sitting room.
Activities Arts & crafts; Cards; Games; Reading groups; Prayer groups; Movies; Shopping trips; Social/Cultural gatherings; Community speakers.

Brighton Place North
1301 N Jefferson, Topeka, KS, 66608
(913) 233-5127
Admin David S Tuttle. *Medical Dir/Dir of Nursing* Glenn O Bair MD; Patricia Hinton DON.
Licensure Intermediate care. *Beds* ICF 34. *Certified* Medicaid.
Owner Proprietary Corp.
Admissions Requirements Minimum age 18; Medical examination; Physician's request.
Staff Physicians 2 (pt); RNs 1 (pt); LPNs 5 (ft), 1 (pt); Nurses aides 7 (ft), 1 (pt); Activities coordinators 1 (ft); Dietitians 3 (ft), 1 (pt).
Facilities Dining room; Physical therapy room; Activities room; Laundry room; Barber/Beauty shop.
Activities Arts & crafts; Cards; Games; Shopping trips; Social/Cultural gatherings; Church visits; Bingo.

Countryside Health Center
3401 Seward, Topeka, KS, 66616
(913) 234-6147
Admin Nancy A Kirk.
Licensure Intermediate care. *Beds* 60. *Certified* Medicaid.
Owner Proprietary Corp.

Eventide Convalescent Center Inc*
2015 E 10th, Topeka, KS, 66607
(913) 233-8918
Admin M Mac Austin. *Medical Dir/Dir of Nursing* Dr Robert Jacoby.
Licensure Skilled care. *Beds* 100. *Certified* Medicaid; Medicare.
Admissions Requirements Medical examination; Physician's request.
Staff Physicians 1 (pt); RNs 2 (ft); LPNs 7 (ft), 1 (pt); Orderlies 9 (ft); Nurses aides 25 (ft); Physical therapists 1 (pt); Occupational therapists 1 (pt); Speech therapists 1 (pt); Activities coordinators 2 (ft); Dietitians 1 (ft), 1 (pt); Dentists 1 (pt); Ophthalmologists 1 (pt); Podiatrists 1 (pt); Audiologists 1 (pt).
Facilities Dining room; Physical therapy room; Activities room; Chapel; Crafts room; Laundry room; Barber/Beauty shop; Library.
Activities Arts & crafts; Cards; Games; Reading groups; Prayer groups; Shopping trips; Social/Cultural gatherings.

Fairlawn Heights Nursing Center
5400 W 7th, Topeka, KS, 66606
(913) 272-6880
Admin Elaine L Wells. *Medical Dir/Dir of Nursing* Dr Doug Gardner; Elaine L Luce RN DON.
Licensure Intermediate care. *Beds* ICF 70. *Certified* Medicaid.
Owner Proprietary Corp.
Admissions Requirements Minimum age 18; Medical examination; Physician's request.
Staff RNs 1 (ft); LPNs 3 (ft), 6 (ft); Orderlies 3 (ft); Nurses aides 15 (ft), 10 (pt); Physical therapists 1 (pt); Occupational therapists; Activities coordinators 1 (ft), 1 (pt); Dietitians 1 (pt).
Facilities Dining room; Physical therapy room; Activities room; Crafts room; Laundry room; Barber/Beauty shop.
Activities Arts & crafts; Cards; Games; Reading groups; Prayer groups; Movies; Shopping trips; Social/Cultural gatherings; Reminiscence therapy.

Glendale Manor*
1334 Buchanan, Topeka, KS, 66604
(913) 235-6258
Admin Brenda Bauman Swank. *Medical Dir/Dir of Nursing* Hazel Craig.
Licensure Intermediate care. *Beds* 53. *Certified* Medicaid.
Staff RNs 1 (pt); LPNs 2 (ft); Orderlies 5 (ft), 1 (pt); Nurses aides 8 (ft), 4 (pt); Physical therapists 1 (pt); Activities coordinators; Dietitians.
Facilities Dining room; Physical therapy room; Activities room; Crafts room; Laundry room; Barber/Beauty shop; Library.
Activities Arts & crafts; Cards; Games; Reading groups; Prayer groups; Movies; Shopping trips; Social/Cultural gatherings.

Highland Villa
1821 E 21st St, Topeka, KS, 66607
(913) 233-9626
Admin William Crego. *Medical Dir/Dir of Nursing* Beverly Clarke RN.
Licensure Skilled care; Intermediate care. *Beds* SNF 50; ICF 50. *Certified* Medicaid.
Owner Proprietary Corp (American Health Care Centers).
Admissions Requirements Minimum age 21; Medical examination; Physician's request.
Staff RNs 2 (ft); LPNs 4 (ft), 5 (pt); Nurses aides 30 (ft), 3 (pt); Physical therapists 1 (pt); Activities coordinators 1 (ft), 1 (pt); Dietitians 1 (ft), 1 (pt); Social worker 1 (ft).

Languages Spanish
Facilities Dining room; Physical therapy room; Activities room; Laundry room; Barber/Beauty shop; 2 lounge areas.
Activities Arts & crafts; Cards; Games; Prayer groups; Movies; Shopping trips; Social/Cultural gatherings.

Hillhaven of Topeka
711 Garfield, Topeka, KS, 66606
(913) 357-6121
Admin Vickey L Foster. *Medical Dir/Dir of Nursing* Jorge Herrera MD; Ruth Johnson RN DON.
Licensure Skilled care; Intermediate care. *Beds* SNF 58; ICF 116. *Certified* Medicaid; Medicare.
Owner Proprietary Corp (Hillhaven Corp).
Admissions Requirements Minimum age 16; Physician's request.
Staff RNs 6 (ft); LPNs 8 (ft); Orderlies 5 (ft); Nurses aides 47 (ft); Physical therapists 1 (ft); Activities coordinators 2 (ft).
Facilities Dining room; Physical therapy room; Activities room; Crafts room; Laundry room; Barber/Beauty shop.
Activities Arts & crafts; Cards; Games; Reading groups; Prayer groups; Movies; Shopping trips; Social/Cultural gatherings.

Indian Trails Mental Health Living Center
1112 Republican, Topeka, KS, 66607
(913) 233-0588
Admin Tanya Williamson. *Medical Dir/Dir of Nursing* Brent Williamson.
Licensure Intermediate care. *Beds* ICF 82. *Certified* Medicaid.
Owner Proprietary Corp.
Admissions Requirements Minimum age 21; Medical examination; Physician's request.
Staff Physicians 2 (ft); RNs 1 (ft); LPNs 6 (ft); Orderlies 6 (ft); Nurses aides 15 (ft); Physical therapists 1 (ft); Occupational therapists 1 (pt); Speech therapists 1 (pt); Activities coordinators 2 (ft); Dietitians 1 (pt); Ophthalmologists 1 (pt); Podiatrists 1 (pt).
Facilities Dining room; Physical therapy room; Activities room; Crafts room; Laundry room; Barber/Beauty shop; Library; 2 Recreation rooms.
Activities Arts & crafts; Cards; Games; Reading groups; Prayer groups; Movies; Shopping trips; Social/Cultural gatherings; Community outings.

The Manor of Topeka
4101 Martin Dr, Topeka, KS, 66609
(913) 267-3100
Admin Sharon L Durrell.
Licensure Intermediate care. *Beds* ICF 120. *Certified* Medicaid.
Owner Proprietary Corp.
Admissions Requirements Minimum age 55; Medical examination; Physician's request.
Staff RNs 2 (ft); LPNs 9 (ft); Orderlies 12 (ft); Nurses aides 30 (ft); Physical therapists 2 (ft); Reality therapists 1 (ft); Recreational therapists 1 (ft); Occupational therapists 1 (ft); Speech therapists 1 (ft); Activities coordinators 2 (ft); Dietitians 1 (ft); Ophthalmologists 1 (ft).
Facilities Dining room; Physical therapy room; Activities room; Chapel; Crafts room; Laundry room; Barber/Beauty shop; Whirlpool.
Activities Arts & crafts; Cards; Games; Reading groups; Prayer groups; Movies; Shopping trips; Social/Cultural gatherings; Supper clubs.

McCrite Plaza Health Center*
1610 W 37th St, Topeka, KS, 66611
(913) 267-2960
Admin Joan Russell.
Licensure Intermediate care. *Beds* 80. *Certified* Medicaid.
Owner Proprietary Corp.

The Oaks
331 Oakley, Topeka, KS, 66606
(913) 232-1212
Admin Milly Ann Briggs. *Medical Dir/Dir of Nursing* Joan Sehdev MD; Betty Bryan LPN.
Licensure ICF-MH. *Beds* ICF-MH 50. *Certified* Medicaid.
Owner Proprietary Corp.
Admissions Requirements Minimum age 50; Medical examination; Physician's request.
Staff RNs 1 (pt); LPNs 4 (ft); Orderlies 4 (ft); Nurses aides 11 (ft); Physical therapists 1 (pt); Recreational therapists 1 (ft); Activities coordinators 1 (pt); Social worker 1 (ft).
Facilities Dining room; Physical therapy room; Activities room; Crafts room; Laundry room; Barber/Beauty shop; Library.
Activities Arts & crafts; Cards; Games; Reading groups; Prayer groups; Movies; Shopping trips; Social/Cultural gatherings.

Pioneer Village I
2209 SE 25th, Topeka, KS, 66605
(913) 267-2927
Admin Kari Ebeling. *Medical Dir/Dir of Nursing* William Wade DO; Linda McWilliams RN DON.
Licensure Intermediate care for mentally retarded. *Beds* ICF/MR 15. *Certified* Medicaid; Medicare.
Owner Nonprofit Corp.
Admissions Requirements Minimum age 18; Medical examination.
Staff Physicians 1 (ft); RNs 1 (ft); LPNs 2 (ft); Nurses aides 12 (ft), 3 (pt); Physical therapists 1 (pt); Occupational therapists 1 (pt); Speech therapists 1 (pt); Activities coordinators 1 (ft); Dietitians 1 (pt); Podiatrists 1 (pt).
Languages Sign
Facilities Dining room; Laundry room.
Activities Arts & crafts; Cards; Games; Movies; Shopping trips; Social/Cultural gatherings; Special Olympics.

Pioneer Village II
2125 SE 25th, Topeka, KS, 66605
(913) 267-2927
Admin Kari Ebeling. *Medical Dir/Dir of Nursing* William Wade DO; Linda McWilliams RN.
Licensure Intermediate care for mentally retarded. *Beds* ICF/MR 15. *Certified* Medicaid; Medicare.
Owner Nonprofit Corp.
Admissions Requirements Minimum age 18; Medical examination.
Staff Physicians 1 (ft); RNs 1 (ft); LPNs 2 (ft); Nurses aides 11 (ft), 2 (pt); Physical therapists 1 (pt); Occupational therapists 1 (pt); Speech therapists 1 (pt); Activities coordinators 1 (ft); Dietitians 1 (pt); Podiatrists 1 (pt).
Languages Sign
Facilities Dining room; Laundry room.
Activities Arts & crafts; Cards; Games; Movies; Shopping trips; Social/Cultural gatherings; Special Olympics.

Pioneer Village III
2209 SE 25th, Topeka, KS, 66605
(913) 267-2927
Admin Richard Shults. *Medical Dir/Dir of Nursing* Linda McWilliams.
Licensure Intermediate care for mentally retarded. *Beds* ICF/MR 60. *Certified* Medicaid.
Owner Nonprofit Corp.
Staff RNs 1 (ft); LPNs 2 (pt); Nurses aides 58 (ft); Recreational therapists 1 (ft).

Pioneer Village IV
2217 SE 25th, Topeka, KS, 66605
(913) 267-2927
Admin Kari Ebeling. *Medical Dir/Dir of Nursing* William Wade DO; Linda McWilliams RN.

Licensure Intermediate care for mentally retarded. *Beds* ICF/MR 15. *Certified* Medicaid; Medicare.
Owner Nonprofit Corp.
Admissions Requirements Minimum age 16; Medical examination.
Staff Physicians 1 (ft); RNs 1 (ft); LPNs 2 (ft); Nurses aides 11 (ft), 2 (pt); Physical therapists 1 (pt); Occupational therapists 1 (pt); Speech therapists 1 (pt); Activities coordinators 1 (ft); Dietitians 1 (pt); Podiatrists 1 (pt).
Languages Sign
Facilities Dining room; Laundry room.
Activities Arts & crafts; Cards; Games; Movies; Shopping trips; Social/Cultural gatherings; Special Olympics.

Samaritan Home Inc
2075 Fillmore, Topeka, KS, 66604
(913) 234-0548
Admin Joseph H Mazur. *Medical Dir/Dir of Nursing* Joan Sehdeu MD.
Licensure Intermediate care. *Beds* 77. *Certified* Medicaid.
Owner Proprietary Corp.
Admissions Requirements Minimum age 22; Medical examination; Physician's request.
Staff RNs 1 (pt); LPNs 4 (ft); Orderlies 3 (ft); Nurses aides 23 (ft); Physical therapists 1 (pt); Occupational therapists 1 (pt); Activities coordinators 1 (ft); Dietitians 1 (pt).
Facilities Dining room; Physical therapy room; Activities room; Chapel; Crafts room; Laundry room; Library.
Activities Arts & crafts; Cards; Games; Reading groups; Prayer groups; Movies; Shopping trips; Social/Cultural gatherings.

Topeka Convalescent Center
515 Horne St, Topeka, KS, 66606
(913) 233-2321
Admin James A Klausman. *Medical Dir/Dir of Nursing* Eric Voth MD; Julie Weber DON.
Licensure Skilled care. *Beds* SNF 100; ICF. *Certified* Medicaid; Medicare.
Owner Proprietary Corp.
Admissions Requirements Physician's request.
Staff Physicians 2 (pt); RNs 3 (ft), 1 (pt); LPNs 6 (ft); Nurses aides 25 (ft), 5 (pt); Physical therapists 1 (ft); Recreational therapists 1 (ft); Occupational therapists 1 (pt); Speech therapists 1 (pt); Activities coordinators 1 (ft), 1 (pt); Dietitians 1 (pt); Dentists 1 (pt); Ophthalmologists 1 (pt); Podiatrists 1 (pt).
Facilities Dining room; Physical therapy room; Activities room; Crafts room; Laundry room; Barber/Beauty shop; Library.
Activities Arts & crafts; Cards; Games; Reading groups; Prayer groups; Movies; Shopping trips; Social/Cultural gatherings.

Topeka Presbyterian Manor Inc
4712 W 6th St, Topeka, KS, 66606
(913) 272-6510
Admin Raymond P Vernon. *Medical Dir/Dir of Nursing* Jo Neill.
Licensure Skilled care; Intermediate care; Personal care. *Beds* SNF 60; ICF 60; Personal 86. *Certified* Medicaid.
Owner Nonprofit organization/foundation.
Admissions Requirements Minimum age 65; Medical examination.
Staff RNs 8 (ft), 8 (pt); LPNs 12 (ft), 4 (pt); Nurses aides 35 (ft), 15 (pt); Physical therapists 2 (ft), 2 (pt); Reality therapists 1 (pt); Recreational therapists 1 (pt); Occupational therapists 1 (ft); Speech therapists 1 (pt); Activities coordinators 3 (ft); Dietitians 1 (ft); Dentists 1 (pt); Ophthalmologists 1 (pt); Podiatrists 1 (pt); Social worker 2 (ft); Chaplain 1 (ft).
Affiliation Presbyterian
Facilities Dining room; Physical therapy room; Activities room; Chapel; Crafts room; Laundry room; Barber/Beauty shop; Library.

Activities Arts & crafts; Cards; Games; Reading groups; Prayer groups; Movies; Shopping trips; Social/Cultural gatherings.

United Methodist Home
1135 College Ave, Topeka, KS, 66604
(913) 234-0421
Admin A Lowell Geelan. *Medical Dir/Dir of Nursing* Gregory Duncan RNC.
Licensure Intermediate care. *Beds* ICF 110. *Certified* Medicaid.
Owner Nonprofit organization/foundation.
Admissions Requirements Minimum age 65; Medical examination; Physician's request.
Staff Physicians 2 (pt); RNs 7 (ft), 4 (pt); LPNs 8 (ft), 4 (pt); Nurses aides 34 (ft), 9 (pt); Physical therapists 1 (pt); Reality therapists 1 (pt); Recreational therapists 1 (ft); Occupational therapists 1 (pt); Speech therapists 1 (pt); Activities coordinators 1 (ft); Dietitians 1 (ft); Dentists 1 (pt); Ophthalmologists 1 (pt); Podiatrists 1 (pt).
Affiliation Methodist
Facilities Dining room; Physical therapy room; Activities room; Chapel; Crafts room; Laundry room; Barber/Beauty shop; Library.
Activities Arts & crafts; Cards; Games; Reading groups; Prayer groups; Movies; Shopping trips; Social/Cultural gatherings.

Westwood Manor
5015 W 28th St, Topeka, KS, 66614
(913) 273-0886
Admin Andrea Kelly.
Licensure Intermediate care. *Beds* 54. *Certified* Medicaid.
Owner Proprietary Corp.

Woodland Health Center
440 Woodland, Topeka, KS, 66607
(913) 233-0544
Admin Dee Klausman. *Medical Dir/Dir of Nursing* Jeffrey Rhoads MD; Scott Teeter MD; Peggy Lemon RN DON.
Licensure Skilled care; Intermediate care. *Beds* SNF 57; ICF 50. *Certified* Medicaid.
Owner Proprietary Corp.
Admissions Requirements Minimum age 16; Medical examination; Physician's request.
Staff RNs 3 (ft), 2 (pt); LPNs 5 (ft), 4 (pt); Nurses aides 30 (ft), 2 (pt); Physical therapists 1 (pt); Occupational therapists 1 (pt); Activities coordinators 1 (ft); Dietitians 1 (ft); Social worker 1 (ft).
Facilities Dining room; Physical therapy room; Activities room; Crafts room; Laundry room; Barber/Beauty shop; Living room.
Activities Arts & crafts; Cards; Games; Reading groups; Prayer groups; Movies; Shopping trips; Social/Cultural gatherings.

TRIBUNE

Helmwood Care Home
311 E Harper, Box 190, Tribune, KS, 67879
(316) 376-4225
Admin Gilbert Booker. *Medical Dir/Dir of Nursing* W F Werner MD.
Licensure Intermediate care. *Beds* ICF 32. *Certified* Medicaid.
Owner Privately owned.
Admissions Requirements Minimum age 18.
Staff RNs 2 (ft); LPNs 1 (ft); Nurses aides 10 (ft), 3 (pt); Physical therapists; Recreational therapists; Activities coordinators 1 (ft); Dentist 1 (pt).
Facilities Dining room; Physical therapy room; Activities room; Chapel; Crafts room; Barber/Beauty shop.
Activities Arts & crafts; Cards; Games; Reading groups; Prayer groups; Movies; Shopping trips; Social/Cultural gatherings.

ULYSSES

Western Prairie Care Home*
300 E Maize, Ulysses, KS, 67880
(316) 356-3331
Admin Paul A Florquist.
Licensure Intermediate care. *Beds* 75.
 Certified Medicaid.
Owner Publicly owned.

UNIONTOWN

Marmaton Valley Home
Box 22, Hwy K-3 & 54, Uniontown, KS,
 66779
(316) 756-4661
Admin Grace Hockett. *Medical Dir/Dir of
 Nursing* Marsha Kumalae.
Licensure Intermediate care. *Beds* ICF 40.
 Certified Medicaid.
Owner Proprietary Corp.
Admissions Requirements Minimum age 18.
Staff RNs 2 (pt); LPNs 1 (ft), 2 (pt); Nurses
 aides 12 (ft), 7 (pt); Physical therapists 1 (ft);
 Activities coordinators 1 (ft); Dietitians 6
 (ft).
Facilities Dining room; Physical therapy
 room; Activities room; Laundry room;
 Barber/Beauty shop.
Activities Arts & crafts; Games; Prayer groups;
 Movies; Shopping trips.

VALLEY CENTER

New Horizons of Valley Center
821 3rd St Terrace, Valley Center, KS, 67147
(316) 755-1288
Admin Paula McHenry. *Medical Dir/Dir of
 Nursing* Helen Chamberlain.
Licensure Intermediate care for mentally
 retarded. *Beds* ICF/MR 100. *Certified*
 Medicaid.
Owner Proprietary Corp (Medicalodges).
Admissions Requirements Minimum age 17;
 Medical examination.
Staff Physicians 1 (pt); RNs 2 (ft), 2 (pt);
 LPNs 7 (ft); Nurses aides 50 (ft); Physical
 therapists 1 (pt); Recreational therapists 1
 (ft); Occupational therapists 1 (pt); Speech
 therapists 1 (ft); Activities coordinators 1
 (ft); Dietitians 1 (ft); Ophthalmologists 1
 (pt); Podiatrists 1 (pt); Resident care 7 (ft).
Facilities Dining room; Physical therapy
 room; Activities room; Crafts room; Laundry
 room; Barber/Beauty shop.
Activities Arts & crafts; Cards; Games;
 Reading groups; Movies; Shopping trips;
 Social/Cultural gatherings; Special Olympics.

VICTORIA

St Johns Rest Home
Box 308, 701 7th St, Victoria, KS, 67671
(913) 735-2208
Admin Donald D Curl. *Medical Dir/Dir of
 Nursing* Dr Pira Rochanayon; Artis Perret
 RN.
Licensure Intermediate care. *Beds* ICF 90.
 Certified Medicaid; Medicare.
Owner Nonprofit organization/foundation.
Admissions Requirements Medical
 examination; Physician's request.
Staff RNs; LPNs; Orderlies; Nurses aides;
 Physical therapists; Reality therapists;
 Recreational therapists; Occupational
 therapists; Speech therapists; Activities
 coordinators; Dietitians.
Languages German
Affiliation Roman Catholic
Facilities Dining room; Physical therapy
 room; Activities room; Chapel; Crafts room;
 Laundry room; Barber/Beauty shop.
Activities Arts & crafts; Cards; Games;
 Reading groups; Prayer groups; Movies;
 Shopping trips; Social/Cultural gatherings.

WAKEENY

Heartland Manor—Wakeeny*
320 South Ave, Box 429, Wakeeny, KS, 67672
(913) 743-2913
Admin Irma G Ell.
Licensure Intermediate care. *Beds* 50.
 Certified Medicaid.
Owner Proprietary Corp (US Care Corp).

WAKEFIELD

Heritage Village of Wakefield
6th & Grove, Wakefield, KS, 67487
(913) 461-5417
Admin Stacy Veh Van Blaricon. *Medical Dir/
 Dir of Nursing* Gloria Hohman.
Licensure Intermediate care. *Beds* ICF 50.
 Certified Medicaid.
Owner Proprietary Corp (Beverly Enterprises).
Admissions Requirements Medical
 examination; Physician's request.
Staff Physicians; LPNs; Nurses aides; Physical
 therapists; Occupational therapists; Speech
 therapists; Activities coordinators; Dietitians;
 Ophthalmologists; Podiatrists.
Facilities Dining room; Physical therapy
 room; Activities room; Chapel; Crafts room;
 Laundry room; Barber/Beauty shop; Library.
Activities Arts & crafts; Cards; Games;
 Reading groups; Prayer groups; Movies;
 Shopping trips.

WAMEGO

Valley Vista Good Samaritan Center*
2011 Grandview Dr, Wamego, KS, 66547
(913) 456-9482
Admin Kimberly Line.
Licensure Intermediate care. *Beds* 50.
 Certified Medicaid.
Owner Nonprofit Corp (Evangelical Lutheran/
 Good Samaritan).
Affiliation Lutheran

WASHINGTON

The Centennial Homestead
311 E 2nd, Washington, KS, 66968
(913) 325-2361
Admin Jane A Magaw. *Medical Dir/Dir of
 Nursing* Terry A Severin RN.
Licensure Intermediate care. *Beds* ICF 50.
 Certified Medicaid.
Owner Proprietary Corp.
Admissions Requirements Minimum age 16;
 Physician's request.
Staff Physicians 1 (pt); RNs 1 (ft); LPNs 4
 (ft), 1 (pt); Orderlies 1 (ft); Nurses aides 17
 (ft), 5 (pt); Physical therapists 1 (pt); Speech
 therapists 1 (pt); Activities coordinators 1
 (ft); Dietitians 4 (ft), 6 (pt);
 Ophthalmologists 1 (pt); Podiatrists 1 (pt).
Facilities Dining room; Physical therapy
 room; Activities room; Crafts room; Laundry
 room; Barber/Beauty shop; Library.
Activities Arts & crafts; Cards; Games;
 Reading groups; Prayer groups; Movies;
 Shopping trips.

WATHENA

Colonial Manor Nursing & Care Center
RR1 Hwy 36, Wathena, KS, 66090
(913) 989-3141
Admin Dawn Gale. *Medical Dir/Dir of
 Nursing* Cynthia Claywell RN.
Licensure Intermediate care. *Beds* ICF 60.
 Certified Medicaid.
Owner Proprietary Corp (Beverly Enterprises).
Staff RNs; LPNs; Nurses aides; Physical
 therapists; Occupational therapists; Speech
 therapists; Activities coordinators.
Facilities Dining room; Physical therapy
 room; Activities room; Laundry room;
 Barber/Beauty shop.

Activities Cards; Games; Movies; Social/
 Cultural gatherings.

WAVERLY

Sunset Manor
Box 246, 128 S Pearson Ave, Waverly, KS,
 66871
(913) 733-2744
Admin Melinda J Arb. *Medical Dir/Dir of
 Nursing* Eunice Bowersox.
Licensure Intermediate care. *Beds* ICF 25.
 Certified Medicaid.
Owner Proprietary Corp.
Admissions Requirements Medical
 examination.
Staff RNs 2 (ft); LPNs 1 (pt); Orderlies 1 (ft);
 Nurses aides 9 (ft), 8 (pt); Activities
 coordinators 1 (ft); Social service designee 1
 (pt); Restorative aide; CMA's 4 (ft), 1 (pt).
Facilities Dining room; Physical therapy
 room; Activities room; Laundry room;
 Barber/Beauty shop.
Activities Arts & crafts; Cards; Games;
 Reading groups; Prayer groups; Movies;
 Shopping trips; Social/Cultural gatherings.

WELLINGTON

Cedar View Nursing Center
RFD 4, 1600 W 8th, Wellington, KS, 67152
(316) 326-2232
Admin Helen Downing.
Licensure Intermediate care. *Beds* 97.
 Certified Medicaid.
Owner Nonprofit Corp (Evangelical Lutheran/
 Good Samaritan).
Admissions Requirements Medical
 examination; Physician's request.
Affiliation Lutheran
Facilities Dining room; Physical therapy
 room; Activities room; Chapel; Crafts room;
 Laundry room; Barber/Beauty shop.
Activities Arts & crafts; Cards; Games;
 Reading groups; Prayer groups; Movies;
 Shopping trips.

Lakeside Lodge*
102 W Botkin, Wellington, KS, 67152
(316) 326-7437
Admin Jeanette Mefford.
Licensure Intermediate care. *Beds* 69.
 Certified Medicaid.
Owner Proprietary Corp (Beverly Enterprises).

WELLSVILLE

Wellsville Manor Care Center*
304 W 7th, Wellsville, KS, 66092
(913) 883-4101
Admin Patrick Hutchens.
Licensure Intermediate care. *Beds* 60.
 Certified Medicaid.
Owner Proprietary Corp.

WESTMORELAND

Westy Community Care Home*
RR 1, Box 9, Westmoreland, KS, 66549
(913) 457-2130
Admin Virginia Roggenkamp. *Medical Dir/Dir
 of Nursing* Dr Thomas Dechairo.
Licensure Intermediate care. *Beds* 52.
 Certified Medicaid.
Admissions Requirements Medical
 examination; Physician's request.
Staff RNs 1 (ft); LPNs 1 (ft), 3 (pt); Orderlies
 1 (pt); Nurses aides 14 (ft), 8 (pt); Physical
 therapists 1 (pt); Occupational therapists 1
 (pt); Speech therapists 1 (pt); Activities
 coordinators 1 (ft); Dietitians 1 (pt); Dentists
 1 (pt); Ophthalmologists 1 (pt); Audiologists
 1 (pt).
Facilities Dining room; Physical therapy
 room; Activities room; Crafts room; Laundry
 room; Barber/Beauty shop.

Activities Arts & crafts; Cards; Games;
Reading groups; Prayer groups; Movies;
Shopping trips; Social/Cultural gatherings.

WHITEWATER

Wheat State Manor Inc
601 S Main, Whitewater, KS, 67154
(316) 799-2181
Admin Norman Durmaskin. *Medical Dir/Dir
of Nursing* Paul Fransen MD; Dorothy Pratt
RN DON.
Licensure Intermediate care. *Beds* ICF 66.
Certified Medicaid.
Owner Nonprofit Corp.
Admissions Requirements Minimum age 16;
Medical examination; Physician's request.
Staff Physicians 1 (pt); RNs 3 (ft), 3 (pt);
LPNs 1 (ft), 1 (pt); Nurses aides 20 (ft), 10
(pt); Physical therapists 1 (pt); Occupational
therapists 1 (pt); Speech therapists 1 (pt);
Activities coordinators 2 (pt); Dietitians 1
(pt); Ophthalmologists 1 (pt); Podiatrists 1
(pt); Dentist 1 (pt).
Facilities Dining room; Physical therapy
room; Activities room; Chapel; Crafts room;
Laundry room; Barber/Beauty shop; Library.
Activities Arts & crafts; Cards; Games;
Reading groups; Prayer groups; Movies;
Shopping trips; Social/Cultural gatherings;
Parties.

WICHITA

Catholic Care Center
3411 E Zimmerly, Wichita, KS, 67218
(316) 681-2118
Admin Patrick D Rackers. *Medical Dir/Dir of
Nursing* Jeanne Ward RN.
Licensure Skilled care; Intermediate care;
Apartments. *Beds* SNF 51; ICF 100; Apts
12. *Certified* Medicaid.
Owner Nonprofit organization/foundation.
Admissions Requirements Minimum age;
Medical examination; Physician's request.
Staff Physicians 1 (pt); RNs 8 (ft), 3 (pt);
LPNs 12 (ft), 3 (pt); Nurses aides 60 (ft);
Physical therapists 1 (pt); Occupational
therapists 1 (pt); Speech therapists 1 (pt);
Activities coordinators 2 (ft); Dietitians 1
(ft); Dentists 1 (pt); Ophthalmologists 1 (pt);
Podiatrists 1 (pt).
Languages Spanish, Hindi
Affiliation Roman Catholic
Facilities Dining room; Physical therapy
room; Activities room; Chapel; Crafts room;
Barber/Beauty shop; Library.
Activities Arts & crafts; Cards; Games;
Reading groups; Prayer groups; Movies;
Shopping trips; Social/Cultural gatherings.

Cherry Creek Village
8100 E Pawnee, Wichita, KS, 67207
(316) 684-1313
Admin Michael P Burke. *Medical Dir/Dir of
Nursing* Dr Robert Fowler; Mary Jane
Schneider DON.
Licensure Skilled care; Intermediate care;
Personal care. *Beds* SNF 30; ICF 112;
Personal 22. *Certified* Medicaid.
Owner Privately owned.
Admissions Requirements Minimum age 16;
Medical examination; Physician's request.
Staff RNs 3 (ft); LPNs 3 (ft); Activities
coordinators 2 (ft).
Facilities Dining room; Physical therapy
room; Activities room; Chapel; Crafts room;
Laundry room; Barber/Beauty shop;
Ceramics area.
Activities Arts & crafts; Cards; Games;
Reading groups; Prayer groups; Movies;
Shopping trips; Social/Cultural gatherings.

Christ Villa Nursing Center
1555 N Meridian, Wichita, KS, 67203
(316) 942-8471

Admin Jim Roylston. *Medical Dir/Dir of
Nursing* Ed Hett MD; Faye Clements DON.
Licensure Skilled care; Intermediate care. *Beds*
SNF 16; ICF 102. *Certified* Medicaid;
Medicare.
Owner Proprietary Corp (Medicalodges).
Admissions Requirements Medical
examination; Physician's request.
Staff Physicians 2 (ft); RNs 6 (ft); LPNs 8 (ft);
Orderlies 10 (ft); Nurses aides 40 (ft);
Physical therapists 1 (pt); Recreational
therapists 1 (pt); Occupational therapists 1
(pt); Speech therapists 1 (pt); Activities
coordinators 1 (ft); Ophthalmologists 1 (pt);
Podiatrists 1 (pt).
Affiliation Church of Christ
Facilities Dining room; Physical therapy
room; Activities room; Chapel; Crafts room;
Laundry room; Barber/Beauty shop; Library.
Activities Arts & crafts; Cards; Games;
Reading groups; Prayer groups; Movies;
Shopping trips; Social/Cultural gatherings.

Heartland Rehabilitation Center
3410 E Funston St, Wichita, KS, 67218
(316) 685-1341
Admin Robin W Lowery. *Medical Dir/Dir of
Nursing* Ann Hatfield.
Licensure Intermediate care. *Beds* ICF 81.
Certified Medicaid.
Owner Proprietary Corp (US Care Corp).
Admissions Requirements Minimum age 18;
Medical examination.
Staff RNs 1 (ft), 3 (pt); LPNs 5 (ft), 3 (pt);
Orderlies 4 (ft), 1 (pt); Nurses aides 12 (ft),
4 (pt); Activities coordinators 1 (ft); Social
worker 1 (ft).
Facilities Dining room; Physical therapy
room; Activities room; Laundry room;
Barber/Beauty shop; Game room; Smoking
room; Quiet room.
Activities Arts & crafts; Cards; Games;
Reading groups; Movies; Shopping trips;
Social/Cultural gatherings; Psyche therapy
groups; Role play groups; Exercise groups;
Social interaction groups.

Heritage Lakewood Health Care Center
1319 Seville, Wichita, KS, 67209
(316) 722-6916
Admin Marcia Mullis.
Licensure Intermediate care. *Beds* ICF 100.
Certified Medicaid.
Owner Proprietary Corp (National Heritage).
Admissions Requirements Medical
examination.
Staff LPNs 9 (ft); Orderlies 3 (ft); Nurses
aides 25 (ft); Activities coordinators 1 (ft).
Facilities Dining room; Physical therapy
room; Activities room; Crafts room; Laundry
room; Barber/Beauty shop.
Activities Arts & crafts; Cards; Games;
Reading groups; Prayer groups; Movies;
Social/Cultural gatherings.

Hillhaven Wichita
932 N Topeka, Wichita, KS, 67214
(316) 262-4261
Admin Keith M Hart. *Medical Dir/Dir of
Nursing* Robert Fowler MD; JoEva Blair
MN DON.
Licensure Skilled care; Intermediate care. *Beds*
SNF 58; ICF 116. *Certified* Medicaid;
Medicare.
Owner Proprietary Corp (Hillhaven Corp).
Admissions Requirements Physician's request.
Staff RNs 7 (ft), 2 (pt); LPNs 18 (ft), 6 (pt);
Nurses aides 58 (ft), 13 (pt); Physical
therapists 1 (ft); Occupational therapists 1
(ft); Speech therapists 1 (ft); Activities
coordinators 2 (ft); Dietitians 1 (ft).
Facilities Dining room; Physical therapy
room; Activities room; Crafts room; Barber/
Beauty shop.
Activities Arts & crafts; Cards; Games;
Reading groups; Prayer groups; Movies;
Shopping trips; Social/Cultural gatherings.

Homestead Health Center Inc
2133 S Elizabeth, Wichita, KS, 67213
(316) 262-4473
Admin Bill L Shook. *Medical Dir/Dir of
Nursing* Kathi S Beeton RN.
Licensure Intermediate care. *Beds* ICF 60.
Certified Medicaid.
Owner Nonprofit Corp.
Admissions Requirements Medical
examination; Physician's request.
Staff RNs; LPNs; Nurses aides; Activities
coordinators.
Affiliation Baptist
Facilities Dining room; Physical therapy
room; Activities room; Crafts room; Laundry
room; Barber/Beauty shop.
Activities Arts & crafts; Cards; Games;
Reading groups; Prayer groups; Movies;
Shopping trips; Social/Cultural gatherings;
Family parties.

Kansas Masonic Home
401 S Seneca, Wichita, KS, 67213
(316) 267-0271
Admin Jerry B Lindenbaum. *Medical Dir/Dir
of Nursing* Dr John Kleady; Betty Fry RN
DON.
Licensure Skilled care; Intermediate care. *Beds*
SNF 270; ICF. *Certified* Medicaid;
Medicare.
Owner Nonprofit Corp.
Admissions Requirements Minimum age 65;
Medical examination.
Staff Physicians 1 (pt); RNs 6 (ft); LPNs 14
(ft); Orderlies 5 (ft); Nurses aides 50 (ft);
Physical therapists 1 (pt); Recreational
therapists 1 (pt); Occupational therapists 1
(ft); Activities coordinators 4 (ft), 1 (pt);
Dietitians 1 (ft).
Affiliation Masons
Facilities Dining room; Physical therapy
room; Activities room; Chapel; Crafts room;
Laundry room; Barber/Beauty shop; Library.
Activities Arts & crafts; Cards; Games;
Reading groups; Prayer groups; Movies;
Shopping trips; Social/Cultural gatherings;
Current events; Religious events; Fraternal
events; Masonic Lodge on premises.

Keen Agers Nursing Home*
2840 S Hillside, Wichita, KS, 67216
(316) 684-7777
Admin Rose A Hand.
Licensure Intermediate care. *Beds* 57.
Certified Medicaid.
Admissions Requirements Minimum age 18.
Staff Physicians 3 (pt); RNs 1 (ft); LPNs 2
(ft); Orderlies 1 (ft); Nurses aides 14 (ft), 2
(pt); Physical therapists 1 (pt); Reality
therapists 1 (pt); Occupational therapists 1
(pt); Activities coordinators 1 (ft); Dietitians
1 (pt).
Facilities Dining room; Physical therapy
room; Activities room; Chapel; Laundry
room; Barber/Beauty shop.
Activities Arts & crafts; Cards; Games;
Reading groups; Prayer groups; Movies;
Shopping trips; Social/Cultural gatherings.

Lincoln East Nursing Home
4007 E Lincoln, Wichita, KS, 67218
(316) 683-7588
Admin Mary Lou Shaft. *Medical Dir/Dir of
Nursing* Angelia Polk LPN DON.
Licensure Intermediate care. *Beds* ICF 60.
Certified Medicaid.
Owner Proprietary Corp (Beverly Enterprises).
Admissions Requirements Medical
examination.
Staff RNs; LPNs; Orderlies; Nurses aides;
Recreational therapists; Activities
coordinators; Dietitians.
Facilities Dining room; Physical therapy
room; Activities room; Chapel; Crafts room;
Laundry room; Barber/Beauty shop; Library.

Activities Arts & crafts; Cards; Games; Reading groups; Prayer groups; Movies; Shopping trips; Social/Cultural gatherings; Quilting; Ceramics.

Medicalodge of Wichita
2280 S Minneapolis, Wichita, KS, 67211
(216) 265-5693
Admin Nadene Oller. *Medical Dir/Dir of Nursing* R D Magsalin MD; Patricia Swartz RN DON.
Licensure Skilled care. *Beds* SNF 100. *Certified* Medicaid; Medicare.
Owner Proprietary Corp (Medicalodges).
Admissions Requirements Minimum age 18; Medical examination.
Staff Physicians 1 (pt); RNs 4 (ft), 1 (pt); LPNs 8 (ft), 4 (pt); Orderlies 4 (ft); Nurses aides 32 (ft), 4 (pt); Physical therapists 1 (ft), 1 (pt); Reality therapists 1 (pt); Recreational therapists 2 (ft); Occupational therapists 1 (pt); Speech therapists 1 (pt); Activities coordinators 1 (ft); Dietitians 8 (ft), 2 (pt); Dentists 1 (pt); Ophthalmologists 1 (pt); Podiatrists 1 (pt).
Languages Spanish
Facilities Dining room; Physical therapy room; Activities room; Chapel; Crafts room; Laundry room; Barber/Beauty shop; Library.
Activities Arts & crafts; Cards; Games; Reading groups; Prayer groups; Movies; Shopping trips; Social/Cultural gatherings.

North Towne Manor
2800 N Hillside, Wichita, KS, 67219
(316) 682-1612
Admin Bonita Williams. *Medical Dir/Dir of Nursing* Jacquelyn Maloney.
Licensure Intermediate care. *Beds* ICF 100. *Certified* Medicaid.
Owner Privately owned.
Admissions Requirements Medical examination; Physician's request.
Staff RNs 1 (ft); LPNs 5 (ft); Nurses aides 25 (ft).
Facilities Dining room; Physical therapy room; Activities room; Chapel; Crafts room; Laundry room; Barber/Beauty shop.
Activities Arts & crafts; Games; Prayer groups; Movies; Shopping trips; Social/Cultural gatherings.

Northeast Health Care Center
5005 E 21st St N, Wichita, KS, 67208
(316) 685-9291
Admin Kathaleen A Crosswhite. *Medical Dir/Dir of Nursing* Dr Robert Fowler.
Licensure Skilled care. *Beds* 100. *Certified* Medicare.
Admissions Requirements Medical examination; Physician's request.
Staff RNs 6 (ft); LPNs 8 (ft); Nurses aides 30 (ft); Physical therapists 1 (pt); Occupational therapists 1 (pt); Speech therapists 1 (pt); Activities coordinators 1 (ft); Dietitians 1 (ft), 1 (pt); Ophthalmologists 1 (pt); Podiatrists 1 (pt).

Regency Health Care Center
1432 N Waco, Wichita, KS, 67203
(316) 262-8481
Admin Carol L Greene. *Medical Dir/Dir of Nursing* Dr A J Wray.
Licensure Skilled care; Intermediate care. *Beds* SNF 24; ICF 103. *Certified* Medicaid.
Owner Proprietary Corp (Regency Health Care Centers).
Admissions Requirements Medical examination; Physician's request.
Facilities Dining room; Physical therapy room; Activities room; Chapel; Crafts room; Laundry room; Barber/Beauty shop; Library.
Activities Arts & crafts; Games; Reading groups; Prayer groups; Movies; Social/Cultural gatherings.

Terrace Gardens Retirement Center
1315 N West St, Wichita, KS, 67203
(316) 943-1294
Admin Chester R West. *Medical Dir/Dir of Nursing* Dr Jon Kardatzke; Betty Bryan RN.
Licensure Skilled care; Intermediate care; Personal care; Retirement apartments. *Beds* SNF 39; ICF 106; Personal 104; Apts 120. *Certified* Medicare.
Owner Proprietary Corp.
Admissions Requirements Medical examination; Physician's request.
Staff Physicians 1 (pt); RNs 3 (ft), 1 (pt); LPNs 12 (ft), 2 (pt); Orderlies 1 (ft); Nurses aides 55 (ft), 6 (pt); Physical therapists 1 (pt); Recreational therapists 3 (ft); Occupational therapists 1 (pt); Speech therapists 1 (pt); Activities coordinators 1 (ft); Dietitians 1 (pt); Podiatrists 1 (pt); Audiologists 1 (pt); Security 1 (ft).
Languages Spanish
Facilities Dining room; Physical therapy room; Activities room; Chapel; Crafts room; Laundry room; Barber/Beauty shop; Library.
Activities Arts & crafts; Cards; Games; Reading groups; Prayer groups; Movies; Social/Cultural gatherings; Bingo.

Wichita Care Center*
1319 W May, Wichita, KS, 67213
(316) 262-1155
Admin Mysel Hall.
Licensure Skilled care; Intermediate care. *Beds* SNF 35; ICF 114. *Certified* Medicaid.
Owner Proprietary Corp (US Care Corp).

Wichita Presbyterian Manor
4700 W 13th, Wichita, KS, 67212
(316) 942-7456
Admin Ronald D Mathis. *Medical Dir/Dir of Nursing* Richard Egelhof MD; Mary Fankhauser RN.
Licensure Skilled care. *Beds* SNF 60. *Certified* Medicaid.
Owner Nonprofit Corp.
Admissions Requirements Minimum age 65; Medical examination; Physician's request.
Staff Physicians 1 (pt); RNs 5 (ft), 2 (pt); LPNs 3 (ft); Orderlies 3 (ft); Nurses aides 30 (ft); Physical therapists 1 (pt); Occupational therapists 1 (pt); Speech therapists 1 (pt); Activities coordinators 2 (ft); Dietitians 1 (ft); Dentists 1 (pt); Ophthalmologists 1 (pt); Podiatrists 1 (pt).
Affiliation Presbyterian
Facilities Dining room; Physical therapy room; Activities room; Chapel; Crafts room; Laundry room; Barber/Beauty shop; Library.
Activities Arts & crafts; Cards; Games; Reading groups; Prayer groups; Movies; Shopping trips; Social/Cultural gatherings; Religious/Spiritual; Support groups.

Woodlawn Nursing Home Inc*
1600 S Woodlawn, Wichita, KS, 67218
(316) 683-4628
Admin John T Wills.
Licensure Skilled care; Intermediate care. *Beds* SNF 58; ICF 67. *Certified* Medicaid; Medicare.

WILSON

Wilson Nursing Home*
PO Box 160, 611 31st St, Wilson, KS, 67490
(913) 658-2505
Admin Barbara J Hladek.
Licensure Intermediate care. *Beds* 50. *Certified* Medicaid.
Owner Proprietary Corp (Beverly Enterprises).

WINFIELD

Good Samaritan Center
1320 Wheat Rd, Winfield, KS, 67156
(316) 221-4660
Admin Roger S Zieg.

Licensure Intermediate care. *Beds* ICF 135. *Certified* Medicaid.
Owner Nonprofit Corp (Evangelical Lutheran/Good Samaritan).
Admissions Requirements Minimum age 16; Medical examination; Physician's request.
Staff RNs 1 (ft); LPNs 2 (ft), 6 (pt); Orderlies 3 (ft); Nurses aides 25 (ft), 20 (pt); Recreational therapists 3 (ft); Activities coordinators 1 (ft).
Affiliation Lutheran
Facilities Dining room; Physical therapy room; Activities room; Chapel; Crafts room; Laundry room; Barber/Beauty shop; Library.
Activities Arts & crafts; Cards; Games; Reading groups; Prayer groups; Movies; Shopping trips; Social/Cultural gatherings.

Heritage House Nursing Home
2720 E 12th St, Winfield, KS, 67156
(316) 221-9120
Admin James J O'Leary. *Medical Dir/Dir of Nursing* Seavard Denkke MD; Lore Vickens LPN HSS.
Licensure Intermediate care. *Beds* ICF 59. *Certified* Medicaid.
Owner Privately owned.
Admissions Requirements Medical examination; Physician's request.
Staff RNs 1 (ft); LPNs 3 (ft); Orderlies 3 (ft); Nurses aides; Physical therapists 1 (ft); Speech therapists 1 (ft); Activities coordinators 2 (ft); Dietitians 1 (ft).
Facilities Dining room; Physical therapy room; Activities room; Chapel; Laundry room; Barber/Beauty shop.
Activities Arts & crafts; Cards; Games; Reading groups; Prayer groups; Movies.

New Horizons of Winfield
2802 E Hwy 160, Winfield, KS, 67156
(316) 221-1747
Admin Paula Fultz. *Medical Dir/Dir of Nursing* Gloria Anderson Health Service Supv.
Licensure Intermediate care for mentally retarded. *Beds* ICF/MR 81. *Certified* Medicaid.
Owner Proprietary Corp (Horizon Healthcare Corp).

Winfield Rest Haven Inc*
1611 Ritchie, Winfield, KS, 67156
(316) 221-9290
Admin Linda Voth. *Medical Dir/Dir of Nursing* Dr S S Daehnke.
Licensure Intermediate care. *Beds* 48.
Admissions Requirements Medical examination; Physician's request.
Staff RNs 1 (ft), 1 (pt); LPNs 1 (ft), 1 (pt); Physical therapists 1 (pt); Occupational therapists 1 (pt); Speech therapists 1 (pt); Dietitians 1 (pt).
Affiliation Church of Christ
Facilities Dining room; Physical therapy room; Activities room; Crafts room; Laundry room; Barber/Beauty shop.
Activities Arts & crafts; Cards; Games; Reading groups; Prayer groups; Movies; Shopping trips.

YATES CENTER

Autumn Manor Inc 2*
801 S Fry St, Yates Center, KS, 66783
(316) 625-2111
Admin Dorothy V Kester.
Licensure Intermediate care. *Beds* 50. *Certified* Medicaid.
Owner Proprietary Corp.

Regency Health Care Center
801 S Fry St, Yates Center, KS, 66783
(316) 625-2111
Admin Dorothy V Kester. *Medical Dir/Dir of Nursing* Beverly Saubers.
Licensure Intermediate care. *Beds* ICF 104. *Certified* Medicaid.

Owner Proprietary Corp (Regency Health Care Centers).
Admissions Requirements Medical examination; Physician's request.

Staff RNs 3 (ft); LPNs 3 (ft), 2 (pt); Nurses aides 24 (ft), 4 (pt); Activities coordinators 2 (ft), 1 (pt).
Facilities Dining room; Physical therapy room; Activities room; Laundry room; Barber/Beauty shop.

Activities Arts & crafts; Cards; Games; Reading groups; Prayer groups; Movies; Shopping trips.

KENTUCKY

ALBANY

Twin Lakes Nursing Home
404 Washington St, Albany, KY, 42602
(606) 387-6623
Admin Deanna D Loy.
Licensure Intermediate care. *Beds* ICF 52.
Certified Medicaid.
Owner Proprietary Corp.
Admissions Requirements Medical
examination; Physician's request.
Staff Physicians 5 (ft); RNs 1 (ft); LPNs 8 (ft);
Orderlies 3 (ft); Nurses aides 21 (ft);
Physical therapists; Speech therapists;
Activities coordinators 1 (ft); Dietitians.
Facilities Dining room; Activities room;
Crafts room; Laundry room.
Activities Arts & crafts; Cards; Games;
Reading groups; Prayer groups; Movies;
Shopping trips; Social/Cultural gatherings.

ASHLAND

Artrips Personal Care Home
3000 Central Ave, Ashland, KY, 41101
(606) 325-3244
Admin Maggie Artrip.
Licensure Personal care. *Beds* 16.
Owner Privately owned.
Admissions Requirements Minimum age 21;
Medical examination; Physician's request.
Staff Orderlies 1 (pt); Nurses aides 6 (pt);
Activities coordinators 2 (pt); Dietitians 1
(pt).
Facilities Dining room; Activities room;
Laundry room; Quiet/Reading area; TV
room.
Activities Cards; Games; Reading groups;
Prayer groups; Social/Cultural gatherings.

Elmwood Village
5400 Apple Blossom Ln, Ashland, KY, 41101
(606) 324-2161
Admin R Morris Stafford. *Medical Dir/Dir of
Nursing* W Rex Duff MD.
Licensure Skilled care; Intermediate care;
Personal care; Adult day care. *Beds* SNF 48;
ICF 99; Personal 14. *Certified* Medicaid;
Medicare.
Owner Nonprofit Corp.
Admissions Requirements Medical
examination; Physician's request.
Staff Physicians 5 (pt); RNs 2 (ft), 5 (pt);
LPNs 20 (ft), 4 (pt); Nurses aides 70 (ft), 10
(pt); Physical therapists 1 (pt); Recreational
therapists 2 (ft), 1 (pt); Speech therapists 1
(pt); Activities coordinators 1 (ft); Dietitians
1 (pt); Dentists 1 (pt); Ophthalmologists 1
(pt) 1 (pt).
Facilities Dining room; Physical therapy
room; Activities room; Chapel; Crafts room;
Laundry room; Barber/Beauty shop; Library;
Covered patio.
Activities Arts & crafts; Cards; Games;
Reading groups; Prayer groups; Movies;
Social/Cultural gatherings.

Hamilton's Personal Care Home
250 W Central Ave, Ashland, KY, 41101
(606) 324-3252
Admin Mrs Ann Hamilton. *Medical Dir/Dir of
Nursing* Ann Hamilton.
Licensure Personal care. *Beds* 22. *Certified*
Medicaid.
Owner Privately owned.
Admissions Requirements Minimum age 18;
Medical examination.
Staff Physicians 3 (ft), 22 (pt); Orderlies 1 (ft),
22 (pt); Nurses aides 7 (ft), 22 (pt);
Activities coordinators 1 (ft), 22 (pt);
Dietitians 1 (ft), 22 (pt).
Facilities Dining room; Activities room;
Crafts room; Laundry room.
Activities Arts & crafts; Cards; Games;
Shopping trips; Social/Cultural gatherings;
Day care program.

**King's Daughters & Sons Home for Aged Men
& Women***
1100 Bath Ave, Ashland, KY, 41101
(606) 324-0343
Admin Vicki Edwards.
Licensure Personal care. *Beds* 36.
Staff Nurses aides 3 (ft); Activities
coordinators 1 (pt); Dietitians 1 (pt).
Affiliation King's Daughters & Sons
Facilities Dining room; Activities room;
Chapel; Laundry room; Barber/Beauty shop;
Library.
Activities Cards; Games; Prayer groups.

Riverview Homes*
38 Russell Rd, Ashland, KY, 41101
(606) 836-3551
Admin Sheila Lemaster.
Licensure Personal care. *Beds* 78.
Staff Physicians 2 (ft); Nurses aides 18 (ft);
Speech therapists 1 (ft); Activities
coordinators 1 (ft); Dietitians 1 (pt);
Podiatrists 1 (pt).
Facilities Dining room; Activities room;
Crafts room; Laundry room.
Activities Arts & crafts; Games; Prayer groups;
Shopping trips; Social/Cultural gatherings.

AUBURN

Auburn Nursing Center Inc
PO Box 128, 121 Pearl St, Auburn, KY,
42206
(502) 542-4111
Admin Grover A Corum. *Medical Dir/Dir of
Nursing* Dr Dewey Wood.
Licensure Skilled care; Intermediate care. *Beds*
SNF 30; ICF 36. *Certified* Medicaid;
Medicare.
Owner Proprietary Corp.
Admissions Requirements Medical
examination.
Staff Physicians; RNs 2 (ft), 1 (pt); LPNs 5
(ft), 1 (pt); Nurses aides 20 (ft), 3 (pt);
Activities coordinators 1 (ft); Dietitians 1
(ft).

Facilities Dining room; Activities room;
Chapel; Crafts room; Laundry room; Barber/
Beauty shop; Library.
Activities Arts & crafts; Cards; Games;
Reading groups; Prayer groups; Movies;
Social/Cultural gatherings.

AUGUSTA

Bracken Center Inc
PO Box 418, Rte 1, Augusta, KY, 41002
(606) 756-2156
Admin Nancy Gallenstein. *Medical Dir/Dir of
Nursing* Milton Brindley MD.
Licensure Intermediate care; Personal care.
Beds ICF 32; Personal 50. *Certified*
Medicaid.
Owner Proprietary Corp.
Admissions Requirements Physician's request.
Staff RNs 1 (ft); LPNs 3 (ft); Orderlies 1 (ft);
Nurses aides 23 (ft); Activities coordinators
1 (ft); Dietitians 2 (pt).
Facilities Dining room; Activities room;
Laundry room; Barber/Beauty shop.
Activities Arts & crafts; Cards; Games; Prayer
groups; Shopping trips.

BARBOURVILLE

Valley Park Conv Center*
117 Shelby St, Barbourville, KY, 40906
(606) 546-5136
Admin Sylvia Carter. *Medical Dir/Dir of
Nursing* Dr Harold Bushey.
Licensure Skilled care; Intermediate care;
Personal care. *Beds* SNF 21; ICF 67;
Personal 25. *Certified* Medicaid.
Owner Proprietary Corp (Health Sys).
Admissions Requirements Medical
examination; Physician's request.
Staff Physicians 7 (ft); RNs 5 (ft); LPNs 11
(ft); Nurses aides 45 (ft); Physical therapists
1 (pt); Speech therapists 1 (pt); Activities
coordinators 2 (ft); Dietitians 12 (ft);
Dentists 1 (ft).
Facilities Dining room; Physical therapy
room; Activities room; Laundry room;
Barber/Beauty shop.
Activities Arts & crafts; Games; Reading
groups; Prayer groups; Shopping trips.

BARDSTOWN

Colonial House*
708 Bartley Ave, Bardstown, KY, 40004
(502) 348-9260
Admin Mary Clark.
Licensure Personal care. *Beds* 96.
Owner Proprietary Corp.

Federal Hill Manor Nurs/Conv Center
PO Box 349, Old Bloomfield Rd, Bardstown,
KY, 40004
(502) 348-4220
Admin Marchetta Beevers.

Licensure Skilled care; Intermediate care; Personal care. *Beds* SNF 15; ICF 79; Personal 6. *Certified* Medicaid; Medicare.
Owner Proprietary Corp.

BEATTYVILLE

Lee County Personal Care Home Inc*
PO Box 245, Lumber St, Beattyville, KY, 41311
(606) 464-3611
Admin Fred Austin. *Medical Dir/Dir of Nursing* Dr J M Smith & Dr A L Taulbee.
Licensure Intermediate care; Personal care. *Beds* ICF 87; Personal 18. *Certified* Medicaid.
Owner Publicly owned.
Staff RNs 2 (ft), 1 (pt); LPNs 2 (ft); Nurses aides 25 (ft), 2 (pt); Activities coordinators 2 (ft); Dietitians 1 (pt).
Facilities Dining room; Activities room; Crafts room; Laundry room; Barber/Beauty shop.
Activities Arts & crafts; Games; Reading groups; Movies; Shopping trips; Social/Cultural gatherings.

BEAVER DAM

Beaver Dam Health Care Manor
Rte 4 Box 119A, Beaver Dam, KY, 42320
(502) 274-9646
Admin Donna Bratcher NHA. *Medical Dir/Dir of Nursing* Kathy Drone.
Licensure Intermediate care; Personal care. *Beds* ICF 58; ICF/MR Personal 50. *Certified* Medicaid.
Owner Proprietary Corp.
Admissions Requirements Minimum age 18; Medical examination; Physician's request.
Staff Physicians 6 (ft); LPNs 6 (ft); Nurses aides 65 (ft), 3 (pt); Activities coordinators 1 (ft).
Facilities Dining room; Activities room; Chapel; Crafts room; Laundry room; Barber/Beauty shop.
Activities Arts & crafts; Games; Reading groups; Prayer groups; Movies; Shopping trips; Social/Cultural gatherings; Homemaker club; Supper club; Cooking class; Storytelling.

BEDFORD

Trimble Nursing Center*
Hwy 42, Box 27, Bedford, KY, 40006
(502) 255-3244
Admin Ann Breitenbach.
Licensure Intermediate care; Personal care. *Beds* ICF 42; Personal 18. *Certified* Medicaid.
Owner Proprietary Corp.

BENTON

Lake Haven Health Care Center*
PO Box 203, US Hwy 641 S, Benton, KY, 42025
(502) 527-3296
Admin Donald R Jury. *Medical Dir/Dir of Nursing* C R Freeman MD.
Licensure Intermediate care; Personal care. *Beds* ICF 76; Personal 24. *Certified* Medicaid.
Owner Proprietary Corp (Hillhaven Corp).
Admissions Requirements Medical examination; Physician's request.
Staff LPNs 2 (ft); Orderlies 28 (ft); Physical therapists 1 (pt); Reality therapists 1 (pt); Speech therapists 1 (pt); Activities coordinators 1 (pt); Dietitians 1 (pt); Dentists 1 (pt); Podiatrists 1 (pt); Audiologists 1 (pt).

Facilities Dining room; Activities room; Laundry room; Barber/Beauty shop.
Activities Arts & crafts; Cards; Games; Reading groups; Shopping trips.

Lake Haven Health Care Center Inc
PO Box 385, US 641 S, Benton, KY, 42025
(502) 527-3296
Admin Donald R Jury. *Medical Dir/Dir of Nursing* C R Freeman; M S Newton RN DON.
Licensure Intermediate care; Personal care. *Beds* ICF 76; Personal 24. *Certified* Medicaid.
Owner Proprietary Corp (Britthaven Inc).
Admissions Requirements Minimum age 18; Physician's request.
Staff RNs 1 (ft); LPNs 4 (ft), 2 (pt); Nurses aides 27 (ft), 12 (pt); Physical therapists 1 (pt); Activities coordinators 1 (ft); Dietitians 1 (pt); Ophthalmologists 1 (pt); Dentist 1 (pt).
Facilities Dining room; Activities room; Laundry room; Barber/Beauty shop.
Activities Arts & crafts; Cards; Games; Reading groups; Prayer groups; Shopping trips; Social/Cultural gatherings.

Marshall County Hospital—SNF
503 George McClain Dr, Benton, KY, 42025
(502) 527-1336
Admin Terry L Skaggs. *Medical Dir/Dir of Nursing* Wendell Gordon MD; Oweata Williams RN.
Licensure Skilled care. *Beds* SNF 34. *Certified* Medicaid; Medicare.
Owner Publicly owned.
Admissions Requirements Physician's request.
Staff Physicians 1 (pt); RNs 2 (ft); LPNs 6 (ft); Orderlies 1 (ft); Nurses aides 9 (ft), 1 (pt); Physical therapists 1 (ft); Speech therapists 1 (pt); Activities coordinators 1 (ft); Dietitians 1 (ft); Ophthalmologists 1 (pt); Dentist 1 (pt).
Facilities Dining room; Physical therapy room; Activities room; Crafts room; Barber/Beauty shop.
Activities Arts & crafts; Games; Reading groups; Prayer groups; Shopping trips; Social/Cultural gatherings.

BEREA

Berea Health Care Center
601 Richmond Rd, Berea, KY, 40403
(606) 986-4710
Admin Audrey Runda. *Medical Dir/Dir of Nursing* Clifford Kerby MD.
Licensure Intermediate care. *Beds* ICF 40. *Certified* Medicaid.
Owner Proprietary Corp.
Admissions Requirements Medical examination.
Staff RNs 1 (ft); LPNs 2 (ft); Orderlies 4 (ft); Nurses aides 20 (ft), 4 (pt); Occupational therapists 1 (pt); Activities coordinators 1 (ft); Dietitians 1 (pt).
Facilities Dining room; Activities room.
Activities Arts & crafts; Cards; Games; Reading groups; Prayer groups; Movies.

Berea Hospital—Skilled Nursing Facility*
PO Box 128, Estill St, Berea, KY, 40403
(606) 986-3151
Admin David E Burgio.
Licensure Skilled care. *Beds* 37. *Certified* Medicaid; Medicare.
Owner Nonprofit Corp.

BOONEVILLE

Owsley County Health Care Center*
Hwy 11, PO Box 157, Booneville, KY, 41314
(606) 593-6302
Admin Judy Terry. *Medical Dir/Dir of Nursing* Dr Larry Mason.

Licensure Intermediate care; Personal care. *Beds* ICF 91; Personal 10. *Certified* Medicaid.
Owner Proprietary Corp (Unicare).
Staff Physicians 4 (pt); RNs 1 (ft), 1 (pt); LPNs 3 (ft); Orderlies 3 (ft), 2 (pt); Nurses aides 21 (ft), 5 (pt); Activities coordinators 1 (ft); Dietitians 1 (pt).
Facilities Dining room; Activities room; Crafts room; Laundry room; Barber/Beauty shop.
Activities Arts & crafts; Cards; Games; Reading groups; Prayer groups; Movies; Shopping trips; Social/Cultural gatherings.

BOWLING GREEN

Britthaven of Bowling Green
PO Box 1719, 5079 Scottsville Rd, Bowling Green, KY, 42101-1719
(502) 782-1125
Admin Don Phelps RN.
Licensure Skilled care; Intermediate care; Personal care. *Beds* SNF 30; ICF 88; Personal 58. *Certified* Medicaid.
Owner Proprietary Corp.
Facilities Dining room; Physical therapy room; Activities room; Chapel; Crafts room; Laundry room; Barber/Beauty shop.
Activities Arts & crafts; Cards; Games; Prayer groups; Movies; Shopping trips; Social/Cultural gatherings.

Colonial Manor Nursing Home*
2365 Nashville Rd, Bowling Green, KY, 42101
(502) 842-1641
Admin Mary P Williams. *Medical Dir/Dir of Nursing* Harold West MD.
Licensure Skilled care; Intermediate care. *Beds* SNF 38; ICF 10. *Certified* Medicaid; Medicare.
Owner Proprietary Corp (Angell Group).
Staff RNs 3 (ft), 3 (pt); LPNs 2 (ft), 3 (pt); Orderlies 1 (ft); Nurses aides 21 (ft), 3 (pt); Physical therapists 1 (pt); Speech therapists 1 (pt); Activities coordinators 1 (pt); Dietitians 1 (pt).
Facilities Dining room; Activities room.
Activities Arts & crafts; Cards; Games; Movies.

Fern Terrace Lodge of Bowling Green
1030 Shive Ln, Bowling Green, KY, 42101
(502) 781-6784
Admin Mollie Banks. *Medical Dir/Dir of Nursing* Monica Blair.
Licensure Personal care. *Beds* 114.
Owner Proprietary Corp.
Admissions Requirements Minimum age 47; Medical examination.
Staff Nurses aides 18 (ft), 2 (pt).
Facilities Dining room; Laundry room; Barber/Beauty shop.
Activities Arts & crafts; Cards; Games; Reading groups; Prayer groups; Movies; Shopping trips; Social/Cultural gatherings.

Medco Center of Bowling Green*
1561 Newton Ave, Bowling Green, KY, 42101
(502) 842-1611
Admin Jerry Alexander.
Licensure Intermediate care. *Beds* 66. *Certified* Medicaid.
Owner Proprietary Corp (Unicare).
Admissions Requirements Medical examination.
Staff Physicians 23 (ft); RNs 1 (ft), 1 (pt); LPNs 5 (ft), 3 (pt); Nurses aides 26 (ft); Speech therapists 1 (ft); Activities coordinators 1 (ft); Dietitians 1 (ft); Dentists 1 (ft); Podiatrists 1 (ft); Audiologists 1 (ft).
Facilities Dining room; Laundry room; Barber/Beauty shop.
Activities Arts & crafts; Cards; Games; Reading groups; Movies; Shopping trips; Social/Cultural gatherings.

Panorama Residential Care
PO Box 1113, US 231 W, Morgantown Rd,
Bowling Green, KY, 42102-1113
(502) 782-7770
Admin Tony Staynings. *Medical Dir/Dir of
Nursing* Dr Larry Green; Tonya York RN.
Licensure Intermediate care for mentally
retarded. *Beds* ICF/MR 58. *Certified*
Medicaid.
Owner Privately owned.
Staff Physicians 1 (pt); RNs 2 (ft); LPNs 3
(ft), 2 (pt); Nurses aides 1 (ft); Physical
therapists 1 (ft); Recreational therapists 2
(ft); Occupational therapists 2 (ft); Speech
therapists 2 (ft); Dietitians 1 (pt).
Facilities Dining room; Physical therapy
room; Activities room; Crafts room; Laundry
room; Library; Occupational therapy room;
Speech therapy rooms.
Activities Arts & crafts; Cards; Games;
Reading groups; Prayer groups; Movies;
Shopping trips; Social/Cultural gatherings;
Community activities; Visits to other
communities.

Rosewood Manor Health Care Center
PO Box 9000, 550 High St, Bowling Green,
KY, 42101-9000
(502) 843-3296
Admin Carmen Downing.
Licensure Skilled care; Intermediate care. *Beds*
SNF 29; ICF 157. *Certified* Medicaid;
Medicare.
Owner Proprietary Corp (Hillhaven Corp).

BRANDENBURG

Medco Center of Brandenburg*
814 Old Ekron Rd, Brandenburg, KY, 40108
(502) 422-2148
Admin Donna Brown.
Licensure Intermediate care; Personal care.
Beds ICF 51; Personal 13. *Certified*
Medicaid.
Owner Proprietary Corp (Unicare).

BRODHEAD

Sowder Nursing Home
PO Box 91-A, Rte 1, Main St, Brodhead, KY,
40409
(606) 758-8711
Admin Linda L Whitt. *Medical Dir/Dir of
Nursing* Jennie L Payne.
Licensure Intermediate care; Personal care.
Beds ICF 82; Personal 10. *Certified*
Medicaid.
Owner Proprietary Corp.
Admissions Requirements Minimum age 16.
Staff RNs 1 (pt); LPNs 5 (ft), 2 (pt); Orderlies
7 (ft), 3 (pt); Nurses aides 31 (ft), 2 (pt);
Activities coordinators 1 (ft), 1 (pt);
Dietitians 1 (pt); Social service 1 (ft).
Facilities Dining room; Activities room;
Barber/Beauty shop; Library Outdoor
garden/picnic area.
Activities Arts & crafts; Games; Reading
groups; Prayer groups; Movies; Shopping
trips; Social/Cultural gatherings;
Homemakers club; Exercise group.

BROWNSVILLE

Joywells*
PO Box 510, Brownsville, KY, 42210
(502) 597-2159
Admin Marie Pasley.
Licensure Personal care. *Beds* 37.
Owner Nonprofit Corp.

BURKESVILLE

Cumberland Valley Manor Inc
PO Box 438, S Main St, Burkesville, KY,
42717
(502) 864-4315

Admin Tim Hicks. *Medical Dir/Dir of Nursing*
Dr Robert Flowers.
Licensure Intermediate care; Personal care.
Beds ICF 64; Personal 16. *Certified*
Medicaid.
Owner Nonprofit organization/foundation.
Admissions Requirements Physician's request.
Staff Physicians 5 (ft); RNs 1 (ft); LPNs 6 (ft),
4 (pt); Orderlies 6 (ft), 6 (pt); Nurses aides
11 (ft), 9 (pt); Activities coordinators 1 (ft),
1 (pt); Dietitians 1 (pt).
Facilities Dining room; Activities room;
Chapel; Crafts room; Laundry room; Barber/
Beauty shop; Country store.
Activities Arts & crafts; Cards; Games; Prayer
groups; Movies; Shopping trips; Social/
Cultural gatherings.

BUTLER

Butler Rest Home Inc
PO Box 131, Front & Main Sts, Butler, KY,
41006
(606) 472-6011
Admin Anne Hosking. *Medical Dir/Dir of
Nursing* Anne Hosking RN.
Licensure Personal care. *Beds* 19.
Owner Proprietary Corp.
Admissions Requirements Medical
examination; Physician's request.
Facilities Dining room.
Activities Arts & crafts; Cards; Games;
Reading groups; Prayer groups; Social/
Cultural gatherings.

Grants Lake I C Home
PO Box 231, 305 Taylor St, Butler, KY,
41006
(606) 472-2217, 472-2671
Admin Anne Hosking. *Medical Dir/Dir of
Nursing* Anne Hosking RN.
Licensure Intermediate care. *Beds* ICF 32.
Certified Medicaid.
Owner Proprietary Corp.
Admissions Requirements Medical
examination; Physician's request.
Staff RNs 1 (ft); LPNs 2 (ft), 1 (pt); Nurses
aides 11 (ft), 6 (pt); Activities coordinators 1
(ft).
Facilities Dining room; Activities room.
Activities Arts & crafts; Cards; Games;
Reading groups; Prayer groups; Social/
Cultural gatherings; Story hour with local
children.

CADIZ

Shady Lawn Nursing Home*
Rte 1, Box 22, Cerulean Rd, Cadiz, KY,
42211
(502) 522-3236
Admin Raymond C Lafser. *Medical Dir/Dir of
Nursing* Dr William Anderson.
Licensure Skilled care; Intermediate care. *Beds*
SNF 15; ICF 35. *Certified* Medicaid;
Medicare.
Owner Proprietary Corp (Unicare).
Admissions Requirements Medical
examination; Physician's request.
Staff RNs 2 (ft), 2 (pt); LPNs 4 (ft), 2 (pt);
Nurses aides 12 (ft), 9 (pt); Activities
coordinators 1 (pt); Dietitians 1 (ft).
Facilities Dining room; Activities room;
Chapel; Crafts room; Laundry room; Barber/
Beauty shop; Lobby; Movie room; TV room.
Activities Arts & crafts; Games; Prayer groups;
Movies; Social/Cultural gatherings; Social
get-togethers; Birthday parties; Holiday
parties.

Trigg County Manor Personal Care Home*
Shelby St, Cadiz, KY, 42211
(502) 522-3711
Admin Dorothy Tooke.
Licensure Personal care. *Beds* 68.
Admissions Requirements Minimum age 15;
Medical examination; Physician's request.

Staff LPNs 1 (ft); Nurses aides 23 (ft);
Activities coordinators 1 (ft).
Facilities Dining room; Activities room;
Laundry room; Barber/Beauty shop; Library.
Activities Arts & crafts; Cards; Games;
Reading groups; Prayer groups; Movies;
Shopping trips; Social/Cultural gatherings.

CALHOUN

McLean County General Hospital—SNU*
Hwy 81 N, Calhoun, KY, 42347
(502) 273-5252
Admin Jim McMahon.
Licensure Skilled care. *Beds* 8. *Certified*
Medicaid; Medicare.
Owner Nonprofit Corp.

Riverside Manor Health Care
PO Box 39, Hwy 136, Calhoun, KY, 42327
(502) 273-5289
Admin Kathy Embry.
Licensure Intermediate care; Personal care.
Beds ICF 51; Personal 33. *Certified*
Medicaid.
Owner Proprietary Corp (Hillhaven Corp).

Sunny Acres*
PO Box 7, Rte 1, Calhoun, KY, 42327
(502) 273-3113
Admin Janette M Ferguson.
Licensure Personal care. *Beds* 20.
Owner Proprietary Corp.

CALVERT CITY

Calvert City Convalescent Center*
PO Box 7, 5th Ave, Calvert City, KY, 42029
(502) 395-4124
Admin Omer Hille.
Licensure Intermediate care; Personal care.
Beds ICF 95; Personal 5. *Certified*
Medicaid.
Owner Nonprofit Corp.

Oakview Manor Health Care Center*
Rte 1, Box 125, Calvert City, KY, 42029
(502) 898-6288
Admin Beverly Arington.
Licensure Intermediate care; Personal care.
Beds ICF 83; Personal 35. *Certified*
Medicaid.
Owner Proprietary Corp.

CAMPBELLSVILLE

Medco Center of Campbellsville
Rt 4 Old Greensburg Rd, Campbellsville, KY,
42718
(502) 465-3506
Admin Amaryllis B Lobb. *Medical Dir/Dir of
Nursing* Mary Jane Karnes.
Licensure Intermediate care. *Beds* 67.
Certified Medicaid.
Owner Proprietary Corp (Unicare).
Admissions Requirements Medical
examination.
Staff Physicians; RNs; LPNs; Orderlies;
Nurses aides; Physical therapists; Speech
therapists; Activities coordinators; Dietitians.
Facilities Dining room; Physical therapy
room; Activities room; Crafts room; Laundry
room; Barber/Beauty shop; Outside areas for
activities.
Activities Arts & crafts; Cards; Games;
Reading groups; Prayer groups; Movies;
Shopping trips; Social/Cultural gatherings.

Metzmeier Nursing Home*
700 N Central Ave, Campbellsville, KY,
42718
(502) 465-4321
Admin Don Metzmeier. *Medical Dir/Dir of
Nursing* Roy E Wilson MD.
Licensure Skilled care; Intermediate care. *Beds*
SNF 55; ICF 16. *Certified* Medicaid;
Medicare.

Staff Physicians 14 (pt); RNs 2 (ft), 1 (pt); LPNs 7 (ft), 1 (pt); Orderlies 3 (ft); Nurses aides 24 (ft), 12 (pt); Speech therapists 1 (pt); Activities coordinators 1 (ft); Dietitians; Dentists 5 (pt); Ophthalmologists.
Facilities Dining room; Physical therapy room; Activities room; Laundry room; Barber/Beauty shop.
Activities Arts & crafts; Cards; Games; Reading groups; Prayer groups; Movies; Shopping trips; Social/Cultural gatherings.

CARLISLE

Johnson-Mathers Health Care Inc
2323 Concrete Rd, Carlisle, KY, 40311
(606) 289-7181
Admin Robert W Hester Jr. *Medical Dir/Dir of Nursing* Jack T Morford MD; Pam Garrison RN DON.
Licensure Skilled care; Intermediate care; Personal care. *Beds* SNF 13; ICF 26; Personal 4. *Certified* Medicaid; Medicare.
Owner Nonprofit Corp.
Admissions Requirements Medical examination; Physician's request.
Staff RNs 2 (ft), 4 (pt); LPNs 5 (ft); Orderlies 4 (ft), 1 (pt); Nurses aides 24 (ft), 26 (pt); Physical therapists 1 (pt); Activities coordinators 1 (ft); Dietitians 1 (pt).
Facilities Dining room; Physical therapy room; Activities room; Chapel; Laundry room; Barber/Beauty shop.
Activities Arts & crafts; Cards; Games; Reading groups; Prayer groups; Movies; Social/Cultural gatherings; Residents council.

CARROLLTON

Carrollton Manor*
205 5th St, Carrollton, KY, 41008
(502) 732-5528
Admin Cathy C Vinson.
Licensure Personal care. *Beds* 32.
Owner Proprietary Corp.

Green Valley Health Care Center*
1206 11th St, Carrollton, KY, 41008
(502) 732-6683
Admin Susan Carlisle. *Medical Dir/Dir of Nursing* Valecia Penick RN.
Licensure Intermediate care; Personal care. *Beds* ICF 55; Personal 8.
Staff RNs 1 (ft); LPNs 1 (ft); Orderlies 20 (ft); Physical therapists 1 (ft); Speech therapists 1 (ft); Activities coordinators 1 (ft); Dietitians 1 (pt); Dentists 1 (pt); Ophthalmologists 1 (pt); Audiologists 1 (pt).
Facilities Dining room; Activities room; Laundry room; Library.
Activities Arts & crafts; Cards; Games; Reading groups; Prayer groups; Social/Cultural gatherings.

CENTRAL CITY

Sparks Nursing Center*
PO Box 387, 5th & Noffsinger Sts, Central City, KY, 42330
(502) 754-4838
Admin Lorene Sparks.
Licensure Personal care. *Beds* 88.
Owner Proprietary Corp.

CLINTON

Clinton-Hickman County Hospital—ICF
359 Washington St, Clinton, KY, 42031
(502) 653-2461
Admin William B Little.
Licensure Intermediate care. *Beds* 46. *Certified* Medicaid.
Owner Nonprofit Corp.

West Kentucky Manor Inc
106 Padgett Dr, Clinton, KY, 42031
(502) 653-2011
Admin Sharon Boaz. *Medical Dir/Dir of Nursing* Hazel Litesy.
Licensure Intermediate care; Personal care. *Beds* ICF 86; Personal 10. *Certified* Medicaid.
Owner Proprietary Corp.
Staff Physicians 3 (pt); RNs 1 (pt); LPNs 2 (ft), 1 (pt); Orderlies 1 (ft); Nurses aides 40 (ft), 3 (pt); Physical therapists 1 (pt); Activities coordinators 1 (ft); Dietitians 1 (ft).
Facilities Dining room; Physical therapy room; Activities room; Crafts room.
Activities Arts & crafts; Cards; Games; Reading groups; Prayer groups; Movies; Shopping trips; Social/Cultural gatherings.

CLOVERPORT

Tindles Personal Care Home
PO Box 108, Hwy 105, Cloverport, KY, 40111
(502) 788-3723
Admin Sue Tindle. *Medical Dir/Dir of Nursing* Sue Tindle.
Licensure Personal care. *Beds* 40.
Owner Proprietary Corp.
Admissions Requirements Minimum age 16; Medical examination; Physician's request.
Staff Nurses aides.
Facilities Dining room; Activities room; Laundry room.
Activities Arts & crafts; Cards; Games; Reading groups; Prayer groups; Shopping trips; Picnics; Dinners; Bible study.

COLUMBIA

Goodin's Rest Home*
Rte 3, Columbia, KY, 42728
(502) 384-2630
Admin Bertha Goodin.
Licensure Personal care. *Beds* 5.

Summit Manor
400 Bomar Heights, Columbia, KY, 42728
(502) 384-2153
Admin Brenda C Williams. *Medical Dir/Dir of Nursing* Dr James Salato; Carol Edwards.
Licensure Skilled care; Intermediate care. *Beds* SNF 38; ICF 66. *Certified* Medicaid; Medicare.
Owner Proprietary Corp.
Facilities Dining room; Physical therapy room; Activities room; Laundry room; Barber/Beauty shop; 2 Lounges.
Activities Arts & crafts; Games; Reading groups; Prayer groups; Movies; Shopping trips.

CORBIN

Christian Health Center—Corbin*
PO Box 1304, Master St & Commonwealth Ave, Corbin, KY, 40701
(606) 528-2886
Admin William Collins.
Licensure Intermediate care; Personal care. *Beds* ICF 92; Personal 23.
Owner Nonprofit Corp.

Hillcrest Nursing Home*
PO Box 556, Rte 7, Corbin, KY, 40701
(606) 528-8917
Admin Carolyn Smith. *Medical Dir/Dir of Nursing* Elmer G Prewitt MD.
Licensure Skilled care; Intermediate care. *Beds* SNF 41; ICF 79. *Certified* Medicaid; Medicare.
Owner Proprietary Corp (Health Sys).
Admissions Requirements Medical examination.

Staff Physicians 8 (ft); RNs 5 (ft); LPNs 9 (ft); Orderlies 2 (ft); Nurses aides 44 (ft); Physical therapists 1 (ft); Speech therapists 1 (pt); Activities coordinators 1 (ft); Dietitians 1 (pt); Dentists 3 (pt).
Facilities Dining room; Physical therapy room; Activities room; Crafts room; Barber/Beauty shop.
Activities Arts & crafts; Cards; Games; Reading groups; Prayer groups; Movies; Social/Cultural gatherings.

Mountain Laurel Manor
PO Box 1190, Rte 7, Corbin, KY, 40701
(606) 528-8822
Admin Cathy J Willis. *Medical Dir/Dir of Nursing* Dr Elmer G Prewitt; Betty Carter DON LPN.
Licensure Intermediate care. *Beds* ICF 50. *Certified* Medicaid.
Owner Proprietary Corp (Health Sys).
Admissions Requirements Medical examination.
Staff Physicians 8 (ft); RNs 1 (pt); LPNs 3 (ft); Orderlies 1 (pt); Nurses aides 10 (ft), 11 (pt); Activities coordinators 1 (ft); Dietitians 3 (ft), 2 (pt); Supervisor 1 (ft).
Facilities Dining room; Laundry room.
Activities Arts & crafts; Cards; Games; Reading groups; Movies; Shopping trips.

COVINGTON

Covington Ladies Home*
702 Garrard St, Covington, KY, 41011
(606) 431-6913
Admin Jackye Kwallek.
Licensure Personal care. *Beds* 36.
Admissions Requirements Minimum age 65; Females only; Medical examination.
Staff LPNs 3 (ft); Nurses aides 6 (ft), 3 (pt); Activities coordinators 1 (ft).
Facilities Dining room; Activities room; Chapel; Laundry room.
Activities Arts & crafts; Cards; Games; Prayer groups; Movies; Shopping trips.

Garrard Convalescent Home
425 Garrard St, Covington, KY, 41011
(606) 581-9393
Admin Ralph Stacy. *Medical Dir/Dir of Nursing* Dr F B Rodriquez.
Licensure Skilled care; Intermediate care. *Beds* SNF 41; ICF 22. *Certified* Medicaid; Medicare.
Staff Physicians 1 (pt); RNs 2 (ft), 1 (pt); LPNs 5 (ft); Nurses aides 28 (ft), 2 (pt); Physical therapists 1 (pt); Speech therapists 1 (pt); Activities coordinators 1 (ft); Dietitians 1 (pt); Ophthalmologists 1 (pt); Podiatrists 1 (pt); Dentist 1 (pt).
Facilities Dining room; Activities room; Laundry room.
Activities Arts & crafts; Cards; Reading groups; Prayer groups; Social/Cultural gatherings; Trips to zoo.

Pavilion Health Care of Covington
800 Highland Ave, Covington, KY, 41017
(606) 491-3800
Admin Peggy Post RN. *Medical Dir/Dir of Nursing* Dr David Suetholtz; Cheryl Menninger RN.
Licensure Skilled care; Intermediate care; Personal care. *Beds* SNF 58; ICF 249; Personal 83. *Certified* Medicaid; Medicare.
Owner Proprietary Corp (Pavillion Care Centers).
Admissions Requirements Minimum age 18.
Staff RNs 2 (ft); LPNs 29 (ft); Nurses aides 169 (ft); Physical therapists 1 (ft); Speech therapists 1 (ft); Activities coordinators 1 (ft); Dietitians 2 (ft).
Facilities Dining room; Physical therapy room; Activities room; Chapel; Crafts room; Barber/Beauty shop; Respiratory therapy; Speech therapy.

Activities Arts & crafts; Cards; Games; Reading groups; Prayer groups; Movies; Shopping trips; Social/Cultural gatherings; Traveling wheelchair volleyball team.

Rosedale Manor
4250 Glenn Ave, Covington, KY, 41015-1699
(606) 431-2244
Admin Arthur W Urlage. *Medical Dir/Dir of Nursing* Kathy Knight RN DON.
Licensure Intermediate care; Personal care. *Beds* ICF 142; Personal 66. *Certified* Medicaid.
Owner Nonprofit Corp.
Admissions Requirements Medical examination; Physician's request.
Staff RNs 1 (ft); LPNs 10 (ft); Orderlies 4 (ft); Activities coordinators 1 (ft); Dietitians 1 (ft).
Facilities Dining room; Activities room; Chapel; Crafts room; Laundry room; Barber/ Beauty shop; Library; Outdoor grounds.
Activities Arts & crafts; Cards; Games; Reading groups; Prayer groups; Movies; Shopping trips; Social/Cultural gatherings; Field trips; Shuffleboard; Picnics; Fishing; Ball games; Bingo; Birthday parties.

St Charles Care Center & Village
500 Farrell Dr, Covington, KY, 41011
(606) 331-3224
Admin Sr Mary Luann Bender. *Medical Dir/ Dir of Nursing* Dr Ralph Huller; Sr Mary Delrita Glaser.
Licensure Skilled care; Intermediate care; Independent living & Adult day health program. *Beds* SNF 54; ICF 93; Independent living 35. *Certified* Medicaid; Medicare.
Owner Nonprofit Corp.
Staff RNs; LPNs; Orderlies; Nurses aides; Physical therapists; Recreational therapists; Activities coordinators; Dietitians.
Facilities Dining room; Physical therapy room; Activities room; Chapel; Crafts room; Laundry room; Barber/Beauty shop; Library.
Activities Arts & crafts; Cards; Games; Reading groups; Prayer groups; Movies; Shopping trips; Social/Cultural gatherings.

CYNTHIANA

Edgemont Manor Nursing Home*
Monticello Heights, Cynthiana, KY, 41031
(606) 234-4595
Admin Joseph Franks.
Licensure Intermediate care; Personal care. *Beds* ICF 68; Personal 2.
Owner Proprietary Corp.

Grand Haven Nursing Home
Rodgers Park, Cynthiana, KY, 41031
(606) 234-2050
Admin Martha Brown. *Medical Dir/Dir of Nursing* Anna Ruth McLoney.
Licensure Intermediate care. *Beds* ICF 54. *Certified* Medicaid.
Owner Proprietary Corp.
Admissions Requirements Medical examination.
Staff RNs 1 (ft), 1 (pt); LPNs 1 (ft), 3 (pt); Nurses aides 8 (ft), 13 (pt); Activities coordinators 1 (ft); Dietitians 1 (ft).
Facilities Dining room; Physical therapy room; Activities room; Laundry room; Barber/Beauty shop.
Activities Games; Prayer groups; Movies; Shopping trips; Social/Cultural gatherings.

Harrison Memorial Hospital
PO Box 250, Millersburg Pike, Cynthiana, KY, 41031
(606) 234-2300
Admin James R Farris. *Medical Dir/Dir of Nursing* Richard Allen MD; Bettye Marshall RN DON.

Licensure Skilled care; Intermediate care. *Beds* SNF 16; ICF 8. *Certified* Medicaid; Medicare.
Owner Nonprofit Corp.
Admissions Requirements Medical examination; Physician's request.
Staff RNs 27 (ft), 7 (pt); LPNs 21 (ft), 2 (pt); Nurses aides 32 (ft), 3 (pt); Physical therapists 1 (ft); Activities coordinators 1 (ft); Dietitians 1 (ft).
Facilities Dining room; Activities room; Outdoor patio.
Activities Cards; Games; Reading groups; Prayer groups; Movies; Social/Cultural gatherings.

Martin's Rest Home Inc
321 Oddville Ave, Cynthiana, KY, 41031
(606) 234-1683
Admin Martha R Brown.
Licensure Personal care. *Beds* 51.
Owner Proprietary Corp.
Staff Nurses aides 11 (ft), 4 (pt); Dietitians 1 (pt).
Facilities Dining room; Activities room; Laundry room.
Activities Games; Shopping trips; Social/ Cultural gatherings.

Shady Lawn Home*
108 Miller St, Cynthiana, KY, 41031
(606) 234-2606
Admin Martha Brown.
Licensure Personal care. *Beds* 75.
Owner Proprietary Corp.

DANVILLE

Autumnfield of Danville*
203 Bruce Ct, Danville, KY, 40422
(606) 236-9292
Admin Shirley Quisenberry.
Licensure Intermediate care; Personal care. *Beds* ICF 74; Personal 16.
Owner Proprietary Corp (OMG Corp).

Fellowship Home
642 N 3rd St, Danville, KY, 40422
(606) 236-3352
Admin Timothy Struttman. *Medical Dir/Dir of Nursing* R Quinn Bailey MD.
Licensure Intermediate care; Personal care. *Beds* ICF 54; Personal 6. *Certified* Medicaid.
Owner Proprietary Corp (Hillhaven Corp).
Admissions Requirements Minimum age 18; Medical examination; Physician's request.
Facilities Dining room; Activities room; Crafts room; Laundry room.
Activities Arts & crafts; Cards; Games; Reading groups; Prayer groups; Movies; Shopping trips; Social/Cultural gatherings.

Friendship House
642 N 3rd St, Danville, KY, 40422
(606) 236-3972
Admin T W Struttman. *Medical Dir/Dir of Nursing* R Quinn Bailey MD.
Licensure Skilled care. *Beds* 50. *Certified* Medicaid; Medicare.
Admissions Requirements Minimum age 18; Medical examination; Physician's request.
Facilities Dining room; Activities room; Crafts room; Laundry room.
Activities Arts & crafts; Cards; Games; Reading groups; Prayer groups; Movies; Shopping trips; Social/Cultural gatherings.

DAWSON SPRINGS

Dawson Springs Health Care Center
PO Box 338, 100 W Ramsey St, Dawson Springs, KY, 42408
(502) 797-8131
Admin Deborah Johnson. *Medical Dir/Dir of Nursing* Dr Herbert Chaney; Ruth Barnett RN DON.

Licensure Skilled care; Intermediate care. *Beds* SNF 20; ICF 60. *Certified* Medicaid; Medicare; JCAH; VA.
Owner Proprietary Corp (National Health Corp).
Staff Physicians 2 (pt); RNs 4 (ft); LPNs 7 (ft); Orderlies 1 (ft); Nurses aides 22 (ft), 7 (pt); Physical therapists 1 (pt); Speech therapists 1 (pt); Activities coordinators 1 (ft); Dietitians 1 (pt).
Facilities Dining room; Physical therapy room; Activities room; Laundry room; Barber/Beauty shop.
Activities Arts & crafts; Games; Movies.

New Dawson Springs Nursing Home
213 Water St, Box 580, Dawson Springs, KY, 42408
(502) 797-2025 or 797-5682
Admin Linda S Thomas.
Licensure Intermediate care; Personal care. *Beds* ICF 69; Personal 35. *Certified* Medicaid.
Owner Proprietary Corp.
Admissions Requirements Medical examination.
Staff RNs 2 (ft); LPNs 5 (ft); Activities coordinators 1 (ft); Social service 1 (ft).
Facilities Dining room; Laundry room.
Activities Arts & crafts; Cards; Games; Reading groups; Prayer groups; Movies; Shopping trips; Social/Cultural gatherings; Picnics; Trips to the lake; Carnivals; Bingo.

Outwood-ICF/MR
Hwy 109, Dawson Springs, KY, 42408
(502) 797-3771
Admin Earl Harris. *Medical Dir/Dir of Nursing* Sophia Logan RN.
Licensure Intermediate care for mentally retarded. *Beds* 80. *Certified* Medicaid.
Owner Publicly owned.
Admissions Requirements Minimum age 6; Medical examination.
Staff Physicians 1 (pt); RNs 4 (ft), 1 (pt); LPNs 3 (ft), 1 (pt); Nurses aides 78 (ft), 6 (pt); Physical therapists 1 (pt); Recreational therapists 1 (ft); Occupational therapists 1 (ft); Speech therapists 1 (ft); Dietitians 1 (ft); Dentists 1 (pt).
Facilities Dining room; Physical therapy room; Activities room; Chapel; Crafts room; Laundry room; Barber/Beauty shop; Library; Classrooms.
Activities Arts & crafts; Games; Movies; Shopping trips; Social/Cultural gatherings.

DRY RIDGE

Carlsbad Nursing Home*
Main St, Dry Ridge, KY, 41035
(606) 823-8201
Admin James Burcham.
Licensure Intermediate care; Personal care. *Beds* ICF 32; Personal 15.
Owner Proprietary Corp.

Dry Ridge Personal Care Home*
Taft Hwy, Dry Ridge, KY, 41035
(606) 824-6164
Admin Ronald B Bennett.
Licensure Personal care. *Beds* 64.
Owner Proprietary Corp.

EDMONTON

Harper Home for the Aged*
Rte 2, Edmonton, KY, 42129
(502) 432-5202
Admin Betty Higginbotham.
Licensure Personal care. *Beds* 29.
Admissions Requirements Minimum age 16; Medical examination.
Staff Nurses aides 5 (ft); Activities coordinators 1 (ft).

Facilities Dining room; Laundry room.
Activities Arts & crafts; Cards; Games; Movies; Shopping trips; Social/Cultural gatherings; Church services; Activities for visually & hearing impaired.

Metcalfe County Nursing Home*
PO Box 115, Skyline Dr, Edmonton, KY, 42129
(502) 432-2921
Admin Lee G Bidwell.
Licensure Intermediate care; Personal care. *Beds* ICF 71; Personal 30. *Certified* Medicaid.
Staff Physicians 2 (pt); RNs 1 (ft); LPNs 5 (ft); Nurses aides 24 (ft), 6 (pt); Activities coordinators 1 (ft); Dietitians 1 (ft); Dentists 1 (pt); Ophthalmologists 1 (pt).
Facilities Dining room; Physical therapy room; Activities room; Crafts room; Laundry room; Barber/Beauty shop.
Activities Arts & crafts; Cards; Games; Reading groups; Prayer groups; Movies; Shopping trips; Social/Cultural gatherings.

ELIZABETHTOWN

Elizabethan Nursing Home
510 Pennsylvania Ave, Elizabethtown, KY, 42701
(502) 769-3314
Admin Rose Marie Tinker. *Medical Dir/Dir of Nursing* Judy Roberts.
Licensure Intermediate care. *Beds* ICF 67. *Certified* Medicaid.
Owner Proprietary Corp.
Admissions Requirements Physician's request.
Staff RNs 1 (ft); Orderlies 1 (ft); Physical therapists 1 (pt); Reality therapists 1 (pt); Recreational therapists 1 (pt); Occupational therapists 1 (pt); Speech therapists 1 (pt); Activities coordinators 1 (ft), 1 (pt); Dietitians 1 (ft).
Facilities Dining room; Activities room; Crafts room.
Activities Arts & crafts; Cards; Games; Reading groups; Prayer groups; Movies; Shopping trips; Social/Cultural gatherings; Ethnic dinners; Residents council.

Medco Center of Elizabethtown
PO Box 604, 108 Laymon Ln, Elizabethtown, KY, 42701
(502) 765-6106
Admin Rebecca S Weaver. *Medical Dir/Dir of Nursing* Dr Godfrey; Ida Watts.
Licensure Intermediate care; Personal care. *Beds* ICF 50; Personal 16. *Certified* Medicaid.
Owner Proprietary Corp (Unicare).
Admissions Requirements Medical examination.
Staff RNs 1 (ft); LPNs 4 (ft); Nurses aides 10 (ft), 10 (pt); Activities coordinators 1 (ft).
Facilities Dining room; Physical therapy room; Activities room; Barber/Beauty shop.
Activities Arts & crafts; Cards; Games; Reading groups; Prayer groups; Movies; Shopping trips; Social/Cultural gatherings; Outings.

Woodland Terrace
1117 Woodland Dr, Elizabethtown, KY, 42701
(502) 769-2363
Admin Ellen Stafford. *Medical Dir/Dir of Nursing* David Lewis.
Licensure Skilled care; Intermediate care; Personal care. *Beds* SNF 50; ICF 62; Personal 6. *Certified* Medicaid; Medicare.
Owner Proprietary Corp (Hillhaven Corp).
Admissions Requirements Medical examination; Physician's request.
Staff RNs 2 (ft); LPNs 8 (ft), 6 (pt); Orderlies; Nurses aides 39 (ft), 16 (pt); Physical therapists 1 (pt); Speech therapists 1 (pt); Activities coordinators 1 (pt); Dietitians 1 (pt); Dentists 1 (pt); Ophthalmologists 1 (pt).

Facilities Dining room; Physical therapy room; Activities room; Laundry room; Barber/Beauty shop.
Activities Arts & crafts; Cards; Games; Reading groups; Prayer groups; Movies; Social/Cultural gatherings.

ELKHORN CITY

Mountain View Health Care Center*
PO Box 650, US Hwy 197, Elkhorn City, KY, 41522
(606) 754-4134
Admin Sharon K Hall.
Licensure Intermediate care; Personal care. *Beds* ICF 106; Personal 20. *Certified* Medicaid.
Owner Proprietary Corp (Angell Group).

ELKTON

Country Manor of Todd County*
PO Box 427, Allensville St, Elkton, KY, 42220
(502) 265-5321
Admin Sarah Slack.
Licensure Personal care. *Beds* 94.

FALMOUTH

Falmouth Rest Home*
406 Barkley St, Falmouth, KY, 41040
(606) 654-4341
Admin James A Burcham.
Licensure Personal care. *Beds* 28.
Owner Proprietary Corp.

Sharps Personal Care Home
307 Maple Ave, Falmouth, KY, 41040
(606) 654-8294
Admin Donna R West. *Medical Dir/Dir of Nursing* Ruth Sharp.
Licensure Personal care. *Beds* 22. *Certified* Medicaid.
Owner Privately owned.
Admissions Requirements Medical examination.
Staff LPNs; Nurses aides; Activities coordinators.
Facilities Dining room; Activities room; Laundry room.
Activities Arts & crafts; Cards; Games; Prayer groups; Shopping trips.

FLATWOODS

Oakmont Manor
1100 Grandview Dr, Flatwoods, KY, 41139
(606) 836-3187
Admin Michael Campbell. *Medical Dir/Dir of Nursing* Oren Justice MD; Barbara McKinney RN.
Licensure Intermediate care. *Beds* ICF 85. *Certified* Medicaid.
Owner Proprietary Corp.
Admissions Requirements Medical examination; Physician's request.
Staff Physicians 5 (pt); RNs 1 (ft); LPNs 5 (ft), 2 (pt); Nurses aides 20 (ft), 10 (pt); Recreational therapists 1 (ft); Dietitians 1 (pt); Podiatrists 1 (pt).
Facilities Dining room; Activities room; Crafts room; Laundry room; Barber/Beauty shop.
Activities Arts & crafts; Games; Reading groups; Prayer groups; Movies; Shopping trips; Social/Cultural gatherings.

FLEMINGSBURG

Pioneer Trace Nursing Home
9115 Pioneer Trace Dr, Flemingsburg, KY, 41041
(606) 845-2131
Admin Mary Ann Campbell. *Medical Dir/Dir of Nursing* Patti Getz DON.

Licensure Intermediate care; Personal care. *Beds* ICF 89; Personal 6. *Certified* Medicaid.
Owner Proprietary Corp.
Admissions Requirements Physician's request.
Staff RNs 3 (ft); LPNs 2 (ft), 1 (pt); Orderlies 4 (ft); Nurses aides 29 (ft), 6 (pt); Activities coordinators 1 (ft); Dietitians 1 (pt).
Facilities Dining room; Activities room; Chapel; Laundry room; Barber/Beauty shop.
Activities Arts & crafts; Games; Reading groups; Prayer groups; Movies.

FLORENCE

Woodspoint Nursing Home*
7300 Woodspoint Dr, Florence, KY, 41042
(606) 371-5731
Admin Alfred J Mollozzi.
Licensure Skilled care; Intermediate care. *Beds* SNF 50; ICF 101. *Certified* Medicaid; Medicare.
Owner Nonprofit Corp.
Facilities Dining room; Physical therapy room; Activities room; Chapel; Laundry room; Barber/Beauty shop.
Activities Arts & crafts; Cards; Games; Reading groups; Prayer groups; Movies; Shopping trips; Social/Cultural gatherings.

FORDSVILLE

Medco Center of Fordsville
PO Box 205, Hwy 54 W, Fordsville, KY, 42343
(502) 276-3603
Admin Teresa Haynes. *Medical Dir/Dir of Nursing* Hettie Johnson DON.
Licensure Intermediate care. *Beds* ICF 67. *Certified* Medicaid.
Owner Proprietary Corp (Unicare).
Admissions Requirements Physician's request.
Staff RNs 1 (ft); LPNs 4 (ft).
Facilities Dining room; Laundry room.
Activities Arts & crafts; Cards; Games; Reading groups; Prayer groups; Movies; Shopping trips; Social/Cultural gatherings.

FORT THOMAS

Carmel Manor
Carmel Manor Rd, Fort Thomas, KY, 41075
(606) 781-5111
Admin Mother Maureen Hughes. *Medical Dir/Dir of Nursing* Dr Edward Stratman.
Licensure Personal care. *Beds* 99.
Admissions Requirements Minimum age 65; Medical examination.
Staff Physicians 2 (pt); RNs 2 (ft); LPNs 6 (pt); Nurses aides 55 (ft), 7 (pt); Activities coordinators 1 (ft); Dietitians 1 (pt).
Affiliation Roman Catholic
Facilities Dining room; Physical therapy room; Activities room; Chapel; Crafts room; Laundry room; Barber/Beauty shop; Library; Coffee shop.
Activities Arts & crafts; Cards; Games; Prayer groups; Movies; Shopping trips; Social/Cultural gatherings.

Horizon House II*
435 River Rd, Fort Thomas, KY, 41075
(606) 491-2752
Admin Mary Beth Meisenhelder.
Owner Nonprofit Corp.

FRANKFORT

Capital Hall*
1040 US 127 S, Frankfort, KY, 40601
(502) 875-5600
Admin Kelley F Owens. *Medical Dir/Dir of Nursing* James T Ramsey MD.
Licensure Skilled care; Intermediate care; Personal care. *Beds* SNF 25; Personal 25. *Certified* Medicaid; Medicare.

Facilities Dining room; Physical therapy room; Activities room; Crafts room; Laundry room; Barber/Beauty shop.
Activities Arts & crafts; Cards; Games; Reading groups; Prayer groups; Movies; Shopping trips; Social/Cultural gatherings.

Franklin Manor*
Old Soldiers Ln, Frankfort, KY, 40601
(502) 875-7272
Admin Steve A Rose. *Medical Dir/Dir of Nursing* Dr William McElwain.
Licensure Skilled care; Intermediate care. *Beds* SNF 50; ICF 50. *Certified* Medicaid; Medicare.
Owner Proprietary Corp (Beverly Enterprises).
Admissions Requirements Medical examination.
Staff RNs 2 (ft), 3 (pt); LPNs 7 (ft), 1 (pt); Orderlies 4 (ft); Nurses aides 30 (ft), 1 (pt); Physical therapists 1 (ft), 1 (pt); Speech therapists 1 (pt); Activities coordinators 1 (ft); Dietitians 1 (ft).
Facilities Dining room; Physical therapy room; Activities room; Crafts room; Laundry room; Barber/Beauty shop; Lobby/lounge.
Activities Arts & crafts; Games; Reading groups; Prayer groups; Social/Cultural gatherings.

FRANKLIN

Franklin Medco Center
PO Box 367, 414 Robey St, Franklin, KY, 42134
(502) 586-7141
Admin Clifton Lake. *Medical Dir/Dir of Nursing* J M Pulliam MD; Carol Frye RN DON.
Licensure Intermediate care. *Beds* ICF 98. *Certified* Medicaid.
Owner Proprietary Corp (Unicare).
Admissions Requirements Medical examination; Physician's request.
Staff RNs 1 (ft); LPNs 10 (ft); Orderlies 1 (ft); Nurses aides 30 (ft); Physical therapists 1 (ft), 2 (pt); Recreational therapists 1 (ft), 1 (pt); Speech therapists 1 (ft), 1 (pt); Dietitians 1 (ft).
Facilities Dining room; Physical therapy room; Activities room; Crafts room; Laundry room; Barber/Beauty shop.
Activities Arts & crafts; Cards; Games; Reading groups; Prayer groups; Movies; Social/Cultural gatherings.

Franklin Personal Care*
214 S College St, Franklin, KY, 42134
(502) 586-5995
Admin W L & Lillie King.
Licensure Personal care. *Beds* 28.
Owner Proprietary Corp.

Lewis Memorial Methodist Home*
Rte 1, Box 376A, Franklin, KY, 42134
(502) 586-3461
Admin Donna Fittze.
Licensure Personal care. *Beds* 15.
Owner Nonprofit Corp.
Affiliation Methodist

FULTON

Haws Memorial Nursing Home*
Holiday Ln, Fulton, KY, 42041
(502) 472-1971
Admin Robert Ambler.
Licensure Skilled care. *Beds* 60. *Certified* Medicaid; Medicare.
Facilities Dining room; Physical therapy room; Activities room; Crafts room; Barber/Beauty shop; Library.
Activities Arts & crafts; Games; Reading groups; Movies; Social/Cultural gatherings.

Parkway Manor*
309 N Highland Dr, Fulton, KY, 42041
(502) 472-3386
Admin Joanne Harper.
Licensure Intermediate care. *Beds* 20. *Certified* Medicaid.
Staff Physicians 4 (ft); RNs 2 (pt); LPNs 1 (ft), 1 (pt); Nurses aides 8 (ft), 2 (pt); Activities coordinators 1 (ft); Dietitians 1 (pt).
Facilities Dining room; Laundry room; Barber/Beauty shop.
Activities Arts & crafts; Cards; Games; Social/Cultural gatherings.

GEORGETOWN

Dover Manor Inc
112 Dover Dr, Georgetown, KY, 40324
(502) 863-9529
Admin Tracey L Martin. *Medical Dir/Dir of Nursing* Laura Shields.
Licensure Intermediate care; Personal care. *Beds* ICF 85; Personal 10. *Certified* Medicaid.
Owner Privately owned.
Admissions Requirements Medical examination.
Staff RNs 1 (ft); LPNs 7 (ft); Nurses aides 50 (ft); Activities coordinators 1 (pt); Dietitians 1 (pt).
Facilities Dining room; Activities room; Chapel; Crafts room; Laundry room; Barber/Beauty shop.
Activities Arts & crafts; Cards; Games; Reading groups; Prayer groups; Movies; Social/Cultural gatherings.

Springhaven Nursing Care*
102 Pocahantos Trail, Georgetown, KY, 40324-1196
(502) 254-3696 or 3983
Admin Gary Hitchings.
Licensure Skilled care; Intermediate care. *Beds* SNF 15; ICF 35. *Certified* Medicaid; Medicare.
Owner Proprietary Corp.

GLASGOW

Barren County Health Care Center*
300 Westwood St, Glasgow, KY, 42141
(502) 651-9131
Admin Steve Brown.
Licensure Intermediate care. *Beds* 94. *Certified* Medicaid.
Owner Proprietary Corp.

Glasgow Rest Home*
220 Westwood St, Glasgow, KY, 42141
(602) 651-6661
Admin Steve Brown.
Licensure Personal care. *Beds* 74.
Owner Proprietary Corp.

Glasgow State—ICF
Box 199, State Ave, Glasgow, KY, 42141
(502) 651-2151
Admin John E Broadbent. *Medical Dir/Dir of Nursing* Phillip Bale MD; Doris Oliver RN.
Licensure Intermediate care. *Beds* ICF 100. *Certified* Medicaid.
Owner Publicly owned.
Admissions Requirements Medical examination.
Staff Physicians 3 (pt); RNs 2 (ft); LPNs 16 (ft); Orderlies 15 (ft), 1 (pt); Nurses aides 30 (ft), 1 (pt); Physical therapists 1 (pt); Recreational therapists 3 (ft); Activities coordinators 1 (ft); Dietitians 1 (ft), 1 (pt).
Facilities Dining room; Activities room; Crafts room; Laundry room; Barber/Beauty shop; Library.
Activities Arts & crafts; Cards; Games; Reading groups; Movies; Shopping trips.

Glenview Manor
1002 Glenview Dr, Glasgow, KY, 42141
(502) 651-8332
Admin Kay Bush. *Medical Dir/Dir of Nursing* Dr John Asriel; Jessica Shaw RN DON.
Licensure Intermediate care. *Beds* ICF 60. *Certified* Medicaid.
Owner Privately owned.
Admissions Requirements Minimum age 30; Medical examination; Physician's request.
Staff RNs 1 (ft); LPNs 3 (ft), 2 (pt); Orderlies 1 (ft), 1 (pt); Nurses aides 18 (ft), 10 (pt); Activities coordinators 1 (ft), 1 (pt); Dietitians 1 (ft).
Facilities Dining room; Activities room; Crafts room; Laundry room; Barber/Beauty shop.
Activities Arts & crafts; Cards; Games; Reading groups; Prayer groups; Movies; Shopping trips; Social/Cultural gatherings.

Homewood Health Care Center
PO Box 297, Homewood Blvd, Glasgow, KY, 42141
(502) 651-6126
Admin Emogene C Stephens. *Medical Dir/Dir of Nursing* Dr William Marrs; Janie Tharp RN.
Licensure Skilled care; Intermediate care; Personal care. *Beds* SNF 80; ICF 104; Personal 22. *Certified* Medicaid; Medicare.
Owner Proprietary Corp (National Health Corp).
Admissions Requirements Medical examination; Physician's request.
Staff RNs 3 (ft), 8 (pt); LPNs 10 (ft), 16 (pt); Nurses aides 70 (ft), 30 (pt); Physical therapists 1 (ft); Speech therapists 1 (ft); Activities coordinators 1 (ft), 4 (pt); Dietitians 1 (ft).
Facilities Dining room; Physical therapy room; Activities room; Chapel; Crafts room; Laundry room; Barber/Beauty shop.
Activities Arts & crafts; Cards; Games; Reading groups; Prayer groups; Movies; Shopping trips; Social/Cultural gatherings.

GREENSBURG

Green Hill Manor
213 Industrial Rd, Greensburg, KY, 42743
(502) 932-4241
Admin Geneva Marcum. *Medical Dir/Dir of Nursing* Patricia Sutton.
Licensure Intermediate care; Personal care. *Beds* ICF 118; Personal 6. *Certified* Medicaid.
Owner Proprietary Corp (Beverly Enterprises).
Admissions Requirements Medical examination.
Staff RNs 3 (ft); LPNs 8 (ft); Orderlies 2 (ft); Nurses aides 40 (ft), 6 (pt); Occupational therapists 1 (ft); Activities coordinators 1 (ft).
Facilities Dining room; Activities room; Laundry room; Barber/Beauty shop.
Activities Arts & crafts; Cards; Games; Reading groups; Prayer groups; Movies; Shopping trips; Social/Cultural gatherings; Fishing trips; Picnics at parks; Outings to amusement parks.

McDowell Skilled Nursing Facility
PO Box 220, 202-206 Milby St, Greensburg, KY, 42743
(502) 932-4211
Admin William Dowe. *Medical Dir/Dir of Nursing* Dr Robert Shuffett.
Licensure Skilled care. *Beds* SNF 26. *Certified* Medicaid; Medicare.
Admissions Requirements Physician's request.
Staff RNs 2 (ft), 1 (pt); LPNs 4 (ft), 8 (pt); Orderlies 3 (ft), 1 (pt); Nurses aides 7 (ft), 6 (pt); Physical therapists 1 (ft); Speech therapists 1 (pt); Activities coordinators 1 (ft); Dietitians 1 (ft).

Facilities Dining room; Physical therapy room; Activities room; Crafts room; Laundry room; Barber/Beauty shop; Patio.
Activities Arts & crafts; Cards; Games; Reading groups; Movies; Church services; Resident council.

GREENVILLE

Belle Meade Home*
521 Greene Dr, PO Box 565, Greenville, KY, 42345
(502) 338-1523
Admin Marlin K Sparks.
Licensure Intermediate care; Personal care. *Beds* ICF 62; Personal 30. *Certified* Medicaid.
Staff RNs 5 (ft); LPNs 6 (ft); Nurses aides 24 (ft); Activities coordinators 1 (ft); Dietitians 1 (ft).
Facilities Dining room; Activities room; Laundry room; Barber/Beauty shop.
Activities Arts & crafts; Cards; Games; Reading groups; Prayer groups; Shopping trips; Social/Cultural gatherings.

Maple Manor Health Care Center*
515 Greene Dr, Greenville, KY, 42345
(502) 338-5400
Admin Martha S Rhoads. *Medical Dir/Dir of Nursing* C J Shipp MD.
Licensure Intermediate care; Personal care. *Beds* ICF 88; Personal 18. *Certified* Medicaid.
Owner Proprietary Corp (Hillhaven Corp).
Staff RNs 2 (ft); LPNs 5 (ft), 4 (pt); Nurses aides 33 (ft), 5 (pt); Physical therapists 1 (pt); Speech therapists 1 (pt); Activities coordinators 1 (ft); Dietitians 1 (pt).
Facilities Dining room; Activities room; Chapel; Crafts room; Laundry room; Barber/Beauty shop.
Activities Arts & crafts; Cards; Games; Reading groups; Prayer groups; Movies; Shopping trips; Social/Cultural gatherings.

Muhlenberg Community Hospital
PO Box 387, 440 Hopkinsville St, Greenville, KY, 42342
(502) 338-4211
Admin C J Perry. *Medical Dir/Dir of Nursing* Andre J Wininger.
Licensure Skilled care. *Beds* SNF 30; Acute 100. *Certified* Medicaid; Medicare.
Owner Nonprofit organization/foundation.
Admissions Requirements Medical examination; Physician's request.
Staff Physicians 30 (ft), 4 (pt); RNs 3 (ft), 3 (pt); LPNs 16 (ft); Orderlies 1 (ft); Nurses aides 6 (ft); Physical therapists 2 (ft); Recreational therapists 1 (ft); Speech therapists 1 (pt); Activities coordinators 1 (ft); Dietitians 1 (ft).
Languages Spanish, German
Facilities Dining room; Physical therapy room; Activities room; Chapel; Barber/Beauty shop; Library; Courtyards.
Activities Arts & crafts; Cards.

Poplar Grove Rest Home*
512 W Campbell St, Greenville, KY, 42345
(502) 338-4592
Admin Lydia Skaggs. *Medical Dir/Dir of Nursing* Dr King.
Licensure Personal care. *Beds* 42.
Admissions Requirements Minimum age 18; Medical examination.
Staff LPNs 1 (ft); Nurses aides 9 (ft); Activities coordinators 1 (pt); Dietitians 1 (pt).
Facilities Dining room; Laundry room.
Activities Arts & crafts; Cards; Games; Reading groups; Prayer groups; Movies; Shopping trips; Social/Cultural gatherings.

HARDINSBURG

Medco Center of Hardinsburg
Rte 1, Box 134, Hardinsburg, KY, 40143
(502) 756-2159
Admin Ann Snyder. *Medical Dir/Dir of Nursing* Norma Combs DON.
Licensure Intermediate care. *Beds* 63. *Certified* Medicaid.
Owner Proprietary Corp (Unicare).
Admissions Requirements Minimum age 18.
Facilities Dining room; Laundry room; Barber/Beauty shop.
Activities Arts & crafts; Cards; Games; Prayer groups; Movies; Social/Cultural gatherings.

HARLAN

Harlan Appalachian Regional Hospital—ECF*
Martin Fork Rd, Harlan, KY, 40831
(606) 573-1433
Admin Leslie Rogers.
Licensure Skilled care. *Beds* 24. *Certified* Medicaid; Medicare.

Harlan Nursing Home Inc
Mounted Rte 1, Hwy 421-S, Harlan, KY, 40831
(606) 573-7250
Admin Resanda S Austin. *Medical Dir/Dir of Nursing* Elmer Prewitt MD; Leta Holden RN DON.
Licensure Skilled care; Intermediate care. *Beds* SNF 24; ICF 119. *Certified* Medicaid; Medicare; VA.
Owner Proprietary Corp (Health Sys).
Admissions Requirements Physician's request.
Staff Physicians 5 (pt); RNs 5 (ft), 1 (pt); LPNs 9 (ft), 5 (pt); Nurses aides 36 (ft), 14 (pt); Activities coordinators 1 (ft); Dietary manager 1 (ft); Dietary consultant 1 (ft); Social services consultant 1 (ft).
Facilities Dining room; Activities room; Crafts room; Laundry room; Barber/Beauty shop; Resident lounge; Outdoor patio/garden.
Activities Arts & crafts; Games; Reading groups; Prayer groups; Movies; Shopping trips; Social/Cultural gatherings; Music; Pet therapy; Special events; Television.

The Laurels Inc
HC 78, Box 285, Harlan, KY, 40831
(606) 573-5105
Admin Claude White.
Licensure Personal care. *Beds* 50. *Certified* Medicare.
Owner Nonprofit Corp.
Admissions Requirements Physician's request.
Staff LPNs 1 (ft); Nurses aides 10 (ft); Dietitians 1 (ft).
Facilities Dining room; Activities room; Laundry room; Barber/Beauty shop.
Activities Arts & crafts; Games; Reading groups; Prayer groups; Movies.

HARRODSBURG

Harrodsburg Health Care Manor
PO Box 39, 853 Lexington Rd, Harrodsburg, KY, 40330
(606) 734-7791
Admin Beth Logue.
Licensure Intermediate care; Personal care. *Beds* ICF 102; Personal 10. *Certified* Medicaid.
Owner Proprietary Corp (Hillhaven Corp).
Staff RNs; LPNs; Orderlies; Nurses aides; Physical therapists; Occupational therapists; Speech therapists; Activities coordinators; Dietitians.
Facilities Dining room; Activities room; Crafts room; Laundry room; Barber/Beauty shop; Outside gazebo.
Activities Arts & crafts; Cards; Games; Prayer groups; Movies.

HARTFORD

Professional Care Home
114 McMurtry Ave, Hartford, KY, 42347
(502) 298-7437
Admin Patricia Donald. *Medical Dir/Dir of Nursing* Frances Coble RN.
Licensure Intermediate care. *Beds* ICF 129. *Certified* Medicaid.
Owner Proprietary Corp.
Staff Physicians 5 (ft); RNs 1 (ft); LPNs 7 (ft), 2 (pt); Nurses aides 24 (ft), 14 (ft); Physical therapists 2 (pt); Speech therapists 1 (pt); Activities coordinators 1 (ft), 1 (pt); Dietitians 1 (ft); Audiologists 1 (pt); Dietary 11 (ft); Housekeeping & laundry 11 (ft); Maintenance 1 (ft); Certified medication aides 6 (ft); Administration 2 (ft).
Facilities Dining room; Activities room; Chapel; Crafts room; Laundry room; Barber/Beauty shop.
Activities Arts & crafts; Cards; Games; Reading groups; Prayer groups; Movies; Shopping trips; Social/Cultural gatherings; Hawaiian Luau; Family picnics; Fall festival.

HAZARD

Hazard Nursing Home
PO Box 1329, Airport Industrial Site, Hazard, KY, 41701
(606) 439-2306
Admin Debra K Reynolds. *Medical Dir/Dir of Nursing* Cordell Williams MD.
Licensure Skilled care; Intermediate care. *Beds* SNF 40; ICF 110. *Certified* Medicaid; Medicare.
Owner Proprietary Corp (Health Sys).
Facilities Dining room; Physical therapy room; Activities room; Crafts room; Laundry room; Barber/Beauty shop.
Activities Arts & crafts; Games; Reading groups; Prayer groups.

HENDERSON

Henderson Rest Home*
201 Watson Ln, Henderson, KY, 42420
(502) 826-2394
Admin Christie Shaver. *Medical Dir/Dir of Nursing* Dr Jack Bland.
Licensure Personal care. *Beds* 64.
Admissions Requirements Medical examination.
Staff RNs 1 (ft); Nurses aides 1 (ft); Recreational therapists 1 (ft).
Facilities Dining room; Laundry room.
Activities Arts & crafts; Cards; Games; Reading groups; Prayer groups; Movies; Shopping trips; Social/Cultural gatherings.

Medco Center of Henderson
2500 N Elm St, Henderson, KY, 42420
(502) 826-9794
Admin Lavine Terry. *Medical Dir/Dir of Nursing* Joyce Klutey RN.
Licensure Intermediate care. *Beds* ICF 100. *Certified* Medicaid; Medicare.
Owner Proprietary Corp (Unicare).

Redbanks
851 Kimsey Ln, Henderson, KY, 42420
(502) 826-6436
Admin Georgene H Fraley. *Medical Dir/Dir of Nursing* Dr Kenneth Eblen.
Licensure Skilled care; Intermediate care; Personal care. *Beds* SNF 76; ICF 146; Personal 49. *Certified* Medicaid; Medicare.
Owner Nonprofit organization/foundation.
Admissions Requirements Minimum age 16; Medical examination; Physician's request.
Staff Physicians 23 (pt); RNs 10 (ft), 4 (pt); LPNs 8 (ft), 4 (pt); Nurses aides 85 (ft), 30 (pt); Physical therapists 1 (ft); Recreational therapists 1 (pt); Occupational therapists 1

(pt); Speech therapists 1 (pt); Activities coordinators 1 (ft); Dietitians 1 (ft); Ophthalmologists 1 (pt).
Facilities Dining room; Physical therapy room; Activities room; Chapel; Laundry room; Barber/Beauty shop; Library.
Activities Arts & crafts; Cards; Games; Reading groups; Prayer groups; Movies; Shopping trips; Social/Cultural gatherings.

HIGHLAND HEIGHTS

Lakeside Place
3510 Alexandria Pike, Highland Heights, KY, 41076
(606) 441-1100
Admin Richard S Kidd. *Medical Dir/Dir of Nursing* Dr Donald Stevens; Betty Ward.
Licensure Skilled care; Intermediate care; Personal care. *Beds* SNF 40; ICF 246; Personal 38. *Certified* Medicaid; Medicare.
Owner Nonprofit Corp.
Admissions Requirements Medical examination; Physician's request.
Staff Physicians 1 (pt); RNs 2 (ft), 2 (pt); LPNs 29 (ft), 4 (pt); Orderlies 6 (ft), 3 (pt); Nurses aides 130 (ft), 6 (pt); Physical therapists 3 (pt); Activities coordinators 1 (ft); Dietitians 1 (ft).
Facilities Dining room; Physical therapy room; Activities room; Chapel; Crafts room; Laundry room; Barber/Beauty shop; Library; 9 TV rooms/solariums; Recreation room.
Activities Arts & crafts; Cards; Games; Reading groups; Prayer groups; Movies; Shopping trips; Monthly birthday parties; Special event banquets; Annual resident/family picnic; Pet therapy.

HINDMAN

June Bluchanan Primary Care Center
PO Box 471, Rte 550, Hindman, KY, 41822
(606) 785-3175
Admin Theresa C Francis FNP Clinic Mgr. *Medical Dir/Dir of Nursing* Dr Denzil G Barker.
Licensure Primary care. *Certified* Medicaid; Medicare.
Owner Nonprofit Corp.
Staff Physicians 3 (ft); RNs 1 (ft); LPNs 2 (ft); Speech therapists 1 (pt); Dietitians 1 (pt).
Languages Spanish, Sign
Facilities Dining room; Lab; ER; Pharmacy; Radiology.

HODGENVILLE

Sunrise Manor Nursing Home
Phillips Ln, Rte 3, Hodgenville, KY, 42748
(502) 358-3103
Admin Hilda Harned. *Medical Dir/Dir of Nursing* Glenn Catlett MD.
Licensure Skilled care; Intermediate care. *Beds* SNF 50; ICF 72. *Certified* Medicaid; Medicare.
Admissions Requirements Medical examination.
Staff Physicians 1 (pt); RNs 5 (ft); LPNs 5 (ft), 3 (pt); Orderlies 1 (ft); Nurses aides 40 (ft), 8 (pt); Physical therapists 1 (ft); Occupational therapists; Speech therapists; Activities coordinators 1 (ft); Dietitians.
Facilities Dining room; Physical therapy room; Activities room; Chapel; Laundry room; Barber/Beauty shop; TV room.
Activities Arts & crafts; Cards; Games; Reading groups; Prayer groups; Social/Cultural gatherings.

HOPKINSVILLE

Brookfield Manor*
Richard St & Henderson Dr, Box 711, Hopkinsville, KY, 42240
(502) 886-8185

Admin Sue Winders.
Licensure Personal care. *Beds* 78.
Staff LPNs 1 (ft); Nurses aides 14 (ft); Activities coordinators 1 (ft); Dietitians 1 (pt).
Facilities Dining room; Activities room; Laundry room; Barber/Beauty shop.
Activities Arts & crafts; Cards; Games; Reading groups; Prayer groups.

Christian Health Center—Hopkinsville*
200 Sterling Dr, Hopkinsville, KY, 42240
(502) 885-1166
Admin Nancy H Steele. *Medical Dir/Dir of Nursing* Guinn Cost MD.
Licensure Skilled care; Intermediate care. *Beds* SNF 30; ICF 86. *Certified* Medicaid; Medicare.
Owner Nonprofit Corp (Christian Ch Campuses).
Staff RNs 3 (ft), 3 (pt); LPNs 11 (ft), 5 (pt); Nurses aides 24 (ft), 19 (pt); Physical therapists 1 (pt); Recreational therapists 1 (ft); Speech therapists 1 (pt); Activities coordinators 1 (ft); Dietitians 1 (pt); Dentists 1 (pt); Podiatrists 1 (pt).
Facilities Dining room; Physical therapy room; Activities room; Chapel; Crafts room; Laundry room; Barber/Beauty shop.
Activities Arts & crafts; Cards; Games; Reading groups; Prayer groups; Movies; Shopping trips; Social/Cultural gatherings.

Covingtons Convalescent Center Inc
115 Cayce St, Hopkinsville, KY, 42240
(502) 886-4403, 6773
Admin William Earl Covington. *Medical Dir/Dir of Nursing* Palmer Covington.
Licensure Intermediate care; Personal care. *Beds* ICF 72; Personal 25. *Certified* Medicaid.
Owner Privately owned.
Activities Arts & crafts; Cards; Games; Reading groups; Prayer groups; Movies; Shopping trips; Social/Cultural gatherings.

Gainesville Manor*
PO Box 4004, Rte 9, Hopkinsville, KY, 42240
(502) 886-0258
Admin Ida Woodard. *Medical Dir/Dir of Nursing* Dr J W Frazier.
Licensure Personal care. *Beds* 102.
Admissions Requirements Minimum age 18; Medical examination; Physician's request.
Staff Physicians; LPNs 1 (ft), 1 (pt); Orderlies 1 (ft); Nurses aides 20 (ft), 2 (pt); Activities coordinators 1 (ft); Dietitians 1 (pt); Dentists 1 (pt); Ophthalmologists 2 (pt); Audiologists 1 (pt).
Facilities Dining room; Activities room; Crafts room; Laundry room; Library.
Activities Arts & crafts; Cards; Games; Reading groups; Prayer groups; Shopping trips; Social/Cultural gatherings.

Pennyrile Home*
502 Noel Ave, Hopkinsville, KY, 42240
(502) 885-9100
Admin Cynthia Kaye Outland.
Licensure Personal care. *Beds* 94.
Owner Proprietary Corp.

Pinecrest Manor*
950 Highpoint Dr, Hopkinsville, KY, 42240
(502) 885-1151
Admin Joe Olson. *Medical Dir/Dir of Nursing* Dr Robert Rose.
Licensure Skilled care; Intermediate care. *Beds* SNF 16; ICF 79. *Certified* Medicaid; Medicare.
Owner Proprietary Corp (Sunbelt Healthcare Centers).
Admissions Requirements Minimum age 21; Physician's request.
Staff Physicians 19 (pt); RNs 3 (ft), 2 (pt); LPNs 7 (ft), 12 (pt); Orderlies 2 (ft), 3 (pt); Nurses aides 26 (ft), 14 (pt); Physical

therapists 1 (ft); Speech therapists 1 (pt); Activities coordinators 1 (ft); Dietitians 1 (ft).
Affiliation Seventh-Day Adventist
Facilities Dining room; Physical therapy room; Activities room; Crafts room; Laundry room; Barber/Beauty shop.
Activities Arts & crafts; Games; Reading groups; Prayer groups; Movies; Social/Cultural gatherings.

INDEPENDENCE

Regency Manor
5716 Madison Pike, Independence, KY, 41051
(606) 356-9294
Admin Patricia C Schroer. *Medical Dir/Dir of Nursing* Melva Jean Elbert.
Licensure Personal care. *Beds* 50.
Owner Proprietary Corp.
Admissions Requirements Minimum age 18; Medical examination.
Staff Nurses aides 9 (ft); Activities coordinators 1 (ft).
Facilities Dining room; Activities room; Crafts room; Barber/Beauty shop.
Activities Arts & crafts; Cards; Games; Prayer groups; Movies; Social/Cultural gatherings.

IRVINE

Irvine Health Care Center
Wallace Dr & Bertha St, Irvine, KY, 40336
(606) 723-5153
Admin David Pendley.
Licensure Intermediate care; Personal care. *Beds* ICF 78; Personal 18. *Certified* Medicaid.
Owner Proprietary Corp (Unicare).
Staff RNs 1 (ft); LPNs 3 (ft); Orderlies 1 (ft); Nurses aides 26 (ft), 4 (pt); Activities coordinators 1 (ft); Dietitians 1 (ft).
Facilities Dining room; Activities room; Crafts room; Laundry room; Barber/Beauty shop.
Activities Arts & crafts; Reading groups; Prayer groups; Movies; Shopping trips.

JACKSON

Nim Henson Geriatric Center
PO Box 636, Jett Subdivision, Jackson, KY, 41339
(606) 666-2456
Admin Ted Manns Jr. *Medical Dir/Dir of Nursing* Emanuel C Turner MD; Maude Coda DON.
Licensure Skilled care; Intermediate care. *Beds* SNF 30; ICF 92. *Certified* Medicaid; Medicare.
Owner Nonprofit Corp.
Admissions Requirements Medical examination; Physician's request.
Staff RNs 2 (ft), 3 (pt); LPNs 7 (ft), 1 (pt); Orderlies 1 (ft), 1 (pt); Nurses aides 41 (ft), 6 (pt); Physical therapists 1 (ft); Activities coordinators 1 (ft); Dietitians 1 (ft).
Facilities Dining room; Activities room; Laundry room; Barber/Beauty shop.
Activities Arts & crafts; Cards; Games; Reading groups; Prayer groups; Movies; Social/Cultural gatherings; Religious services; Entertainment.

JAMESTOWN

Fair Oaks Personal Care Home*
PO Box 140, Hwy 127, Jamestown, KY, 42629
(502) 343-2101
Admin Don Hamlin.
Licensure Intermediate care. *Beds* 94. *Certified* Medicaid.
Owner Proprietary Corp.

JEFFERSONTOWN

Louisville Lutheran Home Inc
10617 E Watterson Trail, Jeffersontown, KY, 40299
(502) 267-7403
Admin Elwood J Culp. *Medical Dir/Dir of Nursing* Shirley Andrew DON.
Licensure Intermediate care; Personal care. *Beds* ICF 60; Personal 38. *Certified* Medicaid.
Owner Nonprofit Corp.
Admissions Requirements Medical examination; Physician's request.
Staff RNs 1 (pt); LPNs 4 (ft); Orderlies 1 (ft); Nurses aides 18 (ft); Recreational therapists 1 (ft); Dietitians 1 (pt).
Affiliation Lutheran
Facilities Dining room; Physical therapy room; Activities room; Chapel; Laundry room; Barber/Beauty shop; Library.
Activities Arts & crafts; Cards; Games; Reading groups; Prayer groups; Movies; Shopping trips; Social/Cultural gatherings.

JENKINS

Letcher County Golden Years Rest Home Inc
PO Box 867, Lakeside Dr, Jenkins, KY, 41537
(606) 832-2123
Admin James F Tackett. *Medical Dir/Dir of Nursing* Anita Taylor.
Licensure Personal care. *Beds* 44.
Owner Nonprofit Corp.
Admissions Requirements Medical examination.
Staff LPNs 1 (ft); Nurses aides 11 (ft).
Facilities Dining room; Activities room; Chapel; Laundry room; Barber/Beauty shop.
Activities Arts & crafts; Cards; Games; Prayer groups; Shopping trips; Social/Cultural gatherings.

JONESVILLE

Jonesville Rest Home*
Rte 36, Jonesville, KY, 41052
(606) 824-4610
Admin Leon Tuttle & Wanda Sue Tuttle.
Licensure Personal care. *Beds* 26.
Owner Proprietary Corp.

KINDMAN

Knott County Nursing Home*
HCR 60, Box 985, Kindman, KY, 41822
(606) 785-5011
Admin Jack Johnson. *Medical Dir/Dir of Nursing* George A Sullivan MD.
Licensure Skilled care; Intermediate care. *Beds* SNF 29; ICF 53. *Certified* Medicaid; Medicare.
Staff Physicians 5 (ft); RNs 3 (ft); LPNs 12 (ft); Orderlies 4 (ft); Nurses aides 28 (ft); Activities coordinators 1 (ft); Dietitians 1 (ft); Dentists 1 (ft).
Facilities Dining room; Physical therapy room; Activities room; Crafts room; Laundry room; Barber/Beauty shop; Library.
Activities Arts & crafts; Cards; Games; Reading groups; Prayer groups; Movies; Shopping trips.

KUTTAWA

Hilltop Nursing Home Inc
PO Box 190, Lake Barkley Dr, Kuttawa, KY, 42055
(502) 388-2291
Admin Nancy J Adams; Clyde S Adams.
Licensure Intermediate care; Personal care. *Beds* ICF 96; Personal 32. *Certified* Medicaid.
Owner Proprietary Corp.
Admissions Requirements Medical examination.

Staff RNs 2 (ft); LPNs 6 (ft); Orderlies 2 (ft); Nurses aides 54 (ft), 2 (pt); Speech therapists 1 (ft); Activities coordinators 1 (ft); Dietitians 1 (ft).
Facilities Dining room; Activities room; Crafts room; Laundry room; Barber/Beauty shop.
Activities Arts & crafts; Cards; Games; Reading groups; Prayer groups; Movies; Shopping trips; Social/Cultural gatherings.

LACENTER

Life Care Center of LaCenter*
5th & Pine Sts, LaCenter, KY, 42056
(502) 665-5681
Admin Marilyn D Ingram.
Licensure Intermediate care; Personal care. *Beds* ICF 70; Personal 21. *Certified* Medicaid.
Owner Proprietary Corp (Life Care Centers of America).
Staff Physicians 4 (pt); RNs 1 (ft); LPNs 4 (ft); Nurses aides 33 (ft); Recreational therapists 1 (pt); Speech therapists 1 (pt); Activities coordinators 1 (ft); Dietitians 1 (pt).
Facilities Dining room; Laundry room; Barber/Beauty shop.
Activities Arts & crafts; Games; Movies; Shopping trips; Social/Cultural gatherings.

LACKEY

Golden Years Rest Home*
HC 80, Box 25, Lackey, KY, 41643
(606) 946-2220
Admin Loveda Snyder Coburn. *Medical Dir/Dir of Nursing* Alberta G Deaton.
Licensure Personal care. *Beds* 84.
Admissions Requirements Minimum age 18; Medical examination; Physician's request.
Staff Physicians 3 (ft), 1 (pt); LPNs 1 (ft); Orderlies 2 (ft); Nurses aides 16 (ft), 4 (pt); Activities coordinators 1 (ft), 1 (pt); Dietitians 1 (ft), 1 (pt); Dentists 1 (pt); Ophthalmologists 1 (pt); Audiologists 1 (pt).
Facilities Dining room; Activities room; Laundry room; Barber/Beauty shop.
Activities Arts & crafts; Cards; Games; Reading groups; Prayer groups; Movies; Shopping trips; Social/Cultural gatherings.

LAGRANGE

Cedar Lake Lodge
PO Box 289, 3301 Jericho Rd, LaGrange, KY, 40031
(502) 222-7157
Admin Clyde D Lang. *Medical Dir/Dir of Nursing* Rose Marie Miller.
Licensure Intermediate care for mentally retarded. *Beds* ICF/MR 76. *Certified* Medicaid.
Owner Nonprofit Corp.
Affiliation Lutheran
Facilities Dining room; Physical therapy room; Activities room; Chapel; Crafts room.
Activities Arts & crafts; Games; Prayer groups; Movies; Shopping trips; Social/Cultural gatherings.

LANCASTER

Garrard County Home for Senior Citizens*
308 W Maple St, Lancaster, KY, 40444
(606) 792-2112
Admin W David MacCool. *Medical Dir/Dir of Nursing* Paul J Sides MD.
Licensure Personal care. *Beds* 48.
Admissions Requirements Minimum age 21; Medical examination.
Staff RNs 1 (pt); LPNs 2 (ft), 2 (pt); Nurses aides 6 (ft); Activities coordinators 1 (ft); Dietitians 1 (pt); Social worker 1 (pt).

Facilities Dining room; Activities room; Laundry room; Barber/Beauty shop.
Activities Arts & crafts; Games; Reading groups; Prayer groups; Movies; Shopping trips.

Garrard County Memorial Hospital—SNF*
308 W Maple St, Lancaster, KY, 40444
(606) 792-2112
Admin W David MacCool.
Licensure Skilled care. *Beds* 34. *Certified* Medicaid; Medicare.
Owner Nonprofit Corp.

LAWRENCEBURG

Heritage Hall Care Center
Box 349, 331 S Main, Lawrenceburg, KY, 40342
(502) 839-7246
Admin Eunice Dorten. *Medical Dir/Dir of Nursing* William P McElwain; Fran Cole RN DON.
Licensure Intermediate care; Personal care. *Beds* ICF 57; Personal 55. *Certified* Medicaid.
Owner Proprietary Corp.
Admissions Requirements Minimum age 16; Medical examination.
Staff RNs 4 (ft), 1 (pt); LPNs 2 (ft); Orderlies 1 (ft); Nurses aides 40 (ft); Physical therapists 1 (pt); Speech therapists 1 (pt); Activities coordinators 1 (ft); Dietitians 1 (pt).
Facilities Dining room; Physical therapy room; Activities room; Chapel; Crafts room; Laundry room; Barber/Beauty shop; Library; 5 patient lounge areas; Park; Courtyard; 2 outdoor patio areas.
Activities Arts & crafts; Cards; Games; Reading groups; Prayer groups; Movies; Shopping trips; Social/Cultural gatherings.

Sunset Hill Home for Aged & Infirm*
1428 Tyrone Rd, Lawrenceburg, KY, 40342
(502) 839-6383
Admin William Crabb.
Licensure Personal care. *Beds* 16.
Owner Nonprofit Corp.

LEBANON

Cedars of Lebanon Rest Home*
S Harrison, Lebanon, KY, 40033
(502) 692-3121
Admin Sandra Creech.
Licensure Intermediate care; Personal care. *Beds* ICF 81; Personal 13. *Certified* Medicaid.
Owner Proprietary Corp (Hillhaven Corp).

Spring View Nursing Home
353 W Walnut St, Lebanon, KY, 40033
(502) 692-3161 ext 223
Admin Marchetta Beevers. *Medical Dir/Dir of Nursing* Tina Fenwick.
Licensure Skilled care; Intermediate care; Intermediate care for mentally retarded; Nursing home. *Beds* 38.
Owner Proprietary Corp.
Admissions Requirements Minimum age 60; Medical examination; Physician's request.
Staff RNs 1 (ft); LPNs 5 (ft); Orderlies 1 (ft); Nurses aides 9 (ft), 3 (pt); Activities coordinators 1 (ft); Dietitians 1 (pt).
Facilities Dining room; Physical therapy room; Activities room; Chapel; Crafts room; Laundry room; Barber/Beauty shop.
Activities Arts & crafts; Cards; Games; Reading groups; Prayer groups; Movies; Shopping trips; Social/Cultural gatherings; Music therapy; Gardening.

LEITCHFIELD

Grayson Manor
349 E Lake Dr, Leitchfield, KY, 42754
(502) 259-4028
Admin Suzanne E Givan. *Medical Dir/Dir of Nursing* Linda Duke RN DON.
Licensure Skilled care; Intermediate care; Personal care. *Beds* SNF 6; ICF 66; Personal 30. *Certified* Medicaid; Medicare.
Owner Nonprofit Corp.
Admissions Requirements Medical examination; Physician's request.
Staff RNs 2 (ft), 1 (pt); LPNs 4 (ft), 2 (pt); Orderlies 3 (ft); Nurses aides 14 (ft); Speech therapists 1 (pt); Activities coordinators 1 (ft); Dietitians 1 (pt).
Facilities Dining room; Activities room; Chapel; Crafts room; Laundry room; Barber/Beauty shop.
Activities Arts & crafts; Cards; Games; Reading groups; Prayer groups; Movies; Shopping trips; Social/Cultural gatherings.

Leithchfield Health Care Manor
PO Box 466, Wallace Ave, Leitchfield, KY, 42754
(502) 259-4036
Admin Margaret Ann Embry. *Medical Dir/Dir of Nursing* Margaret Ann Embry.
Licensure Intermediate care; Personal care. *Beds* ICF 50; Personal 18. *Certified* Medicaid.
Owner Privately owned.
Admissions Requirements Medical examination; Physician's request.
Staff RNs 1 (pt); LPNs 2 (ft), 1 (pt); Orderlies 2 (ft), 1 (pt); Activities coordinators 1 (ft); Dietitians 1 (ft).
Facilities Dining room; Laundry room; Barber/Beauty shop.
Activities Arts & crafts; Cards; Games; Reading groups; Prayer groups; Movies; Shopping trips; Social/Cultural gatherings.

LEWISPORT

Hancock County Rest Haven Inc
Drawer G, Lewisport, KY, 42351
(502) 295-6825
Admin Carla K Jones.
Licensure Personal care. *Beds* 78. *Certified* Medicaid.
Owner Proprietary Corp.
Admissions Requirements Minimum age 18; Medical examination; TB test.
Staff Nurses aides 10 (ft), 11 (pt); Activities coordinators 1 (ft).
Facilities Dining room; Activities room; Laundry room.
Activities Arts & crafts; Cards; Games; Reading groups; Prayer groups; Movies; Shopping trips; Social/Cultural gatherings; Reality & Socialization Groups; Church services provided by 3 different denominations.

LEXINGTON

Ashland Terrace*
475 S Ashland Ave, Lexington, KY, 40502
(606) 266-2581
Admin Leona Coleman.
Licensure Personal care. *Beds* 22.
Owner Nonprofit Corp.

Excepticon—Lexington Campus
1321 Trent Blvd, Lexington, KY, 40502
(606) 272-3496
Admin Jeffrey M Cross.
Licensure Intermediate care for mentally retarded. *Beds* 180. *Certified* Medicaid.
Owner Proprietary Corp.
Admissions Requirements Minimum age 18; Medical examination.

Staff Physicians 2 (pt); RNs 2 (pt); LPNs 7 (pt); Nurses aides 45 (ft), 9 (pt); Physical therapists 1 (pt); Recreational therapists 3 (ft); Occupational therapists 2 (ft); Speech therapists 1 (ft); Dietitians 1 (ft); Dentists 1 (pt).
Facilities Dining room; Activities room; Crafts room; Laundry room.
Activities Arts & crafts; Games; Movies; Shopping trips; Social/Cultural gatherings.

Glen Haven Personal Care Home*
444 Glen Arvin Ave, Lexington, KY, 40508
(606) 233-1833
Admin Hazel Ulrey.
Licensure Personal care. *Beds* 25.

Harrison's Sanitorium
1537 N Limestone St, Lexington, KY, 40505
(606) 252-6673
Admin Beverly Turner. *Medical Dir/Dir of Nursing* James W Mathews MD; Margaret L Harrison RN DON.
Licensure Skilled care. *Beds* SNF 77. *Certified* Medicaid; Medicare.
Owner Proprietary Corp.
Admissions Requirements Physician's request.
Staff RNs 5 (ft); LPNs 7 (ft); Nurses aides 30 (ft); Physical therapists 1 (ft); Reality therapists 1 (ft); Occupational therapists 1 (pt); Speech therapists 1 (pt); Activities coordinators 1 (ft), 1 (pt); Dietitians 1 (pt); Dentists 1 (pt); Ophthalmologists 1 (pt).
Facilities Dining room; Physical therapy room; Activities room; Chapel; Crafts room; Laundry room; Barber/Beauty shop.
Activities Arts & crafts; Cards; Games; Movies; Shopping trips; Social/Cultural gatherings.

Hayden's Personal Care Home*
553 E 3rd St, Lexington, KY, 40508
(606) 233-1944
Admin Lula Hayden.
Licensure Personal care. *Beds* 36.
Owner Proprietary Corp.

Homestead Nursing Center
1608 Versailles Rd, Lexington, KY, 40504
(606) 252-0871
Admin Betty Wells RN.
Licensure Skilled care; Intermediate care. *Beds* SNF 103; ICF 25. *Certified* Medicaid; Medicare.
Owner Proprietary Corp.

Kiva House
201 Mechanic, Lexington, KY, 40507-1096
(606) 252-3676
Admin Nancy Washbaugh.
Licensure Personal care. *Beds* 28.

Lexington Country Place*
700 Mason Headley Rd, Lexington, KY, 40504
(606) 259-3486
Admin David K Rice. *Medical Dir/Dir of Nursing* Kenneth C Tufts MD.
Licensure Skilled care. *Beds* 111. *Certified* Medicaid; Medicare.
Admissions Requirements Minimum age 16; Medical examination; Physician's request.
Staff RNs 6 (ft), 1 (pt); Orderlies 4 (ft); Nurses aides 42 (ft); Physical therapists 1 (ft); Recreational therapists 1 (ft); Speech therapists 1 (pt); Dietitians 1 (ft); Podiatrists 1 (pt).
Facilities Dining room; Physical therapy room; Activities room; Crafts room; Laundry room; Barber/Beauty shop; Library.
Activities Arts & crafts; Cards; Games; Reading groups; Prayer groups; Movies; Shopping trips; Social/Cultural gatherings.

Lexington Manor Health Care Facility
353 Waller Ave, Lexington, KY, 40504
(606) 252-3558

Admin Olive M Peel. *Medical Dir/Dir of Nursing* R M Calbaltica MD; Damie U Castle.
Licensure Skilled care; Intermediate care; SCU. *Beds* SNF 32; ICF 128; SCU 20. *Certified* Medicaid; Medicare VA.
Owner Proprietary Corp (Hillhaven Corp).
Admissions Requirements Minimum age 18; Medical examination; Physician's request.
Staff Physicians 32 (ft); RNs 5 (ft), 1 (pt); LPNs 14 (ft), 8 (pt); Orderlies 9 (ft); Nurses aides 41 (ft), 8 (pt); Physical therapists 2 (ft); Recreational therapists 1 (ft); Occupational therapists 1 (pt); Speech therapists 1 (pt); Activities coordinators 1 (ft), 1 (pt); Dietitians 1 (ft); Dentists 1 (pt); Ophthalmologists 1 (pt).
Facilities Dining room; Physical therapy room; Activities room; Crafts room; Laundry room; Barber/Beauty shop; Enclosed courtyard.
Activities Arts & crafts; Cards; Games; Reading groups; Prayer groups; Movies; Shopping trips; Social/Cultural gatherings.

Julius Marks Home*
866 Georgetown St, Lexington, KY, 40505
(606) 253-2558
Admin Patricia A Taylor.
Licensure Intermediate care; Personal care. *Beds* ICF 73; Personal 34. *Certified* Medicaid.
Admissions Requirements Medical examination; Physician's request.
Staff RNs 1 (ft); LPNs 6 (ft), 1 (pt); Nurses aides 63 (ft); Reality therapists 1 (pt); Recreational therapists 1 (ft); Activities coordinators 1 (ft).
Facilities Dining room; Activities room; Laundry room; Barber/Beauty shop; Library.
Activities Arts & crafts; Cards; Games; Reading groups; Prayer groups; Movies; Shopping trips; Social/Cultural gatherings.

Mayfair Manor
3300 Tates Creek Rd, Lexington, KY, 40502
(606) 266-2126
Admin Renee H Martin. *Medical Dir/Dir of Nursing* Kenneth Tufts MD; Marge Peter DON.
Licensure Skilled care. *Beds* SNF 50; Nursing home beds 50. *Certified* Medicaid; Medicare.
Owner Proprietary Corp (National Heritage).
Admissions Requirements Physician's request.
Staff RNs 4 (ft), 2 (pt); LPNs 10 (ft), 4 (pt); Nurses aides 25 (ft), 20 (pt); Physical therapists 1 (ft), 1 (pt); Activities coordinators 1 (ft), 2 (pt); Dietitians 1 (ft).
Facilities Dining room; Physical therapy room; Activities room; Crafts room; Laundry room; Barber/Beauty shop; Library.
Activities Arts & crafts; Cards; Games; Reading groups; Prayer groups; Movies; Shopping trips; Social/Cultural gatherings.

Meadowbrook Nursing Home*
2020 Cambridge Dr, Lexington, KY, 40504
(606) 252-6747
Admin Beatrice E Hood.
Licensure Intermediate care; Personal care. *Beds* ICF 106; Personal 34. *Certified* Medicaid.
Admissions Requirements Medical examination.
Staff Physicians 10 (pt); RNs 1 (ft), 1 (pt); LPNs 5 (ft), 2 (pt); Orderlies 2 (ft), 2 (pt); Nurses aides 40 (ft), 9 (pt); Physical therapists 2 (pt); Speech therapists 1 (pt); Activities coordinators 1 (ft); Dietitians 1 (ft); Dentists 1 (pt); Podiatrists 1 (pt).
Facilities Dining room; Activities room; Crafts room; Laundry room; Barber/Beauty shop; Library; Sunrooms.
Activities Arts & crafts; Cards; Games; Reading groups; Prayer groups; Movies; Shopping trips; Social/Cultural gatherings.

Rose Manor Rest Home
3057 Cleveland Pike, Lexington, KY, 40505
(606) 299-4117
Admin Alfred E McGregor. *Medical Dir/Dir of Nursing* Nickie Kerr.
Licensure Intermediate care. *Beds* ICF 34.
Certified Medicaid.
Owner Privately owned.
Admissions Requirements Medical examination.
Staff RNs 2 (ft), 5 (pt); LPNs 1 (ft); Nurses aides; Activities coordinators 1 (ft); Dietitians 1 (ft).
Languages Sign
Facilities Dining room; Activities room; Laundry room.
Activities Arts & crafts; Cards; Games; Reading groups; Prayer groups; Movies; Shopping trips; Social/Cultural gatherings.

St Margaret of Cortona Home*
1310 Leestown Pike, Lexington, KY, 40508
(606) 255-4855
Admin Sr Rose Francis Schifferli.
Licensure Personal care. *Beds* 24.
Owner Nonprofit Corp.
Admissions Requirements Minimum age 55; Females only; Medical examination; Physician's request.
Staff RNs 1 (ft); Dietitians 1 (ft).
Affiliation Roman Catholic
Facilities Dining room; Chapel; Laundry room; Library.
Activities Cards; Games; Prayer groups; Movies.

Sayre Christian Village Nursing Home
3840 Camelot Dr, Lexington, KY, 40503
(606) 273 7575
Admin M Eileen Burberry. *Medical Dir/Dir of Nursing* Carol Carpenter RN DON.
Licensure Intermediate care; Personal care. *Beds* ICF 99; Personal 10. *Certified* Medicaid.
Owner Nonprofit Corp.
Admissions Requirements Physician's request.
Staff RNs 2 (ft), 1 (pt); LPNs 8 (ft), 4 (pt); Nurses aides 40 (ft), 4 (pt); Physical therapists 1 (pt); Activities coordinators 2 (ft); Dietitians 1 (pt).
Affiliation Church of Christ
Facilities Dining room; Activities room; Chapel; Laundry room; Barber/Beauty shop.
Activities Arts & crafts; Cards; Games; Reading groups; Prayer groups; Movies; Shopping trips; Social/Cultural gatherings.

Stephens Nursing Home
PO Box 11746, 909 Georgetown St, Lexington, KY, 40577-1746
(606) 254-9602
Admin Susan Lawson. *Medical Dir/Dir of Nursing* Jerzy Wysock MD; Barbara Tucker.
Licensure Intermediate care; Personal care. *Beds* ICF 52; Personal 44. *Certified* Medicaid.
Owner Proprietary Corp.
Admissions Requirements Minimum age 18; Medical examination; Physician's request.
Staff Physicians 1 (pt); RNs 1 (ft); LPNs 7 (ft); Nurses aides 22 (ft), 6 (pt); Physical therapists 1 (pt); Speech therapists 1 (pt); Activities coordinators 1 (pt); Dietitians 1 (pt); Dentists 1 (pt); Ophthalmologists 1 (pt); Social worker 1 (pt).
Facilities Dining room.
Activities Arts & crafts; Cards; Games; Reading groups; Prayer groups; Movies; Shopping trips; Social/Cultural gatherings; Poetry; Basketball; Outside sports; Pet therapy; Music therapy.

Tates Creek Health Care Center
3576 Pimlico Pkwy, Lexington, KY, 40502
(606) 272-0608
Admin Steve Robison. *Medical Dir/Dir of Nursing* Dr Richard French; Tonia Harris RN.

Licensure Intermediate care; Personal care.
Beds ICF 100; Personal 36. *Certified* Medicaid.
Admissions Requirements Females only; Physician's request.
Staff Physicians 20 (pt); RNs 1 (ft), 1 (pt); LPNs 5 (ft), 4 (pt); Orderlies 3 (ft); Nurses aides 37 (ft), 8 (pt); Physical therapists 2 (pt); Speech therapists 1 (pt); Activities coordinators 1 (ft), 1 (pt); Dietitians 1 (ft); Ophthalmologists 1 (pt); Dentists 2 (pt); Podiatrists 1 (pt); Dentist.
Facilities Dining room; Activities room; Crafts room; Laundry room; Barber/Beauty shop; Library; Florida rooms; Van.
Activities Arts & crafts; Cards; Games; Reading groups; Prayer groups; Movies; Shopping trips; Social/Cultural gatherings.

YWCA Arnett Pritchett Foundation Home
319 Duke Rd, Lexington, KY, 40502
(606) 266-6031
Admin Carolyn Danks.
Licensure Personal care. *Beds* 14.
Owner Nonprofit organization/foundation.
Admissions Requirements Minimum age 65; Females only.
Staff Nurses aides 8 (ft); Recreational therapists 1 (ft); Activities coordinators 1 (ft); Dietitians 1 (ft).
Facilities Dining room; Activities room; Laundry room; Library; Home type atmosphere; Private rooms.
Activities Arts & crafts; Cards; Games; Reading groups; Prayer groups; Movies; Shopping trips; Social/Cultural gatherings; Exercise groups; Pet therapy.

LIBERTY

Green River Rest Home*
PO Box G, Liberty, KY, 42539
(606) 787-9256
Admin Anna Lee Tasker.
Licensure Personal care. *Beds* 24.
Owner Nonprofit Corp.

LONDON

Laurel Heights Home for the Elderly
208 W 12th St, London, KY, 40741
(606) 864-4155
Admin Melinda Helton. *Medical Dir/Dir of Nursing* Martha Burns RN.
Licensure Skilled care; Intermediate care; Personal care. *Beds* SNF 42; ICF 93; Personal 62. *Certified* Medicaid; Medicare.
Owner Nonprofit Corp.
Admissions Requirements Medical examination.
Staff Physicians 1 (pt); RNs 3 (ft), 1 (pt); LPNs; Orderlies; Nurses aides; Physical therapists 1 (pt); Speech therapists 1 (pt); Activities coordinators 1 (ft); Dietitians 1 (pt).
Facilities Dining room; Physical therapy room; Activities room; Chapel; Crafts room; Laundry room; Barber/Beauty shop; Library.
Activities Arts & crafts; Cards; Games; Reading groups; Prayer groups; Movies; Shopping trips; Social/Cultural gatherings.

LOUISA

J J Jordan Geriatric Center*
PO Box 726, E Clayton Ln, Louisa, KY, 41230
(606) 638-4586
Admin David McKenzie. *Medical Dir/Dir of Nursing* Lloyd Browning MD & Norman Edwards MD.
Licensure Skilled care; Intermediate care; Personal care. *Beds* SNF 34; Personal 16. *Certified* Medicaid; Medicare.
Admissions Requirements Physician's request.

Staff Physicians 2 (pt); RNs 3 (ft); LPNs 5 (ft); Orderlies 3 (ft); Nurses aides 40 (ft); Physical therapists 1 (ft); Speech therapists 1 (pt); Activities coordinators 1 (ft); Dietitians 1 (pt); Dentists 1 (pt).
Facilities Dining room; Physical therapy room; Activities room; Laundry room; Barber/Beauty shop.
Activities Arts & crafts; Cards; Games; Movies; Shopping trips.

LOUISVILLE

Baptist Home East
3001 Hounz Ln, Louisville, KY, 40222
(502) 426-5531
Admin Larry Jack Butler. *Medical Dir/Dir of Nursing* Virginia Hancock DON.
Licensure Intermediate care; Personal care. *Beds* ICF 90; Personal 20. *Certified* Medicaid.
Owner Nonprofit Corp.
Admissions Requirements Medical examination; Physician's request.
Staff RNs 1 (ft); LPNs 4 (ft); Nurses aides 25 (ft), 15 (pt); Activities coordinators 2 (ft), 1 (pt); Dietitians 1 (ft).
Affiliation Baptist
Facilities Dining room; Activities room; Chapel; Crafts room; Laundry room; Barber/Beauty shop; Library.
Activities Arts & crafts; Cards; Games; Reading groups; Prayer groups; Movies; Shopping trips; Social/Cultural gatherings.

Bashford East Health Care Facility
3535 Bardstown Rd, Louisville, KY, 40218
(502) 459-1400
Admin Patricia Holland. *Medical Dir/Dir of Nursing* Dr Charles Jevec.
Licensure Skilled care; Intermediate care. *Beds* SNF 39; ICF 93. *Certified* Medicaid.
Owner Proprietary Corp (Hillhaven Corp).
Staff RNs; LPNs; Orderlies; Nurses aides; Physical therapists; Occupational therapists; Speech therapists; Activities coordinators; Dietitians.
Facilities Dining room; Physical therapy room; Laundry room; Barber/Beauty shop.
Activities Arts & crafts; Cards; Games; Prayer groups; Shopping trips; Social/Cultural gatherings.

Briarwood Nursing & Convalescent Center
4300 Hazelwood Ave, Louisville, KY, 40215
(502) 367-6139
Admin Mary Campbell.
Licensure Skilled care; Intermediate care. *Beds* SNF 39; ICF 39. *Certified* Medicaid; Medicare.
Owner Proprietary Corp.

Britthaven of South Louisville
9600 Lamborne Blvd, Louisville, KY, 40272
(502) 935-7284
Admin Janis Froman. *Medical Dir/Dir of Nursing* Barry Schlossberg MD; Patricia Chappell.
Licensure Intermediate care. *Beds* ICF 128. *Certified* Medicaid.
Owner Proprietary Corp.
Staff Physicians 1 (pt); RNs 1 (ft); LPNs 1 (ft); Orderlies 1 (ft); Nurses aides 1 (ft); Physical therapists 1 (pt); Occupational therapists 1 (pt); Speech therapists 1 (pt); Activities coordinators 1 (ft); Dietitians 1 (ft); Ophthalmologists 1 (pt).

Brownsboro Hills Nursing Home
2141 Sycamore Ave, Louisville, KY, 40206
(502) 895-5417
Admin Harold V Bomar Jr.
Licensure Skilled care. *Beds* 96.
Owner Proprietary Corp.

Christian Health Center
920 S 4th St, Louisville, KY, 40203
(502) 583-6533

Admin Kim Williams. *Medical Dir/Dir of Nursing* Dr Kenneth Holtzapple & Dr John C Wright.
Licensure Skilled care; Intermediate care; Personal care. *Beds* SNF 27; ICF 137; Personal 70. *Certified* Medicaid; Medicare.
Owner Nonprofit Corp (Christian Ch Campuses).
Admissions Requirements Medical examination.
Staff RNs 5 (ft), 4 (pt); LPNs 8 (ft), 6 (pt); Nurses aides 44 (ft), 34 (pt); Physical therapists 1 (ft); Activities coordinators 1 (ft).
Facilities Dining room; Physical therapy room; Activities room; Chapel; Laundry room; Barber/Beauty shop; Library; Board room.
Activities Arts & crafts; Games; Prayer groups.

Christopher—East Nursing Center*
4200 Browns Ln, Louisville, KY, 40220
(502) 459-8900
Admin Margaret Wulf Brown.
Licensure Intermediate care; Personal care; Nursing home. *Beds* ICF 50; Personal 50; Nursing home 100.
Owner Proprietary Corp.

Eastern Star Home in Kentucky*
923 Cherokee Rd, Louisville, KY, 40204
(502) 451-3535
Admin Martha Durbin.
Licensure Personal care. *Beds* 30.
Owner Nonprofit Corp.
Affiliation Order of Eastern Star

Episcopal Church Home*
1201 Lyndon Ln, Louisville, KY, 40222
(502) 425-8840
Admin J T Horton.
Licensure Intermediate care; Personal care. *Beds* ICF 93; Personal 127. *Certified* Medicaid.
Affiliation Episcopal

Fair Lodge Health Care Center Inc
4522 Winnrose Way, Louisville, KY, 40211
(502) 778-5063
Admin O Howard Silvers. *Medical Dir/Dir of Nursing* James E Redmon MD.
Licensure Personal care. *Beds* 141.
Owner Proprietary Corp.
Admissions Requirements Minimum age 21; Medical examination; Physician's request.
Staff Physicians 1 (ft); LPNs 1 (ft); Nurses aides 15 (ft); Activities coordinators 1 (ft); Dietitians 1 (ft); Ophthalmologists 1 (ft).
Facilities Dining room; Activities room; Laundry room.
Activities Arts & crafts; Cards; Games; Prayer groups.

Four Courts Inc
2100 Millvale Rd, Louisville, KY, 40205
(502) 451-0990
Admin Sharon H Sizemore. *Medical Dir/Dir of Nursing* Dr Harold Kramer MD; Freda G Manion RN.
Licensure Skilled care; Intermediate care; Personal care. *Beds* SNF 3; ICF 50; Personal 22. *Certified* Medicaid; Medicare.
Owner Nonprofit Corp.
Admissions Requirements Medical examination.
Facilities Dining room; Physical therapy room; Activities room; Chapel; Crafts room; Laundry room; Barber/Beauty shop; Library.
Activities Arts & crafts; Cards; Games; Reading groups; Movies; Shopping trips; Social/Cultural gatherings.

Georgetown Manor Health Care Services
900 Gagel Ave, Louisville, KY, 40216
(502) 368-5827
Admin Jeanette Pope. *Medical Dir/Dir of Nursing* E J Brockman MD.

Licensure Skilled care; Intermediate care. *Beds* SNF 96; ICF 24. *Certified* Medicaid; Medicare.
Owner Nonprofit Corp.
Admissions Requirements Minimum age 16; Medical examination; Physician's request.
Staff RNs 7 (ft), 3 (pt); LPNs 13 (ft), 6 (pt); Nurses aides 34 (ft), 40 (pt); Physical therapists 2 (ft); Recreational therapists 3 (ft), 1 (pt); Occupational therapists 1 (pt); Speech therapists 1 (pt); Activities coordinators 1 (pt); Dietitians 1 (ft), 2 (pt); Podiatrists 1 (pt).
Facilities Dining room; Physical therapy room; Activities room; Chapel; Barber/Beauty shop.
Activities Arts & crafts; Games; Reading groups; Prayer groups; Movies.

Hazelwood Intermediate Care Facility for the Mentally Retarded
PO Box 14506, 1800 Bluegrass Ave, Louisville, KY, 40214
(502) 361-2301
Admin Fred Sapp. *Medical Dir/Dir of Nursing* Teresita Layug MD; Linda Knopf RN BSN.
Licensure Intermediate care for mentally retarded. *Beds* ICF/MR 220. *Certified* Medicaid.
Owner Nonprofit Corp.
Admissions Requirements Minimum age 6; Medical examination.
Staff Physicians 3 (ft); RNs 23 (ft), 1 (pt); LPNs 27 (ft), 2 (pt); Nurses aides 202 (ft), 13 (pt); Physical therapists 3 (pt); Recreational therapists 3 (ft); Occupational therapists 1 (ft), 1 (pt); Speech therapists 3 (ft); Dietitians 2 (ft).
Facilities Dining room; Physical therapy room; Activities room; Laundry room; Barber/Beauty shop; Library.
Activities Games; Prayer groups; Movies; Shopping trips; Social/Cultural gatherings.

Hillcreek Manor Convalescent Center*
3116 Breckinridge Ln, Louisville, KY, 40220
(502) 459-9120
Admin Earl Goff. *Medical Dir/Dir of Nursing* Dr Kenneth Hodge.
Licensure Skilled care; Intermediate care; Personal care. *Beds* SNF 28; Personal 30. *Certified* Medicaid; Medicare.
Owner Proprietary Corp (Beverly Enterprises).
Admissions Requirements Medical examination; Physician's request.
Staff RNs 7 (ft), 1 (pt); LPNs 12 (ft), 7 (pt); Nurses aides 42 (ft), 26 (pt); Physical therapists 1 (ft); Speech therapists 1 (pt); Activities coordinators 2 (ft).
Facilities Dining room; Physical therapy room; Activities room; Chapel; Crafts room; Laundry room; Barber/Beauty shop; Library.
Activities Arts & crafts; Cards; Games; Reading groups; Prayer groups; Movies; Social/Cultural gatherings.

Home of the Innocents
485 E Gray St, Louisville, KY, 40202
(502) 582-3769
Admin David A Graves. *Medical Dir/Dir of Nursing* Jeni Seibel DON.
Licensure Skilled care; Intermediate care. *Beds* 40. *Certified* Medicaid; Medicare.
Admissions Requirements Minimum age Birth to 17.
Staff Physicians 1 (pt); RNs 1 (ft), 5 (pt); LPNs 6 (ft), 2 (pt); Nurses aides 10 (ft), 8 (pt); Physical therapists 1 (pt); Activities coordinators 1 (ft); Dietitians 1 (pt); Dentists 1 (pt).
Affiliation Episcopal
Facilities Dining room; Physical therapy room; Activities room; Laundry room; Family Visitation.

Rose Anna Hughes Presbyterian Home
2120 Buechel Bank Rd, Louisville, KY, 40218
(502) 491-3695

Admin Lisa Herzberg. *Medical Dir/Dir of Nursing* Tena Strait.
Licensure Personal care. *Beds* 32.
Owner Nonprofit Corp.
Admissions Requirements Minimum age 62; Medical examination.
Staff LPNs 1 (ft); Nurses aides 5 (ft), 3 (pt); Activities coordinators 1 (ft); CMT 4 (ft), 3 (pt).
Affiliation Presbyterian
Facilities Dining room; Activities room; Crafts room; Laundry room; Barber/Beauty shop; Library.
Activities Arts & crafts; Cards; Games; Reading groups; Prayer groups; Movies; Shopping trips; Social/Cultural gatherings.

Jefferson Manor*
1801 Lynn Way, Louisville, KY, 40222
(502) 426-4513
Admin Deborah Bell. *Medical Dir/Dir of Nursing* Robert L Nold Sr MD.
Licensure Intermediate care.
Admissions Requirements Medical examination; Physician's request.
Staff RNs 5 (ft), 3 (pt); LPNs 7 (ft), 7 (pt); Nurses aides 25 (ft), 25 (pt); Physical therapists 2 (pt); Speech therapists 1 (pt); Activities coordinators 2 (ft); Dietitians 1 (pt); Dentists 1 (pt); Podiatrists 1 (pt); Respiratory therapists 4 (ft), 2 (pt).
Facilities Dining room; Physical therapy room; Activities room; Crafts room; Laundry room; Barber/Beauty shop; Library.
Activities Arts & crafts; Cards; Games; Reading groups; Prayer groups; Movies; Shopping trips; Social/Cultural gatherings; Wine & cheese parties; Family dinners; Guest luncheons.

Kings Daughters & Sons Home
1705 Stevens Ave, Louisville, KY, 40205
(502) 451-7330
Admin Edward L Holley. *Medical Dir/Dir of Nursing* Shelby J Simpson.
Licensure Skilled care; Intermediate care; Personal care. *Beds* SNF 94; ICF 60; Personal 15. *Certified* Medicaid; Medicare.
Admissions Requirements Medical examination; Physician's request.
Staff Physicians 2 (pt); RNs 4 (ft); LPNs 12 (ft); Orderlies 3 (ft); Nurses aides 65 (ft); Physical therapists 1 (ft); Speech therapists 1 (pt); Activities coordinators 1 (ft); Dietitians 1 (ft); Dentists 1 (pt); Ophthalmologists 1 (pt); Podiatrists 1 (pt).
Affiliation King's Daughters & Sons
Facilities Dining room; Physical therapy room; Activities room; Chapel; Crafts room; Laundry room; Barber/Beauty shop; Library.
Activities Arts & crafts; Cards; Games; Reading groups; Prayer groups; Movies; Social/Cultural gatherings.

Klondike Manor
3802 Klondike Ln, Louisville, KY, 40218
(502) 452-1579
Admin Sr Joanne Dewald RN. *Medical Dir/Dir of Nursing* Dr John Lach Jr; Janice Hall RN.
Licensure Intermediate care. *Beds* 62. *Certified* Medicaid.
Owner Proprietary Corp.
Admissions Requirements Medical examination; Physician's request And or Family.
Staff Physicians 1 (pt); RNs 2 (ft), 2 (pt); LPNs 3 (ft); Nurses aides 16 (ft), 6 (pt); Physical therapists 1 (ft); Activities coordinators 1 (ft); Dietitians 1 (pt); Ophthalmologists 1 (pt).
Facilities Dining room; Activities room; Laundry room; Barber/Beauty shop.
Activities Arts & crafts; Cards; Games; Reading groups; Prayer groups; Movies; Shopping trips; Social/Cultural gatherings; Pet therapy & Music therapy.

Louisville Protestant Althenheim
936 Barrett Ave, Louisville, KY, 40204
(502) 584-7417
Admin Joan E Walcutt NHA. *Medical Dir/Dir of Nursing* Doris McGraw DON.
Licensure Intermediate care; Personal care.
Beds ICF 12; Personal 46.
Owner Nonprofit organization/foundation.
Admissions Requirements Minimum age 65;
Medical examination; Physician's request.
Staff RNs 1 (ft); LPNs 2 (ft); Nurses aides 9 (ft), 3 (pt); Activities coordinators 1 (ft); Dietitians 1 (ft); CMT 5 (ft), 1 (pt); CPM 1 (ft).
Facilities Dining room; Activities room; Chapel; Crafts room; Laundry room; Barber/Beauty shop; Library.
Activities Arts & crafts; Cards; Games; Reading groups; Prayer groups; Movies; Shopping trips; Social/Cultural gatherings.

Lyndon Lane Nursing Center
1101 Lyndon Ln, Louisville, KY, 40222
(502) 425-0331
Admin Shirley Roederer. *Medical Dir/Dir of Nursing* Eric Hilgeford MD; Bernadett Stewart RN DON.
Licensure Skilled care; Intermediate care. Beds SNF 29; ICF 136. *Certified* Medicaid; Medicare.
Owner Proprietary Corp (Beverly Enterprises).
Admissions Requirements Minimum age 16;
Medical examination; Physician's request.
Staff RNs 2 (ft); LPNs 15 (ft), 3 (pt); Nurses aides 50 (ft), 7 (pt); Physical therapists 1 (ft), 3 (pt); Occupational therapists 1 (ft), 1 (pt); Speech therapists 1 (ft); Activities coordinators 1 (ft), 1 (pt); Dietitians 1 (ft); Ophthalmologists 1 (ft).
Facilities Dining room; Physical therapy room; Activities room; Chapel; Crafts room; Laundry room; Barber/Beauty shop; Occupational Therapy Room; Speech Therapy Room.
Activities Arts & crafts; Cards; Games; Reading groups; Prayer groups; Movies; Shopping trips; Social/Cultural gatherings.

Marian Home*
3105 Lexington Rd, Louisville, KY, 40206
(502) 893-0121
Admin Sr Assumpta Devine, OSU. *Medical Dir/Dir of Nursing* Walter L Thompson MD.
Licensure Intermediate care; Personal care. Beds ICF 55; Personal 15. *Certified* Medicaid.
Owner Nonprofit Corp.
Admissions Requirements Females only;
Medical examination; Physician's request.
Staff Physicians 1 (pt); RNs 5 (pt); LPNs 1 (ft), 4 (pt); Nurses aides 13 (ft), 10 (pt); Recreational therapists 3 (pt); Activities coordinators 1 (pt); Dietitians 5 (ft), 8 (pt); Podiatrists 1 (pt).
Affiliation Roman Catholic
Facilities Dining room; Physical therapy room; Activities room; Chapel; Crafts room; Laundry room; Barber/Beauty shop; Library.
Activities Arts & crafts; Cards; Games; Reading groups; Prayer groups; Movies; Shopping trips; Social/Cultural gatherings.

Meadows—East*
2529 Six Mile Ln, Louisville, KY, 40220
(502) 491-5560
Admin Debra Finneran.
Licensure Intermediate care; Personal care. Beds ICF 128; Personal 70. *Certified* Medicaid.
Owner Proprietary Corp.

Meadows—South*
1120 Christland Rd, Louisville, KY, 40214
(502) 367-0104
Admin Kathy Fellonneau.
Licensure Intermediate care; Personal care. Beds ICF 100; Personal 32. *Certified* Medicaid.

Owner Proprietary Corp.

Meadowview Nursing & Convalescent Center*
9701 Whipps Mill Rd, Louisville, KY, 40223
(502) 426-2778
Admin Deborah Haering. *Medical Dir/Dir of Nursing* A J Perez MD.
Licensure Intermediate care; Personal care. Beds ICF 100; Personal 32. *Certified* Medicaid.
Admissions Requirements Minimum age 21;
Medical examination; Physician's request.

Melrose Manor Health Care Center
4331 Churchman Ave, Louisville, KY, 40215
(502) 367-6489
Admin Jack Czerkiewicz. *Medical Dir/Dir of Nursing* Dr Manuel Brown; Doris Allison RN DON.
Licensure Nursing home. Beds 45.
Owner Privately owned.
Admissions Requirements Minimum age 18.
Staff Physicians 1 (pt); RNs 1 (ft); LPNs 3 (ft), 5 (pt); Orderlies 1 (ft), 2 (pt); Nurses aides 10 (ft), 6 (pt); Activities coordinators 1 (ft); Dietitians 1 (pt).
Facilities Dining room; Laundry room; Barber/Beauty shop.
Activities Arts & crafts; Cards; Games; Prayer groups; Movies; Shopping trips.

Charles P Moorman Home for Women
966 Cherokee Rd, Louisville, KY, 40204
(502) 451-4424
Admin Lois Irwin. *Medical Dir/Dir of Nursing* M R Rand RN DON.
Licensure Personal care. Beds 81.
Owner Nonprofit Corp.
Admissions Requirements Females only.
Staff Physicians 1 (ft); RNs 2 (ft); Nurses aides 10 (ft); Activities coordinators 1 (ft); Dietitians 1 (ft).
Facilities Dining room.
Activities Arts & crafts; Cards; Games; Reading groups; Prayer groups; Movies; Shopping trips.

Mt Holly Nursing Home
446 Mount Holly Ave, Louisville, KY, 40206
(502) 897-1646
Admin Mary Lou Giovanelli NHA. *Medical Dir/Dir of Nursing* Dr Eric Hilgeford; Myra Fuller RN.
Licensure Skilled care; Nursing home. Beds SNF 20; Nursing home 92. *Certified* Medicaid; Medicare.
Owner Proprietary Corp (Beverly Enterprises).
Admissions Requirements Physician's request.
Staff Physicians; RNs; LPNs; Orderlies; Nurses aides; Physical therapists; Recreational therapists; Occupational therapists; Speech therapists; Activities coordinators; Dietitians; Dentists; Ophthalmologists; Podiatrists.
Facilities Dining room; Physical therapy room; Activities room; Crafts room; Laundry room; Barber/Beauty shop; Library.
Activities Arts & crafts; Cards; Games; Prayer groups; Movies; Shopping trips; Social/Cultural gatherings.

Nazareth Home
2000 Newburg Rd, Louisville, KY, 40205
(502) 459-9681
Admin Sr Gwen McMahon. *Medical Dir/Dir of Nursing* Russell May MD; Rebecca Smith DON.
Licensure Skilled care; Intermediate care; Personal care. Beds SNF 14; ICF 104; Personal 50. *Certified* Medicaid; Medicare.
Staff Physicians 2 (pt); RNs 7 (ft); LPNs 9 (ft), 7 (pt); Orderlies 1 (ft); Nurses aides 41 (ft), 15 (pt); Physical therapists 1 (pt); Speech therapists 1 (pt); Activities coordinators 3 (pt); Dietitians 1 (pt); Ophthalmologists 1 (pt); Dentist 2 (pt).
Affiliation Roman Catholic

Facilities Dining room; Physical therapy room; Activities room; Chapel; Crafts room; Laundry room; Barber/Beauty shop; Library.
Activities Arts & crafts; Cards; Games; Reading groups; Prayer groups; Movies; Shopping trips; Social/Cultural gatherings.

Northfield Manor Health Care Facility*
6000 Hunting Rd, Louisville, KY, 40222
(502) 426-1425
Admin Narda Silon. *Medical Dir/Dir of Nursing* Terry Hagan MD.
Licensure Skilled care. Beds 120. *Certified* Medicaid.
Owner Proprietary Corp (Hillhaven Corp).
Staff Physicians 20 (pt); RNs 4 (ft), 2 (pt); LPNs 4 (ft), 6 (pt); Orderlies 1 (ft); Nurses aides 32 (ft), 8 (pt); Activities coordinators 1 (ft); Dietitians 1 (ft); Dentists 1 (pt); Podiatrists 1 (pt).
Facilities Dining room; Physical therapy room; Activities room; Laundry room; Barber/Beauty shop.
Activities Arts & crafts; Cards; Games; Prayer groups; Movies; Social/Cultural gatherings.

Parkway Medical Center
1155 Eastern Pkwy, Louisville, KY, 40217
(502) 636-5241
Admin Joseph Okruhlica. *Medical Dir/Dir of Nursing* Truman DeMunbrun MD; Barbara Kremer-Schmitt RN DON.
Licensure Skilled care; Intermediate care. Beds SNF 168; ICF 84. *Certified* Medicaid; Medicare.
Owner Privately owned.
Admissions Requirements Physician's request.
Staff Physicians 2 (ft); RNs 15 (ft); LPNs 33 (ft); Nurses aides 112 (ft); Physical therapists 1 (ft), 1 (pt); Speech therapists 1 (pt); Activities coordinators 1 (ft); Dietitians 1 (pt); Ophthalmologists 1 (pt); Dentist 2 (pt).
Facilities Dining room; Physical therapy room; Activities room; Chapel; Barber/Beauty shop; Library; Dental office; X-ray facility; Coffee shop; Pharmacy; Gift shop.
Activities Arts & crafts; Games; Reading groups; Prayer groups; Movies; Social/Cultural gatherings.

Parr's Rest Home*
969 Cherokee Rd, Louisville, KY, 40204
(502) 451-5440
Admin Dorothy Cable. *Medical Dir/Dir of Nursing* Doris Pipkin MD.
Licensure Personal care. Beds 80.
Admissions Requirements Minimum age 65; Medical examination.
Staff Physicians; RNs; Nurses aides 8 (ft), 1 (pt); Activities coordinators 1 (pt); Podiatrists 1 (pt).
Facilities Dining room; Activities room; Chapel; Crafts room; Laundry room; Barber/Beauty shop.
Activities Arts & crafts; Cards; Games; Reading groups; Prayer groups; Movies; Shopping trips; Social/Cultural gatherings.

Pavilion Health Care Center
432 E Jefferson St, Louisville, KY, 40202
(502) 583-2851
Admin Walter J Queen. *Medical Dir/Dir of Nursing* James Redmon MD; Carol Canary RN DON.
Licensure Skilled care; Intermediate care. Beds SNF 62; ICF/MR 124. *Certified* Medicaid; Medicare.
Owner Proprietary Corp (Pavilion Health Care Centers).
Admissions Requirements Medical examination.
Staff RNs 10 (ft), 4 (pt); LPNs 16 (ft), 6 (pt); Nurses aides 60 (ft), 20 (pt); Physical therapists 1 (pt); Occupational therapists 2 (ft); Speech therapists 1 (pt); Activities coordinators 11 (ft); Dietitians 1 (ft).

Facilities Dining room; Physical therapy room; Activities room; Laundry room; Barber/Beauty shop.
Activities Arts & crafts; Cards; Games; Reading groups; Prayer groups; Movies; Shopping trips; Social/Cultural gatherings.

Pine Tree Villa
4604 Lowe Rd, Louisville, KY, 40220
(502) 451-1401
Admin Betty A Appleby. *Medical Dir/Dir of Nursing* Dr Peters, Stober, Copley, Dunaway; Marge Eskridge DON.
Licensure Intermediate care; Personal care. *Beds* ICF 70; Personal 133. *Certified* Medicaid.
Owner Proprietary Corp.
Admissions Requirements Medical examination.
Staff Physicians; RNs; LPNs; Nurses aides; Speech therapists; Activities coordinators; Dietitians; Ophthalmologists.
Facilities Dining room; Activities room; Chapel; Crafts room; Laundry room; Barber/Beauty shop.
Activities Arts & crafts; Cards; Games; Reading groups; Prayer groups; Movies; Shopping trips; Social/Cultural gatherings.

Pleasant Place Home for Care*
12800 Dixie Hwy, Louisville, KY, 40272
(502) 937-4965
Admin Donna Arney.
Licensure Personal care. *Beds* 58.
Owner Proprietary Corp.

Sacred Heart Home
2120 Payne St, Louisville, KY, 40206
(502) 895-9425
Admin Sr Irene Bishop RSM MSSW. *Medical Dir/Dir of Nursing* Betty Gallahue LPN.
Licensure Personal care; Congregate living. *Beds* Personal 64; Congregate living 50.
Owner Nonprofit organization/foundation.
Admissions Requirements Minimum age 65; Medical examination.
Staff LPNs 2 (ft); Nurses aides 4 (ft), 8 (pt); Activities coordinators 1 (ft); Dietitians 1 (ft); Ophthalmologists 1 (ft); Pastoral Care Director 1 (ft); Chaplain 1 (ft).
Affiliation Roman Catholic
Facilities Dining room; Activities room; Chapel; Laundry room; Barber/Beauty shop; Library.
Activities Arts & crafts; Cards; Games; Reading groups; Prayer groups; Movies; Shopping trips; Social/Cultural gatherings; Pet therapy; Resident council.

St Matthews Manor
227 Browns Ln, Louisville, KY, 40207
(502) 897-3402
Admin Mindy D Lowry. *Medical Dir/Dir of Nursing* Eric Hilgeford MD; Barbara Hiland RN.
Licensure Nursing home. *Beds* 125.
Owner Proprietary Corp (Beverly Enterprises).
Admissions Requirements Medical examination.
Staff RNs 12 (ft), 12 (pt); LPNs 1 (ft); Orderlies 2 (pt); Nurses aides 45 (ft), 6 (pt); Physical therapists 1 (pt); Activities coordinators 1 (ft); Dietitians 1 (ft); Podiatrists 1 (pt).
Facilities Dining room; Physical therapy room; Activities room; Crafts room; Laundry room; Barber/Beauty shop; Library.
Activities Arts & crafts; Cards; Games; Prayer groups; Movies; Shopping trips; Social/Cultural gatherings.

W W Spradling Rest Home*
726 S Preston, Louisville, KY, 40203
(502) 585-2426
Admin William H Brown Jr.
Licensure Personal care. *Beds* 24.
Owner Nonprofit Corp.

Summerfield Manor Nursing Home*
1877 Farnsley Rd, Louisville, KY, 40216
(502) 448-8622
Admin James Morris.
Licensure Intermediate care. *Beds* 179. *Certified* Medicaid.
Owner Proprietary Corp.

James S Taylor Memorial Home
1015 Magazine St, Louisville, KY, 40203
(502) 589-0727
Admin Paul A Ferry Jr.
Licensure Intermediate care. *Beds* 117.
Owner Nonprofit Corp.

Twinbrook Nursing Home*
3526 Dutchmans Ln, Louisville, KY, 40205
(502) 452-6331
Admin Brad McCoy.
Licensure Skilled care; Nursing home. *Beds* SNF 25; Nursing home 62. *Certified* Medicaid; Medicare.
Owner Proprietary Corp.

Wesley Manor Retirement Community
PO Box 19258, 5012 E Manslick Rd, Louisville, KY, 40219
(502) 969-3277
Admin Edward D Brandeberry. *Medical Dir/Dir of Nursing* John Stober MD; Joyce Wells DON.
Licensure Skilled care; Intermediate care; Personal care. *Beds* SNF 10; ICF 58; Personal 39. *Certified* Medicaid; Medicare.
Owner Nonprofit Corp.
Admissions Requirements Minimum age 65; Medical examination; Physician's request.
Staff RNs; LPNs; Orderlies; Nurses aides; Activities coordinators; Dietitians.
Affiliation Methodist
Facilities Dining room; Physical therapy room; Activities room; Chapel; Crafts room; Laundry room; Barber/Beauty shop; Library.
Activities Arts & crafts; Cards; Games; Reading groups; Prayer groups; Movies; Shopping trips; Social/Cultural gatherings.

Westminster Terrace
2116 Buechel Bank Rd, Louisville, KY, 40218
(502) 499-9383
Admin Jim Walsh. *Medical Dir/Dir of Nursing* Harold Haller MD; Wilma Marshall DON.
Licensure Skilled care; Intermediate care. *Beds* SNF 31; ICF 81. *Certified* Medicaid; Medicare.
Owner Nonprofit organization/foundation.
Admissions Requirements Minimum age 62; Medical examination; Physician's request.
Staff RNs 6 (ft), 1 (pt); LPNs 12 (ft), 4 (pt); Nurses aides 40 (ft), 18 (pt); Physical therapists 1 (pt); Speech therapists 1 (pt); Activities coordinators 1 (ft); Ophthalmologists 1 (pt).
Affiliation Presbyterian
Facilities Dining room; Physical therapy room; Activities room; Chapel; Crafts room; Laundry room; Barber/Beauty shop; Library.
Activities Arts & crafts; Cards; Games; Reading groups; Prayer groups; Movies; Shopping trips; Social/Cultural gatherings.

LUDLOW

Madonna Manor*
2344 Amsterdam Rd, Ludlow, KY, 41016
(606) 341-3981
Admin Sr M Charles Wolking.
Licensure Intermediate care. *Beds* 38. *Certified* Medicaid.
Owner Nonprofit Corp.

MADISONVILLE

Brown Rest Home*
384 Thompson Ave, Madisonville, KY, 42431
(502) 821-5294
Admin Larry Brown.

Licensure Intermediate care; Personal care. *Beds* ICF 100; Personal 48. *Certified* Medicaid.
Admissions Requirements Medical examination.
Staff RNs 1 (pt); LPNs 6 (ft); Orderlies 3 (ft); Nurses aides 50 (ft), 20 (pt); Speech therapists 1 (pt); Dietitians 1 (pt).
Facilities Dining room; Activities room; Crafts room; Laundry room.
Activities Arts & crafts; Cards; Games; Prayer groups; Movies; Shopping trips; Social/Cultural gatherings.

Clinic Convalescent Center
55 E North St, Madisonville, KY, 42431
(502) 821-1492
Admin Coleen Lovell. *Medical Dir/Dir of Nursing* Dan Martin MD; Jo Ann Ashby RN.
Licensure Skilled care. *Beds* SNF 66. *Certified* Medicaid; Medicare.
Owner Proprietary Corp.
Admissions Requirements Physician's request.
Staff Physicians 20 (pt); RNs 7 (ft), 4 (pt); Nurses aides 24 (ft), 4 (pt); Recreational therapists 1 (pt); Activities coordinators 1 (ft); Dietitians 1 (ft), 1 (pt); Dentists 3 (pt).
Facilities Dining room; Physical therapy room; Activities room; Crafts room; Barber/Beauty shop.
Activities Arts & crafts; Cards; Games; Prayer groups; Social/Cultural gatherings.

Kentucky Rest Haven*
419 N Seminary St, Madisonville, KY, 42431
(502) 821-5564
Admin Danny Belcher.
Licensure Skilled care; Intermediate care. *Beds* SNF 59; ICF 35. *Certified* Medicaid; Medicare.
Owner Proprietary Corp (National Health Corp).

Senior Citizens Nursing Home*
PO Box 743, US Rte 41A & Pride Ave, Madisonville, KY, 42431
(502) 821-1813
Admin Sandra Higgins. *Medical Dir/Dir of Nursing* Dr Richard Dodds.
Licensure Skilled care; Intermediate care. *Beds* SNF 32; ICF 54. *Certified* Medicaid; Medicare.
Admissions Requirements Medical examination; Physician's request.
Facilities Dining room; Physical therapy room; Laundry room; Barber/Beauty shop; Library.
Activities Cards; Games; Movies; Shopping trips; Social/Cultural gatherings.

Watkins Rest Home*
Franklin & Givens Sts, Madisonville, KY, 42431
(502) 821-7232
Admin Frank Ramsey.
Licensure Personal care. *Beds* 86.
Owner Proprietary Corp.

MANCHESTER

Laurel Creek Health Care Center*
Rte 2, Box 254, Manchester, KY, 40962
(606) 598-6163
Admin Deborah Fannin.
Licensure Intermediate care; Personal care. *Beds* ICF 98; Personal 20. *Certified* Medicaid.
Owner Proprietary Corp (Angell Group).

Memorial Hospital—SNF
401 Memorial Dr, Manchester, KY, 40962
(606) 598-5175
Admin Bruce Wickwire. *Medical Dir/Dir of Nursing* Dr Ira Wheeler; Ruby Kane.
Licensure Skilled care. *Beds* SNF 11. *Certified* Medicaid; Medicare.

Owner Nonprofit Corp.
Admissions Requirements Physician's request.
Staff Physicians 12 (ft); RNs 2 (ft); LPNs 3 (ft); Nurses aides 6 (ft); Activities coordinators 1 (pt).
Affiliation Seventh-Day Adventist
Facilities Physical therapy room; Activities room; Chapel; Laundry room.
Activities Movies; Individual activities as needed; Music.

MARION

Crittenden County Convalescence Center
Moore & Watson Sts, Marion, KY, 42064
(502) 965-2218
Admin Marie Yates.
Licensure Intermediate care; Personal care. *Beds* ICF 83; Personal 24. *Certified* Medicaid.
Owner Proprietary Corp.
Admissions Requirements Medical examination; Physician's request.
Facilities Dining room; Activities room; Laundry room; Barber/Beauty shop.
Activities Arts & crafts; Games; Reading groups; Prayer groups; Movies; Shopping trips; Social/Cultural gatherings; Hay rides; Fishing trips.

MASONIC HOME

Masonic Widows & Orphans Home & Infirmary Inc
Masonic Home, KY, 40041
(502) 897-3344
Admin Sally A Bowers Interim Admin. *Medical Dir/Dir of Nursing* Dr Steven Shelton; Sue Rouse RN DON.
Licensure Skilled care; Personal care; Nursing home. *Beds* SNF 38; Personal 129; Nursing home 130.
Owner Nonprofit Corp.
Admissions Requirements Minimum age 60; Females only; Medical examination; Physician's request.
Staff Physicians 4 (pt); RNs 9 (ft), 5 (pt); LPNs 8 (ft), 4 (pt); Nurses aides 48 (ft), 6 (pt); Physical therapists 1 (pt); Activities coordinators 2 (ft), 1 (pt); Dietitians 1 (ft).
Affiliation Masons
Facilities Dining room; Physical therapy room; Activities room; Chapel; Crafts room; Laundry room; Barber/Beauty shop.
Activities Arts & crafts; Cards; Games; Reading groups; Prayer groups; Movies; Shopping trips; Social/Cultural gatherings.

MAYFIELD

Care Inn of Mayfield*
4th & Indiana Ave, Mayfield, KY, 42066
(502) 247-0200
Admin Lanny Harvey.
Licensure Skilled care; Intermediate care. *Beds* SNF 42; ICF 58. *Certified* Medicaid; Medicare.
Owner Proprietary Corp.

Fern Terrace Lodge
Hwy 45 N, Box 325, Mayfield, KY, 42066
(502) 247-3259
Admin Kathryn Baer. *Medical Dir/Dir of Nursing* A Loudean Austin.
Licensure Personal care. *Beds* 140.
Owner Proprietary Corp.
Admissions Requirements Minimum age 42; Medical examination.
Staff Physicians; Activities coordinators; Ophthalmologists.
Facilities Dining room; Activities room; Laundry room; Barber/Beauty shop; Library.
Activities Arts & crafts; Cards; Games; Reading groups; Movies; Shopping trips; Social/Cultural gatherings; Trips.

Green Acres Personal Care Inc
Box 409, 402 W Farthing St, Mayfield, KY, 42066
(502) 247-6477
Admin Samuel Gray.
Licensure Personal care. *Beds* 73. *Certified* Medicaid.
Owner Proprietary Corp.
Admissions Requirements Minimum age 16; Medical examination; Physician's request.
Staff Nurses aides; Activities coordinators; Dietitians.
Facilities Dining room; Activities room; Chapel; Crafts room; Laundry room; Barber/Beauty shop.
Activities Arts & crafts; Cards; Games; Prayer groups; Social/Cultural gatherings.

Meadowview Retirement Home*
Rte 7, Box 64, Mayfield, KY, 42066
(502) 345-2116
Admin Barbara Lamb.
Licensure Personal care. *Beds* 24.
Owner Proprietary Corp.

Mills Manor
500 Beck Lane, Mayfield, KY, 42066
(502) 247-7890
Admin Joseph Robertson. *Medical Dir/Dir of Nursing* Dr Charles Howard; Vivian Goatley RN.
Licensure Intermediate care. *Beds* ICF 98. *Certified* Medicaid.
Owner Nonprofit Corp.
Admissions Requirements Minimum age 21.
Staff Physicians; RNs 2 (ft); LPNs 10 (ft), 2 (pt); Orderlies 1 (ft), 1 (pt); Nurses aides 35 (ft), 10 (pt); Physical therapists 1 (pt); Speech therapists 1 (pt); Dietitians 1 (pt); Ophthalmologists 1 (pt).
Affiliation Seventh-Day Adventist
Facilities Dining room; Physical therapy room; Activities room; Laundry room; Barber/Beauty shop.
Activities Arts & crafts; Cards; Games; Reading groups; Prayer groups; Movies.

Skyview Personal Care Home*
Rte 4, Mayfield, KY, 42066
(502) 623-6696
Admin Nancy Riley.
Licensure Personal care. *Beds* 40.
Owner Proprietary Corp.

MAYSVILLE

Maysville Extended Care Facility
620 Parker Rd, Maysville, KY, 41056
(606) 564-4085
Admin Teresa G Lewis. *Medical Dir/Dir of Nursing* Susan Price RN.
Licensure Skilled care; Intermediate care. *Beds* SNF 18; ICF 82. *Certified* Medicaid.
Owner Proprietary Corp.
Staff Physicians 10 (pt); RNs 2 (ft), 1 (pt); LPNs 8 (ft), 2 (pt); Orderlies 1 (pt); Nurses aides 30 (ft), 10 (pt); Physical therapists 1 (pt); Speech therapists 1 (pt); Activities coordinators 1 (ft), 1 (pt); Dietitians 1 (pt).
Facilities Dining room; Activities room; Laundry room; Barber/Beauty shop.
Activities Arts & crafts; Cards; Games; Reading groups; Prayer groups; Movies; Shopping trips; Social/Cultural gatherings.

MELBER

Melber Rest Home*
Rte 1, General Delivery, Melber, KY, 42069
(502) 856-3210
Admin Bonnie Milgate.
Licensure Personal care. *Beds* 10.
Admissions Requirements Minimum age 16; Medical examination.
Staff Nurses aides 2 (ft); Dietitians 1 (ft).

Facilities Dining room; Activities room; Laundry room.
Activities Arts & crafts; Cards; Games; Prayer groups; Shopping trips; Social/Cultural gatherings.

MIDDLESBORO

Rubys Rest Home Inc
504 S 24th St, Middlesboro, KY, 40965
(606) 248-1540
Admin Ruby Lake. *Medical Dir/Dir of Nursing* Dr Maria Hortillosa; Brenda Jones RN.
Licensure Personal care. *Beds* 64. *Certified* Medicaid.
Owner Proprietary Corp.
Admissions Requirements Minimum age 30; Medical examination; Physician's request.
Staff Physicians 2 (pt); RNs 1 (ft); LPNs 1 (ft); Orderlies 1 (ft); Nurses aides 12 (ft); Activities coordinators 1 (ft); Dietitians 1 (ft).
Facilities Dining room; Activities room; Chapel; Crafts room; Laundry room; TV lounges.
Activities Arts & crafts; Cards; Games; Reading groups; Prayer groups; Movies; Shopping trips; Social/Cultural gatherings; Horseshoes; Badminton.

MONTICELLO

Dishman Personal Care Home*
Warsham Ln, Monticello, KY, 42633
(606) 348-6201
Admin Christine Bybee Goff.
Licensure Personal care. *Beds* 49.
Owner Proprietary Corp.

Hicks Golden Years Nursing Home
Rte 4, Box 121, Monticello, KY, 42633
(606) 348-6034
Admin Darrell Hicks. *Medical Dir/Dir of Nursing* Glenda Turner.
Licensure Intermediate care; Personal care. *Beds* ICF 55; Personal 5. *Certified* Medicaid.
Owner Privately owned.
Staff RNs 2 (ft); LPNs 1 (ft); Nurses aides 20 (ft), 4 (pt); Activities coordinators 2 (ft); Dietitians 1 (ft), 1 (pt).
Facilities Dining room; Activities room; Chapel; Laundry room; Barber/Beauty shop.
Activities Arts & crafts; Cards; Games; Reading groups; Prayer groups; Movies; Shopping trips; Social/Cultural gatherings.

MOREHEAD

Life Care Center of Morehead
PO Box 654, 933 N Tolliver Rd, Morehead, KY, 40351
(606) 784-7518
Admin Virginia H Saunders. *Medical Dir/Dir of Nursing* J Hunter Black MD; Danica Ellington RN.
Licensure Skilled care; Intermediate care; Personal care. *Beds* SNF 30; ICF 67; Personal 14. *Certified* Medicaid; Medicare.
Owner Proprietary Corp (Life Care Centers of America).
Admissions Requirements Minimum age 16; Medical examination; Physician's request.
Staff RNs 2 (ft), 1 (pt); Nurses aides 39 (ft), 8 (pt); Activities coordinators 1 (ft); Social Services Director 1 (ft).
Facilities Dining room; Activities room; Chapel; Crafts room; Laundry room; Barber/Beauty shop.
Activities Arts & crafts; Games; Prayer groups; Social/Cultural gatherings; Residents council; Gourmet club.

MORGANFIELD

Grove Center Rest Home*
Rte 3, Box 118, Morganfield, KY, 42437
(502) 389-2874
Admin Marcus Logsdon.
Licensure Personal care. *Beds* 44.

Higgins Learning Center
PO Box 374, Morganfield, KY, 42437
(502) 389-0822
Admin Robert R Rupsch. *Medical Dir/Dir of Nursing* Joel Haffner MD; Linda Oxford RN.
Licensure Intermediate care for mentally retarded. *Beds* ICF/MR 56. *Certified* Medicaid.
Owner Proprietary Corp.
Admissions Requirements Minimum age 7.
Staff Physicians 1 (pt); RNs 1 (ft), 1 (pt); LPNs 4 (ft), 1 (pt); Nurses aides 28 (ft), 10 (pt); Physical therapists 2 (pt); Recreational therapists 2 (ft); Occupational therapists 2 (ft); Speech therapists 2 (pt); Dietitians 1 (pt).
Facilities Dining room; Physical therapy room; Activities room; Crafts room; Laundry room; Library.
Activities Arts & crafts; Cards; Games; Reading groups; Prayer groups; Movies; Shopping trips; Social/Cultural gatherings.

Medco Center of Morganfield*
Rte 5, Box 24A, 505 N Carrier, Morganfield, KY, 42437
(502) 389-3513
Admin Wanda J Jones.
Licensure Intermediate care. *Beds* 60. *Certified* Medicaid.
Owner Proprietary Corp (Unicare).

MORGANTOWN

Lakeview Nursing Home
Warren St, Box 159, Morgantown, KY, 42261
(502) 526-3368
Admin Ralph Eaton. *Medical Dir/Dir of Nursing* Dr Richard T C Wan; Alice Forgy RN DON.
Licensure Skilled care; Intermediate care; Personal care. *Beds* SNF 38; ICF 96; Personal 35. *Certified* Medicaid; Medicare.
Owner Proprietary Corp (Life Care Centers of America).
Admissions Requirements Medical examination; Physician's request.
Staff Physicians 3 (ft); RNs 7 (ft); LPNs 5 (ft); Nurses aides 6 (ft), 8 (pt); Physical therapists 2 (ft); Recreational therapists 2 (ft); Speech therapists 1 (ft); Activities coordinators 1 (ft); Dietitians 1 (ft).
Facilities Dining room; Physical therapy room; Activities room; Crafts room; Laundry room; Barber/Beauty shop.
Activities Arts & crafts; Cards; Games; Reading groups; Prayer groups; Movies; Shopping trips; Social/Cultural gatherings.

MOUNT STERLING

Annie Walker Nursing Home Inc
PO Box 639, Bridigett Dr, Mount Sterling, KY, 40353
(606) 498-6397
Admin Donna Davis Goodman. *Medical Dir/Dir of Nursing* Dr Robert J Salisbury; Maxine D Huddleston.
Licensure Intermediate care; Personal care. *Beds* ICF 42; Personal 8. *Certified* Medicaid.
Owner Privately owned.
Admissions Requirements Medical examination.
Staff RNs 1 (pt); LPNs 3 (ft); Orderlies 2 (ft); Nurses aides 6 (ft), 3 (pt); Activities coordinators 1 (ft); CMA 3 (ft).

Facilities Dining room; Activities room; Laundry room.
Activities Arts & crafts; Cards; Games; Reading groups; Prayer groups; Movies; Social/Cultural gatherings.

Mary Chiles Hospital*
PO Box 7, 50 Sterling Ave, Mount Sterling, KY, 40353
(606) 498-1220
Admin Alan Newberry.
Licensure Skilled care. *Beds* 30. *Certified* Medicaid; Medicare.
Owner Nonprofit Corp.

Windsor Care Center*
PO Box 251, Rte 460, Widsor Square, Mount Sterling, KY, 40353
(606) 498-3343
Admin James Stephens.
Licensure Intermediate care; Personal care. *Beds* ICF 52; Personal 8. *Certified* Medicaid.
Owner Nonprofit Corp.

MOUNT VERNON

Rockcastle Hospital & Respiratory Care Center
Rte 4, Box 28, Mount Vernon, KY, 40456
(606) 256-2195
Admin Wayne Stewart. *Medical Dir/Dir of Nursing* Cindy Burton.
Licensure Skilled care. *Beds* SNF 32. *Certified* Medicaid; Medicare.
Owner Nonprofit Corp.
Admissions Requirements Medical examination.
Staff Physicians 5 (ft); RNs 8 (ft); LPNs 12 (ft); Orderlies 2 (ft); Nurses aides 16 (ft); Physical therapists 2 (ft); Recreational therapists 2 (ft); Speech therapists 1 (ft); Activities coordinators 1 (ft); Dietitians 2 (ft); Audiologists 1 (pt); Respiratory therapists 25 (ft).
Facilities Dining room; Physical therapy room; Activities room; Chapel; Crafts room; Barber/Beauty shop; Library.
Activities Arts & crafts; Cards; Games; Reading groups; Prayer groups; Movies; Shopping trips; Social/Cultural gatherings; Home trips.

MUNFORDVILLE

TMC Hart County Personal Care Home
Riverview Ct, Munfordville, KY, 42765
(502) 524-4194
Admin Donna Cruse.
Licensure Personal care. *Beds* 54.
Owner Proprietary Corp (Angell Group).
Admissions Requirements Minimum age 16; Medical examination.
Staff Nurses aides 11 (ft); Activities coordinators; Dietitians.
Facilities Dining room; Laundry room; Barber/Beauty shop.
Activities Recreation in afternoon.

MURRAY

Fern Terrace Lodge
1505 Stadium View Dr, Murray, KY, 42071
(502) 753-7109
Admin Glada Dodd.
Licensure Personal care. *Beds* 87. *Certified* Medicaid.
Owner Privately owned.
Admissions Requirements Minimum age 50; Medical examination; Physician's request.
Staff LPNs 1 (ft); Nurses aides 10 (ft), 4 (pt); Activities coordinators 1 (pt).
Facilities Dining room; Activities room; Laundry room; Barber/Beauty shop.
Activities Arts & crafts; Cards; Games; Prayer groups; Shopping trips; Social/Cultural gatherings; Bingo.

Murray-Calloway County Hospital & Long-Term Care Unit
803 Poplar St, Murray, KY, 42071
(502) 753-5131
Admin James Stuart Poston. *Medical Dir/Dir of Nursing* Bonna Yates RN DON.
Licensure Skilled care; Intermediate care. *Beds* SNF 20; ICF 20. *Certified* Medicaid; Medicare.
Owner Nonprofit Corp.
Staff Physicians 35 (ft); RNs 2 (ft), 1 (pt); LPNs 8 (ft), 1 (pt); Orderlies 1 (ft), 1 (pt); Nurses aides 12 (ft); Physical therapists 3 (ft); Speech therapists 1 (pt); Activities coordinators 1 (ft); Dietitians 2 (ft); Dentists 2 (ft); Ophthalmologists 1 (ft); Podiatrists 1 (pt); Dentist 1 (ft).
Facilities Dining room; Physical therapy room; Activities room; Chapel; Laundry room; Barber/Beauty shop; Library.
Activities Arts & crafts; Cards; Games; Reading groups; Prayer groups; Movies; Shopping trips; Social/Cultural gatherings; Pet therapy; Cooking club.

West View Nursing Home*
PO Box 165, 1401 S 16th St, Murray, KY, 42071
(502) 753-1304
Admin Harold G Beaman.
Licensure Skilled care; Intermediate care. *Beds* SNF 56; ICF 118. *Certified* Medicaid; Medicare.
Owner Proprietary Corp.

NAZARETH

Nazareth Infirmary*
Nazareth, KY, 40048
(502) 348-5931
Admin Patricia Farrell.
Licensure Personal care. *Beds* 42.

NERINX

Loretto Motherhouse Infirmary
Hwy 152, Nerinx, KY, 40049
(502) 865-3941, 865-5811
Admin Sr Kay Carlew. *Medical Dir/Dir of Nursing* Sr Marie Lourde Steckler.
Licensure Intermediate care; Personal care. *Beds* ICF 63; Personal 22. *Certified* Medicaid.
Owner Nonprofit Corp.
Admissions Requirements Females only; Medical examination; Physician's request.
Staff RNs 2 (ft); LPNs 4 (ft); Nurses aides 19 (ft), 9 (pt); Activities coordinators 1 (ft); Dietitians 1 (pt).
Affiliation Roman Catholic
Facilities Dining room; Physical therapy room; Activities room; Chapel; Crafts room; Laundry room; Barber/Beauty shop; Library.
Activities Arts & crafts; Games; Reading groups; Prayer groups; Movies; Shopping trips.

NEW CASTLE

Homestead Nursing Center of New Castle*
Box 329, New Castle, KY, 40050
(502) 845-2861
Admin Catherine Foree. *Medical Dir/Dir of Nursing* Dr R Houston.
Licensure Intermediate care. *Beds* 60. *Certified* Medicaid.
Admissions Requirements Minimum age 16.
Staff Physicians 4 (ft); RNs 2 (ft); LPNs 2 (ft); Nurses aides 22 (ft); Physical therapists 1 (ft); Recreational therapists 1 (ft); Activities coordinators 1 (ft); Dietitians 1 (ft); Dentists 1 (ft).
Facilities Dining room; Activities room; Crafts room; Laundry room; Barber/Beauty shop; Library.

Activities Arts & crafts; Cards; Games; Reading groups; Prayer groups; Movies; Social/Cultural gatherings.

NEWPORT

Baptist Convalescent Center
120 Main St, Newport, KY, 41071
(606) 581-1938
Admin Rev Lee Hopkins. *Medical Dir/Dir of Nursing* Dr W V Pierce; Martha Robinson RN DON.
Licensure Skilled care; Intermediate care. *Beds* SNF 59; ICF 108. *Certified* Medicaid; Medicare.
Owner Nonprofit organization/foundation.
Admissions Requirements Medical examination.
Staff Physicians 1 (ft); RNs 6 (ft), 3 (pt); LPNs 9 (ft), 7 (pt); Nurses aides 42 (ft), 25 (pt); Physical therapists 3 (pt); Activities coordinators 1 (ft); Dietitians 1 (ft); Dentists 1 (pt); 1 (pt) Dentist.
Affiliation Baptist
Facilities Dining room; Physical therapy room; Activities room; Chapel; Crafts room; Laundry room; Barber/Beauty shop; Parlor.
Activities Arts & crafts; Cards; Games; Prayer groups; Movies; Shopping trips; Social/ Cultural gatherings; Exercise class; Birthday parties; Sing-alongs; Discussion group; Bookmobile; Rhythm band.

Salvation Army Adult Day Care Center*
10th & Patterson Sts, Newport, KY, 41071
(606) 291-8107
Admin Alice Skirtz.
Licensure Intermediate care.
Owner Nonprofit Corp.
Affiliation Salvation Army

NICHOLASVILLE

Rose Terrace Lodge Inc
401 N 2nd St, Nicholasville, KY, 40356
(606) 885-3821
Admin Sharon Reynolds.
Licensure Personal care. *Beds* 36.
Owner Proprietary Corp.

Royal Manor
100 Sparks Ave, Nicholasville, KY, 40356
(606) 885-4171
Admin Bill Mansfield.
Licensure Intermediate care; Personal care. *Beds* ICF 73; Personal 10. *Certified* Medicaid.
Owner Proprietary Corp.
Admissions Requirements Minimum age 18; Medical examination.
Staff Physicians 1 (pt); RNs 1 (ft); LPNs 5 (ft); Nurses aides 30 (ft); Physical therapists 1 (pt); Reality therapists 1 (pt); Recreational therapists 1 (pt); Activities coordinators 1 (ft); Dietitians 1 (pt); Ophthalmologists 1 (pt); Podiatrists 1 (pt).
Facilities Dining room; Activities room; Crafts room; Laundry room; Barber/Beauty shop.
Activities Arts & crafts; Cards; Games; Reading groups; Prayer groups; Movies; Shopping trips; Social/Cultural gatherings; Parties.

NORTH MIDDLETOWN

Lovely's Rest Home*
PO Box 114, North Middletown, KY, 40357
(606) 362-4560
Admin Allean Platt.
Licensure Personal care. *Beds* 11.
Owner Proprietary Corp.

OWENSBORO

Carmel Home*
2501 Old Hartford Rd, Owensboro, KY, 42301
(502) 683-0227
Admin Sr Mary Andrea Niehaus.
Licensure Intermediate care; Personal care. *Beds* ICF 30; Personal 54. *Certified* Medicaid.
Admissions Requirements Minimum age 65.
Staff RNs 1 (pt); LPNs 5 (ft), 3 (pt); Nurses aides 10 (ft), 11 (pt); Recreational therapists 1 (ft); Activities coordinators 1 (ft).
Facilities Dining room; Activities room; Chapel; Crafts room; Laundry room; Barber/ Beauty shop; Library; Medical services.
Activities Arts & crafts; Cards; Games; Reading groups; Prayer groups; Movies; Shopping trips; Social/Cultural gatherings; Validation therapy groups.

Davco Rest Home*
2526 W 10th St, Owensboro, KY, 42301
(502) 684-1705
Admin Audrey Mason Williams.
Licensure Personal care. *Beds* 92.
Owner Proprietary Corp.

Fern Terrace Lodge of Owensboro
45 Woodford Ave, Owensboro, KY, 42301
(502) 684-7171
Admin Gertrude Cagle. *Medical Dir/Dir of Nursing* Gertrude Cagle.
Licensure Personal care. *Beds* 68. *Certified* Medicaid.
Owner Privately owned.
Admissions Requirements Minimum age 40; Medical examination.
Staff Nurses aides 6 (ft), 3 (pt).
Facilities Dining room; Activities room; Chapel; Crafts room; Laundry room; Barber/ Beauty shop; Outside patio; Enclosed gazebo & porch.
Activities Arts & crafts; Cards; Games; Reading groups; Prayer groups; Movies; Shopping trips; Social/Cultural gatherings.

Wendell Foster Center
PO Box 1668, 815 Triplett St, Owensboro, KY, 42302-1668
(502) 683-4517
Admin Robert G Mobley. *Medical Dir/Dir of Nursing* Anne H Hopwood MD.
Licensure Intermediate care for mentally retarded. *Beds* 63. *Certified* Medicaid.
Owner Nonprofit Corp.
Admissions Requirements Minimum age 16; Medical examination; Physician's request.
Staff Physicians 1 (ft); RNs 2 (ft); LPNs 7 (ft), 1 (pt); Nurses aides 2 (ft); Physical therapists 2 (ft); Recreational therapists 1 (ft); Occupational therapists 1 (ft); Speech therapists 1 (ft); Dietitians 1 (ft).
Facilities Dining room; Physical therapy room; Activities room; Chapel; Crafts room; Laundry room; Barber/Beauty shop; Library.
Activities Arts & crafts; Cards; Games; Reading groups; Prayer groups; Movies; Shopping trips; Social/Cultural gatherings.

Mary Harding Home Inc
1314 W 7th St, Owensboro, KY, 42301
(502) 684-5459
Admin Cynthia Murray. *Medical Dir/Dir of Nursing* Janet Martin LPN Nurses Consultant.
Licensure Personal care. *Beds* 12. *Certified* Medicaid; Medicare.
Owner Nonprofit Corp.
Admissions Requirements Medical examination; Physician's request.
Staff Physicians 6; Nurses aides 3; Activities coordinators 1; Dietitians 3.
Affiliation Baptist

Facilities Dining room; Activities room; Laundry room.
Activities Arts & crafts; Cards; Games; Reading groups; Prayer groups; Social/ Cultural gatherings.

Hermitage Manor*
1614 Parrish Ave, Owensboro, KY, 42301
(502) 684-4559
Admin Jack T Wells. *Medical Dir/Dir of Nursing* Sarah Kamuf.
Licensure Skilled care; Intermediate care. *Beds* SNF 22; ICF 28.
Staff RNs 1 (ft), 1 (pt); LPNs 3 (ft), 3 (pt); Nurses aides 13 (ft), 12 (pt); Activities coordinators 1 (ft); Dietitians 1 (ft).
Facilities Dining room; Activities room; Crafts room; Laundry room; Barber/Beauty shop.
Activities Arts & crafts; Cards; Games; Reading groups; Prayer groups; Movies; Shopping trips; Social/Cultural gatherings.

Hillcrest Healthcare Center
3740 Old Hartford Rd, Owensboro, KY, 42303
(502) 684-7259
Admin Shelia Stallings.
Licensure Skilled care; Intermediate care. *Beds* SNF 32; ICF 124. *Certified* Medicaid; Medicare.
Owner Proprietary Corp (Hillhaven Corp).

Mary Kendall Ladies Home*
199 Phillips Ct, Owensboro, KY, 42301
(502) 683-5044
Admin Donna Anderson.
Licensure Personal care. *Beds* 22.
Admissions Requirements Females only; Medical examination.
Staff Nurses aides 4 (ft), 4 (pt); Activities coordinators 1 (pt); Dietitians 1 (pt).
Facilities Dining room; Laundry room.
Activities Arts & crafts; Cards; Games; Reading groups; Prayer groups; Shopping trips; Weekly church service; Sunday school.

Leisure Years Nursing Home
1205 Leitchfield Rd, Owensboro, KY, 42301
(502) 684-0464
Admin Flora J Norsworthy.
Licensure Intermediate care; Personal care. *Beds* ICF 109; Personal 75. *Certified* Medicaid.
Staff Physicians 45 (pt); RNs 1 (pt); LPNs 13 (ft); Orderlies 5 (ft); Nurses aides 43 (ft), 5 (pt); Physical therapists 2 (ft); Reality therapists 2 (ft); Recreational therapists 2 (ft); Speech therapists 1 (pt); Activities coordinators 1 (ft); Dietitians 1 (pt); Dentists 1 (pt).
Facilities Dining room; Activities room; Laundry room; Barber/Beauty shop.
Activities Arts & crafts; Cards; Games; Reading groups; Prayer groups; Movies; Shopping trips; Social/Cultural gatherings.

Medco Center of Owensboro
2420 W 3rd St, Owensboro, KY, 42301
(502) 685-3141
Admin Gregory E Wells. *Medical Dir/Dir of Nursing* Dr Gary Wahl; Dolores Huff RN.
Licensure Skilled care; Intermediate care. *Beds* SNF 43; ICF 89. *Certified* Medicaid; Medicare; VA.
Owner Proprietary Corp (Unicare).
Admissions Requirements Medical examination.
Staff Physicians 1 (pt); RNs 4 (ft), 4 (pt); LPNs 12 (ft), 8 (pt); Orderlies 2 (ft); Nurses aides 30 (ft), 20 (pt); Physical therapists 1 (ft); Speech therapists 1 (pt); Activities coordinators 1 (ft), 1 (pt); Dietitians 1 (ft).
Facilities Dining room; Physical therapy room; Activities room; Laundry room; Barber/Beauty shop.

Activities Arts & crafts; Cards; Games; Reading groups; Prayer groups; Movies; Shopping trips; Social/Cultural gatherings.

Rosedale Rest Home
415 Sutton Ln, Owensboro, KY, 42301
(502) 684-6753
Admin April Ziemer. *Medical Dir/Dir of Nursing* Teresa Snyder.
Licensure Personal care. *Beds* 50. *Certified* Medicaid.
Owner Privately owned.
Admissions Requirements Minimum age 21; Medical examination; Physician's request.
Staff LPNs 1 (ft); Nurses aides 15 (ft); Dietitians 1 (ft).
Facilities Dining room; Activities room; Laundry room.
Activities Arts & crafts; Cards; Games; Reading groups; Prayer groups; Movies; Shopping trips; Social/Cultural gatherings.

OWENTON

Owenton Manor Inc
PO Box 492, Owenton, KY, 40359
(502) 484-5721
Admin Bernard T Poe.
Licensure Intermediate care. *Beds* 100. *Certified* Medicaid.
Owner Proprietary Corp.
Admissions Requirements Minimum age 18; Medical examination; Physician's request.
Staff RNs 3 (ft); LPNs 4 (ft); Orderlies 3 (ft); Nurses aides 45 (ft); Physical therapists 1 (pt); Speech therapists 1 (pt); Activities coordinators 1 (ft); Dietitians 1 (ft); Ophthalmologists 1 (pt); Podiatrists 1 (pt).
Facilities Dining room; Activities room; Crafts room; Laundry room; Barber/Beauty shop.
Activities Arts & crafts; Cards; Games; Prayer groups; Movies; Social/Cultural gatherings.

OWINGSVILLE

Colonial Rest Home*
E Main St, Owingsville, KY, 40360
(606) 674-2222
Admin Emery V Goodpaster & Joetta Y Goodpaster.
Licensure Personal care. *Beds* 26.
Owner Proprietary Corp.

Hilltop Lodge*
E High St, Box 448, Owingsville, KY, 40360
(606) 674-6062
Admin Jerry Maze.
Licensure Intermediate care. *Beds* 39. *Certified* Medicaid.
Owner Proprietary Corp.

Ridgeway Manor*
PO Box 38, Owingsville, KY, 40360
(606) 674-6613
Admin Thomas Maze.
Licensure Intermediate care. *Beds* 60. *Certified* Medicaid.
Owner Proprietary Corp.

PADUCAH

Life Care Center of Paducah
600 N 4th St, Paducah, KY, 42001
(502) 442-3568
Admin Charles Gallimore. *Medical Dir/Dir of Nursing* Loudel Paul RN.
Licensure Intermediate care; Personal care. *Beds* ICF 102; Personal 40. *Certified* Medicaid.
Owner Proprietary Corp (Life Care Centers of America).
Staff RNs 3 (ft); LPNs 13 (ft); Orderlies 3 (ft); Nurses aides 37 (ft), 15 (pt); Physical therapists 2 (ft); Speech therapists 1 (ft);

Activities coordinators 1 (ft); Dietitians 1 (ft); Ophthalmologists 1 (ft); Podiatrists 1 (ft).
Facilities Dining room; Activities room; Chapel; Crafts room; Barber/Beauty shop; Library.
Activities Arts & crafts; Cards; Games; Prayer groups; Movies; Shopping trips; Social/Cultural gatherings.

McElrath Rest Home*
517 S 5th St, Paducah, KY, 42001
(502) 442-2600
Admin Anna Mae McElrath.
Licensure Personal care. *Beds* 11.
Owner Proprietary Corp.

Medco Center of Paducah*
867 McGuire Ave, Paducah, KY, 42001
(502) 442-6168
Admin Rose Moss.
Licensure Intermediate care. *Beds* 108. *Certified* Medicaid.
Owner Proprietary Corp (Unicare).

Parkview Convalescent Center*
544 Lone Oak Rd, Paducah, KY, 42001
(502) 443-6543
Admin Don Harris.
Licensure Skilled care; Intermediate care. *Beds* SNF 114; ICF 12. *Certified* Medicaid; Medicare.
Owner Proprietary Corp (Life Care Centers of America).

Riverfront Terrace Health Care Facility
PO Box 1137, 501 N 3rd St, Paducah, KY, 42002-1137
(502) 444-9661, 444-9662, 444-9663
Admin Billie Jacobs Tabb. *Medical Dir/Dir of Nursing* Frank Allen Shemwell MD.
Licensure Intermediate care. *Beds* ICF 100. *Certified* Medicaid.
Owner Proprietary Corp (Hillhaven Corp).
Admissions Requirements Medical examination; Physician's request.
Staff Physicians 7 (ft); RNs 3 (ft), 1 (pt); LPNs 6 (ft), 1 (pt); Nurses aides 35 (ft), 10 (pt); Physical therapists 1 (ft); Reality therapists 1 (ft); Occupational therapists 1 (pt); Speech therapists 1 (pt); Activities coordinators 1 (ft); Dietitians 1 (pt); Dentists 1 (pt); Ophthalmologists 1 (pt); Podiatrists 1 (pt).
Facilities Dining room; Activities room; Crafts room; Laundry room; Barber/Beauty shop; Library.
Activities Arts & crafts; Cards; Games; Reading groups; Prayer groups; Movies; Shopping trips; Social/Cultural gatherings; Reality orientation classes; Adopt-a-pet; Adopt-a-resident program.

Superior Care Home*
3100 Clay St, Paducah, KY, 42001
(502) 442-6884
Admin Barbara Davis.
Licensure Intermediate care. *Beds* 85. *Certified* Medicaid.
Owner Proprietary Corp.

PAINTSVILLE

Jennie Wiley Health Care Center*
Mendota Village, Box 138, Paintsville, KY, 41240
(606) 789-5558
Admin Sarah Collins.
Licensure Personal care. *Beds* 51.

Paintsville Health Care Center*
1258 Stafford Ave, Paintsville, KY, 41240
(606) 789-5576
Admin Sarah Collins.
Licensure Personal care. *Beds* 56.
Owner Proprietary Corp.

PARIS

Bourbon Heights Nursing Home
2000 S Main St, Paris, KY, 40361
(606) 987-5750
Admin Emmett R Davis Jr.
Licensure Skilled care; Intermediate care; Personal care; Nursing home. *Beds* SNF 10; ICF 30; Personal 17; Nursing home 32. *Certified* Medicaid.
Owner Nonprofit Corp.

PARKERS LAKE

Cumberland Manor Rest Home*
HC 84, Box 200, Parker's Lake, KY, 42634
(606) 376-5951
Admin Mary A Gordon.
Licensure Personal care. *Beds* 49.
Admissions Requirements Minimum age 16; Medical examination.
Staff LPNs 1 (ft); Orderlies 2 (ft); Nurses aides 8 (ft).
Facilities Dining room; Laundry room.
Activities Games; Prayer groups; Social/Cultural gatherings.

PEMBROKE

Medco Center of Pembroke*
PO Box 149, Hwy 41, Pembroke, KY, 42266
(502) 475-4227
Admin Colleen Foster. *Medical Dir/Dir of Nursing* J C Woodall.
Licensure Intermediate care. *Beds* 64. *Certified* Medicaid.
Owner Proprietary Corp (Unicare).
Staff LPNs 7 (ft); Orderlies 4 (ft); Nurses aides 20 (ft); Speech therapists 1 (pt); Activities coordinators 1 (ft); Dietitians 1 (pt); Dentists 1 (pt).
Facilities Dining room; Activities room; Laundry room.
Activities Arts & crafts; Cards; Games; Reading groups; Prayer groups; Movies; Shopping trips; Social/Cultural gatherings.

PEWEE VALLEY

Friendship Manor Nursing Home
7400 LaGrange Rd, Pewee Valley, KY, 40056-0307
(502) 241-8821
Admin Beth Pearman. *Medical Dir/Dir of Nursing* Irene Walper DON.
Licensure Intermediate care; Nursing home. *Beds* ICF 40; Nursing home 54. *Certified* Medicaid.
Owner Nonprofit Corp.
Admissions Requirements Medical examination; Physician's request.
Staff Physicians 5 (ft); RNs 4 (ft); LPNs 6 (ft); Nurses aides 27 (ft); Activities coordinators 1 (ft).
Affiliation Seventh-Day Adventist
Facilities Dining room; Physical therapy room; Activities room; Chapel; Crafts room; Laundry room; Barber/Beauty shop.
Activities Arts & crafts; Games; Reading groups; Prayer groups; Movies; Shopping trips.

PHELPS

Phelps Community Medical Center
PO Box 424, Hwy 194, Jamboree Rd, Phelps, KY, 41553
(606) 456-8725
Admin Ronald Mann. *Medical Dir/Dir of Nursing* Ronald Mann MD; Henrietta Dotson.
Licensure Intermediate care; Personal care. *Beds* ICF 118; Personal 6. *Certified* Medicaid.
Owner Proprietary Corp.

Admissions Requirements Medical
examination.
Staff Physicians 1 (ft); LPNs 10 (ft); Nurses
aides 45 (ft); Activities coordinators 1 (ft);
Dietitians 1 (ft); Social service director 1
(ft).
Facilities Dining room; Activities room;
Chapel; Crafts room; Laundry room; Barber/
Beauty shop.
Activities Arts & crafts; Cards; Games;
Reading groups; Prayer groups; Movies;
Shopping trips; Social/Cultural gatherings.

PHILPOT

Knottsville Home*
Rte 1, Philpot, KY, 42366
(502) 281-4881
Admin Sr Raymonde Carrot.
Licensure Personal care. *Beds* 68.
Owner Nonprofit Corp.

PIKEVILLE

Mountain Manor Nursing Home
182 S Mayo Trail, Pikeville, KY, 41501
(606) 437-7327
Admin Susan R Arnold. *Medical Dir/Dir of
Nursing* Dr J D Adams; Sue Scott DON.
Licensure Skilled care; Intermediate care. *Beds*
SNF 53; ICF 53. *Certified* Medicaid;
Medicare.
Owner Proprietary Corp.
Facilities Dining room; Physical therapy
room; Activities room; Crafts room; Laundry
room; Barber/Beauty shop.
Activities Arts & crafts; Games; Prayer groups;
Movies; Shopping trips; Social/Cultural
gatherings.

PINEVILLE

Britthaven of Pineville
Rte 1, Box 102, Pineville, KY, 40977
(606) 337-7071
Admin Gwen Golden. *Medical Dir/Dir of
Nursing* Emanuel Rader MD; Sandra Wyatt
DON.
Licensure Intermediate care. *Beds* ICF 114;
Personal Care 8. *Certified* Medicaid;
Medicare.
Owner Proprietary Corp.
Admissions Requirements Minimum age 18;
Medical examination; Physician's request.
Staff Physicians 13 (ft); RNs 1 (ft); LPNs 12
(ft); Orderlies 8 (ft); Nurses aides 36 (ft);
Physical therapists 1 (ft); Speech therapists 1
(ft); Activities coordinators 1 (ft); Dietitians
1 (ft); Ophthalmologists 1 (ft); Podiatrists 1
(ft); Dentist 1 (ft); Respiratory care 1 (ft);
Social worker 1 (ft).
Facilities Dining room; Activities room;
Laundry room; Barber/Beauty shop.
Activities Cards; Games; Reading groups;
Prayer groups; Movies.

PRESTONSBURG

Mountain Manor of Prestonburg*
17 College Ln, Prestonsburg, KY, 41653
(606) 886-2378
Admin Goldie Rorrer.
Licensure Intermediate care. *Beds* 56.
Certified Medicaid.
Admissions Requirements Medical
examination; Physician's request.
Staff Physicians 5 (ft); RNs 1 (ft); LPNs 2 (ft),
1 (pt); Nurses aides 16 (ft); Activities
coordinators 1 (ft); Dietitians 1 (pt); Dentists
5 (pt).
Facilities Dining room; Physical therapy
room; Activities room; Crafts room; Laundry
room; Barber/Beauty shop.
Activities Arts & crafts; Cards; Games;
Reading groups; Prayer groups; Movies;
Shopping trips; Social/Cultural gatherings.

Riverview Manor Nursing Home*
1020 Circle Dr, Prestonsburg, KY, 41653
(606) 886-9178
Admin Charlotte Slone.
Licensure Skilled care; Intermediate care. *Beds*
SNF 56; ICF 60. *Certified* Medicaid;
Medicare.
Owner Proprietary Corp.

PRINCETON

Highlands Homes*
Stevens Ave, PO Box 590, Princeton, KY,
42445
(502) 365-3254
Admin Jo Ann Capps.
Licensure Personal care. *Beds* 88.
Staff LPNs 2 (ft); Nurses aides 22 (ft), 4 (pt);
Recreational therapists 1 (ft).
Facilities Dining room; Activities room;
Laundry room.
Activities Arts & crafts; Games; Prayer groups.

Princeton Health Care Manor Inc
1333 W Main, Princeton, KY, 42445
(502) 365-3541
Admin Mary Jewel Alexander. *Medical Dir/
Dir of Nursing* Jeri Cotton DON.
Licensure Intermediate care; Personal care.
Beds ICF 104; Personal 8. *Certified*
Medicaid.
Owner Proprietary Corp.
Admissions Requirements Minimum age 16.
Staff RNs 1 (ft), 1 (pt); LPNs 3 (ft); Orderlies
1 (ft); Nurses aides 40 (ft); Physical
therapists 1 (pt); Speech therapists 1 (pt);
Activities coordinators 1 (ft); Dietitians 1
(ft).
Facilities Dining room; Physical therapy
room; Activities room; Crafts room; Laundry
room; Barber/Beauty shop.
Activities Arts & crafts; Cards; Games;
Reading groups; Movies; Shopping trips.

PROSPECT

Britthaven of Prospect
PO Box 147, 6301 Bass Rd, Prospect, KY,
40059
(502) 228-8359
Admin Linda L Riffe. *Medical Dir/Dir of
Nursing* Dr A J Perez; Ernestine Williams
DON.
Licensure Intermediate care. *Beds* ICF 100.
Certified Medicaid.
Owner Proprietary Corp (Britthaven Inc).
Admissions Requirements Medical
examination.
Staff RNs 1 (ft), 1 (pt); LPNs 5 (ft); Orderlies
1 (ft); Nurses aides 30 (ft), 10 (pt); Activities
coordinators 1 (ft), 1 (pt); Dietitians 1 (ft).
Facilities Dining room; Activities room;
Chapel; Crafts room; Laundry room; Barber/
Beauty shop; Library.
Activities Arts & crafts; Games; Reading
groups; Prayer groups; Movies; Shopping
trips; Social/Cultural gatherings.

PROVIDENCE

Country Meadows Rest Haven*
Rte 1, Box 98, Providence, KY, 42450
(502) 667-2682
Admin Loeta Tow.
Licensure Personal care. *Beds* 50.
Owner Proprietary Corp.

Shemwell Nursing Home*
805 Princeton St, Providence, KY, 42450
(502) 667-2023
Admin Billie C Cole.
Licensure Skilled care. *Beds* 22.
Owner Proprietary Corp.

RICHMOND

Crestview Personal Care Home*
131 S Meadowlark Dr, Richmond, KY, 40475
(606) 623-5031
Admin Hestel Hibbard.
Licensure Personal care. *Beds* 50.
Owner Proprietary Corp.

Kenwood House*
130 S Meadowlark Dr, Richmond, KY, 40475
(606) 623-9472
Admin Janet Justice.
Licensure Skilled care; Intermediate care. *Beds*
SNF 42; ICF 46. *Certified* Medicaid;
Medicare.
Owner Proprietary Corp.

Madison Manor*
S Meadowlark Dr, Richmond, KY, 40475
(606) 623-3564
Admin Mary Ousley.
Licensure Intermediate care. *Beds* 101.
Certified Medicaid.
Owner Proprietary Corp.

RUSSELL

Russell Convalescent Home*
407 Ferry Rd, Russell, KY, 41169
(606) 836-5616
Admin Carolyn Baumgarden & Oscar
Baumgarden.
Licensure Personal care. *Beds* 28. *Certified*
Medicaid.
Owner Proprietary Corp.

RUSSELLVILLE

Russellville Health Care Manor*
683 E 3rd St, Russellville, KY, 42276
(502) 726-9049
Admin Sarah Slack.
Licensure Intermediate care; Personal care.
Beds ICF 92; Personal 20. *Certified*
Medicaid.
Owner Proprietary Corp.

SAINT CATHERINE

Sansbury Memorial Infirmany
Hwy 150, Bardstown Rd, Saint Catherine,
KY, 40061
(606) 336-3974
Admin Sr Ann Robert Gray.
Licensure Intermediate care; Personal care.
Beds ICF 36; Personal 28. *Certified*
Medicaid.
Admissions Requirements Females only.
Staff Physicians 2 (pt); RNs 1 (ft); LPNs 5
(ft); Nurses aides 18 (ft); Dietitians 1 (ft).
Affiliation Roman Catholic

SALEM

Salem Nursing Home
PO Box 77, Hayden Ave, Hwy 723, Salem,
KY, 42078
(502) 988-2388
Admin Carol Roberts. *Medical Dir/Dir of
Nursing* Stephen Burkhart MD; Janet
Kemper RN.
Licensure Skilled care. *Beds* SNF 50. *Certified*
Medicaid; Medicare.
Owner Privately owned.
Staff Physicians 2 (pt); RNs 4 (ft), 1 (pt);
LPNs 7 (ft), 1 (pt); Physical therapists 1 (pt);
Speech therapists 1 (pt); Activities
coordinators 1 (ft); Dietitians 1 (pt).
Facilities Dining room; Activities room.
Activities Arts & crafts; Cards; Games;
Reading groups; Prayer groups.

SALYERSVILLE

Mountain Valley Rest Home*
PO Box 445, Salyersville, KY, 41465
(606) 349-2014
Admin Mary Bandy.
Licensure Personal care. *Beds* 32.
Owner Proprietary Corp.

Salyersville Health Care Center*
PO Box 819, Hwy 114, Salyersville, KY,
41465
(606) 349-6181
Admin Thomas E Hummer.
Licensure Intermediate care; Personal care.
Beds ICF 147; Personal 21. *Certified*
Medicaid.
Owner Proprietary Corp.

SANDERS

Valley Haven Personal Care Home
PO Box 75, McDaniel St, Sanders, KY, 41083
(502) 347-9355
Admin Patricia Burgess Lewis.
Licensure Personal care. *Beds* 45.
Owner Proprietary Corp.
Admissions Requirements Minimum age 16;
Males only; Medical examination;
Physician's request.
Staff Physicians 1 (pt); Orderlies 4 (ft); Nurses
aides 4 (ft); Activities coordinators 2 (ft);
Dietitians 1 (ft).
Facilities Dining room; Activities room;
Laundry room.
Activities Cards; Games; Movies; Shopping
trips.

SCIENCE HILL

Hilltop Rest Home*
Rte 2, Science Hill, KY, 42553
(606) 423-2555
Admin Ida M Dick.
Licensure Personal care. *Beds* 40.
Owner Proprietary Corp.

SCOTTSVILLE

Friendship Manor*
824 N 4th St, Scottsville, KY, 42164
(502) 237-5182
Admin Mae Foster.
Licensure Personal care. *Beds* 40.
Owner Proprietary Corp.

Hillcrest Home*
515 Water St, Scottsville, KY, 42164
(502) 237-3485
Admin May Foster.
Licensure Personal care. *Beds* 36.
Owner Proprietary Corp.

Hillview Manor*
Hillview Dr, Scottsville, KY, 42164
(502) 237-4164
Admin Sara Threet.
Licensure Personal care. *Beds* 84.
Admissions Requirements Minimum age 16;
Medical examination; Physician's request.
Staff RNs 1 (pt); Nurses aides 35 (ft);
Activities coordinators 1 (ft), 2 (pt).
Facilities Dining room; Laundry room.
Activities Arts & crafts; Cards; Games;
Reading groups; Prayer groups; Movies;
Shopping trips; Social/Cultural gatherings.

SEBREE

Colonial Terrace Nursing Home
S Church St, Sebree, KY, 42455
(502) 835-2533
Admin Kathy Crowley. *Medical Dir/Dir of
Nursing* Jason Samuel MD; Connie Cobb
LPN DON.

Licensure Intermediate care. *Beds* 80.
Certified Medicaid.
Owner Proprietary Corp.
Admissions Requirements Minimum age 20;
Medical examination; Physician's request.
Staff Physicians 7 (pt); LPNs 1 (pt); LPNs 3
(ft); Nurses aides 30 (ft), 10 (pt); Speech
therapists 1 (pt); Activities coordinators 2
(ft), 1 (pt); Dietitians 1 (pt); Dentists 1 (pt);
Ophthalmologists 1 (pt).
Facilities Dining room; Activities room;
Chapel; Crafts room; Laundry room; Barber/
Beauty shop.
Activities Arts & crafts; Cards; Games; Prayer
groups; Movies; Shopping trips; Social/
Cultural gatherings; Bingo; BBQs; Fish fries;
Paper money auction.

SHELBYVILLE

Colonial Hall Manor*
920 Henry Clay St, Shelbyville, KY, 40065
(502) 633-4762
Admin Cathy C Vinson.
Licensure Personal care. *Beds* 57.
Staff RNs 1 (ft); LPNs 1 (pt); Orderlies 1 (ft);
Nurses aides 18 (ft); Activities coordinators
1 (ft); Dietitians 1 (pt).
Facilities Dining room; Activities room;
Chapel; Crafts room; Laundry room;
Library.
Activities Arts & crafts; Cards; Games;
Reading groups; Prayer groups; Movies;
Shopping trips.

Crestview Health Care Center
Rte 6, Box 382, Shelbyville, KY, 40065
(502) 633-2454
Admin Lisa Stoval RN. *Medical Dir/Dir of
Nursing* Dr Donald Chatham MD; Janet
Lawrence RN.
Licensure Nursing home. *Beds* Nursing home
58.
Owner Proprietary Corp.
Admissions Requirements Physician's request.
Staff Physicians 13 (ft); RNs 2 (ft), 1 (pt);
LPNs 4 (ft); Orderlies 1 (ft), 1 (pt); Nurses
aides 15 (ft), 14 (pt); Physical therapists 1
(pt); Speech therapists 1 (pt); Activities
coordinators 1 (ft); Dietitians 1 (pt);
Ophthalmologists 1 (pt).
Facilities Dining room; Physical therapy
room; Activities room; Crafts room; Laundry
room; Barber/Beauty shop.
Activities Arts & crafts; Games; Reading
groups; Prayer groups; Movies; Shopping
trips; Social/Cultural gatherings.

Old Masons' Home of Kentucky*
US Hwy 60, Shelbyville, KY, 40065
(502) 633-3486
Admin O J Simpson.
Licensure Intermediate care; Personal care.
Beds ICF 20; Personal 130. *Certified*
Medicaid.
Owner Nonprofit Corp.
Affiliation Masons

Shelby Manor*
9 Village Plaza, Shelbyville, KY, 40065-1738
(502) 633-2691
Admin Thomas R Hower.
Licensure Intermediate care; Personal care.
Beds ICF 63; Personal 90. *Certified*
Medicaid.
Owner Proprietary Corp.

SHEPHERDSVILLE

Colonial House of Shepherdsville*
Star Rt, Box 64, Shepherdsville, KY, 40165
(502) 543-7042
Admin Sarah M Simpson RN.
Licensure Personal care. *Beds* 62.
Owner Proprietary Corp.

**Patterson's Pleasant View Personal Care
Home***
Hwy 44 E & Loyd's Ln, Shepherdsville, KY,
40165
(502) 543-7995
Admin Pamela Hawkins.
Licensure Personal care. *Beds* 13.
Owner Proprietary Corp.

SHIVELY

Rockford Manor*
4700 Quinn Dr, Shively, KY, 40216
(502) 448-5850
Admin Carol Ann Bottoms.
Licensure Intermediate care. *Beds* 120.
Certified Medicaid.
Owner Proprietary Corp.

SMITHLAND

Livingston County Rest Home
PO Box 280, Rudd & Walnut St, Smithland,
KY, 42081
(502) 928-2137
Admin Dathel & Nora E Ramage. *Medical
Dir/Dir of Nursing* Phyllis Tackwell LPN.
Licensure Personal care. *Beds* 38. *Certified*
Medicare.
Owner Publicly owned.
Admissions Requirements Minimum age 16;
Medical examination.
Staff LPNs 1 (ft); Orderlies 1 (ft); Nurses
aides 7 (ft), 2 (pt); Activities coordinators 1
(ft); Dietitians 1 (pt).
Facilities Dining room; Activities room;
Chapel; Laundry room; Barber/Beauty shop.
Activities Arts & crafts; Games; Prayer groups;
Shopping trips; Social/Cultural gatherings.

SOMERSET

Britthaven of Somerset*
Bourne Ave & Central Ave, Somerset, KY,
42501
(606) 679-7421
Admin Mary Creekmore.
Licensure Skilled care; Intermediate care;
Personal care. *Beds* SNF 36; ICF 116;
Personal 12. *Certified* Medicaid; Medicare.
Owner Proprietary Corp (Britthaven Inc).

Colonial Care Home*
202 N Main St, Somerset, KY, 42501
(606) 679-1504
Admin Joan O Johnson.
Licensure Personal care. *Beds* 50.
Admissions Requirements Minimum age 45;
Medical examination; Physician's request.
Staff Nurses aides 7 (ft), 4 (pt); Dietitians 2
(ft), 2 (pt).
Facilities Dining room; Activities room;
Laundry room.
Activities Arts & crafts; Games; Reading
groups; Prayer groups; Shopping trips.

Crestview Personal Care Home
235 S Richardson Dr, Somerset, KY, 42501
(606) 678-8927
Admin Emma Williamson. *Medical Dir/Dir of
Nursing* Venus B Tanamachi RN DON.
Licensure Personal care. *Beds* 28.
Owner Proprietary Corp.
Admissions Requirements Minimum age 16;
Females only; Medical examination.
Staff RNs; Nurses aides; Activities
coordinators; Dietitians.
Facilities Dining room; Activities room;
Chapel; Crafts room; Laundry room;
Library.
Activities Arts & crafts; Cards; Games;
Reading groups; Prayer groups; Movies.

Crestview Personal Care Home
235 S Richardson Dr, Somerset, KY, 42501
(606) 678-8927

Admin Hiro Tanamachi. *Medical Dir/Dir of Nursing* Venus B Tanamachi RN.
Licensure Personal care. *Beds* 28.
Owner Proprietary Corp.
Admissions Requirements Females only.
Staff RNs 1 (pt); Nurses aides 2 (ft), 5 (pt); Activities coordinators 1 (pt); Dietitians 1 (pt).
Facilities Dining room; Activities room; Laundry room; Library.
Activities Arts & crafts; Cards; Games; Reading groups; Prayer groups; Movies.

Midtown Care Home*
106 Gover St, Somerset, KY, 42501
(606) 679-8331
Admin Brenda Abbott.
Licensure Intermediate care. *Beds* 123.
Certified Medicaid.
Owner Proprietary Corp.

Oakwood Intermediate Care Facility
US 27 S, Somerset, KY, 42501
(606) 679-4361
Admin Mary Warman. *Medical Dir/Dir of Nursing* Alberto Jayme MD.
Licensure Intermediate care for mentally retarded. *Beds* 420. *Certified* Medicaid.
Admissions Requirements Minimum age 6.
Staff Physicians 1 (ft), 1 (pt); RNs 15 (ft); LPNs 13 (ft); Nurses aides; Physical therapists 1 (ft); Recreational therapists 1 (ft); Occupational therapists 1 (ft); Speech therapists 2 (ft); Dietitians 3 (ft); Dentists 1 (pt); Patient aides 457 (ft), 77 (pt).
Facilities Dining room; Physical therapy room; Activities room; Laundry room; Barber/Beauty shop; Library; Residential cottages; Habilitative classrooms; Gym.
Activities Arts & crafts; Cards; Games; Movies; Shopping trips; Social/Cultural gatherings.

Sunrise Manor Nursing Home*
200 Norfleet Dr, Somerset, KY, 42501
(606) 678-5104
Admin Marlene Morgan.
Licensure Skilled care; Intermediate care. *Beds* SNF 64; ICF 29. *Certified* Medicaid; Medicare.
Owner Proprietary Corp (Unicare).

SOUTH SHORE

South Shore Health Care Center
PO Box 489, James E Hannah Dr, South Shore, KY, 41175
(606) 932-6266
Admin Kenneth Morgan. *Medical Dir/Dir of Nursing* Dollie McBrayer.
Licensure Intermediate care. *Beds* ICF 46. *Certified* Medicare.
Owner Privately owned.
Staff Physicians 1 (ft); RNs 1 (ft); LPNs 4 (ft); Orderlies 1 (ft); Activities coordinators 1 (ft); Dietitians 1 (ft).
Facilities Dining room; Activities room; Laundry room.
Activities Arts & crafts; Games; Prayer groups; Social/Cultural gatherings.

SOUTH WILLIAMSON

Williamson Appalachian Regional Hospital*
2000 Central Ave, South Williamson, KY, 41503
(606) 237-1010
Admin W D Crosely.
Licensure Skilled care; Rehabilitation. *Beds* 193.
Owner Nonprofit Corp.

SPRINGFIELD

Medco Center of Springfield
120 E Grundy Ave, Springfield, KY, 40069
(606) 336-7771

Admin Violet Elliott.
Licensure Intermediate care. *Beds* 70. *Certified* Medicaid.
Owner Proprietary Corp (Unicare).
Admissions Requirements Minimum age 21; Medical examination.
Staff LPNs 4 (ft), 3 (pt); Orderlies 2 (ft); Nurses aides 24 (ft), 2 (pt); Activities coordinators 1 (ft).
Facilities Dining room; Activities room; Laundry room; Barber/Beauty shop.
Activities Arts & crafts; Cards; Games; Reading groups; Prayer groups; Movies; Shopping trips; Social/Cultural gatherings.

STANFORD

Fort Logan Hospital—ECF*
124 Portman Ave, Stanford, KY, 40484
(606) 365-2187
Admin Terry C Powers.
Licensure Skilled care. *Beds* 30. *Certified* Medicaid; Medicare.
Owner Nonprofit Corp.

Stanford House*
Harmon Heights, Stanford, KY, 40484
(606) 365-2141
Admin Brenda Williams. *Medical Dir/Dir of Nursing* Dr Joseph Middleton.
Licensure Intermediate care. *Beds* 98. *Certified* Medicaid.
Owner Proprietary Corp (Beverly Enterprises).
Staff Physicians 5 (pt); RNs 1 (pt); LPNs 6 (ft), 1 (pt); Nurses aides 23 (ft); Activities coordinators 1 (ft); Dietitians 1 (pt); Dentists 1 (pt).
Facilities Dining room; Physical therapy room; Activities room; Laundry room; Barber/Beauty shop.
Activities Arts & crafts; Cards; Games; Reading groups; Movies; Shopping trips; Social/Cultural gatherings.

STANTON

Stanton Nursing Center*
Derickson Rd, Stanton, KY, 40380
(606) 663-2846
Admin Dan Dailey.
Licensure Intermediate care; Personal care. *Beds* ICF 81; Personal 9. *Certified* Medicaid.
Owner Proprietary Corp (Unicare).

STURGIS

Sturgis Community Rest Home*
7th & Main Sts, Sturgis, KY, 42459-0304
(502) 333-5508
Admin Minnie Sue Thompson.
Licensure Personal care. *Beds* 27.
Admissions Requirements Medical examination.
Staff Physicians 1 (pt); Nurses aides 3 (ft), 3 (pt); Activities coordinators 1 (ft); Dietitians 1 (pt).
Facilities Dining room; Activities room; Chapel; Crafts room; Laundry room; Barber/Beauty shop.
Activities Arts & crafts; Games; Prayer groups; Movies; Shopping trips; Social/Cultural gatherings.

TOMPKINSVILLE

Monroe Health Care Facility*
706 N Magnolia, Tompkinsville, KY, 42167
(502) 487-6135
Admin Nikki Wright.
Licensure Skilled care; Intermediate care; Personal care. *Beds* SNF 32; ICF 70; Personal 18. *Certified* Medicaid; Medicare.
Owner Proprietary Corp.

VANCEBURG

Vanceburg Health Care Center
PO Box 297, Vanceburg, KY, 41179
(606) 796-3046
Admin Eugena Forman. *Medical Dir/Dir of Nursing* Greg Dick; Joan Pollitt.
Licensure Intermediate care; Personal care. *Beds* ICF 94; Personal 16. *Certified* Medicaid.
Owner Proprietary Corp (Beverly Enterprises).
Admissions Requirements Medical examination.
Staff Physicians 1 (pt); RNs 1 (ft); LPNs 7 (ft); Orderlies 6 (ft); Nurses aides 32 (ft); Activities coordinators 1 (ft); Dietitians 1 (pt).
Facilities Dining room; Activities room; Laundry room; Barber/Beauty shop; Patient lounge.
Activities Arts & crafts; Cards; Games; Reading groups; Prayer groups; Movies; Shopping trips; Social/Cultural gatherings.

VERSAILLES

Taylor Manor Nursing Home
PO Drawer D, Berry Ave, Versailles, KY, 40383
(606) 873-4201
Admin Sr Mary Virginia Sayers SJW. *Medical Dir/Dir of Nursing* Sr Ann Curran RN DON.
Licensure Intermediate care; Personal care; Nursing home. *Beds* ICF 18; Personal 24.
Owner Nonprofit organization/foundation.
Admissions Requirements Minimum age 50; Medical examination.
Staff Physicians 6 (pt); RNs 1 (ft), 2 (pt); LPNs 4 (ft), 3 (pt); Nurses aides 21 (ft), 3 (pt); Activities coordinators 1 (ft), 1 (pt); Dietitians 1 (pt); CMA; Nurse aides 5 (ft).
Affiliation Roman Catholic
Facilities Dining room; Activities room; Chapel; Crafts room; Barber/Beauty shop.
Activities Arts & crafts; Cards; Games; Prayer groups; Shopping trips; Social/Cultural gatherings.

WAYNESBURG

Waynesburg Rest Home
PO Box 68, Waynesburg, KY, 40489
(606) 379-2614
Admin Reva Reynolds.
Licensure Personal care. *Beds* 28.
Owner Proprietary Corp.
Admissions Requirements Minimum age 30; Physician's request.
Staff Nurses aides 10 (ft); Recreational therapists 3 (pt); Activities coordinators 2 (pt); Dietitians 1 (pt).
Facilities Dining room; Activities room; Laundry room; Barber/Beauty shop.

WEST LIBERTY

Allen's Rest Home*
Rte 1, Box 6, West Liberty, KY, 41472
(606) 743-3846
Admin Pamela Burton. *Medical Dir/Dir of Nursing* Loretta Fyffe.
Licensure Intermediate care. *Beds* 29. *Certified* Medicaid.
Staff Physicians 1 (ft); RNs 1 (pt); LPNs 3 (ft); Nurses aides 10 (ft), 3 (pt); Recreational therapists 1 (ft); Activities coordinators 1 (ft); Dietitians 2 (ft), 2 (pt); Dentists 1 (pt).
Facilities Dining room; Activities room; Laundry room.
Activities Arts & crafts; Cards; Games; Reading groups; Movies.

Morgan County Appalachian Regional Hospital Skilled Nursing Facility
PO Box 579, West Liberty, KY, 41472-0545
(606) 743-3186
Admin Raymond Rowlett. *Medical Dir/Dir of Nursing* Morris L Peyton MD; Edith P Blackburn RN DON.
Licensure Skilled care; Hospital. *Beds* SNF 15; Hospital 30. *Certified* Medicaid; Medicare.
Owner Nonprofit Corp.
Admissions Requirements Physician's request.
Staff Physicians 7 (pt); RNs 18 (pt); LPNs 2 (pt); Nurses aides 7 (pt); Physical therapists 1 (pt); Activities coordinators 1 (pt); Dietitians 1 (pt).
Facilities Dining room; Physical therapy room; Activities room; Chapel; Crafts room; Barber/Beauty shop.
Activities Arts & crafts; Cards; Games.

WILLIAMSBURG

Williamsburg Nursing Home*
Rte 4, Box 719, Williamsburg, KY, 40769
(606) 549-4321
Admin Connie Moren.
Licensure Skilled care; Intermediate care. *Beds* SNF 30; ICF 70. *Certified* Medicaid; Medicare.
Owner Proprietary Corp (Health Sys).

WINCHESTER

Winchester Manor Health Care Center*
Rte 7, Van Meter Rd, Winchester, KY, 40391
(606) 744-1800
Admin Wayne Reid.
Licensure Skilled care; Intermediate care; Personal care. *Beds* SNF 50; ICF 131; Personal 15. *Certified* Medicaid; Medicare.
Owner Proprietary Corp (Hillhaven Corp).

WOODBURN

Hopkins Nursing Facility
College St, Woodburn, KY, 42170
(502) 529-2853
Admin Scarlotte Freeman. *Medical Dir/Dir of Nursing* J M Pulliam MD; Lynnda M Peak RN.
Licensure Skilled care; Intermediate care. *Beds* SNF 21; ICF 29. *Certified* Medicaid; Medicare.
Owner Proprietary Corp (Angell Group).
Admissions Requirements Medical examination; Physician's request.
Staff RNs 3 (ft), 1 (pt); LPNs 3 (ft), 1 (pt); Orderlies 1 (ft), 1 (pt); Activities coordinators.
Facilities Dining room; Activities room; Laundry room; Library.
Activities Arts & crafts; Cards; Games; Reading groups; Prayer groups; Movies; Shopping trips; Social/Cultural gatherings.

Twilight Personal Care Home*
Clark St, Woodburn, KY, 42170
(502) 529-2962

Admin Jack Wofford.
Licensure Personal care. *Beds* 25.

Wofford Personal Care Home*
PO Box 100, 311 Clark St, Woodburn, KY, 42170-0100
(502) 529-2962
Admin Jack Wofford.
Licensure Personal care. *Beds* 25.
Owner Proprietary Corp.

WURTLAND

Wurtland Health Care Center
100 Wurtland Ave, Wurtland, KY, 41144
(606) 836-9616
Admin Carl W Cotton. *Medical Dir/Dir of Nursing* Dr Oren Justice; Clara Parker.
Licensure Intermediate care. *Beds* ICF 126. *Certified* Medicaid.
Owner Proprietary Corp.
Staff Physicians 4 (pt); RNs 1 (pt); LPNs 10 (ft); Nurses aides 25 (ft); Physical therapists 1 (pt); Recreational therapists 2 (ft); Speech therapists 1 (pt); Activities coordinators 1 (ft); Dietitians 1 (pt); Dentists 1 (pt); Ophthalmologists 1 (pt); Podiatrists 1 (pt).
Facilities Dining room; Physical therapy room; Activities room; Crafts room; Laundry room; Barber/Beauty shop; Library.
Activities Arts & crafts; Cards; Games; Reading groups; Prayer groups; Movies; Shopping trips; Social/Cultural gatherings; Rock-N-Roll jamboree; 2 festivals.

LOUISIANA

ABBEVILLE

Abbeville Heritage Manor
2403 Alonzo St, Abbeville, LA, 70510
(318) 893-6140
Admin Freddie J Arceneaut. *Medical Dir/Dir of Nursing* Donna Augustus.
Licensure Intermediate care. *Beds* ICF 60.
Certified Medicaid; Medicare.
Owner Proprietary Corp (Southmark Heritage Corp).
Admissions Requirements Medical examination.

ALEXANDRIA

Annie Mae Matthews Memorial Nursing Home
PO Box 12910, 5100 Jackson St, Alexandria, LA, 71301-2910
(318) 445-5215/448-9414
Admin Gloria Carmouche.
Licensure Intermediate care. *Beds* 116.
Certified Medicaid.

Heritage Manor of Alexandria 1*
5115 McArthur Dr, Alexandria, LA, 71302
(318) 442-2340
Admin Bill Blacksher.
Licensure Intermediate care. *Beds* 56.
Certified Medicaid.
Owner Proprietary Corp (Southmark Heritage Corp).

Heritage Manor of Alexandria 2
3343 Masonic Dr, Alexandria, LA, 71301
(318) 445-6508
Admin Wayne L Morris. *Medical Dir/Dir of Nursing* Dr William Brown.
Licensure Intermediate care. *Beds* ICF 124.
Certified Medicaid.
Owner Proprietary Corp (Southmark Heritage Corp).
Admissions Requirements Medical examination; Physician's request.
Staff RNs 1 (ft); LPNs 13 (ft), 2 (pt); Orderlies 3 (ft), 2 (pt); Nurses aides 42 (ft), 4 (pt).
Facilities Dining room; Activities room; Chapel; Crafts room; Laundry room; Barber/Beauty shop.
Activities Arts & crafts; Cards; Games; Reading groups; Prayer groups; Movies; Shopping trips; Social/Cultural gatherings.

Louisiana Special Education Center*
PO Drawer 7797, Alexandria, LA, 71037
(318) 487-5484
Admin Aline Cicardo. *Medical Dir/Dir of Nursing* Dr L J Credeur.
Licensure Intermediate care for Orthopedically Handicapped. *Beds* 75.
Certified Medicaid.
Admissions Requirements Minimum age 3; Medical examination.
Staff Physicians 4 (pt); RNs 6 (ft); LPNs 5 (ft); Nurses aides 44 (ft); Physical therapists 1 (pt); Occupational therapists 1 (ft); Speech

therapists 3 (ft); Activities coordinators 1 (ft); Dietitians 1 (ft); Dentists 1 (ft); Audiologists 1 (pt).
Facilities Dining room; Physical therapy room; Activities room; Crafts room; Laundry room; Barber/Beauty shop; Library.
Activities Arts & crafts; Cards; Games; Reading groups; Movies; Shopping trips; Social/Cultural gatherings.

Naomi Heights Nursing Home*
2421 E Texas Ave, Alexandria, LA, 71301
(318) 448-0175
Admin Finley C Matthews Jr.
Licensure Intermediate care. *Beds* 97.
Certified Medicaid.
Staff RNs 3 (ft); LPNs 7 (ft), 1 (pt); Orderlies 5 (ft); Nurses aides 26 (ft); Dietitians 1 (pt).
Facilities Dining room; Activities room; Laundry room; Barber/Beauty shop.
Activities Arts & crafts; Prayer groups; Movies; Shopping trips; Social/Cultural gatherings.

Pecan Grove Training Center*
5000 Lower 3rd St, Alexandria, LA, 71301
(318) 448-0291
Admin C L Miller.
Licensure Intermediate care for mentally retarded. *Beds* 120. *Certified* Medicaid.

Pleasant Manor Nursing Home*
5908 Skye St, Alexandria, LA, 71303
(318) 445-5984 or 445-4583
Admin Ernest M Smith.
Licensure Intermediate care. *Beds* 160.
Certified Medicaid.

St Mary's Residential Training School
PO Drawer 7768, Hwy 1 N, Alexandria, LA, 71306
(318) 443-6443
Admin Antoinette Baroncini. *Medical Dir/Dir of Nursing* Dr L J Credeur.
Licensure Intermediate care for mentally retarded. *Beds* 152. *Certified* Medicaid.
Owner Nonprofit Corp.
Admissions Requirements Minimum age 3; Medical examination.
Staff Physicians 4 (pt); RNs 1 (ft); LPNs 3 (ft); Nurses aides 5 (ft); Physical therapists 1 (pt); Recreational therapists 2 (ft); Occupational therapists 1 (pt); Speech therapists 2 (ft), 1 (pt); Activities coordinators 2 (ft); Dietitians 1 (ft); Podiatrists 1 (pt); Social workers 2 (ft) Dentist 1 (pt) Psychologists 2 (ft), 1 (pt).
Affiliation Roman Catholic
Facilities Dining room; Activities room; Chapel; Laundry room; Barber/Beauty shop; Library; Gym; Dormitories.
Activities Arts & crafts; Cards; Games; Movies; Shopping trips; Social/Cultural gatherings; Sports.

Wilshire Manor Nursing Home*
1200 Windsor Pl, Alexandria, LA, 71303
(318) 445-9356 or 448-9409
Admin Bob Marshall.

Licensure Intermediate care. *Beds* 110.
Certified Medicaid.

ALGIERS

Touro Shakespeare Home*
2621 General Meyer Ave, Algiers, LA, 70114
(504) 366-9881
Admin Russell J Henry.
Licensure Intermediate care. *Beds* 119.
Certified Medicaid.

Willow Wood*
3700 Behrman Pl, Algiers, LA, 70114
(504) 367-5640
Admin Byron S Arbeit.
Licensure Skilled care; Intermediate care. *Beds* 101. *Certified* Medicaid; Medicare.
Affiliation Jewish

AMITE

Amite Nursing Home Inc*
709 E North Pl, Amite, LA, 70422
(504) 748-9464
Admin Preston J Broussard.
Licensure Intermediate care. *Beds* 100.
Certified Medicaid.

ARABI

Maison Orleans Nursing Home*
2310 Mehle Ave, Arabi, LA, 70032
(504) 393-9595
Admin Frank T Stewart Jr.
Licensure Intermediate care. *Beds* 110.
Certified Medicaid.

St Ann's Convalescent Homes*
633 Mehle St, Arabi, LA, 70032
(504) 279-4461
Admin Hilman Mendoza.
Licensure Intermediate care. *Beds* 70.
Certified Medicaid.

ARCADIA

Arcadia Baptist Home*
PO Box 599, 1109 6th St, Arcadia, LA, 71001
(318) 263-8468
Admin L T Stringer.
Licensure Intermediate care. *Beds* 80.
Certified Medicaid.
Affiliation Baptist

BAKER

Baker Health Care Inc
PO Box 419, 3612 Baker Blvd, Baker, LA, 70714
(504) 778-0573
Admin Kendall L Calhoun. *Medical Dir/Dir of Nursing* Randye Watson DON.
Licensure Intermediate care. *Beds* ICF 136.
Certified Medicaid.
Owner Proprietary Corp.

Staff LPNs 10 (ft), 2 (pt); Nurses aides 47 (ft), 2 (pt); Activities coordinators 1 (ft); Dietitians 1 (ft).
Facilities Dining room; Activities room; Crafts room; Laundry room; Barber/Beauty shop.
Activities Arts & crafts; Cards; Games; Reading groups; Prayer groups; Movies; Shopping trips; Social/Cultural gatherings.

BASILE

Basile Care Center Inc
PO Box 38, 100 Chambers St, Basile, LA, 70515
(318) 432-6663
Admin Joseph P Young NHA. *Medical Dir/ Dir of Nursing* Bernice G Young RN.
Licensure Intermediate care. *Beds* ICF 78.
Certified Medicaid.
Owner Privately owned.
Staff RNs 2 (ft); LPNs 7 (ft); Nurses aides 45 (ft); Activities coordinators 1 (ft); Dietitians 1 (pt).
Languages French
Facilities Dining room; Activities room; Crafts room; Laundry room; Barber/Beauty shop.
Activities Arts & crafts; Cards; Games; Reading groups; Prayer groups; Movies; Social/Cultural gatherings.

BASTROP

Cherry Ridge Guest Care Center
PO Box 941, 1800 Cherry Ridge Rd, Bastrop, LA, 71220
(318) 281-6933
Admin Richard E Boyter. *Medical Dir/Dir of Nursing* Jack Noble MD; Patsy Bing.
Licensure Intermediate care. *Beds* ICF 110.
Certified Medicaid.
Owner Proprietary Corp.
Admissions Requirements Medical examination; Physician's request.
Staff Physicians 1 (pt); RNs 2 (ft); LPNs 10 (ft); Nurses aides 34 (ft); Physical therapists 1 (pt); Speech therapists 1 (pt); Activities coordinators 1 (ft); Dietitians 1 (pt).
Facilities Dining room; Activities room; Chapel; Crafts room; Laundry room; Barber/ Beauty shop.
Activities Arts & crafts; Cards; Games; Reading groups; Prayer groups; Movies; Shopping trips; Social/Cultural gatherings.

Hickory Manor Nursing Home Inc*
360 W Hickory, Bastrop, LA, 71220
(318) 281-6523
Admin John B Williams. *Medical Dir/Dir of Nursing* Dr Bruce Wheeler.
Licensure Intermediate care. *Beds* 106.
Certified Medicaid.
Admissions Requirements Minimum age 21.
Staff Physicians 10 (pt); RNs 1 (ft); LPNs 9 (ft), 3 (pt); Orderlies 5 (ft); Nurses aides 20 (ft); Physical therapists 1 (ft); Activities coordinators 1 (ft); Dietitians 1 (ft); Dentists 2 (pt); Ophthalmologists 2 (pt).
Facilities Dining room; Physical therapy room; Activities room; Chapel; Crafts room; Laundry room; Barber/Beauty shop.
Activities Arts & crafts; Cards; Games; Prayer groups; Movies; Shopping trips; Social/ Cultural gatherings.

Hillview Nursing Home*
Alvin St, Bastrop, LA, 71220
(318) 281-0322
Admin Doris V Johnston. *Medical Dir/Dir of Nursing* Patrica Watson.
Licensure Intermediate care. *Beds* 120.
Certified Medicaid.
Staff RNs 1 (ft); LPNs 10 (ft); Orderlies 4 (ft); Nurses aides 40 (ft); Physical therapists 1 (pt); Dietitians 1 (ft).

Facilities Dining room; Physical therapy room; Activities room; Crafts room; Laundry room.
Activities Arts & crafts; Cards; Games; Reading groups; Prayer groups; Movies; Shopping trips; Social/Cultural gatherings.

Summerlin Lane Nursing Home
1408 Summerlin Ln, Bastrop, LA, 71220
(318) 281-5188
Admin David Holland. *Medical Dir/Dir of Nursing* Dianne Anders.
Licensure Intermediate care. *Beds* 100.
Certified Medicaid.
Owner Privately owned.
Admissions Requirements Medical examination.
Staff RNs; LPNs; Orderlies; Nurses aides; Recreational therapists; Activities coordinators; Dietitians.
Facilities Dining room; Physical therapy room; Activities room; Crafts room; Laundry room; Barber/Beauty shop.
Activities Arts & crafts; Games; Reading groups; Movies; Shopping trips; Social/ Cultural gatherings.

BATON ROUGE

Baton Rouge Extensive Care Facility*
4914 McClelland Dr, Baton Rouge, LA, 70805
(504) 356-3551
Admin Cornelia H Swayze.
Licensure Intermediate care. *Beds* 123.
Certified Medicaid.

Baton Rouge Heritage House II
1335 Wooddale Blvd, Baton Rouge, LA, 70806
(504) 924-2851
Admin Cornelia Swayze. *Medical Dir/Dir of Nursing* Virginia Philmon.
Licensure Intermediate care. *Beds* ICF 160.
Certified Medicaid.
Owner Proprietary Corp.
Admissions Requirements Medical examination.
Staff RNs; LPNs; Orderlies; Nurses aides; Physical therapists; Speech therapists; Activities coordinators; Dietitians.
Facilities Dining room; Activities room; Chapel; Crafts room; Laundry room; Barber/ Beauty shop.
Activities Arts & crafts; Cards; Games; Reading groups; Prayer groups; Movies; Shopping trips; Social/Cultural gatherings.

Ollie Steele Burden Nursing Home
4200 Essen Ln, Baton Rouge, LA, 70809
(504) 926-0091
Admin Sr Rose M Fitzgerald.
Licensure Intermediate care. *Beds* 60.
Owner Nonprofit Corp.

Capitol Nursing Home*
11546 Florida Blvd, Baton Rouge, LA, 70815
(504) 275-0474
Admin Mary Alice Latil. *Medical Dir/Dir of Nursing* Kathy Hagan.
Licensure Intermediate care. *Beds* 85.
Certified Medicaid.
Admissions Requirements Physician's request.
Staff RNs 1 (ft), 1 (pt); LPNs 7 (ft); Nurses aides 25 (ft); Activities coordinators 1 (ft); Dietitians 1 (ft), 1 (pt).
Facilities Dining room; Activities room; Chapel; Crafts room; Laundry room; Barber/ Beauty shop; Library.
Activities Arts & crafts; Cards; Games; Reading groups; Prayer groups; Movies; Shopping trips; Social/Cultural gatherings.

The Care Center
11188 Florida Blvd, Baton Rouge, LA, 70815
(504) 275-7570
Admin Cindy S Quirk. *Medical Dir/Dir of Nursing* Dannette Craft.

Licensure Intermediate care. *Beds* ICF 106.
Certified Medicaid.
Owner Proprietary Corp.
Admissions Requirements Medical examination.
Staff RNs 1 (ft); LPNs 5 (ft), 3 (pt); Nurses aides 64 (ft), 6 (pt); Activities coordinators 1 (ft); Dietitians 1 (pt).
Facilities Dining room; Activities room; Crafts room; Laundry room; Barber/Beauty shop.
Activities Arts & crafts; Cards; Games; Reading groups; Prayer groups; Movies; Shopping trips; Social/Cultural gatherings.

Convention Street Nursing Center*
PO Box 65274, 4660 Convention St, Baton Rouge, LA, 70896
(504) 926-5884
Admin Alan Barnett.
Licensure Intermediate care. *Beds* 54.
Certified Medicaid.

Fountain Lodge Nursing Home*
4005 North Blvd, Baton Rouge, LA, 70806
(504) 387-9848
Admin Muriel L Bates.
Licensure Intermediate care. *Beds* 184.
Certified Medicaid.

Guest House of Baton Rouge*
10145 Florida Blvd, Baton Rouge, LA, 70815
(504) 272-0111
Admin J M Powell & Mary N Powell. *Medical Dir/Dir of Nursing* Dr O P McCutchen.
Licensure Intermediate care. *Beds* 126.
Admissions Requirements Medical examination; Physician's request.
Staff RNs 3 (ft), 2 (pt); LPNs 5 (ft), 3 (pt); Orderlies 5 (ft), 3 (pt); Nurses aides 40 (ft), 8 (pt); Physical therapists 1 (pt); Occupational therapists 1 (ft); Activities coordinators 1 (ft); Dietitians 1 (pt).
Facilities Dining room; Physical therapy room; Activities room; Chapel; Crafts room; Laundry room; Barber/Beauty shop; Library.
Activities Arts & crafts; Games; Reading groups; Prayer groups; Shopping trips; Social/Cultural gatherings.

Hillhaven Rest Home
4100 North Blvd, Baton Rouge, LA, 70806
(504) 387-6704
Admin Marion A Cangelosi Jr. *Medical Dir/ Dir of Nursing* M Landry.
Licensure Intermediate care. *Beds* 123.
Certified Medicaid.
Owner Proprietary Corp (Hillhaven Corp).
Admissions Requirements Minimum age 25; Medical examination; Physician's request.
Staff RNs 2 (ft); LPNs 10 (ft), 3 (pt); Orderlies 2 (ft); Nurses aides 32 (ft); Activities coordinators 1 (ft); Dietitians 1 (ft).
Languages French
Facilities Dining room; Activities room; Laundry room; Barber/Beauty shop.
Activities Arts & crafts; Cards; Games; Reading groups; Prayer groups; Movies; Shopping trips; Social/Cultural gatherings.

Hillhaven Rest Home 1*
170 W Washington St, Baton Rouge, LA, 70802
(504) 343-8770
Admin Elaine S Wells.
Licensure Intermediate care. *Beds* 89.
Certified Medicaid.
Owner Proprietary Corp (Hillhaven Corp).

Jefferson Manor Nursing Home*
9919 Jefferson Hwy, Baton Rouge, LA, 70809
(504) 293-1434
Admin Danny Brown.
Licensure Intermediate care. *Beds* 120.
Certified Medicaid.
Staff RNs 1 (ft); LPNs 6 (ft); Nurses aides 26 (ft); Physical therapists 1 (pt); Reality therapists 1 (pt); Recreational therapists 1

(pt); Occupational therapists 1 (pt); Speech therapists 1 (pt); Activities coordinators 1 (ft), 1 (pt); Dietitians 1 (pt); Dentists 1 (pt); Ophthalmologists 1 (pt); Podiatrists 1 (pt).
Facilities Dining room; Physical therapy room; Activities room; Chapel; Crafts room; Laundry room; Barber/Beauty shop; Library.
Activities Arts & crafts; Cards; Games; Prayer groups; Movies; Shopping trips; Social/Cultural gatherings.

Patio Lodge Nursing Home*
4363 Convention St, Baton Rouge, LA, 70806
(504) 383-6134 or 344-7849
Admin Gordon Jeansonne.
Licensure Intermediate care. *Beds* 141.
Certified Medicaid.

QC II Nursing Care Center of Baton Rouge
7414 Sumrall Dr, Baton Rouge, LA, 70812
(504) 356-0644
Admin Michael Bermes. *Medical Dir/Dir of Nursing* Teresa Harris RN.
Licensure Intermediate care. *Beds* ICF 144.
Certified Medicaid.
Owner Proprietary Corp.
Admissions Requirements Medical examination.
Staff Physicians 1 (ft); RNs 1 (ft); LPNs 9 (ft), 32 (pt); Orderlies 3 (ft); Nurses aides 22 (ft), 11 (pt); Activities coordinators 1 (ft), 1 (pt); Dietitians 1 (pt).
Facilities Dining room; Activities room; Crafts room; Laundry room; Barber/Beauty shop; Doctor's office.
Activities Arts & crafts; Cards; Games; Reading groups; Prayer groups; Movies; Shopping trips; Social/Cultural gatherings.

The Retirement Center
14686 Old Hammond Hwy, Baton Rouge, LA, 70816
(504) 272-9339
Admin Nan Laughlin. *Medical Dir/Dir of Nursing* Pat Chance.
Licensure Skilled care; Intermediate care; Apartments. *Beds* 80.
Owner Proprietary Corp.
Admissions Requirements Medical examination.
Staff RNs 1 (ft); LPNs 7 (ft), 1 (pt); Orderlies 1 (ft); Nurses aides 18 (ft); Activities coordinators 1 (ft).
Facilities Dining room; Activities room; Chapel; Crafts room; Laundry room; Barber/Beauty shop; Library.
Activities Arts & crafts; Cards; Games; Reading groups; Prayer groups; Movies; Shopping trips; Social/Cultural gatherings.

Sterling Place
3888 North Blvd, Baton Rouge, LA, 70806
(504) 344-3551
Admin Jeff Dungan NHA. *Medical Dir/Dir of Nursing* Connie Harig.
Licensure Intermediate care. *Beds* ICF 58.
Certified Medicaid.
Owner Nonprofit Corp.
Admissions Requirements Medical examination.
Staff Physicians 1 (ft); RNs 1 (ft); LPNs; Nurses aides 16 (ft), 3 (pt); Physical therapists 1 (pt); Speech therapists 1 (pt); Activities coordinators 1 (ft); Dietitians 1 (ft).
Facilities Dining room; Activities room; Crafts room; Laundry room; Barber/Beauty shop.
Activities Arts & crafts; Cards; Games; Reading groups; Prayer groups; Movies; Shopping trips; Social/Cultural gatherings.

BELLE CHASSE

Metropolitan Developmental Center
PO Box 7070, Belle Chasse, LA, 70037
(504) 394-1200
Admin Wayne Greenleaf. *Medical Dir/Dir of Nursing* Norman Leslie MD; Sandra G Bryant RN DON.
Licensure Intermediate care for mentally retarded. *Beds* ICF/MR 350.
Owner Publicly owned.
Admissions Requirements Minimum age 7; Medical examination.
Staff Physicians 3 (ft), 6 (pt); RNs; LPNs; Orderlies; Nurses aides; Physical therapists 1 (ft), 2 (pt); Recreational therapists 6 (ft); Occupational therapists 1 (ft); Speech therapists 3 (ft), 1 (pt); Activities coordinators; Dietitians 1 (ft); Dentists 1 (pt); Podiatrists 1 (ft); Audiologists 2 (ft), 2 (pt); Psychologists 10 (ft), 3 (pt); Pharmacists 3 (ft).
Facilities Dining room; Physical therapy room; Activities room; Chapel; Crafts room; Laundry room; Barber/Beauty shop; Library; Theatre; Canteen; Bakery; Gift shop; Clothing store; Workshop; Special school district; Adult education.
Activities Arts & crafts; Cards; Games; Reading groups; Prayer groups; Movies; Shopping trips; Social/Cultural gatherings; Community events.

BERNICE

Pine Crest Manor Nursing Home
101 Reeves St, Bernice, LA, 71222
(318) 285-7600
Admin Helen Campbell. *Medical Dir/Dir of Nursing* W C Reeves MD.
Licensure Intermediate care. *Beds* 126.
Certified Medicaid.
Staff Physicians 1 (pt); RNs 1 (ft); LPNs 10 (ft), 1 (pt); Orderlies 4 (ft); Nurses aides 33 (ft), 4 (pt); Activities coordinators 1 (ft), 1 (pt); Dietitians 1 (pt).
Facilities Dining room; Physical therapy room; Activities room; Chapel; Crafts room; Laundry room; Barber/Beauty shop.
Activities Arts & crafts; Games; Reading groups; Prayer groups; Movies; Shopping trips; Social/Cultural gatherings.

BOGALUSA

Rest Haven Nursing Home*
1301 Harrison St, Bogalusa, LA, 70427
(504) 732-3909
Admin James E Morris.
Licensure Intermediate care. *Beds* 204.
Certified Medicaid.

BOSSIER CITY

Bossier Health Care Center
PO Box 6358, 2901 Douglas Dr, Bossier City, LA, 71111
(318) 747-2700, 747-2701
Admin John B Williams. *Medical Dir/Dir of Nursing* T A Riley MD; Connie Kurz RN.
Licensure Intermediate care. *Beds* ICF 138.
Certified Medicaid; Medicare.
Owner Proprietary Corp.
Admissions Requirements Minimum age 18.
Staff Physicians; RNs; LPNs; Orderlies; Nurses aides; Physical therapists; Recreational therapists; Speech therapists; Activities coordinators; Dietitians; Dentists; Ophthalmologists; Podiatrists.
Facilities Dining room; Activities room; Chapel; Crafts room; Laundry room; Barber/Beauty shop.
Activities Arts & crafts; Cards; Games; Reading groups; Prayer groups; Movies; Shopping trips; Social/Cultural gatherings.

Heritage Manor Nursing Home of Bossier City*
2575 N Airline Dr, Bossier City, LA, 71010
(318) 746-7466
Admin Josey H Nelson.
Licensure Intermediate care. *Beds* 63.
Certified Medicaid.
Owner Proprietary Corp (Southmark Heritage Corp).

Northwest Louisiana State School
5401 Shed Rd B, Bossier City, LA, 71010
(318) 742-6220
Admin Charles Meehan. *Medical Dir/Dir of Nursing* C B Erickson MD.
Licensure Intermediate care for mentally retarded. *Beds* ICF/MR 265. *Certified* Medicaid.
Owner Publicly owned.
Admissions Requirements Medical examination.
Staff Physicians 2 (ft), 4 (pt); RNs 7 (ft); LPNs 18 (ft); Nurses aides 265 (ft); Physical therapists 1 (ft), 1 (pt); Recreational therapists 2 (ft); Occupational therapists 1 (ft); Speech therapists 1 (ft); Activities coordinators 1 (ft); Dietitians 1 (ft).
Facilities Dining room; Physical therapy room; Activities room; Chapel; Crafts room; Laundry room; Barber/Beauty shop; Library.
Activities Arts & crafts; Games; Movies; Shopping trips; Social/Cultural gatherings.

Pilgrim Manor of Bossier City—North
1524 Doctors Dr, Bossier City, LA, 71010
(318) 742-1623
Admin William V Hines. *Medical Dir/Dir of Nursing* Ronald Hines DON.
Licensure Intermediate care. *Beds* ICF 177.
Certified Medicare.
Owner Proprietary Corp.
Admissions Requirements Medical examination; Physician's request.
Staff RNs 3 (ft); LPNs 21 (ft), 2 (pt); Nurses aides 60 (ft); Activities coordinators 1 (ft).
Languages Spanish
Facilities Dining room; Activities room; Chapel; Laundry room; Barber/Beauty shop; Library.
Activities Cards; Games; Reading groups; Movies; Shopping trips; Social/Cultural gatherings.

Pilgrim Manor of Bossier City—South*
1525 Fullilove Dr, Bossier City, LA, 71112
(318) 742-5420
Admin Byron Neal Hines.
Licensure Intermediate care. *Beds* 96.
Certified Medicaid.

BUNKIE

Bayou Vista Manor Nursing Home*
PO Box 270, 323 Evergreen Rd, Bunkie, LA, 71322
(318) 346-2080
Admin Ray Buckner.
Licensure Intermediate care. *Beds* 170.
Certified Medicaid.

CENTERPOINT

Oak Haven Nursing Home*
PO Box 198, Centerpoint, LA, 71323
(318) 253-4601
Admin Linda Scanlan.
Licensure Intermediate care. *Beds* 104.
Certified Medicaid.
Staff Physicians 1 (pt); RNs 1 (ft), 1 (pt); LPNs 5 (ft), 3 (pt); Orderlies 1 (pt); Nurses aides 25 (ft), 11 (pt); Activities coordinators 1 (ft); Dietitians 1 (pt); Dentists 1 (pt).
Facilities Dining room; Crafts room; Laundry room; Barber/Beauty shop.
Activities Arts & crafts; Cards; Games; Prayer groups; Shopping trips; Social/Cultural gatherings.

CHURCH POINT

Acadia—St Landry Guest Home
830 S Broadway St, Church Point, LA, 70525
(318) 684-6316
Admin Carole L Thibodaux RN NHA.
Medical Dir/Dir of Nursing Janis Garber RN.
Licensure Intermediate care. *Beds* ICF 126.
Certified Medicaid.
Owner Proprietary Corp.
Admissions Requirements Medical examination; Physician's request.
Staff RNs 2 (ft); LPNs 10 (ft); Nurses aides 31 (ft), 4 (pt).
Languages French
Facilities Dining room; Activities room; Chapel; Laundry room; Barber/Beauty shop.
Activities Arts & crafts; Cards; Games; Prayer groups; Movies; Shopping trips; Social/Cultural gatherings.

CLINTON

Grace Nursing Home
PO Box 945, Hwy 67 S, Clinton, LA, 70722
(504) 683-8533
Admin Martin M Stott. *Medical Dir/Dir of Nursing* Maydee Rushing.
Licensure Intermediate care. *Beds* ICF 128.
Owner Proprietary Corp.
Admissions Requirements Medical examination.
Staff Physicians 1 (pt); RNs 1 (ft), 1 (pt); LPNs 6 (ft), 3 (pt); Orderlies 2 (ft); Nurses aides 37 (ft), 8 (pt); Physical therapists 1 (pt); Reality therapists 1 (pt); Recreational therapists 1 (pt); Occupational therapists 1 (pt); Speech therapists 1 (pt); Activities coordinators 1 (ft); Dietitians 1 (pt).
Facilities Dining room; Activities room; Crafts room; Laundry room; Barber/Beauty shop.
Activities Arts & crafts; Games; Reading groups; Prayer groups; Movies; Shopping trips; Social/Cultural gatherings.

COLFAX

Grant Manor Nursing Home*
Highway 8, Colfax, LA, 71417
(318) 448-0604
Admin Colene D Bankston. *Medical Dir/Dir of Nursing* Dr G C Bohm.
Licensure Intermediate care. *Beds* 140.
Certified Medicaid.
Admissions Requirements Medical examination; Physician's request.
Staff Physicians 4 (ft), 6 (pt); RNs 2 (ft); LPNs 6 (ft), 4 (pt); Nurses aides 30 (ft), 10 (pt); Physical therapists 2 (ft), 1 (pt); Activities coordinators 1 (ft); Dietitians 1 (ft); Dentists 1 (pt).
Facilities Dining room; Physical therapy room; Activities room; Crafts room; Laundry room; Barber/Beauty shop.
Activities Arts & crafts; Games; Reading groups; Prayer groups; Shopping trips.

COLUMBIA

Columbia Heights Nursing Home Inc
1612 Hwy 165 S, Columbia, LA, 71418
(318) 649-2702
Admin Robert H Causey.
Licensure Intermediate care. *Beds* ICF 157.
Certified Medicaid.
Owner Proprietary Corp.
Admissions Requirements Medical examination.
Staff Physicians 8 (pt); RNs 1 (ft), 2 (pt); LPNs 14 (ft); Nurses aides 46 (ft), 7 (pt); Physical therapists 1 (pt); Recreational therapists 1 (pt); Occupational therapists 1 (pt); Speech therapists 1 (pt); Activities coordinators 2 (pt); Dietitians 1 (pt).

Languages Spanish
Facilities Dining room; Physical therapy room; Activities room; Chapel; Crafts room; Laundry room; Barber/Beauty shop; Library.
Activities Arts & crafts; Games; Prayer groups; Movies; Shopping trips; Social/Cultural gatherings.

Columbia State School
PO Box 1559, Louisiana Hwy 850, Columbia, LA, 71435
(318) 649-2385
Admin Gene I Barrow. *Medical Dir/Dir of Nursing* Sylvia Malcomb.
Licensure Intermediate care for mentally retarded. *Beds* ICF/MR 32. *Certified* Medicaid.
Owner Publicly owned.
Admissions Requirements Minimum age 3; Medical examination.
Staff Physicians 3 (pt); RNs 1 (ft); LPNs 1 (ft); Physical therapists 1 (pt); Occupational therapists 1 (pt); Speech therapists 1 (ft); Dietitians 1 (ft); Dentist 1 (pt).
Facilities Dining room; Physical therapy room; Activities room; Laundry room; Library; Adaptive physical education & diagnostic areas.
Activities Cards; Games; Reading groups; Movies; Shopping trips; Social/Cultural gatherings.

COUSHATTA

Senior Citizens Center*
1108 Ringgold Ave, Coushatta, LA, 71019
(318) 932-5202
Admin Len Stephens. *Medical Dir/Dir of Nursing* Elsie Madden RN.
Licensure Intermediate care. *Beds* 83.
Certified Medicaid.
Admissions Requirements Medical examination.
Staff RNs 1 (ft); LPNs 4 (ft), 1 (pt); Nurses aides 18 (ft), 5 (pt); Physical therapists 1 (pt); Activities coordinators 1 (ft); Dietitians 1 (pt).
Facilities Dining room; Activities room; Laundry room; Barber/Beauty shop.
Activities Cards; Games; Prayer groups; Movies; Shopping trips; Social/Cultural gatherings.

Springville Nursing Center*
Springville Rd, Coushatta, LA, 71019
(318) 932-5006
Admin Len W Stephens. *Medical Dir/Dir of Nursing* Loyce V Plunkett RN.
Licensure Intermediate care. *Beds* 74.
Certified Medicaid.
Admissions Requirements Medical examination.
Staff RNs 1 (ft); LPNs 4 (ft), 1 (pt); Orderlies 3 (ft), 2 (pt); Nurses aides 18 (ft), 3 (pt); Physical therapists 1 (pt); Activities coordinators 1 (ft); Dietitians 1 (pt).
Facilities Dining room; Activities room; Laundry room; Barber/Beauty shop.
Activities Arts & crafts; Games; Prayer groups; Movies; Shopping trips; Social/Cultural gatherings; Field trips.

COVINGTON

Forest Manor Nursing Home
Madisonville Hwy, Covington, LA, 70433
(504) 892-6900
Admin Jon Franzke. *Medical Dir/Dir of Nursing* Brook McDonald.
Licensure Intermediate care. *Beds* ICF 192.
Certified Medicaid.
Owner Proprietary Corp.
Staff RNs; LPNs; Orderlies; Nurses aides; Activities coordinators; Dietitians.
Activities Arts & crafts; Cards; Games; Reading groups; Prayer groups; Movies; Shopping trips.

CROWLEY

Bayou Village Nursing Center*
PO Drawer 387, 1101 S Eastern Ave, Crowley, LA, 70526
(318) 783-2740
Admin Allen Carrier.
Licensure Intermediate care. *Beds* 97.
Certified Medicaid.

Christian Villa*
1120 W Hutchinson, Crowley, LA, 70526
(318) 783-5533
Admin Willie Maynard Jr. *Medical Dir/Dir of Nursing* J C Dauphin MD.
Licensure Intermediate care. *Beds* 73.
Certified Medicaid.
Admissions Requirements Medical examination; Physician's request.
Staff Physicians 1 (ft), 1 (pt); RNs 1 (ft); LPNs 4 (ft), 2 (pt); Orderlies 3 (ft); Nurses aides 41 (ft); Physical therapists 1 (pt); Recreational therapists 1 (ft); Occupational therapists 1 (pt); Activities coordinators 1 (ft); Dietitians 1 (ft); Dentists 1 (pt); Ophthalmologists 1 (pt).
Facilities Dining room; Laundry room; Lounge.
Activities Arts & crafts; Cards; Games; Reading groups; Prayer groups; Movies; Shopping trips; Social/Cultural gatherings.

Crowley Town & Country Nursing Center Inc*
1400 E Elm St, PO Box 1274, Crowley, LA, 70526
(318) 783-8101
Admin Cynthia Lege. *Medical Dir/Dir of Nursing* H Lawrence Gardiner MD.
Licensure Intermediate care. *Beds* 124.
Certified Medicaid.
Owner Proprietary Corp (US Care Corp).
Admissions Requirements Medical examination; Physician's request.
Staff Physicians 1 (ft); RNs 1 (ft); LPNs 9 (ft), 1 (pt); Orderlies 1 (ft); Nurses aides 20 (ft), 5 (pt); Physical therapists 1 (pt); Activities coordinators 1 (ft).
Facilities Dining room; Activities room; Chapel; Crafts room; Laundry room; Library.
Activities Arts & crafts; Cards; Games; Prayer groups; Movies; Social/Cultural gatherings.

Heritage Manor of Crowley*
PO Drawer 1547, 1526 N Ave I, Crowley, LA, 70526
(318) 783-2363
Admin Marian A Trahan.
Licensure Intermediate care. *Beds* 57.
Certified Medicaid.
Owner Proprietary Corp (Southmark Heritage Corp).
Admissions Requirements Medical examination.
Staff RNs 1 (ft); LPNs 3 (ft), 4 (pt); Nurses aides 40 (ft), 3 (pt); Activities coordinators 1 (ft); Dietitians 1 (pt).
Facilities Dining room; Laundry room; Barber/Beauty shop.
Activities Arts & crafts; Cards; Games; Reading groups; Prayer groups; Movies; Shopping trips; Social/Cultural gatherings.

CUT OFF

South Lafourche Nursing Center*
PO Box 338, Cut Off, LA, 70345
(504) 693-8677
Admin Lou Gaspard. *Medical Dir/Dir of Nursing* Dr Seludd.
Licensure Intermediate care. *Beds* 122.
Certified Medicaid.
Admissions Requirements Medical examination.
Staff Physicians 1 (ft); RNs 1 (ft); LPNs 6 (ft); Orderlies 3 (ft); Nurses aides 26 (ft); Physical therapists 1 (ft); Occupational

therapists 1 (pt); Speech therapists 1 (pt); Activities coordinators 1 (ft); Dietitians 1 (pt); Dentists 1 (pt); Ophthalmologists 1 (pt); Podiatrists 1 (pt); Audiologists 1 (pt).
Facilities Dining room; Physical therapy room; Activities room; Chapel; Crafts room; Laundry room; Barber/Beauty shop; Library.
Activities Arts & crafts; Games; Prayer groups; Movies; Shopping trips; Social/Cultural gatherings.

DELHI

Delhi Guest Home
203 Rancher St, Delhi, LA, 71232
(318) 878-5106
Admin Archie B Clayton Jr. *Medical Dir/Dir of Nursing* Lessie Boyett.
Licensure Intermediate care for mentally retarded. *Beds* ICF/MR 145. *Certified* Medicaid; Medicare.
Owner Proprietary Corp.
Admissions Requirements Minimum age 14.
Staff RNs 1 (ft); LPNs 7 (ft); Orderlies 65 (ft); Nurses aides 2 (pt); Recreational therapists 3 (ft); Occupational therapists 1 (pt); Speech therapists 1 (pt); Activities coordinators 7 (ft); Dietitians 1 (ft).
Facilities Dining room; Activities room; Laundry room; Barber/Beauty shop.
Activities Arts & crafts; Games; Reading groups; Movies; Shopping trips; Social/Cultural gatherings.

Richland Nursing Home*
504 N Charter St, Delhi, LA, 71232
(318) 878-2417
Admin Allen S Brown.
Licensure Intermediate care. *Beds* 87. *Certified* Medicaid.
Staff RNs 1 (ft); LPNs 6 (ft); Orderlies 1 (ft); Nurses aides 18 (ft); Physical therapists; Activities coordinators; Dentists; Ophthalmologists.
Facilities Dining room; Barber/Beauty shop.
Activities Arts & crafts; Cards; Games; Reading groups; Prayer groups; Movies.

DENHAM SPRINGS

Golden Age Nursing Home*
4-H Club Rd, Denham Springs, LA, 70726
(504) 665-5544
Admin Cindy Quirk. *Medical Dir/Dir of Nursing* Louise Corkern.
Licensure Intermediate care. *Beds* 175. *Certified* Medicaid.
Staff Physicians 9 (pt); RNs 1 (ft), 1 (pt); LPNs 10 (ft), 3 (pt); Nurses aides 27 (ft), 23 (pt); Physical therapists 1 (pt); Occupational therapists 1 (pt); Speech therapists 1 (pt); Activities coordinators 1 (ft), 1 (pt); Dietitians 1 (pt); Dentists 1 (pt); Ophthalmologists 1 (pt); Podiatrists 1 (pt).
Facilities Dining room; Physical therapy room; Activities room; Crafts room; Laundry room; Barber/Beauty shop; Sunroom.
Activities Arts & crafts; Cards; Games; Reading groups; Prayer groups; Movies; Shopping trips; Social/Cultural gatherings; Field trips.

Harvest Manor Nursing Home
9171 Cockerham Rd, Denham Springs, LA, 70726
(504) 665-8946
Admin Bobby Beebe. *Medical Dir/Dir of Nursing* Bebe Sylar.
Licensure Intermediate care. *Beds* ICF 176. *Certified* Medicaid.
Owner Proprietary Corp.
Admissions Requirements Medical examination.
Staff RNs 2 (ft), 2 (pt); LPNs 8 (ft), 2 (pt); Nurses aides 19 (ft); Activities coordinators 1 (ft); Dietitians 1 (ft).

Facilities Dining room; Activities room; Laundry room; Barber/Beauty shop.
Activities Prayer groups; Movies; Social/Cultural gatherings.

DEQUINCY

Greenhills Nursing Home*
PO Box 1219, 602 N Division, DeQuincy, LA, 70633
(318) 786-2466
Admin Sidney O Sanders.
Licensure Intermediate care. *Beds* 76. *Certified* Medicaid.

DERIDDER

Beauregard Nursing Home*
PO Box 230, 1420 Blankenship Dr, DeRidder, LA, 70630
(318) 463-9022
Admin George Mitchell.
Licensure Intermediate care. *Beds* 142. *Certified* Medicaid.

Westwood Manor Nursing Home*
810 High School Dr, DeRidder, LA, 70634
(318) 463-6293
Admin Benson W Sylvest.
Licensure Intermediate care. *Beds* 76. *Certified* Medicaid.

DONALDSONVILLE

D'Ville House*
PO Box 799, Vatican Dr, Donaldsonville, LA, 70346
(504) 473-8614
Admin Barbara Ourso.
Licensure Intermediate care. *Beds* 133. *Certified* Medicaid.

ERATH

Morris Lahasky Nursing Home*
501 E Conrad St, Erath, LA, 70533
(318) 937-6752
Admin Hazel Hebert. *Medical Dir/Dir of Nursing* Dr Bernard Lahasky.
Licensure Intermediate care. *Beds* 128. *Certified* Medicaid.
Staff Physicians 6 (ft); RNs 1 (ft), 1 (pt); Orderlies 2 (ft), 1 (pt); Nurses aides 32 (ft), 5 (pt); Physical therapists 1 (pt); Activities coordinators 1 (ft); Dietitians 1 (pt).
Languages French
Facilities Dining room; Physical therapy room; Activities room; Chapel; Crafts room; Laundry room; Barber/Beauty shop.
Activities Arts & crafts; Cards; Games; Reading groups; Prayer groups; Movies; Shopping trips; Social/Cultural gatherings.

EUNICE

Nursing Home of Eunice*
1100 Nile St, Eunice, LA, 70535
(318) 457-2681
Admin June Dupuis. *Medical Dir/Dir of Nursing* Dr Brian Heinen.
Licensure Intermediate care. *Beds* 146. *Certified* Medicaid.
Admissions Requirements Medical examination; Physician's request.
Staff Physicians 1 (pt); RNs 1 (ft); LPNs 12 (ft), 4 (pt); Nurses aides 54 (ft), 14 (pt); Physical therapists 1 (pt); Activities coordinators 2 (ft); Dietitians 1 (pt); Dentists 1 (pt).
Facilities Dining room; Activities room; Crafts room; Laundry room; Barber/Beauty shop.
Activities Arts & crafts; Cards; Games; Reading groups; Prayer groups; Movies; Shopping trips; Social/Cultural gatherings.

FARMERVILLE

Lakeview Nursing Home*
110 W Hill St, Farmerville, LA, 71241
(318) 368-3103
Admin Donnice Reynolds. *Medical Dir/Dir of Nursing* Carol Kennedy RN.
Licensure Intermediate care. *Beds* 115. *Certified* Medicaid.
Admissions Requirements Medical examination.
Staff RNs 2 (ft); LPNs 10 (ft); Orderlies 1 (ft); Nurses aides 35 (ft); Physical therapists 1 (pt); Recreational therapists 1 (ft); Activities coordinators 1 (ft); Dietitians 1 (ft).
Facilities Dining room; Physical therapy room; Activities room; Crafts room; Laundry room; Barber/Beauty shop.
Activities Arts & crafts; Cards; Games; Reading groups; Prayer groups; Movies; Shopping trips; Social/Cultural gatherings.

FERRIDAY

Concordia Parish Rest Home
411 N 4th St, Ferriday, LA, 71334
(318) 757-2181
Admin Floyd Thornhill.
Licensure Intermediate care. *Beds* 60. *Certified* Medicaid.

Heritage Manor of Ferriday
PO Box 392, Hwy 65 N, Ferriday, LA, 71334
(318) 757-8671
Admin Tommy L Massey.
Licensure Intermediate care. *Beds* 60. *Certified* Medicaid.
Owner Proprietary Corp (Southmark Heritage Corp).

FRANKLIN

Franklin Nursing Home*
PO Box 1229, 1907 Chinaberry St, Franklin, LA, 70538
(318) 828-1918
Admin Amanda Landry.
Licensure Intermediate care. *Beds* 120. *Certified* Medicaid.

FRANKLINTON

Heritage Manor of Franklinton
Rt 7, Box 31, Franklinton, LA, 70438
(504) 839-4491
Admin George E Gardner Jr. *Medical Dir/Dir of Nursing* Dr Norman Ott MD; Charlotte Sheridan DON.
Licensure Intermediate care. *Beds* ICF 121. *Certified* Medicaid.
Owner Proprietary Corp (Southmark Heritage Corp).
Admissions Requirements Medical examination.
Facilities Dining room; Activities room; Crafts room; Laundry room; Barber/Beauty shop; Library.
Activities Arts & crafts; Cards; Games; Reading groups; Prayer groups; Movies; Social/Cultural gatherings.

GONZALES

Gonzales Health Care Center*
711 W Cornerview Rd, Gonzales, LA, 70737
(504) 644-6581
Admin Preston Broussard.
Licensure Intermediate care. *Beds* 102. *Certified* Medicaid.

Heritage Manor of Gonzales*
PO Box 518, 905 W Cornerview Rd, Gonzales, LA, 70737
(504) 644-5358
Admin Dick Bagwell.

Licensure Intermediate care. *Beds* 104.
Certified Medicaid.
Owner Proprietary Corp (Southmark Heritage Corp).

HAMMOND

Belle Maison Nursing Home
301 7th Ward Medical Plaza, Hammond, LA, 70401
(504) 542-0110
Admin E P Guitreau Jr. *Medical Dir/Dir of Nursing* Collins P Lipcomb MD.
Licensure Intermediate care. *Beds* 132.
Certified Medicaid.
Admissions Requirements Medical examination.
Staff Physicians; RNs 3 (ft); LPNs 10 (ft); Nurses aides 65 (ft); Physical therapists; Reality therapists; Recreational therapists 1 (ft); Speech therapists; Activities coordinators 1 (ft); Dietitians; Podiatrists.
Facilities Dining room; Physical therapy room; Activities room; Chapel; Crafts room; Laundry room; Barber/Beauty shop; Library.
Activities Arts & crafts; Cards; Games; Reading groups; Prayer groups; Movies; Social/Cultural gatherings.

Hammond Nursing Home*
501 Old Covington Hwy, Hammond, LA, 70401
(504) 542-1200
Admin Ray Naquin.
Licensure Intermediate care. *Beds* 120.
Certified Medicaid.

Hammond State School
Rte 3, Box 165-P, Hammond, LA, 70401
(504) 567-3111
Admin Austin H Glass.
Licensure Intermediate care for mentally retarded. *Beds* 750. *Certified* Medicaid.

Heritage Manor of Hammond*
800 S Oak St, Hammond, LA, 70401
(504) 345-7210
Admin Mike Wunnenberg.
Licensure Intermediate care. *Beds* 108.
Certified Medicaid.
Owner Proprietary Corp (Southmark Heritage Corp).

HARRISONBURG

Harrisonburg Nursing Center*
PO Box 307, Sicily St, Harrisonburg, LA, 71340
(318) 744-5954
Admin Beth Willis.
Licensure Intermediate care. *Beds* 104.
Certified Medicaid.

HARVEY

Manhattan Manor Extended Care Facility*
1020 Manhattan Blvd, Harvey, LA, 70058
(504) 362-2020
Admin Minette McCurley. *Medical Dir/Dir of Nursing* David Euans.
Licensure Skilled care; Intermediate care. *Beds* 102. *Certified* Medicaid; Medicare.
Owner Proprietary Corp (ARA Living Centers).
Admissions Requirements Medical examination; Physician's request.
Staff RNs 2 (ft); LPNs 12 (ft), 4 (pt); Orderlies 1 (ft); Nurses aides 35 (ft); Physical therapists 1 (pt); Speech therapists 1 (pt); Activities coordinators 1 (pt); Dietitians 1 (pt); Dentists 1 (pt); Podiatrists 1 (pt).
Facilities Dining room; Activities room; Barber/Beauty shop.
Activities Arts & crafts; Cards; Games; Reading groups; Prayer groups.

Manhattan Manor Guest House
2233 8th St, Harvey, LA, 70058
(504) 362-9522
Admin Ken Pitts. *Medical Dir/Dir of Nursing* Nancy Hembree.
Licensure Intermediate care. *Beds* ICF 100.
Certified Medicaid.
Owner Proprietary Corp (ARA Living Centers).
Staff Physicians 1 (pt); RNs 1 (ft); LPNs 10 (ft); Nurses aides 50 (ft); Physical therapists 1 (pt); Speech therapists 1 (pt); Activities coordinators 1 (ft); Dietitians 1 (pt); Dentists 1 (pt); Ophthalmologists 1 (pt).
Languages French, German
Facilities Dining room; Activities room; Crafts room; Laundry room; Barber/Beauty shop.
Activities Arts & crafts; Cards; Games; Reading groups; Prayer groups; Movies; Shopping trips; Social/Cultural gatherings.

HAYNESVILLE

Heritage Nursing Center
114 Bailey St, Haynesville, LA, 71038
(318) 624-1166
Admin John L Savagge Jr. *Medical Dir/Dir of Nursing* Dr E Butler; Rhonda Ward.
Licensure Intermediate care. *Beds* 38.
Certified Medicaid.
Owner Proprietary Corp.
Staff RNs 1 (ft); LPNs 5 (ft); Orderlies 1 (ft); Nurses aides 13 (ft); Activities coordinators 1 (ft); Dietitians 1 (ft).
Facilities Dining room; Activities room; Crafts room; Laundry room; Barber/Beauty shop.
Activities Arts & crafts; Cards; Games; Reading groups; Prayer groups.

HESSMER

Hessmer Nursing Home Inc
Rte 2, Box 61, Hessmer, LA, 71341
(318) 563-4246
Admin Nell Oliver. *Medical Dir/Dir of Nursing* Dr F P Bordelon; Debra Gaspard RN.
Licensure Intermediate care. *Beds* ICF 92.
Certified Medicaid.
Owner Privately owned.
Admissions Requirements Minimum age 18; Medical examination.
Staff Physicians 1 (ft); RNs 1 (ft); LPNs 6 (ft); Orderlies 2 (ft); Nurses aides 26 (ft); Activities coordinators; Dietitians 1 (ft); Ophthalmologists 1 (ft); Social Service 1 (ft).
Languages French
Facilities Dining room; Activities room; Chapel; Crafts room; Laundry room; Barber/Beauty shop.
Activities Arts & crafts; Games; Reading groups; Prayer groups; Movies; Shopping trips; Social/Cultural gatherings.

HINESTON

Fair Oaks Nursing Home
PO Box 32, Hwy 121, Hineston, LA, 71438
(318) 793-2368/793-8168
Admin Lois Carruth. *Medical Dir/Dir of Nursing* Margaret Guidry.
Licensure Intermediate care. *Beds* ICF 66.
Certified Medicaid; Medicare.
Owner Privately owned.
Admissions Requirements Medical examination.
Staff Physicians 1 (pt); RNs 1 (ft); LPNs 4 (ft), 3 (pt); Nurses aides 16 (ft), 6 (pt); Activities coordinators 1 (ft); Dietitians 1 (pt).
Facilities Dining room; Activities room; Crafts room; Laundry room.
Activities Cards; Games; Prayer groups; Movies; Shopping trips.

HOMER

Presbyterian Village of Homer*
PO Box 149, Homer, LA, 71040
(318) 927-6133
Admin Robert L McGaha. *Medical Dir/Dir of Nursing* Betty Smith.
Licensure Intermediate care. *Beds* 79.
Certified Medicaid.
Admissions Requirements Physician's request.
Staff Physicians 3 (pt); RNs 2 (ft); LPNs 7 (ft); Orderlies 5 (ft); Nurses aides 20 (ft); Recreational therapists 1 (ft), 1 (pt); Activities coordinators 1 (ft); Dietitians 1 (pt); Dentists 1 (pt).
Affiliation Presbyterian

HOUMA

Maranatha Care Center*
1395 W Tunnel Blvd, Houma, LA, 70360
(504) 872-4553
Admin Mary Klein.
Licensure Intermediate care. *Beds* 201.
Certified Medicaid.

Inez Sako Nursing Home II*
107 S Hollywood Rd, Houma, LA, 70360
(504) 876-3250
Admin Robert E Dill III.
Licensure Intermediate care. *Beds* 105.
Certified Medicaid.

IOTA

Southwest Louisiana State School
PO Box 218, Iota, LA, 70543
(318) 779-3305, 824-6250
Admin Samuel K McDaniel. *Medical Dir/Dir of Nursing* Gale Morgan RN.
Licensure Intermediate care for mentally retarded. *Beds* ICF/MR. *Certified* Medicaid; Medicare.
Owner Publicly owned.
Admissions Requirements Minimum age 5; Medical examination.
Staff Physicians 2 (pt); RNs 3 (ft); LPNs 3 (pt); Physical therapists 2 (pt); Recreational therapists 1 (ft); Occupational therapists 1 (pt); Speech therapists 3 (ft); Activities coordinators 1 (ft); Dietitians 1 (ft); Podiatrists 1 (pt).
Languages French
Facilities Dining room; Physical therapy room; Activities room; Crafts room; Laundry room; Barber/Beauty shop; Library; Training/therapy room.
Activities Arts & crafts; Cards; Games; Prayer groups; Movies; Shopping trips; Social/Cultural gatherings; Habilitation training.

JACKSON

Villa Feliciana State Hospital
PO Box 438, Jackson, LA, 70748
(504) 634-7793
Admin John A London.
Licensure Skilled care; Intermediate care. *Beds* 610. *Certified* Medicaid; Medicare.

JEFFERSON

Jefferson Health Care Center*
2200 Jefferson Hwy, Jefferson, LA, 70121
(504) 837-3144
Admin John Robert Laster.
Licensure Intermediate care. *Beds* 288.
Certified Medicaid.
Owner Proprietary Corp (ARA Living Centers).

JENA

Golden Age Nursing Center
PO Drawer 1366, Aimwell Rd, Jena, LA,
71342
(318) 992-4175
Admin V Lynn Conn. *Medical Dir/Dir of
Nursing* Betty Guynes.
Licensure Intermediate care. *Beds* ICF 88.
Certified Medicaid.
Owner Proprietary Corp.
Admissions Requirements Medical
examination.
Staff RNs 1 (ft); LPNs; Nurses aides 22 (ft).
Facilities Dining room; Laundry room;
Barber/Beauty shop.
Activities Arts & crafts; Cards; Games;
Reading groups; Prayer groups; Movies;
Shopping trips; Social/Cultural gatherings.

La Salle Nursing Home Inc
PO Drawer 1510, Hwy 84 W, Jena, LA, 71342
(318) 992-6627
Admin W J Nunnally. *Medical Dir/Dir of
Nursing* Suzanne Harris.
Licensure Intermediate care. *Beds* ICF 133.
Certified Medicaid.
Owner Nonprofit Corp.
Admissions Requirements Minimum age 18;
Medical examination.
Staff Physicians 4 (pt); RNs 3 (ft); LPNs 13
(ft); Nurses aides 56 (ft), 5 (pt); Activities
coordinators 1 (ft); Dietitians 1 (ft).
Facilities Dining room; Activities room;
Crafts room; Barber/Beauty shop; Library.
Activities Arts & crafts; Cards; Games;
Reading groups; Prayer groups; Movies;
Shopping trips; Social/Cultural gatherings.

JENNINGS

Jefferson Davis Nursing Home
PO Box 757, 1338 N Cutting Ave, Jennings,
LA, 70546-0757
(318) 824-3165
Admin Thomas L Qualey Jr. *Medical Dir/Dir
of Nursing* Louis Shirley MD; Tamea Robert
RN.
Licensure Intermediate care. *Beds* 135.
Certified Medicaid.
Owner Proprietary Corp.
Admissions Requirements Medical
examination; Physician's request.
Staff RNs 2 (ft), 1 (pt); LPNs 12 (ft), 2 (pt);
Nurses aides 35 (ft), 18 (pt); Physical
therapists 1 (pt); Activities coordinators 1
(ft); Dietitians 1 (pt); Podiatrists 1 (pt).
Languages French
Facilities Dining room; Physical therapy
room; Activities room; Crafts room; Laundry
room; Barber/Beauty shop; Library.
Activities Arts & crafts; Cards; Games;
Reading groups; Prayer groups; Movies;
Shopping trips; Social/Cultural gatherings;
GED classes.

Jennings Guest House*
203 S Louise St, Jennings, LA, 70546
(318) 824-2466
Admin Bobby R Linscomb.
Licensure Intermediate care. *Beds* 152.
Certified Medicaid.
Owner Proprietary Corp (US Care Corp).

JONESBORO

Carter Nursing Home*
503 W Main St, Jonesboro, LA, 71251
(318) 259-2729
Admin Catherine Walsworth.
Licensure Intermediate care. *Beds* 51.
Certified Medicaid.

Jackson Manor Nursing Home*
PO Box 669, Hwy 167 S, Jonesboro, LA,
71251
(318) 259-7386

Admin Charles E Pogue.
Licensure Intermediate care. *Beds* 84.
Certified Medicaid.

Wyatt Manor Nursing Home
PO Drawer L, Rte 3, Jonesboro, LA, 71251
(318) 259-3290
Admin Harold L Hickey. *Medical Dir/Dir of
Nursing* Judy Andrews RN.
Licensure Intermediate care. *Beds* ICF 62.
Certified Medicaid.
Owner Proprietary Corp.
Staff RNs 1 (ft); LPNs 6 (ft); Orderlies 1 (ft);
Nurses aides 18 (ft); Activities coordinators
1 (ft); Dietitians 1 (ft).

JONESVILLE

Homage Manor*
300 Nasif St, Jonesville, LA, 71343
(318) 339-7374
Admin Floyd Thornhill.
Licensure Intermediate care. *Beds* 54.
Certified Medicaid.

KAPLAN

Heritage Manor of Kaplan*
1300 W 8th St, Kaplan, LA, 70548
(318) 643-7302
Admin Barbara B Hair.
Licensure Intermediate care. *Beds* 120.
Certified Medicaid.
Owner Proprietary Corp (Southmark Heritage
Corp).

Vermilion Health Care Center
PO Box 100, Rte 2, Kaplan, LA, 70548
(318) 643-1949
Admin Al Breaux Jr. *Medical Dir/Dir of
Nursing* Dr George Desormeaux; Darlene
Deshotels RN.
Licensure Intermediate care. *Beds* ICF 120.
Certified Medicaid.
Owner Privately owned.
Admissions Requirements Physician's request.
Staff RNs 1 (ft); LPNs 10 (pt); Nurses aides
35 (ft), 4 (pt); Activities coordinators 1 (ft).
Languages French
Facilities Dining room; Activities room;
Chapel; Crafts room; Barber/Beauty shop.
Activities Arts & crafts; Cards; Games;
Reading groups; Prayer groups; Movies;
Shopping trips; Social/Cultural gatherings.

KENNER

Waldon Healthcare Center*
2401 Idaho Ave, Kenner, LA, 70062
(504) 466-0222
Admin Regina Danner. *Medical Dir/Dir of
Nursing* Dr Paez.
Licensure Intermediate care. *Beds* 205.
Certified Medicaid.
Owner Proprietary Corp (ARA Living
Centers).
Admissions Requirements Medical
examination; Physician's request.
Staff RNs 4 (ft), 2 (pt); LPNs 12 (ft), 5 (pt);
Nurses aides 60 (ft); Activities coordinators
2 (ft); Dietitians 2 (ft).
Facilities Dining room; Activities room;
Crafts room; Laundry room; Barber/Beauty
shop.
Activities Arts & crafts; Cards; Games;
Reading groups; Prayer groups; Movies;
Shopping trips; Social/Cultural gatherings;
Field trips.

KENTWOOD

Kentwood Manor Nursing Home
PO Box 67, Kentwood, LA, 70444
(504) 229-2112
Admin Tim Kirby. *Medical Dir/Dir of Nursing*
Willie M Rogers.

Licensure Intermediate care. *Beds* 134.
Certified Medicaid; Medicare.
Owner Proprietary Corp.
Admissions Requirements Medical
examination.
Staff Physicians; RNs; LPNs; Orderlies;
Nurses aides; Physical therapists; Reality
therapists; Recreational therapists; Speech
therapists; Activities coordinators; Dietitians;
Dentists; Ophthalmologists; Podiatrists.
Facilities Dining room; Physical therapy
room; Activities room; Laundry room;
Barber/Beauty shop.
Activities Arts & crafts; Games; Prayer groups;
Movies; Shopping trips; Social/Cultural
gatherings.

KINDER

Kinder Nursing Home*
Hwy 165 N, Kinder, LA, 70648
(318) 738-5671
Admin Ronnie Smith.
Licensure Intermediate care. *Beds* 100.
Certified Medicaid.
Admissions Requirements Minimum age 30;
Medical examination; Physician's request.
Staff RNs 1 (ft), 1 (pt); LPNs 8 (ft), 2 (pt);
Orderlies 2 (ft); Nurses aides 25 (ft), 8 (pt);
Activities coordinators 1 (ft); Dietitians 1
(pt).
Facilities Dining room; Activities room;
Laundry room; Barber/Beauty shop.
Activities Arts & crafts; Games; Prayer groups;
Movies.

LAFAYETTE

Acadiana Nursing Home
408 SE Evangeline Thruway, Lafayette, LA,
70501
(318) 235-9976
Admin Guy Sarver. *Medical Dir/Dir of
Nursing* Irene Tilbury DON.
Licensure Intermediate care. *Beds* ICF 92.
Certified Medicaid.
Owner Privately owned.
Staff Physicians 1 (ft); RNs 1 (ft); LPNs 6 (ft);
Orderlies 1 (ft); Nurses aides 35 (ft);
Physical therapists 2 (ft); Speech therapists 1
(ft); Activities coordinators 1 (ft); Dietitians
1 (ft).
Languages French
Facilities Dining room; Activities room;
Chapel; Laundry room; Barber/Beauty shop;
Library.
Activities Arts & crafts; Cards; Games;
Reading groups; Prayer groups; Movies;
Shopping trips; Social/Cultural gatherings.

Amelia Manor Nursing Home*
903 Center St, Lafayette, LA, 70501
(318) 234-7331
Admin J B Sarver. *Medical Dir/Dir of Nursing*
William Melencon.
Licensure Intermediate care. *Beds* 150.
Certified Medicaid.
Admissions Requirements Minimum age 40;
Medical examination; Physician's request.
Staff Physicians 3 (pt); RNs 1 (ft); LPNs 10
(ft), 3 (pt); Nurses aides 50 (ft), 5 (pt);
Physical therapists 1 (pt); Recreational
therapists 1 (ft); Occupational therapists 1
(pt); Speech therapists 1 (pt); Activities
coordinators 1 (ft); Dietitians 1 (pt); Dentists
2 (pt).
Facilities Dining room; Activities room;
Crafts room; Laundry room; Barber/Beauty
shop.
Activities Arts & crafts; Cards; Games; Prayer
groups; Movies; Shopping trips; Social/
Cultural gatherings.

Bethany MHS Care Center*
406 Saint Julien St, Lafayette, LA, 70507
(318) 234-2459
Licensure Intermediate care. *Beds* 42.

Affiliation Roman Catholic
Facilities Dining room; Chapel; Crafts room;
Laundry room; Barber/Beauty shop.
Activities Arts & crafts; Cards; Games; Prayer
groups; Movies.

Heritage Manor Nursing Home of Lafayette*
325 Bacque Crescent Dr, Lafayette, LA, 70503
(318) 232-0299
Admin David Reaves.
Licensure Intermediate care. *Beds* 60.
Certified Medicaid.
Owner Proprietary Corp (Southmark Heritage
Corp).
Admissions Requirements Medical
examination.
Staff Physicians 1 (pt); RNs 1 (ft); LPNs 7
(ft), 2 (pt); Nurses aides 20 (ft), 3 (pt);
Physical therapists 1 (pt); Reality therapists
1 (pt); Recreational therapists 1 (pt);
Occupational therapists 1 (pt); Speech
therapists 1 (pt); Activities coordinators 1
(ft); Dietitians 1 (pt); Dentists 1 (pt);
Podiatrists 1 (pt); Audiologists 1 (pt).
Facilities Dining room; Activities room;
Laundry room; Barber/Beauty shop.
Activities Arts & crafts; Cards; Games;
Reading groups; Prayer groups; Movies;
Shopping trips; Social/Cultural gatherings.

Lafayette Guest House*
431 E Lillian, Lafayette, LA, 70501
(318) 233-6855
Admin Cecel P Manuel. *Medical Dir/Dir of
Nursing* Dr Charles Dugal.
Licensure Intermediate care. *Beds* 206.
Certified Medicaid.
Owner Proprietary Corp (US Care Corp).
Admissions Requirements Physician's request.
Staff Physicians 1 (ft); RNs 1 (ft), 1 (pt);
LPNs 16 (ft); Orderlies 2 (ft); Nurses aides
21 (ft); Physical therapists; Reality
therapists; Dietitians 1 (pt); Dentists 1 (pt);
Ophthalmologists 1 (pt); Podiatrists 1 (pt);
Audiologists 1 (pt).

Lafayette Health Care Inc
433 E Lillian Rd, Lafayette, LA, 70501
(318) 233-7235
Admin Arthur O Arnold. *Medical Dir/Dir of
Nursing* Dr Donald Reed; Mrs Debra
Goodly.
Licensure Intermediate care. *Beds* ICF 130.
Certified Medicaid.
Owner Proprietary Corp (US Care Corp).
Admissions Requirements Minimum age 18.
Staff RNs; LPNs; Orderlies; Nurses aides;
Physical therapists; Reality therapists;
Recreational therapists; Occupational
therapists; Speech therapists; Activities
coordinators; Dietitians; Dentists.
Languages Creole, French
Facilities Dining room; Activities room;
Chapel; Laundry room; Barber/Beauty shop.
Activities Arts & crafts; Cards; Games;
Movies; Shopping trips; Social/Cultural
gatherings.

Landry Road Nursing Home*
1005 Landry Rd, Lafayette, LA, 70506
(318) 232-6370
Admin Barbara King. *Medical Dir/Dir of
Nursing* Anita Conner RN.
Licensure Intermediate care. *Beds* 101.
Certified Medicaid.
Admissions Requirements Medical
examination; Physician's request.
Staff RNs 1 (ft); LPNs 4 (ft), 5 (pt); Nurses
aides 18 (ft), 10 (pt); Physical therapists 1
(pt); Speech therapists 1 (pt); Activities
coordinators 1 (ft); Dietitians 1 (pt).
Facilities Dining room; Activities room;
Crafts room; Laundry room; Barber/Beauty
shop; Solarium.
Activities Arts & crafts; Cards; Games;
Reading groups; Prayer groups; Movies;
Social/Cultural gatherings.

Oakwood Village Nurse Care Center Inc
2500 E Simcoe St, Lafayette, LA, 70501
(318) 233-7115
Admin Gordon Doine. *Medical Dir/Dir of
Nursing* Kearney Veazey.
Licensure Intermediate care. *Beds* ICF 160.
Certified Medicaid.
Owner Proprietary Corp.
Admissions Requirements Minimum age 18;
Medical examination; Physician's request.
Staff RNs 1 (ft); LPNs 10 (ft), 9 (pt); Nurses
aides 42 (ft), 11 (pt); Recreational therapists
1 (ft); Activities coordinators 1 (ft), 1 (pt);
Dietitians 1 (pt); Social service director 1
(ft).
Languages French, Arabic
Facilities Dining room; Laundry room;
Barber/Beauty shop; Library; Living room-
Activities room-Chapel; Movie theater.
Activities Arts & crafts; Cards; Games;
Reading groups; Prayer groups; Movies;
Social/Cultural gatherings; Monthly birthday
parties.

LAKE CHARLES

Martin de Porres Multi-Care Center*
200 Teal St, Lake Charles, LA, 70601
(318) 439-5761
Admin Robert Leonards.
Licensure Intermediate care. *Beds* 235.
Certified Medicaid.
Affiliation Roman Catholic

Moss Bluff Manor*
Old Town Rd, Lake Charles, LA, 70601
(318) 436-9527
Admin Jimmy W White.
Licensure Intermediate care. *Beds* 90.
Certified Medicaid.

Oak Park Care Center
PO Box 1851, 2717 1st Ave, Lake Charles,
LA, 70601
(318) 478-2920, 478-2922
Admin Muriel L Bates. *Medical Dir/Dir of
Nursing* Dr Primeaux & Dr LeBeau; Anene
Restow RN.
Licensure Intermediate care. *Beds* ICF 177.
Certified Medicaid.
Owner Proprietary Corp (Manor Care).
Staff Physicians; RNs; LPNs; Nurses aides;
Reality therapists; Recreational therapists;
Activities coordinators; Dietitians.
Languages French
Affiliation Challenge Ministries
Activities Arts & crafts; Cards; Games;
Reading groups; Prayer groups; Movies;
Shopping trips; Social/Cultural gatherings.

Resthaven Nursing Center
PO Box 6736, 4532 Sale Ln, Lake Charles,
LA, 70606
(318) 477-6371
Admin Sereitha M McGee. *Medical Dir/Dir of
Nursing* Alecia Shatluck.
Licensure Intermediate care. *Beds* ICF 160.
Certified Medicaid.
Owner Proprietary Corp.
Admissions Requirements Medical
examination; Physician's request.
Staff Physicians 1 (pt); RNs 1 (ft); LPNs 8
(ft); Nurses aides 45 (ft); Physical therapists
1 (pt); Occupational therapists 1 (pt); Speech
therapists 1 (pt); Activities coordinators 1
(ft); Dietitians 1 (pt).
Languages French
Facilities Dining room; Activities room;
Laundry room; Barber/Beauty shop.
Activities Games; Prayer groups; Movies;
Shopping trips; Social/Cultural gatherings.

Robinswood School
200 Ave C, Lake Charles, LA, 70601
(318) 436-6664
Admin Gordon Propst. *Medical Dir/Dir of
Nursing* Melvin Morris MD; Toni Schell RN
DON.

Licensure Intermediate care for mentally
retarded. *Beds* ICF/MR 120. *Certified*
Medicaid.
Owner Proprietary Corp (Multicare
Management).
Admissions Requirements Minimum age 18;
Medical examination.
Languages Creole
Facilities Dining room; Physical therapy
room; Activities room; Crafts room; Laundry
room; Barber/Beauty shop; Library; Gym;
Classrooms; OT.
Activities Arts & crafts; Cards; Games;
Reading groups; Prayer groups; Movies;
Shopping trips; Social/Cultural gatherings;
Community activites.

Rosewood Nursing Home*
543 15th St, Lake Charles, LA, 70601
(318) 439-8338
Admin Jimmy W White.
Licensure Intermediate care. *Beds* 90.
Certified Medicaid.

LAKE PROVIDENCE

Shady Lake Nursing Home*
Mill St, Lake Providence, LA, 71254
(318) 559-2248
Admin Doris Johnston. *Medical Dir/Dir of
Nursing* Virginia Ratcliff.
Licensure Intermediate care. *Beds* 100.
Certified Medicaid.
Staff RNs 1 (ft); LPNs 8 (ft); Orderlies 4 (ft);
Nurses aides 22 (ft); Activities coordinators
1 (ft); Dietitians 1 (ft).
Facilities Dining room; Physical therapy
room; Activities room; Laundry room;
Barber/Beauty shop.
Activities Arts & crafts; Cards; Games; Prayer
groups; Movies; Shopping trips; Social/
Cultural gatherings.

LAPLACE

Twin Oaks Nursing & Convalescent Home*
1881 W 5th St, LaPlace, LA, 70068
(504) 652-9538
Admin Janet Beaman. *Medical Dir/Dir of
Nursing* S J St Martin MD.
Licensure Intermediate care. *Beds* 152.
Certified Medicaid.
Admissions Requirements Medical
examination; Physician's request.
Staff Physicians 1 (pt); RNs 1 (ft); LPNs 15
(ft); Nurses aides 45 (ft); Physical therapists
1 (pt); Activities coordinators 1 (ft);
Dietitians 1 (pt); Dentists 1 (pt); Podiatrists
1 (pt).
Facilities Dining room; Activities room;
Barber/Beauty shop.
Activities Arts & crafts; Games; Social/
Cultural gatherings.

LEESVILLE

Kurthwood Manor Nursing Home*
PO Box 270, Leesville, LA, 71446
(318) 239-6578
Admin Jerry L Wilson.
Licensure Intermediate care. *Beds* 142.
Certified Medicaid.

Leesville State School*
401 W Texas St, Leesville, LA, 71446
(318) 239-2687
Admin Joseph Martinez.
Licensure Intermediate care for mentally
retarded. *Beds* 96. *Certified* Medicaid.

Pine Haven Nursing Home*
Rte 2, Box 145, Leesville, LA, 71446
(318) 463-8778
Admin Lilly Allen.
Licensure Intermediate care. *Beds* 38.
Certified Medicaid.

LULING

Luling Nursing Home*
Paul Maillard Rd, Luling, LA, 70070
(504) 785-8271
Admin T E McConnell. *Medical Dir/Dir of Nursing* Irene Ham.
Licensure Intermediate care. *Beds* 189. *Certified* Medicaid.
Admissions Requirements Medical examination; Physician's request.
Staff Physicians 1 (pt); RNs 2 (ft), 3 (pt); LPNs 10 (ft); Nurses aides 37 (ft), 13 (pt); Activities coordinators 1 (ft).
Facilities Dining room; Laundry room; Barber/Beauty shop.
Activities Arts & crafts; Cards; Games; Prayer groups; Movies; Social/Cultural gatherings.

LUTCHER

Riverlands Health Care Center*
720 River Rd, Lutcher, LA, 70071
(504) 869-5029
Admin Sam E Narrow Jr.
Licensure Intermediate care. *Beds* 66. *Certified* Medicaid.

MAMOU

Savoy Care Center Inc
801 Poinciana Ave, Mamou, LA, 70554
(318) 468-0348
Admin Frank P Saroy III. *Medical Dir/Dir of Nursing* Laura Fontenot RN.
Licensure Intermediate care. *Beds* 92. *Certified* Medicaid.
Owner Nonprofit Corp.
Admissions Requirements Medical examination; Physician's request.
Staff Physicians; RNs; LPNs; Nurses aides; Physical therapists; Occupational therapists; Speech therapists; Activities coordinators; Dietitians.
Languages French
Facilities Dining room; Activities room; Chapel; Crafts room; Barber/Beauty shop.
Activities Arts & crafts; Cards; Games; Prayer groups; Shopping trips; Social/Cultural gatherings.

MANDEVILLE

Lacombe Nursing Home*
Hwy 190, PO Box 6, Mandeville, LA, 70448
(504) 529-5968
Admin Ronald Goux. *Medical Dir/Dir of Nursing* Dr Gerald Keller.
Licensure Intermediate care. *Beds* 97. *Certified* Medicaid.
Admissions Requirements Medical examination.
Staff Physicians 1 (ft); RNs 2 (ft); LPNs 3 (ft), 3 (pt); Nurses aides 15 (ft), 9 (pt); Activities coordinators.
Facilities Dining room; Activities room; Chapel; Crafts room; Laundry room; Barber/Beauty shop.
Activities Arts & crafts; Cards; Games; Reading groups; Prayer groups; Shopping trips; Social/Cultural gatherings.

Pontchartrain Guest House
PO Box 338, Hwy 190 & Atlin St, Mandeville, LA, 70448
(504) 626-8581
Admin Ronald A Goux. *Medical Dir/Dir of Nursing* Karen Jones.
Licensure Intermediate care. *Beds* ICF 182. *Certified* Medicaid; Medicare.
Owner Privately owned.
Admissions Requirements Medical examination.
Staff RNs 1 (ft); LPNs 8 (ft), 2 (pt); Orderlies 2 (ft); Nurses aides 35 (ft); Activities coordinators 2 (ft); Dietitians 1 (ft).

Facilities Dining room; Activities room; Chapel; Crafts room; Laundry room; Barber/Beauty shop.
Activities Arts & crafts; Cards; Games; Reading groups; Prayer groups; Movies; Shopping trips; Social/Cultural gatherings.

MANSFIELD

Heritage Manor of Mansfield*
102 E Schley St, Mansfield, LA, 71052
(318) 872-0276
Admin Vaughn G Gilbert.
Licensure Intermediate care. *Beds* 135. *Certified* Medicaid.
Owner Proprietary Corp (Southmark Heritage Corp).

MANSURA

Rio-Sol Nursing Home*
PO Box 85, Privot & Zelynne Sts, Mansura, LA, 71350
(318) 964-2198
Admin Laura Spruill.
Licensure Intermediate care. *Beds* 92. *Certified* Medicaid.

MANY

Heritage Manor of Many Number 1
PO Box 360, Natchitoches Hwy, Many, LA, 71449
(318) 256-9233
Admin Edwin E Teal. *Medical Dir/Dir of Nursing* Dr Richard J Oosta.
Licensure Intermediate care. *Beds* ICF 128. *Certified* Medicaid.
Owner Proprietary Corp (National Heritage).
Admissions Requirements Medical examination.
Staff RNs 2 (ft); LPNs 9 (ft), 3 (pt); Nurses aides 40 (ft), 8 (pt); Activities coordinators 1 (ft); Dietitians 1 (pt).
Facilities Dining room; Activities room; Laundry room; Barber/Beauty shop.
Activities Arts & crafts; Cards; Games; Movies; Social/Cultural gatherings.

Heritage Manor of Many Number 2
PO Box 112, Middle Creek Road, Many, LA, 71449
(318) 256-6281
Admin Judy Procell. *Medical Dir/Dir of Nursing* Renee M Blake.
Licensure Intermediate care. *Beds* ICF 60. *Certified* Medicaid.
Owner Proprietary Corp (Southmark Heritage Corp).
Admissions Requirements Medical examination.
Staff RNs 1 (ft); LPNs 5 (ft), 2 (pt); Nurses aides 18 (ft), 3 (pt); Activities coordinators 1 (ft).
Facilities Dining room; Laundry room; Barber/Beauty shop; Day Room.
Activities Arts & crafts; Games; Prayer groups; Movies; Social/Cultural gatherings.

MARION

Marion Nursing Home
PO Box 97, Marion, LA, 71260
(318) 292-4514
Admin Stan Beeson. *Medical Dir/Dir of Nursing* Susan Hiser.
Licensure Intermediate care. *Beds* ICF 77. *Certified* Medicaid.
Owner Privately owned.
Admissions Requirements Minimum age 17; Medical examination.
Staff Physicians 1 (pt); RNs 1 (ft), 1 (pt); LPNs 9 (ft); Orderlies 30 (ft), 10 (pt); Nurses aides; Activities coordinators 2 (ft), 1 (pt); Dietitians 1 (ft), 1 (pt).

Facilities Dining room; Activities room; Laundry room; Barber/Beauty shop.
Activities Arts & crafts; Cards; Games; Reading groups; Prayer groups; Movies; Shopping trips; Social/Cultural gatherings.

MARKSVILLE

Colonial Nursing Home Inc
413 N Washington St, Marksville, LA, 71351
(318) 256-4556
Admin Nell Oliver. *Medical Dir/Dir of Nursing* Karen Barbin RN DON.
Licensure Intermediate care. *Beds* ICF 104. *Certified* Medicaid.
Owner Privately owned.
Admissions Requirements Minimum age 18.
Staff RNs 1 (ft); LPNs 7 (ft); Orderlies 4 (ft); Nurses aides 25 (ft); Activities coordinators 1 (ft); Dietitians 1 (pt).
Languages French
Facilities Dining room; Activities room; Chapel; Crafts room; Laundry room; Barber/Beauty shop.
Activities Arts & crafts; Cards; Games; Reading groups; Prayer groups; Movies; Shopping trips; Social/Cultural gatherings.

Valley View Health Care Facility
PO Box 535, Mansur Hwy, Marksville, LA, 71351
(318) 253-6553
Admin Donna Caubarreaux.
Licensure Intermediate care. *Beds* 100. *Certified* Medicaid.
Staff Physicians; RNs; LPNs; Orderlies; Nurses aides; Activities coordinators; Dietitians.
Facilities Dining room; Activities room; Laundry room; Barber/Beauty shop.
Activities Arts & crafts; Cards; Games; Prayer groups; Movies; Shopping trips; Social/Cultural gatherings.

MARRERO

Heritage Manor Nursing Home of Marrero*
5301 August Ln, Marrero, LA, 70072
(504) 341-3658/347-3746
Admin Michael J Ford.
Licensure Intermediate care. *Beds* 134. *Certified* Medicaid.
Owner Proprietary Corp (Southmark Heritage Corp).

MER ROUGE

The Oak Woods
PO Box 263, Hwy W 165, Mer Rouge, LA, 71261
(318) 647-3691
Admin Ted Parker. *Medical Dir/Dir of Nursing* Dr Joe Williams; Cupid Maroney RN.
Licensure Skilled care; Intermediate care. *Beds* SNF 80; ICF 86. *Certified* Medicaid; Medicare.
Owner Nonprofit organization/foundation.
Admissions Requirements Medical examination; Physician's request.
Staff Physicians 1 (pt); RNs 1 (ft), 2 (pt); LPNs 22 (ft); Orderlies 9 (ft); Nurses aides 44 (ft); Physical therapists 1 (pt); Activities coordinators 1 (ft); Dietitians 1 (ft).
Facilities Dining room; Physical therapy room; Activities room; Chapel; Crafts room; Laundry room; Barber/Beauty shop; Library.
Activities Arts & crafts; Cards; Games; Reading groups; Prayer groups; Movies; Shopping trips; Social/Cultural gatherings.

MERRYVILLE

Merryville Nursing Center*
PO Drawer C, Bryan St, Merryville, LA,
70653
(318) 825-6181
Admin Benson Slyvest.
Licensure Intermediate care. *Beds* 50.
Certified Medicaid.

METAIRIE

Colonial Oaks Nursing Home
4312 Ithaca Street, Metairie, LA, 70006
(504) 887-6414
Admin George Fischer. *Medical Dir/Dir of
Nursing* Dr Samuel Greenberg; Mary Garcia.
Licensure Intermediate care. *Beds* 109.
Certified Medicaid.
Owner Proprietary Corp (ARA Living
Centers).
Admissions Requirements Medical
examination; Physician's request.
Staff Physicians 1 (ft); RNs 5 (ft); LPNs 8 (ft);
Orderlies 1 (ft); Nurses aides 41 (ft);
Physical therapists 1 (ft); Activities
coordinators 1 (ft); Dietitians 1 (ft);
Podiatrists 1 (ft).
Languages Spanish
Facilities Dining room; Activities room;
Laundry room; Barber/Beauty shop;
Whirlpool; Social lounges; patio.
Activities Arts & crafts; Cards; Games;
Reading groups; Prayer groups; Movies;
Shopping trips; Social/Cultural gatherings.

Metairie Healthcare Center*
6401 Riverside Dr, Metairie, LA, 70003
(504) 885-8611
Admin David Hargrave.
Licensure Intermediate care. *Beds* 196.
Certified Medicaid.
Owner Proprietary Corp (ARA Living
Centers).

St Anthony's Nursing Home Inc
6001 Airline Hwy, Metairie, LA, 70003
(504) 733-8448
Admin John S Morvant III. *Medical Dir/Dir
of Nursing* Joyce Ferrier.
Licensure Intermediate care. *Beds* 124.
Certified Medicaid.
Owner Proprietary Corp.
Admissions Requirements Medical
examination; Physician's request.
Staff Physicians 4 (ft); RNs 1 (ft); LPNs 10
(ft), 3 (pt); Nurses aides 65 (ft), 22 (pt);
Physical therapists 1 (pt); Activities
coordinators 1 (ft); Dietitians 1 (ft), 1 (pt);
Podiatrists 1 (pt).
Languages French, Spanish, Italian
Facilities Dining room; Activities room;
Laundry room; Barber/Beauty shop.
Activities Arts & crafts; Cards; Games; Prayer
groups; Movies; Social/Cultural gatherings.

MINDEN

Evergreen Manor
PO Drawer 1177, Rte 3, Minden, LA, 71055-
1177
(318) 377-5405
Admin Harold D Knowles. *Medical Dir/Dir of
Nursing* Penny Thomas RN; Laulie Hobbs
RN DON.
Licensure Intermediate care for mentally
retarded. *Beds* ICF/MR 96. *Certified*
Medicaid.
Owner Nonprofit Corp.
Admissions Requirements Minimum age 15;
Medical examination.
Staff Physicians 1 (pt); RNs 2 (ft); LPNs 9
(ft), 2 (pt); Orderlies 50 (ft); Nurses aides;
Physical therapists 1 (pt); Recreational
therapists 1 (ft); Occupational therapists 1
(pt); Speech therapists 1 (pt); Activities

coordinators 1 (ft); Dietitians 1 (ft); Dentists
1 (pt); Ophthalmologists 1 (pt); Podiatrists 1
(pt); Dentist 1 (pt).
Affiliation Presbyterian
Facilities Dining room; Physical therapy
room; Activities room; Chapel; Crafts room;
Laundry room; Barber/Beauty shop; Dental
Clinic.
Activities Arts & crafts; Games; Prayer groups;
Movies; Shopping trips; Social/Cultural
gatherings.

Meadowview Nursing Home
400 Meadowview Dr, Minden, LA, 71055
(318) 377-1011
Admin Roy Miller. *Medical Dir/Dir of Nursing*
Karen Carter.
Licensure Intermediate care. *Beds* ICF 230.
Certified Medicaid.
Owner Proprietary Corp (National Heritage).
Admissions Requirements Minimum age 60;
Medical examination.
Staff Physicians 1 (pt); RNs 3 (ft); LPNs 17
(ft), 5 (pt); Nurses aides 74 (ft), 9 (pt);
Physical therapists 1 (pt); Occupational
therapists 1 (pt); Speech therapists 1 (pt);
Activities coordinators 2 (ft); Dietitians 1
(ft).
Facilities Dining room; Activities room;
Chapel; Crafts room; Laundry room; Barber/
Beauty shop; Atrium.
Activities Arts & crafts; Cards; Games;
Reading groups; Prayer groups; Movies;
Shopping trips; Social/Cultural gatherings.

Town & Country Nursing Center*
614 Weston St, Minden, LA, 71055
(318) 377-5148
Admin Walter Ledig.
Licensure Intermediate care. *Beds* 128.
Certified Medicaid.

MONROE

Bayou Heath Care Center
2700 Georgia St, Monroe, LA, 71202
(318) 323-9671
Admin Erik Hellstrom. *Medical Dir/Dir of
Nursing* Bruce Wheeler MD; Betty Bishop
RN.
Licensure Intermediate care. *Beds* 94.
Certified Medicaid.
Admissions Requirements Medical
examination.
Staff Physicians 1 (ft), 4 (pt); RNs 1 (ft), 2
(pt); LPNs 10 (ft), 3 (pt); Orderlies 8 (ft), 2
(pt); Nurses aides 20 (ft), 4 (pt); Physical
therapists 1 (ft), 1 (pt); Reality therapists 1
(ft); Recreational therapists 1 (ft);
Occupational therapists 1 (pt); Speech
therapists 1 (pt); Activities coordinators 1
(ft), 1 (pt); Dietitians 1 (ft), 1 (pt); Dentists 1
(pt); Ophthalmologists 1 (pt); Podiatrists 1
(pt); Dentist 1 (pt).
Facilities Dining room; Physical therapy
room; Activities room; Chapel; Crafts room;
Laundry room.
Activities Arts & crafts; Cards; Games;
Reading groups; Prayer groups; Movies;
Shopping trips; Social/Cultural gatherings.

Mary Goss Nursing Home*
3300 White St, Monroe, LA, 71201
(318) 323-9013
Admin Louise G Tucker.
Licensure Intermediate care. *Beds* 91.
Certified Medicaid.

Lincoln Park Nursing Home*
4600 Burg Jones Ln, Monroe, LA, 71202
(318) 387-0683
Admin John T Parnell.
Licensure Intermediate care. *Beds* 96.
Certified Medicaid.

Monroe Manor Nursing Home*
PO Box 3148, 4201 S Grand St, Monroe, LA,
71202
(318) 325-8244
Admin Jacqueline Burnette.
Licensure Intermediate care. *Beds* 108.
Certified Medicaid.
Owner Proprietary Corp (Southmark Heritage
Corp).

Riverside Nursing Home Inc
PO Box 1841, 3001 S Grand St, Monroe, LA,
71202
(318) 388-3200
Admin James C Houston. *Medical Dir/Dir of
Nursing* Francis Sanders RN DON.
Licensure Intermediate care. *Beds* ICF 166.
Certified Medicaid.
Owner Proprietary Corp; Privately owned.
Admissions Requirements Medical
examination; Physician's request.
Staff Physicians 1 (pt); RNs 1 (ft), 1 (pt);
LPNs 12 (ft), 3 (pt); Orderlies 5 (ft); Nurses
aides 30 (ft), 12 (pt); Activities coordinators
2 (ft); Dietitians 1 (ft).
Facilities Dining room; Physical therapy
room; Activities room; Chapel; Crafts room;
Laundry room; Barber/Beauty shop.
Activities Arts & crafts; Cards; Games;
Reading groups; Prayer groups; Movies;
Shopping trips; Social/Cultural gatherings.

St Joseph's Home
2301 Sterlington Rd, Monroe, LA, 71211
(318) 323-3426
Admin Joy Anderson. *Medical Dir/Dir of
Nursing* Symira Cupit.
Licensure Intermediate care. *Beds* ICF 132.
Certified Medicaid.
Owner Nonprofit Corp.
Admissions Requirements Medical
examination; Physician's request.
Staff RNs 3 (ft); LPNs 16 (ft), 3 (pt); Nurses
aides 36 (ft), 3 (pt); Activities coordinators 1
(ft).
Affiliation Roman Catholic
Facilities Dining room; Activities room;
Chapel; Crafts room; Laundry room; Barber/
Beauty shop.
Activities Arts & crafts; Cards; Games;
Reading groups; Prayer groups; Movies;
Shopping trips.

Shady Oaks Nursing Home*
4310 Grand S, Monroe, LA, 71202
(318) 322-2616
Admin Jacob O Strickland. *Medical Dir/Dir of
Nursing* Dr Doyle Hamilton.
Licensure Intermediate care. *Beds* 108.
Certified Medicaid.
Admissions Requirements Medical
examination; Physician's request.
Staff Physicians 10 (pt); RNs 1 (ft); LPNs 7
(ft), 1 (pt); Orderlies 2 (ft); Nurses aides 28
(ft), 2 (pt); Physical therapists 1 (pt);
Occupational therapists 1 (pt); Speech
therapists 1 (pt); Activities coordinators 1
(ft); Dietitians 1 (pt); Dentists 1 (pt);
Podiatrists 1 (pt).
Facilities Dining room; Activities room;
Chapel; Crafts room; Laundry room; Barber/
Beauty shop.
Activities Arts & crafts; Cards; Games;
Reading groups; Prayer groups; Shopping
trips; Social/Cultural gatherings.

MORGAN CITY

St Mary's Guest Home*
Justa St, Morgan City, LA, 70380
(504) 384-1726
Admin Nolan Ledet.
Licensure Intermediate care. *Beds* 87.
Certified Medicaid.

NAPOLEONVILLE

Assumption Health Care Center Inc
PO Box 669, Napoleonville, LA, 70390
(504) 369-6011
Admin Tracy Brouillette. *Medical Dir/Dir of Nursing* Dr Charles Bollotte; Marilyn Vernetti RN DON.
Licensure Intermediate care. *Beds* ICF 170.
Certified Medicaid.
Owner Proprietary Corp.
Admissions Requirements Medical examination.
Staff Physicians 1 (ft); RNs 1 (ft); LPNs 8 (ft), 3 (pt); Orderlies 5 (ft), 3 (pt); Nurses aides 34 (ft), 10 (pt); Physical therapists 1 (pt); Recreational therapists 1 (pt); Occupational therapists 1 (pt); Speech therapists 1 (pt); Activities coordinators 1 (ft); Dietitians 1 (pt); Dentists 1 (pt); Ophthalmologists 1 (pt); Dentist 1 (pt).
Languages French
Facilities Dining room; Physical therapy room; Activities room; Chapel; Crafts room; Laundry room; Barber/Beauty shop; Library.
Activities Arts & crafts; Cards; Games; Reading groups; Prayer groups; Movies; Shopping trips; Social/Cultural gatherings; Crawfish boils; Fishing trips; Style shows.

NATCHITOCHES

Natchitoches Manor Nursing Home
PO Box 2178, 720 Keyser Ave, Natchitoches, LA, 71457-2178
(318) 352-8296
Admin Charles L Watson. *Medical Dir/Dir of Nursing* Dr I L Campbell.
Licensure Intermediate care. *Beds* 160.
Certified Medicaid.
Staff RNs 2 (ft), 1 (pt); LPNs 6 (ft); Orderlies 5 (ft); Nurses aides 25 (ft); Activities coordinators 1 (ft); Dietitians 1 (pt).
Facilities Dining room; Physical therapy room; Activities room; Crafts room; Laundry room; Barber/Beauty shop.
Activities Arts & crafts; Cards; Games; Reading groups; Prayer groups; Movies; Shopping trips; Social/Cultural gatherings.

Natchitoches Parish Hospital—Long-Term Care Unit
PO Box 2009, 501 Keyser Ave, Natchitoches, LA, 71457-2009
(318) 352-1200
Admin Eugene Spillman.
Licensure Intermediate care. *Beds* 108.
Certified Medicaid.
Owner Publicly owned.
Staff Physicians 5 (ft); RNs 9 (ft); LPNs 9 (ft); Orderlies 5 (ft); Nurses aides 10 (ft); Speech therapists 1 (ft); Activities coordinators 2 (ft); Dietitians 1 (ft).
Facilities Dining room; Physical therapy room; Activities room; Chapel; Barber/Beauty shop.
Activities Arts & crafts; Games; Reading groups.

Riverside Guest Care Center*
650 Keyser Ave, Natchitoches, LA, 71457
(318) 352-8779
Admin Billy P Plunkett.
Licensure Intermediate care. *Beds* 102.
Certified Medicaid.

NEW IBERIA

Azalea Villa Nursing Home*
1002 Admiral Doyle, PO Box 777, New Iberia, LA, 70560
(318) 364-5472
Admin Norma D Dupre. *Medical Dir/Dir of Nursing* Dr J C Musso.
Licensure Intermediate care. *Beds* 150.
Certified Medicaid.

Admissions Requirements Medical examination; Physician's request.
Facilities Dining room; Activities room; Laundry room; Barber/Beauty shop.
Activities Arts & crafts; Cards; Games; Reading groups; Prayer groups; Movies; Shopping trips; Social/Cultural gatherings.

Consolata Home
2319 E Main St, New Iberia, LA, 70560
(318) 365-8226
Admin David Landry. *Medical Dir/Dir of Nursing* Dr Oscar Alvarez.
Licensure Intermediate care. *Beds* 114.
Certified Medicaid.
Admissions Requirements Medical examination.
Staff Physicians 1 (pt); RNs 1 (ft), 2 (pt); LPNs 8 (ft), 6 (pt); Nurses aides 30 (ft), 10 (pt); Activities coordinators 1 (ft); Dietitians 1 (pt).
Affiliation Roman Catholic
Facilities Dining room; Activities room; Chapel; Crafts room; Laundry room; Barber/Beauty shop.
Activities Arts & crafts; Cards; Games; Prayer groups; Movies; Social/Cultural gatherings.

Heritage Manor of New Iberia—North*
PO Box 957, 1803 Jane St, New Iberia, LA, 70560
(318) 365-2466
Admin Larry Viator.
Licensure Intermediate care. *Beds* 121.
Certified Medicaid.
Owner Proprietary Corp (Southmark Heritage Corp).

Heritage Manor of New Iberia—South*
PO Box 967, 600 Bayard St, New Iberia, LA, 70560
(318) 365-3441
Admin Harvey W Koenig II.
Licensure Intermediate care. *Beds* 80.
Certified Medicaid.
Owner Proprietary Corp (Southmark Heritage Corp).

NEW ORLEANS

Audubon Health Care Center
13500 Chef Menteur Hwy, New Orleans, LA, 70129
(504) 254-9431
Admin J Erik Engberg. *Medical Dir/Dir of Nursing* Gordon McHardy MD; Ronny Monterio RN.
Licensure Intermediate care; Alzheimer's unit. *Beds* ICF 207. *Certified* Medicaid.
Owner Proprietary Corp.
Admissions Requirements Medical examination.
Staff Physicians 2 (pt); RNs 1 (ft); LPNs; Orderlies; Nurses aides; Physical therapists 1 (pt); Recreational therapists 3 (pt); Speech therapists 1 (pt); Activities coordinators 1 (ft); Dietitians 1 (ft); Dentists 1 (pt); Ophthalmologists 1 (pt).
Languages Vietnamese, Spanish
Facilities Dining room; Physical therapy room; Activities room; Crafts room; Laundry room; Barber/Beauty shop; Greenhouse.
Activities Arts & crafts; Cards; Games; Reading groups; Prayer groups; Movies; Shopping trips; Social/Cultural gatherings.

Bethany Home
2535 Esplanade Ave, New Orleans, LA, 70119
(504) 949-1738
Admin Timothy A Bains. *Medical Dir/Dir of Nursing* William LaCorte MD; Elizabeth Sturdevant.
Licensure Skilled care; Intermediate care. *Beds* SNF; ICF 117. *Certified* Medicaid.
Owner Nonprofit Corp.
Admissions Requirements Minimum age 65; Medical examination.

Staff RNs 2 (ft); LPNs 11 (ft), 6 (pt); Nurses aides 35 (ft), 13 (pt); Activities coordinators 1 (ft).
Facilities Dining room; Physical therapy room; Activities room; Library.
Activities Arts & crafts; Cards; Games; Prayer groups; Movies.

Chateau de Notre Dame*
2832 Burdette St, New Orleans, LA, 70125
(504) 866-2741
Admin Dolly More.
Beds 180.
Owner Nonprofit Corp.

Coliseum Medical Center*
3601 Coliseum St, New Orleans, LA, 70115
(504) 897-9700
Admin Fredrick R Mirmelstein.
Licensure Skilled care. *Beds* 78. *Certified* Medicare.

Covenant Home*
5919 Magazine St, New Orleans, LA, 70115
(504) 897-6216
Admin Charles Killion. *Medical Dir/Dir of Nursing* Howard Russell MD.
Licensure Intermediate care. *Beds* 84.
Certified Medicaid.
Admissions Requirements Medical examination; Physician's request.
Staff RNs 1 (ft); LPNs 7 (ft), 3 (pt); Nurses aides 25 (ft), 3 (pt); Activities coordinators 1 (ft).
Facilities Dining room; Physical therapy room; Activities room; Chapel; Crafts room; Laundry room; Barber/Beauty shop; Library.
Activities Arts & crafts; Cards; Games; Prayer groups; Movies.

F Edward Hebert Hospital—SNF
1 Sanctuary Dr, New Orleans, LA, 70114
(504) 363-2664
Admin Patricia Miller. *Medical Dir/Dir of Nursing* Frank Wagner MD; Barbara Riley RN DON.
Licensure Skilled care. *Beds* SNF 44. *Certified* Medicare.
Owner Proprietary Corp.
Admissions Requirements Medical examination; Physician's request.
Staff RNs 4 (ft), 20 (pt); LPNs 8 (ft), 20 (pt); Orderlies 3 (ft), 20 (pt); Nurses aides 3 (ft), 20 (pt); Physical therapists 2 (ft), 20 (pt); Recreational therapists 1 (ft), 20 (pt); Occupational therapists 2 (ft), 20 (pt); Speech therapists 5 (ft), 4 (pt); Dietitians 1 (ft), 20 (pt).
Facilities Dining room; Physical therapy room; Activities room; Chapel; Laundry room; Barber/Beauty shop.
Activities Arts & crafts; Cards; Games; Reading groups; Prayer groups; Movies.

Lafon Nursing Home of the Holy Family
6900 Chef Menteur Hwy, New Orleans, LA, 70126
(504) 246-1100
Admin Sr Augustine McDaniel. *Medical Dir/Dir of Nursing* Dr William Stallworth; Karen Fasone.
Licensure Intermediate care. *Beds* ICF 171.
Certified Medicaid.
Owner Nonprofit Corp.
Admissions Requirements Medical examination; Physician's request.
Staff RNs 3 (ft), 5 (pt); LPNs 12 (ft), 12 (pt); Orderlies 2 (pt); Nurses aides 26 (ft), 20 (pt); Physical therapists 2 (pt); Speech therapists 1 (pt); Activities coordinators 3 (ft), 1 (pt); Dietitians 1 (ft), 1 (pt); Dentists 1 (pt); Ophthalmologists 1 (pt); Dentist.
Affiliation Roman Catholic
Facilities Dining room; Physical therapy room; Activities room; Chapel; Crafts room; Laundry room; Barber/Beauty shop; Library.

Activities Arts & crafts; Cards; Games; Prayer groups; Movies; Shopping trips; Social/ Cultural gatherings.

Lafon United Methodist Nursing Home
4021 Cadillac St, New Orleans, LA, 70122
(504) 288-2314
Admin Edward J Lang. *Medical Dir/Dir of Nursing* Winniefred A Jones RN.
Licensure Intermediate care. *Beds* ICF 104.
 Certified Medicaid; Medicare.
Owner Nonprofit organization/foundation.
Admissions Requirements Medical examination; Physician's request.
Staff Physicians; RNs; LPNs; Nurses aides; Activities coordinators; Dietitians.
Affiliation Methodist
Facilities Dining room; Activities room; Chapel; Crafts room; Laundry room; Barber/ Beauty shop.
Activities Arts & crafts; Cards; Games; Reading groups; Social/Cultural gatherings.

Lutheran Home of New Orleans
6400 Hayne Blvd, New Orleans, LA, 70126
(504) 246-7900
Admin Thomas E Schuetz.
Licensure Intermediate care. *Beds* 208.
 Certified Medicaid.
Affiliation Lutheran

Maison Hospiere*
1220 Dauphine, New Orleans, LA, 70116
(504) 524-4309
Admin Joyce Flynn.
Licensure Intermediate care. *Beds* 87.
 Certified Medicaid.

Mary-Joseph Residence for the Elderly
4201 Woodland Dr, New Orleans, LA, 70131
(504) 394-2200
Admin Sr Mary Vincent. *Medical Dir/Dir of Nursing* Henry White MD; Sr Clare DON.
Licensure Intermediate care. *Beds* ICF 122.
 Certified Medicaid.
Owner Nonprofit Corp.
Admissions Requirements Minimum age 62.
Staff Physicians 5 (pt); RNs 4 (ft); LPNs 8 (ft), 6 (pt); Nurses aides 30 (ft), 8 (pt); Physical therapists 1 (pt); Recreational therapists 1 (ft), 1 (pt); Speech therapists 1 (pt); Activities coordinators 1 (ft); Dietitians 1 (pt); Dentists 1 (pt); Ophthalmologists 1 (pt); Podiatrists 1 (pt).
Affiliation Roman Catholic
Facilities Dining room; Physical therapy room; Activities room; Chapel; Crafts room; Laundry room; Barber/Beauty shop; Library.
Activities Arts & crafts; Cards; Games; Reading groups; Prayer groups; Movies; Shopping trips; Social/Cultural gatherings.

New Orleans Home & Rehabilitation Center
612 Henry Clay Ave, New Orleans, LA, 70118
(504) 895-4833
Admin Harry A Cicero Sr NHA. *Medical Dir/ Dir of Nursing* Henry Rothschild MD; Jackie Beary DON.
Licensure Skilled care; Intermediate care. *Beds* SNF 101; ICF 101. *Certified* Medicaid; Medicare.
Owner Nonprofit organization/foundation.
Admissions Requirements Minimum age 18; Medical examination; Physician's request.
Staff RNs 8 (ft); LPNs 22 (ft); Nurses aides 59 (ft); Recreational therapists 1 (ft); Speech therapists 1 (ft).
Facilities Dining room; Physical therapy room; Activities room; Chapel; Crafts room; Laundry room; Barber/Beauty shop; Library.
Activities Arts & crafts; Cards; Games; Reading groups; Prayer groups; Movies; Shopping trips; Social/Cultural gatherings.

Poydras Home for Elderly Ladies
5354 Magazine St, New Orleans, LA, 70115
(504) 897-0535
Admin Phyllis Maness. *Medical Dir/Dir of Nursing* Dr John Phillips; Maureen Cutillo.

Licensure Intermediate care. *Beds* ICF 44.
Owner Nonprofit organization/foundation.
Admissions Requirements Females only; Medical examination.
Staff Physicians 1 (pt); RNs 1 (ft), 2 (pt); LPNs 2 (ft), 5 (pt); Nurses aides 8 (ft), 4 (pt); Activities coordinators 1 (pt); Dietitians 1 (pt); Social worker 1 (pt); Food Service Supervisor 1 (ft); Kitchen 3 (ft), 4 (pt); Housekeeper 2 (ft); Secretary 1 (ft); Maintenance 1 (ft).
Facilities Dining room; Activities room; Chapel; Crafts room; Laundry room; Barber/ Beauty shop; Library.
Activities Arts & crafts; Cards; Games; Prayer groups; Movies; Shopping trips; Social activities.

Prayer Tower Rest Home
3316 Pine St, New Orleans, LA, 70125
(504) 486-1235
Admin Thelma Harper. *Medical Dir/Dir of Nursing* Lucille Cavitt.
Licensure Intermediate care. *Beds* ICF 104.
 Certified Medicaid; Medicare.
Owner Privately owned.
Admissions Requirements Medical examination; Physician's request.
Staff Physicians 1 (ft); RNs 1 (ft); LPNs 10 (ft); Orderlies 8 (ft); Nurses aides 30 (ft); Activities coordinators 3 (ft); Dietitians 1 (ft).
Affiliation Church of God
Facilities Dining room; Activities room; Chapel; Crafts room; Laundry room; Barber/ Beauty shop.
Activities Arts & crafts; Cards; Games; Reading groups; Prayer groups; Movies; Shopping trips.

St Anna's Asylum*
1823 Prytania St, New Orleans, LA, 70130
(504) 523-3466
Admin Barbara S Nicolas.
Beds 88.
Owner Nonprofit Corp.

St Charles Health Care Center*
1539 Delachaise, New Orleans, LA, 70115
(504) 895-3953
Admin Peggy Resor.
Licensure Skilled care; Intermediate care. *Beds* 115. *Certified* Medicaid; Medicare.

St Margaret's Daughters Nursing Home
6220 Chartres St, New Orleans, LA, 70117
(504) 279-6414
Admin Patricia Heintz. *Medical Dir/Dir of Nursing* Dianne Candebat RN.
Licensure Intermediate care. *Beds* ICF 112.
 Certified Medicaid.
Owner Nonprofit Corp.
Admissions Requirements Females only; Medical examination; Physician's request.
Staff Physicians 1 (ft); RNs 1 (ft); LPNs 15 (ft); Activities coordinators 2 (ft); Ophthalmologists 1 (pt).
Affiliation Roman Catholic
Facilities Dining room; Activities room; Chapel; Laundry room; Barber/Beauty shop.
Activities Arts & crafts; Cards; Games; Reading groups; Prayer groups; Movies; Shopping trips; Social/Cultural gatherings.

NEW ROADS

Lakeview Manor
400 Hospital Rd, New Roads, LA, 70760
(504) 638-4404
Admin Myron Chatelain. *Medical Dir/Dir of Nursing* Phyllis Chatelain DON.
Licensure Intermediate care. *Beds* ICF 120.
 Certified Medicaid.
Owner Proprietary Corp.
Staff RNs 1 (ft); LPNs 7 (ft), 2 (pt); Nurses aides 27 (ft), 5 (pt); Activities coordinators 1 (ft); Dietitians 1 (pt).

Facilities Dining room; Activities room; Laundry room; Barber/Beauty shop; 2 TV lobbies; 2 patios.
Activities Arts & crafts; Cards; Games; Prayer groups; Movies; Shopping trips.

Pointe Coupee Parish Nursing Home
2202-A Hospital Rd, New Roads, LA, 70760
(504) 638-4431
Admin Betty L Vosburg. *Medical Dir/Dir of Nursing* Pamela M Firmin RN.
Licensure Intermediate care. *Beds* ICF 120.
 Certified Medicaid.
Owner Publicly owned.
Admissions Requirements Medical examination.
Staff RNs 2 (ft); LPNs 10 (ft), 7 (pt); Orderlies 1 (ft); Nurses aides 39 (ft), 5 (pt); Physical therapists 1 (pt); Speech therapists 1 (pt); Activities coordinators 1 (ft); Dietitians 1 (ft); Dentists 1 (pt).
Languages French
Facilities Dining room; Physical therapy room; Activities room; Crafts room; Laundry room; Barber/Beauty shop; Library.
Activities Arts & crafts; Cards; Games; Reading groups; Prayer groups; Movies; Shopping trips; Social/Cultural gatherings.

NEWELLTON

St Charles Nursing Home*
Hwy 4, Newellton, LA, 71357
(318) 467-9442
Admin Louise Crane.
Licensure Intermediate care. *Beds* 56.
 Certified Medicaid.

Tensas Care Center
PO Box 508, 901 Verona Street, Newellton, LA, 71357
(318) 467-5919
Admin Charlene Rountree. *Medical Dir/Dir of Nursing* Christine A Hulett RN.
Licensure Intermediate care. *Beds* 60.
 Certified Medicaid.
Owner Nonprofit Corp.
Admissions Requirements Medical examination; Physician's request.
Staff Physicians 3 (pt); RNs 1 (ft); LPNs 4 (ft), 2 (pt); Nurses aides 13 (ft), 5 (pt); Activities coordinators 1 (ft); Dietitians 1 (pt); Clerical 1 (ft).
Facilities Dining room; Crafts room; Barber/ Beauty shop; TV Room.
Activities Arts & crafts; Games; Prayer groups; Movies.

OAK GROVE

Carroll Nursing Home*
N Castleman St, Oak Grove, LA, 71263
(318) 428-3249
Admin Elvyn N Dumas.
Licensure Intermediate care. *Beds* 106.
 Certified Medicaid.
Admissions Requirements Medical examination; Physician's request.
Staff Physicians 1 (pt); RNs 1 (ft); LPNs 7 (ft), 1 (pt); Orderlies 1 (ft), 1 (pt); Nurses aides 40 (ft), 3 (pt); Recreational therapists 1 (ft); Activities coordinators 1 (ft); Dietitians 1 (pt); Dentists 1 (pt).
Facilities Dining room; Activities room; Crafts room; Laundry room; Barber/Beauty shop; Library.
Activities Arts & crafts; Cards; Games; Reading groups; Prayer groups; Movies; Shopping trips; Social/Cultural gatherings.

OAKDALE

Care Nursing Home Inc
PO Box 683, Oakdale, LA, 71463
(318) 335-1469 or 335-1484

Admin Michael R Hathorn. *Medical Dir/Dir
of Nursing* George B Mowad MD; Tammy
Moore DON.
Licensure Intermediate care. *Beds* ICF 77.
Owner Privately owned.
Admissions Requirements Medical
examination.
Staff Physicians 1 (ft), 3 (pt); RNs 1 (ft);
LPNs 4 (ft); Orderlies 3 (ft); Nurses aides 11
(ft); Physical therapists 1 (ft); Recreational
therapists 1 (pt); Activities coordinators 1
(ft); Dietitians 1 (ft).
Facilities Dining room; Activities room;
Laundry room; Barber/Beauty shop.
Activities Arts & crafts; Games; Movies;
Social/Cultural gatherings.

OPELOUSAS

Opelousas Health Care Inc
328 W Grolee St, Opelousas, LA, 70570
(318) 942-7588
Admin Mary E Thurmond. *Medical Dir/Dir of
Nursing* James McCarthy; Rosemary Roy.
Licensure Intermediate care. *Beds* ICF 71.
Certified Medicaid.
Owner Proprietary Corp (Southeastern Health
Care Inc).
Admissions Requirements Medical
examination.
Staff Physicians 1 (pt); RNs 1 (ft); LPNs 6
(ft), 3 (pt); Activities coordinators 1 (ft);
Dietitians 1 (pt).
Languages French
Facilities Dining room; Laundry room;
Barber/Beauty shop.
Activities Arts & crafts; Cards; Games; Prayer
groups; Movies; Social/Cultural gatherings.

Prompt Succor Nursing Home*
751 Prudhomme Ln, Opelousas, LA, 70570
(318) 948-3634
Admin Sr Margaret M Lafleur. *Medical Dir/
Dir of Nursing* Dr Donald Gremillion.
Licensure Skilled care. *Beds* 80. *Certified*
Medicare.
Staff RNs 4 (ft); LPNs 6 (ft), 2 (pt); Nurses
aides 30 (ft), 4 (pt); Physical therapists 1
(pt); Speech therapists 1 (pt); Activities
coordinators 1 (pt); Dietitians 1 (pt);
Dentists 1 (pt); Audiologists 1 (pt).
Affiliation Roman Catholic
Facilities Dining room; Activities room;
Chapel; Laundry room; Barber/Beauty shop.
Activities Arts & crafts; Cards; Games;
Reading groups; Prayer groups; Shopping
trips; Social/Cultural gatherings.

Senior Village Nursing Home*
160 Ducharme Rd, Opelousas, LA, 70570
(318) 948-4486
Admin Susan Bourgogne.
Licensure Intermediate care. *Beds* 208.
Certified Medicaid.
Owner Proprietary Corp (Southmark Heritage
Corp).

PINEVILLE

Camellia Garden Nursing Home
PO Box 3728, 701 Bayou Marie Rd, Pineville,
LA, 71361
(318) 445-4251
Admin Ralph Hargrove. *Medical Dir/Dir of
Nursing* Kathy Baker RN.
Licensure Intermediate care. *Beds* ICF 93.
Certified Medicaid.
Owner Proprietary Corp.
Admissions Requirements Minimum age 16;
Medical examination; Physician's request.
Staff Physicians 1 (ft), 8 (pt); RNs 1 (ft);
LPNs 6 (ft), 3 (pt); Nurses aides 20 (ft), 10
(pt); Physical therapists 1 (pt); Speech
therapists 1 (pt); Activities coordinators 1
(ft); Dietitians 1 (pt).
Languages French

Facilities Dining room; Activities room;
Laundry room; Barber/Beauty shop.
Activities Arts & crafts; Cards; Games;
Reading groups; Prayer groups; Movies;
Shopping trips; Social/Cultural gatherings.

Heritage Manor North Nursing Home
1709 Odom St, Pineville, LA, 71301
(318) 445-6355
Admin Otey M Dear. *Medical Dir/Dir of
Nursing* Dr M Khokhar; Peggy Bihm RN
DON.
Licensure Intermediate care. *Beds* ICF 75.
Certified Medicaid; Medicare.
Owner Proprietary Corp (National Heritage).
Admissions Requirements Medical
examination.
Staff RNs 1 (ft); LPNs 5 (ft), 4 (pt); Orderlies
2 (ft), 1 (pt); Nurses aides 21 (ft), 6 (pt);
Activities coordinators 1 (ft); Dietitians 1
(pt).
Facilities Dining room; Laundry room;
Barber/Beauty shop.
Activities Arts & crafts; Cards; Games; Prayer
groups; Movies; Shopping trips; Social/
Cultural gatherings; Resident Council.

Hilltop Nursing Center No II
PO Box 4177, 1100 Bayou Marie Rd,
Pineville, LA, 71360
(318) 487-9400
Admin A A Kelley Jr. *Medical Dir/Dir of
Nursing* Carrie Graves.
Licensure Intermediate care. *Beds* ICF 102.
Certified Medicaid.
Owner Proprietary Corp.
Admissions Requirements Minimum age 21;
Medical examination; Physician's request.
Staff RNs 1 (ft), 2 (pt); LPNs 6 (ft), 4 (pt);
Orderlies 1 (ft); Nurses aides 28 (ft);
Activities coordinators 1 (ft); Dietitians 1
(ft).
Facilities Dining room; Activities room;
Laundry room; Barber/Beauty shop.
Activities Arts & crafts; Cards; Games; Prayer
groups; Movies; Shopping trips; Social/
Cultural gatherings.

Hilltop Nursing Home No I*
500 Dupree St, Pineville, LA, 71360
(318) 442-9552
Admin Juanita B Kelley. *Medical Dir/Dir of
Nursing* Dr Grover Bahm.
Licensure Intermediate care. *Beds* 98.
Certified Medicaid.
Admissions Requirements Medical
examination; Physician's request.
Staff Physicians 1 (ft), 6 (pt); RNs 2 (ft);
LPNs 10 (ft); Orderlies 2 (ft); Nurses aides
25 (ft), 4 (pt); Physical therapists 1 (pt);
Activities coordinators 1 (ft); Dietitians 1
(pt).
Facilities Dining room; Activities room;
Laundry room; Barber/Beauty shop.
Activities Arts & crafts; Cards; Games; Prayer
groups; Movies; Shopping trips; Social/
Cultural gatherings.

Lakeland Nursing Home*
PO Box 933, Hillsdale Dr, Pineville, LA,
71360
(318) 448-0141
Admin Herman P Marshall.
Licensure Intermediate care. *Beds* 140.
Certified Medicaid.

Pilgrim Manor Nursing Home of Pineville
200 Gordon St, PO Box 4208, Pineville, LA,
71361
(318) 442-4364
Admin Edward Rose. *Medical Dir/Dir of
Nursing* Ken Rose.
Licensure Intermediate care. *Beds* ICF 152.
Certified Medicaid.
Owner Privately owned.

Staff RNs 1 (ft), 1 (pt); LPNs 14 (ft), 1 (pt);
Orderlies 2 (ft), 1 (pt); Nurses aides 56 (ft),
3 (pt); Physical therapists 1 (pt); Activities
coordinators 1 (ft).
Languages French
Facilities Dining room; Activities room;
Chapel; Crafts room; Laundry room; Barber/
Beauty shop.
Activities Arts & crafts; Cards; Games;
Reading groups; Prayer groups; Movies;
Shopping trips; Social/Cultural gatherings.

Pinecrest State School*
PO Drawer 191, Pineville, LA, 71360
(318) 640-0754
Admin Coates Stuckey.
Licensure Intermediate care for mentally
retarded. *Beds* 1688. *Certified* Medicaid.

PLAIN DEALING

Whispering Pines Nursing Home*
Hwy 3 S, PO Box 147, Plain Dealing, LA,
71064
(318) 326-4259
Admin Louis A Dye Sr.
Licensure Intermediate care. *Beds* 77.
Certified Medicaid.

PLAQUEMINE

Iberville Living Center
1601 Riverwest Dr, Plaquemine, LA, 70764
(504) 687-0240
Admin Janice A Handwerk. *Medical Dir/Dir
of Nursing* Dr B F Trosclair; Yvonne Hasten
RN DON.
Licensure Skilled care. *Beds* SNF 180.
Certified Medicaid; Medicare; VA.
Owner Proprietary Corp (ARA Living
Centers).
Admissions Requirements Minimum age 16.
Staff RNs 2 (ft); LPNs 8 (ft), 1 (pt); Orderlies
2 (ft); Nurses aides 18 (ft), 1 (pt); Activities
coordinators 1 (ft); Dietitians 1 (ft).
Languages French
Facilities Dining room; Physical therapy
room; Activities room; Chapel; Crafts room;
Laundry room; Barber/Beauty shop; Library;
Van with wheelchair lift.
Activities Arts & crafts; Cards; Games; Prayer
groups; Movies; Shopping trips; Social/
Cultural gatherings; Outings to participate in
local activities.

Plaquemine Nursing Home*
1202 Ferdinand St, Plaquemine, LA, 70764
(504) 387-1345 or 292-1947
Admin Bruno E Egros Jr.
Licensure Intermediate care. *Beds* 106.
Certified Medicaid.

PLAUCHEVILLE

Avoyelles Manor Nursing Home*
Rte 1, Box 215, LA Hwy 107, Plaucheville,
LA, 71362
(318) 922-3404
Admin Donald Scallan.
Licensure Intermediate care. *Beds* 104.
Certified Medicaid.

PLEASANT HILL

North Sabine Nursing Home*
PO Box 245, Hwy 174, Pleasant Hill, LA,
71065
(318) 796-3316
Admin Elizabeth Durr.
Licensure Intermediate care. *Beds* 90.
Certified Medicaid.

POLLOCK

Woods Haven Senior Citizens Home
PO Box 469, Pollock, LA, 71467
(318) 765-3557
Admin Rev H P Tarpley.
Licensure Intermediate care. *Beds* ICF 103.
Certified Medicaid.
Owner Proprietary Corp.
Admissions Requirements Medical
examination.
Staff RNs; LPNs; Nurses aides; Activities
coordinators; Dietitians.
Facilities Dining room; Activities room;
Laundry room; Barber/Beauty shop.
Activities Arts & crafts; Cards; Games;
Reading groups; Prayer groups; Movies;
Shopping trips; Social/Cultural gatherings.

PORT ALLEN

Port Allen Care Center Inc*
403 15th St, Port Allen, LA, 70767
(504) 346-8815
Admin Barbara Anne King.
Licensure Intermediate care. *Beds* 50.
Certified Medicaid.

POYDRAS

Poydras Manor*
Massicot St, Poydras, LA, 70085
(504) 682-0012
Admin Vallie B White.
Licensure Intermediate care. *Beds* 36.
Certified Medicaid.

QUITMAN

Pine Hill Senior Citizens Center*
Rte 2, Box 54, Quitman, LA, 71268
(318) 259-4474
Admin Billy M Roberson.
Licensure Intermediate care. *Beds* 80.
Certified Medicaid.

RAYNE

Rayne Guest House*
PO Box 54, 308 Amelia St, Rayne, LA, 70578
(318) 334-5111
Admin Leroy Richard.
Licensure Intermediate care. *Beds* 80.
Certified Medicaid.

RAYVILLE

Colonial Manor Guest House*
505 E 4th St, Rayville, LA, 71269
(318) 728-3251
Admin David E Barr.
Licensure Intermediate care. *Beds* 130.
Certified Medicaid.

Community Comfort Cottage
PO Box 60, 717 Madeline St, Rayville, LA,
71269
(318) 728-5373
Admin Claude H Minor. *Medical Dir/Dir of
Nursing* Barbara Foster.
Licensure Intermediate care. *Beds* 85.
Certified Medicaid; Medicare.
Owner Nonprofit organization/foundation.
Admissions Requirements Physician's request.
Staff RNs 1 (ft); LPNs 7 (ft), 4 (pt); Orderlies
2 (ft), 2 (pt); Nurses aides 25 (ft), 4 (pt);
Activities coordinators 1 (ft); Dietitians 1
(pt).
Facilities Dining room; Activities room;
Crafts room; Laundry room; Barber/Beauty
shop.
Activities Arts & crafts; Cards; Games; Prayer
groups; Movies; Shopping trips; Social/
Cultural gatherings.

Rayville Guest House Inc*
PO Box 875, Rayville, LA, 71269
(318) 728-2089
Admin Edmond Boudreaux.
Licensure Intermediate care. *Beds* 125.
Certified Medicaid.

RUSTON

Alpine Guest Care Center*
PO Box 1385, Hwy 80, Ruston, LA, 71270
(318) 255-9818
Admin Elton Dugan.
Licensure Intermediate care. *Beds* 117.
Certified Medicaid.

Longleaf Nursing Home*
PO Box 849, Hwy 80 E, Ruston, LA, 71270
(318) 255-5001
Admin Henry S Roane III.
Licensure Intermediate care. *Beds* 92.
Certified Medicaid.

Ruston State School
PO Box 907, Ruston, LA, 71270
(318) 247-3721
Admin George E Bostick. *Medical Dir/Dir of
Nursing* Temple Douglas MD; Alverne
Martin RN DON.
Licensure Intermediate care for mentally
retarded. *Beds* ICF/MR 148. *Certified*
Medicaid; Medicare.
Owner Publicly owned.
Admissions Requirements Minimum age 13;
Medical examination.
Staff RNs 2 (ft); LPNs 2 (ft); Occupational
therapists 2 (ft); Speech therapists 2 (ft);
Dietitians 1 (ft).
Facilities Dining room; Activities room;
Crafts room; Laundry room.
Activities Arts & crafts; Cards; Games;
Movies; Shopping trips; Social/Cultural
gatherings; Church services.

Towne Oaks Nursing Center*
1405 White St, Ruston, LA, 71270
(318) 255-4400
Admin Bill Copeland.
Licensure Intermediate care. *Beds* 119.
Certified Medicaid.

SAINT FRANCISVILLE

Idlewood Nursing Center*
PO Box 249, Hwy 10, Saint Francisville, LA,
70775
(504) 635-3346
Admin Tom McVea.
Licensure Intermediate care. *Beds* 128.
Certified Medicaid.

SAINT MARTINVILLE

St Martinville Nursing Home
PO Box 787, 200 Claire Dr, Saint Martinville,
LA, 70582
(318) 394-6044
Admin Larry Baker.
Licensure Intermediate care. *Beds* 94.
Certified Medicaid.

SHREVEPORT

Centenary Heritage Manor
225 Wyandotte St, Shreveport, LA, 71101
(318) 221-3591
Admin Debbie Brooks. *Medical Dir/Dir of
Nursing* Mary Johnson.
Licensure Intermediate care. *Beds* ICF 101.
Certified Medicaid.
Owner Proprietary Corp (Southmark Heritage
Corp).
Admissions Requirements Medical
examination; Physician's request.

Staff Physicians; RNs; LPNs; Nurses aides;
Physical therapists; Speech therapists;
Activities coordinators; Dietitians;
Ophthalmologists.
Facilities Dining room; Laundry room;
Barber/Beauty shop.
Activities Arts & crafts; Cards; Games;
Reading groups; Prayer groups; Movies;
Shopping trips; Social/Cultural gatherings.

Eden Gardens Nursing Center
PO Box 6045, 7923 Line Ave, Shreveport, LA,
71106
(318) 865-0261
Admin Elaine B Kirby. *Medical Dir/Dir of
Nursing* C R Teagle MD; Donna Areaux RN
DON.
Licensure Intermediate care. *Beds* 74.
Certified Medicaid.
Owner Proprietary Corp.
Admissions Requirements Medical
examination.
Staff RNs 2 (ft); LPNs 11 (ft); Orderlies 3 (ft);
Nurses aides 45 (ft); Activities coordinators
1 (ft); Dietitians 1 (pt).
Facilities Dining room; Activities room;
Laundry room.
Activities Arts & crafts; Cards; Games;
Reading groups; Prayer groups; Movies;
Shopping trips; Social/Cultural gatherings.

Glen Oaks Retirement Home
1524 Glen Oak Pl, Shreveport, LA, 71103
(318) 221-0911
Admin Jean McCarty. *Medical Dir/Dir of
Nursing* Nora McCoy.
Licensure Intermediate care. *Beds* ICF 60.
Certified Medicaid.
Owner Nonprofit Corp.
Admissions Requirements Minimum age 65;
Medical examination.
Staff Physicians 1 (pt); RNs 1 (ft); LPNs 3
(ft), 3 (pt); Nurses aides 18 (ft), 1 (pt);
Physical therapists 1 (pt); Activities
coordinators 2 (ft); Dietitians 1 (pt);
Ophthalmologists 1 (pt); Dentist 1 (pt).
Facilities Dining room; Activities room;
Laundry room; Barber/Beauty shop.
Activities Arts & crafts; Cards; Games; Prayer
groups; Movies; Shopping trips; Social/
Cultural gatherings; Field trips.

The Glen Retirement Village
403 E Flournoy Lucas Rd, Shreveport, LA,
71115
(318) 798-3500
Admin Peggy Newell. *Medical Dir/Dir of
Nursing* Margaret Bell DON.
Licensure Intermediate care. *Beds* 126.
Certified Medicaid.
Owner Nonprofit Corp.
Admissions Requirements Minimum age 62;
Medical examination; Physician's request.
Staff Physicians 1 (pt); RNs 1 (ft); LPNs 10
(ft), 8 (pt); Nurses aides 38 (ft), 18 (pt);
Physical therapists 1 (pt); Reality therapists;
Activities coordinators 1 (ft); Dietitians 1
(pt); Ophthalmologists 1 (pt); Dentist 1 (pt).
Facilities Dining room; Physical therapy
room; Activities room; Chapel; Crafts room;
Laundry room; Barber/Beauty shop; Game
room; Medical suite; Sweet shop; Village
store; Gift shop; Fishing pier.
Activities Arts & crafts; Cards; Games; Prayer
groups; Movies; Shopping trips; Social/
Cultural gatherings; Field trips.

The Guest House
9225 Normandie Dr, Shreveport, LA, 71118
(318) 686-0515
Admin Rory W Beckman. *Medical Dir/Dir of
Nursing* Dr Robert Braswell; Helen Brewton
DON.
Licensure Intermediate care. *Beds* ICF 117.
Certified Medicaid.
Owner Proprietary Corp (Convalescent
Services).

Admissions Requirements Medical
examination; Physician's request.
Staff RNs 1 (ft), 1 (pt); LPNs 8 (ft); Orderlies
1 (ft); Nurses aides 36 (ft), 6 (pt); Activities
coordinators 1 (ft).
Facilities Dining room; Activities room;
Crafts room; Laundry room; Barber/Beauty
shop.
Activities Arts & crafts; Cards; Games;
Reading groups; Prayer groups; Movies;
Social/Cultural gatherings.

Harmony House Nursing Home*
1825 Laurel St, Shreveport, LA, 71103
(318) 424-5251
Admin G Wayne Hopper.
Licensure Intermediate care. *Beds* 115.
Certified Medicaid.
Staff Physicians 2 (pt); RNs 1 (ft); LPNs 6
(ft), 2 (pt); Orderlies 2 (ft), 1 (pt); Nurses
aides 30 (ft); Physical therapists 1 (pt);
Speech therapists 1 (ft), 1 (pt); Activities
coordinators 1 (ft); Dietitians 1 (ft); Dentists
1 (ft); Ophthalmologists 1 (pt); Audiologists
1 (pt).

**Harrison's Booker T Washington Nursing
Home***
PO Box 6021, 610 Turner Ln, Shreveport, LA,
71106
(318) 861-0223
Admin Hattie Mae Scott.
Licensure Intermediate care. *Beds* 54.
Certified Medicaid.

Heritage Manor Nursing Home of Shreveport*
1536 Claiborne Ave, Shreveport, LA, 71103
(318) 631-3426
Admin Sandra Elliott.
Licensure Intermediate care. *Beds* 86.
Certified Medicaid.
Owner Proprietary Corp (Southmark Heritage
Corp).

Highland Guest Care Center*
453 Jordan St, Shreveport, LA, 71101
(318) 222-2261
Admin Kathryn C Gamble.
Licensure Intermediate care. *Beds* 38.
Certified Medicaid.

Live Oak Multi Faith Retirement Center
600 E Flournoy-Lucas Rd, Shreveport, LA,
71115
(318) 797-1900
Admin Jay P Irby. *Medical Dir/Dir of Nursing*
Dr Fred Robberson.
Licensure Intermediate care. *Beds* ICF 130.
Certified Medicaid.
Owner Nonprofit Corp.
Admissions Requirements Minimum age 62;
Medical examination; Physician's request.
Staff Physicians 1 (pt); RNs 2 (ft);
LPNs 14 (ft), 5 (pt); Orderlies 3 (ft), 2 (pt);
Nurses aides 26 (ft), 12 (pt); Physical
therapists 1 (pt); Reality therapists 1 (ft);
Recreational therapists 1 (pt); Occupational
therapists 1 (ft); Activities coordinators 2
(ft); Dietitians 1 (pt); Ophthalmologists 1
(pt).
Facilities Dining room; Physical therapy
room; Activities room; Chapel; Crafts room;
Laundry room; Barber/Beauty shop; Library;
Convenience store; Gift shop.
Activities Arts & crafts; Cards; Games;
Reading groups; Prayer groups; Movies;
Shopping trips; Social/Cultural gatherings.

Magnolia Manor Nursing Home Inc*
1411 Claiborne Ave, Shreveport, LA, 71103
(318) 868-4421
Admin John L Colvin.
Licensure Intermediate care. *Beds* 98.
Certified Medicaid.

Midway Manor Nursing Home*
2150 Midway Ave, Shreveport, LA, 71108
(318) 635-5314

Admin Jean S McCarty. *Medical Dir/Dir of
Nursing* Dr J F Hawkins.
Licensure Intermediate care. *Beds* 212.
Certified Medicaid.
Admissions Requirements Medical
examination.
Staff RNs 4 (ft); LPNs 16 (ft), 2 (pt);
Orderlies 8 (ft), 2 (pt); Nurses aides 58 (ft),
12 (pt); Activities coordinators 2 (ft);
Dietitians 2 (ft).
Facilities Dining room; Activities room;
Crafts room; Laundry room; Barber/Beauty
shop.
Activities Arts & crafts; Cards; Games; Prayer
groups; Movies; Shopping trips; Social/
Cultural gatherings.

Nursecare of Shreveport
1736 Irving Pl, Shreveport, LA, 71101
(318) 221-1983
Admin Patricia T Daron. *Medical Dir/Dir of
Nursing* Robert Braswell MD; Debbie Fon
RN DON.
Licensure Skilled care; Intermediate care. *Beds*
SNF 29; ICF 199. *Certified* Medicaid;
Medicare; VA.
Owner Proprietary Corp.
Admissions Requirements Medical
examination; Physician's request.
Staff Physicians; RNs; LPNs; Orderlies;
Nurses aides; Physical therapists;
Occupational therapists; Speech therapists;
Activities coordinators; Dietitians;
Ophthalmologists; Podiatrists; Chaplains 2
(pt).
Languages French
Facilities Dining room; Activities room;
Chapel; Barber/Beauty shop.
Activities Arts & crafts; Cards; Games; Prayer
groups; Movies; Social/Cultural gatherings.

Pierremont Heritage Manor
725 Mitchell Ln, Shreveport, LA, 71106
(318) 868-2789
Admin Carolyn Fultz. *Medical Dir/Dir of
Nursing* Dr David Henry; Betty Youngblood
DON.
Licensure Intermediate care. *Beds* ICF 196.
Certified Medicaid.
Owner Proprietary Corp (National Heritage).
Admissions Requirements Minimum age 53;
Medical examination.
Staff RNs 3 (ft); LPNs 16 (ft), 2 (pt); Nurses
aides 54 (ft), 4 (pt); Activities coordinators 2
(ft); Dietitians 1 (ft).
Facilities Dining room; Activities room;
Crafts room; Laundry room; Barber/Beauty
shop; Library.
Activities Arts & crafts; Cards; Games;
Reading groups; Prayer groups; Movies;
Shopping trips; Social/Cultural gatherings;
Picnics; Fishing trips; Baseball games.

Roseview Nursing Center*
3405 Mansfield Rd, Shreveport, LA, 71103
(318) 222-3100
Admin Mary Ann Schaefer.
Licensure Intermediate care. *Beds* 124.
Certified Medicaid.

Shreveport Manor Guest Care Center*
3302 Mansfield Rd, Shreveport, LA, 71103
(318) 222-9482
Admin Ralph Balentine.
Licensure Intermediate care. *Beds* 124.
Certified Medicaid.

South Park Guest Care Center*
3050 Baird Rd, Shreveport, LA, 71118
(318) 688-1010
Admin Claude Pasquier.
Licensure Intermediate care. *Beds* 120.
Certified Medicaid.

Virginia Hall*
2715 Virginia Ave, Shreveport, LA, 71103
(318) 425-3247
Admin Rosalind B Foster.

Licensure Skilled care; Intermediate care. *Beds*
155. *Certified* Medicaid; Medicare.

Westwood Heritage Manor*
1 Westwood Circle, Shreveport, LA, 71109
(318) 631-1846
Admin Betty Stuart.
Licensure Intermediate care. *Beds* 82.
Certified Medicaid.
Owner Proprietary Corp (Southmark Heritage
Corp).

SIMMESPORT

Bayou Chateau Nursing Center
PO Box 390, Route 1, Simmesport, LA, 71369
(318) 941-2294
Admin Dorothy Anne Lacour. *Medical Dir/Dir
of Nursing* Leon F Beridon MD; Lela
Normand DON.
Licensure Intermediate care. *Beds* 104.
Certified Medicaid.
Owner Proprietary Corp.
Admissions Requirements Medical
examination; Physician's request.
Staff Physicians 1 (pt); RNs 1 (ft); LPNs 8
(ft), 4 (pt); Nurses aides; Activities
coordinators 1 (ft); Dietitians 1 (ft).
Languages French
Facilities Dining room; Activities room;
Crafts room; Laundry room; Barber/Beauty
shop; Library; Sun & recreation rooms
lounges.
Activities Arts & crafts; Cards; Games;
Reading groups; Prayer groups; Movies;
Shopping trips; Social/Cultural gatherings.

SLIDELL

Greenbriar Nursing & Convalescent Home*
505 Robert Rd, Slidell, LA, 70458
(504) 581-1272
Admin Jon W Franzke.
Licensure Intermediate care. *Beds* 124.
Certified Medicaid.

Guest House of Slidell Nursing Home*
1051 Robert Rd, Slidell, LA, 70458
(504) 566-7697
Admin Thomas G Beck Jr.
Licensure Intermediate care. *Beds* 90.
Certified Medicaid.

SPRINGHILL

Fountain View Nursing Home*
215 1st St NE, Springhill, LA, 71075
(318) 539-3527
Admin L M Cadenhead Jr.
Licensure Intermediate care. *Beds* 93.
Certified Medicaid.

SULPHUR

High Hope Care Center
PO Box 1460, Sulphur, LA, 70664
(318) 527-8140
Admin Paul C Reed. *Medical Dir/Dir of
Nursing* Dr H B Lovejoy; Denise Ardon RN.
Licensure Intermediate care. *Beds* ICF 101.
Certified Medicaid.
Owner Proprietary Corp.
Admissions Requirements Minimum age 18;
Medical examination.
Staff Physicians; RNs; LPNs; Nurses aides;
Physical therapists; Reality therapists;
Speech therapists; Activities coordinators;
Dietitians.
Languages French
Facilities Dining room; Activities room;
Crafts room; Laundry room; Barber/Beauty
shop.
Activities Arts & crafts; Cards; Games; Prayer
groups; Movies; Shopping trips; Social/
Cultural gatherings.

Holly Hill House*
100 Kingston Rd, Sulphur, LA, 70663
(318) 625-5843
Admin Ray Green. *Medical Dir/Dir of Nursing*
C L Fellows MD.
Licensure Skilled care. *Beds* 235. *Certified*
Medicaid; Medicare.
Admissions Requirements Medical
examination; Physician's request.
Staff Physicians 1 (pt); RNs 4 (ft), 1 (pt);
LPNs 18 (ft), 5 (pt); Orderlies 1 (ft); Nurses
aides 40 (ft), 10 (pt); Physical therapists 1
(pt); Occupational therapists 1 (pt); Speech
therapists 1 (pt); Activities coordinators 2
(ft); Dietitians 1 (ft); Dentists 1 (pt);
Podiatrists 1 (pt); Audiologists 1 (pt).
Facilities Dining room; Activities room;
Chapel; Crafts room; Laundry room; Barber/
Beauty shop; Library.
Activities Arts & crafts; Cards; Games;
Reading groups; Prayer groups; Movies;
Shopping trips; Social/Cultural gatherings;
Pet therapy.

TALLULAH

Delta Haven Nursing Home
201 Lee St, Tallulah, LA, 71282
(318) 574-4621
Admin Richard Snow NHA, MA. *Medical
Dir/Dir of Nursing* Marla Cummins RN.
Licensure Intermediate care for mentally
retarded. *Beds* ICF 146. *Certified* Medicaid.
Owner Proprietary Corp.
Admissions Requirements Medical
examination.
Staff RNs; LPNs; Orderlies; Nurses aides;
Activities coordinators.
Facilities Dining room; Activities room;
Chapel; Crafts room; Laundry room; Barber/
Beauty shop.
Activities Arts & crafts; Cards; Games;
Reading groups; Movies; Exercise; Music;
Church.

Madison Parish Baptist Nursing Home
701 N Chestnut St, Tallulah, LA, 71282
(318) 574-1541, 574-1545
Admin Georgia Mae C Johnson. *Medical Dir/
Dir of Nursing* Reba Rinicker.
Licensure Intermediate care. *Beds* ICF 43.
Certified Medicaid; Medicare.
Owner Nonprofit Corp.
Admissions Requirements Medical
examination; Physician's request.
Staff Physicians 4 (pt); RNs 1 (ft); LPNs 3
(ft), 3 (pt); Nurses aides 8 (ft), 4 (pt);
Activities coordinators 1 (ft); Dietitians 1
(pt).
Affiliation Baptist
Facilities Dining room; Activities room;
Laundry room.
Activities Arts & crafts; Cards; Games; Prayer
groups; Shopping trips.

THIBODAUX

Heritage Manor of Thibodaux*
1300 Lafourche St, Thibodaux, LA, 70301
(504) 446-1332
Admin Ollie Hymel.
Licensure Intermediate care. *Beds* 58.
Certified Medicaid.
Owner Proprietary Corp (Southmark Heritage
Corp).

Lafourche Home for the Aged
1002 Tiger Dr, Thibodaux, LA, 70301
(504) 447-2205
Admin Ann Howell. *Medical Dir/Dir of
Nursing* Richard A Morvant MD.
Licensure Intermediate care. *Beds* 64.
Certified Medicaid.
Owner Nonprofit Corp.
Admissions Requirements Medical
examination.

Staff RNs 1 (ft), 1 (pt); LPNs 4 (ft), 3 (pt);
Nurses aides 35 (ft), 15 (pt); Activities
coordinators 1 (ft); Dietitians 1 (ft).
Facilities Dining room; Activities room;
Crafts room; Laundry room; Barber/Beauty
shop.
Activities Arts & crafts; Cards; Games; Prayer
groups; Movies; Shopping trips; Social/
Cultural gatherings.

TIOGA

Tioga Manor Nursing Center
PO Box 1097, 5201 Shreveport Hwy, Tioga,
LA, 71477
(318) 640-3014
Admin Iris Winegeart. *Medical Dir/Dir of
Nursing* Dr Jajinda Verma MD; Karen Z
Williams RN BS.
Licensure Intermediate care. *Beds* ICF 120.
Certified Medicaid.
Owner Privately owned.
Admissions Requirements Medical
examination; Physician's request.
Staff Physicians 6 (pt); RNs 1 (ft), 1 (pt);
LPNs 8 (ft), 3 (pt); Nurses aides 40 (ft), 7
(pt); Physical therapists 1 (pt); Speech
therapists 1 (pt); Dietitians 1 (pt).
Facilities Dining room; Activities room;
Barber/Beauty shop; Library.
Activities Arts & crafts; Cards; Games;
Reading groups; Prayer groups; Movies;
Shopping trips; Social/Cultural gatherings;
Pet shows; Exercise classes.

VILLE PLATTE

Maison de Sante*
220 S Thompson St, Ville Platte, LA, 70586
(318) 363-4048
Admin Matthus M West Sr.
Licensure Intermediate care. *Beds* 171.
Certified Medicaid.

VIOLET

Simmons Nursing Home Inc
2309 "A" St, Violet, LA, 70092
(504) 682-2505, 682-2506
Admin Jeannie J Simmons. *Medical Dir/Dir of
Nursing* Samuel D Huddleston; Rosemary
James RN.
Licensure Skilled care. *Beds* SNF 48. *Certified*
Medicaid; Medicare.
Owner Proprietary Corp.
Admissions Requirements Medical
examination; Physician's request.
Staff Physicians 2 (pt); RNs 1 (ft), 1 (pt);
LPNs 6 (ft), 2 (pt); Orderlies 2 (ft); Nurses
aides 10 (ft); Physical therapists 1 (pt);
Recreational therapists 1 (pt); Activities
coordinators 1 (ft).
Languages French
Facilities Dining room; Laundry room.
Activities Arts & crafts; Cards; Games; Prayer
groups; Social/Cultural gatherings.

VIVIAN

Heritage Manor Vivian
Box 111, Rte 1, Camp Rd, Vivian, LA, 71082
(318) 375-2203
Admin Ben T Stogsdill. *Medical Dir/Dir of
Nursing* John Haymes MD; Melinda Baker
RN.
Licensure Intermediate care. *Beds* ICF 80.
Certified Medicaid.
Owner Proprietary Corp (National Heritage).
Admissions Requirements Medical
examination; Physician's request.
Staff Physicians 3 (pt); RNs 1 (ft); LPNs 4
(ft), 1 (pt); Nurses aides 16 (ft), 4 (pt);
Physical therapists 1 (pt); Occupational
therapists 1 (pt); Activities coordinators 1
(ft); Dietitians 1 (pt).

Facilities Dining room; Activities room;
Chapel; Crafts room; Laundry room; Barber/
Beauty shop; Library.
Activities Arts & crafts; Cards; Games;
Movies; Shopping trips; Social/Cultural
gatherings.

WELSH

Welsh Nursing Facility
PO Box 918, 410 Simmons St, Welsh, LA,
70591
(318) 734-2550
Admin Jean Paul LeJeune.
Licensure Intermediate care. *Beds* 60.
Certified Medicaid.

WEST MONROE

G B Cooley Hospital for Retarded Citizens
PO Box 93, Rte 8, 364 Cooley Rd, West
Monroe, LA, 71291
(318) 396-6300
Admin H Larry Parks. *Medical Dir/Dir of
Nursing* Dr Joseph Keyes.
Licensure Intermediate care for mentally
retarded Community homes 36 Supervised
apartments 5 Residential 85. *Beds* 126.
Certified Medicaid.
Owner Proprietary Corp (Forum Grp).
Admissions Requirements Minimum age 6.
Staff Physicians 1 (pt); RNs 1 (pt); LPNs 7
(ft), 1 (pt); Physical therapists 1 (ft);
Recreational therapists 1 (ft); Occupational
therapists 1 (pt); Speech therapists 1 (ft);
Dietitians 1 (ft).
Facilities Dining room; Physical therapy
room; Activities room; Laundry room;
Library.
Activities Arts & crafts; Games; Shopping
trips.

Ridgecrest Nursing Home*
100 Landrum Dr, West Monroe, LA, 71291
(318) 387-2577
Admin Carolyn Jeansonne. *Medical Dir/Dir of
Nursing* Cathy Goatley D.O.N..
Licensure Intermediate care. *Beds* 114.
Certified Medicaid.
Admissions Requirements Medical
examination; Physician's request.
Staff RNs 1 (ft); LPNs 8 (ft), 1 (pt); Orderlies
2 (ft); Nurses aides 34 (ft); Activities
coordinators 1 (ft); Dietitians 1 (pt).
Facilities Dining room; Activities room;
Crafts room; Laundry room; Barber/Beauty
shop; Sun porch.
Activities Arts & crafts; Cards; Games;
Reading groups; Prayer groups; Movies;
Shopping trips; Social/Cultural gatherings;
Fishing; Picnics; Senior Olympics.

West Monroe Guest House Inc*
1007 Glenwood Dr, West Monroe, LA, 71291
(318) 387-3900
Admin Virginia B Coplin.
Licensure Intermediate care. *Beds* 182.
Certified Medicaid.

WINNFIELD

Autumn Leaves Nursing Home*
167 North St, Winnfield, LA, 71483
(318) 628-4152
Admin Jimmy Dale Zimmerman.
Licensure Intermediate care. *Beds* 114.
Certified Medicaid.

Parkview Guest Care Center*
PO Box 948, 701 1st St, Winnfield, LA, 71483
(318) 628-3533
Admin Ron Frazier.
Licensure Intermediate care. *Beds* 88.
Certified Medicaid.

WINNSBORO

Franklin Guest Home*
2400 Ellis St, Winnsboro, LA, 71295
(318) 435-5026
Admin Lois J Evans.
Licensure Intermediate care. *Beds* 108.
  Certified Medicaid.

King's Guest Home*
1216 Prairie Rd, Winnsboro, LA, 71295
(318) 435-5194
Admin A A Kelley Jr.
Licensure Intermediate care. *Beds* 67.
  Certified Medicaid.

Winnsboro Manor Nursing Center*
Lone Cedar Rd, Winnsboro, LA, 71295
(318) 435-4536
Admin James D Sikes.
Licensure Intermediate care. *Beds* 111.
  Certified Medicaid.

WISNER

Mary Anna Nursing Home*
PO Drawer B, Wisner, LA, 71378
(318) 724-7244

Admin Carl D Batey.
Licensure Intermediate care. *Beds* 80.
  Certified Medicaid.

Rosalie Nursing Home
PO Box 190, Wisner, LA, 71378
(318) 724-7493
Admin Thelma G Sanders. *Medical Dir/Dir of
  Nursing* Barbara Harris RN.
Licensure Intermediate care. *Beds* ICF 75.
  Certified Medicaid; Medicare.
Owner Proprietary Corp.
Admissions Requirements Medical
  examination.
Staff RNs 1 (ft); LPNs 4 (ft), 1 (pt); Orderlies
  1 (ft); Nurses aides 22 (ft), 3 (pt); Activities
  coordinators 1 (pt); Dietitians 1 (pt).
Facilities Dining room; Activities room;
  Crafts room; Laundry room.
Activities Arts & crafts; Cards; Games;
  Reading groups; Prayer groups; Movies;
  Shopping trips; Social/Cultural gatherings;
  Bingo; Fishing trips/fries; Car excursions.

ZACHARY

Lane Memorial Hospital—Geriatric Unit
6300 Main St, Zachary, LA, 70791
(504) 654-4511
Admin Charlie L Massey. *Medical Dir/Dir of
  Nursing* Linda Long RN DON.
Licensure Intermediate care. *Beds* ICF 39.
  Certified Medicaid.
Owner Nonprofit organization/foundation.
Staff Physicians 30 (ft), 50 (pt); RNs 1 (ft), 3
  (pt); LPNs 4 (ft), 2 (pt); Orderlies 1 (ft), 2
  (pt); Nurses aides 8 (ft), 4 (pt); Physical
  therapists 1 (ft), 1 (pt); Activities
  coordinators 1 (pt); Dietitians 1 (ft);
  Dentists.
Facilities Dining room; Physical therapy
  room; Activities room; Chapel; Crafts room;
  Barber/Beauty shop.
Activities Arts & crafts; Games.

Zachary Manor Nursing Home*
6161 Main St, Zachary, LA, 70791
(504) 654-6893
Admin Billie F Dean.
Licensure Intermediate care. *Beds* 110.
  Certified Medicaid.

MAINE

ABBOT

Abbot Group Home
PO Box 141, West Rd, Abbot, ME, 04406
(207) 876-3703
Admin Carol Sylvester.
Licensure Intermediate care for mentally retarded. *Beds* ICF/MR 6. *Certified* Medicaid.
Owner Nonprofit Corp.
Admissions Requirements Minimum age 18.
Staff Activities coordinators 2 (pt); Dietitians 1 (ft); 4 (ft), 6 (pt) QMPP 1 (pt) Administration 3 (pt).
Facilities Dining room; Activities room; Laundry room; Library; Living room; TV room; Kitchen; Large yard.
Activities Arts & crafts; Games; Reading groups; Movies; Shopping trips; Social/Cultural gatherings; Bowling; Camping; Picnics; Museums; Community activities.

ALBION

Bethany Inc*
Hussey Rd, Albion, ME, 04910
(207) 437-4294
Admin Kathryn Sawtelle.
Licensure Intermediate care. *Beds* 25.
Certified Medicaid.

ATHENS

Athens Group Home
PO Box 4640, Rte 1, Athens, ME, 04912
(207) 654-2629
Admin Christy Provost.
Licensure Intermediate care for mentally retarded. *Beds* ICF/MR 6.
Owner Nonprofit organization/foundation.
Staff ADL Counselors 7 (ft), 1 (pt).

AUBURN

Auburn Nursing Home
185 Summer St, Auburn, ME, 04210
(207) 786-0111
Admin Donald Powers. *Medical Dir/Dir of Nursing* Elissa Louze.
Licensure Intermediate care. *Beds* ICF 42. *Certified* Medicaid.
Owner Privately owned.
Staff RNs 3 (ft), 2 (pt); LPNs 4 (ft); Nurses aides 15 (ft), 6 (pt); Activities coordinators 1 (pt).
Languages French
Facilities Dining room; Physical therapy room; Activities room; Laundry room; Barber/Beauty shop.
Activities Arts & crafts; Cards; Games; Reading groups; Prayer groups; Movies; Shopping trips; Social/Cultural gatherings; Cooking; Exercises.

Bolster Heights Health Care Facility*
26 Bolster St, Auburn, ME, 04210
(207) 784-1364

Admin Gailene Buckley.
Licensure Intermediate care. *Beds* 70.
Certified Medicaid.

Bon Air Nursing Home*
109 Davis Ave, Auburn, ME, 04210
(207) 783-0550
Admin Pauline Robertson.
Licensure Intermediate care. *Beds* 13.
Certified Medicaid.

Clover Manor Inc
440 Minot Ave, Auburn, ME, 04210
(207) 784-3573
Admin William Gillis. *Medical Dir/Dir of Nursing* Dr Carl Wolf.
Licensure Intermediate care; Alzheimer's units; Child day care; Personal adult day care; Congregate housing. *Beds* 120;; Hospice beds 5; Child day care 20; Personal adult day care 20; Congregate housing 91. *Certified* Medicaid.
Staff Physicians 2 (pt); RNs 7 (ft), 5 (pt); LPNs 6 (ft), 3 (pt); Nurses aides 52 (ft), 33 (pt); Physical therapists 1 (ft); Occupational therapists 1 (pt); Speech therapists 1 (pt); Activities coordinators 1 (ft); Dietitians 1 (ft), 1 (pt).
Facilities Dining room; Physical therapy room; Activities room; Crafts room; Laundry room; Barber/Beauty shop; Greenhouse.
Activities Arts & crafts; Cards; Games; Reading groups; Prayer groups; Movies; Shopping trips; Social/Cultural gatherings; Cocktail party.

Lovelett Health Care Center*
392 Turner St, Auburn, ME, 04210
(207) 784-4773
Admin Ann Lally.
Licensure Intermediate care. *Beds* 22.
Certified Medicaid.

Promenade Health Care Facility
27 Charles St, Auburn, ME, 04210
(207) 782-1621
Admin Peter Mauro. *Medical Dir/Dir of Nursing* Rita Wilson.
Licensure Intermediate care. *Beds* ICF 29. *Certified* Medicaid.
Staff RNs; LPNs; Orderlies; Nurses aides; Activities coordinators; Podiatrists.
Facilities Dining room; Laundry room.
Activities Arts & crafts; Cards; Games; Prayer groups; Movies; Shopping trips.

AUGUSTA

Augusta Convalescent Center*
187 Eastern Ave, Augusta, ME, 04330
(207) 622-3121
Admin Rosemary Rowe.
Licensure Intermediate care. *Beds* 78.
Certified Medicaid.
Owner Proprietary Corp (Hillhaven Corp).

Augusta Mental Health Institute
PO Box 724, Arsenal St, Augusta, ME, 04330
(207) 289-7230

Admin William C Daumueller. *Medical Dir/ Dir of Nursing* Jose Castellanos MD.
Licensure Intermediate care. *Beds* 70.
Certified Medicaid.
Staff Physicians 1 (ft); RNs 3 (ft), 1 (pt); LPNs 6 (ft); Nurses aides 39 (ft); Physical therapists 1 (pt); Recreational therapists 1 (ft); Dietitians 1 (pt).
Facilities Dining room; Physical therapy room; Chapel; Crafts room; Laundry room; Barber/Beauty shop; Library; Gift shop; Canteen.
Activities Arts & crafts; Cards; Games; Reading groups; Movies; Shopping trips; Social/Cultural gatherings.

Maine Veterans Home*
Cony Rd, Augusta, ME, 04330
(207) 622-2454
Admin William Carney.
Licensure Intermediate care. *Beds* 120.

Williams Health Care
Gray Birch Dr, Augusta, ME, 04330
(207) 622-6226
Admin Gregory B Gravel. *Medical Dir/Dir of Nursing* Roy Miller MD; Charlene Dorsky RN DON.
Licensure Skilled care; Intermediate care. *Beds* SNF 20; ICF 100. *Certified* Medicaid; Medicare.
Owner Nonprofit Corp.
Admissions Requirements Medical examination; Physician's request.
Staff RNs 6 (ft), 3 (pt); LPNs 2 (ft), 1 (pt); Nurses aides 39 (ft), 7 (pt); Physical therapists 1 (ft); Reality therapists 1 (pt); Recreational therapists 1 (ft), 4 (pt); Activities coordinators 1 (ft); Dietitians 1 (pt).
Languages French
Facilities Dining room; Physical therapy room; Activities room; Crafts room; Laundry room; Barber/Beauty shop.
Activities Arts & crafts; Cards; Games; Reading groups; Prayer groups; Movies; Social/Cultural gatherings.

Williams Health Care
Glenridge Dr, Augusta, ME, 04330
(207) 623-2593
Admin Nola B Ribe. *Medical Dir/Dir of Nursing* Roy Miller MD; Judy McGrail RN DON.
Licensure Intermediate care. *Beds* ICF 120. *Certified* Medicaid; Medicare.
Owner Nonprofit Corp.
Admissions Requirements Medical examination; Physician's request.
Staff RNs 6 (ft), 7 (pt); LPNs 2 (ft), 1 (pt); Nurses aides 39 (ft), 9 (pt); Physical therapists 1 (ft); Activities coordinators 1 (ft); Dietitians 1 (ft).
Languages French
Facilities Dining room; Physical therapy room; Activities room; Chapel; Crafts room; Laundry room; Barber/Beauty shop.

Activities Arts & crafts; Cards; Games; Reading groups; Prayer groups; Movies; Social/Cultural gatherings.

BANGOR

Bangor City Nursing Facility
103 Texas Ave, Bangor, ME, 04401
(207) 947-4557
Admin Judith B Roscetti. *Medical Dir/Dir of Nursing* Edward Babcock MD; Sharon Miner RN.
Licensure Skilled care. *Beds* SNF 54. *Certified* Medicaid; Medicare.
Owner Publicly owned.
Staff Physicians 1 (pt); RNs 3 (ft), 6 (pt); Physical therapists 1 (pt); Activities coordinators 1 (ft); Dietitians 1 (pt); Social worker 1 (ft).
Facilities Dining room; Physical therapy room; Activities room; Crafts room; Laundry room; Barber/Beauty shop.
Activities Arts & crafts; Cards; Games; Reading groups; Prayer groups; Movies; Shopping trips; Social/Cultural gatherings; Bowling; Birthday parties; Religious services for all denominations.

Bangor Convalescent Center*
516 Mount Hope Ave, Bangor, ME, 04401
(207) 947-6131
Admin Jean Green. *Medical Dir/Dir of Nursing* Michael Bruhel MD.
Licensure Intermediate care. *Beds* 80. *Certified* Medicaid.
Owner Proprietary Corp (Hillhaven Corp).
Admissions Requirements Medical examination.
Staff Physicians 12 (pt); RNs 2 (ft), 1 (pt); LPNs 8 (ft), 2 (pt); Nurses aides 25 (ft), 10 (pt); Physical therapists 1 (pt); Occupational therapists 1 (pt); Speech therapists 1 (pt); Activities coordinators 1 (ft), 1 (pt); Dietitians 1 (ft), 1 (pt).
Facilities Dining room; Physical therapy room; Activities room; Crafts room; Laundry room; Barber/Beauty shop; Library; Living rooms.
Activities Arts & crafts; Cards; Games; Reading groups; Prayer groups; Movies; Shopping trips; Social/Cultural gatherings; Field trips; Family dinners.

Bangor Mental Health Institute
PO Box 926, 656 State St, Bangor, ME, 04401
(207) 941-4289
Admin Hope A Richards. *Medical Dir/Dir of Nursing* Roger M Wilson MD; Frances Vanecek Asst DON.
Licensure Intermediate care. *Beds* ICF 130. *Certified* Medicaid.
Owner Publicly owned.
Staff Physicians 5 (ft), 5 (pt); RNs 46 (ft); LPNs 27 (ft); Nurses aides 226 (ft); Physical therapists 1 (ft); Reality therapists 1 (ft); Recreational therapists 2 (ft); Occupational therapists 1 (ft).
Facilities Dining room; Physical therapy room; Activities room; Chapel; Crafts room; Laundry room; Barber/Beauty shop; Library; Occupational therapy; Home living skills area.
Activities Arts & crafts; Cards; Games; Reading groups; Prayer groups; Movies; Shopping trips; Social/Cultural gatherings.

Eastern Maine Medical Center
489 State St, Bangor, ME, 04401
(207) 947-3711
Admin Robert Brandow. *Medical Dir/Dir of Nursing* Dr Phillip Mossman.
Licensure Skilled care. *Beds* 15. *Certified* Medicaid; Medicare.
Admissions Requirements Medical examination; Physician's request.

Staff RNs 4 (ft), 4 (pt); Nurses aides 7 (ft), 8 (pt); Physical therapists 2 (ft); Occupational therapists 1 (pt); Speech therapists 1 (pt); Activities coordinators 1 (ft); Dietitians 1 (pt).
Facilities Dining room; Physical therapy room; Activities room; Chapel; Crafts room; Laundry room; Barber/Beauty shop.
Activities Arts & crafts; Cards; Games; Reading groups; Movies; Social/Cultural gatherings.

Elizabeth Levinson Center
159 Hogan Rd, Bangor, ME, 04401-5697
(207) 941-4400
Admin Robert Durgan PhD. *Medical Dir/Dir of Nursing* Kathi Murray RN.
Licensure Intermediate care for mentally retarded. *Beds* ICF/MR 17 11D Respite care 3. *Certified* Medicaid.
Owner Publicly owned.
Admissions Requirements Minimum age 0-20; Medical examination; Physician's request.
Staff RNs 3 (ft), 3 (pt); LPNs 3 (ft), 2 (pt); Physical therapists 1 (pt); Recreational therapists 1 (pt); Occupational therapists 1 (ft); Psychologist 1 (pt).
Facilities Dining room; Physical therapy room; Activities room; Laundry room.
Activities Arts & crafts; Games; Movies; Shopping trips; Social/Cultural gatherings.

Pine Street Group Home
188 Pine St, Bangor, ME, 04401
(207) 947-6634
Admin Raymond B Hart.
Licensure Intermediate care for mentally retarded. *Beds* ICF/MR 6. *Certified* Medicaid.
Owner Nonprofit Corp.
Admissions Requirements Minimum age 21; Medical examination; Physician's request.
Staff Recreational therapists 1 (ft).
Facilities Dining room; Activities room; Laundry room.
Activities Arts & crafts; Cards; Games; Movies; Shopping trips; Social/Cultural gatherings.

Stillwater Health Care
335 Stillwater Ave, Bangor, ME, 04401
(207) 947-1111
Admin Gerard H Cyr. *Medical Dir/Dir of Nursing* Dr Henry Atkins.
Licensure Intermediate care. *Beds* 67. *Certified* Medicaid.
Owner Proprietary Corp.
Facilities Dining room; Physical therapy room; Activities room; Chapel; Laundry room; Barber/Beauty shop.
Activities Arts & crafts; Cards; Games; Reading groups; Prayer groups; Movies; Shopping trips; Picnics.

Taylor Hospital*
268 Stillwater Ave, Bangor, ME, 04401
(207) 942-5286
Admin Philip J Stoner. *Medical Dir/Dir of Nursing* Koster K Peter DO.
Licensure Intermediate care. *Beds* 38. *Certified* Medicaid.
Admissions Requirements Physician's request.
Staff RNs 2 (ft); LPNs 5 (ft); Nurses aides 14 (ft); Physical therapists 1 (pt); Activities coordinators 1 (pt); Dietitians 1 (ft).
Facilities Dining room; Activities room; Chapel; Laundry room.
Activities Arts & crafts; Cards; Games; Movies; Shopping trips.

Westgate Manor
750 Union St, Bangor, ME, 04401
(207) 942-7336
Admin Susan C Cirone. *Medical Dir/Dir of Nursing* Henry Atkins MD; Donna Ireland RN.
Licensure Intermediate care. *Beds* ICF 115. *Certified* Medicaid.

Owner Proprietary Corp (Hillhaven Corp).
Admissions Requirements Medical examination; Physician's request.
Staff RNs; LPNs; Nurses aides; Activities coordinators 2 (ft); Dietitians 1 (pt).
Facilities Dining room; Physical therapy room; Activities room; Chapel; Crafts room; Laundry room; Barber/Beauty shop; Library.
Activities Arts & crafts; Cards; Games; Reading groups; Prayer groups; Movies; Shopping trips; Social/Cultural gatherings.

BAR HARBOR

Sonogee Estates
131 Eden St, Bar Harbor, ME, 04609
(207) 288-5833
Admin Richard V Collier. *Medical Dir/Dir of Nursing* Donna Cameron RN.
Licensure Intermediate care. *Beds* ICF 83. *Certified* Medicaid.
Owner Proprietary Corp.
Admissions Requirements Minimum age 60; Physician's request.
Staff RNs 5 (ft); LPNs 9 (ft); Nurses aides 35 (ft), 8 (pt); Activities coordinators 2 (ft); Dietitians 1 (ft).
Facilities Dining room; Physical therapy room; Activities room; Chapel; Crafts room; Laundry room; Barber/Beauty shop.
Activities Arts & crafts; Cards; Games; Reading groups; Prayer groups; Movies; Shopping trips; Social/Cultural gatherings.

Summit House Health Care Center*
Norman Rd, Bar Harbor, ME, 04609
(207) 288-5856
Admin David Waldron.
Licensure Intermediate care. *Beds* 88. *Certified* Medicaid.

BATH

Bath Nursing Home*
PO Box 138, Winship St, Bath, ME, 04530
(207) 443-9772
Admin Carol Sharp. *Medical Dir/Dir of Nursing* Anthony Keating MD.
Licensure Intermediate care. *Beds* 72. *Certified* Medicaid.
Owner Proprietary Corp (Hillhaven Corp).
Admissions Requirements Medical examination; Physician's request.
Staff Physicians 16 (pt); RNs 3 (ft), 4 (pt); LPNs 3 (ft), 2 (pt); Nurses aides 22 (ft), 12 (pt); Physical therapists; Occupational therapists; Speech therapists; Activities coordinators 1 (ft), 1 (pt); Dietitians 1 (pt); Dentists 3 (pt); Ophthalmologists 3 (pt); Podiatrists 1 (pt).
Facilities Dining room; Physical therapy room; Activities room; Chapel; Crafts room; Laundry room; Barber/Beauty shop.
Activities Arts & crafts; Cards; Games; Reading groups; Prayer groups; Movies; Shopping trips; Social/Cultural gatherings.

Hillhouse Convalescent Home*
Box 98, Whiskeag Rd, Bath, ME, 04530
(207) 443-6301
Admin Marjorie Voorhees.
Licensure Intermediate care. *Beds* 37. *Certified* Medicaid.

BELFAST

Bradbury Manor*
32 High St, Belfast, ME, 04915
(207) 338-3666
Admin Edward A Bonenfant.
Licensure Intermediate care. *Beds* 60. *Certified* Medicaid.

BIDDEFORD

Good Shepherd Villa Inc*
173 South St, Biddeford, ME, 04005
(207) 282-4138
Admin Ralph Ham. *Medical Dir/Dir of Nursing* M P Houle MD.
Licensure Intermediate care. *Beds* 124.
Certified Medicaid.
Staff RNs 5 (ft); LPNs 11 (ft); Nurses aides 36 (ft); Activities coordinators 2 (ft); Dietitians 2 (ft).
Facilities Dining room; Physical therapy room; Activities room; Chapel; Crafts room; Laundry room; Barber/Beauty shop.
Activities Arts & crafts; Cards; Games; Reading groups; Prayer groups; Movies; Shopping trips; Social/Cultural gatherings.

Greenhill Residence*
1 Green St, Biddeford, ME, 04005
(207) 282-3741
Admin Anne Waterhouse.
Licensure Intermediate care for mentally retarded. *Beds* 6.
Admissions Requirements Minimum age 16; Medical examination; Physician's request.
Staff RNs 1 (pt); Activities coordinators 1 (ft).
Facilities Dining room; Activities room; Laundry room.
Activities Arts & crafts; Cards; Games; Movies; Shopping trips; Social/Cultural gatherings.

Riverwood Health Care Center
PO Box 364, 355 Pool Rd, Biddeford, ME, 04005
(207) 283-3646
Admin Daniel Sowerby. *Medical Dir/Dir of Nursing* Linda Owen RN.
Licensure Intermediate care. *Beds* ICF 61.
Certified Medicaid.
Owner Proprietary Corp.
Admissions Requirements Medical examination.
Staff RNs 5 (ft), 2 (pt); LPNs 4 (ft), 3 (pt); Orderlies 2 (ft); Nurses aides 14 (ft), 8 (pt); Activities coordinators 1 (ft), 1 (pt); Med tech 2 (ft).
Languages French, Greek
Facilities Dining room; Physical therapy room; Activities room; Chapel; Crafts room; Laundry room; Barber/Beauty shop; Library.
Activities Arts & crafts; Cards; Games; Reading groups; Prayer groups; Movies; Shopping trips; Social/Cultural gatherings.

St Andre Health Care Facility
PO Box 601, 407 Pool St, Biddeford, ME, 04005
(207) 282-5171
Admin Sr Madeleine D'Anjou. *Medical Dir/Dir of Nursing* Sarah Moore MD; Michelle Fecteau DON.
Licensure Intermediate care. *Beds* ICF 96.
Certified Medicaid.
Owner Nonprofit Corp.
Admissions Requirements Medical examination; Physician's request.
Staff RNs 4 (ft), 9 (pt); LPNs 3 (ft), 5 (pt); Orderlies 1 (pt); Nurses aides 25 (ft), 33 (pt); Physical therapists 1 (pt); Reality therapists 3 (pt); Activities coordinators 3 (ft).
Languages French
Affiliation Roman Catholic
Facilities Dining room; Physical therapy room; Activities room; Chapel; Laundry room; Barber/Beauty shop; Library.
Activities Arts & crafts; Games; Movies; Shopping trips; Social/Cultural gatherings.

Trull Nursing Home*
15 May St, Biddeford, ME, 04005
(207) 284-4507
Admin Marion Stickney.
Licensure Intermediate care. *Beds* 49.
Certified Medicaid.

BINGHAM

Somerset Manor Inc
Owen St, Bingham, ME, 04920
(207) 672-4041
Admin Mary Anne Albano. *Medical Dir/Dir of Nursing* Molly Williams.
Licensure Intermediate care. *Beds* ICF 34.
Certified Medicaid.
Owner Proprietary Corp (Continental Health Systems).
Staff RNs 2 (ft); LPNs 2 (ft), 1 (pt); Nurses aides 10 (ft), 14 (pt).
Facilities Dining room; Activities room; Laundry room; Barber/Beauty shop.
Activities Arts & crafts; Cards; Games; Reading groups; Prayer groups; Movies; Shopping trips; Social/Cultural gatherings; Van rides; Bell ringing; Adopt-a-grandchild.

BREWER

Brewer Conv Center*
174 Parkway S, Brewer, ME, 04412
(207) 989-7300
Admin Penelope Sargent. *Medical Dir/Dir of Nursing* Richard Sagall.
Licensure Intermediate care. *Beds* 116.
Certified Medicaid.
Owner Proprietary Corp (Hillhaven Corp).
Staff Physicians 1 (ft); RNs 5 (ft), 2 (pt); LPNs 9 (ft), 1 (pt); Nurses aides 30 (ft), 20 (pt); Physical therapists 1 (pt); Speech therapists 1 (pt); Activities coordinators 2 (ft), 1 (pt); Dietitians 1 (ft); Podiatrists 1 (pt).
Facilities Dining room; Physical therapy room; Activities room; Crafts room; Laundry room; Barber/Beauty shop; Library.
Activities Arts & crafts; Cards; Games; Reading groups; Prayer groups; Movies; Shopping trips; Social/Cultural gatherings; Fund raising; Resident council.

Eddington Group Home
PO Box 82, Rte 2, Brewer, ME, 04412
(207) 989-1303
Admin Jacqueline L Turner. *Medical Dir/Dir of Nursing* Gail Sinclair RN.
Licensure Intermediate care for mentally retarded. *Beds* 6. *Certified* Medicaid.
Owner Nonprofit Corp.
Admissions Requirements Minimum age 18; Medical examination.
Staff RNs 1 (pt); Nurses aides 12 (ft); Speech therapists 1 (pt); Activities coordinators 1 (ft); Dietitians 1 (pt).
Activities Arts & crafts; Cards; Games; Reading groups; Prayer groups; Movies; Shopping trips; Social/Cultural gatherings.

Penobscot Valley Nursing Home*
23 Holyoke St, Brewer, ME, 04412
(207) 989-3100
Admin Sally Lord.
Licensure Intermediate care. *Beds* 26.
Certified Medicaid.

BRIDGTON

Good Neighbors Inc*
PO Box 119, S High St, Bridgton, ME, 04009
(207) 647-8244
Admin Rebecca Shanor.
Licensure Intermediate care for mentally retarded. *Beds* 12. *Certified* Medicaid.

BRUNSWICK

Brunswick Conv Center
Baribeau Dr, Brunswick, ME, 04011
(207) 725-4379
Admin Mitchell Rousseau. *Medical Dir/Dir of Nursing* E Schmidt MD.
Licensure Intermediate care. *Beds* 82.
Certified Medicaid.

Admissions Requirements Medical examination.
Staff RNs 3 (ft), 4 (pt); LPNs 1 (ft), 7 (pt); Orderlies 1 (ft); Nurses aides 21 (ft), 28 (pt); Activities coordinators 1 (ft); Dietitians 1 (ft).
Facilities Dining room; Activities room; Crafts room; Laundry room; Barber/Beauty shop; Library.
Activities Arts & crafts; Reading groups; Prayer groups; Movies; Shopping trips; Social/Cultural gatherings.

Brunswick Manor
26 Cumberland Ave, Brunswick, ME, 04011
(207) 725-5801
Admin Kathleen A McGhee. *Medical Dir/Dir of Nursing* Marion A Roy RN DON.
Licensure Intermediate care. *Beds* ICF 51.
Certified Medicaid.
Owner Privately owned.
Admissions Requirements Physician's request.
Staff RNs; LPNs; Nurses aides; Activities coordinators; Dietitians.
Facilities Activities room; Laundry room; Barber/Beauty shop; Library.
Activities Arts & crafts; Cards; Games; Reading groups; Prayer groups; Movies; Shopping trips; Social/Cultural gatherings; Resident council.

Mere Point Nursing Home*
Mere Point Rd, Brunswick, ME, 04011
(207) 725-2870
Admin Thomas E Edwards.
Licensure Intermediate care. *Beds* 26.
Certified Medicaid.

Regional Memorial Hospital SNF
58 Baribeau Dr, Brunswick, ME, 04011
(207) 729-0181
Admin David Dix. *Medical Dir/Dir of Nursing* Dr Montegut.
Licensure Skilled care. *Beds* 8. *Certified* Medicaid; Medicare.
Owner Nonprofit Corp.
Admissions Requirements Medical examination.
Staff RNs 2 (ft), 2 (pt); LPNs 1 (ft), 2 (pt); Nurses aides 4 (ft), 2 (pt); Activities coordinators 1 (pt).
Languages French
Facilities Dining room; Physical therapy room; Activities room.
Activities Arts & crafts; Cards; Games; Movies; Shopping trips; Home cooked meals.

CALAIS

Barnard Nursing Home
Palmer St, Calais, ME, 04619
(207) 454-2366
Admin Edward Fournier. *Medical Dir/Dir of Nursing* Ann Lyons.
Licensure Intermediate care. *Beds* ICF 100.
Certified Medicaid.
Owner Privately owned.
Staff RNs; LPNs; Nurses aides; Activities coordinators; Dietitians.
Facilities Dining room; Activities room; Crafts room; Laundry room; Barber/Beauty shop.
Activities Arts & crafts; Cards; Games; Reading groups; Prayer groups; Movies; Shopping trips; Social/Cultural gatherings; Student reading; Volunteer programs; Cooking.

CAMDEN

Camden Health Care Center
108 Elm St, Camden, ME, 04843
(207) 236-8381
Admin Jefferson Ackor. *Medical Dir/Dir of Nursing* Marjorie Smith RN.

Licensure Skilled care; Intermediate care. *Beds* SNF 20; ICF 178. *Certified* Medicaid; Medicare; VA.
Owner Nonprofit Corp.
Admissions Requirements Medical examination; Physician's request.
Staff Physicians 2 (pt); RNs 3 (ft), 10 (pt); LPNs 2 (ft), 10 (pt); Nurses aides 80 (ft), 40 (pt); Physical therapists 3 (ft), 2 (pt); Occupational therapists 2 (ft), 2 (pt); Speech therapists 2 (ft), 1 (pt); Activities coordinators 1 (ft), 3 (pt); Dietitians 1 (pt); Dentists 3 (pt); Ophthalmologists 2 (pt); Podiatrists 1 (ft).
Facilities Dining room; Physical therapy room; Activities room; Chapel; Crafts room; Laundry room; Barber/Beauty shop; Library; Outdoor patio; Park & BBQ area.
Activities Arts & crafts; Cards; Games; Reading groups; Prayer groups; Movies; Shopping trips; Social/Cultural gatherings.

Camden Nursing Home
19 Mountain St, Camden, ME, 04843
(207) 236-2900
Admin Barbara Baranello. *Medical Dir/Dir of Nursing* Thelma Dean RN.
Licensure Intermediate care. *Beds* 29.
Certified Medicaid.
Owner Proprietary Corp.
Admissions Requirements Minimum age 65.
Staff RNs 2 (ft); LPNs 2 (ft); Nurses aides 23 (ft); Activities coordinators 1 (ft).
Facilities Dining room; Activities room; Laundry room.
Activities Arts & crafts; Cards; Games; Reading groups; Movies; Shopping trips; Social/Cultural gatherings.

CANTON

Victorian Villa
Pleasant St, Canton, ME, 04221
(207) 597-2115
Admin Aiden E Redding. *Medical Dir/Dir of Nursing* Pat Coyne DN.
Licensure Intermediate care. *Beds* 36.
Certified Medicaid.
Staff RNs 2 (ft); LPNs 3 (ft); Nurses aides 10 (ft), 12 (pt); Recreational therapists 1 (pt); Activities coordinators 1 (pt).
Facilities Dining room; Physical therapy room; Laundry room; Barber/Beauty shop.
Activities Arts & crafts; Games; Reading groups; Prayer groups; Movies; Shopping trips; Social/Cultural gatherings.

CAPE ELIZABETH

The Viking Intermediate Care Facility
Scott Dyer Rd, Cape Elizabeth, ME, 04107
(207) 767-3373
Admin Duane Rancourt. *Medical Dir/Dir of Nursing* Nancy Littlefield.
Licensure Intermediate care. *Beds* ICF 60.
Certified Medicaid.
Owner Proprietary Corp.
Staff RNs 4 (ft), 5 (pt); LPNs 2 (ft), 4 (pt); Nurses aides 14 (ft), 19 (pt).
Facilities Dining room; Activities room; Laundry room; Barber/Beauty shop.
Activities Arts & crafts; Cards; Games; Reading groups; Prayer groups; Movies; Shopping trips.

CARIBOU

Caribou Nursing Home*
10 Bernadette St, Caribou, ME, 04736
(207) 498-3102
Admin Philip Cyr.
Licensure Intermediate care. *Beds* 110.
Certified Medicaid.
Admissions Requirements Medical examination.

Staff RNs 1 (ft), 7 (pt); LPNs 1 (ft), 10 (pt); Nurses aides 16 (ft), 67 (pt); Physical therapists 1 (ft); Activities coordinators 2 (ft); Diet tians 1 (pt).
Facilities Dining room; Physical therapy room; Activities room; Crafts room; Laundry room; Barber/Beauty shop.
Activities Arts & crafts; Cards; Games; Prayer groups; Movies; Social/Cultural gatherings.

COOPERS MILLS

Country Manor Nursing Home
PO Box 76, Coopers Mills, ME, 04341
(204) 549-7471
Admin Kenneth J Weber. *Medical Dir/Dir of Nursing* Linda Bradford RN DON.
Licensure Intermediate care. *Beds* ICF 53.
Certified Medicaid.
Owner Proprietary Corp.
Admissions Requirements Minimum age 65; Medical examination; Physician's request.
Staff RNs 2 (ft), 1 (pt); LPNs 1 (ft), 2 (pt); Orderlies 1 (ft); Nurses aides 12 (ft), 9 (pt); Activities coordinators 1 (pt).
Facilities Dining room; Activities room; Laundry room.
Activities Arts & crafts; Cards; Games; Reading groups; Prayer groups; Movies; Shopping trips.

Sheepscot Valley Health Center*
Main St, Coopers Mills, ME, 04341
(207) 549-7581
Admin David N Fenton.

DANFORTH

Danforth Nursing Home*
Depot St, Danforth, ME, 04424
(207) 448-2383
Admin Anna Schillinger. *Medical Dir/Dir of Nursing* John Madigan MD.
Licensure Intermediate care. *Beds* 18.
Certified Medicaid.
Staff Physicians 2 (pt); RNs 1 (ft), 1 (pt); Nurses aides 6 (ft), 8 (pt); Physical therapists 1 (pt); Occupational therapists 1 (pt); Activities coordinators 1 (pt); Dietitians 1 (pt).
Facilities Dining room; Activities room; Crafts room; Laundry room.
Activities Arts & crafts; Cards; Games; Reading groups.

Still Waters Nursing Home*
Main St, Danforth, ME, 04424
(207) 448-2327
Admin Gertrude M Ripley.
Licensure Intermediate care. *Beds* 21.
Certified Medicaid.

DEER ISLE

Island Nursing Home
Rte 15, Box 124, Deer Isle, ME, 04627
(207) 348-2351
Admin Laurna Griffin. *Medical Dir/Dir of Nursing* Dr Daniel; Arlene Hasbell DON.
Licensure Intermediate care. *Beds* ICF 50.
Certified Medicaid.
Owner Nonprofit Corp.
Admissions Requirements Minimum age 16; Physician's request.
Staff RNs 2 (ft), 1 (pt); LPNs 3 (ft), 2 (pt); Nurses aides 23 (ft), 15 (pt); Speech therapists 1 (pt); Activities coordinators 1 (ft), 1 (pt); Dietitians 1 (pt).
Facilities Dining room; Activities room; Crafts room; Laundry room; Barber/Beauty shop; Library.
Activities Arts & crafts; Cards; Games; Reading groups; Prayer groups; Movies; Shopping trips; Dine out trips.

Island Nursing Home Inc
Rte 15, PO Box 124, Deer Isle, ME, 04627
(207) 348-6847
Admin Laura Griffin. *Medical Dir/Dir of Nursing* Daniel Rissi MD; Sarah Bloy MSN.
Licensure Intermediate care. *Beds* ICF 50.
Certified Medicaid.
Owner Nonprofit Corp.
Admissions Requirements Minimum age 18.
Staff RNs 2 (ft), 2 (pt); LPNs 3 (ft), 3 (pt); Nurses aides 17 (ft), 18 (pt); Activities coordinators 1 (ft), 1 (pt); Dietitians; Ophthalmologists; Social workers.
Facilities Dining room; Activities room; Crafts room; Laundry room; Barber/Beauty shop; Library.
Activities Arts & crafts; Cards; Games; Reading groups; Prayer groups; Movies; Shopping trips.

DEXTER

Dexter Nursing Home*
PO Box 347, 64 Park St, Dexter, ME, 04930
(207) 924-5516
Admin Belle V Chandler.
Licensure Intermediate care. *Beds* 66.
Certified Medicaid.
Owner Proprietary Corp (Angell Group).

DIXFIELD

Dixfield Health Care Center*
100 Weld St, Dixfield, ME, 04224
(207) 562-4922
Admin Paula Varney.
Licensure Intermediate care. *Beds* 55.
Certified Medicaid.
Owner Proprietary Corp (Hillhaven Corp).

DOVERFOXCROFT

Hibbard Nursing Home*
Guilford Rd, Dover-Foxcroft, ME, 04426
(207) 564-8129
Admin Jane M Hibbard. *Medical Dir/Dir of Nursing* L J Stitham MD.
Licensure Skilled care; Intermediate care. *Beds* SNF 12; ICF 66. *Certified* Medicaid; Medicare.
Staff Physicians 10 (ft), 3 (pt); RNs 3 (ft), 3 (pt); LPNs 4 (ft), 2 (pt); Nurses aides 31 (ft), 13 (pt); Physical therapists 1 (pt); Speech therapists 1 (pt); Activities coordinators 2 (ft); Dietitians 1 (pt); Dentists 1 (pt); Ophthalmologists 1 (pt); Podiatrists 1 (pt).
Facilities Dining room; Physical therapy room; Activities room; Crafts room; Laundry room; Barber/Beauty shop; Library.
Activities Arts & crafts; Cards; Games; Reading groups; Prayer groups; Movies; Shopping trips; Social/Cultural gatherings.

EAGLE LAKE

Eagle Lake Nursing Home
Church St, Eagle Lake, ME, 04739
(207) 444-5152
Admin Gerald Frenette. *Medical Dir/Dir of Nursing* Jeanne Charette RN.
Licensure Intermediate care. *Beds* ICF 60.
Certified Medicaid.
Owner Nonprofit Corp.
Admissions Requirements Minimum age 16; Medical examination; Physician's request.
Staff RNs 7 (ft), 1 (pt); LPNs 1 (ft), 1 (pt); Nurses aides 12 (ft), 30 (pt); Recreational therapists 1 (pt); Speech therapists 1 (pt); Activities coordinators 1 (pt); Dietitians 1 (ft); Ophthalmologists 1 (pt); Podiatrists 1 (pt).
Languages French
Facilities Dining room; Physical therapy room; Activities room; Chapel; Crafts room; Laundry room; Barber/Beauty shop; Library.

Activities Arts & crafts; Cards; Games;
Reading groups; Movies; Shopping trips;
Social/Cultural gatherings.

EAST LEBANON

Greenwood Nursing Care Center Inc*
Little River Rd, East Lebanon, ME, 04027
(207) 457-1033
Admin Christine Boisvert.
Licensure Intermediate care. *Beds* 31.
Certified Medicaid.

EASTPORT

Eastport Memorial Nursing Home
23 Boynton St, Eastport, ME, 04631
(207) 853-2531
Admin Marlene Salig.
Licensure Intermediate care. *Beds* 26.
Certified Medicaid.
Admissions Requirements Medical
examination.
Staff RNs 3 (ft); LPNs 3 (ft), 1 (pt); Nurses
aides 7 (ft), 1 (pt); Activities coordinators 1
(pt); Dietitians 1 (pt); Social worker.
Facilities Dining room; Activities room;
Crafts room; Barber/Beauty shop.
Activities Arts & crafts; Cards; Games;
Reading groups; Prayer groups; Shopping
trips; Exercise; Religious services weekly;
Resident council; Cooking class; Regular &
special family style dinners; cook-outs;
Special group (confused residents); All
American ice cream cone give away to
public; Letters to Santa; Resident council;
Individualized activity program.

ELLSWORTH

Agape House ICF/MR
360 E Main St, Ellsworth, ME, 04605
(207) 667-3028
Admin Peter S Vacca. *Medical Dir/Dir of
Nursing* John C Van Pelt MD.
Licensure Intermediate care for mentally
retarded. *Beds* ICF/MR. *Certified* Medicaid.
Owner Nonprofit Corp.
Admissions Requirements Minimum age 20;
Medical examination.
Staff RNs 2 (ft), 1 (pt); LPNs 2 (ft), 2 (pt);
Nurses aides 28 (ft), 2 (pt); Activities
coordinators 1 (ft); Dietitians 3 (ft), 1 (pt).
Languages Sign
Facilities Dining room; Activities room;
Crafts room; Laundry room.
Activities Arts & crafts; Cards; Games;
Reading groups; Movies; Shopping trips;
Social/Cultural gatherings.

Collier's Nursing Home
33 Birch Ave, Ellsworth, ME, 04605
(207) 667-9336
Admin William L Collier. *Medical Dir/Dir of
Nursing* Dr Joseph LaCasce; Mrs Sigrid
Stevens.
Licensure Intermediate care. *Beds* ICF 44.
Certified Medicaid.
Owner Proprietary Corp.
Admissions Requirements Medical
examination.
Staff RNs 2 (ft); LPNs 4 (ft), 5 (pt); Nurses
aides 21 (ft), 5 (pt); Activities coordinators 1
(pt).
Languages French
Facilities Activities room; Laundry room.
Activities Arts & crafts; Cards; Games; Prayer
groups; Movies; Special meals.

Ellsworth Conv Center*
38 Court St, Ellsworth, ME, 04605
(207) 667-9036
Admin Stanley R Martin. *Medical Dir/Dir of
Nursing* Charles Alexander MD.
Licensure Intermediate care. *Beds* 94.
Certified Medicaid.

Admissions Requirements Medical
examination; Physician's request.
Staff RNs 4 (ft), 1 (pt); LPNs 5 (ft), 2 (pt);
Nurses aides 39 (ft); Physical therapists 1
(pt); Speech therapists 1 (pt); Activities
coordinators 1 (ft); Dietitians 1 (ft).
Facilities Dining room; Physical therapy
room; Activities room; Laundry room;
Barber/Beauty shop; Library.
Activities Arts & crafts; Cards; Games;
Reading groups; Prayer groups; Movies;
Shopping trips; Social/Cultural gatherings.

FAIRFIELD

Klearview Manor*
RFD 1, Shawmut Rd, Fairfield, ME, 04937
(207) 453-2112
Admin Carroll Marston.
Licensure Intermediate care for mentally
retarded. *Beds* 29.

Pleasant Hill Health Facility
PO Box 350, RR 1, Mountain Ave, Fairfield,
ME, 04937
(207) 453-2511
Admin Tammy Burnham. *Medical Dir/Dir of
Nursing* Marion Strickland MD.
Licensure Intermediate care. *Beds* 95.
Certified Medicaid.
Staff RNs 4 (ft); LPNs 6 (ft), 3 (pt); Orderlies
2 (ft); Nurses aides 32 (ft), 10 (pt); Activities
coordinators 1 (ft), 1 (pt); Dietitians 1 (pt).
Facilities Dining room; Activities room;
Crafts room; Barber/Beauty shop.
Activities Arts & crafts; Cards; Games;
Reading groups; Prayer groups; Movies;
Shopping trips; Social/Cultural gatherings;
Cooking; Gardening.

FALMOUTH

Falmouth Convalescent Center*
191 Foreside Rd, Falmouth, ME, 04105
(207) 781-4714
Admin Sandra Tate.
Licensure Intermediate care. *Beds* 70.
Certified Medicaid.

FARMINGTON

Edgewood Manor*
70 N Main St, Farmington, ME, 04938
(207) 778-3386
Admin Carey Davis. *Medical Dir/Dir of
Nursing* K Gooch MD.
Licensure Intermediate care. *Beds* 53.
Certified Medicaid.
Admissions Requirements Medical
examination; Physician's request.
Staff RNs 4 (ft), 2 (pt); LPNs 6 (ft), 2 (pt);
Orderlies 2 (ft); Nurses aides 23 (ft), 16 (pt);
Physical therapists 1 (pt); Recreational
therapists 1 (ft); Activities coordinators 1
(ft); Dietitians 1 (pt).
Facilities Dining room; Activities room;
Chapel; Crafts room; Laundry room; Barber/
Beauty shop; Library.
Activities Arts & crafts; Cards; Games;
Reading groups; Prayer groups; Movies;
Shopping trips; Social/Cultural gatherings.

Franklin Manor II Inc*
18 Orchard St, Farmington, ME, 04938
(207) 778-4416
Admin Sherrill Brann. *Medical Dir/Dir of
Nursing* Paul Taylor MD.
Licensure Intermediate care. *Beds* 32.
Certified Medicaid.
Admissions Requirements Medical
examination.
Staff RNs 1 (ft), 1 (pt); LPNs 3 (ft), 3 (pt);
Nurses aides 10 (ft), 8 (pt); Activities
coordinators 1 (pt).

Facilities Dining room; Laundry room.
Activities Arts & crafts; Cards; Games;
Reading groups; Prayer groups; Movies;
Shopping trips; Social/Cultural gatherings.

**Our House/Western Medical Association for
Retarded Citizens**
8 Anson St, Farmington, ME, 04955
(207) 778-2602
Admin Kathleen Cordes.
Licensure Intermediate care for mentally
retarded. *Beds* ICF/MR 6. *Certified*
Medicaid.
Owner Nonprofit Corp.
Admissions Requirements Minimum age 18;
Medical examination; Physician's request.
Staff Activities coordinators 1 (pt); Residential
counselors 5 (ft), 3 (pt); QMRP 1 (ft).
Facilities Dining room; Laundry room;
Normal household setting; In-town location;
pool.
Activities Arts & crafts; Games; Movies;
Shopping trips; Social/Cultural gatherings;
Instruction & supervision in activities of
daily living.

Sandy River Nursing Care Center
PO Box 5121, RFD 4, Farmington, ME,
04938
(207) 778-6591, 945-3752
Admin Mary Bayer. *Medical Dir/Dir of
Nursing* Anne Hunter MD; Susanne
Heeschen RN DON.
Licensure Intermediate care. *Beds* ICF 95.
Certified Medicaid.
Owner Proprietary Corp.
Admissions Requirements Minimum age 16;
Medical examination; Physician's request.
Staff RNs 8 (ft), 3 (pt); LPNs 1 (ft), 4 (pt);
Nurses aides 25 (ft), 28 (pt); Physical
therapists 1 (pt); Recreational therapists 1
(ft), 1 (pt); Occupational therapists 1 (pt);
Speech therapists 1 (pt); Ophthalmologists 1
(pt).
Facilities Dining room; Physical therapy
room; Activities room; Barber/Beauty shop.
Activities Arts & crafts; Cards; Games;
Reading groups; Prayer groups; Movies;
Shopping trips; Social/Cultural gatherings.

FORT FAIRFIELD

**The Aroostook Medical Center-Community
General Hospital Division**
3 Green St, Fort Fairfield, ME, 04742
(207) 768-4779
Admin William E Nettles. *Medical Dir/Dir of
Nursing* Arthur Pendleton MD; Brenda
Roope RN DON.
Licensure Skilled care; Intermediate care. *Beds*
SNF 10; ICF 16. *Certified* Medicaid;
Medicare.
Owner Nonprofit organization/foundation.
Admissions Requirements Medical
examination; Physician's request.
Staff RNs 2 (ft), 1 (pt); LPNs 2 (ft), 5 (pt);
Nurses aides 11 (ft), 12 (pt); Activities
coordinators 1 (pt); Dietitians 1 (pt).
Languages French, Spanish
Facilities Dining room; Activities room;
Barber/Beauty shop.
Activities Arts & crafts; Cards; Games;
Movies; Shopping trips; Social/Cultural
gatherings; Dining out.

FORT KENT

Forest Hill Manor Inc
20 Bolduc Ave, Fort Kent, ME, 04743
(207) 834-3915
Admin James Leuasseur. *Medical Dir/Dir of
Nursing* Rosanne Paradis RN.
Licensure Intermediate care. *Beds* ICF 45.
Certified Medicaid.
Owner Proprietary Corp.
Admissions Requirements Medical
examination; Physician's request.

Staff RNs 4 (ft), 1 (pt); LPNs 2 (ft), 1 (pt); Nurses aides 26 (ft); Activities coordinators 1 (ft).
Languages French
Facilities Dining room; Activities room; Chapel; Crafts room; Laundry room; Barber/ Beauty shop.
Activities Arts & crafts; Cards; Prayer groups; Movies.

FREEPORT

Freeport Convalescent Center
Old County Rd, Freeport, ME, 04032
(207) 865-4782
Admin Peter Morneault. *Medical Dir/Dir of Nursing* Sandra Keith RN.
Licensure Intermediate care. *Beds* ICF 82. *Certified* Medicaid.
Owner Proprietary Corp.
Admissions Requirements Medical examination.
Staff RNs 4 (ft); LPNs 4 (ft); Nurses aides 14 (ft); Activities coordinators 1 (ft).
Languages French
Facilities Dining room; Activities room; Crafts room; Laundry room; Barber/Beauty shop.
Activities Arts & crafts; Games; Reading groups; Prayer groups; Movies; Shopping trips; Social/Cultural gatherings.

The Freeport Nursing Home Inc
PO Box K, 3 East St, Freeport, ME, 04032
(207) 865-4713
Admin Douglas N Powers. *Medical Dir/Dir of Nursing* Michael Contartese; Shelly Kinsman.
Licensure Intermediate care. *Beds* 60. *Certified* Medicaid.
Owner Privately owned.
Staff RNs; LPNs; Nurses aides; Physical therapists; Reality therapists; Recreational therapists; Occupational therapists; Speech therapists; Activities coordinators; Dietitians; Ophthalmologists.
Languages French
Facilities Dining room; Activities room; Laundry room; Barber/Beauty shop; Library.
Activities Arts & crafts; Cards; Games; Reading groups; Prayer groups; Movies; Shopping trips; Social/Cultural gatherings.

Freeport Towne Square I*
Lower Main St, Freeport, ME, 04032
(207) 865-4876
Admin Eric Gilliam.
Licensure Intermediate care for mentally retarded. *Beds* 6.

Freeport Towne Square II*
Lower Main St, Freeport, ME, 04032
(207) 865-6060
Admin Eric Gilliam.
Licensure Intermediate care for mentally retarded. *Beds* 8.

FRYEBURG

Fryeburg Health Care Center*
77 Fairview Dr, Fryeburg, ME, 04037
(207) 935-3351
Admin David R Hicks.
Licensure Intermediate care. *Beds* 82. *Certified* Medicaid.

Hicks Nursing Home*
PO Box 170, 27 Oxford St, Fryeburg, ME, 04037
(207) 935-2985
Admin Erna Hicks.
Licensure Intermediate care. *Beds* 27. *Certified* Medicaid.

GARDINER

Gardiner Group Home*
23 River Rd, Gardiner, ME, 04345
(207) 582-7355
Admin Deborah Dixon.
Licensure Intermediate care for mentally retarded. *Beds* 6.

Merrill Memorial Manor
146 Dresden Ave, Gardiner, ME, 04345
(207) 582-2114
Admin Krista S Weber. *Medical Dir/Dir of Nursing* Dr Stanley Painter; Barbara Seaman.
Licensure Intermediate care. *Beds* ICF 64. *Certified* Medicaid.
Owner Proprietary Corp.
Admissions Requirements Minimum age 60.
Staff RNs 2 (ft); LPNs 3 (ft), 2 (pt); Orderlies 4 (ft), 1 (pt); Nurses aides 13 (ft), 15 (pt); Activities coordinators 1 (ft); Dietitians 1 (pt).
Languages French
Facilities Dining room; Activities room; Chapel; Crafts room; Laundry room; Barber/ Beauty shop; Library.
Activities Arts & crafts; Cards; Games; Reading groups; Prayer groups; Movies; Shopping trips; Social/Cultural gatherings.

Robinson's Health Care Facility
PO Box 478, 284 Brunswick Ave, Gardiner, ME, 04345
(207) 582-6250
Admin Shirley M Shaw. *Medical Dir/Dir of Nursing* Barbara Gray RN.
Licensure Intermediate care. *Beds* 50. *Certified* Medicare.
Owner Privately owned.
Staff RNs 2 (ft), 3 (pt); LPNs 2 (pt); Nurses aides 12 (ft), 17 (pt); Activities coordinators 1 (ft); Dietitians 1 (pt); Social service 1 (pt).
Languages Russian, French
Facilities Dining room; Physical therapy room; Activities room; Laundry room.
Activities Arts & crafts; Games; Reading groups; Prayer groups; Movies.

Willowcrest Home Inc*
Rte 4, Gardiner, ME, 04345
(207) 582-3632
Admin Donald Palleschi. *Medical Dir/Dir of Nursing* Maurice Guillemette MD.
Licensure Intermediate care. *Beds* 42. *Certified* Medicaid.
Admissions Requirements Minimum age 16.
Staff Physicians 1 (pt); RNs 1 (ft); LPNs 2 (ft), 2 (pt); Orderlies 11 (ft), 14 (pt); Physical therapists 1 (pt); Speech therapists 1 (pt); Activities coordinators 1 (ft); Dietitians 1 (pt); Dentists 1 (pt); Podiatrists 1 (pt).
Facilities Dining room; Activities room.
Activities Arts & crafts; Cards; Games; Reading groups; Prayer groups; Movies; Shopping trips; Social/Cultural gatherings; Outside trips.

GORHAM

Gorham Manor*
30 New Portland Rd, Gorham, ME, 04038
(207) 839-3732
Admin Arlene Cooper.
Licensure Intermediate care. *Beds* 24. *Certified* Medicaid.
Admissions Requirements Minimum age 16; Medical examination.
Staff RNs 1 (ft); LPNs 2 (ft), 1 (pt); Nurses aides 5 (ft), 9 (pt); Activities coordinators 1 (ft); Social workers 1 (ft).
Facilities Dining room; Activities room; Crafts room; Laundry room.
Activities Arts & crafts; Cards; Games; Reading groups; Prayer groups; Movies; Shopping trips; Social/Cultural gatherings.

GREENE

Greene Acres Manor Inc*
PO Box 160, Rte 202, Greene, ME, 04236
(207) 946-5225
Admin Rachel Alward.
Licensure Intermediate care. *Beds* 59. *Certified* Medicaid.

GREENVILLE

Mid-Maine Medical Center—Charles A Dean Div*
Pritham Ave, Greenville, ME, 04442
(207) 695-2223
Admin Ralph Gabarro.
Licensure Intermediate care. *Beds* 28. *Certified* Medicaid.

HALLOWELL

Hayden House*
Winthrop St, Hallowell, ME, 04347
(207) 622-6712
Admin Charlene Kinnelly.
Licensure Intermediate care for mentally retarded. *Beds* 15. *Certified* Medicaid.

HARTLAND

Sanfield Manor*
PO Box 234, Main St, Hartland, ME, 04943
(207) 938-4455
Admin George Petty. *Medical Dir/Dir of Nursing* Marion Strickland MD.
Licensure Intermediate care. *Beds* 47. *Certified* Medicaid.
Staff RNs 1 (ft), 1 (pt); LPNs 3 (ft); Nurses aides 26 (ft); Activities coordinators 1 (ft); Social workers 1 (ft).
Facilities Dining room; Physical therapy room; Laundry room.
Activities Arts & crafts; Cards; Games; Prayer groups.

HOULTON

Crest View Manor Inc*
Rte 2, Calais Rd, Houlton, ME, 04730
(207) 532-3498
Admin Pierre Morneault. *Medical Dir/Dir of Nursing* Dr Ted Sussman.
Licensure Intermediate care; Boarding care. *Beds* ICF 20; Boarding care 17. *Certified* Medicaid.
Admissions Requirements Medical examination.
Staff RNs 1 (ft), 1 (pt); LPNs 1 (ft); Nurses aides 10 (ft), 15 (pt); Activities coordinators 1 (ft).
Facilities Activities room; Laundry room.
Activities Arts & crafts; Cards; Games; Movies; Shopping trips; Social/Cultural gatherings.

Gardiner Nursing Home*
8 Holland St, Box 520, Houlton, ME, 04730
(702) 532-3323
Admin Mark Anderson.
Licensure Intermediate care. *Beds* 55. *Certified* Medicaid.
Staff RNs 1 (ft); LPNs 4 (ft), 3 (pt); Nurses aides 30 (ft), 4 (pt); Activities coordinators 1 (ft); Dietitians 1 (pt).
Facilities Dining room; Activities room; Laundry room; Barber/Beauty shop; Library.
Activities Arts & crafts; Cards; Games; Reading groups; Prayer groups; Movies; Social/Cultural gatherings.

Houlton Regional Hospital
20 Hartford St, Houlton, ME, 04730
(207) 532-9471
Admin Bradley C Bean. *Medical Dir/Dir of Nursing* Donald Brushett MD.

Licensure Skilled care. *Beds* SNF 24. *Certified* Medicaid; Medicare.
Owner Nonprofit Corp.
Admissions Requirements Medical examination; Physician's request.
Staff Physicians 1 (pt); RNs 1 (ft), 1 (pt); LPNs 5 (ft), 5 (pt); Nurses aides 5 (ft), 9 (pt); Physical therapists 3 (pt); Occupational therapists 1 (pt); Activities coordinators 1 (ft); Dietitians 1 (pt).
Facilities Dining room; Activities room; Crafts room; Laundry room.
Activities Arts & crafts; Cards; Games; Reading groups; Prayer groups; Movies.

Houlton Residential Center
45 School St, Houlton, ME, 04730
(207) 532-9446
Admin Ron Langworthy.
Licensure Intermediate care for mentally retarded. *Beds* 28. *Certified* Medicaid.
Owner Nonprofit Corp.
Admissions Requirements Minimum age 18.
Staff RNs 1 (ft); LPNs 1 (ft), 6 (pt); Nurses aides 20 (ft), 20 (pt); Activities coordinators 1 (ft).
Facilities Dining room; Physical therapy room; Activities room; Crafts room; Laundry room.
Activities Arts & crafts; Cards; Games; Movies; Shopping trips; Social/Cultural gatherings.

Madigan Estates
Military St, Houlton, ME, 04730
(207) 532-6593
Admin Brenda L Brown. *Medical Dir/Dir of Nursing* Carol Swallow RN.
Licensure Intermediate care. *Beds* ICF 50. *Certified* Medicaid.
Owner Privately owned.
Admissions Requirements Medical examination.
Staff Physicians 8 (pt); RNs 3 (ft); LPNs 6 (ft); Nurses aides 25 (ft); Recreational therapists 1 (ft); Activities coordinators 1 (ft); Dietitians 1 (ft); Dentists 1 (pt).
Facilities Dining room; Activities room; Laundry room; Barber/Beauty shop.
Activities Arts & crafts; Cards; Games; Reading groups; Prayer groups; Movies; Shopping trips; Social/Cultural gatherings.

Park Street Group Home
7 Park St, Houlton, ME, 04730
(207) 532-7150
Admin Terry Hutchinson.
Licensure Intermediate care for mentally retarded. *Beds* ICF/MR 6. *Certified* Medicaid.
Owner Nonprofit Corp.
Admissions Requirements Minimum age 18.
Staff RNs; Activities coordinators; Dietitians.
Facilities Dining room; Activities room; Laundry room.
Activities Arts & crafts; Cards; Games; Reading groups; Movies; Shopping trips; Social/Cultural gatherings.

HOWLAND

Cummings Health Care Facility Inc
Crocker St Ext, Howland, ME, 04448
(207) 732-4121
Admin Fern P Cummings. *Medical Dir/Dir of Nursing* Susan Bailey RN.
Licensure Intermediate care. *Beds* ICF 40. *Certified* Medicaid.
Owner Privately owned.
Admissions Requirements Physician's request.
Staff RNs 6 (ft); LPNs 3 (ft); Nurses aides 25 (ft); Activities coordinators 1 (ft); Dietitians 1 (ft).
Facilities Dining room; Physical therapy room; Activities room; Chapel; Crafts room; Laundry room; Barber/Beauty shop.

Activities Arts & crafts; Cards; Games; Reading groups; Prayer groups; Movies; Shopping trips.

ISLAND FALLS

Green Valley Group
Box 127, Sewall St, Island Falls, ME, 04747
(207) 463-2823
Admin Dale Lowe.
Licensure Intermediate care for mentally retarded. *Beds* ICF/MR 6. *Certified* Medicaid.
Owner Nonprofit Corp.
Admissions Requirements Minimum age 20; Medical examination; Physician's request.
Staff Speech therapists; Activities coordinators 1 (pt); Direct care staff 6 (ft), 7 (pt).
Facilities Dining room; Activities room; Laundry room.
Activities Arts & crafts; Cards; Games; Movies; Shopping trips; Social/Cultural gatherings; Hiking club; Outing club; Cross country ski team; Running races.

JACKMAN

Jackman Region Health Center
Rte 201, Main St, Jackman, ME, 04945
(207) 668-2691
Admin Marcia Seavey. *Medical Dir/Dir of Nursing* Patricia Doyle MD; Marcia Seavey DON.
Licensure Intermediate care; Ambulatory care facility. *Beds* ICF 18. *Certified* Medicaid; Medicare.
Owner Nonprofit Corp.
Admissions Requirements Medical examination.
Staff Physicians 1 (ft); RNs 3 (pt); LPNs 1 (pt); Nurses aides 8 (ft), 11 (pt); Activities coordinators; Dietitians; Ophthalmologists.
Languages French
Facilities Dining room; Activities room; Laundry room; Library; Sitting room.
Activities Cards; Games; Prayer groups; Movies; Social/Cultural gatherings; Maple sugar parties; Pets.

Northland Manor*
Main St, Jackman, ME, 04945
(207) 668-3221
Admin George R Petty.
Licensure Intermediate care for mentally retarded. *Beds* 25.
Admissions Requirements Minimum age 18; Medical examination.
Staff RNs 1 (ft); LPNs 3 (ft); Nurses aides 10 (ft), 3 (pt); Activities coordinators 1 (ft); Dietitians 1 (pt).
Facilities Dining room; Activities room; Laundry room.
Activities Arts & crafts; Cards; Games; Reading groups; Prayer groups; Movies; Shopping trips.

JONESPORT

Resthaven Nursing Home Inc
Ocean St, Jonesport, ME, 04649
(207) 497-2363
Admin Donald J Palleschi. *Medical Dir/Dir of Nursing* Dr S Weisberger; Helen Wass RN DON.
Licensure Intermediate care. *Beds* ICF 22. *Certified* Medicaid; Medicare.
Owner Nonprofit organization/foundation.
Admissions Requirements Physician's request.
Staff RNs 1 (ft); LPNs 2 (ft); Nurses aides 7 (ft), 11 (pt); Activities coordinators 1 (pt); Dietitians 1 (pt); Ophthalmologists 1 (pt); Social service director 1 (pt).
Facilities Dining room; Activities room.
Activities Arts & crafts; Cards; Games; Reading groups; Prayer groups; Movies.

KENNEBUNK

Beach Wood*
77 Brown St, Kennebunk, ME, 04043
(207) 985-7959
Admin Karen Miller.
Licensure Intermediate care for mentally retarded. *Beds* 6.
Admissions Requirements Medical examination.
Staff RNs 1 (pt); Physical therapists 1 (pt); Occupational therapists 1 (pt); Speech therapists 1 (pt); Activities coordinators 1 (ft); Dietitians 1 (pt).
Facilities Dining room; Laundry room.
Activities Arts & crafts; Games; Movies; Shopping trips; Social/Cultural gatherings.

Kennebunk Nursing Home*
PO Box 797, Ross Rd, Kennebunk, ME, 04043
(207) 985-7141
Admin Patricia Small.
Licensure Intermediate care. *Beds* 70. *Certified* Medicaid.
Owner Proprietary Corp (Hillhaven Corp).
Admissions Requirements Medical examination; Physician's request.
Staff RNs 3 (ft), 4 (pt); LPNs 2 (ft), 3 (pt); Nurses aides 17 (ft), 16 (pt); Physical therapists 1 (pt); Recreational therapists 1 (ft); Speech therapists 1 (pt); Activities coordinators 1 (ft); Dietitians 1 (pt); Podiatrists 1 (pt).
Facilities Dining room; Physical therapy room; Activities room; Crafts room; Laundry room; Barber/Beauty shop; Library.
Activities Arts & crafts; Cards; Games; Reading groups; Prayer groups; Movies; Shopping trips.

KEZAR FALLS

Greenhill Farm*
Rte 2, Box 421, Kezar Falls, ME, 04047
(207) 625-8644
Admin Doug DuBois.
Licensure Intermediate care for mentally retarded. *Beds* 6.
Admissions Requirements Minimum age 18; Medical examination; Physician's request.
Staff RNs; Activities coordinators 1 (ft).
Facilities Dining room; Activities room; Crafts room; Laundry room.
Activities Arts & crafts; Cards; Games; Reading groups; Shopping trips; Social/Cultural gatherings.

KITTERY

Homestead*
RFD 1, Box 735, Kittery, ME, 03904
(207) 439-2100
Admin David Sowerby. *Medical Dir/Dir of Nursing* Dr William Gilbert.
Licensure Intermediate care. *Beds* 56. *Certified* Medicaid.
Admissions Requirements Minimum age 55; Medical examination.
Staff RNs 2 (ft), 2 (pt); LPNs 2 (ft), 3 (pt); Orderlies 1 (pt); Nurses aides 13 (ft), 17 (pt); Physical therapists; Reality therapists 1 (pt); Occupational therapists; Speech therapists; Activities coordinators 1 (ft); Social workers 1 (ft).
Facilities Dining room; Activities room; Barber/Beauty shop.
Activities Arts & crafts; Prayer groups; Movies; Shopping trips; Social/Cultural gatherings; Happy hour; Church service; Bingo; Cooking club; Exercise.

LEWISTON

d'Youville Pavilion Nursing Home
102 Campus Ave, Lewiston, ME, 04240
(207) 783-1471
Admin Roger Dumont. *Medical Dir/Dir of Nursing* Dr Betty Keneddy; Kathy Murphy.
Licensure Skilled care; Intermediate care. *Beds* SNF 30; ICF 250. *Certified* Medicaid; Medicare.
Owner Nonprofit Corp.
Admissions Requirements Minimum age 16; Medical examination.
Staff RNs 18 (ft), 9 (pt); LPNs 13 (ft), 10 (pt); Nurses aides 53 (ft), 70 (pt); Physical therapists 1 (pt); Recreational therapists 4 (ft); Occupational therapists 1 (pt); Speech therapists 1 (pt); Activities coordinators 1 (ft); Dietitians 1 (ft); Ophthalmologists 1 (pt).
Languages French
Affiliation Roman Catholic
Facilities Dining room; Physical therapy room; Activities room; Chapel; Crafts room; Laundry room; Barber/Beauty shop; Library.
Activities Arts & crafts; Cards; Games; Reading groups; Prayer groups; Movies; Shopping trips; Social/Cultural gatherings.

Good Shepherd Health Care Facility
67 Webster St, Lewiston, ME, 04240
(207) 782-3922
Admin Steven F Sasseville. *Medical Dir/Dir of Nursing* Anne Lacourse.
Licensure Intermediate care. *Beds* ICF 20. *Certified* Medicaid.
Owner Proprietary Corp.
Admissions Requirements Medical examination; Physician's request.
Staff RNs 1 (ft); LPNs 3 (ft), 1 (pt); Nurses aides 9 (ft); Recreational therapists 1 (pt).
Languages French
Facilities Dining room; Activities room; Laundry room; Barber/Beauty shop.
Activities Arts & crafts; Cards; Games; Prayer groups; Movies; Shopping trips; Social/Cultural gatherings.

Marshwood Nursing Care Center
Roger Ave, Lewiston, ME, 04240
(207) 784-0108
Admin Leon Bresloff. *Medical Dir/Dir of Nursing* Dr S Rosenblatt; Mrs H Noel.
Licensure Intermediate care. *Beds* ICF 120. *Certified* Medicaid.
Owner Proprietary Corp.
Admissions Requirements Minimum age 18.
Staff RNs 7 (ft), 6 (pt); LPNs 1 (ft), 3 (pt); Recreational therapists 7 (pt); Activities coordinators 1 (ft); Dietitians 1 (pt).
Languages French
Facilities Dining room; Physical therapy room; Activities room; Crafts room; Laundry room; Barber/Beauty shop.
Activities Arts & crafts; Cards; Games; Reading groups; Prayer groups; Movies; Shopping trips; Social/Cultural gatherings.

Montello Manor Nursing Home
540 College St, Lewiston, ME, 04240
(207) 783-2039
Admin Cecil Adams. *Medical Dir/Dir of Nursing* John Mendros.
Licensure Skilled care; Intermediate care. *Beds* SNF 71; ICF 72. *Certified* Medicaid; Medicare.
Staff Physicians 1 (pt); RNs 15 (ft), 5 (pt); LPNs 9 (ft), 2 (pt); Orderlies 3 (ft), 1 (pt); Nurses aides 30 (ft), 20 (pt); Physical therapists 2 (pt); Occupational therapists 1 (pt); Speech therapists 1 (pt); Activities coordinators 2 (pt); Dietitians 1 (pt); Dentists 1 (pt); Ophthalmologists 1 (pt); Podiatrists 1 (pt).
Facilities Dining room; Physical therapy room; Activities room; Crafts room; Laundry room; Barber/Beauty shop.

Activities Arts & crafts; Cards; Games; Reading groups; Prayer groups; Movies; Shopping trips; Social/Cultural gatherings; Newsletter.

Russell Park Manor*
158-178 Russell St, Lewiston, ME, 04240
(207) 786-0691
Admin Maurice Labbe.
Licensure Skilled care; Intermediate care. *Beds* SNF 30; ICF 90.

St Casimir Health Care Facility*
69 Horton St, Lewiston, ME, 04240
(207) 784-5273
Admin Charles Cook.
Licensure Intermediate care. *Beds* 21. *Certified* Medicaid.
Staff LPNs 3 (ft), 2 (pt); Nurses aides 7 (ft), 5 (pt); Activities coordinators 1 (ft).
Affiliation Roman Catholic
Facilities Dining room; Activities room; Crafts room; Laundry room.
Activities Arts & crafts; Cards; Games; Prayer groups; Movies; Shopping trips; Social/Cultural gatherings; Various outings.

LINCOLN

Colonial Acres Nursing Home*
Workman Terrace, Lincoln, ME, 04457
(207) 794-6534
Admin R Eugene Libby. *Medical Dir/Dir of Nursing* Bourcard Nesin MD.
Licensure Intermediate care. *Beds* 78. *Certified* Medicaid.
Admissions Requirements Medical examination; Physician's request.
Staff RNs 3 (ft), 3 (pt); LPNs 4 (ft), 2 (pt); Nurses aides 23 (ft), 25 (pt); Activities coordinators 1 (ft).
Facilities Dining room; Physical therapy room; Activities room; Chapel; Crafts room; Laundry room; Barber/Beauty shop.
Activities Arts & crafts; Cards; Games; Reading groups; Prayer groups; Movies; Shopping trips; Social/Cultural gatherings.

LISBON

The Lamp Nursing Home*
RFD 2, Box 33, Lisbon Rd, Lisbon, ME, 04250
(207) 353-4318
Admin Shirley A Quinlan. *Medical Dir/Dir of Nursing* Joseph M Mendes MD.
Licensure Intermediate care. *Beds* 37. *Certified* Medicaid.
Admissions Requirements Medical examination.
Staff RNs 3 (ft); LPNs 1 (pt); Nurses aides 13 (ft), 6 (pt); Physical therapists; Speech therapists; Activities coordinators 1 (ft); Dietitians 1 (pt); Dentists; Podiatrists.
Facilities Dining room; Activities room; Crafts room; Barber/Beauty shop; Library.
Activities Arts & crafts; Cards; Games; Reading groups; Prayer groups; Movies; Shopping trips; Social/Cultural gatherings.

LIVERMORE FALLS

Pomeroy Hill Nursing Home*
RFD 1, Livermore Falls, ME, 04254
(207) 897-6748
Admin Arthur Upton. *Medical Dir/Dir of Nursing* Dr Joseph DeGrinney.
Licensure Intermediate care. *Beds* 60. *Certified* Medicaid.
Staff RNs 5 (ft), 2 (pt); LPNs 3 (ft), 4 (pt); Nurses aides 17 (ft), 17 (pt); Physical therapists 1 (pt); Reality therapists 1 (ft); Recreational therapists 1 (ft); Occupational therapists 1 (pt); Activities coordinators 1 (ft); Dietitians 1 (pt); Podiatrists 1 (pt).

Facilities Dining room; Physical therapy room; Activities room; Crafts room; Laundry room; Barber/Beauty shop.
Activities Arts & crafts; Cards; Games; Reading groups; Prayer groups; Movies; Shopping trips; Social/Cultural gatherings; Outside trips.

LUBEC

Oceanview Nursing Home
48 Washington St, Lubec, ME, 04652
(207) 733-4900
Admin Margaret Brown. *Medical Dir/Dir of Nursing* Dr Robert G MacBride; Carole Webber RN DON.
Licensure Intermediate care. *Beds* ICF 50. *Certified* Medicaid.
Owner Proprietary Corp.
Admissions Requirements Physician's request.
Staff Physicians 4 (pt); RNs 3 (ft), 2 (pt); LPNs 2 (ft); Orderlies 1 (ft); Nurses aides 24 (ft), 3 (pt); Physical therapists 1 (pt); Activities coordinators 1 (ft), 2 (pt); Dietitians 1 (pt); Ophthalmologists 1 (pt).
Facilities Dining room; Activities room; Barber/Beauty shop.
Activities Arts & crafts; Cards; Games; Reading groups; Prayer groups; Movies; Shopping trips; Social/Cultural gatherings; Potluck dinners with families; Picnics; Restaurant dinners.

MACHIAS

Marshall Health Care Facility*
High St Ext, Machias, ME, 04654
(207) 255-3387
Admin Vaughn Marshall. *Medical Dir/Dir of Nursing* Karl V Larson MD.
Licensure Intermediate care. *Beds* 62. *Certified* Medicaid.
Admissions Requirements Medical examination.
Staff Physicians 4 (pt); RNs 4 (ft), 3 (pt); LPNs 2 (ft), 1 (pt); Nurses aides 42 (ft).
Facilities Dining room; Activities room; Chapel; Crafts room; Laundry room; Barber/Beauty shop; Library.
Activities Arts & crafts; Cards; Games; Reading groups; Prayer groups; Movies.

MADAWASKA

Highview Manor
40 Riverview St, Madawaska, ME, 04756
(207) 728-3338
Admin George Dugal.
Licensure Intermediate care. *Beds* 78. *Certified* Medicaid.

MADISON

Maplecrest Manor Inc.
174 Main St, Madison, ME, 04950
(207) 696-3033
Admin Paula Varney.
Licensure Intermediate care. *Beds* 58. *Certified* Medicaid.
Owner Proprietary Corp.
Staff RNs 2 (ft), 1 (pt); LPNs 3 (ft), 1 (pt); Nurses aides 20 (ft), 10 (pt); Recreational therapists 1 (ft).

MARS HILL

The Aroostook Medical Center
Highland Ave, Mars Hill, ME, 04758
(207) 768-4913
Admin James Kemer. *Medical Dir/Dir of Nursing* Eric Nicolas MD.
Licensure Skilled care; Intermediate care. *Beds* SNF 14; ICF 50. *Certified* Medicaid; Medicare.

Staff Physicians 2 (ft); RNs 2 (ft), 3 (pt); LPNs 7 (ft), 8 (pt); Nurses aides 17 (ft), 37 (pt); Physical therapists 1 (ft); Occupational therapists 1 (pt); Speech therapists 1 (pt); Activities coordinators 1 (ft), 1 (pt); Dietitians 1 (ft).
Facilities Dining room; Physical therapy room; Activities room; Barber/Beauty shop.
Activities Arts & crafts; Cards; Games; Reading groups; Prayer groups; Shopping trips; Social/Cultural gatherings.

MILBRIDGE

Marchalin*
Main St, Milbridge, ME, 04658
(207) 546-2371
Admin Alan Matterson. *Medical Dir/Dir of Nursing* Carl Aselton MD.
Licensure Intermediate care. *Beds* 65. *Certified* Medicaid.
Owner Proprietary Corp (Beverly Enterprises).
Admissions Requirements Medical examination.
Staff RNs 1 (ft); LPNs 2 (ft), 6 (pt); Orderlies 1 (pt); Nurses aides 12 (ft), 20 (pt); Physical therapists; Speech therapists; Activities coordinators 1 (ft); Dietitians.
Facilities Dining room; Physical therapy room; Activities room; Crafts room; Laundry room; Barber/Beauty shop.
Activities Arts & crafts; Cards; Games; Reading groups; Prayer groups; Movies; Shopping trips; Social/Cultural gatherings.

MILLINOCKET

Katahdin Nursing Home
22 Walnut St, Millinocket, ME, 04462
(207) 723-4711
Admin Donald J Palleschi. *Medical Dir/Dir of Nursing* Elaine Niles DON.
Licensure Intermediate care. *Beds* ICF 50. *Certified* Medicaid.
Owner Proprietary Corp.
Staff RNs 3 (ft); LPNs 2 (ft); Nurses aides 23 (ft); Activities coordinators 1 (ft); Social service 1 (ft).
Languages French
Facilities Dining room; Physical therapy room; Activities room; Laundry room.
Activities Arts & crafts; Cards; Games; Reading groups; Prayer groups; Movies; Shopping trips; Social/Cultural gatherings; Outings.

MINOT

Western Maine Association for Retarded Citizens
Box 87, Central Office, 30 Broadway, Farmington, ME 04938, Minot, ME, 04258
(207) 345-9752
Admin Bryan Erskine. *Medical Dir/Dir of Nursing* Genise Bugal.
Licensure Intermediate care for mentally retarded; Duel diagnosis group home MR/MI adult. *Beds* ICF/MR 6. *Certified* Medicaid.
Owner Nonprofit organization/foundation.
Admissions Requirements Minimum age 20.
Staff Direct Care 25 (ft), 15 (pt).
Facilities Dining room; Activities room; Crafts room; Laundry room.
Activities Arts & crafts; Cards; Games; Shopping trips; Social/Cultural gatherings.

NORTH BERWICK

North Berwick Nursing Home*
45 Elm St, North Berwick, ME, 03906
(207) 676-2242
Admin Frances Lacourse.
Licensure Intermediate care. *Beds* 48. *Certified* Medicaid.

NORTH VASSALBORO

Volmer Nursing Home*
Rte 1, Box 1190, North Vassalboro, ME, 04962
(207) 873-2040
Admin Roland E Drovin.
Licensure Intermediate care. *Beds* 32. *Certified* Medicaid.
Staff RNs 1 (ft); LPNs 2 (ft); Nurses aides 9 (ft), 6 (pt); Activities coordinators 1 (ft); Dietitians 1 (ft), 1 (pt).
Facilities Dining room; Activities room; Crafts room; Laundry room; Barber/Beauty shop; Library.
Activities Arts & crafts; Cards; Games; Prayer groups; Shopping trips.

NORTH WINDHAM

Ledgewood Manor
PO Box 760, 200 Rte 115, North Windham, ME, 04062
(702) 892-2261
Admin Edison Bennett.
Licensure Intermediate care. *Beds* ICF 60. *Certified* Medicaid.
Owner Proprietary Corp.
Admissions Requirements Minimum age 60; Physician's request.
Staff RNs 5 (ft); LPNs 8 (ft); Nurses aides 36 (ft); Activities coordinators 1 (ft); Dietitians 1 (ft).
Facilities Dining room; Physical therapy room; Activities room; Crafts room; Laundry room; Barber/Beauty shop.
Activities Arts & crafts; Games; Reading groups; Prayer groups; Movies.

NORWAY

Norway Nursing Home*
Marion Ave, Norway, ME, 04268
(207) 743-7075
Admin Julie Hermans.
Licensure Intermediate care. *Beds* 70. *Certified* Medicaid.
Owner Proprietary Corp (Hillhaven Corp).
Admissions Requirements Minimum age 16; Medical examination.
Staff RNs 4 (ft), 2 (pt); LPNs 3 (ft), 3 (pt); Nurses aides 15 (ft), 23 (pt); Physical therapists 1 (pt); Activities coordinators 1 (ft), 1 (pt); Dietitians 1 (pt).
Facilities Dining room; Physical therapy room; Activities room; Laundry room; Barber/Beauty shop.
Activities Arts & crafts; Cards; Games; Reading groups; Prayer groups; Movies; Shopping trips; Social/Cultural gatherings.

OLD ORCHARD BEACH

The Elms Residence Nursing Home*
28 Portland Ave, Old Orchard Beach, ME, 04604
(207) 934-2174
Admin Roger Painchaud.
Licensure Intermediate care. *Beds* 26. *Certified* Medicaid.
Staff RNs 3 (ft); LPNs 2 (ft); Nurses aides 6 (ft), 10 (pt); Activities coordinators 1 (ft).
Facilities Dining room; Activities room; Crafts room; Laundry room.
Activities Arts & crafts; Cards; Games; Reading groups; Movies; Social/Cultural gatherings.

ORONO

Orono Nursing Home
PO Box 430, Bennoch Rd, Orono, ME, 04473
(207) 866-4914
Admin William Shirley. *Medical Dir/Dir of Nursing* Michael Bruehl MD.

Licensure Skilled care; Intermediate care. *Beds* SNF 12; ICF 60. *Certified* Medicaid; Medicare.
Staff Physicians 6 (pt); RNs 10 (ft), 6 (pt); LPNs 1 (ft), 2 (pt); Nurses aides 30 (ft), 25 (pt); Physical therapists 1 (pt); Activities coordinators 1 (ft), 1 (pt); Dietitians 1 (pt); Podiatrists 1 (pt).
Facilities Dining room; Physical therapy room; Activities room; Laundry room; Barber/Beauty shop.
Activities Arts & crafts; Cards; Games; Reading groups; Prayer groups; Movies; Shopping trips; Social/Cultural gatherings.

Treats Falls
PO Box 10, 2 Hill St, Orono, ME, 04473
(207) 866-3769
Admin Dick Valentine.
Licensure Intermediate care for mentally retarded. *Beds* 20. *Certified* Medicaid.
Admissions Requirements Minimum age 18; Medical examination.
Staff Physicians 1 (pt); RNs 1 (pt); LPNs 1 (pt); Nurses aides 23 (ft); Physical therapists 1 (pt); Occupational therapists 1 (pt); Activities coordinators 1 (pt); Dietitians 1 (pt).
Facilities Dining room; Activities room; Crafts room; Laundry room.
Activities Arts & crafts; Cards; Games; Movies; Shopping trips; Social/Cultural gatherings.

ORRINGTON

Orrington Group Home*
RFD 2, Box 125, Orrington, ME, 04474
(207) 825-3557
Admin Patrick Roger.
Licensure Intermediate care for mentally retarded. *Beds* 6. *Certified* Medicaid.

PATTEN

Green Valley Patten Group House
PO Box 127, Katahdin St, Patten, ME, (04747)
(207) 528-2929
Admin Rebecca Baltzer.
Licensure Intermediate care for mentally retarded. *Beds* ICF/MR 6. *Certified* Medicaid; Medicare.
Owner Nonprofit organization/foundation.
Admissions Requirements Minimum age 18; Medical examination; Physician's request.
Facilities Dining room; Activities room; Crafts room; Laundry room.
Activities Arts & crafts; Cards; Games; Reading groups; Movies; Shopping trips; Social/Cultural gatherings; Hikes; Trips; Swimming; Walk/Jog races; Nature groups; Hobby clubs; Social/sexuality club.

Resthaven Nursing Home
10 Houlton St, Patten, ME, 04765
(207) 528-2200
Admin Justine Michaud. *Medical Dir/Dir of Nursing* Ronald Blum.
Licensure Intermediate care. *Beds* 25. *Certified* Medicaid.
Staff RNs 1 (ft), 2 (pt); LPNs 2 (pt); Nurses aides 3 (ft), 4 (pt); Activities coordinators 1 (ft); Dietitians 1 (pt).
Facilities Dining room; Activities room; Laundry room.
Activities Arts & crafts; Cards; Games; Prayer groups; Movies; Shopping trips.

PENOBSCOT

Penobscot Nursing Home
Main St, Penobscot, ME, 04476
(207) 326-4344
Admin Wendell Dennison. *Medical Dir/Dir of Nursing* Dr Dale Walter; Elizabeth Sawyer RN DON.

Licensure Intermediate care. *Beds* ICF 93.
Certified Medicaid.
Owner Proprietary Corp.
Staff RNs 3 (ft); LPNs 13 (ft); Nurses aides 27
(ft); Physical therapists 1 (ft); Occupational
therapists 1 (ft); Activities coordinators 1
(ft); Dietitians 1 (ft).
Facilities Dining room; Physical therapy
room; Activities room; Crafts room; Laundry
room; Barber/Beauty shop.
Activities Arts & crafts; Cards; Games;
Reading groups; Prayer groups; Movies;
Foliage tours; Outings.

PITTSFIELD

Pittsfield Convalescent Center*
Leighton St, Pittsfield, ME, 04967
(207) 487-3182
Admin Lynn Jordan.
Licensure Intermediate care. *Beds* 30.
Certified Medicaid.
Owner Proprietary Corp (Hillhaven Corp).

Sebasticook Valley Health Care Facility
Leighton St, Pittsfield, ME, 04967
(207) 487-3131
Admin Barbara Steller. *Medical Dir/Dir of
Nursing* Cheryl West RN.
Licensure Intermediate care. *Beds* ICF 64.
Certified Medicaid.
Owner Privately owned.
Admissions Requirements Physician's request.
Staff RNs 2 (ft), 1 (pt); LPNs 5 (ft), 1 (pt);
Nurses aides 25 (ft), 13 (pt); Activities
coordinators 1 (ft).
Facilities Dining room; Physical therapy
room; Activities room; Laundry room;
Barber/Beauty shop; Library.
Activities Arts & crafts; Cards; Games;
Reading groups; Prayer groups; Movies;
Shopping trips; Social/Cultural gatherings;
Remotivation groups.

PORTLAND

Barron Center
1145 Brighton Ave, Portland, ME, 04102
(207) 774-2623
Admin Anthony Forgione. *Medical Dir/Dir of
Nursing* Benjamin Zolou MD; Jeanne
Delicata RN DON.
Licensure Skilled care; Intermediate care. *Beds*
SNF 20; ICF 165. *Certified* Medicaid;
Medicare.
Owner Publicly owned.
Admissions Requirements Minimum age 18;
Medical examination; Physician's request.
Staff Physicians 4 (ft); RNs 18 (ft); LPNs 16
(ft); Nurses aides 92 (ft); Physical therapists
3 (ft); Recreational therapists 6 (ft);
Occupational therapists 1 (pt); Speech
therapists 1 (pt); Dietitians 1 (pt); Dentists 1
(pt); Ophthalmologists 1 (pt); Dentist 1 (pt).
Facilities Dining room; Physical therapy
room; Activities room; Chapel; Crafts room;
Laundry room; Barber/Beauty shop.
Activities Arts & crafts; Cards; Games;
Reading groups; Prayer groups; Movies;
Shopping trips; Social/Cultural gatherings.

Devonshire Manor
68 Devonshire St, Portland, ME, 04101
(207) 772-2893
Admin Betty Edwards.
Licensure Intermediate care. *Beds* 149.
Certified Medicaid.

Emery Street Community Residence*
72 Emery St, Portland, ME, 04102
(207) 772-6332
Admin Lisa J MacDonald.
Licensure Intermediate care for mentally
retarded. *Beds* 6. *Certified* Medicaid.

Jewish Home for the Aged*
158 North St, Portland, ME, 04101
(207) 772-5456
Admin C Gail MacLean.
Licensure Skilled care; Intermediate care. *Beds*
SNF 18; ICF 70. *Certified* Medicaid;
Medicare.
Affiliation Jewish

St Joseph's Manor
1133 Washington Ave, Portland, ME, 04103
(207) 797-0600
Admin Ronald Tardif. *Medical Dir/Dir of
Nursing* Sr Margurite Carignan.
Licensure Intermediate care. *Beds* ICF 200.
Certified Medicaid.
Owner Nonprofit Corp.
Admissions Requirements Medical
examination; Physician's request.
Staff RNs; LPNs; Nurses aides; Physical
therapists; Recreational therapists; Activities
coordinators; Dietitians.
Languages French
Affiliation Roman Catholic
Facilities Dining room; Physical therapy
room; Activities room; Chapel; Crafts room;
Laundry room; Barber/Beauty shop.
Activities Arts & crafts; Cards; Games;
Movies; Shopping trips; Social/Cultural
gatherings.

Seaside Nursing & Retirement Home*
850 Baxter Blvd, Portland, ME, 04101
(207) 774-7878
Admin Eleanor Matterson.
Licensure Skilled care; Intermediate care. *Beds*
SNF 38; ICF 76. *Certified* Medicaid.

Woodfords Group Home I*
342 Woodfords St, Portland, ME, 04103
(207) 871-1209
Admin Marjorie Smith.
Licensure Intermediate care for mentally
retarded. *Beds* 6. *Certified* Medicaid.

Woodfords Group Home II*
388 Woodfords St, Portland, ME, 04103
(207) 774-3331
Admin Melvin Richards.
Licensure Intermediate care for mentally
retarded. *Beds* 4. *Certified* Medicaid.

POWNAL

Pineland Center
Box C, Pownal, ME, 04069-0902
(207) 688-4811
Admin Spenser A Moore. *Medical Dir/Dir of
Nursing* Hecter A Arrache MD; Julie L
Biggs RN.
Licensure Intermediate care for mentally
retarded. *Beds* ICF/MR 295. *Certified*
Medicaid.
Owner Publicly owned.
Admissions Requirements Minimum age 5;
Physician's request; Court commitment.
Staff Physicians 3 (ft), 1 (pt); RNs 19 (ft), 1
(pt); LPNs 14 (ft), 1 (pt); Nurses aides 300
(ft), 2 (pt); Physical therapists 3 (ft);
Recreational therapists 4 (ft); Occupational
therapists 6 (ft); Speech therapists 3 (ft);
Dietitians 1 (ft).
Facilities Dining room; Physical therapy
room; Activities room; Chapel; Crafts room;
Laundry room; Barber/Beauty shop; Library.
Activities Arts & crafts; Games; Prayer groups;
Movies; Shopping trips; Social/Cultural
gatherings; Developmental training centers.

PRESQUE ISLE

Aroostook Residential Center
PO Box 1285, Presque Isle, ME, 04769
(207) 764-2010
Admin Terry L Sandusky.

Licensure Intermediate care for mentally
retarded. *Beds* ICF/MR 15. *Certified*
Medicaid.
Owner Publicly owned.
Admissions Requirements Minimum age 16.
Staff Physicians 1 (pt); RNs 1 (pt);
Occupational therapists 1 (pt); Speech
therapists 1 (pt); Activities coordinators 1
(pt); Dietitians 1 (pt).
Facilities Dining room; Activities room;
Laundry room; Library.
Activities Arts & crafts; Games; Movies;
Shopping trips; Social/Cultural gatherings;
Swimming.

Presque Isle Nursing Home Inc*
162 Academy St, Presque Isle, ME, 04769
(207) 764-0145
Admin Albert G Cyr.
Licensure Intermediate care. *Beds* 82.
Certified Medicaid.

ROCKLAND

Camden Health Care Center
108 Elm St, Rockland, ME, 04843
(207) 236-8381
Admin Jefferson Ackor. *Medical Dir/Dir of
Nursing* David Bradeen MD; Peggy Smith
RN DON.
Licensure Skilled care; Intermediate care. *Beds*
SNF; ICF 198. *Certified* Medicaid;
Medicare.
Owner Nonprofit Corp.
Staff RNs 11 (ft), 11 (pt); LPNs 2 (ft), 8 (pt);
Nurses aides 35 (ft), 64 (pt); Recreational
therapists 1 (ft); Activities coordinators 3
(ft); Dietitians 1 (pt).
Facilities Dining room; Physical therapy
room; Activities room; Chapel; Crafts room;
Laundry room; Barber/Beauty shop; Library.
Activities Arts & crafts; Cards; Games;
Reading groups; Prayer groups; Movies;
Shopping trips; Social/Cultural gatherings;
Gardening.

Rockland Convalescent Center*
201 Camden St, Rockland, ME, 04841
(207) 596-6423
Admin Nola B Ribe.
Licensure Intermediate care. *Beds* 64.
Certified Medicaid.
Owner Proprietary Corp (Hillhaven Corp).

RUMFORD

Cozy Inn Nursing Home*
Eaton Hill Rd, Box 430, Rumford, ME, 04276
(207) 364-7863
Admin John Ford. *Medical Dir/Dir of Nursing*
David Phillips MD.
Licensure Intermediate care. *Beds* 57.
Certified Medicaid.
Staff RNs 6 (ft); LPNs 3 (ft); Nurses aides 27
(ft); Activities coordinators 1 (ft); Dietitians
1 (pt).
Facilities Dining room; Activities room;
Chapel; Crafts room; Laundry room; Barber/
Beauty shop.
Activities Arts & crafts; Cards; Games; Prayer
groups; Movies.

SACO

Evergreen Manor
328 North St, Saco, ME, 04072
(207) 282-5161
Admin Robert E Wolter. *Medical Dir/Dir of
Nursing* Andre Fortier MD.
Licensure Intermediate care. *Beds* ICF 42.
Certified Medicaid.
Owner Proprietary Corp.
Staff RNs 2 (ft), 3 (pt); LPNs 3 (ft), 5 (pt);
Nurses aides 15 (ft), 11 (pt); Recreational
therapists 1 (ft); Activities coordinators 1
(ft).
Languages French

Facilities Dining room; Activities room; Chapel; Crafts room; Laundry room; Barber/ Beauty shop; Library.
Activities Arts & crafts; Cards; Games; Reading groups; Prayer groups; Movies; Shopping trips; Social/Cultural gatherings.

SAINT ALBANS

Square Road ICF/MR Group Home
Box 65, Square Rd, Saint Albans, ME, 04971
(207) 938-2046
Admin Christy Provost.
Licensure Intermediate care for mentally retarded. *Beds* ICF/MR 6.
Owner Nonprofit organization/foundation.
Admissions Requirements Minimum age 18; Medical examination.
Staff ADL staff 7 (ft), 2 (pt).
Facilities Dining room; Activities room; Laundry room; Home setting.
Activities Arts & crafts; Cards; Games; Reading groups; Movies; Shopping trips; Social/Cultural gatherings.

SANFORD

Hillcrest Skilled Care Div*
Hillcrest Dr, Sanford, ME, 04073
(207) 324-4310
Admin Peter Booth. *Medical Dir/Dir of Nursing* Carl E Richards MD.
Licensure Skilled care; Intermediate care. *Beds* SNF 25; ICF 77. *Certified* Medicaid; Medicare.
Admissions Requirements Medical examination; Physician's request.
Staff RNs 3 (ft), 6 (pt); LPNs 9 (ft), 8 (pt); Nurses aides 27 (ft), 12 (pt); Physical therapists 3 (pt); Recreational therapists 1 (ft); Occupational therapists 1 (pt); Speech therapists 1 (pt); Activities coordinators 1 (ft); Dietitians 1 (pt); Audiologists 1 (pt).
Facilities Dining room; Physical therapy room; Activities room; Laundry room; Barber/Beauty shop.
Activities Arts & crafts; Cards; Games; Reading groups; Movies; Shopping trips; Social/Cultural gatherings.

Maine Stay Nursing Home*
291 Main St, Sanford, ME, 04073
(207) 324-7999
Admin Doyle T Sowerby.
Licensure Intermediate care; Lodging care. *Beds* ICF 45; Lodging care 11. *Certified* Medicaid.
Staff RNs 3 (ft); LPNs 2 (ft), 2 (pt); Orderlies 1 (ft); Nurses aides 17 (ft); Activities coordinators 1 (ft), 1 (pt); Dietitians 1 (pt); Podiatrists 1 (pt).
Facilities Dining room; Activities room; Chapel; Crafts room; Laundry room; Barber/ Beauty shop.
Activities Arts & crafts; Cards; Games; Reading groups; Prayer groups; Movies; Shopping trips; Social/Cultural gatherings.

Sanford Health Care Facility*
179 Main St, Sanford, ME, 04073
(207) 324-6818
Admin Doyle Sowerby.
Licensure Intermediate care. *Beds* 31. *Certified* Medicaid.

SCARBOROUGH

Casa Inc
PO Box 58, 148 Gorham Rd, Scarborough, ME, 04074
(207) 883-6333
Admin Anne D Walsh Walp. *Medical Dir/Dir of Nursing* Dorothy Bender RN.
Licensure Intermediate care for mentally retarded. *Beds* ICF/MR 8. *Certified* Medicaid.
Owner Nonprofit Corp.

Admissions Requirements Minimum age 8-15; Medical examination; Physician's request.
Staff RNs 1 (ft); LPNs 3 (ft), 2 (pt); Nurses aides 6 (ft), 6 (pt); Recreational therapists 1 (pt).
Facilities Dining room; Activities room; Laundry room.
Activities Arts & crafts; Games; Reading groups; Movies; Shopping trips; Social/ Cultural gatherings.

SKOWHEGAN

Cedar Ridge Inc*
234 Maidson Ave, Skowhegan, ME, 04976
(207) 474-9686
Admin David Sylvester. *Medical Dir/Dir of Nursing* Robert Kaschub MD.
Licensure Intermediate care. *Beds* 50. *Certified* Medicaid.
Admissions Requirements Medical examination.
Staff RNs 3 (ft), 1 (pt); LPNs 3 (ft); Nurses aides 35 (ft); Physical therapists 1 (pt); Recreational therapists 1 (ft); Activities coordinators 1 (ft); Dietitians 1 (ft).
Facilities Dining room; Physical therapy room; Activities room; Crafts room; Laundry room; Barber/Beauty shop.
Activities Arts & crafts; Cards; Games; Reading groups; Prayer groups; Movies; Shopping trips; Social/Cultural gatherings.

Woodlawn Nursing Home*
91 W Front St, Skowhegan, ME, 04976
(207) 474-9300
Admin Anthony Belliveau Jr.
Licensure Intermediate care. *Beds* 50. *Certified* Medicaid.

SOUTH PARIS

Market Square Health Care Facility*
12 Market Square, Box 280, South Paris, ME, 04281
(207) 743-7086
Admin Frank M Drigotas Jr.
Licensure Intermediate care. *Beds* 99. *Certified* Medicaid.
Staff Physicians 6 (pt); RNs 6 (ft); LPNs 12 (ft); Orderlies 42 (ft); Occupational therapists 1 (pt); Speech therapists 1 (pt); Activities coordinators 1 (ft); Dietitians 1 (ft); Dentists 1 (pt); Ophthalmologists 1 (pt); Podiatrists 1 (pt); Audiologists 1 (pt).
Facilities Dining room; Physical therapy room; Activities room; Crafts room; Laundry room; Library.
Activities Arts & crafts; Cards; Games; Reading groups; Prayer groups; Movies; Shopping trips; Social/Cultural gatherings.

SOUTH PORTLAND

Hillside Rest & Nursing Home Inc
161 Preble St, South Portland, ME, 04106
(207) 799-2245
Admin Betty M Guay. *Medical Dir/Dir of Nursing* Douglas Hill MD; Rita Adams RN.
Licensure Intermediate care. *Beds* ICF 18. *Certified* Medicaid.
Owner Proprietary Corp.
Admissions Requirements Medical examination; Physician's request.
Staff Physicians 1 (pt); RNs 1 (ft); LPNs 5 (pt); Nurses aides 4 (ft), 6 (pt); Activities coordinators 1 (pt); Dietitians 1 (pt); Podiatrists 1 (pt).
Facilities Dining room; Activities room; Crafts room; Laundry room.
Activities Arts & crafts; Cards; Games; Reading groups; Prayer groups; Shopping trips; Social/Cultural gatherings.

Manden Nursing Home*
1060 Broadway, South Portland, ME, 04106
(207) 799-1945

Admin Dawn Wursthorne.
Licensure Intermediate care. *Beds* 10. *Certified* Medicaid.

South Portland Nursing Home Inc*
42 Anthoine St 2413, South Portland, ME, 04106
(207) 799-8561
Admin Donald Johnson.
Licensure Intermediate care. *Beds* 73. *Certified* Medicaid.

SOUTH WINDHAM

Swampscotta Nursing Home*
Rte 302, Box 387, South Windham, ME, 04082
(207) 892-6922
Admin Florence Mayberry. *Medical Dir/Dir of Nursing* Walter Penta MD.
Licensure Intermediate care. *Beds* 36. *Certified* Medicaid.

STRONG

Strong Nursing Home
Box 249, Main St, Strong, ME, 04983
(207) 684-3341
Admin Glenna Barden. *Medical Dir/Dir of Nursing* Mary Evelyn Gregor RN DON.
Licensure Intermediate care for mentally retarded. *Beds* ICF/MR 20. *Certified* Medicaid.
Owner Proprietary Corp.
Admissions Requirements Medical examination.
Staff Physicians 1 (pt); RNs 2 (pt); LPNs 4 (pt); Nurses aides 35 (pt); Physical therapists 1 (pt); Recreational therapists 1 (pt); Speech therapists 1 (pt) 13K 1 (pt); Dietitians 1 (pt).
Facilities Dining room; Physical therapy room; Activities room; Laundry room.
Activities Arts & crafts; Games; Reading groups; Movies; Shopping trips; Social/ Cultural gatherings.

SULLIVAN

Maplecrest Nursing Home
Rte 1, Box 50, Sullivan, ME, 04689
(207) 422-3345
Admin Martha Scott. *Medical Dir/Dir of Nursing* Dr Richard LaRocco; Dr Kerri Crowley; Joyce D Jamison RN.
Licensure Intermediate care. *Beds* 34. *Certified* Medicaid.
Owner Proprietary Corp.
Admissions Requirements Medical examination; Physician's request.
Staff Physicians 2 (pt); RNs 1 (ft); LPNs 1 (ft), 1 (pt); Orderlies 1 (ft); Nurses aides 12 (ft), 2 (pt); Physical therapists 1 (pt); Activities coordinators 1 (ft), 1 (pt); Dietitians 1 (pt); Dentists 1 (pt); MSW 1 (ft).
Facilities Dining room; Activities room; Crafts room; Laundry room.
Activities Arts & crafts; Cards; Games; Reading groups; Movies.

TOPSHAM

Amenity Manor*
29 Elm St, Topsham, ME, 04086
(207) 725-7495
Admin Robert Colarusso.
Licensure Intermediate care. *Beds* 69. *Certified* Medicaid.

Gregory House
1 Middlesex Rd, Topsham, ME, 04086
(207) 729-4371
Admin Deborah Sloan Libby.
Licensure Intermediate care for mentally retarded. *Beds* 8. *Certified* Medicaid.

Admissions Requirements Minimum age 18.
Activities Arts & crafts; Cards; Games;
Reading groups; Prayer groups; Movies;
Shopping trips; Social/Cultural gatherings.

UPPER FRENCHVILLE

St Joseph Nursing Home
PO Box 605, Main St, Upper Frenchville, ME,
04784
(207) 543-6648
Admin Clovis Daigle. *Medical Dir/Dir of
Nursing* Dr Zui Sun Tao.
Licensure Intermediate care. *Beds* 37.
Certified Medicaid.
Admissions Requirements Medical
examination; Physician's request.
Staff Physicians 1 (pt); RNs 1 (ft), 2 (pt);
LPNs 3 (ft), 1 (pt); Orderlies 1 (pt); Nurses
aides 12 (ft), 8 (pt); Activities coordinators 1
(pt); Dietitians 1 (ft).
Affiliation Roman Catholic
Facilities Dining room; Activities room;
Chapel; Crafts room; Laundry room; Barber/
Beauty shop.
Activities Arts & crafts; Cards; Games; Prayer
groups; Movies; Social/Cultural gatherings.

VAN BUREN

Borderview Manor Inc
90 State St, Van Buren, ME, 04785
(207) 868-5211
Admin John B Pelletier. *Medical Dir/Dir of
Nursing* Maxima A Corriveau RN DON.
Licensure Intermediate care; Boarding care.
Beds ICF 82; Boarding care 36. *Certified*
Medicaid.
Owner Proprietary Corp.
Staff RNs; LPNs; Nurses aides; Activities
coordinators; Dietitians.
Languages French
Facilities Dining room; Physical therapy
room; Activities room; Chapel; Crafts room;
Laundry room; Barber/Beauty shop.
Activities Arts & crafts; Cards; Games; Prayer
groups; Movies; Shopping trips; Social/
Cultural gatherings.

WALDOBORO

Fieldcrest Manor Inc
RR 1, Box 34, Depot St, Waldoboro, ME,
04572
(207) 832-5343
Admin Wayde Rankin. *Medical Dir/Dir of
Nursing* Jack Waterman MD; Phyllis Tonry
DON.
Licensure Intermediate care. *Beds* ICF 70.
Certified Medicaid.
Owner Proprietary Corp (Hillhaven Corp).
Staff Physicians 9 (pt); RNs 2 (ft), 4 (pt);
LPNs 3 (ft), 4 (pt); Nurses aides 20 (ft), 23
(pt); Activities coordinators 1 (ft); Dietitians
1 (pt); Podiatrists 1 (pt).
Facilities Dining room; Physical therapy
room; Activities room; Laundry room;
Barber/Beauty shop.
Activities Arts & crafts; Games; Reading
groups; Prayer groups; Movies; Shopping
trips; Social/Cultural gatherings.

WATERVILLE

Colonial House Manor
110 College Ave, Waterville, ME, 04901
(207) 873-0641
Admin Rev Bruce Alexander. *Medical Dir/Dir
of Nursing* John M Szala DO; Kathleen
Crawford RN.
Licensure Intermediate care. *Beds* ICF 74.
Certified Medicaid.
Owner Proprietary Corp (Hillhaven Corp).
Admissions Requirements Medical
examination; Physician's request.

Staff Physicians 19 (pt); RNs 3 (ft), 2 (pt);
LPNs 2 (ft), 4 (pt); Orderlies 18 (ft), 20 (pt);
Nurses aides; Activities coordinators 1 (ft);
Dietitians 1 (pt); Social services 1 (ft).
Languages French
Facilities Dining room; Activities room;
Chapel; Crafts room; Laundry room; Barber/
Beauty shop; Library.
Activities Arts & crafts; Cards; Games;
Reading groups; Prayer groups; Movies;
Shopping trips; Social/Cultural gatherings.

Lakewood Manor*
220 Kennedy Memorial Dr, Waterville, ME,
04901
(207) 873-5125
Admin Norma Pearl. *Medical Dir/Dir of
Nursing* Dr Stanley Beckerman.
Licensure Intermediate care. *Beds* 75.
Certified Medicaid.
Staff Physicians 14 (pt); RNs 5 (ft), 1 (pt);
LPNs 4 (ft), 4 (pt); Orderlies 2 (ft); Nurses
aides 26 (ft), 5 (pt); Physical therapists 1
(pt); Reality therapists 1 (pt); Recreational
therapists 1 (pt); Occupational therapists 1
(pt); Speech therapists 1 (pt); Activities
coordinators 1 (ft); Dietitians 1 (pt); Dentists
1 (pt); Ophthalmologists 1 (pt); Podiatrists 1
(pt); Audiologists 1 (pt).
Facilities Dining room; Physical therapy
room; Activities room; Chapel; Crafts room;
Laundry room; Barber/Beauty shop; Library;
Living rooms.
Activities Arts & crafts; Cards; Games;
Reading groups; Prayer groups; Movies;
Shopping trips; Social/Cultural gatherings;
Bean & cheese parties.

Mt St Joseph Nursing Home
Highwood St, Waterville, ME, 04901
(207) 873-0705
Admin Patricia Berger. *Medical Dir/Dir of
Nursing* Jeannette Leighton DON.
Licensure Intermediate care. *Beds* ICF 77.
Certified Medicaid.
Owner Nonprofit Corp.
Admissions Requirements Physician's request.
Staff RNs 4 (ft), 2 (pt); LPNs 7 (ft), 2 (pt);
Nurses aides 45 (ft), 4 (pt); Physical
therapists 2 (ft); Activities coordinators 1
(ft), 1 (pt); Dietitians 1 (pt).
Languages French
Facilities Dining room; Physical therapy
room; Activities room; Chapel; Crafts room;
Laundry room; Barber/Beauty shop.
Activities Arts & crafts; Cards; Games;
Reading groups; Prayer groups; Movies;
Shopping trips; Social/Cultural gatherings.

Waterville Convalescent Center*
Cool St, Waterville, ME, 04901
(207) 873-0721
Admin Linda Kane.
Licensure Intermediate care. *Beds* 78.
Certified Medicaid.
Owner Proprietary Corp (Hillhaven Corp).

Western Avenue Residence*
101 Western Ave, Waterville, ME, 04901
(207) 872-8195
Admin Donna Moore.
Licensure Intermediate care for mentally
retarded. *Beds* 6.

WEST PARIS

Ledgeview Memorial Home*
Rte 26, Box 3420, West Paris, ME, 04289
(207) 674-2250
Admin Lawrence Wilday. *Medical Dir/Dir of
Nursing* Thomas Nangle MD.
Licensure Intermediate care. *Beds* 124.
Certified Medicaid.
Admissions Requirements Medical
examination; Physician's request.
Staff RNs 2 (ft), 5 (pt); LPNs 8 (ft), 4 (pt);
Orderlies 1 (ft); Nurses aides 34 (ft), 27 (pt);
Physical therapists 1 (pt); Speech therapists

1 (pt); Activities coordinators 2 (ft);
Dietitians 1 (pt); Dentists 1 (pt); Podiatrists
1 (pt); Audiologists 1 (pt).
Affiliation Seventh-Day Adventist
Facilities Dining room; Physical therapy
room; Activities room; Chapel; Crafts room;
Laundry room; Barber/Beauty shop; Library;
Dental.
Activities Arts & crafts; Cards; Games;
Reading groups; Prayer groups; Movies;
Shopping trips; Social/Cultural gatherings;
Day trips; Cookouts.

WEST SCARBOROUGH

Pine Point Manor*
Pine Point Rd, Box 127, West Scarborough,
ME, 04074
(207) 883-2468
Admin Beverly Malpass.
Licensure Intermediate care. *Beds* 62.
Certified Medicaid.

WINTHROP

Heritage Manor Inc
Box 1220, RFD 3, Old Lewiston Rd,
Winthrop, ME, 04364
(207) 377-8453, 377-9965
Admin Jessie E Jacques. *Medical Dir/Dir of
Nursing* Dr R E Barron; Alberta Chick RN.
Licensure Intermediate care. *Beds* ICF 56.
Certified Medicaid.
Owner Proprietary Corp.
Staff RNs 2 (ft), 1 (pt); LPNs 2 (ft), 6 (pt);
Nurses aides 15 (ft), 10 (pt); Recreational
therapists 1 (ft); Activities coordinators 1
(ft); Dietitians 1 (pt); Social worker 1 (ft).
Facilities Dining room; Activities room;
Crafts room; Laundry room; Barber/Beauty
shop.
Activities Arts & crafts; Cards; Games;
Reading groups; Prayer groups; Movies;
Shopping trips; Social/Cultural gatherings.

Nicholson's Nursing Home*
11 Western Ave, Winthrop, ME, 04364
(207) 377-8184
Admin Constance Burnham.
Licensure Intermediate care. *Beds* 45.
Certified Medicaid.

YARMOUTH

Brentwood Manor*
122 Portland St, Yarmouth, ME, 04096
(207) 846-9021
Admin Robert Lezer.
Licensure Intermediate care. *Beds* 73.
Certified Medicaid.
Owner Proprietary Corp (Hillhaven Corp).

Coastal Manor*
PO Box 475, 10 W Main St, Yarmouth, ME,
04096
(207) 846-5013
Admin Cindy N Scott.
Licensure Intermediate care. *Beds* 46.
Certified Medicaid.

YORK

**York Hospital—Henry Strater Skilled Nursing
Facility**
15 Hospital Dr, York, ME, 03909
(207) 363-4321
Admin Jud Knox. *Medical Dir/Dir of Nursing*
Jill Fargo RN.
Licensure Skilled care. *Beds* SNF 18. *Certified*
Medicare.
Owner Nonprofit Corp.
Facilities Dining room; Physical therapy
room; Activities room; Barber/Beauty shop.
Activities Arts & crafts; Cards; Games;
Movies; Shopping trips.

YORK HARBOR

Harbor Home
PO Box 96, Norwood Farms Rd, York
 Harbor, ME, 03911
(207) 363-2422

Admin Marcella Sowerby.
Licensure Intermediate care. *Beds* ICF 79.
 Certified Medicaid.

Facilities Dining room; Laundry room;
 Barber/Beauty shop.
Activities Arts & crafts; Cards; Games;
 Reading groups; Prayer groups; Movies;
 Shopping trips; Social/Cultural gatherings.

MARYLAND

ADELPHI

Hillhaven Nursing Home
3210 Powder Mill Rd, Adelphi, MD, 20783
(301) 937-3939
Admin Joyce A Malin. *Medical Dir/Dir of Nursing* Charles Benner MD; Judy Dolecek BSN.
Licensure Intermediate care. *Beds* ICF 60. *Certified* Medicaid.
Owner Proprietary Corp (Hillhaven Corp).
Staff RNs 4 (ft), 2 (pt); LPNs 2 (ft), 7 (pt); Nurses aides 17 (ft), 8 (pt); Physical therapists 1 (pt); Recreational therapists 1 (pt); Occupational therapists 1 (ft); Speech therapists 1 (pt); Activities coordinators 1 (pt); Dietitians 1 (pt); Dentists 1 (pt); Ophthalmologists 1 (pt).
Facilities Dining room; Physical therapy room; Activities room; Crafts room; Laundry room; Barber/Beauty shop.
Activities Arts & crafts; Cards; Games; Reading groups; Prayer groups; Movies.

Presidential Woods Health Care Center
1801 Metzerott Rd, Adelphi, MD, 20783
(301) 434-0500
Admin Marjorie S Lambdin. *Medical Dir/Dir of Nursing* Dr Myron Lenkin; Nancy L Petersen RN.
Licensure Skilled care; Intermediate care. *Beds* Comprehensive 210. *Certified* Medicaid; Medicare.
Owner Proprietary Corp (Health Care & Retirement Corp).
Admissions Requirements Minimum age 18.
Staff RNs 4 (ft), 2 (pt); LPNs 10 (ft); Nurses aides 90 (ft); Physical therapists 1 (ft); Recreational therapists 2 (ft) Occupational therapists 1 (ft); Speech therapists 1 (ft); Dietitians 2 (ft).
Languages Spanish
Facilities Dining room; Physical therapy room; Activities room; Crafts room; Laundry room; Barber/Beauty shop.
Activities Arts & crafts; Cards; Games; Reading groups; Prayer groups; Movies; Shopping trips; Social/Cultural gatherings.

ANNAPOLIS

Annapolis Convalescent Center*
Bay Ridge Ave & Van Buren St, Annapolis, MD, 21403
(301) 269-0444
Admin Loretta J Davis. *Medical Dir/Dir of Nursing* Richard Hochman MD.
Licensure Skilled care; Intermediate care. *Beds* 91. *Certified* Medicaid; Medicare.
Owner Proprietary Corp.
Admissions Requirements Minimum age 54; Medical examination; Physician's request.
Staff Physicians 22 (pt); RNs 3 (ft), 3 (pt); LPNs 5 (ft), 4 (pt); Nurses aides 26 (ft), 16 (pt); Physical therapists 2 (ft), 2 (pt); Speech therapists 1 (pt); Activities coordinators 1 (ft); Dietitians 1 (pt); Dentists 1 (pt); Podiatrists 3 (pt).

Facilities Dining room; Physical therapy room; Activities room; Crafts room; Laundry room; Barber/Beauty shop.
Activities Arts & crafts; Games; Reading groups; Movies; Shopping trips; Social/ Cultural gatherings.

Bay Manor Nursing Home Inc
509 Revell Hwy, Annapolis, MD, 21401
(301) 757-2069
Admin Vickie Fila. *Medical Dir/Dir of Nursing* Dr C V Cyriac; Chris Ellzey RN DON.
Licensure Intermediate care. *Beds* ICF 74. *Certified* Medicaid.
Owner Proprietary Corp.
Admissions Requirements Medical examination; Physician's request.
Staff Physicians 1 (ft); RNs 2 (ft), 4 (pt); LPNs 5 (pt); Nurses aides 28 (ft); Physical therapists; Occupational therapists; Speech therapists; Activities coordinators 2 (pt); Dietitians.
Facilities Dining room; Laundry room; TV room.
Activities Arts & crafts; Cards; Games; Reading groups; Prayer groups; Movies; Shopping trips; Social/Cultural gatherings; Music; Resident council; Cooking; Exercise.

BALTIMORE

Ardleigh Nursing Home Inc*
2095 Rockrose Ave, Baltimore, MD, 21211
(301) 243-7458
Admin Benjamin H Roffman. *Medical Dir/Dir of Nursing* Dr L Kemper Owens.
Licensure Intermediate care. *Beds* 33. *Certified* Medicaid.
Owner Proprietary Corp.
Admissions Requirements Minimum age 14; Medical examination.
Staff Physicians; RNs; LPNs; Nurses aides; Activities coordinators; Dietitians.
Activities Arts & crafts; Cards; Games; Reading groups; Prayer groups; Movies; Shopping trips; Social/Cultural gatherings.

Armacost Nursing Home Inc
812 Regester Ave, Baltimore, MD, 21239
(301) 377-5225
Admin Ira Dennis Greene. *Medical Dir/Dir of Nursing* Mark Davis MD.
Licensure Intermediate care. *Beds* 45. *Certified* Medicaid.
Owner Proprietary Corp.
Admissions Requirements Medical examination.
Staff RNs 2 (ft), 1 (pt); LPNs 2 (ft), 2 (pt); Orderlies 2 (ft); Nurses aides 12 (ft), 10 (pt); Activities coordinators 1 (ft).
Facilities Dining room; Activities room; Crafts room; Laundry room.
Activities Arts & crafts; Cards; Games; Reading groups; Prayer groups; Movies; Shopping trips; Social/Cultural gatherings; Picnics; Outings; Bowling; Restaurant lunches.

Ashburton Nursing Home*
3520 N Hilton Rd, Baltimore, MD, 21215
(301) 466-2400
Admin Teresa M Kelly. *Medical Dir/Dir of Nursing* Allan H Macht MD.
Licensure Intermediate care. *Beds* 37. *Certified* Medicaid.
Owner Proprietary Corp.
Admissions Requirements Minimum age 21; Medical examination; Physician's request.
Staff Physicians 1 (ft); RNs 2 (ft); LPNs 1 (ft), 3 (pt); Nurses aides 7 (ft), 4 (pt); Physical therapists 1 (ft); Reality therapists 1 (ft); Recreational therapists 1 (ft); Speech therapists 1 (pt); Activities coordinators 1 (ft); Dietitians 1 (pt); Dentists 1 (pt); Ophthalmologists 1 (pt); Podiatrists 1 (pt).
Facilities Dining room; Physical therapy room; Activities room; Laundry room.
Activities Arts & crafts; Cards; Games; Reading groups; Prayer groups; Shopping trips; Social/Cultural gatherings; Outdoor picnics; Various trips.

The Belair Convalesarium*
6116 Belair Rd, Baltimore, MD, 21206
(301) 426-1424
Admin Robert R Ross. *Medical Dir/Dir of Nursing* Luis E Rivera MD.
Licensure Skilled care; Intermediate care. *Beds* 196. *Certified* Medicaid; Medicare.
Owner Proprietary Corp.

Walter P Carter Center—Intensive Behavior Management Program
630 W Fayette St, Baltimore, MD, 21201
(301) 328-2119
Admin Mark Quinn. *Medical Dir/Dir of Nursing* Shirly Thomas.
Licensure Intermediate care for mentally retarded. *Beds* ICF/MR 12. *Certified* Medicaid.
Owner Publicly owned.
Admissions Requirements Minimum age 18.
Staff Physicians; RNs; LPNs; Recreational therapists; Occupational therapists; Speech therapists; Activities coordinators; Dietitians.
Languages Spanish
Facilities Dining room; Activities room; Crafts room; Laundry room.
Activities Arts & crafts; Cards; Games; Reading groups; Prayer groups; Movies; Shopping trips; Social/Cultural gatherings.

Century Home Inc
102 N Paca St, Baltimore, MD, 21201
(301) 727-2050
Admin Oscar Newman. *Medical Dir/Dir of Nursing* Moges Gebremaniam.
Licensure Intermediate care. *Beds* ICF 82. *Certified* Medicaid.
Owner Proprietary Corp.
Admissions Requirements Minimum age 17.
Staff Physicians; RNs; LPNs; Orderlies; Nurses aides; Physical therapists; Speech therapists; Activities coordinators; Dietitians; Dentists; Ophthalmologists; Podiatrists.

Facilities Dining room; Activities room.
Activities Arts & crafts; Cards; Games;
Reading groups; Prayer groups; Movies;
Shopping trips.

Crawford Retreat Inc
2117 Denison St, Baltimore, MD, 21216
(301) 566-0160
Admin Marie A Fox. *Medical Dir/Dir of
Nursing* Edward Hunt Jr MD.
Licensure Intermediate care. *Beds* 23.
Certified Medicaid.
Owner Proprietary Corp.

John L Deaton Medical Center Inc
611 S Charles St, Baltimore, MD, 21230
(301) 547-8500
Admin Noel E Kroncke. *Medical Dir/Dir of
Nursing* Julian W Reed MD; Joanne Shafik
RN.
Licensure Speciality Hospital; Long-term care
facility. *Beds* Chronic 120; Comprehensive
200. *Certified* Medicaid; Medicare.
Owner Nonprofit Corp.
Admissions Requirements Minimum age 14.
Staff Physicians 2 (pt); RNs 29 (ft), 16 (pt);
LPNs 80 (ft), 15 (pt); Nurses aides 79 (ft),
27 (pt); Physical therapists 2 (ft);
Occupational therapists 3 (ft); Activities
coordinators 1 (ft); Speech therapists 3 (ft).
Affiliation Lutheran
Facilities Dining room; Physical therapy
room; Activities room; Chapel; Crafts room;
Laundry room; Barber/Beauty shop.
Activities Arts & crafts; Games; Reading
groups; Movies; Shopping trips; Trips to
Inner Harbor.

**Dukeland Nursing Home & Convalescent
Center**
1501 N Dukeland St, Baltimore, MD, 21216
(301) 945-7433
Admin Michael A Sabo. *Medical Dir/Dir of
Nursing* Dr Davis MD; Gary Halliburton
RN DON.
Licensure Intermediate care. *Beds* 104.
Certified Medicaid.
Owner Proprietary Corp.
Facilities Dining room; Physical therapy
room; Activities room; Crafts room; Laundry
room; Barber/Beauty shop.
Activities Arts & crafts; Cards; Games;
Reading groups; Prayer groups; Movies.

Friedler's Guest House*
2449 Shirley Ave, Baltimore, MD, 21215
(301) 466-0061
Admin Nathan Rofsky. *Medical Dir/Dir of
Nursing* Manuel Levin MD.
Licensure Intermediate care. *Beds* 31.
Certified Medicaid.
Owner Proprietary Corp.

Garrison Nursing Home Inc
2803 Garrison Blvd, Baltimore, MD, 21216
(301) 367-6726
Admin Teresa M Friend. *Medical Dir/Dir of
Nursing* Mark Davis MD; Gwendolyn
Lopez-Rodriquez DON.
Licensure Intermediate care. *Beds* ICF 22.
Certified Medicaid.
Owner Proprietary Corp.
Admissions Requirements Minimum age 45;
Medical examination; Physician's request.
Staff Physicians 1 (ft); RNs 1 (ft); LPNs 4 (ft);
Nurses aides 6 (ft); Activities coordinators 1
(pt); Dietitians 1 (pt).
Facilities Dining room; Activities room;
Laundry room.
Activities Arts & crafts; Cards; Games;
Reading groups; Prayer groups; Trips to
senior center weekly.

Granada Nursing Center*
4017 Liberty Heights Ave, Baltimore, MD,
21207
(301) 542-5306
Admin Robert T DeFontes. *Medical Dir/Dir of
Nursing* Hollis Seunaring MD.

Licensure Intermediate care. *Beds* 112.
Certified Medicaid.
Owner Proprietary Corp.

Greater Pennsylvania Ave Nursing Center Inc*
607 Pennsylvania Ave, Baltimore, MD, 21201
(301) 728-3344
Admin John Murphy. *Medical Dir/Dir of
Nursing* Richard Tyson.
Licensure Intermediate care. *Beds* 124.
Certified Medicaid.
Owner Proprietary Corp.
Admissions Requirements Minimum age 21;
Medical examination; Physician's request.
Staff Physicians 5 (pt); RNs 4 (ft), 1 (pt);
LPNs 10 (ft), 3 (pt); Nurses aides 43 (ft);
Physical therapists 2 (pt); Speech therapists
1 (pt); Activities coordinators 1 (ft);
Dietitians 1 (pt); Dentists 1 (pt);
Ophthalmologists 1 (pt); Podiatrists 1 (pt).
Facilities Dining room; Physical therapy
room; Activities room; Barber/Beauty shop.
Activities Arts & crafts; Cards; Games;
Reading groups; Prayer groups; Movies;
Shopping trips; Social/Cultural gatherings.

Greenwood Acres Nursing Home*
3706 Nortonia Rd, Baltimore, MD, 21216
(301) 947-1444
Admin Delzora S Johnson. *Medical Dir/Dir of
Nursing* Shaukat Y Kahn MD.
Licensure Intermediate care. *Beds* 23.
Certified Medicaid.
Owner Proprietary Corp.

Harford Gardens Nursing Center
4700 Harford Rd, Baltimore, MD, 21214
(301) 254-3012
Admin Janice Mattare. *Medical Dir/Dir of
Nursing* Arthur Lebson.
Licensure Intermediate care. *Beds* ICF 58.
Certified Medicaid.
Owner Proprietary Corp.
Staff Physicians 1 (ft); RNs; LPNs; Nurses
aides; Physical therapists; Recreational
therapists; Speech therapists; Activities
coordinators; Dietitians; Dentists;
Ophthalmologists.
Facilities Dining room; Laundry room.
Activities Arts & crafts; Cards; Games;
Reading groups; Prayer groups; Movies;
Shopping trips; Social/Cultural gatherings.

Haven Nursing Home
3939 Penhurst Ave, Baltimore, MD, 21215
(301) 664-9535
Admin Evelyn Bennett. *Medical Dir/Dir of
Nursing* Richard Bennett MD.
Licensure Intermediate care. *Beds* 22.
Certified Medicaid.
Owner Proprietary Corp.
Admissions Requirements Minimum age 45;
Medical examination; Physician's request.
Staff Physicians 1 (pt); RNs 1 (ft), 1 (pt);
LPNs 3 (ft), 2 (pt); Nurses aides 6 (ft);
Recreational therapists 1 (ft); Activities
coordinators 1 (ft); Dietitians 1 (pt);
Podiatrists 1 (pt).
Facilities Dining room; Activities room;
Crafts room; Laundry room.
Activities Arts & crafts; Cards; Games;
Reading groups; Prayer groups; Movies;
Shopping trips; Social/Cultural gatherings.

Hayes Care Home
3001 Garrison Blvd, Baltimore, MD, 21216
(301) 542-9694
Admin Queen E Hayes. *Medical Dir/Dir of
Nursing* Azalee Foreman.
Licensure Intermediate care; Domiciliary care.
Beds ICF 15; Domiciliary care 4. *Certified*
Medicaid.
Owner Privately owned.
Facilities Dining room; Activities room;
Chapel; Crafts room; Laundry room;
Library.

Activities Arts & crafts; Cards; Games;
Reading groups; Prayer groups; Movies;
Shopping trips; Social/Cultural gatherings.

**Highland Health Facility-Mental Retardation
Unit**
5200 Eastern Ave, Bldg D, Baltimore, MD,
21224
(301) 276-7000
Admin Deloris M Miller. *Medical Dir/Dir of
Nursing* Patricia Mildvan MD.
Licensure Intermediate care for mentally
retarded. *Beds* ICF/MR 99. *Certified*
Medicaid.
Owner Publicly owned.
Admissions Requirements Closed admissions
at this time.
Staff Physicians 1 (ft); RNs 3 (ft); LPNs 14
(ft); Nurses aides 59 (ft); Physical therapists
1 (pt); Recreational therapists 1 (ft);
Occupational therapists 1 (pt); Speech
therapists 1 (pt); Activities coordinators 1
(ft); Dietitians 1 (ft).
Facilities Dining room; Physical therapy
room; Activities room; Crafts room; Laundry
room.
Activities Arts & crafts; Games; Movies;
Shopping trips; Social/Cultural gatherings.

Hurwitz House*
133 Slade Ave, Baltimore, MD, 21208
(301) 466-8700
Admin Louis M Balk. *Medical Dir/Dir of
Nursing* Steven Levinson.
Licensure Intermediate care. *Beds* 23.
Certified Medicaid.
Owner Nonprofit Corp.
Admissions Requirements Minimum age 60;
Medical examination.
Staff LPNs 3 (ft), 3 (pt); Nurses aides 3 (ft), 3
(pt).
Affiliation Jewish
Facilities Dining room; Activities room;
Laundry room.
Activities Arts & crafts; Cards; Games;
Reading groups; Movies; Shopping trips.

Inglenook Nursing Center
333 Harlem Ln, Baltimore, MD, 21228
(301) 744-1020
Admin Roselyn L Scott. *Medical Dir/Dir of
Nursing* Dr Mark Davis; Alice Lepson DON.
Licensure Skilled care; Intermediate care. *Beds*
96. *Certified* Medicaid; Medicare.
Owner Proprietary Corp.

Inns of Evergreen-Central
140 W Lafayette Ave, Baltimore, MD, 21217
(301) 523-3400
Admin Patricia K Scherch. *Medical Dir/Dir of
Nursing* Richard F Tyson MD; Patricia
Woolson RN DON.
Licensure Intermediate care. *Beds* ICF 264.
Certified Medicaid.
Owner Proprietary Corp.
Staff Physicians 9 (pt); RNs 5 (ft), 1 (pt);
LPNs 20 (ft), 3 (pt); Nurses aides 140 (ft),
20 (pt); Physical therapists 4 (pt);
Recreational therapists 5 (ft); Speech
therapists 1 (pt); Dietitians 1 (ft); Dentists 1
(pt); Ophthalmologists 1 (pt); Podiatrists 1
(pt); Dentist 1 (pt).
Facilities Dining room; Physical therapy
room; Activities room; Chapel; Crafts room;
Laundry room; Barber/Beauty shop; Library;
Art gallery.
Activities Arts & crafts; Cards; Games;
Reading groups; Prayer groups; Movies;
Social/Cultural gatherings; Outside activities
trips.

Inns of Evergreen Northeast
5837 Belair Rd, Baltimore, MD, 21206
(301) 483-5800
Admin Susan Mooneyhan. *Medical Dir/Dir of
Nursing* Albert Bradley MD; Peggy Nearhoof
RN DON.

Licensure Skilled care; Intermediate care. *Beds* SNF; ICF 99. *Certified* Medicaid; Medicare.
Owner Proprietary Corp.
Facilities Dining room; Activities room; Laundry room.
Activities Arts & crafts; Games; Prayer groups; Movies.

Inns of Evergreen-South
1213 Light St, Baltimore, MD, 21230
(301) 727-1600
Admin Sandra Mennerick. *Medical Dir/Dir of Nursing* Robert Gober DO MD; Sandra Williams RN.
Licensure Intermediate care. *Beds* ICF 314. *Certified* Medicaid.
Owner Proprietary Corp.
Admissions Requirements Minimum age 21; Medical examination; Physician's request.
Staff Physicians 12 (pt); RNs 9 (ft), 2 (pt); LPNs 15 (ft), 5 (pt); Orderlies 3 (ft); Nurses aides 90 (ft), 20 (pt); Physical therapists 3 (pt); Recreational therapists 1 (ft); Speech therapists 1 (pt); Activities coordinators 6 (ft); Dietitians 1 (pt); Dentists 1 (pt); Ophthalmologists 1 (pt); Podiatrists 1 (pt).
Facilities Dining room; Physical therapy room; Activities room; Chapel; Crafts room; Laundry room; Barber/Beauty shop; Library.
Activities Arts & crafts; Cards; Games; Reading groups; Prayer groups; Movies; Shopping trips; Social/Cultural gatherings.

Ivy Hall Geriatric Center
1300 Windlass Dr, Baltimore, MD, 21220
(301) 687-1383
Admin Darell R Cammack Jr. *Medical Dir/Dir of Nursing* Dr Firozui; Barbara Anderson.
Licensure Intermediate care. *Beds* ICF 60. *Certified* Medicaid.
Owner Proprietary Corp.
Admissions Requirements Medical examination.
Staff Physicians 3 (ft); RNs 4 (ft); LPNs 4 (ft), 2 (pt); Nurses aides 10 (ft); Activities coordinators 1 (ft); Dietitians 1 (ft); Social worker 1 (ft).
Facilities Dining room; Physical therapy room; Activities room; Crafts room; Laundry room; Barber/Beauty shop; Library; Quiet room; Pleasant wooded environment.
Activities Arts & crafts; Cards; Games; Reading groups; Prayer groups; Movies; Shopping trips; Social/Cultural gatherings; Bingo; Sing-along; Current events.

Jenkins Memorial Nursing Home
1000 S Caton Ave, Baltimore, MD, 212295294
(301) 644-7100
Admin Sr Catherine Sanders. *Medical Dir/Dir of Nursing* John F Hartman MD; Nina Cheuvront RN DON.
Licensure Skilled care; Comprehensive care. *Beds* SNF 83; Comprehensive care 43. *Certified* Medicaid; Medicare.
Owner Nonprofit Corp.
Admissions Requirements Medical examination.
Staff RNs 1 (ft), 2 (pt); RNs 3 (ft), 3 (pt); LPNs 8 (ft), 2 (pt); Nurses aides 40 (ft), 19 (pt); Physical therapists 2 (pt); Activities coordinators 2 (ft), 1 (pt); Dietitians 1 (pt); Ophthalmologists 1 (pt); Podiatrists 1 (pt).
Affiliation Roman Catholic
Facilities Dining room; Physical therapy room; Activities room; Chapel; Crafts room; Laundry room; Barber/Beauty shop; Library.
Activities Arts & crafts; Cards; Games; Reading groups; Prayer groups; Movies; Shopping trips; Social/Cultural gatherings.

Jewish Convalescent & Nursing Home Inc
7920 Scotts Level Rd, Baltimore, MD, 21208
(301) 521-3600
Admin Bernard Fishbein. *Medical Dir/Dir of Nursing* Ian Sunshine MD.

Licensure Skilled care; Intermediate care. *Beds* 151. *Certified* Medicaid; Medicare.
Owner Nonprofit Corp.
Affiliation Jewish

Kenesaw Nursing Home Inc*
2601 Roslyn Ave, Baltimore, MD, 21216
(301) 466-3900
Admin Doris P Gordon. *Medical Dir/Dir of Nursing* Edward Hunt Jr MD.
Licensure Intermediate care. *Beds* 27. *Certified* Medicaid.
Owner Proprietary Corp.

Kenson Nursing Home*
2914-2922 Arunah Ave, Baltimore, MD, 21216
(301) 947-3566
Admin Benjamin Roffman. *Medical Dir/Dir of Nursing* Dr S Liau MD.
Licensure Intermediate care. *Beds* 38. *Certified* Medicaid.
Owner Proprietary Corp.
Admissions Requirements Minimum age 12.
Staff Physicians 2 (ft); RNs 2 (ft); LPNs 11 (ft); Orderlies 4 (ft); Nurses aides 10 (ft); Physical therapists 1 (ft); Reality therapists 1 (ft); Recreational therapists 1 (ft); Occupational therapists 1 (ft); Speech therapists 1 (ft); Activities coordinators 2 (ft); Dietitians 1 (ft); Dentists 1 (ft); Ophthalmologists 1 (ft); Podiatrists 1 (ft); Audiologists 1 (ft).
Facilities Dining room; Activities room; Chapel; Crafts room; Laundry room.
Activities Arts & crafts; Cards; Games; Reading groups; Prayer groups; Movies; Shopping trips; Social/Cultural gatherings.

Keswick Home for Incurables of Baltimore City
700 W 40th St, Baltimore, MD, 21211-2199
(301) 235-8860
Admin Brooks R Major. *Medical Dir/Dir of Nursing* M Isabelle MacGregor MD; Chere Bosley RN.
Licensure Skilled care; Intermediate care; Chronic hospital. *Beds* 216. *Certified* Medicaid; Medicare.
Owner Nonprofit organization/foundation.
Admissions Requirements Minimum age 18; Medical examination.
Staff Physicians 1 (ft), 19 (pt); RNs 34 (ft); LPNs 17 (ft); Nurses aides 127 (ft); Physical therapists 1 (ft); Recreational therapists 3 (ft); Occupational therapists 3 (ft); Speech therapists 2 (pt); Activities coordinators 4 (ft); Dietitians 1 (ft); Dentists 1 (pt); Ophthalmologists 1 (pt); Podiatrists 1 (pt).
Facilities Dining room; Physical therapy room; Activities room; Chapel; Crafts room; Laundry room; Barber/Beauty shop; Library; Pharmacy; Clinic; X-Ray; Dental dept; OT clinic; Adult day care.
Activities Arts & crafts; Cards; Games; Reading groups; Movies; Shopping trips; Social/Cultural gatherings.

Key Circle Hospice Inc
1214 Eutaw Pl, Baltimore, MD, 21217
(301) 523-7800
Admin Bertram Zimmerman. *Medical Dir/Dir of Nursing* Richard R Rigler MD; Howard G Chaney RN.
Licensure Intermediate care. *Beds* ICF 121. *Certified* Medicaid.
Owner Proprietary Corp.
Admissions Requirements Minimum age 18; Medical examination; Physician's request.
Staff Physicians 1 (pt); RNs 1 (ft), 1 (pt); LPNs 6 (ft), 2 (pt); Nurses aides 40 (ft), 42 (pt); Activities coordinators 1 (ft), 1 (pt); Dietitians 1 (pt); Social worker 1 (ft).
Languages Russian, Hungarian
Facilities Dining room; Physical therapy room; Activities room; Laundry room; Barber/Beauty shop.

Activities Arts & crafts; Cards; Games; Prayer groups; Movies; Shopping trips; Social/Cultural gatherings; Exercise group.

Lake Drive Nursing Home Inc
200 E Lexington St, Baltimore, MD, 21202-3522
(301) 669-4444
Admin Wallace Dow. *Medical Dir/Dir of Nursing* Arthur Lebson MD.
Licensure Intermediate care. *Beds* 50. *Certified* Medicaid.
Owner Proprietary Corp.

Levindale Hebrew Geriatric Center & Hospital
2434 W Belvedere Ave, Baltimore, MD, 21215
(301) 466-8700
Admin Stanford A Alliker. *Medical Dir/Dir of Nursing* Steven A Levenson MD; Nina Glomski RN DON.
Licensure Skilled care; Intermediate care; Chronic hospital. *Beds* SNF 65; ICF 165; Chronic hospital 53. *Certified* Medicaid; Medicare.
Owner Nonprofit organization/foundation.
Admissions Requirements Medical examination.
Staff Physicians 5 (ft); RNs 20 (ft); LPNs 46 (ft); Nurses aides 101 (ft); Physical therapists 3 (ft); Reality therapists 1 (pt); Occupational therapists 2 (ft), 1 (pt); Dietitians 2 (ft), 1 (pt); Creative arts therapists 3 (ft); physical therapy aide 1 (ft); Psychologist 1 (pt).
Languages Yiddish, Hebrew
Affiliation Jewish
Facilities Dining room; Physical therapy room; Activities room; Chapel; Crafts room; Laundry room; Barber/Beauty shop.
Activities Arts & crafts; Cards; Games; Reading groups; Prayer groups; Movies; Shopping trips; Social/Cultural gatherings.

Lincoln Convalescent Center Inc*
1217 W Fayette St, Baltimore, MD, 21223
(301) 727-3947
Admin Mildred L Pipkin. *Medical Dir/Dir of Nursing* Ali Baykaler MD.
Licensure Skilled care; Intermediate care. *Beds* 224. *Certified* Medicaid.
Owner Proprietary Corp.

Little Sisters of the Poor—St Martin's*
601 Maiden Choice Ln, Baltimore, MD, 21228
(301) 744-9367
Admin Sr Margaret R Halloran. *Medical Dir/Dir of Nursing* Stanley Ankudas MD.
Licensure Intermediate care; Domiciliary care. *Beds* ICF 157; Domiciliary care 103. *Certified* Medicaid.
Owner Nonprofit Corp.
Affiliation Roman Catholic

Mason F Lord Chronic Hospital & Nursing Facility
5200 Eastern Ave, Baltimore, MD, 21224
(301) 955-0756
Admin Cleve Laub Jr. *Medical Dir/Dir of Nursing* Susan Denman MD; Anita Langford RN DON.
Licensure Skilled care; Intermediate care; Chronic hospital; Comprehensive care. *Beds* SNF 233; ICF; Chronic hospital 55; Comprehensive care 178. *Certified* Medicaid; Medicare.
Owner Nonprofit Corp.
Admissions Requirements Minimum age 14; Females only; Medical examination; Physician's request.
Staff Physicians 1 (ft), 5 (pt); RNs 15 (ft), 1 (pt); LPNs 6 (ft); Nurses aides 96 (ft); Physical therapists 3 (ft); Recreational therapists 4 (ft); Occupational therapists 3 (ft); Speech therapists 1 (pt); Dietitians 1 (ft); Podiatrists 1 (pt).
Languages Greek

Facilities Dining room; Physical therapy room; Activities room; Chapel; Crafts room; Laundry room; Library Occupational therapy room; clinics; Adult day care.
Activities Arts & crafts; Cards; Games; Reading groups; Prayer groups; Movies; Shopping trips; Social/Cultural gatherings.

Manor Care—Rossville*
6600 Ridge Rd, Baltimore, MD, 21237
(301) 574-4950
Admin Patricia Megary. *Medical Dir/Dir of Nursing* Walter Kees MD.
Licensure Intermediate care. *Beds* 204. *Certified* Medicaid.
Owner Proprietary Corp (Manor Care).

Maryland Baptist Aged Home
2801 Rayner Ave, Baltimore, MD, 21216
(301) 624-3964
Admin Angeline Byrd. *Medical Dir/Dir of Nursing* Dr Hollis Seunarine.
Licensure Intermediate care. *Beds* ICF 33. *Certified* Medicaid.
Owner Nonprofit organization/foundation.
Admissions Requirements Minimum age 35; Medical examination; Physician's request.
Staff Physicians 1 (ft); RNs 1 (ft); LPNs 5 (ft), 5 (pt); Nurses aides 7 (ft), 3 (pt); Activities coordinators 1 (ft); Dietitians 1 (pt); Dentists 1 (pt); Ophthalmologists 1 (pt).
Affiliation Baptist
Facilities Dining room; Activities room; Chapel; Laundry room; Library.
Activities Arts & crafts; Cards; Games; Reading groups; Prayer groups; Movies; Shopping trips.

Maryland Intensive Behavior Management Program
630 W Fayette St, Baltimore, MD, 21228
(301) 328-2358
Admin Mark Quinn. *Medical Dir/Dir of Nursing* Dr Olmpia Aybar.
Licensure Intermediate care for mentally retarded. *Beds* 12. *Certified* Medicaid.
Owner Publicly owned.
Admissions Requirements Minimum age 18.
Staff Physicians 1 (ft); RNs 3 (ft); LPNs 1 (ft); Nurses aides 1 (ft); Reality therapists 1 (pt); Recreational therapists 1 (ft); Occupational therapists 1 (ft); Speech therapists 1 (pt); Activities coordinators 1 (ft); Dietitians 1 (pt); Podiatrists 1 (pt).
Facilities Dining room; Activities room; Crafts room; Laundry room; Barber/Beauty shop.
Activities Arts & crafts; Games; Movies; Shopping trips; Social/Cultural gatherings.

Melchor Nursing Home*
2327 N Charles St, Baltimore, MD, 21218
(301) 235-8997
Admin P Ramona Fearins.
Licensure Intermediate care. *Beds* 50. *Certified* Medicaid.
Owner Proprietary Corp.
Admissions Requirements Minimum age 18; Medical examination; Physician's request.
Facilities Dining room; Activities room; Laundry room.
Activities Arts & crafts; Cards; Games; Reading groups; Prayer groups; Movies; Shopping trips; Social/Cultural gatherings.

Meridian Nursing Center—Caton Manor*
3330 Wilkens Ave, Baltimore, MD, 21229
(301) 525-1544
Admin Robert Kincaid. *Medical Dir/Dir of Nursing* Herbert Levickas.
Licensure Skilled care; Intermediate care. *Beds* SNF 184; ICF 150. *Certified* Medicaid; Medicare.
Owner Proprietary Corp (Meridan Healthcare).
Admissions Requirements Minimum age 14; Medical examination.

Facilities Dining room; Activities room; Laundry room; Barber/Beauty shop.
Activities Arts & crafts; Cards; Games; Reading groups; Prayer groups; Movies; Shopping trips; Social/Cultural gatherings.

Meridian Nursing Center—Hamilton*
6040 Harford Rd, Baltimore, MD, 21214
(301) 426-8855
Admin Karen Pressman. *Medical Dir/Dir of Nursing* Ingeborg Fromm MD.
Licensure Skilled care; Intermediate care. *Beds* 104. *Certified* Medicaid; Medicare.
Owner Proprietary Corp (Meridan Healthcare).

Meridian Nursing Center—Heritage
7232 German Hill Rd, Baltimore, MD, 21222
(301) 282-6310
Admin Pamela E Fisher. *Medical Dir/Dir of Nursing* Theodore C Patterson MD; Rita Stewart DON.
Licensure Skilled care; Intermediate care. *Beds* 181. *Certified* Medicaid; Medicare.
Owner Proprietary Corp (Meridan Healthcare).
Admissions Requirements Medical examination.
Staff Physicians 1 (pt); RNs 8 (ft), 4 (pt) 13C 8 (ft), 13 (pt); Nurses aides 45 (ft), 40 (pt); Activities coordinators 4 (ft).
Facilities Dining room; Physical therapy room; Activities room; Crafts room; Laundry room; Barber/Beauty shop; TV Lounges.
Activities Arts & crafts; Cards; Games; Prayer groups; Movies; Shopping trips; Social/Cultural gatherings; College courses; Intergenerational programs.

Meridian Nursing Center—Homewood
6000 Bellona Ave, Baltimore, MD, 21212
(301) 323-4223
Admin Joseph R Fuchs. *Medical Dir/Dir of Nursing* Anthony Cazozza MD; Mary Ann Rodavitch RN DON.
Licensure Skilled care. *Beds* SNF 127. *Certified* Medicaid; Medicare.
Owner Proprietary Corp.
Admissions Requirements Medical examination.
Staff Physicians 1 (pt); RNs 6 (ft), 9 (pt); LPNs 8 (ft), 4 (pt); Nurses aides 35 (ft), 23 (pt); Physical therapists 2 (pt); Occupational therapists 1 (pt); Speech therapists 1 (pt); Activities coordinators 2 (ft); Dietitians 1 (pt).
Facilities Dining room; Physical therapy room; Activities room; Crafts room; Laundry room; Barber/Beauty shop.
Activities Arts & crafts; Cards; Games; Reading groups; Prayer groups; Movies; Shopping trips; Social/Cultural gatherings.

Meridian Nursing Center—Long Green
115 E Melrose Ave, Baltimore, MD, 21212
(301) 435-9073
Admin Michael R Baker. *Medical Dir/Dir of Nursing* Norman Freeman MD; Eileen Timms RN.
Licensure Skilled care; Intermediate care. *Beds* SNF 156; ICF. *Certified* Medicaid; Medicare.
Owner Proprietary Corp (Meridan Healthcare).
Admissions Requirements Minimum age 14; Medical examination.
Facilities Dining room; Physical therapy room; Activities room; Crafts room; Laundry room; Barber/Beauty shop; Library.
Activities Arts & crafts; Cards; Games; Reading groups; Prayer groups; Movies; Shopping trips; Social/Cultural gatherings.

Milford Manor Nursing Home
4204 Old Milford Mill Rd, Baltimore, MD, 21208
(301) 486-1500

Admin Joan Arthur. *Medical Dir/Dir of Nursing* Dr Naomi Cutler; Beth Yarnold RN DN.
Licensure Skilled care. *Beds* SNF 99. *Certified* Medicaid; Medicare.
Owner Proprietary Corp.
Admissions Requirements Medical examination.
Staff RNs 3 (ft), 1 (pt); LPNs 7 (ft), 1 (pt); Nurses aides 42 (ft); Physical therapists; Recreational therapists; Speech therapists; Activities coordinators; Dietitians; Dentists; Podiatrists.
Languages Yiddish, Hebrew, Russian, German
Affiliation Jewish
Facilities Dining room; Physical therapy room; Activities room; Chapel; Crafts room; Laundry room; Barber/Beauty shop; TV lounges.
Activities Arts & crafts; Cards; Games; Reading groups; Prayer groups; Movies; Shopping trips; Social/Cultural gatherings.

Mt Sinai Nursing Home Inc*
4613 Park Heights Ave, Baltimore, MD, 21215
(301) 367-5300
Admin Maury J Leibowtiz. *Medical Dir/Dir of Nursing* Arthur Lebson MD.
Licensure Intermediate care. *Beds* 59. *Certified* Medicaid.
Owner Proprietary Corp.

Mt Vernon Care Center
808 Saint Paul St, Baltimore, MD, 21202
(301) 685-6766
Admin Jeffrey Pepper. *Medical Dir/Dir of Nursing* Alex Enrique MD; Theresa Peet.
Licensure Intermediate care. *Beds* ICF 137. *Certified* Medicaid; VA.
Owner Proprietary Corp.
Admissions Requirements Minimum age 21; Medical examination.
Staff Physicians 5 (pt); RNs 4 (ft); LPNs 11 (ft); Orderlies 9 (ft); Nurses aides 64 (ft); Physical therapists 1 (pt); Reality therapists 1 (pt); Speech therapists 1 (pt); Activities coordinators 1 (ft), 2 (pt); Dietitians 1 (ft); Dentists 1 (pt); Ophthalmologists 1 (pt); Podiatrists 1 (pt).
Facilities Dining room; Physical therapy room; Activities room; Library.
Activities Arts & crafts; Cards; Games; Reading groups; Prayer groups; Movies; Social/Cultural gatherings.

Northwest Nursing & Convalescent Center
4601 Pall Mall Rd, Baltimore, MD, 21215
(301) 664-5551
Admin Darrell Reich. *Medical Dir/Dir of Nursing* Mark Davis MD; June Heseldach RN.
Licensure Intermediate care. *Beds* ICF 91. *Certified* Medicaid.
Owner Nonprofit Corp.
Admissions Requirements Minimum age 21; Medical examination.
Staff RNs 6 (ft); LPNs 10 (ft), 4 (pt); Nurses aides 60 (ft), 15 (pt); Activities coordinators 1 (ft).
Facilities Dining room; Physical therapy room; Activities room; Crafts room.
Activities Arts & crafts; Cards; Games; Reading groups; Prayer groups; Movies; Shopping trips; Social/Cultural gatherings.

Park Manor Nursing Home*
1802 Eutaw Pl, Baltimore, MD, 21217
(301) 523-4370
Admin Henry Goldbaum. *Medical Dir/Dir of Nursing* Richard Tyson.
Licensure Intermediate care. *Beds* 50. *Certified* Medicaid.
Owner Proprietary Corp.

Perring Parkway Nursing Home Inc*
1801 Wentworth Rd, Baltimore, MD, 21234
(301) 661-5717
Admin Lucy Monninger. *Medical Dir/Dir of Nursing* Anthony Carozza MD.
Licensure Skilled care; Intermediate care. *Beds* 130. *Certified* Medicaid; Medicare.
Owner Proprietary Corp.

Pimlico Manor*
2525 W Belvedere Ave, Baltimore, MD, 21215
(301) 367-9100
Admin Amelia Hague. *Medical Dir/Dir of Nursing* Leon Kochman MD.
Licensure Skilled care; Intermediate care. *Beds* 70. *Certified* Medicaid; Medicare.
Owner Proprietary Corp.

Pleasant Manor Nursing & Convalescent Center*
4615 Park Heights Ave, Baltimore, MD, 21215
(301) 542-4800
Admin Henry Reitberger. *Medical Dir/Dir of Nursing* Jamie Punzalan MD.
Licensure Skilled care; Intermediate care. *Beds* 137. *Certified* Medicaid; Medicare.
Owner Proprietary Corp.

Poplar Manor Nursing Home
3313 Poplar St, Baltimore, MD, 21216
(301) 566-7700
Admin Philip Greene. *Medical Dir/Dir of Nursing* Dr Mark Davis; Shirley Wright.
Licensure Skilled care; Intermediate care. *Beds* 157. *Certified* Medicaid; Medicare.
Owner Proprietary Corp.
Admissions Requirements Physician's request.
Staff Physicians 1 (ft), 1 (pt); RNs 6 (ft), 1 (pt); LPNs 8 (ft), 3 (pt); Orderlies 6 (ft), 1 (pt); Nurses aides 36 (ft), 6 (pt); Physical therapists; Speech therapists 1 (pt); Activities coordinators 1 (ft); Dietitians 1 (pt); Ophthalmologists 1 (pt).
Facilities Dining room; Physical therapy room; Activities room; Laundry room; Barber/Beauty shop; Outside community activities; Wheelchair van; Physical therapy room.
Activities Arts & crafts; Cards; Games; Reading groups; Prayer groups; Movies; Shopping trips; Social/Cultural gatherings.

Riverview Nursing Centre*
One Eastern Blvd, Baltimore, MD, 21221
(301) 574-1400
Admin Wayne K DeFontes. *Medical Dir/Dir of Nursing* Morris Rainess MD.
Licensure Intermediate care. *Beds* 305. *Certified* Medicaid.
Owner Proprietary Corp.
Admissions Requirements Minimum age 14; Medical examination.
Staff Physicians 2 (pt); RNs 8 (ft), 2 (pt); LPNs 20 (ft), 10 (pt); Orderlies 8 (ft), 4 (pt); Nurses aides 150 (ft), 30 (pt); Physical therapists 2 (ft); Recreational therapists 3 (ft), 2 (pt); Speech therapists 1 (pt); Activities coordinators 1 (ft), 2 (pt); Dietitians 1 (pt); Dentists 1 (pt); Ophthalmologists 1 (pt); Podiatrists 1 (pt); Audiologists 1 (pt).
Facilities Dining room; Physical therapy room; Activities room; Chapel; Crafts room; Laundry room; Barber/Beauty shop; Library.
Activities Arts & crafts; Cards; Games; Reading groups; Prayer groups; Movies; Shopping trips; Social/Cultural gatherings.

Roland Park Place
830 West 40th Street, Baltimore, MD, 21211
243-5800
Admin Frank Bailey. *Medical Dir/Dir of Nursing* Dr K A Peter van Berkum; Adrienne M Brunn RN.
Licensure Intermediate care. *Beds* ICF 18. *Certified* Medicare.

Owner Nonprofit Corp.
Admissions Requirements Medical examination.
Staff RNs 6 (ft); Physical therapists 2 (pt); Recreational therapists; Occupational therapists; Speech therapists; Activities coordinators 1 (ft); Dietitians 1 (pt); Podiatrists 1 (pt).
Affiliation Lutheran
Facilities Dining room; Physical therapy room; Activities room; Crafts room; Laundry room; Barber/Beauty shop; Library; Den; Board room.
Activities Arts & crafts; Cards; Games; Reading groups; Prayer groups; Movies; Social/Cultural gatherings.

St Luke Lutheran Home
7600 Clays Ln, Baltimore, MD, 21207-7699
(301) 298-1400
Admin Stanley D Selenski. *Medical Dir/Dir of Nursing* Dr Darshan Saluja.
Licensure Domiciliary care; Comprehensive care. *Beds* Domiciliary care 60; Comprehensive care 61. *Certified* Medicaid.
Owner Nonprofit Corp.
Admissions Requirements Medical examination.
Staff Physicians 1 (ft), 5 (pt); RNs 2 (ft), 3 (pt); LPNs 4 (ft), 2 (pt); Nurses aides 17 (ft), 17 (pt); Physical therapists 2 (pt); Activities coordinators 1 (ft), 1 (pt); Dietitians 1 (ft); Ophthalmologists 1 (pt).
Affiliation Lutheran
Facilities Dining room; Physical therapy room; Activities room; Chapel; Crafts room; Laundry room; Barber/Beauty shop; Library.
Activities Arts & crafts; Cards; Games; Reading groups; Prayer groups; Movies; Shopping trips; Social/Cultural gatherings; Bible study.

Seton Hill Manor
501 W Franklin St, Baltimore, MD, 21201
(301) 837-4990
Admin Lorraine Raffel. *Medical Dir/Dir of Nursing* Jamie Punzalan MD; William Peddicord RN DON.
Licensure Skilled care. *Beds* 300. *Certified* Medicaid; Medicare.
Owner Privately owned.
Admissions Requirements Medical examination; Physician's request.
Staff RNs; LPNs; Orderlies; Nurses aides; Recreational therapists; Activities coordinators; Dietitians.
Facilities Dining room; Physical therapy room; Activities room; Chapel; Crafts room; Laundry room; Barber/Beauty shop; Library.
Activities Arts & crafts; Cards; Games; Reading groups; Prayer groups; Movies; Shopping trips; Social/Cultural gatherings; Bus trips; Sporting events.

Stella Maris
Dulaney Valley Rd, Baltimore, MD, 21204
(301) 252-4500
Admin Sr Louis Mary Battle RSN. *Medical Dir/Dir of Nursing* Dr Eddie Nakhuda; Dr Carla Alexdander.
Licensure Skilled care; Intermediate care; Hospice. *Beds* SNF 181; ICF 213; Hospice 13. *Certified* Medicaid; Medicare.
Owner Nonprofit organization/foundation.
Admissions Requirements Minimum age 65; Medical examination; Physician's request.
Staff Physicians 2 (ft), 38 (pt); RNs 15 (ft), 38 (pt); LPNs 5 (ft), 4 (pt); Orderlies 16 (ft); Nurses aides 104 (ft), 55 (pt); Physical therapists 1 (ft); Recreational therapists 2 (ft); Occupational therapists 1 (ft); Speech therapists 1 (ft); Activities coordinators 1 (ft); Dietitians 4 (ft); Dentists 2 (pt); Ophthalmologists 2 (pt).
Affiliation Roman Catholic
Facilities Dining room; Physical therapy room; Activities room; Chapel; Crafts room; Laundry room; Barber/Beauty shop; Library.

Activities Arts & crafts; Cards; Games; Reading groups; Prayer groups; Movies; Shopping trips; Social/Cultural gatherings.

Uplands Home for Church Women*
4501 Old Frederick Rd, Baltimore, MD, 21229
(301) 945-1900
Admin Richard Buck. *Medical Dir/Dir of Nursing* Dr Alva Baker.
Licensure Domiciliary care. *Beds* 48.
Owner Nonprofit Corp.
Admissions Requirements Minimum age 65; Females only; Medical examination; Physician's request.
Staff Physicians 1 (pt); RNs 1 (ft); LPNs 2 (ft), 2 (pt); Nurses aides 6 (ft), 5 (pt); Activities coordinators 1 (pt); Dietitians 1 (pt).
Affiliation Episcopal
Facilities Dining room; Activities room; Chapel; Crafts room; Laundry room; Barber/Beauty shop; Library.
Activities Arts & crafts; Cards; Games; Movies; Shopping trips; Social/Cultural gatherings.

Valley Nursing & Convalescent Center Inc*
8710 Emge Rd, Baltimore, MD, 21234
(301) 661-5995
Admin Jeffrey Berenbach. *Medical Dir/Dir of Nursing* Marion Kowaleski MD.
Licensure Skilled care; Intermediate care. *Beds* 173. *Certified* Medicaid; Medicare.
Owner Proprietary Corp.

Valley View Nursing Home*
8720 Emge Rd, Baltimore, MD, 21234
(301) 668-1961
Admin Brian Klausmeyer. *Medical Dir/Dir of Nursing* Anthony Carozza MD.
Licensure Skilled care; Intermediate care. *Beds* 130. *Certified* Medicaid; Medicare.
Owner Proprietary Corp.

Wesley Home Inc
2211 W Rogers Ave, Baltimore, MD, 21209
(301) 664-4006
Admin Anne M Schisler. *Medical Dir/Dir of Nursing* Robert Roby MD; Robert Liberto MD; Wendy A Warner RN.
Licensure Life care. *Beds* Domiciliary 223; Comprehensive 65.
Owner Nonprofit organization/foundation.
Admissions Requirements Minimum age 65; Medical examination; Physician's request.
Staff Physicians 2 (pt); RNs 4 (ft), 1 (pt); LPNs 4 (ft), 2 (pt); Orderlies 3 (ft); Nurses aides 35 (ft), 15 (pt); Activities coordinators 1 (ft); Music Therapist 1 (pt).
Affiliation Methodist
Facilities Dining room; Physical therapy room; Activities room; Chapel; Crafts room; Laundry room; Barber/Beauty shop; Library; Solarium.
Activities Arts & crafts; Cards; Games; Reading groups; Prayer groups; Movies; Shopping trips; Social/Cultural gatherings; Rhythm band; Choir; Community college program; Hospital volunteer program; Ceramics; Canning classes.

BEL AIR

Bel Air Convalescent Center Inc
410 MacPhail Rd, Bel Air, MD, 21014
(301) 879-1120
Admin Phyllis M Kelley. *Medical Dir/Dir of Nursing* Dr Andrew Nowakowski.
Licensure Skilled care; Intermediate care. *Beds* 150. *Certified* Medicaid; Medicare.
Owner Proprietary Corp.
Staff Physicians 14 (pt); RNs 11 (pt); Nurses aides 80 (pt); Physical therapists 3 (pt); Recreational therapists 2 (pt); Speech therapists 1 (pt); Activities coordinators 1 (pt); Dietitians 1 (pt); Dentists 1 (pt); Podiatrists 1 (pt).

Facilities Dining room; Physical therapy room; Laundry room; Barber/Beauty shop; Lounges.
Activities Arts & crafts; Cards; Games; Reading groups; Prayer groups; Movies; Shopping trips; Social/Cultural gatherings.

BERLIN

Berlin Nursing Home Inc
Rte 3, Box 13, Berlin, MD, 21811
(301) 641-4400
Admin Philip Lang. *Medical Dir/Dir of Nursing* Federico Arthes MD; Jeanine Hooper, RN DON.
Licensure Skilled care; Comprehensive care; Domiciliary care. *Beds* SNF 153; Domicillary 18. *Certified* Medicaid; Medicare.
Owner Proprietary Corp.
Admissions Requirements Minimum age 15; Medical examination; Physician's request.
Staff Physicians 2 (pt); RNs 8 (ft), 5 (pt); LPNs 8 (ft), 2 (pt); Orderlies 7 (ft), 2 (pt); Nurses aides 37 (ft), 15 (pt); Physical therapists 1 (pt); Recreational therapists 1 (pt); Occupational therapists 1 (pt); Activities coordinators 1 (ft); Dietitians 1 (ft); Dentists 1 (pt); Ophthalmologists 1 (pt); Podiatrists 1 (pt).
Facilities Dining room; Physical therapy room; Activities room; Chapel; Crafts room; Laundry room; Barber/Beauty shop; Library; Enclosed outdoor patio.
Activities Arts & crafts; Cards; Games; Reading groups; Movies; Prayer groups; Shopping trips; Social/Cultural gatherings; Picnics; Zoo trips; Parades.

BETHESDA

Carriage Hill—Bethesda Inc
5215 Cedar Lane Ave, Bethesda, MD, 20814
(301) 897-5500
Admin Ruth Reynolds. *Medical Dir/Dir of Nursing* John Umhau MD; Claire Malden RN.
Licensure Skilled care. *Beds* 81.
Owner Proprietary Corp.
Admissions Requirements Minimum age 18; Medical examination.
Staff Physicians 35 (pt); RNs 14 (pt); LPNs 3 (pt); Nurses aides 36 (pt); Physical therapists 3 (pt); Speech therapists 1 (pt); Activities coordinators 3 (pt); Dietitians 1 (pt); Dentists 4 (pt); Ophthalmologists 6 (pt); Podiatrists 1 (pt).
Languages Spanish, French, German
Facilities Dining room; Physical therapy room; Activities room; Chapel; Crafts room; Laundry room; Barber/Beauty shop; Library.
Activities Arts & crafts; Cards; Games; Reading groups; Prayer groups; Movies; Social/Cultural gatherings.

Fernwood House Retirement & Nursing Center*
6530 Democracy Blvd, Bethesda, MD, 20817
(301) 530-9000
Admin Sandra L Wood. *Medical Dir/Dir of Nursing* J Blaine Fitzgerald MD.
Licensure Skilled care; Intermediate care. *Beds* 100. *Certified* Medicaid; Medicare.
Owner Proprietary Corp.

Grosvenor Health Care Center Inc
5721 Grosvenor Ln, Bethesda, MD, 20814
(301) 530-1600
Admin Gregg Plaster. *Medical Dir/Dir of Nursing* Dr Thomas Ward; Claire Cummings RN.
Licensure Skilled care. *Beds* 180. *Certified* Medicaid; Medicare.
Owner Proprietary Corp.
Admissions Requirements Medical examination; Physician's request.

Staff RNs 21 (ft); LPNs 14 (ft); Nurses aides 103 (ft); Physical therapists 1 (ft); Recreational therapists 1 (ft); Speech therapists 1 (ft); Activities coordinators 1 (ft); Dietitians 1 (ft); Ophthalmologists 1 (ft).
Facilities Dining room; Physical therapy room; Activities room; Laundry room; Barber/Beauty shop.
Activities Arts & crafts; Cards; Games; Reading groups; Prayer groups; Movies; Shopping trips; Social/Cultural gatherings.

BOONSBORO

Faheney-Keedy Memorial Home Inc
Maryland Rte 66, Boonsboro, MD, 21713-9001
(301) 733-6284
Admin Richard A Bowman. *Medical Dir/Dir of Nursing* A Waheed; Cheri Shives.
Licensure Intermediate care; Domiciliary care. *Beds* ICF 102; Domiciliary care 40. *Certified* Medicaid.
Owner Nonprofit Corp.
Admissions Requirements Minimum age 62; Medical examination.
Staff Physicians 1 (pt); RNs 2 (ft); LPNs 11 (ft); Orderlies 1 (ft); Nurses aides 51 (ft), 20 (pt); Physical therapists 1 (pt); Reality therapists 1 (pt); Recreational therapists 2 (ft); Activities coordinators 1 (ft); Dietitians 1 (pt); Dentists 1 (pt); Podiatrists 1 (pt).
Affiliation Church of the Brethren
Facilities Dining room; Physical therapy room; Activities room; Chapel; Crafts room; Laundry room; Barber/Beauty shop; Library.
Activities Arts & crafts; Cards; Games; Reading groups; Prayer groups; Shopping trips; Social/Cultural gatherings.

Reeders Memorial Home*
141 S Main St, Boonsboro, MD, 21713
(301) 432-5457
Admin Nancy E Stocks. *Medical Dir/Dir of Nursing* R Lawrence Kugler MD.
Licensure Skilled care; Intermediate care. *Beds* 150. *Certified* Medicaid.
Owner Nonprofit Corp.

BRADDOCK HEIGHTS

Vindobona Nursing Home Inc
6012 Jefferson Blvd, Braddock Heights, MD, 21714
(301) 371-7160
Admin Nayoda E Kefauver. *Medical Dir/Dir of Nursing* Dr Wayne Allgaier.
Licensure Intermediate care; Comprehensive care. *Beds* 61. *Certified* Medicaid.
Owner Proprietary Corp.
Admissions Requirements Minimum age 16.
Staff RNs 4 (ft), 4 (pt); LPNs 4 (ft), 4 (pt); Nurses aides 21 (ft), 15 (pt); Activities coordinators 1 (ft), 1 (pt); Dietitians 1 (pt); Ophthalmologists 1 (pt).
Facilities Dining room; Activities room; Crafts room; Laundry room; Barber/Beauty shop; Library; Examining & treatment room.
Activities Arts & crafts; Cards; Games; Reading groups; Prayer groups; Movies; Shopping trips; Social/Cultural gatherings; Monthly parties; Group band; Croquet; Horseshoes; Picnics; Family style dinners; Sing-alongs; Bingo; Resident council; Pets; Church services.

BROOKLYN PARK

Meridian Nursing Center, Hammonds Lane
Hammonds Ln & Robinswood Rd, Brooklyn Park, MD, 21225
(301) 636-3400
Admin Deborah Skwiercz. *Medical Dir/Dir of Nursing* Michael Schwartz MD; Margaret Schmitt RN-C DON.

Licensure Skilled care; Intermediate care. *Beds* SNF 50; ICF 79. *Certified* Medicaid; Medicare.
Owner Proprietary Corp (Meridan Healthcare).
Admissions Requirements Medical examination.
Staff Physicians 1 (pt); RNs 6 (ft), 4 (pt); LPNs 5 (ft), 5 (pt); Nurses aides 45 (ft), 20 (pt); Physical therapists 1 (ft); Occupational therapists 1 (pt); Speech therapists 1 (pt); Activities coordinators 1 (ft), 1 (pt); Dietitians 1 (ft); Dentists 1 (ft); Ophthalmologists 1 (ft); Podiatrists 1 (ft).
Facilities Dining room; Physical therapy room; Activities room; Barber/Beauty shop.
Activities Arts & crafts; Cards; Games; Reading groups; Prayer groups; Movies; Shopping trips; Social/Cultural gatherings; Bingo.

CAMBRIDGE

Cambridge House
PO Box 597, 520 Glenburn Ave, Cambridge, MD, 21613
(301) 228-9191
Admin Cynthia L Woodard. *Medical Dir/Dir of Nursing* Dr Eyup Tanman.
Licensure Skilled care; Intermediate care. *Beds* 180. *Certified* Medicaid; Medicare.
Owner Proprietary Corp.
Staff Physicians 2 (pt); RNs 5 (ft), 1 (pt); LPNs 14 (ft), 6 (pt); Orderlies 5 (ft); Nurses aides 55 (ft), 5 (pt); Physical therapists 2 (pt); Speech therapists 1 (pt); Activities coordinators 2 (ft); Dietitians 1 (pt).
Facilities Dining room; Physical therapy room; Activities room; Laundry room; Barber/Beauty shop.
Activities Arts & crafts; Cards; Games; Reading groups; Prayer groups; Movies; Shopping trips; Social/Cultural gatherings; Country rides; Outdoor theater; Picnics; BBQs.

Glasgow Nursing Home Inc
311 Glenburn Ave, Cambridge, MD, 21613
(301) 228-3780
Admin Esther Russell. *Medical Dir/Dir of Nursing* Herbert Fiery MD; Barbara Rolf RN.
Licensure Intermediate care. *Beds* ICF 35. *Certified* Medicaid.
Owner Proprietary Corp.
Admissions Requirements Physician's request.
Staff Physicians 2 (pt); RNs 1 (ft), 2 (pt); LPNs 3 (ft), 3 (pt); Orderlies 1 (pt); Nurses aides 9 (ft), 5 (pt); Dietitians 1 (pt).
Facilities Dining room; Laundry room; Barber/Beauty shop.
Activities Arts & crafts; Games; Reading groups; Prayer groups; Movies.

CATONSVILLE

Forest Haven Nursing Home
315 Ingleside Ave, Catonsville, MD, 21228
(301) 747-7425
Admin Faye L Maguire. *Medical Dir/Dir of Nursing* Allan Macht MD; Mary Schell RN.
Licensure Skilled care. *Beds* SNF 172. *Certified* Medicaid; Medicare.
Owner Privately owned.
Admissions Requirements Medical examination.
Staff RNs 5 (ft), 1 (pt); LPNs 16 (ft), 2 (pt); Nurses aides 66 (ft); Physical therapists 1 (pt); Speech therapists; Activities coordinators 3 (pt); Dietitians 1 (pt); Dentists 1 (pt); Ophthalmologists 1 (pt); Podiatrists 1 (pt).
Facilities Dining room; Physical therapy room; Activities room; Chapel; Crafts room; Barber/Beauty shop.

Activities Arts & crafts; Cards; Games; Reading groups; Prayer groups; Movies; Shopping trips; Social/Cultural gatherings.

Frederick Villa Nursing Center
711 Academy Rd, Catonsville, MD, 21228
(301) 788-3300
Admin Lois A McGovern. *Medical Dir/Dir of Nursing* Elmo Gayoso MD.
Licensure Intermediate care. *Beds* ICF 125. *Certified* Medicaid; VA.
Owner Proprietary Corp.
Admissions Requirements Minimum age 14; Medical examination.
Staff Physicians 1 (pt); RNs 3 (ft), 2 (pt); LPNs 9 (ft), 1 (pt); Nurses aides 35 (ft), 30 (pt); Reality therapists 1 (pt); Recreational therapists 4 (pt); Activities coordinators 1 (ft); Dietitians 1 (pt).
Facilities Dining room; Physical therapy room; Activities room; Barber/Beauty shop; Library.
Activities Arts & crafts; Cards; Games; Prayer groups; Movies; Social/Cultural gatherings.

Meridian Nursing Center—Catonsville*
16 Fusting Ave, Catonsville, MD, 21228
(301) 747-1800
Admin Pamela E Fisher. *Medical Dir/Dir of Nursing* Herbert J Levickas.
Licensure Skilled care; Intermediate care. *Beds* SNF 37; ICF 160. *Certified* Medicaid; Medicare.
Owner Proprietary Corp (Meridan Healthcare).
Staff Physicians 1 (pt); RNs 5 (ft), 5 (pt); LPNs 8 (ft), 4 (pt); Nurses aides 58 (ft), 20 (pt); Speech therapists; Activities coordinators 2 (ft); Dietitians 1 (pt); Dentists; Ophthalmologists; Podiatrists.
Facilities Dining room; Physical therapy room; Activities room; Crafts room; Laundry room; Barber/Beauty shop.
Activities Arts & crafts; Cards; Games; Prayer groups; Movies; Shopping trips; Social/Cultural gatherings.

Ridgeway Manor Nursing Home*
5743 Edmondson Ave, Catonsville, MD, 21228
(301) 747-5250
Admin John E Burleigh Jr.
Licensure Intermediate care. *Beds* 45. *Certified* Medicaid.
Owner Proprietary Corp.
Staff Physicians 2 (pt); RNs 1 (ft), 3 (pt); LPNs 1 (ft), 8 (pt); Nurses aides 7 (ft), 15 (pt); Physical therapists 1 (pt); Reality therapists 1 (pt); Recreational therapists 3 (pt); Occupational therapists 1 (pt); Speech therapists 1 (pt); Activities coordinators 1 (pt); Dietitians 1 (pt); Dentists 1 (pt); Ophthalmologists 1 (pt); Podiatrists 1 (pt); Audiologists 1 (pt).
Facilities Dining room; Physical therapy room; Activities room; Crafts room; Laundry room; Barber/Beauty shop; Library.
Activities Arts & crafts; Cards; Games; Reading groups; Prayer groups; Movies; Shopping trips.

St Joseph's Nursing Home
1222 Tugwell Dr, Catonsville, MD, 21228
(301) 747-0026
Admin Sr Carolyn Carne. *Medical Dir/Dir of Nursing* J Nelson McKay MD; Sr Krystyna Mroczek RN DON.
Licensure Intermediate care. *Beds* ICF 40. *Certified* Medicaid.
Owner Nonprofit Corp.
Admissions Requirements Medical examination.
Staff Physicians 1 (ft), 3 (pt); RNs 3 (ft), 2 (pt); LPNs 1 (ft), 2 (pt); Nurses aides 10 (ft), 25 (pt); Physical therapists 1 (pt); Recreational therapists 1 (ft); Activities coordinators 1 (ft); Dietitians 1 (ft); Dentist 1 (pt); Psychologist 1 (pt).

Languages Polish
Affiliation Roman Catholic
Facilities Dining room; Activities room; Chapel; Crafts room; Laundry room; Barber/Beauty shop; Library; Enclosed outdoor porch; 3 acres of lovely grounds.
Activities Arts & crafts; Cards; Games; Reading groups; Prayer groups; Movies; Social/Cultural gatherings; Picnics; Musical events; Daily mass & rosary.

Summit Nursing Home Inc*
98 Smithwood Ave, Catonsville, MD, 21228
(301) 747-3287
Admin Lawrence J Repetti. *Medical Dir/Dir of Nursing* James E Rowe MD.
Licensure Skilled care. *Beds* 141. *Certified* Medicare.
Owner Proprietary Corp.
Staff RNs 7 (ft), 20 (pt); LPNs 2 (ft), 9 (pt); Nurses aides 103 (ft), 24 (pt); Physical therapists 1 (pt); Recreational therapists 1 (ft); Speech therapists 1 (pt); Activities coordinators 1 (ft); Dietitians 1 (pt); Dentists 1 (pt); Podiatrists 1 (pt).
Facilities Dining room; Physical therapy room; Activities room; Chapel; Crafts room; Laundry room; Barber/Beauty shop.
Activities Arts & crafts; Games; Reading groups; Prayer groups; Movies; Social/Cultural gatherings.

Tawes/Bland Bryant Nursing Center*
Wade Ave, Spring Grove Hospital, Catonsville, MD, 21228
(301) 455-7603
Admin Haywood R Ammons. *Medical Dir/Dir of Nursing* Carl Fischer MD.
Licensure Skilled care. *Beds* 296. *Certified* Medicaid; Medicare.
Owner Publicly owned.

CENTREVILLE

Meridian Nursing Center—Corsica Hills*
PO Box 50, Rte 213, Centreville, MD, 21617
(301) 758-2323
Admin Harold Ackermann. *Medical Dir/Dir of Nursing* John Smith Jr MD.
Licensure Skilled care; Intermediate care. *Beds* 139. *Certified* Medicaid; Medicare.
Owner Proprietary Corp.

CHESTERTOWN

Magnolia Hall Inc
Morgnec Rd, Chestertown, MD, 21620
(301) 778-4550
Admin Pauline E Lindauer. *Medical Dir/Dir of Nursing* Harry P Ross MD; Carol A Miller DON.
Licensure Intermediate care. *Beds* 74. *Certified* Medicaid.
Owner Nonprofit Corp.
Admissions Requirements Medical examination; Physician's request.
Staff RNs 2 (ft), 2 (pt); LPNs 8 (ft), 6 (pt); Nurses aides 40 (ft), 20 (pt); Recreational therapists 1 (ft); Activities coordinators 1 (ft); Dietitians 1 (pt).
Facilities Dining room; Physical therapy room; Activities room; Chapel; Laundry room; Barber/Beauty shop; Enclosed courtyard.
Activities Arts & crafts; Cards; Games; Reading groups; Prayer groups; Movies; Social/Cultural gatherings.

CHEVERLY

Gladys Spellman Nursing Center
3035 Hospital Dr, Cheverly, MD, 20785
(301) 341-3350
Admin Roger D Larson. *Medical Dir/Dir of Nursing* Dorothy Lucas.

Licensure Skilled care; Intermediate care. *Beds* SNF 20; ICF 80. *Certified* Medicaid; Medicare.
Owner Publicly owned.
Admissions Requirements Minimum age 16.
Staff RNs 14 (ft); LPNs 11 (ft); Nurses aides 24 (ft); Reality therapists 1 (ft); Recreational therapists 2 (ft); Dietitians 5 (pt).
Facilities Dining room; Physical therapy room; Activities room; Crafts room; Barber/Beauty shop.
Activities Arts & crafts; Games; Reading groups; Prayer groups; Movies; Social/Cultural gatherings.

CHEVY CHASE

Bethesda Retirement Nursing Center*
8700 Jones Mill Rd, Chevy Chase, MD, 20815
(301) 657-8686
Admin Jeanetta M Manuel. *Medical Dir/Dir of Nursing* J Blaine Fitzgerald.
Beds 166. *Certified* Medicare.
Owner Proprietary Corp.
Admissions Requirements Minimum age 16; Medical examination.
Staff RNs 19 (ft); LPNs 3 (ft); Orderlies 3 (pt); Nurses aides 55 (ft); Physical therapists 1 (pt); Recreational therapists 3 (ft); Occupational therapists 1 (pt); Speech therapists 1 (pt); Activities coordinators 1 (ft); Dietitians 1 (pt); Dentists 1 (pt); Podiatrists 1 (pt); Audiologists 1 (pt).
Facilities Dining room; Physical therapy room; Activities room; Chapel; Crafts room; Barber/Beauty shop; Library; Lounges; Lobbies; Patios.
Activities Arts & crafts; Cards; Games; Reading groups; Prayer groups; Movies; Shopping trips; Social/Cultural gatherings.

CLINTON

Clinton Convalescent Center*
9211 Stuart Ln, Clinton, MD, 20735
(301) 868-3600
Admin Patricia Doherty. *Medical Dir/Dir of Nursing* Frank Ryan MD.
Licensure Skilled care; Intermediate care. *Beds* 275. *Certified* Medicaid; Medicare.
Owner Proprietary Corp (Beverly Enterprises).
Staff RNs 15 (pt); LPNs 24 (pt); Nurses aides 150 (pt); Physical therapists 2 (pt); Speech therapists 1 (ft); Activities coordinators 4 (ft), 1 (pt); Dietitians 1 (ft).
Facilities Dining room; Physical therapy room; Activities room; Chapel; Crafts room; Laundry room; Barber/Beauty shop.
Activities Arts & crafts; Cards; Games; Reading groups; Prayer groups; Movies; Social/Cultural gatherings.

COCKEYSVILLE

Broadmead
13801 York Rd, Cockeysville, MD, 21030
(301) 628-6900
Admin Thomas Mondloch. *Medical Dir/Dir of Nursing* D Thomas Crawford; Debra Titus.
Licensure Comprehensive care. *Beds* Comprehensive care 66. *Certified* Medicare.
Owner Nonprofit Corp.
Admissions Requirements Minimum age 65; Medical examination.
Staff Physicians 3 (pt); RNs 8 (ft), 11 (pt); LPNs 5 (ft), 1 (pt); Nurses aides 20 (ft), 15 (pt); Physical therapists 1 (pt); Recreational therapists 1 (pt); Occupational therapists 1 (pt); Speech therapists 1 (pt); Activities coordinators 1 (pt); Dietitians 1 (pt); Dentists 1 (pt); Ophthalmologists 1 (pt); Dentist 1 (pt).
Affiliation Society of Friends
Facilities Dining room; Physical therapy room; Activities room; Crafts room; Laundry room; Barber/Beauty shop; Library.

Activities Arts & crafts; Cards; Games; Reading groups; Prayer groups; Movies; Shopping trips; Social/Cultural gatherings.

Maryland Masonic Homes
300 International Circle, Cockeysville, MD, 21030
(301) 666-2222
Admin George A Dailey NHA. *Medical Dir/Dir of Nursing* Dr Paul Rivas; Marie Slaysman RN.
Licensure Intermediate care; Domiciliary care. *Beds* 220.
Owner Nonprofit organization/foundation.
Admissions Requirements Minimum age 60; Medical examination.
Staff Physicians 1 (pt); RNs 1 (ft), 2 (pt); LPNs 5 (ft), 3 (pt); Orderlies 1 (ft); Nurses aides 30 (ft), 2 (pt); Physical therapists 1 (pt); Recreational therapists 1 (pt); Speech therapists 1 (pt); Activities coordinators 2 (ft); Dentists 1 (pt); Podiatrists 1 (pt); Social workers 1 (ft).
Affiliation Masons
Facilities Dining room; Physical therapy room; Activities room; Chapel; Crafts room; Laundry room; Barber/Beauty shop; Library.
Activities Arts & crafts; Cards; Games; Reading groups; Prayer groups; Movies; Shopping trips; Social/Cultural gatherings; Fraternal oriented activities; Picnics; Watermelon parties.

COLUMBIA

Lorien Nursing & Convalescent Home*
6334 Cedar Ln, Columbia, MD, 21044
(301) 531-5151
Admin Louis Grimmel. *Medical Dir/Dir of Nursing* Jerome Hantman MD.
Licensure Intermediate care. *Beds* 120. *Certified* Medicaid; Medicare.
Owner Proprietary Corp.
Staff Physicians 60 (pt); RNs 15 (ft), 8 (pt); LPNs 18 (ft), 4 (pt); Orderlies 2 (ft), 4 (pt); Nurses aides 76 (ft), 18 (pt); Physical therapists 1 (pt); Recreational therapists 2 (pt); Occupational therapists 1 (pt); Speech therapists 1 (pt); Activities coordinators 1 (ft), 1 (pt); Dietitians 2 (ft); Dentists 1 (pt); Ophthalmologists 1 (pt); Podiatrists 1 (pt); Audiologists 1 (pt).
Facilities Dining room; Physical therapy room; Activities room; Chapel; Laundry room; Barber/Beauty shop.
Activities Arts & crafts; Games; Reading groups; Prayer groups; Movies.

CRISFIELD

Alice Byrd Tawes Nursing Home
1923 Hall Hwy, Crisfield, MD, 21817
(301) 968-1200
Admin Geraldine M Schmidlin. *Medical Dir/Dir of Nursing* James Sterling MD.
Licensure Skilled care; Intermediate care. *Beds* 64. *Certified* Medicaid; Medicare.
Owner Nonprofit organization/foundation.
Admissions Requirements Minimum age 14; Medical examination.
Staff Physicians 2 (pt); RNs 3 (ft), 2 (pt); LPNs 6 (ft), 6 (pt); Nurses aides 13 (ft), 17 (pt); Physical therapists 1 (pt); Occupational therapists 1 (pt); Speech therapists 1 (pt); Activities coordinators 1 (ft); Dietitians 1 (pt); Ophthalmologists 1 (pt); Dentist 1 (pt).
Facilities Dining room; Physical therapy room; Activities room; Crafts room; Laundry room; Barber/Beauty shop.
Activities Arts & crafts; Games; Reading groups; Prayer groups; Shopping trips; Social/Cultural gatherings.

CROFTON

Crofton Convalescent Center
2131 Davidsonville Rd, Crofton, MD, 21114
(301) 721-1000, 793-0123, 261-3634
Admin Barbara Klein. *Medical Dir/Dir of Nursing* Max C Frank MD; Dorothy L Cox RN DON.
Licensure Skilled care; Intermediate care. *Beds* 134. *Certified* Medicaid; Medicare.
Owner Privately owned.
Admissions Requirements Minimum age 14; Medical examination; Physician's request.
Staff Physicians 2 (ft), 20 (pt); RNs 9 (ft), 12 (pt); LPNs 5 (ft), 15 (pt); Nurses aides 37 (ft), 17 (pt); Physical therapists 2 (pt); Reality therapists 1 (pt); Recreational therapists 1 (ft); Occupational therapists 1 (pt); Speech therapists 1 (pt); Activities coordinators 1 (ft), 3 (pt); Dietitians 1 (pt); Dentists 1 (pt); Ophthalmologists 1 (pt); Podiatrists 1 (pt).
Facilities Dining room; Physical therapy room; Activities room; Chapel; Laundry room; Barber/Beauty shop; Day rooms; Enclosed courtyard & patio; Visitor's lounge.
Activities Arts & crafts; Cards; Games; Reading groups; Prayer groups; Movies; Shopping trips; Social/Cultural gatherings.

CROWNSVILLE

Arundel Nursing Center Inc
1454 Fairfield Loop Rd, Crownsville, MD, 21032
(301) 987-6338 or 923-6820
Admin Calvin W Parker. *Medical Dir/Dir of Nursing* Richard Hochman MD; Barbara Newton RN DN.
Licensure Skilled care; Intermediate care. *Beds* 142. *Certified* Medicaid; Medicare.
Owner Nonprofit Corp.
Admissions Requirements Minimum age 19; Physician's request.
Staff Physicians 26 (pt); RNs 4 (ft), 6 (pt); LPNs 7 (ft), 8 (pt); Nurses aides 42 (ft), 43 (pt); Physical therapists 1 (ft); Occupational therapists 1 (pt); Speech therapists 1 (pt); Activities coordinators 1 (ft); Dietitians 1 (pt); Ophthalmologists 1 (pt).
Facilities Dining room; Physical therapy room; Activities room; Crafts room; Laundry room; Barber/Beauty shop; Library.
Activities Arts & crafts; Cards; Games; Reading groups; Movies; Shopping trips; Social/Cultural gatherings.

CUMBERLAND

Allegany County Nursing Home
PO Box 599, Furnace St, Cumberland, MD, 21502
(301) 777-5941
Admin Bertie M Stotler. *Medical Dir/Dir of Nursing* Dr Robustiano J Barrera.
Licensure Intermediate care. *Beds* 153. *Certified* Medicaid.
Owner Publicly owned.
Staff Physicians 1 (ft), 1 (pt); RNs 4 (ft), 2 (pt); LPNs 10 (ft), 9 (pt); Orderlies 9 (ft), 9 (pt); Nurses aides 29 (ft), 27 (pt); Physical therapists 1 (ft); Activities coordinators 1 (ft), 1 (pt); Dietitians 1 (ft); Dentists 1 (ft); Podiatrists 1 (ft).
Facilities Dining room; Physical therapy room; Activities room; Crafts room; Laundry room; Barber/Beauty shop.
Activities Arts & crafts; Cards; Games; Prayer groups; Movies; Social/Cultural gatherings; Birthday parties.

Joseph D Brandenburg Center*
Country Club Rd, PO Box 1722, Cumberland, MD, 21502
(301) 777-2250
Admin Dennis George. *Medical Dir/Dir of Nursing* Dr Gary Wagoner.

Licensure Intermediate care for mentally retarded. *Beds* 50. *Certified* Medicaid.
Owner Publicly owned.
Admissions Requirements Minimum age 18.
Staff Physicians 1 (pt); RNs 6 (ft); LPNs 3 (ft); Physical therapists 1 (pt); Recreational therapists 2 (ft); Occupational therapists 1 (ft); Speech therapists 1 (ft), 1 (pt); Audiologists 2 (pt).
Facilities Dining room; Physical therapy room; Activities room; Crafts room; Laundry room; Barber/Beauty shop; Library.
Activities Arts & crafts; Games; Movies; Shopping trips; Social/Cultural gatherings.

Cumberland Villa Nursing Center*
510 Winifred Rd, Cumberland, MD, 21502
(301) 724-6066
Admin Shirley E Paulus. *Medical Dir/Dir of Nursing* Peter B Halmos.
Licensure Skilled care; Intermediate care. *Beds* 135. *Certified* Medicaid.
Owner Proprietary Corp (Beverly Enterprises).

Lions Manor Nursing Home
Seton Dr Ext, Cumberland, MD, 21502
(301) 722-6272
Admin Leo J Bechtold. *Medical Dir/Dir of Nursing* Dr Vimala Ranjithan.
Licensure Skilled care; Intermediate care. *Beds* SNF 101; ICF. *Certified* Medicaid; Medicare.
Owner Nonprofit organization/foundation.
Admissions Requirements Minimum age 14; Medical examination.
Staff Physicians 3 (pt); RNs 7 (ft), 1 (pt); LPNs 5 (ft), 3 (pt); Orderlies 2 (ft); Nurses aides 27 (ft), 10 (pt); Physical therapists 1 (pt); Reality therapists 1 (pt); Recreational therapists 1 (pt); Occupational therapists; Activities coordinators 2 (ft); Dietitians 1 (pt); Social service director 1 (ft).
Languages Spanish
Facilities Dining room; Physical therapy room; Activities room; Crafts room; Laundry room; Barber/Beauty shop; Library.
Activities Arts & crafts; Cards; Games; Reading groups; Prayer groups; Movies; Shopping trips; Social/Cultural gatherings; Birthday & holiday parties; Resident Council; Outings in handicap vehicle; Religious services; Volunteer Corps.

DENTON

Caroline Nursing Home Inc*
520 Kerr Ave, Denton, MD, 21629
(301) 479-2130
Admin Karen L Potter. *Medical Dir/Dir of Nursing* Cynthia Lipsitz MD.
Licensure Skilled care; Intermediate care. *Beds* 76. *Certified* Medicaid; Medicare.
Owner Nonprofit Corp.
Admissions Requirements Minimum age 18.
Staff Physicians 6 (pt); RNs 4 (ft), 4 (pt); LPNs 4 (ft), 5 (pt); Nurses aides 24 (ft), 26 (pt); Physical therapists 1 (pt); Occupational therapists 1 (pt); Speech therapists 1 (pt); Activities coordinators 1 (ft); Dietitians 1 (pt); Dentists 1 (pt); Ophthalmologists 1 (pt); Podiatrists 1 (pt).
Facilities Dining room; Physical therapy room; Activities room; Chapel; Crafts room; Laundry room; Barber/Beauty shop.
Activities Arts & crafts; Cards; Games; Reading groups; Prayer groups; Movies; Shopping trips.

Wesleyan Health Care Center Inc*
PO Box 15, 280 Camp Rd, Denton, MD, 21629
(601) 479-4400
Admin Bruce Goodpaster. *Medical Dir/Dir of Nursing* Philip Felipe MD.
Beds 120.
Owner Proprietary Corp (US Care Corp).

EASTON

William Hill Manor
501 Dutchmans Ln, Easton, MD, 21601
(301) 822-8888
Admin Donna S Taylor. *Medical Dir/Dir of Nursing* Albert T Dawkins MD; Susan M Sullivan RN DON.
Licensure Skilled care; Intermediate care. *Beds* 60. *Certified* Medicaid; Medicare.
Owner Proprietary Corp.
Admissions Requirements Minimum age 55; Medical examination; Physician's request.
Staff Physicians 1 (pt); RNs 5 (ft); LPNs 5 (ft); Nurses aides 19 (ft); Physical therapists 1 (ft); Recreational therapists 1 (ft); Activities coordinators 1 (ft); Dietitians 1 (pt).
Facilities Dining room; Physical therapy room; Activities room; Laundry room; Barber/Beauty shop; Cocktail lounge/bar; Gift shop; Post office/mail room; Full service bank.
Activities Arts & crafts; Cards; Games; Reading groups; Prayer groups; Movies; Social/Cultural gatherings; Guest speakers; Special dinners; Parties; Exercise classes.

Memorial Hospital at Easton Maryland Inc
219 S Washington St, Easton, MD, 21601
(301) 822-1000
Admin Nick Rajacich. *Medical Dir/Dir of Nursing* Albert T Dawkins MD.
Licensure Skilled care; Intermediate care. *Beds* SNF 33; ICF. *Certified* Medicaid; Medicare.
Owner Nonprofit Corp.
Admissions Requirements Minimum age 14; Physician's request.
Staff Physicians 1 (pt); RNs 4 (ft), 2 (pt); LPNs 1 (ft), 3 (pt); Nurses aides 15 (ft); Physical therapists 3 (ft); Occupational therapists 1 (ft); Speech therapists 1 (pt); Dietitians 3 (ft); Dentists 2 (ft).
Facilities Dining room; Physical therapy room; Activities room; Chapel; Library.
Activities Arts & crafts; Cards; Reading groups; Movies.

Meridian Nursing Center—The Pines*
Rte 50 & Dutchman's Ln, Easton, MD, 21601
(301) 822-4000
Admin Bruce Levin. *Medical Dir/Dir of Nursing* Stephen P Carney MD.
Licensure Skilled care; Intermediate care; Domiciliary care. *Beds* SNF 181; ICF 42; Domiciliary care 22. *Certified* Medicaid; Medicare.
Owner Proprietary Corp (Meridan Healthcare).

EDGEWATER

Pleasant Living Convalescent Center
144 Washington Rd, Edgewater, MD, 21037
(301) 956-5000
Admin Howard Waltz Jr. *Medical Dir/Dir of Nursing* Charles W Kinzer MD; Nancy Youngblood RN DON.
Licensure Skilled care; Intermediate care. *Beds* 120. *Certified* Medicaid; Medicare.
Owner Proprietary Corp.
Admissions Requirements Minimum age 14; Medical examination; Physician's request.
Staff Physicians 17 (pt); RNs 6 (ft), 4 (pt); LPNs 5 (ft), 7 (pt); Orderlies 6 (ft); Nurses aides 37 (ft), 28 (pt); Physical therapists 1 (pt); Recreational therapists 1 (ft); Speech therapists 1 (pt); Activities coordinators 2 (ft); Dietitians 1 (pt); Dentists 1 (pt); Ophthalmologists 1 (pt); Podiatrists 1 (pt).
Facilities Dining room; Physical therapy room; Activities room; Chapel; Crafts room; Laundry room; Barber/Beauty shop; Library.
Activities Arts & crafts; Cards; Games; Reading groups; Prayer groups; Movies; Shopping trips; Social/Cultural gatherings; Picnic outings; Dining affair twice monthly, local restaurants provide their specialty & wine w/their chef & assistants.

ELKTON

Devine Haven Convalescent Home*
224 E Main St, Elkton, MD, 21921
(301) 398-4550
Admin Ronald Sohl. *Medical Dir/Dir of Nursing* S Ralph Andrews Jr MD.
Licensure Intermediate care. *Beds* 43. *Certified* Medicaid.
Owner Proprietary Corp.

Laurelwood Nursing Center
100 Laurel Dr, Elkton, MD, 21921
(301) 398-8800
Admin Carole McMullen.
Beds 133.
Owner Proprietary Corp (TJ Rock).

ELLICOTT CITY

Bon Secours Extended Care Facility
3000 N Ridge Rd, Ellicott City, MD, 21043
(301) 461-6660
Admin Leslie D Goldschmidt. *Medical Dir/Dir of Nursing* Randy Reese MD; Ward Murray RN DON.
Licensure Skilled care; Intermediate care. *Beds* SNF 30; ICF 66. *Certified* Medicaid; Medicare.
Owner Nonprofit Corp (Bon Secours Health Sys).
Admissions Requirements Minimum age 21; Medical examination; Physician's request.
Staff Physicians 1 (pt); RNs 12 (ft), 8 (pt); LPNs 5 (ft), 3 (pt); Nurses aides 30 (ft), 12 (pt); Physical therapists 1 (pt); Recreational therapists 1 (ft), 1 (pt); Occupational therapists 1 (pt); Speech therapists 1 (pt); Dietitians 1 (pt); Dentists 1 (pt); Ophthalmologists 1 (pt); Podiatrists 1 (pt).
Affiliation Roman Catholic
Facilities Dining room; Physical therapy room; Activities room; Chapel; Crafts room; Laundry room; Barber/Beauty shop; Library.
Activities Arts & crafts; Cards; Games; Reading groups; Prayer groups; Movies; Shopping trips; Social/Cultural gatherings.

FORESTVILLE

Regency Nursing & Rehabilitation Center
7420 Marlboro Pike, Forestville, MD, 20028
(301) 736-0240
Admin Robert Bristol. *Medical Dir/Dir of Nursing* Kelvin L Minchin MD.
Licensure Skilled care; Intermediate care. *Beds* 160. *Certified* Medicaid; Medicare.
Owner Proprietary Corp.
Admissions Requirements Minimum age 14; Medical examination.
Staff RNs 4 (ft), 6 (pt); LPNs 5 (ft), 4 (pt); Orderlies 61 (ft), 11 (pt); Recreational therapists 1 (ft); Activities coordinators 1 (ft).
Facilities Dining room; Physical therapy room; Activities room; Crafts room; Laundry room; Barber/Beauty shop; Library.
Activities Arts & crafts; Cards; Games; Reading groups; Prayer groups; Movies; Shopping trips; Social/Cultural gatherings.

FORT WASHINGTON

Fort Washington Rehabilitation Center
12021 Livingston Rd, Fort Washington, MD, 20744
(301) 292-0300
Admin Marvin Rabovsky. *Medical Dir/Dir of Nursing* William Furst MD; Diana Adinig RN.
Licensure Skilled care; Intermediate care. *Beds* 150. *Certified* Medicaid; Medicare.
Owner Proprietary Corp.
Admissions Requirements Minimum age 14; Medical examination.
Staff Physicians 7 (pt); RNs 8 (ft), 3 (pt); LPNs 9 (ft), 3 (pt); Orderlies; Nurses aides 30 (ft), 7 (pt); Physical therapists 1 (ft); Reality therapists 1 (ft); Recreational therapists 2 (ft); Occupational therapists 1 (ft); Speech therapists 1 (pt); Activities coordinators 1 (ft); Dietitians 1 (ft); Dentists 1 (pt); Ophthalmologists 1 (pt); Podiatrists 1 (pt).
Facilities Dining room; Physical therapy room; Activities room; Crafts room; Laundry room; Barber/Beauty shop.
Activities Arts & crafts; Cards; Games; Reading groups; Prayer groups; Movies; Shopping trips; Social/Cultural gatherings.

FREDERICK

Citizens Nursing Home of Frederick County*
2200 Rosemont Ave, Frederick, MD, 21701
(301) 694-1550
Admin William P Hill Jr. *Medical Dir/Dir of Nursing* B O Thomas Jr MD.
Licensure Skilled care; Intermediate care. *Beds* 170. *Certified* Medicaid; Medicare.
Owner Publicly owned.
Staff Physicians 1 (pt); RNs 12 (ft), 8 (pt); LPNs 7 (ft), 10 (pt); Nurses aides 50 (ft), 35 (pt); Physical therapists 2 (pt); Speech therapists 1 (pt); Activities coordinators 1 (ft); Dietitians 1 (ft), 1 (pt).
Facilities Dining room; Physical therapy room; Activities room; Chapel; Crafts room; Laundry room; Barber/Beauty shop; Library.
Activities Arts & crafts; Cards; Games; Reading groups; Prayer groups; Movies; Shopping trips.

Home for the Aged—Frederick
115 Record St, Frederick, MD, 21701
(301) 663-6822
Admin Robert Woodard. *Medical Dir/Dir of Nursing* Leroy T Davis MD.
Licensure Intermediate care; Domiciliary care. *Beds* ICF 6; Domiciliary care 23.
Owner Nonprofit Corp.

Homewood Retirement Center—Frederick
31 W Patrick St, Frederick, MD, 21701
(301) 694-7292
Admin Joseph H Clem. *Medical Dir/Dir of Nursing* George I Smith Jr MD; Patsy Clark Grimes RN.
Licensure Skilled care; Domiciliary care. *Beds* SNF 102; Domiciliary 58. *Certified* Medicaid.
Owner Nonprofit Corp (Homewood Retire Centers/UCC).
Admissions Requirements Minimum age 60; Medical examination; Physician's request.
Staff RNs 8 (ft), 6 (pt); LPNs 10 (ft), 4 (pt); Nurses aides 34 (ft), 11 (pt); Physical therapists 1 (pt); Speech therapists 1 (pt); Activities coordinators 1 (ft); Dietitians 1 (ft); Dentists 1 (pt); Podiatrists 1 (pt).
Affiliation Church of Christ
Facilities Dining room; Physical therapy room; Activities room; Chapel; Crafts room; Laundry room; Barber/Beauty shop; Library; Game room; Sunshine room.
Activities Arts & crafts; Cards; Games; Reading groups; Prayer groups; Movies; Shopping trips; Social/Cultural gatherings; Bingo; Birthday parties.

Meridian Nursing Center—Frederick
400 North Ave, Frederick, MD, 21701
(301) 663-5181
Admin Bruce E Boyer. *Medical Dir/Dir of Nursing* Gilcin Meadors MD; Anne Skow RN DON.
Licensure Skilled care; Intermediate care; Domiciliary. *Beds* SNF 92; ICF 66; Domiciliary 8. *Certified* Medicaid; Medicare.

Owner Proprietary Corp (Meridan Healthcare).
Admissions Requirements Minimum age 14; Physician's request.
Staff Physicians 1 (pt); RNs 7 (ft), 6 (pt); LPNs 7 (ft), 5 (pt); Nurses aides 54 (ft), 11 (pt); Physical therapists 3 (pt); Occupational therapists 1 (pt); Speech therapists 1 (pt); Activities coordinators 2 (ft), 1 (pt); Dietitians 1 (pt); Ophthalmologists 1 (pt).
Facilities Dining room; Physical therapy room; Activities room; Chapel; Crafts room; Laundry room; Barber/Beauty shop; Patio garden.
Activities Arts & crafts; Cards; Games; Reading groups; Prayer groups; Movies; Shopping trips; Social/Cultural gatherings; Daylong bus trips; Pet therapy; Educational classes.

FROSTBURG

Frostburg Village Nursing Home of Allegany County
1 Kaylor Circle, Frostburg, MD, 21532
(301) 689-2425
Admin Leo J Cyr. *Medical Dir/Dir of Nursing* S L Sanshir MD; Phyllis Roque RN.
Licensure Skilled care. *Beds* SNF 170. *Certified* Medicaid; Medicare.
Owner Nonprofit Corp (Tressler-Luthren Services Assoc).
Admissions Requirements Minimum age 65.
Staff RNs; LPNs; Orderlies; Nurses aides; Recreational therapists; Activities coordinators; Dietitians.
Affiliation Lutheran
Facilities Dining room; Physical therapy room; Activities room; Chapel; Crafts room; Laundry room; Barber/Beauty shop; Library.
Activities Arts & crafts; Cards; Games; Reading groups; Prayer groups; Movies; Shopping trips; Social/Cultural gatherings.

GAITHERSBURG

Herman M Wilson Health Care Center*
201-301 Russell Ave, Gaithersburg, MD, 20760
(301) 330-3000
Admin Alan W Porterfield. *Medical Dir/Dir of Nursing* Henry Scruggs MD.
Licensure Skilled care; Intermediate care. *Beds* 279. *Certified* Medicaid; Medicare.
Owner Nonprofit Corp.

GARRISON

Garrison Valley Center Inc
9600 Reisterstown Rd, Garrison, MD, 21055
(301) 363-3337
Admin Ida M Campanella. *Medical Dir/Dir of Nursing* Allan H Macht MD; Ms Josephine Mungin RN DON.
Licensure Intermediate care. *Beds* ICF 76. *Certified* Medicaid.
Owner Proprietary Corp.
Admissions Requirements Minimum age 16; Medical examination; Physician's request.
Staff Physicians 2 (ft); RNs 3 (ft); LPNs 4 (ft), 4 (pt); Physical therapists 1 (pt); Activities coordinators 1 (ft); Dietitians 1 (pt).
Facilities Dining room; Physical therapy room; Activities room; Chapel; Crafts room; Laundry room; Library.
Activities Arts & crafts; Cards; Games; Prayer groups; Movies; Shopping trips.

GLEN BURNIE

Arundel Geriatric & Nursing Center
7355 Furnace Branch Rd E, Glen Burnie, MD, 21061
(301) 766-3460
Admin Vida Sullivan. *Medical Dir/Dir of Nursing* Elmo Gayoso; Mary Jo Neal.

Licensure Intermediate care. *Beds* 115. *Certified* Medicaid.
Owner Proprietary Corp.
Admissions Requirements Minimum age 14.
Staff RNs; LPNs; Orderlies; Nurses aides; Recreational therapists; Activities coordinators.
Facilities Dining room; Activities room; Laundry room.
Activities Arts & crafts; Cards; Games; Reading groups; Prayer groups; Movies; Shopping trips; Social/Cultural gatherings.

Maryland Manor of Glen Burnie
7575 E Howard St, Glen Burnie, MD, 21061
(301) 768-8200
Admin Paul J Robertson. *Medical Dir/Dir of Nursing* Peter Rheinstein MD.
Licensure Skilled care. *Beds* 99. *Certified* Medicaid; Medicare.
Admissions Requirements Minimum age 18; Medical examination.
Staff Physicians; RNs; LPNs; Orderlies; Nurses aides; Physical therapists; Speech therapists; Activities coordinators; Dietitians; Dentists; Ophthalmologists; Podiatrists.
Facilities Dining room; Physical therapy room; Activities room; Chapel; Crafts room; Laundry room; Barber/Beauty shop; Library.
Activities Arts & crafts; Cards; Games; Reading groups; Prayer groups; Movies; Shopping trips; Social/Cultural gatherings.

North Arundel Nursing & Convalescent Center Inc*
313 Hospital Dr, Glen Burnie, MD, 21061
(301) 761-1222
Admin Shirley McKnight. *Medical Dir/Dir of Nursing* Mustafa C Oz MD.
Licensure Skilled care; Intermediate care. *Beds* 101. *Certified* Medicaid; Medicare.
Owner Proprietary Corp.

GRANTSVILLE

Goodwill Mennonite Home Inc*
Dorsey Hotel Rd, Grantsville, MD, 21536
(301) 895-5194
Admin R Henry Diller. *Medical Dir/Dir of Nursing* George Stoltzfus MD.
Licensure Intermediate care. *Beds* 81. *Certified* Medicaid.
Owner Nonprofit Corp.
Admissions Requirements Medical examination.
Staff RNs 1 (ft); LPNs 5 (ft); Orderlies 4 (ft), 1 (pt); Nurses aides 20 (ft); Activities coordinators 1 (ft).
Affiliation Mennonite
Facilities Dining room; Physical therapy room; Activities room; Chapel; Crafts room; Laundry room; Barber/Beauty shop.
Activities Arts & crafts; Games; Movies.

GREENBELT

Greenbelt Nursing Center
7010 Greenbelt Rd, Greenbelt, MD, 20770
(301) 345-9595
Admin Daniel C Frost. *Medical Dir/Dir of Nursing* Dr Jeffrey Kelman; Bonnie Baker RN.
Licensure Skilled care; Intermediate care. *Beds* SNF 132; ICF. *Certified* Medicaid; Medicare.
Owner Proprietary Corp (Unicare).
Admissions Requirements Minimum age 18.
Staff RNs 5 (ft), 5 (pt); LPNs 9 (ft), 9 (pt); Nurses aides 50 (ft), 25 (pt); Physical therapists 1 (ft); Recreational therapists 1 (ft); Occupational therapists 1 (ft); Speech therapists 1 (ft); Activities coordinators 1 (ft); Dietitians 1 (ft); Podiatrists 1 (pt).

Facilities Dining room; Physical therapy room; Barber/Beauty shop.
Activities Arts & crafts; Cards; Games; Reading groups; Prayer groups; Movies; Shopping trips; Social/Cultural gatherings.

HAGERSTOWN

Avalon Manor
Marsh Pike & Eden Rd, Hagerstown, MD, 21740
(301) 739-9360
Admin Stuart Reiker. *Medical Dir/Dir of Nursing* Dr William Lesh.
Licensure Intermediate care. *Beds* 221. *Certified* Medicaid.
Owner Proprietary Corp.
Admissions Requirements Minimum age 14; Medical examination; Physician's request.
Staff Physicians 4 (pt); RNs 7 (ft); LPNs 19 (ft); Orderlies 3 (ft); Nurses aides 94 (ft), 3 (pt); Recreational therapists 1 (ft), 2 (pt); Activities coordinators 1 (ft); Dietitians 1 (ft).
Facilities Dining room; Activities room; Crafts room; Laundry room; Barber/Beauty shop; Library.
Activities Arts & crafts; Cards; Games; Prayer groups; Movies; Shopping trips; Social/Cultural gatherings; Ceramics.

Clearview Nursing Home Inc*
Rte 3, Box 144, Hagerstown, MD, 21740
(301) 582-1654
Admin Willa Jean Vaters. *Medical Dir/Dir of Nursing* John D Wilson MD.
Licensure Intermediate care. *Beds* 49. *Certified* Medicaid.
Owner Proprietary Corp.

Coffman Home for the Aging Inc*
1304 Pennsylvania Ave, Hagerstown, MD, 21740
(301) 733-2914
Admin Ruth Yvonne Eyler. *Medical Dir/Dir of Nursing* J D Wilson MD.
Licensure Intermediate care. *Beds* 51. *Certified* Medicaid.
Owner Publicly owned.

Colton Villa Nursing Center
750 Dual Hwy, Hagerstown, MD, 21740
(301) 797-4020
Admin Margaret V Saylor. *Medical Dir/Dir of Nursing* Dr Abdul Waheed.
Licensure Skilled care; Intermediate care. *Beds* 160. *Certified* Medicaid; Medicare.
Owner Proprietary Corp (Beverly Enterprises).
Admissions Requirements Minimum age 18; Medical examination; Physician's request.
Staff Physicians 1 (pt); RNs 8 (ft), 3 (pt); LPNs 9 (ft), 3 (pt); Nurses aides 60 (ft), 4 (pt); Physical therapists 1 (pt); Speech therapists 2 (pt); Activities coordinators 2 (ft); Dietitians 1 (pt); Podiatrists 1 (pt).
Facilities Dining room; Activities room; Laundry room; Barber/Beauty shop.
Activities Arts & crafts; Cards; Games; Reading groups; Prayer groups; Movies; Shopping trips; Social/Cultural gatherings.

Garlock Memorial Convalescent Home Inc*
241 N Prospect St, Hagerstown, MD, 21740
(301) 733-3310
Admin Louis Vogel. *Medical Dir/Dir of Nursing* Sidney Novenstein MD.
Licensure Intermediate care. *Beds* 37. *Certified* Medicaid.
Owner Proprietary Corp.

Potomac Center*
1380 Marshall St, Hagerstown, MD, 21740
(301) 791-4650
Admin Steven J Smith. *Medical Dir/Dir of Nursing* J Ramsey Farah MD.
Licensure Intermediate care for mentally retarded. *Beds* 150. *Certified* Medicaid.
Owner Publicly owned.

Ravenwood Lutheran Village Nursing Home*
1183 Luther Dr, Hagerstown, MD, 21740
(301) 790-1000
Admin Carole L Malin.
Licensure Skilled care; Intermediate care. *Beds*
86. *Certified* Medicaid; Medicare.
Owner Nonprofit Corp (Tressler-Lutheran
Services Assoc).
Affiliation Lutheran

Western Maryland Center*
1500 Pennsylvania Ave, Hagerstown, MD,
21740
(301) 791-4430
Admin Carl Fischer, MD. *Medical Dir/Dir of
Nursing* F U Porciumcula MD.
Licensure Skilled care; Intermediate care. *Beds*
SNF 62; ICF 92. *Certified* Medicaid;
Medicare.
Owner Publicly owned.

HAVRE DE GRACE

Brevin Nursing Home Inc*
421 S Union Ave, Havre de Grace, MD,
21078
(301) 935-1740
Admin Jerrold F Bress.
Licensure Intermediate care. *Beds* 40.
Certified Medicaid.
Owner Proprietary Corp.

Citizens Nursing Home of Harford County
415 S Market St, Havre de Grace, MD, 21078
(301) 939-5500
Admin John C Fisher. *Medical Dir/Dir of
Nursing* John D Yun MD.
Licensure Skilled care; Intermediate care. *Beds*
200. *Certified* Medicaid; Medicare.
Owner Publicly owned.
Admissions Requirements Minimum age 14;
Medical examination; Physician's request.
Staff RNs 4 (ft), 6 (pt); LPNs 14 (ft), 11 (pt);
Nurses aides 48 (ft), 42 (pt); Activities
coordinators 1 (ft); Dietitians 1 (ft).
Facilities Dining room; Physical therapy
room; Activities room; Chapel; Crafts room;
Laundry room; Barber/Beauty shop;
Enclosed courtyard.
Activities Arts & crafts; Cards; Games; Prayer
groups; Movies; Shopping trips; Social/
Cultural gatherings; Outside entertainment;
College programs.

HYATTSVILLE

Carroll Manor Inc
4922 LaSalle Rd, Hyattsville, MD, 20782
(301) 864-2333
Admin Sr Mary Robert Romano. *Medical Dir/
Dir of Nursing* Dr Thomas E Curtin;
Carmella Walsh RN DON.
Licensure Skilled care; Intermediate care. *Beds*
SNF (20 swing beds) 232; ICF. *Certified*
Medicaid; Medicare.
Owner Nonprofit Corp.
Admissions Requirements Minimum age 60;
Medical examination; Physician's request.
Staff Physicians 1 (pt); RNs 6 (ft), 9 (pt);
LPNs 23 (ft), 3 (pt); Orderlies 1 (ft); Nurses
aides 76 (ft), 31 (pt); Physical therapists 1
(pt); Recreational therapists 1 (ft); Activities
coordinators 1 (ft); Dietitians 1 (ft);
Ophthalmologists 2 (pt).
Affiliation Roman Catholic
Facilities Dining room; Physical therapy
room; Activities room; Chapel; Crafts room;
Laundry room; Barber/Beauty shop; Library;
Cocktail lounge; Auditorium.
Activities Arts & crafts; Cards; Games;
Reading groups; Prayer groups; Movies;
Shopping trips; Social/Cultural gatherings.

Hyattsville Manor
6500 Riggs Rd, Hyattsville, MD, 20783
(301) 559-0300

Admin Richard Balogh. *Medical Dir/Dir of
Nursing* Myron Lenkin MD; Ronald
Bowlyou.
Licensure Skilled care; Intermediate care. *Beds*
SNF 10; ICF 140. *Certified* Medicaid;
Medicare.
Owner Proprietary Corp (Health Care &
Retirement Corp).
Admissions Requirements Minimum age 16.
Staff Physicians 1 (pt); RNs 8 (ft); LPNs 12
(ft), 4 (pt); Nurses aides 25 (ft), 10 (pt);
Physical therapists 1 (pt); Recreational
therapists 1 (ft); Occupational therapists 1
(pt); Speech therapists 1 (pt); Activities
coordinators 1 (ft); Dietitians 1 (ft);
Ophthalmologists 1 (pt).
Facilities Dining room; Physical therapy
room; Activities room; Crafts room; Laundry
room; Barber/Beauty shop.
Activities Arts & crafts; Cards; Games;
Reading groups; Prayer groups; Movies;
Shopping trips; Social/Cultural gatherings.

Madison Manor Nursing Home
5801 42nd Ave, Hyattsville, MD, 20781
(301) 864-8800
Admin Mayther Brackins. *Medical Dir/Dir of
Nursing* B Arora MD; Brenda Mauney Rian.
Licensure Intermediate care. *Beds* 27.
Certified Medicaid.
Owner Proprietary Corp.
Admissions Requirements Medical
examination.
Staff Physicians 3 (ft), 1 (pt); RNs 1 (ft);
LPNs 3 (ft), 3 (pt); Nurses aides 5 (ft), 5
(pt); Activities coordinators 1 (ft); Dietitians
1 (ft); Ophthalmologists 1 (pt).
Facilities Dining room; Activities room;
Laundry room.
Activities Arts & crafts; Games; Reading
groups; Shopping trips.

Sacred Heart Home Inc
5805 Queens Chapel Rd, Hyattsville, MD,
20782
(301) 277-6500
Admin Sr Mary Agnes Fahrland. *Medical Dir/
Dir of Nursing* Ibrahim Khatri MD.
Licensure Intermediate care. *Beds* 102.
Certified Medicaid.
Owner Nonprofit Corp.

KENSINGTON

Circle Manor Nursing Home
10231 Carroll Pl, Kensington, MD, 20895
(301) 949-0230
Admin Gary Sudhalter. *Medical Dir/Dir of
Nursing* Dr Rosenbaum & Dr Shargel; Judy
Pelton RN DON.
Licensure Intermediate care. *Beds* 86.
Certified Medicaid.
Owner Proprietary Corp.
Admissions Requirements Medical
examination.
Staff RNs 3 (ft), 1 (pt); LPNs 4 (ft), 4 (pt);
Nurses aides 30 (ft), 5 (pt); Physical
therapists 1 (pt); Recreational therapists 1
(ft); Occupational therapists 1 (pt); Speech
therapists 1 (pt); Activities coordinators 1
(ft); Dietitians 1 (pt).
Facilities Dining room; Activities room;
Laundry room; Barber/Beauty shop.
Activities Arts & crafts; Games; Reading
groups; Prayer groups; Movies; Social/
Cultural gatherings; Summerfest picnic;
Holiday parties.

Kensington Gardens Nursing Center
3000 McComas Ave, Kensington, MD, 20795
(301) 933-0060
Admin Anne Souders. *Medical Dir/Dir of
Nursing* DR David Kessler; Norma Fraley
DON.
Licensure Intermediate care; Comprehensive
care. *Beds* 170. *Certified* Medicaid;
Medicare.
Owner Proprietary Corp.

Admissions Requirements Minimum age 17;
Medical examination.
Staff RNs 16 (ft), 4 (pt); LPNs 8 (ft), 1 (pt);
Orderlies 22 (ft); Nurses aides 16 (ft);
Physical therapists 1 (ft); Recreational
therapists 4 (ft); Speech therapists 1 (pt);
Activities coordinators 1 (ft); Dietitians 1
(pt); Dentists 1 (pt); Podiatrists 1 (pt).
Facilities Dining room; Physical therapy
room; Activities room; Crafts room; Laundry
room; Barber/Beauty shop.
Activities Arts & crafts; Cards; Games;
Reading groups; Prayer groups; Movies;
Shopping trips; Social/Cultural gatherings.

LA PLATA

Charles County Nursing Home
Rte 488, Box 1320, La Plata, MD, 20646
(301) 934-1900
Admin Michael E Morin. *Medical Dir/Dir of
Nursing* Paul Prichard MD; Barbara Howard
RN.
Licensure Skilled care; Intermediate care. *Beds*
105. *Certified* Medicaid; Medicare.
Owner Nonprofit Corp.
Facilities Dining room; Physical therapy
room; Activities room; Chapel; Crafts room;
Laundry room; Barber/Beauty shop.
Activities Arts & crafts; Cards; Games;
Reading groups; Prayer groups; Movies;
Social/Cultural gatherings.

LANHAM

Magnolia Gardens Nursing Home*
8200 Good Luck Rd, Lanham, MD, 20801
(301) 552-2000
Admin Margaret O'Hare. *Medical Dir/Dir of
Nursing* Leon Levitsky MD.
Licensure Skilled care; Intermediate care. *Beds*
104. *Certified* Medicaid; Medicare.
Owner Proprietary Corp.

LARGO

Largo Manor Care
Rte 2, 600 Largo Rd, Largo, MD, 20772
(301) 350-5555
Admin Barry Grofic. *Medical Dir/Dir of
Nursing* Norton Elson; Denise Laurion
DON.
Licensure Skilled care; Intermediate care. *Beds*
120. *Certified* Medicaid; Medicare.
Owner Proprietary Corp.
Admissions Requirements Minimum age 16.
Staff Physicians; RNs; LPNs; Nurses aides;
Physical therapists; Reality therapists;
Recreational therapists; Occupational
therapists; Speech therapists; Activities
coordinators; Dietitians; Dentists;
Ophthalmologists; Podiatrists; Dentist.
Facilities Dining room; Physical therapy
room; Activities room; Barber/Beauty shop;
Library.
Activities Arts & crafts; Cards; Games;
Reading groups; Prayer groups; Movies;
Shopping trips; Social/Cultural gatherings.

LAUREL

Bureau of Habilitation Services-Forest Haven
3360 Center Ave, Laurel, MD, 20707
(301) 725-3600
Admin Clifford Hubbard. *Medical Dir/Dir of
Nursing* Robert L Baird MD.
Licensure Intermediate care for mentally
retarded. *Beds* (day treatment center).
Certified Medicaid.
Owner Publicly owned.
Admissions Requirements Admission closed.
Staff Physicians 7 (ft); RNs 28 (ft); LPNs 18
(ft); Physical therapists 8 (ft); Recreational
therapists 10 (ft); Occupational therapists 5

(ft); Speech therapists 3 (ft); Dietitians 3 (ft); Dentists 1 (ft); Ophthalmologists 1 (ft); Podiatrists 1 (ft).
Facilities Dining room; Physical therapy room; Activities room; Chapel; Crafts room; Laundry room; Barber/Beauty shop; Comprehensive complex.
Activities Arts & crafts; Cards; Games; Reading groups; Prayer groups; Movies; Shopping trips; Social/Cultural gatherings.

Greater Laurel Nursing Home*
14200 Laurel Pk Dr, Laurel, MD, 20707
(601) 792-4717
Admin Stanley Savitz. *Medical Dir/Dir of Nursing* Gregory Compton MD.
Beds 131.
Owner Proprietary Corp.

LEONARDTOWN

St Mary's Nursing Center
PO Box 518, Leonardtown, MD, 20650
(301) 475-2139
Admin George E Smith. *Medical Dir/Dir of Nursing* J Roy Guyther MD; Stephanie Meyers RN.
Licensure Skilled care; Intermediate care. *Beds* SNF 36; ICF 102. *Certified* Medicaid; Medicare.
Owner Nonprofit Corp.
Admissions Requirements Minimum age 14; Medical examination.
Staff RNs 3 (ft), 2 (pt); LPNs 8 (ft), 1 (pt); Orderlies; Nurses aides 19 (ft), 14 (pt); Physical therapists 1 (pt); Reality therapists; Recreational therapists; Occupational therapists; Activities coordinators 1 (ft); Dietitians 1 (pt); Ophthalmologists 1 (pt).
Facilities Dining room; Physical therapy room; Activities room; Crafts room; Laundry room; Barber/Beauty shop.
Activities Arts & crafts; Cards; Games; Reading groups; Prayer groups; Movies; Social/Cultural gatherings.

LEXINGTON PARK

Amber House
Great Mills Rd, PO Box 620, Lexington Park, MD, 20653
(301) 863-7244
Admin Sharon Kidwell. *Medical Dir/Dir of Nursing* Dr James Boyd.
Licensure Skilled care; Intermediate care. *Beds* 123. *Certified* Medicaid; Medicare.
Owner Proprietary Corp (TJ Rock).
Admissions Requirements Minimum age 14; Physician's request.
Staff Physicians 1 (pt); RNs 5 (ft); LPNs 12 (ft), 6 (pt); Orderlies 3 (ft); Nurses aides 45 (ft), 13 (pt); Physical therapists 1 (pt); Speech therapists 1 (pt); Activities coordinators 1 (ft), 2 (pt); Dietitians 1 (ft); Dentists 1 (pt); Ophthalmologists 1 (pt); Podiatrists 1 (pt).
Facilities Dining room; Physical therapy room; Activities room; Crafts room; Laundry room; Barber/Beauty shop; Library.
Activities Arts & crafts; Cards; Games; Reading groups; Prayer groups; Movies; Shopping trips; Social/Cultural gatherings.

Bayside Nursing Center
PO Box 620, Great Mills Rd, Lexington Park, MD, 20653
(301) 863-7244
Admin William Delaney.
Beds 123.
Owner Proprietary Corp (Genesis Health Ventures).

LONACONING

Egle Nursing Home*
57 Jackson St, Lonaconing, MD, 21539
(301) 463-5451

Admin Vera Clark Egle. *Medical Dir/Dir of Nursing* Donald Manger MD.
Licensure Intermediate care. *Beds* 24. *Certified* Medicaid.
Owner Proprietary Corp.
Admissions Requirements Minimum age 16.
Staff Physicians; RNs; LPNs; Nurses aides; Physical therapists; Reality therapists; Recreational therapists; Occupational therapists; Speech therapists; Activities coordinators; Dietitians; Dentists; Ophthalmologists; Podiatrists.
Facilities Dining room; Activities room; Crafts room; Laundry room.
Activities Arts & crafts; Cards; Games; Reading groups; Prayer groups; Movies; Shopping trips; Social/Cultural gatherings.

MANCHESTER

Long View Nursing Home
128 N Main St, Manchester, MD, 21102
(301) 374-6271
Admin Martha J Tarutis. *Medical Dir/Dir of Nursing* Wilbur Foard MD.
Licensure Skilled care; Intermediate care. *Beds* 58. *Certified* Medicaid; Medicare.
Owner Proprietary Corp.

MAUGANSVILLE

Mennonite Old People's Home
Maugansville Rd, Maugansville, MD, 21767
(301) 733-5899
Admin Allen Martin. *Medical Dir/Dir of Nursing* Ada Burkholder LPN.
Licensure Domiciliary care. *Beds* 17.
Owner Nonprofit organization/foundation.
Staff Physicians 1 (pt); LPNs 1 (ft); Nurses aides 11 (pt); 4 (pt).
Affiliation Mennonite
Facilities Dining room; Laundry room.
Activities Arts & crafts.

MILLERSVILLE

Knollwood Manor
899 Cecil Ave, Millersville, MD, 21108
(301) 923-2020
Admin Kathy Gelzhiser. *Medical Dir/Dir of Nursing* Howard Martin.
Licensure Skilled care; Intermediate care. *Beds* 97. *Certified* Medicaid; Medicare.
Owner Proprietary Corp.
Admissions Requirements Minimum age 14; Medical examination; Physician's request.
Staff Physicians 1 (ft); RNs 4 (ft); LPNs 6 (ft); CNA 32 (ft); CMA 3 (ft).
Facilities Dining room; Activities room; Barber/Beauty shop.
Activities Arts & crafts; Cards; Games; Reading groups; Prayer groups; Movies; Shopping trips; Social/Cultural gatherings; Activities Program.

MITCHELLVILLE

Villa Rosa Nursing Home
3800 Lottsford Vista Rd, Mitchellville, MD, 20716
(301) 459-4700
Admin Rev Anthony Dal Balcon. *Medical Dir/Dir of Nursing* Ciro Montanez MD; Marion Bendt RN.
Licensure Skilled care; Intermediate care. *Beds* 101.
Owner Nonprofit organization/foundation.
Admissions Requirements Minimum age 14; Medical examination; Physician's request.
Staff RNs 3 (ft), 1 (pt); LPNs 6 (ft), 1 (pt); Nurses aides 39 (ft), 3 (pt); Occupational therapists 1 (ft), 3 (pt); Dietitians 1 (pt).
Languages Italian, Portuguese, Spanish, German, French

Affiliation Roman Catholic
Activities Arts & crafts; Cards; Games; Reading groups; Prayer groups; Movies; Shopping trips; Social/Cultural gatherings.

MOUNT AIRY

Pleasant View Nursing Home
4101 Baltimore National Pike, Mount Airy, MD, 21771
(301) 829-0800, 442-1621, 831-5850
Admin Karen A Nichols. *Medical Dir/Dir of Nursing* Melvin Kordon MD; Patricia Keaton DON.
Licensure Intermediate care. *Beds* ICF. *Certified* Medicaid.
Admissions Requirements Physician's request.
Staff Physicians; RNs 3 (ft), 1 (pt); LPNs 7 (ft), 7 (pt); Orderlies 1 (ft), 1 (pt); Nurses aides 24 (ft), 24 (pt); Recreational therapists; Occupational therapists; Activities coordinators 1 (ft); Dietitians 1 (ft); Dentists; Ophthalmologists 1 (pt).
Facilities Dining room; Activities room; Crafts room; Laundry room; Barber/Beauty shop Hair care room; Library Mobile.
Activities Arts & crafts; Cards; Games; Reading groups; Prayer groups; Movies; Social/Cultural gatherings.

OAKLAND

Cuppett & Weeks Nursing Home Inc
706 E Alder St, Oakland, MD, 21550
(301) 334-2333
Admin James E Cuppett. *Medical Dir/Dir of Nursing* W Nauman MD; C Simpson DON.
Licensure Intermediate care. *Beds* ICF 155. *Certified* Medicaid.
Owner Proprietary Corp.
Admissions Requirements Minimum age 14; Medical examination.
Staff Physicians 10 (pt); RNs 5 (ft), 1 (pt); LPNs 7 (ft), 3 (pt); Nurses aides 53 (ft), 8 (pt); Physical therapists 1 (pt); Occupational therapists 1 (pt); Activities coordinators 1 (ft); Dietitians 1 (pt); Dentists 1 (pt).
Facilities Dining room; Physical therapy room; Barber/Beauty shop.
Activities Arts & crafts; Cards; Games; Reading groups; Prayer groups; Movies; Shopping trips; Social/Cultural gatherings.

Dennett Road Manor Inc*
1113 Mary Dr, Mountain Lake Park, Oakland, MD, 21550
(301) 334-8346
Admin Thomas U Cuppett. *Medical Dir/Dir of Nursing* James H Feaster Jr MD.
Licensure Intermediate care. *Beds* 100. *Certified* Medicaid.
Owner Proprietary Corp.
Admissions Requirements Minimum age 60; Medical examination; Physician's request.
Staff Physicians 10 (pt); RNs 5 (ft), 1 (pt); LPNs 5 (ft), 2 (pt); Nurses aides 23 (ft), 27 (pt); Activities coordinators 2 (ft); Dietitians 1 (ft), 1 (pt); Dentists 1 (pt); Podiatrists 1 (pt).
Facilities Dining room; Activities room; Crafts room; Laundry room; Barber/Beauty shop; Library.
Activities Arts & crafts; Games; Reading groups; Prayer groups; Movies.

OLNEY

Brooke Grove Nursing Home
18430 Brooke Grove Rd, Olney, MD, 20832
(301) 924-4475
Admin Florence Hallman. *Medical Dir/Dir of Nursing* Ted E Howe MD; Marge Jennings RN.
Licensure Intermediate care. *Beds* 99. *Certified* Medicaid.
Owner Nonprofit Corp.

Staff Physicians 1 (ft), 1 (pt); RNs 6 (ft), 3 (pt); LPNs 2 (ft), 1 (pt); Nurses aides 27 (ft), 16 (pt); Recreational therapists 2 (ft); Activities coordinators 1 (ft); Dietitians 1 (pt).
Facilities Dining room; Physical therapy room; Activities room; Laundry room; Barber/Beauty shop.
Activities Games; Prayer groups; Shopping trips; Restaurants.

Sharon Nursing Home*
18201 Marden Ln, Olney, MD, 20832
(301) 924-4475
Admin Judith Sines. *Medical Dir/Dir of Nursing* Charles Ligon MD.
Licensure Intermediate care. *Beds* 45. *Certified* Medicaid.
Owner Nonprofit Corp.

OWINGS MILLS

The Baptist Home of Maryland Del Inc
10729 Park Heights Ave, Owings Mills, MD, 21117-3098
(301) 484-3324
Admin Vlasta A Stadler. *Medical Dir/Dir of Nursing* Dr John G Lavin; Carol F Woodland DON.
Licensure Intermediate care; Domiciliary care. *Beds* ICF 17; Domiciliary care 47.
Owner Nonprofit Corp.
Admissions Requirements Minimum age 65; Medical examination.
Staff Physicians; RNs; LPNs; Nurses aides; Physical therapists; Recreational therapists; Occupational therapists; Activities coordinators; Dietitians; Ophthalmologists.
Affiliation Baptist
Facilities Dining room; Activities room; Chapel; Crafts room; Laundry room; Barber/Beauty shop.
Activities Arts & crafts; Prayer groups; Movies; Shopping trips; Music; Physical education.

Rosewood Center
Rosewood Ln, Owings Mills, MD, 21117
(301) 363-0300
Admin Harry G Beck Jr. *Medical Dir/Dir of Nursing* Melanie A Vaughy Health Services Admin; Mary Jane Pieterson DON.
Licensure Intermediate care for mentally retarded. *Beds* ICF/MR 600. *Certified* Medicaid.
Owner Publicly owned.
Admissions Requirements Medical examination.
Staff Physicians 9 (ft), 4 (pt); RNs 33 (ft); LPNs 58 (ft); Nurses aides 660 (ft), 56 (pt); Physical therapists 4 (ft); Recreational therapists 50 (ft); Occupational therapists 9 (ft), 4 (pt); Speech therapists; Activities coordinators 2 (ft); Dietitians 7 (ft), 2 (pt); Ophthalmologists 2 (ft); Podiatrists 12 (ft), 1 (pt).
Facilities Dining room; Physical therapy room; Activities room; Chapel; Crafts room; Laundry room; Barber/Beauty shop; Library.
Activities Arts & crafts; Cards; Games; Reading groups; Prayer groups; Movies; Shopping trips; Social/Cultural gatherings.

PIKESVILLE

Augsburg Lutheran Home of Maryland Inc
6811 Campfield Rd, Pikesville, MD, 21207
(301) 486-4573
Admin Norman O Payne. *Medical Dir/Dir of Nursing* Arthur M Lebson MD.
Licensure Intermediate care. *Beds* 78. *Certified* Medicaid.
Owner Nonprofit Corp.
Admissions Requirements Minimum age 65; Medical examination.

Staff Physicians 1 (ft); RNs 2 (ft), 5 (pt); LPNs 6 (ft), 5 (pt); Nurses aides 22 (ft), 15 (pt); Physical therapists 1 (ft); Reality therapists 1 (ft); Recreational therapists 1 (ft); Speech therapists 1 (ft); Activities coordinators 1 (ft); Dietitians 1 (ft); Dentists 2 (ft); Ophthalmologists 1 (ft); Podiatrists 1 (ft).
Affiliation Lutheran
Facilities Dining room; Activities room; Chapel; Crafts room; Laundry room; Barber/Beauty shop; Library.
Activities Arts & crafts; Cards; Games; Reading groups; Prayer groups; Movies; Shopping trips; Social/Cultural gatherings.

Pikesville Nursing & Convalescent Center*
7 Sudbrook Ln, Pikesville, MD, 21208
(301) 486-8771
Admin Fred DiBartolo. *Medical Dir/Dir of Nursing* Dr Harold Bob.
Licensure Skilled care; Intermediate care. *Beds* 174. *Certified* Medicaid; Medicare.
Owner Proprietary Corp.
Admissions Requirements Minimum age 14; Medical examination.
Staff RNs 6 (ft); LPNs 12 (ft), 5 (pt); Orderlies 5 (ft); Nurses aides 60 (ft), 23 (pt); Physical therapists 1 (pt); Recreational therapists 1 (ft); Activities coordinators 1 (ft).
Affiliation Jewish
Facilities Dining room; Physical therapy room; Activities room; Chapel; Barber/Beauty shop; Library; Four separate TV lounges (one on each unit).
Activities Arts & crafts; Prayer groups; Movies; Numerous volunteer groups provide entertainment.

POCOMOKE

Hartley Hall Nursing Home
1006 Market St, Pocomoke, MD, 21851
(301) 957-2252
Admin George W Anderson. *Medical Dir/Dir of Nursing* Dr Mary Fleury; Rebecca Sutton DON.
Licensure Skilled care. *Beds* SNF 50. *Certified* Medicaid; Medicare.
Owner Nonprofit Corp.
Admissions Requirements Minimum age 16.
Staff Physicians 3 (pt); RNs 1 (ft), 3 (pt); LPNs 2 (ft), 6 (pt); Orderlies 1 (ft); Nurses aides 20 (ft), 7 (pt); Physical therapists 1 (pt); Speech therapists 1 (pt); Activities coordinators 1 (pt); Dietitians 1 (pt); Ophthalmologists 1 (pt); Dentist 1 (pt).
Facilities Dining room; Physical therapy room; Activities room; Chapel; Laundry room; Barber/Beauty shop.
Activities Arts & crafts; Cards; Games; Reading groups; Prayer groups; Movies; Shopping trips; Social/Cultural gatherings.

PRINCE FREDERICK

Calvert County Nursing Center Inc
85 Hospital Rd, Prince Frederick, MD, 20678-9u69
(301) 535-2300 or 855-1325
Admin John A Olmstead. *Medical Dir/Dir of Nursing* Thomas Lusby MD; Priscilla Baker RN DON.
Licensure Intermediate care. *Beds* ICF 100. *Certified* Medicaid.
Owner Nonprofit Corp.
Admissions Requirements Medical examination; Physician's request.
Staff RNs 5 (ft), 5 (pt); LPNs 6 (ft), 5 (pt); Nurses aides 26 (ft), 31 (pt); Dietitians 1 (pt).
Facilities Dining room; Activities room; Chapel; Barber/Beauty shop.
Activities Arts & crafts; Cards; Games; Reading groups; Prayer groups; Movies; Social/Cultural gatherings.

Calvert House Corp*
Rte 1, Box 1, Prince Frederick, MD, 20678
(301) 535-0984
Admin Helen P Marsellas. *Medical Dir/Dir of Nursing* George J Weems MD.
Licensure Intermediate care. *Beds* 50. *Certified* Medicaid.
Owner Proprietary Corp.
Admissions Requirements Minimum age 14; Medical examination; Physician's request.
Staff Physicians 3 (pt); RNs 3 (pt); LPNs 2 (ft); Nurses aides 22 (ft), 2 (pt); Physical therapists 1 (pt); Activities coordinators 1 (ft); Dietitians 1 (pt); Dentists 1 (pt); Podiatrists 1 (pt).
Facilities Dining room; Physical therapy room; Laundry room.
Activities Arts & crafts; Cards; Games; Prayer groups; Movies.

RANDALLSTOWN

Chapel Hill Convalescent Home
4511 Robosson Rd, Randallstown, MD, 21133
(301) 922-2443
Admin Frances Gosnay. *Medical Dir/Dir of Nursing* Dr Renzo Ricci; Barbara Harris DON.
Licensure Intermediate care. *Beds* 71. *Certified* Medicaid.
Owner Proprietary Corp.
Admissions Requirements Medical examination; Physician's request.
Staff Physicians 9 (pt); RNs 1 (ft), 1 (pt); LPNs 5 (ft), 1 (pt); Orderlies 3 (ft), 1 (pt); Nurses aides 25 (ft), 4 (pt); Physical therapists 1 (pt); Speech therapists 1 (pt); Activities coordinators 1 (ft); Dietitians 1 (ft); Dentists 1 (pt); Ophthalmologists 2 (pt); Podiatrists 1 (pt); Social worker 1 (ft), 1 (pt) Dentist 1 (pt) Pharmacist 1 (pt).
Facilities Dining room; Physical therapy room; Activities room; Crafts room; Laundry room; Barber/Beauty shop; Library.
Activities Arts & crafts; Cards; Games; Reading groups; Prayer groups; Movies; Social/Cultural gatherings; Bus trips; Special luncheons; Open house; Pool parties.

Meridian Nursing Center—Randallstown
9109 Liberty Rd, Randallstown, MD, 21133
(301) 655-7373
Admin Richard Hanauer. *Medical Dir/Dir of Nursing* H Gerald Oster MD; Margaret A Leonard RN.
Licensure Skilled care; Intermediate care; Domiciliary. *Beds* SNF 56; ICF 246; 4. *Certified* Medicaid; Medicare.
Owner Proprietary Corp (Meridan Healthcare).
Admissions Requirements Medical examination.
Staff Physicians 46 (pt); RNs 8 (ft), 4 (pt); LPNs 14 (ft), 13 (pt); Nurses aides 67 (ft), 42 (pt); Physical therapists 1 (ft); Occupational therapists 1 (pt); Speech therapists 1 (pt); Activities coordinators 3 (ft), 2 (pt); Dietitians 2 (ft); Dentists 1 (pt); Ophthalmologists 1 (pt); Podiatrists 1 (pt).
Facilities Dining room; Physical therapy room; Activities room; Crafts room; Barber/Beauty shop; Library.
Activities Arts & crafts; Cards; Games; Reading groups; Prayer groups; Movies; Shopping trips; Social/Cultural gatherings; Overnight outings; Special functions.

Old Court Nursing Center*
5412 Old Court Rd, Randallstown, MD, 21133
(301) 922-3200
Admin Albert H Radtke. *Medical Dir/Dir of Nursing* Michael Pearlman MD.
Licensure Skilled care; Intermediate care. *Beds* 144. *Certified* Medicaid; Medicare.
Owner Proprietary Corp.

REISTERSTOWN

Bent Nursing Home Inc*
12020 Reisterstown Rd, Reisterstown, MD, 21136
(301) 833-3141
Admin Dennis R Melchor. *Medical Dir/Dir of Nursing* Dr C E McWilliams.
Licensure Intermediate care. *Beds* 51. *Certified* Medicaid.
Owner Proprietary Corp.
Admissions Requirements Minimum age 21; Medical examination; Physician's request.
Staff Physicians 1 (ft), 1 (pt); RNs 4 (ft), 2 (pt); LPNs 6 (ft), 3 (pt); Nurses aides 21 (ft), 8 (pt); Physical therapists 1 (pt); Recreational therapists 1 (ft); Occupational therapists 1 (pt); Speech therapists 1 (pt); Dietitians 1 (pt); Dentists 1 (pt); Ophthalmologists 1 (pt); Podiatrists 1 (pt); Audiologists 1 (pt).

Breightonwood
PO Box 375, Reisterstown, MD, 21236-0375
(301) 747-0689
Admin Kathy Gelzhiser. *Medical Dir/Dir of Nursing* David Moseman.
Licensure Intermediate care. *Beds* 34. *Certified* Medicaid.
Owner Proprietary Corp.
Admissions Requirements Minimum age 14; Medical examination; Physician's request.
Staff Physicians 1 (pt); RNs 1 (ft), 1 (pt); LPNs 3 (ft), 3 (pt); Orderlies 1 (pt); Nurses aides 8 (ft); Activities coordinators 1 (ft); Dietitians 1 (pt).
Facilities Dining room; Activities room.
Activities Arts & crafts; Games; Reading groups; Prayer groups.

RISING SUN

Calvert Manor Nursing Home Inc
1881 Telegraph Rd, Rising Sun, MD, 21911
(301) 658-6555
Admin Ruth N Graybeal. *Medical Dir/Dir of Nursing* Neil Taylor Jr MD; Carol Darby.
Licensure Skilled care; Domiciliary. *Beds* ICF 118; Domiciliary 36. *Certified* Medicaid.
Owner Proprietary Corp.
Staff Physicians; RNs; LPNs; Nurses aides; Physical therapists; Occupational therapists; Speech therapists; Activities coordinators; Dietitians; Ophthalmologists.
Facilities Dining room; Physical therapy room; Activities room; Chapel; Crafts room; Laundry room; Barber/Beauty shop; Library.
Activities Arts & crafts; Cards; Games; Movies.

ROCKVILLE

Collingswood Nursing Center
299 Hurley Ave, Rockville, MD, 20850
(301) 762-8900
Admin Carol A Baker. *Medical Dir/Dir of Nursing* Walter Goozh MD.
Licensure Skilled care; Intermediate care. *Beds* 157. *Certified* Medicaid; Medicare.
Owner Proprietary Corp (TJ Rock).
Staff RNs 8 (ft), 6 (pt); LPNs 4 (ft), 2 (pt); Orderlies 7 (ft), 1 (pt); Nurses aides 38 (ft), 11 (pt); Physical therapists 1 (pt); Activities coordinators 1 (ft); Dietitians 1 (pt).
Facilities Dining room; Physical therapy room; Activities room; Laundry room; Barber/Beauty shop.
Activities Arts & crafts; Cards; Games; Reading groups; Prayer groups; Movies; Social/Cultural gatherings.

Hebrew Home of Greater Washington
6121 Montrose Rd, Rockville, MD, 20852
(301) 881-0300
Admin Michael Weinfield. *Medical Dir/Dir of Nursing* Steven Lipson MD; Judith Braun RN DON.
Licensure Skilled care; Intermediate care. *Beds* 550. *Certified* Medicaid; Medicare.
Owner Nonprofit organization/foundation.
Admissions Requirements Minimum age 65 (long term); 40 (short stay); Medical examination.
Staff Physicians 5 (ft); RNs 11 (ft), 9 (pt); LPNs 21 (ft), 5 (pt); Nurses aides 160 (ft), 30 (pt); Physical therapists 3 (ft), 1 (pt); Recreational therapists 4 (ft), 6 (pt); Occupational therapists 2 (ft); Speech therapists 1 (ft); Activities coordinators 1 (ft), 1 (pt); Dietitians 2 (ft); Dentists 1 (pt); Ophthalmologists 10 (pt); Podiatrists 1 (pt); Dentist 1 (pt); Physiatrist 1 (pt).
Languages Yiddish, Hebrew, Russian, German, Hungarian, Polish
Affiliation Jewish
Facilities Dining room; Physical therapy room; Activities room; Chapel; Crafts room; Laundry room; Barber/Beauty shop; Library; Soda shop; Occupatinal therapy room; Social hall.
Activities Arts & crafts; Cards; Games; Reading groups; Prayer groups; Movies; Shopping trips; Social/Cultural gatherings; Outside lunches; Day camp.

National Lutheran Home for the Aged
9701 Viers Dr, Rockville, MD, 20850
(301) 424-9560
Admin Richard Reichard. *Medical Dir/Dir of Nursing* Harold McCann MD.
Licensure Skilled care; Intermediate care; Independent living program. *Beds* 300; Independent living 51. *Certified* Medicaid; Medicare.
Owner Nonprofit Corp.
Affiliation Lutheran

Potomac Valley Nursing Center
1235 Potomac Valley Rd, Rockville, MD, 20850
(301) 762-0700
Admin Roxanne L Stigers RN LNHA. *Medical Dir/Dir of Nursing* Walter Goozh MD and Pat Kellog MD; Penny Brasher RN DON.
Licensure Skilled care; Intermediate care. *Beds* 171. *Certified* Medicaid; Medicare.
Owner Proprietary Corp (TJ Rock).
Admissions Requirements Minimum age 18.
Staff RNs 8 (ft), 20 (pt); LPNs 2 (ft), 4 (pt); Orderlies; Nurses aides 56 (ft), 18 (pt); Physical therapists 2 (pt); Occupational therapists; Speech therapists; Activities coordinators 2 (ft), 2 (pt); Dietitians; Ophthalmologists; Podiatrists; 1 (pt) Chaplain; Supportive staff; Laundry; Dietary.
Facilities Physical therapy room; Activities room; Chapel; Crafts room; Laundry room; Barber/Beauty shop; Library.
Activities Arts & crafts; Cards; Games; Reading groups; Prayer groups; Movies; Shopping trips; Social/Cultural gatherings.

Rockville Nursing Home Inc*
303 Adclare Rd, Rockville, MD, 20850
(301) 279-9000
Admin Ray Cromwell. *Medical Dir/Dir of Nursing* Frauke Westphal MD.
Licensure Skilled care; Intermediate care. *Beds* 100. *Certified* Medicaid; Medicare.
Owner Nonprofit Corp.

SABILLASVILLE

Victor Cullen Center
6000 Cullen Dr, Sabillasville, MD, 21780
(301) 241-3131
Admin Steven M Haigh. *Medical Dir/Dir of Nursing* Robert Brull MD.
Licensure Intermediate care for mentally retarded. *Beds* ICF/MR 90. *Certified* Medicaid; Medicare.
Owner Publicly owned.
Admissions Requirements Minimum age 18.

Staff RNs; LPNs; Recreational therapists; Occupational therapists; Speech therapists; Dietitians.
Facilities Dining room; Activities room; Chapel; Crafts room; Library.
Activities Arts & crafts; Movies; Shopping trips; Social/Cultural gatherings.

SALISBURY

Deers Head Center Comprehensive Care Facility
PO Box 2018, Emerson Ave, Salisbury, MD, 21801
(301) 742-2164
Medical Dir/Dir of Nursing Maheswari Shrestha MD; Theresa Myer RN.
Licensure Skilled care; Intermediate care. *Beds* 14. *Certified* Medicaid; Medicare.
Owner Publicly owned.
Admissions Requirements Physician's request.
Staff Physicians 1 (ft); RNs 3 (ft); LPNs 3 (ft); Orderlies 4 (ft); Nurses aides 2 (ft); Physical therapists 1 (ft); Recreational therapists 1 (ft); Occupational therapists 1 (ft); Speech therapists 1 (ft); Activities coordinators 1 (ft); Dietitians 1 (ft); Dentists 1 (pt); Ophthalmologists 1 (pt); Dentist 1 (pt).
Facilities Dining room; Physical therapy room; Activities room; Chapel; Crafts room; Laundry room; Barber/Beauty shop; Library.
Activities Arts & crafts; Cards; Games; Reading groups; Prayer groups; Movies; Shopping trips; Social/Cultural gatherings.

Holly Center*
PO Box 2358, Snow Hill Rd, Salisbury, MD, 21801
(301) 546-2181
Admin Frank Gibson. *Medical Dir/Dir of Nursing* Hilda Houlihan MD.
Licensure Intermediate care for mentally retarded. *Beds* 250. *Certified* Medicaid.
Owner Publicly owned.

River Walk Manor
105 Times Square, Salisbury, MD, 21801
(301) 749-2474
Admin Dennis K Chappell. *Medical Dir/Dir of Nursing* Thomas C Hill Jr MD.
Licensure Intermediate care. *Beds* ICF 150. *Certified* Medicaid.
Owner Privately owned.
Admissions Requirements Physician's request.
Staff RNs 4 (ft), 2 (pt); LPNs 13 (ft), 6 (pt); Nurses aides 47 (ft), 5 (pt).
Facilities Dining room; Physical therapy room; Activities room; Crafts room; Laundry room; Barber/Beauty shop; Day room on each floor.
Activities Arts & crafts; Cards; Games; Reading groups; Prayer groups; Movies; Shopping trips; Social/Cultural gatherings.

Salisbury Nursing Home*
US 50 at Civic Ave, Salisbury, MD, 21801
(301) 749-1466
Admin Dennis Nooner. *Medical Dir/Dir of Nursing* Dr Earl Beardsley.
Licensure Intermediate care. *Beds* 310. *Certified* Medicaid; Medicare.
Owner Proprietary Corp.
Admissions Requirements Minimum age 14; Physician's request.
Staff Physicians 2 (pt); RNs 23 (pt); LPNs 12 (pt); Orderlies 20 (pt); Nurses aides 80 (pt); Physical therapists 1 (pt); Activities coordinators 1 (pt); Dietitians 1 (pt).
Facilities Dining room; Physical therapy room; Activities room; Crafts room; Laundry room; Barber/Beauty shop; Library.
Activities Arts & crafts; Cards; Games; Reading groups; Prayer groups; Movies; Shopping trips.

Wicomico Nursing Home
PO Box 2378, Booth St, Salisbury, MD, 21801
(301) 742-8896

Admin Mary E Schwartz. *Medical Dir/Dir of Nursing* Frederico G Arthes MD; Audrey Lang.
Licensure Skilled care; Intermediate care. *Beds* 82. *Certified* Medicaid; Medicare.
Owner Publicly owned.
Admissions Requirements Minimum age 14; Medical examination; Physician's request.
Staff RNs 4 (ft), 3 (pt); LPNs 5 (ft), 3 (pt); Orderlies; Nurses aides 22 (ft), 17 (pt); Physical therapists 1 (pt); Activities coordinators 1 (ft), 1 (pt); Dietitians 1 (pt).
Facilities Dining room; Physical therapy room; Activities room; Laundry room; Barber/Beauty shop.
Activities Arts & crafts; Cards; Games; Reading groups; Prayer groups; Movies; Shopping trips; Social/Cultural gatherings.

SANDY SPRING

Friends Nursing Home Inc
17340 Quaker Ln, Sandy Spring, MD, 20860
(301) 924-4900
Admin Darryl Clemmer. *Medical Dir/Dir of Nursing* Charles Ligon MD.
Licensure Intermediate care. *Beds* 80. *Certified* Medicaid.
Owner Nonprofit Corp.
Staff Physicians 1 (pt); RNs 2 (ft), 12 (pt); LPNs 2 (ft); Nurses aides 35 (ft), 10 (pt); Physical therapists 1 (pt); Recreational therapists 1 (ft), 2 (pt); Speech therapists 1 (pt); Dietitians 1 (pt); Podiatrists 1 (pt).
Affiliation Society of Friends
Facilities Dining room; Physical therapy room; Activities room; Crafts room; Laundry room; Barber/Beauty shop; Library.
Activities Arts & crafts; Cards; Games; Reading groups; Prayer groups; Movies; Shopping trips.

SEVERNA PARK

Meridian Nursing Center—Severna Park*
24 Truck House Rd, Severna Park, MD, 21146
(301) 544-4220
Admin Martha Clingman. *Medical Dir/Dir of Nursing* Thomas Walsh MD.
Beds 141.
Owner Proprietary Corp (Meridan Healthcare).

SILVER SPRING

Althea Woodland Nursing Home
1000 Daleview Dr, Silver Spring, MD, 20901
(301) 434-2646
Admin Ron Carsell. *Medical Dir/Dir of Nursing* B Fitzgerald MD; R Robertson RN DON.
Licensure Skilled care; Intermediate care. *Beds* SNF; ICF.
Owner Proprietary Corp.
Admissions Requirements Minimum age 18; Medical examination.
Staff Physicians 8 (pt); RNs 4 (ft), 2 (pt); LPNs 1 (ft); Nurses aides 25 (ft), 1 (pt); Physical therapists 2 (pt); Recreational therapists 1 (ft); Occupational therapists 1 (pt); Speech therapists 1 (pt); Activities coordinators 1 (ft); Dietitians 1 (ft); Dentists 1 (pt); Ophthalmologists 1 (pt); Podiatrists 1 (pt).
Facilities Dining room; Activities room; Crafts room; Laundry room; Barber/Beauty shop.
Activities Arts & crafts; Cards; Games; Reading groups; Prayer groups; Movies; Shopping trips; Social/Cultural gatherings.

Bel Pre Health Care Center*
2601 Bel Pre Rd, Silver Spring, MD, 20906
(301) 598-6000
Admin Irvin Gershowitz. *Medical Dir/Dir of Nursing* Raymond Benack MD.
Licensure Skilled care; Intermediate care. *Beds* 100. *Certified* Medicaid.
Owner Proprietary Corp.
Admissions Requirements Minimum age 18; Medical examination.
Staff RNs 7 (ft), 6 (pt); LPNs 1 (ft), 2 (pt); Nurses aides 43 (ft); Physical therapists 2 (pt); Recreational therapists 1 (pt); Speech therapists 1 (pt); Activities coordinators 1 (ft); Dietitians 1 (pt); Podiatrists 1 (pt).
Facilities Dining room; Activities room; Crafts room; Laundry room; Barber/Beauty shop.
Activities Arts & crafts; Cards; Games; Reading groups; Prayer groups; Movies; Shopping trips; Social/Cultural gatherings.

Carriage Hill—Silver Spring*
9101 2nd Ave, Silver Spring, MD, 20910
(301) 588-5544
Admin Flora Luckett. *Medical Dir/Dir of Nursing* John Umhau MD.
Licensure Skilled care; Intermediate care. *Beds* 97. *Certified* Medicare.
Owner Proprietary Corp.

Chevy Chase Retirement & Nursing Center
2015 East-West Hwy, Silver Spring, MD, 20910
(301) 587-2400
Admin Basil F Boyce. *Medical Dir/Dir of Nursing* Stephanie D Evers RN.
Licensure Skilled care 10B. *Beds* SNF 19 11B 68. *Certified* Medicare.
Owner Proprietary Corp (Continental Medical Systems).
Admissions Requirements Minimum age 18; Medical examination; Physician's request.
Staff Physicians 18 (pt); RNs 6 (ft), 6 (pt); LPNs 10 (ft), 4 (pt); Nurses aides 14 (ft); Physical therapists 1 (ft), 1 (pt); Recreational therapists 1 (ft); Occupational therapists 1 (ft); Speech therapists 1 (pt); Activities coordinators 1 (ft); Dietitians 1 (pt); Ophthalmologists 1 (pt); Podiatrists 1 (pt).
Languages German, Spanish
Facilities Dining room; Physical therapy room; Activities room; Crafts room; Laundry room; Barber/Beauty shop; Library.
Activities Arts & crafts; Cards; Games; Reading groups; Prayer groups; Movies; Shopping trips; Social/Cultural gatherings.

Colonial Villa Nursing Home
12325 New Hampshire Ave, Silver Spring, MD, 20904
(301) 622-4600
Admin Steven H Haynal. *Medical Dir/Dir of Nursing* Dr Michael Leiboloitz; Marjorie Beheydt RN.
Licensure Skilled care; Intermediate care. *Beds* 92. *Certified* Medicaid; Medicare.
Owner Proprietary Corp (Beverly Enterprises).
Admissions Requirements Minimum age 14; Medical examination.
Staff RNs 15 (ft); LPNs 4 (ft); Orderlies 1 (ft); Nurses aides 25 (ft); Recreational therapists 1 (ft); Activities coordinators 1 (ft); Dietitians 1 (ft); Housekeeping; Dietary; Laundry; General office.

Facilities Dining room; Physical therapy room; Activities room; Crafts room; Laundry room; Barber/Beauty shop; Living room; Independent living area (12 beds).
Activities Arts & crafts; Cards; Games; Reading groups; Prayer groups; Movies; Shopping trips; Social/Cultural gatherings.

Fairland Nursing Home*
2101 Fairland Rd, Silver Spring, MD, 20904
(301) 384-6161
Admin Scotty Lawyer. *Medical Dir/Dir of Nursing* Thomas Ward MD.
Licensure Skilled care; Intermediate care. *Beds* 83. *Certified* Medicaid; Medicare.
Owner Proprietary Corp.

Great Oaks Center
3100 Gracefield Rd, Silver Spring, MD, 20904-1899
(301) 595-5000
Admin Marvin Malcotti PhD. *Medical Dir/Dir of Nursing* Stefano Kenessey MD.
Licensure Intermediate care for mentally retarded. *Beds* 500. *Certified* Medicaid.
Owner Publicly owned.
Staff Physicians 2 (ft), 1 (pt); RNs 33 (ft), 4 (pt); LPNs 8 (ft); Nurses aides 297 (ft); Physical therapists 5 (ft); Recreational therapists 26 (ft); Occupational therapists 5 (ft); Speech therapists 6 (ft); Activities coordinators 2 (ft); Dietitians 4 (ft); Podiatrists 1 (ft).
Facilities Dining room; Activities room; Laundry room.
Activities Arts & crafts; Cards; Games; Movies; Shopping trips; Social/Cultural gatherings.

Sylvan Manor Health Care Center*
2700 Barker St, Silver Spring, MD, 20910
(301) 565-0300
Admin Gary G Waitt. *Medical Dir/Dir of Nursing* Martin Shargel MD.
Licensure Skilled care; Intermediate care. *Beds* 137. *Certified* Medicaid.
Owner Proprietary Corp.

SMITHSBURG

Kemp Horn Home*
Rte 1, Box 39, Smithsburg, MD, 21783
(301) 824-3121
Admin Margot R Payne. *Medical Dir/Dir of Nursing* Ramsey Farah MD.
Licensure Intermediate care for mentally retarded. *Beds* 17. *Certified* Medicaid.
Owner Nonprofit Corp.
Staff Physicians 1 (ft), 1 (pt); RNs 2 (ft); LPNs 2 (ft); Orderlies 6 (ft); Physical therapists 1 (ft); Occupational therapists 1 (ft); Speech therapists 1 (ft); Dietitians 1 (ft).
Facilities Dining room; Activities room.
Activities Arts & crafts; Cards; Games; Reading groups; Movies; Shopping trips; Social/Cultural gatherings.

SNOW HILL

Harrison House
430 W Market St, Snow Hill, MD, 21863
(301) 632-3755
Admin Jeannine C Aydelotte. *Medical Dir/Dir of Nursing* Dorothy C Holzworth MD; Rebecca Wheaton DON.
Licensure Skilled care; Intermediate care. *Beds* SNF 58; ICF 60. *Certified* Medicaid; Medicare.
Owner Proprietary Corp.

Admissions Requirements Minimum age 14; Medical examination; Physician's request.
Staff Physicians 3 (pt); RNs 3 (pt); LPNs 5 (ft), 4 (pt); Nurses aides 24 (ft), 11 (pt); Physical therapists 1 (pt); Speech therapists 1 (pt); Activities coordinators 1 (ft); Dietitians 1 (pt); Ophthalmologists 1 (pt).
Facilities Dining room; Physical therapy room; Activities room; Laundry room; Barber/Beauty shop.
Activities Arts & crafts; Cards; Games; Reading groups; Prayer groups; Movies; Shopping trips.

SYKESVILLE

Fairhaven Nursing Home*
7200 3rd Ave, Sykesville, MD, 21784
(301) 795-8800
Admin James Melhorn. *Medical Dir/Dir of Nursing* Alva Baker MD.
Licensure Skilled care; Intermediate care. *Beds* 99.
Owner Nonprofit Corp.

Golden Age Guest Home Inc
1442 Buckhorn Rd, Sykesville, MD, 21784
795-2737
Admin James C Talbott. *Medical Dir/Dir of Nursing* Patrick Turnes MD; Nancy Greasky RN DON.
Licensure Intermediate care; DOM. *Beds* ICF 20; DOM 5. *Certified* Medicaid.
Owner Proprietary Corp.
Staff Physicians 1 (pt); RNs 1 (ft), 3 (pt); LPNs 2 (ft), 5 (pt); Nurses aides 6 (ft), 3 (pt); Activities coordinators 2 (pt); Dietitians 1 (pt).
Facilities Dining room; Activities room; Laundry room.
Activities Arts & crafts; Cards; Games; Reading groups; Prayer groups; Movies; Shopping trips; Social/Cultural gatherings.

Sykesville Eldercare Center
7309 Second Ave, Sykesville, MD, 21784
(301) 795-1100
Admin Robert L Killett. *Medical Dir/Dir of Nursing* Jose' Chapulle MD; Mary E Killett.
Licensure Skilled care; Intermediate care. *Beds* 135. *Certified* Medicaid; Medicare.
Owner Proprietary Corp.
Admissions Requirements Minimum age 21.
Staff RNs 5 (ft), 4 (pt); LPNs 10 (ft), 4 (pt); Nurses aides 42 (ft), 4 (pt); Activities coordinators 1 (ft).
Facilities Dining room; Physical therapy room; Activities room; Crafts room; Laundry room; Barber/Beauty shop.
Activities Arts & crafts; Cards; Games; Reading groups; Prayer groups; Movies; Shopping trips; Social/Cultural gatherings; Exercise classes.

TAKOMA PARK

Heritage Health Care Center
7525 Carroll Ave, Takoma Park, MD, 20912
(301) 270-4200
Admin Scotty A Lawyer. *Medical Dir/Dir of Nursing* Dr Jeffrey Kelman; Kitty Brown RN.
Licensure Skilled care; Intermediate care. *Beds* SNF 15; ICF 102. *Certified* Medicaid; Medicare.
Owner Proprietary Corp (Beverly Enterprises).
Admissions Requirements Medical examination; Physician's request.
Staff RNs 6 (ft), 9 (pt); LPNs 1 (ft), 6 (pt); Orderlies 3 (pt); Nurses aides 29 (ft), 24 (pt); Physical therapists 1 (ft), 1 (pt); Recreational therapists 1 (ft), 1 (pt); Occupational therapists 1 (pt); Speech therapists 1 (pt); Activities coordinators 1 (ft); Dietitians 1 (pt).

Facilities Dining room; Physical therapy room; Activities room; Crafts room; Laundry room; Barber/Beauty shop; Library.
Activities Arts & crafts; Cards; Games; Reading groups; Prayer groups; Movies; Shopping trips; Social/Cultural gatherings; Intergenerational activities; Pets on wheels.

TOWSON

Cardinal Shehan Center for the Aging
2300 Dulaney Valley Rd, Towson, MD, 21204
(301) 252-4500
Admin Sr Louis Mary Battle. *Medical Dir/Dir of Nursing* Eddie Nakhuda MD; Margaret Wall.
Licensure Skilled care; Intermediate care; Hospice. *Beds* SNF 46; ICF 377; Hospice 13. *Certified* Medicaid; Medicare.
Owner Nonprofit organization/foundation.
Admissions Requirements Minimum age 62; Medical examination; Physician's request.
Staff Physicians; RNs; LPNs; Orderlies; Nurses aides; Physical therapists; Reality therapists; Recreational therapists; Occupational therapists; Speech therapists; Activities coordinators; Dietitians; Ophthalmologists; Podiatrists.
Affiliation Roman Catholic
Facilities Dining room; Physical therapy room; Activities room; Chapel; Crafts room; Laundry room; Barber/Beauty shop; Library; Pharmacy.
Activities Arts & crafts; Cards; Games; Reading groups; Prayer groups; Movies; Shopping trips; Social/Cultural gatherings.

Dulaney Towson Nursing & Convalescent Center*
111 West Rd, Towson, MD, 21204
(301) 828-6500
Admin Phyllis Belmonte. *Medical Dir/Dir of Nursing* Charles O'Donnell MD.
Licensure Skilled care; Intermediate care. *Beds* 151. *Certified* Medicaid; Medicare.
Owner Proprietary Corp.

Edenwald
800 Southerly Rd, Towson, MD, 21204
(301) 339-6000
Admin Patricia S Martin Admin, Housing Division; Carol A Baker Admin, Health Care Division. *Medical Dir/Dir of Nursing* Marcelino Albuerne MD; Josephine Ziek DON.
Licensure Comprehensive care unit; Domiciliary care. *Beds* Comprehensive 57; Domiciliary 58.
Owner Nonprofit Corp.
Admissions Requirements Minimum age 65; Medical examination.
Staff RNs 4 (ft), 3 (pt); LPNs 6 (ft); Nurses aides 20 (ft), 10 (pt); Recreational therapists 1 (ft); Dietitians 1 (ft).
Languages German
Facilities Dining room; Physical therapy room; Activities room; Crafts room; Laundry room; Barber/Beauty shop; Library.
Activities Arts & crafts; Cards; Games; Reading groups; Prayer groups; Movies; Shopping trips; Social/Cultural gatherings.

Holly Hill Manor Inc
531 Stevenson Ln, Towson, MD, 21204
(301) 823-5310
Admin M L Cursey Jr. *Medical Dir/Dir of Nursing* Theresa Walter RN DON.
Licensure Intermediate care. *Beds* 55. *Certified* Medicaid.
Owner Proprietary Corp.

Manor Care—Ruxton*
7001 Charles St, Towson, MD, 21204
(301) 821-9600
Admin Thomas A Keiser. *Medical Dir/Dir of Nursing* Walter T Kees MD.
Licensure Intermediate care. *Beds* 200. *Certified* Medicaid; Medicare.

Owner Proprietary Corp (Manor Care).
Staff Physicians; RNs; LPNs; Orderlies; Nurses aides; Physical therapists 1 (ft); Reality therapists 3 (ft); Recreational therapists 3 (ft); Occupational therapists 2 (ft); Speech therapists 1 (ft); Activities coordinators 3 (ft); Dietitians 2 (ft); Dentists 1 (ft); Podiatrists 1 (ft); Audiologists 1 (ft).
Facilities Dining room; Physical therapy room; Activities room; Crafts room; Laundry room; Barber/Beauty shop; Library.
Activities Arts & crafts; Cards; Games; Reading groups; Prayer groups; Movies; Shopping trips; Social/Cultural gatherings.

Manor Care—Towson*
509 E Joppa Rd, Towson, MD, 21204
(301) 828-9494
Admin Robert Harris. *Medical Dir/Dir of Nursing* Walter T Kees MD.
Licensure Skilled care; Comprehensive care. *Beds* 115. *Certified* Medicaid; Medicare.
Owner Proprietary Corp (Manor Care).
Admissions Requirements Medical examination.
Staff Physicians 1 (pt); RNs 7 (ft), 10 (pt); LPNs 3 (ft), 2 (pt); Nurses aides 28 (ft), 23 (pt); Recreational therapists 1 (ft), 1 (pt); Audiologists 8 (ft), 8 (pt).
Facilities Dining room; Physical therapy room; Activities room; Crafts room; Laundry room; Barber/Beauty shop.
Activities Arts & crafts; Cards; Games; Reading groups; Prayer groups; Movies; Shopping trips; Social/Cultural gatherings.

Meridian Multi-Medical Nursing Center
7700 York Rd, Towson, MD, 21204
(301) 821-5500
Admin John S Allard Jr. *Medical Dir/Dir of Nursing* Carl Friedman; Bonnie Brill.
Licensure Skilled care. *Beds* 120. *Certified* Medicare.
Owner Proprietary Corp (Meridan Healthcare).
Admissions Requirements Minimum age 15.
Staff RNs 7 (ft), 2 (pt); LPNs 9 (ft), 4 (pt); Nurses aides 75 (ft), 20 (pt); Physical therapists 2 (ft); Recreational therapists 3 (ft); Occupational therapists 1 (ft); Speech therapists 1 (pt); Dietitians 1 (ft).
Facilities Dining room; Physical therapy room; Activities room; Laundry room; Barber/Beauty shop.
Activities Arts & crafts; Cards; Games; Movies; Shopping trips; Social/Cultural gatherings.

Pickersgill
615 Chestnut Ave, Towson, MD, 21204
(301) 825-7423
Admin Brantley Hart Jr. *Medical Dir/Dir of Nursing* Dr Keith Manley; Val Litsch RN.
Licensure Intermediate care; Domiciliary. *Beds* 169. *Certified* Medicaid.
Owner Nonprofit Corp.
Admissions Requirements Minimum age 65; Medical examination.
Staff Physicians 1 (pt); RNs 7 (ft), 4 (pt); LPNs 6 (ft), 3 (pt); Nurses aides 32 (ft), 10 (pt); Physical therapists 1 (pt); Recreational therapists 1 (ft), 1 (pt); Speech therapists 1 (pt); Activities coordinators 1 (ft); Dietitians 1 (pt); Dentists 1 (pt); Ophthalmologists 2 (pt); Podiatrists 1 (pt).
Facilities Dining room; Physical therapy room; Activities room; Crafts room; Laundry room; Barber/Beauty shop; Library.
Activities Arts & crafts; Cards; Games; Reading groups; Prayer groups; Movies; Shopping trips; Social/Cultural gatherings.

Presbyterian Home of Maryland Inc*
400 Georgia Ct, Towson, MD, 21204
(301) 823-4622
Admin Rosa Lee Robertson.
Licensure Intermediate care; Domiciliary care. *Beds* ICF 22; Domiciliary 80.

Owner Nonprofit Corp.
Affiliation Presbyterian

Towson Convalescent Home Inc*
301 W Chesapeake Ave, Towson, MD, 21204
(301) 296-3191
Admin Lee S Rose.
Licensure Intermediate care. *Beds* 34.
Owner Proprietary Corp.
Staff RNs 2 (ft), 1 (pt); LPNs 4 (pt); Nurses
aides 24 (ft), 3 (pt); Activities coordinators 1
(pt); Dietitians 1 (pt).
Facilities Dining room; Activities room.
Activities Arts & crafts; Games; Prayer groups;
Movies.

WESTMINSTER

Fairhaven Nursing Home*
200 St Luke's Circle, Westminster, MD, 21157
(601) 795-8800
Admin Lyle E Peters. *Medical Dir/Dir of
Nursing* John Lehigh MD.
Beds 99.
Owner Nonprofit Corp.

**Westminster Villa Nursing & Convalescent
Center***
1234 Washington Rd, Westminster, MD,
21157
(301) 848-0700
Admin Lorrie Custodio. *Medical Dir/Dir of
Nursing* Daniel Welliver MD.
Licensure Skilled care; Intermediate care. *Beds*
170. *Certified* Medicaid; Medicare.
Owner Proprietary Corp (Beverly Enterprises).

WHEATON

Manor Care—Wheaton
11901 Georgia Ave, Wheaton, MD, 20902
(301) 942-2500
Admin Cherilyn Poulsen. *Medical Dir/Dir of
Nursing* Walter Goozh MD; Elaine
Fairweather RN DON.

Licensure Skilled care. *Beds* SNF 102.
Certified Medicare.
Owner Proprietary Corp (Manor Care).
Admissions Requirements Minimum age 16;
Medical examination.
Facilities Dining room; Physical therapy
room; Activities room; Laundry room;
Barber/Beauty shop; Library; Living room;
Lobby.
Activities Arts & crafts; Cards; Games;
Reading groups; Prayer groups; Movies;
Shopping trips; Social/Cultural gatherings;
Resident council; Monthly newsletter.

Randolph Hills Nursing Home
4011 Randolph Rd, Wheaton, MD, 20902
(301) 933-2500
Admin Harvey R Wertlieb. *Medical Dir/Dir of
Nursing* Dr Barry Rosenbahm.
Licensure Skilled care; Intermediate care. *Beds*
95. *Certified* Medicaid; Medicare.
Owner Proprietary Corp.
Admissions Requirements Minimum age 14;
Medical examination; Physician's request.
Staff RNs 13 (ft); LPNs 2 (ft); Nurses aides 33
(ft); Physical therapists 1 (ft); Recreational
therapists 1 (ft); Occupational therapists 1
(pt); Speech therapists 1 (pt); Activities
coordinators 2 (ft); Dietitians 1 (pt); Dentists
1 (pt); Ophthalmologists 1 (pt); Podiatrists 1
(pt).
Facilities Dining room; Physical therapy
room; Activities room; Crafts room; Laundry
room; Barber/Beauty shop; Library.
Activities Arts & crafts; Cards; Games;
Reading groups; Prayer groups; Movies;
Shopping trips; Social/Cultural gatherings.

University Convalescent & Nursing Home Inc*
901 Arcola Ave, Wheaton, MD, 20902
(301) 649-2400
Admin Marjorie Lambdin. *Medical Dir/Dir of
Nursing* Myron L Lenkin MD.
Licensure Skilled care; Intermediate care. *Beds*
150. *Certified* Medicaid; Medicare.

Owner Proprietary Corp.
Admissions Requirements Minimum age 16;
Medical examination.
Staff RNs 25 (ft), 8 (pt); LPNs 10 (ft), 2 (pt);
Nurses aides 65 (ft), 5 (pt); Physical
therapists 1 (ft).
Facilities Dining room; Physical therapy
room; Activities room; Crafts room; Barber/
Beauty shop.
Activities Arts & crafts; Cards; Games;
Reading groups; Prayer groups; Movies;
Social/Cultural gatherings; Resident Council.

WILLIAMSPORT

Homewood Retirement Center—Williamsport
2750 Virginia Ave, Williamsport, MD, 21795
(301) 582-1628
Admin Timothy Johnson.
Licensure Intermediate care; Domiciliary.
Beds ICF 100; Domiciliary care 45. *Certified*
Medicaid.
Owner Nonprofit Corp (Homewood Retire
Centers/UCC).

Williamsport Nursing Home
154 N Artizan St, Williamsport, MD, 21795
(301) 223-7971
Admin David Benton. *Medical Dir/Dir of
Nursing* Ted Howe MD.
Licensure Intermediate care. *Beds* 97.
Certified Medicaid.
Owner Nonprofit Corp.
Staff Physicians 2 (pt); RNs 6 (ft), 3 (pt);
LPNs 6 (ft), 3 (pt); Nurses aides 60 (ft), 8
(pt); Physical therapists 1 (pt); Speech
therapists 1 (pt); Activities coordinators 2
(ft); Dietitians 1 (pt); Podiatrists 1 (pt).
Facilities Dining room; Activities room;
Crafts room; Laundry room; Barber/Beauty
shop.
Activities Arts & crafts; Cards; Games;
Movies; Wheelchair accessible van.

MASSACHUSETTS

ABINGTON

Mildred Alford Nursing Home*
81 Birch St, Abington, MA, 02351
(617) 878-4660
Admin Gilbert Rocha.
Licensure Skilled care; Intermediate care. *Beds*
99. *Certified* Medicaid.

Colony House Healthcare Nursing Home
277 Washington St, Abington, MA, 02351
(617) 871-0200
Admin Russell H Dumas. *Medical Dir/Dir of
Nursing* Edward Welch MD; Claire Kelly
RN DON.
Licensure Skilled care; Intermediate care. *Beds*
SNF 36; ICF 66. *Certified* Medicaid.
Owner Proprietary Corp (Hillhaven Corp).
Admissions Requirements Medical
examination.
Staff RNs 2 (ft), 15 (pt); LPNs 1 (ft), 8 (pt);
Orderlies 1 (pt); Nurses aides 7 (ft), 40 (pt);
Physical therapists 1 (pt); Occupational
therapists 1 (pt); Speech therapists 1 (pt);
Activities coordinators 1 (ft); Dietitians 1
(pt); Ophthalmologists 1 (pt).
Facilities Dining room; Activities room;
Crafts room; Laundry room; Barber/Beauty
shop.
Activities Arts & crafts; Cards; Games;
Reading groups; Prayer groups; Movies;
Shopping trips; Social/Cultural gatherings;
Reality orientation program; Creative
reflections grooming groups; Restorative
feeding program.

ACTON

**Suburban Manor Convalescent & Nursing
Home***
1 Great Rd, Acton, MA, 01720
(617) 263-9101
Admin Vincent M Polo.
Licensure Skilled care; Intermediate care. *Beds*
122. *Certified* Medicaid; Medicare.

Surburan Manor Nursing Home
1 Great Rd, Acton, MA, 01720
(617) 263-9101
Admin James D Campbell. *Medical Dir/Dir of
Nursing* Edwin Knights MD; Sharon Staley
DON.
Licensure Skilled care; Intermediate care. *Beds*
SNF 82; ICF 40. *Certified* Medicaid;
Medicare.
Owner Privately owned.
Admissions Requirements Minimum age 18;
Females only.
Staff Physicians 1 (pt); RNs 6 (ft), 7 (pt);
LPNs 2 (ft), 3 (pt); Orderlies 3 (pt); Nurses
aides 22 (ft), 16 (pt); Physical therapists 1
(ft), 1 (pt); Recreational therapists 1 (pt);
Occupational therapists 1 (pt); Speech
therapists 1 (pt); Activities coordinators 1
(ft), 1 (pt); Dietitians 1 (pt); Dentists 1 (pt);
Ophthalmologists 1 (pt); Podiatrists 1 (pt).
Languages Spanish, Russian

Facilities Dining room; Physical therapy
room; Activities room; Chapel; Crafts room;
Laundry room; Barber/Beauty shop; Library.
Activities Arts & crafts; Cards; Games;
Reading groups; Prayer groups; Movies;
Shopping trips; Social/Cultural gatherings.

ACUSHNET

Acushnet Nursing Home
127 S Main St, Acushnet, MA, 02743
(617) 995-1857
Admin Mary G Laughlin. *Medical Dir/Dir of
Nursing* Lorraine Travers LPN.
Licensure Intermediate care. *Beds* ICF 28.
Certified Medicaid.
Owner Proprietary Corp.
Admissions Requirements Minimum age 30;
Physician's request.
Staff RNs 1 (pt); LPNs 6 (pt); Nurses aides;
Physical therapists 1 (pt); Speech therapists
1 (pt); Activities coordinators 1 (pt);
Dietitians 1 (pt); Dentists 1 (pt);
Ophthalmologists 1 (pt).
Languages Portuguese
Facilities Dining room; Activities room;
Crafts room; Laundry room.
Activities Arts & crafts; Games; Reading
groups; Prayer groups; Movies; Social/
Cultural gatherings.

ADAMS

Adams Rest Home Inc*
17 Commercial St, Adams, MA, 01220
(413) 743-1132
Admin Harold Stein.
Licensure Rest home. *Beds* 45.

Rest Haven Rest Home Inc
395 Old Columbia St, Adams, MA, 01220
(413) 743-2115
Admin Sandra L Bisson. *Medical Dir/Dir of
Nursing* Dr Ronald Durning.
Licensure Rest home. *Beds* 29. *Certified*
Medicaid; Medicare.
Owner Proprietary Corp.
Admissions Requirements Minimum age 40;
Medical examination.
Staff Physicians; RNs; Nurses aides; Physical
therapists; Activities coordinators; Dietitians;
Dentists; Ophthalmologists; Podiatrists.
Languages Polish
Facilities Dining room; Activities room;
Laundry room.
Activities Arts & crafts; Cards; Games;
Reading groups; Prayer groups; Shopping
trips.

AGAWAM

Heritage Hall East
464 Main St, Agawam, MA, 01001
(413) 786-8000
Admin Carol Katz.

Beds 123.
Owner Proprietary Corp (Genesis Health
Ventures).

Heritage Hall North
55 Cooper St, Agawam, MA, 01001
(413) 786-8000
Admin Regina A Bossig RN. *Medical Dir/Dir
of Nursing* A Dores MD; Sandra Pothul RN.
Licensure Intermediate care; Retirement care.
Beds ICF 62; Retirement care 62. *Certified*
Medicaid.
Owner Proprietary Corp (Genesis Health
Ventures).
Admissions Requirements Minimum age 21.
Staff Physicians; RNs; LPNs; Nurses aides;
Physical therapists; Recreational therapists;
Occupational therapists; Speech therapists;
Activities coordinators; Dietitians;
Ophthalmologists; Podiatrists.
Languages Italian, Polish, French
Facilities Dining room; Activities room;
Crafts room; Laundry room; Barber/Beauty
shop; Library.
Activities Arts & crafts; Cards; Games;
Reading groups; Prayer groups; Movies;
Shopping trips; Social/Cultural gatherings.

Heritage Hall South
100 Harvey Johnson Dr, Agawam, MA, 01001
(413) 786-8000
Admin Constance A Henning. *Medical Dir/Dir
of Nursing* Dr Antonio Dores; Roslyn
Nooney.
Licensure Skilled care; Intermediate care. *Beds*
SNF 82; ICF 40. *Certified* Medicaid;
Medicare.
Owner Proprietary Corp (Genesis Health
Ventures).
Admissions Requirements Medical
examination.
Staff RNs; LPNs; Nurses aides; Physical
therapists; Reality therapists; Recreational
therapists; Occupational therapists; Speech
therapists; Activities coordinators; Dietitians;
Podiatrists.
Languages Spanish, Polish, Italian, German
Facilities Dining room; Physical therapy
room; Activities room; Chapel; Crafts room;
Laundry room; Barber/Beauty shop; Library.
Activities Arts & crafts; Cards; Games;
Reading groups; Prayer groups; Movies;
Shopping trips.

Heritage Hall West
61 Cooper St, Agawam, MA, 01001
(413) 786-8000
Admin Richard Circosta.
Licensure Skilled care. *Beds* 164. *Certified*
Medicaid; Medicare.

Kelley Rest Home*
808 Suffield St, Agawam, MA, 01001
(413) 786-2177
Admin C Burns.
Licensure Rest home. *Beds* 10.

ALLSTON

Allston Manor Nursing Home
533 Cambridge St, Allston, MA, 02134
(617) 782-2053
Admin Elaine Addlespurger. *Medical Dir/Dir of Nursing* Walter Lee MD; Richard Levesque RN CNAA.
Licensure Intermediate care. *Beds* ICF 150. *Certified* Medicaid.
Owner Proprietary Corp (Health Care & Retirement Corp).
Admissions Requirements Minimum age 21; Medical examination.
Staff Physicians 12 (pt); RNs 5 (ft), 3 (pt); LPNs 3 (ft), 8 (pt); Orderlies 1 (ft); Nurses aides 24 (ft), 1 (pt); Physical therapists 1 (pt); Recreational therapists 2 (pt); Occupational therapists 1 (pt); Speech therapists 1 (pt); Activities coordinators 1 (ft); Dietitians 1 (pt); Ophthalmologists 1 (pt); Podiatrists 1 (pt); Audiologists 1 (pt); Rehabilitation Assistant 1 (ft).
Facilities Dining room; Activities room; Laundry room; Barber/Beauty shop.
Activities Arts & crafts; Cards; Games; Reading groups; Movies; Shopping trips.

AMESBURY

Amesbury Nursing & Retirement Home
22 Maple St, Amesbury, MA, 01913
(617) 388-4682
Admin Marilyn Garfinkle.
Licensure Skilled care; Intermediate care. *Beds* 124. *Certified* Medicaid.

Eastwood Rest Home Inc
PO Box 647, 39 High St, Amesbury, MA, 01913
(617) 388-1749
Admin Jane E Rochon.
Licensure Rest home. *Beds* 33.
Owner Proprietary Corp.
Admissions Requirements Medical examination.
Facilities Dining room; Activities room; Laundry room.
Activities Cards; Games; Prayer groups; Shopping trips; Social/Cultural gatherings.

Hillside Rest Home*
29 Hillside Ave, Amesbury, MA, 01913
(617) 388-1010
Admin William E Ring.
Licensure Rest home. *Beds* 28.

Maplewood Manor Nursing Home
6 Morrill Pl, Amesbury, MA, 01913
(617) 388-3500
Admin Robert M Shaughnessy. *Medical Dir/ Dir of Nursing* Barrie Paster MD; Nancy Piecewicz RN DON.
Licensure Skilled care; Intermediate care. *Beds* SNF 60; ICF 60. *Certified* Medicaid; Medicare.
Owner Proprietary Corp.
Admissions Requirements Minimum age 21.
Staff Physicians 2 (pt); RNs 6 (ft), 14 (pt); LPNs 8 (ft), 7 (pt); Orderlies 1 (ft); Nurses aides 34 (ft), 27 (pt); Physical therapists 1 (pt); Recreational therapists 1 (ft), 5 (pt); Occupational therapists 1 (pt); Speech therapists 1 (pt); Activities coordinators 1 (ft); Dietitians 1 (pt).
Facilities Dining room; Physical therapy room; Activities room; Chapel; Crafts room; Laundry room; Barber/Beauty shop; TV rooms.
Activities Arts & crafts; Cards; Games; Reading groups; Prayer groups; Movies; Shopping trips; Social/Cultural gatherings; Exercise; Restaurant outings; Sightseeing; Musical entertainment.

AMHERST

Amherst Home for Aged Women*
1165 N Pleasant St, Amherst, MA, 01002
(413) 549-0115
Admin Walter C Jones.
Licensure Charitable home. *Beds* 6.
Admissions Requirements Females only.

Amherst Nursing Home Inc
150 University Dr, Amherst, MA, 01002
(413) 256-8185
Admin Bettie S Kravetz & Sharon E Meyers.
Licensure Skilled care; Intermediate care. *Beds* SNF 40; ICF 41. *Certified* Medicaid.
Facilities Dining room; Physical therapy room; Activities room; Crafts room; Laundry room; Barber/Beauty shop; Rotunda.
Activities Arts & crafts; Cards; Games; Reading groups; Prayer groups; Movies; Social/Cultural gatherings.

ANDOVER

Academy Manor of Andover
89 Morton St, Andover, MA, 01810
(617) 475-0944
Admin David Solomont. *Medical Dir/Dir of Nursing* Dr Edward Broddus.
Licensure Skilled care; Intermediate care. *Beds* 87. *Certified* Medicaid.
Admissions Requirements Medical examination; Physician's request.
Staff RNs 11 (ft); LPNs 7 (ft); Nurses aides 16 (ft), 10 (pt); Physical therapists 1 (pt); Recreational therapists 2 (ft); Occupational therapists 1 (pt); Speech therapists 2 (pt); Activities coordinators 2 (ft); Dietitians 1 (pt); Dentists 1 (pt); Ophthalmologists 1 (pt); Podiatrists 1 (pt).
Facilities Dining room; Physical therapy room; Activities room; Chapel; Crafts room; Laundry room; Barber/Beauty shop; Library.
Activities Arts & crafts; Cards; Games; Reading groups; Prayer groups; Movies; Shopping trips; Social/Cultural gatherings.

Randolph Nursing Home*
102 Burnham Rd, Andover, MA, 01810
(617) 475-2092
Admin Frank Andreoli.
Licensure Intermediate care. *Beds* 17. *Certified* Medicaid.

ARLINGTON

Arlington Rest Home Inc
129 Lake St, Arlington, MA, 02174
(617) 643-8761
Admin Eloise C Milligan. *Medical Dir/Dir of Nursing* Janice Hilson RN.
Licensure Rest home. *Beds* 19. *Certified* Medicaid.
Owner Privately owned.
Admissions Requirements Minimum age 21; Females only; Medical examination.
Staff RNs 1 (ft), 1 (pt); Nurses aides 1 (ft), 2 (pt); Recreational therapists 1 (pt); Dietitians 1 (pt); Dentists 1 (pt); Ophthalmologists 1 (pt).
Facilities Dining room; Activities room; Laundry room; Barber/Beauty shop.
Activities Arts & crafts; Cards; Games; Reading groups; Prayer groups; Movies; Shopping trips.

Jefferson Rest Home*
149 Hillside Ave, Arlington, MA, 02174
(617) 648-0085
Admin Vasco Lima.
Licensure Rest home. *Beds* 23.

Park Avenue Nurs, Convalescent & Retirement Home*
146 Park Ave, Arlington, MA, 02174
(617) 648-9530
Admin Joseph J Alessandroni.

Licensure Skilled care; Intermediate care. *Beds* 80. *Certified* Medicaid.

Wellington Manor Nursing Home*
8 Wellington St, Arlington, MA, 02174
(617) 648-7300
Admin Mary A Carroll.
Licensure Intermediate care. *Beds* 42. *Certified* Medicaid.

ASHBURNHAM

Collins Rest Home Inc*
10 Lawrence St, Ashburnham, MA, 01430
(617) 827-4351
Admin Louise A Gilligan.
Licensure Rest home. *Beds* 20.

Sunnyvale Rest Home
10 Central St, Ashburnham, MA, 01430
(617) 827-4212
Admin Deepak Desai.
Beds 19. *Certified* Medicaid; Medicare.
Owner Privately owned.
Admissions Requirements Minimum age 50; Medical examination; Physician's request.
Staff RNs; Orderlies; Nurses aides; Recreational therapists; Activities coordinators.
Facilities Dining room; Activities room; Laundry room.
Activities Arts & crafts; Cards; Games; Reading groups; Prayer groups; Movies; Shopping trips; Social/Cultural gatherings.

ASHLAND

Ashland Manor Nursing Home*
25 Central St, Ashland, MA, 01721
(617) 881-1044
Admin Sabina Milman.
Licensure Intermediate care. *Beds* 29. *Certified* Medicaid.

Mill Pond Rest Home*
84 Myrtle St, Ashland, MA, 01721
(617) 881-1360
Admin A Bridget Trainor.
Licensure Rest home. *Beds* 27.
Admissions Requirements Minimum age 50; Medical examination.
Staff LPNs 1 (ft); Orderlies 3 (ft), 1 (pt); Nurses aides 1 (ft); Activities coordinators 1 (pt); Dietitians 1 (pt).
Facilities Dining room; Activities room; Laundry room; Barber/Beauty shop.
Activities Arts & crafts; Cards; Games; Prayer groups; Movies; Shopping trips; Social/ Cultural gatherings.

ATHOL

Fleetwood Nursing Home*
821 Daniel Shay Hwy, Athol, MA, 01331
(617) 249-3717
Admin Francis F Krupa.
Licensure Skilled care; Intermediate care. *Beds* 126. *Certified* Medicaid.

Tully Brook Rest Home*
232 N Orange Rd, Athol, MA, 01331
(617) 249-4482
Admin Helen M Bisbee.
Licensure Rest home. *Beds* 9.

ATTLEBORO

Attleboro Retirement Center Inc
144 Pleasant St, Attleboro, MA, 02703
(617) 222-1532
Admin Carlton C Albritton Jr. *Medical Dir/ Dir of Nursing* Jane Chadwick.
Licensure Retirement Center. *Beds* 60. *Certified* Medicaid.
Owner Proprietary Corp.
Admissions Requirements Medical examination; Physician's request.

Staff Physicians 1 (pt); RNs 1 (pt); LPNs 1 (ft); Nurses aides 6 (ft); Recreational therapists 1 (ft); Activities coordinators 1 (ft); Dietitians 1 (pt); Ophthalmologists 1 (pt).
Languages French, Portuguese
Facilities Dining room; Activities room; Crafts room; Laundry room; Barber/Beauty shop.
Activities Arts & crafts; Cards; Games; Prayer groups; Shopping trips; Music entertainment.

Bristol Nursing Home
1000 Oak Hill Ave, Attleboro, MA, 02703
(617) 222-6400
Admin Ann E Kelley PhD. *Medical Dir/Dir of Nursing* Harry Mayer MD; Linda Teixeira RN.
Licensure Intermediate care. *Beds* 68. *Certified* Medicaid.
Owner Privately owned.
Admissions Requirements Medical examination.
Staff Physicians; RNs; LPNs; Orderlies; Nurses aides; Physical therapists; Recreational therapists; Occupational therapists; Speech therapists; Activities coordinators; Dietitians; Ophthalmologists.
Facilities Dining room; Activities room; Chapel; Crafts room; Laundry room; Barber/Beauty shop; Library.
Activities Arts & crafts; Cards; Games; Reading groups; Prayer groups; Movies; Shopping trips; Social/Cultural gatherings.

Pleasant Manor Nursing Home
193-195 Pleasant St, Attleboro, MA, 02703
(617) 222-4950
Admin Arthur C Taylor. *Medical Dir/Dir of Nursing* J Allen Bryer MD.
Licensure Skilled care; Intermediate care. *Beds* SNF 82; ICF 51. *Certified* Medicaid; Medicare.
Owner Proprietary Corp (Beverly Enterprises).
Admissions Requirements Minimum age 21; Medical examination; Physician's request.
Staff Physicians 1 (pt); RNs 8 (ft), 4 (pt); LPNs 4 (ft), 9 (pt); Orderlies 4 (ft); Nurses aides 25 (ft), 20 (pt); Physical therapists 2 (pt); Reality therapists 1 (ft); Occupational therapists 1 (pt); Speech therapists 1 (pt); Activities coordinators 2 (pt); Dietitians 1 (pt); Ophthalmologists 1 (pt); Podiatrists 1 (pt).
Facilities Dining room; Physical therapy room; Activities room; Chapel; Crafts room; Laundry room; Barber/Beauty shop.
Activities Arts & crafts; Cards; Games; Reading groups; Prayer groups; Movies; Shopping trips; Social/Cultural gatherings.

Ridgewood Court Nursing Home
27 George St, Attleboro, MA, 02703
(617) 226-1650
Admin Mark O'Flaherty. *Medical Dir/Dir of Nursing* Joseph Gelineau.
Licensure Skilled care; Intermediate care. *Beds* SNF 120; ICF. *Certified* Medicaid; Medicare.
Owner Proprietary Corp (Beverly Enterprises).
Admissions Requirements Minimum age 21; Medical examination; Physician's request.
Staff RNs; LPNs; Orderlies; Nurses aides; Physical therapists; Recreational therapists; Occupational therapists; Speech therapists; Activities coordinators; Dietitians; Dentists; Ophthalmologists; Podiatrists.
Facilities Dining room; Physical therapy room; Activities room; Chapel; Crafts room; Laundry room; Barber/Beauty shop.
Activities Arts & crafts; Cards; Games; Reading groups; Prayer groups; Movies.

Victorian Mansion Retirement Home*
574 Newport Ave, Attleboro, MA, 02703
(617) 761-5115
Admin Jodie Seidl.
Licensure Rest home. *Beds* 18.

AYER

Shady Glade Rest Home*
44 E Main St, Ayer, MA, 01432
(617) 772-2330
Admin Barbara A Rice.
Licensure Rest home. *Beds* 16.

Woodford of Ayer Long-Term Care Facility
15 Winthrop St, Ayer, MA, 01432
(617) 772-0409
Admin Harold Schwartz. *Medical Dir/Dir of Nursing* Dr Barttleson; Sally Moniz RN.
Licensure Intermediate care. *Beds* 71. *Certified* Medicaid.
Admissions Requirements Medical examination.
Staff RNs 1 (ft), 3 (pt); LPNs 8 (ft), 3 (pt); Orderlies 1 (ft); Nurses aides 30 (ft), 10 (pt).
Facilities Dining room; Activities room; Laundry room; Barber/Beauty shop; Whirlpools.
Activities Arts & crafts; Cards; Games; Reading groups; Prayer groups; Movies; Shopping trips.

BARNSTABLE

Cape Regency Nursing Home*
120 S Main St, Barnstable, MA, 02630
(617) 387-6560
Admin Charles Peterman.
Licensure Skilled care; Intermediate care. *Beds* SNF 80; ICF 40.

Fraser Rest Home of Hyannis*
349 Sea St, Hyannis, Barnstable, MA, 02601
(617) 775-4881
Admin Charles R Fraser.
Licensure Rest home. *Beds* 37. *Certified* Medicare.

Lewis Bay Convalescent Home*
89 Lewis Bay Rd, Barnstable, MA, 02601
(617) 775-7601
Admin Michael T Kelly. *Medical Dir/Dir of Nursing* Arthur Bickford MD.
Licensure Skilled care; Intermediate care. *Beds* 142. *Certified* Medicaid; Medicare.
Admissions Requirements Minimum age 21; Medical examination; Physician's request.
Facilities Dining room; Physical therapy room; Activities room; Laundry room; Barber/Beauty shop; Library.
Activities Arts & crafts; Cards; Games; Reading groups; Prayer groups; Movies; Shopping trips; Social/Cultural gatherings; Remotivation; Sensitivity stimulation; Exercise to music; Radio interviews; Annual fair.

Village Haven Rest Home
PO Box 335, 3401 Main St, Barnstable, MA, 02630
362-3042
Admin Benjamin Spadaro. *Medical Dir/Dir of Nursing* Glenn Williams RN.
Licensure Intermediate care. *Beds* ICF 24. *Certified* Medicaid; Medicare.
Owner Proprietary Corp.
Admissions Requirements Medical examination; Physician's request.
Staff Physicians 3 (pt); RNs 1 (ft); LPNs 1 (ft); Nurses aides 14 (ft); Activities coordinators 1 (pt); Dietitians 1 (pt); Ophthalmologists 1 (pt).
Facilities Dining room; Activities room; Crafts room; Laundry room; Barber/Beauty shop.
Activities Arts & crafts; Cards; Games; Reading groups; Movies; Shopping trips; Social/Cultural gatherings; Whale watching cruises; Specialized activities; Trips.

BARRE

Christian Hill Rest Home*
Christian Hill Dr, Barre, MA, 01005
(617) 355-4491
Admin May E Danahy.
Licensure Rest home. *Beds* 18.

BEDFORD

Carleton-Willard Retirement & Nursing Center*
100 Old Billerica Rd, Bedford, MA, 01730
(617) 275-8700
Admin Barbara A Doyle. *Medical Dir/Dir of Nursing* John W Bergin MD.
Licensure Charitable home. *Beds* 337.
Owner Nonprofit Corp.
Admissions Requirements Minimum age 65; Medical examination; Physician's request.
Staff Physicians 1 (ft), 16 (pt); RNs 6 (ft), 16 (pt); LPNs 10 (ft), 15 (pt); Nurses aides 46 (ft), 23 (pt); Physical therapists 2 (ft); Recreational therapists 1 (ft); Occupational therapists; Activities coordinators 2 (ft); Dietitians 1 (ft).
Facilities Dining room; Physical therapy room; Activities room; Crafts room; Laundry room; Barber/Beauty shop; Library.
Activities Arts & crafts; Cards; Games; Reading groups; Prayer groups; Movies; Shopping trips; Social/Cultural gatherings; Day trips; Workshop; Ceramics.

BELCHERTOWN

Belchertown State School*
Box 446, Belchertown, MA, 01007
(413) 326-3111
Admin William Jones. *Medical Dir/Dir of Nursing* Aran Kasparyan MD.
Licensure Intermediate care for mentally retarded. *Beds* 415. *Certified* Medicaid.
Owner Publicly owned.
Admissions Requirements Minimum age 6.
Staff Physicians 3 (ft); RNs 50 (ft), 2 (pt); LPNs 52 (ft), 10 (pt); Nurses aides 243 (ft), 9 (pt); Physical therapists 4 (ft); Recreational therapists 27 (ft), 15 (pt); Occupational therapists 6 (ft), 1 (pt); Speech therapists 14 (ft); Dietitians 4 (ft); Dentists 1 (ft).
Facilities Dining room; Physical therapy room; Activities room; Chapel; Crafts room; Laundry room; Barber/Beauty shop; Library.
Activities Arts & crafts; Cards; Games; Reading groups; Prayer groups; Movies; Shopping trips; Social/Cultural gatherings.

BELMONT

Belmont Manor Nursing Home
34 Agassiz Ave, Belmont, MA, 02178
(617) 489-1200
Admin Stewart A Karger. *Medical Dir/Dir of Nursing* David Barrasso MD; Zosh Mierzloarndus.
Licensure Skilled care; Intermediate care. *Beds* SNF 57; ICF 62. *Certified* Medicaid.
Owner Proprietary Corp.
Admissions Requirements Minimum age 21; Medical examination; Physician's request.
Staff RNs; LPNs; Orderlies; Nurses aides; Physical therapists; Reality therapists; Recreational therapists; Occupational therapists; Speech therapists; Activities coordinators; Dietitians; Dentists; Ophthalmologists.
Languages French, Spanish, Italian
Facilities Dining room; Physical therapy room; Activities room; Chapel; Crafts room; Laundry room; Barber/Beauty shop; Living room.
Activities Arts & crafts; Cards; Games; Reading groups; Prayer groups; Movies; Shopping trips; Social/Cultural gatherings.

BEVERLY

Beverly Nursing Home
40 Heather St, Beverly, MA, 01915
(617) 927-6220
Admin James F Smith.
Licensure Skilled care; Intermediate care. *Beds*
160. *Certified* Medicaid; Medicare.
Owner Proprietary Corp (Greenery Rehab
Grp).

Blueberry Hill Healthcare Nursing Home*
75 Brimbal Ave, Beverly, MA, 01915
(617) 927-2020
Admin Philip S Sher. *Medical Dir/Dir of
Nursing* F Carbone MD.
Licensure Skilled care; Intermediate care. *Beds*
94. *Certified* Medicaid; Medicare.
Owner Proprietary Corp (Hillhaven Corp).
Staff Physicians 19 (pt); RNs 6 (ft), 10 (pt);
LPNs 2 (ft), 8 (pt); Nurses aides 16 (ft), 28
(pt); Physical therapists 1 (pt); Occupational
therapists 1 (pt); Speech therapists 1 (pt);
Activities coordinators 2 (ft); Dietitians 1
(pt); Dentists 1 (pt); Ophthalmologists 1 (pt);
Podiatrists 2 (pt); Audiologists 1 (pt).
Facilities Dining room; Physical therapy
room; Activities room; Chapel; Crafts room;
Laundry room; Barber/Beauty shop; Library.
Activities Arts & crafts; Cards; Games;
Reading groups; Prayer groups; Movies;
Shopping trips; Social/Cultural gatherings.

Girdler House
78 Lothrop St, Beverly, MA, 01915
(617) 922-0346
Admin Margaret Shea. *Medical Dir/Dir of
Nursing* M Sadie Reid.
Licensure Self care. *Beds* 11.
Owner Nonprofit organization/foundation.
Admissions Requirements Minimum age 65;
Females only; Medical examination;
Physician's request.
Staff RNs 3 (pt); LPNs 1 (pt); Nurses aides 1
(pt).
Facilities Dining room; Activities room;
Laundry room; Barber/Beauty shop; Library.
Activities Cards; Games; Movies; Shopping
trips; Social/Cultural gatherings.

**Mediplex of Beverly: A Long-Term Care
Facility**
265 Essex St, Beverly, MA, 01915
(617) 927-3260
Admin Mr Kardenetz. *Medical Dir/Dir of
Nursing* Dr Taylor; Mrs Myers RN DON.
Licensure Skilled care; Intermediate care. *Beds*
SNF 80; ICF 110. *Certified* Medicaid;
Medicare.
Owner Proprietary Corp.
Admissions Requirements Minimum age 16;
Medical examination.
Staff RNs 10 (ft), 6 (pt); LPNs 8 (ft), 18 (pt);
Orderlies 2 (ft), 2 (pt); Nurses aides 38 (ft),
46 (pt); Physical therapists 1 (pt); Reality
therapists 1 (pt); Recreational therapists 3
(ft); Occupational therapists 1 (pt); Speech
therapists 1 (pt); Activities coordinators 1
(ft); Dietitians 1 (pt); Dentists 1 (pt);
Ophthalmologists 1 (pt); Podiatrists 1 (pt);
Social workers 2 (pt).
Facilities Dining room; Physical therapy
room; Activities room; Chapel; Crafts room;
Barber/Beauty shop; Library.
Activities Arts & crafts; Cards; Games;
Reading groups; Prayer groups; Movies;
Shopping trips; Social/Cultural gatherings.

BILLERICA

Bay State Rehabilitation Care*
78 Boston Rd, Billerica, MA, 01862
(617) 667-5123
Admin Charles W Merriam Jr.
Licensure Intermediate care. *Beds* 80.
Certified Medicaid.

Country View Nursing Home*
Boston Rd, Rte 3A, Billerica, MA, 01821
(617) 667-2166
Admin Carl E Moeller.
Licensure Intermediate care. *Beds* 121.
Certified Medicaid.
Owner Proprietary Corp (Life Care Centers of
America).

Simmons Nursing Home Inc
PO Box 345, 317 Boston Rd, Billerica, MA,
01862
(617) 663-3538
Admin Christine C Wilkins. *Medical Dir/Dir
of Nursing* Dr J ohn Q Marshall.
Licensure Intermediate care. *Beds* 44.
Certified Medicare.
Owner Proprietary Corp.
Admissions Requirements Females only;
Medical examination.
Staff Physicians 6 (ft); RNs 2 (ft); LPNs 7 (ft);
Nurses aides 20 (ft); Recreational therapists
2 (ft); Activities coordinators 1 (ft);
Dietitians 2 (ft).
Facilities Dining room; Activities room;
Crafts room; Laundry room.
Activities Arts & crafts; Cards; Games;
Reading groups; Prayer groups; Movies;
Shopping trips; Social/Cultural gatherings;
Cookouts; Dances.

BLACKSTONE

Blackstone Nursing Home
8 Butler St, Blackstone, MA, 01504
(617) 883-5818
Admin Beverly J McIntyre RN. *Medical Dir/
Dir of Nursing* Janice Flinton RN.
Licensure Intermediate care. *Beds* 33.
Certified Medicaid.
Owner Proprietary Corp.
Admissions Requirements Minimum age 25.
Staff Physicians 1 (pt); RNs 2 (ft), 2 (pt);
LPNs 4 (ft), 4 (pt); Nurses aides 12 (ft), 5
(pt); Physical therapists 1 (pt); Recreational
therapists 1 (ft); Occupational therapists 1
(pt); Speech therapists 1 (pt); Activities
coordinators 1 (pt); Dietitians 1 (pt);
Dentists 1 (pt); Ophthalmologists 1 (pt);
Podiatrists 1 (pt).
Languages French
Facilities Dining room; Activities room;
Barber/Beauty shop.
Activities Arts & crafts; Cards; Games;
Reading groups; Prayer groups; Movies;
Shopping trips; Social/Cultural gatherings;
Exercise groups.

BOSTON

Almeida Rest Home*
69 Robinson St, Jamaica Plain, Boston, MA,
02130
(617) 522-1904
Admin Vernard N Granderson.
Licensure Rest home. *Beds* 30.

Arborway Manor Convalescent Home*
55 Burroughs St, Boston, MA, 02130
(617) 524-2155
Admin Marilyn M Maher. *Medical Dir/Dir of
Nursing* Arlene Rego.
Licensure Intermediate care. *Beds* 32.
Admissions Requirements Medical
examination; Physician's request.
Facilities Dining room; Activities room;
Crafts room; Laundry room; Barber/Beauty
shop.
Activities Arts & crafts; Cards; Games;
Reading groups; Prayer groups; Movies;
Shopping trips; Social/Cultural gatherings.

Auburn House Nursing Home*
9 Revere St, Boston, MA, 02130
(617) 524-2822
Admin Jane G Spear.

Licensure Intermediate care. *Beds* 71.
Certified Medicaid.
Admissions Requirements Minimum age 21;
Medical examination; Physician's request.
Staff Physicians 2 (pt); RNs 1 (ft), 3 (pt);
LPNs 2 (ft), 4 (pt); Nurses aides 14 (ft), 4
(pt); Physical therapists 1 (pt); Recreational
therapists 1 (ft), 1 (pt); Occupational
therapists 1 (pt); Speech therapists 1 (pt);
Dietitians 1 (pt); Dentists 1 (pt); Podiatrists
1 (pt).
Facilities Dining room; Activities room;
Crafts room; Laundry room; Library.
Activities Arts & crafts; Cards; Games;
Reading groups; Prayer groups; Movies;
Shopping trips; Social/Cultural gatherings.

Frances Merry Barnard Home*
50 Beacon St, Boston, MA, 02136
(617) 361-0156
Admin Elizabeth Haley.
Licensure Rest home. *Beds* 11.

Bayside Nursing Home*
804 E 7th St, Boston, MA, 02127
(617) 268-1833
Admin Joseph Vilimas Jr.
Licensure Intermediate care. *Beds* 103.
Certified Medicaid.

Beatrice Catherine Rest Home*
47 Ocean St, Boston, MA, 02124
(617) 825-4862
Admin Marguerite I Munster.
Licensure Rest home. *Beds* 18.
Admissions Requirements Minimum age 75;
Females only.
Staff RNs 2 (ft); Nurses aides 4 (ft), 1 (pt);
Activities coordinators 1 (pt).
Facilities Activities room; Laundry room.
Activities Arts & crafts; Cards; Games;
Movies; Exercises.

Boston Home Inc
2049-61 Dorchester Ave, Boston, MA, 02124
(617) 825-3905
Admin Cletus A Carr. *Medical Dir/Dir of
Nursing* Eugene F McAuliffe MD; Irene
Reynolds RN DON.
Licensure Skilled care. *Beds* SNF 42. *Certified*
Medicaid.
Owner Nonprofit Corp.
Admissions Requirements Minimum age 21;
Females only; Medical examination;
Physician's request.
Staff Physicians 4 (pt); RNs 1 (ft), 7 (pt);
LPNs 4 (ft), 2 (pt); Nurses aides 17 (ft), 15
(pt); Physical therapists 1 (pt); Occupational
therapists 1 (pt); Activities coordinators 1
(ft); Dietitians 1 (pt); Dentists 1 (pt);
Ophthalmologists 1 (pt); Podiatrists 1 (pt);
Dentist 1 (pt); Rehabilitation aide 1 (ft);
Social worker 1 (ft).
Facilities Physical therapy room; Activities
room; Chapel; Barber/Beauty shop; Library.
Activities Arts & crafts; Cards; Games;
Reading groups; Prayer groups; Movies;
Shopping trips; Social/Cultural gatherings;
Resident run store.

Bostonian Nursing Care Center
337 Neponset Ave, Boston, MA, 02122
(617) 265-2350
Admin Thomas F Healy. *Medical Dir/Dir of
Nursing* John Jainchill MD.
Licensure Skilled care; Intermediate care. *Beds*
109. *Certified* Medicaid.
Admissions Requirements Minimum age 21;
Medical examination; Physician's request.
Staff RNs 4 (ft), 2 (pt); LPNs 10 (ft), 7 (pt);
Orderlies 3 (ft), 1 (pt); Nurses aides 24 (ft),
26 (pt); Activities coordinators 2 (ft), 2 (pt).
Facilities Dining room; Activities room;
Crafts room; Barber/Beauty shop; Gift shop;
Cafe.

Activities Arts & crafts; Cards; Games; Reading groups; Prayer groups; Movies; Shopping trips; Social/Cultural gatherings; Ceramics; Cooking; Field trips; BBQs.

Bradlee Rest Home*
33 Bradlee St, Boston, MA, 02124
(617) 436-3560
Admin Toni L Bullock.
Licensure Rest home. *Beds* 17.

Burgoyne Rest Home
53 Hartford St, Boston, MA, 02125
(617) 445-1868
Admin Willard L Basler.
Licensure Rest home. *Beds* 11.
Admissions Requirements Minimum age 21.
Facilities Activities room.
Activities Movies.

Charles House Convalescent Home
10 Bellamy St, Boston, MA, 02135
(617) 782-8113
Admin David Potvin.
Licensure Skilled care; Intermediate care. *Beds* 121. *Certified* Medicaid.

Circle Manor Nursing Home
29 Chestnut Hill Ave, Boston, MA, 02135
(617) 254-7655
Admin Clifford Blake. *Medical Dir/Dir of Nursing* Margaret Brennan RN.
Licensure Intermediate care. *Beds* 64. *Certified* Medicaid.
Admissions Requirements Medical examination.
Staff Physicians; RNs 1 (ft), 3 (pt); LPNs 6 (pt); Nurses aides 11 (ft), 9 (pt); Physical therapists; Recreational therapists 1 (ft); Dietitians.
Facilities Dining room; Activities room; Chapel; Crafts room; Laundry room; Barber/Beauty shop.
Activities Arts & crafts; Cards; Games; Reading groups; Prayer groups; Movies; Shopping trips; Social/Cultural gatherings.

Columbus Nursing Home
910 Saratoga St, Boston, MA, 02128
(617) 569-1157
Admin Valerie Williamson. *Medical Dir/Dir of Nursing* Carl Sterpi; Denise Kress.
Licensure Skilled care; Intermediate care. *Beds* SNF 54; ICF 56. *Certified* Medicaid; Medicare.
Owner Proprietary Corp (New Medico Assoc).
Admissions Requirements Minimum age 21.
Staff RNs; LPNs; Orderlies; Nurses aides; Recreational therapists; Occupational therapists; Speech therapists; Activities coordinators.
Facilities Dining room; Physical therapy room; Activities room; Chapel; Crafts room; Laundry room; Barber/Beauty shop.
Activities Arts & crafts; Cards; Games; Reading groups; Prayer groups; Movies; Shopping trips; Social/Cultural gatherings.

Corey Hill Nursing Home*
249 Corey Rd, Boston, MA, 02135
(617) 734-7138
Admin Louis Dronge. *Medical Dir/Dir of Nursing* Dr Herbert Leventhal.
Licensure Intermediate care. *Beds* 43. *Certified* Medicaid.
Admissions Requirements Minimum age 60; Medical examination; Physician's request.
Staff RNs 2 (ft), 1 (pt); LPNs 2 (ft), 1 (pt); Nurses aides 14 (ft), 6 (pt); Activities coordinators 1 (ft); Dietitians 1 (pt).

Cushing Manor Rest Home*
20 Cushing Ave, Dorchester, Boston, MA, 02125
(617) 436-9608
Admin Natalie I Batchelder.
Licensure Rest home. *Beds* 36. *Certified* Medicaid.

Don Orione Nursing Home*
111 Orient Ave, Boston, MA, 02128
(617) 569-2100
Admin Rocco Crescenzi.
Licensure Intermediate care. *Beds* 197. *Certified* Medicaid.

Duplex Nursing Home Inc*
12 Harris Ave, Boston, MA, 02130
(617) 522-0588
Admin Janet C Murphy.
Licensure Intermediate care. *Beds* 46. *Certified* Medicaid.
Admissions Requirements Minimum age 21; Males only.
Staff RNs 1 (ft), 3 (pt); LPNs 2 (ft), 2 (pt); Nurses aides 7 (ft), 3 (pt); Activities coordinators 1 (pt); Dietitians 1 (pt); Dentists 1 (pt); Ophthalmologists 1 (pt); Podiatrists 1 (pt).
Facilities Dining room; Activities room.
Activities Arts & crafts; Cards; Games; Reading groups; Prayer groups; Movies; Shopping trips; Social/Cultural gatherings.

Elizabeth Carelton House*
2055 Columbus Ave, Boston, MA, 02119
(617) 522-2100
Admin Hilda Jane Miller.
Licensure Intermediate care. *Beds* 110. *Certified* Medicaid.

Elm Hill Nursing Home*
237-241 Walnut Ave, Boston, MA, 02119
(617) 427-4798
Admin Jeanette Savoie.
Licensure Intermediate care. *Beds* 55. *Certified* Medicaid.

Englewood Nursing Home*
27 Howland St, Boston, MA, 02121
(617) 427-2332
Admin Lillian B Granderson.
Licensure Intermediate care. *Beds* 35. *Certified* Medicaid.

Fairfax Rest Home*
15 Fairfax St, Boston, MA, 02124
(617) 265-8431
Admin Andrew Basler.
Licensure Rest home. *Beds* 17.

Fairmount Rest Home Inc*
172 Fairmount Ave, Hyde Park, Boston, MA, 02136
(617) 361-5150
Admin Mildred Marden.
Licensure Rest home. *Beds* 32.

Franida House Nursing Home*
65 Glen Rd, Boston, MA, 02130
(617) 522-8714
Admin Barbara A Smith.
Licensure Intermediate care. *Beds* 22. *Certified* Medicaid.

Gardner House Rest Home
47 Centre St, Boston, MA, 02119
(617) 445-1727
Admin Phillip P Cohen. *Medical Dir/Dir of Nursing* Dr Rubin.
Licensure Retirement home. *Beds* 24. *Certified* Medicaid.
Owner Nonprofit Corp.
Admissions Requirements Minimum age 40; Physician's request.
Staff LPNs; Orderlies; Nurses aides; Recreational therapists; Dietitians; Ophthalmologists.
Languages Greek, Spanish
Facilities Dining room; Activities room; Crafts room; Laundry room.
Activities Arts & crafts; Cards; Games; Reading groups; Prayer groups; Movies; Shopping trips.

Gardner Pierce Nursing & Rest Home*
333 Commonwealth Ave, Boston, MA, 02115
(617) 266-3300

Admin Edward M Levitt.
Licensure Intermediate care. *Beds* 38. *Certified* Medicaid.

Greenery Rehabilitation & Skilled Nursing Center
99 Chestnut Hill Ave, Boston, MA, 02135
(617) 787-3390
Admin Laurie Tolarico. *Medical Dir/Dir of Nursing* William Garvin MD; Elizabeth Berry DON.
Licensure Skilled care; Rehabilitation for head injured individuals. *Beds* 201. *Certified* Medicaid; Medicare.
Owner Proprietary Corp (Greenery Rehab Grp).
Admissions Requirements Minimum age 15; Medical examination.
Staff Physicians 2 (ft), 2 (pt); RNs 26 (ft); LPNs 26 (ft); Nurses aides 88 (ft); Physical therapists 17 (ft); Recreational therapists 10 (ft); Occupational therapists 12 (ft); Speech therapists 15 (ft); Dietitians 1 (ft); Dentists 1 (pt); Ophthalmologists 1 (pt); Podiatrists 1 (pt); Special education 6 (ft); Neuropsychologists 6 (ft); Behavioral therapists 3 (ft); Vocational rehabilitation therapists 6 (ft).
Languages French, Spanish
Facilities Dining room; Physical therapy room; Activities room; Crafts room; Laundry room; Barber/Beauty shop; Library; Vocational rehabilitation; Special education classrooms.
Activities Arts & crafts; Cards; Games; Reading groups; Prayer groups; Movies; Shopping trips; Social/Cultural gatherings.

Hale-Barnard Home*
273 Clarendon St, Boston, MA, 02116
(617) 536-3726
Admin Rebekah Richardson. *Medical Dir/Dir of Nursing* Christine Wolford.
Licensure Charitable home. *Beds* 60.
Admissions Requirements Minimum age 65; Medical examination.
Staff RNs 2 (ft); LPNs 6 (pt); Nurses aides 1 (ft), 1 (pt); Activities coordinators 1 (pt).
Facilities Dining room; Activities room; Laundry room; Barber/Beauty shop; Library.
Activities Cards; Games; Reading groups; Movies; Shopping trips; Social/Cultural gatherings.

Harris Avenue Rest Home*
7 Harris Ave, Jamaica Plain, Boston, MA, 02130
(617) 524-9796
Admin Dianne Lilis.
Licensure Rest home. *Beds* 23. *Certified* Medicaid.

Haven Nursing Home*
44 Peter Parley Rd, Boston, MA, 02130
(617) 524-3150
Admin Donald J MacQuarrie.
Licensure Intermediate care. *Beds* 20. *Certified* Medicaid.

Highland Rest Home
516 Warren St, Boston, MA, 02121
(617) 427-6640
Admin Barbara Wade. *Medical Dir/Dir of Nursing* Frances Valentine.
Licensure Rest home. *Beds* 41.
Admissions Requirements Minimum age 40; Medical examination.
Staff LPNs 1 (ft); Nurses aides 3 (ft), 8 (pt); Activities coordinators 1 (pt); Activities coordinators 1 (pt).
Facilities Dining room; Laundry room.
Activities Arts & crafts; Cards; Games; Prayer groups; Movies; Shopping trips; Social/Cultural gatherings.

Hodgdon Rest Home*
95 Moreland St, Roxbury, Boston, MA, 02121
(617) 445-8864
Admin Adolphus G Bullock.

Licensure Rest home. *Beds* 60.

Home for Aged Women*
201-05 S Huntington Ave, Boston, MA, 02130
(617) 522-3080
Admin Andrew J Comeau. *Medical Dir/Dir of Nursing* Kim Bowman MD.
Licensure Intermediate care. *Beds* 145.
Certified Medicaid.
Owner Nonprofit Corp.
Admissions Requirements Minimum age 60;
Females only; Medical examination.
Staff RNs 1 (ft); LPNs 5 (ft), 1 (pt); Nurses aides 29 (ft), 6 (pt); Activities coordinators 2 (ft).
Facilities Dining room; Physical therapy room; Activities room; Crafts room; Laundry room; Barber/Beauty shop; Library.
Activities Arts & crafts; Cards; Games; Reading groups; Prayer groups; Movies; Shopping trips; Social/Cultural gatherings.

Hyde Park Convalescent Home
113 Central Ave, Boston, MA, 02136
(617) 364-1135
Admin Arthur D Kruskall.
Licensure Skilled care; Intermediate care. *Beds* SNF 25; ICF 28. *Certified* Medicaid.
Staff RNs 6 (ft), 2 (pt); LPNs 4 (ft), 3 (pt); Nurses aides 23 (ft), 8 (pt).
Facilities Dining room; Activities room; Crafts room; Laundry room; Barber/Beauty shop.
Activities Arts & crafts; Cards; Games; Reading groups; Prayer groups; Movies; Shopping trips; Social/Cultural gatherings; Mens club; Cooking club; Garden club; Exercise bike club.

Jamaica Towers Nursing Home*
174 Forest Hills St, Boston, MA, 02130
(617) 522-6675
Admin Alfred J Souza. *Medical Dir/Dir of Nursing* Saripalli V Subbaraju MD.
Licensure Skilled care; Intermediate care. *Beds* 120. *Certified* Medicaid; Medicare.
Owner Proprietary Corp (Hillhaven Corp).
Admissions Requirements Minimum age 21;
Physician's request.
Staff Physicians 18 (pt); RNs 5 (ft), 2 (pt); LPNs 7 (ft), 9 (pt); Orderlies 4 (ft); Nurses aides 60 (ft), 1 (pt); Physical therapists 1 (pt); Occupational therapists 1 (pt); Speech therapists 1 (pt); Activities coordinators 2 (ft); Dietitians 1 (pt); Dentists 1 (pt); Ophthalmologists 1 (pt); Podiatrists 1 (pt); Audiologists 1 (pt).
Facilities Dining room; Physical therapy room; Activities room; Crafts room; Laundry room; Barber/Beauty shop.
Activities Arts & crafts; Cards; Games; Reading groups; Prayer groups; Movies; Shopping trips; Social/Cultural gatherings.

Ellen James Rest Home*
42 Elm Hill Ave, Roxbury, Boston, MA, 02121
(617) 427-7464
Admin Jeanette Savoie.
Licensure Rest home. *Beds* 40.

Johnson Nursing Home*
46 Wren St, Boston, MA, 02132
(617) 325-5006
Admin Louis J Furash.
Licensure Intermediate care. *Beds* 32.
Certified Medicaid.

Lynmark Nursing Home Inc*
15 Robinwood Ave, Boston, MA, 02130
(617) 522-9044
Admin Marilyn Maher.
Licensure Intermediate care. *Beds* 20.
Certified Medicaid.

Marco Polo Rest Home Inc*
Box 501, Boston, MA, 02128
(617) 567-7500

Admin Richard J Diamond. *Medical Dir/Dir of Nursing* Glenn Rothfeld MD.
Licensure Rest home. *Beds* 62.
Admission Requirements Minimum age 45;
Medical examination.
Staff Nurses aides 4 (ft), 6 (pt); Activities coordinators 1 (pt).
Facilities Dining room; Activities room; Laundry room.
Activities Arts & crafts; Cards; Games; Social/Cultural gatherings.

Martin Nursing Home*
415 Columbia Rd, Boston, MA, 02125
(617) 436-4170
Admin Susanna Sheppard.
Licensure Intermediate care. *Beds* 150.
Certified Medicaid.

Melville Rest Home*
3 Melville Ave, Boston, MA, 02124
(617) 288-5816
Admin Margaret T Murray. *Medical Dir/Dir of Nursing* Dr Boderick.
Licensure Rest home. *Beds* 23.
Admissions Requirements Minimum age 18;
Medical examination.
Staff LPNs 1 (pt); Activities coordinators 1 (pt).
Facilities Dining room; Activities room; Laundry room; Kitchen.
Activities Arts & crafts; Cards; Games; Reading groups; Prayer groups; Movies; Shopping trips; Social/Cultural gatherings.

Milton View Nursing Home*
150 River St, Mattapan, Boston, MA, 02126
(617) 296-0140
Admin Thomas B Dresser.
Licensure Intermediate care. *Beds* 64.
Certified Medicaid.

Mt Pleasant Home*
301 S Huntington Ave, Boston, MA, 02130
(617) 522-7600
Admin Harriet H Caton.
Licensure Rest home. *Beds* 44.

Mary Murphy Nursing Home*
70 Rockview St, Boston, MA, 02130
(617) 524-6200
Admin Ethel Peters. *Medical Dir/Dir of Nursing* Dr Louis Kassler.
Licensure Intermediate care. *Beds* 91.
Certified Medicaid.
Admissions Requirements Minimum age 21;
Medical examination; Physician's request.
Staff Physicians 4 (pt); RNs 2 (ft), 2 (pt); LPNs 4 (ft), 2 (pt); Orderlies 1 (ft); Nurses aides 18 (ft), 8 (pt); Physical therapists 1 (pt); Recreational therapists 1 (pt); Speech therapists 1 (pt); Activities coordinators 1 (ft), 1 (pt); Dietitians 1 (pt); Dentists 1 (pt); Ophthalmologists 1 (pt); Podiatrists 1 (pt).
Activities Arts & crafts; Cards; Games; Reading groups; Prayer groups; Movies; Shopping trips.

Nelson Manor Nursing Home*
3 Aspinwall Rd, Dorchester, Boston, MA, 02124
(617) 288-4100
Admin Barbara Cohen.
Licensure Intermediate care. *Beds* 47.
Certified Medicaid.

Norwegian Old Peoples Home*
1205 Centre St, Boston, MA, 02131
(617) 325-9439
Admin Olaf A Ness.
Licensure Charitable home. *Beds* 18.

Oak Haven Nursing Home
74 Howland St, Boston, MA, 02121
(617) 427-8080
Admin Loretta Murphy.
Licensure Intermediate care. *Beds* 38.
Certified Medicaid.

Park Dale Rest Home*
36 Elm Hill Ave, Boston, MA, 02121
(617) 427-9649
Admin L B Granderson.
Licensure Rest home. *Beds* 27.

Parkway Nursing Home*
1190 VFW Pkwy, Boston, MA, 02132
(617) 325-1688
Admin Burton K Lipsky.
Licensure Intermediate care. *Beds* 140.
Certified Medicaid.

Parkwell Nursing Home*
745 Truman Hwy, Boston, MA, 02136
(617) 361-8300
Admin Patrick O'Connor.
Licensure Skilled care; Intermediate care. *Beds* 124. *Certified* Medicaid; Medicare.

Resthaven Corporation*
120 Fisher Ave, Boston, MA, 02120
(617) 738-1500
Admin Felix F Albano.
Licensure Skilled care; Intermediate care. *Beds* 240. *Certified* Medicaid.

Riverside Nursing Home
405 River St, Boston, MA, 02126
(617) 296-5585
Admin Stephen J Kelly. *Medical Dir/Dir of Nursing* Barbra Collins.
Licensure Skilled care. *Beds* SNF 85. *Certified* Medicaid.
Owner Proprietary Corp.
Admissions Requirements Minimum age 65.
Staff RNs 8 (ft); LPNs 10 (pt); Nurses aides 20 (ft), 10 (pt); Physical therapists 1 (pt); Recreational therapists 3 (ft); Occupational therapists 1 (pt); Activities coordinators 1 (ft); Dietitians 1 (pt); Dentists 1 (pt); Ophthalmologists 1 (pt); Podiatrists 1 (pt).
Languages French
Facilities Dining room; Activities room; Chapel; Crafts room; Laundry room; Barber/Beauty shop.
Activities Arts & crafts; Cards; Games; Reading groups; Prayer groups; Movies; Shopping trips; Social/Cultural gatherings.

Riverview Nursing Home*
142 Bigelow St, Boston, MA, 02135
(617) 782-3424
Admin Barry Chiler.
Licensure Intermediate care. *Beds* 143.
Certified Medicaid.

Rodger Rest Home*
54 Bowdoin St, Dorchester, Boston, MA, 02124
(617) 825-1771
Admin Lillian B Granderson.
Licensure Rest home. *Beds* 20.

Rodgerson House
434 Jamaica Way, Boston, MA, 02130
(617) 522-7230
Admin James F Seagle Jr. *Medical Dir/Dir of Nursing* Dr Amnon Wachman.
Licensure Intermediate care; Level IV Rest Home. *Beds* ICF 16; 40 Rest Home.
Certified Medicaid.
Owner Nonprofit organization/foundation.
Admissions Requirements Minimum age 55;
Males only; Medical examination.
Staff Physicians 1 (pt); RNs 1 (pt); LPNs 3 (ft), 3 (pt); Nurses aides 5 (ft), 4 (pt); Activities coordinators 1 (ft), 1 (pt); Dietitians 1 (pt).
Facilities Dining room; Physical therapy room; Activities room; Laundry room; Library; Pub; Billiard room; Smoking lounges; TV room.
Activities Arts & crafts; Games; Reading groups; Movies; Shopping trips; Social/Cultural gatherings.

St Joseph's Manor*
321 Centre St, Boston, MA, 02122
(617) 825-6320
Admin Sr James Frances Powers.
Licensure Charitable home. *Beds* 77.
Admissions Requirements Minimum age 70;
Females only; Medical examination;
Physician's request.
Staff RNs 1 (pt); LPNs 1 (ft); Orderlies 3 (ft),
5 (pt); Activities coordinators 1 (ft);
Dietitians 1 (pt); Podiatrists 1 (pt).
Affiliation Roman Catholic
Facilities Dining room; Activities room;
Chapel; Laundry room; Barber/Beauty shop.
Activities Arts & crafts; Cards; Games;
Reading groups; Prayer groups; Movies;
Shopping trips; Social/Cultural gatherings.

Sheriff Manor Nursing Home*
176 Humboldt, Boston, MA, 02121
(617) 445-5224
Admin Roger T Dillingham.
Licensure Intermediate care. *Beds* 60.
Certified Medicaid.

Sherrill House Inc
135 S Huntington Ave, Boston, MA, 02130
(617) 731-2400
Admin Donald M Powell. *Medical Dir/Dir of
Nursing* Dr Jens Tougorg; Mrs Betty
Mollica.
Licensure Skilled care; Intermediate care;
Charitable home. *Beds* SNF; ICF 164.
Certified Medicaid; Medicare.
Staff RNs 15 (ft), 10 (pt); LPNs 10 (ft), 10
(pt); Orderlies 5 (ft), 1 (pt); Nurses aides 60
(ft), 30 (pt).
Facilities Dining room; Physical therapy
room; Activities room; Chapel; Crafts room;
Laundry room; Barber/Beauty shop; Library.
Activities Arts & crafts; Cards; Games;
Reading groups; Prayer groups; Movies;
Shopping trips.

Stadium Manor Nursing Home*
461 Walnut Ave, Boston, MA, 02130
(617) 522-1170
Admin James D Regan.
Licensure Intermediate care. *Beds* 120.
Certified Medicaid.

Star of David Convalescent Home*
1100 VFW Parkway, Boston, MA, 02132
(617) 325-8100
Admin Richard Sabounjiam. *Medical Dir/Dir
of Nursing* Dr Joseph Pines.
Licensure Intermediate care. *Beds* 146.
Certified Medicaid.
Admissions Requirements Medical
examination.
Staff RNs 18 (ft); LPNs 6 (ft); Orderlies 4 (ft);
Nurses aides 38 (ft); Physical therapists 2
(ft), 1 (pt); Reality therapists 2 (ft);
Occupational therapists 1 (pt); Speech
therapists 1 (pt); Activities coordinators 1
(ft), 2 (pt); Dietitians 1 (pt).
Facilities Dining room; Physical therapy
room; Activities room; Chapel; Crafts room;
Laundry room; Barber/Beauty shop; Library;
Lounges; Auditorium.
Activities Arts & crafts; Cards; Reading
groups; Prayer groups; Movies; Shopping
trips; Social/Cultural gatherings.

Stonehedge Nursing Home*
5 Redlands Rd, Boston, MA, 02132
(617) 327-6325
Admin Lawrence E Warner.
Licensure Intermediate care. *Beds* 79.
Certified Medicaid.

Tara Nursing Home*
52 Alban St, Boston, MA, 02124
(617) 436-5048
Admin Robert D Wilkins. *Medical Dir/Dir of
Nursing* Dr G Bonderman.
Licensure Intermediate care. *Beds* 22.
Certified Medicaid.

Admissions Requirements Females only;
Medical examination.
Staff RNs 1 (ft); LPNs 1 (ft), 2 (pt); Nurses
aides 5 (ft), 3 (pt); Activities coordinators 1
(ft).
Facilities Dining room; Activities room;
Laundry room.
Activities Arts & crafts; Cards; Games;
Reading groups; Prayer groups; Movies;
Shopping trips.

Village Manor Nursing Home
25 Alpine St, Boston, MA, 02126
(617) 361-5400
Admin John J Power. *Medical Dir/Dir of
Nursing* David Chen; Steve Kolodziej RN.
Licensure Skilled care; Intermediate care. *Beds*
SNF 82; ICF 41. *Certified* Medicaid.
Owner Nonprofit Corp.
Admissions Requirements Minimum age 21.
Staff Physicians 1 (pt); RNs 7 (ft), 3 (pt);
LPNs 11 (ft), 5 (pt); Nurses aides 35 (ft), 25
(pt); Physical therapists 1 (pt); Reality
therapists 1 (pt); Occupational therapists 1
(pt); Speech therapists 1 (pt); Activities
coordinators 1 (ft), 2 (pt); Dietitians 1 (pt);
Dentists 1 (pt); Ophthalmologists 2 (pt);
Podiatrists 1 (pt).
Facilities Dining room; Physical therapy
room; Activities room; Crafts room; Laundry
room; Barber/Beauty shop; TV rooms.
Activities Arts & crafts; Cards; Games;
Reading groups; Prayer groups; Movies;
Shopping trips; Social/Cultural gatherings.

Wayne Manor Nursing Home*
133 Hancock St, Boston, MA, 02125
(617) 265-5220
Admin Barbara Cohen.
Licensure Intermediate care. *Beds* 78.
Certified Medicaid.

West Roxbury Manor Nursing Home*
5060 Washington St, Boston, MA, 02132
(617) 323-5440
Admin Burton K Lipsky. *Medical Dir/Dir of
Nursing* James Harrison MD.
Licensure Skilled care; Intermediate care. *Beds*
76. *Certified* Medicaid.
Admissions Requirements Minimum age 50;
Medical examination; Physician's request.
Staff Physicians 12 (pt); RNs 5 (ft); LPNs 8
(ft); Orderlies 1 (ft); Nurses aides 25 (ft);
Physical therapists 1 (pt); Reality therapists
1 (pt); Recreational therapists 1 (ft), 1 (pt);
Occupational therapists 1 (pt); Speech
therapists 1 (pt); Activities coordinators 1
(ft); Dietitians 1 (pt); Dentists 1 (pt);
Ophthalmologists 1 (pt); Podiatrists 1 (pt);
Audiologists 1 (pt).
Facilities Dining room; Laundry room;
Library.
Activities Arts & crafts; Cards; Games;
Reading groups; Movies; Shopping trips;
Social/Cultural gatherings.

Frank Wood Convalescent Home*
1135 Morton St, Boston, MA, 02126
(617) 298-8003
Admin Dennis F Sullivan.
Licensure Skilled care. *Beds* 58. *Certified*
Medicaid; Medicare.

BRAINTREE

**Braintree Manor Nursing & Retirement
Center***
1102 Washington St, Braintree, MA, 02185
(617) 848-3100
Admin Francis J Pattavina.
Licensure Skilled care; Intermediate care. *Beds*
247. *Certified* Medicaid; Medicare.

Franklin Nursing Home
149 Franklin St, Braintree, MA, 02184
(617) 843-3136, 843-3121

Admin Andrew J Comeau. *Medical Dir/Dir of
Nursing* Dr Floyd Wolff MD; Diane Fell
RN.
Licensure Intermediate care. *Beds* ICF 27.
Certified Medicaid.
Owner Privately owned.
Admissions Requirements Minimum age 50;
Females only; Medical examination.
Staff RNs 2 (ft), 3 (pt); LPNs 2 (pt); Nurses
aides 5 (ft), 9 (pt); Activities coordinators 1
(ft); Dietitians 1 (pt).
Facilities Dining room; Laundry room; Living
room.
Activities Arts & crafts; Cards; Games;
Reading groups; Prayer groups; Movies;
Shopping trips; Social/Cultural gatherings.

Franvale Nursing Home
20 Pond St, Braintree, MA, 02184
(617) 848-1616
Admin Ann F Masterson. *Medical Dir/Dir of
Nursing* Dr Jay Portnow; Patricia Chase RN
DON.
Licensure Skilled care; Intermediate care. *Beds*
SNF 91; ICF. *Certified* Medicaid; Medicare.
Owner Proprietary Corp.
Admissions Requirements Physician's request.
Staff Physicians 1 (pt); RNs; LPNs; Orderlies;
Nurses aides; Physical therapists 1 (pt);
Recreational therapists 1 (ft); Occupational
therapists 1 (pt); Speech therapists 1 (pt);
Dietitians 1 (pt); Ophthalmologists 1 (pt).
Facilities Dining room; Physical therapy
room; Activities room; Crafts room; Laundry
room; Barber/Beauty shop.
Activities Arts & crafts; Cards; Games;
Reading groups; Prayer groups; Movies;
Social/Cultural gatherings.

Hollingsworth House
1120 Washington St, Braintree, MA, 02184
(617) 848-4710
Admin Elizabeth A Pattavina. *Medical Dir/Dir
of Nursing* Mark Ostrem MD; Margaret
Nelson RN.
Licensure Intermediate care. *Beds* ICF 120.
Certified Medicaid.
Owner Proprietary Corp.
Admissions Requirements Minimum age 60.
Staff RNs 16 (ft), 4 (pt); LPNs 12 (ft), 6 (pt);
Nurses aides 15 (ft), 20 (pt); Physical
therapists 1 (pt); Recreational therapists 4
(ft), 2 (pt); Activities coordinators 1 (ft);
Dietitians 1 (pt); Hairdresser 1 (pt); Barber 1
(pt).
Facilities Dining room; Activities room;
Crafts room; Barber/Beauty shop; Library.
Activities Arts & crafts; Cards; Games;
Reading groups; Prayer groups; Movies;
Shopping trips; Social/Cultural gatherings;
Slide shows; Happy hour.

**John Scott House Nursing & Rehabilitation
Center***
233 Middle St, Braintree, MA, 02184
(617) 843-1860
Admin Michael Welch.
Licensure Skilled care; Intermediate care. *Beds*
200. *Certified* Medicaid; Medicare.

Elihu White Nursing & Rehabilitation Center*
95 Commercial St, Braintree, MA, 02184
(617) 848-3678
Admin Florence E Logan.
Licensure Skilled care; Intermediate care. *Beds*
189. *Certified* Medicaid; Medicare.

BREWSTER

Brewster Manor Nursing & Retirement Home
873 Harwich Rd, Brewster, MA, 02631
(617) 896-7046
Admin Dorothea L Maloney. *Medical Dir/Dir
of Nursing* Carol Topolewski MD; Elinore
Swansen RN.
Licensure Skilled care; Intermediate care. *Beds*
SNF 121; ICF 82. *Certified* Medicaid.
Owner Privately owned.

Staff Physicians 1 (pt); RNs 21 (ft), 8 (pt);
LPNs 6 (ft), 1 (pt); Orderlies 2 (ft), 2 (pt);
Nurses aides 47 (ft), 25 (pt); Physical
therapists 1 (pt); Reality therapists 2 (pt);
Recreational therapists 1 (ft), 2 (pt);
Occupational therapists 1 (pt); Speech
therapists 1 (pt); Activities coordinators 1
(ft), 1 (pt); Dietitians 1 (pt);
Ophthalmologists 1 (pt); Podiatrists 1 (pt).
Facilities Dining room; Physical therapy
room; Activities room; Chapel; Crafts room;
Laundry room; Barber/Beauty shop; Library.
Activities Arts & crafts; Cards; Games;
Reading groups; Prayer groups; Movies;
Shopping trips; Social/Cultural gatherings.

BRIDGEWATER

Bridgewater Nursing Home*
16 Pleasant St, Bridgewater, MA, 02324
(617) 697-4616
Admin William Gold.
Licensure Intermediate care. *Beds* 43.
Certified Medicaid.

BRIGHTON

Provident Nursing Home
1501 Commonwealth Ave, Brighton, MA,
02135
(617) 782-1320
Admin John C Marshall. *Medical Dir/Dir of
Nursing* Jeffrey Kang MD; Charlene Ayers.
Licensure Psychiatric ICF. *Beds* Psychiatric
ICF 100. *Certified* Medicaid.
Admissions Requirements Minimum age 65 or
Waiver; Medical examination.
Staff Physicians 5 (pt); RNs 15 (ft); Nurses
aides 73 (ft); Recreational therapists 2 (ft);
Occupational therapists 1 (ft); Activities
coordinators 1 (ft); Dietitians 1 (pt);
Podiatrists 1 (pt).
Facilities Dining room; Activities room;
Crafts room; Laundry room; Barber/Beauty
shop.
Activities Arts & crafts; Cards; Games;
Reading groups; Movies; Shopping trips;
Social/Cultural gatherings.

BROCKTON

Quincy Adams Nursing Home*
130 Quincy Ave, Brockton, MA, 02402
(617) 588-4700
Admin Martha A Munies.
Licensure Skilled care; Intermediate care. *Beds*
125. *Certified* Medicaid.

Braemoor Nursing Home Inc
34 N Pearl St, Brockton, MA, 02401
(617) 586-3696
Admin Michael J Roland. *Medical Dir/Dir of
Nursing* Dr Craig Wannick; Christine
Cossigan.
Licensure Skilled care; Intermediate care;
Level I. *Beds* SNF 40/80; ICF 40; Level I
40. *Certified* Medicaid; Medicare.
Owner Privately owned.
Staff Physicians 3 (pt); RNs 4 (ft), 4 (pt);
LPNs 10 (ft), 8 (pt).
Facilities Dining room; Physical therapy
room; Activities room; Chapel; Crafts room;
Laundry room; Barber/Beauty shop; Library.
Activities Arts & crafts; Cards; Games;
Reading groups; Prayer groups; Movies;
Shopping trips; Social/Cultural gatherings.

Embassy House Healthcare Nursing Home
2 Beaumont Ave, Brockton, MA, 02402
(617) 588-8550
Admin Lewis B Rosen. *Medical Dir/Dir of
Nursing* Dr Elliot Korim.
Licensure Skilled care; Intermediate care. *Beds*
123. *Certified* Medicaid; Medicare.
Owner Proprietary Corp (Hillhaven Corp).
Admissions Requirements Minimum age 21;
Medical examination; Physician's request.

Staff Physicians 15 (pt); RNs 14 (ft), 18 (pt);
LPNs 5 (ft), 8 (pt); Orderlies 1 (pt); Nurses
aides 14 (ft), 38 (pt); Physical therapists 1
(pt); Recreational therapists 1 (pt);
Occupational therapists 1 (pt); Speech
therapists 1 (pt); Activities coordinators 1
(ft), 1 (pt); Dietitians 1 (pt); Dentists 1 (pt);
Podiatrists 1 (pt).
Facilities Dining room; Physical therapy
room; Activities room; Crafts room; Laundry
room; Barber/Beauty shop; Library; TV
rooms; Solariums.
Activities Arts & crafts; Cards; Games;
Reading groups; Prayer groups; Movies;
Shopping trips; Social/Cultural gatherings;
Fishing for men; Bus tours.

Fairview Rest Home*
197 W Chestnut St, Brockton, MA, 02401
(617) 586-7704
Admin Marguerite Donato.
Licensure Rest home. *Beds* 14.
Admissions Requirements Minimum age 40;
Females only; Medical examination;
Physician's request.
Staff Nurses aides 1 (ft), 4 (pt); Dietitians 1
(pt); Podiatrists 1 (pt).
Facilities Dining room; Laundry room.
Activities Cards; Games; Prayer groups;
Church groups.

Green Oak Nursing Home
947 N Main St, Brockton, MA, 02401
(617) 587-9367
Admin Shirley Lajoie. *Medical Dir/Dir of
Nursing* Virginia Foster DON.
Licensure Intermediate care. *Beds* ICF 83.
Certified Medicaid.
Admissions Requirements Minimum age 40;
Females only.
Staff RNs 2 (ft); LPNs 4 (ft), 6 (pt); Nurses
aides 17 (ft), 8 (pt); Recreational therapists 1
(ft), 1 (pt); Dietitians 1 (pt); Social worker 1
(ft).
Languages French
Facilities Dining room; Activities room;
Crafts room; Laundry room; Barber/Beauty
shop.
Activities Arts & crafts; Cards; Games;
Reading groups; Prayer groups; Movies;
Shopping trips; Social/Cultural gatherings.

Lutheran Home of Brockton Inc
888 N Main St, Brockton, MA, 02401
(617) 587-6556
Admin Rev William S Eaton. *Medical Dir/Dir
of Nursing* Mayer Rubenstein MD; Carol
Glazier RN.
Licensure Skilled care; Intermediate care;
Outpatient Geriatric Center. *Beds* SNF 82;
ICF 41. *Certified* Medicaid.
Admissions Requirements Minimum age 65;
Medical examination.
Staff Physicians 1 (pt); RNs 3 (ft), 14 (pt);
LPNs 12 (ft), 4 (pt); Orderlies 2 (pt); Nurses
aides 36 (ft), 23 (pt); Physical therapists 3
(ft); Reality therapists 1 (ft), 1 (pt); Activities
coordinators 1 (ft); Social worker 1 (ft).
Affiliation Lutheran
Facilities Dining room; Physical therapy
room; Activities room; Chapel; Crafts room;
Laundry room; Barber/Beauty shop; Library.
Activities Arts & crafts; Games; Reading
groups; Prayer groups; Movies; Shopping
trips; Social/Cultural gatherings; Music;
Short plays; Dancing shows; In-house
shopping.

Madalawn Nursing Home
1330 Main St, Brockton, MA, 02401
(617) 583-1070
Admin Thomas F Shields.
Licensure Intermediate care. *Beds* 50.
Certified Medicaid.

Regent Park Long-Term Care Center
41 Libby St, Brockton, MA, 02402
(617) 588-1450

Admin F Roy Fitzsimmons. *Medical Dir/Dir
of Nursing* Peter C Roos MD; Nancy
McComas RN.
Licensure Skilled care; Intermediate care. *Beds*
SNF 60; ICF 60. *Certified* Medicaid.
Owner Privately owned.
Admissions Requirements Medical
examination; Physician's request.
Staff RNs 4 (ft), 5 (pt); LPNs 7 (ft), 5 (pt);
Orderlies 2 (ft); Nurses aides 29 (ft);
Physical therapists 1 (pt); Occupational
therapists 1 (pt); Activities coordinators 2
(ft); Dietitians 1 (ft).
Facilities Dining room; Activities room;
Laundry room; Barber/Beauty shop; Day
rooms.
Activities Arts & crafts; Cards; Games;
Reading groups; Prayer groups; Movies;
Shopping trips; Social/Cultural gatherings.

St John Rest Home*
25 Simmons Ave, Brockton, MA, 02401
(617) 586-2746
Admin John H Keeney.
Licensure Rest home. *Beds* 21.

St Joseph Manor*
215 Thatcher St, Brockton, MA, 02402
(617) 583-5834
Admin Sr Geraldine Nevaras.
Licensure Skilled care; Intermediate care. *Beds*
120. *Certified* Medicaid.

West Acres Nursing Home*
804 Pleasant St, Brockton, MA, 02401
(617) 583-6000
Admin Emanuel Freddura.
Licensure Skilled care; Intermediate care. *Beds*
109. *Certified* Medicaid; Medicare.

West Elm Nursing Home
PO Box 4156, 227 W Elm St, Brockton, MA,
02403
(617) 583-2203
Admin Mary J Tomlinson.
Licensure Intermediate care. *Beds* 54.
Certified Medicaid.
Admissions Requirements Minimum age 21;
Medical examination; Physician's request.
Staff RNs 2 (ft), 1 (pt); LPNs 1 (ft), 2 (pt);
Nurses aides 10 (ft), 4 (pt); Recreational
therapists 1 (pt); Dietitians 1 (pt).
Facilities Dining room; Activities room;
Laundry room.
Activities Arts & crafts; Cards; Games;
Reading groups; Prayer groups; Movies;
Shopping trips; Social/Cultural gatherings;
Outside dinners.

Woodridge House Nursing Home*
596 Summer St, Brockton, MA, 02402
(617) 586-1467
Admin John G Soule.
Licensure Skilled care; Intermediate care. *Beds*
123. *Certified* Medicaid; Medicare.
Owner Proprietary Corp (Hillhaven Corp).

BROOKLINE

Brentwood Nursing Home Inc
34-36 Francis St, Brookline, MA, 02146
(617) 277-0722
Admin Mary Kathryn Bittner. *Medical Dir/Dir
of Nursing* Vivian Evers RN.
Licensure Intermediate care. *Beds* ICF 23.
Owner Privately owned.
Staff Physicians 1 (pt); RNs 2 (ft), 3 (pt);
LPNs 2 (ft); Orderlies 1 (ft); Nurses aides 8
(ft), 6 (pt); Activities coordinators 1 (pt);
Dietitians 1 (pt).
Languages French
Activities Cards; Games; Reading groups;
Prayer groups; Movies.

Chamberlain Nursing Home*
123 Gardner Rd, Brookline, MA, 02146
(617) 277-0225
Admin Barbara A Smith.

Licensure Intermediate care. *Beds* 27.
  Certified Medicaid.
Staff RNs 2 (ft), 1 (pt); LPNs 1 (ft); Nurses
  aides 4 (ft), 2 (pt); Activities coordinators 1
  (ft); Dietitians 1 (pt).
Facilities Dining room; Activities room;
  Laundry room.
Activities Arts & crafts; Games; Movies;
  Shopping trips; Social/Cultural gatherings;
  Overnight trips.

City View Nursing Home Inc*
PO Box 446, 232 Summit Ave, Brookline,
MA, 02146-0004
(617) 232-8266
Admin Leon Backenroth.
Licensure Intermediate care. *Beds* 80.
  Certified Medicaid.

Coolidge Street Rest Home
41 Coolidge St, Brookline, MA, 02146
(617) 566-6636
Admin Nancy A Winer.
Licensure Community support rest homes.
  Beds 24. *Certified* Medicaid.
Owner Proprietary Corp.
Admissions Requirements Females only.
Staff Physicians 1 (pt); RNs 1 (pt); Orderlies 1
  (pt); Nurses aides 3 (ft), 2 (pt); Activities
  coordinators 1 (pt); Dietitians 1 (pt);
  Ophthalmologists 1 (pt); Podiatrists 1 (pt);
  Social worker; Community support
  coordinator.
Facilities Dining room; Activities room;
  Crafts room; Laundry room; Library.
Activities Arts & crafts; Cards; Games;
  Reading groups; Prayer groups; Movies;
  Shopping trips; Social/Cultural gatherings.

Mason Terrace Rest Home
12 Mason Terrace, Brookline, MA, 02146
(617) 277-0655
Admin Elaine K Porter.
Licensure Rest home. *Beds* Rest home 26.
  Certified Medicaid.
Owner Proprietary Corp.
Admissions Requirements Minimum age 30;
  Medical examination; Physician's request.
Staff Orderlies 1 (ft); Nurses aides 4 (ft), 2
  (pt); Activities coordinators 1 (pt).
Facilities Dining room; Activities room.
Activities Arts & crafts; Cards; Games;
  Reading groups.

Park Marion Nursing Centre
99 Park St, Brookline, MA, 02146
(617) 731-1050
Admin Kathy W Lesar.
Licensure Skilled care. *Beds* SNF 120.
  Certified Medicaid.
Owner Nonprofit Corp.
Admissions Requirements Medical
  examination; Physician's request.
Staff RNs 18 (ft); Nurses aides 54 (ft);
  Physical therapists 1 (ft); Recreational
  therapists 1 (ft); Occupational therapists 1
  (ft); Speech therapists 1 (ft); Activities
  coordinators 1 (ft); Dietitians 1 (ft);
  Ophthalmologists 1 (ft).
Languages French, Spanish
Facilities Dining room; Physical therapy
  room; Activities room; Crafts room; Laundry
  room; Barber/Beauty shop.
Activities Arts & crafts; Cards; Games;
  Reading groups; Prayer groups; Movies;
  Shopping trips; Social/Cultural gatherings.

Regent Nursing Home
74 Corey Rd, Brighton, Brookline, MA, 02146
(617) 277-2782
Admin Harold Schwartz.
Licensure Intermediate care. *Beds* ICF 41.
  Certified Medicaid.
Owner Privately owned.
Staff RNs 1 (ft); LPNs 1 (ft); Nurses aides 8
  (ft), 4 (pt); Activities coordinators 1 (ft);
  Dietitians 1 (pt).

Facilities Dining room; Activities room;
  Laundry room.
Activities Arts & crafts; Games; Prayer groups.

Wellman House Rest Home*
35-37 Winchester St, Brookline, MA, 02146
(617) 277-4081
Admin Albert V Reynolds.
Licensure Rest home. *Beds* 20.

Winthrop Road Rest Home*
24 Winthrop Rd, Brookline, MA, 02146
(617) 277-5504
Admin Arthur V Reynolds.
Licensure Rest home. *Beds* 31.

BUZZARDS BAY

Cape Cod Nursing & Retirement Home
Lewis Point Rd, Buzzards Bay, MA, 02532
759-5752
Admin Lori N Charles. *Medical Dir/Dir of
  Nursing* Dr Wm Bowers; Mary Rainville
  RN.
Licensure Intermediate care. *Beds* ICF 97.
  Certified Medicaid.
Owner Proprietary Corp (Beverly Enterprises).
Admissions Requirements Minimum age 21;
  Medical examination.
Staff RNs 4 (ft), 2 (pt); LPNs 8 (ft), 4 (pt);
  Nurses aides 10 (ft), 10 (pt); Recreational
  therapists 1 (ft); Activities coordinators 1
  (pt); Dietitians 1 (pt).
Languages Chinese
Facilities Dining room; Activities room;
  Laundry room; Barber/Beauty shop; Outdoor
  walks; Putting green.
Activities Arts & crafts; Cards; Games;
  Reading groups; Prayer groups; Social/
  Cultural gatherings; Exercise groups.

CAMBRIDGE

The Cambridge Homes
360 Mount Auburn St, Cambridge, MA,
02138
(617) 876-0369
Admin Miriam S Klapper. *Medical Dir/Dir of
  Nursing* Dr Aram Tomasian; Lorraine
  Nicholls.
Licensure Intermediate care; Retirement home
  with an Infirmary. *Beds* Level III 12; Level
  IV 38.
Owner Nonprofit organization/foundation.
Admissions Requirements Minimum age 65;
  Medical examination.
Staff Physicians 2 (pt); RNs 2 (ft), 4 (pt);
  LPNs 2 (ft), 2 (pt); Orderlies 1 (pt); Nurses
  aides 3 (ft), 7 (pt); Activities coordinators 1
  (pt); Dietitians 1 (pt); Dentists 1 (pt);
  Ophthalmologists 1 (pt).
Languages French
Facilities Dining room; Activities room;
  Crafts room; Laundry room; Barber/Beauty
  shop; Library; Card room; Guest bedroom; 4
  living rooms; Reading room.
Activities Arts & crafts; Cards; Games;
  Reading groups; Prayer groups; Movies;
  Shopping trips; Social/Cultural gatherings.

Cambridge Nursing Home*
1 Russell St, Cambridge, MA, 02140
(617) 491-6110
Admin Madelyn Dolliver.
Licensure Skilled care; Intermediate care. *Beds*
  119. *Certified* Medicaid.

Cantabridgia Health Care Inc
195 Prospect St, Cambridge, MA, 02139
(617) 491-6363
Admin Barry Chiler. *Medical Dir/Dir of
  Nursing* Eileen Ireton DON.
Licensure Skilled care; Intermediate care. *Beds*
  SNF 49; ICF 50. *Certified* Medicaid.
Owner Proprietary Corp.
Admissions Requirements Minimum age 21.

Staff RNs; LPNs; Orderlies; Nurses aides;
  Physical therapists; Reality therapists;
  Recreational therapists; Occupational
  therapists; Activities coordinators; Dietitians;
  Ophthalmologists.
Languages Portuguese
Facilities Dining room; Activities room;
  Crafts room; Laundry room; Barber/Beauty
  shop.
Activities Arts & crafts; Cards; Games;
  Reading groups; Prayer groups; Movies;
  Shopping trips; Social/Cultural gatherings.

Chester Manor Rest Home*
10 Chester St, Cambridge, MA, 02140
(617) 876-1863
Admin Richard D Pacifico.
Licensure Rest home. *Beds* 36.

The Jane Elizabeth House Nursing Home*
6 Prentiss St, Cambridge, MA, 02140
(617) 354-9018
Admin Bradley McDermott.
Licensure Intermediate care. *Beds* 53.
  Certified Medicaid.

Harvard Manor Nursing Home
273 Harvard St, Cambridge, MA, 02139
(617) 547-4291
Admin Saul Tobias. *Medical Dir/Dir of
  Nursing* M Norah Murray.
Licensure Intermediate care. *Beds* 95.
  Certified Medicaid.
Owner Privately owned.
Admissions Requirements Minimum age 45;
  Medical examination.
Staff RNs 3 (ft); LPNs 7 (ft); Nurses aides 25
  (ft); Recreational therapists 1 (ft); Dietitians
  1 (ft).
Facilities Activities room; Laundry room.
Activities Arts & crafts; Cards; Games; Prayer
  groups; Movies; Shopping trips; Social/
  Cultural gatherings.

**Mayor Michael J Neville Manor Nursing
Home**
650 Concord Ave, Cambridge, MA, 02138
(617) 492-6310
Admin Gerald L MacDonald. *Medical Dir/Dir
  of Nursing* Ilan P Abrams MD; Teresa
  Clunan RN DON.
Licensure Skilled care; Intermediate care. *Beds*
  SNF 97; ICF 83. *Certified* Medicaid.
Owner Nonprofit organization/foundation.
Admissions Requirements Minimum age 21;
  Medical examination.
Staff Physicians 1 (pt); RNs 7 (ft), 5 (pt);
  LPNs 10 (ft), 6 (pt); Orderlies 6 (ft), 1 (pt);
  Nurses aides 41 (ft), 16 (pt); Physical
  therapists 1 (ft); Recreational therapists 3
  (ft); Occupational therapists 1 (pt); Speech
  therapists 1 (pt); Dietitians 1 (pt); Dentists 1
  (pt); Ophthalmologists 1 (pt); Podiatrists 1
  (pt).
Facilities Dining room; Physical therapy
  room; Activities room; Laundry room;
  Barber/Beauty shop; Library; Gift shop.
Activities Arts & crafts; Cards; Games;
  Reading groups; Prayer groups; Movies;
  Shopping trips; Social/Cultural gatherings;
  Bus trips.

Vernon Hall Inc*
8 Dana St, Cambridge, MA, 02138
(617) 864-4267
Admin Joseph G Pallotta.
Licensure Skilled care; Intermediate care. *Beds*
  83. *Certified* Medicaid.

CANTON

Hellenic Nursing Home for The Aged
601 Sherman St, Canton, MA, 02021-2098
(617) 828-7450
Admin Mary Jarvis. *Medical Dir/Dir of
  Nursing* George A Hasiotis; Elaine Luchini.
Licensure Skilled care; Intermediate care. *Beds*
  SNF 80; ICF 80. *Certified* Medicaid.

Owner Nonprofit Corp.
Admissions Requirements Minimum age 65.
Staff Physicians; RNs; LPNs; Orderlies;
Nurses aides; Physical therapists;
Recreational therapists; Occupational
therapists; Speech therapists; Activities
coordinators; Dietitians; Dentists;
Ophthalmologists.
Languages Greek
Affiliation Hellenic Women's Benevolent
Society
Facilities Dining room; Physical therapy
room; Activities room; Chapel; Crafts room;
Laundry room; Barber/Beauty shop.
Activities Arts & crafts; Cards; Games;
Reading groups; Prayer groups; Movies;
Shopping trips; Social/Cultural gatherings.

CARVER

Hilltop Rest Home
Lakeview St, Carver, MA, 02330
(617) 866-4548
Admin Mildred D Weeden.
Licensure Rest home. *Beds* 14.
Admissions Requirements Medical
examination; Physician's request.
Staff Physicians 1 (ft), 1 (pt); RNs 1 (pt);
Nurses aides 1 (ft); Dietitians 1 (pt);
Dentists 1 (pt); Ophthalmologists 1 (pt);
Podiatrists 1 (pt).
Facilities Dining room; Activities room;
Chapel; Laundry room.
Activities Cards; Games; Prayer groups;
Shopping trips; Social/Cultural gatherings.

CENTERVILLE

Centerville Nursing Home Corp
22 Richardson Rd, Centerville, MA, 02632
(617) 775-5050
Admin Ronald W Morris. *Medical Dir/Dir of
Nursing* John F Berry MD; Wilhelmina Cuff
RN DON.
Licensure Skilled care. *Beds* SNF 115.
Certified Medicaid.
Owner Privately owned.
Admissions Requirements Minimum age 21;
Medical examination; Physician's request.
Staff RNs 4 (ft), 8 (pt); LPNs 4 (ft), 2 (pt);
Orderlies 4 (ft); Nurses aides 22 (ft), 12 (pt);
Physical therapists 2 (ft); Recreational
therapists 1 (ft); Speech therapists 1 (pt);
Activities coordinators 1 (ft); Dietitians 1
(pt); Ophthalmologists 1 (pt).
Facilities Dining room; Physical therapy
room; Activities room; Chapel; Crafts room;
Laundry room; Barber/Beauty shop; Library.
Activities Arts & crafts; Games; Reading
groups; Prayer groups; Movies; Social/
Cultural gatherings.

CHARLTON

Charlton Manor Rest Home*
Town Farm Rd, Charlton, MA, 01507
(617) 248-5136
Admin Caroline G Iandoli.
Licensure Rest home. *Beds* 35.

Masonic Home
Masonic Home Rd, Charlton, MA, 01507
(617) 248-7344
Admin James L Parker. *Medical Dir/Dir of
Nursing* Edmond Koury MD; Carol J Mason
DON.
Licensure Skilled care; Residential care. *Beds*
ICF 100; Residential 69. *Certified* Medicaid.
Owner Nonprofit Corp.
Admissions Requirements Minimum age 65;
Medical examination.
Staff Physicians 3 (pt); RNs 7 (ft), 5 (pt);
LPNs 6 (ft), 5 (pt); Nurses aides 40 (ft), 20
(pt); Reality therapists 1 (ft), 1 (pt);
Recreational therapists 1 (ft), 1 (pt);

Activities coordinators 1 (ft); Dietitians 1
(ft); Ophthalmologists 1 (pt); Podiatrists 1
(pt).
Affiliation Masons
Facilities Dining room; Physical therapy
room; Activities room; Chapel; Crafts room;
Laundry room; Barber/Beauty shop; Library;
Music & game room; Greenhouse; Shop;
Dentist office; Auditorium.
Activities Arts & crafts; Cards; Games;
Reading groups; Prayer groups; Movies;
Shopping trips; Social/Cultural gatherings.

CHELMSFORD

Alpine Nursing Home*
83 Middlesex St, Chelmsford, MA, 01863
(617) 251-3472
Admin John G Metcalf Jr. *Medical Dir/Dir of
Nursing* Susan Black MD.
Licensure Intermediate care. *Beds* 23.
Admissions Requirements Medical
examination.
Staff RNs 1 (ft); LPNs 1 (ft), 3 (pt); Orderlies
1 (ft); Nurses aides 2 (ft), 6 (pt); Physical
therapists 1 (pt); Occupational therapists 1
(pt); Speech therapists 1 (pt); Activities
coordinators 1 (ft); Dietitians 1 (pt); Dentists
1 (pt); Ophthalmologists 1 (pt); Podiatrists 1
(pt); Audiologists 1 (pt).
Facilities Dining room; Activities room;
Crafts room; Laundry room; Barber/Beauty
shop; Library.
Activities Arts & crafts; Cards; Games; Prayer
groups; Movies; Shopping trips; Social/
Cultural gatherings.

Palm Manor Nursing Home Inc*
40 Parkhurst Rd, Chelmsford, MA, 01824
(617) 256-3151
Admin Nels A Palm III. *Medical Dir/Dir of
Nursing* Dr Thomas Fitzpatrick.
Licensure Skilled care; Intermediate care. *Beds*
120. *Certified* Medicaid.
Facilities Dining room; Physical therapy
room; Activities room; Chapel; Laundry
room; Barber/Beauty shop; Library.
Activities Arts & crafts; Cards; Games;
Reading groups; Prayer groups; Movies;
Shopping trips; Social/Cultural gatherings.

Serenity Rest Home*
146 Tynsboro Rd, Chelmsford, MA, 01863
(617) 251-4420
Admin Henry H Martell.
Licensure Rest home. *Beds* 21.

Sunny Acres Nursing Home*
254 Billerica Rd, Chelmsford, MA, 01824
(617) 256-0231
Admin Shirley Schwartz.
Licensure Intermediate care. *Beds* 40.
Certified Medicaid.

CHELSEA

Chelsea Jewish Nursing Home*
17 Lafayette Ave, Chelsea, MA, 02150
(617) 884-6766
Admin Barry Berman.
Licensure Intermediate care; Charitable home.
Beds 94. *Certified* Medicaid.
Affiliation Jewish

Cottage Manor Nursing Home
148 Shawmut St, Chelsea, MA, 02150
(617) 889-2250
Admin Marjorie A Minichello.
Licensure Intermediate care. *Beds* 34.
Certified Medicaid.
Admissions Requirements Minimum age 21;
Medical examination.
Staff RNs 2 (ft); LPNs 4 (pt); Orderlies 1 (pt);
Nurses aides 9 (ft), 4 (pt); Recreational
therapists 1 (ft); Activities coordinators 1
(ft); Dietitians 1 (pt).

Facilities Dining room; Activities room;
Crafts room; Laundry room; Barber/Beauty
shop.
Activities Arts & crafts; Cards; Games;
Reading groups; Prayer groups; Movies;
Shopping trips; Social/Cultural gatherings.

**L F Quigley Memorial Skilled Nursing
Facility***
100 Summit Ave, Chelsea, MA, 02150
(617) 884-5660
Admin John L Quigley.
Licensure Skilled care. *Beds* 82. *Certified*
Medicaid; Medicare.

CHICOPEE

Birch Manor Nursing Home
44 New Lombard Rd, Chicopee, MA, 01021
(413) 592-7738
Admin Mary L Harris. *Medical Dir/Dir of
Nursing* Trudy Atteridge.
Licensure Intermediate care. *Beds* ICF 56.
Certified Medicaid.
Owner Proprietary Corp (Health Care &
Retirement Corp).
Staff RNs; LPNs; Nurses aides; Activities
coordinators.
Activities Arts & crafts; Cards; Games;
Reading groups; Prayer groups; Movies;
Shopping trips; Social/Cultural gatherings.

Chicopee Municipal Home
820 Front St, Chicopee, MA, 01020
(413) 598-8455
Admin David F Leitl. *Medical Dir/Dir of
Nursing* Dr Raymond Gagnon; Margaret
Yopak RN.
Licensure Intermediate care. *Beds* ICF 74.
Certified Medicaid.
Owner Nonprofit organization/foundation.
Admissions Requirements Minimum age 60;
Medical examination.
Staff Physicians 1 (pt); RNs 4 (ft), 2 (pt);
LPNs 5 (ft), 1 (pt); Nurses aides 22 (ft), 10
(pt); Recreational therapists 1 (ft);
Occupational therapists 1 (pt); Speech
therapists 1 (pt); Activities coordinators 1
(ft); Dietitians 1 (pt); Ophthalmologists 1
(pt).
Languages French, Polish
Facilities Dining room; Activities room;
Chapel; Crafts room; Laundry room; Barber/
Beauty shop; Library.
Activities Arts & crafts; Cards; Games;
Reading groups; Prayer groups; Movies;
Shopping trips; Social/Cultural gatherings.

Chicopee Rest Home Inc
12 Dallaire Ave, Chicopee, MA, 01020
(413) 532-4004
Admin Ruth I Mercer. *Medical Dir/Dir of
Nursing* Judith Ratkiewicz House Mgr.
Licensure Rest home. *Beds* 38. *Certified*
Medicaid.
Owner Proprietary Corp.
Admissions Requirements Minimum age 50.
Staff RNs 1 (pt); LPNs 1 (pt); Nurses aides 2
(ft), 7 (pt); Activities coordinators 1 (pt);
Dietitians 1 (pt).
Languages French
Facilities Dining room.
Activities Arts & crafts; Cards; Games; Prayer
groups; Shopping trips; Social/Cultural
gatherings.

Elms Manor Nursing Home*
269 Moore St, Chicopee, MA, 01013
(413) 592-7736
Admin Jeffrey Kline.
Licensure Intermediate care. *Beds* 85.
Certified Medicaid.
Owner Proprietary Corp (Health Care &
Retirement Corp).
Admissions Requirements Minimum age 21.
Staff RNs 2 (ft); LPNs 2 (ft), 5 (pt); Nurses
aides 10 (ft), 8 (pt); Physical therapists 1
(pt); Reality therapists 1 (pt); Recreational

therapists 1 (ft); Occupational therapists 1 (pt); Speech therapists 1 (pt); Activities coordinators 1 (ft); Dietitians 1 (pt); Podiatrists 1 (pt).
Facilities Dining room; Activities room; Laundry room; Barber/Beauty shop.
Activities Arts & crafts; Cards; Games; Reading groups; Prayer groups; Movies; Shopping trips; Social/Cultural gatherings.

Willimansett East Nursing Home
11 St Anthony St, Chicopee, MA, 01013
(413) 536-2540
Admin Virginia F Motsky RN. *Medical Dir/Dir of Nursing* William J Dean Jr MD; Eileen C Plante RN DNS.
Licensure Skilled care. *Beds* SNF 85. *Certified* Medicaid; Medicare.
Owner Proprietary Corp (Genesis Health Ventures).
Admissions Requirements Medical examination.
Staff Physicians; RNs; LPNs; Nurses aides; Physical therapists; Recreational therapists; Occupational therapists; Speech therapists; Activities coordinators; Dietitians; Dentists; Ophthalmologists; Podiatrists.
Languages Polish, French
Facilities Dining room; Physical therapy room; Activities room; Chapel; Laundry room; Barber/Beauty shop; Library.
Activities Arts & crafts; Cards; Games; Prayer groups; Movies; Social/Cultural gatherings.

Willimansett West Nursing Home
545 Chicopee St, Chicopee, MA, 01013
(413) 536-2540
Admin E Leo Attella Jr. *Medical Dir/Dir of Nursing* Dr William Dean; Marilyn Dunpity RN.
Licensure Skilled care; Intermediate care. *Beds* SNF 43; ICF 60; 13 Short term rehab. *Certified* Medicaid; Medicare.
Owner Proprietary Corp (Genesis Health Ventures).
Admissions Requirements Physician's request.
Staff RNs; LPNs; Orderlies; Nurses aides; Physical therapists; Recreational therapists; Occupational therapists; Speech therapists; Activities coordinators; Dietitians; Ophthalmologists; Podiatrists.
Languages Polish, French, Spanish, Portuguese
Facilities Dining room; Physical therapy room; Activities room; Chapel; Crafts room; Barber/Beauty shop; Solarium; Beautiful landscaped outdoor area with patio & garden.
Activities Arts & crafts; Cards; Games; Reading groups; Prayer groups; Movies; Shopping trips; Social/Cultural gatherings; Field trips; Outings; Red Sox games; Pet therapy; Bingo.

CLINTON

Clinton Home for Aged People*
271 Church St, Clinton, MA, 01510
(617) 365-4872
Admin Marjorie C Stake.
Licensure Rest home. *Beds* 12.
Admissions Requirements Minimum age 65; Medical examination.
Staff RNs 1 (pt).
Facilities Dining room; Living room.

Clinton Manor Nursing Home
250 Main St, Clinton, MA, 01510
(617) 368-0171
Admin John A Holt. *Medical Dir/Dir of Nursing* Dr Allan Ramey; Patricia P Dwyer DNS.
Licensure Skilled care; Intermediate care. *Beds* SNF 49; ICF 30. *Certified* Medicaid.
Owner Privately owned.
Admissions Requirements Medical examination; Physician's request.

Staff RNs; LPNs; Orderlies; Nurses aides; Activities coordinators; Dietitians.
Languages Italian
Facilities Dining room; Physical therapy room; Laundry room; Barber/Beauty shop.
Activities Arts & crafts; Cards; Games; Reading groups; Prayer groups; Movies; Social/Cultural gatherings; Garden; Cooking; Trivia; One on one visits; Slides; Pet therapy; Adopt-a-grandparent program; Pen & Palette sittercise; & more.

Ferguson Rest Home*
88 Walnut St, Clinton, MA, 01510
(617) 365-3552
Admin Duncan Ferguson. *Medical Dir/Dir of Nursing* Dr William Jacobson.
Licensure Rest home. *Beds* 17.
Admissions Requirements Minimum age 50; Females only; Medical examination; Physician's request.
Staff LPNs 1 (pt); Nurses aides 6 (pt).
Facilities Dining room; Laundry room; Barber/Beauty shop; Library.
Activities Arts & crafts; Games; Movies; Shopping trips.

COHASSET

Cohasset Knoll Nursing Home*
Rte 3A, Cohasset, MA, 02025
(617) 383-9060
Admin Arthur C Taylor. *Medical Dir/Dir of Nursing* Albert Cline.
Licensure Skilled care. *Beds* 80. *Certified* Medicare.
Owner Proprietary Corp (Beverly Enterprises).
Admissions Requirements Minimum age 21; Medical examination; Physician's request.
Staff Physicians 16 (pt); RNs 5 (ft), 4 (pt); LPNs 2 (ft), 3 (pt); Nurses aides 21 (ft), 20 (pt); Physical therapists 1 (pt); Occupational therapists 1 (pt); Speech therapists 1 (pt); Activities coordinators 1 (ft), 1 (pt); Dietitians 1 (pt); Dentists 1 (pt); Podiatrists 2 (pt).
Facilities Dining room; Physical therapy room; Activities room; Crafts room; Laundry room; Barber/Beauty shop; Library; Sitting rooms.
Activities Arts & crafts; Cards; Games; Reading groups; Prayer groups; Movies; Shopping trips; Social/Cultural gatherings.

Ripley Road Nursing Home Inc*
25 Ripley Rd, Cohasset, MA, 02025
(617) 383-0419
Admin Kathleen R Logan.
Licensure Intermediate care. *Beds* 22. *Certified* Medicaid.
Owner Proprietary Corp.

CONCORD

Rivercrest Long-Term Care Facility
80 Deaconess Rd, Concord, MA, 01742
(617) 369-5151
Admin Cathy B Smith. *Medical Dir/Dir of Nursing* Dr Henry Vaillant.
Licensure Skilled care; Intermediate care. *Beds* SNF 41; ICF 39. *Certified* Medicaid; Medicare.
Owner Nonprofit Corp.
Admissions Requirements Minimum age 65.
Staff Physicians 3 (pt); RNs 8 (ft), 21 (pt); LPNs 9 (ft), 2 (pt); Nurses aides 20 (ft), 19 (pt); Physical therapists 1 (pt); Reality therapists 1 (ft); Occupational therapists 1 (pt); Speech therapists 1 (pt); Activities coordinators 1 (ft); Dietitians 1 (ft); Ophthalmologists 1 (pt).
Affiliation Methodist
Facilities Dining room; Physical therapy room; Activities room; Chapel; Crafts room; Barber/Beauty shop; Library.

Activities Arts & crafts; Cards; Games; Reading groups; Prayer groups; Movies; Shopping trips; Social/Cultural gatherings.

Walden House Healthcare Nursing Home
785 Main St, Concord, MA, 01742
(617) 369-6889
Admin Ira R Lipshutz. *Medical Dir/Dir of Nursing* Mary Donald MD; Helen McNabola RN DON.
Licensure Skilled care. *Beds* SNF 123; ICF; ICF 123. *Certified* Medicaid; Medicare.
Owner Proprietary Corp (Hillhaven Corp).
Admissions Requirements Medical examination; Physician's request.
Staff RNs 6 (ft), 12 (pt); LPNs 4 (ft), 5 (pt); Nurses aides 30 (ft), 10 (pt); Physical therapists 1 (pt); Recreational therapists 2 (ft); Occupational therapists 1 (pt); Speech therapists 1 (pt); Activities coordinators 1 (ft); Dietitians 1 (pt); Ophthalmologists 1 (pt).
Languages Spanish, Portuguese
Facilities Dining room; Physical therapy room; Activities room; Chapel; Crafts room; Laundry room; Barber/Beauty shop; Library.
Activities Arts & crafts; Cards; Games; Prayer groups; Movies; Shopping trips; Social/Cultural gatherings.

DALTON

Curtis Manor Retirement Home*
83 Curtis Ave, Dalton, MA, 01226
(413) 684-0218
Admin Bradford Jameson.
Licensure Rest home. *Beds* 23.

Dalton Nursing Home Inc*
265 Main St, Dalton, MA, 01226
(413) 684-3212
Admin Harry S Chapman. *Medical Dir/Dir of Nursing* Wilfren A Blais MD.
Licensure Skilled care. *Beds* 77. *Certified* Medicaid.
Staff RNs 3 (ft), 4 (pt); LPNs 5 (ft), 5 (pt); Orderlies 2 (ft); Nurses aides 14 (ft), 19 (pt); Physical therapists 2 (ft); Activities coordinators 1 (ft); Dietitians 1 (pt); Podiatrists 1 (pt).
Facilities Dining room; Physical therapy room; Activities room; Crafts room; Laundry room; Barber/Beauty shop.
Activities Arts & crafts; Games; Reading groups; Prayer groups; Movies; Shopping trips; Social/Cultural gatherings.

DANVERS

Blakedale Rest Home
49 Coolidge Rd, Danvers, MA, 01923
(617) 774-4391
Admin Jill H Pidgeon.
Licensure Level IV Rest home. *Beds* ICF/MR 13. *Certified* Medicaid; Medicare.
Owner Privately owned.
Staff RNs 1 (pt); Nurses aides 8 (pt); Activities coordinators 1 (pt); Dietitians 1 (pt).
Facilities Dining room; Laundry room.
Activities Arts & crafts; Cards; Prayer groups; Movies.

Cedar Glen Nursing Home
44 Summer St, Danvers, MA, 01923
(617) 774-6955
Admin Linda Barrington.
Licensure Skilled care; Intermediate care; Residential care. *Beds* 100. *Certified* Medicaid.

Danvers Twin Oaks Nursing Home
63 Locust St, Danvers, MA, 01923
(617) 777-0011
Admin Beth Casso. *Medical Dir/Dir of Nursing* John Hazelton MD; Barbara Pasquariello RN.

Licensure Skilled care; Intermediate care. *Beds*
SNF 65; ICF 36. *Certified* Medicaid;
Medicare.
Owner Proprietary Corp.
Staff RNs; LPNs; Orderlies; Nurses aides;
Physical therapists; Recreational therapists;
Occupational therapists; Speech therapists;
Activities coordinators; Dietitians.
Facilities Dining room; Physical therapy
room; Activities room; Crafts room; Laundry
room; Barber/Beauty shop; Library; Day
rooms.
Activities Arts & crafts; Cards; Games;
Reading groups; Prayer groups; Movies;
Shopping trips; Social/Cultural gatherings;
Hospitality program; Student volunteers;
Adult volunteers.

Heritage House Nursing Home
11 Sylvan St, Danvers, MA, 01923
(617) 774-1763
Admin David W Bittner.
Licensure Intermediate care. *Beds* 46.
Certified Medicaid.
Owner Proprietary Corp.
Admissions Requirements Minimum age 21.
Staff RNs 2 (ft), 4 (pt); LPNs 2 (ft), 6 (pt);
Nurses aides 6 (ft), 12 (pt); Recreational
therapists 1 (pt); Activities coordinators 1
(ft), 1 (pt); Dietitians 1 (pt);
Ophthalmologists 1 (pt).
Facilities Dining room; Activities room;
Laundry room.
Activities Arts & crafts; Cards; Games;
Reading groups; Prayer groups; Movies;
Shopping trips; Social/Cultural gatherings.

**Charles V Hogan Regional Center & John T
Berry Rehabilitation Center**
PO Box A, Danvers, MA, 01937
(617) 774-5000
Admin Edward W Budelmann. *Medical Dir/
Dir of Nursing* Zsuzanna Dallos MD;
Dorothy Mullen DON.
Licensure Intermediate care for mentally
retarded. *Beds* 325. *Certified* Medicaid.
Owner Publicly owned.
Staff Physicians; RNs; LPNs; Physical
therapists; Recreational therapists;
Occupational therapists; Speech therapists;
Activities coordinators; Dietitians;
Ophthalmologists; Podiatrists.
Facilities Dining room; Physical therapy
room; Activities room; Chapel; Crafts room;
Laundry room; Barber/Beauty shop; Library.
Activities Arts & crafts; Cards; Games;
Reading groups; Prayer groups; Movies;
Shopping trips; Social/Cultural gatherings.

Hunt Nursing & Retirement Home Inc*
90 Lindall St, Danvers, MA, 01923
(617) 777-3740
Admin Daniel Micherone. *Medical Dir/Dir of
Nursing* B Geoffrey Piken MD.
Licensure Skilled care; Intermediate care. *Beds*
120. *Certified* Medicaid.
Owner Proprietary Corp (Hannover
Healthcare).
Admissions Requirements Minimum age 60.
Staff Physicians 3 (pt); RNs 18 (pt); LPNs 6
(pt); Orderlies 5 (pt); Nurses aides 65 (pt);
Physical therapists 1 (pt); Recreational
therapists 1 (pt); Occupational therapists 1
(pt); Speech therapists 1 (pt); Activities
coordinators 2 (pt); Dietitians 1 (pt);
Dentists 1 (pt); Ophthalmologists 1 (pt);
Podiatrists 1 (pt); Audiologists 1 (pt).
Facilities Dining room; Physical therapy
room; Activities room; Crafts room; Laundry
room; Barber/Beauty shop; Library; Patios.
Activities Arts & crafts; Cards; Games;
Reading groups; Prayer groups; Movies;
Shopping trips; Social/Cultural gatherings;
Community program.

Liberty Pavilion Nursing Home
56 Liberty St, Danvers, MA, 01923
(617) 777-2700

Admin Jean Heffernan. *Medical Dir/Dir of
Nursing* John Hazelton MD; Melba
Wharton.
Licensure Skilled care; Intermediate care. *Beds*
SNF 80; ICF 80. *Certified* Medicaid;
Medicare.
Owner Proprietary Corp (Greenery Rehab
Grp).
Admissions Requirements Minimum age 18;
Medical examination; Physician's request.
Staff Physicians 25 (pt); RNs 6 (ft), 5 (pt);
LPNs 7 (ft), 4 (pt); Orderlies 1 (ft), 2 (pt);
Nurses aides 31 (ft), 70 (pt); Physical
therapists 1 (pt); Occupational therapists 1
(pt); Speech therapists 1 (pt); Activities
coordinators 1 (ft); Dietitians 1 (pt); Dentists
1 (pt); Ophthalmologists 1 (pt); Podiatrists 1
(pt); Psychiatrist 1 (pt).
Facilities Dining room; Physical therapy
room; Activities room; Crafts room; Laundry
room; Barber/Beauty shop.
Activities Arts & crafts; Cards; Games;
Reading groups; Prayer groups; Movies;
Social/Cultural gatherings.

New England Home for the Deaf
154 Water St, Danvers, MA, 01923
(617) 774-0445
Admin Eddy F Laird.
Licensure Residential care. *Beds* Residential
30.
Owner Nonprofit Corp.
Staff RNs 1 (pt); Nurses aides 6 (ft), 6 (pt);
Activities coordinators 2 (ft), 2 (pt).

DARTMOUTH

Brandon Woods of Dartmouth
567 Dartmouth St, Dartmouth, MA, 02748
(617) 997-7787
Admin Robert E Arsenault. *Medical Dir/Dir of
Nursing* James W Ross MD; Elaine
Tetreault RN.
Licensure Skilled care; Intermediate care. *Beds*
SNF 37; ICF 71. *Certified* Medicaid.
Owner Proprietary Corp.
Admissions Requirements Minimum age 65;
Medical examination.
Staff RNs; LPNs; Nurses aides; Physical
therapists; Recreational therapists;
Occupational therapists; Speech therapists;
Activities coordinators; Dietitians.
Facilities Dining room; Physical therapy
room; Activities room; Chapel; Crafts room;
Laundry room; Barber/Beauty shop.
Activities Arts & crafts; Cards; Games; Prayer
groups; Movies; Shopping trips; Social/
Cultural gatherings.

Country Rest Home
263 Bakerville Rd, Dartmouth, MA, 02714
(617) 992-9280
Admin Elsie M Niemac.
Licensure Rest home. *Beds* 25.

Dartmouth Manor Rest Home*
70 State Rd, Dartmouth, MA, 02747
(617) 993-9255
Admin James Casey.
Licensure Rest home. *Beds* 25.

DEDHAM

Eastwood at Dedham Convalescent Center*
1007 East St, Dedham, MA, 02026
(617) 329-1520
Admin Julie A Secord.
Licensure Skilled care; Intermediate care. *Beds*
142. *Certified* Medicaid.
Owner Proprietary Corp (Beverly Enterprises).

DEERFIELD

Hillside Nursing Home*
N Hillside Rd, Deerfield, MA, 01373
(413) 665-2200
Admin Robert S Page Jr.

Licensure Intermediate care. *Beds* 54.
Certified Medicaid.

DIGHTON

Dighton Nursing & Convalescent Home*
907 Centre St, Dighton, MA, 02764
(617) 669-6741
Admin Henry J Keenan.
Licensure Intermediate care. *Beds* 30.
Certified Medicaid.

DORCHESTER

Ann's Rest Home
66 Bowdoin Ave, Dorchester, MA, 02121-
3997
(617) 825-1793
Admin Willard L Basler.
Licensure Intermediate care. *Beds* ICF 13.
Certified Medicaid; Medicare.
Owner Privately owned.
Admissions Requirements Minimum age 21;
Medical examination; Physician's request.
Staff Activities coordinators;
Ophthalmologists.
Facilities Dining room; Activities room;
Crafts room; Library.
Activities Arts & crafts; Cards; Games;
Movies.

Edgewood Convalescent Home*
637 Washington St, Dorchester, MA, 02124
(617) 436-6210
Admin Brian T Hurley. *Medical Dir/Dir of
Nursing* Mark Ostrem MD.
Licensure Skilled care; Intermediate care. *Beds*
SNF 48; ICF 50. *Certified* Medicaid.
Owner Proprietary Corp (Hillhaven Corp).
Admissions Requirements Physician's request.
Staff RNs 5 (ft); LPNs 5 (ft); Orderlies 2 (ft);
Nurses aides 30 (ft), 15 (pt); Physical
therapists 1 (ft), 1 (pt); Occupational therapists 1 (pt);
Speech therapists 1 (pt); Dietitians 1 (pt);
Dentists 1 (pt); Ophthalmologists 1 (pt);
Podiatrists 1 (pt).
Facilities Dining room; Physical therapy
room; Activities room; Crafts room; Laundry
room; Barber/Beauty shop.
Activities Arts & crafts; Cards; Games;
Reading groups; Prayer groups; Movies;
Shopping trips.

Grampian Nursing Home
33 Grampian Way, Dorchester, MA, 02125
(617) 436-3331
Admin Louis Furash. *Medical Dir/Dir of
Nursing* Kathleen A Maffie.
Licensure Intermediate care. *Beds* ICF 26.
Certified Medicaid; Medicare.
Owner Proprietary Corp.
Admissions Requirements Minimum age 18;
Females only; Medical examination;
Physician's request.
Staff Physicians 4 (pt); RNs 2 (pt); LPNs 3
(ft), 3 (pt); Nurses aides 8 (ft), 5 (pt);
Physical therapists 1 (pt); Reality therapists
1 (pt); Recreational therapists 1 (pt);
Occupational therapists 1 (pt); Speech
therapists 1 (pt); Activities coordinators 1
(pt); Dietitians 1 (pt); Dentists 1 (pt);
Ophthalmologists 1 (pt); Podiatrists 1 (pt).
Languages French
Facilities Laundry room; Barber/Beauty shop.
Activities Arts & crafts; Cards; Games;
Reading groups; Movies; Shopping trips;
Social/Cultural gatherings.

Long-Term Care at Neponset—Ashmont Manor
45 Coffey St, Neponset, Dorchester, MA,
02122
(617) 282-9700
Admin Peter S Gordon. *Medical Dir/Dir of
Nursing* Sharon Acker.
Licensure Intermediate care. *Beds* ICF 77.
Owner Proprietary Corp.

Staff RNs 2 (ft), 1 (pt); LPNs 5 (ft), 6 (pt); Nurses aides 20 (ft), 20 (pt); Physical therapists 1 (pt); Reality therapists 2 (ft); Recreational therapists 2 (ft), 2 (pt); Occupational therapists 1 (pt); Activities coordinators 1 (ft); Dietitians 1 (pt).
Facilities Dining room; Activities room; Crafts room; Laundry room; Barber/Beauty shop.
Activities Arts & crafts; Cards; Games; Reading groups; Prayer groups; Movies; Shopping trips; Social/Cultural gatherings.

Long-Term Care at Neponset—Neponset Hall
35 Coffey St, Neponset, Dorchester, MA, 02171
(617) 282-3600
Admin Peter S Gordon. *Medical Dir/Dir of Nursing* Sharon Acker.
Licensure Intermediate care. *Beds* ICF 98.
Owner Proprietary Corp.
Staff RNs 2 (ft), 2 (pt); LPNs 5 (ft), 6 (pt); Nurses aides 20 (ft), 25 (pt); Physical therapists 1 (pt); Reality therapists 1 (ft), 1 (pt); Recreational therapists 1 (ft), 1 (pt); Occupational therapists 1 (pt); Activities coordinators 1 (ft); Dietitians 1 (pt).
Facilities Dining room; Activities room; Laundry room; Barber/Beauty shop.
Activities Arts & crafts; Cards; Games; Reading groups; Prayer groups; Movies; Shopping trips; Social/Cultural gatherings.

DUXBURY

Duxbury House Nursing Home
298 Kings Town Way, Duxbury, MA, 02332
(617) 585-2397
Admin Ruth St John.
Licensure Intermediate care. *Beds* ICF 23. *Certified* Medicaid.
Owner Privately owned.
Admissions Requirements Minimum age 21; Medical examination; Physician's request.
Staff RNs 1 (ft); LPNs 4 (ft); Orderlies 5 (ft); Activities coordinators 1 (ft).
Facilities Dining room; Activities room; Laundry room.
Activities Arts & crafts; Cards; Games; Prayer groups; Movies; Shopping trips; Social/Cultural gatherings.

EAST BRAINTREE

Resthaven Nursing Home
155 Quincy Ave, East Braintree, MA, 02184
(617) 843-2155
Admin Ruth E Houde.
Licensure Skilled care. *Beds* 72. *Certified* Medicaid.
Activities Arts & crafts; Games; Reading groups; Prayer groups; Movies.

EAST BRIDGEWATER

Forge Pond Nursing Home
66 Central St, East Bridgewater, MA, 02333-1999
(617) 378-7227
Admin Bruce Kaiser. *Medical Dir/Dir of Nursing* George Gagne MD; Claire Wheeler RN DON.
Licensure Skilled care; Intermediate care. *Beds* SNF 82; ICF 41. *Certified* Medicaid.
Owner Proprietary Corp.
Admissions Requirements Minimum age 21; Medical examination; Physician's request.
Staff Physicians 2 (pt); RNs 3 (ft), 5 (pt); LPNs 3 (ft), 10 (pt); Orderlies 3 (pt); Nurses aides 29 (ft), 31 (pt); Physical therapists 1 (pt); Occupational therapists 1 (pt); Speech therapists 1 (pt); Activities coordinators 2 (ft); Dietitians 1 (pt); Dentists 1 (pt); Ophthalmologists 1 (pt); Podiatrists 1 (pt).

Facilities Dining room; Activities room; Crafts room; Laundry room; Barber/Beauty shop; Screened porch; Outside patio; Gardens.
Activities Arts & crafts; Cards; Games; Reading groups; Prayer groups; Movies; Shopping trips; Social/Cultural gatherings.

Westview Rest Home*
446 West St, East Bridgewater, MA, 02333
(617) 378-2451
Admin Robert W Carey Jr.
Licensure Rest home. *Beds* 18.

EAST LONGMEADOW

East Longmeadow Nursing Center/ Longmeadow House
305 Maple St, East Longmeadow, MA, 01028
(413) 525-6361
Admin Russell J Firewicz. *Medical Dir/Dir of Nursing* Dr John Quinn; Ann Sleith.
Licensure Skilled care; Intermediate care. *Beds* SNF 78; ICF 41. *Certified* Medicaid.
Owner Proprietary Corp (Hannover Healthcare).
Admissions Requirements Minimum age 60.
Staff RNs 5 (ft), 13 (pt); LPNs 2 (ft), 3 (pt); Nurses aides; Physical therapists 1 (ft), 2 (pt); Occupational therapists 1 (pt); Speech therapists 1 (pt); Activities coordinators 2 (ft); Dietitians 1 (pt); Ophthalmologists 1 (pt).
Facilities Dining room; Physical therapy room; Activities room; Crafts room; Laundry room; Barber/Beauty shop.
Activities Arts & crafts; Cards; Games; Reading groups; Movies; Shopping trips.

EASTHAMPTON

Hampshire Manor Nursing Home
Rte 10, Easthampton, MA, 01027
(413) 584-2213
Admin David LaBroad.
Licensure Intermediate care. *Beds* 42. *Certified* Medicaid.

EASTON

Easton-Lincoln Nursing Home
184 Lincoln St, Easton, MA, 02356
(617) 238-7053
Admin Sharmalee Bernhardt. *Medical Dir/Dir of Nursing* Nancy Sylvia DON.
Licensure Skilled care; Intermediate care. *Beds* SNF 41; ICF 46. *Certified* Medicaid; Medicare.
Owner Proprietary Corp (Oakwood Living Centers).
Admissions Requirements Minimum age 21.
Staff RNs; LPNs; Nurses aides; Activities coordinators.
Languages Portuguese, Indonesian
Facilities Dining room; Physical therapy room; Activities room; Crafts room; Laundry room; Barber/Beauty shop; TV rooms; Community rooms.
Activities Arts & crafts; Cards; Games; Prayer groups; Movies; Shopping trips; Cooking class; Coffee hours; Bowling.

Village Rest Home*
22 Main St, Easton, MA, 02356
(617) 238-7262
Admin Carol L Audette.
Licensure Rest home. *Beds* 14.
Admissions Requirements Females only; Medical examination; Physician's request.
Staff LPNs 1 (pt); Nurses aides 5 (pt); Dietitians 1 (pt).
Facilities Dining room; Activities room; Laundry room.
Activities Arts & crafts; Cards; Games; Movies; Shopping trips; Social/Cultural gatherings.

EVERETT

Robert Appleton Nursing Home*
153 Linden St, Everett, MA, 02149
(617) 389-3699
Admin Miriam S Clapper.
Licensure Intermediate care. *Beds* 23. *Certified* Medicaid.

Parkway Manor Nursing Home*
13 School St, Everett, MA, 02149
(617) 387-1200
Admin Lillian M Murray.
Licensure Intermediate care. *Beds* 57. *Certified* Medicaid.
Admissions Requirements Minimum age 21; Medical examination; Physician's request.
Staff RNs 2 (ft), 2 (pt); LPNs 5 (ft), 3 (pt); Nurses aides 16 (ft), 9 (pt); Activities coordinators 1 (ft); Dietitians 1 (pt).
Facilities Dining room; Activities room.
Activities Arts & crafts; Cards; Games; Reading groups; Prayer groups; Movies; Social/Cultural gatherings.

Woodlawn Manor Nursing Home*
289 Elm St, Everett, MA, 02149
(617) 387-6560
Admin James R Plunkett.
Licensure Skilled care; Intermediate care. *Beds* 144. *Certified* Medicaid.

FAIRHAVEN

Bailie's Rest Home*
125 New Boston Rd, Fairhaven, MA, 02719
(617) 993-4106
Admin Eleanor M Charpentier.
Licensure Rest home. *Beds* 12.

Center Green Rest Home
109 Green St, Fairhaven, MA, 02719
(617) 994-7653
Licensure Intermediate care. *Beds* ICF 27.
Owner Proprietary Corp.
Admissions Requirements Minimum age 18; Medical examination.
Staff LPNs 1 (pt); Nurses aides 3 (ft), 3 (pt); Activities coordinators 1 (pt); Dietitians 1 (pt); Podiatrists 1 (pt).
Facilities Dining room; Activities room; Laundry room.
Activities Arts & crafts; Cards; Games; Movies; Shopping trips; Social/Cultural gatherings.

McCormack Rest Home*
88 Fort St, Fairhaven, MA, 02719
(617) 993-3277
Admin Teresa Ann Vieira.
Licensure Rest home. *Beds* 13.

Nichols House Nursing Home*
184 Main St, Fairhaven, MA, 02719
(617) 997-3193
Admin W B Glass. *Medical Dir/Dir of Nursing* Edward D Mackler MD.
Licensure Skilled care; Intermediate care. *Beds* 107. *Certified* Medicaid; Medicare.
Staff RNs 8 (ft), 5 (pt); LPNs 6 (ft), 3 (pt); Nurses aides 31 (ft), 17 (pt); Reality therapists 1 (ft); Occupational therapists 1 (pt); Speech therapists 1 (pt); Activities coordinators 2 (ft), 1 (pt); Dietitians 1 (pt); Dentists 1 (pt); Ophthalmologists 1 (pt); Podiatrists 1 (pt); Audiologists 1 (pt).
Facilities Dining room; Physical therapy room; Activities room; Laundry room; Barber/Beauty shop; Library.
Activities Arts & crafts; Cards; Games; Reading groups; Prayer groups; Movies; Shopping trips; Social/Cultural gatherings.

Our Lady's Haven
71 Center St, Fairhaven, MA, 02719
(617) 999-4561
Admin Martha J Daneault.

Licensure Intermediate care. *Beds* ICF 38.
Certified Medicaid.
Owner Nonprofit Corp.
Admissions Requirements Minimum age 65;
Medical examination.
Staff Physicians; RNs 3 (ft), 8 (pt); LPNs 6
(ft), 12 (pt); Orderlies 2 (ft); Nurses aides 35
(ft), 13 (pt); Physical therapists; Reality
therapists; Recreational therapists;
Occupational therapists; Speech therapists;
Activities coordinators 1 (pt); Dietitians;
Dentists; Ophthalmologists; Podiatrists.
Affiliation Roman Catholic
Facilities Dining room; Physical therapy
room; Activities room; Chapel; Crafts room;
Laundry room; Barber/Beauty shop; Library.
Activities Arts & crafts; Cards; Games;
Reading groups; Prayer groups; Movies;
Shopping trips; Social/Cultural gatherings.

FALL RIVER

Catholic Memorial Home Inc
2446 Highland Ave, Fall River, MA, 02720
(617) 679-0011
Admin Sister Shawn Flynn. *Medical Dir/Dir of
Nursing* Robert J Rubano MD; Jean M
Quigley RNBSN.
Licensure Skilled care; Intermediate care. *Beds*
SNF; ICF 288. *Certified* Medicaid;
Medicare.
Owner Nonprofit Corp.
Admissions Requirements Minimum age 65;
Medical examination; Physician's request.
Staff RNs 5 (ft), 15 (pt); LPNs 14 (ft), 19 (pt);
Orderlies 1 (pt); Nurses aides 100 (ft), 73
(pt); Reality therapists 1 (ft); Activities
coordinators 6 (ft), 1 (pt).
Languages Portuguese, French, Spanish
Affiliation Roman Catholic
Facilities Dining room; Physical therapy
room; Activities room; Chapel; Crafts room;
Laundry room; Barber/Beauty shop; Library;
Wood shop; Dentist office.
Activities Arts & crafts; Cards; Games;
Reading groups; Prayer groups; Movies;
Shopping trips; Social/Cultural gatherings;
Gourmet cooking class.

Cliff Gables Nursing Home*
423 Middle St, Fall River, MA, 02724
(617) 687-4855
Admin Linda Valenzano.
Licensure Intermediate care. *Beds* 39.
Certified Medicaid.

Cliff Haven Nursing Home*
745 Highland Ave, Fall River, MA, 02720
(617) 674-3354
Admin Linda Valenzano.
Licensure Intermediate care. *Beds* 31.
Certified Medicaid.

Cliff Heights Nursing Home*
635 Rock St, Fall River, MA, 02720
(617) 674-7509
Admin Linda Valenzano.
Licensure Intermediate care. *Beds* 34.
Certified Medicaid.

Cliff Lawn Nursing Home*
851 Highland Ave, Fall River, MA, 02720
(617) 678-6100
Admin Linda Valenzano.
Licensure Intermediate care. *Beds* 26.
Certified Medicaid.

Cliff Manor Nursing Home*
431 Rock St, Fall River, MA, 02720
(617) 678-8011
Admin Linda Valenzano.
Licensure Intermediate care. *Beds* 37.
Certified Medicaid.

Crawford House Convalescent Home*
273 Oak Grove Ave, Fall River, MA, 02723
(617) 679-4866
Admin Gilberto Reis.

Licensure Skilled care; Intermediate care. *Beds*
123. *Certified* Medicaid.
Owner Proprietary Corp (Hillhaven Corp).

Crestwood Convalescent Home*
170 Oak Grove Ave, Fall River, MA, 02723
(617) 678-5234
Admin Joyce Pinto.
Licensure Skilled care; Intermediate care. *Beds*
102. *Certified* Medicaid.
Owner Proprietary Corp (Hillhaven Corp).

Fall River Jewish Home for the Aged*
538 Robeson St, Fall River, MA, 02720
(617) 679-6172
Admin Ellen Feldman.
Licensure Skilled care; Intermediate care. *Beds*
60. *Certified* Medicaid.
Affiliation Jewish

Fall River Nursing Home Inc*
1748 Highland Ave, Fall River, MA, 02720
(617) 675-1131
Admin James A Jackson. *Medical Dir/Dir of
Nursing* N Kenneth Shand MD.
Licensure Skilled care; Intermediate care. *Beds*
164. *Certified* Medicaid.
Admissions Requirements Minimum age 16.
Staff Physicians 1 (pt); RNs 14 (ft), 5 (pt);
LPNs 11 (ft), 5 (pt); Orderlies 2 (ft); Nurses
aides 48 (ft), 31 (pt); Physical therapists 1
(ft), 1 (pt); Recreational therapists 1 (ft), 2
(pt); Occupational therapists 1 (pt);
Dietitians 1 (pt); Dentists 1 (pt); Podiatrists
2 (pt).
Facilities Dining room; Physical therapy
room; Activities room; Chapel; Crafts room;
Laundry room; Barber/Beauty shop; Library.
Activities Arts & crafts; Cards; Games;
Reading groups; Prayer groups; Movies;
Shopping trips; Social/Cultural gatherings.

Hanover House Retirement Facility*
391 Hanover St, Fall River, MA, 02720
(617) 675-7583
Admin Irma Lentenore.
Licensure Rest home. *Beds* 35.

Highland Manor Nursing Home Inc*
761 Highland Ave, Fall River, MA, 02720
(617) 679-1411
Admin Michael F Cummings.
Licensure Intermediate care. *Beds* 26.
Certified Medicaid.

Home for Aged People in Fall River*
1168 Highland Ave, Fall River, MA, 02720
(617) 679-0144
Admin Yolanda E McAuliffe.
Licensure Rest home. *Beds* 59.
Admissions Requirements Minimum age 68;
Medical examination; Physician's request.

Kimwell Health Care Center
495 New Boston Rd, Fall River, MA, 02720
(617) 679-0106
Admin Michael E Isabella. *Medical Dir/Dir of
Nursing* N Kenneth Shand MD; Sharon
Lounsbury.
Licensure Skilled care; Intermediate care. *Beds*
SNF 82; ICF 42. *Certified* Medicaid;
Medicare.
Owner Privately owned.
Admissions Requirements Medical
examination.
Staff Physicians 3 (pt); RNs 8 (ft), 2 (pt);
LPNs 7 (ft), 8 (pt); Orderlies 2 (ft); Nurses
aides 20 (ft), 27 (pt); Physical therapists 1
(pt); Reality therapists 1 (pt); Recreational
therapists 2 (ft), 2 (pt); Occupational
therapists 1 (pt); Speech therapists 1 (pt);
Dietitians 1 (pt); Dentists 1 (pt);
Ophthalmologists 1 (pt); Podiatrists 1 (pt).
Facilities Dining room; Physical therapy
room; Activities room; Chapel; Crafts room;
Laundry room; Barber/Beauty shop; Library.
Activities Arts & crafts; Cards; Games;
Reading groups; Prayer groups; Movies;
Shopping trips; Social/Cultural gatherings.

Rose Hawthorne Lathrop Home
1600 Bay St, Fall River, MA, 02724
(617) 673-2322
Admin Sr M Denise. *Medical Dir/Dir of
Nursing* Sr M Imelda.
Licensure Intermediate care. *Beds* 35.
Certified Medicaid.
Owner Nonprofit Corp.
Staff Physicians 1 (pt); RNs 2 (ft); LPNs 2
(ft); Orderlies 5 (ft); Nurses aides 7 (ft);
Dietitians 1 (pt); Social worker 1 (pt).
Facilities Dining room; Chapel; Laundry
room.

Rosewood Manor Rest Home*
547 Highland Ave, Fall River, MA, 02720
(617) 678-6075
Licensure Rest home. *Beds* 60.
Admissions Requirements Minimum age 21;
Medical examination.
Staff Nurses aides 6 (ft), 6 (pt); Activities
coordinators 1 (ft); Dietitians 1 (pt); Dentists
1 (pt); Ophthalmologists 1 (pt); Podiatrists 1
(pt).
Facilities Dining room; Activities room;
Laundry room; Barber/Beauty shop.
Activities Arts & crafts; Cards; Games;
Reading groups; Prayer groups; Movies;
Shopping trips; Social/Cultural gatherings.

FALMOUTH

Falmouth Nursing Home
545 Main St, Falmouth, MA, 02540
(617) 548-3800
Admin John J Hedderson. *Medical Dir/Dir of
Nursing* Virgina Biddle MD; Jean E
Throckmorton RN DNS.
Licensure Skilled care; Intermediate care. *Beds*
SNF 80; ICF 41. *Certified* Medicaid.
Owner Proprietary Corp.
Admissions Requirements Minimum age 21;
Medical examination.
Staff Physicians 1 (pt); RNs 8 (ft), 9 (pt);
LPNs 10 (ft), 1 (pt); Nurses aides 34 (ft), 16
(pt); Physical therapists 1 (ft); Recreational
therapists 2 (ft), 1 (pt); Occupational
therapists 1 (pt); Speech therapists 1 (pt);
Activities coordinators 1 (ft); Dietitians 1
(pt); Dentists 1 (pt); Ophthalmologists 1 (pt);
Podiatrists 1 (pt).
Facilities Dining room; Physical therapy
room; Activities room; Chapel; Crafts room;
Laundry room; Barber/Beauty shop.
Activities Arts & crafts; Cards; Games;
Reading groups; Prayer groups; Movies;
Shopping trips; Social/Cultural gatherings.

Fraser Rest Home of Falmouth*
17 Pine St, Falmouth, MA, 02540
(617) 563-3522
Admin Caleb Fraser.
Licensure Rest home. *Beds* 23.

Royal Megansett Nursing Home*
209 County Rd, Falmouth, MA, 02556
(617) 563-5913
Admin Robert H Warner.
Licensure Intermediate care. *Beds* 85.
Certified Medicaid.

FITCHBURG

Birchwood Manor Nursing Home*
1199 John Fitch Hwy, Fitchburg, MA, 01420
(617) 345-0146
Admin Angelino J Rollo.
Licensure Skilled care; Intermediate care. *Beds*
160. *Certified* Medicaid; Medicare.
Owner Proprietary Corp (Beverly Enterprises).

Cedar Street Home Inc
30 Cedar St, Fitchburg, MA, 01420
(617) 342-0527
Admin B Hollows.
Licensure Retirement home. *Beds* Level IV
28.

Owner Nonprofit Corp.
Admissions Requirements Minimum age 62;
Medical examination; Physician's request.
Staff Physicians 1 (pt); RNs 2 (pt); LPNs 1
(pt); Nurses aides 8 (pt); Activities
coordinators 1 (pt); Dietitians 1 (pt);
Ophthalmologists 1 (pt).
Facilities Dining room; Activities room;
Crafts room; Laundry room; Barber/Beauty
shop; Library; Large screened porches.
Activities Arts & crafts; Cards; Games;
Reading groups; Prayer groups; Movies;
Shopping trips; Social/Cultural gatherings;
Recreational outings.

Grand View Rest Home*
55 Garnet St, Fitchburg, MA, 01420
(617) 342-3030
Admin Donald & Claudette Richards. *Medical
Dir/Dir of Nursing* Dr Parnes.
Licensure Rest home. *Beds* 21.
Admissions Requirements Minimum age 30;
Medical examination.
Staff RNs 1 (pt); Nurses aides 4 (ft), 3 (pt);
Activities coordinators 1 (pt); Dietitians 1
(pt).
Facilities Dining room; Activities room;
Laundry room.
Activities Arts & crafts; Cards; Games;
Reading groups; Prayer groups; Movies;
Shopping trips; Social/Cultural gatherings.

High Street Rest Home*
69 High St, Fitchburg, MA, 01420
(617) 342-7962
Admin Kathryn E Salafia.
Licensure Rest home. *Beds* 16.

Hillcrest Nursing Home
94 Summer St, Fitchburg, MA, 01420
(617) 343-3374
Admin Jean Corley. *Medical Dir/Dir of
Nursing* Raymond Wolejko; Elizabeth
Sigmon.
Licensure Skilled care; Intermediate care. *Beds*
96. *Certified* Medicaid.
Owner Proprietary Corp (Hillhaven Corp).
Admissions Requirements Minimum age 21;
Medical examination; Physician's request.
Staff RNs 6 (ft), 4 (pt); LPNs 5 (ft), 5 (pt);
Nurses aides 20 (ft), 25 (pt); Physical
therapists 1 (pt); Occupational therapists 1
(pt); Speech therapists 1 (pt); Activities
coordinators 1 (ft), 1 (pt); Dietitians 1 (pt);
Dentists 1 (pt); Ophthalmologists 4 (pt);
Podiatrists 1 (pt).
Facilities Dining room; Physical therapy
room; Activities room; Chapel; Crafts room;
Laundry room; Barber/Beauty shop; Library.
Activities Arts & crafts; Cards; Games;
Reading groups; Prayer groups; Movies;
Shopping trips; Social/Cultural gatherings.

James Manor Rest Home*
222 South St, Fitchburg, MA, 01420
(617) 342-5041
Admin Ann Dumont.
Licensure Rest home. *Beds* 28.

Magnolia Rest Home*
159 Summer St, Fitchburg, MA, 01420
(617) 342-5372
Admin Anthony W Sciabarrasi. *Medical Dir/
Dir of Nursing* Eric L Knutson.
Licensure Rest home. *Beds* 16.
Admissions Requirements Minimum age 50.
Staff Physicians 1 (ft); LPNs 1 (pt); Nurses
aides 6 (pt); Dietitians 2 (pt); Dentists 1 (ft);
Podiatrists 1 (ft).
Facilities Dining room; Activities room;
Crafts room; Laundry room.
Activities Arts & crafts; Cards; Games;
Reading groups.

New Bunker Rest Home
82 Mechanic St, Fitchburg, MA, 01420
(617) 345-5701
Admin Esther E Ogilvie.

Licensure Rest home. *Beds* 17. *Certified*
Medicaid; Medicare.
Owner Proprietary Corp.
Admissions Requirements Minimum age 21.
Staff RNs; Nurses aides; Recreational
therapists; Dietitians.
Facilities Laundry room.
Activities Arts & crafts; Cards; Games;
Reading groups; Prayer groups; Movies;
Shopping trips; Social/Cultural gatherings;
Trips.

Tower Hill Rest Home
PO Box 943, 20 Myrtle Ave, Fitchburg, MA,
01420
(617) 342-4242
Admin Pauline J Stockwell. *Medical Dir/Dir of
Nursing* Dr Babineau.
Licensure Level IV care. *Beds* Level IV care
21. *Certified* Medicaid; Medicare.
Owner Privately owned.
Admissions Requirements Medical
examination.
Staff RNs 1 (pt); Nurses aides 2 (ft), 6 (pt);
Activities coordinators 1 (pt); Dietitians 1
(pt); Ophthalmologists 1 (pt).
Affiliation Roman Catholic
Facilities Dining room; Activities room;
Laundry room; Barber/Beauty shop;
Smoking room.
Activities Arts & crafts; Cards; Games;
Reading groups; Prayer groups; Movies;
Shopping trips; Social/Cultural gatherings;
Cooking classes; Trips to McDonalds.

Woodbury Manor Nursing Home
360 Electric Ave, Fitchburg, MA, 01420
(617) 342-3242
Admin Phyllis Madigan. *Medical Dir/Dir of
Nursing* Eric Knutson MD; Jacqueline
Woicieschowski DON.
Licensure Skilled care. *Beds* 99. *Certified*
Medicaid; Medicare.
Owner Proprietary Corp (Integrated Health
Services Inc).
Admissions Requirements Medical
examination; Physician's request.
Staff Physicians 1 (pt); RNs 4 (ft), 9 (pt);
LPNs 5 (ft), 2 (pt); Orderlies 1 (ft), 3 (pt);
Nurses aides 17 (ft), 22 (pt); Physical
therapists 1 (pt); Occupational therapists 1
(pt); Speech therapists 1 (pt); Activities
coordinators 1 (ft); Dietitians 1 (pt);
Ophthalmologists 1 (pt); Podiatrists 1 (pt);
Recreational assistants 1 (ft), 2 (pt);
Rehabilitation assistants 1 (ft).
Facilities Dining room; Physical therapy
room; Activities room; Laundry room;
Barber/Beauty shop.
Activities Arts & crafts; Cards; Games;
Reading groups; Prayer groups; Movies;
Shopping trips; Social/Cultural gatherings.

Wright Rest Home
10 Prospect St, Fitchburg, MA, 01420
(617) 345-5827
Admin Rosalyn J Piro.
Licensure Residential custodial care. *Beds*
Residential custodial care 28. *Certified*
Medicaid.
Owner Proprietary Corp.
Admissions Requirements Minimum age 60;
Medical examination; Physician's request.
Staff RNs 1 (ft), 1 (pt); Nurses aides 5 (ft);
Activities coordinators 1 (pt); Dietitians 1
(pt).
Facilities Dining room; Activities room;
Laundry room.
Activities Arts & crafts; Cards; Games;
Reading groups; Prayer groups; Movies;
Shopping trips.

FOXBORO

Doolittle Home Inc
16 Bird St, Foxboro, MA, 02035
(617) 543-2694

Admin Joan Marsh. *Medical Dir/Dir of
Nursing* Dr John MacDonald; Sheila Miller
RN.
Licensure Retirement home. *Beds* Retirement
home 33. *Certified* Medicare.
Owner Nonprofit Corp.
Admissions Requirements Minimum age 65.
Staff Physicians 1 (pt); RNs 2 (ft), 3 (pt);
LPNs 1 (ft), 8 (pt); Nurses aides 3 (ft), 5
(pt); Physical therapists 1 (pt); Recreational
therapists 1 (pt); Activities coordinators 1
(pt); Dietitians 1 (pt); Dentists 1 (pt);
Ophthalmologists 1 (pt); Podiatrists 1 (pt).
Affiliation Unitarian Universalist
Facilities Dining room; Crafts room; Laundry
room; Barber/Beauty shop.
Activities Arts & crafts; Games; Prayer groups;
Shopping trips.

Van Dora Nursing Home Inc*
67 Central St, Foxboro, MA, 02035
(617) 543-8000
Admin Joseph G Ranieri.
Licensure Intermediate care. *Beds* 67.
Certified Medicaid.

FRAMINGHAM

Clearview Nursing Home*
162 Old Connecticut Path, Framingham, MA,
01701
(617) 875-5096
Admin Sarah M Katz.
Licensure Intermediate care. *Beds* 18.
Certified Medicaid.

Countryside Nursing Home Inc*
153 Winter St, Framingham, MA, 01701
(617) 872-5250
Admin John Steacie.
Licensure Intermediate care. *Beds* 30.
Certified Medicaid.
Admissions Requirements Females only.
Staff RNs 1 (ft); LPNs 4 (pt); Nurses aides 30
(pt); Physical therapists 1 (pt); Occupational
therapists 1 (pt); Speech therapists 1 (pt);
Activities coordinators 1 (ft); Dietitians 1
(pt).
Facilities Dining room; Activities room;
Laundry room.
Activities Arts & crafts; Cards; Games; Prayer
groups; Shopping trips.

Kathleen Daniel Health Care Center
485 Franklin St, Framingham, MA, 01701
(617) 872-8801
Admin Ethel Peters. *Medical Dir/Dir of
Nursing* Arthur Freedman MD; Joan Parent
DON.
Licensure Skilled care; Intermediate care. *Beds*
124. *Certified* Medicaid; Medicare.
Staff Physicians 20 (pt); RNs 10 (ft), 4 (pt);
LPNs 6 (ft), 6 (pt); Orderlies 2 (ft); Nurses
aides 35 (ft), 17 (pt); Physical therapists 1
(pt); Reality therapists 2 (ft); Recreational
therapists 2 (ft), 2 (pt); Occupational
therapists 1 (pt); Speech therapists 1 (pt);
Activities coordinators 1 (ft); Dietitians 1
(pt); Dentists 1 (pt); Ophthalmologists 1 (pt);
Podiatrists 1 (pt); Audiologists 1 (pt);
Psychologist 1 (pt).
Facilities Dining room; Physical therapy
room; Activities room; Chapel; Crafts room;
Laundry room; Barber/Beauty shop.
Activities Arts & crafts; Cards; Games;
Reading groups; Prayer groups; Movies;
Shopping trips; Social/Cultural gatherings.

Edgell Rest Home*
248 Edgell Rd, Framingham, MA, 01701
(617) 875-5454
Admin James J Battles.
Licensure Rest home. *Beds* 14.

Framingham Nursing Home
517 Winter St, Framingham, MA, 01701
(617) 875-0607

Admin Beverly McIntyre. *Medical Dir/Dir of Nursing* Pramod Chira MD.
Licensure Skilled care. *Beds* 43. *Certified* Medicaid.
Admissions Requirements Minimum age 21; Medical examination.
Staff Physicians 1 (pt); RNs 4 (ft); LPNs 4 (ft); Nurses aides 20 (ft); Physical therapists 1 (pt); Reality therapists 1 (pt); Recreational therapists 1 (ft), 1 (pt); Occupational therapists 1 (pt); Speech therapists 1 (pt); Activities coordinators 1 (pt); Dietitians 1 (pt); Dentists 1 (pt); Ophthalmologists 1 (pt); Podiatrists 1 (pt).
Facilities Dining room; Activities room; Crafts room; Laundry room.
Activities Arts & crafts; Cards; Games; Reading groups; Prayer groups; Movies; Shopping trips; Social/Cultural gatherings.

Middlesex Manor Nursing Home*
228 Concord St, Framingham, MA, 01701
(617) 237-2799
Admin Robert D Brennan.
Licensure Intermediate care. *Beds* 97. *Certified* Medicaid.
Staff RNs 4 (ft), 2 (pt); LPNs 4 (ft), 4 (pt); Nurses aides 15 (ft), 10 (pt); Physical therapists 1 (pt); Recreational therapists 1 (pt); Activities coordinators 1 (ft), 1 (pt); Dietitians 1 (pt); Dentists 1 (pt); Ophthalmologists 1 (pt); Podiatrists 1 (pt); Audiologists 1 (pt).

St Patricks Manor Inc
863 Central Ave, Framingham, MA, 01701
(617) 879-8000
Admin Sr M Joseph Augustine.
Licensure Skilled care; Intermediate care. *Beds* 292. *Certified* Medicaid.
Affiliation Roman Catholic

Vernon House Inc
20 Vernon St, Framingham, MA, 01701
875-7556
Admin David J McGuire.
Licensure Level IV Rest home. *Beds* Level IV Rest home 14.
Owner Nonprofit Corp.
Admissions Requirements Females only; Medical examination; Physician's request.
Staff Physicians 5 (pt); RNs 2 (ft), 3 (pt); LPNs 2 (pt); Nurses aides 2 (ft), 3 (pt); Activities coordinators 1 (pt); Ophthalmologists 1 (pt).
Facilities Dining room; Laundry room; Library.
Activities Arts & crafts; Cards; Games; Prayer groups; Shopping trips; Social/Cultural gatherings.

Winter Gables Nursing Home*
342 Winter St, Framingham, MA, 01701
(617) 879-6100
Admin Caroline M Kreshpane.
Licensure Intermediate care. *Beds* 43. *Certified* Medicaid.

Winter Gables Rest Home*
340 Winter St, Framingham, MA, 01701
(617) 879-6100
Admin Caroline M Kreshpane.
Licensure Rest home. *Beds* 30.

FRANKLIN

Franklin House Health Care
130 Chestnut St, Franklin, MA, 02038
(617) 528-4600
Admin Cary Corley. *Medical Dir/Dir of Nursing* Leslie Silverstone; Diane Paster.
Licensure Skilled care; Intermediate care. *Beds* SNF 41; ICF 41. *Certified* Medicaid.
Owner Proprietary Corp (Hillhaven Corp).
Admissions Requirements Medical examination; Physician's request.

Staff Physicians; RNs; LPNs; Orderlies; Nurses aides; Physical therapists; Recreational therapists; Occupational therapists; Speech therapists; Activities coordinators; Dietitians; Dentists; Ophthalmologists; Podiatrists.
Facilities Dining room; Activities room; Crafts room; Laundry room; Barber/Beauty shop.
Activities Arts & crafts; Cards; Games; Reading groups; Prayer groups; Movies; Shopping trips; Social/Cultural gatherings; Bowling; Horse racing game; Bingo.

GARDNER

Eastwood Pines Nursing Home*
Eastwood Circle, Gardner, MA, 01440
(617) 632-8776
Admin Abe Treshinsky.
Licensure Skilled care; Intermediate care. *Beds* 128. *Certified* Medicaid; Medicare.

Gallant Rest Home*
381 E Broadway, Gardner, MA, 01440
(617) 632-6175
Admin Robert W LeBlanc. *Medical Dir/Dir of Nursing* Dr John Denman.
Licensure Rest home. *Beds* 13.
Admissions Requirements Minimum age 18.
Staff Physicians 1 (ft); LPNs 1 (ft); Dentists 1 (pt); Podiatrists 1 (pt).
Facilities Dining room; Activities room; Laundry room.
Activities Arts & crafts; Cards; Games; Prayer groups; Movies; Shopping trips.

Gardner Manor Nursing Home
155 Green St, Gardner, MA, 01440
(617) 632-2900
Admin Annie A Greene.
Licensure Skilled care; Intermediate care. *Beds* SNF 38; ICF 36. *Certified* Medicaid.
Owner Proprietary Corp.
Admissions Requirements Minimum age 18; Physician's request.
Staff Physicians; RNs; LPNs; Orderlies; Nurses aides; Activities coordinators.
Languages Polish, French, Spanish
Facilities Dining room; Physical therapy room; Activities room; Crafts room; Laundry room; Barber/Beauty shop.
Activities Arts & crafts; Cards; Games; Prayer groups; Movies; Birthday parties; Wine & cheese parties; BBQs.

Wachusett Manor
32 Hospital Hll Rd, Gardner, MA, 01440
(617) 632-5477
Admin Eleanor Landa. *Medical Dir/Dir of Nursing* Judith Rose RN.
Licensure Intermediate care. *Beds* 89. *Certified* Medicaid.
Owner Privately owned.
Admissions Requirements Minimum age 60; Medical examination; Physician's request.
Staff RNs; LPNs; Nurses aides; Physical therapists; Recreational therapists; Occupational therapists; Speech therapists; Activities coordinators; Dietitians; Ophthalmologists; Podiatrists.
Languages French
Facilities Dining room; Activities room; Crafts room; Laundry room; Barber/Beauty shop; Library.
Activities Arts & crafts; Cards; Games; Reading groups; Prayer groups; Movies; Shopping trips; Social/Cultural gatherings.

GLOUCESTER

Greycliff at Cape Ann Nursing Home*
272 Washington St, Gloucester, MA, 01930
(617) 281-0333
Admin Thomas B Dresser. *Medical Dir/Dir of Nursing* Dr Douglas Fiero.

Licensure Skilled care; Intermediate care. *Beds* 101. *Certified* Medicaid.
Owner Proprietary Corp (Beverly Enterprises).
Admissions Requirements Medical examination.
Staff RNs 5 (ft), 2 (pt); LPNs 3 (ft), 3 (pt); Nurses aides 20 (ft), 25 (pt); Physical therapists 1 (pt); Occupational therapists 1 (pt); Activities coordinators 2 (ft); Dietitians 1 (pt); Podiatrists 1 (pt).
Facilities Dining room; Activities room; Crafts room; Laundry room; Barber/Beauty shop; Library.
Activities Arts & crafts; Cards; Games; Reading groups; Prayer groups; Movies; Shopping trips; Social/Cultural gatherings.

Hillcrest Rest Home*
374 Washington St, Gloucester, MA, 01930
(617) 283-1032
Admin June B Cahoon. *Medical Dir/Dir of Nursing* David Cohen MD.
Licensure Rest home. *Beds* 14.
Admissions Requirements Minimum age 50; Females only; Medical examination; Physician's request.
Staff RNs 2 (ft), 1 (pt); LPNs 3 (ft), 1 (pt); Nurses aides 4 (ft), 3 (pt); Recreational therapists 1 (pt); Occupational therapists; Speech therapists; Activities coordinators; Dietitians; Podiatrists.

Shore Cliff*
Cliff Rd, Gloucester, MA, 01930
(617) 525-3456
Admin Mary L Barnett.
Licensure Charitable home. *Beds* 34.
Admissions Requirements Minimum age 65; Medical examination.
Staff RNs 2 (ft); LPNs 5 (pt); Nurses aides 1 (ft), 3 (pt); Activities coordinators 1 (pt).
Facilities Dining room; Activities room; Laundry room; Barber/Beauty shop; Library.
Activities Arts & crafts; Cards; Games; Reading groups; Prayer groups; Movies; Shopping trips; Social/Cultural gatherings; Field trips; Exercise program.

GRAFTON

Crescent Manor Rest Home*
5 Crescent St, Grafton, MA, 01519
(617) 839-2124
Admin Robert Waters.
Licensure Rest home. *Beds* 58.

Edgewood Nursing Home Inc*
23 N Brigham Hill Rd, Grafton, MA, 01536
(617) 839-4980
Admin Mark Awed.
Licensure Intermediate care. *Beds* 36. *Certified* Medicaid.
Admissions Requirements Minimum age 16.
Staff RNs 1 (pt); LPNs 2 (ft), 4 (pt); Nurses aides 4 (ft), 4 (pt); Activities coordinators 1 (pt); Dietitians 1 (pt).
Facilities Dining room; Activities room; Laundry room; Barber/Beauty shop.
Activities Arts & crafts; Cards; Games; Reading groups; Prayer groups; Movies; Social/Cultural gatherings.

Keith Hill Nursing Home Inc*
44 Old Upton Rd, Grafton, MA, 01519
(617) 839-2195
Admin Richard J Carlson.
Licensure Skilled care; Intermediate care. *Beds* 43. *Certified* Medicaid.

GREAT BARRINGTON

Great Barrington Healthcare Nursing Home*
148 Maple Ave, Great Barrington, MA, 01230
(413) 528-3320
Admin Robert Schwenk.

Licensure Skilled care; Intermediate care. *Beds* 106. *Certified* Medicaid; Medicare.
Owner Proprietary Corp (Hillhaven Corp).

Timberlyn Heights
320 Maple Ave, Great Barrington, MA, 01230
(413) 528-2650
Admin Edward M Lenz. *Medical Dir/Dir of Nursing* Joanne Marshall.
Licensure Skilled care; Intermediate care. *Beds* 78. *Certified* Medicaid.
Owner Proprietary Corp (Hillhaven Corp).
Facilities Dining room; Physical therapy room; Activities room; Chapel; Laundry room; Barber/Beauty shop.
Activities Arts & crafts; Cards; Games; Reading groups; Prayer groups; Movies; Shopping trips; Social/Cultural gatherings.

Willowood Nursing & Retirement Facility*
Christian Hill Rd, Great Barrington, MA, 01230
(413) 528-4560
Admin Curtis L Ivey.
Licensure Skilled care; Intermediate care. *Beds* 130. *Certified* Medicaid; Medicare.

GREENFIELD

Franklin Nursing & Rehabilitation Center
329 Conway St, Greenfield, MA, 01301
(413) 772-0811
Admin Doris Garbose.
Licensure Skilled care; Intermediate care. *Beds* 250. *Certified* Medicaid.
Facilities Dining room; Physical therapy room; Activities room; Laundry room; Barber/Beauty shop.
Activities Arts & crafts; Cards; Games; Reading groups; Prayer groups; Movies; Shopping trips; Social/Cultural gatherings.

Pioneer Valley Manor Rest Home*
148 Montague City Rd, Greenfield, MA, 01301
(413) 773-8589
Admin Simone McDonald.
Licensure Rest home. *Beds* 37.

Poet's Seat Nursing Home*
359 High St, Greenfield, MA, 01301
(413) 774-2253
Admin Mary L Harris.
Licensure Skilled care. *Beds* 63. *Certified* Medicaid.

GROTON

Children's Extended Care Center
22 Hillside Ave, Groton, MA, 01450
(617) 448-3388
Admin Carol S Lobron MS. *Medical Dir/Dir of Nursing* I Leslie Rubin MD; Jessie Munn RN MS.
Licensure Skilled care. *Beds* 73. *Certified* Medicaid.
Owner Nonprofit Corp.
Admissions Requirements Through Massachusetts Department of Public Health.
Staff Physicians 3 (pt); RNs 11 (ft), 11 (pt); LPNs 7 (ft), 11 (pt); Nurses aides 31 (ft), 43 (pt); Physical therapists 3 (ft); Occupational therapists 1 (ft); Speech therapists 1 (pt); Dietitians 1 (pt); Podiatrists 1 (pt).

Hale Convalescent & Nursing Home Inc*
58 Main St, Groton, MA, 01472
(617) 448-6802
Admin Paul R Chernov.
Licensure Intermediate care. *Beds* 36. *Certified* Medicaid.

HADLEY

Shady Lawn Rest Home Inc
90 Middle St, Hadley, MA, 01035
(413) 584-4018

Admin Anna Thompson. *Medical Dir/Dir of Nursing* David Artzerounian; Peter Betjemann.
Licensure Intermediate care; Self care. *Beds* ICF 5; Self care 17. *Certified* Medicaid.
Owner Privately owned.
Admissions Requirements Minimum age 36; Medical examination.
Staff Physicians 1 (pt); LPNs 1 (ft), 1 (pt); Nurses aides 7 (ft), 2 (pt); Physical therapists 1 (pt); Activities coordinators 1 (pt); Dietitians 1 (pt); Ophthalmologists 1 (pt).
Languages Polish, Spanish
Facilities Dining room; Activities room; Chapel; Laundry room; Barber/Beauty shop; Library.
Activities Arts & crafts; Cards; Games; Prayer groups; Shopping trips; Lunch trips; Trips to flower shows; Parks; Picnics; Dinner trips.

HAMPDEN

Mary Lyon Nursing Home
34 W Main St, Hampden, MA, 01036
(413) 566-5511
Admin C L Verrill. *Medical Dir/Dir of Nursing* Dr Fred Schwendenmann.
Licensure Skilled care. *Beds* SNF 40; ICF 60. *Certified* Medicaid; Medicare.
Owner Proprietary Corp (Continental Medical Systems).
Admissions Requirements Minimum age 16; Medical examination; Physician's request.
Staff Physicians 12 (ft); RNs 6 (ft), 10 (pt); LPNs 5 (ft), 6 (pt); Orderlies 1 (ft); Nurses aides 24 (ft), 11 (pt); Physical therapists 1 (ft), 1 (pt); Occupational therapists 1 (pt); Speech therapists 1 (pt); Activities coordinators 1 (ft); Dietitians 1 (pt).
Languages French, Spanish, Italian
Facilities Dining room; Physical therapy room; Activities room; Laundry room; Barber/Beauty shop.
Activities Arts & crafts; Cards; Games; Prayer groups; Movies; Shopping trips; Social/Cultural gatherings.

HANOVER

Mill Pond Rest Home*
974 Main St, Hanover, MA, 02339
(617) 871-0171
Admin Edward R Hammond Jr. *Medical Dir/Dir of Nursing* Donna Buckley RN.
Licensure Rest home. *Beds* 38.
Admissions Requirements Minimum age 55; Medical examination; Physician's request.
Staff Orderlies 1 (pt); Nurses aides 10 (ft), 4 (pt); Recreational therapists 1 (pt); Activities coordinators 1 (pt); Dietitians 1 (pt).
Facilities Dining room; Activities room; Chapel; Barber/Beauty shop.
Activities Cards; Games; Movies; Shopping trips; Social/Cultural gatherings.

North River Nursing Home*
Box 11, Washington St, Hanover, MA, 02339
(617) 826-4521
Admin Maryanne Sullivan.
Licensure Intermediate care. *Beds* 39. *Certified* Medicaid.

HARDWICK

Hilltop Rest Home*
31 Prospect St, Gilbertville, Hardwick, MA, 01031
(413) 477-6601
Admin Richard J Muise.
Licensure Rest home. *Beds* 22.

HAVERHILL

Baker Katz Nursing Home
194 Boardman St, Haverhill, MA, 01830
(617) 373-5697

Admin David M Baker.
Licensure Intermediate care. *Beds* 77. *Certified* Medicaid.

Churchview Health Center Retirement Home*
35-37 Arlington St, Box 150, Haverhill, MA, 01830
(617) 372-3675
Admin Ann Azzarito. *Medical Dir/Dir of Nursing* Arnold George MD.
Licensure Rest home. *Beds* 22.
Admissions Requirements Minimum age 21; Medical examination; Physician's request.
Facilities Dining room; Activities room; Laundry room.
Activities Arts & crafts; Prayer groups.

Glynn Memorial Nursing Home
61 Brown St, Haverhill, MA, 01830
(617) 374-2378
Admin Stanley T Trocki Jr. *Medical Dir/Dir of Nursing* Dr Charles Chaput; Mrs Janine Bloomfield RN.
Licensure Intermediate care. *Beds* ICF 48. *Certified* Medicaid.
Owner Publicly owned.
Admissions Requirements Minimum age 21.
Staff RNs 4 (ft), 2 (pt); LPNs 4 (ft), 1 (pt); Nurses aides 18 (ft), 4 (pt); Activities coordinators 1 (ft); Dietitians 1 (pt).
Languages Polish, French
Facilities Dining room; Activities room; Chapel; Crafts room; Laundry room; Barber/ Beauty shop; Library.
Activities Arts & crafts; Cards; Games; Reading groups; Prayer groups; Movies; Shopping trips; Social/Cultural gatherings.

Hannah Duston Long-Term Health Care Facility*
126 Monument St, Haverhill, MA, 01830
(617) 373-1747
Admin Robert Bastck. *Medical Dir/Dir of Nursing* Homode Habhab MD.
Licensure Skilled care; Intermediate care. *Beds* 80. *Certified* Medicaid; Medicare.
Admissions Requirements Minimum age 50; Medical examination; Physician's request.
Staff Physicians 3 (ft), 7 (pt); RNs 5 (ft), 3 (pt); LPNs 5 (ft), 6 (pt); Orderlies 1 (ft); Nurses aides 20 (ft), 17 (pt); Physical therapists 1 (ft), 1 (pt); Reality therapists 1 (ft); Recreational therapists 1 (ft), 1 (pt); Occupational therapists 1 (pt); Speech therapists 1 (pt); Activities coordinators 1 (ft), 1 (pt); Dietitians 1 (pt); Dentists 1 (pt); Ophthalmologists 1 (pt); Podiatrists 1 (pt); Audiologists 1 (pt).
Facilities Dining room; Physical therapy room; Activities room; Chapel; Crafts room; Laundry room; Barber/Beauty shop; Library.
Activities Arts & crafts; Cards; Games; Reading groups; Prayer groups; Movies; Shopping trips; Social/Cultural gatherings.

Haverhill Manor Nursing Home
100 Lawrence St, Haverhill, MA, 01830
(617) 374-0356
Admin Timothy G Barry. *Medical Dir/Dir of Nursing* Charles Chaput; Jane Merrow.
Licensure Skilled care; Intermediate care. *Beds* SNF 47; ICF 53. *Certified* Medicaid.
Owner Proprietary Corp (American Health Centers Inc).
Admissions Requirements Minimum age 21; Physician's request.
Staff Physicians 1 (pt); RNs 8 (ft), 2 (pt); LPNs 12 (ft), 4 (pt); Orderlies 4 (ft), 1 (pt); Nurses aides 22 (ft), 5 (pt); Physical therapists 1 (pt); Occupational therapists 1 (pt); Speech therapists 1 (pt); Activities coordinators 1 (ft); Dietitians 1 (pt); Ophthalmologists 1 (pt); Podiatrists 1 (pt).
Facilities Dining room; Physical therapy room; Activities room; Laundry room; Barber/Beauty shop; TV room.

Activities Arts & crafts; Cards; Games;
Reading groups; Prayer groups; Movies;
Shopping trips; Social/Cultural gatherings;
Community events; Outings; Lunch groups;
Fairs; Sports; Pets; Gardening.

Kenoza Hillcrest Nursing Home*
186 North Ave, Haverhill, MA, 01830
(617) 373-5121
Admin Leo Curtin.
Licensure Intermediate care. *Beds* 21.
Certified Medicaid.
Owner Proprietary Corp (American Health
Centers Inc).

Kenoza Manor Convalescent Center
190 North Ave, Haverhill, MA, 01830
(617) 372-7700
Admin Diane C Tessier-Efstathiou. *Medical
Dir/Dir of Nursing* Dr David Byrne; Darlene
Ryan.
Licensure Skilled care; Intermediate care. *Beds*
SNF 40; ICF 60. *Certified* Medicare.
Owner Proprietary Corp (American Health
Care Inc).
Admissions Requirements Minimum age 18;
Physician's request.
Staff Physicians 12 (pt); RNs 6 (ft), 3 (pt);
LPNs 7 (ft), 2 (pt); Orderlies 2 (ft); Nurses
aides 29 (ft), 13 (pt); Physical therapists 1
(pt); Recreational therapists 1 (pt);
Occupational therapists 1 (pt).
Facilities Dining room; Activities room;
Crafts room; Laundry room; Barber/Beauty
shop.
Activities Arts & crafts; Cards; Games;
Reading groups; Prayer groups; Movies;
Shopping trips; Social/Cultural gatherings;
Continental breakfast; Dance exercise class;
Mens group; Sensory stimulation; Bowling;
Basketball; Painting; Baking.

Kenoza Nursing Home*
87 Shattuck Rd, Haverhill, MA, 01830
(617) 372-1081
Admin Jon R Guarino.
Licensure Skilled care. *Beds* 87. *Certified*
Medicaid.

Lenox Nursing Home Inc*
378 S Main St, Haverhill, MA, 01830
(617) 374-7953
Admin Marion A Thisse.
Licensure Intermediate care. *Beds* 27.
Certified Medicaid.

Oxford Manor Nursing Home
689 Main St, Haverhill, MA, 01830
(617) 373-1131
Admin Leo W McCarron Jr NHA. *Medical
Dir/Dir of Nursing* David Byrne MD;
Kathleen Silva RN.
Licensure Skilled care; Intermediate care. *Beds*
SNF 60; ICF 60. *Certified* Medicaid;
Medicare.
Owner Proprietary Corp.
Admissions Requirements Minimum age 21;
Medical examination; Physician's request.
Staff RNs; LPNs; Nurses aides; Physical
therapists 1 (pt); Occupational therapists 1
(pt); Activities coordinators 1 (ft), 2 (pt);
Dietitians 1 (pt).
Facilities Dining room; Physical therapy
room; Activities room; Laundry room;
Barber/Beauty shop.
Activities Arts & crafts; Cards; Games;
Reading groups; Prayer groups; Movies;
Shopping trips; Social/Cultural gatherings.

St Johns Nursing Home of Lowell Inc
500 Wentworth Ave, Haverhill, MA, 01852
(617) 458-1271
Admin Raymond V Mailloux. *Medical Dir/Dir
of Nursing* Edward Saba MD; Janet
Sweeney.
Licensure Skilled care; Intermediate care. *Beds*
SNF 69; ICF 34. *Certified* Medicaid;
Medicare.
Owner Nonprofit Corp.

Staff Physicians; RNs; LPNs; Orderlies;
Nurses aides; Physical therapists;
Occupational therapists; Speech therapists;
Activities coordinators; Dietitians; Dentists;
Ophthalmologists; Podiatrists.
Languages Spanish, Portuguese
Facilities Dining room; Activities room;
Chapel; Crafts room; Laundry room; Barber/
Beauty shop.
Activities Arts & crafts; Cards; Games;
Reading groups; Prayer groups; Movies;
Shopping trips; Social/Cultural gatherings.

Scotts Rest Home
69 Keeley St, Haverhill, MA, 01830-6694
(617) 374-4535
Admin Era M Scott.
Licensure Rest home. *Beds* 10. *Certified*
Medicaid.
Owner Privately owned.
Admissions Requirements Minimum age 60.
Staff Physicians; LPNs.
Facilities Dining room; Laundry room; Beauty
shop chair & dryer.
Activities Arts & crafts; Cards; Movies.

Stevens-Bennett Home Inc
337 Main St, Haverhill, MA, 01830
(617) 374-8861
Admin Sandra A Favor. *Medical Dir/Dir of
Nursing* Dr David Byrne.
Licensure Skilled care. *Beds* SNF 30. *Certified*
Medicaid; Medicare.
Owner Nonprofit organization/foundation.
Admissions Requirements Minimum age 65;
Females only; Medical examination;
Physician's request.
Staff Physicians 1 (ft); RNs 1 (pt); Nurses
aides 6 (pt); Activities coordinators 1 (pt);
Dietitians 1 (pt).
Facilities Dining room; Activities room;
Crafts room; Laundry room; Barber/Beauty
shop; Library.
Activities Arts & crafts; Cards; Games;
Movies; Shopping trips; Social/Cultural
gatherings.

Union Mission Nursing Home Inc
150 Water St, Haverhill, MA, 01830
(617) 374-0707
Admin Dr Eugene Tillock. *Medical Dir/Dir of
Nursing* Ulrich Ehrig MD; Marcia Kent RN.
Licensure Skilled care; Intermediate care;
Social day care Program M-F; Respite care
for short term admissions. *Beds* 160.
Certified Medicaid.
Owner Nonprofit Corp.
Admissions Requirements Medical
examination; Physician's request.
Staff Physicians 15 (pt); RNs 8 (ft); LPNs 6
(ft); Nurses aides 48 (ft); Physical therapists
1 (pt); Recreational therapists 1 (ft);
Occupational therapists 1 (pt); Speech
therapists 1 (pt); Activities coordinators 1
(ft); Dietitians 1 (pt); Dentists 2 (pt);
Ophthalmologists 1 (pt); Podiatrists 3 (pt).
Facilities Dining room; Physical therapy
room; Activities room; Crafts room; Barber/
Beauty shop; Library; Lounges.
Activities Arts & crafts; Cards; Games;
Reading groups; Prayer groups; Movies;
Shopping trips; Social/Cultural gatherings;
Continuing education.

**Griffin White Home for Aged Men & Aged
Couples**
170 Main St, Haverhill, MA, 01830
(617) 372-1501
Admin Virginia Guyot.
Licensure Charitable home. *Beds* 16.
Owner Nonprofit Corp.
Admissions Requirements Minimum age 60;
Males only & married couples.

HAYDENVILLE

Colonial Rest Home
18 S Main St, Haydenville, MA, 01039
(413) 268-7321
Admin Collin S Campbell.
Licensure Rest home. *Beds* 18.

HINGHAM

Deering Nursing Home Inc*
1192 Main St, Hingham, MA, 02043
(617) 749-2285
Admin Lorraine A Starr.
Licensure Intermediate care. *Beds* 54.
Certified Medicaid.

New England Friends Home*
Turkey Hill Ln, Hingham, MA, 02043
(617) 749-3556
Admin Brian Drayton.
Licensure Rest home. *Beds* 15.
Affiliation Society of Friends
Facilities Dining room; Activities room;
Library.
Activities Cards; Games; Prayer groups;
Movies; Social/Cultural gatherings.

Queen Anne Nursing Home*
50 Recreation Park Dr, Hingham, MA, 02043
(617) 749-4983
Admin Peter H Starr.
Licensure Skilled care; Intermediate care. *Beds*
94. *Certified* Medicaid; Medicare.

HINSDALE

Ashmere Manor Nursing Home
George Schnopp Rd, Hinsdale, MA, 01235
(413) 655-2920 or 655-2929
Admin Linda Hamilton. *Medical Dir/Dir of
Nursing* Michael J Murray MD; Linda
Letourneau RN DON.
Licensure Skilled care. *Beds* SNF 22; ICF 60.
Certified Medicaid.
Owner Privately owned.
Admissions Requirements Medical
examination; Physician's request.
Staff Physicians 1 (ft), 3 (pt); RNs 7 (ft), 3
(pt); LPNs 6 (ft), 4 (pt); Nurses aides 25 (ft),
15 (pt); Physical therapists 1 (ft);
Recreational therapists 1 (ft), 1 (pt);
Occupational therapists 1 (ft); Speech
therapists 1 (ft); Activities coordinators 1
(ft), 1 (pt); Dietitians 1 (pt);
Ophthalmologists 1 (pt).
Languages Polish, Italian
Facilities Dining room; Physical therapy
room; Activities room; Chapel; Laundry
room; Barber/Beauty shop.
Activities Arts & crafts; Cards; Games;
Reading groups; Prayer groups; Movies;
Shopping trips; Social/Cultural gatherings;
Fall & spring tours.

HOLBROOK

Holbrook Nursing Home*
45 S Franklin St, Holbrook, MA, 02343
(617) 767-1915
Admin Margaret Pomeroy.
Licensure Intermediate care. *Beds* 43.
Certified Medicaid.

HOLDEN

Holden Nursing Home Inc*
32 Mayo Rd, Holden, MA, 01520
(617) 829-4327
Admin John L Knight. *Medical Dir/Dir of
Nursing* Henry Kramer.
Licensure Intermediate care. *Beds* 88.
Certified Medicaid.
Admissions Requirements Minimum age 21;
Medical examination; Physician's request.

Staff Physicians 1 (pt); RNs 6 (ft), 6 (pt); LPNs 4 (ft), 5 (pt); Nurses aides 23 (ft), 18 (pt); Physical therapists 1 (ft); Recreational therapists 1 (ft); Occupational therapists 1 (pt); Dietitians 2 (ft), 1 (pt).
Facilities Dining room; Physical therapy room; Activities room; Chapel; Laundry room; Barber/Beauty shop; Library.
Activities Arts & crafts; Cards; Games; Reading groups; Prayer groups; Movies; Shopping trips; Social/Cultural gatherings; Church services.

Stonehouse Hill Nursing Home
Stonehouse Hill Rd, Holden, MA, 01520
(617) 755-5345
Admin Anthony J Penny MD. *Medical Dir/ Dir of Nursing* James Finale; Donna Allen RN.
Licensure Intermediate care. *Beds* ICF 48. *Certified* Medicaid.
Owner Proprietary Corp.
Facilities Dining room; Crafts room; Laundry room.
Activities Arts & crafts; Cards; Games; Reading groups; Prayer groups; Movies; Shopping trips; Social/Cultural gatherings.

HOLLISTON

Holliston Manor Nursing Home*
84 Elm St, Holliston, MA, 01746
(617) 429-4566
Admin V Jean Cohen. *Medical Dir/Dir of Nursing* John LaRossa MD.
Licensure Intermediate care. *Beds* 40. *Certified* Medicaid.
Admissions Requirements Minimum age 21.
Staff Physicians 3 (pt); RNs 1 (ft), 4 (pt); LPNs 1 (ft), 3 (pt); Orderlies 1 (pt); Nurses aides 7 (ft), 6 (pt); Physical therapists 1 (pt); Activities coordinators 1 (ft); Dietitians 1 (pt); Podiatrists 1 (pt).
Facilities Dining room; Activities room.
Activities Arts & crafts; Games; Prayer groups; Movies; Shopping trips; Social/Cultural gatherings.

HOLYOKE

Beaven-Kelly Rest Home
1245 Main St, Holyoke, MA, 01040
(413) 532-4892
Admin Sr Mary of Providence SP. *Medical Dir/Dir of Nursing* Cynthia Brown.
Licensure Rest home. *Beds* 55.
Owner Nonprofit Corp.
Admissions Requirements Minimum age 65; Medical examination.
Staff LPNs 2 (ft); Nurses aides 4 (ft); Activities coordinators 1 (ft); Pastoral Care 1 (pt).
Affiliation Roman Catholic
Facilities Dining room; Activities room; Chapel; Crafts room; Laundry room; Barber/ Beauty shop; Spacious grounds; Private area.
Activities Arts & crafts; Cards; Games; Reading groups; Prayer groups; Movies; Shopping trips; Social/Cultural gatherings.

Brookwood Court Nursing Home*
260 Easthampton Rd, Holyoke, MA, 01040
(413) 538-9733
Admin Mary Jane Roeder. *Medical Dir/Dir of Nursing* Thomas Gartman MD.
Licensure Skilled care; Intermediate care. *Beds* 164. *Certified* Medicaid; Medicare.
Admissions Requirements Physician's request.
Staff Physicians 1 (pt); RNs 8 (ft), 8 (pt); LPNs 9 (ft), 5 (pt); Orderlies 2 (ft), 1 (pt); Nurses aides 48 (ft), 27 (pt); Physical therapists 1 (pt); Occupational therapists 1 (pt); Speech therapists 1 (pt); Activities coordinators 1 (ft), 2 (pt); Dietitians 1 (pt); Dentists 1 (pt); Podiatrists 1 (pt).

Facilities Dining room; Physical therapy room; Activities room; Chapel; Crafts room; Laundry room; Barber/Beauty shop.
Activities Arts & crafts; Cards; Games; Reading groups; Prayer groups; Movies; Shopping trips; Social/Cultural gatherings.

Buckley Nursing & Retirement Home
PO Box 6257, 282 Cabot St, Holyoke, MA, 01040
(413) 538-7470
Admin William M Hartt. *Medical Dir/Dir of Nursing* Margaret Thieme RN.
Licensure Skilled care; Intermediate care. *Beds* 102. *Certified* Medicaid; Medicare; JCAH.
Owner Proprietary Corp.
Admissions Requirements Minimum age 18; Physician's request.
Staff Physicians; RNs; LPNs; Orderlies; Nurses aides; Physical therapists; Reality therapists; Recreational therapists; Occupational therapists; Speech therapists; Activities coordinators; Dietitians; Ophthalmologists; Podiatrists.
Facilities Dining room; Physical therapy room; Activities room; Crafts room; Laundry room; Barber/Beauty shop; Library.
Activities Arts & crafts; Cards; Games; Reading groups; Prayer groups; Movies; Shopping trips; Social/Cultural gatherings; Daily exercise groups; Sensory integration.

Chapel Hill Nursing Home*
100 Locust St, Holyoke, MA, 01040
(413) 536-3435
Admin Rosemary Dubuc.
Licensure Skilled care. *Beds* 61. *Certified* Medicaid.

Holyoke Geriatric & Convalescent Center*
45 Lower Westfield Rd, Holyoke, MA, 01040
(413) 536-8110
Admin Timothy V Cotz. *Medical Dir/Dir of Nursing* Robert Mausel MD.
Licensure Skilled care; Intermediate care. *Beds* 240. *Certified* Medicaid; Medicare.
Admissions Requirements Medical examination.
Staff Physicians 14 (pt); RNs 20 (ft); LPNs 14 (ft); Nurses aides 100 (ft); Physical therapists 1 (ft); Recreational therapists 7 (ft); Occupational therapists 1 (ft); Speech therapists 1 (pt); Activities coordinators 7 (ft); Dietitians 1 (ft); Dentists 1 (pt); Ophthalmologists 1 (pt); Podiatrists 3 (pt).
Facilities Dining room; Physical therapy room; Activities room; Chapel; Crafts room; Laundry room; Barber/Beauty shop; Library; Bar; Gift shop.
Activities Arts & crafts; Cards; Games; Reading groups; Prayer groups; Movies; Shopping trips; Social/Cultural gatherings.

Holyoke Nursing Home
1913 Northampton St, Holyoke, MA, 01040
(413) 536-7110
Admin Theodore Baldwin. *Medical Dir/Dir of Nursing* Norman Halpern MD; Susan Brooks RN DON.
Licensure Skilled care; Intermediate care. *Beds* SNF 50; ICF 50. *Certified* Medicaid.
Owner Proprietary Corp.
Staff RNs 3 (ft), 3 (pt); LPNs 6 (ft), 2 (pt); Nurses aides 28 (ft), 9 (pt); Activities coordinators 1 (ft); Dietitians 1 (pt).
Facilities Dining room; Physical therapy room; Activities room; Chapel; Crafts room; Laundry room; Barber/Beauty shop.
Activities Arts & crafts; Cards; Games; Reading groups; Prayer groups; Movies; Shopping trips; Social/Cultural gatherings.

Loomis House Nursing Center
298 Jarvis Ave, Holyoke, MA, 01040
(413) 538-7551
Admin Richard S Huddy. *Medical Dir/Dir of Nursing* Dr Brian Akers & Dr David Clinton; Theresa Peltier RN DON.

Licensure Skilled care; Intermediate care. *Beds* SNF 41; ICF 39. *Certified* Medicaid; Medicare.
Owner Nonprofit Corp.
Admissions Requirements Physician's request.
Staff RNs 4 (ft), 5 (pt); LPNs 4 (ft), 1 (pt); Nurses aides 14 (ft), 15 (pt); Physical therapists 1 (pt); Recreational therapists 1 (ft), 2 (pt); Occupational therapists 1 (pt); Dietitians 1 (pt); Ophthalmologists 1 (pt).
Languages Polish, French
Facilities Dining room; Activities room; Crafts room; Laundry room; Barber/Beauty shop; Library.
Activities Arts & crafts; Cards; Games; Prayer groups; Movies; Shopping trips; Social/ Cultural gatherings; Art therapy; Exercise class.

Mt St Vincent Nursing Home Inc
Holy Family Rd, Holyoke, MA, 01040
(413) 532-3246
Admin Patricia A Tiernan. *Medical Dir/Dir of Nursing* Michael A Rosner MD; Margaret Fay RN.
Licensure Skilled care; Intermediate care. *Beds* SNF 43; ICF 82. *Certified* Medicaid.
Owner Nonprofit Corp.
Admissions Requirements Minimum age 65.
Staff Physicians 1 (pt); RNs 6 (ft), 8 (pt); LPNs 5 (ft), 2 (pt); Nurses aides 35 (ft), 13 (pt); Physical therapists 1 (ft); Occupational therapists 1 (pt); Activities coordinators 1 (ft); Dietitians 1 (pt).
Affiliation Roman Catholic
Facilities Dining room; Physical therapy room; Activities room; Chapel; Crafts room; Laundry room; Barber/Beauty shop; Library; Auditorium; Sundeck.
Activities Arts & crafts; Cards; Games; Reading groups; Prayer groups; Movies; Shopping trips; Social/Cultural gatherings.

Oak Manor Nursing Home*
19 Quirk Ave, Holyoke, MA, 01040
(413) 532-1415
Admin Beth McCauley-Dupre.
Licensure Intermediate care. *Beds* 60. *Certified* Medicaid.
Owner Proprietary Corp (Health Care & Retirement Corp).

HOPEDALE

Adin Manor Nursing Home
34 Adin St, Hopedale, MA, 01747
(617) 473-0171
Admin Robert Brennan. *Medical Dir/Dir of Nursing* Faheem Farooq MD.
Licensure Intermediate care. *Beds* 56. *Certified* Medicaid.
Admissions Requirements Minimum age 21; Medical examination.
Staff Physicians 4 (pt); RNs 2 (ft); LPNs 8 (ft), 2 (pt); Nurses aides 20 (ft); Physical therapists 1 (pt); Recreational therapists 1 (pt); Occupational therapists 1 (pt); Speech therapists 1 (pt); Activities coordinators 1 (ft); Dietitians 1 (pt); Dentists 1 (pt); Ophthalmologists 1 (pt); Podiatrists 1 (pt).
Facilities Dining room; Activities room; Laundry room; Barber/Beauty shop; Library.
Activities Arts & crafts; Cards; Games; Reading groups; Prayer groups; Movies; Shopping trips; Social/Cultural gatherings.

Hopedale Garden Nursing Home*
325 S Main St, Hopedale, MA, 01747
(617) 473-9600
Admin Sidney Croll.
Licensure Intermediate care. *Beds* 70. *Certified* Medicaid.

HUDSON

St Jude Convalescent Home
53 Church St, Hudson, MA, 01749
(617) 961-2374
Admin Beverly Singer. *Medical Dir/Dir of Nursing* Dr Michelle Ricard; Pearl Prevoir.
Licensure Intermediate care. *Beds* ICF 43. *Certified* Medicaid.
Owner Proprietary Corp.
Admissions Requirements Minimum age 50.
Staff RNs 3 (ft), 3 (pt); LPNs 2 (ft), 4 (pt); Nurses aides 9 (ft), 6 (pt); Activities coordinators 1 (pt); Dietitians 1 (pt).
Facilities Activities room; Laundry room; Multi-purpose room.
Activities Arts & crafts; Cards; Games; Reading groups; Prayer groups; Movies.

HYANNIS

Resthaven Nursing Home
82 School St, Hyannis, MA, 02601
(617) 775-3616
Admin Nicholas H Thisse. *Medical Dir/Dir of Nursing* Arthur F Bickford MD; Barbara V Massoni RH.
Licensure Private. *Beds* Private 44.
Owner Proprietary Corp.
Admissions Requirements Minimum age 21; Medical examination.
Staff Physicians 1 (pt); RNs 2 (ft), 2 (pt); LPNs 2 (ft); Nurses aides 7 (ft), 6 (pt); Physical therapists 1 (pt); Activities coordinators 1 (ft); Dietitians 1 (pt); Ophthalmologists 1 (pt).
Facilities Dining room; Physical therapy room; Activities room; Crafts room; Laundry room.
Activities Arts & crafts; Cards; Games; Reading groups; Prayer groups; Movies; Shopping trips; Shopping trips Dining out.

Whitehall Health Care Facilities
Falmouth Rd, PO Box 979, Hyannis, MA, 02601
(617) 775-6662
Admin Allen J White & Dr David K White. *Medical Dir/Dir of Nursing* Dr Forrest Beame.
Licensure Skilled care; Intermediate care. *Beds* 187. *Certified* Medicaid; Medicare.
Owner Proprietary Corp (Columbia Corp).
Staff Physicians; RNs 25 (ft); LPNs 6 (ft); Orderlies 6 (ft); Nurses aides 60 (ft); Physical therapists; Reality therapists 1 (ft); Recreational therapists 4 (ft); Occupational therapists 2 (pt); Speech therapists 1 (pt); Activities coordinators 2 (ft); Dietitians 1 (ft); Dentists 1 (ft); Ophthalmologists 1 (pt); Podiatrists 1 (pt).
Facilities Dining room; Physical therapy room; Activities room; Chapel; Crafts room; Laundry room; Barber/Beauty shop; Library.
Activities Arts & crafts; Cards; Games; Reading groups; Prayer groups; Movies; Shopping trips; Social/Cultural gatherings.

IPSWICH

Coburn Charitable Society
20 N Main St, Ipswich, MA, 01938
(617) 356-3571
Admin Helen Fraga.
Licensure Rest home. *Beds* 9.
Owner Nonprofit Corp.
Admissions Requirements Minimum age 60; Medical examination.
Staff LPNs 1 (pt); Nurses aides 1 (ft), 1 (pt); Ophthalmologists 1 (pt).
Facilities Dining room; Activities room; Laundry room.
Activities Shopping trips.

Stephen Caldwell Memorial Convalescent Home Inc
16 Green St, Ipswich, MA, 01938
(617) 356-5460; 356-2526
Admin Jeannette O Connor. *Medical Dir/Dir of Nursing* Thomas Sullivan MD; Donald Frances RN DON.
Licensure Skilled care. *Beds* SNF 60. *Certified* Medicaid; Medicare.
Owner Nonprofit Corp.
Admissions Requirements Minimum age 21; Medical examination; Physician's request.
Staff Physicians 10 (pt); RNs 5 (ft), 3 (pt); LPNs 6 (pt); Nurses aides 15 (ft), 7 (pt); Physical therapists 1 (pt); Occupational therapists 1 (pt); Speech therapists 1 (pt); Activities coordinators 2 (ft); Dietitians 1 (pt); Dentists 2 (pt); Ophthalmologists 1 (pt); Podiatrists 1 (pt).
Facilities Dining room; Physical therapy room; Activities room; Barber/Beauty shop; Library.
Activities Arts & crafts; Cards; Games; Reading groups; Prayer groups; Movies; Shopping trips; Social/Cultural gatherings.

JAMAICA PLAIN

The Armenian Nursing Home
431 Pond St, Jamaica Plain, MA, 02130
(617) 552-2600
Admin Kathy LeSar. *Medical Dir/Dir of Nursing* Terrence Murphy.
Licensure Skilled care; Intermediate care. *Beds* SNF 41; ICF 42. *Certified* Medicaid.
Owner Nonprofit Corp.
Admissions Requirements Medical examination; Physician's request.
Staff Physicians 2 (ft); RNs 3 (ft); LPNs 6 (ft); Nurses aides 36 (ft); Physical therapists 1 (pt); Reality therapists 1 (pt); Recreational therapists 2 (ft); Occupational therapists 1 (pt); Speech therapists 1 (pt); Dietitians 1 (ft), 1 (pt); Dentists 1 (pt); Ophthalmologists 1 (pt); Podiatrists 1 (pt).
Languages Armenian, Russian, Turkish, Farsi
Facilities Dining room; Physical therapy room; Activities room; Chapel; Crafts room; Laundry room; Barber/Beauty shop.
Activities Arts & crafts; Cards; Games; Reading groups; Prayer groups; Movies; Shopping trips; Social/Cultural gatherings.

Bradley Nursing Home
495 Walnut Ave, Jamaica Plain, MA, 02130
(617) 522-0660
Admin Joseph C Novak. *Medical Dir/Dir of Nursing* Hazel Butler RN DON.
Licensure Skilled care; Intermediate care. *Beds* SNF; ICF 26. *Certified* Medicaid; Medicare.
Owner Privately owned.
Admissions Requirements Females only; Medical examination.
Staff Physicians 6 (pt); RNs 1 (ft), 1 (pt); LPNs 1 (ft), 5 (pt); Nurses aides 8 (ft), 4 (pt); Reality therapists 2 (pt); Recreational therapists 1 (pt); Activities coordinators 1 (ft); Dietitians 1 (pt); Dentists 2 (pt); Ophthalmologists 1 (pt).
Facilities Activities room; Laundry room.
Activities Games; Prayer groups; Movies; Social/Cultural gatherings.

Tudor House Nursing Home*
81 S Huntington Ave, Jamaica Plain, MA, 02130
(617) 277-2633
Admin Herbert D Fisher.
Licensure Intermediate care. *Beds* 43. *Certified* Medicaid.

KINGSTON

Blueberry Hill Rest Home
PO Box 185, 15 Foster Ln, Kingston, MA, 02364
(617) 585-3657

Admin Bonnie Robinson. *Medical Dir/Dir of Nursing* Bonnie Robinson.
Licensure Custodial care. *Beds* Custodial care 15. *Certified* Medicaid.
Owner Proprietary Corp.
Admissions Requirements Minimum age 50; Males only; Medical examination.
Staff Physicians 2 (ft); LPNs 1 (ft); Nurses aides 10 (ft); Recreational therapists 1 (ft); Activities coordinators 1 (ft); Dietitians 1 (ft); Dentists 2 (ft); Ophthalmologists 2 (ft); Podiatrists 1 (ft).
Facilities Dining room; Activities room; Laundry room.
Activities Arts & crafts; Cards; Games; Reading groups; Prayer groups; Movies; Shopping trips; Social/Cultural gatherings.

LAKEVILLE

Island Terrace Nursing Home
Long Point Rd, PO Box 232, Lakeville, MA, 02346
(617) 947-0151
Admin Lucille Tolles. *Medical Dir/Dir of Nursing* Bernard Beuthner MD.
Licensure Skilled care 10B. *Beds* 73. *Certified* Medicaid.
Staff RNs 3 (ft); LPNs 6 (ft); Nurses aides 23 (ft); Physical therapists 1 (pt); Occupational therapists 1 (pt); Activities coordinators 1 (ft); Dietitians 1 (pt); Podiatrists 1 (pt).
Facilities Dining room; Physical therapy room; Activities room; Crafts room; Laundry room; Barber/Beauty shop; Library.
Activities Arts & crafts; Games; Reading groups; Prayer groups; Movies; Shopping trips.

Meadow View Nursing Home*
18 Crooked Ln, Lakeville, MA, 02346
(617) 947-2793
Admin Ora Mae Torres.
Licensure Intermediate care. *Beds* 29. *Certified* Medicaid.

LANCASTER

River Terrace Healthcare Nursing Home
Ballard Hill, Rte 117, Lancaster, MA, 01523
(617) 365-4537
Admin Linda E Weldon. *Medical Dir/Dir of Nursing* Dr Robert Fraser; Phyllis Mortimer RN.
Licensure Skilled care; Intermediate care. *Beds* SNF 41; ICF 41. *Certified* Medicaid.
Owner Proprietary Corp (Hillhaven Corp).

LAWRENCE

Anlaw Nursing Home*
555 S Union St, Lawrence, MA, 01843
(617) 682-5281
Admin Carmella M Mancini.
Licensure Skilled care; Intermediate care. *Beds* 90. *Certified* Medicaid; Medicare.
Owner Proprietary Corp (Hillhaven Corp).

Berkley Retirement Home
150 Berkley St, Lawrence, MA, 01841
(617) 682-1614
Admin Nancy J Herrmann. *Medical Dir/Dir of Nursing* Edward Broaddus MD.
Licensure Rest home. *Beds* 32.
Admissions Requirements Minimum age 70; Medical examination.
Staff Physicians 1 (pt); RNs 1 (ft); LPNs 5 (pt); Nurses aides 5 (pt); Recreational therapists 1 (pt); Activities coordinators 1 (pt); Dietitians 1 (pt); Podiatrists 1 (pt).
Facilities Dining room; Activities room; Chapel; Crafts room; Laundry room; Barber/Beauty shop; Library.
Activities Arts & crafts; Cards; Games; Reading groups; Prayer groups; Movies; Shopping trips; Social/Cultural gatherings.

German Old Folks Home Inc
374 Howard St, Lawrence, MA, 01841
(617) 682-5593
Admin Valerie Emerton.
Licensure Rest home. *Beds* 31. *Certified*
Medicaid.
Owner Nonprofit Corp.
Admissions Requirements Minimum age 50;
Medical examination; Physician's request.
Staff RNs 1 (pt); Orderlies 1 (pt); Nurses
aides 7 (pt); Reality therapists 1 (pt);
Recreational therapists; Dietitians 1 (pt).
Facilities Dining room; Activities room;
Crafts room; Laundry room.
Activities Arts & crafts; Cards; Games; Prayer
groups; Movies; Shopping trips; Social/
Cultural gatherings.

MI Nursing & Restorative Center
0 Bennington St, Lawrence, MA, 01841
(617) 685-6321
Admin Richard J Hamilton. *Medical Dir/Dir
of Nursing* Alan Miller MD; Bette McNabb
RN.
Licensure Skilled care; Intermediate care. *Beds*
SNF 208; ICF 42. *Certified* Medicaid;
Medicare.
Owner Nonprofit Corp.
Admissions Requirements Minimum age 21;
Medical examination.
Staff Physicians 18 (pt); RNs 20 (ft), 5 (pt);
LPNs 32 (ft), 25 (pt); Orderlies 6 (ft), 6 (pt);
Nurses aides 70 (ft), 35 (pt); Physical
therapists 6 (ft), 1 (pt); Recreational
therapists 4 (ft), 1 (pt); Occupational
therapists 2 (ft); Speech therapists 1 (ft);
Activities coordinators 1 (ft); Dietitians 3
(ft), 1 (pt); Ophthalmologists 1 (pt).
Languages Spanish, French, Lebanese
Affiliation Roman Catholic
Facilities Dining room; Physical therapy
room; Activities room; Chapel; Crafts room;
Laundry room; Barber/Beauty shop; Library;
Outside patio; Wheelchair garden; Patient
bar; Podiatry & dental treatment rooms.
Activities Arts & crafts; Cards; Games;
Reading groups; Prayer groups; Movies;
Shopping trips; Social/Cultural gatherings;
Bus/Van.

Town Manor Nursing Home Inc*
55 Lowell St, Lawrence, MA, 01840
(617) 688-6056
Admin Robert F Belluche.
Licensure Skilled care; Intermediate care. *Beds*
111. *Certified* Medicaid.
Owner Proprietary Corp (Hillhaven Corp).

Wood Mill Convalescent Home
800 Essex St, Lawrence, MA, 01841
(617) 686-2994
Admin Stephen A Witt. *Medical Dir/Dir of
Nursing* Dr Walter Jacobs; Joanne Ferguson.
Licensure Skilled care; Intermediate care. *Beds*
SNF 48; ICF 46. *Certified* Medicaid.
Owner Proprietary Corp (Hillhaven Corp).
Admissions Requirements Minimum age 21;
Medical examination; Physician's request.
Staff Physicians; RNs 5 (ft); LPNs 6 (pt);
Nurses aides 31 (ft), 5 (pt); Physical
therapists; Occupational therapists; Activities
coordinators; Dietitians.
Languages Spanish
Facilities Dining room; Physical therapy
room; Activities room; Crafts room; Laundry
room; Barber/Beauty shop.
Activities Arts & crafts; Cards; Games;
Reading groups; Prayer groups; Movies;
Shopping trips; Social/Cultural gatherings.

LEE

Berkshire Hills Nursing Home—North*
19 Prospect St, Lee, MA, 01238
(413) 243-2010
Admin Paul R Chernov. *Medical Dir/Dir of
Nursing* Charles W Stratton MD.

Licensure Intermediate care. *Beds* 73.
Certified Medicaid.
Staff Physicians; RNs; LPNs; Orderlies;
Nurses aides; Physical therapists;
Recreational therapists; Occupational
therapists; Speech therapists; Dietitians;
Dentists; Ophthalmologists; Podiatrists;
Audiologists.
Facilities Dining room; Physical therapy
room; Activities room; Laundry room;
Barber/Beauty shop.
Activities Arts & crafts; Cards; Games;
Reading groups; Prayer groups; Movies;
Shopping trips.

LENOX

Edgecombe Nursing & Convalescent Home*
40 Sunset Ave, Lenox, MA, 01240
(413) 637-0622
Admin James Bednarski.
Licensure Skilled care; Intermediate care. *Beds*
124. *Certified* Medicaid.
Admissions Requirements Minimum age 21;
Physician's request.
Staff Physicians 1 (pt); RNs 6 (ft), 4 (pt);
LPNs 5 (ft), 1 (pt); Orderlies 3 (ft); Nurses
aides 40 (ft), 9 (pt); Physical therapists 1
(pt); Recreational therapists 2 (ft);
Occupational therapists 1 (pt); Speech
therapists 1 (pt); Dietitians 1 (pt); Dentists 1
(pt); Podiatrists 2 (pt).
Facilities Dining room; Physical therapy
room; Activities room; Chapel; Crafts room;
Laundry room; Barber/Beauty shop.
Activities Arts & crafts; Cards; Games;
Reading groups; Prayer groups; Movies;
Social/Cultural gatherings.

Edgecombe Nursing Home
40 Sunset Ave, Lenox, MA, 02140
(413) 637-0622
Admin Mel Hitt. *Medical Dir/Dir of Nursing*
Dr Asta Potter; Vicki Stone DON.
Licensure Skilled care; Intermediate care. *Beds*
SNF 28; ICF 95.
Owner Proprietary Corp.
Admissions Requirements Minimum age 18;
Medical examination; Physician's request.
Staff RNs 7 (ft), 1 (pt); LPNs 9 (ft), 2 (pt);
Orderlies 3 (ft); Nurses aides 25 (ft), 9 (pt);
Physical therapists 1 (pt); Activities
coordinators 1 (ft).
Facilities Dining room; Physical therapy
room; Barber/Beauty shop.
Activities Arts & crafts; Cards; Games; Prayer
groups; Movies; Shopping trips; Social/
Cultural gatherings.

Valley View Nursing Home*
540 Pittsfield Rd, Lenox, MA, 01240
(413) 637-1221
Admin Kim P Murphy.
Licensure Intermediate care. *Beds* 140.
Certified Medicaid.
Owner Proprietary Corp (Health Care &
Retirement Corp).
Staff Physicians 2 (pt); RNs 3 (ft), 2 (pt);
LPNs 6 (ft), 4 (pt); Nurses aides 25 (ft), 17
(pt); Occupational therapists 1 (pt);
Activities coordinators 1 (ft); Dietitians 1
(pt); Dentists 1 (pt); Ophthalmologists 1 (pt);
Podiatrists 1 (pt).
Facilities Dining room; Physical therapy
room; Activities room; Chapel; Crafts room;
Laundry room; Barber/Beauty shop; Library.
Activities Arts & crafts; Cards; Games;
Reading groups; Prayer groups; Movies;
Shopping trips; Social/Cultural gatherings;
Exercise program.

LEOMINSTER

Fairlawn Nursing Home Inc
370 West St, Leominster, MA, 01453
(617) 537-0771

Admin James M Oliver. *Medical Dir/Dir of
Nursing* Edward Kamens MD; Judith
Raichle RN.
Licensure Skilled care; Intermediate care. *Beds*
SNF 80; ICF 41. *Certified* Medicaid;
Medicare.
Owner Proprietary Corp.
Admissions Requirements Minimum age 21.
Staff Physicians 8 (pt); RNs; LPNs; Orderlies;
Nurses aides; Physical therapists 2 (ft), 1
(pt); Recreational therapists 2 (ft);
Occupational therapists 1 (pt); Speech
therapists 1 (pt); Activities coordinators 1
(ft); Dietitians 1 (ft); Dentists 1 (pt);
Ophthalmologists 1 (pt); Podiatrists 1 (pt).
Facilities Dining room; Physical therapy
room; Activities room; Chapel; Crafts room;
Laundry room; Barber/Beauty shop; Library.
Activities Arts & crafts; Cards; Games;
Reading groups; Prayer groups; Movies;
Shopping trips; Social/Cultural gatherings.

Fairmount Rest Home*
34 Fairmount St, Leominster, MA, 01453
(617) 537-5472
Admin Mary A Gagne.
Licensure Rest home. *Beds* 20.

Homestead Rest Home*
226 Main St, Leominster, MA, 03453
(617) 537-7202
Admin Richard Ryan.
Licensure Rest home. *Beds* 21.
Admissions Requirements Medical
examination; Physician's request.
Facilities Dining room; Laundry room;
Barber/Beauty shop.
Activities Arts & crafts; Cards; Games;
Movies; Shopping trips.

Keystone Nursing Home Inc
44 Keystone Dr, Leominster, MA, 01453
(617) 537-9327
Admin Robert Sugar. *Medical Dir/Dir of
Nursing* John J Murphy MD; Lisa Smith
DON.
Licensure Intermediate care. *Beds* ICF 106.
Certified Medicaid.
Owner Proprietary Corp.
Admissions Requirements Physician's request.
Staff RNs; LPNs; Nurses aides; Physical
therapists; Reality therapists; Recreational
therapists; Occupational therapists; Speech
therapists; Activities coordinators; Dietitians;
Dentists; Ophthalmologists; Podiatrists.
Languages French, Italian, Finnish
Facilities Dining room; Physical therapy
room; Activities room; Chapel; Crafts room;
Laundry room; Barber/Beauty shop; Library;
Solarium.
Activities Arts & crafts; Cards; Games;
Reading groups; Prayer groups; Movies;
Shopping trips; Social/Cultural gatherings.

The Nancy Patch Retirement Home
16 Pearl St, Leominster, MA, 01453
(617) 537-3022
Admin Kathleen Flanagan Bergeron. *Medical
Dir/Dir of Nursing* Helen Kline RN.
Licensure Retirement home. *Beds* 12.
Owner Nonprofit Corp.
Admissions Requirements Minimum age 65;
Medical examination.
Staff Physicians; RNs; Nurses aides; Activities
coordinators; Dietitians; Ophthalmologists.
Facilities Dining room; Activities room;
Laundry room; Barber/Beauty shop.
Activities Arts & crafts; Cards; Games;
Reading groups; Prayer groups; Movies;
Shopping trips; Social/Cultural gatherings.

Village Rest Home
446 Main St, Leominster, MA, 01453
(617) 534-6270
Admin Matilda Iandoli.
Licensure Rest home. *Beds* 25.
Owner Privately owned.
Admissions Requirements Minimum age 32.

Staff LPNs 1 (ft); Nurses aides 5 (ft);
  Recreational therapists 1 (ft); Activities
  coordinators 1 (ft); Ophthalmologists 1 (ft).
Facilities Dining room; Activities room;
  Crafts room; Laundry room; Barber/Beauty
  shop; Library.
Activities Arts & crafts; Cards; Games;
  Reading groups; Prayer groups; Movies;
  Shopping trips; Social/Cultural gatherings.

LEXINGTON

Dana Home of Lexington
2027 Massachusetts Ave, Lexington, MA,
  02173
(617) 861-0131, 862-0222
Admin Mrs Rafi.
Licensure Rest home. *Beds* 15.
Owner Nonprofit organization/foundation.
Admissions Requirements Medical
  examination.
Facilities Dining room.
Activities Arts & crafts; Cards; Games;
  Movies; Shopping trips.

East Village Nursing Home*
140 Emerson St, Lexington, MA, 02173
(617) 861-8630
Admin Robert Cataldo.
Licensure Skilled care; Intermediate care. *Beds*
  162. *Certified* Medicaid.
Owner Proprietary Corp (Beverly Enterprises).

Fairlawn Nursing Home Inc
265 Lowell St, Lexington, MA, 02173
(617) 862-7640
Admin Thomas R Walsh. *Medical Dir/Dir of
  Nursing* Robert Stewart MD.
Licensure Intermediate care. *Beds* ICF 104.
Owner Proprietary Corp.
Admissions Requirements Medical
  examination; Physician's request.
Staff RNs; LPNs; Nurses aides; Activities
  coordinators; Dietitians.
Facilities Dining room; Physical therapy
  room; Activities room; Laundry room;
  Barber/Beauty shop; Library.
Activities Arts & crafts; Cards; Games; Prayer
  groups; Movies; Shopping trips; Social/
  Cultural gatherings.

**Mediplex at Lexington—Long-Term Care
Facility***
178 Lowell St, Lexington, MA, 02173
(617) 862-7400
Admin Sylvia J Chiasson.
Licensure Intermediate care. *Beds* 120.
  Certified Medicaid.

Pine Knoll Nursing Home
30 Watertown St, Lexington, MA, 02173
(617) 862-8151
Admin Edward F Cataldo.
Licensure Skilled care. *Beds* 81. *Certified*
  Medicaid; Medicare.
Owner Proprietary Corp.
Admissions Requirements Physician's request.
Staff RNs; LPNs; Orderlies; Nurses aides;
  Physical therapists; Occupational therapists;
  Speech therapists; Activities coordinators;
  Dietitians; Dentists; Ophthalmologists.
Languages Greek, French
Facilities Dining room; Physical therapy
  room; Activities room; Chapel; Crafts room;
  Laundry room; Barber/Beauty shop.
Activities Arts & crafts; Cards; Games;
  Reading groups; Prayer groups; Movies;
  Shopping trips.

LINCOLN

Lincoln Rest Home*
Farrar Rd, Lincoln, MA, 01773
(617) 259-8128
Admin Joseph S Sulomont.
Licensure Rest home. *Beds* 12.

LITTLETON

Littleton House Nursing Home*
191 Foster St, Littleton, MA, 01460
(617) 486-3512
Admin Andrew MacLeod.
Licensure Intermediate care. *Beds* 120.
  Certified Medicaid.
Owner Proprietary Corp (Life Care Centers of
  America).

LONGMEADOW

**Jewish Nursing Home of Western
Massachusetts**
770 Converse St, Longmeadow, MA, 01106
(413) 567-6211
Admin Howard L Braverman. *Medical Dir/Dir
  of Nursing* Dr Irving Hoff MD; Janet Pope
  RN DON.
Licensure Skilled care; Intermediate care. *Beds*
  SNF 160; ICF 40. *Certified* Medicaid;
  Medicare.
Owner Nonprofit Corp.
Admissions Requirements Minimum age 21;
  Medical examination.
Staff Physicians 1 (ft); RNs 20 (ft), 10 (pt);
  LPNs 13 (ft), 7 (pt); Orderlies 5 (ft), 2 (pt);
  Nurses aides 58 (ft), 26 (pt); Physical
  therapists 2 (ft); Recreational therapists 2
  (ft); Occupational therapists 2 (ft); Speech
  therapists 1 (pt); Activities coordinators 1
  (ft); Dietitians 1 (pt); Dentists 1 (pt);
  Ophthalmologists 1 (pt); 108 (ft).
Languages Hebrew, Yiddish
Affiliation Jewish
Facilities Dining room; Physical therapy
  room; Activities room; Chapel; Crafts room;
  Laundry room; Barber/Beauty shop; Library.
Activities Arts & crafts; Cards; Games;
  Reading groups; Prayer groups; Movies;
  Shopping trips; Social/Cultural gatherings;
  Continuing education classes.

LOWELL

Arcadia Nursing Home*
841 Merrimack St, Lowell, MA, 01854
(617) 459-0546
Admin Isabel R Donovan.
Licensure Skilled care; Intermediate care. *Beds*
  142. *Certified* Medicaid.

Battles Home
236 Fairmount St, Lowell, MA, 01852
(617) 453-2531
Admin Clifford R Jennings.
Licensure Rest home. *Beds* 12.
Admissions Requirements Males only; Medical
  examination.
Facilities Dining room; Activities room;
  Laundry room; Library Living room; Pool
  room.

Christian Hill Convalescent Home
19 Varnum St, Lowell, MA, 01850
(617) 454-5644
Admin Frank P Miller. *Medical Dir/Dir of
  Nursing* Lawrence Newman MD; Rachel
  Eiserman DON.
Licensure Skilled care; Intermediate care. *Beds*
  SNF 160; ICF. *Certified* Medicaid;
  Medicare.
Owner Proprietary Corp (New Medico Assoc).
Staff RNs 9 (ft), 12 (pt); LPNs 17 (ft), 11 (pt);
  Nurses aides 46 (ft), 37 (pt); Physical
  therapists 1 (pt); Activities coordinators 1
  (ft); Dietitians 2 (ft).
Facilities Dining room; Physical therapy
  room; Activities room; Chapel; Crafts room;
  Laundry room; Barber/Beauty shop.
Activities Arts & crafts; Cards; Games;
  Reading groups; Prayer groups; Movies;
  Shopping trips; Social/Cultural gatherings.

Colonial Rest Home*
945 Middlesex St, Lowell, MA, 01851
(617) 454-5644
Admin Elliott C Williams.
Licensure Rest home. *Beds* 22.

D'Youville Manor
981 Varnum Ave, Lowell, MA, 01854-1997
(617) 454-5681
Admin Pauline Beauchesne. *Medical Dir/Dir
  of Nursing* Stephen R Brovender MD; Ruth
  MacKinnon RN DON.
Licensure Skilled care; Intermediate care;
  Adult day care. *Beds* SNF 196; ICF; Adult
  day care 20. *Certified* Medicaid.
Owner Nonprofit Corp.
Admissions Requirements Minimum age 55;
  Medical examination; Physician's request.
Staff RNs 3 (ft), 6 (pt); LPNs 12 (ft), 22 (pt);
  Orderlies 6 (ft), 4 (pt); Nurses aides 43 (ft),
  37 (pt); Physical therapists 1 (pt);
  Recreational therapists 1 (ft); Occupational
  therapists 1 (ft); Activities coordinators 1
  (ft); Dietitians 1 (ft); Ophthalmologists 6
  (pt); Social worker 1 (ft), 1 (pt).
Affiliation Roman Catholic
Facilities Dining room; Physical therapy
  room; Activities room; Chapel; Crafts room;
  Laundry room; Barber/Beauty shop; Library;
  Podiatrists room; Pastoral room.
Activities Arts & crafts; Cards; Games;
  Reading groups; Prayer groups; Movies;
  Shopping trips; Social/Cultural gatherings;
  Music movement; Daily Mass.

Fairhaven Nursing Home*
476 Varnum Ave, Lowell, MA, 01854
(617) 458-3388
Admin Margaret H Larkin.
Licensure Skilled care; Intermediate care. *Beds*
  166. *Certified* Medicaid.

Glenwood Manor Convalescent Home
577 Varnum Ave, Lowell, MA, 01854
(617) 455-5444
Admin Scott Elsass. *Medical Dir/Dir of
  Nursing* Dr Susan Black.
Licensure Intermediate care. *Beds* 101.
  Certified Medicaid.
Owner Proprietary Corp (Hillhaven Corp).
Admissions Requirements Minimum age 21;
  Medical examination; Physician's request.
Staff RNs; LPNs; Orderlies; Nurses aides;
  Physical therapists; Reality therapists;
  Recreational therapists; Occupational
  therapists; Speech therapists; Activities
  coordinators; Dietitians; Dentists;
  Ophthalmologists; Podiatrists.
Facilities Dining room; Activities room;
  Crafts room; Barber/Beauty shop.
Activities Arts & crafts; Cards; Games;
  Reading groups; Prayer groups; Movies;
  Shopping trips; Social/Cultural gatherings.

Horn Home for Aged
98 Smith St, Lowell, MA, 01851
(617) 452-9571
Admin David M Bennett. *Medical Dir/Dir of
  Nursing* Dr John J Droescher Jr.
Licensure Retirement home. *Beds* Retirement
  home 14.
Owner Nonprofit organization/foundation.
Admissions Requirements Minimum age 65;
  Females only; Medical examination;
  Physician's request.
Staff Physicians 1 (pt); RNs 1 (pt); Dietitians
  1 (pt); Podiatrists 1 (pt).
Languages French
Facilities Dining room; Activities room;
  Laundry room; Library; Recreation & Social
  Communal areas.
Activities Games; Prayer groups; Music
  performances; Holiday celebrations.

Merrimack River Valley House
5320 Fletcher St, Lowell, MA, 01854
(617) 452-6071

Admin Jane I Bellegarde. *Medical Dir/Dir of Nursing* Dr Benjamin Gaieski; Linda Bellegarde.
Licensure Retirement home level IV. *Beds* 28.
Owner Nonprofit Corp.
Admissions Requirements Minimum age 62; Females only; Medical examination.
Staff Physicians 1 (pt); LPNs 1 (ft); Nurses aides 5 (ft), 6 (pt); Activities coordinators 1 (pt); Dietitians 1 (pt); Ophthalmologists 1 (pt).
Facilities Dining room; Activities room; Crafts room; Laundry room; Barber/Beauty shop; Library.
Activities Arts & crafts; Cards; Games; Prayer groups; Movies; Shopping trips; Social/Cultural gatherings.

Merrimack Valley Retirement Home*
360 Pawtucket St, Lowell, MA, 01854
(617) 453-6412
Admin Yale Canter.
Licensure Rest home. *Beds* 19.

Northwood Convalescent Center*
1010 Varnum Ave, Lowell, MA, 01854
(617) 458-8773
Admin Richard Wallace. *Medical Dir/Dir of Nursing* John Korbowniczak MD.
Licensure Skilled care; Intermediate care. *Beds* 123. *Certified* Medicaid; Medicare.
Admissions Requirements Medical examination.
Staff Physicians 5 (pt); RNs; LPNs; Orderlies; Physical therapists 1 (pt); Recreational therapists 2 (ft), 1 (pt); Occupational therapists 1 (pt); Speech therapists 1 (pt); Activities coordinators 1 (ft); Dietitians 1 (pt); Dentists 1 (pt); Podiatrists 1 (pt).
Facilities Dining room; Physical therapy room; Activities room; Crafts room; Laundry room; Barber/Beauty shop.
Activities Arts & crafts; Cards; Games; Reading groups; Prayer groups; Movies; Shopping trips; Social/Cultural gatherings.

Princeton House Rest Home*
94-100 Priceton Blvd, Lowell, MA, 01853
(617) 458-4056
Admin Jeanette F Savoie.
Licensure Rest home. *Beds* 56.

Town & Country Nursing Home
915 Westford St, Lowell, MA, 01851
(617) 459-7262, 454-5438
Admin Alexander E Struzziero. *Medical Dir/Dir of Nursing* Patricia Struzziero.
Licensure Intermediate care. *Beds* ICF 50. *Certified* Medicaid.
Owner Proprietary Corp.
Admissions Requirements Minimum age 16.
Staff RNs 2 (ft); LPNs 3 (ft), 5 (pt); Orderlies 1 (pt); Nurses aides 12 (ft), 11 (pt); Activities coordinators 1 (ft), 1 (pt); Dietitians 1 (pt).
Facilities Dining room; Laundry room; Barber/Beauty shop.
Activities Arts & crafts; Cards; Games; Reading groups; Prayer groups; Movies; Shopping trips; Social/Cultural gatherings.

Willow Manor Nursing Home*
30 Princeton Blvd, Lowell, MA, 01851
(617) 454-8086
Admin S Joseph S Solomont.
Licensure Skilled care; Intermediate care. *Beds* 84. *Certified* Medicaid.

LYNN

Abbott House Nursing Home
28 Essex St, Lynn, MA, 01902
(617) 595-5500
Admin Richard C Bane.
Licensure Skilled care. *Beds* SNF 47. *Certified* Medicaid; Medicare.
Owner Proprietary Corp.

Alba Nursing Home
12 Park St, Lynn, MA, 01905
(617) 599-3993
Admin William A Sherman, Jr.
Licensure Intermediate care. *Beds* 34. *Certified* Medicaid.

Atlantic Rest Home*
60 Atlantic St, Lynn, MA, 01902
(617) 598-0609
Admin David J Solimine Jr.
Licensure Rest home. *Beds* 21.
Admissions Requirements Minimum age 60; Females only; Medical examination; Physician's request.
Staff Nurses aides 3 (ft), 5 (pt); Podiatrists.
Facilities Dining room.
Activities Cards; Games.

Avalon Nursing Home
24 Baker St, Lynn, MA, 01902
(617) 598-1142
Admin Richard C Bane.
Licensure Intermediate care. *Beds* 29. *Certified* Medicaid.

Baker Manor Rest Home
16 Baker St, Lynn, MA, 01902
(617) 592-7033
Admin Michael W Mosho. *Medical Dir/Dir of Nursing* Diane F Fuller.
Licensure Rest home. *Beds* 15. *Certified* Medicaid.
Owner Proprietary Corp.
Admissions Requirements Minimum age 50; Females only; Medical examination.
Staff Physicians 2 (pt); RNs 1 (pt); Nurses aides 2 (ft), 5 (pt); Activities coordinators 1 (pt); Dietitians 1 (pt); Ophthalmologists 1 (pt); Podiatrists 1 (pt).
Facilities Dining room; Activities room; Laundry room.
Activities Arts & crafts; Cards; Games; Prayer groups; Shopping trips; Social/Cultural gatherings.

Ann Carroll Nursing Home
66 Johnson St, Lynn, MA, 01902
(615) 592-5849
Admin Robert Douglas. *Medical Dir/Dir of Nursing* Marilyn Arsenault LPN.
Licensure Intermediate care. *Beds* ICF 28. *Certified* Medicaid.
Owner Proprietary Corp.
Admissions Requirements Medical examination; Physician's request.
Staff Physicians 3 (pt); LPNs 3 (pt); Orderlies 2 (pt); Nurses aides 5 (pt); Physical therapists 1 (pt); Recreational therapists 1 (pt); Activities coordinators 1 (pt); Dietitians 1 (pt); Podiatrists 1 (pt); Audiologists 1 (pt).
Facilities Dining room; Activities room; Laundry room; Dining rooms double as activity rooms for services & crafts.
Activities Arts & crafts; Cards; Games; Reading groups; Prayer groups; Shopping trips; Social/Cultural gatherings.

Crestview Manor Nursing Home
72 Nahant St, Lynn, MA, 01902
(617) 598-6363
Admin William A Sherman Jr.
Licensure Intermediate care. *Beds* 29. *Certified* Medicaid.

Joseph B Devlin Public Medical Institute
179 Holyoke St, Lynn, MA, 01905
(617) 595-3743
Admin Garry Mayo. *Medical Dir/Dir of Nursing* Stephen P Weglarz MD; Barbara Spencer RN DON.
Licensure Skilled care. *Beds* SNF 54. *Certified* Medicaid.
Owner Publicly owned.
Admissions Requirements Physician's request.

Staff Physicians 1 (pt); RNs 4 (ft), 3 (pt); LPNs 2 (ft), 3 (pt); Nurses aides 26 (ft); Physical therapists 1 (pt); Occupational therapists 1 (pt); Activities coordinators 1 (ft); Dietitians 1 (pt).
Facilities Dining room; Activities room; Laundry room; Barber/Beauty shop.
Activities Arts & crafts; Games; Reading groups; Prayer groups; Movies; Social/Cultural gatherings.

Essex Convalescent Home
94 Franklin St, Lynn, MA, 01902
(617) 592-7758
Admin William Mantzoukas. *Medical Dir/Dir of Nursing* James Gottschall MD; Clestorine Madden RN DON.
Licensure Intermediate care. *Beds* ICF 62. *Certified* Medicaid.
Owner Proprietary Corp.
Admissions Requirements Minimum age 40; Medical examination.
Staff RNs 3 (ft), 3 (pt); LPNs 1 (pt); Nurses aides 14 (ft), 8 (pt); Physical therapists 1 (pt); Recreational therapists 1 (pt); Activities coordinators 1 (pt); Dietitians 1 (pt).
Languages Greek, Spanish, French
Facilities Dining room; Activities room; Laundry room.
Activities Arts & crafts; Cards; Games; Reading groups; Prayer groups; Movies; Shopping trips.

Family Rest Home*
13 Essex St, Lynn, MA, 01902
(617) 595-7644
Admin James B Kerwin.
Licensure Intermediate care. *Beds* 22. *Certified* Medicaid.
Admissions Requirements Medical examination.
Facilities Dining room; Activities room; Laundry room.
Activities Arts & crafts; Cards; Games; Shopping trips.

Karlson Rest Home Inc*
73 Baker St, Lynn, MA, 01902
(617) 595-8931
Admin Maureen Callahan.
Licensure Rest home. *Beds* 15.
Staff Physicians 1 (pt); RNs 1 (pt); Nurses aides 1 (ft), 6 (pt); Activities coordinators 1 (pt); Dietitians 1 (pt); Dentists 1 (pt); Ophthalmologists 1 (pt); Podiatrists 1 (pt).

Lawrence Manor Nursing Home
26 Henry Ave, Lynn, MA, 01902
(617) 595-2941
Admin Albert Dukatz.
Licensure Intermediate care. *Beds* 39. *Certified* Medicaid.

Lenox Hill Nursing & Rehabilitation Care Facility*
70 Granite St, Lynn, MA, 01904
(617) 581-2400
Admin Robert N Murphy.
Licensure Skilled care; Intermediate care. *Beds* 218. *Certified* Medicaid; Medicare.

Lynn Home for Elderly Persons
Atlantic Terrace, Lynn, MA, 01902
(617) 593-8099
Admin Barbara L Pinkham. *Medical Dir/Dir of Nursing* G Fred Jackson MD.
Licensure Rest home. *Beds* 39.
Admissions Requirements Minimum age 65; Medical examination.
Staff RNs 1 (pt); LPNs 1 (ft), 4 (pt); Nurses aides 3 (ft), 5 (pt); Activities coordinators 1 (ft).
Facilities Dining room; Activities room; Crafts room; Laundry room; Barber/Beauty shop; Library; Sewing room; Card room; Ceramic shop.

Activities Arts & crafts; Cards; Games; Reading groups; Prayer groups; Movies; Shopping trips; Social/Cultural gatherings; Ceramics; Cooking.

Lynn Home & Infirmary*
655 Boston St, Lynn, MA, 01905
(617) 593-4347
Admin Donald P Dixon. *Medical Dir/Dir of Nursing* Dr Milton Helsel.
Licensure Intermediate care. *Beds* 105. *Certified* Medicaid.
Admissions Requirements Medical examination; Physician's request.
Staff Physicians 1 (pt); RNs 9 (ft); LPNs 4 (ft); Nurses aides 30 (ft); Physical therapists 1 (pt); Occupational therapists 1 (pt); Activities coordinators 1 (ft), 1 (pt); Dietitians 1 (pt).
Facilities Activities room; Laundry room.
Activities Arts & crafts; Games; Prayer groups; Movies.

Lynn Shore Rest Home*
37 Breed St, Lynn, MA, 01902
(617) 595-7110
Admin David J Solimine Jr.
Licensure Rest home. *Beds* 34.
Admissions Requirements Minimum age 60; Medical examination; Physician's request.
Staff Nurses aides 3 (ft), 3 (pt); Podiatrists.
Facilities Dining room; Activities room.
Activities Cards; Games.

Phillips Manor Nursing Home*
28 Linwood Rd, Lynn, MA, 01905
(617) 592-8000
Admin Anna Freehling.
Licensure Intermediate care. *Beds* 20. *Certified* Medicaid.

Pine Hill Rest Home*
341 Linwood St, Lynn, MA, 01905
(617) 598-6256
Admin Charles Dandaneau.
Licensure Rest home. *Beds* 12.

Twomey Rest Home*
54 Tudor St, Lynn, MA, 01902
(617) 593-4567
Admin Timothy Twomey.
Licensure Rest home. *Beds* 30.

MALDEN

Bartlett Manor Nursing Home
180 Summer St, Malden, MA, 02148
(617) 321-8752
Admin John DiPirro. *Medical Dir/Dir of Nursing* Donna Hurd RN.
Licensure Intermediate care; Level III. *Beds* ICF 40. *Certified* Medicaid.
Owner Privately owned.
Admissions Requirements Medical examination; Physician's request.
Staff RNs 2 (ft), 3 (pt); LPNs 2 (pt); Nurses aides 8 (ft), 6 (pt); Activities coordinators 1 (pt).
Languages French
Facilities Dining room; Activities room.
Activities Arts & crafts; Cards; Games; Prayer groups; Shopping trips; Social/Cultural gatherings.

Buchanan Nursing Home Inc
190 Summer St, Malden, MA, 02148
(617) 321-4157
Admin John DiPirro. *Medical Dir/Dir of Nursing* Lillian McCarthy.
Licensure Intermediate care. *Beds* ICF 35. *Certified* Medicaid; Medicare.
Owner Privately owned.
Admissions Requirements Females only.
Staff RNs 2 (ft); LPNs 3 (ft); Nurses aides 12 (ft); Activities coordinators.

Facilities Dining room; Activities room; Crafts room; Laundry room.
Activities Arts & crafts; Cards; Games; Social/Cultural gatherings; Van rides.

Care Well Manor Nursing Home*
203 Summer St, Malden, MA, 02148
(617) 324-3663
Admin Neil B McCole.
Licensure Intermediate care. *Beds* 23. *Certified* Medicaid.
Admissions Requirements Minimum age 21; Females only; Medical examination.
Staff RNs 1 (ft); LPNs 1 (ft), 2 (pt); Nurses aides 3 (ft), 4 (pt); Activities coordinators; Dietitians.
Facilities Dining room; Activities room; Crafts room; Laundry room.
Activities Arts & crafts; Cards; Games; Reading groups; Prayer groups; Movies; Shopping trips; Social/Cultural gatherings; Outings for lunches & dinners.

Davenport Memorial Home
70 Salem St, Malden, MA, 02148-9998
(617) 324-0150
Admin Beth E Walsh.
Licensure Level IV. *Beds* Level IV 20.
Owner Nonprofit organization/foundation.
Admissions Requirements Minimum age 65; Medical examination.
Staff RNs 1 (pt); LPNs 1 (pt); Nurses aides 6 (pt).
Facilities Dining room; Laundry room; Barber/Beauty shop; Library; Social rooms.
Activities Games; Movies; Shopping trips; Social/Cultural gatherings.

Dexter House Nursing Facility*
120 Main St, Malden, MA, 02148
(617) 324-5600
Admin Gerald A Sohn.
Licensure Skilled care; Intermediate care. *Beds* 130. *Certified* Medicaid.
Owner Proprietary Corp (Beverly Enterprises).
Admissions Requirements Minimum age 21; Medical examination; Physician's request.
Staff Physicians 1 (pt); RNs 13 (ft); LPNs 9 (ft); Nurses aides 55 (ft); Physical therapists 1 (ft); Reality therapists 1 (ft); Recreational therapists 1 (ft); Occupational therapists 1 (pt); Speech therapists 1 (pt); Dietitians 1 (ft); Dentists 1 (pt); Ophthalmologists 1 (pt); Podiatrists 1 (pt); Audiologists 1 (pt); Social workers 1 (ft).
Facilities Dining room; Physical therapy room; Activities room; Crafts room; Barber/Beauty shop; Library.
Activities Arts & crafts; Cards; Games; Reading groups; Prayer groups; Movies; Shopping trips; Social/Cultural gatherings.

Forestdale Nusing Home*
342 Forest St, Malden, MA, 02148
(617) 322-1716
Admin Clyde L Tyler Jr.
Licensure Intermediate care. *Beds* 69. *Certified* Medicaid.

Malden Home for Aged Persons*
578 Main St, Malden, MA, 02148
(617) 321-3740
Admin Bridget Berk. *Medical Dir/Dir of Nursing* H Portman MD.
Licensure Intermediate care. *Beds* 25.
Owner Nonprofit Corp.
Admissions Requirements Minimum age 65; Females only; Medical examination.
Staff RNs 2 (ft), 1 (pt); LPNs 4 (pt); Nurses aides 2 (ft), 4 (pt); Activities coordinators 1 (pt); Dietitians 1 (pt).
Facilities Dining room; Activities room; Crafts room; Laundry room; Barber/Beauty shop; Store.
Activities Arts & crafts; Cards; Games; Shopping trips; Annual fair.

Malden Nursing Home*
255 Clifton St, Malden, MA, 02148
(617) 324-2620
Admin Clyde L Tyler Jr.
Licensure Intermediate care. *Beds* 52. *Certified* Medicaid.

Mansion Rest Home*
14 Rockland Ave, Malden, MA, 02148
(617) 322-4634
Admin Reta C Mackinnon.
Licensure Rest home. *Beds* 27. *Certified* Medicaid.

McFadden Memorial Manor*
341 Forest St, Malden, MA, 02148
(617) 322-1700
Admin Harry E Munro.
Licensure Intermediate care. *Beds* 61. *Certified* Medicaid.

San Filippo Rest Home
53 James St, Malden, MA, 02148
(617) 324-7233
Admin Carol Wallace. *Medical Dir/Dir of Nursing* Elizabeth Banks RN.
Licensure Rest home. *Beds* Rest home 17. *Certified* Medicaid; Medicare.
Owner Privately owned.
Admissions Requirements Medical examination.
Staff Physicians 3 (pt); LPNs 1 (pt); Nurses aides 3 (ft), 3 (pt); Activities coordinators 1 (pt); Dietitians 1 (pt); Ophthalmologists 1 (pt).
Languages Italian
Facilities Dining room; Activities room; Laundry room.
Activities Arts & crafts; Cards; Games; Social/Cultural gatherings.

MANCHESTER

Oakwood Nursing Home*
601 Summer St, Manchester, MA, 01944
(617) 526-4653
Admin Joanne E O'Day.
Licensure Intermediate care. *Beds* 29. *Certified* Medicaid.
Owner Proprietary Corp (Beverly Enterprises).

MARBLEHEAD

Devereux House Nursing Home Inc
39 Lafayette St, Marblehead, MA, 01945
(617) 631-6120
Admin Melvin A Rose. *Medical Dir/Dir of Nursing* Dr Elliot Strauss; Clara M Donahue RN.
Licensure Skilled care. *Beds* SNF 64. *Certified* Medicaid.
Owner Proprietary Corp.
Admissions Requirements Minimum age 18.
Staff Physicians 13 (pt); RNs 9 (ft); LPNs 7 (ft); Orderlies; Nurses aides 19 (ft), 18 (pt); Physical therapists 1 (pt); Reality therapists 1 (ft), 2 (pt); Recreational therapists 1 (ft), 2 (pt); Occupational therapists 1 (pt); Speech therapists 1 (pt); Activities coordinators; Dietitians 1 (pt); Dentists 4 (pt); Ophthalmologists 2 (pt); Podiatrists 3 (pt).
Facilities Dining room; Physical therapy room; Activities room; Chapel; Crafts room; Laundry room; Barber/Beauty shop; Library; Patio.
Activities Arts & crafts; Cards; Games; Reading groups; Prayer groups; Movies; Shopping trips; Social/Cultural gatherings.

Lafayette Convalescent Home*
25 Lafayette St, Marblehead, MA, 01945
(617) 631-4535
Admin Beatrice G Breitstein.
Licensure Skilled care; Intermediate care. *Beds* 62. *Certified* Medicaid.

MARLBOROUGH

Bolton Manor Nursing Home
400 Bolton Rd, Marlborough, MA, 01752
481-6123
Admin John Rossetti. *Medical Dir/Dir of Nursing* Elizabeth Mocklow RN.
Licensure Skilled care; Intermediate care. *Beds* SNF 80; ICF 80. *Certified* Medicaid.
Owner Proprietary Corp (Hillhaven Corp).
Admissions Requirements Minimum age 50.
Staff RNs; LPNs; Orderlies; Nurses aides; Activities coordinators; Dietitians.
Languages French, Portuguese, Spanish
Facilities Dining room; Physical therapy room; Activities room; Chapel; Crafts room; Laundry room; Barber/Beauty shop.
Activities Arts & crafts; Cards; Games; Reading groups; Prayer groups; Movies; Shopping trips; Social/Cultural gatherings.

Pine Grove Rest Home*
455 Northboro Rd, Marlborough, MA, 01752
(617) 481-6562
Admin Alice M McGee. *Medical Dir/Dir of Nursing* Dr C Levin.
Licensure Rest home. *Beds* 28.
Admissions Requirements Minimum age 25; Males only; Medical examination; Physician's request.
Staff RNs 1 (ft); Nurses aides 4 (ft); Recreational therapists 1 (pt).
Languages French, Spanish
Facilities Dining room; Activities room; Crafts room; Laundry room; Library.
Activities Arts & crafts; Cards; Games; Movies; Shopping trips; Social/Cultural gatherings; Holiday parties; Bingo.

Westridge Health Care Center
121 Northboro Rd, Marlborough, MA, 01752
(617) 485-4040
Admin Philip Quillard. *Medical Dir/Dir of Nursing* Dr Richard McMahon.
Licensure Skilled care; Intermediate care. *Beds* SNF 139; ICF 57. *Certified* Medicaid; Medicare.
Owner Proprietary Corp (Hillhaven Corp).
Admissions Requirements Medical examination.
Staff RNs 8 (ft), 6 (pt); LPNs 15 (ft), 5 (pt); Orderlies 5 (ft), 5 (pt); Nurses aides 41 (ft), 30 (pt); Physical therapists 1 (ft); Recreational therapists 3 (pt); Occupational therapists 1 (pt); Speech therapists 1 (pt); Activities coordinators 1 (pt); Dentists 1 (pt); Ophthalmologists 1 (pt); Podiatrists 1 (pt).
Facilities Dining room; Physical therapy room; Activities room; Chapel; Crafts room; Laundry room; Barber/Beauty shop; Library.
Activities Arts & crafts; Cards; Games; Reading groups; Prayer groups; Movies; Shopping trips; Social/Cultural gatherings.

MASHPEE

Pilgrim's Pride Nursing Home
Rte 28 at Noisy Hole Rd, Mashpee, MA, 02649
(617) 477-1310
Admin Margaret E Kelly. *Medical Dir/Dir of Nursing* Abraham Dietz MD.
Licensure Intermediate care. *Beds* 120. *Certified* Medicaid.
Admissions Requirements Minimum age 21; Medical examination; Physician's request.
Staff Physicians 1 (pt); RNs 5 (ft), 1 (pt); LPNs 6 (ft), 5 (pt); Nurses aides 30 (ft), 15 (pt); Activities coordinators 2 (ft); Dietitians 1 (pt); Ophthalmologists 1 (pt).
Facilities Dining room; Physical therapy room; Activities room; Chapel; Crafts room; Laundry room; Barber/Beauty shop; Library; Dental office.
Activities Arts & crafts; Cards; Games; Reading groups; Prayer groups; Movies; Shopping trips; Social/Cultural gatherings; Field trips.

MATTAPOISETT

Mattapoisett Nursing Home Inc
79 N St, Mattapoisett, MA, 02739
(617) 758-2512
Admin Norman L Turcotte. *Medical Dir/Dir of Nursing* Ruth M Hart RN.
Licensure Intermediate care. *Beds* ICF 42. *Certified* Medicaid; Medicare.
Owner Proprietary Corp.
Admissions Requirements Minimum age 21.
Staff RNs 2 (ft), 2 (pt); LPNs 1 (ft), 1 (pt); Nurses aides 6 (ft), 11 (pt); Activities coordinators 1 (pt); Dietitians 1 (pt); Dietary, Laundry, Housekeeping 4 (ft), 5 (pt).
Languages Portuguese, Cape Verdean
Facilities Dining room; Activities room; Laundry room; Kitchen.
Activities Arts & crafts; Cards; Games; Prayer groups; Movies; Shopping trips; Social/Cultural gatherings.

MEDFIELD

Med-Vale Nursing Home
519 Main St, Medfield, MA, 02052
(617) 359-6050
Admin John Corliss. *Medical Dir/Dir of Nursing* A Stagg MD; Janice Hathaway.
Licensure Intermediate care. *Beds* ICF 49. *Certified* Medicaid.
Owner Proprietary Corp.
Admissions Requirements Minimum age 21.
Staff RNs; LPNs; Nurses aides; Activities coordinators; Dietitians; Ophthalmologists.
Facilities Laundry room.
Activities Arts & crafts; Cards; Games; Reading groups; Prayer groups; Movies; Shopping trips; Social/Cultural gatherings.

MEDFORD

Emery Retirement & Convalescent Home*
34 Grove St, Medford, MA, 02155
(617) 488-7117
Admin Thomas J McNulty Jr.
Licensure Intermediate care. *Beds* 31. *Certified* Medicaid.

Magoun Manor Nursing Home
68 Magoun Ave, Medford, MA, 02155
(617) 488-7117
Admin K R Kaffenberger.
Licensure Intermediate care. *Beds* 29. *Certified* Medicaid.
Admissions Requirements Medical examination; Physician's request.
Staff RNs; LPNs; Nurses aides; Recreational therapists; Activities coordinators; Dietitians 1 (pt); Podiatrists 1 (pt).
Facilities Dining room; Activities room; Crafts room; Laundry room.
Activities Arts & crafts; Cards; Games; Reading groups; Prayer groups; Movies; Shopping trips; Social/Cultural gatherings; Bowling; Life program.

Medford Rest Home*
2 Central St, Medford, MA, 02155
(617) 391-4741
Admin Mary Jane Allen.
Licensure Rest home. *Beds* 28. *Certified* Medicaid.
Staff Physicians 3 (pt); RNs 1 (pt); Activities coordinators 1 (pt); Dietitians 1 (pt).
Facilities Dining room; Crafts room; Laundry room.
Activities Arts & crafts; Movies.

Rest Haven Nursing Home
96 Mystic St, Medford, MA, 02155
(617) 396-3632
Admin David A Niles.
Licensure Intermediate care. *Beds* ICF 33. *Certified* Medicaid; Medicare.

Winthrop House Nursing Home
300 Winthrop St, Medford, MA, 02155
(617) 396-4400
Admin David L Bell. *Medical Dir/Dir of Nursing* Ralph Goldstein MD; Angela Derrivan RN DNS.
Licensure Skilled care; Intermediate care. *Beds* SNF 82; ICF 60. *Certified* Medicaid.
Owner Privately owned.
Admissions Requirements Physician's request.
Staff RNs 9 (ft), 5 (pt); LPNs 3 (ft), 5 (pt); Orderlies 6 (ft); Nurses aides 39 (ft), 12 (pt).
Facilities Dining room; Physical therapy room; Activities room; Chapel; Barber/Beauty shop.
Activities Arts & crafts; Games; Prayer groups; Movies; Social/Cultural gatherings.

MEDWAY

Mary-Land Rest Home
17 Holliston St, Medway, MA, 02053
(617) 533-2900
Admin Gertrude A O'Connor.
Licensure Residential care. *Beds* Residential 32. *Certified* Medicaid.
Owner Proprietary Corp.
Admissions Requirements Minimum age 50; Medical examination.
Staff RNs 1 (pt); Nurses aides 5 (ft), 2 (pt); Activities coordinators 1 (ft).
Languages French
Facilities Dining room; Laundry room.
Activities Arts & crafts; Cards; Games; Reading groups; Prayer groups; Movies; Shopping trips; Social/Cultural gatherings; Parties; Cookouts; Trips.

Medway Country Manor Nursing Home
Holliston St, Medway, MA, 02053
(617) 533-6634
Admin John Peters.
Licensure Skilled care; Intermediate care. *Beds* 82. *Certified* Medicaid.

MELROSE

Elmhurst Nursing & Retirement Home*
743 Main St, Melrose, MA, 02176
(617) 622-7500
Admin Joanne E O'Day.
Licensure Intermediate care. *Beds* 43. *Certified* Medicaid.
Owner Proprietary Corp (Beverly Enterprises).

The Fitch Home Inc
75 Lake Ave, Melrose, MA, 02176
(617) 665-0521 & 665-0522
Admin Joyce M Lamb. *Medical Dir/Dir of Nursing* Rose Pica RN.
Licensure Level IV Rest home. *Beds* Level IV Rest home 28.
Owner Nonprofit Corp.
Admissions Requirements Minimum age 65; Medical examination.
Staff Physicians 1 (pt); RNs 1 (ft); LPNs 4 (pt); Nurses aides 7 (pt); Activities coordinators 1 (pt); Dietitians 1 (pt).
Facilities Dining room; Activities room; Crafts room; Barber/Beauty shop.
Activities Cards; Games; Movies; Shopping trips.

Mackenzie Nursing Home
24 Vine St, Melrose, MA, 02176
(617) 665-4419
Admin Harry G Meline. *Medical Dir/Dir of Nursing* Lisa Cadigan.
Licensure Intermediate care. *Beds* ICF 29. *Certified* Medicaid.

Owner Proprietary Corp.
Admissions Requirements Females only;
Medical examination.
Staff Physicians; RNs; LPNs; Orderlies;
Nurses aides; Activities coordinators;
Dietitians; Social worker; Kitchen staff;
Maintenance; Housekeeper; Laundry.
Languages French
Facilities Dining room; Activities room;
Laundry room.
Activities Arts & crafts; Cards; Games;
Reading groups; Prayer groups; Movies;
Shopping trips; Social/Cultural gatherings.

Middlesex Fells Nursing Home*
40 Martin St, Melrose, MA, 02176
(617) 665-7050
Admin Charles A Holden Jr. *Medical Dir/Dir
of Nursing* Dr Robert Holden.
Licensure Skilled care; Intermediate care. *Beds*
106. *Certified* Medicaid; Medicare.
Owner Proprietary Corp (Beverly Enterprises).
Admissions Requirements Medical
examination.
Staff Physicians 3 (pt); RNs 13 (ft), 10 (pt);
LPNs 4 (ft), 2 (pt); Orderlies 1 (ft); Nurses
aides 20 (ft), 26 (pt); Physical therapists 2
(pt); Occupational therapists 1 (pt); Speech
therapists 1 (pt); Activities coordinators 1
(ft), 1 (pt); Dietitians 1 (pt); Dentists 1 (pt);
Podiatrists 1 (pt); Audiologists 1 (pt).
Facilities Dining room; Physical therapy
room; Activities room; Crafts room; Laundry
room; Barber/Beauty shop.
Activities Arts & crafts; Cards; Games;
Reading groups; Prayer groups; Movies;
Shopping trips.

Normandy House Nursing Home*
15 Green St, Melrose, MA, 02176
(617) 665-3950
Admin Bonnie-Jean McLean.
Licensure Skilled care; Intermediate care. *Beds*
82. *Certified* Medicaid.

Oosterman Rest Home
93 Laurel St, Melrose, MA, 02176
(617) 665-3188
Admin Troy Oosterman. *Medical Dir/Dir of
Nursing* Gladys Foster RN.
Licensure Rest home. *Beds* 20.
Owner Privately owned.
Admissions Requirements Females only;
Medical examination; Physician's request.
Staff RNs 1 (pt); Orderlies 1 (ft), 1 (pt);
Nurses aides 4 (ft), 6 (pt); Dietitians 2 (ft).
Facilities Dining room; Activities room;
Crafts room; Laundry room; Library.
Activities Arts & crafts; Cards; Games;
Movies; Shopping trips.

Tuell Nursing Home Inc
92 Franklin St, Melrose, MA, 02176
(617) 665-0764
Admin Francis J Cummings. *Medical Dir/Dir
of Nursing* Ruth Bougas RN.
Licensure Intermediate care. *Beds* 28.
Certified Medicaid.
Owner Proprietary Corp.
Admissions Requirements Females only.
Staff RNs 1 (ft), 4 (pt); LPNs 4 (pt); Nurses
aides 6 (ft), 8 (pt); Physical therapists 1 (pt);
Activities coordinators 1 (pt); Dietitians 1
(pt); Ophthalmologists 1 (pt).
Facilities Dining room; Activities room.
Activities Arts & crafts; Cards; Games;
Reading groups; Prayer groups; Movies.

METHUEN

Blenwood Nursing Home*
302 Broadway, Methuen, MA, 01844
(617) 682-8113
Admin Marion A Thisse.
Licensure Intermediate care. *Beds* 41.
Certified Medicaid.

Broadway Convalescent Home*
281 Broadway, Methuen, MA, 01844
(617) 682-5373
Admin Linda E Weldon.
Licensure Skilled care; Intermediate care. *Beds*
52. *Certified* Medicaid.
Owner Proprietary Corp (Hillhaven Corp).

Halcyon House Rest Home*
175 Berkeley St, Methuen, MA, 01844
(617) 685-5505
Admin Elizabeth L Bonde.
Licensure Rest home. *Beds* 20.
Staff LPNs 1 (pt); Nurses aides 10 (ft);
Physical therapists 1 (pt); Speech therapists
1 (pt); Activities coordinators 1 (pt);
Dietitians 1 (pt); Podiatrists 1 (pt).
Facilities Dining room; Activities room.
Activities Arts & crafts; Cards; Games;
Reading groups; Movies; Shopping trips.

McGowan Nursing Home*
489 Prospect St, Methuen, MA, 01844
(617) 682-4342
Admin Mary R Kim.
Licensure Intermediate care. *Beds* 41.
Certified Medicaid.

**Methuen House Nursing & Convalescent
Center***
480 Jackson St, Methuen, MA, 01844
(617) 686-3906
Admin Joseph O'Rourke.
Licensure Skilled care; Intermediate care. *Beds*
101. *Certified* Medicaid.

Henry C Nevins Home Inc*
10 Ingalls Ct, Methuen, MA, 01844
(617) 682-7611
Admin Kenneth C Mermer.
Licensure Charitable home. *Beds* 133.
Certified Medicaid.

MIDDLEBORO

Alpha Village Long-Term Care Facility
PO Box 798, 312 Marion Rd, Middleboro,
MA, 02346
(617) 947-8632
Admin Ora Mae Torres.
Licensure Intermediate care. *Beds* ICF 50.
Certified Medicaid.
Owner Proprietary Corp.
Admissions Requirements Elderly people
requiring Level III care.
Staff RNs; LPNs; Orderlies; Nurses aides;
Recreational therapists; Activities
coordinators; Dietitians; Social worker.
Languages Portuguese
Facilities Dining room; Activities room.
Activities Arts & crafts; Cards; Games;
Movies; Shopping trips; Social/Cultural
gatherings.

Fair Havens Rest Home Inc
334 Marion Rd, Middleboro, MA, 02346
(617) 947-1660
Admin Sharon Copeland. *Medical Dir/Dir of
Nursing* Carol Sologaistoa.
Licensure Intermediate care; Rest home Level
IV. *Beds* ICF 28. *Certified* Medicaid;
Medicare.
Owner Nonprofit Corp.
Admissions Requirements Minimum age 45;
Medical examination.
Staff LPNs 2 (ft); Nurses aides 10 (ft), 10 (pt);
Reality therapists 1 (ft); Recreational
therapists 1 (ft); Activities coordinators 1
(ft).
Affiliation Lutheran
Facilities Dining room; Activities room;
Chapel; Crafts room; Laundry room; Barber/
Beauty shop; Library.
Activities Arts & crafts; Cards; Games; Prayer
groups; Movies; Shopping trips; Social/
Cultural gatherings.

Forest Manor Long-Term Care Facility
PO Box 1330, Isaac St, Middleboro, MA,
02346
(617) 947-9295
Admin Sharon R Kellegrew. *Medical Dir/Dir
of Nursing* Sylvio Landry MD.
Licensure Skilled care; Intermediate care. *Beds*
SNF 124; ICF. *Certified* Medicaid;
Medicare.
Owner Privately owned.
Languages Sign
Facilities Dining room; Physical therapy
room; Activities room; Crafts room; Laundry
room; Barber/Beauty shop.
Activities Arts & crafts; Cards; Games;
Reading groups; Prayer groups; Movies;
Shopping trips; Social/Cultural gatherings.

Greenlawn Nursing Home
14 E Grove St, Middleboro, MA, 02346
(617) 947-1172
Admin Dorothy Hoult. *Medical Dir/Dir of
Nursing* Shirley Dionne.
Licensure Intermediate care; Intermediate care
for mentally retarded. *Beds* ICF/MR 47.
Certified Medicaid.
Owner Privately owned.
Admissions Requirements Minimum age 18;
Medical examination.
Staff LPNs; Nurses aides; Physical therapists;
Recreational therapists; Occupational
therapists; Speech therapists; Dietitians.
Facilities Dining room; Activities room;
Laundry room.
Activities Arts & crafts; Cards; Games;
Reading groups; Prayer groups; Movies;
Shopping trips; Social/Cultural gatherings;
School sessions.

Middleboro Rest Home*
5 Barrows St, Middleboro, MA, 02346
(617) 947-4120
Admin Roger L Plante.
Licensure Rest home. *Beds* 17.
Staff Physicians 1 (pt); RNs 6 (pt); Nurses
aides 2 (ft), 2 (pt); Recreational therapists 1
(pt); Dietitians 1 (pt); Dentists 1 (pt);
Podiatrists 1 (pt).
Facilities Dining room; Activities room;
Laundry room.
Activities Arts & crafts; Cards; Games;
Reading groups; Prayer groups; Shopping
trips; Social/Cultural gatherings.

Oak Hill Nursing Home*
76 North St, Middleboro, MA, 02346
(617) 947-4775
Admin Frances G Comeau. *Medical Dir/Dir of
Nursing* Bernard Beuthner.
Licensure Skilled care; Intermediate care. *Beds*
126. *Certified* Medicaid; Medicare.
Owner Proprietary Corp (Beverly Enterprises).
Facilities Dining room; Physical therapy
room; Activities room; Crafts room; Laundry
room; Barber/Beauty shop; Library.
Activities Arts & crafts; Cards; Games;
Reading groups; Prayer groups; Movies;
Social/Cultural gatherings.

Hannah B G Shaw Home for the Aged Inc
PO Box 390, 299 Wareham St, Middleboro,
MA, 02346
(617) 947-1184
Admin Lenore Baldwin. *Medical Dir/Dir of
Nursing* Thelma Hayden RN.
Licensure Level IV with Level III for residents
of Level IV only/No admission to Level III
from outside source. *Beds* Level III 8; Level
IV 42.
Owner Nonprofit Corp.
Admissions Requirements Minimum age 65;
Medical examination.
Staff RNs 1 (ft), 5 (pt); LPNs 2 (ft), 3 (pt);
Nurses aides 2 (ft), 2 (pt); Activities
coordinators 1 (ft), 1 (pt); Dietitians 1 (pt).
Facilities Dining room; Activities room;
Chapel; Crafts room; Laundry room; Barber/
Beauty shop; Library.

Activities Arts & crafts; Cards; Games;
Reading groups; Prayer groups; Movies;
Shopping trips; Social/Cultural gatherings.

Susan Welch Rest Home*
98 S Main St, Middleboro, MA, 02346
(617) 947-2155
Admin Marion F Pattison.
Licensure Rest home. *Beds* 24.
Admissions Requirements Medical
examination; Physician's request.
Staff LPNs 1 (ft), 3 (pt); Activities
coordinators 1 (pt); Dietitians 1 (pt).
Facilities Dining room; Activities room;
Laundry room.
Activities Arts & crafts; Cards; Games; Prayer
groups; Movies; Shopping trips.

MILFORD

Blair House of Milford
20 Claflin St, Milford, MA, 01757
(617) 473-1272
Admin Martha A Forsher. *Medical Dir/Dir of
Nursing* Dr Faheem Farooq; Kathleen
Derocher RN DON.
Licensure Skilled care. *Beds* SNF 61. *Certified*
Medicaid; Medicare.
Owner Proprietary Corp.
Admissions Requirements Minimum age 50;
Medical examination; Physician's request.
Staff RNs 5 (ft), 1 (pt); LPNs 5 (ft), 2 (pt);
Nurses aides 21 (ft), 10 (pt).
Facilities Dining room; Physical therapy
room; Activities room; Laundry room;
Barber/Beauty shop.
Activities Arts & crafts; Cards; Games;
Reading groups; Prayer groups; Movies;
Social/Cultural gatherings; Bowling;
Cookouts; Music programs.

Geriatric Authority of Milford
Countryside Dr, Milford, MA, 01757
(617) 473-0435
Admin Michael R Smith.
Licensure Skilled care; Intermediate care. *Beds*
SNF 39; ICF 34. *Certified* Medicaid.

Milford Manor Rest Home Inc
16 Claflin St, Milford, MA, 01757
(617) 473-2896
Admin Kalidas R Patel.
Licensure Rest home. *Beds* 27.
Admissions Requirements Minimum age 30;
Medical examination; Physician's request.
Staff Physicians 2 (pt); LPNs 1 (pt); Nurses
aides 4 (ft), 4 (pt); Activities coordinators 1
(ft); Dietitians 1 (pt); Podiatrists 1 (pt).
Facilities Dining room; Activities room;
Crafts room; Laundry room.
Activities Arts & crafts; Cards; Games;
Reading groups; Prayer groups; Shopping
trips; Social/Cultural gatherings.

MILLBURY

The New Pine Grove Villa Nursing Home
5 Rhodes St, Millbury, MA, 01527
(617) 865-9490
Admin Steven Hochhauser. *Medical Dir/Dir of
Nursing* Dr Susan Moran; Terry Kitteredge.
Licensure Intermediate care. *Beds* ICF 41.
Certified Medicaid.
Owner Proprietary Corp.
Admissions Requirements Minimum age 18;
Physician's request.
Staff Physicians; RNs; LPNs; Nurses aides;
Activities coordinators; Dietitians.
Facilities Dining room; Activities room;
Laundry room.
Activities Arts & crafts; Cards; Games;
Reading groups; Prayer groups; Movies;
Shopping trips; Social/Cultural gatherings.

Smith Nursing Home*
29 Main St, Millbury, MA, 01527
(617) 865-6825

Admin Anthony E Penny.
Licensure Skilled care; Intermediate care. *Beds*
44. *Certified* Medicaid.

MILLIS

Four Seasons Rest Home*
71 Union St, Millis, MA, 02054
(617) 376-5083
Admin Gabriel Gabrielli.
Licensure Rest home. *Beds* 34.

MILTON

Milton Health Care Facility*
1200 Brush Mill Rd, Milton, MA, 02186
(617) 333-0600
Admin Donald Gresh.
Licensure Skilled care; Intermediate care. *Beds*
SNF 40; ICF 40.

MONSON

Buckwell Rest Home*
300 Main St, Monson, MA, 01057
(413) 267-9285
Admin Donna Swist.
Licensure Rest home. *Beds* 17.

MONTGOMERY

Mountain View Nursing Home*
Rte 1, Montgomery, MA, 01085
(413) 562-0097
Admin Mary Uschmann.
Licensure Intermediate care. *Beds* 27.
Certified Medicaid.

NAHANT

Jesmond Nursing Home
271 Nahant Rd, Nahant, MA, 01908
(617) 581-0420
Admin Rosemary C Costin. *Medical Dir/Dir
of Nursing* Lorraine A Desrosier RN.
Licensure Skilled care; Intermediate care. *Beds*
SNF 29; ICF 28. *Certified* Medicaid.
Owner Proprietary Corp.
Admissions Requirements Medical
examination; Physician's request.
Staff Physicians 1 (pt); RNs 3 (ft), 1 (pt);
LPNs 5 (ft), 2 (pt); Nurses aides 12 (ft), 9
(pt); Physical therapists 1 (pt); Occupational
therapists 1 (pt); Speech therapists 1 (pt);
Activities coordinators 1 (ft); Dietitians 1
(pt).
Facilities Dining room; Physical therapy
room; Activities room; Crafts room; Laundry
room; Barber/Beauty shop.
Activities Arts & crafts; Cards; Games;
Reading groups; Prayer groups; Movies.

Rockledge Manor Nursing Home*
162 Willow Rd, Nahant, MA, 01908
(617) 581-0249
Admin Robert D Brennan.
Licensure Intermediate care. *Beds* 43.
Certified Medicaid.

NANTUCKET

Our Island Home
E Creek Rd, Nantucket, MA, 02554
(617) 228-3953
Admin Mrs M L Smith. *Medical Dir/Dir of
Nursing* Dr C C Briggs MD; Mrs Eleanor E
MacVicar RN DNS.
Licensure Skilled care; Intermediate care. *Beds*
SNF 22; ICF 23. *Certified* Medicaid.
Owner Publicly owned.
Admissions Requirements Medical
examination; Physician's request.
Staff RNs 4 (ft), 2 (pt); LPNs 3 (pt); Nurses
aides 11 (ft), 3 (pt); Activities coordinators 1
(ft); Dietitians 1 (pt); Social workers 2 (pt).

Languages Portuguese
Facilities Dining room; Physical therapy
room; Activities room; Laundry room;
Barber/Beauty shop.
Activities Arts & crafts; Cards; Games; Prayer
groups; Movies; Shopping trips; Social/
Cultural gatherings; Van rides.

NATICK

Brittany Convalescent Home
168 W Central St, Natick, MA, 01706
(617) 655-1000
Admin Marc A Neustadt. *Medical Dir/Dir of
Nursing* Dr Alan Engel; Barbara Kane DON.
Licensure Skilled care; Intermediate care; Rest
home. *Beds* SNF 40; ICF 40; Rest home 40.
Certified Medicaid.
Owner Proprietary Corp (Hillhaven Corp).
Admissions Requirements Minimum age 20.
Staff RNs 3 (ft), 5 (pt); LPNs 3 (ft), 1 (pt);
Orderlies 1 (ft), 1 (pt); Nurses aides 24 (ft),
10 (pt); Physical therapists 1 (pt); Reality
therapists 1 (pt); Recreational therapists 1
(ft); Occupational therapists 1 (pt); Speech
therapists 1 (pt); Activities coordinators 1
(ft); Dietitians 1 (pt); Dentists 1 (pt).
Facilities Dining room; Physical therapy
room; Activities room; Crafts room; Laundry
room; Barber/Beauty shop; Library.
Activities Arts & crafts; Cards; Games; Prayer
groups; Movies; Shopping trips; Social/
Cultural gatherings.

Hanson Nursing Home*
30 Pleasant St, Natick, MA, 01760
(617) 653-1543
Admin Robert L Douglas.
Licensure Intermediate care. *Beds* 13.
Certified Medicaid.

Nims Rest Home*
38 Fiske St, Natick, MA, 01760
(617) 653-0382
Admin Helen Nims. *Medical Dir/Dir of
Nursing* Muriel Baim.
Licensure Rest home. *Beds* 21.
Admissions Requirements Minimum age 35;
Medical examination; Physician's request.
Staff RNs 1 (pt); Nurses aides 4 (ft);
Dietitians 1 (ft); Podiatrists 1 (pt).
Facilities Dining room; Activities room;
Laundry room.
Activities Arts & crafts; Cards; Games; Prayer
groups; Shopping trips; Social/Cultural
gatherings; A group comes the first of every
month for singing & prayers.

Phillips House Nursing Home*
10 Phillips St, Natick, MA, 01760
(617) 653-1543
Admin Robert L Douglas.
Licensure Intermediate care. *Beds* 9.

Riverbend Convalescent Center
34 Lincoln St, Natick, MA, 01760
(617) 653-8330
Admin Beverly McIntyre RN. *Medical Dir/Dir
of Nursing* Cynthia Wade RN.
Licensure Intermediate care. *Beds* ICF 55.
Certified Medicaid.
Owner Proprietary Corp.
Staff Physicians 1 (pt); RNs 4 (ft); LPNs 3
(ft), 1 (pt); Orderlies 1 (ft); Nurses aides 20
(ft), 6 (pt); Physical therapists 1 (pt);
Recreational therapists 2 (ft); Occupational
therapists 1 (pt); Speech therapists 1 (pt);
Dietitians 1 (pt); Dentists 1 (pt);
Ophthalmologists 1 (pt); Podiatrists 1 (pt);
Social service 1 (pt).
Facilities Dining room; Activities room;
Crafts room; Laundry room; Barber/Beauty
shop; Library.
Activities Arts & crafts; Cards; Games;
Reading groups; Movies; Shopping trips;
Social/Cultural gatherings; Drama Club takes
musicals to other homes & hospitals.

White Gables Rest Home of Natick*
50 Pleasant St, Natick, MA, 01760
(617) 653-2733
Admin Jean Sprague.
Licensure Rest home. *Beds* 12.

NEEDHAM

Briarwood Convalescent Center
26 Garfield St, Needham, MA, 02192
(617) 449-4040
Admin Linda M Murphy. *Medical Dir/Dir of Nursing* Simon Weitzman MD; Mary M Morrissey RN DON.
Licensure Skilled care; Intermediate care. *Beds* SNF 80; ICF 40. *Certified* Medicaid.
Owner Proprietary Corp (Hillhaven Corp).
Admissions Requirements Minimum age 65; Medical examination.
Facilities Dining room; Physical therapy room; Activities room; Chapel; Crafts room; Barber/Beauty shop.
Activities Arts & crafts; Cards; Games; Reading groups; Prayer groups; Movies; Shopping trips; Social/Cultural gatherings; Luncheons; Residents council; Music therapy.

Daystar Home*
1180 Great Plain Ave, Needham, MA, 02192
(617) 449-1149
Admin Ethel F Blettner.
Licensure Rest home. *Beds* 20.

Hamilton House Nursing Home*
141 Chestnut St, Needham, MA, 02192
(617) 444-9114
Admin Anita M Chevrette. *Medical Dir/Dir of Nursing* John Fernald MD & Asha Wallace MD.
Licensure Skilled care; Intermediate care. *Beds* 80. *Certified* Medicaid; Medicare.
Admissions Requirements Minimum age 21.
Staff RNs 6 (ft), 9 (pt); LPNs 2 (ft), 2 (pt); Orderlies 1 (ft); Nurses aides 18 (ft), 34 (pt).
Facilities Dining room; Physical therapy room; Activities room; Chapel; Crafts room; Laundry room; Barber/Beauty shop.
Activities Arts & crafts; Cards; Games; Reading groups; Prayer groups; Movies; Shopping trips; Social/Cultural gatherings.

The Skilled Nursing Facility at North Hill
865 Central Ave, Needham, MA, 02192
(617) 444-9910
Admin Patrick T Zoerner. *Medical Dir/Dir of Nursing* Simon Weitzman MD; Barbara Gerstein RN DON.
Licensure Skilled care; Intermediate care. *Beds* SNF 40; ICF 20. *Certified* Medicaid; Medicare.
Owner Nonprofit Corp (Life Care Services Corp).
Admissions Requirements Medical examination; Physician's request.
Staff Physicians 1 (pt); RNs 6 (ft), 7 (pt); LPNs 2 (ft), 3 (pt); Orderlies 2 (ft); Nurses aides 20 (ft), 8 (pt); Physical therapists 1 (ft), 1 (pt); Recreational therapists 1 (ft); Activities coordinators 1 (pt); Dietitians 1 (pt); Social worker 1 (pt).
Facilities Dining room; Physical therapy room; Activities room; Crafts room; Barber/Beauty shop; Library; Pool; Extensive walkways.
Activities Arts & crafts; Cards; Games; Reading groups; Prayer groups; Movies; Shopping trips; Social/Cultural gatherings; Restaurant trips.

NEW BEDFORD

Arbourway Rest Home*
875 Plainville Rd, New Bedford, MA, 02745
(617) 995-8229
Admin James A Casey.
Licensure Rest home. *Beds* 24.

Blaire House LTCF of New Bedford
397 County St, New Bedford, MA, 02740
(617) 997-9396
Admin Linda R Valenzono. *Medical Dir/Dir of Nursing* Sheldon Davis MD; Nancy Lawrence RN.
Licensure Skilled care; Intermediate care. *Beds* SNF 82; ICF 41. *Certified* Medicaid; Medicare.
Owner Proprietary Corp.
Admissions Requirements Minimum age 65.
Staff RNs; LPNs; Orderlies; Nurses aides; Physical therapists; Recreational therapists; Occupational therapists; Speech therapists; Activities coordinators; Dietitians; Ophthalmologists.
Facilities Dining room; Physical therapy room; Activities room; Crafts room; Laundry room; Barber/Beauty shop.
Activities Arts & crafts; Cards; Games; Reading groups; Prayer groups; Movies; Shopping trips; Social/Cultural gatherings.

Bristol Nursing & Convalescent Home*
9 Pope St, New Bedford, MA, 02740
(617) 997-3358
Admin Ashley Clark.
Licensure Intermediate care. *Beds* 73.
Certified Medicaid.

The Cottage Rest Home*
434 Cottage St, New Bedford, MA, 02740
(617) 997-7678
Admin Teresa Ann Vieira.
Licensure Intermediate care. *Beds* 13.
Certified Medicaid.

Hallmark Nursing Home of New Bedford
1123 Rockdale Ave, New Bedford, MA, 02740
(617) 997-7448
Admin Mark S Nussman. *Medical Dir/Dir of Nursing* Nancy S Clark RN.
Licensure Skilled care; Intermediate care. *Beds* 124. *Certified* Medicaid.
Owner Proprietary Corp (Hillhaven Corp).
Admissions Requirements Minimum age 16; Medical examination; Physician's request.
Staff Physicians 5 (pt); Physical therapists 1 (pt); Reality therapists 1 (ft); Recreational therapists 1 (pt); Occupational therapists 1 (pt); Speech therapists 1 (pt); Activities coordinators 1 (ft), 1 (pt); Dietitians 1 (pt); Dentists 1 (pt); Ophthalmologists 1 (pt); Podiatrists 1 (pt).
Languages Portuguese, German
Facilities Dining room; Activities room; Crafts room; Laundry room; Barber/Beauty shop.
Activities Arts & crafts; Cards; Games; Reading groups; Prayer groups; Movies; Shopping trips; Social/Cultural gatherings.

Havenwood Rest Home
251 Walnut St, New Bedford, MA, 02740
(617) 994-3120
Admin Donald L Di Santi.
Licensure Skilled care. *Beds* SNF 41. *Certified* Medicaid; Medicare.
Owner Proprietary Corp.
Admissions Requirements Minimum age 21.
Staff Physicians 1 (pt); LPNs 1 (pt); Nurses aides 4 (ft), 2 (pt); Activities coordinators 1 (pt); Dietitians 1 (pt); Ophthalmologists 1 (pt).
Languages Spanish, Portuguese
Facilities Dining room; Activities room; Laundry room; Barber/Beauty shop; TV room.
Activities Arts & crafts; Cards; Games; Shopping trips; Social/Cultural gatherings.

Kristen Beth Nursing Home Inc*
713 Shawmut Ave, New Bedford, MA, 02746
(617) 999-6456
Admin Irene C Awed. *Medical Dir/Dir of Nursing* Dr John Barnes.
Licensure Skilled care; Intermediate care. *Beds* 93. *Certified* Medicaid.

Admissions Requirements Minimum age 21.
Staff RNs 6 (ft); LPNs 5 (ft), 2 (pt); Nurses aides 37 (ft); Physical therapists 1 (pt); Occupational therapists 1 (pt); Speech therapists 1 (pt); Dietitians 1 (pt); Dentists 1 (pt); Ophthalmologists 1 (pt); Podiatrists 1 (pt).
Facilities Dining room; Physical therapy room; Activities room; Crafts room; Laundry room; Barber/Beauty shop.
Activities Arts & crafts; Cards; Games; Reading groups; Prayer groups; Movies; Shopping trips; Social/Cultural gatherings.

New Bedford Jewish Convalescent Home
200 Hawthorn St, New Bedford, MA, 02740
(617) 997-9314
Admin Estelle R Shanbrun.
Licensure Skilled care; Intermediate care. *Beds* SNF 40; ICF 40. *Certified* Medicaid; Medicare.
Owner Nonprofit Corp.
Admissions Requirements Minimum age 22.
Languages Portuguese, Polish, Yiddish, Hebrew
Affiliation Jewish
Facilities Dining room; Physical therapy room; Activities room; Chapel; Crafts room; Barber/Beauty shop; Library; Patio.
Activities Arts & crafts; Cards; Games; Reading groups; Prayer groups; Movies; Shopping trips; Social/Cultural gatherings; Birthday parties; Music; Lunch outings; Pet therapy; Cooking; Baking.

Rita's Rest Home*
49 Desautels St, New Bedford, MA, 02745
(617) 992-6074
Admin Rita Rouke.
Licensure Rest home. *Beds* 10.

Rol-Ann Rest Home*
31 7th St, New Bedford, MA, 02740
(617) 996-1730
Admin Florence T Tavano.
Licensure Rest home. *Beds* 17.

Sacred Heart Nursing Home
359 Summer St, New Bedford, MA, 02740
(617) 996-6751
Admin Blandine d'Amours. *Medical Dir/Dir of Nursing* Dr William A Jeffrey; Therese Bergeron.
Licensure Skilled care; Intermediate care. *Beds* SNF 217; ICF. *Certified* Medicaid.
Owner Nonprofit Corp.
Admissions Requirements Minimum age 65; Medical examination; Physician's request.
Staff Physicians 1 (pt); RNs 17 (ft), 10 (pt); LPNs 28 (ft), 14 (pt); Orderlies 2 (ft); Nurses aides 28 (ft), 15 (pt); Physical therapists 3 (ft), 1 (pt); Reality therapists 1 (ft), 1 (pt); Recreational therapists 2 (ft), 2 (pt); Occupational therapists 1 (pt); Speech therapists 1 (pt); Activities coordinators 1 (ft); Dietitians 1 (pt); Ophthalmologists 2 (pt); Dentist 1 (ft).
Affiliation Roman Catholic
Facilities Dining room; Physical therapy room; Activities room; Chapel; Crafts room; Laundry room; Barber/Beauty shop; Library.
Activities Arts & crafts; Cards; Games; Reading groups; Prayer groups; Movies; Shopping trips; Social/Cultural gatherings.

Sassaquin Nursing Home Inc
4586 Acushnet Ave, New Bedford, MA, 02745
(617) 998-1188
Admin Irwin Kalmer. *Medical Dir/Dir of Nursing* Sheldon Caplan MD; Kathryn Carter RN.
Licensure Skilled care; Intermediate care. *Beds* SNF; ICF 120. *Certified* Medicaid.
Owner Privately owned.
Admissions Requirements Minimum age 21; Physician's request.

Staff RNs; LPNs; Nurses aides; Physical
therapists; Occupational therapists; Speech
therapists; Activities coordinators; Dietitians;
Dentists; Ophthalmologists.
Facilities Dining room; Physical therapy
room; Activities room; Crafts room; Laundry
room; Barber/Beauty shop.
Activities Arts & crafts; Cards; Games;
Reading groups; Prayer groups; Movies;
Social/Cultural gatherings.

Savoy Convalescent Home*
670 County St, New Bedford, MA, 02743
(617) 994-2400
Admin Nancy A Winer.
Licensure Skilled care. *Beds* 39. *Certified*
Medicaid.

Taber Street Nursing Home
19 Taber St, New Bedford, MA, 02740
(617) 997-0791
Admin Laurence Reed. *Medical Dir/Dir of
Nursing* Kathleen M Douris RN DON.
Licensure Intermediate care. *Beds* ICF 56.
Certified Medicaid.
Owner Proprietary Corp (Beverly Enterprises).
Admissions Requirements Minimum age 65;
Medical examination.
Staff Physicians 1 (pt); RNs 3 (ft), 2 (pt);
LPNs 2 (ft), 2 (pt); Orderlies 2 (ft); Nurses
aides 15 (ft), 10 (pt); Activities coordinators
1 (ft); Dietitians 1 (pt); Podiatrists 1 (pt).
Languages Portuguese, French
Affiliation Episcopal
Facilities Dining room; Activities room;
Chapel; Crafts room; Laundry room; Barber/
Beauty shop; Library.
Activities Arts & crafts; Cards; Games;
Reading groups; Prayer groups; Movies;
Shopping trips; Social/Cultural gatherings.

NEWBURYPORT

Brigham Manor Convalescent Home
77 High St, Newburyport, MA, 01950
(617) 462-4221
Admin Jennifer Hummel. *Medical Dir/Dir of
Nursing* Claire Lawrence.
Licensure Intermediate care. *Beds* ICF 64.
Certified Medicaid.
Owner Proprietary Corp (Hillhaven Corp).
Admissions Requirements Medical
examination.
Staff RNs; LPNs; Orderlies; Nurses aides;
Activities coordinators; Dietitians.
Facilities Dining room; Barber/Beauty shop;
Porch.
Activities Arts & crafts; Cards; Games;
Reading groups; Prayer groups; Movies;
Shopping trips; Social/Cultural gatherings.

Country Manor Convalescent Home
180 Low St, Newburyport, MA, 01950
(617) 465-5361
Admin Thomas B Dresser. *Medical Dir/Dir of
Nursing* Dr Christopher Harris; Marion
Chabot RN DON.
Licensure Skilled care; Intermediate care. *Beds*
SNF 82; ICF 41. *Certified* Medicaid.
Owner Proprietary Corp (Hillhaven Corp).
Admissions Requirements Minimum age 21;
Medical examination; Physician's request.
Staff Physicians 1 (pt); RNs 4 (ft), 4 (pt);
LPNs 4 (ft), 2 (pt); Nurses aides 23 (ft), 11
(pt); Physical therapists 1 (pt); Occupational
therapists 1 (pt); Activities coordinators 1
(ft), 1 (pt); Dietitians 1 (pt).
Facilities Dining room; Activities room;
Chapel; Laundry room; Barber/Beauty shop.
Activities Arts & crafts; Games; Reading
groups; Prayer groups; Movies; Shopping
trips.

Newburyport Society Home for Aged Men*
361 High St, Newburyport, MA, 01950
(617) 465-7091
Admin Patricia C Messinger.
Licensure Rest home. *Beds* 9.

Admissions Requirements Minimum age 65;
Males only; Medical examination.
Staff RNs; Nurses aides; Dietitians.
Facilities Dining room; Activities room;
Laundry room.

Port Manor Nursing Home*
Hale & Low Sts, Newburyport, MA, 01950
(617) 462-7373
Admin David Madigan.
Licensure Skilled care. *Beds* 102.

Wheelwright House
75 High St, Newburyport, MA, 01950
(617) 465-7102
Admin Susanne Roaf Flaherty.
Licensure Conventional Rest home. *Beds*
Level IV; Supervisory care 10.
Owner Nonprofit organization/foundation.
Admissions Requirements Minimum age 65;
Females only; Medical examination.
Staff RNs; Nurses aides; Podiatrists.
Facilities Dining room; Laundry room;
Barber/Beauty shop.
Activities Arts & crafts; Cards; Games;
Movies; Shopping trips; Social/Cultural
gatherings.

NEWTON

Baptist Home of Massachusetts*
66 Commonwealth Ave, Newton, MA, 02167
(617) 969-9380
Admin Cathy B Smith. *Medical Dir/Dir of
Nursing* Allen Ergel MD.
Licensure Intermediate care. *Beds* 131.
Certified Medicaid.
Admissions Requirements Minimum age 65;
Medical examination.
Staff Physicians 1 (pt); RNs 7 (ft), 1 (pt);
LPNs 3 (ft), 4 (pt); Orderlies 1 (pt); Nurses
aides 21 (ft), 4 (pt); Physical therapists 1
(pt); Recreational therapists 1 (ft);
Occupational therapists 1 (pt); Activities
coordinators 1 (ft), 1 (pt); Dietitians 1 (pt);
Dentists 1 (pt); Ophthalmologists 1 (pt);
Podiatrists 1 (pt); Audiologists 1 (pt).
Affiliation Baptist
Facilities Dining room; Activities room;
Chapel; Crafts room; Laundry room; Barber/
Beauty shop; Library.
Activities Arts & crafts; Games; Reading
groups; Prayer groups; Movies; Shopping
trips; Social/Cultural gatherings; Field trips.

Burton Convalescent Home Corp*
11 Washington St, Newton, MA, 02158
(617)964-9342
Licensure Intermediate care. *Beds* 30.
Certified Medicaid.

Chetwynde Convalescent Home*
1660 Washington St, Newton, MA, 02165
(617) 244-1137
Admin Charlene B Ferriera.
Licensure Intermediate care. *Beds* 27.
Certified Medicaid.

Chetwynde Nursing Home*
1650 Washington St, Newton, MA, 02165
(617) 244-5407
Admin Eleanor B Lanoa.
Licensure Skilled care; Intermediate care. *Beds*
75. *Certified* Medicaid.
Owner Proprietary Corp (Beverly Enterprises).

Elliot Manor Nursing Home
25 Mechanic St, Newton, MA, 02164
(617) 527-1750
Admin Andrew Comeau. *Medical Dir/Dir of
Nursing* Dr Carl Levison; Ann Keon RN.
Licensure Intermediate care. *Beds* ICF 53.
Certified Medicaid.
Admissions Requirements Minimum age 21;
Medical examination; Physician's request.
Staff RNs 3 (ft), 3 (pt); LPNs 2 (ft), 1 (pt);
Nurses aides 18 (ft), 6 (pt); Recreational
therapists 1 (ft), 1 (pt); Dietitians 1 (pt).

Activities Arts & crafts; Games; Reading
groups; Prayer groups; Movies; Shopping
trips.

Garland Rest Home*
217 Bellevue St, Newton, MA, 02158
(617) 527-0381
Admin Rosemary Omelite.
Licensure Rest home. *Beds* 9.

Heathwood Nursing Home*
188 Florence St, Newton, MA, 02167
(617) 332-4730
Admin Janet S Urdang.
Licensure Intermediate care. *Beds* 74.
Certified Medicaid.

Lakeview Rest Home
38 Lake Ave, Newton, MA, 02159
(617) 244-9179
Admin N Joan Sterndale.
Licensure Rest home. *Beds* 12.
Owner Proprietary Corp.
Admissions Requirements Medical
examination; Physician's request.
Staff RNs 1 (pt); Nurses aides 2 (pt);
Activities coordinators 1 (pt); Dietitians 1
(pt).
Facilities Activities room; Library; Solarium;
Gazebo.
Activities Cards; Games; Movies; Social/
Cultural gatherings; Music.

**Mediplex of Newton—Long-Term Care
Facility***
2101 Washington St, Newton, MA, 02162
(617) 969-4660
Admin Gerald S LaBourene.
Licensure Skilled care; Intermediate care. *Beds*
190. *Certified* Medicaid.

Mt Ida Rest Home
32 Newtonville Ave, Newton, MA, 02160
(617) 572-5657
Admin Indira Upadhyay. *Medical Dir/Dir of
Nursing* Ann Lennihan RN.
Licensure Rest home. *Beds* 18. *Certified*
Medicaid; Medicare.
Owner Privately owned.
Admissions Requirements Minimum age 21;
Males only.
Staff Physicians; RNs; LPNs; Orderlies;
Nurses aides; Recreational therapists;
Activities coordinators; Dietitians; Dentists;
Ophthalmologists; Podiatrists; Social worker.
Facilities Dining room; Physical therapy
room; Activities room; Laundry room;
Barber/Beauty shop.
Activities Arts & crafts; Cards; Games;
Reading groups; Prayer groups; Movies;
Shopping trips; Social/Cultural gatherings;
Cooking classes.

Pelham House Nursing Home
45 Pelham St, Newton, MA, 02159
(617) 527-5833
Admin Michael J Galatis. *Medical Dir/Dir of
Nursing* Dr Mark Rohrer; Gail Bekebrede
DON.
Licensure Intermediate care. *Beds* ICF 18.
Certified Medicare.
Owner Proprietary Corp.
Admissions Requirements Minimum age 21;
Medical examination; Physician's request.
Staff Physicians 1 (pt); RNs 3 (ft); LPNs 2
(ft), 2 (pt); Nurses aides 1 (ft), 2 (pt);
Physical therapists 1 (pt); Reality therapists
1 (pt); Recreational therapists 1 (ft);
Occupational therapists 1 (pt); Speech
therapists 1 (pt); Activities coordinators 1
(ft); Dietitians 1 (pt); Dentists 1 (pt);
Ophthalmologists 1 (pt); Podiatrists 1 (pt).
Facilities Dining room; Activities room;
Crafts room; Laundry room; Barber/Beauty
shop; Library.
Activities Arts & crafts; Cards; Games;
Reading groups; Prayer groups; Movies;
Shopping trips; Social/Cultural gatherings;
Entertainment.

Stone Institution & Newton Home for Aged People
277 Elliott St, Newton, MA, 02164
(617) 527-0023
Admin Joan McMullin Luthy. *Medical Dir/Dir of Nursing* Charles A Thompson MD.
Licensure Retirement home. *Beds* 23.
Owner Nonprofit Corp.
Admissions Requirements Minimum age 65; Medical examination.
Staff Physicians 1 (pt); RNs 1 (pt); Activities coordinators 2 (pt); Dietitians 1 (pt); Ophthalmologists 1 (pt).
Facilities Dining room; Activities room; Laundry room; Barber/Beauty shop; Library.
Activities Cards; Games; Reading groups; Movies; Social/Cultural gatherings; Teas.

Swedish Home for the Aged*
206 Waltham St, Newton, MA, 02165
(617) 527-6566
Admin Mildred Lundstrom. *Medical Dir/Dir of Nursing* David W Duhone MD.
Licensure Charitable home. *Beds* 30.
Admissions Requirements Minimum age 65.
Staff RNs 1 (pt); LPNs 1 (ft), 1 (pt); Nurses aides 1 (ft), 2 (pt).
Facilities Dining room; Activities room; Barber/Beauty shop.
Activities Movies; Shopping trips; Exercise class.

Vanderklish Hall Nursing Home*
929 Beacon St, Newton, MA, 02159
(617) 244-5063
Admin Duncan Vanderklish. *Medical Dir/Dir of Nursing* Nancy Kirrane RN.
Licensure Intermediate care. *Beds* ICF 22.
Owner Proprietary Corp.
Admissions Requirements Medical examination; Physician's request.
Staff RNs 3 (ft), 2 (pt); LPNs 1 (ft), 1 (pt); Nurses aides 1 (ft), 6 (pt); Recreational therapists 1 (pt); Dietitians 1 (pt).
Activities Arts & crafts; Cards; Games; Reading groups; Prayer groups; Movies.

NORTH ADAMS

Homestead Rest Home*
215 E Main St, North Adams, MA, 01247
(413) 663-6885
Admin Henry Dargie.
Licensure Rest home. *Beds* 36.

Richardson Rest Home Inc*
767 S Church St, North Adams, MA, 01247
(413) 663-8035
Admin Ruth M Richardson.
Licensure Rest home. *Beds* 26.

Willowood of North Adams
175 Franklin St, North Adams, MA, 01247
(413) 664-4041
Admin J Michael Rivers. *Medical Dir/Dir of Nursing* Douglas Herr MD; Susan Chalifoux RN.
Licensure Skilled care; Intermediate care. *Beds* SNF 83; ICF. *Certified* Medicaid.
Owner Proprietary Corp.
Staff RNs; LPNs; Nurses aides; Physical therapists; Occupational therapists; Activities coordinators; Dietitians.
Facilities Dining room; Physical therapy room; Activities room; Laundry room; Barber/Beauty shop.
Activities Arts & crafts; Cards; Games; Prayer groups; Movies.

NORTH ANDOVER

Prescott House Nursing Home
140 Prescott St, North Andover, MA, 01845
(617) 685-8086
Admin Robert Whitkin. *Medical Dir/Dir of Nursing* Edward Broaddus MD; Kathleen Melia RN DON.

Licensure Skilled care; Intermediate care. *Beds* SNF 126; ICF. *Certified* Medicaid.
Owner Proprietary Corp.
Admissions Requirements Minimum age 21.
Staff Physicians 1 (pt); RNs 15 (ft); LPNs 9 (ft); Nurses aides 37 (ft); Physical therapists 1 (pt); Recreational therapists 1 (ft), 1 (pt); Occupational therapists 1 (pt); Speech therapists 1 (pt); Activities coordinators 1 (ft); Dietitians 1 (pt).
Facilities Dining room; Physical therapy room; Activities room; Crafts room; Laundry room; Barber/Beauty shop; Library.
Activities Arts & crafts; Cards; Games; Reading groups; Prayer groups; Movies; Shopping trips; Social/Cultural gatherings.

Stevens Hall Long-Term Care Facility*
75 Park St, North Andover, MA, 01845
(617) 685-3372
Admin Timothy Barry. *Medical Dir/Dir of Nursing* Matthew Cushing MD.
Licensure Skilled care; Intermediate care. *Beds* 122. *Certified* Medicaid; Medicare.
Admissions Requirements Minimum age 21.
Staff Physicians 1 (ft), 4 (pt); RNs 7 (ft), 12 (pt); LPNs 5 (ft), 4 (pt); Orderlies 2 (ft); Nurses aides 27 (ft), 13 (pt); Physical therapists 1 (ft); Recreational therapists 1 (ft); Occupational therapists 1 (pt); Speech therapists 1 (pt); Activities coordinators 1 (ft); Dietitians 1 (pt); Dentists 1 (pt); Ophthalmologists 2 (pt); Podiatrists 2 (pt); Audiologists 1 (pt).
Facilities Dining room; Physical therapy room; Activities room; Crafts room; Laundry room; Barber/Beauty shop; Library; TV rooms; Sitting rooms.
Activities Arts & crafts; Cards; Games; Reading groups; Prayer groups; Movies; Shopping trips; Social/Cultural gatherings; Bowling; Happy hour; Traveling store; Various bus trips; Sunday ice cream; Parties; Morning coffee, tea, hot chocolate, donuts, English muffins.

NORTH ATTLEBORO

Madonna Manor*
N Washington St, North Attleboro, MA, 02760
(617) 699-2740
Admin Sr M Thomas More. *Medical Dir/Dir of Nursing* J Allen Bryer MD.
Licensure Skilled care; Intermediate care. *Beds* 121. *Certified* Medicaid.
Admissions Requirements Minimum age 65; Medical examination.
Staff RNs 6 (ft), 9 (pt); LPNs 4 (ft), 10 (pt); Orderlies 2 (ft); Nurses aides 10 (ft), 30 (pt); Physical therapists 1 (ft); Recreational therapists 1 (ft), 3 (pt); Activities coordinators 1 (ft), 3 (pt); Dietitians 4 (ft), 12 (pt).
Affiliation Roman Catholic
Facilities Dining room; Physical therapy room; Activities room; Chapel; Laundry room; Barber/Beauty shop; Library.
Activities Arts & crafts; Cards; Games; Reading groups; Prayer groups; Movies; Shopping trips; Social/Cultural gatherings.

NORTH EASTON

Stonehill Manor Nursing & Retirement Home
231 Main St, North Easton, MA, 02356
(617) 238-6511
Admin Arthur S Logan. *Medical Dir/Dir of Nursing* Elaine Rogers LPN.
Licensure Intermediate care. *Beds* 26. *Certified* Medicaid.
Admissions Requirements Minimum age 21; Females only; Medical examination.

Staff Physicians 5 (pt); RNs 2 (pt); LPNs 5 (pt); Nurses aides 12 (pt); Physical therapists 1 (pt); Activities coordinators 1 (pt); Dietitians 1 (pt); Dentists 1 (pt); Ophthalmologists 1 (pt); Podiatrists 1 (pt).
Facilities Dining room; Activities room; Laundry room.
Activities Arts & crafts; Cards; Games; Reading groups; Prayer groups; Movies; Shopping trips; Social/Cultural gatherings.

NORTH HAMPTON

Hampshire Charitable Hospital*
Off River Rd, North Hampton, MA, 01053
(413) 584-8457
Admin Edwin Warner.
Licensure Skilled care.

NORTH READING

Meadow View Convalescent Home
134 North St, North Reading, MA, 01864
Admin Carl Anderson. *Medical Dir/Dir of Nursing* Dr John Kidd; Karen Graham DNS.
Licensure Skilled care; Intermediate care. *Beds* SNF 52; ICF 49. *Certified* Medicaid.
Owner Proprietary Corp (Hillhaven Corp).
Admissions Requirements Minimum age 21.
Staff Physicians; RNs; LPNs; Orderlies; Nurses aides; Physical therapists; Recreational therapists; Occupational therapists; Speech therapists; Activities coordinators; Dietitians; Dentists; Ophthalmologists.
Facilities Dining room; Activities room; Crafts room; Laundry room; Barber/Beauty shop.
Activities Arts & crafts; Cards; Games; Reading groups; Prayer groups; Movies; Shopping trips; Social/Cultural gatherings.

NORTHAMPTON

Florence Rest Home*
29 N Main St, Northampton, MA, 01060
(413) 584-2418
Admin Marguerite Tuperkeizsis.
Licensure Rest home. *Beds* 26.
Admissions Requirements Minimum age 21; Medical examination; Physician's request.
Staff Activities coordinators 1 (ft).
Facilities Dining room; Activities room; Laundry room; Porch/enclosed in winter with glass; screened in summer.
Activities Arts & crafts; Cards; Games; Reading groups; Prayer groups; Movies; Shopping trips; Social/Cultural gatherings.

Lathrop Home for Aged Women
215 South St, Northampton, MA, 01060
(413) 584-2865
Admin Elizabeth Gallant. *Medical Dir/Dir of Nursing* Barbara Parsons.
Licensure Level IV. *Beds* Level IV 40. *Certified* Medicaid.
Owner Nonprofit organization/foundation.
Admissions Requirements Minimum age 65; Females only; Medical examination.
Staff RNs 1 (ft), 3 (pt); LPNs 7 (pt); Nurses aides 3 (ft), 6 (pt); Activities coordinators 1 (pt); Ophthalmologists 1 (pt).
Facilities Dining room; Activities room; Crafts room; Laundry room; Barber/Beauty shop; Library; Screened porch.
Activities Arts & crafts; Cards; Games; Reading groups; Prayer groups; Movies; Shopping trips; Social/Cultural gatherings.

Northampton Nursing Home Inc*
737 Bridge Rd, Northampton, MA, 01060
(413) 586-3300
Admin A Benson Walen. *Medical Dir/Dir of Nursing* Bernard St John DO.
Licensure Skilled care; Intermediate care. *Beds* 123. *Certified* Medicaid.

Admissions Requirements Minimum age 6
months; Medical examination; Physician's
request.
Staff Physicians 1 (pt); RNs 16 (ft), 15 (pt);
LPNs 12 (ft), 17 (pt); Nurses aides 20 (ft),
23 (pt); Physical therapists 3 (pt);
Occupational therapists 2 (pt); Speech
therapists 1 (pt); Activities coordinators 1
(ft), 1 (pt); Dietitians 1 (pt); Dentists 1 (pt);
Podiatrists 3 (pt).
Facilities Dining room; Physical therapy
room; Activities room; Chapel; Crafts room;
Laundry room; Barber/Beauty shop; Library.
Activities Arts & crafts; Cards; Games;
Reading groups; Prayer groups; Movies;
Shopping trips; Social/Cultural gatherings.

Pine Rest Nursing Home*
5 Franklin St, Northampton, MA, 01060
(413) 584-2369
Admin Leon L Dickinson. *Medical Dir/Dir of
Nursing* Donald B Rogers MD.
Licensure Intermediate care. *Beds* 47.
Certified Medicaid.
Staff RNs 1 (ft); LPNs 3 (ft), 2 (pt); Orderlies
2 (ft); Nurses aides 12 (ft), 6 (pt); Activities
coordinators 1 (ft); Dietitians 1 (pt).
Facilities Dining room; Activities room;
Library.
Activities Arts & crafts; Cards; Games;
Reading groups; Movies; Shopping trips;
Social/Cultural gatherings.

Pioneer Valley Nursing Home
548 Elm St, Northampton, MA, 01060
(413) 586-3150
Admin Chris Alexander. *Medical Dir/Dir of
Nursing* Elizabeth Podolak.
Licensure Skilled care; Intermediate care. *Beds*
SNF 43; ICF 82. *Certified* Medicaid;
Medicare.
Owner Proprietary Corp (New Medico Assoc).
Facilities Dining room; Physical therapy
room; Activities room; Crafts room; Laundry
room; Barber/Beauty shop.
Activities Arts & crafts; Cards; Games;
Reading groups; Prayer groups; Movies;
Shopping trips; Social/Cultural gatherings.

River Valley Rest Home
159 Pine St, Northampton, MA, 01060
(413) 584-3776
Admin Monroe L Bethea Jr. *Medical Dir/Dir
of Nursing* Anna W Thompson.
Licensure Rest home. *Beds* 29. *Certified*
Medicaid; Medicare.
Admissions Requirements Medical
examination.
Staff LPNs 1 (pt); Nurses aides 3 (ft), 4 (pt);
Activities coordinators 1 (pt).
Facilities Dining room; Activities room;
Laundry room; Barber/Beauty shop.
Activities Arts & crafts; Cards; Games;
Reading groups; Movies; Shopping trips;
Social/Cultural gatherings; Cooking class.

Rockridge at Laurel Park
25 Coles Meadow Rd, Northampton, MA,
01060
(413) 586-2902
Admin Dorothea V Munro. *Medical Dir/Dir of
Nursing* Patricia Sokop.
Licensure Rest home Level IV. *Beds* Rest
home Level IV 61.
Owner Nonprofit Corp.
Admissions Requirements Minimum age 65;
Medical examination.
Staff RNs 2 (ft), 5 (pt); LPNs 2 (pt); Nurses
aides 2 (ft), 7 (pt); Recreational therapists 1
(ft); Dietitians 1 (pt); Ophthalmologists 1
(pt).
Facilities Dining room; Activities room;
Chapel; Crafts room; Laundry room; Barber/
Beauty shop; Library.
Activities Arts & crafts; Cards; Games;
Reading groups; Prayer groups; Movies;
Shopping trips; Social/Cultural gatherings.

NORTHBOROUGH

Grangers Nursing Home
112 W Main St, Northborough, MA, 01532
(617) 393-2382
Admin Clifford Blake. *Medical Dir/Dir of
Nursing* Christian W Aussenheimer MD;
Pearl Gibbs RN DON.
Licensure Skilled care; Intermediate care. *Beds*
33. *Certified* Medicaid.
Owner Privately owned.
Admissions Requirements Minimum age 16.
Staff Physicians; RNs; LPNs; Nurses aides;
Physical therapists; Reality therapists;
Recreational therapists; Occupational
therapists; Speech therapists; Activities
coordinators; Dietitians; Dentists;
Ophthalmologists; Podiatrists; Dentist.
Facilities Dining room; Physical therapy
room; Activities room; Crafts room; Laundry
room; Barber/Beauty shop; Library.
Activities Arts & crafts; Cards; Games;
Reading groups; Prayer groups; Movies;
Shopping trips; Social/Cultural gatherings.

Northboro Rest Home*
238 W Main St, Northborough, MA, 01532
(617) 393-3304
Admin Edward F Thorton Jr.
Licensure Rest home. *Beds* 20.

Thornton Nursing Home*
238 1/2 W Main St, Northborough, MA,
01532
(617) 393-2368
Admin Edward F Thornton Jr.
Licensure Skilled care; Intermediate care. *Beds*
84. *Certified* Medicaid.

NORTHBRIDGE

Beaumont Nursing Home*
85 Beaumont Dr, Northbridge, MA, 01534
(617) 234-9771
Admin Daniel J Salmon. *Medical Dir/Dir of
Nursing* James Kuehan MD.
Licensure Skilled care; Intermediate care. *Beds*
142. *Certified* Medicaid; Medicare.
Staff Physicians; RNs; LPNs; Orderlies;
Nurses aides; Physical therapists;
Recreational therapists; Occupational
therapists; Speech therapists; Activities
coordinators; Dietitians; Dentists;
Ophthalmologists; Podiatrists; Audiologists.
Facilities Dining room; Physical therapy
room; Activities room; Crafts room; Laundry
room; Barber/Beauty shop; Library.

Northbridge Nursing Home
2356 Providence Rd, Northbridge, MA, 01534
(617) 234-8778
Admin Scott P Rabideau.
Licensure Skilled care; Intermediate care. *Beds*
SNF 58; ICF 60. *Certified* Medicaid.
Owner Proprietary Corp (Oakwood Living
Centers).

NORTON

Country Haven Nursing Home*
184 Mansfield Ave, Norton, MA, 02766
(617) 285-7745
Admin Thomas D Ward.
Licensure Skilled care; Intermediate care. *Beds*
94. *Certified* Medicaid.

Daggett Crandall Newcomb Home
55 Newland St, Norton, MA, 02766
(617) 285-7944
Admin Cheryl J Larson. *Medical Dir/Dir of
Nursing* Dr Timothy Whiting; Susan
Campbell RN.
Licensure Retirement home. *Beds* 30.
Certified Medicare.
Owner Nonprofit Corp.
Admissions Requirements Minimum age 65;
Physician's request.

Staff Physicians 1 (ft); RNs 5 (ft); LPNs 6 (ft);
Nurses aides 8 (ft).
Facilities Dining room; Activities room;
Laundry room; Barber/Beauty shop; Library.
Activities Arts & crafts; Cards; Shopping trips;
Play; Musicals.

Old Colony Road Rest Home
377 Old Colony Rd, Norton, MA, 02766
(617) 222-1074
Admin Robert J Devlin.
Licensure Rest home. *Beds* 50.

NORWELL

Norwell Knoll Nursing Home*
329 Washington St, Norwell, MA, 02061
(617) 659-4901
Admin Brian G Geany. *Medical Dir/Dir of
Nursing* Dr Clifford Ward.
Licensure Skilled care; Intermediate care. *Beds*
80. *Certified* Medicaid.
Admissions Requirements Medical
examination; Physician's request.
Staff Physicians 22 (pt); RNs 7 (ft); LPNs 2
(ft); Nurses aides 32 (ft), 6 (pt); Physical
therapists 1 (pt); Recreational therapists 1
(ft); Occupational therapists 1 (pt); Speech
therapists 1 (pt); Activities coordinators 1
(ft); Dietitians 1 (pt); Dentists 1 (pt);
Ophthalmologists 1 (pt); Podiatrists 1 (pt);
Audiologists 1 (pt).
Facilities Dining room; Physical therapy
room; Activities room; Chapel; Crafts room;
Laundry room; Barber/Beauty shop.
Activities Arts & crafts; Cards; Games;
Reading groups; Prayer groups; Movies;
Shopping trips; Social/Cultural gatherings;
Fashion shows.

Stetson Manor Nursing Home*
12 Barstow Ave, Norwell, MA, 02061
(617) 826-2311
Admin Martha Mello.
Licensure Intermediate care. *Beds* 17.
Certified Medicaid.

NORWOOD

Charlwell House Nursing Home
305 Walpole St, Norwood, MA, 02062
(617) 762-7700
Admin Stephen L Esdale. *Medical Dir/Dir of
Nursing* Prya Nandi MD; Susan Chace RN
DON.
Licensure Skilled care; Intermediate care. *Beds*
SNF 41; ICF 83. *Certified* Medicaid;
Medicare.
Owner Proprietary Corp.
Staff Physicians 1 (pt); RNs 10 (ft), 15 (pt);
LPNs 15 (ft), 10 (pt); Orderlies 2 (ft); Nurses
aides 60 (ft), 25 (pt); Physical therapists 1
(pt); Reality therapists 1 (pt); Recreational
therapists 1 (ft); Occupational therapists 1
(pt); Speech therapists 1 (pt); Activities
coordinators 2 (ft); Dietitians 1 (pt); Dentists
1 (pt); Ophthalmologists 1 (pt).
Facilities Dining room; Physical therapy
room; Activities room; Crafts room; Laundry
room; Barber/Beauty shop; Library; Gift
shop; Meeting room; Porch & patios;
Transportation.
Activities Arts & crafts; Cards; Games;
Reading groups; Prayer groups; Movies;
Shopping trips; Social/Cultural gatherings;
Gardening outside; Greenhouse gardening;
Exercise & walk clubs; Cooking clubs.

Denny House Nursing Home Inc
PO Box 336, 86 Saunders Rd, Norwood, MA,
02062
(617) 762-4426
Admin Maurice M Denny. *Medical Dir/Dir of
Nursing* Maureen Miller LPN.
Licensure Intermediate care. *Beds* ICF 38.
Certified Medicaid.
Owner Proprietary Corp.

Admissions Requirements Minimum age 35; Medical examination; Physician's request.
Staff LPNs 3 (ft), 3 (pt); Nurses aides 6 (ft), 2 (pt); Activities coordinators 1 (ft); Dietitians 1 (pt); LSW 1 (pt).
Facilities Dining room; Activities room; Laundry room.
Activities Arts & crafts; Cards; Games; Reading groups; Prayer groups; Movies; Shopping trips; Social/Cultural gatherings; Shows; Singing & dancing; Guitar & accordion players.

The Ellis Nursing Center
135 Ellis Ave, Norwood, MA, 02062
(617) 762-6880
Admin Mark W Tobin. *Medical Dir/Dir of Nursing* Elizabeth Goughan RN.
Licensure Skilled care; Intermediate care. *Beds* SNF 112; ICF 79. *Certified* Medicaid; Medicare.
Owner Proprietary Corp.
Admissions Requirements Minimum age 21; Physician's request.
Staff Physicians; RNs 14 (ft); LPNs 12 (ft); Orderlies 2 (ft); Nurses aides 75 (ft); Physical therapists; Occupational therapists 1 (pt); Speech therapists; Activities coordinators 4 (ft); Dietitians.
Languages Italian, Yiddish, French, Spanish
Facilities Dining room; Physical therapy room; Activities room; Chapel; Crafts room; Laundry room; Barber/Beauty shop; Library.
Activities Arts & crafts; Cards; Games; Reading groups; Prayer groups; Movies; Shopping trips; Social/Cultural gatherings.

Maple Grove Manor Convalescent Home
460 Washington St, Norwood, MA, 02062
(617) 769-2200
Admin Mary E Brooks. *Medical Dir/Dir of Nursing* Dr P Nandi; F Palmieri RN DON.
Licensure Skilled care; Intermediate care. *Beds* SNF 134; ICF 46. *Certified* Medicaid.
Owner Proprietary Corp (Beverly Enterprises).
Staff RNs; LPNs; Orderlies; Nurses aides; Physical therapists; Recreational therapists; Occupational therapists; Speech therapists; Activities coordinators; Dietitians.

Norwood Nursing & Retirement Home
767 Washington St, Norwood, MA, 02062
(617) 769-3704
Admin Kathleen F McKenna. *Medical Dir/Dir of Nursing* Carol B Quinn.
Licensure Intermediate care; Level III; DPH. *Beds* ICF 48.
Owner Proprietary Corp (Beverly Enterprises).
Staff RNs; LPNs; Orderlies; Nurses aides; Activities coordinators; Dietitians.
Facilities Dining room; Activities room; Barber/Beauty shop; Library.
Activities Arts & crafts; Cards; Games; Reading groups; Movies; Shopping trips; Entertainment; Dinner parties.

Victoria Haven Nursing Facility*
137 Nichols St, Norwood, MA, 02062
(617) 762-0858
Admin William Gold.
Licensure Intermediate care. *Beds* 31. *Certified* Medicaid.

OAK BLUFFS

Marthas Vineyard Hospital—Skilled & Intermediate Care Facility
Linton Ln, Oak Bluffs, MA, 02557
(617) 693-0410
Admin Robert L Langlois.
Licensure Skilled care; Intermediate care. *Beds* 40. *Certified* Medicaid.

ORANGE

Eastern Star Home*
75 E Main St, Orange, MA, 01364
(617) 544-6695
Admin Dorothy E Stackhouse.
Licensure Rest home. *Beds* 17.
Affiliation Order of Eastern Star

ORLEANS

Orleans Convalescent & Retirement Home*
Daley Terrace, Orleans, MA, 02563
(617) 255-2328
Admin Peter J Meade.
Licensure Skilled care. *Beds* 50. *Certified* Medicaid.

OXBRIDGE

Sunnyside Rest Home*
Old Millville Rd, Oxbridge, MA, 01569
(617) 278-3357
Admin Dorothy F Moore.
Licensure Intermediate care for mentally retarded. *Beds* 37.

OXFORD

Sandalwood Convalescent Home*
3 Pine St, Oxford, MA, 01540
(617) 987-8417
Admin Mary A Graham.
Licensure Skilled care; Intermediate care. *Beds* 77. *Certified* Medicaid.
Owner Proprietary Corp (Hillhaven Corp).

PALMER

Monson State Hospital*
Box F, Palmer, MA, 01069
(413) 283-3411
Admin Ron Rosen.
Licensure Intermediate care for mentally retarded. *Beds* 851. *Certified* Medicaid.
Owner Publicly owned.

Palmer House Healthcare Nursing Home
Shearer St, Palmer, MA, 01069
(413) 283-8361
Admin Bonnie J Davis.
Licensure Intermediate care. *Beds* 61. *Certified* Medicaid.
Owner Proprietary Corp (Hillhaven Corp).

PEABODY

Farnsworth Nursing Home*
28 Bowditch St, Peabody, MA, 01960
(617) 532-0768
Admin Gerald Swartz.
Licensure Intermediate care. *Beds* 74. *Certified* Medicaid.

Parkside Rest Home
210 Lowell St, Peabody, MA, 01960-4201
(617) 388-2446
Admin William L Twomey.
Licensure Rest home. *Beds* 30.

Pilgrim Rehabilitation & Skilled Nursing Center
96 Forest St, Peabody, MA, 01960
(617) 532-0303 or 884-8383
Admin W Bruce Glass. *Medical Dir/Dir of Nursing* Stephen Price MD; Deborah Levesque RN.
Licensure Skilled care. *Beds* SNF 144. *Certified* Medicaid; Medicare.
Owner Proprietary Corp (Hannover Healthcare).
Staff RNs 10 (ft), 8 (pt); LPNs 16 (ft), 8 (pt); Nurses aides 48 (ft), 44 (pt); Physical therapists 2 (ft), 1 (pt); Recreational

therapists 2 (ft), 1 (pt); Occupational therapists 2 (ft), 1 (pt); Speech therapists 1 (ft); Dietitians 1 (pt).
Languages Spanish, Portuguese, Greek
Facilities Dining room; Physical therapy room; Activities room; Chapel; Crafts room; Laundry room; Barber/Beauty shop; Library.
Activities Arts & crafts; Cards; Games; Reading groups; Prayer groups; Movies; Shopping trips; Social/Cultural gatherings.

Rainbow Nursing Home
210 Lowell St, Peabody, MA, 01960
(617) 531-2499
Admin John Di Pirro. *Medical Dir/Dir of Nursing* Gail Cochran RN.
Licensure Intermediate care. *Beds* ICF 35. *Certified* Medicaid.
Owner Proprietary Corp.
Admissions Requirements Minimum age 18; Medical examination.
Staff RNs 1 (ft), 1 (pt); LPNs 3 (ft); Nurses aides 5 (ft); Activities coordinators 1 (pt); Dietitians 1 (pt).
Facilities Dining room; Activities room; Chapel; Crafts room; Laundry room.
Activities Arts & crafts; Cards; Games; Reading groups; Prayer groups; Movies; Shopping trips; Social/Cultural gatherings.

PEPPERELL

Freeman Nursing Home
17 Main St, Pepperell, MA, 01463
(617) 433-2461
Admin Esther P Elliott. *Medical Dir/Dir of Nursing* Linda Sheehan LPN.
Licensure Intermediate care. *Beds* ICF 17. *Certified* Medicaid.
Owner Privately owned.
Admissions Requirements Minimum age 40; Medical examination; Physician's request.
Staff RNs 2 (pt); LPNs 1 (ft), 2 (pt); Nurses aides 5 (ft), 6 (pt); Recreational therapists 1 (pt); Activities coordinators 1 (pt); Dietitians 1 (pt).
Facilities Dining room; Activities room; Crafts room; Laundry room.
Activities Arts & crafts; Cards; Games; Reading groups; Prayer groups; Movies; Shopping trips; Social/Cultural gatherings.

Park Manor Nursing Home
13 Park St, Pepperell, MA, 01463
(617) 433-2490
Admin Esther P Elliott. *Medical Dir/Dir of Nursing* Debra P Walsh RN.
Licensure Intermediate care. *Beds* ICF 32. *Certified* Medicaid.
Owner Proprietary Corp.
Admissions Requirements Minimum age 40; Medical examination.
Staff RNs 1 (ft), 1 (pt); LPNs 1 (ft), 2 (pt); Nurses aides 8 (ft), 5 (pt); Recreational therapists 1 (pt); Activities coordinators 1 (pt); Dietitians 1 (pt).
Facilities Dining room; Activities room; Laundry room.
Activities Arts & crafts; Cards; Games; Reading groups; Prayer groups; Movies; Shopping trips; Social/Cultural gatherings; Cookouts; Picnics; Swimming; Hay rides; Sleigh rides.

PITTSFIELD

Berkshire Nursing Home Inc
360 W Housatonic St, Pittsfield, MA, 01201
(413) 442-4841
Admin Michael Stroetzel.
Licensure Skilled care; Intermediate care. *Beds* 84. *Certified* Medicaid.

Berkshire Place*
89 South St, Pittsfield, MA, 01201
(413) 445-4056
Admin Marion Nielsen.

Licensure Intermediate care; Charitable home. *Beds* 38. *Certified* Medicaid.
Admissions Requirements Minimum age 65; Females only; Medical examination.
Staff RNs 8 (pt); LPNs 4 (ft); Nurses aides 1 (ft), 4 (pt); Physical therapists 1 (pt); Recreational therapists 1 (pt); Activities coordinators 1 (ft); Dietitians 1 (pt); Podiatrists 1 (pt).
Facilities Dining room; Laundry room; Barber/Beauty shop.
Activities Arts & crafts; Cards; Games; Shopping trips; Social/Cultural gatherings.

Edgewood Rest Home*
50 Edgewood Rd, Pittsfield, MA, 01201
(413) 442-1004
Admin Dorothy E Studley.
Licensure Rest home. *Beds* 13.

Springside of Pittsfield Long-Term Care Facility*
255 Lebanon Ave, Pittsfield, MA, 01201
(413) 499-2334
Admin David Carlson.
Licensure Intermediate care. *Beds* 100.
Certified Medicaid.

Bertha M Young Rest Home*
261 South St, Pittsfield, MA, 01201
(413) 448-8801
Admin Doris T Hogan.
Licensure Rest home. *Beds* 20.

PLAINVILLE

Plainville Nursing Home
62 South St, Plainville, MA, 02762
(617) 695-1434
Admin Louis Furash. *Medical Dir/Dir of Nursing* Jane Sellmayer.
Licensure Intermediate care. *Beds* ICF 60.
Certified Medicaid.
Owner Proprietary Corp.
Admissions Requirements Physician's request.
Staff RNs; LPNs; Orderlies; Nurses aides; Activities coordinators 1 (ft); Dietitians 1 (pt).
Facilities Dining room; Activities room; Chapel; Crafts room; Laundry room; Barber/ Beauty shop; Library.
Activities Arts & crafts; Cards; Games; Reading groups; Prayer groups; Movies; Shopping trips; Social/Cultural gatherings.

PLYMOUTH

Mayflower House Nursing Home & Child Care Center
123 South St, Plymouth, MA, 02360
(617) 746-4343
Admin Burton K Lipsky. *Medical Dir/Dir of Nursing* Marie McDonald.
Licensure Skilled care; Intermediate care; Child care unit. *Beds* SNF 62; ICF 62.
Certified Medicaid; Medicare.
Owner Proprietary Corp (Oakwood Living Centers).
Admissions Requirements Minimum age 21; Medical examination; Physician's request.
Staff Physicians 1 (pt); RNs 23 (ft), 5 (pt); LPNs 10 (ft); Nurses aides 60 (ft), 20 (pt); Physical therapists 1 (ft), 1 (pt); Recreational therapists 1 (ft); Occupational therapists 1 (ft), 1 (pt); Speech therapists 2 (pt); Activities coordinators 1 (ft); Dietitians 1 (pt).
Facilities Dining room; Physical therapy room; Activities room; Laundry room; Barber/Beauty shop; Library.
Activities Arts & crafts; Cards; Games; Reading groups; Prayer groups; Movies; Shopping trips; Social/Cultural gatherings.

Newfield House Inc
19 Newfield St, Plymouth, MA, 02360
(617) 746-2912

Admin Geoffrey T Stewart. *Medical Dir/Dir of Nursing* Catherine D Maher RN DNS.
Licensure Intermediate care. *Beds* 100.
Owner Proprietary Corp.
Facilities Dining room; Physical therapy room; Activities room; Laundry room; Barber/Beauty shop.
Activities Arts & crafts; Cards; Games; Reading groups; Prayer groups; Movies; Social/Cultural gatherings.

Pilgrim Manor Nursing Home
60 Stafford St, Plymouth, MA, 02360
(617) 746-7016
Admin Bonnie A Burke. *Medical Dir/Dir of Nursing* John T O'Neil MD; Cal Dearinger DON.
Licensure Skilled care; Intermediate care. *Beds* SNF 120; ICF 56. *Certified* Medicaid; Medicare.
Owner Proprietary Corp.
Admissions Requirements Minimum age 50.
Staff Physicians 1 (pt); RNs 8 (ft), 9 (pt); LPNs 5 (ft), 11 (pt); Nurses aides 40 (ft), 49 (pt); Physical therapists 2 (pt); Recreational therapists 2 (ft), 1 (pt); Occupational therapists 1 (pt); Speech therapists 1 (pt); Activities coordinators 1 (pt); Dietitians 1 (pt); Dentists 1 (pt); Ophthalmologists 2 (pt).
Facilities Dining room; Physical therapy room; Activities room; Chapel; Crafts room; Barber/Beauty shop; Library.
Activities Arts & crafts; Cards; Games; Reading groups; Prayer groups; Movies; Shopping trips; Social/Cultural gatherings; Luncheon trips.

Plymouth Nursing Home
35 Warren Ave, Plymouth, MA, 02360
(617) 746-2085
Admin Salvatore Freddura.
Licensure Intermediate care; Level III. *Beds* ICF 37. *Certified* Medicaid.
Owner Privately owned.
Admissions Requirements Minimum age 21; Physician's request.
Staff LPNs 1 (ft), 2 (pt); Nurses aides 6 (ft), 3 (pt); Activities coordinators 1 (ft).
Facilities Dining room; Activities room; Laundry room.
Activities Arts & crafts; Cards; Games; Prayer groups; Movies; Social/Cultural gatherings; Special Olympics.

PROVINCETOWN

Cape End Manor Nursing Home
100 Alden St, Provincetown, MA, 02657
(617) 487-0235
Admin David M Maloney. *Medical Dir/Dir of Nursing* Brian O'Malley MD.
Licensure Intermediate care. *Beds* ICF 57.
Certified Medicaid.
Owner Publicly owned.
Admissions Requirements Minimum age 60 w/ exceptions; Medical examination; Physician's request No primary Psyc or ETOM Diagnosis.
Staff Physicians 1 (pt); RNs 2 (ft), 2 (pt); LPNs 1 (ft), 4 (pt); Nurses aides 18 (ft), 10 (pt); Physical therapists 1 (pt); Activities coordinators 1 (ft), 1 (pt); Dietitians 1 (pt); Ophthalmologists 1 (pt).
Languages Portuguese
Facilities Dining room; Activities room; Laundry room; Barber/Beauty shop.
Activities Arts & crafts; Cards; Games; Reading groups; Prayer groups; Movies; Shopping trips; Social/Cultural gatherings; Luncheons; Cocktail parties; Local sightseeing trips; Picnics.

QUINCY

John Adams Nursing Home*
211 Franklin St, Quincy, MA, 02169
(617) 479-0837

Admin Muriel F Finn.
Licensure Skilled care. *Beds* 49. *Certified* Medicaid.

Almana Rest Home*
8 Old Colony Ave, Quincy, MA, 02170
(617) 479-5912
Admin Jackelene M Walton.
Licensure Rest home. *Beds* 22.
Admissions Requirements Medical examination; Physician's request.
Staff RNs 1 (pt); Orderlies 2 (ft), 3 (pt); Dietitians 1 (pt).
Facilities Activities room.
Activities Cards; Games; Prayer groups; Shopping trips.

Crestview Nursing Home*
86 Greenleaf St, Quincy, MA, 02169
(617) 472-9721
Admin Stephen J Clinton.
Licensure Intermediate care. *Beds* 49.
Certified Medicaid.
Admissions Requirements Medical examination; Physician's request.
Staff RNs 1 (ft), 1 (pt); LPNs 5 (ft), 4 (pt); Nurses aides 8 (ft), 20 (pt); Activities coordinators 1 (ft), 1 (pt); Dietitians 1 (pt).
Facilities Dining room; Activities room; Laundry room; Barber/Beauty shop; 2 Living rooms.
Activities Arts & crafts; Cards; Games; Reading groups; Prayer groups; Movies; Shopping trips; Social/Cultural gatherings; Auto drives; Corsages on Mother's Day; Daily walks by those able, on nice days.

Merrymount Manor Nursing Home*
38 Edgemere Rd, Quincy, MA, 02169
(617) 472-1704
Admin John G Murphy.
Licensure Intermediate care. *Beds* 24.
Certified Medicaid.
Staff RNs 1 (ft), 1 (pt); LPNs 2 (ft), 2 (pt); Nurses aides 4 (ft), 8 (pt); Dietitians 1 (pt).
Facilities Dining room; Laundry room; Library.
Activities Arts & crafts; Cards; Games; Reading groups; Movies; Shopping trips; Social/Cultural gatherings.

Oceanside Nursing Home*
445 Quincy Shore Dr, Quincy, MA, 02171
(617) 472-4618
Admin Harry J Minassian.
Licensure Intermediate care. *Beds* 25.
Certified Medicaid.

Presidential Convalescent Home Inc
43 Old Colony Ave, Quincy, MA, 02170
(617) 471-0155
Admin Carl A Awed. *Medical Dir/Dir of Nursing* Dr Joseph Carella.
Licensure Skilled care; Intermediate care. *Beds* 89. *Certified* Medicaid.
Staff RNs 8 (ft), 3 (pt); LPNs 3 (ft), 4 (pt); Nurses aides 27 (ft); Physical therapists 1 (pt); Occupational therapists 1 (pt); Speech therapists 1 (pt); Activities coordinators 1 (ft), 1 (pt); Dietitians 1 (pt); Dentists 1 (pt); Ophthalmologists 1 (pt); Podiatrists 1 (pt).
Facilities Dining room; Activities room; Crafts room; Laundry room; Barber/Beauty shop.
Activities Arts & crafts; Cards; Games; Reading groups; Prayer groups; Movies; Shopping trips; Social/Cultural gatherings.

Quincy Nursing Home*
11 Thomas J McGrath Hwy, Quincy, MA, 02169
(617) 479-2820
Admin Mabel S Hurley.
Licensure Skilled care; Intermediate care. *Beds* 139. *Certified* Medicaid; Medicare.
Owner Proprietary Corp (Hillhaven Corp).

William B Rice Eventide Home*
215 Adams St, Quincy, MA, 02169
(617) 472-8300
Admin Priscilla Urann.
Licensure Intermediate care. *Beds* 53.
Certified Medicaid.

Robbin House Convalescent Home
205 Elm St, Quincy, MA, 02169
(617) 471-1750
Admin Timothy Brainerd. *Medical Dir/Dir of Nursing* Jane Kimball.
Licensure Skilled care; Intermediate care. *Beds* SNF 49; ICF 65. *Certified* Medicaid.
Owner Proprietary Corp (Hillhaven Corp).
Admissions Requirements Medical examination.
Facilities Dining room; Laundry room; Patio.
Activities Arts & crafts; Cards; Games; Reading groups; Prayer groups; Movies; Shopping trips; Social/Cultural gatherings; Therapeutic groups.

Wollaston Nursing & Retirement Home*
210 Arlington St, Quincy, MA, 02170
(617) 773-6362
Admin Edna F Rand.
Licensure Intermediate care. *Beds* 21.
Certified Medicaid.

RANDOLPH

Hollywell Nursing Home*
975 N Main St, Randolph, MA, 02368
(617) 963-8800
Admin William F Lee.
Licensure Skilled care; Intermediate care. *Beds* 139. *Certified* Medicaid; Medicare.

Seth Mann II Home for the Aged*
349 N Main St, Randolph, MA, 02368
(617) 963-9116
Admin Evelyn McLeer.
Licensure Charitable home. *Beds* 5.

READING

Daniel's Nursing Home Inc*
59 Middlesex Ave, Reading, MA, 01867
(617) 944-0198
Admin D Lee Rorick.
Beds 30. *Certified* Medicaid.

REVERE

Annemark Nursing Home Inc
133 Salem St, Revere, MA, 02151
(617) 322-4861
Admin Elena A Bean. *Medical Dir/Dir of Nursing* Haren Desai MD; Kathleen M Bibo RN BSN.
Licensure Skilled care; Intermediate care. *Beds* SNF 80; ICF 60. *Certified* Medicaid.
Owner Proprietary Corp; Privately owned.
Admissions Requirements Minimum age 50; Physician's request.
Staff RNs 8 (ft), 3 (pt); LPNs 8 (ft), 3 (pt); Orderlies 4 (ft); Nurses aides 48 (ft), 6 (pt); Physical therapists 1 (pt); Recreational therapists 1 (ft); Occupational therapists 1 (pt); Speech therapists 1 (pt); Activities coordinators 1 (ft); Dietitians 1 (pt); Dentists 1 (pt); Ophthalmologists 1 (pt); Podiatrists 1 (pt).
Languages Spanish, Italian, Polish
Facilities Dining room; Physical therapy room; Activities room; Crafts room; Laundry room; Barber/Beauty shop; Day rooms.
Activities Arts & crafts; Cards; Games; Reading groups; Prayer groups; Movies; Shopping trips; Social/Cultural gatherings.

Oak Island Skilled Nursing Facility
400 Revere Beach Blvd, Revere, MA, 02151
(617) 284-1958
Admin Felix F Albano Jr. *Medical Dir/Dir of Nursing* Carl Sterpi; Joan Buckley.

Licensure Skilled care; Intermediate care; Level II; Level III. *Beds* SNF 66; ICF 70. *Certified* Medicaid.
Owner Proprietary Corp.
Admissions Requirements Minimum age 60; Medical examination.
Staff Physicians; RNs; LPNs; Orderlies; Nurses aides; Physical therapists; Recreational therapists; Occupational therapists; Speech therapists; Activities coordinators; Dietitians; Dentists; Ophthalmologists; Podiatrists.
Languages Italian
Facilities Dining room; Activities room; Crafts room; Laundry room; Barber/Beauty shop.
Activities Arts & crafts; Cards; Games; Reading groups; Prayer groups; Movies; Shopping trips; Social/Cultural gatherings.

ROCKLAND

Del Manor Nursing Home
56 Webster St, Rockland, MA, 02370
(617) 871-0555
Admin Edmund W Del Prete. *Medical Dir/Dir of Nursing* Brian Battista MD; Ann Hession RN.
Licensure Skilled care. *Beds* 110. *Certified* Medicaid.

Linden Nursing & Retirement Home*
167 W Water St, Rockland, MA, 02370
(617) 878-3728
Admin Arthur S Logan.
Licensure Intermediate care. *Beds* 19. *Certified* Medicaid.

Rockland Nursing Home*
384 Union St, Rockland, MA, 02370
(617) 878-4405
Admin Janet M Williams.
Licensure Intermediate care. *Beds* 21. *Certified* Medicaid.

South Shore Nursing Facility
115 North Ave, Rockland, MA, 02370
(617) 878-3308
Admin Charles O Williams Jr. *Medical Dir/Dir of Nursing* John Carpenter MD; Susan Keaney RN DON.
Licensure Skilled care; Intermediate care. *Beds* SNF 40; ICF 44. *Certified* Medicaid; Medicare.
Owner Proprietary Corp.
Staff RNs 3 (ft), 13 (pt); LPNs 2 (ft), 4 (pt); Nurses aides 20 (ft), 13 (pt); Physical therapists 1 (pt); Recreational therapists 1 (ft), 1 (pt); Occupational therapists 1 (pt); Speech therapists 1 (pt); Dietitians 1 (pt); Dentists 1 (pt); Ophthalmologists 1 (pt).
Facilities Dining room; Physical therapy room; Activities room; Crafts room; Laundry room; Barber/Beauty shop.
Activities Arts & crafts; Cards; Games; Reading groups; Prayer groups; Movies; Shopping trips; Social/Cultural gatherings; Cookouts; Local events trips.

Tiffany Rest & Retirement Home
5 Union St, Rockland, MA, 02370
(617) 878-3757
Admin Diane B Gillis.
Licensure Retirement. *Beds* Retirement 43. *Certified* Medicaid.
Owner Privately owned.
Admissions Requirements Minimum age 50.
Staff LPNs 1 (ft), 1 (pt); Nurses aides 3 (ft), 3 (pt).
Facilities Dining room; Laundry room; Library.
Activities Arts & crafts; Cards; Games; Prayer groups; Movies; Shopping trips.

Tiffany II Rest Home*
56 W Water St, Rockland, MA, 02370
(617) 878-0676
Admin Donna M Zaccardi.

Licensure Rest home. *Beds* 16.

ROCKPORT

Den-Mar Nursing Home
44 South St, Rockport, MA, 01966
(617) 546-6311
Admin Kimberley A Edmands.
Licensure Skilled care; Intermediate care. *Beds* 80. *Certified* Medicaid.
Owner Proprietary Corp (Hillhaven Corp).
Admissions Requirements Medical examination.
Staff RNs 4 (ft), 2 (pt); LPNs 6 (ft), 2 (pt); Orderlies 1 (ft), 1 (pt); Nurses aides 8 (ft), 13 (pt); Activities coordinators 1 (ft), 1 (pt); Dietitians 1 (ft).
Facilities Dining room; Activities room; Laundry room; Barber/Beauty shop.
Activities Arts & crafts; Games; Reading groups; Prayer groups; Movies; Shopping trips; Social/Cultural gatherings; Cooking; Awareness & exercise group; Manicures; Residents council; For Men Only group.

ROSLINDALE

The Recuperative Center
1245 Centre St, Roslindale, MA, 02131
(617) 325-5400
Admin Gregory C Karr. *Medical Dir/Dir of Nursing* Lester Steinberg MD; Betty Hern RN.
Licensure Skilled care. *Beds* SNF 81. *Certified* Medicaid; Medicare.
Owner Nonprofit Corp.
Admissions Requirements Minimum age 21.
Staff Physicians 1 (pt); RNs 15 (ft); LPNs 2 (ft), 2 (pt); Orderlies 4 (pt); Nurses aides 20 (ft), 20 (pt); Physical therapists 2 (ft); Recreational therapists 2 (ft); Occupational therapists 3 (ft); Speech therapists 1 (pt); Activities coordinators 1 (ft); Dietitians 1 (ft); Ophthalmologists 1 (pt).
Languages Yiddish, Hebrew
Facilities Dining room; Physical therapy room; Activities room; Chapel; Crafts room; Barber/Beauty shop; Library.
Activities Arts & crafts; Cards; Games; Reading groups; Prayer groups; Movies; Social/Cultural gatherings; Current events.

Roxbury Home for Aged Women*
1215 Centre St, Roslindale, MA, 02131
(617) 323-0373
Admin Alice Runci. *Medical Dir/Dir of Nursing* Dr Alice Rogado.
Licensure Intermediate care; Charitable home. *Beds* 24.
Admissions Requirements Minimum age 65; Females only; Medical examination.
Staff Physicians 1 (pt); RNs 1 (pt); LPNs 1 (ft), 1 (pt); Nurses aides 7 (pt); Activities coordinators 1 (pt); Dietitians 1 (pt); Dentists 1 (pt); Ophthalmologists 1 (pt); Podiatrists 1 (pt); Audiologists 1 (pt).

ROWLEY

Sea View Convalescent & Nursing Home
Mansion Dr, Rowley, MA, 01969
(617) 948-7440
Admin Stephen B Comley. *Medical Dir/Dir of Nursing* Dr William Wigglesworth.
Licensure Intermediate care. *Beds* 61. *Certified* Medicaid.
Admissions Requirements Minimum age 45; Physician's request.
Staff RNs 2 (ft), 4 (pt); LPNs 6 (pt); Nurses aides 14 (ft), 8 (pt); Physical therapists 1 (pt); Recreational therapists 1 (pt); Activities coordinators 1 (ft), 1 (pt); Dietitians 1 (pt); Podiatrists 1 (pt); Social workers 1 (pt).

Facilities Dining room; Physical therapy room; Activities room; Chapel; Crafts room; Laundry room; Barber/Beauty shop; Library; Classroom; Garden; Greenhouse; Elevator; Residents' kitchen; Kiln & pottery workshop.
Activities Arts & crafts; Games; Reading groups; Prayer groups; Movies; Shopping trips; Social/Cultural gatherings; Outings in van; Gardening & plant care; Ceramics.

ROXBURY

St Monica's Home
17 Highland Park St, Roxbury, MA, 02119
(617) 445-8961
Admin Donald S Lindsay.
Licensure Skilled care. *Beds* 42. *Certified* Medicaid.
Admissions Requirements Females only.
Affiliation Episcopal

RUTLAND

Rutland Heights Hospital—Skilled Nursing Facility
86 Maple Ave, Rutland, MA, 01543
(617) 886-4711
Admin Donald J Rutherford. *Medical Dir/Dir of Nursing* Priscilla Hele MD; Bonnie Fauteux DON.
Licensure Skilled care; Intermediate care; Respite. *Beds* SNF 36; Respite 4. *Certified* Medicaid; Medicare.
Owner Publicly owned.
Admissions Requirements Minimum age 16; Physician's request.
Staff Physicians 4 (ft); RNs; Physical therapists 1 (ft); Recreational therapists 2 (ft); Occupational therapists 1 (ft); Speech therapists 1 (ft); Dietitians 2 (ft); Ophthalmologists 1 (pt).
Facilities Dining room; Physical therapy room; Activities room; Crafts room; Barber/Beauty shop; Library.
Activities Arts & crafts; Cards; Games; Prayer groups; Movies; Shopping trips; Social/Cultural gatherings.

SALEM

Bertran Home for Aged Men*
29 Washington Square, Salem, MA, 01970
(617) 744-1002
Admin Eugene M Mater.
Licensure Charitable home. *Beds* 61.
Admissions Requirements Males only.

Home for Aged Women in Salem*
180 Derby St, Salem, MA, 01970
(617) 744-0219
Admin Arthur Webster.
Licensure Rest home. *Beds* 36.

Ivy Manor Rest Home*
204 Lafayette St, Salem, MA, 01970
(617) 745-2920
Admin Shirley A Phillips.
Licensure Rest home. *Beds* 17.

Newhall Nursing Home*
7 Carpenter St, Salem, MA, 01970
(617) 744-3844
Admin Betsey D Marcus.
Licensure Intermediate care. *Beds* 47. *Certified* Medicaid.
Admissions Requirements Minimum age 21; Medical examination; Physician's request.
Staff RNs 3 (pt); LPNs 4 (ft), 2 (pt); Nurses aides 13 (ft), 6 (pt); Activities coordinators; Dietitians.
Facilities Dining room; Activities room.
Activities Arts & crafts; Cards; Games; Reading groups; Prayer groups; Movies; Shopping trips.

Shaughnessy—Kaplan Rehabilitation Hospital
Dove Ave, Salem, MA, 01970
(617) 745-9000
Admin James A Lomastro. *Medical Dir/Dir of Nursing* Frederic O Buckley Jr MD; Linda Henlotter RN DON.
Beds SNF 40; Rehabilitation 120. *Certified* Medicaid; Medicare.
Owner Publicly owned.
Admissions Requirements Physician's request.
Staff Physicians; RNs; LPNs; Nurses aides; Physical therapists; Reality therapists; Recreational therapists; Occupational therapists; Speech therapists; Activities coordinators; Dietitians.
Facilities Dining room; Physical therapy room; Activities room; Chapel; Crafts room; Barber/Beauty shop.
Activities Arts & crafts; Cards; Games; Reading groups; Prayer groups; Movies; Shopping trips; Social/Cultural gatherings.

SANDISFIELD

New Boston Nursing Home Inc*
Rte 57, Sandisfield, MA, 01255
(413) 258-4731
Admin Brian J Foohey.
Licensure Intermediate care. *Beds* 49. *Certified* Medicaid.

SANDWICH

Fraser Rest Home of Sandwich*
125 Old Maine St, Sandwich, MA, 02563
(617) 888-0880
Admin David P Fraser.
Licensure Rest home. *Beds* 20.

SAUGUS

Abbey Hill Nursing Home*
163 Hamilton St, Saugus, MA, 01906
(617) 233-2522
Admin Patrick J Fahy. *Medical Dir/Dir of Nursing* Dr J Stanley Carp.
Licensure Intermediate care. *Beds* 30. *Certified* Medicaid.
Admissions Requirements Minimum age 55.
Staff RNs 1 (ft), 4 (pt); LPNs 4 (pt); Nurses aides 3 (ft), 6 (pt); Physical therapists 1 (pt); Activities coordinators 1 (ft); Dietitians 1 (pt); Dentists 1 (ft); Ophthalmologists 1 (ft); Podiatrists 1 (ft); Social workers 1 (pt).
Facilities Dining room; Activities room; Laundry room.
Activities Arts & crafts; Cards; Games; Reading groups; Prayer groups; Movies; Shopping trips; Social/Cultural gatherings.

Louise Caroline Rehabilitation & Nursing Center
266 Lincoln Ave, Saugus, MA, 01906
(617) 233-6830
Admin Patrice E Pelletier. *Medical Dir/Dir of Nursing* Terrance O'Malley MD.
Licensure Skilled care; Intermediate care. *Beds* 80. *Certified* Medicaid; Medicare.
Admissions Requirements Minimum age 65.
Staff Physicians 6 (pt); RNs 5 (ft), 9 (pt); LPNs 4 (ft), 2 (pt); Nurses aides 22 (ft), 19 (pt); Physical therapists 1 (pt); Recreational therapists 1 (pt); Occupational therapists 1 (pt); Speech therapists 1 (pt); Activities coordinators 1 (ft); Dietitians 2 (pt).
Facilities Dining room; Physical therapy room; Activities room; Crafts room; Laundry room; Barber/Beauty shop.
Activities Arts & crafts; Cards; Games; Reading groups; Prayer groups; Movies; Shopping trips; Restaurant outings.

North Shore Convalescent Home*
73 Chestnut St, Saugus, MA, 01906
(617) 233-8123
Admin Edward Y Serro. *Medical Dir/Dir of Nursing* J Stanley Carp MD.

Licensure Skilled care; Intermediate care. *Beds* 100. *Certified* Medicaid.
Owner Proprietary Corp (Hillhaven Corp).
Admissions Requirements Minimum age 21.
Staff Nurses aides 60 (ft); Physical therapists 1 (pt); Reality therapists 1 (pt); Recreational therapists 2 (ft), 1 (pt); Occupational therapists 1 (pt); Speech therapists 1 (pt); Activities coordinators 1 (ft); Dietitians 1 (ft); Dentists 1 (pt); Ophthalmologists 1 (pt); Podiatrists 1 (pt); Audiologists 1 (pt).
Facilities Dining room; Physical therapy room; Activities room; Chapel; Crafts room; Laundry room; Barber/Beauty shop.
Activities Arts & crafts; Cards; Games; Reading groups; Prayer groups; Movies; Shopping trips; Social/Cultural gatherings.

SCITUATE

Cardigan Nursing Home*
59 Country Way, Scituate, MA, 02040
(617) 545-9477
Admin John H Hilton Jr.
Licensure Intermediate care. *Beds* 65. *Certified* Medicaid.

Scituate Ocean Manor*
309 Driftway, Scituate, MA, 02066
(617) 545-1370
Admin James Oliver. *Medical Dir/Dir of Nursing* Tod Forman MD.
Licensure Skilled care; Intermediate care. *Beds* 113. *Certified* Medicaid.
Staff Physicians 2 (ft); RNs 5 (ft), 12 (pt); LPNs 6 (ft), 9 (pt); Orderlies 2 (ft); Nurses aides 22 (ft), 53 (pt); Physical therapists 2 (ft), 1 (pt); Recreational therapists 2 (ft); Occupational therapists 1 (pt); Speech therapists 1 (pt); Activities coordinators 1 (ft), 1 (pt); Dietitians 1 (pt); Dentists 1 (pt); Ophthalmologists 1 (pt); Podiatrists 1 (pt); Audiologists 1 (pt).
Facilities Dining room; Physical therapy room; Activities room; Chapel; Crafts room; Laundry room; Barber/Beauty shop; Library.
Activities Arts & crafts; Cards; Games; Reading groups; Prayer groups; Movies; Shopping trips; Social/Cultural gatherings.

SHARON

Sharon Manor Nursing Home*
259 Norwood St, Sharon, MA, 02067
(617) 784-6781
Admin John J Ribeiro.
Licensure Skilled care. *Beds* 58. *Certified* Medicaid; Medicare.

SHELBURNE

Anchorage Nursing Home
Mohawk Trail, Rte 2, Shelburne, MA, 01370
(413) 625-2305
Admin Franics B Caldwell.
Licensure Intermediate care. *Beds* 35. *Certified* Medicaid.

Mohawk Manor Rest Home Inc
45 Water St, Shelburne, MA, 01370
(413) 625-6860
Admin Gail A Bissell.
Licensure Rest home. *Beds* 24.
Admissions Requirements Minimum age 35; Medical examination; Physician's request.
Staff RNs 1 (pt); LPNs 1 (ft); Nurses aides 9 (pt); Activities coordinators 1 (pt); Dietitians 1 (pt).
Facilities Dining room; Laundry room.
Activities Arts & crafts; Cards; Games; Prayer groups; Movies; Shopping trips.

SHELBURNE FALLS

La Belle's Rest Home
3 High St, Shelburne Falls, MA, 01370
(413) 625-6560
Admin Haren B Upadhyay.
Licensure Residential care. *Beds* Residential
32. *Certified* Medicaid; Medicare.
Owner Privately owned.
Admissions Requirements Minimum age 18.
Staff RNs; LPNs; Nurses aides; Activities
coordinators; Dietitians; Ophthalmologists.
Facilities Dining room; Activities room;
Laundry room.
Activities Arts & crafts; Cards; Games;
Reading groups; Prayer groups; Movies;
Shopping trips; Social/Cultural gatherings.

SHREWSBURY

Shrewsbury Nursing Home Inc*
66 South St, Shrewsbury, MA, 01545
(617) 845-6786
Admin Betty L Stratford.
Licensure Skilled care; Intermediate care. *Beds*
123. *Certified* Medicaid.

SOMERSET

**Clifton Geriatric Center Long-Term Care
Facility***
500 Wilbur Ave, Somerset, MA, 02725
(617) 675-7589
Admin Clifton O Greenwood.
Licensure Skilled care; Intermediate care. *Beds*
130. *Certified* Medicaid.

SOMERVILLE

Chandler Manor Rest Home*
38 Chandler St, Somerville, MA, 02144
(617) 666-1519
Admin Janina Elmaleh.
Licensure Rest home. *Beds* 21.

Clarendon Hill Nursing Home*
1323 Broadway, Somerville, MA, 02144
(617) 623-6700
Admin Burton F Faulkner Jr.
Licensure Intermediate care. *Beds* 58.
Certified Medicaid.

Jeanne Jugan Residence*
186 Highland Ave, Somerville, MA, 02143
(617) 776-4420
Admin Angelique Roth.
Licensure Skilled care; Intermediate care. *Beds*
120. *Certified* Medicaid.

Mary Ellen Nursing Home*
170 Highland Ave, Somerville, MA, 02143
(617) 625-7764
Admin Martha L Ditucci.
Licensure Intermediate care. *Beds* 23.
Certified Medicaid.

Prospect Hill Manor Nursing Home
37 Munroe St, Somerville, MA, 02143
(617) 666-9891
Admin Richard S Percoco. *Medical Dir/Dir of
Nursing* June Baker.
Licensure Intermediate care. *Beds* ICF 40.
Certified Medicaid.
Owner Proprietary Corp.
Staff RNs; LPNs; Nurses aides; Speech
therapists; Activities coordinators; Dietitians;
Dentists; Ophthalmologists.
Activities Arts & crafts; Cards; Games;
Picnics.

Reagan's Resident Care Facility
174 Morrison Ave, Somerville, MA, 02144
(617) 666-0380
Admin Victoria Stone. *Medical Dir/Dir of
Nursing* Dorothy Bradley.
Licensure Rest home Level IV. *Beds*
Supervised care 42. *Certified* Medicaid; SSI.

Owner Privately owned.
Admissions Requirements Minimum age 50;
Medical examination; Physician's request.
Staff LPNs; Nurses aides; Activities
coordinators; Dietitians.
Facilities Dining room; Activities room; TV
rooms.
Activities Arts & crafts; Cards; Games; Prayer
groups; Shopping trips.

Somerville Home for the Aged
117 Summer St, Somerville, MA, 02143
(617) 776-0260
Admin Elsa E Lewis RN.
Licensure Rest home. *Beds* 59 Retirement
home.
Owner Nonprofit Corp.
Admissions Requirements Minimum age 65;
Medical examination; Physician's request.
Staff RNs 1 (ft); LPNs 1 (pt); Nurses aides 3
(ft), 5 (pt); Activities coordinators 1 (pt);
Dietitians 1 (pt); Ophthalmologists 1 (pt).
Facilities Dining room; Activities room;
Chapel; Laundry room; Barber/Beauty shop;
Library.
Activities Arts & crafts; Cards; Games;
Reading groups; Prayer groups; Movies;
Shopping trips; Social/Cultural gatherings;
Exercise classes.

Sunrise Nursing Home*
26 Adams St, Somerville, MA, 02145
(617) 625-2233
Admin Jacob M Volensky.
Licensure Intermediate care. *Beds* 40.
Certified Medicaid.

Winter Hill Nursing Home*
50 Evergreen Ave, Somerville, MA, 02145
(617) 628-0110
Admin Robert D Brennan. *Medical Dir/Dir of
Nursing* Dr Herbert Leventhal.
Licensure Intermediate care. *Beds* 78.
Certified Medicaid.
Admissions Requirements Minimum age 21;
Medical examination; Physician's request.
Staff RNs 1 (ft), 1 (pt); LPNs 4 (ft), 4 (pt);
Nurses aides 21 (ft), 10 (pt); Recreational
therapists 1 (ft), 1 (pt); Dietitians 1 (pt).
Facilities Dining room; Activities room;
Laundry room.
Activities Arts & crafts; Cards; Games;
Reading groups; Prayer groups; Movies;
Shopping trips; Social/Cultural gatherings.

SOUTH BOSTON

Harbor Inn Nursing Home Inc
1380 Columbia Rd, South Boston, MA, 02127
(617) 268-5450
Admin Lillian Ruth Talcof. *Medical Dir/Dir of
Nursing* Veronica Boderick MD; Hinda
Abrams RN DON.
Licensure Intermediate care. *Beds* ICF 111.
Certified Medicaid.
Owner Privately owned.
Admissions Requirements Minimum age 30.
Staff RNs 2 (ft); LPNs 5 (ft), 1 (pt); Nurses
aides 18 (ft), 3 (pt); Recreational therapists 1
(ft); Social worker 1 (pt).
Languages Italian, Hebrew, Yiddish,
Lithuanian, Polish
Facilities Dining room; Activities room;
Chapel; Crafts room; Laundry room; Barber/
Beauty shop; Boston Public Library
distributes books & magazines.
Activities Arts & crafts; Cards; Games;
Reading groups; Prayer groups; Movies;
Shopping trips; Social/Cultural gatherings;
Dining out.

Marian Manor Nursing Home
130 Dorchester St, South Boston, MA, 02127
(617) 268-3333
Admin Sr Andre Marie. *Medical Dir/Dir of
Nursing* Ernesto Waingortin MD; Anne
Marie Perry RN DON.

Licensure Skilled care; Intermediate care;
Level IV. *Beds* SNF 376; ICF; Level IV.
Certified Medicaid.
Owner Nonprofit organization/foundation.
Admissions Requirements Minimum age 65;
Physician's request.
Staff Physicians; RNs; LPNs; Orderlies;
Nurses aides; Physical therapists; Reality
therapists; Recreational therapists;
Occupational therapists; Speech therapists;
Activities coordinators; Dietitians; Dentists;
Ophthalmologists; Podiatrists.
Languages Spanish, Lithuanian, Polish
Affiliation Roman Catholic
Facilities Dining room; Physical therapy
room; Activities room; Chapel; Crafts room;
Laundry room; Barber/Beauty shop; Library.
Activities Arts & crafts; Cards; Games;
Reading groups; Prayer groups; Movies;
Shopping trips; Social/Cultural gatherings.

SOUTH DARTMOUTH

Harborview Manor Nursing Home
173 Smith Neck Rd, South Dartmouth, MA,
02748
(617) 992-8901
Admin Joyce Finkenstein. *Medical Dir/Dir of
Nursing* Dr Stewart Kirknedy; Sandra
Wrench.
Licensure Intermediate care. *Beds* ICF 29.
Certified Medicaid.
Owner Proprietary Corp (Beverly Enterprises).
Admissions Requirements Medical
examination.
Staff Physicians 1 (ft); RNs 2 (ft), 2 (pt);
LPNs 2 (ft); Nurses aides 7 (ft), 7 (pt);
Activities coordinators 1 (ft); Dietitians 1
(ft); Ophthalmologists 1 (pt).
Languages French, Spanish, Portuguese
Affiliation Roman Catholic
Facilities Dining room; Crafts room; Laundry
room; Barber/Beauty shop; Library.
Activities Arts & crafts; Cards; Games;
Reading groups; Prayer groups; Movies;
Shopping trips; Social/Cultural gatherings.

SOUTH EASTON

Happiness House Rest Home
11 Nancy Rd, South Easton, MA, 02375-1623
(617) 746-2982
Admin Harry McCabe.
Licensure Rest home. *Beds* 36.
Admissions Requirements Medical
examination; Physician's request.
Staff LPNs 2 (pt); Orderlies 2 (ft), 7 (pt);
Recreational therapists 1 (pt); Activities
coordinators 1 (pt).
Facilities Dining room; Activities room;
Crafts room.
Activities Arts & crafts; Cards; Games; Prayer
groups; Movies; Shopping trips.

SOUTH HADLEY

Falls Nursing Home*
18 Hartford St, South Hadley, MA, 01075
(413) 538-8403
Admin Angelina T Savko.
Licensure Intermediate care. *Beds* 44.
Certified Medicaid.

SOUTH YARMOUTH

Windsor Nursing & Retirement Home
265 N Main St, South Yarmouth, MA, 02664
(617) 394-3514
Admin Judith A Welling. *Medical Dir/Dir of
Nursing* Charles Derrick MD; Virginia
Robinson RN DON.
Licensure Skilled care; Intermediate care. *Beds*
SNF 60; ICF 60. *Certified* Medicaid.
Owner Proprietary Corp (Hannover
Healthcare).

Admissions Requirements Minimum age 21;
Physician's request.
Staff Physicians 1 (pt); RNs 4 (ft), 13 (pt);
LPNs 1 (ft), 4 (pt); Nurses aides 17 (ft), 25
(pt); Physical therapists 1 (pt); Occupational
therapists 1 (pt); Activities coordinators 2
(ft); Dietitians 1 (pt); Dentists 1 (pt);
Podiatrists 1 (pt).
Facilities Dining room; Physical therapy
room; Activities room; Chapel; Crafts room;
Laundry room; Barber/Beauty shop.
Activities Arts & crafts; Cards; Games;
Reading groups; Prayer groups; Movies;
Shopping trips; Social/Cultural gatherings;
Sensory.

SOUTHBRIDGE

Liberty House Nursing Home*
84 Chapin St, Southbridge, MA, 01550
(617) 765-9133
Admin James A Neustadt.
Licensure Skilled care; Intermediate care. *Beds*
246. *Certified* Medicaid.

SPENCER

Coventry Hall Nursing Home*
500 Main St, Spencer, MA, 01562
(617) 885-2277
Admin Glynes Hunter.
Licensure Intermediate care. *Beds* 31.
Certified Medicaid.

Lincoln Hill Manor Rest Home*
53 Lincoln St, Spencer, MA, 01562
(617) 885-3338
Admin Joan M Lynds. *Medical Dir/Dir of
Nursing* Dr Richard Fowler.
Licensure Rest home. *Beds* 30.
Admissions Requirements Minimum age 30;
Medical examination; Physician's request.
Staff Physicians 5 (ft); RNs 1 (pt);
Recreational therapists 1 (ft); Dietitians 1
(pt); Podiatrists 1 (pt).
Facilities Dining room; Laundry room.
Activities Cards; Games; Reading groups;
Prayer groups.

SPRINGFIELD

Beech Manor Rest Home
38 Warner St, Springfield, MA, 01108
(413) 733-7162
Admin Ellen N Rice.
Licensure Rest home level II. *Beds* ICF; 12.
Certified Medicaid.
Owner Privately owned.
Admissions Requirements Minimum age 50;
Females only; Medical examination;
Physician's request.
Staff LPNs 1 (pt); Nurses aides 1 (pt);
Activities coordinators 1 (pt).
Facilities Dining room; Activities room;
Crafts room.
Activities Arts & crafts; Cards; Games;
Reading groups; Shopping trips.

Blue Spruce Rest Home*
175 Bowdoin St, Springfield, MA, 01109
(413) 739-2373
Admin Nathan H Rice.
Licensure Rest home. *Beds* 19.
Admissions Requirements Medical
examination; Physician's request.
Facilities Dining room; Activities room;
Laundry room; Barber/Beauty shop.
Activities Arts & crafts; Cards; Games;
Shopping trips.

Campbell's Ingersoll Rest Home
29 Ingersoll Grove St, Springfield, MA, 01109
(413) 732-1068
Admin Collin A Campbell. *Medical Dir/Dir of
Nursing* Marilyn Campbell.
Licensure Rest home. *Beds* Resident care
facility 36. *Certified* Medicaid.

Owner Proprietary Corp.
Admissions Requirements Minimum age 50;
Medical examination.
Staff RNs; Nurses aides; Activities
coordinators; Dietitians; Social services.
Facilities Dining room; Activities room;
Crafts room; Laundry room.
Activities Arts & crafts; Cards; Games;
Reading groups; Prayer groups; Movies.

Chapin Center
200 Kendall St, Springfield, MA, 01104
(413) 737-4756
Admin James Clifford.
Beds 160.
Owner Proprietary Corp (Genesis Health
Ventures).

Chapin Center Skilled Nursing Facility*
200 Kendall St, Springfield, MA, 01104
(413) 737-4756
Admin Robert Denson. *Medical Dir/Dir of
Nursing* Alphonse Calvanese MD.
Licensure Skilled care; Intermediate care. *Beds*
160. *Certified* Medicaid.
Admissions Requirements Minimum age 55;
Medical examination; Physician's request.
Staff Physicians 13 (pt); RNs 5 (ft), 10 (pt);
LPNs 7 (ft), 8 (pt); Orderlies 1 (ft), 1 (pt);
Nurses aides 31 (ft), 22 (pt); Physical
therapists 1 (pt); Occupational therapists 1
(pt); Speech therapists 1 (pt); Activities
coordinators 1 (ft); Dietitians 1 (pt); Dentists
1 (pt); Ophthalmologists 1 (pt); Podiatrists 1
(pt).
Facilities Dining room; Physical therapy
room; Activities room; Crafts room; Barber/
Beauty shop.
Activities Arts & crafts; Cards; Games;
Reading groups; Prayer groups; Movies;
Social/Cultural gatherings; Reality
orientation.

Chestnut Knoll Inc
471 Chestnut St, Springfield, MA, 01107
(413) 732-7817
Admin Sandra Golec.
Licensure Intermediate care; Retirement
home; Level III Infirmary. *Beds* ICF 13.
Certified Medicaid.
Owner Nonprofit Corp.
Admissions Requirements Minimum age 65;
Females only; Medical examination.
Staff Physicians 1 (pt); RNs 1 (ft); LPNs 4
(ft); Nurses aides 6 (ft); Activities
coordinators; Dietitians 1 (pt);
Ophthalmologists.
Facilities Dining room; Activities room;
Chapel; Laundry room; Barber/Beauty shop;
Library.
Activities Cards; Games; Reading groups;
Movies; Shopping trips; Social/Cultural
gatherings; Gardening.

Crescent Hill Nursing Center*
370 Pine St, Springfield, MA, 01105
(413) 781-5290
Admin David Johnson. *Medical Dir/Dir of
Nursing* Jack Skelskie MD.
Licensure Skilled care; Intermediate care. *Beds*
SNF 41; ICF 129. *Certified* Medicaid.
Owner Proprietary Corp (Health Care &
Retirement Corp).
Admissions Requirements Minimum age 16.
Staff Physicians 21 (pt); RNs 6 (ft), 2 (pt);
LPNs 8 (ft), 8 (pt); Orderlies 2 (ft), 1 (pt);
Nurses aides 24 (ft), 27 (pt); Physical
therapists 2 (ft), 1 (pt); Reality therapists 1
(ft), 1 (pt); Occupational therapists 1 (pt);
Speech therapists 1 (pt); Activities
coordinators 2 (pt); Dietitians 1 (pt); Dentists
1 (pt); Ophthalmologists 1 (pt); Podiatrists 1
(pt); Audiologists 1 (pt).
Facilities Dining room; Physical therapy
room; Activities room; Crafts room; Laundry
room; Barber/Beauty shop.

Activities Arts & crafts; Cards; Games;
Reading groups; Prayer groups; Movies;
Shopping trips; Social/Cultural gatherings.

Evergreen Place A Rest Home
175 Mill St, Springfield, MA, 01108
(413) 737-5964
Admin Warren C Laborde. *Medical Dir/Dir of
Nursing* Shirley J Laborde.
Licensure Rest home. *Beds* 18. *Certified*
Medicaid.
Owner Privately owned.
Admissions Requirements Minimum age 21;
Medical examination; Physician's request.
Staff RNs.
Facilities Dining room; Activities room;
Crafts room; Laundry room; Barber/Beauty
shop.
Activities Arts & crafts; Cards; Games; Prayer
groups; Shopping trips.

Hahn Rest Home*
178 Thompson St, Springfield, MA, 01109
(413) 737-5124
Admin Kathleen M Hahn.
Licensure Rest home. *Beds* 13.

Hampden House Retirement Home
190 Kendall St, Springfield, MA, 01104
(413) 733-6617
Admin Bestey Brooks. *Medical Dir/Dir of
Nursing* Alphonse Calvanese.
Licensure Rest home. *Beds* 160.
Owner Proprietary Corp.
Admissions Requirements Minimum age 50;
Medical examination.
Staff LPNs 3 (ft), 2 (pt); Nurses aides 9 (ft), 1
(pt); Activities coordinators 1 (ft); Dietitians
1 (ft).
Facilities Dining room; Activities room;
Laundry room; Barber/Beauty shop.
Activities Arts & crafts; Games; Reading
groups; Prayer groups; Movies; Shopping
trips; Social/Cultural gatherings.

Hilltop Rest Home*
103 Bowdoin St, Springfield, MA, 01109
(413) 739-6377
Admin Edith Gibby.
Licensure Rest home. *Beds* 19.

Hodges Rest Home*
69 Bowdoin St, Springfield, MA, 01109
(413) 788-4850
Admin Della M Hodges.
Licensure Rest home. *Beds* 14.

Hurstdale Rest Home*
181 Acorn St, Springfield, MA, 01109
(413) 734-0177
Admin M Z Barksdale. *Medical Dir/Dir of
Nursing* Dr Jack Skelskie.
Licensure Rest home. *Beds* 15.
Admissions Requirements Minimum age 21;
Medical examination; Physician's request.
Staff Physicians 1 (pt); RNs 1 (pt); LPNs 2
(pt); Orderlies 1 (pt); Nurses aides 2 (pt);
Recreational therapists 1 (pt); Occupational
therapists 1 (pt); Activities coordinators 1
(pt); Dietitians 1 (pt); Podiatrists 1 (pt).
Affiliation Afro-American
Facilities Dining room; Activities room;
Crafts room; Library.
Activities Arts & crafts; Cards; Games;
Reading groups; Prayer groups; Shopping
trips; Social/Cultural gatherings.

Ivy Manor Rest Home*
368 St James Ave, Springfield, MA, 01109
(413) 788-6783
Admin Roger F Thomas.
Licensure Rest home. *Beds* 12.

Maple Hill Rest Home*
156 Mill St, Springfield, MA, 01108
(413) 737-2148
Admin Michael H Joseph.
Licensure Rest home. *Beds* 32.

Pine Manor Nursing Home*
1190 Liberty St, Springfield, MA, 01104
(413) 781-0831
Admin Joseph P Kennedy Jr.
Licensure Intermediate care. *Beds* 101.
 Certified Medicaid.
Owner Proprietary Corp (Health Care &
 Retirement Corp).
Admissions Requirements Minimum age 21;
 Medical examination.
Facilities Dining room; Activities room;
 Laundry room; Barber/Beauty shop.
Activities Arts & crafts; Cards; Games;
 Movies; Shopping trips; Social/Cultural
 gatherings.

Primus Mason Manor
74 Walnut St, Springfield, MA, 01105
(413) 733-1517
Admin Elizabeth L Hogan.
Licensure Rest home. *Beds* 20.
Admissions Requirements Minimum age 60;
 Medical examination; Physician's request.
Staff Physicians 1 (pt); LPNs 1 (pt); Nurses
 aides 2 (pt); Activities coordinators 1 (pt);
 Dietitians 1 (pt); Dentists 1 (pt);
 Ophthalmologists 1 (pt); Podiatrists 1 (pt).
Facilities Dining room; Activities room;
 Laundry room; Barber/Beauty shop; Library.
Activities Arts & crafts; Cards; Games;
 Movies; Shopping trips; Social/Cultural
 gatherings.

Ring Nursing Home—Ridgewood*
22 Ridgewood Pl, Springfield, MA, 01105
(413) 781-1141
Admin Sheila M Leahey.
Licensure Intermediate care. *Beds* 126.
 Certified Medicaid.
Staff RNs 1 (ft), 1 (pt); LPNs 7 (ft), 7 (pt);
 Nurses aides 25 (ft), 18 (pt); Activities
 coordinators 1 (ft), 1 (pt); Dietitians 1 (pt).
Facilities Dining room; Physical therapy
 room; Activities room; Chapel; Laundry
 room; Barber/Beauty shop.
Activities Arts & crafts; Cards; Games;
 Reading groups; Prayer groups; Movies;
 Social/Cultural gatherings.

Ring Nursing Home—South
155 Mill St, Springfield, MA, 01105
(413) 734-1122
Admin Jean Clifford.
Licensure Skilled care; Intermediate care. *Beds*
 110. *Certified* Medicaid.
Staff RNs 6 (ft), 2 (pt); LPNs 4 (ft), 2 (pt);
 Nurses aides 28 (ft), 30 (pt); Physical
 therapists 1 (pt); Recreational therapists 2
 (ft); Dietitians 1 (pt).

St Lukes Home*
79-85 Spring St, Springfield, MA, 01105
(413) 736-5494
Admin Sr Mary of Providence.
Licensure Rest home. *Beds* 92.
Admissions Requirements Minimum age 60;
 Medical examination; Physician's request.
Staff Physicians 1 (pt); RNs 2 (ft); LPNs 1
 (ft), 1 (pt); Nurses aides 8 (ft), 8 (pt);
 Activities coordinators 1 (ft); Dietitians 1
 (pt); Podiatrists 1 (pt).
Affiliation Roman Catholic
Facilities Dining room; Activities room;
 Chapel; Laundry room; Barber/Beauty shop.
Activities Arts & crafts; Cards; Games;
 Reading groups; Prayer groups; Movies;
 Shopping trips; Social/Cultural gatherings.

Springfield Municipal Hospital*
1400 State St, Springfield, MA, 01109
(413) 787-6700
Admin George H Lane.
Licensure Skilled care; Intermediate care. *Beds*
 438. *Certified* Medicaid.
Admissions Requirements Medical
 examination; Physician's request.

Facilities Dining room; Physical therapy
 room; Activities room; Chapel; Crafts room;
 Laundry room; Barber/Beauty shop; Library.
Activities Arts & crafts; Cards; Games; Prayer
 groups; Movies; Shopping trips; Social/
 Cultural gatherings.

Spruce Manor Nursing Home*
388 Central St, Springfield, MA, 01105
(413) 734-4986
Admin Amelia Fournier.
Licensure Intermediate care. *Beds* 150.
 Certified Medicaid.
Owner Proprietary Corp (Health Care &
 Retirement Corp).

Stone Acre Rest Home Inc*
120 Mill St, Springfield, MA, 01108
(413) 734-3054
Admin Conrad E Wertheim.
Licensure Rest home. *Beds* 26.
Admissions Requirements Minimum age 21;
 Medical examination.
Staff Physicians 1 (pt); LPNs 1 (ft); Nurses
 aides 3 (ft), 1 (pt); Activities coordinators 1
 (pt); Dietitians 1 (pt).
Facilities Dining room; Activities room;
 Crafts room; Laundry room; Barber/Beauty
 shop.
Activities Cards; Games; Movies; Shopping
 trips.

STONEHAM

Arnold House Inc
490 William St, Stoneham, MA, 02180
(617) 438-1116
Admin Loretta Marino.
Licensure Intermediate care. *Beds* 22.
Owner Proprietary Corp.
Admissions Requirements Females only.
Staff Physicians; RNs; LPNs; Nurses aides;
 Physical therapists; Recreational therapists;
 Occupational therapists; Activities
 coordinators; Dietitians; Dentists;
 Ophthalmologists; Podiatrists.
Facilities Dining room; Living rooms; Music
 room; Solarium.
Activities Arts & crafts; Cards; Games; Prayer
 groups; Movies; Shopping trips; Social/
 Cultural gatherings.

Bear Hill Nursing Center at Wakefield*
Enter 11 North St, Stoneham, MA, 02180
Medical Dir/Dir of Nursing John Danis MD.
Admissions Requirements Minimum age 21;
 Physician's request.
Staff Physicians; RNs 10 (ft); LPNs 10 (ft);
 Orderlies 2 (ft); Nurses aides 30 (ft);
 Physical therapists 1 (pt); Reality therapists
 1 (pt); Recreational therapists 2 (ft);
 Occupational therapists 1 (pt); Speech
 therapists 1 (pt); Activities coordinators 1
 (ft); Dietitians 1 (pt); Dentists 1 (pt);
 Ophthalmologists 1 (pt); Podiatrists 1 (pt);
 Audiologists 1 (pt).
Facilities Dining room; Physical therapy
 room; Activities room; Chapel; Crafts room;
 Laundry room; Barber/Beauty shop; Library;
 Pub; Greenhouse; Cinema.
Activities Arts & crafts; Cards; Games;
 Reading groups; Prayer groups; Movies;
 Shopping trips; Social/Cultural gatherings.

Home for Aged People*
32 Franklin St, Stoneham, MA, 02180
(617) 438-0580
Licensure Rest home. *Beds* 11.
Admissions Requirements Minimum age 65;
 Medical examination; Physician's request.
Staff Dietitians 1 (pt); Podiatrists 1 (pt).
Facilities Dining room; Laundry room.

Sunshine Nursing Home Inc
12 Benton St, Stoneham, MA, 02180
(617) 438-9305, 438-9357
Admin Lillian I Price. *Medical Dir/Dir of
 Nursing* Dr Hinnendael; Marie Walker.

Licensure Intermediate care. *Beds* ICF 36.
 Certified Medicaid.
Owner Proprietary Corp.
Admissions Requirements Minimum age 18.
Staff RNs 2 (ft), 1 (pt); LPNs 2 (ft), 1 (pt);
 Nurses aides 5 (ft), 7 (pt); Activities
 coordinators 1 (ft); Dietitians 1 (pt).
Facilities Dining room; Activities room;
 Laundry room; Barber/Beauty shop.
Activities Arts & crafts; Cards; Games;
 Movies; Shopping trips.

STOUGHTON

Blue Hills Convalescent Home
1044 Park St, Stoughton, MA, 02072
(617) 344-7300
Admin Judith D Cunningham. *Medical Dir/
 Dir of Nursing* Dr Karl Stammen; Barbara
 Despres RN.
Licensure Skilled care; Intermediate care. *Beds*
 SNF 41; ICF 60. *Certified* Medicaid.
Owner Proprietary Corp (Hillhaven Corp).
Staff Physicians; RNs; LPNs; Orderlies;
 Nurses aides; Physical therapists;
 Recreational therapists; Occupational
 therapists; Speech therapists; Activities
 coordinators; Dietitians; Podiatrists.
Facilities Dining room; Activities room;
 Barber/Beauty shop.
Activities Arts & crafts; Cards; Games; Prayer
 groups; Movies; Social/Cultural gatherings.

Francis T Crimmins Rest Home*
239 Pleasant St, Stoughton, MA, 02072
(617) 344-2451
Admin Lorraine Roche.
Licensure Rest home. *Beds* 20.
Admissions Requirements Females only;
 Medical examination.

Norfolk Nursing Home*
94 Prospect St, Stoughton, MA, 02072
(617) 344-3645
Admin Catherine Warner.
Licensure Intermediate care. *Beds* 59.
 Certified Medicaid.

STOW

Stow Rest Home*
Wheeler Rd, Stow, MA, 01775
(617) 897-7923
Admin Charles L Alves.
Licensure Rest home. *Beds* 18.

Whitney Homestead Rest Home*
Great Rd, Stow, MA, 01775
(617) 756-1515
Admin Bonnie Fredette.
Licensure Skilled care; Intermediate care. *Beds*
 SNF 40; ICF 40.

SUDBURY

Sudbury Pines Nursing Home
642 Boston Post Rd, Sudbury, MA, 01776
(617) 443-9000
Admin Roberta C Henderson. *Medical Dir/Dir
 of Nursing* Dr Melvin Kramer; Ellen
 Pennington DON.
Licensure Skilled care; Intermediate care. *Beds*
 SNF 40; ICF 40. *Certified* Medicaid.
Owner Proprietary Corp.
Admissions Requirements Minimum age 21;
 Medical examination; Physician's request.
Staff Physicians 3 (pt); RNs 4 (ft), 8 (pt);
 LPNs 9 (pt); Orderlies; Nurses aides 19 (ft),
 25 (pt); Physical therapists 1 (ft), 1 (pt);
 Reality therapists 1 (ft), 1 (pt); Recreational
 therapists 1 (ft), 1 (pt); Occupational
 therapists 1 (pt); Speech therapists 1 (pt);
 Activities coordinators 1 (ft), 3 (pt);
 Dietitians 1 (pt); Dentists 1 (pt);
 Ophthalmologists 1 (pt); Podiatrists 1 (pt);
 Dentist 1 (pt).

Languages Italian, French, Spanish, Sign, Hebrew, Yiddish
Facilities Dining room; Physical therapy room; Activities room; Chapel; Crafts room; Laundry room; Barber/Beauty shop; Library; Patient lounges; Child care rooms; Alarmed & secured areas inside & outside.
Activities Arts & crafts; Cards; Games; Reading groups; Prayer groups; Movies; Shopping trips; Resident council; Monthly newspaper; Current events; Baking; Child day care.

SUNDERLAND

Cozy Corner Nursing Home Inc*
Old Amherst Rd, PO Box 405, Sunderland, MA, 01375
(413) 665-2740
Admin I James Bednarski III. *Medical Dir/Dir of Nursing* Samuel Hunter MD.
Licensure Intermediate care. *Beds* 57. *Certified* Medicaid.
Admissions Requirements Minimum age 21; Medical examination.
Staff Physicians 14 (pt); RNs 4 (ft), 3 (pt); LPNs 1 (ft), 1 (pt); Nurses aides 12 (ft), 8 (pt); Physical therapists 1 (pt); Recreational therapists 1 (pt); Occupational therapists 1 (pt); Speech therapists 1 (pt); Activities coordinators 1 (ft); Dietitians 1 (pt); Dentists 1 (pt); Podiatrists 1 (pt).
Facilities Dining room; Activities room; Chapel; Crafts room; Laundry room; Barber/Beauty shop.
Activities Arts & crafts; Cards; Games; Reading groups; Prayer groups; Movies; Shopping trips.

SWAMPSCOTT

Jewish Rehabilitation Center for Aged of the North Shore Inc
330 Paradise Rd, Swampscott, MA, 01907
(617) 598-5310
Admin Greg Aqua. *Medical Dir/Dir of Nursing* David Levy MD; Carolann Crowe.
Licensure Intermediate care. *Beds* ICF 171. *Certified* Medicaid.
Owner Nonprofit organization/foundation.
Admissions Requirements Minimum age 65; Medical examination; Physician's request.
Staff Physicians 1 (pt); RNs 12 (ft), 6 (pt); LPNs 7 (ft), 9 (pt); Orderlies 2 (ft), 1 (pt); Nurses aides 58 (ft), 15 (pt); Physical therapists 1 (pt); Recreational therapists 3 (ft), 2 (pt); Occupational therapists 1 (pt); Speech therapists 1 (pt); Activities coordinators 1 (ft); Dietitians 1 (ft); Dentists 1 (pt); Ophthalmologists 1 (pt); Podiatrists 1 (pt).
Affiliation Jewish
Facilities Dining room; Physical therapy room; Activities room; Chapel; Crafts room; Laundry room; Barber/Beauty shop; Library.
Activities Arts & crafts; Cards; Games; Reading groups; Prayer groups; Movies.

SWANSEA

Country Gardens Nursing Home
2045 Grand Army Hwy, Swansea, MA, 02777
(617) 379-9700
Admin Scott M Sanborn. *Medical Dir/Dir of Nursing* Dr Daniel Sullivan; Elaine A Downs RN MS.
Licensure Skilled care. *Beds* SNF 86. *Certified* Medicaid; Medicare.
Owner Proprietary Corp (Hillhaven Corp).
Languages Portuguese
Facilities Dining room; Physical therapy room; Activities room; Chapel; Laundry room; Barber/Beauty shop.
Activities Arts & crafts; Cards; Games; Reading groups; Prayer groups; Movies; Social/Cultural gatherings; Outings.

Gardner's Grove Nursing Home*
924 Gardner's Neck Rd, Swansea, MA, 02777
(617) 674-1717
Admin Evelyn H Purdy.
Licensure Intermediate care. *Beds* 27. *Certified* Medicaid.

Swansea Rest Home Inc
115 Wilbur Ave, Swansea, MA, 02777
(617) 678-8661
Admin Marion G Albritton. *Medical Dir/Dir of Nursing* Paula Robidoux RN.
Licensure Rest home. *Beds* 16. *Certified* Medicaid.
Owner Proprietary Corp.
Admissions Requirements Minimum age 21; Medical examination.
Staff Physicians 1 (pt); RNs 1 (pt); Nurses aides; Activities coordinators 1 (pt); Dietitians 1 (pt); Dentists; Ophthalmologists 1 (pt); Podiatrists.
Languages French
Facilities Dining room; Activities room; Laundry room.
Activities Arts & crafts; Cards; Games; Prayer groups; Movies; Shopping trips.

TAUNTON

Paul A Dever State School*
1380 Bay St, Box 631, Taunton, MA, 02780
(617) 824-5881
Admin Anne Lewis.
Licensure Skilled care. *Beds* 20.
Owner Publicly owned.

Longmeadow of Taunton A Skilled Facility
68 Dean St, Taunton, MA, 02780
(617) 824-1467
Licensure Skilled care; Intermediate care. *Beds* 100. *Certified* Medicaid.

Marian Manor of Taunton*
33 Summer St, Taunton, MA, 02780
(617) 822-4885
Admin Sr Marie Therese.
Licensure Intermediate care. *Beds* 83. *Certified* Medicaid.

Taunton Female Charity Association Inc*
96 Broadway, Taunton, MA, 02780
(617) 824-7747
Admin Mary A Conteras.
Licensure Charitable home. *Beds* 12.
Admissions Requirements Females only.

Taunton Nursing Home*
350 Norton Ave, Taunton, MA, 02780
(617) 822-6404
Admin Peter F Tardo.
Licensure Intermediate care. *Beds* 39. *Certified* Medicaid.

Wedgemere Convalescent Home
146 Dean St, Taunton, MA, 02780
(617) 823-0767
Admin Ruth A Vital. *Medical Dir/Dir of Nursing* David Pottier MD; Mary Hennique RN.
Licensure Skilled care. *Beds* 82. *Certified* Medicaid; Medicare.
Owner Proprietary Corp (Beverly Enterprises).
Admissions Requirements Minimum age 21.
Staff RNs 5 (ft); LPNs 8 (ft), 4 (pt); Orderlies 1 (ft); Nurses aides 20 (ft), 16 (pt); Recreational therapists 1 (ft); Dietitians 2 (pt).
Facilities Dining room; Physical therapy room; Activities room; Crafts room; Laundry room; Barber/Beauty shop; Library.
Activities Arts & crafts; Cards; Games; Reading groups; Prayer groups; Movies; Shopping trips; Social/Cultural gatherings; Pet visits.

TEMPLETON

Baldwinville Nursing Home*
Hospital Rd, Baldwinville, Templeton, MA, 01436
(617) 939-2196
Admin Leighton S Cheney.
Licensure Skilled care; Intermediate care. *Beds* 82. *Certified* Medicaid.

TEWKSBURY

Casa Grande Long-Term Care Facility*
10 Erlin Terrace, Tewksbury, MA, 01876
(617) 851-3121
Admin Richard T Forsley.
Licensure Skilled care; Intermediate care. *Beds* 124. *Certified* Medicaid; Medicare.

Castle Nursing Home*
553 North St, Tewksbury, MA, 01876
(617) 851-9621
Admin Benjamin L Benson. *Medical Dir/Dir of Nursing* Dr Ralph LePase.
Licensure Intermediate care. *Beds* 26. *Certified* Medicaid.
Admissions Requirements Minimum age 21; Females only.
Staff Physicians 2 (pt); LPNs 3 (ft), 3 (pt); Nurses aides 7 (ft), 6 (pt); Activities coordinators 2 (pt); Dietitians 1 (ft); Dentists 1 (ft).
Facilities Dining room; Activities room.
Activities Arts & crafts; Cards; Games; Reading groups; Prayer groups; Movies; Shopping trips; Social/Cultural gatherings.

WABAN

Braeburn Nursing Home
20 Kinmonth Rd, Waban, MA, 02168
(617) 332-8481
Admin Peter H DiFoggio. *Medical Dir/Dir of Nursing* Roberta S Golledge.
Licensure Intermediate care. *Beds* ICF 84. *Certified* Medicaid.
Owner Proprietary Corp.
Admissions Requirements Minimum age 40; Medical examination.
Staff RNs 7 (ft), 3 (pt); LPNs 1 (pt); Nurses aides 27 (ft), 4 (pt); Activities coordinators 1 (ft); Dentist 1 (pt); SS 1 (pt).
Languages Italian, Spanish, French
Facilities Dining room; Physical therapy room; Activities room; Chapel; Crafts room; Laundry room; Barber/Beauty shop; Library.
Activities Arts & crafts; Cards; Games; Reading groups; Prayer groups; Movies; Shopping trips; Social/Cultural gatherings.

WAKEFIELD

Elizabeth E Boit Home
5 Bennett St, Wakefield, MA, 01880
(617) 245-0008
Admin B Joy Alderman.
Licensure Rest home. *Beds* 12.
Owner Nonprofit Corp.
Admissions Requirements Minimum age 65; Females only.
Staff Resident Director.
Facilities Dining room; Library; Livingroom.
Activities Arts & crafts; Games; Entertainment; Outings.

Greenview Manor Nursing Home
Bathol St, Wakefield, MA, 01880
(617) 245-7600
Admin Judith J Gordon. *Medical Dir/Dir of Nursing* Alexander Latty MD; Norene Gachienard RN.
Licensure Skilled care; Intermediate care. *Beds* SNF 48; ICF 60. *Certified* Medicaid.
Owner Privately owned.
Admissions Requirements Medical examination; Physician's request.

Staff Physicians 2 (pt); RNs 6 (ft), 7 (pt);
LPNs 3 (ft), 2 (pt); Orderlies 3 (pt); Nurses
aides 25 (ft), 32 (pt); Physical therapists 1
(pt); Recreational therapists 2 (pt);
Occupational therapists 1 (pt); Activities
coordinators 1 (ft); Dietitians 1 (pt); Dentists
1 (pt); Ophthalmologists 4 (pt).
Facilities Dining room; Physical therapy
room; Activities room; Crafts room; Laundry
room; Barber/Beauty shop.
Activities Arts & crafts; Cards; Games; Prayer
groups; Movies; Shopping trips; Social/
Cultural gatherings; Minibus trips.

Greenwood Nursing Home
90 Greenwood St, Wakefield, MA, 01880
(617) 246-0211
Admin Merna E Morse. *Medical Dir/Dir of
Nursing* Claire Carlin.
Licensure Intermediate care. *Beds* ICF 36.
Certified Medicaid.
Owner Proprietary Corp.
Staff RNs 1 (ft); LPNs 2 (ft), 2 (pt); Nurses
aides 6 (ft), 9 (pt); Recreational therapists;
Dietitians 1 (pt).
Facilities Dining room; Activities room;
Laundry room.
Activities Arts & crafts; Cards; Games;
Reading groups; Prayer groups; Movies;
Social/Cultural gatherings.

Kirkwood Nursing Home*
202 Main St, Wakefield, MA, 01880
(617) 245-4129
Admin Bettiann Wells.
Licensure Intermediate care. *Beds* 32.
Certified Medicaid.

Oosterman Rest Home
706 Main St, Wakefield, MA, 01880
(617) 245-4778
Admin Troy Oosterman. *Medical Dir/Dir of
Nursing* Gladys Foster RN.
Licensure Rest home. *Beds* 20.
Owner Privately owned.
Admissions Requirements Females only;
Physician's request.
Staff RNs 1 (ft); LPNs 2 (ft); Nurses aides 6
(ft); Activities coordinators 1 (ft); Dietitians
1 (ft); Ophthalmologists 1 (ft).
Facilities Dining room; Activities room;
Laundry room.
Activities Cards; Prayer groups; Movies;
Exercise.

WALLASTON

Friel Nursing Home Inc
58 Beach St, Wallaston, MA, 02170
(617) 479-7722
Admin Isabel Friel RN. *Medical Dir/Dir of
Nursing* Isabel Friel RN.
Licensure Intermediate care. *Beds* ICF 29.
Certified Medicaid.
Owner Proprietary Corp.
Admissions Requirements Females only;
Medical examination.
Staff Physicians 1 (pt); RNs 1 (ft), 3 (pt);
LPNs 1 (ft), 2 (pt); Nurses aides 5 (ft), 10
(pt); Physical therapists 1 (pt); Reality
therapists 1 (pt); Recreational therapists 1
(ft); Activities coordinators 1 (ft); Dietitians
1 (pt).
Facilities Dining room; Laundry room.
Activities Arts & crafts; Cards; Games;
Reading groups; Prayer groups; Movies;
Shopping trips; Social/Cultural gatherings;
Entertainment; Parties.

WALTHAM

Abbey Forest Nursing Home*
50 Forest St, Waltham, MA, 02154
(617) 893-3453
Admin Patrick J Fahy.
Licensure Intermediate care. *Beds* 40.
Certified Medicaid.

Hopkins Nursing Home*
508 Lexington St, Waltham, MA, 02154
(617) 893-7841
Admin Paul G Hopkins.
Licensure Intermediate care. *Beds* 19.
Certified Medicaid.

Larchwood Lodge Nursing Home*
221 Worcester Lane, Waltham, MA, 02154
(617) 894-4720
Admin G Paul Hopkins.
Licensure Intermediate care. *Beds* 32.
Certified Medicaid.

Lee Rest Home*
222 Bacon St, Waltham, MA, 02154
(617) 894-0645
Admin William F Lee.
Licensure Rest home. *Beds* 27.

The Leland Home
21 Newton St, Waltham, MA, 02154
(617) 893-2557
Admin Maureen T Murray. *Medical Dir/Dir of
Nursing* David Duhme MD.
Licensure Resident care; Supportive care
infirmary. *Beds* Level IV 33 Level III 8.
Certified Medicare.
Owner Nonprofit Corp.
Admissions Requirements Minimum age 65;
Medical examination; Physician's request.
Staff Physicians 32 (pt); RNs 1 (ft), 32 (pt);
LPNs 1 (ft), 32 (pt); Orderlies 32 (pt);
Nurses aides 1 (ft), 32 (pt); Physical
therapists 32 (pt); Reality therapists 32 (pt);
Dentist 1 (pt).
Facilities Dining room; Laundry room;
Barber/Beauty shop; Library; Library
services.
Activities Cards; Games; Social/Cultural
gatherings.

Maristhill Nursing Home
66 Newton St, Waltham, MA, 02154
(617) 893-0240
Admin Anne Dupuis Sr. *Medical Dir/Dir of
Nursing* Dr Joseph Riley; Suzanne O'Brien
RN DON.
Licensure Skilled care; Intermediate care. *Beds*
SNF 82; ICF 41. *Certified* Medicaid.
Owner Nonprofit Corp.

Piety Corner Nursing Home
325 Bacon St, Waltham, MA, 02154
(617) 894-5264
Admin Guy D'Amore.
Licensure Intermediate care. *Beds* 34.
Certified Medicaid.

Prospect Hill Nursing Home
31 Woodland Rd, Waltham, MA, 02154
(617) 893-6916
Admin Vasco A Lima Jr. *Medical Dir/Dir of
Nursing* Albert Levinson.
Licensure Intermediate care. *Beds* 28.
Certified Medicaid; Medicare.
Admissions Requirements Females only;
Medical examination; Physician's request.
Staff RNs 1 (ft); LPNs 4 (ft); Nurses aides 6
(ft); Physical therapists 1 (pt); Reality
therapists 1 (pt); Recreational therapists 1
(pt); Occupational therapists 1 (pt); Speech
therapists 1 (pt); Activities coordinators 1
(ft); Dietitians 1 (pt); Ophthalmologists 1
(pt); Dentist 1 (pt).
Languages French, Spanish.
Facilities Dining room; Activities room;
Laundry room.
Activities Arts & crafts; Cards; Games;
Reading groups; Prayer groups; Movies;
Shopping trips; Social/Cultural gatherings.

Reservoir Nursing Home Inc*
1841 Trapelo Rd, Waltham, MA, 02154
(617) 890-5000
Admin Dorothy S Hill.
Licensure Skilled care; Intermediate care. *Beds*
120. *Certified* Medicaid; Medicare.

Varnum Park Rest Home*
249 Bacon St, Waltham, MA, 02154
(617) 894-3320
Admin Doris M Lee.
Licensure Rest home. *Beds* 31.

Waltham Nursing Home Inc
91 Summer St, Waltham, MA, 02154
(617) 893-6944
Admin Deborah A Hagar. *Medical Dir/Dir of
Nursing* Marilyn Brown.
Licensure Intermediate care. *Beds* ICF 29.
Certified Medicaid.
Owner Proprietary Corp.
Admissions Requirements Females only.
Facilities Dining room; Activities room.
Activities Arts & crafts; Cards; Games;
Reading groups; Prayer groups; Movies;
Shopping trips; Social/Cultural gatherings.

WAREHAM

Lake View Rest Home*
2 Depot St, Wareham, MA, 02538
(617) 295-1440
Admin Sandra McCubrey.
Licensure Rest home. *Beds* 16.

Roland Thatcher Nursing Home*
Main St, Wareham, MA, 02571
(617) 295-1040
Admin Charlotte A Strong.
Licensure Skilled care; Intermediate care. *Beds*
108. *Certified* Medicaid.

WASHINGTON

Maple View Nursing Home*
Lover's Lane Rd, Washington, MA, 01201
(413) 623-8936
Admin Elizabeth Jones.
Licensure Intermediate care. *Beds* 57.
Certified Medicaid.
Owner Proprietary Corp (Health Care &
Retirement Corp).

WATERTOWN

Charlesgate Manor Convalescent Home Inc
590 Main St, Watertown, MA, 02172
(617) 924-1966
Admin Philip M Altsher. *Medical Dir/Dir of
Nursing* Mark B Rohrer; Marcia McNamara.
Licensure Skilled care; Intermediate care. *Beds*
SNF 50; ICF 52. *Certified* Medicaid.
Owner Proprietary Corp.
Admissions Requirements Medical
examination; Physician's request.
Staff Physicians 3 (pt); RNs 3 (ft), 6 (pt);
LPNs 6 (ft), 2 (pt); Orderlies 1 (ft); Nurses
aides 25 (ft), 18 (pt); Physical therapists 1
(pt); Reality therapists 1 (pt); Occupational
therapists 1 (pt); Speech therapists 1 (pt);
Activities coordinators 1, 1 (pt);
Dietitians 1 (pt); Ophthalmologists 1 (pt);
Dentist 1 (pt).
Facilities Dining room; Physical therapy
room; Activities room; Chapel; Laundry
room; Barber/Beauty shop.
Activities Arts & crafts; Cards; Games;
Reading groups; Prayer groups; Movies.

Emerson Convalescent Home Inc
59 Coolidge Hill Rd, Watertown, MA, 02172
(617) 924-1130
Admin Norman J Duffy. *Medical Dir/Dir of
Nursing* Alan M Barron MD; Clare McNally
RN.
Licensure Skilled care; Intermediate care. *Beds*
163. *Certified* Medicaid.
Owner Proprietary Corp.
Admissions Requirements Minimum age 60;
Medical examination.
Staff RNs 8 (ft), 6 (pt); LPNs 11 (ft), 10 (pt);
Orderlies 3 (ft), 3 (pt); Orderlies 70 (ft), 45
(pt); Physical therapists 2 (ft); Reality
therapists 1 (ft); Recreational therapists 2

(ft), 2 (pt); Occupational therapists 1 (ft); Activities coordinators 1 (ft); Dietitians 1 (pt).
Facilities Dining room; Physical therapy room; Activities room; Chapel; Crafts room; Laundry room; Barber/Beauty shop.
Activities Arts & crafts; Cards; Games; Reading groups; Prayer groups; Movies; Shopping trips; Social/Cultural gatherings.

Marshall Home
120 Mount Auburn St, Watertown, MA, 02172
(617) 924-4510
Admin Julie Brandlen.
Licensure Rest home. *Beds* Rest home 19. *Certified* Medicaid.
Owner Nonprofit Corp.
Admissions Requirements Minimum age 65; Medical examination.
Staff RNs 1 (pt); Nurses aides 2 (ft), 6 (pt); Recreational therapists 1 (ft).
Facilities Dining room; Activities room; Laundry room; Barber/Beauty shop; Living rooms; Patio; Sitting room.
Activities Arts & crafts; Cards; Games; Movies; Shopping trips; Social/Cultural gatherings; Exercise class; Intergenerational events.

WAYLAND

Kathryn Barton Nursing Home*
373 Commonwealth Rd, Wayland, MA, 01778
(617) 653-5401
Admin Susan Corman Burnett. *Medical Dir/ Dir of Nursing* Joyce Vettraino MD.
Licensure Skilled care. *Beds* 55. *Certified* Medicaid; Medicare.
Staff Physicians 1 (pt); RNs 4 (ft), 3 (pt); LPNs 2 (ft), 6 (pt); Nurses aides 24 (ft), 12 (pt); Physical therapists 1 (pt); Speech therapists 1 (pt); Activities coordinators 1 (ft); Dietitians 1 (pt); Dentists 1 (pt); Podiatrists 1 (pt).
Facilities Dining room; Physical therapy room; Crafts room; Laundry room; Barber/ Beauty shop.
Activities Arts & crafts; Games; Prayer groups; Movies; Shopping trips; Social/Cultural gatherings; Sculpture group; Painting class; Weekly cookout in summer; Musical group; Exercise aerobics.

Cochituate Nursing Home Inc
188 Commonwealth Rd, Wayland, MA, 01778
(617) 653-8500
Admin Alan A Guidrey. *Medical Dir/Dir of Nursing* Sandra O'Leary RN.
Licensure Intermediate care. *Beds* ICF 40. *Certified* Medicaid.
Owner Proprietary Corp.
Admissions Requirements Minimum age 65.
Staff RNs 3 (ft), 2 (pt); LPNs 4 (ft), 1 (pt); Nurses aides 8 (ft), 8 (pt); Activities coordinators 1 (ft); Dietitians 1 (pt).
Facilities Dining room; Physical therapy room; Activities room; Laundry room; Barber/Beauty shop.
Activities Arts & crafts; Cards; Games; Reading groups; Shopping trips; Social/ Cultural gatherings.

WEBSTER

Oakwood Convalescent Home*
86 Hartley St, Webster, MA, 01570-1699
(617) 943-3889
Admin Daniel A O'Neil.
Licensure Skilled care; Intermediate care. *Beds* 81. *Certified* Medicaid.
Owner Proprietary Corp (Hillhaven Corp).
Admissions Requirements Minimum age 21.
Staff Physicians; RNs 4 (ft), 2 (pt); LPNs 3 (ft), 4 (pt); Orderlies; Nurses aides; Physical therapists; Occupational therapists; Speech

therapists; Activities coordinators; Dietitians; Dentists; Ophthalmologists; Podiatrists; Audiologists.
Facilities Dining room; Activities room; Chapel; Laundry room; Barber/Beauty shop.
Activities Arts & crafts; Cards; Games; Reading groups; Movies; Shopping trips; Social/Cultural gatherings.

Webster Manor LTCF*
749 School St, Webster, MA, 10570
(617) 949-0644
Admin Richard Wentzel.
Licensure Skilled care; Intermediate care. *Beds* 123. *Certified* Medicaid.
Admissions Requirements Minimum age 21.
Staff Physicians 1 (pt); Orderlies 2 (ft); Physical therapists 1 (ft), 1 (pt); Reality therapists 1 (pt); Recreational therapists 1 (pt); Occupational therapists 1 (ft), 1 (pt); Speech therapists 1 (pt); Activities coordinators 1 (ft); Dietitians 1 (pt); Dentists 1 (pt); Ophthalmologists 1 (pt); Podiatrists 1 (pt); Audiologists 1 (pt).
Facilities Dining room; Physical therapy room; Activities room; Chapel; Crafts room; Laundry room; Barber/Beauty shop; Library.
Activities Arts & crafts; Cards; Games; Reading groups; Prayer groups; Movies; Shopping trips; Social/Cultural gatherings.

WELLESLEY

Newton & Wellesley Nursing Home
694 Worcester Rd, Wellesley, MA, 02181
(617) 237-6400
Admin Muriel Baum. *Medical Dir/Dir of Nursing* David Kaufman MD; Mary Gallo RN.
Licensure Skilled care; Intermediate care. *Beds* 120 (includes 34 Alzheimer's patients). *Certified* Medicaid; Medicare.
Owner Proprietary Corp (Hillhaven Corp).
Admissions Requirements Medical examination.
Staff RNs 8 (ft), 10 (pt); LPNs 6 (ft), 4 (pt); Orderlies 4 (ft); Nurses aides 20 (ft), 30 (pt); Recreational therapists 3 (ft); Dietitians 1 (pt).
Languages French, Italian, Yiddish, Spanish
Facilities Dining room; Activities room; Crafts room; Laundry room; Barber/Beauty shop.
Activities Arts & crafts; Cards; Games; Reading groups; Prayer groups; Movies; Shopping trips; Social/Cultural gatherings; Music therapy.

Wellesley Manor Nursing Home
878 Worcester St, Wellesley, MA, 02181
(617) 235-6699
Admin Joanne Cooper.
Licensure Skilled care. *Beds* 97. *Certified* Medicare.
Owner Proprietary Corp (Beverly Enterprises).
Facilities Dining room; Physical therapy room; Activities room; Crafts room; Laundry room; Barber/Beauty shop.
Activities Arts & crafts; Cards; Games; Reading groups; Prayer groups; Movies.

WEST BOYLSTON

Oakdale Nursing Home
86 N Main St, West Boylston, MA, 01583-1130
(617) 835-6076
Admin David H Oriol.
Licensure Skilled care; Intermediate care. *Beds* 80. *Certified* Medicaid.

WEST BROOKFIELD

Brook Haven Rest Home*
Main St, West Brookfield, MA, 01585
(617) 867-3325
Admin Madaline D Smith-Papison.

Licensure Rest home. *Beds* 22.

Quaboag Nursing Home*
32 Main St, West Brookfield, MA, 01585
(617) 867-7716
Admin James J Moran.
Licensure Skilled care; Intermediate care. *Beds* 129. *Certified* Medicaid.

Westbrook Heights Rest Home
PO Box 581, Brookfield Rd, West Brookfield, MA, 01585
(617) 867-2062
Admin Annette Dorman. *Medical Dir/Dir of Nursing* Richard Fowler MD.
Licensure Intermediate care. *Beds* ICF 26. *Certified* Medicaid; Medicare.
Owner Privately owned.
Admissions Requirements Minimum age 35; Medical examination; Physician's request.
Staff Physicians 2 (pt); RNs 1 (pt); Orderlies 3 (ft); Nurses aides 2 (ft), 2 (pt); Activities coordinators 1 (ft); Dietitians 1 (pt); Dentists 1 (pt); Ophthalmologists 1 (pt).
Facilities Dining room; Activities room; Crafts room; Laundry room; Barber/Beauty shop.
Activities Arts & crafts; Cards; Games; Prayer groups; Movies; Shopping trips; Social/ Cultural gatherings.

WEST NEWTON

Newton Convalescent Home
25 Armory St, West Newton, MA, 02165
(617) 969-2300
Admin George Elkins. *Medical Dir/Dir of Nursing* Dr David Kaufman; Lorene Welsh RN DON.
Licensure Skilled care; Intermediate care. *Beds* SNF 82; ICF 41. *Certified* Medicaid.
Owner Proprietary Corp (Beverly Enterprises).

WEST ROXBURY

Deutsches Altenheim Inc
2222 Centre St, West Roxbury, MA, 02132
(617) 325-1230
Admin Donna Lee McLean. *Medical Dir/Dir of Nursing* Dr Robert Mullins; Carolyn Anderson RN.
Licensure Intermediate care. *Beds* 40. *Certified* Medicaid.
Owner Nonprofit Corp.
Admissions Requirements Minimum age 65; Medical examination; Physician's request.
Staff RNs 3 (ft), 1 (pt); LPNs 3 (ft), 1 (pt); Nurses aides 10 (ft), 9 (pt); Activities coordinators 1 (ft); Dietitians 1 (pt).
Languages German
Affiliation German Ladies Aid Society
Facilities Dining room; Activities room; Chapel; Crafts room; Laundry room; Barber/ Beauty shop; Library; 12 Acres.
Activities Arts & crafts; Cards; Games; Reading groups; Prayer groups; Movies; Shopping trips; Social/Cultural gatherings; Reality orientation; Choir; German cultural activities.

WEST SPRINGFIELD

Riverdale Gardens Nursing Home Inc
42 Prospect Ave, West Springfield, MA, 01089
(413) 733-3151
Admin James Cameron McNeill. *Medical Dir/ Dir of Nursing* Laurie A McNeill DON.
Licensure Skilled care; Intermediate care. *Beds* SNF 84; ICF 84. *Certified* Medicaid; Medicare.
Owner Proprietary Corp.
Facilities Dining room; Physical therapy room; Activities room; Crafts room; Laundry room; Barber/Beauty shop; Library.
Activities Arts & crafts; Cards; Games; Reading groups; Prayer groups; Movies; Shopping trips; Social/Cultural gatherings.

West Springfield Nursing Home
217 Westfield St, PO Box 1017, West
Springfield, MA, 01089
(413) 788-6126
Admin Ronald Slosek. *Medical Dir/Dir of
Nursing* Joseph T Bagamary MD.
Licensure Skilled care. *Beds* SNF 120.
Certified Medicaid.
Owner Privately owned.
Admissions Requirements Minimum age 21.
Staff RNs 7 (ft), 4 (pt); LPNs 3 (ft), 4 (pt);
Orderlies 2 (ft); Nurses aides 40 (ft), 20 (pt);
Physical therapists 1 (pt); Reality therapists
1 (pt); Occupational therapists 1 (pt); Speech
therapists 1 (pt); Activities coordinators 1
(ft); Dietitians 1 (pt); Ophthalmologists 1
(pt).
Facilities Dining room; Activities room;
Crafts room; Laundry room; Barber/Beauty
shop; Library.
Activities Arts & crafts; Cards; Games; Prayer
groups; Movies; Shopping trips; Social/
Cultural gatherings.

WEST UPTON

Knowlton Manor Nursing Home
Box 453, 145 Main St, West Upton, MA,
01587
(617) 529-6983
Admin Anthony D'Amore. *Medical Dir/Dir of
Nursing* Barbara Sperry RN.
Licensure Intermediate care. *Beds* ICF 37.
Certified Medicaid.
Owner Privately owned.
Admissions Requirements Minimum age 50;
Physician's request.
Staff RNs 2 (ft), 3 (pt); LPNs 2 (pt); Orderlies
1 (ft); Nurses aides 8 (ft), 4 (pt);
Recreational therapists 1 (pt); Activities
coordinators 1 (ft); Dietitians 1 (pt).
Facilities Dining room; Activities room;
Laundry room.
Activities Arts & crafts; Cards; Games;
Reading groups; Prayer groups; Movies;
Shopping trips; Social/Cultural gatherings.

WESTBOROUGH

Beaumont at the Willows
1 Lyman St, Westborough, MA, 01581
366-4730
Admin Stephen R Roizen. *Medical Dir/Dir of
Nursing* Karen Brennan RN DON.
Licensure Skilled care; Intermediate care. *Beds*
140. *Certified* Medicaid; Medicare.
Owner Proprietary Corp.
Staff RNs 11 (ft), 1 (pt); LPNs 10 (ft), 6 (pt);
Orderlies 3 (ft); Nurses aides 32 (ft), 25 (pt);
Recreational therapists 3 (ft); Activities
coordinators 3 (ft).
Facilities Dining room; Physical therapy
room; Activities room; Laundry room;
Barber/Beauty shop.
Activities Arts & crafts; Cards; Games; Reading
groups; Prayer groups; Movies; Shopping
trips; Social/Cultural gatherings.

Westborough Nursing Home*
Colonial Dr, Westborough, MA, 01581
(617) 366-9131
Admin Anthony J Penny. *Medical Dir/Dir of
Nursing* Robert Klugman MD.
Licensure Skilled care; Intermediate care. *Beds*
123. *Certified* Medicaid; Medicare.
Owner Proprietary Corp (Hillhaven Corp).
Staff RNs 6 (ft), 14 (pt); LPNs 4 (ft), 5 (pt);
Nurses aides 28 (ft), 28 (pt); Activities
coordinators 2 (ft), 1 (pt).
Facilities Dining room; Physical therapy
room; Activities room; Crafts room; Laundry
room; Barber/Beauty shop.
Activities Arts & crafts; Cards; Games;
Reading groups; Prayer groups; Movies;
Shopping trips; Social/Cultural gatherings.

WESTFIELD

Barnard Rest Home*
160 Franklin St, Westfield, MA, 01085
(413) 562-2931
Admin Ivan K Barnard.
Licensure Rest home. *Beds* 84.

Governor's House Nursing Home
66 Broad St, Westfield, MA, 01085
(413) 562-5464
Admin Ann E Maher. *Medical Dir/Dir of
Nursing* Paul Bothner MD; Charlene
Whitaker.
Licensure Skilled care; Intermediate care. *Beds*
SNF 40; ICF 60. *Certified* Medicaid.
Owner Proprietary Corp.
Admissions Requirements Minimum age 21;
Medical examination; Physician's request.
Staff Physicians 1 (pt); RNs 3 (ft), 3 (pt);
LPNs 4 (ft), 5 (pt); Nurses aides 19 (ft), 21
(pt); Physical therapists 1 (ft), 1 (pt);
Occupational therapists 1 (pt); Activities
coordinators 1 (ft), 1 (pt); Dietitians 1 (pt).
Facilities Dining room; Physical therapy
room; Activities room; Crafts room; Laundry
room; Barber/Beauty shop; Library.
Activities Arts & crafts; Cards; Games;
Reading groups; Prayer groups; Movies;
Shopping trips; Social/Cultural gatherings;
Picnics.

Valley View Nursing Home
PO Box 578, 37 Feeding Hill Rd, Westfield,
MA, 01086
(413) 568-2341
Admin Mark Cerveny. *Medical Dir/Dir of
Nursing* Joseph T Bagamary MD; Lucille
Harding RN.
Licensure Skilled care. *Beds* SNF 80. *Certified*
Medicaid.
Owner Proprietary Corp.
Admissions Requirements Minimum age 21.
Staff RNs 5 (ft), 1 (pt); LPNs 5 (ft), 3 (pt);
Orderlies 1 (ft); Nurses aides 23 (ft), 8 (pt);
Physical therapists 1 (pt); Recreational
therapists 1 (ft), 1 (pt); Occupational
therapists 1 (pt); Dietitians 1 (pt);
Ophthalmologists 1 (pt).
Facilities Dining room; Physical therapy
room; Activities room; Crafts room; Laundry
room; Barber/Beauty shop; Library.
Activities Arts & crafts; Cards; Games;
Reading groups; Prayer groups; Movies;
Shopping trips; Social/Cultural gatherings.

Westfield Manor Nursing Home
PO Box 785, 60 E Silver St, Westfield, MA,
01086
(413) 562-5121
Admin Richard E Furlong. *Medical Dir/Dir of
Nursing* Ms Simmons.
Licensure Skilled care; Intermediate care. *Beds*
SNF 42; ICF 62. *Certified* Medicaid.
Owner Privately owned.
Admissions Requirements Minimum age 16;
Medical examination.
Staff RNs; LPNs; Orderlies; Nurses aides;
Physical therapists; Occupational therapists;
Activities coordinators; Dietitians;
Ophthalmologists.
Languages Spanish, Polish
Facilities Dining room; Activities room;
Chapel; Laundry room; Barber/Beauty shop.
Activities Arts & crafts; Cards; Games;
Reading groups; Prayer groups; Movies;
Shopping trips; Social/Cultural gatherings.

WESTFORD

Westford Nursing Home Inc
39 Main St, Westford, MA, 01886
(617) 692-4787
Admin Mary E Johnson. *Medical Dir/Dir of
Nursing* Thomas Fitzpatrick MD; Cynthia
O'Leary RN DON.

Licensure Intermediate care. *Beds* ICF 58.
Certified Medicaid.
Owner Privately owned.
Admissions Requirements Medical
examination; Physician's request.
Staff Physicians 1 (pt); RNs 2 (ft); LPNs 4
(pt); Orderlies 3 (ft); Nurses aides 20 (pt);
Physical therapists 1 (pt); Recreational
therapists 1 (ft); Activities coordinators 1
(ft); Dietitians 1 (pt); Ophthalmologists 1
(pt).
Languages French, Spanish
Facilities Dining room; Activities room;
Laundry room; Barber/Beauty shop.
Activities Arts & crafts; Cards; Games;
Reading groups; Prayer groups; Movies;
Shopping trips; Social/Cultural gatherings.

WESTMINISTER

Maranatha Rest Home*
99 State Rd, Westminister, MA, 01473
(617) 632-0985
Admin Richard R Boucher.
Licensure Rest home. *Beds* 12.
Admissions Requirements Medical
examination; Physician's request.
Staff Nurses aides 8 (ft); Recreational
therapists 1 (ft); Activities coordinators 1
(ft); Dietitians 1 (pt).
Facilities Dining room; Activities room;
Laundry room; Library.
Activities Cards; Games; Reading groups;
Prayer groups; Shopping trips.

WESTON

Campion Residence & Renewal Center
319 Concord Rd, Weston, MA, 02193
(617) 894-0751
Admin Rev Richard T Cleary. *Medical Dir/
Dir of Nursing* Dr John E Doherty; Jayne
Strunk RN DON.
Licensure Skilled care. *Beds* SNF 15.
Owner Nonprofit Corp.
Admissions Requirements Males only.
Staff Physicians 1 (pt); RNs 4 (ft), 3 (pt);
LPNs 1 (ft); Orderlies 3 (ft), 1 (pt); Nurses
aides 2 (ft), 3 (pt); Physical therapists 1 (pt);
Activities coordinators 1 (ft); Dietitians 1
(ft).
Languages Spanish
Affiliation Roman Catholic
Facilities Dining room; Physical therapy
room; Activities room; Chapel; Crafts room;
Laundry room; Barber/Beauty shop; Library.
Activities Arts & crafts; Cards; Games; Prayer
groups; Movies; Special trips & outings.

Weston Manor Nursing & Retirement*
75 Norumbega Rd, Weston, MA, 02193
(617) 891-6100
Admin Benjamin Shuman. *Medical Dir/Dir of
Nursing* Jerome Tanzer MD.
Licensure Intermediate care. *Beds* 120.
Certified Medicaid.
Staff Physicians 1 (pt); RNs 8 (ft), 9 (pt);
LPNs 4 (ft), 3 (pt); Orderlies 3 (ft), 2 (pt);
Nurses aides 25 (ft), 35 (pt); Physical
therapists 2 (pt); Recreational therapists 2
(ft); Occupational therapists 1 (pt); Speech
therapists 1 (pt); Activities coordinators 1
(ft); Dietitians 1 (pt); Dentists 1 (pt);
Ophthalmologists 1 (pt); Podiatrists 1 (pt);
Audiologists 1 (pt).
Facilities Dining room; Physical therapy
room; Activities room; Chapel; Crafts room;
Laundry room; Barber/Beauty shop.
Activities Arts & crafts; Cards; Games;
Reading groups; Movies; Shopping trips;
Social/Cultural gatherings.

WEYMOUTH

Bradley Manor Nursing Home*
861 Main St, Weymouth, MA, 02190
(617) 337-0678
Admin Joseph Aristide.
Licensure Skilled care; Intermediate care. *Beds* 72. *Certified* Medicaid.

Brookbend Rest Home*
27 Front St, Weymouth, MA, 02188
(617) 335-2596
Admin Alice L Chappel.
Licensure Rest home. *Beds* 33.

Colonial Nursing & Rehabilitation Center*
125 Broad St, Weymouth, MA, 02188
(617) 337-3121
Admin Rita M Welch.
Licensure Skilled care; Intermediate care. *Beds* 211. *Certified* Medicaid; Medicare.

Samuel Marcus Nursing & Retirement Home*
28 Front St, Weymouth, MA, 02188
(617) 337-9074
Admin Arthur S Logan.
Licensure Intermediate care. *Beds* 22. *Certified* Medicaid.

Pope Nursing Home*
140 Webb St, Weymouth, MA, 02188
(617) 335-4352
Admin Margaret Pomerdy.
Licensure Intermediate care. *Beds* 37. *Certified* Medicaid.

Weymouth Manor Nursing Home*
188 Summer St, Weymouth, MA, 02188
(617) 337-6900
Admin Patrick O'Connor.
Licensure Skilled care; Intermediate care. *Beds* 84. *Certified* Medicaid.

Whittaker Rest Home*
46 Union St, Weymouth, MA, 02190
(617) 335-5885
Admin Robert S Whittaker.
Licensure Rest home. *Beds* 34.

WHITMAN

Brae Burn Nursing Home
146 South Ave, Whitman, MA, 02382
(617) 447-5541
Admin Francis J Cummings. *Medical Dir/Dir of Nursing* Elaine Hawley RN DON.
Licensure Intermediate care. *Beds* 60. *Certified* Medicaid.
Owner Proprietary Corp.
Admissions Requirements Minimum age.
Staff RNs; LPNs; Nurses aides; Recreational therapists 1 (pt); Occupational therapists 1 (pt); Speech therapists 1 (pt); Dietitians 1 (pt).
Facilities Dining room; Activities room; Laundry room.
Activities Arts & crafts; Cards; Games; Reading groups; Prayer groups; Movies; Shopping trips; Social/Cultural gatherings.

WILLIAMSBURG

Sunny Acres Nursing Home*
Rte 9, Haydenville, Williamsburg, MA, 01039
(413) 268-7291
Admin James R Wade.
Licensure Intermediate care. *Beds* 30. *Certified* Medicaid.

WILLIAMSTOWN

Sweet Brook Nursing Home Inc
Cold Spring Rd, Williamstown, MA, 01267
(413) 458-8127
Admin K Elaine Neely. *Medical Dir/Dir of Nursing* Dr Robert Wicksman; Connie Hvizda RN.

Licensure Skilled care. *Beds* 123. *Certified* Medicaid; Medicare.
Owner Proprietary Corp.
Admissions Requirements Minimum age 18.

Willowood Nursing Home of Williamstown
Adams Rd, Williamstown, MA, 01267
(413) 458-2111
Admin J Michael Rivers. *Medical Dir/Dir of Nursing* Dr Ronald Durning; Rhonda Hartlage DON.
Licensure Skilled care. *Beds* SNF 72. *Certified* Medicaid.
Owner Privately owned.
Admissions Requirements Minimum age 18; Medical examination.
Staff Physicians 3 (pt); RNs 2 (ft), 2 (pt); LPNs 7 (ft), 1 (pt); Orderlies 1 (ft); Nurses aides 213 (ft), 4 (pt); Physical therapists 1 (pt); Recreational therapists 1 (pt); Occupational therapists 1 (pt); Speech therapists 1 (pt); Activities coordinators 2 (ft); Dietitians 1 (ft), 1 (pt); Ophthalmologists 1 (pt); Podiatrists 1 (pt); Social worker 1 (pt).
Facilities Dining room; Physical therapy room; Activities room; Crafts room; Laundry room; Barber/Beauty shop.
Activities Arts & crafts; Cards; Games; Reading groups; Prayer groups; Movies; Shopping trips; Social/Cultural gatherings.

WINCHENDON

Hillside Rest Home
547 Central St, Winchendon, MA, 01475
(617) 297-2333
Admin Stanley S Smith.
Licensure Intermediate care. *Beds* ICF 18. *Certified* Medicaid; Medicare.
Owner Proprietary Corp.
Admissions Requirements Minimum age Elderly; Medical examination.
Staff Physicians; RNs; Activities coordinators; Dietitians; Ophthalmologists.
Facilities Dining room; Activities room; Crafts room; Laundry room.
Activities Arts & crafts; Cards; Games; Reading groups; Prayer groups; Movies; Shopping trips; Social/Cultural gatherings.

Open Arms Nursing Home Inc
PO Box 280, 163 Brown St, Winchendon, MA, 01475
(617) 297-2458
Admin Edith A Hallet. *Medical Dir/Dir of Nursing* Barbara Sibley.
Licensure Intermediate care. *Beds* 43. *Certified* Medicaid.
Owner Proprietary Corp.
Admissions Requirements Minimum age 55.
Staff RNs 3 (ft), 3 (pt); Nurses aides 7 (ft), 7 (pt); Recreational therapists 2 (ft).
Facilities Dining room; Activities room; Crafts room; Laundry room; Barber/Beauty shop.
Activities Arts & crafts; Cards; Games; Reading groups; Prayer groups; Movies; Social/Cultural gatherings.

Pleasant View Rest Home
PO Box 7, 271 High St, Winchendon, MA, 01475
(617) 297-0325
Admin Robert J Grady. *Medical Dir/Dir of Nursing* John Harrington MD; Kathleen Ouellette.
Licensure Rest home Level IV. *Beds* Rest home Level IV 19. *Certified* Medicaid; Medicare.
Owner Privately owned.
Admissions Requirements Medical examination; Physician's request.
Staff RNs; LPNs; Nurses aides; Recreational therapists; Activities coordinators; Dietitians; Ophthalmologists; Podiatrists; Administrator; Assistant administrator.
Languages French

Facilities Dining room; Activities room; Laundry room; Library.
Activities Arts & crafts; Cards; Games; Reading groups; Prayer groups; Movies; Shopping trips; Social/Cultural gatherings; Pleasure & vacation trips.

WINCHESTER

Aberjona Nursing Home Inc*
Box 490, 184 Swanton St, Winchester, MA, 01890
(617) 729-9370
Admin Robert Salter.
Licensure Skilled care; Intermediate care. *Beds* 123. *Certified* Medicaid.

Home for Aged People*
110 Mount Vernon St, Winchester, MA, 01890
(617) 729-0497
Admin Grace P Phillips.
Licensure Rest home. *Beds* 17.
Admissions Requirements Minimum age 65; Medical examination.
Staff RNs 1 (ft).
Facilities Dining room; Activities room; Crafts room; Laundry room; Barber/Beauty shop; Library.
Activities Games; Movies.

Winchester Nursing Center
Box 490, 223 Swanton St, Winchester, MA, 01890
(617) 729-9595
Admin Richard Salter.
Licensure Skilled care; Intermediate care. *Beds* SNF 92; ICF 28. *Certified* Medicaid; Medicare.
Owner Proprietary Corp.
Admissions Requirements Minimum age 25; Physician's request.
Staff Physicians; RNs; LPNs; Orderlies; Nurses aides; Physical therapists; Recreational therapists; Occupational therapists; Speech therapists; Activities coordinators; Dietitians.
Languages French
Facilities Dining room; Physical therapy room; Activities room; Crafts room; Laundry room; Barber/Beauty shop; Library.
Activities Arts & crafts; Cards; Games; Reading groups; Prayer groups; Movies; Shopping trips; Social/Cultural gatherings; Van trips.

WINDSOR

Elizabeth Seton Residence*
125 Oakland St, Windsor, MA, 02181
(617) 251-2161
Admin Margaret Coyle.
Licensure Skilled care. *Beds* 32. *Certified* Medicaid.

WINTHROP

Bay View Nursing Home
26 Sturgis St, Winthrop, MA, 02152
(617) 846-2060
Admin Leonard Small. *Medical Dir/Dir of Nursing* Louise Boucher.
Licensure Intermediate care. *Beds* ICF 78. *Certified* Medicaid.
Owner Proprietary Corp.
Admissions Requirements Minimum age 65; Medical examination; Physician's request.
Staff Physicians 6 (pt); RNs 6 (ft), 1 (pt); LPNs 6 (ft); Nurses aides 28 (ft), 6 (pt); Physical therapists 2 (ft), 1 (pt); Reality therapists 1 (ft); Speech therapists 2 (ft), 1 (pt); Activities coordinators 1 (ft); Dietitians 1 (pt); Dentists 1 (pt); Ophthalmologists 1 (pt).
Activities Arts & crafts; Cards; Reading groups; Prayer groups; Movies; Shopping trips; Social/Cultural gatherings.

Cliff House Nursing Home Inc*
170 Cliff Ave, Winthrop, MA, 02152
(617) 846-0500
Admin C H Anderson. *Medical Dir/Dir of Nursing* John Coyle MD.
Licensure Skilled care; Intermediate care. *Beds* 88. *Certified* Medicaid.
Staff RNs; LPNs; Orderlies; Nurses aides; Physical therapists; Reality therapists; Occupational therapists; Speech therapists; Activities coordinators; Dietitians; Dentists; Podiatrists; Audiologists.
Facilities Dining room; Activities room; Crafts room; Laundry room; Barber/Beauty shop.
Activities Arts & crafts; Cards; Games; Shopping trips.

Governor Winthop Nursing Home
142 Pleasant St, Winthrop, MA, 02152
(617) 846-7750
Admin Robert D Wilkins. *Medical Dir/Dir of Nursing* William Moore RN DON.
Licensure Intermediate care. *Beds* ICF 87. *Certified* Medicaid.
Owner Privately owned.
Admissions Requirements Minimum age 21; Physician's request.
Staff RNs 7 (ft), 2 (pt); LPNs 2 (ft), 2 (pt); Nurses aides 18 (ft), 6 (pt); Physical therapists 1 (pt); Recreational therapists 1 (ft); Speech therapists 1 (pt); Activities coordinators 1 (ft); Dietitians 1 (pt); Dentists 1 (pt); Ophthalmologists 2 (pt).
Facilities Dining room; Physical therapy room; Activities room; Crafts room; Laundry room; Barber/Beauty shop.
Activities Arts & crafts; Games; Reading groups; Prayer groups; Movies; Shopping trips; Social/Cultural gatherings; Ceramics.

WOBURN

Glendale Nursing Home*
171 Cambridge Rd, Woburn, MA, 01801
(617) 933-7080
Admin Mary Carroll.
Licensure Intermediate care. *Beds* 49. *Certified* Medicaid.

New England Rehabilitation Hospital*
Rehabilitation Way, Woburn, MA, 01801
(617) 935-5050
Admin Sr Joan Cassidy.
Licensure Skilled care. *Beds* 120. *Certified* Medicaid; Medicare.

Tidd Home*
74 Elm St, Woburn, MA, 01801
(617) 933-0248
Admin Beverly Whalen.
Licensure Charitable home. *Beds* 14.
Admissions Requirements Minimum age 65; Females only; Medical examination.
Facilities Dining room; Laundry room.
Activities Cards; Movies; Shopping trips.

Woburn Nursing Center
18 Frances St, Woburn, MA, 01801
(617) 933-8175
Admin Edythe Salter. *Medical Dir/Dir of Nursing* Thomas Hirschfeld MD; Patricia Devercaux RN.
Licensure Skilled care; Intermediate care. *Beds* SNF 71; ICF 39. *Certified* Medicaid.
Owner Privately owned.
Admissions Requirements Minimum age 21; Males only; Females only; Medical examination; Physician's request.
Staff Physicians 2 (pt); RNs 8 (ft); LPNs 8 (ft); Physical therapists 1 (pt); Recreational therapists 1 (pt); Occupational therapists 1 (pt); Activities coordinators 1 (ft), 1 (pt); Dietitians 1 (ft); Ophthalmologists 1 (pt).
Facilities Dining room; Physical therapy room; Activities room; Crafts room; Barber/Beauty shop.

Activities Arts & crafts; Cards; Games; Reading groups; Prayer groups; Movies; Shopping trips; Social/Cultural gatherings.

WORCESTER

Anna Maria Rest Home
1398 Main St, Worcester, MA, 01603
(617) 756-1515
Admin Florence E Stearns.
Licensure Rest home. *Beds* Rest home 64. *Certified* Medicaid.
Owner Proprietary Corp.
Admissions Requirements Minimum age 21.
Staff RNs 1 (ft); LPNs 1 (ft); Nurses aides 8 (ft), 1 (pt); Recreational therapists 1 (pt); Activities coordinators 1 (pt); Dietitians.
Facilities Dining room; Activities room; Crafts room; Laundry room; Barber/Beauty shop; 2 Lounges with color TVs.
Activities Arts & crafts; Cards; Games; Prayer groups; Movies; Shopping trips; Social/Cultural gatherings; Planned trips; Entertainment groups.

Armstrong Nursing Home*
119 Forest St, Worcester, MA, 01609
(617) 754-6190
Admin James M Meola. *Medical Dir/Dir of Nursing* Dr Arthur Ward.
Licensure Intermediate care. *Beds* 17. *Certified* Medicaid.
Admissions Requirements Minimum age 50; Males only; Medical examination; Physician's request.
Staff Physicians 1 (pt); RNs 1 (ft), 2 (pt); LPNs 1 (ft), 5 (pt); Nurses aides 1 (ft), 2 (pt); Activities coordinators 1 (pt); Dietitians 1 (pt).
Facilities Dining room; Laundry room.
Activities Arts & crafts; Cards; Games; Movies; Shopping trips.

Bancroft House Healthcare Nursing Home*
835 Main St, Worcester, MA, 01610
(617) 757-6311
Admin John Mahoney. *Medical Dir/Dir of Nursing* Carl Marsh MD.
Licensure Skilled care; Intermediate care. *Beds* 120. *Certified* Medicaid; Medicare.
Owner Proprietary Corp (Hillhaven Corp).
Admissions Requirements Minimum age 18.
Staff RNs 4 (ft), 13 (pt); LPNs 3 (ft), 6 (pt); Nurses aides 19 (ft), 26 (pt); Activities coordinators 1 (ft), 1 (pt); 14 (ft), 16 (pt).
Facilities Dining room; Physical therapy room; Activities room; Crafts room; Laundry room; Barber/Beauty shop.
Activities Arts & crafts; Cards; Games; Reading groups; Prayer groups; Movies; Shopping trips; Social/Cultural gatherings.

Beechaven Nursing Home*
133 Paine St, Worcester, MA, 01605
(617) 752-3029
Admin Leo H Roberge Jr.
Licensure Intermediate care. *Beds* 19. *Certified* Medicaid.

Belmont Home*
255 Belmont St, Worcester, MA, 01605
(617) 799-1554
Admin Arthur Firella.
Licensure Skilled care; Intermediate care. *Beds* 184. *Certified* Medicaid.

Blaire House of Worcester
116 Houghton St, Worcester, MA, 01604
(617) 791-5543
Admin Mary Keating. *Medical Dir/Dir of Nursing* Dr Subarraju; Mary Lou Cross DON.
Licensure Skilled care; Intermediate care. *Beds* 75. *Certified* Medicaid.
Owner Proprietary Corp.
Staff Physicians 12 (pt); RNs 4 (ft), 4 (pt); LPNs 4 (ft), 2 (pt); Orderlies 3 (ft), 1 (pt); Nurses aides 10 (ft), 12 (pt); Physical

therapists 1 (pt); Occupational therapists 1 (ft); Activities coordinators 1 (ft), 2 (pt); Dietitians 1 (pt); Dentists 1 (pt); Ophthalmologists 1 (pt); Podiatrists 1 (pt); Dentist 1 (pt).
Facilities Dining room; Activities room; Crafts room; Laundry room; Barber/Beauty shop; Library.
Activities Arts & crafts; Cards; Games; Reading groups; Prayer groups; Movies; Shopping trips; Social/Cultural gatherings.

Burncoat Plains Rest Home*
572 Burncoat St, Worcester, MA, 01606
(617) 853-0021
Admin William J Lange.
Licensure Rest home. *Beds* 35.

Castle Park Nursing Home
22-24 King, Worcester, MA, 01610
(617) 752-8910
Admin Janet P Waller RN LNHA. *Medical Dir/Dir of Nursing* Rita Reilly RN.
Licensure Intermediate care. *Beds* ICF 30. *Certified* Medicaid.
Owner Proprietary Corp.
Admissions Requirements Minimum age 60.
Staff RNs; LPNs; Nurses aides; Activities coordinators; Dietitians.
Languages Greek, French
Facilities Activities room; Laundry room; Barber/Beauty shop.
Activities Arts & crafts; Cards; Games; Prayer groups; Movies; Shopping trips.

Catherine Rest Home
27 Catherine St, Worcester, MA, 01605
(617) 756-3954
Admin Richard F Alarie. *Medical Dir/Dir of Nursing* Eric Dunphy RN.
Licensure Long-term care. *Beds* 27. *Certified* Medicaid.
Owner Privately owned.
Admissions Requirements Minimum age 50.
Staff RNs 1 (pt); Orderlies 3 (pt); Nurses aides 2 (ft), 3 (pt); Activities coordinators; Dietitians.
Facilities Dining room; Activities room; Laundry room.
Activities Arts & crafts; Cards; Games; Reading groups; Prayer groups; Movies; Shopping trips.

Catherine-Windsor Rest Home
25 Catherine St, Worcester, MA, 01605
(617) 791-5166
Admin Richard F Alarie. *Medical Dir/Dir of Nursing* Eric Durphy RN.
Licensure Long term care; Level IV facility. *Beds* 36. *Certified* Medicaid.
Owner Privately owned.
Admissions Requirements Minimum age 50; Medical examination; Physician's request.
Staff RNs 1 (pt); Orderlies 2 (ft), 3 (pt); Nurses aides 2 (ft), 3 (pt); Activities coordinators 1 (pt); Dietitians 1 (pt).
Facilities Dining room; Activities room; Laundry room.
Activities Arts & crafts; Cards; Games; Reading groups; Movies; Social/Cultural gatherings.

Clark Manor Nursing Home*
1350 Main St, Worcester, MA, 01603
(617) 791-4200
Admin Morris Sibulkin Jr.
Licensure Skilled care; Intermediate care. *Beds* 162. *Certified* Medicaid.

Dalton Rest Home*
453 Cambridge St, Worcester, MA, 01610
(617) 756-7310
Admin William J Lange.
Licensure Rest home. *Beds* 34.

Dodge Park Rest Home*
101 Randolph Rd, Worcester, MA, 01606
(617) 853-8180
Admin Anthony E Penny.

Licensure Rest home. *Beds* 32.

Donna Kay Rest Home Inc
16 Marble St, Worcester, MA, 01603
(617) 755-6667
Admin Barbara J Duffy.
Licensure Rest home level IV. *Beds* 60.
Certified Medicaid.
Owner Privately owned.
Admissions Requirements Minimum age 50;
Physician's request.
Staff LPNs 1 (pt); Nurses aides 10 (ft);
Activities coordinators 1 (ft); Dietitians 1
(pt).
Facilities Dining room; Activities room;
Laundry room; Barber/Beauty shop; Library.
Activities Arts & crafts; Cards; Games;
Reading groups; Prayer groups; Movies;
Shopping trips; Social/Cultural gatherings.

Elmwood Manor Nursing Home
21 Catherine St, Worcester, MA, 01605
(617) 756-4875
Admin John G Bastille.
Licensure Intermediate care. *Beds* ICF 31.
Certified Medicaid.
Owner Privately owned.
Admissions Requirements Physician's request.
Staff RNs 1 (pt); LPNs 3 (ft); Orderlies 8 (ft),
2 (pt); Physical therapists 1 (pt);
Recreational therapists 1 (pt); Occupational
therapists 1 (pt); Speech therapists 1 (pt);
Activities coordinators 1 (pt); Dietitians 1
(pt); Ophthalmologists 1 (pt); Podiatrists 1
(pt).
Languages Polish, French
Facilities Dining room; Activities room;
Crafts room; Barber/Beauty shop.
Activities Arts & crafts; Cards; Games;
Movies; Shopping trips; Social/Cultural
gatherings.

Evamor Manor*
23 May St, Worcester, MA, 01610
(617) 799-4043
Admin Josephine M Morrow.
Licensure Intermediate care. *Beds* 28.
Certified Medicaid.
Admissions Requirements Minimum age 21;
Medical examination; Physician's request.
Staff RNs 1 (pt); LPNs 1 (pt); Orderlies 1 (pt);
Nurses aides 3 (ft), 3 (pt); Activities
coordinators 1 (pt); Dietitians 1 (pt).
Facilities Dining room; Activities room;
Crafts room; Laundry room; Barber/Beauty
shop; Library.
Activities Arts & crafts; Cards; Games;
Reading groups; Prayer groups; Movies;
Shopping trips; Social/Cultural gatherings.

Evans Manor Nursing Home*
27 Tirrell St, Worcester, MA, 01603
(617) 755-4255
Admin Clifton N LaFrenier.
Licensure Intermediate care. *Beds* 18.
Certified Medicaid.

**Goddard Homestead Inc A Community for
Elders**
1199 Main St, Worcester, MA, 01603
(617) 753-4890
Admin Margaret P Naylor.
Licensure Level IV Rest home; Congregate
housing. *Beds* Level IV 30; Congregate units
36.
Owner Nonprofit Corp.
Admissions Requirements Minimum age 65;
Medical examination.
Staff RNs; Activities coordinators; Dietitians.
Facilities Dining room; Activities room;
Chapel; Crafts room; Laundry room; Barber/
Beauty shop; Library; Living room.
Activities Arts & crafts; Cards; Games;
Reading groups; Prayer groups; Movies;
Shopping trips; Social/Cultural gatherings.

Hammond House Convalescent Home*
18 Hammond St, Worcester, MA, 01610
(617) 799-7991

Admin Esther Travers.
Licensure Intermediate care. *Beds* 70.
Certified Medicaid.
Owner Proprietary Corp (Hillhaven Corp).

Harvard Nursing Home Inc*
14 John St, Worcester, MA, 01609
(619) 755-7268
Admin Frithiof B Carlson.
Licensure Intermediate care. *Beds* 42.
Certified Medicaid.

Hermitage Nursing Home*
383 Mill St, Worcester, MA, 01602
(617) 791-8131
Admin Stephen C Warner.
Licensure Skilled care; Intermediate care. *Beds*
101. *Certified* Medicaid; Medicare.
Owner Proprietary Corp (Beverly Enterprises).

Heywood Valley Nursing Home
59 Acton St, Worcester, MA, 01604
(617) 791-3147
Admin Steven Haase. *Medical Dir/Dir of
Nursing* Dr Robert McGan; Elizabeth
Howard RN.
Licensure Skilled care; Intermediate care. *Beds*
SNF 82; ICF 79. *Certified* Medicaid;
Medicare.
Owner Proprietary Corp (Greenery Rehab
Grp).
Admissions Requirements Medical
examination.
Staff Physicians 2 (pt); RNs 7 (ft), 3 (pt);
LPNs 12 (ft), 5 (pt); Orderlies 15 (ft), 3 (pt);
Nurses aides 60 (ft), 12 (pt); Physical
therapists 8 (ft); Recreational therapists 5
(ft); Occupational therapists 9 (ft); Speech
therapists 4 (ft); Activities coordinators 1
(ft).
Facilities Dining room; Physical therapy
room; Activities room; Barber/Beauty shop;
Library.
Activities Arts & crafts; Cards; Games;
Reading groups; Prayer groups; Movies;
Shopping trips; Social/Cultural gatherings.

Highland Manor Rest Home
41 Lancaster St, Worcester, MA, 01609
(617) 753-0184
Admin Richard B Bastille.
Licensure Rest home. *Beds* 30.
Owner Privately owned.
Admissions Requirements Minimum age 50;
Medical examination.
Staff LPNs 1 (pt); Nurses aides 4 (ft), 4 (pt);
Activities coordinators 1 (pt); Dietitians 1
(pt).
Facilities Dining room; Activities room;
Laundry room.
Activities Arts & crafts; Cards; Games;
Movies; Shopping trips; Social/Cultural
gatherings.

Homestead Hall*
10 Homestead Ave, Worcester, MA, 01610
(617) 755-7915
Admin D Patricia Johnson.
Licensure Rest home. *Beds* 30.

Jewish Home for the Aged*
629 Salisbury St, Worcester, MA, 01609
(617) 798-8653
Admin Marvin A Goldberg.
Licensure Skilled care; Intermediate care. *Beds*
141. *Certified* Medicaid; Medicare.
Affiliation Jewish

Knollwood Nursing Home Inc
271 E Mountain St, Worcester, MA, 01606
(617) 853-6910
Admin Paula Ann Kuzdzal. *Medical Dir/Dir of
Nursing* Betsy Moody MD; Diane Inzerillo
RN DNS.
Licensure Skilled care. *Beds* SNF 70. *Certified*
Medicaid; Medicare.
Owner Proprietary Corp.
Admissions Requirements Physician's request.

Staff RNs 7 (ft), 3 (pt); LPNs 1 (ft), 2 (pt);
Orderlies 2 (ft), 1 (pt); Nurses aides 14 (ft),
5 (pt); Activities coordinators 1 (ft).
Facilities Dining room; Physical therapy
room; Activities room; Laundry room;
Barber/Beauty shop.
Activities Cards; Games; Reading groups;
Prayer groups; Movies; Social/Cultural
gatherings.

Linda Lee Rest Home
30 Institute Rd, Worcester, MA, 01609
(616) 753-3718
Admin Olga C Burdett. *Medical Dir/Dir of
Nursing* Dr Ageonavritis Demosthenes; Olga
C Burdett LPN.
Licensure Intermediate care for mentally
retarded; Rest home. *Beds* 11. *Certified*
Medicaid.
Owner Privately owned.
Admissions Requirements Minimum age 21;
Females only; Medical examination;
Physician's request.
Staff Physicians 1 (ft); LPNs 2 (ft); Nurses
aides 4 (ft); Activities coordinators 1 (ft);
Dietitians 1 (ft); Ophthalmologists 1 (ft).
Facilities Dining room; Activities room;
Laundry room.
Activities Arts & crafts; Cards; Games;
Reading groups; Movies; Shopping trips.

Lincoln Nursing Home*
299 Lincoln St, Worcester, MA, 01605
(617) 852-2001
Admin Sarli J Battista.
Licensure Skilled care; Intermediate care. *Beds*
130. *Certified* Medicaid; Medicare.

Lutheran Home of Worcester Inc
26 Harvard St, Worcester, MA, 01609
(617) 754-8877
Admin Rev Richard E Olson. *Medical Dir/Dir
of Nursing* Lorenzo Campos MD.
Licensure Skilled care; Intermediate care. *Beds*
141. *Certified* Medicaid.
Admissions Requirements Minimum age 65;
Medical examination.
Staff Physicians 1 (pt); RNs 6 (ft), 12 (pt);
LPNs 4 (ft), 8 (pt); Orderlies 1 (ft), 1 (pt);
Nurses aides 17 (ft), 48 (pt); Physical
therapists 2 (pt); Reality therapists 2 (ft);
Recreational therapists 1 (ft); Occupational
therapists 2 (pt); Speech therapists 1 (pt);
Dietitians 1 (pt).
Affiliation Lutheran
Facilities Dining room; Physical therapy
room; Activities room; Chapel; Crafts room;
Laundry room; Barber/Beauty shop; Outdoor
gazebo.
Activities Arts & crafts; Cards; Games;
Reading groups; Prayer groups; Movies;
Shopping trips; Social/Cultural gatherings.

Maple Hall Nursing Home*
19 King St, Worcester, MA, 01610
(617) 753-4380
Admin Lloyd W Buckley.
Licensure Intermediate care. *Beds* 56.
Certified Medicaid.

Meadowbrook Manor*
856 Main St, Worcester, MA, 01610
(617) 756-7822
Admin Anne Jette.
Licensure Rest home. *Beds* 25.

Mill Hill Nursing Home Inc*
215 Mill St, Worcester, MA, 01602
(617) 791-3168
Admin F E Kuzdzal.
Licensure Skilled care; Intermediate care. *Beds*
101. *Certified* Medicaid.

Newton Manor Rest Home
710 Pleasant St, Worcester, MA, 01602
(617) 753-4024
Admin Marie Callahan.
Licensure Rest home. *Beds* 25. *Certified*
Medicaid; Medicare.

Staff Physicians 1 (ft); RNs 1 (ft); Nurses aides 6 (ft); Activities coordinators 1 (ft).
Facilities Dining room; Laundry room; Barber/Beauty shop; Library.
Activities Arts & crafts; Games; Reading groups.

Northeast Care Center
39 Queen St, Worcester, MA, 01610
(617) 753-4791
Admin Jeanne Y Caron RN. *Medical Dir/Dir of Nursing* Dr Jeffrey Burl; Marie Lanzillotti RN DON.
Licensure Skilled care; Intermediate care. *Beds* SNF 80; ICF 80. *Certified* Medicaid; Medicare.
Owner Proprietary Corp.
Admissions Requirements Minimum age 21; Medical examination; Physician's request.
Staff Physicians 1 (pt); RNs 10 (ft); LPNs 10 (ft); Orderlies 5 (ft); Nurses aides 50 (ft), 20 (pt); Physical therapists 1 (ft), 1 (pt); Reality therapists 1 (ft); Recreational therapists 3 (ft); Occupational therapists 1 (pt); Speech therapists 1 (pt); Activities coordinators 1 (ft); Dietitians 1 (pt); Dentists 1 (pt); Ophthalmologists 1 (pt); Podiatrists 1 (pt); Medical Records.
Facilities Dining room; Physical therapy room; Activities room; Chapel; Crafts room; Laundry room; Barber/Beauty shop; Patio w/furniture.
Activities Arts & crafts; Cards; Games; Reading groups; Prayer groups; Movies; Shopping trips; Social/Cultural gatherings; Birds & fish.

Odd Fellows Home of Massachusetts
104 Randolph Rd, Worcester, MA, 01606
(617) 853-6687
Admin George E Shaw. *Medical Dir/Dir of Nursing* Dr Steven R Rozak; Shirley Platts DON.
Licensure Intermediate care; Rest home. *Beds* 75. *Certified* Medicaid.
Owner Nonprofit organization/foundation.
Admissions Requirements Medical examination.
Staff Physicians 1 (pt); RNs 2 (ft); LPNs 3 (ft), 2 (pt); Orderlies 1 (ft); Nurses aides 12 (ft), 6 (pt); Physical therapists 1 (pt); Activities coordinators 1 (ft); Dietitians 1 (pt).
Affiliation Independent Order of Odd Fellows & Rebekahs
Facilities Dining room; Activities room; Chapel; Crafts room; Laundry room; Barber/Beauty shop; Library.
Activities Arts & crafts; Cards; Games; Reading groups; Prayer groups; Movies; Shopping trips; Social/Cultural gatherings; Trips.

Park Hill Manor Nursing Home
1 Gorham St, Worcester, MA, 01605
(617) 825-1267
Admin Edward MacLeod.
Licensure Intermediate care. *Beds* 101. *Certified* Medicaid.

Pleasant Acres Rest Home*
107 E Mountain St, Worcester, MA, 01606
(617) 853-8333
Admin Bernadette Wilcox.
Licensure Rest home. *Beds* 10.

Providence House Nursing Home*
119 Providence St, Worcester, MA, 01604
(617) 791-7881
Admin Eugene L Oriol.
Licensure Skilled care; Intermediate care. *Beds* 160. *Certified* Medicaid; Medicare.

St Francis Home
101 Plantation St, Worcester, MA, 01604
(617) 755-8605
Admin Sr Jacquelyn Alix. *Medical Dir/Dir of Nursing* Stanley L Kocot MD; Sr Frances Emond RN.

Licensure Skilled care; Intermediate care; Rest home. *Beds* SNF 40; ICF 60; Rest home 40; Adult day care 75. *Certified* Medicaid.
Owner Nonprofit Corp.
Admissions Requirements Medical examination.
Staff RNs 1 (ft); LPNs 4 (ft); Orderlies; Nurses aides 10 (ft), 6 (pt); Physical therapists; Recreational therapists 1 (ft); Occupational therapists; Activities coordinators 1 (ft); Dietitians; Ophthalmologists.
Languages French
Affiliation Roman Catholic
Facilities Dining room; Physical therapy room; Activities room; Chapel; Crafts room; Laundry room; Barber/Beauty shop; Library; Occupational therapy room.
Activities Arts & crafts; Cards; Games; Reading groups; Prayer groups; Movies; Social/Cultural gatherings; Exercise group; Music.

Salisbury Nursing Home*
25 Oriol Dr, Worcester, MA, 01605
(617) 852-3330
Admin Donald F Flanagan.
Licensure Skilled care; Intermediate care. *Beds* 160. *Certified* Medicaid.

Schussler Rest Home
1 Schussler Rd, Worcester, MA, 01609
(617) 757-6759
Admin Richard F Alarie. *Medical Dir/Dir of Nursing* Eric Dunphy RN.
Licensure Rest home. *Beds* 25. *Certified* Medicaid.
Owner Privately owned.
Admissions Requirements Minimum age 50; Medical examination.
Staff RNs 1 (pt); Orderlies 2 (ft), 3 (pt); Nurses aides 2 (ft), 3 (pt); Activities coordinators 1 (pt); Dietitians 1 (pt).
Facilities Dining room; Activities room; Crafts room; Laundry room.
Activities Arts & crafts; Cards; Games; Reading groups; Prayer groups; Movies.

Smiths Rest Home*
25 Sturgis St, Worcester, MA, 01605
(617) 755-8711
Admin George H Gross.
Licensure Rest home. *Beds* 27.

Spring Valley Convalescent Home*
81 Chatham St, Worcester, MA, 01069
(617) 754-3276
Admin Jeffrey Kline.
Licensure Skilled care; Intermediate care. *Beds* 82. *Certified* Medicaid.
Owner Proprietary Corp (Hillhaven Corp).

Washburn House-Home For Aged Women
1183 Main St, Worcester, MA, 01602
(617) 756-3810
Admin Hilda-Jane Miller. *Medical Dir/Dir of Nursing* Dr Horatio Turner.
Licensure Intermediate care; Level III; Level IV. *Beds* ICF 48. *Certified* Medicaid.
Owner Nonprofit organization/foundation.
Admissions Requirements Females only.
Staff Physicians; RNs; LPNs; Nurses aides; Recreational therapists; Activities coordinators; Dietitians.
Facilities Dining room; Activities room; Chapel; Crafts room; Laundry room; Barber/Beauty shop; Library.
Activities Arts & crafts; Games; Prayer groups; Movies; Shopping trips.

Wayside Nursing Home Inc*
751 Grove St, Worcester, MA, 01605
(617) 852-4365
Admin Edith C Cobb.
Licensure Skilled care. *Beds* 69. *Certified* Medicaid; Medicare.

West Side Nursing Home*
35 Fruit St, Worcester, MA, 01609
(617) 752-6763
Admin Jeanne M Care. *Medical Dir/Dir of Nursing* Merle Ingraham.
Licensure Skilled care; Intermediate care. *Beds* 90. *Certified* Medicaid.
Admissions Requirements Minimum age 65.
Staff Physicians 6 (pt); RNs 24 (ft); LPNs 18 (ft); Orderlies 10 (ft); Nurses aides 50 (ft); Physical therapists 1 (ft); Reality therapists 2 (pt); Recreational therapists 4 (pt); Occupational therapists 1 (pt); Speech therapists 1 (pt); Activities coordinators 1 (ft); Dietitians 1 (ft); Dentists 1 (pt); Ophthalmologists 1 (pt); Audiologists 1 (pt).
Facilities Dining room; Activities room; Crafts room; Laundry room; Barber/Beauty shop.
Activities Arts & crafts; Cards; Games; Reading groups; Movies; Shopping trips; Social/Cultural gatherings; Therapy groups.

Winter Hill Rest Home*
24 Chester St, Worcester, MA, 01605
(617) 852-2438
Admin William J Lange. *Medical Dir/Dir of Nursing* Dr Carl Marsh.
Licensure Rest home. *Beds* 15.
Admissions Requirements Females only; Medical examination; Physician's request.
Facilities Dining room; Activities room.
Activities Arts & crafts; Cards; Games; Reading groups; Movies; Shopping trips; Social/Cultural gatherings.

WRENTHAM

Kings Daughters & Sons Home for the Aged in Norfolk County
289 East St, Wrentham, MA, 02093
(617) 384-3531
Admin DeAnna E Willis. *Medical Dir/Dir of Nursing* Dorothy B Abrams DON.
Licensure Level IV & Level III Infirmary. *Beds* Level IV 25; Level III 6.
Owner Nonprofit Corp.
Admissions Requirements Minimum age 65; Medical examination.
Staff Physicians 1 (pt); LPNs 2 (ft), 6 (pt); Nurses aides 3 (ft), 8 (pt); Physical therapists 1 (pt); Recreational therapists 1 (pt); Speech therapists 1 (pt); Activities coordinators 1 (ft); Dietitians 1 (pt); Dentists 1 (pt); Ophthalmologists 1 (pt).
Facilities Dining room; Laundry room; Barber/Beauty shop; Library; Living room; Multi-sitting rooms & porches; 10 acres of grounds.
Activities Arts & crafts; Cards; Games; Prayer groups; Movies; Shopping trips; Outings to restaurants & parks etc.

Maples Convalescent Home
24 Common St, Wrentham, MA, 02093
(617) 384-7977
Admin Sigmund A Capachin.
Licensure Intermediate care. *Beds* ICF 50. *Certified* Medicaid.
Owner Proprietary Corp.
Admissions Requirements Minimum age 60; Medical examination; Physician's request.
Staff RNs 1 (ft), 1 (pt); LPNs 3 (ft), 3 (pt); Orderlies 2 (ft); Nurses aides 9 (ft), 9 (pt); Activities coordinators 1 (ft); Dietitians 1 (pt).
Facilities Dining room; Activities room; Laundry room; Barber/Beauty shop.
Activities Arts & crafts; Cards; Games; Reading groups; Prayer groups; Movies; Shopping trips; Social/Cultural gatherings.

Serenity Hill Nursing Home*
655 Dedham St, Wrentham, MA, 02093
(617) 384-3400
Admin Deanna Willis.
Licensure Intermediate care. *Beds* 44. *Certified* Medicaid.

Admissions Requirements Minimum age 60; Medical examination; Physician's request.
Staff RNs 1 (ft), 2 (pt); LPNs 5 (pt); Nurses aides 5 (ft), 22 (pt); Recreational therapists 1 (ft); Dietitians 1 (pt).
Facilities Dining room; Activities room; Crafts room; Laundry room.
Activities Arts & crafts; Cards; Games; Reading groups; Prayer groups; Movies; Shopping trips; Social/Cultural gatherings.

Sheldonville Nursing Home*
1022 West St, Wrentham, MA, 02070
(617) 384-2421
Admin Barbara Horowitz.
Licensure Intermediate care. *Beds* 50.
  Certified Medicaid.
Staff Physicians; RNs; LPNs; Nurses aides; Physical therapists; Reality therapists; Recreational therapists; Occupational therapists; Speech therapists; Activities coordinators; Dietitians; Dentists; Ophthalmologists; Podiatrists; Audiologists.
Facilities Dining room; Activities room; Chapel; Crafts room; Barber/Beauty shop; TV sitting room.
Activities Arts & crafts; Cards; Games; Reading groups; Prayer groups; Movies; Shopping trips; Social/Cultural gatherings.

MICHIGAN

ADRIAN

Hillhaven Convalescent Center
730 Kimole Ln, Adrian, MI, 49221
(517) 263-6771
Admin Penny J Place. *Medical Dir/Dir of Nursing* Richard Burns DO; L Joyce Heesen RN DON.
Licensure Skilled care; Intermediate care. *Beds* 98. *Certified* Medicaid; Medicare.
Owner Proprietary Corp (Hillhaven Corp).
Admissions Requirements Minimum age 13; Medical examination; Physician's request.
Staff RNs 2 (ft), 2 (pt); LPNs 4 (ft), 4 (pt); Nurses aides 8 (ft), 35 (pt); Physical therapists 1 (ft), 1 (pt); Recreational therapists 1 (ft); Speech therapists 1 (pt); Dietitians 1 (ft).
Facilities Dining room; Physical therapy room; Activities room; Chapel; Crafts room; Laundry room; Barber/Beauty shop.
Activities Arts & crafts; Cards; Games; Prayer groups; Movies; Social/Cultural gatherings; Bingo; Craft classes.

Lenawee Medical Care Facility
200 Sand Creek Hwy, Adrian, MI, 49221
(517) 263-6794
Admin Mark C Wendt. *Medical Dir/Dir of Nursing* Randall De Arment DO; Alice Schultz RN.
Licensure Skilled care; Intermediate care. *Beds* 136. *Certified* Medicaid; Medicare.
Owner Publicly owned.
Admissions Requirements Medical examination; Physician's request.
Staff Physicians 1 (pt); RNs 6 (ft), 6 (pt); LPNs 6 (ft), 6 (pt); Nurses aides 15 (ft), 58 (pt); Physical therapists 1 (pt); Activities coordinators 1 (ft), 1 (pt); Dietitians 1 (pt); Ophthalmologists 1 (pt).
Languages Spanish, Polish, German
Facilities Dining room; Physical therapy room; Activities room; Laundry room; Barber/Beauty shop.
Activities Arts & crafts; Cards; Games; Reading groups; Prayer groups; Movies; Shopping trips; Social/Cultural gatherings.

Provincial House—Adrian*
700 Lakeshire Trail, Adrian, MI, 49221
(517) 263-0781
Medical Dir/Dir of Nursing Dr Michael Worzniak.
Licensure Skilled care; Intermediate care. *Beds* 117. *Certified* Medicaid; Medicare.
Owner Proprietary Corp (Beverly Enterprises).
Admissions Requirements Medical examination; Physician's request.
Staff RNs 5 (ft), 1 (pt); LPNs 8 (ft); Orderlies 65 (ft); Physical therapists 1 (pt); Occupational therapists 1 (pt); Speech therapists 1 (pt); Activities coordinators 1 (ft); Dietitians 1 (pt); Audiologists 1 (pt).

Facilities Dining room; Physical therapy room; Activities room; Barber/Beauty shop.
Activities Arts & crafts; Cards; Games; Reading groups; Prayer groups; Movies; Shopping trips; Social/Cultural gatherings.

ALBION

Albion Manor*
1000 W Erie St, Albion, MI, 49224
(517) 629-5501
Medical Dir/Dir of Nursing Dr Horace Davis.
Licensure Skilled care; Intermediate care. *Beds* 80. *Certified* Medicaid.
Owner Proprietary Corp (Vantage Healthcare).
Admissions Requirements Minimum age 15; Medical examination; Physician's request.
Staff Physicians 8 (pt); RNs 1 (ft), 2 (pt); LPNs 4 (ft), 5 (pt); Orderlies 1 (ft); Nurses aides 26 (ft), 11 (pt); Physical therapists 1 (pt); Occupational therapists 1 (pt); Speech therapists 1 (pt); Activities coordinators 1 (ft); Dietitians 1 (pt); Dentists 1 (pt).
Facilities Dining room; Physical therapy room; Activities room; Crafts room; Laundry room; Barber/Beauty shop.
Activities Arts & crafts; Cards; Games; Reading groups; Prayer groups; Movies; Shopping trips; Social/Cultural gatherings.

ALLEGAN

Allegan County Medical Care Facility*
3265 122nd Ave, Allegan, MI, 49010
(616) 673-2102
Admin Keith M Miller.
Licensure Skilled care. *Beds* 60. *Certified* Medicaid; Medicare.

Pine Oaks Nursing Center*
1200 Ely St, Allegan, MI, 49010
Licensure Intermediate care. *Beds* 123. *Certified* Medicaid; Medicare.

ALLEN PARK

Allen Park Convalescent Home*
9150 Allen Rd, Allen Park, MI, 48101
(313) 386-2150
Licensure Skilled care; Intermediate care. *Beds* 180.

Inter-City Christian Manor
4600 Allen Rd, Allen Park, MI, 48101
(313) 383-6226
Admin Robert G Hopper. *Medical Dir/Dir of Nursing* Catherine Bork DON.
Licensure Intermediate care. *Beds* ICF 17.
Owner Nonprofit Corp.
Admissions Requirements Minimum age 62; Medical examination.
Staff RNs 5 (ft), 5 (pt); LPNs 2 (ft), 3 (pt); Nurses aides 10 (ft), 10 (pt); Activities coordinators 1 (ft); Dietitians 1 (ft).
Affiliation Baptist

Facilities Dining room; Physical therapy room; Activities room; Barber/Beauty shop.
Activities Arts & crafts; Cards; Games; Reading groups; Prayer groups; Movies; Shopping trips; Social/Cultural gatherings.

ALLENDALE

West Michigan Care Center
11007 Radcliff Dr, Allendale, MI, 49401
(616) 895-6688
Admin Philip B Turlington. *Medical Dir/Dir of Nursing* Roger Holman DO.
Licensure Skilled care. *Beds* SNF 72. *Certified* Medicaid; Medicare.
Owner Privately owned.
Admissions Requirements Minimum age 17; Physician's request.
Staff RNs 2 (ft), 4 (pt); LPNs 2 (ft), 6 (pt); Orderlies 2 (pt); Nurses aides 12 (ft), 16 (pt); Activities coordinators 1 (ft).
Facilities Dining room; Activities room; Laundry room; Barber/Beauty shop.
Activities Arts & crafts; Cards; Games; Reading groups; Prayer groups; Movies; Social/Cultural gatherings.

ALMA

Michigan Masonic Home
1200 Wright Ave, Alma, MI, 48801
(517) 463-3141
Admin Roger L Myers. *Medical Dir/Dir of Nursing* Dr Richard Remsberg; Yvonne Sweeney DON.
Licensure Skilled care; Intermediate care; Home for aged. *Beds* 409. *Certified* Medicaid; Medicare.
Admissions Requirements Medical examination.
Staff Physicians 3 (ft); RNs 8 (ft); LPNs 55 (ft); Nurses aides 70 (ft); Physical therapists 3 (ft); Recreational therapists 1 (ft); Occupational therapists 6 (ft); Dietitians 1 (ft); Dentists 1 (ft); Ophthalmologists 1 (ft); Podiatrists 1 (ft); Dentist 1 (ft).
Affiliation Masons
Facilities Dining room; Physical therapy room; Activities room; Chapel; Crafts room; Laundry room; Barber/Beauty shop; Library.
Activities Arts & crafts; Cards; Games; Reading groups; Prayer groups; Movies.

Wilcox Nursing Home*
525 N State St, Alma, MI, 48801
(517) 463-4000
Licensure Intermediate care. *Beds* 45. *Certified* Medicaid.

ALPENA

Pierce Nursing Home
1234 Golf Course Rd, Alpena, MI, 49707
(517) 356-1030
Admin Donald J Wisniewski. *Medical Dir/Dir of Nursing* Mary R Wisniewski.
Licensure Intermediate care. *Beds* ICF 36. *Certified* Medicaid.

Owner Proprietary Corp.
Admissions Requirements Physician's request.
Staff RNs 1 (ft); LPNs 4 (ft), 2 (pt); Nurses aides 9 (ft), 6 (pt); Activities coordinators 1 (ft); Dietitians 1 (pt).
Facilities Dining room; Activities room; Crafts room; Laundry room.
Activities Arts & crafts; Cards; Games; Prayer groups.

Provincial House—Alpena
301 Long Rapids Rd, Alpena, MI, 49707
(517) 356-2194
Admin Sylvia Owens. *Medical Dir/Dir of Nursing* Roma Dean RN DON.
Licensure Skilled care. *Beds* SNF 117. *Certified* Medicaid; Medicare.
Owner Proprietary Corp (Beverly Enterprises).
Admissions Requirements Minimum age 18; Medical examination.
Staff RNs 6 (ft); LPNs 15 (ft); Orderlies 8 (ft); Nurses aides 100 (ft); Physical therapists 1 (ft); Speech therapists 1 (ft); Activities coordinators 1 (ft); Dietitians 1 (ft); Ophthalmologists 1 (ft); Social worker 1 (ft).
Facilities Dining room; Physical therapy room; Activities room; Laundry room; Barber/Beauty shop; TV room.
Activities Arts & crafts; Cards; Games; Reading groups; Prayer groups; Movies; Shopping trips; Social/Cultural gatherings.

ANN ARBOR

Glacier Hills Nursing Center
1200 Earhart Rd, Ann Arbor, MI, 48105
(313) 769-6410
Admin Nicholas Meima. *Medical Dir/Dir of Nursing* John Sautinga MD; Alan Deugiz MD; Terri Durkin Williams RN DON.
Licensure Skilled care. *Beds* SNF 86. *Certified* Medicaid; Medicare.
Owner Nonprofit Corp.
Admissions Requirements Minimum age 15; Medical examination; Physician's request.
Staff Physicians 14 (pt); RNs 12 (ft), 6 (pt); LPNs 6 (ft), 3 (pt); Orderlies 2 (ft); Nurses aides 35 (ft), 8 (pt); Physical therapists 3 (pt); Reality therapists 1 (pt); Occupational therapists 1 (ft); Speech therapists 1 (pt); Activities coordinators 1 (ft); Dietitians 1 (ft); Dentists 1 (pt); Ophthalmologists 1 (pt).
Facilities Dining room; Physical therapy room; Activities room; Laundry room; Barber/Beauty shop; Library.
Activities Arts & crafts; Cards; Games; Reading groups; Prayer groups; Movies; Shopping trips; Social/Cultural gatherings.

Hillside Terrace Retirement Home*
1939 Jackson, Ann Arbor, MI, 48103
(313) 761-4451
Licensure Intermediate care. *Beds* 23. *Certified* Medicaid.

Huron View Lodge
355 Huron View Blvd, Ann Arbor, MI, 48103
(313) 761-3800
Admin Ronald Head. *Medical Dir/Dir of Nursing* Lynette Nearon RN DON.
Licensure Skilled care; Intermediate care. *Beds* SNF 71; ICF. *Certified* Medicaid; Medicare.
Owner Proprietary Corp (Columbia Corp).
Admissions Requirements Medical examination; Physician's request.
Staff RNs; LPNs; Orderlies; Nurses aides; Physical therapists; Reality therapists; Recreational therapists; Occupational therapists; Speech therapists; Activities coordinators; Dietitians.
Facilities Dining room; Physical therapy room; Activities room; Laundry room; Barber/Beauty shop.
Activities Arts & crafts; Cards; Games; Reading groups; Prayer groups; Movies.

Whitehall Convalescent Home
3370 Morgan Rd, Ann Arbor, MI, 48104
(313) 971-3230
Medical Dir/Dir of Nursing Russell Achison MD; Mabel K Johnson RN DON.
Licensure Intermediate care. *Beds* 102. *Certified* Medicaid.
Admissions Requirements Minimum age 18; Medical examination; Physician's request.
Staff RNs 6 (ft), 2 (pt); LPNs 8 (ft), 2 (pt); Nurses aides 60 (ft), 14 (pt); Physical therapists 1 (pt); Recreational therapists 1 (ft); Activities coordinators 1 (ft); Dietitians 1 (pt).
Facilities Dining room; Physical therapy room; Activities room; Crafts room; Laundry room; Barber/Beauty shop.
Activities Arts & crafts; Cards; Games; Reading groups; Prayer groups; Movies.

ARMADA

Fair Acres Nursing Home
PO Box 559, 22600 Armada Ride, Armada, MI, 48005
(313) 784-5322
Admin Diane M Ewald. *Medical Dir/Dir of Nursing* Patricia Falk RN DON.
Licensure Intermediate care. *Beds* ICF 49. *Certified* Medicaid.
Owner Privately owned.
Admissions Requirements Minimum age 18; Medical examination; Physician's request.
Staff RNs 1 (ft), 3 (pt); LPNs 2 (ft), 3 (pt); Orderlies 1 (ft); Nurses aides 10 (ft), 20 (pt); Activities coordinators 1 (ft); Dietitians 1 (pt).
Facilities Dining room; Activities room; Barber/Beauty shop; Beautiful grounds.
Activities Arts & crafts; Cards; Games; Reading groups; Prayer groups; Movies; Shopping trips; Social/Cultural gatherings.

ASHLEY

Maple Valley Nursing Home*
211 W Wallace, Ashley, MI, 48806
(517) 847-2011
Licensure Intermediate care. *Beds* 49. *Certified* Medicaid.

BAD AXE

Huron County Medical Care Facility
1116 S Van Dyke Rd, Bad Axe, MI, 48413
(517) 269-6425
Admin Arthur J Woelke. *Medical Dir/Dir of Nursing* R A Lockard MD; Gwen McLachlan RN DON.
Licensure Skilled care; Intermediate care. *Beds* 112. *Certified* Medicaid; Medicare.
Owner Publicly owned.
Admissions Requirements Medical examination; Physician's request.
Staff Physicians 2 (pt); RNs 6 (ft), 8 (pt); LPNs 6 (ft), 4 (pt); Nurses aides 44 (ft), 20 (pt); Physical therapists 1 (pt); Recreational therapists 1 (ft); Occupational therapists 1 (pt); Speech therapists 1 (pt); Dietitians 1 (ft).
Facilities Dining room; Physical therapy room; Activities room; Crafts room; Laundry room; Barber/Beauty shop.
Activities Arts & crafts; Cards; Games; Reading groups; Prayer groups; Movies; Social/Cultural gatherings; Bus tours; County fair; Gardening.

Sunny Acres Nursing Center Inc
2762 Pigeon Rd, Bad Axe, MI, 48413
(517) 269-9138
Admin Patricia Patterson. *Medical Dir/Dir of Nursing* O Kay Seiting.
Licensure Intermediate care. *Beds* ICF 30. *Certified* Medicaid.
Owner Proprietary Corp.

Admissions Requirements Medical examination.
Staff RNs 2 (ft), 2 (pt); LPNs 3 (ft), 5 (pt); Nurses aides 2 (ft), 8 (pt); Activities coordinators 1 (pt); Dietitians 1 (ft).
Languages German, Polish
Facilities Dining room; Activities room; Laundry room.
Activities Arts & crafts; Cards; Games; Reading groups; Prayer groups; Movies; Shopping trips; Social/Cultural gatherings.

BALDWIN

Oak Village Care Center*
4153 S M-37, Baldwin, MI, 49304
(616) 745-4648d
Licensure Skilled care; Intermediate care. *Beds* 90. *Certified* Medicaid; Medicare.

BATTLE CREEK

Arrowood Nursing Center
270 N Bedford Rd, Battle Creek, MI, 49017
(616) 968-2296
Licensure Skilled care; Intermediate care. *Beds* 123. *Certified* Medicaid; Medicare.

Calhoun County Medical Care Facility
1150 E Michigan Ave, Battle Creek, MI, 49017
(616) 962-5458
Admin Joanne J Konkle. *Medical Dir/Dir of Nursing* Robert Oakes MD; Pam Pope RN DON.
Licensure Skilled care; Intermediate care. *Beds* SNF 120. *Certified* Medicaid; Medicare.
Owner Publicly owned.
Admissions Requirements Minimum age 18; Medical examination.
Staff Physicians 8 (pt); RNs 13 (ft), 1 (pt); LPNs 2 (ft), 15 (pt); Nurses aides 45 (ft), 21 (pt); Physical therapists 1 (pt); Speech therapists 1 (pt); Activities coordinators; Dietitians 1 (pt); Podiatrists; Audiologists 1 (pt); Optometrist.
Facilities Dining room; Physical therapy room; Activities room; Chapel; Crafts room; Laundry room; Barber/Beauty shop; TV rooms.
Activities Arts & crafts; Cards; Games; Reading groups; Prayer groups; Movies; Shopping trips; Social/Cultural gatherings; Cook outs; Social hour; Dinner trips.

Provincial House—Battle Creek*
111 Evergreen Rd, Battle Creek, MI, 49017
Admin Helen Gastian. *Medical Dir/Dir of Nursing* Gerald Rutledge DO.
Licensure Skilled care. *Beds* 117. *Certified* Medicaid; Medicare.
Owner Proprietary Corp (Beverly Enterprises).
Admissions Requirements Medical examination; Physician's request.
Staff RNs 5 (ft), 1 (pt); LPNs 6 (ft), 4 (pt); Orderlies 3 (ft), 3 (pt); Nurses aides 32 (ft), 15 (pt); Activities coordinators 1 (ft); Dietitians 1 (ft).
Facilities Dining room; Physical therapy room; Activities room; Chapel; Crafts room; Laundry room; Barber/Beauty shop; Library.
Activities Arts & crafts; Cards; Games; Reading groups; Prayer groups; Movies; Shopping trips; Social/Cultural gatherings.

Riverside Manor
675 Wagner Dr, Battle Creek, MI, 49017
(616) 962-6244
Admin Marian M Hart.
Licensure Intermediate care. *Beds* ICF 107. *Certified* Medicaid.
Owner Proprietary Corp.
Admissions Requirements Minimum age 15.
Staff RNs 1 (ft); LPNs; Orderlies; Nurses aides; Activities coordinators.

Facilities Dining room; Activities room; Chapel; Barber/Beauty shop; Library.
Activities Arts & crafts; Cards; Games; Reading groups; Prayer groups; Movies; Shopping trips; Social/Cultural gatherings.

Springhill Manor
200 E Roosevelt Ave, Battle Creek, MI, 49017
(616) 965-3327
Admin Betty J Martin. *Medical Dir/Dir of Nursing* Paul Diamante MD; Donna D Bunce RN.
Licensure Skilled care. *Beds* SNF 65. *Certified* Medicaid; Medicare.
Owner Proprietary Corp (Health Care & Retire Corp).
Admissions Requirements Medical examination; Physician's request.
Staff RNs 4 (ft), 4 (pt); LPNs 2 (ft), 6 (pt); Orderlies 2 (ft), 3 (pt); Nurses aides 17 (ft), 20 (pt); Physical therapists 1 (pt); Speech therapists 1 (pt); Activities coordinators 1 (ft); Dietitians 1 (ft); Ophthalmologists 1 (pt); Podiatrists 1 (pt).
Facilities Dining room; Laundry room; Barber/Beauty shop.
Activities Arts & crafts; Cards; Games; Reading groups; Prayer groups; Movies; Shopping trips; Social/Cultural gatherings; Bus tours twice per year.

BAY CITY

Colonial Rest Home*
2394 Midland Rd, Bay City, MI, 48706
(517) 684-2303
Licensure Intermediate care. *Beds* 52.

Hampton Manor
800 Mulholland St, Bay City, MI, 48708
(517) 895-8539
Admin Nancy J Walker. *Medical Dir/Dir of Nursing* L Berta DO; Julie Osling RN DON.
Licensure Skilled care. *Beds* SNF 51. *Certified* Medicaid; Medicare.
Owner Proprietary Corp (Health Care & Retirement Corp).
Admissions Requirements Minimum age 18; Physician's request.
Staff RNs 1 (ft), 2 (pt); LPNs 3 (ft), 2 (pt); Nurses aides 15 (ft), 11 (pt); Activities coordinators 1 (ft).
Facilities Dining room; Physical therapy room; Laundry room; Barber/Beauty shop.
Activities Arts & crafts; Cards; Games; Reading groups; Prayer groups; Movies; Shopping trips; Social/Cultural gatherings.

Rach Sovereign Memorial Home*
1014 Center Ave, Bay City, MI, 48706
(517) 892-8493
Licensure Intermediate care. *Beds* 7. *Certified* Medicaid.

Tri-City Nursing Center
3254 E Midland Rd, Bay City, MI, 48706
(517) 686-3770
Medical Dir/Dir of Nursing Ronald Koehler DO.
Licensure Skilled care; Intermediate care. *Beds* 126. *Certified* Medicaid; Medicare.
Owner Proprietary Corp (International Health Care Management).
Admissions Requirements Minimum age 15; Medical examination; Physician's request.
Staff RNs 6 (ft), 2 (pt); LPNs 12 (ft), 6 (pt); Nurses aides 80 (ft), 60 (pt); Physical therapists 1 (ft); Recreational therapists 1 (ft); Speech therapists 1 (pt); Activities coordinators 1 (ft); Dietitians 1 (pt).

BELDING

Belding Christian Home*
414 E State St, Belding, MI, 48809
(616) 794-0406

Licensure Skilled care; Intermediate care. *Beds* 123. *Certified* Medicaid; Medicare.

BELLAIRE

Meadow Brook Medical Care Facility
4543 Scenic Hwy, Bellaire, MI, 49615
(616) 533-8661
Admin Mrs LaVerne Sheneman RN. *Medical Dir/Dir of Nursing* Donald Bills DO; Patsy Marshall RN DON.
Licensure Skilled care. *Beds* SNF 113. *Certified* Medicaid.
Owner Publicly owned.
Admissions Requirements Minimum age 15; Physician's request.
Staff Physicians 4 (pt); RNs 4 (ft), 5 (pt); LPNs 6 (ft), 5 (pt); Orderlies 1 (ft); Nurses aides 52 (ft), 6 (pt); Physical therapists 1 (pt); Recreational therapists 1 (ft); Activities coordinators 1 (ft); Dietitians 1 (pt); Ophthalmologists 1 (pt); Podiatrists 1 (pt); Physical therapy aides 1 (pt) Recreational therapy aides 1 (pt).
Facilities Dining room; Physical therapy room; Activities room; Chapel; Crafts room; Laundry room; Barber/Beauty shop; Library; Bingo; Picnics; Fishing; Catholic mass; Theme dinners.
Activities Arts & crafts; Cards; Games; Movies; Social/Cultural gatherings.

BELLEVILLE

Van Buren Convalescent Center
44401 Willow Run Expwy, Belleville, MI, 48111
(313) 697-8051
Licensure Skilled care; Intermediate care. *Beds* 222. *Certified* Medicaid; Medicare.
Owner Proprietary Corp (International Health Care Management).

BENTON HARBOR

Blossom Care Center
1385 E Empire Ave, Benton Harbor, MI, 49022
(616) 925-0033
Admin Sheila McNees. *Medical Dir/Dir of Nursing* Lynn Gray MD.
Licensure Skilled care; Intermediate care. *Beds* SNF 123; ICF. *Certified* Medicaid; Medicare.
Owner Proprietary Corp.
Admissions Requirements Medical examination; Physician's request.
Staff RNs 3 (ft), 6 (pt); LPNs 5 (ft), 2 (pt); Orderlies 3 (ft), 2 (pt); Nurses aides 32 (ft), 32 (pt); Activities coordinators 1 (ft), 2 (pt).
Facilities Dining room; Physical therapy room; Activities room; Crafts room; Barber/Beauty shop.
Activities Arts & crafts; Cards; Games; Reading groups; Prayer groups; Movies; Shopping trips; Social/Cultural gatherings; Happy hour; Pet therapy.

BERRIEN CENTER

Berrien General Hospital
1250 Deanshill Rd, Berrien Center, MI, 49102
(616) 471-7761
Medical Dir/Dir of Nursing Dwain Silvernale MD.
Licensure Skilled care; Intermediate care. *Beds* 189. *Certified* Medicaid; Medicare.
Admissions Requirements Minimum age 18; Physician's request.
Staff Physicians 14 (ft), 1 (pt); RNs 7 (ft), 3 (pt); LPNs 13 (ft), 7 (pt); Orderlies 51 (ft), 18 (pt); Physical therapists 2 (ft); Recreational therapists 1 (ft); Speech therapists 1 (ft); Activities coordinators 1 (ft); Dietitians 1 (ft); Dentists 1 (pt); Ophthalmologists 1 (pt).

Facilities Dining room; Physical therapy room; Activities room; Chapel; Crafts room; Laundry room; Barber/Beauty shop; Living center.
Activities Arts & crafts; Cards; Games; Reading groups; Prayer groups; Movies; Shopping trips; Social/Cultural gatherings.

Bry Fern Care Center*
Deans Hill, PO Box 68, Berrien Center, MI, 49102
(616) 473-4911
Medical Dir/Dir of Nursing Dr Richard Roach.
Licensure Intermediate care. *Beds* 62. *Certified* Medicaid.
Admissions Requirements Minimum age 15; Medical examination.
Staff RNs 3 (ft); LPNs 5 (ft); Orderlies 2 (pt); Nurses aides 12 (ft), 18 (pt); Physical therapists; Occupational therapists; Speech therapists; Activities coordinators 1 (ft); Dietitians 1 (ft); Ophthalmologists.
Facilities Dining room; Activities room; Crafts room; Laundry room; Barber/Beauty shop; Library.
Activities Arts & crafts; Cards; Games; Reading groups; Prayer groups; Movies; Shopping trips; Social/Cultural gatherings.

BIG RAPIDS

Greenridge Nursing Center
725 W Fuller, Big Rapids, MI, 49307
(616) 796-2631
Admin Janet L Worthington. *Medical Dir/Dir of Nursing* Leona Spedoski Rn DON.
Licensure Skilled care. *Beds* 126. *Certified* Medicaid; Medicare.
Owner Proprietary Corp.
Admissions Requirements Minimum age 15; Medical examination; Physician's request.
Staff RNs 2 (ft), 3 (pt); LPNs 9 (ft); Nurses aides 50 (ft), 20 (pt); Physical therapists 1 (ft), 1 (pt); Occupational therapists 1 (pt); Speech therapists 1 (pt); Activities coordinators 1 (ft); Dietitians 1 (ft).
Facilities Dining room; Physical therapy room; Activities room; Crafts room; Laundry room; Barber/Beauty shop.
Activities Arts & crafts; Cards; Games; Reading groups; Prayer groups; Movies; Shopping trips; Social/Cultural gatherings.

BIRMINGHAM

Cambridge Nursing Center—South
18200 W 13 Mile Rd, Birmingham, MI, 48009
(313) 647-6500
Licensure Skilled care; Intermediate care. *Beds* 102. *Certified* Medicaid; Medicare.
Owner Proprietary Corp (International Health Care Management).

BLOOMFIELD HILLS

Bloomfield Hills Care Center*
50 Square Lake Rd, Bloomfield Hills, MI, 48013
(313) 338-0345
Licensure Skilled care; Intermediate care. *Beds* 366. *Certified* Medicaid; Medicare.

Brae Burn Inc
1312 N Woodward Ave, Bloomfield Hills, MI, 48013
(313) 644-8015
Admin Jim Albright. *Medical Dir/Dir of Nursing* Dr Harley J Robinson; William Lass.
Licensure Intermediate care. *Beds* ICF 115. *Certified* Medicaid.
Owner Proprietary Corp.
Admissions Requirements Medical examination.

Staff Physicians 5 (pt); RNs 5 (ft), 3 (pt); LPNs 6 (ft), 4 (pt); Orderlies 10 (ft); Nurses aides 30 (ft); Physical therapists 2 (pt); Recreational therapists 1 (pt); Occupational therapists 1 (pt); Speech therapists 1 (pt); Activities coordinators 2 (ft); Dietitians 1 (ft); Dentists 1 (pt); Ophthalmologists 1 (pt); Podiatrists 1 (pt).
Facilities Dining room; Physical therapy room; Activities room; Crafts room; Laundry room; Barber/Beauty shop; Library.
Activities Arts & crafts; Cards; Games; Reading groups; Prayer groups; Movies; Shopping trips; Social/Cultural gatherings.

Georgian—Bloomfield*
2975 N Adams Rd, Bloomfield Hills, MI, 48013
(313) 645-2900
Medical Dir/Dir of Nursing Dr John Dzuiba.
Licensure Skilled care; Intermediate care. *Beds* 274. *Certified* Medicaid; Medicare.
Staff Physicians 7 (pt); RNs 16 (ft), 9 (pt); LPNs 8 (ft), 5 (pt); Orderlies 6 (ft); Nurses aides 60 (ft), 18 (pt); Recreational therapists 1 (ft), 1 (pt); Activities coordinators 1 (ft); Dietitians 1 (ft), 1 (pt).
Facilities Dining room; Physical therapy room; Activities room; Chapel; Laundry room; Barber/Beauty shop.
Activities Arts & crafts; Cards; Games; Reading groups; Prayer groups; Movies; Social/Cultural gatherings.

BLOOMINGDALE

Bethany Nursing Home Inc
42235 County Rd 665, Bloomingdale, MI, 49026
(616) 521-3383
Admin Delmon M Esh Jr. *Medical Dir/Dir of Nursing* Daniel Ekkens MD; Imelda Fuster RN.
Licensure Skilled care; Intermediate care. *Beds* 78. *Certified* Medicaid; Medicare.
Owner Proprietary Corp.
Admissions Requirements Minimum age 15; Medical examination; Physician's request.
Staff Physicians 1 (pt); RNs 3 (ft), 6 (pt); LPNs 3 (ft), 1 (pt); Orderlies 3 (ft); Nurses aides 28 (ft), 12 (pt); Physical therapists 1 (pt); Occupational therapists 1 (pt); Speech therapists 1 (pt); Activities coordinators 1 (ft), 1 (pt); Dietitians 1 (pt).
Languages Tagalog, Spanish
Facilities Dining room; Physical therapy room; Activities room; Crafts room; Laundry room; Barber/Beauty shop; Library.
Activities Arts & crafts; Cards; Games; Reading groups; Prayer groups; Movies; Social/Cultural gatherings.

BRIDGMAN

Jordan's Nursing Home
PO Box 607, 9935 Red Arrow Hwy, Bridgman, MI, 49106
(616) 465-3017
Admin Larry Olson.
Licensure Intermediate care. *Beds* 105. *Certified* Medicaid.
Admissions Requirements Minimum age 15; Medical examination; Physician's request.
Staff Physicians 4 (pt); RNs 1 (ft), 4 (pt); LPNs 2 (ft), 4 (pt); Nurses aides 31 (ft), 28 (pt); Reality therapists 1 (ft); Recreational therapists 1 (ft); Activities coordinators 1 (ft), 1 (pt); Dietitians 1 (ft); Dentists 1 (pt).
Facilities Dining room; Activities room; Chapel; Crafts room; Laundry room; Barber/Beauty shop.
Activities Arts & crafts; Games; Prayer groups; Movies.

CADILLAC

Lakeview Manor Nursing Home*
460 Pearl St, Cadillac, MI, 49601
(313) 775-0101
Medical Dir/Dir of Nursing Wendell Hyink MD.
Licensure Skilled care; Intermediate care. *Beds* 218. *Certified* Medicaid; Medicare.
Admissions Requirements Minimum age 16; Medical examination; Physician's request.
Staff Physicians 1 (pt); RNs 7 (ft), 4 (pt); LPNs 16 (ft), 13 (pt); Nurses aides 66 (ft), 24 (pt); Physical therapists; Activities coordinators 1 (ft); Dietitians 1 (ft).
Facilities Dining room; Physical therapy room; Activities room; Crafts room; Barber/Beauty shop; 5 lounges.
Activities Arts & crafts; Cards; Games; Reading groups; Prayer groups; Movies; Shopping trips; Social/Cultural gatherings.

CARO

Tuscola County Medical Care Facility
1285 Cleaver Rd, Caro, MI, 48723
(517) 673-4117
Admin Darlene N Davidson. *Medical Dir/Dir of Nursing* Edward N Elmendorf MD; Nancy Hack RN BSN.
Licensure Skilled care. *Beds* SNF 123. *Certified* Medicaid; Medicare.
Owner Publicly owned.
Admissions Requirements Minimum age 15; Medical examination; Physician's request.
Staff Physicians 1 (ft); RNs 5 (ft), 1 (pt); LPNs 4 (ft), 4 (pt); Orderlies 3 (ft); Nurses aides 60 (ft), 25 (pt); Physical therapists 1 (pt); Occupational therapists 1 (pt); Speech therapists 1 (pt); Activities coordinators 1 (ft); Dietitians 1 (pt); Dentists 1 (pt); Ophthalmologists 1 (pt); Podiatrists 1 (pt).
Facilities Dining room; Physical therapy room; Activities room; Chapel; Crafts room; Laundry room; Barber/Beauty shop.
Activities Arts & crafts; Cards; Games; Reading groups; Prayer groups; Movies; Shopping trips; Social/Cultural gatherings.

CASS CITY

Provincial House—Cass City*
Hospital Dr, Cass City, MI, 48726
(517) 872-2174
Admin Alan J Sward. *Medical Dir/Dir of Nursing* Dr Zuzga.
Licensure Skilled care; Intermediate care. *Beds* 117. *Certified* Medicaid; Medicare.
Owner Proprietary Corp (Beverly Enterprises).
Staff Physicians 5 (pt); RNs 4 (ft), 2 (pt); LPNs 7 (ft), 2 (pt); Nurses aides 57 (ft), 18 (pt); Physical therapists 1 (pt); Occupational therapists 1 (pt); Speech therapists 1 (pt); Activities coordinators 1 (ft); Dietitians 1 (pt); Dentists 1 (pt); Ophthalmologists 1 (pt); Podiatrists 1 (pt).
Facilities Dining room; Physical therapy room; Activities room; Crafts room; Laundry room; Barber/Beauty shop.
Activities Arts & crafts; Cards; Games; Reading groups; Movies; Shopping trips; Social/Cultural gatherings.

CASSOPOLIS

Cass County Medical Care Facility
Rte 2, 23770 Hospital St, Cassopolis, MI, 49031
(616) 445-3801
Admin Norma J Weaver. *Medical Dir/Dir of Nursing* Aaron K Warren MD; Janet L Huffman RN.
Licensure Skilled care; Intermediate care. *Beds* SNF 80; ICF. *Certified* Medicaid; Medicare.
Owner Publicly owned.

Admissions Requirements Minimum age 16; Medical examination; Physician's request.
Staff Physicians 2 (pt); RNs 4 (ft), 1 (pt); LPNs 7 (ft), 2 (pt); Orderlies 1 (pt); Nurses aides 39 (ft), 6 (pt); Physical therapists 1 (pt); Activities coordinators 1 (ft).
Languages German, Hungarian
Facilities Dining room; Physical therapy room; Activities room; Chapel; Crafts room; Laundry room; Barber/Beauty shop.
Activities Arts & crafts; Cards; Games; Reading groups; Prayer groups; Movies; Social/Cultural gatherings.

CEDAR SPRINGS

Cedar Springs Nursing Center*
RR 3, 280 Marie, Cedar Springs, MI, 49319-9509
(616) 696-0170
Licensure Skilled care; Intermediate care. *Beds* 77. *Certified* Medicaid; Medicare.

CENTERLINE

Father Murray Nursing Center
8444 Engleman, Centerline, MI, 48015
(313) 755-2400
Admin Catherine T Bertolini. *Medical Dir/Dir of Nursing* Barry Szczesny DO; Nettie Rickerman RN.
Licensure Skilled care; Intermediate care. *Beds* SNF 234; ICF. *Certified* Medicaid; Medicare.
Owner Nonprofit Corp.
Admissions Requirements Minimum age 16; Medical examination; Physician's request.
Languages Polish, Italian, German
Facilities Dining room; Physical therapy room; Activities room; Laundry room; Barber/Beauty shop; Dentist office.
Activities Arts & crafts; Cards; Games; Reading groups; Prayer groups; Movies; Social/Cultural gatherings; Holiday parties including residents families.

CENTREVILLE

Fairview Medical Care Facility
441 E Main P.O. Box 97, Centreville, MI, 49032
(616) 467-9575
Admin Jeanette M Schirs. *Medical Dir/Dir of Nursing* Dr R Smith, Dr D Colberg, Dr O Lepard; Phyllis Bonebright RN DON.
Licensure Skilled care; Intermediate care. *Beds* SNF 64; ICF. *Certified* Medicaid; Medicare.
Owner Publicly owned.
Admissions Requirements Medical examination; Physician's request.
Staff RNs 4 (ft), 2 (pt); LPNs 7 (ft), 3 (pt); Nurses aides 15 (ft), 12 (pt); Activities coordinators 1 (ft).
Facilities Dining room; Physical therapy room; Activities room; Chapel; Crafts room; Barber/Beauty shop; Occupational therapy room.
Activities Arts & crafts; Cards; Games; Prayer groups; Movies; Shopping trips; Social/Cultural gatherings.

CHARLOTTE

Eaton County Medical Care Facility*
530 W Beech St, Charlotte, MI, 48813
(517) 543-2940
Licensure Skilled care; Intermediate care. *Beds* 100. *Certified* Medicaid; Medicare.
Owner Publicly owned.

Immanuel Nursing Home*
511 E Sheperd, Charlotte, MI, 48813
(517) 543-4750
Licensure Intermediate care. *Beds* 49. *Certified* Medicaid.

CHEBOYGAN

Community Memorial Hospital-Extended Care Facility
748 S Main St, Cheboygan, MI, 49721
(616) 627-5601
Admin Howard Purcell Jr. *Medical Dir/Dir of Nursing* Michael Bacon DO; Sandra Dunlap RN DON.
Licensure Skilled care; Intermediate care. *Beds* 50. *Certified* Medicaid; Medicare.
Owner Nonprofit Corp.
Admissions Requirements Medical examination; Physician's request.
Staff RNs 1 (ft), 4 (pt); LPNs 3 (ft), 5 (pt); Nurses aides 12 (ft), 16 (pt); Physical therapists 1 (ft); Activities coordinators 1 (pt); Dietitians 1 (ft).
Facilities Dining room; Physical therapy room; Activities room; Crafts room; Barber/ Beauty shop; Recreation room; 2 outdoor patios; Fenced outdoor area.
Activities Arts & crafts; Cards; Games; Reading groups; Prayer groups; Movies; Shopping trips; Social/Cultural gatherings; Exercise class; Life review group; Annual picnic; Open house.

Green Meadows Nursing Home
824 S Huron St, Cheboygan, MI, 49721
(616) 627-4347
Admin Edward L Bohnow. *Medical Dir/Dir of Nursing* Richard Knecht MD; Julie Jewell RN DON.
Licensure Intermediate care. *Beds* ICF 112; Home for aged 8. *Certified* Medicaid.
Owner Privately owned.
Admissions Requirements Medical examination.
Staff LPNs; Orderlies; Nurses aides; Activities coordinators.
Facilities Dining room; Barber/Beauty shop.
Activities Arts & crafts; Cards; Games; Prayer groups; Social/Cultural gatherings.

CHELSEA

Chelsea United Methodist Retirement Home
W Middle St, Chelsea, MI, 48118
(313) 475-8633
Admin Jack L Steiner. *Medical Dir/Dir of Nursing* James Peggs MD; Carol Peckham RN DON.
Licensure Skilled care; Intermediate care; Retirement; Independent living; Alzheimer's unit. *Beds* SNF; ICF 110; Retirement 173; Independent living 26. *Certified* Medicaid; Medicare.
Owner Nonprofit Corp.
Admissions Requirements Minimum age 62; Medical examination.
Staff Physicians 1 (pt); Physical therapists; Reality therapists; Recreational therapists; Occupational therapists; Speech therapists; Dentists; Ophthalmologists; Podiatrists.
Affiliation Methodist
Facilities Dining room; Physical therapy room; Activities room; Chapel; Crafts room; Laundry room; Barber/Beauty shop; Library; Ice cream parlor; Ceramic shop; Woodworking shop.
Activities Arts & crafts; Cards; Games; Reading groups; Prayer groups; Movies; Shopping trips; Social/Cultural gatherings; Outside groups with socials & entertainment; Special dinners; Girl Scout troop.

CHESANING

Chesaning Nursing Care Center Inc
201 S Front St, Chesaning, MI, 48616
(517) 845-6602
Admin Maria A Janveja. *Medical Dir/Dir of Nursing* Dawn McBride RN.
Licensure Intermediate care. *Beds* ICF 30; Home for Aged 9. *Certified* Medicaid.
Owner Proprietary Corp.

Admissions Requirements Minimum age 18; Medical examination; Physician's request.
Staff Physicians 4 (pt); RNs 1 (ft), 2 (pt); LPNs 3 (ft), 5 (pt); Nurses aides 7 (ft), 15 (pt); Recreational therapists 1 (ft), 1 (pt); Dietitians 1 (pt); Ophthalmologists 1 (pt).
Facilities Dining room; Activities room; Crafts room; Laundry room; Barber/Beauty shop.
Activities Arts & crafts; Cards; Games; Reading groups; Prayer groups; Movies; Shopping trips; Social/Cultural gatherings; Music programs; Clown programs.

CLARE

Clare Nursing Home*
600 SE 4th St, Clare, MI, 48617
(517) 386-7723
Admin Wilma Shurlow. *Medical Dir/Dir of Nursing* Dr E C Shurlow.
Licensure Skilled care; Intermediate care. *Beds* 129. *Certified* Medicaid; Medicare.
Staff RNs 2 (ft), 4 (pt); LPNs 12 (ft), 4 (pt); Orderlies 3 (ft), 1 (pt); Nurses aides 41 (ft), 36 (pt); Physical therapists 1 (pt); Speech therapists; Activities coordinators 1 (ft); Dietitians 1 (pt); Dentists.
Facilities Dining room; Physical therapy room; Activities room; Chapel; Crafts room; Laundry room; Barber/Beauty shop; 3 Day rooms.
Activities Arts & crafts; Cards; Games; Reading groups; Prayer groups; Movies; Shopping trips; Social/Cultural gatherings.

CLAWSON

Cambridge North Inc
535 N Main, Clawson, MI, 48017
(313) 435-5200
Admin Barbara L Iseppi. *Medical Dir/Dir of Nursing* Ronald Knauff DO; Jane Brunt RN.
Licensure Skilled care; Intermediate care. *Beds* 120. *Certified* Medicaid; Medicare.
Owner Proprietary Corp (International Health Care Management).
Staff Physicians; RNs; LPNs; Orderlies; Nurses aides; Physical therapists; Recreational therapists; Speech therapists; Activities coordinators; Dietitians; Dentists; Ophthalmologists; Dentist.
Facilities Dining room; Physical therapy room; Activities room; Crafts room; Barber/ Beauty shop.
Activities Arts & crafts; Cards; Games; Prayer groups; Movies; Parties.

CLIO

Clio Convalescent Center Inc
13137 N Clio Rd, Clio, MI, 48420
(313) 686-2600
Admin Pearl Fredell. *Medical Dir/Dir of Nursing* Gerald Whalen DO; Roberta Kennedy RN DON.
Licensure Intermediate care. *Beds* ICF 151. *Certified* Medicaid.
Owner Proprietary Corp.
Admissions Requirements Minimum age 15; Medical examination; Physician's request.
Staff Physicians 7 (pt); RNs 4 (ft); LPNs 7 (ft), 6 (pt); Nurses aides 32 (ft), 38 (pt); Physical therapists 1 (pt); Speech therapists 1 (pt); Activities coordinators 2 (ft); Dietitians 1 (ft); Dentists 2 (pt); Ophthalmologists 1 (pt).
Languages Hungarian
Facilities Dining room; Physical therapy room; Activities room; Chapel; Crafts room; Laundry room; Barber/Beauty shop.
Activities Arts & crafts; Cards; Games; Reading groups; Prayer groups; Movies; Social/Cultural gatherings.

COLDWATER

Carriage Inn Convalescent Center
90 N Michigan Ave, Coldwater, MI, 49036
(517) 278-4819
Admin F Harold Creal. *Medical Dir/Dir of Nursing* L J Creal.
Licensure Skilled care. *Beds* SNF 169. *Certified* Medicaid; Medicare.
Owner Proprietary Corp.
Admissions Requirements Medical examination.
Staff RNs; LPNs; Orderlies; Nurses aides; Physical therapists; Occupational therapists; Speech therapists; Activities coordinators.
Facilities Dining room; Physical therapy room; Activities room; Crafts room; Laundry room; Barber/Beauty shop.
Activities Arts & crafts; Cards; Games; Reading groups; Prayer groups; Movies; Shopping trips; Social/Cultural gatherings; High school courses.

Maple Lawn Medical Care Facility
841 Marshall Rd, Coldwater, MI, 49036
(517) 279-9587
Admin C Eldon Loney. *Medical Dir/Dir of Nursing* L F Chapman MD; Darlene Starr Acting DON.
Licensure Skilled care; Intermediate care; VA. *Beds* SNF 114. *Certified* Medicaid; Medicare; VA.
Owner Publicly owned.
Admissions Requirements Physician's request.
Facilities Dining room; Physical therapy room; Activities room; Chapel; Crafts room; Laundry room; Barber/Beauty shop.
Activities Arts & crafts; Cards; Games; Reading groups; Prayer groups; Movies; Social/Cultural gatherings.

CORUNNA

Shiawassee County Medical Care Facility
729 S Norton St, Corunna, MI, 48817
(517) 743-3491
Admin Anne Hark RN BA MS. *Medical Dir/ Dir of Nursing* P J Moore MD; Linda Gall RN BS MA.
Licensure Skilled care; Intermediate care. *Beds* SNF 152; ICF. *Certified* Medicaid; Medicare.
Owner Publicly owned.
Admissions Requirements Minimum age 16; Medical examination; Physician's request.
Staff Physicians 2 (pt); RNs; LPNs 40 (ft); Nurses aides 80 (ft); Physical therapists 1 (pt); Activities coordinators 1 (ft); Dietitians 1 (pt).
Facilities Dining room; Physical therapy room; Activities room; Chapel; Crafts room; Barber/Beauty shop.
Activities Arts & crafts; Cards; Games; Reading groups; Prayer groups; Movies.

CRYSTAL FALLS

Crystal Manor*
400 Superior Ave, Crystal Falls, MI, 49920
(906) 875-6663
Licensure Intermediate care. *Beds* 71. *Certified* Medicaid.

Iron County Medical Care Facility
1523 W US 2, Crystal Falls, MI, 49920
(906) 875-6671
Admin Chester E Pintarelli. *Medical Dir/Dir of Nursing* Robert F Han MD; Maxine M Tokoly RN DON.
Licensure Skilled care; Intermediate care. *Beds* 109. *Certified* Medicaid; Medicare.
Owner Publicly owned.
Admissions Requirements Physician's request.

Staff Physicians 1 (pt); RNs 2 (ft), 5 (pt); LPNs 9 (ft), 3 (pt); Nurses aides 38 (ft), 22 (pt); Physical therapists 2 (pt); Occupational therapists 2 (ft); Activities coordinators 1 (pt).
Facilities Dining room; Physical therapy room; Activities room; Chapel; Crafts room; Laundry room; Barber/Beauty shop; Library; Smoking & TV areas.
Activities Arts & crafts; Cards; Games; Reading groups; Prayer groups; Movies; Social/Cultural gatherings; Woodworking; Ceramics; Parties; Picnics; Fair outings.

DEARBORN HEIGHTS

Dearborn Heights Convalescent Center*
26001 Ford Rd, Dearborn Heights, MI, 48127
Licensure Intermediate care. *Beds* 151. *Certified* Medicaid.

DETROIT

Alpha Annex Nursing Center*
609 E Grand Blvd, Detroit, MI, 48207
(313) 923-0300
Licensure Skilled care; Intermediate care. *Beds* 103. *Certified* Medicaid; Medicare.

Alpha Manor Nursing Home*
440 E Grand Blvd, Detroit, MI, 48207
(313) 579-2900
Licensure Intermediate care. *Beds* 100.

Ambassador Nursing Center*
9146 Woodward Ave, Detroit, MI, 48203
(313) 875-1263
Licensure Skilled care. *Beds* 195. *Certified* Medicaid; Medicare.

Americare Convalescent Center*
19211 Anglin St, Detroit, MI, 48234
(313) 893-9745
Licensure Intermediate care. *Beds* 139. *Certified* Medicaid.

Anchorage Convalescent Home Inc
13850 Grand River Ave, Detroit, MI, 48227
(313) 273-2470
Admin Virginia Sampson. *Medical Dir/Dir of Nursing* Clabon Densley.
Licensure Intermediate care. *Beds* ICF 53. *Certified* Medicaid.
Owner Proprietary Corp.
Admissions Requirements Minimum age 18; Medical examination; Physician's request.
Staff RNs 1 (ft); LPNs 3 (ft), 3 (pt); Nurses aides 18 (ft), 6 (pt); Activities coordinators 1 (ft); Dietitians 1 (pt); Dentists 1 (pt); Ophthalmologists 1 (pt).
Facilities Dining room; Activities room; Laundry room; Barber/Beauty shop.
Activities Arts & crafts; Cards; Games; Reading groups; Prayer groups; Movies; Shopping trips; Social/Cultural gatherings.

Arnold Home Inc
18520 W 7 Mile Rd, Detroit, MI, 48219
(313) 531-4001
Admin Chester E Pearson. *Medical Dir/Dir of Nursing* Meyer J Elman MD; Mildred Angelillo RN DON.
Licensure Skilled care; Intermediate care; Independent living; Home for aged. *Beds* SNF 224; ICF; Independent living; Home for aged 165. *Certified* Medicaid; Medicare.
Owner Nonprofit Corp.
Admissions Requirements Minimum age 15; Home for Aged 60; Medical examination; Physician's request.
Staff Physicians 3 (pt); RNs 5 (ft), 7 (pt); LPNs 12 (ft), 9 (pt); Nurses aides 87 (ft); Physical therapists 1 (pt); Reality therapists 1 (pt); Recreational therapists 2 (ft); Occupational therapists 1 (ft), 1 (pt); Speech therapists 1 (pt); Activities coordinators 1

(ft); Dietitians 1 (ft); Dentists 1 (pt); Ophthalmologists 1 (pt); Podiatrists 1 (pt); Dentist 1 (pt).
Facilities Dining room; Physical therapy room; Activities room; Chapel; Crafts room; Laundry room; Barber/Beauty shop; Library; Pharmacy.
Activities Arts & crafts; Cards; Games; Reading groups; Prayer groups; Movies; Shopping trips; Social/Cultural gatherings.

Avonside Nursing Home*
791 E Grand Blvd, Detroit, MI, 48207
(313) 9211-1332
Licensure Intermediate care. *Beds* 42. *Certified* Medicaid.

Barton Nursing Home Inc
722 E Grand Blvd, Detroit, MI, 48207
(313) 923-8080
Admin Daniel W James. *Medical Dir/Dir of Nursing* Eleanor James.
Licensure Intermediate care. *Beds* ICF 50. *Certified* Medicaid.
Owner Proprietary Corp.
Admissions Requirements Physician's request.
Staff RNs 1 (ft), 1 (pt); LPNs 2 (ft), 14 (pt); Nurses aides 16 (ft), 8 (pt); Dietitians 1 (pt).
Languages Polish, Tagalog
Facilities Dining room; Activities room; Crafts room; Barber/Beauty shop; Library.
Activities Arts & crafts; Cards; Games; Reading groups; Prayer groups; Movies; Shopping trips; Social/Cultural gatherings.

Boulevard Temple United Methodist Retirement Home
2567 W Grand Blvd, Detroit, MI, 48208
(313) 895-5340
Admin Wanda R Wooten. *Medical Dir/Dir of Nursing* Caroline Blaum MD.
Licensure Intermediate care; Home for aged. *Beds* ICF 124; Alzheimer's 11; Home for aged 45; Apts 33. *Certified* Medicaid.
Owner Nonprofit Corp.
Admissions Requirements Medical examination.
Staff Physicians 3 (ft); RNs 6 (ft); LPNs 8 (ft), 6 (pt); Nurses aides 42 (ft), 31 (pt); Physical therapists 1 (ft); Occupational therapists 1 (ft); Speech therapists 1 (ft); Activities coordinators 2 (ft); Dietitians 1 (ft); Podiatrists 1 (pt).
Affiliation Methodist
Facilities Dining room; Physical therapy room; Activities room; Chapel; Crafts room; Laundry room; Barber/Beauty shop; Library.
Activities Arts & crafts; Games; Reading groups; Prayer groups; Movies; Shopping trips; Social/Cultural gatherings.

Broadstreet Nursing Center
12040 Broadstreet, Detroit, MI, 48204
(313) 931-2800
Admin James Norcross. *Medical Dir/Dir of Nursing* Fred Gold DO; Marilyn Mayville RN DON.
Licensure Intermediate care. *Beds* ICF 97. *Certified* Medicaid.
Owner Proprietary Corp.
Admissions Requirements Minimum age 21; Physician's request.
Staff Physicians 1 (pt); RNs 1 (ft), 1 (pt); LPNs 7 (ft), 4 (pt); Orderlies 3 (ft); Nurses aides 27 (ft), 11 (pt); Physical therapists 1 (pt); Occupational therapists 1 (pt); Speech therapists 1 (pt); Activities coordinators 1 (ft), 1 (pt); Dietitians 1 (pt); Dentists 1 (pt); Ophthalmologists 1 (pt); Podiatrists 1 (pt).
Facilities Dining room; Physical therapy room; Activities room; Laundry room; Barber/Beauty shop; Library.
Activities Arts & crafts; Cards; Games; Reading groups; Prayer groups; Movies; Shopping trips; Social/Cultural gatherings; Music therapy.

Cadillac Nursing Home
1533 Cadillac Blvd, Detroit, MI, 48214
(313) 823-0435
Admin James T McCuish. *Medical Dir/Dir of Nursing* Dr D Dreyfuss; A Lumarque DON.
Licensure Skilled care; Intermediate care. *Beds* SNF 47; ICF 50. *Certified* Medicaid; Medicare.
Owner Proprietary Corp.
Staff Physicians 1 (pt); RNs 4 (ft); LPNs 6 (ft); Nurses aides 40 (ft); Physical therapists 1 (pt); Recreational therapists 1 (pt); Speech therapists 1 (pt); Activities coordinators 2 (ft); Dietitians 1 (pt); Dentists 1 (pt); Ophthalmologists 1 (pt); Podiatrists 1 (pt).
Languages Italian, Spanish, Tagalog
Activities Arts & crafts; Cards; Games; Reading groups; Prayer groups; Movies; Social/Cultural gatherings.

Coplin Manor Convalescent Home*
4721 Coplin, Detroit, MI, 48215
(313) 823-0330
Medical Dir/Dir of Nursing Arthur Cooper DO.
Licensure Intermediate care. *Beds* 38. *Certified* Medicaid.
Admissions Requirements Minimum age 18; Females only; Medical examination; Physician's request.
Staff RNs; LPNs; Orderlies; Nurses aides; Physical therapists; Reality therapists; Recreational therapists; Occupational therapists; Speech therapists; Activities coordinators; Dietitians; Dentists; Ophthalmologists; Podiatrists; Audiologists.
Facilities Dining room; Physical therapy room; Activities room; Crafts room; Laundry room; Barber/Beauty shop.
Activities Arts & crafts; Cards; Games; Reading groups; Prayer groups; Movies; Shopping trips; Social/Cultural gatherings.

Cranbrook Nursing Home*
5000 E 7 Mile Rd, Detroit, MI, 48234
(313) 366-8500
Licensure Skilled care; Intermediate care. *Beds* 91. *Certified* Medicaid; Medicare.
Admissions Requirements Minimum age 15; Medical examination; Physician's request.
Staff RNs; LPNs; Orderlies; Nurses aides; Physical therapists 1 (pt); Occupational therapists 1 (pt); Activities coordinators 1 (ft); Dietitians 1 (pt).
Facilities Dining room; Physical therapy room; Activities room; Crafts room; Barber/Beauty shop.
Activities Arts & crafts; Cards; Games; Reading groups; Prayer groups; Movies; Shopping trips; Social/Cultural gatherings.

David Nursing Home*
13241 W Chicago, Detroit, MI, 48228
(313) 834-6670 & 834-1192
Licensure Skilled care. *Beds* 57. *Certified* Medicaid.

Detroiter Residence*
2560 Woodward, Detroit, MI, 48201
(313) 963-3545
Licensure Intermediate care. *Beds* 300. *Certified* Medicaid.
Staff Physicians 5 (pt); RNs 3 (ft); LPNs 18 (ft); Orderlies 12 (ft); Nurses aides 150 (ft); Physical therapists 4 (ft); Reality therapists 2 (ft); Recreational therapists 4 (ft); Occupational therapists 1 (pt); Speech therapists 1 (pt); Activities coordinators 1 (ft); Dietitians 3 (ft), 1 (pt); Dentists 1 (pt); Ophthalmologists 1 (pt); Podiatrists 1 (pt).
Facilities Dining room; Physical therapy room; Activities room; Chapel; Crafts room; Laundry room; Barber/Beauty shop; Library.
Activities Arts & crafts; Games; Reading groups; Prayer groups; Shopping trips; Social/Cultural gatherings.

East Grand Nursing Home*
130 E Grand Blvd, Detroit, MI, 48207
(313) 824-8224
Licensure Skilled care; Intermediate care. *Beds* 94.

Eastwood Nursing Center
626 E Grand Blvd, Detroit, MI, 48207
(313) 923-5816
Admin Michele T Chare. *Medical Dir/Dir of Nursing* Sharon Dale DON.
Licensure Skilled care; Intermediate care. *Beds* SNF 47; ICF 39. *Certified* Medicaid; Medicare.
Owner Proprietary Corp.
Admissions Requirements Physician's request.
Facilities Dining room; Activities room.
Activities Arts & crafts; Cards; Prayer groups; Movies; Social/Cultural gatherings.

Elmwood Geriatric Village
1881 E Grand Blvd, Detroit, MI, 48211
(313) 922-1600
Admin Jacqueline E Nave. *Medical Dir/Dir of Nursing* Lawrence Usher DO; Dorothy Cheit RN DON.
Licensure Skilled care. *Beds* SNF 120. *Certified* Medicaid; Medicare.
Owner Privately owned.
Admissions Requirements Minimum age 18; Medical examination; Physician's request.
Staff Physicians 2 (pt); RNs 2 (ft), 4 (pt); LPNs 10 (ft), 10 (pt); Orderlies 4 (ft), 2 (pt); Nurses aides 30 (ft), 15 (pt); Activities coordinators 1 (ft).
Facilities Dining room; Physical therapy room; Activities room; Chapel; Crafts room; Laundry room; Barber/Beauty shop.
Activities Arts & crafts; Cards; Games; Reading groups; Prayer groups; Movies; Shopping trips; Social/Cultural gatherings.

Evangelical Home—Detroit
6700 W Outer Dr, Detroit, MI, 48235
(313) 836-1700
Admin Vito A Bommarito. *Medical Dir/Dir of Nursing* Donald Visscher MD; Jeanne Legge-Taylor RN.
Licensure Skilled care; Intermediate care; Independent living HFA apts. *Certified* Medicaid; Medicare.
Owner Nonprofit Corp.
Admissions Requirements Minimum age 60; Medical examination.
Staff Physicians; RNs; LPNs; Nurses aides; Physical therapists; Occupational therapists; Speech therapists; Activities coordinators; Dietitians; Dentists; Ophthalmologists.
Affiliation Church of Christ
Facilities Dining room; Physical therapy room; Activities room; Chapel; Crafts room; Laundry room; Barber/Beauty shop; Library.
Activities Arts & crafts; Games; Prayer groups; Movies; Shopping trips; Social/Cultural gatherings.

Fairlane Nursing Center
15750 Joy Rd, Detroit, MI, 48228
(313) 273-6850
Admin James R Branscum. *Medical Dir/Dir of Nursing* Jack Mayer DO; Ronda Kuzmanovich RN.
Licensure Skilled care; Intermediate care. *Beds* SNF 179; ICF 146. *Certified* Medicaid; Medicare.
Owner Proprietary Corp.
Admissions Requirements Minimum age 18; Physician's request.
Staff Physicians 4 (pt); RNs 4 (ft); LPNs 20 (ft); Orderlies 5 (ft); Nurses aides 100 (ft); Physical therapists 2 (ft); Reality therapists 3 (ft); Recreational therapists 2 (ft); Occupational therapists 1 (ft); Speech therapists 1 (ft); Activities coordinators 1 (ft); Dietitians 1 (ft); Dentists 1 (ft); Ophthalmologists 1 (ft); Podiatrists 1 (ft); Dentist 1 (ft).
Languages Polish

Facilities Dining room; Physical therapy room; Activities room; Chapel; Crafts room; Laundry room; Barber/Beauty shop; Library.
Activities Arts & crafts; Cards; Games; Reading groups; Prayer groups; Movies; Shopping trips; Social/Cultural gatherings.

Friendship Manor Nursing Home
3950 Beaubien Ave, Detroit, MI, 48201
(313) 833-7600
Licensure Intermediate care. *Beds* 170. *Certified* Medicaid.

Grace Convalescent Center*
18901 Meyers Rd, Detroit, MI, 48235
(313) 864-8481
Licensure Skilled care; Intermediate care. *Beds* 226. *Certified* Medicaid; Medicare.

Great Lakes Convalescent Center*
12900 W Chicago, Detroit, MI, 48228
(313) 491-6400
Licensure Skilled care; Intermediate care. *Beds* 164. *Certified* Medicaid; Medicare.
Owner Proprietary Corp (Beverly Enterprises).

Hadley Manor
535 E Grand Blvd, Detroit, MI, 48207
(313) 923-2020
Admin Timothy Korlson. *Medical Dir/Dir of Nursing* William Silverstone MD; Georgia Gray RN DON.
Licensure Intermediate care. *Beds* ICF 38. *Certified* Medicaid.
Staff Physicians 1 (pt); RNs 1 (ft); LPNs 3 (ft), 4 (pt); Nurses aides 20 (ft); Activities coordinators 1 (ft); Dietitians 1 (pt); Dentists 1 (pt); Ophthalmologists 1 (pt).
Facilities Dining room; Activities room; Crafts room; Laundry room.
Activities Arts & crafts; Cards; Games; Prayer groups; Movies; Shopping trips; Social/ Cultural gatherings; Outings.

Hamilton Nursing Home*
590 E Grand Blvd, Detroit, MI, 48207
(313) 921-1580
Licensure Skilled care. *Beds* 55. *Certified* Medicaid; Medicare.

Hillcrest Convalescent Center*
E12535 Harper, Detroit, MI, 48213
(313) 371-5520
Licensure Skilled care; Intermediate care. *Beds* 79. *Certified* Medicaid; Medicare.

Ingleside Convalescent Center*
9155 Woodward Ave, Detroit, MI, 48202
(313) 872-1420
Licensure Intermediate care. *Beds* 141.

Jewish Home for the Aged 2*
19100 W 7 Mile Rd, Detroit, MI, 48219
(313) 532-7112
Medical Dir/Dir of Nursing William Solomon MD.
Licensure Skilled care; Intermediate care. *Beds* 212. *Certified* Medicaid; Medicare.
Staff Physicians 1 (ft), 3 (pt); RNs 5 (ft), 4 (pt); LPNs 10 (ft), 3 (pt); Nurses aides 77 (ft), 24 (pt); Physical therapists 1 (pt); Occupational therapists 4 (ft); Speech therapists 1 (pt); Activities coordinators 1 (ft); Dietitians 1 (pt); Dentists 1 (pt); Ophthalmologists 1 (pt); Podiatrists 1 (pt).
Affiliation Jewish
Facilities Dining room; Physical therapy room; Activities room; Chapel; Crafts room; Laundry room; Barber/Beauty shop; Library.
Activities Arts & crafts; Cards; Games; Reading groups; Prayer groups; Movies; Shopping trips; Social/Cultural gatherings.

La Villa Nursing Center
660 E Grand Blvd, Detroit, MI, 48207
(313) 923-5800
Admin Pierce S Morton Jr. *Medical Dir/Dir of Nursing* Dr W Silverstone.

Licensure Skilled care; Intermediate care. *Beds* 95. *Certified* Medicaid; Medicare.
Owner Proprietary Corp; Privately owned.
Admissions Requirements Minimum age 30.
Staff RNs; LPNs; Nurses aides; Activities coordinators.
Facilities Dining room; Activities room; Barber/Beauty shop.
Activities Arts & crafts; Cards; Games; Reading groups; Prayer groups; Movies; Shopping trips; Social/Cultural gatherings.

Lakeland Convalescent Center*
751 E Grand Blvd, Detroit, MI, 48207
(313) 921-0998
Licensure Intermediate care. *Beds* 92. *Certified* Medicaid.

LaSalle Nursing Home
2411 W Grand Blvd, Detroit, MI, 48208
(313) 897-5144
Admin Clair K Lewis. *Medical Dir/Dir of Nursing* Dr Auther Cooper; Pamela McCants RN.
Licensure Skilled care. *Beds* SNF 100. *Certified* Medicaid; Medicare.
Owner Privately owned.
Admissions Requirements Minimum age 18; Medical examination; Physician's request.
Staff Physicians 1 (ft), 2 (pt); RNs 5 (ft); LPNs 10 (ft), 10 (pt); Orderlies 4 (ft), 1 (pt); Nurses aides 70 (ft), 5 (pt); Physical therapists 1 (ft); Recreational therapists 1 (ft); Occupational therapists 1 (ft); Speech therapists 1 (ft); Activities coordinators 1 (ft); Dietitians 1 (ft), 1 (pt); Dentists 1 (ft); Ophthalmologists 1 (ft); Podiatrists 1 (ft).
Languages Polish, Spanish, Tagalog
Facilities Dining room; Physical therapy room; Activities room; Crafts room; Laundry room; Barber/Beauty shop; Library.
Activities Arts & crafts; Cards; Games; Reading groups; Prayer groups; Movies; Shopping trips.

Law-Den Nursing Home
1640 Webb Ave, Detroit, MI, 48206
(313) 867-1719
Admin Lawrence D Johnson.
Licensure Intermediate care. *Beds* ICF 100. *Certified* Medicaid.
Owner Proprietary Corp.
Admissions Requirements Minimum age 18.
Staff RNs 2 (ft); LPNs 8 (ft), 2 (pt); Orderlies 2 (ft); Nurses aides 42 (ft); Recreational therapists 1 (ft); Activities coordinators 1 (ft); Dietitians 1 (pt).
Languages Spanish
Facilities Dining room; Activities room; Chapel; Crafts room; Laundry room.
Activities Arts & crafts; Cards; Games; Reading groups; Prayer groups; Movies; Social/Cultural gatherings; Baseball games.

Lincoln Care Center
13001 W Chicago Blvd, Detroit, MI, 48228
(313) 834-1204
Admin Genevieve Stratton. *Medical Dir/Dir of Nursing* Raymond Weitzman MD; Genevieve Albright RN DON.
Licensure Skilled care; Intermediate care. *Beds* 118. *Certified* Medicaid; Medicare.
Owner Proprietary Corp.
Admissions Requirements Minimum age 15; Medical examination; Physician's request.
Staff Physicians; RNs; LPNs; Orderlies; Nurses aides; Physical therapists; Reality therapists; Recreational therapists; Occupational therapists; Speech therapists; Activities coordinators; Dietitians; Dentists; Ophthalmologists; Podiatrists.
Facilities Dining room; Physical therapy room; Activities room; Crafts room; Laundry room; Barber/Beauty shop.
Activities Arts & crafts; Cards; Games; Reading groups; Prayer groups; Movies; Shopping trips; Social/Cultural gatherings; Camping trips; Library services.

Little Sisters of the Poor*
17550 Southfield Rd, Detroit, MI, 48235
(313) 531-1565
Medical Dir/Dir of Nursing Frank Prokop
MD.
Licensure Skilled care; Intermediate care. *Beds*
76. *Certified* Medicaid; Medicare.
Affiliation Roman Catholic
Facilities Dining room; Physical therapy
room; Activities room; Chapel; Crafts room;
Laundry room; Barber/Beauty shop; Library;
Kitchen; Gift shop; Auditorium.
Activities Arts & crafts; Cards; Games;
Reading groups; Prayer groups; Movies;
Shopping trips; Social/Cultural gatherings;
Occupational therapy.

Luther Haven
464 E Grand Blvd, Detroit, MI, 48207
(313) 882-7529
Admin Dave Houtomaki. *Medical Dir/Dir of
Nursing* A Bedwell MD; Sharon Furtow RN.
Licensure Skilled care; Intermediate care;
Personal care. *Beds* SNF 89; ICF 89;
Personal 52. *Certified* Medicaid; Medicare.
Owner Nonprofit organization/foundation.
Admissions Requirements Minimum age 65;
Medical examination; Physician's request.
Staff RNs 1 (ft); LPNs 7 (ft); Nurses aides 35
(ft); Activities coordinators 1 (ft).
Affiliation Lutheran
Facilities Dining room; Physical therapy
room; Activities room; Chapel; Crafts room;
Laundry room; Barber/Beauty shop.
Activities Arts & crafts; Cards; Games;
Reading groups; Prayer groups; Movies;
Shopping trips; Social/Cultural gatherings.

Madonna Nursing Center
15311 Schaefer St, Detroit, MI, 48227
(313) 835-4775
Licensure Skilled care; Intermediate care. *Beds*
138. *Certified* Medicaid.
Owner Proprietary Corp (International Health
Care Management).

Medicos Recovery Care Center
22355 W 8 Mile Rd, Detroit, MI, 48219
(313) 255-6450
Admin Shirley A St Souver. *Medical Dir/Dir
of Nursing* Marvin Klein MD; C Littleton
RN DON.
Licensure Skilled care. *Beds* SNF 180.
Certified Medicaid; Medicare.
Owner Proprietary Corp.
Admissions Requirements Minimum age 18.
Staff RNs 4 (ft), 4 (pt); LPNs 12 (ft), 10 (pt);
Orderlies 4 (ft); Nurses aides 90 (ft), 10 (pt);
Physical therapists 1 (ft); Activities
coordinators 1 (ft), 1 (pt); Dietitians 1 (pt);
Podiatrists 1 (pt).
Facilities Dining room; Physical therapy
room; Activities room; Crafts room; Laundry
room; Barber/Beauty shop.
Activities Arts & crafts; Cards; Games; Prayer
groups; Movies; Shopping trips; Social/
Cultural gatherings.

Moroun Nursing Home*
8045 E Jefferson, Detroit, MI, 48214
(313) 821-3525
Medical Dir/Dir of Nursing Remedios Doctor
RN DON.
Licensure Skilled care; Intermediate care. *Beds*
189. *Certified* Medicaid; Medicare.

New Detroit Nursing Center
716 E Grand Blvd, Detroit, MI, 48207
(313) 923-0300
Admin Thelma J Scott. *Medical Dir/Dir of
Nursing* Dr M Williams; M Miller RN.
Licensure Intermediate care. *Beds* ICF 50.
Certified Medicaid.
Owner Proprietary Corp.
Admissions Requirements Minimum age 18;
Physician's request.

Staff Physicians 1 (pt); RNs 1 (ft), 1 (pt);
LPNs 3 (ft), 3 (pt); Nurses aides 20 (ft), 20
(pt); Reality therapists 1 (pt); Recreational
therapists 1 (ft); Activities coordinators 1
(ft); Dietitians 1 (pt); Dentists 1 (pt);
Ophthalmologists 1 (pt).
Facilities Dining room; Activities room;
Laundry room; Barber/Beauty shop.
Activities Arts & crafts; Cards; Games;
Reading groups; Prayer groups; Movies;
Shopping trips; Social/Cultural gatherings.

New Light Baptist Church Nursing Home Inc
9500 Grand River Ave, Detroit, MI, 48204
(313) 491-7920
Admin George B Talley. *Medical Dir/Dir of .
Nursing* I Jan MD; N Blair RN.
Licensure Skilled care; Intermediate care. *Beds*
189. *Certified* Medicaid; Medicare.
Owner Nonprofit Corp.
Admissions Requirements Minimum age 18;
Medical examination; Physician's request.
Staff Physicians; RNs; LPNs; Orderlies;
Nurses aides; Physical therapists; Reality
therapists; Recreational therapists; Activities
coordinators; Dietitians; Dentists;
Ophthalmologists.
Facilities Dining room; Physical therapy
room; Activities room; Chapel; Crafts room;
Laundry room; Barber/Beauty shop.
Activities Arts & crafts; Cards; Games;
Reading groups; Prayer groups; Movies;
Shopping trips; Social/Cultural gatherings.

Northland Nursing Center*
21630 Hessel, Detroit, MI, 48219
(313) 534-8400
Licensure Skilled care; Intermediate care. *Beds*
110. *Certified* Medicaid; Medicare.

Northwest Care Center*
16181 Hubbell, Detroit, MI, 48235
(313) 273-8764
Licensure Skilled care; Intermediate care. *Beds*
154. *Certified* Medicaid; Medicare.
Owner Proprietary Corp (Beverly Enterprises).

Qualicare Nursing Home
695 E Grand Blvd, Detroit, MI, 48207
(313) 925-6655
Admin Jeri Ribant. *Medical Dir/Dir of
Nursing* Jean Sherman.
Licensure Skilled care; Intermediate care. *Beds*
SNF 115; ICF. *Certified* Medicaid;
Medicare.
Owner Proprietary Corp.
Admissions Requirements Minimum age 21;
Medical examination; Physician's request.
Staff RNs; LPNs; Orderlies; Nurses aides;
Activities coordinators; Dietitians.
Facilities Dining room; Physical therapy
room; Activities room; Crafts room; Barber/
Beauty shop.
Activities Arts & crafts; Cards; Games;
Reading groups; Prayer groups; Movies;
Shopping trips; Social/Cultural gatherings.

Redford Geriatric Village
22811 W Seven Mile Rd, Detroit, MI, 48219
(313) 534-1440
Admin W T Beardsley. *Medical Dir/Dir of
Nursing* Lawrence Usher; V Farris.
Licensure Skilled care; Intermediate care. *Beds*
SNF 106; ICF. *Certified* Medicaid;
Medicare.
Owner Privately owned.
Admissions Requirements Minimum age 18;
Medical examination; Physician's request.
Staff Physicians; RNs; LPNs; Orderlies;
Nurses aides; Physical therapists;
Occupational therapists; Speech therapists;
Activities coordinators; Dietitians; Dentists;
Ophthalmologists; Podiatrists; Dentist.
Facilities Dining room; Physical therapy
room; Activities room; Crafts room; Laundry
room; Barber/Beauty shop.

Activities Arts & crafts; Cards; Games;
Reading groups; Prayer groups; Movies;
Shopping trips; Social/Cultural gatherings;
Lunch outings.

Regency Park Convalescent Center
5201 Conner Ave, Detroit, MI, 48213
(313) 571-5555
Admin Beverly Court. *Medical Dir/Dir of
Nursing* Pearlie Mae Brown.
Licensure Intermediate care. *Beds* ICF 234.
Certified Medicaid.
Owner Proprietary Corp.
Admissions Requirements Medical
examination; Physician's request.
Staff Physicians 1 (ft); RNs 1 (ft); LPNs 8 (ft),
2 (pt); Nurses aides 50 (ft), 25 (pt); Physical
therapists 2 (ft); Activities coordinators 1
(ft); Dietitians 1 (ft); Ophthalmologists 1 (ft).
Facilities Dining room; Physical therapy
room; Activities room; Crafts room; Laundry
room; Barber/Beauty shop.
Activities Arts & crafts; Cards; Games;
Reading groups; Prayer groups; Movies;
Shopping trips; Social/Cultural gatherings.

St Annes Convalescent Center
6232 Cadieux Rd, Detroit, MI, 48224
(313) 886-2500
Admin Mary E Gallagher. *Medical Dir/Dir of
Nursing* Catherine McEntee RN DON.
Licensure Skilled care. *Beds* SNF 105.
Certified Medicaid; Medicare.
Owner Proprietary Corp.
Admissions Requirements Physician's request.
Staff RNs; LPNs; Nurses aides; Dietitians.
Languages German, Polish, Tagalog, Spanish
Facilities Dining room; Physical therapy
room; Activities room; Chapel; Laundry
room; Library.
Activities Arts & crafts; Cards; Games;
Reading groups; Prayer groups; Movies;
Shopping trips; Social/Cultural gatherings.

St Benedict Nursing Home*
281 W Grand Blvd, Detroit, MI, 48216
(313) 554-2700
Licensure Skilled care; Intermediate care. *Beds*
258. *Certified* Medicaid; Medicare.
Owner Proprietary Corp (Beverly Enterprises).

St Clare Convalescent Center*
15063 Gratiot, Detroit, MI, 48205
(313) 372-4065
Licensure Skilled care; Intermediate care. *Beds*
150. *Certified* Medicaid; Medicare.

St Josephs Home for the Aged*
4800 Cadieux Rd, Detroit, MI, 48224
(313) 882-3800
Licensure Home for aged. *Beds* 25.

St Martin Deporres Nursing Home*
1880 E Grand Blvd, Detroit, MI, 48211
(313) 925-6868
Licensure Skilled care; Intermediate care. *Beds*
81. *Certified* Medicaid; Medicare.
Affiliation Roman Catholic

Jessie Thompson Convalescent Home Inc
650 E Grand Blvd, Detroit, MI, 48207
(313) 925-6651
Admin James Allen Jr. *Medical Dir/Dir of
Nursing* Michael A Williams.
Licensure Intermediate care. *Beds* ICF 42.
Certified Medicaid.
Owner Proprietary Corp.
Admissions Requirements Minimum age 18;
Medical examination; Physician's request.
Staff RNs; LPNs; Nurses aides; Physical
therapists; Recreational therapists 1 (ft);
Occupational therapists; Activities
coordinators 1 (ft); Dietitians 2 (ft);
Ophthalmologists 1 (ft); Dentists 1 (ft).
Facilities Dining room; Activities room;
Crafts room; Laundry room.
Activities Arts & crafts; Cards; Games; Prayer
groups; Shopping trips; Social/Cultural
gatherings.

Westwood Nursing Center*
16588 Schaefer, Detroit, MI, 48235
(313) 925-6655
Licensure Skilled care; Intermediate care. *Beds* 139. *Certified* Medicaid; Medicare.

DEWITT

Avon Nursing Home*
477 Solon Rd, Dewitt, MI, 48820
(517) 484-0164
Licensure Intermediate care. *Beds* 24.
Certified Medicaid.

DIMONDALE

St Lawrence Diamondale Center
4000 N Michigan Rd, Dimondale, MI, 48821
(517) 646-6258
Admin Sr Mary Ricardo Gentle RSM. *Medical Dir/Dir of Nursing* Rodman Jacobi MD; Janet L Graham RN DON.
Licensure Skilled care; Intermediate care. *Beds* SNF 20; ICF 171. *Certified* Medicaid; Medicare.
Owner Nonprofit Corp.
Admissions Requirements Medical examination; Physician's request.
Staff Physicians; RNs 2 (ft), 3 (pt); LPNs 14 (ft), 2 (pt); Orderlies; Nurses aides 35 (ft), 25 (pt); Recreational therapists 1 (ft); Activities coordinators 2 (ft); Dietitians 11 (ft); Dentists; Podiatrists; Dermotologist.
Affiliation Roman Catholic
Facilities Dining room; Physical therapy room; Activities room; Chapel; Crafts room; Laundry room; Barber/Beauty shop; Lobby; Large garden area.
Activities Arts & crafts; Cards; Games; Reading groups; Prayer groups; Movies; Shopping trips; Social/Cultural gatherings.

DOWAGIAC

Dowagiac Nursing Home
610 Uneta St, Dowagiac, MI, 49047
(616) 782-3471
Admin Alex Miskiewicz. *Medical Dir/Dir of Nursing* Pat Parker DON.
Licensure Skilled care; Intermediate care. *Beds* 150. *Certified* Medicaid; Medicare.
Owner Nonprofit organization/foundation.
Admissions Requirements Minimum age 18; Medical examination; Physician's request.
Staff RNs 7 (ft); LPNs 7 (ft), 8 (pt); Nurses aides 60 (ft), 25 (pt); Physical therapists 1 (pt); Recreational therapists 2 (ft); Speech therapists 1 (pt); Activities coordinators 2 (ft); Dietitians 1 (pt); Ophthalmologists 1 (pt); Podiatrists 1 (pt).
Affiliation Roman Catholic
Facilities Dining room; Physical therapy room; Activities room; Chapel; Laundry room; Barber/Beauty shop.
Activities Arts & crafts; Cards; Games; Reading groups; Prayer groups; Movies; Social/Cultural gatherings.

DURAND

Durand Convalescent Center*
8750 E Monroe Rd, Durand, MI, 48429
(517) 288-3166
Licensure Skilled care; Intermediate care. *Beds* 119. *Certified* Medicaid; Medicare.

EAST JORDAN

Grandvue Medical Care Facility
East Jordan, MI, 49727
(616) 536-2286
Licensure Skilled care; Intermediate care. *Beds* 73. *Certified* Medicaid; Medicare.

EAST LANSING

Burcham Hills Retirement Center
2700 Burcham Dr, East Lansing, MI, 48823
(517) 337-9580
Admin Frank Salimbene. *Medical Dir/Dir of Nursing* Gordon Baustian MD; Sue Maschke RN DON.
Licensure Skilled care; Intermediate care. *Beds* SNF 53; ICF 36. *Certified* Medicaid; Medicare.
Owner Proprietary Corp.
Staff RNs; LPNs; Nurses aides; Physical therapists; Recreational therapists; Activities coordinators; Dietitians; Ophthalmologists.
Facilities Dining room; Physical therapy room; Activities room; Crafts room; Barber/Beauty shop.
Activities Arts & crafts; Cards; Games; Reading groups; Prayer groups; Movies; Shopping trips; Social/Cultural gatherings.

Provincial House—East*
2815 Northwind Dr, East Lansing, MI, 48823
(517) 332-0817
Medical Dir/Dir of Nursing E Rittenhouse DO.
Licensure Intermediate care. *Beds* 113.
Certified Medicaid.
Admissions Requirements Minimum age 21; Medical examination; Physician's request.
Staff RNs 3 (ft), 2 (pt); LPNs 4 (ft), 6 (pt); Orderlies 4 (ft), 1 (pt); Nurses aides 38 (ft), 10 (pt); Activities coordinators 1 (ft).
Facilities Dining room; Activities room; Laundry room; Barber/Beauty shop.
Activities Arts & crafts; Cards; Games; Reading groups; Prayer groups; Movies; Shopping trips; Social/Cultural gatherings.

Provincial House—Whitehills*
1843 N Hagadorn Rd, East Lansing, MI, 48823
(517) 332-5061
Licensure Skilled care; Intermediate care. *Beds* 115. *Certified* Medicaid; Medicare.

ESCANABA

Bishop Noa Home for Senior Citizens
624 Ludington St, Escanaba, MI, 49829
(906) 786-5810
Admin Daniel H Ross. *Medical Dir/Dir of Nursing* Janet Cutter RN DON.
Licensure Intermediate care; Home for aged. *Beds* ICF 81; Home for aged 28. *Certified* Medicaid.
Owner Nonprofit Corp.
Admissions Requirements Minimum age 15; Medical examination; Physician's request.
Staff RNs 1 (ft); LPNs 5 (ft), 5 (pt); Orderlies 2 (ft), 2 (pt); Nurses aides 35 (ft), 17 (pt); Activities coordinators 1 (ft), 1 (pt).
Affiliation Roman Catholic
Facilities Dining room; Activities room; Chapel; Crafts room; Laundry room; Library.
Activities Arts & crafts; Cards; Games; Reading groups; Prayer groups; Movies; Shopping trips; Social/Cultural gatherings; Bingo.

Northwoods Manor
2415 5th Ave S, Escanaba, MI, 49829
(906) 786-6907
Admin Thomas E Lenhard. *Medical Dir/Dir of Nursing* Steven Dosh MD; MaryLou Lancour RN.
Licensure Skilled care. *Beds* SNF 99. *Certified* Medicaid; Medicare.
Owner Proprietary Corp (Health Care & Retirement Corp).
Staff RNs 4 (ft), 4 (pt); LPNs 8 (ft), 4 (pt); Nurses aides 22 (ft), 10 (pt); Physical therapists 1 (pt); Occupational therapists 1 (pt); Speech therapists 1 (pt); Activities coordinators 1 (ft); Dietitians 1 (ft); Ophthalmologists 1 (pt).

Northwoods Manor Annex
2525 7th Ave S, Escanaba, MI, 49829
(906) 786-0408
Admin Jane A Verhamme. *Medical Dir/Dir of Nursing* Stephen Dosh MD; Linda Harm RN DON.
Licensure Skilled care; Intermediate care. *Beds* 59. *Certified* Medicaid; Medicare.
Owner Proprietary Corp (Health Care & Retire Corp).
Admissions Requirements Minimum age 15.
Staff RNs 4 (ft), 2 (pt); LPNs 4 (ft), 3 (pt); Nurses aides 12 (ft), 7 (pt); Physical therapists 1 (pt); Occupational therapists 1 (pt); Speech therapists 1 (pt); Activities coordinators 1 (ft); Dietitians 1 (ft); Ophthalmologists 1 (pt).
Facilities Dining room; Physical therapy room; Activities room; Laundry room; Barber/Beauty shop.
Activities Arts & crafts; Cards; Games; Reading groups; Prayer groups; Movies; Shopping trips; Social/Cultural gatherings; Bingo; Picnics.

ESSEXVILLE

Bay County Medical Care Facility
564 W Hampton Rd, Essexville, MI, 48732
(517) 892-3591
Admin W R Mahoney. *Medical Dir/Dir of Nursing* B W Webb DO; G VanTol RN.
Licensure Skilled care; Intermediate care. *Beds* 206. *Certified* Medicaid; Medicare.
Owner Publicly owned.
Admissions Requirements Medical examination; Physician's request.
Staff Physicians; RNs; LPNs; Orderlies; Nurses aides; Physical therapists; Occupational therapists; Speech therapists; Activities coordinators; Dietitians; Dentists; Ophthalmologists.
Facilities Dining room; Physical therapy room; Activities room; Chapel; Crafts room; Barber/Beauty shop; Library.
Activities Arts & crafts; Cards; Games; Prayer groups; Movies; Social/Cultural gatherings; Crafts.

EVART

Brown Nursing Home
PO Box 591, Evart, MI, 49631-0591
(517) 236-7348
Licensure Intermediate care. *Beds* 50.
Certified Medicaid.

FAIRVIEW

Ausable Valley Home
Box 8, Fairview, MI, 48621-0008
(517) 848-2241
Admin Wayne M Miller. *Medical Dir/Dir of Nursing* Leta Gerber RN.
Licensure Skilled care; Intermediate care. *Beds* SNF 62; ICF. *Certified* Medicaid; Medicare.
Owner Nonprofit Corp.
Admissions Requirements Medical examination; Physician's request.
Staff RNs 3 (ft), 2 (pt); LPNs 3 (ft), 2 (pt); Nurses aides 20 (ft), 7 (pt); Physical therapists 1 (pt); Speech therapists 1 (pt); Activities coordinators 1 (ft), 1 (pt); Dietitians 1 (pt).
Languages German
Affiliation Mennonite
Facilities Dining room; Physical therapy room; Activities room; Laundry room; Barber/Beauty shop.
Activities Arts & crafts; Cards; Games; Reading groups; Prayer groups; Movies.

FARMINGTON

Oak Hill Care Center
34225 Grand River, Farmington, MI, 48024
(313) 477-7373
Licensure Skilled care; Intermediate care. *Beds*
137. *Certified* Medicaid; Medicare.

Oak Hill Nursing Home Annex
34225 Grand River, Farmington, MI, 48024
(313) 474-6750
Licensure Intermediate care. *Beds* 16.
Certified Medicaid.

FARMINGTON HILLS

Farmington Nursing Home
30405 Folsom Rd, Farmington Hills, MI,
48024
(313) 477-7400
Admin Ruth Farrell. *Medical Dir/Dir of
Nursing* Harold Wasserman MD; Barbara
Blair RN DON.
Licensure Skilled care; Intermediate care. *Beds*
Concurrent certification 179. *Certified*
Medicaid.
Owner Nonprofit Corp.
Admissions Requirements Minimum age 18.
Facilities Dining room; Physical therapy
room; Activities room; Crafts room; Laundry
room; Barber/Beauty shop.
Activities Arts & crafts; Cards; Games; Prayer
groups; Movies; Social/Cultural gatherings;
Alzheimer's support group.

FARMINGTON TOWNSHIP

Williamsburg Convalescent Center*
21017 Middlebelt Rd, Farmington Township,
MI, 48024
(313) 476-8300
Admin Ruth Bard. *Medical Dir/Dir of Nursing*
Richard Knight DO.
Licensure Skilled care; Intermediate care. *Beds*
112. *Certified* Medicaid; Medicare.
Owner Proprietary Corp (Beverly Enterprises).
Admissions Requirements Minimum age 18;
Medical examination; Physician's request.
Staff Physicians 9 (pt); RNs 6 (ft); LPNs 7
(ft); Orderlies 6 (ft); Nurses aides 37 (ft);
Physical therapists 1 (pt); Recreational
therapists 1 (pt); Occupational therapists 1
(pt); Speech therapists 1 (pt); Activities
coordinators 1 (ft); Dietitians 1 (ft); Dentists
1 (pt); Ophthalmologists 1 (pt); Podiatrists 1
(pt); Audiologists 1 (pt).
Facilities Dining room; Physical therapy
room; Activities room; Crafts room; Laundry
room; Barber/Beauty shop; Library.
Activities Arts & crafts; Cards; Games;
Reading groups; Prayer groups; Movies;
Shopping trips; Social/Cultural gatherings.

FARWELL

Ardis Nursing Home Inc
PO Box 579, Farwell, MI, 48622
(517) 588-9928
Admin Grant Walter. *Medical Dir/Dir of
Nursing* C McGowen.
Licensure Skilled care; Intermediate care. *Beds*
71. *Certified* Medicaid; Medicare.
Owner Proprietary Corp.
Admissions Requirements Minimum age 18;
Medical examination.
Staff RNs; LPNs; Orderlies; Nurses aides;
Physical therapists; Recreational therapists;
Occupational therapists; Speech therapists;
Activities coordinators.
Languages Sign, Spanish
Facilities Dining room; Physical therapy
room; Activities room; Crafts room; Laundry
room; Barber/Beauty shop.
Activities Arts & crafts; Cards; Games;
Reading groups; Prayer groups; Movies;
Social/Cultural gatherings.

FENTON

Crestmont Medical Care Facility
111 Trealout, Fenton, MI, 48430
(313) 629-4105
Medical Dir/Dir of Nursing W Buchanan MD.
Licensure Skilled care; Intermediate care. *Beds*
136. *Certified* Medicaid; Medicare.
Owner Proprietary Corp (International Health
Care Management).
Staff Physicians 6 (pt); RNs 8 (ft), 5 (pt);
LPNs 5 (ft); Orderlies 3 (ft); Nurses aides 51
(ft), 14 (pt); Physical therapists 1 (pt);
Occupational therapists 1 (pt); Speech
therapists 1 (pt); Activities coordinators 2
(ft); Dietitians 1 (pt); Dentists 1 (pt);
Podiatrists 1 (pt); Physical therapy assistants
1 (ft).
Facilities Dining room; Physical therapy
room; Activities room; Chapel; Crafts room;
Laundry room; Barber/Beauty shop; Family
room; Day room; Classroom.
Activities Arts & crafts; Cards; Games; Prayer
groups; Movies; Shopping trips; Social/
Cultural gatherings; Picnics; Happy hour.

Elder House*
202 Shiawassee Ave, Fenton, MI, 48430
(313) 629-6391
Licensure Home for aged. *Beds* 36.
Admissions Requirements Minimum age 60;
Medical examination; Physician's request.
Staff RNs 1 (pt); Nurses aides 6 (ft); Activities
coordinators 1 (ft); Dietitians 1 (pt).
Facilities Dining room; Activities room;
Crafts room; Barber/Beauty shop; Library;
Outdoor activity area.
Activities Arts & crafts; Cards; Games;
Reading groups; Prayer groups; Movies;
Shopping trips; Social/Cultural gatherings;
Cookouts; Bowling.

Fenton Extended Care Center*
512 Beach St, Fenton, MI, 48430
(313) 629-4117
Licensure Intermediate care. *Beds* 121.
Certified Medicaid.

Hammond Rest Home
700 S Adelaide St, Fenton, MI, 48430
(313) 629-9641
Admin Anna M Charles. *Medical Dir/Dir of
Nursing* Anna M Charles DON.
Licensure Intermediate care. *Beds* ICF 25.
Certified Medicaid.
Owner Proprietary Corp.
Admissions Requirements Minimum age 15;
Females only; Medical examination.
Staff RNs 1 (ft), 1 (pt); LPNs 3 (ft), 4 (pt);
Nurses aides 7 (ft), 4 (pt); Activities
coordinators 1 (ft); Dietitians 1 (pt).
Facilities Dining room; Activities room;
Laundry room.
Activities Arts & crafts; Cards; Games; Prayer
groups; Movies.

FERNDALE

Hilton Convalescent Home*
3161 Hilton Rd, Ferndale, MI, 48220
(313) 547-6227
Licensure Skilled care; Intermediate care. *Beds*
78. *Certified* Medicaid; Medicare.

FLINT

Briarwood Manor
3011 N Center Rd, Flint, MI, 48506
(313) 736-0600
Admin Glenn J Porterfield. *Medical Dir/Dir of
Nursing* Thomas E Lewis MD; Leslie
Goodell RN DON.
Licensure Skilled care; Intermediate care. *Beds*
97. *Certified* Medicaid; Medicare.
Owner Proprietary Corp (Health Care &
Retire Corp).

Admissions Requirements Minimum age 21;
Medical examination; Physician's request.
Staff RNs 3 (ft); LPNs 3 (ft), 10 (pt); Nurses
aides 15 (ft), 25 (pt); Recreational therapists
1 (ft), 1 (pt); Activities coordinators.
Facilities Dining room; Physical therapy
room; Activities room; Laundry room;
Barber/Beauty shop.
Activities Cards; Games; Reading groups;
Prayer groups; Movies; Social/Cultural
gatherings.

Chateau Gardens
627 Begole St, Flint, MI, 48503
(313) 234-1667
Medical Dir/Dir of Nursing Richard Dykewicz
MD.
Licensure Skilled care; Intermediate care. *Beds*
222. *Certified* Medicaid; Medicare.
Admissions Requirements Physician's request.
Staff RNs 6 (ft), 8 (pt); LPNs 13 (ft), 2 (pt);
Orderlies 2 (ft), 3 (pt); Nurses aides 60 (ft),
33 (pt); Physical therapists 1 (pt);
Occupational therapists 1 (pt); Speech
therapists 1 (pt); Activities coordinators 1
(ft), 2 (pt); Dietitians 1 (pt).
Facilities Dining room; Physical therapy
room; Activities room; Chapel; Crafts room;
Laundry room; Barber/Beauty shop; Library.
Activities Arts & crafts; Cards; Games;
Reading groups; Prayer groups; Movies;
Shopping trips; Social/Cultural gatherings.

Clara Barton Terrace Convalescent Home
1801 E Atherton Rd, Flint, MI, 48507
(313) 742-5850
Admin Diane Blick RN. *Medical Dir/Dir of
Nursing* Maurice Chapin MD; Barbara Start
RN.
Licensure Intermediate care. *Beds* 149.
Certified Medicaid.
Owner Proprietary Corp (Hillhaven Corp).
Admissions Requirements Minimum age 15;
Medical examination.
Staff RNs 4 (ft), 3 (pt); LPNs 9 (ft), 10 (pt);
Nurses aides 50 (ft), 40 (pt); Activities
coordinators 1 (ft).
Facilities Dining room; Activities room;
Chapel; Crafts room; Laundry room; Barber/
Beauty shop; Library.
Activities Arts & crafts; Cards; Games;
Reading groups; Prayer groups; Movies;
Shopping trips; Social/Cultural gatherings.

Genesee Care Center*
G-4436 Beecher Rd, Flint, MI, 48504
(313) 733-0290
Licensure Skilled care; Intermediate care. *Beds*
101. *Certified* Medicaid.

Heritage Manor Convalescent Center*
G-3201 Beecher Rd, Flint, MI, 48504
(313) 732-9200
Medical Dir/Dir of Nursing Kenneth Jordan
MD.
Licensure Skilled care; Intermediate care. *Beds*
180. *Certified* Medicaid; Medicare.
Admissions Requirements Minimum age 17;
Medical examination; Physician's request.
Facilities Dining room; Physical therapy
room; Activities room; Library.
Activities Arts & crafts; Cards; Games;
Reading groups; Prayer groups; Movies;
Shopping trips; Social/Cultural gatherings.

Kith Haven*
G-1069 Ballenger Hwy, Flint, MI, 48505
(313) 235-6676
Licensure Skilled care; Intermediate care. *Beds*
167. *Certified* Medicaid; Medicare.

FLUSHING

Fostrian Manor*
540 Sunnyside Dr, Flushing, MI, 48433
(313) 659-5695

Licensure Skilled care; Intermediate care. *Beds* 101. *Certified* Medicaid; Medicare.
Owner Proprietary Corp (Health Care & Retirement Corp).

FRANKENMUTH

Frankenmuth Convalescent Center*
500 W Genesee, Frankenmuth, MI, 48734
(517) 652-6101
Licensure Skilled care; Intermediate care. *Beds* 126. *Certified* Medicaid; Medicare.

The Lutheran Home
725 W Genesee, Frankenmuth, MI, 48734
(517) 652-9951
Admin C Douglas Anderson. *Medical Dir/Dir of Nursing* J F Shetlar MD.
Licensure Skilled care; Intermediate care. *Beds* 112. *Certified* Medicaid; Medicare.
Owner Proprietary Corp (Vantage Healthcare).
Admissions Requirements Minimum age 65; Medical examination.
Staff RNs 7 (ft), 14 (pt); LPNs 4 (pt); Nurses aides 24 (ft), 30 (pt); Physical therapists 1 (pt); Activities coordinators 1 (ft), 2 (pt); Dietitians 1 (ft).
Languages German
Affiliation Lutheran
Facilities Dining room; Physical therapy room; Activities room; Chapel; Crafts room; Laundry room; Barber/Beauty shop; Library.
Activities Arts & crafts; Cards; Games; Reading groups; Prayer groups; Movies; Shopping trips; Social/Cultural gatherings.

FRANKFORT

Benzie County Medical Care Facility
210 Maple St, Frankfort, MI, 49635
(616) 352-9674
Admin Vickie Burlew RN. *Medical Dir/Dir of Nursing* James N Kaufman MD; Theresa Schmeichel RN DON.
Licensure Skilled care; Intermediate care. *Beds* SNF 62. *Certified* Medicaid; Medicare.
Owner Publicly owned.
Admissions Requirements Minimum age 16; Physician's request.
Staff Physicians 1 (ft); RNs 2 (ft), 3 (pt); LPNs 4 (ft), 2 (pt); Orderlies 1 (ft); Nurses aides 23 (ft), 6 (pt); Physical therapists 1 (pt); Activities coordinators 1 (ft); Dietitians 1 (pt).
Facilities Dining room; Physical therapy room; Activities room; Crafts room; Laundry room; Barber/Beauty shop.
Activities Arts & crafts; Games; Reading groups; Prayer groups; Movies; Shopping trips; Social/Cultural gatherings.

FREMONT

Meadows Nursing Home*
4554 48th St, Fremont, MI, 49412
(616) 924-3990
Licensure Skilled care; Intermediate care. *Beds* 129. *Certified* Medicaid; Medicare.

Newaygo Medical Care Facility
4465 W 48th St, Rte 1, Fremont, MI, 49412
(616) 924-2020
Admin Michael B Shira. *Medical Dir/Dir of Nursing* Lorraine DeKan RN.
Licensure Skilled care. *Beds* SNF 116. *Certified* Medicaid; Medicare.
Owner Publicly owned.
Admissions Requirements Physician's request.
Staff Physicians 1 (pt); RNs 4 (ft), 6 (pt); LPNs 6 (ft), 5 (pt); Nurses aides 35 (ft), 23 (pt); Physical therapists 1 (pt); Recreational therapists 1 (ft); Occupational therapists 1 (pt); Speech therapists 1 (pt); Activities coordinators 1 (pt); Dietitians 1 (pt); Dentists 1 (pt); Ophthalmologists 1 (pt); Podiatrists 1 (pt); Dentist 1 (pt).

Facilities Dining room; Physical therapy room; Activities room; Crafts room; Laundry room; Barber/Beauty shop.
Activities Arts & crafts; Cards; Games; Reading groups; Prayer groups; Movies; Social/Cultural gatherings; Music therapy; Exercise classes.

GALESBURG

Matheson Nursing Home*
1080 N 35th St, Galesburg, MI, 49503
(616) 665-7043
Licensure Skilled care; Intermediate care. *Beds* 93. *Certified* Medicaid; Medicare.

GAYLORD

Otsego County Memorial—Intermediate Care Facility
825 N Center St, Gaylord, MI, 49735
(517) 732-1731
Licensure Skilled care; Intermediate care. *Beds* 34. *Certified* Medicaid; Medicare.

Provincial House
508 Random Ln, Gaylord, MI, 49735
(517) 732-3508
Admin Deborah Horn. *Medical Dir/Dir of Nursing* Irineo Matias MD; Fran Kuntz RN DON.
Licensure Skilled care; Long-term care. *Beds* SNF 120; Ventilator beds 8. *Certified* Medicaid; Medicare.
Owner Proprietary Corp (Beverly Enterprises).
Admissions Requirements Medical examination.
Staff Physicians 1 (ft), 6 (pt); RNs 6 (ft); Orderlies 10 (ft); Nurses aides 50 (ft), 10 (pt); Physical therapists 1 (ft), 1 (pt); Reality therapists 1 (ft); Recreational therapists 1 (ft); Occupational therapists 1 (ft); Speech therapists 1 (ft); Activities coordinators 1 (ft), 1 (pt); Dietitians 1 (ft), 1 (pt); Dentists 1 (pt); Ophthalmologists 1 (pt); Podiatrists 1 (pt); Respiratory therapists 4 (ft), 2 (pt).
Facilities Dining room; Physical therapy room; Activities room; Crafts room; Laundry room; Barber/Beauty shop; Library; 2 Day rooms.
Activities Arts & crafts; Cards; Games; Reading groups; Prayer groups; Movies; Shopping trips; Social/Cultural gatherings; Family nights; Picnics; Gardening; Adopt-a-grandparent.

GLADWIN

Gladwin Nursing Home*
3270 Pratt Lake Rd, Gladwin, MI, 48624
(517) 426-7275
Medical Dir/Dir of Nursing H A Timreck MD.
Licensure Skilled care; Intermediate care. *Beds* 60. *Certified* Medicaid; Medicare.
Admissions Requirements Minimum age 15; Medical examination; Physician's request.
Staff RNs 4 (ft), 3 (pt); LPNs 2 (ft), 4 (pt); Nurses aides 15 (ft), 7 (pt).
Facilities Dining room; Physical therapy room; Activities room.
Activities Arts & crafts; Cards; Games; Reading groups; Social/Cultural gatherings.

GOODELLS

St Clair County Medical Centre
8332 County Park Dr, Goodells, MI, 48027
(313) 325-1291
Admin Cora M Urquhart. *Medical Dir/Dir of Nursing* Frederick E Ludwig MD; Cornelia Smith RN.
Licensure Skilled care; Intermediate care. *Beds* SNF 75; ICF. *Certified* Medicaid; Medicare.
Owner Publicly owned.
Admissions Requirements Minimum age 15; Medical examination; Physician's request.

Staff Physicians 1 (pt); RNs 3 (ft), 4 (pt); LPNs 4 (ft), 2 (pt); Nurses aides 19 (ft), 20 (pt); Physical therapists 1 (pt); Occupational therapists 1 (pt); Speech therapists 1 (pt); Activities coordinators 1 (ft); Dietitians 1 (pt); Ophthalmologists 1 (pt); Podiatrists 1 (pt).
Languages French
Facilities Dining room; Physical therapy room; Activities room; Laundry room; Barber/Beauty shop; Library.
Activities Arts & crafts; Cards; Games; Reading groups; Prayer groups; Movies; Shopping trips; Social/Cultural gatherings; Bowling; Bingo; Diners club.

GRAND BLANC

Grand Blanc Convalescent Center Inc
8481 Holly Rd, Grand Blanc, MI, 48439
(313) 694-1711
Admin Paul N Wright. *Medical Dir/Dir of Nursing* Dr Joseph T Batdorf; Marilynn Brainard RNC DON.
Licensure Skilled care. *Beds* SNF 95. *Certified* Medicaid; Medicare.
Owner Nonprofit Corp.
Admissions Requirements Minimum age 25; Medical examination; Physician's request.
Staff RNs 3 (ft), 9 (pt); LPNs 4 (ft), 4 (pt); Orderlies 2 (pt); Nurses aides 30 (ft), 24 (pt); Physical therapists 1 (pt); Occupational therapists 1 (pt); Speech therapists 1 (pt); Activities coordinators 1 (ft), 1 (pt); Dietitians 1 (ft); Dentists 1 (pt); Ophthalmologists 1 (pt); Dentist 1 (pt); Pastoral care 1 (pt).
Affiliation Roman Catholic
Facilities Dining room; Physical therapy room; Activities room; Chapel; Crafts room; Barber/Beauty shop; Library; Patient lounges.
Activities Arts & crafts; Cards; Games; Reading groups; Prayer groups; Movies; Shopping trips; Social/Cultural gatherings; Music & cooking classes; Gardening.

Riverbend Nursing Home Inc
11941 Belsay Rd, Grand Blanc, MI, 48439
(313) 694-1970
Admin M Ellen Knickerbocker. *Medical Dir/Dir of Nursing* Thomas B Marwil MD; Rosemary E Sedgewick RN BSN.
Licensure Skilled care; Intermediate care; Home for aged. *Beds* SNF 30; ICF 127; 20. *Certified* Medicaid; Medicare.
Owner Proprietary Corp.
Admissions Requirements Minimum age 16; Medical examination; Physician's request.
Staff Physicians 3 (pt); RNs 7 (ft), 4 (pt); LPNs 12 (ft), 4 (pt); Nurses aides 55 (ft), 24 (pt); Physical therapists 1 (pt); Occupational therapists 1 (pt); Speech therapists 2 (pt); Activities coordinators 1 (ft); Dietitians 1 (ft), 1 (pt); Dentists 1 (pt); Ophthalmologists 1 (pt); Social worker 1 (ft).
Facilities Dining room; Physical therapy room; Activities room; Crafts room; Laundry room; Barber/Beauty shop; Library; Lounges.
Activities Arts & crafts; Cards; Games; Reading groups; Prayer groups; Movies; Shopping trips; Social/Cultural gatherings.

GRAND HAVEN

North Ottawa Care Center
1615 S Despelder St, Grand Haven, MI, 49417
(616) 842-0770
Licensure Skilled care. *Beds* 64. *Certified* Medicaid; Medicare.

Riverside Nursing Home
415 Friant St, Grand Haven, MI, 49417
(616) 842-4120
Admin James A Winkle. *Medical Dir/Dir of Nursing* Debbie Krebs RN.

Licensure Intermediate care. *Beds* ICF 34.
Certified Medicaid.
Owner Proprietary Corp.
Admissions Requirements Minimum age 15;
Medical examination; Physician's request.
Staff RNs; LPNs; Nurses aides; Recreational
therapists; Activities coordinators; Dietitians.
Facilities Dining room; Activities room;
Laundry room; Barber/Beauty shop.
Activities Arts & crafts; Cards; Games;
Reading groups; Prayer groups; Movies;
Shopping trips; Social/Cultural gatherings.

Shore Haven Nursing Home*
900 S Beacon, Grand Haven, MI, 49417
(616) 846-1850
Licensure Skilled care; Intermediate care. *Beds*
126. *Certified* Medicaid; Medicare.
Owner Proprietary Corp (International Health
Care Management).

GRAND RAPIDS

Cascade Care Center
1095 Medical Park SE, Grand Rapids, MI,
49506
(616) 949-7220
Admin Sylvia Jean Mosher. *Medical Dir/Dir
of Nursing* Edith Miller DON.
Licensure Skilled care. *Beds* SNF 123.
Certified Medicaid; Medicare.
Owner Proprietary Corp.
Admissions Requirements Minimum age 18.
Staff RNs; LPNs; Orderlies; Nurses aides;
Physical therapists; Recreational therapists;
Occupational therapists; Speech therapists;
Activities coordinators.
Facilities Dining room; Physical therapy
room; Activities room; Crafts room; Laundry
room; Barber/Beauty shop.
Activities Arts & crafts; Cards; Games; Prayer
groups; Movies; Shopping trips; Social/
Cultural gatherings.

Christian Nursing Center
2589 44th St SE, Grand Rapids, MI, 49508-
3877
(616) 452-8992 & 452-7206
Licensure Intermediate care. *Beds* 42.
Certified Medicaid.

Christian Rest Home Association*
1000 Edison Ave NW, Grand Rapids, MI,
49504
(616) 453-2475
Admin John Rurter. *Medical Dir/Dir of
Nursing* John Vander Molen MD.
Licensure Skilled care; Intermediate care. *Beds*
153. *Certified* Medicaid; Medicare.
Admissions Requirements Minimum age 15;
Medical examination; Physician's request.
Staff RNs 1 (ft), 12 (pt); LPNs 1 (ft), 10 (pt);
Orderlies 1 (pt); Nurses aides 45 (ft), 45 (pt);
Physical therapists 1 (ft); Recreational
therapists 2 (ft), 1 (pt); Occupational
therapists 1 (pt).
Facilities Dining room; Physical therapy
room; Activities room; Chapel; Crafts room;
Laundry room; Barber/Beauty shop; Library.
Activities Arts & crafts; Cards; Games;
Reading groups; Prayer groups; Movies;
Shopping trips; Social/Cultural gatherings.

M J Clark Memorial Home*
1546 Sherman SE, Grand Rapids, MI, 49506
(616) 452-7206
Licensure Skilled care; Intermediate care. *Beds*
111. *Certified* Medicaid; Medicare.

Grand Valley Nursing Center*
4118 Kalamazoo Ave SE, Grand Rapids, MI,
49508
(616) 455-7300
Medical Dir/Dir of Nursing Dr Dirk Mouw.
Licensure Skilled care; Intermediate care. *Beds*
165. *Certified* Medicaid; Medicare.
Admissions Requirements Minimum age 3;
Medical examination; Physician's request.

Staff RNs 9 (ft), 15 (pt); LPNs 10 (ft), 10 (pt);
Nurses aides 46 (ft), 38 (pt); Physical
therapists 1 (ft); Recreational therapists 1
(ft); Occupational therapists 1 (ft); Speech
therapists 1 (ft); Activities coordinators 1
(ft); Dietitians 1 (ft); Dentists 1 (pt);
Ophthalmologists 1 (pt); Podiatrists 1 (pt);
Social workers 2 (ft), 1 (pt); Psychologists 1
(ft).
Facilities Dining room; Physical therapy
room; Activities room; Chapel; Crafts room;
Barber/Beauty shop; Library.
Activities Arts & crafts; Cards; Games;
Reading groups; Prayer groups; Movies;
Shopping trips; Social/Cultural gatherings;
Luncheon trips.

Greenview Nursing Home
1708 Leonard St NE, Grand Rapids, MI,
49505
(616) 456-7243
Admin Bill Hekker. *Medical Dir/Dir of
Nursing* Shirley Carter RN.
Licensure Skilled care. *Beds* SNF 69. *Certified*
Medicaid; Medicare.
Owner Proprietary Corp (Health Care &
Retirement Corp).
Admissions Requirements Medical
examination; Physician's request.
Facilities Dining room; Activities room;
Crafts room; Laundry room; Barber/Beauty
shop.
Activities Arts & crafts; Cards; Games;
Reading groups; Prayer groups; Movies;
Shopping trips; Social/Cultural gatherings.

Holland Home—Brown Home*
1435 E Fulton, Grand Rapids, MI, 49503
(616) 459-2717
Licensure Intermediate care. *Beds* 11.
Certified Medicaid.

Holland Home—Fulton Manor
1450 E Fulton St, Grand Rapids, MI, 49503
(616) 459-3495
Admin Irvin G Van Dyke. *Medical Dir/Dir of
Nursing* Joyce A Rottman.
Licensure Skilled care; Home for aged. *Beds*
SNF 79; Home for aged 290. *Certified*
Medicaid; Medicare.
Owner Nonprofit Corp.
Admissions Requirements Minimum age 60;
Medical examination.
Staff RNs; LPNs; Orderlies; Orderlies; Nurses
aides; Recreational therapists; Activities
coordinators.
Languages Dutch
Facilities Dining room; Physical therapy
room; Activities room; Chapel; Crafts room;
Laundry room; Barber/Beauty shop; Library.
Activities Arts & crafts; Cards; Games;
Reading groups; Prayer groups; Movies;
Shopping trips; Social/Cultural gatherings.

Holland Home—Raybrook Manor
2121 Raybrook Ave SE, Grand Rapids, MI,
49506
(616) 949-6656
Admin Gary G Ellens. *Medical Dir/Dir of
Nursing* Dr Keith Crane; Margaret Dekker
RN.
Licensure Skilled care; Intermediate care
Concurrently Licensed. *Beds* SNF 101; ICF
Concurrently licensed. *Certified* Medicaid;
Medicare.
Owner Nonprofit Corp.
Admissions Requirements Minimum age 16;
Medical examination; Physician's request.
Staff RNs 7 (ft), 7 (pt); LPNs 11 (ft), 10 (pt);
Nurses aides 46 (ft), 31 (pt); Activities
coordinators 2 (ft).
Languages Dutch
Affiliation Christian Reformed
Facilities Dining room; Physical therapy
room; Activities room; Chapel; Crafts room;
Laundry room; Barber/Beauty shop; Library.

Activities Arts & crafts; Cards; Games;
Reading groups; Prayer groups; Movies;
Shopping trips; Social/Cultural gatherings.

Jefferson Christian Nursing Home
2589 44th St SE, Grand Rapids, MI, 49508-
3877
(616) 452-9198
Licensure Intermediate care. *Beds* 30.
Certified Medicaid.

Kent Community Hospital Complex
750 Fuller Ave NE, Grand Rapids, MI, 49503
(616) 774-3300
Licensure Skilled care; Intermediate care. *Beds*
338. *Certified* Medicaid; Medicare.

Lafayette Christian Nursing Home
1001 Lafayette SE, Grand Rapids, MI, 49507
(616) 452-9673
Admin Doyle R Melton. *Medical Dir/Dir of
Nursing* Maxine Rogers.
Licensure Intermediate care. *Beds* ICF 61.
Certified Medicaid.
Owner Proprietary Corp.
Staff Physicians 1 (pt); RNs 1 (ft); LPNs 3
(ft); Orderlies 2 (ft); Nurses aides 8 (ft);
Physical therapists 1 (pt); Recreational
therapists 1 (ft); Activities coordinators 1
(ft); Dietitians 1 (ft); Dentists 1 (pt);
Ophthalmologists 1 (pt); Podiatrists 1 (pt).
Facilities Dining room; Activities room;
Laundry room; Barber/Beauty shop.
Activities Arts & crafts; Cards; Games; Social/
Cultural gatherings.

Luther Home
1950 32nd St SE, Grand Rapids, MI, 49508-
1504
(616) 243-0252
Licensure Intermediate care. *Beds* 52.
Certified Medicaid.
Affiliation Lutheran

Michigan Christian Home
1845 Boston St SE, Grand Rapids, MI, 49506
(616) 245-9179
Admin Byron G Wild. *Medical Dir/Dir of
Nursing* Sue Vanderberg DON.
Licensure Skilled care; Home for aged;
Independent Apartments. *Beds* SNF 29;
Home for aged 72; Apts 20. *Certified*
Medicaid; Medicare.
Owner Nonprofit Corp.
Admissions Requirements Minimum age 62;
Medical examination.
Staff RNs; LPNs; Nurses aides; Recreational
therapists; Activities coordinators; Dietitians.
Affiliation Baptist
Facilities Dining room; Activities room;
Chapel; Crafts room; Laundry room; Barber/
Beauty shop; Library.
Activities Arts & crafts; Games; Reading
groups; Prayer groups; Movies; Shopping
trips.

Olds Manor
201 Michigan NW, Grand Rapids, MI, 49502
(616) 429-0101
Medical Dir/Dir of Nursing John N Campbell
MD.
Licensure Intermediate care. *Beds* 44.
Certified Medicaid.
Admissions Requirements Medical
examination; Physician's request.
Staff Physicians 2 (pt); RNs 2 (ft); LPNs 10
(ft); Orderlies 3 (ft); Nurses aides 11 (ft), 15
(pt); Activities coordinators 1 (ft); Dietitians
1 (ft); Ophthalmologists 1 (ft); Podiatrists 1
(ft).
Facilities Dining room; Activities room;
Chapel; Crafts room; Laundry room; Barber/
Beauty shop; Library.
Activities Arts & crafts; Games; Prayer groups;
Movies; Shopping trips.

Pilgrim Manor Inc
2000 Leonard NE, Grand Rapids, MI, 49505
(616) 458-1133

Admin John H Pylman. *Medical Dir/Dir of
Nursing* Keith Crane MD; Mrs Bartz DON.
Licensure Skilled care; Intermediate care. *Beds*
42. *Certified* Medicaid; Medicare.
Owner Nonprofit Corp.
Admissions Requirements Minimum age 62;
Medical examination.
Staff Physicians 1 (pt); RNs 2 (ft), 4 (pt);
LPNs 4 (ft), 5 (pt); Nurses aides 21 (ft), 10
(pt); Activities coordinators 1 (ft); Dietitians
1 (pt); Podiatrists 1 (pt).
Affiliation Church of Christ
Facilities Dining room; Activities room;
Chapel; Crafts room; Laundry room; Barber/
Beauty shop; Library.
Activities Arts & crafts; Cards; Games;
Reading groups; Prayer groups; Movies;
Shopping trips; Social/Cultural gatherings.

Porter Hills Presbyterian Village Inc
3600 Fulton St E, Grand Rapids, MI, 49506
(616) 949-4971
Admin David B Douma. *Medical Dir/Dir of
Nursing* Dr Grace; Kay Downs DON.
Licensure Skilled care; Intermediate care. *Beds*
101. *Certified* Medicaid; Medicare.
Owner Nonprofit Corp.
Admissions Requirements Minimum age 62;
Medical examination; Physician's request.
Staff RNs 3 (ft), 8 (pt); LPNs 4 (ft), 15 (pt);
Orderlies 3 (ft); Nurses aides 8 (ft), 33 (pt);
Activities coordinators 3 (ft); Dietitians 1
(pt).
Affiliation Presbyterian
Facilities Dining room; Physical therapy
room; Activities room; Chapel; Crafts room;
Laundry room; Barber/Beauty shop; Library.
Activities Arts & crafts; Cards; Games;
Reading groups; Prayer groups; Movies;
Shopping trips; Social/Cultural gatherings.

St Ann's Home
2161 Leonard St NW, Grand Rapids, MI,
49504
(616) 453-7715
Admin Mary Therese Esselman. *Medical Dir/
Dir of Nursing* Ellen Kuligoski RN DON.
Licensure Intermediate care; Residential. *Beds*
SNF 37; Residential 85. *Certified* Medicaid.
Owner Nonprofit organization/foundation.
Admissions Requirements Minimum age 65;
Medical examination; Physician's request.
Staff RNs; LPNs; Nurses aides; Occupational
therapists; Dietitians.
Facilities Dining room; Physical therapy
room; Activities room; Chapel; Crafts room;
Laundry room; Barber/Beauty shop; Library;
Large recreation rooms.
Activities Arts & crafts; Cards; Games;
Reading groups; Prayer groups; Movies;
Shopping trips; Social/Cultural gatherings.

Sherbrooke Nursing Home*
1157 Medical Park Dr, Grand Rapids, MI,
49506
(616) 949-7310
Licensure Skilled care. *Beds* 71.

Springbrook Manor*
2320 E Beltline SE, Grand Rapids, MI, 49506
(616) 949-3000
Licensure Skilled care; Intermediate care. *Beds*
205. *Certified* Medicaid; Medicare.
Owner Proprietary Corp (Health Care &
Retirement Corp).

Villa Elizabeth Inc
2100 Leonard NE, Grand Rapids, MI, 49505
(616) 454-8273
Admin Sr Mary Norbertine Zacharias. *Medical
Dir/Dir of Nursing* Dr J D Maskill MD;
Mary Ann Greenhoe RN DON.
Licensure Skilled care; Country villa. *Beds*
SNF 136; Residential assisted living units
48. *Certified* Medicaid; Medicare.
Owner Nonprofit Corp.

Admissions Requirements Minimum age 65
Villa Elizabeth, 60 Country Villa; Medical
examination; Physician's request for Villa
Elizabeth.
Staff RNs 4 (ft), 8 (pt); LPNs 2 (ft), 6 (pt);
Nurses aides 36 (ft), 38 (pt); Physical
therapists 1 (ft); Activities coordinators 2
(ft); Dietitians 1 (pt); Social worker 1 (ft);
Pastoral care 1 (ft).
Affiliation Roman Catholic
Facilities Dining room; Physical therapy
room; Activities room; Chapel; Laundry
room; Barber/Beauty shop.
Activities Arts & crafts; Cards; Games;
Reading groups; Prayer groups; Movies;
Shopping trips; Parties.

Walker Care Center*
1050 4 Mile Rd NW, Grand Rapids, MI,
49504
(616) 784-0646
Medical Dir/Dir of Nursing Dr James O'Brien.
Licensure Skilled care; Intermediate care. *Beds*
207. *Certified* Medicaid; Medicare.
Admissions Requirements Minimum age 17;
Medical examination; Physician's request.
Staff Physicians 3 (pt); RNs 8 (ft), 4 (pt);
LPNs 4 (ft), 11 (pt); Orderlies 1 (ft), 2 (pt);
Nurses aides 52 (ft), 30 (pt); Physical
therapists 1 (ft); Reality therapists 1 (ft);
Recreational therapists 1 (ft).
Facilities Dining room; Physical therapy
room; Activities room; Chapel; Crafts room;
Laundry room; Barber/Beauty shop; Library;
Cooking kitchen; Men's workshop.
Activities Arts & crafts; Cards; Games;
Reading groups; Prayer groups; Movies;
Shopping trips; Social/Cultural gatherings;
Outside visits to community functions;
Bowling; Pet shows; Educational
opportunities.

GRANDVILLE

Brookcrest Nursing Home*
3400 Wilson Ave SW, Grandville, MI, 49418
(616) 534-5487
Licensure Skilled care. *Beds* 153. *Certified*
Medicaid; Medicare.

GRASS LAKE

Cedar Knoll Rest Home Inc
9230 Cedar Knoll Dr, Grass Lake, MI, 49240
(517) 522-8471
Admin Janet M Smith. *Medical Dir/Dir of
Nursing* E E Vivirski MD; Donna Myers
DON.
Licensure Skilled care; Intermediate care. *Beds*
SNF 142; ICF 27. *Certified* Medicaid;
Medicare.
Owner Proprietary Corp.
Admissions Requirements Minimum age 16;
Medical examination; Physician's request.
Staff RNs 5 (ft), 1 (pt); LPNs 15 (ft), 3 (pt);
Orderlies 12 (ft); Nurses aides 62 (ft), 3 (pt);
Activities coordinators 3 (ft).
Facilities Dining room; Physical therapy
room; Activities room; Crafts room; Laundry
room; Barber/Beauty shop.
Activities Arts & crafts; Cards; Games;
Reading groups; Prayer groups; Movies;
Shopping trips.

GRAYLING

Mercy Hospital*
1100 Michigan Ave, Grayling, MI, 49738
(517) 348-5461
Licensure Skilled care; Intermediate care. *Beds*
40. *Certified* Medicaid; Medicare.

GREENVILLE

Christensen's Nursing Home*
828 E Washington Ave, Greenville, MI, 48838
(616) 754-7186
Medical Dir/Dir of Nursing Gerald L Tovatt
DO.
Licensure Skilled care; Intermediate care. *Beds*
106. *Certified* Medicaid; Medicare.
Admissions Requirements Minimum age 18;
Medical examination; Physician's request.
Staff RNs 4 (ft), 2 (pt); LPNs 6 (ft), 4 (pt);
Nurses aides 40 (ft), 20 (pt); Physical
therapists 1 (ft), 1 (pt); Recreational
therapists 1 (ft), 1 (pt); Activities
coordinators 1 (ft), 1 (pt); Dietitians 1 (pt).
Facilities Dining room; Physical therapy
room; Activities room; Crafts room; Laundry
room; Barber/Beauty shop.
Activities Arts & crafts; Cards; Games;
Reading groups; Prayer groups; Movies;
Shopping trips; Social/Cultural gatherings.

United Memorial Hospital
615 S Bower St, Greenville, MI, 48838
(616) 754-4691
Admin Wilfrid L Hufton. *Medical Dir/Dir of
Nursing* Helen E Harms RN.
Licensure Skilled care. *Beds* SNF 40. *Certified*
Medicaid; Medicare.
Owner Nonprofit Corp.
Admissions Requirements Physician's request.
Staff RNs 4 (ft), 1 (pt); LPNs 6 (ft), 6 (pt);
Nurses aides 16 (ft), 10 (pt); Activities
coordinators 1 (ft).
Facilities Dining room; Physical therapy
room; Activities room; Barber/Beauty shop.
Activities Arts & crafts; Cards; Games;
Reading groups; Prayer groups; Movies;
Shopping trips; Church service.

GROSSE POINTE WOODS

Georgian East*
21401 Mack Ave, Grosse Pointe Woods, MI,
48236
(313) 778-0800
Licensure Intermediate care. *Beds* 80.
Certified Medicare.

HAMTRAMCK

St Joseph Nursing Home
9400 Conant, Hamtramck, MI, 48212
(313) 874-4500
Admin Rosanne Ruehlen. *Medical Dir/Dir of
Nursing* Diane Cottle RN DON.
Licensure Skilled care; Intermediate care;
Intermediate care for mentally retarded.
Beds SNF 27; ICF 27; ICF/MR 120.
Certified Medicaid; Medicare.
Owner Proprietary Corp.
Admissions Requirements Medical
examination; Physician's request.
Staff RNs 7 (ft), 2 (pt); LPNs 18 (ft), 3 (pt);
Orderlies 2 (pt); Nurses aides 48 (ft), 25 (pt);
Physical therapists 2 (pt); Speech therapists
1 (pt); Activities coordinators 2 (ft);
Dietitians 1 (ft), 2 (pt); Ophthalmologists 2
(pt).
Languages Polish, Arabic
Facilities Dining room; Physical therapy
room; Activities room; Chapel; Crafts room;
Laundry room; Barber/Beauty shop.
Activities Arts & crafts; Cards; Games;
Reading groups; Prayer groups; Movies.

HANCOCK

Cypress Manor
1400 Poplar St, Hancock, MI, 49930
(906) 482-6644
Admin Kathleen L Dube. *Medical Dir/Dir of
Nursing* Terry Kinzel MD; Miriam Kipina
RN DON.

Licensure Intermediate care. *Beds* ICF 63.
Certified Medicaid.
Owner Proprietary Corp (Health Concepts
Corp).
Admissions Requirements Minimum age 18;
Medical examination; Physician's request.
Staff Physicians 4 (ft); RNs 2 (ft); LPNs 4 (ft);
Nurses aides 25 (ft); Physical therapists 1
(pt); Reality therapists 1 (pt); Recreational
therapists 1 (pt); Occupational therapists 1
(pt); Speech therapists 1 (pt); Activities
coordinators 1 (ft); Dietitians 1 (pt); Dentists
1 (pt); Ophthalmologists 1 (pt); Podiatrists 1
(pt).
Facilities Dining room; Physical therapy
room; Activities room; Laundry room;
Barber/Beauty shop.
Activities Arts & crafts; Cards; Games;
Reading groups; Prayer groups; Movies;
Shopping trips; Social/Cultural gatherings.

Houghton County Medical Care Facility
1100 Quincy St, Hancock, MI, 49930
(906) 482-5050
Medical Dir/Dir of Nursing Hororatio Barrios
MD.
Licensure Skilled care; Intermediate care. *Beds*
197. *Certified* Medicaid; Medicare.
Admissions Requirements Minimum age 18;
Medical examination; Physician's request.
Staff Physicians 9 (pt); RNs 8 (ft), 6 (pt);
LPNs 7 (ft), 4 (pt); Orderlies 5 (ft), 4 (pt);
Nurses aides 66 (ft), 14 (pt); Physical
therapists 1 (pt); Speech therapists 1 (pt);
Activities coordinators 2 (ft); Dietitians 1
(pt); Dentists 1 (pt); Ophthalmologists 1 (pt).
Facilities Dining room; Physical therapy
room; Activities room; Chapel; Crafts room;
Barber/Beauty shop; Library.
Activities Arts & crafts; Cards; Games;
Reading groups; Movies; Shopping trips;
Social/Cultural gatherings.

Portage View Hospital*
200-10 Michigan St, Hancock, MI, 49930
(517) 482-1122
Medical Dir/Dir of Nursing Marko V Beley.
Licensure Skilled care. *Beds* 30. *Certified*
Medicare.
Admissions Requirements Minimum age 15;
Medical examination; Physician's request.
Staff Physicians 9 (pt); RNs 1 (ft); LPNs 2
(ft), 6 (pt); Nurses aides 6 (ft), 9 (pt);
Physical therapists 2 (ft), 1 (pt); Speech
therapists 1 (pt); Activities coordinators 1
(pt); Dietitians 2 (ft); Dentists 5 (pt);
Ophthalmologists 2 (ft).
Facilities Activities room; Crafts room.
Activities Arts & crafts; Cards; Games;
Movies; Shopping trips.

HARBOR BEACH

Harbor Beach Community Hospital*
1st & Broad Sts, Harbor Beach, MI, 48441
(517) 479-3201
Licensure Skilled care; Intermediate care. *Beds*
40. *Certified* Medicaid; Medicare.

HARBOR SPRINGS

Emmet County Medical Care Facility
750 E Main St, Harbor Springs, MI, 49740
(616) 526-2161
Admin Paula Kebrzycki. *Medical Dir/Dir of
Nursing* Richard A Knecht MD; Ann
Bodzick DON.
Licensure Skilled care. *Beds* SNF 110.
Certified Medicaid; Medicare.
Owner Publicly owned.
Admissions Requirements Minimum age 16;
Medical examination; Physician's request.
Staff Physicians 4 (pt); RNs 10 (ft), 4 (pt);
LPNs 2 (ft); Orderlies 2 (ft), 1 (pt); Nurses
aides 43 (ft), 12 (pt); Physical therapists 1
(pt); Occupational therapists 1 (pt); Speech

therapists 1 (pt); Activities coordinators 1
(ft), 2 (pt); Dietitians 1 (ft);
Ophthalmologists 1 (pt).
Facilities Dining room; Physical therapy
room; Activities room; Chapel; Crafts room;
Laundry room; Barber/Beauty shop.
Activities Arts & crafts; Cards; Games;
Reading groups; Prayer groups; Movies;
Social/Cultural gatherings.

HARPER WOODS

Cottage-Belmont Nursing Center Inc
19840 Harper Ave, Harper Woods, MI, 48225
(313) 881-9556
Admin William T Barr. *Medical Dir/Dir of
Nursing* Dorothy Pankowski RN DON.
Licensure Skilled care; Intermediate care. *Beds*
153.
Owner Nonprofit Corp.
Admissions Requirements Minimum age 50;
Medical examination; Physician's request.
Staff Physicians 5 (pt); RNs 5 (ft), 5 (pt);
LPNs 5 (ft), 5 (pt); Orderlies 2 (ft), 2 (pt);
Nurses aides 50 (ft), 25 (pt); Physical
therapists 2 (pt); Reality therapists 1 (pt);
Recreational therapists 1 (ft); Occupational
therapists 1 (pt); Speech therapists 1 (pt);
Activities coordinators 2 (ft), 2 (pt);
Dietitians 1 (pt); Ophthalmologists 1 (pt).
Languages Polish
Activities Arts & crafts; Cards; Games;
Reading groups; Prayer groups; Movies;
Shopping trips; Social/Cultural gatherings.

HARRISVILLE

Jamieson Nursing Home
790 S US 23, Harrisville, MI, 48740
(517) 724-6889
Admin Sally J Smith. *Medical Dir/Dir of
Nursing* Neda Joyce RN.
Licensure Intermediate care. *Beds* ICF 51.
Certified Medicaid.
Owner Proprietary Corp.
Admissions Requirements Minimum age 15;
Physician's request.
Staff Physicians; RNs; LPNs; Orderlies;
Nurses aides; Physical therapists; Reality
therapists; Recreational therapists;
Occupational therapists; Speech therapists;
Activities coordinators; Dietitians; Dentists;
Ophthalmologists; Podiatrists.
Facilities Dining room; Activities room;
Chapel; Crafts room; Laundry room; Barber/
Beauty shop; Library.
Activities Arts & crafts; Cards; Games;
Reading groups; Prayer groups; Movies;
Shopping trips; Social/Cultural gatherings;
Gardening.

HART

Oceana County Medical Care Facility*
701 E Main St, Hart, MI, 49420
(313) 873-2148
Licensure Skilled care; Intermediate care. *Beds*
113. *Certified* Medicaid; Medicare.
Owner Publicly owned.

HASTINGS

Provincial House—Hastings
240 N East St, Hastings, MI, 49058
(616) 945-9564
Admin Joyce F Weinbrecht. *Medical Dir/Dir
of Nursing* Joseph C Roth DO; Kay Rowley
RN DON.
Licensure Skilled care. *Beds* SNF 114.
Certified Medicaid; Medicare.
Owner Proprietary Corp (Beverly Enterprises).
Admissions Requirements Minimum age 16;
Medical examination; Physician's request.
Staff Physicians 17 (pt); RNs 4 (ft), 5 (pt);
LPNs 5 (ft), 3 (pt); Nurses aides 35 (ft), 31
(pt); Physical therapists 1 (pt); Occupational

therapists 1 (ft); Speech therapists 1 (pt);
Activities coordinators 1 (ft), 1 (pt);
Dietitians 1 (pt); Dentists 1 (pt);
Ophthalmologists 1 (pt).
Facilities Dining room; Physical therapy
room; Activities room; Crafts room; Laundry
room; Barber/Beauty shop.
Activities Arts & crafts; Cards; Games;
Reading groups; Prayer groups; Movies;
Shopping trips; Social/Cultural gatherings.

Thornapple Manor
2700 Nashville Rd, Hastings, MI, 49058
(616) 945-2407
Admin Lynn Sommerfeld. *Medical Dir/Dir of
Nursing* Lawrence Hawkings MD; Bonita
Laverty RN DON.
Licensure Skilled care. *Beds* SNF 138.
Certified Medicaid; Medicare.
Owner Publicly owned.
Admissions Requirements Physician's request.
Staff RNs; LPNs; Nurses aides; Physical
therapists; Occupational therapists; Speech
therapists; Activities coordinators; Dietitians;
Ophthalmologists.
Facilities Dining room; Physical therapy
room; Activities room; Crafts room; Laundry
room; Barber/Beauty shop.

HIGHLAND PARK

Park Geriatric Village
111 Ford Ave, Highland Park, MI, 48203
(313) 883-3585
Admin Paul C Holliday. *Medical Dir/Dir of
Nursing* E Pistain MD; B Cash RN.
Licensure Intermediate care. *Beds* ICF 137.
Certified Medicaid.
Owner Privately owned.
Admissions Requirements Minimum age 18;
Medical examination; Physician's request.
Staff Physicians 2 (ft); RNs 3 (ft), 3 (pt);
LPNs 7 (ft), 10 (pt); Orderlies 6 (ft), 8 (pt);
Nurses aides 36 (ft), 25 (pt); Activities
coordinators 1 (ft).
Facilities Dining room; Physical therapy
room; Activities room; Laundry room;
Barber/Beauty shop; Library.
Activities Arts & crafts; Cards; Games;
Reading groups; Prayer groups; Movies.

Royal Nursing Center*
91 Glendale Ave, Highland Park, MI, 48203
(313) 869-7711
Licensure Skilled care; Intermediate care. *Beds*
183. *Certified* Medicaid; Medicare.

St Lukes Episcopal Home
224 Highland Ave, Highland Park, MI, 48203
(313) 868-1445
Admin Philip C Fischer. *Medical Dir/Dir of
Nursing* Mary I Caragay RN.
Licensure Intermediate care. *Beds* ICF 22.
Certified Medicaid.
Owner Nonprofit Corp.
Admissions Requirements Minimum age 65;
Medical examination.
Staff Physicians 4 (pt); RNs 1 (ft), 1 (pt);
LPNs 2 (ft), 3 (pt); Nurses aides 3 (ft), 15
(pt); Activities coordinators 1 (ft); Dietitians
1 (pt).
Affiliation Episcopal
Facilities Dining room; Activities room;
Chapel; Crafts room; Laundry room; Barber/
Beauty shop.
Activities Arts & crafts; Cards; Games;
Reading groups; Prayer groups; Movies;
Shopping trips; Social/Cultural gatherings.

HILLMAN

Pineview of Hillman*
631 Caring St, Hillman, MI, 49746
Licensure Intermediate care. *Beds* 70.
Certified Medicaid; Medicare.
Owner Proprietary Corp (Hillhaven Corp).

HILLSDALE

Hillsdale County Medical Care Facility*
140 W Mechanic St, Hillsdale, MI, 49242
(517) 439-9341
Admin Keith Van Oosterhout MD. *Medical Dir/Dir of Nursing* Dr Frank Monti.
Licensure Skilled care; Intermediate care. *Beds* 160. *Certified* Medicaid; Medicare.
Admissions Requirements Minimum age 15; Medical examination; Physician's request.
Staff Physicians 1 (ft), 1 (pt); RNs 6 (ft), 2 (pt); LPNs 20 (ft), 10 (pt); Nurses aides 50 (ft), 50 (pt); Physical therapists 1 (pt); Recreational therapists 3 (ft); Occupational therapists 1 (pt); Speech therapists 1 (pt); Activities coordinators 1 (ft); Dietitians 1 (ft); Dentists 1 (pt); Ophthalmologists 1 (pt); Podiatrists 1 (pt).
Facilities Dining room; Physical therapy room; Activities room; Chapel; Crafts room; Laundry room; Barber/Beauty shop.
Activities Arts & crafts; Cards; Games; Reading groups; Prayer groups; Movies; Social/Cultural gatherings.

HOLLAND

Birchwood Manor*
493 W 32nd St, Holland, MI, 49423
(616) 396-1438
Licensure Skilled care; Intermediate care. *Beds* 111. *Certified* Medicaid; Medicare.
Owner Proprietary Corp (Health Care & Retirement Corp).

Meadowbrook Care Center
280 W 40th, Holland, MI, 49423
(616) 392-7161
Admin Richard A Myers. *Medical Dir/Dir of Nursing* Dr Leppink; Bernice Catson.
Licensure Skilled care; Intermediate care. *Beds* SNF 125; ICF. *Certified* Medicaid; Medicare.
Owner Proprietary Corp (Beverly Enterprises).
Admissions Requirements Medical examination; Physician's request.
Staff Physicians 5 (pt); RNs 4 (ft), 4 (pt); LPNs 9 (ft), 6 (pt); Nurses aides 75 (ft), 50 (pt); Physical therapists 1 (ft); Occupational therapists 1 (pt); Speech therapists 1 (pt); Activities coordinators 1 (ft), 1 (pt); Dietitians 1 (ft); Dentists 1 (pt); Ophthalmologists 1 (pt); Podiatrists 1 (pt).
Languages Dutch
Facilities Dining room; Physical therapy room; Activities room; Laundry room; Barber/Beauty shop.
Activities Arts & crafts; Cards; Games; Reading groups; Prayer groups; Movies.

HOLT

Martin Luther Holt Home
5091 Willoughby Rd, Holt, MI, 48842
(517) 694-2144
Admin Ben Larsen. *Medical Dir/Dir of Nursing* Dr Elizabeth Imeson; Marcelene Morris RN DON.
Licensure Skilled care. *Beds* SNF 84. *Certified* Medicaid; Medicare.
Owner Nonprofit organization/foundation.
Admissions Requirements Medical examination.
Staff RNs 3 (ft), 6 (pt); LPNs 2 (ft), 5 (pt); Orderlies 2 (pt); Nurses aides 16 (ft), 45 (pt); Activities coordinators 1 (ft); Dietitians 1 (ft).
Affiliation Lutheran
Facilities Dining room; Activities room; Crafts room; Barber/Beauty shop.
Activities Arts & crafts; Games; Reading groups; Prayer groups; Movies; Shopping trips.

HOUGHTON LAKE

King Nursing Home*
206 Tower Hill Rd, Houghton Lake, MI, 48629
(517) 422-5153
Licensure Intermediate care. *Beds* 49. *Certified* Medicaid.

HOWELL

Greenbriar Care Center
3003 W Grand River, Howell, MI, 48843
(517) 546-4210
Admin Sheryl Purcell. *Medical Dir/Dir of Nursing* Edwin C Blumberg MD; Kathy Bonfiglio RN.
Licensure Skilled care; Intermediate care. *Beds* 189. *Certified* Medicaid; Medicare; VA.
Owner Proprietary Corp.
Admissions Requirements Medical examination; Physician's request.
Facilities Dining room; Physical therapy room; Activities room; Crafts room; Laundry room; Barber/Beauty shop.
Activities Arts & crafts; Cards; Games; Reading groups; Prayer groups; Movies; Shopping trips; Social/Cultural gatherings.

Livingston Care Center Inc
1333 W Grand River, Howell, MI, 48843
(517) 548-1900
Admin Harold Trend. *Medical Dir/Dir of Nursing* Edwin C Blumberg DO; Marlene Smith END.
Licensure Skilled care; Intermediate care. *Beds* 210. *Certified* Medicaid; Medicare.
Owner Proprietary Corp.
Admissions Requirements Minimum age 16; Medical examination; Physician's request.
Staff RNs; LPNs; Orderlies; Nurses aides; Activities coordinators 3 (ft).
Facilities Dining room; Physical therapy room; Activities room; Chapel; Crafts room; Laundry room; Barber/Beauty shop; Library.
Activities Arts & crafts; Cards; Games; Reading groups; Prayer groups; Movies.

HUBBELL

Our Lady of Mercy Convalescent Home Inc
Box 369, 1201 Grant St, Hubbell, MI, 49934
(906) 296-3301 & 296-9601
Admin Raymond E Dube. *Medical Dir/Dir of Nursing* Dr Jerry Luoma & Dr Gary Mikel; Deborah Little RN DON.
Licensure Intermediate care. *Beds* ICF 45. *Certified* Medicaid.
Owner Proprietary Corp.
Admissions Requirements Minimum age 18; Medical examination.
Staff Physicians 2 (ft); RNs 2 (ft), 2 (pt); LPNs 1 (ft), 3 (pt); Nurses aides 12 (ft), 7 (pt); Activities coordinators 1 (ft), 1 (pt); Dietitians 1 (pt).
Languages French, Croatian, Finnish
Affiliation Roman Catholic
Facilities Dining room; Activities room; Laundry room; Barber/Beauty shop; Library.
Activities Arts & crafts; Cards; Games; Reading groups; Prayer groups; Movies; Social/Cultural gatherings; Library services.

HUDSONVILLE

Hudsonville Christian Nursing Home*
3650 Van Buren, Hudsonville, MI, 49426
(616) 669-1520
Licensure Skilled care; Intermediate care. *Beds* 113. *Certified* Medicaid; Medicare.

INKSTER

Advance Nursing Center*
2936 S John Daley Rd, Inkster, MI, 48141
(313) 278-7272
Licensure Skilled care; Intermediate care. *Beds* 92. *Certified* Medicaid; Medicare.

City & Country Convalescent Homes Inc
28355 Michigan Ave, Inkster, MI, 48141
(313) 274-0310
Admin Mr Jessie T Joyner. *Medical Dir/Dir of Nursing* Lawrence Usher; Loretta Mulzer.
Licensure Intermediate care. *Beds* ICF 79. *Certified* Medicaid.
Owner Proprietary Corp.
Admissions Requirements Minimum age 18; Medical examination; Physician's request.
Staff Physicians 1 (ft); RNs 1 (ft); LPNs 5 (ft), 8 (pt); Orderlies 6 (ft); Nurses aides 23 (ft), 1 (pt); Activities coordinators 1 (ft), 1 (pt); Dietitians 1 (ft).
Facilities Dining room; Activities room; Crafts room; Laundry room; Barber/Beauty shop.
Activities Arts & crafts; Cards; Games; Reading groups; Prayer groups; Movies; Shopping trips; Social/Cultural gatherings.

IONIA

Ionia Manor*
814 Lincoln, Ionia, MI, 48846
(616) 527-0080
Licensure Skilled care; Intermediate care. *Beds* 120. *Certified* Medicaid; Medicare.
Owner Proprietary Corp (Health Care & Retirement Corp).

IRON MOUNTAIN

Freeman Convalescent Home*
Box 130, Star Rte 3, Iron Mountain, MI, 49801
(906) 774-1530
Licensure Intermediate care. *Beds* 45. *Certified* Medicaid.

Hyland Convalescent Home*
601 E "G" St, Iron Mountain, MI, 49801
(906) 774-9333
Licensure Intermediate care. *Beds* 51.

IRON RIVER

Iron River Nursing Home Inc
330 Lincoln Ave, Iron River, MI, 49935
(906) 265-5168
Admin Philip Laturi. *Medical Dir/Dir of Nursing* Robert Han MD; Karen Patton DON.
Licensure Intermediate care. *Beds* ICF 69. *Certified* Medicaid.
Owner Proprietary Corp.
Staff LPNs 3 (ft), 3 (pt); Orderlies 2 (ft); Nurses aides 18 (ft), 15 (pt); Activities coordinators 1 (ft), 1 (pt); Dietitians 1 (pt).

IRONWOOD

Hautamaki Westgate Rest Home*
1500 N Lowell St, Ironwood, MI, 49938
(906) 932-3867
Licensure Intermediate care. *Beds* 65. *Certified* Medicaid.

Josephson Nursing Home*
634 E Ayer St, Ironwood, MI, 49938
(906) 932-2006
Medical Dir/Dir of Nursing Allen C Gorrilca MD.
Licensure Intermediate care. *Beds* 47. *Certified* Medicaid.
Staff Physicians 9 (pt); RNs 1 (ft); LPNs 8 (pt); Nurses aides 20 (ft), 30 (pt); Physical therapists 1 (pt); Reality therapists 1 (pt); Recreational therapists 1 (pt); Activities coordinators 1 (ft); Dietitians 1 (pt); Dentists 1 (pt); Ophthalmologists 1 (pt); Podiatrists 1 (pt); Audiologists 1 (pt).

Facilities Dining room; Activities room; Laundry room.
Activities Arts & crafts; Cards; Games; Reading groups; Prayer groups; Movies; Shopping trips; Social/Cultural gatherings; Fishing trips; Picnics; Swimming.

ISHPEMING

Mather Nursing Center
435 Stoneville Rd, Ishpeming, MI, 49849
(906) 485-1073
Admin Sue Cieslinski. *Medical Dir/Dir of Nursing* Barbara Lyons MD; Judith Nagel DON.
Licensure Skilled care. *Beds* SNF 122. *Certified* Medicaid; Medicare.
Owner Proprietary Corp (Health Concepts Corp).
Staff Physicians; RNs; LPNs; Orderlies; Nurses aides; Physical therapists; Reality therapists; Recreational therapists; Occupational therapists; Speech therapists; Activities coordinators; Dietitians; Podiatrists.
Facilities Dining room; Physical therapy room; Activities room; Crafts room; Laundry room; Barber/Beauty shop.
Activities Arts & crafts; Cards; Games; Reading groups; Prayer groups; Movies; Shopping trips; Social/Cultural gatherings.

JACKSON

Faith Haven Care Center*
6531 W Michigan Ave, Jackson, MI, 49201
(517) 750-3822
Licensure Skilled care; Intermediate care. *Beds* 88. *Certified* Medicaid; Medicare.

Jackson County Medical Care Facility*
1715 Lansing Ave, Jackson, MI, 49202
(517) 783-2726
Licensure Skilled care; Intermediate care. *Beds* 194. *Certified* Medicaid; Medicare.
Owner Publicly owned.

Marlin Manor*
434 W North St, Jackson, MI, 49202
(517) 787-3250
Licensure Skilled care. *Beds* 100. *Certified* Medicaid; Medicare.
Owner Proprietary Corp (Health Care & Retirement Corp).

Odd Fellow & Rebekah Home
2388 W Michigan, Jackson, MI, 49202
(517) 787-5140
Admin Ann E O'Dell. *Medical Dir/Dir of Nursing* Pat Balaze RN.
Licensure Intermediate care; Home for aged. *Beds* ICF 50; Home for aged 20. *Certified* Medicaid.
Owner Nonprofit Corp.
Admissions Requirements Minimum age 16; Medical examination.
Staff Physicians; RNs; LPNs; Orderlies; Nurses aides; Recreational therapists; Activities coordinators; Dietitians; Ophthalmologists.
Affiliation Independent Order of Odd Fellows & Rebekahs
Facilities Dining room; Physical therapy room; Activities room; Chapel; Crafts room; Laundry room; Barber/Beauty shop; Library.
Activities Arts & crafts; Cards; Games; Reading groups; Prayer groups; Movies; Shopping trips; Social/Cultural gatherings.

Vista Grande Villa
2251 Springport Rd, Jackson, MI, 49202
(517) 787-0222
Admin Donald Johansen. *Medical Dir/Dir of Nursing* I H Butt MD; Blanche Knight RN DON.
Licensure Skilled care; Intermediate care. *Beds* 60. *Certified* Medicaid; Medicare.

Owner Nonprofit organization/foundation.
Admissions Requirements Minimum age 62; Females only; Medical examination.
Staff Physicians 1 (ft), 2 (pt); RNs 2 (ft), 5 (pt); LPNs 3 (ft), 8 (pt); Nurses aides 18 (ft), 16 (pt); Physical therapists 1 (pt); Speech therapists 1 (pt); Activities coordinators 1 (ft), 2 (pt); Dietitians 1 (ft), 1 (pt); Ophthalmologists 1 (pt); Podiatrists 1 (pt).
Facilities Dining room; Physical therapy room; Activities room; Chapel; Crafts room; Laundry room; Barber/Beauty shop; Library; Pharmacy.
Activities Arts & crafts; Cards; Games; Reading groups; Prayer groups; Movies; Shopping trips; Social/Cultural gatherings.

KALAMAZOO

Alamo Nursing Home, Inc
8290 W "C" Ave, Kalamazoo, MI, 49009
(616) 343-2587
Admin Fern Enos, Catherine Preston. *Medical Dir/Dir of Nursing* E R Topp MD; Carol Allor DON.
Licensure Skilled care; Intermediate care. *Beds* 100. *Certified* Medicaid; Medicare.
Owner Proprietary Corp.
Admissions Requirements Minimum age 15.
Staff Physicians 2 (pt); RNs 3 (ft), 2 (pt); LPNs 5 (ft), 4 (pt); Orderlies 2 (ft), 1 (pt); Nurses aides 31 (ft), 12 (pt); Physical therapists 1 (pt); Activities coordinators 1 (ft), 1 (pt).
Facilities Dining room; Physical therapy room; Activities room; Crafts room; Laundry room; Barber/Beauty shop; Library.
Activities Arts & crafts; Cards; Games; Reading groups; Prayer groups; Movies; Shopping trips; Social/Cultural gatherings; Poetry class; Picnics; Outings; Monthly birthday parties; Holiday parties.

Birch Manor*
537 Chicago Ave, Kalamazoo, MI, 49001
(616) 382-2392
Medical Dir/Dir of Nursing Frank Harrell MD.
Licensure Skilled care; Intermediate care. *Beds* 121. *Certified* Medicaid; Medicare.
Admissions Requirements Minimum age 15; Medical examination; Physician's request.
Staff RNs 14 (ft); LPNs 8 (ft); Orderlies 4 (ft); Nurses aides 100 (ft); Reality therapists 1 (pt); Recreational therapists 4 (ft); Occupational therapists 1 (pt); Activities coordinators 1 (ft); Dietitians 1 (pt).
Facilities Dining room; Physical therapy room; Activities room; Chapel; Crafts room; Laundry room; Barber/Beauty shop; Library.
Activities Arts & crafts; Cards; Games; Reading groups; Prayer groups; Movies; Social/Cultural gatherings; Outdoor picnics; Tours by bus.

Brookhaven Care Facility*
1701 Olmstead Rd, Kalamazoo, MI, 49001
(616) 349-9694
Licensure Intermediate care. *Beds* 50. *Certified* Medicaid.

Friendship Village*
1400 N Drake Rd, Kalamazoo, MI, 49007
(616) 381-0560
Medical Dir/Dir of Nursing Dr Bennard Dowd.
Licensure Skilled care; Intermediate care. *Beds* 57. *Certified* Medicaid; Medicare.
Admissions Requirements Minimum age 62; Medical examination; Physician's request.
Staff Physicians 3 (pt); RNs 1 (ft), 6 (pt); LPNs 4 (ft), 3 (pt); Nurses aides 22 (ft), 8 (pt); Physical therapists 1 (pt); Speech therapists 1 (pt); Activities coordinators 1 (ft); Dietitians 1 (pt); Dentists 1 (pt); Ophthalmologists 1 (pt); Podiatrists 1 (pt); Audiologists 1 (pt).

Facilities Dining room; Physical therapy room; Activities room; Chapel; Crafts room; Laundry room; Barber/Beauty shop; Library.
Activities Arts & crafts; Cards; Games; Reading groups; Prayer groups; Movies; Shopping trips; Social/Cultural gatherings.

Provincial House
1701 S 11th St, Kalamazoo, MI, 49009
(616) 375-2020
Admin Thomas M Bourisseau. *Medical Dir/Dir of Nursing* Simon Hoogendyk; Pat Bushouse DON.
Licensure Skilled care; Intermediate care. *Beds* SNF 117. *Certified* Medicaid; Medicare.
Owner Proprietary Corp (Beverly Enterprises).
Admissions Requirements Medical examination; Physician's request.
Staff Physicians 23 (pt); RNs 4 (ft), 2 (pt); LPNs 8 (ft), 1 (pt); Orderlies 2 (ft); Nurses aides 50 (ft), 5 (pt); Physical therapists 1 (pt); Recreational therapists 1 (pt); Occupational therapists 1 (pt); Speech therapists 1 (pt); Speech therapists J; Activities coordinators 1 (ft), 1 (pt); Dietitians 1 (ft); Ophthalmologists 1 (pt); Podiatrists 1 (pt).
Facilities Dining room; Physical therapy room; Activities room; Crafts room; Laundry room; Barber/Beauty shop; Library.
Activities Arts & crafts; Cards; Games; Reading groups; Prayer groups; Movies; Social/Cultural gatherings.

Provincial House—Kalamazoo Total Living Center
2575 N Drake Rd, Kalamazoo, MI, 49007
(616) 342-0206
Admin Sonya Scarff. *Medical Dir/Dir of Nursing* Dr H Sidney Helrsma MD; Sally Leiterman RN DON.
Licensure Skilled care. *Beds* SNF 117. *Certified* Medicaid.
Owner Proprietary Corp (Beverly Enterprises).
Admissions Requirements Minimum age 18.
Staff RNs 6 (ft), 1 (pt); LPNs 15 (ft); Nurses aides 90 (ft), 10 (pt); Recreational therapists 1 (ft).
Facilities Dining room; Activities room; Crafts room; Barber/Beauty shop.
Activities Arts & crafts; Games; Reading groups; Movies; Shopping trips.

Provincial House—Portage*
7855 Currier Dr, Kalamazoo, MI, 49002
(616) 323-7748
Medical Dir/Dir of Nursing Dr Simon Hoogendyk.
Licensure Skilled care; Intermediate care. *Beds* 120. *Certified* Medicaid; Medicare.
Owner Proprietary Corp (Beverly Enterprises).
Admissions Requirements Medical examination; Physician's request.
Staff RNs 8 (ft), 3 (pt); LPNs 6 (ft), 2 (pt); Orderlies 2 (ft), 2 (pt); Nurses aides 40 (ft), 30 (pt); Physical therapists 1 (pt); Recreational therapists 1 (ft); Occupational therapists 1 (pt); Speech therapists 1 (pt); Activities coordinators 1 (ft); Dietitians 1 (ft); Dentists 1 (pt); Podiatrists 1 (pt); Audiologists 1 (pt).
Facilities Dining room; Physical therapy room; Activities room; Crafts room; Laundry room; Barber/Beauty shop; Library.
Activities Arts & crafts; Games; Reading groups; Prayer groups; Movies; Shopping trips.

Ridgeview Manor
3625 W Michigan Ave, Kalamazoo, MI, 49007
(616) 375-4550
Admin Donald J Kitchin. *Medical Dir/Dir of Nursing* Dr J T Cerovski; Mar Driskill.
Licensure Skilled care; Intermediate care. *Beds* SNF 114; ICF 66. *Certified* Medicaid; Medicare.

Owner Proprietary Corp (Health Care & Retire Corp).
Admissions Requirements Medical examination; Physician's request.
Staff RNs; LPNs; Orderlies; Nurses aides; Activities coordinators; Dietitians.
Facilities Dining room; Physical therapy room; Activities room; Crafts room; Laundry room; Barber/Beauty shop.
Activities Arts & crafts; Cards; Games; Reading groups; Prayer groups; Movies; Shopping trips; Social/Cultural gatherings; Youth activities; College courses.

Upjohn Community Nursing Home
2400 Portage St, Kalamazoo, MI, 49001
(616) 381-4290
Admin Donna Menchinger. *Medical Dir/Dir of Nursing* Donna Menchinger RN DON.
Licensure Skilled care; Intermediate care. *Beds* SNF 130; ICF 130. *Certified* Medicaid; Medicare.
Owner Nonprofit Corp.
Admissions Requirements Medical examination; Physician's request.
Staff Physicians 1 (pt); RNs 6 (ft), 10 (pt); LPNs 5 (ft), 6 (pt); Orderlies 2 (ft); Nurses aides 38 (ft), 61 (pt); Physical therapists 1 (pt); Occupational therapists 1 (ft); Activities coordinators 1 (ft); Dietitians 1 (ft); Volunteer coordinator 1 (ft).
Facilities Dining room; Physical therapy room; Activities room; Chapel; Crafts room; Laundry room; Barber/Beauty shop; Library.
Activities Arts & crafts; Cards; Games; Reading groups; Prayer groups; Movies; Shopping trips; Social/Cultural gatherings; Gardening; Baking.

Verdries Nursing Home*
1430 Alamo Ave, Kalamazoo, MI, 49007
(616) 349-2661
Licensure Skilled care; Intermediate care. *Beds* 140. *Certified* Medicaid; Medicare.
Owner Proprietary Corp (Comprehensive Health Care Assn).

Westbrook Manor
6203 W Michigan Ave, Kalamazoo, MI, 49009
(616) 375-1204
Admin William R Becker. *Medical Dir/Dir of Nursing* Helen Kroemlien.
Licensure Skilled care. *Beds* SNF 101. *Certified* Medicaid; Medicare.
Owner Privately owned.
Admissions Requirements Medical examination.
Staff Physicians 2 (ft); RNs 2 (ft); LPNs 8 (ft); Orderlies 3 (ft); Nurses aides 20 (ft); Occupational therapists 1 (ft); Activities coordinators 1 (ft); Dietitians 1 (ft); Ophthalmologists 1 (ft).
Facilities Dining room; Physical therapy room; Activities room; Crafts room; Laundry room; Barber/Beauty shop.
Activities Arts & crafts; Cards; Games; Reading groups; Prayer groups; Movies; Shopping trips; Social/Cultural gatherings.

KALKASKA

Kalkaska Memorial Hospital
PO Box 249, 419 S Coral, Kalkaska, MI, 49646
(616) 258-9142
Admin Harvey Norris. *Medical Dir/Dir of Nursing* Dr Richard E Hodgman; Lynn Quail RN.
Licensure Concurrent. *Beds* 8. *Certified* Medicaid; Medicare.
Admissions Requirements Minimum age 15; Medical examination; Physician's request.
Staff Physicians 4 (pt); RNs 8 (pt); LPNs 10 (pt); Nurses aides 6 (pt); Physical therapists 1 (ft); Activities coordinators 1 (pt); Dietitians 1 (pt); Podiatrists 1 (pt).

Facilities Physical therapy room; Activities room.
Activities Arts & crafts; Games; Reading groups; Prayer groups; Movies; Shopping trips; Social/Cultural gatherings.

KAWKAWLIN

Huron Woods Nursing Home*
1395 S Huron, Kawkawlin, MI, 48631
(517) 684-3213
Licensure Intermediate care. *Beds* 51. *Certified* Medicaid.

KINGSFORD

Americana Healthcare Center
1225 Woodward Ave, Kingsford, MI, 49801
(906) 774-4805
Admin Helen R Roach. *Medical Dir/Dir of Nursing* Dr Donald J Jacobs; Dorothy Saler RN DON.
Licensure Skilled care. *Beds* SNF 107. *Certified* Medicaid; Medicare.
Owner Proprietary Corp (Manor Care).
Admissions Requirements Minimum age 17.
Staff RNs 1 (ft), 4 (pt); LPNs 1 (ft), 5 (pt); Nurses aides 25 (ft), 30 (pt); Physical therapists 1 (pt); Activities coordinators; Dietitians 1 (pt).
Facilities Dining room; Physical therapy room; Activities room; Crafts room; Laundry room; Barber/Beauty shop.
Activities Arts & crafts; Cards; Games; Reading groups; Prayer groups; Movies; Shopping trips.

LAKEVIEW

Kelsey Memorial Hospital
418 Washington, Lakeview, MI, 48850
(517) 352-7211
Admin Melvin R Creeley. *Medical Dir/Dir of Nursing* John L London MD; Marlene Schalm RN DON.
Licensure Skilled care. *Beds* SNF 42. *Certified* Medicaid; Medicare.
Owner Nonprofit organization/foundation.
Admissions Requirements Medical examination; Physician's request.
Staff Physicians 13 (ft); RNs 2 (ft); LPNs 12 (ft), 8 (pt); Nurses aides 9 (ft), 10 (pt); Physical therapists 1 (ft), 1 (pt); Reality therapists 1 (ft); Occupational therapists 1 (pt); Speech therapists 1 (pt); Activities coordinators 1 (ft), 1 (pt); Dentists 1 (pt); Ophthalmologists 1 (pt).
Facilities Dining room; Physical therapy room; Activities room; Barber/Beauty shop.
Activities Arts & crafts; Cards; Games; Reading groups; Prayer groups; Movies; Shopping trips; Social/Cultural gatherings; Parties; Picnics; Museum trips; Weekly excursions in handicapped-equipped van.

LAMONT

Glenwood Christian Nursing Home
13030 44th Ave, Lamont, MI, 49430
(616) 677-1243
Medical Dir/Dir of Nursing Mary S Kitchel MD.
Licensure Skilled care; Intermediate care. *Beds* 66. *Certified* Medicaid; Medicare.
Admissions Requirements Minimum age 17; Medical examination; Physician's request.
Staff Physicians 7 (ft); RNs 11 (ft); LPNs 5 (ft); Nurses aides 50 (ft); Physical therapists 1 (ft); Recreational therapists 1 (ft); Occupational therapists 1 (pt); Speech therapists 1 (pt); Activities coordinators 1 (ft); Dietitians 1 (pt); Dentists 1 (pt); Ophthalmologists 1 (pt); Podiatrists 1 (pt).
Facilities Dining room; Physical therapy room; Activities room; Crafts room; Laundry room; Barber/Beauty shop.

Activities Arts & crafts; Cards; Games; Reading groups; Prayer groups; Movies; Shopping trips.

LANSE

Baraga County Memorial Hospital
770 N Main St, Lanse, MI, 49946
(906) 524-6166
Admin John P Tembreull. *Medical Dir/Dir of Nursing* Mary Hulkonen RN.
Licensure Skilled care; Intermediate care. *Beds* 28. *Certified* Medicaid; Medicare.
Owner Publicly owned.
Admissions Requirements Minimum age 14; Medical examination; Physician's request.
Staff RNs; LPNs; Nurses aides; Physical therapists; Speech therapists; Activities coordinators; Dietitians.
Languages Finnish
Facilities Dining room; Physical therapy room; Activities room; Crafts room; Barber/Beauty shop.
Activities Arts & crafts; Cards; Games; Reading groups; Prayer groups; Movies; Shopping trips; Social/Cultural gatherings.

Winkler Nursing Home
833 Sicotte Ave, L'anse, MI, 49946
(906) 524-6531
Admin Catherine Kinsey. *Medical Dir/Dir of Nursing* P E Carmody MD; Jennie Jukkala RN.
Licensure Skilled care. *Beds* 59. *Certified* Medicaid; Medicare.
Owner Proprietary Corp.
Admissions Requirements Medical examination; Only admitted by order of a physician.
Staff RNs 1 (ft), 3 (pt); LPNs 2 (ft), 5 (pt); Nurses aides 18 (ft), 11 (pt); Activities coordinators 1 (ft), 1 (pt); Dietitians 1 (pt).
Facilities Dining room; Activities room; Crafts room; Laundry room.
Activities Arts & crafts; Cards; Games; Reading groups; Prayer groups; Movies; Shopping trips; Social/Cultural gatherings; Rides; Visit other facilities; Outings to lunch & dinner.

LANSING

NHE—Lansing*
1313 Mary Ave, Lansing, MI, 48910
(517) 393-6130
Medical Dir/Dir of Nursing Willard J Miller MD.
Licensure Skilled care; Intermediate care. *Beds* 134. *Certified* Medicaid; Medicare.
Admissions Requirements Minimum age 17; Medical examination; Physician's request.
Staff Physicians 2 (ft), 4 (pt); LPNs 6 (pt); Nurses aides 42 (ft), 16 (pt); Activities coordinators 1 (ft); Dietitians 1 (ft).
Facilities Dining room; Physical therapy room; Activities room; Laundry room.
Activities Arts & crafts; Reading groups; Movies; Social/Cultural gatherings.

Provincial House South
2100 Provincial Dr, Lansing, MI, 48917
(517) 882-2458
Admin Markham T Farrell. *Medical Dir/Dir of Nursing* Stephen Tepastee MD; Linda Wagner RN DON.
Licensure Skilled care; Intermediate care. *Beds* 120. *Certified* Medicaid; Medicare.
Owner Proprietary Corp (Beverly Enterprises).
Staff Physicians 1 (pt); RNs 8 (ft), 2 (pt); LPNs 7 (ft), 5 (pt); Nurses aides 45 (ft), 11 (pt); Physical therapists 1 (pt); Occupational therapists 1 (pt); Speech therapists 1 (pt); Activities coordinators 1 (ft); Dietitians 1 (pt); Dentists 1 (pt); Ophthalmologists 1 (pt); Podiatrists 1 (pt).

Facilities Dining room; Physical therapy
room; Activities room; Crafts room; Laundry
room; Barber/Beauty shop.
Activities Arts & crafts; Cards; Games;
Reading groups; Prayer groups; Movies;
Shopping trips; Social/Cultural gatherings.

Provincial House—West*
731 Starkweather Dr, Lansing, MI, 48917
(517) 323-9133
Medical Dir/Dir of Nursing Dr John Neuman.
Licensure Skilled care; Intermediate care. *Beds*
117. *Certified* Medicaid; Medicare.
Owner Proprietary Corp (Beverly Enterprises).
Admissions Requirements Medical
examination.
Staff Physicians 1 (ft), 14 (pt); RNs 4 (ft), 4
(pt); LPNs 4 (ft), 4 (pt); Nurses aides 30 (ft),
35 (pt); Physical therapists 1 (pt);
Occupational therapists 1 (pt); Speech
therapists 1 (pt); Activities coordinators 1
(ft); Dietitians 1 (ft); Dentists 1 (pt);
Podiatrists 1 (pt).
Facilities Dining room; Physical therapy
room; Activities room; Laundry room;
Barber/Beauty shop; TV lounge.
Activities Arts & crafts; Cards; Games;
Reading groups; Prayer groups; Movies;
Shopping trips; Social/Cultural gatherings;
Musical programs.

Roselawn Manor*
707 Armstrong Rd, Lansing, MI, 48910
(517) 393-5680
Licensure Skilled care. *Beds* 234. *Certified*
Medicaid; Medicare.
Staff Physicians 4 (pt); RNs 8 (pt); LPNs 14
(pt); Physical therapists 3 (ft), 3 (pt); Recreational
therapists 3 (ft), 3 (pt); Occupational
therapists 1 (pt); Speech therapists 1 (pt);
Activities coordinators 1 (ft); Dietitians 2
(ft); Dentists 1 (pt); Ophthalmologists 1 (pt);
Podiatrists 1 (pt); Audiologists 1 (pt).
Facilities Dining room; Physical therapy
room; Activities room; Crafts room; Laundry
room; Barber/Beauty shop.
Activities Arts & crafts; Cards; Games;
Reading groups; Prayer groups; Movies;
Shopping trips; Social/Cultural gatherings.

LAPEER

Ferguson Convalescent Home*
239 S Main, Lapeer, MI, 48446
(313) 664-6611
Licensure Intermediate care. *Beds* 91.
Certified Medicaid.

Lapeer County Medical Care Facility*
1455 Suncrest Dr, Lapeer, MI, 48446
(313) 664-8571
Medical Dir/Dir of Nursing Jules Reinhardt
DO.
Licensure Skilled care; Intermediate care. *Beds*
162. *Certified* Medicaid; Medicare.
Owner Publicly owned.
Admissions Requirements Minimum age 16;
Physician's request.
Staff Physicians 2 (pt); RNs 10 (ft), 1 (pt);
LPNs 17 (ft), 12 (pt); Physical therapists 1
(pt); Recreational therapists 1 (ft);
Occupational therapists 1 (pt); Speech
therapists 1 (pt); Activities coordinators 1
(ft); Dietitians 1 (pt); Dentists 1 (pt);
Ophthalmologists 1 (pt); Podiatrists 1 (pt).
Facilities Dining room; Physical therapy
room; Activities room; Chapel; Laundry
room; Barber/Beauty shop.
Activities Arts & crafts; Cards; Games;
Reading groups; Prayer groups; Movies;
Shopping trips; Social/Cultural gatherings.

LAWTON

Lake View Community Nursing Home
99 Walker St, Lawton, MI, 49065
(616) 624-4311

Admin Edward Alderman. *Medical Dir/Dir of
Nursing* Dr E Lean MD; Ms E Lanphear
RN.
Licensure Skilled care; Intermediate care. *Beds*
SNF 120; ICF. *Certified* Medicaid;
Medicare.
Owner Nonprofit organization/foundation.
Admissions Requirements Minimum age 16;
Medical examination; Physician's request.
Staff Physicians 3 (pt); RNs 3 (ft), 3 (pt);
LPNs 6 (ft), 8 (pt); Orderlies 1 (ft), 4 (pt);
Nurses aides 15 (ft), 35 (pt); Physical
therapists 1 (pt); Speech therapists 1 (pt);
Activities coordinators 1 (ft); Dietitians 1
(pt); Ophthalmologists 1 (pt).
Facilities Dining room; Physical therapy
room; Activities room; Crafts room; Laundry
room; Barber/Beauty shop.
Activities Arts & crafts; Cards; Games;
Reading groups; Prayer groups; Movies;
Social/Cultural gatherings.

LINCOLN

Lincoln Haven Rest Home*
950 Barlow Rd, Lincoln, MI, 48742
(517) 736-8481
Licensure Intermediate care. *Beds* 36.
Certified Medicaid.

LINDEN

Stanmarie*
9051 Silver Lake Rd, Linden, MI, 48451
(313) 735-7413
Licensure Intermediate care. *Beds* 50.
Certified Medicaid.

LITCHFIELD

Litchfield Nursing Center
527 Marshall Rd M-99, Litchfield, MI, 49252
(517) 542-2323
Admin Martha Brownlee. *Medical Dir/Dir of
Nursing* Billie Bushre DON.
Licensure Intermediate care. *Beds* ICF 81.
Certified Medicaid.
Owner Proprietary Corp.
Admissions Requirements Minimum age 18;
Medical examination.
Staff RNs 1 (ft), 1 (pt); LPNs 6 (ft), 4 (pt);
Nurses aides 18 (ft), 15 (pt); Recreational
therapists 1 (ft).
Facilities Dining room; Activities room;
Laundry room; Barber/Beauty shop.
Activities Arts & crafts; Cards; Games;
Reading groups; Prayer groups.

LIVONIA

Camelot Hall Convalescent Centre
35100 Ann Arbor Trail, Livonia, MI, 48150
(313) 522-1444
Admin Nancy J Mix. *Medical Dir/Dir of
Nursing* David Miller MD; Mrs Martha
Felosak RN DON.
Licensure Skilled care. *Beds* SNF 166.
Certified Medicaid; Medicare; VA.
Owner Proprietary Corp.
Admissions Requirements Minimum age 55;
Medical examination; Physician's request.
Staff Physicians 3 (pt); RNs 10 (ft), 4 (pt);
LPNs 12 (ft), 5 (pt); Orderlies 10 (ft), 5 (pt);
Nurses aides 60 (ft), 10 (pt); Physical
therapists 1 (ft); Recreational therapists 3
(ft); Occupational therapists 1 (pt); Speech
therapists 1 (pt); Activities coordinators 1
(ft); Dietitians 1 (pt); Ophthalmologists 1
(pt); Restorative nursing 4 (ft).
Facilities Dining room; Physical therapy
room; Activities room; Laundry room;
Barber/Beauty shop; Library; Patio.
Activities Arts & crafts; Cards; Games;
Reading groups; Prayer groups; Movies;
Shopping trips; Social/Cultural gatherings;
Field trips.

Dorvin Convalescent & Nursing Center
29270 Morlock, Livonia, MI, 48152
(313) 476-0550
Admin Julie Cameron Kaslly. *Medical Dir/Dir
of Nursing* Leslie Mandel MD; Ellen Basmaji
RN DON.
Licensure Skilled care; Intermediate care;
Short-term rehabilitation. *Beds* 132.
Certified Medicaid; Medicare.
Owner Proprietary Corp (Health Care &
Retirement Corp).
Admissions Requirements Medical
examination.
Staff Physicians 2 (ft), 3 (pt); RNs 8 (ft), 5
(pt); LPNs 7 (ft), 3 (pt); Orderlies 1 (pt);
Nurses aides 80 (ft), 20 (pt); Physical
therapists 2 (ft), 2 (pt); Reality therapists 1
(ft), 2 (pt); Recreational therapists 1 (ft), 2
(pt); Occupational therapists 2 (pt); Speech
therapists 1 (pt); Activities coordinators 1
(ft), 2 (pt); Dietitians 1 (ft); Dentists 1 (pt);
Ophthalmologists 1 (pt); Podiatrists 1 (pt).
Facilities Dining room; Physical therapy
room; Activities room; Crafts room; Laundry
room; Barber/Beauty shop; Library; 2
Lounges; Patio areas.
Activities Arts & crafts; Cards; Games;
Reading groups; Prayer groups; Movies;
Shopping trips; Social/Cultural gatherings;
Religious services; Sensory stimulation;
Current events; Pet therapy; Resident
council; Volunteer program.

Livonia Nursing Center
28910 Plymouth Rd, Livonia, MI, 48150
(313) 522-8970
Licensure Intermediate care. *Beds* 88.
Certified Medicaid.

Marycrest Manor*
15475 Middlebelt Rd, Livonia, MI, 48154
(313) 427-9175
Licensure Skilled care; Intermediate care. *Beds*
55. *Certified* Medicaid; Medicare.

Middlebelt Nursing Centre
14900 Middlebelt Rd, Livonia, MI, 48154
(313) 425-4200
Admin Charles A Gutkowski. *Medical Dir/Dir
of Nursing* Donald Albert MD.
Licensure Skilled care; Intermediate care. *Beds*
162. *Certified* Medicaid; Medicare.
Owner Proprietary Corp (International Health
Care Management).
Admissions Requirements Minimum age 16;
Medical examination; Physician's request.
Staff Physicians 4 (pt); RNs 4 (ft), 6 (pt);
LPNs 6 (ft), 4 (pt); Orderlies 2 (ft); Nurses
aides 70 (ft), 20 (pt); Reality therapists 2 (ft);
Recreational therapists 2 (ft); Occupational
therapists 1 (pt); Speech therapists 1 (pt);
Activities coordinators 1 (ft); Dietitians 1
(ft), 1 (pt); Dentists 1 (pt); Ophthalmologists
1 (pt); Podiatrists 1 (pt).
Facilities Dining room; Physical therapy
room; Activities room; Chapel; Crafts room;
Laundry room; Barber/Beauty shop; Library.
Activities Arts & crafts; Cards; Games;
Reading groups; Prayer groups; Movies;
Shopping trips; Social/Cultural gatherings;
Sports; Entertainment events; Fishing -
outside facility; Marching in parades.

St Jude Convalescent Center*
34350 Ann Arbor Trail, Livonia, MI, 48150
(313) 261-4800
Licensure Skilled care; Intermediate care. *Beds*
64. *Certified* Medicaid; Medicare.
Affiliation Roman Catholic

University Convalescent & Nursing Home
28550 5 Mile Rd, Livonia, MI, 48154
(313) 427-8270
Admin Kay Kermode. *Medical Dir/Dir of
Nursing* George Pappas DO; Linda
Hirschfield RN.
Licensure Skilled care. *Beds* SNF 184.
Certified Medicaid; Medicare.

Owner Proprietary Corp (Health Care & Retirement Corp).
Admissions Requirements Medical examination; Physician's request.
Staff RNs 12 (ft); LPNs 18 (ft); Nurses aides 70 (ft); Physical therapists 1 (ft); Activities coordinators 2 (ft), 1 (pt); Dietitians 1 (ft).
Languages French
Facilities Dining room; Physical therapy room; Activities room; Chapel; Crafts room; Laundry room; Barber/Beauty shop.
Activities Arts & crafts; Cards; Games; Reading groups; Prayer groups; Movies; Shopping trips; Social/Cultural gatherings.

LOWELL

Lowell Medical Care Center*
350 N Center St, Lowell, MI, 49331
(616) 897-8473
Licensure Skilled care; Intermediate care. *Beds* 153. *Certified* Medicaid; Medicare.

LUDINGTON

Baywood Nursing Home*
1000 Tinkham Ave, Ludington, MI, 49431
(616) 845-6291
Licensure Skilled care; Intermediate care. *Beds* 126. *Certified* Medicaid; Medicare.
Owner Proprietary Corp (Beverly Enterprises).

Oakview Medical Care Facility
1000 Diana St, Ludington, MI, 49431
(616) 845-5185
Admin Jeffery L Welch. *Medical Dir/Dir of Nursing* William Sutter MD; Dianne Eisenlohr RN DON.
Licensure Skilled care; Intermediate care. *Beds* SNF 76. *Certified* Medicaid; Medicare.
Owner Publicly owned.
Admissions Requirements Minimum age 14; Medical examination; Physician's request.
Staff Physicians 3 (pt); RNs 3 (ft), 5 (pt); LPNs 5 (ft), 8 (pt); Nurses aides 28 (ft), 29 (pt); Physical therapists 1 (ft); Occupational therapists 1 (ft); Speech therapists 1 (pt); Activities coordinators 1 (ft); Dietitians 1 (pt); Dentist 1 (pt).
Facilities Dining room; Physical therapy room; Activities room; Crafts room; Laundry room; Barber/Beauty shop; Library; Multi-purpose rooms.
Activities Arts & crafts; Cards; Games; Prayer groups; Movies; Social/Cultural gatherings; Tours.

MADISON HEIGHTS

Cambridge Nursing Center—East
31155 DeQuindre, Madison Heights, MI, 48071
(313) 585-7010
Admin H L Ostrow. *Medical Dir/Dir of Nursing* Dr S Wollock; J Kowal RN DON.
Licensure Skilled care; Intermediate care. *Beds* SNF 160; ICF. *Certified* Medicaid; Medicare.
Owner Proprietary Corp.
Staff RNs 10 (ft), 5 (pt); LPNs 10 (ft), 5 (pt); Orderlies; Nurses aides 125 (ft), 25 (pt); Activities coordinators 1 (ft), 1 (pt).

MANISTEE

Manistee County Medical Care Facility
1505 E Parkdale Ave, Manistee, MI, 49660
(616) 723-2543
Admin Ronald R Schimke. *Medical Dir/Dir of Nursing* David A Wild MD; Joan Schaefer RN DON.
Licensure Skilled care; Intermediate care. *Beds* 102. *Certified* Medicaid; Medicare.
Owner Publicly owned.
Admissions Requirements Physician's request.

Staff Physicians; RNs; LPNs; Nurses aides; Physical therapists; Occupational therapists; Speech therapists; Activities coordinators; Dietitians.
Facilities Dining room; Physical therapy room; Activities room; Chapel; Crafts room; Laundry room; Barber/Beauty shop.
Activities Arts & crafts; Cards; Games; Reading groups; Prayer groups; Movies; Social/Cultural gatherings.

Manistee Heights Care Center
300 Care Center Dr, Manistee, MI, 49660
(313) 723-6262
Admin Shirley Abfalter. *Medical Dir/Dir of Nursing* Dr John Long DO; Anne Reed RN.
Licensure Intermediate care. *Beds* ICF 119. *Certified* Medicaid.
Owner Proprietary Corp (Beverly Enterprises).
Admissions Requirements Minimum age 16; Medical examination.
Staff RNs 6 (ft), 2 (pt); LPNs 3 (ft), 1 (pt); Orderlies 1 (ft); Nurses aides 40 (ft), 20 (pt); Recreational therapists 1 (ft); Activities coordinators 1 (ft).
Facilities Dining room; Physical therapy room; Activities room; Chapel; Crafts room; Laundry room; Barber/Beauty shop; Patio.
Activities Arts & crafts; Cards; Games; Reading groups; Prayer groups; Movies; Shopping trips; Social/Cultural gatherings.

MANISTIQUE

Schoolcraft Medical Care Facility
520 Main St, Manistique, MI, 49854
(906) 341-6921, 341-6922
Admin Dennis K Boyd. *Medical Dir/Dir of Nursing* Neil Grossmikle MD; Charlotte Schwartz RN DON.
Licensure Skilled care. *Beds* SNF 75. *Certified* Medicaid; Medicare.
Owner Publicly owned.
Admissions Requirements Medical examination; Physician's request.
Staff RNs 3 (ft); LPNs 8 (ft); Orderlies 3 (ft); Nurses aides 41 (ft); Recreational therapists 1 (ft).
Facilities Dining room; Physical therapy room; Activities room; Chapel; Laundry room; Barber/Beauty shop; TV areas; Smoking areas.
Activities Arts & crafts; Cards; Games; Reading groups; Prayer groups; Movies; Shopping trips; Social/Cultural gatherings; Exercise classes.

MAPLE CITY

Maple Valley Nursing Home
PO Box 7, Rte 2, Maple City, MI, 49664
(616) 228-5895
Admin Alan J Caron. *Medical Dir/Dir of Nursing* Donna Kasber RN.
Licensure Intermediate care. *Beds* ICF 25. *Certified* Medicaid.
Owner Privately owned.
Admissions Requirements Minimum age 15; Medical examination; Physician's request.
Staff Physicians; RNs; LPNs; Nurses aides; Recreational therapists; Activities coordinators; Dietitians.
Facilities Dining room; Activities room; Laundry room.
Activities Arts & crafts; Cards; Games; Reading groups; Prayer groups; Movies; Shopping trips; Social/Cultural gatherings; Outings.

MARLETTE

Marlette Community Hospital
2770 Main St, Marlette, MI, 48453
(517) 635-7491

Admin Darwin Root. *Medical Dir/Dir of Nursing* Duane Smith MD; Florence Elston RN DON.
Licensure Skilled care; Intermediate care. *Beds* 43. *Certified* Medicaid; Medicare.
Owner Nonprofit organization/foundation.
Admissions Requirements Medical examination.
Staff Physicians; RNs; LPNs; Nurses aides; Physical therapists; Occupational therapists; Speech therapists; Activities coordinators; Dietitians; Ophthalmologists.
Facilities Dining room; Physical therapy room; Activities room; Chapel; Crafts room; Laundry room; Barber/Beauty shop.
Activities Arts & crafts; Cards; Games; Reading groups; Prayer groups; Movies; Shopping trips; Social/Cultural gatherings.

MARNE

Birchwood Care Center
15140 16th Ave, Marne, MI, 49435
(616) 667-1215
Admin Lawana S Parks. *Medical Dir/Dir of Nursing* Earl Reynolds DO; Carolyn VanBoven RN DON.
Licensure Skilled care. *Beds* 239. *Certified* Medicaid; Medicare.
Owner Proprietary Corp (Hillhaven Corp).
Admissions Requirements Minimum age 16; Medical examination; Physician's request.
Staff RNs 5 (ft), 2 (pt); LPNs 11 (ft), 8 (pt); Nurses aides 46 (ft), 22 (pt); Activities coordinators 1 (ft), 3 (pt); Dietitians 1 (ft).
Facilities Dining room; Physical therapy room; Activities room; Chapel; Crafts room; Laundry room; Barber/Beauty shop; Library.
Activities Arts & crafts; Games; Reading groups; Prayer groups; Movies; Social/Cultural gatherings.

MARQUETTE

Acocks Medical Facility
PO Box 160, Acocks Dr, Marquette, MI, 49855
(906) 226-3586
Admin Harry G Scott. *Medical Dir/Dir of Nursing* Dr B Lyons; Ruby Cheatham RN DON.
Licensure Skilled care. *Beds* SNF 98. *Certified* Medicaid; Medicare.
Owner Publicly owned.
Admissions Requirements Minimum age 18; Males only; Females only; Medical examination.
Staff Physicians 8 (pt); RNs 6 (ft), 1 (pt); LPNs 4 (ft), 5 (pt); Orderlies 4 (ft), 2 (pt); Nurses aides 43 (ft), 4 (pt); Recreational therapists 1 (ft); Activities coordinators 1 (ft); Dietitians 1 (pt); Ophthalmologists 1 (pt); Podiatrists 1 (pt); Social worker 1 (ft).
Facilities Physical therapy room; Activities room; Crafts room; Laundry room.
Activities Arts & crafts; Cards; Games; Reading groups; Prayer groups; Movies; Shopping trips.

Brooks Center Health Care Facility*
S Rte 41, Marquette, MI, 49855
Admin Grace E McCarthy. *Medical Dir/Dir of Nursing* Benjamin T Ulep.
Licensure Skilled care; Intermediate care. *Beds* 11. *Certified* Medicaid; Medicare.
Admissions Requirements Males only; Medical examination; Physician's request.
Staff Physicians 1 (ft); RNs 10 (ft); LPNs 4 (ft); Physical therapists; Reality therapists; Recreational therapists; Occupational therapists; Speech therapists; Activities coordinators; Dietitians 1 (pt); Dentists 1 (pt); Ophthalmologists; Podiatrists; Audiologists; Laboratory workers 1 (ft); Physical aides 1 (ft).

Norlite Nursing Center*
701 Homestead St, Marquette, MI, 49855
(906) 228-9252
Licensure Skilled care; Intermediate care. *Beds*
99. *Certified* Medicaid; Medicare.

MARSHALL

Marshall Manor
575 N Madison St, Marshall, MI, 49068
(616) 781-4281
Admin Deborah Culp. *Medical Dir/Dir of
Nursing* Thomas Neidlinger MD.
Licensure Skilled care; Intermediate care. *Beds*
SNF 71; ICF. *Certified* Medicaid; Medicare.
Owner Proprietary Corp.
Admissions Requirements Minimum age 21;
Physician's request.
Staff RNs 2 (ft), 1 (pt); LPNs 7 (ft), 5 (pt);
Orderlies 1 (ft), 3 (pt); Nurses aides 13 (ft),
21 (pt); Physical therapists 1 (pt); Speech
therapists 1 (pt); Activities coordinators 1
(ft), 1 (pt); Dietitians 1 (pt);
Ophthalmologists 1 (pt).
Facilities Dining room; Physical therapy
room; Activities room; Chapel; Crafts room;
Laundry room; Barber/Beauty shop.
Activities Arts & crafts; Cards; Games;
Reading groups; Prayer groups; Movies;
Shopping trips; Social/Cultural gatherings.

Provincial House—Marshall*
879 E Michigan Ave, Marshall, MI, 49068
(616) 781-4251
Licensure Intermediate care. *Beds* 114.
Certified Medicaid.
Owner Proprietary Corp (Beverly Enterprises).
Admissions Requirements Minimum age 15;
Medical examination; Physician's request.
Staff Physicians 16 (pt); RNs 3 (ft), 3 (pt);
LPNs 1 (ft), 9 (pt); Orderlies 2 (pt); Nurses
aides 24 (ft), 42 (pt); Physical therapists 1
(pt); Reality therapists 1 (pt); Recreational
therapists 1 (ft); Occupational therapists 1
(pt); Speech therapists 1 (pt); Activities
coordinators 1 (ft); Dietitians 1 (ft); Dentists
1 (pt); Ophthalmologists 1 (pt); Podiatrists 1
(pt); Audiologists 1 (pt).
Facilities Dining room; Physical therapy
room; Activities room; Crafts room; Laundry
room; Barber/Beauty shop.
Activities Arts & crafts; Cards; Games;
Reading groups; Prayer groups; Movies;
Social/Cultural gatherings.

MAYVILLE

Fisher Convalescent Home*
521 Ohmer Rd, M-24, Mayville, MI, 48744
(517) 843-6185
Licensure Intermediate care. *Beds* 38.
Certified Medicaid.

MCMILLAN

Applewood Manor Inc*
Rte 3, Box 2347, McMillan, MI, 49853
(906) 586-9641
Licensure Intermediate care. *Beds* 30.
Certified Medicaid.

MENOMINEE

Good Samaritan Home
501 2nd St, Menominee, MI, 49858
(906) 863-9941
Admin Gerard A Buser.
Licensure Intermediate care; Home for aged.
Beds ICF 39; Home for aged 18. *Certified*
Medicaid.
Owner Nonprofit Corp.
Admissions Requirements Minimum age 16;
Medical examination; Physician's request.
Staff RNs 1 (ft), 1 (pt); LPNs 7 (pt); Nurses
aides 5 (ft), 18 (pt); Activities coordinators 1
(ft); Dietitians 1 (ft); Social worker 1 (ft).

Facilities Dining room; Activities room;
Crafts room; Barber/Beauty shop.
Activities Arts & crafts; Cards; Games;
Reading groups; Prayer groups; Movies;
Shopping trips; Social/Cultural gatherings;
Musicals.

MIDLAND

Midland Hospital Center—Skilled Care Unit
4005 Orchard Dr, Midland, MI, 48670
(517) 839-3000
Admin C Fraser. *Medical Dir/Dir of Nursing* J
Christopher Hough MD; J Wenglikowski RN
DON.
Licensure Skilled care; Intermediate care. *Beds*
48. *Certified* Medicaid; Medicare.
Owner Nonprofit Corp.
Admissions Requirements Medical
examination; Physician's request.
Staff Physicians 1 (pt); RNs 5 (ft), 6 (pt);
LPNs 8 (ft), 9 (pt); Orderlies 1 (ft); Nurses
aides 7 (ft), 5 (pt); Physical therapists 3 (ft),
2 (pt); Recreational therapists 1 (pt);
Occupational therapists 6 (ft), 2 (pt); Speech
therapists 3 (ft), 1 (pt); Dietitians 8 (pt);
Podiatrists 1 (pt).
Facilities Dining room; Physical therapy
room; Activities room; Chapel; Laundry
room; Barber/Beauty shop.
Activities Arts & crafts; Cards; Games;
Reading groups; Prayer groups; Movies;
Social/Cultural gatherings; Cooking classes;
Bowling; Fun & fitness classes.

Midland Kings Daughters*
2410 Rodd St, Midland, MI, 48640
Licensure Intermediate care. *Beds* 31.

Provincial House—Midland*
4900 Hedgewood, Midland, MI, 48640
(517) 631-9670
Licensure Skilled care; Intermediate care. *Beds*
120. *Certified* Medicaid; Medicare.
Owner Proprietary Corp (Beverly Enterprises).

Town & Country Nursing Home*
3615 E Ashman St, Midland, MI, 48640
(517) 631-0460
Medical Dir/Dir of Nursing John E Vargas
DO.
Licensure Skilled care; Intermediate care. *Beds*
153. *Certified* Medicaid; Medicare.
Admissions Requirements Medical
examination; Physician's request.
Staff RNs 6 (ft), 1 (pt); LPNs 5 (ft), 8 (pt);
Orderlies 4 (ft), 6 (pt); Nurses aides 17 (ft),
64 (pt); Activities coordinators 1 (ft);
Dietitians 1 (ft).
Facilities Dining room; Activities room;
Crafts room; Laundry room; Barber/Beauty
shop.
Activities Arts & crafts; Cards; Games;
Reading groups; Prayer groups; Shopping
trips; Social/Cultural gatherings.

MILFORD

West Hickory Haven
3310 W Commerce Rd, Milford, MI, 48042
(313) 685-1400
Admin Wanda Baad RN. *Medical Dir/Dir of
Nursing* William Kolbe DO; Donna Beebe
RN.
Licensure Skilled care; Intermediate care. *Beds*
SNF 101; ICF. *Certified* Medicaid;
Medicare.
Owner Proprietary Corp.
Admissions Requirements Minimum age
Geriatric; Medical examination.
Staff RNs 4 (ft), 4 (pt); LPNs 3 (ft), 14 (pt);
Orderlies 2 (pt); Nurses aides 10 (ft), 35 (pt);
Physical therapists 1 (pt); Recreational
therapists 1 (ft); Speech therapists 1 (pt);
Activities coordinators 1 (ft), 1 (pt);
Dietitians 1 (pt).

Facilities Dining room; Physical therapy
room; Activities room; Barber/Beauty shop;
Library.

MIO

White Oak Manor
PO Box 430, 205 E 11th, Mio, MI, 48647
(517) 826-3983
Admin Peter Costa. *Medical Dir/Dir of
Nursing* E Kauffman.
Licensure Intermediate care. *Beds* ICF 28.
Certified Medicaid.
Owner Privately owned.
Admissions Requirements Medical
examination; Physician's request.
Staff Physicians 8 (pt); RNs 1 (ft); LPNs 5
(ft); Nurses aides 12 (ft); Physical therapists
1 (pt); Speech therapists 1 (pt); Activities
coordinators 1 (ft); Dietitians 4 (ft), 1 (pt);
Ophthalmologists 1 (pt); Podiatrists 1 (pt).
Facilities Dining room; Activities room;
Crafts room; Laundry room.
Activities Arts & crafts; Cards; Games;
Reading groups; Prayer groups; Movies;
Shopping trips; Social/Cultural gatherings.

MONROE

Beach Nursing Home
1215 N Telegraph Rd, Monroe, MI, 48161
(313) 242-4848
Admin Joan Rasegan. *Medical Dir/Dir of
Nursing* Elaine Evans RN DON.
Licensure Skilled care; Intermediate care. *Beds*
189. *Certified* Medicaid; Medicare.
Owner Proprietary Corp (Beverly Enterprises).
Admissions Requirements Minimum age 18.
Staff RNs; LPNs; Orderlies; Nurses aides;
Activities coordinators 1 (ft), 2 (pt).
Facilities Dining room; Physical therapy
room; Activities room; Barber/Beauty shop.
Activities Arts & crafts; Cards; Games;
Reading groups; Prayer groups; Movies;
Social/Cultural gatherings; Intergenerational
groups; Adult education.

Frenchtown Convalescent Center
3250 N Monroe, Monroe, MI, 48161
(517) 243-5100
Licensure Skilled care; Intermediate care. *Beds*
229. *Certified* Medicaid; Medicare.
Owner Proprietary Corp (International Health
Care Management).

Lutheran Home—Monroe
1236 S Monroe St, Monroe, MI, 48161
(313) 241-9533
Admin Edward G Kurtz. *Medical Dir/Dir of
Nursing* John J Burroughs MD; Marie
Schlump RN DON.
Licensure Skilled care; Intermediate care. *Beds*
SNF 30; ICF 72. *Certified* Medicaid;
Medicare.
Owner Nonprofit Corp.
Admissions Requirements Minimum age 62;
Medical examination.
Affiliation Lutheran.
Facilities Dining room; Activities room;
Chapel; Crafts room; Laundry room; Barber/
Beauty shop.
Activities Arts & crafts; Cards; Games;
Reading groups; Prayer groups; Movies;
Shopping trips; Social/Cultural gatherings.

Monroe Care Center*
481 Village Green Ln, Monroe, MI, 48161
(517) 242-6282
Licensure Skilled care. *Beds* 103. *Certified*
Medicare.

Monroe Convalescent Center
120 Maple Blvd, Monroe, MI, 48161
(313) 242-5656
Admin Mary Jo Szandrowsky. *Medical Dir/Dir
of Nursing* Dr Hyun Steward; Cathy Ledford
RN DON.

Licensure Intermediate care. *Beds* ICF 70.
Certified Medicaid.
Owner Proprietary Corp.
Admissions Requirements Minimum age 16;
Medical examination; Physician's request.
Staff Physicians 1 (pt); RNs 1 (ft), 2 (pt);
LPNs 3 (ft), 6 (pt); Orderlies 4 (pt); Nurses
aides 13 (ft), 12 (pt); Physical therapists 1
(pt); Occupational therapists 1 (pt) 13J 1
(pt); Activities coordinators 1 (ft); Dietitians
1 (pt); Dentists 1 (pt); Ophthalmologists 1
(pt); Podiatrists 1 (pt).
Facilities Dining room; Activities room;
Crafts room; Laundry room; Barber/Beauty
shop.
Activities Arts & crafts; Cards; Games;
Reading groups; Prayer groups; Movies;
Shopping trips.

MONTROSE

Mary James Nursing Home*
13476 Duffield Rd, Montrose, MI, 48457
(313) 639-6113
Medical Dir/Dir of Nursing John T Block DO.
Licensure Skilled care; Intermediate care. *Beds*
63. *Certified* Medicaid; Medicare.
Admissions Requirements Minimum age 18;
Medical examination; Physician's request.
Staff Physicians 2 (pt); RNs 3 (ft), 1 (pt);
LPNs 1 (ft), 3 (pt); Nurses aides 19 (ft), 17
(pt); Recreational therapists 1 (ft); Activities
coordinators 1 (ft); Dietitians 1 (ft);
Podiatrists 1 (pt).
Facilities Dining room.
Activities Arts & crafts; Cards; Games;
Reading groups; Prayer groups; Movies;
Shopping trips; Social/Cultural gatherings.

Montrose Nursing Home*
9317 W Vienna Rd, Montrose, MI, 48457
Admin Gale E Neff.
Licensure Intermediate care. *Beds* 71.
Certified Medicaid.
Owner Proprietary Corp.
Admissions Requirements Minimum age 15;
Medical examination.
Staff RNs 1 (ft), 1 (pt); LPNs 3 (ft), 5 (pt);
Orderlies 1 (pt); Nurses aides 20 (ft), 12 (pt);
Activities coordinators 1 (ft); Dietitians 1
(pt).
Facilities Dining room; Activities room;
Laundry room; Barber/Beauty shop.
Activities Arts & crafts; Cards; Games;
Reading groups; Prayer groups; Movies;
Shopping trips; Social/Cultural gatherings.

MOUNT CLEMENS

Martha T Berry Medical Care Facility
43533 Elizabeth Rd, Mount Clemens, MI,
48043
(313) 469-5265
Admin Raymond D Pietrzak. *Medical Dir/Dir
of Nursing* Donald Dreyfuss DO; Marjorie
Kelley RN.
Licensure Skilled care; Intermediate care. *Beds*
SNF 218; ICF. *Certified* Medicaid;
Medicare.
Owner Publicly owned.
Admissions Requirements Medical
examination; Physician's request.
Staff Physicians 2 (pt); RNs 17 (ft), 2 (pt);
LPNs 14 (ft), 4 (pt); Orderlies 2 (ft), 1 (pt);
Nurses aides 81 (ft), 13 (pt); Physical
therapists 1 (ft); Recreational therapists 1
(ft); Occupational therapists 1 (pt); Speech
therapists 1 (pt); Activities coordinators 1
(ft); Dietitians 1 (pt); Podiatrists 1 (pt).
Facilities Dining room; Physical therapy
room; Activities room; Crafts room; Laundry
room; Library.
Activities Arts & crafts; Cards; Games;
Reading groups; Prayer groups; Movies;
Shopping trips; Social/Cultural gatherings;
Community parties; Musical groups; Basic
adult education; Horticultural therapy;

Exercise program; One-to-one contacts;
Patient council; Picnics; BBQs; Monthly
newspaper & calendar.

Church of Christ Care Center
23575 15 Mile Rd, Mount Clemens, MI,
48043
(313) 791-2470
Admin Louis D Elliott. *Medical Dir/Dir of
Nursing* Dr Stanley Pesta DO.
Licensure Intermediate care. *Beds* ICF 130.
Certified Medicaid.
Owner Nonprofit Corp.
Admissions Requirements Physician's request.
Staff Physicians 1 (pt); RNs 6 (ft), 4 (pt);
LPNs 7 (ft), 5 (pt); Orderlies 1 (ft); Nurses
aides 40 (ft), 30 (pt); Activities coordinators
1 (ft); Dietitians 1 (pt).
Affiliation Church of Christ
Facilities Dining room; Activities room;
Laundry room; Barber/Beauty shop.
Activities Arts & crafts; Cards; Games;
Reading groups; Prayer groups; Movies.

Clinton Aire Nursing Center
17001 17 Mile Rd, Mount Clemens, MI,
48043
(313) 286-7100
Medical Dir/Dir of Nursing Sonjai Poonpanij
MD.
Licensure Skilled care; Intermediate care. *Beds*
150. *Certified* Medicaid; Medicare.
Owner Proprietary Corp (International Health
Care Management).
Admissions Requirements Minimum age 15.
Staff RNs 3 (ft), 6 (pt); LPNs 3 (ft), 11 (pt);
Orderlies 5 (ft), 2 (pt); Nurses aides 37 (ft),
19 (pt); Physical therapists 1 (pt);
Recreational therapists 1 (ft); Occupational
therapists 1 (pt); Speech therapists 1 (pt);
Activities coordinators 1 (ft); Dietitians 1
(ft); Dentists 1 (pt); Ophthalmologists 1 (pt);
Podiatrists 1 (pt).
Facilities Dining room; Physical therapy
room; Activities room; Chapel; Laundry
room; Barber/Beauty shop.
Activities Arts & crafts; Cards; Games;
Reading groups; Prayer groups; Movies;
Shopping trips.

Clintonview Care
37700 Harper Ave, Mount Clemens, MI,
48043
(313) 468-0827
Medical Dir/Dir of Nursing M Shiffman MD.
Licensure Skilled care; Intermediate care. *Beds*
264. *Certified* Medicaid; Medicare.
Owner Proprietary Corp (International Health
Care Management).
Admissions Requirements Minimum age 17;
Medical examination; Physician's request.
Staff Physicians 4 (pt); RNs 16 (ft), 4 (pt);
LPNs 10 (ft), 3 (pt); Orderlies 6 (ft); Nurses
aides 120 (ft), 5 (pt); Physical therapists 1
(ft); Recreational therapists 1 (ft);
Occupational therapists 1 (ft); Speech
therapists 1 (pt); Activities coordinators 1
(ft); Dietitians 1 (pt); Dentists 3 (pt);
Ophthalmologists 2 (pt); Podiatrists 1 (pt).
Facilities Dining room; Physical therapy
room; Activities room; Chapel; Crafts room;
Laundry room; Barber/Beauty shop; Library.
Activities Arts & crafts; Cards; Games;
Reading groups; Prayer groups; Movies;
Shopping trips; Social/Cultural gatherings.

MOUNT PLEASANT

Isabella County Medical Care Facility
1222 N Drive, Mount Pleasant, MI, 48858
(517) 772-2957
Admin John P Verwey. *Medical Dir/Dir of
Nursing* Dr Dan C Dean DO; Louis S Rank
RN.
Licensure Skilled care. *Beds* SNF 80. *Certified*
Medicaid; Medicare.
Owner Publicly owned.

Admissions Requirements Medical
examination; Physician's request.
Staff Physicians 30 (pt); RNs 6 (ft), 5 (pt);
LPNs 6 (ft), 5 (pt); Nurses aides 30 (ft), 14
(pt); Physical therapists 3 (ft); Occupational
therapists 1 (ft); Speech therapists 1 (pt);
Activities coordinators 1 (pt); Dietitians 1
(pt).
Languages Flemish, French, Spanish
Facilities Dining room; Physical therapy
room; Activities room; Chapel; Crafts room;
Laundry room; Barber/Beauty shop.
Activities Arts & crafts; Cards; Games;
Reading groups; Prayer groups; Movies;
Shopping trips; Social/Cultural gatherings.

Mt Pleasant Total Living Center
1524 Portabella Rd, Mount Pleasant, MI,
48858
(517) 772-2967
Admin Rosemary Shuette. *Medical Dir/Dir of
Nursing* Dan Radawski MD; Beverly Curtiss
RN DON.
Licensure Skilled care; Intermediate care. *Beds*
SNF 117; ICF. *Certified* Medicaid.
Staff Physicians 5 (ft); RNs 3 (ft), 1 (pt);
Nurses aides 50 (ft), 10 (pt); Physical
therapists 1 (ft); Occupational therapists 1
(pt); Speech therapists 1 (pt); Activities
coordinators 1 (ft), 1 (pt); Dietitians 1 (ft);
Dentists 1 (pt); Ophthalmologists 1 (pt);
Podiatrists 1 (pt).
Facilities Dining room; Physical therapy
room; Activities room; Laundry room;
Barber/Beauty shop.
Activities Arts & crafts; Cards; Games;
Reading groups; Prayer groups; Movies;
Shopping trips; Social/Cultural gatherings.

Pleasant Manor Inc
400 S Crapo St, Mount Pleasant, MI, 48858
(517) 773-5918
Admin Sandra Caul. *Medical Dir/Dir of
Nursing* Dr Leo Wickert MD; Shirley
Schafer RN DON.
Licensure Skilled care; Intermediate care. *Beds*
SNF 112; ICF. *Certified* Medicaid;
Medicare.
Owner Proprietary Corp.
Admissions Requirements Minimum age 15;
Medical examination; Physician's request.
Staff RNs 4 (ft), 5 (pt); LPNs 6 (ft), 1 (pt);
Physical therapists 1 (pt); Recreational
therapists 1 (ft); Occupational therapists 1
(pt); Speech therapists 1 (pt); Activities
coordinators 1 (ft); Dietitians 1 (ft), 1 (pt);
Dentists 1 (pt); Ophthalmologists 1 (pt);
Podiatrists 1 (pt).
Facilities Dining room; Physical therapy
room; Activities room; Barber/Beauty shop;
Library.
Activities Arts & crafts; Cards; Games;
Reading groups; Prayer groups; Movies;
Shopping trips; Social/Cultural gatherings;
Exercise class; Stroke club; Monthly special
event; Outings each week; Art study classes;
Lunch outings.

MUNISING

Superior Shores Nursing Center
300 W City Park Dr, Munising, MI, 49862
(906) 387-2273
Admin Denis C Harbath. *Medical Dir/Dir of
Nursing* Cindy Carl.
Licensure Skilled care; Intermediate care. *Beds*
SNF 106; ICF. *Certified* Medicaid;
Medicare.
Owner Proprietary Corp (Health Concepts
Corp).
Admissions Requirements Minimum age 18;
Medical examination; Physician's request.
Staff RNs 2 (ft), 1 (pt); LPNs 1 (ft), 14 (pt);
Nurses aides 21 (ft), 45 (pt); Physical
therapists 1 (pt); Activities coordinators 1
(ft).

Facilities Dining room; Physical therapy room; Activities room; Laundry room; Barber/Beauty shop; TV lounges.
Activities Arts & crafts; Games; Reading groups; Prayer groups; Movies; Shopping trips; Social/Cultural gatherings; Bingo; Exercises; Reality orientation sessions.

MUSKEGON

Brookhaven Medical Care Facility
1890 Apple Ave, Muskegon, MI, 49442
(616) 773-9146
Admin Bertram G Hanson. *Medical Dir/Dir of Nursing* Erwin Grasman MD; Wilma Overweg RN.
Licensure Skilled care. *Beds* SNF 218. *Certified* Medicaid; Medicare.
Owner Nonprofit organization/foundation.
Admissions Requirements Minimum age 18; Physician's request.
Staff Physicians 2 (pt); RNs 9 (ft); LPNs 20 (ft), 16 (pt); Orderlies 2 (pt); Nurses aides 48 (ft), 68 (pt); Physical therapists 1 (pt); Occupational therapists 1 (ft); Speech therapists 1 (pt); Activities coordinators 1 (ft); Dietitians 1 (ft); Podiatrists 1 (pt).
Facilities Dining room; Physical therapy room; Activities room; Chapel; Crafts room; Laundry room; Barber/Beauty shop; Large enclosed courtyard.
Activities Arts & crafts; Cards; Games; Reading groups; Prayer groups; Movies; Shopping trips; Social/Cultural gatherings.

Christian Convalescent Home*
1275 Kenneth Ave, Muskegon, MI, 49442
(616) 722-7165
Licensure Intermediate care. *Beds* 49.

DeBoer Nursing Home
1684 Vulcan St, Muskegon, MI, 49442
(616) 777-2511
Admin Samuel T DeBoer. *Medical Dir/Dir of Nursing* Dale W Heeres MD Med Dir; Robert G Willis RN DON.
Licensure Skilled care. *Beds* SNF 90. *Certified* Medicaid; Medicare.
Owner Proprietary Corp.
Admissions Requirements Medical examination; Physician's request.
Staff Physicians; RNs; LPNs; Nurses aides; Physical therapists; Recreational therapists; Occupational therapists; Speech therapists; Activities coordinators; Dietitians; Ophthalmologists.
Facilities Dining room; Physical therapy room; Activities room; Chapel; Crafts room; Laundry room; Barber/Beauty shop; Library.
Activities Arts & crafts; Cards; Games; Reading groups; Prayer groups; Movies; Shopping trips.

Knollview Manor Nursing Home*
1061 W Hackley Ave, Muskegon, MI, 49441
(616) 755-2255
Licensure Skilled care. *Beds* 107. *Certified* Medicaid; Medicare.
Owner Proprietary Corp (Health Care & Retirement Corp).

Muskegon Correctional Facility*
2400 S Sheridan, Muskegon, MI, 49442
Admin Diane Haynor. *Medical Dir/Dir of Nursing* Richard G Huff DO.
Licensure Skilled care. *Beds* 7.
Owner Publicly owned.
Admissions Requirements Minimum age 18; Males only; Medical examination; Physician's request.
Staff Physicians 1 (pt); RNs 8 (ft); Dietitians 1 (ft); Dentists 1 (ft); Physician's aides 1 (ft).
Facilities Physical therapy room; Activities room; Crafts room; Laundry room; Barber/Beauty shop; Library.
Activities Games; Movies.

Seaway Care Center*
1300 Broadway, Muskegon, MI, 49441
(616) 755-2221
Licensure Intermediate care. *Beds* 69.
Certified Medicaid.

Sherman Oaks Care Center
1380 E Sherman Blvd, Muskegon, MI, 49444
(616) 733-2578
Licensure Skilled care. *Beds* 98. *Certified* Medicaid; Medicare.
Owner Proprietary Corp (Beverly Enterprises).

University Park Care Center*
570 S Harvey St, Muskegon, MI, 49442
(616) 773-9121
Licensure Intermediate care. *Beds* 99.
Certified Medicaid.
Owner Proprietary Corp (Beverly Enterprises).

MUSKEGON HEIGHTS

Park Manor Care Center
2333 Jarman, Muskegon Heights, MI, 49444
(616) 733-9423
Admin David Timmer. *Medical Dir/Dir of Nursing* Valorie Brooks.
Licensure Intermediate care. *Beds* ICF 27. *Certified* Medicaid.
Owner Proprietary Corp (Manor Care).
Admissions Requirements Medical examination; Physician's request.
Staff RNs 1 (ft); LPNs 3 (ft), 3 (pt); Orderlies 2 (pt); Nurses aides 5 (ft), 12 (pt); Activities coordinators 1 (ft).
Facilities Dining room; Laundry room; Barber/Beauty shop.
Activities Arts & crafts; Games; Reading groups; Prayer groups; Movies.

NEWBERRY

Helen Newberry Joy Hospital Annex
502 W Harrie, Newberry, MI, 49868
(906) 293-5181
Admin Tom Hicks. *Medical Dir/Dir of Nursing* Theresa Shiffutt.
Licensure Skilled care; Intermediate care. *Beds* 31. *Certified* Medicaid; Medicare.
Owner Publicly owned.
Staff RNs 1 (ft); LPNs 6 (ft), 4 (pt); Nurses aides 20 (ft), 10 (pt); Physical therapists 1 (ft); Recreational therapists 1 (ft); Occupational therapists 1 (pt); Speech therapists 1 (pt); Dietitians 1 (pt); Dentists 1 (pt); Ophthalmologists 1 (pt); Podiatrists 1 (pt).
Activities Arts & crafts; Cards; Games; Reading groups; Prayer groups; Movies; Shopping trips; Social/Cultural gatherings.

NILES

Michigan Skilled Care*
Box 417, 911 S 3rd St, Niles, MI, 49120
(616) 684-4320
Licensure Skilled care; Intermediate care. *Beds* 100. *Certified* Medicaid; Medicare.

Oak Grove Manor
1217 Stateline Rd, Niles, MI, 49120
(616) 683-4143
Admin Phillip Stephan. *Medical Dir/Dir of Nursing* Kent D Hassan MD; Brenda Scott DON.
Licensure Intermediate care. *Beds* ICF 15. *Certified* Medicaid.
Owner Privately owned.
Admissions Requirements Medical examination Chest x-ray; Physician's request.
Staff RNs 1 (ft), 1 (pt); LPNs 2 (ft), 2 (pt); Nurses aides 3 (ft), 3 (pt); Physical therapists 1 (pt); Recreational therapists 1 (pt); Speech therapists 1 (pt); Activities coordinators 1 (ft); Dietitians 1 (pt); Ophthalmologists 1 (pt); Dentist 1 (pt).

Facilities Dining room; Activities room.
Activities Arts & crafts; Cards; Games; Prayer groups; Movies; Social/Cultural gatherings.

Riveridge Manor, Inc
1333 Wells St, Niles, MI, 49120
(616) 684-1111
Admin Pauline M Westman, RN. *Medical Dir/Dir of Nursing* Helen Rhodes, RN.
Licensure Intermediate care; Intermediate care for mentally retarded. *Beds* ICF 84; Home for aged 10. *Certified* Medicaid.
Owner Proprietary Corp.
Admissions Requirements Medical examination; Physician's request.
Staff RNs 1 (ft); LPNs 5 (ft), 2 (pt); Nurses aides 46 (ft), 3 (pt); Activities coordinators 1 (ft).
Affiliation Seventh-Day Adventist
Facilities Dining room; Activities room; Laundry room; Barber/Beauty shop.
Activities Arts & crafts; Games; Reading groups; Prayer groups; Movies.

Woodfield Manor Inc
1211 State Line Rd, Niles, MI, 49120
(616) 684-2810
Admin Phillip Stephan. *Medical Dir/Dir of Nursing* Kent D Hassan MD.
Licensure Skilled care; Intermediate care. *Beds* SNF 89; ICF. *Certified* Medicaid; Medicare.
Owner Proprietary Corp.
Admissions Requirements Minimum age 15; Medical examination; Physician's request.
Staff Physicians 1 (pt); RNs 2 (ft), 1 (pt); LPNs 4 (ft), 1 (pt); Orderlies 4 (ft); Nurses aides 30 (ft), 2 (pt); Physical therapists 1 (pt); Speech therapists 1 (pt); Activities coordinators 1 (ft), 2 (pt); Dietitians 1 (pt); Dentists 1 (pt); Ophthalmologists 1 (pt).
Facilities Dining room; Activities room; Crafts room; Laundry room; Barber/Beauty shop.
Activities Arts & crafts; Cards; Games; Prayer groups; Movies; Shopping trips; Social/Cultural gatherings.

NORTH MUSKEGON

Hillcrest Nursing Home*
695 Mitzi Dr, North Muskegon, MI, 49445
(616) 744-1641
Licensure Intermediate care. *Beds* 63.
Certified Medicaid.

NORTHPORT

Leelanau Memorial Hospital
High St, Northport, MI, 49670
(616) 386-5101
Admin Kathleen Putnam. *Medical Dir/Dir of Nursing* J M Wood MD; Kathy Garthern MSN.
Licensure Skilled care; Intermediate care; Adult day care. *Beds* SNF; ICF 61. *Certified* Medicaid; Medicare.
Owner Nonprofit organization/foundation.
Staff Physicians 1 (pt); RNs 2 (ft), 2 (pt); LPNs 7 (ft), 3 (pt); Orderlies 1 (ft); Nurses aides 18 (ft), 6 (pt); Physical therapists 1 (pt); Activities coordinators 1 (ft), 1 (pt); Dietitians 1 (pt).

NORTHVILLE

Wishing Well Manor, Inc
520 W Main St, Northville, MI, 48167
(313) 349-4290
Admin Donald J Nowka. *Medical Dir/Dir of Nursing* Constance J Nowka RN.
Licensure Intermediate care. *Beds* ICF 37. *Certified* Medicaid.
Owner Proprietary Corp.
Admissions Requirements Minimum age 60; Medical examination; Physician's request.

Staff Physicians 1 (pt); RNs 1 (ft); LPNs 3 (ft), 3 (pt); Nurses aides 12 (ft); Activities coordinators 1 (ft); Dietitians 1 (pt); Social worker 1 (pt).
Facilities Dining room; Activities room; Crafts room; Laundry room; Barber/Beauty shop.
Activities Arts & crafts; Cards; Games; Reading groups; Prayer groups; Movies; Social/Cultural gatherings.

NOVI

Novi Care Center
24500 Meadowbrook Rd, Novi, MI, 48050
(313) 447-2000
Admin James L Tiffin. *Medical Dir/Dir of Nursing* Kathy Bonfiglio DON.
Licensure Skilled care. *Beds* 144. *Certified* Medicaid.
Owner Proprietary Corp (Beverly Enterprises).
Admissions Requirements Minimum age 15; Medical examination.
Staff Physicians; RNs; LPNs; Orderlies; Nurses aides; Physical therapists; Recreational therapists; Speech therapists; Dietitians; Ophthalmologists; Podiatrists.
Facilities Dining room; Physical therapy room; Activities room; Crafts room; Laundry room; Barber/Beauty shop.
Activities Arts & crafts; Cards; Prayer groups; Movies; Shopping trips.

Whitehall Convalescent Home 2*
43455 W 10 Mile Rd, Novi, MI, 48050
(313) 349-2200
Medical Dir/Dir of Nursing R M Atchison MD.
Licensure Intermediate care. *Beds* 82. *Certified* Medicaid.
Admissions Requirements Minimum age 18; Medical examination; Physician's request.
Staff RNs 4 (ft), 2 (pt); LPNs 2 (ft), 4 (pt); Nurses aides 50 (ft), 6 (pt); Recreational therapists 1 (ft); Activities coordinators 1 (ft); Dietitians 1 (pt).
Affiliation Royal Order of Moose
Facilities Dining room; Activities room; Crafts room; Laundry room; Barber/Beauty shop; Library.
Activities Arts & crafts; Cards; Games; Reading groups; Prayer groups; Movies.

OKEMOS

Ingham County Medical Care Facility
3860 Dobie Rd, Okemos, MI, 48864
(517) 349-1050
Admin D Vande Vusse. *Medical Dir/Dir of Nursing* John Strandmark MD.
Licensure Skilled care; Intermediate care. *Beds* 204. *Certified* Medicaid; Medicare.
Admissions Requirements Minimum age 12; Medical examination; Physician's request.
Staff Physicians 3 (pt); RNs 15 (ft); LPNs 20 (ft); Nurses aides 145 (ft); Physical therapists 1 (pt); Recreational therapists 1 (pt); Occupational therapists 1 (pt); Speech therapists 3 (pt); Activities coordinators 1 (ft); Dietitians 1 (ft); Dentists 1 (pt); Ophthalmologists 1 (pt); Podiatrists 1 (pt); Dentist 2 (pt).
Facilities Dining room; Physical therapy room; Activities room; Crafts room; Laundry room; Barber/Beauty shop; Library.
Activities Arts & crafts; Cards; Games; Reading groups; Prayer groups; Movies; Shopping trips; Social/Cultural gatherings.

ONTONAGON

Maple Manor Nursing Center*
102 2nd St, Ontonagon, MI, 49953
Licensure Intermediate care. *Beds* 64. *Certified* Medicaid.

Ontonagon Memorial Hospital*
601 7th St, Ontonagon, MI, 49953
(906) 884-2811
Licensure Skilled care; Intermediate care. *Beds* 46. *Certified* Medicaid; Medicare.

ORTONVILLE

Ortonville Nursing Home
Box 160, 330 Sherman Ct, Ortonville, MI, 48462
(313) 627-2420
Licensure Intermediate care. *Beds* 51. *Certified* Medicaid.

OVID

Ovid Convalescent Manor*
9480 M 21 W, Ovid, MI, 48866
(517) 834-2228
Licensure Intermediate care. *Beds* 63. *Certified* Medicaid.

PETOSKEY

Bortz Health Care of Petoskey
1500 Spring St, Petoskey, MI, 49770
(616) 347-5500
Admin Ray W Persall. *Medical Dir/Dir of Nursing* Bradley Haas MD; Regina Shafer RN DON.
Licensure Skilled care; Intermediate care. *Beds* 120. *Certified* Medicaid; Medicare.
Owner Proprietary Corp.
Admissions Requirements Minimum age 15; Medical examination; Physician's request.
Staff RNs 6 (ft), 2 (pt); LPNs 7 (ft), 4 (pt); Orderlies 2 (ft), 4 (pt); Nurses aides 28 (ft), 11 (pt); Activities coordinators 1 (ft), 1 (pt).
Languages Tagalog
Facilities Dining room; Physical therapy room; Activities room; Laundry room; Barber/Beauty shop.
Activities Games; Reading groups; Prayer groups; Movies; Shopping trips; Social/Cultural gatherings.

PIGEON

Scheuber Hospital*
170 N Caseville Rd, Pigeon, MI, 48755
(517) 453-3223
Licensure Intermediate care. *Beds* 19. *Certified* Medicaid.

PLAINWELL

Bridgewood Manor Inc*
320 Brigham St, Box 28, Plainwell, MI, 49080
(616) 685-5390
Licensure Intermediate care. *Beds* 124. *Certified* Medicaid.

PLYMOUTH

Plymouth Court
105 Haggerty Rd, Plymouth, MI, 48170
(313) 455-0510
Admin Ralph Corvino. *Medical Dir/Dir of Nursing* Louis Schwartz MD; Kathleen Hervian DON.
Licensure Skilled care. *Beds* SNF 129. *Certified* Medicare.
Owner Proprietary Corp (Health Care & Retirement Corp).
Admissions Requirements Minimum age 18; Physician's request.

West Trail Nursing Home*
395 W Ann Arbor Trail, Plymouth, MI, 48170
(313) 453-3983
Medical Dir/Dir of Nursing Joseph Gadbaw MD.
Licensure Intermediate care. *Beds* 46. *Certified* Medicaid.

Admissions Requirements Medical examination; Physician's request.
Staff Physicians 1 (pt); RNs 2 (ft); LPNs 3 (ft); Nurses aides 14 (ft); Recreational therapists 1 (ft); Activities coordinators 1 (ft); Dietitians 1 (ft); Dentists 1 (pt); Podiatrists 1 (pt).
Facilities Dining room; Activities room; Laundry room; Barber/Beauty shop; Library.
Activities Arts & crafts; Cards; Games; Reading groups; Prayer groups; Movies; Shopping trips; Social/Cultural gatherings.

PONTIAC

Grovecrest Convalescent Center
1121 Prall St, Pontiac, MI, 48053
(313) 334-4732
Licensure Skilled care; Intermediate care. *Beds* 57. *Certified* Medicare.

Lourdes Inc
2300 Watkins Lake Rd, Pontiac, MI, 48054
(313) 674-2241
Admin Sr Frances Mary Kernasovich. *Medical Dir/Dir of Nursing* W P Richards MD; Elaine Sawchuk RN.
Licensure Skilled care; Intermediate care. *Beds* 108. *Certified* Medicaid; Medicare.
Owner Nonprofit Corp.
Admissions Requirements Minimum age 65; Medical examination; Physician's request.
Staff Physicians 4 (pt); RNs 4 (ft), 13 (pt); LPNs 6 (ft), 6 (pt); Nurses aides 36 (ft), 19 (pt); Physical therapists 1 (pt); Activities coordinators 1 (ft), 2 (pt); Dentists 1 (pt); Podiatrists 1 (pt).
Affiliation Roman Catholic
Facilities Dining room; Physical therapy room; Activities room; Chapel; Crafts room; Laundry room; Barber/Beauty shop.
Activities Arts & crafts; Cards; Games; Reading groups; Prayer groups; Movies; Social/Cultural gatherings; Pet therapy; Bowling; Music; Sing-alongs; Entertainment; Residents' council; Current events; Library on wheels; Quarterly newsletter.

Oakland County Medical Care Facility
2200 N Telegraph Rd, Pontiac, MI, 48053
(313) 858-1415
Admin James A Eddy. *Medical Dir/Dir of Nursing* Antonio Nucum MD.
Licensure Skilled care. *Beds* SNF 120. *Certified* Medicaid; Medicare.
Owner Publicly owned.
Admissions Requirements Physician's request.
Staff Physicians 1 (ft), 1 (pt); RNs 9 (ft), 4 (pt); LPNs 6 (ft), 8 (pt); Nurses aides 25 (ft), 40 (pt); Physical therapists 2 (pt); Occupational therapists 1 (pt); Speech therapists 1 (pt); Activities coordinators 1 (ft); Dietitians 2 (pt); Ophthalmologists 1 (pt); Podiatrists 1 (pt).
Facilities Dining room; Physical therapy room; Activities room; Chapel; Crafts room; Laundry room; Barber/Beauty shop; Library.
Activities Arts & crafts; Cards; Games; Reading groups; Prayer groups; Movies; Shopping trips; Social/Cultural gatherings.

Oakland Geriatric Village*
1255 Silver Bell, Pontiac, MI, 48057
(313) 391-0900
Medical Dir/Dir of Nursing Dr Janicke DO.
Licensure Skilled care; Intermediate care. *Beds* 106. *Certified* Medicaid; Medicare.
Admissions Requirements Medical examination; Physician's request.
Staff Physicians 6 (pt); RNs 2 (ft), 7 (pt); LPNs 3 (ft), 14 (pt); Nurses aides 60 (pt); Physical therapists 1 (pt); Recreational therapists 1 (ft); Occupational therapists 1 (pt); Speech therapists 1 (pt); Activities coordinators 1 (ft); Dietitians 1 (ft); Dentists 1 (pt); Ophthalmologists 1 (pt); Podiatrists 1 (pt).

Facilities Dining room; Physical therapy room; Activities room; Crafts room; Laundry room; Barber/Beauty shop.
Activities Arts & crafts; Cards; Reading groups; Prayer groups; Movies; Shopping trips; Social/Cultural gatherings; Bowling; Senior citizens' center visited weekly.

Pontiac Nursing Center
532 Orchard Lake Rd, Pontiac, MI, 48053
(313) 338-7151
Admin Morsy F Morsy Sr Adm; Marianne Mikkelsen, Barbara Lawson Asst Adm. *Medical Dir/Dir of Nursing* Marie Bell RN DON.
Licensure Skilled care; Intermediate care. *Beds* 360. *Certified* Medicaid; Medicare.
Owner Proprietary Corp (Beverly Enterprises).
Admissions Requirements Minimum age 15.
Staff Physicians 10 (pt); RNs 5 (ft); LPNs 22 (ft), 11 (pt); Orderlies 1 (ft); Nurses aides 78 (ft), 5 (pt); Physical therapists 1 (ft); Activities coordinators 1 (ft); Dietitians 1 (ft).
Languages Arabic, Spanish, Tagalog
Facilities Dining room; Physical therapy room; Activities room; Chapel; Crafts room; Laundry room; Barber/Beauty shop; Library; Patios; Recreation rooms.
Activities Arts & crafts; Cards; Games; Reading groups; Prayer groups; Movies; Shopping trips; Social/Cultural gatherings; Adopt-a-grandparent program; Entertainment by community groups.

PORT HURON

Evangelical Home Port Huron
5635 Lakeshore Rd, Port Huron, MI, 48060
(313) 385-7447
Admin Catherine M Durkin. *Medical Dir/Dir of Nursing* Douglas A Krause MD; Katherine Schlichting RNC.
Licensure Skilled care; Intermediate care. *Beds* 182. *Certified* Medicaid; Medicare.
Owner Nonprofit organization/foundation.
Admissions Requirements Minimum age 18; Medical examination; Physician's request.
Staff RNs 9 (ft); LPNs 12 (ft); Orderlies 2 (ft); Nurses aides 60 (ft); Physical therapists 1 (pt); Recreational therapists 1 (pt); Occupational therapists 1 (pt); Speech therapists 1 (pt); Activities coordinators 1 (pt); Dietitians 1 (pt); Dentists 1 (pt); Ophthalmologists 1 (pt); Podiatrists 1 (pt).
Affiliation Church of Christ
Facilities Dining room; Physical therapy room; Activities room; Crafts room; Laundry room; Barber/Beauty shop.
Activities Arts & crafts; Cards; Games; Reading groups; Prayer groups; Movies; Shopping trips; Social/Cultural gatherings; Baking, Cooking.

Marwood Manor Nursing Home
1300 Beard St, Port Huron, MI, 48060
(313) 982-8591
Admin Peter Cangemi. *Medical Dir/Dir of Nursing* Frederick E Ludwig MD.
Licensure Skilled care; Intermediate care. *Beds* 252. *Certified* Medicaid; Medicare.
Owner Nonprofit Corp.
Admissions Requirements Minimum age 17; Medical examination; Physician's request.
Staff RNs 3 (ft), 5 (pt); LPNs 13 (ft), 11 (pt); Orderlies 2 (pt); Nurses aides 84 (ft), 17 (pt); Physical therapists 1 (ft); Occupational therapists 1 (pt); Speech therapists 1 (pt); Activities coordinators 1 (ft), 1 (pt).
Facilities Dining room; Physical therapy room; Activities room; Crafts room; Laundry room; Barber/Beauty shop; Library.
Activities Arts & crafts; Cards; Games; Prayer groups; Movies; Social/Cultural gatherings; Live bands; Cookouts; Christmas teas; Popcorn parties; Ice cream socials; Bingo.

POWERS

Pinecrest Medical Care Facility
Box 603, Powers, MI, 49874
(906) 497-5244
Admin Gerald Betters. *Medical Dir/Dir of Nursing* Michael Feltes; D Smith RN DON.
Licensure Skilled care. *Beds* SNF 160. *Certified* Medicaid; Medicare.
Owner Nonprofit organization/foundation.
Admissions Requirements Minimum age 14.
Staff Physicians 1 (ft); RNs 3 (ft), 3 (pt); LPNs 14 (ft), 12 (pt); Orderlies 1 (ft); Nurses aides 42 (ft), 32 (pt); Physical therapists 1 (ft); Occupational therapists 1 (pt); Speech therapists 1 (pt); Activities coordinators 1 (ft); Dietitians 1 (ft).
Facilities Dining room; Physical therapy room; Activities room; Chapel; Crafts room; Laundry room; Barber/Beauty shop.
Activities Arts & crafts; Cards; Games; Prayer groups; Movies; Shopping trips; Social/Cultural gatherings.

REDFORD TOWNSHIP

Cambridge West Nursing Centre
18633 Beech Daly Rd, Redford Township, MI, 48240
(313) 255-1010
Admin Betty Shore. *Medical Dir/Dir of Nursing* David Rosenberg DO; Shirley Maxwell RN.
Licensure Skilled care. *Beds* SNF 121. *Certified* Medicaid; Medicare.
Owner Proprietary Corp (International Health Care Management).
Admissions Requirements Minimum age 15; Medical examination; Physician's request.
Staff Physicians 3 (pt); RNs 3 (ft), 3 (pt); LPNs 10 (ft), 3 (pt); Orderlies 3 (ft); Nurses aides 32 (ft), 6 (pt); Physical therapists 1 (ft); Speech therapists 1 (ft); Activities coordinators 1 (ft); Dietitians 1 (ft).
Facilities Dining room; Physical therapy room; Activities room; Laundry room; Barber/Beauty shop; Library.
Activities Arts & crafts; Cards; Games; Reading groups; Prayer groups; Movies; Shopping trips; Social/Cultural gatherings.

REED CITY

Reed City Hospital Long-Term Care Facility
7665 Patterson Rd, Reed City, MI, 49677
(616) 832-3271
Admin Jack L Haybarker RPH. *Medical Dir/Dir of Nursing* Richard Karns RN DON.
Licensure Skilled care. *Beds* SNF 54. *Certified* Medicaid; Medicare.
Owner Publicly owned.
Admissions Requirements Physician's request.
Staff Physicians; RNs; LPNs; Orderlies; Nurses aides; Physical therapists; Occupational therapists; Speech therapists; Activities coordinators; Dietitians; Dentists; Ophthalmologists.
Facilities Dining room; Activities room.
Activities Arts & crafts; Cards; Games; Reading groups; Prayer groups.

RICHMOND

Medilodge of Richmond*
34901 Division Rd, Richmond, MI, 48062
(313) 727-7562
Licensure Intermediate care. *Beds* 126. *Certified* Medicaid.

RIVERVIEW

Marian Manor Nursing Care Center
18591 Quarry Rd, Riverview, MI, 48192
(313) 282-2100

Admin Alexander D Duonch. *Medical Dir/Dir of Nursing* Gerald Lammers MD; Virginia LePla RN DON.
Licensure Skilled care; Substance abuse. *Beds* SNF 83; Substance abuse 57. *Certified* Medicaid; Medicare.
Owner Proprietary Corp (International Health Care Management).
Admissions Requirements Minimum age 18; Medical examination; Physician's request.
Staff Podiatrists 1 (pt); Physicians 2 (ft), 1 (pt); RNs 4 (ft); LPNs 7 (ft), 3 (pt); Orderlies 3 (ft); Nurses aides 23 (ft), 10 (pt); Physical therapists 1 (ft), 1 (pt); Reality therapists 1 (ft); Recreational therapists 1 (ft), 1 (pt); Occupational therapists 1 (ft); Speech therapists 1 (ft); Activities coordinators 1 (ft), 1 (pt); Dietitians 1 (ft), 1 (pt); Dentists 1 (pt); Ophthalmologists 1 (pt).
Facilities Dining room; Physical therapy room; Activities room; Laundry room; Barber/Beauty shop; Library.
Activities Arts & crafts; Cards; Games; Reading groups; Prayer groups; Movies; Shopping trips; Social/Cultural gatherings; Off site trips; Zoo.

Rivergate Convalescent Center*
14041 Pennsylvania, Riverview, MI, 48192
(313) 284-7200
Licensure Skilled care; Intermediate care. *Beds* 223. *Certified* Medicaid; Medicare.

The Rivergate Terrace—Intermediate Care Facility*
14141 Pennsylvania, Riverview, MI, 48192
(313) 284-8000, 283-6244
Licensure Intermediate care. *Beds* 221. *Certified* Medicaid.

ROCHESTER

Avondale Convalescent Home
PO Box 70, 1480 Walton Blvd, Rochester, MI, 48309
(313) 651-4422
Admin Michael G Ardelean. *Medical Dir/Dir of Nursing* C E Hendershott DO; Marsha Ackerman RN.
Licensure Skilled care; Intermediate care. *Beds* SNF 166; ICF. *Certified* Medicaid; Medicare.
Owner Privately owned.
Admissions Requirements Minimum age 16; Medical examination; Physician's request.
Staff RNs 4 (ft), 21 (pt); LPNs 2 (ft), 5 (pt); Orderlies 3 (ft); Nurses aides 80 (ft); Physical therapists 1 (ft); Activities coordinators 1 (ft); Dietitians 1 (ft).
Facilities Dining room; Physical therapy room; Activities room; Chapel; Crafts room; Laundry room; Barber/Beauty shop; Library.
Activities Arts & crafts; Cards; Games; Reading groups; Prayer groups; Movies; Social/Cultural gatherings.

ROGERS CITY

Rogers City Hospital LTCU
555 N Bradley Hwy, Rogers City, MI, 49779
(517) 734-2151
Admin Samuel Gregory. *Medical Dir/Dir of Nursing* Karen Meyers RN.
Licensure Skilled care. *Beds* SNF 49. *Certified* Medicaid; Medicare.
Owner Publicly owned.
Admissions Requirements Medical examination; Physician's request.
Staff Physicians 5 (ft); RNs 2 (ft), 1 (pt); LPNs 3 (ft), 6 (pt); Nurses aides 6 (ft), 29 (pt); Physical therapists 1 (ft); Recreational therapists 1 (ft); Speech therapists 1 (pt); Activities coordinators 1 (ft); Dietitians 1 (ft).

Facilities Dining room; Physical therapy room; Activities room; Chapel; Crafts room; Barber/Beauty shop; Library; TV-Visiting room.
Activities Arts & crafts; Cards; Games; Reading groups; Prayer groups; Movies; Shopping trips; Social/Cultural gatherings; Color tours.

ROMEO

Medilodge of Romeo
309 S Bailey, Romeo, MI, 48065
(313) 752-2581
Admin Dennis Prost. *Medical Dir/Dir of Nursing* Mary Marvin.
Licensure Intermediate care. *Beds* 33. *Certified* Medicaid.
Owner Proprietary Corp.
Admissions Requirements Minimum age 17; Medical examination.
Staff RNs 1 (ft); LPNs 4 (ft), 6 (pt); Orderlies 2 (pt); Nurses aides 26 (ft); Activities coordinators 1 (pt).
Facilities Dining room; Activities room; Crafts room; Laundry room; Barber/Beauty shop.
Activities Arts & crafts; Cards; Games; Reading groups; Prayer groups; Movies; Shopping trips; Social/Cultural gatherings.

Romeo Nursing Center*
250 Denby St, PO Box 306, Romeo, MI, 48065
(313) 752-3571
Licensure Intermediate care. *Beds* 35. *Certified* Medicaid.
Admissions Requirements Minimum age 18; Medical examination.
Staff Physicians 1 (ft); RNs 1 (ft), 2 (pt); LPNs 4 (pt); Nurses aides 8 (ft), 6 (pt); Activities coordinators 1 (ft); Dietitians 1 (pt); Dentists 1 (pt); Ophthalmologists 1 (pt); Podiatrists 1 (pt).
Facilities Dining room; Activities room.
Activities Arts & crafts; Cards; Games; Social/Cultural gatherings.

ROMULUS

Apple Tree Lane Convalescent Home*
39000 Chase Rd, Romulus, MI, 48174
(313) 941-1142
Licensure Intermediate care. *Beds* 43. *Certified* Medicaid.

ROSE CITY

Ogemaw Valley Medical Facility*
517 W Page St, Rose City, MI, 48654
(313) 685-25656
Licensure Skilled care; Intermediate care. *Beds* 140. *Certified* Medicaid; Medicare.

ROSEVILLE

Rose Villa Nursing Center*
25375 Kelly Rd, Roseville, MI, 48066
(313) 773-6022
Licensure Skilled care; Intermediate care. *Beds* 172. *Certified* Medicaid; Medicare.

ROYAL OAK

Alexander Continuing Care Center
718 W 4th St, Royal Oak, MI, 48067
(313) 545-0571
Admin Helen Harmon. *Medical Dir/Dir of Nursing* Harold Wasserman MD; Beverly Bilge RN.
Licensure Skilled care. *Beds* 96. *Certified* Medicaid; Medicare.
Owner Proprietary Corp (Beverly Enterprises).
Admissions Requirements Minimum age 18; Medical examination; Physician's request.

Staff Physicians 1 (ft), 3 (pt); RNs 2 (ft), 2 (pt); LPNs 6 (pt); Orderlies 2 (ft); Nurses aides 28 (ft), 4 (pt); Physical therapists 1 (pt); Speech therapists 1 (pt); Activities coordinators 1 (ft), 1 (pt); Dietitians 1 (ft); Dentists 1 (pt); Ophthalmologists 1 (pt); Podiatrists 1 (pt).
Facilities Dining room; Physical therapy room; Laundry room.
Activities Arts & crafts; Cards; Games; Reading groups; Prayer groups; Movies; Shopping trips; Social/Cultural gatherings.

Oakland Care Center*
3030 Greenfield, Royal Oak, MI, 48072
(313) 288-6610
Medical Dir/Dir of Nursing Edwin Blumberg DO.
Licensure Skilled care; Intermediate care. *Beds* 151. *Certified* Medicaid; Medicare.
Admissions Requirements Minimum age 15.
Staff Physicians 1 (ft), 8 (pt); RNs 1 (ft), 6 (pt); LPNs 10 (ft), 6 (pt); Nurses aides 36 (ft), 27 (pt); Physical therapists 1 (ft); Reality therapists 1 (pt); Recreational therapists 1 (pt); Occupational therapists 1 (pt); Speech therapists 1 (pt); Activities coordinators 1 (ft), 1 (pt); Dietitians 1 (ft); Dentists 2 (pt); Ophthalmologists 2 (pt); Podiatrists 1 (pt); Audiologists 1 (pt).
Facilities Dining room; Physical therapy room; Activities room; Crafts room; Laundry room; Barber/Beauty shop; Library.
Activities Arts & crafts; Cards; Games; Reading groups; Prayer groups; Movies; Shopping trips; Social/Cultural gatherings; Sightseeing.

SAGINAW

Hoyt Nursing Home*
1202 Weiss St, Saginaw, MI, 48602
Licensure Intermediate care. *Beds* 69. *Certified* Medicaid; Medicare.

Luther Manor
3161 Davenport, Saginaw, MI, 48602
(517) 799-1902
Admin Mr Gere L Ablett. *Medical Dir/Dir of Nursing* Dr Frederick Rosin; Mrs Jean Roe DON.
Licensure Skilled care. *Beds* SNF 98. *Certified* Medicaid; Medicare.
Owner Nonprofit organization/foundation.
Admissions Requirements Medical examination; Physician's request.
Staff RNs 1 (ft), 6 (pt); LPNs 3 (ft), 6 (pt); Nurses aides 28 (ft), 26 (pt); Chaplain 1 (ft).
Affiliation Lutheran
Facilities Dining room; Activities room; Chapel; Crafts room; Barber/Beauty shop; Courtyards; Living room; 79 private rooms.
Activities Arts & crafts; Cards; Games; Prayer groups; Movies; Shopping trips; Social/Cultural gatherings.

Martin Luther Saginaw Home
4322 Mackinaw Rd, Saginaw, MI, 48603
(517) 792-8729
Admin Werner H Rosenbaum. *Medical Dir/Dir of Nursing* James Brasseur DO; Anna Suhr RN DON.
Licensure Skilled care; Intermediate care. *Beds* SNF 71; ICF. *Certified* Medicaid; Medicare.
Owner Nonprofit Corp.
Admissions Requirements Medical examination.
Staff RNs 3 (ft), 3 (pt); LPNs 4 (ft), 4 (pt); Orderlies 1 (ft), 1 (pt); Nurses aides 20 (ft), 14 (pt); Activities coordinators 1 (ft); Dietitians 1 (pt).
Languages German, Spanish
Affiliation Lutheran
Facilities Dining room; Physical therapy room; Activities room; Chapel; Crafts room; Laundry room; Barber/Beauty shop.

Activities Arts & crafts; Cards; Games; Reading groups; Movies; Shopping trips; Social/Cultural gatherings.

Maccabee Gardens
2160 N Center Rd, Saginaw, MI, 48603
(517) 799-2996
Admin Daniel Echler. *Medical Dir/Dir of Nursing* Dr Ellis; Ann Phillips DON.
Licensure Skilled care; Intermediate care. *Beds* 98. *Certified* Medicaid; Medicare.
Owner Proprietary Corp (Beverly Enterprises).
Admissions Requirements Minimum age 15.
Staff Physicians; RNs; LPNs; Orderlies; Nurses aides; Physical therapists; Occupational therapists; Speech therapists; Activities coordinators; Dietitians.
Facilities Dining room; Physical therapy room; Activities room; Chapel; Crafts room; Barber/Beauty shop.
Activities Arts & crafts; Cards; Games; Reading groups; Prayer groups; Movies.

Saginaw Community Hospital
PO Box 6280, Saginaw, MI, 48608-6280
(517) 790-1234
Licensure Skilled care; Intermediate care. *Beds* 208. *Certified* Medicaid; Medicare.

Saginaw Geriatric Home*
1413 Gratiot, Saginaw, MI, 48602
(517) 793-3471
Licensure Intermediate care. *Beds* 55. *Certified* Medicaid.

St Francis Home
915 N River Rd, Saginaw, MI, 48603
(517) 781-3150
Admin Sr Jane Marie. *Medical Dir/Dir of Nursing* Dr Ronald Jensen; Ann Suhr.
Licensure Skilled care. *Beds* SNF 100. *Certified* Medicaid; Medicare.
Owner Nonprofit Corp.
Admissions Requirements Medical examination.
Staff RNs 13 (ft); LPNs 7 (ft); Nurses aides 45 (pt); Physical therapists 1 (ft); Activities coordinators 1 (ft); Dietitians 1 (ft); Ophthalmologists 1 (ft).
Affiliation Roman Catholic
Facilities Dining room; Physical therapy room; Activities room; Chapel; Crafts room; Laundry room; Barber/Beauty shop.
Activities Arts & crafts; Cards; Games; Reading groups; Prayer groups; Movies.

Sun Valley Manor
2901 Galaxy Dr, Saginaw, MI, 48601
(517) 777-5110
Admin Corinne Douglas RN. *Medical Dir/Dir of Nursing* James Brasseur DO; Sally Carigan RN.
Licensure Skilled care; Home for aged with concurrent intermediate. *Beds* SNF 103; Home for aged 26. *Certified* Medicaid; Medicare.
Owner Proprietary Corp (Health Care & Retire Corp).
Admissions Requirements Medical examination.
Staff RNs 4 (ft), 2 (pt); LPNs 10 (ft); Nurses aides 27 (ft), 29 (pt); Activities coordinators 1 (ft).
Facilities Dining room; Physical therapy room; Activities room; Laundry room; Barber/Beauty shop.
Activities Arts & crafts; Cards; Games; Reading groups; Prayer groups; Movies; Shopping trips; Social/Cultural gatherings.

SAINT CLAIR

Faith Medical Care Center
4220 S Hospital Dr, Saint Clair, MI, 48079
(313) 329-4736
Medical Dir/Dir of Nursing Gordon H Webb MD.

Licensure Skilled care; Intermediate care. *Beds*
125. *Certified* Medicaid; Medicare.
Admissions Requirements Minimum age 16;
Medical examination.
Staff Physicians 14 (pt); RNs 4 (ft), 2 (pt);
LPNs 6 (ft), 4 (pt); Orderlies 1 (ft); Nurses
aides 39 (ft), 10 (pt); Recreational therapists
2 (ft); Activities coordinators 1 (ft);
Dietitians 2 (ft); Dentists 1 (pt); Podiatrists
1 (pt).
Facilities Dining room; Activities room;
Crafts room; Laundry room; Barber/Beauty
shop.
Activities Arts & crafts; Cards; Games;
Reading groups; Prayer groups; Movies;
Social/Cultural gatherings.

SAINT CLAIR SHORES

St Mary Nursing Home*
22601 E 9 Mile Rd, Saint Clair Shores, MI,
48080
(313) 772-4300
Admin C T Bertolini. *Medical Dir/Dir of
Nursing* Harry Latos DO.
Licensure Skilled care; Intermediate care. *Beds*
SNF 103; ICF 4. *Certified* Medicaid;
Medicare.
Admissions Requirements Minimum age 15;
Medical examination; Physician's request.
Staff Physicians 13 (pt); RNs 5 (ft), 1 (pt);
LPNs 1 (ft), 6 (pt); Orderlies 2 (ft), 1 (pt);
Nurses aides 30 (ft), 10 (pt); Physical
therapists; Recreational therapists;
Occupational therapists; Speech therapists;
Dietitians; Dentists; Ophthalmologists;
Podiatrists.
Facilities Dining room; Physical therapy
room; Activities room; Laundry room;
Barber/Beauty shop.
Activities Arts & crafts; Cards; Games;
Reading groups; Prayer groups; Movies;
Shopping trips; Social/Cultural gatherings.

SAINT IGNACE

Mackinac County Medical Care Facility*
Hombach St, Saint Ignace, MI, 49781
(906) 643-7788
Licensure Skilled care; Intermediate care. *Beds*
60. *Certified* Medicaid; Medicare.
Owner Publicly owned.

SAINT JOHNS

Hazel I Findlay Country Manor
1101 S Scott Rd, Saint Johns, MI, 48879
(517) 224-8936
Admin Mark Stapelman MBA NHA. *Medical
Dir/Dir of Nursing* Mary Ann Bond RN.
Licensure Intermediate care. *Beds* ICF 108.
Certified Medicaid.
Owner Nonprofit Corp.
Admissions Requirements Minimum age 15;
Medical examination; Physician's request.
Staff RNs 4 (ft), 1 (pt); LPNs 3 (ft), 8 (pt);
Orderlies 6 (ft); Nurses aides 39 (ft), 24 (pt);
Physical therapists 1 (ft), 1 (pt); Recreational
therapists 2 (ft); Occupational therapists 1
(pt); Speech therapists 1 (pt); Dietitians 1
(pt); Ophthalmologists 1 (pt); Podiatrists 1
(pt); Social worker 1 (ft).
Languages Spanish
Facilities Dining room; Physical therapy
room; Activities room; Crafts room; Barber/
Beauty shop; Library; Courtyards; Resident
gardens.
Activities Arts & crafts; Cards; Games;
Reading groups; Prayer groups; Movies;
Shopping trips; Social/Cultural gatherings;
King & Queen annually; Adult education;
Garden grant winner.

SAINT JOSEPH

Shoreham Terrace Inc
3425 Lake Shore Dr, Saint Joseph, MI, 49085
(616) 983-6501
Admin Judith E Hoese. *Medical Dir/Dir of
Nursing* Mary Bauer RN.
Licensure Skilled care; Intermediate care. *Beds*
SNF 112; ICF; Medicare 33. *Certified*
Medicaid; Medicare.
Owner Proprietary Corp (Beverly Enterprises).
Staff RNs; LPNs; Nurses aides; Activities
coordinators.

SAINT LOUIS

Schnepps Health Care Center
4527 E Washington Ave, Saint Louis, MI,
48880
(517) 681-5721
Admin David Roslund. *Medical Dir/Dir of
Nursing* Cind Bosley DON.
Licensure Skilled care. *Beds* SNF 127.
Certified Medicaid; Medicare.
Owner Privately owned.
Admissions Requirements Physician's request.
Staff RNs 4 (ft); LPNs 18 (ft); Nurses aides 74
(ft); Physical therapists 1 (pt).
Facilities Dining room; Physical therapy
room; Activities room; Barber/Beauty shop.
Activities Arts & crafts; Cards; Games;
Reading groups.

Westgate Manor Nursing Home
1149 W Monroe Rd, Saint Louis, MI, 48880
(517) 681-3852
Admin Joyce Feldkamp. *Medical Dir/Dir of
Nursing* Jeanne Wernette RN DON.
Licensure Skilled care. *Beds* SNF 81. *Certified*
Medicaid; Medicare.
Owner Proprietary Corp.
Admissions Requirements Minimum age 15;
Medical examination; Physician's request.
Staff RNs; LPNs; Orderlies; Nurses aides;
Physical therapists; Recreational therapists;
Occupational therapists; Speech therapists;
Activities coordinators; Dietitians;
Ophthalmologists.
Facilities Dining room; Activities room;
Barber/Beauty shop.
Activities Arts & crafts; Cards; Games;
Reading groups; Prayer groups; Movies;
Shopping trips; Social/Cultural gatherings.

SALINE

Evangelical Home*
440 W Russell, Saline, MI, 48176
(313) 429-9401
Licensure Skilled care; Intermediate care. *Beds*
215. *Certified* Medicaid; Medicare.

SANDUSKY

Sanilac Medical Care Facility*
137 N Elk St, Sandusky, MI, 48471
(313) 648-3017
Licensure Skilled care; Intermediate care. *Beds*
84. *Certified* Medicaid; Medicare.

SAULT SAINTE MARIE

Chippewa County War Memorial Hospital
500 Osborn Blvd, Sault Sainte Marie, MI,
49783
(906) 635-4410
Admin Lewis Herrero. *Medical Dir/Dir of
Nursing* E J Ranta MD; Beverly Stewart
RN.
Licensure Skilled care; Intermediate care. *Beds*
SNF 31; ICF 20. *Certified* Medicaid;
Medicare.
Owner Publicly owned.
Admissions Requirements Medical
examination; Physician's request.

Staff Physicians 12 (pt); RNs 3 (ft); LPNs 3
(ft); Orderlies 1 (pt); Nurses aides 15 (ft), 1
(pt); Physical therapists 2 (pt); Occupational
therapists 1 (pt); Activities coordinators 1
(ft); Dietitians 1 (ft); Dentists 1 (pt); Dentist
1 (pt); Clerk 1 (ft).
Facilities Dining room; Physical therapy
room; Activities room; Chapel; Crafts room;
Barber/Beauty shop; Library.
Activities Arts & crafts; Cards; Games;
Reading groups; Prayer groups; Movies;
Shopping trips; Social/Cultural gatherings;
Senior living classes through the community
schools; Exercise class; Special parties.

Provincial House—Sault Ste Marie*
1011 Meridian, Sault Sainte Marie, MI, 49783
(906) 635-1518
Licensure Skilled care. *Beds* 117. *Certified*
Medicaid; Medicare.
Owner Proprietary Corp (Beverly Enterprises).

SOUTH HAVEN

Countryside Nursing Home*
120 Baseline Rd, South Haven, MI, 49090
(616) 637-8411
Medical Dir/Dir of Nursing Thomas Burns
MD.
Licensure Intermediate care. *Beds* 63.
Certified Medicaid.
Admissions Requirements Medical
examination.
Staff RNs 3 (pt); LPNs 6 (ft), 2 (pt); Orderlies
9 (ft); Nurses aides 25 (ft), 20 (pt);
Recreational therapists 1 (ft), 2 (pt);
Activities coordinators 1 (ft); Dietitians 1
(pt).
Facilities Dining room; Activities room;
Laundry room; Barber/Beauty shop.
Activities Arts & crafts; Cards; Games;
Reading groups; Prayer groups; Movies;
Shopping trips; Social/Cultural gatherings.

Martin Luther Memorial Home
850 Phillips St, South Haven, MI, 49090
(616) 637-5147
Admin Richard F Hennig. *Medical Dir/Dir of
Nursing* Dale Morgan MD; Anita Behncke
RN.
Licensure Skilled care; Intermediate care. *Beds*
125. *Certified* Medicaid; Medicare.
Owner Nonprofit Corp.
Admissions Requirements Minimum age 15;
Medical examination; Physician's request.
Staff Physicians 10 (pt); RNs 6 (ft); LPNs 8
(ft); Nurses aides 60 (ft); Physical therapists
1 (pt); Occupational therapists 1 (pt); Speech
therapists 1 (ft); Activities coordinators 1
(pt); Dietitians 1 (ft), 1 (pt); Dentists 1 (pt);
Ophthalmologists 1 (pt); Social worker 1 (ft).
Affiliation Lutheran
Facilities Dining room; Physical therapy
room; Activities room; Chapel; Laundry
room; Barber/Beauty shop; Library.
Activities Arts & crafts; Cards; Games;
Reading groups; Prayer groups; Movies;
Shopping trips.

SOUTH LYON

Martin Luther Memorial Home*
307 Elm Place, South Lyon, MI, 48178
(313) 437-2048
Medical Dir/Dir of Nursing Dr Barbara
Mercer.
Licensure Skilled care; Intermediate care. *Beds*
44. *Certified* Medicaid; Medicare.
Admissions Requirements Medical
examination.
Staff RNs 4 (pt); LPNs 2 (ft), 2 (pt); Orderlies
1 (pt); Nurses aides 24 (ft), 10 (pt);
Activities coordinators 2 (pt).
Affiliation Lutheran
Facilities Dining room; Physical therapy
room; Crafts room; Laundry room; Barber/
Beauty shop.

Activities Arts & crafts; Games; Reading
groups; Prayer groups; Movies.

SOUTHFIELD

Bedford Villa Nursing Center
16240 W 12 Mile Rd, Southfield, MI, 48075
(313) 557-3333
Medical Dir/Dir of Nursing Dr Knauff.
Licensure Skilled care; Intermediate care. *Beds*
61.
Owner Proprietary Corp.
Admissions Requirements Physician's request.
Staff Physicians 1 (ft); Physical therapists 1
(pt); Reality therapists 1 (pt); Recreational
therapists 1 (pt); Occupational therapists 1
(pt); Speech therapists 1 (pt); Activities
coordinators 1 (pt); Dietitians 1 (ft); Dentists
1 (pt); Podiatrists 1 (pt).
Facilities Dining room; Activities room;
Crafts room; Laundry room; Barber/Beauty
shop; Library; TV room.
Activities Arts & crafts; Cards; Games;
Reading groups; Prayer groups; Movies;
Social/Cultural gatherings; Outings; Pet on
premises.

Franklin Manor Convalescent Center*
26900 Franklin Rd, Southfield, MI, 48034
(313) 352-7390
Licensure Intermediate care. *Beds* 107.
Certified Medicaid.

Hospice of Southeastern Michigan
16250 Northland Dr, Suite 212, Southfield,
MI, 48075
(313) 559-9209
Admin Paul Werner. *Medical Dir/Dir of
Nursing* Paul Werner MD.
Licensure Skilled care; Hospice care. *Beds* 42.
Certified Medicaid; Medicare.
Owner Nonprofit Corp.
Admissions Requirements Life expectancy 6
mos or less.
Staff Physicians 4 (ft); RNs; LPNs; Nurses
aides; Physical therapists; Occupational
therapists; Speech therapists; Dietitians.
Facilities Dining room; Activities room;
Chapel.
Activities Arts & crafts; Cards; Games.

Lahser Hills Nursing Center
25300 Lahser Rd, Southfield, MI, 48034
(313) 354-3222
Admin Belle Eisenberg. *Medical Dir/Dir of
Nursing* Dianne Casagrande RN.
Licensure Skilled care; Intermediate care. *Beds*
SNF 161; ICF. *Certified* Medicaid;
Medicare.
Admissions Requirements Minimum age 60;
Medical examination; Physician's request.
Staff Physicians; RNs; LPNs; Nurses aides;
Physical therapists; Occupational therapists;
Speech therapists; Activities coordinators;
Dietitians; Dentists; Ophthalmologists;
Podiatrists.
Facilities Dining room; Physical therapy
room; Activities room; Barber/Beauty shop.
Activities Arts & crafts; Cards; Games;
Reading groups; Prayer groups; Movies;
Shopping trips; Social/Cultural gatherings.

Mt Vernon Nursing Center*
26715 Greenfield Rd, Southfield, MI, 48075
(313) 557-0050
Licensure Skilled care; Intermediate care. *Beds*
228. *Certified* Medicaid; Medicare.

Prentis Manor Jewish Home for Aged 1
26051 Lahser Rd, Southfield, MI, 48034
(313) 352-2336
Admin Marcia Mittelman. *Medical Dir/Dir of
Nursing* William Solomon MD; Sandra
Nutten DON.
Licensure Skilled care; Intermediate care. *Beds*
SNF 100; ICF. *Certified* Medicaid;
Medicare.
Owner Nonprofit Corp.

Staff Physicians 1 (ft), 1 (pt); RNs 10 (ft);
LPNs 11 (ft); Nurses aides 40 (ft); Physical
therapists 1 (pt); Recreational therapists 1
(pt); Occupational therapists 4 (ft); Dietitians
1 (ft); Dentists; Ophthalmologists.
Affiliation Jewish

Southfield Rehabilitation Hospital
22401 Foster Winter Dr, Southfield, MI,
48075
(313) 569-1500
Admin Marcia Thomas-Brown. *Medical Dir/
Dir of Nursing* J Chatfield MD; Janet Rippy
RN.
Licensure Skilled care; Rehabilitation hospital.
Beds SNF 75; Rehabilitation hospital 75.
Certified Medicaid; Medicare.
Owner Proprietary Corp.
Admissions Requirements Minimum age 16;
Medical examination; Physician's request.
Staff Physicians 10 (ft); RNs 9 (ft), 13 (pt);
LPNs 15 (ft), 3 (pt); Nurses aides 16 (ft), 8
(pt); Physical therapists 6 (ft), 2 (pt);
Occupational therapists 4 (ft), 1 (pt); Speech
therapists 3 (ft), 4 (pt).
Facilities Dining room; Physical therapy
room; Activities room; Crafts room; Laundry
room; Barber/Beauty shop.
Activities Arts & crafts; Cards; Games;
Reading groups; Prayer groups.

SOUTHGATE

Beverly Manor Convalescent Center
15400 Trenton Rd, Southgate, MI, 48195
(313) 284-4620
Licensure Skilled care; Intermediate care. *Beds*
100. *Certified* Medicaid; Medicare.
Owner Proprietary Corp (Beverly Enterprises).

SPRING ARBOR

Arbor Manor Care Center
151 2nd St, Spring Arbor, MI, 49283
(517) 750-1900
Admin Kevin J Ganton. *Medical Dir/Dir of
Nursing* Barbara A. Buikema RN DON.
Licensure Skilled care. *Beds* SNF 123; ICF.
Certified Medicaid; Medicare.
Owner Privately owned.
Admissions Requirements Minimum age 15;
Medical examination; Physician's request.
Staff Physicians 6 (pt); RNs 4 (ft), 4 (pt);
LPNs 7 (ft), 9 (pt); Orderlies 1 (ft), 2 (pt);
Nurses aides 33 (ft), 25 (pt); Physical
therapists 1 (pt); Recreational therapists 1
(ft); Occupational therapists 1 (pt); Speech
therapists 1 (pt); Activities coordinators 1
(ft), 1 (pt); Dietitians 1 (ft), 1 (pt);
Ophthalmologists 1 (pt); Social worker 1 (ft).
Languages Polish, Yiddish
Facilities Dining room; Physical therapy
room; Activities room; Crafts room; Laundry
room; Barber/Beauty shop; Library;
Occupational Therapy.
Activities Arts & crafts; Cards; Games;
Reading groups; Prayer groups; Movies;
Shopping trips; Social/Cultural gatherings;
Bingo; Bible study; Music; Stroke club; Mens
club; Pet day; Church.

SPRINGFIELD

Provincial House—Battle Creek*
111 Evergreen Rd, Springfield, MI, 49017
(616) 965-1308
Medical Dir/Dir of Nursing Dr Gerald
Rutledge.
Licensure Skilled care; Intermediate care. *Beds*
117. *Certified* Medicaid; Medicare.
Admissions Requirements Minimum age 17;
Physician's request.
Staff RNs 5 (ft), 1 (pt); LPNs 6 (ft), 4 (pt);
Nurses aides 26 (ft), 25 (pt); Activities
coordinators 1 (ft); Dietitians 1 (ft).

Facilities Dining room; Physical therapy
room; Activities room; Crafts room; Laundry
room; Barber/Beauty shop.
Activities Arts & crafts; Cards; Games;
Reading groups; Prayer groups; Movies;
Shopping trips; Social/Cultural gatherings.

STANDISH

Standish Community Hospital
PO Box 579, 805 W Cedar, Standish, MI,
48658
(517) 846-4521
Admin James J Polonis. *Medical Dir/Dir of
Nursing* Antonio F Mendiola, Jr MD; Laurel
P Borylo RN.
Licensure Skilled care. *Beds* SNF 44. *Certified*
Medicaid; Medicare.
Owner Nonprofit Corp.
Admissions Requirements Physician's request.
Staff Physicians 1 (ft); RNs 1 (ft); LPNs 8 (ft),
4 (pt); Nurses aides 18 (ft), 9 (pt); Physical
therapists 1 (pt); Recreational therapists 1
(pt); Speech therapists 1 (pt); Dietitians 1
(pt).
Facilities Dining room; Physical therapy
room; Activities room; Crafts room; Barber/
Beauty shop.
Activities Arts & crafts; Cards; Games;
Reading groups; Prayer groups; Movies;
Shopping trips; Social/Cultural gatherings.

STEPHENSON

Roubals Nursing Home
PO Box 32, Rte 1, Stephenson, MI, 49887
(906) 753-2231
Admin William Rosner. *Medical Dir/Dir of
Nursing* Karen Raether.
Licensure Intermediate care. *Beds* ICF 88.
Certified Medicaid.
Owner Proprietary Corp.
Admissions Requirements Minimum age 18;
Medical examination; Physician's request.
Staff RNs 1 (ft), 1 (pt); LPNs 6 (ft), 6 (pt);
Nurses aides 46 (ft), 15 (pt); Activities
coordinators 1 (ft), 2 (pt); Dietitians 1 (ft).
Facilities Dining room; Activities room;
Crafts room; Laundry room; Barber/Beauty
shop.
Activities Arts & crafts; Cards; Games;
Reading groups; Prayer groups; Movies;
Shopping trips; Social/Cultural gatherings.

STERLING

Greenbriar Nursing Home*
500 School Rd, Sterling, MI, 48659
Admin John H Swaffield. *Medical Dir/Dir of
Nursing* Gordon A Page Jr MD.
Licensure Skilled care; Intermediate care. *Beds*
104. *Certified* Medicaid; Medicare.
Owner Proprietary Corp.
Admissions Requirements Minimum age 15.
Staff Physical therapists 1 (pt); Occupational
therapists 1 (pt); Speech therapists 1 (pt);
Activities coordinators 1 (ft); Dietitians 1
(ft).
Facilities Dining room; Physical therapy
room; Activities room; Chapel; Crafts room;
Laundry room; Barber/Beauty shop.
Activities Arts & crafts; Cards; Games;
Reading groups; Prayer groups; Movies;
Shopping trips.

STERLING HEIGHTS

Nightingale North*
14151 15 Mile, Sterling Heights, MI, 48077
(313) 939-0200
Licensure Skilled care; Intermediate care. *Beds*
257. *Certified* Medicaid; Medicare.

STOCKBRIDGE

Geriatric Center of Stockbridge Inc
406 W Main St, Stockbridge, MI, 49285
(517) 851-7700
Admin Joyce A Novak. *Medical Dir/Dir of Nursing* Michael Smith MD; Jennifer Rooney RN DON.
Licensure Intermediate care. *Beds* ICF 53. *Certified* Medicaid.
Owner Proprietary Corp.
Staff RNs 2 (ft); LPNs 2 (ft), 3 (pt); Nurses aides 13 (ft), 9 (pt); Activities coordinators 1 (ft).
Facilities Dining room; Activities room; Crafts room; Barber/Beauty shop.
Activities Arts & crafts; Cards; Games; Reading groups; Prayer groups; Movies; Shopping trips; Social/Cultural gatherings.

STURGIS

Thurston Woods Village-Nursing Center
307 Spruce St, Sturgis, MI, 49091
(616) 651-7841
Admin Don Snyder. *Medical Dir/Dir of Nursing* Dr Lepard & Dr Smith; Joyce Nottoli DON.
Licensure Skilled care; Intermediate care; Home for Aged; Apartments. *Beds* SNF; ICF; Home for the aged; Apartments 241. *Certified* Medicaid; Medicare.
Owner Nonprofit Corp.
Admissions Requirements Minimum age 16; Medical examination; Physician's request.
Staff Physicians 3 (pt); RNs 4 (ft), 3 (pt); LPNs 9 (ft), 5 (pt); Orderlies 1 (ft), 1 (pt); Nurses aides 37 (ft), 16 (pt); Physical therapists 1 (pt); Reality therapists 1 (ft); Recreational therapists 1 (ft), 3 (pt); Activities coordinators 1 (ft); Dietitians 1 (pt); Ophthalmologists 1 (pt).
Languages German, Spanish
Affiliation Mennonite
Facilities Dining room; Physical therapy room; Activities room; Chapel; Crafts room; Laundry room; Barber/Beauty shop; Library; Outdoor recreation.
Activities Arts & crafts; Cards; Games; Reading groups; Prayer groups; Movies; Shopping trips; Social/Cultural gatherings; Pontoon rides on lake.

TAWAS CITY

Iosco County Medical Care Facility*
1201 Harris Ave, Tawas City, MI, 48763
(517) 362-4424
Licensure Skilled care; Intermediate care. *Beds* 64. *Certified* Medicaid; Medicare.
Owner Publicly owned.

Provincial House—Tawas City*
400 W North St, Tawas City, MI, 48763
(517) 362-8645
Licensure Skilled care; Intermediate care. *Beds* 120. *Certified* Medicaid; Medicare.
Owner Proprietary Corp (Beverly Enterprises).

TAYLOR

Park Nursing Center
12575 S Telegraph Rd, Taylor, MI, 48180
(313) 287-4710
Admin Juanita W Brannock. *Medical Dir/Dir of Nursing* Carol O'Brien DON.
Licensure Skilled care; Intermediate care. *Beds* SNF 265; ICF. *Certified* Medicaid; Medicare.
Owner Proprietary Corp.
Admissions Requirements Minimum age 15; Medical examination; Physician's request.

Staff Physicians; RNs; LPNs; Nurses aides; Physical therapists; Recreational therapists; Speech therapists; Activities coordinators; Dietitians; Dentists; Ophthalmologists; Podiatrists.
Languages French, Spanish, Polish
Facilities Dining room; Physical therapy room; Activities room; Crafts room; Laundry room; Barber/Beauty shop.
Activities Arts & crafts; Cards; Games; Reading groups; Movies; Shopping trips.

Pine Knoll Convalescent Center Inc
23600 Northline Rd, Taylor, MI, 48180
(313) 287-8580
Admin Diane Tackett. *Medical Dir/Dir of Nursing* M Elanjian DO; B Shellhammer RN.
Licensure Skilled care. *Beds* 142. *Certified* Medicaid; Medicare.
Owner Privately owned.
Admissions Requirements Minimum age 15; Medical examination; Physician's request.
Staff RNs; LPNs; Nurses aides; Physical therapists; Reality therapists; Occupational therapists; Speech therapists; Activities coordinators; Dietitians; Dentists; Ophthalmologists.
Facilities Dining room; Physical therapy room; Activities room; Chapel; Crafts room; Laundry room; Barber/Beauty shop; Day rooms.
Activities Arts & crafts; Cards; Games; Prayer groups; Movies.

Taylor Total Living Center*
22950 Northline Rd, Taylor, MI, 48180
Licensure Intermediate care. *Beds* 150. *Certified* Medicaid.

TECUMSEH

Herrick Nursing Home
500 E Pottawatomie St, Tecumseh, MI, 49286
(517) 423-2141
Admin Philip M Sullivan. *Medical Dir/Dir of Nursing* Carlton Cook MD; Terri Durkin Williams RN.
Licensure Intermediate care. *Beds* ICF 25. *Certified* Medicaid.
Owner Nonprofit organization/foundation.
Admissions Requirements Minimum age 15; Physician's request.
Staff Physicians; RNs; LPNs; Orderlies; Nurses aides; Physical therapists; Occupational therapists; Speech therapists; Activities coordinators; Dietitians; Dentists; Ophthalmologists.
Facilities Dining room; Physical therapy room; Activities room; Chapel; Crafts room; Laundry room; Barber/Beauty shop.
Activities Arts & crafts; Cards; Games; Reading groups; Prayer groups; Movies; Shopping trips; Social/Cultural gatherings.

THREE RIVERS

River Forest Nursing Care Center
55378 Wilbur Rd, Three Rivers, MI, 49093
(616) 279-7441
Admin Ron Boothby. *Medical Dir/Dir of Nursing* Dr Bas Mutnal; Don Makela.
Licensure Skilled care; Intermediate care; Home for aged; Adult Foster care. *Beds* SNF 87; ICF; Home for aged; Adult Foster care 30. *Certified* Medicaid; Medicare.
Owner Nonprofit organization/foundation.
Admissions Requirements Minimum age 16; Medical examination; Physician's request.
Staff Physicians 6 (pt); RNs 2 (ft), 3 (pt); LPNs 5 (ft), 3 (pt); Nurses aides 30 (ft), 20 (pt); Physical therapists 1 (pt); Recreational therapists 1 (pt); Occupational therapists 11 (pt); Speech therapists 1 (pt); Activities coordinators 1 (ft); Dietitians 1 (pt); Dentists 1 (pt); Ophthalmologists 1 (pt); Podiatrists 1 (pt).

Affiliation Roman Catholic
Facilities Dining room; Physical therapy room; Activities room; Chapel; Crafts room; Laundry room; Barber/Beauty shop; Library.
Activities Arts & crafts; Cards; Games; Reading groups; Prayer groups; Movies; Shopping trips; Social/Cultural gatherings.

Three Rivers Manor*
517 Erie St, Three Rivers, MI, 49093
(616) 273-8661
Medical Dir/Dir of Nursing B Mutnal MD.
Licensure Skilled care; Intermediate care. *Beds* 100. *Certified* Medicaid; Medicare.
Owner Proprietary Corp (Health Care & Retirement Corp).
Admissions Requirements Minimum age 17.
Facilities Dining room; Physical therapy room; Activities room; Chapel; Crafts room; Laundry room; Barber/Beauty shop.
Activities Arts & crafts; Cards; Games; Reading groups; Prayer groups; Movies; Social/Cultural gatherings.

TRAVERSE CITY

Birchwood Nursing Center
2950 LaFranier Rd, Traverse City, MI, 49684
(616) 947-0506
Licensure Skilled care; Intermediate care. *Beds* 155. *Certified* Medicaid; Medicare.

Bortz Health Care of Traverse City
2828 Concord, Traverse City, MI, 49684
(616) 941-1200
Admin John F Walz. *Medical Dir/Dir of Nursing* Dr D Webster MD; Marilyn Redman RN.
Licensure Skilled care; Intermediate care. *Beds* SNF 37; ICF 59. *Certified* Medicaid; Medicare.
Owner Proprietary Corp.
Admissions Requirements Minimum age 15; Medical examination; Physician's request.
Staff RNs 10 (ft), 3 (pt); LPNs 5 (ft), 2 (pt); Orderlies 1 (ft); Nurses aides 40 (ft), 15 (pt); Physical therapists 1 (pt); Occupational therapists 1 (pt); Speech therapists 1 (pt); Activities coordinators 1 (ft), 2 (pt); Dietitians 1 (ft); Dentists 1 (pt); Ophthalmologists 1 (pt); Podiatrists 1 (pt).
Facilities Dining room; Physical therapy room; Activities room; Crafts room; Laundry room; Barber/Beauty shop.
Activities Arts & crafts; Cards; Games; Reading groups; Prayer groups; Movies; Shopping trips; Social/Cultural gatherings.

Grand Traverse County Medical Care Facility*
410 S Elwood, Traverse City, MI, 49684
(616) 947-4750
Medical Dir/Dir of Nursing Robert Johnson MD.
Licensure Skilled care; Intermediate care. *Beds* 181. *Certified* Medicaid; Medicare.
Staff Physicians 1 (pt); RNs 10 (ft), 5 (pt); LPNs 10 (ft), 10 (pt); Orderlies 5 (ft), 5 (pt); Nurses aides 75 (ft), 25 (pt).
Facilities Dining room; Physical therapy room; Activities room; Chapel; Crafts room; Laundry room; Barber/Beauty shop; Library.
Activities Arts & crafts; Cards; Games; Reading groups; Prayer groups; Movies; Shopping trips; Social/Cultural gatherings.

Provincial House—Traverse City
2585 S LaFranier Rd, Traverse City, MI, 49684
(616) 947-9511
Admin Judy Petieff. *Medical Dir/Dir of Nursing* Wm Thomos MD; Katie Thomos RN DON.
Licensure Skilled care; Intermediate care. *Beds* SNF 120; ICF 120. *Certified* Medicaid; Medicare.
Owner Proprietary Corp (Beverly Enterprises).
Admissions Requirements Minimum age 15; Physician's request.

Staff Physicians 41 (pt); RNs 3 (ft), 1 (pt); LPNs 9 (ft), 4 (pt); Nurses aides 108 (ft), 10 (pt); Physical therapists 1 (pt); Recreational therapists 1 (ft); Occupational therapists 2 (pt); Speech therapists 1 (pt); Activities coordinators 1 (ft); Dietitians 1 (pt); Ophthalmologists 1 (pt); Podiatrists 1 (pt).
Facilities Dining room; Physical therapy room; Activities room; Chapel; Crafts room; Laundry room; Barber/Beauty shop; Library.
Activities Arts & crafts; Games; Reading groups; Prayer groups; Movies.

TRENTON

Balmoral Skilled Nursing Home*
5500 Fort St, Trenton, MI, 48183
(313) 675-1600
Medical Dir/Dir of Nursing Dr S Kwasiborski.
Licensure Skilled care; Intermediate care. *Beds* 209. *Certified* Medicaid; Medicare.
Owner Proprietary Corp (Comprehensive Health Care Assn).
Admissions Requirements Minimum age 16.
Staff Physicians 50 (pt); RNs 5 (ft), 6 (pt); LPNs 7 (ft), 7 (pt); Nurses aides 51 (ft), 14 (pt); Physical therapists 1 (ft); Occupational therapists 1 (pt); Speech therapists 1 (pt); Activities coordinators 1 (ft); Dietitians 1 (ft); Dentists 1 (pt); Ophthalmologists 1 (pt); Podiatrists 1 (pt).
Facilities Dining room; Physical therapy room; Activities room; Laundry room; Barber/Beauty shop; Library.
Activities Arts & crafts; Cards; Games; Prayer groups; Movies; Social/Cultural gatherings; Classes; Cooking.

Trenton Convalescent Center*
406 Elm St, Trenton, MI, 48183
(313) 676-3232
Licensure Intermediate care. *Beds* 51.
Certified Medicaid.

UNION LAKE

West Winds Nursing Home*
10765 Bogie Lake Rd, Union Lake, MI, 48085
(313) 363-9400
Admin Daniel C Page. *Medical Dir/Dir of Nursing* J J Johnstone DO.
Licensure Intermediate care. *Beds* 50.
Certified Medicaid.
Admissions Requirements Minimum age 60.
Staff Physicians 2 (pt); RNs 7 (ft); LPNs 3 (ft); Nurses aides 13 (ft), 24 (pt); Physical therapists; Reality therapists; Recreational therapists; Occupational therapists; Speech therapists; Activities coordinators 1 (ft); Dietitians 1 (pt); Dentists; Ophthalmologists; Podiatrists; Audiologists.
Facilities Dining room; Activities room; Crafts room; Laundry room; Barber/Beauty shop.
Activities Arts & crafts; Cards; Games; Reading groups; Prayer groups; Movies; Social/Cultural gatherings.

UTICA

Wil Mar Convalescent Home*
45305 Cass Ave, Utica, MI, 48087
Licensure Intermediate care. *Beds* 52.
Certified Medicaid.

WAKEFIELD

Gogebic County Medical Care Facility*
Rte 1, Box 3, Wakefield, MI, 49968
(906) 224-9811
Medical Dir/Dir of Nursing Bruce D Gordon MD.
Licensure Skilled care; Intermediate care. *Beds* 109. *Certified* Medicaid; Medicare.
Admissions Requirements Minimum age 15; Medical examination; Physician's request.

Staff Physicians 6 (pt); RNs 3 (ft), 5 (pt); LPNs 5 (ft), 7 (pt); Orderlies 1 (ft), 1 (pt); Nurses aides 42 (ft), 18 (pt); Physical therapists 1 (ft), 1 (pt); Reality therapists 2 (ft); Recreational therapists 1 (ft), 2 (pt); Activities coordinators 1 (pt); Dietitians 1 (ft); Dentists 1 (ft), 1 (pt); Ophthalmologists 1 (pt); Podiatrists 1 (pt); Audiologists 1 (pt).
Facilities Dining room; Physical therapy room; Activities room; Chapel; Crafts room; Laundry room; Barber/Beauty shop; Library.
Activities Arts & crafts; Games; Reading groups; Prayer groups; Movies; Shopping trips; Social/Cultural gatherings.

WARREN

Abbey Convalescent & Nursing Home*
12250 E 12 Mile Rd, Warren, MI, 48093
(313) 751-6200
Admin Juanita A Majishe. *Medical Dir/Dir of Nursing* Barry Szczesny DO.
Licensure Skilled care; Intermediate care. *Beds* 201. *Certified* Medicaid; Medicare.
Owner Proprietary Corp (Beverly Enterprises).
Admissions Requirements Minimum age 21; Medical examination; Physician's request.
Staff Physicians; RNs 12 (ft); LPNs 14 (ft); Nurses aides 40 (ft), 25 (pt); Physical therapists 1 (pt); Recreational therapists 2 (ft); Speech therapists 1 (pt); Activities coordinators 1 (ft); Dietitians 1 (pt); Dentists 1 (pt); Ophthalmologists 1 (pt); Podiatrists 1 (pt); Audiologists 1 (pt).
Facilities Dining room; Physical therapy room; Activities room; Laundry room; Barber/Beauty shop.
Activities Arts & crafts; Cards; Games; Reading groups; Prayer groups; Movies; Shopping trips; Social/Cultural gatherings.

Nightingale Nursing Home
11525 E 10 Mile Rd, Warren, MI, 48089
(313) 759-0700
Admin Lois J Klaus. *Medical Dir/Dir of Nursing* Martha Dettloff DON.
Licensure Skilled care. *Beds* SNF 185. *Certified* Medicaid; Medicare.
Owner Proprietary Corp (International Health Care Management).
Admissions Requirements Medical examination.
Staff Physicians 1 (ft), 1 (pt); RNs 6 (ft), 2 (pt); LPNs 11 (ft), 4 (pt); Orderlies 10 (ft); Nurses aides 78 (ft), 22 (pt); Physical therapists 1 (ft); Reality therapists 1 (ft); Recreational therapists 3 (ft), 1 (pt); Speech therapists 1 (ft); Activities coordinators 1 (ft); Dietitians 1 (ft); Dentists 1 (ft); Ophthalmologists 1 (ft); Podiatrists 1 (ft).
Facilities Dining room; Physical therapy room; Activities room; Crafts room; Laundry room; Barber/Beauty shop.
Activities Arts & crafts; Cards; Games; Reading groups; Prayer groups; Movies; Shopping trips; Social/Cultural gatherings.

St Anthony Nursing Center*
31830 Ryan Rd, Warren, MI, 48092
(313) 977-6700
Licensure Skilled care; Intermediate care. *Beds* 72. *Certified* Medicaid; Medicare.
Owner Proprietary Corp (International Health Care Management).
Affiliation Roman Catholic

Warren Geriatric Village
11700 E 10 Mile Rd, Warren, MI, 48089
(313) 759-5960
Licensure Skilled care; Intermediate care. *Beds* 304. *Certified* Medicaid; Medicare.

WAYLAND

Sandy Creek Nursing Center Inc
425 E Elm St, Wayland, MI, 49348
(616) 792-2249

Admin Evelyn L Hampel. *Medical Dir/Dir of Nursing* Daniel F Kreuzer MD.
Licensure Skilled care; Intermediate care; Residential care. *Beds* 119. *Certified* Medicaid; Medicare.
Owner Proprietary Corp.
Admissions Requirements Minimum age 16; Medical examination; Physician's request.
Staff RNs 4 (ft), 3 (pt); LPNs 7 (ft), 3 (pt); Nurses aides 45 (ft), 40 (pt); Activities coordinators 3 (ft).
Facilities Dining room; Physical therapy room; Activities room; Laundry room; Barber/Beauty shop; TV room.
Activities Arts & crafts; Games; Reading groups; Prayer groups; Movies; Outside musical groups; Sing-alongs.

WAYNE

Venoy Continued Care Center
3999 Venoy Rd, Wayne, MI, 48184
(313) 326-6600
Admin David E Herbel. *Medical Dir/Dir of Nursing* Rosa Redmond RN.
Licensure Skilled care; Medicare Distinct unit. *Beds* SNF 161; 49. *Certified* Medicaid; Medicare.
Owner Proprietary Corp (Beverly Enterprises).
Admissions Requirements Minimum age 17; Medical examination; Physician's request.
Staff Physicians 1 (pt); RNs 4 (ft), 3 (pt); LPNs 5 (ft), 19 (pt); Nurses aides 107 (ft), 8 (pt); Physical therapists 2 (pt); Occupational therapists 2 (pt); Speech therapists 1 (pt); Activities coordinators 1 (ft); Dietitians 1 (ft); Dentists 1 (pt); Ophthalmologists 1 (pt); Podiatrists 1 (pt).
Languages Spanish, Chinese
Facilities Dining room; Physical therapy room; Activities room; Chapel; Crafts room; Laundry room; Barber/Beauty shop; Library.
Activities Arts & crafts; Cards; Games; Reading groups; Prayer groups; Movies; Shopping trips; Social/Cultural gatherings.

Wayne Convalescent Center*
34330 Van Born Rd, Wayne, MI, 48184
(313) 721-0740
Medical Dir/Dir of Nursing Fredrick Kroot DO.
Licensure Intermediate care. *Beds* 53.
Certified Medicaid.
Owner Proprietary Corp.
Admissions Requirements Minimum age 15; Medical examination; Physician's request.
Staff RNs 2 (ft); LPNs 4 (ft), 2 (pt); Orderlies 3 (ft); Nurses aides 30 (ft), 10 (pt); Recreational therapists 1 (ft); Speech therapists; Activities coordinators 1 (ft); Dietitians; Dentists; Ophthalmologists; Podiatrists.

Wayne Total Living Center*
4427 Venoy Rd, Wayne, MI, 48184
Licensure Intermediate care. *Beds* 150.
Certified Medicaid.
Owner Proprietary Corp (Beverly Enterprises).

WEST BLOOMFIELD

West Bloomfield Geriatric Center*
6470 Alden Dr, West Bloomfield, MI, 48033
(313) 363-4121
Admin F Taker. *Medical Dir/Dir of Nursing* Dr J Janicke.
Licensure Intermediate care. *Beds* 56.
Certified Medicaid.
Admissions Requirements Minimum age 21.
Staff Physicians 1 (ft); RNs 1 (ft), 3 (pt); LPNs 2 (ft), 4 (pt); Nurses aides 35 (ft); Activities coordinators 1 (ft); Dietitians 1 (pt); Dentists 1 (pt); Ophthalmologists 1 (pt); Podiatrists 1 (pt).
Facilities Dining room; Barber/Beauty shop.
Activities Arts & crafts; Games; Reading groups; Prayer groups; Movies.

WEST BRANCH

Bortz Health Care of West Branch
445 S Valley St, West Branch, MI, 48661
(313) 345-3600
Admin Pats;y Hardaway NHA. *Medical Dir/
Dir of Nursing* Patricia Yost DON.
Licensure Skilled care; Intermediate care. *Beds*
SNF 41; ICF 52. *Certified* Medicaid;
Medicare.
Owner Proprietary Corp.
Admissions Requirements Medical
examination; Physician's request.
Staff RNs 3 (ft), 1 (pt); LPNs 6 (ft), 1 (pt);
Orderlies 2 (ft); Nurses aides 25 (ft), 10 (pt);
Activities coordinators 1 (ft), 1 (pt);
Dietitians 1 (ft).
Facilities Dining room; Physical therapy
room; Activities room; Chapel; Crafts room;
Barber/Beauty shop; Library.
Activities Arts & crafts; Cards; Games;
Reading groups; Prayer groups; Movies;
Shopping trips; Social/Cultural gatherings;
Garden clubs; Resident of the month;
Annual king & queen.

WESTLAND

Four Chaplains Convalescent Home
28349 Joy Rd, Westland, MI, 48185
(313) 261-9500
Admin Dr Larry L Ruehlen. *Medical Dir/Dir
of Nursing* Dr Michael Gambel MD; Diane
Pryslak RN DON.
Licensure Skilled care; Residential. *Beds* SNF
111; Residential 50. *Certified* Medicaid;
Medicare.
Owner Proprietary Corp (Beverly Enterprises).
Admissions Requirements Minimum age 21;
Medical examination; Physician's request.
Staff Physicians; RNs; LPNs; Nurses aides;
Physical therapists; Activities coordinators;
Dietitians.
Facilities Dining room; Physical therapy
room; Activities room; Chapel; Crafts room;
Laundry room; Barber/Beauty shop; Library.
Activities Arts & crafts; Cards; Games;
Reading groups; Prayer groups; Movies;
Shopping trips; Social/Cultural gatherings;
Exercises; Current events; Cooking classes.

Middlebelt-Hope Nursing Center
38410 Cherry Hill Rd, Westland, MI, 48184
(313) 326-1200
Admin Patricia Ostland. *Medical Dir/Dir of
Nursing* J Mobladi MD.
Licensure Skilled care; Intermediate care. *Beds*
142. *Certified* Medicaid; Medicare.
Owner Proprietary Corp (International Health
Care Management).
Admissions Requirements Minimum age 15;
Physician's request.
Staff Physicians 2 (ft); RNs 6 (ft), 2 (pt);
LPNs 7 (ft), 5 (pt); Orderlies 2 (ft); Nurses
aides 54 (ft), 27 (pt); Physical therapists 1
(ft); Reality therapists 3 (ft); Recreational
therapists 3 (ft); Occupational therapists 1
(ft); Speech therapists 1 (ft); Activities
coordinators 1 (ft); Dietitians 1 (pt); Dentists
1 (pt); Podiatrists 1 (pt).
Facilities Dining room; Physical therapy
room; Activities room; Crafts room; Laundry
room; Barber/Beauty shop; TV room.
Activities Arts & crafts; Cards; Games;
Reading groups; Prayer groups; Movies;
Social/Cultural gatherings; Picnics.

Nightingale West*
8365 Newburgh Rd, Westland, MI, 48185
(313) 261-5300
Licensure Skilled care; Intermediate care. *Beds*
236. *Certified* Medicaid; Medicare.

Westland Convalescent Center
36137 W Warren, Westland, MI, 48187
(313) 728-6100

Admin Judith G Caroselli. *Medical Dir/Dir of
Nursing* Leonard Rosenberg MD; Judith
Smith DON.
Licensure Skilled care. *Beds* SNF 230.
Certified Medicaid; Medicare.
Owner Proprietary Corp.
Admissions Requirements Minimum age 15;
Medical examination; Physician's request.
Staff RNs 20 (ft), 6 (pt); LPNs 16 (ft), 4 (pt);
Orderlies 10 (ft); Nurses aides 150 (ft);
Physical therapists 1 (ft); Reality therapists 4
(ft); Occupational therapists 1 (ft); Speech
therapists 1 (ft); Activities coordinators 3
(ft); Dietitians 2 (ft); Dentists 1 (pt);
Ophthalmologists 1 (pt); Podiatrists 2 (pt).
Facilities Dining room; Physical therapy
room; Activities room; Chapel; Crafts room;
Laundry room; Barber/Beauty shop; Library;
Private dining room.
Activities Arts & crafts; Cards; Games;
Reading groups; Prayer groups; Movies;
Shopping trips; Social/Cultural gatherings;
M.S. club; Greeters group; Men's only night;
Community council.

WHITEHALL

Whitehall Manor*
916 Lewis St, Whitehall, MI, 49461
(616) 894-4056
Medical Dir/Dir of Nursing Albert Engstrom
MD.
Licensure Skilled care; Intermediate care. *Beds*
125. *Certified* Medicaid; Medicare.
Owner Proprietary Corp (Health Care &
Retirement Corp).
Admissions Requirements Minimum age 15;
Medical examination; Physician's request.
Staff Physicians 7 (pt); RNs 3 (ft), 4 (pt);
LPNs 7 (ft), 16 (pt); Orderlies 2 (pt); Nurses
aides 43 (ft), 25 (pt); Physical therapists 1
(pt); Occupational therapists 1 (pt); Speech
therapists 1 (pt); Activities coordinators 1
(ft); Dietitians 1 (pt); Dentists 1 (pt);
Podiatrists 1 (pt); Audiologists 1 (pt).
Facilities Dining room; Physical therapy
room; Activities room; Crafts room; Laundry
room; Barber/Beauty shop.
Activities Arts & crafts; Cards; Games;
Reading groups; Prayer groups; Movies;
Shopping trips; Social/Cultural gatherings.

WHITMORE LAKE

Whitmore Lake Convalescent Center
8633 N Main St, Whitmore Lake, MI, 48189
(313) 449-4431
Admin Sara J Schaden. *Medical Dir/Dir of
Nursing* George Fischmann MD; Pamela J
Thorp RN.
Licensure Intermediate care. *Beds* ICF 212.
Certified Medicaid.
Owner Proprietary Corp.
Admissions Requirements Minimum age 15;
Medical examination; Physician's request.
Staff Physicians 2 (pt); RNs 3 (ft), 7 (pt);
LPNs 11 (ft), 3 (pt); Orderlies 15 (ft), 2 (pt);
Nurses aides 35 (ft), 8 (pt); Activities
coordinators 2 (pt); Dietitians 12 (ft), 5 (pt).
Facilities Dining room; Physical therapy
room; Activities room; Laundry room;
Barber/Beauty shop; Library; Privacy room;
Gift shop.
Activities Arts & crafts; Cards; Games;
Reading groups; Prayer groups; Movies;
Social/Cultural gatherings; GED program;
Outings; Pets in-house; Wood shop.

WOODHAVEN

Applewood Nursing Center*
18500 Van Horn Rd, Woodhaven, MI, 48183
(313) 676-7575
Medical Dir/Dir of Nursing Craig Kwalton
DO.

Licensure Skilled care; Intermediate care. *Beds*
150. *Certified* Medicaid; Medicare.
Admissions Requirements Medical
examination; Physician's request.
Facilities Dining room; Physical therapy
room; Activities room; Crafts room; Laundry
room; Barber/Beauty shop.
Activities Arts & crafts; Cards; Games;
Reading groups; Prayer groups; Movies;
Social/Cultural gatherings.

WYOMING

Holland Home—Crestview Nursing Center*
625 36th St, Wyoming, MI, 49509
(616) 531-0200
Licensure Intermediate care. *Beds* 120.
Certified Medicaid.

YALE

Medilodge of Yale*
90 Jean St, Yale, MI, 48097
(313) 387-3226
Licensure Skilled care. *Beds* 88. *Certified*
Medicaid; Medicare.

YPSILANTI

Evergreen Hills Nursing Center
1045 Ware Court, Ypsilanti, MI, 48197
(313) 483-5421
Admin Diane Haugh. *Medical Dir/Dir of
Nursing* Yvonne Koniowka.
Licensure Intermediate care. *Beds* 108.
Certified Medicaid.
Owner Proprietary Corp.
Staff RNs 2 (ft); LPNs 6 (ft), 4 (pt); Orderlies
6 (ft); Nurses aides 25 (ft), 5 (pt); Activities
coordinators 1 (ft); Dietitians 1 (ft).
Facilities Dining room; Physical therapy
room; Activities room; Laundry room;
Barber/Beauty shop.
Activities Arts & crafts; Games; Reading
groups; Prayer groups; Movies; Shopping
trips.

Gilbert Old People's Home*
203 S Huron St, Ypsilanti, MI, 48197
(313) 482-9498
Medical Dir/Dir of Nursing William Barss
MD.
Licensure Intermediate care. *Beds* 32.
Certified Medicaid.
Admissions Requirements Minimum age 65;
Medical examination.
Facilities Dining room; Activities room;
Laundry room; Barber/Beauty shop; Library.
Activities Arts & crafts; Games; Prayer groups;
Movies; Shopping trips.

Huron Valley Nursing Facility
3201 Bemis Rd, Ypsilanti, MI, 48197
(313) 434-7775
Licensure Intermediate care. *Beds* 16.

Prospect Park Convalescent Center
28 S Prospect St, Ypsilanti, MI, 48197
(313) 483-6125
Admin Herbert E Harrington. *Medical Dir/Dir
of Nursing* Athar Siddiqui MD.
Licensure Skilled care. *Beds* SNF 180.
Certified Medicaid; Medicare.
Owner Proprietary Corp.
Admissions Requirements Minimum age 18;
Physician's request.
Staff Physicians 1 (pt); RNs 4 (ft); LPNs 15
(ft), 3 (pt); Physical therapists 1 (pt);
Occupational therapists 1 (pt); Speech
therapists 1 (pt); Activities coordinators 1
(ft); Dietitians 1 (pt); Ophthalmologists 1
(pt).
Facilities Dining room; Physical therapy
room; Activities room; Crafts room; Barber/
Beauty shop.

Activities Arts & crafts; Cards; Games;
   Reading groups; Prayer groups; Movies;
   Shopping trips; Social/Cultural gatherings.

ZEELAND

Haven Park Nursing Center
285 N State St, Zeeland, MI, 49464
(616) 772-4641
Admin Valerie Powell RN. *Medical Dir/Dir of
   Nursing* Dr Nasim Yacob; Hazel Fik RN.
Licensure Skilled care. *Beds* SNF 153; ICF.
   Certified Medicaid; Medicare.
Owner Proprietary Corp (Comprehensive
   Health Care Assn).

Admissions Requirements Medical
   examination; Physician's request.
Staff RNs; LPNs; Orderlies; Nurses aides;
   Activities coordinators.
Languages Dutch
Facilities Dining room; Physical therapy
   room; Activities room; Laundry room;
   Barber/Beauty shop.
Activities Arts & crafts; Cards; Games;
   Reading groups; Prayer groups; Movies.

Heritage Healthcare Centre
320 E Central Ave, Zeeland, MI, 49464
(616) 772-9191

Admin Marsha Van Norman. *Medical Dir/Dir
   of Nursing* Marge Bergsma.
Licensure Intermediate care. *Beds* ICF 45.
   Certified Medicaid.
Owner Proprietary Corp.
Admissions Requirements Medical
   examination; Physician's request.
Staff Physicians 1 (pt); RNs 1 (ft); LPNs 1
   (ft), 6 (pt); Nurses aides; Activities
   coordinators 2 (pt); Dietitians 1 (pt).
Facilities Dining room; Activities room;
   Chapel; Crafts room; Laundry room; Barber/
   Beauty shop; Library.
Activities Arts & crafts; Cards; Games; Prayer
   groups; Movies.

MINNESOTA

ADA

Ada Municipal Hospital*
405 E 2nd Ave, Ada, MN, 56510
(218) 784-2561
Admin Robert Cameron.
Licensure Intermediate care. *Beds* 53.
  Certified Medicaid; Medicare.
Owner Publicly owned.

Ada I
207 Jamison Dr, Ada, MN, 56510
(218) 784-2219
Admin Vernon C Nordmark. *Medical Dir/Dir
of Nursing* Josette C Nordmark MD.
Licensure Intermediate care for mentally
  retarded. *Beds* ICF/MR 6. *Certified*
  Medicaid.
Owner Nonprofit Corp.
Admissions Requirements Minimum age 18;
  Medical examination.
Staff RNs 1 (pt); Activities coordinators 1 (ft);
  Direct care 3 (ft), 6 (pt).
Facilities Dining room; Laundry room.
Activities Arts & crafts; Cards; Games;
  Movies; Shopping trips; Social/Cultural
  gatherings; Community recreation.

Project New Hope-Ada 2*
21 E 4th Ave, Ada, MN, 58510
(218) 784-2217
Admin Gerald Cascioli.
Licensure Intermediate care for mentally
  retarded. *Beds* 6. *Certified* Medicaid.
Owner Nonprofit Corp.

ADAMS

Adams Group Home
407 6th St NW, Adams, MN, 55909
(507) 582-3482
Admin Vicki Evenson.
Licensure Intermediate care for mentally
  retarded. *Beds* ICF/MR 16. *Certified*
  Medicaid.
Owner Nonprofit Corp.
Admissions Requirements Minimum age 16;
  Medical examination.
Staff LPNs 3 (pt); Nurses aides 8 (ft), 12 (pt).
Affiliation Lutheran
Facilities Dining room; Laundry room.
Activities Arts & crafts; Cards; Games; Prayer
  groups; Movies; Shopping trips; Social/
  Cultural gatherings; Dinner out; Concerts.

Adams Health Care Center*
Rte 2, Box 300, Adams, MN, 55909
(507) 582-3263
Admin James Thalberg.
Licensure Skilled care; Intermediate care. *Beds*
  SNF 55; ICF 11. *Certified* Medicaid.
Owner Publicly owned.

ADRIAN

Arnold Memorial Nursing Home
601 Louisiana Ave, Adrian, MN, 56110-0279
(507) 483-2668

Admin Charlotte D Heitkamp. *Medical Dir/
Dir of Nursing* T E Nealy MD; Virginia
Simonich RN DON.
Licensure Intermediate care. *Beds* ICF 41.
  Certified Medicaid.
Owner Publicly owned.
Admissions Requirements Physician's request.
Staff RNs 1 (ft); LPNs 2 (ft), 3 (pt); Nurses
  aides 3 (ft), 15 (pt); Recreational therapists 1
  (pt); Activities coordinators 1 (ft), 1 (pt).
Facilities Dining room; Activities room;
  Chapel; Crafts room; Laundry room; Barber/
  Beauty shop.
Activities Arts & crafts; Cards; Games;
  Reading groups; Prayer groups; Movies;
  Shopping trips; Trips; Fishing; Zoo; Baseball
  games.

AH-GWAH-CHING

Ah-Gwah-Ching
Ah-Gwah-Ching, MN, 56430
(218) 547-1250
Admin John Grimley. *Medical Dir/Dir of
Nursing* Dr Burton Haugen; Nancy Dahl
DON.
Licensure Skilled care; Intermediate care. *Beds*
  SNF 179; ICF 164. *Certified* Medicaid.
Owner Publicly owned.
Admissions Requirements Minimum age 65;
  Medical examination.
Staff RNs 19 (ft), 2 (pt); LPNs 42 (ft); Nurses
  aides 88 (ft), 26 (pt); Physical therapists 2
  (ft); Recreational therapists 13 (ft); Activities
  coordinators 1 (ft); Dietitians 1 (ft);
  Psychologist 2 (ft); Social workers 5 (ft);
  RNP (Geriatric Specialty) 1 (ft).
Facilities Dining room; Physical therapy
  room; Activities room; Chapel; Crafts room;
  Barber/Beauty shop.
Activities Arts & crafts; Cards; Games;
  Reading groups; Prayer groups; Movies;
  Shopping trips; Social/Cultural gatherings;
  Pantoon rides; Fishing.

AITKIN

Aicota Nursing Home*
820 2nd St SW, Aitkin, MN, 56431
(218) 927-2164
Admin Barry Foss.
Licensure Skilled care; Intermediate care. *Beds*
  106. *Certified* Medicaid.
Owner Proprietary Corp.

ALBANY

**Mother of Mercy Nursing Home & Retirement
Center**
320 Church Ave, Albany, MN, 56307
(612) 845-2195
Admin Patrick F Mitchell. *Medical Dir/Dir of
Nursing* Bertha Schiller DON.
Licensure Skilled care; Intermediate care;
  Residential. *Beds* SNF 72; ICF 12;
  Residential 30. *Certified* Medicaid;
  Medicare.

Owner Nonprofit Corp.
Staff Physicians 1 (ft); RNs 3 (ft), 4 (pt);
  LPNs 4 (ft), 3 (pt); Orderlies 1 (ft); Nurses
  aides 33 (ft), 17 (pt); Physical therapists 1
  (ft); Reality therapists 4 (ft); Recreational
  therapists 4 (ft); Recreational therapists 4
  (ft); Occupational therapists 1 (pt); Speech
  therapists 1 (pt); Activities coordinators 1
  (ft); Dietitians 1 (ft).
Languages German
Affiliation Roman Catholic
Facilities Dining room; Physical therapy
  room; Activities room; Chapel; Crafts room;
  Laundry room; Barber/Beauty shop; Library.
Activities Arts & crafts; Cards; Games;
  Reading groups; Prayer groups; Movies;
  Shopping trips; Social/Cultural gatherings;
  Fishing; Golf.

ALBERT LEA

Albert Lea Good Samaritan Center*
Rte 2, PO Box 217, Albert Lea, MN, 56007
(507) 373-0684
Admin Craig Johnson. *Medical Dir/Dir of
Nursing* Dr Thoburn Thompson.
Licensure Skilled care; Intermediate care;
  Boarding care. *Beds* 182. *Certified*
  Medicaid.
Owner Nonprofit Corp (Evangelical Lutheran/
  Good Samaritan).
Admissions Requirements Minimum age 16;
  Medical examination; Physician's request.
Staff RNs 2 (ft), 9 (pt); LPNs 4 (ft), 7 (pt);
  Orderlies 1 (pt); Nurses aides 21 (ft), 83 (pt);
  Physical therapists 1 (pt); Recreational
  therapists 4 (ft); Activities coordinators 1
  (ft); Dietitians 1 (ft).
Affiliation Lutheran
Facilities Dining room; Physical therapy
  room; Activities room; Chapel; Crafts room;
  Laundry room; Barber/Beauty shop; Library.
Activities Arts & crafts; Cards; Games;
  Reading groups; Prayer groups; Movies;
  Shopping trips; Social/Cultural gatherings.

Albert Lea Health Care Center
617 10th St, Albert Lea, MN, 56007
(507) 373-7600
Admin David R Blum. *Medical Dir/Dir of
Nursing* Dr D Birkhofer; Judy Eidness.
Licensure Skilled care. *Beds* SNF 28. *Certified*
  Medicaid.
Owner Privately owned.
Admissions Requirements Medical
  examination.
Staff RNs 1 (ft), 1 (pt); LPNs 6 (pt); Orderlies
  15 (pt); Activities coordinators 1 (pt).
Activities Arts & crafts; Reading groups;
  Prayer groups; Movies; Shopping trips;
  Social/Cultural gatherings.

Broadway Care Home*
512 S Broadway, Albert Lea, MN, 56007
(507) 373-2909
Admin Annabelle Frazier.
Licensure Boarding care. *Beds* 11.
Owner Proprietary Corp.

Admissions Requirements Medical examination; Physician's request.
Staff RNs 1 (pt); LPNs 1 (ft); Nurses aides 5 (ft); Dietitians 1 (pt).
Facilities Dining room; Activities room; Laundry room.
Activities Arts & crafts; Cards; Games; Reading groups; Prayer groups; Movies; Shopping trips; Social/Cultural gatherings.

Crest Home of Albert Lea
1205 Garfield Ave, Albert Lea, MN, 56007
(507) 373-0188
Admin Bonnie Malloy.
Licensure Intermediate care for mentally retarded. *Beds* ICF/MR 15. *Certified* Medicaid.
Owner Nonprofit Corp.
Staff RNs consultant; Recreational therapists consultant; Speech therapists consultant; Dietitians consultant.

Golden Age Guest Home
601 E 5th St, Albert Lea, MN, 56007
(507) 373-0949
Admin LaVerne Peters. *Medical Dir/Dir of Nursing* Vicky Thompson.
Licensure Ambulatory residents. *Beds* Ambulatory 9. *Certified* Medicare.
Owner Privately owned.
Admissions Requirements Medical examination.
Staff Nurses aides; Activities coordinators; Dietitians.
Facilities Dining room; Laundry room; Large porch.
Activities Arts & crafts; Cards; Games; Prayer groups; Movies; Shopping trips.

Albert Lea Boarding Care Center
315 Park Ave, Albert Lea, MN, 56007
(507) 373-9616
Admin Myrtle Dahl RN. *Medical Dir/Dir of Nursing* Gail Harty LPN; Myrtle Dahl RN.
Licensure Boarding care. *Beds* 21.
Owner Privately owned.
Admissions Requirements Medical examination; Physician's request.
Staff RNs 1 (ft); LPNs 1 (ft); Nurses aides 13 (ft); Physical therapists; Activities coordinators 1 (pt); Dietitians 1 (pt).
Facilities Dining room; Activities room; Laundry room; Library.
Activities Arts & crafts; Cards; Games; Reading groups; Prayer groups; Movies; Shopping trips.

St Johns Lutheran Home
901 Luther Place, Albert Lea, MN, 56007
(507) 373-8226
Admin Roger W Paulsberg. *Medical Dir/Dir of Nursing* L E Shelhamer MD.
Licensure Skilled care; Intermediate care. *Beds* 206. *Certified* Medicaid; Medicare.
Owner Nonprofit Corp.
Admissions Requirements Minimum age 21; Medical examination; Physician's request.
Staff RNs 7 (ft), 9 (pt); LPNs 4 (ft), 13 (pt); Orderlies 1 (pt); Nurses aides 45 (ft), 60 (pt); Physical therapists 3 (ft); Occupational therapists 2 (ft), 2 (pt); Speech therapists 1 (pt); Activities coordinators 1 (pt); Dietitians 1 (ft).
Affiliation Lutheran
Facilities Dining room; Physical therapy room; Activities room; Chapel; Crafts room; Laundry room; Barber/Beauty shop; Library.
Activities Arts & crafts; Cards; Games; Reading groups; Prayer groups; Movies; Shopping trips; Social/Cultural gatherings.

Thorne Crest Retirement Center
1201 Garfield Ave, Albert Lea, MN, 56007
(507) 373-2311
Admin Dale L Rippey.
Licensure Skilled care; Intermediate care. *Beds* 52. *Certified* Medicaid.

Owner Nonprofit Corp (American Baptist Homes).
Admissions Requirements Medical examination.
Staff RNs 3 (ft), 5 (pt); LPNs 2 (ft), 4 (pt); Orderlies 1 (pt); Nurses aides 10 (ft), 20 (pt); Activities coordinators 1 (ft), 2 (pt).
Affiliation Baptist
Facilities Dining room; Physical therapy room; Activities room; Chapel; Crafts room; Laundry room; Barber/Beauty shop; Library.
Activities Arts & crafts; Cards; Games; Reading groups; Prayer groups; Movies; Shopping trips; Social/Cultural gatherings.

Woodvale V*
1204 Plainview Ln, Albert Lea, MN, 56007
(507) 373-7629
Admin Richard Turcotte.
Licensure Intermediate care for mentally retarded. *Beds* 32. *Certified* Medicaid.
Owner Proprietary Corp.

Woodvale VII*
PO Box 650, 1432 Spartan Ave, Albert Lea, MN, 56007
(507) 373-7629
Admin Walter Baldus.
Licensure Skilled care; Intermediate care. *Beds* SNF 10; ICF 10. *Certified* Medicaid.
Owner Proprietary Corp.

ALEXANDRIA

Bethany Home/Bethel Manors
1020 Lark St, Alexandria, MN, 56308
(612) 762-1567
Admin Delbert G Clark. *Medical Dir/Dir of Nursing* Dr Mark Odland; Julie Sterk.
Licensure Skilled care; Board & Lodging. *Beds* SNF 181; Board & Lodging 30; Apts 132. *Certified* Medicaid; Medicare.
Owner Nonprofit Corp (MN Synod/Lutheran Ch Board).
Admissions Requirements Medical examination; Physician's request.
Staff RNs; LPNs; Orderlies; Nurses aides; Physical therapists 1 (ft); Activities coordinators 1 (ft); Dietitians 1 (ft); Chaplain 1 (ft).
Affiliation Lutheran
Facilities Dining room; Physical therapy room; Activities room; Chapel; Crafts room; Laundry room; Barber/Beauty shop; Library.
Activities Arts & crafts; Cards; Games; Reading groups; Prayer groups; Movies; Shopping trips; Social/Cultural gatherings.

Knute Nelson Memorial Home*
420 12th Ave E, Alexandria, MN, 56308
(612) 763-6653
Admin David L Sorbel.
Licensure Skilled care; Intermediate care. *Beds* SNF 97; ICF 70. *Certified* Medicaid.
Owner Nonprofit Corp.

Project New Hope 1-5
PO Box 368, Quincy & Glendale, Alexandria, MN, 56308
(612) 763-6528
Admin Gerry Cascioli. *Medical Dir/Dir of Nursing* Nancy School RN.
Licensure Intermediate care for mentally retarded. *Beds* ICF/MR 30 (5 facilities of 6 residents each). *Certified* Medicaid.
Owner Nonprofit Corp.
Admissions Requirements Minimum age 18; Medical examination.
Staff RNs 1 (pt); LPNs 1 (pt).
Activities Arts & crafts; Cards; Games; Reading groups; Movies; Shopping trips; Social/Cultural gatherings.

Project New Hope 6
1007 High St, Alexandria, MN, 56308
(612) 763-6528
Admin Gerry Cascioli. *Medical Dir/Dir of Nursing* Nancy Scholl RN.

Licensure Intermediate care for mentally retarded. *Beds* ICF/MR 6. *Certified* Medicaid.
Owner Nonprofit Corp.
Admissions Requirements Minimum age 18; Medical examination.
Staff RNs 1 (pt); LPNs 1 (pt).
Activities Arts & crafts; Cards; Games; Reading groups; Movies; Shopping trips; Social/Cultural gatherings.

Project New Hope 7
Rte 8, Scenic Heights Rd, Alexandria, MN, 56308
(612) 763-6528
Admin Gerry Cascioli. *Medical Dir/Dir of Nursing* Nancy Scholl RN.
Licensure Intermediate care for mentally retarded. *Beds* ICF/MR 6. *Certified* Medicaid.
Owner Nonprofit Corp.
Admissions Requirements Minimum age 18; Medical examination.
Staff RNs 1 (pt); LPNs 1 (pt).
Activities Arts & crafts; Cards; Games; Reading groups; Movies; Shopping trips; Social/Cultural gatherings.

ANNANDALE

Annandale Care Center*
RR 4, Box 57, Hwy 24 E, Annandale, MN, 55302
(612) 274-3737
Admin John Nelson.
Licensure Skilled care; Intermediate care. *Beds* SNF 41; ICF 19. *Certified* Medicaid; Medicare.
Owner Proprietary Corp.

ANOKA

Anoka Maple Manor Care Center*
1040 Madison St, Anoka, MN, 55303
(612) 421-2311
Admin Steven Felsenberg.
Licensure Skilled care; Intermediate care. *Beds* SNF 71; ICF 54. *Certified* Medicaid; Medicare.
Owner Proprietary Corp.

Twin Rivers Care Center
305 Fremont St, Anoka, MN, 55303
(612) 421-5660
Admin Barbara A Christen. *Medical Dir/Dir of Nursing* R Sonnetag MD; Carol Jacobson.
Licensure Skilled care. *Beds* 66. *Certified* Medicaid; Medicare.
Owner Proprietary Corp (Beverly Enterprises).
Admissions Requirements Minimum age 16; Medical examination; Physician's request.
Staff RNs 6 (ft), 4 (pt); LPNs 8 (ft), 4 (pt); Nurses aides 13 (ft), 14 (pt); Physical therapists 1 (ft); Occupational therapists 1 (ft); Speech therapists 1 (ft); Activities coordinators 1 (ft); Dietitians 1 (pt).
Facilities Dining room; Physical therapy room; Activities room; Barber/Beauty shop.
Activities Arts & crafts; Cards; Games; Reading groups; Prayer groups; Movies; Shopping trips; Social/Cultural gatherings.

APPLE VALLEY

Apple Valley Health Center
14650 Garrett Ave, Apple Valley, MN, 55124
(612) 431-7700
Admin Pearl A Lemieux. *Medical Dir/Dir of Nursing* E J English MD; Lois A Duffy RN DON.
Licensure Skilled care; Intermediate care. *Beds* SNF 168; ICF 32. *Certified* Medicaid; Medicare.
Owner Privately owned.
Admissions Requirements Minimum age 16; Medical examination.

Staff Physicians; RNs; LPNs; Orderlies;
Nurses aides; Physical therapists;
Recreational therapists; Occupational
therapists; Speech therapists; Activities
coordinators; Dietitians.
Facilities Dining room; Physical therapy
room; Activities room; Crafts room; Laundry
room; Barber/Beauty shop; Therapeutic pool.
Activities Arts & crafts; Cards; Games;
Reading groups; Prayer groups; Movies;
Shopping trips; Social/Cultural gatherings.

APPLETON

Appleton Municipal Hospital & Nursing Home
30 S Behl St, Appleton, MN, 56208
(612) 289-2400
Admin Mark Paulson. *Medical Dir/Dir of
Nursing* R V Kabatay MD; Marti Croatt
DON.
Licensure Skilled care; Intermediate care. *Beds*
SNF 40; ICF 44. *Certified* Medicaid;
Medicare.
Owner Publicly owned.
Admissions Requirements Females only;
Medical examination.
Staff RNs 6 (ft); LPNs 10 (ft); Nurses aides 25
(ft); Activities coordinators 1 (ft).
Languages Norwegian
Facilities Dining room; Physical therapy
room; Activities room; Chapel; Crafts room;
Laundry room; Barber/Beauty shop.
Activities Arts & crafts; Cards; Games;
Reading groups; Prayer groups; Movies;
Shopping trips; Social/Cultural gatherings.

ARDEN HILLS

ARC Homes on Cummings*
1385 Cummings Ln, Arden Hills, MN, 55112
(612) 636-7537
Admin James Nelson.
Licensure Intermediate care for mentally
retarded. *Beds* 6. *Certified* Medicaid.
Owner Proprietary Corp.

Presbyterian Homes-Johanna Shores
3220 Lake Johanna Blvd, Arden Hills, MN,
55112
(612) 631-6000
Admin Fred Strandberg. *Medical Dir/Dir of
Nursing* Robert Blomberg MD.
Licensure Skilled care; Intermediate care;
Retirement care. *Beds* SNF 158; ICF 50;
Board & lodging 178; Apts 19. *Certified*
Medicaid; Medicare.
Owner Nonprofit Corp.
Admissions Requirements Medical
examination.
Staff Physicians; RNs; LPNs; Nurses aides;
Physical therapists; Recreational therapists;
Occupational therapists; Speech therapists;
Activities coordinators; Dietitians; Dentists;
Podiatrists; X-ray technician; Aquatics
instructor.
Affiliation Presbyterian
Facilities Dining room; Physical therapy
room; Activities room; Chapel; Crafts room;
Laundry room; Barber/Beauty shop; Library;
Medical clinic (Ophthomolgy; X ray; Dental;
Podiatry; Audiology; Speech) Swimming
pool; Whirlpool.
Activities Arts & crafts; Cards; Games;
Reading groups; Prayer groups; Movies;
Shopping trips; Social/Cultural gatherings.

ARLINGTON

Arlington Good Samaritan Center
411 7th Ave NW, Box 645, Arlington, MN,
55307
(612) 964-2251
Admin Dale Miller.
Licensure Intermediate care. *Beds* 63.
Certified Medicaid.

Owner Nonprofit Corp (Evangelical Lutheran/
Good Samaritan).
Affiliation Lutheran

ASHBY

Pelican Lake Health Care Center
305 Melba, Box 227, Ashby, MN, 56309
(218) 747-2224
Admin John Elleffson. *Medical Dir/Dir of
Nursing* Paul Jacobson MD.
Licensure Skilled care; Intermediate care. *Beds*
78. *Certified* Medicaid; Medicare; VA.
Owner Proprietary Corp.
Admissions Requirements Medical
examination.
Staff Physicians 2 (ft); RNs 3 (ft); LPNs 2 (ft),
5 (pt); Nurses aides 4 (ft), 30 (pt); Activities
coordinators 1 (ft), 1 (pt).
Facilities Dining room; Activities room;
Crafts room; Laundry room; Barber/Beauty
shop.
Activities Arts & crafts; Cards; Games;
Reading groups; Prayer groups; Movies;
Social/Cultural gatherings.

ATWATER

Atwater House
5th & Minnesota Ave, Atwater, MN, 56201
(612) 974-8070
Admin Kathryn Selseth-Kill. *Medical Dir/Dir
of Nursing* Ronald Holmgien MD; Linda
Nelson RN DON.
Licensure Intermediate care for mentally
retarded. *Beds* ICF/MR 15. *Certified*
Medicaid.
Owner Nonprofit Corp.
Admissions Requirements Minimum age 18;
Females only; Medical examination.
Staff Physicians 1 (pt); RNs 1 (pt); Activities
coordinators 1 (ft).
Languages Spanish
Facilities Dining room; Activities room;
Laundry room.
Activities Arts & crafts; Cards; Games;
Reading groups; Movies; Shopping trips;
Social/Cultural gatherings; Travel.

AURORA

Salmi Boarding Home*
Rte 1, Box 237-B, Aurora, MN, 55705
(218) 638-2990
Admin Clyde E Salmi.
Licensure Intermediate care for mentally
retarded. *Beds* 15. *Certified* Medicaid.
Owner Proprietary Corp.

White Community Hospital*
320 Hwy 110 E, Aurora, MN, 55705
(218) 229-2211
Admin Albert Briggs.
Licensure Skilled care; Intermediate care. *Beds*
SNF 28; ICF 43. *Certified* Medicaid;
Medicare.
Owner Nonprofit Corp.

AUSTIN

Agape Halfway House Inc
200 SW 5th St, Austin, MN, 55912
(507) 433-8819
Admin Dan Ecklund Dir.
Licensure Supervised living facility. *Beds*
Supervised living 15.
Owner Nonprofit organization/foundation.
Admissions Requirements Minimum age 15;
Medical examination.
Staff Reality therapists 2 (ft); Dietitians 1 (ft),
1 (pt).
Facilities Dining room; Physical therapy
room; Activities room; Laundry room.
Activities Arts & crafts; Cards; Games;
Reading groups; Movies; Shopping trips;
Social/Cultural gatherings.

Burr Oak Manor
400 10th Ave NW, Austin, MN, 55912
(507) 433-7391
Admin Aaron Chatterson. *Medical Dir/Dir of
Nursing* Dr C Jones; Jolene Alexander
DON.
Licensure Skilled care; Intermediate care. *Beds*
SNF 106; ICF 31. *Certified* Medicaid;
Medicare.
Owner Proprietary Corp (Hillhaven Corp).
Admissions Requirements Minimum age 18.
Staff RNs 3 (ft), 9 (pt); LPNs 2 (ft), 8 (pt);
Nurses aides 6 (ft), 9 (pt).
Facilities Dining room; Physical therapy
room; Activities room; Crafts room; Barber/
Beauty shop.
Activities Arts & crafts; Cards; Games; Prayer
groups; Movies; Shopping trips; Social/
Cultural gatherings.

Cedar I
207 1st Ave SW, Austin, MN, 55912
(507) 433-7301
Admin Steve Thorson. *Medical Dir/Dir of
Nursing* Pam Ollman.
Licensure Intermediate care for mentally
retarded. *Beds* 10. *Certified* Medicaid.
Owner Proprietary Corp.
Admissions Requirements Minimum age 5.
Staff LPNs 2 (pt).
Activities Arts & crafts; Cards; Games;
Movies; Shopping trips; Social/Cultural
gatherings.

Cedar II
601 13th Ave SE, Austin, MN, 55912
(507) 433-7301
Admin Steve Thorson.
Licensure Intermediate care for mentally
retarded. *Beds* 9. *Certified* Medicaid;
Medicare.
Owner Proprietary Corp.
Admissions Requirements Medical
examination; Physician's request; Maximum
Age 25.
Staff RNs; LPNs; Orderlies; Nurses aides;
Physical therapists; Recreational therapists;
Occupational therapists; Speech therapists;
Activities coordinators; Dietitians.
Facilities Dining room; Activities room;
Crafts room; Laundry room.
Activities Arts & crafts; Cards; Games;
Reading groups; Movies; Shopping trips;
Social/Cultural gatherings.

Cedar III
1921 6th Ave NW, Austin, MN, 55912
(507) 433-7301
Admin Steve Thorson. *Medical Dir/Dir of
Nursing* Pam Ollman.
Licensure Intermediate care for mentally
retarded. *Beds* ICF/MR 6. *Certified*
Medicaid.
Owner Proprietary Corp.
Admissions Requirements Minimum age 5.
Staff LPNs 2 (pt).
Facilities Regular homes.
Activities Arts & crafts; Cards; Games;
Movies; Shopping trips; Social/Cultural
gatherings.

Cedar IV
108 16th St SE, Austin, MN, 55912
(507) 433-7301
Admin Steve Thorson. *Medical Dir/Dir of
Nursing* Pam Ollman.
Licensure Intermediate care for mentally
retarded. *Beds* ICF/MR 6. *Certified*
Medicaid.
Owner Proprietary Corp.
Admissions Requirements Minimum age 5.
Staff LPNs 2 (pt).
Facilities Regular homes.

Comforcare Care Center
205 14th St NW, Austin, MN, 55912
(507) 437-4526

Admin Dan Colgan. *Medical Dir/Dir of Nursing* Michele Gemmel DON.
Licensure Skilled care. *Beds* SNF 45. *Certified* Medicaid; Medicare.
Owner Proprietary Corp (Good Neighbor Services).
Admissions Requirements Medical examination; Physician's request.
Staff RNs 2 (ft), 4 (pt); LPNs 2 (ft), 2 (pt); Nurses aides 2 (ft), 22 (pt); Recreational therapists 1 (ft), 1 (pt).
Facilities Dining room; Physical therapy room; Activities room; Crafts room; Barber/Beauty shop.
Activities Arts & crafts; Cards; Games; Reading groups; Prayer groups; Movies; Shopping trips; Social/Cultural gatherings; Resident council; Family council.

Sacred Heart Hospice*
1200 12th St SW, Austin, MN, 55912
(507) 433-1808
Admin Madonna Waletzke. *Medical Dir/Dir of Nursing* Dr Thomas Seery.
Licensure Skilled care; Intermediate care. *Beds* SNF 49; ICF 10. *Certified* Medicaid.
Owner Nonprofit Corp.
Admissions Requirements Physician's request.
Staff RNs 1 (ft), 6 (pt); LPNs 13 (pt); Orderlies 1 (pt); Nurses aides 34 (pt); Recreational therapists 2 (ft); Occupational therapists 1 (ft).
Affiliation Roman Catholic

St Marks Lutheran Home
400 15th Ave SW, Austin, MN, 55912
(507) 437-4594
Admin Glenn E Mair. *Medical Dir/Dir of Nursing* Dr Reginald Isele; Connie Priebe.
Licensure Skilled care. *Beds* SNF 169. *Certified* Medicare.
Owner Nonprofit Corp.
Admissions Requirements Minimum age 18; Medical examination; Physician's request.
Staff Physicians 1 (pt); RNs 1 (ft), 14 (pt); LPNs 2 (ft), 13 (pt); Nurses aides 125 (pt); Physical therapists 1 (pt); Recreational therapists 1 (pt); Activities coordinators 1 (pt); Dietitians 1 (pt).
Affiliation Lutheran
Facilities Dining room; Physical therapy room; Activities room; Chapel; Crafts room; Laundry room; Barber/Beauty shop; Library.
Activities Arts & crafts; Cards; Games; Reading groups; Prayer groups; Movies; Shopping trips; Social/Cultural gatherings.

Woodvale III*
1209 1st St NE, Austin, MN, 55912
(507) 437-7621
Admin Walter A Baldus.
Licensure Supervised living facility. *Beds* 41. *Certified* Medicaid.
Owner Proprietary Corp.
Admissions Requirements Minimum age 18; Medical examination.
Staff RNs 1 (pt); LPNs 1 (ft), 1 (pt); Orderlies 8 (ft), 13 (pt); Recreational therapists 1 (ft).
Facilities Dining room; Laundry room.
Activities Arts & crafts; Cards; Games; Reading groups; Movies; Shopping trips; Social/Cultural gatherings.

BAGLEY

Greensview Nursing Home
Rte 1, Bagley, MN, 56621
(218) 694-6552
Admin Jan Otness. *Medical Dir/Dir of Nursing* Fred Martin MD.
Licensure Skilled care. *Beds* 70. *Certified* Medicaid.
Owner Proprietary Corp.
Admissions Requirements Medical examination; Physician's request.
Staff RNs 5 (ft); LPNs 8 (ft); Nurses aides 20 (ft).

Facilities Dining room; Activities room; Crafts room; Barber/Beauty shop.
Activities Arts & crafts; Cards; Games; Reading groups; Prayer groups; Movies; Shopping trips; Social/Cultural gatherings.

Pine Ridge Residence
Box 29, 8th St & Hallan Ave, Bagley, MN, 56621
(218) 694-6716
Admin Donald L Blooflat.
Licensure Intermediate care for mentally retarded. *Beds* ICF/MR 15. *Certified* Medicaid.
Owner Nonprofit Corp.
Admissions Requirements Minimum age 18; Medical examination.
Staff RNs 1 (pt); Physical therapists 1 (pt); Occupational therapists 1 (pt); Speech therapists 1 (pt); Dietitians 1 (pt); Podiatrists 1 (pt); 8 (ft), 4 (pt).
Facilities Dining room; Activities room; Crafts room; Laundry room.
Activities Arts & crafts; Cards; Games; Reading groups; Prayer groups; Movies; Shopping trips; Social/Cultural gatherings.

BALATON

Colonial Manor of Balaton
PO Box 375, Hwy 14 E, Balaton, MN, 56115
(507) 734-3511
Admin Kara Johnson. *Medical Dir/Dir of Nursing* Dr O'Rourke; Mary Lebert.
Licensure Intermediate care. *Beds* ICF 78. *Certified* Medicaid.
Owner Proprietary Corp (Beverly Enterprises).
Admissions Requirements Physician's request.
Staff RNs 2 (ft); LPNs 3 (ft), 3 (pt); Nurses aides 30 (ft), 22 (pt); Physical therapists 1 (pt); Activities coordinators 1 (ft), 2 (pt); Dietitians 1 (pt).
Facilities Dining room; Physical therapy room; Activities room; Crafts room; Laundry room; Barber/Beauty shop.
Activities Arts & crafts; Cards; Games; Reading groups; Prayer groups; Movies; Social/Cultural gatherings.

BARNESVILLE

Barnesville Care Center
PO Box 129, 600 5th St SE, Barnesville, MN, 56514
(218) 354-2254
Admin Michael D Pattee. *Medical Dir/Dir of Nursing* Beth Desing RN.
Licensure Skilled care. *Beds* SNF 76. *Certified* Medicaid; Medicare.
Owner Proprietary Corp (Good Neighbor Services).
Staff RNs 2 (ft), 3 (pt); LPNs 2 (ft), 7 (pt); Orderlies 1 (pt); Nurses aides 12 (ft), 26 (pt); Recreational therapists 1 (ft), 1 (pt); Rehab Nurses 4 (pt).
Facilities Dining room; Activities room; Crafts room; Laundry room; Barber/Beauty shop.
Activities Arts & crafts; Cards; Games; Reading groups; Prayer groups; Movies; Shopping trips; Social/Cultural gatherings.

BARRETT

Barrett Care Center Inc
Hwy 55 & 59 South, Barrett, MN, 56311
(612) 528-2527
Admin Betty De Clercq. *Medical Dir/Dir of Nursing* Dr Larry Rapp; Vi Melin.
Licensure Intermediate care. *Beds* 60. *Certified* Medicaid.
Owner Proprietary Corp.
Admissions Requirements Medical examination; Physician's request.

Staff RNs 3 (ft), 2 (pt); LPNs 2 (ft), 5 (pt); Nurses aides 10 (ft), 18 (pt); Activities coordinators 1 (ft), 1 (pt); Dietitians 1 (pt).
Facilities Dining room; Activities room; Crafts room; Laundry room; Barber/Beauty shop; Library.
Activities Arts & crafts; Cards; Games; Reading groups; Prayer groups; Movies; Social/Cultural gatherings; Reality orientation groups; Remotivation groups; Music.

Steffen Group Home
PO Box 63, Barrett, MN, 56311
(612) 528-2533
Admin Julia Solein Mortenson. *Medical Dir/Dir of Nursing* Ronna Steffen.
Licensure Intermediate care for mentally retarded. *Beds* ICF/MR 6. *Certified* Medicaid.
Owner Privately owned.
Admissions Requirements Minimum age 18; Medical examination.
Staff LPNs 1 (ft); Recreational therapists 1 (pt); Speech therapists 1 (pt); Activities coordinators 1 (ft).
Facilities Dining room; Activities room; Crafts room; Laundry room.
Activities Arts & crafts; Cards; Games; Reading groups; Movies; Shopping trips; Social/Cultural gatherings.

BATTLE LAKE

Battle Lake Care Center
PO Box 68, Glenhaven Dr, Battle Lake, MN, 56515
(218) 864-5231
Admin John Rieke. *Medical Dir/Dir of Nursing* Charles McGraw MD; Mildred Mitzel RN.
Licensure Skilled care. *Beds* SNF 65. *Certified* Medicaid; Medicare.
Owner Proprietary Corp (Good Neighbor Services).
Admissions Requirements Medical examination.
Staff RNs 2 (ft), 2 (pt); LPNs 5 (ft), 4 (pt); Orderlies 1 (ft); Nurses aides 18 (ft), 14 (pt); Physical therapists 1 (pt); Recreational therapists 1 (ft); Speech therapists 1 (pt); Dietitians 1 (pt).
Facilities Dining room; Physical therapy room; Activities room; Chapel; Crafts room; Laundry room; Barber/Beauty shop.
Activities Arts & crafts; Cards; Games; Reading groups; Prayer groups; Movies; Shopping trips; Social/Cultural gatherings.

Otter Tail Nursing Home
PO Box 257R, Rte 2, Battle Lake, MN, 56515
(218) 495-2992
Admin Mark Tysver. *Medical Dir/Dir of Nursing* June Shearer RN.
Licensure Intermediate care. *Beds* ICF 62. *Certified* Medicaid.
Owner Proprietary Corp (Beverly Enterprises).
Admissions Requirements Medical examination; Physician's request.
Staff RNs 2 (ft), 2 (pt); LPNs 2 (ft), 4 (pt); Nurses aides 10 (ft), 18 (pt).
Facilities Dining room; Activities room; Crafts room; Laundry room; Barber/Beauty shop; Library.
Activities Arts & crafts; Cards; Games; Reading groups; Prayer groups; Movies; Shopping trips.

BAUDETTE

Pioneer Nursing Home
410 3rd Ave SE, Baudette, MN, 56623
(218) 634-1588
Admin David A Nelson.
Licensure Intermediate care. *Certified* Medicaid.
Owner Nonprofit organization/foundation.

Staff RNs 2 (ft); LPNs 7 (ft); Nurses aides 12 (ft), 12 (pt); Physical therapists 1 (ft), 2 (pt); Activities coordinators 1 (ft), 2 (pt).
Facilities Dining room; Physical therapy room; Activities room; Crafts room.
Activities Arts & crafts; Games; Reading groups; Movies; Shopping trips; Social/ Cultural gatherings.

BAXTER

Baxter Group Home ICF/MR
551 Birchwood St S, Baxter, MN, 56401
(218) 828-4383
Admin John Peterson.
Licensure Skilled care; Intermediate care; Intermediate care for mentally retarded. *Beds* SNF 12; ICF 12. *Certified* MN Dept of Human Services.
Owner Nonprofit Corp.
Admissions Requirements Minimum age 18; Medical examination; Physician's request.
Staff RNs; Residential counselors.
Affiliation Lutheran
Facilities Dining room; Activities room; Crafts room; Laundry room.
Activities Arts & crafts; Cards; Games; Movies; Shopping trips; Social/Cultural gatherings.

BAYPORT

Croixdale Residence
334 N 7th Ave, Bayport, MN, 55003
(612) 439-4946
Admin Margaret Day Juhl.
Licensure Boarding care. *Beds* 50.
Owner Nonprofit Corp.

BELGRADE

Belgrade Nursing Home
Box 340, Belgrade, MN, 56312
(612) 254-8215
Admin Philip Lord. *Medical Dir/Dir of Nursing* G R Savelkoul MD.
Licensure Skilled care; Intermediate care. *Beds* 64. *Certified* Medicaid.
Owner Nonprofit Corp.
Admissions Requirements Minimum age 16; Medical examination; Physician's request.
Staff Physicians 1 (pt); RNs 1 (ft), 3 (pt); LPNs 1 (ft), 7 (pt); Physical therapists 1 (pt); Speech therapists 1 (pt); Activities coordinators 1 (ft), 2 (pt); Dietitians 1 (pt); Dentists 1 (pt).
Facilities Dining room; Physical therapy room; Activities room; Chapel; Crafts room; Laundry room; Barber/Beauty shop; TV/Day room.
Activities Arts & crafts; Cards; Games; Reading groups; Prayer groups; Movies; Shopping trips; Social/Cultural gatherings; Outside entertainment groups.

BELLE PLAINE

The Lutheran Home & Hope Residence
611 W Main St, Belle Plaine, MN, 56011
(612) 873-2215
Admin Rev Robert W Schlicht.
Licensure Intermediate care; Intermediate care for mentally retarded. *Beds* ICF 128; ICF/ MR 52. *Certified* Medicaid.
Owner Nonprofit Corp.
Affiliation Lutheran

BELVIEW

Parkview Home
401 County State Aid Hwy 9, Belview, MN, 56214
(507) 938-4151

Admin Madonna C Keavney. *Medical Dir/Dir of Nursing* Steve Medrud MD; Ruth Gjermundson RN DON.
Licensure Skilled care. *Beds* SNF 62. *Certified* Medicaid; Medicare.
Owner Publicly owned.
Admissions Requirements Medical examination.
Staff RNs 3 (ft), 2 (pt); LPNs 3 (ft), 2 (pt); Orderlies 2 (ft), 3 (pt); Nurses aides 13 (ft), 31 (pt); Activities coordinators 1 (ft), 2 (pt); Dietitians 1 (pt); Chaplains 20 (pt).
Languages Swedish, Norwegian, German
Facilities Dining room; Physical therapy room; Activities room; Chapel; Crafts room; Laundry room; Barber/Beauty shop; Library; Conference rooms; Large & small lounges.
Activities Arts & crafts; Cards; Games; Reading groups; Prayer groups; Movies; Shopping trips; Social/Cultural gatherings; Community interaction; Remotivation groups; Senior citizens group; Adopted grandparents.

BEMIDJI

Beltrami Nursing Home
1633 Delton Ave, Bemidji, MN, 56601
(218) 751-1024
Admin Larry Schuette. *Medical Dir/Dir of Nursing* Steve Liebhard RN DON.
Licensure Skilled care; Intermediate care; Boarding care. *Beds* SNF 113; Boarding care 20. *Certified* Medicaid; Medicare.
Owner Publicly owned.
Admissions Requirements Medical examination; Physician's request.
Staff RNs 5 (ft), 5 (pt); LPNs 8 (ft), 8 (pt); Nurses aides 25 (ft), 27 (pt); Physical therapists 1 (pt); Recreational therapists 3 (ft), 2 (pt); Occupational therapists 1 (pt); Speech therapists 1 (pt); Activities coordinators 1 (ft); Dietitians 1 (pt); Dentists 1 (pt).
Facilities Dining room; Physical therapy room; Activities room; Chapel; Crafts room; Laundry room; Barber/Beauty shop; Library.
Activities Arts & crafts; Cards; Games; Reading groups; Prayer groups; Movies; Shopping trips; Social/Cultural gatherings.

Mississippi Home
PO Box 1537, 1001 Mississippi Ave, Bemidji, MN, 56601
(218) 751-0957
Admin Barbara R Stensland.
Licensure Intermediate care for mentally retarded. *Beds* 8. *Certified* Medicaid.
Owner Proprietary Corp.
Admissions Requirements Minimum age 18; Medical examination.
Facilities Dining room; Activities room; Laundry room.
Activities Arts & crafts; Movies; Shopping trips; Social/Cultural gatherings.

North Country Nursing & Rehabilitation Center
109 E 8th St, Bemidji, MN, 56601
(218) 751-0220
Admin Eunice Ulshafer. *Medical Dir/Dir of Nursing* James F Hatch MD; Colleen Lubken RN DON.
Licensure Skilled care; Respite care. *Beds* SNF 78; Respite care. *Certified* Medicaid; Medicare.
Owner Nonprofit Corp.
Admissions Requirements Physician's request.
Staff RNs 5 (ft), 6 (pt); LPNs 16 (pt); Nurses aides 5 (ft), 26 (pt); Physical therapists 2 (ft); Activities coordinators 1 (ft), 4 (pt); Dentist 1 (pt); Chaplain.
Facilities Dining room; Physical therapy room; Activities room; Chapel; Crafts room; Barber/Beauty shop.
Activities Arts & crafts; Cards; Games; Movies; Reality orientation.

North Star Homes*
2528 Park Ave, Bemidji, MN, 56601
(218) 751-5876
Admin Judith M Thorson. *Medical Dir/Dir of Nursing* Grant Christopher.
Licensure Intermediate care for mentally retarded. *Beds* 14. *Certified* Medicare.
Owner Nonprofit Corp.
Admissions Requirements Minimum age 18; Medical examination; Physician's request.
Staff LPNs 1 (pt); House parents 10 (ft), 10 (pt).
Facilities Dining room; Activities room; Laundry room.
Activities Arts & crafts; Cards; Games; Reading groups; Movies; Shopping trips; Social/Cultural gatherings.

REM Bemidji
PO Box 197-E, Rte 5, Bemidji, MN, 56601
(218) 586-2573
Admin David Petersen.
Licensure Intermediate care for mentally retarded. *Beds* ICF/MR 10. *Certified* Medicaid.
Owner Proprietary Corp.
Admissions Requirements Minimum age 16; Medical examination.
Facilities Dining room; Activities room; Laundry room.
Activities Arts & crafts; Cards; Games; Reading groups; Movies; Shopping trips; Social/Cultural gatherings.

BENSON

Meadowlane Healthcare Center
W Hwy 9, Benson, MN, 56215
(612) 843-2225
Admin Dale Nibbe. *Medical Dir/Dir of Nursing* Roger Horeka; Mary Ann Hogguist.
Licensure Skilled care; Intermediate care; Board & care. *Beds* 94. *Certified* Medicaid; Medicare.
Owner Proprietary Corp (Beverly Enterprises).
Admissions Requirements Medical examination; Physician's request.
Staff Physicians 3 (ft); RNs 2 (ft), 4 (pt); LPNs 4 (ft), 3 (pt); Nurses aides 25 (ft), 15 (pt); Physical therapists 1 (ft); Recreational therapists 1 (ft); Occupational therapists 1 (ft); Speech therapists 1 (pt); Activities coordinators 1 (pt); Dietitians 1 (pt); Dentists 1 (pt); Ophthalmologists 1 (pt); Podiatrists 1 (pt).
Facilities Dining room; Physical therapy room; Activities room; Laundry room; Barber/Beauty shop.
Activities Cards; Games; Reading groups; Prayer groups; Movies; Social/Cultural gatherings.

Swift County Home*
1650 Stone Ave, Benson, MN, 56215
(612) 843-3509
Admin Margaret Demarce.
Licensure Skilled care; Intermediate care for mentally retarded. *Beds* SNF 10; ICF/MR 10. *Certified* Medicaid.
Owner Nonprofit Corp.

BERTHA

Memorial Community Hospital*
Box 97, Bertha, MN, 56437
(218) 924-2700
Admin Harriet Smith.
Licensure Skilled care; Intermediate care. *Beds* SNF 10; ICF 16. *Certified* Medicaid.
Owner Publicly owned.

BIG LAKE

Residential Alternatives VII
150 Powell Circle W, Big Lake, MN, 55309
(612) 263-6503

Admin Peter Jacobsen. *Medical Dir/Dir of Nursing* Sharon Robideau Consultant RN.
Licensure Intermediate care for mentally retarded. *Certified* Medicare.
Owner Privately owned.
Admissions Requirements Minimum age 18.
Staff RNs.
Facilities Dining room; Activities room; Laundry room.
Activities Arts & crafts; Games; Movies; Shopping trips; Social/Cultural gatherings.

BIGFORK

Northern Itasca Health Care Center
258 Pine Tree Dr, Bigfork, MN, 56628
(218) 743-3177
Admin Lillian M Krueger. *Medical Dir/Dir of Nursing* J Scrivner MD; Pearl Aakhus DON.
Licensure Skilled care; Intermediate care. *Beds* 40. *Certified* Medicaid; Medicare.
Owner Publicly owned.
Staff Physicians; RNs; LPNs; Nurses aides; Physical therapists; Activities coordinators; Dietitians.
Facilities Dining room; Physical therapy room; Activities room; Barber/Beauty shop.
Activities Arts & crafts; Cards; Games; Reading groups; Prayer groups; Movies; Shopping trips; Social/Cultural gatherings.

BIRD ISLAND

Bird Island Manor Healthcare Center*
421 S 11th St, Bird Island, MN, 55310
(612) 365-4141
Admin Mark Rust.
Licensure Intermediate care. *Beds* 24. *Certified* Medicaid.
Owner Proprietary Corp (Beverly Enterprises).

Renville County Community Residence
PO Box 520, 831 Grove Ave, Bird Island, MN, 55310
(612) 365-3748
Admin Mark Glesener MSW. *Medical Dir/Dir of Nursing* Bonnie Peterson RN.
Licensure Intermediate care for mentally retarded. *Beds* ICF/MR 15. *Certified* Medicaid.
Owner Nonprofit Corp.
Admissions Requirements Minimum age 18.
Staff RNs 1 (pt); Activities coordinators 1 (pt); Home skill instructor.
Facilities Dining room; Physical therapy room; Activities room; Crafts room; Laundry room.
Activities Arts & crafts; Cards; Games; Movies; Shopping trips; Social/Cultural gatherings; Cooking; Personal hygiene; Housekeeping; Speech.

BLACKDUCK

Northern Pines Good Samaritan Center
PO Box 190, Rte 1, Blackduck, MN, 56630
(218) 835-4218
Admin Jon Kosiak. *Medical Dir/Dir of Nursing* Dr G W Mouser.
Licensure Intermediate care. *Beds* ICF 70. *Certified* Medicaid.
Owner Nonprofit Corp (Evangelical Lutheran/ Good Samaritan).
Admissions Requirements Minimum age 16; Physician's request.
Staff RNs 2 (ft), 2 (pt); LPNs 1 (ft), 6 (pt); Nurses aides 17 (ft), 20 (pt); Activities coordinators 1 (ft).
Affiliation Lutheran
Facilities Dining room; Physical therapy room; Activities room; Crafts room; Laundry room.

Activities Arts & crafts; Cards; Games; Reading groups; Prayer groups; Movies; Shopping trips; Social/Cultural gatherings; Devotions daily; Bible study; Choir; Walking group.

BLOOMING PRAIRIE

Prairie Manor Inc
220 3rd St NW, Blooming Prairie, MN, 55917
(507) 583-4434
Admin Michelle Gemmel. *Medical Dir/Dir of Nursing* Mary Jane Simonson.
Licensure Skilled care; Intermediate care. *Beds* 82. *Certified* Medicaid; Medicare.
Owner Nonprofit Corp.
Admissions Requirements Medical examination; Physician's request.
Staff Physicians; RNs; LPNs; Orderlies; Nurses aides; Physical therapists; Reality therapists; Recreational therapists; Activities coordinators; Dietitians.
Facilities Dining room; Physical therapy room; Activities room; Chapel; Crafts room; Laundry room; Barber/Beauty shop; Family visiting room; Resident's kitchen.
Activities Arts & crafts; Cards; Games; Reading groups; Prayer groups; Movies; Shopping trips; Social/Cultural gatherings; Sing-alongs; Cooking; Church services; Family nights; Picnics.

BLOOMINGTON

Bloomington Maple Manor Care Center
8916 Lyndale Ave S, Bloomington, MN, 55420
(612) 881-5803
Admin James A Jasper. *Medical Dir/Dir of Nursing* J P Carlson MD; Mary Mellenbruch RN.
Licensure Skilled care. *Beds* SNF 63. *Certified* Medicaid; Medicare.
Owner Proprietary Corp (Good Neighbor Services).
Admissions Requirements Minimum age 16; Medical examination; Physician's request.
Staff RNs 6 (ft), 5 (pt); LPNs 1 (ft), 3 (pt); Nurses aides 16 (ft), 21 (pt); Physical therapists 1 (pt); Reality therapists 1 (ft); Recreational therapists 1 (ft), 1 (pt); Occupational therapists 1 (pt); Speech therapists 1 (pt); Activities coordinators 1 (ft); Dietitians 1 (pt); Dentists 1 (pt); Ophthalmologists 1 (pt); Podiatrists 1 (pt).
Facilities Dining room; Physical therapy room; Activities room; Laundry room; Barber/Beauty shop.
Activities Arts & crafts; Cards; Games; Reading groups; Prayer groups; Movies; Shopping trips; Social/Cultural gatherings; Music therapy.

Bloomington Nursing Home*
9200 Nicollet Ave S, Bloomington, MN, 55406
(612) 881-8676
Admin Shirley E Heim. *Medical Dir/Dir of Nursing* Dr Lorraine Kretchman.
Licensure Skilled care; Intermediate care. *Beds* 80. *Certified* Medicaid.
Owner Proprietary Corp (Beverly Enterprises).
Admissions Requirements Minimum age 18; Medical examination.
Staff Physicians 2 (pt); RNs 2 (ft), 8 (pt); LPNs 6 (pt); Nurses aides 9 (ft), 26 (pt); Physical therapists 1 (pt); Recreational therapists 1 (ft); Occupational therapists 1 (pt); Speech therapists 1 (pt); Dietitians 1 (ft); Dentists 1 (pt); Podiatrists 1 (pt); Audiologists 1 (pt); Respiratory aides 2 (pt); Social workers 1 (pt); Others 15 (ft), 19 (pt).
Facilities Dining room; Physical therapy room; Activities room; Laundry room.
Activities Arts & crafts; Cards; Games; Reading groups; Prayer groups; Movies; Shopping trips; Social/Cultural gatherings.

Eagle Nursing Home*
401 W 95th St, Bloomington, MN, 55420
(612) 888-9461
Admin William J Eagle.
Licensure Intermediate care. *Beds* 80. *Certified* Medicaid.
Owner Proprietary Corp.

Forestview Sunlen*
400 E 99th St, Bloomington, MN, 55420
(612) 888-0897
Admin Mary M Hill.
Licensure Intermediate care for mentally retarded. *Beds* 6. *Certified* Medicaid.
Owner Proprietary Corp.

Friendship Village*
8100 Highwood Dr, Bloomington, MN, 55438
(612) 831-7500
Admin Elinor Gent. *Medical Dir/Dir of Nursing* Paul Kaldor MD.
Licensure Skilled care. *Beds* 66. *Certified* Medicare.
Owner Nonprofit Corp (Life Care Services Corp).
Admissions Requirements Minimum age 62; Medical examination; Physician's request.
Staff Physicians 1 (ft); RNs 3 (ft), 4 (pt); LPNs 6 (ft), 4 (pt); Nurses aides 21 (ft), 8 (pt); Physical therapists 1 (pt); Activities coordinators 1 (ft), 2 (pt); Dietitians 1 (ft); Podiatrists 1 (pt).
Facilities Dining room; Physical therapy room; Activities room; Chapel; Crafts room; Laundry room; Barber/Beauty shop; Library.
Activities Arts & crafts; Cards; Games; Reading groups; Prayer groups; Movies; Shopping trips; Social/Cultural gatherings.

Gerarda House*
6001 W 106th St, Bloomington, MN, 55438
(612) 888-9741
Admin Roberta Miller Rosenow.
Licensure Supervised care facility. *Beds* 6.
Owner Proprietary Corp.

Martin Luther Manor
1401 E 100th St, Bloomington, MN, 55420
(612) 888-7751
Admin Thomas Goeritz. *Medical Dir/Dir of Nursing* Doris Larkin DON.
Licensure Skilled care; Intermediate care; Board & care. *Beds* SNF 158; ICF; Board & care 60. *Certified* Medicaid; Medicare.
Owner Nonprofit Corp (MN Synod/Lutheran Ch Board).
Admissions Requirements Minimum age 18; Medical examination; Physician's request.
Staff Physical therapists 1 (ft); Recreational therapists 2 (ft); Occupational therapists 1 (ft); Speech therapists 1 (pt); Activities coordinators 1 (ft); Dietitians 1 (ft); Dentists 1 (pt); Ophthalmologists 1 (pt); Podiatrists 1 (pt).
Affiliation Lutheran
Facilities Dining room; Physical therapy room; Activities room; Chapel; Crafts room; Laundry room; Barber/Beauty shop; Library; Adult Day Care.
Activities Arts & crafts; Cards; Games; Reading groups; Prayer groups; Movies; Shopping trips; Social/Cultural gatherings.

Minnesota Masonic Care Center*
11400 Normandale Blvd, Bloomington, MN, 55437
(612) 881-8665
Admin Edwin A Martini.
Licensure Skilled care; Intermediate care. *Beds* SNF 157; ICF 249. *Certified* Medicaid.
Owner Nonprofit Corp.
Affiliation Masons

Outreach-Bloomington
10633 Kell Ave S, Bloomington, MN, 55437
(612) 881-2848
Admin Eileen L Harris.

Licensure Intermediate care for mentally retarded. *Beds* ICF/MR 6. *Certified* Medicare.
Owner Nonprofit Corp.
Admissions Requirements Minimum age 19; Medical examination.
Facilities Dining room; Activities room; Crafts room; Laundry room; Kitchen; 4 Bedrooms; 2 Bath.
Activities Arts & crafts; Cards; Games; Reading groups; Prayer groups; Movies; Shopping trips; Social/Cultural gatherings; Vacations.

REM Bloomington*
9201 Cedar Ave S, Bloomington, MN, 55420
(612) 854-1800
Admin Karen Sebesta.
Licensure Skilled care; Intermediate care. *Beds* SNF 15; ICF 15. *Certified* Medicaid.
Owner Proprietary Corp.

St Stephen Group Homes A & B
8450 France Ave S, Bloomington, MN, 55431
(612) 831-1011
Admin Norman Doeden. *Medical Dir/Dir of Nursing* Jane Knudsen.
Licensure Intermediate care for mentally retarded. *Beds* ICF/MR 24. *Certified* Medicaid; Title XIX.
Owner Nonprofit Corp.
Admissions Requirements Minimum age 18; Medical examination; M-R Primary disability.
Staff RNs 1 (pt); Residential counselors 10 (ft), 15 (pt).
Affiliation Lutheran
Facilities Dining room; Activities room; Laundry room.
Activities Arts & crafts; Cards; Games; Movies; Shopping trips; Social/Cultural gatherings; Community related for daily living.

BLUE EARTH

Assisi Residences of Fairbault County Inc
PO Box 353, 325 W 2nd, Blue Earth, MN, 56013
(507) 526-5629
Admin Sharon Hoefs. *Medical Dir/Dir of Nursing* Virginia Fischer.
Licensure Intermediate care for mentally retarded. *Beds* ICF/MR 7. *Certified* Medicaid.
Owner Nonprofit Corp.
Admissions Requirements Minimum age 18; Medical examination.
Staff RNs 1 (pt); Nurses aides 7 (ft), 7 (pt); Recreational therapists 1 (pt).
Facilities Dining room; Laundry room.
Activities Arts & crafts; Cards; Games; Movies; Shopping trips; Social/Cultural gatherings.

St Lukes Lutheran Home
1217 S Ramsey, Blue Earth, MN, 56013
(507) 526-2184
Admin Mark G Robinson. *Medical Dir/Dir of Nursing* Dr George Drexler; Mary Jo Hill DON.
Licensure Skilled care; Intermediate care. *Beds* SNF 131; ICF 49. *Certified* Medicaid; Medicare.
Owner Nonprofit Corp.
Admissions Requirements Medical examination; Physician's request.
Staff Physicians; RNs; LPNs; Orderlies; Nurses aides; Physical therapists; Recreational therapists; Occupational therapists; Speech therapists; Activities coordinators; Dietitians; Dentists; Ophthalmologists; Podiatrists.
Languages Norwegian, Danish
Facilities Dining room; Physical therapy room; Activities room; Chapel; Crafts room; Laundry room; Barber/Beauty shop; Library.

Activities Arts & crafts; Cards; Games; Reading groups; Prayer groups; Movies; Shopping trips; Social/Cultural gatherings.

BOVEY

Hawthorne House*
Rte 1, Box 189, Bovey, MN, 55709
(218) 245-1853
Admin Gregory A White.
Licensure Intermediate care for mentally retarded. *Beds* 23. *Certified* Medicaid.
Owner Proprietary Corp.

BRAINERD

Bethany Good Samaritan Center
804 Wright St, Brainerd, MN, 56401
(218) 829-1407
Admin Dale Backhaus. *Medical Dir/Dir of Nursing* Mike Musty.
Licensure Skilled care; Intermediate care. *Beds* 160. *Certified* Medicaid; Medicare.
Owner Nonprofit Corp (Evangelical Lutheran/ Good Samaritan).
Admissions Requirements Minimum age 16.
Staff RNs 6 (ft), 7 (pt); LPNs 6 (ft), 7 (pt); Orderlies 6 (ft), 3 (pt); Nurses aides 30 (ft), 60 (pt); Physical therapists 1 (pt); Recreational therapists 1 (pt); Activities coordinators 1 (ft); Dietitians 1 (ft); Chaplain 1 (ft).
Affiliation Lutheran
Facilities Dining room; Physical therapy room; Activities room; Crafts room; Laundry room; Barber/Beauty shop; Library.
Activities Cards; Games; Reading groups; Prayer groups; Movies; Shopping trips; Social/Cultural gatherings.

Brainerd Good Samaritan Center*
803 Kingwood St, Brainerd, MN, 56401
(218) 829-8711
Admin Mary Feig. *Medical Dir/Dir of Nursing* Dr Peter Dunphy.
Licensure Skilled care; Intermediate care; Boarding care. *Beds* SNF 24; Boarding care 32. *Certified* Medicaid.
Owner Nonprofit Corp (Evangelical Lutheran/ Good Samaritan).
Admissions Requirements Medical examination; Physician's request.
Staff RNs 1 (ft), 4 (pt); LPNs 2 (ft), 7 (pt); Nurses aides 6 (ft), 14 (pt); Activities coordinators 1 (ft), 2 (pt); Dietitians 1 (ft), 1 (pt).
Affiliation Lutheran
Facilities Dining room; Activities room; Chapel; Crafts room; Laundry room; Barber/ Beauty shop; Library.
Activities Arts & crafts; Cards; Games; Reading groups; Prayer groups; Movies; Shopping trips; Social/Cultural gatherings.

Charis House*
1008 S 10th St, Brainerd, MN, 58401
(218) 828-4823
Admin John D Peterson.
Licensure Skilled care; Intermediate care. *Beds* SNF 12; ICF 12. *Certified* Medicaid.
Owner Nonprofit Corp.

BRECKENRIDGE

St Francis Home
501 Oak St, Breckenridge, MN, 56520
(218) 643-7661
Admin Kalvin G Michels.
Licensure Skilled care; Intermediate care. *Beds* SNF 85; ICF 39. *Certified* Medicaid; Medicare.
Owner Nonprofit organization/foundation.
Admissions Requirements Medical examination; Physician's request.
Affiliation Roman Catholic

Facilities Dining room; Physical therapy room; Activities room; Chapel; Crafts room; Laundry room; Barber/Beauty shop; Library.
Activities Arts & crafts; Cards; Games; Reading groups; Prayer groups; Movies; Shopping trips; Social/Cultural gatherings.

Wilkin County Group Home Inc
732 S 5th St, Breckenridge, MN, 56520
(218) 643-5952
Admin Addie Kuznia-Kroshus. *Medical Dir/ Dir of Nursing* Floss Kempfer RN.
Licensure Intermediate care for mentally retarded. *Beds* ICF/MR 6. *Certified* Medicaid.
Owner Nonprofit Corp.
Admissions Requirements Minimum age 18.
Facilities Dining room; Activities room; Laundry room.
Activities Arts & crafts; Cards; Games; Movies; Shopping trips; Social/Cultural gatherings.

BRIANERD

Woodland Acres Health Care Center
100 Buffalo Hills Ln, Brianerd, MN, 56401
(218) 829-1429
Admin Sharon Kramer. *Medical Dir/Dir of Nursing* Stephen Hanska MD.
Licensure Skilled care. *Beds* SNF 80. *Certified* Medicaid; Medicare.
Owner Proprietary Corp.
Admissions Requirements Minimum age 16; Medical examination; Physician's request.
Staff RNs; LPNs; Orderlies; Nurses aides; Physical therapists; Occupational therapists 1 (ft); Activities coordinators 1 (ft), 2 (pt); Dietitians; Social workers 1 (ft); Physical therapy aides 1 (ft).
Facilities Dining room; Physical therapy room; Activities room; Chapel; Crafts room; Laundry room; Barber/Beauty shop.
Activities Arts & crafts; Cards; Games; Reading groups; Prayer groups; Movies; Shopping trips; Social/Cultural gatherings.

BROOKLYN CENTER

Brooklyn Center Outreach Home*
507 69th Ave N, Brooklyn Center, MN, 55430
(612) 561-9030
Admin Eileen Harris.
Licensure Intermediate care for mentally retarded. *Beds* 6. *Certified* Medicaid.
Owner Nonprofit Corp.

Maranatha Baptist Care Center
5401 69th Ave N, Brooklyn Center, MN, 55429
(612) 561-0477
Admin David V Viland. *Medical Dir/Dir of Nursing* Eva Oldenborg RN DON.
Licensure Skilled care. *Beds* SNF 106. *Certified* Medicaid; Medicare.
Owner Nonprofit organization/foundation.
Admissions Requirements Minimum age 18; Medical examination; Physician's request.
Staff Physicians 1 (pt); RNs 5 (ft), 5 (pt); LPNs 3 (ft), 5 (pt); Orderlies 2 (ft), 2 (pt); Nurses aides 15 (ft), 25 (pt); Physical therapists 2 (pt); Recreational therapists 3 (ft); Occupational therapists 1 (ft); Speech therapists 1 (pt); Activities coordinators 1 (ft); Dietitians 1 (ft).
Affiliation Baptist
Facilities Dining room; Physical therapy room; Activities room; Chapel; Crafts room; Laundry room; Barber/Beauty shop.
Activities Arts & crafts; Cards; Games; Reading groups; Prayer groups; Shopping trips; Social/Cultural gatherings.

Residential Alternatives II*
5449 Lyndale Ave N, Brooklyn Center, MN, 55430
(612) 560-2220

Admin Peter Jacobson.
Licensure Intermediate care for mentally retarded. *Beds* 8. *Certified* Medicaid.

BROOKLYN PARK

Homeward Bound—Brooklyn Park*
7839 Brooklyn Blvd, Brooklyn Park, MN, 55445
(612) 566-7860
Admin James Glasoe.
Licensure Intermediate care for mentally retarded. *Beds* 32. *Certified* Medicaid.
Owner Nonprofit Corp.

Residential Alternatives III*
6525 Edgewood Ave N, Brooklyn Park, MN, 55428
(612) 533-5104
Admin Peter Jacobson.
Licensure Intermediate care for mentally retarded. *Beds* 8. *Certified* Medicaid.
Owner Proprietary Corp.

BROOKSTON

Aneskarn IV*
Star Rt, Box 630, Brookston, MN, 55711
(218) 879-3296
Admin Lawrence Tunell.
Licensure Intermediate care for mentally retarded; Supervised living facility. *Beds* ICF/MR 28; Supervised living 28. *Certified* Medicaid.
Owner Proprietary Corp.

Hilltop Manor*
Box 338, Brookston, MN, 55711
(218) 453-5622
Admin Elizabeth Demenge.
Licensure Supervised living facility. *Beds* 10. *Certified* Medicaid.
Owner Proprietary Corp.
Admissions Requirements Minimum age 18; Medical examination.
Staff RNs 1 (pt); Activities coordinators 1 (pt).
Facilities Dining room; Activities room; Crafts room; Laundry room.
Activities Arts & crafts; Cards; Games; Reading groups; Prayer groups; Movies; Shopping trips; Social/Cultural gatherings.

BROWNS VALLEY

Browns Valley Community Nursing Home
PO Box 340, Jefferson St, Browns Valley, MN, 56219
(612) 695-2165
Admin Robert B Marx. *Medical Dir/Dir of Nursing* Dorothy Nelson RN.
Licensure Intermediate care. *Beds* 63. *Certified* Medicaid.
Owner Proprietary Corp.
Admissions Requirements Minimum age 18; Medical examination; Physician's request.
Staff Physicians 12 (pt); RNs 2 (ft), 1 (pt); LPNs 3 (ft), 2 (pt); Orderlies 1 (pt); Nurses aides 17 (ft), 15 (pt); Physical therapists 1 (pt); Reality therapists 1 (pt); Recreational therapists 1 (ft), 3 (pt); Occupational therapists 1 (pt); Activities coordinators 1 (ft); Dietitians 1 (pt).
Facilities Dining room; Physical therapy room; Activities room; Crafts room; Laundry room; Barber/Beauty shop; Garden; Workshop.
Activities Arts & crafts; Cards; Games; Prayer groups; Movies; Shopping trips; Social/Cultural gatherings; Dinner trips; Van trips.

BUFFALO

Ebenezer Covenant Home
310 Lake Blvd, Buffalo, MN, 55313
(612) 682-1434
Admin John Daniel Engels. *Medical Dir/Dir of Nursing* Dr Robert Sandeen; Darlene A Nyquist RN.
Licensure Skilled care. *Beds* SNF 65. *Certified* Medicaid; Medicare.
Owner Nonprofit Corp (Covenant Benevolent Inst).
Admissions Requirements Medical examination.
Staff RNs 3 (ft), 3 (pt); LPNs 1 (ft), 4 (pt); Orderlies 1 (ft); Nurses aides 12 (ft), 30 (pt); Activities coordinators 1 (ft), 2 (pt).
Affiliation Evangelical Covenant Church
Facilities Dining room; Physical therapy room; Activities room; Chapel; Crafts room; Laundry room; Barber/Beauty shop; Library.
Activities Arts & crafts; Cards; Games; Reading groups; Prayer groups; Movies; Shopping trips; Social/Cultural gatherings.

REM-Buffalo*
914 3rd Ave NE, Buffalo, MN, 55313
(612) 682-3960
Admin Juanita Turner.
Licensure Intermediate care for mentally retarded. *Beds* 15. *Certified* Medicaid.
Owner Proprietary Corp.

Residential Alternatives V*
1804 Sakenda Rd, Buffalo, MN, 55313
(612) 682-5868
Admin Peter Jacobson.
Licensure Intermediate care. *Beds* 8. *Certified* Medicaid.
Owner Proprietary Corp.

Retirement Center of Wright County
200 Park Ln, Buffalo, MN, 55313
(612) 682-1131
Admin Roger E Lundeen. *Medical Dir/Dir of Nursing* Dr Milligan; Joyce Smith.
Licensure Skilled care; Intermediate care. *Beds* SNF 107; ICF 47. *Certified* Medicaid; Medicare.
Owner Nonprofit Corp.
Admissions Requirements Physician's request.
Staff RNs 10 (ft), 10 (pt); LPNs 10 (ft), 8 (pt); Orderlies 4 (ft); Nurses aides 40 (ft), 40 (pt); Physical therapists 1 (ft); Occupational therapists 1 (ft); Speech therapists 1 (pt); Activities coordinators 1 (ft); Dietitians 1 (pt).
Facilities Dining room; Physical therapy room; Activities room; Laundry room; Barber/Beauty shop.
Activities Arts & crafts; Cards; Games; Reading groups; Prayer groups; Movies; Shopping trips; Social/Cultural gatherings; Happy hour; Pet program; Child day care.

BUFFALO LAKE

Buffalo Lake Nursing Home Inc
PO Box 368, 703 W Yellowstone Trail, Buffalo Lake, MN, 55314
(612) 833-5364
Admin Stanley Gallup. *Medical Dir/Dir of Nursing* Dan Huebert MD; Janet Scharmer RN DON.
Licensure Intermediate care. *Beds* ICF 66. *Certified* Medicaid.
Owner Proprietary Corp.
Staff RNs 1 (ft), 2 (pt); LPNs 6 (ft); Nurses aides 8 (ft), 24 (pt); Physical therapists 1 (pt); Activities coordinators 1 (ft); Dietitians 1 (ft).
Languages Swedish, Norwegian, German
Facilities Dining room; Activities room; Laundry room; Barber/Beauty shop.
Activities Arts & crafts; Cards; Games; Reading groups; Prayer groups; Movies; Shopping trips; Social/Cultural gatherings.

BUHL

Mesabi Home
PO Box 703, 501 Jones Ave, Buhl, MN, 55713
(218) 258-3253
Admin Betty Holmes. *Medical Dir/Dir of Nursing* Esther Lakso.
Licensure Intermediate care. *Beds* ICF 31. *Certified* Medicaid.
Owner Nonprofit Corp.
Admissions Requirements Medical examination; Physician's request.
Staff RNs 1 (ft), 2 (pt); LPNs 2 (pt); Nurses aides 5 (ft), 6 (pt); Activities coordinators 1 (pt); Dietitians 1 (pt).
Facilities Dining room; Activities room; Laundry room; TV room.
Activities Arts & crafts; Cards; Games; Reading groups; Prayer groups; Movies; Shopping trips; Social/Cultural gatherings.

CALEDONIA

Houston County Group Home
109 S Winnebago St, Caledonia, MN, 55921
(507) 724-5259
Admin Dennis Theede. *Medical Dir/Dir of Nursing* Janice Storlie.
Licensure Intermediate care for mentally retarded. *Beds* ICF/MR 13. *Certified* Medicaid.
Owner Nonprofit Corp.
Admissions Requirements Minimum age 18; Medical examination.
Staff RNs 1 (pt); LPNs 1 (pt); Activities coordinators 1 (ft), 2 (pt).
Facilities Dining room; Activities room; Laundry room.
Activities Arts & crafts; Cards; Games; Prayer groups; Movies; Shopping trips; Social/Cultural gatherings.

CAMBRIDGE

Cambridge Health Care Center*
548 W 1st Ave, Cambridge, MN, 55008
(612) 689-2323
Admin Dale Thompson. *Medical Dir/Dir of Nursing* P S Sanders MD.
Licensure Skilled care; Intermediate care. *Beds* SNF 110; ICF 47. *Certified* Medicaid; Medicare.
Owner Proprietary Corp.
Admissions Requirements Medical examination; Physician's request.
Staff RNs 8 (ft); LPNs 5 (ft); Nurses aides 40 (ft); Physical therapists 1 (ft); Occupational therapists 1 (ft); Speech therapists 1 (pt); Activities coordinators 1 (ft); Dietitians 1 (pt); Dentists 1 (pt); Podiatrists 1 (pt); Audiologists 1 (pt).
Facilities Dining room; Physical therapy room; Activities room; Chapel; Crafts room; Laundry room; Barber/Beauty shop; Library.
Activities Arts & crafts; Cards; Games; Reading groups; Prayer groups; Movies; Shopping trips; Social/Cultural gatherings; Resident council; Family council.

Cambridge Regional Human Services Center
Cambridge, MN, 55008
(612) 689-2121
Admin Kenneth Gossert.
Licensure Intermediate care for mentally retarded. *Beds* 588. *Certified* Medicaid.
Owner Publicly owned.

Grandview Christian Home
800 NW 2nd Ave, Cambridge, MN, 55008
(612) 689-1474
Admin Greg Carlson.
Licensure Skilled care; Intermediate care. *Beds* SNF 83; ICF 95. *Certified* Medicare.
Owner Nonprofit Corp.

Residential Alternatives VI
RR 3 Box 268, Cambridge, MN, 55008
(612) 689-3794
Admin Peter Jacobson.
Licensure Intermediate care for mentally
retarded. *Beds* ICF/MR 6. *Certified*
Medicaid.
Owner Proprietary Corp.
Admissions Requirements Minimum age 18;
Medical examination.
Staff RNs 1 (pt); Dietitians 1 (pt).

CANBY

Canby Community Health Services
112 Saint Olaf Ave S, Canby, MN, 56220
(507) 223-7277
Admin Robert J Salmon. *Medical Dir/Dir of
Nursing* Robert T Olson MD.
Licensure Skilled care. *Beds* SNF 75. *Certified*
Medicaid; Medicare.
Owner Nonprofit Corp.
Admissions Requirements Minimum age 16;
Medical examination.
Staff Physicians 3 (ft); RNs 1 (ft), 3 (pt);
LPNs 3 (ft), 10 (pt); Nurses aides 9 (ft), 32
(pt); Physical therapists 1 (pt); Occupational
therapists; Speech therapists 1 (pt); Activities
coordinators 1 (ft), 2 (pt); Dietitians 1 (ft);
Dentists 1 (pt); Podiatrists 1 (pt).
Facilities Dining room; Physical therapy
room; Activities room; Chapel; Crafts room;
Laundry room; Barber/Beauty shop; Library.
Activities Arts & crafts; Cards; Games;
Reading groups; Prayer groups; Movies;
Social/Cultural gatherings; Entertainment
groups; Picnics.

REM Canby A & B*
1201 Haarfagar Ave N, Canby, MN, 56220
(507) 223-7271
Admin Craig Miller.
Licensure Intermediate care for mentally
retarded. *Beds* 30. *Certified* Medicaid.
Owner Proprietary Corp.

CANNON FALLS

Cannon Falls Manor Nursing Home*
300 N Dow St, Cannon Falls, MN, 55009
(507) 263-4658
Admin Bonnie Campeau. *Medical Dir/Dir of
Nursing* Lloyd Klefstad.
Licensure Skilled care; Intermediate care;
Boarding care. *Beds* SNF 76; ICF 10;
Boarding care 2. *Certified* Medicaid.
Owner Proprietary Corp.
Admissions Requirements Minimum age 16;
Staff Physicians 2 (ft); RNs 1 (ft), 6 (pt);
LPNs 3 (ft), 6 (pt); Nurses aides 7 (ft), 45
(pt); Physical therapists 1 (pt); Dietitians 1
(pt).
Facilities Dining room; Physical therapy
room; Activities room; Crafts room; Laundry
room; Barber/Beauty shop; Conference
room.
Activities Arts & crafts; Cards; Games;
Reading groups; Prayer groups; Movies;
Shopping trips; Social/Cultural gatherings.

CARLTON

Carlton Nursing Home*
810 3rd St, Carlton, MN, 55718
(218) 384-4258
Admin Larry C Penk. *Medical Dir/Dir of
Nursing* Dr Vickie Anderson.
Licensure Skilled care; Intermediate care. *Beds*
96. *Certified* Medicaid; Medicare.
Owner Nonprofit Corp.
Admissions Requirements Minimum age 16;
Medical examination.
Staff Physicians 2 (pt); RNs 1 (ft), 3 (pt);
LPNs 10 (pt); Orderlies 1 (pt); Nurses aides
42 (pt); Physical therapists 1 (ft); Speech

therapists 1 (pt); Activities coordinators 1
(ft); Dietitians 1 (pt); Dentists 1 (pt);
Ophthalmologists 1 (pt); Podiatrists 1 (pt).
Facilities Dining room; Physical therapy
room; Activities room; Crafts room; Laundry
room; Barber/Beauty shop.
Activities Arts & crafts; Cards; Games;
Reading groups; Prayer groups; Movies;
Shopping trips; Social/Cultural gatherings.

CENTER CITY

Hazelden Foundation
Box 11, Pleasant Valley Rd, Center City, MN,
55012
(612) 257-4010
Admin Harold A Swift.
Licensure Skilled care; Intermediate care. *Beds*
SNF 15; ICF 15. *Certified* Medicaid.
Owner Nonprofit organization/foundation.
Admissions Requirements Medical
examination.
Staff Physicians 3 (ft); RNs 34 (ft);
Recreational therapists 7 (ft); Occupational
therapists 3 (ft); Dietitians 1 (ft).
Facilities Dining room; Crafts room; Laundry
room; Barber/Beauty shop; Library;
Recreational facility including swimming
pool.
Activities Arts & crafts; Movies.

South Center Manor Inc
Park Island, Center City, MN, 55012
(612) 257-1686
Admin Lowell J Petersen. *Medical Dir/Dir of
Nursing* Caroline M Petersen.
Licensure Intermediate care for mentally
retarded. *Beds* ICF/MR 15. *Certified*
Medicaid; Medicare.
Owner Proprietary Corp.
Admissions Requirements Minimum age 18.
Staff RNs 1 (pt); LPNs 1 (ft); Dietitians 1
(pt).
Facilities Dining room; Activities room;
Crafts room; Laundry room.
Activities Arts & crafts; Cards; Games;
Movies; Shopping trips.

CEYLON

Schmidtke Rest Home
Ceylon, MN, 56121
(507) 632-4348
Admin Clark Schmidtke.
Licensure Boarding care. *Beds* 11.
Owner Proprietary Corp.
Admissions Requirements Medical
examination.
Staff RNs 1 (pt); Nurses aides 3 (ft), 1 (pt);
Activities coordinators 1 (ft); Dietitians 1
(pt).
Facilities Dining room; Laundry room.
Activities Cards; Games; Reading groups;
Prayer groups; Movies; Social/Cultural
gatherings.

CHANHASSEN

Chanhassen Center*
7701 Arboretum Blvd, Chanhassen, MN,
55317
(612) 934-3264
Admin William J Gregg.
Licensure Supervised living facility. *Beds* 70.
Owner Nonprofit Corp.

CHATFIELD

Chosen Valley Care Center*
1102 Liberty St SE, Chatfield, MN, 55923
(507) 867-4220
Admin Ruth Jensen.
Licensure Skilled care. *Beds* 86. *Certified*
Medicaid.
Owner Publicly owned.

CHISAGO CITY

Linnea Residential Home*
28770 Old Town Rd, Chisago City, MN,
55013
(612) 257-2211
Admin Donna Hoverman.
Licensure Intermediate care for mentally
retarded. *Beds* 12. *Certified* Medicaid.
Owner Nonprofit Corp.

Margaret S Parmly Residence
28210 Old Towne Rd, Chisago City, MN,
55013
(612) 257-5620
Admin Charles Zimmerman. *Medical Dir/Dir
of Nursing* Shari Larson DON.
Licensure Skilled care; Intermediate care. *Beds*
SNF 77; ICF 24. *Certified* Medicaid;
Medicare.
Owner Nonprofit Corp (MN Synod/Lutheran
Ch Board).
Admissions Requirements Minimum age 18;
Medical examination; Physician's request.
Staff RNs 2 (ft), 6 (pt); LPNs 2 (ft), 12 (pt);
Nurses aides 10 (ft), 15 (pt); Recreational
therapists 1 (ft), 2 (pt).
Facilities Dining room; Activities room;
Chapel; Crafts room; Laundry room; Barber/
Beauty shop.
Activities Arts & crafts; Cards; Games;
Reading groups; Prayer groups; Movies;
Shopping trips; Social/Cultural gatherings.

CHISHOLM

Buchanan Nursing Home*
PO Box 549, 30 1st St NW, Chisholm, MN,
55719
(218) 254-3614
Admin John Buchanan.
Licensure Intermediate care. *Beds* 39.
Certified Medicaid.
Owner Proprietary Corp.

Heritage Manor Health Care Center
321 NE 6th St, Chisholm, MN, 55719
(218) 254-5765
Admin Robert Koepcke. *Medical Dir/Dir of
Nursing* Jack Greene MD; Carol McVicars
RN DON.
Licensure Skilled care; Intermediate care;
Board & lodging. *Beds* SNF 76; ICF; Board
& lodging 26. *Certified* Medicaid; Medicare.
Owner Nonprofit Corp.
Admissions Requirements Medical
examination; Physician's request.
Staff Physicians 9 (pt); RNs 3 (ft), 5 (pt);
LPNs 2 (ft), 5 (pt); Orderlies 5 (pt); Nurses
aides 11 (ft), 22 (pt); Physical therapists 1
(pt); Occupational therapists 1 (pt); Speech
therapists 1 (pt); Activities coordinators 1
(ft); Dietitians 1 (pt); Ophthalmologists 1
(pt).
Facilities Dining room; Physical therapy
room; Activities room; Children's center.
Activities Arts & crafts; Games; Prayer groups;
Movies; Shopping trips; Social/Cultural
gatherings; Field trips; Outings to
restaurants; Cooking.

Range Center Inc
PO Box 629, 1001 NW 8th Ave, Chisholm,
MN, 55719
(218) 254-3347
Admin Neil Boyum.
Licensure Intermediate care for mentally
retarded. *Beds* ICF/MR 47. *Certified*
Medicaid.
Owner Nonprofit Corp.
Admissions Requirements Physician's request
Social worker referral.
Staff RNs 1 (ft); LPNs 3 (pt); Physical
therapists 1 (pt); Occupational therapists 1
(pt); Speech therapists 1 (ft).
Languages Sign

Facilities Dining room; Physical therapy room; Crafts room; Laundry room; Library; Candle factory (DAC portion).
Activities Work activity; Habilitation services.

Range Center—Oakwood Home*
28 NE 11th St, Chisholm, MN, 55719
(218) 254-3347
Admin Timothy Larson.
Licensure Supervised living facility. *Beds* 6. *Certified* Medicaid.
Owner Nonprofit Corp.
Admissions Requirements Minimum age 3.
Staff RNs 1 (pt).
Facilities Dining room; Activities room; Laundry room; Typical family living home.
Activities Arts & crafts; Cards; Games; Reading groups; Movies; Shopping trips; Social/Cultural gatherings.

CLARA CITY

Clara City Community Nursing Home*
1012 Division St N, Clara City, MN, 56222
(612) 847-3553
Admin Mark Rossi.
Licensure Intermediate care. *Beds* 95. *Certified* Medicaid.
Owner Publicly owned.
Admissions Requirements Medical examination; Physician's request.
Staff Physicians 3 (pt); RNs 2 (ft); LPNs 3 (ft), 6 (pt); Orderlies 1 (pt); Physical therapists 1 (pt); Activities coordinators 1 (ft); Dietitians 1 (pt).
Facilities Dining room; Physical therapy room; Activities room; Chapel; Crafts room; Laundry room; Barber/Beauty shop.
Activities Arts & crafts; Cards; Games; Reading groups; Movies; Shopping trips; Social/Cultural gatherings.

CLARISSA

Central Todd County Care Center
S Hwy 71, Clarissa, MN, 56440
(218) 756-3636
Admin Margaret Taggart. *Medical Dir/Dir of Nursing* Judy Ladwig RN.
Licensure Skilled care. *Beds* SNF 78. *Certified* Medicaid.
Owner Nonprofit Corp.
Admissions Requirements Minimum age 16; Medical examination.
Staff RNs; LPNs; Nurses aides; Activities coordinators; Dietitians.
Facilities Dining room; Physical therapy room; Activities room; Chapel; Crafts room; Laundry room; Barber/Beauty shop; Library.
Activities Arts & crafts; Cards; Games; Reading groups; Prayer groups; Movies; Shopping trips; Social/Cultural gatherings.

CLARKFIELD

Clarkfield Care Center*
805 5th St, Clarkfield, MN, 56223
(612) 669-7561
Admin Arthur Brown.
Licensure Intermediate care. *Beds* 86. *Certified* Medicaid.
Owner Publicly owned.

CLEAR LAKE

High Point Lodge Nursing Home
11050 49th St, Clear Lake, MN, 55319
(612) 743-2695
Admin Hazel L Bollinger. *Medical Dir/Dir of Nursing* Bernie Bieledeldt RN DON.
Licensure Intermediate care. *Beds* 26. *Certified* Medicaid.
Owner Proprietary Corp.
Admissions Requirements Minimum age 18; Medical examination; Physician's request.

Staff RNs 1 (pt); LPNs 3 (pt); Nurses aides 9 (pt).
Facilities Dining room; Activities room; Laundry room.
Activities Arts & crafts; Cards; Games; Movies; Shopping trips; Social/Cultural gatherings; Bowling; Boating; Fishing.

CLEARBROOK

Good Samaritan Center
PO Box 47, Clearbrook, MN, 56634
(218) 776-3157
Admin Collin Eid. *Medical Dir/Dir of Nursing* Sherry Torgerson.
Licensure Intermediate care. *Beds* 96. *Certified* Medicaid.
Owner Nonprofit Corp.
Admissions Requirements Medical examination.
Staff RNs 1 (ft), 2 (pt); LPNs 6 (ft), 5 (pt); Nurses aides 9 (ft), 29 (pt); Physical therapists 1 (ft), 1 (pt); Activities coordinators 1 (ft); Dietitians 1 (pt).
Affiliation Lutheran
Facilities Dining room; Activities room; Chapel; Crafts room; Laundry room; Barber/Beauty shop.
Activities Arts & crafts; Cards; Games; Reading groups; Prayer groups; Movies; Shopping trips; Social/Cultural gatherings.

CLINTON

Clinton Good Samaritan Center*
PO Box 379, Hwy 75, Cty Rd 6, Clinton, MN, 56225
(612) 325-5414
Admin Patrick Kelly.
Licensure Intermediate care. *Beds* 54. *Certified* Medicaid.
Owner Nonprofit Corp (Evangelical Lutheran/Good Samaritan).
Staff RNs 1 (ft); LPNs 2 (ft), 1 (pt); Orderlies 1 (ft); Nurses aides 9 (ft), 11 (pt); Activities coordinators 1 (ft), 1 (pt).
Affiliation Lutheran
Facilities Dining room; Activities room; Laundry room.
Activities Arts & crafts; Cards; Games; Reading groups.

CLOQUET

Pine Ridge Home 1*
413 Broadway, Cloquet, MN, 55720
(218) 879-1168
Admin David Felske.
Licensure Intermediate care for mentally retarded. *Beds* 6. *Certified* Medicaid.
Owner Nonprofit Corp.

Pine Ridge Home 2*
16 11th St, Cloquet, MN, 55720
(218) 879-8395
Admin David Felske.
Licensure Intermediate care for mentally retarded. *Beds* 6. *Certified* Medicaid.
Owner Nonprofit Corp.

Pine Ridge Home 3*
1509 14th St, Cloquet, MN, 55720
(218) 879-1281
Admin David Felske.
Licensure Intermediate care for mentally retarded. *Beds* 13. *Certified* Medicaid.
Owner Nonprofit Corp.

COKATO

Cokato Manor Inc
W Hwy 12, Cokato, MN, 55321
(612) 286-2158
Admin Larry S Petersen. *Medical Dir/Dir of Nursing* Tracy Wolf MD; Jan Ostlund DON.

Licensure Skilled care. *Beds* 66. *Certified* Medicaid; Medicare.
Owner Proprietary Corp.
Admissions Requirements Minimum age 16; Medical examination; Physician's request.
Staff RNs 2 (ft), 3 (pt); LPNs 1 (ft), 4 (pt); Orderlies 1 (pt); Nurses aides 8 (ft), 30 (pt); Physical therapists 1 (pt); Activities coordinators 1 (ft), 2 (pt).
Facilities Dining room; Physical therapy room; Activities room; Laundry room; Barber/Beauty shop.
Activities Arts & crafts; Cards; Games; Reading groups; Prayer groups; Movies; Shopping trips; Social/Cultural gatherings.

Warner Care Home 1*
325 Swanson Ave, Cokato, MN, 55321
(612) 286-2843
Admin Martin McGraw.
Licensure Intermediate care for mentally retarded. *Beds* 15. *Certified* Medicaid.
Owner Proprietary Corp.

Warner Care Home 2*
180 6th St W, Cokato, MN, 55321
(612) 286-2955
Admin Martin McGraw.
Licensure Intermediate care for mentally retarded. *Beds* 7. *Certified* Medicaid.
Owner Proprietary Corp.

Warner Care Home 3*
370 W 3rd St, Cokato, MN, 55321
(612) 286-2185
Admin Martin McGraw.
Licensure Intermediate care for mentally retarded. *Beds* 7. *Certified* Medicaid.
Owner Proprietary Corp.

COLD SPRING

Assumption Home
715 N 1st St, Cold Spring, MN, 56320
(612) 685-3693
Admin Reta Patri. *Medical Dir/Dir of Nursing* Dr John Kelly.
Licensure Skilled care. *Beds* SNF 95. *Certified* Medicaid; Medicare.
Owner Nonprofit Corp.
Admissions Requirements Medical examination; Physician's request.
Staff RNs 2 (ft), 5 (pt); LPNs 1 (ft), 6 (pt); Nurses aides 18 (ft), 21 (pt); Physical therapists 1 (pt); Reality therapists 1 (pt); Recreational therapists 3 (ft); Activities coordinators 1 (ft); Dietitians 1 (pt).
Affiliation Roman Catholic
Facilities Dining room; Physical therapy room; Activities room; Chapel; Crafts room; Barber/Beauty shop; Library.
Activities Arts & crafts; Cards; Games; Prayer groups; Movies; Shopping trips; Social/Cultural gatherings.

Mother Teresa Home
101 10th Ave N, Cold Spring, MN, 56320
(612) 685-8626
Admin Rev Timothy Wentzel.
Licensure Intermediate care for mentally retarded. *Beds* ICF/MR 14. *Certified* Medicare.
Owner Nonprofit organization/foundation.
Admissions Requirements Minimum age 18.
Staff RNs 1 (pt); LPNs 1 (pt).
Affiliation Roman Catholic
Facilities Dining room; Laundry room.
Activities Arts & crafts; Cards; Games; Movies; Shopping trips; Social/Cultural gatherings.

COLUMBIA HEIGHTS

Crest View Lutheran Home*
4444 Reservoir Blvd NE, Columbia Heights, MN, 55421
(612) 788-1678

Admin Thomas W Paul.
Licensure Skilled care. *Beds* 122. *Certified*
  Medicaid; Medicare.
Owner Nonprofit Corp.
Affiliation Lutheran

COOK

Cook Community Hospital
3rd St & Cedar Ave, Cook, MN, 55723
(218) 666-5945
Admin Lineta Scott. *Medical Dir/Dir of*
  Nursing Margie Hyppa.
Licensure Skilled care. *Beds* SNF 41. *Certified*
  Medicaid; Medicare.
Owner Publicly owned.
Admissions Requirements Physician's request.
Staff RNs 10 (ft), 7 (pt); LPNs 3 (ft), 7 (pt);
  Orderlies 1 (pt); Nurses aides 10 (ft), 14 (pt);
  Physical therapists 1 (ft), 1 (pt);
  Occupational therapists 1 (pt); Speech
  therapists 1 (pt); Activities coordinators 1
  (ft); Dietitians 2 (pt).
Languages Swedish, Finnish, German
Facilities Dining room; Physical therapy
  room; Activities room; Crafts room; Laundry
  room; Barber/Beauty shop; Library.
Activities Arts & crafts; Cards; Games;
  Reading groups; Prayer groups; Movies;
  Shopping trips; Social/Cultural gatherings.

COON RAPIDS

Camilia Rose Convalescent Center
11800 Xeon Blvd, Coon Rapids, MN, 55433
(612) 755-8400
Admin Norma Brendle. *Medical Dir/Dir of*
  Nursing William Rodman MD; Janice
  Villella RN.
Licensure Skilled care. *Beds* SNF 94. *Certified*
  Medicaid; Medicare.
Owner Proprietary Corp.
Admissions Requirements Minimum age 16;
  Medical examination; Physician's request.
Staff RNs 3 (ft), 10 (pt); LPNs 15 (pt);
  Orderlies 2 (pt); Nurses aides 10 (ft), 32 (pt);
  Physical therapists 1 (ft); Recreational
  therapists 3 (ft); Occupational therapists 1
  (ft); Speech therapists 1 (pt); Dietitians 1
  (pt).
Facilities Dining room; Physical therapy
  room; Chapel; Laundry room; Barber/Beauty
  shop; Artist studio; Family lounges.
Activities Arts & crafts; Cards; Games;
  Reading groups; Prayer groups; Movies;
  Shopping trips; Social/Cultural gatherings;
  Music therapy; Lunch outings; Picnics.

Camilia Rose Group Home
11820 Xeon Blvd NW, Coon Rapids, MN,
  55433
(612) 755-8489
Admin Dr Mary M Tjosvold. *Medical Dir/Dir*
  of Nursing Vicky Baulkner.
Licensure Intermediate care for mentally
  retarded. *Beds* ICF/MR 35. *Certified*
  Medicaid.
Owner Proprietary Corp.
Admissions Requirements Minimum age 18;
  Medical examination; Physician's request
  Diagnosis of MR.
Staff RNs 1 (ft); LPNs 2 (ft), 1 (pt); Physical
  therapists 1 (pt); Occupational therapists 1
  (pt); Activities coordinators 1 (ft), 1 (pt);
  Dietitians 1 (pt); Direct care 10 (ft), 25 (pt);
  Program planner 2 (ft); Program director 1
  (ft); Lead advisors 5 (ft).
Facilities Dining room; Physical therapy
  room; Activities room; Crafts room; Laundry
  room; Barber/Beauty shop.
Activities Arts & crafts; Cards; Games;
  Reading groups; Movies; Shopping trips;
  Social/Cultural gatherings.

Community Living
2483 109th Ave NW, Coon Rapids, MN,
  55433
(612) 757-6248
Admin Jerry Gross.
Licensure Intermediate care for mentally
  retarded. *Beds* 24. *Certified* Medicaid.
Owner Proprietary Corp.

Demars Childrens Home
11777 Xeon Blvd, Coon Rapids, MN, 55433
(612) 755-8174
Admin Dr Mary Tjosvold.
Licensure Intermediate care for mentally
  retarded. *Beds* ICF/MR 20.
Owner Privately owned.
Admissions Requirements Minimum age 21
  yrs & under; Medical examination;
  Physician's request.
Staff RNs 1 (ft); LPNs 1 (ft); Nurses aides 25
  (ft); Physical therapists; Recreational
  therapists 1 (ft); Occupational therapists 1
  (ft); Dietitians.
Facilities Dining room; Physical therapy
  room; Activities room; Crafts room; Laundry
  room; Living room.
Activities Arts & crafts; Cards; Games;
  Reading groups; Movies; Shopping trips;
  Social/Cultural gatherings; Dance therapy;
  Music therapy; Camp; Communication
  groups; Learning groups; Sports.

Park River Estates Care Center
9899 Avocet St NW, Coon Rapids, MN,
  55433
(612) 757-2320
Admin Steven Chies. *Medical Dir/Dir of*
  Nursing Dr Mark Brakke; Cindy McClintock
  RN DON.
Licensure Skilled care; Intermediate care. *Beds*
  SNF 91; ICF 13. *Certified* Medicaid;
  Medicare.
Owner Proprietary Corp.
Admissions Requirements Medical
  examination; Physician's request.
Staff Physicians 2 (pt); RNs 1 (ft), 8 (pt);
  LPNs 1 (ft), 12 (pt); Nurses aides 34 (ft), 18
  (pt); Physical therapists 1 (ft); Occupational
  therapists 1 (pt); Activities coordinators 1
  (ft); Dietitians 1 (pt).
Facilities Dining room; Physical therapy
  room; Activities room; Chapel; Crafts room;
  Laundry room; Barber/Beauty shop; Library.
Activities Arts & crafts; Cards; Games;
  Reading groups; Prayer groups; Movies;
  Shopping trips; Social/Cultural gatherings.

COSMOS

Cosmos Healthcare Center*
Neptune & Pegasus, Cosmos, MN, 56228
(612) 877-7227
Admin Mark Rust.
Licensure Skilled care; Intermediate care. *Beds*
  SNF 29; ICF 29. *Certified* Medicaid.
Owner Proprietary Corp (Beverly Enterprises).

COTTAGE GROVE

Forestview Hemingway
8045 Hemingway Ave S, Cottage Grove, MN,
  55016
(612) 459-7747
Admin Eileen Harris. *Medical Dir/Dir of*
  Nursing Mary Ellen Hanson.
Licensure Intermediate care for mentally
  retarded. *Beds* ICF/MR 6. *Certified*
  Medicaid.
Owner Proprietary Corp.
Admissions Requirements Minimum age 18;
  Medical examination; Physician's request.
Staff RNs 1 (pt).
Facilities Dining room; Activities room.
Activities Arts & crafts; Cards; Games;
  Movies; Shopping trips; Social/Cultural
  gatherings.

CROMWELL

Villa Vista Inc
PO Box 98, N Hwy 73, Cromwell, MN, 55726
(218) 644-3331
Admin Raymond M Lally. *Medical Dir/Dir of*
  Nursing Gail V Dahl.
Licensure Intermediate care. *Beds* 51.
  Certified Medicaid.
Owner Proprietary Corp.
Admissions Requirements Medical
  examination.
Staff RNs 2 (ft); LPNs 2 (ft); Nurses aides 6
  (ft), 6 (pt); Activities coordinators 1 (ft), 1
  (pt); Dietitians 1 (pt).
Facilities Dining room; Activities room;
  Crafts room; Laundry room; Barber/Beauty
  shop; Sauna; Smoking room.
Activities Arts & crafts; Cards; Games;
  Reading groups; Prayer groups; Movies;
  Shopping trips; Social/Cultural gatherings.

CROOKSTON

Crookston Group Home 1
315 Summit Ave, Crookston, MN, 56716
(218) 281-7245
Admin Vernon Nordmark. *Medical Dir/Dir of*
  Nursing Josette C Nordmark MD.
Licensure Intermediate care for mentally
  retarded. *Beds* ICF/MR 10. *Certified*
  Medicaid.
Owner Nonprofit Corp.
Admissions Requirements Minimum age 18;
  Medical examination.
Staff RNs 1 (pt); Activities coordinators 1 (ft).
Facilities Dining room; Activities room;
  Laundry room.
Activities Arts & crafts; Cards; Games;
  Movies; Shopping trips; Social/Cultural
  gatherings.

Crookston Group Home 2
1423 Foskett Ave, Crookston, MN, 56716
(218) 281-1904
Admin Dr Vernon Nordmark. *Medical Dir/Dir*
  of Nursing Josette C Nordmark MD.
Licensure Intermediate care for mentally
  retarded. *Beds* 10. *Certified* Medicaid.
Owner Nonprofit Corp.
Admissions Requirements Minimum age 18;
  Females only.
Facilities Dining room; Activities room;
  Laundry room.
Activities Arts & crafts; Cards; Games;
  Movies; Shopping trips; Social/Cultural
  gatherings.

Crookston Group Home 3
220 Johnson Pl, Crookston, MN, 56716
(218) 281-5642
Admin Vernon C Nordmark PhD. *Medical*
  Dir/Dir of Nursing Josette C Nordmark MD.
Licensure Intermediate care for mentally
  retarded. *Beds* ICF/MR 8. *Certified*
  Medicaid.
Owner Nonprofit Corp.
Admissions Requirements Minimum age 18;
  Medical examination.
Staff RNs 1 (pt); Activities coordinators 1 (ft);
  Direct care staff.
Facilities Dining room; Activities room;
  Laundry room.
Activities Arts & crafts; Cards; Games;
  Movies; Shopping trips; Social/Cultural
  gatherings; Community recreation.

East Grand Forks Group Home I
1924 5th Ave NW, Crookston, MN, 56716
(218) 773-7439
Admin Vernon Nordmark. *Medical Dir/Dir of*
  Nursing Josette C Nordmark.
Licensure Intermediate care for mentally
  retarded. *Beds* ICF/MR 10. *Certified*
  Medicaid.
Owner Nonprofit Corp.

Admissions Requirements Minimum age 15; Medical examination.
Staff RNs 1 (pt); Activities coordinators 1 (pt).
Facilities Dining room; Laundry room; Resident bedrooms; Living area.
Activities Arts & crafts; Cards; Games; Reading groups; Prayer groups; Movies; Shopping trips; Social/Cultural gatherings.

Riverview Nursing Home
323 S Minnesota, Crookston, MN, 56716-1866
(218) 281-4682
Admin Thomas Lenertz. *Medical Dir/Dir of Nursing* A Chadwick MD; LouCeil Myrold RN.
Licensure Skilled care. *Beds* SNF 100. *Certified* Medicaid.
Owner Nonprofit Corp.
Admissions Requirements Physician's request.
Staff RNs 2 (ft), 1 (pt); LPNs 7 (ft), 7 (pt); Nurses aides 21 (ft), 30 (pt); Physical therapists 1 (pt); Recreational therapists 3 (ft), 1 (pt); Occupational therapists 1 (pt); Speech therapists 1 (pt); Activities coordinators 1 (ft); Dietitians 1 (pt).
Facilities Dining room; Physical therapy room; Activities room; Chapel; Crafts room; Barber/Beauty shop.
Activities Arts & crafts; Cards; Games; Reading groups; Prayer groups; Movies; Shopping trips; Social/Cultural gatherings.

Villa St Vincent
516 Walsh St, Crookston, MN, 56716
(218) 281-3424
Admin Michael D Siekas. *Medical Dir/Dir of Nursing* Dr R T Martin; Judy Hulst RN.
Licensure Skilled care; ICF II. *Beds* SNF 80; ICF II 95. *Certified* Medicaid; Medicare.
Owner Nonprofit Corp.
Admissions Requirements Medical examination; Physician's request.
Staff RNs 5 (ft), 3 (pt); LPNs 9 (ft), 4 (pt); Nurses aides 63 (ft), 36 (pt); Recreational therapists 6 (ft); Dietitians 1 (pt).
Affiliation Roman Catholic
Facilities Dining room; Activities room; Chapel; Crafts room; Laundry room; Barber/Beauty shop; Library; Woodworking shop; Darkroom; Kiln for ceramics.
Activities Arts & crafts; Cards; Games; Prayer groups; Movies; Social/Cultural gatherings.

CRYSTAL

Crystal Care Center
3245 Vera Cruz Ave N, Crystal, MN, 55422
(612) 535-6260
Admin Patricia Kalaidis. *Medical Dir/Dir of Nursing* Dr Keith Kubasch; Terri Ritten.
Licensure Skilled care. *Beds* 192. *Certified* Medicaid.
Owner Nonprofit Corp (Volunteers of America Care).
Admissions Requirements Minimum age 21; Medical examination; Physician's request.
Staff Physicians 1 (pt); RNs 12 (ft), 3 (pt); LPNs 13 (ft), 15 (pt); Nurses aides 45 (ft), 25 (pt); Physical therapists 1 (ft), 2 (pt); Recreational therapists 4 (ft); Occupational therapists 2 (ft), 1 (pt); Activities coordinators 1 (ft); Dietitians 1 (pt).
Affiliation Volunteers of America
Facilities Dining room; Physical therapy room; Activities room; Chapel; Crafts room; Laundry room; Barber/Beauty shop; Library.
Activities Arts & crafts; Cards; Games; Reading groups; Prayer groups; Movies; Shopping trips; Social/Cultural gatherings.

Dungarvin V—Tyrothy
3157 Douglas Dr, Crystal, MN, 55422
(612) 545-8757
Admin Deborah Sheehan.
Licensure Supervised living facility. *Beds* 6. *Certified* Medicaid.
Owner Proprietary Corp.

Staff RNs 1 (pt); Activities coordinators 1 (ft).
Facilities Laundry room.
Activities Games; Movies; Shopping trips; Social/Cultural gatherings.

Forestview Kentucky*
4806 Kentucky Ave N, Crystal, MN, 55428
(612) 535-3116
Admin Mary M Hill.
Licensure Intermediate care for mentally retarded. *Beds* 6. *Certified* Medicaid.
Owner Proprietary Corp.

DASSEL

Dassel Lakeside Community Home
441 William Ave, Dassel, MN, 55325
(612) 275-3433
Admin William D Ward. *Medical Dir/Dir of Nursing* Marilyn Nelson.
Licensure Intermediate care. *Beds* ICF 64. *Certified* Medicaid.
Owner Publicly owned.
Admissions Requirements Minimum age 16; Medical examination; Physician's request.
Staff RNs 2 (ft), 3 (pt); LPNs 5 (ft), 3 (pt); Nurses aides 18 (ft), 20 (pt); Recreational therapists 1 (ft), 1 (pt); Activities coordinators 1 (ft); Dietitians 1 (pt).
Facilities Dining room; Activities room; Chapel; Crafts room; Laundry room; Barber/Beauty shop.
Activities Arts & crafts; Games; Reading groups; Prayer groups; Movies; Social/Cultural gatherings.

DAWSON

Johnson Memorial Hospital Home*
Walnut St & Memorial Pl, Dawson, MN, 56232
(612) 769-4323
Admin Mark Rinehardt. *Medical Dir/Dir of Nursing* Dr P W Maus.
Licensure Skilled care; Intermediate care. *Beds* 70. *Certified* Medicaid.
Owner Nonprofit Corp.
Admissions Requirements Medical examination.
Staff Physicians 2 (ft); RNs 1 (ft), 3 (pt); LPNs 4 (ft), 5 (pt); Nurses aides 17 (ft), 22 (pt); Physical therapists 1 (pt); Occupational therapists 1 (ft); Activities coordinators 1 (ft); Dietitians 1 (pt); Dentists 2 (pt); Activity assistants 5 (ft).
Facilities Dining room; Physical therapy room; Activities room; Chapel; Barber/Beauty shop; Day room.
Activities Arts & crafts; Cards; Games; Reading groups; Prayer groups; Social/Cultural gatherings; Weekly bingo.

DEER RIVER

Homestead Nursing Home
1002 Comstock Dr, Deer River, MN, 56636
(218) 246-2900
Admin William Eckblad. *Medical Dir/Dir of Nursing* John Ward MD; Sharyn Rohder RN DON.
Licensure Skilled care. *Beds* SNF 50. *Certified* Medicaid; Medicare.
Owner Nonprofit Corp.
Admissions Requirements Medical examination; Physician's request.
Staff Physicians 5 (pt); RNs 4 (pt); LPNs 2 (ft), 6 (pt); Nurses aides 7 (ft), 20 (pt); Physical therapists 1 (ft); Activities coordinators 1 (ft); Dietitians 1 (ft).
Languages Chippewa, Ojibway
Facilities Dining room; Physical therapy room; Activities room; Crafts room; Laundry room; Barber/Beauty shop.

Activities Arts & crafts; Cards; Games; Reading groups; Prayer groups; Movies; Shopping trips; Social/Cultural gatherings; Exclusive outings.

DELANO

Delano Healthcare Center
433 County Rd 30, Delano, MN, 55328
(612) 972-2987
Admin Kristi Olmanson. *Medical Dir/Dir of Nursing* Joann Hubbard DON.
Licensure Skilled care; Intermediate care. *Beds* 64. *Certified* Medicaid; Medicare.
Owner Proprietary Corp (Beverly Enterprises).
Admissions Requirements Physician's request.
Staff RNs 3 (ft), 1 (pt); LPNs 2 (ft), 3 (pt); Nurses aides 9 (ft), 31 (pt); Physical therapists 1 (ft); Recreational therapists 2 (ft); Occupational therapists 1 (ft); Speech therapists 1 (pt).
Facilities Dining room; Physical therapy room; Activities room; Barber/Beauty shop; Library; Patio.
Activities Arts & crafts; Cards; Games; Reading groups; Prayer groups; Movies; Shopping trips; Social/Cultural gatherings.

The Dells Place Inc
235 S 2nd St, Delano, MN, 55328
(612) 972-3664
Admin Vernon Wahlstrom.
Licensure Intermediate care for mentally retarded. *Beds* ICF/MR 9. *Certified* Medicaid.
Owner Nonprofit Corp.
Admissions Requirements Minimum age 18; Medical examination.
Staff RNs 1 (pt); Activities coordinators 1 (ft).
Facilities Dining room; Activities room; Laundry room; Kitchen; Living room; Day room.
Activities Arts & crafts; Cards; Games; Movies; Shopping trips; Social/Cultural gatherings.

DENT

Peleske Group Home*
Rte 1, Dent, MN, 56528
(218) 758-2570
Admin Mary Peleske.
Licensure Intermediate care for mentally retarded. *Beds* 8.
Owner Proprietary Corp.

DETROIT LAKES

Emmanuel Nursing Home
1415 Madison Ave, Detroit Lakes, MN, 56501
(218) 847-9215
Admin Mark Hoplin. *Medical Dir/Dir of Nursing* Dr Bill Henke.
Licensure Skilled care. *Beds* 144. *Certified* Medicaid; Medicare.
Owner Nonprofit Corp.
Staff RNs 6 (ft); LPNs 22 (ft); Orderlies 2 (ft); Nurses aides 50 (ft), 40 (pt); Physical therapists 1 (ft), 1 (pt); Speech therapists 1 (pt); Activities coordinators 1 (ft); Dietitians 1 (ft).
Affiliation Lutheran
Facilities Dining room; Physical therapy room; Activities room; Chapel; Crafts room; Laundry room; Barber/Beauty shop; Library.
Activities Arts & crafts; Cards; Games; Reading groups; Prayer groups; Movies; Shopping trips; Social/Cultural gatherings.

St Marys Nursing Center*
1014 Lincoln Ave, Detroit Lakes, MN, 56501
(218) 847-5611
Admin John Korzenderfer.
Licensure Skilled care. *Beds* 103. *Certified* Medicaid; Medicare.
Owner Proprietary Corp.

Summit Home*
920 Summit Ave, Detroit Lakes, MN, 56501
(218) 847-7176
Admin Thomas Reiffenberger.
Licensure Intermediate care for mentally retarded. *Beds* 9. *Certified* Medicaid.
Owner Nonprofit Corp.

West Home*
1118 West Ave, Detroit Lakes, MN, 56501
(218) 847-5642
Admin Thomas Reiffenberger.
Licensure Intermediate care for mentally retarded. *Beds* 9. *Certified* Medicaid.
Owner Nonprofit Corp.

DODGE CENTER

Fairview Nursing Home*
Rte 1, Box 334, Dodge Center, MN, 55927
(507) 374-2578
Admin Donald W Bakke. *Medical Dir/Dir of Nursing* O S Kulstad.
Licensure Skilled care. *Beds* 72. *Certified* Medicaid; Medicare.
Owner Publicly owned.
Admissions Requirements Minimum age 16; Medical examination.
Staff RNs 3 (ft), 4 (pt); LPNs 3 (ft), 4 (pt); Nurses aides 15 (ft), 23 (pt); Physical therapists 1 (pt); Occupational therapists 1 (pt); Activities coordinators 1 (ft); Dietitians 1 (ft).
Facilities Dining room; Physical therapy room; Activities room; Chapel; Laundry room; Barber/Beauty shop.
Activities Arts & crafts; Cards; Games; Prayer groups; Movies.

Woodvak Dodge Center*
503 5th Ave NW, Dodge Center, MN, 55927
(507) 374-2836
Admin Walter Baldus.
Licensure Intermediate care for mentally retarded. *Beds* 8. *Certified* Medicaid.
Owner Proprietary Corp.

DULUTH

Aftenro Home
510 W College St, Duluth, MN, 55811
(218) 728-6864
Admin Hildegarde Ricci. *Medical Dir/Dir of Nursing* Catherine Watt.
Licensure Intermediate care; Boarding care. *Beds* ICF 65. *Certified* Medicaid.
Owner Nonprofit Corp.
Admissions Requirements Medical examination.
Staff LPNs 8 (ft); Nurses aides 7 (ft); Activities coordinators 1 (ft).
Facilities Dining room; Activities room; Chapel; Crafts room; Laundry room; Barber/Beauty shop.
Activities Arts & crafts; Cards; Games; Reading groups; Prayer groups; Movies; Shopping trips; Social/Cultural gatherings.

Baldwin House
2232 E 1st St, Duluth, MN, 55812
(218) 728-5569
Admin Clyde Johnson.
Licensure Intermediate care for mentally retarded. *Beds* ICF/MR 10. *Certified* Medicaid.
Owner Nonprofit organization/foundation.
Admissions Requirements Minimum age 17.
Facilities Dining room; Activities room; Laundry room.
Activities Cards; Games; Movies; Shopping trips; Social/Cultural gatherings.

Caromin House—Dodge*
4620 Dodge St, Duluth, MN, 55804
(218) 525-6995
Admin Trudy Carlson.
Licensure Supervised living facility. *Beds* 6.
Certified Medicaid.
Owner Proprietary Corp.
Admissions Requirements Minimum age 18.

Caromin House—Tioga*
6009 Tioga St, Duluth, MN, 55804
(218) 525-5650
Admin Trudy Carlson.
Licensure Supervised living facility. *Beds* 15.
Certified Medicaid.
Owner Proprietary Corp.
Admissions Requirements Minimum age 18; Females only.

Champion Childrens Home*
1889 Lester River Rd, Duluth, MN, 55804
(218) 525-1165
Admin Gordon Atol.
Licensure Supervised living facility. *Beds* 16.
Certified Medicaid.
Owner Proprietary Corp.
Admissions Requirements Medical examination.
Staff RNs 1 (pt); LPNs 1 (ft), 1 (pt); Nurses aides 2 (ft), 15 (pt); Dietitians 1 (pt).
Facilities Dining room; Activities room; Laundry room; Music room; Living room.
Activities Arts & crafts; Games; Reading groups; Movies; Shopping trips; Social/Cultural gatherings.

Cliff House*
1707 Cliff Ave, Duluth, MN, 55803
(218) 525-3075
Admin Judy Johnson.
Licensure Intermediate care for mentally retarded. *Beds* 6. *Certified* Medicaid.
Owner Proprietary Corp.

Duluth Regional Care Center II*
323 90th Ave W, Duluth, MN, 55808
(218) 626-1784
Admin Clyde Johnson.
Licensure Supervised living facility. *Beds* 6.
Certified Medicaid.
Owner Nonprofit Corp.
Admissions Requirements Minimum age 17; Medical examination.
Facilities Dining room; Activities room; Laundry room.
Activities Arts & crafts; Cards; Games; Movies; Shopping trips; Social/Cultural gatherings.

Duluth Regional Care Center III
631 W Skyline Blvd, Duluth, MN, 55805
(218) 727-5984
Admin Clyde Johnson.
Licensure Intermediate care for mentally retarded. *Beds* ICF/MR 10. *Certified* Medicaid.
Owner Privately owned.
Admissions Requirements Minimum age 18.
Staff Program director 1 (ft); Program coordinator 2 (ft); Program implementer 4 (ft).
Facilities Three complete apartments.
Activities Cards; Games; Movies; Shopping trips; Social/Cultural gatherings; Teach day-to-day living skills.

Duluth Regional Care Center IV*
2502 W 2nd St, Duluth, MN, 55807
(218) 727-4423
Admin Clyde Johnson.
Licensure Intermediate care for mentally retarded. *Beds* 6. *Certified* Medicaid.
Owner Nonprofit Corp.

Chris Jensen Nursing Home
2501 Rice Lake Rd, Duluth, MN, 55811
(218) 720-1500
Admin Ronald J Johnson. *Medical Dir/Dir of Nursing* William A Stein MD; Beverly Nordwall DON.
Licensure Skilled care; Intermediate care. *Beds* 247. *Certified* Medicaid; Medicare.
Owner Publicly owned.

Admissions Requirements Minimum age 16.
Staff Physicians 3 (ft); RNs 10 (ft), 12 (pt); LPNs 17 (ft), 14 (pt); Nurses aides 59 (ft), 71 (pt); Physical therapists 1 (ft); Activities coordinators 1 (ft); Dietitians 2 (ft).
Languages Finnish, Swedish
Facilities Dining room; Physical therapy room; Activities room; Chapel; Crafts room; Barber/Beauty shop.
Activities Arts & crafts; Cards; Games; Reading groups; Prayer groups; Movies; Shopping trips; Social/Cultural gatherings.

Lake Haven Manor
7700 Grand Ave, Duluth, MN, 55807
(218) 628-2341
Admin Barbara H Korpela. *Medical Dir/Dir of Nursing* Dr Douglas J Hiza; Virginia McDonnell.
Licensure Skilled care; Intermediate care. *Beds* 132. *Certified* Medicaid; Medicare.
Owner Privately owned.
Admissions Requirements Minimum age 18; Medical examination.
Staff RNs 1 (ft), 14 (pt); LPNs 1 (ft), 7 (pt); Orderlies 1 (pt); Nurses aides 5 (ft), 60 (pt); Physical therapists 1 (ft), 2 (pt); Occupational therapists 1 (ft), 2 (pt); Activities coordinators 3 (ft); Dietitians 1 (pt); Social services 2 (ft).
Facilities Dining room; Physical therapy room; Activities room; Chapel; Crafts room; Laundry room; Barber/Beauty shop; Occupational therapy room.
Activities Arts & crafts; Cards; Games; Prayer groups; Movies; Shopping trips; Social/Cultural gatherings.

Lakeshore Lutheran Home*
4002 London Rd, Duluth, MN, 55804
(218) 525-1951
Admin Alden G Adams.
Licensure Skilled care; Intermediate care. *Beds* SNF 160; ICF 69. *Certified* Medicaid; Medicare.
Owner Nonprofit Corp (MN Synod/Lutheran Ch Board).
Affiliation Lutheran

Nekton on Greysolon*
3518 Greysolon Rd, Duluth, MN, 55804
(218) 724-9373
Admin Joe Modec.
Licensure Supervised living facility. *Beds* 6.
Certified Medicaid.
Owner Proprietary Corp.
Admissions Requirements Minimum age 4; Medical examination; Physician's request.
Staff Physicians 4 (pt); RNs 1 (pt); Physical therapists 1 (pt); Recreational therapists 2 (pt); Occupational therapists 1 (pt); Speech therapists 1 (pt); Activities coordinators 1 (pt); Dietitians 1 (pt); Dentists 1 (pt); Ophthalmologists 1 (pt); Podiatrists 1 (pt); Audiologists 1 (pt).
Facilities Dining room; Activities room; Laundry room; Library.
Activities Arts & crafts; Cards; Games; Reading groups; Movies; Shopping trips; Social/Cultural gatherings.

Nekton on London Road*
4515 London Rd, Duluth, MN, 55804
(218) 525-3632
Admin Joe Modec.
Licensure Intermediate care for mentally retarded. *Beds* 6. *Certified* Medicaid.
Owner Proprietary Corp.

Nekton on Springvale*
2214 Springvale Rd, Duluth, MN, 55811
(218) 722-7280
Admin Joe Modec.
Licensure Intermediate care for mentally retarded. *Beds* 6. *Certified* Medicaid.
Owner Proprietary Corp.

Nekton on Wallace*
1702 Wallace Ave, Duluth, MN, 55803
(218) 726-6224
Admin Joe Modec.
Licensure Intermediate care for mentally
retarded. *Beds* 6. *Certified* Medicaid.
Owner Proprietary Corp.

Park Point Manor
1601 St Louis Ave, Duluth, MN, 55802
(218) 727-8651
Admin Mark Norgard. *Medical Dir/Dir of
Nursing* Dr Hiza; Shelly Hanson DON.
Licensure Skilled care; Intermediate care. *Beds*
SNF 216; ICF 24. *Certified* Medicaid;
Medicare.
Owner Proprietary Corp.
Admissions Requirements Minimum age 16;
Medical examination; Physician's request.
Staff Physicians 1 (pt); RNs 8 (ft), 10 (pt);
LPNs 10 (ft), 20 (pt); Nurses aides 70 (ft),
90 (pt); Physical therapists 3 (ft);
Recreational therapists 5 (ft); Occupational
therapists 1 (ft); Speech therapists 1 (pt);
Activities coordinators 1 (ft); Dietitians 1
(pt); Ophthalmologists 1 (pt).
Facilities Dining room; Physical therapy
room; Activities room; Chapel; Crafts room;
Laundry room; Barber/Beauty shop; Library;
Courtyard.
Activities Arts & crafts; Cards; Games;
Reading groups; Prayer groups; Movies;
Shopping trips; Social/Cultural gatherings;
Concerts; Horse back riding; Swimming.

Residential Services of Northeast Minnesota I
PO Box 3008, 2048 E 8th St, Duluth, MN,
55803
(218) 728-6819
Admin Timothy S Mowbray.
Licensure Intermediate care for mentally
retarded. *Beds* 13. *Certified* Medicaid.
Owner Nonprofit Corp.

Residential Services of Northeast Minnesota II
707 Arrowhead Rd, Duluth, MN, 55811
(218) 728-6871
Admin Jon Nelson.
Licensure Intermediate care for mentally
retarded. *Beds* ICF/MR 16. *Certified*
Medicaid.
Owner Nonprofit Corp.
Admissions Requirements Medical
examination.
Staff RNs 1 (pt); LPNs 1 (ft); Activities
coordinators 1 (ft).

Surf & Sand Health Center*
3910 Minnesota Ave, Duluth, MN, 55802
(218) 727-8933
Admin William Buchanan.
Licensure Skilled care; Intermediate care. *Beds*
SNF 42; ICF 14. *Certified* Medicaid;
Medicare.
Owner Proprietary Corp.

Thunderbird House*
229 N 4th Ave W, Duluth, MN, 55806
(218) 727-1476
Admin Edwin J Benton.
Licensure Supervised living facility. *Beds* 10.
Owner Nonprofit Corp.

Viewcrest Nursing Home*
3111 Church St, Duluth, MN, 55811
(218) 727-8801
Admin Gerald Buchanan.
Licensure Skilled care; Intermediate care. *Beds*
SNF 98; ICF 40. *Certified* Medicaid.
Owner Proprietary Corp.

EAGAN

Orvilla Inc*
3430 Westcott Hills Dr, Eagan, MN, 55123
(612) 454-8501
Admin James Driscoll.

Licensure Intermediate care for mentally
retarded. *Beds* 54. *Certified* Medicaid.
Owner Proprietary Corp.

EAST GRAND FORKS

East Grand Forks II
2138 9th Ave NW, East Grand Forks, MN,
56721
(218) 773-8338
Admin Vernon C Nordmark PhD. *Medical
Dir/Dir of Nursing* Josette C Nordmark MD.
Licensure Intermediate care for mentally
retarded. *Beds* ICF/MR 8. *Certified*
Medicaid.
Owner Nonprofit Corp.
Admissions Requirements Minimum age 18;
Medical examination.
Staff RNs 1 (pt); Activities coordinators 1 (ft);
Direct care staff 6 (ft), 3 (pt).
Facilities Dining room; Activities room;
Laundry room.
Activities Arts & crafts; Cards; Games;
Movies; Shopping trips; Social/Cultural
gatherings; Community recreation.

Good Samaritan Nursing Center
1414 20th St NW, East Grand Forks, MN,
56721
(218) 773-7484
Admin Sandra Bentley. *Medical Dir/Dir of
Nursing* Dr Dale Moquist; Mary Johnson
RN.
Licensure Skilled care; Intermediate care. *Beds*
129. *Certified* Medicaid; Medicare.
Owner Nonprofit Corp (Evangelical Lutheran/
Good Samaritan).
Admissions Requirements Minimum age 16;
Medical examination; Physician's request.
Staff RNs 4 (ft), 4 (pt); LPNs 6 (ft), 10 (pt);
Orderlies 4 (ft), 2 (pt); Nurses aides 34 (ft),
33 (pt); Activities coordinators.
Affiliation Lutheran
Facilities Dining room; Physical therapy
room; Activities room; Chapel; Laundry
room; Barber/Beauty shop.
Activities Arts & crafts; Cards; Games;
Reading groups; Prayer groups; Shopping
trips; Social/Cultural gatherings.

EDEN PRAIRIE

Castle Ridge Care Center & Manor House
625 Prairie Center Dr, Eden Prairie, MN,
55344
(612) 944-8982
Admin Jean Mulder. *Medical Dir/Dir of
Nursing* David Olson MD; Jean Mulder
DON.
Licensure Skilled care. *Beds* SNF 60. *Certified*
Medicaid; Medicare.
Owner Nonprofit organization/foundation.
Admissions Requirements Medical
examination; Physician's request.
Staff RNs 5 (ft), 5 (pt); LPNs 3 (ft), 3 (pt);
Nurses aides 17 (ft), 17 (pt); Physical
therapists 1 (ft); Recreational therapists 1
(ft); Occupational therapists 1 (ft); Speech
therapists 1 (ft); Dietitians 1 (ft);
Ophthalmologists 1 (ft).
Affiliation Baptist
Facilities Dining room; Physical therapy
room; Activities room; Chapel; Crafts room;
Laundry room; Barber/Beauty shop; Library.
Activities Arts & crafts; Cards; Games;
Reading groups; Prayer groups; Movies;
Shopping trips; Social/Cultural gatherings.

EDEN VALLEY

Valley Rest Home
PO Box 485, Eden Valley, MN, 55329
(612) 453-6747
Admin Maryann Ruhland.
Licensure Boarding care. *Beds* 21.
Owner Proprietary Corp.

EDGERTON

Edgebrook Rest Center Inc
505 Trosky Rd W, Edgerton, MN, 56128
(507) 442-7121
Admin Larry Oberloh. *Medical Dir/Dir of
Nursing* Roland Beckering MD; Audrey
Vander Maten DON.
Licensure Intermediate care. *Beds* ICF 61.
Certified Medicaid.
Owner Nonprofit Corp.
Admissions Requirements Medical
examination; Physician's request.
Staff RNs 2 (ft), 3 (pt); LPNs 2 (ft), 3 (pt);
Nurses aides 10 (ft), 20 (pt); Physical
therapists 1 (pt); Activities coordinators 1
(ft); Dietitians 1 (pt).
Languages Dutch
Facilities Dining room; Activities room;
Chapel; Crafts room; Laundry room; Barber/
Beauty shop.
Activities Arts & crafts; Cards; Games;
Reading groups; Prayer groups; Movies;
Shopping trips; Social/Cultural gatherings;
Groups trips; Zoo outings.

EDINA

Edina Care Center
6200 Xerxes Ave S, Edina, MN, 55423
(612) 925-4810
Admin Leila E Campbell. *Medical Dir/Dir of
Nursing* Dr K M Kubasch; Chris Gorder.
Licensure Skilled care; Intermediate care. *Beds*
161. *Certified* Medicaid; Medicare.
Owner Nonprofit Corp (Volunteers of
America Care).
Admissions Requirements Physician's request.
Facilities Dining room; Physical therapy
room; Activities room; Chapel; Crafts room;
Laundry room; Barber/Beauty shop; Library;
Dental office.
Activities Arts & crafts; Cards; Games;
Reading groups; Prayer groups; Movies;
Shopping trips; Social/Cultural gatherings.

Heritage of Edina
3456 Heritage Dr, Edina, MN, 55435
(612) 927-5656
Admin Sylvia Triden. *Medical Dir/Dir of
Nursing* Dr Albert Fetzek.
Licensure Nursing home. *Beds* 121.
Owner Proprietary Corp.
Staff RNs 3 (ft), 12 (pt); LPNs 2 (ft), 8 (pt);
Orderlies 5 (ft), 6 (pt); Nurses aides 17 (ft),
32 (pt); Physical therapists 2 (ft); Speech
therapists 1 (pt); Activities coordinators 1
(ft); Dietitians 1 (ft); Dentists 1 (pt);
Podiatrists 1 (pt).
Facilities Dining room; Physical therapy
room; Activities room; Chapel; Crafts room;
Laundry room; Barber/Beauty shop.
Activities Arts & crafts; Cards; Games;
Reading groups; Prayer groups; Movies;
Shopping trips; Social/Cultural gatherings.

Nekton on William*
5100 William Ave, Edina, MN, 55436
(612) 925-3292
Admin Milton Conrath.
Licensure Intermediate care for mentally
retarded. *Beds* 6. *Certified* Medicaid.
Owner Proprietary Corp.

ELK RIVER

Elk River Nursing Home*
400 Evans Ave, Elk River, MN, 55330
(612) 441-1213
Admin Timothy J O'Brien.
Licensure Skilled care; Intermediate care. *Beds*
SNF 60; ICF 60. *Certified* Medicaid;
Medicare.
Owner Nonprofit Corp.

The Shire—Dungarvin IV*
9607 201st Ave NE, Elk River, MN, 55330
(612) 441-6043
Admin Deborah Sheehan.
Licensure Intermediate care for mentally
retarded. *Beds* 12. *Certified* Medicaid.
Owner Proprietary Corp.

ELLSWORTH

Parkview Manor Nursing Home
PO Box 152, RR 1, Ellsworth, MN, 56129
(507) 967-2482
Admin Michael Werner.
Licensure Intermediate care. *Beds* 60.
Certified Medicaid.
Owner Publicly owned.
Admissions Requirements Medical
examination.
Staff RNs 1 (ft), 3 (pt); LPNs 1 (ft), 3 (pt);
Nurses aides 8 (ft), 23 (pt); Physical
therapists 1 (pt); Activities coordinators 1
(ft), 1 (pt); Dietitians 1 (pt).
Languages German, Dutch
Facilities Dining room; Physical therapy
room; Activities room; Crafts room; Laundry
room; Barber/Beauty shop.
Activities Arts & crafts; Cards; Games;
Reading groups; Prayer groups; Movies.

ELY

**Ely Bloomenson Community Hospital &
Nursing Home**
328 W Conan St, Ely, MN, 55731
(218) 365-3271
Admin John Perushek. *Medical Dir/Dir of
Nursing* Dr Walter B Leino; Mary E
Reichensperger RN DON.
Licensure Skilled care; Intermediate care. *Beds*
99. *Certified* Medicaid; Medicare.
Owner Nonprofit Corp.
Admissions Requirements Minimum age 16;
Medical examination; Physician's request.
Staff Physicians 1 (ft), 3 (pt); RNs 1 (ft), 1
(pt); LPNs 7 (ft), 5 (pt); Orderlies 3 (ft), 3
(pt); Nurses aides 22 (ft), 16 (pt); Physical
therapists 1 (ft); Speech therapists 1 (pt);
Activities coordinators 1 (ft), 3 (pt);
Dietitians 3 (ft), 1 (pt); Dentists 1 (pt);
Ophthalmologists 1 (pt); Podiatrists 1 (pt).
Languages Finnish, Slavic, Swedish,
Norwegian, German, Italian
Facilities Dining room; Physical therapy
room; Activities room; Chapel; Crafts room;
Laundry room; Barber/Beauty shop.
Activities Arts & crafts; Cards; Games;
Reading groups; Prayer groups; Movies;
Shopping trips; Social/Cultural gatherings;
Bingo outings.

ERSKINE

Johnson Rest Home*
Vance Ave N, Erskine, MN, 56535
(218) 687-3955
Admin Palma C Johnson.
Licensure Intermediate care. *Beds* 8.
Owner Proprietary Corp.

Pioneer Memorial Care Center
Rte 2, Box 148, Erskine, MN, 56535
(218) 687-2365
Admin Dorothy Sandahl.
Licensure Skilled care. *Beds* 75. *Certified*
Medicaid; Medicare.
Owner Nonprofit Corp.

EVANSVILLE

Crestview Manor Inc*
649 State St, Evansville, MN, 56326
(218) 948-2219
Admin Richard Beadling. *Medical Dir/Dir of
Nursing* Dr James Lueders.

Licensure Skilled care; Intermediate care. *Beds*
70. *Certified* Medicaid.
Owner Proprietary Corp.
Staff Physicians 1 (pt); RNs 1 (ft), 2 (pt);
LPNs 2 (ft), 6 (pt); Nurses aides 9 (ft), 24
(pt); Activities coordinators 1 (ft).
Facilities Dining room; Physical therapy
room; Crafts room; Laundry room; Barber/
Beauty shop.
Activities Arts & crafts; Cards; Games;
Reading groups; Prayer groups; Movies;
Shopping trips; Social/Cultural gatherings.

EVELETH

Arrowhead Health Care Center—Eveleth*
601 Grant Ave, Eveleth, MN, 55734
(218) 741-2550
Admin Phyllis J King.
Licensure Skilled care; Intermediate care. *Beds*
SNF 85; ICF 37. *Certified* Medicaid.
Owner Proprietary Corp (Beverly Enterprises).

**Eveleth Fitzgerald Community Hospital C &
NC**
227 McKinley Ave, Eveleth, MN, 55734
(218) 744-1950
Admin Rosalyn Karosich. *Medical Dir/Dir of
Nursing* R M Martinson MD; Linda
Kolochek RN DON.
Licensure Skilled care. *Beds* SNF 24. *Certified*
Medicaid; Medicare.
Owner Nonprofit Corp.
Admissions Requirements Minimum age 18;
Medical examination.
Staff Physicians 7 (ft); RNs 4 (ft), 5 (pt);
LPNs 3 (ft); Nurses aides 8 (ft), 1 (pt);
Activities coordinators 1 (ft); Dietitians 1
(ft).
Facilities Dining room; Activities room;
Crafts room; Laundry room.
Activities Arts & crafts; Cards; Games;
Reading groups; Prayer groups; Movies.

Range Center—Birchwood Home*
1016 W 1st St, Eveleth, MN, 55734
(218) 254-3347
Admin Timothy Larson.
Licensure Intermediate care for mentally
retarded. *Beds* 6. *Certified* Medicaid.
Owner Nonprofit Corp.

EXCELSIOR

Excelsior Nursing Home
515 Division St, Excelsior, MN, 55331
(612) 464-5488
Admin Lawrence D Whalen Jr. *Medical Dir/
Dir of Nursing* William Jefferies MD; Joan
Nolan RN DON.
Licensure Skilled care. *Beds* SNF 66. *Certified*
Medicare.
Owner Proprietary Corp (Beverly Enterprises).
Admissions Requirements Medical
examination; Physician's request.
Staff RNs 4 (ft), 2 (pt); LPNs 2 (ft), 4 (pt);
Nurses aides 8 (ft), 31 (pt); Activities
coordinators 1 (ft); Dietitians 1 (ft).
Facilities Dining room; Physical therapy
room; Activities room; Chapel; Crafts room;
Laundry room; Barber/Beauty shop.
Activities Arts & crafts; Games; Reading
groups; Prayer groups; Movies; Shopping
trips; Social/Cultural gatherings.

Lake Auburn Home for Aged
7555 Victoria Dr, Excelsior, MN, 55331
(612) 443-2421
Admin Marvel Heath. *Medical Dir/Dir of
Nursing* Jan Carlson.
Licensure Boarding care. *Beds* Boarding care
22.
Owner Nonprofit Corp.
Admissions Requirements Minimum age 45;
Medical examination.
Staff RNs 2 (pt); Nurses aides 9 (pt);
Activities coordinators 1 (pt).

Languages German
Affiliation Moravian
Facilities Dining room; Activities room;
Laundry room; Community living room.
Activities Arts & crafts; Cards; Games;
Reading groups; Prayer groups; Movies;
Shopping trips; Social/Cultural gatherings.

Minnetonka Health Care Center Inc
20395 Summerville Rd, Excelsior, MN, 55331
(612) 474-4474
Admin Kathleen Melin; Michael Cooling.
Medical Dir/Dir of Nursing Milton H Seifert
MD; Karen Sprinkel RN.
Licensure Intermediate care. *Beds* ICF 21.
Certified Medicaid; Medicare.
Owner Privately owned.
Admissions Requirements Minimum age 18;
Medical examination; Physician's request.
Staff RNs 1 (ft), 1 (pt); LPNs 2 (ft), 1 (pt);
Nurses aides 2 (ft), 2 (pt); Activities
coordinators 1 (pt); Dietitians 1 (pt).
Facilities Dining room; Activities room;
Laundry room.
Activities Arts & crafts; Cards; Games;
Reading groups; Prayer groups; Movies;
Shopping trips; Social/Cultural gatherings;
Bowling trips; Library trips.

Mt Olivet Rolling Acres*
7200 Rolling Acres Rd, Excelsior, MN, 55331
(612) 474-5974
Admin Gerald F Walsh.
Licensure Intermediate care for mentally
retarded. *Beds* 74. *Certified* Medicaid.
Owner Nonprofit Corp.

FAIRFAX

Fairfax Community Home Inc
10th Ave SE, Fairfax, MN, 55332
(507) 426-8241
Admin Emly Larsen. *Medical Dir/Dir of
Nursing* Dr Thomas Gilles; Mary Anderson.
Licensure Skilled care. *Beds* SNF 65. *Certified*
Medicaid; Medicare.
Owner Proprietary Corp.
Staff Physicians 1 (pt); RNs 3 (ft), 3 (pt);
LPNs 3 (ft), 3 (pt); Nurses aides 10 (ft), 15
(pt); Physical therapists 1 (pt); Occupational
therapists 1 (ft), 1 (pt); Speech therapists 1
(pt); Activities coordinators 1 (pt); Dietitians
1 (pt); Dentists 1 (pt); Podiatrists 1 (pt);
Dentist 1 (pt).
Facilities Dining room; Activities room;
Chapel; Crafts room; Laundry room; Barber/
Beauty shop.
Activities Arts & crafts; Cards; Games;
Reading groups; Prayer groups; Movies;
Shopping trips; Social/Cultural gatherings.

FAIRMONT

**Fairmont Community Hospital & Lutz Wing
Nursing Home**
RR 1, Box 21, 835 Johnson St, Fairmont,
MN, 56031
(507) 238-4254
Admin Gerry Gilbertson. *Medical Dir/Dir of
Nursing* Gayle Hansen.
Licensure Skilled care. *Beds* 40. *Certified*
Medicaid; Medicare.
Owner Nonprofit Corp.
Staff Physicians 16 (ft); RNs 19 (ft), 33 (pt);
LPNs 8 (ft), 11 (pt); Nurses aides 17 (ft), 28
(pt); Physical therapists 1 (ft), 1 (pt);
Activities coordinators 1 (ft); Dietitians 1
(ft); Dentists 1 (ft).
Activities Arts & crafts; Cards; Games;
Reading groups; Prayer groups; Movies;
Shopping trips; Social/Cultural gatherings.

Lakeview Methodist Health Care Center*
610 Summit Dr, Fairmont, MN, 56031
(507) 235-6606
Admin George W Klus. *Medical Dir/Dir of
Nursing* Dr H A Williamson.

Licensure Skilled care; Intermediate care; Boarding care. *Beds* SNF 81; ICF 60; Boarding care 18. *Certified* Medicaid.
Owner Nonprofit Corp.
Admissions Requirements Medical examination; Physician's request.
Staff RNs 5 (ft), 7 (pt); LPNs 8 (ft), 6 (pt); Orderlies 1 (ft), 3 (pt); Nurses aides 17 (ft), 36 (pt); Physical therapists 2 (ft); Reality therapists 1 (ft); Recreational therapists 2 (ft); Activities coordinators 1 (ft); Dietitians 1 (ft).
Affiliation Methodist
Facilities Dining room; Physical therapy room; Activities room; Chapel; Laundry room; Barber/Beauty shop; Library.
Activities Arts & crafts; Cards; Games; Reading groups; Prayer groups; Movies; Shopping trips; Social/Cultural gatherings.

REM Fairmont A
107 Dorothy St, Fairmont, MN, 56031
(507) 238-4751
Admin Douglas Miller.
Licensure Supervised living facility. *Beds* 30. *Certified* Medicaid.
Owner Proprietary Corp.
Admissions Requirements Minimum age 16; Medical examination.
Staff Direct care 10 (ft), 14 (pt).
Facilities Dining room; Activities room; Crafts room; Laundry room.
Activities Arts & crafts; Cards; Games; Reading groups; Movies; Shopping trips; Social/Cultural gatherings.

REM Fairmont Inc B
107 Dorothy St, Fairmont, MN, 56031
(507) 238-4751
Admin Douglas Miller. *Medical Dir/Dir of Nursing* Gayle Zoch.
Licensure Intermediate care for mentally retarded. *Beds* ICF/MR 15. *Certified* Medicaid; Medicare.
Owner Proprietary Corp.
Admissions Requirements Minimum age 16; Medical examination.
Staff RNs 1 (pt); Activities coordinators 1 (pt).
Facilities Dining room; Activities room; Crafts room; Laundry room.
Activities Arts & crafts; Cards; Games; Movies; Shopping trips; Social/Cultural gatherings.

FARIBAULT

Faribault Manor Nursing Home*
1738 Hulett Ave, Faribault, MN, 55021
(507) 334-3919
Admin David Westbrook. *Medical Dir/Dir of Nursing* Dr Goode.
Licensure Skilled care. *Beds* 94. *Certified* Medicaid; Medicare.
Owner Proprietary Corp (Beverly Enterprises).
Admissions Requirements Minimum age 18.
Staff Physicians 1 (pt); RNs 3 (ft), 4 (pt); LPNs 6 (ft), 3 (pt); Nurses aides 23 (ft), 19 (pt); Physical therapists 1 (pt); Reality therapists 1 (pt); Occupational therapists 1 (pt); Speech therapists 1 (pt); Activities coordinators 2 (ft), 1 (pt); Dietitians 1 (pt); Dentists 1 (pt); Ophthalmologists 1 (pt); Podiatrists 1 (pt); Audiologists 1 (pt).
Facilities Dining room; Physical therapy room; Activities room; Laundry room; Barber/Beauty shop.
Activities Arts & crafts; Cards; Games; Reading groups; Prayer groups; Movies; Shopping trips; Social/Cultural gatherings.

Faribault Regional Center
802 Circle Drive, Faribault, MN, 55021
(507) 332-3000
Admin William C Saufferer. *Medical Dir of Nursing* Iancu Foni MD; Mary Zabel RN.

Licensure Skilled care; Intermediate care for mentally retarded; Medical hospital. *Beds* SNF 35; ICF/MR 775; Medical hospital 35. *Certified* Medicaid; Medicare.
Owner Publicly owned.
Admissions Requirements Minimum age 18; Medical examination; Physician's request.
Staff Physicians 4 (ft), 1 (pt); RNs 53 (ft); LPNs 87 (ft); Orderlies 475 (ft); Physical therapists 1 (ft), 1 (pt); Recreational therapists 26 (ft); Occupational therapists 4 (ft); Speech therapists 6 (ft); Activities coordinators 12 (ft); Dietitians 2 (ft); Dentists 1 (pt); Ophthalmologists 1 (pt); Podiatrists 1 (ft).
Languages Cambodian, Sign
Facilities Dining room; Physical therapy room; Activities room; Chapel; Crafts room; Laundry room; Barber/Beauty shop; Library.
Activities Arts & crafts; Cards; Games; Reading groups; Prayer groups; Movies; Shopping trips; Social/Cultural gatherings.

Park Avenue Home*
214 Park Ave, Faribault, MN, 55021
(507) 334-7808
Admin George Johnson.
Licensure Intermediate care for mentally retarded. *Beds* 15.
Owner Proprietary Corp.

Pleasant Manor Inc
27 Brand Ave, Faribault, MN, 55021
(507) 334-2036
Admin David E Meillier. *Medical Dir/Dir of Nursing* Dr Robert C Speckhals.
Licensure Skilled care; Intermediate care. *Beds* SNF 77; ICF 26. *Certified* Medicaid; Medicare.
Owner Proprietary Corp.
Admissions Requirements Minimum age 18; Medical examination.
Staff Physicians 12 (ft); RNs 2 (ft), 7 (pt); LPNs 9 (ft), 7 (pt); Nurses aides 19 (ft), 44 (pt); Physical therapists 1 (pt); Recreational therapists 3 (ft); Occupational therapists 1 (pt); Speech therapists 1 (pt); Activities coordinators 1 (pt); Dietitians 1 (pt); Dentists 1 (pt); Podiatrists 1 (pt).
Facilities Dining room; Physical therapy room; Activities room; Crafts room; Laundry room; Barber/Beauty shop.
Activities Arts & crafts; Cards; Games; Reading groups; Prayer groups; Movies; Shopping trips; Social/Cultural gatherings.

Region Park Hall*
1150 SW 3rd St, Faribault, MN, 55021
(507) 334-6292
Admin Charles A Kroeger.
Licensure Intermediate care for mentally retarded. *Beds* 12. *Certified* Medicaid.
Owner Proprietary Corp.

Resident Homes Inc—Harmony*
611 NW 5th St, Faribault, MN, 55021
(507) 334-5262
Admin Richard Northrop. *Medical Dir/Dir of Nursing* Helen Dahlstedt.
Licensure Supervised living facility. *Beds* 8. *Certified* Medicaid.
Owner Nonprofit Corp.
Admissions Requirements Minimum age 18; Females only.
Staff RNs 1 (pt); Activities coordinators 1 (pt).
Facilities Dining room; Laundry room.
Activities Arts & crafts; Cards; Games; Reading groups; Movies; Shopping trips; Social/Cultural gatherings.

Resident Homes Inc—Haven*
538 NW 2nd St, Faribault, MN, 55021
(507) 332-8320
Admin Robert Northrop. *Medical Dir/Dir of Nursing* Helen Dahlstedt.
Licensure Supervised living facility. *Beds* 9. *Certified* Medicaid.

Owner Nonprofit Corp.
Admissions Requirements Minimum age 18; Medical examination; Physician's request.
Staff RNs 1 (pt); Recreational therapists 1 (ft).
Facilities Dining room; Laundry room.
Activities Arts & crafts; Cards; Games; Reading groups; Movies; Shopping trips; Social/Cultural gatherings.

St Lucas Convalescent & Geriatric Center
503 E Division St, Faribault, MN, 55021
(507) 334-4314
Admin Joseph Stanislav. *Medical Dir/Dir of Nursing* R P Meyer MD; Betty Judd RN.
Licensure Skilled care. *Beds* 148. *Certified* Medicaid; Medicare.
Owner Nonprofit Corp.
Admissions Requirements Medical examination.
Staff RNs 7 (ft); LPNs 12 (ft); Nurses aides 40 (ft); Physical therapists 1 (ft); Occupational therapists 1 (ft); Activities coordinators 3 (ft); Dietitians 1 (ft).
Affiliation Church of Christ
Facilities Dining room; Physical therapy room; Activities room; Chapel; Crafts room; Laundry room; Barber/Beauty shop; Occupational therapy room.
Activities Arts & crafts; Cards; Games; Reading groups; Prayer groups; Movies; Shopping trips; Social/Cultural gatherings.

Seventh Street House*
216 7th St NW, Faribault, MN, 55021
(507) 334-8985
Admin George Johnson.
Licensure Intermediate care for mentally retarded. *Beds* 15. *Certified* Medicaid.
Owner Proprietary Corp.

FARMINGTON

Sanford Memorial Nursing Home/Hospital
913 Main St, Farmington, MN, 55024
(612) 463-7825
Admin Robert D Johnson. *Medical Dir/Dir of Nursing* Dr Joseph Emond; C Robin Schmitz RN.
Licensure Skilled care; Intermediate care. *Beds* SNF 65; ICF. *Certified* Medicaid; Medicare.
Owner Nonprofit Corp.
Admissions Requirements Minimum age 50; Medical examination; Physician's request.
Staff RNs 1 (ft), 8 (pt); LPNs 2 (ft), 8 (pt); Nurses aides 19 (ft), 22 (pt); Physical therapists 1 (ft); Activities coordinators 1 (ft), 1 (pt); Dietitians 1 (ft); Dietitians 1 (ft); Social worker 1 (ft).
Facilities Dining room; Physical therapy room; Activities room; Chapel; Crafts room; Laundry room; Barber/Beauty shop; Library.
Activities Arts & crafts; Cards; Games; Reading groups; Prayer groups; Movies; Shopping trips; Social/Cultural gatherings; Luncheon trips; Daytime trips (other than shopping).

FERGUS FALLS

Broen Memorial Home
824 S Sheridan E, Fergus Falls, MN, 56537
(218) 736-5441
Admin Ina M Larson. *Medical Dir/Dir of Nursing* Dr R Beck; Becky Odden RN.
Licensure Skilled care; Intermediate care; Board & care. *Beds* 207. *Certified* Medicaid; Medicare.
Owner Nonprofit organization/foundation.
Admissions Requirements Medical examination; Physician's request.
Staff RNs; LPNs; Nurses aides.
Affiliation Lutheran
Facilities Dining room; Physical therapy room; Activities room; Chapel; Crafts room; Laundry room; Barber/Beauty shop; Library.

Activities Arts & crafts; Games; Reading groups; Prayer groups; Movies; Shopping trips.

Fergus Falls Regional Treatment Center
N Union Ave, Box 157, Fergus Falls, MN, 56537-0157
(218) 739-7200
Admin Elaine Timmer.
Licensure Intermediate care for mentally retarded. *Beds* 270. *Certified* Medicaid.
Owner Publicly owned.

Koep Group Homes Inc
PO Box 764, Rte 3, Box 220, Fergus Falls, MN, 56537
(218) 736-6312
Admin Ione Koep. *Medical Dir/Dir of Nursing* LaRie Hull.
Licensure Intermediate care for mentally retarded. *Beds* ICF/MR 8. *Certified* Medicaid; Medicare.
Owner Proprietary Corp.
Admissions Requirements Minimum age 14; Medical examination; Physician's request.
Staff RNs 1 (pt); LPNs 1 (ft).
Facilities Dining room; Activities room; Crafts room; Laundry room.
Activities Cards; Games; Movies; Shopping trips; Social/Cultural gatherings; Developmental training.

Lake Region Hospital & Nursing Home
712 S Cascade, Fergus Falls, MN, 56537
(218) 736-5475
Admin Edward J Mehl. *Medical Dir/Dir of Nursing* Dr K Rau; Annette McBeth DON.
Licensure Skilled care. *Beds* SNF 44. *Certified* Medicaid; Medicare.
Owner Nonprofit Corp.
Admissions Requirements Minimum age 18; Medical examination; Physician's request.
Staff RNs 2 (ft), 6 (pt); LPNs 5 (ft), 9 (pt); Orderlies; Nurses aides 8 (ft), 15 (pt); Physical therapists 4 (ft); Occupational therapists 1 (ft), 1 (pt); Activities coordinators 1 (ft); Dietitians 1 (ft), 1 (pt).
Facilities Dining room; Activities room; Chapel; Laundry room; Barber/Beauty shop.
Activities Arts & crafts; Cards; Games; Reading groups; Prayer groups Bible Study; Movies; Pet therapy; Exercises; Bingo; Van rides; Discussion groups.

Pioneer Home Inc
1006 S Sheridan St, Fergus Falls, MN, 56537
(218) 739-3361
Admin Carmon D Jackson. *Medical Dir/Dir of Nursing* David Bjork MD; Barb Lorsung RN.
Licensure Skilled care; Intermediate care. *Beds* 110. *Certified* Medicaid; Medicare.
Owner Nonprofit Corp.
Admissions Requirements Minimum age 16; Medical examination.
Staff RNs 3 (ft), 2 (pt); LPNs 9 (ft), 3 (pt); Orderlies 4 (ft), 2 (pt); Nurses aides 28 (ft), 27 (pt); Recreational therapists 2 (ft), 1 (pt); Occupational therapists 1 (pt); Activities coordinators 1 (ft).
Affiliation Lutheran
Facilities Dining room; Physical therapy room; Activities room; Chapel; Crafts room; Laundry room; Barber/Beauty shop; Garden court; Craft kitchen.
Activities Arts & crafts; Cards; Games; Reading groups; Prayer groups; Movies; Shopping trips; Social/Cultural gatherings; Dinner groups.

Piper Group Home
PO Box 167, Rte 6, Fergus Falls, MN, 56537
(218) 736-6612
Admin Catherine Piper. *Medical Dir/Dir of Nursing* L Hull.
Licensure Intermediate care for mentally retarded. *Beds* ICF/MR 6. *Certified* Medicaid.

Owner Privately owned.
Admissions Requirements Minimum age 18; Medical examination; Physician's request.
Facilities Dining room; Activities room; Crafts room; Laundry room.
Activities Arts & crafts; Cards; Games; Movies; Shopping trips; Social/Cultural gatherings.

FERTILE

Fair Meadow Nursing Home
PO Box 8, Fertile, MN, 56540
(218) 945-6194
Admin Barry J Robertson. *Medical Dir/Dir of Nursing* Bruce Ring MD; Marian Cerkowniak DON.
Licensure Intermediate care. *Beds* ICF 83. *Certified* Medicaid.
Owner Publicly owned.
Staff RNs; LPNs; Nurses aides; Activities coordinators.
Facilities Dining room; Physical therapy room; Activities room; Chapel; Crafts room; Laundry room; Barber/Beauty shop.
Activities Arts & crafts; Cards; Games; Reading groups; Movies; Shopping trips; Social/Cultural gatherings.

FOLEY

Foley Nursing Center
PO Box 260, Rte 2, Foley, MN, 56329
(612) 968-6201
Admin Walter E Bahner. *Medical Dir/Dir of Nursing* Dean Weber RN.
Licensure Skilled care; Intermediate care. *Beds* SNF 97; ICF 20. *Certified* Medicaid; Medicare.
Owner Proprietary Corp.
Admissions Requirements Minimum age 16; Medical examination; Physician's request.
Staff RNs 4 (ft), 7 (pt); LPNs 4 (ft), 8 (pt); Nurses aides 5 (ft), 50 (pt); Physical therapists 1 (ft).
Facilities Dining room; Physical therapy room; Activities room; Chapel; Crafts room; Laundry room; Barber/Beauty shop; Library; Country store.
Activities Arts & crafts; Cards; Games; Reading groups; Prayer groups; Movies; Shopping trips; Social/Cultural gatherings; Religious services; Stroke group; Remotivation group; Outings; Special birthday rememberances.

FOREST LAKE

Birchwood Health Care Center
604 NE 1st St, Forest Lake, MN, 55025
(612) 464-5600
Admin Barbara Christen. *Medical Dir/Dir of Nursing* Carl Peikert; Voni Gervais DON.
Licensure Skilled care; Intermediate care. *Beds* 161. *Certified* Medicaid; Medicare.
Owner Proprietary Corp.
Admissions Requirements Minimum age 16; Medical examination; Physician's request.
Staff Physicians 4 (pt); RNs 7 (ft), 10 (pt); LPNs 2 (ft), 15 (pt); Nurses aides 22 (ft), 55 (pt); Physical therapists 2 (ft); Recreational therapists 1 (ft), 3 (pt); Occupational therapists 2 (ft); Speech therapists 1 (pt); Dietitians 1 (pt); Dentists 1 (pt); Ophthalmologists 1 (pt); Podiatrists 1 (pt).
Facilities Dining room; Physical therapy room; Activities room; Chapel; Crafts room; Laundry room; Barber/Beauty shop; Library.
Activities Arts & crafts; Cards; Games; Reading groups; Prayer groups; Movies; Shopping trips; Social/Cultural gatherings.

FOSSTON

Fosston Group Home
N Mark Ave, Fosston, MN, 56542
(218) 435-6088
Admin Dr Vernon C Nordmark. *Medical Dir/Dir of Nursing* Josette C Nordmark MD.
Licensure Intermediate care for mentally retarded. *Beds* ICF/MR 10. *Certified* Medicaid.
Owner Nonprofit Corp.
Admissions Requirements Minimum age 18; Medical examination.
Staff RNs 1 (pt); Activities coordinators 1 (ft).
Facilities Dining room; Activities room; Laundry room.
Activities Arts & crafts; Cards; Games; Movies; Shopping trips; Social/Cultural gatherings.

Fosston Municipal Nursing Home
900 S Hilligoss Blvd E, Fosston, MN, 56542
(218) 435-1133
Admin David Hubbard. *Medical Dir/Dir of Nursing* Wes Ofstedal MD; Stefanie Reed RN.
Licensure Skilled care; Intermediate care. *Beds* SNF 50; ICF. *Certified* Medicaid; Medicare.
Owner Nonprofit Corp.
Admissions Requirements Physician's request.
Staff Physicians; RNs; LPNs; Nurses aides; Physical therapists; Recreational therapists; Occupational therapists; Speech therapists; Activities coordinators; Dietitians.
Facilities Dining room; Physical therapy room; Activities room; Chapel; Laundry room; Barber/Beauty shop; Library.
Activities Arts & crafts; Cards; Games; Reading groups; Prayer groups; Movies; Shopping trips; Social/Cultural gatherings.

Johnson Rest Home*
516 2nd St NE, Fosston, MN, 56542
(218) 435-1494
Admin Palma C Johnson. *Medical Dir/Dir of Nursing* Dr Haven.
Licensure Intermediate care; Boarding care. *Beds* ICF 20; Boarding care 20. *Certified* Medicaid.
Owner Proprietary Corp.
Admissions Requirements Medical examination; Physician's request.
Staff RNs 1 (ft), 1 (pt); LPNs 1 (pt); Nurses aides 10 (pt); Recreational therapists 1 (ft); Dietitians 1 (pt).
Facilities Dining room; Activities room; Crafts room.
Activities Arts & crafts; Cards; Games; Reading groups; Prayer groups; Movies; Shopping trips; Social/Cultural gatherings.

Midway Care Center
114 2nd St NE, Fosston, MN, 56542
(218) 435-1272
Admin Allen G Potvin. *Medical Dir/Dir of Nursing* Mary West RN.
Licensure Intermediate care. *Beds* 32. *Certified* Medicaid.
Owner Proprietary Corp.
Admissions Requirements Minimum age 16; Medical examination; Physician's request.
Staff RNs 1 (ft); LPNs 2 (ft); Nurses aides 3 (ft), 8 (pt); Recreational therapists 1 (ft), 1 (pt); Activities coordinators 1 (ft); Dietitians 1 (pt).
Facilities Dining room; Activities room; Laundry room; Barber/Beauty shop.
Activities Arts & crafts; Cards; Games; Reading groups; Prayer groups; Movies; Shopping trips; Social/Cultural gatherings.

FRANKLIN

Franklin Healthcare Center
900 3rd St E, Franklin, MN, 55333
(507) 557-2211

Admin Lamberta Doll. *Medical Dir/Dir of Nursing* Dr Buhr & Dr Thompson.
Licensure Skilled care. *Beds* SNF 58. *Certified* Medicaid; Medicare.
Owner Proprietary Corp (Beverly Enterprises).
Admissions Requirements Minimum age 16; Medical examination.
Staff RNs 1 (ft), 3 (pt); LPNs 1 (ft), 10 (pt); Nurses aides 11 (ft), 40 (pt); Physical therapists 1 (pt); Occupational therapists 1 (pt); Activities coordinators 1 (ft), 1 (pt); Dietitians 1 (ft).
Facilities Dining room; Physical therapy room; Activities room; Chapel; Crafts room; Laundry room; Barber/Beauty shop; Fireside room.
Activities Arts & crafts; Cards; Games; Reading groups; Prayer groups; Movies; Shopping trips; Social/Cultural gatherings; International days; Adopt-a-grandparent program.

FRAZEE

Frazee Retirement Center
Box 96, 2nd St SW, Frazee, MN, 56544
(218) 334-4501
Admin Robert B McTaggert. *Medical Dir/Dir of Nursing* Dr J Emery; Jan Riewer DON.
Licensure Skilled care; Intermediate care. *Beds* 102. *Certified* Medicaid; Medicare.
Owner Proprietary Corp.
Admissions Requirements Minimum age 18; Medical examination; Physician's request.
Staff RNs 3 (ft), 2 (pt); LPNs 6 (ft), 4 (pt); Orderlies 1 (ft), 2 (pt); Nurses aides 31 (ft), 26 (pt); Physical therapists 1 (pt); Speech therapists 1 (pt); Activities coordinators 1 (ft).
Facilities Dining room; Physical therapy room; Activities room; Chapel; Crafts room; Laundry room; Barber/Beauty shop.
Activities Arts & crafts; Cards; Games; Reading groups; Prayer groups; Movies; Shopping trips; Social/Cultural gatherings; Dinner outings.

Smith Group Home
Rte 1, Box 36, Frazee, MN, 56544
(218) 334-5651
Admin Leona Smith.
Licensure Intermediate care for mentally retarded. *Beds* ICF/MR 7. *Certified* Medicare.
Owner Privately owned.
Admissions Requirements Minimum age 21; Females only.
Facilities Dining room; Laundry room.
Activities Arts & crafts; Cards; Games; Reading groups; Movies; Shopping trips; Social/Cultural gatherings; Vacations.

FRIDLEY

Fridley Convalescent Home*
7590 Lyric Ln, Fridley, MN, 55432
(612) 786-7700
Admin Jackie Jedlicki.
Licensure Skilled care. *Beds* 129. *Certified* Medicaid.
Owner Nonprofit Corp.

Lynwood Healthcare Center
5700 E River Rd, Fridley, MN, 55432
(612) 571-3150
Admin Lois A Center. *Medical Dir/Dir of Nursing* Dr C E Turbak; Nancy Dierks RN.
Licensure Skilled care. *Beds* SNF 55. *Certified* Medicaid; Medicare.
Owner Proprietary Corp (Beverly Enterprises).
Admissions Requirements Minimum age 18; Medical examination; Physician's request.
Staff Physicians 2 (pt); RNs 2 (ft), 1 (pt); LPNs 2 (ft), 2 (pt); Nurses aides 11 (ft), 17 (pt); Physical therapists 1 (ft); Occupational therapists 1 (ft); Speech therapists 1 (pt);

Activities coordinators 1 (ft); Dietitians 1 (pt); Dentists 1 (pt); Ophthalmologists 1 (pt); Podiatrists 1 (pt).
Facilities Dining room; Physical therapy room; Activities room; Barber/Beauty shop; Occupational therapy room; Smoking area.
Activities Arts & crafts; Games; Prayer groups; Movies; Shopping trips; Social/Cultural gatherings.

FULDA

Maple Lawn Nursing Home Inc
400 7th St, Fulda, MN, 56131
(507) 425-2571
Admin Lisa M Abicht.
Licensure Intermediate care. *Beds* ICF 62. *Certified* Medicaid.
Owner Nonprofit Corp.
Admissions Requirements Medical examination; Physician's request.
Staff RNs 1 (ft), 2 (pt); LPNs 8 (pt); Nurses aides 6 (ft), 29 (pt); Reality therapists 3 (pt); Speech therapists 1 (pt); Activities coordinators 1 (ft); Dietitians 1 (pt).
Languages Sign
Facilities Dining room; Activities room; Chapel; Crafts room; Laundry room.
Activities Arts & crafts; Cards; Games; Reading groups; Prayer groups; Movies; Shopping trips; Social/Cultural gatherings; Dining out; Football outings; County Fair exhibitors etc.

New Dawn Inc
Box G, 307 S Lafayette Ave, Fulda, MN, 56131
(507) 425-3278
Admin Stephen D Lee. *Medical Dir/Dir of Nursing* Kathy Thurston.
Licensure Intermediate care for mentally retarded. *Beds* ICF/MR 15. *Certified* Medicaid.
Owner Nonprofit Corp.
Admissions Requirements Minimum age 18; Medical examination; Physician's request.
Staff RNs 1 (ft); LPNs 1 (ft); Nurses aides 8 (ft); Physical therapists 1 (ft); Recreational therapists 1 (ft); Occupational therapists 1 (ft); Speech therapists 1 (ft); Dietitians 1 (ft).
Facilities Dining room; Activities room; Crafts room; Laundry room.
Activities Arts & crafts; Cards; Games; Movies; Shopping trips; Social/Cultural gatherings.

GAYLORD

Gaylord Lakeview Home
640 3rd St, Gaylord, MN, 55334
(612) 237-2911
Admin Richard C Kons. *Medical Dir/Dir of Nursing* Dr H A Knoche; Betty Henke RN DON.
Licensure Skilled care; Intermediate care. *Beds* SNF 52; ICF 6. *Certified* Medicaid; Medicare.
Owner Publicly owned.
Admissions Requirements Minimum age 16; Medical examination; Physician's request.
Staff Physicians 5 (ft); RNs 2 (ft); LPNs 10 (ft); Nurses aides 26 (ft); Physical therapists 1 (ft); Recreational therapists 1 (ft); Occupational therapists 1 (ft); Speech therapists 1 (ft); Activities coordinators 1 (ft); Dietitians 1 (ft).
Facilities Dining room; Physical therapy room; Activities room; Crafts room; Laundry room; Barber/Beauty shop; Library.
Activities Arts & crafts; Cards; Games; Prayer groups; Movies; Shopping trips; Social/Cultural gatherings.

GLENCOE

Glencoe Area Health Center
705 E 18th St, Glencoe, MN, 55336
(612) 864-3121
Admin John C Doidge. *Medical Dir/Dir of Nursing* Dr Donald Rudy; Glenora Hoversten DON.
Licensure Skilled care. *Beds* SNF 110. *Certified* Medicaid; Medicare.
Owner Publicly owned.
Admissions Requirements Physician's request.
Staff Physicians 7 (ft); RNs 3 (ft), 5 (pt); LPNs 2 (ft), 13 (pt); Orderlies 4 (pt); Nurses aides 13 (ft), 37 (pt); Physical therapists 1 (ft); Occupational therapists 1 (pt); Speech therapists 1 (pt); Activities coordinators 4 (ft), 1 (pt); Dietitians 2 (ft).
Facilities Dining room; Physical therapy room; Activities room; Chapel; Crafts room; Laundry room; Barber/Beauty shop; Library.
Activities Arts & crafts; Cards; Games; Reading groups; Prayer groups; Movies; Shopping trips; Social/Cultural gatherings.

GLENWOOD

Glenwood Retirement Home Inc
719 SE 2nd St, Glenwood, MN, 56334
(612) 634-5131
Admin Gordon H Amble. *Medical Dir/Dir of Nursing* Dr Schuster; Mrs Bymere DON.
Licensure Skilled care; Intermediate care; Board & care ICF III. *Beds* SNF 53; ICF 12; BC ICF III 35. *Certified* Medicaid; Medicare.
Owner Nonprofit organization/foundation.
Admissions Requirements Medical examination.
Affiliation Lutheran
Facilities Dining room; Physical therapy room; Activities room; Chapel; Crafts room; Barber/Beauty shop; Library.
Activities Arts & crafts; Cards; Reading groups; Prayer groups; Movies; Social/Cultural gatherings.

Lakeview Care Center
Franklin at Lakeshore Dr, Glenwood, MN, 56334
(612) 634-4553
Admin Ruth Gunderson. *Medical Dir/Dir of Nursing* Dr Jeffrey Schlueter; Jean Cosgriff RN.
Licensure Skilled care. *Beds* SNF 69. *Certified* Medicaid; Medicare.
Owner Proprietary Corp (Good Neighbor Services).
Admissions Requirements Minimum age 18; Medical examination; Physician's request.
Staff RNs 2 (ft), 2 (pt); LPNs 2 (ft), 3 (pt); Nurses aides 11 (ft), 18 (pt); Physical therapists 1 (ft); Occupational therapists 1 (pt); Activities coordinators 1 (ft).
Facilities Dining room; Physical therapy room; Activities room; Chapel; Crafts room; Laundry room; Barber/Beauty shop.
Activities Arts & crafts; Cards; Games; Reading groups; Prayer groups; Movies; Shopping trips; Social/Cultural gatherings.

GOLDEN VALLEY

Colonial Acres Health Care Center*
5825 Saint Croix Ave, Golden Valley, MN, 55422
(612) 544-1555
Admin Timothy Wenberg. *Medical Dir/Dir of Nursing* Dr Roger Grimm.
Licensure Skilled care; Intermediate care. *Beds* 151. *Certified* Medicaid.
Owner Nonprofit Corp (Covenant Benevolent Inst).
Admissions Requirements Medical examination; Physician's request.

Staff Physicians 1 (pt); RNs 7 (ft), 13 (pt); LPNs 8 (ft), 8 (pt); Orderlies 5 (ft), 13 (pt); Nurses aides 21 (ft), 42 (pt); Physical therapists 1 (ft); Occupational therapists 1 (ft); Speech therapists 1 (pt); Activities coordinators 1 (ft); Dietitians 1 (pt).
Affiliation Evangelical Covenant Church
Facilities Dining room; Physical therapy room; Activities room; Chapel; Crafts room; Laundry room; Barber/Beauty shop; Library.
Activities Arts & crafts; Games; Reading groups; Prayer groups; Movies; Shopping trips; Social/Cultural gatherings.

Courage Residence
3915 Golden Valley Rd, Golden Valley, MN, 55422
(612) 588-0811 Ext 300
Admin Kathy Bakkenist. *Medical Dir/Dir of Nursing* Dr Arthur Quiggle; Janet Quarn.
Licensure Skilled care. *Beds* SNF 64. *Certified* Medicaid.
Owner Nonprofit Corp.
Admissions Requirements Minimum age 18.
Staff Physicians 5 (pt); RNs 3 (ft), 8 (pt); LPNs 2 (ft), 4 (pt); Nurses aides 11 (ft), 20 (pt); Physical therapists 2 (ft), 1 (pt); Recreational therapists 2 (ft); Occupational therapists 3 (ft), 1 (pt); Speech therapists 1 (ft), 1 (pt); Dietitians 1 (ft); Podiatrists 1 (pt).
Facilities Dining room; Physical therapy room; Activities room; Chapel; Laundry room; Barber/Beauty shop.
Activities Arts & crafts; Cards; Games; Reading groups; Prayer groups; Movies; Shopping trips; Social/Cultural gatherings.

Trevilla of Golden Valley*
7505 Country Club Rd, Golden Valley, MN, 55427
(612) 545-0416
Admin Sharon Bertsch.
Licensure Skilled care; Intermediate care. *Beds* SNF 218; ICF 35. *Certified* Medicaid; Medicare.
Owner Proprietary Corp (Unicare).

Weldwood Health Care Center
5411 Circle Downs, Golden Valley, MN, 55416
(612) 545-5633
Admin Janice L Palmer. *Medical Dir/Dir of Nursing* William Shimp MD; Diane Sjogren.
Licensure Skilled care; Intermediate care. *Beds* 88. *Certified* Medicaid; Medicare.
Owner Proprietary Corp (Good Neighbor Services).
Admissions Requirements Minimum age 18.
Staff Physicians; RNs 5 (ft), 3 (pt); LPNs 3 (ft), 4 (pt); Nurses aides 11 (ft), 15 (pt); Physical therapists 2 (pt); Recreational therapists 2 (ft); Occupational therapists 2 (pt).
Facilities Dining room; Activities room; Crafts room; Laundry room; Barber/Beauty shop.
Activities Arts & crafts; Cards; Games; Reading groups; Prayer groups; Movies; Shopping trips; Social/Cultural gatherings; Camping trips.

GRACEVILLE

Grace Home*
116 W 2nd St, Graceville, MN, 56240
(612) 748-7261
Admin Charles E Lund.
Licensure Intermediate care. *Beds* 60. *Certified* Medicaid.
Owner Nonprofit Corp.

GRAND MARAIS

Cook County Northshore Hospital—Care & Nursing Center
Gunflint Trail, Grand Marais, MN, 55604
(218) 387-1500
Admin Craig Kantos. *Medical Dir/Dir of Nursing* Dr Bill Gallea; Donna Clothier.
Licensure Skilled care. *Beds* 47. *Certified* Medicaid; Medicare.
Owner Nonprofit Corp.
Staff RNs 1 (ft), 4 (pt); LPNs 1 (ft), 3 (pt); Nurses aides 11 (ft), 12 (pt); Physical therapists 1 (ft); Activities coordinators 1 (ft); Dietitians 1 (pt).
Facilities Dining room; Physical therapy room; Activities room; Laundry room; Barber/Beauty shop.
Activities Arts & crafts; Cards; Games; Reading groups; Prayer groups; Movies; Shopping trips; Social/Cultural gatherings.

GRAND MEADOW

Meadow Manor Nursing Home
PO Box 365, 210 E Grand Ave, Grand Meadow, MN, 55936
(507) 754-5212
Admin Robert A Lamp. *Medical Dir/Dir of Nursing* B D Westra MD.
Licensure Skilled care. *Beds* 50. *Certified* Medicaid; Medicare.
Owner Nonprofit Corp.
Admissions Requirements Minimum age 18; Medical examination; Physician's request.
Facilities Dining room; Physical therapy room; Activities room; Chapel; Crafts room; Laundry room; Barber/Beauty shop; Library.
Activities Arts & crafts; Cards; Games; Reading groups; Prayer groups; Movies; Shopping trips; Social/Cultural gatherings.

GRAND RAPIDS

Christus Group Home*
510 13th St SE, Grand Rapids, MN, 55744
(218) 326-8095
Admin Sandra Johnson. *Medical Dir/Dir of Nursing* Carolyn Lorbiecki RN.
Licensure Supervised care facility. *Beds* 12. *Certified* Medicaid.
Owner Nonprofit Corp.
Admissions Requirements Minimum age 18; Medical examination.
Staff RNs 1 (pt); Dietitians 1 (pt); Counselors 5 (ft), 4 (pt).
Affiliation Lutheran
Facilities Dining room; Crafts room; Laundry room.
Activities Arts & crafts; Cards; Games; Movies; Shopping trips; Social/Cultural gatherings.

Itasca Nursing Home
923 County Home Rd, Grand Rapids, MN, 55744
(218) 326-0543
Admin Anthony J Ogdahl. *Medical Dir/Dir of Nursing* Dr L E Karges; Don Gaalaas RN DON.
Licensure Skilled care; Intermediate care; Adult day care; Head Start 3-5 yr old children. *Beds* SNF 60; ICF 58; Adult day care 22. *Certified* Medicaid; Medicare.
Owner Publicly owned.
Admissions Requirements Minimum age 12; Medical examination.
Staff RNs 4 (ft), 2 (pt); LPNs 7 (ft), 8 (pt); Nurses aides 22 (ft), 10 (pt); Physical therapists 1 (pt); Activities coordinators 1 (ft); Dietitians 1 (ft).
Facilities Dining room; Physical therapy room; Activities room; Chapel; Crafts room; Laundry room; Barber/Beauty shop.
Activities Arts & crafts; Cards; Games; Reading groups; Movies; Shopping trips; Social/Cultural gatherings.

Leisure Hills Inc*
2801 S Pokegama, Grand Rapids, MN, 55744
(218) 326-3431
Admin Ronald Evensen.
Licensure Skilled care. *Beds* 124. *Certified* Medicaid.
Owner Proprietary Corp.

GRANITE FALLS

Granite Falls Municipal Hospital & Manor
345 10th Ave, Granite Falls, MN, 56241
(612) 564-3111
Admin George Gerlach. *Medical Dir/Dir of Nursing* Patti Kile MD; Nancy St Sauver RN DON.
Licensure Skilled care; Intermediate care. *Beds* 64. *Certified* Medicaid; Medicare.
Owner Publicly owned.
Admissions Requirements Medical examination; Physician's request.
Facilities Dining room; Physical therapy room; Activities room; Laundry room; Barber/Beauty shop; Library.
Activities Arts & crafts; Cards; Games; Reading groups; Prayer groups; Movies; Shopping trips; Social/Cultural gatherings.

Project Turnabout
660 18th St, Granite Falls, MN, 56241
(612) 564-4911
Admin Philip S Kelly. *Medical Dir/Dir of Nursing* Peggy Gatz.
Licensure Supervised living facility. *Beds* 44.
Owner Nonprofit Corp.
Staff RNs 1 (ft); LPNs 3 (ft); Nurses aides 4 (ft); Counselors 8 (ft).
Facilities Dining room; Activities room; Laundry room; Group therapy rooms; Lecture hall.
Activities Arts & crafts; Movies; Chemical dependency treatment.

HALLOCK

Kittson County Nursing Home*
410 Cedar Ave S, Hallock, MN, 56728
(218) 843-2633
Admin John A Nelson.
Licensure Intermediate care. *Beds* 36. *Certified* Medicaid.
Owner Publicly owned.

Kittson Memorial Hospital*
1010 S Birch, Hallock, MN, 56728
(218) 843-3612
Admin Bruce Berg.
Licensure Skilled care; Intermediate care. *Beds* 95. *Certified* Medicaid.
Owner Nonprofit Corp.

HALSTAD

Halstad Lutheran Memorial Home
133 4th Ave E, Halstad, MN, 56548
(218) 456-2105
Admin Kurt S Hansen. *Medical Dir/Dir of Nursing* Dr G Brown.
Licensure Intermediate care. *Beds* 68. *Certified* Medicaid.
Owner Nonprofit Corp.
Admissions Requirements Medical examination; Physician's request.
Staff RNs 1 (pt); LPNs 7 (ft).
Affiliation Lutheran
Facilities Dining room; Physical therapy room; Activities room; Chapel; Crafts room; Laundry room; Barber/Beauty shop; Library; Garden & gazebo area.
Activities Arts & crafts; Cards; Games; Reading groups; Prayer groups; Movies; Shopping trips; Social/Cultural gatherings.

HARMONY

Harmony Community Hospital
Rte 1 Box 173, Harmony, MN, 55939
(507) 886-6544
Admin Greg Braun. *Medical Dir/Dir of Nursing* John D Nehring MD; Shirley Browning RN DON.
Licensure Skilled care; Intermediate care. *Beds* 45. *Certified* Medicaid.
Owner Nonprofit Corp.
Admissions Requirements Medical examination.
Staff Physicians 1 (ft); RNs 1 (ft), 1 (pt); LPNs 2 (ft), 9 (pt); Nurses aides 9 (ft), 18 (pt); Physical therapists 1 (pt); Activities coordinators 1 (ft), 1 (pt); Dietitians 1 (pt); Ophthalmologists 1 (pt); Podiatrists 1 (pt).
Facilities Dining room; Physical therapy room; Activities room; Chapel; Crafts room; Laundry room; Barber/Beauty shop.
Activities Arts & crafts; Cards; Games; Reading groups; Prayer groups; Movies; Social/Cultural gatherings.

Sunshine Place
135 Center St E, Harmony, MN, 55939
(507) 886-2220
Admin Luwayne Ommen.
Licensure Intermediate care for mentally retarded. *Beds* ICF/MR 10. *Certified* Medicaid.
Owner Nonprofit Corp.
Activities Arts & crafts; Cards; Games; Reading groups; Prayer groups; Movies; Shopping trips; Social/Cultural gatherings.

HASTINGS

Henry Hagen Residence
19845 Lillehei Ave, Hastings, MN, 55033
(612) 437-9363
Admin Laura L Reynolds.
Licensure Intermediate care for mentally retarded. *Beds* ICF/MR 6. *Certified* Medicaid.
Owner Privately owned.
Admissions Requirements Minimum age 18; Medical examination; Physician's request.
Staff RNs 1 (pt); Activities coordinators 1 (pt).
Facilities Dining room; Activities room; Crafts room; Laundry room.
Activities Arts & crafts; Cards; Games; Movies; Shopping trips; Social/Cultural gatherings.

Haven Homes Health Center
930 W 16th St, Hastings, MN, 55033
(612) 437-6176
Admin Rev Lester Fair. *Medical Dir/Dir of Nursing* David Ecker MD; Jeanne Menard DON.
Licensure Skilled care; Intermediate care; Rehabilitation services. *Beds* 107. *Certified* Medicaid; Medicare.
Owner Proprietary Corp.
Admissions Requirements Minimum age 55; Medical examination; Physician's request.
Staff Physicians; RNs; LPNs; Orderlies; Nurses aides; Physical therapists 1 (ft); Recreational therapists 1 (ft); Occupational therapists 1 (ft); Speech therapists 1 (pt); Dietitians 1 (ft).
Facilities Dining room; Physical therapy room; Activities room; Chapel; Crafts room; Laundry room; Barber/Beauty shop.
Activities Arts & crafts; Cards; Games; Reading groups; Prayer groups; Movies; Social/Cultural gatherings.

Micoll Residence
926 W 2nd St, Hastings, MN, 55033
(612) 437-1967
Admin James Driscoll.

Licensure Intermediate care for mentally retarded. *Beds* 6.
Owner Proprietary Corp.

Minnesota Veterans Home—Hastings*
1200 E 18th St, Hastings, MN, 55033
(612) 437-3111
Admin James Ertz. *Medical Dir/Dir of Nursing* Ralph D Rayner MD.
Licensure Boarding care. *Beds* 200.
Owner Publicly owned.
Admissions Requirements Medical examination.
Staff Physicians 1 (pt); RNs 3 (ft); LPNs 5 (ft); Recreational therapists 1 (ft); Activities coordinators 1 (ft); Dietitians 1 (pt); Dentists 1 (pt); Ophthalmologists 1 (pt); Podiatrists 1 (pt); Chiropractors 1 (pt); Social workers 2 (ft); Counselors 2 (ft).
Facilities Dining room; Physical therapy room; Activities room; Chapel; Crafts room; Laundry room; Barber/Beauty shop; Library.
Activities Arts & crafts; Cards; Games; Reading groups; Prayer groups; Movies; Shopping trips; Social/Cultural gatherings; Sports activities; Fishing trips; Golf.

Regina Convalescent & Nursing Care Unit
1260 Nininger Rd, Hastings, MN, 55033
(612) 437-3121
Admin John W Junkman. *Medical Dir/Dir of Nursing* Susan Simon.
Licensure Skilled care; Intermediate care. *Beds* 61. *Certified* Medicaid; Medicare.
Owner Nonprofit organization/foundation.
Admissions Requirements Minimum age 55; Medical examination.
Staff RNs; LPNs; Orderlies; Nurses aides; Physical therapists; Activities coordinators; Dietitians.
Facilities Dining room; Physical therapy room; Activities room; Chapel; Crafts room; Laundry room; Barber/Beauty shop; Library.
Activities Arts & crafts; Cards; Games; Reading groups; Prayer groups; Movies; Shopping trips; Social/Cultural gatherings.

HAWLEY

Clay County Residence*
1358 Main St, Hawley, MN, 56549
(218) 233-5949
Admin Douglas E Johnson.
Licensure Supervised living facility. *Beds* 8. *Certified* Medicaid.
Owner Nonprofit Corp.
Admissions Requirements Minimum age 18; Medical examination.
Staff RNs 1 (pt).
Facilities Dining room; Activities room; Crafts room; Laundry room.
Activities Arts & crafts; Cards; Games; Movies; Shopping trips.

HAYFIELD

Field Crest Nursing Home
Rte 2, Box 6A, Hayfield, MN, 55940
(507) 477-3266
Admin Steven E Moss. *Medical Dir/Dir of Nursing* Dr Joan Knight; Dorothy Gesme RN DON.
Licensure Skilled care. *Beds* SNF 84. *Certified* Medicaid; Medicare.
Owner Publicly owned.
Admissions Requirements Medical examination; Physician's request.
Staff Physicians 1 (pt); RNs 4 (ft), 5 (pt); LPNs 4 (ft), 6 (pt); Nurses aides 27 (ft), 16 (pt); Physical therapists 1 (pt); Activities coordinators 1 (ft).
Facilities Dining room; Physical therapy room; Activities room; Crafts room; Laundry room; Barber/Beauty shop.
Activities Arts & crafts; Cards; Games; Reading groups; Prayer groups; Movies; Shopping trips; Social/Cultural gatherings.

HENDRICKS

Hendricks Nursing Home
503 E Lincoln St, Hendricks, MN, 56136
(507) 275-3134 or 275-3135
Admin Betty Buseth. *Medical Dir/Dir of Nursing* Dr LeRoy Mueller; Barbara Oerter DON.
Licensure Skilled care; Intermediate care. *Beds* SNF 40; ICF 30. *Certified* Medicaid.
Owner Nonprofit Corp.
Admissions Requirements Medical examination; Physician's request.
Staff Physicians 2 (ft); RNs 3 (ft), 5 (pt); LPNs 1 (ft), 8 (pt); Orderlies 1 (pt); Nurses aides 4 (ft), 40 (pt); Physical therapists 2 (pt); Activities coordinators 1 (ft); Dietitians 1 (pt); Aides 1 (ft), 1 (pt).
Languages Norwegian, Danish, German
Facilities Dining room; Physical therapy room; Activities room; Chapel; Crafts room; Laundry room.
Activities Arts & crafts; Cards; Games; Reading groups; Prayer groups; Movies; Shopping trips; Social/Cultural gatherings; Bingo; Horseshoe; Bowling; Sensory stimulation.

HENNING

Henning Nursing Home
907 Marshall Ave, Henning, MN, 56551
(218) 583-2965
Admin Richard Cloeter. *Medical Dir/Dir of Nursing* Jon Wigert MD; Joan Johnson RN DON.
Licensure Intermediate care. *Beds* ICF 64. *Certified* Medicaid.
Owner Proprietary Corp (Beverly Enterprises).
Admissions Requirements Minimum age 16; Medical examination.
Staff RNs 1 (ft), 1 (pt); LPNs 3 (ft), 5 (pt); Nurses aides 14 (ft), 24 (pt); Activities coordinators 1 (ft), 1 (pt).
Languages German, Norwegian
Facilities Dining room; Activities room; Crafts room; Laundry room.
Activities Arts & crafts; Cards; Games; Reading groups; Prayer groups; Shopping trips.

HIBBING

Golden Crest
2413 1st Ave W, Hibbing, MN, 55746
(218) 262-1081
Admin Mark S Noble. *Medical Dir/Dir of Nursing* Bayard French MD; Delores Rootes DON.
Licensure Skilled care. *Beds* SNF 84. *Certified* Medicaid; Medicare.
Owner Proprietary Corp (Beverly Enterprises).
Admissions Requirements Minimum age 16; Medical examination; Physician's request.
Staff RNs 4 (ft), 5 (pt); LPNs 4 (ft), 3 (pt); Orderlies 3 (pt); Nurses aides 15 (ft), 24 (pt); Occupational therapists 1 (ft); Activities coordinators 1 (ft).
Facilities Dining room; Physical therapy room; Activities room; Laundry room; Barber/Beauty shop; Library.
Activities Arts & crafts; Cards; Games; Movies; Shopping trips; Social/Cultural gatherings; Evening activities; Adopt-a-grandparent program.

Leisure Hills Healthcare Center*
1500 3rd Ave E, Hibbing, MN, 55746
(218) 263-7583
Admin Kenneth W Steiger.
Licensure Skilled care; Intermediate care. *Beds* SNF 203; ICF 12. *Certified* Medicaid.
Owner Proprietary Corp.

Range Center—Mapleview*
506 W 47th St, Hibbing, MN, 55748
(218) 263-4573

Admin Timothy Larson.
Licensure Skilled care; Intermediate care for mentally retarded. *Beds* SNF 6; ICF/MR 6. *Certified* Medicaid.
Owner Nonprofit Corp.

HILLS

Tuff Memorial Home
RR 1, Box 10, Hills, MN, 56138
(507) 962-3275
Admin Dana Dahlquist. *Medical Dir/Dir of Nursing* Dr L E Lyon; Karen Sandager RN DON.
Licensure Intermediate care. *Beds* ICF 52. *Certified* Medicaid.
Owner Nonprofit Corp.
Admissions Requirements Minimum age 19; Medical examination; Physician's request.
Staff RNs 2 (ft), 2 (pt); LPNs 1 (ft), 3 (pt); Nurses aides 4 (ft), 25 (pt); Activities coordinators 1 (ft), 1 (pt); Dietitians 1 (pt).
Affiliation Lutheran
Facilities Dining room; Chapel; Crafts room; Laundry room; Barber/Beauty shop.
Activities Arts & crafts; Games; Reading groups; Movies; Shopping trips; Social/Cultural gatherings.

HOFFMAN

Hoffman Care Center
104 S 6th St, Hoffman, MN, 56339
(612) 986-2047
Admin Douglas Aretz. *Medical Dir/Dir of Nursing* R Sampson DO; Debra Nelson RN DON.
Licensure Skilled care. *Beds* SNF 54. *Certified* Medicaid; Medicare.
Owner Proprietary Corp.
Admissions Requirements Medical examination; Physician's request.
Staff RNs 2 (ft); LPNs 5 (ft); Nurses aides 38 (ft); Physical therapists 1 (ft); Recreational therapists 1 (ft); Activities coordinators 1 (ft); Dietitians 1 (ft).
Facilities Dining room; Physical therapy room; Activities room; Crafts room; Laundry room; Barber/Beauty shop; Day room in conjunction with Chapel.
Activities Arts & crafts; Cards; Games; Reading groups; Prayer groups; Movies; Shopping trips; Social/Cultural gatherings; Sensory stimulation; Discussion groups.

HOPKINS

Chapel View Inc
615 Minnetonka Mills Rd, Hopkins, MN, 55343
(612) 938-2761
Admin Steven J Fritzke. *Medical Dir/Dir of Nursing* Margaret Schroeder DON.
Licensure Skilled care. *Beds* SNF 104; ICF 24. *Certified* Medicaid; Medicare.
Owner Nonprofit organization/foundation.
Admissions Requirements Minimum age 65.
Affiliation Methodist
Facilities Dining room; Physical therapy room; Activities room; Chapel; Crafts room; Laundry room; Barber/Beauty shop; Library.
Activities Arts & crafts; Cards; Games; Reading groups; Prayer groups; Movies; Shopping trips; Social/Cultural gatherings.

Edgewood Nursing Center
725 Second Ave S, Hopkins, MN, 55343
(612) 935-3338
Admin Mark A Wiener. *Medical Dir/Dir of Nursing* April Anderson.
Licensure Skilled care; Intermediate care. *Beds* 183. *Certified* Medicaid; Medicare.
Owner Proprietary Corp (Beverly Enterprises).
Admissions Requirements Medical examination.

Staff Physicians; RNs; LPNs; Nurses aides; Physical therapists; Occupational therapists; Speech therapists; Activities coordinators; Dietitians; Dentists; Ophthalmologists; Podiatrists; Dentist.
Facilities Dining room; Physical therapy room; Activities room; Crafts room; Laundry room; Barber/Beauty shop; Library.
Activities Arts & crafts; Cards; Games; Reading groups; Prayer groups; Movies; Shopping trips; Social/Cultural gatherings; Diners club.

HOUSTON

Valley View Nursing Home*
510 E Cedar St, Houston, MN, 55943
(507) 895-3125
Admin Rick Buechner.
Licensure Intermediate care. *Beds* 68. *Certified* Medicaid.
Owner Nonprofit Corp.

HOWARD LAKE

Howard Lake Care Center
413 13th Ave, Howard Lake, MN, 55349
(612) 543-3800
Admin Timothy Ryden. *Medical Dir/Dir of Nursing* Dr Mary Stiles; Marilyn Augle RN DON.
Licensure Skilled care. *Beds* SNF 73. *Certified* Medicaid.
Owner Proprietary Corp (Good Neighbor Services).
Admissions Requirements Minimum age 18; Medical examination; Physician's request.
Staff RNs 2 (ft), 4 (pt); LPNs 3 (ft), 4 (pt); Nurses aides 8 (ft), 39 (pt); Physical therapists 1 (pt); Occupational therapists 1 (pt); Speech therapists 1 (pt); Activities coordinators 1 (ft); Dietitians 1 (pt).
Facilities Dining room; Physical therapy room; Activities room; Laundry room; Barber/Beauty shop; Dayroom; Courtyard.
Activities Arts & crafts; Cards; Games; Reading groups; Movies; Shopping trips; Social/Cultural gatherings; Bible studies; Intergenerational activities.

HUTCHINSON

Aveyron Homes Inc
851 Dale St, Hutchinson, MN, 55350
(612) 587-6277
Admin Peggy LaDue. *Medical Dir/Dir of Nursing* Jane Larter.
Licensure Intermediate care for mentally retarded. *Beds* 14. *Certified* Medicaid.
Owner Nonprofit Corp.
Admissions Requirements Minimum age; Medical examination.
Staff RNs 1 (pt).
Facilities Dining room; Activities room; Laundry room.
Activities Arts & crafts; Cards; Games; Movies; Shopping trips; Social/Cultural gatherings.

Burns Manor Nursing Home*
N High Dr, Hutchinson, MN, 55350
(612) 587-4919
Admin Mavis J Geier.
Licensure Skilled care; Intermediate care. *Beds* SNF 65; ICF 64. *Certified* Medicaid; Medicare.
Owner Publicly owned.

INTERNATIONAL FALLS

Falls Care Center
Hwy 11-71, International Falls, MN, 56649
(218) 283-8313
Admin Rose M Matthews. *Medical Dir/Dir of Nursing* Charles Helleloid MD.

Licensure Skilled care; Intermediate care. *Beds* SNF 90; ICF 10. *Certified* Medicaid; Medicare; VA.
Owner Proprietary Corp (Good Neighbor Services).
Admissions Requirements Minimum age 18; Medical examination; Physician's request.
Staff RNs 4 (ft); LPNs 16 (ft); Nurses aides 48 (ft); Activities coordinators 3 (ft); Social services 1 (ft).
Facilities Dining room; Activities room; Chapel; Crafts room; Laundry room; Barber/Beauty shop.
Activities Arts & crafts; Cards; Games; Reading groups; Prayer groups; Movies; Shopping trips; Social/Cultural gatherings.

International Falls Group Home*
2000 Spruce St, International Falls, MN, 56649
(218) 285-7264
Admin Sandra Johnson.
Licensure Skilled care; Intermediate care. *Beds* SNF 11; ICF 12. *Certified* Medicaid.
Owner Nonprofit Corp.

INVER GROVE HEIGHTS

Inver Grove Care Center
4700 S Robert Trail, Inver Grove Heights, MN, 55075
(612) 451-1853
Admin Caryl Crozier. *Medical Dir/Dir of Nursing* Dr A Ferrara; Caroline Frascone RN DON.
Licensure Skilled care; Intermediate care. *Beds* SNF 70; ICF 6. *Certified* Medicaid; Medicare.
Owner Proprietary Corp (Good Neighbor Services).
Staff RNs 4 (ft), 4 (pt); LPNs 1 (ft), 9 (pt); Nurses aides 12 (ft), 20 (pt); Physical therapists 2 (pt); Recreational therapists 2 (ft); Occupational therapists 1 (ft); Speech therapists 1 (pt).
Languages Spanish
Facilities Dining room; Physical therapy room; Activities room; Chapel; Crafts room; Laundry room; Barber/Beauty shop.
Activities Arts & crafts; Cards; Games; Reading groups; Prayer groups; Movies; Shopping trips; Social/Cultural gatherings.

Wedgewood Health Care Center
2060 Upper 55th St E, Inver Grove Heights, MN, 55075
(612) 451-1881
Admin Edward W Lehmann. *Medical Dir/Dir of Nursing* Mary Wangsness MD; Sandra Van Beck RN DON.
Licensure Skilled care; Intermediate care. *Beds* SNF 141; ICF 29. *Certified* Medicaid; Medicare.
Owner Proprietary Corp.
Admissions Requirements Minimum age 16; Medical examination; Physician's request.
Staff RNs 7 (ft), 6 (pt); LPNs 6 (ft), 4 (pt); Nurses aides 36 (ft), 48 (pt); Recreational therapists 1 (ft).
Facilities Dining room; Physical therapy room; Activities room; Chapel; Crafts room; Laundry room; Barber/Beauty shop.
Activities Arts & crafts; Cards; Games; Reading groups; Prayer groups; Movies; Shopping trips; Social/Cultural gatherings.

IVANHOE

Divine Providence Hospital & Home
312 George St, Ivanhoe, MN, 56142
(507) 694-1414
Admin Sr Mariette. *Medical Dir/Dir of Nursing* Sr Cynthia.
Licensure Skilled care. *Beds* SNF 51. *Certified* Medicaid; Medicare.
Owner Nonprofit Corp.

Admissions Requirements Minimum age 18;
Physician's request.
Staff RNs 2 (ft), 2 (pt); LPNs 3 (ft), 4 (pt);
Orderlies 1 (ft); Nurses aides 12 (ft), 20 (pt);
Physical therapists 1 (pt); Speech therapists
1 (pt); Activities coordinators 2 (ft), 1 (pt);
Dietitians 1 (ft).
Languages Polish, German, Spanish
Affiliation Roman Catholic
Facilities Dining room; Physical therapy
room; Activities room; Chapel; Crafts room;
Laundry room; Barber/Beauty shop; Library.
Activities Arts & crafts; Cards; Games;
Reading groups; Prayer groups; Movies;
Shopping trips; Social/Cultural gatherings;
Outings.

JACKSON

Good Samaritan Center
600 W Street, Jackson, MN, 56143
(507) 847-3100
Admin Michael T Cranny. *Medical Dir/Dir of
Nursing* Dr Marianne Clinton; Lois
Stensland.
Licensure Skilled care; Intermediate care. *Beds*
SNF; ICF 89. *Certified* Medicaid; Medicare.
Owner Nonprofit Corp (Evangelical Lutheran/
Good Samaritan).
Staff Physicians 1 (pt); RNs 7 (ft), 4 (pt);
LPNs 5 (ft), 2 (pt).
Affiliation Lutheran
Facilities Dining room; Physical therapy
room; Activities room; Chapel; Crafts room;
Laundry room; Barber/Beauty shop; Library.
Activities Arts & crafts; Cards; Games;
Reading groups; Prayer groups; Movies;
Shopping trips; Social/Cultural gatherings.

Jackson Municipal Hospital C&CN
N Hwy, Jackson, MN, 56143
(507) 847-2247
Admin Sr Patricia Glowski RN. *Medical Dir/
Dir of Nursing* Dr M Clinton.
Licensure Intermediate care. *Beds* ICF 21.
Certified Medicaid.
Owner Publicly owned.
Admissions Requirements Medical
examination; Physician's request.
Staff RNs 1 (pt); LPNs 2 (ft), 4 (pt); Nurses
aides 2 (ft), 8 (pt); Physical therapists 1 (pt);
Activities coordinators 1 (ft); Dietitians 1
(ft).
Facilities Dining room; Physical therapy
room; Activities room; Crafts room; Laundry
room; Barber/Beauty shop.
Activities Arts & crafts; Cards; Games;
Reading groups; Prayer groups; Movies;
Social/Cultural gatherings.

JANESVILLE

The Janesville Nursing Home
102 E North St, Janesville, MN, 56048
(507) 234-5113
Admin Jennifer D Pfeffer. *Medical Dir/Dir of
Nursing* David Pope MD; Cynthia Cahill
RN DON.
Licensure Skilled care. *Beds* SNF 45. *Certified*
Medicaid; Medicare.
Owner Publicly owned.
Admissions Requirements Medical
examination; Physician's request.
Staff RNs 1 (ft), 2 (pt); LPNs 5 (pt); Nurses
aides 5 (ft), 19 (pt); Activities coordinators 2
(pt); Dietitians 1 (pt).
Facilities Dining room; Activities room;
Laundry room; Barber/Beauty shop.
Activities Cards; Games; Reading groups;
Prayer groups; Movies.

JORDAN

Valleyview Health Care Center
4061 W 173rd St, Jordan, MN, 55352
(612) 492-6160

Admin Ralph A Olinger. *Medical Dir/Dir of
Nursing* Dr W N Amra; LaDonna Battcher
RN.
Licensure Skilled care; Intermediate care. *Beds*
SNF 75; ICF 27. *Certified* Medicaid;
Medicare.
Owner Proprietary Corp.
Admissions Requirements Minimum age 21;
Medical examination.
Staff Physicians 19 (pt); RNs 4 (ft), 3 (pt);
LPNs 4 (ft), 11 (pt); Nurses aides 23 (ft), 36
(pt); Physical therapists 1 (pt); Speech
therapists 1 (pt); Activities coordinators 1
(ft); Dietitians 1 (pt); Ophthalmologists 1
(pt).
Facilities Dining room; Physical therapy
room; Activities room; Chapel; Crafts room;
Laundry room; Barber/Beauty shop.
Activities Arts & crafts; Cards; Games;
Reading groups; Prayer groups; Movies;
Shopping trips; Social/Cultural gatherings.

KARLSTAD

Karlstad Memorial Nursing Center
3rd & Washington, Karlstad, MN, 56732
(218) 436-2161
Admin Jerry D Peak. *Medical Dir/Dir of
Nursing* Ruben Thorbus MD; Kristen
Pagnac RN.
Licensure Skilled care; Intermediate care. *Beds*
SNF 71. *Certified* Medicaid; Medicare.
Owner Nonprofit Corp.
Admissions Requirements Minimum age 21;
Medical examination; Physician's request.
Staff RNs 3 (ft), 4 (pt); LPNs 3 (ft), 2 (pt);
Orderlies 1 (ft); Nurses aides 35 (ft), 20 (pt);
Physical therapists 1 (pt); Activities
coordinators 1 (ft); Dietitians 1 (pt).
Facilities Dining room; Physical therapy
room; Activities room; Chapel; Crafts room;
Laundry room; Barber/Beauty shop; Library.
Activities Arts & crafts; Cards; Games;
Reading groups; Prayer groups; Movies;
Shopping trips; Social/Cultural gatherings.

Valley Group Home 2
Main St S, Karlstad, MN, 56732
(218) 436-2518
Admin Vernon C Nordmark. *Medical Dir/Dir
of Nursing* Josette C Nordmark MD.
Licensure Intermediate care for mentally
retarded. *Beds* ICF/MR 10. *Certified*
Medicaid.
Owner Proprietary Corp.
Admissions Requirements Minimum age 18;
Medical examination.
Staff RNs 1 (pt); Activities coordinators 1 (ft).
Facilities Dining room; Activities room;
Laundry room.
Activities Arts & crafts; Cards; Games;
Movies; Shopping trips; Social/Cultural
gatherings.

KASSON

Woodvale Kasson*
17 4th St SW, Kasson, MN, 55944
(507) 634-4430
Admin Walter Baldus.
Licensure Intermediate care for mentally
retarded. *Beds* 14. *Certified* Medicaid.
Owner Proprietary Corp.

KELLIHER

Kelliher Good Samaritan Center
PO Box 189, Main St, Kelliher, MN, 56650
(218) 647-8251; 647-8258
Admin Susan K Utter.
Licensure Intermediate care. *Beds* ICF 36.
Certified Medicaid.
Owner Nonprofit Corp (Evangelical Lutheran/
Good Samaritan).
Admissions Requirements Minimum age 17;
Medical examination.

Staff RNs 1 (ft); LPNs 3 (ft), 2 (pt); Nurses
aides 3 (ft), 10 (pt); Activities coordinators 1
(ft).
Languages Chippewa
Facilities Dining room; Activities room;
Laundry room; Barber/Beauty shop; Rehab
social services.
Activities Arts & crafts; Cards; Games; Prayer
groups; Movies; Shopping trips; Social/
Cultural gatherings.

KENYON

Kenyon Sunset Home
127 Gunderson Blvd, Kenyon, MN, 55946
(507) 789-6134
Admin Gary E Flatgard. *Medical Dir/Dir of
Nursing* Dr William Walter; Beverly Olson
RN DON.
Licensure Skilled care; Intermediate care. *Beds*
SNF 62; ICF 17. *Certified* Medicaid;
Medicare.
Owner Nonprofit Corp.
Staff RNs; LPNs; Orderlies; Nurses aides;
Activities coordinators.
Affiliation Lutheran
Facilities Dining room; Activities room;
Chapel; Crafts room; Laundry room; Barber/
Beauty shop.
Activities Arts & crafts; Cards; Games;
Reading groups; Prayer groups; Movies;
Social/Cultural gatherings.

KERKHOVEN

Lindberg Rest Home*
Kerkhoven, MN, 56252
(612) 264-2601
Admin Florence E Lindberg.
Licensure Boarding care. *Beds* 26.
Owner Proprietary Corp.

KIMBALL

Madden Kimball Home
PO Box 129, Kimball, MN, 55353
(612) 398-5678
Admin Dolores Madden. *Medical Dir/Dir of
Nursing* D Krengel RN.
Licensure Intermediate care for mentally
retarded. *Beds* 32. *Certified* Medicaid.
Owner Proprietary Corp.
Admissions Requirements Minimum age 18;
Medical examination.
Staff RNs; LPNs; Speech therapists;
Dietitians.
Facilities Dining room; Activities room;
Independent kitchens.
Activities Arts & crafts; Cards; Games;
Shopping trips; Social/Cultural gatherings.

LACRESCENT

Houston County Group Home
1700 Lancer Blvd, LaCrescent, MN, 55947
(507) 895-8111
Admin Dennis Theede. *Medical Dir/Dir of
Nursing* Janice Larsen.
Licensure Intermediate care for mentally
retarded. *Beds* ICF/MR 15. *Certified*
Medicaid.
Owner Nonprofit Corp.
Admissions Requirements Minimum age 3.
Staff RNs 1 (ft), 2 (pt); LPNs 1 (ft); Activities
coordinators 3 (ft).
Facilities Dining room; Activities room;
Laundry room.
Activities Arts & crafts; Cards; Games;
Reading groups; Prayer groups; Movies;
Shopping trips.

LaCrescent Healthcare Center
701 Main St, LaCrescent, MN, 55947
(507) 895-4445

Admin Gale A Bruessel. *Medical Dir/Dir of Nursing* Dr Bruce Carlson; Dixie Johnson RN.
Licensure Skilled care. *Beds* 77. *Certified* Medicaid; Medicare.
Owner Proprietary Corp (Beverly Enterprises).
Admissions Requirements Medical examination; Physician's request.
Staff RNs 4 (ft); LPNs 2 (ft), 8 (pt); Nurses aides 6 (ft), 34 (pt); Physical therapists 1 (pt); Recreational therapists 1 (pt); Occupational therapists 1 (pt); Speech therapists 1 (pt).
Facilities Dining room; Physical therapy room; Activities room; Chapel; Crafts room; Laundry room; Barber/Beauty shop.
Activities Arts & crafts; Cards; Games; Prayer groups; Movies; Shopping trips; Social/Cultural gatherings; Birthday parties; Bingo; Happy hours; Memorial services.

LAFAYETTE

Lafayette Good Samaritan Center
Box 19, Esther Ave, Lafayette, MN, 56054
(507) 228-8238
Admin Lane Anderson. *Medical Dir/Dir of Nursing* Julie Pace RN DNS.
Licensure Intermediate care. *Beds* 40. *Certified* Medicaid.
Owner Nonprofit Corp (Evangelical Lutheran/Good Samaritan).
Staff RNs 3 (ft); LPNs 4 (ft); Nurses aides 18 (ft); Physical therapists 1 (ft); Activities coordinators 2 (ft); Dietitians 1 (ft).
Affiliation Lutheran
Facilities Dining room; Activities room; Chapel; Crafts room; Laundry room; Barber/Beauty shop; Library.
Activities Arts & crafts; Cards; Games; Reading groups; Prayer groups; Movies; Shopping trips; Social/Cultural gatherings.

LAKE CITY

Great River Homes Inc
711 N High St, Lake City, MN, 55041
(612) 345-2625
Admin Michael Weinandt.
Licensure Intermediate care for mentally retarded. *Beds* ICF/MR 8. *Certified* Medicare.
Owner Nonprofit Corp.
Admissions Requirements Minimum age 18.
Staff RNs 1 (pt); LPNs 1 (pt).
Facilities Dining room; Laundry room.

Lake City Nursing Home
405 W Grant St, Lake City, MN, 55041
(612) 345-5366
Admin Mariann K Wiebusch. *Medical Dir/Dir of Nursing* Frank Thorngren MD; Jeanette Hoops DON.
Licensure Skilled care. *Beds* SNF 115. *Certified* Medicare.
Owner Publicly owned.
Admissions Requirements Minimum age 16.
Staff Physicians 5 (pt); RNs 6 (ft), 5 (pt); LPNs 3 (ft), 10 (pt); Orderlies 4 (pt); Nurses aides 11 (ft), 35 (pt); Physical therapists 1 (pt); Occupational therapists 1 (pt); Speech therapists 1 (pt); Activities coordinators 1 (pt); Dietitians 1 (pt).
Facilities Dining room; Physical therapy room; Activities room; Crafts room; Laundry room; Barber/Beauty shop; Greenhouse; Lounges.
Activities Arts & crafts; Cards; Games; Reading groups; Prayer groups; Movies; Shopping trips; Social/Cultural gatherings.

River Oaks Health Care Center*
815 N High St, Lake City, MN, 55041
(612) 345-5336
Admin James E Range.
Licensure Nursing home. *Beds* 36.
Owner Proprietary Corp.

Admissions Requirements Minimum age 21; Medical examination.
Staff RNs 1 (ft), 1 (pt); LPNs 3 (ft), 3 (pt); Nurses aides 10 (ft), 12 (pt); Recreational therapists 1 (pt); Activities coordinators 1 (pt); Dietitians 1 (pt).
Facilities Dining room; Activities room; Chapel; Crafts room; Family room.
Activities Arts & crafts; Cards; Games; Prayer groups; Movies; Shopping trips.

LAKE CRYSTAL

Lake Crystal Healthcare Center*
202 Laclaire, Lake Crystal, MN, 56055
(507) 726-2669
Admin David Gislason.
Licensure Skilled care; Intermediate care. *Beds* SNF 40; ICF 24. *Certified* Medicaid.
Owner Proprietary Corp (Thro Co).

LAKE ELMO

Nekton on Stillwater Lane
10092 Stillwater Ln, Lake Elmo, MN, 55042
(612) 777-1907
Admin Omar Othman. *Medical Dir/Dir of Nursing* Jeanne Kube RN.
Licensure Intermediate care for mentally retarded. *Beds* 6. *Certified* Medicaid.
Owner Proprietary Corp.
Admissions Requirements Medical examination; Physician's request.
Staff RNs 1 (ft).
Languages Sign
Facilities Dining room; Activities room; Laundry room.
Activities Arts & crafts; Cards; Games; Movies; Shopping trips; Social/Cultural gatherings.

LAKE PARK

Sunnyside Nursing Home*
Rte 2, Lake Park, MN, 56544
(218) 238-5944
Admin Gary Ask.
Licensure Intermediate care. *Beds* 63. *Certified* Medicaid.
Owner Publicly owned.

LAKEFIELD

Colonial Manor Nursing Home
RR 1 Box 370, Manor Dr, Lakefield, MN, 56150
(507) 662-6646
Admin Geraldine Burmeister. *Medical Dir/Dir of Nursing* B Carleton MD; Lee Ann Bauer DON.
Licensure Intermediate care. *Beds* ICF 54. *Certified* Medicaid.
Owner Publicly owned.
Admissions Requirements Medical examination; Physician's request.
Staff Physicians 2 (pt); RNs 1 (ft), 2 (pt); LPNs 3 (ft), 6 (pt); Nurses aides 3 (ft), 20 (pt); Recreational therapists 1 (ft); Activities coordinators 1 (ft); Dietitians 1 (pt).
Facilities Dining room; Activities room; Chapel; Crafts room; Laundry room; Barber/Beauty shop.
Activities Arts & crafts; Cards; Games; Reading groups; Prayer groups; Movies; Shopping trips; Social/Cultural gatherings.

LAKEVILLE

Ebenezer Ridges Geriatric Care Center
13820 Community Dr, Lakeville, MN, 55337
(612) 435-8116
Admin Mark Broman. *Medical Dir/Dir of Nursing* Dr Brian Ebeling; Mary Hoeppner.
Licensure Skilled care. *Beds* SNF 104. *Certified* Medicaid; Medicare.

Owner Nonprofit Corp.
Admissions Requirements Minimum age 62; Medical examination.
Staff RNs 4 (ft), 14 (pt); LPNs 2 (ft), 10 (pt); Orderlies; Nurses aides 15 (ft), 50 (pt); Physical therapists 1 (ft); Occupational therapists 1 (ft); Speech therapists 1 (pt); Activities coordinators 1 (pt); Dietitians 1 (ft).
Affiliation Lutheran
Facilities Dining room; Physical therapy room; Crafts room; Laundry room; Barber/Beauty shop; Occupational therapy room; Multi-purpose room; Patio & garden area.
Activities Arts & crafts; Cards; Games; Prayer groups; Movies; Shopping trips; Social/Cultural gatherings.

Zenith Apartments
20345 Iberia Ave W, Lakeville, MN, 55044
(612) 469-4000
Admin James Driscoll.
Licensure Skilled care; Intermediate care for mentally retarded. *Beds* ICF/MR 15. *Certified* Medicaid.
Owner Proprietary Corp.

LAMBERTON

Valley View Manor
Box 126, 9th & Birch, Lamberton, MN, 56152
(507) 752-7346
Admin James Broich. *Medical Dir/Dir of Nursing* Dr Mearl Keithahn; Susan Swan.
Licensure Skilled care; Intermediate care. *Beds* SNF 65; ICF 15. *Certified* Medicaid; Medicare; VA.
Owner Publicly owned.
Admissions Requirements Minimum age 18; Medical examination; Physician's request.
Staff RNs 2 (ft), 4 (pt); LPNs 8 (pt); Nurses aides 5 (ft), 40 (pt); Physical therapists 1 (pt); Recreational therapists 1 (ft), 3 (pt); Activities coordinators 1 (ft); Dietitians 1 (pt).
Languages German, Norweigan
Facilities Dining room; Physical therapy room; Activities room; Crafts room; Laundry room; Barber/Beauty shop.
Activities Arts & crafts; Cards; Games; Reading groups; Prayer groups; Movies; Shopping trips; Social/Cultural gatherings.

LE CENTER

Central Health Care
444 N Cordova St, Le Center, MN, 56057
(612) 357-2275
Admin Scott Jackson. *Medical Dir/Dir of Nursing* Dr Michael Wilcox; Mary Lynn Schatz DON.
Licensure Skilled care. *Beds* 110. *Certified* Medicaid; Medicare; VA.
Owner Privately owned.
Admissions Requirements Medical examination; Physician's request.
Staff RNs 6 (ft), 1 (pt); LPNs 7 (ft), 1 (pt); Orderlies 2 (ft), 4 (pt); Nurses aides 19 (ft), 42 (pt); Physical therapists 1 (ft), 3 (pt); Recreational therapists 1 (ft), 1 (pt); Dietitians 1 (ft).
Facilities Dining room; Physical therapy room; Activities room; Chapel; Laundry room; Barber/Beauty shop; Library.
Activities Arts & crafts; Cards; Games; Reading groups; Prayer groups; Movies; Shopping trips; Social/Cultural gatherings.

LESTER PRAIRIE

Dungarvin X Alice Haney Annex*
100 S Maple St, Lester Prairie, MN, 55354
(612) 395-2517
Admin Jan Carver.

Licensure Intermediate care for mentally retarded. *Beds* 15. *Certified* Medicaid.
Owner Proprietary Corp.

LEWISTON

Lewiston Villa Nursing Home
505 E Main St, Lewiston, MN, 55952
(507) 523-2123
Admin Thomas Johnsrud. *Medical Dir/Dir of Nursing* Dr Donald Morris; Roger Wertanen.
Licensure Skilled care. *Beds* SNF 58. *Certified* Medicaid; Medicare.
Owner Proprietary Corp (Beverly Enterprises).
Admissions Requirements Minimum age 16; Medical examination; Physician's request.
Staff RNs 1 (ft), 3 (pt); LPNs 3 (ft), 5 (pt); Orderlies 1 (pt); Nurses aides 8 (ft), 10 (pt); Activities coordinators 1 (ft), 1 (pt).
Facilities Dining room; Physical therapy room; Activities room; Chapel; Crafts room; Laundry room; Barber/Beauty shop; Library.
Activities Arts & crafts; Cards; Games; Reading groups; Prayer groups; Movies; Shopping trips; Social/Cultural gatherings; Outings.

LEXINGTON

Forestview Lexington*
9329 Dunlap Ave N, Lexington, MN, 55112
(612) 546-1969
Admin Mary M Hill.
Licensure Supervised living facility. *Beds* 6. *Certified* Medicaid.
Staff RNs 1 (pt).
Facilities Laundry room.
Activities Arts & crafts; Cards; Games; Movies; Shopping trips; Social/Cultural gatherings; Camping & other outdoor activities.

LITCHFIELD

Bethany Home
203 N Armstrong, Litchfield, MN, 55355
(612) 693-2423
Admin Brandon Pietsch. *Medical Dir/Dir of Nursing* Dr Ted Loftness; Joan Kuechle RN.
Licensure Intermediate care. *Beds* ICF 52. *Certified* Medicaid.
Owner Nonprofit Corp.
Admissions Requirements Medical examination; Physician's request.
Staff RNs; LPNs; Nurses aides; Activities coordinators; Dietitians.
Affiliation Lutheran
Facilities Dining room; Activities room; Chapel; Crafts room; Laundry room; Barber/Beauty shop.
Activities Arts & crafts; Cards; Games; Reading groups; Prayer groups; Movies; Shopping trips; Social/Cultural gatherings.

Emmanuel Home*
600 S Davis, Litchfield, MN, 55355
(612) 693-2472
Admin Michael Boyle. *Medical Dir/Dir of Nursing* Cecil Leitch MD.
Licensure Skilled care. *Beds* 120. *Certified* Medicaid.
Owner Nonprofit Corp.
Staff RNs 10 (ft); LPNs 18 (ft); Nurses aides 90 (ft); Physical therapists 1 (ft); Activities coordinators 1 (ft).
Affiliation Lutheran
Facilities Dining room; Physical therapy room; Activities room; Chapel; Crafts room; Laundry room; Barber/Beauty shop.
Activities Arts & crafts; Cards; Games; Reading groups; Prayer groups; Movies; Shopping trips; Social/Cultural gatherings.

Meeker County Community Home
504 S Marshall Ave, Litchfield, MN, 55355
(612) 693-8836

Admin Ron Monson.
Licensure Supervised care facility. *Beds* 15. *Certified* Medicaid.
Owner Nonprofit Corp.
Admissions Requirements Minimum age 18.
Staff RNs 1 (pt).
Facilities Dining room; Activities room; Laundry room; Living room; Kitchen.
Activities Arts & crafts; Cards; Games; Reading groups; Movies; Shopping trips; Social/Cultural gatherings.

LITTLE CANADA

Nekton on Sextant*
332 Sextant, Little Canada, MN, 55117
(612) 483-3093
Admin Lynda Meadir.
Licensure Intermediate care for mentally retarded. *Beds* 6. *Certified* Medicaid.
Owner Proprietary Corp.

LITTLE FALLS

Christus Group Home*
315 SW 6th St, Little Falls, MN, 56345
(612) 632-2240
Admin John D Peterson.
Licensure Intermediate care for mentally retarded. *Beds* 13. *Certified* Medicaid.
Owner Nonprofit Corp.

Lutheran Senior Citizen Home Inc
1200 1st Ave NE, Little Falls, MN, 56345
(612) 632-9211
Admin Hubert T Zyvoloski. *Medical Dir/Dir of Nursing* Dr Royden Belcher; Albina Perowitz RN DON.
Licensure Skilled care. *Beds* SNF 118. *Certified* Medicaid; Medicare.
Owner Nonprofit Corp.
Admissions Requirements Physician's request.
Staff Physicians 1 (pt); RNs 5 (ft), 4 (pt); LPNs 9 (ft); Orderlies 3 (ft); Nurses aides 30 (ft), 25 (pt); Reality therapists 2 (ft), 1 (pt); Recreational therapists 5 (ft), 3 (pt); Activities coordinators 2 (ft); Dietitians 1 (pt).
Facilities Dining room; Physical therapy room; Activities room; Chapel; Crafts room; Laundry room; Barber/Beauty shop; Library; 5 acres; Park; Woodworking shop; 2 resident vans.
Activities Arts & crafts; Cards; Games; Reading groups; Prayer groups; Movies; Shopping trips; Social/Cultural gatherings.

St Otto's Home
920 SE 4th St, Little Falls, MN, 56345
(612) 632-9281
Admin Sr Susan Knutson OSF. *Medical Dir/Dir of Nursing* Helen Sundquist RN DON.
Licensure Skilled care; Intermediate care. *Beds* SNF 134; ICF 25. *Certified* Medicaid; Medicare.
Owner Nonprofit Corp.
Admissions Requirements Physician's request.
Staff RNs 3 (ft), 9 (pt); LPNs 7 (ft), 11 (pt); Nurses aides 18 (ft), 56 (pt); Physical therapists 1 (ft); Activities coordinators 1 (ft).
Affiliation Roman Catholic
Facilities Dining room; Physical therapy room; Activities room; Chapel; Crafts room; Laundry room; Barber/Beauty shop; Parlor; Day rooms.
Activities Arts & crafts; Cards; Games; Reading groups; Prayer groups; Movies; Shopping trips; Social/Cultural gatherings.

LONG LAKE

Long Lake Nursing Home
345 S Brown Rd, Long Lake, MN, 55356
(612) 473-2527
Admin James S O'Connell. *Medical Dir/Dir of Nursing* Tamara Staska.

Licensure Skilled care; Intermediate care. *Beds* 52. *Certified* Medicaid; Medicare.
Owner Proprietary Corp (Beverly Enterprises).
Admissions Requirements Minimum age 60; Medical examination; Physician's request.
Staff RNs 3 (ft); LPNs 6 (ft); Nurses aides 18 (ft); Physical therapists 1 (pt); Recreational therapists 1 (ft); Occupational therapists 1 (ft); Speech therapists 1 (pt); Activities coordinators 1 (ft); Dietitians 1 (ft).
Languages Swedish
Facilities Dining room; Physical therapy room; Laundry room; Barber/Beauty shop; Library; Day rooms.
Activities Arts & crafts; Cards; Games; Reading groups; Prayer groups; Movies; Social/Cultural gatherings; Adopt-a-grandchild.

LONG PRAIRIE

Long Prairie Memorial Hospital*
20 9th St SE, Long Prairie, MN, 56347
(612) 732-2141
Admin Kevin Smith.
Licensure Skilled care; Intermediate care. *Beds* SNF 64; ICF 29. *Certified* Medicaid; Medicare.
Owner Nonprofit Corp.

LUVERNE

Mary J Brown Good Samaritan Center
110 S Walnut Ave, Luverne, MN, 56156
(507) 283-2375
Admin Rev Daniel Fuelling. *Medical Dir/Dir of Nursing* Dr Larry Lyon.
Licensure Intermediate care; Boarding care. *Beds* ICF 70; Boarding care 4. *Certified* Medicaid.
Owner Nonprofit Corp (Evangelical Lutheran/ Good Samaritan).
Admissions Requirements Medical examination.
Staff RNs 1 (ft), 2 (pt); LPNs 3 (ft), 2 (pt); Nurses aides 10 (ft), 15 (ft); Physical therapists 2 (ft), 1 (pt); Activities coordinators 1 (ft), 1 (pt); Dietitians 1 (pt).
Affiliation Lutheran
Facilities Dining room; Physical therapy room; Activities room; Chapel; Crafts room; Laundry room; Barber/Beauty shop.
Activities Arts & crafts; Cards; Games; Reading groups; Prayer groups; Movies; Shopping trips; Social/Cultural gatherings.

MABEL

Green Lea Manor Nursing Home
PO Box 306, Mabel, MN, 55954
(507) 493-5436
Admin Jon P Tagatz.
Licensure Intermediate care. *Beds* 79. *Certified* Medicaid.
Staff RNs 2 (ft); LPNs 7 (ft); Orderlies 1 (ft); Nurses aides 30 (ft), 15 (pt); Activities coordinators 1 (ft); Dietitians 1 (pt).

MADELIA

Luther Memorial Home
221 6th St SW, Madelia, MN, 56062
(507) 642-3271
Admin Timothy J Samuelson. *Medical Dir/Dir of Nursing* William Halverson MD; Elizabeth Sondt.
Licensure Skilled care; Intermediate care. *Beds* 89. *Certified* Medicaid; Medicare.
Owner Nonprofit organization/foundation.
Admissions Requirements Medical examination.
Staff RNs 1 (ft), 3 (pt); LPNs 6 (ft); Activities coordinators 1 (ft), 1 (pt).
Affiliation Lutheran

Facilities Dining room; Activities room; Chapel; Crafts room; Laundry room; Barber/Beauty shop; Library.
Activities Arts & crafts; Cards; Games; Reading groups; Prayer groups; Movies; Shopping trips; Social/Cultural gatherings.

MADISON

Madison Lutheran Home
900 2nd Ave, Madison, MN, 56256
(612) 598-7536
Admin Stephen H Johnson. *Medical Dir/Dir of Nursing* Norval Westby MD; Shirley Hanson DON.
Licensure Skilled care; Intermediate care. *Beds* 140. *Certified* Medicaid; Medicare.
Owner Nonprofit Corp.
Admissions Requirements Minimum age 16; Medical examination; Physician's request.
Staff RNs 9 (pt); LPNs 16 (pt); Nurses aides 74 (pt); Occupational therapists 1 (ft).
Facilities Dining room; Physical therapy room; Activities room; Chapel; Crafts room; Barber/Beauty shop; Library.
Activities Arts & crafts; Cards; Games; Reading groups; Prayer groups; Movies; Shopping trips; Social/Cultural gatherings.

MANKATO

Family House*
328 N 6th St, Mankato, MN, 56001
(507) 345-1652
Admin Paul Hagen.
Licensure Supervised living facility. *Beds* 7.
Owner Nonprofit Corp.
Admissions Requirements Minimum age 5.
Facilities Dining room; Activities room; Crafts room; Laundry room.
Activities Arts & crafts; Cards; Games; Reading groups; Prayer groups; Movies; Shopping trips; Social/Cultural gatherings.

Harry Meyering Center Inc
109 Homestead Dr, Mankato, MN, 56001
(507) 387-8281
Admin Carol Lee.
Licensure Supervised living facility. *Beds* 44.
Owner Nonprofit Corp.
Admissions Requirements Minimum age 18; Medical examination; Screening.
Staff LPNs 1 (ft), 1 (pt); Activities coordinators 1 (ft).
Languages Sign
Facilities Laundry room.
Activities Arts & crafts; Cards; Games; Reading groups; Movies; Shopping trips; Social/Cultural gatherings; Community focused recreation.

Hillcrest Health Care Center*
Rte 9, Box 3, Mankato, MN, 56001
(507) 387-3491
Admin Dorothy Leduc.
Licensure Skilled care; Intermediate care. *Beds* SNF 98; ICF 60. *Certified* Medicaid.
Owner Proprietary Corp (Thro Co).

Mankato House Health Care Center*
700 James Ave, Mankato, MN, 56001
(507) 345-4631
Admin Kevin W King. *Medical Dir/Dir of Nursing* Dr Harry Brauer.
Licensure Skilled care; Intermediate care. *Beds* 97. *Certified* Medicaid.
Owner Proprietary Corp (Thro Co).
Admissions Requirements Minimum age 18; Medical examination; Physician's request.
Staff Physicians 1 (pt); RNs 4 (ft), 11 (pt); LPNs 6 (ft), 14 (pt); Orderlies 2 (pt); Nurses aides 23 (ft), 26 (pt); Physical therapists 1 (pt); Recreational therapists 2 (ft); Occupational therapists 1 (pt); Activities coordinators 1 (ft); Dietitians 1 (pt).

Mankato Lutheran Home
718 Mound Ave, Mankato, MN, 56001
(507) 345-4576
Admin Kevin A Anderson. *Medical Dir/Dir of Nursing* John J Heimark MD; Bonnie Betts DON.
Licensure Skilled care; Boarding care. *Beds* SNF 45; Boarding care 23. *Certified* Medicaid; Medicare.
Owner Nonprofit Corp (MN Synod/Lutheran Ch Board).
Admissions Requirements Medical examination; Physician's request.
Staff RNs 1 (ft), 4 (pt); LPNs 4 (ft), 6 (pt); Nurses aides 9 (ft), 10 (pt); Physical therapists 1 (pt); Recreational therapists 3 (pt); Occupational therapists 1 (pt); Activities coordinators 1 (ft); Dietitians 1 (ft).
Affiliation Lutheran
Facilities Dining room; Physical therapy room; Activities room; Crafts room; Laundry room; Barber/Beauty shop.
Activities Arts & crafts; Cards; Games; Reading groups; Prayer groups; Movies; Social/Cultural gatherings.

Oaklawn Health Care Center
1112 Mulberry, Mankato, MN, 56001
(507) 388-2913
Admin Chris Thro.
Licensure Skilled care. *Beds* SNF 63. *Certified* Medicaid.
Owner Proprietary Corp (Thro Co).
Staff RNs; LPNs; Orderlies; Nurses aides; Recreational therapists; Activities coordinators; Dietitians.
Facilities Dining room.
Activities Arts & crafts; Cards; Games; Reading groups; Prayer groups; Movies; Shopping trips; Social/Cultural gatherings.

REM Mankato
210 Thomas Dr, Mankato, MN, 56001
(612) 387-3181
Admin Thomas Miller.
Licensure Supervised living facility. *Beds* 45. *Certified* Medicaid.
Owner Proprietary Corp.
Admissions Requirements Minimum age 18; Medical examination.
Staff RNs 1 (ft); LPNs 1 (pt).
Facilities Dining room; Activities room; Laundry room.
Activities Arts & crafts; Cards; Games; Movies; Shopping trips; Social/Cultural gatherings; Sporting & other community events.

MAPLE PLAIN

Haven Homes of Maple Plain
1520 Wyman Avenue, Maple Plain, MN, 55359
(612) 479-1993
Admin Daniel Fair. *Medical Dir/Dir of Nursing* Jo Berger MD.
Licensure Skilled care; Intermediate care. *Beds* 67. *Certified* Medicaid; Medicare.
Owner Proprietary Corp.
Admissions Requirements Medical examination; Physician's request.
Staff Physicians 8 (pt); RNs 2 (ft), 7 (pt); LPNs 2 (ft), 3 (pt); Orderlies 1 (pt); Nurses aides 4 (ft), 28 (pt); Physical therapists 1 (ft), 2 (pt); Recreational therapists 1 (ft); Occupational therapists 1 (pt); Speech therapists 1 (pt); Dietitians 1 (pt); Dentists 1 (pt); Ophthalmologists 1 (pt); Podiatrists 1 (pt).
Facilities Dining room; Physical therapy room; Barber/Beauty shop.
Activities Arts & crafts; Cards; Games; Reading groups; Movies.

MAPLETON

Mapleton Community Home*
301 Troendel St, Mapleton, MN, 56065
(507) 524-3315
Admin Calvin Ward. *Medical Dir/Dir of Nursing* Dr John Lester.
Licensure Skilled care; Intermediate care. *Beds* 80. *Certified* Medicaid.
Owner Nonprofit Corp.
Admissions Requirements Medical examination; Physician's request.
Staff RNs 2 (ft), 5 (pt); LPNs 10 (pt); Nurses aides 14 (ft), 38 (pt); Activities coordinators 1 (ft), 2 (pt); Dietitians 1 (pt).
Facilities Dining room; Activities room; Chapel; Crafts room; Laundry room; Barber/Beauty shop; Library.
Activities Arts & crafts; Cards; Games; Reading groups; Prayer groups; Movies; Shopping trips.

MAPLEWOOD

Maplewood Maple Manor Care Center
550 E Roselawn Ave, Maplewood, MN, 55117
(612) 774-9765
Admin Claudia Sajevic. *Medical Dir/Dir of Nursing* Leon Nesvicil MD; Mary Flaherty.
Licensure Skilled care; Intermediate care. *Beds* 162. *Certified* Medicaid; Medicare.
Owner Proprietary Corp (Good Neighbor Services).
Admissions Requirements Medical examination; Physician's request.
Staff RNs 7 (ft), 15 (pt); LPNs 3 (ft), 10 (pt); Nurses aides 31 (ft), 49 (pt); Physical therapists 1 (ft); Recreational therapists 3 (ft), 2 (pt); Occupational therapists 1 (ft); Speech therapists 1 (ft); Dietitians 2 (pt); Volunteer coordinator 1 (ft).
Facilities Dining room; Physical therapy room; Activities room; Crafts room; Laundry room; Barber/Beauty shop; Library; Meeting rooms.
Activities Arts & crafts; Cards; Games; Reading groups; Prayer groups; Movies; Shopping trips; Social/Cultural gatherings; Poetry; Art; Camping; Exercise.

Nekton on Frost*
1695 Frost Ave, Maplewood, MN, 55109
(612) 770-5370
Admin Elizabeth Porter.
Licensure Intermediate care for mentally retarded. *Beds* 6. *Certified* Medicaid.
Owner Proprietary Corp.

Sur La Rue de Skillman*
373 Skillman Ave, Maplewood, MN, 55117
(612) 488-6956
Admin Peter Sajevic.
Licensure Intermediate care for mentally retarded. *Beds* 6. *Certified* Medicaid.
Owner Proprietary Corp.

MARSHALL

REM Marshall A, B, & C*
1005 N 4th St, Marshall, MN, 56258
(507) 532-1458
Admin Craig Miller.
Licensure Intermediate care for mentally retarded. *Beds* 45. *Certified* Medicaid.
Owner Proprietary Corp.

Wiener Memorial Medical Center*
300 S Bruce St, Marshall, MN, 56258
(507) 532-9661
Admin Ronald L Jensen.
Licensure Skilled care. *Beds* 76. *Certified* Medicaid; Medicare.
Owner Publicly owned.

MCINTOSH

McIntosh
700 NE Riverside Ave, McIntosh, MN, 56556
(218) 563-2715
Admin Robert Kleinschmidt. *Medical Dir/Dir of Nursing* Pam Kerssen RN DON.
Licensure Skilled care; Intermediate care. *Beds* 89. *Certified* Medicaid; Medicare.
Owner Proprietary Corp.
Facilities Dining room; Physical therapy room; Activities room; Chapel; Laundry room; Barber/Beauty shop.
Activities Arts & crafts; Cards; Games; Reading groups; Prayer groups; Movies; Shopping trips; Social/Cultural gatherings.

Riverside Board & Care*
240 1st St NE, McIntosh, MN, 56556
(218) 563-4451
Admin Dennis Ekeberg.
Licensure Boarding care. *Beds* 11.
Owner Proprietary Corp.

MENAHGA

Green Pine Acres Nursing Home
PO Box 130, Menahga, MN, 56464
(218) 564-4101
Admin Clair Erickson.
Licensure Intermediate care. *Beds* 91. *Certified* Medicaid.
Owner Publicly owned.

MENDOTA HEIGHTS

DCI Dakota Adults
2031 S Victoria Rd, Mendota Heights, MN, 55118
(612) 452-4295
Admin Kathleen Pine.
Licensure Intermediate care; Intermediate care for mentally retarded. *Beds* ICF/MR 12. *Certified* Medicaid.
Owner Nonprofit Corp.

MILACA

Elim Home*
730 2nd St SE, Milaca, MN, 56353
(612) 983-2185
Admin Linda Letich. *Medical Dir/Dir of Nursing* Dr Bruce Gersterkorn.
Licensure Skilled care. *Beds* 119. *Certified* Medicaid.
Owner Nonprofit Corp.
Admissions Requirements Medical examination; Physician's request.
Staff RNs 2 (ft), 8 (pt); LPNs 1 (ft), 5 (pt); Nurses aides 8 (ft), 57 (pt); Physical therapists 1 (ft); Reality therapists 1 (ft); Activities coordinators 1 (ft), 2 (pt); Dietitians 1 (ft).
Affiliation Evangelical Free Church
Facilities Dining room; Physical therapy room; Activities room; Chapel; Crafts room; Laundry room; Barber/Beauty shop; Library.
Activities Arts & crafts; Cards; Games; Reading groups; Prayer groups; Movies; Shopping trips; Social/Cultural gatherings.

Stepping Stones Group Home
560 SE 3rd St, Milaca, MN, 56353
(612) 983-2550
Admin Tim Barkett.
Licensure Skilled care; Intermediate care. *Beds* SNF 4; ICF 8. *Certified* Medicaid.
Owner Nonprofit Corp.

MINNEAPOLIS

Aldrich Board & Care
3101 Aldrich Ave S, Minneapolis, MN, 55408
(612) 825-4488
Admin D W Thistlewood. *Medical Dir/Dir of Nursing* Jan Stenzel.

Licensure Board & care. *Beds* Board & care 25.
Owner Privately owned.
Admissions Requirements Females only.
Staff LPNs 1 (ft); Activities coordinators 1 (pt).
Facilities Dining room; Activities room; Crafts room; Laundry room.
Activities Arts & crafts; Cards; Games; Reading groups; Movies; Shopping trips; Social/Cultural gatherings; Ball games; Picnics.

Andrew Residence
1215 S 9th St, Minneapolis, MN, 55404
(612) 333-0111
Admin Karen M Foy. *Medical Dir/Dir of Nursing* Phyllis Goranson DON.
Licensure Intermediate care. *Beds* ICF. *Certified* Medicaid.
Owner Proprietary Corp (Beverly Enterprises).
Admissions Requirements Minimum age 18; Medical examination; Physician's request.
Staff Physicians 7 (ft); LPNs 2 (ft), 2 (pt); Recreational therapists 8 (ft); Dietitians 1 (pt); Mental health staff 60 (ft), 20 (pt).
Facilities Dining room; Activities room; Crafts room; Library Group & training areas.
Activities Living skills; Interpersonal skills; Health education; Use of leisure time; Vocational training & employment.

Angelus Convalescent Home*
4544 4th Ave S, Minneapolis, MN, 55409
(612) 827-3526
Admin Todd Carsen.
Licensure Skilled care; Intermediate care. *Beds* SNF 62; ICF 22. *Certified* Medicaid.
Owner Proprietary Corp (Beverly Enterprises).

Augustana Home of Minneapolis
1007 E 14th St, Minneapolis, MN, 55404
(612) 333-1551
Admin John C Hult. *Medical Dir/Dir of Nursing* Dr Henry Quist MD; Margaret Sorenson DON.
Licensure Skilled care; Intermediate care. *Beds* SNF 290; ICF 92. *Certified* Medicaid; Medicare.
Owner Nonprofit organization/foundation; Nonprofit Corp.
Admissions Requirements Medical examination; Physician's request.
Staff Physicians 1 (pt); RNs 17 (ft), 18 (pt); LPNs 12 (ft), 8 (pt); Nurses aides 58 (ft), 125 (pt); Physical therapists 3 (ft); Reality therapists 2 (ft); Recreational therapists 8 (ft); Activities coordinators 1 (ft).
Affiliation Lutheran
Facilities Dining room; Physical therapy room; Activities room; Chapel; Crafts room; Laundry room; Barber/Beauty shop.
Activities Arts & crafts; Cards; Games; Reading groups; Prayer groups; Movies; Shopping trips; Social/Cultural gatherings.

Bannochie Nursing Home*
3515 2nd Ave S, Minneapolis, MN, 55408
(612) 822-3600
Admin Douglas W Bannochie.
Licensure Intermediate care. *Beds* 43. *Certified* Medicaid.
Owner Proprietary Corp.

Baptist Residence*
512 49th Ave N, Minneapolis, MN, 55430
(612) 529-7747
Admin David Nelson.
Licensure Intermediate care. *Beds* 87. *Certified* Medicaid.
Owner Nonprofit Corp (American Baptist Homes).

Bethany Covenant Home
2309 Hayes St NE, Minneapolis, MN, 55418
(612) 781-2691
Admin Scott T Mixer. *Medical Dir/Dir of Nursing* Theone L Klausler.

Licensure Intermediate care. *Beds* ICF 66. *Certified* Medicaid.
Owner Nonprofit Corp (Covenant Benevolent Inst).
Admissions Requirements Minimum age 62; Medical examination; Physician's request.
Staff RNs 3 (ft), 6 (pt); LPNs 1 (ft), 8 (pt); Orderlies 1 (pt); Nurses aides 7 (ft), 20 (pt); Physical therapists 1 (pt); Activities coordinators 1 (ft), 2 (pt); Dietitians 1 (ft).
Languages Swedish, German
Facilities Dining room; Activities room; Chapel; Crafts room; Laundry room; Barber/Beauty shop; Library; Parlor; Park.
Activities Arts & crafts; Games; Reading groups; Prayer groups; Movies; Shopping trips; Social/Cultural gatherings; Sunday chapel services.

Birchwood Care Home
715 W 31st St, Minneapolis, MN, 55408
(612) 823-7286
Admin Donald E Fowler; Randal L Halemeyer.
Licensure Intermediate care. *Beds* ICF 60. *Certified* Medicaid.
Owner Proprietary Corp.
Admissions Requirements Minimum age 21; Medical examination; Physician's request.
Staff LPNs 3 (ft); Nurses aides 2 (ft); Activities coordinators 1 (ft), 1 (pt).
Facilities Dining room; Activities room; Laundry room; Barber/Beauty shop.
Activities Arts & crafts; Cards; Games; Reading groups; Prayer groups; Movies; Shopping trips; Social/Cultural gatherings; Community outings.

Bryn Mawr Nursing Home
275 Penn Ave N, Minneapolis, MN, 55405
(612) 377-4723
Admin Mary Rosch. *Medical Dir/Dir of Nursing* Dr Stephen Carlson; Mary Abbey RN.
Licensure Skilled care; Intermediate care. *Beds* SNF 178. *Certified* Medicaid; Medicare.
Owner Proprietary Corp.
Admissions Requirements Minimum age 16.
Staff Physicians 35 (pt); RNs 10 (ft), 12 (pt); LPNs 10 (ft), 10 (pt); Nurses aides 40 (ft), 20 (pt); Physical therapists 1 (ft); Recreational therapists 4 (ft), 1 (pt); Occupational therapists 2 (ft); Speech therapists 1 (ft); Activities coordinators 1 (ft); Dietitians 1 (ft); Ophthalmologists 1 (pt).
Facilities Dining room; Physical therapy room; Activities room; Crafts room; Laundry room; Barber/Beauty shop.
Activities Arts & crafts; Cards; Games; Reading groups; Prayer groups; Movies; Shopping trips; Social/Cultural gatherings; Events designed for our special young adult unit.

Bywood East Health Care
3427 Central Ave NE, Minneapolis, MN, 55418
(612) 788-9757
Admin Richard C Werner. *Medical Dir/Dir of Nursing* Mary Lundquist DON.
Licensure Intermediate care. *Beds* ICF 105. *Certified* Medicaid.
Owner Proprietary Corp.
Admissions Requirements Minimum age 17.
Staff RNs 2 (ft), 3 (pt); LPNs 9 (ft), 10 (pt); Nurses aides 3 (ft); Activities coordinators 1 (ft); Dietitians 1 (pt); 12 (ft), 15 (pt).
Facilities Dining room; Activities room; Crafts room; Barber/Beauty shop; Library; Patio in yard.
Activities Arts & crafts; Cards; Games; Reading groups; Prayer groups; Movies; Shopping trips; Social/Cultural gatherings; Breakfast club; Fishing trips; Camping trips; Bus tours; Bowling team as well as a variety of unique activities.

Camden Care Center
4659 Lyndale Ave N, Minneapolis, MN, 55412
(612) 529-9152
Admin Richard Johnson. *Medical Dir/Dir of Nursing* Susan Thistlewood.
Licensure Intermediate care. *Beds* ICF 44. *Certified* Medicaid.
Owner Proprietary Corp.
Admissions Requirements Medical examination.
Staff Physicians 1 (pt); RNs 2 (pt); LPNs 4 (pt); Nurses aides 16 (pt); Physical therapists 2 (pt); Occupational therapists 3 (pt); Activities coordinators 1 (pt); Dietitians 1 (pt); Ophthalmologists 1 (pt).
Facilities Dining room; Physical therapy room; Laundry room; Barber/Beauty shop.
Activities Arts & crafts; Cards; Games; Movies; Shopping trips.

Careview Home Inc*
5517 Lyndale Ave S, Minneapolis, MN, 55419
(612) 827-5677
Admin James Kaiser.
Licensure Skilled care. *Beds* 150. *Certified* Medicaid; Medicare.
Owner Nonprofit Corp.

Cedar Pines Health Care Facility
2739 Cedar Ave S, Minneapolis, MN, 55407
(612) 724-5491
Admin Deborah L Rose. *Medical Dir/Dir of Nursing* Dr Robert Breitenbucher; Adelle Winkels DON.
Licensure Skilled care. *Beds* SNF 131. *Certified* Medicaid; Medicare.
Owner Privately owned.
Admissions Requirements Medical examination; Physician's request.
Facilities Dining room; Physical therapy room; Activities room; Laundry room; Barber/Beauty shop.
Activities Arts & crafts; Cards; Games; Reading groups; Prayer groups; Movies; Shopping trips; Social/Cultural gatherings.

Central Care Center
1828 Central Ave NE, Minneapolis, MN, 55418
(612) 781-3118
Admin Christie Hutchens. *Medical Dir/Dir of Nursing* Dr John Doyle; Ron Kaylor DON.
Licensure Skilled care; Intermediate care. *Beds* SNF 101; ICF 48. *Certified* Medicaid; Medicare.
Owner Proprietary Corp (Beverly Enterprises).
Admissions Requirements Medical examination.
Staff RNs; LPNs; Orderlies; Nurses aides; Physical therapists; Recreational therapists; Occupational therapists; Speech therapists; Activities coordinators; Dietitians.
Facilities Dining room; Physical therapy room; Activities room; Crafts room; Laundry room; Barber/Beauty shop.
Activities Arts & crafts; Cards; Games; Reading groups; Prayer groups; Movies; Shopping trips; Social/Cultural gatherings.

Chateau Healthcare Center
2106 2nd Ave S, Minneapolis, MN, 55404
(612) 874-1603
Admin Kara M Johnson.
Licensure Skilled care; Intermediate care. *Beds* SNF 80; ICF 13. *Certified* Medicaid; Medicare.
Owner Proprietary Corp (Beverly Enterprises).
Staff Physicians 2 (pt); RNs 2 (ft); LPNs 3 (ft), 3 (pt); Orderlies; Nurses aides; Physical therapists 1 (ft); Occupational therapists 1 (ft); Speech therapists 1 (ft); Activities coordinators 1 (ft); Dietitians 1 (ft); Dentists; Ophthalmologists.
Facilities Dining room; Physical therapy room; Activities room; Laundry room; Barber/Beauty shop.

Activities Arts & crafts; Cards; Games; Reading groups; Prayer groups; Movies; Shopping trips; Social/Cultural gatherings.

Christian Union Home
1507 Lowry Ave NE, Minneapolis, MN, 55418
(612) 781-4871
Admin Ruthanne Mussetter. *Medical Dir/Dir of Nursing* Eleanore Spraungel RN.
Licensure Boarding care. *Beds* Boarding care 53.
Owner Nonprofit Corp.
Admissions Requirements Minimum age 17; Medical examination.
Staff RNs 1 (ft); LPNs 1 (ft), 1 (pt); Nurses aides 6 (ft), 4 (pt); Activities coordinators 1 (pt); Dietitians 1 (pt).
Facilities Dining room; Activities room; Chapel; Crafts room; Laundry room; Barber/Beauty shop; Library.
Activities Arts & crafts; Cards; Games; Reading groups; Prayer groups; Movies; Shopping trips; Social/Cultural gatherings; Picnics; Lunch outings.

Clara Doerr-Lindley Hall
1717 2nd Ave S, Minneapolis, MN, 55403
(612) 870-4440
Admin David Wiencke.
Licensure Intermediate care for mentally retarded. *Beds* 103. *Certified* Medicaid.
Owner Nonprofit Corp.

Clifton House
301 Clifton Ave, Minneapolis, MN, 55403
(612) 870-8111
Admin Neal H Frank Jr.
Licensure Skilled care. *Beds* 13.
Owner Nonprofit Corp.
Affiliation Christian Science
Facilities Dining room; Laundry room; Barber/Beauty shop; Library.
Activities Arts & crafts; Reading groups.

Ebenezer Hall
2545 Portland Ave S, Minneapolis, MN, 55404
(612) 879-2261
Admin Ruth M Lunde. *Medical Dir/Dir of Nursing* Dr Robert Tierney.
Licensure Intermediate care; Boarding care. *Beds* 172. *Certified* Medicaid.
Owner Nonprofit Corp (Ebenezer Soc).
Admissions Requirements Minimum age 65.
Affiliation Lutheran
Facilities Dining room; Physical therapy room; Activities room; Chapel; Crafts room; Laundry room; Barber/Beauty shop; Library.
Activities Arts & crafts; Cards; Games; Reading groups; Prayer groups; Movies; Shopping trips; Social/Cultural gatherings.

Ebenezer Society Luther & Field
2636 Park Ave, Minneapolis, MN, 55407
(612) 879-2200
Admin Susan O'Shea. *Medical Dir/Dir of Nursing* Robert Tierney MD.
Licensure Skilled care; Intermediate care. *Beds* SNF 179; ICF 131. *Certified* Medicaid; Medicare.
Owner Nonprofit Corp (Ebenezer Soc).
Admissions Requirements Minimum age 62.
Affiliation Lutheran
Facilities Dining room; Physical therapy room; Activities room; Chapel; Crafts room; Laundry room; Barber/Beauty shop.
Activities Arts & crafts; Cards; Games; Reading groups; Prayer groups; Movies; Shopping trips; Social/Cultural gatherings.

Elliot Avenue Boarding Care Home
1500 Elliot Ave S, Minneapolis, MN, 55404
(612) 339-2291
Admin Barbara Bester. *Medical Dir/Dir of Nursing* Kimberly Louricas.
Licensure Intermediate care; Mentally ill only. *Beds* ICF 15. *Certified* Medicaid; Medicare.
Owner Privately owned.

Admissions Requirements Minimum age 21; Medical examination.
Staff RNs 1 (pt); LPNs 1 (ft), 1 (pt); Nurses aides 1 (ft), 1 (pt); Activities coordinators 1 (ft).
Facilities Dining room; Activities room.
Activities Arts & crafts; Cards; Games; Reading groups; Movies; Shopping trips; Social/Cultural gatherings; Exercise group.

Emerson Boarding Care Home*
2708 Emerson Ave S, Minneapolis, MN, 55408
(612) 872-7100
Admin Muriel Ganje.
Licensure Intermediate care. *Beds* 10. *Certified* Medicaid.
Owner Proprietary Corp.

Emerson Place North*
2304 Emerson Ave N, Minneapolis, MN, 55411
(612) 521-3679
Admin Stephen Klappa.
Licensure Intermediate care. *Beds* 68. *Certified* Medicaid.
Admissions Requirements Physician's request.
Staff Physicians 2 (pt); RNs 3 (ft); LPNs 3 (ft); Nurses aides 16 (ft), 16 (pt); Physical therapists 1 (pt); Recreational therapists 4 (ft); Occupational therapists 1 (ft), 2 (pt); Speech therapists 1 (pt); Dietitians 1 (pt); Dentists 1 (pt); Ophthalmologists 1 (pt); Podiatrists 1 (pt).
Facilities Dining room; Activities room; Crafts room; Laundry room; Occupational therapy room.
Activities Arts & crafts; Cards; Games; Reading groups; Prayer groups; Movies; Shopping trips; Social/Cultural gatherings.

First Christian Church Residence
2300 Stevens Ave S, Minneapolis, MN, 55041
(612) 870-1811
Admin JoAnne Angier. *Medical Dir/Dir of Nursing* Janet Gulsuig.
Licensure Intermediate care. *Beds* 65. *Certified* Medicaid.
Owner Nonprofit Corp.
Staff RNs 6 (ft); LPNs 3 (ft); Nurses aides 15 (ft); Activities coordinators 1 (ft).

Flambeau-Aneskarn 1*
1446 W 34th St, Minneapolis, MN, 55408
(612) 823-3927
Admin Julia Hanson.
Licensure Intermediate care for mentally retarded. *Beds* 7.
Owner Nonprofit Corp.

Forestview James*
1616 James Ave N, Minneapolis, MN, 55411
(612) 521-6116
Admin Mary M Hill.
Licensure Intermediate care for mentally retarded. *Beds* 6.
Owner Proprietary Corp.

Four Seasons Care Center—Metro
321 E 25th St, Minneapolis, MN, 55404
(612) 874-1701
Admin Thomas Thompson. *Medical Dir/Dir of Nursing* Dr Richard Pfohl; Dorothy Smith.
Licensure Skilled care; Intermediate care. *Beds* 114. *Certified* Medicaid.
Owner Proprietary Corp.
Admissions Requirements Medical examination; Physician's request.
Staff RNs 6 (ft), 6 (pt); LPNs 4 (ft), 2 (pt); Nurses aides 25 (ft), 25 (pt); Physical therapists 2 (ft); Occupational therapists 2 (ft); Speech therapists 1 (pt); Activities coordinators 2 (ft); Dietitians 1 (pt); Dentists 1 (pt); Ophthalmologists 1 (pt); Podiatrists 1 (pt).
Facilities Dining room; Physical therapy room; Laundry room; Barber/Beauty shop; Library.

Activities Arts & crafts; Cards; Games; Reading groups; Prayer groups; Movies; Shopping trips; Social/Cultural gatherings.

Franklin Place East
2100 1st Ave S, Minneapolis, MN, 55404
(612) 874-1101
Admin Debra Campbell. *Medical Dir/Dir of Nursing* Keith Kubasch; Mary Kellett.
Licensure Intermediate care. *Beds* ICF 35. *Certified* Medicaid.
Owner Proprietary Corp.
Admissions Requirements Minimum age 16; Medical examination.
Staff RNs 1 (ft), 2 (pt); LPNs 1 (ft), 2 (pt); Nurses aides 10 (ft), 5 (pt); Recreational therapists 1 (ft); Occupational therapists 1 (ft); Dietitians 1 (ft).
Facilities Dining room; Activities room; Crafts room.
Activities Arts & crafts; Cards; Games; Reading groups; Movies; Shopping trips; Social/Cultural gatherings.

Grand Avenue Rest Home
3956 Grand Ave S, Minneapolis, MN, 55409
(612) 824-1434
Admin Richard Johnson. *Medical Dir/Dir of Nursing* Nancy Winslow.
Licensure Intermediate care. *Beds* 21. *Certified* Medicaid; Medicare.
Owner Proprietary Corp.

David Herman Health Care Center*
2401 Chicago Ave S, Minneapolis, MN, 55404
(612) 871-3661
Admin Marion L Resnick. *Medical Dir/Dir of Nursing* Thomas J Bloss MD.
Licensure Skilled care; Intermediate care. *Beds* SNF 130; ICF 17. *Certified* Medicaid.
Owner Proprietary Corp.
Admissions Requirements Minimum age 18; Medical examination; Physician's request.
Staff Physicians 3 (pt); RNs 9 (ft); LPNs 12 (ft), 2 (pt); Nurses aides 51 (ft), 6 (pt); Physical therapists 3 (ft); Recreational therapists 3 (ft), 1 (pt); Occupational therapists 1 (ft), 1 (pt); Speech therapists 1 (pt); Activities coordinators 4 (ft); Dietitians 1 (pt); Dentists 1 (pt); Ophthalmologists 1 (pt); Podiatrists 1 (pt); Audiologists 1 (pt); Clinical psychologist 1 (pt).
Facilities Dining room; Physical therapy room; Activities room; Chapel; Crafts room; Barber/Beauty shop; Library.
Activities Arts & crafts; Cards; Games; Movies; Social/Cultural gatherings; Birthday parties.

Horizon West Health Care Center
1620 Oak Park Ave N, Minneapolis, MN, 55411
(612) 588-0804
Admin Margaret Stewart. *Medical Dir/Dir of Nursing* Keith Kubasch; Cindy Yaklich.
Licensure Skilled care. *Beds* SNF 96. *Certified* Medicaid; Medicare.
Owner Proprietary Corp.
Admissions Requirements Minimum age 18; Medical examination.
Staff RNs; LPNs; Nurses aides; Physical therapists; Recreational therapists; Occupational therapists; Speech therapists; Dietitians; Dentists; Ophthalmologists; Podiatrists; Psychologist.
Facilities Dining room; Physical therapy room; Activities room; Crafts room; Laundry room; Barber/Beauty shop.
Activities Arts & crafts; Cards; Games; Reading groups; Prayer groups; Movies; Shopping trips; Social/Cultural gatherings.

Jones-Harrison Residence
3700 Cedar Lake Ave, Minneapolis, MN, 55416
(612) 920-2030
Admin Gloria Fiebiger. *Medical Dir/Dir of Nursing* Dr John Cardle; Leslie Martens.

Licensure Skilled care; Intermediate care; Boarding care. *Beds* SNF; ICF 66; Boarding care 97. *Certified* Medicaid; Medicare.
Owner Nonprofit Corp.
Admissions Requirements Medical examination; Physician's request.
Staff Physicians 2 (pt); RNs 6 (ft), 9 (pt); LPNs 5 (ft), 7 (pt); Orderlies 4 (ft), 3 (pt); Nurses aides 11 (ft), 17 (pt); Physical therapists 1 (pt); Recreational therapists 2 (ft); Occupational therapists 1 (pt); Speech therapists 1 (pt); Dietitians 1 (pt); Dentists 1 (pt); Ophthalmologists 1 (pt); Podiatrists 1 (pt); Dentist 1 (pt).
Facilities Dining room; Physical therapy room; Activities room; Chapel; Crafts room; Laundry room; Barber/Beauty shop; Library; Lounges; Living room.
Activities Arts & crafts; Cards; Games; Reading groups; Prayer groups; Movies; Shopping trips; Social/Cultural gatherings; Educational opportunities; Ceramics; Gardening.

LaSalle Convalescent Home
1920 Lasalle Ave, Minneapolis, MN, 55403
(612) 870-8611
Admin Steven Tjeltveit. *Medical Dir/Dir of Nursing* Dr John Dunn; Ms Bette Martinson RN DON.
Licensure Skilled care; Intermediate care; Chemically dependent; Mentally ill. *Beds* SNF 106; ICF 33. *Certified* Medicaid.
Owner Proprietary Corp (Beverly Enterprises).
Admissions Requirements Medical examination; Physician's request.
Staff RNs 6 (ft), 3 (pt); LPNs 11 (ft), 7 (pt); Nurses aides 28 (ft), 14 (pt); Physical therapists 2 (ft), 1 (pt); Reality therapists 1 (pt); Recreational therapists 1 (ft), 1 (pt); Occupational therapists 3 (ft), 2 (pt); Activities coordinators 1 (ft); Social worker 1 (ft), 1 (pt).
Languages Spanish, German, Polish
Facilities Dining room; Physical therapy room; Activities room; Laundry room; Barber/Beauty shop; Library; Occupational therapy room.
Activities Arts & crafts; Cards; Games; Reading groups; Prayer groups; Movies; Shopping trips; Social/Cultural gatherings; Resident council; Therapeutic work programs.

Maria Home*
420 Ridgewood Ave S, Minneapolis, MN, 55403
(612) 871-0805
Admin Sheldon Schneider.
Licensure Supervised living facility. *Beds* 9. *Certified* Medicaid.
Owner Proprietary Corp.
Admissions Requirements Minimum age 18; Medical examination.
Staff RNs 1 (pt); Activities coordinators 1 (pt); Counselors 2 (ft), 1 (pt).
Facilities Dining room; Activities room; Laundry room.
Activities Arts & crafts; Cards; Games; Movies; Shopping trips; Social/Cultural gatherings.

Medallion II Board & Lodge Home*
2430 Pillsbury Ave S, Minneapolis, MN, 55404
(612) 871-8306
Admin Robert Servold.
Licensure Intermediate care. *Beds* 25. *Certified* Medicaid.
Owner Proprietary Corp.
Admissions Requirements Minimum age 18.
Staff CookMgr 1 (ft), 1 (pt); Housekeepers 2 (pt).
Facilities Dining room; Laundry room.

Metro Care Center
1300 Olson Memorial Hwy, Minneapolis, MN, 55411
(612) 374-5660
Admin Becky Brenna.
Licensure Skilled care; Intermediate care. *Beds* SNF 128; ICF 8. *Certified* Medicaid.
Owner Proprietary Corp (Beverly Enterprises).

Minneapolis Outreach Home*
5304 Stevens Ave S, Minneapolis, MN, 55419
(612) 823-9241
Admin Eileen Harris.
Licensure Supervised living facility. *Beds* 6. *Certified* Medicaid.
Owner Nonprofit Corp.
Admissions Requirements Minimum age 18; Medical examination.
Staff Physicians 1 (pt); RNs 1 (pt).
Affiliation Presbyterian
Facilities Dining room; Activities room; Laundry room.
Activities Arts & crafts; Cards; Games; Prayer groups; Movies; Shopping trips; Social/Cultural gatherings.

Minnesota Veterans Home
5101 Minnehaha Ave S, Minneapolis, MN, 55417
(612) 721-0600
Admin James E Ertz. *Medical Dir/Dir of Nursing* Jean Timmermann DON.
Licensure Long-term nursing care. *Beds* Nursing care 346; Domiciliary 194.
Owner Publicly owned.
Admissions Requirements Medical examination; Physician's request.
Staff Physicians; RNs; LPNs; Nurses aides; Physical therapists; Recreational therapists; Activities coordinators; Dietitians.
Facilities Dining room; Physical therapy room; Activities room; Chapel; Crafts room; Laundry room; Barber/Beauty shop; Library.
Activities Arts & crafts; Cards; Games; Reading groups; Movies; Shopping trips; Social/Cultural gatherings.

Mt Olivet Homes Inc*
5517 Lyndale Ave S, Minneapolis, MN, 55419
(612) 827-5677
Admin James Kaiser.
Licensure Intermediate care. *Beds* 97. *Certified* Medicaid.
Owner Nonprofit Corp.

Nekton on Minnehaha Park*
3822 E 49th St, Minneapolis, MN, 55417
(612) 729-5526
Admin Milton Conrath.
Licensure Intermediate care for mentally retarded. *Beds* 6. *Certified* Medicaid.

Nekton on Queen*
614 Queen Ave S, Minneapolis, MN, 55404
(612) 377-5587
Admin Milton Conrath.
Licensure Intermediate care for mentally retarded. *Beds* 6. *Certified* Medicaid.
Owner Proprietary Corp.

Nicollet Health Care Center Inc*
4429 Nicollet Ave S, Minneapolis, MN, 55409
(612) 827-5667
Admin Joan Bangasser. *Medical Dir/Dir of Nursing* Stuart Lancer MD.
Licensure Skilled care; Intermediate care. *Beds* SNF 88; ICF 59. *Certified* Medicaid; Medicare.
Admissions Requirements Minimum age 16; Medical examination; Physician's request.
Facilities Dining room; Physical therapy room; Activities room; Crafts room; Laundry room; Barber/Beauty shop; Library.
Activities Arts & crafts; Cards; Games; Reading groups; Prayer groups; Movies; Shopping trips; Social/Cultural gatherings.

Nile Health Care Center
3720 23rd Ave S, Minneapolis, MN, 55407
(612) 724-5495
Admin Julie L Ditzler. *Medical Dir/Dir of
Nursing* Dr Robert Breitenbucher; Lou
Murphy RN DON.
Licensure Skilled care. *Beds* SNF 125.
Certified Medicaid; Medicare.
Owner Proprietary Corp.
Admissions Requirements Minimum age 60;
Physician's request.
Staff RNs 7 (ft), 13 (pt); LPNs 8 (ft), 8 (pt);
Nurses aides 40 (ft), 25 (pt); Physical
therapists 1 (ft); Recreational therapists 1
(ft); Occupational therapists 1 (ft); Activities
coordinators 2 (ft); Dietitians 1 (ft).
Facilities Dining room; Physical therapy
room; Activities room; Crafts room; Laundry
room; Barber/Beauty shop; Private lounges;
Community room.
Activities Arts & crafts; Games; Reading
groups; Prayer groups; Movies; Shopping
trips; Social/Cultural gatherings.

Northeast House Inc
1918 19th Ave NE, Minneapolis, MN, 55418
(612) 789-8841
Admin Donald G Levin. *Medical Dir/Dir of
Nursing* Dr V K Arora; Jeanette Oleary RN
DON.
Licensure Intermediate care for mentally
retarded; Supervised living facility. *Beds* 24.
Certified Medicaid; Medicare.
Owner Privately owned.
Admissions Requirements Minimum age 30;
Medical examination; Physician's request.
Staff Physicians 2 (pt); RNs 1 (ft), 1 (pt);
LPNs 1 (pt); Physical therapists 2 (pt);
Reality therapists 2 (pt); Recreational
therapists 1 (ft); Occupational therapists 1
(pt); Speech therapists 1 (pt); Activities
coordinators 2 (ft), 1 (pt); Dietitians 1 (pt);
Dentists 2 (pt); Ophthalmologists 1 (pt);
Podiatrists 1 (pt); Psychiatrists 2 (pt);
Psychologists 2 (pt); Program director 1 (ft).
Facilities Dining room; Activities room;
Crafts room; Laundry room; 2-season
screened porch; Nature trails.
Activities Arts & crafts; Cards; Games;
Reading groups; Movies; Shopping trips;
Social/Cultural gatherings.

Oak Grove Resident Treatment Center*
131 Oak Grove, Minneapolis, MN, 55403
(612) 871-5800
Admin Tom Paul.
Licensure Boarding care. *Beds* 21.
Owner Proprietary Corp.
Admissions Requirements Minimum age 30;
Medical examination.
Staff LPNs 1 (ft), 2 (pt); Nurses aides 1 (ft), 2
(pt); Reality therapists 2 (ft); Recreational
therapists 1 (ft); Dietitians 1 (pt).
Facilities Dining room; Activities room;
Crafts room; Laundry room.
Activities Arts & crafts; Cards; Games;
Movies; Shopping trips; Social/Cultural
gatherings.

Outreach Northeast Group Home
729 Adams St NE, Minneapolis, MN, 55413
(612) 379-8897
Admin Eileen Harris. *Medical Dir/Dir of
Nursing* Carole Pitrowski RN.
Licensure Intermediate care for mentally
retarded. *Beds* ICF/MR 7. *Certified*
Medicaid.
Owner Nonprofit organization/foundation.
Admissions Requirements Minimum age 18;
Medical examination.
Staff RNs 1 (pt).
Facilities Dining room; Activities room;
Laundry room.
Activities Arts & crafts; Cards; Games;
Movies; Shopping trips; Social/Cultural
gatherings.

Pillsbury Board & Care Home
2500 Pillsbury Ave S, Minneapolis, MN,
55404
(612) 872-8363
Admin Karen A Fournier.
Licensure Intermediate care. *Beds* 22.
Certified Medicaid.
Owner Proprietary Corp.
Admissions Requirements Minimum age 21;
Medical examination; Physician's request.
Staff RNs 1 (ft); LPNs 1 (ft), 1 (pt); Nurses
aides 3 (pt); Activities coordinators 1 (ft);
Dietitians 1 (pt).
Facilities Dining room.
Activities Arts & crafts; Cards; Games;
Reading groups; Prayer groups; Shopping
trips; Social/Cultural gatherings.

Portland Residence Inc
1619 Portland Ave, Minneapolis, MN, 55404
(612) 332-8300
Admin Leonard Jankowski. *Medical Dir/Dir of
Nursing* Sandy Wessman.
Licensure Intermediate care for mentally
retarded. *Beds* ICF/MR 101. *Certified*
Medicaid.
Owner Proprietary Corp.
Admissions Requirements Minimum age 18;
Medical examination.
Staff RNs 2 (ft); Nurses aides 60 (ft);
Recreational therapists 2 (ft); Speech
therapists 2 (ft); Activities coordinators 1
(ft); Dietitians 1 (ft).
Languages Sign
Facilities Dining room; Activities room;
Chapel; Crafts room; Laundry room;
Auditorium; Exercise patio; Weight room;
Gym; Kitchen.
Activities Arts & crafts; Cards; Games;
Reading groups; Prayer groups; Movies;
Shopping trips; Social/Cultural gatherings.

Queen Nursing Home*
300 Queen Ave N, Minneapolis, MN, 55405
(612) 374-3380
Admin G Raymond Thiss. *Medical Dir/Dir of
Nursing* Kenneth Kubasch.
Licensure Skilled care; Intermediate care;
Boarding care. *Beds* SNF 58; ICF 5;
Boarding care 12. *Certified* Medicaid;
Medicare.
Owner Proprietary Corp.
Staff Physicians 1 (pt); RNs 4 (ft); LPNs 10
(ft); Orderlies 6 (ft); Nurses aides 24 (ft);
Physical therapists 1 (ft); Reality therapists 1
(ft); Recreational therapists 4 (ft);
Occupational therapists 1 (ft); Speech
therapists 1 (ft); Activities coordinators 1
(ft); Dietitians 1 (ft); Dentists 1 (pt);
Ophthalmologists 1 (pt); Podiatrists 1 (pt);
Audiologists 1 (pt).
Facilities Dining room; Activities room;
Laundry room; Barber/Beauty shop.
Activities Arts & crafts; Cards; Games; Prayer
groups; Movies; Shopping trips; Social/
Cultural gatherings; AA meetings.

Redeemer Residence Inc
3111 Lyndale Ave S, Minneapolis, MN, 55408
(612) 827-2555
Admin William E Brown. *Medical Dir/Dir of
Nursing* James Struve; Mary Adams.
Licensure Skilled care; Intermediate care;
Certified boarding care. *Beds* SNF 54; ICF
109. *Certified* Medicaid; Medicare.
Owner Nonprofit Corp.
Admissions Requirements Minimum age 65.
Staff RNs 5 (ft), 8 (pt); LPNs 4 (ft), 2 (pt);
Orderlies; Nurses aides 29 (ft), 21 (pt);
Activities coordinators 3 (ft), 2 (pt).
Facilities Dining room; Physical therapy
room; Activities room; Chapel; Crafts room;
Laundry room; Barber/Beauty shop.
Activities Arts & crafts; Games; Reading
groups; Prayer groups; Movies.

REM Lyndale Inc
2210 Lyndale Ave N, Minneapolis, MN,
55411
(612) 522-6689
Admin David Petersen. *Medical Dir/Dir of
Nursing* Laura Sissala.
Licensure Intermediate care for mentally
retarded. *Beds* ICF/MR 10. *Certified*
Medicaid.
Owner Proprietary Corp.
Admissions Requirements Minimum age 18;
Males only.
Staff RNs 1 (pt).
Facilities Dining room; Laundry room.
Activities Arts & crafts; Cards; Games;
Reading groups; Prayer groups; Movies;
Shopping trips; Social/Cultural gatherings;
Sports.

REM Pillsbury*
2311 Pillsbury Ave S, Minneapolis, MN,
55404
(612) 871-1954
Admin Craig Miller.
Licensure Intermediate care for mentally
retarded. *Beds* 34. *Certified* Medicaid.
Owner Proprietary Corp.

REM Pleasant*
2548 Pleasant Ave S, Minneapolis, MN,
55404
(612) 872-7800
Admin Douglas Miller.
Licensure Intermediate care for mentally
retarded. *Beds* 15. *Certified* Medicaid.
Owner Proprietary Corp.

REM Southeast Inc
1307 6th St SE, Minneapolis, MN, 55414
(612) 378-1556
Admin Douglas Miller. *Medical Dir/Dir of
Nursing* Diane Violett.
Licensure Intermediate care for mentally
retarded. *Beds* ICF/MR 10. *Certified*
Medicaid.
Owner Proprietary Corp.
Admissions Requirements Minimum age 50;
Medical examination.
Staff RNs 1 (pt); Coordinators 3 (ft), 8 (pt).
Activities Cards; Games; Movies; Shopping
trips; Social/Cultural gatherings.

St Anns Residence
2120 Clinton Ave S, Minneapolis, MN, 55428
(612) 871-0666
Admin Annette Rowland.
Licensure Intermediate care for mentally
retarded. *Beds* ICF/MR 30. *Certified*
Medicaid.
Owner Nonprofit organization/foundation.
Staff RNs 1 (ft); LPNs 1 (pt); Dietitians 1
(pt).
Facilities Dining room; Activities room;
Crafts room; Laundry room; Barber/Beauty
shop.
Activities Arts & crafts; Cards; Games;
Reading groups; Prayer groups; Movies;
Shopping trips; Social/Cultural gatherings.

St Anthony Eldercenter on Main
817 Man St NE, Minneapolis, MN, 55413
(612) 379-1370
Admin David Westbrook. *Medical Dir/Dir of
Nursing* Gene Ott MD; Florence Zamor RN.
Licensure Skilled care; Intermediate care. *Beds*
SNF 100; ICF 50. *Certified* Medicaid;
Medicare.
Owner Nonprofit Corp.
Admissions Requirements Medical
examination; Physician's request.
Staff RNs; LPNs; Orderlies; Nurses aides;
Physical therapists; Recreational therapists;
Occupational therapists; Speech therapists;
Activities coordinators; Dietitians.
Languages Polish, German, Slavic, Russian,
French
Affiliation Roman Catholic

Facilities Dining room; Physical therapy
room; Activities room; Chapel; Crafts room;
Laundry room; Barber/Beauty shop; Library.
Activities Arts & crafts; Cards; Games;
Reading groups; Prayer groups; Movies;
Shopping trips; Social/Cultural gatherings.

St Olaf Residence
2912 Fremont Ave N, Minneapolis, MN,
55411
(612) 522-6561
Admin Richard F Holy. *Medical Dir/Dir of
Nursing* Dr John J Salchert; Ms Mary Lou
Tkalcich DON.
Licensure Skilled care; Boarding care. *Beds*
SNF 63; Boarding care 122. *Certified*
Medicaid; Medicare.
Owner Nonprofit Corp.
Admissions Requirements Medical
examination.
Staff RNs 3 (ft), 8 (pt); LPNs 3 (ft), 1 (pt);
Nurses aides 1 (ft), 37 (pt); Recreational
therapists 3 (ft); Dietitians 1 (ft).
Affiliation Lutheran
Facilities Dining room; Activities room;
Chapel; Crafts room; Laundry room; Barber/
Beauty shop; Library.
Activities Arts & crafts; Cards; Games;
Reading groups; Prayer groups; Movies;
Shopping trips.

Southside Care Center*
2644 Aldrich Ave S, Minneapolis, MN, 55408
(612) 872-4233
Admin Philip Seidenfeld.
Licensure Boarding care. *Beds* ICF 20;
Boarding care 20. *Certified* Medicaid.
Admissions Requirements Medical
examination.
Staff RNs 1 (pt); LPNs 2 (ft), 1 (pt); Nurses
aides 2 (ft), 2 (pt); Recreational therapists 1
(ft); Activities coordinators 1 (pt); Dietitians
1 (pt).
Facilities Dining room; Activities room;
Laundry room; Barber/Beauty shop.
Activities Arts & crafts; Cards; Games; Prayer
groups.

Stevens Square
101 E 32nd St, Minneapolis, MN, 55408
(612) 823-5201
Admin Rachel Rustad.
Licensure Skilled care; Intermediate care. *Beds*
SNF 15; ICF 51. *Certified* Medicaid.
Owner Nonprofit Corp.

Teachers Home Care Center
2625 Park Ave, Minneapolis, MN, 55407
(507) 871-4594
Admin David Hjartland. *Medical Dir/Dir of
Nursing* Marilyn Westlin RN DON.
Licensure Skilled care; Intermediate care. *Beds*
SNF 13; ICF.
Owner Nonprofit Corp.
Admissions Requirements Medical
examination; Physician's request.
Staff RNs 2 (ft), 3 (pt); LPNs 4 (pt); Nurses
aides 4 (pt); Dietitians 1 (pt).
Facilities Dining room; Activities room;
Laundry room; Barber/Beauty shop; Library.
Activities Arts & crafts; Cards; Games;
Reading groups; Prayer groups; Movies.

Three Thirty-Five Ridgewood*
335 Ridgewood Ave S, Minneapolis, MN,
55403
(612) 871-0805
Admin Sheldon Schneider.
Licensure Supervised living facility. *Beds* 9.
Certified Medicaid.
Owner Proprietary Corp.
Admissions Requirements Minimum age 18;
Medical examination.
Staff RNs 1 (pt); Activities coordinators 1
(pt); Counselors 1 (ft), 2 (pt).

Facilities Dining room; Activities room;
Laundry room.
Activities Arts & crafts; Cards; Games;
Movies; Shopping trips; Social/Cultural
gatherings.

University Health Care Center
22 27th Ave SE, Minneapolis, MN, 55414
(612) 332-4262
Admin Paula Kneisl. *Medical Dir/Dir of
Nursing* John Mielke MD; Joanna Nordseth
RN DON.
Licensure Skilled care. *Beds* SNF 358.
Certified Medicaid; Medicare.
Owner Proprietary Corp.
Admissions Requirements Minimum age 16;
Physician's request.
Staff Recreational therapists 2 (pt);
Occupational therapists 3 (ft); Speech
therapists 1 (ft); Activities coordinators 1
(ft); Dietitians 3 (ft); Counselors 4 (ft); Social
workers 10 (ft).
Facilities Dining room; Physical therapy
room; Activities room; Crafts room; Laundry
room; Barber/Beauty shop; Library.
Activities Arts & crafts; Cards; Games;
Reading groups; Prayer groups; Movies;
Shopping trips; Social/Cultural gatherings;
Community events.

Walker Methodist Health Center Inc
3737 Bryant Ave S, Minneapolis, MN, 55409
(612) 827-5931
Admin Paul Mikelson. *Medical Dir/Dir of
Nursing* Dr Thomas M Recht; Elizabeth
Colloton.
Licensure Skilled care; Intermediate care. *Beds*
SNF 240; ICF 250. *Certified* Medicaid;
Medicare.
Owner Nonprofit organization/foundation.
Admissions Requirements Minimum age 65;
Medical examination; Physician's request.
Staff Physicians 1 (pt); RNs 29 (ft), 14 (pt);
LPNs 23 (ft), 14 (pt); Nurses aides 115 (ft),
95 (pt); Recreational therapists 6 (ft), 1 (pt);
Occupational therapists; Speech therapists;
Activities coordinators 1 (ft); Dietitians 1
(ft); Dentists; Ophthalmologists.
Affiliation Methodist
Facilities Dining room; Physical therapy
room; Activities room; Chapel; Crafts room;
Laundry room; Barber/Beauty shop; Library;
Terrace/Green house.
Activities Arts & crafts; Cards; Games;
Reading groups; Prayer groups; Movies;
Shopping trips; Social/Cultural gatherings;
Support groups.

Willows Convalescent Center Central
625 E 16th St, Minneapolis, MN, 55419
(612) 332-3541
Admin Dorothy Ragland. *Medical Dir/Dir of
Nursing* Henry Smith MD.
Licensure Intermediate care; Boarding care.
Beds ICF 150; Boarding care 22. *Certified*
Medicaid.
Owner Proprietary Corp.
Admissions Requirements Minimum age 16;
Medical examination.
Staff RNs 10 (ft), 1 (pt); LPNs 6 (ft), 8 (pt);
Orderlies 11 (ft), 3 (pt); Nurses aides 22 (ft),
14 (pt); Physical therapists 1 (ft);
Recreational therapists 1 (ft); Occupational
therapists 2 (ft); Speech therapists 1 (pt);
Activities coordinators 2 (ft); Dietitians 1
(pt); Podiatrists 1 (pt); Social workers 3 (ft).
Facilities Dining room; Physical therapy
room; Activities room; Chapel; Crafts room;
Laundry room; Barber/Beauty shop; Library.
Activities Arts & crafts; Cards; Games;
Reading groups; Prayer groups; Movies;
Shopping trips; Social/Cultural gatherings.

Willows Convalescent Center South
6130 Lyndale Ave S, Minneapolis, MN, 55419
(612) 866-3095
Admin Sharon Klefsaas. *Medical Dir/Dir of
Nursing* Diane Klefsaas.

Licensure Skilled care; Intermediate care. *Beds*
SNF 144; ICF. *Certified* Medicaid;
Medicare.
Owner Privately owned.
Admissions Requirements Minimum age 16;
Medical examination; Physician's request.
Staff RNs; LPNs; Orderlies; Nurses aides;
Physical therapists; Reality therapists;
Recreational therapists; Occupational
therapists; Speech therapists; Activities
coordinators; Dietitians; Dentists;
Ophthalmologists; Podiatrists.
Facilities Dining room; Physical therapy
room; Activities room; Laundry room;
Barber/Beauty shop.
Activities Arts & crafts; Cards; Games;
Reading groups; Prayer groups; Movies;
Shopping trips; Social/Cultural gatherings.

Willows East Health Care Center
719 E 16th St, Minneapolis, MN, 55404
(612) 339-7281
Admin Patrick J Rafferty.
Licensure Skilled care. *Beds* SNF 170.
Certified Medicaid; Medicare.
Owner Proprietary Corp.
Admissions Requirements Minimum age 18.
Staff RNs 12 (ft); LPNs 7 (ft); Nurses aides 36
(ft); Physical therapists 1 (ft); Recreational
therapists 4 (ft); Occupational therapists 1
(ft); Speech therapists 1 (pt).
Facilities Dining room; Physical therapy
room; Activities room; Chapel; Crafts room;
Laundry room; Barber/Beauty shop.
Activities Arts & crafts; Cards; Games;
Reading groups; Prayer groups; Movies;
Shopping trips; Social/Cultural gatherings.

Yorkshire Manor Health Care Facility
2200 Park Ave S, Minneapolis, MN, 55404
(612) 871-2200
Admin Jenean Erickson. *Medical Dir/Dir of
Nursing* C D Townes MD; Marlice Finch
DON.
Licensure Skilled care; Intermediate care. *Beds*
SNF 45; ICF 39. *Certified* Medicaid;
Medicare.
Owner Proprietary Corp.
Admissions Requirements Medical
examination; Physician's request.
Staff Physicians 1 (pt); RNs 4 (ft), 1 (pt);
LPNs 1 (ft), 2 (pt); Nurses aides 7 (ft), 18
(pt); Occupational therapists 2 (ft); Activities
coordinators 1 (ft); Dietitians 1 (pt).
Facilities Dining room; Physical therapy
room; Activities room; Crafts room; Laundry
room; Barber/Beauty shop.
Activities Arts & crafts; Cards; Games;
Reading groups; Prayer groups; Movies;
Shopping trips; Social/Cultural gatherings.

MINNEOTA

Minneota Manor Health Care Center
700 N Monroe St, Minneota, MN, 56264
(507) 872-6166
Admin Rev Richard Erickson. *Medical Dir/
Dir of Nursing* Dr M J Bird; Mary Ann Full
DON.
Licensure Skilled care; Intermediate care. *Beds*
SNF 51; ICF 36. *Certified* Medicaid.
Owner Proprietary Corp.
Staff RNs 1 (ft), 5 (pt); LPNs 1 (ft), 6 (pt);
Nurses aides 8 (ft), 49 (pt); Activities
coordinators 1 (ft), 1 (pt); Dietitians 1 (pt).
Facilities Dining room; Activities room;
Laundry room; Barber/Beauty shop; Library.
Activities Arts & crafts; Cards; Games;
Reading groups; Movies; Shopping trips.

MINNETONKA

Forestview Minnetonka*
14212 Excelsior Blvd, Minnetonka, MN,
55345
(612) 938-7203
Admin Mary M Hill.

Licensure Intermediate care for mentally retarded. *Beds* 6. *Certified* Medicaid.
Owner Proprietary Corp.

Oak Terrace Nursing Home
14500 County Rd 67, Minnetonka, MN, 55345
(612) 934-4100
Admin Faye B Christensen. *Medical Dir/Dir of Nursing* Dr Auril Sulciner; Doris Thomas DON.
Licensure Skilled care. *Beds* SNF 350. *Certified* Medicaid; Medicare.
Owner Publicly owned.
Admissions Requirements Minimum age 65; Medical examination.
Staff Physicians 2 (ft); RNs 22 (ft), 5 (pt); LPNs 24 (ft), 4 (pt); Nurses aides; Physical therapists 1 (ft); Recreational therapists 4 (ft), 1 (pt); Occupational therapists 1 (ft); Dietitians 3 (ft); COTA 1 (ft); Social workers 4 (ft).
Facilities Dining room; Physical therapy room; Activities room; Chapel; Crafts room; Laundry room; Barber/Beauty shop; Library.
Activities Arts & crafts; Cards; Games; Reading groups; Prayer groups; Movies; Shopping trips; Social/Cultural gatherings.

Oakwood Residence, Inc
13403 McGinty Rd E, Minnetonka, MN, 55343
(612) 938-8130
Admin Sandra L Singer. *Medical Dir/Dir of Nursing* Irene Moore.
Licensure Intermediate care for mentally retarded. *Beds* ICF/MR 15. *Certified* Medicare.
Owner Nonprofit Corp.
Admissions Requirements Minimum age 15.
Staff RNs 1 (pt); Activities coordinators 1 (ft).
Facilities Dining room; Laundry room.
Activities Arts & crafts; Cards; Games; Movies; Shopping trips; Programs for independent leisure skills in community.

REM Minnetonka Inc
21 Westwood Rd, Minnetonka, MN, 55443
(612) 541-9421
Admin Douglas Miller.
Licensure Intermediate care for mentally retarded. *Beds* ICF/MR 15. *Certified* Medicaid.
Owner Proprietary Corp.
Admissions Requirements Minimum age 16.
Staff RNs 1 (ft); Activities coordinators 1 (pt); Coordinators 8 (ft).
Facilities Dining room; Activities room; Laundry room.
Activities Arts & crafts; Cards; Games; Movies; Shopping trips.

Resa On Eden Prarie Rd
5601 Eden Prairie Rd, Minnetonka, MN, 55345
(612) 933-3348
Admin Jean Searles. *Medical Dir/Dir of Nursing* Health Counseling Consultant.
Licensure Intermediate care for mentally retarded; Supervised living facility. *Beds* 6. *Certified* Medicaid.
Owner Proprietary Corp.
Admissions Requirements Minimum age 40.
Staff RNs 1 (pt).
Facilities Dining room; Laundry room; Library; Dining room; Living room; Recreation room; Kitchen.
Activities Arts & crafts; Cards; Games; Reading groups; Movies; Shopping trips; Social/Cultural gatherings; Vacations; Church; Visitation; Walks; Fishing.

MONTEVIDEO

Luther Haven Nursing Home*
1109 E Hwy 7, Montevideo, MN, 56265
(612) 269-6517
Admin James Flaherty.

Licensure Skilled care; Intermediate care. *Beds* SNF 65; ICF 55. *Certified* Medicaid.
Owner Nonprofit Corp.
Affiliation Lutheran

REM Montevideo Inc*
585 Gravel Rd, Montevideo, MN, 56265
(612) 269-6479
Admin Craig Miller.
Licensure Supervised living facility. *Beds* 15. *Certified* Medicaid.
Owner Proprietary Corp.
Admissions Requirements Minimum age 16; Medical examination; Physician's request.
Staff RNs 1 (pt); Nurses aides 3 (ft), 8 (pt); Recreational therapists 1 (pt); Activities coordinators 1 (pt).
Facilities Dining room; Activities room; Laundry room.
Activities Arts & crafts; Cards; Games; Reading groups; Movies; Shopping trips; Social/Cultural gatherings; Camping; Bowling; Swimming; Fishing.

MONTGOMERY

Siemers Board & Care
211 Spruce Ave, Montgomery, MN, 56069
(612) 364-8831
Admin David Mann. *Medical Dir/Dir of Nursing* Diane Dokken DON.
Licensure Intermediate care. *Beds* ICF 12. *Certified* Medicaid.
Owner Privately owned.
Admissions Requirements Medical examination.
Staff RNs 1 (pt); LPNs 1 (ft), 1 (pt); Orderlies 1 (pt); Nurses aides 5 (pt); Dietitians 1 (pt).
Languages German, Czech
Facilities Dining room; Activities room; Chapel; Laundry room.
Activities Arts & crafts; Cards; Games; Shopping trips; Social/Cultural gatherings.

MONTICELLO

Monticello Big Lake Community Nursing Home
PO Box 480, 1013 Hart Blvd, Monticello, MN, 55362
(612) 295-2945
Admin Barbara Schwientek. *Medical Dir/Dir of Nursing* Dr M Smorstok; Olive Krahl RN DON.
Licensure Skilled care. *Beds* SNF 91. *Certified* Medicaid; Medicare.
Owner Publicly owned.
Staff RNs 6 (pt); LPNs 12 (pt); Nurses aides 5 (ft), 44 (pt); Recreational therapists 1 (ft).
Facilities Dining room; Activities room; Laundry room; Barber/Beauty shop; Outdoor patios; 2 screened gazebos; Senior walking & exercise course.
Activities Arts & crafts; Cards; Games; Reading groups; Prayer groups; Movies; Shopping trips; Social/Cultural gatherings; Annual overnite experience at handicap 'camp' facility.

MOORHEAD

Clay County Residence II*
2842 Village Green Dr, Moorhead, MN, 56560
(218) 233-5949
Admin Douglas Johnson.
Licensure Intermediate care for mentally retarded. *Beds* 6. *Certified* Medicaid; Medicare.
Owner Nonprofit Corp.
Admissions Requirements Minimum age 16; Medical examination.
Staff RNs 1 (pt).

Facilities Dining room; Activities room; Crafts room; Laundry room.
Activities Arts & crafts; Cards; Games; Movies; Shopping trips.

Eventide Lutheran Home
1405 S 7th St, Moorhead, MN, 56560
(218) 233-7508
Admin David Torkildson. *Medical Dir/Dir of Nursing* Dr John R Holten.
Licensure Skilled care; Intermediate care. *Beds* 195. *Certified* Medicaid; Medicare.
Owner Nonprofit Corp.
Admissions Requirements Medical examination.
Staff RNs 8 (ft), 5 (pt); LPNs 5 (ft), 12 (pt); Nurses aides 40 (ft), 65 (pt); Physical therapists 1 (ft), 1 (pt); Recreational therapists 5 (pt); Activities coordinators 1 (ft); Dietitians 1 (ft).
Affiliation Lutheran
Facilities Dining room; Physical therapy room; Activities room; Chapel; Crafts room; Laundry room; Barber/Beauty shop; Library; Coffee shop; Formal family dining; Senior day care.
Activities Arts & crafts; Cards; Games; Prayer groups; Movies; Shopping trips; Social/Cultural gatherings.

Moorhead Healthcare Center*
2810 N 2nd Ave, Moorhead, MN, 56560
(218) 233-7578
Admin Roger Paulsberg. *Medical Dir/Dir of Nursing* Dr Craychee.
Licensure Skilled care; Intermediate care. *Beds* 89. *Certified* Medicaid; Medicare.
Owner Proprietary Corp (Beverly Enterprises).
Admissions Requirements Medical examination; Physician's request.
Facilities Dining room; Physical therapy room; Activities room; Chapel; Crafts room; Laundry room; Barber/Beauty shop.
Activities Arts & crafts; Cards; Games; Reading groups; Prayer groups; Movies; Shopping trips; Social/Cultural gatherings.

Valley Group Home 1
1330 2nd Ave N, Moorhead, MN, 56560
(218) 236-9805
Admin Dr Vernon C Nordmark Phd. *Medical Dir/Dir of Nursing* Josette Nordmark MD.
Licensure Intermediate care for mentally retarded. *Beds* ICF/MR 10. *Certified* Medicaid.
Owner Proprietary Corp.
Admissions Requirements Minimum age 18; Medical examination.
Staff RNs 1 (pt); Activities coordinators 1 (ft); Direct care staff 3 (ft), 8 (pt).
Facilities Dining room; Activities room; Activities room; Laundry room.
Activities Arts & crafts; Cards; Games; Movies; Shopping trips; Social/Cultural gatherings.

MOOSE LAKE

Moose Lake Regional Treatment Center*
1000 Lakeshore Dr, Moose Lake, MN, 55767
(618) 485-4411
Admin Frank R Milczark.
Licensure Skilled care; Intermediate care. *Beds* SNF 245; ICF/MR 203. *Certified* Medicaid; Medicare.
Owner Publicly owned.

MORA

Brighter Day Residence*
620 N Wood St, Mora, MN, 55051
(612) 679-3840
Admin Louis Nelson.
Licensure Intermediate care for mentally retarded. *Beds* 8. *Certified* Medicaid.
Owner Nonprofit Corp.

Fireside Foster Inn*
114 W Maple St, Mora, MN, 55051
(612) 679-2822
Admin Robert Sandberg.
Licensure Board care & Board lodging. *Beds*
29. *Certified* Medicaid.
Owner Proprietary Corp.
Staff LPNs 1 (ft), 2 (pt); Nurses aides 9 (pt);
Activities coordinators 1 (pt); Dietitians 1
(pt).

Sunshine Villa
Birch-Mor Medical Park, Mora, MN, 55051
(612) 679-1411
Admin Charles Huyink. *Medical Dir/Dir of
Nursing* Larry Brettingen; Anna Norgaard
DON.
Licensure Skilled care. *Beds* 87. *Certified*
Medicaid; Medicare.
Owner Proprietary Corp.
Admissions Requirements Medical
examination.
Staff RNs 4 (ft), 5 (pt); LPNs 4 (ft), 6 (pt);
Orderlies 1 (pt); Nurses aides 12 (ft), 24 (pt);
Physical therapists 1 (pt); Occupational
therapists 1 (pt); Activities coordinators 1
(ft).
Facilities Dining room; Physical therapy
room; Activities room; Crafts room; Laundry
room; Barber/Beauty shop.
Activities Arts & crafts; Cards; Games;
Reading groups; Prayer groups; Movies;
Shopping trips; Social/Cultural gatherings.

MORGAN

Gil Mor Manor
Morgan, MN, 56266
(507) 249-3144
Admin Rita Sabatino. *Medical Dir/Dir of
Nursing* C M Galvin.
Licensure Intermediate care. *Beds* 49.
Certified Medicaid.
Owner Nonprofit Corp.
Admissions Requirements Physician's request.
Staff RNs 1 (ft); LPNs 4 (ft), 1 (pt); Nurses
aides 10 (ft), 10 (pt); Activities coordinators
1 (ft); Dietitians 1 (pt).
Facilities Dining room; Activities room;
Chapel; Crafts room; Laundry room; Barber/
Beauty shop; Library.
Activities Arts & crafts; Cards; Games;
Reading groups; Prayer groups; Movies;
Shopping trips.

MORRIS

Aneskarm III—Inisteige*
210 W 7th, Morris, MN, 56267
(612) 589-2057
Admin Deborah Sheehan.
Licensure Intermediate care for mentally
retarded. *Beds* 10. *Certified* Medicaid.
Owner Nonprofit Corp.

Villa of St Francis Nursing Home
1001 Scott Ave, Morris, MN, 56267
(612) 589-1133
Admin Luverne Hoffman. *Medical Dir/Dir of
Nursing* Dr Raymond Rossberg; Mary
Garmer.
Licensure Skilled care; Intermediate care. *Beds*
SNF 98; ICF 42. *Certified* Medicaid;
Medicare.
Owner Nonprofit Corp.
Admissions Requirements Minimum age 16;
Medical examination; Physician's request.
Staff Physicians 8 (pt); RNs 7 (pt); LPNs 8
(ft), 13 (pt); Nurses aides 22 (ft), 44 (pt);
Recreational therapists 1 (ft); Activities
coordinators 1 (ft); Dietitians 1 (pt).
Affiliation Roman Catholic
Facilities Dining room; Physical therapy
room; Activities room; Chapel; Barber/
Beauty shop.

Activities Arts & crafts; Cards; Games;
Movies; Shopping trips; Discussion club;
Bible discussion.

MOUNTAIN LAKE

Eventide Home
810 3rd Ave, Mountain Lake, MN, 56159
(507) 427-3221
Admin Jane Ramiller.
Licensure Intermediate care. *Beds* 50.
Certified Medicaid.
Owner Nonprofit Corp.

Good Samaritan Village
745 Basinger Memorial Dr, Mountain Lake,
MN, 56159
(507) 427-2464
Admin Gary R Baumgartner.
Licensure Intermediate care. *Beds* ICF 80.
Certified Medicaid.
Owner Nonprofit Corp (Evangelical Lutheran/
Good Samaritan).
Staff RNs; LPNs; Orderlies; Nurses aides;
Activities coordinators.
Languages German
Affiliation Lutheran
Facilities Dining room; Activities room;
Chapel; Barber/Beauty shop.
Activities Arts & crafts; Cards; Games;
Reading groups; Prayer groups; Movies;
Shopping trips.

NEW BRIGHTON

Innsbruck Healthcare Center*
2800 Hwy 694, New Brighton, MN, 55112
(612) 633-1686
Admin Michael Goblirsch.
Licensure Skilled care. *Beds* 130. *Certified*
Medicaid.
Owner Proprietary Corp (Beverly Enterprises).

New Brighton Care Center
550 8th St NW, New Brighton, MN, 55112
(612) 633-7200
Admin Michael Chies. *Medical Dir/Dir of
Nursing* Arella Saretle DON.
Licensure Skilled care. *Beds* SNF 64. *Certified*
Medicaid; Medicare.
Owner Proprietary Corp.
Admissions Requirements Physician's request.
Staff Physicians 3 (pt); RNs 5 (ft); LPNs 6
(ft); Orderlies 11 (ft); Nurses aides 15 (ft);
Physical therapists 1 (pt); Reality therapists
1 (pt); Recreational therapists 1 (pt);
Occupational therapists 1 (pt); Speech
therapists 1 (pt); Activities coordinators 1
(ft); Dietitians 1 (ft), 1 (pt); Dentists 1 (pt);
Ophthalmologists 1 (pt); Podiatrists 1 (pt).
Facilities Dining room; Activities room;
Chapel; Crafts room; Barber/Beauty shop.
Activities Arts & crafts; Cards; Games;
Reading groups; Prayer groups; Movies;
Shopping trips.

Trevilla of New Brighton
825 1st Ave NW, New Brighton, MN, 55112
(612) 633-7875
Admin Charlotte Samuelson. *Medical Dir/Dir
of Nursing* Dr Mary Wangsness.
Licensure Skilled care; Intermediate care. *Beds*
SNF 177; ICF 12. *Certified* Medicaid;
Medicare.
Owner Proprietary Corp (Unicare).
Admissions Requirements Minimum age 16;
Medical examination; Physician's request.
Staff Physicians 1 (pt); RNs; LPNs; Nurses
aides; Physical therapists; Reality therapists;
Recreational therapists; Occupational
therapists; Speech therapists; Activities
coordinators.
Facilities Dining room; Physical therapy
room; Activities room; Chapel; Crafts room;
Barber/Beauty shop.

Activities Arts & crafts; Cards; Games;
Reading groups; Prayer groups; Movies;
Shopping trips; Social/Cultural gatherings.

NEW HOPE

Ambassador Healthcare Center
8100 Medicine Lake Rd, New Hope, MN,
55427
(612) 544-4171
Admin Jon Lundberg. *Medical Dir/Dir of
Nursing* Diane Dahl MD; Shirley Stiener
DON.
Licensure Skilled care. *Beds* SNF 114.
Certified Medicaid; Medicare.
Owner Proprietary Corp (Good Neighbor
Services).
Admissions Requirements Minimum age 18;
Medical examination.
Staff RNs 5 (ft), 7 (pt); LPNs 3 (ft), 12 (pt);
Nurses aides 21 (ft), 20 (pt); Physical
therapists 1 (ft); Activities coordinators 1
(ft), 1 (pt); Social workers 1 (ft), 1 (pt).
Facilities Dining room; Physical therapy
room; Activities room; Crafts room; Laundry
room; Barber/Beauty shop; OT room;
Gazebo; Large patio.
Activities Arts & crafts; Games; Reading
groups; Prayer groups; Movies; Shopping
trips; Social/Cultural gatherings.

Homeward Bound*
4741 Zealand Ave N, New Hope, MN, 55428
(612) 535-6171
Admin James L Glasoe. *Medical Dir/Dir of
Nursing* Arnold Anderson MD.
Licensure Supervised living facility. *Beds* 64.
Certified Medicaid.
Owner Nonprofit Corp.
Staff RNs 3 (ft); LPNs 6 (ft), 12 (pt); Nurses
aides 14 (ft), 30 (pt); Physical therapists 1
(ft); Recreational therapists 1 (ft);
Occupational therapists 2 (ft); Speech
therapists 1 (ft); Activities coordinators 1
(ft).

North Ridge Care Center
5430 Boone Ave N, New Hope, MN, 55428
(612) 536-7000
Admin Charles P Thompson. *Medical Dir/Dir
of Nursing* Dr James J Pattee; Catherine A
Lloyd RN DON.
Licensure Skilled care; Intermediate care. *Beds*
SNF 559. *Certified* Medicaid; Medicare.
Owner Privately owned.
Admissions Requirements Medical
examination; Physician's request.
Staff Physicians 1 (pt); RNs 38 (ft); LPNs 37
(ft), 40 (pt); Nurses aides 85 (ft), 175 (pt);
Physical therapists 1 (ft); Occupational
therapists 1 (ft); Activities coordinators 1
(ft); Recreational aides 7 (ft), 15 (pt).
Facilities Dining room; Physical therapy
room; Activities room; Chapel; Crafts room;
Laundry room; Barber/Beauty shop;; Dental
office; Occupational therapy room.
Activities Arts & crafts; Cards; Games;
Reading groups; Prayer groups; Movies;
Shopping trips; Social/Cultural gatherings;
Bazaars; Mini-golf course; Bell ringer band;
Theatre group.

St Therese Home
8000 Bass Lake Rd, New Hope, MN, 55428
(612) 537-4503
Admin Kenneth Gallus. *Medical Dir/Dir of
Nursing* C Dwight Townes; Dianne
Crawford.
Licensure Skilled care; Intermediate care;
Board care. *Beds* SNF 202; ICF 50;
Boarding care 50. *Certified* Medicaid.
Owner Nonprofit Corp.
Admissions Requirements Minimum age 65;
Medical examination.
Staff RNs 4 (ft), 23 (pt); LPNs 2 (ft), 19 (pt);
Orderlies; Nurses aides 19 (ft), 131 (pt);
Physical therapists 2 (ft), 2 (pt); Reality
therapists 1 (ft); Recreational therapists 5

(ft), 3 (pt); Occupational therapists 1 (ft), 1 (pt); Speech therapists 1 (pt); Activities coordinators 1 (ft); Dietitians 1 (ft); Dentists 1 (pt); Ophthalmologists 1 (pt); Podiatrists 1 (pt); Pharmacist 1 (ft); Psychologist 11 (pt).
Affiliation Roman Catholic
Facilities Dining room; Physical therapy room; Activities room; Chapel; Crafts room; Laundry room; Barber/Beauty shop; Library; Gift shop; Coffee shop.
Activities Arts & crafts; Cards; Games; Prayer groups; Movies; Social/Cultural gatherings; Rosary; Parties; Gardening.

NEW LONDON

Glen Oaks Care Center
Box B, 207 Main St N, Rte 3, New London, MN, 56273
(612) 354-2231
Admin Larry E Juhl. *Medical Dir/Dir of Nursing* Jock A Guy MD; Louise Ziemer RN.
Licensure Skilled care. *Beds* SNF 62; Apts 36. *Certified* Medicaid; Medicare.
Owner Proprietary Corp.
Admissions Requirements Minimum age 16; Medical examination.
Staff Physicians 1 (pt); RNs 4 (ft), 4 (pt); Orderlies 8 (pt); Nurses aides 5 (ft), 31 (pt); Physical therapists 1 (pt); Occupational therapists 1 (pt); Activities coordinators 1 (ft); Dietitians 1 (pt).
Facilities Dining room; Physical therapy room; Activities room; Chapel; Crafts room; Laundry room; Barber/Beauty shop; Library.
Activities Arts & crafts; Cards; Games; Reading groups; Prayer groups; Movies; Shopping trips; Social/Cultural gatherings.

NEW PRAGUE

Mala Strana Health Care Center
1001 Columbus Ave N, New Prague, MN, 56071
(612) 758-2511
Admin Jacqueline J Henle. *Medical Dir/Dir of Nursing* Michael Wilcox MD; Fay Kohnert DON.
Licensure Skilled care. *Beds* 120. *Certified* Medicaid.
Owner Proprietary Corp (Thro Co).
Admissions Requirements Medical examination; Physician's request.
Languages Czech
Facilities Dining room; Physical therapy room; Activities room; Chapel; Crafts room; Laundry room; Barber/Beauty shop; Library.
Activities Arts & crafts; Cards; Games; Reading groups; Prayer groups; Movies; Shopping trips; Social/Cultural gatherings.

NEW RICHLAND

New Richland Care Center
PO Box 477, 312 1st Street North East, New Richland, MN, 56072
(507) 465-3292
Admin Obie L Reese Jr. *Medical Dir/Dir of Nursing* Tamyra Williams RN.
Licensure Skilled care; Intermediate care. *Beds* SNF 60; ICF. *Certified* Medicaid; Medicare.
Owner Publicly owned.
Admissions Requirements Medical examination.
Staff RNs 3 (ft), 3 (pt); LPNs 1 (ft), 6 (pt); Nurses aides 2 (ft), 26 (pt); Recreational therapists 1 (ft); Social service director 1 (ft).
Facilities Dining room; Physical therapy room; Activities room; Chapel; Crafts room; Laundry room; Barber/Beauty shop.
Activities Arts & crafts; Cards; Games; Reading groups; Prayer groups; Movies; Social/Cultural gatherings; Physical activities; Exercise; Bowling; Baking.

NEW ULM

Eleven Seven
117 S Minnesota, New Ulm, MN, 56073
(612) 359-7812
Admin Mark Wiger.
Licensure Skilled care; Intermediate care for mentally retarded. *Beds* 16. *Certified* Medicaid.
Owner Proprietary Corp.

Highland Manor
405 N Highland Ave, New Ulm, MN, 56073
(507) 359-2026
Admin Elroy E Ubl. *Medical Dir/Dir of Nursing* Karen Stoite DON.
Licensure Skilled care. *Beds* 98. *Certified* Medicaid; Medicare.
Owner Nonprofit organization/foundation.
Admissions Requirements Medical examination; Physician's request.
Languages German
Facilities Dining room; Activities room; Crafts room; Laundry room; Barber/Beauty shop.
Activities Arts & crafts; Cards; Games; Reading groups; Prayer groups; Movies; Shopping trips; Social/Cultural gatherings.

MBW on Center
801 Center St, New Ulm, MN, 56073
(507) 354-3808
Admin Mark Wiger. *Medical Dir/Dir of Nursing* Brenda Wiger.
Licensure Intermediate care for mentally retarded. *Beds* 8. *Certified* Medicaid.
Owner Proprietary Corp.
Staff RNs 1 (pt); Orderlies 2 (pt); Nurses aides; Recreational therapists 4 (ft); Activities coordinators 1 (ft).

New Ulm CRF I
327 N German, New Ulm, MN, 56073
(507) 359-2892
Admin D Bill Olson. *Medical Dir/Dir of Nursing* Devin Nelson.
Licensure Intermediate care for mentally retarded. *Beds* ICF/MR 6. *Certified* Medicaid.
Owner Proprietary Corp.
Admissions Requirements Minimum age 18; State screening.
Facilities Laundry room.

New Ulm CRF II
1708 N Garden, New Ulm, MN, 56073
(507) 359-2892
Admin D Bill Olson. *Medical Dir/Dir of Nursing* Devin Nelson.
Licensure Intermediate care for mentally retarded. *Beds* ICF/MR 6. *Certified* Medicaid.
Owner Proprietary Corp.
Admissions Requirements Minimum age 18; State screening.
Facilities Laundry room.

NEW YORK MILLS

Elders Home Inc
PO Box 188, S Tousley Ave, New York Mills, MN, 56567
(218) 385-2005
Admin Andrew Tumberg. *Medical Dir/Dir of Nursing* Tom Wachlarowicz RN DON.
Licensure Intermediate care. *Beds* ICF 70. *Certified* Medicaid.
Owner Nonprofit Corp.
Admissions Requirements Minimum age 60 or less depending on need; Medical examination; Physician's request.
Staff RNs 1 (ft); LPNs 6 (ft), 4 (pt); Orderlies 1 (ft), 1 (pt); Nurses aides 20 (ft), 10 (pt); Activities coordinators 1 (ft).
Languages Finnish
Affiliation Lutheran

Facilities Dining room; Physical therapy room; Activities room; Chapel; Crafts room; Laundry room; Barber/Beauty shop; Sauna.
Activities Arts & crafts; Cards; Games; Reading groups; Prayer groups; Movies; Shopping trips; Transportation to social events, athletic events, other medical facilites, & other outings; Picnics.

NOPEMING

Nopeming Nursing Home
Nopeming, MN, 55810
(218) 628-2381
Admin Dick Jokinen. *Medical Dir/Dir of Nursing* Dr William Stein; Mrs Nancy Parkko RN.
Licensure Skilled care. *Beds* SNF 212. *Certified* Medicaid; Medicare.
Owner Publicly owned.
Admissions Requirements Medical examination; Physician's request.
Staff RNs 9 (ft), 8 (pt); LPNs 11 (ft), 30 (pt); Nurses aides 44 (ft), 66 (pt); Physical therapists 1 (ft), 1 (pt); Activities coordinators 1 (ft); Dietitians 1 (ft), 1 (pt).
Languages Finnish, Polish, Swedish, Serbian, Slavic, Norwegian
Facilities Dining room; Physical therapy room; Activities room; Chapel; Crafts room; Laundry room; Barber/Beauty shop; Library; Cafeteria.
Activities Arts & crafts; Cards; Games; Reading groups; Prayer groups; Movies; Shopping trips; Social/Cultural gatherings; Church; Band; Dining club.

NORTH BRANCH

Green Acres Nursing Home*
North Branch, MN, 55056
(612) 674-7068
Admin Ellis R Johnson.
Licensure Skilled care; Intermediate care. *Beds* SNF 67; ICF 68. *Certified* Medicaid.
Owner Publicly owned.

NORTH SAINT PAUL

Maplewood Care Center
1900 Sherren Ave E, North Saint Paul, MN, 55109
(612) 770-1365
Admin Angeline H Sewall. *Medical Dir/Dir of Nursing* Dr James Nolin; Mary Beth Lacina DON.
Licensure Skilled care. *Beds* 176. *Certified* Medicaid; Medicare.
Owner Nonprofit Corp (Volunteers of America).
Admissions Requirements Minimum age 65; Physician's request.
Staff RNs 16 (ft), 24 (pt); LPNs 5 (ft), 9 (pt); Nurses aides 65 (ft), 97 (pt); Physical therapists 1 (ft); Recreational therapists 4 (ft); Occupational therapists 1 (ft); Dietitians 2 (ft).
Facilities Dining room; Physical therapy room; Activities room; Chapel; Laundry room; Barber/Beauty shop; Library; Occupational therapy room.
Activities Arts & crafts; Cards; Games; Reading groups; Prayer groups; Movies; Shopping trips; Social/Cultural gatherings; Live music; Outside entertainment.

North St Paul Care Center
2375 Skillman Ave E, North Saint Paul, MN, 55109
(612) 777-7435
Admin Ms J Jankowski. *Medical Dir/Dir of Nursing* William Schroeder MD.
Licensure Skilled care. *Beds* SNF 47. *Certified* Medicaid.
Owner Proprietary Corp (King Care Centers Inc).

Admissions Requirements Minimum age 18; Medical examination; Physician's request.
Staff RNs 1 (ft), 5 (pt); LPNs 1 (ft), 6 (pt); Orderlies 1 (ft); Nurses aides 8 (ft), 9 (pt); Recreational therapists 1 (ft).
Languages Polish, Norwegian
Facilities Dining room; Physical therapy room; Activities room; Chapel; Crafts room; Laundry room; Barber/Beauty shop.
Activities Arts & crafts; Cards; Games; Reading groups; Prayer groups; Movies; Shopping trips; Social/Cultural gatherings.

NORTHFIELD

Minnesota Odd Fellows Home
815 Forest Ave, Northfield, MN, 55057
(507) 645-6611
Admin Carlton Sather. *Medical Dir/Dir of Nursing* Patricia Vincent.
Licensure Skilled care; Intermediate care; Board & lodging; Adult day care. *Beds* 120. *Certified* Medicaid.
Owner Nonprofit Corp.
Admissions Requirements Medical examination.
Staff Physicians 1 (pt); RNs 6 (ft); LPNs 12 (ft); Nurses aides 80 (ft); Physical therapists 1 (pt); Occupational therapists 2 (ft); Speech therapists 1 (pt); Dietitians 1 (pt); Dentists 1 (pt); Ophthalmologists 1 (pt); Podiatrists 1 (pt).
Affiliation Independent Order of Odd Fellows & Rebekahs
Facilities Dining room; Physical therapy room; Activities room; Chapel; Crafts room; Laundry room; Barber/Beauty shop; Library.
Activities Arts & crafts; Cards; Games; Reading groups; Prayer groups; Movies; Shopping trips; Social/Cultural gatherings.

Northfield Retirement Center
900 Cannon Valley Dr, Northfield, MN, 55057
(507) 645-9511
Admin Rev Gerhard J Nygaard. *Medical Dir/Dir of Nursing* Corrine Hanson RN.
Licensure Intermediate care. *Beds* ICF 80. *Certified* Medicaid.
Owner Nonprofit Corp.
Admissions Requirements Minimum age 18; Medical examination.
Staff RNs 1 (ft), 2 (pt); LPNs 4 (ft), 1 (pt); Nurses aides 7 (ft), 18 (pt); Recreational therapists 1 (ft), 2 (pt); Activities coordinators 1 (ft); Dietitians 1 (pt).
Affiliation Lutheran
Facilities Dining room; Activities room; Chapel; Crafts room; Laundry room; Barber/Beauty shop; Library.
Activities Arts & crafts; Cards; Games; Reading groups; Prayer groups; Movies; Shopping trips; Social/Cultural gatherings.

NORTHOME

Northome Nursing Home
PO Box 138, Northome, MN, 56661
(218) 897-5235
Admin Paul Raygor. *Medical Dir/Dir of Nursing* Dr G W Franklin; N Leseman RN.
Licensure Skilled care; Intermediate care for mentally retarded. *Beds* SNF 42; ICF/MR 16. *Certified* Medicaid; Medicare.
Owner Proprietary Corp (King Care Centers Inc).
Admissions Requirements Minimum age 18; Medical examination; Physician's request.
Staff RNs 3 (ft), 1 (pt); LPNs 3 (ft), 1 (pt); Nurses aides 12 (ft), 9 (pt); Physical therapists 1 (ft); Activities coordinators 1 (ft), 5 (pt).
Facilities Dining room; Physical therapy room; Activities room; Laundry room.
Activities Arts & crafts; Cards; Games; Reading groups; Prayer groups; Movies; Shopping trips.

OLIVIA

Olivia Healthcare Center Inc
1003 W Maple, Olivia, MN, 56277
(612) 523-1652
Admin David D Lamb. *Medical Dir/Dir of Nursing* C A Anderson MD; Susan Meyer RN.
Licensure Skilled care; Intermediate care. *Beds* SNF 94. *Certified* Medicaid; Medicare.
Owner Proprietary Corp (Beverly Enterprises).
Staff Physicians 6 (pt); RNs 2 (ft), 1 (pt); LPNs 7 (ft), 5 (pt); Nurses aides 21 (ft), 31 (pt); Physical therapists 1 (pt); Occupational therapists 1 (pt); Activities coordinators 1 (ft).
Facilities Dining room; Physical therapy room; Activities room; Crafts room; Laundry room; Barber/Beauty shop.
Activities Arts & crafts; Cards; Games; Reading groups; Prayer groups; Movies; Shopping trips; Social/Cultural gatherings; Reminiscence group.

ONAMIA

Mille Lacs Nursing Home
200 N Elm St, Onamia, MN, 56359
(612) 532-3154
Admin John Haines. *Medical Dir/Dir of Nursing* Dr Dennis Jacobson; Kathryn E Mickus RN DON.
Licensure Skilled care. *Beds* SNF 80. *Certified* Medicaid; Medicare.
Owner Nonprofit Corp.
Admissions Requirements Medical examination; Physician's request.
Staff Physicians 4 (ft); RNs 5 (ft), 1 (pt); LPNs 6 (ft), 2 (pt); Nurses aides 30 (ft), 10 (pt); Physical therapists 1 (ft); Activities coordinators 1 (ft).
Languages Chippewa
Affiliation Roman Catholic
Facilities Dining room; Physical therapy room; Activities room; Chapel; Crafts room; Barber/Beauty shop.
Activities Arts & crafts; Cards; Games; Reading groups; Prayer groups; Movies; Shopping trips; Social/Cultural gatherings.

ORTONVILLE

Monarch Heights
501 Burdick Ave, Ortonville, MN, 56278
(612) 839-6139
Admin Ernest Guillemette. *Medical Dir/Dir of Nursing* Karen Russman RN.
Licensure Intermediate care for mentally retarded. *Beds* ICF/MR 12. *Certified* Medicaid.
Owner Nonprofit Corp.
Admissions Requirements Minimum age 18; Medical examination; Physician's request.
Staff Physicians 1 (pt); RNs 1 (pt); Physical therapists 1 (pt); Occupational therapists 1 (pt); Speech therapists 1 (pt); Dietitians 1 (pt); Dentists 1 (pt); Podiatrists 1 (pt); Direct care 12 (ft), 7 (pt).
Facilities Dining room; Activities room; Crafts room; Laundry room; Training kitchen.
Activities Arts & crafts; Cards; Games; Reading groups; Prayer groups; Movies; Shopping trips; Social/Cultural gatherings.

Northridge Residence
1075 Roy St, Ortonville, MN, 56278
(612) 839-6113
Admin Dan Olson. *Medical Dir/Dir of Nursing* Robert S Ross MD.
Licensure Skilled care. *Beds* SNF 74. *Certified* Medicaid; Medicare.
Owner Publicly owned.
Admissions Requirements Medical examination; Physician's request.

Staff Physicians 3 (pt); RNs 3 (ft), 2 (pt); LPNs 3 (ft), 4 (pt); Nurses aides 20, 20 (pt); Physical therapists 1 (pt); Activities coordinators 4 (pt); Dietitians 1 (ft).
Facilities Dining room; Physical therapy room; Activities room; Chapel; Crafts room; Laundry room; Barber/Beauty shop.
Activities Arts & crafts; Cards; Games; Reading groups; Prayer groups; Movies; Shopping trips; Social/Cultural gatherings.

OSAKIS

Community Memorial Home
410 Main St SW, Osakis, MN, 56360
(612) 859-2142
Admin Gary Larson. *Medical Dir/Dir of Nursing* Paul E Van Garp MD.
Licensure Skilled care. *Beds* SNF 62. *Certified* Medicaid; Medicare.
Owner Nonprofit Corp.
Admissions Requirements Minimum age 18; Medical examination.
Staff RNs 2 (ft), 4 (pt); Physical therapists 1 (pt); Occupational therapists 1 (pt); Activities coordinators 1 (ft); Dietitians 1 (pt).
Facilities Dining room; Physical therapy room; Activities room; Crafts room; Laundry room; Barber/Beauty shop.
Activities Arts & crafts; Cards; Games; Reading groups; Prayer groups; Movies; Social/Cultural gatherings.

REM Osakis Inc*
405 Lake St, Osakis, MN, 56360
(612) 859-4200
Admin Thomas Miller.
Licensure Intermediate care for mentally retarded. *Beds* 13. *Certified* Medicaid.
Owner Proprietary Corp.

OSSEO

Berkshire Residence
501 2nd St SE, Osseo, MN, 55369
(612) 425-3939
Admin Sonja Johnson. *Medical Dir/Dir of Nursing* Sheila Gahr DON.
Licensure Intermediate care. *Beds* ICF 150. *Certified* Medicaid.
Owner Privately owned.
Admissions Requirements Minimum age; Medical examination; Physician's request.
Staff RNs 2 (ft), 9 (pt); LPNs 2 (ft), 12 (pt); Orderlies 1 (pt); Nurses aides 4 (ft), 12 (pt) 1 (ft); Recreational therapists 3 (pt); Activities coordinators 1 (ft); Dietitians 1 (ft); Dentists 1 (ft); Ophthalmologists 1 (ft); Podiatrists 1 (ft).
Facilities Dining room; Activities room; Chapel; Crafts room; Laundry room; Barber/Beauty shop; Library.
Activities Arts & crafts; Cards; Games; Reading groups; Prayer groups; Movies; Shopping trips; Social/Cultural gatherings; Dinners; Clubs; Choir.

Osseo Health Care*
525 2nd St SE, Osseo, MN, 53369
(612) 425-2128
Admin Joe Stanislav.
Licensure Skilled care; Intermediate care. *Beds* SNF 96; ICF 41. *Certified* Medicaid.
Owner Proprietary Corp (Unicare).

OSTRANDER

Ostrander Nursing Home*
PO Box 36, Ostrander, MN, 55961
(507) 657-2231
Admin Dotty Liebold. *Medical Dir/Dir of Nursing* Dr R Matson & Dr B Westra.
Licensure Skilled care; Intermediate care. *Beds* 57. *Certified* Medicaid.
Owner Proprietary Corp.

Admissions Requirements Medical
examination; Physician's request.
Staff RNs 1 (ft), 5 (pt); LPNs 2 (ft), 5 (pt);
Nurses aides 9 (ft), 15 (pt); Activities
coordinators 1 (ft); Dietitians 1 (pt).
Facilities Dining room; Activities room;
Laundry room; Barber/Beauty shop.
Activities Arts & crafts; Cards; Games;
Reading groups; Prayer groups; Movies;
Shopping trips; Social/Cultural gatherings.

OWATONNA

Cedarview Nursing Home
1409 S Cedar St, Owatonna, MN, 55060
(507) 451-7240
Admin Greg M Johnson. *Medical Dir/Dir of
Nursing* Dr A J Olson MD; Toni Anderson
RN DON.
Licensure Skilled care. *Beds* SNF 108.
Certified Medicaid; Medicare.
Owner Publicly owned.
Admissions Requirements Minimum age 18;
Medical examination; Physician's request.
Staff Physicians 1 (pt); RNs 2 (ft), 2 (pt);
LPNs 2 (ft), 12 (pt); Nurses aides 10 (ft), 50
(pt); Physical therapists 1 (pt); Reality
therapists 1 (pt); Recreational therapists 1
(pt); Speech therapists 1 (pt); Activities
coordinators 1 (ft); Dietitians 1 (ft); Dentists
1 (pt); Ophthalmologists 1 (pt); Podiatrists 1
(pt).
Facilities Dining room; Physical therapy
room; Activities room; Chapel; Crafts room;
Laundry room; Barber/Beauty shop; Library;
Lobbies.
Activities Arts & crafts; Cards; Games;
Reading groups; Prayer groups; Movies;
Shopping trips; Social/Cultural gatherings;
Bingo; Fishing trips; Outings; Picnics.

Owatonna Health Care Center*
201 SW 18th St, Owatonna, MN, 55060
(507) 451-6800
Admin Karl Pelovsky.
Licensure Skilled care; Intermediate care. *Beds*
SNF 90; ICF 20. *Certified* Medicaid.
Owner Proprietary Corp.

West Hills Lodge*
545 Florence Ave, Owatonna, MN, 55060
(507) 451-1172
Admin W H Taylor.
Licensure Supervised living facility. *Beds* 14.
Owner Nonprofit Corp.

Westside Boarding Care Home*
Rte 1, Owatonna, MN, 55060
(507) 451-0832
Admin Margaret Striemer.
Licensure Boarding care. *Beds* 13.

Woodvale VI
592 Adams St, Owatonna, MN, 55060
(507) 451-1296
Admin Ross Jacobson.
Licensure Intermediate care for mentally
retarded. *Beds* ICF/MR 15. *Certified*
Medicaid.
Owner Proprietary Corp.
Admissions Requirements Minimum age 18;
Medical examination; Physician's request.
Staff Psychologist; Resident supervisors 9 (ft),
7 (pt).
Facilities Laundry room.
Activities Arts & crafts; Cards; Games;
Movies; Shopping trips; Social/Cultural
gatherings.

PARK RAPIDS

Heartland Home*
609 W 7th St, Box 214, Park Rapids, MN,
56470
(218) 732-4572
Admin Raylene Kimball.

Licensure Intermediate care for mentally
retarded. *Beds* 8. *Certified* Medicaid.
Owner Nonprofit Corp.

Sunset Nursing Home*
W 5th St, Park Rapids, MN, 56470
(218) 732-3329
Admin Dale Jackson.
Licensure Skilled care. *Beds* 130. *Certified*
Medicaid.
Owner Publicly owned.
Admissions Requirements Medical
examination; Physician's request.
Facilities Dining room; Physical therapy
room; Activities room; Chapel; Crafts room;
Laundry room; Barber/Beauty shop.
Activities Arts & crafts; Cards; Games;
Reading groups; Prayer groups; Movies;
Social/Cultural gatherings.

PARKERS PRAIRIE

St Williams Nursing Home*
Soo St, Parkers Prairie, MN, 56361
(218) 338-4671
Admin Cyrilla Bitzan.
Licensure Intermediate care. *Beds* 70.
Certified Medicaid.
Owner Nonprofit Corp.

PAYNESVILLE

**Paynesville Community Hospital/Koronis
Manor**
200 1st St W, Paynesville, MN, 56362
(612) 243-3767
Admin William LaCroix. *Medical Dir/Dir of
Nursing* Beverly Mueller.
Licensure Skilled care. *Beds* SNF 64. *Certified*
Medicaid; Medicare.
Owner Publicly owned.
Admissions Requirements Physician's request.
Staff RNs 3 (ft), 5 (pt); LPNs 5 (ft), 3 (pt);
Nurses aides 16 (ft), 18 (pt); Occupational
therapists 1 (pt); Activities coordinators 1
(ft); Dietitians 1 (ft).
Facilities Dining room; Physical therapy
room; Activities room; Chapel; Barber/
Beauty room.
Activities Arts & crafts; Cards; Games;
Movies; Shopping trips; Social/Cultural
gatherings.

Paynesville Good Samaritan Center
311 Washburn Ave, Paynesville, MN, 56362
(612) 243-7451
Admin Elizabeth Crusoe. *Medical Dir/Dir of
Nursing* Sandra Christle.
Licensure Intermediate care. *Beds* ICF 46.
Certified Medicaid.
Owner Nonprofit Corp (Evangelical Lutheran/
Good Samaritan).
Admissions Requirements Minimum age 21;
Medical examination.
Staff RNs 1 (ft), 1 (pt); LPNs 4 (pt); Nurses
aides 3 (ft), 9 (pt); Recreational therapists;
Activities coordinators 1 (ft); Dietitians 1
(pt).
Affiliation Lutheran
Facilities Dining room; Activities room;
Chapel; Crafts room; Laundry room; 3
lounges.
Activities Arts & crafts; Cards; Games;
Reading groups; Prayer groups; Movies;
Shopping trips; Social/Cultural gatherings;
Discussion groups; Study groups; Resident
council.

PELICAN RAPIDS

Pelican Rapids Good Samaritan Center
119 N Broadway, Pelican Rapids, MN, 56572
(218) 863-2401
Admin Rev Arthur Gustafson. *Medical Dir/
Dir of Nursing* Owen Thompson MD; E
Dellaneva DON.

Licensure Intermediate care. *Beds* ICF 70.
Certified Medicare.
Owner Nonprofit Corp (Evangelical Lutheran/
Good Samaritan).
Admissions Requirements Medical
examination; Physician's request.
Staff RNs 1 (ft), 2 (pt); LPNs 6 (ft); Nurses
aides 24 (ft), 12 (pt); Physical therapists 1
(pt); Recreational therapists 2 (ft); Activities
coordinators 1 (ft); Dietitians 1 (pt).
Affiliation Lutheran
Facilities Dining room; Activities room;
Chapel; Crafts room; Laundry room; Barber/
Beauty shop; Smoking day room with TV.
Activities Cards; Games; Reading groups;
Prayer groups; Movies; Social/Cultural
gatherings.

Pelican Valley Health Center
211 E Mill St, Pelican Rapids, MN, 56572
(218) 863-3111
Admin Charles F Harms. *Medical Dir/Dir of
Nursing* Gary Kennedy MD.
Licensure Skilled care; Intermediate care;
Hospital—home health agency. *Beds* SNF
46; Hospital—home health agency 13.
Certified Medicaid; Medicare.
Owner Publicly owned.
Admissions Requirements Medical
examination.
Staff RNs 8 (ft), 4 (pt); LPNs 6 (ft), 4 (pt);
Nurses aides 15 (ft), 15 (pt); Physical
therapists 1 (ft); Recreational therapists 2
(ft); Occupational therapists 1 (pt); Speech
therapists 1 (pt); Activities coordinators 1
(ft); Dietitians 1 (pt).
Languages Norwegian, Swedish
Affiliation Lutheran
Facilities Dining room; Physical therapy
room; Activities room; Chapel; Crafts room;
Laundry room; Barber/Beauty shop.
Activities Arts & crafts; Cards; Games;
Reading groups; Prayer groups; Movies;
Shopping trips; Social/Cultural gatherings.

PERHAM

Memorial Hospital & Home
665 3rd St SW, Perham, MN, 56573
(218) 346-4500
Admin Rick Failing. *Medical Dir/Dir of
Nursing* Elaine Beyer DON.
Licensure Skilled care; Intermediate care. *Beds*
SNF 68; ICF 34. *Certified* Medicaid;
Medicare.
Owner Publicly owned.
Staff RNs 1 (ft), 2 (pt); LPNs 13 (ft), 4 (pt);
Nurses aides 32 (ft), 15 (pt); Activities
coordinators 1 (ft).
Facilities Dining room; Physical therapy
room; Activities room; Chapel; Crafts room;
Barber/Beauty shop.
Activities Arts & crafts; Cards; Games;
Reading groups; Prayer groups; Movies;
Shopping trips; Social/Cultural gatherings.

PIERZ

St Marys Villa Nursing Home
1st Ave S & Faust St, Pierz, MN, 56364
(612) 468-6405
Admin James B Birchem. *Medical Dir/Dir of
Nursing* Dr Michael Neudecker.
Licensure Skilled care; Intermediate care. *Beds*
101. *Certified* Medicaid; Medicare.
Owner Nonprofit organization/foundation.
Admissions Requirements Medical
examination; Physician's request.
Staff RNs 7 (ft), 2 (pt); LPNs 6 (ft), 5 (pt);
Orderlies 1 (pt); Nurses aides 22 (ft), 18 (pt);
Activities coordinators 1 (ft); Dietitians 1
(ft).
Affiliation Roman Catholic
Facilities Dining room; Physical therapy
room; Activities room; Chapel; Crafts room;
Laundry room; Barber/Beauty shop.

Activities Arts & crafts; Cards; Games;
Reading groups; Prayer groups; Movies;
Shopping trips; Social/Cultural gatherings.

PINE CITY

Lakeside Medical Center*
129 E 6th St, Pine City, MN, 55063
(612) 629-2542
Admin Mary Blaufuss. *Medical Dir/Dir of
Nursing* R F Mach MD.
Licensure Skilled care; Intermediate care. *Beds*
SNF 93; ICF 42. *Certified* Medicaid.
Owner Proprietary Corp.
Admissions Requirements Minimum age 16;
Medical examination.
Staff RNs 2 (ft), 4 (pt); LPNs 3 (ft), 9 (pt);
Nurses aides 17 (ft), 40 (pt); Physical
therapists 1 (pt); Recreational therapists 1
(ft); Dietitians 1 (ft).
Facilities Dining room; Physical therapy
room; Activities room; Chapel; Crafts room;
Laundry room; Barber/Beauty shop.
Activities Arts & crafts; Reading groups;
Movies; Social/Cultural gatherings; Reality
orientation & remotivation.

PINE ISLAND

Pine Haven Care Center
PO Box 768, 210 NW 3rd St, Pine Island,
MN, 55963
(507) 356-8304
Admin Sharon Brenny. *Medical Dir/Dir of
Nursing* O E H Larson MD; Sandi
Lamphere DON.
Licensure Skilled care. *Beds* SNF 74. *Certified*
Medicaid; Medicare.
Owner Nonprofit organization/foundation.
Admissions Requirements Medical
examination; Physician's request.
Staff RNs 5 (pt); LPNs 1 (ft), 10 (pt); Nurses
aides 6 (ft), 36 (pt); Physical therapists 1
(pt); Recreational therapists 1 (ft);
Occupational therapists 1 (pt); Speech
therapists 1 (pt).
Facilities Dining room; Activities room;
Crafts room; Barber/Beauty shop.
Activities Arts & crafts; Cards; Games;
Reading groups; Prayer groups; Movies;
Shopping trips; Social/Cultural gatherings;
Bible studies.

PINE RIVER

Pine River Group Home*
PO Box 96, Pine River, MN, 56474
(218) 587-4888
Admin Bruce Winder.
Licensure Intermediate care for mentally
retarded. *Beds* 11. *Certified* Medicaid.
Owner Nonprofit Corp.

Whispering Pines Good Samaritan Center
PO Box 29, Pine River, MN, 56474
(218) 587-4423
Admin Jim Wolf. *Medical Dir/Dir of Nursing*
Dr C R Pelzl; Judy Goldberg RN DON.
Licensure Skilled care. *Beds* SNF 113.
Certified Medicaid; Medicare.
Owner Nonprofit Corp (Evangelical Lutheran/
Good Samaritan).
Admissions Requirements Medical
examination; Physician's request.
Staff RNs 4 (ft), 3 (pt); LPNs 10 (ft), 5 (pt);
Orderlies 2 (pt); Nurses aides 25 (ft), 20 (pt);
Physical therapists 2 (pt); Occupational
therapists 1 (pt); Speech therapists 1 (pt);
Activities coordinators 1 (ft).
Affiliation Lutheran
Facilities Dining room; Physical therapy
room; Activities room; Chapel; Crafts room;
Laundry room; Barber/Beauty shop; Library.
Activities Arts & crafts; Cards; Games;
Reading groups; Prayer groups; Movies;
Shopping trips; Social/Cultural gatherings.

PIPESTONE

Good Samaritan Village
Rte 1, N Hiawatha, Pipestone, MN, 56164
(507) 825-5428
Admin Bruce A Stratman. *Medical Dir/Dir of
Nursing* Karen Amdahl DNS.
Licensure Intermediate care; Boarding care.
Beds ICF 96; Boarding care 30. *Certified*
Medicaid.
Owner Nonprofit Corp (Evangelical Lutheran/
Good Samaritan).
Admissions Requirements Medical
examination.
Staff RNs; LPNs; Nurses aides; Physical
therapists; Occupational therapists; Activities
coordinators; Dietitians; Chaplain; Art
therapists; Music therapist.
Affiliation Lutheran
Facilities Dining room; Physical therapy
room; Activities room; Chapel; Crafts room;
Laundry room; Barber/Beauty shop; Library;
Covered patio; Art therapy room.
Activities Arts & crafts; Cards; Games;
Reading groups; Prayer groups; Movies;
Shopping trips; Social/Cultural gatherings;
Art therapy; Music therapy; Exercise group;
Van rides; Fishing; Birthday dinners.

Hiawatha Manor
107 5th Ave NE, Pipestone, MN, 56164
(507) 825-5697
Admin Llinda Loven. *Medical Dir/Dir of
Nursing* Ruth Kluis.
Licensure Intermediate care for mentally
retarded. *Beds* ICF/MR 10. *Certified*
Medicaid.
Owner Nonprofit Corp.
Admissions Requirements Minimum age 18.
Staff RNs 1 (pt); Nurses aides 9 (pt).
Facilities Dining room; Activities room;
Laundry room.
Activities Arts & crafts; Cards; Games;
Reading groups; Prayer groups; Movies;
Shopping trips; Social/Cultural gatherings.

Pipestone County Medical Center
PO Box 370, 911 5th Ave SW, Pipestone,
MN, 56164
(507) 825-5811
Admin Allan J Christensen. *Medical Dir/Dir
of Nursing* Dr R W Keyes.
Licensure Skilled care. *Beds* SNF 43. *Certified*
Medicaid; Medicare.
Owner Publicly owned.
Admissions Requirements Medical
examination.
Staff Physicians 9 (pt); RNs 2 (ft), 5 (pt);
LPNs 2 (ft); Nurses aides 7 (ft), 15 (pt);
Physical therapists 1 (pt); Activities
coordinators 1 (ft); Dietitians 1 (pt).
Facilities Dining room; Physical therapy
room; Activities room; Chapel; Barber/
Beauty shop.
Activities Arts & crafts; Cards; Games;
Movies; Social/Cultural gatherings.

PLAINVIEW

Hillcrest Nursing Home
800 2nd Ave NW, Plainview, MN, 55964
(507) 534-3191
Admin Jim Pederson. *Medical Dir/Dir of
Nursing* Kathy Martig.
Licensure Skilled care. *Beds* SNF 71. *Certified*
Medicaid; Medicare.
Owner Publicly owned.
Admissions Requirements Minimum age 16;
Medical examination; Physician's request.
Staff RNs 4 (ft), 4 (pt); LPNs 5 (ft), 4 (pt);
Nurses aides 20 (ft), 26 (pt); Activities
coordinators 1 (ft), 2 (pt).
Facilities Dining room; Physical therapy
room; Activities room; Chapel; Laundry
room; Barber/Beauty shop.

Activities Arts & crafts; Cards; Games;
Reading groups; Prayer groups; Movies;
Shopping trips; Trips.

PLYMOUTH

Hazelden Pioneer House
11505 36th Ave N, Plymouth, MN, 55012
(612) 559-2022
Admin Harold Swift.
Licensure Skilled care. *Beds* SNF 60.
Owner Nonprofit organization/foundation.
Admissions Requirements Minimum age 14;
Medical examination.
Facilities Dining room; Activities room;
Laundry room; Library.
Activities Games; Movies; Social/Cultural
gatherings.

Anthony Louis Center—Plymouth
115 Forestview Ln, Plymouth, MN, 55441
(612) 546-8008
Admin Jon D Benson. *Medical Dir/Dir of
Nursing* Shar Benson.
Licensure Adolescent Primary C D Treatment.
Beds Evaluation/Treatment 15.
Owner Privately owned.
Admissions Requirements Minimum age 12.
Staff Physicians 1 (pt); RNs 1 (ft); Nurses
aides 6 (ft); Reality therapists 4 (ft);
Recreational therapists 1 (ft); Dietitians 2
(ft).
Facilities Dining room; Activities room;
Laundry room; Library.
Activities Games; YMCA/Softball; Football.

Mission Farms Nursing Home
3401 Medicine Lake Blvd, Plymouth, MN,
55441
(612) 559-3123
Admin James M Pearson. *Medical Dir/Dir of
Nursing* M M Millis MD; Sanmdra Kaske
RN.
Licensure Intermediate care; Boarding care.
Beds ICF 72; Boarding care 32. *Certified*
Medicaid.
Owner Nonprofit organization/foundation.
Admissions Requirements Males only; Medical
examination.
Staff RNs 3 (ft); LPNs 5 (ft), 2 (pt); Orderlies;
Nurses aides 14 (ft), 13 (pt); Recreational
therapists 2 (ft), 1 (pt); Activities
coordinators 1 (ft); Dietitians 1 (pt).
Languages Korean
Facilities Dining room; Activities room;
Chapel; Crafts room; Library.
Activities Arts & crafts; Cards; Games; Prayer
groups; Movies; Shopping trips; Social/
Cultural gatherings; Special tours; Bowling;
Pool; Circus; Ball games; Special music
programs; Church services.

Outreach Group Homes Inc Plymouth West
2735 Olive Ln North, Plymouth, MN, 55447
(612) 473-7182
Admin Eileen Harris.
Licensure Intermediate care for mentally
retarded. *Beds* 6. *Certified* Medicaid;
Medicare.
Owner Nonprofit organization/foundation.
Admissions Requirements Minimum age 21.
Staff RNs 1 (pt).
Facilities Dining room; Activities room;
Laundry room.
Activities Arts & crafts; Cards; Games; Prayer
groups; Movies; Shopping trips; Social/
Cultural gatherings; Golf; Swimming.

Vanguard Extended Care*
3401 E Medicine Lake Blvd, Plymouth, MN,
55441
(612) 559-4249
Admin Leonard Boche.
Licensure Supervised living facility. *Beds* 65.
Owner Nonprofit Corp.

PRESTON

Fillmore Place
PO Box 15A, Preston, MN, 55965
(507) 765-3848
Admin Lu Ommen. *Medical Dir/Dir of Nursing* Betty Johnson.
Licensure Intermediate care for mentally retarded. *Beds* ICF/MR 16. *Certified* Medicare.
Owner Nonprofit organization/foundation.
Admissions Requirements Minimum age 16; Medical examination.
Staff Physicians 1 (pt); RNs 1 (ft); LPNs 3 (pt); Orderlies 5 (ft), 34 (pt); Physical therapists 1 (pt); Speech therapists 1 (pt); Dietitians 1 (pt).
Facilities Activities room; Laundry room; 3 apartments.
Activities Arts & crafts; Cards; Games; Movies; Shopping trips; Social/Cultural gatherings.

Preston Care Center
608 Winona St, Preston, MN, 55965
(507) 765-3837
Admin James Framstad. *Medical Dir/Dir of Nursing* Dr John Nehring; Dianne Schmidt.
Licensure Skilled care; Intermediate care. *Beds* SNF 79; ICF. *Certified* Medicaid; Medicare; VA.
Owner Proprietary Corp (Good Neighbor Services).
Admissions Requirements Medical examination.
Staff RNs 2 (ft), 2 (pt); LPNs 7 (ft), 2 (pt); Nurses aides 23 (ft), 15 (pt); Physical therapists 1 (pt); Recreational therapists 1 (ft); Activities coordinators 1 (ft); Dietitians 1 (ft), 1 (pt).
Facilities Dining room; Physical therapy room; Activities room; Laundry room; Barber/Beauty shop.
Activities Arts & crafts; Cards; Games; Reading groups; Prayer groups; Movies; Shopping trips; Social/Cultural gatherings; Woodcrafts; Dining out; Picnics.

PRINCETON

Elim Home
101 7th Ave S, Princeton, MN, 55371
(612) 389-1171
Admin August "Augie" Pepple. *Medical Dir/ Dir of Nursing* Mike Metcalf MD; Mark Thyen DON.
Licensure Skilled care. *Beds* SNF 140. *Certified* Medicaid; Medicare.
Owner Nonprofit Corp.
Admissions Requirements Minimum age 16; Medical examination; Physician's request.
Staff RNs 2 (ft), 6 (pt); LPNs 4 (ft), 8 (pt); Nurses aides 20 (ft), 40 (pt); Physical therapists 1 (pt); Recreational therapists 2 (ft), 1 (pt); Occupational therapists 1 (pt); Speech therapists 1 (pt); Activities coordinators 1 (ft); Dietitians 1 (ft); Ophthalmologists 1 (pt); Podiatrists 1 (pt); Chaplain 1 (pt).
Affiliation Evangelical Free Church
Facilities Dining room; Physical therapy room; Activities room; Chapel; Crafts room; Laundry room; Barber/Beauty shop; Speech; Psychological.
Activities Arts & crafts; Cards; Games; Reading groups; Prayer groups; Movies; Shopping trips; Social/Cultural gatherings.

Sahara House
407 LaGrande Ave S, Princeton, MN, 55371
(612) 389-5703
Admin Jerry A Johnson.
Licensure Supervised living facility. *Beds* 13.
Owner Nonprofit Corp.
Admissions Requirements Minimum age 15; Males only; Medical examination; Physician's request.

Staff Reality therapists 3 (ft); Recreational therapists 1 (ft); Dietitians 2 (ft).
Facilities Dining room; Activities room; Laundry room.
Activities Cards; Games; Reading groups; Prayer groups; Movies; Shopping trips; Social/Cultural gatherings; AA/NA meetings.

RED LAKE FALLS

Hillcrest Nursing Home*
311 Broadway, Red Lake Falls, MN, 56750
(218) 253-2157
Admin L W Larson.
Licensure Intermediate care. *Beds* 74. *Certified* Medicaid.
Owner Publicly owned.

RED WING

Haven Health Center
213 Pioneer Rd, Red Wing, MN, 55066
(612) 388-4752
Admin John Boughton. *Medical Dir/Dir of Nursing* Tom Witt MD.
Licensure Skilled care. *Beds* SNF 85. *Certified* Medicaid; Medicare.
Owner Proprietary Corp.
Admissions Requirements Minimum age 18; Medical examination.
Staff RNs 2 (ft), 2 (pt); LPNs 4 (ft), 7 (pt); Nurses aides 12 (ft), 15 (pt); Physical therapists 1 (pt); Recreational therapists 1 (pt); Occupational therapists 1 (ft); Speech therapists 1 (pt); Activities coordinators 1 (ft); Dietitians 1 (pt).
Facilities Dining room; Physical therapy room; Activities room; Laundry room; Barber/Beauty shop.
Activities Arts & crafts; Cards; Games; Reading groups; Prayer groups; Movies; Shopping trips.

Red Wing Group Home
4911 W Hwy 61, Red Wing, MN, 55066
(612) 388-9446
Admin Roy A Harley.
Licensure Intermediate care for mentally retarded. *Beds* ICF/MR 12. *Certified* Medicare.
Owner Nonprofit Corp.
Admissions Requirements Minimum age 16.
Staff Nurses aides 12 (pt); Speech therapists 1 (pt).
Affiliation Lutheran
Facilities Laundry room.
Activities Arts & crafts; Cards; Games; Movies; Shopping trips; Social/Cultural gatherings; Special Olympics.

Red Wing Health Center
1400 W 4th St, Red Wing, MN, 55066
(612) 388-2843
Admin Donna Van Loon. *Medical Dir/Dir of Nursing* Dr Charles Roth.
Licensure Skilled care; Intermediate care. *Beds* 215. *Certified* Medicaid; Medicare.
Owner Proprietary Corp.
Staff Physicians 10 (pt); RNs 5 (ft), 7 (pt); LPNs 10 (ft), 11 (pt); Nurses aides 44 (ft), 86 (pt); Physical therapists 1 (ft); Occupational therapists 2 (ft), 3 (pt); Speech therapists 2 (ft), 2 (pt); Activities coordinators 1 (ft); Dietitians 1 (pt); Recreational staff 7 (ft).
Facilities Dining room; Physical therapy room; Activities room; Chapel; Crafts room; Laundry room; Barber/Beauty shop; Library; Child day care.
Activities Arts & crafts; Cards; Games; Reading groups; Prayer groups; Movies; Shopping trips; Social/Cultural gatherings; Adopt-a-grandparent.

Seminary Memorial Home
906 College Ave, Red Wing, MN, 55066
(612) 388-1591

Admin Kyle Nordine. *Medical Dir/Dir of Nursing* Dr D R Bruns; Judy Barfiend RN.
Licensure Skilled care; Intermediate care. *Beds* 112. *Certified* Medicaid; Medicare.
Owner Nonprofit Corp.
Admissions Requirements Minimum age 16.
Staff RNs 4 (ft), 8 (pt); LPNs 11 (ft), 6 (pt); Nurses aides 12 (ft), 33 (pt); Recreational therapists; Activities coordinators 1 (ft); Dietitians 1 (ft).
Affiliation Lutheran
Facilities Dining room; Physical therapy room; Activities room; Chapel; Crafts room; Barber/Beauty shop; Library.
Activities Arts & crafts; Cards; Games; Reading groups; Prayer groups; Movies; Shopping trips; Social/Cultural gatherings.

Vasa Lutheran Home
5225 W Hwy 61, Red Wing, MN, 55066
(612) 388-8845
Admin Roy A Harley. *Medical Dir/Dir of Nursing* Kay Kermig.
Licensure Intermediate care for mentally retarded. *Beds* ICF/MR 52. *Certified* Medicaid.
Owner Nonprofit Corp.
Admissions Requirements Minimum age 5; Medical examination.
Staff RNs 1 (ft); LPNs 2 (pt); Recreational therapists 1 (pt); Activities coordinators 1 (ft); Social workers 3 (ft).
Affiliation Lutheran
Facilities Dining room; Activities room; Crafts room; Laundry room; Library.
Activities Arts & crafts; Special Olympics.

REDWOOD FALLS

REM Redwood Falls, Inc; A & B
1011 E Elm St, Redwood Falls, MN, 56283
(507) 637-3541
Admin Dr Robert Miller.
Licensure Intermediate care for mentally retarded. *Beds* ICF/MR 132. *Certified* Medicaid.
Owner Proprietary Corp.
Admissions Requirements Minimum age 18.
Staff RNs; LPNs 413E; Physical therapists; Recreational therapists; Dietitians; Podiatrists.
Facilities Dining room; Laundry room; Barber/Beauty shop.
Activities Arts & crafts; Cards; Games; Movies; Shopping trips; Social/Cultural gatherings.

Sunwood Care Center
200 S DeKalb, Redwood Falls, MN, 56283
(507) 637-5711
Admin Vernon Junker. *Medical Dir/Dir of Nursing* Dr Dennis Nelson; Jan Gibson RN.
Licensure Skilled care. *Beds* SNF 92. *Certified* Medicaid; Medicare.
Owner Proprietary Corp (Good Neighbor Services).
Admissions Requirements Minimum age 16; Medical examination; Physician's request.
Staff RNs; LPNs; Orderlies; Nurses aides; Physical therapists; Recreational therapists; Speech therapists; Activities coordinators; Dietitians.
Activities Arts & crafts; Cards; Games; Reading groups; Prayer groups; Movies; Shopping trips; Social/Cultural gatherings.

Wood Dale Home Inc
600 Sunrise Blvd, Redwood Falls, MN, 56283
(507) 637-3587
Admin Alma J Little. *Medical Dir/Dir of Nursing* J B Flinn MD; Christy Melzer RN DON.
Licensure Skilled care. *Beds* SNF 60. *Certified* Medicaid; Medicare.
Owner Proprietary Corp.
Staff Physicians 5 (pt); RNs 2 (ft), 5 (pt); LPNs 3 (ft), 5 (pt); Nurses aides 12 (ft), 18 (pt); Physical therapists 1 (pt); Reality

therapists 1 (pt); Recreational therapists 1 (pt); Occupational therapists 1 (pt); Speech therapists 1 (pt); Activities coordinators 2 (ft); Dietitians 1 (pt); Dentists 1 (pt); Ophthalmologists 1 (pt); Podiatrists 1 (pt).
Facilities Dining room; Physical therapy room; Activities room; Crafts room; Laundry room; Barber/Beauty shop.
Activities Arts & crafts; Cards; Games; Reading groups; Prayer groups; Movies; Shopping trips; Social/Cultural gatherings; Seasonal sightseeing trips.

RENVILLE

Ren-Villa
205 SE Elm St, Renville, MN, 56284
(612) 329-8304
Admin Craig Doughty. *Medical Dir/Dir of Nursing* Jennie Lee Wurm DON.
Licensure Intermediate care. *Beds* ICF 76. *Certified* Medicaid.
Owner Publicly owned.
Staff RNs 2 (ft); LPNs 1 (ft), 9 (pt); Orderlies 1 (pt); Nurses aides 6 (ft), 35 (pt); Activities coordinators 1 (ft).
Facilities Dining room; Physical therapy room; Activities room; Crafts room; Laundry room; Library; Residents park.
Activities Arts & crafts; Cards; Games; Reading groups; Prayer groups; Movies; Social/Cultural gatherings; Adopt-a-grandparent program; Active volunteer visitation program.

REVERE

Revere Home
202 S Main, Revere, MN, 56166
(507) 752-7182
Admin David Reynolds. *Medical Dir/Dir of Nursing* Bev MaKarrall.
Licensure Board & care. *Beds* Board & care 22.
Owner Proprietary Corp.
Admissions Requirements Minimum age 18.
Staff Nurses aides; Activities coordinators; Dietitians.
Facilities Dining room; Activities room; Laundry room; Barber/Beauty shop.
Activities Arts & crafts; Cards; Games; Reading groups; Movies; Shopping trips; Bingo; Sightseeing trips.

RICHFIELD

Forestview Vincent*
7615 Vincent Ave S, Richfield, MN, 55423
(612) 861-4373
Admin Mary M Hill.
Licensure Intermediate care for mentally retarded. *Beds* 6. *Certified* Medicaid.
Owner Proprietary Corp.

Progress Valley II*
308 E 78th St, Richfield, MN, 55423
(612) 869-3223
Admin Mary Thorpe-Mease.
Licensure Supervised living facility. *Beds* 24.
Owner Nonprofit Corp.

Richfield Outreach Group Home*
7425 4th Ave S, Richfield, MN, 55423
(612) 866-2035
Admin Eileen Harris.
Licensure Intermediate care for mentally retarded. *Beds* 6. *Certified* Medicaid.
Owner Nonprofit Corp.

Richview*
7727 Portland Ave S, Richfield, MN, 55423
(612) 861-1691
Admin James Laine. *Medical Dir/Dir of Nursing* John Lamey MD.
Licensure Skilled care; Intermediate care. *Beds* SNF 126; ICF 49. *Certified* Medicaid.
Owner Proprietary Corp.

Admissions Requirements Medical examination; Physician's request.
Staff RNs 8 (ft), 5 (pt); LPNs 6 (ft), 6 (pt); Nurses aides 36 (ft), 36 (pt); Physical therapists 1 (ft); Occupational therapists 1 (ft); Speech therapists 1 (pt); Activities coordinators 1 (ft); Dietitians 1 (pt); Audiologists 1 (pt).
Facilities Dining room; Physical therapy room; Activities room; Chapel; Crafts room; Laundry room; Barber/Beauty shop.
Activities Arts & crafts; Cards; Games; Reading groups; Prayer groups; Movies; Shopping trips; Social/Cultural gatherings; Sightseeing outings.

RICHVILLE

Shelton Group Home*
Rte 1, Richville, MN, 56576
(218) 758-2438
Admin Carol Shelton.
Licensure Intermediate care for mentally retarded. *Beds* 8. *Certified* Medicaid.
Owner Proprietary Corp.

ROBBINSDALE

Crystal Lake Health Care Center
3815 W Broadway, Robbinsdale, MN, 55422
(612) 588-4635
Admin Pam Guyer. *Medical Dir/Dir of Nursing* Dr Kephart; Andrea Sadowski.
Licensure Skilled care. *Beds* SNF 166. *Certified* Medicaid; Medicare.
Owner Proprietary Corp.
Admissions Requirements Medical examination; Physician's request.
Staff Physicians; RNs; LPNs; Orderlies; Nurses aides; Physical therapists; Reality therapists; Recreational therapists; Occupational therapists; Speech therapists; Activities coordinators; Dietitians; Dentists; Ophthalmologists; Podiatrists.
Facilities Dining room; Physical therapy room; Activities room; Crafts room; Laundry room; Barber/Beauty shop; Occupational therapy room.
Activities Arts & crafts; Cards; Games; Reading groups; Prayer groups; Movies; Shopping trips; Social/Cultural gatherings.

Erinkay-Aneskarn II*
3349 Chowen Ave N, Robbinsdale, MN, 55422
(612) 529-7480
Admin Julie Hanson.
Licensure Intermediate care for mentally retarded. *Beds* 6. *Certified* Medicaid.
Owner Nonprofit Corp.

Residential Alternatives IV*
2759 France Ave N, Robbinsdale, MN, 55422
(612) 521-0387
Admin Peter Jacobson.
Licensure Intermediate care for mentally retarded. *Beds* 6. *Certified* Medicaid.
Owner Proprietary Corp.

Residential Alternatives VIII
3801 W Broadway, Robbinsdale, MN, 55422
(612) 522-6363 or 522-7556
Admin Peter Jacobson.
Licensure Intermediate care for mentally retarded. *Beds* ICF 9. *Certified* Medicaid.
Owner Proprietary Corp.
Admissions Requirements Minimum age 18; Medical examination.
Staff LPNs 1 (pt); Dietitians 1 (pt); 3 (ft), 6 (pt).
Facilities Laundry room; There are 3 separate; self-sustaining apartments-3 residents per apartment.
Activities Routine social & domestic program for 9 relatively high functioning persons with mental retardation.

Trevilla of Robbinsdale
3130 Grimes Ave N, Robbinsdale, MN, 55422
(612) 588-0771
Admin Mark S Linz. *Medical Dir/Dir of Nursing* R Batemen MD; Adeline Stanoch DON.
Licensure Skilled care; Intermediate care for mentally retarded. *Beds* SNF 132; ICF/MR 32. *Certified* Medicaid; Medicare.
Owner Proprietary Corp (Unicare).
Admissions Requirements Minimum age 18; Medical examination.
Staff RNs 13 (ft), 5 (pt); LPNs 13 (ft), 5 (pt); Nurses aides 72 (ft), 24 (pt); Recreational therapists 8 (ft); Occupational therapists 1 (ft); Speech therapists 1 (ft); Activities coordinators 1 (ft); Dietitians 1 (pt).
Facilities Dining room; Physical therapy room; Activities room; Crafts room; Laundry room; Barber/Beauty shop; Library.
Activities Arts & crafts; Cards; Games; Reading groups; Prayer groups; Movies; Shopping trips; Social/Cultural gatherings.

ROCHESTER

Bear Creek House*
812 10th Ave SE, Rochester, MN, 55901
(507) 288-0531
Admin Steven Larson.
Licensure Intermediate care for mentally retarded. *Beds* 6. *Certified* Medicaid.
Owner Nonprofit Corp.

Bethany Samaritan Heights
PO Box 5947, 1530 11th Ave NW, Rochester, MN, 55903
(507) 289-3336
Admin Paul Rengstorf. *Medical Dir/Dir of Nursing* Eric Tangelos; Diane Russell.
Licensure Skilled care. *Beds* SNF 120. *Certified* Medicaid; Medicare.
Owner Nonprofit Corp.
Admissions Requirements Minimum age 18.
Staff RNs 6 (ft), 3 (pt); LPNs 12 (ft), 6 (pt); Nurses aides 24 (ft), 13 (pt); Activities coordinators 1 (ft).
Affiliation Lutheran
Facilities Dining room; Physical therapy room; Activities room; Chapel; Laundry room; Barber/Beauty shop.
Activities Arts & crafts; Cards; Games; Reading groups; Prayer groups; Movies; Shopping trips; Social/Cultural gatherings.

Guest House/Rochester Treatment Center
PO Box 954, 4800 48th St NE, Rochester, MN, 55903
(507) 288-4693
Admin Richard Frisch ACSW CCDP. *Medical Dir/Dir of Nursing* Russell F Smith MD CAC.
Licensure Boarding care. *Beds* 35.
Owner Nonprofit Corp.
Staff Physicians 1 (ft); RNs 1 (ft); Physical therapists; Recreational therapists; Activities coordinators 1 (ft); Dietitians; Dentists.

Hiawatha Childrens Home*
1820 Valkyrie Dr NW, Rochester, MN, 55901
(507) 289-7222
Admin Douglas H Butler.
Licensure Intermediate care for mentally retarded. *Beds* 44. *Certified* Medicaid.
Owner Nonprofit Corp.

Madonna Towers Inc
4001 19th Ave NW, Rochester, MN, 55901
(507) 288-3911
Admin Alice J McHale. *Medical Dir/Dir of Nursing* Guy Daugherty MD.
Licensure Skilled care. *Beds* SNF 62; Apartments 139. *Certified* Medicaid; Medicare.
Owner Nonprofit Corp (Missionary Oblates of Mary Imm).
Admissions Requirements Minimum age 62; Medical examination.

Staff Physicians 1 (pt); RNs; LPNs; Nurses
aides; Physical therapists; Speech therapists;
Activities coordinators; Dietitians; Dentists;
Podiatrists.
Affiliation Roman Catholic
Facilities Dining room; Activities room;
Chapel; Crafts room; Laundry room; Barber/
Beauty shop; Library.
Activities Arts & crafts; Cards; Games;
Reading groups; Prayer groups; Movies;
Shopping trips; Social/Cultural gatherings.

Maple Manor Nursing Home
1875 19th St NW, Rochester, MN, 55901
(507) 282-9449
Admin Patrick Blum. *Medical Dir/Dir of
Nursing* Donna Manbeck.
Licensure Skilled care; Intermediate care. *Beds*
109. *Certified* Medicaid; Medicare.
Owner Privately owned.
Admissions Requirements Minimum age 16;
Medical examination; Physician's request.
Staff RNs 4 (ft); LPNs 12 (ft); Nurses aides 47
(ft); Physical therapists 1 (ft), 1 (pt);
Activities coordinators 3 (ft); Dietitians 13
(ft).
Facilities Dining room; Physical therapy
room; Activities room; Chapel; Crafts room;
Laundry room; Barber/Beauty shop.
Activities Arts & crafts; Games; Prayer groups;
Movies; Shopping trips; Social/Cultural
gatherings.

Meadow Park House*
1605 8th Ave SE, Rochester, MN, 55901
(507) 288-3893
Admin Steven Larson.
Licensure Intermediate care for mentally
retarded. *Beds* 6. *Certified* Medicaid.
Owner Nonprofit Corp.

REM Rochester
2509 55th St NW, Rochester, MN, 55901
(507) 281-1105
Admin Thomas Miller. *Medical Dir/Dir of
Nursing* Jack Priggen.
Licensure Intermediate care for mentally
retarded. *Beds* ICF/MR 30. *Certified*
Medicaid.
Owner Privately owned.
Admissions Requirements Minimum age 16;
Medical examination.
Staff RNs 1 (pt); Nurses aides 10 (ft), 10 (pt);
Activities coordinators 1 (pt); Dietitians.
Facilities Dining room; Activities room;
Laundry room; 10 apartments.
Activities Arts & crafts; Cards; Games;
Reading groups; Movies; Shopping trips;
Social/Cultural gatherings.

Rochester Health Care Center
2215 Hwy 52 N, Rochester, MN, 55901
(507) 288-1818 or 288-1819
Admin Joseph G Gubbels. *Medical Dir/Dir of
Nursing* Dr Victoria Beckett; Deb Miller.
Licensure Skilled care. *Beds* SNF 68. *Certified*
Medicaid; Medicare.
Owner Proprietary Corp (Beverly Enterprises).
Admissions Requirements Minimum age 18.
Staff Physicians 1 (pt); RNs 3 (ft), 2 (pt);
LPNs 4 (ft), 2 (pt); Orderlies 4 (ft); Nurses
aides 20 (ft), 7 (pt); Physical therapists 1
(pt); Occupational therapists 1 (pt);
Activities coordinators 1 (ft), 1 (pt);
Dietitians 1 (pt); Dentists 1 (pt);
Ophthalmologists 1 (pt); Podiatrists 1 (pt).
Facilities Dining room; Physical therapy
room; Activities room; Crafts room; Laundry
room; Barber/Beauty shop.
Activities Arts & crafts; Cards; Games;
Reading groups; Prayer groups; Movies;
Shopping trips; Social/Cultural gatherings.

Samaritan Bethany Home
PO Box 5947, 24 8th St NW, Rochester, MN,
55901
(507) 289-4031

Admin Earl Schillo. *Medical Dir/Dir of
Nursing* Peter Cross MD.
Licensure Skilled care. *Beds* 122. *Certified*
Medicaid.
Owner Nonprofit Corp.
Admissions Requirements Minimum age 16;
Medical examination; Physician's request.
Staff RNs; LPNs; Nurses aides; Physical
therapists; Recreational therapists; Speech
therapists; Activities coordinators; Dietitians.
Affiliation Church of Christ
Facilities Dining room; Physical therapy
room; Activities room; Chapel; Crafts room;
Laundry room; Barber/Beauty shop.
Activities Arts & crafts; Cards; Games;
Reading groups; Prayer groups; Movies;
Shopping trips; Social/Cultural gatherings.

Sixth Street House*
805 6th St SE, Rochester, MN, 55904
(507) 288-4138
Admin Steven Larson.
Licensure Intermediate care for mentally
retarded. *Beds* 6. *Certified* Medicaid.
Owner Nonprofit Corp.

Southside House
1416 4th St SE, Rochester, MN, 55904
(507) 281-2523
Admin Robert Hafdahl.
Licensure Intermediate care for mentally
retarded. *Beds* ICF/MR 6.
Owner Nonprofit organization/foundation.
Admissions Requirements Minimum age 45;
Medical examination.
Staff RNs 1 (ft); LPNs 2 (pt); Resident
counselors 5 (ft), 2 (pt).
Languages Sign
Facilities Dining room; Activities room;
Laundry room.
Activities Arts & crafts; Movies; Shopping
trips; Social/Cultural gatherings.

Town Hall Estates Retirement Center
607 E Center St, Rochester, MN, 55901
(507) 288-3615
Admin Arnold C Swanson. *Medical Dir/Dir of
Nursing* Geraldine Lotero.
Licensure Boarding care. *Beds* Boarding care
75.
Owner Nonprofit Corp.
Admissions Requirements Medical
examination.
Staff RNs 1 (ft), 1 (pt); LPNs 3 (pt); Nurses
aides 1 (ft), 1 (pt); Activities coordinators 1
(ft); Dietitians 1 (pt).
Facilities Dining room; Activities room;
Chapel; Crafts room; Laundry room; Barber/
Beauty shop; Library.
Activities Arts & crafts; Cards; Games;
Reading groups; Prayer groups; Movies;
Shopping trips; Social/Cultural gatherings.

Woodside Convalescent Center*
501 8th Ave SE, Rochester, MN, 55901
(507) 288-6514
Admin Patrick J Rafferty.
Licensure Skilled care; Intermediate care. *Beds*
SNF 129; ICF 30. *Certified* Medicaid;
Medicare.
Owner Proprietary Corp (Hillhaven Corp).

ROSEAU

Eventide Home
307 3rd Ave NW, Roseau, MN, 56751
(218) 463-1447
Admin Alice Halvorson.
Licensure Board & care. *Beds* Board & care
26.
Owner Nonprofit Corp.
Admissions Requirements Minimum age 18.
Staff Physicians; RNs; Nurses aides; Activities
coordinators.
Facilities Dining room; Activities room;
Chapel; Crafts room; Laundry room;
Library.

Activities Arts & crafts; Cards; Games;
Reading groups; Prayer groups; Movies;
Shopping trips; Social/Cultural gatherings;
Picnics.

REM Roseau Inc
208 2nd Ave NE, Roseau, MN, 56751
(218) 463-1031
Admin David Petersen.
Licensure Intermediate care for mentally
retarded. *Beds* ICF/MR 33. *Certified*
Medicaid.
Owner Nonprofit organization/foundation.
Staff LPNs 2 (ft), 3 (pt); Nurses aides 25 (ft),
26 (pt); Physical therapists 2 (pt); Activities
coordinators 2 (pt); Dietitians 1 (pt).

ROSEVILLE

Dungarvin II Camara
3101 W Owasso Blvd, Roseville, MN, 55112
(612) 483-8377
Admin Diane Jones Madden.
Licensure Intermediate care for mentally
retarded. *Beds* ICF/MR 6. *Certified*
Medicaid.
Owner Proprietary Corp.
Admissions Requirements Medical
examination; Physician's request.
Staff RNs 1 (pt).
Facilities Dining room; Laundry room.
Activities Arts & crafts; Cards; Games;
Reading groups; Movies; Shopping trips;
Social/Cultural gatherings.

Golden Age Health Care Center
1415 W County Rd B, Roseville, MN, 55113
(612) 631-1616
Admin Tim Middendorf. *Medical Dir/Dir of
Nursing* Sue Willemssen.
Licensure Skilled care; Intermediate care. *Beds*
SNF 133. *Certified* Medicaid; Medicare.
Owner Proprietary Corp (Good Neighbor
Services).
Admissions Requirements Minimum age;
Males only; Females only; Physician's
request.
Staff RNs; LPNs; Orderlies; Nurses aides;
Physical therapists; Recreational therapists;
Occupational therapists; Speech therapists;
Activities coordinators; Dietitians.
Activities Arts & crafts; Cards; Games;
Reading groups; Prayer groups; Movies;
Social/Cultural gatherings.

Lake Ridge Health Care Center*
2727 N Victoria, Roseville, MN, 55113
(612) 483-5431
Admin Lynne Glasrud. *Medical Dir/Dir of
Nursing* Dr Timothy F Lane.
Licensure Skilled care. *Beds* 240. *Certified*
Medicare.
Owner Proprietary Corp (Beverly Enterprises).
Admissions Requirements Minimum age 18;
Medical examination; Physician's request.
Staff RNs 10 (ft), 35 (pt); LPNs 5 (ft), 7 (pt);
Orderlies 1 (ft), 8 (pt); Nurses aides 34 (ft),
75 (pt); Physical therapists 1 (ft); Speech
therapists 1 (pt); Activities coordinators 1
(ft); Dietitians 1 (pt); Dentists 1 (pt);
Podiatrists 1 (pt); Audiologists 1 (pt).
Facilities Dining room; Physical therapy
room; Activities room; Chapel; Crafts room;
Barber/Beauty shop; Library; Dental office.
Activities Arts & crafts; Cards; Games;
Reading groups; Prayer groups; Movies;
Shopping trips; Social/Cultural gatherings;
Exploration activities outside facility.

Rose of Sharon Manor
1000 Lovell Ave, Roseville, MN, 55113
(612) 484-3378
Admin Vivian Trettin. *Medical Dir/Dir of
Nursing* J Richard Burton MD; Darla Hill
RN.
Licensure Skilled care. *Beds* SNF 85. *Certified*
Medicaid; Medicare.
Owner Proprietary Corp (Unicare).

Admissions Requirements Minimum age 18;
Medical examination; Physician's request.
Staff Physicians 1 (pt); RNs 3 (ft), 4 (pt);
LPNs 1 (ft), 5 (pt); Nurses aides 13 (ft), 32
(pt); Physical therapists 1 (pt); Recreational
therapists 1 (ft); Occupational therapists 1
(pt); Speech therapists 1 (pt); Activities
coordinators 1 (ft); Dietitians 1 (pt);
Ophthalmologists 1 (pt); Podiatrists 1 (pt);
Dentist 1 (pt); Optometrist 1 (pt).
Facilities Dining room; Physical therapy
room; Activities room; Crafts room; Barber/
Beauty shop; Occupational therapy.
Activities Arts & crafts; Cards; Games;
Reading groups; Prayer groups; Movies;
Shopping trips; Social/Cultural gatherings;
Science hours.

Whitehouse Health Care Center
563 W County Rd B, Roseville, MN, 55113
(612) 489-8851
Admin Pamela Schultz. *Medical Dir/Dir of
Nursing* David Gilbertson DO; Donna
Hartwig RN.
Licensure Skilled care. *Beds* 79. *Certified*
Medicaid; Medicare.
Owner Proprietary Corp (Good Neighbor
Services).
Admissions Requirements Medical
examination; Physician's request.
Staff RNs 3 (ft), 7 (pt); LPNs 2 (ft), 3 (pt);
Nurses aides 12 (ft), 33 (pt); Physical
therapists 1 (pt); Recreational therapists 1
(ft), 2 (pt); Occupational therapists 1 (pt);
Speech therapists 1 (pt); Dietitians 1 (ft);
Ophthalmologists 1 (pt).
Facilities Dining room; Activities room;
Laundry room; Barber/Beauty shop.
Activities Arts & crafts; Cards; Games;
Reading groups; Prayer groups; Movies;
Shopping trips; Social/Cultural gatherings.

RUSH CITY

Hillcrest Health Care Center
PO Box 606, 650 Bremer Ave S, Rush City,
MN, 55069
(612) 358-4765
Admin Patricia A Behrendt. *Medical Dir/Dir
of Nursing* James M Giefer MD; Sandy
Olson RN DON.
Licensure Skilled care; Intermediate care. *Beds*
SNF; ICF 65. *Certified* Medicaid; Medicare.
Owner Proprietary Corp (Beverly Enterprises).
Admissions Requirements Medical
examination; Physician's request.
Staff Physicians; RNs; LPNs; Orderlies;
Nurses aides; Physical therapists; Reality
therapists; Recreational therapists;
Occupational therapists; Speech therapists;
Activities coordinators; Dietitians; Dentists;
Ophthalmologists; Podiatrists.
Facilities Dining room; Physical therapy
room; Activities room; Crafts room; Laundry
room; Barber/Beauty shop; Library.
Activities Arts & crafts; Cards; Games;
Reading groups; Prayer groups; Movies;
Shopping trips; Social/Cultural gatherings.

RUSHFORD

Good Shepherd Lutheran Home
PO Box 747, 800 Home, Rushford, MN,
55971
(507) 864-7714
Admin Robert Letich. *Medical Dir/Dir of
Nursing* Dr John R Peterson.
Licensure Skilled care. *Beds* SNF 98. *Certified*
Medicaid; Medicare.
Owner Nonprofit organization/foundation.
Admissions Requirements Medical
examination; Physician's request.
Staff Physicians 1 (pt); RNs; LPNs; Nurses
aides; Physical therapists; Activities
coordinators; Dietitians.
Affiliation Lutheran

Facilities Dining room; Physical therapy
room; Activities room; Chapel; Crafts room;
Laundry room; Barber/Beauty shop.
Activities Arts & crafts; Cards; Games;
Reading groups; Prayer groups; Movies;
Shopping trips; Social/Cultural gatherings.

SAINT ANTHONY VILLAGE

St Anthony Health Center
3700 Foss Rd NE, Saint Anthony Village,
MN, 55421
(612) 788-9673
Admin Michael Milder. *Medical Dir/Dir of
Nursing* Bernice Anderson.
Licensure Skilled care; Intermediate care. *Beds*
SNF 128; ICF 26. *Certified* Medicaid;
Medicare.
Owner Proprietary Corp.
Staff Physicians; RNs; LPNs; Orderlies;
Nurses aides; Physical therapists;
Recreational therapists; Occupational
therapists; Speech therapists; Activities
coordinators; Dietitians; Ophthalmologists.

SAINT CHARLES

Whitewater Healthcare Center
525 Bluff Ave, Saint Charles, MN, 55972
(507) 932-3283
Admin Faye Manee. *Medical Dir/Dir of
Nursing* Richard Christiana MD; Loretta
Schillo DON.
Licensure Skilled care; Board & care. *Beds*
SNF 79; Board & care 7. *Certified* Medicaid;
Medicare.
Owner Proprietary Corp (Beverly Enterprises).
Admissions Requirements Minimum age
Adult; Medical examination; Physician's
request.
Facilities Dining room; Physical therapy
room; Activities room; Chapel; Crafts room;
Laundry room; Barber/Beauty shop.
Activities Arts & crafts; Cards; Games;
Reading groups; Prayer groups; Movies;
Shopping trips; Social/Cultural gatherings.

SAINT CLOUD

Dan's Boarding Care Home
1101 3rd St North, Saint Cloud, MN, 56301
(612) 251-6567
Admin Doreen Murphy.
Beds 12.
Owner Privately owned.
Admissions Requirements Minimum age 18;
Males only; Medical examination.
Staff RNs; Orderlies; Nurses aides; Dietitians.
Facilities Dining room; Activities room.
Activities Cards; Games; Movies; Shopping
trips.

Opportunity Manor II*
1311 13th Ave SE, Saint Cloud, MN, 56301
(612) 255-0135
Admin James Steiner.
Licensure Skilled care; Intermediate care for
mentally retarded. *Beds* SNF 15; ICF/MR
15. *Certified* Medicaid.
Owner Nonprofit Corp.

REM St Cloud*
1506 33rd Ave N, Saint Cloud, MN, 56301
(612) 252-8875
Admin Juanita Turner.
Licensure Skilled care; Intermediate care for
mentally retarded. *Beds* SNF 15; ICF/MR
15. *Certified* Medicaid.
Owner Proprietary Corp.

St Benedicts Center
1810 Minnesota Blvd SE, Saint Cloud, MN,
56301
(612) 252-0010
Admin Sr Rita Budig. *Medical Dir/Dir of
Nursing* Sr Juliana Lauer DON.

Licensure Skilled care; Intermediate care;
Residential Apartments. *Beds* SNF 167; ICF
55. *Certified* Medicaid; Medicare.
Owner Nonprofit Corp.
Admissions Requirements Minimum age 16;
Medical examination; Physician's request.
Staff RNs 9 (ft), 9 (pt); LPNs 14 (ft), 16 (pt);
Nurses aides 39 (ft), 81 (pt); Physical
therapists 1 (ft); Occupational therapists 1
(ft); Activities coordinators 1 (ft).
Languages German, Polish, French
Affiliation Roman Catholic
Facilities Dining room; Physical therapy
room; Activities room; Chapel; Crafts room;
Laundry room; Barber/Beauty shop; Library.
Activities Arts & crafts; Cards; Games;
Reading groups; Prayer groups; Movies;
Shopping trips; Social/Cultural gatherings.

St Cloud Manor
1717 Michigan Ave SE, Saint Cloud, MN,
56301
(612) 251-9120
Admin Darwin Schwantes. *Medical Dir/Dir of
Nursing* Dr R L Thienes; Jon Hendrickson
DNS.
Licensure Skilled care; Intermediate care. *Beds*
108. *Certified* Medicaid; Medicare.
Owner Proprietary Corp.
Admissions Requirements Minimum age 16;
Medical examination; Physician's request.
Staff Physicians 9 (pt); RNs 5 (ft), 5 (pt);
LPNs 5 (ft), 3 (pt); Orderlies 6 (pt); Nurses
aides 15 (ft), 46 (pt); Physical therapists 1
(pt); Reality therapists 1 (pt); Recreational
therapists 1 (ft); Occupational therapists 1
(pt); Speech therapists 1 (pt); Activities
coordinators 1 (ft), 1 (pt); Dietitians 1 (pt);
Ophthalmologists 1 (pt); Podiatrists 1 (pt);
Social workers 2 (ft).
Facilities Dining room; Physical therapy
room; Activities room; Chapel; Crafts room;
Laundry room; Barber/Beauty shop; Library.

St Elizabeth Home*
306 15th Ave N, Saint Cloud, MN, 56301
(612) 252-8350
Admin Rev Richard Leisen.
Licensure Intermediate care for mentally
retarded. *Beds* 14. *Certified* Medicaid.
Owner Nonprofit Corp.

SAINT JAMES

Pleasant View Good Samaritan Center
1000 S 2nd St, Saint James, MN, 56081
(507) 375-3286
Admin Rosalyn G Wielenga. *Medical Dir/Dir
of Nursing* Dorothy Christianson RN.
Licensure Intermediate care. *Beds* ICF 79.
Certified Medicaid.
Owner Nonprofit Corp (Evangelical Lutheran/
Good Samaritan).
Admissions Requirements Minimum age 18.
Staff RNs 1 (ft), 1 (pt); LPNs 3 (ft), 3 (pt);
Nurses aides 9 (ft), 29 (pt); Activities
coordinators 1 (ft).
Affiliation Lutheran
Facilities Dining room; Activities room;
Chapel; Crafts room; Laundry room; Barber/
Beauty shop; Library.
Activities Arts & crafts; Cards; Games;
Reading groups; Prayer groups; Movies;
Shopping trips.

SAINT LOUIS PARK

Greenwood Residence West*
6019 W 39th St, Saint Louis Park, MN, 55416
(612) 929-4681
Admin Norman Bollinger. *Medical Dir/Dir of
Nursing* Dorothy Prickeril.
Licensure Intermediate care for mentally
retarded. *Beds* 14. *Certified* Medicaid.
Owner Proprietary Corp.

Admissions Requirements Minimum age 18;
Medical examination; Physician's request.
Staff RNs 1 (ft), 1 (pt); LPNs 2 (ft), 2 (pt);
Nurses aides 1 (ft), 1 (pt); Recreational
therapists 1 (ft); Dietitians 1 (pt); 6 (pt).

Methodist Hospital Extended Care Facility
6500 Excelsior Blvd, Saint Louis Park, MN,
55426
(612) 932-5325
Admin Sandra Toy. *Medical Dir/Dir of
Nursing* Dr Hugh Edmondson MD; Ruth
Towey RN DON.
Licensure Skilled care. *Beds* SNF 35. *Certified*
Medicaid; Medicare.
Owner Nonprofit Corp.
Admissions Requirements Minimum age 16;
Medical examination; Physician's request.
Staff Physicians; RNs; LPNs; Orderlies;
Nurses aides; Physical therapists;
Occupational therapists; Speech therapists;
Activities coordinators; Dietitians.
Affiliation Methodist
Facilities Dining room; Physical therapy
room; Activities room; Chapel.
Activities Arts & crafts; Cards; Games;
Movies; Social/Cultural gatherings.

Minnesota Jewish Group Home 1—Chai House
8101 Westwood Hills Dr, Saint Louis Park,
MN, 55426
(612) 544-7030
Admin Deborah Sheehan. *Medical Dir/Dir of
Nursing* Janice K Martland.
Licensure Intermediate care for mentally
retarded. *Beds* ICF/MR 6. *Certified*
Medicaid.
Owner Nonprofit Corp.
Staff RNs 1 (pt); Household coordinators 2
(ft); Program counselors 6 (pt); Program
director 1 (pt).
Affiliation Jewish

Park Nursing & Convalescent Center*
4415 W 36 1/2 St, Saint Louis Park, MN,
55416
(612) 927-9717
Admin Thomas Chamberlain.
Licensure Skilled care; Intermediate care. *Beds*
SNF 102; ICF 19. *Certified* Medicaid;
Medicare.
Owner Proprietary Corp (Unicare).

St Louis Park Plaza Healthcare Center
3201 Virginia Ave South, Saint Louis Park,
MN, 55426
(612) 935-0333
Admin Tod Carsen. *Medical Dir/Dir of
Nursing* Richard Bick MD; Theresa Lang
RN.
Licensure Skilled care. *Beds* 300. *Certified*
Medicaid; Medicare.
Owner Proprietary Corp (Beverly Enterprises).
Admissions Requirements Medical
examination; Physician's request.
Staff RNs; LPNs; Nurses aides; Physical
therapists; Recreational therapists;
Occupational therapists; Speech therapists;
Activities coordinators; Dietitians.
Languages Russian, Spanish
Facilities Dining room; Physical therapy
room; Activities room; Chapel; Barber/
Beauty shop.
Activities Arts & crafts; Cards; Games;
Reading groups; Prayer groups; Movies;
Shopping trips.

Summit House II
4600 Minnetonka Blvd, Saint Louis Park,
MN, 55416
(612) 926-5553
Admin Carol Robson. *Medical Dir/Dir of
Nursing* Leroy Geis MD; Scott Skobe RN
DON.
Licensure Intermediate care for mentally
retarded. *Beds* ICF/MR 6. *Certified*
Medicaid.

Owner Proprietary Corp.
Staff RNs; Skilled counselors 14 (ft); Program
directors 2 (ft).

Texas Terrace Convalescent Center
7900 W 28th St, Saint Louis Park, MN, 55426
(612) 920-8380
Admin James C Platten. *Medical Dir/Dir of
Nursing* Jesse Barron MD; Linda Duos RN
DON.
Licensure Skilled care. *Beds* SNF 194.
Owner Proprietary Corp (Unicare).
Admissions Requirements Minimum age 18;
Medical examination; Physician's request.
Staff Physicians 1 (pt); Nurses aides 60 (ft);
Physical therapists 1 (ft); Recreational
therapists 6 (ft); Occupational therapists 1
(ft); Speech therapists 1 (ft); Activities
coordinators 1 (ft); Dietitians 1 (ft).
Languages Russian, Yiddish, Hebrew
Facilities Dining room; Physical therapy
room; Activities room; Chapel; Crafts room;
Laundry room; Barber/Beauty shop; Library.
Activities Arts & crafts; Cards; Games;
Reading groups; Prayer groups; Movies;
Shopping trips; Social/Cultural gatherings.

Westwood Nursing Home
7500 W 22nd St, Saint Louis Park, MN,
55426
(612) 546-4261
Admin Cheryl Stinski. *Medical Dir/Dir of
Nursing* Dr Robert Sonntag; Andrea Levich
RN DON.
Licensure Skilled care. *Beds* SNF 212.
Certified Medicaid; Medicare.
Owner Proprietary Corp.
Admissions Requirements Minimum age 16;
Medical examination; Physician's request.
Staff RNs 25 (ft); LPNs 13 (ft); Orderlies 12
(ft); Nurses aides 60 (ft); Physical therapists
1 (ft); Recreational therapists 2 (ft);
Occupational therapists 1 (ft); Speech
therapists 1 (ft); Activities coordinators 1
(ft); Dietitians 1 (ft); Dentists 1 (pt);
Ophthalmologists 1 (pt); Podiatrists 1 (pt);
Chaplain 1 (ft); Volunteer coord 1 (ft);
Music therapists 2 (ft).
Facilities Dining room; Physical therapy
room; Activities room; Crafts room; Laundry
room; Barber/Beauty shop; Coffee Shop;
Smoking & nonsmoking lounges.
Activities Arts & crafts; Cards; Games;
Reading groups; Prayer groups; Movies;
Shopping trips; Social/Cultural gatherings;
Annual camping trip; Ceramics; Woodshop;
Music, pet, occupational, & speech therapies.

SAINT PAUL

Aurora House
2134 Marshall Ave, Saint Paul, MN, 55104
(612) 645-8622
Admin Terry Forss. *Medical Dir/Dir of
Nursing* Greg Cottle RN.
Licensure Intermediate care for mentally
retarded. *Beds* ICF/MR 6. *Certified*
Medicaid.
Owner Proprietary Corp.
Admissions Requirements Minimum age 18;
Medical examination; Physician's request.
Staff RNs; Reality therapists 2 (ft), 8 (pt);
Recreational therapists 1 (ft).
Facilities Dining room; Laundry room.
Activities Arts & crafts; Cards; Games;
Reading groups; Movies; Shopping trips;
Social/Cultural gatherings; Leisure services
focus on treatment & education.

Bethel Care Center*
420 Marshall Ave, Saint Paul, MN, 55102
(612) 224-2368
Admin Ona Orth.
Licensure Skilled care; Intermediate care. *Beds*
SNF 127; ICF 22. *Certified* Medicaid.
Owner Proprietary Corp.

Bethesda Lutheran Care Center*
558 Capitol Blvd, Saint Paul, MN, 55103
(612) 221-2347
Admin Nancy Herbeck.
Licensure Skilled care. *Beds* 138. *Certified*
Medicaid; Medicare.
Owner Nonprofit Corp.
Affiliation Lutheran

Board of Social Ministry
3881 Highland Ave, Saint Paul, MN, 55110
(612) 426-5013
Admin Robert Armitage.
Licensure Skilled care; Intermediate care. *Beds*
2100. *Certified* Medicaid; Medicare.
Owner Nonprofit organization/foundation.
Admissions Requirements Medical
examination; Physician's request.
Languages Swedish, Norwegian, German
Affiliation Lutheran
Facilities Dining room; Physical therapy
room; Activities room; Chapel; Crafts room;
Laundry room; Barber/Beauty shop; Library.
Activities Arts & crafts; Cards; Games;
Reading groups; Prayer groups; Movies;
Shopping trips; Social/Cultural gatherings.

Chez Nous—St Anthony Park*
2248 Carter Ave, Saint Paul, MN, 55108
(612) 644-2326
Admin Dan Kastrul.
Licensure Skilled care; Intermediate care for
mentally retarded. *Beds* SNF 6; ICF/MR 6.
Certified Medicaid.
Owner Proprietary Corp.

Commonwealth Healthcare Center
2237 Commonwealth Ave, Saint Paul, MN,
55108
(612) 646-7486
Admin Kathe Bolinder. *Medical Dir/Dir of
Nursing* Dr Carolyn Johnson; Jan Pope RN.
Licensure Skilled care; Intermediate care. *Beds*
SNF 86; ICF 22. *Certified* Medicaid;
Medicare.
Owner Proprietary Corp (Vantage Healthcare).
Admissions Requirements Physician's request.
Staff RNs; LPNs; Nurses aides; Physical
therapists; Recreational therapists;
Occupational therapists; Speech therapists.
Facilities Dining room; Physical therapy
room; Activities room; Laundry room;
Barber/Beauty shop.
Activities Arts & crafts; Cards; Games;
Reading groups; Prayer groups; Movies;
Shopping trips; Social/Cultural gatherings.

Dayton Boarding Care Home*
740 Dayton Ave, Saint Paul, MN, 55104
(612) 226-1051
Admin Stephen R Scalzo.
Licensure Boarding care. *Beds* 26.
Owner Proprietary Corp.

Dungarvin I*
1086 Como Place, Saint Paul, MN, 55103
(612) 489-0745
Admin Diane Jones-Madden. *Medical Dir/Dir
of Nursing* Dr D Current.
Licensure Intermediate care for mentally
retarded. *Beds* 15. *Certified* Medicaid.
Owner Proprietary Corp.
Admissions Requirements Minimum age 18;
Medical examination; Physician's request.
Staff RNs 1 (pt); Activities coordinators 1 (ft);
Dietitians 1 (pt).
Facilities Dining room; Crafts room; Laundry
room; Library.
Activities Arts & crafts; Cards; Games;
Reading groups; Movies; Shopping trips;
Social/Cultural gatherings.

Dungarvin III—Balbriggen*
1270 Larpenteur Ave E, Saint Paul, MN,
55109
(612) 776-2044
Admin Diane Jones-Madden. *Medical Dir/Dir
of Nursing* Dr D Current.

Licensure Supervised living facility. *Beds* 6.
Certified Medicaid.
Owner Proprietary Corp.
Admissions Requirements Minimum age 18.
Facilities Dining room; Laundry room.
Activities Arts & crafts; Games; Movies;
Shopping trips; Social/Cultural gatherings;
Wide variety of activities as per resident
interest.

Episcopal Church Home of Minnesota
1879 Feronia Ave, Saint Paul, MN, 55104
(612) 646-4061
Admin David Bredenberg. *Medical Dir/Dir of
Nursing* Jack Beaird; Sharon Lewis.
Licensure Skilled care; Boarding care. *Beds*
SNF 67; Boarding care 64. *Certified*
Medicaid; Medicare.
Owner Nonprofit organization/foundation.
Admissions Requirements Medical
examination.
Staff Physicians 1 (pt); RNs 5 (ft), 4 (pt);
LPNs 3 (ft), 2 (pt); Orderlies 2 (ft), 2 (pt);
Nurses aides 14 (ft), 5 (pt); Physical
therapists 1 (ft); Occupational therapists 1
(ft), 1 (pt); Speech therapists 1 (pt);
Activities coordinators 1 (ft); Dietitians 1
(pt); Ophthalmologists 1 (pt); Podiatrists 1
(pt).
Affiliation Episcopal
Facilities Dining room; Activities room;
Chapel; Crafts room; Laundry room; Barber/
Beauty shop; Library.
Activities Arts & crafts; Cards; Games;
Reading groups; Prayer groups; Movies;
Shopping trips; Social/Cultural gatherings.

Familystyle Home
398 Duke St, Saint Paul, MN, 55102
(612) 291-2612
Admin Dr James Janecek. *Medical Dir/Dir of
Nursing* James Janecek MD.
Licensure Boarding care. *Beds* 21.
Owner Proprietary Corp.
Admissions Requirements Minimum age 18;
Medical examination; Physician's request.
Staff RNs 1 (ft); LPNs 2 (ft); Nurses aides 3
(ft); Activities coordinators 1 (ft); Dietitians
1 (ft); Mental health counselors 4 (ft);
Mental health workers 15 (ft).
Facilities Dining room; Activities room;
Crafts room; Laundry room; Library; 23
Residential houses & duplexes.
Activities Arts & crafts; Cards; Games; Prayer
groups; Movies; Shopping trips; Social/
Cultural gatherings; Camping; Jogging.

Fellowship Club*
680 Stewart Ave, Saint Paul, MN, 55102
(612) 227-7637
Admin Harold Swift.
Licensure Supervised living facility. *Beds* 55.
Owner Nonprofit Corp.

Four Seasons Care Center—Central
375 N Lexington Pkwy, Saint Paul, MN,
55104
(612) 645-0577
Admin Frank Robinson. *Medical Dir/Dir of
Nursing* Fred Webber MD; Kim Vikstrom
RN DON.
Licensure Skilled care; Intermediate care. *Beds*
SNF 128; ICF 58. *Certified* Medicaid;
Medicare.
Owner Proprietary Corp.
Admissions Requirements Minimum age 18;
Medical examination; Physician's request.
Staff Physicians 1 (ft); RNs 8 (ft), 7 (pt);
LPNs 9 (ft), 9 (pt); Nurses aides 50 (ft), 60
(pt); Physical therapists 1 (ft); Occupational
therapists 1 (ft); Activities coordinators 1
(ft); Dietitians 1 (ft); Ophthalmologists 1
(pt); Podiatrists 1 (pt).
Facilities Dining room; Physical therapy
room; Activities room; Chapel; Laundry
room; Barber/Beauty shop; Library.

Activities Arts & crafts; Cards; Games;
Reading groups; Prayer groups; Movies;
Shopping trips; Social/Cultural gatherings.

Frances Residence I
1735 Arlington Ave E, Saint Paul, MN, 55106
(612) 771-3578
Admin Jeffrey T Boston. *Medical Dir/Dir of
Nursing* Jeffery T Boston.
Licensure Intermediate care for mentally
retarded. *Beds* ICF/MR 6. *Certified*
Medicaid.
Owner Proprietary Corp.
Admissions Requirements Minimum age 18.
Staff RNs 1 (pt); LPNs 1 (pt); Physical
therapists 1 (pt); Activities coordinators 1
(pt).
Activities Community activities.

Good Neighbor Home—Fairmount
1081 Fairmount Ave, Saint Paul, MN, 55105
(612) 641-0041
Admin Gerald Glomb.
Licensure Intermediate care for mentally
retarded. *Beds* 6. *Certified* Medicaid.
Owner Proprietary Corp.

Greenbrier Home Inc*
941 Birmingham St, Saint Paul, MN, 55106
(612) 771-5531
Admin Claudia Sajevic.
Licensure Intermediate care for mentally
retarded. *Beds* 165. *Certified* Medicaid.
Owner Nonprofit Corp.

Greenwood Residence East
1609 Jackson St, Saint Paul, MN, 55117
(612) 488-2561
Admin Norman Bollinger. *Medical Dir/Dir of
Nursing* Deborah Dunn.
Licensure Intermediate care for mentally
retarded. *Beds* ICF/MR 16. *Certified*
Medicaid.
Owner Proprietary Corp.
Admissions Requirements Minimum age 18;
Medical examination; Physician's request.
Staff RNs 1 (ft); LPNs 2 (ft), 2 (pt); Nurses
aides 1 (ft), 2 (pt); Physical therapists 1 (pt);
Recreational therapists 1 (ft), 1 (pt).
Facilities Dining room; Physical therapy
room; Activities room; Crafts room; Laundry
room.
Activities Arts & crafts; Cards; Games;
Movies; Shopping trips; Social/Cultural
gatherings.

Harmony Nursing Home*
135 Geranium Ave, Saint Paul, MN, 55117
(612) 488-6658
Admin Richard Ludwigson.
Licensure Skilled care. *Beds* 150. *Certified*
Medicaid.
Owner Proprietary Corp (King Care Centers
Inc).

Hayes Residence
1620 Randolph Ave, Saint Paul, MN, 55105
(612) 690-4458
Admin Helen B Jennen.
Licensure Intermediate care. *Beds* 40.
Certified Medicaid.
Owner Proprietary Corp.
Admissions Requirements Medical
examination; Physician's request.
Staff RNs 2 (pt); LPNs 3 (pt); Nurses aides 2
(ft), 5 (pt); Recreational therapists 1 (ft);
Dietitians 1 (pt).
Facilities Dining room; Activities room;
Crafts room; Laundry room.
Activities Arts & crafts; Cards; Games;
Reading groups; Prayer groups; Movies;
Shopping trips; Social/Cultural gatherings;
Parties.

Highland Chateau Health Care Center
2319 W 7th St, Saint Paul, MN, 55116
(612) 648-0793

Admin Doug Beardsley. *Medical Dir/Dir of
Nursing* Wayne Thalhuber MD; Kathy Riley
DON.
Licensure Skilled care; Intermediate care. *Beds*
SNF 111. *Certified* Medicare.
Owner Proprietary Corp.
Admissions Requirements Minimum age 18;
Medical examination; Physician's request.
Staff RNs 8 (ft), 5 (pt); LPNs 7 (ft), 5 (pt);
Nurses aides 28 (ft), 26 (pt); Physical
therapists 1 (ft); Recreational therapists 2
(ft); Activities coordinators 1 (ft); Dietitians
1 (pt).
Facilities Dining room; Physical therapy
room; Activities room; Laundry room;
Barber/Beauty shop.
Activities Arts & crafts; Cards; Games;
Reading groups; Prayer groups; Movies;
Shopping trips.

Hoikka House Inc
393 Chestnut St, Saint Paul, MN, 55102
(612) 222-7491
Admin Rhoda Miller. *Medical Dir/Dir of
Nursing* Dr Thomas Smith.
Licensure Intermediate care for mentally
retarded. *Beds* ICF/MR 117.
Owner Proprietary Corp.
Admissions Requirements Minimum age 18.
Staff Physicians 2 (pt); RNs 2 (pt); LPNs 7
(ft); Recreational therapists 3 (ft); Activities
coordinators 1 (ft); Dietitians 1 (pt).
Facilities Dining room; Activities room;
Crafts room; Laundry room.
Activities Arts & crafts; Cards; Games;
Reading groups; Prayer groups; Movies;
Shopping trips; Social/Cultural gatherings.

Hoikka House Inc
238 Pleasant Ave, Saint Paul, MN, 55102
(612) 222-7491
Admin Rhoda E Miller. *Medical Dir/Dir of
Nursing* Thomas Smith MD.
Licensure Boarding care for mentally ill. *Beds*
Boarding care 108.
Owner Proprietary Corp.
Admissions Requirements Minimum age 18;
Medical examination; Physician's request.
Staff Physicians 2 (pt); RNs 2 (pt); LPNs 7
(ft); Recreational therapists 1 (ft); Activities
coordinators 2 (ft).
Facilities Dining room; Activities room;
Crafts room; Laundry room; 2 TV lounges; 2
Conference rooms; Exercise room.
Activities Arts & crafts; Cards; Games;
Reading groups; Movies; Shopping trips;
Social/Cultural gatherings.

Amy Johnson Residence
89 Virginia St, Saint Paul, MN, 55102
(612) 227-0574
Admin Donetta Johnson.
Licensure Boarding care. *Beds* 25.
Owner Proprietary Corp.
Admissions Requirements Medical
examination.
Staff Nurses aides 8 (pt); Activities
coordinators 2 (pt).
Facilities Dining room; Laundry room.
Activities Arts & crafts; Cards; Games;
Reading groups; Prayer groups; Movies;
Shopping trips; Social/Cultural gatherings;
Music; Resident council; Field trips.

Little Sisters of the Poor
330 S Exchange St, Saint Paul, MN, 55102
(612) 227-0336
Admin Sr Catherine Williamson. *Medical Dir/
Dir of Nursing* Dr Cecil Warren.
Licensure Skilled care; Intermediate care. *Beds*
SNF 62; ICF 56. *Certified* Medicaid.
Owner Nonprofit Corp.
Admissions Requirements Minimum age 62;
Medical examination.
Affiliation Roman Catholic
Facilities Dining room; Physical therapy
room; Activities room; Chapel; Crafts room;
Laundry room; Barber/Beauty shop; Library.

Activities Arts & crafts; Cards; Games;
Reading groups; Prayer groups; Movies;
Shopping trips; Social/Cultural gatherings.

Lyngblomsten Care Center*
1415 Almond Ave, Saint Paul, MN, 55108
(612) 646-2941
Admin Evelyn Halverson. *Medical Dir/Dir of
Nursing* Dr Donald Severson.
Licensure Skilled care; Intermediate care. *Beds*
SNF 184; ICF 72. *Certified* Medicaid.
Owner Nonprofit Corp.
Admissions Requirements Medical
examination.
Staff Physical therapists 1 (ft), 1 (pt);
Occupational therapists 1 (ft); Activities
coordinators 1 (ft); Dietitians 3 (ft).
Affiliation Lutheran
Facilities Dining room; Physical therapy
room; Activities room; Chapel; Crafts room;
Laundry room; Barber/Beauty shop; Library.
Activities Arts & crafts; Cards; Games;
Reading groups; Prayer groups; Movies;
Shopping trips; Social/Cultural gatherings.

Lynhurst Healthcare Center*
471 Lynnhurst Ave W, Saint Paul, MN, 55104
(612) 645-6453
Admin Joleen Waalen.
Licensure Skilled care. *Beds* 84. *Certified*
Medicaid.
Owner Proprietary Corp (Beverly Enterprises).

Minnesota Jewish Group Home II—Tivah*
1778 Rome Ave, Saint Paul, MN, 55103
(612) 690-1566
Admin Deborah Sheehan.
Licensure Skilled care; Intermediate care for
mentally retarded. *Beds* SNF 6; ICF/MR 6.
Certified Medicaid.
Owner Nonprofit Corp.
Affiliation Jewish

Mounds Park Residence*
908 Mound St, Saint Paul, MN, 55106
(612) 776-7170
Admin Frederick Brumm. *Medical Dir/Dir of
Nursing* Dr Paul Dyrdal.
Licensure Boarding care. *Beds* 37.
Owner Proprietary Corp.
Admissions Requirements Minimum age 18;
Medical examination.
Staff Physicians 3 (pt); LPNs 2 (ft), 1 (pt);
Nurses aides 5 (ft), 1 (pt); Recreational
therapists 1 (ft), 1 (pt); Speech therapists 1
(ft); Activities coordinators 1 (ft), 1 (pt);
Dietitians 1 (pt); Dentists 1 (pt);
Ophthalmologists 1 (pt); Podiatrists 1 (pt);
Audiologists 1 (pt).
Facilities Dining room; Activities room;
Crafts room; Barber/Beauty shop; Library;
Lounges.
Activities Arts & crafts; Cards; Games;
Reading groups; Prayer groups; Movies;
Shopping trips; Social/Cultural gatherings;
Resident council.

Nekton Inc
296 N Snelling, Saint Paul, MN, 55104
(612) 644-7680
Admin Steve Kodluboy.
Licensure Intermediate care for mentally
retarded. *Beds* ICF/MR 6. *Certified*
Medicaid.
Owner Proprietary Corp.
Admissions Requirements Medical
examination.
Staff RNs 1 (ft).
Facilities Regular community homes.
Activities Arts & crafts; Cards; Games;
Reading groups; Prayer groups; Movies;
Shopping trips; Social/Cultural gatherings.

Nekton on Goodrich*
917 Goodrich Ave, Saint Paul, MN, 55105
(612) 221-0180
Admin Laurel Zieman.

Licensure Intermediate care for mentally
retarded. *Beds* 8. *Certified* Medicaid.
Owner Proprietary Corp.

Nekton on Wheeler*
148 Wheeler Ave S, Saint Paul, MN, 55105
(612) 690-0120
Admin Milton Conrath.
Licensure Intermediate care for mentally
retarded. *Beds* 6. *Certified* Medicaid.
Owner Proprietary Corp.

Nekton on Wyoming*
445 E Wyoming, Saint Paul, MN, 55107
(612) 291-8054
Admin Milton Conrath.
Licensure Intermediate care for mentally
retarded. *Beds* 6.
Owner Proprietary Corp.

Norhaven
1394 Jackson St, Saint Paul, MN, 55117
(612) 488-0275
Admin Peter Sajevic.
Licensure Intermediate care for mentally
retarded. *Beds* 106. *Certified* Medicaid.
Owner Proprietary Corp.

Our House of Minnesota I*
1846 Dayton Ave, Saint Paul, MN, 55104
(612) 646-1104
Admin Georgine Busch.
Licensure Supervised living facility. *Beds* 6.
Certified Medicaid.
Owner Nonprofit Corp.
Admissions Requirements Minimum age 18;
Medical examination; Physician's request.
Facilities Dining room; Laundry room.
Activities Arts & crafts; Cards; Games;
Reading groups; Prayer groups; Movies;
Shopping trips; Social/Cultural gatherings;
Adult education.

Our Lady of Good Counsel Home
2076 St Anthony Ave, Saint Paul, MN, 55104
(612) 646-2797
Admin Sr Mary Daniel King. *Medical Dir/Dir
of Nursing* Dr Wayne H Thalhuber, Dr
LeRoy Geis; Sr Marie Edward RN DON.
Licensure Intermediate care. *Beds* ICF 40.
Certified No charge to patients.
Owner Nonprofit Corp.
Admissions Requirements Minimum age 16;
Limited to terminal cancer patients.
Staff Physicians 2 (pt); RNs 4 (ft), 1 (pt);
LPNs 5 (ft); Orderlies 2 (ft), 2 (pt); Nurses
aides 1 (ft); Activities coordinators 1 (pt);
Dietitians 1 (pt); Ophthalmologists 1 (pt);
Dentist 1 (pt).
Languages Spanish
Affiliation Roman Catholic
Facilities Dining room Combined with
solarium; Chapel; Laundry room; Barber/
Beauty shop; Library; Enclosed screen
porches; Patio.
Activities Arts & crafts; Cards; Games; Prayer
groups; Movies; Social/Cultural gatherings;
Families on 4th of July picnic, Thanksgiving,
Christmas.

Parkway Manor Health Care Center*
324 Johnson Pkwy, Saint Paul, MN, 55106
(612) 774-9737
Admin Jack D Houston.
Licensure Skilled care. *Beds* 239. *Certified*
Medicaid; Medicare.
Owner Proprietary Corp (Beverly Enterprises).

People Inc—Dayton House
565 Dayton Avenue, Saint Paul, MN, 55102
(612) 222-1009
Admin Mary Kay McJilton.
Licensure Intermediate care. *Beds* 15.
Owner Nonprofit Corp.
Admissions Requirements Minimum age 18-
65; Males only.

Staff Program director 1 (ft); Chemical
dependency counselor 1 (ft); Basic living
daily coordinator 1 (ft); Chemical
dependency technicians 6 (pt).
Facilities Dining room; Physical therapy
room; Activities room; Laundry room;
Kitchen; Living room.
Activities Recreation events; Individual &
group counseling.

Peoples Child Care Residence
1611 Ames Ave, Saint Paul, MN, 55106
(612) 774-5940
Admin Margaret Foley. *Medical Dir/Dir of
Nursing* Eunice A Davis MD.
Licensure Intermediate care for mentally
retarded. *Beds* ICF/MR 32. *Certified*
Medicaid.
Owner Nonprofit Corp.
Admissions Requirements Medical
examination.
Staff Physicians 1 (pt); RNs 2 (ft), 2 (pt);
LPNs 3 (ft), 1 (pt); Nurses aides 6 (ft), 60
(pt); Physical therapists 1 (pt); Reality
therapists 6 (ft); Recreational therapists 1
(ft), 4 (pt); Occupational therapists 1 (pt);
Activities coordinators 1 (pt); Dietitians 1
(pt).
Facilities Physical therapy room; Activities
room; Crafts room; Laundry room; Barber/
Beauty shop.
Activities Arts & crafts; Games; Movies;
Shopping trips; Social/Cultural gatherings.

Phoenix Residence Inc
135 E Colorado St, Saint Paul, MN, 55107
(612) 227-7655
Admin Judy Douglas. *Medical Dir/Dir of
Nursing* Judith Rikala.
Licensure Intermediate care for mentally
retarded. *Beds* ICF/MR 51; Foster care 6.
Certified Medicaid.
Owner Nonprofit organization/foundation.
Admissions Requirements Minimum age 18;
Medical examination; Physician's request.
Staff RNs 1 (ft), 2 (pt); LPNs 1 (ft), 4 (pt);
Nurses aides 28 (ft), 32 (pt); Physical
therapists 2 (pt); Occupational therapists 1
(pt); Speech therapists 1 (pt); Activities
coordinators 1 (ft), 2 (pt); Dietitians 1 (pt);
Dentists 1 (pt); Podiatrists 1 (pt).
Facilities Dining room; Physical therapy
room; Activities room; Laundry room;
Library.
Activities Arts & crafts; Reading groups;
Movies; Shopping trips; Social/Cultural
gatherings; Bowling; Outings.

Pineview Residence*
69 N Milton, Saint Paul, MN, 55104
(612) 227-1333
Admin Joanne Chapman.
Licensure Boarding care. *Beds* 22.
Owner Proprietary Corp.
Admissions Requirements Minimum age 55;
Medical examination.
Staff Physicians; RNs; Nurses aides;
Recreational therapists; Activities
coordinators; Dietitians.
Facilities Dining room; Activities room;
Crafts room; Laundry room; Barber/Beauty
shop.
Activities Arts & crafts; Cards; Games; Prayer
groups; Movies; Shopping trips; Social/
Cultural gatherings.

Pleasant Hill Care Center
391 Pleasant Ave, Saint Paul, MN, 55102
(612) 224-3837
Admin Patti Paist. *Medical Dir/Dir of Nursing*
Dr Tom Altemeir; Gloria Wilkie DON.
Licensure Skilled care. *Beds* SNF 90. *Certified*
Medicaid; Medicare.
Owner Proprietary Corp (Health East).
Facilities Dining room; Physical therapy
room; Activities room; Crafts room; Laundry
room; Barber/Beauty shop; Library; Patio.

Activities Arts & crafts; Cards; Games;
Reading groups; Prayer groups; Movies;
Shopping trips; Social/Cultural gatherings.

Presbyterian Homes Johanna Shores
3220 Lake Johanna Blvd, Saint Paul, MN,
55112
(612) 631-6000
Admin Fred Strandberg. *Medical Dir/Dir of
Nursing* R Blomberg MD; Marj Kuhl DON.
Licensure Skilled care. *Beds* 208.
Owner Nonprofit Corp.
Admissions Requirements Minimum age 65.
Staff Physicians 15 (pt); RNs 22 (ft), 18 (pt);
LPNs 9 (ft), 7 (pt); Nurses aides 75 (ft);
Physical therapists 2 (ft), 2 (pt); Recreational
therapists 3 (pt); Occupational therapists 5
(pt); Speech therapists 1 (pt); Activities
coordinators 1 (ft); Ophthalmologists 1 (pt);
Podiatrists 1 (pt).
Affiliation Presbyterian
Facilities Dining room; Physical therapy
room; Activities room; Chapel; Crafts room;
Laundry room; Barber/Beauty shop; Library;
Pool; Whirlpool; Handicapped gardens; 1
mile paved walkways; Lake front; Gazebo;
Woods & trails; Shuffleboard; Exercise
rooms; Private dining rooms; Sidewalk cafe;
Gift shop; Medical & dental clinic.
Activities Arts & crafts; Cards; Games;
Reading groups; Prayer groups; Movies;
Shopping trips; Social/Cultural gatherings;
Wellness program.

Presbyterian Homes Langton Place
1910 W County Rd B, Saint Paul, MN, 55112
(612) 631-6200
Admin David Ross. *Medical Dir/Dir of
Nursing* Cindy Richter DON.
Licensure Skilled care. *Beds* SNF 165.
Owner Nonprofit Corp.
Admissions Requirements Minimum age 65;
Medical examination; Physician's request.
Staff RNs 30 (ft), 6 (pt); LPNs 15 (ft), 7 (pt);
Orderlies 47 (pt); Nurses aides 53 (ft);
Physical therapists 2 (ft), 1 (pt); Recreational
therapists 2 (ft), 1 (pt); Occupational
therapists 2 (ft); Activities coordinators 1
(ft).
Affiliation Presbyterian
Facilities Dining room; Physical therapy
room; Activities room; Chapel; Crafts room;
Laundry room; Barber/Beauty shop; Library;
Aquatic pool; Sidewalk cafe; Open
courtyards.
Activities Arts & crafts; Cards; Games;
Reading groups; Prayer groups; Movies;
Shopping trips; Social/Cultural gatherings.

Quinlan Home
233 W 5th St, Saint Paul, MN, 55102
(612) 222-7200
Admin Laura Reynolds.
Licensure Boarding care. *Beds* Boarding care
26.
Owner Proprietary Corp.
Admissions Requirements Minimum age 18;
Medical examination.
Staff Nurses aides 5 (ft), 3 (pt); Activities
coordinators 1 (pt).
Facilities Dining room; Activities room;
Laundry room.
Activities Arts & crafts; Cards; Games;
Reading groups; Prayer groups; Movies;
Shopping trips; Social/Cultural gatherings.

Ramsey Nursing Home
2000 White Bear Ave, Saint Paul, MN, 55109
(612) 777-7486
Admin David J Berres. *Medical Dir/Dir of
Nursing* Dr Robert L Powers; Karen
Wierenga DON.
Licensure Skilled care. *Beds* 180. *Certified*
Medicaid; Medicare.
Owner Publicly owned.
Admissions Requirements Minimum age 18.

Staff RNs 3 (ft), 8 (pt); LPNs 1 (ft), 11 (pt);
Nurses aides 32 (ft), 52 (pt); Physical
therapists 1 (pt); Occupational therapists 1
(ft); Speech therapists 1 (pt); Activities
coordinators 1 (ft); Dietitians 1 (ft).
Facilities Dining room; Physical therapy
room; Activities room; Crafts room; Laundry
room; Barber/Beauty shop.
Activities Arts & crafts; Cards; Games;
Reading groups; Prayer groups; Movies;
Shopping trips; Social/Cultural gatherings.

Regency Manor Inc
445 Galtier St, Saint Paul, MN, 55103
(612) 224-1848
Admin Gary D Dalzell.
Licensure Skilled care; Intermediate care. *Beds*
SNF 94; ICF 51. *Certified* Medicaid.
Owner Proprietary Corp.

The Residence III
1968 Foxridge Rd, Saint Paul, MN, 55119
(612) 735-9269
Admin Dennis M Holman.
Licensure Supervised living facility. *Beds* 6.
Certified Medicaid.
Owner Nonprofit Corp.
Admissions Requirements Minimum age 15.
Facilities Dining room; Laundry room.

St Marys Home
1925 Norfolk Ave, Saint Paul, MN, 55116
(612) 698-5508
Admin Thomas Fauskee. *Medical Dir/Dir of
Nursing* Dr Barry Bershow; Phyllis Kirk.
Licensure Skilled care; Intermediate care. *Beds*
140. *Certified* Medicaid; Medicare.
Owner Nonprofit organization/foundation.
Admissions Requirements Medical
examination; Physician's request.
Staff Physicians 49 (pt); RNs 7 (ft); LPNs 9
(ft), 10 (pt); Nurses aides 18 (ft), 22 (pt);
Physical therapists 1 (pt); Recreational
therapists 2 (ft), 1 (pt); Occupational
therapists 2 (ft); Speech therapists 1 (pt);
Activities coordinators 1 (ft); Dietitians 1
(pt); Dentists 1 (pt); Ophthalmologists 1 (pt);
Dental 1 (pt).
Languages German
Facilities Dining room; Physical therapy
room; Activities room; Chapel; Crafts room;
Laundry room; Barber/Beauty shop; Library;
Auditorium.
Activities Arts & crafts; Cards; Games;
Reading groups; Prayer groups; Movies;
Social/Cultural gatherings; Outside field
trips; Human society visits; Mens breakfast;
Manicures; Sensory groups; Nauslexercise;
Music groups.

St Pauls Church Home
484 Ashland Ave, Saint Paul, MN, 55102
(612) 227-8351
Admin Lionel Jadoo. *Medical Dir/Dir of
Nursing* Dr Mario Garcia; Melody Volek
DON.
Licensure Skilled care; Intermediate care. *Beds*
SNF 89; ICF 23; Private pay 16. *Certified*
Medicaid.
Owner Nonprofit Corp.
Admissions Requirements Minimum age 65;
Medical examination; Physician's request.
Staff RNs 4 (ft), 4 (pt); LPNs 10 (ft), 4 (pt);
Nurses aides 20 (ft), 29 (pt); Physical
therapists 1 (ft), 1 (pt); Occupational
therapists 1 (ft), 1 (pt); Speech therapists 1
(ft); Activities coordinators 2 (ft), 1 (pt);
Dietitians 1 (ft), 1 (pt); Dentists 1 (pt);
Ophthalmologists 1 (pt); Podiatrists 1 (pt).
Affiliation Church of Christ
Facilities Dining room; Physical therapy
room; Activities room; Chapel; Crafts room;
Laundry room; Barber/Beauty shop; Library;
Solarium.

Activities Arts & crafts; Cards; Games;
Reading groups; Prayer groups; Movies;
Shopping trips; Social/Cultural gatherings;
Community outings; Resident council;
Family council.

Sholom Home
1554 Midway Pkwy, Saint Paul, MN, 55108
(612) 646-6311
Admin Marshall Silberstein. *Medical Dir/Dir
of Nursing* Dr George Battis; Ann Lutterman
DNS.
Licensure Skilled care; Intermediate care. *Beds*
SNF 274; ICF 28. *Certified* Medicaid;
Medicare.
Owner Nonprofit Corp.
Admissions Requirements Minimum age 60;
Medical examination; Physician's request.
Languages Yiddish, Hebrew, German,
Russian
Affiliation Jewish
Facilities Dining room; Physical therapy
room; Activities room; Chapel; Laundry
room; Barber/Beauty shop; Library;
Occupational therapy room; Day care.
Activities Arts & crafts; Cards; Games;
Reading groups; Prayer groups; Movies;
Shopping trips; Social/Cultural gatherings;
Choir; Horticulture; Exercise; Closed circuit
TV network in-house.

Stevencroft
1436 Ashland Ave, Saint Paul, MN, 55104
(612) 644-2514
Admin Sandra Sorensen.
Licensure Skilled care; Intermediate care for
mentally retarded. *Beds* SNF 6; ICF/MR 11.
Certified Medicaid.
Owner Proprietary Corp.

Summit Manor Health Care Center
80 Western Ave N, Saint Paul, MN, 55102
(612) 227-8988
Admin Joanne Volden.
Licensure Skilled care. *Beds* SNF 120.
Certified Medicaid.
Owner Proprietary Corp (Thro Co).
Admissions Requirements Minimum age 18;
Medical examination; Physician's request.
Staff RNs 10 (ft), 12 (pt); LPNs 5 (ft), 5 (pt);
Nurses aides 25 (ft), 25 (pt); Physical
therapists 1 (ft); Recreational therapists 2
(ft); Occupational therapists 2 (ft); Speech
therapists 1 (pt); Activities coordinators 1
(ft); Ophthalmologists 1 (pt).
Facilities Dining room; Physical therapy
room; Activities room; Chapel; Laundry
room; Barber/Beauty shop.
Activities Arts & crafts; Cards; Games;
Reading groups; Prayer groups; Movies;
Shopping trips; Social/Cultural gatherings.

Sur La Rue de Breen*
1174 Breen St, Saint Paul, MN, 55106
(612) 488-6956
Admin Peter Sajevic.
Licensure Intermediate care for mentally
retarded. *Beds* 6. *Certified* Medicaid.
Owner Proprietary Corp.

Sur La Rue De Wheelock Ridge*
1561 Wheelock Ridge, Saint Paul, MN, 55102
(612) 771-3162
Admin Peter Sajevic.
Licensure Supervised living facility. *Beds* 6.
Certified Medicaid.
Owner Proprietary Corp.

Twin City Linnea Home*
2040 W Como Ave, Saint Paul, MN, 55108
(612) 646-2544
Admin Keith Johnson.
Licensure Intermediate care. *Beds* 73.
Certified Medicaid.
Owner Nonprofit Corp.

Twin Town Treatment Center
1706 University Ave, Saint Paul, MN, 55104
(612) 645-3661

Admin Robert L Haven. *Medical Dir/Dir of Nursing* Jerry Schulz MD.
Licensure Chemical dependency treatment. *Beds* Chemical dependency treatment 50. *Certified* JCAH.
Owner Proprietary Corp.
Admissions Requirements Minimum age 15; Medical examination.
Staff Physicians; RNs; LPNs; Nurses aides; Reality therapists; Dietitians; Chemical dependency counselors 9 (ft).
Facilities Dining room; Group therapy rooms; Lounges; Lecture room.
Activities YMCA; Aerobics; Relaxation therapy.

Wilder Residence East*
696 Dellwood Pl, Saint Paul, MN, 55106
(612) 776-4107
Admin Ted A Schmidt. *Medical Dir/Dir of Nursing* Madeline Adcock.
Licensure Skilled care; Intermediate care; Boarding care. *Beds* 108. *Certified* Medicaid.
Owner Nonprofit Corp.
Admissions Requirements Minimum age 60; Medical examination; Physician's request.
Staff RNs 8 (ft); LPNs 12 (ft); Orderlies 2 (ft); Nurses aides 98 (ft); Physical therapists 1 (pt); Recreational therapists 1 (ft), 2 (pt); Occupational therapists; Speech therapists; Activities coordinators; Dietitians.
Facilities Dining room; Physical therapy room; Activities room; Chapel; Crafts room; Laundry room; Barber/Beauty shop; Library; Solarium.
Activities Arts & crafts; Cards; Games; Reading groups; Prayer groups; Movies; Shopping trips; Social/Cultural gatherings.

Wilder Residence West
512 Humboldt Ave, Saint Paul, MN, 55107
(612) 227-6684
Admin Rick T Johnson. *Medical Dir/Dir of Nursing* Dr Patrick Irvine; Bonnie Peterson.
Licensure Skilled care; Board & lodging. *Beds* SNF 50; Board & lodging 125. *Certified* Medicaid; Medicare.
Owner Nonprofit organization/foundation.
Admissions Requirements Minimum age 60.
Staff RNs 3 (ft), 4 (pt); LPNs 1 (ft), 3 (pt); Nurses aides 15 (ft), 10 (pt); Physical therapists 1 (pt); Recreational therapists 1 (ft), 3 (pt); Occupational therapists 1 (pt); Activities coordinators 1 (ft).
Facilities Dining room; Physical therapy room; Activities room; Chapel; Crafts room; Laundry room; Barber/Beauty shop; Library; Gift shop.
Activities Arts & crafts; Cards; Games; Reading groups; Prayer groups; Movies; Shopping trips; Social/Cultural gatherings; Happy hour; Outings; Horticulture; Life review & enrichment.

Wilson Apartments*
1975 Wilson Ave, Saint Paul, MN, 55119
(612) 738-6603
Admin James Driscoll.
Licensure Skilled care; Intermediate care for mentally retarded. *Beds* SNF 15; ICF/MR 15. *Certified* Medicaid.
Owner Proprietary Corp.

SAINT PETER

Community Hospital & Health Care Center
618 W Broadway, Saint Peter, MN, 56082
(507) 931-2200
Admin David L Larson. *Medical Dir/Dir of Nursing* M D Olmanson; Maureen Pearson RN BSN.
Licensure Skilled care. *Beds* 85. *Certified* Medicaid; Medicare.
Owner Nonprofit Corp.
Admissions Requirements Minimum age 16; Medical examination; Prescreen by county.

Staff Physicians 8 (ft); RNs 5 (pt); LPNs 3 (ft), 11 (pt); Nurses aides 8 (ft), 38 (pt); Physical therapists 1 (ft); Recreational therapists 1 (ft); Occupational therapists 1 (ft); Dietitians 1 (ft), 1 (pt).
Facilities Dining room; Physical therapy room; Activities room; Chapel; Crafts room; Laundry room; Barber/Beauty shop; Library.
Activities Arts & crafts; Cards; Games; Reading groups; Prayer groups; Movies; Shopping trips; Social/Cultural gatherings; Happy hour; Special activities for Alzheimer's disease unit; Lunch away from facility; Weekly church & Mass; Exercises; Physical activites; Resident council.

Grandview Care Center
830 N Sunrise Dr, Saint Peter, MN, 56082
(507) 931-9021
Admin Sherry Fisher. *Medical Dir/Dir of Nursing* M D Olmanson; Jennifer Lammert RN DON.
Licensure Skilled care; Intermediate care. *Beds* SNF 74; ICF 2. *Certified* Medicaid; Medicare.
Owner Proprietary Corp (Good Neighbor Services).
Admissions Requirements Minimum age 16; Medical examination; Physician's request.
Staff Physicians 7 (pt); RNs 4 (ft), 1 (pt); LPNs 3 (ft), 2 (pt); Orderlies 1 (ft); Nurses aides 10 (ft), 20 (pt); Physical therapists 1 (ft); Occupational therapists 1 (pt); Speech therapists 1 (pt); Activities coordinators 1 (ft); Dietitians 1 (pt); Dentists 1 (pt); Podiatrists 1 (pt); Dentist 1 (pt).
Facilities Dining room; Physical therapy room; Activities room; Laundry room; Barber/Beauty shop; Library; Lounge.
Activities Arts & crafts; Cards; Games; Reading groups; Prayer groups; Movies; Shopping trips; Social/Cultural gatherings.

SARTELL

Country Manor Nursing Home
520 1st St NE, Sartell, MN, 56377
(812) 253-1920
Admin Hollis Helgeson. *Medical Dir/Dir of Nursing* Sue Schwartz DON.
Licensure Skilled care. *Beds* SNF 187. *Certified* Medicaid; Medicare.
Owner Proprietary Corp.
Admissions Requirements Medical examination; Physician's request.
Staff RNs; LPNs; Nurses aides; Physical therapists; Occupational therapists; Activities coordinators; Dietitians.
Facilities Dining room; Physical therapy room; Activities room; Chapel; Crafts room; Laundry room; Barber/Beauty shop.
Activities Arts & crafts; Cards; Games; Reading groups; Prayer groups; Movies; Shopping trips; Social/Cultural gatherings.

SAUK CENTRE

Dorothe Lane Home*
205 6th St, Sauk Centre, MN, 56378
(612) 352-3653
Admin Joseph M Bartsh.
Licensure Supervised living facility. *Beds* 8. *Certified* Medicaid.
Owner Proprietary Corp.
Admissions Requirements Minimum age 13; Medical examination.
Staff RNs 1 (pt); LPNs 1 (pt); Activities coordinators 1 (ft).
Facilities Dining room; Activities room; Laundry room.
Activities Arts & crafts; Cards; Games; Movies; Shopping trips; Social/Cultural gatherings.

Lakeview Childrens Home*
Lincoln & W 2nd St, Sauk Centre, MN, 56378
(612) 352-3081

Admin Joseph M Bartsh.
Licensure Supervised living facility. *Beds* 7. *Certified* Medicaid.
Owner Proprietary Corp.
Admissions Requirements Minimum age 3; Medical examination.
Staff RNs 1 (pt); LPNs 1 (ft).
Facilities Dining room; Activities room; Laundry room.
Activities Arts & crafts; Games; Movies; Shopping trips; Social/Cultural gatherings.

Pettit Childrens Home*
812 S Main St, Sauk Centre, MN, 56378
(612) 352-2844
Admin Cathy Marthaler.
Licensure Intermediate care for mentally retarded. *Beds* 15. *Certified* Medicaid.
Owner Proprietary Corp.

St Michaels Hospital & Nursing Home
425 N Elm St, Sauk Centre, MN, 56378
(612) 352-2221
Admin Roy Provo. *Medical Dir/Dir of Nursing* A B Nietfeld; Gail Ostrom.
Licensure Skilled care; Intermediate care. *Beds* SNF 56; ICF 4. *Certified* Medicaid; Medicare.
Owner Publicly owned.
Admissions Requirements Physician's request.
Staff RNs; LPNs; Orderlies; Nurses aides; Activities coordinators.
Facilities Dining room; Physical therapy room; Activities room; Chapel; Barber/Beauty shop.
Activities Arts & crafts; Cards; Games; Reading groups; Movies; Social/Cultural gatherings.

SAUK RAPIDS

Good Shepherd Lutheran Home
1115 4th Ave N, Sauk Rapids, MN, 56379
(612) 252-6525
Admin Tim Steller. *Medical Dir/Dir of Nursing* Dr Vernon E Neils.
Licensure Skilled care. *Beds* 174. *Certified* Medicaid.
Owner Nonprofit Corp.
Admissions Requirements Minimum age 16; Medical examination; Physician's request.
Staff RNs 7 (ft), 7 (pt); LPNs 15 (ft), 9 (pt); Orderlies 2 (ft), 5 (pt); Nurses aides 24 (ft), 39 (pt); Activities coordinators 1 (ft).
Affiliation Lutheran
Facilities Dining room; Physical therapy room; Activities room; Chapel; Crafts room; Laundry room; Barber/Beauty shop.
Activities Arts & crafts; Cards; Games; Reading groups; Prayer groups; Movies; Shopping trips; Social/Cultural gatherings.

Granite Care Home*
202 2nd Ave S, Sauk Rapids, MN, 56379
(612) 251-4736
Admin Quinton W Hommerding.
Licensure Intermediate care for mentally retarded. *Beds* 23. *Certified* Medicaid.
Owner Proprietary Corp.

SHAKOPEE

Delphi*
1411 E Shakopee Ave, Shakopee, MN, 55379
(612) 445-1680
Admin Betsy Nelson.
Licensure Intermediate care for mentally retarded. *Beds* 10. *Certified* Medicaid.
Owner Proprietary Corp.

Shakopee Friendship Manor
1340 3rd Ave W, Shakopee, MN, 55379
(612) 445-4155
Admin Timothy A Riffe. *Medical Dir/Dir of Nursing* R D Pistulka MD; Barbara Barry RN.

Licensure Skilled care; Intermediate care. *Beds* SNF; ICF 116. *Certified* Medicaid; Medicare.
Owner Proprietary Corp.
Admissions Requirements Minimum age 16; Medical examination.
Facilities Dining room; Physical therapy room; Activities room; Crafts room; Laundry room; Barber/Beauty shop.
Activities Arts & crafts; Cards; Games; Reading groups; Prayer groups; Movies; Shopping trips; Social/Cultural gatherings.

SHERBURN

Friendship Haven I
Fox Lake Rd, Sherburn, MN, 56171
(507) 764-3311
Admin Ruth Kirschmann.
Licensure Intermediate care for mentally retarded. *Beds* 14. *Certified* Medicaid.
Owner Nonprofit Corp.

Friendship Haven II
Fox Lake Rd, Sherburn, MN, 56171
(507) 764-2421
Admin Ruth Kirschmann.
Licensure Intermediate care for mentally retarded. *Beds* 6. *Certified* Medicaid.
Owner Nonprofit Corp.

SHOREVIEW

Dungarvin VI—Moores Haven*
3490 N Victoria, Shoreview, MN, 55112
(612) 482-8029
Admin Sandra Lee Henry.
Licensure Intermediate care for mentally retarded. *Beds* 6. *Certified* Medicaid.
Owner Publicly owned.

Lake Owasso Residence*
210 Owasso Blvd N, Shoreview, MN, 55112
(612) 484-2234
Admin Louis Speggen.
Licensure Intermediate care for mentally retarded. *Beds* 64. *Certified* Medicaid.
Owner Publicly owned.

Nekton-Hodgson Rd
5091 Hodgson Rd, Shoreview, MN, 55126
(612) 483-4024
Admin Peter Sajevic. *Medical Dir/Dir of Nursing* Jean Kube DON.
Licensure Intermediate care for mentally retarded. *Beds* ICF/MR 6. *Certified* Medicaid.
Owner Proprietary Corp.
Admissions Requirements Minimum age.
Facilities Ranch style home.
Activities Arts & crafts; Cards; Games; Reading groups; Movies; Shopping trips; Social/Cultural gatherings; Hiking; Biking.

The Residence I
935 Amble Rd, Shoreview, MN, 55126
(612) 484-0985
Admin Dennis Holman.
Licensure Supervised living facility. *Beds* ICF/MR 8. *Certified* Medicaid.
Owner Nonprofit Corp.
Admissions Requirements Minimum age 18; Medical examination; Physician's request Mental retardation.
Staff RNs 1 (pt); Activities coordinators 2 (ft).
Facilities Dining room; Activities room.
Activities Cards; Games; Reading groups; Prayer groups; Movies; Shopping trips; Social/Cultural gatherings.

The Residence II*
925 Amble Rd, Shoreview, MN, 51126
(612) 484-6718
Admin Dennis Holman.
Licensure Supervised living facility. *Beds* ICF/MR 8. *Certified* Medicaid.
Owner Nonprofit Corp.
Staff RNs 1 (pt); Activities coordinators 2 (ft).

Facilities Dining room; Activities room; Laundry room.
Activities Cards; Games; Reading groups; Prayer groups; Shopping trips; Social/Cultural gatherings.

SLAUTON

Prairie View Inc
2220 27th St, Slauton, MN, 56131
(507) 836-8955
Admin Louis R Nelson. *Medical Dir/Dir of Nursing* Kasey Lou Wagie.
Licensure Intermediate care for mentally retarded. *Beds* ICF/MR 18. *Certified* Medicaid.
Owner Privately owned.
Admissions Requirements Minimum age 18.
Staff Physicians 1 (pt); RNs 1 (ft), 1 (pt); LPNs 4 (ft); Nurses aides 13 (ft), 6 (pt); Physical therapists 1 (pt); Recreational therapists 1 (pt); Occupational therapists 1 (pt); Speech therapists 1 (pt); Activities coordinators 1 (ft); Dietitians 1 (pt); Dentists 1 (pt); Ophthalmologists 1 (pt); Podiatrists 1 (pt).
Facilities Dining room; Laundry room; Living rooms; Lounges; Kitchenettes.
Activities Arts & crafts; Cards; Games; Reading groups; Prayer groups; Movies; Shopping trips; Social/Cultural gatherings; Community outings weekly.

SLAYTON

Slayton Manor Care Center
2957 Redwood Ave, Slayton, MN, 56172
(507) 836-6135
Admin W Dru Fischgrabe. *Medical Dir/Dir of Nursing* Larry B Okerlund MD; Cheryl Gerth DON.
Licensure Skilled care. *Beds* SNF 64. *Certified* Medicaid; Medicare.
Owner Proprietary Corp (Beverly Enterprises).
Admissions Requirements Medical examination; Physician's request.
Staff RNs 1 (ft), 3 (pt); LPNs 6 (ft); Nurses aides 16 (ft), 16 (pt); Physical therapists 1 (pt); Occupational therapists; Speech therapists; Activities coordinators 1 (ft), 2 (pt); Dietitians; Social worker 1 (ft).
Facilities Dining room; Physical therapy room; Activities room; Chapel; Crafts room; Laundry room; Barber/Beauty shop; Library; Whirlpool bath.
Activities Arts & crafts; Cards; Games; Reading groups; Prayer groups; Movies; Shopping trips; Social/Cultural gatherings.

SLEEPY EYE

Divine Providence Community Home
700 3rd Ave NW, Sleepy Eye, MN, 56085
(507) 794-3011
Admin Sr Margaret Mary Schissler. *Medical Dir/Dir of Nursing* Dr Michael Ecker; Sr Mary Lynn.
Licensure Intermediate care. *Beds* ICF 58. *Certified* Medicaid.
Owner Nonprofit Corp.
Admissions Requirements Medical examination; Physician's request.
Staff Physicians 3 (pt); RNs 2 (ft), 1 (pt); LPNs 2 (ft), 4 (pt); Nurses aides 14 (ft), 25 (pt); Activities coordinators 2 (ft), 1 (pt).
Affiliation Roman Catholic
Facilities Dining room; Activities room; Chapel; Crafts room; Barber/Beauty shop.
Activities Arts & crafts; Cards; Games; Reading groups; Prayer groups; Movies; Shopping trips; Social/Cultural gatherings.

Sleepy Eye Care Center
1105 3rd Ave SW, Sleepy Eye, MN, 56085
(507) 794-7995

Admin Del Begalka. *Medical Dir/Dir of Nursing* C M Galvin MD; Ethel Roth.
Licensure Skilled care. *Beds* SNF 86. *Certified* Medicaid; Medicare.
Owner Nonprofit Corp (Volunteers of America Care).
Admissions Requirements Medical examination; Physician's request.
Staff RNs 5 (ft); LPNs 3 (ft), 7 (pt); Orderlies 2 (ft); Nurses aides 20 (ft), 16 (ft); Physical therapists 2 (pt); Recreational therapists 1 (ft); Activities coordinators 1 (ft); Dietitians 1 (ft).
Affiliation Volunteers of America
Facilities Dining room; Physical therapy room; Activities room; Chapel; Crafts room; Laundry room; Barber/Beauty shop.
Activities Arts & crafts; Cards; Games; Reading groups; Prayer groups; Shopping trips; Social/Cultural gatherings.

SOUTH SAINT PAUL

Bryant Avenue Residence*
1120 Bryant Ave, South Saint Paul, MN, 55075
(612) 451-1344
Admin Sarah Cosgrove.
Licensure Supervised living facility. *Beds* 30. *Certified* Medicaid.
Owner Proprietary Corp.
Admissions Requirements Minimum age 18.
Staff RNs 1 (ft).
Facilities Dining room; Activities room; Laundry room; Separate self-contained apartment units.
Activities Arts & crafts; Cards; Games; Reading groups; Movies; Shopping trips; Social/Cultural gatherings.

Golden Oaks Nursing Home
1025 9th Ave S, South Saint Paul, MN, 55075
(612) 455-6615
Admin Otto J Olson. *Medical Dir/Dir of Nursing* Mary Wangs Ness MD; Barbara Dentinger RN DON.
Licensure Skilled care. *Beds* SNF 98. *Certified* Medicaid; Medicare.
Owner Proprietary Corp.
Admissions Requirements Minimum age 16; Medical examination; Physician's request.
Staff RNs; LPNs; Nurses aides; Activities coordinators.
Facilities Dining room; Physical therapy room; Activities room; Chapel; Crafts room; Laundry room; Barber/Beauty shop; Library.
Activities Arts & crafts; Cards; Games; Reading groups; Prayer groups; Movies; Shopping trips; Social/Cultural gatherings.

Maclare Residence*
630 15th Ave N, South Saint Paul, MN, 55075
(612) 457-4898
Admin James Driscoll. *Medical Dir/Dir of Nursing* Angela Pelequin.
Licensure Intermediate care for mentally retarded. *Beds* 6. *Certified* Medicaid.
Owner Proprietary Corp.
Admissions Requirements Minimum age 18; Medical examination.
Staff RNs 1 (ft); LPNs 1 (pt).

Spruce Avenue Residence
1249 8th Ave N, South Saint Paul, MN, 55075
(612) 455-0578
Admin James Driscoll.
Licensure Skilled care; Intermediate care. *Beds* SNF 6; ICF 6. *Certified* Medicaid.
Owner Proprietary Corp.

Summit Avenue Residence*
920 Summit Ave, South Saint Paul, MN, 55075
(612) 455-5335
Admin Sarah Cosgrove.

Licensure Skilled care; Intermediate care. *Beds* SNF 15; ICF 15. *Certified* Medicaid.
Owner Proprietary Corp.

SPICER

Alpha Home*
137 Lake Ave N, Spicer, MN, 56288
(612) 796-5792
Admin Barbara Ulman.
Licensure Supervised living facility. *Beds* 15. *Certified* Medicaid.
Owner Proprietary Corp.
Admissions Requirements Minimum age 18.
Staff RNs 1 (pt); LPNs 1 (ft).
Facilities Dining room; Activities room; Crafts room; Laundry room.
Activities Arts & crafts; Cards; Games; Shopping trips; Social/Cultural gatherings.

SPRING GROVE

Tweeten Memorial Hospital—Nurs Home
125 5th Ave SE, Spring Grove, MN, 55974
(507) 498-3211
Admin Robert J Schmidt. *Medical Dir/Dir of Nursing* Glenn McCarty DO; Jan Kraabel RN.
Licensure Skilled care; Intermediate care. *Beds* SNF 32; ICF 47. *Certified* Medicaid; Medicare.
Owner Nonprofit Corp.
Admissions Requirements Medical examination; Physician's request.
Staff Physicians 1 (ft); RNs 4 (ft), 6 (pt); LPNs 3 (ft), 3 (pt); Nurses aides 10 (ft), 29 (pt); Recreational therapists 1 (ft); Activities coordinators 1 (ft), 1 (pt); Dietitians 1 (ft).
Affiliation Lutheran
Facilities Dining room; Activities room; Chapel; Crafts room; Laundry room; Barber/Beauty shop.
Activities Arts & crafts; Cards; Games; Reading groups; Prayer groups; Movies; Shopping trips; Social/Cultural gatherings.

SPRING PARK

Twin Birch Health Care Center
4527 Shoreline Dr, Spring Park, MN, 55384
(612) 471-8411
Admin Cynthia Morris. *Medical Dir/Dir of Nursing* Dr Jerry Petersen; Karen Dotson.
Licensure Skilled care; Intermediate care. *Beds* SNF 140; ICF 52. *Certified* Medicaid; Medicare.
Owner Proprietary Corp.
Admissions Requirements Minimum age 16; Medical examination; Physician's request.
Staff Physicians; RNs; LPNs; Orderlies; Nurses aides; Physical therapists; Recreational therapists; Occupational therapists; Speech therapists; Activities coordinators; Dietitians; Dentists; Ophthalmologists; Podiatrists.
Facilities Dining room; Physical therapy room; Activities room; Chapel; Crafts room; Laundry room; Barber/Beauty shop; Library.
Activities Arts & crafts; Cards; Games; Reading groups; Prayer groups; Movies; Shopping trips; Social/Cultural gatherings.

SPRINGFIELD

St John Lutheran Home
PO Box 167, 710 E Walnut, Springfield, MN, 56087
(507) 723-6251
Admin Randy D Snyder. *Medical Dir/Dir of Nursing* Francis J Boyle MD; Mary S Krueger RN DON.
Licensure Skilled care; Intermediate care; Board & Lodging care. *Beds* SNF 108; ICF 8; Board care 11;; Board & Lodging 12. *Certified* Medicaid; Medicare.
Owner Nonprofit Corp.

Admissions Requirements Medical examination; Physician's request.
Staff RNs 4 (ft), 3 (pt); LPNs 9 (ft), 10 (pt); Orderlies 1 (ft), 1 (pt); Nurses aides 26 (ft), 45 (pt); Physical therapists 1 (ft); Recreational therapists 2 (ft), 4 (pt); Activities coordinators 1 (ft); Dietitians 1 (ft).
Affiliation Lutheran
Facilities Dining room; Physical therapy room; Activities room; Chapel; Crafts room; Barber/Beauty shop; Library.
Activities Arts & crafts; Cards; Games; Reading groups; Prayer groups; Movies; Shopping trips; Social/Cultural gatherings.

STAPLES

United District Hospital & Home
401 Prairie Ave N, Staples, MN, 56479
(218) 894-1515
Admin Tim Rice. *Medical Dir/Dir of Nursing* T J Lelwica MD; Karen Noetzelman DON.
Licensure Skilled care. *Beds* SNF 100. *Certified* Medicaid; Medicare.
Owner Publicly owned.
Admissions Requirements Minimum age 16; Medical examination; Physician's request.
Staff Physicians 4 (pt); RNs 4 (ft), 3 (pt); LPNs 2 (ft), 13 (pt); Orderlies 1 (pt); Nurses aides 13 (ft), 60 (pt); Physical therapists 2 (pt); Activities coordinators 1 (ft); Dietitians 1 (ft).
Languages Finnish, Bohemian
Facilities Dining room; Physical therapy room; Activities room; Chapel; Crafts room; Barber/Beauty shop; Library.
Activities Arts & crafts; Cards; Games; Reading groups; Prayer groups; Movies; Shopping trips; Social/Cultural gatherings; Social services 32 hours per week.

STARBUCK

Minnewaska Lutheran Home
Box 40, 605 Main St, Starbuck, MN, 56381
(612) 239-2217
Admin Bruce Prause. *Medical Dir/Dir of Nursing* Starbuck Clinic; Andrea Hilden.
Licensure Intermediate care; Boarding care. *Beds* ICF 60; Boarding care 16. *Certified* Medicaid.
Owner Nonprofit Corp.
Admissions Requirements Minimum age 16; Medical examination; Physician's request.
Staff RNs 2 (ft), 1 (pt); LPNs 6 (ft), 2 (pt); Nurses aides 15 (ft), 15 (pt); Recreational therapists 1 (pt); Speech therapists 1 (pt); Activities coordinators 1 (ft); Dietitians 1 (pt).
Affiliation Lutheran
Facilities Dining room; Activities room; Chapel; Crafts room; Barber/Beauty shop.
Activities Arts & crafts; Cards; Games; Reading groups; Prayer groups; Movies; Shopping trips; Social/Cultural gatherings.

Project New Hope—Starbuck
707 8th St E, Starbuck, MN, 56381
(612) 763-6528
Admin Gerry Cascioli. *Medical Dir/Dir of Nursing* Nancy Scholl RN.
Licensure Intermediate care for mentally retarded. *Beds* ICF/MR 6. *Certified* Medicaid.
Owner Nonprofit Corp.
Admissions Requirements Minimum age 18; Medical examination.
Staff RNs 1 (pt); LPNs 1 (pt).
Facilities Dining room.
Activities Arts & crafts; Cards; Games; Reading groups; Movies; Shopping trips; Social/Cultural gatherings.

STEWARTVILLE

Stewartville Nursing Home
120 4th St NE, Stewartville, MN, 55976
(507) 533-4288
Admin Francis A Jensen. *Medical Dir/Dir of Nursing* Craig D Thauwald MD; Ruth Sherman RN DON.
Licensure Skilled care. *Beds* SNF 109. *Certified* Medicaid; Medicare.
Owner Publicly owned.
Admissions Requirements Medical examination; Physician's request.
Staff RNs 4 (ft), 5 (pt); LPNs 4 (ft), 9 (pt); Orderlies 1 (ft); Nurses aides 16 (ft), 26 (pt); Physical therapists 1 (pt); Reality therapists 1 (pt); Recreational therapists 1 (ft), 2 (pt); Activities coordinators 1 (ft); Dietitians 1 (pt).
Facilities Dining room; Physical therapy room; Activities room; Chapel; Crafts room; Laundry room; Barber/Beauty shop; Library.
Activities Arts & crafts; Cards; Games; Reading groups; Prayer groups; Movies; Shopping trips; Social/Cultural gatherings; Sight-seeing trips.

STILLWATER

Greeley Healthcare Center
313 S Greeley St, Stillwater, MN, 55082
(612) 439-5775
Admin Nancy Saatzer. *Medical Dir/Dir of Nursing* H V Pearson MD; Gail Geisenhoff DON.
Licensure Skilled care. *Beds* 83. *Certified* Medicaid; Medicare.
Owner Proprietary Corp (Beverly Enterprises).
Admissions Requirements Minimum age 16; Medical examination; Physician's request.
Staff RNs; LPNs; Orderlies; Nurses aides; Physical therapists; Recreational therapists; Occupational therapists; Speech therapists; Dietitians; Social worker.
Facilities Physical therapy room.
Activities Arts & crafts; Cards; Games; Reading groups; Prayer groups; Movies; Shopping trips; Social/Cultural gatherings.

Linden Healthcare Center
105 W Linden St, Stillwater, MN, 55082
(612) 439-5004
Admin Hilda Gooding. *Medical Dir/Dir of Nursing* James Hart MD; Kathleen Davis DON.
Licensure Skilled care. *Beds* SNF 75. *Certified* Medicaid; Medicare.
Owner Proprietary Corp (Beverly Enterprises).
Admissions Requirements Minimum age 16; Medical examination.
Staff Physicians 1 (pt); RNs 2 (pt); LPNs 6 (ft); Nurses aides 8 (ft), 23 (pt); Physical therapists 1 (pt); Occupational therapists 1 (pt); Speech therapists 1 (pt); Activities coordinators 1 (ft), 1 (pt); Podiatrists 1 (pt).
Facilities Dining room; Physical therapy room; Activities room; Crafts room; Laundry room; Barber/Beauty shop.
Activities Arts & crafts; Cards; Games; Reading groups; Prayer groups; Movies; Shopping trips; Social/Cultural gatherings.

Nekton on Imperial Court*
8050 Imperial Court, Stillwater, MN, 55802
(612) 429-0079
Admin Milton Conrath.
Licensure Intermediate care for mentally retarded. *Beds* 6. *Certified* Medicaid.
Owner Proprietary Corp.

Stillwater Maple Manor Health Care Center Inc
1119 N Owens St, Stillwater, MN, 55082
(612) 439-7180
Admin Douglas Dolinsky. *Medical Dir/Dir of Nursing* Dr Paul Spilseth.

Licensure Skilled care; Intermediate care. *Beds* SNF 105; ICF 27. *Certified* Medicaid; Medicare.
Owner Proprietary Corp.
Staff RNs 17 (ft), 17 (pt); LPNs 10 (ft), 10 (pt); Nurses aides 26 (ft), 60 (pt); Physical therapists 1 (ft); Recreational therapists 1 (ft); Occupational therapists 1 (pt); Speech therapists 1 (ft); Activities coordinators 1 (ft); Dietitians 1 (ft); Ophthalmologists 1 (pt); Music therapists 1 (ft), 1 (pt).
Facilities Dining room; Physical therapy room; Activities room; Chapel; Crafts room; Laundry room; Barber/Beauty shop.
Activities Arts & crafts; Cards; Games; Reading groups; Prayer groups; Movies; Shopping trips; Social/Cultural gatherings.

Stillwater Residence
220 W Olive St, Stillwater, MN, 55082
(612) 439-1601
Admin Laura L Reynolds.
Licensure Intermediate care; Board & lodging. *Beds* ICF 23; Board & lodging 8. *Certified* Medicaid.
Owner Proprietary Corp.
Admissions Requirements Minimum age 18; Medical examination; Physician's request.
Staff RNs 1 (pt); LPNs 3 (pt); Nurses aides 4 (ft), 5 (pt); Activities coordinators 1 (pt); Dietitians 1 (pt).
Facilities Dining room; Activities room; Crafts room; Laundry room.
Activities Arts & crafts; Cards; Games; Movies; Shopping trips; Social/Cultural gatherings; Resident council; AA Meetings.

THIEF RIVER FALLS

Crestview Home*
101 S State Ave, Thief River Falls, MN, 56701
(218) 681-3484
Admin Patricia Norberg.
Licensure Intermediate care. *Beds* 15.
Owner Proprietary Corp.

Johnsons Riverside Boarding Care Home
PO Box 21, Rte 4, Thief River Falls, MN, 56701
(218) 681-1278
Admin Paul Johnson. *Medical Dir/Dir of Nursing* Irene Dosser.
Licensure Intermediate care for mentally retarded. *Beds* ICF/MR 15. *Certified* Medicaid.
Owner Proprietary Corp.
Admissions Requirements Minimum age 18; Medical examination.
Staff RNs 1 (pt); Orderlies 1 (ft), 1 (pt).
Facilities Dining room; Activities room; Laundry room.
Activities Arts & crafts; Cards; Games; Reading groups; Movies; Shopping trips; Social/Cultural gatherings; Fishing; Snowmobiling; Gardening; Pontoon rides; Picnics; Vacations.

Oakland Park Nursing Home*
123 Baken St, Thief River Falls, MN, 56701
(218) 681-1675
Admin Sherryll C Irvine.
Licensure Intermediate care. *Beds* 75. *Certified* Medicaid.
Owner Publicly owned.

Valley Home
Hwy 32, S Arnold, Thief River Falls, MN, 56701
(218) 681-3286
Admin Mildred Brekke.
Licensure Boarding care. *Beds* Board & care 136.
Owner Nonprofit Corp.
Admissions Requirements Minimum age 62; Medical examination.
Staff LPNs 2 (ft); Nurses aides 10 (ft), 3 (pt); Dietitians 1 (pt).

Languages Norwegian
Activities Arts & crafts; Cards; Games; Reading groups; Prayer groups; Movies; Shopping trips; Social/Cultural gatherings.

TOWER

Hearthside Homes*
Pike Bay Dr, Tower, MN, 55790
(218) 753-2700
Admin Ronald L Abrahamson.
Licensure Supervised living facility. *Beds* 40. *Certified* Medicaid.
Owner Proprietary Corp.
Admissions Requirements Minimum age 18; Medical examination.
Staff RNs 1 (ft); LPNs 1 (pt); Nurses aides 4 (ft), 6 (pt); Recreational therapists 2 (ft).
Facilities Dining room; Crafts room.
Activities Arts & crafts; Cards; Games; Prayer groups; Movies; Shopping trips; Social/Cultural gatherings.

TRACY

Christian Manor Nursing Home
502 5th St E, Tracy, MN, 56175
(507) 629-3331
Admin Rev Homer Dobson. *Medical Dir/Dir of Nursing* Dr James O'Rourke.
Licensure Skilled care. *Beds* SNF 67. *Certified* Medicaid; Medicare.
Owner Nonprofit Corp.
Admissions Requirements Medical examination; Physician's request.
Staff Physicians 2 (pt); RNs 2 (ft), 2 (pt); LPNs 5 (ft), 2 (pt); Orderlies 1 (ft); Nurses aides 14 (ft), 7 (pt); Physical therapists 1 (pt); Activities coordinators 2 (ft), 1 (pt); Dietitians 2 (ft).
Affiliation Church of Christ
Facilities Dining room; Physical therapy room; Activities room; Chapel; Crafts room; Laundry room.
Activities Arts & crafts; Cards; Games; Prayer groups; Movies; Social/Cultural gatherings.

Tracy Nursing Home Inc
487 2nd St, Tracy, MN, 56175
(507) 629-4857
Admin Goldie Wilking. *Medical Dir/Dir of Nursing* Pam Baumann DON.
Licensure Intermediate care; Boarding care. *Beds* ICF 50; Boarding care 8. *Certified* Medicaid.
Owner Nonprofit Corp.
Admissions Requirements Minimum age 18; Medical examination; Physician's request.
Staff Physicians 2 (pt); RNs 2 (ft), 2 (pt); LPNs 1 (ft), 1 (pt); Nurses aides 7 (ft), 16 (pt); Activities coordinators 1 (ft), 2 (pt); Dietitians 1 (ft).
Facilities Dining room; Activities room; Chapel; Laundry room.
Activities Arts & crafts; Cards; Games; Reading groups; Prayer groups; Movies; Shopping trips; Social/Cultural gatherings.

TRIMONT

Trimont Nursing Home
303 Broadway Ave S, Trimont, MN, 56176
(507) 639-2381
Admin Thomas Tallant. *Medical Dir/Dir of Nursing* Dr K L Reddy; Margaret Theobald RN.
Licensure Skilled care. *Beds* SNF 41. *Certified* Medicaid; Medicare.
Owner Publicly owned.
Admissions Requirements Medical examination.
Staff RNs 1 (ft), 3 (pt); LPNs 3 (ft), 3 (pt); Nurses aides 5 (ft), 16 (pt); Recreational therapists 2 (pt); Dietitians 1 (pt).

Facilities Dining room; Activities room; Laundry room; Barber/Beauty shop; Library.
Activities Arts & crafts; Cards; Games; Reading groups; Movies.

TRUMAN

Lutheran Retirement Home of Southern Minnesota
400 N 4th Ave E, Truman, MN, 56088
(507) 776-2031
Admin Rodney Dahlberg. *Medical Dir/Dir of Nursing* Dr M J Lester.
Licensure Skilled care; Intermediate care. *Beds* 113. *Certified* Medicaid.
Owner Nonprofit Corp.
Admissions Requirements Minimum age 62; Medical examination; Physician's request.
Staff RNs 2 (ft), 4 (pt); LPNs 4 (ft), 5 (pt); Orderlies 1 (ft); Nurses aides 21 (ft), 36 (pt); Activities coordinators 1 (ft); Dietitians 1 (pt); Rehabilitation aides 2 (ft), 1 (pt).
Affiliation Lutheran
Facilities Dining room; Physical therapy room; Activities room; Chapel; Crafts room; Laundry room; Barber/Beauty shop; Library.
Activities Arts & crafts; Cards; Games; Reading groups; Prayer groups; Movies; Shopping trips; Social/Cultural gatherings.

TWIN VALLEY

Lutheran Memorial Nursing Home*
Hwy 32 N, Twin Valley, MN, 56584
(218) 584-5181
Admin Dwight Fuglie.
Licensure Skilled care; Intermediate care. *Beds* SNF 40; ICF 64. *Certified* Medicaid.
Owner Nonprofit Corp.
Affiliation Lutheran

Lutheran Memorial Retirement Center*
205 3rd St NW, Twin Valley, MN, 56584
(218) 584-5181
Admin Dwight Fuglie.
Licensure Skilled care; Intermediate care. *Beds* SNF 44; ICF 44. *Certified* Medicaid.
Owner Nonprofit Corp.

TWO HARBORS

Sunrise Home
13th Ave & 4th St, Two Harbors, MN, 55616
(218) 834-5574
Admin Jack L'Heureux. *Medical Dir/Dir of Nursing* Dr Eugene Rondeau.
Licensure Skilled care. *Beds* SNF 55. *Certified* Medicaid; Medicare.
Owner Publicly owned.
Admissions Requirements Minimum age 16; Medical examination; Physician's request.
Staff RNs 2 (ft), 2 (pt); LPNs 2 (ft), 5 (pt); Nurses aides 14 (ft), 21 (pt); Physical therapists 1 (pt); Activities coordinators 1 (ft); Dietitians 1 (pt).
Facilities Dining room; Activities room; Crafts room; Laundry room; Barber/Beauty shop.
Activities Arts & crafts; Cards; Games; Reading groups; Prayer groups; Movies; Shopping trips; Social/Cultural gatherings.

TYLER

REM Tyler*
303 Highland Ct, Tyler, MN, 56178
(507) 247-5568
Admin Craig Miller.
Licensure Intermediate care for mentally retarded. *Beds* 15.
Owner Proprietary Corp.

Sunrise Manor
240 Willow St, Tyler, MN, 56178
(507) 247-5521

Admin Pam Gilchrist. *Medical Dir/Dir of Nursing* Keith Carlson MD; Paula Hansen RN.
Licensure Skilled care. *Beds* SNF 43. *Certified* Medicaid; Medicare.
Owner Nonprofit Corp.
Admissions Requirements Medical examination.
Staff RNs 1 (ft), 2 (pt); LPNs 3 (ft); Nurses aides 8 (ft), 13 (pt); Physical therapists 1 (pt); Activities coordinators 1 (ft); Dietitians 1 (pt).
Facilities Dining room; Activities room; Barber/Beauty shop.
Activities Arts & crafts; Cards; Games; Movies; Bingo.

VICTORIA

Community Living
1501 82nd St, Victoria, MN, 55386
(612) 443-2048
Admin Jerry Gross.
Licensure Supervised living facility. *Beds* 66. *Certified* Medicaid.
Owner Proprietary Corp.
Admissions Requirements Minimum age 18; Medical examination; Physician's request.
Staff RNs 2 (ft).
Facilities Dining room; Activities room; Laundry room.
Activities Arts & crafts; Cards; Games; Reading groups; Movies; Shopping trips; Social/Cultural gatherings.

VILLARD

Jennies Retirement Home*
620 Washington Ave, Villard, MN, 56385
(612) 554-3311
Admin Virginia Grussing.
Licensure Boarding care. *Beds* 10.
Owner Proprietary Corp.

VIRGINIA

Arrowhead Health Care Center—Virginia*
1201 8-1/2 St S, Virginia, MN, 55792
(218) 741-4590
Admin Philip K Schumacher. *Medical Dir/Dir of Nursing* Dr Mathew Weir.
Licensure Skilled care; Intermediate care. *Beds* SNF 84; ICF 26. *Certified* Medicaid.
Owner Proprietary Corp (Beverly Enterprises).
Admissions Requirements Physician's request.
Facilities Dining room; Physical therapy room; Activities room; Crafts room; Laundry room; Barber/Beauty shop.
Activities Arts & crafts; Cards; Games; Reading groups; Prayer groups; Movies; Shopping trips; Social/Cultural gatherings.

Gethsemane Group Home*
507 9th Ave S, Virginia, MN, 55792
(218) 741-9437
Admin Sandra Johnson. *Medical Dir/Dir of Nursing* Valborg Pepelnjak RN.
Licensure Intermediate care for mentally retarded. *Beds* ICF/MR 12. *Certified* Medicaid.
Owner Nonprofit Corp.
Admissions Requirements Minimum age 18; Medical examination.
Staff RNs 1 (pt); Residential counselors 3 (ft), 5 (pt); Others 1 (ft), 1 (pt).
Affiliation Lutheran
Facilities Dining room; Activities room; Crafts room; Laundry room.
Activities Arts & crafts; Cards; Games; Movies; Shopping trips; Social/Cultural gatherings.

Virginia Regional Medical Center-Conv Center
901 N 9th St, Virginia, MN, 55792
(218) 741-3340

Admin Joyce A Fleming. *Medical Dir/Dir of Nursing* Dr Donald Werner; Connie Devereux RN.
Licensure Skilled care; Intermediate care. *Beds* 116. *Certified* Medicaid; Medicare.
Owner Publicly owned.
Admissions Requirements Minimum age 16; Medical examination; Physician's request.
Staff RNs; LPNs; Nurses aides; Physical therapists; Activities coordinators; Dietitians.
Languages Finnish
Facilities Dining room; Physical therapy room; Activities room; Chapel; Crafts room; Laundry room; Barber/Beauty shop; Library; Lounges; Atrium.
Activities Arts & crafts; Cards; Games; Reading groups; Prayer groups; Movies; Shopping trips; Social/Cultural gatherings.

WABASHA

St Elizabeth Nursing Home
1200 5th Grant Blvd W, Wabasha, MN, 55981
(612) 565-4531
Admin Tom Crowley. *Medical Dir/Dir of Nursing* Mary Tentis.
Licensure Skilled care; Intermediate care. *Beds* 52. *Certified* Medicaid; Medicare.
Owner Nonprofit Corp.
Admissions Requirements Minimum age; Medical examination; Physician's request.
Affiliation Roman Catholic
Facilities Dining room; Physical therapy room; Chapel; Crafts room; Laundry room.
Activities Arts & crafts; Cards; Games; Reading groups; Prayer groups; Movies; Shopping trips; Social/Cultural gatherings.

Wabasha Nursing Home*
626 Shields Ave, Wabasha, MN, 55981
(612) 565-4581
Admin Debra Mikelson. *Medical Dir/Dir of Nursing* Max Bachhuber.
Licensure Skilled care. *Beds* 125. *Certified* Medicaid.
Owner Publicly owned.
Admissions Requirements Medical examination.
Staff RNs 6 (ft), 5 (pt); LPNs 6 (ft), 4 (pt); Orderlies 3 (ft); Nurses aides 28 (ft), 16 (pt); Activities coordinators 1 (pt).

WABASSO

Wabasso Health Care Center
Maple & May Sts, Wabasso, MN, 56293
(507) 342-5166
Admin Brad Gauger. *Medical Dir/Dir of Nursing* David Dekert MD; Carol Bratsch RN DON.
Licensure Skilled care. *Beds* SNF 50. *Certified* Medicaid; Medicare.
Owner Proprietary Corp (Beverly Enterprises).
Admissions Requirements Minimum age 21; Medical examination; Physician's request.
Staff RNs 1 (ft), 1 (pt); LPNs 2 (ft), 4 (pt); Nurses aides 10 (ft), 16 (pt); Activities coordinators 1 (ft).
Facilities Dining room; Physical therapy room; Activities room; Laundry room; Barber/Beauty shop.
Activities Arts & crafts; Cards; Games; Reading groups; Movies; Social/Cultural gatherings.

WACONIA

Nightingale Nursing Home
232 S Elm St, Waconia, MN, 55387
(612) 442-2546
Admin Muriel Maass. *Medical Dir/Dir of Nursing* Russel Heagle MD; Ruth Goetz RN DONf.

Licensure Intermediate care; Boarding care. *Beds* ICF 36; Boarding care 4. *Certified* Medicaid.
Owner Nonprofit Corp.
Admissions Requirements Minimum age 21; Medical examination; Physician's request.
Staff RNs 1 (ft), 2 (pt); LPNs 4 (ft); Nurses aides 10 (ft), 10 (pt); Activities coordinators 1 (ft), 1 (pt); Dietitians 1 (pt).
Languages German
Facilities Dining room; Activities room; Crafts room; Laundry room.
Activities Arts & crafts; Cards; Games; Reading groups; Prayer groups; Movies; Shopping trips; Social/Cultural gatherings.

Waconia Healthcare Center*
333 W 5th St, Waconia, MN, 55387
(612) 442-5111
Admin Jim Duchene.
Licensure Skilled care; Intermediate care. *Beds* SNF 70; ICF 30. *Certified* Medicaid; Medicare.
Owner Proprietary Corp.

WADENA

Pembina Trail Group Home Inc
PO Box 127, Rte 1, Wadena, MN, 56482
(218) 631-1853
Admin Karen Crandall. *Medical Dir/Dir of Nursing* Karen Crandall.
Licensure Intermediate care for mentally retarded. *Beds* 8.
Owner Nonprofit Corp.
Admissions Requirements Minimum age 18; Medical examination; Physician's request.
Activities Arts & crafts; Cards; Games; Reading groups; Prayer groups; Movies; Shopping trips; Social/Cultural gatherings.

Shady Lane Nursing Home
RR 2 Box 12BB, Wadena, MN, 56482
(218) 631-1391
Admin Michael M Gibson. *Medical Dir/Dir of Nursing* Jane Uselman RN.
Licensure Intermediate care. *Beds* ICF 115. *Certified* Medicaid.
Owner Publicly owned.
Staff RNs; LPNs; Nurses aides; Activities coordinators; Dietitians.
Facilities Dining room; Physical therapy room; Activities room; Chapel; Crafts room; Barber/Beauty shop.
Activities Arts & crafts; Games; Reading groups; Movies; Shopping trips; Social/Cultural gatherings.

WAITE PARK

REM Waite Park Inc*
46 9th Ave N, Waite Park, MN, 56387
(612) 251-6142
Admin Juanita Turner.
Licensure Intermediate care for mentally retarded. *Beds* 9. *Certified* Medicaid.
Owner Proprietary Corp.

St Francis Home*
25 2nd St N, Waite Park, MN, 56387
(612) 251-7630
Admin Eugene Theisen.
Licensure Skilled care; Intermediate care for mentally retarded. *Beds* SNF 6; ICF 6. *Certified* Medicaid; Medicare.
Owner Publicly owned.
Affiliation Roman Catholic

Waite Park Nursing Home Inc
142 NW 1st St, Waite Park, MN, 56387
(612) 252-9595
Admin Marlene Nyquist. *Medical Dir/Dir of Nursing* Dr Thienes.
Licensure Skilled care. *Beds* 74. *Certified* Medicaid; Medicare.
Owner Proprietary Corp.

Admissions Requirements Medical
examination; Physician's request.
Staff Physicians; RNs; LPNs; Nurses aides;
Physical therapists; Recreational therapists;
Occupational therapists; Speech therapists;
Activities coordinators; Dietitians;
Ophthalmologists.
Languages German
Facilities Dining room; Physical therapy
room; Activities room; Laundry room;
Barber/Beauty shop.
Activities Arts & crafts; Cards; Games;
Reading groups; Prayer groups; Movies;
Shopping trips; Social/Cultural gatherings.

WALKER

Johnsons Long Lake Home*
PO Box 687, Walker, MN, 56484
(218) 547-1352
Admin George A Johnson.
Licensure Intermediate care for mentally
retarded. *Beds* 6. *Certified* Medicaid.
Owner Proprietary Corp.

Woodrest Nursing Home*
Box J, Walker, MN, 56484
(218) 547-1855
Admin Shirley Ziegler.
Licensure Skilled care; Intermediate care. *Beds*
SNF 50; ICF 16. *Certified* Medicaid.
Owner Proprietary Corp (Beverly Enterprises).

WANAMINGO

Riverview Manor Inc
Box 102A, RR 1, Wanamingo, MN, 55983
(507) 824-2910
Admin Betty Malchow.
Licensure Intermediate care for mentally
retarded. *Beds* ICF/MR 15. *Certified*
Medicaid.
Owner Nonprofit Corp.
Admissions Requirements Minimum age 18.
Staff Recreational therapists 1 (pt).
Facilities Dining room; Activities room;
Laundry room.
Activities Arts & crafts; Cards; Games;
Reading groups; Prayer groups; Movies;
Shopping trips; Social/Cultural gatherings.

WARREN

Good Samaritan Center*
410 S McKinley St, Warren, MN, 56762
(218) 745-5282
Admin Dwight Voigt.
Licensure Intermediate care. *Beds* 102.
Certified Medicaid.
Owner Nonprofit Corp (Evangelical Lutheran/
Good Samaritan).

WARROAD

Warroad Care Center*
611 E Lake St, Warroad, MN, 56763
(218) 386-1234
Admin Jack L Heureux. *Medical Dir/Dir of
Nursing* Dr Michael Clark.
Licensure Skilled care; Intermediate care. *Beds*
SNF 30; ICF 19. *Certified* Medicaid.
Owner Publicly owned.
Staff Physicians 2 (ft); RNs 4 (ft); LPNs 5 (ft);
Nurses aides 25 (ft); Recreational therapists
2 (ft); Activities coordinators 1 (ft);
Dietitians 1 (ft); Dentists 1 (ft); Audiologists
1 (pt).
Facilities Dining room; Activities room;
Chapel; Laundry room; Barber/Beauty shop;
Library.
Activities Arts & crafts; Cards; Games;
Reading groups; Prayer groups; Movies;
Shopping trips; Social/Cultural gatherings.

WASECA

Larry James Home
404 2nd St NE, Waseca, MN, 56093
(507) 835-3580
Admin E L Miller. *Medical Dir/Dir of Nursing*
Maryl Scott RN.
Licensure Supervised living facility. *Beds* ICF/
MR 8. *Certified* Medicaid.
Owner Proprietary Corp.
Admissions Requirements Minimum age 18;
Medical examination.
Staff RNs 2 (pt); LPNs 1 (pt).
Facilities Dining room; Activities room;
Laundry room.
Activities Arts & crafts; Games; Movies;
Shopping trips; Social/Cultural gatherings.

Lakeshore Inn Nursing Home*
108 8th St NW, Waseca, MN, 56093
(507) 835-2800
Admin R P Madel Jr.
Licensure Skilled care. *Beds* 94. *Certified*
Medicaid.
Owner Proprietary Corp.

WATERTOWN

Elim Home
PO Box 638, 409 Jefferson Ave SW, Hwy 25,
Watertown, MN, 55388
(612) 955-2691
Admin Trenton Carlson. *Medical Dir/Dir of
Nursing* Dr D R Philip; Joy Drawert.
Licensure Skilled care. *Beds* SNF 55. *Certified*
Medicaid; Medicare.
Owner Nonprofit Corp.
Admissions Requirements Minimum age 18;
Medical examination; Physician's request.
Staff Physicians 3 (pt); RNs 1 (ft), 4 (pt);
LPNs 3 (ft), 5 (pt); Nurses aides 10 (ft), 27
(pt); Physical therapists 1 (pt); Occupational
therapists 1 (pt); Activities coordinators 1
(ft); Dietitians 1 (pt).
Affiliation Evangelical Free Church
Facilities Dining room; Physical therapy
room; Activities room; Crafts room; Laundry
room; Barber/Beauty shop; Outdoor patio.
Activities Arts & crafts; Cards; Games;
Reading groups; Prayer groups; Movies;
Shopping trips; One-on-one LEEP program.

WATERVILLE

Hope Residences Inc
Box 63, Paquin & Herbert, Waterville, MN,
56096
(507) 362-8243
Admin Douglas Scharfe.
Licensure Intermediate care for mentally
retarded. *Beds* ICF/MR 14. *Certified*
Medicaid; Medicare.
Owner Nonprofit Corp.
Admissions Requirements Minimum age 18.
Staff LPNs 1 (ft).
Facilities Dining room; Laundry room.
Activities Arts & crafts; Cards; Games;
Movies; Shopping trips; Social/Cultural
gatherings.

Waterville Care Center
205 1st St N, Waterville, MN, 56096
(507) 362-4245
Admin Jeffrey D Bomberger. *Medical Dir/Dir
of Nursing* Dr Burton Grimes; Kathleen
Nosbush.
Licensure Skilled care. *Beds* SNF 56. *Certified*
Medicaid; Medicare.
Owner Proprietary Corp (Good Neighbor
Services).
Admissions Requirements Minimum age 16.
Staff RNs 1 (ft), 7 (pt); LPNs 5 (pt); Nurses
aides 5 (ft), 20 (pt); Physical therapists 1
(pt); Recreational therapists 2 (pt);
Occupational therapists 1 (pt); Speech
therapists 1 (pt); Activities coordinators 1
(pt); Dietitians 1 (pt).

Facilities Dining room; Physical therapy
room; Activities room; Chapel; Laundry
room; Barber/Beauty shop.
Activities Arts & crafts; Cards; Games;
Movies; Shopping trips; Social/Cultural
gatherings.

WATKINS

Hilltop Care Center
PO Box H, Rte 1, Watkins, MN, 55389
(612) 764-2300
Admin Daniel Waage. *Medical Dir/Dir of
Nursing* Dr Gardner.
Licensure Skilled care; Intermediate care. *Beds*
SNF 65; ICF. *Certified* Medicaid.
Owner Privately owned.
Admissions Requirements Medical
examination; Physician's request.
Staff RNs 1 (ft), 3 (pt); LPNs 4 (ft), 4 (pt);
Nurses aides 16 (ft), 15 (pt); Physical
therapists 1 (pt); Occupational therapists 1
(pt); Activities coordinators 1 (ft); Dietitians
1 (pt).
Facilities Dining room; Physical therapy
room; Activities room; Crafts room; Laundry
room; Barber/Beauty shop.
Activities Arts & crafts; Cards; Games;
Reading groups; Prayer groups; Movies;
Shopping trips; Social/Cultural gatherings.

WAYZATA

Hammer Residence—Gleason Lake Residence*
16325 County Rd 15, Wayzata, MN, 55391
(612) 473-1261
Admin Roger A Deneen.
Licensure Supervised care facility. *Beds* 6.
Certified Medicaid.
Owner Nonprofit Corp.

Hillcrest Health Care Center*
15409 Wayzata Blvd, Wayzata, MN, 55391
(612) 473-5466
Admin Lavonne Hagemeyer.
Licensure Skilled care. *Beds* 155. *Certified*
Medicaid; Medicare.
Owner Proprietary Corp (Beverly Enterprises).

Shadyway Group Home*
522 Shadyway Rd, Wayzata, MN, 55391
(612) 475-1825
Admin Eileen Harris.
Licensure Supervised living facility. *Beds* 6.
Certified Medicaid.
Owner Nonprofit Corp.

Way Twelve Halfway House
645 E Wayzata Blvd, Wayzata, MN, 55391
(612) 473-7371
Admin Karen Mattson.
Licensure Boarding care. *Beds* Boarding care
20.
Owner Nonprofit Corp.
Admissions Requirements Minimum age 16-
25; Medical examination.
Facilities Laundry room.
Activities Arts & crafts; Games; Movies;
Shopping trips; Social/Cultural gatherings;
Individual & group therapy; Lectures;
Independent living skills.

WELLS

Naeve Parkview Home
55 10th St SE, Wells, MN, 56097
(507) 553-3115
Admin Cathrine A Hagen RN. *Medical Dir/
Dir of Nursing* Dr Kenneth Haycraft; Jean
Steinhauer RN DON.
Licensure Skilled care. *Beds* SNF 61. *Certified*
Medicaid; Medicare.
Owner Nonprofit organization/foundation.
Admissions Requirements Medical
examination; Physician's request.

Staff Physicians 3 (pt); RNs 2 (ft), 10 (pt);
LPNs 8 (pt); Orderlies 1 (pt); Nurses aides
52 (pt); Physical therapists 10 (pt); Activities
coordinators 1 (ft), 1 (pt); Dietitians 1 (pt).
Languages German
Facilities Dining room; Physical therapy
room; Activities room; Chapel; Crafts room;
Laundry room; Barber/Beauty shop.
Activities Arts & crafts; Cards; Games;
Reading groups; Prayer groups; Movies;
Shopping trips; Social/Cultural gatherings.

WEST SAINT PAUL

Dakotas Childrens Home
400 W Marie Ave, West Saint Paul, MN,
55118
(612) 455-1286
Admin Kathleen Pine.
Licensure Supervised living facility. *Beds* 48.
Certified Medicaid.
Owner Nonprofit Corp.
Admissions Requirements Minimum age 3;
Medical examination; Physician's request.
Staff RNs 2 (ft), 1 (pt); LPNs 1 (ft), 1 (pt);
Recreational therapists 1 (ft); Occupational
therapists 2 (ft); Activities coordinators 2
(ft); Dietitians 1 (ft).
Facilities Dining room; Activities room;
Crafts room; Laundry room.
Activities Arts & crafts; Games; Reading
groups; Movies; Shopping trips; Social/
Cultural gatherings; Developmental
programming.

Horizon Apartments*
1094 Waterloo St, West Saint Paul, MN,
55118
(612) 455-6285
Admin James R Driscoll.
Licensure Intermediate care for mentally
retarded. *Beds* 15. *Certified* Medicaid.

OCI-Thompson Avenue Group Home
219 E Thompson Ave, West Saint Paul, MN,
55118
(612) 455-1286
Admin Kathleen Pine.
Licensure Intermediate care for mentally
retarded. *Beds* 9. *Certified* Medicaid.
Owner Nonprofit Corp.

Southview Acres Health Care Center*
2000 Oakdale Ave, West Saint Paul, MN,
55118
(612) 451-1821
Admin Harry J Lemieux.
Licensure Skilled care; Intermediate care. *Beds*
SNF 218; ICF 44. *Certified* Medicaid;
Medicare.
Owner Proprietary Corp.

WESTBROOK

Westbrook Good Samaritan Center*
149 1st Ave, Box 218, Westbrook, MN, 56183
(507) 274-6155
Admin Gary Hofer.
Licensure Intermediate care. *Beds* 49.
Certified Medicaid.
Owner Nonprofit Corp (Evangelical Lutheran/
Good Samaritan).

WHEATON

Traverse County Nursing Home
303 7th St S, Wheaton, MN, 56296
(612) 563-8124
Admin Gael A Coleman. *Medical Dir/Dir of
Nursing* Audrey Mitteness RN DON.
Licensure Intermediate care. *Beds* ICF 64.
Certified Medicaid.
Owner Publicly owned.
Admissions Requirements Medical
examination.

Staff RNs 2 (ft); LPNs 2 (ft), 3 (pt); Orderlies
1 (ft); Nurses aides 12 (ft), 21 (pt);
Recreational therapists 1 (ft); Activities
coordinators 2 (ft), 1 (pt); Dietitians 1 (pt).
Facilities Dining room; Activities room;
Chapel; Crafts room; Laundry room; Barber/
Beauty shop; Library.
Activities Arts & crafts; Cards; Games;
Reading groups; Prayer groups; Movies;
Shopping trips; Social/Cultural gatherings.

WHITE BEAR LAKE

Northeast Residence Inc
4680 Bald Eagle Ave, White Bear Lake, MN,
55110
(612) 426-1210
Admin Mary Joe Dolan.
Licensure Intermediate care for mentally
retarded. *Beds* ICF/MR 9. *Certified*
Medicaid.
Owner Nonprofit Corp.
Admissions Requirements Minimum age 16;
Medical examination; Physician's request.
Facilities Dining room; Activities room;
Crafts room; Laundry room.
Activities Arts & crafts; Movies; Shopping
trips; Social/Cultural gatherings.

Northeast Respite Care
1995 Oak Knoll Drive, White Bear Lake, MN,
55110
(612) 426-4306
Admin Mary Joe Dolan. *Medical Dir/Dir of
Nursing* Judy Zech.
Licensure Intermediate care for mentally
retarded. *Beds* 6. *Certified* Medicaid.
Owner Nonprofit Corp.
Admissions Requirements Minimum age 5;
Medical examination.
Staff RNs 1 (pt).
Facilities Dining room; Activities room;
Crafts room; Laundry room.
Activities Arts & crafts; Cards; Games;
Movies; Shopping trips; Shopping trips;
Social/Cultural gatherings; Swimming;
Community gymnasium; Hayrides; Music.

White Bear Lake Care Center
1891 Florence St, White Bear Lake, MN,
55110
(612) 426-1361
Admin Barbara DeLaHunt. *Medical Dir/Dir of
Nursing* T Altemeier MD.
Licensure Skilled care. *Beds* SNF 201.
Certified Medicaid; Medicare.
Owner Proprietary Corp (Health East).
Admissions Requirements Minimum age 18;
Medical examination.
Staff RNs 7 (ft), 8 (pt); LPNs 13 (ft), 25 (pt);
Orderlies 4 (ft), 8 (pt); Nurses aides 32 (ft),
68 (pt); Physical therapists 1 (ft);
Recreational therapists 2 (ft); Occupational
therapists 1 (ft); Speech therapists 1 (pt);
Activities coordinators 1 (ft); Dietitians 1
(pt).
Facilities Dining room; Physical therapy
room; Activities room; Crafts room; Laundry
room; Barber/Beauty shop; Meditation room;
Carpentry room.
Activities Arts & crafts; Cards; Games;
Reading groups; Prayer groups; Movies;
Shopping trips; Social/Cultural gatherings;
Resident job program; Chaplain services.

WILLMAR

Alexander Home
901 Memorial Pkwy, Willmar, MN, 56201
(612) 235-8315
Admin Kathryn Selseth-Kill. *Medical Dir/Dir
of Nursing* Dr Ronald Holmgren; Linda
Nelson RN RN.
Licensure Intermediate care for mentally
retarded. *Beds* ICF/MR 15. *Certified*
Medicaid.
Owner Nonprofit Corp.

Admissions Requirements Minimum age 18;
Medical examination.
Staff Physicians 1 (pt); RNs 1 (pt); Activities
coordinators 1 (pt).
Languages Spanish
Facilities Dining room; Laundry room.
Activities Arts & crafts; Cards; Games;
Reading groups; Movies; Shopping trips;
Social/Cultural gatherings; Travel.

Bethesda Heritage Center*
1012 E 3rd St, Willmar, MN, 56201
(612) 235-3924
Admin Douglas Dewane.
Licensure Intermediate care. *Beds* ICF 130.
Certified Medicaid.
Owner Nonprofit Corp.

Bethesda Nursing Home—Pleasantview*
901 Willmar Ave SE, Willmar, MN, 56201
(612) 235-9532
Admin Warren Becken.
Licensure Skilled care. *Beds* 120. *Certified*
Medicaid.
Owner Nonprofit Corp.

Christian Nursing Center
1801 Willmar Ave, Willmar, MN, 56201
(612) 235-0050
Admin Dennis Kamstra. *Medical Dir/Dir of
Nursing* Robert P Hodapp MD; Renee Aro
RN.
Licensure Skilled care. *Beds* SNF 86. *Certified*
Medicaid; Medicare.
Owner Proprietary Corp.
Admissions Requirements Medical
examination; Physician's request.
Staff Physicians 1 (pt); RNs 8 (ft); LPNs 11
(ft); Nurses aides 5 (ft), 20 (pt); Physical
therapists 1 (pt); Recreational therapists 3
(ft); Activities coordinators 1 (ft); Dietitians
1 (pt); Dentist 1 (pt).
Facilities Dining room; Physical therapy
room; Activities room; Laundry room;
Barber/Beauty shop; Library.
Activities Arts & crafts; Cards; Games;
Reading groups; Prayer groups; Movies;
Shopping trips; Social/Cultural gatherings.

Friendship House
901 Memorial Pkwy, Willmar, MN, 56201
(612) 235-8444
Admin Kathryn Selseth-Kill. *Medical Dir/Dir
of Nursing* Ronald Holmgren MD; Linda
Nelson RN DON.
Licensure Intermediate care for mentally
retarded. *Beds* ICF/MR 15. *Certified*
Medicaid.
Owner Nonprofit Corp.
Admissions Requirements Minimum age 18;
Females only.
Staff Physicians 1 (pt); RNs 1 (pt); Activities
coordinators 1 (ft).
Facilities Dining room; Activities room;
Laundry room.
Activities Arts & crafts; Cards; Games;
Reading groups; Movies; Shopping trips;
Social/Cultural gatherings; Travel.

Heather Hill
901 Memorial Pkwy, Willmar, MN, 56201
(612) 235-4373
Admin Kathryn Selseth-Kill. *Medical Dir/Dir
of Nursing* Ronald Holmgren MD; Linda
Nelson RN DON.
Licensure Intermediate care for mentally
retarded. *Beds* ICF/MR 15. *Certified*
Medicaid.
Owner Nonprofit Corp.
Admissions Requirements Minimum age 18.
Staff Physicians 1 (pt); RNs 1 (pt); Activities
coordinators 1 (ft).
Facilities Dining room; Activities room;
Laundry room.
Activities Arts & crafts; Cards; Games;
Reading groups; Movies; Shopping trips;
Social/Cultural gatherings; Travel.

Kindlehope
1217 7th St SE, Willmar, MN, 56201
(612) 235-2838
Admin David Meillier. *Medical Dir/Dir of Nursing* Dr Michael T Anderson.
Licensure Supervised living facility. *Beds* 64. *Certified* Medicaid.
Owner Proprietary Corp.
Admissions Requirements Minimum age 16; Medical examination; Physician's request.
Staff RNs 1 (pt); LPNs 2 (ft), 2 (pt); Nurses aides 9 (ft), 21 (pt); Recreational therapists 1 (ft); Dietitians 4 (ft); Social workers 4 (ft), 1 (pt).
Facilities Dining room; Laundry room.
Activities Arts & crafts; Cards; Games; Movies; Shopping trips; Social/Cultural gatherings; Trips to zoo; Dinner theatre; Camping; Cross-country skiing.

Willmar Health Care Center
500 Russell St, Willmar, MN, 56201
(612) 235-3181
Admin Phyllis Saunders. *Medical Dir/Dir of Nursing* Dr Michael T Anderson; Bev Jibbens RN.
Licensure Skilled care; Intermediate care. *Beds* SNF 99; ICF. *Certified* Medicaid; Medicare.
Owner Proprietary Corp (Beverly Enterprises).
Admissions Requirements Minimum age 18; Medical examination; Physician's request.
Staff RNs 2 (ft), 2 (pt); LPNs 3 (ft), 3 (pt); Nurses aides 20 (ft), 13 (pt); Physical therapists 1 (pt); Occupational therapists 1 (pt); Speech therapists 1 (pt); Activities coordinators 1 (ft), 2 (pt).
Facilities Dining room; Physical therapy room; Activities room; Crafts room; Laundry room; Barber/Beauty shop.
Activities Arts & crafts; Cards; Games; Reading groups; Prayer groups; Movies; Shopping trips; Social/Cultural gatherings; Picnics.

Willmar Regional Treatment Center
PO Box 1128, Willmar, MN, 56201
(612) 231-5100
Admin Gregory G Spartz. *Medical Dir/Dir of Nursing* Larry Olson MD; Dennis Butler RN DON.
Licensure Supervised living facility. *Beds* 170. *Certified* Medicaid.
Owner Publicly owned.

WINDOM

Home for Creative Living
108 9th St, Windom, MN, 56101
(507) 831-5033
Admin D Bill Olson.
Licensure Supervised living facility. *Beds* 45. *Certified* Medicaid.
Owner Proprietary Corp.
Admissions Requirements Medical examination.
Staff RNs 1 (ft); LPNs 4 (ft); Physical therapists 1 (pt); Occupational therapists 1 (pt); Speech therapists 1 (pt); Dietitians 1 (pt); Corrective therapist 1 (ft).
Facilities Dining room; Physical therapy room; Activities room; Laundry room; Library.
Activities Arts & crafts; Cards; Games; Reading groups; Movies; Shopping trips.

Sogge Memorial Good Samaritan Center
705 Sixth St, Windom, MN, 56101
(507) 831-1788
Admin Wayne O Brodland. *Medical Dir/Dir of Nursing* Dr James Dokken; Linda Dulaney RN DNS.
Licensure Intermediate care. *Beds* ICF 93. *Certified* Medicaid.
Owner Nonprofit Corp (Evangelical Lutheran/ Good Samaritan).
Admissions Requirements Minimum age 16; Medical examination; Physician's request.

Staff RNs 2 (ft), 5 (pt); LPNs 7 (pt); Orderlies 2 (pt); Nurses aides 11 (ft), 30 (pt); Activities coordinators 1 (ft).
Affiliation Lutheran
Facilities Dining room; Physical therapy room; Activities room; Crafts room; Laundry room; Barber/Beauty shop; Library.
Activities Arts & crafts; Cards; Games; Reading groups; Prayer groups; Movies; Shopping trips; Social/Cultural gatherings.

Windom CRF
945 Prospect, Windom, MN, 56101
(507) 831-3804
Admin D Bill Olson.
Licensure Supervised living facility. *Beds* 12. *Certified* Medicaid.
Owner Proprietary Corp.
Admissions Requirements Minimum age 18; Medical examination.
Staff Resident advisors 4 (ft), 5 (pt); Relief staff 3 (pt).
Facilities Activities room; Laundry room.

WINNEBAGO

Winnebago Baptist Home
211 6th St NW, Winnebago, MN, 56098
(507) 893-3171
Admin Kenneth E Presley. *Medical Dir/Dir of Nursing* Robin Lintelman DON.
Licensure Skilled care; Intermediate care; Boarding care. *Beds* SNF 20; ICF 41; Boarding care 27. *Certified* Medicaid; Medicare.
Owner Nonprofit Corp (American Baptist Homes).
Admissions Requirements Medical examination.
Languages Spanish, Sign
Affiliation Baptist
Activities Arts & crafts; Games; Reading groups; Prayer groups; Movies; Shopping trips; Social/Cultural gatherings.

WINONA

Community Memorial Hospital*
855 Mankato Ave, Winona, MN, 55987
(507) 454-3650
Admin Roger L Metz.
Licensure Skilled care. *Beds* 145. *Certified* Medicaid; Medicare.
Owner Nonprofit Corp.

St Annes Hospice
1347 W Broadway, Winona, MN, 55987
(507) 454-3621
Admin Robert Boyd. *Medical Dir/Dir of Nursing* Sidney O Hughes MD.
Licensure Skilled care; Intermediate care; Boarding care. *Beds* SNF 81; ICF 33; Boarding care 20. *Certified* Medicaid; Medicare.
Owner Nonprofit Corp.
Admissions Requirements Minimum age 60; Medical examination.
Staff RNs 4 (ft), 10 (pt); LPNs 4 (ft), 17 (pt); Nurses aides 24 (ft), 51 (pt); Physical therapists 1 (pt); Activities coordinators 3 (ft); Dietitians 1 (pt).
Affiliation Roman Catholic
Facilities Dining room; Physical therapy room; Activities room; Chapel; Crafts room; Laundry room; Barber/Beauty shop; Library; Wheelchair van; Adult day care center.
Activities Arts & crafts; Cards; Games; Reading groups; Prayer groups; Movies; Shopping trips; Social/Cultural gatherings; Imaginary 3 day trips.

Sauer Memorial Home
1635 Service Dr, Winona, MN, 55987
(507) 454-5540
Admin William H English. *Medical Dir/Dir of Nursing* Dr H J Andersen.

Licensure Skilled care. *Beds* 114. *Certified* Medicaid; Medicare.
Owner Nonprofit Corp.
Admissions Requirements Minimum age 16; Medical examination.
Staff RNs 2 (ft), 3 (pt); LPNs 5 (ft), 7 (pt); Nurses aides 20 (ft), 27 (pt); Physical therapists 1 (pt); Speech therapists 1 (pt); Activities coordinators 2 (ft), 2 (pt).
Facilities Dining room; Physical therapy room; Activities room; Chapel; Crafts room; Laundry room; Barber/Beauty shop; Library.
Activities Arts & crafts; Cards; Games; Reading groups; Prayer groups; Social/ Cultural gatherings.

Starzecki Boarding Care Home*
123 E 8th St, Winona, MN, 55987
(507) 452-4798
Admin Shirley Bronk.
Licensure Supervised living facility. *Beds* 11.
Owner Proprietary Corp.

377 Main Street
377 Main St, Winona, MN, 55987
(507) 452-5909
Admin Sharon Kannenberg.
Licensure Intermediate care for mentally retarded. *Beds* ICF/MR 11. *Certified* Medicaid.
Owner Nonprofit Corp.
Admissions Requirements Minimum age 18; Medical examination; Physician's request.
Facilities Dining room; Laundry room; Living room; Kitchen; Recreation room.
Activities Arts & crafts; Cards; Games; Movies; Shopping trips; Social/Cultural gatherings; Individualized skills training; Community based activities; Recreation.

Two Fifty Two West Wabasha Street
252 W Wabasha St, Winona, MN, 55987
(507) 454-5377
Admin Sharon Kannenberg.
Licensure Intermediate care for mentally retarded. *Beds* ICF/MR 10. *Certified* Medicaid.
Owner Nonprofit Corp.
Facilities Dining room; Activities room; Laundry room; Living room; Kitchen.
Activities Arts & crafts; Cards; Games; Movies; Shopping trips; Social/Cultural gatherings; Skills training; Community-based activities; Recreation.

The Watkins Home*
175 E Wabasha, Winona, MN, 55987
(507) 454-4670
Admin Charles A Barclay.
Licensure Skilled care; Intermediate care. *Beds* SNF 42; ICF 99. *Certified* Medicaid.
Owner Nonprofit Corp.

WINSTED

St Marys Hospital & Home
PO Box 750, 551 4th St N, Winsted, MN, 55395
(612) 485-2151
Admin Jeanne Johnson. *Medical Dir/Dir of Nursing* Dr Ted Akers.
Licensure Skilled care. *Beds* 95. *Certified* Medicaid; Medicare.
Owner Nonprofit Corp.
Admissions Requirements Minimum age 18; Medical examination.
Staff Physicians 29 (ft); RNs 4 (ft); LPNs 10 (ft); Physical therapists 1 (ft); Recreational therapists 1 (ft); Occupational therapists 1 (ft); Activities coordinators 1 (ft); Dietitians 1 (ft); Podiatrists 1 (ft).
Facilities Dining room; Physical therapy room; Activities room; Chapel; Crafts room; Laundry room; Barber/Beauty shop; Library; Medical clinic.

Activities Arts & crafts; Cards; Games; Reading groups; Prayer groups; Movies; Shopping trips; Social/Cultural gatherings; Daily religious services; Reality & music therapy; Exercise.

WINTHROP

Winthrop Care Center
506 High St, Winthrop, MN, 55396
(507) 647-5391
Admin Terri Kruger. *Medical Dir/Dir of Nursing* Dean Bergerson MD; Peggy Forstner DON.
Licensure Skilled care. *Beds* SNF 52. *Certified* Medicaid; Medicare.
Owner Proprietary Corp (Good Neighbor Services).
Admissions Requirements Minimum age 18; Medical examination; Physician's request.
Staff RNs 1 (ft), 3 (pt); LPNs 4 (pt); Nurses aides 7 (ft), 34 (pt); Activities coordinators 1 (ft), 1 (pt); Dietitians.
Facilities Dining room; Physical therapy room; Activities room; Crafts room; Laundry room; Barber/Beauty shop.
Activities Cards; Games; Reading groups; Prayer groups; Movies; Shopping trips; Social/Cultural gatherings.

WOODBURY

Jane Dickman House*
1665 Woodbury Dr, Woodbury, MN, 55125
(612) 739-4927
Admin Arlene Kelly.
Licensure Intermediate care for mentally retarded. *Beds* 35. *Certified* Medicaid.
Owner Nonprofit Corp.

Woodbury Health Care Center
7012 Lake Rd, Woodbury, MN, 55125
(612) 735-6000
Admin Dallas C Reese. *Medical Dir/Dir of Nursing* Dr Kuhlenkamp; Marion Johnson DON.
Licensure Skilled care. *Beds* SNF 212. *Certified* Medicaid; Medicare; VA.
Owner Proprietary Corp.
Admissions Requirements Minimum age 16; Physician's request.
Staff Physicians 56 (pt); RNs 9 (ft), 20 (pt); LPNs 10 (ft), 9 (pt); Orderlies 2 (ft), 2 (pt); Nurses aides 36 (ft), 40 (pt); Physical therapists 1 (ft), 1 (pt); Recreational therapists 2 (ft); Occupational therapists 1 (ft); Speech therapists 1 (pt); Activities coordinators 1 (ft); Music therapists 2 (ft), 6 (pt); Chaplain 1 (ft).
Facilities Dining room; Physical therapy room; Activities room; Chapel; Crafts room; Laundry room; Barber/Beauty shop; Doctor's examination office.
Activities Arts & crafts; Cards; Games; Reading groups; Prayer groups; Movies; Shopping trips; Social/Cultural gatherings.

WOODSTOCK

New Life Treatment Center
PO Box 38, Woodstock, MN, 56186
(507) 777-4321

Admin Wes Van Essen. *Medical Dir/Dir of Nursing* Pamela Talsma RN.
Licensure Supervised living facility. *Beds* 18.
Owner Nonprofit Corp.
Admissions Requirements Minimum age 18.
Staff Physicians 1 (pt); RNs 1 (ft); LPNs 1 (ft); Nurses aides 1 (ft); Dentist 1 (pt).
Facilities Dining room; Chapel; Laundry room.
Activities Movies.

WORTHINGTON

CLA—Southwest Manor
921 7th Ave, Worthington, MN, 56187
(507) 372-7278
Admin Donna Bruns. *Medical Dir/Dir of Nursing* Donna Bruns.
Licensure Intermediate care for mentally retarded. *Beds* 4. *Certified* Medicaid.
Owner Nonprofit organization/foundation.
Admissions Requirements Minimum age 18; Medical examination.
Staff RNs 1 (pt); LPNs 1 (pt).
Facilities Dining room; Laundry room.
Activities Arts & crafts; Cards; Games; Movies; Shopping trips; Social/Cultural gatherings.

Fauskee Nursing Home Inc
965 McMillan St, Worthington, MN, 56187
(507) 376-5312
Admin Betty Atchison RN BA. *Medical Dir/Dir of Nursing* Dr M W Plucker; Patricia Terhaar RN.
Licensure Skilled care; Intermediate care. *Beds* SNF 62; ICF 2. *Certified* Medicaid.
Owner Privately owned.
Admissions Requirements Minimum age 18; Medical examination.
Staff RNs; LPNs; Nurses aides; Recreational therapists; Activities coordinators; Dietitians.
Facilities Dining room; Activities room; Chapel; Crafts room; Laundry room; Barber/Beauty shop; Library.
Activities Arts & crafts; Cards; Games; Reading groups; Prayer groups; Movies; Social/Cultural gatherings; Hobby groups.

Lake Haven Nursing Home
PO Box 69, 1307 S Shore Dr, Worthington, MN, 56187
(507) 376-3175
Admin Richard Atchison. *Medical Dir/Dir of Nursing* Avis Torgrimson RN DON.
Licensure Intermediate care. *Beds* ICF 88; Board & Lodging 14. *Certified* Medicaid.
Owner Proprietary Corp.
Admissions Requirements Medical examination; Physician's request.
Staff RNs 3 (ft), 1 (pt); LPNs 6 (ft), 4 (pt); Nurses aides 25 (ft), 25 (pt); Recreational therapists 2 (ft), 1 (pt); Activities coordinators 1 (ft); 10 (ft), 20 (pt).
Facilities Dining room; Activities room; Laundry room; Barber/Beauty shop.
Activities Arts & crafts; Cards; Games; Reading groups; Prayer groups; Movies; Shopping trips; Social/Cultural gatherings.

Project Independence McMillan Home
PO Box 23, 1205 Burlington Ave, Worthington, MN, 56187
(507) 376-9555

Admin Donna Bruns. *Medical Dir/Dir of Nursing* Donna Bruns.
Licensure Intermediate care for mentally retarded. *Beds* ICF/MR 8. *Certified* Medicaid.
Owner Nonprofit Corp.
Admissions Requirements Minimum age 16.
Staff RNs 1 (pt); LPNs 1 (pt).
Facilities Dining room; Laundry room.
Activities Arts & crafts; Cards; Games; Movies; Shopping trips; Social/Cultural gatherings.

Project Independence Ridgewood
1381 Knollwood Dr, Worthington, MN, 56187
(507) 376-6095
Admin Donna Bruns.
Licensure Intermediate care for mentally retarded. *Beds* ICF/MR 15. *Certified* Medicaid.
Owner Nonprofit Corp.
Admissions Requirements Minimum age 16; Medical examination.
Staff RNs 1 (ft); LPNs 1 (ft), 1 (pt).
Facilities Dining room; Laundry room; Library; Living rooms.
Activities Arts & crafts; Cards; Games; Movies; Shopping trips; Social/Cultural gatherings; Daytime program outside facility.

Unity House
1224 4th Ave, Worthington, MN, 56187
(507) 372-7671
Admin Clark Guhiw.
Licensure Supervised living facility. *Beds* 12. *Certified* Medicaid.
Owner Nonprofit Corp.
Admissions Requirements Minimum age 12; Medical examination.
Staff Physicians; Reality therapists 6 (ft); Activities coordinators.
Facilities Dining room; Crafts room; Laundry room.
Activities Arts & crafts; Cards; Games; Reading groups; Movies; Shopping trips; Social/Cultural gatherings.

Worthington Regional Hospital*
1018 6th Ave, Worthington, MN, 56187
(507) 372-2941
Admin John C Albaugh.
Licensure Skilled care. *Beds* 95.
Owner Publicly owned.

ZUMBROTA

Zumbrota Nursing Home*
433 Mill St, Zumbrota, MN, 55992
(507) 732-5139
Admin Jerry L Hoganson. *Medical Dir/Dir of Nursing* William Walter MD.
Licensure Skilled care; Boarding care. *Beds* SNF 65; Boarding Home 8. *Certified* Medicaid.
Owner Proprietary Corp.
Staff RNs 2 (ft), 3 (pt); LPNs 1 (ft), 5 (pt); Nurses aides 11 (ft), 26 (pt); Physical therapists 1 (pt); Activities coordinators 1 (ft), 2 (pt); Dietitians 1 (ft).
Facilities Dining room; Activities room; Chapel; Barber/Beauty shop.
Activities Arts & crafts; Cards; Games; Reading groups; Prayer groups; Movies; Shopping trips; Social/Cultural gatherings.

MISSISSIPPI

ABERDEEN

Hillcrest Manor Inc*
PO Box 211, Jackson & Chestnut Sts,
Aberdeen, MS, 39730
(601) 369-6431
Admin Rita Faye Roberts.
Licensure Skilled care; Intermediate care. *Beds*
120. *Certified* Medicaid.
Owner Proprietary Corp.

Monroe County Rest Home
Box 394, Rte 2, Aberdeen, MS, 39730
(601) 369-4485
Admin Barbara Mabry. *Medical Dir/Dir of
Nursing* Dr L R Murphree.
Licensure Intermediate care. *Beds* ICF 12.
Owner Publicly owned.
Admissions Requirements Medical
examination.
Staff Physicians; Nurses aides 3 (ft); Activities
coordinators 1 (ft).
Facilities Dining room; Activities room;
Chapel; Laundry room; Barber/Beauty shop.
Activities Church groups provide most
activities at this facility.

ACKERMAN

Choctaw County Nursing Home
PO Drawer 417, 148 W Cherry St, Ackerman,
MS, 39735
(601) 285-3275
Admin Robert B Hughes. *Medical Dir/Dir of
Nursing* Dr Edward Pennington.
Licensure Skilled care; Intermediate care. *Beds*
SNF; ICF 60. *Certified* Medicaid.
Owner Publicly owned.
Admissions Requirements Medical
examination; Physician's request.
Staff Physicians 4 (ft); RNs 2 (ft); LPNs 6 (ft),
2 (pt); Orderlies 2 (ft); Nurses aides 14 (ft),
3 (pt); Activities coordinators 1 (ft);
Dietitians 1 (ft); Social services 1 (ft).
Facilities Dining room; Activities room;
Crafts room; Laundry room; Barber/Beauty
shop; Porch; TV-lobby.
Activities Arts & crafts; Cards; Games;
Reading groups; Prayer groups; Social/
Cultural gatherings; Outings; Pet therapy.

AMORY

Amory Manor Nursing Home*
1215 S Boulevard Dr, Amory, MS, 38821
(601) 256-9344
Admin Kelly Faulkner.
Licensure Intermediate care. *Beds* 60.
Certified Medicaid.
Owner Proprietary Corp (Beverly Enterprises).

BALDWYN

Oakview Nursing Home*
423 N 2nd St, Baldwyn, MS, 38824
(601) 365-5276
Admin Lana Maxey.

Licensure Skilled care. *Beds* 36. *Certified*
Medicaid.
Owner Proprietary Corp.

BATESVILLE

Batesville Manor Nursing Home*
Rte 1, Hospital Rd, Batesville, MS, 38606
(601) 563-5636
Admin James McCauley.
Licensure Intermediate care. *Beds* 120.
Certified Medicaid.
Owner Proprietary Corp (Beverly Enterprises).

BAY SAINT LOUIS

Hotel Reed Nursing Center*
400 N Beach Blvd, Bay Saint Louis, MS,
39520
(601) 467-5462
Admin Avonna Z Cain.
Licensure Skilled care; Intermediate care. *Beds*
88. *Certified* Medicaid.
Owner Proprietary Corp.

BAY SPRINGS

Jasper County Nursing Home*
PO Box 527, 6th St, Bay Springs, MS, 39422
(601) 764-2101
Admin Noel Hart.
Licensure Skilled care; Intermediate care. *Beds*
SNF 35; ICF 20. *Certified* Medicaid.
Owner Publicly owned.

BELZONI

Humphreys County Nursing Home*
500 CC Rd, Belzoni, MS, 39038
(601) 247-1821
Admin Mary T Gammons.
Licensure Skilled care; Intermediate care. *Beds*
48. *Certified* Medicaid.
Owner Proprietary Corp (Southmark Heritage
Corp).

BOONEVILLE

Aletha Lodge Nursing Home Inc*
200 Long St, PO Box 326, Booneville, MS,
38829
(601) 728-6234
Admin Juanita Evetts. *Medical Dir/Dir of
Nursing* Joseph Lewis Hurst MD.
Licensure Skilled care. *Beds* 64. *Certified*
Medicaid.
Owner Proprietary Corp.
Admissions Requirements Medical
examination; Physician's request.
Staff Physicians 1 (ft); RNs 1 (ft), 2 (pt);
LPNs 6 (ft), 4 (pt); Nurses aides 18 (ft), 3
(pt); Physical therapists 1 (ft); Speech
therapists; Activities coordinators; Dietitians;
Dentists.

Facilities Dining room; Activities room;
Crafts room; Laundry room; Barber/Beauty
shop; Library.
Activities Arts & crafts; Cards; Games;
Reading groups; Prayer groups; Movies;
Social/Cultural gatherings.

BRANDON

Crossgate Manor Inc*
PO Box 795, 335 Crossgate Blvd, Brandon,
MS, 39042
(601) 825-3192
Admin Shirley Allen.
Licensure Skilled care; Intermediate care. *Beds*
230. *Certified* Medicaid.
Owner Proprietary Corp (Beverly Enterprises).

BROOKHAVEN

Brook Manor Nursing Center*
Brookman Dr, Brookhaven, MS, 39601
(601) 833-2881
Admin Carolyn Wilson.
Licensure Skilled care; Intermediate care. *Beds*
58. *Certified* Medicaid.
Owner Proprietary Corp (Beverly Enterprises).

Cartwheel Lodge Nursing Home*
525 Brookman Dr, Brookhaven, MS, 39601
(601) 833-2330
Admin Scholber Roberts.
Licensure Skilled care; Intermediate care. *Beds*
120. *Certified* Medicaid.
Owner Proprietary Corp.

Haven Hall Nursing Center*
PO Box 848, 101 Mills St, Brookhaven, MS,
39601
(601) 833-5608
Admin Cindy Freeman.
Licensure Intermediate care. *Beds* 60.
Certified Medicaid.
Owner Proprietary Corp.

Lincoln Residential Center*
524 Brookman Dr, Brookhaven, MS, 39601
(601) 835-1884
Admin Deborah Ratcliff. *Medical Dir/Dir of
Nursing* Jim Barnett MD.
Licensure Intermediate care for mentally
retarded. *Beds* 120. *Certified* Medicaid.
Owner Proprietary Corp.
Admissions Requirements Minimum age 18;
Medical examination.
Staff Physicians 1 (ft); RNs 1 (ft), 1 (pt);
LPNs 4 (ft), 5 (pt); Nurses aides 54 (ft), 4
(pt); Physical therapists 1 (pt); Recreational
therapists 1 (ft); Occupational therapists 1
(ft); Speech therapists 1 (ft), 1 (pt); Activities
coordinators 1 (ft); Dietitians 1 (ft); Dentists
1 (pt); Ophthalmologists 1 (pt); Audiologists
1 (pt).
Facilities Dining room; Physical therapy
room; Activities room; Crafts room; Laundry
room; Barber/Beauty shop.

Activities Arts & crafts; Cards; Games; Reading groups; Movies; Shopping trips; Social/Cultural gatherings; Vocational programs.

Silver Cross Home
303 N Jackson St, Brookhaven, MS, 39601
(601) 833-2361
Admin Gussie W Ashley. *Medical Dir/Dir of Nursing* David Strong; Peggie Applewhite.
Licensure Skilled care; Intermediate care. *Beds* SNF 60; ICF. *Certified* Medicaid.
Owner Nonprofit Corp.
Admissions Requirements Medical examination; Physician's request.
Staff Physicians 1 (pt); RNs 1 (ft), 3 (pt); LPNs 8 (ft); Nurses aides 26 (ft); Physical therapists 1 (pt); Activities coordinators 1 (ft); Dietitians 1 (pt).
Facilities Dining room; Physical therapy room; Activities room; Chapel; Crafts room; Laundry room; Barber/Beauty shop.
Activities Arts & crafts; Cards; Games; Reading groups; Prayer groups; Movies; Shopping trips; Social/Cultural gatherings.

CALHOUN

Calhoun County Nursing Home*
Burke Rd, PO Box 110, Calhoun, MS, 38916
(601) 628-6651
Admin M B Martin. *Medical Dir/Dir of Nursing* Guy Farmer MD.
Licensure Skilled care; Intermediate care. *Beds* 120. *Certified* Medicaid.
Owner Publicly owned.
Admissions Requirements Medical examination; Physician's request.
Staff RNs 3 (ft); LPNs 10 (ft), 3 (pt); Orderlies 4 (ft), 2 (pt); Nurses aides 32 (ft), 6 (pt); Activities coordinators 1 (ft).
Facilities Dining room; Physical therapy room; Activities room; Laundry room; Barber/Beauty shop.
Activities Arts & crafts; Cards; Games; Social/Cultural gatherings.

CANTON

Canton Manor
PO Box 269, 1145 E Tisdale Ave, Canton, MS, 39046
(601) 859-6712
Admin Raymond Dailey. *Medical Dir/Dir of Nursing* Clyde McLaurin MD.
Licensure Intermediate care for mentally retarded. *Beds* ICF/MR 120. *Certified* Medicaid; Medicare.
Owner Proprietary Corp (Unicare).
Admissions Requirements Minimum age 18; Medical examination.
Staff Physicians 1 (ft); RNs 1 (ft); LPNs 10 (ft); Orderlies 69 (ft); Physical therapists 1 (ft); Recreational therapists 1 (ft); Occupational therapists 1 (ft); Speech therapists 1 (ft); Activities coordinators 1 (ft); Dietitians 1 (ft); Ophthalmologists 1 (ft); Podiatrists 1 (ft).
Facilities Dining room; Physical therapy room; Activities room; Crafts room; Laundry room; Vocational training center.
Activities Arts & crafts; Cards; Games; Movies; Shopping trips; Social/Cultural gatherings.

Madison County Nursing Home
PO Box 281, 411 S Liberty St, Canton, MS, 39046
(601) 948-6960, 859-1172
Admin Sidney L Whittington. *Medical Dir/Dir of Nursing* Joy Dilmore RN DON.
Licensure Skilled care. *Beds* SNF 60. *Certified* Medicaid; Medicare.
Owner Nonprofit organization/foundation.
Admissions Requirements Physician's request.

Staff RNs 1 (ft), 2 (pt); LPNs 8 (ft), 2 (pt); Orderlies 3 (ft), 9 (pt); Nurses aides 13 (ft), 9 (pt); Physical therapists 1 (ft); Activities coordinators 1 (ft); Dietitians 1 (ft).
Facilities Dining room; Activities room; Laundry room; Barber/Beauty shop.
Activities Arts & crafts; Cards; Games; Reading groups; Prayer groups; Bingo.

CARTHAGE

Carthage Health Care Center Inc*
1101 E Franklin St, Carthage, MS, 39051
(601) 267-4551
Admin Robert D Faulkner.
Licensure Skilled care; Intermediate care. *Beds* 90. *Certified* Medicaid.
Owner Proprietary Corp (Beverly Enterprises).

Leake County Skilled Nursing Facility*
300 Ellis St, Carthage, MS, 39051
(601) 267-4511
Admin Joe H Cooper.
Licensure Skilled care. *Beds* 37. *Certified* Medicaid.
Owner Publicly owned.

CENTREVILLE

Centreville Health Care Center*
PO Box 69, Lafayette St, Centreville, MS, 39631
(601) 645-5253
Admin Debbie Spence.
Licensure Skilled care; Intermediate care. *Beds* 96. *Certified* Medicaid.
Owner Proprietary Corp (Beverly Enterprises).

CHARLESTON

Tallahatchie General Hospital—Extended Care Facility
PO Box F, Charleston, MS, 38921
(601) 647-5535
Admin F W Ergle Jr. *Medical Dir/Dir of Nursing* Peggy Cole RN.
Licensure Skilled care. *Beds* SNF 40. *Certified* Medicaid.
Owner Publicly owned.
Staff RNs 1 (ft), 2 (pt); LPNs 7 (ft), 2 (pt); Orderlies 2 (ft), 1 (pt); Nurses aides 16 (ft); Physical therapists 1 (pt); Activities coordinators 1 (ft); Dietitians 1 (ft), 1 (pt).
Facilities Dining room; Activities room; Barber/Beauty shop.
Activities Arts & crafts; Games; Movies.

CLARKSDALE

Delta Manor Nursing Center
PO Box 338, 701 US Hwy 322 W, Clarksdale, MS, 38614
(601) 627-2212
Admin James Melvin Anderson. *Medical Dir/Dir of Nursing* Dr P W Hill Jr; Yvonne Ashley.
Licensure Intermediate care for mentally retarded. *Beds* ICF/MR 120. *Certified* Medicaid.
Owner Proprietary Corp (Unicare).
Admissions Requirements Minimum age 18; Medical examination.
Staff Physicians 1 (pt); RNs 1 (ft); LPNs 7 (ft), 5 (pt); Orderlies 54 (ft), 20 (pt); Physical therapists 1 (pt); Recreational therapists 1 (ft); Occupational therapists 1 (pt); Speech therapists 1 (pt); Dietitians 7 (ft), 2 (pt); Dentists 1 (pt); Ophthalmologists 1 (pt); Podiatrists 1 (pt); Dentist 1 (pt).
Facilities Dining room; Physical therapy room; Activities room; Crafts room; Laundry room; Barber/Beauty shop; Library.
Activities Arts & crafts; Cards; Games; Reading groups; Movies; Shopping trips; Social/Cultural gatherings.

Greenbough Nursing Center*
340 DeSoto Ave Extension, Clarksdale, MS, 38614
(601) 627-3486
Admin Shirley J Adcock.
Licensure Skilled care; Intermediate care. *Beds* 66. *Certified* Medicaid.
Owner Proprietary Corp.

CLEVELAND

Bolivar County Hospital—Long-Term Care Facility*
Hwy 8 E, Cleveland, MS, 38732
(601) 846-0061
Admin James L Townsend. *Medical Dir/Dir of Nursing* Dr S D Austin.
Licensure Skilled care. *Beds* 33. *Certified* Medicaid.
Owner Publicly owned.
Admissions Requirements Medical examination.
Staff RNs 1 (ft); LPNs 5 (ft), 2 (pt); Orderlies 1 (ft); Nurses aides 17 (ft), 3 (pt); Activities coordinators 1 (ft).
Facilities Dining room; Activities room; Barber/Beauty shop.
Activities Arts & crafts; Games; Prayer groups; Movies; Shopping trips; Social/Cultural gatherings.

Cleveland Health Care Center
PO Box 1688, Cleveland, MS, 38732
(601) 843-4014
Admin Tommy Herndon. *Medical Dir/Dir of Nursing* Bennie Wright MD; Christine Lacy DON.
Licensure Skilled care; Intermediate care. *Beds* SNF 60; ICF 60. *Certified* Medicaid.
Owner Proprietary Corp (Beverly Enterprises).
Admissions Requirements Medical examination; Physician's request.
Staff Physicians; RNs; LPNs; Orderlies; Nurses aides; Speech therapists; Activities coordinators; Dietitians; Ophthalmologists.
Facilities Dining room; Activities room; Laundry room; Barber/Beauty shop; Library.
Activities Arts & crafts; Games; Reading groups; Prayer groups; Movies; Shopping trips; Social/Cultural gatherings.

Heritage Manor
200 Dr Martin L King Jr Dr, Cleveland, MS, 38732
(601) 843-5347
Admin Sharon W Sauerwein. *Medical Dir/Dir of Nursing* John T Milam MD; Patti Bailey RN.
Licensure Skilled care; Intermediate care. *Beds* 75. *Certified* Medicaid.
Owner Proprietary Corp (National Heritage).
Admissions Requirements Physician's request.
Staff RNs 2 (ft), 2 (pt); LPNs 7 (ft), 8 (pt); Nurses aides 24 (ft), 9 (pt); Activities coordinators 1 (ft); Dietitians 1 (ft).
Facilities Dining room; Activities room; Laundry room; Barber/Beauty shop.
Activities Arts & crafts; Cards; Games; Reading groups; Movies; Social/Cultural gatherings.

CLINTON

Care Inn—Clinton*
101 W Northside Dr, Clinton, MS, 39056
(601) 924-7043
Admin Linda Stephens.
Licensure Skilled care; Intermediate care. *Beds* 135. *Certified* Medicaid.
Owner Proprietary Corp (Southmark Heritage Corp).

Clinton Country Manor*
1251 Pinehaven Rd, Clinton, MS, 39056
(601) 924-0627
Admin Darwin Martin. *Medical Dir/Dir of Nursing* Dr Robert Estess.

Licensure Skilled care; Intermediate care. *Beds* 120. *Certified* Medicaid.
Owner Proprietary Corp.
Admissions Requirements Medical examination.
Staff Physicians 1 (ft), 5 (pt); RNs 2 (ft), 3 (pt); LPNs 8 (ft), 2 (pt); Orderlies 1 (ft); Nurses aides 36 (ft), 12 (pt); Physical therapists 1 (pt); Activities coordinators 1 (ft); Dentists 1 (pt); Podiatrists 1 (pt).
Facilities Dining room; Activities room; Crafts room; Laundry room; Barber/Beauty shop.
Activities Arts & crafts; Cards; Games; Prayer groups; Movies; Shopping trips; Social/Cultural gatherings.

COLLINS

Covington County Nursing Center
PO Box 1089, 1207 Old Hiway 49 S, Collins, MS, 39428
(601) 765-8262
Admin Ms Bronze Walker. *Medical Dir/Dir of Nursing* Dr E P Reeves; Chris Kelly RN DON.
Licensure Skilled care; Intermediate care. *Beds* 60. *Certified* Medicaid.
Owner Proprietary Corp (Southmark Heritage Corp).
Admissions Requirements Medical examination; Physician's request.
Staff Physicians 4 (pt); RNs 2 (ft), 3 (pt); LPNs 5 (ft), 4 (pt); Nurses aides 18 (ft), 4 (pt); Physical therapists 1 (pt); Recreational therapists 1 (ft); Activities coordinators 1 (ft); Dietitians 1 (ft).
Facilities Dining room; Activities room; Crafts room; Laundry room; Barber/Beauty shop; Whirlpool; Living room; Lobby; Patio.
Activities Arts & crafts; Cards; Games; Reading groups; Prayer groups; Movies; Shopping trips; Social/Cultural gatherings.

COLUMBIA

The Cedars Intermediate Care Facility
511 S Main St, Columbia, MS, 39429
(601) 736-4747
Admin Jack Bradshaw. *Medical Dir/Dir of Nursing* Dr Robert Herrington; Vicky Burge RN DON.
Licensure Intermediate care. *Beds* ICF 32. *Certified* Medicare.
Owner Proprietary Corp.
Admissions Requirements Medical examination.
Staff Physicians 1 (pt); RNs 1 (pt); LPNs 1 (ft), 2 (pt); Orderlies 2 (ft); Nurses aides 10 (ft); Recreational therapists 1 (pt); Activities coordinators 1 (ft); Dietitians 1 (pt).
Facilities Dining room; Activities room; Laundry room.
Activities Arts & crafts; Cards; Games; Reading groups; Prayer groups; Movies; Shopping trips; Social/Cultural gatherings.

Floadrian Manor*
PO Box 70, N Main St, Columbia, MS, 39429
(601) 736-9557
Admin Harold Creecy.
Licensure Skilled care; Intermediate care. *Beds* 119. *Certified* Medicaid.
Owner Proprietary Corp (Southmark Heritage Corp).

The Myrtles Health Care Facility*
1018 Alberta Ave, Columbia, MS, 39429
(601) 736-8040
Admin Jeanne H Jones.
Licensure Intermediate care. *Beds* 66. *Certified* Medicaid.
Owner Proprietary Corp.

COLUMBUS

Aurora Australis Lodge*
310 N 20th St E, Columbus, MS, 39701
(601) 327-8021
Admin Betty Meadows.
Licensure Skilled care; Intermediate care. *Beds* 120. *Certified* Medicaid.
Owner Proprietary Corp.

Magnolia Manor Nursing Home
2002 5th St N, Columbus, MS, 39701
(601) 328-1133
Admin Lowell D Scales.
Licensure Skilled care; Intermediate care. *Beds* 60. *Certified* Medicaid.
Owner Proprietary Corp.
Staff RNs 2 (ft); LPNs 10 (ft), 1 (pt); Nurses aides 20 (ft); Activities coordinators 1 (ft); Dietitians 1 (ft).
Facilities Dining room; Physical therapy room; Activities room; Crafts room; Laundry room; Barber/Beauty shop.
Activities Arts & crafts; Games; Shopping trips.

CORINTH

Alcorn County Care Inn*
PO Box 751, Alcorn Dr, Corinth, MS, 38834
(610) 287-8071
Admin Richard Atkins.
Licensure Skilled care; Intermediate care. *Beds* 120. *Certified* Medicaid.
Owner Proprietary Corp.

Care Inn—Corinth
PO Box 1417, Alcorn Dr, Corinth, MS, 38834
(610) 286-2286
Admin Mary F Mullens.
Licensure Skilled care; Intermediate care. *Beds* 95. *Certified* Medicaid.
Owner Proprietary Corp (Southmark Heritage Corp).

Whitfield Nursing Home Inc
PO Drawer 1437, 2101 E Proper St, Corinth, MS, 38834
(601) 286-3331
Admin Erit L Burns. *Medical Dir/Dir of Nursing* Eloise Drinkard.
Licensure Intermediate care. *Beds* ICF 44. *Certified* Medicaid.
Owner Proprietary Corp.
Admissions Requirements Medical examination; Physician's request.
Staff RNs 1 (ft); LPNs 1 (ft), 4 (pt); Orderlies 3 (ft), 3 (pt); Nurses aides 9 (ft); Physical therapists 1 (pt); Reality therapists 1 (pt); Recreational therapists 1 (pt); Occupational therapists 1 (pt); Speech therapists 1 (pt); Activities coordinators 1 (ft); Dietitians 1 (pt).
Facilities Dining room; Activities room; Crafts room; Barber/Beauty shop.
Activities Arts & crafts; Cards; Games; Reading groups; Prayer groups; Movies; Shopping trips; Gardening; Walking.

DEKALB

Kemper County Nursing Home*
PO Box 577, DeKalb, MS, 39328
(601) 743-5888
Admin Patty C Nester. *Medical Dir/Dir of Nursing* Dr Jim Smith.
Licensure Skilled care; Intermediate care. *Beds* 60. *Certified* Medicaid.
Staff Physicians 3 (pt); RNs 3 (ft); LPNs 6 (ft); Nurses aides 19 (ft); Physical therapists 1 (pt); Activities coordinators 1 (pt); Dietitians 1 (pt); Dentists 1 (pt).
Facilities Dining room; Activities room; Laundry room; Barber/Beauty shop.
Activities Reading groups; Prayer groups; Movies; Social/Cultural gatherings.

DUNCAN

Oak Grove Retirement Home*
430 Oak Ave, Duncan, MS, 38740
(601) 395-2577
Admin Charles E Smith. *Medical Dir/Dir of Nursing* R T Hollingsworth MD.
Licensure Skilled care. *Beds* 59. *Certified* Medicaid.
Owner Proprietary Corp.
Staff Physicians 1 (pt); RNs 1 (pt); LPNs 2 (ft), 1 (pt); Orderlies 1 (ft), 1 (pt); Nurses aides 9 (ft), 6 (pt); Activities coordinators 1 (ft); Dietitians 1 (pt); Dentists 1 (pt).
Facilities Dining room; Activities room; Laundry room; Barber/Beauty shop; Library.
Activities Arts & crafts; Cards; Games; Reading groups; Prayer groups; Movies; Social/Cultural gatherings.

ELLISVILLE

Ellisville State School-Clover Circle ICF/MR*
Hwy 11 S, Ellisville, MS, 39437
(601) 477-9834
Admin Danny Lamier. *Medical Dir/Dir of Nursing* E Mangaoang MD.
Licensure Intermediate care for mentally retarded. *Beds* 132. *Certified* Medicaid.
Owner Publicly owned.
Admissions Requirements Medical examination; Physician's request.
Staff Physicians 1 (ft), 2 (pt); RNs 3 (ft); LPNs 11 (ft); Orderlies 3 (ft); Nurses aides 121 (ft); Physical therapists 1 (pt); Recreational therapists 3 (ft); Occupational therapists 1 (pt); Speech therapists 1 (ft), 1 (pt); Dietitians 1 (pt); Audiologists 1 (pt).
Facilities Dining room; Physical therapy room; Activities room; Chapel; Crafts room; Laundry room; Barber/Beauty shop.
Activities Arts & crafts; Cards; Games; Reading groups; Prayer groups; Movies; Shopping trips; Social/Cultural gatherings.

Ellisville State School-Hillside SNF/ICF*
Hwy 11 S, Ellisville, MS, 39437
(601) 477-9384
Admin Willie Jefferson. *Medical Dir/Dir of Nursing* Dr Rolando Estrella Vilar.
Licensure Skilled care; Intermediate care. *Beds* 88. *Certified* Medicaid.
Owner Publicly owned.
Admissions Requirements Minimum age 55; Medical examination; Physician's request.
Staff Physicians 1 (pt); RNs 3 (ft); LPNs 11 (ft); Nurses aides 45 (ft); Physical therapists 1 (pt); Reality therapists 1 (pt); Occupational therapists 1 (pt); Speech therapists 1 (pt); Activities coordinators 1 (ft); Dietitians 1 (pt); Dentists 2 (pt); Audiologists 2 (pt).
Facilities Dining room; Physical therapy room; Activities room; Chapel; Crafts room; Laundry room; Barber/Beauty shop; Library.
Activities Arts & crafts; Cards; Games; Reading groups; Movies; Shopping trips; Social/Cultural gatherings.

Ellisville State School-Pecan Grove*
Hwy 11 S, Ellisville, MS, 39437
(601) 477-8541
Admin Virginia Rendon. *Medical Dir/Dir of Nursing* Evangelina Paulino MD.
Licensure Intermediate care for mentally retarded. *Beds* 217. *Certified* Medicaid.
Owner Publicly owned.
Staff Physicians 1 (pt); RNs 2 (ft); LPNs 13 (ft); Nurses aides 157 (ft); Physical therapists 1 (pt); Recreational therapists 2 (ft); Occupational therapists 1 (pt); Speech therapists 1 (ft), 1 (pt); Activities coordinators 1 (ft); Dietitians 1 (pt); Dentists 3 (pt).
Facilities Dining room; Physical therapy room; Chapel; Laundry room; Barber/Beauty shop; Library.

Activities Arts & crafts; Cards; Games;
Reading groups; Prayer groups; Movies;
Shopping trips; Social/Cultural gatherings.

Jones County Rest Home*
Rte 2, Box 198, Ellisville, MS, 39437
(601) 477-3334
Admin Charles T Smith.
Licensure Skilled care; Intermediate care. *Beds*
114. *Certified* Medicaid.
Owner Publicly owned.

EUPORA

Eupora Health Care Center Inc
PO Box 918, 200 Walnut St, Eupora, MS,
39744
(601) 258-8293
Admin Gerald C Gary. *Medical Dir/Dir of
Nursing* Dr Charles A Ozborn.
Licensure Skilled care; Intermediate care. *Beds*
SNF 45; ICF 45. *Certified* Medicaid.
Owner Proprietary Corp (Beverly Enterprises).
Admissions Requirements Medical
examination; Physician's request.
Staff Physicians 4 (pt); RNs 6 (ft), 1 (pt);
LPNs 6 (ft), 5 (pt); Orderlies 2 (pt); Nurses
aides 27 (ft), 8 (pt); Physical therapists 1
(pt); Speech therapists 1 (pt); Activities
coordinators 1 (ft); Dietitians 1 (pt).
Facilities Dining room; Physical therapy
room; Activities room; Laundry room;
Barber/Beauty shop.
Activities Arts & crafts; Cards; Games;
Reading groups; Prayer groups; Movies;
Shopping trips; Social/Cultural gatherings.

FLORENCE

Briar Hill Rest Home Inc
Rte 1, Box 157, Florence, MS, 39073
(601) 939-6371
Admin Barbara M Bridges. *Medical Dir/Dir of
Nursing* Dr Terry K Brantley.
Licensure Skilled care; Intermediate care. *Beds*
55. *Certified* Medicaid.
Owner Proprietary Corp.
Admissions Requirements Medical
examination; Physician's request.
Staff Physicians 2 (pt); RNs 1 (ft), 2 (pt);
LPNs 4 (ft), 3 (pt); Orderlies 1 (pt); Nurses
aides 18 (ft); Physical therapists 1 (pt);
Speech therapists 1 (pt); Activities
coordinators 1 (ft); Dietitians 1 (ft), 1 (pt);
Dentists 1 (pt).
Facilities Dining room; Laundry room;
Barber/Beauty shop.
Activities Arts & crafts; Cards; Games;
Reading groups; Prayer groups; Movies;
Shopping trips; Social/Cultural gatherings.

FOREST

Lackey Convalescent Home
266 1st Ave, Forest, MS, 39074
(601) 469-4151
Admin Virginia F Mangum. *Medical Dir/Dir
of Nursing* Martha Adcox RN.
Licensure Skilled care. *Beds* SNF 30.
Owner Publicly owned.
Admissions Requirements Medical
examination; Physician's request.
Staff RNs 2 (ft), 3 (pt); LPNs 1 (ft), 1 (pt);
Orderlies 1 (ft); Nurses aides 10 (ft), 1 (pt);
Physical therapists 1 (pt); Speech therapists
1 (pt); Activities coordinators 1 (ft);
Dietitians 1 (ft).
Facilities Dining room; Activities room;
Crafts room; Laundry room; Barber/Beauty
shop.
Activities Arts & crafts; Cards; Games;
Reading groups; Prayer groups; Movies;
Social/Cultural gatherings.

FULTON

Daniel Nursing Home*
Rte 5, Box 219, Fulton, MS, 38843
(601) 862-2165
Admin James C Holland. *Medical Dir/Dir of
Nursing* Grayden Tubb MD.
Licensure Skilled care; Intermediate care. *Beds*
120. *Certified* Medicaid.
Owner Proprietary Corp.
Admissions Requirements Medical
examination; Physician's request.
Staff Physicians 1 (pt); RNs 2 (ft), 1 (pt);
LPNs 12 (ft), 2 (pt); Orderlies 3 (ft); Nurses
aides 38 (ft), 3 (pt); Physical therapists 1
(pt); Activities coordinators 1 (pt); Dietitians
1 (pt); Dentists 1 (pt).
Facilities Dining room; Activities room;
Laundry room; Barber/Beauty shop.
Activities Cards; Games; Reading groups;
Prayer groups; Movies; Social/Cultural
gatherings.

GREENVILLE

Arnold Avenue Nursing Home*
205 E Starling St, Greenville, MS, 38701
(601) 332-0318
Admin D D Felts.
Licensure Skilled care; Intermediate care. *Beds*
41. *Certified* Medicaid.
Owner Proprietary Corp.

Autumn Leaves Nursing Home Inc
PO Box 4042, 570 N Solomon St, Greenville,
MS, 38701
(601) 335-5863
Admin Ernest E McKinney.
Licensure Skilled care; Intermediate care. *Beds*
60. *Certified* Medicaid.
Owner Proprietary Corp.

Greenville Convalescent Home Inc*
1935 N Theobald Extended, Greenville, MS,
38701
(601) 334-4501
Admin Alvin L Freeman.
Licensure Skilled care; Intermediate care. *Beds*
120. *Certified* Medicaid.
Owner Proprietary Corp.

Mississippi Extended Care of Greenville Inc*
1221 E Union St, Greenville, MS, 38701
(601) 335-5811
Admin Jimmy W Hayes. *Medical Dir/Dir of
Nursing* Dr J Edward Hill.
Licensure Skilled care; Intermediate care. *Beds*
116. *Certified* Medicaid.
Owner Proprietary Corp.
Admissions Requirements Minimum age 18;
Medical examination; Physician's request.
Staff Physicians 14 (pt); RNs 2 (ft), 2 (pt);
LPNs 10 (ft), 1 (pt); Nurses aides 35 (ft), 10
(pt); Physical therapists 1 (pt); Reality
therapists 1 (pt); Speech therapists 1 (pt);
Activities coordinators 1 (ft); Dietitians 1
(ft); Dentists 1 (pt).
Facilities Dining room; Physical therapy
room; Activities room; Crafts room; Laundry
room; Barber/Beauty shop.
Activities Arts & crafts; Cards; Games; Prayer
groups; Movies.

GREENWOOD

Care Inn—Greenwood*
PO Box 1670, Hwy 82 By-Pass, Greenwood,
MS, 38930
(601) 453-9173
Admin Mark Waldrop.
Licensure Skilled care; Intermediate care. *Beds*
110. *Certified* Medicaid.
Owner Proprietary Corp (Southmark Heritage
Corp).

Golden Age Nursing Home*
Hwy 82 E, PO Box 853, Greenwood, MS,
38930
(601) 453-6323
Admin Alvin Loewenberg.
Licensure Skilled care; Intermediate care. *Beds*
180. *Certified* Medicaid.
Owner Nonprofit Corp.

Pemberton Manor Nursing Home
PO Box 1958, W Claiborne Ext, Greenwood,
MS, 38930
(601) 453-8140
Admin Kathy B Buford. *Medical Dir/Dir of
Nursing* J Edward Hill MD; Willie B Young
RN DON.
Licensure Skilled care; Intermediate care. *Beds*
120. *Certified* Medicaid.
Owner Privately owned.
Admissions Requirements Medical
examination; Physician's request.
Staff Physicians 1 (pt); RNs 2 (ft), 9 (pt);
LPNs 5 (ft), 16 (pt); Orderlies 1 (ft), 2 (pt);
Physical therapists 2 (pt); Speech therapists
2 (pt); Activities coordinators 2 (ft);
Dietitians 1 (ft), 1 (pt).
Facilities Dining room; Activities room;
Crafts room; Laundry room; Barber/Beauty
shop.
Activities Arts & crafts; Cards; Games;
Reading groups; Prayer groups; Movies;
Shopping trips; Social/Cultural gatherings.

GRENADA

Care Inn—Grenada*
PO Box 1210, 1966 Hill Dr, Grenada, MS,
38901
(601) 226-2442
Admin Joe Bannon.
Licensure Skilled care; Intermediate care. *Beds*
137. *Certified* Medicaid.
Owner Proprietary Corp (Southmark Heritage
Corp).

Grandview Health Care Center*
1950 Grandview Dr, Grenada, MS, 38901
(601) 226-9554
Admin Larry Schrader.
Licensure Skilled care; Intermediate care. *Beds*
120. *Certified* Medicaid.
Owner Proprietary Corp.

GULFPORT

Driftwood Nursing Center
4520 15th St, Gulfport, MS, 39501
(601) 868-1314
Admin Avonna Cain. *Medical Dir/Dir of
Nursing* Dr C D Taylor; Ranelle Hiley.
Licensure Skilled care. *Beds* SNF 131.
Certified Medicaid.
Owner Proprietary Corp.
Staff RNs; LPNs; Orderlies; Nurses aides;
Physical therapists; Recreational therapists;
Activities coordinators; Dietitians.
Facilities Dining room; Activities room;
Crafts room; Laundry room; Barber/Beauty
shop; Library.
Activities Arts & crafts; Cards; Games;
Reading groups; Prayer groups; Movies;
Shopping trips; Social/Cultural gatherings.

Gulfport Convalescent Center*
1530 Broad St, Gulfport, MS, 39501
(601) 864-6544
Admin Terri Reynolds.
Licensure Skilled care; Intermediate care. *Beds*
120. *Certified* Medicaid.
Owner Proprietary Corp (Hillhaven Corp).

Tender Care Home*
01512 Pass Rd, Gulfport, MS, 39501
(601) 896-1302
Admin Aubrey F Dryden.
Licensure Personal care. *Beds* 8.
Owner Proprietary Corp.

HATTIESBURG

Conva-Rest North Gate—Warren Hall
300 Cahal St, Hattiesburg, MS, 39401
(601) 582-9157
Admin Roy A Dumas. *Medical Dir/Dir of Nursing* Dr A J Carrol.
Licensure Skilled care. *Beds* SNF 120. *Certified* Medicaid.
Owner Proprietary Corp.
Admissions Requirements Medical examination; Physician's request.
Staff RNs 4 (ft); LPNs 13 (ft); Orderlies 5 (ft); Nurses aides 30 (ft); Recreational therapists 1 (ft); Activities coordinators 1 (ft); Dietitians 1 (ft).
Facilities Dining room; Activities room; Crafts room; Laundry room; Barber/Beauty shop.
Activities Arts & crafts; Cards; Games; Reading groups; Prayer groups; Movies; Social/Cultural gatherings.

Conva-Rest of Hattiesburg*
Medical Blvd, Hattiesburg, MS, 39401
(601) 264-3709
Admin Michael E McElroy.
Licensure Skilled care. *Beds* 192. *Certified* Medicaid.
Owner Proprietary Corp.

For-Rest Convalescent Home*
907 E Hardy St, Hattiesburg, MS, 39401
(601) 584-7218
Admin Vera Mae Davis.
Licensure Personal care. *Beds* 7.
Owner Proprietary Corp.

Green Forest Convalescent Home*
300 Cahal St, Hattiesburg, MS, 39401
(601) 544-5300
Admin Jack Gibson.
Licensure Intermediate care. *Beds* 100. *Certified* Medicaid.
Owner Proprietary Corp.

Hattiesburg Convalescent Center
514 Bay St, Hattiesburg, MS, 39401
(601) 544-4230
Admin Jewell McMahan. *Medical Dir/Dir of Nursing* Dr Clayton Cook; Louise Rounsaville.
Licensure Skilled care. *Beds* SNF 174. *Certified* Medicaid; Medicare.
Owner Proprietary Corp.
Admissions Requirements Medical examination; Physician's request.
Staff Physicians 4 (ft); RNs 20 (ft); LPNs 40 (ft); Orderlies 4 (ft); Nurses aides 70 (ft); Physical therapists 2 (pt); Recreational therapists 2 (ft); Speech therapists 1 (ft); Activities coordinators 1 (ft); Dietitians 1 (ft); Ophthalmologists 1 (pt).
Facilities Dining room; Physical therapy room; Activities room.
Activities Arts & crafts; Cards; Games; Reading groups; Prayer groups; Movies; Shopping trips; Social/Cultural gatherings; Fishing; Ball games; Music recitals; Dinner outings.

HAZLEHURST

Pine Crest Guest Home
133 Pine St, Hazlehurst, MS, 39083
(601) 894-1411
Admin Peggy Gaddy. *Medical Dir/Dir of Nursing* Dr Fred McDonnell; Lucy Tomicich DON.
Licensure Skilled care; Intermediate care. *Beds* 120. *Certified* Medicaid.
Owner Proprietary Corp.
Admissions Requirements Medical examination.
Staff Physicians 1 (pt); RNs 3 (ft), 1 (pt); LPNs 9 (ft), 3 (pt); Nurses aides 31 (ft), 11 (pt); Physical therapists 2 (pt); Recreational

therapists 1 (pt); Speech therapists 1 (pt); Activities coordinators 1 (ft); Dietitians 1 (ft), 1 (pt).
Facilities Dining room; Activities room; Crafts room; Laundry room; Barber/Beauty shop.
Activities Arts & crafts; Cards; Games; Reading groups; Prayer groups; Movies; Shopping trips; Social/Cultural gatherings.

HOLLY SPRINGS

Care Inn—Holly Springs*
PO Box 640, 960 E Salem Ave, Holly Springs, MS, 38635
(601) 252-1141
Admin Jerry Beck.
Licensure Skilled care; Intermediate care. *Beds* 120. *Certified* Medicaid.
Owner Proprietary Corp (Southmark Heritage Corp).

Heritage Manor of Holly Springs
960 E Salem Ave, Holly Springs, MS, 38635
(601) 252-1141
Admin Jerry Beck. *Medical Dir/Dir of Nursing* Marion Green MD; Geraldine Gholson RN DON.
Licensure Skilled care; Intermediate care.
Owner Proprietary Corp.
Staff RNs.

HOUSTON

Floy Dyer Manor*
Hwy 8 E, Houston, MS, 38851
(601) 456-3701
Admin Ruth Rhodes. *Medical Dir/Dir of Nursing* Dr Edward Gore.
Licensure Skilled care; Intermediate care. *Beds* 60. *Certified* Medicaid.
Owner Proprietary Corp.
Admissions Requirements Medical examination; Physician's request.
Staff RNs 2 (ft), 1 (pt); LPNs 4 (ft), 5 (pt); Orderlies 5 (ft), 1 (pt); Nurses aides 14 (ft), 2 (pt); Activities coordinators 1 (ft); Dietitians 1 (pt).
Facilities Dining room; Activities room; Barber/Beauty shop.
Activities Arts & crafts; Cards; Games; Movies; Shopping trips; Social/Cultural gatherings.

INDIANOLA

Care Inn-Indianola
401 Hwy 82 W, Indianola, MS, 38751
(601) 887-2682
Admin David Brinkley. *Medical Dir/Dir of Nursing* Dr Joe Hull; Linda Fike RN DON.
Licensure Skilled care; Intermediate care. *Beds* SNF 75; ICF. *Certified* Medicaid.
Owner Proprietary Corp (National Heritage).
Staff Physicians 7 (pt); RNs 3 (ft); LPNs 8 (ft), 4 (pt); Nurses aides 23 (ft), 6 (pt); Activities coordinators 1 (ft); Dietitians 1 (pt).
Facilities Dining room; Activities room; Laundry room; Barber/Beauty shop.
Activities Arts & crafts; Cards; Games; Reading groups; Prayer groups; Movies; Shopping trips; Social/Cultural gatherings; Bus trips; Fishing.

IUKA

Pickwick Manor Nursing Home*
230 Kaki St, Iuka, MS, 38852
(601) 423-9112
Admin Leonard C Goodin. *Medical Dir/Dir of Nursing* Dr Kelly Segars.
Licensure Skilled care; Intermediate care. *Beds* 120. *Certified* Medicaid.
Owner Proprietary Corp (Beverly Enterprises).

Admissions Requirements Medical examination; Physician's request.
Staff Physicians 6 (ft); RNs 2 (ft), 2 (pt); LPNs 13 (ft); Orderlies 1 (pt); Nurses aides 32 (ft), 10 (pt); Physical therapists 1 (pt); Speech therapists 1 (pt); Activities coordinators 1 (ft); Dietitians 1 (pt); Dentists 1 (pt); Ophthalmologists 1 (pt).
Facilities Dining room; Activities room; Chapel; Laundry room; Barber/Beauty shop.
Activities Arts & crafts; Games; Prayer groups; Movies; Shopping trips; Social/Cultural gatherings.

Tishomingo County Rest Home
Rte 4, Box 914, Iuka, MS, 38852
(601) 423-6728
Admin Arwilla Wilson.
Licensure Personal care. *Beds* 27.
Owner Publicly owned.

JACKSON

Albemarle Health Care Center*
3454 Albemarle Rd, Jackson, MS, 39213
(601) 362-5394
Admin Debbie Spence. *Medical Dir/Dir of Nursing* Dr Aaron Shirley & Dr James Anderson.
Licensure Skilled care; Intermediate care. *Beds* 119. *Certified* Medicaid; Medicare.
Owner Proprietary Corp (Beverly Enterprises).
Admissions Requirements Physician's request.
Staff RNs 6 (ft); LPNs 14 (ft); Orderlies 3 (ft); Nurses aides 43 (ft); Activities coordinators 1 (ft); Dietitians 1 (ft).
Facilities Dining room; Activities room; Crafts room; Laundry room; Barber/Beauty shop.
Activities Arts & crafts; Cards; Games; Reading groups; Prayer groups; Movies; Shopping trips; Social/Cultural gatherings.

Alpha & Omega Personal Care Home*
131 S Prentiss St, Jackson, MS, 39203
(601) 354-0783
Admin Myrtle McAllister.
Licensure Personal care. *Beds* 13.
Owner Proprietary Corp.

Ann's Personal Care Home
3137 James Hill St, Jackson, MS, 39213
981-5963 or 362-2182
Admin Ann Fleming Coleman.
Licensure Intermediate care for mentally retarded. *Beds* ICF 15.
Owner Privately owned.
Admissions Requirements Medical examination; Physician's request.
Facilities Dining room; Activities room; Laundry room.
Activities Cards; Prayer groups.

Armstrong's Personal Care Home I*
129 Poindexter St, Jackson, MS, 39203
(601) 355-7029
Admin Minnie Armstrong.
Licensure Personal care. *Beds* 11.
Owner Proprietary Corp.

Armstrong's Personal Care Home II*
227 Poindexter St, Jackson, MS, 39203
(601) 355-0364
Admin Minnie Armstrong.
Licensure Personal care. *Beds* 10.
Owner Proprietary Corp.

Beehaven Nursing Home
1004 North St, Jackson, MS, 39202
(601) 355-0763
Admin Billie T Trussell.
Licensure Intermediate care. *Beds* ICF 60. *Certified* Medicaid.
Owner Proprietary Corp.
Admissions Requirements Medical examination.

Staff RNs; LPNs 4 (ft), 1 (pt); Orderlies 1 (ft); Nurses aides 11 (ft), 2 (pt); Activities coordinators 1 (ft); Dietitians 1 (ft).
Facilities Dining room; Physical therapy room; Activities room; Chapel; Crafts room; Laundry room; Barber/Beauty shop.
Activities Arts & crafts; Cards; Games; Reading groups; Prayer groups; Movies; Shopping trips; Social/Cultural gatherings.

Carter's Guest Home Inc*
941 Cooper Rd, Jackson, MS, 39212
(601) 372-6931
Admin Aline P Carter.
Licensure Skilled care; Intermediate care. *Beds* 53. *Certified* Medicaid.
Owner Proprietary Corp.

Coleman's Personal Care Home*
219 Poindexter St, Jackson, MS, 39203
(601) 355-3390
Admin Theola Coleman.
Licensure Personal care. *Beds* 9.
Owner Proprietary Corp.

Community Nursing Home
1129 Langley Ave, Jackson, MS, 39204
(601) 355-0617
Admin Dillie Myrick. *Medical Dir/Dir of Nursing* J Daniel Mitchell MD; Blanche Reed DON.
Licensure Intermediate care. *Beds* ICF 60. *Certified* Medicaid.
Owner Nonprofit Corp.
Admissions Requirements Medical examination; Physician's request.
Staff RNs 1 (ft), 5 (pt); LPNs 5 (ft), 1 (pt); Nurses aides 18 (ft), 1 (pt); Activities coordinators 1 (ft), 1 (pt); Dietitians 1 (ft), 1 (pt).
Facilities Dining room; Activities room; Crafts room; Laundry room.
Activities Arts & crafts; Cards; Games; Prayer groups; Movies; Shopping trips; Social/Cultural gatherings.

Compere's Nursing Home Inc*
865 North St, Jackson, MS, 39202
(601) 948-6531
Admin Robert F Burkett.
Licensure Skilled care; Intermediate care. *Beds* 60. *Certified* Medicaid.
Owner Proprietary Corp.

Cottage Grove Nursing Home*
3636 Lampton Ave, Jackson, MS, 39213
(601) 366-6461
Admin Juadine Cleveland.
Licensure Intermediate care. *Beds* 28. *Certified* Medicaid.
Owner Proprietary Corp.

Crawford Nursing Home Inc
927 Cooper Rd, Jackson, MS, 39212
(601) 372-8662
Medical Dir/Dir of Nursing Robert Lowe MD.
Licensure Intermediate care. *Beds* 71. *Certified* Medicaid.
Owner Proprietary Corp.
Admissions Requirements Minimum age 21; Medical examination; Physician's request.
Staff Physicians 2 (pt); RNs 1 (ft), 1 (pt); LPNs 5 (ft), 1 (pt); Orderlies 2 (ft); Nurses aides 30 (ft), 2 (pt); Physical therapists 1 (pt); Reality therapists 1 (pt); Recreational therapists 1 (pt); Occupational therapists 1 (pt); Speech therapists 1 (pt); Activities coordinators 1 (ft); Dietitians 1 (pt); Dentists 1 (pt); Ophthalmologists 1 (pt); Podiatrists 1 (pt); 1 (pt).
Affiliation Baptist.
Facilities Dining room; Physical therapy room; Activities room; Chapel; Crafts room; Laundry room; Barber/Beauty shop.
Activities Arts & crafts; Cards; Games; Reading groups; Prayer groups; Movies; Shopping trips; Social/Cultural gatherings; Trips.

Earle Street Personal Care Home
438 Earle St, Jackson, MS, 39203
(601) 352-3478
Admin Izora Wells.
Licensure Personal care. *Beds* 11. *Certified* Medicaid; Medicare.
Owner Privately owned.
Admissions Requirements Minimum age 18; Males only.
Facilities Dining room; Laundry room.
Activities Cards; Games; Social/Cultural gatherings.

Henderson's Personal Care*
3908 Skyline, Jackson, MS, 39213
(601) 366-1953
Admin Mary Alice Henderson.
Licensure Personal care. *Beds* 6.
Owner Proprietary Corp.

Hunt Street Personal Care Home*
933 Hunt St, Jackson, MS, 39203
(601) 352-0046
Admin Mary A Henderson.
Licensure Personal care. *Beds* 12.
Owner Proprietary Corp.

Inglewood Manor Nursing Home*
1900 Chadwick Dr, Jackson, MS, 39204
(601) 372-0231
Admin Sylvia Smith.
Licensure Skilled care; Intermediate care. *Beds* 103. *Certified* Medicaid.
Owner Proprietary Corp (Beverly Enterprises).

Lakeland Nursing Center*
3680 Lakeland Ln, Jackson, MS, 39216
(601) 982-5505
Admin Cynthia Herdry.
Licensure Skilled care; Intermediate care. *Beds* 105. *Certified* Medicaid; Medicare.
Owner Proprietary Corp (Beverly Enterprises).

Magnolia Nursing Home*
942 North St, Jackson, MS, 39202
(601) 353-6447
Admin Mildred Spell.
Licensure Intermediate care. *Beds* 33. *Certified* Medicaid.
Owner Proprietary Corp.

Manhattan Health Care Center
4540 Manhattan Rd, Jackson, MS, 39206
(601) 982-7421
Admin Gwen Harper. *Medical Dir/Dir of Nursing* Hardy B Woodbridge MD; Jean Bible CRNA.
Licensure Skilled care; Intermediate care. *Beds* 180. *Certified* Medicaid.
Owner Proprietary Corp (Beverly Enterprises).
Admissions Requirements Medical examination.
Staff RNs 5 (ft), 2 (pt); LPNs 22 (ft), 3 (pt); Orderlies 3 (ft); Nurses aides 60 (ft), 5 (pt); Activities coordinators 2 (ft); Dietitians 1 (ft).
Facilities Dining room; Activities room; Laundry room; Barber/Beauty shop.
Activities Arts & crafts; Games; Reading groups; Prayer groups; Movies; Shopping trips; Social/Cultural gatherings.

Mississippi Children's Rehabilitation Center*
777 Lakeland Dr, Jackson, MS, 39216
(601) 982-2911
Admin David Lightwine. *Medical Dir/Dir of Nursing* Marilyn Graves MD.
Licensure Intermediate care. *Beds* 60. *Certified* Medicaid.
Owner Publicly owned.
Admissions Requirements Minimum age Birth; Physician's request.
Staff RNs 4 (ft), 1 (pt); LPNs 4 (ft); Nurses aides 16 (ft); Physical therapists 5 (ft); Recreational therapists 2 (ft); Occupational therapists 2 (ft); Speech therapists 1 (ft); Dietitians 1 (pt).

Facilities Dining room; Physical therapy room; Activities room; Crafts room; Laundry room; Library; Outpatient physical therapy room; Classrooms.
Activities Arts & crafts; Games; Movies; Field trips.

Northside Haven Personal Care Home*
3125 W Northside Dr, Jackson, MS, 39213
(601) 362-1574
Admin J C Marshall.
Licensure Personal care. *Beds* 12.

Old Ladies Home*
2902 W Capitol St, Jackson, MS, 39209
(601) 355-4581
Admin Grace H Auwater.
Licensure Skilled care; Personal care. *Beds* SNF 19; Personal 21.
Owner Nonprofit Corp.

Pleasant Hills Health Center
1600 Raymond Rd, Jackson, MS, 39204
(601) 371-1700
Admin Catherine Brinson. *Medical Dir/Dir of Nursing* William Gregory; Peggy Gregory.
Licensure Skilled care; Intermediate care. *Beds* 60. *Certified* Medicaid.
Owner Privately owned.
Admissions Requirements Minimum age 78.
Staff Physicians 1 (pt); RNs 2 (ft); LPNs 5 (ft), 3 (pt); Nurses aides 17 (ft), 3 (pt); Physical therapists 1 (pt); Activities coordinators 1 (ft), 1 (pt); Dietitians 1 (pt); Ophthalmologists 1 (pt).
Facilities Dining room; Physical therapy room; Activities room; Chapel; Laundry room; Barber/Beauty shop.
Activities Arts & crafts; Cards; Games; Reading groups; Prayer groups; Movies; Shopping trips; Social/Cultural gatherings.

Richmond's Boarding Home*
852 Crawford St, Jackson, MS, 39213
(601) 353-7694
Admin R M Richmond Sr.
Licensure Personal care. *Beds* 14.
Owner Proprietary Corp.

Spencer's Personal Care Home*
117 Clairborne St, Jackson, MS, 39209
(601) 355-4390
Admin Barbara Spencer.
Licensure Personal care. *Beds* 9.

Teat Personal Care Home*
3227 Edwards Ave, Jackson, MS, 39213
(601) 982-2872
Admin Ms Eddie L Teat.
Licensure Personal care. *Beds* 13.
Owner Proprietary Corp.

Wells Personal Care Home
2403 Rutledge, Jackson, MS, 39213
(601) 362-4032
Admin Izora Wells.
Licensure Personal care. *Beds* 5.
Owner Proprietary Corp.

Westhaven Home*
Rte 2, Box 170, Jackson, MS, 29209
(601) 922-2363
Admin John Lea.
Licensure Personal care. *Beds* 32.
Owner Proprietary Corp.

Whispering Pines Nursing Home*
1480 Raymond Rd, Jackson, MS, 39204
(601) 373-2472
Admin A D Buffington.
Licensure Skilled care; Intermediate care. *Beds* 50. *Certified* Medicaid.
Owner Proprietary Corp.
Admissions Requirements Medical examination.
Staff Physicians 1 (pt); RNs 2 (ft); LPNs 5 (ft), 1 (pt); Nurses aides 17 (ft), 1 (pt); Physical therapists 1 (pt); Reality therapists 1 (pt); Recreational therapists 1 (ft); Speech

therapists 1 (pt); Activities coordinators 1 (ft); Dietitians 1 (pt); Dentists 1 (pt); Ophthalmologists 1 (pt); Podiatrists 1 (pt); Audiologists 1 (pt).
Facilities Dining room; Activities room; Barber/Beauty shop.
Activities Arts & crafts; Games; Reading groups; Prayer groups; Movies.

KOSCIUSKO

Attala County Nursing Center*
Hwy 12 W, Kosciusko, MS, 39090
(601) 289-1200
Admin Myren Hughes.
Licensure Skilled care; Intermediate care. *Beds* 119. *Certified* Medicaid.
Owner Proprietary Corp (Southmark Heritage Corp).

LAUREL

Davison Rest Home Inc
PO Box 4476, 616 E 19th St, Laurel, MS, 39441
(601) 426-3201
Admin George Harold Huff.
Licensure Skilled care; Intermediate care. *Beds* 40. *Certified* Medicaid.
Owner Proprietary Corp.

Heathside Haven Inc*
935 West Dr, Laurel, MS, 39440
(601) 428-0571
Admin J D Mayfield.
Licensure Skilled care. *Beds* 130. *Certified* Medicaid.
Owner Proprietary Corp.
Staff RNs 4 (ft); LPNs 14 (ft), 3 (pt); Nurses aides 50 (ft), 15 (pt); Activities coordinators 1 (ft).
Facilities Dining room; Physical therapy room; Activities room; Chapel; Crafts room; Barber/Beauty shop.
Activities Arts & crafts; Games; Reading groups; Prayer groups; Movies; Shopping trips; Social/Cultural gatherings.

Nucare Convalescent Center
1036 West Dr, Laurel, MS, 39440
(601) 425-3191
Admin Bobby Welborn. *Medical Dir/Dir of Nursing* James Waites MD; Betty Spann DON.
Licensure Skilled care. *Beds* SNF 60. *Certified* Medicaid.
Owner Proprietary Corp.
Admissions Requirements Medical examination; Physician's request.
Staff Physicians 4 (pt); RNs 1 (ft), 1 (pt); LPNs 7 (ft), 1 (pt); Orderlies 1 (ft); Nurses aides 17 (ft), 5 (pt); Physical therapists 1 (pt); Recreational therapists 1 (pt); Occupational therapists 1 (pt); Speech therapists 1 (pt); Activities coordinators 1 (ft), 1 (pt); Dietitians 1 (pt); Ophthalmologists 1 (pt).
Facilities Dining room; Physical therapy room; Activities room; Laundry room; Barber/Beauty shop.
Activities Arts & crafts; Cards; Games; Reading groups; Movies; Shopping trips.

LEAKESVILLE

Greene County Hospital—Extended Care Facility*
PO Box 137, Leakesville, MS, 39451
(601) 394-2371
Admin L Earl Debose.
Licensure Skilled care; Intermediate care. *Beds* 22. *Certified* Medicaid.
Owner Publicly owned.

Melody Manor Convalescent Center*
PO Box 640, Leakesville, MS, 39451
(601) 394-2331

Admin Myrna Green. *Medical Dir/Dir of Nursing* Dr Alvaro Moreno.
Licensure Skilled care; Intermediate care. *Beds* 60. *Certified* Medicaid.
Owner Proprietary Corp.
Admissions Requirements Medical examination; Physician's request.
Staff RNs 1 (ft), 1 (pt); LPNs 7 (ft), 1 (pt); Nurses aides 16 (ft), 3 (pt); Activities coordinators 1 (ft), 1 (pt); Dietitians 1 (pt).
Facilities Dining room; Activities room; Crafts room; Laundry room; Barber/Beauty shop.
Activities Arts & crafts; Cards; Games; Reading groups; Prayer groups; Movies; Shopping trips.

LONG BEACH

South Mississippi Retardation Center
1170 W Railroad St, Long Beach, MS, 39560
(601) 868-2923
Admin Dr Pamela C Baker. *Medical Dir/Dir of Nursing* Dr Pamela C Baker; Gerry Braden RN DON.
Licensure Intermediate care for mentally retarded. *Beds* ICF/MR 12; Transitional cottages 15. *Certified* Medicaid.
Owner Publicly owned.
Staff Physicians 3 (pt); RNs 7 (ft); LPNs 9 (ft); Orderlies 88 (ft); Physical therapists 1 (pt); Recreational therapists 6 (ft); Occupational therapists 1 (pt); Speech therapists 2 (ft); Activities coordinators 1 (ft); Dietitians 1 (ft); Podiatrists 1 (pt); Dentist 1 (pt); Pharmacist.
Activities Arts & crafts; Cards; Games; Reading groups; Prayer groups; Movies; Shopping trips; Social/Cultural gatherings; Special Olympics.

LOUISVILLE

Tri-County Nursing Home Inc
PO Box 542, Louisville, MS, 39339
(601) 773-8048
Admin Bruce Stone. *Medical Dir/Dir of Nursing* Dewitt G Crawford MD; Pamela D Thomas DON.
Licensure Skilled care. *Beds* SNF 60. *Certified* Medicaid; Medicare.
Owner Proprietary Corp.
Admissions Requirements Medical examination; Physician's request.
Staff RNs 3 (ft), 2 (pt); LPNs 4 (ft), 4 (pt); Orderlies 3 (ft), 2 (pt); Nurses aides 13 (ft), 6 (pt).
Facilities Dining room; Activities room; Chapel; Crafts room; Laundry room; Barber/ Beauty shop.
Activities Arts & crafts; Cards; Games; Reading groups; Prayer groups; Social/ Cultural gatherings; Singing.

Winston County Nursing Home
PO Box 670, Louisville, MS, 39339
(601) 773-6211
Admin Paul Wood.
Licensure Skilled care; Intermediate care. *Beds* 42. *Certified* Medicaid; Medicare.
Owner Publicly owned.

LUCEDALE

Glen Oaks Nursing Home*
220 Glenoaks Dr, Lucedale, MS, 39452
(601) 947-2783
Admin John Stinson.
Licensure Skilled care; Intermediate care. *Beds* 60. *Certified* Medicaid.
Owner Proprietary Corp.

LUMBERTON

Adventist Health Center
Rte 2, Box 79, Lumberton, MS, 39455
(601) 794-8566
Admin Kenneth A Becker. *Medical Dir/Dir of Nursing* Dr Thomas McFarland.
Licensure Skilled care; Intermediate care. *Beds* 120. *Certified* Medicaid.
Owner Nonprofit Corp.
Admissions Requirements Medical examination.
Staff Physicians 3 (pt); RNs 3 (ft), 2 (pt); LPNs 11 (ft), 4 (pt); Orderlies 7 (ft), 2 (pt); Nurses aides 30 (ft), 24 (pt); Reality therapists 1 (ft), 1 (pt); Recreational therapists 2 (ft), 6 (pt); Activities coordinators 1 (ft); Dietitians 9 (ft), 4 (pt); Dentists 1 (pt).
Affiliation Seventh-Day Adventist
Facilities Dining room; Physical therapy room; Activities room; Crafts room; Laundry room; Barber/Beauty shop.
Activities Arts & crafts; Games; Reading groups; Prayer groups; Movies; Shopping trips.

MADISON

Willard F Bond Home*
Rte 1, Box 284, Madison, MS, 39110
(601) 856-8041
Admin Thomas Nichols.
Licensure Intermediate care. *Beds* 60. *Certified* Medicaid.
Owner Nonprofit Corp.

MAGEE

Hillcrest Health Center Inc*
1401 1st Ave NE, Magee, MS, 39111
(601) 849-5443
Admin Mary Wilson. *Medical Dir/Dir of Nursing* Charles Pruitt Jr MD.
Licensure Skilled care; Intermediate care. *Beds* 120. *Certified* Medicaid.
Owner Proprietary Corp.
Staff Physicians 6 (pt); RNs 1 (ft), 1 (pt); Physical therapists 1 (pt); Activities coordinators 1 (ft); Dietitians 1 (pt); Podiatrists 1 (pt).
Facilities Dining room; Activities room; Chapel; Laundry room; Barber/Beauty shop.
Activities Arts & crafts; Games; Reading groups; Prayer groups.

Rehabilitation Centers Inc
PO Box 697, 900 1st Ave NE, Magee, MS, 39111
(601) 849-4221
Admin Joseph L Stephens. *Medical Dir/Dir of Nursing* Dr James O Stephens; Lisa Hilton DON.
Licensure Intermediate care for mentally retarded. *Beds* ICF/MR 125. *Certified* Medicaid.
Owner Proprietary Corp.
Admissions Requirements Minimum age 5; Medical examination.
Staff Physicians 1 (ft); RNs 1 (ft), 1 (pt); LPNs 6 (ft), 2 (pt); Orderlies 50 (ft), 39 (pt); Nurses aides 6 (ft); Physical therapists 1 (pt); Recreational therapists 1 (ft); Occupational therapists 1 (pt); Speech therapists 1 (ft), 1 (pt); Activities coordinators 1 (ft); Dietitians 1 (pt); Podiatrists 1 (pt).
Facilities Dining room; Physical therapy room; Activities room; Crafts room; Laundry room; Library.
Activities Arts & crafts; Games; Movies; Shopping trips; Social/Cultural gatherings; Peer interactions & socialization; Recreational activities.

MARKS

Quitman County Nursing Home
PO Box 350, 340 Getwell Dr, Marks, MS, 38646
(601) 326-8031
Admin David W Fuller. *Medical Dir/Dir of Nursing* Dr Waller.
Licensure Intermediate care. *Beds* ICF 60. *Certified* Medicaid.
Owner Publicly owned.
Admissions Requirements Medical examination; Physician's request.
Staff Physicians 5 (pt); RNs 1 (ft); LPNs 5 (ft); Orderlies 2 (ft); Nurses aides 9 (ft); Physical therapists 1 (pt); Recreational therapists 1 (ft); Speech therapists 1 (pt); Activities coordinators 1 (ft); Dietitians 1 (pt); Podiatrists 1 (pt).
Facilities Dining room; Physical therapy room; Activities room; Chapel; Crafts room; Laundry room; Barber/Beauty shop; Library.
Activities Arts & crafts; Cards; Games; Reading groups; Prayer groups; Movies; Shopping trips; Social/Cultural gatherings; Field trips; Picnics; Guest speakers.

MCCOMB

McComb Extended Care & Nursing Home*
501 S Locust St, McComb, MS, 39648
(601) 684-8111
Admin Elton Beebe.
Licensure Skilled care; Intermediate care. *Beds* 136. *Certified* Medicaid.
Owner Proprietary Corp (Southmark Heritage Corp).

Southwest Extended Care Center*
415 Marion Ave, McComb, MS, 39648
(601) 684-8700
Admin Ronald J Smith.
Licensure Skilled care; Intermediate care. *Beds* 120. *Certified* Medicaid.
Owner Proprietary Corp (Beverly Enterprises).

MEADVILLE

Meadville Nursing Home
PO Box 233, Rte 2, Meadville, MS, 39653
(601) 384-5861
Admin Ellen P Harrigill. *Medical Dir/Dir of Nursing* E P Gabbert MD; Dora Hester RN DON.
Licensure Skilled care; Intermediate care. *Beds* 60. *Certified* Medicaid.
Owner Proprietary Corp (Southeastern Health Care Inc).
Admissions Requirements Medical examination; Physician's request.
Staff RNs 2 (ft); LPNs 8 (ft); Orderlies 3 (ft); Nurses aides 20 (ft); Physical therapists 1 (pt); Recreational therapists 1 (pt); Speech therapists 1 (pt); Activities coordinators 1 (ft), 1 (pt); Dietitians 1 (pt).
Facilities Dining room; Activities room; Chapel; Crafts room; Laundry room; Barber/Beauty shop.
Activities Arts & crafts; Cards; Games; Reading groups; Prayer groups; Movies; Shopping trips.

MENDENHALL

Mendenhall Nursing Home Inc*
PO Box 308, Mangum St, Mendenhall, MS, 39114
(601) 847-1311
Admin Carolyn Davis.
Licensure Skilled care; Intermediate care. *Beds* 60. *Certified* Medicaid.
Owner Proprietary Corp.

MERIDIAN

Broadmoor Health Care Center Inc*
4728 Hwy 39 N, Meridian, MS, 39301
(601) 482-8151
Admin Barbara Nester.
Licensure Skilled care; Intermediate care. *Beds* 120. *Certified* Medicaid.
Owner Proprietary Corp (Beverly Enterprises).

East Mississippi State Nursing Home*
PO Box 4128, West Station, Meridian, MS, 39301
(601) 482-6186
Admin Brent Jackson. *Medical Dir/Dir of Nursing* James E Gracey.
Licensure Skilled care. *Beds* 119. *Certified* Medicaid.
Owner Publicly owned.
Staff Physicians 1 (ft); RNs 4 (ft); LPNs 13 (ft); Nurses aides 57 (ft); Physical therapists 1 (pt); Activities coordinators 1 (ft); Dietitians 1 (pt); Dentists 1 (pt).
Facilities Dining room; Physical therapy room; Activities room; Laundry room; Barber/Beauty shop; Library.
Activities Arts & crafts; Cards; Games; Prayer groups; Movies; Shopping trips; Social/Cultural gatherings.

Golden Sunset Guest Home*
Rte 5, Box 178, Hwy 11 S, Meridian, MS, 39301
(601) 482-3684
Admin Guy J Howard. *Medical Dir/Dir of Nursing* Dr Fred R Hunt.
Licensure Intermediate care. *Beds* 46. *Certified* Medicaid.
Owner Proprietary Corp.
Admissions Requirements Medical examination; Physician's request.
Staff Physicians 1 (pt); RNs 1 (pt); LPNs 2 (ft), 3 (pt); Orderlies 1 (ft); Nurses aides 16 (ft); Physical therapists 1 (pt); Reality therapists 1 (pt); Recreational therapists 1 (pt); Occupational therapists 1 (pt); Speech therapists 1 (pt); Activities coordinators 1 (ft); Dietitians 1 (ft); Dentists 1 (pt); Ophthalmologists 1 (pt); Podiatrists 1 (pt); Audiologists 1 (pt).
Facilities Dining room; Activities room; Chapel; Crafts room; Laundry room; Barber/Beauty shop.
Activities Arts & crafts; Cards; Games; Reading groups; Prayer groups; Movies; Shopping trips; Social/Cultural gatherings.

King's Daughters & Sons Rest Home Inc*
PO Box 3623, Hwy 39 N, Meridian, MS, 39301
(601) 483-5256
Admin Lange F Butler.
Licensure Intermediate care. *Beds* 120.
Owner Nonprofit Corp.
Affiliation King's Daughters & Sons

Meridian Convalescent Home*
517 33rd St, Meridian, MS, 39301
(601) 483-3916
Admin Sue Ward.
Licensure Skilled care; Intermediate care. *Beds* 58. *Certified* Medicaid.
Owner Proprietary Corp.

Meridian Nursing Center*
3716 Hwy 39 N, Meridian, MS, 39301
(601) 482-7164
Admin Sam R Sturges.
Licensure Skilled care; Intermediate care. *Beds* 75. *Certified* Medicaid; Medicare.
Owner Proprietary Corp.

Queen City Nursing Center*
1201 28th Ave, Meridian, MS, 39301
(601) 483-1467
Admin Michael W Howard.
Licensure Skilled care. *Beds* 60. *Certified* Medicaid.
Owner Proprietary Corp.

MONTICELLO

Lawrence County Medical Center Inc*
PO Box 398, 700 S Jefferson St, Monticello, MS, 39654
(601) 587-2593
Admin James Todd.
Licensure Skilled care; Intermediate care. *Beds* 60. *Certified* Medicaid.
Owner Proprietary Corp (Southmark Heritage Corp).

MORTON

Scott County Nursing Home*
Old Hwy 80 E, Morton, MS, 39117
(601) 732-6361
Admin Gary Pace.
Licensure Skilled care; Intermediate care. *Beds* 100. *Certified* Medicaid.
Owner Proprietary Corp.

NATCHEZ

Glenburney Nursing Home
555 John R Jukin Dr, Natchez, MS, 39120
(601) 442-4395
Admin Sammy Gore. *Medical Dir/Dir of Nursing* Teresa Loomis.
Licensure Skilled care; Intermediate care. *Beds* SNF 60; ICF 36. *Certified* Medicaid.
Owner Proprietary Corp (Southmark Heritage Corp).
Admissions Requirements Medical examination; Physician's request.
Staff RNs 2 (ft); LPNs 11 (ft), 1 (pt); Nurses aides 31 (ft), 6 (pt); Activities coordinators 1 (ft); Dietitians 1 (ft).
Facilities Dining room; Laundry room; Barber/Beauty shop; Lobby.
Activities Arts & crafts; Games; Prayer groups; Movies; Shopping trips; Social/Cultural gatherings.

Oakwood Lodge of Natchez*
587 John R Junkin Dr, Natchez, MS, 39120
(601) 446-8426
Admin Barbara Evans.
Licensure Skilled care; Intermediate care. *Beds* 120. *Certified* Medicaid.
Owner Proprietary Corp.

Trace Haven Nursing Home*
344 Arlington Ave, Natchez, MS, 39120
(601) 442-4393
Admin Kathryn Conn.
Licensure Skilled care; Intermediate care. *Beds* 58. *Certified* Medicaid.
Owner Proprietary Corp (Southmark Heritage Corp).

NEW ALBANY

Roselawn Retirement Home
118 S Glenfield Rd, New Albany, MS, 38652
(601) 534-9506
Admin Walter J Grace. *Medical Dir/Dir of Nursing* Richard Russell MD; Betty Carter, RN DON.
Licensure Skilled care; Intermediate care. *Beds* SNF 120; ICF. *Certified* Medicaid.
Owner Privately owned.
Admissions Requirements Minimum age 18; Medical examination; Physician's request.
Staff Physicians 6 (pt); RNs 3 (ft); LPNs 15 (ft); Nurses aides 40 (ft); Physical therapists 1 (pt); Reality therapists 1 (pt); Recreational therapists 1 (pt); Occupational therapists 1 (pt); Speech therapists 1 (pt); Activities coordinators 1 (ft); Dietitians 1 (pt); Ophthalmologists 1 (pt).
Facilities Dining room; Activities room; Laundry room; Barber/Beauty shop.
Activities Arts & crafts; Cards; Games; Reading groups; Prayer groups; Social/Cultural gatherings.

NEWTON

Conva-Rest of Newton Inc
1009 S Main St, Newton, MS, 39345
(601) 683-6601
Admin Marilyn M Rainer. *Medical Dir/Dir of
Nursing* Dr Austin P Boggan.
Licensure Skilled care; Intermediate care. *Beds*
SNF 120; ICF. *Certified* Medicaid.
Owner Proprietary Corp.
Admissions Requirements Medical
examination.
Staff Physicians 1 (ft), 5 (pt); RNs 4 (ft), 1
(pt); LPNs 10 (ft); Orderlies 1 (ft); Nurses
aides 35 (ft), 2 (pt); Physical therapists 1
(pt); Speech therapists 1 (pt); Activities
coordinators 1 (ft); Dietitians 1 (ft), 1 (pt);
Dentist 1 (pt); Social workers 1 (ft).
Facilities Dining room; Activities room;
Crafts room; Laundry room; Barber/Beauty
shop; Library; Day room; TV room; 2
patios.
Activities Arts & crafts; Cards; Games;
Reading groups; Prayer groups; Movies;
Shopping trips; Social/Cultural gatherings;
Fishing trips; Coffee hour; Ladies tea; Bus
rides.

OCEAN SPRINGS

Ocean Springs Nursing Center*
Vancleave Rd, Ocean Springs, MS, 39564
(601) 875-9363
Admin Jeanette Walker.
Licensure Skilled care. *Beds* 60. *Certified*
Medicaid.
Owner Proprietary Corp.
Staff Physical therapists 1 (pt); Recreational
therapists 1 (ft); Activities coordinators 1
(ft); Dietitians 1 (pt); Dentists 1 (pt);
Podiatrists 1 (pt).
Facilities Dining room; Activities room;
Chapel; Crafts room; Laundry room; Barber/
Beauty shop.
Activities Arts & crafts; Cards; Games;
Reading groups; Prayer groups; Movies;
Shopping trips.

TLC Home for the Elderly*
9002 Travis Ave, Ocean Springs, MS, 39564
(601) 875-9525
Admin Marie H McMillian.
Licensure Personal care. *Beds* 11.

OKOLONA

Shearer-Richardson Memorial Nursing Home*
Rockwell Dr, Okolona, MS, 38860
(601) 447-5463
Admin Brenda Wise. *Medical Dir/Dir of
Nursing* Dr J H Shoemaker.
Licensure Skilled care; Intermediate care. *Beds*
43. *Certified* Medicaid.
Owner Publicly owned.
Staff Physicians 2 (pt); RNs 2 (ft); LPNs 4
(ft), 2 (pt); Nurses aides 18 (ft), 4 (pt);
Activities coordinators 1 (ft); Dietitians 1
(pt).
Facilities Dining room; Activities room;
Crafts room; Laundry room; Barber/Beauty
shop.
Activities Arts & crafts; Cards; Games.

Young at Heart Personal Care Center*
Rte 1, Box 211-3, Okolona, MS, 38860
(601) 447-2388
Admin Ruby Hollimon.
Licensure Personal care. *Beds* 8.
Owner Proprietary Corp.

OXFORD

Golden Years Retirement Center*
606 Van Buren Ave, Oxford, MS, 38655
(601) 234-4245
Admin Katie M Overstreet.

Licensure Intermediate care. *Beds* 37.
Certified Medicaid.
Owner Proprietary Corp.

Gracelands Inc*
1300 Belk St, Oxford, MS, 38655
(601) 234-7821
Admin James D Braswell. *Medical Dir/Dir of
Nursing* J O Gilmore MD.
Licensure Skilled care; Intermediate care. *Beds*
135. *Certified* Medicaid.
Owner Proprietary Corp.
Admissions Requirements Minimum age 21;
Medical examination; Physician's request.
Staff Physicians 8 (pt); RNs 3 (ft), 1 (pt);
LPNs 15 (ft), 2 (pt); Nurses aides 60 (ft), 10
(pt); Physical therapists 1 (pt); Activities
coordinators 1 (ft), 1 (pt); Dietitians 2 (ft), 1
(pt); Dentists 1 (pt).
Facilities Dining room; Activities room;
Chapel; Crafts room; Laundry room; Barber/
Beauty shop.
Activities Arts & crafts; Cards; Games;
Movies.

**Wood Lane—North Mississippi Retardation
Center***
PO Box 967, Hwy 7 By-Pass, Oxford, MS,
38655
(601) 234-1476
Admin William J Lawhorn.
Licensure Intermediate care for mentally
retarded. *Beds* 204. *Certified* Medicaid.
Owner Publicly owned.

**Woodlea Skilled Nursing Home—North
Mississippi Retardation Center***
PO Box 967, Hwy 7 By-Pass, Oxford, MS,
38655
(601) 234-1476
Admin William J Lawhorn.
Licensure Skilled care. *Beds* 61. *Certified*
Medicaid.
Owner Publicly owned.

PASCAGOULA

Gulf Coast Nursing Home of Moss Point Inc*
4501 Jefferson Ave, Pascagoula, MS, 39567
(601) 762-7451
Admin Robert E Sevier.
Licensure Intermediate care. *Beds* 84.
Certified Medicaid.
Owner Proprietary Corp.

Jackson County Personal Care Home*
Rte 2, Box 286, Pascagoula, MS, 39567
(601) 588-6227
Admin Norma Coleman.
Licensure Personal care. *Beds* 20.
Owner Publicly owned.

Plaza Nursing Center*
4403 Hospital Rd, Pascagoula, MS, 39567
(601) 762-8960
Admin Vic Price.
Licensure Skilled care; Intermediate care. *Beds*
120. *Certified* Medicaid.
Owner Proprietary Corp.

**Singing River Hospital System—Extended Care
Facility***
2809 Denny Ave, Pascagoula, MS, 39567
(601) 938-5000
Admin Robert L Lingle.
Licensure Skilled care. *Beds* 10. *Certified*
Medicare.
Owner Publicly owned.

PASS CHRISTIAN

Dixie White House Nursing Home Inc*
PO Box 515, Menge Ave, Pass Christian, MS,
39571
(601) 452-4344
Admin Tommie Ann Felts.

Licensure Skilled care; Intermediate care. *Beds*
57. *Certified* Medicaid.
Owner Proprietary Corp.

Miramar Lodge Nursing Home*
216 W Beach Blvd, Pass Christian, MS, 39571
(601) 452-2416
Admin Billy F Reed. *Medical Dir/Dir of
Nursing* C D Taylor Jr.
Licensure Skilled care; Intermediate care. *Beds*
180. *Certified* Medicaid.
Owner Proprietary Corp.
Admissions Requirements Medical
examination; Physician's request.
Staff Physicians 5 (pt); RNs 3 (ft), 1 (pt);
LPNs 18 (ft); Orderlies 3 (ft); Nurses aides
76 (ft); Physical therapists 2 (pt); Reality
therapists 1 (ft); Speech therapists 1 (pt);
Activities coordinators 3 (ft); Dietitians 1
(ft); Audiologists 1 (pt).

PETAL

Conva-Rest of Petal*
201 10th Ave, Petal, MS, 39465
(601) 544-7441
Admin Johnnie W Walters Jr.
Licensure Skilled care; Intermediate care. *Beds*
60. *Certified* Medicaid.
Owner Proprietary Corp.

PHILADELPHIA

Neshoba County Nursing Home
PO Box 648, Hwy 19 S, Philadelphia, MS,
39350
(601) 656-3554
Admin Tommy L Dearing. *Medical Dir/Dir of
Nursing* Mary Barrier.
Licensure Skilled care; Intermediate care. *Beds*
SNF 70; ICF 10. *Certified* Medicaid.
Owner Publicly owned.
Admissions Requirements Medical
examination; Physician's request.
Staff Physicians 6 (ft); RNs 6 (ft); LPNs 7 (ft),
1 (pt); Orderlies 4 (ft); Nurses aides 36 (ft),
2 (pt); Physical therapists 1 (ft); Dietitians 1
(ft).
Facilities Dining room; Physical therapy
room; Activities room; Chapel; Crafts room;
Laundry room; Barber/Beauty shop.
Activities Arts & crafts; Cards; Games;
Reading groups; Prayer groups.

PICAYUNE

Picayune Convalescent Home
PO Box 937, 1620 Read Rd, Picayune, MS,
39466
(601) 798-1811
Admin Edna Gibson.
Licensure Skilled care; Intermediate care. *Beds*
120. *Certified* Medicaid.
Owner Proprietary Corp (Southmark Heritage
Corp).

PONTOTOC

Gracelands of Pontotoc
PO Drawer 547, 278 8th St, Pontotoc, MS,
38863
(601) 489-6411
Admin Jane B Price. *Medical Dir/Dir of
Nursing* James R Howard MD; Mimi
Hughes RN DON.
Licensure Skilled care; Intermediate care. *Beds*
60. *Certified* Medicaid.
Owner Privately owned.
Admissions Requirements Medical
examination; Physician's request.
Staff RNs 1 (ft), 1 (pt); LPNs 7 (ft), 1 (pt);
Nurses aides 17 (ft), 3 (pt); Physical
therapists 1 (pt); Activities coordinators 1
(ft); Dietitians 1 (ft).

Facilities Dining room; Activities room; Laundry room; Barber/Beauty shop; Library.
Activities Arts & crafts; Cards; Games; Reading groups; Prayer groups; Movies; Shopping trips; Social/Cultural gatherings; Residents council; Cooking classes; Exercise classes.

Pontotoc Community Hospital—Extended Care Facility*
176 S Main St, Pontotoc, MS, 38863
(601) 489-5510
Admin Carl Parrish.
Licensure Skilled care; Intermediate care. *Beds* 14. *Certified* Medicaid; Medicare.
Owner Publicly owned.

Sunshine Rest Home*
Rte 60, Box 443, Pontotoc, MS, 38863
(601) 489-1189
Admin James Westmoreland.
Licensure Intermediate care. *Beds* 27. *Certified* Medicaid.
Owner Publicly owned.

POPLARVILLE

Pearl River County Hospital-Nurs Home
PO Box 392, W Moody St, Poplarville, MS, 39470
(601) 795-4543
Admin Dorthy C Bilbo. *Medical Dir/Dir of Nursing* Dr W F Stringer.
Licensure Skilled care; Intermediate care. *Beds* 60. *Certified* Medicaid.
Owner Publicly owned.
Staff Physicians 4 (ft); RNs 3 (ft); LPNs 6 (ft); Orderlies 6 (ft), 2 (pt); Nurses aides 10 (ft), 4 (pt); Physical therapists 1 (ft); Recreational therapists 1 (pt); Speech therapists 1 (pt); Activities coordinators 2 (ft); Dietitians 2 (ft).
Facilities Dining room; Physical therapy room; Activities room; Chapel; Crafts room; Laundry room; Barber/Beauty shop.
Activities Arts & crafts; Games; Prayer groups; Movies; Shopping trips; Social/Cultural gatherings.

PRENTISS

Jefferson Davis County—Extended Care Facility
PO Box 1289, Berry St, Prentiss, MS, 39474
(601) 792-4276
Admin Dale Saulters.
Licensure Skilled care; Intermediate care. *Beds* 60. *Certified* Medicaid; Medicare.
Owner Publicly owned.

QUITMAN

Archusa Convalescent Center Inc
Hwy 511 E, Quitman, MS, 39355
(601) 776-2141
Admin Harmon Knight. *Medical Dir/Dir of Nursing* Walter Gunn MD.
Licensure Skilled care; Intermediate care. *Beds* 120. *Certified* Medicaid.
Owner Proprietary Corp.
Admissions Requirements Medical examination; Physician's request.
Staff Physicians 5 (pt); RNs 3 (ft); LPNs 7 (ft); Orderlies 2 (ft); Nurses aides 27 (ft); Physical therapists 1 (pt); Reality therapists 1 (pt); Recreational therapists 1 (ft); Occupational therapists 1 (pt); Speech therapists 1 (pt); Activities coordinators 1 (ft); Dietitians 1 (pt); Dentists 1 (pt).
Facilities Dining room; Physical therapy room; Activities room; Crafts room; Laundry room; Barber/Beauty shop.
Activities Arts & crafts; Cards; Games; Reading groups; Prayer groups; Movies; Shopping trips; Social/Cultural gatherings.

RALEIGH

Rolling Acres Retirement Center Inc*
PO Box 128, Raleigh, MS, 39153
(601) 782-4244
Admin Cleta Mullins. *Medical Dir/Dir of Nursing* Vance Baucum MD.
Licensure Skilled care; Intermediate care. *Beds* 120. *Certified* Medicaid.
Admissions Requirements Medical examination.
Staff Physicians 4 (pt); RNs 2 (ft); LPNs 10 (ft); Nurses aides 29 (ft), 13 (pt); Physical therapists 1 (pt); Activities coordinators 1 (ft); Dietitians 2 (ft), 1 (pt); Dentists 2 (pt); Podiatrists 1 (pt).
Facilities Dining room; Activities room; Crafts room; Laundry room; Barber/Beauty shop.
Activities Arts & crafts; Cards; Games; Reading groups; Prayer groups; Movies; Social/Cultural gatherings.

RIPLEY

Rest Haven Nursing Home
103 Cunningham Dr, Ripley, MS, 38663
(601) 837-3062
Admin Mildred Murphree. *Medical Dir/Dir of Nursing* Thomas L Ketchum MD.
Licensure Skilled care; Intermediate care. *Beds* SNF; ICF 60. *Certified* Medicaid.
Owner Proprietary Corp.
Staff Physicians 7 (ft); RNs 1 (ft), 1 (pt); LPNs 5 (ft), 4 (pt); Orderlies 1 (ft); Nurses aides 14 (ft), 8 (pt); Speech therapists 1 (pt); Activities coordinators 1 (ft); Dietitians 1 (pt); Dentists 1 (pt).
Facilities Dining room; Physical therapy room; Activities room; Chapel; Crafts room; Laundry room; Barber/Beauty shop.
Activities Arts & crafts; Games; Reading groups; Prayer groups; Movies; Shopping trips.

Ripley Manor Nursing Home
1010 Cunningham Dr, Ripley, MS, 38663
(601) 837-3011
Admin Bobbye Wells.
Licensure Skilled care; Intermediate care. *Beds* 120.
Owner Proprietary Corp (Beverly Enterprises).

ROLLING FORK

Care Inn—Rolling Fork*
PO Box 189, 506 W Race St, Rolling Fork, MS, 39159
(601) 873-6218
Admin Kyle Patton.
Licensure Skilled care; Intermediate care. *Beds* 60. *Certified* Medicaid.
Owner Proprietary Corp (Southmark Heritage Corp).

RULEVILLE

Ruleville Health Care Center
800 Stansel Dr, Ruleville, MS, 38771
(601) 756-4361
Admin Rosal Burden. *Medical Dir/Dir of Nursing* Bennie Wright MD; Nell Sandidge RN DON.
Licensure Skilled care; Intermediate care. *Beds* SNF 45; ICF 45. *Certified* Medicaid.
Owner Proprietary Corp (Beverly Enterprises).
Admissions Requirements Physician's request.
Staff RNs 3 (ft); LPNs 9 (ft), 2 (pt); Orderlies 3 (ft), 1 (pt); Nurses aides 24 (ft), 5 (pt); Activities coordinators 1 (ft), 1 (pt); Dietitians 1 (ft), 1 (pt).
Facilities Dining room; Activities room; Crafts room; Laundry room; Barber/Beauty shop.

Activities Arts & crafts; Cards; Games; Reading groups; Prayer groups; Movies; Shopping trips; Social/Cultural gatherings.

SANATORIUM

W L Jaquith ICF/MR
PO Box 128, Sanatorium, MS, 39112
(601) 849-3321
Admin Bruce Womack. *Medical Dir/Dir of Nursing* Paul D Cotten MD; Patsy Burris RN.
Licensure Intermediate care for mentally retarded. *Beds* ICF/MR 84. *Certified* Medicaid.
Owner Publicly owned.
Admissions Requirements Medical examination; Physician's request.
Staff Physicians 4 (pt); RNs 3 (ft); LPNs 8 (ft); Orderlies 56 (ft); Physical therapists 1 (pt); Recreational therapists 1 (pt); Occupational therapists 1 (pt); Speech therapists 1 (pt); Activities coordinators 1 (ft); Dietitians 1 (pt); Ophthalmologists 1 (pt).
Facilities Dining room; Physical therapy room; Activities room; Chapel; Barber/Beauty shop.
Activities Arts & crafts; Cards; Games; Movies; Shopping trips; Social/Cultural gatherings; Daily living; Horticultural therapy; Animal husbandry.

SARDIS

North Panola Regional Hospital & Nursing Center Inc
PO Box 160, I-55 at Hwy 315, Sardis, MS, 38666
(601) 487-2720
Admin Robert L Gillespie. *Medical Dir/Dir of Nursing* Michael E Shaheen MD; Valera Mothershed RN.
Licensure Skilled care. *Beds* SNF 60. *Certified* Medicaid.
Owner Nonprofit Corp.
Facilities Dining room; Activities room; Crafts room; Laundry room; Barber/Beauty shop.
Activities Arts & crafts; Cards; Games; Reading groups; Prayer groups; Movies; Shopping trips.

SENATOBIA

Senatobia Convalescent Center*
402 Getwell Dr, Senatobia, MS, 38668
(601) 562-5664
Admin Denver Northrip.
Licensure Skilled care; Intermediate care. *Beds* 120. *Certified* Medicaid.
Owner Proprietary Corp.

SHELBY

Zion Grove Nursing Center
PO Drawer 7, Church St Extention, Shelby, MS, 38774
(601) 398-5117
Admin Diwana Sanders. *Medical Dir/Dir of Nursing* James Warrington MD; Louise Hicks RN DON.
Licensure Skilled care; Intermediate care. *Beds* 120. *Certified* Medicaid.
Owner Proprietary Corp.
Admissions Requirements Medical examination; Physician's request.
Staff Physicians 1 (ft), 1 (pt); RNs 1 (ft), 3 (pt); LPNs 13 (ft); Orderlies 9 (ft), 5 (pt); Nurses aides 29 (ft), 9 (pt); Physical therapists 1 (pt); Speech therapists 1 (pt); Activities coordinators 1 (ft); Dietitians 1 (ft); Ophthalmologists 1 (pt).
Facilities Dining room; Physical therapy room; Activities room; Chapel; Crafts room; Laundry room; Barber/Beauty shop.

Activities Arts & crafts; Cards; Games; Reading groups; Prayer groups; Movies; Shopping trips; Social/Cultural gatherings.

SOUTHAVEN

Southhaven Health Care Center*
1730 Dorchester Dr, Southaven, MS, 38671
(601) 393-0050
Admin James Williams.
Licensure Skilled care; Intermediate care. *Beds* 120. *Certified* Medicaid.
Owner Proprietary Corp (Beverly Enterprises).

STARKVILLE

Rolling Hills Nursing Center*
PO Drawer 1566, 200 Womack St, Starkville, MS, 39759
(601) 323-9183
Admin Ann Thompson.
Licensure Intermediate care for mentally retarded. *Beds* 120. *Certified* Medicaid.
Owner Proprietary Corp (Unicare).

Starkville Manor Nursing Home
PO Box 1466, Starkville, MS, 39759
(601) 323-6360
Admin Mark S Clay. *Medical Dir/Dir of Nursing* Vicki B Clay.
Licensure Skilled care; Intermediate care. *Beds* SNF 119; ICF. *Certified* Medicaid.
Owner Proprietary Corp (Southmark Heritage Corp).

TUPELO

Cedars Health Center
2800 W Main St, Tupelo, MS, 38801
(601) 842-8555
Admin Paul Young.
Licensure Skilled care; Intermediate care. *Beds* SNF 60; ICF 60. *Certified* Medicaid.
Owner Nonprofit Corp.

Lee Manor Nursing Home*
1901 Briar Ridge Rd, Tupelo, MS, 38801
(601) 844-0675
Admin Franklin C Lowe. *Medical Dir/Dir of Nursing* Dr James L Brown.
Licensure Intermediate care. *Beds* 120. *Certified* Medicaid.
Owner Proprietary Corp (Beverly Enterprises).
Admissions Requirements Medical examination; Physician's request.
Staff Physicians 12 (pt); RNs 1 (ft); LPNs 8 (ft), 1 (pt); Orderlies 3 (ft); Nurses aides 23 (ft); Physical therapists 1 (pt); Speech therapists 1 (pt); Activities coordinators 1 (ft), 1 (pt); Dietitians 1 (pt).
Facilities Dining room; Activities room; Chapel; Crafts room; Laundry room; Barber/Beauty shop; Library; Outside patio.
Activities Arts & crafts; Cards; Games; Reading groups; Prayer groups; Movies; Shopping trips; Social/Cultural gatherings; Cookouts; Picnics.

Tupelo Manor Nursing Home*
646 Eason Blvd, Tupelo, MS, 38801
(601) 842-2461
Admin Mike Bass. *Medical Dir/Dir of Nursing* James Brown MD.
Licensure Skilled care. *Beds* 120. *Certified* Medicaid.
Owner Proprietary Corp.
Admissions Requirements Medical examination; Physician's request.
Activities Arts & crafts; Cards; Games; Reading groups; Prayer groups; Movies; Shopping trips.

TYLERTOWN

Billdora Rest Home
314 Enochs St, Tylertown, MS, 39667
(601) 876-2173
Admin Bill Brent. *Medical Dir/Dir of Nursing* Betty Knippers DON.
Licensure Skilled care. *Beds* SNF 48. *Certified* Medicaid.
Owner Proprietary Corp.
Staff RNs; LPNs; Nurses aides; Activities coordinators.

Tylertown Extended Care Center*
200 Medical Circle, Tylertown, MS, 39667
(601) 876-2107
Admin Arline Dillon. *Medical Dir/Dir of Nursing* Dr Ben Crawford.
Licensure Skilled care; Intermediate care. *Beds* 60. *Certified* Medicaid; Medicare.
Owner Proprietary Corp (Beverly Enterprises).
Admissions Requirements Medical examination; Physician's request.
Staff Physicians 8 (ft); RNs 2 (ft), 1 (pt); LPNs 6 (ft); Nurses aides 22 (ft); Activities coordinators 1 (ft); Dietitians 1 (ft).
Facilities Dining room; Activities room; Laundry room; Barber/Beauty shop; Day room.
Activities Arts & crafts; Cards; Games; Reading groups; Prayer groups; Movies; Shopping trips; Social/Cultural gatherings.

UNION

Hilltop Manor Inc
PO Box 266, County Line St, Union, MS, 39365
(601) 774-8233
Admin Dewanda S Page. *Medical Dir/Dir of Nursing* A P Boggan MD; Glenda Barrett RN DON.
Licensure Skilled care; Intermediate care. *Beds* 60. *Certified* Medicaid.
Owner Proprietary Corp (National Heritage).
Staff Physicians 6 (pt); RNs 2 (ft), 2 (pt); LPNs 4 (ft), 4 (pt); Nurses aides 16 (ft), 3 (pt); Physical therapists 1 (pt); Speech therapists 1 (pt); Activities coordinators 1 (ft), 1 (pt); Dietitians 1 (pt).
Facilities Dining room; Activities room; Laundry room; Barber/Beauty shop.
Activities Arts & crafts; Cards; Games; Reading groups; Prayer groups; Movies; Shopping trips; Social/Cultural gatherings.

VICKSBURG

Mercy Extended Care Facility
100 McAuley Dr, Vicksburg, MS, 39180
(601) 631-2131
Admin Carl E Barry. *Medical Dir/Dir of Nursing* Joe M Ross MD; Charlie Jean Newton RN DON.
Licensure Skilled care. *Beds* SNF 28. *Certified* Medicare.
Owner Nonprofit organization/foundation.
Admissions Requirements Medical examination; Physician's request.
Staff Physicians; RNs; LPNs; Nurses aides; Physical therapists; Speech therapists; Activities coordinators; Dietitians; Dentists.
Facilities Dining room; Activities room; Chapel; Crafts room; Barber/Beauty shop.
Activities Arts & crafts; Cards; Games; Prayer groups; Movies.

Shady Lawn Nursing Home Inc
23 Porters Chapel Rd, Vicksburg, MS, 39180
(601) 636-1448
Admin Jean Corbin. *Medical Dir/Dir of Nursing* Joe M Ross Jr MD.
Licensure Skilled care; Intermediate care. *Beds* 81. *Certified* Medicaid.
Owner Proprietary Corp.
Admissions Requirements Medical examination.

Staff Physicians 1 (pt); RNs 2 (ft), 1 (pt); LPNs 8 (ft), 2 (pt); Nurses aides 28 (ft), 2 (pt); Activities coordinators 1 (ft); Dietitians 1 (ft).
Facilities Dining room; Activities room; Chapel; Crafts room; Laundry room; Barber/Beauty shop.
Activities Arts & crafts; Cards; Games; Reading groups; Prayer groups; Movies; Shopping trips; Social/Cultural gatherings.

Sydney House
PO Box 949, 900 Crawford St, Vicksburg, MS, 39180
(601) 638-1514, 638-1598
Admin Mary Dell Greer. *Medical Dir/Dir of Nursing* Dr J Russell Barnes; Mable L Cox RN DON.
Licensure Intermediate care. *Beds* ICF 55.
Owner Proprietary Corp (Integrated Health Services Inc).
Admissions Requirements Medical examination.
Staff RNs 1 (ft); LPNs 7 (ft); Nurses aides 17 (ft), 5 (pt); Activities coordinators 1 (ft); Dietary Manager 1 (ft), 1 (pt).
Facilities Dining room; Activities room; Laundry room; Barber/Beauty shop.
Activities Arts & crafts; Games; Reading groups; Prayer groups; Movies; Social/Cultural gatherings.

Vicksburg Convalescent Home*
1708 Cherry St, Vicksburg, MS, 39180
(601) 638-3632
Admin Lola Snyder. *Medical Dir/Dir of Nursing* M E Hinman.
Licensure Skilled care; Intermediate care. *Beds* 100. *Certified* Medicaid.
Owner Proprietary Corp.
Admissions Requirements Medical examination.
Staff RNs 2 (ft), 2 (pt); LPNs 11 (ft), 2 (pt); Nurses aides 32 (ft), 5 (pt); Activities coordinator, 1 (ft); Dietitians 1 (pt).
Facilities Dining room; Laundry room; Patio.
Activities Arts & crafts; Games; Prayer groups; Movies; Social/Cultural gatherings.

Vicksburg Trace Haven*
40 Porter's Chapel Rd, Vicksburg, MS, 39180
(601) 638-9211
Admin Eva Williams.
Licensure Skilled care; Intermediate care. *Beds* 120. *Certified* Medicaid.
Owner Proprietary Corp (Southmark Heritage Corp).

WATER VALLEY

Yalobusha County Nursing Home
PO Box 728, Hwy 7 S, Water Valley, MS, 38965
(601) 473-1411
Admin James H Ivy. *Medical Dir/Dir of Nursing* Dr Harold Sexton; Linda Sehmitz RN DON.
Licensure Skilled care. *Beds* SNF 53. *Certified* Medicaid.
Owner Publicly owned.
Admissions Requirements Medical examination; Physician's request.
Staff Physicians 3 (ft); RNs 4 (ft); LPNs 14 (ft); Orderlies 2 (ft); Nurses aides 21 (ft); Physical therapists 1 (ft); Reality therapists 1 (ft); Recreational therapists 1 (ft); Activities coordinators 1 (ft); Dietitians 1 (ft).
Facilities Dining room; Activities room; Chapel; Crafts room; Laundry room; Barber/Beauty shop; Patio with garden.
Activities Arts & crafts; Games; Movies; Social/Cultural gatherings.

WAYNESBORO

Restful Acres Nursing Home Inc*
1304 Walnut St, Waynesboro, MS, 39367
(601) 735-9025
Admin Karen S Williams.
Licensure Skilled care; Intermediate care. *Beds* 60. *Certified* Medicaid.
Owner Proprietary Corp.

WEST POINT

Care Inn—West Point*
PO Box 817, West Point, MS, 39773
(601) 494-6011
Admin Roger Strickland. *Medical Dir/Dir of Nursing* William Billington DO.
Licensure Skilled care; Intermediate care. *Beds* 120. *Certified* Medicaid.
Owner Proprietary Corp.
Admissions Requirements Minimum age 17; Medical examination; Physician's request.
Staff Physicians 1 (pt); RNs 5 (ft); LPNs 9 (ft), 4 (pt); Orderlies 2 (ft); Nurses aides 40 (ft), 4 (pt); Physical therapists 1 (pt); Activities coordinators 1 (ft); Dietitians 1 (pt); Dentists 1 (pt); Ophthalmologists 1 (pt); Podiatrists 1 (pt).
Facilities Dining room; Activities room; Crafts room; Laundry room; Barber/Beauty shop.
Activities Arts & crafts; Cards; Games; Reading groups; Prayer groups; Movies; Shopping trips; Social/Cultural gatherings.

Dugan Memorial Home
804 E Main St, West Point, MS, 39773
(601) 494-3640
Admin Royce Fulgham. *Medical Dir/Dir of Nursing* Dr T M Braddock; Mrs M L Vozzo.
Licensure Skilled care. *Beds* SNF 60.
Owner Proprietary Corp.
Admissions Requirements Medical examination; Physician's request.
Staff Physicians 1 (ft); RNs 4 (ft); LPNs 4 (ft), 3 (pt); Nurses aides 21 (ft), 6 (pt); Activities coordinators 1 (ft).
Facilities Dining room; Activities room; Chapel; Laundry room; Barber/Beauty shop.
Activities Cards; Games; Reading groups; Prayer groups; Shopping trips; Social/ Cultural gatherings; Therapy (exercise & validation); Newsletter; Sightseeing.

WHITFIELD

Hudspeth Center Azalea Intermediate Care Facility
PO Box 127-B, Whitfield, MS, 39193
(601) 939-8640 Ext 463

Admin Edwin C LeGrand III. *Medical Dir/Dir of Nursing* Margaret Batson MD; Ladell Hamilton RN DON.
Licensure Intermediate care. *Beds* ICF 30. *Certified* Medicaid.
Owner Publicly owned.
Admissions Requirements Minimum age 5; Medical examination.
Staff Physicians 2 (ft), 1 (pt); RNs 1 (ft), 1 (pt); LPNs 3 (ft); Physical therapists 1 (ft), 1 (pt); Recreational therapists 2 (ft); Occupational therapists 1 (ft), 1 (pt); Speech therapists 1 (pt); Dietitians 1 (ft), 1 (pt); Dentists 1 (pt); Ophthalmologists 1 (pt); Podiatrists 2 (pt).
Facilities Dining room; Physical therapy room; Activities room; Chapel; Crafts room; Laundry room; Barber/Beauty shop; Library.
Activities Arts & crafts; Games; Movies; Shopping trips; Social/Cultural gatherings; Therapeutic self-help activities.

Hudspeth Center-Rosewood Skilled Nursing Facility
PO Box 127-B, Whitfield, MS, 39193
(601) 939-8640
Admin Edwin C LeGrand III. *Medical Dir/Dir of Nursing* Margaret Batson MD; Ladell Hamilton RN DON.
Licensure Skilled care. *Beds* SNF 55. *Certified* Medicaid.
Owner Publicly owned.
Admissions Requirements Minimum age 5; Medical examination.
Staff Physicians 2 (ft), 1 (pt); RNs 2 (ft), 1 (pt); LPNs 7 (ft), 1 (pt); Physical therapists 1 (ft), 1 (pt); Recreational therapists 2 (ft); Occupational therapists 1 (ft), 1 (pt); Speech therapists 1 (ft); Dietitians 1 (ft), 1 (pt); Dentists 1 (pt); Ophthalmologists 1 (pt); Podiatrists 2 (pt).
Facilities Dining room; Physical therapy room; Activities room; Chapel; Crafts room; Laundry room; Barber/Beauty shop; Library.
Activities Arts & crafts; Games; Movies; Shopping trips; Social/Cultural gatherings; Education & training activities as appropriate for severe & profound multihandicapped persons.

Jaquith Nursing Home—Adams Inn
PO Box 7, Whitfield, MS, 39193
(601) 939-1221, Exten 364
Admin Robert E Brister. *Medical Dir/Dir of Nursing* Charles Sledge MD; Sarah Pittman RN.
Licensure Intermediate care. *Beds* ICF 243. *Certified* Medicaid.
Owner Publicly owned.

Jaquith Nursing Home—Washington Inn
PO Box 7, Whitfield, MS, 39193
(601) 939-1221, Exten 364

Admin Robert E Brister. *Medical Dir/Dir of Nursing* Charles Sledge MD; Sarah Pittman RN.
Licensure Skilled care. *Beds* SNF 134. *Certified* Medicaid.
Owner Publicly owned.

WIGGINS

Azalea Gardens Nursing Center*
530 Hall St, Wiggins, MS, 39577
(601) 928-5281
Admin Bambi Breland.
Licensure Skilled care; Intermediate care. *Beds* 127. *Certified* Medicaid.
Owner Proprietary Corp.

WINONA

Winona Manor Nursing Home*
PO Box 311, Hwy 82 W, Winona, MS, 38967
(601) 283-1260
Admin Marvell Morgan.
Licensure Skilled care; Intermediate care. *Beds* 120. *Certified* Medicaid.
Owner Proprietary Corp (Southmark Heritage Corp).

YAZOO CITY

Care Inn—Yazoo City*
925 Calhoun Ave, Yazoo City, MS, 39194
(601) 746-6651
Admin Bob Knott.
Licensure Skilled care; Intermediate care. *Beds* 180. *Certified* Medicaid.
Owner Proprietary Corp (Southmark Heritage Corp).

Martha Coker Convalescent Home
401 E 9th St, Yazoo City, MS, 39194
(601) 746-4621
Admin Anita S Boyd. *Medical Dir/Dir of Nursing* Dr Charles R Hogue.
Licensure Skilled care. *Beds* 41.
Owner Nonprofit Corp.
Admissions Requirements Medical examination.
Staff Physicians 6 (ft); RNs 1 (ft), 1 (pt); LPNs 3 (ft), 2 (pt); Orderlies 1 (ft), 1 (pt); Nurses aides 9 (ft), 3 (pt); Physical therapists 1 (pt); Reality therapists 1 (pt); Recreational therapists 1 (pt); Activities coordinators 1 (pt); Dietitians 1 (ft), 1 (pt); Dentists 1 (pt).
Facilities Dining room; Physical therapy room; Activities room; Chapel; Crafts room; Laundry room; Barber/Beauty shop.
Activities Arts & crafts; Cards; Games; Reading groups; Prayer groups; Movies; Shopping trips; Social/Cultural gatherings.

MISSOURI

ADRIAN

Adrian Manor Nursing Home Inc
Box 425, 403 W 3rd St, Adrian, MO, 64720
(816) 297-2107
Admin Clarence B Price. *Medical Dir/Dir of Nursing* Mary Harmon RN.
Licensure Skilled care. *Beds* SNF 60. *Certified* Medicaid.
Owner Nonprofit Corp.
Admissions Requirements Medical examination.
Staff RNs 3 (ft); LPNs 5 (ft), 1 (pt); Nurses aides 21 (ft), 4 (pt); Physical therapists 1 (pt); Occupational therapists 1 (pt); Speech therapists 1 (pt); Activities coordinators 1 (ft); Dietitians 1 (pt) 13O 1 (pt); Social services 1 (ft); Social services consultant 1 (pt); Medical records 1 (pt).
Facilities Dining room; Physical therapy room; Activities room; Crafts room; Laundry room; Barber/Beauty shop.
Activities Arts & crafts; Cards; Games; Reading groups; Prayer groups; Movies; Social/Cultural gatherings.

ALBANY

Colonial Manor of Albany
Box 244, Hwy E 136, Albany, MO, 64402
(816) 726-5297
Admin Shirley Ann Talmadge.
Licensure Intermediate care. *Beds* 60. *Certified* Medicaid.
Owner Proprietary Corp (Beverly Enterprises).

ANDERSON

Woodlawn Manor Residential Care Facility*
PO Box 81, Anderson, MO, 64831
(417) 845-3326
Admin Suzanne & Paul Peak.
Licensure Residential care. *Beds* 20.
Owner Proprietary Corp.

APPLETON CITY

Colonial Manor Nursing Home*
600 N Ohio, Box 98, Appleton City, MO, 64724
(816) 476-2128
Admin Paul S Wheeler. *Medical Dir/Dir of Nursing* Glen H Reed MD.
Licensure Intermediate care. *Beds* 60. *Certified* Medicaid.
Owner Proprietary Corp.
Staff LPNs 3 (ft); Nurses aides 30 (ft); Activities coordinators 1 (ft).
Facilities Dining room; Physical therapy room; Activities room; Crafts room; Laundry room; Barber/Beauty shop.
Activities Arts & crafts; Games; Prayer groups; Movies; Shopping trips; Social/Cultural gatherings; Bingo; Dominos; Bowling.

ARNOLD

Hillview Lodge*
Rte 2, Hwy 21, PO Box 802A, Arnold, MO, 64010
(314) 296-5141
Admin Marian Kling. *Medical Dir/Dir of Nursing* M Equil Abelardo MD.
Licensure Intermediate care. *Beds* 155.
Owner Proprietary Corp.
Admissions Requirements Medical examination; Physician's request.
Staff Physicians 2 (ft); RNs 1 (ft); LPNs 3 (ft), 2 (pt); Nurses aides 51 (ft); Physical therapists 3 (ft), 1 (pt); Recreational therapists 1 (ft), 1 (pt); Occupational therapists 1 (ft), 1 (pt); Speech therapists 1 (pt); Activities coordinators 1 (ft); Dietitians 1 (pt); Dentists 1 (pt); Ophthalmologists 1 (pt); Podiatrists 1 (pt).
Facilities Dining room; Physical therapy room; Crafts room; Laundry room; Barber/Beauty shop.
Activities Arts & crafts; Cards; Games; Prayer groups; Social/Cultural gatherings.

ASH GROVE

Ash Grove Nursing Home Inc
PO Box 247, 400 Meadowview, Ash Grove, MO, 65604
(417) 672-2575
Admin Jimmy L Frieze. *Medical Dir/Dir of Nursing* Wilma Gray RN.
Licensure Intermediate care. *Beds* 60. *Certified* Medicaid.
Owner Proprietary Corp.
Admissions Requirements Minimum age 18.
Staff RNs 1 (ft); LPNs 3 (ft), 4 (pt); Nurses aides 16 (ft), 4 (pt); Activities coordinators 1 (ft).
Facilities Dining room; Physical therapy room; Activities room; Barber/Beauty shop.
Activities Arts & crafts; Games; Prayer groups; Movies.

AURORA

Aurora Nursing Center
PO Box 438, 1700 S Hudson, Aurora, MO, 65605
(417) 678-2165
Admin Edward James Hitt. *Medical Dir/Dir of Nursing* William P Hamilton MD; Melisa Teague RN DON.
Licensure Skilled care; Intermediate care. *Beds* SNF 127; ICF. *Certified* Medicaid; Medicare.
Owner Privately owned.
Admissions Requirements Minimum age 18; Medical examination; Physician's request.
Staff Physicians; RNs 4 (ft), 1 (pt); LPNs 7 (ft), 1 (pt); Orderlies 3 (ft); Nurses aides 28 (ft); Physical therapists 2 (ft), 1 (pt); Recreational therapists 3 (ft); Occupational therapists 1 (pt); Speech therapists 1 (pt); Activities coordinators 1 (ft); Dietitians 1 (ft), 1 (pt).
Facilities Dining room; Physical therapy room; Activities room; Chapel; Crafts room; Laundry room; Barber/Beauty shop; Library; Living room.
Activities Arts & crafts; Cards; Games; Reading groups; Prayer groups; Movies; Shopping trips; Social/Cultural gatherings.

Hudson House
1700-B S Hudson, Aurora, MO, 65605
(417) 678-2169
Admin E James Hitt.
Licensure Residential care. *Beds* Residential 38.
Owner Proprietary Corp.
Admissions Requirements Minimum age 16; Physician's request.
Staff RNs 1 (pt); Nurses aides 3 (ft), 5 (pt); Activities coordinators 1 (pt); Dietitians 1 (ft), 1 (pt).
Facilities Dining room; Laundry room; Barber/Beauty shop; Whirlpool bath; Outside sitting area.
Activities Arts & crafts; Games; Prayer groups; Movies; Shopping trips; Discussion group.

AVA

Crestview Healthcare
2001 St Jefferson St, Ava, MO, 65608
(417) 683-4129
Admin Nancy J Kissee. *Medical Dir/Dir of Nursing* M S Chern MD; Kristi McIntosh RN DON.
Licensure Skilled care. *Beds* SNF 120. *Certified* Medicaid; Medicare.
Owner Proprietary Corp (Hillhaven Corp).
Staff Physicians 2 (pt); RNs; LPNs; Orderlies; Nurses aides; Physical therapists 1 (pt); Speech therapists 1 (pt); Activities coordinators; Dietitians 1 (pt).
Facilities Dining room; Physical therapy room; Activities room; Chapel; Crafts room; Laundry room; Barber/Beauty shop; Library.
Activities Arts & crafts; Cards; Games; Reading groups; Prayer groups; Movies; Shopping trips.

BALLWIN

Clayton House Healthcare
13995 Clayton Rd, Ballwin, MO, 63011
(601) 227-5070
Admin Michael A Van Meter. *Medical Dir/Dir of Nursing* James Sertl MD; Robin Storey RN DON.
Licensure Skilled care; Intermediate care; Residential care. *Beds* SNF 178; ICF 48; Residential 52. *Certified* Medicaid; Medicare.
Owner Proprietary Corp (Hillhaven Corp).
Admissions Requirements Medical examination.

Staff Physicians; RNs; LPNs; Nurses aides; Physical therapists; Reality therapists; Recreational therapists; Occupational therapists; Speech therapists; Activities coordinators; Dietitians; Ophthalmologists.
Languages Spanish
Facilities Dining room; Physical therapy room; Activities room; Chapel; Crafts room; Laundry room; Barber/Beauty shop; Library; Cocktail lounge; Private dining room; Atrium; Rotunda; Big screen TV room.
Activities Arts & crafts; Cards; Games; Reading groups; Prayer groups; Movies; Shopping trips; Social/Cultural gatherings; Animal visits.

Clayton-on-the-Green Nursing Center
477 Clayton Rd, Ballwin, MO, 63011
(314) 394-7515
Admin Catherine J Bono. *Medical Dir/Dir of Nursing* Dr Virgil Fish.
Licensure Skilled care; Intermediate care. *Beds* SNF 180; ICF. *Certified* Medicaid; Medicare.
Owner Proprietary Corp.
Admissions Requirements Minimum age 21; Medical examination; Physician's request.
Staff Physicians; RNs 5 (ft), 10 (pt); LPNs 3 (ft), 5 (pt); Nurses aides 50 (ft); Physical therapists 1 (ft); Recreational therapists 2 (ft); Occupational therapists 1 (pt); Speech therapists 1 (pt); Activities coordinators 1 (ft); Dietitians 1 (pt); Ophthalmologists 1 (pt).
Facilities Dining room; Physical therapy room; Activities room; Chapel; Crafts room; Laundry room; Barber/Beauty shop.
Activities Arts & crafts; Cards; Games; Reading groups; Prayer groups; Movies; Shopping trips; Social/Cultural gatherings.

Manchester Nursing Home*
PO Box 1407, Ballwin, MO, 63011
(314) 391-0666
Admin Ron Rogers. *Medical Dir/Dir of Nursing* Donald C Walkenhorst DO.
Licensure Intermediate care. *Beds* 130. *Certified* Medicaid.
Owner Proprietary Corp.
Admissions Requirements Minimum age 21.
Staff Physicians 1 (pt); RNs 4 (ft); LPNs 3 (ft), 2 (pt).
Facilities Dining room; Physical therapy room; Activities room; Crafts room; Laundry room; Barber/Beauty shop.
Activities Arts & crafts; Cards; Games; Reading groups; Prayer groups; Movies; Social/Cultural gatherings.

BELL CITY

Shetley Nursing Home*
PO Box 123, N Walnut St, Bell City, MO, 63735
(314) 733-4426
Admin Joyce Gilles.
Licensure Intermediate care. *Beds* 29.
Owner Proprietary Corp.

BELLEVIEW

Belleview Valley Nursing Homes Inc
Hc Rte 63, Box 34, Belleview, MO, 63623
(314) 697-5311
Admin Wilma Davis. *Medical Dir/Dir of Nursing* Harriett Cramer DON.
Licensure Skilled care. *Beds* 122. *Certified* Medicaid; Medicare.
Owner Proprietary Corp.
Admissions Requirements Medical examination.
Staff Physicians 3 (pt); RNs 1 (ft), 1 (pt); LPNs 5 (ft), 1 (pt); Orderlies 2 (ft); Nurses aides 40 (ft), 15 (pt); Physical therapists 1 (pt); Reality therapists 1 (ft); Recreational

therapists 1 (ft); Occupational therapists 1 (pt); Speech therapists 1 (pt); Activities coordinators 1 (ft); Dietitians 1 (pt).
Facilities Dining room; Physical therapy room; Activities room; Chapel; Crafts room; Laundry room; Barber/Beauty shop.
Activities Arts & crafts; Cards; Games; Reading groups; Prayer groups; Movies; Shopping trips; Social/Cultural gatherings.

BELTON

Beautiful Savior Home
Rte 2, Box 306, Belton, MO, 64012
(816) 331-0781
Admin Mary Anderson. *Medical Dir/Dir of Nursing* Ronald La Hue; Georgia Spearman.
Licensure Intermediate care; Residential care. *Beds* ICF 82; Residential 42. *Certified* Medicaid.
Owner Nonprofit Corp.
Admissions Requirements Medical examination.
Staff RNs 2 (ft); LPNs 4 (ft), 2 (pt); Nurses aides 26 (ft); Activities coordinators 1 (ft); Dietitians 1 (ft).
Affiliation Lutheran
Facilities Dining room; Physical therapy room; Activities room; Chapel; Laundry room; Barber/Beauty shop.
Activities Arts & crafts; Cards; Games; Reading groups; Prayer groups; Movies; Social/Cultural gatherings.

BERKELEY

Wood-Acre Inc*
9732 Natural Bridge Rd, Berkeley, MO, 63134
(314) 428-4725
Admin Michael Woodard.
Licensure Intermediate care. *Beds* 24.
Owner Proprietary Corp.

BERTRAND

Bertrand Retirement Home Inc*
Rte 1, Bertrand, MO, 63823
(314) 471-6161
Admin Charlotte York.
Licensure Intermediate care. *Beds* 40. *Certified* Medicaid.
Owner Proprietary Corp.

BETHANY

Crestview Home Inc
Box 430, Jct Hwy 69 & 13, Bethany, MO, 64424
(816) 425-6337
Admin Dorothy Underwood. *Medical Dir/Dir of Nursing* G F Scamahorn DO; Carla Greene RN DON.
Licensure Skilled care; Intermediate care. *Beds* 120. *Certified* Medicaid.
Owner Nonprofit Corp.
Staff RNs 3 (ft); LPNs 7 (ft), 1 (pt); Orderlies 3 (ft), 1 (pt); Nurses aides 42 (ft), 7 (pt); Activities coordinators 1 (ft), 1 (pt); Dietitians 13 (ft).
Facilities Dining room; Physical therapy room; Activities room; Chapel; Crafts room; Laundry room; Barber/Beauty shop; Library.
Activities Arts & crafts; Cards; Games; Reading groups; Prayer groups; Movies; Social/Cultural gatherings.

BIRCH TREE

Birch View Nursing Home
PO Box 180, Hwy 60 W, Birch Tree, MO, 65438
(314) 292-3212
Admin Sharon L Bockman. *Medical Dir/Dir of Nursing* Jon W Roberts DO; Sarah Skinner RN DON.

Licensure Intermediate care. *Beds* 90. *Certified* Medicaid.
Owner Proprietary Corp (Americare Corp).
Admissions Requirements Minimum age 18; Medical examination.
Staff Physicians 4 (pt); RNs 1 (ft); LPNs 9 (ft); Nurses aides 25 (ft); Physical therapists 1 (pt); Occupational therapists 1 (pt); Speech therapists 1 (pt); Activities coordinators 1 (ft); Dietitians 1 (pt); Dentists 1 (pt).
Facilities Dining room; Activities room; Chapel; Crafts room; Laundry room; Barber/Beauty shop.
Activities Arts & crafts; Cards; Games; Reading groups; Prayer groups; Movies; Shopping trips; Social/Cultural gatherings.

BISMARCK

Colonial Retirement Center Inc
PO Box 727, 1162 Cedar St, Bismarck, MO, 63624
(314) 734-2846
Admin Teresa Watkins. *Medical Dir/Dir of Nursing* Carol Fear.
Licensure Intermediate care. *Beds* ICF 23.
Owner Proprietary Corp.
Admissions Requirements Minimum age 21; Medical examination.
Staff Physicians 1 (pt); RNs 1 (pt); LPNs 1 (ft), 1 (pt); Nurses aides 6 (ft), 5 (pt); Activities coordinators 1 (pt); Dietitians 1 (pt).
Activities Arts & crafts; Cards; Games; Reading groups; Movies; Shopping trips.

BLOOMFIELD

Bloomfield Nursing Center
502 W Missouri St, Bloomfield, MO, 63825
(314) 568-2137
Admin Anthony L Erickson. *Medical Dir/Dir of Nursing* Carole McCall.
Licensure Skilled care. *Beds* 60. *Certified* Medicaid.
Owner Proprietary Corp (Beverly Enterprises).
Facilities Dining room; Physical therapy room; Activities room; Crafts room; Laundry room; Barber/Beauty shop.

BLUE SPRINGS

Blue Springs Care Center*
PO Box 425, 930 Duncan Rd, Blue Springs, MO, 64015
(816) 229-6677
Admin Barbara Hill.
Licensure Intermediate care. *Beds* 120. *Certified* Medicaid.
Owner Proprietary Corp.

Golden Age Project—Boarding Home*
630 Lakeview Dr, Blue Springs, MO, 64015
Admin Delores L Wieners.
Licensure Boarding care. *Beds* 12. *Certified* Medicaid.
Owner Nonprofit Corp.
Admissions Requirements Minimum age 18; Medical examination.
Staff RNs 1 (ft); Orderlies 1 (ft); Nurses aides 1 (ft), 1 (pt); Physical therapists 1 (pt); Recreational therapists 1 (pt); Dietitians 1 (pt).
Facilities Dining room; Laundry room.
Activities Arts & crafts; Cards; Games; Reading groups; Prayer groups; Movies; Shopping trips; Social/Cultural gatherings; Bowling; Bible study groups.

BOLIVAR

Bolivar Nursing Home Inc
1218 W Locust, Bolivar, MO, 65613
(417) 326-7648
Admin Frank Follis. *Medical Dir/Dir of Nursing* Monte Kahler MD.

Licensure Skilled care. *Beds* SNF 108.
Certified Medicare.
Owner Nonprofit organization/foundation.
Admissions Requirements Medical
examination; Physician's request.
Staff Physicians 5 (pt); RNs 3 (ft); LPNs 7
(ft); Orderlies 3 (ft); Nurses aides 1 (pt);
Physical therapists 1 (pt); Recreational
therapists 1 (pt); Occupational therapists 1
(pt); Speech therapists 1 (pt); Activities
coordinators 1 (ft); Dietitians 1 (pt);
Podiatrists 1 (pt).
Facilities Dining room; Physical therapy
room; Activities room; Chapel; Crafts room;
Laundry room; Barber/Beauty shop; Library.
Activities Arts & crafts; Cards; Games;
Reading groups; Prayer groups; Movies;
Shopping trips.

Manor House Residential Care Inc
PO Box 387, 404 E Broadway, Bolivar, MO,
65613
(417) 326-7873
Admin Nancy E Havens. *Medical Dir/Dir of
Nursing* Nancy E Havens.
Licensure Residential care. *Beds* 20. *Certified*
Medicaid; Medicare.
Owner Proprietary Corp.
Admissions Requirements Minimum age 18;
Medical examination.
Staff LPNs; Orderlies 1 (ft); Nurses aides 3
(ft), 1 (pt); Recreational therapists 1 (pt).
Facilities Dining room; Activities room.
Activities Arts & crafts; Cards; Games; Prayer
groups; Movies; Shopping trips; Social/
Cultural gatherings.

BONNE TERRE

Bonne Terre Rest Home Inc*
518 Grove St, Bonne Terre, MO, 63628
(314) 358-3400
Admin Thomas W McDowell.
Licensure Intermediate care. *Beds* 27.
Owner Proprietary Corp.

BOONVILLE

Ashley Manor Care Center
PO Box 106, Radio Hill Rd, Boonville, MO,
65233
(816) 882-6584
Admin Sandy Smith. *Medical Dir/Dir of
Nursing* Dennis Handley MD; Pam Morton
LPN DON.
Licensure Intermediate care. *Beds* ICF 52.
Certified Medicaid.
Owner Proprietary Corp.
Admissions Requirements Minimum age
Adult.
Staff Physicians 4 (ft); RNs 1 (pt); LPNs 5
(ft); Orderlies 1 (ft); Nurses aides 20 (ft);
Physical therapists 1 (pt); Occupational
therapists 1 (pt); Speech therapists 1 (pt);
Activities coordinators 1 (ft); Dietitians 1
(pt).
Facilities Dining room; Activities room;
Laundry room; Barber/Beauty shop.
Activities Arts & crafts; Cards; Games;
Reading groups; Prayer groups; Movies;
Shopping trips; Social/Cultural gatherings.

Colonial Gardens Retirement Center
Hwy 5, Boonville, MO, 65233
(816) 882-7007
Admin Ardell Myer. *Medical Dir/Dir of
Nursing* Janice DeGraffenreid RN.
Licensure Skilled care; Intermediate care;
Residential care. *Beds* SNF 60; ICF 19;
Residential 17. *Certified* Medicaid.
Owner Privately owned.
Admissions Requirements Medical
examination.
Staff Physicians 8 (pt); RNs 1 (ft), 1 (pt);
LPNs 5 (ft), 1 (pt); Orderlies 2 (ft); Nurses
aides 20 (ft), 7 (pt); Physical therapists 1
(pt); Occupational therapists 1 (pt); Speech

therapists 1 (pt); Activities coordinators 1
(ft); Dietitians 1 (pt); Dentists 1 (pt);
Ophthalmologists 1 (pt); Podiatrists 1 (pt).
Facilities Dining room; Physical therapy
room; Activities room; Chapel; Crafts room;
Laundry room; Barber/Beauty shop.
Activities Arts & crafts; Cards; Games;
Reading groups; Prayer groups; Movies;
Social/Cultural gatherings.

Cooper County Rest Haven Nursing Home*
PO Box 374, 1121 11th St, Boonville, MO,
65233
(816) 882-7600
Admin Dorothy Young.
Licensure Intermediate care. *Beds* 57.
Owner Proprietary Corp.

River Heights Retirement Center Inc*
PO Box 63, Boonville, MO, 65233
(816) 882-2328
Admin Robert Clausen.
Licensure Residential care. *Beds* 120.
Owner Proprietary Corp.

BOWLING GREEN

Moore & Pike County Nursing Home*
400 S Saint Charles St, Bowling Green, MO,
63334
(314) 324-5281
Admin Martha E Moore.
Licensure Intermediate care. *Beds* 68.
Owner Proprietary Corp.

Sunset Nursing & Retirement
PO Box 398, N Main Cross, Bowling Green,
MO, 63334
(314) 324-5191
Admin Judith A Barteau. *Medical Dir/Dir of
Nursing* Carley Lovell DON.
Licensure Intermediate care; Intermediate care
for mentally retarded. *Beds* 46. *Certified*
Nursing care grant only.
Owner Proprietary Corp.
Admissions Requirements Minimum age 18;
Medical examination.
Staff Physicians 1 (ft); RNs 1 (pt); LPNs 3
(ft), 1 (pt); Orderlies 1 (pt); Nurses aides 13
(ft); Activities coordinators 1 (ft).
Facilities Dining room; Activities room;
Barber/Beauty shop.
Activities Arts & crafts; Cards; Games;
Reading groups; Prayer groups; Movies;
Shopping trips; Social/Cultural gatherings;
Dining out.

BRANSON

Rolling Hills Nursing Center
PO Box 1249, Hwy 248 W, Branson, MO,
65616
(417) 334-6431
Admin Dan West. *Medical Dir/Dir of Nursing*
O K Broughton MD; Nancy Howard RN
DON.
Licensure Skilled care. *Beds* SNF 100.
Certified Medicaid.
Owner Proprietary Corp (Beverly Enterprises).
Admissions Requirements Minimum age 16.
Staff Physicians 6 (pt); RNs 2 (ft), 2 (pt);
LPNs 5 (ft), 2 (pt); Orderlies 5 (ft); Nurses
aides 30 (ft), 5 (pt); Physical therapists 1
(pt); Reality therapists 1 (pt); Recreational
therapists 1 (pt); Occupational therapists 1
(pt); Speech therapists 1 (pt); Activities
coordinators 1 (ft); Dietitians 1 (pt); Dentists
1 (pt); Ophthalmologists 1 (pt); Podiatrists 1
(pt).
Facilities Dining room; Physical therapy
room; Activities room; Crafts room; Laundry
room; Barber/Beauty shop.
Activities Arts & crafts; Cards; Games;
Reading groups; Prayer groups; Movies;
Shopping trips; Social/Cultural gatherings;
Cooking classes; Music shows.

BRAYMER

Golden Age Nursing Home District*
Hwy 116, Braymer, MO, 64624
(816) 645-2243
Admin Cara Herring.
Licensure Intermediate care. *Beds* 110.
Certified Medicaid.
Owner Publicly owned.

BRIDGETON

DePaul Health Center St Anne's Division
12303 DePaul Dr, Bridgeton, MO, 63044
(314) 344-6000
Admin Frank A Petrich. *Medical Dir/Dir of
Nursing* Frank R Mohs MD.
Licensure Skilled care; Intermediate care. *Beds*
SNF 18; ICF 68. *Certified* Medicaid;
Medicare.
Owner Nonprofit Corp.
Admissions Requirements Medical
examination; Physician's request.
Staff RNs 8 (ft), 12 (pt); LPNs 7 (ft), 3 (pt);
Nurses aides 26 (ft), 17 (pt);
Ophthalmologists 1 (pt).
Affiliation Roman Catholic
Facilities Dining room; Physical therapy
room; Activities room; Chapel; Crafts room;
Laundry room; Barber/Beauty shop; Library.
Activities Arts & crafts; Cards; Games;
Reading groups; Prayer groups; Movies;
Shopping trips; Social/Cultural gatherings.

Mark Twain Manor
11988 Mark Twain Ln, Bridgeton, MO, 63044
(314) 291-8240
Admin Alfred J Jewson. *Medical Dir/Dir of
Nursing* Arnold Tepper MD; Barbara Brown
RN DON.
Licensure Skilled care. *Beds* SNF 120.
Certified Medicaid; Medicare.
Owner Proprietary Corp.
Admissions Requirements Minimum age 18;
Medical examination.
Staff RNs 4 (ft); LPNs 8 (ft), 2 (pt); Nurses
aides 35 (ft), 1 (pt); Activities coordinators 1
(ft), 2 (pt).
Facilities Dining room; Physical therapy
room; Activities room; Crafts room; Laundry
room; Barber/Beauty shop.
Activities Arts & crafts; Cards; Games;
Reading groups; Prayer groups; Movies;
Shopping trips; Social/Cultural gatherings.

BROOKFIELD

Brookfield Nursing Center*
315 Hunt, Brookfield, MO, 64628
(816) 258-3367
Admin Dennis F Sever. *Medical Dir/Dir of
Nursing* Robert Smith MD.
Licensure Skilled care. *Beds* 120. *Certified*
Medicaid; Medicare.
Owner Proprietary Corp (Beverly Enterprises).
Admissions Requirements Medical
examination; Physician's request.
Staff Physicians 3 (pt); RNs 4 (ft), 1 (pt);
LPNs 6 (ft), 2 (pt); Orderlies 2 (ft); Nurses
aides 23 (ft), 4 (pt); Physical therapists 1
(pt); Recreational therapists 1 (pt);
Occupational therapists 1 (pt); Speech
therapists 1 (pt); Activities coordinators 1
(ft); Dietitians 1 (pt); Dentists 1 (pt);
Ophthalmologists 1 (pt); Podiatrists 1 (pt);
Audiologists 1 (pt).
Facilities Dining room; Physical therapy
room; Activities room; Chapel; Crafts room;
Laundry room; Barber/Beauty shop.
Activities Arts & crafts; Cards; Games;
Reading groups; Prayer groups; Movies;
Shopping trips; Social/Cultural gatherings.

Maranatha Manor
620 West Ave, Brookfield, MO, 64628
(816) 258-2212
Admin Janet Robinson.

Licensure Intermediate care; Residential care. *Beds* ICF 27; Residential 44.
Owner Proprietary Corp.
Staff RNs 1 (ft), 1 (pt); LPNs 2 (ft); Orderlies 1 (ft); Nurses aides 18 (ft); Physical therapists 1 (pt); Speech therapists 1 (pt); Activities coordinators 1 (pt); Dentist 1 (pt).
Facilities Dining room; Activities room; Laundry room; Barber/Beauty shop.
Activities Cards; Games; Prayer groups; Movies; Shopping trips.

McLarney Manor
PO Box 129, 116 E Pratt, Brookfield, MO, 64628
(816) 258-7402
Admin Judith Lewis. *Medical Dir/Dir of Nursing* B D Howell MD; Doris James RN DON.
Licensure Skilled care; Intermediate care. *Beds* 60. *Certified* Medicaid.
Owner Proprietary Corp (Tiffany Care Centers).
Admissions Requirements Minimum age 21; Medical examination; Physician's request.
Staff Physicians 1 (pt); RNs 1 (ft), 1 (pt); LPNs 3 (ft), 3 (pt); Orderlies 1 (ft), 1 (pt); Nurses aides 12 (ft), 6 (pt); Physical therapists 1 (pt); Reality therapists 1 (pt); Occupational therapists 1 (pt); Speech therapists 1 (pt); Activities coordinators 1 (ft); Dietitians 1 (pt); Dentists 1 (pt); Ophthalmologists 1 (pt); Podiatrists 1 (pt).
Facilities Dining room; Physical therapy room; Activities room; Laundry room; Barber/Beauty shop.
Activities Arts & crafts; Cards; Games; Reading groups; Prayer groups; Movies; Shopping trips; Social/Cultural gatherings.

BRUNSWICK

Grand Chariton Manor Inc*
Rte 2, Box 11, 721 W Filmore, Brunswick, MO, 65236
(816) 548-3182
Admin Sarah F Breshears.
Licensure Intermediate care. *Beds* 60.
Owner Proprietary Corp.

BUFFALO

Chastain's of Buffalo Inc*
PO Box 449, Hickory & Cooper Sts, Buffalo, MO, 65622
(417) 345-2228
Admin Barbara Lee Myers.
Licensure Intermediate care. *Beds* 120. *Certified* Medicaid.
Owner Proprietary Corp (Hillhaven Corp).

BUTLER

Heartland Willow Lane Nursing Center
416 S High, Butler, MO, 64730
(816) 679-6157
Admin Melba J Swope. *Medical Dir/Dir of Nursing* Donna Short RN.
Licensure Skilled care. *Beds* SNF 100. *Certified* Medicaid; Medicare.
Owner Proprietary Corp (Health Care & Retirement Corp).
Admissions Requirements Medical examination; Physician's request.
Staff RNs 3 (ft), 3 (pt); LPNs 17 (ft), 5 (pt); Orderlies 3 (ft), 2 (pt); Nurses aides 29 (ft), 3 (pt); Physical therapists 1 (pt); Reality therapists 1 (pt); Recreational therapists 1 (pt); Occupational therapists 1 (pt); Speech therapists 1 (pt); Activities coordinators 1 (ft); Dietitians 1 (ft), 1 (pt); Ophthalmologists 1 (pt).
Facilities Dining room; Physical therapy room; Activities room; Crafts room; Laundry room; Barber/Beauty shop.

Activities Arts & crafts; Cards; Games; Reading groups; Prayer groups; Movies; Shopping trips; Social/Cultural gatherings.

Medicalodge of Butler*
Rte 4, Box 130, Butler, MO, 64730
(816) 679-3179
Admin Vicky Petty.
Licensure Intermediate care. *Beds* 120. *Certified* Medicaid.
Owner Proprietary Corp (Medicalodges).

Pine Tree Nursing Home
Rte 3, Box 208, Butler, MO, 64730
(816) 679-4807
Admin Mildred Reynolds.
Licensure Intermediate care. *Beds* 59.
Owner Proprietary Corp.

CABOOL

Kabul Nursing Home*
920 W Main, Cabool, MO, 65689
(417) 962-3713
Admin Robert K Cameron.
Licensure Skilled care; Intermediate care. *Beds* 82. *Certified* Medicaid; Medicare.
Owner Nonprofit Corp.

CALIFORNIA

California Care Center
Rte 3 Box 875 Hwy 875, California, MO, 65018
(314) 796-3127
Admin Jo Ann Cantriel. *Medical Dir/Dir of Nursing* Dr Richard Fulks MD; Mary Farris RN DON.
Licensure Skilled care; Intermediate care. *Beds* 60; ICF. *Certified* Medicaid.
Owner Proprietary Corp.
Admissions Requirements Minimum age 18; Medical examination.
Staff Physicians 1 (pt); RNs 2 (ft); LPNs 3 (ft), 2 (pt); Orderlies 2 (ft), 1 (pt); Nurses aides 16 (ft), 12 (pt); Physical therapists 1 (pt); Recreational therapists 1 (pt); Occupational therapists 1 (pt); Speech therapists 1 (pt); Activities coordinators 1 (ft), 1 (pt); Dietitians 1 (ft), 1 (pt); Ophthalmologists 1 (pt); Podiatrists 1 (pt).
Languages Spanish
Facilities Dining room; Physical therapy room; Activities room; Crafts room; Laundry room; Barber/Beauty shop; Library.
Activities Arts & crafts; Cards; Games; Reading groups; Prayer groups; Movies; Shopping trips; Social/Cultural gatherings.

Latham Care Center Inc
109 N High, California, MO, 65018
(314) 796-3944
Admin Dennis C Tilton; Janice Claas. *Medical Dir/Dir of Nursing* Barbara Peoples DON.
Licensure Intermediate care. *Beds* ICF 44.
Owner Proprietary Corp.
Staff RNs; LPNs; Orderlies; Nurses aides; Activities coordinators.
Facilities Dining room; Activities room; Crafts room; Laundry room; Barber/Beauty shop.
Activities Arts & crafts; Cards; Games; Reading groups; Prayer groups; Movies; Shopping trips.

Tilton Nursing Home Inc
PO Box 19, 201 N Oak St, California, MO, 65018
(314) 796-4791
Admin Marion A Tilton. *Medical Dir/Dir of Nursing* Dr Honeywell; Gladys Wordelman.
Licensure Residential care facility. *Beds* Residential 44.
Owner Privately owned.
Admissions Requirements Minimum age 16; Medical examination.

Staff Physicians 3 (pt); LPNs 1 (ft), 1 (pt); Orderlies 1 (pt); Nurses aides 5 (ft); Recreational therapists 1 (pt); Activities coordinators 1 (ft).
Facilities Dining room; Activities room; Laundry room.
Activities Arts & crafts; Cards; Games; Reading groups; Prayer groups; Movies; Shopping trips; Picnics.

CAMDENTON

Mozark Health Resort
PO Box 1345, Camdenton, MO, 65020
(314) 346-2445
Admin Joyce L Shaffer. *Medical Dir/Dir of Nursing* R R Porter DO.
Licensure Intermediate care. *Beds* ICF 32.
Owner Privately owned.
Admissions Requirements Minimum age 18.
Staff Physicians 1 (pt); RNs 1 (pt); LPNs 1 (pt); Nurses aides 8 (pt); Recreational therapists 1 (pt).
Facilities Dining room; Activities room; Laundry room.
Activities Arts & crafts; Cards; Games; Reading groups; Movies; Shopping trips; Social/Cultural gatherings.

Windsor Estates Convalescent Center*
PO Box 812, Hwy 5 N, Camdenton, MO, 65020
(314) 346-5654
Admin John S Freeman.
Licensure Skilled care; Intermediate care. *Beds* 60. *Certified* Medicaid; Medicare.
Owner Proprietary Corp.

CAMERON

Cameron Manor Nursing Home
PO Box 210A, Rte 1, 801 Euclid St, Cameron, MO, 64429
(816) 632-7254
Admin Betty A Smith. *Medical Dir/Dir of Nursing* Dr E R Schmidt DO; Sally Temple.
Licensure Intermediate care. *Beds* ICF 60. *Certified* Medicaid.
Owner Proprietary Corp.
Admissions Requirements Minimum age 17.
Staff Physicians 5 (pt); RNs 1 (pt); LPNs 3 (ft); Nurses aides 20 (ft); Physical therapists 2 (pt); Occupational therapists 1 (pt); Speech therapists 1 (pt); Activities coordinators 1 (ft), 1 (pt); Dietitians 1 (pt).
Languages Korean
Facilities Dining room; Activities room; Laundry room; Barber/Beauty shop.
Activities Arts & crafts; Reading groups; Prayer groups; Movies.

Indian Hills Nursing Center
PO Box 373, 1405 Grand Ave, Cameron, MO, 64429
(816) 632-2151
Admin Carmelita R Green. *Medical Dir/Dir of Nursing* E R Schmidt; Barbara Barnes.
Licensure Skilled care. *Beds* SNF 84. *Certified* Medicaid.
Owner Proprietary Corp (Beverly Enterprises).
Admissions Requirements Minimum age 21; Medical examination.
Staff RNs 3 (ft), 2 (pt); LPNs 5 (ft), 2 (pt); Orderlies 3 (ft); Nurses aides 36 (ft), 5 (pt); Activities coordinators 1 (ft); Dietitians 1 (ft).
Facilities Dining room; Physical therapy room; Activities room; Crafts room; Laundry room; Barber/Beauty shop.
Activities Arts & crafts; Cards; Games; Reading groups; Prayer groups; Movies; Social/Cultural gatherings.

The Village Health Care Center
320 Little Brick Rd, Cameron, MO, 64429
(816) 632-7611

Admin Ronnie Wilkinson. *Medical Dir/Dir of Nursing* Sue Coy.
Licensure Intermediate care; Residential care. *Beds* ICF 20; Residential 25. *Certified* Medicaid.
Owner Proprietary Corp.
Admissions Requirements Minimum age 21; Medical examination.
Staff Physicians 1 (pt); RNs 2 (ft); LPNs 2 (pt); Nurses aides 9 (ft); Physical therapists 1 (pt); Reality therapists 1 (pt); Recreational therapists 1 (pt); Occupational therapists 1 (pt); Speech therapists 1 (pt); Activities coordinators 1 (ft).
Facilities Dining room; Physical therapy room; Activities room; Laundry room; Barber/Beauty shop.
Activities Cards; Games; Prayer groups.

CAMPBELL

General Baptist Nursing Home Inc
Hwy 62 W, Rte 2, Box 650, Campbell, MO, 63933
(314) 246-2155
Admin Wanda Britt. *Medical Dir/Dir of Nursing* Diana Burchell RN DON.
Licensure Intermediate care. *Beds* 90. *Certified* Medicaid.
Owner Nonprofit Corp.
Admissions Requirements Minimum age 16; Medical examination; Physician's request.
Staff RNs 1 (ft); LPNs 7 (ft), 1 (pt).
Affiliation Baptist
Facilities Dining room; Physical therapy room; Activities room; Chapel; Crafts room; Laundry room; Barber/Beauty shop; Residents lounge.
Activities Arts & crafts; Cards; Games; Reading groups; Prayer groups; Movies; Shopping trips.

CANTON

Lewis County Nursing Home Dist
RR 2, Canton, MO, 63435
(314) 288-4454
Admin Patricia L Hardin-Cummings. *Medical Dir/Dir of Nursing* Dr Buening; Ella M Dochterman.
Licensure Skilled care; Intermediate care. *Beds* 90. *Certified* Medicaid.
Owner Nonprofit organization/foundation.
Admissions Requirements Minimum age 16.
Staff RNs 4 (ft); LPNs 10 (ft); Orderlies 3 (ft); Nurses aides 4 (ft); Recreational therapists 2 (ft); Activities coordinators 1 (ft), 1 (pt); Dietitians 1 (ft).
Facilities Dining room; Physical therapy room; Activities room; Laundry room; Barber/Beauty shop.
Activities Arts & crafts; Cards; Games; Reading groups; Prayer groups; Movies; Shopping trips; Social/Cultural gatherings.

CAPE GIRARDEAU

Cape Girardeau Care Center
2525 Boutin Dr, Cape Girardeau, MO, 63701
(314) 334-5225
Admin Katherine M Lane. *Medical Dir/Dir of Nursing* W W Hutton DO; Helen Gwin.
Licensure Intermediate care. *Beds* ICF 120. *Certified* Medicaid.
Owner Nonprofit Corp.
Admissions Requirements Minimum age 19; Medical examination.
Staff RNs 1 (ft); LPNs 9 (ft); Orderlies 5 (ft); Nurses aides 61 (ft); Activities coordinators 3 (ft); Dietitians.
Facilities Dining room; Physical therapy room; Laundry room; Barber/Beauty shop.
Activities Arts & crafts; Cards; Games; Reading groups; Prayer groups; Movies; Shopping trips; Social/Cultural gatherings.

Cape Girardeau Nursing Center
2852 Independence St, Cape Girardeau, MO, 63701
(314) 335-2086
Admin Dianne Walker. *Medical Dir/Dir of Nursing* Patty Schmarje DON.
Licensure Skilled care. *Beds* SNF 120. *Certified* Medicaid; Medicare.
Owner Proprietary Corp (Beverly Enterprises).
Admissions Requirements Medical examination; Physician's request.
Staff Physicians 26 (pt); RNs 6 (ft); LPNs 15 (ft); Orderlies 4 (ft); Nurses aides 40 (ft); Physical therapists 1 (ft); Recreational therapists 1 (ft); Occupational therapists 1 (pt); Speech therapists 1 (pt); Activities coordinators 1 (ft); Dietitians 1 (ft); Dentists 1 (pt); Ophthalmologists 1 (pt); Podiatrists 1 (pt); Social worker 1 (ft).
Facilities Dining room; Physical therapy room; Activities room; Crafts room; Laundry room; Barber/Beauty shop; Library.
Activities Arts & crafts; Cards; Games; Reading groups; Prayer groups; Movies; Shopping trips; Social/Cultural gatherings.

Chateau Girardeau
3120 Independence St, Cape Girardeau, MO, 63701
(314) 335-1281
Admin Barbara N Calvin. *Medical Dir/Dir of Nursing* Phyllis T Watkins RN.
Licensure Skilled care; Life/Continuing care; Retirement community. *Beds* SNF 38; Life/Continuing care apts 151. *Certified* Medicare.
Owner Nonprofit Corp.
Admissions Requirements Minimum age 62; Medical examination.
Staff RNs 4 (ft), 1 (pt); LPNs 4 (ft), 1 (pt); Nurses aides 17 (ft), 5 (pt); Activities coordinators 1 (ft), 1 (pt).
Facilities Dining room; Physical therapy room; Activities room; Chapel; Crafts room; Laundry room; Barber/Beauty shop; Library; Billiards room; Woodworking shop.
Activities Arts & crafts; Cards; Games; Reading groups; Prayer groups; Movies; Shopping trips; Social/Cultural gatherings; Trips; Residents committees.

Hill Top Residential Care Facility*
430 N Frederick, Cape Girardeau, MO, 63701
(314) 334-2662
Admin Donald McMullin.
Licensure Intermediate care. *Beds* 30.
Owner Proprietary Corp.

The Lutheran Home*
2825 Bloomfield Rd, Cape Girardeau, MO, 63701
(314) 335-0158
Admin Janice T Unger.
Licensure Intermediate care. *Beds* 120. *Certified* Medicaid.
Owner Nonprofit Corp.
Affiliation Lutheran

Ratliff Nursing Home*
717 N Spriggs, Cape Girardeau, MO, 63701
(314) 335-5810
Admin Emmagene Ratliff.
Licensure Intermediate care. *Beds* 17.
Owner Proprietary Corp.

CARROLLTON

Carrollton Nursing Center
1500 N Jefferson, Carrollton, MO, 64633
(816) 542-0155
Admin Loretta Stigall. *Medical Dir/Dir of Nursing* Marvin E Ross DO; Aimee Harris RN DON.
Licensure Skilled care; Intermediate care. *Beds* SNF; ICF 10; Medicare 110. *Certified* Medicaid; Medicare.
Owner Proprietary Corp.

Admissions Requirements Minimum age 18; Medical examination.
Staff Physicians 5 (pt); RNs 2 (ft), 2 (pt); LPNs 11 (ft), 1 (pt); Nurses aides 45 (ft), 5 (pt); Physical therapists 3 (pt); Recreational therapists 1 (pt); Occupational therapists 1 (pt); Speech therapists 1 (pt); Activities coordinators 2 (ft); Dietitians 1 (pt); Dentists 1 (pt); Podiatrists 1 (pt).
Facilities Dining room; Physical therapy room; Activities room; Chapel; Crafts room; Laundry room; Barber/Beauty shop; 2 courtyards.
Activities Arts & crafts; Cards; Games; Reading groups; Prayer groups; Movies; Social/Cultural gatherings.

Carrollton's Resthaven Inc
307 Grand, Carrollton, MO, 64633
(816) 542-0588
Admin Ruth Ann Hayes. *Medical Dir/Dir of Nursing* June Schenk DON.
Licensure Intermediate care. *Beds* ICF 63.
Owner Proprietary Corp.
Admissions Requirements Minimum age 17; Medical examination.
Staff RNs 1 (pt); LPNs 2 (ft); Nurses aides 20 (ft); Activities coordinators 1 (pt); Dietitians 1 (pt).
Facilities Dining room; Activities room; Laundry room; Barber/Beauty shop.
Activities Arts & crafts; Games; Prayer groups; Movies.

CARTHAGE

Drake Residential Care Facility*
406 Howard, Carthage, MO, 64836
Admin Manny Brandt.
Licensure Intermediate care for mentally retarded. *Beds* 88. *Certified* Medicaid; Medicare.
Owner Nonprofit Corp.
Staff Orderlies 7 (ft); Nurses aides 11 (ft); Activities coordinators 1 (ft); Dietitians 1 (ft).
Facilities Dining room; Activities room; Crafts room; Laundry room; Barber/Beauty shop.
Activities Arts & crafts; Cards; Games; Reading groups; Movies; Shopping trips; Social/Cultural gatherings.

Fair Acres*
Rte 3, Carthage, MO, 64836
(417) 358-4514
Admin Noel Kenneth Derrick Sr. *Medical Dir/Dir of Nursing* J J Royce MD.
Licensure Intermediate care. *Beds* 140.
Owner Nonprofit Corp.
Admissions Requirements Minimum age 18; Medical examination; Physician's request.
Staff Physicians 1 (pt); RNs 2 (pt); LPNs 8 (ft); Orderlies 10 (ft); Nurses aides 50 (ft), 3 (pt); Recreational therapists 3 (pt); Activities coordinators 1 (ft); Dietitians 1 (pt).
Facilities Dining room; Activities room; Chapel; Laundry room; Barber/Beauty shop; Library.
Activities Arts & crafts; Cards; Games; Reading groups; Prayer groups; Movies; Shopping trips; Social/Cultural gatherings.

Maryetta's Rest Home*
316 S Fulton, Carthage, MO, 64836
(417) 358-6672
Admin Eldred F Gilbreath.
Licensure Intermediate care. *Beds* 17.
Owner Proprietary Corp.

St Luke's Nursing Center*
1220 E Fairview, Carthage, MO, 64836
(417) 358-9084
Admin John L Montgomery.
Licensure Skilled care; Intermediate care. *Beds* 120. *Certified* Medicaid.
Owner Nonprofit Corp.

CARUTHERSVILLE

Caruthersville Nursing Center
500 Truman Blvd, Caruthersville, MO, 63830
(314) 333-5150
Admin Judson R Schultz.
Licensure Skilled care; Intermediate care. *Beds* SNF 120. *Certified* Medicaid.
Owner Proprietary Corp (Beverly Enterprises).
Admissions Requirements Minimum age 21; Medical examination; Physician's request.
Staff Physicians 1 (pt); RNs 3 (ft); LPNs 10 (ft), 5 (pt); Orderlies 2 (ft); Nurses aides 30 (ft), 30 (pt); Physical therapists 1 (pt); Recreational therapists 1 (ft); Activities coordinators 1 (ft); Dietitians 1 (pt); Ophthalmologists 1 (pt).
Facilities Dining room; Physical therapy room; Activities room; Crafts room; Barber/Beauty shop.
Activities Arts & crafts; Cards; Games; Reading groups; Prayer groups; Movies; Shopping trips; Social/Cultural gatherings.

CASSVILLE

Cassville Nursing Center*
Country Farm Rd, PO Box 117, Cassville, MO, 65625
(417) 847-3386
Admin Mildred Shuster. *Medical Dir/Dir of Nursing* W G Barns DO & Herman Sardjano MD.
Licensure Intermediate care. *Beds* 32.
Owner Proprietary Corp.
Admissions Requirements Minimum age 18; Medical examination; Physician's request.
Staff Physicians 2 (pt); RNs 1 (pt); LPNs 2 (ft); Nurses aides 12 (ft); Activities coordinators 1 (ft); Dietitians 1 (pt).
Facilities Dining room; Activities room; Laundry room.
Activities Arts & crafts; Games; Reading groups; Movies; Shopping trips; Social/Cultural gatherings.

Red Rose Inn
PO Box 289-A, Rte 1, Cassville, MO, 65625
(417) 847-2184
Admin Jane Prier. *Medical Dir/Dir of Nursing* Dr Ricky Kime; Kaye Learned RN DON.
Licensure Skilled care; Intermediate care. *Beds* SNF 90; ICF. *Certified* Medicaid.
Owner Privately owned.
Staff RNs; LPNs; Orderlies; Nurses aides; Activities coordinators.
Facilities Dining room; Physical therapy room; Laundry room; Barber/Beauty shop.
Activities Arts & crafts; Cards; Games; Reading groups; Prayer groups; Movies.

Sunset Valley Nursing Home*
11th St, Cassville, MO, 65625
(417) 847-4607
Admin Kenneth L Bemis.
Licensure Intermediate care. *Beds* 25.
Owner Proprietary Corp.

CENTRALIA

Heritage Hall Nursing Center
750 E Hwy 22, Centralia, MO, 65240
(314) 682-5551
Admin Rita Hampton. *Medical Dir/Dir of Nursing* Jamie Eryart.
Licensure Intermediate care. *Beds* 60. *Certified* Medicaid.
Owner Proprietary Corp (Beverly Enterprises).
Admissions Requirements Minimum age 18; Medical examination; Physician's request.
Staff RNs 1 (pt); LPNs 2 (ft), 2 (pt); Orderlies 1 (ft); Nurses aides 28 (ft), 6 (pt); Activities coordinators 1 (ft).
Facilities Dining room; Physical therapy room; Activities room; Chapel; Crafts room; Laundry room; Barber/Beauty shop.

Activities Arts & crafts; Cards; Games; Reading groups; Prayer groups; Movies; Social/Cultural gatherings.

CHARLESTON

Russell Retirement RCFI
200 E Commercial St, Charleston, MO, 63834
(314) 683-3353, 683-8643
Admin Nina McWilliams.
Licensure Residential care. *Beds* 50.
Owner Privately owned.
Admissions Requirements Minimum age 18; Minimum age 18; Medical examination.
Staff Physicians; LPNs; Orderlies; Nurses aides; Activities coordinators; Dietitians.
Facilities Dining room; Activities room; Chapel; Crafts room; Laundry room; Barber/Beauty shop; Library.
Activities Arts & crafts; Cards; Games; Reading groups; Movies; Shopping trips.

CHESTERFIELD

Chesterfield Manor Inc
14001 Olive Street Rd, Chesterfield, MO, 63017
(314) 469-3500
Admin Penny Griffin. *Medical Dir/Dir of Nursing* Ted Vargas MD.
Licensure Skilled care; Intermediate care. *Beds* SNF 72; ICF 64. *Certified* Medicaid.
Admissions Requirements Medical examination.
Staff RNs 2 (ft), 2 (pt); LPNs 2 (ft), 4 (pt); Orderlies 4 (ft), 3 (pt); Nurses aides 10 (ft), 15 (pt); Physical therapists 1 (pt); Speech therapists 1 (pt); Activities coordinators 1 (ft); Dietitians 1 (pt); Dentists 1 (pt); Ophthalmologists 1 (pt); Podiatrists 1 (pt).
Facilities Dining room; Physical therapy room; Activities room; Chapel; Crafts room; Laundry room; Barber/Beauty shop.
Activities Arts & crafts; Cards; Games; Prayer groups; Movies.

Delmar Gardens of Chesterfield*
14855 N Outer 40 Rd, Chesterfield, MO, 63017
(314) 532-0150
Admin Gabe Grossberg.
Licensure Skilled care; Intermediate care. *Beds* 180. *Certified* Medicaid.
Owner Proprietary Corp.

Delmar Gardens West*
13550 S Outer Forty Rd, Chesterfield, MO, 63017
(314) 878-1330
Admin Barbara Grossberg.
Licensure Skilled care; Intermediate care. *Beds* 330. *Certified* Medicaid; Medicare.
Owner Proprietary Corp.

Friendship Village West County
15201 Olive Street Rd, Chesterfield, MO, 63017
(314) 532-1515
Admin Wes Sperr. *Medical Dir/Dir of Nursing* Grant Izmirlian MD; Judy Thorp DON.
Licensure Skilled care. *Beds* SNF 60. *Certified* Medicare.
Owner Nonprofit Corp.
Admissions Requirements Minimum age 62.
Staff Physicians; RNs; LPNs; Orderlies; Nurses aides; Physical therapists; Reality therapists; Recreational therapists; Occupational therapists; Speech therapists; Activities coordinators; Dietitians; Dentists; Ophthalmologists; Podiatrists; Dentist.
Facilities Dining room; Physical therapy room; Activities room; Chapel; Crafts room; Laundry room; Barber/Beauty shop; Library.
Activities Arts & crafts; Cards; Games; Reading groups; Prayer groups; Movies; Shopping trips; Social/Cultural gatherings; Grandparents day; Residents council.

Jewish Center for Aged
13190 S Outer Forty Rd, Chesterfield, MO, 63017
(314) 434-3330
Admin Miner Brown. *Medical Dir/Dir of Nursing* Ellen Binder MD; Marva Reese Abdul-Hamid MS RN DON.
Licensure Skilled care. *Beds* SNF 276. *Certified* Medicaid; Medicare.
Owner Nonprofit Corp.
Admissions Requirements Medical examination.
Staff RNs 10 (ft), 12 (pt); LPNs 3 (ft), 3 (pt); Nurses aides 93 (ft), 18 (pt); Physical therapists 1 (ft); Recreational therapists 1 (ft); Occupational therapists 1 (ft).
Affiliation Jewish
Facilities Dining room; Physical therapy room; Activities room; Chapel; Crafts room; Laundry room; Barber/Beauty shop; Library; Occupational therapy, speech, dental/podiatry, medical exam, and conference rooms; Gardens.
Activities Arts & crafts; Cards; Games; Reading groups; Prayer groups; Movies; Shopping trips; Social/Cultural gatherings; Music instruction/appreciation.

Westchester House*
550 White Rd, Chesterfield, MO, 63017
(314) 469-1200
Admin Darlena Voegele. *Medical Dir/Dir of Nursing* Dr Jamie Aquinaldo.
Licensure Skilled care. *Beds* 76.
Owner Proprietary Corp (Life Care Centers of America).
Admissions Requirements Minimum age 18.
Staff Physicians 1 (pt); RNs 6 (ft), 4 (pt); LPNs 3 (ft), 3 (pt); Nurses aides 24 (ft), 22 (pt); Physical therapists 1 (pt); Activities coordinators 1 (ft), 1 (pt).
Facilities Dining room; Physical therapy room; Activities room; Crafts room; Laundry room; Barber/Beauty shop; Library.
Activities Arts & crafts; Cards; Games; Reading groups; Prayer groups; Movies; Shopping trips; Social/Cultural gatherings.

CHILLICOTHE

Indian Hills Nursing Home Inc*
2601 Fair St, Chillicothe, MO, 64601
(816) 646-1230
Admin Marilyn Wever.
Licensure Intermediate care. *Beds* 60. *Certified* Medicaid.
Owner Proprietary Corp.
Staff RNs 1 (ft); LPNs 4 (ft), 2 (pt); Nurses aides 21 (ft), 3 (pt); Physical therapists 1 (pt); Occupational therapists 1 (pt); Speech therapists 1 (pt); Activities coordinators 1 (ft); Dietitians 1 (pt); Audiologists 1 (pt).
Facilities Dining room; Physical therapy room; Activities room; Chapel; Crafts room; Laundry room; Barber/Beauty shop; Library.
Activities Arts & crafts; Cards; Games; Reading groups; Prayer groups; Movies; Shopping trips; Social/Cultural gatherings.

Livingston Manor Care Center
PO Box 28, Hwy 36 E, Chillicothe, MO, 64601
(816) 646-5177
Admin Shirley A Moreland. *Medical Dir/Dir of Nursing* Dr Sensenich DO; Nancy Gamble DON.
Licensure Skilled care. *Beds* 94. *Certified* Medicaid.
Owner Proprietary Corp.
Admissions Requirements Minimum age 16; Medical examination.
Staff Physicians; RNs; LPNs; Nurses aides; Physical therapists; Reality therapists; Recreational therapists; Occupational therapists; Speech therapists; Activities coordinators; Dietitians.

Facilities Dining room; Physical therapy room; Activities room; Crafts room; Laundry room; Barber/Beauty shop.
Activities Arts & crafts; Cards; Games; Reading groups; Prayer groups; Movies; Shopping trips; Social/Cultural gatherings.

Long-Blum Retirement Center*
1301 Monroe, Chillicothe, MO, 64601
(816) 646-5180
Admin Barbara S White.
Licensure Residential care. *Beds* 64.
Owner Proprietary Corp.

Morningside Center
1700 Morningside Dr, Chillicothe, MO, 64601
(816) 646-0170
Admin Joan K Kimberling. *Medical Dir/Dir of Nursing* Denise Lingen RN.
Licensure Intermediate care. *Beds* ICF 60.
Certified Medicaid.
Owner Publicly owned.
Admissions Requirements Medical examination.
Staff RNs 1 (ft); LPNs 1 (ft), 6 (pt); Nurses aides 12 (ft), 20 (pt); Activities coordinators 1 (ft).
Facilities Dining room; Physical therapy room; Activities room; Laundry room; Barber/Beauty shop.
Activities Arts & crafts; Cards; Games; Reading groups; Prayer groups; Movies; Shopping trips; Social/Cultural gatherings.

Suncrest Nursing Center
505 2nd St, Chillicothe, MO, 64601
(816) 646-3476
Admin Retha Emerich. *Medical Dir/Dir of Nursing* Sheryl Oneth DON.
Licensure Intermediate care. *Beds* ICF 60.
Owner Proprietary Corp.
Admissions Requirements Minimum age 18; Medical examination.
Staff RNs 1 (pt); LPNs 1 (ft), 1 (pt); Nurses aides 13 (ft), 3 (pt); Activities coordinators 1 (ft), 1 (pt).
Facilities Dining room; Activities room; Crafts room; Laundry room.
Activities Arts & crafts; Cards; Games; Reading groups; Prayer groups; Movies; Shopping trips; Social/Cultural gatherings; Van for outside field trips; Doctors visits.

CLARENCE

Clarence Nursing Home District
PO Box 250, 307 East St, Clarence, MO, 63437
(816) 699-2118
Admin Michael O'Neal. *Medical Dir/Dir of Nursing* Dr D R Hull; Carolyn Garnett.
Licensure Intermediate care. *Beds* ICF 60.
Certified Medicaid.
Owner Proprietary Corp.
Admissions Requirements Minimum age 17; Medical examination.
Staff Physicians 1 (pt); RNs 1 (pt); LPNs 3 (ft), 2 (pt); Nurses aides 25 (ft), 9 (pt); Physical therapists 1 (ft), 1 (pt); Reality therapists 1 (ft); Recreational therapists 1 (ft); Occupational therapists 1 (pt); Speech therapists 1 (pt); Activities coordinators 1 (ft); Dietitians 1 (ft).
Facilities Dining room; Physical therapy room; Activities room; Crafts room; Laundry room; Barber/Beauty shop.
Activities Arts & crafts; Cards; Games; Reading groups; Prayer groups; Movies.

CLINTON

Golden Valley Nursing Home*
302 E Ohio, Clinton, MO, 64735
(816) 931-4024
Admin Frances Hardy.
Licensure Intermediate care. *Beds* 29.
Owner Proprietary Corp.

Sycamore View Healthcare
1009 E Ohio St, Clinton, MO, 64735
(816) 885-5571
Admin Richard E Clarke. *Medical Dir/Dir of Nursing* Dr Kenneth Scot; Wanda Kimble RN.
Licensure Skilled care. *Beds* SNF 120.
Certified Medicaid; Medicare.
Owner Proprietary Corp (Hillhaven Corp).
Admissions Requirements Minimum age 18; Medical examination.
Staff RNs 2 (ft), 2 (pt); LPNs 8 (ft), 2 (pt); Orderlies 30 (ft), 5 (pt); Activities coordinators 1 (ft).
Facilities Dining room; Physical therapy room; Activities room; Crafts room; Laundry room; Barber/Beauty shop.
Activities Arts & crafts; Cards; Games; Reading groups; Movies; Social/Cultural gatherings.

Truman Health Center*
614 S Main, Clinton, MO, 64735
(816) 885-8328
Admin Ernestine Gray.
Licensure Residential care. *Beds* 25.
Owner Proprietary Corp.

Westwood Home Inc
Hwy 13 N, Clinton, MO, 64735
(816) 885-8196
Admin Melva Dean Hart. *Medical Dir/Dir of Nursing* R J Powell DO.
Licensure Skilled care; Intermediate care. *Beds* 100. *Certified* Medicaid; Medicare.
Owner Proprietary Corp (Beverly Enterprises).
Admissions Requirements Minimum age 21; Physician's request.
Staff Physicians 1 (pt); RNs 2 (ft), 1 (pt); LPNs 5 (ft), 3 (pt); Nurses aides 27 (ft), 18 (pt); Physical therapists 2 (ft), 2 (pt); Recreational therapists 1 (pt); Occupational therapists 1 (pt); Speech therapists 1 (pt); Activities coordinators 1 (pt); Dietitians 1 (pt); Dentists 1 (pt); Dentist 1 (pt).
Facilities Dining room; Physical therapy room; Activities room; Chapel; Crafts room; Laundry room; Barber/Beauty shop.
Activities Arts & crafts; Cards; Games; Reading groups; Prayer groups; Movies; Social/Cultural gatherings.

COLE CAMP

Good Samaritan Nursing Home
1st & Grother, Cole Camp, MO, 65325
(816) 668-4515
Admin Donald D Wuebbold.
Licensure Intermediate care. *Beds* 60.
Certified Medicaid.
Owner Publicly owned.

COLUMBIA

Autumn Court Nursing Center
300 Portland, Columbia, MO, 65201
(314) 875-3033
Admin Carolyn Cantrell. *Medical Dir/Dir of Nursing* Caroline Jackson RN DON.
Licensure Skilled care; Intermediate care. *Beds* 120. *Certified* Medicaid.
Owner Proprietary Corp (Beverly Enterprises).
Admissions Requirements Minimum age 18; Medical examination; Physician's request.
Staff RNs 3 (ft); LPNs 12 (ft); Orderlies 6 (ft); Nurses aides 30 (ft); Reality therapists 1 (ft), 1 (pt); Recreational therapists 1 (pt) 1 (pt); Occupational therapists 1 (ft), 1 (pt); Speech therapists 1 (pt); Activities coordinators 1 (ft); Dietitians 1 (ft); Ophthalmologists 1 (pt); Podiatrists 1 (pt).
Facilities Dining room; Physical therapy room; Activities room; Crafts room; Laundry room; Barber/Beauty shop; Library.
Activities Arts & crafts; Cards; Games; Reading groups; Prayer groups; Movies; Shopping trips; Social/Cultural gatherings.

Boone Retirement Center Inc
1623 Anthony St, Columbia, MO, 65201
(314) 449-6105
Admin John Lloyd Jones. *Medical Dir/Dir of Nursing* David Mehr MD.
Licensure Intermediate care. *Beds* ICF 122.
Certified Medicaid.
Owner Nonprofit Corp.
Admissions Requirements Minimum age 21; Medical examination.
Staff Physicians 1 (pt); RNs 2 (ft), 1 (pt); LPNs 13 (ft); Orderlies 18 (ft); Nurses aides 22 (ft), 12 (pt); Physical therapists 3 (ft); Recreational therapists 1 (ft), 1 (pt); Occupational therapists 1 (pt); Speech therapists 1 (pt); Dietitians 1 (ft); Dentists 1 (pt).
Facilities Dining room; Physical therapy room; Activities room; Crafts room; Laundry room; Barber/Beauty shop; Library.
Activities Arts & crafts; Cards; Games; Prayer groups; Movies; Shopping trips; Social/Cultural gatherings.

Candle Light Lodge Retirement Center*
1406 Business Loop 70 W, Columbia, MO, 65202
(314) 449-5287
Admin Randall P Gross.
Licensure Intermediate care. *Beds* 45.
Owner Proprietary Corp.

Columbia House Healthcare
1801 Towne Dr, Columbia, MO, 65202
(314) 474-6111
Admin John D Sullivan. *Medical Dir/Dir of Nursing* Jeff Beldon MD; Judy Morgan RN DON.
Licensure Skilled care; Intermediate care. *Beds* SNF 47; ICF 94. *Certified* Medicaid; Medicare.
Owner Proprietary Corp (Hillhaven Corp).
Admissions Requirements Minimum age 18; Medical examination.
Staff RNs 3 (ft); LPNs 9 (ft); Nurses aides 66 (ft); Activities coordinators 1 (ft); Dietitians 4 (ft).
Facilities Dining room; Physical therapy room; Activities room; Chapel; Laundry room; Barber/Beauty shop.
Activities Cards; Games; Reading groups; Prayer groups; Movies; Shopping trips; Social/Cultural gatherings.

Columbia Manor Care Center
2012 Nifong Blvd, Columbia, MO, 65201
(314) 449-1246
Admin Robert H Rogers. *Medical Dir/Dir of Nursing* Mary Smith RN.
Licensure Intermediate care. *Beds* ICF 52.
Owner Proprietary Corp.
Admissions Requirements Minimum age 16.
Staff RNs 1 (ft), 1 (pt); LPNs 3 (ft), 2 (pt); Orderlies 2 (ft); Nurses aides 6 (ft), 3 (pt); Physical therapists 1 (ft); Activities coordinators 1 (ft).
Facilities Dining room; Physical therapy room; Activities room; Crafts room; Laundry room; Barber/Beauty shop; Library.
Activities Arts & crafts; Cards; Games; Reading groups; Movies; Social/Cultural gatherings.

Lenoir Health Care Center
3300 New Haven Rd, Columbia, MO, 65201
(314) 443-2478
Admin J Robert Brennan. *Medical Dir/Dir of Nursing* David Mehr MD.
Licensure Skilled care; Intermediate care; Resident care II. *Beds* SNF 47; ICF 30; Residential II 22.
Owner Nonprofit Corp.
Admissions Requirements Minimum age 60; Medical examination; Physician's request.
Staff Physicians 1 (ft); RNs 5 (ft); LPNs 10 (ft); Nurses aides 38 (ft); Physical therapists 1 (ft); Recreational therapists 3 (ft); Occupational therapists 1 (ft); Speech

therapists 1 (ft); Activities coordinators 2 (ft); Dietitians 1 (ft); Ophthalmologists 1 (ft); Podiatrists 1 (ft).
Affiliation Disciples of Christ
Facilities Dining room; Physical therapy room; Activities room; Chapel; Crafts room; Laundry room; Barber/Beauty shop; Library; Occupational therapy room; Speech therapy room; Child day care.
Activities Arts & crafts; Cards; Games; Reading groups; Prayer groups; Movies; Shopping trips; Social/Cultural gatherings; Book discussions; Oil painting; Outings.

CONCORDIA

Lutheran Good Shepherd Home*
3rd & West Sts, Concordia, MO, 64020
(816) 463-2267
Admin Paul R Brackman. *Medical Dir/Dir of Nursing* Dr Robert LaHue.
Licensure Intermediate care. *Beds* 22.
Owner Nonprofit Corp.
Staff Physicians 5 (pt); RNs 3 (ft); LPNs 1 (pt); Nurses aides 12 (ft), 5 (pt); Physical therapists 2 (pt); Occupational therapists 1 (pt); Speech therapists 1 (pt); Activities coordinators 1 (ft); Dietitians 1 (ft); Dentists 1 (pt).
Affiliation Lutheran
Facilities Dining room; Physical therapy room; Activities room; Chapel; Crafts room; Barber/Beauty shop.
Activities Arts & crafts; Cards; Games; Reading groups; Movies.

COOL VALLEY

Bell Crest Inc
1301 S Florissant Rd, Cool Valley, MO, 63121
(314) 521-6060
Admin Gayla Bentley. *Medical Dir/Dir of Nursing* Ranore Davison.
Licensure Intermediate care. *Beds* 51.
Owner Proprietary Corp.
Admissions Requirements Medical examination.
Staff Physicians 1 (pt); RNs 1 (ft), 2 (pt); LPNs 1 (ft); Nurses aides 20 (ft), 10 (pt); Physical therapists 1 (pt); Recreational therapists 1 (ft); Occupational therapists 1 (pt); Speech therapists 1 (pt); Activities coordinators 1 (ft); Dietitians 1 (pt); Ophthalmologists 1 (pt).
Facilities Dining room; Activities room; Crafts room; Laundry room; Barber/Beauty shop; Van.
Activities Arts & crafts; Cards; Games; Reading groups; Prayer groups; Shopping trips; Social/Cultural gatherings.

CREVE COEUR

Evergreen Nursing Home & Rehabilitation Center Inc*
12705 Olive Street Rd, Creve Coeur, MO, 63141
(314) 434-8361
Admin Maurice Abrams. *Medical Dir/Dir of Nursing* Thomas Margulies.
Licensure Skilled care; Intermediate care. *Beds* 147. *Certified* Medicaid; Medicare.
Owner Proprietary Corp.
Admissions Requirements Medical examination.
Facilities Dining room; Physical therapy room; Activities room; Chapel; Crafts room; Laundry room; Barber/Beauty shop; Library; Enclosed open air courtyard.
Activities Arts & crafts; Cards; Games; Reading groups; Prayer groups; Movies.

CUBA

Community Care Center of Cuba
410 N Franklin, Cuba, MO, 65453
(314) 885-3516
Admin Leigh Ann McGuirk. *Medical Dir/Dir of Nursing* Dr G Riffel; Joan Jolley.
Licensure Skilled care; Intermediate care. *Beds* 65. *Certified* Medicaid; Medicare.
Owner Proprietary Corp (Community Care Centers).
Admissions Requirements Minimum age 21; Medical examination.
Staff Physicians 1 (pt); RNs 2 (ft); LPNs 3 (ft), 5 (pt); Orderlies; Nurses aides 38 (ft); Physical therapists 1 (pt); Occupational therapists 1 (pt); Speech therapists 1 (pt); Activities coordinators 1 (ft); Dietitians 1 (pt); Dentists 1 (pt); Ophthalmologists 1 (pt); Podiatrists 1 (pt).
Facilities Dining room; Physical therapy room; Activities room; Chapel; Crafts room; Laundry room; Barber/Beauty shop.
Activities Arts & crafts; Cards; Games; Reading groups; Prayer groups; Movies; Shopping trips; Social/Cultural gatherings.

DES PERES

Des Peres Health Care
11692 Manchester Rd, Des Peres, MO, 63131
(314) 966-3350
Admin Cathy Johnson. *Medical Dir/Dir of Nursing* Dr Don DiPasco.
Licensure Skilled care. *Beds* SNF 143. *Certified* Medicaid.
Owner Proprietary Corp (Hillhaven Corp).
Staff Physicians; RNs; LPNs; Orderlies; Nurses aides; Reality therapists; Recreational therapists; Activities coordinators; Dietitians.
Facilities Dining room; Physical therapy room; Activities room; Chapel; Laundry room; Barber/Beauty shop.
Activities Arts & crafts; Cards; Games; Prayer groups; Movies; Shopping trips; Social/Cultural gatherings.

DESLOGE

Desloge Health Care Center
801 Brim St, Desloge, MO, 63601
(314) 431-0223
Admin W Bruce Bible. *Medical Dir/Dir of Nursing* C W Chastain MD; Debbie Thomas RN.
Licensure Skilled care. *Beds* 120. *Certified* Medicaid; Medicare.
Owner Proprietary Corp (National Health Corp).
Admissions Requirements Minimum age 18.
Staff Physicians 1 (pt); RNs 4 (ft); LPNs 14 (ft), 6 (pt); Orderlies 1 (ft); Nurses aides 30 (ft), 12 (pt); Physical therapists 2 (pt); Occupational therapists 1 (pt); Speech therapists 1 (pt); Activities coordinators 1 (ft); Dietitians 1 (pt).
Facilities Dining room; Physical therapy room; Activities room; Crafts room; Laundry room; Barber/Beauty shop.
Activities Arts & crafts; Cards; Games; Reading groups; Prayer groups; Movies; Shopping trips; Social/Cultural gatherings.

DESOTO

Burt Manor Nursing Home
Rte 1, Box 214A, Hwy 67, DeSoto, MO, 63020
(314) 586-2291
Admin Mary K Baisch. *Medical Dir/Dir of Nursing* Michael K Blank MD; Monica Pashia RN DON.
Licensure Intermediate care. *Beds* ICF 61.
Owner Proprietary Corp.
Admissions Requirements Minimum age 18; Medical examination; Physician's request.

Staff Physicians 2 (pt); RNs 1 (ft); LPNs 5 (ft); Nurses aides 16 (ft), 10 (pt); Physical therapists; Occupational therapists; Speech therapists; Activities coordinators; Dietitians.
Facilities Dining room; Activities room; Barber/Beauty shop.
Activities Cards; Games; Prayer groups; Shopping trips; Social/Cultural gatherings.

DEXTER

Dexter Nursing Center
PO Box 517, Dexter, MO, 63841
(314) 624-7491
Admin Jacqueline McCollom.
Licensure Skilled care; Intermediate care. *Beds* 83. *Certified* Medicaid.
Owner Proprietary Corp (Beverly Enterprises).

Sunshine Manor I
Star Rte Box 150-B, Dexter, MO, 63841
568-2050
Admin Patsy Davis.
Licensure Intermediate care for mentally retarded. *Beds* 20. *Certified* Medicaid; Medicare.
Owner Privately owned.
Admissions Requirements Minimum age 18.
Facilities Dining room; Activities room; Laundry room; Barber/Beauty shop.
Activities Arts & crafts; Bowling; Movie theatres; Dining out.

Sunshine Manor II
108 Nelson, Dexter, MO, 63841
624-4792
Beds 11.
Owner Privately owned.

Vintage Villa Nursing Home
228 E Market St, Dexter, MO, 63841
(314) 624-8908
Admin Vicki McCrackin. *Medical Dir/Dir of Nursing* Mella Parker DON.
Licensure Intermediate care. *Beds* ICF 60. *Certified* Medicaid.
Owner Proprietary Corp.
Admissions Requirements Minimum age 21.
Staff Physicians; RNs 1 (pt); LPNs 5 (ft), 2 (pt); Nurses aides 16 (ft), 5 (pt); Physical therapists 1 (pt); Occupational therapists 1 (pt); Activities coordinators 1 (ft), 1 (pt); Dietitians 1 (pt).
Facilities Dining room; Physical therapy room; Activities room; Laundry room; Barber/Beauty shop.
Activities Arts & crafts; Cards; Games; Reading groups; Prayer groups; Movies; Shopping trips; Social/Cultural gatherings.

DONIPHAN

Doniphan Retirement Home Inc*
PO Box 130, Hwy 142, Doniphan, MO, 63935
(314) 996-2191, 785-0858
Admin Edward Kinworthy.
Licensure Skilled care; Intermediate care. *Beds* 90. *Certified* Medicaid.
Owner Proprietary Corp.

EAST PRAIRIE

Charleston Manor
1220 E Marshall, East Prairie, MO, 63845
(314) 683-3721
Admin David Mercier. *Medical Dir/Dir of Nursing* David Pfefferhoin; Beverly Julian.
Licensure Skilled care; Intermediate care. *Beds* 120. *Certified* Medicaid; Medicare.
Owner Proprietary Corp (Americare Corp).
Admissions Requirements Minimum age 18; Medical examination.
Staff Physicians 5 (pt); RNs 3 (ft); LPNs 12 (ft); Orderlies 1 (ft); Nurses aides 53 (ft); Physical therapists 1 (pt); Recreational therapists 1 (pt); Occupational therapists 1 (pt); Speech therapists 1 (pt); Activities

coordinators 2 (ft); Dietitians 1 (pt); Dentists 1 (pt); Ophthalmologists 1 (pt); Podiatrists 1 (pt).
Facilities Dining room; Physical therapy room; Activities room; Laundry room; Barber/Beauty shop.
Activities Arts & crafts; Cards; Games; Reading groups; Prayer groups; Movies; Shopping trips; Social/Cultural gatherings.

EDINA

Hostel House*
300-302 N Main St, Edina, MO, 63537
(816) 397-3404
Admin Ina Marie Small.
Licensure Residential care. *Beds* 23.
Owner Proprietary Corp.

Knox County Nursing Home
Hwy 6 E, Edina, MO, 63537
(816) 397-2282
Admin Gerald Foreman. *Medical Dir/Dir of Nursing* Helen Karhoff LPN.
Licensure Intermediate care. *Beds* 60.
Certified Medicaid.
Owner Proprietary Corp.
Staff Physicians 3 (pt); RNs 1 (pt); LPNs 1 (ft), 2 (pt); Nurses aides 6 (ft), 35 (pt); Physical therapists 1 (pt); Occupational therapists 1 (pt); Speech therapists 1 (pt); Activities coordinators 1 (ft).
Facilities Dining room; Activities room; Chapel; Crafts room; Laundry room; Barber/Beauty shop.
Activities Arts & crafts; Cards; Games; Reading groups; Prayer groups; Movies.

EL DORADO SPRINGS

Community Nursing Home*
400 E Hospital Rd, El Dorado Springs, MO, 64744
(417) 876-2531
Admin David B Richardson.
Licensure Intermediate care. *Beds* 120.
Certified Medicaid.
Owner Proprietary Corp (Beverly Enterprises).

ELDON

Osage Manor Nursing & Care Center*
Rte 1, Box 450, Eldon, MO, 65026
(314) 392-3164
Admin Carolyn Nichols. *Medical Dir/Dir of Nursing* Dr Robert Mason.
Licensure Intermediate care. *Beds* 60.
Certified Medicaid.
Owner Proprietary Corp.
Admissions Requirements Minimum age 16; Medical examination; Physician's request.
Staff RNs 1 (ft); LPNs 2 (ft), 1 (pt); Nurses aides 11 (ft), 16 (pt); Activities coordinators 1 (ft).
Facilities Dining room; Physical therapy room; Laundry room; Barber/Beauty shop; Library; Living room; Solarium; Whirlpool bath.
Activities Arts & crafts; Cards; Games; Reading groups; Prayer groups; Movies; Shopping trips; Social/Cultural gatherings; Book & newspaper reading; Birthday parties monthly; Music programs; Special meals & holiday parties; Exercise group; Coffee group; Resident council; Active community auxilliary; Special pet visitor (dog).

ELLISVILLE

Westwinds Geriatric Center*
1460 Manchester Rd, Ellisville, MO, 63011
(314) 227-5000
Admin Ronald E Rogers.
Licensure Intermediate care. *Beds* 120.
Certified Medicaid.
Owner Proprietary Corp.

ELSBERRY

Elsberry Health Care Center
PO Box 26, Rte 2, Elsberry, MO, 63343
(314) 898-2880
Admin Perry Stonebraker. *Medical Dir/Dir of Nursing* Hazel Gladney DON.
Licensure Intermediate care. *Beds* ICF 60.
Certified Medicaid.
Owner Nonprofit Corp.
Admissions Requirements Minimum age 18; Medical examination.
Staff RNs 1 (pt); LPNs 3 (ft), 1 (pt); Nurses aides 17 (ft), 7 (pt); Physical therapists 1 (pt); Occupational therapists 1 (pt); Speech therapists 1 (pt); Activities coordinators 1 (ft); Dietitians 1 (pt).
Facilities Dining room; Physical therapy room; Laundry room; Barber/Beauty shop.
Activities Arts & crafts; Cards; Games; Reading groups; Prayer groups; Movies; Shopping trips; Social/Cultural gatherings.

Sunset Nursing & Retirement Home of Elsberry*
415 N 5th, Elsberry, MO, 63343
(314) 898-5604
Admin Judith Jordan.
Licensure Intermediate care. *Beds* 29.
Owner Proprietary Corp.
Admissions Requirements Minimum age 18.

ESSEX

Martin Hills Retirement Village
Rte 2, Essex, MO, 63846
(314) 568-2780
Admin Greta E Martin. *Medical Dir/Dir of Nursing* Judy Garner DON.
Licensure RCF II. *Beds* 50. *Certified* Medicaid.
Owner Proprietary Corp.
Admissions Requirements Minimum age 18.
Staff LPNs; Nurses aides; Activities coordinators.
Facilities Dining room; Laundry room; Barber/Beauty shop; Coffee shop.
Activities Arts & crafts; Cards; Games; Movies; Shopping trips; Social/Cultural gatherings.

EUREKA

Marymount Manor
313 Augustine Rd, Eureka, MO, 63114
(314) 938-6770
Admin Charles J Riley. *Medical Dir/Dir of Nursing* R Gavini MD; Thelma Gand RN DON.
Licensure Skilled care; Intermediate care; Residential care Nursing. *Beds* 280. *Certified* Medicaid; Medicare.
Owner Privately owned.
Admissions Requirements Minimum age 21; Medical examination; Physician's request.
Staff Physicians 2 (pt); RNs 3 (ft), 3 (pt); LPNs 8 (ft), 4 (pt); Orderlies 2 (ft), 1 (pt); Nurses aides 48 (ft), 10 (pt); Physical therapists 1 (pt); Reality therapists 1 (pt); Occupational therapists 1 (pt); Speech therapists 1 (ft), 2 (pt); Activities coordinators 3 (ft), 2 (pt); Dietitians 1 (pt); Ophthalmologists 1 (pt).
Facilities Dining room; Physical therapy room; Activities room; Crafts room; Laundry room; Barber/Beauty shop; Library; Visiting rooms.
Activities Arts & crafts; Cards; Games; Reading groups; Prayer groups; Movies; Shopping trips; Social/Cultural gatherings.

Price Memorial*
PO Box 476, Forby Rd, Eureka, MO, 63025
(314) 587-3200
Admin Joseph Spila.

Licensure Skilled care. *Beds* 120. *Certified* Medicaid.
Owner Nonprofit Corp.

St Joseph's Hill Infirmary Inc*
Saint Joseph's Rd, Eureka, MO, 63025
(314) 587-3661
Admin Br Bernardo Trosa.
Licensure Skilled care. *Beds* 130.
Owner Nonprofit Corp.
Affiliation Roman Catholic

EXCELSIOR SPRINGS

Excelsior Springs Care Center*
1410 Hospital Dr, Excelsior Springs, MO, 64024
Admin Thomas Bechtel. *Medical Dir/Dir of Nursing* James Soeldner MD.
Licensure Skilled care. *Beds* 120. *Certified* Medicaid; Medicare.
Owner Proprietary Corp (Beverly Enterprises).
Staff RNs 2 (ft), 2 (pt); LPNs 7 (ft), 2 (pt); Orderlies 2 (ft), 1 (pt); Nurses aides 35 (ft), 10 (pt); Activities coordinators 1 (ft), 1 (pt).
Facilities Dining room; Physical therapy room; Activities room; Barber/Beauty shop.
Activities Arts & crafts; Games; Reading groups; Prayer groups; Shopping trips; Social/Cultural gatherings.

Spa View Nursing Home Inc
120 Bluff St, Excelsior Springs, MO, 64024
(816) 637-3145
Admin Jesse J. Hwang. *Medical Dir/Dir of Nursing* Dr Aram Lila; Esther Hwang.
Licensure Intermediate care. *Beds* 111.
Owner Privately owned.
Admissions Requirements Medical examination.
Staff Physicians 3 (pt); RNs 1 (ft); LPNs 1 (ft), 2 (pt); Nurses aides 17 (ft), 4 (pt); Physical therapists 1 (pt); Activities coordinators 1 (ft); Dietitians 1 (pt).
Facilities Dining room; Activities room; Chapel; Crafts room; Laundry room; Barber/Beauty shop; Library.
Activities Arts & crafts; Cards; Games; Reading groups; Prayer groups; Movies; Shopping trips; Social/Cultural gatherings.

FARMINGTON

Bayless Boarding Home
PO Box 288, Rte 3, Farmington, MO, 63640
(314) 756-2856
Admin Emma Lee Bayless.
Licensure Intermediate care. *Beds* ICF 4.
Owner Privately owned.
Admissions Requirements Males only.
Facilities Dining room; Activities room; Laundry room.
Activities Arts & crafts; Cards; Games; Movies; Shopping trips; Social/Cultural gatherings.

Camelot Nursing Home*
705 Grand Canyon Dr, Farmington, MO, 63640
(314) 756-8911
Admin Carroll Allen.
Licensure Skilled care; Intermediate care. *Beds* 90. *Certified* Medicaid.
Owner Proprietary Corp (Beverly Enterprises).

Thomas Dell Nursing Home Inc*
Box 452, Farmington, MO, 63640
(314) 756-6716, 6717
Admin Lester J Straughan & Janet Straughan.
Licensure Intermediate care. *Beds* 70.
Owner Proprietary Corp.

Easter's Home of Ruth Inc*
401 S Henry, Farmington, MO, 63640
(314) 756-4559
Admin Sandra L Straughan.
Licensure Intermediate care; ABF. *Beds* ICF 42; ABF 12.

Owner Proprietary Corp.
Admissions Requirements Minimum age 17.
Staff RNs 1 (ft); LPNs 1 (ft), 2 (pt); Nurses aides 12 (ft), 3 (pt); Physical therapists 2 (pt); Recreational therapists 1 (ft); Speech therapists 2 (pt); Activities coordinators 1 (ft); Dietitians 1 (pt).
Facilities Dining room; Activities room; Chapel; Crafts room; Laundry room; Barber/Beauty shop.
Activities Arts & crafts; Cards; Games; Reading groups; Prayer groups; Movies; Shopping trips; Social/Cultural gatherings.

Fleur de Lis
1108 W Liberty St, Farmington, MO, 63640
(314) 756-6658
Admin Pearl Underwood. *Medical Dir/Dir of Nursing* Martha Young DON.
Licensure Intermediate care. *Beds* ICF 104. *Certified* Medicaid.
Owner Proprietary Corp (Beverly Enterprises).
Admissions Requirements Minimum age 18; Medical examination; Physician's request.
Staff Physicians; RNs 1 (ft), 1 (pt); LPNs 6 (ft), 1 (pt); Orderlies 4 (ft); Nurses aides 26 (ft); Activities coordinators 1 (ft); Dietitians 1 (ft).
Facilities Dining room; Physical therapy room; Activities room; Crafts room; Laundry room; Barber/Beauty shop; Library.
Activities Arts & crafts; Cards; Games; Reading groups; Prayer groups; Movies; Shopping trips; Social/Cultural gatherings.

Presbyterian Manor at Farmington
500 Cayce, Farmington, MO, 63640
(314) 756-6768
Admin Peter W F Adgie. *Medical Dir/Dir of Nursing* Lana Jinkerson RN.
Licensure Intermediate care. *Beds* 79.
Owner Nonprofit Corp.
Admissions Requirements Minimum age 65; Medical examination.
Staff Physicians 1 (pt); RNs 1 (ft), 1 (pt); LPNs 4 (ft), 2 (pt); Nurses aides 37 (ft), 3 (pt); Physical therapists 1 (pt); Occupational therapists 3 (pt); Activities coordinators 2 (ft); Dietitians 1 (pt); Dentists 1 (pt); Podiatrists 1 (pt).
Affiliation Presbyterian

Sunset Nursing & Retirement Home of Farmington*
508 N Washington, Farmington, MO, 63640
(314) 756-5376
Admin Freda Huston.
Licensure Intermediate care. *Beds* 31.
Owner Proprietary Corp.

FAYETTE

The Greenbriar Home
PO Box 249, 306 S Main St, Fayette, MO, 65248
(816) 248-2091
Admin Charma E Blount.
Licensure Residential care facility II. *Beds* MR/DD MI 24. *Certified* Medicaid.
Owner Proprietary Corp.
Admissions Requirements Minimum age 17; Medical examination.
Staff LPNs 1 (pt); Orderlies 4 (ft); Nurses aides 4 (ft); Activities coordinators 1 (pt).
Facilities Dining room; Activities room; Laundry room; Sitting and/or Quiet room.
Activities Arts & crafts; Cards; Games; Reading groups; Prayer groups; Movies; Shopping trips; Social/Cultural gatherings; Musical groups.

Maple Lawn Rest Home Inc
PO Box 65, Rte 1, Fayette, MO, 65248
(816) 248-3626
Admin Kathy Kauffman. *Medical Dir/Dir of Nursing* Debbie Carr LPN DON.
Licensure RCF II. *Beds* 39.
Owner Proprietary Corp.

Admissions Requirements Minimum age 18.
Staff LPNs 1 (pt); Nurses aides.
Facilities Dining room; Activities room; Crafts room; Laundry room; Barber/Beauty shop.
Activities Arts & crafts; Cards; Games; Reading groups; Prayer groups; Movies; Shopping trips; Social/Cultural gatherings; Outings; Cookouts.

The Phillips Home*
303 S Main, Fayette, MO, 65248
(816) 248-3333
Admin Lawrence Sapp Jr & Pegi Phillips-Sapp.
Licensure Intermediate care. *Beds* 30.
Owner Proprietary Corp.

Rest Haven Residential Care
400 N Mulberry, Fayette, MO, 65248
(816) 248-2277
Admin Chris Losey. *Medical Dir/Dir of Nursing* L W Lawhorne MD; Jeanette Inness RN DON.
Licensure RCF. *Beds* RCF 27. *Certified* Medicaid; Medicare.
Owner Proprietary Corp.
Admissions Requirements Minimum age 21; Medical examination; Physician's request.
Staff Physicians 1 (pt); RNs 1 (pt); Nurses aides 6 (ft), 7 (pt); Activities coordinators 1 (pt).
Facilities Dining room; Activities room; Crafts room; Laundry room; Barber/Beauty shop; Library.
Activities Arts & crafts; Cards; Games; Reading groups; Prayer groups; Movies; Shopping trips.

Vogue Retirement Residence
301 S Main St, Fayette, MO, 65248
Admin Zeda Eaton-Wiehardt & Theda Stidham.
Licensure Adult Boarding care. *Beds* 11.
Owner Proprietary Corp.
Admissions Requirements Medical examination.
Staff Nurses aides 2 (pt).
Facilities Dining room; Crafts room; Barber/Beauty shop.
Activities Arts & crafts; Cards; Games; Reading groups; Prayer groups; Shopping trips.

FENTON

Cori Manor Nursing Home
560 Corisande Hill Rd, Fenton, MO, 63026
(314) 343-2282
Admin Connie Radvin. *Medical Dir/Dir of Nursing* Dr Robert Dorton; Kathy Lorey RN DON.
Licensure Skilled care; RCF II.
Owner Proprietary Corp (Life Care Centers of America).
Admissions Requirements Medical examination.
Staff Physicians 1 (ft), 3 (pt); RNs 2 (ft), 2 (pt); LPNs 7 (ft); Orderlies 5 (ft); Nurses aides 52 (ft); Physical therapists 1 (ft); Recreational therapists 1 (ft); Occupational therapists 1 (ft); Activities coordinators 1 (ft), 1 (pt); Dietitians 1 (ft); Dentists 1 (ft); Ophthalmologists 1 (ft).
Facilities Dining room; Physical therapy room; Activities room; Crafts room; Laundry room; Barber/Beauty shop; Library.
Activities Arts & crafts; Cards; Games; Reading groups; Prayer groups; Movies; Shopping trips; Social/Cultural gatherings.

Fieser Nursing Home
404 Main St, Fenton, MO, 63026
(314) 343-4344
Admin Glen E Fieser. *Medical Dir/Dir of Nursing* R Kaza MD; Gwen Stevens RN DON.
Licensure Intermediate care. *Beds* 60.

Owner Proprietary Corp.
Admissions Requirements Medical examination.
Staff Physicians 1 (pt); RNs 3 (ft); LPNs 1 (pt); Nurses aides 18 (ft), 2 (pt); Physical therapists 1 (pt); Reality therapists 1 (pt); Recreational therapists 1 (pt); Occupational therapists 1 (pt); Speech therapists 1 (pt); Dietitians 1 (pt); Ophthalmologists 1 (pt); Podiatrists 1 (pt).
Facilities Dining room; Physical therapy room; Activities room; Crafts room; Laundry room; Barber/Beauty shop.
Activities Arts & crafts; Cards; Games; Reading groups; Prayer groups; Movies; Shopping trips; Social/Cultural gatherings.

FERGUSON

Christian Old Peoples Home
800 Chambers Rd, Ferguson, MO, 63135
(314) 522-8100
Admin Richard Klug. *Medical Dir/Dir of Nursing* D Rosenberg MD; T Gestring RN.
Licensure Skilled care. *Beds* 180. *Certified* Medicaid.
Admissions Requirements Minimum age 65.
Staff Physicians 4 (pt); RNs 5 (ft), 4 (pt); LPNs 4 (ft), 8 (pt); Nurses aides 39 (ft), 19 (pt); Physical therapists 2 (ft); Activities coordinators 3 (ft); Dietitians 1 (ft); Dentists 1 (pt); Podiatrists 1 (pt).
Facilities Dining room; Physical therapy room; Activities room; Chapel; Crafts room; Laundry room; Barber/Beauty shop; Library.
Activities Arts & crafts; Cards; Games; Reading groups; Prayer groups; Movies; Shopping trips; Social/Cultural gatherings.

Oak Knoll Nursing Home
37 N Clark Ave, Ferguson, MO, 63135
(314) 521-7419
Admin Eunice Schvermann. *Medical Dir/Dir of Nursing* R A Latorpe MD; Ida Johnson DON.
Licensure Intermediate care. *Beds* ICF 60. *Certified* Private pay.
Owner Proprietary Corp.
Staff Physicians 1 (ft); RNs 2 (ft), 1 (pt); LPNs 1 (ft), 3 (pt); Dietitians 1 (ft).
Facilities Dining room; Activities room; Chapel; Crafts room; Laundry room; Barber/Beauty shop; Library.
Activities Arts & crafts; Cards; Games; Reading groups; Prayer groups; Movies; Shopping trips; Social/Cultural gatherings; Garden club.

FESTUS

Bolle's Boarding Home Inc*
500 Sunshine Dr, Festus, MO, 63028
Admin Louisa E Bolle. *Medical Dir/Dir of Nursing* M Charles MD.
Licensure Intermediate care. *Beds* 28. *Certified* Medicaid.
Owner Proprietary Corp.
Admissions Requirements Medical examination.
Staff Physicians 1 (pt); LPNs 2 (ft); Nurses aides 6 (ft), 2 (pt); Physical therapists 1 (ft); Recreational therapists 1 (ft); Activities coordinators 1 (ft); Dietitians 1 (pt); Dentists 1 (pt); Ophthalmologists 1 (pt); Podiatrists 1 (pt); Audiologists 1 (pt).
Facilities Dining room; Physical therapy room; Activities room; Crafts room; Laundry room; Barber/Beauty shop.
Activities Arts & crafts; Cards; Games; Reading groups; Prayer groups; Movies; Shopping trips; Exercise sessions.

Community Care Center of Festus
PO Box 427, Rte 2, Festus, MO, 63028
(314) 937-3150
Admin Connie D Marshall.

Licensure Skilled care. *Beds* SNF 81. *Certified* Medicaid.
Owner Privately owned.
Admissions Requirements Minimum age 18.
Staff Physicians; RNs; LPNs; Nurses aides; Physical therapists; Speech therapists; Activities coordinators; Dietitians.
Facilities Dining room; Physical therapy room; Activities room; Laundry room; Barber/Beauty shop.
Activities Arts & crafts; Cards; Games; Reading groups; Prayer groups; Movies; Shopping trips; Social/Cultural gatherings.

Festus Nursing Center
627 Westwoods S Dr, Festus, MO, 63028
(314) 937-9066, 464-0194
Admin Sharon Greco. *Medical Dir/Dir of Nursing* Dr Moorthy; Joanne Nash RN DON.
Licensure Skilled care. *Beds* SNF 120. *Certified* Medicaid.
Owner Proprietary Corp (Beverly Enterprises).
Admissions Requirements Minimum age 16.
Staff RNs 7 (ft); LPNs 8 (ft); Orderlies 2 (ft); Nurses aides 55 (ft), 6 (pt); Activities coordinators 1 (ft); Dietitians 1 (ft).
Facilities Dining room; Physical therapy room; Activities room; Crafts room; Laundry room; Barber/Beauty shop; Library.
Activities Arts & crafts; Cards; Games; Reading groups; Prayer groups; Movies; Shopping trips; Social/Cultural gatherings.

Festus Rest Home
705 Moore St, Festus, MO, 63028
(314) 937-7125
Admin Harry J Reiter.
Licensure Residential care II. *Beds* 21.
Owner Privately owned.

FLAT RIVER

Peach Residential Care Facility
301 Roosevelt, Flat River, MO, 63601
(?) 431-4874
Admin Deborah K Franks. *Medical Dir/Dir of Nursing* Lorretta Statham.
Licensure RCF II. *Beds* RCF II 16. *Certified* Medicaid; Medicare.
Owner Privately owned.
Admissions Requirements Minimum age 18; Medical examination.
Staff Physicians 1 (ft), 16 (pt); RNs 1 (ft), 16 (pt); LPNs 1 (ft), 16 (pt); Nurses aides 7 (ft), 16 (pt); Recreational therapists 1 (ft), 16 (pt); Occupational therapists 1 (ft), 16 (pt); Speech therapists 1 (ft), 16 (pt); Activities coordinators 1 (ft), 16 (pt); Dietitians 1 (ft), 16 (pt).
Facilities Dining room; Activities room; Laundry room.
Activities Cards; Games; Prayer groups; Shopping trips.

FLORISSANT

Americana Healthcare Center
1200 Graham Rd, Florissant, MO, 63031
(314) 838-6555
Admin Judith Sutton. *Medical Dir/Dir of Nursing* Dr Light; Jackie Proctor DON.
Licensure Skilled care. *Beds* SNF 98. *Certified* Medicaid; Medicare.
Owner Proprietary Corp (Manor Care).
Admissions Requirements Minimum age 18; Medical examination.
Facilities Dining room; Physical therapy room; Activities room; Laundry room; Barber/Beauty shop.
Activities Arts & crafts; Cards; Games; Reading groups; Prayer groups; Movies; Shopping trips; Social/Cultural gatherings.

Florissant Nursing Center*
Rancho & Patterson, Florissant, MO, 63031
(314) 839-2150

Admin Lawrence Boshert.
Licensure Skilled care. *Beds* 120. *Certified* Medicaid.
Owner Proprietary Corp (Beverly Enterprises).

Northgate Park Nursing Home
250 S New Florissant Rd, Florissant, MO, 63031
(314) 838-2211
Admin Yvonne Hopmann RN. *Medical Dir/Dir of Nursing* Lucy Trautmann RN.
Licensure Skilled care; Intermediate care. *Beds* 180.
Owner Proprietary Corp.
Staff Physicians; RNs; LPNs; Orderlies; Nurses aides; Physical therapists; Occupational therapists; Speech therapists; Activities coordinators; Dietitians; Dentists; Ophthalmologists; Podiatrists.
Facilities Dining room; Physical therapy room; Activities room; Crafts room; Laundry room; Barber/Beauty shop.
Activities Arts & crafts; Cards; Games; Reading groups; Prayer groups; Movies; Shopping trips; Social/Cultural gatherings.

Park Terrace Resident Center
300 New Florissant Rd S, Florissant, MO, 63031
(314) 921-1700
Admin David L Nolting. *Medical Dir/Dir of Nursing* Lori Hemenway DON.
Licensure Residential care. *Beds* 160.
Owner Proprietary Corp.
Staff RNs 1 (ft), 1 (pt); LPNs 2 (ft), 3 (pt); Nurses aides 7 (ft), 7 (pt); Activities coordinators 1 (ft), 1 (pt); Dietitians 5 (ft), 7 (pt); Medical technicians 5 (ft), 5 (pt).
Facilities Dining room; Activities room; Crafts room; Laundry room; Barber/Beauty shop; Library.
Activities Arts & crafts; Cards; Games; Reading groups; Prayer groups; Movies; Shopping trips; Social/Cultural gatherings.

St Sophia Geriatric Center*
936 Charbonier Rd, Florissant, MO, 63031
(314) 831-4800
Admin Edward Dering.
Licensure Skilled care; Intermediate care. *Beds* 240. *Certified* Medicaid; Medicare.
Owner Proprietary Corp.

Spanish Lake Nursing Center
13700 Old Halls Ferry, Florissant, MO, 63033
(314) 355-6660
Admin David G Mixon. *Medical Dir/Dir of Nursing* Dr V Philips; Sharon Coulborn RN DON.
Licensure Skilled care. *Beds* SNF 120. *Certified* Medicaid.
Owner Proprietary Corp (Beverly Enterprises).
Staff Physicians; RNs; LPNs; Orderlies; Nurses aides; Physical therapists; Occupational therapists; Speech therapists; Activities coordinators; Dietitians; Dentists; Ophthalmologists; Podiatrists.
Languages Italian, German
Facilities Dining room; Physical therapy room; Activities room; Laundry room; Barber/Beauty shop.
Activities Arts & crafts; Cards; Games; Reading groups; Prayer groups; Movies; Shopping trips; Social/Cultural gatherings.

FORSYTH

Lakeview Rest Home Inc*
PO Box 276, Forsyth, MO, 65653
(417) 546-3081
Admin Carolyn K Blevins.
Licensure Intermediate care. *Beds* 67.
Owner Proprietary Corp.

FREDERICKTOWN

Madison Memorial Hospital*
College at Wood Ave, Box 431, Fredericktown, MO, 63645
(314) 783-3341
Admin Bill M Seek. *Medical Dir/Dir of Nursing* Arthur Newcomb MD.
Licensure Intermediate care. *Beds* 9.
Owner Publicly owned.
Staff Physicians 12 (ft); RNs 2 (ft); LPNs 4 (ft), 2 (pt); Orderlies 3 (ft); Nurses aides 38 (ft); Physical therapists 1 (ft); Speech therapists 1 (pt); Activities coordinators 1 (ft); Dietitians 2 (pt).
Facilities Dining room; Physical therapy room; Activities room; Chapel; Crafts room; Laundry room; Barber/Beauty shop.
Activities Arts & crafts; Games; Reading groups; Prayer groups; Movies; Social/Cultural gatherings.

Ozark Nursing Home*
700 S Main St, Fredericktown, MO, 63645
(314) 783-6833
Admin Florence Wanner.
Licensure Intermediate care. *Beds* 42.
Owner Proprietary Corp.
Admissions Requirements Minimum age 40; Medical examination.
Staff Physicians 1 (pt); RNs 1 (pt); LPNs 2 (ft), 1 (pt); Orderlies 1 (ft), 2 (pt); Nurses aides 12 (ft), 5 (pt); Recreational therapists 1 (pt); Dietitians 1 (pt).

FULTON

Fulton Manor Care Center*
520 Manor Dr, Fulton, MO, 65251
(314) 642-6834
Admin Charlotte Henderson. *Medical Dir/Dir of Nursing* Dr George Grace.
Licensure Intermediate care. *Beds* 52.
Owner Proprietary Corp.
Admissions Requirements Minimum age Birth; Medical examination; Physician's request.
Staff RNs 1 (pt); LPNs 3 (ft), 1 (pt); Nurses aides 10 (ft), 4 (pt); Activities coordinators 1 (pt).
Facilities Dining room; Activities room; Laundry room.
Activities Arts & crafts; Cards; Games; Reading groups; Prayer groups; Movies.

Fulton Presbyterian Manor
802 Court St, Fulton, MO, 65251
(314) 642-6646
Admin Jane E Daniell-Mitchel.
Licensure Intermediate care; Boarding care. *Beds* ICF 30; Boarding care 37.
Owner Nonprofit Corp.
Affiliation Presbyterian

Kingdom Nursing Home Association Inc
Rte 6, 501 Collier Lane, Fulton, MO, 65251-2022
(314) 642-2022
Admin Pat Burton LPN. *Medical Dir/Dir of Nursing* Sheila Pattillo LPN.
Licensure Intermediate care. *Beds* ICF 28. *Certified* Medicaid.
Owner Nonprofit organization/foundation.
Admissions Requirements Medical examination.
Staff Physicians 5 (pt); RNs 1 (pt); LPNs 2 (ft), 2 (pt); Nurses aides 6 (ft), 11 (pt); Physical therapists 1 (pt); Reality therapists 1 (pt); Recreational therapists 01; Occupational therapists 1 (pt); Speech therapists 1 (pt); Activities coordinators 1 (pt); Dietitians 1 (pt); Dentists 1 (pt); Ophthalmologists 1 (pt); Podiatrists 1 (pt).
Facilities Dining room; Physical therapy room; Activities room; Laundry room; Barber/Beauty shop.

Activities Arts & crafts; Cards; Games;
Reading groups; Prayer groups; Movies;
Shopping trips; Social/Cultural gatherings.

Modern Acre Home*
Rte 2, Fulton, MO, 65251
(314) 642-3160
Admin Sodonia Logan.
Licensure Intermediate care. *Beds* 22.
Owner Proprietary Corp.

Sodonia's Home*
222 E 6th, Fulton, MO, 65251
(314) 642-3160
Admin Warren T Robinson.
Licensure Intermediate care. *Beds* 22.
Owner Proprietary Corp.

GALLATIN

Daviess County Nursing Home Corp
Hwy 6 W, Gallatin, MO, 64640
(816) 663-2197
Admin Evelyn Morrissey. *Medical Dir/Dir of
Nursing* Sheldon Dunkin DON.
Licensure Intermediate care. *Beds* ICF 97.
Certified Medicaid.
Owner Nonprofit Corp.
Admissions Requirements Medical
examination.
Staff RNs 1 (ft), 2 (pt); LPNs 5 (ft); Nurses
aides 35 (ft), 8 (pt); Physical therapists 1 (ft);
Recreational therapists 1 (ft), 2 (pt);
Occupational therapists 1 (pt); Speech
therapists 1 (pt); Activities coordinators 1
(pt); Dietitians 1 (pt).
Facilities Dining room; Physical therapy
room; Activities room; Chapel; Crafts room;
Laundry room; Barber/Beauty shop; Library.
Activities Arts & crafts; Cards; Games;
Reading groups; Prayer groups; Movies;
Shopping trips; Social/Cultural gatherings.

GLADSTONE

Kendallwood Trails Nursing Center*
2900 Kendallwood Pkwy, Gladstone, MO,
64119
(816) 453-1222
Admin William D Burford.
Licensure Skilled care; Intermediate care. *Beds*
280. *Certified* Medicaid; Medicare.
Owner Proprietary Corp.

GLASGOW

Colonial Manor of Glasgow
100 Audsley Dr, Glasgow, MO, 65254
(816) 339-2297
Admin Nell Hensiek. *Medical Dir/Dir of
Nursing* William Marshall MD.
Licensure Intermediate care; Intermediate care
for mentally retarded. *Beds* 59. *Certified*
Medicaid.
Owner Proprietary Corp (Beverly Enterprises).
Admissions Requirements Medical
examination; Physician's request.
Staff Physicians; RNs 1 (ft); LPNs 2 (ft), 1
(pt); Orderlies 1 (ft); Nurses aides 13 (ft), 3
(pt); Physical therapists 1 (ft); Recreational
therapists 1 (ft); Occupational therapists 1
(ft); Speech therapists 1 (ft); Activities
coordinators 1 (ft); Dietitians 1 (ft); Dentists
1 (pt); Ophthalmologists 1 (pt); Podiatrists 1
(pt); Dentist 1 (pt).
Facilities Dining room; Physical therapy
room; Activities room; Chapel; Crafts room;
Laundry room; Barber/Beauty shop; Library.
Activities Arts & crafts; Cards; Games;
Reading groups; Prayer groups; Movies;
Shopping trips; Social/Cultural gatherings.

GOWER

Gower Convalescent Center Inc
Hwy 169 S, Gower, MO, 64454
(816) 424-6483
Admin John Ronald Murawski. *Medical Dir/
Dir of Nursing* Dorothy Kretzer RN.
Licensure Intermediate care. *Beds* ICF 74.
Certified Medicaid.
Owner Nonprofit Corp.
Admissions Requirements Minimum age 18.
Staff Physicians 2 (pt); RNs 1 (ft); LPNs 3
(ft); Orderlies 2 (ft); Nurses aides 32 (ft);
Physical therapists 1 (pt); Recreational
therapists 2 (ft); Occupational therapists 1
(pt); Speech therapists 1 (pt); Activities
coordinators 1 (ft); Dietitians 1 (pt);
Podiatrists 1 (pt).
Facilities Dining room; Physical therapy
room; Activities room; Crafts room; Laundry
room; Barber/Beauty shop; Library.
Activities Arts & crafts; Cards; Games; Prayer
groups; Movies; Social/Cultural gatherings.

GRANDVIEW

Geriatric Center of Grandview*
13111 Spring St, Grandview, MO, 64030
(816) 761-4333
Admin Tom Mason. *Medical Dir/Dir of
Nursing* Dr Kirk Barnett.
Licensure Intermediate care. *Beds* 52.
Owner Proprietary Corp.
Admissions Requirements Medical
examination.
Staff Physicians 2 (pt); RNs 1 (pt); LPNs 3
(ft), 1 (pt); Nurses aides 18 (ft), 5 (pt);
Physical therapists 3 (pt); Reality therapists
1 (pt); Occupational therapists 1 (pt); Speech
therapists 1 (pt); Activities coordinators 2
(pt); Dietitians 1 (pt); Dentists 1 (pt);
Podiatrists 1 (pt).
Facilities Dining room; Laundry room.
Activities Arts & crafts; Cards; Games; Prayer
groups.

Grandview Manor Care Center
5301 E 125th St, Grandview, MO, 64030
(816) 763-2855
Admin Vada Mae Eder RN MA. *Medical Dir/
Dir of Nursing* Mary Bragulla DON.
Licensure Intermediate care. *Beds* 102.
Owner Proprietary Corp (Beverly Enterprises).
Staff RNs 1 (ft), 3 (pt); LPNs 4 (ft), 2 (pt);
Orderlies 1 (ft); Nurses aides 20 (ft), 8 (pt);
Physical therapists 1 (pt); Reality therapists
1 (pt); Recreational therapists 1 (pt);
Occupational therapists 1 (pt); Speech
therapists 1 (pt); Activities coordinators 1
(ft), 1 (pt); Dietitians 1 (pt);
Ophthalmologists 1 (pt).

GRANT CITY

Wilkinsons Residential Care Facility
PO Box 130, Rte 1, Grant City, MO, 64456
(816) 564-3304
Admin Susan Holzfaster. *Medical Dir/Dir of
Nursing* Susan Holzfaster.
Licensure Residential care. *Beds* 15.
Owner Privately owned.
Admissions Requirements Minimum age 21;
Medical examination.
Staff Physicians; LPNs; Nurses aides;
Dietitians; Dentists.
Facilities Dining room; Activities room;
Laundry room.
Activities Cards; Games; Reading groups;
Prayer groups; Music; Field trips.

Worth County Convalescent Center
503 E 4th, Grant City, MO, 64456
(816) 564-3304
Admin Mary Weaver. *Medical Dir/Dir of
Nursing* Marcia Henry RN DON.
Licensure Intermediate care. *Beds* ICF 60.
Certified Medicaid.

Owner Nonprofit organization/foundation.
Admissions Requirements Medical
examination; Physician's request.
Staff Physicians 2 (pt); RNs 4 (pt); LPNs 3
(ft); Nurses aides 15 (ft), 10 (pt); Physical
therapists 1 (pt); Occupational therapists 1
(pt); Speech therapists 1 (pt); Activities
coordinators 1 (pt); Dietitians 1 (pt);
Podiatrists 1 (pt).
Facilities Dining room; Physical therapy
room; Activities room; Chapel; Crafts room;
Laundry room; Barber/Beauty shop; TV;
Living room.
Activities Arts & crafts; Cards; Games;
Reading groups; Prayer groups; Movies;
Shopping trips; Social/Cultural gatherings.

GREENFIELD

Dade County Nursing Home
400 S Broad St, Greenfield, MO, 65661
(417) 637-5315
Admin Brenda Dodson. *Medical Dir/Dir of
Nursing* Barbara Evans RN DON.
Licensure Intermediate care; Residential care.
Beds ICF 120; Residential 24. *Certified*
Medicaid.
Owner Publicly owned.
Admissions Requirements Minimum age 18.
Staff RNs 1 (ft), 1 (pt); LPNs 8 (ft), 3 (pt);
Nurses aides 41 (ft); Physical therapists 2
(ft); Activities coordinators 2 (ft); Dietitians
1 (ft).
Facilities Dining room; Physical therapy
room; Activities room; Chapel; Crafts room;
Laundry room; Barber/Beauty shop; Library.
Activities Arts & crafts; Cards; Games;
Reading groups; Prayer groups; Movies;
Shopping trips; Social/Cultural gatherings.

HALLSVILLE

Arah's Acres
Box J, Elizabeth St, Hallsville, MO, 65255
(314) 696-2541
Admin Arah Kathryn Hubbard Grimes.
Medical Dir/Dir of Nursing Mick Bryon RN.
Licensure Intermediate care. *Beds* ICF 18.
Owner Privately owned.
Admissions Requirements Medical
examination.
Staff RNs 1 (pt); LPNs 1 (ft), 1 (pt); Nurses
aides 9 (ft); Activities coordinators 1 (ft), 1
(pt); Cook 1 (ft), 1 (pt); Housekeeper 1 (ft).
Facilities Dining room; Laundry room;
Barber/Beauty shop.
Activities Cards; Games; Prayer groups;
Shopping trips.

HAMILTON

Hamilton Hill Crest Manor*
Irwin & Colby Sts, Hamilton, MO, 64644
(816) 583-2364
Admin Katharine Ensign.
Licensure Intermediate care. *Beds* 60.
Certified Medicaid.
Owner Proprietary Corp.
Staff Physicians 1 (ft); LPNs 4 (pt); Physical
therapists 2 (pt); Occupational therapists 2
(pt); Speech therapists 1 (pt); Activities
coordinators 1 (ft); Dietitians 1 (pt).
Facilities Dining room; Activities room;
Crafts room; Laundry room; Barber/Beauty
shop.
Activities Arts & crafts; Cards; Games;
Reading groups; Movies; Shopping trips;
Social/Cultural gatherings.

HANNIBAL

Becky Thatcher Nursing Home*
711 Church St, Hannibal, MO, 63401
(314) 221-4288
Admin Bill Callicott.

Licensure Intermediate care. *Beds* 23.
Owner Proprietary Corp.

Beth Haven Nursing Home
2500 Pleasant St, Hannibal, MO, 63401
(314) 221-6000
Admin Paul Ewert.
Licensure Skilled care; Intermediate care. *Beds*
66. *Certified* Medicaid; Medicare.
Owner Nonprofit Corp.

Luther Manor Retirement & Nursing Center
RFD 2, Hwy 61 N, Hannibal, MO, 63401
(314) 221-5533
Admin Mary E Greening. *Medical Dir/Dir of
Nursing* Gerry Higgins RN DON.
Licensure Intermediate care. *Beds* ICF 60.
Certified Medicaid.
Owner Nonprofit Corp (Evangelical Lutheran/
Good Samaritan).
Admissions Requirements Medical
examination.
Staff RNs 1 (ft); LPNs 4 (ft), 2 (pt); Nurses
aides 16 (ft), 8 (pt); Physical therapists 1 (ft);
Recreational therapists 1 (ft); Speech
therapists 1 (pt); Activities coordinators 1
(ft); Dietitians 1 (ft), 1 (pt).
Affiliation Lutheran
Facilities Dining room; Physical therapy
room; Activities room; Chapel; Crafts room;
Laundry room; Barber/Beauty shop; Library;
Solarium.
Activities Arts & crafts; Cards; Games;
Reading groups; Prayer groups; Movies;
Shopping trips; Social/Cultural gatherings;
Public buffets; Daily exercises.

River View Manor Home*
Box 894, 408 Rock St, Hannibal, MO, 63401
(314) 221-5910
Admin Phyllis Rupp.
Licensure Intermediate care. *Beds* 39.
Owner Proprietary Corp.

Willow Care Center
328 Munger Ln, Hannibal, MO, 63401
(314) 221-9122
Admin James McBride. *Medical Dir/Dir of
Nursing* J H Walterscheid MD.
Licensure Skilled care. *Beds* SNF 120.
Certified Medicaid.
Owner Proprietary Corp (Beverly Enterprises).
Admissions Requirements Medical
examination; Physician's request.
Facilities Dining room; Physical therapy
room; Activities room; Laundry room;
Barber/Beauty shop; Library.
Activities Arts & crafts; Cards; Games;
Reading groups; Prayer groups; Movies;
Social/Cultural gatherings.

HARRISONVILLE

ABC Health Center
307 E South St, Harrisonville, MO, 64701
(816) 884-3413
Admin Gary Holmes. *Medical Dir/Dir of
Nursing* Lauri Higgins.
Licensure Intermediate care. *Beds* ICF 60.
Certified Medicaid.
Owner Proprietary Corp (Horizon Healthcare
Corp).
Admissions Requirements Minimum age 18.
Staff Physicians 4 (pt); RNs 1 (ft); LPNs 4
(pt); Nurses aides 18 (ft); Physical therapists
1 (pt); Recreational therapists 1 (pt);
Occupational therapists 1 (pt); Speech
therapists 1 (pt); Activities coordinators 1
(pt); Dietitians 1 (pt).
Facilities Dining room; Physical therapy
room; Activities room; Chapel; Crafts room;
Laundry room; Barber/Beauty shop.
Activities Arts & crafts; Cards; Games;
Reading groups; Prayer groups; Movies;
Social/Cultural gatherings.

Camden Health Center*
2203 E Mechanic, Harrisonville, MO, 64701
(816) 884-2622
Admin Virginia Samuelson. *Medical Dir/Dir
of Nursing* Richard Price.
Licensure Intermediate care. *Beds* 60.
Certified Medicaid.
Owner Proprietary Corp.
Admissions Requirements Minimum age 16;
Medical examination.
Staff RNs 1 (ft), 1 (pt); LPNs 3 (ft); Orderlies
1 (pt); Nurses aides 17 (ft); Recreational
therapists 1 (ft); Activities coordinators 1
(ft).
Facilities Dining room; Physical therapy
room; Activities room; Crafts room; Laundry
room; Barber/Beauty shop.
Activities Arts & crafts; Cards; Games; Prayer
groups; Movies; Shopping trips; Social/
Cultural gatherings.

Dunsworth Estates*
104 W Pearl, Harrisonville, MO, 64701
(816) 884-6300
Admin Melvin Dunsworth, Jr.
Licensure Residential care. *Beds* 51.
Owner Proprietary Corp.

Dunsworth Manor
2001 Jefferson Pkwy, Harrisonville, MO,
64701
(816) 884-4731
Admin Kevin W Wood. *Medical Dir/Dir of
Nursing* Richard C Price MD; Renee
Endicott RN DON.
Licensure Intermediate care. *Beds* ICF 49.
Certified Medicaid.
Owner Privately owned.
Admissions Requirements Medical
examination.
Staff RNs 3 (ft); LPNs 4 (ft); Nurses aides 20
(ft); Physical therapists 1 (pt); Dietitians 1
(ft).
Facilities Dining room; Activities room;
Laundry room; Barber/Beauty shop.
Activities Arts & crafts; Cards; Games;
Reading groups; Prayer groups; Movies;
Shopping trips; Social/Cultural gatherings.

Pleasant View Rest Home*
PO Box 423, Rte 2, 2001 County Home Rd,
Harrisonville, MO, 64701
(816) 884-4731
Admin ALice C Reed.
Licensure Intermediate care. *Beds* 43.
Owner Proprietary Corp.

HAYTI

**Pemiscot County Memorial Hospital Long-
Term Care Unit**
PO Box 489, Hayti, MO, 63851
(314) 359-1372
Admin Glenn D Haynes. *Medical Dir/Dir of
Nursing* Sanan Saengsamran MD; Gearl V
Adams RN.
Licensure Skilled care; Intermediate care. *Beds*
SNF 60; ICF. *Certified* Medicaid; Medicare.
Owner Publicly owned.
Admissions Requirements Minimum age 18;
Medical examination; Physician's request.
Staff Physicians 15 (ft); RNs 2 (ft), 1 (pt);
LPNs 5 (ft), 2 (pt); Orderlies 4 (ft); Nurses
aides 12 (ft), 5 (pt); Activities coordinators 1
(ft).
Facilities Dining room; Activities room;
Barber/Beauty shop.
Activities Arts & crafts; Cards; Games;
Reading groups; Prayer groups; Movies;
Shopping trips.

HERCULANEUM

Westview Nursing Center
1333 Scenic Dr, Herculaneum, MO, 63048
(314) 937-7333

Admin Elizabeth Shannon RN. *Medical Dir/
Dir of Nursing* Dr Joseph Elterman MD;
Darryl Powell RN DON.
Licensure Skilled care. *Beds* SNF 136.
Certified Medicaid; Medicare.
Owner Privately owned Partnership.
Staff RNs; LPNs; Orderlies; Nurses aides;
Physical therapists 1 (pt); Occupational
therapists 1 (pt); Activities coordinators;
Dietitians 1 (pt); Dentists 1 (pt);
Ophthalmologists 1 (pt); Psychiatrist 3 (pt).
Facilities Dining room; Physical therapy
room; Activities room; Crafts room; Barber/
Beauty shop; Library.
Activities Arts & crafts; Cards; Games;
Reading groups; Prayer groups; Movies;
Shopping trips; Social/Cultural gatherings.

HERMANN

Frene Valley Geriatric & Rehabilitation Center
18th/Jefferson St, Rte 1, Box 30C, Hermann,
MO, 65041
(314) 486-3193
Admin Robert H Lloyd. *Medical Dir/Dir of
Nursing* George Workman MD; Marty
Steiner RN DON.
Licensure Intermediate care. *Beds* 60.
Certified Medicaid.
Owner Proprietary Corp.
Admissions Requirements Minimum age 18.
Staff Physicians 6 (pt); RNs 1 (ft); LPNs 2
(ft); Nurses aides 19 (ft), 4 (pt); Physical
therapists 1 (pt); Speech therapists 1 (pt);
Activities coordinators 1 (ft); Dietitians 1
(pt); Dentists 2 (pt); Ophthalmologists 1 (pt);
Podiatrists 1 (pt).
Languages German
Facilities Dining room; Physical therapy
room; Activities room; Crafts room; Laundry
room; Barber/Beauty shop; Library.
Activities Arts & crafts; Cards; Games;
Reading groups; Prayer groups; Movies;
Shopping trips; Social/Cultural gatherings;
Community activities; Lunch out.

Frene Valley Health Center*
Rte 1, Box 75A, Hermann, MO, 65041
(314) 486-3155
Admin Gary E Lloyd. *Medical Dir/Dir of
Nursing* G M Workman MD.
Licensure Intermediate care. *Beds* 88.
Owner Proprietary Corp.
Admissions Requirements Minimum age 18;
Medical examination.
Staff RNs 1 (ft); LPNs 3 (ft); Nurses aides 16
(ft), 6 (pt); Activities coordinators 1 (ft).
Facilities Dining room; Physical therapy
room; Activities room; Crafts room; Laundry
room; Barber/Beauty shop.
Activities Arts & crafts; Games; Prayer groups;
Movies; Shopping trips; Social/Cultural
gatherings; Exercises; Church services.

HIGGINSVILLE

Higginsville State School & Hospital*
Box 522, Higginsville, MO, 64037
(816) 584-2142
Admin Ara L Morris.
Licensure Intermediate care for mentally
retarded. *Beds* 310.

Meyer Care Center
Truman Rd & 13 Hwy, PO Box 512,
Higginsville, MO, 64037
(816) 584-4224
Admin Frank F Haston.
Licensure Intermediate care. *Beds* 60.
Owner Nonprofit Corp.
Admissions Requirements Minimum age 16;
Medical examination.
Staff Physicians 4 (pt); RNs 1 (ft), 2 (pt);
LPNs 3 (ft); Nurses aides 22 (ft), 12 (ft);
Physical therapists 1 (pt); Occupational
therapists 1 (pt); Speech therapists 1 (pt);
Activities coordinators 1 (ft), 1 (pt).

Facilities Dining room; Activities room;
Chapel; Laundry room; Barber/Beauty shop.
Activities Cards; Games; Reading groups;
Movies; Exercise program for all patients.

Parkview Nursing Home*
PO Box 471, 214 E 13th St, Higginsville, MO,
64037
(816) 584-2543
Admin William W Popp.
Licensure Intermediate care. *Beds* 18.
Owner Proprietary Corp.

HILLSBORO

Castle Acres Nursing Home Inc*
PO Box 308, Hillsboro, MO, 63050
(314) 789-2882
Admin Mary E Ouhrabka.
Licensure Intermediate care. *Beds* 29.
Owner Proprietary Corp.

Cedar Grove Nursing Home*
Box 367, Hillsboro, MO, 63050
(314) 789-2481
Admin Carolyn Dahle. *Medical Dir/Dir of
Nursing* Dr Dandamudi.
Licensure Intermediate care. *Beds* 64.
Owner Proprietary Corp.
Admissions Requirements Minimum age 18.
Staff Physicians 1 (pt); RNs 1 (pt); LPNs 2
(ft); Orderlies 1 (ft); Nurses aides 13 (ft), 2
(pt); Physical therapists 1 (pt); Speech
therapists 1 (pt); Activities coordinators 1
(ft); Dietitians 1 (pt); Dentists 1 (pt);
Audiologists 1 (pt).
Facilities Dining room; Activities room;
Crafts room; Laundry room.
Activities Arts & crafts; Cards; Games; Prayer
groups; Movies; Shopping trips; Social/
Cultural gatherings.

HOLDEN

Holden Manor Care Center
2005 S Lexington, Holden, MO, 64040
(816) 732-4138
Admin Jim Clayton. *Medical Dir/Dir of
Nursing* Dr Wm Rhode; Darlene Clayton
DON.
Licensure Intermediate care. *Beds* ICF 52.
Owner Proprietary Corp.
Staff Physicians 1 (pt); RNs 1 (pt); LPNs 5
(ft); Nurses aides 20 (ft); Physical therapists
1 (pt); Reality therapists 1 (pt); Recreational
therapists 1 (pt); Occupational therapists 1
(pt); Speech therapists 1 (pt); Activities
coordinators 1 (ft); Dietitians 2 (ft), 1 (pt).

HOUSTON

Texas County Rest Home Inc*
Rte 1, Houston, MO, 65483
(417) 967-2983
Admin Delores Bowlin.
Licensure Residential care. *Beds* 30.
Owner Proprietary Corp.

HUMANSVILLE

Big Springs Nursing Home
203 E Mill St, Humansville, MO, 65674
(417) 754-2450
Admin Norma Pitts. *Medical Dir/Dir of
Nursing* Darline Peebles DON.
Licensure Intermediate care. *Beds* ICF 38.
Certified Medicaid.
Owner Privately owned.
Admissions Requirements Minimum age 18.
Staff Physicians 5 (pt); RNs 1 (pt); LPNs 1
(ft), 1 (pt); Nurses aides 12 (ft), 2 (pt);
Recreational therapists 1 (pt); Activities
coordinators 1 (pt).

Facilities Dining room; Activities room;
Laundry room.
Activities Arts & crafts; Games; Prayer groups;
Movies; Shopping trips.

HUNTSVILLE

Pleasant View Nursing Home*
PO Box 162, Rte JJ, Huntsville, MO, 65259
(816) 277-4455
Admin Leonard Fish.
Licensure Intermediate care. *Beds* 67.
Owner Proprietary Corp.

IMPERIAL

Four Oaks Rest Home Inc*
Rte 2, Imperial, MO, 63052
(314) 464-1313
Admin Veronica M Ziegelmeyer.
Licensure Intermediate care. *Beds* 46.
Owner Proprietary Corp.

INDEPENDENCE

Carmel Hills
200 N Crane, Independence, MO,
(816) 252-1110
Admin Diane Flowers.
Licensure Residential care facility II. *Beds*
RCF I 20; RCF II 64.
Owner Privately owned Partnership.
Admissions Requirements Medical
examination.
Staff LPNs; Nurses aides; Activities
coordinators.
Facilities Dining room; Activities room;
Crafts room; Laundry room; Barber/Beauty
shop; Library.
Activities Arts & crafts; Cards; Games;
Reading groups; Prayer groups; Movies;
Shopping trips; Social/Cultural gatherings.

The Country House
1400 N River, Independence, MO, 64050
(816) 252-2737
Admin Bernard G Vaughan. *Medical Dir/Dir
of Nursing* Linda Chapman.
Licensure Residential care II. *Beds*
Residential II 30.
Owner Proprietary Corp.
Admissions Requirements Medical
examination.
Staff Physicians 1 (pt); LPNs 1 (pt); Nurses
aides 6 (ft); Physical therapists 1 (pt);
Recreational therapists 1 (pt); Reality
therapists 1 (pt); Occupational therapists 1
(pt); Speech therapists 1 (pt); Dietitians 1
(pt); Ophthalmologists 1 (pt); Podiatrists 1
(pt).
Facilities Dining room; Activities room;
Chapel; Crafts room; Laundry room; Barber/
Beauty shop; Library.
Activities Cards; Games; Reading groups;
Prayer groups; Movies; Shopping trips;
Social/Cultural gatherings.

Four Pines Retirement Home Inc*
3713 Hardy, Independence, MO, 64052
(816) 353-2737
Admin Evelyn Spangler. *Medical Dir/Dir of
Nursing* Ron LaHue DO.
Licensure Intermediate care. *Beds* 45.
Owner Proprietary Corp.
Admissions Requirements Medical
examination; Physician's request.
Staff RNs 1 (ft); LPNs 2 (ft), 1 (pt); Nurses
aides 13 (ft), 2 (pt); Activities coordinators 1
(pt); Dietitians 1 (pt).
Facilities Dining room; Physical therapy
room; Activities room; Laundry room.
Activities Games; Reading groups; Prayer
groups; Movies; Shopping trips.

General Baptist Nursing Home
419 N Hocker, Independence, MO, 64050
(816) 252-4019

Admin Alberta Marshall, Charlotte Jennings.
Medical Dir/Dir of Nursing Sharon Miles.
Licensure Intermediate care. *Beds* 27.
Owner Nonprofit organization/foundation.
Staff Physicians 1 (pt); RNs 2 (pt); LPNs 2
(pt); Nurses aides 13 (pt); Dietitians 1 (pt).
Affiliation Baptist
Facilities Dining room; Chapel; Laundry
room.
Activities Arts & crafts; Games; Reading
groups; Prayer groups.

Independence Health Care Center*
17451 E Medical Center Pkwy, Independence,
MO, 64050
(816) 373-7795
Admin Mary Beth Alpers. *Medical Dir/Dir of
Nursing* Keith Broughton DO.
Licensure Skilled care; Intermediate care. *Beds*
120. *Certified* Medicaid; Medicare.
Owner Proprietary Corp (Beverly Enterprises).
Staff Physicians 1 (pt); RNs 4 (ft), 1 (pt);
LPNs 7 (ft), 2 (pt); Orderlies 2 (ft); Nurses
aides 40 (ft); Physical therapists 1 (pt);
Occupational therapists 1 (pt); Speech
therapists 1 (pt); Activities coordinators 1
(ft); Dietitians 1 (pt); Dentists 1 (pt);
Podiatrists 1 (pt).
Facilities Dining room; Physical therapy
room; Activities room; Crafts room; Laundry
room; Barber/Beauty shop.
Activities Arts & crafts; Cards; Games;
Reading groups; Prayer groups; Movies;
Shopping trips; Social/Cultural gatherings.

Independence Manor Care Center
1600 S Kingshighway, Independence, MO,
64050
(816) 833-4777
Admin Kim Collins.
Licensure Intermediate care. *Beds* 102.
Owner Proprietary Corp.
Admissions Requirements Medical
examination; Physician's request.
Staff Physicians 1 (ft), 9 (pt); RNs 1 (ft), 1
(pt); LPNs 4 (ft), 3 (pt); Orderlies 1 (pt);
Nurses aides 22 (ft), 14 (pt); Physical
therapists 1 (ft); Reality therapists 1 (ft), 1
(pt); Recreational therapists 1 (ft), 1 (pt);
Occupational therapists 1 (pt); Speech
therapists 1 (pt); Activities coordinators 1
(ft), 1 (pt); Dietitians 1 (pt);
Ophthalmologists 1 (pt); Dentist 1 (pt).
Facilities Dining room; Physical therapy
room; Activities room; Crafts room; Laundry
room; Barber/Beauty shop.
Activities Arts & crafts; Cards; Games;
Reading groups; Prayer groups; Movies; Out-
to-lunch bunch; Classic cooks; Daily
exercise.

**Independence Regional Health
Center—Extended Care**
1509 W Truman Rd, Independence, MO,
64050
(816) 836-8100
Admin Carole Ferguson. *Medical Dir/Dir of
Nursing* Dr Frank Lewis; Teresa Halling
RN.
Licensure Skilled care. *Beds* SNF 72. *Certified*
Medicare.
Owner Nonprofit organization/foundation.
Admissions Requirements Medical
examination; Physician's request.
Staff RNs 9 (ft); LPNs 5 (ft), 4 (pt); Nurses
aides 20 (ft), 1 (pt); Physical therapists 2 (ft);
Occupational therapists 3 (ft); Speech
therapists 2 (ft); Activities coordinators 1
(pt); Dietitians 1 (ft); Social worker 1 (pt).
Languages Spanish
Affiliation Reorganized Church of Jesus Christ
of Latter-Day Saints
Facilities Dining room; Physical therapy
room; Activities room; Chapel; Crafts room;
Laundry room.
Activities Arts & crafts; Cards; Games;
Reading groups; Prayer groups; Movies.

Resthaven*
1500 W Truman Rd, Independence, MO, 64050
(816) 254-3500
Admin Homer D Spiers.
Licensure Skilled care; Intermediate care. *Beds* 259. *Certified* Medicaid.
Owner Nonprofit Corp.

Windsor Estates of Independence*
10300 Truman Rd, Independence, MO, 64052
(816) 836-1250
Admin Denny Barnett. *Medical Dir/Dir of Nursing* C M Cernech DO.
Licensure Skilled care; Intermediate care. *Beds* 83. *Certified* Medicaid; Medicare.
Owner Proprietary Corp (Beverly Enterprises).
Admissions Requirements Minimum age 18.
Staff Physicians 1 (ft), 3 (pt); RNs 2 (ft), 1 (pt); LPNs 6 (ft), 2 (pt); Nurses aides 34 (ft), 6 (pt); Physical therapists 1 (ft); Occupational therapists 1 (pt); Speech therapists 1 (pt); Activities coordinators 1 (ft); Dietitians 1 (pt); Dentists 1 (pt); Podiatrists 1 (pt).
Facilities Dining room; Physical therapy room; Activities room; Crafts room; Laundry room; Barber/Beauty shop.
Activities Arts & crafts; Games; Reading groups; Prayer groups; Movies; Social/Cultural gatherings.

IRONTON

The Baptist Home
PO Box 87, Ironton, MO, 63650
(314) 546-7429
Admin Edward C Goodwin. *Medical Dir/Dir of Nursing* Retha Keller DON.
Licensure Intermediate care; RCF. *Beds* 210.
Owner Nonprofit Corp.
Staff Physicians 3 (pt); RNs 5 (ft); LPNs 5 (ft); Nurses aides 75 (ft); Physical therapists 2 (ft); Activities coordinators 5 (ft).
Affiliation Baptist
Activities Arts & crafts; Cards; Games; Reading groups; Prayer groups; Movies; Shopping trips; Social/Cultural gatherings.

Crawford's Boarding Home*
101 S Knob, Ironton, MO, 63650
(314) 546-3080
Admin Violet J Crawford.
Licensure Adult Boarding facility. *Beds* 8.
Owner Nonprofit Corp.
Admissions Requirements Males only.
Facilities Dining room; Laundry room.
Activities Games; Shopping trips.

Lone Pine Congregate Center
321 S Main St, Ironton, MO, 63650
(314) 546-7283
Admin Sharon Gamble.
Licensure Residential care I. *Beds* 60.
Certified Medicaid.
Owner Proprietary Corp.
Admissions Requirements Minimum age 18; Medical examination.
Staff LPNs; Nurses aides; Recreational therapists; Activities coordinators; Dietitians.
Facilities Dining room; Activities room; Crafts room; Laundry room; Library.
Activities Arts & crafts; Cards; Games; Reading groups; Prayer groups; Movies; Shopping trips; Social/Cultural gatherings; Monthly band.

JACKSON

Deal Nursing Home Inc*
PO Box 371, Jackson, MO, 63755
(314) 243-3121
Admin Billy Joe Thompson.
Licensure Intermediate care. *Beds* 75.
Owner Proprietary Corp.

Jackson Manor Nursing Home
710 Broadridge, Jackson, MO, 63755
(314) 243-3101
Admin Karen F Young.
Licensure Skilled care. *Beds* 90. *Certified* Medicaid.
Owner Proprietary Corp (Angell Group).

JEFFERSON CITY

Chastain's of Jefferson City*
1024 Adams St, Jefferson City, MO, 65101
(314) 635-8191
Admin Marie Anders.
Licensure Intermediate care. *Beds* 120. *Certified* Medicaid.
Owner Proprietary Corp (Hillhaven Corp).

Jefferson City Manor Care Center
1720 Vieth Dr, Jefferson City, MO, 65101
(314) 635-6193
Admin Carol Sims. *Medical Dir/Dir of Nursing* Robert Tanner MD; Mary Chigwidden RN DON.
Licensure Skilled care; Intermediate care. *Beds* SNF 40; ICF 62. *Certified* Medicaid; Medicare.
Owner Nonprofit organization/foundation.
Staff RNs 2 (ft), 3 (pt); LPNs 8 (ft), 3 (pt); Orderlies 2 (ft), 2 (pt); Nurses aides 25 (ft), 15 (pt); Physical therapists 1 (ft), 2 (pt); Recreational therapists 1 (pt); Occupational therapists 1 (pt); Speech therapists 1 (pt); Activities coordinators 1 (ft), 1 (pt); Dietitians 1 (ft), 1 (pt).
Languages German
Facilities Dining room; Physical therapy room; Laundry room; Barber/Beauty shop; Library.
Activities Arts & crafts; Cards; Games; Reading groups; Prayer groups; Movies; Shopping trips; Social/Cultural gatherings; Pet therapy; Reality orientation.

Lincoln Nursing Center
3038 W Truman Blvd, Jefferson City, MO, 65101
(314) 893-3404
Admin Donna Hurt. *Medical Dir/Dir of Nursing* Helen Goetz RN DON.
Licensure Skilled care; Intermediate care. *Beds* SNF 100; ICF. *Certified* Medicaid.
Owner Proprietary Corp (Beverly Enterprises).
Admissions Requirements Medical examination.
Staff RNs 3 (ft); LPNs 6 (ft), 1 (pt); Nurses aides 23 (ft), 6 (pt); Activities coordinators 1 (ft); CMTs 4 (ft), 1 (pt).
Facilities Dining room; Physical therapy room; Activities room; Laundry room; Barber/Beauty shop.
Activities Arts & crafts; Prayer groups; Movies.

St Joseph's Home for the Aged*
1306 W Main, Jefferson City, MO, 65101
(314) 635-0166
Admin Sr M Bernardine Moors.
Licensure Intermediate care. *Beds* 125.
Owner Nonprofit Corp.

Southgate Nursing Center*
1207 Stadium Rd, Jefferson City, MO, 65101
(314) 635-3131
Admin Tom Hoeferlin.
Licensure Skilled care. *Beds* 120. *Certified* Medicaid.
Owner Proprietary Corp (Beverly Enterprises).

Villa Marie Skilled Nursing Facility
PO Box 1801, 1030 Edmonds St, Jefferson City, MO, 65102
(314) 635-3381
Admin John J Driscoll. *Medical Dir/Dir of Nursing* John I Matthews MD: Barbara L Lowry DON.

Licensure Skilled care; Intermediate care. *Beds* SNF 120; ICF. *Certified* Medicaid; Medicare; VA.
Owner Nonprofit Corp.
Staff Physicians 4 (pt); RNs 11 (ft); LPNs 11 (ft); Orderlies 7 (ft); Nurses aides 38 (ft), 14 (pt); Physical therapists 4 (pt); Recreational therapists 2 (ft); Occupational therapists 2 (pt); Activities coordinators 1 (ft); Dietitians 1 (ft); Music therapist 1 (ft).
Facilities Dining room; Physical therapy room; Activities room; Chapel; Crafts room; Laundry room; Barber/Beauty shop.
Activities Arts & crafts; Cards; Games; Reading groups; Prayer groups; Movies; Shopping trips; Social/Cultural gatherings; Band; Choir; Rhythm band; Tone bell band.

JENNINGS

Jennings Caring Center*
2520 McLaran, Jennings, MO, 63136
(314) 867-5748
Admin Bobby F Reed Jr. *Medical Dir/Dir of Nursing* Arnold S Tepper MD.
Licensure Intermediate care. *Beds* 41.
Owner Proprietary Corp.
Staff Physicians 1 (ft); RNs 1 (pt); LPNs 1 (ft), 1 (pt); Nurses aides 8 (ft); Activities coordinators 1 (ft); Dietitians 1 (pt); Podiatrists 1 (pt).
Facilities Dining room; Activities room; Laundry room.
Activities Arts & crafts; Cards; Games; Reading groups; Prayer groups; Movies; Shopping trips; Social/Cultural gatherings.

JONESBURG

Jonesburg Caring Center
PO Box 218, Cedar Ave & William Tell, Jonesburg, MO, 63351
(314) 488-5400
Admin Joseph Cusic. *Medical Dir/Dir of Nursing* Costantino Carpio MD; Kathy Wright DON.
Licensure Skilled care; Intermediate care. *Beds* 60.
Owner Proprietary Corp.
Admissions Requirements Minimum age 18; Medical examination; Physician's request.
Staff Physicians 1 (pt); RNs 1 (ft); LPNs 1 (ft), 1 (pt); Orderlies 1 (ft); Nurses aides 10 (ft), 1 (pt); Activities coordinators 1 (ft); Dietitians 1 (ft).
Facilities Dining room; Activities room; Laundry room.
Activities Arts & crafts; Cards; Games; Prayer groups; Movies; Shopping trips.

JOPLIN

Chastain's Joplin House Nursing Home*
2502 Moffet, Joplin, MO, 64801
(417) 623-3264
Admin Frank Manning. *Medical Dir/Dir of Nursing* W W Hurst MD.
Licensure Skilled care. *Beds* 120. *Certified* Medicaid.
Owner Proprietary Corp (Hillhaven Corp).
Staff Physicians 1 (ft), 10 (pt); RNs 4 (ft); LPNs 7 (ft); Nurses aides 36 (ft), 1 (pt); Physical therapists 1 (ft); Occupational therapists 1 (ft); Speech therapists 1 (ft); Activities coordinators 2 (ft); Dietitians 1 (ft); Dentists 1 (pt); Ophthalmologists 1 (pt); Podiatrists 1 (pt); Audiologists 1 (pt).
Facilities Dining room; Physical therapy room; Activities room; Laundry room; Barber/Beauty shop.
Activities Arts & crafts; Cards; Games; Reading groups; Prayer groups; Movies; Shopping trips; Social/Cultural gatherings.

Chastain's Tradition House Nursing Home*
PO Box 2353, 2810 Jackson St, Joplin, MO,
64801
(417) 624-2061
Admin Peggy R Frisinger.
Licensure Intermediate care. *Beds* 92.
Certified Medicaid.
Owner Proprietary Corp (Hillhaven Corp).

Empire Nursing Home*
2215 Empire Ave, Joplin, MO, 64801
(417)624-8141
Admin Mary F Turner.
Licensure Intermediate care. *Beds* 15.
Owner Proprietary Corp.
Admissions Requirements Minimum age 50;
Medical examination.
Staff LPNs 1 (ft), 1 (pt); Orderlies 1 (pt);
Nurses aides 4 (ft), 2 (pt); Recreational
therapists 1 (pt); Occupational therapists 1
(pt).

Hope Manor*
1402 Rex, Joplin, MO, 64801
(417) 623-5551
Admin Pat Fenix.
Licensure Intermediate care. *Beds* 24.
Owner Proprietary Corp.
Admissions Requirements Minimum age 18;
Medical examination.
Staff RNs 1 (pt); LPNs 1 (ft), 1 (pt); Nurses
aides 12 (ft).
Facilities Dining room; Activities room;
Crafts room; Laundry room; Barber/Beauty
shop.
Activities Arts & crafts; Games; Prayer groups.

Joplin Health Care Center
PO Box 2877, 2700 E 34th, Joplin, MO,
64803
(417) 781-1737
Admin Tim Haynes. *Medical Dir/Dir of
Nursing* O A Mehaffy MD; Jan Walker RN
DON.
Licensure Skilled care; Intermediate care. *Beds*
126. *Certified* Medicaid.
Owner Privately owned.
Staff RNs 4 (ft), 1 (pt); LPNs 10 (ft), 3 (pt);
Orderlies 4 (ft); Nurses aides 39 (ft), 6 (pt);
Physical therapists 1 (pt); Occupational
therapists 1 (pt); Speech therapists 1 (pt);
Activities coordinators 1 (ft), 1 (pt).

Meadow View Nursing Center
1805 W 32nd St, Joplin, MO, 64804
(417) 782-0114
Admin Jeffrey R Carter. *Medical Dir/Dir of
Nursing* Stephen Bazzano DO; Carol
McGinn RN.
Licensure Skilled care; Intermediate care. *Beds*
120. *Certified* Medicaid; Medicare.
Owner Proprietary Corp (Beverly Enterprises).
Admissions Requirements Minimum age 16;
Medical examination; Physician's request.
Staff Physicians 1 (pt); RNs 3 (ft); LPNs 10
(ft), 2 (pt); Orderlies 3 (ft); Nurses aides 41
(ft); Physical therapists 1 (pt); Occupational
therapists 1 (pt); Speech therapists 1 (pt);
Activities coordinators 1 (ft); Dietitians 1
(pt); Dentists 1 (pt); Ophthalmologists 1 (pt);
Podiatrists 1 (pt); Dentist 1 (pt).
Facilities Dining room; Physical therapy
room; Activities room; Laundry room;
Barber/Beauty shop; 3 Living rooms.
Activities Arts & crafts; Cards; Games;
Reading groups; Prayer groups; Movies;
Shopping trips; Social/Cultural gatherings.

KAHOKA

Clark County Nursing Home
Rte 2, Hwy 81 N, Kahoka, MO, 63445
(816) 727-3303
Admin James S Holmes. *Medical Dir/Dir of
Nursing* Dr John Beckert DO.
Licensure Intermediate care. *Beds* 120.
Certified Medicaid.
Owner Publicly owned.

Admissions Requirements Physician's request.
Staff Physicians 2 (pt); RNs 1 (ft), 1 (pt);
LPNs 10 (pt); Nurses aides 12 (ft), 51 (pt);
Physical therapists 2 (ft), 2 (pt); Dietitians 1
(pt).
Facilities Dining room; Physical therapy
room; Activities room; Crafts room; Barber/
Beauty shop.
Activities Arts & crafts; Cards; Games;
Reading groups; Prayer groups; Movies;
Shopping trips; Social/Cultural gatherings.

KANSAS

Meldonia Residential Care Facility*
503-505 Olive St, Kansas, MO, 64124
(816) 483-2911
Admin Nathan Friedman.
Licensure Residential care. *Beds* 47.
Owner Proprietary Corp.

KANSAS CITY

Armour Home
8100 Wornall Rd, Kansas City, MO, 64114
(816) 363-1510
Admin R Larry Louthain. *Medical Dir/Dir of
Nursing* Dr Robert Lahue; M Alice Mitchell.
Licensure Skilled care; Residential II;
Independent living. *Beds* SNF 34;
Residential II 44; Independent living 24.
Certified Medicaid.
Owner Nonprofit Corp.
Admissions Requirements Minimum age 65;
Medical examination.
Staff Physicians 2 (pt); RNs 2 (ft); LPNs 7
(ft); Nurses aides 12 (ft); Physical therapists
1 (pt); Activities coordinators 2 (ft);
Dietitians 1 (pt); Ophthalmologists 1 (pt).
Facilities Dining room; Physical therapy
room; Activities room; Chapel; Crafts room;
Laundry room; Barber/Beauty shop; Library.
Activities Arts & crafts; Cards; Games;
Reading groups; Prayer groups; Movies;
Shopping trips; Social/Cultural gatherings.

Beacon Hill Nursing Home*
2905 Campbell, Kansas City, MO, 64109
(816) 531-6168
Admin Christena Nicholson. *Medical Dir/Dir
of Nursing* Leroy Williams DO.
Licensure Intermediate care. *Beds* 35.
Owner Proprietary Corp.
Admissions Requirements Minimum age 25;
Medical examination.
Staff Physicians 1 (pt); RNs 1 (pt); LPNs 2
(ft); Orderlies 2 (ft); Nurses aides 18 (ft);
Activities coordinators 1 (pt).
Facilities Dining room; Laundry room.
Activities Arts & crafts; Cards; Games; Prayer
groups; Movies; Social/Cultural gatherings.

Benton Care Center
622 Benton Blvd, Kansas City, MO, 64124
(816) 241-5856
Admin Nancy Cole. *Medical Dir/Dir of
Nursing* Ray Baker MD, Harvey Munshaw
MD; Ruth Stafford DON.
Licensure Intermediate care. *Beds* ICF 46.
Owner Privately owned.
Staff Physicians 3 (ft); RNs 1 (ft); LPNs 3 (ft);
Orderlies 2 (ft); Nurses aides 25 (ft);
Physical therapists 1 (ft); Occupational
therapists 1 (ft); Activities coordinators 1
(ft); Dietitians 1 (ft); Ophthalmologists 1 (ft).
Facilities Activities room; Laundry room.
Activities Arts & crafts; Games; Reading
groups; Movies.

Blue Hills Centre
12942 Wornall Rd, Kansas City, MO, 64145
(816) 941-0250
Admin Michael L Barnes. *Medical Dir/Dir of
Nursing* Dr Ron Lahve; Linda Maniscalco
DON.
Licensure Skilled care. *Beds* SNF 183.
Certified Medicaid; Medicare.

Owner Proprietary Corp (Hillhaven Corp).
Staff Physicians 2 (ft); RNs 5 (ft); LPNs 10
(ft); Orderlies 10 (ft); Nurses aides 80 (ft);
Physical therapists 1 (ft); Recreational
therapists 2 (ft); Occupational therapists 1
(ft); Speech therapists 1 (ft); Activities
coordinators 1 (ft); Dietitians 1 (ft).
Facilities Dining room; Physical therapy
room; Activities room; Chapel; Crafts room;
Laundry room; Barber/Beauty shop; Library.
Activities Arts & crafts; Cards; Games;
Reading groups; Prayer groups; Movies;
Shopping trips; Social/Cultural gatherings.

Blue Ridge Nursing Home Inc
7505 E 87th St, Kansas City, MO, 64138
(816) 761-6838
Admin Eleanor Mochel. *Medical Dir/Dir of
Nursing* Bernadine Patel LPN.
Licensure Intermediate care. *Beds* ICF 28.
Certified Medicaid.
Owner Proprietary Corp.
Admissions Requirements Minimum age 18.
Facilities Dining room; Physical therapy
room; Activities room; Crafts room; Laundry
room; Barber/Beauty shop; Library.
Activities Arts & crafts; Cards; Games;
Reading groups; Prayer groups; Movies;
Shopping trips.

Bra-Ton Nursing Home Inc
3400 Campbell, Kansas City, MO, 64109
(816) 531-5746
Admin Ronald G Putz.
Licensure Intermediate care. *Beds* 40.
Owner Proprietary Corp.

Caldwell Manor Nursing Home*
101 E 36th, Kansas City, MO, 64111
(816) 753-6553
Admin Evelyn Caldwell.
Licensure Intermediate care. *Beds* 49.
Owner Proprietary Corp.

Chippendale Nursing Home
3240 Norledge, Kansas City, MO, 64123
(816) 231-1161
Admin Jenifer LaRose. *Medical Dir/Dir of
Nursing* R L Williams DO; Jenny Jeffries
DON.
Licensure Intermediate care. *Beds* ICF 36.
Owner Proprietary Corp.
Admissions Requirements Minimum age 60;
Medical examination.
Staff Physicians 3 (ft); RNs 1 (pt); LPNs 3
(ft); Orderlies 4 (ft); Nurses aides 18 (ft), 4
(pt); Physical therapists 1 (pt); Reality
therapists 1 (ft); Recreational therapists 1
(ft); Occupational therapists 1 (pt); Speech
therapists 1 (pt); Activities coordinators 1
(ft); Ophthalmologists 1 (ft); Podiatrists 1
(ft).
Facilities Dining room; Activities room;
Crafts room; Laundry room; Barber/Beauty
shop.
Activities Arts & crafts; Cards; Games;
Reading groups; Prayer groups; Movies;
Shopping trips; Social/Cultural gatherings.

Cleveland Health Care Center
7001 Cleveland Ave, Kansas City, MO, 64132
(816) 333-0700
Admin Laura Briggs MPA. *Medical Dir/Dir of
Nursing* Dr Ron Lahue.
Licensure Skilled care; Intermediate care; RCF
II. *Beds* 150. *Certified* Medicaid; Medicare.
Owner Proprietary Corp.
Admissions Requirements Minimum age 18.
Staff Physicians 1 (ft); RNs 3 (ft); LPNs 9 (ft);
Orderlies 1 (ft); Nurses aides 60 (ft);
Physical therapists 1 (pt); Occupational
therapists 1 (pt); Speech therapists 1 (pt);
Activities coordinators 2 (ft); Dietitians 1
(ft); Ophthalmologists 1 (ft).

Facilities Dining room; Physical therapy room; Laundry room.
Activities Arts & crafts; Cards; Games; Reading groups; Prayer groups; Movies; Social/Cultural gatherings.

Cliff Manor Inc*
4700 Cliff View Dr, Kansas City, MO, 64150
(816) 741-5105
Admin Norman Springer.
Licensure Skilled care. *Beds* 186.
Owner Proprietary Corp.

Colonial Nursing Home
100 E 36th, Kansas City, MO, 64111
(816) 561-5624
Admin Lori Hamill. *Medical Dir/Dir of Nursing* Sue Shanks.
Licensure Intermediate care. *Beds* ICF 51.
Owner Proprietary Corp.
Admissions Requirements Minimum age 60; Medical examination.
Staff Physicians 6 (ft); RNs 1 (pt); LPNs 2 (ft); Orderlies 4 (ft); Nurses aides 18 (ft), 4 (pt); Physical therapists 1 (pt); Reality therapists 1 (ft); Recreational therapists 1 (ft); Occupational therapists 1 (pt); Speech therapists 1 (pt); Activities coordinators 1 (ft); Ophthalmologists 1 (pt).
Facilities Dining room; Activities room; Crafts room; Laundry room; Barber/Beauty shop.
Activities Arts & crafts; Cards; Games; Reading groups; Prayer groups; Movies; Shopping trips; Social/Cultural gatherings.

Cresthaven Nursing Home*
3516 Summit, Kansas City, MO, 64111
(816) 931-4024
Admin Charles F Hardy.
Licensure Intermediate care. *Beds* 42.
Owner Proprietary Corp.

Garden Grove Nursing Home*
3522 Walnut St, Kansas City, MO, 64111
(816) 561-9344
Admin Jo Ann Gropper.
Licensure Intermediate care. *Beds* 36.
Owner Proprietary Corp.

Gladstone Nursing Home*
435 Gladstone Blvd, Kansas City, MO, 64124
(816) 531-1089
Admin Josephine Whiteley. *Medical Dir/Dir of Nursing* Dr Robert LaHue.
Licensure Intermediate care. *Beds* 28.
Owner Proprietary Corp.
Admissions Requirements Females only.
Staff Physicians 3 (ft); RNs 1 (pt); LPNs 1 (ft), 2 (pt); Physical therapists 1 (ft); Recreational therapists 1 (pt); Dietitians 1 (pt).
Facilities Activities room; Chapel; Crafts room; Laundry room.
Activities Arts & crafts; Cards; Games; Prayer groups; Movies.

Glennon Place*
128 N Hardesty Ave, Kansas City, MO, 64123
(816) 241-2020
Admin James L Webb.
Licensure Skilled care; Intermediate care. *Beds* 120. *Certified* Medicaid.
Owner Proprietary Corp (Beverly Enterprises).

Great Oaks Inc
115 E 83rd St, Kansas City, MO, 64114
(816) 363-2900
Admin Marion V Pike. *Medical Dir/Dir of Nursing* Lydia Abercrombie.
Licensure Intermediate care. *Beds* ICF 12. *Certified* Medicare.
Owner Nonprofit Corp.
Admissions Requirements Minimum age 18.
Staff RNs 3 (ft), 2 (pt); LPNs 3 (ft), 2 (pt); Nurses aides 1 (ft); Activities coordinators 1 (ft); Dietitians 1 (ft), 4 (pt).
Affiliation Christian Science

Facilities Dining room; Activities room; Laundry room; Barber/Beauty shop.
Activities Arts & crafts; Reading groups; Prayer groups; Movies; Singing.

Grosse Nursing Home Inc
3918 Charlotte, Kansas City, MO, 64110
(816) 931-0306
Admin J Ruth Richardson.
Licensure Intermediate care. *Beds* 32.
Owner Proprietary Corp.

Guardian Angel Nursing Home Inc*
5234 N E Munger Ave, Kansas City, MO, 64119
(816) 452-2654
Admin Thomas Misasi.
Licensure Intermediate care. *Beds* 19.
Owner Proprietary Corp.

Harvest Home Estates*
2905 Forest Ave, Kansas City, MO, 64109
(816) 531-7356
Admin Hazel Thompson.
Licensure Intermediate care. *Beds* 55.
Owner Proprietary Corp.

Haven Manor Nursing Home
3526 Walnut, Kansas City, MO, 64111
(816) 931-9579
Admin Katherine Littlewood. *Medical Dir/Dir of Nursing* Bob La Hue MD.
Licensure Intermediate care; Intermediate care for mentally retarded; Mental health facility. *Beds* 29. *Certified* Medicaid.
Owner Proprietary Corp.
Admissions Requirements Minimum age 29; Medical examination; Physician's request.
Staff Physicians 1 (ft); RNs 1 (pt); LPNs 1 (ft), 3 (pt); Nurses aides 6 (ft), 6 (pt); Physical therapists 3 (pt); Reality therapists 1 (pt); Recreational therapists 1 (pt); Occupational therapists 1 (pt); Speech therapists 1 (pt); Activities coordinators 1 (pt); Dentists 1 (pt); Ophthalmologists 1 (pt); Podiatrists 1 (pt); Dentist 1 (ft).
Facilities Dining room; Laundry room.
Activities Arts & crafts; Cards; Games; Reading groups; Prayer groups; Movies; Shopping trips; Social/Cultural gatherings.

Holmesdale Convalescent Center
8039 Holmes, Kansas City, MO, 64131
(816) 363-6222
Admin Madeline Ryan. *Medical Dir/Dir of Nursing* Mary Miller DON.
Licensure Skilled care. *Beds* SNF 100. *Certified* Medicare.
Owner Privately owned.
Staff RNs 4 (ft), 3 (pt); LPNs 2 (ft), 6 (pt); Orderlies 1 (ft); Nurses aides 25 (ft); Physical therapists 1 (ft); Recreational therapists 1 (ft); Activities coordinators 1 (ft); Dietitians 1 (ft).
Facilities Dining room; Physical therapy room; Activities room; Laundry room; Barber/Beauty shop; 2 Solariums.
Activities Arts & crafts; Games; Reading groups; Prayer groups; Movies; Social/Cultural gatherings; Bingo; Happy hour; Birthday parties.

Hyde Park Nursing Home*
401 E 36th St, Kansas City, MO, 64109
(816) 931-6378
Admin Cheryl Bauer.
Licensure Intermediate care. *Beds* 45.
Owner Proprietary Corp.

Indian Creek Nursing Center of Missouri*
12000 Wornall Rd, Kansas City, MO, 64145
(816) 942-1676
Admin James M Sanner.
Licensure Skilled care. *Beds* 240.
Owner Proprietary Corp.

Kelly Nursing Home*
4123 Independence Ave, Kansas City, MO, 64124
(816) 241-3232
Admin Edith M Eckenroed. *Medical Dir/Dir of Nursing* Robert C LaHue DO.
Licensure Intermediate care; Residential care. *Beds* 28.
Owner Proprietary Corp.
Admissions Requirements Minimum age 18.
Staff RNs 1 (pt); LPNs 1 (ft), 1 (pt); Nurses aides 14 (ft); Physical therapists; Reality therapists; Recreational therapists 1 (ft); Occupational therapists; Speech therapists; Activities coordinators 1 (ft), 2 (pt); Dentists 1 (pt); Ophthalmologists 1 (pt); Podiatrists 1 (pt); Audiologists.
Facilities Physical therapy room; Activities room; Crafts room; Laundry room; Barber/Beauty shop; Library.
Activities Arts & crafts; Cards; Games; Reading groups; Prayer groups; Movies; Shopping trips; Social/Cultural gatherings.

King's Nursing Home*
2836 Benton Blvd, Kansas City, MO, 64128
(816) 924-5662
Admin Opal Lavern King.
Licensure Intermediate care. *Beds* 34.
Owner Proprietary Corp.

Little Sisters of the Poor—St Alexis Home*
5331 Highland Ave, Kansas City, MO, 64110
(816) 444-9164
Admin Cecilia Honigfort.
Licensure Intermediate care. *Beds* 140. *Certified* Medicaid.
Owner Nonprofit Corp.
Affiliation Roman Catholic

Midtown Manor Nursing Home*
2700 Tracy, Kansas City, MO, 64109
(816) 421-1272
Admin Claudia McDaniel.
Licensure Intermediate care. *Beds* 55.
Owner Proprietary Corp.

Myers Nursing & Convalescent Center Inc
2315 Walrond Ave, Kansas City, MO, 64127
(816) 231-3180
Admin Agnes Dodd. *Medical Dir/Dir of Nursing* Connie Harkness RN DON.
Licensure Intermediate care. *Beds* ICF 84. *Certified* Medicaid.
Owner Proprietary Corp.
Staff RNs 1 (ft); LPNs 5 (ft); Activities coordinators 1 (ft); Dietitians 1 (ft).
Facilities Dining room; Activities room; Laundry room.
Activities Arts & crafts; Cards; Games; Reading groups; Prayer groups; Movies; Shopping trips; Social/Cultural gatherings; Outings.

George H Nettleton Home
5125 Swope Pkwy, Kansas City, MO, 64130
(816) 924-5641
Admin Patricia Rodina MA. *Medical Dir/Dir of Nursing* Robert Raich; Jeannette Harris LPN.
Licensure Intermediate care; Residential care. *Beds* ICF 30; Residential 43.
Owner Nonprofit Corp.
Admissions Requirements Females only.
Staff Physicians 1 (pt); RNs 1 (pt); LPNs 2 (ft), 1 (pt); Nurses aides 9 (ft), 15 (pt); Physical therapists 1 (pt); Reality therapists 1 (pt); Recreational therapists 1 (ft); Occupational therapists 1 (pt); Speech therapists 1 (pt); Dietitians 1 (pt); Ophthalmologists 1 (pt); Podiatrists 1 (pt); Social service 1 (pt).
Facilities Dining room; Activities room; Chapel; Laundry room; Barber/Beauty shop; Library; Sunroom; Large parlor.

Activities Arts & crafts; Cards; Games; Reading groups; Prayer groups; Movies; Shopping trips; Social/Cultural gatherings; Shopping trips; Van.

Newberry Nursing Home*
3215 Campbell, Kansas City, MO, 64109
(816) 561-5282
Admin Patrick Reznak. *Medical Dir/Dir of Nursing* Dr Robert LaHue.
Licensure Intermediate care. *Beds* 45.
Owner Proprietary Corp.
Staff RNs 1 (pt); LPNs 1 (ft), 2 (pt); Orderlies 3 (ft), 1 (pt); Nurses aides 18 (ft), 2 (pt); Physical therapists 1 (pt); Recreational therapists 1 (ft).
Facilities Dining room; Activities room; Laundry room.
Activities Arts & crafts; Cards; Games; Reading groups; Prayer groups; Movies; Shopping trips; Social/Cultural gatherings.

Oak Park Manor
724 NE 79th Terrace, Kansas City, MO, 64118
(816) 436-8940
Admin Paul Harper. *Medical Dir/Dir of Nursing* Ruth Hershey.
Licensure Skilled care. *Beds* SNF 120. *Certified* Medicaid.
Owner Proprietary Corp (Beverly Enterprises).
Admissions Requirements Minimum age 18.
Staff RNs 4 (ft); LPNs 7 (ft); Orderlies 2 (ft); Nurses aides 50 (ft); Physical therapists 1 (ft); Recreational therapists 1 (ft).
Facilities Dining room; Physical therapy room; Activities room; Laundry room; Barber/Beauty shop.
Activities Arts & crafts; Games; Prayer groups; Movies; Shopping trips.

Oak Ridge Manor Nursing Home
512 Woodland, Kansas City, MO, 64124
(816) 474-6869
Admin Beryl Pegues. *Medical Dir/Dir of Nursing* Minnie Jones DON.
Licensure Intermediate care. *Beds* ICF 46. *Certified* Medicaid.
Owner Proprietary Corp.
Admissions Requirements Minimum age 18; Medical examination.
Staff Physicians 2 (pt); RNs 1 (pt); LPNs 1 (ft), 1 (pt); Orderlies 1 (ft); Nurses aides 15 (ft), 3 (pt); Activities coordinators 1 (pt); Dietitians 1 (pt).
Facilities Dining room; Day room.
Activities Arts & crafts; Cards; Games; Social/ Cultural gatherings.

Our Lady of Mercy Home
918 E 9th St, Kansas City, MO, 64106
(816) 842-6518
Admin Sr Mary Margaret Sneddon. *Medical Dir/Dir of Nursing* Elsie Hunter RN.
Licensure Intermediate care. *Beds* 153. *Certified* Medicaid.
Owner Nonprofit Corp.
Admissions Requirements Females only; Medical examination; Physician's request.
Staff RNs 2 (ft), 2 (pt); LPNs 3 (ft); Nurses aides 22 (ft); Recreational therapists 1 (ft), 3 (pt); Occupational therapists 1 (ft); Activities coordinators 1 (ft), 2 (pt); Dietitians 1 (ft).
Languages Spanish
Affiliation Roman Catholic
Facilities Dining room; Activities room; Chapel; Crafts room; Laundry room; Barber/ Beauty shop; Library.
Activities Arts & crafts; Cards; Games; Prayer groups; Movies; Shopping trips; Social/ Cultural gatherings.

Paseo Nursing Home*
3433 Paseo, Kansas City, MO, 64109
(816) 921-4938
Admin Charlotte S Hosie. *Medical Dir/Dir of Nursing* Elizabeth Channel.
Licensure Intermediate care. *Beds* 29.

Owner Proprietary Corp.
Staff RNs 1 (pt); LPNs 1 (ft); Nurses aides 6 (ft); Physical therapists 1 (pt); Reality therapists 1 (pt); Speech therapists 1 (pt); Activities coordinators 1 (ft); Dentists 1 (pt); Ophthalmologists 1 (pt); Podiatrists 1 (pt).
Facilities Dining room; Activities room; Laundry room.
Activities Arts & crafts; Cards; Games; Reading groups; Prayer groups; Movies; Shopping trips.

Pleasant View Nursing Home*
4400 St John, Kansas City, MO, 64124
(816) 231-1790
Admin Cynthia Marvine.
Licensure Residential care. *Beds* 16.
Owner Proprietary Corp.

Red Bridge Health Care Center
11515 Troost, Kansas City, MO, 66131
(816) 942-6700
Admin Mary E Marnett. *Medical Dir/Dir of Nursing* D D Zimmerman MD.
Licensure Skilled care. *Beds* SNF 180; RCF. *Certified* Medicaid; Medicare.
Owner Proprietary Corp.
Admissions Requirements Minimum age 18.
Staff RNs 4 (ft), 3 (pt); LPNs 3 (ft); Orderlies 28 (ft), 2 (pt); Nurses aides 2 (ft); Physical therapists 1 (pt); Activities coordinators 1 (ft), 1 (pt).
Facilities Dining room; Physical therapy room; Activities room; Chapel; Crafts room; Laundry room; Barber/Beauty shop.
Activities Arts & crafts; Cards; Games; Reading groups; Prayer groups; Movies; Shopping trips; Social/Cultural gatherings.

Roanoke Manor Nursing Home*
3660 Summit, Kansas City, MO, 64111
(816) 753-6566
Admin Miriam J Zwiegel.
Licensure Intermediate care. *Beds* 43.
Owner Proprietary Corp.

Rockhill Healthcare Center*
904 E 68th St, Kansas City, MO, 64131
(816) 333-5485
Admin Marshall Grant. *Medical Dir/Dir of Nursing* Harold Keairnes MD.
Licensure Skilled care; Intermediate care. *Beds* 174. *Certified* Medicaid; Medicare.
Owner Proprietary Corp (Southmark Heritage Corp).
Admissions Requirements Minimum age 18.
Staff Physicians 1 (ft); RNs 7 (ft); LPNs 21 (ft); Orderlies 15 (ft); Nurses aides 59 (ft); Physical therapists 4 (ft); Reality therapists 1 (pt); Recreational therapists 1 (pt); Occupational therapists 1 (pt); Speech therapists 1 (pt); Activities coordinators 3 (ft); Dietitians 1 (pt).
Facilities Dining room; Physical therapy room; Activities room; Chapel; Crafts room; Laundry room; Barber/Beauty shop; Library.
Activities Arts & crafts; Cards; Games; Prayer groups; Movies; Shopping trips; Social/ Cultural gatherings.

Senior Estates
2323 Swope Pkwy, Kansas City, MO, 64063
(816) 924-1122
Admin Patricia L Stickler. *Medical Dir/Dir of Nursing* Ron LaHue MD; Norma Anderson DON.
Licensure Skilled care; Intermediate care; Residential care. *Beds* 96.
Owner Privately owned.
Admissions Requirements Minimum age 17; Medical examination; Physician's request.
Staff RNs 2 (ft); LPNs 7 (ft); Orderlies 3 (ft); Nurses aides 23 (ft); Activities coordinators 1 (ft).
Activities Arts & crafts; Cards; Games; Reading groups; Prayer groups; Movies; Shopping trips; Social/Cultural gatherings; Camping.

Shalom Geriatric Center
7801 Holmes, Kansas City, MO, 64131
(816) 333-7800
Admin Melvyn Weissman. *Medical Dir/Dir of Nursing* Dr Harry Cohen; Marge Groves DON.
Licensure Skilled care. *Beds* SNF 192. *Certified* Medicaid; Medicare.
Owner Nonprofit Corp.
Admissions Requirements Minimum age 18; Medical examination; Physician's request.
Staff RNs 6 (ft), 3 (pt); LPNs 19 (ft), 10 (pt); Orderlies 4 (ft); Nurses aides 54 (ft), 16 (pt); Physical therapists 1 (ft); Recreational therapists 1 (ft); Occupational therapists 1 (ft); Activities coordinators 1 (ft); Dietitians 1 (ft); Art therapist 1 (ft).
Affiliation Jewish
Facilities Dining room; Physical therapy room; Activities room; Chapel; Crafts room; Laundry room; Barber/Beauty shop; Library.
Activities Arts & crafts; Cards; Games; Reading groups; Prayer groups; Movies; Social/Cultural gatherings.

Swope Ridge Health Care Center
5900 Swope Pkwy, Kansas City, MO, 64130
(816) 333-2700
Admin Charles Nigro.
Licensure Skilled care; Intermediate care. *Beds* 236. *Certified* Medicaid; Medicare.
Owner Nonprofit Corp.

Troost Avenue Nursing Home*
2839 Troost Ave, Kansas City, MO, 64109
(816) 931-1047
Admin Jerry Shaw & Wendy Morgan.
Licensure Intermediate care. *Beds* 41.
Owner Proprietary Corp.

Truman Medical Center
7900 Lees Summit Rd, Kansas City, MO, 64139
(816) 373-4415
Admin Clifford Browne Jr. *Medical Dir/Dir of Nursing* Jack Mulligan MD; Barbara Quirk RN DON.
Licensure Skilled care; Intermediate care; Psychiatric rehab ICF. *Beds* SNF 24; ICF 187; Psychiatric rehab ICF 15. *Certified* Medicaid; Medicare.
Owner Nonprofit organization/foundation.
Admissions Requirements Medical examination.
Staff Physicians 1 (ft); RNs 12 (ft); LPNs 22 (ft); Nurses aides 81 (ft); Physical therapists 1 (ft); Recreational therapists 1 (ft); Occupational therapists 1 (ft); Speech therapists 1 (ft); Dietitians 1 (ft).
Facilities Dining room; Physical therapy room; Activities room; Chapel; Crafts room; Laundry room; Barber/Beauty shop; Library.
Activities Arts & crafts; Cards; Games; Reading groups; Prayer groups; Movies; Shopping trips; Social/Cultural gatherings.

Vista Del Rio Medical Center*
615 E 6th St, Kansas City, MO, 64106
(816) 234-7800
Admin Willa Hughes.
Licensure Skilled care. *Beds* 50.
Owner Nonprofit Corp.

KENNETT

Kennett Health Care Center
Rte 1 South, Kennett, MO, 63857
(314) 888-1150
Admin Larry Baker. *Medical Dir/Dir of Nursing* Wuthisak Soonattrakul MD; Patty Borchers DON.
Licensure Skilled care; Intermediate care. *Beds* 120. *Certified* Medicaid; Medicare.
Owner Proprietary Corp.
Admissions Requirements Medical examination; Physician's request.

Staff Physicians 1 (pt); RNs 4 (ft), 3 (pt); LPNs 13 (ft), 4 (pt); Orderlies 2 (pt); Nurses aides 53 (ft), 3 (pt); Physical therapists 1 (pt); Occupational therapists 1 (pt); Speech therapists 1 (pt); Activities coordinators 1 (ft); Dietitians 1 (pt).
Facilities Dining room; Physical therapy room; Activities room; Laundry room; Barber/Beauty shop.
Activities Arts & crafts; Games; Prayer groups.

KEYTESVILLE

Chariton County Rest Home*
Rte 2, Box 5, Keytesville, MO, 65261
(816) 288-3791
Admin Mildred Coy.
Licensure Residential care. *Beds* 37.
Owner Proprietary Corp.

KIMBERLING CITY

Table Rock Health Care Center*
Table Rock Village, Kimberling City, MO, 65686
(417) 739-2481
Admin A L Schluter.
Licensure Skilled care. *Beds* 60. *Certified* Medicaid.
Owner Proprietary Corp.

KING CITY

King City Manor
300 W Fairview, King City, MO, 64463
(816) 535-4325
Admin Carolyn Stegman. *Medical Dir/Dir of Nursing* Bev Culver RN.
Licensure Intermediate care. *Beds* ICF 60. *Certified* Medicaid.
Owner Proprietary Corp (Tiffany Care Centers).
Staff RNs 2 (ft); Orderlies 1 (ft); Nurses aides 17 (ft), 4 (pt); Activities coordinators 1 (ft).
Facilities Dining room; Physical therapy room; Laundry room; Barber/Beauty shop; Library.
Activities Arts & crafts; Cards; Games; Reading groups; Prayer groups; Movies; Shopping trips; Social/Cultural gatherings.

KIRKSVILLE

Countryside Rehabilitation
RRte 4, E Normal, Kirksville, MO, 63501
(816) 665-6135
Admin Wilma Bramhall.
Licensure RCF II. *Beds* RCF II 54.
Owner Proprietary Corp.
Admissions Requirements Minimum age 18; Medical examination.
Staff Physicians 35 (pt); LPNs 1 (ft); Nurses aides 5 (ft); Activities coordinators 1 (ft), 35 (pt); Dietitians 2 (ft); Medical technician 3 (ft).
Languages Sign
Facilities Dining room; Activities room; Crafts room; Laundry room.
Activities Arts & crafts; Cards; Games; Reading groups; Prayer groups; Shopping trips; Social/Cultural gatherings; Picnics; Fairs; Concerts; Garden; Counseling.

Kirksville Manor Care Center
1705 E LaHarpe, Kirksville, MO, 63501
(816) 665-3774
Admin Robert Redman. *Medical Dir/Dir of Nursing* Nancy Bradley.
Licensure Skilled care; Intermediate care. *Beds* SNF 132; ICF. *Certified* Medicaid; Medicare.
Owner Proprietary Corp.
Admissions Requirements Minimum age 16; Medical examination; Physician's request.

Staff Physicians 3 (pt); RNs 4 (ft), 3 (pt); LPNs 14 (ft); Orderlies 6 (ft); Nurses aides 35 (ft), 15 (pt); Physical therapists 2 (pt); Occupational therapists 1 (pt); Speech therapists 1 (pt); Activities coordinators 1 (ft); Dentists 1 (pt); Podiatrists 1 (pt); Ophthalmologists 1 (pt).
Facilities Dining room; Physical therapy room; Activities room; Chapel; Crafts room; Laundry room; Barber/Beauty shop; Library.
Activities Arts & crafts; Cards; Games; Reading groups; Prayer groups; Movies; Social/Cultural gatherings.

Twin Pines Adult Care Center
316 S Osteopathy, Kirksville, MO, 63501
(816) 665-2887
Admin Marilyn Powell. *Medical Dir/Dir of Nursing* Marlene Wager MD; Marilyn Stull RN DON.
Licensure Skilled care. *Beds* 126. *Certified* Medicare.
Owner Nonprofit Corp.
Admissions Requirements Minimum age 18.
Staff Physicians 1 (ft); RNs 4 (ft), 1 (pt); LPNs 20 (ft), 4 (pt); Nurses aides 60 (ft), 25 (pt); Physical therapists 1 (pt); Recreational therapists 2 (ft); Occupational therapists 1 (pt); Speech therapists 1 (pt); Dietitians 1 (pt); Dentists 1 (pt); Ophthalmologists; Podiatrists.
Facilities Dining room; Physical therapy room; Activities room; Crafts room; Laundry room; Barber/Beauty shop.
Activities Arts & crafts; Cards; Games; Reading groups; Prayer groups; Movies; Shopping trips; Social/Cultural gatherings.

KIRKWOOD

Blind Girl's Home*
221 W Washington Ave, Kirkwood, MO, 63122
(314) 966-6033
Admin Colleen L Hill. *Medical Dir/Dir of Nursing* Dr Aaron Bernstein.
Licensure Intermediate care. *Beds* 28.
Owner Nonprofit Corp.
Admissions Requirements Minimum age 21; Females only; Medical examination; Physician's request.
Staff Physicians 1 (ft); RNs 1 (ft), 1 (pt); LPNs 3 (pt); Nurses aides 5 (ft), 12 (pt); Recreational therapists 1 (pt); Activities coordinators 1 (pt); Dietitians 1 (ft).
Facilities Dining room; Physical therapy room; Activities room; Chapel; Laundry room; Barber/Beauty shop; Auditorium.
Activities Arts & crafts; Cards; Games; Reading groups; Shopping trips; Social/Cultural gatherings; Music programs.

Manor Grove*
711 S Kirkwood Rd, Kirkwood, MO, 63122
(314) 965-0864
Admin Carolyn Ellerbusch. *Medical Dir/Dir of Nursing* Dr David Schoenwalder.
Licensure Skilled care. *Beds* 97.
Owner Nonprofit Corp.
Staff Physicians 19 (pt); RNs 4 (ft), 8 (pt); LPNs 1 (ft), 3 (pt); Orderlies 1 (pt); Nurses aides 20 (ft), 9 (pt); Physical therapists 1 (pt); Occupational therapists 1 (pt); Speech therapists 1 (pt); Activities coordinators 1 (ft); Dietitians 1 (ft); Dentists 1 (pt); Ophthalmologists 1 (pt); Podiatrists 1 (pt); Audiologists 1 (pt).
Facilities Dining room; Physical therapy room; Activities room; Chapel; Crafts room; Laundry room; Barber/Beauty shop; Library.
Activities Arts & crafts; Cards; Games; Reading groups; Prayer groups; Movies; Shopping trips; Social/Cultural gatherings.

St Agnes Home
10341 Manchester Rd, Kirkwood, MO, 63122
(314) 965-7616
Admin Sr Mary Patrick Gruber.

Licensure Intermediate care. *Beds* 150.
Owner Nonprofit Corp.
Admissions Requirements Minimum age 65; Medical examination; Physician's request.
Staff Physicians 2 (pt); RNs 1 (ft), 1 (pt); LPNs 7 (pt); Orderlies 53 (ft); Physical therapists 2 (pt); Activities coordinators 1 (ft); Dietitians 1 (pt); Ophthalmologists 1 (pt).
Affiliation Roman Catholic
Facilities Dining room; Physical therapy room; Activities room; Chapel; Crafts room; Laundry room; Barber/Beauty shop; Library.
Activities Arts & crafts; Cards; Games; Reading groups; Prayer groups; Movies; Shopping trips; Social/Cultural gatherings; Weekly happy hour; Monthly salad luncheon.

LABELLE

La Belle Manor
Hwy 6 W, LaBelle, MO, 63447
(816) 462-3234
Admin Eva Coleman. *Medical Dir/Dir of Nursing* Beverly Greehagen.
Licensure Intermediate care. *Beds* SNF 92.
Owner Proprietary Corp.
Admissions Requirements Minimum age 18.
Staff Physicians 4 (ft); RNs 2 (ft), 3 (pt); Orderlies 3 (ft); Nurses aides 54 (ft), 24 (pt); Physical therapists 1 (ft), 4 (pt); Recreational therapists 1 (ft); Speech therapists 1 (ft); Activities coordinators 1 (ft); Dietitians 1 (ft), 1 (pt); Dentists 1 (ft).
Languages German
Facilities Dining room; Physical therapy room; Activities room; Chapel; Laundry room; Barber/Beauty shop.
Activities Arts & crafts; Cards; Games; Prayer groups; Movies; Shopping trips; Social/Cultural gatherings.

LAMAR

Chastain's of Lamar Inc*
206 W 1st St, Lamar, MO, 64759
(417) 682-3315
Admin Alvin L Forester.
Licensure Intermediate care. *Beds* 123. *Certified* Medicaid.
Owner Proprietary Corp (Hillhaven Corp).

Lamar Boarding & Rest Home*
505 E 8th St, Lamar, MO, 64759
Admin Tom Dale. *Medical Dir/Dir of Nursing* Catherine Boyer Dale.
Licensure Intermediate care for mentally retarded. *Beds* 60. *Certified* Medicaid.
Owner Nonprofit Corp.
Admissions Requirements Medical examination.
Staff LPNs 1 (ft); Orderlies 1 (ft); Nurses aides 7 (ft); Physical therapists 2 (pt); Recreational therapists 2 (pt); Activities coordinators 1 (pt).
Facilities Dining room; Physical therapy room; Activities room; Chapel; Crafts room; Laundry room; Barber/Beauty shop; Pool room.
Activities Cards; Games; Movies; Social/Cultural gatherings.

LANAGAN

Cinnamon Hill Manor Inc*
PO Box 146, Lanagan, MO, 64847
(417) 436-2231
Admin Joetta Jenkins.
Licensure Intermediate care. *Beds* 43.
Owner Proprietary Corp.

LAPLATA

LaPlata Nursing Home District
Old Stagecoach Rd, LaPlata, MO, 63549
(816) 332-4315
Admin Wanda L Smith. *Medical Dir/Dir of Nursing* O L Woodward DO; Connie Delaney LPN DON.
Licensure Intermediate care. *Beds* ICF 52. *Certified* Medicaid.
Owner Nonprofit Corp.
Admissions Requirements Minimum age 21; Medical examination.
Staff RNs 1 (pt); LPNs 3 (ft), 3 (pt); Orderlies 1 (ft); Nurses aides 12 (ft), 12 (pt); Physical therapists 1 (pt); Occupational therapists 1 (pt); Speech therapists 1 (pt); Activities coordinators 1 (ft); Dietitians 1 (pt).
Facilities Dining room; Physical therapy room; Activities room; Laundry room.
Activities Arts & crafts; Cards; Games; Reading groups; Prayer groups; Movies; Shopping trips; Social/Cultural gatherings.

LATHROP

Lathrop Health Facility Inc
PO Box 285, 702 Center St, Lathrop, MO, 64465
(816) 528-4257
Admin Evelyn L Spiers.
Licensure Intermediate care. *Beds* ICF 84.
Owner Nonprofit Corp.
Staff RNs 1 (ft), 2 (pt); LPNs 4 (ft), 1 (pt); Nurses aides 28 (ft); Activities coordinators 1 (ft); Dietitians 6 (ft), 1 (pt).
Facilities Dining room; Activities room; Chapel; Laundry room; Barber/Beauty shop.
Activities Arts & crafts; Cards; Games; Reading groups; Prayer groups; Movies; Social/Cultural gatherings; Bus tours.

LAURIE

Laurie Nursing Home*
State Rd O, Laurie, MO, 65038
Admin Ethel G Jones. *Medical Dir/Dir of Nursing* Dr H Petry.
Licensure Intermediate care. *Beds* 60. *Certified* Medicaid.
Owner Nonprofit Corp.
Admissions Requirements Minimum age 18; Medical examination; Physician's request.
Staff Physicians 4 (ft); RNs 2 (ft), 1 (pt); LPNs 1 (ft); Nurses aides 16 (ft), 5 (pt); Physical therapists 1 (ft), 1 (pt); Activities coordinators 1 (ft); Dentists 2 (ft); Ophthalmologists 2 (ft); Podiatrists 1 (ft); Audiologists 2 (ft); Dietary workers 3 (ft), 4 (pt).
Facilities Dining room; Physical therapy room; Activities room; Laundry room; Barber/Beauty shop; Library.
Activities Arts & crafts; Cards; Games; Prayer groups; Movies; Shopping trips; Social/Cultural gatherings.

LAWSON

Graceland Manor*
Rte 1, Box 460, Lawson, MO, 64062
Admissions Requirements Medical examination.
Staff Nurses aides 2 (ft).
Facilities Dining room; Activities room; Chapel; Laundry room.
Activities Arts & crafts; Games; Reading groups; Prayer groups; Shopping trips; Social/Cultural gatherings.

Smithview Manor Nursing Home
210 8th Terrace, Lawson, MO, 64062
(816) 296-3269
Admin Genevie M Herndon.
Licensure Intermediate care. *Beds* 60.
Owner Proprietary Corp.

Staff RNs 1 (pt); LPNs 3 (ft), 1 (pt); Orderlies 1 (ft); Nurses aides 21 (ft), 4 (pt); Physical therapists 1 (pt); Occupational therapists 1 (pt); Speech therapists 1 (pt); Activities coordinators 1 (ft); Dietitians 1 (pt).
Facilities Dining room; Activities room; Laundry room; Barber/Beauty shop; TV room.
Activities Arts & crafts; Cards; Games; Reading groups; Prayer groups; Movies; Shopping trips; Social/Cultural gatherings; Musical entertainment.

LEBANON

Lebanon Care Center*
596 Morton Rd, Lebanon, MO, 65536
(417) 532-9173
Admin John D Foster.
Licensure Skilled care; Intermediate care. *Beds* 180. *Certified* Medicaid; Medicare.
Owner Proprietary Corp.

Lebanon Nursing Home*
175 Morton Rd, Lebanon, MO, 65536
(417) 532-5351
Admin Phyllis Appleberry.
Licensure Intermediate care. *Beds* 29.
Owner Proprietary Corp.

LEES SUMMIT

Lees Summit Nursing Center
615 SW Oldham Pkwy, Lees Summit, MO, 64063
(816) 524-3328
Admin Agatha M Forck. *Medical Dir/Dir of Nursing* Dr Robert LaHue; Sharon Byers.
Licensure Skilled care; Intermediate care. *Beds* SNF 120; ICF. *Certified* Medicaid.
Owner Proprietary Corp (Beverly Enterprises).
Admissions Requirements Minimum age 21.
Staff Physicians 8 (pt); RNs 2 (ft), 2 (pt); LPNs 9 (ft), 3 (pt); Orderlies 7 (ft); Nurses aides 36 (ft); Physical therapists 1 (ft); Recreational therapists 1 (ft); Occupational therapists 1 (pt); Speech therapists 1 (pt); Activities coordinators 1 (ft); Dietitians 1 (pt); Dentists 1 (pt); Ophthalmologists 1 (pt); Podiatrists 1 (pt); Psychologist 1 (pt); Certified dietary manager 1 (ft).
Facilities Dining room; Physical therapy room; Activities room; Crafts room; Laundry room; Barber/Beauty shop.
Activities Arts & crafts; Cards; Games; Reading groups; Prayer groups; Movies; Shopping trips; Social/Cultural gatherings.

Village Care Center
500 N Murray, Lee's Summit, MO, 64063
(816) 524-8400
Admin Sandra Grant. *Medical Dir/Dir of Nursing* John Murphy MD; Bernice Holtgrewe RN DON.
Licensure Skilled care; Intermediate care. *Beds* 312. *Certified* Medicaid; Medicare.
Owner Nonprofit Corp.
Admissions Requirements Physician's request.
Staff Physicians 2 (pt); RNs 13 (ft), 2 (pt); LPNs 8 (ft), 2 (pt); Nurses aides 132 (ft), 9 (pt); Physical therapists 9 (pt); Occupational therapists 1 (pt); Speech therapists 1 (pt); Activities coordinators 4 (ft), 1 (pt); Dietitians 1 (pt); Dentists 1 (pt); Ophthalmologists 1 (pt); Dentist 1 (pt).
Facilities Dining room; Physical therapy room; Activities room; Chapel; Crafts room; Laundry room; Barber/Beauty shop; Library.
Activities Arts & crafts; Cards; Games; Reading groups; Prayer groups; Movies; Shopping trips; Social/Cultural gatherings.

LEMAY

Lemay Nursing Home
PO Box 99, 1204 Telegraph Rd, Lemay, MO, 63841-0099
(314) 544-2380
Admin Charlotte Sczepanski. *Medical Dir/Dir of Nursing* Juan Castro.
Licensure Intermediate care. *Beds* 38.
Owner Proprietary Corp.
Staff Physicians 2 (ft); RNs 1 (pt); LPNs 2 (ft), 1 (pt); Orderlies 1 (ft); Nurses aides 15 (ft); Activities coordinators 1 (ft).
Facilities Dining room; Barber/Beauty shop.
Activities Arts & crafts; Shopping trips.

LEWISTOWN

Prairie View Rest Home Inc
Rte 2, Lewistown, MO, 63452
(314) 497-2424
Admin Mildred L Huebotter. *Medical Dir/Dir of Nursing* Gene Childress DO; Janet Richardson DON.
Licensure Intermediate care. *Beds* ICF 69.
Owner Nonprofit Corp.
Admissions Requirements Minimum age 21.
Staff RNs 2 (pt); LPNs 5 (ft); Nurses aides 20 (ft); Occupational therapists 1 (ft); Activities coordinators 2 (ft); Dietitians 1 (pt).
Facilities Dining room; Activities room; Laundry room; Barber/Beauty shop.
Activities Arts & crafts; Cards; Games; Prayer groups; Movies; Shopping trips; Social/Cultural gatherings.

Stone Haven
401 S Oak, Lewistown, MO, 63452
Admin Jesse Stone & Betty Stone.
Licensure Intermediate care. *Certified* Medicaid.
Owner Proprietary Corp.
Admissions Requirements Minimum age 18; Medical examination.
Staff Physicians; RNs; LPNs; Nurses aides; Activities coordinators.
Facilities Dining room; Activities room; Laundry room.
Activities Arts & crafts; Cards; Games; Prayer groups; Movies; Shopping trips.

LEXINGTON

Lafayette Manor Nursing Home
PO Box 499, Hwy 13 S, Lexington, MO, 64067
(816) 259-4697
Admin Harold T Ainsworth Jr. *Medical Dir/Dir of Nursing* David Pullium DO; Connie McPherson RN DON.
Licensure Intermediate care. *Beds* ICF 148. *Certified* Medicaid.
Owner Proprietary Corp (Beverly Enterprises).
Admissions Requirements Minimum age 17; Medical examination.
Staff Physicians 6 (pt); RNs 1 (ft); LPNs 3 (ft); Orderlies 2 (ft); Nurses aides 58 (ft), 4 (pt); Physical therapists 1 (pt); Occupational therapists 1 (pt); Speech therapists 1 (pt); Activities coordinators 1 (ft); Dietitians 1 (pt); Podiatrists 1 (pt); Dentist 1 (pt).
Facilities Dining room; Physical therapy room; Activities room; Chapel; Crafts room; Laundry room; Barber/Beauty shop.
Activities Arts & crafts; Games; Reading groups; Movies; Shopping trips; Social/Cultural gatherings; Resident council.

LIBERTY

Heartland of Liberty
1200 W College, Liberty, MO, 64068
(816) 781-3020
Admin Rob Dvorak. *Medical Dir/Dir of Nursing* Dr Ron LaHue; Michelle Boudreaux.

Licensure Intermediate care. *Beds* ICF 140. *Certified* Medicaid.
Owner Proprietary Corp.
Admissions Requirements Medical examination; Physician's request.
Staff RNs 2 (ft); LPNs 21 (ft), 7 (pt); Nurses aides 38 (ft), 6 (pt); Activities coordinators 1 (ft), 1 (pt); Social worker 1 (pt).
Languages Spanish
Facilities Dining room; Physical therapy room; Activities room; Crafts room; Laundry room; Barber/Beauty shop.
Activities Arts & crafts; Cards; Games; Reading groups; Prayer groups; Movies; Shopping trips; Social/Cultural gatherings.

Odd Fellows Home*
Rte 6, Box 194, Liberty, MO, 64068
(816) 781-4880
Admin Helen Jo White.
Licensure Intermediate care; Boarding care. *Beds* ICF 20; Boarding care 45.
Owner Nonprofit Corp.
Affiliation Independent Order of Odd Fellows & Rebekahs

Pleasant Valley Manor Care Center*
6814 Sobbie Rd, Liberty, MO, 64068
Medical Dir/Dir of Nursing Dr Nancy Russell.
Staff Physicians 2 (ft); RNs 1 (ft); LPNs 6 (ft), 1 (pt); Nurses aides 22 (ft), 4 (pt); Physical therapists 3 (ft); Reality therapists 1 (ft); Recreational therapists 1 (ft); Occupational therapists 1 (ft); Activities coordinators 1 (ft); Dietitians 1 (ft); Dentists 1 (ft); Podiatrists 1 (ft).
Facilities Dining room; Physical therapy room; Activities room; Chapel; Laundry room; Barber/Beauty shop; Library.
Activities Arts & crafts; Games; Reading groups; Prayer groups; Movies; Shopping trips; Social/Cultural gatherings.

LICKING

Texas County Missouri Health Care Center Inc*
600 Hickory, Licking, MO, 65542
(314) 674-2111
Admin Raymond O Wood.
Licensure Intermediate care. *Beds* 60. *Certified* Medicaid.
Owner Nonprofit Corp.

LINCOLN

Lincoln Community Nursing Home
PO Box 302, RT 1, Lincoln, MO, 65338
(816) 547-3322
Admin Ruth Proctor. *Medical Dir/Dir of Nursing* D K Allcorn MD.
Licensure Intermediate care. *Beds* ICF 60. *Certified* Medicaid.
Owner Nonprofit Corp.
Admissions Requirements Minimum age 16; Medical examination; Physician's request.
Staff RNs 1 (ft); LPNs 2 (ft), 2 (pt); Nurses aides 15 (ft), 8 (pt); Activities coordinators 1 (ft); Dietitians 1 (ft).
Facilities Dining room; Physical therapy room; Activities room; Chapel; Laundry room; Barber/Beauty shop; Library.
Activities Arts & crafts; Cards; Games; Reading groups; Prayer groups; Movies; Social/Cultural gatherings; Monthly birthday parties.

LINN

Green Meadows Health Care Center
PO Box 499, Linn, MO, 65051
(314) 897-2218
Admin Weldon Curry. *Medical Dir/Dir of Nursing* Dorothy Curry.
Licensure Skilled care; Intermediate care. *Beds* SNF 30; ICF 60. *Certified* Medicaid.
Owner Proprietary Corp.

Admissions Requirements Minimum age 21; Medical examination.
Facilities Dining room; Physical therapy room; Activities room; Chapel; Crafts room; Laundry room; Barber/Beauty shop; Library.
Activities Arts & crafts; Cards; Games; Reading groups; Prayer groups; Movies; Shopping trips; Social/Cultural gatherings.

Linn Manor Nursing Home
Box 499, Linn, MO, 65051
(314) 897-2247
Admin Dorothy Curry & Weldon Curry.
Licensure Intermediate care. *Beds* 41.
Owner Proprietary Corp.

LOCKWOOD

Good Shepherd Nursing Home
200 W 12th, Lockwood, MO, 65682
(417) 232-4571
Admin Doris Lilienkamp. *Medical Dir/Dir of Nursing* Beth Paschall RN DON.
Licensure Intermediate care. *Beds* 66. *Certified* Medicaid.
Owner Nonprofit Corp.
Admissions Requirements Minimum age 14.
Staff Physicians 4 (pt); RNs 1 (ft); LPNs 3 (ft), 2 (pt); Nurses aides 18 (ft), 6 (pt); Physical therapists 1 (pt); Recreational therapists 1 (ft); Occupational therapists 1 (pt); Activities coordinators 1 (ft); Dietitians 1 (ft).
Facilities Dining room; Activities room; Chapel; Laundry room; Barber/Beauty shop; Library.
Activities Arts & crafts; Cards; Games; Prayer groups; Movies.

LOUISIANA

Louisiana Nursing Home
600 Nebraska, Louisiana, MO, 63353
(314) 754-4556, 754-4557
Admin Dorothy Payne. *Medical Dir/Dir of Nursing* Lois Turner.
Licensure Intermediate care. *Beds* 29.
Owner Privately owned.
Admissions Requirements Minimum age 21; Medical examination.
Staff Physicians 2 (ft); RNs; LPNs 2 (ft), 2 (pt); Nurses aides 7 (ft), 2 (pt); Activities coordinators 1 (pt).
Facilities Dining room; Activities room; Laundry room.
Activities Arts & crafts; Cards; Games; Reading groups; Movies; Shopping trips; Social/Cultural gatherings.

Maple Grove Lodge Inc
PO Box 370, 2407 Kentucky St, Louisiana, MO, 63353
(314) 754-5456
Admin Joanne K Rucker. *Medical Dir/Dir of Nursing* L G Stuerman MD; Darline Bange DON.
Licensure Intermediate care. *Beds* ICF 60. *Certified* Medicaid.
Owner Proprietary Corp.
Admissions Requirements Minimum age 18; Medical examination.
Staff RNs 1 (pt); LPNs 3 (ft), 1 (pt); Orderlies 1 (ft); Nurses aides 15 (ft), 3 (pt); Activities coordinators 1 (ft); Dietitians 1 (pt).
Facilities Dining room; Laundry room; Barber/Beauty shop.
Activities Arts & crafts; Prayer groups; Movies; Social/Cultural gatherings.

Smith-Barr Manor Nursing Home
2407 W Georgia, Louisiana, MO, 63353
(314) 754-6279
Admin Charles Ulry Jr. *Medical Dir/Dir of Nursing* Larry Stuerman MD; Karen Lynn RN.
Licensure Skilled care. *Beds* SNF 71. *Certified* Medicaid; Medicare.

Admissions Requirements Minimum age 21.
Staff RNs 2 (ft), 1 (pt); LPNs 7 (ft), 1 (pt); Nurses aides 23 (ft); Recreational therapists 1 (ft); Activities coordinators 1 (ft); Dietitians 1 (pt).
Facilities Dining room; Physical therapy room; Activities room; Laundry room; Barber/Beauty shop; Library.
Activities Arts & crafts; Games; Reading groups; Prayer groups; Movies; Social/Cultural gatherings.

LOWRY CITY

Truman Lake Manor Inc*
600 E 7th, Box 188, Lowry City, MO, 64763
(417) 644-2248
Admin Robert O Scott. *Medical Dir/Dir of Nursing* Mark Snell DO.
Licensure Intermediate care. *Beds* 60. *Certified* Medicaid.
Owner Proprietary Corp.
Admissions Requirements Minimum age 18; Medical examination; Physician's request.
Staff Physicians 3 (pt); RNs 1 (ft), 1 (pt); LPNs 4 (ft), 1 (pt); Nurses aides 18 (ft), 2 (pt); Physical therapists 1 (pt); Occupational therapists 1 (pt); Speech therapists 1 (pt); Activities coordinators 1 (pt); Dietitians 1 (pt); Dentists 1 (pt).
Facilities Dining room; Physical therapy room; Activities room; Chapel; Crafts room; Laundry room; Barber/Beauty shop; Library.
Activities Arts & crafts; Cards; Games; Reading groups; Movies; Shopping trips; Social/Cultural gatherings.

MACON

Macon County Nursing Home District—Loch Haven
PO Box 187, Sunset Hills Dr, Macon, MO, 63552
(816) 385-3113
Admin Richard S Waller. *Medical Dir/Dir of Nursing* Dr J E Campbell; Barbara Primm RN DON.
Licensure Skilled care; Intermediate care; Residential apartments. *Beds* SNF 60; ICF 120; Residential apts 24. *Certified* Medicaid; Medicare.
Owner Nonprofit organization/foundation.
Admissions Requirements Minimum age 18.
Staff Physicians 1 (pt); RNs 5 (ft), 1 (pt); LPNs 10 (ft), 2 (pt); Orderlies 5 (ft); Nurses aides 98 (ft); Physical therapists 1 (ft); Occupational therapists 1 (pt); Speech therapists 1 (pt); Activities coordinators 1 (ft), 2 (pt); Dietitians 1 (pt).
Languages Spanish, Italian
Facilities Dining room; Physical therapy room; Activities room; Chapel; Crafts room; Laundry room; Barber/Beauty shop.
Activities Arts & crafts; Cards; Games; Reading groups; Prayer groups; Movies; Shopping trips; Social/Cultural gatherings; Music.

Macon Health Care Center
PO Box 465, Hwy 36E, Macon, MO, 63552
(816) 385-5797
Admin Jim Kurtz. *Medical Dir/Dir of Nursing* Joseph Quaranto MD; Linda Conner RN DON.
Licensure Skilled care; Intermediate care; Residential care. *Beds* 120. *Certified* Medicaid; Medicare.
Owner Proprietary Corp.
Admissions Requirements Minimum age 18; Medical examination.
Staff Physicians 7 (pt); RNs 4 (ft), 1 (pt); LPNs 6 (ft), 3 (pt); Nurses aides 19 (ft), 8 (pt); Physical therapists 1 (pt); Occupational therapists 1 (pt); Speech therapists 1 (pt); Activities coordinators 1 (ft); Dietitians 1 (pt).

Facilities Dining room; Physical therapy room; Activities room; Chapel; Crafts room; Laundry room; Barber/Beauty shop.
Activities Arts & crafts; Cards; Games; Reading groups; Prayer groups; Movies; Shopping trips; Social/Cultural gatherings.

MADISON

Wildwood Nursing Home
Rte 2 Hwy 151, Madison, MO, 65263
(816) 291-8636
Admin Margery Sue Waller. *Medical Dir/Dir of Nursing* Dr Robert Warbritton; Judy Hollingsworth.
Licensure Intermediate care. *Beds* ICF 32. *Certified* Medicaid.
Owner Privately owned.
Staff Physicians; RNs; LPNs; Orderlies; Nurses aides; Activities coordinators; Dietitians.
Facilities Dining room; Activities room; Laundry room.
Activities Arts & crafts; Cards; Games; Reading groups; Prayer groups; Movies; Shopping trips; Social/Cultural gatherings.

MALDEN

Ridgeview Manor Nursing Home*
500 Barrett Dr, Malden, MO, 63863
(314) 276-3843
Admin John Hisaw. *Medical Dir/Dir of Nursing* Tom Henderson.
Licensure Intermediate care. *Beds* 120. *Certified* Medicaid.
Owner Proprietary Corp (Beverly Enterprises).
Admissions Requirements Minimum age 21.
Staff Physicians 5 (ft), 4 (pt); RNs 1 (ft), 2 (pt); LPNs 5 (ft), 3 (pt); Nurses aides 43 (ft), 8 (pt); Physical therapists 2 (ft), 1 (pt); Recreational therapists 2 (ft); Occupational therapists 1 (pt); Speech therapists 1 (pt); Dietitians 1 (pt); Dentists 1 (pt); Ophthalmologists 1 (pt).
Facilities Dining room; Physical therapy room; Activities room; Laundry room; Barber/Beauty shop; Library.
Activities Arts & crafts; Cards; Games; Reading groups; Prayer groups; Movies; Shopping trips; Social/Cultural gatherings.

MANCHESTER

Clayton House Healthcare*
1251 E Clayton Rd, Manchester, MO, 63011
(314) 227-5070
Admin Mark D Lee.
Licensure Skilled care; Intermediate care; Residential. *Beds* 282. *Certified* Medicaid; Medicare.
Owner Proprietary Corp (Hillhaven Corp).
Staff RNs; LPNs; Nurses aides; Physical therapists; Reality therapists; Recreational therapists; Occupational therapists; Speech therapists; Activities coordinators; Dietitians; Dentists; Podiatrists.
Facilities Dining room; Physical therapy room; Activities room; Chapel; Crafts room; Laundry room; Barber/Beauty shop; Library.
Activities Arts & crafts; Cards; Games; Reading groups; Prayer groups; Movies; Shopping trips; Social/Cultural gatherings.

Mari de Villa Retirement Center Inc*
13900 Clayton Rd, Manchester, MO, 63011
(314) 227-5347
Admin Joseph L Linneman.
Licensure Skilled care. *Beds* 224.
Owner Proprietary Corp.

MANSFIELD

Mansfield Nursing Home
Rte 1, Mansfield, MO, 65704
(417) 724-8116

Admin Michael D Baldus. *Medical Dir/Dir of Nursing* Efraim Reyes MD; Mary Ann Heib DON.
Licensure Intermediate care. *Beds* ICF 45. *Certified* Medicaid.
Owner Proprietary Corp.
Admissions Requirements Minimum age 18; Medical examination.
Staff Physicians 1 (ft), 2 (pt); RNs 1 (pt); LPNs 2 (ft); Orderlies 2 (ft); Nurses aides 14 (ft), 1 (pt); Physical therapists 1 (pt); Activities coordinators 1 (ft), 1 (pt); Dietitians 1 (pt); Dentists 1 (pt); Podiatrists 1 (pt).
Facilities Dining room; Physical therapy room; Activities room; Laundry room; Deck for outdoor parties.
Activities Arts & crafts; Cards; Games; Prayer groups; Movies; Shopping trips; Sunshine day; Wilder day; Ice cream socials; Fish day & fry; Tours.

MARCELINE

Chastain's of Marceline Nursing Home*
108 E Howell St, Marceline, MO, 64658
(816) 376-3579
Admin Shirley White.
Licensure Intermediate care. *Beds* 81. *Certified* Medicaid.
Owner Proprietary Corp (Hillhaven Corp).

King Rest Home*
215 W Walker St, Marceline, MO, 64658
(816) 376-2165
Admin Thelma Braley.
Licensure Intermediate care. *Beds* 14.
Owner Proprietary Corp.

Pioneer Health Center*
Rte 1, PO Box 477, Marceline, MO, 64658
(816) 376-2001
Admin Phil McAnulty. *Medical Dir/Dir of Nursing* S P Galvez MD.
Licensure Skilled care; Intermediate care. *Beds* 84. *Certified* Medicaid; Medicare.
Owner Proprietary Corp.
Admissions Requirements Minimum age 18; Medical examination; Physician's request.
Staff Physicians 1 (pt); RNs 2 (ft); LPNs 5 (ft), 1 (pt); Orderlies 3 (ft); Nurses aides 26 (ft), 7 (pt); Physical therapists 1 (pt); Occupational therapists 1 (pt); Speech therapists 1 (pt); Activities coordinators 1 (ft), 1 (pt); Dietitians 1 (pt); Dentists 1 (pt); Podiatrists 1 (pt).
Facilities Dining room; Physical therapy room; Activities room; Laundry room; Barber/Beauty shop; Fire protection sprinkler; Individual room controlled heat; Central air conditioning; Cable television.
Activities Arts & crafts; Cards; Games; Movies; Shopping trips; Social/Cultural gatherings.

St Francis Hopital—SNF/ICF Care Facility*
225 W Hayden St, Marceline, MO, 64658
(816) 376-3521
Admin Estelle M Vosen. *Medical Dir/Dir of Nursing* David Armin MD.
Licensure Skilled care; Intermediate care. *Beds* 42.
Owner Nonprofit Corp.
Admissions Requirements Medical examination.
Staff Physicians 2 (ft), 10 (pt); RNs 4 (ft), 7 (pt); LPNs 12 (ft), 6 (pt); Nurses aides 16 (ft), 3 (pt); Physical therapists 1 (pt); Recreational therapists 1 (ft); Occupational therapists 1 (pt); Speech therapists 1 (pt); Dietitians 1 (ft); Dentists 1 (pt); Ophthalmologists 1 (pt); Podiatrists 1 (pt); Audiologists 1 (pt).
Affiliation Roman Catholic
Facilities Dining room; Physical therapy room; Activities room; Chapel; Crafts room; Barber/Beauty shop.

Activities Arts & crafts; Cards; Games; Reading groups; Prayer groups; Movies; Shopping trips; Social/Cultural gatherings.

MARIONVILLE

The Ozarks Methodist Manor
PO Box C, 205 S College, Marionville, MO, 65705
(417) 463-2573, 463-7622
Admin Beryl R Gourley. *Medical Dir/Dir of Nursing* Pam Fite DON.
Licensure Intermediate care. *Beds* 78.
Owner Nonprofit organization/foundation.
Admissions Requirements Minimum age 60; Medical examination.
Staff Physicians 1 (pt); RNs 2 (ft), 1 (pt); LPNs 7 (ft), 3 (pt); Nurses aides 35 (ft), 33 (pt); Physical therapists 5 (ft), 1 (pt); Dietitians 1 (ft); Ophthalmologists 1 (pt).
Affiliation Methodist
Facilities Dining room; Physical therapy room; Activities room; Chapel; Crafts room; Laundry room; Barber/Beauty shop; Library.
Activities Arts & crafts; Cards; Games; Reading groups; Prayer groups; Movies; Shopping trips.

MARSHALL

Mar-Saline Manor Care Center*
809 E Gordon St, Marshall, MO, 65340
(816) 886-2247
Admin R Nadine Ozias. *Medical Dir/Dir of Nursing* Jane Coleman LPN.
Licensure Intermediate care. *Beds* 92.
Owner Proprietary Corp.
Admissions Requirements Medical examination.
Staff Physicians 1 (ft); RNs 1 (pt); LPNs 6 (ft); Orderlies 30 (ft); Physical therapists 1 (pt); Speech therapists 1 (pt); Activities coordinators 1 (ft); Dietitians 1 (pt); Dentists 1 (pt); Podiatrists 1 (pt).
Facilities Dining room; Activities room; Crafts room; Laundry room; Barber/Beauty shop.
Activities Arts & crafts; Cards; Games; Reading groups; Prayer groups; Movies; Shopping trips; Social/Cultural gatherings.

Marshall State School & Hospital*
PO Box 190, Marshall, MO, 65340
(816) 886-2202
Admin Adriene McKenna.
Licensure Intermediate care for mentally retarded. *Beds* 734.

Saline County Rest Home Inc*
Rte 1, Marshall, MO, 65340
(816) 886-9676
Admin D Castle.
Licensure Intermediate care. *Beds* 82.
Owner Publicly owned.

MARSHFIELD

Webco Manor
1657 W Washington, Marshfield, MO, 65706
(417) 468-5144
Admin Jo Walker. *Medical Dir/Dir of Nursing* Dr T M Macdonnell; Laura Sullivan DON.
Licensure Skilled care; Residential care. *Beds* SNF 100; Residential 24. *Certified* Medicaid.
Owner Nonprofit Corp.
Admissions Requirements Medical examination; Physician's request.
Staff Physicians 1 (pt); RNs 4 (ft), 1 (pt); LPNs 6 (ft), 2 (pt); Nurses aides 40 (ft), 20 (pt); Physical therapists 1 (pt); Occupational therapists 1 (pt); Speech therapists 1 (pt); Activities coordinators 1 (ft); Dietitians 1 (pt).
Facilities Dining room; Physical therapy room; Activities room; Chapel; Crafts room; Laundry room; Barber/Beauty shop.

Activities Arts & crafts; Cards; Games; Reading groups; Prayer groups; Movies; Shopping trips; Social/Cultural gatherings.

MARYLAND HEIGHTS

Brook View Nursing Home Inc
2963 Doddridge, Maryland Heights, MO, 63043
(314) 291-4557
Admin Gloria Lierman. *Medical Dir/Dir of Nursing* Marilyn Kuebrich RN.
Licensure Skilled care. *Beds* SNF 116.
Owner Proprietary Corp.
Facilities Dining room; Activities room; Crafts room; Barber/Beauty shop.
Activities Arts & crafts; Cards; Games; Reading groups; Prayer groups; Movies; Social/Cultural gatherings.

Fairways Caring Center
3201 Parkwood Ln, Maryland Heights, MO, 63043
(314) 291-1356
Admin Mathias P Dasal. *Medical Dir/Dir of Nursing* Arnold S Tepper MD.
Licensure Skilled care; Intermediate care. *Beds* 120. *Certified* Medicaid.
Owner Proprietary Corp.
Admissions Requirements Medical examination.
Staff Physicians 3 (pt); RNs 3 (ft), 4 (pt); LPNs 5 (ft), 1 (pt); Orderlies 1 (ft), 1 (pt); Nurses aides 36 (ft), 5 (pt); Physical therapists 1 (ft); Reality therapists 1 (pt); Recreational therapists 1 (pt); Occupational therapists 1 (pt); Speech therapists 1 (ft); Activities coordinators 1 (ft); Dietitians 1 (pt); Dentists 1 (pt); Ophthalmologists 1 (pt); Podiatrists 1 (pt).
Facilities Dining room; Physical therapy room; Activities room; Chapel; Crafts room; Laundry room; Barber/Beauty shop; Library.
Activities Arts & crafts; Games; Reading groups; Prayer groups; Movies; Shopping trips; Social/Cultural gatherings.

Villa Capri Manor*
2920 Fee Rd, Maryland Heights, MO, 63043
(314) 291-0121
Admin Jane Forness. *Medical Dir/Dir of Nursing* Varkey Philip MD.
Licensure Skilled care; Intermediate care. *Beds* 220. *Certified* Medicaid.
Owner Proprietary Corp (Beverly Enterprises).
Admissions Requirements Minimum age 18.
Staff RNs 9 (ft); LPNs 14 (ft), 2 (pt); Nurses aides 135 (ft), 10 (pt); Physical therapists 2 (ft); Occupational therapists 1 (pt); Speech therapists 1 (pt); Activities coordinators 2 (ft); Dietitians 1 (ft); Dentists 1 (pt); Ophthalmologists 1 (pt); Podiatrists 1 (pt).
Facilities Dining room; Physical therapy room; Laundry room; Barber/Beauty shop.
Activities Arts & crafts; Games; Prayer groups; Movies; Shopping trips; Social/Cultural gatherings.

MARYVILLE

Maryville Health Care Center
524 N Laura, Maryville, MO, 64468
(816) 582-7447
Admin Keith K Stanton. *Medical Dir/Dir of Nursing* Pat Harr MD; Shirlie Bunkowski RN DON.
Licensure Skilled care. *Beds* SNF 108. *Certified* Medicaid.
Owner Proprietary Corp (Beverly Enterprises).
Admissions Requirements Minimum age 16; Medical examination; Physician's request.
Staff Physicians 7 (pt); RNs 4 (pt); LPNs 6 (ft); Nurses aides 35 (ft); Physical therapists 1 (pt); Occupational therapists 1 (pt); Speech therapists 1 (pt); Activities coordinators 1 (ft); Dietitians 1 (pt); Ophthalmologists 1 (pt).

Facilities Dining room; Physical therapy room; Activities room; Crafts room; Laundry room; Barber/Beauty shop.
Activities Arts & crafts; Cards; Games; Reading groups; Prayer groups; Movies; Shopping trips; Social/Cultural gatherings.

Nodaway Nursing Home Inc
Hwy 46 W, Maryville, MO, 64468
(816) 582-5658
Admin Betsy Stevens. *Medical Dir/Dir of Nursing* Bernetta Younger RN DON.
Licensure Skilled care; Intermediate care; RCF. *Beds* SNF; ICF 60; RCF 30. *Certified* Medicaid.
Owner Proprietary Corp (Tiffany Care Centers).
Admissions Requirements Minimum age 21.
Staff RNs 2 (ft); LPNs 3 (ft), 2 (pt); Activities coordinators 1 (ft).
Facilities Dining room; Physical therapy room; Activities room; Crafts room; Laundry room; Barber/Beauty shop.
Activities Arts & crafts; Cards; Games; Reading groups; Prayer groups; Movies; Shopping trips; Social/Cultural gatherings.

Parkdale Manor Care Center
Route V & Munn Ave, Maryville, MO, 64468
(816) 582-8161
Admin Wallis Ann Gray. *Medical Dir/Dir of Nursing* Barbara J O'Connell RN.
Licensure Skilled care. *Beds* 92.
Owner Proprietary Corp.
Admissions Requirements Minimum age 16; Medical examination.
Staff RNs 2 (ft); LPNs 8 (ft); Nurses aides 30 (ft), 1 (pt); Physical therapists 1 (pt); Activities coordinators 1 (ft), 1 (pt); Dietitians 1 (pt).
Facilities Dining room; Activities room; Laundry room; Barber/Beauty shop; Conference room.
Activities Arts & crafts; Cards; Games; Reading groups; Prayer groups; Movies; Social/Cultural gatherings.

MATTHEWS

Sells Rest Home Inc*
Rte 1, Box 6A, Matthews, MO, 63867
(314) 471-7861
Admin Annie Lee Sells.
Licensure Intermediate care. *Beds* 94. *Certified* Medicaid.
Owner Proprietary Corp.

MAYSVILLE

Sunset Home Inc*
Hwy 33, Maysville, MO, 64469
(816) 449-2158
Admin Roy Trussell.
Licensure Intermediate care. *Beds* 119. *Certified* Medicaid.
Owner Publicly owned.
Staff RNs 1 (ft), 1 (pt); LPNs 2 (ft), 1 (pt); Activities coordinators 1 (ft), 1 (pt).

MEMPHIS

Scotland County Nursing Home District
Box 52 RR 1, Memphis, MO, 63555
(816) 467-7221
Admin Gerald L Vice. *Medical Dir/Dir of Nursing* Mary Ann Kerr RN.
Licensure Skilled care. *Beds* 120. *Certified* Medicaid.
Owner Publicly owned.
Staff Physicians 4 (pt); RNs 2 (ft), 3 (pt); LPNs 4 (ft), 4 (pt); Orderlies 1 (ft); Nurses aides 40 (ft), 30 (pt); Physical therapists 2 (pt); Recreational therapists 2 (pt); Activities coordinators 1 (ft); Dietitians 1 (pt).
Activities Arts & crafts; Games; Movies; Shopping trips; Out trips.

Scottland Company Community Home*
361 Grand Ave, Memphis, MO, 63555
(816) 465-2203
Admin Catherine Aldridge.
Licensure Residential care. *Beds* 24.
Owner Proprietary Corp.

MEXICO

Allen Home*
219 E Bolivar, Mexico, MO, 65265
(314) 581-1815
Admin Virginia Walker.
Licensure Intermediate care. *Beds* 31.
Owner Proprietary Corp.
Admissions Requirements Minimum age 18; Medical examination.
Staff RNs 1 (pt); LPNs 2 (ft); Nurses aides 18 (ft); Dentists 1 (ft).
Facilities Activities room; Laundry room.
Activities Games; Movies; Shopping trips.

Coldwell Nursing Home
Rte 2 , Hwy 22 W, Mexico, MO, 65265
(314) 581-2752
Admin Frances Weber LPN. *Medical Dir/Dir of Nursing* J E Taft DO; Helen McMellen.
Licensure Intermediate care. *Beds* 64.
Owner Privately owned.
Admissions Requirements Minimum age 21; Medical examination.
Staff Physicians 1 (ft); RNs 1 (pt); LPNs 3 (ft); Nurses aides 12 (ft), 1 (pt); Activities coordinators 1 (ft); Dietitians 1 (ft); Ophthalmologists 1 (pt).
Facilities Dining room; Activities room; Chapel; Crafts room; Laundry room; Barber/Beauty shop; Library.
Activities Arts & crafts; Cards; Games; Reading groups; Prayer groups; Movies; Social/Cultural gatherings.

King's Daughters Home*
620 West Blvd, Mexico, MO, 65265
(314) 581-1577
Admin Joan C Talley.
Licensure Intermediate care. *Beds* 29.
Owner Nonprofit Corp.
Admissions Requirements Minimum age 65; Females only; Medical examination.
Staff RNs 1 (pt); LPNs 1 (ft), 2 (pt); Nurses aides 8 (ft), 3 (pt); Activities coordinators 1 (pt); Dietitians 1 (pt).
Affiliation King's Daughters & Sons
Facilities Dining room; Activities room; Chapel; Crafts room; Laundry room; Barber/Beauty shop; Library.
Activities Arts & crafts; Games; Prayer groups; Movies; Shopping trips.

Pin Oaks Nursing Center
Hwy 22 at Curtis Ave, Mexico, MO, 65265
(314) 581-7261
Admin Fern Walker. *Medical Dir/Dir of Nursing* Marty Wilsoncroft RN DON.
Licensure Skilled care. *Beds* SNF 164. *Certified* Medicaid.
Owner Proprietary Corp (Beverly Enterprises).
Admissions Requirements Medical examination.
Staff Physicians 1 (pt); RNs 3 (ft); LPNs; Orderlies 5 (ft); Nurses aides 51 (ft); Physical therapists 1 (pt); Reality therapists 1 (pt); Recreational therapists 2 (ft); Occupational therapists 1 (pt); Speech therapists 1 (pt); Activities coordinators 1 (ft); Dietitians 1 (ft); Dentists 1 (pt); Ophthalmologists 1 (pt); Podiatrists 1 (pt).
Facilities Dining room; Physical therapy room; Activities room; Chapel; Crafts room; Laundry room; Barber/Beauty shop.
Activities Arts & crafts; Cards; Games; Reading groups; Prayer groups; Movies; Shopping trips; Social/Cultural gatherings.

MILAN

Leewood Manor Nursing Home Inc*
W 3rd, Milan, MO, 63556
(816) 265-4433
Admin Harley E Reece.
Licensure Intermediate care. *Beds* 81.
Certified Medicaid.
Owner Proprietary Corp.
Admissions Requirements Minimum age 17;
Medical examination.
Staff RNs 1 (ft); LPNs 3 (ft); Nurses aides 30
(ft); Physical therapists 1 (pt); Occupational
therapists 1 (pt); Speech therapists 1 (pt);
Activities coordinators 1 (ft); Dietitians 1
(pt).
Facilities Dining room; Laundry room;
Barber/Beauty shop.
Activities Arts & crafts; Cards; Games;
Movies; Shopping trips; Social/Cultural
gatherings.

Milan Care Center Inc*
Rte 3, Box 16, Milan, MO, 63556
(816) 265-3168
Admin Wayne Wheeler.
Licensure Intermediate care. *Beds* 100.
Owner Proprietary Corp.
Admissions Requirements Minimum age 16.
Staff Physicians 4 (pt); RNs 2 (ft), 1 (pt);
LPNs 6 (ft); Orderlies 2 (ft); Nurses aides 30
(ft), 10 (pt); Physical therapists 1 (pt);
Occupational therapists 1 (pt); Speech
therapists 1 (pt); Activities coordinators 1
(pt); Dietitians 1 (pt); Dentists 1 (pt).
Facilities Dining room; Physical therapy
room; Activities room; Crafts room; Laundry
room; Barber/Beauty shop.
Activities Arts & crafts; Cards; Games;
Reading groups; Prayer groups; Movies;
Shopping trips; Social/Cultural gatherings.

MINERAL POINT

Rainbow Springs Care Center*
Rte 1, Box 666, Mineral Point, MO, 63660
(314) 438-3398
Admin Donald H Bohr.
Licensure Intermediate care. *Beds* 15.
Owner Proprietary Corp.

MOBERLY

Maple Lawn Lodge*
415 Woodland Ave, Moberly, MO, 65270
(816) 263-5652
Admin Melba Swope.
Licensure Intermediate care. *Beds* 49.
Owner Proprietary Corp.

North Village Manor*
Box 40, 2041 Silva Ln, Moberly, MO, 65270
(816) 263-1894
Admin Carol Wright.
Licensure Intermediate care. *Beds* 184.
Certified Medicaid.
Owner Proprietary Corp.

MOKANE

Riverview Nursing Center
Rte 1, Mokane, MO, 65059
(314) 676-3136
Admin S Jay Hitt. *Medical Dir/Dir of Nursing*
Mel Hector.
Licensure Intermediate care. *Beds* 60.
Certified Medicaid.
Owner Proprietary Corp.
Admissions Requirements Medical
examination.
Staff Physicians 1 (pt); RNs 2 (pt); LPNs 2
(ft), 2 (pt); Orderlies 3 (ft); Nurses aides 17
(ft); Physical therapists 1 (pt); Reality
therapists 1 (pt); Recreational therapists 2

(ft); Occupational therapists 1 (pt); Speech
therapists 1 (pt); Activities coordinators 1
(pt); Dietitians 1 (pt); Dentist 1 (pt).
Facilities Dining room; Physical therapy
room; Activities room; Laundry room;
Barber/Beauty shop; Lounge.
Activities Arts & crafts; Cards; Games;
Reading groups; Prayer groups; Movies;
Shopping trips; Social/Cultural gatherings.

MONETT

Camden Health Care Center*
410 W Benton St, Monett, MO, 65708
(417) 235-6031
Admin Kerry D Soncrant.
Licensure Intermediate care. *Beds* 120.
Certified Medicaid.
Owner Proprietary Corp.

LaCoba Homes Inc*
Rte 2, Monett, MO, 65708
(417) 235-7895
Admin Bill L Stout.
Licensure Intermediate care. *Beds* 60.
Owner Nonprofit Corp.

Rest Haven Nursing Home
PO Box 166, 910 4th St, Monett, MO, 65708
(417) 235-7243
Admin Stella Bolles.
Licensure Intermediate care. *Beds* 26.
Owner Proprietary Corp.

MONROE CITY

Monroe City Manor Care Center*
Hwy 36 E & Z Rd, Monroe City, MO, 63456
(314) 735-4850
Admin Lillian M Edwards.
Licensure Intermediate care. *Beds* 52.
Owner Proprietary Corp.

MONTGOMERY CITY

Bellflower Nursing Home
PO Box 157, Montgomery City, MO, 63361-0157
(314) 929-3617
Admin Nancy Fisher.
Licensure Intermediate care. *Beds* 27.
Owner Proprietary Corp.

Montgomery Manor Inc
230 Pickering St, Box 157, Montgomery City,
MO, 63361
(314) 564-7986 or 564-3825
Admin Homer Branham. *Medical Dir/Dir of
Nursing* Bonnie Williams.
Licensure Residential care. *Beds* Residential
II 40.
Owner Privately owned.
Admissions Requirements Minimum age 18;
Medical examination.
Staff Physicians 1 (pt); LPNs 2 (ft); Nurses
aides 3 (ft), 2 (pt).
Facilities Dining room; Activities room;
Crafts room; Laundry room.
Activities Cards; Games; Movies; Shopping
trips; Social/Cultural gatherings.

Owens Home
100 S Wentz, Montgomery City, MO, 63361
(314) 564-2207
Admin Sue Owens.
Licensure Residential care facility II. *Beds*
RCF II 14.
Owner Privately owned.
Staff RNs; Nurses aides.
Facilities Dining room.
Activities Arts & crafts; Cards; Games.

MOSCOW MILLS

Four Seasons Nursing Home
PO Box 40, Moscow Mills, MO, 63362
(314) 356-4231

Admin Shirley Quiroz.
Licensure Intermediate care. *Beds* ICF 30;
Residential care facility 23; Group home 6.
Owner Privately owned.
Staff Physicians 1 (pt); RNs 1 (ft); LPNs 1
(ft); Nurses aides 25 (ft); Activities
coordinators 1 (ft), 1 (pt).
Facilities Dining room; Activities room;
Laundry room; Barber/Beauty shop.
Activities Arts & crafts; Cards; Games;
Shopping trips; Social/Cultural gatherings;
Bowling.

MOUND CITY

Tiffany Heights
1531 Nebraska, PO Box 208, Mound City,
MO, 64470
(816) 442-3146
Admin P R Northup.
Licensure Intermediate care. *Beds* 60.
Certified Medicaid.
Owner Proprietary Corp.
Staff RNs 3 (pt); LPNs 2 (ft); Orderlies 1 (ft);
Nurses aides 15 (ft), 4 (pt); Physical
therapists 1 (pt); Occupational therapists 1
(pt); Speech therapists 1 (pt); Activities
coordinators 1 (ft); Dietitians 1 (pt).
Facilities Dining room; Physical therapy
room; Activities room; Crafts room; Laundry
room; Barber/Beauty shop.
Activities Arts & crafts; Cards; Games;
Reading groups; Prayer groups; Movies;
Social/Cultural gatherings.

MOUNT VERNON

Lawrence County Nursing Home District
PO Box 191, Carol Allen Dr, Mount Vernon,
MO, 65712
(417) 466-2183
Admin Alberta T Ford. *Medical Dir/Dir of
Nursing* Ronald Williams DO MD; Carol
Sue Houston RN DON.
Licensure Skilled care. *Beds* SNF 120.
Certified Medicaid.
Owner Publicly owned.
Admissions Requirements Minimum age 16;
Medical examination; Physician's request.
Staff Physicians 5 (pt); RNs 2 (ft), 1 (pt);
LPNs 14 (ft), 2 (pt); Orderlies 2 (ft); Nurses
aides 44 (ft); Physical therapists 1 (pt);
Occupational therapists 1 (pt); Speech
therapists 1 (pt); Activities coordinators 1
(ft); Dietitians 1 (pt).
Facilities Dining room; Physical therapy
room; Activities room; Crafts room; Laundry
room; Barber/Beauty shop.
Activities Arts & crafts; Cards; Games;
Reading groups; Prayer groups; Movies;
Shopping trips; Social/Cultural gatherings;
Reality orientation; Remotivation.

MOUNTAIN GROVE

Heritage Manor of Mountain Grove
13th & Hovis, Mountain Grove, MO, 65711
(417) 926-5128
Admin Max Benton. *Medical Dir/Dir of
Nursing* David Barbe MD; Helen Beard RN
DON.
Licensure Intermediate care. *Beds* ICF 120.
Certified Medicaid.
Owner Privately owned.
Staff Physicians 1 (pt); RNs 2 (ft); LPNs 10
(ft), 1 (pt); Orderlies 1 (ft); Nurses aides 43
(ft); Physical therapists 1 (pt); Speech
therapists 1 (pt); Activities coordinators 1
(ft); Dietitians 1 (pt).
Facilities Dining room; Physical therapy
room; Activities room; Crafts room; Laundry
room; Barber/Beauty shop; Library.
Activities Arts & crafts; Cards; Games; Prayer
groups; Shopping trips; Social/Cultural
gatherings.

NEOSHO

Medicalodge of Neosho
PO Box 153, Rte 6, Neosho, MO, 64850
(417) 451-2544
Admin Theresa Theas.
Licensure Skilled care. *Beds* 120. *Certified* Medicare.
Owner Proprietary Corp (Medicalodges).

Neosho Senior Center Inc*
330 S Wood, Neosho, MO, 64850
(417) 451-3600
Admin Barbara Johnson.
Licensure Intermediate care. *Beds* 94.
Certified Medicaid.
Owner Proprietary Corp (Beverly Enterprises).

NEVADA

Nevada City Nursing Home*
815 S Adams, Nevada, MO, 64772
(417) 667-3355
Admin Shirley Baxter & Albert Ban Jr.
Medical Dir/Dir of Nursing Dr F L Thompson.
Licensure Skilled care; Intermediate care. *Beds* 80. *Certified* Medicaid; Medicare.
Owner Publicly owned.
Admissions Requirements Medical examination; Physician's request.
Staff Physicians 1 (pt); RNs 1 (ft), 1 (pt); LPNs 7 (ft), 4 (pt); Orderlies 1 (ft); Nurses aides 26 (ft), 8 (pt); Physical therapists 1 (pt); Occupational therapists 1 (pt); Speech therapists 1 (pt); Activities coordinators 1 (ft); Dietitians 1 (pt); Dentists 1 (pt); Ophthalmologists 1 (pt); Podiatrists 1 (pt); Audiologists 1 (pt).
Facilities Dining room; Physical therapy room; Activities room; Chapel; Crafts room; Laundry room; Barber/Beauty shop; Library.
Activities Arts & crafts; Cards; Games; Reading groups; Prayer groups; Movies; Shopping trips; Social/Cultural gatherings.

Nevada Habilitation Center
Ash & Highland, Nevada, MO, 64772
(417) 667-7833
Admin Orvis D Salrin Jr. *Medical Dir/Dir of Nursing* John E Byrne MD.
Licensure Skilled care; Intermediate care for mentally retarded. *Beds* SNF; ICF/MR 383. *Certified* Medicaid.
Owner Publicly owned.
Staff Physicians 4 (ft); RNs 31 (ft); LPNs 29 (ft); Nurses aides 424 (ft); Physical therapists 2 (ft); Recreational therapists 1 (ft); Occupational therapists 2 (ft); Speech therapists 4 (ft); Activities coordinators 1 (ft); Dietitians 2 (ft); Ophthalmologists 1 (ft); Podiatrists 1 (ft).
Facilities Dining room; Activities room; Chapel; Crafts room; Barber/Beauty shop; Library.
Activities Arts & crafts; Games; Movies; Shopping trips; Social/Cultural gatherings.

Nevada Manor Nursing Home
1210 W Ashland, Nevada, MO, 64772
(417) 667-5064
Admin Virginia Nash.
Licensure Skilled care; Intermediate care. *Beds* 100. *Certified* Medicaid.
Owner Proprietary Corp (Beverly Enterprises).

Senior Citizen's Nursing Home*
614 N Washington St, Nevada, MO, 64772
(417) 667-2786
Admin Lola Trego.
Licensure Intermediate care. *Beds* 17.
Owner Proprietary Corp.

NEW FLORENCE

New Florence Nursing & Care Center
Rte 1, Box 30, New Florence, MO, 63363
(314) 835-2025
Admin Lauri Tiala. *Medical Dir/Dir of Nursing* George Workman MD; Janet Hall RN DON.
Licensure Intermediate care. *Beds* ICF 60. *Certified* Medicaid.
Owner Publicly owned.
Admissions Requirements Minimum age 18.
Staff RNs 1 (ft); LPNs 1 (ft), 2 (pt); Nurses aides 17 (ft), 7 (pt); Activities coordinators 1 (ft); Dietitians 1 (ft); Dentist 2 (pt).
Facilities Dining room; Physical therapy room; Activities room; Chapel; Crafts room; Laundry room; Barber/Beauty shop.
Activities Arts & crafts; Cards; Games; Reading groups; Prayer groups; Movies; Social/Cultural gatherings; Resident supper clubs.

NEW MADRID

Magnolia Manor*
1050 Dawson Rd, New Madrid, MO, 63869
Medical Dir/Dir of Nursing Dr Pattaropong.
Staff RNs 1 (ft), 1 (pt); LPNs 5 (ft), 1 (pt); Nurses aides 22 (ft); Physical therapists 2 (ft); Activities coordinators 1 (ft); Dietitians 1 (ft); Dentists 1 (pt).
Facilities Dining room; Physical therapy room; Activities room; Laundry room; Barber/Beauty shop.
Activities Arts & crafts; Cards; Games; Reading groups; Prayer groups; Shopping trips; Social/Cultural gatherings.

NORMANDY

Bell Manor Inc*
3715 Saint Ann's Ln, Normandy, MO, 63121
(314) 383-3353
Admin David Joe Bentley.
Licensure Intermediate care. *Beds* 61.
Owner Proprietary Corp.
Admissions Requirements Minimum age 18; Medical examination.
Staff Physicians 1 (pt); RNs 1 (ft), 1 (pt); LPNs 1 (pt); Nurses aides 25 (ft), 5 (pt); Physical therapists 1 (pt); Occupational therapists 1 (pt); Speech therapists 1 (pt); Activities coordinators 1 (ft); Dietitians 1 (pt); Dentists 1 (pt); Podiatrists 1 (pt).
Facilities Dining room; Activities room; Crafts room; Laundry room; Barber/Beauty shop.
Activities Arts & crafts; Cards; Games; Reading groups; Prayer groups; Movies; Shopping trips; Social/Cultural gatherings.

Castle Park Professional Care Center
7301 St Charles Rock Rd, Normandy, MO, 63133
(314) 726-5514
Admin Ruby P Jackson. *Medical Dir/Dir of Nursing* Dr D Walkenhorst DO; Annette Ruffin.
Licensure Skilled care. *Beds* 116. *Certified* Medicaid; Medicare.
Owner Proprietary Corp.
Staff Physicians 2 (pt); RNs 2 (ft), 1 (pt); Nurses aides; Physical therapists 2 (pt); Activities coordinators 1 (ft); Dietitians.
Facilities Dining room; Physical therapy room; Activities room; Laundry room; Barber/Beauty shop.
Activities Arts & crafts; Cards; Games; Movies; Shopping trips; Social/Cultural gatherings.

Medigroup Castle Park Professional Care Center
7301 St Charles Rock Rd, Normandy, MO, 63133
(314) 726-5514

Admin Ruby P Burks. *Medical Dir/Dir of Nursing* D Walkenhorst DO; Don A Ruffin.
Licensure Skilled care; Intermediate care. *Beds* SNF 116; ICF 116. *Certified* Medicaid; Medicare.
Owner Privately owned.
Staff Physicians 1 (pt); RNs 2 (ft), 2 (pt); LPNs 8 (ft), 5 (pt); Nurses aides 67 (ft); Physical therapists 2 (pt); Occupational therapists 2 (pt); Speech therapists 1 (pt); Activities coordinators 1 (ft); Dietitians 1 (ft).
Facilities Dining room; Physical therapy room; Activities room; Laundry room; Barber/Beauty shop.
Activities Arts & crafts; Cards; Games; Reading groups; Prayer groups; Movies; Shopping trips; Social/Cultural gatherings.

OAK GROVE

Oak Grove Health Care Center
21st & Mitchell Sts, Oak Grove, MO, 64075
(816) 625-4118, 229-7935
Admin Jerry L Eisenhauer. *Medical Dir/Dir of Nursing* Stephan Griffith MD; Darlene Burns RN DON.
Licensure Skilled care; Intermediate care. *Beds* SNF 90; ICF 90. *Certified* Medicaid.
Owner Proprietary Corp (Angell Group).
Admissions Requirements Minimum age 17; Medical examination.
Staff Physicians 13 (pt); RNs 3 (ft), 1 (pt); LPNs 3 (ft), 1 (pt); Orderlies 3 (ft); Nurses aides 33 (ft), 3 (pt); Physical therapists 3 (pt); Reality therapists 1 (pt); Recreational therapists 1 (pt); Occupational therapists 1 (pt); Speech therapists 1 (pt); Activities coordinators 1 (ft), 2 (pt); Dietitians 1 (pt); Dentists 1 (pt); Ophthalmologists 1 (pt); Podiatrists 1 (pt).
Facilities Dining room; Physical therapy room; Activities room; Crafts room; Laundry room; Barber/Beauty shop; Library.
Activities Arts & crafts; Cards; Games; Reading groups; Prayer groups; Movies; Shopping trips; Social/Cultural gatherings; Bowling; Spelling bees.

ODESSA

New Haven Nursing Home
609 Golf St, Odessa, MO, 64076
(816) 633-7539
Admin Leigh Helfers.
Licensure Intermediate care. *Beds* 60.
Certified Medicaid.
Owner Proprietary Corp (Beverly Enterprises).
Facilities Dining room; Activities room; Crafts room; Laundry room; Barber/Beauty shop.
Activities Arts & crafts; Cards; Games; Reading groups; Prayer groups; Movies; Shopping trips; Social/Cultural gatherings.

OFALLON

Twin Oaks Estate Inc
707 Enge Rd, O'Fallon, MO, 63366
( ) 272-8959
Admin Mary A Huber.
Licensure Residential care. *Beds* 42.
Owner Proprietary Corp.
Admissions Requirements Medical examination.
Staff RNs 1 (ft), 1 (pt); Nurses aides 4 (ft), 6 (pt); Activities coordinators 1 (pt); Dietitians 1 (ft), 3 (pt).
Facilities Dining room; Activities room; Chapel; Laundry room; Barber/Beauty shop.
Activities Arts & crafts; Cards; Games; Prayer groups; Movies; Shopping trips; Social/Cultural gatherings; Outings by van.

OREGON

Oregon Health Care Center*
501 S Monroe, Oregon, MO, 64473
(816) 446-3355
Admin John Stein.
Licensure Intermediate care. *Beds* 60.
Owner Proprietary Corp.
Staff Physicians 2 (ft); RNs 1 (pt); LPNs 1
(ft), 1 (pt); Orderlies 1 (ft); Nurses aides 31
(ft), 12 (pt); Physical therapists 1 (pt);
Occupational therapists 1 (pt); Speech
therapists 1 (pt); Activities coordinators 2
(ft); Dietitians 1 (pt); Dentists 1 (pt);
Audiologists 1 (pt).
Facilities Dining room; Physical therapy
room; Activities room; Chapel; Crafts room;
Laundry room; Barber/Beauty shop.
Activities Arts & crafts; Cards; Games; Prayer
groups; Movies; Social/Cultural gatherings.

Pleasant Hill Nursing Home*
Rte 1, Oregon, MO, 64473
(816) 446-2281
Admin Dorothy Boehm.
Licensure Intermediate care. *Beds* 32.
Owner Proprietary Corp.

OSAGE BEACH

Osage Beach Health Care Center
Lake Rd 54-29, Osage Beach, MO, 65065
(314) 348-2225
Admin Charles Shorter. *Medical Dir/Dir of
Nursing* Dr Clemmons Haggerty; Judi
Grimes RN DON.
Licensure Skilled care; Intermediate care. *Beds*
120. *Certified* Medicaid; Medicare.
Owner Proprietary Corp.
Admissions Requirements Minimum age 18;
Medical examination.
Staff Physicians 3 (pt); RNs 4 (ft), 2 (pt);
LPNs 9 (ft), 4 (pt); Nurses aides 22 (ft), 3
(pt); Physical therapists 1 (pt); Occupational
therapists 1 (pt); Speech therapists 1 (pt);
Activities coordinators 1 (ft); Dietitians 1
(pt).
Facilities Dining room; Physical therapy
room; Activities room; Laundry room;
Barber/Beauty shop; Library.
Activities Arts & crafts; Cards; Games;
Reading groups; Prayer groups; Movies;
Shopping trips; Social/Cultural gatherings;
Community functions.

Ozark Care Center Inc
PO Box 278, Osage Beach, MO, 65065
(314) 348-1711
Admin Katherine Fisch. *Medical Dir/Dir of
Nursing* T W Garrison MD; Michael DeClue
RN DON.
Licensure Skilled care; Intermediate care. *Beds*
60. *Certified* Medicaid; Medicare.
Owner Proprietary Corp.
Admissions Requirements Minimum age 17;
Medical examination; Physician's request.
Staff Physicians 1 (pt); RNs 2 (ft), 1 (pt);
LPNs 4 (ft), 2 (pt); Nurses aides 17 (ft), 5
(pt); Physical therapists 3 (pt); Occupational
therapists 1 (pt); Speech therapists 1 (pt);
Activities coordinators 1 (pt); Dietitians 1
(pt); Ophthalmologists 1 (pt); Podiatrists 1
(pt).
Facilities Dining room; Physical therapy
room; Activities room; Chapel; Crafts room;
Laundry room; Barber/Beauty shop.
Activities Arts & crafts; Cards; Games;
Reading groups; Prayer groups; Movies;
Shopping trips; Social/Cultural gatherings.

OWENSVILLE

Gasconade Manor Nursing Home
PO Box 520, Hwy 19 & Springfield Rd,
Owensville, MO, 65066
(314) 437-4101

Admin Dale Grunewald. *Medical Dir/Dir of
Nursing* Dr Robert LaHue; Donna Bond
RON DON.
Licensure Skilled care. *Beds* 60. *Certified*
Medicaid.
Owner Nonprofit organization/foundation.
Admissions Requirements Minimum age 16;
Medical examination.
Staff RNs 2 (ft), 2 (pt); LPNs 3 (ft), 2 (pt);
Orderlies 1 (ft); Nurses aides 16 (ft), 6 (pt);
Activities coordinators 1 (pt).
Facilities Dining room; Physical therapy
room; Activities room; Laundry room;
Barber/Beauty shop.
Activities Arts & crafts; Cards; Games; Prayer
groups; Movies; Shopping trips; Social/
Cultural gatherings.

OZARK

Ozark Nursing & Care Center
1106 N 3rd Ave, Ozark, MO, 65721
(417) 485-7126
Admin John Harrison. *Medical Dir/Dir of
Nursing* Randall Halley DO; Joeha
Schnetzler RN DON.
Licensure Skilled care. *Beds* SNF 120.
Certified Medicaid; Medicare.
Owner Proprietary Corp.
Admissions Requirements Medical
examination.
Staff Physicians 2 (pt); RNs 1 (ft), 1 (pt);
LPNs 9 (ft); Orderlies 1 (ft); Physical
therapists 1 (pt); Occupational therapists 1
(pt); Speech therapists 1 (pt); Activities
coordinators 1 (ft), 2 (pt); Dietitians 1 (pt);
Ophthalmologists 1 (pt).
Facilities Dining room; Physical therapy
room; Activities room; Crafts room; Laundry
room; Barber/Beauty shop; Library; Century
tub.
Activities Arts & crafts; Cards; Games;
Reading groups; Prayer groups; Movies;
Shopping trips; Social/Cultural gatherings.

Ozark Riverview Manor
PO Box 157, 1400 W Hall, Ozark, MO, 65721
(417) 485-6025
Admin Daniel L Serven.
Licensure Intermediate care. *Beds* ICF 56.
Owner Proprietary Corp.

PARIS

Monroe Manor
200 South St, Paris, MO, 65275
(816) 327-4125
Admin Norma Gritton. *Medical Dir/Dir of
Nursing* Dr C R Warbritton; Joyce Riedesel
LPN.
Licensure Intermediate care. *Beds* 120.
Certified Medicaid.
Owner Nonprofit organization/foundation.
Staff RNs 1 (pt); LPNs 9 (ft); Orderlies 3 (ft);
Nurses aides 48 (ft); Physical therapists 1
(pt); Recreational therapists 4 (ft);
Occupational therapists 1 (pt); Speech
therapists 1 (pt); Activities coordinators 1
(ft); Dietitians 1 (pt).
Facilities Dining room; Physical therapy
room; Activities room; Chapel; Crafts room;
Laundry room; Barber/Beauty shop; Library.
Activities Arts & crafts; Cards; Games;
Reading groups; Prayer groups; Movies;
Shopping trips; Social/Cultural gatherings;
Family meals.

PERRY

Twain Haven Nursing Home
Hwy 154 E, Perry, MO, 63462
(314) 565-2217
Admin Doris G Moore.
Licensure Intermediate care. *Beds* 50.
Owner Proprietary Corp.
Admissions Requirements Minimum age 16.

Staff RNs 1 (pt); LPNs 1 (ft), 2 (pt); Nurses
aides 12 (ft), 14 (pt); Activities coordinators
1 (pt).
Facilities Dining room; Crafts room.
Activities Games; Prayer groups; Movies;
Weekly church services.

PERRYVILLE

American Care Center
430 Northwest St, Perryville, MO, 63775
(314) 547-1011
Admin Norma Jean Steffens.
Licensure Skilled care. *Beds* 156. *Certified*
Medicaid; Medicare.
Owner Nonprofit Corp.

Perry County Nursing Home
Rte 2, 800 S Kingshighway, Perryville, MO,
63775
(314) 547-6546
Admin Frank Bergman. *Medical Dir/Dir of
Nursing* Dr L Medrano; S Freand RN.
Licensure Intermediate care. *Beds* ICF 123.
Certified Medicaid.
Owner Publicly owned.
Admissions Requirements Minimum age 18;
Medical examination.
Staff RNs 1 (ft), 2 (pt); LPNs 4 (ft), 2 (pt);
Orderlies 1 (ft); Nurses aides 32 (ft), 30 (pt);
Activities coordinators 1 (ft).
Languages German
Facilities Dining room; Physical therapy
room; Activities room; Chapel; Crafts room;
Laundry room; Barber/Beauty shop.
Activities Arts & crafts; Cards; Games;
Reading groups; Prayer groups; Movies;
Shopping trips; Social/Cultural gatherings.

PIEDMONT

Clark's Mountain Nursing Center
2100 Barnes St, Piedmont, MO, 63957
(314) 223-4297
Admin Linda L Vandergriff. *Medical Dir/Dir
of Nursing* Rhonda Payton RN.
Licensure Intermediate care. *Beds* ICF 90.
Certified Medicaid.
Owner Proprietary Corp (Americare Corp).
Admissions Requirements Minimum age 18;
Medical examination; Physician's request.
Staff Physicians 4 (pt); RNs 1 (ft); LPNs 6
(ft); Orderlies 5 (ft); Nurses aides 31 (ft);
Physical therapists 1 (pt); Occupational
therapists 1 (pt); Speech therapists 1 (pt);
Activities coordinators 1 (ft); Dietitians 1
(pt).
Facilities Dining room; Physical therapy
room; Activities room; Laundry room;
Barber/Beauty shop.
Activities Arts & crafts; Games; Reading
groups; Prayer groups; Movies; Shopping
trips.

PLATTSBURG

Clinton Manor Inc*
Hwy 116, Plattsburg, MO, 64477
(816) 539-2713
Admin Yvonne Breckenridge.
Licensure Intermediate care. *Beds* 64.
Owner Proprietary Corp.

Oakridge of Plattsburg
PO Box 247, E Clay Ave, Plattsburg, MO,
64477
(816) 539-2128
Admin Gene Davidson. *Medical Dir/Dir of
Nursing* Judy Davidson RN DON.
Licensure Intermediate care. *Beds* ICF 60.
Owner Nonprofit Corp.
Staff Physicians 4 (ft); RNs 1 (ft); LPNs 1 (ft),
1 (pt); Nurses aides 30 (ft), 2 (pt); Activities
coordinators 1 (ft); Dietitians 1 (pt).
Facilities Dining room; Activities room;
Crafts room; Laundry room; Barber/Beauty
shop.

Activities Arts & crafts; Cards; Games;
Reading groups; Prayer groups; Shopping
trips; Social/Cultural gatherings.

POPLAR BLUFF

Assembly Nursing Home of Poplar Bluff Inc
203 N "B" St, Poplar Bluff, MO, 63901
(314) 785-6155
Admin Lillian Haley.
Licensure Intermediate care. *Beds* 48.
Owner Proprietary Corp.
Admissions Requirements Minimum age 18.
Staff RNs 1 (pt); LPNs 1 (ft), 1 (pt); Orderlies
1 (ft); Nurses aides 13 (ft), 4 (pt); Activities
coordinators 1 (ft), 1 (pt).
Facilities Dining room; Activities room;
Laundry room; Barber/Beauty shop.
Activities Arts & crafts; Games; Prayer groups;
Movies.

Bluff Manor Nursing Home*
2071 Barron Rd, PO Box 1066, Poplar Bluff,
MO, 63901
(314) 686-1147
Admin Samuel D Vancil. *Medical Dir/Dir of
Nursing* Barry B White MD.
Licensure Skilled care; Intermediate care. *Beds*
90. *Certified* Medicaid; Medicare.
Owner Proprietary Corp (Beverly Enterprises).
Admissions Requirements Physician's request.
Staff Physicians 2 (ft); RNs 2 (ft), 1 (pt);
LPNs 4 (ft), 4 (pt); Nurses aides 36 (ft), 8
(pt); Physical therapists 1 (pt); Reality
therapists 1 (pt); Recreational therapists 1
(pt); Occupational therapists 1 (pt); Speech
therapists 1 (pt); Activities coordinators 1
(ft); Dietitians 1 (ft); Dentists 1 (pt);
Ophthalmologists 1 (pt); Podiatrists 1 (pt);
Audiologists 1 (pt).

Cedargate
Hwy PP, PO Box 608, Poplar Bluff, MO,
63901
(314) 785-0188
Admin Ruth Warren. *Medical Dir/Dir of
Nursing* Fred Caldwell MD.
Licensure Skilled care; Intermediate care. *Beds*
108. *Certified* Medicaid; Medicare.
Owner Proprietary Corp.
Admissions Requirements Minimum age 16.
Staff Physicians 15 (pt); RNs 2 (ft), 2 (pt);
LPNs 12 (ft), 2 (pt); Nurses aides 34 (ft), 4
(pt); Physical therapists 1 (pt); Reality
therapists 1 (pt); Recreational therapists 1
(pt); Occupational therapists 1 (pt); Speech
therapists 1 (pt); Activities coordinators 1
(ft); Dietitians 1 (pt); Dentists 1 (pt);
Ophthalmologists 1 (pt); Podiatrists 1 (pt).
Facilities Dining room; Physical therapy
room; Activities room; Crafts room; Laundry
room; Barber/Beauty shop.
Activities Arts & crafts; Cards; Games;
Reading groups; Prayer groups; Movies;
Shopping trips; Social/Cultural gatherings.

Golden Years Boarding Facility*
307 Broadway, Poplar Bluff, MO, 63901
Admin Donald R Johnson. *Medical Dir/Dir of
Nursing* Lue Ella Mason.
Licensure Residential care. *Beds* 17.
Owner Proprietary Corp.
Admissions Requirements Minimum age 21;
Medical examination.
Staff Physicians 1 (pt); RNs 1 (pt).
Facilities Dining room; Activities room;
Chapel; Laundry room; Barber/Beauty shop.
Activities Games; Prayer groups; Movies;
Shopping trips.

Westwood Hills Health Care Center
PO Box 1328, Hwy 67, Poplar Bluff, MO,
63901
(314) 785-0851
Admin Michael Young BS MS. *Medical Dir/
Dir of Nursing* Dr Ben Till; Janet Glass RN
DON.

Licensure Skilled care; Intermediate care. *Beds*
SNF 120; ICF. *Certified* Medicaid;
Medicare.
Owner Proprietary Corp.
Admissions Requirements Physician's request.
Staff RNs 3 (ft); LPNs 10 (ft); Orderlies 3 (ft);
Nurses aides 25 (ft).
Facilities Dining room; Physical therapy
room; Activities room; Laundry room;
Barber/Beauty shop.
Activities Arts & crafts; Games; Prayer groups;
Movies; Shopping trips; Social/Cultural
gatherings.

POTOSI

Moses Austin Group Care Home*
217 E Citadel, Potosi, MO, 63665
(314) 438-3736
Admin Rick J Hurst.
Licensure Intermediate care for mentally
retarded. *Beds* 9.
Owner Publicly owned.

PRINCETON

Princeton Care Center Inc*
Rte 2, Box 147, Princeton, MO, 64673
(816) 748-3228
Admin Karen Rockhold.
Licensure Intermediate care. *Beds* 52.
Certified Medicaid.
Owner Proprietary Corp.
Staff Physicians; RNs; LPNs; Nurses aides;
Physical therapists; Recreational therapists;
Occupational therapists; Speech therapists;
Activities coordinators; Dietitians; Dentists;
Audiologists.
Facilities Dining room; Physical therapy
room; Activities room; Laundry room;
Barber/Beauty shop; Library.
Activities Arts & crafts; Cards; Games;
Reading groups; Prayer groups; Movies;
Shopping trips; Social/Cultural gatherings.

PUXICO

Puxico Nursing Center
PO Box 218, Highway 51 N, Puxico, MO,
63960
(314) 222-3125, 222-3176
Admin Shirley Stewart. *Medical Dir/Dir of
Nursing* Elaine Lemons RN DON.
Licensure Intermediate care. *Beds* ICF 60.
Certified Medicaid.
Owner Proprietary Corp (Beverly Enterprises).
Admissions Requirements Medical
examination; Physician's request.
Staff RNs; LPNs 4 (ft), 2 (pt); Orderlies 13
(ft), 3 (pt); Nurses aides; Physical therapists
1 (ft); Activities coordinators 1 (ft);
Dietitians 1 (ft).
Facilities Dining room; Physical therapy
room; Activities room; Laundry room;
Barber/Beauty shop; Sitting room; TV room.
Activities Arts & crafts; Games; Prayer groups;
Movies; Shopping trips; Social/Cultural
gatherings.

QUEEN CITY

Schuyler County Nursing Home
Rte 1, Hwy 63 N, Queen City, MO, 63561
(816) 766-2291
Admin Robert Seamster. *Medical Dir/Dir of
Nursing* Dr E M Roberts; Anna J March RN
DON.
Licensure Intermediate care. *Beds* ICF 60.
Certified Medicaid.
Owner Publicly owned.
Admissions Requirements Minimum age 17;
Medical examination.
Staff RNs 2 (ft); LPNs 2 (ft), 1 (pt); Orderlies
2 (ft), 1 (pt); Nurses aides 18 (ft), 13 (pt);
Physical therapists 1 (ft); Occupational

therapists 1 (pt); Speech therapists 1 (pt);
Activities coordinators 1 (ft); Dietitians 1
(pt).
Facilities Dining room; Physical therapy
room; Activities room; Crafts room; Laundry
room; Barber/Beauty shop; Library.
Activities Arts & crafts; Games; Reading
groups; Prayer groups; Movies; Shopping
trips.

RAYMORE

Foxwood Springs Living Center
Box 370, 2500 W Foxwood Dr, Raymore,
MO, 64083
(816) 331-3111
Admin Thomas R Williams. *Medical Dir/Dir
of Nursing* Dr George K Landis MD; Trudy
DeLuca RN.
Licensure Skilled care; Intermediate care;
Residential care. *Beds* SNF 122; ICF.
Certified Medicaid.
Owner Nonprofit Corp (Natl Bnvlnt Assn of
Chrstn Homes).
Staff Physicians 4 (pt); RNs 4 (ft), 1 (pt);
LPNs 5 (ft), 5 (pt); Nurses aides 20 (ft), 10
(pt); Physical therapists 1 (pt); Activities
coordinators 2 (ft), 1 (pt); Dietitians 2 (ft);
Dentists 1 (pt); Ophthalmologists 1 (pt).
Affiliation Disciples of Christ
Facilities Dining room; Physical therapy
room; Activities room; Crafts room; Laundry
room; Barber/Beauty shop; Library.
Activities Arts & crafts; Cards; Games;
Reading groups; Prayer groups; Movies;
Shopping trips; Social/Cultural gatherings.

RAYTOWN

Bowen Health Center*
6124 Raytown Rd, Raytown, MO, 64133
(816) 358-8222
Admin Ervin E Smith.
Licensure Intermediate care. *Beds* 60.
Certified Medicaid.
Owner Proprietary Corp.

Heritage Village at Park Place Meadows
11901 Jessica Ln, Raytown, MO, 64138
(816) 358-3535
Admin Nell M Schmidt. *Medical Dir/Dir of
Nursing* Doris Johnson.
Licensure Skilled care; Intermediate care. *Beds*
SNF 60; ICF 60. *Certified* Medicaid.
Owner Proprietary Corp.
Admissions Requirements Minimum age 18;
Medical examination.
Staff Physicians; RNs; LPNs; Orderlies;
Nurses aides; Physical therapists 1 (pt);
Reality therapists; Recreational therapists;
Occupational therapists; Activities
coordinators; Dietitians; Dentists;
Ophthalmologists; Podiatrists.
Facilities Dining room; Physical therapy
room; Activities room; Chapel; Crafts room;
Laundry room; Barber/Beauty shop; Library.
Activities Arts & crafts; Cards; Games;
Reading groups; Prayer groups; Movies.

RICHLAND

Tri-County Nursing Home Inc
PO Box 756, Richland, MO, 65556
(314) 765-3243
Admin Dorothy J Setser. *Medical Dir/Dir of
Nursing* Ruth P Zeigenbein.
Licensure Intermediate care. *Beds* ICF 86.
Owner Nonprofit Corp.
Staff RNs 1 (pt); LPNs 4 (ft), 1 (pt); Nurses
aides 23 (ft), 2 (pt); Activities coordinators;
CMT 4 (ft), 1 (pt).

RICHMOND

Shirkey Leisure Acres*
Hwy 13 S, Richmond, MO, 64085
(816) 766-5403
Admin M L Hopkins. *Medical Dir/Dir of Nursing* Dr Robert LaHue.
Licensure Intermediate care. *Beds* 140.
Owner Nonprofit Corp.
Staff RNs 1 (ft); LPNs 4 (ft), 1 (pt); Orderlies 3 (ft); Nurses aides 84 (ft); Physical therapists 1 (pt); Recreational therapists 1 (ft); Occupational therapists 1 (pt); Speech therapists 1 (pt); Activities coordinators 1 (ft), 1 (pt); Dietitians 1 (ft); Audiologists 1 (pt).
Facilities Dining room; Physical therapy room; Activities room; Chapel; Crafts room; Laundry room; Barber/Beauty shop; Library.
Activities Arts & crafts; Games; Reading groups; Prayer groups; Movies; Social/Cultural gatherings.

ROCK PORT

Pleasant View
Rte 1, Box B, Rock Port, MO, 64482
(816) 744-6252
Admin Charles Loucks. *Medical Dir/Dir of Nursing* Billie Debuhr RN.
Licensure Intermediate care. *Beds* ICF 100. *Certified* Medicaid.
Owner Proprietary Corp (Tiffany Care Centers).
Admissions Requirements Minimum age 18.
Staff RNs; LPNs; Orderlies; Nurses aides; Physical therapists; Reality therapists; Recreational therapists; Occupational therapists; Speech therapists; Dietitians.
Facilities Dining room; Physical therapy room; Activities room; Chapel; Crafts room; Laundry room; Barber/Beauty shop; Library.
Activities Arts & crafts; Cards; Games; Reading groups; Prayer groups; Movies; Shopping trips; Social/Cultural gatherings.

ROLLA

Medigroup Heritage Park
1200 McCutchen Rd, Rolla, MO, 65401
(314) 364-2311
Admin Claire Meinert. *Medical Dir/Dir of Nursing* Dr John James; Joann Goldberg.
Licensure Skilled care; Intermediate care. *Beds* 120. *Certified* Medicaid; Medicare.
Owner Privately owned.
Facilities Dining room; Physical therapy room; Activities room; Barber/Beauty shop.
Activities Arts & crafts; Games; Reading groups; Prayer groups; Movies; Shopping trips; Social/Cultural gatherings.

Presbyterian Manor at Rolla*
1200 Homelife Plaza, Rolla, MO, 65401
Admin Pat Look.
Beds 38.
Owner Nonprofit Corp.
Admissions Requirements Minimum age 65; Medical examination.
Staff RNs; LPNs; Nurses aides 2 (pt); Activities coordinators; Dietitians; Podiatrists.
Affiliation Presbyterian

Rolla Manor Care Center*
1800 White Columns Dr, Rolla, MO, 65401
(314) 364-7766
Admin Maria E Carroll.
Licensure Intermediate care. *Beds* 102.
Owner Proprietary Corp.

SAINT CHARLES

Charlevoix Professional Nursing Home*
1221 Boonslick Rd, Saint Charles, MO, 63301
(314) 723-1600
Admin William B Mahon.
Licensure Skilled care; Intermediate care. *Beds* 115. *Certified* Medicaid.
Owner Proprietary Corp (Hillhaven Corp).

Claywest House
2840 W Clay, Saint Charles, MO, 63301
(314) 925-1500, 946-6100
Admin Sue Damrell. *Medical Dir/Dir of Nursing* Judy Strasser RN DON.
Licensure Skilled care. *Beds* 180. *Certified* Medicaid; Medicare.
Owner Proprietary Corp.
Admissions Requirements Minimum age 18; Medical examination; Physician's request.
Staff Physicians; RNs; LPNs; Orderlies; Nurses aides; Physical therapists; Occupational therapists; Speech therapists; Activities coordinators; Dietitians; Ophthalmologists.
Facilities Dining room; Physical therapy room; Activities room; Crafts room; Laundry room; Barber/Beauty shop; Sunroom; Decks; Gazebos; Enclosed courtyard.
Activities Arts & crafts; Cards; Games; Reading groups; Prayer groups; Movies; Shopping trips; Social/Cultural gatherings.

Colonial Rest Home*
404 McDonough, Saint Charles, MO, 63301
(314) 724-1147
Admin Lydia Rosenstengel. *Medical Dir/Dir of Nursing* Dr Poggemeier.
Licensure Intermediate care. *Beds* 21.
Owner Proprietary Corp.
Admissions Requirements Medical examination.
Staff Physicians 1 (ft); RNs 1 (ft); LPNs 1 (ft), 1 (pt); Nurses aides 8 (ft), 2 (pt); Activities coordinators 1 (pt); Dietitians 1 (pt).

Jefferson Street Nursing Home
1014 Jefferson St, Saint Charles, MO, 63301
(314) 724-1565
Admin Kaye Allen. *Medical Dir/Dir of Nursing* Kaye Allen RN.
Licensure Intermediate care. *Beds* ICF 10.
Owner Proprietary Corp.
Admissions Requirements Females only.
Staff RNs 1 (ft); Nurses aides 3 (ft), 2 (pt).
Activities Arts & crafts; Cards; Games; Prayer groups; Movies.

Parkside Meadows Inc
PO Box 430, 2150 Randolph St, Saint Charles, MO, 63301
(314) 724-7800 or 946-4966
Admin G Herbert Gessert. *Medical Dir/Dir of Nursing* Gene Roxas MD; Mary Bratcher DON.
Licensure Intermediate care; Residential care. *Beds* ICF 60; Residential 15. *Certified* Medicaid.
Owner Nonprofit Corp.
Admissions Requirements Medical examination; Physician's request.
Staff RNs 1 (ft), 6 (pt); LPNs 1 (ft), 7 (pt); Nurses aides 21 (ft), 4 (pt); Activities coordinators 1 (ft); Dietitians 1 (ft); Certified medical technician 5 (ft).
Affiliation Church of Christ
Facilities Dining room; Physical therapy room; Activities room; Crafts room; Laundry room; Barber/Beauty shop; Library.
Activities Arts & crafts; Cards; Games; Reading groups; Prayer groups; Movies; Shopping trips; Social/Cultural gatherings.

St Charles Health Care Center*
Sugar Maple Ln, Saint Charles, MO, 63301
(314) 946-8887
Admin Melvin Rector.
Licensure Skilled care; Intermediate care. *Beds* 120. *Certified* Medicaid; Medicare.
Owner Proprietary Corp.

St Joseph's Home*
723 First Capitol Dr, Saint Charles, MO, 63301
(314) 946-4140
Admin Dianne Mossberger. *Medical Dir/Dir of Nursing* Dr Brian Stuffelbam.
Licensure Intermediate care. *Beds* 103.
Owner Nonprofit Corp.
Admissions Requirements Minimum age 65; Medical examination.
Staff RNs 2 (ft), 1 (pt); LPNs 5 (ft); Nurses aides 25 (ft), 15 (pt); Physical therapists 1 (pt); Speech therapists 1 (pt); Activities coordinators 3 (pt); Dietitians 1 (pt); Dentists 1 (pt); Podiatrists 1 (pt).
Facilities Dining room; Physical therapy room; Activities room; Chapel; Crafts room; Laundry room; Barber/Beauty shop.
Activities Arts & crafts; Cards; Games; Reading groups; Prayer groups; Movies; Shopping trips; Social/Cultural gatherings.

Walton Caring Center
1392 S 5th St, Saint Charles, MO, 63301-2444
(314) 361-3424
Admin Lucy H Gordon.
Licensure Intermediate care. *Beds* 40.
Owner Proprietary Corp.
Admissions Requirements Medical examination; Physician's request.
Staff RNs 1 (pt); LPNs 2 (ft); Nurses aides 12 (ft); Activities coordinators 1 (pt); Dietitians 1 (pt).
Facilities Dining room; Activities room; Barber/Beauty shop.
Activities Arts & crafts; Cards; Games; Movies; Shopping trips.

SAINT ELIZABETH

St Elizabeth Manor Inc
Rte 1, Box 22, Saint Elizabeth, MO, 65075
(314) 493-2215
Admin Frederick Doerhoff. *Medical Dir/Dir of Nursing* Elizabeth Conley DON; Helen True LPN.
Licensure Intermediate care. *Beds* ICF 60. *Certified* Medicaid.
Owner Proprietary Corp.
Admissions Requirements Physician's request.
Staff Physicians 1 (pt); RNs 1 (pt); LPNs 4 (ft), 2 (pt); Nurses aides 18 (ft), 8 (pt); Physical therapists 1 (pt); Occupational therapists 1 (pt); Speech therapists 1 (pt); Activities coordinators 1 (ft); Dietitians 1 (pt).
Facilities Dining room; Physical therapy room; Activities room; Laundry room; Barber/Beauty shop.
Activities Arts & crafts; Games; Reading groups; Prayer groups; Movies; Shopping trips.

SAINT JAMES

Country Valley Home
Rte 3, Box 356, Saint James, MO, 65559
(314) 265-8250
Admin Mary V Auten. *Medical Dir/Dir of Nursing* Mary V Auten.
Licensure Residential care. *Beds* 23.
Owner Proprietary Corp.
Admissions Requirements Minimum age 18; Females only.
Staff RNs 1 (ft); Nurses aides 6 (ft), 4 (pt); Activities coordinators 1 (pt).
Facilities Dining room; Laundry room; Barber/Beauty shop.
Activities Arts & crafts; Prayer groups; Movies; Shopping trips; Social/Cultural gatherings; Exercise.

Meadow Manor Nursing Home*
Sidney St, Box 69, Saint James, MO, 65559
(314) 265-8921
Admin Jo Hancock.

Licensure Skilled care. *Beds* 90. *Certified*
Medicaid; Medicare.
Owner Proprietary Corp (Beverly Enterprises).
Staff RNs 3 (ft); LPNs 8 (ft); Orderlies 1 (ft);
Nurses aides 60 (ft); Physical therapists 1
(ft); Reality therapists 1 (ft); Recreational
therapists 1 (ft); Occupational therapists 1
(ft); Speech therapists 1 (ft); Activities
coordinators 1 (ft); Dietitians 1 (ft); Dentists
1 (ft); Podiatrists 1 (ft); Audiologists 1 (ft).
Facilities Dining room; Physical therapy
room; Activities room; Chapel; Crafts room;
Laundry room; Barber/Beauty shop.
Activities Arts & crafts; Cards; Games;
Reading groups; Prayer groups; Movies;
Shopping trips; Social/Cultural gatherings.

Woodland Estates*
Rte 1, Box 127, Saint James, MO, 65559
Admin Mel Matlock II. *Medical Dir/Dir of
Nursing* Dr P Pander.
Licensure Residential care. *Beds* 50. *Certified*
Medicaid.
Owner Proprietary Corp.
Admissions Requirements Minimum age 18.
Staff Physicians 1 (pt); RNs 1 (pt); LPNs 1
(pt); Orderlies 1 (ft); Nurses aides 3 (ft), 1
(pt); Activities coordinators 1 (ft); Dentists 1
(pt).
Facilities Dining room; Physical therapy
room; Activities room; Crafts room; Laundry
room; Barber/Beauty shop; Library.
Activities Arts & crafts; Cards; Games; Prayer
groups; Movies; Shopping trips; Social/
Cultural gatherings.

SAINT JOSEPH

Beverly Manor
1317 N 36th St, Saint Joseph, MO, 64506
(816) 233-8085
Admin Beverly Jean Cathcart. *Medical Dir/Dir
of Nursing* Dr David Cathcart.
Licensure Skilled care. *Beds* SNF 120.
Certified Medicaid; Medicare.
Owner Proprietary Corp (Beverly Enterprises).
Admissions Requirements Minimum age 18;
Medical examination.
Staff Physicians; RNs; LPNs; Nurses aides;
Physical therapists; Recreational therapists;
Occupational therapists; Speech therapists;
Activities coordinators; Dietitians; Dentists;
Ophthalmologists; Podiatrists.
Facilities Dining room; Physical therapy
room; Activities room; Crafts room; Laundry
room; Barber/Beauty shop; Library.
Activities Arts & crafts; Cards; Games;
Reading groups; Prayer groups; Movies;
Shopping trips; Social/Cultural gatherings.

Bliss Manor
2929 Lafayette, Saint Joseph, MO, 64507
(816) 233-2418
Admin Bernice Vandever.
Licensure Intermediate care. *Beds* 90.
Owner Proprietary Corp.
Admissions Requirements Minimum age 18;
Medical examination.
Staff LPNs 1 (ft); Nurses aides 4 (ft);
Activities coordinators 1 (ft).
Facilities Dining room; Activities room;
Laundry room; Barber/Beauty shop.
Activities Cards; Games; Prayer groups;
Movies; Shopping trips; Social/Cultural
gatherings.

Bright Horizon*
701 S 11th, Saint Joseph, MO, 64501
(816) 279-7687
Admin Margaret Pike.
Licensure Residential care. *Beds* 20.
Owner Proprietary Corp.
Admissions Requirements Medical
examination.
Staff LPNs 1 (pt); Nurses aides 5 (ft), 2 (pt).

Carriage Square Health Care Center*
Woodbine & Gene Field Rds, Saint Joseph,
MO, 64506
(816) 364-1526
Admin Clara Lash. *Medical Dir/Dir of Nursing*
Dr C C DuMont.
Licensure Skilled care; Intermediate care. *Beds*
120. *Certified* Medicaid.
Owner Proprietary Corp (Beverly Enterprises).
Admissions Requirements Medical
examination.
Staff RNs 4 (ft); LPNs 5 (pt); Nurses aides 38
(pt); Physical therapists 1 (pt); Occupational
therapists 1 (pt); Speech therapists 1 (pt);
Activities coordinators 1 (ft); Dietitians 1
(ft); Dentists 1 (pt); Audiologists 1 (pt).
Facilities Dining room; Physical therapy
room; Activities room; Crafts room; Laundry
room; Barber/Beauty shop.
Activities Arts & crafts; Cards; Games;
Reading groups; Prayer groups; Movies;
Social/Cultural gatherings.

Church Street Manor*
611 N 11th, Saint Joseph, MO, 64501
(816) 232-3740
Admin Veda Sollars.
Licensure Intermediate care. *Beds* 30.
Owner Proprietary Corp.

Citadel Health Care Pavilion*
5026 Faraon, Saint Joseph, MO, 64506
(816) 279-1591
Admin Myrtle Wright.
Licensure Intermediate care. *Beds* 100.
Certified Medicaid.
Owner Proprietary Corp.

Green Acres
5215 Green Acres Rd, Saint Joseph, MO,
64506
(816) 232-4540
Admin John & Margaret Moffet. *Medical Dir/
Dir of Nursing* Margaret Moffet RN.
Licensure Residential care facility II. *Beds* 87.
Owner Nonprofit Corp.
Admissions Requirements Minimum age 21;
Medical examination; Physician's request.
Staff RNs 1 (ft); LPNs 1 (ft), 1 (pt); Orderlies
1 (ft); Nurses aides 8 (ft), 8 (pt); Activities
coordinators 1 (ft).
Facilities Dining room; Activities room;
Chapel; Crafts room; Laundry room; Barber/
Beauty shop; Library.
Activities Arts & crafts; Cards; Games;
Reading groups; Prayer groups; Movies;
Shopping trips; Social/Cultural gatherings;
Field trips; Programs from outside groups.

Heartland Centre
701 Faraon St, Saint Joseph, MO, 64501
(816) 271-7376
Admin J William Crittenden. *Medical Dir/Dir
of Nursing* Carlyn Kline MD; Landis L
Downing DON.
Licensure Skilled care; Intermediate care. *Beds*
SNF 46; ICF 104. *Certified* Medicaid;
Medicare.
Owner Nonprofit Corp.
Admissions Requirements Medical
examination.
Staff RNs 7 (ft), 2 (pt); LPNs 12 (ft), 21 (pt);
Nurses aides 29 (ft), 18 (pt); Physical
therapists 3 (ft), 3 (pt); Recreational
therapists 2 (ft); Occupational therapists 3
(ft), 1 (pt); Speech therapists 2 (ft), 1 (pt);
Dietitians 3 (pt); Podiatrists 1 (ft); Chaplain
1 (ft); Dentist 2 (pt).
Facilities Dining room; Physical therapy
room; Activities room; Chapel; Crafts room;
Laundry room; Barber/Beauty shop; Library.
Activities Arts & crafts; Cards; Games;
Reading groups; Prayer groups; Movies;
Shopping trips; Social/Cultural gatherings.

Lucas Boarding Home
1218-1220 North 3, Saint Joseph, MO, 64501
(314) 233-0946

Admin Mrs John M Lucas.
Licensure Intermediate care. *Beds* 15.
Owner Privately owned.
Admissions Requirements Medical
examination; Physician's request.
Facilities Dining room.
Activities Prayer groups.

St Joseph Convalescent Center*
811 N 9th, PO Box 207 Fairleigh Station,
Saint Joseph, MO, 64501
(816) 233-5164
Admin Dorothy Blakesley. *Medical Dir/Dir of
Nursing* Dr Donald Sklenar.
Licensure Skilled care. *Beds* 69. *Certified*
Medicaid.
Owner Proprietary Corp.
Admissions Requirements Medical
examination.
Staff RNs 1 (ft); LPNs 7 (ft); Nurses aides 27
(ft); Physical therapists 1 (ft), 1 (ft);
Occupational therapists 1 (ft); Speech
therapists 1 (pt); Activities coordinators 1
(ft).
Facilities Dining room; Activities room;
Chapel; Crafts room; Laundry room; Barber/
Beauty shop.
Activities Arts & crafts; Cards; Games;
Reading groups; Prayer groups; Social/
Cultural gatherings.

Saxton Nursing Home*
2421 Francis, Saint Joseph, MO, 64501
(816) 232-9874
Admin Edna Jessica Saxton. *Medical Dir/Dir
of Nursing* Dr Sklenar & Dr Christ.
Licensure Intermediate care. *Beds* 20.
Owner Proprietary Corp.
Admissions Requirements Minimum age 18;
Medical examination; Physician's request.
Staff RNs; LPNs 2 (ft).
Facilities Dining room.

Tiffany Square Convalescent Center
PO Box 1308, 3002 N 18th, Saint Joseph,
MO, 64505
(816) 364-4200
Admin S Marian Wilson. *Medical Dir/Dir of
Nursing* Kathryn Rhodes.
Licensure Intermediate care. *Beds* ICF 210;
RC 30. *Certified* Medicaid.
Owner Proprietary Corp.
Admissions Requirements Medical
examination.
Staff RNs 6 (ft); LPNs 12 (ft), 2 (pt); Nurses
aides 72 (ft); Physical therapists 1 (ft), 1 (pt);
Occupational therapists 1 (pt); Speech
therapists 1 (pt); Activities coordinators 2
(ft); Dietitians 1 (pt).
Facilities Dining room; Physical therapy
room; Activities room; Chapel; Laundry
room; Barber/Beauty shop.
Activities Arts & crafts; Cards; Games;
Reading groups; Prayer groups; Movies;
Shopping trips; Social/Cultural gatherings.

SAINT LOUIS

Affton Care Center
9009 Gravois, Saint Louis, MO, 63123
(314) 832-4833
Admin Rev Wooten. *Medical Dir/Dir of
Nursing* J Redding.
Licensure Intermediate care. *Beds* 19.
Certified Medicaid.
Owner Proprietary Corp.
Admissions Requirements Medical
examination.
Staff Physicians 4 (ft); LPNs 1 (ft); Nurses
aides 4 (ft); Dietitians 1 (ft); Dentists 1 (ft);
Ophthalmologists 1 (ft).
Facilities Dining room; Laundry room; Sun
porch.
Activities Games.

Barry Alan Nursing Home
3326-38 Eminence Ave, Saint Louis, MO, 63114
(314) 427-0988
Admin Deanna M Dotson. *Medical Dir/Dir of Nursing* Loretta Smith LPN.
Licensure Intermediate care. *Beds* 34.
Owner Proprietary Corp.
Admissions Requirements Minimum age 40; Medical examination.
Staff Physicians 1 (pt); RNs 1 (pt); LPNs 1 (ft), 1 (pt); Nurses aides 9 (ft), 5 (pt); Recreational therapists 1 (pt); Occupational therapists 1 (pt); Activities coordinators 1 (pt); Ophthalmologists 1 (pt).
Facilities Activities room; Crafts room.
Activities Arts & crafts; Cards; Games; Reading groups; Prayer groups; Movies.

Alcazar Home for the Aged Inc
1935 Park Ave, Saint Louis, MO, 63104
(314) 371-5172
Admin Edwin Wayne Cook.
Licensure Residential care. *Beds* 145.
Owner Proprietary Corp.

Arena Manor Inc*
3300 Texas Ave, Saint Louis, MO, 63118
(314) 773-3408
Admin Joseph S Arena.
Licensure Intermediate care. *Beds* 32.
Owner Proprietary Corp.

Avalon Nursing Home
4359 Taft Ave, Saint Louis, MO, 63149
(314) 752-2022
Admin Gayle Rhee. *Medical Dir/Dir of Nursing* Seoung E Rhee MD.
Licensure Intermediate care. *Beds* 64.
Owner Proprietary Corp.
Admissions Requirements Minimum age 16; Medical examination.
Staff Physicians 1 (ft); RNs 1 (ft); LPNs 2 (ft); Nurses aides 22 (ft), 4 (pt); Physical therapists 1 (ft); Reality therapists 1 (ft); Recreational therapists 1 (pt); Occupational therapists 1 (pt); Speech therapists 1 (pt); Activities coordinators 1 (ft); Dietitians 1 (pt); Podiatrists 1 (pt).
Facilities Dining room; Physical therapy room; Activities room; Chapel; Crafts room; Laundry room; Barber/Beauty shop.
Activities Arts & crafts; Cards; Games; Prayer groups; Movies; Social/Cultural gatherings.

Bernard West Pine Nursing Home*
4335 W Pine, Saint Louis, MO, 63108
(314) 371-0200
Admin Patti Crockarell. *Medical Dir/Dir of Nursing* Miguel Abelcuda.
Licensure Skilled care; Intermediate care. *Beds* 141. *Certified* Medicaid; Medicare.
Owner Proprietary Corp.
Admissions Requirements Minimum age 18; Medical examination; Physician's request.
Staff Physicians 16 (pt); RNs 2 (ft), 3 (pt); LPNs 7 (ft), 1 (pt); Orderlies 4 (ft); Nurses aides 37 (ft), 7 (pt); Physical therapists 2 (ft), 1 (pt); Occupational therapists 1 (pt); Speech therapists 1 (pt); Activities coordinators 1 (ft); Dietitians 1 (pt); Dentists 1 (pt); Ophthalmologists 1 (pt); Podiatrists 1 (pt); Audiologists 1 (pt).
Facilities Dining room; Physical therapy room; Activities room; Crafts room; Laundry room; Barber/Beauty shop; Enclosed patios.
Activities Arts & crafts; Games; Reading groups; Prayer groups; Social/Cultural gatherings; Outings to area sights.

Bethesda-Dilworth Memorial Home
9645 Big Bend Rd, Saint Louis, MO, 63122
(314) 968-5460
Admin Fletcher W Carter. *Medical Dir/Dir of Nursing* Patrick Majors MD; Elaine McCluggage DON.
Licensure Skilled care. *Beds* SNF 490. *Certified* Medicaid; Medicare.

Owner Nonprofit Corp.
Admissions Requirements Medical examination.
Staff Physicians 1 (ft); RNs 33 (ft); LPNs 32 (ft); Nurses aides 150 (ft); Physical therapists 1 (ft); Recreational therapists 1 (ft); Occupational therapists 1 (ft); Activities coordinators 1 (ft); Dietitians 1 (ft).
Facilities Dining room; Physical therapy room; Activities room; Chapel; Crafts room; Laundry room; Barber/Beauty shop; Library.
Activities Arts & crafts; Cards; Games; Reading groups; Prayer groups; Movies; Shopping trips; Social/Cultural gatherings.

Bethesda Skilled Nursing Facility*
3655 Vista Ave, Saint Louis, MO, 63110
(314) 772-9200
Admin Connie Siffring. *Medical Dir/Dir of Nursing* B Dandamudi MD.
Licensure Skilled care. *Beds* 30. *Certified* Medicare.
Owner Nonprofit Corp.
Admissions Requirements Medical examination; Physician's request.
Staff Physicians 1 (pt); RNs 2 (ft); LPNs 6 (ft); Orderlies 2 (pt); Nurses aides 10 (ft); Physical therapists 3 (ft); Occupational therapists; Speech therapists; Activities coordinators 1 (pt); Dietitians 1 (ft); Podiatrists 1 (pt); Audiologists 1 (pt).
Facilities Dining room; Physical therapy room; Chapel.
Activities Arts & crafts; Cards; Games; Reading groups; Prayer groups.

Birchway Nursing Home*
4373 W Pine Blvd, Saint Louis, MO, 63108
(314) 531-2644
Admin Ellen Goodrich. *Medical Dir/Dir of Nursing* Varkey Philip MD.
Licensure Skilled care; Intermediate care. *Beds* 65.
Owner Proprietary Corp.
Admissions Requirements Medical examination; Physician's request.
Facilities Dining room; Activities room; Crafts room; Laundry room; Barber/Beauty shop.
Activities Arts & crafts; Cards; Games; Prayer groups; Shopping trips; Social/Cultural gatherings.

Charles the First Medical Center*
5303 Bermuda Rd, Saint Louis, MO, 63121
(314) 385-0910
Admin Charles L Twedell.
Licensure Skilled care. *Beds* 52.
Owner Proprietary Corp.

The Charless Home
4431 S Broadway, Saint Louis, MO, 63111
(314) 481-4840
Admin Joseph Berry. *Medical Dir/Dir of Nursing* Dr Leonhardt & Dr Brody; Ella Altman DON.
Licensure Intermediate care. *Beds* ICF 40.
Owner Nonprofit organization/foundation.
Admissions Requirements Minimum age 55; Females only.
Staff RNs 1 (ft); LPNs 8 (ft); Nurses aides 30 (ft); Physical therapists 1 (pt); Recreational therapists 1 (ft); Occupational therapists 1 (pt); Speech therapists 1 (pt); Dietitians 1 (pt); Dentists 1 (pt); Ophthalmologists 1 (pt).
Languages German
Facilities Dining room; Barber/Beauty shop; Library.
Activities Arts & crafts; Cards; Games; Reading groups; Prayer groups; Movies; Shopping trips; Social/Cultural gatherings; Tours.

Community Care Center of Lemay
9353 S Broadway, Saint Louis, MO, 63125
(314) 631-0540
Admin Jean Price. *Medical Dir/Dir of Nursing* Lori Uroste.

Licensure Intermediate care. *Beds* ICF 42. *Certified* Medicaid.
Owner Proprietary Corp.
Admissions Requirements Minimum age 60; Medical examination.
Staff Physicians 1 (pt); RNs 1 (pt); LPNs 3 (pt); Nurses aides 15 (pt); Activities coordinators 1 (ft), 1 (pt); Dietitians 1 (ft).
Languages Italian
Facilities Dining room; Activities room; Laundry room; Barber/Beauty shop.
Activities Arts & crafts; Cards; Games; Reading groups; Prayer groups; Movies; Shopping trips; Social/Cultural gatherings.

Deaconess Manor*
6220 Oakland Ave, Saint Louis, MO, 63139
(314) 647-7350
Admin Stanley R Ekrem.
Licensure Skilled care. *Beds* 117. *Certified* Medicaid; Medicare.
Owner Nonprofit Corp.

Delhaven Nursing Center
5460 Delmar Blvd, Saint Louis, MO, 63112
(314) 361-2902
Admin Reece Cunningham. *Medical Dir/Dir of Nursing* Glynis Warters DON.
Licensure Skilled care. *Beds* SNF 156. *Certified* Medicaid.
Owner Proprietary Corp (Beverly Enterprises).
Admissions Requirements Medical examination.
Staff Physicians 3 (pt); RNs 5 (ft); LPNs 14 (ft); Nurses aides 65 (ft); Physical therapists 1 (pt); Occupational therapists 1 (pt); Activities coordinators 1 (ft); Dietitians 2 (ft); Dentists 1 (pt); Ophthalmologists 1 (pt); Podiatrists 1 (pt).
Facilities Dining room; Physical therapy room; Activities room; Crafts room; Laundry room; Barber/Beauty shop.
Activities Arts & crafts; Cards; Games; Reading groups; Prayer groups; Movies; Shopping trips; Social/Cultural gatherings; Bingo; Talent & fashion shows.

Edgewater Home Inc
5500 S Broadway, Saint Louis, MO, 63111
(314) 832-5800
Admin Georgia C Lisitano. *Medical Dir/Dir of Nursing* J Castro MD; E Murphy RN DON.
Licensure Skilled care. *Beds* SNF 151.
Owner Proprietary Corp.
Admissions Requirements Minimum age 21.
Staff RNs 4 (ft); LPNs 8 (ft); Orderlies 4 (ft); Nurses aides 75 (ft); Physical therapists 1 (ft); Occupational therapists 1 (ft); Speech therapists 1 (ft); Activities coordinators 1 (ft); Dietitians 1 (ft).
Facilities Dining room; Activities room; Crafts room; Laundry room; Barber/Beauty shop.
Activities Arts & crafts; Cards; Games.

Fairview Gardens
850 Country Manor Ln, Saint Louis, MO, 63141-6651
(314) 434-5900
Admin Carole L White.
Licensure Intermediate care. *Beds* 152. *Certified* Medicaid.
Owner Proprietary Corp.

Ferrier Harris Home for Aged*
3636 Page Ave, Saint Louis, MO, 63106
(314) 531-5549
Admin Bettye Dawson. *Medical Dir/Dir of Nursing* Dr Dunet F Belancourt.
Licensure Intermediate care. *Beds* 30.
Owner Nonprofit Corp.
Admissions Requirements Minimum age 45.
Staff Physicians 1 (pt); RNs 1 (pt); LPNs 2 (ft), 1 (pt).
Facilities Dining room; Physical therapy room; Activities room; Chapel; Crafts room; Laundry room; Barber/Beauty shop.

Activities Arts & crafts; Cards; Games; Reading groups; Prayer groups; Shopping trips; Social/Cultural gatherings.

Fontaine Woods Nursing Home*
9500 Bellefontaine Rd, Saint Louis, MO, 63137
(314) 868-1400
Admin Gladys Sullivan. *Medical Dir/Dir of Nursing* Dr David Light.
Licensure Skilled care. *Beds* 97.
Owner Proprietary Corp.
Admissions Requirements Minimum age 50.
Staff RNs 2 (ft), 5 (pt); LPNs 2 (ft), 6 (pt); Orderlies 1 (ft); Physical therapists 1 (pt); Activities coordinators 2 (ft); Dietitians 1 (pt).
Facilities Dining room; Physical therapy room; Activities room; Crafts room; Laundry room; Barber/Beauty shop.
Activities Arts & crafts; Cards; Games; Reading groups; Prayer groups; Movies; Shopping trips; Social/Cultural gatherings.

Frazier Nursing Home
4512 W Pine, Saint Louis, MO, 63108
(314) 367-8516
Admin Mabel Frazier. *Medical Dir/Dir of Nursing* Dr Nathan Kimelman; Joan Schmidt DON.
Licensure Intermediate care. *Beds* ICF 36.
Owner Privately owned.
Admissions Requirements Medical examination; Physician's request.
Staff Physicians 2 (pt); RNs 4 (pt); LPNs 2 (ft); Orderlies 1 (ft); Nurses aides 12 (ft), 3 (pt); Recreational therapists 2 (ft); Activities coordinators 1 (ft); Dietitians 1 (pt); Ophthalmologists 1 (pt).
Facilities Dining room; Activities room; Crafts room; Laundry room; Barber/Beauty shop; Library.
Activities Arts & crafts; Cards; Games; Reading groups; Prayer groups; Movies; Shopping trips; Social/Cultural gatherings; Van trips; Clubhouse available June-Oct.

Friendship Village
12503 Village Circle Dr, Saint Louis, MO, 63127
(314) 842-6840
Admin Dave Heeter. *Medical Dir/Dir of Nursing* Grant I Zmirlian MD.
Licensure Skilled care; Intermediate care. *Beds* 60. *Certified* Medicaid; Medicare.
Owner Nonprofit Corp (Life Care Services Corp).
Admissions Requirements Minimum age 21; Medical examination; Physician's request.
Staff RNs 2 (ft), 1 (pt); LPNs 4 (ft), 3 (pt); Nurses aides 30 (ft), 2 (pt); Physical therapists 1 (pt); Recreational therapists 1 (ft).
Facilities Dining room; Physical therapy room; Activities room; Crafts room; Laundry room; Barber/Beauty shop; Library.
Activities Arts & crafts; Cards; Games; Reading groups; Prayer groups.

Fueller Nursing Home*
5512 Kerth Rd, Saint Louis, MO, 63128
(314) 487-5929
Admin Doris Fueller.
Licensure Intermediate care. *Beds* 21.
Owner Proprietary Corp.

Carrie Elligson Gietner Home Inc
5000 S Broadway Ave, Saint Louis, MO, 63111
(314) 752-0000
Admin Althea H Wilson. *Medical Dir/Dir of Nursing* Norman P Knowlton MD.
Licensure Intermediate care; Residential care I & II. *Beds* ICF 75; Residential I 85; Residential II 25.
Owner Nonprofit Corp.
Admissions Requirements Minimum age 69; Medical examination.

Staff Physicians 1 (ft), 1 (pt); RNs 1 (ft), 1 (pt); LPNs 4 (ft); Nurses aides 35 (ft), 15 (pt); Physical therapists 2 (pt); Recreational therapists 2 (pt); Activities coordinators 1 (pt); Dietitians 1 (ft); Dentists 1 (pt); Ophthalmologists 1 (pt).
Facilities Dining room; Activities room; Chapel; Laundry room; Barber/Beauty shop; Library.
Activities Arts & crafts; Cards; Games; Reading groups; Prayer groups; Movies; Social/Cultural gatherings; Discussion groups.

Good Samaritan Home
5200 S Boardway, Saint Louis, MO, 63111
(314) 352-2400
Admin Charles Lockyear. *Medical Dir/Dir of Nursing* C E Mueller MD; Janine Potrzeboski DON.
Licensure Intermediate care. *Beds* ICF 86.
Owner Nonprofit organization/foundation.
Admissions Requirements Minimum age 60; Medical examination.
Staff Physicians 1 (ft); RNs 4 (ft), 1 (pt); LPNs 5 (ft), 2 (pt); Nurses aides 38 (ft), 4 (pt); Activities coordinators 1 (ft); Dietitians 1 (ft); Dentists 1 (pt); Ophthalmologists 1 (pt); Social service designee 1 (ft); CMT 11 (ft), 7 (pt).
Affiliation Church of Christ
Facilities Dining room; Physical therapy room; Activities room; Chapel; Crafts room; Laundry room; Barber/Beauty shop; Library.
Activities Arts & crafts; Cards; Games; Prayer groups; Movies; Shopping trips; Social/ Cultural gatherings; Outings to municipal opera, Ice Capades, Ballgames, Church camp, State park, and Fishing.

Grand Manor
3400 S Grand, Saint Louis, MO, 63118
(314) 865-2600
Admin Darlene Sredl RN MA. *Medical Dir/ Dir of Nursing* Peggy Winkler RN.
Licensure Intermediate care; Residential care. *Beds* ICF 177; Residential 32. *Certified* Medicaid.
Owner Proprietary Corp.
Admissions Requirements Minimum age 21; Medical examination; Physician's request.
Staff Physicians 2 (pt); RNs 4 (ft), 1 (pt); LPNs 3 (ft), 1 (pt); Nurses aides 110 (ft); Physical therapists 1 (pt); Recreational therapists 1 (pt); Speech therapists 1 (pt); Activities coordinators 4 (ft); Dietitians 1 (pt); Dentists 1 (pt); Podiatrists 1 (pt).
Affiliation Roman Catholic
Facilities Dining room; Physical therapy room; Activities room; Chapel; Crafts room; Laundry room; Barber/Beauty shop; Library.
Activities Arts & crafts; Reading groups; Prayer groups; Movies; Social/Cultural gatherings.

Gravois Rest Haven Inc
10954 Kennerly Rd, Saint Louis, MO, 63128
(314) 843-4242
Admin Barbara M Wagner. *Medical Dir/Dir of Nursing* Rebecca Bernard RN.
Licensure Skilled care. *Beds* SNF 167.
Owner Proprietary Corp.
Admissions Requirements Minimum age 18.
Staff RNs 7 (ft), 2 (pt); LPNs 9 (ft), 1 (pt); Orderlies 8 (ft); Nurses aides 75 (ft), 1 (pt); Physical therapists 1 (pt); Activities coordinators 1 (ft), 2 (pt).
Facilities Dining room; Physical therapy room; Activities room; Crafts room; Laundry room; Barber/Beauty shop.
Activities Arts & crafts; Cards; Games; Reading groups; Prayer groups; Movies; Social/Cultural gatherings.

Heritage of St Louis
4401 N Hanley, Saint Louis, MO, 63121
(314) 521-6211

Admin Suzanne Westhoff. *Medical Dir/Dir of Nursing* David Rosenberg MD; Sue Sullivan RN DON.
Licensure Skilled care; Intermediate care. *Beds* 120. *Certified* Medicaid.
Owner Proprietary Corp.
Admissions Requirements Minimum age 65; Medical examination; Physician's request.
Staff Physicians 1 (ft), 1 (pt); RNs 2 (ft), 3 (pt); LPNs 4 (ft), 2 (pt); Orderlies 7 (ft), 1 (pt); Nurses aides 20 (ft), 10 (pt); Physical therapists 1 (pt); Reality therapists 1 (pt); Recreational therapists 1 (pt); Occupational therapists 1 (pt); Speech therapists 1 (pt); Activities coordinators 1 (ft), 1 (pt); Dietitians 1 (ft), 1 (pt).
Facilities Dining room; Physical therapy room; Activities room; Laundry room; Barber/Beauty shop.
Activities Arts & crafts; Cards; Games; Reading groups; Prayer groups; Movies.

Jerri's Benevolent Manor*
730 Hodiamont, Saint Louis, MO, 63112
(314)727-5219
Admin Laverne Haulcy.
Licensure Residential care. *Beds* 22.
Owner Proprietary Corp.

Ranken Jordan Home for Convalescent Crippled Children
10621 Ladue Rd, Saint Louis, MO, 63141
(314) 993-1207
Admin Johann L Ellerbrake. *Medical Dir/Dir of Nursing* Anthony J Rejent MD; Ann A Young DON.
Licensure Skilled care. *Beds* SNF 26.
Owner Nonprofit organization/foundation.

K F J Manor Inc 2*
5415 Thelka, Saint Louis, MO, 63136
(314) 385-8180
Admin Willie Jammer.
Licensure Residential care. *Beds* 25.
Owner Proprietary Corp.

Robert Koch Hospital*
4101 Koch Rd, Saint Louis, MO, 63129
(314) 622-5800
Admin Thomas J Purcell.
Licensure Intermediate care. *Beds* 428.
Owner Publicly owned.

Little Flower Nursing Home*
2500 S 18th, Saint Louis, MO, 63104
(314) 664-2267
Admin Roxie Lavine. *Medical Dir/Dir of Nursing* Leonard Piccione MD.
Licensure Intermediate care. *Beds* 90.
Owner Proprietary Corp.
Staff Physicians 1 (ft), 6 (pt); RNs 3 (ft); LPNs 2 (ft), 2 (pt); Nurses aides 21 (ft), 5 (pt); Physical therapists 1 (ft); Reality therapists 1 (pt); Recreational therapists 1 (ft); Occupational therapists 1 (pt); Speech therapists 1 (pt); Activities coordinators 1 (ft); Dietitians 1 (pt); Dentists 1 (pt); Ophthalmologists 1 (pt); Audiologists 1 (pt).
Facilities Dining room; Activities room; Chapel; Crafts room; Laundry room; Barber/ Beauty shop.
Activities Arts & crafts; Cards; Games; Reading groups; Prayer groups; Movies; Shopping trips; Social/Cultural gatherings.

Little Sisters of the Poor
3225 N Florissant Ave, Saint Louis, MO, 63107
(314) 421-6022
Admin Marguerite Marie. *Medical Dir/Dir of Nursing* Sr Carolyn RN BSN.
Licensure Intermediate care; HUD Housing. *Beds* ICF 112; HUD Housing 68. *Certified* Medicaid.
Owner Nonprofit Corp.
Admissions Requirements Minimum age 60; Medical examination.

Staff Physicians 8 (pt); RNs 3 (ft); LPNs 5 (ft), 3 (pt); Nurses aides 60 (ft), 10 (pt); Physical therapists 1 (pt); Recreational therapists 1 (pt); Occupational therapists 1 (pt); Speech therapists 1 (pt); Activities coordinators 1 (pt); Dietitians 1 (pt); Dentists 2 (pt); Ophthalmologists 2 (pt); Podiatrists 1 (pt).
Affiliation Roman Catholic
Facilities Dining room; Physical therapy room; Activities room; Chapel; Crafts room; Laundry room; Barber/Beauty shop; Library.
Activities Arts & crafts; Cards; Games; Reading groups; Prayer groups; Movies; Shopping trips; Social/Cultural gatherings.

Lutheran Altenheim Society of Missouri*
1265 McLaran Ave, Saint Louis, MO, 63147
(314) 388-2867
Admin E Willis Piehl.
Licensure Skilled care; Intermediate care; Residential care. *Beds* SNF 60; ICF 68; Residential 78. *Certified* Medicaid.
Owner Nonprofit Corp.
Affiliation Lutheran

Marquette Manor Nursing Home
3419 Gasconade St, Saint Louis, MO, 63118
(314) 351-7512
Admin Lawrence A Pulas. *Medical Dir/Dir of Nursing* Gerri Villaire.
Licensure Intermediate care; Residential care. *Beds* ICF 125; Residential 22. *Certified* Medicaid.
Owner Proprietary Corp.
Admissions Requirements Medical examination.
Staff Physicians 1 (pt); RNs 1 (ft); LPNs 12 (ft); Orderlies 10 (ft); Nurses aides 50 (ft); Physical therapists 1 (pt); Occupational therapists 1 (pt); Speech therapists 1 (pt); Activities coordinators 1 (ft); Dietitians 1 (ft); Dentists 1 (pt); Ophthalmologists 1 (pt).
Facilities Dining room; Physical therapy room; Activities room; Chapel; Barber/ Beauty shop; Rooftop patio; Rose garden.
Activities Arts & crafts; Games; Reading groups; Prayer groups; Movies.

Mary, Queen & Mother Center
7601 Watson Rd, Saint Louis, MO, 63119
(314) 961-8485
Admin Sr Jeanne McGovern. *Medical Dir/Dir of Nursing* Rajendraprasad Dandamudi MD; Gail Marchesi RN DON.
Licensure Skilled care; Intermediate care. *Beds* 220. *Certified* Medicaid; Medicare.
Owner Nonprofit Corp.
Admissions Requirements Minimum age 62; Medical examination; Physician's request.
Staff Physicians 1 (pt); RNs 12 (ft), 4 (pt); LPNs 17 (ft), 5 (pt); Orderlies 3 (ft); Nurses aides 94 (ft), 7 (pt); Physical therapists 1 (pt); Recreational therapists 1 (pt); Occupational therapists 1 (pt); Speech therapists 1 (pt); Activities coordinators 1 (ft); Dietitians 1 (ft); Dentists 1 (pt); Ophthalmologists 1 (pt); Podiatrists 1 (pt).
Affiliation Roman Catholic
Facilities Dining room; Physical therapy room; Activities room; Chapel; Crafts room; Laundry room; Barber/Beauty shop.
Activities Arts & crafts; Cards; Games; Reading groups; Prayer groups; Movies.

Medicalodge of Halls Ferry
2115 Kappel Dr, Saint Louis, MO, 63136
(314) 867-7474
Admin Charlene Hale. *Medical Dir/Dir of Nursing* Terrell Mulford DO; Mildred Spencer RNC DON.
Licensure Skilled care; Intermediate care. *Beds* SNF 100; ICF 48. *Certified* Medicaid; Medicare.
Owner Proprietary Corp (Medicalodges).
Admissions Requirements Minimum age 16; Medical examination; Physician's request.

Staff Physicians 1 (ft), 7 (pt); RNs 5 (ft), 2 (pt); LPNs 8 (ft), 3 (pt); Orderlies 1 (ft); Nurses aides 47 (ft), 5 (pt); Physical therapists 1 (ft); Reality therapists 1 (ft); Recreational therapists 2 (ft); Occupational therapists 1 (pt); Speech therapists 1 (pt); Dietitians 1 (pt); Dentists 1 (pt); Ophthalmologists 1 (pt); Podiatrists 1 (pt).
Facilities Dining room; Physical therapy room; Activities room; Crafts room; Laundry room; Barber/Beauty shop.
Activities Arts & crafts; Cards; Games; Reading groups; Prayer groups; Movies; Shopping trips; Social/Cultural gatherings.

Medigroup Oak Park Nursing Home*
6637 Berthold, Saint Louis, MO, 63139
(314) 781-3444
Admin Marian Kling.
Licensure Skilled care. *Beds* 120. *Certified* Medicaid.
Owner Proprietary Corp.

Mercy Convalescent Center*
3450 Russell, Saint Louis, MO, 63104
(314) 664-1020
Admin Matthew P Puchta.
Licensure Intermediate care. *Beds* 254. *Certified* Medicaid.
Owner Proprietary Corp.

Mother of Good Counsel Nursing Home
6825 Natural Bridge, Saint Louis, MO, 63121
(314) 383-4765
Admin Sr M Silvana Budde. *Medical Dir/Dir of Nursing* Dr Walter Kutryb; Sr M Stephanie Belgeri DON.
Licensure Skilled care. *Beds* SNF 110. *Certified* Medicaid.
Owner Nonprofit Corp.
Admissions Requirements Females only.
Staff RNs 3 (ft), 3 (pt); LPNs 5 (ft), 3 (pt); Nurses aides 38 (ft), 18 (pt); Physical therapists 1 (ft), 2 (pt); Recreational therapists 1 (ft); Activities coordinators 1 (ft); Dietitians 1 (ft); Ophthalmologists 1 (pt).
Languages German, Portuguese
Affiliation Roman Catholic
Facilities Dining room; Physical therapy room; Activities room; Chapel; Crafts room; Barber/Beauty shop; Library; Several solariums.
Activities Arts & crafts; Cards; Games; Reading groups; Prayer groups; Movies; Social/Cultural gatherings.

Oak Park Professional Care Center*
6637 Berthold Ave, Saint Louis, MO, 63139
Admin Mona Hilliard. *Medical Dir/Dir of Nursing* Dr James F Sertl.
Licensure Skilled care; Intermediate care. *Beds* 120. *Certified* Medicaid.
Owner Proprietary Corp.
Admissions Requirements Minimum age 16.
Staff Physicians 1 (pt); RNs 2 (ft), 1 (pt); LPNs 10 (ft), 3 (pt); Nurses aides 35 (ft), 6 (pt); Physical therapists 1 (ft), 1 (pt); Reality therapists 2 (ft); Recreational therapists 2 (ft), 2 (pt); Occupational therapists 2 (pt); Speech therapists 1 (pt); Activities coordinators 1 (pt); Dietitians 1 (pt); Dentists 1 (pt); Ophthalmologists 1 (pt); Podiatrists 1 (pt).
Facilities Dining room; Physical therapy room; Activities room; Crafts room; Laundry room; Barber/Beauty shop.
Activities Arts & crafts; Cards; Games; Prayer groups; Movies; Shopping trips; Social/ Cultural gatherings.

Parkside Towers
4960 Laclede Ave, Saint Louis, MO, 63108
(314) 361-6240
Admin Libby S Routman. *Medical Dir/Dir of Nursing* Aaron Birenbaum MD; Sue Hardin RN DON.

Licensure Skilled care; Intermediate care. *Beds* SNF 47; ICF 119. *Certified* Medicaid.
Owner Proprietary Corp.
Staff RNs 3 (ft); LPNs 14 (ft); Orderlies 17 (ft), 1 (pt); Nurses aides 65 (ft), 3 (pt); Physical therapists 1 (ft); Reality therapists 1 (ft).

Mary Ryder Home for the Aged
4341 Westminister Pl, Saint Louis, MO, 63108
(314) 533-9018
Admin Catherine Jones. *Medical Dir/Dir of Nursing* Douglas F Biggs MD.
Licensure Residential care II. *Beds* 31.
Owner Nonprofit Corp.
Admissions Requirements Females only; Medical examination.
Staff LPNs 1 (pt); Nurses aides 10 (ft); Recreational therapists 1 (ft); Dietitians 1 (pt).
Facilities Dining room; Laundry room; Barber/Beauty shop; Library.
Activities Arts & crafts; Cards; Games; Reading groups; Prayer groups; Movies; Shopping trips; Social/Cultural gatherings.

Mary Ryder Home for the Aged
4360 Olive St, Saint Louis, MO, 63108
(314) 531-2981
Admin Ethel M Ryder.
Licensure Residential care II. *Beds* Residential Care II 37.
Owner Nonprofit Corp.
Staff LPNs 1 (ft); Nurses aides 2 (ft); Activities coordinators 1 (ft); Certified Medical Technicians 6 (ft).

St Anthony's Medical Center-Rehab Center
10010 Kennerly Rd, Saint Louis, MO, 63128
(314) 525-1770
Admin Thomas P Long. *Medical Dir/Dir of Nursing* Bartolome Kairuz MD; Ellen Douty RN.
Licensure Skilled care; Rehabilitation Ventilator unit. *Beds* SNF 74. *Certified* Medicaid; Medicare.
Owner Nonprofit Corp.
Admissions Requirements Physician's request.
Staff Physicians 1 (pt); RNs 11 (ft); LPNs 5 (ft); Nurses aides 20 (ft); Physical therapists 5 (ft); Recreational therapists 2 (ft); Occupational therapists 3 (ft); Speech therapists 1 (ft); Dietitians 1 (ft); Podiatrists 2 (ft).
Facilities Dining room; Physical therapy room; Activities room; Chapel; Barber/ Beauty shop.
Activities Arts & crafts; Cards; Games; Prayer groups; Movies.

St Louis Altenheim*
5408 S Broadway, Saint Louis, MO, 63111
(314) 353-7225
Admin Albert R Emmerth.
Licensure Intermediate care; Residential care. *Beds* ICF 42; Residential 108.
Owner Nonprofit Corp.

St Louis Developmental Disabilities Treatment Center*
5400 Arsenal, Saint Louis, MO, 63139
(314) 644-5400
Admin John Twehaus. *Medical Dir/Dir of Nursing* Kyu Her MD.
Licensure Intermediate care for mentally retarded. *Beds* 300.
Staff Physicians 4 (ft), 2 (pt); RNs 31 (ft), 1 (pt); LPNs 5 (ft), 1 (pt); Physical therapists 1 (ft), 1 (pt); Recreational therapists 4 (ft); Occupational therapists 4 (ft), 1 (pt); Speech therapists 4 (ft), 1 (pt); Dietitians 3 (ft); Dentists 1 (ft); Psychologists 7 (ft), 1 (pt).
Facilities Dining room; Physical therapy room; Activities room; Laundry room; Classrooms/modules.

Activities Arts & crafts; Cards; Games; Movies; Shopping trips; Social/Cultural gatherings; Community trips.

St Louis Good Shepherd Homes Inc*
9444 Midland Blvd, Saint Louis, MO, 63114
(314) 427-8795
Admin Ed Anthonis Jr.
Licensure Intermediate care. *Beds* 34.
Owner Proprietary Corp.

South Gate Care Center
5943 S Telegraph Rd, Saint Louis, MO, 63129
(314) 846-2000
Admin C Michael Roth. *Medical Dir/Dir of Nursing* Carla Jurgensen DON.
Licensure Skilled care. *Beds* SNF 180. *Certified* Medicaid.
Owner Proprietary Corp.
Admissions Requirements Medical examination; Physician's request.
Staff Physicians 3 (ft); RNs 5 (ft), 8 (pt); LPNs 10 (ft), 7 (pt); Nurses aides 200 (ft), 50 (pt); Physical therapists 2 (ft); Recreational therapists 1 (ft), 1 (pt); Activities coordinators 1 (ft); Dietitians 1 (ft); Podiatrists 1 (pt).
Facilities Dining room; Physical therapy room; Activities room; Crafts room; Laundry room; Barber/Beauty shop; Library; Outdoor gazebo.
Activities Arts & crafts; Cards; Games; Reading groups; Prayer groups; Movies; Shopping trips; Social/Cultural gatherings.

Stellar Homes Inc*
4336 Lindell, Saint Louis, MO, 63108
(314) 652-4828
Admin Viola J Huskey.
Licensure Residential care. *Beds* 24.
Owner Proprietary Corp.

Tower Village Inc
4518 Blair Ave, Saint Louis, MO, 63107
(314) 534-4000
Admin Charles T Gooden. *Medical Dir/Dir of Nursing* Alphonso Hillard MD; Beverly Davis RN DON.
Licensure Skilled care; Intermediate care. *Beds* 268. *Certified* Medicaid.
Owner Nonprofit Corp.
Admissions Requirements Medical examination.
Staff Physicians 3 (pt); RNs 6 (ft); LPNs 30 (ft); Nurses aides 78 (ft); Physical therapists 1 (pt); Recreational therapists 1 (pt); Occupational therapists 1 (pt); Speech therapists 1 (pt); Activities coordinators 2 (ft); Dietitians 1 (ft); Dentists 1 (pt); Ophthalmologists 1 (pt); Podiatrists 1 (pt); Dentist 1 (pt).
Facilities Dining room; Physical therapy room; Activities room; Chapel; Crafts room; Laundry room; Barber/Beauty shop; Library; Gift shop; Living room.
Activities Arts & crafts; Cards; Games; Reading groups; Prayer groups; Movies; Shopping trips.

Village North Inc
11160 Village North Dr, Saint Louis, MO, 63136
(314) 355-8010
Admin Dorothy Espenschied. *Medical Dir/Dir of Nursing* David Smuckler MD; Grace O White RN DON.
Licensure Skilled care; Independent living. *Beds* SNF 60; Independent living apts 213. *Certified* Medicaid; Medicare.
Owner Nonprofit Corp.
Admissions Requirements Minimum age 18; Medical examination; Physician's request.
Staff Physicians 1 (pt); RNs 1 (ft), 2 (pt); LPNs 7 (ft), 4 (pt); Orderlies 1 (ft); Nurses aides 10 (ft), 10 (pt); Physical therapists 1 (ft); Reality therapists 1 (pt); Recreational therapists 1 (pt); Occupational therapists 1 (pt); Speech therapists 1 (pt); Activities

coordinators 1 (ft); Dietitians 1 (pt); Dentists 1 (pt); Ophthalmologists 1 (pt); Podiatrists 1 (pt).
Facilities Dining room; Physical therapy room; Activities room; Crafts room; Laundry room; Barber/Beauty shop; Library.
Activities Arts & crafts; Cards; Games; Reading groups; Prayer groups; Movies; Shopping trips; Social/Cultural gatherings; Billiards; Pitch & putt golf.

SAINT PETERS

St Peters Manor Care Center*
150 Spencer Rd, Saint Peters, MO, 63376
Admin Bennie Wiegand. *Medical Dir/Dir of Nursing* Dr Martin Walsch.
Licensure Intermediate care. *Beds* 102.
Owner Nonprofit Corp.
Admissions Requirements Medical examination; Physician's request.
Staff RNs 2 (pt); LPNs 6 (ft); Physical therapists 1 (pt); Occupational therapists 1 (pt); Speech therapists 1 (pt); Activities coordinators 1 (ft), 1 (pt); Podiatrists 1 (pt).
Facilities Dining room; Barber/Beauty shop.
Activities Arts & crafts; Games; Reading groups; Movies; Shopping trips; Social/ Cultural gatherings; Adopt-a-grandparent program.

SAINTE GENEVIEVE

Greenfields Nursing Home*
PO Box 346, Little Rock Rd, Sainte Genevieve, MO, 63670
(314) 883-3124
Admin Janet Kemper.
Licensure Intermediate care. *Beds* 36.
Owner Proprietary Corp.

Riverview Manor Nursing Home
PO Box 151, N 4th St & Matthews Dr, Sainte Genevieve, MO, 63670
(314) 883-3454
Admin Martin F Radmer. *Medical Dir/Dir of Nursing* Dr Joseph F Lutkewitte; Betty Grobe.
Licensure Intermediate care. *Beds* 120. *Certified* Medicaid.
Owner Publicly owned.
Admissions Requirements Minimum age 18; Medical examination; Physician's request.
Staff Physicians 1 (pt); RNs 3 (ft); LPNs 2 (ft); Orderlies 2 (ft); Nurses aides 49 (ft), 16 (pt); Recreational therapists 2 (ft).
Facilities Dining room; Physical therapy room; Activities room; Laundry room; Barber/Beauty shop; Solarium.
Activities Arts & crafts; Cards; Games; Reading groups; Prayer groups; Movies; Shopping trips; Social/Cultural gatherings.

SALEM

Elwood Nursing Home*
1000 N Jackson, Salem, MO, 65560
(314) 729-3011
Admin Virginia A Elwood.
Licensure Intermediate care. *Beds* 36.
Owner Proprietary Corp.

Seville Nursing Home*
Hwy 72 W, PO Box 311, Salem, MO, 65560
(314) 729-6141
Admin Mary Wilson. *Medical Dir/Dir of Nursing* James Bass MD.
Licensure Skilled care; Intermediate care. *Beds* 90. *Certified* Medicaid; Medicare.
Owner Proprietary Corp (Beverly Enterprises).
Admissions Requirements Minimum age 21.
Staff Physicians 1 (pt); RNs 2 (ft), 2 (pt); LPNs 3 (ft), 3 (pt); Nurses aides 20 (ft), 6 (pt); Physical therapists 2 (pt); Recreational therapists 1 (pt); Occupational therapists 1

(pt); Speech therapists 1 (pt); Activities coordinators 1 (pt); Dietitians 1 (pt); Dentists 1 (pt); Podiatrists 1 (pt).
Facilities Dining room; Physical therapy room; Activities room; Crafts room; Laundry room; Barber/Beauty shop; Library.
Activities Arts & crafts; Cards; Games; Reading groups; Prayer groups; Movies; Shopping trips; Social/Cultural gatherings; Outings.

SALISBURY

Chariton Park Care Center
902 Manor Dr, Salisbury, MO, 65281
(816) 388-6486
Admin Sandy Smith. *Medical Dir/Dir of Nursing* Donald Pressley & George Quinn; Patricia Bell DON.
Licensure Intermediate care; Residential care. *Beds* ICF/MR 88; Residential 12. *Certified* Medicaid.
Owner Proprietary Corp.
Admissions Requirements Minimum age 18.
Staff Physicians; RNs; LPNs; Orderlies; Nurses aides; Physical therapists; Occupational therapists; Speech therapists; Activities coordinators; Dietitians.
Facilities Dining room; Physical therapy room; Activities room; Crafts room; Laundry room; Barber/Beauty shop.
Activities Arts & crafts; Cards; Games; Reading groups; Prayer groups; Shopping trips; Social/Cultural gatherings.

SARCOXIE

Royce Manor
16th & Miner, Sarcoxie, MO, 64862
(417) 548-3434
Admin Ann Royce & James J Royce. *Medical Dir/Dir of Nursing* J J Royce MD.
Licensure Skilled care. *Beds* 37.
Admissions Requirements Medical examination.
Staff Physicians 1 (ft); RNs 2 (ft), 1 (pt); LPNs 3 (ft), 1 (pt); Nurses aides 10 (ft), 4 (pt); Activities coordinators 2 (pt).
Facilities Dining room; Activities room; Chapel; Crafts room; Laundry room; Barber/ Beauty shop; Library.
Activities Arts & crafts; Cards; Games; Prayer groups; Movies; Shopping trips; Social/ Cultural gatherings.

SAVANNAH

LaVerna Heights
194 E Park Ave, Savannah, MO, 64485
(816) 324-3179
Admin Sr M Magdelene Bergmann. *Medical Dir/Dir of Nursing* Pauline Youngblood LPN.
Licensure Intermediate care. *Beds* ICF 40.
Owner Nonprofit Corp.
Admissions Requirements Minimum age 45; Females only; Medical examination.
Staff RNs 1 (pt); LPNs 3 (ft); Nurses aides 16 (ft), 6 (pt); Activities coordinators 1 (pt); Dietitians 1 (pt).
Languages German
Affiliation Roman Catholic
Facilities Dining room; Physical therapy room; Activities room; Chapel; Laundry room; Barber/Beauty shop; Library.
Activities Arts & crafts; Cards; Games; Reading groups; Prayer groups; Movies; Shopping trips; Social/Cultural gatherings.

LaVerna Village Nursing Home*
904 Hall Ave, Savannah, MO, 64485
(816) 324-3185
Admin Leon T Jennings.
Licensure Intermediate care. *Beds* 120. *Certified* Medicaid.
Owner Nonprofit Corp.

Staff RNs 1 (ft), 2 (pt); LPNs 9 (ft); Nurses aides 58 (ft), 4 (pt); Activities coordinators 3 (ft).
Affiliation Roman Catholic
Facilities Dining room; Activities room; Chapel; Crafts room; Laundry room; Barber/Beauty shop; Library.
Activities Arts & crafts; Cards; Games; Reading groups; Prayer groups; Social/Cultural gatherings.

Shady Lawn
PO Box 209, Savannah, MO, 64485
(816) 324-5991
Admin Brenda Elifrits. *Medical Dir/Dir of Nursing* Barbara Huff, RN DON.
Licensure Intermediate care; Residential care. *Beds* ICF 88; Residential 30. *Certified* Medicaid.
Owner Proprietary Corp (Tiffany Care Centers).
Admissions Requirements Minimum age 21; Medical examination.
Staff Physicians 3 (pt); RNs 1 (ft); LPNs 4 (ft); Orderlies 1 (ft); Nurses aides 30 (ft), 3 (pt); Physical therapists 1 (ft), 1 (pt); Occupational therapists 1 (pt); Speech therapists 1 (pt); Activities coordinators 1 (ft), 1 (pt); Dietitians 1 (ft), 1 (pt); Ophthalmologists 1 (pt); Podiatrists 1 (pt).
Facilities Dining room; Physical therapy room; Activities room; Crafts room; Laundry room; Barber/Beauty shop; Enclosed garden; Courtyard.
Activities Arts & crafts; Cards; Games; Prayer groups; Movies; Shopping trips; Social/Cultural gatherings.

SEDALIA

Brooking Park Geriatric Center Inc
PO Box 1667, Sedalia, MO, 65301
(816) 826-8803
Admin R H "Hank" Monsees. *Medical Dir/Dir of Nursing* Kenneth Azan MD.
Licensure Skilled care; Intermediate care; Residential care. *Beds* 180. *Certified* Medicaid; Medicare.
Owner Proprietary Corp.
Admissions Requirements Medical examination.
Staff Physicians 1 (pt); RNs 4 (ft), 4 (pt); LPNs 14 (ft), 2 (pt); Orderlies 5 (ft), 1 (pt); Nurses aides 60 (ft), 16 (pt); Physical therapists 1 (pt); Reality therapists; Recreational therapists; Occupational therapists 1 (pt); Speech therapists 1 (pt); Activities coordinators 2 (ft); Dietitians 1 (ft); Chaplain; Social worker.
Facilities Dining room; Physical therapy room; Activities room; Crafts room; Barber/Beauty shop; Library; Game room.
Activities Arts & crafts; Cards; Games; Reading groups; Prayer groups; Movies; Shopping trips; Social/Cultural gatherings; Cooking; Exercise; Bingo; News & views.

Buena Vista Home for the Aged
Rte 4, Georgetown Rd, Sedalia, MO, 65301
(816) 826-5159
Admin Arlene M Benn. *Medical Dir/Dir of Nursing* Dr Donald Allcorn.
Licensure Intermediate care. *Beds* 48.
Owner Nonprofit Corp.
Staff Physicians 1 (ft); RNs 1 (ft); LPNs 3 (ft); Orderlies 2 (ft); Nurses aides 21 (ft); Physical therapists 1 (ft); Activities coordinators 1 (ft); Dietitians 3 (ft).
Facilities Dining room; Physical therapy room; Activities room; Chapel; Laundry room; Barber/Beauty shop.
Activities Arts & crafts; Cards; Games; Prayer groups; Social/Cultural gatherings.

Burt Manor Nursing Home*
711 N Missouri, Sedalia, MO, 65301
(816) 826-3593
Admin Belva Morney.

Licensure Intermediate care. *Beds* 33.
Owner Proprietary Corp.

Fair View Nursing Home*
1714 W 16th St, Sedalia, MO, 65301
(816) 827-1594
Admin Constance Johnson Pope.
Licensure Intermediate care. *Beds* 58.
Owner Proprietary Corp.

Gina's Granny Home*
1105 E 6th St, Sedalia, MO, 65301
Admin Doris Riley.
Beds 6. *Certified* Medicaid; Medicare.
Owner Proprietary Corp.
Admissions Requirements Medical examination.
Facilities Dining room.
Activities Prayer groups.

Hawthorne House*
1401 W 3rd St, Sedalia, MO, 65301
(816) 826-2080
Admin Brenda Thompson.
Licensure Intermediate care. *Beds* 31.
Owner Proprietary Corp.

Rest Haven Convalescent & Retirement Home*
1800 S Ingram, Sedalia, MO, 65301
(816) 827-0845
Admin Lee Stormer & John C Finley.
Licensure Skilled care; Intermediate care. *Beds* 81. *Certified* Medicaid.
Owner Proprietary Corp.

SENATH

Senath Nursing Home*
Hwy 25, Box Q, Senath, MO, 63876
(314) 738-2068
Admin George W Krone.
Licensure Skilled care; Intermediate care. *Beds* 120. *Certified* Medicaid.
Owner Proprietary Corp.

SHELBINA

Aladdin's of Shelbina*
310 E Walnut, Shelbina, MO, 63468
(314) 588-7749
Admin Mildred Wheeler.
Licensure Residential care. *Beds* 31.
Owner Proprietary Corp.

Salt River Nursing Home*
Box 529, Shelbina, MO, 63468
(314) 588-4175
Admin Floyd Sims.
Licensure Skilled care. *Beds* 120.
Owner Publicly owned.

SIKESTON

Shuffit Nursing Home 1 Inc*
PO Box 827, 509 Ruth St, Sikeston, MO, 63801
(314) 471-2565
Admin Ira B Shuffit.
Licensure Intermediate care. *Beds* 82. *Certified* Medicaid.
Owner Proprietary Corp.

Shuffit Nursing Home 3 Inc*
Rte 3, PO Box 827, Sikeston, MO, 63801
(314) 471-1174
Admin Randol M York. *Medical Dir/Dir of Nursing* A L Weaver.
Licensure Intermediate care. *Beds* 100. *Certified* Medicaid.
Owner Proprietary Corp.
Admissions Requirements Minimum age 21.
Staff Physicians 1 (pt); RNs 1 (ft), 1 (pt); LPNs 8 (ft), 3 (pt); Orderlies &; Nurses aides 37 (ft), 6 (pt); Physical therapists 1 (ft), 1 (pt); Occupational therapists 1 (pt); Speech therapists 1 (pt); Activities coordinators 1 (ft); Dietitians 1 (ft), 1 (pt); Dentists 1 (pt); 16 (ft), 6 (pt).

Facilities Dining room; Physical therapy room; Activities room; Crafts room; Laundry room; Barber/Beauty shop.
Activities Arts & crafts; Cards; Games; Prayer groups; Movies; Shopping trips; Social/Cultural gatherings.

Sikeston Convalescent Center
103 Kennedy Dr, Sikeston, MO, 63801
(314) 471-6900
Admin Robert J Hodges. *Medical Dir/Dir of Nursing* M Critchlow MD; Marie Muench RN DON.
Licensure Skilled care; Intermediate care. *Beds* 120. *Certified* Medicaid.
Owner Proprietary Corp.
Admissions Requirements Minimum age 17; Medical examination; Physician's request.
Staff Physicians 2 (pt); RNs 2 (ft), 1 (pt); LPNs 10 (ft); Orderlies 35 (ft); Physical therapists 1 (ft); Occupational therapists 1 (pt); Speech therapists 1 (pt); Activities coordinators 1 (ft); Dietitians 1 (ft); Ophthalmologists 1 (pt); Podiatrists 1 (pt).
Facilities Dining room; Physical therapy room; Activities room; Crafts room; Laundry room; Barber/Beauty shop.
Activities Arts & crafts; Cards; Games; Reading groups; Prayer groups; Movies; Shopping trips; Social/Cultural gatherings.

Sikeston Manor Nursing Home
628 N West, Sikeston, MO, 63801
(314) 471-7130
Admin W Charles New. *Medical Dir/Dir of Nursing* Edwin J Masters MD.
Licensure Skilled care; Intermediate care. *Beds* 120. *Certified* Medicaid.
Owner Proprietary Corp (Beverly Enterprises).
Admissions Requirements Minimum age 21; Medical examination; Physician's request.
Staff Physicians 1 (pt); RNs 2 (ft); LPNs 4 (ft), 2 (pt); Nurses aides 74 (ft), 22 (pt); Physical therapists 1 (pt); Occupational therapists 1 (pt); Speech therapists 1 (pt); Activities coordinators 1 (ft), 1 (pt); Dietitians 1 (pt); Dentists 1 (pt).
Facilities Dining room; Physical therapy room; Activities room; Crafts room; Laundry room; Barber/Beauty shop; Library.
Activities Arts & crafts; Cards; Games; Reading groups; Prayer groups; Movies; Shopping trips; Social/Cultural gatherings.

SILEX

Rosedale Nursing Home*
Rte 1, Box 108, Silex, MO, 63377
(314) 384-5213
Admin Clarence E & Juanita L Beck. *Medical Dir/Dir of Nursing* Jose M A Navato MD.
Licensure Intermediate care. *Beds* 60.
Owner Proprietary Corp.
Admissions Requirements Minimum age 16; Medical examination; Physician's request.
Staff RNs 1 (ft); LPNs 2 (ft), 1 (pt); Nurses aides 7 (ft), 22 (pt); Activities coordinators 1 (ft).
Facilities Dining room; Physical therapy room; Activities room; Laundry room.
Activities Arts & crafts; Cards; Games; Reading groups; Prayer groups; Movies; Shopping trips; Social/Cultural gatherings.

SMITHVILLE

Smithville Convalescent Center
Box F, Smithville, MO, 64089
(816) 532-0888
Admin Gordon L Dille. *Medical Dir/Dir of Nursing* Jan Clark RN DON.
Licensure Skilled care; Intermediate care. *Beds* 120. *Certified* Medicaid; Medicare.
Owner Proprietary Corp (Beverly Enterprises).
Staff Physicians 1 (pt); RNs 5 (ft); LPNs 12 (ft); Orderlies 5 (ft); Nurses aides 45 (ft); Physical therapists 1 (pt); Reality therapists

1 (pt); Recreational therapists 2 (ft); Occupational therapists 1 (pt); Speech therapists 1 (pt); Activities coordinators 1 (ft); Dietitians 1 (pt); Ophthalmologists 1 (pt); Podiatrists 1 (pt).

SPRINGFIELD

Americana Fremont Healthcare Center
2915 S Fremont, Springfield, MO, 65804
(417) 883-4022
Admin Betty Luckie. *Medical Dir/Dir of Nursing* Stanley S Peterson MD; Anne Moore RN DON.
Licensure Skilled care; Intermediate care. *Beds* SNF 146; ICF; Residential I 40. *Certified* Medicaid; Medicare.
Owner Proprietary Corp (Manor Care).
Admissions Requirements Medical examination; Physician's request.
Staff Physicians 1 (pt); RNs 6 (ft); LPNs 20 (ft); Orderlies 4 (ft); Nurses aides 53 (ft), 4 (pt); Physical therapists 1 (pt); Recreational therapists 1 (pt); Occupational therapists 1 (pt); Speech therapists 1 (pt); Activities coordinators 1 (ft), 2 (pt); Dietitians 1 (ft); Ophthalmologists 1 (pt).
Facilities Dining room; Physical therapy room; Activities room; Chapel; Crafts room; Laundry room; Barber/Beauty shop; Library.
Activities Arts & crafts; Cards; Games; Reading groups; Prayer groups; Movies; Shopping trips; Social/Cultural gatherings; Service projects.

Cherry Care Centre Inc
1330 E Cherry St, Springfield, MO, 65802
(417) 862-3753
Admin John H Simmons. *Medical Dir/Dir of Nursing* Kay Simmons DON.
Licensure Intermediate care; Residential care. *Beds* ICF 56; Residential 10.
Owner Privately owned.
Admissions Requirements Minimum age 18; Medical examination.
Staff Physicians 1 (pt); RNs 1 (ft); LPNs 2 (ft), 6 (pt); Orderlies 2 (ft), 2 (pt); Nurses aides 3 (pt).
Languages French, Spanish, Tagalog
Facilities Dining room; Laundry room.
Activities Prayer groups.

Greene Haven
910 S West Ave, Springfield, MO, 65802
(417) 865-8741
Admin Bernard A Olson. *Medical Dir/Dir of Nursing* Richard T Honderick DO; Jill Beard RN.
Licensure Skilled care. *Beds* 120. *Certified* Medicaid.
Owner Nonprofit Corp.
Admissions Requirements Physician's request.
Staff Physicians 1 (pt); RNs 4 (ft); LPNs 11 (ft), 2 (pt); Orderlies 4 (ft), 1 (pt); Nurses aides 36 (ft), 5 (pt); Physical therapists 1 (pt); Occupational therapists 1 (pt); Speech therapists 1 (pt); Activities coordinators 1 (ft); Dietitians 1 (pt); Ophthalmologists 1 (pt).
Facilities Dining room; Physical therapy room; Activities room; Crafts room; Laundry room; Barber/Beauty shop.
Activities Arts & crafts; Cards; Games; Reading groups; Prayer groups; Movies; Shopping trips; Social/Cultural gatherings; Music; Van rides; Outings.

Heritage Manor of Springfield
2323 W Grand, Springfield, MO, 65802
(417) 862-7445
Admin Patricia Uhlis RN. *Medical Dir/Dir of Nursing* Charlotte Jenkins RN DON.
Licensure Skilled care; Intermediate care. *Beds* SNF 100; ICF.
Owner Proprietary Corp (National Heritage).
Admissions Requirements Medical examination.

Staff RNs 1 (ft); LPNs 9 (ft); Orderlies 2 (ft); Nurses aides 35 (ft), 2 (pt); Physical therapists 1 (pt); Activities coordinators 1 (ft); Dietitians 2 (pt); Ophthalmologists 1 (pt).
Facilities Dining room; Physical therapy room; Activities room; Crafts room; Laundry room; Barber/Beauty shop; Library Service.
Activities Arts & crafts; Cards; Games; Reading groups; Prayer groups; Movies; Shopping trips; Social/Cultural gatherings; Exercise groups; Pet therapy.

Kimbrough Nursing Home
519 Cherry, Springfield, MO, 65806
(417) 862-2109
Admin Jeanne Paris. *Medical Dir/Dir of Nursing* Cheryl McCall DON.
Licensure Intermediate care. *Beds* ICF 66.
Owner Proprietary Corp.
Admissions Requirements Medical examination.
Staff RNs; LPNs; Orderlies; Nurses aides; Activities coordinators.
Activities Games; Prayer groups.

Maranatha Manor*
233 E Norton, Springfield, MO, 65803
(417) 833-0016
Admin Charles W Davis. *Medical Dir/Dir of Nursing* K DeWayne Piker MD.
Licensure Skilled care; Intermediate care. *Beds* 180. *Certified* Medicaid.
Owner Nonprofit Corp.
Staff Physicians 2 (pt); RNs 2 (ft); LPNs 8 (ft), 3 (pt); Orderlies 7 (ft), 1 (pt); Nurses aides 55 (ft), 7 (pt); Physical therapists 1 (pt); Occupational therapists 1 (pt); Activities coordinators 1 (ft); Dietitians 1 (ft); Dentists 1 (pt).
Affiliation Assembly of God
Facilities Dining room; Physical therapy room; Activities room; Chapel; Crafts room; Laundry room; Barber/Beauty shop; Library.
Activities Arts & crafts; Games; Prayer groups; Shopping trips; Social/Cultural gatherings.

Medicenter—Springfield*
1911 S National, Springfield, MO, 65804
(417) 883-6521
Admin Charles L Yates.
Licensure Skilled care; Intermediate care. *Beds* 168. *Certified* Medicaid; Medicare.
Owner Proprietary Corp.

Mt Vernon Park Care Center*
3403 W Mount Vernon, Springfield, MO, 65802
(417) 866-3533
Admin Bill Foster.
Licensure Skilled care; Intermediate care. *Beds* 180. *Certified* Medicaid; Medicare.
Owner Proprietary Corp.

National Care Centers of America Inc
1610 N Broadway, Springfield, MO, 65803
(417) 866-3533
Admin Kaye Foster-Gibson. *Medical Dir/Dir of Nursing* Efriam Reyes MD; Cindy Foster RN DON.
Licensure Skilled care. *Beds* SNF 100. *Certified* Medicaid.
Owner Proprietary Corp.
Admissions Requirements Minimum age 16.
Staff Physicians 2 (pt); RNs 3 (ft); LPNs 7 (ft); Orderlies 2 (ft); Nurses aides 56 (ft), 4 (pt); Physical therapists 1 (pt); Recreational therapists 1 (pt); Occupational therapists 1 (pt); Speech therapists 1 (pt); Activities coordinators 1 (ft); Dietitians 1 (pt).
Facilities Dining room; Laundry room; Barber/Beauty shop.
Activities Arts & crafts; Games; Reading groups; Prayer groups; Movies; Shopping trips; Social/Cultural gatherings.

Northside Nursing Center
1347 E Valley Water Mill Rd, Springfield, MO, 65803
(417) 833-1220
Admin Leesa A Pendleton. *Medical Dir/Dir of Nursing* Dennis Morrison DO; Shirley Smith RN DON.
Licensure Skilled care. *Beds* SNF 180. *Certified* Medicaid; Medicare.
Owner Proprietary Corp.
Admissions Requirements Minimum age 18; Medical examination.
Staff Physicians 1 (ft); RNs 3 (ft), 1 (pt); LPNs 12 (ft), 2 (pt); Orderlies 22 (ft); Nurses aides 52 (ft); Activities coordinators 1 (ft).
Facilities Dining room; Physical therapy room; Activities room; Crafts room; Barber/Beauty shop; Movie/video room.
Activities Arts & crafts; Games; Movies; Shopping trips; Social/Cultural gatherings; Outings; Church; Bingo.

Primrose Place Health Care Inc
1115 E Primrose St, Springfield, MO, 65807
(417) 883-1546
Admin Sharon Warren. *Medical Dir/Dir of Nursing* Wayne Stine MD; Leveta Longley RN DON.
Licensure Skilled care. *Beds* 130.
Owner Nonprofit Corp.
Admissions Requirements Minimum age 18; Medical examination; Physician's request.
Staff Physicians 1 (pt); RNs 4 (ft), 1 (pt); LPNs 16 (ft), 5 (pt); Orderlies 12 (ft); Nurses aides 40 (ft), 5 (pt); Physical therapists 2 (pt); Reality therapists 1 (pt); Activities coordinators 1 (ft), 2 (pt); Dietitians 1 (ft), 1 (pt).
Facilities Dining room; Physical therapy room; Activities room; Crafts room; Laundry room; Barber/Beauty shop; Library; Senior walking course; Miniature golf course.
Activities Arts & crafts; Games; Reading groups; Movies; Shopping trips; Social/Cultural gatherings; Exercise groups.

St Johns Mercy Villa
1100 E Montclair, Springfield, MO, 65807
(417) 882-3992
Admin Donald Swafford. *Medical Dir/Dir of Nursing* W Timothy Wilson DO; Liz Tourville RN.
Licensure Skilled care. *Beds* SNF 150.
Owner Nonprofit organization/foundation.
Admissions Requirements Minimum age 18; Medical examination; Physician's request.
Staff Physicians 1 (pt); RNs 6 (ft), 2 (pt); LPNs 6 (ft); Nurses aides 40 (ft), 5 (pt); Physical therapists 1 (pt); Reality therapists 1 (pt); Recreational therapists 1 (pt); Occupational therapists 1 (pt); Speech therapists 1 (pt); Activities coordinators 1 (ft); Dietitians 1 (ft).
Affiliation Roman Catholic
Facilities Dining room; Physical therapy room; Activities room; Chapel; Crafts room; Laundry room; Barber/Beauty shop.
Activities Arts & crafts; Cards; Games; Reading groups; Prayer groups; Movies; Shopping trips; Social/Cultural gatherings; Pet therapy; Music therapy; Country store where residents sell crafts.

Springfield Health Care Center
PO Box 3438, 2800 S Fort St, Springfield, MO, 65807
(417) 882-0035
Admin Carolyn Smith. *Medical Dir/Dir of Nursing* Dr William Rosen MD; Sherlyn Show RN.
Licensure Skilled care. *Beds* 120. *Certified* Medicaid; Medicare.
Owner Proprietary Corp (National Health Corp).
Staff RNs 2 (ft), 2 (pt); LPNs 13 (ft); Physical therapists 1 (ft); Activities coordinators 1 (ft), 1 (pt); Dietitians 1 (pt).

Springfield Rest Home
2323 W Grand, Springfield, MO, 65802
(417) 862-7445
Admin Patricia J Uhlis.
Licensure Intermediate care. *Beds* 100.
Admissions Requirements Medical
examination.
Staff RNs 1 (ft); LPNs 8 (ft); Nurses aides 30
(ft), 2 (pt); Activities coordinators 1 (ft);
Dietitians 1 (pt).
Facilities Dining room; Physical therapy
room; Activities room; Crafts room; Laundry
room; Barber/Beauty shop.
Activities Arts & crafts; Cards; Games;
Reading groups; Prayer groups; Movies.

Mary E Wilson Home for the Aged
924 N Main, Springfield, MO, 65802
(417) 869-7236
Admin Nancy Blankenship. *Medical Dir/Dir of
Nursing* Diane Hardin RN DON.
Licensure Residential care II. *Beds* 28.
Owner Nonprofit organization/foundation.
Admissions Requirements Females only;
Medical examination.
Staff RNs 1 (pt); Nurses aides 6 (ft), 3 (pt);
Recreational therapists 1 (pt); Activities
coordinators 1 (pt).
Facilities Dining room; Activities room;
Crafts room; Laundry room; Barber/Beauty
shop; Library.
Activities Arts & crafts; Games; Prayer groups.

STANBERRY

Concerned Services Inc
PO Box 6, RR 2, Stanberry, MO, 64489
(816) 783-2897
Admin Benjamin Rogers.
Licensure Intermediate care for mentally
retarded. *Beds* ICF/MR 9. *Certified*
Medicaid.
Owner Proprietary Corp.
Admissions Requirements Minimum age 16;
Medical examination.
Facilities Dining room; Activities room;
Laundry room.
Activities Arts & crafts; Games; Movies;
Shopping trips; Social/Cultural gatherings.

Pine View Manor Inc
Rte 2, Stanberry, MO, 64489
(816) 783-2118
Admin Robert L Adams. *Medical Dir/Dir of
Nursing* Dr A L Carlin; Betty Wilson.
Licensure Intermediate care. *Beds* 80.
Certified Medicaid.
Owner Publicly owned.
Admissions Requirements Physician's request.
Staff LPNs 6 (ft); Orderlies 1 (ft); Nurses
aides 25 (ft); Activities coordinators 1 (ft).
Affiliation Lutheran
Facilities Dining room; Physical therapy
room; Activities room; Chapel; Laundry
room; Barber/Beauty shop.
Activities Games; Reading groups; Prayer
groups; Movies; Bingo.

STEELE

River Oaks Nursing Home
Box 247, Hwy 164, Steele, MO, 63877
(314) 695-2121
Admin Marvin Haynes.
Licensure Skilled care. *Beds* SNF 90. *Certified*
Medicaid; Medicare.
Owner Proprietary Corp.
Admissions Requirements Minimum age 18;
Medical examination.
Staff Physicians 3 (pt); RNs 4 (ft); LPNs 8
(ft); Orderlies 2 (ft); Nurses aides 30 (ft);
Physical therapists 1 (pt); Recreational
therapists 1 (pt); Occupational therapists 1
(pt); Speech therapists 1 (pt); Activities
coordinators 1 (ft); Dietitians 1 (pt).

Facilities Dining room; Physical therapy
room; Laundry room; Barber/Beauty shop.
Activities Arts & crafts; Cards; Games;
Reading groups; Prayer groups; Movies;
Shopping trips; Social/Cultural gatherings.

STEELVILLE

Gibbs Care Center
Rte 2, Box 590, Steelville, MO, 65565
(314) 775-5815
Admin Phillip C Marzluf. *Medical Dir/Dir of
Nursing* Mike Elders MD; Mary Major
DON.
Licensure Intermediate care; RCF II. *Beds*
ICF 60; RCF II 24. *Certified* Medicaid.
Owner Nonprofit Corp.
Admissions Requirements Minimum age 21;
Medical examination.
Staff RNs 1 (ft); LPNs 3 (ft), 1 (pt); Nurses
aides 24 (ft), 2 (pt); Activities coordinators 1
(ft).
Facilities Dining room; Physical therapy
room; Activities room; Chapel; Crafts room;
Laundry room; Barber/Beauty shop; Library.
Activities Arts & crafts; Cards; Games; Prayer
groups; Movies; Shopping trips.

STOCKTON

Stockton Nursing Home Inc*
Drawer W, Stockton, MO, 65785
(417) 276-5126
Admin Gilbert W York.
Licensure Intermediate care. *Beds* 120.
Certified Medicaid.
Owner Nonprofit Corp.
Admissions Requirements Minimum age 18.
Staff RNs 1 (ft); LPNs 3 (ft), 2 (pt); Orderlies
2 (ft); Nurses aides 45 (ft), 8 (pt); Activities
coordinators 2 (pt).
Facilities Dining room; Activities room;
Crafts room; Laundry room; Barber/Beauty
shop; Library.
Activities Arts & crafts; Cards; Games;
Reading groups; Movies.

STOVER

Golden Age Nursing Home District 1
3rd & Mimosa Sts, Stover, MO, 65078
(314) 377-4521
Admin Rosalie Craig. *Medical Dir/Dir of
Nursing* Rose Suttmoller.
Licensure Intermediate care. *Beds* ICF 60.
Certified Medicaid.
Owner Nonprofit Corp.
Admissions Requirements Minimum age 21;
Medical examination; Physician's request.
Staff Physicians 1 (pt); RNs 1 (pt); LPNs 3
(ft), 2 (pt); Orderlies 1 (ft); Nurses aides 15
(ft), 10 (pt); Physical therapists 1 (pt);
Recreational therapists 1 (ft); Activities
coordinators 1 (ft); Dietitians 1 (ft).
Languages German
Facilities Dining room; Activities room;
Crafts room; Laundry room; Barber/Beauty
shop.
Activities Arts & crafts; Cards; Games;
Reading groups; Prayer groups; Movies.

SULLIVAN

Ridgeway Nursing Home
PO Box 267, 431 Russell Rd, Sullivan, MO,
63080
(314) 468-4318
Admin Joy J DeLuca.
Licensure RCF II. *Beds* 20.
Owner Privately owned.
Admissions Requirements Minimum age 21;
Medical examination.
Staff Physicians 1 (pt); LPNs 1 (pt); Nurses
aides 3 (ft), 1 (pt); Activities coordinators 1
(ft).

Facilities Activities room; Crafts room;
Laundry room.
Activities Arts & crafts; Cards; Games;
Reading groups; Movies; Shopping trips.

Sullivan Nursing Center
Dunsford Dr, Sullivan, MO, 63080
(314) 468-3128
Admin Joyce Oberle.
Licensure Skilled care; Intermediate care. *Beds*
120. *Certified* Medicaid.
Owner Proprietary Corp (Beverly Enterprises).

SWEET SPRINGS

Sweet Springs Caring Center
518 E Marshall, Sweet Springs, MO, 65351
(816) 335-6391
Admin Bobby F Reed Jr. *Medical Dir/Dir of
Nursing* Dorothy Bertrand RN DON.
Licensure Skilled care; Intermediate care. *Beds*
100. *Certified* Medicaid; Medicare.
Owner Proprietary Corp.
Admissions Requirements Minimum age 17;
Medical examination.
Staff RNs 2 (ft); LPNs 9 (ft), 1 (pt); Nurses
aides 21 (ft), 4 (pt); Activities coordinators 1
(ft), 1 (pt); Dietitians 1 (pt).
Facilities Dining room; Activities room;
Laundry room; Barber/Beauty shop.
Activities Arts & crafts; Cards; Games;
Reading groups; Movies; Shopping trips;
Social/Cultural gatherings; Bible study;
Church; Exercise groups.

TARKIO

Bethesda Care Center
N 3rd & Cedar Sts, Tarkio, MO, 64491
(816) 736-4116
Admin Bernard F Correll. *Medical Dir/Dir of
Nursing* Dr E F Bare; Carol Walter.
Licensure Intermediate care for mentally
retarded. *Beds* ICF/MR 95. *Certified*
Medicaid.
Owner Nonprofit Corp (Bethesda Care
Centers).
Staff RNs 1 (ft); LPNs 3 (ft), 2 (pt); Nurses
aides 25 (ft), 5 (pt); Physical therapists 1
(pt); Activities coordinators 1 (ft), 1 (pt);
Dietitians 1 (ft).
Facilities Dining room; Physical therapy
room; Activities room; Chapel; Laundry
room; Barber/Beauty shop.
Activities Arts & crafts; Cards; Games;
Reading groups; Prayer groups; Movies;
Shopping trips; Social/Cultural gatherings.

THAYER

Chastain's of Thayer Inc*
PO Box 77, Hwy 142 at 8th St, Thayer, MO,
65791
(417) 264-7256
Admin Phyllis Stayton.
Licensure Intermediate care. *Beds* 120.
Certified Medicaid.
Owner Proprietary Corp.

TIPTON

Tipton Manor
W Morgan St, PO Box 599, Tipton, MO,
65081
(816) 433-5574
Admin John Arth. *Medical Dir/Dir of Nursing*
Johannes Schokker MD.
Licensure Intermediate care. *Beds* 60.
Certified Medicaid.
Owner Nonprofit Corp.
Admissions Requirements Minimum age 16;
Medical examination; Physician's request.

Staff RNs 1 (ft); LPNs 3 (ft); Orderlies 2 (ft); Nurses aides 22 (ft); Physical therapists 1 (pt); Occupational therapists 1 (pt); Speech therapists 1 (pt); Activities coordinators 1 (ft); Dietitians 1 (pt); Dentists 1 (pt).
Facilities Dining room; Physical therapy room; Activities room; Laundry room; Barber/Beauty shop.
Activities Arts & crafts; Cards; Games; Reading groups; Prayer groups; Movies; Shopping trips.

TRENTON

Eastview Manor Care Center
1622 E 28th St, Trenton, MO, 64683
(816) 359-2251
Admin Mildred Linhart. Medical Dir/Dir of Nursing Donna Grisamore.
Licensure Skilled care. Beds SNF 90; ICF. Certified Medicaid.
Owner Proprietary Corp.
Admissions Requirements Minimum age 21; Medical examination; Physician's request.
Staff RNs 1 (ft), 2 (pt); LPNs 1 (ft), 7 (pt); Nurses aides 23 (ft), 19 (pt); Physical therapists 1 (ft), 1 (pt); Occupational therapists 1 (ft), 1 (pt); Speech therapists 1 (pt); Activities coordinators 1 (ft); Dietitians 1 (ft); Podiatrists 1 (pt).
Facilities Dining room; Physical therapy room; Activities room; Crafts room; Laundry room; Barber/Beauty shop.
Activities Arts & crafts; Cards; Games; Reading groups; Prayer groups; Movies.

Sunnyview Nursing Home & Apartments
1311 E 28th St, Trenton, MO, 64683
(816) 359-5647
Admin Brenda Thexton.
Licensure Skilled care. Beds SNF 154; Residential care apartments 30. Certified Medicaid.
Owner Publicly owned.
Admissions Requirements Minimum age 16.
Staff RNs 4 (ft); LPNs 7 (ft), 1 (pt); Nurses aides 49 (ft), 16 (pt); Physical therapists 1 (pt); Occupational therapists 1 (pt); Speech therapists 1 (pt); Activities coordinators 3 (ft); Dietitians 1 (pt); Podiatrists 1 (pt); Social service director 1 (ft).
Facilities Dining room; Physical therapy room; Chapel; Barber/Beauty shop; Living rooms; Lift van transportation.
Activities Prayer groups; Movies; Sheltered workshop, Cooking classes.

TROY

Medicalodge of Troy
RR1 Box 605, 200 Thompson Dr, Troy, MO, 63379
(314) 528-8446
Admin Joyce Hopkins. Medical Dir/Dir of Nursing Donald Mogerman DO; Debra Herps RN DON.
Licensure Skilled care. Beds SNF 120.
Owner Proprietary Corp (Medicalodges).
Staff RNs 3 (ft); LPNs 10 (ft); Nurses aides 60 (ft); Physical therapists 1 (ft), 1 (pt); Occupational therapists 1 (pt); Speech therapists 1 (pt); Activities coordinators 2 (ft); Dietitians 1 (pt).
Facilities Dining room; Physical therapy room; Activities room; Chapel; Crafts room; Laundry room; Barber/Beauty shop.
Activities Arts & crafts; Cards; Games; Reading groups; Prayer groups; Shopping trips; Social/Cultural gatherings.

Troy House Inc
PO Box 271, 350 Cap-au-Gris, Troy, MO, 63379-0271
(314) 528-4915
Admin Betty O Wermuth.
Licensure Residential care. Beds 15.
Owner Proprietary Corp.

TUSCUMBIA

Miller County Nursing Home
PO Box 20, Star Rte, Tuscumbia, MO, 65082
(314) 369-2318
Admin Beulah Cotten. Medical Dir/Dir of Nursing Holly Martin.
Licensure Intermediate care. Beds ICF 60. Certified Medicaid.
Owner Nonprofit organization/foundation.
Admissions Requirements Minimum age 18; Medical examination.
Staff RNs 1 (pt); LPNs 5 (ft); Nurses aides 19 (ft); Physical therapists 1 (ft); Activities coordinators 1 (ft); Dietitians 1 (ft).
Facilities Dining room; Physical therapy room; Activities room; Chapel; Crafts room; Laundry room; Barber/Beauty shop.
Activities Arts & crafts; Cards; Games; Reading groups; Prayer groups; Movies; Social/Cultural gatherings; Yearly carnival; Dress up days; Birthday parties.

UNION

Sunset Nursing & Retirement Home of Union
400 W Park Ave, Union, MO, 63084
(314) 583-2252
Admin Ronald F Davis. Medical Dir/Dir of Nursing Donald L Baker MD; Delores M Muisket LPN DON.
Licensure Intermediate care. Beds ICF 165. Certified Medicaid.
Owner Proprietary Corp.
Admissions Requirements Minimum age 19; Medical examination.
Staff Physicians 1 (pt); RNs 1 (pt); LPNs 6 (ft), 2 (pt); Nurses aides 60 (ft), 1 (pt); Physical therapists 1 (pt); Reality therapists 5 (ft); Recreational therapists 1 (pt); Occupational therapists 1 (pt); Activities coordinators 2 (ft); Dietitians 1 (pt); Psychiatrist 1 (pt).
Languages Sign, German
Facilities Dining room; Physical therapy room; Activities room; Chapel; Crafts room; Laundry room; Barber/Beauty shop; Library; TV rooms; Outside patios; Covered porches.
Activities Arts & crafts; Cards; Games; Reading groups; Prayer groups; Movies; Shopping trips; Social/Cultural gatherings; Outings.

UNIONVILLE

Putnam County Nursing Home
1814 Oak, Unionville, MO, 63565
(816) 947-2492 947-2493
Admin Nancy J Dory. Medical Dir/Dir of Nursing Mark O'Brien.
Licensure Intermediate care. Beds ICF 46. Certified Medicaid.
Owner Nonprofit organization/foundation.
Admissions Requirements Medical examination.
Staff Physicians; RNs; LPNs; Nurses aides; Physical therapists; Occupational therapists; Speech therapists; Activities coordinators; Dietitians.
Facilities Dining room; Physical therapy room; Activities room; Barber/Beauty shop.
Activities Arts & crafts; Cards; Games; Prayer groups; Movies; Shopping trips.

UNIVERSITY CITY

Delmar Gardens East Inc*
894 Leland, University City, MO, 63130
(314) 726-4767
Admin Florine Korlin.
Licensure Skilled care; Intermediate care. Beds 128. Certified Medicaid; Medicare.
Owner Proprietary Corp.

VALLEY PARK

Cedarcroft Nursing Home
110 Highland Ave, Valley Park, MO, 63088
(314) 225-5144
Admin Gloria J Osbourn. Medical Dir/Dir of Nursing Conrad Abinoja MD; Mary Jo Maple RN DON.
Licensure Skilled care; Intermediate care; Intermediate care for mentally retarded. Beds SNF 176; ICF 176; ICF/MR 176. Certified Medicaid; Medicare.
Owner Proprietary Corp.
Admissions Requirements Minimum age 21; Medical examination; Physician's request.
Staff Physicians 20 (pt); RNs 6 (ft), 2 (pt); LPNs 10 (ft); Orderlies 4 (ft); Nurses aides 70 (ft); Physical therapists 1 (pt); Reality therapists 1 (pt); Recreational therapists 3 (ft); Occupational therapists 1 (pt); Speech therapists 1 (pt); Activities coordinators 1 (ft); Dietitians 2 (ft), 1 (pt); Dentists 1 (pt); Ophthalmologists 1 (pt); Podiatrists 1 (pt).
Facilities Dining room; Physical therapy room; Activities room; Chapel; Crafts room; Laundry room; Barber/Beauty shop; Library.
Activities Arts & crafts; Cards; Games; Prayer groups; Movies; Social/Cultural gatherings.

Valley Park Nursing Home*
332 Benton Ave, Valley Park, MO, 63088
(314) 225-5105
Admin Barbara Branson Rikard.
Licensure Intermediate care. Beds 76. Certified Medicaid.
Owner Proprietary Corp.

VAN BUREN

Riverways Manor Nursing Home*
PO Box 116, Van Buren, MO, 63965
(314) 323-4282
Admin Helen Jackson.
Licensure Intermediate care. Beds 60. Certified Medicaid.
Owner Proprietary Corp (Angell Group).

VANDALIA

Country Side Manor
1415 E Hwy 54, Vandalia, MO, 63382
(314) 594-6215
Admin Virginia Walker. Medical Dir/Dir of Nursing Virginia Walker.
Licensure RCF II. Beds 18. Certified Medicaid.
Owner Privately owned.
Admissions Requirements Minimum age 18; Medical examination.
Staff RNs 1 (pt); LPNs 1 (pt); Nurses aides 3 (ft), 4 (pt).
Facilities Dining room; Laundry room; Barber/Beauty shop; Library.
Activities Games; Prayer groups; Movies; Shopping trips.

Tri County Nursing Home
601 N Galloway Rd, Vandalia, MO, 63382
(314) 594-6468
Admin Shirley Whetstine. Medical Dir/Dir of Nursing Rex D Carter DO; Cathy James DON.
Licensure Intermediate care. Beds ICF 60. Certified Medicaid.
Owner Publicly owned.
Admissions Requirements Minimum age 16; Medical examination.
Staff Physicians 4 (pt); RNs 1 (pt); LPNs 7 (ft); Orderlies 2 (pt); Nurses aides 20 (ft), 13 (pt); Physical therapists 1 (pt); Occupational therapists 1 (pt); Speech therapists 1 (pt); Activities coordinators 1 (ft), 1 (pt); Dietitians 1 (ft), 1 (pt).
Facilities Dining room; Physical therapy room; Chapel; Laundry room; Barber/Beauty shop.

Activities Arts & crafts; Cards; Games; Reading groups; Prayer groups; Movies; Shopping trips; Social/Cultural gatherings; Bus rides; Carry-in smorgasbords (every 3 months with families).

VERSAILLES

Good Shepherd Nursing Home
PO Box M, Fairground Rd, Versailles, MO, 65084
(314) 378-5411
Admin Dolores Jones. *Medical Dir/Dir of Nursing* Ruth Kauffman.
Licensure Skilled care; Intermediate care. *Beds* 120.
Owner Proprietary Corp.
Admissions Requirements Minimum age 16.
Staff Physicians 3 (pt); RNs 3 (ft); LPNs 7 (ft); Orderlies 3 (ft); Physical therapists 1 (ft); Recreational therapists 1 (pt); Occupational therapists 1 (pt); Speech therapists 1 (pt); Activities coordinators 1 (ft); Dietitians 1 (pt); Dentists 1 (pt); Ophthalmologists 1 (pt); Podiatrists 1 (pt).
Facilities Dining room; Physical therapy room; Activities room; Chapel; Crafts room; Laundry room; Barber/Beauty shop; Library.
Activities Arts & crafts; Games; Reading groups; Prayer groups; Movies; Shopping trips; Social/Cultural gatherings.

WARRENSBURG

Messick Nursing Home Inc*
122 E Market, Warrensburg, MO, 64093
(816) 747-8101
Admin Valerie Whiteman.
Licensure Intermediate care. *Beds* 87.
Certified Medicaid.
Owner Proprietary Corp.
Staff Physicians 1 (ft); RNs 1 (ft); LPNs 3 (ft), 2 (pt); Nurses aides 30 (ft); Physical therapists 1 (ft); Recreational therapists 1 (ft); Occupational therapists 1 (ft); Speech therapists 1 (ft); Activities coordinators 1 (ft); Dietitians 1 (ft); Dentists 1 (pt); Podiatrists 1 (pt); Audiologists 1 (pt).
Facilities Dining room; Physical therapy room; Activities room; Laundry room; Barber/Beauty shop.
Activities Arts & crafts; Cards; Games; Prayer groups; Movies; Social/Cultural gatherings.

Pleasantview Care Center
Rte 2, Hwy 50 E, Warrensburg, MO, 64093
(816) 747-6457
Admin Ethel L Jackson. *Medical Dir/Dir of Nursing* Robert LaHue DO.
Licensure Intermediate care; Residential care. *Beds* ICF 41; Residential 11.
Owner Proprietary Corp.
Admissions Requirements Minimum age 18; Medical examination.
Staff RNs 1 (pt); LPNs 2 (pt); Orderlies 4 (ft); Nurses aides 10 (ft), 3 (pt); Activities coordinators 1 (ft).
Facilities Dining room; Activities room; Laundry room.
Activities Arts & crafts; Cards; Games; Reading groups; Prayer groups; Movies; Shopping trips; Social/Cultural gatherings; Field trips.

Ridge Crest Adult Care Center*
706 S Mitchell, Warrensburg, MO, 64093
(816) 429-2177
Admin Ivan R Wilson.
Licensure Skilled care; Intermediate care. *Beds* 120. *Certified* Medicaid.
Owner Proprietary Corp (Beverly Enterprises).

Warrensburg Manor Care Center
East Gay St & Manor Dr, Warrensburg, MO, 64093
(816) 747-2216, 747-2217

Admin Melba A Jones. *Medical Dir/Dir of Nursing* Doris Newkirk LPN.
Licensure Intermediate care. *Beds* ICF 52.
Owner Proprietary Corp.
Admissions Requirements Minimum age 20; Medical examination.
Staff RNs 1 (pt); LPNs 2 (ft), 2 (pt); Nurses aides 18 (ft), 2 (pt); Activities coordinators 1 (pt); Dietitians 1 (pt); Office staff 1 (ft); Dietary staff 3 (ft), 5 (pt); Housekeeper 3 (ft), 1 (pt); Maintenance 1 (ft), 1 (pt).
Facilities Dining room; Laundry room; Barber/Beauty shop.
Activities Arts & crafts; Games.

WARRENTON

Fellowship Nursing Home
Hwy AA, Warrenton, MO, 63383
(314) 456-4183
Admin Charlotte M Fink. *Medical Dir/Dir of Nursing* Dr M Baig.
Licensure Skilled care. *Beds* SNF 120.
Certified Medicaid; Medicare.
Owner Proprietary Corp.
Admissions Requirements Minimum age 18; Medical examination; Physician's request.
Staff Physicians 5 (pt); RNs 4 (ft), 3 (pt); LPNs 6 (ft), 4 (pt); Nurses aides 70 (ft), 12 (pt); Physical therapists 1 (pt); Occupational therapists 1 (pt); Speech therapists 1 (pt); Activities coordinators 3 (ft); Dietitians 1 (pt); Podiatrists 1 (pt).
Facilities Dining room; Physical therapy room; Activities room; Laundry room; Barber/Beauty shop.
Activities Arts & crafts; Cards; Games; Reading groups; Prayer groups; Movies; Shopping trips; Social/Cultural gatherings.

Katie Jane Memorial Home
PO Box 160, 607 E Main St, Warrenton, MO, 63383
(314) 456-3401, 456-2566
Admin Thomas A Daniels. *Medical Dir/Dir of Nursing* J O'Conner MD; Bonnie Hune DON.
Licensure Intermediate care. *Beds* ICF 75.
Owner Proprietary Corp.
Admissions Requirements Minimum age 21.
Staff Physicians 4 (pt); RNs 1 (pt); LPNs 3 (ft); Orderlies 1 (ft); Nurses aides 16 (ft), 6 (pt); Activities coordinators 1 (ft); Dietitians Dietary Aides 3 (ft), 2 (pt).
Facilities Activities room; Laundry room.
Activities Arts & crafts; Cards; Games; Reading groups; Prayer groups; Social/Cultural gatherings.

West Boarding Home
707 E Boonslick Rd, Warrenton, MO, 63383
(314) 456-2290
Admin Donald D West.
Licensure RCF I. *Beds* 34. *Certified* Medicaid.
Owner Privately owned.
Admissions Requirements Minimum age 18; Medical examination.
Staff Nurses aides.
Facilities Dining room; Activities room; Chapel; Crafts room; Laundry room.
Activities Arts & crafts; Games; Prayer groups.

WARSAW

Oakhaven Manor
810 Kennedy Dr, Warsaw, MO, 65355
(816) 438-5135
Admin Glenda Foster. *Medical Dir/Dir of Nursing* Julie Fletcher.
Licensure Intermediate care. *Beds* ICF 35.
Owner Proprietary Corp.
Admissions Requirements Minimum age 18.

Staff Physicians 3 (ft); RNs 2 (pt); LPNs 1 (ft); Orderlies 2 (ft); Nurses aides 8 (ft); Physical therapists 1 (pt); Activities coordinators 1 (ft); Dietitians 1 (pt); CMT 2 (ft), 1 (pt); Dentist 1 (pt).
Facilities Dining room; Barber/Beauty shop.
Activities Arts & crafts; Cards; Games; Prayer groups; Social/Cultural gatherings.

WASHINGTON

Cedarcrest Manor Inc
324 W 5th St, Washington, MO, 63090
(314) 239-7848
Admin Edward R Maschmann. *Medical Dir/Dir of Nursing* Dr Kenneth Smith MD, Dr David Brunworth MD; Mary Ann Newbanks DON.
Licensure Skilled care. *Beds* SNF 184.
Certified Medicaid; Medicare.
Owner Privately owned.
Admissions Requirements Minimum age 16; Medical examination; Physician's request.
Staff Physicians 2 (pt); RNs 6 (ft), 2 (pt); LPNs 9 (ft), 1 (pt); Nurses aides 60 (ft), 15 (pt); Physical therapists 3 (ft); Recreational therapists 2 (ft); Speech therapists 1 (pt); Activities coordinators 2 (ft); Dietitians 1 (pt); Ophthalmologists 1 (pt).
Languages German
Facilities Dining room; Physical therapy room; Activities room; Chapel; Crafts room; Laundry room; Barber/Beauty shop.
Activities Arts & crafts; Cards; Games; Reading groups; Prayer groups; Movies; Shopping trips; Social/Cultural gatherings.

WAVERLY

Riverview Heights Nursing Home*
Box 181, Waverly, MO, 64096
(816) 493-2232
Admin Gordon L Dille. *Medical Dir/Dir of Nursing* Dr Gene McFadden.
Licensure Intermediate care. *Beds* 60.
Certified Medicaid.
Owner Proprietary Corp (Beverly Enterprises).
Staff Physicians 1 (pt); RNs 1 (ft); LPNs 5 (ft); Orderlies 1 (ft); Nurses aides 26 (ft); Physical therapists 1 (pt); Reality therapists 1 (pt); Recreational therapists 1 (pt); Occupational therapists 1 (pt); Speech therapists 1 (pt); Activities coordinators 1 (ft); Dietitians 1 (pt); Dentists 1 (pt); Podiatrists 1 (pt); Audiologists 1 (pt).
Facilities Dining room; Physical therapy room; Activities room; Chapel; Crafts room; Laundry room; Barber/Beauty shop.
Activities Arts & crafts; Cards; Games; Reading groups; Prayer groups; Movies; Social/Cultural gatherings.

WAYNESVILLE

Sunset Village of the Ozarks
PO Box 60, Rte 2, Waynesville, MO, 65583
(314) 336-4322
Admin Pan Opperman. *Medical Dir/Dir of Nursing* C R Jenkins MD; Joy Petrich RN DON.
Licensure Skilled care; Intermediate care. *Beds* SNF 33; ICF. *Certified* Medicaid; Medicare.
Owner Privately owned Partnership.
Admissions Requirements Minimum age 18; Medical examination; Physician's request.
Staff Physicians 1 (ft); RNs 2 (ft), 4 (pt); LPNs 4 (ft), 2 (pt); Nurses aides 13 (ft); Physical therapists 1 (pt); Occupational therapists 1 (pt); Speech therapists 1 (pt); Activities coordinators 1 (pt); Dietitians 1 (pt); Dentists 1 (pt); Ophthalmologists 1 (pt); Dentist 1 (pt); Pharmacist 1 (pt).
Facilities Dining room; Physical therapy room; Activities room; Chapel; Laundry room; Barber/Beauty shop; Library; Indoor pool; Workshop.

Activities Arts & crafts; Cards; Games; Prayer groups; Movies; Shopping trips; Social/ Cultural gatherings; Tours.

Waynesville Nursing Center*
700 Birch Ln, Waynesville, MO, 65583
(314) 774-6456
Admin Jerry Snobl.
Licensure Skilled care; Intermediate care. *Beds* 120. *Certified* Medicaid.
Owner Proprietary Corp (Beverly Enterprises).

WEBB CITY

Country Living Residential Care
710 Cardinal Dr, Webb City, MO, 64870
(417) 673-5559
Admin Wes Watkins. *Medical Dir/Dir of Nursing* Kathy Watkins.
Licensure Residential care facility Level I. *Beds* 10. *Certified* Medicaid.
Owner Privately owned.
Admissions Requirements Females only.
Staff LPNs 1 (ft); Nurses aides 2 (pt).
Facilities Dining room; Laundry room.
Activities Cards; Games; Prayer groups.

Elmhurst Nursing Home*
Rte 1, Box 100-C, Webb City, MO, 64870
(417) 673-4626
Admin Larry G Cole. *Medical Dir/Dir of Nursing* Robert Ferguson MD.
Licensure Skilled care. *Beds* 144.
Owner Nonprofit Corp.
Admissions Requirements Minimum age 21; Medical examination.
Staff RNs 2 (ft); LPNs 14 (ft); Orderlies 4 (ft); Nurses aides 48 (ft), 4 (pt); Physical therapists 1 (pt); Speech therapists 1 (pt); Activities coordinators 3 (ft); Dietitians 1 (pt).
Facilities Dining room; Physical therapy room; Activities room; Chapel; Crafts room; Laundry room; Barber/Beauty shop; Patio.
Activities Arts & crafts; Cards; Games; Reading groups; Prayer groups; Movies; Shopping trips; Social/Cultural gatherings; Adult basic education.

WEBSTER GROVE

Lutheran Health Care Association Extended Care Facility
723 S Laclede Station Rd, Webster Grove, MO, 63119
(314) 968-5570
Admin Patricia A Woodward NHA. *Medical Dir/Dir of Nursing* Sharon Rullkoeter RN DON.
Licensure Skilled care; Intermediate care. *Beds* SNF 143; ICF; RCF 15. *Certified* Medicaid.
Owner Nonprofit organization/foundation.
Admissions Requirements Medical examination.
Staff Physicians 1 (ft); RNs 11 (ft), 6 (pt); LPNs 10 (ft), 1 (pt); Nurses aides 35 (ft), 45 (pt); Physical therapists 1 (ft), 2 (pt); Recreational therapists 1 (ft); Speech therapists 1 (pt); Activities coordinators 1 (ft), 1 (pt); Dietitians 1 (ft), 1 (pt); Dentists 1 (pt); Ophthalmologists 1 (pt).
Affiliation Lutheran
Facilities Dining room; Physical therapy room; Activities room; Chapel; Crafts room; Laundry room; Barber/Beauty shop; Library.

Activities Arts & crafts; Games; Reading groups; Prayer groups; Movies; BBQs; Musical Events.

WELLSTON

Rockwood Manor Nursing Home Inc*
6470 Plymouth Ave, Wellston, MO, 63133
(314) 726-0306
Admin Thelma Craig.
Licensure Intermediate care. *Beds* 36.
Owner Proprietary Corp.

WELLSVILLE

Gamma Road Lodge*
250 Gamma Rd, Wellsville, MO, 63384
(314) 684-2002
Admin Fay Walden. *Medical Dir/Dir of Nursing* Donald Shoup DO.
Licensure Skilled care. *Beds* 120. *Certified* Medicaid.
Owner Proprietary Corp (Beverly Enterprises).
Admissions Requirements Medical examination; Physician's request.
Staff Physicians 3 (ft); RNs 4 (ft); Nurses aides 2 (ft); Nurses aides 33 (ft), 23 (pt); Physical therapists 1 (ft), 1 (pt); Recreational therapists 1 (ft); Occupational therapists 1 (pt); Speech therapists 1 (pt); Dietitians 1 (ft); Dentists 1 (pt).
Facilities Dining room; Physical therapy room; Activities room; Chapel; Crafts room; Laundry room; Barber/Beauty shop; Library.
Activities Arts & crafts; Cards; Games; Reading groups; Prayer groups; Movies; Shopping trips; Monthly birthday parties.

WENTZVILLE

Mar-Le Nursing Home*
401 Mar-Le Dr, Wentzville, MO, 63385
(314) 327-5274
Admin Dave Richardson.
Licensure Skilled care. *Beds* 120.
Owner Proprietary Corp.

WEST PLAINS

Ozark Nursing Center
1410 Kentucky St, West Plains, MO, 65775
(417) 256-7975
Admin Barbara Young.
Licensure Skilled care. *Beds* 120.
Owner Proprietary Corp (Beverly Enterprises).

West Plains Nursing Home*
919 Grace Ave, West Plains, MO, 65775
Admin V Walene O'Dell & Paganini Baet.
Licensure Intermediate care for mentally retarded. *Beds* 25. *Certified* Medicaid; Medicare.
Admissions Requirements Minimum age 21; Medical examination; Physician's request.
Staff Physicians 2 (pt); LPNs 1 (pt); Nurses aides 5 (ft); Activities coordinators 1 (pt); Dietitians 1 (pt); Dentists 1 (pt).
Facilities Dining room; Activities room; Laundry room.
Activities Cards; Games; Prayer groups; Shopping trips.

West Vue Home Inc
909 Kentucky St, West Plains, MO, 65775
(417) 256-2152
Admin Warren Fletcher. *Medical Dir/Dir of Nursing* M L Fowler MD; Ruth Fletcher RN DON.
Licensure Skilled care; Intermediate care; Residential apartments. *Beds* 191. *Certified* Medicaid; Medicare.
Owner Nonprofit Corp.
Admissions Requirements Medical examination; Physician's request.
Staff Physicians 1 (pt); RNs 6 (ft); LPNs 10 (ft), 2 (pt); Orderlies 2 (ft); Nurses aides 65 (ft); Physical therapists 1 (pt); Occupational therapists 1 (pt); Speech therapists 1 (pt); Activities coordinators 2 (ft); Dietitians 1 (pt); Dentists 1 (pt); Podiatrists 1 (pt).
Affiliation Baptist
Facilities Dining room; Physical therapy room; Activities room; Crafts room; Laundry room; Barber/Beauty shop.
Activities Arts & crafts; Cards; Games; Reading groups; Prayer groups; Movies; Shopping trips; Social/Cultural gatherings; Adult education.

WILLOW SPRINGS

Willow Care Nursing Home
PO Box 309, S Hwy 76, Willow Springs, MO, 65793
(417) 469-3152
Admin Jack Whitaker. *Medical Dir/Dir of Nursing* C F Smith MD; Barbara Murphy RN DON.
Licensure Skilled care; RCF II. *Beds* SNF 120; RCF II 24. *Certified* Medicaid.
Owner Nonprofit Corp.
Admissions Requirements Minimum age 16; Medical examination; Physician's request.
Staff Physicians 6 (pt); RNs 6 (ft); LPNs 11 (ft); Nurses aides 74 (ft); Physical therapists 1 (ft), 1 (pt); Occupational therapists 1 (pt); Speech therapists 1 (ft); Activities coordinators 1 (ft); Dietitians 1 (pt); Podiatrists 1 (pt).
Facilities Dining room; Physical therapy room; Activities room; Crafts room; Laundry room; Barber/Beauty shop; Multipurpose room.
Activities Arts & crafts; Cards; Games; Reading groups; Prayer groups; Movies; Shopping trips; Social/Cultural gatherings.

WINDSOR

Windsor's Resthaven Inc
206 E Jackson St, Windsor, MO, 65360
(816) 647-3312
Admin Jim Fetters. *Medical Dir/Dir of Nursing* Mary Dugger.
Licensure Intermediate care. *Beds* ICF 60. *Certified* Medicaid.
Owner Proprietary Corp.
Admissions Requirements Medical examination.
Staff RNs 1 (pt); LPNs 2 (pt); Nurses aides 31 (pt).
Facilities Dining room; Activities room; Chapel; Laundry room; Library.
Activities Cards; Games.

MONTANA

ANACONDA

Community Nursing Home of Anaconda*
600 Main St, Anaconda, MT, 59711
(406) 563-8417
Admin Warren L Croston.
Licensure Skilled care; Intermediate care. *Beds*
SNF 40; ICF 28. *Certified* Medicaid;
Medicare.

BAKER

Fallon Memorial Nursing Home*
Box 820, 320 Hospital Dr, Baker, MT, 59313
(406) 778-3331
Admin Dan McLeod.
Licensure Skilled care. *Beds* 32. *Certified*
Medicaid; Medicare.

BIG SANDY

Sande Convalescent Home Inc
PO Box F, Big Sandy, MT, 59520
(406) 378-2402
Admin David R Sande. *Medical Dir/Dir of
Nursing* David R Sande.
Licensure Intermediate care. *Beds* 29.
Certified Medicaid.
Owner Proprietary Corp.
Admissions Requirements Medical
examination; Physician's request.
Staff RNs 1 (pt); LPNs 3 (ft), 1 (pt); Orderlies
1 (ft); Nurses aides 4 (ft), 2 (pt);
Recreational therapists 1 (pt); Activities
coordinators 1 (pt); 3 (ft).
Facilities Dining room; Activities room;
Laundry room.
Activities Arts & crafts; Cards; Games; Prayer
groups; Movies; Shopping trips; Social/
Cultural gatherings.

BIG TIMBER

Pioneer Nursing Home
W 7th, Big Timber, MT, 59011
(406) 932-4603
Admin Karen Herman. *Medical Dir/Dir of
Nursing* Dr Thomas Ivey.
Licensure Skilled care; Intermediate care. *Beds*
SNF 35; ICF 13. *Certified* Medicaid.
Owner Publicly owned.
Admissions Requirements Physician's request.
Staff RNs 1 (ft), 1 (pt); LPNs 3 (ft), 2 (pt);
Nurses aides 10 (ft), 9 (pt); Activities
coordinators 1 (ft).
Facilities Dining room; Activities room;
Laundry room.
Activities Arts & crafts; Cards; Games;
Reading groups; Prayer groups; Movies;
Shopping trips; Social/Cultural gatherings.

BIGFORK

Lake View Care Center
PO Box 338, 1050 Grand Ave, Bigfork, MT,
59911
(406) 837-5041, 755-5414
Admin Ed McCart. *Medical Dir/Dir of
Nursing* Thomas Jenko MD.
Licensure Skilled care; Intermediate care. *Beds*
SNF 40; ICF 43. *Certified* Medicaid;
Medicare.
Owner Proprietary Corp.
Admissions Requirements Medical
examination; Physician's request.
Staff Physicians 1 (pt); RNs 4 (ft), 3 (pt);
LPNs 2 (ft), 3 (pt); Nurses aides 17 (ft), 19
(pt); Physical therapists 1 (pt); Recreational
therapists 1 (pt); Occupational therapists 1
(pt); Speech therapists 1 (pt); Activities
coordinators 1 (pt); Dietitians 1 (pt);
Dentists 1 (pt); Ophthalmologists 1 (pt);
Podiatrists 1 (pt).
Facilities Dining room; Physical therapy
room; Activities room; Crafts room; Laundry
room; Barber/Beauty shop.
Activities Arts & crafts; Cards; Games;
Reading groups; Prayer groups; Movies;
Shopping trips; Social/Cultural gatherings.

BILLINGS

Glendeen Nursing Home
4001 Rosebud Ln, Billings, MT, 59101
(406) 252-6135
Admin Robert P Gilstrap. *Medical Dir/Dir of
Nursing* Dr Ross Lemire.
Licensure Skilled care; Intermediate care. *Beds*
36. *Certified* Medicaid; Medicare.
Admissions Requirements Medical
examination.

St John's Lutheran Home*
3940 Rimrock Rd, Billings, MT, 59102
(406) 656-2710
Admin Steven F Olson. *Medical Dir/Dir of
Nursing* Dr John Schaeffer.
Licensure Skilled care; Intermediate care. *Beds*
SNF 84; ICF 92. *Certified* Medicaid;
Medicare.
Admissions Requirements Medical
examination; Physician's request.
Staff Physicians 1 (pt); RNs 7 (ft), 9 (pt);
LPNs 11 (ft), 12 (pt); Nurses aides 55 (ft), 1
(pt); Physical therapists 2 (pt); Dietitians 1
(pt).
Affiliation Lutheran
Facilities Dining room; Physical therapy
room; Activities room; Chapel; Laundry
room; Barber/Beauty shop; Library.
Activities Arts & crafts; Cards; Games;
Reading groups; Prayer groups; Movies;
Shopping trips; Social/Cultural gatherings.

Valley Nursing Home
1807 24th St W, Billings, MT, 59102
(406) 656-5010
Admin Joyce Fisher.

Licensure Skilled care. *Beds* 100. *Certified*
Medicaid; Medicare.

Western Manor Nursing Home*
2115 Central Ave, Billings, MT, 59102
(406) 656-6500
Admin Ruth Strickler. *Medical Dir/Dir of
Nursing* John Schaeffer MD.
Licensure Skilled care; Intermediate care. *Beds*
158. *Certified* Medicaid; Medicare.
Admissions Requirements Medical
examination.
Staff RNs 6 (ft), 6 (pt); LPNs 7 (ft), 2 (pt);
Orderlies 3 (ft); Nurses aides 35 (ft), 20 (pt);
Physical therapists 1 (pt); Activities
coordinators 2 (ft); Dietitians 1 (pt).
Facilities Dining room; Physical therapy
room; Activities room; Crafts room; Laundry
room; Barber/Beauty shop.
Activities Arts & crafts; Cards; Games;
Reading groups; Prayer groups; Movies;
Shopping trips; Social/Cultural gatherings.

Yellowstone County Nursing Home
1415 Yellowstone River Rd, Billings, MT,
59105
(406) 256-6816
Admin R P Gilstrap. *Medical Dir/Dir of
Nursing* Dr R C Nelson; Marilyn Miller.
Licensure Skilled care; Intermediate care. *Beds*
SNF 59; ICF. *Certified* Medicaid.
Owner Nonprofit organization/foundation.
Admissions Requirements Physician's request.
Staff Physicians 1 (pt); RNs 5 (ft), 2 (pt);
LPNs 3 (ft); Orderlies 1 (ft); Nurses aides 23
(ft); Physical therapists 1 (pt); Recreational
therapists 1 (pt); Activities coordinators 1
(ft); Dentist 1 (pt).
Facilities Dining room; Physical therapy
room; Activities room; Chapel; Laundry
room; Barber/Beauty shop.
Activities Arts & crafts; Cards; Games;
Reading groups; Prayer groups; Movies;
Shopping trips; Social/Cultural gatherings.

BOULDER

Montana Developmental Center
Box 87, Boulder, MT, 59632
(406) 225-3311, Exten 2241
Admin Richard L Heard. *Medical Dir/Dir of
Nursing* Dr Gilbert Preston; Margaret
Keating RN.
Licensure Intermediate care for mentally
retarded. *Beds* ICF/MR 228. *Certified*
Medicaid.
Owner Publicly owned.
Staff RNs 9 (ft); LPNs 18 (ft); Nurses aides
166 (ft); Physical therapists 2 (ft);
Recreational therapists 4 (ft); Occupational
therapists 2 (ft); Speech therapists 3 (ft);
Dietitians 1 (ft); Podiatrists 1 (ft).
Activities Arts & crafts; Cards; Games;
Movies; Shopping trips; Social/Cultural
gatherings; Trips; Special olympics;
Camping; Bowling.

BOZEMAN

Bozeman Convalescent Center
321 N 5th Ave, Bozeman, MT, 59715
(406) 587-4404
Admin Gayle Cook. *Medical Dir/Dir of
Nursing* Dr C Kurtz; Julie Graden DON.
Licensure Intermediate care. *Beds* 94.
Certified Medicaid; Medicare.
Owner Proprietary Corp (Hillhaven Corp).
Admissions Requirements Physician's request.
Facilities Dining room; Physical therapy
room; Activities room; Laundry room;
Barber/Beauty shop; Living room.
Activities Arts & crafts; Cards; Games;
Reading groups; Prayer groups; Movies;
Shopping trips; Social/Cultural gatherings;
Adopt-a-grandparent.

**Bozeman Deaconess Hospital—Extended Care
Facility**
15 W Lamme, Bozeman, MT, 59715
(406) 585-5000
Admin Gary Kenner. *Medical Dir/Dir of
Nursing* Dr Timothy Adams.
Licensure Skilled care; Intermediate care. *Beds*
SNF 30; ICF 30. *Certified* Medicare.
Admissions Requirements Minimum age 16;
Medical examination; Physician's request.
Staff RNs 2 (ft), 1 (pt); LPNs 5 (ft), 5 (pt);
Nurses aides 30 (ft), 16 (pt); Recreational
therapists 1 (pt); Activities coordinators 1
(ft).
Facilities Dining room; Physical therapy
room; Activities room; Enclosed outside
patio with area to garden.
Activities Arts & crafts; Cards; Games;
Reading groups; Prayer groups; Movies;
Social/Cultural gatherings; Special painting
sessions weekly.

Gallatin County Nursing Home
1221 W Durston Rd, Bozeman, MT, 59715
(406) 585-1470
Admin James Spady. *Medical Dir/Dir of
Nursing* Edward L King MD; Connie
Wagner RN DON.
Licensure Skilled care. *Beds* SNF 56. *Certified*
Medicaid; Medicare.
Owner Publicly owned.
Admissions Requirements Medical
examination; Physician's request.
Staff RNs 4 (ft), 5 (pt); LPNs 1 (ft); Orderlies
1 (ft); Nurses aides 9 (ft), 20 (pt); Activities
coordinators 1 (ft); Dietitians 1 (ft).
Facilities Dining room; Physical therapy
room; Activities room; Laundry room.
Activities Arts & crafts; Cards; Games;
Reading groups; Prayer groups; Movies;
Shopping trips; Social/Cultural gatherings.

Hillcrest Retirement Community
1201 Highland Blvd, Bozeman, MT, 59715
(406) 587-4411
Admin Lotis L Thorsen.
Licensure Personal care. *Beds* 10.
Owner Nonprofit organization/foundation.
Admissions Requirements Minimum age 55;
Medical examination.
Staff Nurses aides 2 (ft), 4 (pt).
Facilities Dining room; Activities room;
Chapel; Laundry room; Barber/Beauty shop;
Library.
Activities Arts & crafts; Cards; Games;
Reading groups; Prayer groups; Movies;
Shopping trips; Social/Cultural gatherings.

BROADUS

Powder River Nursing Home
Box 70, Broadus, MT, 59317
(406) 436-2646
Admin Jim Tavary. *Medical Dir/Dir of
Nursing* Dr Patty Huguley.
Licensure Skilled care; Intermediate care. *Beds*
SNF 19; ICF 21. *Certified* Medicaid;
Medicare; VA.

Admissions Requirements Medical
examination; Physician's request.
Staff Physicians 1 (pt); RNs 1 (ft), 4 (pt);
LPNs 3 (ft); Nurses aides 9 (ft), 4 (pt);
Physical therapists 1 (pt); Activities
coordinators 1 (ft); Dietitians 1 (ft); Dentist
1 (pt).
Facilities Dining room; Physical therapy
room; Activities room; Crafts room; Laundry
room; Barber/Beauty shop.
Activities Arts & crafts; Cards; Games; Prayer
groups; Movies; Shopping trips; Social/
Cultural gatherings.

BROWNING

Blackfeet Nursing Home*
Box 728, Browning, MT, 59417
(406) 338-2686
Admin Fae Shelby.
Licensure Skilled care; Intermediate care. *Beds*
SNF 29; ICF 20. *Certified* Medicaid.

BUTTE

Butte Park Royal Convalescent Center Inc
3251 Nettie St, Butte, MT, 59701
(406) 723-3225
Admin David J Murphy. *Medical Dir/Dir of
Nursing* Dr Gilbert Preston.
Licensure Skilled care; Intermediate care. *Beds*
SNF 50; ICF 150. *Certified* Medicaid;
Medicare.
Admissions Requirements Medical
examination; Physician's request.
Staff RNs 4 (ft), 2 (pt); LPNs 12 (ft), 7 (pt);
Orderlies 4 (ft), 1 (pt); Nurses aides 67 (ft),
8 (pt); Physical therapists 1 (ft), 1 (pt);
Recreational therapists 1 (ft); Occupational
therapists 1 (pt); Activities coordinators 2
(ft).
Facilities Dining room; Physical therapy
room; Activities room; Barber/Beauty shop;
Library.
Activities Arts & crafts; Cards; Games; Prayer
groups; Movies; Shopping trips; Social/
Cultural gatherings.

Crest Nursing Home Inc
3131 Amherst Ave, Butte, MT, 59701
(406) 494-7035
Admin Colleen R Broderick.
Licensure Skilled care; Intermediate care. *Beds*
SNF 40; ICF 63. *Certified* Medicaid.
Admissions Requirements Minimum age 21;
Medical examination; Physician's request.
Staff RNs; LPNs; Nurses aides; Physical
therapists; Activities coordinators; Dietitians.
Activities Arts & crafts; Cards; Games;
Reading groups; Prayer groups; Movies;
Shopping trips; Social/Cultural gatherings.

CHESTER

Liberty County Nursing Home
Monroe Ave, Chester, MT, 59522
(406) 759-5181
Admin Richard O Brown. *Medical Dir/Dir of
Nursing* Dr Richard S Buker Jr; Ann
Ruddick.
Licensure Skilled care. *Beds* SNF 40. *Certified*
Medicaid; Medicare.
Owner Publicly owned.
Staff RNs 2 (ft); LPNs 4 (ft), 2 (pt); Nurses
aides 15 (ft), 8 (pt); Physical therapists 1
(pt); Activities coordinators 1 (ft); Dietitians
1 (pt); Dentist 1 (pt).
Facilities Dining room; Physical therapy
room; Activities room; Chapel; Crafts room;
Laundry room; Barber/Beauty shop; Library.
Activities Arts & crafts; Cards; Games;
Reading groups; Prayer groups; Movies;
Shopping trips; Social/Cultural gatherings.

CHINOOK

Sweet Memorial Nursing Home*
Chinook, MT, 59523
(406) 357-2549
Admin Norma Fraser. *Medical Dir/Dir of
Nursing* James Begg MD.
Licensure Skilled care; Intermediate care. *Beds*
SNF 34; ICF 6. *Certified* Medicaid.
Admissions Requirements Physician's request.
Staff RNs 1 (ft), 1 (pt); LPNs 1 (ft), 4 (pt);
Nurses aides 11 (ft), 4 (pt); Activities
coordinators 2 (pt).
Facilities Dining room; Activities room;
Laundry room; Barber/Beauty shop.
Activities Arts & crafts; Cards; Games;
Reading groups; Prayer groups; Movies;
Shopping trips; Social/Cultural gatherings;
Meals at senior citizen centers.

CHOTEAU

Teton Nursing Home
24 Main Ave N, Choteau, MT, 59422
(406) 466-5338
Admin Arlene Wolbaum. *Medical Dir/Dir of
Nursing* M A Johnson MD; Georgia Buck
RN DON.
Licensure Skilled care; Intermediate care. *Beds*
SNF 38; ICF 3. *Certified* Medicaid;
Medicare.
Owner Publicly owned.
Admissions Requirements Medical
examination; Physician's request.
Staff RNs 2 (ft), 4 (pt); LPNs 2 (pt); Nurses
aides 14 (ft), 5 (pt); Activities coordinators 1
(ft), 1 (pt).
Facilities Dining room; Physical therapy
room; Activities room; Barber/Beauty shop.
Activities Arts & crafts; Cards; Games;
Reading groups; Prayer groups; Movies;
Shopping trips; Social/Cultural gatherings.

CIRCLE

McCone County Nursing Home
PO Box 48, Circle, MT, 59215
(406) 485-3381
Admin Nancy A Berry. *Medical Dir/Dir of
Nursing* Sandra Rueb RN DON.
Licensure Skilled care; Intermediate care;
Adult day care; Respite care. *Beds* SNF 10;
ICF 30. *Certified* Medicaid; Medicare; VA.
Owner Nonprofit Corp.
Admissions Requirements Medical
examination; Physician's request.
Staff Physicians 1 (pt); RNs 2 (ft), 4 (pt);
LPNs 1 (ft), 1 (pt); Nurses aides 6 (ft), 12
(pt); Activities coordinators 1 (ft); Dietitians
1 (pt); Mental health specialist 1 (pt).
Facilities Dining room; Physical therapy
room; Activities room; Crafts room; Laundry
room; Barber/Beauty shop; TV room.
Activities Arts & crafts; Cards; Games;
Reading groups; Prayer groups; Movies;
Shopping trips; Social/Cultural gatherings;
Group discussion; walks.

CLANCY

Hillbrook Nursing Home
Rte 2, Clancy, MT, 59634
(406) 933-8311
Admin William Chapek. *Medical Dir/Dir of
Nursing* Dr Etter; Sharon Butler DON.
Licensure Skilled care; Intermediate care. *Beds*
SNF 24; ICF 43. *Certified* Medicaid;
Medicare.
Owner Proprietary Corp.
Staff Physicians 1 (pt); RNs 4 (ft), 2 (pt);
LPNs 6 (ft); Orderlies 1 (ft), 1 (pt); Nurses
aides 36 (ft); Physical therapists 1 (pt);
Activities coordinators; Dietitians.
Facilities Dining room; Physical therapy
room; Activities room; Crafts room; Laundry
room; Barber/Beauty shop.

Activities Arts & crafts; Cards; Games; Reading groups; Prayer groups; Movies; Shopping trips; Social/Cultural gatherings; Boat trips; Picnics; Outings; Volleyball; Horseshoes.

COLUMBIA FALLS

Montana Veterans Home
Box 250, Columbia Falls, MT, 59912
(406) 892-3256
Admin Michael Patrick Estenson. *Medical Dir/Dir of Nursing* Libby Yeats DON.
Licensure Skilled care; Intermediate care. *Beds* SNF 20; ICF 70. *Certified* Medicaid; Medicare; VA.
Owner Publicly owned.
Admissions Requirements Honorably discharged veteran or spouse.
Staff Physicians 3 (pt); RNs 5 (ft); LPNs 8 (ft); Nurses aides 28 (ft); Physical therapists 1 (pt); Activities coordinators 1 (ft); Dietitians 1 (pt).
Facilities Dining room; Physical therapy room; Activities room; Chapel; Crafts room; Laundry room; Barber/Beauty shop; Library.
Activities Arts & crafts; Cards; Games; Reading groups; Prayer groups; Movies; Shopping trips; Social/Cultural gatherings.

COLUMBUS

Stillwater Convalescent Center*
350 W Pike Ave, Columbus, MT, 59019
(406) 322-5342
Admin Ronald I Borgman. *Medical Dir/Dir of Nursing* Dr Jack Exley.
Licensure Skilled care; Intermediate care. *Beds* SNF 31; ICF 50. *Certified* Medicaid; Medicare.
Staff Physicians 3 (pt); RNs 3 (ft), 3 (pt); LPNs 5 (ft), 2 (pt); Nurses aides 26 (ft), 6 (pt); Physical therapists 1 (pt); Speech therapists 1 (pt); Activities coordinators 1 (ft); Dietitians 1 (pt).
Facilities Dining room; Physical therapy room; Activities room; Crafts room; Laundry room; Barber/Beauty shop.
Activities Arts & crafts; Cards; Games; Reading groups; Prayer groups; Movies; Shopping trips; Social/Cultural gatherings.

CONRAD

Pondera Pioneer Nursing Home*
Conrad, MT, 59425
(406) 278-7581
Admin Esther Johnson.
Licensure Skilled care; Intermediate care. *Beds* SNF 43; ICF 20. *Certified* Medicaid; Medicare.

CULBERTSON

Roosevelt Memorial Nursing Home
PO Box 419, Culbertson, MT, 59218
(406) 787-6621
Admin Michael D Schafer. *Medical Dir/Dir of Nursing* Cheryl Hofman RN DON.
Licensure Skilled care. *Beds* SNF 40. *Certified* Medicaid; Medicare; VA.
Owner Nonprofit Corp.
Admissions Requirements Physician's request.
Staff Physicians 3 (pt); RNs 3 (pt); LPNs 6 (ft); Orderlies 1 (ft); Nurses aides 10 (ft), 10 (pt); Physical therapists 1 (pt); Activities coordinators 1 (ft); Dietitians 1 (pt).
Facilities Dining room; Physical therapy room; Activities room; Chapel; Barber/Beauty shop.
Activities Arts & crafts; Cards; Games; Reading groups; Prayer groups; Movies; Shopping trips; Social/Cultural gatherings.

CUT BANK

Glacier County Medical Center
802-2nd Street SE, Cut Bank, MT, 59427
(406) 873-2251
Admin Mack Simpson. *Medical Dir/Dir of Nursing* Dr L Hemmer.
Licensure Skilled care; Intermediate care. *Beds* SNF 23; ICF 16; Certified Medicare 16. *Certified* Medicaid; Medicare.
Owner Publicly owned.
Admissions Requirements Medical examination.
Staff RNs 2 (ft), 1 (pt); LPNs 4 (ft); Orderlies 1 (ft), 1 (pt); Nurses aides 12 (ft), 2 (pt); Activities coordinators 1 (ft); Dietitians 1 (pt).
Facilities Dining room; Physical therapy room; Activities room; Chapel; Laundry room; Barber/Beauty shop.
Activities Arts & crafts; Cards; Games; Prayer groups; Movies; Shopping trips; Social/Cultural gatherings.

DEER LODGE

Colonial Manor of Deer Lodge*
1100 Texas Ave, Deer Lodge, MT, 59722
(406) 846-1655
Admin Fern Knight.
Licensure Skilled care; Intermediate care. *Beds* SNF 40; ICF 20. *Certified* Medicaid.
Owner Proprietary Corp (Beverly Enterprises).

Galen State Hospital*
Rte 1, Galen, Deer Lodge, MT, 59722
(406) 693-2281
Admin Joseph M Balkovatz.
Licensure Intermediate care. *Beds* 185. *Certified* Medicaid.

Powell County Memorial Hospital & LTC Unit
1101 Texas Ave, Deer Lodge, MT, 59722
(406) 846-2212
Admin Jon Frantsvog. *Medical Dir/Dir of Nursing* Peggy Madore.
Licensure Skilled care. *Beds* SNF 12. *Certified* Medicaid; Medicare.
Owner Publicly owned.
Admissions Requirements Medical examination; Physician's request.
Staff RNs 5 (ft), 3 (pt); LPNs 4 (ft), 2 (pt); Nurses aides 5 (ft), 1 (pt); Physical therapists 1 (pt); Activities coordinators 1 (pt).
Facilities Dining room; Physical therapy room; Activities room; Barber/Beauty shop; Library.
Activities Arts & crafts; Cards; Games; Reading groups; Prayer groups; Movies; Social/Cultural gatherings.

DILLON

Parkview Acres Convalescent Center*
200 Oregon St, Dillon, MT, 59725
(406) 683-5105
Admin George Montrose.
Licensure Skilled care; Intermediate care; Personal care. *Beds* SNF 4; ICF 94; Personal 10. *Certified* Medicaid.
Owner Proprietary Corp (Hillhaven Corp).

EKALAKA

Dahl Memorial Nursing Home
PO Box 46, Ekalaka, MT, 59324
(406) 775-8730/8739
Admin Scott W Haycock. *Medical Dir/Dir of Nursing* Dan Harper MD; Pat Keith RN.
Licensure Skilled care. *Beds* SNF 21. *Certified* Medicaid.
Owner Nonprofit organization/foundation.
Admissions Requirements Medical examination.

Staff Physicians 1 (ft); RNs 8 (ft); LPNs 1 (ft); Nurses aides 7 (ft), 2 (pt); Activities coordinators 1 (ft); Dietitians 1 (ft).
Facilities Dining room; Activities room; Laundry room.
Activities Arts & crafts; Cards; Games; Reading groups; Prayer groups; Movies.

ENNIS

Madison County Nursing Home-Ennis
PO Box 335, Ennis, MT, 59729
(406) 682-7271
Admin J Page Puckett. *Medical Dir/Dir of Nursing* Dr Gene C Wilkins; Jeanne Bodine RN DON.
Licensure Skilled care; Intermediate care. *Beds* SNF 20; ICF 20. *Certified* Medicaid.
Owner Publicly owned.
Admissions Requirements Medical examination; Physician's request.
Staff Physicians 2 (pt); RNs 2 (ft); LPNs 3 (ft), 1 (pt); Orderlies 1 (ft); Nurses aides 10 (ft), 4 (pt); Activities coordinators 1 (ft); Dietitians 1 (ft); Dentist 1 (pt).
Facilities Dining room; Activities room; Laundry room; Barber/Beauty shop.
Activities Arts & crafts; Cards; Games; Reading groups; Prayer groups; Movies; Shopping trips; Social/Cultural gatherings; Exercising.

EUREKA

Mountain View Manor Nursing Center
PO Box 327, Eureka, MT, 59917
(406) 296-2541
Admin Mark Bichler. *Medical Dir/Dir of Nursing* Dr Andy Ivy Jr; Shirley Appleby RN DON.
Licensure Skilled care; Intermediate care. *Beds* SNF 30; ICF 10. *Certified* Medicaid; Medicare.
Owner Nonprofit Corp.
Admissions Requirements Medical examination.
Staff RNs 1 (ft), 6 (pt); LPNs 5 (pt); Nurses aides 4 (ft), 15 (pt); Recreational therapists 1 (pt); Occupational therapists 1 (pt); Activities coordinators 1 (ft); Dietitians 1 (pt).
Affiliation Lutheran
Facilities Dining room; Physical therapy room; Activities room; Chapel; Crafts room; Laundry room; Barber/Beauty shop; Fish/duck pond.
Activities Arts & crafts; Cards; Games; Reading groups; Prayer groups; Movies; Shopping trips; Social/Cultural gatherings; Camping; Fishing; Rides; Parades; Ceramics; Devotions; Singing.

FORSYTH

Rosebud Health Care Center
383 N 17th St, Forsyth, MT, 59327
(406) 356-2161
Admin Joyce Asay. *Medical Dir/Dir of Nursing* Marilyn Kanta RN.
Licensure Skilled care; Intermediate care. *Beds* SNF 10; ICF 45; Swing beds 8. *Certified* Medicaid; Medicare.
Owner Nonprofit Corp.
Admissions Requirements Medical examination; Physician's request.
Staff Physicians 4 (ft); RNs 7 (ft); LPNs 1 (ft), 2 (pt); Nurses aides 30 (ft), 10 (pt); Activities coordinators 1 (ft), 1 (pt); Dietitians 1 (ft).
Facilities Dining room; Physical therapy room; Activities room; Laundry room; Barber/Beauty shop.
Activities Arts & crafts; Cards; Games; Reading groups; Prayer groups; Movies; Shopping trips; Social/Cultural gatherings.

FORT BENTON

Chouteau County District Nursing Home
1512 Saint Charles St, Fort Benton, MT, 59442
(406) 622-3331
Admin Robert E Smith. *Medical Dir/Dir of Nursing* W F Gertson MD; Maxine McDede RN.
Licensure Skilled care. *Beds* SNF 22. *Certified* Medicaid; Medicare.
Owner Publicly owned.
Admissions Requirements Physician's request.
Staff Physicians 2 (ft); RNs 3 (ft), 6 (pt); LPNs 2 (ft), 1 (pt); Nurses aides 8 (ft), 11 (pt); Physical therapists 1 (ft); Activities coordinators 1 (ft); Dietitians 1 (pt).
Facilities Dining room; Physical therapy room; Activities room; Crafts room; Barber/Beauty shop.
Activities Arts & crafts; Cards; Games; Reading groups; Movies; Shopping trips; Social/Cultural gatherings.

GLASGOW

Frances Mahon Deaconess Hospital—Extended Care Facility*
621 2nd St S, Glasgow, MT, 59230
(406) 228-4351
Admin Kyle Hosptad. *Medical Dir/Dir of Nursing* Louise Johnston.
Licensure Skilled care. *Beds* 6. *Certified* Medicaid; Medicare.

Valley View Home
1225 Perry Ln, Glasgow, MT, 59230
(406) 228-2461
Admin Mary Newton. *Medical Dir/Dir of Nursing* Dr O'Dea.
Licensure Skilled care; Intermediate care. *Beds* SNF 34; ICF 58. *Certified* Medicaid; Medicare.
Staff RNs 1 (ft), 3 (pt); LPNs 4 (ft), 3 (pt); Orderlies 1 (pt); Nurses aides 25 (ft), 8 (pt); Physical therapists 1 (pt); Activities coordinators 1 (ft); Dietitians 1 (ft).
Affiliation Lutheran
Facilities Dining room; Activities room; Laundry room; Barber/Beauty shop.
Activities Arts & crafts; Cards; Games; Reading groups; Prayer groups; Movies; Shopping trips; Social/Cultural gatherings.

GLENDIVE

Eastmont Human Services Center
Box 1383, 700 E Little St, Glendive, MT, 59330
(406) 365-6001
Admin Sylvia Y Hammer. *Medical Dir/Dir of Nursing* Sylvia Hammer; Patricia Holm; Ann Sveen.
Licensure Intermediate care for mentally retarded. *Beds* ICF/MR 55. *Certified* Medicaid.
Owner Publicly owned.
Admissions Requirements Court Committed.
Staff RNs 2 (ft); LPNs 5 (ft); Recreational therapists 1 (ft); Speech therapists 1 (ft); Dietitians 1 (ft).
Languages Sign
Facilities Dining room; Activities room; Crafts room.
Activities Arts & crafts; Games; Movies; Shopping trips; Social/Cultural gatherings.

Glendive Coummunity Nursing Home*
Ames & Prospect, Glendive, MT, 59330
(406) 365-5692
Admin John Nordwick. *Medical Dir/Dir of Nursing* Dr N H Rausch.
Licensure Skilled care; Intermediate care. *Beds* SNF 30; ICF 45. *Certified* Medicaid; Medicare.
Admissions Requirements Minimum age 18; Medical examination; Physician's request.

Staff Physicians 6 (ft); RNs 3 (ft), 4 (pt); LPNs 3 (ft), 3 (pt); Nurses aides 18 (ft), 18 (pt); Recreational therapists 1 (ft); Activities coordinators 1 (ft); Dietitians 1 (ft).
Facilities Dining room; Physical therapy room; Activities room; Chapel; Crafts room; Laundry room; Barber/Beauty shop.
Activities Arts & crafts; Cards; Games; Reading groups; Prayer groups; Movies; Shopping trips; Social/Cultural gatherings.

GREAT FALLS

Cascade County Convalescent Nursing Home
1130 17th Ave S, Great Falls, MT, 59405
(406) 761-6467
Admin Donald E Pizzini. *Medical Dir/Dir of Nursing* Dr John Hickes; Doris Odegard.
Licensure Skilled care; Intermediate care. *Beds* SNF 232. *Certified* Medicaid; Medicare.
Owner Publicly owned.
Admissions Requirements Medical examination; Physician's request.
Staff Physicians 1 (ft), 1 (pt); RNs 12 (ft), 11 (pt); LPNs 11 (ft), 9 (pt); Orderlies 5 (ft), 1 (pt); Nurses aides 80 (ft); Physical therapists 1 (ft); Activities coordinators 2 (ft); Dietitians 1 (pt); Dentists 1 (pt); Pharmacists 2 (ft); Dentist 1 (ft), 1 (pt).
Languages Spanish
Facilities Dining room; Physical therapy room; Activities room; Chapel; Crafts room; Laundry room; Barber/Beauty shop; Library.
Activities Arts & crafts; Cards; Games; Reading groups; Prayer groups; Movies; Shopping trips; Social/Cultural gatherings.

Deaconess Skilled Nursing Center*
1109 6th Ave N, Great Falls, MT, 59405
(406) 761-1200
Admin Margaret Weedman. *Medical Dir/Dir of Nursing* Dr L L Howard.
Licensure Skilled care. *Beds* 90. *Certified* Medicaid; Medicare.
Admissions Requirements Medical examination; Physician's request.
Facilities Dining room; Physical therapy room; Activities room; Chapel; Crafts room; Laundry room; Barber/Beauty shop; Library; Outside garden area; Enclosed sun porches; On-site doctor's office.
Activities Arts & crafts; Cards; Games; Reading groups; Prayer groups; Movies; Shopping trips; Social/Cultural gatherings; Bus; Wheelchair van.

McAuley Nursing Home*
1009 3rd Ave N, Great Falls, MT, 59401
(406) 452-6302
Admin George B Eusterman Jr. *Medical Dir/Dir of Nursing* Mary Freeman.
Licensure Skilled care. *Beds* 42. *Certified* Medicaid; Medicare.

Park Place Health Care Center*
15th Ave S & 32nd St, PO Box 5001, Great Falls, MT, 59405
(406) 761-4300
Admin Dale Zulauf. *Medical Dir/Dir of Nursing* Dorothy V Boettcher.
Licensure Skilled care; Intermediate care. *Beds* SNF 105; ICF 70. *Certified* Medicaid; Medicare.
Owner Proprietary Corp (Hillhaven Corp).
Facilities Dining room; Physical therapy room; Activities room; Crafts room; Laundry room; Barber/Beauty shop; Library.
Activities Arts & crafts; Cards; Games; Reading groups; Prayer groups; Movies; Shopping trips; Social/Cultural gatherings.

HAMILTON

Valley View Estates Nursing Home*
225 N 8th St, Hamilton, MT, 59840
(406) 363-1144
Admin John B Muir.

Licensure Skilled care; Intermediate care. *Beds* SNF 58; ICF 40. *Certified* Medicaid.

HARDIN

Big Horn County Memorial Nursing Home*
17 N Miles, Hardin, MT, 59034
(406) 665-2310
Admin Michael N Sinclair.
Licensure Skilled care. *Beds* 34. *Certified* Medicaid; Medicare.

Heritage Acres
200 N Mitchell Ave, Hardin, MT, 59034
(406) 665-2802
Admin Jackie Suko. *Medical Dir/Dir of Nursing* Veryl Ann Balckel.
Licensure Intermediate care. *Beds* ICF 36. *Certified* Medicaid.
Owner Publicly owned.
Admissions Requirements Minimum age 16; Physician's request.
Staff RNs 3 (ft), 1 (pt); LPNs 3 (ft), 2 (pt); Orderlies 1 (ft), 4 (pt); Nurses aides 9 (ft), 4 (pt); Activities coordinators 1 (ft); 12 (ft), 10 (pt).
Languages Native American languages
Facilities Dining room; Activities room; Laundry room; Barber/Beauty shop; Library.
Activities Arts & crafts; Cards; Games; Prayer groups; Movies; Shopping trips; Social/Cultural gatherings; Bus rides; Exercise.

HARLEM

Harlem Rest Home
112 S Main, Harlem, MT, 59526-0279
(406) 353-2421
Admin A J Fuzesi. *Medical Dir/Dir of Nursing* K Fuzesy.
Licensure Intermediate care. *Beds* ICF 55. *Certified* Medicaid.
Owner Privately owned.
Staff RNs 2 (ft), 1 (pt); LPNs 1 (ft); Nurses aides 12 (ft), 2 (pt); Activities coordinators 1 (ft).
Facilities Dining room; Activities room; Crafts room; Laundry room; Library.
Activities Arts & crafts; Cards; Games; Reading groups; Prayer groups; Movies; Shopping trips; Social/Cultural gatherings.

HARLOWTON

Wheatland Memorial Nursing Home*
530 3rd St NW, Harlowton, MT, 59036
(406) 632-4351
Admin Robert B Holmes.
Licensure Skilled care. *Beds* 33. *Certified* Medicaid; Medicare.

HAVRE

Lutheran Home of the Good Shepherd
2229 5th Ave, Havre, MT, 59501
(406) 265-2238
Admin Carol Ann Andrews. *Medical Dir/Dir of Nursing* Dr Tom Booth; Cathy Bender RN.
Licensure Skilled care. *Beds* 102. *Certified* Medicaid; Medicare.
Owner Nonprofit Corp.
Admissions Requirements Medical examination; Physician's request.
Staff RNs 6 (ft), 4 (pt); LPNs 3 (ft), 3 (pt); Orderlies 1 (pt); Nurses aides 26 (ft), 13 (pt); Recreational therapists 1 (ft), 3 (pt); Activities coordinators 1 (ft); Dietitians 1 (ft).
Affiliation Lutheran
Facilities Dining room; Activities room; Chapel; Crafts room; Laundry room; Barber/Beauty shop.
Activities Arts & crafts; Cards; Games; Reading groups; Prayer groups; Movies; Shopping trips; Social/Cultural gatherings.

HELENA

Cedar Street Home*
721 Cedar St, Helena, MT, 59601
(406) 442-1676
Admin Janet Ford. *Medical Dir/Dir of Nursing* Elizabeth Henry.
Licensure Intermediate care. *Beds* 7. *Certified* Medicaid.

Cooney Convalescent Home
2555 Broadway, Helena, MT, 59601
(406) 442-0572
Admin Joan Ashley. *Medical Dir/Dir of Nursing* Martin Skinner MD; Joan Lester RN DON.
Licensure Skilled care; Intermediate care; Adult day care. *Beds* SNF 62; ICF 14. *Certified* Medicaid; Medicare.
Owner Publicly owned.
Admissions Requirements Minimum age 55; Medical examination; Physician's request.
Staff Physicians 1 (pt); RNs 5 (ft), 5 (pt); LPNs 2 (ft), 4 (pt); Orderlies 8 (ft), 2 (pt); Nurses aides 27 (ft), 6 (pt); Physical therapists 2 (pt); Occupational therapists 1 (pt); Speech therapists 1 (pt); Activities coordinators 1 (ft); Dietitians 1 (pt).
Facilities Dining room; Physical therapy room; Activities room; Crafts room; Laundry room; Barber/Beauty shop; Religious services.
Activities Arts & crafts; Cards; Games; Reading groups; Prayer groups; Movies; Shopping trips; Social/Cultural gatherings; Reality orientation; Exercise; Gardening.

Helena Nursing Home Co
25 S Ewing, Helena, MT, 59601
(406) 443-5880
Admin Gerald Hughes. *Medical Dir/Dir of Nursing* David Jordan MD; Helen Tamol RN DON.
Licensure Skilled care; Intermediate care. *Beds* SNF 32; ICF 31. *Certified* Medicaid; Medicare.
Owner Privately owned.
Admissions Requirements Physician's request.
Staff Physicians 1 (pt); RNs 3 (ft), 2 (pt); LPNs 7 (ft); Orderlies 6 (ft), 1 (pt); Nurses aides 13 (ft), 1 (pt); Activities coordinators 1 (ft), 1 (pt); Dietitians 1 (pt); Kitchen staff 9 (ft).
Facilities Dining room; Physical therapy room; Activities room; Crafts room; Barber/Beauty shop.
Activities Arts & crafts; Cards; Games; Reading groups; Prayer groups; Movies; Shopping trips; Social/Cultural gatherings; Exercise.

Western Care Nursing Home*
2475 Winne Ave, Helena, MT, 59601
(406) 442-1350
Admin Page Puckett.
Licensure Skilled care; Intermediate care. *Beds* SNF 12; ICF 96. *Certified* Medicaid; Medicare.
Owner Proprietary Corp (Hillhaven Corp).

HOT SPRINGS

Hot Springs Convalescent Inc*
Drawer U, Hot Springs, MT, 59845
(406) 741-2992
Admin H Kent Ferguson. *Medical Dir/Dir of Nursing* Jacob V Lulack MD.
Licensure Skilled care; Intermediate care. *Beds* SNF 18; ICF 54. *Certified* Medicaid; Medicare.
Admissions Requirements Medical examination; Physician's request.
Staff RNs 4 (ft), 2 (pt); LPNs 1 (pt); Orderlies 2 (ft), 1 (pt); Nurses aides 9 (ft).
Facilities Dining room; Physical therapy room; Activities room; Laundry room; Barber/Beauty shop.

Activities Arts & crafts; Cards; Games; Reading groups; Prayer groups; Movies; Shopping trips; Social/Cultural gatherings.

JORDAN

Garfield County Health Center Inc
PO Box 389, Jordan, MT, 59337
(406) 557-2465
Admin Michael Piper. *Medical Dir/Dir of Nursing* Sheila Johnson.
Licensure Skilled care; Intermediate care. *Beds* SNF 4; ICF 9. *Certified* Medicaid; Medicare.
Owner Nonprofit Corp.
Staff Physicians 1 (ft), 1 (pt); RNs 2 (ft), 4 (pt); LPNs 1 (ft), 3 (pt); Nurses aides 1 (ft), 9 (pt); Activities coordinators 1 (pt).

KALISPELL

Brendan House Skilled Nursing Facility
350 Conway Dr, Kalispell, MT, 59912
(406) 752-5460
Admin Karen E Black. *Medical Dir/Dir of Nursing* Richard Wise MD; Judy Leigh RN DON.
Licensure Skilled care. *Beds* SNF 76. *Certified* Medicaid; Medicare.
Owner Nonprofit organization/foundation.
Admissions Requirements Physician's request.
Staff Physicians 1 (ft); RNs 9 (ft); LPNs 6 (ft); Nurses aides 27 (ft); Physical therapists 2 (ft); Occupational therapists 1 (ft); Speech therapists 1 (ft); Activities coordinators 2 (ft); Dietitians 1 (ft).
Activities Arts & crafts; Cards; Games; Reading groups; Prayer groups; Movies; Shopping trips; Social/Cultural gatherings.

Flathead County Nursing Home*
1251 Willow Glen Dr, Kalispell, MT, 59901
(406) 257-5575
Admin Marguerite Watne. *Medical Dir/Dir of Nursing* Anna Drew.
Licensure Skilled care; Intermediate care. *Beds* SNF 49; ICF 17. *Certified* Medicaid; Medicare.
Admissions Requirements Physician's request.
Staff RNs 3 (ft), 3 (pt); LPNs 2 (ft); Nurses aides 18 (ft), 5 (pt); Activities coordinators 1 (ft).
Facilities Dining room; Activities room; Crafts room; Laundry room; Library.
Activities Arts & crafts; Movies; Shopping trips; Church.

Immanuel Lutheran Home
Buffalo Hill, Kalispell, MT, 59901
(406) 752-9622
Admin Lorraine Wagnild. *Medical Dir/Dir of Nursing* Dr Alfred V Swanberg; Marge Keith.
Licensure Skilled care; Intermediate care. *Beds* SNF 50; ICF 90. *Certified* Medicaid.
Owner Nonprofit Corp.
Admissions Requirements Medical examination; Physician's request.
Staff RNs 7 (ft), 6 (pt); LPNs 9 (ft), 5 (pt); Orderlies; Nurses aides 46 (ft), 22 (pt); Activities coordinators 3 (ft), 1 (pt); Dietitians 1 (ft).
Affiliation Lutheran
Facilities Dining room; Activities room; Chapel; Crafts room; Laundry room; Barber/Beauty shop.
Activities Arts & crafts; Cards; Games; Reading groups; Prayer groups; Movies; Shopping trips; Social/Cultural gatherings; Educational groups with college teachers.

LAUREL

Laurel Care Center
820 3rd Ave, Laurel, MT, 59044
(406) 628-8251
Admin Phillip Gorby. *Medical Dir/Dir of Nursing* Virla Kober DON.

Licensure Skilled care; Personal care. *Beds* SNF 40; Personal 15. *Certified* Medicaid; Medicare; VA.
Owner Proprietary Corp.
Admissions Requirements Minimum age 18.
Staff RNs 2 (ft), 1 (pt); LPNs 5 (ft), 2 (pt); Orderlies 2 (ft); Nurses aides 20 (ft), 6 (pt); Activities coordinators 1 (ft), 1 (pt); Dietitians 1 (ft).
Facilities Dining room; Physical therapy room; Activities room; Chapel; Laundry room; Barber/Beauty shop.
Activities Arts & crafts; Cards; Games; Reading groups; Prayer groups; Movies; Shopping trips; Social/Cultural gatherings.

LEWISTOWN

Central Montana Nursing Home
PO Box 580, 408 Wendell Ave, Lewistown, MT, 59457
(406) 538-7711
Admin Robert G Conrad. *Medical Dir/Dir of Nursing* Phyllis Taylor RN.
Licensure Skilled care. *Beds* SNF 70. *Certified* Medicaid; Medicare.
Owner Nonprofit Corp.
Admissions Requirements Minimum age 18; Medical examination; Physician's request.
Staff Physicians 11 (pt); RNs 5 (ft), 4 (pt); LPNs 3 (ft), 2 (pt); Orderlies 1 (pt); Nurses aides 15 (ft), 26 (pt); Physical therapists 1 (pt); Activities coordinators 1 (ft), 1 (pt); Dietitians 1 (pt); Dentists 1 (pt); Ophthalmologists 1 (pt); Dentist 1 (pt).
Facilities Dining room; Physical therapy room; Activities room; Chapel; Crafts room; Laundry room; Barber/Beauty shop; Library; Courtyard.
Activities Arts & crafts; Cards; Games; Reading groups; Prayer groups; Movies; Social/Cultural gatherings; Weekly restaurant outings.

Montana Center for the Aged
Box 820, 800 Casino Creek Drive, Lewistown, MT, 59457
(406) 538-7451
Admin Gerald F Butcher. *Medical Dir/Dir of Nursing* Kay Brooks DON.
Licensure Intermediate care. *Beds* ICF 191. *Certified* Medicaid.
Owner Publicly owned.
Admissions Requirements Minimum age 55.
Staff RNs 6 (ft), 3 (pt); LPNs 3 (ft), 2 (pt); Nurses aides 31 (ft), 5 (pt).
Facilities Dining room; Activities room; Laundry room; Barber/Beauty shop.
Activities Arts & crafts; Cards; Games; Prayer groups; Movies; Shopping trips; Social/Cultural gatherings.

Valle Vista Manor*
Summit Ave, Lewistown, MT, 59457
(406) 538-8775
Admin Bill McLain. *Medical Dir/Dir of Nursing* Dr Paul Gans.
Licensure Skilled care; Intermediate care. *Beds* SNF 29; ICF 66. *Certified* Medicaid; Medicare.
Staff RNs 5 (ft), 4 (pt); LPNs 5 (ft), 3 (pt); Nurses aides 33 (ft), 16 (pt); Activities coordinators 1 (ft), 1 (pt); Dietitians 1 (pt); Dentists 1 (pt).
Facilities Dining room; Activities room; Chapel; Crafts room; Laundry room; Barber/Beauty shop.
Activities Arts & crafts; Cards; Games; Movies; Shopping trips; Social/Cultural gatherings.

LIBBY

Libby Care Center
308 E 3rd, Libby, MT, 59923
(406) 293-6285

Admin Joan Croucher. *Medical Dir/Dir of Nursing* Roger Brus MD; Thelma Blackwell.
Licensure Skilled care; Intermediate care. *Beds* SNF 40; ICF 40. *Certified* Medicaid; Medicare.
Owner Proprietary Corp (National Heritage).
Admissions Requirements Medical examination; Physician's request.
Staff RNs 3 (ft), 1 (pt); LPNs 5 (ft), 4 (pt); Nurses aides 24 (ft), 12 (pt); Physical therapists 1 (pt); Activities coordinators 1 (ft), 1 (pt); Dietitians 1 (ft).
Facilities Dining room; Activities room; Laundry room; Barber/Beauty shop; Multi purpose room.
Activities Arts & crafts; Cards; Games; Reading groups; Prayer groups; Movies; Shopping trips; Social/Cultural gatherings; Church services.

LIVINGSTON

Livingston Convalescent Center*
510 S 14th St, Livingston, MT, 59047
(406) 222-0672
Admin Judith A Melin. *Medical Dir/Dir of Nursing* Dr L M Baskett.
Licensure Skilled care; Intermediate care. *Beds* SNF 9; ICF 116. *Certified* Medicaid; Medicare.
Owner Proprietary Corp (Hillhaven Corp).
Staff RNs 6 (ft); LPNs 7 (ft); Orderlies 2 (ft); Nurses aides 30 (ft); Physical therapists 1 (ft); Reality therapists 1 (ft); Recreational therapists 1 (ft); Occupational therapists 1 (ft); Speech therapists 1 (ft); Activities coordinators 1 (ft); Dietitians 1 (ft); Dentists 1 (ft).
Facilities Dining room; Activities room; Laundry room; Barber/Beauty shop.
Activities Arts & crafts; Cards; Games; Reading groups; Prayer groups; Movies; Shopping trips; Social/Cultural gatherings.

MALTA

Phillips County Good Samaritan Retirement Center*
Box P, Malta, MT, 59538
(406) 654-1190
Admin Henryka Shelton. *Medical Dir/Dir of Nursing* Michael Emond.
Licensure Skilled care; Intermediate care. *Beds* SNF 40; ICF 20. *Certified* Medicaid.
Owner Nonprofit Corp (Evangelical Lutheran/ Good Samaritan).

MILES CITY

Custer County Rest Home
PO Box 130, Miles City, MT, 59301
(406) 232-1035
Admin Milton E Benge. *Medical Dir/Dir of Nursing* Patricia Neiffer.
Licensure Skilled care; Intermediate care; Intermediate care for mentally retarded. *Beds* SNF 40; ICF 81. *Certified* Medicaid; Medicare.
Owner Publicly owned.
Admissions Requirements Physician's request.
Staff RNs 6 (ft), 5 (pt); LPNs 6 (ft), 4 (pt); Orderlies 9 (ft), 3 (pt); Nurses aides 49 (ft), 4 (pt); Activities coordinators 1 (ft); Dietitians 1 (ft).
Facilities Dining room; Physical therapy room; Activities room; Chapel; Crafts room; Laundry room; Barber/Beauty shop; Library.
Activities Arts & crafts; Cards; Games; Reading groups; Prayer groups; Movies; Shopping trips.

Friendship Villa Care Center
Rte 2, Box 3001, 1242 S Strevell, Miles City, MT, 59301
(406) 232-2687

Admin Charles J Blando. *Medical Dir/Dir of Nursing* Dr Campodonico; Myrna Hillier DON.
Licensure Skilled care; Intermediate care. *Beds* SNF 40; ICF 27. *Certified* Medicaid; Medicare.
Owner Proprietary Corp.
Admissions Requirements Medical examination; Physician's request.
Staff RNs; LPNs; Orderlies; Nurses aides; Physical therapists; Activities coordinators.
Facilities Dining room; Physical therapy room; Activities room; Chapel; Crafts room; Laundry room; Barber/Beauty shop.
Activities Arts & crafts; Cards; Games; Reading groups; Prayer groups; Movies; Shopping trips; Social/Cultural gatherings.

MISSOULA

Community Nursing & Rehabilitation Facility
2823 Fort Missoula Rd, Missoula, MT, 59803
(406) 728-9162, 728-9216
Admin Danna J Miller. *Medical Dir/Dir of Nursing* R Ratigan MD; Sandra Leischner RN DON.
Licensure Skilled care. *Beds* SNF 149. *Certified* Medicaid; Medicare; VA.
Owner Privately owned.
Admissions Requirements Minimum age 16; Medical examination; Physician's request.
Staff RNs 5 (ft), 6 (pt); LPNs 9 (ft), 7 (pt); Nurses aides 53 (ft), 17 (pt); Recreational therapists 2 (ft); Activities coordinators 1 (ft); Dietitians 1 (pt).
Facilities Dining room; Physical therapy room; Activities room; Crafts room; Laundry room; Barber/Beauty shop; Library.
Activities Arts & crafts; Cards; Games; Reading groups; Prayer groups; Movies; Shopping trips; Social/Cultural gatherings.

Hillside Manor
4720 23rd Ave, Missoula, MT, 59803
(406) 251-5100
Admin Connie Thisselle. *Medical Dir/Dir of Nursing* T H Roberts MD; Joanne Verlanic-Scherger.
Licensure Skilled care. *Beds* SNF 102. *Certified* Medicaid; Medicare.
Owner Privately owned.
Admissions Requirements Medical examination; Physician's request.
Staff RNs 4 (ft), 6 (pt); LPNs 5 (ft), 5 (pt); Orderlies 3 (ft), 4 (pt); Nurses aides 17 (ft), 12 (pt); Activities coordinators 2 (ft), 1 (pt); Dietitians 1 (ft).
Facilities Dining room; Physical therapy room; Activities room; Crafts room; Laundry room; Barber/Beauty shop; Library.
Activities Arts & crafts; Cards; Games; Reading groups; Prayer groups; Movies.

Royal Manor Care Center
3018 Rattlesnake Dr, Missoula, MT, 59802
(406) 549-0988
Admin Gregory A Miller. *Medical Dir/Dir of Nursing* Mary Kloser.
Licensure Skilled care; Intermediate care. *Beds* SNF 31; ICF 20. *Certified* Medicaid; Medicare.
Owner Proprietary Corp (Manor Care).
Admissions Requirements Physician's request.
Staff RNs 2 (pt); LPNs 3 (ft), 1 (pt); Nurses aides 17 (ft), 4 (pt); Activities coordinators 1 (ft), 1 (pt); Dietitians 1 (pt).
Facilities Dining room; Laundry room.
Activities Arts & crafts; Cards; Games; Reading groups; Prayer groups; Movies; Shopping trips; Social/Cultural gatherings.

Wayside Nursing Care Facility*
2222 Rattlesnake, Missoula, MT, 59802
(406) 549-6158
Admin Jo Waldbillig. *Medical Dir/Dir of Nursing* Dr D Hubbard.

Licensure Skilled care; Intermediate care. *Beds* SNF 40; ICF 4. *Certified* Medicaid; Medicare.
Admissions Requirements Physician's request.
Staff Physicians 1 (pt); RNs 2 (pt); LPNs 5 (ft); Orderlies 1 (ft); Nurses aides 13 (ft), 6 (pt); Physical therapists 1 (pt); Activities coordinators 1 (pt); Dietitians 1 (pt); Dentists 1 (pt).
Facilities Dining room; Activities room; Crafts room; Laundry room; Barber/Beauty shop.
Activities Arts & crafts; Cards; Games; Reading groups; Prayer groups; Movies; Shopping trips; Social/Cultural gatherings.

PHILIPSBURG

Granite County Memorial Nursing Home
Box 729, Philipsburg, MT, 59858
(406) 859-3271
Admin Mike Kahoe. *Medical Dir/Dir of Nursing* Margery Metesh RN.
Licensure Skilled care. *Beds* 13. *Certified* Medicaid; Medicare.
Activities Arts & crafts; Cards; Games; Reading groups; Prayer groups; Movies.

PLAINS

Clark Fort Valley Nursing Home*
Kruger Rd, PO Box 768, Plains, MT, 59859
(406) 826-3601
Admin Mike Billing. *Medical Dir/Dir of Nursing* Jacob Lulack MD.
Licensure Skilled care; Intermediate care. *Beds* 24. *Certified* Medicaid; Medicare.
Staff Physicians 4 (ft); RNs 3 (ft), 4 (pt); LPNs 3 (ft); Nurses aides 7 (ft), 8 (pt); Physical therapists 1 (pt); Activities coordinators 1 (ft); Dietitians 1 (ft); Dentists 1 (pt).
Facilities Dining room; Physical therapy room; Activities room; Crafts room; Laundry room; Barber/Beauty shop.
Activities Arts & crafts; Games; Reading groups; Prayer groups; Movies; Shopping trips; Social/Cultural gatherings.

PLENTYWOOD

Sheridan Memorial Nursing Home*
440 W Laurel Ave, Plentywood, MT, 59254
(406) 765-1423
Admin Mark Rinehardt. *Medical Dir/Dir of Nursing* Dr Kirk Stoner.
Licensure Skilled care; Intermediate care. *Beds* SNF 34; ICF 31. *Certified* Medicaid; Medicare.
Admissions Requirements Medical examination.
Staff Physicians 2 (ft); RNs 6 (pt); LPNs 2 (ft), 3 (pt); Nurses aides 8 (ft), 28 (pt); Occupational therapists 1 (pt); Activities coordinators 1 (pt); Dietitians 1 (pt); Dentists 1 (pt).
Facilities Dining room; Physical therapy room; Activities room; Crafts room; Laundry room; Barber/Beauty shop.
Activities Arts & crafts; Games; Reading groups; Prayer groups; Movies; Social/ Cultural gatherings.

POLSON

St Joseph Convalescent Center*
PO Box 1530, 1st & 14th Ave, Polson, MT, 59860
(406) 883-4378
Admin William McDonald.
Licensure Skilled care; Intermediate care. *Beds* SNF 40; ICF 72. *Certified* Medicaid; Medicare.

POPLAR

Community Hospital & Nursing Home
PO Box 38, Corner of H & Court, Poplar,
MT, 59255
(406) 768-3452
Admin Margaret B Sage. *Medical Dir/Dir of
Nursing* Juanita Martin.
Licensure Skilled care. *Beds* SNF 22. *Certified*
Medicaid; Medicare.
Owner Nonprofit organization/foundation.
Admissions Requirements Physician's request.
Staff Physicians 6 (ft); RNs 5 (ft); LPNs 4 (ft),
3 (pt); Orderlies 2 (ft); Nurses aides 14 (ft),
11 (pt); Activities coordinators 1 (pt);
Dietitians 1 (pt).
Languages Sioux
Facilities Dining room; Physical therapy
room; Activities room; Crafts room; Barber/
Beauty shop.
Activities Arts & crafts; Cards; Games;
Reading groups; Prayer groups; Movies;
Shopping trips; Social/Cultural gatherings.

RED LODGE

Carbon County Health Care Center
PO Box 430, 1 S Oaks, Red Lodge, MT,
59068
(406) 446-2525
Admin Henry M Rae. *Medical Dir/Dir of
Nursing* Dr James J Kane; Darlene Huseby
RN.
Licensure Skilled care; Intermediate care. *Beds*
SNF 36; ICF 44. *Certified* Medicaid;
Medicare.
Owner Proprietary Corp (Hillhaven Corp).
Admissions Requirements Medical
examination.
Staff RNs 5 (ft); LPNs 7 (ft); Nurses aides 37
(ft).
Facilities Dining room; Physical therapy
room; Activities room; Crafts room; Laundry
room; Barber/Beauty shop.
Activities Arts & crafts; Cards; Games;
Reading groups; Prayer groups; Movies;
Social/Cultural gatherings.

Carbon County Memorial Nursing Home
PO Box 590, 600 W 21st St, Red Lodge, MT,
59068
(406) 446-2345
Admin Mark Teckmeyer.
Licensure Skilled care. *Beds* SNF 30. *Certified*
Medicaid; Medicare.
Owner Nonprofit Corp.
Admissions Requirements Physician's request.
Staff Physicians 5 (ft), 2 (pt); RNs 3 (ft);
LPNs 5 (ft); Nurses aides 10 (ft); Activities
coordinators 1 (ft).
Affiliation Lutheran
Facilities Dining room; Physical therapy
room; Activities room; Barber/Beauty shop.
Activities Arts & crafts; Games; Prayer groups;
Movies.

RONAN

Happy Acres Home
919 Main St SW, Ronan, MT, 59864
(406) 676-3934
Admin Judith A Frame. *Medical Dir/Dir of
Nursing* Dr Jay L Ballhagen.
Licensure Intermediate care for mentally
retarded. *Beds* ICF/MR 10. *Certified*
Medicaid.
Owner Privately owned.
Admissions Requirements Minimum age 18;
Females only; Medical examination.
Staff RNs; Nurses aides 2 (ft), 4 (pt); Social
worker 1 (pt).
Facilities Dining room; Activities room;
Laundry room; Library.
Activities Arts & crafts; Cards; Games;
Reading groups; Prayer groups; Shopping
trips; Social/Cultural gatherings; Community
activities.

St Luke Community Nursing Home*
901 26th St, Ronan, MT, 59864
(406) 676-3934
Admin James Oliverson.
Licensure Skilled care; Intermediate care. *Beds*
SNF 20; ICF 23. *Certified* Medicaid;
Medicare.

West Side Rest Home
Box 787, 829 Main St SW, Ronan, MT, 59864
(406) 676-5510
Admin Faye Abrahamson. *Medical Dir/Dir of
Nursing* Dr S T McDonald; Wendella
Draper.
Licensure Intermediate care. *Beds* ICF 23.
Certified Medicaid.
Owner Privately owned.
Admissions Requirements Medical
examination.
Staff RNs 1 (ft); LPNs 3 (pt); Nurses aides 8
(pt); Activities coordinators 1 (ft).
Facilities Dining room; Activities room;
Crafts room; Laundry room; Barber/Beauty
shop; Library.
Activities Arts & crafts; Cards; Games;
Reading groups; Prayer groups; Movies;
Shopping trips; Social/Cultural gatherings.

ROUNDUP

Roundup Memorial Nursing Home
1202 3rd St W, Roundup, MT, 59072
(406) 323-2302
Admin Fern Mikkelson. *Medical Dir/Dir of
Nursing* Dorothy F Harper RN DON.
Licensure Skilled care. *Beds* 37. *Certified*
Medicaid; Medicare.
Owner Publicly owned.
Admissions Requirements Females only;
Medical examination.
Staff Physicians 1 (ft); RNs 4 (ft), 2 (pt);
LPNs 3 (ft), 4 (pt); Nurses aides 4 (ft), 11
(pt); Physical therapists 1 (pt); Activities
coordinators 1 (ft), 1 (pt); Dietitians 1 (pt).
Facilities Dining room; Physical therapy
room; Activities room; Chapel; Laundry
room; Barber/Beauty shop.
Activities Arts & crafts; Cards; Games;
Reading groups; Prayer groups; Movies;
Shopping trips; Social/Cultural gatherings.

SCOBEY

Daniels Memorial Nursing Home
PO Box 400, 105 5th Ave, Scobey, MT, 59263
(406) 487-2296
Admin Curtis Leibrand. *Medical Dir/Dir of
Nursing* Merle Fitz MD; Naomi Stentoft
DON.
Licensure Skilled care; Intermediate care. *Beds*
SNF 45. *Certified* Medicaid; Medicare; VA.
Owner Nonprofit organization/foundation.
Admissions Requirements Physician's request.
Staff RNs; LPNs; Nurses aides; Activities
coordinators; Dietitians; Dentist.
Facilities Dining room; Activities room;
Chapel; Crafts room; Laundry room; Barber/
Beauty shop; Library.
Activities Arts & crafts; Cards; Games;
Reading groups; Prayer groups; Movies;
Shopping trips; Bingo; Cooking; Bus rides.

SHELBY

Toole County Nursing Home
PO Box P, 640 Park Dr, Shelby, MT, 59474
(406) 434-5536
Admin Todd Hansen. *Medical Dir/Dir of
Nursing* Marian Hultin.
Licensure Skilled care; Intermediate care. *Beds*
43. *Certified* Medicaid; Medicare.
Owner Publicly owned.
Admissions Requirements Physician's request.
Staff Physicians; RNs; LPNs; Nurses aides;
Physical therapists; Activities coordinators.

Facilities Dining room; Physical therapy
room; Activities room; Crafts room;
Laundry room; Barber/Beauty shop.
Activities Arts & crafts; Cards; Games;
Shopping trips.

SHERIDAN

Madison County Nursing Home*
Sheridan, MT, 59749
(406) 842-5600
Admin James Mantz. *Medical Dir/Dir of
Nursing* H D Rossiter MD.
Licensure Intermediate care. *Beds* 39.
Certified Medicaid.
Admissions Requirements Medical
examination.
Staff Physicians 3 (pt); RNs 2 (ft), 2 (pt);
LPNs 4 (pt); Nurses aides 11 (ft), 10 (pt);
Recreational therapists 1 (pt); Activities
coordinators 1 (ft), 1 (pt); Dietitians 1 (pt);
Dentists 1 (pt).
Facilities Dining room; Activities room;
Crafts room; Laundry room; Barber/Beauty
shop.
Activities Arts & crafts; Cards; Games; Prayer
groups; Movies; Shopping trips; Social/
Cultural gatherings.

SIDNEY

Richland Homes Inc
PO Box 5001, Girard Rte, Sidney, MT, 59270
(406) 482-2120
Admin Judy Linder. *Medical Dir/Dir of
Nursing* Dr Ashcraft.
Licensure Intermediate care. *Beds* SNF 10;
ICF 75. *Certified* Medicaid.
Owner Nonprofit Corp.
Admissions Requirements Medical
examination; Physician's request.
Staff Physicians 8 (ft); RNs 3 (ft), 3 (pt);
LPNs 2 (ft), 6 (pt); Nurses aides 40 (ft), 16
(pt); Activities coordinators 1 (ft); Podiatrists
1 (ft).
Facilities Dining room; Chapel; Laundry
room; Barber/Beauty shop.
Activities Arts & crafts; Cards; Games;
Reading groups; Prayer groups; Movies;
Shopping trips; Social/Cultural gatherings;
Adopted grandparents; Outings; Animal
visits; Musical entertainment.

STEVENSVILLE

North Valley Nursing Home*
63 Main, Stevensville, MT, 59870
(406) 777-5411
Admin Nancy Summers. *Medical Dir/Dir of
Nursing* W R Spencer MD.
Licensure Skilled care; Intermediate care. *Beds*
SNF 37; ICF 20. *Certified* Medicaid.
Staff Physicians 2 (pt); RNs 1 (ft), 2 (pt);
LPNs 4 (ft), 2 (pt); Nurses aides 15 (ft), 7
(pt); Activities coordinators 1 (ft).
Facilities Dining room; Activities room;
Crafts room; Laundry room; Barber/Beauty
shop.
Activities Arts & crafts; Cards; Games;
Reading groups; Prayer groups; Movies;
Shopping trips; Social/Cultural gatherings.

SUPERIOR

Mineral County Nursing Home*
Brooklyn & Roosevelt, PO Box 66, Superior,
MT, 59872
(406) 822-4841
Admin Robert E Smith. *Medical Dir/Dir of
Nursing* James P Hoyne MD.
Licensure Skilled care. *Beds* 20. *Certified*
Medicaid; Medicare.
Admissions Requirements Medical
examination; Physician's request.

Staff Physicians 3 (pt); RNs 7 (pt); LPNs 5 (pt); Orderlies 2 (pt); Nurses aides 9 (pt); Physical therapists 1 (pt); Recreational therapists 1 (pt); Activities coordinators 1 (pt); Dietitians 1 (pt); Dentists 1 (pt).
Facilities Dining room; Physical therapy room; Activities room; Crafts room; Laundry room; Barber/Beauty shop.
Activities Arts & crafts; Cards; Games; Reading groups; Prayer groups; Movies; Shopping trips; Social/Cultural gatherings.

TERRY

Prairie Community Nursing Home
PO Box 156, Terry, MT, 59349
(406) 637-5511
Admin Mark Johnson. *Medical Dir/Dir of Nursing* Adele Lukaszewicz MD; Carleen Gaub RN DON.
Licensure Skilled care; Intermediate care. *Beds* 14. *Certified* Medicaid; Medicare.
Owner Publicly owned.
Admissions Requirements Medical examination; Physician's request.
Staff Physicians 1 (ft); RNs 2 (ft), 5 (pt); Nurses aides 3 (ft), 6 (pt); Activities coordinators 1 (ft), 1 (pt); Dietitians 1 (ft).
Facilities Dining room; Laundry room.
Activities Arts & crafts; Games; Reading groups; Prayer groups; Movies.

TOWNSEND

Broadwater County Rest Home
PO Box G, Townsend, MT, 59644
(406) 266-3711
Admin Audrey A Solberg.
Licensure Personal care. *Beds* 16. *Certified* Medicaid.
Owner Publicly owned.
Admissions Requirements Minimum age 18; Medical examination; Physician's request.
Staff Nurses aides 3 (ft), 3 (pt); Activities coordinators 1 (ft); Dietitians 1 (ft), 1 (pt).
Facilities Dining room; Activities room; Crafts room; Laundry room; Barber/Beauty shop.

Activities Arts & crafts; Cards; Games; Reading groups; Prayer groups; Movies; Shopping trips; Social/Cultural gatherings; Crafts; Exercise groups; Singing; Music.

WARM SPRINGS

Warm Springs State Hospital*
Bldg 219, Warm Springs, MT, 59756
(406) 693-2221
Admin Richard Moore.
Licensure Skilled care; Intermediate care. *Beds* SNF 8; ICF 52. *Certified* Medicaid; Medicare.

WHITE SULPHUR SPRINGS

Mountainview Memorial Hospital & Nursing Home
Box Q, White Sulphur Springs, MT, 59645
(406) 547-3321
Admin Larry Putnam. *Medical Dir/Dir of Nursing* Dr Pam Hiebert; Mary Hamel RN.
Licensure Skilled care; Intermediate care. *Beds* 31. *Certified* Medicaid; Medicare.
Owner Nonprofit Corp.
Admissions Requirements Physician's request.
Staff RNs 6 (ft); LPNs 3 (ft); Nurses aides 6 (ft), 2 (pt); Physical therapists 1 (pt); Activities coordinators 1 (ft); Dietitians 1 (pt).
Affiliation Lutheran
Facilities Dining room; Physical therapy room; Laundry room.
Activities Arts & crafts; Cards; Games; Reading groups; Movies.

WHITEFISH

Colonial Manor Nursing Home*
PO Box 1359, E 7th St, Whitefish, MT, 59937
(406) 862-3557
Admin Betty Elder.
Licensure Intermediate care. *Beds* 60. *Certified* Medicaid.
Owner Proprietary Corp (Beverly Enterprises).

North Valley Hospital & Extended Care Center*
PO Box 68, Hwy 93 S, Whitefish, MT, 59937
(406) 862-2501

Admin Dale Jessup.
Licensure Skilled care; Intermediate care. *Beds* SNF 50; ICF 6. *Certified* Medicaid; Medicare.

WIBAUX

Wibaux County Nursing Home
601 S Wibaux St, Wibaux, MT, 59353
(406) 795-2429
Admin Bill O'Hara. *Medical Dir/Dir of Nursing* Dr Nancy Rausch MD; Barbara Stockwell RN DON.
Licensure Skilled care. *Beds* SNF 40. *Certified* Medicaid; Medicare.
Owner Publicly owned.
Admissions Requirements Medical examination; Physician's request.
Staff RNs 2 (ft), 3 (pt); LPNs 2 (ft); Orderlies 1 (ft); Nurses aides 5 (ft), 14 (pt); Activities coordinators 1 (ft).
Facilities Dining room; Activities room; Chapel; Crafts room; Laundry room; Barber/Beauty shop.
Activities Arts & crafts; Cards; Games; Reading groups; Movies.

WOLF POINT

Faith Lutheran Home
1000 6th Ave N, Wolf Point, MT, 59201
(406) 653-1400
Admin Greg Sorum. *Medical Dir/Dir of Nursing* Elaine Keane.
Licensure Intermediate care. *Beds* ICF 60. *Certified* Medicaid.
Owner Nonprofit Corp.
Admissions Requirements Medical examination.
Staff RNs 1 (ft); LPNs 3 (ft), 3 (pt); Orderlies 1 (ft), 1 (pt); Nurses aides 10 (ft), 15 (pt); Activities coordinators 1 (ft).
Affiliation Lutheran
Facilities Dining room; Physical therapy room; Activities room; Chapel; Crafts room; Laundry room; Barber/Beauty shop; Library.
Activities Arts & crafts; Cards; Games; Reading groups; Prayer groups; Movies; Shopping trips; Social/Cultural gatherings.

NEBRASKA

ADAMS

Gold Crest Retirement Center
PO Box 78, Adams, NE, 68301
(402) 988-7115
Admin James M Helmink. *Medical Dir/Dir of Nursing* Dr Monroe Dowling.
Licensure Skilled care; Intermediate care; Residential care. *Beds* SNF 52; ICF; Residential 40.
Owner Nonprofit Corp.
Admissions Requirements Medical examination; Physician's request.
Staff Physicians 1 (ft); RNs 5 (ft); LPNs 3 (ft); Nurses aides 20 (ft); Physical therapists 1 (ft); Activities coordinators 2 (ft); Dietitians 1 (ft).
Languages German, Swedish, Danish
Facilities Dining room; Physical therapy room; Activities room; Chapel; Crafts room; Laundry room; Barber/Beauty shop; Library.
Activities Arts & crafts; Cards; Games; Reading groups; Prayer groups; Movies; Shopping trips.

AINSWORTH

Bethesda Care Center
143 N Fullerton St, Ainsworth, NE, 69210
(402) 387-2500
Admin Melanie Palmer. *Medical Dir/Dir of Nursing* Dr F Shiffermiler; Diana Syfie.
Licensure Intermediate care. *Beds* ICF 47. *Certified* Medicaid.
Owner Nonprofit Corp (Bethesda Care Centers).
Admissions Requirements Medical examination; Physician's request.
Staff RNs 1 (ft), 1 (pt); LPNs 2 (ft), 2 (pt); Nurses aides 12 (ft), 6 (pt); Physical therapists 1 (ft); Activities coordinators 1 (ft), 1 (pt).
Facilities Dining room; Activities room; Laundry room; Barber/Beauty shop.
Activities Arts & crafts; Cards; Games; Reading groups; Prayer groups; Shopping trips; Social/Cultural gatherings.

ALBION

Wolf Memorial Good Samaritan Center
1222 S 7th St, Albion, NE, 68620
(402) 395-5050
Admin Shelly Henderson. *Medical Dir/Dir of Nursing* Shirley Price DNS.
Licensure Intermediate care. *Beds* ICF 62. *Certified* Medicaid.
Owner Nonprofit Corp (Evangelical Lutheran/ Good Samaritan).
Admissions Requirements Medical examination; Physician's request.
Staff RNs 2 (ft); LPNs 8 (ft); Nurses aides 35 (ft); Physical therapists 3 (ft); Recreational therapists 1 (ft); Occupational therapists; Speech therapists; Activities coordinators 1 (ft); Dietitians 1 (ft); Ophthalmologists 1 (ft); Podiatrists.

Affiliation Lutheran
Facilities Dining room; Physical therapy room; Activities room; Chapel; Crafts room; Laundry room; Barber/Beauty shop.
Activities Arts & crafts; Cards; Games; Reading groups; Prayer groups; Movies; Social/Cultural gatherings.

ALLIANCE

Good Samaritan Village
1016 E 6th St, Alliance, NE, 69301
(308) 762-5675
Admin Jerry Walker. *Medical Dir/Dir of Nursing* Magda Greene RN DON.
Licensure Intermediate care. *Beds* 106. *Certified* Medicaid.
Owner Nonprofit Corp (Evangelical Lutheran/ Good Samaritan).
Admissions Requirements Medical examination.
Staff RNs 3 (ft), 3 (pt); LPNs 4 (ft), 6 (pt); Nurses aides 15 (ft), 24 (pt); Physical therapists 1 (pt); Activities coordinators 2 (ft), 1 (pt).
Affiliation Lutheran
Facilities Dining room; Physical therapy room; Activities room; Chapel; Crafts room; Laundry room; Barber/Beauty shop; Library.
Activities Arts & crafts; Cards; Games; Reading groups; Prayer groups; Movies; Social/Cultural gatherings.

St Joseph Gerontology Center
416 W 11th St, Alliance, NE, 69301
(308) 762-2525
Admin Cheryl Mundt. *Medical Dir/Dir of Nursing* Dr John Ruffing; Betty Leistritz.
Licensure Skilled care; Intermediate care. *Beds* 61. *Certified* Medicaid; Medicare.
Owner Nonprofit Corp.
Admissions Requirements Medical examination; Physician's request.
Staff RNs; LPNs; Orderlies; Nurses aides; Activities coordinators.
Affiliation Roman Catholic
Facilities Dining room; Activities room; Chapel; Crafts room; Laundry room; Barber/ Beauty shop; Library; Hospitality room; Special dining room.
Activities Arts & crafts; Cards; Games; Reading groups; Prayer groups; Movies; Shopping trips; Social/Cultural gatherings; Birthday parties; News & exercise class.

ALMA

Colonial Villa Good Samaritan Center
719 N Brown, Alma, NE, 68920
(308) 928-2128
Admin Peggy Hodde. *Medical Dir/Dir of Nursing* Mary W Goessling.
Licensure Intermediate care. *Beds* 61. *Certified* Medicaid.
Owner Nonprofit Corp (Evangelical Lutheran/ Good Samaritan).

Admissions Requirements Medical examination; Physician's request.
Staff RNs 1 (ft), 1 (pt); LPNs 5 (pt); Nurses aides 10 (ft), 20 (pt); Physical therapists 1 (pt); Occupational therapists 1 (pt); Speech therapists 1 (pt); Activities coordinators 1 (ft); Dietitians 3 (ft), 4 (pt).
Affiliation Lutheran
Facilities Dining room; Activities room; Chapel; Crafts room; Laundry room; Barber/ Beauty shop.
Activities Arts & crafts; Cards; Games; Reading groups; Prayer groups; Movies; Shopping trips.

ARAPAHOE

C A Mues Memorial Good Samaritan Center
601 Main St, Arapahoe, NE, 68922
(308) 962-5230
Admin Lawrence Eickhoff. *Medical Dir/Dir of Nursing* Beverly Anderson.
Licensure Intermediate care. *Beds* ICF 53. *Certified* Medicaid.
Owner Nonprofit Corp (Evangelical Lutheran/ Good Samaritan).
Admissions Requirements Medical examination; Physician's request.
Staff RNs 2 (ft); LPNs 3 (ft), 2 (pt); Nurses aides 18 (ft), 8 (pt); Activities coordinators 1 (ft); Dietitians 1 (pt).
Affiliation Lutheran
Facilities Dining room; Physical therapy room; Activities room; Chapel; Laundry room; Barber/Beauty shop; Prayer garden.
Activities Arts & crafts; Cards; Games; Reading groups; Prayer groups; Movies; Social/Cultural gatherings; Gardening; Fishing trips.

ASHLAND

Bethesda Care Center of Ashland
1700 Furnas St, Ashland, NE, 68003
(402) 944-7031
Admin Shirley L Hemke. *Medical Dir/Dir of Nursing* Betsy Lynch DON.
Licensure Intermediate care. *Beds* ICF 100. *Certified* Medicaid.
Owner Nonprofit Corp (Bethesda Care Centers).
Admissions Requirements Medical examination; Physician's request.
Staff RNs 2 (ft), 1 (pt); LPNs 5 (ft); Orderlies 1 (ft); Nurses aides 24 (ft), 6 (pt); Physical therapists 2 (ft); Activities coordinators 2 (ft), 1 (pt); Dietitians 1 (pt); Ophthalmologists 1 (pt).
Facilities Dining room; Physical therapy room; Activities room; Chapel; Crafts room; Laundry room; Barber/Beauty shop; Large dayroom.
Activities Arts & crafts; Cards; Games; Reading groups; Prayer groups; Movies; Shopping trips; Social/Cultural gatherings; Hand bell choirs; Van rides; Picnics.

ATKINSON

Atkinson Good Samaritan Center
PO Box 699, Atkinson, NE, 68713
(402) 925-2875
Admin Phyllis Langan. *Medical Dir/Dir of
Nursing* Sharon Spangler RN.
Licensure Intermediate care. *Beds* 62.
Certified Medicaid.
Owner Nonprofit Corp (Evangelical Lutheran/
Good Samaritan).
Admissions Requirements Medical
examination.
Staff RNs 2 (ft), 1 (pt); LPNs 1 (ft), 4 (pt);
Nurses aides 3 (ft), 18 (pt); Activities
coordinators 1 (ft).
Affiliation Lutheran
Facilities Dining room; Activities room;
Chapel; Laundry room.
Activities Arts & crafts; Cards; Games;
Reading groups; Prayer groups; Movies;
Shopping trips; Social/Cultural gatherings.

AUBURN

Nemaha County Good Samaritan Center*
Rte 1, Box 4, Auburn, NE, 68305
(402) 274-3109
Admin Daniel H Guenther.
Licensure Intermediate care. *Beds* 113.
Certified Medicaid.
Owner Nonprofit Corp (Evangelical Lutheran/
Good Samaritan).
Affiliation Lutheran

AURORA

Bethesda Care Center
610-616 13th St, Aurora, NE, 68818
(402) 694-6905
Admin Diane Schlotman. *Medical Dir/Dir of
Nursing* Judith Trumble.
Licensure Intermediate care. *Beds* ICF 45.
Certified Medicaid.
Owner Nonprofit Corp (Bethesda Care
Centers).
Admissions Requirements Physician's request.
Staff RNs; LPNs; Orderlies; Nurses aides;
Recreational therapists; Activities
coordinators; Dietitians.
Languages German
Facilities Dining room; Activities room;
Laundry room; Barber/Beauty shop; Library.
Activities Arts & crafts; Cards; Games;
Reading groups; Prayer groups; Movies;
Shopping trips; Social/Cultural gatherings.

Hamilton Manor*
1515 5th St, Aurora, NE, 68818
(402) 694-2128
Admin Barry D Robertshaw.
Licensure Intermediate care. *Beds* 109.
Certified Medicaid.
Owner Publicly owned.

AXTELL

Bethpage at Axtell
1 N Mission Rd, Axtell, NE, 68924
(308) 743-2401
Admin Sherril R Hansen. *Medical Dir/Dir of
Nursing* Linda Mattson.
Licensure Intermediate care for mentally
retarded. *Beds* ICF/MR 180. *Certified*
Medicaid; Medicare.
Owner Nonprofit Corp.
Admissions Requirements Medical
examination; Physician's request.
Staff Physicians; RNs; LPNs; Nurses aides;
Physical therapists; Recreational therapists;
Occupational therapists; Speech therapists;
Activities coordinators; Dietitians;
Podiatrists.
Languages Spanish
Affiliation Lutheran

Facilities Dining room; Physical therapy
room; Activities room; Chapel; Crafts room;
Laundry room; Barber/Beauty shop; Library;
Classrooms; Swimming pool.
Activities Arts & crafts; Cards; Games;
Reading groups; Movies; Shopping trips;
Social/Cultural gatherings; Training; Cultural
gatherings; Swimming; Outdoor sports.

BASSETT

Bethesda Care Center of Bassett
519 Fort St, Bassett, NE, 68714
(402) 684-3388
Admin Sonya Phillis. *Medical Dir/Dir of
Nursing* Catherine S Clark RN DON.
Licensure Intermediate care. *Beds* ICF 30.
Certified Medicaid.
Owner Nonprofit Corp (Bethesda Care
Centers).
Admissions Requirements Medical
examination; Physician's request.
Staff RNs 1 (ft), 1 (pt); LPNs 1 (ft), 1 (pt);
Nurses aides 8 (ft), 3 (pt); Activities
coordinators 1 (ft).
Facilities Dining room; Activities room;
Laundry room; Barber/Beauty shop.
Activities Arts & crafts; Cards; Games;
Reading groups; Prayer groups; Movies;
Shopping trips; Social/Cultural gatherings;
Weekly van rides.

BAYARD

Chimney Rock Villa
106 E 13th St, Bayard, NE, 69334
(308) 586-1142
Admin Alexander Beninger. *Medical Dir/Dir
of Nursing* Diana Stevens RN DON.
Licensure Intermediate care. *Beds* ICF 47.
Certified Medicaid.
Owner Proprietary Corp.
Admissions Requirements Medical
examination; Physician's request.
Staff RNs 1 (ft); LPNs 4 (ft); Nurses aides 8
(ft), 8 (pt); Physical therapists 1 (pt);
Occupational therapists 1 (pt); Activities
coordinators 1 (ft); Dietitians 1 (ft).
Facilities Dining room; Activities room;
Laundry room; Barber/Beauty shop; Library.
Activities Arts & crafts; Cards; Games;
Reading groups; Prayer groups; Movies.

BEATRICE

Beatrice Manor Care Center*
1800 Irving, Beatrice, NE, 68310
(402) 223-2311
Admin Allen Siebert.
Licensure Intermediate care. *Beds* 62.
Certified Medicaid.
Owner Proprietary Corp.
Admissions Requirements Medical
examination; Physician's request.
Staff LPNs 5 (ft); Nurses aides 15 (ft), 10 (pt);
Activities coordinators 1 (ft).
Facilities Dining room; Activities room;
Laundry room; Barber/Beauty shop.
Activities Arts & crafts; Cards; Games;
Reading groups; Prayer groups; Movies;
Shopping trips; Social/Cultural gatherings.

Good Samaritan Home & Center*
1306 S 9th St, Beatrice, NE, 68310
(402) 223-3304
Admin William S Kubat Jr.
Licensure Intermediate care. *Beds* 130.
Certified Medicaid.
Owner Nonprofit Corp (Evangelical Lutheran/
Good Samaritan).
Affiliation Lutheran

Martin Luther Home
804 S 12th St, Beatrice, NE, 68310
(402) 223-4066
Admin Donna C Johnsen. *Medical Dir/Dir of
Nursing* Janice Grummert.

Licensure Intermediate care for mentally
retarded. *Beds* ICF/MR 146. *Certified*
Medicaid.
Owner Nonprofit organization/foundation.
Admissions Requirements Minimum age 5;
Medical examination.
Staff RNs 2 (ft); LPNs 4 (ft); Nurses aides 94
(ft); Speech therapists 1 (ft); Activities
coordinators 1 (ft); Dietitians 1 (ft).
Affiliation Lutheran
Facilities Dining room; Physical therapy
room; Activities room; Chapel; Crafts room;
Laundry room; Barber/Beauty shop; Library.
Activities Arts & crafts; Cards; Games;
Reading groups; Movies; Shopping trips;
Social/Cultural gatherings; Special olympics.

BEAVER CITY

Beaver City Manor*
905 Floyd St, Beaver City, NE, 68926
(308) 268-5111
Admin Thomas D Hardin.
Licensure Intermediate care. *Beds* 52.
Certified Medicaid.
Owner Publicly owned.

BEEMER

Colonial Haven
RR 1, Beemer, NE, 68716
(402) 528-3268. 528-3269
Admin Thomas J Schulte. *Medical Dir/Dir of
Nursing* Marian Brockmann RN.
Licensure Intermediate care. *Beds* 55.
Certified Medicaid.
Owner Publicly owned.
Admissions Requirements Medical
examination.
Staff Physicians 6 (pt); RNs 1 (ft), 4 (pt);
LPNs 1 (ft), 3 (pt); Orderlies 2 (pt); Nurses
aides 3 (ft), 40 (pt); Physical therapists 1
(pt); Occupational therapists 1 (pt); Speech
therapists 2 (pt); Activities coordinators 3
(pt); Dietitians 1 (pt); Dentists 3 (pt);
Ophthalmologists 1 (pt); Podiatrists 1 (pt).
Facilities Dining room; Physical therapy
room; Activities room; Chapel; Crafts room;
Laundry room; Barber/Beauty shop.
Activities Arts & crafts; Cards; Games;
Reading groups; Prayer groups; Movies;
Shopping trips; Social/Cultural gatherings.

BELLEVUE

Hillcrest Care Center Inc
1702 N Hillcrest Dr, Bellevue, NE, 68005
(402) 291-8500
Admin Martha L Tiller. *Medical Dir/Dir of
Nursing* Joan Mitchell.
Licensure Intermediate care. *Beds* ICF 116.
Certified Medicaid.
Owner Privately owned.
Admissions Requirements Medical
examination; Physician's request.
Staff RNs 3 (ft); LPNs; Physical therapists;
Reality therapists; Recreational therapists;
Occupational therapists; Speech therapists;
Activities coordinators; Dietitians;
Ophthalmologists.
Facilities Dining room; Activities room;
Laundry room; Barber/Beauty shop.
Activities Arts & crafts; Cards; Games;
Reading groups; Prayer groups; Movies;
Shopping trips.

BENKELMAN

Sarah Ann Hester Memorial Home
350 East St SW, Benkelman, NE, 69021
(308) 423-2179
Admin Marvin L Zimbelman.
Licensure Intermediate care. *Beds* 58.
Certified Medicaid.
Owner Nonprofit Corp.

Admissions Requirements Medical
examination; Physician's request.
Staff RNs 2 (ft); LPNs 3 (ft); Orderlies 1 (ft);
Nurses aides 22 (ft); Activities coordinators
1 (ft).
Facilities Dining room; Activities room;
Chapel; Crafts room; Laundry room; Barber/
Beauty shop.
Activities Arts & crafts; Cards; Games;
Reading groups; Movies.

BERTRAND

Bertrand Nursing Home*
100 Minor Ave, Bertrand, NE, 68927
(308) 472-3341
Admin Ray Hanson. *Medical Dir/Dir of
Nursing* Sylvia Sattler.
Licensure Intermediate care. *Beds* 47.
Certified Medicaid.
Owner Publicly owned.
Admissions Requirements Medical
examination; Physician's request.
Facilities Dining room; Activities room;
Chapel; Crafts room; Laundry room; Barber/
Beauty shop; Library.
Activities Arts & crafts; Cards; Games;
Reading groups; Prayer groups; Movies.

BLAIR

Crowell Memorial Home*
245 S 22nd St, Blair, NE, 68008
(402) 426-2177
Admin Morland Adell.
Licensure Intermediate care. *Beds* 127.
Certified Medicaid.
Owner Nonprofit Corp.

Good Shepherd Lutheran Home
2242 Wright St, Blair, NE, 68008
(402) 426-3377
Admin Marlys Horky. *Medical Dir/Dir of
Nursing* Kathy Cox RN DON.
Licensure Skilled care; Intermediate care;
Residential. *Beds* 104. *Certified* Medicaid.
Owner Nonprofit organization/foundation.
Admissions Requirements Medical
examination; Physician's request.
Staff RNs 3 (ft), 2 (pt); LPNs 5 (ft), 5 (pt);
Nurses aides 20 (ft), 15 (pt); Physical
therapists 1 (pt); Speech therapists 1 (pt);
Dietitians 1 (pt).
Affiliation Lutheran
Facilities Dining room; Activities room;
Chapel; Crafts room; Laundry room; Barber/
Beauty shop.
Activities Arts & crafts; Cards; Games;
Reading groups; Prayer groups; Movies;
Shopping trips; Social/Cultural gatherings.

BLOOMFIELD

Bloomfield Good Samaritan Center
300 North Second, Bloomfield, NE, 68718
(402) 373-4506
Admin Timothy M Dardis. *Medical Dir/Dir of
Nursing* Dr D J Nagengast; Dolores Broders
RN DON.
Licensure Skilled care; Intermediate care. *Beds*
80. *Certified* Medicaid.
Owner Nonprofit Corp (Evangelical Lutheran/
Good Samaritan).
Admissions Requirements Medical
examination.
Staff RNs 1 (ft), 3 (pt); LPNs 2 (ft), 3 (pt);
Nurses aides; Physical therapists;
Occupational therapists 1 (pt); Speech
therapists 1 (pt); Activities coordinators 1
(ft); Dietitians 1 (pt); Dentists 1 (pt);
Ophthalmologists 1 (pt); Podiatrists 1 (pt).
Affiliation Lutheran
Facilities Dining room; Physical therapy
room; Activities room; Chapel; Crafts room;
Laundry room; Barber/Beauty shop.

Activities Arts & crafts; Cards; Games;
Reading groups; Prayer groups; Movies;
Shopping trips; Social/Cultural gatherings.

BLUE HILL

Bethesda Care Center of Blue Hill
Box 156, 414 N Wilson, Blue Hill, NE, 68930
(402) 756-2080
Admin Diann M Schmidt. *Medical Dir/Dir of
Nursing* Frank Kamm MD; Debra Krueger
DON.
Licensure Intermediate care. *Beds* ICF 81.
Certified Medicaid.
Owner Nonprofit Corp (Bethesda Care
Centers).
Admissions Requirements Medical
examination.
Staff RNs 1 (ft); LPNs 2 (ft), 1 (pt); Nurses
aides 24 (ft), 9 (pt); Physical therapists 1
(pt); Occupational therapists 1 (pt); Speech
therapists 1 (pt); Recreational therapists 2
(ft); Activities coordinators 1 (ft); Dietitians
1 (pt); Podiatrists 1 (pt).
Facilities Dining room; Activities room;
Chapel; Crafts room; Barber/Beauty shop.
Activities Arts & crafts; Cards; Games;
Reading groups; Prayer groups; Movies;
Shopping trips; Baking; Recreational trips.

BRIDGEPORT

Heritage of Bridgeport
5th & N Sts, Bridgeport, NE, 69336
(308) 262-0725
Admin David Creal. *Medical Dir/Dir of
Nursing* Evelyn Rose RN DON.
Licensure Intermediate care. *Beds* ICF 61.
Certified Medicaid.
Owner Proprietary Corp (Vetter Health
Services).
Admissions Requirements Medical
examination.
Staff RNs 2 (ft); LPNs 2 (ft), 1 (pt); Nurses
aides 12 (ft), 5 (pt); Reality therapists 1 (ft);
Activities coordinators 1 (ft).
Facilities Dining room; Activities room;
Barber/Beauty shop.
Activities Arts & crafts; Games; Prayer groups;
Movies; Shopping trips; Social/Cultural
gatherings.

BROKEN BOW

Sandhills Manor
E Hwy 2, Broken Bow, NE, 68822
(308) 872-6421
Admin Clarine Dickinson. *Medical Dir/Dir of
Nursing* Jodi McCoy RN DON.
Licensure Intermediate care. *Beds* ICF 105.
Certified Medicaid.
Owner Proprietary Corp (Beverly Enterprises).
Admissions Requirements Medical
examination; Physician's request.
Staff RNs; LPNs; Orderlies; Nurses aides;
Activities coordinators.
Facilities Dining room; Physical therapy
room; Activities room; Chapel; Crafts room;
Laundry room; Barber/Beauty shop.
Activities Arts & crafts; Cards; Games;
Reading groups; Prayer groups; Movies;
Shopping trips; Social/Cultural gatherings.

BUTTE

Butte Nursing Home
Box 49, Butte, NE, 68722
(402) 775-2355
Admin Myron Armfield. *Medical Dir/Dir of
Nursing* Susan Lechtenberg.
Licensure Intermediate care. *Beds* ICF 62.
Certified Medicaid.
Owner Publicly owned.
Admissions Requirements Medical
examination.

Staff Physicians 2 (pt); RNs 2 (ft); LPNs 1
(ft), 2 (pt); Nurses aides 10 (ft), 15 (pt);
Physical therapists 1 (pt); Activities
coordinators 1 (ft); Dietitians 1 (ft).
Facilities Dining room; Activities room;
Laundry room; Barber/Beauty shop.
Activities Arts & crafts; Cards; Games;
Reading groups; Prayer groups; Movies;
Shopping trips; Social/Cultural gatherings.

CALLAWAY

Callaway Good Samaritan Home
PO Box 398, Callaway, NE, 68825
(308) 836-2267
Admin Greg C Staudenmaier. *Medical Dir/Dir
of Nursing* Joann Farmer.
Licensure Intermediate care. *Beds* ICF 45.
Certified Medicaid.
Owner Nonprofit Corp (Evangelical Lutheran/
Good Samaritan).
Staff RNs 1 (ft), 1 (pt); LPNs 2 (ft), 3 (pt);
Nurses aides 5 (ft), 10 (pt); Activities
coordinators 1 (ft).
Affiliation Lutheran
Facilities Dining room; Activities room;
Laundry room; Barber/Beauty shop; Library.
Activities Arts & crafts; Cards; Games;
Movies; Social/Cultural gatherings.

CAMPBELL

Grandview Manor Nursing Home
Broad St & Hwy 4, Campbell, NE, 68932
(402) 756-8701
Admin Shirley L'Heureux. *Medical Dir/Dir of
Nursing* Diani Brooks.
Licensure Intermediate care. *Beds* ICF 49.
Certified Medicaid.
Owner Nonprofit Corp (Bethesda Care
Centers).
Staff RNs; LPNs; Nurses aides.
Facilities Dining room; Activities room;
Chapel; Laundry room; Barber/Beauty shop.
Activities Arts & crafts; Cards; Games;
Reading groups; Prayer groups; Movies.

CENTRAL CITY

Bethesda Care Center
S 17th Ave, Central City, NE, 68826
(308) 946-3088
Admin Donice Woodworth. *Medical Dir/Dir
of Nursing* Linda Tyler RN.
Licensure Intermediate care. *Beds* ICF 72.
Certified Medicaid.
Owner Nonprofit Corp (Bethesda Care
Centers).
Admissions Requirements Physician's request.
Staff RNs 1 (ft), 2 (pt); LPNs 2 (ft), 1 (pt);
Nurses aides 8 (ft), 16 (pt); Physical
therapists 1 (pt); Speech therapists 1 (pt);
Activities coordinators 1 (ft), 1 (pt);
Dietitians 1 (pt).
Facilities Dining room; Activities room;
Chapel; Crafts room; Laundry room; Barber/
Beauty shop.
Activities Arts & crafts; Cards; Games;
Reading groups; Prayer groups; Movies;
Shopping trips; Social/Cultural gatherings;
Picnics; Resident council group; Alzheimer
support group.

CHADRON

Crest View Manor*
420 Gordon Ave, Chadron, NE, 69337
(308) 432-3355
Admin John Bray. *Medical Dir/Dir of Nursing*
R H Rasmussen MD.
Licensure Skilled care; Intermediate care. *Beds*
70. *Certified* Medicaid.
Owner Proprietary Corp (Beverly Enterprises).
Staff RNs 2 (ft), 1 (pt); LPNs 6 (ft), 2 (pt);
Nurses aides 25 (ft), 5 (pt); Activities
coordinators 1 (ft); Dietitians 1 (pt).

Facilities Dining room; Activities room;
Chapel; Crafts room; Laundry room; Barber/
Beauty shop.
Activities Arts & crafts; Cards; Games;
Reading groups; Prayer groups; Movies;
Social/Cultural gatherings.

CHAPPELL

Miller Memorial Nursing Home
589 Vincent Ave, Chappell, NE, 69129
(308) 874-2292
Admin Patricia Livengood. *Medical Dir/Dir of
Nursing* Mary Groves RN.
Licensure Intermediate care; Residential care.
Beds ICF 24; Residential 12. *Certified*
Medicaid.
Owner Publicly owned.
Admissions Requirements Medical
examination; Physician's request.
Staff RNs 1 (ft); LPNs 2 (ft), 2 (pt); Nurses
aides 3 (ft), 10 (pt); Activities coordinators 1
(pt).
Facilities Dining room; Activities room;
Crafts room; Laundry room; Barber/Beauty
shop; Solarium.
Activities Arts & crafts; Cards; Games;
Reading groups; Movies; Social/Cultural
gatherings.

CLARKSON

Colonial Manor of Clarkson
PO Box J, W 3rd Sunrise Dr, Clarkson, NE,
68629
(402) 892-3494
Admin William M Harris. *Medical Dir/Dir of
Nursing* John O'Neal MD; Elaine
Roggenstein RN DON.
Licensure Intermediate care. Beds ICF 60.
Certified Medicaid.
Owner Proprietary Corp (Beverly Enterprises).
Admissions Requirements Medical
examination; Physician's request.
Staff RNs; LPNs; Nurses aides; Activities
coordinators.
Languages Czech
Facilities Dining room; Physical therapy
room; Activities room; Chapel; Laundry
room; Barber/Beauty shop.
Activities Arts & crafts; Cards; Games;
Reading groups; Prayer groups; Movies;
Shopping trips; Social/Cultural gatherings.

COLERIDGE

Parkview Haven*
PO Box 39, 325 N Madison, Coleridge, NE,
68727
(402) 283-4224
Admin Terry Sharron.
Licensure Intermediate care. Beds 67.
Certified Medicaid.
Owner Publicly owned.

COLUMBUS

Columbus Manor*
3918 27th St, Columbus, NE, 68601
(402) 564-8014
Admin Carl Haase.
Licensure Skilled care; Intermediate care. Beds
145. *Certified* Medicaid.
Owner Proprietary Corp.

Val Morys Haven
1112 15th St, Columbus, NE, 68601
(402) 564-3197
Admin Joe Hageman. *Medical Dir/Dir of
Nursing* Donna Wasco RN DON.
Licensure Intermediate care. Beds ICF 46.
Certified Medicaid.
Owner Nonprofit organization/foundation.
Admissions Requirements Medical
examination; Physician's request.

Staff RNs 1 (ft), 4 (pt) 13C 4 (ft), 2 (pt);
Nurses aides 7 (ft), 15 (pt); Activities
coordinators 1 (ft).
Facilities Dining room; Activities room;
Chapel; Crafts room; Laundry room.
Activities Arts & crafts; Cards; Games;
Reading groups; Prayer groups; Movies;
Shopping trips; Social/Cultural gatherings.

CRAWFORD

Ponderosa Villa
1st & Paddock, Crawford, NE, 69339
(308) 655-1224
Admin Dixie G Moody.
Licensure Intermediate care. Beds 55.
Certified Medicaid.
Owner Publicly owned.
Admissions Requirements Medical
examination; Physician's request.
Staff RNs 1 (ft), 3 (pt); LPNs 2 (ft), 2 (pt);
Activities coordinators 1 (ft); Dietitians 1
(pt).
Facilities Dining room; Activities room;
Chapel; Crafts room; Laundry room; Barber/
Beauty shop; Library.
Activities Arts & crafts; Cards; Games;
Reading groups; Prayer groups; Movies;
Shopping trips; Social/Cultural gatherings.

CREIGHTON

Creighton Care Centre*
Main St at Lundberg Dr, Creighton, NE,
68729
(402) 358-3232
Admin Delberta Peterson.
Licensure Intermediate care. Beds 50.
Certified Medicaid.
Owner Proprietary Corp.

CRETE

Crete Manor
1st & Boswell Sts, Crete, NE, 68333
(402) 826-4325
Admin John C Snyder. *Medical Dir/Dir of
Nursing* Jan Clark RN DON.
Licensure Intermediate care. Beds 96; Locked
Alzheimer's unit 14. *Certified* Medicaid.
Owner Proprietary Corp (ARA Living
Centers).
Admissions Requirements Medical
examination.
Staff RNs 1 (ft), 1 (pt); LPNs 6 (ft); Orderlies
1 (ft), 4 (pt); Nurses aides 18 (ft), 20 (pt);
Physical therapists 1 (pt); Occupational
therapists 1 (pt); Speech therapists 1 (pt);
Activities coordinators 1 (ft), 1 (pt);
Dietitians 1 (pt).
Facilities Dining room; Chapel; Barber/Beauty
shop; Library; Lounges.
Activities Arts & crafts; Cards; Games; Prayer
groups; Movies; Social/Cultural gatherings.

CURTIS

Sunset Haven Nursing Home*
902 Howard St, Curtis, NE, 69025
(308) 367-8388
Admin Elda Roethemeyer.
Licensure Intermediate care. Beds 49.
Certified Medicaid.
Owner Nonprofit Corp.
Admissions Requirements Medical
examination.
Staff RNs 1 (pt); LPNs 1 (ft), 4 (pt); Nurses
aides 6 (ft), 6 (pt); Activities coordinators 1
(ft); Dietitians 1 (pt).
Facilities Dining room; Activities room;
Chapel; Laundry room; Barber/Beauty shop.
Activities Arts & crafts; Cards; Games;
Reading groups.

CUZAD

Southview Manor Care Center
318 W 18th St, Cuzad, NE, 69130
(308) 784-3715
Admin Bernard Correll. *Medical Dir/Dir of
Nursing* Judy Gibson RN.
Licensure Skilled care. Beds SNF 12; ICF 78.
Certified Medicaid.
Owner Proprietary Corp (Beverly Enterprises).
Admissions Requirements Medical
examination; Physician's request.
Staff RNs 2 (ft), 2 (pt); LPNs 11 (ft), 3 (pt);
Nurses aides 20 (ft), 8 (pt); Physical
therapists 1 (ft); Activities coordinators 1
(ft), 1 (pt); Dietitians 1 (ft).
Facilities Dining room; Physical therapy
room; Activities room; Chapel; Laundry
room; Barber/Beauty shop.
Activities Arts & crafts; Cards; Games;
Reading groups; Prayer groups; Movies;
Shopping trips; Social/Cultural gatherings.

DAVID CITY

Heritage of David City
PO Box 321, 260 S 10th, David City, NE,
68632
(402) 367-3144
Admin Mary Lee High. *Medical Dir/Dir of
Nursing* Gerald Luckey MD; Mary
Steinberger DON.
Licensure Skilled care; Intermediate care. Beds
93. *Certified* Medicaid; Medicare; VA.
Owner Proprietary Corp (Vetter Health
Services).
Admissions Requirements Medical
examination; Physician's request.
Staff RNs 20 (ft); LPNs 3 (ft); Nurses aides 35
(ft); Activities coordinators 1 (ft).
Facilities Dining room; Physical therapy
room; Activities room; Chapel; Crafts room;
Laundry room; Barber/Beauty shop.
Activities Arts & crafts; Cards; Games;
Reading groups; Prayer groups; Shopping
trips; Social/Cultural gatherings.

St Josephs Villa Inc
927 7th St, David City, NE, 68632
(402) 367-3045
Admin Sr Esther Marie Miller. *Medical Dir/
Dir of Nursing* Dr G Luckey; Sr Flora
Jentgen.
Licensure Intermediate care. Beds 65.
Certified Medicaid.
Owner Nonprofit Corp.
Admissions Requirements Minimum age 65;
Medical examination; Physician's request.
Staff RNs; LPNs; Nurses aides; Activities
coordinators; Dietitians.
Affiliation Roman Catholic
Facilities Dining room; Activities room;
Chapel; Crafts room; Laundry room; Barber/
Beauty shop.
Activities Arts & crafts; Cards; Games;
Reading groups; Prayer groups; Movies;
Shopping trips; Social/Cultural gatherings.

DESHLER

Parkview Haven*
1203 S 4th St, Deshler, NE, 68340
(402) 365-7812
Admin Richard K Kjar.
Licensure Intermediate care. Beds 52.
Certified Medicaid.
Owner Publicly owned.

DODGE

Parkview Home Inc
RR 2 Box 414, Dodge, NE, 68633
(402) 693-2212
Admin Dwaine E Lauer. *Medical Dir/Dir of
Nursing* Donna Uher DON.

Licensure Intermediate care. *Beds* SNF 80.
Certified Medicaid.
Owner Proprietary Corp.
Admissions Requirements Medical
examination; Physician's request.
Staff RNs 4 (ft), 3 (pt); LPNs 1 (ft), 2 (pt);
Nurses aides 11 (ft), 16 (pt); Reality
therapists 4 (pt); Activities coordinators 1
(ft).
Facilities Dining room; Physical therapy
room; Activities room; Chapel; Crafts room;
Laundry room; Barber/Beauty shop; Library.
Activities Arts & crafts; Cards; Games;
Reading groups; Prayer groups; Movies;
Social/Cultural gatherings.

EDGAR

Bethesda Care Center of Edgar
Box 1183, Rte 1, 106 5th St, Edgar, NE,
68935
(402) 224-5015
Admin David A Schlegel. *Medical Dir/Dir of
Nursing* Frank Kamm MD; Mary Ann Lang
RN DON.
Licensure Intermediate care. *Beds* ICF 54.
Certified Medicaid.
Owner Nonprofit Corp (Bethesda Care
Centers).
Admissions Requirements Medical
examination; Physician's request.
Staff RNs 1 (ft), 2 (pt); LPNs 1 (ft), 3 (pt);
Nurses aides 10 (ft), 5 (pt); Activities
coordinators 1 (ft); Dietitians 1 (pt).
Facilities Dining room; Chapel; Laundry
room; Barber/Beauty shop.
Activities Arts & crafts; Games; Reading
groups; Prayer groups; Movies; Shopping
trips; Social/Cultural gatherings.

ELKHORN

Elkhorn Manor
315 Hopper St, Elkhorn, NE, 68022
(402) 289-2572
Admin Tim Hagerty. *Medical Dir/Dir of
Nursing* Donald Darst MD; Willene
Strickland RN DON.
Licensure Intermediate care. *Beds* ICF 132.
Certified Medicaid.
Owner Proprietary Corp (Life Care Centers of
America).
Admissions Requirements Medical
examination; Physician's request.
Staff RNs 4 (ft); LPNs 12 (ft); Orderlies 4 (ft);
Nurses aides 32 (ft); Recreational therapists
2 (ft); Occupational therapists 1 (pt);
Activities coordinators 1 (ft); Dietitians 1
(ft).
Facilities Dining room; Activities room;
Crafts room; Laundry room; Barber/Beauty
shop.
Activities Arts & crafts; Cards; Games;
Reading groups; Prayer groups; Movies;
Shopping trips; Social/Cultural gatherings.

ELWOOD

Elwood Care Center
613 Smith, Elwood, NE, 68937
(308) 785-3302
Admin D Maxine Misterek. *Medical Dir/Dir
of Nursing* Barbara J Foss DON.
Licensure Intermediate care. *Beds* ICF 51.
Certified Medicaid.
Owner Nonprofit organization/foundation.
Admissions Requirements Minimum age 18;
Medical examination.
Staff RNs 1 (ft), 1 (pt); LPNs 5 (ft), 1 (pt);
Physical therapists 1 (pt); Activities
coordinators 1 (pt); Dietitians 1 (pt).
Facilities Dining room; Activities room;
Chapel; Crafts room; Laundry room; Barber/
Beauty shop; Library.
Activities Arts & crafts; Cards; Games;
Reading groups; Prayer groups; Movies.

EMERSON

Heritage of Emerson
PO Box 310, 6th & Ne St, Emerson, NE,
68733-9801
(402) 695-2683
Admin Jeannia J Bottger. *Medical Dir/Dir of
Nursing* Vicki Summerfield RN DON.
Licensure Intermediate care. *Beds* ICF 63.
Certified Medicaid.
Owner Proprietary Corp (Vetter Health
Services).
Admissions Requirements Medical
examination; Physician's request.
Staff Physicians 1 (ft); RNs; LPNs; Orderlies;
Nurses aides; Physical therapists; Activities
coordinators; Dietitians.
Facilities Dining room; Physical therapy
room; Activities room; Chapel; Crafts room;
Laundry room; Barber/Beauty shop; Library.
Activities Arts & crafts; Cards; Games;
Reading groups; Prayer groups; Movies;
Shopping trips; Social/Cultural gatherings.

EXETER

Bethesda Care Center
425 S Empire Ave, Exeter, NE, 68351
(402) 266-4501
Admin Elaine Thornton. *Medical Dir/Dir of
Nursing* Ruth Ekler RN.
Licensure Intermediate care. *Beds* 60.
Certified Medicaid.
Owner Nonprofit Corp (Bethesda Care
Centers).
Admissions Requirements Medical
examination.
Staff RNs 1 (ft); LPNs 3 (ft), 1 (pt); Orderlies
1 (ft); Nurses aides 14 (ft), 1 (pt); Physical
therapists 1 (pt); Occupational therapists 1
(pt); Speech therapists 1 (pt); Activities
coordinators 1 (ft), 1 (pt); Dietitians 1 (pt).
Facilities Dining room; Activities room;
Chapel; Crafts room; Laundry room; Barber/
Beauty shop; Living room setting with 45
inch TV & VCR; Screened in porch & patio;
Van used for resident transportation.
Activities Arts & crafts; Cards; Games;
Reading groups; Prayer groups; Movies;
Shopping trips; Social/Cultural gatherings;
Bowling; Fishing; Ceramics.

FAIRBURY

Heritage of Fairbury
909 17th St, Fairbury, NE, 68352
(402) 729-2289
Admin Michael G Steele. *Medical Dir/Dir of
Nursing* Janet F Steele DON.
Licensure Intermediate care. *Beds* ICF 96.
Certified Medicaid.
Owner Proprietary Corp (Vetter Health
Services).
Admissions Requirements Minimum age 18;
Medical examination; Physician's request.
Staff RNs 1 (ft), 1 (pt); LPNs 5 (pt); Nurses
aides 12 (ft), 24 (pt).
Facilities Dining room; Physical therapy
room; Activities room; Chapel; Crafts room;
Laundry room; Barber/Beauty shop; Library.
Activities Arts & crafts; Cards; Games; Prayer
groups; Movies; Shopping trips; Social/
Cultural gatherings; Mother-daughter tea;
Father-son barbecue; Ice cream social;
Family resident picnic.

FAIRMONT

Fairview Manor
255 F Street, Fairmont, NE, 68354
(402) 268-2271
Admin Larry L Eichelberger NHA. *Medical
Dir/Dir of Nursing* Charlotte M Hall RN.
Licensure Intermediate care. *Beds* ICF 54.
Certified Medicaid.
Owner Publicly owned.

examination; Physician's request.
Staff RNs 2 (ft), 1 (pt); LPNs 1 (ft), 3 (pt);
Nurses aides 8 (ft), 9 (pt); Activities
coordinators 1 (ft); Dietitians 1 (pt).
Languages Czech
Facilities Dining room; Activities room;
Chapel; Crafts room; Laundry room; Barber/
Beauty shop.
Activities Cards; Games; Reading groups;
Prayer groups; Movies; Shopping trips;
Bingo.

FALLS CITY

Ketter Manor Inc
1010 E 21st St, Falls City, NE, 68355
(402) 245-3700
Admin Vern B Ketter. *Medical Dir/Dir of
Nursing* Janet Bletscher RN.
Licensure Intermediate care. *Beds* ICF 61.
Certified Medicaid.
Owner Proprietary Corp.
Admissions Requirements Minimum age 30;
Medical examination; Physician's request.
Staff RNs 1 (ft); LPNs 1 (pt); Orderlies 15
(ft), 10 (pt); Activities coordinators 1 (ft);
Dietitians 1 (ft).
Facilities Dining room; Laundry room;
Barber/Beauty shop.
Activities Cards; Games; Prayer groups;
Movies; Shopping trips.

Midland Villa
East 19th & Burton St, Rte 2, Falls City, NE,
68355
(402) 245-4466
Admin JoAnn Kolina. *Medical Dir/Dir of
Nursing* Dr David E Borg; Nelda Godwin
RN DON.
Licensure Skilled care. *Beds* SNF 70;
Medicare 8. *Certified* Medicaid; Medicare.
Owner Proprietary Corp.
Admissions Requirements Minimum age 21;
Medical examination; Physician's request.
Staff Physicians; RNs 3 (ft), 3 (pt); LPNs 3
(pt); Nurses aides 20 (ft), 15 (pt); Dietitians
1 (pt); Ophthalmologists 1 (pt).
Facilities Dining room; Physical therapy
room; Activities room; Crafts room; Laundry
room; Barber/Beauty shop.
Activities Arts & crafts; Cards; Games; Prayer
groups; Movies; Social/Cultural gatherings;
Sing-along.

Northview Care Center*
28th & Towle, Falls City, NE, 68355
(402) 245-5252
Admin Betty Ann Harmon. *Medical Dir/Dir of
Nursing* R L Burghart MD.
Licensure Intermediate care. *Beds* 100.
Certified Medicaid.
Owner Proprietary Corp (Beverly Enterprises).
Staff RNs; LPNs; Orderlies; Nurses aides;
Physical therapists; Recreational therapists;
Occupational therapists; Speech therapists;
Activities coordinators; Dietitians; Dentists;
Ophthalmologists; Podiatrists; Audiologists.
Facilities Dining room; Physical therapy
room; Activities room; Chapel; Crafts room;
Laundry room; Barber/Beauty shop.
Activities Arts & crafts; Cards; Games;
Reading groups; Prayer groups; Movies;
Shopping trips; Social/Cultural gatherings.

FIRTH

Lakeview Rest Home*
Firth, NE, 68357
(402) 791-5588
Admin Gary S Nelson. *Medical Dir/Dir of
Nursing* Yvonne Wilder LPN.
Licensure Intermediate care. *Beds* 56.
Certified Medicaid.
Owner Nonprofit Corp.
Admissions Requirements Medical
examination; Physician's request.

Staff Physicians 1 (pt); RNs 3 (pt); LPNs 1
(ft), 4 (pt); Nurses aides 5 (ft), 13 (pt);
Activities coordinators 1 (ft), 1 (pt);
Dietitians 1 (pt).
Affiliation Reformed Church
Facilities Dining room; Activities room;
Chapel; Laundry room; Barber/Beauty shop.
Activities Cards; Games; Prayer groups;
Movies; Shopping trips; Social/Cultural
gatherings.

FRANKLIN

Franklin Nursing Center
PO Box 167, W Hwy 136, Franklin, NE,
68939
(308) 425-6262
Admin Dorothy Sweet. *Medical Dir/Dir of
Nursing* R A Houston MD; Dian Rogers RN
DON.
Licensure Intermediate care. *Beds* ICF 72.
Certified Medicaid.
Owner Proprietary Corp (Beverly Enterprises).
Admissions Requirements Medical
examination; Physician's request.
Staff RNs 1 (ft); LPNs 4 (ft); Nurses aides 14
(ft), 8 (pt); Activities coordinators 1 (ft);
Social service 1 (ft).
Facilities Dining room; Activities room;
Chapel; Crafts room; Laundry room; Barber/
Beauty shop.
Activities Arts & crafts; Cards; Games;
Reading groups; Prayer groups; Movies;
Shopping trips; Social/Cultural gatherings.

FREMONT

Arbor Manor Inc*
26th & N Nye Ave, Fremont, NE, 68025
(402) 727-1710
Admin Marguerite McCardle.
Licensure Intermediate care. *Beds* 151.
Certified Medicaid.
Owner Proprietary Corp (ARA Living
Centers).

Fremont Care Center*
2700 LaVerna St, Fremont, NE, 68025
(402) 727-4900
Admin Jeffrey D Harmon.
Licensure Intermediate care. *Beds* 60.
Owner Proprietary Corp.

FRIEND

Friend Manor
905 2nd St, Friend, NE, 68359
(402) 947-2541
Admin Leonard Torson. *Medical Dir/Dir of
Nursing* Naomi Larka.
Licensure Intermediate care. *Beds* ICF 58.
Certified Medicaid.
Owner Publicly owned.
Staff Physicians 1 (ft); RNs 3 (ft); LPNs 3 (ft),
1 (pt); Nurses aides 10 (ft), 8 (pt); Physical
therapists 1 (pt); Dietitians 1 (ft).

FULLERTON

Fullerton Manor
202 N Esther, Fullerton, NE, 68638
(308) 536-2225
Admin Mason Cash Benn. *Medical Dir/Dir of
Nursing* Norma J Wilke RN.
Licensure Intermediate care. *Beds* ICF 94.
Certified Medicaid.
Owner Proprietary Corp (Beverly Enterprises).
Admissions Requirements Minimum age 21;
Medical examination; Physician's request.
Staff RNs 1 (ft); LPNs 4 (ft); Orderlies 1 (pt);
Nurses aides 18 (ft), 17 (pt); Activities
coordinators 1 (ft), 1 (pt); Social Service 1
(ft), 1 (pt).
Facilities Dining room; Activities room;
Chapel; Laundry room; Barber/Beauty shop;
Covered patio.

Activities Arts & crafts; Cards; Games; Prayer
groups; Movies; Shopping trips; Social/
Cultural gatherings; City swimming pool.

GENEVA

Fillmore County Long-Term Care*
1325 H St, Geneva, NE, 68361
(402) 759-3167
Admin Larry G Warrelman.
Licensure Intermediate care. *Beds* 20.
Certified Medicaid.
Owner Publicly owned.

Heritage of Geneva
501 N 13th St, Geneva, NE, 68361
(402) 759-3194
Admin Chester R Frey. *Medical Dir/Dir of
Nursing* Joyce Belau RN.
Licensure Intermediate care. *Beds* ICF 75.
Certified Medicare.
Owner Proprietary Corp (Vetter Health
Services).
Staff RNs 1 (ft), 1 (pt); LPNs 2 (ft), 1 (pt);
Nurses aides 11 (ft), 11 (pt); Activities
coordinators 1 (ft).
Facilities Dining room; Activities room;
Laundry room; Barber/Beauty shop.
Activities Cards; Games; Reading groups;
Prayer groups; Movies; Shopping trips.

GERING

Heritage Health Care Center
PO Box 518; 2025 21st St, Gering, NE, 69341
(308) 436-5007
Admin Charles K Gulley. *Medical Dir/Dir of
Nursing* Dr Alan Johnson; Lynn Bigner RN.
Licensure Skilled care. *Beds* SNF 101.
Certified Medicaid; Medicare.
Owner Proprietary Corp (Vetter Health
Services).
Admissions Requirements Medical
examination; Physician's request.
Staff RNs 5 (ft), 2 (pt); LPNs 6 (ft), 2 (pt);
Activities coordinators 1 (ft).
Languages Spanish translation available
Facilities Dining room; Chapel; Laundry
room; Barber/Beauty shop; Lounges; TV
room.
Activities Arts & crafts; Cards; Games;
Reading groups; Prayer groups; Movies;
Shopping trips; Social/Cultural gatherings.

Northfield Villa Inc
2550 21st St, Gering, NE, 69341
(308) 436-3101
Admin Floyd J Sauer. *Medical Dir/Dir of
Nursing* Verene Lane DON.
Licensure Skilled care; Intermediate care. *Beds*
41.
Owner Nonprofit Corp.
Staff RNs; LPNs; Nurses aides; Physical
therapists; Recreational therapists;
Occupational therapists; Speech therapists;
Activities coordinators; Dietitians; Dentist.
Facilities Dining room; Activities room;
Chapel; Crafts room; Laundry room; Barber/
Beauty shop; Library.
Activities Arts & crafts; Cards; Games; Prayer
groups.

GIBBON

Good Samaritan Center
PO Box 670, 7th & Court, Gibbon, NE, 68840
(308) 468-5353
Admin Margaret Krause. *Medical Dir/Dir of
Nursing* Dorothy Rayburn RN DON.
Licensure Intermediate care. *Beds* ICF 47.
Certified Medicaid.
Owner Nonprofit Corp (Evangelical Lutheran/
Good Samaritan).
Admissions Requirements Physician's request.
Staff RNs 1 (ft), 1 (pt); LPNs 4 (pt); Orderlies
1 (pt); Nurses aides 21 (pt); Activities
coordinators 1 (ft); Dietitians 1 (pt).

Languages Spanish
Facilities Dining room; Activities room;
Chapel; Crafts room; Laundry room; Barber/
Beauty shop; Library.
Activities Arts & crafts; Cards; Games;
Movies; Social/Cultural gatherings.

GORDON

Gordon Good Samaritan Center*
500 E 10th St, Gordon, NE, 69343
(308) 282-0806
Admin Rollen E Knapp.
Licensure Intermediate care. *Beds* 61.
Certified Medicaid.
Owner Nonprofit Corp (Evangelical Lutheran/
Good Samaritan).
Affiliation Lutheran

GOTHENBURG

Slack Nursing Home Inc
121 6th St, Gothenburg, NE, 69138
(308) 537-7136
Admin Richard D Slack. *Medical Dir/Dir of
Nursing* Marg Miller RN.
Licensure Intermediate care. *Beds* ICF 69.
Certified Medicaid.
Owner Proprietary Corp.
Admissions Requirements Medical
examination; Physician's request.
Staff Physicians 4 (pt); RNs 2 (ft); LPNs 3
(ft), 2 (pt); Nurses aides 10 (ft), 12 (pt);
Physical therapists 1 (pt); Recreational
therapists 1 (pt); Occupational therapists 1
(pt); Speech therapists 1 (pt); Activities
coordinators 1 (ft); Dietitians 1 (pt); Dentists
1 (pt); Ophthalmologists 1 (pt); Podiatrists 1
(pt).
Facilities Dining room; Activities room;
Chapel; Crafts room; Laundry room; Barber/
Beauty shop.
Activities Arts & crafts; Cards; Games;
Reading groups; Prayer groups; Movies;
Shopping trips; Social/Cultural gatherings.

GRAND ISLAND

Heritage Village of Grand Island—North*
610 N Darr St, Grand Island, NE, 68801
(308) 382-2635
Admin Robert D Steffen.
Licensure Intermediate care. *Beds* 97.
Certified Medicaid.
Owner Proprietary Corp (Beverly Enterprises).
Admissions Requirements Medical
examination.
Staff RNs 1 (pt); LPNs 8 (ft); Orderlies 2 (ft);
Nurses aides 11 (ft), 12 (pt); Physical
therapists 1 (pt); Recreational therapists 1
(ft); Occupational therapists 1 (pt); Speech
therapists 1 (pt); Activities coordinators 1
(ft); Dietitians 1 (pt); Dentists 1 (pt);
Ophthalmologists 1 (pt); Podiatrists 1 (pt);
Audiologists 1 (pt).
Facilities Dining room; Laundry room;
Barber/Beauty shop.
Activities Arts & crafts; Cards; Games;
Reading groups; Movies; Shopping trips;
Social/Cultural gatherings.

Lakeview Nursing Center
1405 W Hwy 34, Grand Island, NE, 68801
(308) 382-6397
Admin James R Falk. *Medical Dir/Dir of
Nursing* Donna Jorgensen.
Licensure Intermediate care. *Beds* ICF 96.
Certified Medicaid.
Owner Proprietary Corp (Beverly Enterprises).
Staff RNs 2 (ft), 1 (pt); LPNs 8 (ft), 2 (pt);
Nurses aides 25 (ft), 7 (pt); Physical
therapists 1 (pt); Recreational therapists 1
(pt); Occupational therapists 1 (pt); Speech
therapists 1 (pt); Activities coordinators 1
(ft); Dietitians 1 (ft).

Facilities Dining room; Physical therapy room; Activities room; Chapel; Crafts room; Laundry room; Barber/Beauty shop; Library; Private family dining area; Lakefront country atmosphere.
Activities Arts & crafts; Cards; Games; Reading groups; Prayer groups; Movies; Shopping trips; Social/Cultural gatherings.

Nebraska Veterans Home
Burkett Station, Grand Island, NE, 68803-2097
(308) 382-9420
Admin Richard L Terrell. *Medical Dir/Dir of Nursing* Richard DeMay MD; Barbara Abernethy RN DON.
Licensure Skilled care; Intermediate care; Domiciliary. *Beds* 449.
Owner Publicly owned.
Admissions Requirements Medical examination; Admission is limited to Veterans and/or their eligible dependents; No age limit for Veterans.
Staff Physicians 2 (ft); RNs 19 (ft), 8 (pt); LPNs 17 (ft), 6 (pt); Orderlies; Nurses aides 175 (ft), 8 (pt); Activities coordinators 1 (ft); Dietitians 1 (ft).
Facilities Dining room; Physical therapy room; Activities room; Chapel; Crafts room; Laundry room; Barber/Beauty shop; Library; Canteen; Post office.
Activities Arts & crafts; Cards; Games; Reading groups; Prayer groups; Movies; Shopping trips; Social/Cultural gatherings; Dining out trips; Fishing; Bowling; Field trips; Band concerts; Bingos; Bus tours; Las Vegas nights; Musical events.

Wedgewood*
800 Stoeger Dr, Grand Island, NE, 68801
(308) 382-5400
Admin Patricia E Wissel.
Licensure Intermediate care. *Beds* 71.
Owner Proprietary Corp.
Admissions Requirements Medical examination.
Staff RNs 1 (ft); Physical therapists 1 (pt); Activities coordinators 1 (ft); Dietitians 1 (ft).
Facilities Dining room; Physical therapy room; Activities room; Crafts room; Laundry room; Barber/Beauty shop; Library.
Activities Arts & crafts; Cards; Games; Reading groups; Prayer groups; Movies; Shopping trips; Social/Cultural gatherings.

GREELEY

Greeley Care Home*
Greeley, NE, 68842
(308) 428-5145
Admin Mary Haschke.
Licensure Intermediate care. *Beds* 48. *Certified* Medicaid.
Owner Publicly owned.

GRETNA

Bethesda Care Center of Gretna
700 Hwy 6, Gretna, NE, 68028
(402) 332-3446
Admin Alan Cooper. *Medical Dir/Dir of Nursing* Mary Stewart RN.
Licensure Intermediate care. *Beds* ICF 63. *Certified* Medicaid.
Owner Nonprofit Corp (Bethesda Care Centers).
Admissions Requirements Medical examination; Physician's request.
Staff RNs 3 (ft); LPNs 3 (ft); Nurses aides 30 (ft); Physical therapists 1 (pt); Reality therapists 1 (pt); Recreational therapists 1 (pt); Occupational therapists 1 (pt); Speech therapists 1 (ft), 1 (pt); Activities coordinators 1 (pt); Dietitians.

Facilities Dining room; Activities room; Chapel; Crafts room; Laundry room; Barber/ Beauty shop.
Activities Arts & crafts; Cards; Games; Reading groups; Prayer groups; Movies; Shopping trips; Social/Cultural gatherings.

HARTINGTON

Hartington Nursing Center
401 W Darline St, Hartington, NE, 68739
(402) 254-3905
Admin Elvera Lewis. *Medical Dir/Dir of Nursing* Dr C J Vlach; Alice Uhing.
Licensure Skilled care; Intermediate care. *Beds* 74. *Certified* Medicaid.
Owner Proprietary Corp (Beverly Enterprises).
Admissions Requirements Medical examination.
Staff Physicians 1 (pt); RNs 3 (ft), 2 (pt); LPNs 2 (ft), 1 (pt); Nurses aides 13 (ft), 12 (pt); Activities coordinators 1 (ft), 1 (pt); Dietitians 1 (ft), 1 (pt).
Facilities Dining room; Physical therapy room; Activities room; Chapel; Crafts room; Laundry room; Barber/Beauty shop; Van w/ wheelchair lift.
Activities Arts & crafts; Cards; Games; Reading groups; Prayer groups; Movies; Shopping trips; Social/Cultural gatherings; Sight seeing trips; Fishing trips; Outdoor picnics; Dinner trips.

HARVARD

Harvard Rest Haven*
400 E 7th St, Harvard, NE, 68944
(402) 772-7591
Admin Ronald E Crosby.
Licensure Intermediate care. *Beds* 60. *Certified* Medicaid.
Owner Publicly owned.

HASTINGS

Good Samaritan Village—Perkins Pavilion
300 S 1st Ave, Hastings, NE, 68901
(402) 463-3181
Admin G E Doughty. *Medical Dir/Dir of Nursing* Dr Gerald Kuehn; Judith Prentiss RN.
Licensure Skilled care; Intermediate care; Basic care. *Beds* SNF 59; ICF 89; Basic care 59. *Certified* Medicaid.
Owner Nonprofit Corp (Evangelical Lutheran/ Good Samaritan).
Staff Physicians 1 (pt); RNs 6 (ft), 3 (pt); LPNs 5 (ft), 8 (pt); Orderlies 1 (ft), 5 (pt); Nurses aides 24 (ft), 35 (pt); Physical therapists 1 (pt); Recreational therapists 1 (ft); Occupational therapists 1 (pt); Speech therapists 1 (pt); Dietitians 1 (pt); Podiatrists 1 (pt); Dentist 1 (pt).
Affiliation Lutheran
Facilities Dining room; Physical therapy room; Activities room; Chapel; Crafts room; Laundry room; Barber/Beauty shop; Library.
Activities Arts & crafts; Cards; Games; Reading groups; Prayer groups; Movies; Shopping trips; Social/Cultural gatherings.

Hastings Regional Center*
PO Box 579, Hastings, NE, 68901
(402) 463-2471
Admin Charles W Landgraf Jr.
Licensure Intermediate care; Intermediate care for mentally retarded. *Beds* 20.
Owner Publicly owned.

Villa Grace Good Samaritan Village
926 E "E" St, Box 2149, Hastings, NE, 68901
(402) 463-3181
Admin Donna Valentine. *Medical Dir/Dir of Nursing* Rebecca Smith RN DON.
Licensure Intermediate care. *Beds* ICF 150. *Certified* Medicaid.

Owner Nonprofit Corp (Evangelical Lutheran/ Good Samaritan).
Admissions Requirements Medical examination; Physician's request.
Staff RNs 7 (ft), 1 (pt); LPNs 2 (ft), 3 (pt); Nurses aides 30 (ft), 38 (pt); Activities coordinators 3 (ft); Dietitians 1 (ft); Social services 1 (ft), 2 (pt).
Affiliation Lutheran
Facilities Dining room; Physical therapy room; Activities room; Chapel; Crafts room; Laundry room; Barber/Beauty shop; Library.
Activities Arts & crafts; Cards; Games; Reading groups; Prayer groups; Movies; Shopping trips; Social/Cultural gatherings.

HAY SPRINGS

Pioneer Manor
Box 310, E Line Ave, Hay Springs, NE, 69347
(308) 638-4483
Admin Patsy A Bridge. *Medical Dir/Dir of Nursing* Connie Stannard RN.
Licensure Intermediate care. *Beds* ICF 51. *Certified* Medicaid.
Owner Nonprofit organization/foundation.
Admissions Requirements Medical examination.
Staff RNs 1 (ft), 1 (pt); LPNs 4 (ft), 2 (pt); Orderlies 2 (ft); Nurses aides 10 (ft), 2 (pt); Physical therapists 1 (pt); Occupational therapists 1 (pt); Speech therapists 1 (pt); Activities coordinators 1 (ft); Dietitians 1 (pt); Dentists 1 (pt); Ophthalmologists 1 (pt); Podiatrists 1 (pt).
Facilities Dining room; Activities room; Laundry room; Barber/Beauty shop.
Activities Arts & crafts; Cards; Games; Reading groups; Prayer groups; Movies; Shopping trips; Social/Cultural gatherings.

HEBRON

Blue Valley Lutheran Home Society Inc
4th & Park Ave, Box 166, Hebron, NE, 68370
(402) 768-6045
Admin LaVern L Poppe. *Medical Dir/Dir of Nursing* Ruth Kripal RN.
Licensure Intermediate care. *Beds* ICF 178.
Owner Nonprofit Corp.
Staff Physicians; RNs; LPNs; Nurses aides; Physical therapists; Recreational therapists; Occupational therapists; Speech therapists; Activities coordinators; Dietitians.
Affiliation Lutheran
Facilities Dining room; Activities room; Chapel; Crafts room; Laundry room; Barber/ Beauty shop.
Activities Arts & crafts; Cards; Games; Reading groups; Prayer groups; Movies; Shopping trips.

HOLDREGE

Christian Homes Inc
Rte 2 Box 24, Holdrege, NE, 68949
(308) 995-4493
Admin Dick Bauer. *Medical Dir/Dir of Nursing* Nancy Hanson DON.
Licensure Intermediate care; Residential care. *Beds* ICF 82; Residential 53. *Certified* Medicaid.
Owner Nonprofit Corp (Christian Homes).
Admissions Requirements Medical examination; Physician's request.
Staff RNs 3 (ft), 1 (pt); LPNs 6 (ft), 1 (pt); Nurses aides 26 (ft), 15 (pt); Physical therapists 1 (ft); Activities coordinators 1 (ft), 1 (pt).
Affiliation Evangelical Free Church
Facilities Dining room; Activities room; Crafts room; Laundry room; Barber/Beauty shop; Library.

Activities Arts & crafts; Games; Reading
groups; Prayer groups; Movies; Shopping
trips; Social/Cultural gatherings; Sing time;
Exercise; Hayrides; Senior olympics; Social
gatherings; Rhythm band.

Methodist Memorial Homes Inc
1320 11th Ave, Holdrege, NE, 68949
(308) 995-8631
Admin James S McClure. *Medical Dir/Dir of
Nursing* W Reiner MD; Margo Walker RN.
Licensure Skilled care; Intermediate care. *Beds*
59. *Certified* Medicaid; Medicare.
Owner Nonprofit Corp.
Admissions Requirements Medical
examination.
Staff Physicians 1 (ft); RNs 4 (ft), 8 (pt);
LPNs 3 (ft), 6 (pt); Nurses aides 16 (ft), 9
(pt); Physical therapists 1 (pt); Speech
therapists 1 (pt); Activities coordinators 1
(ft); Dietitians 1 (pt).
Affiliation Methodist
Facilities Dining room; Physical therapy
room; Activities room; Chapel; Crafts room;
Laundry room; Barber/Beauty shop; Library;
Gift shop.
Activities Arts & crafts; Cards; Games;
Reading groups; Prayer groups; Movies;
Shopping trips; Social/Cultural gatherings.

HOOPER

Hooper Care Center
Box 447, Hooper, NE, 68031
(402) 654-3362
Admin Sally R Stecher. *Medical Dir/Dir of
Nursing* Terri Nilles RN DON.
Licensure Intermediate care. *Beds* ICF 64.
Certified Medicaid.
Owner Proprietary Corp.
Admissions Requirements Medical
examination; Physician's request.
Staff RNs 1 (ft), 2 (pt); LPNs 3 (ft), 3 (pt);
Nurses aides 10 (ft), 13 (pt); Physical
therapists 1 (ft); Recreational therapists 1
(ft); Activities coordinators 1 (ft), 1 (pt);
Dietitians 1 (ft); Podiatrists 1 (ft).
Facilities Dining room; Physical therapy
room; Activities room; Chapel; Laundry
room; Barber/Beauty shop; Library.
Activities Arts & crafts; Cards; Games;
Reading groups; Prayer groups; Movies;
Shopping trips; Social/Cultural gatherings.

HUMBOLDT

Colonial Acres Nursing Home
RR 2, Humboldt, NE, 68376
(402) 862-3123
Admin John L Fischer. *Medical Dir/Dir of
Nursing* Carol Leuenberger RN DON.
Licensure Intermediate care. *Beds* ICF 68.
Certified Medicaid.
Owner Publicly owned.
Admissions Requirements Medical
examination; Physician's request.
Staff RNs 1 (ft), 2 (pt); LPNs 2 (ft), 2 (pt);
Nurses aides 14 (ft), 3 (pt); Physical
therapists 1 (pt); Activities coordinators 1
(ft); Dietitians 1 (pt).
Facilities Dining room; Activities room;
Chapel; Crafts room; Laundry room; Barber/
Beauty shop.
Activities Arts & crafts; Cards; Games;
Reading groups; Prayer groups; Movies;
Shopping trips.

IMPERIAL

Imperial Manor
933 Grant, Imperial, NE, 69033
(308) 882-5333, 882-5656
Admin Richard L Terrell. *Medical Dir/Dir of
Nursing* Kate Langenfeld RN DON.
Licensure Intermediate care. *Beds* ICF 70.
Certified Medicaid.

Owner Publicly owned.
Admissions Requirements Medical
examination; Physician's request.
Staff RNs 1 (ft); LPNs 4 (ft); Nurses aides 17
(ft), 4 (pt); Activities coordinators 2 (pt).
Facilities Dining room; Activities room;
Chapel; Laundry room; Barber/Beauty shop.
Activities Cards; Games; Reading groups;
Prayer groups; Movies; Shopping trips;
Social/Cultural gatherings.

KEARNEY

Mother Hull Home
125 E 23rd St, Kearney, NE, 68847
(308) 234-2447
Admin Richard D Reuhle. *Medical Dir/Dir of
Nursing* Sue Grubbs.
Licensure Intermediate care. *Beds* ICF 52.
Certified Medicaid.
Owner Nonprofit Corp.
Admissions Requirements Medical
examination; Physician's request.
Staff RNs 1 (ft); LPNs 5 (ft), 5 (pt); Nurses
aides 9 (ft), 9 (pt); Physical therapists;
Occupational therapists; Speech therapists;
Activities coordinators 1 (ft); Dietitians 1
(ft).
Affiliation Women's Christian Temperance
Union
Facilities Dining room; Laundry room;
Barber/Beauty shop; Resident lounge.
Activities Arts & crafts; Games; Reading
groups; Prayer groups; Movies; Shopping
trips.

Mt Carmel Home—Keens Memorial
412 W 18th St, Kearney, NE, 68847
(308) 237-2287
Admin Sr Ann Mary Schmidt. *Medical Dir/
Dir of Nursing* Colleen O'Connor RN.
Licensure Intermediate care. *Beds* ICF 76.
Certified Medicaid.
Owner Nonprofit Corp.
Admissions Requirements Medical
examination.
Staff RNs 1 (ft); LPNs 4 (ft), 6 (pt); Nurses
aides 21 (ft), 11 (pt); Recreational therapists
1 (ft); Activities coordinators 1 (ft).
Affiliation Roman Catholic
Facilities Dining room; Physical therapy
room; Activities room; Chapel; Laundry
room; Barber/Beauty shop; Family room.
Activities Cards; Games; Reading groups;
Prayer groups; Movies.

St John's Center
3410 N Central Ave, Kearney, NE, 68847
(308) 234-1888
Admin Harry A Carlsen. *Medical Dir/Dir of
Nursing* S McCammond MD; Donna Foster
RN.
Licensure Skilled care. *Beds* SNF 72. *Certified*
Medicaid.
Owner Nonprofit Corp (Evangelical Lutheran/
Good Samaritan).
Admissions Requirements Medical
examination; Physician's request.
Staff Physicians 1 (ft); RNs 3 (ft); LPNs 8 (ft),
5 (pt); Orderlies 9 (ft), 5 (pt); Nurses aides 9
(ft), 5 (pt); Recreational therapists 1 (ft), 1
(pt); Activities coordinators 1 (ft); Dietitians
1 (pt).
Affiliation Lutheran
Facilities Dining room; Physical therapy
room; Activities room; Chapel; Crafts room;
Laundry room; Barber/Beauty shop; Library.
Activities Arts & crafts; Cards; Games;
Reading groups; Prayer groups; Movies;
Shopping trips; Social/Cultural gatherings.

St Luke's Good Samaritan Village*
2300 E 32nd St, Kearney, NE, 68847
(308) 237-3108
Admin Steven R Wolff.
Licensure Intermediate care. *Beds* 60.
Certified Medicaid.

Owner Nonprofit Corp (Evangelical Lutheran/
Good Samaritan).
Affiliation Lutheran

KENESAW

Haven Home of Kenesaw*
Box 10, Kenesaw, NE, 68956
(402) 752-3212
Admin Robert E Williams.
Licensure Intermediate care. *Beds* 84.
Certified Medicaid.
Owner Proprietary Corp.

KIMBALL

Kimball County Manor*
810 E 7th St, Kimball, NE, 69145
(308) 235-4693
Admin Earl L Baker.
Licensure Intermediate care; Domiciliary care.
Beds 70. *Certified* Medicaid.
Owner Publicly owned.
Admissions Requirements Medical
examination; Physician's request.
Staff Physicians 3 (pt); RNs 2 (ft), 2 (pt);
LPNs 3 (ft), 2 (pt); Orderlies 1 (pt); Nurses
aides 10 (ft), 12 (pt); Physical therapists 1
(pt); Occupational therapists 12 (pt); Speech
therapists 1 (pt); Activities coordinators 1
(ft), 1 (pt); Dietitians 1 (pt); Dentists 1 (pt).
Facilities Dining room; Activities room;
Chapel; Crafts room; Laundry room; Barber/
Beauty shop.
Activities Arts & crafts; Cards; Games;
Reading groups; Prayer groups; Movies;
Shopping trips.

LAUREL

Hillcrest Care Center*
Oak St, Laurel, NE, 68745
(402) 256-3961
Admin Marcia Haisch.
Licensure Intermediate care. *Beds* 51.
Certified Medicaid.
Owner Publicly owned.

LEWELLEN

Garden County Lewellen Nursing Home
PO Box E, Lewellen, NE, 69147
(308) 778-5351
Admin Jody L Roberson. *Medical Dir/Dir of
Nursing* Louanne Toepfer RN DON.
Licensure Intermediate care. *Beds* ICF 37.
Certified Medicaid.
Owner Publicly owned.
Admissions Requirements Medical
examination.
Staff Physicians 8 (ft); RNs 2 (ft); LPNs 6 (ft),
1 (pt); Nurses aides 6 (ft), 2 (pt); Activities
coordinators 1 (ft); Dietitians 1 (pt); Dentists
1 (pt); Ophthalmologists 1 (pt); Podiatrists 1
(pt).
Facilities Dining room; Activities room;
Crafts room; Laundry room; Barber/Beauty
shop; Library.
Activities Arts & crafts; Cards; Games;
Reading groups; Prayer groups; Movies;
Shopping trips; Social/Cultural gatherings.

LEXINGTON

Westside Home Inc*
1505 N Adams St, Lexington, NE, 68850
(308) 324-5531
Admin Susan M Appelt.
Licensure Intermediate care. *Beds* 124.
Certified Medicaid.
Owner Proprietary Corp.
Admissions Requirements Medical
examination; Physician's request.

Staff RNs 1 (ft), 3 (pt); LPNs 4 (ft), 2 (pt); Nurses aides 17 (ft), 10 (pt); Activities coordinators 1 (ft); Dietitians 1 (pt).
Facilities Dining room; Activities room; Chapel; Crafts room; Laundry room; Barber/ Beauty shop.
Activities Arts & crafts; Cards; Games; Reading groups; Prayer groups; Movies; Shopping trips; Social/Cultural gatherings.

LINCOLN

Bethphage at Lincoln
904 Sumner St, Lincoln, NE, 68502
(402) 475-5895
Admin Charlene K Swanson NHA. *Medical Dir/Dir of Nursing* Darla Duran RN.
Licensure Intermediate care for mentally retarded. *Beds* ICF/MR 38. *Certified* Medicaid.
Owner Nonprofit Corp.
Admissions Requirements Minimum age 21; MR or DD diagnosis/occurring prior to age 22.
Staff Physicians; RNs 1 (ft); LPNs 2 (ft), 1 (pt); Orderlies 3 (ft), 1 (pt); Nurses aides 22 (ft); Physical therapists; Occupational therapists; Speech therapists; Activities coordinators 1 (pt); Dietitians; Psychologist; Religious Education Coord 1 (ft); Staff Dev Coord 1 (ft); Pharmacist; Social worker 1 (ft); Dietary Mgr 1 (ft).
Languages Sign
Affiliation Lutheran
Facilities Dining room; Activities room; Laundry room.

Eastmont Tower*
6315 O St, Lincoln, NE, 68510
(402) 489-6591
Admin Cecil Wissink. *Medical Dir/Dir of Nursing* J R Thomsen.
Licensure Skilled care; Intermediate care. *Beds* 50. *Certified* Medicaid.
Owner Nonprofit Corp.
Admissions Requirements Minimum age 62.
Staff RNs; LPNs; Nurses aides; Physical therapists; Activities coordinators.
Facilities Dining room; Activities room; Chapel; Laundry room; Barber/Beauty shop; Library.
Activities Arts & crafts; Cards; Games; Reading groups; Movies; Shopping trips.

Gateway Manor Inc
225 N 56th St, Lincoln, NE, 68504
(402) 464-6371
Admin Mary Lou Philippi. *Medical Dir/Dir of Nursing* Dr Fred Hathaway; Beverly Anderson RN DON.
Licensure Skilled care. *Beds* SNF 18. *Certified* Medicaid.
Admissions Requirements Minimum age 62; Medical examination.
Staff RNs 2 (ft), 4 (pt); LPNs 1 (ft); Nurses aides 4 (ft), 3 (pt); Activities coordinators 1 (pt); Social services 1 (pt).
Facilities Dining room; Activities room; Laundry room; Barber/Beauty shop; Library; Penthouse; Auditorium.
Activities Arts & crafts; Games; Movies; Shopping trips; Religious activities; Current topics—speakers & programs.

Holmes Lake Manor
6101 Normal Blvd, Lincoln, NE, 68506
(402) 489-7175
Admin Margaret E Cole.
Licensure Skilled care; Intermediate care. *Beds* 120.
Owner Privately owned.
Admissions Requirements Medical examination; Physician's request.
Staff RNs 5 (ft), 1 (pt); LPNs 6 (ft); Orderlies 3 (ft); Nurses aides 40 (ft), 12 (pt); Activities coordinators 1 (ft), 3 (pt); Social Services 1 (ft), 1 (pt).

Facilities Dining room; Activities room; Chapel; Crafts room; Laundry room; Barber/ Beauty shop; Library.
Activities Arts & crafts; Cards; Games; Reading groups; Prayer groups; Movies; Shopping trips; Social/Cultural gatherings; Couple club; Social night.

Homestead Nursing Home
4735 S 54th St, Lincoln, NE, 68516
(402) 488-0977
Admin Mary Morris. *Medical Dir/Dir of Nursing* Marjorie Kwan MD; Dona Quimby RN DON.
Licensure Skilled care. *Beds* SNF 147. *Certified* Medicaid; Medicare.
Owner Proprietary Corp (Hillhaven Corp).
Admissions Requirements Medical examination.
Staff RNs 6 (ft), 7 (pt); LPNs 5 (ft), 6 (pt); Nurses aides 28 (ft), 26 (pt); Activities coordinators 1 (ft), 1 (pt); Dietitians 1 (pt).
Languages Spanish
Facilities Dining room; Physical therapy room; Activities room; Chapel; Laundry room; Barber/Beauty shop.
Activities Arts & crafts; Cards; Games; Reading groups; Prayer groups; Movies; Shopping trips; Social/Cultural gatherings.

Lancaster Manor
1001 South St, Lincoln, NE, 68502
(402) 471-7101
Admin Richard Diba. *Medical Dir/Dir of Nursing* Kathy Eslinger DON.
Licensure Skilled care; Intermediate care. *Beds* SNF 60; ICF 240. *Certified* Medicaid.
Owner Publicly owned.
Admissions Requirements Minimum age 18; Medical examination.
Staff Physicians 1 (pt); RNs 12 (ft), 2 (pt); LPNs 14 (ft), 1 (pt); Orderlies 10 (ft), 4 (pt); Nurses aides 112 (ft), 14 (pt); Physical therapists 1 (ft), 2 (pt); Occupational therapists 1 (pt); Speech therapists 1 (pt); Activities coordinators 5 (ft); Dietitians 2 (ft); Ophthalmologists 1 (pt).
Facilities Dining room; Physical therapy room; Activities room; Chapel; Crafts room; Laundry room; Barber/Beauty shop; Library.
Activities Arts & crafts; Cards; Games; Reading groups; Prayer groups; Movies; Shopping trips; Social/Cultural gatherings.

Madonna Centers
2200 S 52nd St, Lincoln, NE, 68506
(402) 489-7102
Admin Sr M Phyllis Hunhoff. *Medical Dir/Dir of Nursing* Dr George Wolcott; Jackie Lageson.
Licensure Skilled care; Intermediate care. *Beds* 201. *Certified* Medicaid; Medicare.
Owner Nonprofit organization/foundation.
Admissions Requirements Medical examination; Physician's request.
Staff Physicians 1 (ft); RNs 48 (ft), 27 (pt); LPNs 38 (ft), 18 (pt); Orderlies 95 (ft), 69 (pt); Nurses aides; Physical therapists 10 (ft), 2 (pt); Recreational therapists 4 (ft); Occupational therapists 10 (ft), 2 (pt); Speech therapists 6 (ft), 2 (pt); Dietitians 2 (ft), 1 (pt); Podiatrists 1 (ft).
Affiliation Roman Catholic
Facilities Dining room; Physical therapy room; Activities room; Chapel; Crafts room; Laundry room; Barber/Beauty shop; Library.
Activities Arts & crafts; Cards; Games; Reading groups; Prayer groups; Movies; Shopping trips; Social/Cultural gatherings.

Maplewood Care Center
4405 Normal Blvd, Lincoln, NE, 68506
(402) 488-2355
Admin Jill D Molzahn. *Medical Dir/Dir of Nursing* Dr D E Michels.
Licensure Skilled care; Specialty respiratory care unit. *Beds* 120. *Certified* Medicaid; Medicare.

Owner Proprietary Corp.
Admissions Requirements Medical examination; Physician's request.
Staff Physicians 5 (ft); RNs 9 (ft), 2 (pt); LPNs 15 (ft), 31 (pt); Nurses aides 36 (ft); Physical therapists 1 (pt); Occupational therapists 1 (pt); Speech therapists 1 (pt); Activities coordinators 2 (ft); Dietitians 1 (ft).
Languages Spanish, German
Facilities Dining room; Activities room; Crafts room; Laundry room; Barber/Beauty shop; Library.
Activities Arts & crafts; Cards; Games; Reading groups; Prayer groups; Movies; Shopping trips; Social/Cultural gatherings.

Milder Manor Nursing Home*
1750 S 20th St, Lincoln, NE, 68502
(402) 475-6791
Admin Jerome J Milder.
Licensure Skilled care. *Beds* 154. *Certified* Medicaid; Medicare.
Owner Proprietary Corp.

Tabitha Home
4720 Randolph St, Lincoln, NE, 68510
(402) 483-7671
Admin Robert E Moore Jr. *Medical Dir/Dir of Nursing* James Carlson MD; Catherine Kinnaman RN DON.
Licensure Skilled care; Intermediate care. *Beds* SNF 109; ICF 127. *Certified* Medicaid; Medicare; VA.
Owner Nonprofit Corp.
Admissions Requirements Medical examination; Physician's request.
Staff Physicians 1 (pt); RNs 27 (ft); RNs 24 (ft); Nurses aides 57 (ft); Physical therapists 2 (ft); Occupational therapists 1 (ft); Speech therapists 1 (pt); Activities coordinators 5 (ft); Dietitians 2 (ft); Ophthalmologists 1 (pt).
Affiliation Lutheran
Facilities Dining room; Physical therapy room; Activities room; Chapel; Crafts room; Laundry room; Barber/Beauty shop; Library.
Activities Arts & crafts; Cards; Games; Reading groups; Prayer groups; Movies; Shopping trips; Social/Cultural gatherings; Bingo; Parades; Fishing; Special meals; Trivia; Resident council.

Village Manor Nursing Home*
3220 N 14th St, Lincoln, NE, 68521
(402) 476-3274
Admin Virgil L Carner.
Licensure Intermediate care. *Beds* 50. *Certified* Medicaid.
Owner Proprietary Corp.

LOUISVILLE

Louisville Care Center
6th & Hazel St, Louisville, NE, 68037
(402) 234-2125
Admin Elaine Storovich. *Medical Dir/Dir of Nursing* Barbara Ross RN.
Licensure Intermediate care. *Beds* ICF 55. *Certified* Medicaid.
Owner Publicly owned.
Admissions Requirements Medical examination; Physician's request.
Staff RNs 1 (ft), 2 (pt); Nurses aides 8 (ft), 16 (pt); Physical therapists; Occupational therapists; Speech therapists; Activities coordinators 1 (ft); Dietitians 1 (pt); Ophthalmologists; Social Services 1 (ft).
Facilities Dining room; Activities room; Chapel; Crafts room; Laundry room; Barber/ Beauty shop.
Activities Arts & crafts; Cards; Games; Reading groups; Prayer groups; Movies; Shopping trips; Social/Cultural gatherings.

LOUP CITY

Rose Lane Nursing Home
PO Box 46, Route 2, Loup City, NE, 68853
(308) 745-0303
Admin Tom Youngquist. *Medical Dir/Dir of Nursing* Delores Treffer.
Licensure Intermediate care. *Beds* 77.
Certified Medicaid.
Owner Publicly owned.
Staff Physicians 1 (pt); RNs 2 (ft); LPNs 4 (ft); Nurses aides 30 (ft), 9 (pt); Physical therapists 1 (pt); Occupational therapists 1 (pt); Speech therapists 1 (pt); Activities coordinators 1 (ft); Dietitians 1 (ft); Ophthalmologists 1 (pt); 1 (pt) Social services.
Facilities Dining room; Physical therapy room; Crafts room; Laundry room; Barber/Beauty shop.
Activities Arts & crafts; Cards; Games; Reading groups; Prayer groups; Movies; Shopping trips; Social/Cultural gatherings.

LYONS

Logan Valley Manor
PO Box 48, RR 1, Lyons, NE, 68038
(402) 687-2121
Admin Lois Vavra. *Medical Dir/Dir of Nursing* Sandra Anderson.
Licensure Skilled care; Intermediate care. *Beds* 90. *Certified* Medicaid.
Owner Proprietary Corp.
Admissions Requirements Medical examination.
Staff RNs 4 (ft), 2 (pt); LPNs 1 (ft), 2 (pt); Nurses aides 16 (ft), 17 (pt); Activities coordinators 1 (ft), 1 (pt).
Facilities Dining room; Physical therapy room; Activities room; Chapel; Crafts room; Laundry room; Barber/Beauty shop.
Activities Arts & crafts; Cards; Games; Reading groups; Prayer groups; Movies; Shopping trips; Social/Cultural gatherings.

MACY

Carl T Curtis Health Education Center
PO Box 250, Macy, NE, 68039
(402) 837-5381
Admin June Cook. *Medical Dir/Dir of Nursing* J E Nicolas MD; June Cook.
Licensure Skilled care. *Beds* SNF 25. *Certified* Medicaid.
Owner Nonprofit organization/foundation.
Admissions Requirements Medical examination.
Staff Physicians 3 (pt); RNs 6 (ft); LPNs 3 (pt); Orderlies 3 (ft); Nurses aides 7 (ft); Physical therapists 1 (pt); Recreational therapists 1 (pt); Occupational therapists 1 (pt); Speech therapists 1 (pt); Activities coordinators 1 (ft); Dietitians 1 (ft); Dentists 1 (pt); Ophthalmologists 1 (pt); Podiatrists 1 (pt).
Languages Omaha, Winnebago
Facilities Dining room; Physical therapy room; Activities room; Laundry room; Barber/Beauty shop.
Activities Arts & crafts; Cards; Games; Prayer groups; Movies; Shopping trips; Social/Cultural gatherings.

MADISON

Countryside Home
PO Box 3A, N Pearl St, Madison, NE, 68748
(402) 454-3373
Admin Fern J Salmen RN. *Medical Dir/Dir of Nursing* Jan K Hake DON.
Licensure Intermediate care. *Beds* 72.
Certified Medicaid.
Owner Publicly owned.
Admissions Requirements Medical examination; Physician's request.

Staff RNs 1 (ft), 1 (pt); LPNs 2 (ft), 7 (pt); Physical therapists 1 (pt); Activities coordinators 1 (ft); Dietitians 1 (pt); Social Service 1 (pt); Physical Therapy Aide 1 (ft); Dentist 1 (pt).
Facilities Dining room; Physical therapy room; Activities room; Chapel; Laundry room; Barber/Beauty shop.
Activities Arts & crafts; Cards; Games; Prayer groups; Movies; Shopping trips; Social/Cultural gatherings.

MCCOOK

Hillcrest Nursing Home
309 W 7th St, McCook, NE, 69001
(308) 345-4600
Admin Don Harpst. *Medical Dir/Dir of Nursing* Joyce Hinze.
Licensure Intermediate care. *Beds* ICF 96.
Certified Medicaid.
Owner Publicly owned.
Admissions Requirements Medical examination; Physician's request.
Staff RNs 3 (ft), 1 (pt); LPNs 8 (ft), 3 (pt); Nurses aides 39 (ft), 9 (pt); Physical therapists 1 (pt); Occupational therapists 1 (pt); Speech therapists 1 (pt); Dietitians 1 (pt); Ophthalmologists 1 (pt).
Facilities Dining room; Physical therapy room; Activities room; Chapel; Crafts room; Laundry room; Barber/Beauty shop.
Activities Arts & crafts; Cards; Games; Reading groups; Prayer groups; Movies; Shopping trips; Social/Cultural gatherings.

MILFORD

Crestview Care Center
PO Box D, 1100 W First St, Milford, NE, 68405
(402) 761-2261
Admin Edith E Wymore RN. *Medical Dir/Dir of Nursing* Collette Carothers RN.
Licensure Intermediate care. *Beds* ICF 66.
Certified Medicaid.
Owner Proprietary Corp.
Admissions Requirements Medical examination.
Staff RNs 2 (ft); LPNs 2 (ft), 1 (pt); Orderlies; Nurses aides; Physical therapists; Activities coordinators 1 (ft); Dietitians; Social Service.
Activities Arts & crafts; Cards; Games; Reading groups; Prayer groups; Movies; Shopping trips; Social/Cultural gatherings.

Milford Rest Home Inc*
Rte 2, Milford, NE, 68405
(402) 761-3230
Admin Wanetta Stabenow.
Licensure Intermediate care. *Beds* 72.
Certified Medicaid.
Owner Proprietary Corp.

MINDEN

Bethany Home*
515 W 1st St, Minden, NE, 68959
(308) 832-1594
Admin Wesley K Anderson.
Licensure Intermediate care. *Beds* 61.
Certified Medicaid.
Owner Nonprofit Corp.

MITCHELL

Western Nebraska Rest Home*
1508 22nd Ave, Mitchell, NE, 69357
(308) 623-1212
Admin Clara Reisig.
Licensure Intermediate care. *Beds* 50.
Certified Medicaid.
Owner Proprietary Corp.

NEBRASKA CITY

Duff Memorial Nursing Home
1104 3rd Ave, Nebraska City, NE, 68410
(402) 873-3304
Admin Diane Schneider.
Licensure Intermediate care. *Beds* 63.
Certified Medicaid.
Owner Publicly owned.

Nebraska City Manor
1420 N 10th St, Nebraska City, NE, 68410
(402) 873-3304
Admin Tom Mason. *Medical Dir/Dir of Nursing* Portia Voelker.
Licensure Intermediate care. *Beds* 122.
Certified Medicaid.
Owner Proprietary Corp (Beverly Enterprises).
Admissions Requirements Minimum age 18.
Staff RNs 2 (ft), 1 (pt); LPNs 6 (ft); Orderlies 3 (ft); Nurses aides 38 (ft), 5 (pt); Physical therapists 1 (ft); Recreational therapists 1 (ft); Activities coordinators 1 (ft), 2 (pt); Dietitians 1 (pt).
Facilities Dining room; Physical therapy room; Activities room; Chapel; Crafts room; Laundry room; Barber/Beauty shop; Library.
Activities Arts & crafts; Cards; Games; Reading groups; Prayer groups; Movies; Shopping trips; Social/Cultural gatherings; Music; Puppet play; Family gathering.

Valley View Care Inc
1800 14th St, Nebraska City, NE, 68410
(402) 873-6650
Admin Lois Rakes.
Licensure Intermediate care. *Beds* 74.
Certified Medicaid.
Owner Proprietary Corp.
Admissions Requirements Minimum age 16; Medical examination.
Staff RNs 1 (ft), 3 (pt); LPNs 2 (ft), 1 (pt); Orderlies 1 (pt); Nurses aides 17 (ft), 5 (pt); Activities coordinators 1 (ft), 1 (pt); Dentists 11 (ft).
Facilities Dining room; Activities room; Laundry room; Barber/Beauty shop; Bathing area.
Activities Arts & crafts; Cards; Games; Reading groups; Prayer groups; Movies; Shopping trips; Social/Cultural gatherings.

NELIGH

Heritage Village of Neligh*
PO Box 66, Neligh, NE, 68756
(402) 887-4101
Admin Patsy Uttecht.
Licensure Intermediate care. *Beds* 97.
Certified Medicaid.
Owner Proprietary Corp (Beverly Enterprises).

NELSON

Good Samaritan Center
150 W 8th St, Nelson, NE, 68961
(402) 225-2411
Admin Gloria Sigler. *Medical Dir/Dir of Nursing* Chris Stemper RN.
Licensure Intermediate care. *Beds* ICF 48.
Certified Medicaid.
Owner Nonprofit Corp (Evangelical Lutheran/ Good Samaritan).
Staff RNs 1 (ft), 2 (pt); LPNs 2 (ft); Nurses aides 14 (ft), 7 (pt).
Affiliation Lutheran
Facilities Dining room; Crafts room; Laundry room; Barber/Beauty shop.
Activities Arts & crafts; Cards; Games; Prayer groups.

NEWMAN GROVE

Mid-Nebraska Lutheran Home Inc
109 N 2nd St, Newman Grove, NE, 68758
(402) 447-6204

Admin Lee A Jenkins. *Medical Dir/Dir of Nursing* Dr Gary Smith MD; Marcia Knust RN DON.
Licensure Intermediate care. *Beds* ICF 55; Apartments 4. *Certified* Medicaid.
Owner Nonprofit Corp.
Admissions Requirements Medical examination; Physician's request.
Staff RNs 1 (ft); LPNs 1 (ft), 4 (pt); Nurses aides 2 (ft), 24 (pt); Physical therapists 1 (ft), 1 (pt); Activities coordinators 1 (ft), 4 (pt); Dietitians 1 (ft), 12 (pt).
Affiliation Lutheran
Facilities Dining room; Activities room; Chapel; Crafts room; Laundry room; Barber/ Beauty shop.
Activities Arts & crafts; Cards; Games; Reading groups; Prayer groups; Movies; Shopping trips; Social/Cultural gatherings; Woodworking.

NORFOLK

Heritage of Bel Air
13th & Bel Air Rd, Norfolk, NE, 68701
(402) 371-4991
Admin Linda Bomar. *Medical Dir/Dir of Nursing* Sheryl Kyriss.
Licensure Intermediate care. *Beds* ICF 89. *Certified* Medicaid.
Owner Proprietary Corp (Vetter Health Services).
Staff RNs; LPNs 8 (ft), 2 (pt); Orderlies 1 (ft); Nurses aides 20 (ft), 8 (pt); Physical therapists 1 (ft); Recreational therapists; Occupational therapists; Speech therapists; Activities coordinators 1 (ft); Dietitians 1 (pt).
Facilities Dining room; Activities room; Crafts room; Laundry room; Barber/Beauty shop.
Activities Arts & crafts; Cards; Games; Reading groups; Prayer groups; Movies; Shopping trips; Social/Cultural gatherings.

Nebraska Veterans Home Annex
Box 409, Norfolk, NE, 68701
(402) 371-2701
Admin Duane J Hodge. *Medical Dir/Dir of Nursing* Dr Harold Dahlheim.
Licensure Skilled care; Intermediate care. *Beds* SNF 42; ICF 118. *Certified* Medicare; VA.
Owner Publicly owned.
Admissions Requirements Medical examination.
Staff Physicians 1 (ft), 1 (pt); RNs 7 (ft), 4 (pt); LPNs 8 (ft), 1 (pt); Nurses aides 42 (ft), 10 (pt); Physical therapists; Recreational therapists 1 (ft); Occupational therapists 1 (ft); Speech therapists; Activities coordinators 1 (ft); Dietitians; Dentists; Ophthalmologists.
Facilities Dining room; Activities room; Chapel; Crafts room; Library.
Activities Arts & crafts; Cards; Games; Reading groups; Prayer groups; Movies; Shopping trips; Social/Cultural gatherings.

Norfolk Nursing Center
1900 Vicki Ln, Norfolk, NE, 68701
(402) 371-2303
Admin Shirley Kraemer. *Medical Dir/Dir of Nursing* Darleen Nickless RN DON.
Licensure Skilled care. *Beds* SNF 102. *Certified* Medicaid.
Owner Proprietary Corp (Beverly Enterprises).
Admissions Requirements Medical examination; Physician's request.
Staff RNs 3 (ft); LPNs 6 (ft); Nurses aides 27 (ft), 3 (pt); Activities coordinators 1 (ft), 1 (pt).
Facilities Dining room; Physical therapy room; Activities room; Chapel; Crafts room; Laundry room; Barber/Beauty shop.
Activities Arts & crafts; Cards; Games; Reading groups; Prayer groups; Movies; Shopping trips; Social/Cultural gatherings.

St Joseph's Nursing Home*
401 N 18th St, Norfolk, NE, 68701
(402) 371-9404
Admin Sr M Rita Hess.
Licensure Intermediate care. *Beds* 70. *Certified* Medicaid.
Owner Nonprofit Corp.

NORTH BEND

Birchwood Manor
1120 N Walnut, North Bend, NE, 68649
(402) 652-3242
Admin Donald A Hruza. *Medical Dir/Dir of Nursing* Marilyn Heauigan.
Licensure Intermediate care. *Beds* ICF 67. *Certified* Medicaid.
Owner Proprietary Corp.
Admissions Requirements Minimum age 18; Medical examination; Physician's request.
Staff Physicians 3 (pt); RNs 1 (ft), 2 (pt); LPNs 5 (pt); Nurses aides 20 (ft), 3 (pt); Physical therapists 1 (pt); Occupational therapists 1 (pt); Speech therapists 1 (pt); Activities coordinators 1 (ft); Dietitians 1 (pt).
Languages Slavic, German
Facilities Dining room; Physical therapy room; Activities room; Chapel; Crafts room; Laundry room; Barber/Beauty shop; Library.
Activities Arts & crafts; Cards; Games; Reading groups; Prayer groups; Movies; Shopping trips; Social/Cultural gatherings.

NORTH PLATTE

Linden Manor Nursing Home*
420 W 4th St, North Platte, NE, 69101
(308) 532-5774
Admin William J Wagner.
Licensure Skilled care; Intermediate care. *Beds* 100. *Certified* Medicaid.
Owner Proprietary Corp.

Valley View Care Centre*
3001 W "E" St, North Platte, NE, 69101
(308) 534-2200
Admin Charles Richards. *Medical Dir/Dir of Nursing* Elayne Underwood.
Licensure Intermediate care. *Beds* 92. *Certified* Medicaid.
Owner Proprietary Corp.
Admissions Requirements Medical examination.
Staff RNs 1 (ft), 1 (pt); LPNs 4 (ft), 4 (pt); Physical therapists 1 (pt); Occupational therapists 1 (pt); Speech therapists 1 (pt); Dietitians 1 (ft).
Facilities Dining room; Activities room; Laundry room; Barber/Beauty shop.
Activities Arts & crafts; Cards; Games; Reading groups; Prayer groups; Shopping trips.

OAKLAND

Oakland Heights
PO Box 86, 207 S Engdahl St, Oakland, NE, 68045
(402) 685-5683
Admin Barbara C Anderson.
Licensure Intermediate care. *Beds* ICF 57. *Certified* Medicaid.
Owner Nonprofit organization/foundation.
Admissions Requirements Medical examination; Physician's request.
Staff RNs 1 (ft), 1 (pt); LPNs 1 (ft), 3 (pt); Nurses aides 9 (ft), 11 (pt); Activities coordinators 2 (ft), 1 (pt).
Facilities Dining room; Activities room; Chapel; Crafts room; Laundry room; Barber/ Beauty shop.
Activities Arts & crafts; Cards; Games; Reading groups; Prayer groups; Movies; Shopping trips; Social/Cultural gatherings.

OGALLALA

Indian Hills Manor
RR 2, Box 35A, Ogallala, NE, 69153
(308) 284-4068
Admin Cheri Bruckner. *Medical Dir/Dir of Nursing* Chris Malmkar RN DON.
Licensure Intermediate care. *Beds* ICF 82. *Certified* Medicaid.
Owner Proprietary Corp.
Admissions Requirements Minimum age 21; Medical examination.
Staff RNs 2 (ft), 2 (pt); LPNs 4 (ft), 4 (pt); Orderlies 4 (ft); Nurses aides 11 (ft), 10 (pt); Activities coordinators 1 (ft), 1 (pt); Dietitians 1 (pt).
Facilities Dining room; Physical therapy room; Activities room; Chapel; Laundry room; Barber/Beauty shop; Visiting room.
Activities Arts & crafts; Cards; Games; Prayer groups; Movies; Social/Cultural gatherings; Van rides.

OMAHA

Rose Blumkin Jewish Home
323 S 132nd St, Omaha, NE, 68154
(402) 330-4272
Admin Eugene H Brandt. *Medical Dir/Dir of Nursing* Thomas B Cotton MD; Cherill Samson RN DON.
Licensure Skilled care. *Beds* 97. *Certified* Medicaid; Medicare.
Owner Nonprofit Corp.
Admissions Requirements Minimum age 65; Medical examination.
Staff Physicians 1 (pt); RNs 4 (ft), 4 (pt); LPNs 4 (ft), 4 (pt); Nurses aides 16 (ft), 16 (pt); Recreational therapists 1 (ft), 1 (pt); Dietitians 1 (ft), 1 (pt).
Affiliation Jewish
Facilities Dining room; Physical therapy room; Activities room; Chapel; Crafts room; Barber/Beauty shop; Library.
Activities Arts & crafts; Games; Movies; Shopping trips; Social/Cultural gatherings.

Thomas Fitzgerald Veterans Home
156th & Maple Rd, Omaha, NE, 68164
(402) 554-2180
Admin Gerald N Rhone. *Medical Dir/Dir of Nursing* Haskell Morris MD; Julie Holling RN DON.
Licensure Skilled care. *Beds* SNF 182; Boarding home 10. *Certified* Medicare.
Admissions Requirements Minimum age 50 for non-vets (widows & wives).
Staff Physicians 2 (pt); RNs 9 (pt); LPNs 14 (pt); Nurses aides 42 (ft), 10 (pt); Physical therapists 1 (ft), 1 (pt); Recreational therapists 1 (ft); Occupational therapists 1 (ft); Activities coordinators 1 (ft); Dietitians 1 (pt).
Facilities Dining room; Physical therapy room; Activities room; Chapel; Crafts room; Laundry room; Barber/Beauty shop; Library; Kitchenette; Game room; Pavilion; Canteen; Pharmacy; Dental laboratory.
Activities Arts & crafts; Cards; Games; Reading groups; Prayer groups; Movies; Shopping trips; Social/Cultural gatherings; Bingo; Luncheons; Exercise programs; Horse races twice yearly; Riverboat cruise.

Florence Height Village Nursing Center Inc*
3220 Scott St, Omaha, NE, 68112
(402) 455-6333
Admin Mary Pratkelis. *Medical Dir/Dir of Nursing* Charles M Bressman MD.
Licensure Skilled care; Intermediate care. *Beds* 80. *Certified* Medicaid.
Owner Proprietary Corp.
Admissions Requirements Medical examination; Physician's request.
Staff RNs 3 (ft); LPNs 2 (ft), 2 (pt); Orderlies 1 (ft); Nurses aides 20 (ft), 14 (pt); Physical therapists 1 (pt); Reality therapists 1 (pt);

Recreational therapists 1 (pt); Activities coordinators 1 (ft); Dietitians 1 (pt); Dentists 1 (pt).
Facilities Dining room; Physical therapy room; Activities room; Chapel; Crafts room; Laundry room; Barber/Beauty shop; Library.
Activities Arts & crafts; Cards; Games; Prayer groups; Movies; Shopping trips.

Florence Home
7915 N 30th St, Omaha, NE, 68112
(402) 457-4111
Admin Richard J Booth. *Medical Dir/Dir of Nursing* Marian Peterson RN.
Licensure Intermediate care. *Beds* ICF 128. *Certified* Medicaid.
Owner Nonprofit Corp.
Admissions Requirements Minimum age 60; Medical examination.
Staff Physicians 1 (ft); RNs 3 (ft); LPNs 7 (ft); Nurses aides 45 (ft); Physical therapists 1 (pt); Reality therapists 1 (pt); Recreational therapists 1 (ft); Activities coordinators 1 (pt).
Facilities Dining room; Physical therapy room; Activities room; Chapel; Crafts room; Barber/Beauty shop; Library; Pharmacy; Gift shop.
Activities Arts & crafts; Cards; Games; Reading groups; Prayer groups; Movies; Shopping trips; Social/Cultural gatherings.

Hallmark Care Center*
5505 Grover St, Omaha, NE, 68106
(402) 558-0225
Admin John Miller.
Licensure Intermediate care. *Beds* 168. *Certified* Medicaid.
Owner Proprietary Corp.

Haven House
1540 N 72nd St, Omaha, NE, 68114
(402) 393-6500
Admin Jolene M Kemp MSW. *Medical Dir/Dir of Nursing* Dr Jane F Potter; Betty Lamb RN DON.
Licensure Intermediate care. *Beds* ICF 165. *Certified* Medicaid.
Owner Proprietary Corp.
Admissions Requirements Medical examination; Physician's request.
Staff Physicians; RNs; LPNs; Orderlies; Nurses aides; Physical therapists; Recreational therapists; Occupational therapists; Speech therapists; Activities coordinators; Dietitians; Dentists; Ophthalmologists; Podiatrists.
Facilities Dining room; Chapel; Laundry room; Barber/Beauty shop; Library.
Activities Arts & crafts; Cards; Games; Reading groups; Prayer groups; Movies; Shopping trips; Social/Cultural gatherings.

Hillhaven—Omaha*
7410 Mercy Rd, Omaha, NE, 68124
(402) 397-1220
Admin Jean E Mazanec. *Medical Dir/Dir of Nursing* Thomas Cotton MD.
Licensure Skilled care; Intermediate care. *Beds* 174. *Certified* Medicaid; Medicare.
Owner Proprietary Corp (Hillhaven Corp).
Admissions Requirements Minimum age 18; Medical examination.
Staff Physicians 1 (pt); RNs 5 (ft), 4 (pt); LPNs 8 (ft), 2 (pt); Orderlies 5 (ft), 1 (pt); Nurses aides 36 (ft), 5 (pt); Physical therapists 1 (ft), 1 (pt); Recreational therapists 1 (ft); Occupational therapists 1 (pt); Speech therapists 1 (pt); Dentists 1 (pt); Ophthalmologists 1 (pt); Podiatrists 1 (pt); Audiologists 1 (pt).
Facilities Dining room; Physical therapy room; Activities room; Chapel; Laundry room; Barber/Beauty shop.
Activities Arts & crafts; Cards; Games; Prayer groups; Movies; Shopping trips; Social/Cultural gatherings.

Lindenwood Nursing Home Inc*
910 S 40th St, Omaha, NE, 68105
(402) 342-2015
Admin Charlene Toland. *Medical Dir/Dir of Nursing* Daniel Halm MD.
Licensure Intermediate care. *Beds* 65. *Certified* Medicaid.
Owner Proprietary Corp.
Staff RNs 1 (ft), 4 (pt); LPNs 5 (ft), 3 (pt); Nurses aides 18 (ft), 15 (pt); Physical therapists 1 (pt); Recreational therapists 1 (ft); Occupational therapists 1 (pt); Activities coordinators 1 (ft); Dietitians 1 (ft); Podiatrists 1 (pt).
Facilities Dining room; Activities room; Crafts room; Laundry room; Barber/Beauty shop.
Activities Arts & crafts; Cards; Games; Reading groups; Prayer groups; Movies.

The Lutheran Home*
530 S 26th St, Omaha, NE, 68105
(402) 346-3344
Admin Byron G Will.
Licensure Skilled care; Intermediate care. *Beds* 177. *Certified* Medicaid.
Owner Nonprofit Corp.
Affiliation Lutheran

Maple-Crest
2824 N 66th Ave, Omaha, NE, 68104
(402) 551-2110
Admin Richard A Peterson. *Medical Dir/Dir of Nursing* Lyle Nilson MD; Virginia DeFord.
Licensure Skilled care; Intermediate care. *Beds* 184. *Certified* Medicaid.
Owner Nonprofit Corp (American Baptist Homes).
Admissions Requirements Medical examination.
Staff RNs 6 (ft), 6 (pt); LPNs 14 (ft), 12 (pt); Orderlies 4 (ft); Nurses aides 55 (ft), 30 (pt); Physical therapists 1 (pt); Activities coordinators 2 (ft), 1 (pt); Dietitians 1 (pt).
Affiliation Baptist
Facilities Dining room; Physical therapy room; Activities room; Chapel; Crafts room; Laundry room; Barber/Beauty shop; Library.
Activities Arts & crafts; Cards; Games; Reading groups; Prayer groups; Movies; Shopping trips; Social/Cultural gatherings; Music.

Mercy Care Center
1870 S 75th St, Omaha, NE, 68124
(402) 398-6800
Admin Joyce Gibbs. *Medical Dir/Dir of Nursing* V W Meyers MD; Carol Smith RN DON.
Licensure Skilled care. *Beds* SNF 250. *Certified* Medicaid; Medicare.
Owner Nonprofit Corp.
Staff Physicians 1 (ft); RNs 20 (ft), 20 (pt); LPNs 40 (ft), 40 (pt); Orderlies 55 (ft), 55 (pt) 13E 55 (ft), 55 (pt); Physical therapists 2 (ft), 1 (pt); Recreational therapists 2 (ft); Occupational therapists 1 (ft); Speech therapists 1 (ft); Dietitians 1 (ft); Ophthalmologists 1 (pt); Dentist 1 (pt); Social worker 2 (ft); Pastoral care 1 (ft); Admissions RN 2 (ft), 1 (pt).

Millard Good Samaritan Center
12856 Deauville Dr, Omaha, NE, 68137
(402) 895-2266
Admin Luann Foos. *Medical Dir/Dir of Nursing* Dr Fred Schwartz; Kris Sullivan RN DON.
Licensure Skilled care; Intermediate care. *Beds* 113. *Certified* Medicaid.
Owner Nonprofit Corp (Evangelical Lutheran/ Good Samaritan).
Staff RNs 6 (ft), 6 (pt); LPNs 2 (ft), 4 (pt); Nurses aides 32 (ft), 29 (pt); Recreational therapists 1 (pt); Dietitians 1 (ft).
Affiliation Lutheran

Facilities Dining room; Physical therapy room; Activities room; Chapel; Crafts room; Laundry room; Barber/Beauty shop.
Activities Arts & crafts; Cards; Games; Reading groups; Prayer groups; Movies; Shopping trips; Social/Cultural gatherings.

Montclair Nursing Center
2525 S 135th Ave, Omaha, NE, 68144
(402) 333-2304
Admin Eileen J Corns. *Medical Dir/Dir of Nursing* Donald J Darst; Dianna Averill RN.
Licensure Skilled care; Intermediate care; Hospice. *Beds* 179. *Certified* Medicare.
Owner Proprietary Corp (Life Care Centers of America).
Admissions Requirements Medical examination; Physician's request.
Staff Physicians; RNs; LPNs; Orderlies; Nurses aides; Physical therapists; Reality therapists; Occupational therapists; Speech therapists; Activities coordinators; Dietitians; Dentists; Podiatrists; Social workers.
Facilities Dining room; Physical therapy room; Activities room; Crafts room; Laundry room; Barber/Beauty shop; Library; Family room; Meeting space.
Activities Arts & crafts; Cards; Games; Reading groups; Prayer groups; Movies; Shopping trips; Social/Cultural gatherings; Fishing trips.

Omaha Manor Inc*
2406 Fowler Ave, Omaha, NE, 68111
(402) 457-4488
Admin William L Anderson. *Medical Dir/Dir of Nursing* William D Murphy MD.
Licensure Intermediate care; Intermediate care for mentally retarded. *Beds* 49.
Owner Proprietary Corp.
Admissions Requirements Minimum age 19; Medical examination.
Staff Physicians; RNs; LPNs; Orderlies; Nurses aides; Physical therapists; Reality therapists; Recreational therapists; Occupational therapists; Speech therapists; Activities coordinators; Dietitians; Dentists; Ophthalmologists; Podiatrists; Audiologists.
Facilities Dining room; Activities room.
Activities Arts & crafts; Cards; Games; Reading groups; Prayer groups; Movies; Shopping trips; Social/Cultural gatherings.

Omaha Nursing Home Inc*
4835 S 49th St, Omaha, NE, 68117
(402) 733-7200
Admin Emelie Jonusas.
Licensure Intermediate care. *Beds* 83. *Certified* Medicaid.
Owner Proprietary Corp.

Orchard Hill Nursing Home*
3853 Decatur St, Omaha, NE, 68111
(402) 556-8878
Admin Joe Hageman.
Licensure Intermediate care. *Beds* 49. *Certified* Medicaid.
Owner Proprietary Corp.

Redman Nursing Home*
4809 Redman Ave, Omaha, NE, 68104
(402) 455-5025
Admin Brian Farrell.
Licensure Intermediate care. *Beds* 122. *Certified* Medicaid.
Owner Proprietary Corp.
Staff RNs 4 (ft), 2 (pt); LPNs 4 (ft), 4 (pt); Orderlies 4 (ft), 1 (pt); Nurses aides 21 (ft), 9 (pt); Activities coordinators 1 (ft), 1 (pt).
Facilities Dining room; Activities room; Crafts room; Laundry room; Barber/Beauty shop.
Activities Arts & crafts; Cards; Games; Reading groups; Prayer groups; Movies; Shopping trips; Social/Cultural gatherings.

Doctor Philip Sher Jewish Home*
4801 N 52nd St, Omaha, NE, 68104
(402) 451-7220

Admin Allan Greene.
Licensure Intermediate care. *Beds* 80.
  Certified Medicaid.
Owner Nonprofit Corp.
Affiliation Jewish

Skyline Manor & Skyline Villa
7300 Graceland Dr, Omaha, NE, 68134
(402) 572-5753
Admin Jacqueline W Fatheree. *Medical Dir/
  Dir of Nursing* Dr Robert Underriner; Rita
  Bachtell DON.
Licensure Intermediate care; Apartments. *Beds*
  ICF 84; Apts 468.
Owner Nonprofit Corp.
Admissions Requirements Minimum age 65;
  Medical examination.
Staff RNs; LPNs; Orderlies; Nurses aides;
  Physical therapists; Reality therapists;
  Recreational therapists; Activities
  coordinators; Dietitians; Podiatrists;
  Chaplain.
Facilities Dining room; Activities room;
  Chapel; Crafts room; Laundry room; Barber/
  Beauty shop; Library.
Activities Arts & crafts; Cards; Games;
  Reading groups; Prayer groups; Movies;
  Shopping trips; Social/Cultural gatherings;
  Ceramic shop; Gardens.

Ville de Sante Nursing Home*
6032 Ville de Sante Dr, Omaha, NE, 68104
(402) 571-6770
Admin Donna Suing. *Medical Dir/Dir of
  Nursing* Joan Arnold.
Licensure Intermediate care. *Beds* 128.
  Certified Medicaid.
Owner Proprietary Corp (Southmark Heritage
  Corp).
Admissions Requirements Minimum age 50;
  Medical examination; Physician's request.
Staff RNs 3 (ft), 2 (pt); LPNs 4 (ft), 2 (pt);
  Nurses aides 25 (ft), 20 (pt); Activities
  coordinators 1 (ft), 1 (pt).
Facilities Dining room; Activities room;
  Chapel; Crafts room; Laundry room; Barber/
  Beauty shop; Library.
Activities Arts & crafts; Cards; Games;
  Reading groups; Prayer groups; Movies;
  Shopping trips; Social/Cultural gatherings.

Williams Care Manor
3525 Evans St, Omaha, NE, 68111
(402) 451-5060
Admin Kinze M Williams. *Medical Dir/Dir of
  Nursing* Lillian E Rogers RN DON.
Licensure Intermediate care. *Beds* 60.
  Certified Medicaid.
Owner Proprietary Corp.
Admissions Requirements Medical
  examination; Physician's request.
Staff Physicians; RNs 2 (ft); LPNs 4 (ft), 2
  (pt); Orderlies 4 (ft); Nurses aides 20 (ft), 6
  (pt); Physical therapists; Recreational
  therapists; Occupational therapists; Activities
  coordinators; Dietitians; Podiatrists.
Facilities Dining room; Activities room;
  Chapel; Crafts room; Laundry room; Barber/
  Beauty shop.
Activities Arts & crafts; Cards; Games;
  Reading groups; Prayer groups; Movies;
  Shopping trips; Social/Cultural gatherings.

ONEILL

O'Neill Senior Citizen's Home*
Box 756, O'Neill, NE, 68763
(402) 336-2384
Admin James R Falk.
Licensure Intermediate care. *Beds* 72.
  Certified Medicaid.
Owner Proprietary Corp.
Staff RNs 2 (ft); LPNs 3 (ft); Nurses aides 20
  (ft), 5 (pt); Physical therapists 1 (pt);
  Activities coordinators 1 (ft); Dietitians 1
  (ft).

Facilities Dining room; Physical therapy
  room; Activities room; Chapel; Crafts room;
  Laundry room; Barber/Beauty shop.
Activities Arts & crafts; Cards; Games;
  Reading groups; Prayer groups; Movies;
  Shopping trips; Social/Cultural gatherings.

OSCEOLA

Osceola Good Samaritan Center*
Box 507, Osceola, NE, 68651
(402) 747-2691
Admin James W Barta.
Licensure Intermediate care. *Beds* 65.
  Certified Medicaid.
Owner Nonprofit Corp (Evangelical Lutheran/
  Good Samaritan).
Admissions Requirements Medical
  examination; Physician's request.
Staff Physicians 2 (pt); RNs 2 (pt); LPNs 2
  (ft), 6 (pt); Nurses aides 9 (ft), 19 (pt);
  Physical therapists 1 (pt); Activities
  coordinators 1 (ft); Dietitians 1 (pt).
Facilities Dining room; Physical therapy
  room; Activities room; Chapel; Crafts room;
  Laundry room; Barber/Beauty shop.
Activities Arts & crafts; Cards; Games;
  Reading groups; Prayer groups; Movies;
  Shopping trips; Social/Cultural gatherings;
  Community activities; Annual special events;
  Annual bazaar.

OXFORD

Walker Post Manor
PO Box 98, Oxford, NE, 68967
(308) 824-3293
Admin Dolores J Woodruff.
Licensure Intermediate care. *Beds* 56.
  Certified Medicaid.
Owner Proprietary Corp.

PALMER

The Coolidge Center
RR2 Box 8, Palmer, NE, 68864
(308) 894-2735
Admin Shirley Stratman. *Medical Dir/Dir of
  Nursing* Kristine K Moeller DON.
Licensure Intermediate care. *Beds* ICF 42.
  Certified Medicaid.
Owner Privately owned.
Admissions Requirements Medical
  examination.
Facilities Dining room; Activities room;
  Laundry room; Barber/Beauty shop.
Activities Arts & crafts; Cards; Games;
  Reading groups; Prayer groups; Movies;
  Social/Cultural gatherings.

PAPILLION

Huntington Park Care Center
1507 Gold Coast Rd, Papillion, NE, 68046
(402) 339-6010
Admin Susan E Anagnostou. *Medical Dir/Dir
  of Nursing* Ruth Ticknor RN DON.
Licensure Intermediate care. *Beds* ICF 112.
  Certified Medicaid.
Owner Proprietary Corp.
Admissions Requirements Minimum age 55;
  Medical examination; Physician's request.
Staff Physicians 1 (pt); RNs 3 (ft), 1 (pt);
  LPNs 5 (ft), 2 (pt); Nurses aides 30 (ft), 20
  (pt); Physical therapists 1 (pt); Recreational
  therapists 1 (ft); Occupational therapists 1
  (pt); Speech therapists 1 (pt); Activities
  coordinators 1 (ft); Dietitians 1 (pt).
Facilities Dining room; Activities room;
  Crafts room; Laundry room; Barber/Beauty
  shop.
Activities Arts & crafts; Cards; Games;
  Reading groups; Prayer groups; Movies;
  Shopping trips; Social/Cultural gatherings;
  Exercise; Discussion groups; Alzheimers
  therapy group.

Papillion Manor Inc
610 S Polk St, Papillion, NE, 68046
(402) 339-7700
Admin Virginia Chase. *Medical Dir/Dir of
  Nursing* Nancy Harpster RN.
Licensure Intermediate care. *Beds* ICF 83.
Owner Proprietary Corp (Vetter Health
  Services).
Admissions Requirements Medical
  examination.
Staff RNs 3 (ft), 3 (pt); LPNs 3 (ft), 1 (pt);
  Orderlies 1 (ft); Nurses aides 15 (ft), 15 (pt);
  Activities coordinators 1 (ft); Dietitians 1
  (ft).
Facilities Dining room; Physical therapy
  room; Activities room; Chapel; Laundry
  room; Barber/Beauty shop.
Activities Arts & crafts; Cards; Games;
  Reading groups; Prayer groups; Movies;
  Shopping trips.

PAWNEE CITY

Pawnee Manor Inc
438 12th St, Pawnee City, NE, 68420
(402) 852-2975
Admin Jenett Reed. *Medical Dir/Dir of
  Nursing* Debra Schultz DON.
Licensure Intermediate care. *Beds* ICF 66.
  Certified Medicaid.
Owner Proprietary Corp (ARA Living
  Centers).
Staff RNs 1 (ft), 1 (pt); LPNs 3 (pt); Nurses
  aides 19 (pt); Activities coordinators 1 (ft).
Facilities Dining room; Activities room;
  Chapel; Laundry room; Barber/Beauty shop.
Activities Arts & crafts; Cards; Games;
  Reading groups; Prayer groups; Movies;
  Shopping trips; Social/Cultural gatherings;
  Banquets.

PENDER

Pender Care Centre
200 Valley View Dr, Pender, NE, 68047
(402) 385-3072
Admin Bernice Heath. *Medical Dir/Dir of
  Nursing* Cindy Lierman RN DON.
Licensure Intermediate care. *Beds* ICF 62.
  Certified Medicaid.
Owner Proprietary Corp.
Admissions Requirements Minimum age 16;
  Medical examination; Physician's request.
Staff RNs 1 (ft), 2 (pt); LPNs 5 (pt); Nurses
  aides 5 (ft), 19 (pt); Physical therapists 1
  (pt); Activities coordinators 1 (pt); Dietitians
  1 (pt); Ophthalmologists 1 (pt).
Facilities Dining room; Physical therapy
  room; Laundry room; Barber/Beauty shop.
Activities Arts & crafts; Cards; Games;
  Reading groups; Prayer groups; Movies;
  Shopping trips; Social/Cultural gatherings.

PIERCE

Pierce Manor
515 E Main St, Pierce, NE, 68767
(402) 329-6228
Admin Janet Zierke. *Medical Dir/Dir of
  Nursing* Laurrie Steele.
Licensure Intermediate care. *Beds* ICF 86.
  Certified Medicaid.
Owner Proprietary Corp (ARA Living
  Centers).
Staff RNs 1 (ft); LPNs 1 (ft), 6 (pt); Nurses
  aides 6 (ft), 26 (pt); Physical therapists 1
  (pt); Occupational therapists 1 (pt); Speech
  therapists 1 (pt); Activities coordinators 1
  (ft); Dietitians 1 (pt).
Facilities Dining room; Activities room;
  Chapel; Crafts room; Laundry room; Barber/
  Beauty shop; Library.
Activities Arts & crafts; Cards; Games;
  Reading groups; Prayer groups; Movies;
  Shopping trips; Social/Cultural gatherings;
  Awareness groups.

PLAINVIEW

Plainview Manor
PO Box 219, Plainview, NE, 68769-0219
(402) 582-3849
Admin Berkley E Homstedt.
Licensure Intermediate care. *Beds* 60.
 Certified Medicaid.
Owner Proprietary Corp.

PLATTSMOUTH

Plattsmouth Manor*
602 S 18th St, Plattsmouth, NE, 68048
(402) 296-2800
Admin Ivan Craft.
Licensure Intermediate care. *Beds* 140.
 Certified Medicaid.
Owner Proprietary Corp.

PONCA

Elms Health Care Center Inc*
Ponca, NE, 68770
(402) 755-2233
Admin Rozanne Elliott.
Licensure Intermediate care. *Beds* 52.
 Certified Medicaid.
Owner Proprietary Corp.

RANDOLPH

Colonial Manor of Randolph Inc
Box D, 811 S Main, Randolph, NE, 68771
(402) 337-0444
Admin Roger E Johnson. *Medical Dir/Dir of
 Nursing* Kathie Keefer.
Licensure Intermediate care. *Beds* ICF 64.
 Certified Medicaid.
Owner Proprietary Corp.
Staff RNs 1 (pt); LPNs 2 (ft), 1 (pt); Orderlies
 1 (ft), 1 (pt); Nurses aides 12 (ft), 1 (pt);
 Physical therapists 1 (ft), 1 (pt);
 Occupational therapists 1 (pt); Activities
 coordinators 1 (ft), 1 (pt); Dietitians 1 (pt);
 Dentists 1 (pt).
Facilities Dining room; Chapel; Crafts room;
 Laundry room; Barber/Beauty shop.
Activities Arts & crafts; Cards; Games; Prayer
 groups; Movies; Shopping trips; Social/
 Cultural gatherings.

RAVENNA

Ravenna Good Samaritan Home
411 W Genoa, Ravenna, NE, 68869
(308) 452-3230
Admin Eleanor M Deines. *Medical Dir/Dir of
 Nursing* Janet Campbell RN.
Licensure Intermediate care. *Beds* ICF 83.
 Certified Medicaid.
Owner Nonprofit Corp (Evangelical Lutheran/
 Good Samaritan).
Admissions Requirements Minimum age 50;
 Medical examination; Physician's request.
Staff RNs 1 (ft), 2 (pt); LPNs 6 (ft); Nurses
 aides 20 (ft), 5 (pt); Activities coordinators 1
 (ft), 2 (pt); Dietitians 1 (ft).
Affiliation Lutheran
Facilities Dining room; Physical therapy
 room; Activities room; Crafts room; Laundry
 room; Barber/Beauty shop; Library; Lounge
 area.
Activities Arts & crafts; Cards; Games;
 Reading groups; Prayer groups; Movies;
 Shopping trips; Social/Cultural gatherings;
 Hymm sings; Van trips.

RED CLOUD

Sprague Nursing Home*
7th & Locust Sts, Red Cloud, NE, 68970
(402) 746-3414
Admin Harry M Sprague.

Licensure Intermediate care. *Beds* 52.
 Certified Medicaid.
Owner Proprietary Corp.

SAINT EDWARD

Cloverlodge Care Center
Box B, 301 N 13th St, Saint Edward, NE,
 68660
(402) 678-2294
Admin Helen A Zona. *Medical Dir/Dir of
 Nursing* Deb Zarek.
Licensure Intermediate care. *Beds* ICF 65.
 Certified Medicaid.
Owner Proprietary Corp (Vetter Health
 Services).
Admissions Requirements Physician's request.
Staff RNs; LPNs; Nurses aides; Physical
 therapists; Reality therapists; Recreational
 therapists; Occupational therapists; Speech
 therapists; Activities coordinators; Dietitians;
 Ophthalmologists; Podiatrists.
Facilities Dining room; Activities room;
 Chapel; Laundry room; Barber/Beauty shop.
Activities Arts & crafts; Cards; Games; Prayer
 groups; Movies; Shopping trips.

SAINT PAUL

Heritage Living Center
920 Jackson St, Saint Paul, NE, 68873
(308) 754-5430
Admin Kevin Sauberzweig. *Medical Dir/Dir of
 Nursing* Pat Swanson.
Licensure Intermediate care. *Beds* ICF 74.
 Certified Medicaid.
Owner Proprietary Corp (Vetter Health
 Services).
Admissions Requirements Medical
 examination; Physician's request.
Staff LPNs; Orderlies; Nurses aides; Activities
 coordinators.
Languages Polish, Czech
Facilities Dining room; Laundry room;
 Barber/Beauty shop.
Activities Arts & crafts; Cards; Games; Prayer
 groups; Movies; Social/Cultural gatherings.

SARGENT

Sargent Nursing Home
PO Box 480, S Hwy 183, Sargent, NE, 68874
(308) 527-4201
Admin Connie Disbrow. *Medical Dir/Dir of
 Nursing* Mary Harvey DON.
Licensure Intermediate care; Domiciliary care.
 Beds ICF 33; Domiciliary care 9. *Certified*
 Medicaid.
Owner Proprietary Corp (Beverly Enterprises).
Admissions Requirements Medical
 examination; Physician's request.
Staff RNs 1 (pt); LPNs 2 (ft), 1 (pt); Nurses
 aides 7 (ft), 3 (pt); Activities coordinators 1
 (ft); Dietary 3 (ft), 3 (pt); Social services 1
 (pt).
Facilities Dining room; Activities room;
 Laundry room; Barber/Beauty shop; TV
 room.
Activities Arts & crafts; Cards; Games; Prayer
 groups; Movies; Shopping trips; Social/
 Cultural gatherings; Group exercise; Current
 events; Bingo.

SCHUYLER

Schuyler Senior Citizen's Home
2023 Colfax Ave, Schuyler, NE, 68661
(402) 352-3977
Admin Eric M Stewart. *Medical Dir/Dir of
 Nursing* Veria Wilson RN.
Licensure Intermediate care. *Beds* 72.
 Certified Medicaid.
Owner Proprietary Corp (Beverly Enterprises).
Admissions Requirements Medical
 examination.

Staff Physicians 5 (ft); RNs 2 (ft), 3 (pt);
 LPNs 3 (ft), 3 (pt); Nurses aides 14 (ft), 10
 (pt); Physical therapists 1 (pt); Speech
 therapists 1 (pt); Activities coordinators 1
 (ft), 1 (pt); Dietitians 1 (pt); Podiatrists 1
 (pt); Audiologists 1 (pt); Restorative aides 1
 (ft), 1 (pt); Social Services 1 (ft).
Facilities Dining room; Activities room;
 Chapel; Laundry room; Barber/Beauty shop;
 Library; TV; Card playing rooms.
Activities Arts & crafts; Cards; Games;
 Reading groups; Prayer groups; Movies;
 Social/Cultural gatherings; Intergenerational
 programs; Beauty groups.

SCOTTSBLUFF

Scottsbluff Villa*
111 W 36th St, Scottsbluff, NE, 69361
(308) 635-2019
Admin Melvin Williams.
Licensure Intermediate care. *Beds* 134.
 Certified Medicaid.
Owner Proprietary Corp (Beverly Enterprises).

SCRIBNER

Scribner Good Samaritan Center
815 Logan St, Scribner, NE, 68057
(402) 664-2527
Admin Clarence R Wegenast. *Medical Dir/Dir
 of Nursing* Marge Zieg RN.
Licensure Intermediate care. *Beds* ICF 83.
 Certified Medicaid.
Owner Nonprofit Corp (Evangelical Lutheran/
 Good Samaritan).
Admissions Requirements Physician's request.
Staff RNs 1 (ft), 3 (pt); LPNs 5 (pt); Orderlies
 1 (pt); Nurses aides 41 (pt); Physical
 therapists 3 (pt); Occupational therapists;
 Activities coordinators 2 (pt); Dietitians 1
 (pt); Ophthalmologists.
Languages German
Affiliation Lutheran
Facilities Dining room; Physical therapy
 room; Activities room; Chapel; Crafts room;
 Laundry room; Barber/Beauty shop.
Activities Arts & crafts; Cards; Games;
 Reading groups; Prayer groups; Movies;
 Shopping trips; Social/Cultural gatherings.

SEWARD

Bethesda Care Center of Seward
624 Pinewood Ave, Seward, NE, 68434
(402) 643-4561
Admin Larry Lavelle. *Medical Dir/Dir of
 Nursing* Lori Wehrs.
Licensure Intermediate care. *Beds* ICF 56.
 Certified Medicaid.
Owner Nonprofit Corp (Bethesda Care
 Centers).
Admissions Requirements Medical
 examination.
Staff RNs 2 (ft), 1 (pt); LPNs 2 (ft), 2 (pt);
 Nurses aides 10 (ft), 13 (pt).
Facilities Dining room; Activities room;
 Chapel; Laundry room; Barber/Beauty shop.
Activities Arts & crafts; Cards; Games;
 Reading groups; Prayer groups; Movies;
 Shopping trips; Social/Cultural gatherings.

Anna Sundermann Home
446 Pinewood Ave, Seward, NE, 68434
(402) 643-2902
Admin Karen E McConnell. *Medical Dir/Dir
 of Nursing* Kris Sanberzweig.
Licensure Intermediate care. *Beds* ICF 62.
 Certified Medicaid.
Owner Nonprofit Corp.
Admissions Requirements Minimum age 55;
 Medical examination.
Facilities Dining room; Activities room;
 Chapel; Crafts room; Laundry room; Barber/
 Beauty shop.

Activities Arts & crafts; Cards; Games;
Reading groups; Prayer groups; Movies;
Shopping trips; Social/Cultural gatherings;
Adult day care; Van service.

SIDNEY

Lodgepole Plaza Nursing Home*
1435 Toledo, Sidney, NE, 69162
(308) 254-4756
Admin Charlotte Fleming.
Licensure Intermediate care. *Beds* 54.
Certified Medicaid.
Owner Proprietary Corp.
Admissions Requirements Medical
examination.
Staff RNs 1 (ft), 2 (pt); LPNs 3 (ft), 2 (pt);
Nurses aides 11 (ft); Recreational therapists
1 (ft); Activities coordinators 1 (ft);
Dietitians 1 (ft).
Facilities Dining room; Physical therapy
room; Activities room; Crafts room; Laundry
room; Barber/Beauty shop; Library.
Activities Arts & crafts; Cards; Games;
Reading groups; Prayer groups; Movies;
Social/Cultural gatherings.

SOUTH SIOUX CITY

Green Acres Nursing Home*
3501 Dakota Ave, South Sioux City, NE,
68776
(402) 494-4273
Admin Jerry Albright.
Licensure Intermediate care. *Beds* 84.
Certified Medicaid.
Owner Proprietary Corp.

Matney's Colonial Manor*
3200 G St, South Sioux City, NE, 68776
(402) 494-3043
Admin Edward H Matney.
Licensure Intermediate care. *Beds* 66.
Certified Medicaid.
Owner Proprietary Corp.

SPALDING

Friendship Villa of Spalding
PO Box 190, Spalding, NE, 68665
(308) 497-2426
Admin Karen Simmons. *Medical Dir/Dir of
Nursing* Peg Fairbanks RN.
Licensure Intermediate care. *Beds* ICF 48.
Certified Medicaid.
Owner Proprietary Corp (Vetter Health
Services).
Admissions Requirements Medical
examination; Physician's request.
Staff RNs 1 (ft); LPNs 3 (ft); Nurses aides 18
(ft); Physical therapists 1 (pt); Activities
coordinators 1 (pt); Dietitians 1 (pt); Social
Service 1 (pt).
Facilities Dining room; Physical therapy
room; Activities room; Chapel; Crafts room;
Laundry room; Barber/Beauty shop.
Activities Arts & crafts; Games; Reading
groups; Movies; Shopping trips.

STANTON

Stanton Nursing Home
PO Box 407, 301 17th St, Stanton, NE, 68779
(402) 439-2201
Admin Ted Boese. *Medical Dir/Dir of Nursing*
Stephanie Wymer DON.
Licensure Intermediate care. *Beds* ICF 69.
Certified Medicaid.
Owner Publicly owned.
Admissions Requirements Medical
examination; Physician's request.
Staff RNs; LPNs; Nurses aides.
Facilities Dining room; Physical therapy
room; Activities room; Chapel; Laundry
room; Barber/Beauty shop; Library;
Solariums.

STROMSBURG

Midwest Covenant Home Inc
615 E 9th St, Stromsburg, NE, 68666
(402) 764-2711
Admin Robert L Greenwall. *Medical Dir/Dir
of Nursing* Ruth Hanson DON.
Licensure Skilled care; Intermediate care. *Beds*
SNF 65; ICF 35. *Certified* Medicaid;
Medicare.
Owner Nonprofit Corp.
Staff RNs 3 (ft), 5 (pt); LPNs 4 (ft), 11 (pt);
Nurses aides 9 (ft), 38 (pt); Physical
therapists 1 (pt); Speech therapists 1 (pt);
Activities coordinators 1 (ft), 2 (pt);
Dietitians 1 (pt).
Facilities Dining room; Physical therapy
room; Activities room; Chapel; Crafts room;
Laundry room; Barber/Beauty shop; Library.
Activities Arts & crafts; Cards; Games;
Reading groups; Prayer groups; Movies;
Shopping trips; Social/Cultural gatherings.

STUART

Parkside Manor
PO Box A, N Main, Stuart, NE, 68780
(402) 924-3601
Admin Ruth Ann Walter. *Medical Dir/Dir of
Nursing* Kris Cobb DON.
Licensure Intermediate care. *Beds* ICF 55.
Certified Medicaid.
Owner Nonprofit organization/foundation.
Admissions Requirements Medical
examination; Physician's request.
Staff RNs 1 (ft); LPNs 4 (ft); Orderlies 3 (ft);
Nurses aides 10 (ft), 12 (pt); Physical
therapists 1 (ft); Activities coordinators 1
(ft); Dietitians 1 (ft); Dentists 1 (pt);
Ophthalmologists 1 (pt); Podiatrists 1 (pt).
Facilities Dining room; Physical therapy
room; Activities room; Chapel; Crafts room;
Laundry room; Barber/Beauty shop.
Activities Arts & crafts; Cards; Games;
Reading groups; Prayer groups; Movies;
Shopping trips; Social/Cultural gatherings.

SUPERIOR

Good Samaritan Center*
Hwy 14 N, Superior, NE, 68978
(402) 879-4791
Admin Diane Berens.
Licensure Intermediate care. *Beds* 84.
Certified Medicaid.
Owner Nonprofit Corp (Evangelical Lutheran/
Good Samaritan).
Affiliation Lutheran

SUTHERLAND

Bethesda Care Center
333 Maple, Sutherland, NE, 69101
(308) 386-4393
Admin Joan L Anderson. *Medical Dir/Dir of
Nursing* Joan H Spurgin.
Licensure Intermediate care. *Beds* ICF 62.
Certified Medicaid.
Owner Nonprofit Corp (Bethesda Care
Centers).
Admissions Requirements Medical
examination; Physician's request.
Staff RNs; LPNs; Nurses aides; Activities
coordinators.
Facilities Dining room; Physical therapy
room; Activities room; Crafts room; Laundry
room; Barber/Beauty shop.
Activities Arts & crafts; Cards; Games;
Reading groups; Prayer groups; Movies;
Shopping trips; Social/Cultural gatherings.

SUTTON

Sutton Community Home
1106 N Sauders St, Sutton, NE, 68979
(402) 773-5557
Admin Bernadette Thiel. *Medical Dir/Dir of
Nursing* Carol Spahn DON.
Licensure Intermediate care. *Beds* ICF 46.
Certified Medicaid.
Owner Proprietary Corp.
Staff RNs; LPNs; Nurses aides; Physical
therapists; Occupational therapists; Activities
coordinators; Dietitians.
Facilities Dining room; Laundry room;
Barber/Beauty shop.
Activities Arts & crafts; Cards; Games;
Reading groups; Prayer groups; Movies;
Shopping trips.

SYRACUSE

Good Samaritan Center
1622 Walnut St, Syracuse, NE, 68446
(402) 269-2251
Admin Mary Kraus. *Medical Dir/Dir of
Nursing* Jackie Wooster RN.
Licensure Intermediate care. *Beds* ICF 113.
Certified Medicaid.
Owner Nonprofit Corp (Evangelical Lutheran/
Good Samaritan).
Admissions Requirements Medical
examination; Physician's request.
Staff RNs 1 (ft), 3 (pt); LPNs 2 (ft), 4 (pt);
Nurses aides 10 (ft), 48 (pt); Activities
coordinators 1 (ft); Dietitians 1 (pt).
Affiliation Lutheran
Facilities Dining room; Physical therapy
room; Activities room; Chapel; Crafts room;
Laundry room; Barber/Beauty shop; Library.
Activities Arts & crafts; Cards; Games;
Reading groups; Prayer groups; Movies;
Social/Cultural gatherings.

TECUMSEH

Maple Grove Home
Rte 2 Box 225, Tecumseh, NE, 68450
(402) 335-2885
Admin Dorothy J Babel. *Medical Dir/Dir of
Nursing* Doris Teet.
Licensure Intermediate care. *Beds* ICF 30.
Certified Medicaid.
Owner Nonprofit Corp.
Staff Physicians; RNs; LPNs; Nurses aides;
Activities coordinators.
Facilities Dining room; Activities room;
Chapel; Laundry room; Barber/Beauty shop.
Activities Arts & crafts; Cards; Games;
Reading groups; Prayer groups; Movies.

Tecumseh Care Center*
3rd St, Tecumseh, NE, 68450
(402) 335-3357
Admin Charles Haas & Mary C Haas.
Licensure Intermediate care. *Beds* 73.
Certified Medicaid.
Owner Proprietary Corp.

TEKAMAH

Takamah Nursing Center
823 M St, Tekamah, NE, 68061
(402) 374-1414
Admin Lisa Teager. *Medical Dir/Dir of
Nursing* Mary Jo Malone RN DON.
Licensure Intermediate care. *Beds* ICF 63.
Certified Medicaid.
Owner Proprietary Corp (Beverly Enterprises).
Facilities Dining room; Activities room;
Chapel; Crafts room; Laundry room; Barber/
Beauty shop.

TILDEN

Tilden Nursing Center
401 Park, Tilden, NE, 68781
(402) 368-5388
Admin Rose Nathan. *Medical Dir/Dir of Nursing* Leona Shrader.
Licensure Intermediate care. *Beds* ICF 52. *Certified* Medicaid.
Owner Proprietary Corp (Beverly Enterprises).
Admissions Requirements Medical examination.
Staff Physicians 8 (pt); RNs 1 (ft); LPNs 3 (ft), 3 (pt); Physical therapists 1 (pt); Recreational therapists 1 (pt); Occupational therapists 1 (pt); Speech therapists 1 (pt); Activities coordinators 1 (ft); Dietitians 1 (pt); Ophthalmologists 1 (pt); Podiatrists 1 (pt).
Facilities Dining room; Activities room; Laundry room; Barber/Beauty shop.
Activities Arts & crafts; Cards; Games; Reading groups; Prayer groups; Movies; Social/Cultural gatherings.

TRENTON

El Dorado Manor Nursing Home
Jct Hwys 25 & 34, Trenton, NE, 69044
(308) 334-5242
Admin Virginia L McClure. *Medical Dir/Dir of Nursing* Nan Shimek DON.
Licensure Intermediate care; Residential care; Day care. *Beds* ICF; Residential 20; Day care 2. *Certified* Medicaid.
Owner Nonprofit organization/foundation.
Admissions Requirements Minimum age 35; Medical examination; Physician's request.
Staff RNs 1 (ft), 1 (pt); LPNs 5 (ft); Nurses aides 14 (ft), 3 (pt); Physical therapists 1 (pt); Activities coordinators 1 (ft).
Facilities Dining room; Physical therapy room; Activities room; Chapel; Crafts room; Laundry room; Barber/Beauty shop; Library.
Activities Arts & crafts; Cards; Games; Reading groups; Prayer groups; Movies; Shopping trips; Social hour; Style shows.

UTICA

Bethesda Care Center
1350 Centennial Ave, Utica, NE, 68456
(402) 534-2041
Admin Alene E Dittmar. *Medical Dir/Dir of Nursing* Donna D Tomes.
Licensure Intermediate care. *Beds* ICF 47. *Certified* Medicaid.
Owner Nonprofit Corp (Bethesda Care Centers).
Admissions Requirements Medical examination.
Staff RNs 1 (ft), 2 (pt); LPNs 4 (pt); Nurses aides 10 (ft), 10 (pt); Recreational therapists 1 (pt); Activities coordinators 1 (ft).
Languages German
Facilities Dining room; Physical therapy room; Activities room; Chapel; Crafts room; Laundry room; Barber/Beauty shop; Library.
Activities Arts & crafts; Cards; Games; Reading groups; Prayer groups; Movies; Shopping trips; Social/Cultural gatherings.

VALENTINE

Pine View Good Samaritan Center*
W Hwy 83, Valentine, NE, 69201
(402) 376-1260
Admin Marvin Sackschewsky.
Licensure Intermediate care. *Beds* 66. *Certified* Medicaid.
Owner Nonprofit Corp (Evangelical Lutheran/Good Samaritan).
Admissions Requirements Medical examination; Physician's request.
Staff RNs 2 (ft), 1 (pt).
Affiliation Lutheran

Facilities Dining room; Physical therapy room; Activities room; Chapel; Crafts room; Laundry room; Barber/Beauty shop.
Activities Arts & crafts; Cards; Games; Prayer groups; Movies; Shopping trips; Social/Cultural gatherings.

VALLEY

Colonial Manor*
PO Box 375, 300 W Meigs, Valley, NE, 68064
(402) 359-2533
Admin Linda Boddy.
Licensure Intermediate care. *Beds* 60. *Certified* Medicaid.
Owner Proprietary Corp (Beverly Enterprises).

VERDIGRE

Alpine Village
706 James, Verdigre, NE, 68783
(402) 668-2209
Admin Patricia McElhose. *Medical Dir/Dir of Nursing* Marc Vakoc RN DON.
Licensure Intermediate care. *Beds* ICF 65. *Certified* Medicaid.
Owner Publicly owned.
Admissions Requirements Medical examination; Physician's request.
Staff Physicians; RNs 2 (ft), 1 (pt); LPNs 2 (ft), 1 (pt); Nurses aides 15 (ft), 13 (pt); Physical therapists 1 (ft), 1 (pt); Activities coordinators 1 (ft), 1 (pt); Social worker 1 (ft) Physical therapy aides 2 (pt).
Facilities Dining room; Physical therapy room; Activities room; Chapel; Crafts room; Laundry room; Barber/Beauty shop; Pool room with TV; Living room with TV; Family room; Solarium.
Activities Arts & crafts; Cards; Games; Reading groups; Prayer groups; Movies; Shopping trips; Social/Cultural gatherings; Numerous clubs; Resident's Council; Exercise groups.

WAHOO

Haven House
1145 Laurel St, Wahoo, NE, 68066
(402) 443-3737
Admin Maxine V Pflieger. *Medical Dir/Dir of Nursing* Dr Brian Elliot; Judy Merkel RN.
Licensure Intermediate care. *Beds* 75. *Certified* Medicaid.
Owner Proprietary Corp.
Admissions Requirements Medical examination; Physician's request.
Languages Czech
Facilities Dining room; Activities room; Laundry room; Barber/Beauty shop.
Activities Arts & crafts; Cards; Games; Reading groups; Prayer groups; Movies; Shopping trips; Social/Cultural gatherings.

Saunders County Care Center
PO Box 307, 844 W 9th St, Wahoo, NE, 68066
(402) 443-4685
Admin Lorraine Syverson. *Medical Dir/Dir of Nursing* Leann Jeppson RN.
Licensure Intermediate care. *Beds* ICF 75. *Certified* Medicaid.
Owner Nonprofit organization/foundation.
Admissions Requirements Medical examination.
Staff RNs 1 (ft), 3 (pt); LPNs 2 (ft), 4 (pt); Nurses aides 16 (ft), 20 (pt); Physical therapists; Recreational therapists; Occupational therapists; Speech therapists; Activities coordinators 1 (ft), 1 (pt); Dietitians; Dentists.
Languages Czech, Swedish, German
Facilities Dining room; Activities room; Chapel; Crafts room; Laundry room; Barber/Beauty shop.

Activities Arts & crafts; Cards; Games; Reading groups; Prayer groups; Movies; Shopping trips; Social/Cultural gatherings.

WAKEFIELD

Wakefield Health Care Center*
306 Ash St, Wakefield, NE, 68784
(402) 287-2244
Admin W Russell Swigart Jr.
Licensure Intermediate care. *Beds* 65. *Certified* Medicaid.
Owner Publicly owned.

WAUNETA

Heritage of Wauneta
Box 1204, 427 Legion St, Wauneta, NE, 69045
(308) 394-5738
Admin Elaine E Hink. *Medical Dir/Dir of Nursing* Donna Taylor RN DON.
Licensure Intermediate care. *Beds* ICF 52. *Certified* Medicaid.
Owner Proprietary Corp (Vetter Health Services).
Admissions Requirements Medical examination.
Staff RNs 1 (ft), 1 (pt); LPNs 1 (ft), 3 (pt); Nurses aides 10 (ft), 5 (pt).
Facilities Dining room; Activities room; Chapel; Laundry room; Barber/Beauty shop.
Activities Arts & crafts; Cards; Games; Reading groups; Prayer groups; Movies; Shopping trips.

WAUSA

Valley View Home*
703 S Vivian Rd, Wausa, NE, 68786
(402) 586-2010
Admin Phyllis Hoy.
Licensure Intermediate care. *Beds* 52. *Certified* Medicaid.
Owner Proprietary Corp (Beverly Enterprises).
Staff RNs 1 (ft), 2 (pt); LPNs 1 (ft); Activities coordinators 1 (ft).
Facilities Dining room; Activities room; Crafts room; Laundry room; Barber/Beauty shop.
Activities Arts & crafts; Cards; Games; Reading groups; Prayer groups; Movies; Shopping trips; Social/Cultural gatherings.

WAYNE

Wayne Care Center*
918 Main St, Wayne, NE, 68787
(402) 375-1922
Admin Alan P Cooper.
Licensure Intermediate care. *Beds* 94. *Certified* Medicaid.
Owner Proprietary Corp.

WEST POINT

West Point Nursing Home
Rte 3, Prospect Rd, West Point, NE, 68788
(402) 372-2441
Admin Mary L Bernhardt. *Medical Dir/Dir of Nursing* Susan Reppert.
Licensure Intermediate care. *Beds* ICF 72. *Certified* Medicaid.
Owner Proprietary Corp (ARA Living Centers).
Admissions Requirements Medical examination.
Staff Physicians 5 (pt); RNs 4 (ft); LPNs 4 (pt); Nurses aides 20 (pt); Physical therapists 1 (pt); Recreational therapists 1 (ft); Occupational therapists 1 (pt); Speech therapists 1 (pt); Activities coordinators 1 (ft); Dietitians 1 (pt); Dentists 1 (pt).

Facilities Dining room; Physical therapy room; Activities room; Laundry room; Barber/Beauty shop.

Activities Arts & crafts; Cards; Games; Reading groups; Prayer groups; Movies; Social/Cultural gatherings.

WILBER

Wilber Nursing Home
610 N Main, Wilber, NE, 68465
(402) 821-2331
Admin Patricia A Wait. *Medical Dir/Dir of Nursing* Carmon Kubicek.
Licensure Intermediate care. *Beds* ICF 120. *Certified* Medicaid.
Owner Publicly owned.
Admissions Requirements Medical examination; Physician's request.
Staff RNs 4 (ft), 2 (pt); LPNs 2 (ft), 2 (pt); Nurses aides 34 (ft), 21 (pt); Activities coordinators 1 (ft), 1 (pt); Social service Dietary supervisor 2 (ft).
Languages Czech
Facilities Dining room; Physical therapy room; Activities room; Crafts room; Laundry room; Barber/Beauty shop; Recreation room; Fenced-in gazebo.
Activities Arts & crafts; Cards; Games; Reading groups; Prayer groups; Movies; Shopping trips; Social/Cultural gatherings; Summer outings.

WISNER

Wisner Manor
PO Box 629, N 9th, Wisner, NE, 68791
(402) 529-3286
Admin Bonnie McGinnis. *Medical Dir/Dir of Nursing* Erdine Moeller RN.
Licensure Intermediate care. *Beds* ICF 65. *Certified* Medicaid.

Owner Nonprofit organization/foundation.
Admissions Requirements Medical examination.
Staff RNs 1 (ft), 2 (pt); LPNs 1 (ft), 4 (pt); Orderlies 4 (ft), 3 (pt); Nurses aides 15 (pt); Physical therapists 1 (pt); Reality therapists 1 (pt); Recreational therapists 1 (pt); Activities coordinators 1 (ft); Dietitians 1 (pt); Dentist 1 (pt).
Facilities Dining room; Physical therapy room; Activities room; Chapel; Crafts room; Laundry room; Barber/Beauty shop; Library.
Activities Arts & crafts; Cards; Games; Reading groups; Prayer groups; Movies; Shopping trips; Social/Cultural gatherings; Fishing trips; Picnics; Fish fry.

WOOD RIVER

Western Hall Good Samaritan Center
PO Box 517, 1401 East St, Wood River, NE, 68883-0517
(308) 583-2214
Admin A Verle Ralston. *Medical Dir/Dir of Nursing* Marian Hensley.
Licensure Intermediate care. *Beds* ICF 72. *Certified* Medicaid.
Owner Nonprofit Corp (Evangelical Lutheran/ Good Samaritan).
Admissions Requirements Medical examination; Physician's request.
Staff RNs 1 (ft), 1 (pt); LPNs 1 (ft), 4 (pt); Nurses aides 6 (ft), 12 (pt); Activities coordinators 1 (ft), 1 (pt); Dietitians 1 (ft).
Languages Spanish
Facilities Dining room; Physical therapy room; Activities room; Chapel; Crafts room; Laundry room; Barber/Beauty shop; Library.
Activities Arts & crafts; Cards; Games; Reading groups; Prayer groups; Movies; Shopping trips; Social/Cultural gatherings; Daily services.

WYMORE

Wymore Good Samaritan Center
105 E "D" St, Wymore, NE, 68466
(402) 645-3355
Admin Michael R Larson. *Medical Dir/Dir of Nursing* Peggy Engle RN.
Licensure Intermediate care. *Beds* ICF 59. *Certified* Medicaid.
Owner Nonprofit Corp (Evangelical Lutheran/ Good Samaritan).
Staff RNs 1 (ft); LPNs 1 (ft), 6 (pt); Orderlies 2 (pt); Nurses aides 5 (ft), 20 (pt); Physical therapists 1 (ft), 1 (pt); Speech therapists 1 (pt); Activities coordinators 1 (ft), 1 (pt); Dietitians 1 (pt).
Affiliation Lutheran
Facilities Dining room; Activities room; Chapel; Crafts room; Laundry room; Barber/ Beauty shop; Library.
Activities Arts & crafts; Cards; Games; Reading groups; Prayer groups; Movies; Shopping trips; Social/Cultural gatherings; Therapeutic projects.

YORK

The Hearthstone Inc
2319 Lincoln Ave, York, NE, 68467
(402) 362-4333
Admin Lyle Hight. *Medical Dir/Dir of Nursing* Johanna Cass RN DON.
Licensure Intermediate care. *Beds* ICF 168. *Certified* Medicaid.
Owner Nonprofit Corp.
Staff Physicians 6 (ft); RNs 4 (ft), 4 (pt); LPNs 6 (ft), 6 (pt); Orderlies 2 (pt); Nurses aides 36 (ft), 35 (pt); Physical therapists 1 (pt); Activities coordinators 1 (ft), 2 (pt); Dietitians 1 (pt); Dentist 1 (pt), Social service 1 (ft).

NEVADA

BOULDER CITY

Boulder City Care Center*
601 Adams Blvd, Boulder City, NV, 89005
(702) 293-5151
Admin Susan Cabral.
Licensure Skilled care. *Beds* 84. *Certified*
Medicaid; Medicare.

CALIENTE

Grover C Dils Medical Center
PO Box 38, Hwy 93 N, Caliente, NV, 89008
(702) 726-3171
Admin Dorine Soper. *Medical Dir/Dir of*
Nursing Joseph Wilkin MD; Pam Finley
DON.
Licensure Skilled care; Intermediate care. *Beds*
SNF 12. *Certified* Medicaid; Medicare.
Owner Publicly owned.
Staff Physicians 2 (pt); RNs 4 (ft), 2 (pt);
LPNs 4 (ft); Nurses aides 7 (ft); Activities
coordinators 1 (ft); Dietitians 1 (pt).
Facilities Dining room; Activities room.
Activities Arts & crafts; Cards; Games; Prayer
groups.

CARSON CITY

Carson Convalescent Center
2898 Hwy 50 E, Carson City, NV, 89701
(702) 882-3301
Admin Donna Rose Santini. *Medical Dir/Dir*
of Nursing William King MD.
Licensure Skilled care. *Beds* SNF 74. *Certified*
Medicaid; Medicare.
Owner Proprietary Corp (Hillhaven Corp).
Admissions Requirements Medical
examination.
Staff RNs 6 (ft), 6 (pt); LPNs 8 (ft), 8 (pt);
Orderlies 5 (ft), 5 (pt); Nurses aides 30 (ft),
10 (pt); Physical therapists 3 (pt); Reality
therapists 1 (pt); Recreational therapists 1
(pt); Occupational therapists 1 (pt); Speech
therapists 1 (pt); Activities coordinators 1
(ft); Dietitians 3 (pt); Dentists 1 (pt);
Ophthalmologists 1 (pt); Podiatrists 1 (pt).
Facilities Dining room; Physical therapy
room; Activities room; Laundry room;
Barber/Beauty shop.
Activities Arts & crafts; Cards; Games;
Reading groups; Prayer groups; Movies;
Shopping trips; Social/Cultural gatherings.

Eagle Valley Children's Home
PO Box 755, Rte 1, Carson City, NV, 89701
(702) 882-1188
Admin Dianna Hoover. *Medical Dir/Dir of*
Nursing Thomas A Good MD; Tena
Howard RN DON.
Licensure Intermediate care for mentally
retarded. *Beds* ICF/MR 15. *Certified*
Medicaid.
Owner Nonprofit organization/foundation.
Admissions Requirements Medical
examination; Physician's request.

Staff Physicians 1 (pt); RNs 1 (ft); LPNs 4
(ft), 13 (pt); Nurses aides 15 (ft), 6 (pt);
Physical therapists 1 (pt); Recreational
therapists 1 (ft); Occupational therapists 1
(pt); Speech therapists 1 (ft); Dietitians 1
(ft).
Languages Spanish, German
Facilities Dining room; Physical therapy
room; Activities room; Crafts room; Laundry
room; Library; Speech therapy room.
Activities Arts & crafts; Games; Reading
groups; Movies; Shopping trips; Social/
Cultural gatherings.

Sierra Convalescent Center
201 Koontz Ln, Carson City, NV, 89701
(702) 883-3622
Admin Janey Mallow. *Medical Dir/Dir of*
Nursing Shirly Paul RN DON.
Licensure Skilled care; Intermediate care. *Beds*
147. *Certified* Medicaid; Medicare.
Owner Proprietary Corp (Beverly Enterprises).
Admissions Requirements Medical
examination; Physician's request.
Staff RNs; LPNs; Nurses aides.
Facilities Dining room; Physical therapy
room; Activities room.
Activities Arts & crafts; Cards; Games;
Reading groups; Prayer groups; Movies;
Shopping trips; Social/Cultural gatherings.

EAST ELY

White Pine Care Center*
1500 Ave G, East Ely, NV, 89315
(702) 289-8801
Admin Russell D Fay.
Licensure Skilled care. *Beds* 99. *Certified*
Medicaid; Medicare.
Staff Physicians 4 (pt); RNs 4 (ft), 1 (pt);
LPNs 10 (ft); Orderlies 3 (ft); Nurses aides
32 (ft); Physical therapists 1 (pt); Activities
coordinators 1 (ft).
Facilities Dining room; Physical therapy
room; Activities room; Laundry room;
Barber/Beauty shop.
Activities Arts & crafts; Cards; Games; Prayer
groups; Movies; Birthday parties; Picnics.

ELKO

Ruby Mountains Manor
701 Walnut St, Elko, NV, 89801
(702) 738-8051
Admin Larry Roberts. *Medical Dir/Dir of*
Nursing Judy Saunders RN DON.
Licensure Skilled care; Intermediate care. *Beds*
SNF 50; ICF 23. *Certified* Medicaid;
Medicare.
Owner Proprietary Corp.
Admissions Requirements Minimum age 21;
Medical examination; Physician's request.
Staff RNs; LPNs; Orderlies; Nurses aides;
Activities coordinators; Dietitians.
Facilities Dining room; Physical therapy
room; Activities room; Chapel; Crafts room;
Laundry room; Barber/Beauty shop; Library.

Activities Arts & crafts; Cards; Games;
Reading groups; Prayer groups; Movies;
Shopping trips; Social/Cultural gatherings.

FALLON

Fallon Convalescent Center
365 W "A" St, Fallon, NV, 89406
(702) 423-6551
Admin Liz Martin RN. *Medical Dir/Dir of*
Nursing Dr Kurt Carlson; Joan McLaughlin
DON.
Licensure Skilled care. *Beds* SNF 147.
Certified Medicaid; Medicare.
Owner Proprietary Corp.
Admissions Requirements Medical
examination; Physician's request.
Staff Physicians 10 (ft); RNs 10 (ft); LPNs 14
(ft); Orderlies 4 (ft); Nurses aides 50 (ft);
Physical therapists 2 (ft); Recreational
therapists 2 (ft); Speech therapists 1 (ft);
Activities coordinators 1 (ft); Dietitians 1
(ft); Dentist 1 (ft).
Facilities Dining room; Physical therapy
room; Activities room; Crafts room; Laundry
room; Barber/Beauty shop; Conference
room; Patios.
Activities Arts & crafts; Cards; Games;
Reading groups; Prayer groups; Movies;
Shopping trips; Social/Cultural gatherings.

GARDNERVILLE

Cottonwood Care Center
806 Tillman Ln, Gardnerville, NV, 89410
(702) 265-3571
Admin Diana Roberts. *Medical Dir/Dir of*
Nursing J K Toth MD; Charlotte Johnson
RN DON.
Licensure Skilled care. *Beds* SNF 109.
Certified Medicaid; Medicare.
Owner Privately owned.
Staff RNs; LPNs; Orderlies; Nurses aides;
Recreational therapists 2 (ft); Activities
coordinators 1 (ft); Dietitians 1 (ft).
Facilities Dining room; Physical therapy
room; Activities room; Crafts room; Laundry
room; Barber/Beauty shop.
Activities Arts & crafts; Cards; Games;
Reading groups; Prayer groups; Movies;
Shopping trips; Social/Cultural gatherings.

HAWTHORNE

Lefa L Seran Skilled Nursing Facility
PO Box 1510, 1st & A Sts, Hawthorne, NV,
89415-1570
(702) 945-2461
Admin Richard N Munger.
Licensure Skilled care. *Beds* 20. *Certified*
Medicaid; Medicare.

HENDERSON

Glen Halla Intermediate Care Facility
1745 Athol St, Henderson, NV, 89015
(702) 565-8748
Admin Paul S Besser. *Medical Dir/Dir of Nursing* Jeanne Heki RN.
Licensure Intermediate care. *Beds* ICF 48. *Certified* Medicaid.
Owner Proprietary Corp.
Admissions Requirements Physician's request.
Staff Physicians 5 (ft), 1 (pt); RNs 2 (ft), 3 (pt); LPNs 4 (ft); Nurses aides 9 (ft), 2 (pt); Recreational therapists 1 (ft); Activities coordinators 1 (ft); Dietitians 1 (ft).
Languages Spanish
Facilities Dining room; Activities room; Crafts room; Laundry room; Barber/Beauty shop; Spacious outdoor area.
Activities Arts & crafts; Cards; Games; Reading groups; Prayer groups; Movies; Shopping trips; Social/Cultural gatherings; Outings.

Henderson Convalescent Hospital
1180 E Lake Mead Dr, Henderson, NV, 89105
(702) 565-8555
Admin Charles C Perry Jr. *Medical Dir/Dir of Nursing* Al Waters MD; Helen Tyning RN DON.
Licensure Skilled care. *Beds* SNF 124. *Certified* Medicaid; Medicare.
Owner Proprietary Corp (Americare Corp).
Admissions Requirements Medical examination; Physician's request.
Staff RNs 8 (ft), 2 (pt); LPNs 9 (ft), 3 (pt); Orderlies 4 (ft), 2 (pt); Nurses aides 44 (ft), 5 (pt); Physical therapists 1 (ft); Recreational therapists 1 (ft); Occupational therapists 1 (pt); Speech therapists 2 (pt); Activities coordinators 1 (ft), 2 (pt); Dietitians 1 (pt); Ophthalmologists 1 (pt); Podiatrists 2 (pt).
Languages Spanish, German, French, Italian, Polish
Facilities Dining room; Physical therapy room; Activities room; Chapel; Crafts room; Laundry room; Barber/Beauty shop; Library.
Activities Arts & crafts; Cards; Games; Reading groups; Prayer groups; Movies; Shopping trips; Social/Cultural gatherings.

LAS VEGAS

Beverly Manor Convalescent Hospital
660 Desert Ln, Las Vegas, NV, 89106
(702) 382-5580
Admin Dale A Moore. *Medical Dir/Dir of Nursing* Arthur Pitterman MD; JoAnn Good RN DON.
Licensure Skilled care; Intermediate care; Dependent life support. *Beds* SNF 208; ICF; Dependent life support. *Certified* Medicaid; Medicare.
Owner Proprietary Corp (Beverly Enterprises).
Admissions Requirements Medical examination; Physician's request.
Staff RNs 20 (ft), 2 (pt); LPNs 18 (ft), 1 (pt); Orderlies 4 (ft); Nurses aides 73 (ft), 8 (pt); Dietitians 1 (ft); Dietary assts 15 (ft), 4 (pt); Laundry 4 (ft); Office 8 (ft); Maintenance 3 (ft); Central supply 2 (ft); Medical records 4 (ft); Housekeeping 12 (ft); Social services 4 (ft); Activities 3 (ft).
Languages Tagalog, German
Facilities Dining room; Physical therapy room; Activities room; Crafts room; Laundry room; Barber/Beauty shop.
Activities Arts & crafts; Cards; Games; Reading groups; Prayer groups; Movies; Shopping trips; Social/Cultural gatherings.

Charleston Health Care Center*
2035 W Charleston Blvd, Las Vegas, NV, 89102
(702) 386-7980

Admin Marian Nielson. *Medical Dir/Dir of Nursing* Thomas Quam MD.
Licensure Skilled care. *Beds* 100. *Certified* Medicaid; Medicare.
Admissions Requirements Medical examination; Physician's request.
Staff Physical therapists 1 (pt); Reality therapists 1 (ft); Recreational therapists 1 (ft); Occupational therapists 1 (pt); Speech therapists 1 (ft); Activities coordinators 1 (ft); Dietitians 1 (ft); Dentists 1 (pt); Ophthalmologists 1 (pt); Podiatrists 1 (pt); Audiologists 1 (pt).
Facilities Dining room; Physical therapy room; Activities room; Crafts room; Laundry room; Barber/Beauty shop; Central courtyard; Cable TV.
Activities Arts & crafts; Cards; Games; Reading groups; Prayer groups; Movies; Shopping trips; Social/Cultural gatherings.

El Jen Convalescent Hospital*
5538 W Duncan Dr, Las Vegas, NV, 89106
(702) 645-2606
Admin James M Toomey. *Medical Dir/Dir of Nursing* LeRoy Wolever MD.
Licensure Skilled care. *Beds* 74. *Certified* Medicaid; Medicare.
Staff Physicians 10 (pt); RNs 8 (ft), 1 (pt); LPNs 2 (ft), 1 (pt); Orderlies 2 (ft); Nurses aides 45 (ft); Physical therapists 1 (pt); Reality therapists 1 (pt); Recreational therapists 1 (pt); Occupational therapists 1 (pt); Speech therapists 1 (pt); Activities coordinators 2 (ft); Dietitians 1 (ft), 1 (pt); Dentists 1 (pt); Ophthalmologists 1 (pt); Podiatrists 1 (pt); Audiologists 1 (pt); Social workers 1 (ft).
Facilities Dining room; Physical therapy room; Activities room; Crafts room; Laundry room; Barber/Beauty shop.
Activities Arts & crafts; Cards; Games; Reading groups; Prayer groups; Movies; Shopping trips; Social/Cultural gatherings.

Gaye Haven Intermediate Care Facility Inc
1813 Betty Ln, Las Vegas, NV, 89115
(702) 452-8399
Admin Sandra V Manetas. *Medical Dir/Dir of Nursing* Amanda Blount DO.
Licensure Intermediate care. *Beds* ICF 20. *Certified* Medicaid.
Owner Proprietary Corp; Privately owned.
Admissions Requirements Minimum age 20.
Staff Physicians 1 (pt); RNs 1 (pt); LPNs 5 (ft); Reality therapists 1 (ft); Recreational therapists 1 (ft); Activities coordinators 1 (ft), 1 (pt); Dietitians 1 (ft), 1 (pt).
Facilities Dining room; Activities room; Crafts room; Laundry room.
Activities Arts & crafts; Cards; Games; Movies; Shopping trips.

Hillhaven Convalescent Center*
5659 Duncan Dr, Las Vegas, NV, 89130
(702) 645-1900
Admin Judy A Clark.
Licensure Skilled care. *Beds* 125. *Certified* Medicaid; Medicare.
Owner Proprietary Corp (Hillhaven Corp).

Las Vegas Convalescent Center*
2832 Maryland Pkwy, Las Vegas, NV, 89109
(702) 735-5848
Admin Myra G Stade.
Licensure Skilled care. *Beds* 77. *Certified* Medicaid; Medicare.
Owner Proprietary Corp (Hillhaven Corp).

Torrey Pines Care Center
1701 S Torrey Pines Dr, Las Vegas, NV, 89102-2999
(702) 871-0005
Admin Sam Sparks. *Medical Dir/Dir of Nursing* Elizabeth Mongeau.
Licensure Intermediate care. *Beds* 116. *Certified* Medicaid.

Owner Proprietary Corp (Hillhaven Corp).
Staff RNs 6 (ft), 2 (pt); LPNs 10 (ft); Nurses aides 34 (ft), 1 (pt); Activities coordinators 2 (ft); Dietitians 1 (ft).

Vegas Valley Convalescent Hospital
2945 Casa Vegas St, Las Vegas, NV, 89109
(702) 735-7179
Admin Charles C Perry III. *Medical Dir/Dir of Nursing* Dr Robert Shreck.
Licensure Skilled care. *Beds* 102. *Certified* Medicaid; Medicare.
Admissions Requirements Medical examination; Physician's request.
Staff RNs 10 (ft), 2 (pt); LPNs 15 (ft), 4 (pt); Orderlies 5 (ft); Nurses aides 50 (ft), 5 (pt); Physical therapists 1 (pt); Occupational therapists 1 (pt); Activities coordinators 2 (pt); Dietitians 2 (pt).
Facilities Dining room; Physical therapy room; Activities room; Crafts room; Laundry room; Barber/Beauty shop.
Activities Arts & crafts; Cards; Games; Movies; Shopping trips; Social/Cultural gatherings.

LOVELOCK

Pershing County Hospital & Nursing Home
PO Box 661, 855 6th St, Lovelock, NV, 89419
(702) 273-2621
Admin Myra B Garland. *Medical Dir/Dir of Nursing* Meridith Kelleher.
Licensure Skilled care. *Beds* SNF 33. *Certified* Medicaid; Medicare.
Owner Nonprofit organization/foundation.
Admissions Requirements Physician's request.
Staff Physicians 2 (ft); RNs 7 (ft); LPNs 1 (ft); Nurses aides 21 (ft); Physical therapists 1 (pt); Activities coordinators 1 (ft).
Facilities Dining room; Activities room; Crafts room; Laundry room.
Activities Arts & crafts; Cards; Games; Prayer groups; Movies; Group singing.

NORTH LAS VEGAS

North Las Vegas Care Center
3215 Cheyenne Ave, North Las Vegas, NV, 89030
(702) 649-7800
Admin Paul M Boyar. *Medical Dir/Dir of Nursing* Gary DesAuzo DO; Louise Hampton RN DON.
Licensure Skilled care. *Beds* SNF 182. *Certified* Medicaid; Medicare.
Owner Proprietary Corp (Beverly Enterprises).
Admissions Requirements Medical examination.
Facilities Dining room; Physical therapy room; Activities room; Crafts room; Laundry room; Barber/Beauty shop; Outside patios.
Activities Arts & crafts; Cards; Games; Reading groups; Prayer groups; Movies; Shopping trips; Social/Cultural gatherings.

RENO

Physician's Hospital for Extended Care*
2045 Silverada Blvd, Reno, NV, 89512
(702) 359-3161
Admin Kathy L Wagner.
Licensure Skilled care. *Beds* 100. *Certified* Medicaid; Medicare.

Reno Convalescent Center*
1300 Mill St, Reno, NV, 89502
(702) 786-1933
Admin Norma J Beales.
Licensure Skilled care. *Beds* 119. *Certified* Medicaid; Medicare.
Owner Proprietary Corp (Hillhaven Corp).

Riverside Hospital for Skilled Care
2865 Idlewild Dr, Reno, NV, 89509
(702) 329-0691

Admin Norma J Beales. *Medical Dir/Dir of Nursing* Grant Anderson MD; Harriet Beaman DON.
Licensure Skilled care; Intermediate care. *Beds* 182. *Certified* Medicaid; Medicare.
Owner Privately owned.
Admissions Requirements Physician's request.
Facilities Dining room; Physical therapy room; Activities room; Laundry room; Barber/Beauty shop.
Activities Arts & crafts; Cards; Games; Reading groups; Prayer groups; Movies; Shopping trips; Social/Cultural gatherings.

SPARKS

Sierra Developmental Center
605 S 21st St, Sparks, NV, 89431
(702) 359-6100
Admin David E Luke. *Medical Dir/Dir of Nursing* Dr David Koroshec; Janice Young RN.
Licensure Intermediate care for mentally retarded. *Beds* 84. *Certified* Medicaid.
Owner Publicly owned.
Staff RNs 5 (ft); LPNs 6 (ft); Physical therapists 1 (ft); Recreational therapists 1 (ft); Occupational therapists 1 (ft); Speech therapists 1 (ft); Activities coordinators 1 (ft); Dietitians 1 (ft).
Languages Sign

Sierra Health Center*
1835 Oddie Blvd, Sparks, NV, 89431
(702) 359-5420

Admin Tom W Morton.
Licensure Skilled care; Intermediate care. *Beds* SNF 50; ICF 100. *Certified* Medicaid; Medicare.

Washoe Care Center
1375 Baring Blvd, Sparks, NV, 89431
(702) 356-2707
Admin Jeanne Stone. *Medical Dir/Dir of Nursing* Dr J Forsythe; Genny Dixon RN DON.
Licensure Skilled care; Intermediate care. *Beds* SNF 130; ICF. *Certified* Medicaid; Medicare.
Owner Proprietary Corp.
Admissions Requirements Physician's request.
Staff Physicians 1 (ft); RNs 12 (ft); LPNs 10 (ft); Nurses aides 30 (ft), 2 (pt); Physical therapists 1 (ft), 2 (pt); Speech therapists 1 (pt); Activities coordinators 1 (ft); Dietitians 1 (ft).
Facilities Dining room; Physical therapy room; Activities room; Laundry room; Barber/Beauty shop.
Activities Arts & crafts; Reading groups; Movies; Social/Cultural gatherings.

TONOPAH

Nye General Hospital
PO Box 391, 825 Erie Main, Tonopah, NV, 89049
(702) 482-6233

Admin Richard L Kilburn. *Medical Dir/Dir of Nursing* Gerald Peterson DO; Elizabeth Deweese RN DON.
Licensure Skilled care; Intermediate care. *Beds* SNF 24; ICF. *Certified* Medicaid; Medicare.
Owner Publicly owned.
Admissions Requirements Physician's request.
Staff Physicians 1 (ft); RNs 3 (ft); LPNs 3 (ft); Nurses aides 10 (ft); Activities coordinators 1 (ft); Dietitians 1 (pt).
Languages Spanish
Facilities Dining room; Activities room; Crafts room; Laundry room.
Activities Arts & crafts; Cards; Games; Reading groups; Movies; Social/Cultural gatherings.

WINNEMUCCA

Humboldt General Hospital*
118 E Haskell St, Winnemucca, NV, 89445
(702) 623-5222
Admin E J Hanssen.
Licensure Skilled care. *Beds* 14. *Certified* Medicaid; Medicare.

YERINGTON

Lyon Health Center*
PO Box 940, Suprise at Whitacre, Yerington, NV, 89447
(702) 463-2301
Admin Paul E LeCave.
Licensure Skilled care. *Beds* 18. *Certified* Medicaid; Medicare.

NEW HAMPSHIRE

BEDFORD

Bedford Nursing Home*
480 Donald St, Bedford, NH, 03102
(603) 627-4147
Admin Norman L Tiercotti. *Medical Dir/Dir of Nursing* Dr William Heslin.
Licensure Intermediate care. *Beds* 102. *Certified* Medicaid.
Staff Physicians 1 (pt); RNs 8 (ft), 10 (pt); LPNs 6 (pt); Nurses aides 15 (ft), 34 (pt); Physical therapists 1 (pt); Reality therapists 1 (pt); Recreational therapists 1 (ft); Occupational therapists 1 (pt); Speech therapists 1 (pt); Activities coordinators 1 (ft); Dietitians 1 (pt); Dentists 1 (pt); Ophthalmologists 1 (pt); Podiatrists 1 (pt); Audiologists 1 (pt).
Facilities Dining room; Physical therapy room; Activities room; Crafts room; Laundry room; Barber/Beauty shop; Library.
Activities Arts & crafts; Cards; Games; Prayer groups; Movies; Shopping trips; Social/Cultural gatherings.

BERLIN

Coos County Nursing Home*
Rte 2, Cates Hill Rd, Berlin, NH, 03570
(603) 752-2343
Admin John Langell.
Licensure Intermediate care. *Beds* 100. *Certified* Medicaid.

St Vincent de Paul Nursing Home
29 Providence Ave, Berlin, NH, 03570
(603) 752-1820
Admin Sr Lorraine Boyer. *Medical Dir/Dir of Nursing* Priscilla Gazey.
Licensure Intermediate care. *Beds* 80. *Certified* Medicaid.
Owner Nonprofit organization/foundation.
Admissions Requirements Minimum age 65; Physician's request.
Staff Physicians; RNs; LPNs; Nurses aides; Physical therapists; Recreational therapists; Occupational therapists; Speech therapists; Activities coordinators; Dietitians; Dentists; Ophthalmologists.
Languages French
Facilities Dining room; Physical therapy room; Activities room; Chapel; Crafts room; Laundry room; Barber/Beauty shop; Library.
Activities Arts & crafts; Cards; Games; Reading groups; Prayer groups; Movies; Social/Cultural gatherings.

CENTER OSSIPEE

Ossipee House
PO Box 10B, RR 1 Moultonville Rd, Center Ossipee, NH, 03814
(603) 323-7759
Admin Sandy Boothby RN. *Medical Dir/Dir of Nursing* Danield Melville MD.

Licensure Intermediate care for mentally retarded. *Beds* ICF/MR 8. *Certified* Medicaid; Medicare.
Owner Nonprofit organization/foundation.
Admissions Requirements Minimum age 21; Medical examination.
Staff Physicians 1 (pt); RNs 2 (ft); LPNs 4 (pt); Physical therapists 1 (pt); Occupational therapists 1 (pt); Speech therapists 1 (pt); Program Managers 6- 8 (ft), 2 (pt); Program coordinator 2 (ft).
Languages Sign
Facilities Dining room; Physical therapy room; Activities room; Laundry room; Living room; Enclosed yard & patio.
Activities Arts & crafts; Cards; Games; Movies; Shopping trips; Social/Cultural gatherings; Beach trips.

CHESTER

Jodoin Home*
RFD 1, Box 45, Chester, NH, 03036
(603) 483-5508
Admin Anita Jodoin.
Licensure Skilled care. *Beds* 4.

CLAREMONT

McKerley Health Care Center
Hanover St Extension, Claremont, NH, 03743
(603) 542-2606 or (800) 722-0197
Admin Jean Jenkins. *Medical Dir/Dir of Nursing* Louella Graham RN DON.
Licensure Intermediate care. *Beds* ICF 51. *Certified* Medicaid.
Owner Privately owned.
Admissions Requirements Medical examination; Physician's request.
Staff Physicians 4 (pt); RNs 12 (pt); LPNs 12 (pt); Nurses aides 14 (pt); Physical therapists 1 (pt); Occupational therapists 1 (pt); Speech therapists 1 (pt); Activities coordinators 1 (pt); Dietitians 1 (pt); Ophthalmologists 1 (pt).
Facilities Dining room; Laundry room; Barber/Beauty shop.
Activities Arts & crafts; Games; Prayer groups; Movies; Social/Cultural gatherings; Bingo.

Sullivan County Nursing Home
PO Box 392, RFD 1, Claremont, NH, 03743
(603) 542-9511
Admin Mary Louise Horn. *Medical Dir/Dir of Nursing* Richard Hutchins MD; Judith B Brogren RN.
Licensure Intermediate care. *Beds* ICF 190. *Certified* Medicaid.
Owner Publicly owned.
Admissions Requirements Medical examination; Physician's request.
Staff Physicians 2 (pt); RNs 9 (ft), 3 (pt); LPNs 5 (ft), 5 (pt); Nurses aides 48 (ft), 20 (pt); Recreational therapists 1 (ft); Activities coordinators 1 (ft); Dietitians 1 (pt); RPTA 2 (pt); COTA 1 (pt).
Languages French

Facilities Dining room; Physical therapy room; Activities room; Crafts room; Laundry room; Barber/Beauty shop; Library; Courtyard.
Activities Arts & crafts; Cards; Games; Reading groups; Prayer groups; Movies; Shopping trips; Social/Cultural gatherings.

CONCORD

Havenwood-Heritage Heights Retirement Community
33 Christian Ave, Concord, NH, 03301
(603) 224-5363
Admin Albert B Dwyer. *Medical Dir/Dir of Nursing* Frankie Pugh.
Licensure Skilled care; Intermediate care. *Beds* 58. *Certified* Medicaid; Medicare.
Owner Nonprofit Corp.
Admissions Requirements Minimum age 62.
Staff RNs; LPNs; Nurses aides; Physical therapists; Recreational therapists; Activities coordinators; Dietitians; Ophthalmologists.
Affiliation Church of Christ
Facilities Dining room; Physical therapy room; Activities room; Chapel; Crafts room; Laundry room; Barber/Beauty shop; Library.
Activities Arts & crafts; Cards; Games; Reading groups; Prayer groups; Movies; Shopping trips; Social/Cultural gatherings.

McKerley Nursing Home*
20 Maitland St, Concord, NH, 03301
(603) 224-6561
Admin James McKerley.
Licensure Skilled care; Intermediate care. *Beds* SNF 49; ICF 152. *Certified* Medicaid; Medicare.

New Hampshire Centennial Home for the Aged
96 Pleasant St, Concord, NH, 03301
(603) 225-2021
Admin Arthur Bruemmer.
Licensure Home for aged; Life care. *Beds* 45.
Owner Nonprofit Corp.
Admissions Requirements Minimum age 65; Females only; Medical examination.
Facilities Dining room; Laundry room; Barber/Beauty shop; Library.

New Hampshire Odd Fellows Home
200 Pleasant St, Concord, NH, 03301
(603) 225-6644
Admin Leslie Sherman. *Medical Dir/Dir of Nursing* Kathleen Nickerson.
Licensure Intermediate care; Sheltered care facility with nursing unit. *Beds* ICF 47; Sheltered care facility with nursing unit 73. *Certified* Medicaid.
Owner Nonprofit Corp.
Admissions Requirements Minimum age 60; Medical examination; Physician's request.
Staff RNs; LPNs; Nurses aides; Activities coordinators; Dietitians.
Affiliation Independent Order of Odd Fellows & Rebekahs

Facilities Dining room; Physical therapy room; Activities room; Chapel; Crafts room; Laundry room; Barber/Beauty shop; Library; Living room; Solarium; Auditorium.
Activities Arts & crafts; Cards; Games; Reading groups; Prayer groups; Movies; Shopping trips; Social/Cultural gatherings.

DERRY

Birchwood Nursing Home*
20 Chester Rd, Derry, NH, 03038
(603) 432-3801
Admin Dorothy Bimpson.
Licensure Intermediate care. *Beds* 52.
Certified Medicaid.

Hoodkroft Convalescent Center*
Peabody Rd, Derry, NH, 03038
(603) 434-1566
Admin Joan McGorry.
Licensure Intermediate care. *Beds* 100.
Certified Medicaid; Medicare.

DOVER

Dover House Healthcare
307 Plaza Dr, Dover, NH, 03820
(603) 742-2676
Admin Verne L Rice. *Medical Dir/Dir of Nursing* Vito Molori MD; Kate Rockey DON.
Licensure Skilled care; Intermediate care. *Beds* SNF 11; ICF 91. *Certified* Medicaid; Medicare.
Owner Proprietary Corp (Hillhaven Corp).
Admissions Requirements Medical examination.
Staff RNs; LPNs; Orderlies; Nurses aides; Physical therapists; Recreational therapists; Activities coordinators; Dietitians.
Facilities Dining room; Physical therapy room; Activities room; Chapel; Crafts room; Laundry room; Barber/Beauty shop; Library.
Activities Arts & crafts; Cards; Games; Reading groups; Prayer groups; Movies; Shopping trips; Social/Cultural gatherings.

St Ann Home
195 Dover Point Rd, Dover, NH, 03820
(603) 742-2612
Admin Sr M Madeline.
Licensure Intermediate care. *Beds* 53.
Certified Medicaid.

Strafford County Home*
Rte 3, Dover, NH, 03820
(603) 742-1348
Admin Mary Louise Horn.
Licensure Intermediate care. *Beds* 205.
Certified Medicaid.

Wentworth Home for the Aged*
795 Central Ave, Dover, NH, 03820
(603) 742-1915
Admin Mary Jane Allen.
Licensure Skilled care. *Beds* 36.

EPPING

Rockingham County Nursing Home
PO Box 427, Epping, NH, 03042
(603) 679-5335
Admin William Sturtevant. *Medical Dir/Dir of Nursing* Karl Singer; Norma Dodge DON.
Licensure Intermediate care. *Beds* ICF 290. *Certified* Medicaid.
Owner Nonprofit organization/foundation.
Admissions Requirements Medical examination.
Staff Physicians 5 (pt); RNs 365 (ft); LPNs 22 (ft); Orderlies 2 (ft); Nurses aides 120 (ft), 37 (pt); Physical therapists 2 (ft); Recreational therapists 1 (ft); Occupational therapists 1 (ft); Speech therapists 1 (pt); Dietitians 1 (ft); Ophthalmologists 1 (pt); Podiatrists 1 (pt); Dentist 1 (pt).

Facilities Dining room; Physical therapy room; Activities room; Chapel; Crafts room; Laundry room; Barber/Beauty shop; Library; Snack bar; Speech therapy; Dental office.
Activities Arts & crafts; Cards; Games; Reading groups; Prayer groups; Movies; Shopping trips; Social/Cultural gatherings; Bingo; Cocktail parties; Picnics.

EPSOM

Epsom Manor
RR 2 Box 107, Epsom, NH, 03234
(603) 736-4772
Admin Lynn G Guenther. *Medical Dir/Dir of Nursing* Carole Dionne.
Licensure Intermediate care. *Beds* ICF 108. *Certified* Medicaid.
Owner Proprietary Corp (Lemire Enterprises).
Admissions Requirements Medical examination.
Staff RNs; LPNs; Nurses aides; Activities coordinators 1 (ft); Dietitians 1 (pt).
Languages French
Facilities Dining room; Activities room; Crafts room; Laundry room; Barber/Beauty shop.
Activities Arts & crafts; Games; Prayer groups.

EXETER

Eventide Home Inc
81 High St, Exeter, NH, 03833
(603) 772-5743
Admin Sandra Cross. *Medical Dir/Dir of Nursing* Mary Kelly.
Licensure Intermediate care. *Beds* ICF 19. *Certified* Medicaid.
Owner Nonprofit Corp.
Admissions Requirements Minimum age 65; Females only; Medical examination.
Staff RNs 3 (ft), 3 (pt); LPNs 2 (pt); Nurses aides 3 (ft), 3 (pt); Activities coordinators 1 (pt); Dietitians 1 (pt).
Facilities Dining room; Activities room; Barber/Beauty shop; Library.
Activities Arts & crafts; Cards; Games; Reading groups; Shopping trips.

Exeter Healthcare Inc
131 Court St, Exeter, NH, 03833
778-1668
Admin Frances Comeau. *Medical Dir/Dir of Nursing* Suzanne Robinson.
Licensure Skilled care; Intermediate care. *Beds* SNF 115; ICF. *Certified* Medicaid; Medicare.
Owner Nonprofit Corp.
Admissions Requirements Medical examination.
Staff RNs 7 (ft), 3 (pt); LPNs 9 (ft), 7 (pt); Orderlies; Nurses aides; Physical therapists 1 (ft); Occupational therapists 1 (pt); Speech therapists 1 (pt); Activities coordinators; Dietitians; Ophthalmologists 1 (pt).
Facilities Dining room; Physical therapy room; Activities room; Chapel; Crafts room; Laundry room; Barber/Beauty shop; Library; Family room for personal gatherings for such occasions as birthdays & anniversaries.
Activities Arts & crafts; Cards; Games; Reading groups; Prayer groups; Movies; Shopping trips; Social/Cultural gatherings; Monthly birthday parties; Weekly teas; Dietary specials; Bingo; Cooking; Canning.

Goodwin's of Exeter*
Hampton Rd, Exeter, NH, 03833
(603) 778-0531
Admin William Gilmore.
Licensure Intermediate care. *Beds* 81.
Certified Medicaid.

FRANCONIA

North Country Rehabilitation Center
148 Main St, Franconia, NH, 03580
(603) 823-5502
Admin Maria J Troisi. *Medical Dir/Dir of Nursing* Linda M Keller RN.
Licensure Skilled care; Intermediate care. *Beds* SNF 62; ICF. *Certified* Medicare.
Owner Proprietary Corp (Beverly Enterprises).
Admissions Requirements Minimum age 18; Physician's request.
Staff Physicians; RNs; LPNs; Orderlies; Nurses aides; Physical therapists; Occupational therapists; Speech therapists; Activities coordinators; Dietitians; Ophthalmologists.
Facilities Dining room; Physical therapy room; Activities room; Laundry room; Barber/Beauty shop.
Activities Arts & crafts; Games; Reading groups; Prayer groups; Movies; Social/Cultural gatherings.

FRANKLIN

Peabody Home*
24 Peabody Pl, Franklin, NH, 03235
(603) 934-3718
Admin Arthur Swenson.
Licensure Intermediate care. *Beds* 29.

Sunny Knoll Retirement Home Inc
221 Victory Dr, Franklin, NH, 03265
(603) 934-5447
Admin Donna Holden. *Medical Dir/Dir of Nursing* Donna Holden.
Licensure Sheltered care. *Beds* 35. *Certified* Medicare.
Owner Proprietary Corp.
Admissions Requirements Medical examination; Physician's request.
Staff Physicians; RNs; Nurses aides; Activities coordinators; Dietitians.
Facilities Dining room; Activities room; Laundry room; Barber/Beauty shop; Library.
Activities Arts & crafts; Cards; Games; Reading groups; Prayer groups; Movies; Shopping trips; Social/Cultural gatherings.

FREMONT

Colonial Manor*
PO Box 101, Main St, Fremont, NH, 03044
(603) 895-2911
Admin Russell Philbrick.
Licensure Skilled care; Intermediate care. *Beds* SNF 18; ICF 50.

GOFFSTOWN

Hillsborough County Nursing Home
Rte 2, Goffstown, NH, 03045
(603) 627-5540
Admin Robert Curran. *Medical Dir/Dir of Nursing* Dr Marcel Dupuis MD; Emily Mercier RN DON.
Licensure Intermediate care. *Beds* ICF 300. *Certified* Medicaid.
Owner Publicly owned.
Admissions Requirements Medical examination; Physician's request.
Staff Physicians 2 (pt); RNs 43 (ft); LPNs 9 (ft); Nurses aides 126 (ft); Physical therapists 1 (ft); Recreational therapists 1 (ft); Activities coordinators 1 (ft); Dietitians 1 (pt); Ophthalmologists 1 (pt).
Languages French, Greek
Facilities Dining room; Physical therapy room; Activities room; Chapel; Crafts room; Laundry room; Barber/Beauty shop; Library.
Activities Arts & crafts; Cards; Games; Reading groups; Prayer groups; Movies; Shopping trips; Social/Cultural gatherings; Ceramics; Woodworking; Leather; Cooking.

GRASMERE

Bel-Air Nursing Home
19 Center St, Grasmere, NH, 03045
(603) 497-4871
Admin Ellen Mitchell. *Medical Dir/Dir of Nursing* Rota Krape.
Licensure Intermediate care. *Beds* 32.
Certified Medicaid.
Owner Privately owned.
Staff RNs 2 (ft), 1 (pt); LPNs 1 (ft), 2 (pt); Nurses aides 7 (ft), 9 (pt); Recreational therapists 1 (pt).
Languages French
Facilities Dining room; Laundry room.
Activities Arts & crafts; Cards; Games; Prayer groups; Movies.

HAMPSHIRE

St Frances Home for the Aged
PO Box 1699, Court St, Hampshire, NH, 03247-1699
(603) 524-0466
Admin Julieann R Fay. *Medical Dir/Dir of Nursing* Dr E C Squires MD; Claire P Falardeau RN.
Licensure Intermediate care. *Beds* 51.
Certified Medicaid; Medicare.
Owner Nonprofit Corp.
Admissions Requirements Minimum age 65; Medical examination.
Staff Physicians 1 (ft), 3 (pt); RNs 4 (ft), 5 (pt); LPNs 2 (ft), 1 (pt); Nurses aides 19 (ft), 1 (pt); Physical therapists 1 (ft); Reality therapists 1 (ft); Occupational therapists 1 (ft); Speech therapists 1 (ft); Activities coordinators 1 (ft), 1 (pt); Dietitians 1 (ft); Dentists 1 (ft); Ophthalmologists 1 (ft); Podiatrists 1 (ft); Chaplain 1 (ft); Pastoral minister 1 (ft).
Languages French
Affiliation Roman Catholic
Facilities Dining room; Physical therapy room; Activities room; Chapel; Crafts room; Laundry room; Barber/Beauty shop; Lounge.
Activities Arts & crafts; Cards; Games; Prayer groups; Movies; Shopping trips; Social/Cultural gatherings; Discussion group; Library services.

HAMPTON

Seacoast Health Center
22 Tuck Rd, Hampton, NH, 03842-1298
(603) 926-4551
Admin Daniel P Trahan.
Licensure Intermediate care. *Beds* ICF 107.
Certified Medicaid.
Owner Proprietary Corp.
Admissions Requirements Physician's request.
Staff RNs 5 (ft); LPNs 10 (ft); Nurses aides 20 (ft); Recreational therapists 2 (ft); Activities coordinators 1 (ft); Dietitians 1 (ft).
Facilities Dining room; Activities room; Crafts room; Laundry room; Barber/Beauty shop; Gathering rooms.
Activities Arts & crafts; Cards; Games; Reading groups; Prayer groups; Movies; Shopping trips; Social/Cultural gatherings.

HANOVER

Hanover Terrace Healthcare
Lyme Rd, Hanover, NH, 03755
(603) 643-2854
Admin Edward Golas. *Medical Dir/Dir of Nursing* Dr Richard Whiting; Rosemary Hinton.
Licensure Skilled care; Intermediate care. *Beds* 100. *Certified* Medicaid; Medicare.
Owner Proprietary Corp (Hillhaven Corp).
Staff Physicians 1 (pt); RNs 7 (ft), 1 (pt); LPNs 6 (ft), 1 (pt); Nurses aides 28 (ft); Physical therapists 1 (pt); Occupational therapists 1 (ft); Speech therapists 1 (pt);

Activities coordinators 1 (pt); Dietitians 1 (pt); Dentists 1 (pt); Podiatrists 1 (pt); Audiologists 1 (pt); Social workers 1 (ft); Staff Coordinator 1 (ft).
Facilities Dining room; Physical therapy room; Activities room; Chapel; Crafts room; Laundry room; Barber/Beauty shop; Library.
Activities Arts & crafts; Cards; Games; Reading groups; Movies; Shopping trips; Social/Cultural gatherings.

HILLSBOROUGH

Hillsboro House Nursing Home*
School St, Hillsborough, NH, 03244
(603) 464-5561
Admin David Irwin.
Licensure Intermediate care. *Beds* 30.
Certified Medicaid.

HUDSON

Fairview Nursing Home
203 Lowell Rd, Hudson, NH, 03051
(603) 882-5261
Admin Brian Courville. *Medical Dir/Dir of Nursing* Peter Hacker MD.
Licensure Intermediate care. *Beds* ICF 101.
Certified Medicaid.
Owner Proprietary Corp.
Admissions Requirements Minimum age 62; Medical examination.
Staff RNs; LPNs; Orderlies; Nurses aides 413F; Reality therapists; Recreational therapists; Occupational therapists; Speech therapists; Activities coordinators; Dietitians.
Facilities Dining room; Physical therapy room; Activities room; Chapel; Crafts room; Laundry room; Barber/Beauty shop; Library.
Activities Arts & crafts; Cards; Games; Reading groups; Prayer groups; Movies; Shopping trips; Social/Cultural gatherings.

JAFFREY

Monadnock Christian Nursing Home
PO Box 410, Jaffrey, NH, 03452
(603) 532-8762
Admin Benson Walen CFACHA. *Medical Dir/Dir of Nursing* Ursula Schribner RN.
Licensure Intermediate care. *Beds* ICF 51.
Certified Medicaid.
Owner Nonprofit organization/foundation.
Admissions Requirements Medical examination; Physician's request.
Staff RNs 6 (ft); LPNs 5 (ft); Nurses aides 30 (ft); Activities coordinators 1 (ft); Dietitians 1 (pt).
Facilities Dining room; Activities room; Chapel; Crafts room; Laundry room; Barber/Beauty shop.
Activities Arts & crafts; Games; Reading groups; Prayer groups; Movies; Shopping trips; Social/Cultural gatherings; Music; Bingo; Pets.

KEENE

Country Way Retirement Care Center
677 Court St, Keene, NH, 03431
(603) 357-3800
Admin Paul E Clements. *Medical Dir/Dir of Nursing* Walter Griffiths; M Denise Southgate.
Licensure Intermediate care. *Beds* ICF 100.
Certified Medicaid.
Owner Proprietary Corp (Beverly Enterprises).
Admissions Requirements Medical examination; Physician's request.
Staff RNs 6 (ft), 2 (pt); LPNs 9 (ft), 2 (pt); Nurses aides 35 (ft), 10 (pt); Recreational therapists 1 (ft), 1 (pt); Activities coordinators 1 (ft).
Languages French

Facilities Dining room; Physical therapy room; Activities room; Crafts room; Barber/Beauty shop; Library.
Activities Arts & crafts; Cards; Games; Reading groups; Prayer groups; Movies; Shopping trips; Social/Cultural gatherings.

Monadnock Nursing Home*
428 Main St, Keene, NH, 03431
(603) 352-0257
Admin Arthur Bottomley. *Medical Dir/Dir of Nursing* Dr Ballou Jr.
Licensure Intermediate care. *Beds* 35.
Certified Medicaid.
Staff RNs 2 (ft); LPNs 5 (ft); Nurses aides 9 (ft); Occupational therapists 1 (pt); Activities coordinators 1 (ft); Social workers 1 (ft).
Facilities Dining room; Activities room; Laundry room.
Activities Arts & crafts; Cards; Games; Reading groups; Prayer groups; Movies; Shopping trips; Social/Cultural gatherings.

One-Eighty Court
180 Court St, Keene, NH, 03431
(603) 352-7755
Admin Mary Lund.
Licensure Intermediate care. *Beds* ICF 15.
Owner Proprietary Corp.
Staff RNs 3 (ft), 2 (pt); LPNs 2 (ft), 3 (pt); Nurses aides 4 (ft), 4 (pt).

One-Fifty-One Court
151 Court St, Keene, NH, 03431
(603) 352-7755
Admin Earl & Mary Lund.
Licensure Sheltered care. *Beds* 10.
Owner Proprietary Corp.
Staff RNs 1 (pt); LPNs 1 (pt); Nurses aides 3 (ft), 3 (pt); Dietitians 1 (pt).

Prospect Hill Home*
361 Court St, Keene, NH, 03431
(603) 352-0323
Admin Mary-Lou Hodgdon.
Licensure Skilled care. *Beds* 20.

Thirty-Nine Summer
39 Summer St, Keene, NH, 03431
(603) 352-7755
Admin Earl E Lund.
Licensure Intermediate care. *Beds* ICF 12.
Owner Proprietary Corp.
Staff RNs 2 (ft), 3 (pt); LPNs 2 (ft), 2 (pt); Nurses aides 4 (ft), 4 (pt).

Westwood Healthcare Center*
298 Main St, Keene, NH, 03431
(603) 352-7311
Admin Lillian Watkins.
Licensure Skilled care; Intermediate care. *Beds* 72. *Certified* Medicaid; Medicare.

LACONIA

Belknap County Nursing Home
1152 N Main St, Laconia, NH, 03246
(603) 524-4048
Admin Donald D Drouin Sr. *Medical Dir/Dir of Nursing* Kathleen M Lord RN.
Licensure Intermediate care. *Beds* ICF 85.
Certified Medicaid.
Owner Publicly owned.
Admissions Requirements Medical examination; Physician's request.
Staff Physicians 1 (pt); RNs 11 (ft), 3 (pt); LPNs 5 (ft), 1 (pt); Orderlies 5 (ft), 1 (pt); Nurses aides 41 (ft), 3 (pt); Physical therapists 1 (pt); Recreational therapists 3 (pt); Activities coordinators 1 (ft); Dietitians 1 (ft).
Languages French
Facilities Dining room; Physical therapy room; Activities room; Chapel; Crafts room; Laundry room; Barber/Beauty shop.

Activities Arts & crafts; Cards; Games; Reading groups; Prayer groups; Movies; Shopping trips; Social/Cultural gatherings; Quilting; Church.

McKerley Health Care Center*
175 Blueberry Ln, Laconia, NH, 03246
(603) 524-3340
Admin Harold Baldwin.
Licensure Skilled care; Intermediate care. *Beds* SNF 26; ICF 82. *Certified* Medicaid; Medicare.

St Francis Home
PO Box 1699, Court St, Laconia, NH, 03247-1699
(603) 524-0466
Admin Julieann R Fay. *Medical Dir/Dir of Nursing* E C Squires MD; Claire Falardeau RN DNS.
Licensure Intermediate care. *Beds* 51. *Certified* Medicaid.
Owner Nonprofit Corp.
Admissions Requirements Minimum age 65; Medical examination.
Staff Physicians 1 (ft); RNs 4 (ft), 5 (pt); LPNs 2 (ft), 1 (pt); Nurses aides 21 (ft), 2 (pt); Physical therapists 1 (ft); Speech therapists 1 (ft); Activities coordinators 1 (ft); Dietitians 1 (ft); Dentists 1 (ft); Ophthalmologists 1 (ft).
Languages French
Affiliation Roman Catholic
Facilities Dining room; Physical therapy room; Activities room; Chapel; Laundry room; Barber/Beauty shop; Lounge; Coffee shop.
Activities Arts & crafts; Cards; Games; Reading groups; Prayer groups; Movies; Shopping trips; Social/Cultural gatherings; Ceramics.

Taylor Home*
435 Union Ave, Laconia, NH, 03246
(603) 524-3409
Admin Howard Chandler.
Licensure Skilled care. *Beds* 42.

LANCASTER

Country Village Health Care Center
24 N Main St, Lancaster, NH, 03584
(603) 788-4935
Admin Kirt D Sampson. *Medical Dir/Dir of Nursing* Ruth Meek DON.
Licensure Intermediate care. *Beds* ICF 86. *Certified* Medicaid.
Owner Privately owned.
Admissions Requirements Medical examination.
Staff Physicians 8 (pt); RNs 6 (ft), 4 (pt); LPNs 2 (ft), 2 (pt); Orderlies 1 (ft); Nurses aides 15 (ft), 10 (pt); Physical therapists 1 (pt); Occupational therapists 1 (pt); Speech therapists 1 (pt); Activities coordinators 1 (ft); Dietitians 1 (pt); Dentists 1 (pt).
Facilities Dining room; Physical therapy room; Activities room; Chapel; Crafts room; Laundry room; Barber/Beauty shop.
Activities Arts & crafts; Cards; Games; Reading groups; Prayer groups; Movies; Shopping trips; Social/Cultural gatherings.

LEBANON

Etna Valley Health Center
PO Box 131K, RR 1, Lebanon, NH, 03766
(603) 448-2234
Admin John H King. *Medical Dir/Dir of Nursing* Jo West RN DON.
Licensure Intermediate care. *Beds* ICF 110. *Certified* Medicaid.
Owner Proprietary Corp (Lemire Enterprises).
Admissions Requirements Physician's request.

Staff RNs 5 (ft); LPNs 13 (ft); Orderlies 1 (ft); Nurses aides 50 (ft); Physical therapists 1 (pt); Recreational therapists 2 (ft); Activities coordinators 1 (ft); Dietitians 1 (pt).
Facilities Dining room; Physical therapy room; Activities room; Barber/Beauty shop.
Activities Arts & crafts; Cards; Games; Reading groups; Social/Cultural gatherings.

LITTLETON

Oak Hill Residence
8 Oak Hill Ave, Littleton, NH, 03561
(603) 444-5590
Admin Bryon & Rita Cascadden.
Licensure Shared. *Beds* 4.
Owner Privately owned.
Languages French

LONDONDERRY

Guardian Nursing Home
PO Box 1290, Londonderry, NH, 03053-1290
(617) 245-2483
Licensure Intermediate care. *Beds* 24. *Certified* Medicaid.

MANCHESTER

Gale Home*
133 Ash St, Manchester, NH, 03103
(603) 622-6632
Admin Joan Lemire. *Medical Dir/Dir of Nursing* Dr Gregory White.
Licensure Intermediate care. *Beds* 24. *Certified* Medicaid.
Admissions Requirements Females only; Medical examination.
Staff Physicians; RNs 2 (ft), 2 (pt); LPNs 2 (ft), 1 (pt); Nurses aides 3 (ft), 5 (pt); Physical therapists; Reality therapists; Recreational therapists 1 (pt); Occupational therapists; Speech therapists; Dietitians 3 (ft); Dentists; Ophthalmologists.
Facilities Dining room; Physical therapy room; Activities room; Crafts room; Laundry room; Barber/Beauty shop.
Activities Arts & crafts; Cards; Games; Prayer groups; Movies; Shopping trips; Weekly entertainment.

Hanover Hill Healthcare Center*
700 Hanover St, Manchester, NH, 03104
(603) 627-3826
Admin Theodore Lee.
Licensure Skilled care; Intermediate care. *Beds* SNF 6; ICF 115. *Certified* Medicaid; Medicare.

Mammoth Nursing Home*
1 Mammoth Rd, Manchester, NH, 03103
(603) 625-9891
Admin Ralph Allard.
Licensure Intermediate care. *Beds* 55. *Certified* Medicaid.
Owner Proprietary Corp (Courville Management).

Maple Leaf Health Care Center*
198 Pearl St, Manchester, NH, 03104
(603) 669-1660
Admin Rita Miville.
Licensure Skilled care; Intermediate care. *Beds* SNF 27; ICF 81. *Certified* Medicaid.
Owner Proprietary Corp (Lemire Enterprises).

Maple Leaf Nursing Home*
593 Maple St, Manchester, NH, 03104
(603) 669-1452
Admin Claire Lemire.
Licensure Intermediate care. *Beds* 63. *Certified* Medicaid.

Masonic Home
813 Beech St, Manchester, NH, 03104
(603) 669-7361

Admin Rene G Lemire. *Medical Dir/Dir of Nursing* Toni Gray RN DNS.
Licensure Skilled care; Sheltered care with Infirmary. *Beds* 52.
Owner Nonprofit Corp.
Admissions Requirements Medical examination; Physician's request.
Staff RNs; LPNs; Nurses aides; Activities coordinators; Dietitians; Ophthalmologists.
Affiliation Masons
Facilities Dining room; Activities room; Chapel; Crafts room; Laundry room; Barber/Beauty shop; Library.
Activities Arts & crafts; Cards; Games; Reading groups; Prayer groups; Movies; Shopping trips; Bus trips; BBQs; Birthday parties.

McKerley Health Care Center—Manchester Inc
191 Hackett Hill Rd, Manchester, NH, 03103
(603) 668-8161
Admin Warren E Lapham. *Medical Dir/Dir of Nursing* Meg Welch.
Licensure Intermediate care; Sheltered care. *Beds* ICF 68.
Owner Proprietary Corp.
Staff RNs 2 (ft), 5 (pt); LPNs 4 (ft), 6 (pt); Nurses aides 20 (ft), 16 (pt); Recreational therapists 1 (ft); Activities coordinators 1 (ft); Dietitians 1 (ft).
Facilities Dining room; Activities room; Crafts room; Laundry room; Barber/Beauty shop; Library.
Activities Arts & crafts; Cards; Games; Movies; Social/Cultural gatherings.

Mt Carmel Nursing Home
235 Myrtle St, Manchester, NH, 03104
(603) 627-3811
Admin Sr Mark Louis. *Medical Dir/Dir of Nursing* Dr Parker Wheat; Sr Joseph Jude RN.
Licensure Intermediate care. *Beds* ICF 120. *Certified* Medicaid.
Owner Nonprofit Corp.
Admissions Requirements Minimum age 65.
Languages French
Affiliation Roman Catholic
Facilities Dining room; Physical therapy room; Activities room; Chapel; Crafts room; Laundry room; Barber/Beauty shop; Library.
Activities Arts & crafts; Cards; Games; Reading groups; Prayer groups; Movies; Shopping trips; Social/Cultural gatherings.

Myrtle Convalescent Home
1276 Hanover St, Manchester, NH, 03104-5623
(603) 623-7110
Admin Grace Trahan.
Licensure Intermediate care. *Beds* 34. *Certified* Medicaid.

Northwood Nursing Home*
668 Amherst St, Manchester, NH, 03104
(603) 625-6462
Admin Cynthia DuBois.
Licensure Intermediate care. *Beds* 51. *Certified* Medicaid.

St Teresa's Manor*
519 Bridge St, Manchester, NH, 03103
(603) 668-2373
Admin Sr Andre Marie Ross. *Medical Dir/Dir of Nursing* Jonathan Jaffe.
Licensure Intermediate care. *Beds* 51. *Certified* Medicaid.

Women's Aid Home*
180 Pearl St, Manchester, NH, 03104
(603) 669-6991
Admin Marjorie Huckabee.
Licensure Skilled care. *Beds* 39.

MEREDITH

Golden View Health Care Center
Rte 104 RFD 3 Box 51, Meredith, NH, 03253
(603) 279-8111
Admin Jeanne Sanders.
Licensure Intermediate care. *Beds* ICF 100.
Certified Medicaid.
Owner Proprietary Corp (Lemire Enterprises).
Admissions Requirements Medical
examination; Physician's request.
Staff RNs; LPNs; Nurses aides; Physical
therapists; Occupational therapists; Speech
therapists; Activities coordinators; Dietitians.
Facilities Dining room; Physical therapy
room; Activities room; Crafts room; Laundry
room; Barber/Beauty shop.
Activities Arts & crafts; Cards; Games;
Reading groups; Prayer groups; Movies;
Shopping trips; Social/Cultural gatherings.

MILFORD

Crestwood Health Care Center—Milford
18 Crosby St, Milford, NH, 03055
(603) 673-7061
Admin Alain J Bernard.
Licensure Intermediate care. *Beds* ICF 79.
Certified VA.

Milford Nursing Home
41 Elm St, Milford, NH, 03055
(603) 673-2907
Admin Zofia Long.
Licensure Intermediate care. *Beds* 49.
Certified Medicaid.

MILTON

Kraus House*
41 Old Wakefield Rd, Milton, NH, 03851
(603) 652-9977
Admin Donna Kraus.
Licensure Skilled care. *Beds* 4.

NASHUA

The Courville at Nashua*
22 Hunt St, Nashua, NH, 03060
(603) 889-5450
Admin Richard Courville. *Medical Dir/Dir of
Nursing* Dr John Posner.
Licensure Skilled care; Intermediate care. *Beds*
SNF 50; ICF.
Owner Proprietary Corp (Courville
Management).
Admissions Requirements Physician's request.
Staff RNs 10 (ft); LPNs 14 (ft); Orderlies 1
(ft); Nurses aides 26 (ft); Physical therapists
2 (pt); Recreational therapists 1 (ft);
Occupational therapists 1 (pt); Speech
therapists 1 (pt); Activities coordinators 1
(ft); Dietitians 1 (ft); Dentists 1 (pt).
Facilities Dining room; Physical therapy
room; Activities room; Chapel; Crafts room;
Laundry room; Barber/Beauty shop; Library.
Activities Arts & crafts; Cards; Games;
Reading groups; Prayer groups; Movies;
Shopping trips; Social/Cultural gatherings;
Current events.

Greenbriar Terrace Healthcare
55 Harris Rd, Nashua, NH, 03062
(603) 888-1573
Admin Philip S Sher.
Licensure Skilled care; Intermediate care. *Beds*
SNF 25; ICF 275. *Certified* Medicaid;
Medicare.
Owner Proprietary Corp (Hillhaven Corp).
Admissions Requirements Medical
examination.
Languages French
Facilities Dining room; Physical therapy
room; Activities room; Chapel; Crafts room;
Laundry room; Barber/Beauty shop; Library.

Activities Arts & crafts; Cards; Games;
Reading groups; Prayer groups; Movies;
Shopping trips; Social/Cultural gatherings.

Hunt Community
10 Allds St, Nashua, NH, 03060
(603) 882-6511
Admin Christine C Hallock. *Medical Dir/Dir
of Nursing* Barbara Carey.
Licensure Intermediate care; Independent
living units; Personal care beds. *Beds* ICF
40; Level V 75; Personal 40.
Owner Nonprofit Corp.
Admissions Requirements Minimum age 62;
Medical examination.
Facilities Dining room; Physical therapy
room; Activities room; Chapel; Crafts room;
Laundry room; Barber/Beauty shop; Library.
Activities Arts & crafts; Cards; Games;
Reading groups; Prayer groups; Movies;
Shopping trips; Social/Cultural gatherings.

Nightingale Home
381 Main St, Nashua, NH, 03060
(603) 882-1770
Admin Paul Donnelly.
Licensure Self care. *Beds* 10.

NEWPORT

Woodlawn Nursing Home
84 Pine St, Newport, NH, 03773
(603) 863-1020
Admin Prey F Gadway. *Medical Dir/Dir of
Nursing* Denis T Maryn MD; May Berner
RN.
Licensure Intermediate care. *Beds* 51.
Certified Medicaid; Medicare.
Owner Proprietary Corp.
Admissions Requirements Medical
examination; Physician's request.
Staff RNs 1 (ft), 4 (pt); LPNs 4 (ft), 2 (pt);
Orderlies 2 (ft); Nurses aides 7 (ft), 16 (pt);
Recreational therapists 1 (ft); Activities
coordinators 1 (ft); Dietitians 1 (pt).
Facilities Dining room; Activities room;
Laundry room; Barber/Beauty shop; Library.
Activities Arts & crafts; Cards; Games;
Reading groups; Prayer groups; Movies;
Shopping trips; Musical programs.

NORTH CONWAY

Merriman House
The Memorial Hospital, Intervale Rd, North
Conway, NH, 03860
(603) 356-5461
Admin Susan Kuemmerle. *Medical Dir/Dir of
Nursing* Dr Miles Waltz; Gaye Ekberg RN.
Licensure Intermediate care. *Beds* ICF 21.
Certified Medicaid; Medicare.
Owner Nonprofit Corp.
Staff Physicians; RNs; LPNs; Nurses aides;
Occupational therapists; Speech therapists;
Activities coordinators; Dietitians;
Ophthalmologists.
Facilities Dining room; Physical therapy
room; Activities room; Chapel; Crafts room;
Laundry room; Barber/Beauty shop; Sun
porch; Yard; Acute care; Skilled care;
Hospital.
Activities Arts & crafts; Cards; Games;
Reading groups; Prayer groups; Movies;
Shopping trips; Social/Cultural gatherings;
Sightseeing trips; Restaurant trips;
Participation in community's Senior Center.

OSSIPEE

Mountain View Nursing Home
Rte 171, Ossipee, NH, 03864
(603) 539-7511
Admin Gregory F Froton Sr. *Medical Dir/Dir
of Nursing* Gerald Bozuwa MD; Colleen
Bagley RN DNS.
Licensure Intermediate care. *Beds* ICF 103.
Certified Medicaid.

Owner Publicly owned.
Admissions Requirements Minimum age 20;
Physician's request.
Staff RNs 8 (ft); LPNs 11 (ft); Nurses aides 53
(ft); Physical therapists 1 (ft); Recreational
therapists 2 (ft); Activities coordinators 1
(ft).
Languages French
Facilities Dining room; Physical therapy
room; Activities room; Laundry room;
Barber/Beauty shop.
Activities Arts & crafts; Cards; Games; Prayer
groups; Movies; Shopping trips; Social/
Cultural gatherings.

PENACOOK

McKerley Harris Hill Nursing Home*
30 Tremont St, Penacook, NH, 03303
(603) 753-6551
Admin Daniel Estee.
Licensure Skilled care. *Beds* 11.

Merrimack County Nursing Home*
PO Box 9, Penacook, NH, 03303
(603) 224-2284
Admin Howard Teaf.
Licensure Intermediate care. *Beds* 312.
Certified Medicaid.

PETERBOROUGH

Pheasant Wood Nursing Home
Pheasant Rd, Peterborough, NH, 03458
(603) 924-7267
Admin Walter Hoszkiewicz. *Medical Dir/Dir
of Nursing* Sylvia St John.
Licensure Intermediate care. *Beds* ICF 101.
Certified Medicaid.
Owner Proprietary Corp.
Staff RNs 4 (ft), 3 (pt); LPNs 12 (ft), 4 (pt);
Nurses aides 35 (ft); Physical therapists 1
(ft); Activities coordinators 1 (ft); Dietitians
1 (ft).
Facilities Dining room; Physical therapy
room; Activities room; Laundry room;
Barber/Beauty shop.
Activities Arts & crafts; Cards; Games;
Reading groups; Movies; Shopping trips;
Social/Cultural gatherings.

PORTSMOUTH

Clipper Home*
188 Jones Ave, Portsmouth, NH, 03801
(603) 431-2530
Admin Douglas Stockbridge.
Licensure Intermediate care. *Beds* 78.

The Edgewood Centre
928 South St, Portsmouth, NH, 03801
(603) 436-0099
Admin Patricia M Ramsey. *Medical Dir/Dir of
Nursing* Dr Richard Altenborough; Sharon
Plante RN.
Licensure Skilled care; Intermediate care;
Outpatient therapy services. *Beds* SNF 50;
ICF 102. *Certified* Medicaid; Medicare; VA.
Owner Proprietary Corp.
Staff RNs; LPNs; Nurses aides; Physical
therapists; Recreational therapists;
Occupational therapists; Speech therapists;
Activities coordinators; Dietitians;
Ophthalmologists.
Facilities Dining room; Physical therapy
room; Activities room; Chapel; Crafts room;
Laundry room; Barber/Beauty shop.
Activities Arts & crafts; Cards; Games;
Reading groups; Prayer groups; Movies;
Shopping trips; Social/Cultural gatherings.

Mark H Wentworth Home
346 Pleasant St, Portsmouth, NH, 03801
(603) 436-7236
Admin Donald E Reeves. *Medical Dir/Dir of
Nursing* Dr Richard Attenborough; Anne
Levesque.

Licensure Intermediate care. *Beds* ICF 57.
Owner Nonprofit Corp.
Staff Physicians 1 (pt); RNs 2 (ft), 2 (pt);
LPNs 4 (ft), 2 (pt); Nurses aides 38 (ft), 6
(pt); Physical therapists; Reality therapists;
Recreational therapists; Occupational
therapists; Speech therapists; Activities
coordinators; Dietitians; Dentists;
Ophthalmologists; Podiatrists.

Parrott Avenue Home
127 Parrott Ave, Portsmouth, NH, 03801
(603) 436-2435
Admin Sharon J Christianson. *Medical Dir/
Dir of Nursing* Richard Attenborough MD.
Licensure Sheltered care with nursing unit.
Beds 22.
Owner Nonprofit organization/foundation.
Admissions Requirements Medical
examination; Physician's request.
Staff RNs 1 (ft), 2 (pt); LPNs 3 (pt); Nurses
aides 3 (ft), 4 (pt).
Facilities Dining room; Laundry room;
Barber/Beauty shop; Library.
Activities Games; Shopping trips.

ROCHESTER

Gafney Home for the Aged
90 Wakefield St, Rochester, NH, 03867
(603) 332-2705
Admin Laurie J Woodman. *Medical Dir/Dir of
Nursing* Nancy Weeks.
Licensure Sheltered care facility. *Beds* 20.
Owner Nonprofit Corp.
Admissions Requirements Minimum age 65;
Medical examination.
Staff RNs 2 (pt); LPNs 1 (ft); Orderlies 4 (pt);
Nurses aides 2 (pt).
Facilities Dining room; Laundry room;
Barber/Beauty shop; Library.
Activities Prayer groups.

Rochester Manor*
Whitehall Rd, Rochester, NH, 03867
(603) 332-7711
Admin Mary Flynn.
Licensure Intermediate care. *Beds* SNF 25;
ICF 83. *Certified* Medicaid.

SALEM

Salemhaven*
23 Geremonty Dr, Salem, NH, 03079
(603) 893-5586
Admin Bruce Freeman.
Licensure Intermediate care. *Beds* 100.
Certified Medicaid.
Owner Proprietary Corp (Hillhaven Corp).

WARNER

The Austin Home Inc
White Plains Rd, Warner, NH, 03278
(603) 456-3525
Admin Kathleen Y Fifield. *Medical Dir/Dir of
Nursing* William Fifield; Kathleen Fifield,
Dorothea Young.
Licensure Sheltered care. *Beds* 15.
Owner Privately owned.
Admissions Requirements Medical
examination.
Staff Nurses aides.
Facilities Dining room; Laundry room;
Barber/Beauty shop; Library; Living room
with TV.
Activities Prayer groups; Shopping trips;
Social/Cultural gatherings; Church functions;
Fairs.

Pine Rock Farm*
Denny Hill Rd, Box 266, Warner, NH, 03278
(603) 456-3181
Admin Judith Waschsmuth.
Licensure Skilled care. *Beds* 15.

WEST CHESTERFIELD

Bert Anne Annex*
PO Box 144, West Chesterfield, NH, 03466
(603) 256-6277
Admin Bertha Bergeron.
Licensure Skilled care. *Beds* 6.

Bert Anne Home for the Aged
PO Box 144, West Chesterfield, NH, 03466
(603) 256-6277
Admin Bertha M Bergeron. *Medical Dir/Dir of
Nursing* Gertrude Kung RN.
Licensure Sheltered care. *Beds* 6. *Certified*
Medicare.
Owner Privately owned.
Admissions Requirements Minimum age 45.
Staff Physicians; RNs; Orderlies; Nurses aides.
Languages German, French
Facilities Dining room; Activities room;
Chapel; Crafts room; Laundry room; Barber/
Beauty shop.
Activities Cards; Games.

WEST STEWARTSTOWN

Coos County Nursing Hospital
PO Box 10, West Stewartstown, NH, 03597
(603) 246-3321
Admin Jerilyn Pelch. *Medical Dir/Dir of
Nursing* Joseph Capobianco MD.
Licensure Intermediate care. *Beds* ICF 101.
Certified Medicaid.
Owner Publicly owned.
Admissions Requirements Medical
examination; Physician's request.
Staff Physicians 4 (pt); RNs 5 (ft), 5 (pt);
LPNs 4 (ft), 2 (pt); Nurses aides 29 (ft), 14
(pt); Physical therapists 1 (pt); Occupational
therapists 1 (pt); Speech therapists 1 (pt);
Activities coordinators 1 (ft); Dietitians 1
(pt).
Languages French
Facilities Dining room; Physical therapy
room; Activities room; Chapel; Crafts room;
Laundry room; Barber/Beauty shop; Outside
patio with cookout; Picnic facilities; Secure
care system.
Activities Arts & crafts; Cards; Games;
Reading groups; Prayer groups; Movies;
Shopping trips; Social/Cultural gatherings.

WESTMORELAND

Cedarcrest Inc
Aldrich Rd, Westmoreland, NH, 03467
(603) 399-4446
Admin Sharon Ann Kaiser NHA RN. *Medical
Dir/Dir of Nursing* Sharon Ann Kaiser NHA
RN.
Licensure Intermediate care for mentally
retarded. *Beds* ICF/MR 21. *Certified*
Medicaid.
Owner Nonprofit Corp.
Admissions Requirements Minimum age 16.
Staff Physicians 1 (pt); RNs 2 (ft), 3 (pt);
LPNs 3 (ft), 3 (pt); Nurses aides 12 (ft), 20
(pt); Physical therapists 1 (pt); Occupational
therapists 2 (pt); Speech therapists 1 (pt);
Activities coordinators 1 (pt); Dietitians 1
(pt).

Facilities Dining room; Laundry room;
School.
Activities Arts & crafts; Movies; Shopping
trips; Social/Cultural gatherings.

Cheshire County Maplewood Nursing Home
River Road, Westmoreland, NH, 03467
(603) 399-4912
Admin Patrick F McManus. *Medical Dir/Dir
of Nursing* Harriet T Davenport RN DON.
Licensure Intermediate care. *Beds* ICF 150.
Certified Medicaid.
Owner Publicly owned.
Admissions Requirements Minimum age 16;
Medical examination; Physician's request.
Staff RNs 8 (ft), 6 (pt); LPNs 8 (ft), 13 (pt);
Nurses aides 42 (ft), 30 (pt); Physical
therapists 1 (ft); Activities coordinators 1
(ft); Dietitians 1 (ft); Pharmacist 1 (ft);
Social worker 1 (ft).
Facilities Dining room; Physical therapy
room; Activities room; Chapel; Crafts room;
Laundry room; Barber/Beauty shop; Library;
Gift shop.
Activities Arts & crafts; Cards; Games;
Reading groups; Prayer groups; Movies;
Shopping trips; Social/Cultural gatherings;
Gourmet dining; Parties; Men's club;
Exercise groups; Cooking.

WHITEFIELD

Morrison Nursing Home
2-6 Terrace St, Whitefield, NH, 03598
(603) 837-2541
Admin Paul V Kaminski. *Medical Dir/Dir of
Nursing* Dr Jorge deVillafane.
Licensure Intermediate care. *Beds* ICF 51.
Certified Medicaid.
Owner Nonprofit organization/foundation.
Admissions Requirements Physician's request.
Staff Physicians 4 (pt); RNs 3 (ft), 3 (pt);
LPNs 3 (ft), 3 (pt); Nurses aides 21 (ft), 4
(pt); Physical therapists 1 (pt); Activities
coordinators 1 (ft); Dietitians 1 (pt); Dentists
1 (pt); Podiatrists 1 (pt).
Facilities Dining room; Activities room;
Laundry room; Barber/Beauty shop; Library.
Activities Arts & crafts; Cards; Games;
Reading groups; Movies.

WOODSVILLE

Grafton County Nursing Home
PO Box 276, Woodsville, NH, 03785
(603) 787-6971
Admin William Siegmund. *Medical Dir/Dir of
Nursing* Evelyn Biglow RN DON.
Licensure Intermediate care. *Beds* ICF 136.
Certified Medicaid.
Owner Publicly owned.
Admissions Requirements Medical
examination; Physician's request.
Staff Physicians 2 (pt); RNs 5 (ft), 6 (pt);
LPNs 11 (ft), 5 (pt); Nurses aides 62 (ft), 10
(pt); Physical therapists 1 (pt); Occupational
therapists 1 (pt); Speech therapists 1 (pt);
Activities coordinators 1 (ft); Dietitians 1
(pt); Dentists 1 (pt); Ophthalmologists 1 (pt);
Podiatrists 1 (pt).
Facilities Dining room; Physical therapy
room; Activities room; Chapel; Crafts room;
Laundry room; Barber/Beauty shop; Library.
Activities Arts & crafts; Cards; Games;
Reading groups; Prayer groups; Movies;
Shopping trips; Social/Cultural gatherings.

NEW JERSEY

ALLENDALE

Allendale Nursing Home*
55 Harreton Rd, Allendale, NJ, 07401
(201) 825-0660
Admin Hecter Giancarlo MD.
Licensure Skilled care; Intermediate care. *Beds*
SNF 50; ICF 120. *Certified* Medicaid;
Medicare.

Wiersma's Nursing Home*
703 Franklin Turnpike, Allendale, NJ, 07401
(201) 327-3150
Admin Louis Wiersma, Pres.
Licensure Long-Term care. *Beds* 18.

ALLENWOOD

Geraldine L Thompson Medical Home
Hospital Rd, Allenwood, NJ, 08720
(201) 938-5250
Admin Diana L Jargowski. *Medical Dir/Dir of*
Nursing Dr James Cashman.
Licensure Skilled care. *Beds* 73. *Certified*
Medicaid.
Owner Publicly owned.
Admissions Requirements Minimum age 18.
Staff Physicians 2 (pt); RNs 5 (ft), 2 (pt);
LPNs 3 (ft), 1 (pt); Nurses aides 28 (ft), 6
(pt); Physical therapists 1 (pt); Recreational
therapists 3 (ft); Activities coordinators 1
(ft); Dietitians 1 (pt); Podiatrists 1 (pt).
Facilities Dining room; Activities room;
Chapel; Crafts room; Laundry room; Barber/
Beauty shop.
Activities Arts & crafts; Cards; Games;
Reading groups; Prayer groups; Movies;
Shopping trips; Social/Cultural gatherings;
Video games; Community trips.

ANDOVER

Andover Intermediate Care Center
Mulford Creamery, Andover, NJ, 07821
(201) 383-6200
Admin Jeryl Turco. *Medical Dir/Dir of*
Nursing Dr Pavle Topalovic.
Licensure Intermediate care. *Beds* 540.
Certified Medicaid.
Admissions Requirements Physician's request.
Staff Physicians 1 (ft), 22 (pt); RNs 42 (ft), 21
(pt); LPNs 17 (ft), 10 (pt); Orderlies &;
Nurses aides 142 (ft), 27 (pt); Physical
therapists 1 (ft); Recreational therapists 10
(ft), 3 (pt); Speech therapists 1 (pt);
Activities coordinators 1 (ft); Dietitians 2
(ft); Podiatrists 3 (pt); Physical therapy
assistants 4 (ft).
Facilities Dining room; Physical therapy
room; Activities room; Chapel; Crafts room;
Laundry room; Barber/Beauty shop;
Swimming pool; Miniature golf course.
Activities Arts & crafts; Cards; Games;
Reading groups; Prayer groups; Movies;
Shopping trips; Social/Cultural gatherings;
Plays; Validation-fantasy groups; Sensory
retraining; Aerobics.

ANNANDALE

Union Forge Nursing Home
184 Cratetown Road, Annandale, NJ, 08801
(201) 236-2011
Admin Irene Pasternak. *Medical Dir/Dir of*
Nursing Alan Kelsey MD; Cathy Bodine
RN.
Licensure Skilled care. *Beds* 60.
Owner Proprietary Corp.
Admissions Requirements Medical
examination.
Facilities Dining room; Activities room;
Laundry room; Barber/Beauty shop.
Activities Arts & crafts; Cards; Games;
Reading groups; Prayer groups; Movies;
Social/Cultural gatherings.

ATLANTIC CITY

Golden Crest Nursing Home*
29 & 33 N Vermont Ave, Atlantic City, NJ,
08401
(609) 344-8911
Admin William B Calvin.
Licensure Skilled care; Intermediate care. *Beds*
208. *Certified* Medicaid.

King David Care Center of Atlantic City
166 S South Carolina Ave, Atlantic City, NJ,
08401
(609) 344-2181
Admin Leonora C Pilao. *Medical Dir/Dir of*
Nursing Harry A Sweeney DO; Jane O'Brien
RN.
Licensure Skilled care; Intermediate care. *Beds*
372. *Certified* Medicaid.
Owner Proprietary Corp.
Staff Physicians; RNs; LPNs; Orderlies;
Nurses aides; Physical therapists;
Recreational therapists; Occupational
therapists; Speech therapists; Activities
coordinators; Dietitians; Ophthalmologists.
Languages Spanish
Facilities Dining room; Physical therapy
room; Activities room; Chapel; Crafts room;
Barber/Beauty shop; Bookmobile.
Activities Arts & crafts; Cards; Games;
Reading groups; Prayer groups; Movies;
Shopping trips; Social/Cultural gatherings.

**Oceanside Convalescent & Rehabilitation
Center**
401 Boardwalk, Atlantic City, NJ, 08401
(609) 348-0171
Admin Ray Welsh. *Medical Dir/Dir of Nursing*
Harry Sweeney MD; Marietta Stewart.
Licensure Skilled care; Intermediate care. *Beds*
104. *Certified* Medicaid; Medicare.
Owner Proprietary Corp.
Admissions Requirements Physician's request.
Staff Physicians 5 (pt); RNs 14 (ft), 5 (pt);
LPNs 3 (ft), 1 (pt); Orderlies 7 (ft); Nurses
aides 33 (ft); Physical therapists 1 (ft);
Occupational therapists 1 (pt); Speech
therapists 1 (pt); Activities coordinators 1
(ft); Dietitians 1 (pt); Dentists 1 (pt);
Ophthalmologists 2 (pt); Podiatrists 1 (pt).

Languages Spanish, Tagalog
Facilities Dining room; Physical therapy
room; Laundry room; TV lounge; Screened
porch with ocean view.
Activities Arts & crafts; Cards; Games; Prayer
groups; Movies; Shopping trips; Social/
Cultural gatherings; Boardwalk trips.

**Presbyterian Home of Atlantic City—Madison
House***
123 S Illinois Ave, Atlantic City, NJ, 08401
(609) 344-8191
Admin Edward Conklin.
Licensure Intermediate care. *Beds* 26.
Certified Medicaid.
Affiliation Presbyterian

Westside Convalescent Center*
2153 Venice Ave, Atlantic City, NJ, 08401
(609) 348-2656
Admin Mary Wilson.
Licensure Skilled care; Intermediate care. *Beds*
30. *Certified* Medicaid.

ATLANTIC HIGHLANDS

Atlantic Highlands Nursing Home*
8 Middletown Ave, Atlantic Highlands, NJ,
07716
(201) 291-0600
Admin Gezor Kaszierer.
Licensure Skilled care; Intermediate care. *Beds*
155. *Certified* Medicaid; Medicare.

BARNEGAT

Barnegat Nursing Center
859 W Bay Ave, Barnegat, NJ, 08005
(609) 698-1400
Admin Michael D Gentile. *Medical Dir/Dir of*
Nursing Dr Philip Varner; Natalie Lawless
DON.
Licensure Skilled care. *Beds* SNF 120.
Certified Medicaid; Medicare.
Owner Proprietary Corp.
Admissions Requirements Minimum age 18;
Medical examination; Physician's request.
Staff RNs 8 (ft), 3 (pt); LPNs 5 (ft), 1 (pt);
Orderlies 1 (ft), 1 (pt); Nurses aides 25 (ft),
10 (pt); Physical therapists 1 (pt);
Recreational therapists 1 (ft); Occupational
therapists 1 (pt); Speech therapists 1 (pt);
Activities coordinators 1 (ft); Dietitians 1
(pt).
Languages Italian, German
Facilities Dining room; Physical therapy
room; Activities room; Crafts room; Laundry
room; Barber/Beauty shop.
Activities Arts & crafts; Cards; Games;
Reading groups; Prayer groups; Movies;
Shopping trips; Social/Cultural gatherings.

BAYVILLE

Bayview Convalescent Center
Lakeside Blvd, Bayville, NJ, 08721
(201) 269-0500

Admin Oscar Heller. *Medical Dir/Dir of Nursing* William Jones DO; Shirley Libby RN.
Licensure Skilled care; Intermediate care. *Beds* SNF 323. *Certified* Medicaid; Medicare.
Owner Proprietary Corp.
Admissions Requirements Minimum age 18; Physician's request.
Staff Physicians 3 (pt); RNs 11 (ft), 7 (pt); LPNs 13 (ft), 17 (pt); Orderlies 3 (ft); Nurses aides 78 (ft), 31 (pt); Physical therapists 1 (ft); Recreational therapists 7 (ft); Occupational therapists 1 (pt); Speech therapists 1 (pt); Activities coordinators 1 (ft); Dietitians 1 (pt); Dentists 1 (pt); Ophthalmologists 1 (pt); Podiatrists 1 (pt).
Facilities Dining room; Physical therapy room; Activities room; Crafts room; Laundry room; Barber/Beauty shop; Library; Outdoor barbeque.
Activities Arts & crafts; Cards; Games; Reading groups; Prayer groups; Movies; Shopping trips; Social/Cultural gatherings.

BELLEVILLE

Essex County Geriatrics Center*
Belleville & Franklin Avenues, Belleville, NJ, 07109
(201) 751-7200
Admin Robert Hilsen. *Medical Dir/Dir of Nursing* Ricardo P Alzadon.
Licensure Skilled care; Intermediate care. *Beds* 332. *Certified* Medicaid.
Owner Publicly owned.
Admissions Requirements Minimum age 18; Medical examination; Physician's request.
Staff RNs 43 (ft); LPNs 50 (ft); Nurses aides 158 (ft); Physical therapists 1 (ft); Activities coordinators 1 (ft); Dietitians 2 (ft).
Facilities Dining room; Physical therapy room; Activities room; Crafts room; Barber/Beauty shop.
Activities Arts & crafts; Prayer groups; Movies; Social/Cultural gatherings.

BERKELEY HEIGHTS

Berkeley Hall Nursing Home*
311 Springfield Ave, Berkeley Heights, NJ, 07922
(201) 464-9260
Admin Noel W Swan. *Medical Dir/Dir of Nursing* Dr J J Aquino.
Licensure Long-Term care. *Beds* 67.
Admissions Requirements Medical examination.
Staff Physicians 10 (pt); RNs 6 (ft), 5 (pt); LPNs 8 (ft), 2 (pt); Nurses aides 11 (ft), 8 (pt); Physical therapists 1 (pt); Recreational therapists 1 (ft); Occupational therapists 1 (pt); Speech therapists 1 (pt); Activities coordinators 1 (ft); Dietitians 1 (pt); Dentists 1 (pt); Ophthalmologists 1 (pt); Podiatrists 1 (pt); Audiologists 1 (pt).
Facilities Dining room; Physical therapy room; Activities room; Chapel; Crafts room; Laundry room; Barber/Beauty shop.
Activities Arts & crafts; Cards; Games; Reading groups; Prayer groups; Movies; Shopping trips; Social/Cultural gatherings.

Berkeley Heights Convalescent Center
35 Cottage St, Berkeley Heights, NJ, 07922
(201) 464-0048
Admin Mimail Davidovich. *Medical Dir/Dir of Nursing* Dr Donald Kent.
Licensure Skilled care; Intermediate care. *Beds* SNF 120; ICF. *Certified* Medicaid; Medicare.
Owner Proprietary Corp.
Admissions Requirements Minimum age 60.
Staff Physicians 10 (pt); RNs 10 (ft); LPNs 15 (ft); Nurses aides 30 (ft); Recreational therapists 3 (ft); Dietitians 1 (ft).
Languages Russian

Facilities Dining room; Physical therapy room; Activities room; Crafts room; Laundry room; Barber/Beauty shop; Library; Patio.
Activities Arts & crafts; Cards; Games; Reading groups; Prayer groups; Movies; Shopping trips; Social/Cultural gatherings.

BERNARDSVILLE

Fellowship Deaconry Inc*
Shannon Lodge, Old Army Rd, Bernardsville, NJ, 07924
(201) 766-0832
Admin Roy Gaida.
Licensure Long-Term care; Residential care. *Beds* 74.
Owner Nonprofit Corp.

BLACKWOOD

Camden County Health Service Center
Lakeland, Blackwood, NJ, 08012
(609) 227-3000
Admin Rose Simpson. *Medical Dir/Dir of Nursing* William Hingston MD; Romayne Gallagher RN DON.
Licensure Skilled care; Intermediate care; Medical day care. *Beds* SNF 122; ICF 159; Medical day care 35. *Certified* Medicaid; Medicare.
Owner Publicly owned.
Admissions Requirements Minimum age 18; Medical examination; Physician's request.
Facilities Dining room; Physical therapy room; Activities room; Chapel; Crafts room; Barber/Beauty shop.
Activities Arts & crafts; Cards; Games; Reading groups; Prayer groups; Movies; Shopping trips; Social/Cultural gatherings.

BLOOMFIELD

Hazelcrest Manor Nursing Home*
60 Hazelwood Rd, Bloomfield, NJ, 07003
(201) 743-2366
Admin Richard Del Vecchio Jr. *Medical Dir/Dir of Nursing* R Chhabria MD.
Licensure Long-Term care. *Beds* 18.
Admissions Requirements Physician's request.
Staff Physicians 2 (pt); RNs 1 (ft), 4 (pt); LPNs 3 (ft), 3 (pt); Nurses aides 4 (ft), 3 (pt); Recreational therapists 1 (pt); Activities coordinators 1 (pt); Dietitians 1 (pt); Dentists 1 (pt); Ophthalmologists 1 (pt); Podiatrists 1 (pt); Audiologists 1 (pt).
Facilities Dining room; Activities room; Laundry room.
Activities Arts & crafts; Cards; Games; Reading groups; Prayer groups.

Park Manor Nursing Home*
23 Park Pl, Bloomfield, NJ, 07003
(201) 743-7772
Admin Peter Peterson.
Licensure Long-Term care. *Beds* 61.

Parklane Nursing Home Inc*
15 Church St, Bloomfield, NJ, 07003
(201) 748-4074
Admin Richard Del Vecchio Jr.
Licensure Intermediate care. *Beds* 30. *Certified* Medicaid.

BOONTON

Sarah Frances/Tally-Ho Manor
PO Box 84, Boonton, NJ, 07005
(201) 334-2454, 334-2455
Admin Timothy D Doyle. *Medical Dir/Dir of Nursing* Fran Benning RN DON.
Licensure Skilled care; Intermediate care; Residential care. *Beds* SNF 22; ICF 41; Residential 68.
Owner Proprietary Corp.
Admissions Requirements Minimum age 18; Medical examination.

Staff Physicians 22 (pt); RNs 14 (ft); LPNs 3 (ft); Nurses aides 22 (ft); Physical therapists 1 (pt); Recreational therapists 2 (pt); Activities coordinators 3 (ft); Dietitians 1 (ft).
Languages Italian, Spanish, German
Facilities Dining room; Activities room; Chapel; Crafts room; Laundry room; Barber/Beauty shop; Library.
Activities Arts & crafts; Cards; Games; Reading groups; Prayer groups; Movies; Shopping trips; Social/Cultural gatherings.

New Jersey Firemen's Home*
565 Lathrop Ave, Boonton, NJ, 07005
(201) 334-0024
Admin L George Hoth.
Licensure Long-Term care; Residential care. *Beds* 77.
Admissions Requirements Medical examination.
Staff Physicians; RNs; LPNs; Orderlies; Nurses aides; Activities coordinators.
Facilities Dining room; Activities room; Chapel; Laundry room; Barber/Beauty shop; Library.
Activities Arts & crafts; Cards; Games; Movies.

Tally Ho Manor*
RD 1, Powerville Rd, Boonton, NJ, 07005
(201) 334-2454
Admin Timothy Doyle.
Licensure Long-Term care; Residential care. *Beds* 109.

BOUND BROOK

Somerset Valley Nursing Home*
1621 Rte 22, Bound Brook, NJ, 08805
(201) 469-2000
Admin Robert Armbruster Jr.
Licensure Skilled care. *Beds* 58. *Certified* Medicaid; Medicare.

BRIDGETON

Bridgeton Nursing Centre
99 Manheim Ave, Bridgeton, NJ, 08302
(609) 455-2100
Admin Christopher Gillies.
Licensure Skilled care; Intermediate care. *Beds* 185. *Certified* Medicaid; Medicare.
Facilities Dining room; Physical therapy room; Activities room; Chapel; Laundry room; Barber/Beauty shop.
Activities Arts & crafts; Cards; Games; Reading groups; Prayer groups; Movies; Shopping trips; Social/Cultural gatherings.

Cumberland Manor*
Rte 2, Cumberland Dr, Bridgeton, NJ, 08302
(609) 455-8000
Admin Starret L Hill.
Licensure Skilled care; Intermediate care. *Beds* 196. *Certified* Medicaid.

Rainbow Nursing Center
Big Oak Rd RD 8, Box 318, Bridgeton, NJ, 08302
(609) 451-5000
Admin Janice R Friday. *Medical Dir/Dir of Nursing* Dr Leshner (Stanley) MD; T Dennis De Mary DON.
Licensure Skilled care; Intermediate care. *Beds* 84. *Certified* Medicaid; Medicare.
Owner Proprietary Corp (Unicare).
Admissions Requirements Minimum age 21; Medical examination.
Staff Physicians 3 (ft), 3 (pt); RNs 5 (ft), 5 (pt); LPNs 5 (ft), 5 (pt); Orderlies 2 (ft), 1 (pt); Nurses aides 21 (ft), 16 (pt); Activities coordinators 1 (ft), 1 (pt); Dentists 1 (pt); Ophthalmologists 1 (pt).

Facilities Dining room; Physical therapy room; Activities room; Crafts room; Laundry room; Barber/Beauty shop; Book delivery from library.
Activities Arts & crafts; Cards; Games; Reading groups; Prayer groups; Movies; Shopping trips; Social/Cultural gatherings.

BRIDGEWATER

Bridgeway Convalescent Center
270 Rte 28, Bridgewater, NJ, 08807
(201) 722-7022
Admin Lucille A Link. *Medical Dir/Dir of Nursing* Chik Chin MD; Julie Murphy RN DON.
Licensure Skilled care; Intermediate care. *Beds* 120. *Certified* Medicaid; Medicare.
Owner Proprietary Corp.
Staff RNs 2 (ft), 8 (pt); LPNs 7 (ft), 1 (pt); Orderlies 4 (ft); Nurses aides 29 (ft), 10 (pt); Physical therapists 1 (pt); Recreational therapists 2 (ft), 2 (pt); Occupational therapists 1 (pt); Speech therapists 1 (pt); Dietitians 1 (ft).
Facilities Dining room; Physical therapy room; Activities room; Chapel; Crafts room; Laundry room; Barber/Beauty shop.
Activities Arts & crafts; Cards; Games; Reading groups; Prayer groups; Movies; Shopping trips; Social/Cultural gatherings.

BRIDGEWATER TOWNSHIP

Greenfield Convalescent Center*
875 Rte 202-206 N, Bridgewater Township, NJ, 08876
(201) 526-8600
Admin Linda Reid. *Medical Dir/Dir of Nursing* Dr Brewster Miller.
Licensure Skilled care; Intermediate care. *Beds* 162. *Certified* Medicaid; Medicare.
Admissions Requirements Minimum age 18.
Facilities Dining room; Physical therapy room; Activities room; Chapel; Crafts room; Laundry room; Barber/Beauty shop; Library.
Activities Arts & crafts; Cards; Games; Reading groups; Prayer groups; Movies; Social/Cultural gatherings.

BURLINGTON

Burlington Woods Convalescent Center*
115 Sunset Rd, Burlington, NJ, 08016
(609) 387-3620
Admin Martha Schneider.
Licensure Skilled care; Intermediate care. *Beds* 168. *Certified* Medicaid; Medicare.
Owner Proprietary Corp (Geriatric & Medical Centerss).

Masonic Home of New Jersey
Jacksonville Rd, Burlington, NJ, 08016
(609) 386-0300
Admin T F Small III. *Medical Dir/Dir of Nursing* Jhin J Cynn MD; Marjorie Powell RN DON.
Licensure Skilled care; Intermediate care; Residential health care. *Beds* SNF 46; ICF 293; Residential health care 112. *Certified* Medicaid; Medicare.
Owner Nonprofit organization/foundation.
Admissions Requirements Medical examination.
Staff Physicians 1 (ft), 2 (pt); RNs 9 (ft), 11 (pt); LPNs 14 (ft), 21 (pt); Nurses aides 88 (ft), 34 (pt); Physical therapists 1 (pt); Occupational therapists 1 (pt); Speech therapists 1 (pt); Activities coordinators 1 (ft); Dietitians 1 (ft); Dentists 1 (pt); Ophthalmologists 1 (pt); Podiatrists 1 (pt); Dentist 1 (pt).
Affiliation Masons

Facilities Dining room; Physical therapy room; Activities room; Chapel; Crafts room; Laundry room; Barber/Beauty shop; Library; Auditorium; Picnic pavilion; Gift shop.
Activities Arts & crafts; Cards; Games; Reading groups; Prayer groups; Movies; Shopping trips; Social/Cultural gatherings; Woodworking shop; Cultural exchange programs; Trips; Ceramics; Bell choir; Gardening.

CALIFON

Little Brook Nursing & Convalescent Center
PO Box 398, Sliker Rd, Califon, NJ, 07830
(201) 832-2220
Admin Andrea Berry Shawn. *Medical Dir/Dir of Nursing* Raymond Byrd MD; Sue Sabatina RN.
Licensure Skilled care; Intermediate care. *Beds* 30. *Certified* Medicaid; Medicare.
Owner Proprietary Corp.
Staff Physicians; RNs; LPNs; Nurses aides; Physical therapists; Reality therapists; Recreational therapists; Occupational therapists; Speech therapists; Activities coordinators; Dietitians; Podiatrists.
Facilities Dining room; Activities room; Crafts room; Laundry room.
Activities Arts & crafts; Cards; Games.

CAPE MAY COURT HOUSE

Cape May Care Center*
Shore Rd, Rte 9, Cape May Court House, NJ, 08210
(609) 465-7633
Admin David M Slutzker. *Medical Dir/Dir of Nursing* S Melita MD.
Licensure Skilled care. *Beds* 116. *Certified* Medicaid; Medicare.
Admissions Requirements Minimum age 21.
Facilities Dining room; Physical therapy room; Activities room; Chapel; Crafts room; Laundry room; Barber/Beauty shop.
Activities Arts & crafts; Cards; Games; Reading groups; Prayer groups; Movies; Shopping trips; Social/Cultural gatherings; Casino trips.

Courthouse Convalescent Center
144 Magnolia Dr, Cape May Court House, NJ, 08210
(609) 465-7171
Admin Karen K Bayer. *Medical Dir/Dir of Nursing* Robert G Beitman MD; G Cavagnaro RN DON.
Licensure Skilled care; Intermediate care. *Beds* SNF 120; ICF. *Certified* Medicaid; Medicare.
Owner Proprietary Corp.
Admissions Requirements Minimum age 18; Physician's request.
Staff Physicians 6 (pt); RNs; LPNs 14 (ft), 3 (pt); Orderlies; Nurses aides 42 (ft), 2 (pt); Physical therapists 1 (pt); Recreational therapists 2 (ft); Occupational therapists 1 (pt); Speech therapists 1 (pt); Dietitians 1 (pt); Dentists 1 (pt); Dentists 1 (pt); Ophthalmologists 1 (pt); Podiatrists 1 (pt).
Languages Spanish
Facilities Dining room; Physical therapy room; Activities room; Laundry room; Barber/Beauty shop.
Activities Arts & crafts; Cards; Games; Reading groups; Prayer groups; Movies; Social/Cultural gatherings; Lunches out; Trip to boardwalk.

Crest Haven Nursing Home
Rte 9, Garden State Parkway, Cape May Court House, NJ, 08210
(609) 465-1184
Admin Robert A Pastoria. *Medical Dir/Dir of Nursing* Dr Clayton F Carr; Mary Lea Mills RN.

Licensure Skilled care; Intermediate care. *Beds* SNF 140; ICF. *Certified* Medicaid.
Owner Publicly owned.
Staff Physicians 1 (ft); RNs 15 (ft); LPNs 14 (ft); Nurses aides 82 (ft); Recreational therapists 2 (ft); Activities coordinators 1 (ft); Dietitians 1 (pt); Dentist 1 (pt).
Facilities Dining room; Activities room; Barber/Beauty shop.
Activities Arts & crafts; Cards; Games; Reading groups; Prayer groups; Movies; Shopping trips; Social/Cultural gatherings.

South Cape Nursing Home*
Stites Ave, Cape May Court House, NJ, 08210
(609) 465-5335
Admin Larry Powell.
Licensure Skilled care; Intermediate care. *Beds* 40. *Certified* Medicaid.

CARNEYS POINT

Park View Health Care Center
5th & Park Ave, Carney's Point, NJ, 08069
(609) 299-6800
Admin Paul T Andrews. *Medical Dir/Dir of Nursing* A Auerbach DO.
Licensure Skilled care; Intermediate care; Residential. *Beds* SNF; ICF 180; Residential 19. *Certified* Medicaid; Medicare.
Owner Proprietary Corp.
Admissions Requirements Minimum age 18.
Staff Physicians 2 (pt); RNs 8 (ft), 13 (pt); LPNs 9 (ft), 5 (pt); Orderlies 2 (ft), 2 (pt); Nurses aides 43 (ft), 38 (pt); Physical therapists 1 (pt); Reality therapists 1 (ft); Recreational therapists 2 (ft), 1 (pt); Occupational therapists 1 (pt); Speech therapists 1 (pt); Activities coordinators 1 (ft); Dietitians 1 (pt); Dentists 1 (pt); Ophthalmologists 1 (pt); Podiatrists 1 (pt).
Languages Spanish, Italian, German
Facilities Dining room; Physical therapy room; Activities room; Chapel; Crafts room; Laundry room; Barber/Beauty shop; Library.
Activities Arts & crafts; Cards; Games; Reading groups; Prayer groups; Movies; Shopping trips; Social/Cultural gatherings.

CEDAR GROVE

Hartwyck West Nursing Convalescent & Rehabilitation Center
Pompton Ave & E Lindsley Rd, Cedar Grove, NJ, 07009
(201) 256-7220
Admin Donald E Lynch. *Medical Dir/Dir of Nursing* Daniel Burbank MD; Amy Berkemyer RN DON.
Licensure Skilled care. *Beds* SNF 113. *Certified* Medicaid; Medicare.
Owner Nonprofit organization/foundation.
Admissions Requirements Physician's request.
Staff RNs; LPNs; Nurses aides; Physical therapists; Recreational therapists; Occupational therapists; Speech therapists; Activities coordinators; Dietitians.
Facilities Dining room; Physical therapy room; Activities room; Chapel; Crafts room; Laundry room; Barber/Beauty shop; Library.
Activities Arts & crafts; Cards; Games; Reading groups; Prayer groups; Movies; Shopping trips.

Waterview Nursing Center
536 Ridge Rd, Cedar Grove, NJ, 07009
(201) 239-9300
Admin Carolyn Handler. *Medical Dir/Dir of Nursing* Alfred R Dardis MD; Dorothy De Block RN DON.
Licensure Skilled care. *Beds* SNF 180; ICF. *Certified* Medicaid; Medicare.
Owner Proprietary Corp (Multicare Management).
Admissions Requirements Minimum age 18.

Staff RNs 12 (ft); LPNs 8 (ft); Nurses aides 45
(ft); Physical therapists; Recreational
therapists 2 (ft); Occupational therapists;
Activities coordinators 1 (ft); Dietitians 1
(ft); Dentists; Podiatrists.
Facilities Dining room; Physical therapy
room; Activities room; Barber/Beauty shop;
Library.
Activities Arts & crafts; Cards; Games;
Reading groups; Games; Movies;
Shopping trips; Social/Cultural gatherings.

CHATHAM

King James Care Center of Chatham
415 Southern Blvd, Chatham, NJ, 07928
(201) 822-1500
Admin Joseph Desher. *Medical Dir/Dir of
Nursing* Joseph Fennely MD.
Licensure Skilled care. *Beds* 104. *Certified*
Medicare.
Admissions Requirements Minimum age 50;
Medical examination; Physician's request.
Staff Physicians 17 (pt); RNs 15 (pt); LPNs 5
(pt); Orderlies 1 (pt); Nurses aides 42 (pt);
Physical therapists 1 (ft); Recreational
therapists 2 (ft); Occupational therapists 1
(pt); Speech therapists 1 (pt); Activities
coordinators 1 (ft); Dietitians 1 (pt);
Podiatrists 1 (pt).
Facilities Dining room; Physical therapy
room; Activities room; Crafts room; Laundry
room; Barber/Beauty shop.
Activities Arts & crafts; Games; Reading
groups; Movies; Shopping trips; Social/
Cultural gatherings.

CHERRY HILL

Cadbury Health Care Center
2150 Rte 38, Cherry Hill, NJ, 08002
(609) 667-4550
Admin Franklin Gillet. *Medical Dir/Dir of
Nursing* Joseph Termini MD; Marilyn
Elliott RN.
Licensure Skilled care; Intermediate care. *Beds*
SNF 60; ICF 60. *Certified* Medicaid;
Medicare.
Owner Nonprofit Corp.
Admissions Requirements Minimum age 65.
Staff Physicians 4 (pt); RNs 10 (ft), 1 (pt);
LPNs 4 (ft), 2 (pt); Nurses aides 39 (ft), 12
(pt); Physical therapists 1 (pt); Recreational
therapists F 1 (ft); Occupational therapists 1
(pt); Speech therapists 1 (pt); Activities
coordinators 1 (ft); Dietitians 1 (ft); Dentists
1 (pt); Ophthalmologists 1 (pt); Podiatrists 1
(pt).
Affiliation Society of Friends
Facilities Dining room; Physical therapy
room; Activities room; Laundry room;
Barber/Beauty shop; Library.
Activities Arts & crafts; Cards; Games;
Reading groups; Prayer groups; Movies;
Shopping trips; Social/Cultural gatherings.

Heritage House of Cherry Hill*
100 Arbor Ave, Cherry Hill, NJ, 08034
(609) 795-3131
Admin Edward Rudow. *Medical Dir/Dir of
Nursing* Dr R N Wells.
Licensure Intermediate care. *Beds* 126.
Certified Medicaid.
Admissions Requirements Physician's request.
Staff Physicians 4 (pt); RNs 9 (ft), 4 (pt);
LPNs 5 (pt), 3 (pt); Orderlies 4 (ft); Nurses
aides 19 (ft), 11 (pt); Reality therapists 1
(pt); Recreational therapists 2 (pt), 4 (pt);
Occupational therapists 1 (pt); Activities
coordinators 1 (ft).
Facilities Dining room; Activities room;
Crafts room; Laundry room.
Activities Arts & crafts; Cards; Games;
Reading groups; Prayer groups; Movies;
Shopping trips; Social/Cultural gatherings.

Jewish Geriatric Center
3025 W Chapel Ave, Cherry Hill, NJ, 08002
(609) 667-3100
Admin Isadore Tennenberg.
Licensure Skilled care; Intermediate care. *Beds*
171. *Certified* Medicaid; Medicare.
Owner Nonprofit Corp.
Affiliation Jewish

Leader Nursing & Rehabilitation Center
1412 Marlton Pike, Cherry Hill, NJ, 08034
(609) 428-6100
Admin Lyla Walsh. *Medical Dir/Dir of
Nursing* Frank Addugo MD; Lee Meeker
RN DON.
Licensure Skilled care; Intermediate care. *Beds*
SNF 98. *Certified* Medicare.
Owner Proprietary Corp (Manor Care).
Staff Physicians 32 (pt); RNs 7 (ft), 5 (pt);
LPNs 5 (ft), 3 (pt); Orderlies 1 (ft); Nurses
aides 31 (ft), 4 (pt); Physical therapists 1 (ft);
Recreational therapists 1 (ft); Occupational
therapists 1 (pt); Speech therapists 1 (pt);
Dietitians 1 (pt); Dentists 1 (pt);
Ophthalmologists 1 (pt); Podiatrists 1 (pt);
Dentist; Patient aides 6 (pt).
Facilities Dining room; Physical therapy
room; Activities room; Laundry room;
Barber/Beauty shop; Lounge areas; TV
rooms.
Activities Arts & crafts; Cards; Games;
Reading groups; Prayer groups; Movies;
Shopping trips; Social/Cultural gatherings;
Intergenerational activities.

CHESTER

Glenlora Nursing Home
PO Box 367, Rte 24, Chester, NJ, 07930
(201) 879-5055
Admin Ray C Walborn Jr. *Medical Dir/Dir of
Nursing* Dr Alan Chanin.
Licensure Skilled care. *Beds* SNF 26.
Owner Privately owned.
Admissions Requirements Minimum age 16;
Medical examination; Physician's request.
Staff RNs 3 (ft), 5 (pt); LPNs 3 (ft); Orderlies
1 (ft); Nurses aides 10 (ft), 8 (pt); Physical
therapists 1 (pt); Recreational therapists 1
(ft); Speech therapists 1 (pt); Activities
coordinators 1 (ft); Dietitians 1 (pt);
Ophthalmologists 1 (pt).
Facilities Dining room; Activities room;
Crafts room; Laundry room; Barber/Beauty
shop; Library.
Activities Arts & crafts; Cards; Games;
Reading groups; Prayer groups; Movies;
Shopping trips; Social/Cultural gatherings.

CINNAMINSON

Cinnaminson Manor Nursing Center
1700 Wynwood Dr, Cinnaminson, NJ, 08077
(609) 829-3812
Admin John W Francks.
Licensure Skilled care; Intermediate care. *Beds*
SNF 104; ICF. *Certified* Medicare.
Owner Proprietary Corp (Multicare
Management).
Staff RNs 8 (ft), 14 (pt); LPNs 1 (ft), 1 (pt);
Orderlies 2 (ft); Nurses aides 36 (ft), 6 (pt);
Physical therapists 1 (ft); Recreational
therapists 1 (ft); Occupational therapists 1
(pt); Speech therapists 1 (pt); Activities
coordinators 1 (ft); Dietitians 1 (pt).
Facilities Dining room; Physical therapy
room; Activities room; Crafts room; Laundry
room; Barber/Beauty shop; Library.
Activities Arts & crafts; Cards; Games;
Reading groups; Prayer groups; Movies;
Shopping trips; Social/Cultural gatherings.

CLARKSBORO

Shady Lane Gloucester County Home*
County House Rd & Shady Lane, Clarksboro,
NJ, 08020
(609) 423-0020
Admin Jospeh Varelli. *Medical Dir/Dir of
Nursing* D B Weems Jr MD.
Licensure Intermediate care. *Beds* 121.
Certified Medicaid.
Owner Publicly owned.
Admissions Requirements Minimum age 60;
Medical examination; Physician's request.
Staff Physicians 1 (pt); RNs 6 (ft), 1 (pt);
LPNs 13 (ft), 1 (pt); Nurses aides 60 (ft), 6
(pt); Physical therapists 1 (pt); Recreational
therapists 3 (ft); Speech therapists 1 (pt);
Activities coordinators 1 (ft); Dietitians 1
(pt); Dentists 1 (pt); Podiatrists 1 (pt).
Facilities Dining room; Physical therapy
room; Activities room; Crafts room; Laundry
room; Barber/Beauty shop.
Activities Arts & crafts; Cards; Games;
Reading groups; Movies; Shopping trips;
Social/Cultural gatherings.

CLIFTON

Dolly Mt Nursing Home*
20 Valley Rd, Clifton, NJ, 07013
(201) 278-8781
Admin Sylvia Bolster RN.
Licensure Skilled care; Intermediate care. *Beds*
32. *Certified* Medicaid.

COLUMBIA

Clover Rest Home*
Washington & Green Sts, Columbia, NJ,
07836
(201) 496-4307
Admin Linda Dinolfo.
Licensure Intermediate care; Residential care.
Beds ICF 30; Residential 20. *Certified*
Medicaid.

CRANBURY

The Elms
65 N Main St, Cranbury, NJ, 08512
(609) 395-0725
Admin Anita M Dietrick. *Medical Dir/Dir of
Nursing* Syed S Ali MD.
Licensure Intermediate care. *Beds* ICF 16.
Owner Proprietary Corp.
Admissions Requirements Medical
examination.
Staff Physicians 2 (pt); RNs 2 (ft), 2 (pt);
LPNs 2 (ft); Nurses aides 3 (ft), 5 (pt);
Physical therapists 1 (pt); Reality therapists
1 (pt); Recreational therapists 1 (pt);
Occupational therapists 1 (pt); Speech
therapists 1 (pt); Activities coordinators 1
(pt); Dietitians 1 (pt); Dentists 1 (pt);
Ophthalmologists 1 (pt); Podiatrists 1 (pt).
Facilities Dining room; Activities room;
Laundry room.
Activities Arts & crafts; Cards; Games;
Reading groups; Prayer groups; Movies;
Shopping trips; Social/Cultural gatherings;
Talking books; Exercise groups.

Sunnyfield Nursing Home Inc
61 Maplewood Ave, Cranbury, NJ, 08521
(609) 395-0641
Admin George E Conley. *Medical Dir/Dir of
Nursing* Elizabeth Decrease RN DON.
Licensure Intermediate care. *Beds* ICF 28.
Certified Medicaid.
Owner Proprietary Corp.
Admissions Requirements Minimum age 18;
Medical examination; Physician's request.
Staff Physicians 3 (pt); RNs 1 (ft), 6 (pt);
LPNs 2 (pt); Nurses aides 6 (ft), 8 (pt);
Recreational therapists 1 (pt); Activities
coordinators 1 (pt); Dietitians 1 (pt).

Facilities Dining room; Activities room;
Crafts room.
Activities Arts & crafts; Cards; Games; Prayer
groups.

CRANFORD

Cranford Hall Nursing Home
600 Lincoln Park E, Cranford, NJ, 07016
(201) 276-7100
Admin Maryanne Lyons. *Medical Dir/Dir of
Nursing* Virginia Quintone MD; Marie Wells
RN DON.
Licensure Skilled care; Intermediate care. *Beds*
120. *Certified* Medicaid.
Owner Proprietary Corp.
Staff Physicians 9 (pt); RNs 9 (ft), 3 (pt);
LPNs 9 (ft), 3 (pt); Nurses aides 40 (ft), 15
(pt); Physical therapists 1 (pt); Reality
therapists 1 (pt); Recreational therapists 1
(pt); Occupational therapists 1 (pt);
Activities coordinators 2 (ft), 2 (pt);
Dietitians 1 (ft); Dentists 1 (pt);
Ophthalmologists 1 (pt); Podiatrists 1 (pt).
Languages French, Spanish, Italian
Facilities Dining room; Activities room;
Crafts room; Laundry room; Barber/Beauty
shop; 5 acres of grounds.
Activities Arts & crafts; Cards; Games;
Reading groups; Prayer groups; Movies;
Shopping trips; Social/Cultural gatherings;
Van with wheelchair lift.

Cranford Health & Extended Care Center
205 Birchwood Ave, Cranford, NJ, 07016
(201) 272-6660
Admin Edward Gorczynski. *Medical Dir/Dir
of Nursing* Dr Elim; Carole Mitchell DON.
Licensure Skilled care. *Beds* SNF 188.
Certified Medicaid; Medicare.
Owner Proprietary Corp.
Admissions Requirements Physician's request.
Staff RNs 18 (ft), 8 (pt); LPNs 12 (ft), 6 (pt);
Orderlies 4 (ft); Nurses aides 45 (ft), 15 (pt);
Recreational therapists 4 (ft); Activities
coordinators 1 (ft); Dietitians 1 (pt).
Facilities Dining room; Physical therapy
room; Activities room; Crafts room; Laundry
room; Barber/Beauty shop; Library.
Activities Arts & crafts; Cards; Games;
Reading groups; Prayer groups; Movies;
Shopping trips; Social/Cultural gatherings.

CRESSKILL

Dunroven Nursing Home
221 County Rd, Cresskill, NJ, 07626
(201) 567-9310
Admin Donald C DeVries. *Medical Dir/Dir of
Nursing* Harry Roselle MD.
Licensure Skilled care. *Beds* SNF 100.
Owner Proprietary Corp.
Admissions Requirements Minimum age 16.
Staff Physicians 1 (pt); RNs 14 (ft); LPNs 18
(ft); Nurses aides 38 (ft); Physical therapists
1 (pt); Occupational therapists 1 (pt); Speech
therapists 1 (pt); Activities coordinators 3
(ft); Dietitians 1 (pt); Ophthalmologists 1
(pt).
Languages German
Facilities Dining room; Physical therapy
room; Activities room; Laundry room;
Barber/Beauty shop.
Activities Arts & crafts; Cards; Games;
Reading groups; Prayer groups; Movies;
Shopping trips; Social/Cultural gatherings.

DEPTFORD

Greenbriar-East Nursing Center
1511 Clements Bridge Rd, Deptford, NJ,
08096
(609) 845-9400
Admin Ruth E Gandek. *Medical Dir/Dir of
Nursing* James G Kehler MD.

Licensure Skilled care; Intermediate care. *Beds*
167. *Certified* Medicaid; Medicare.
Staff Physicians; RNs; LPNs; Orderlies;
Nurses aides; Physical therapists; Speech
therapists; Activities coordinators; Dietitians;
Dentist.
Facilities Dining room; Physical therapy
room; Activities room; Laundry room;
Barber/Beauty shop; Library; TV rooms;
Reading rooms; Lounge.
Activities Arts & crafts; Cards; Games; Prayer
groups; Movies; Social/Cultural gatherings;
Trips.

EAST ORANGE

East Orange Nursing Home*
101 N Grove St, East Orange, NJ, 07017
(201) 672-1700
Admin Joseph Cohen.
Licensure Skilled care; Intermediate care. *Beds*
195. *Certified* Medicaid; Medicare.

Garden State Health Care Center*
140 Park Ave, East Orange, NJ, 07017
(201) 677-1500
Admin Charles Yaker. *Medical Dir/Dir of
Nursing* Pasquale Cumpanile.
Licensure Long-Term care. *Beds* 228.
Staff Physical therapists 1 (pt); Speech
therapists 1 (pt); Dentists 1 (pt);
Ophthalmologists 1 (pt); Podiatrists 1 (pt);
Audiologists 1 (pt); Psychologist 1 (pt).
Facilities Dining room; Physical therapy
room; Activities room; Crafts room; Laundry
room; Barber/Beauty shop.
Activities Arts & crafts; Cards; Games;
Reading groups; Prayer groups; Movies.

EATONTOWN

Eatontown Convalescent Center
139 Grant Ave, Eatontown, NJ, 07724
(201) 542-4700
Admin Nancy Lessard. *Medical Dir/Dir of
Nursing* Roger Quinlan DO; Edith Bonado
RN DON.
Licensure Skilled care; Intermediate care. *Beds*
SNF 108; ICF. *Certified* Medicaid;
Medicare.
Owner Proprietary Corp.
Admissions Requirements Minimum age 16;
Medical examination; Physician's request.
Staff Physicians 1 (ft), 15 (pt); RNs 6 (ft), 3
(pt); LPNs 5 (ft), 4 (pt); Nurses aides 34 (ft),
12 (pt); Recreational therapists 3 (ft);
Activities coordinators 1 (ft); Dietitians 1
(ft).
Facilities Dining room; Activities room;
Crafts room; Laundry room; Barber/Beauty
shop.
Activities Arts & crafts; Cards; Games;
Reading groups; Prayer groups; Movies;
Shopping trips; Social/Cultural gatherings.

EDISON

Birchwood Nursing & Convalescent Center
1350 Inman Ave, Edison, NJ, 08817
(201) 754-7100
Admin Gerald Roth. *Medical Dir/Dir of
Nursing* Amarjit Saini MD; Marian Matlaga
RN DON.
Licensure Skilled care; Intermediate care. *Beds*
84. *Certified* Medicaid; Medicare.
Admissions Requirements Minimum age 18.
Staff Physicians; RNs; LPNs; Orderlies;
Nurses aides; Physical therapists; Reality
therapists; Recreational therapists;
Occupational therapists; Speech therapists;
Activities coordinators; Dietitians; Dentists;
Ophthalmologists; Podiatrists.
Facilities Dining room; Physical therapy
room; Activities room; Crafts room; Laundry
room; Barber/Beauty shop; Library.

Activities Arts & crafts; Cards; Games;
Reading groups; Prayer groups; Movies;
Shopping trips; Social/Cultural gatherings.

Edison Estates Inc
465 Plainfield Ave, Edison, NJ, 08817
(201) 985-1500
Admin Howard A Sukoff.
Licensure Skilled care. *Beds* 348. *Certified*
Medicaid.
Admissions Requirements Minimum age 65;
Medical examination; Physician's request.
Staff Physicians 12 (pt); RNs 30 (ft), 3 (pt);
LPNs 14 (ft), 7 (pt); Nurses aides 108 (ft),
46 (pt); Physical therapists 5 (pt);
Recreational therapists 6 (pt); Occupational
therapists 2 (pt); Speech therapists 1 (pt);
Activities coordinators 1 (ft); Dietitians 3
(ft); Dentists 1 (pt); Podiatrists 1 (pt); Social
workers 2 (ft), 2 (pt).
Facilities Dining room; Physical therapy
room; Activities room; Crafts room; Laundry
room; Barber/Beauty shop; Library.
Activities Arts & crafts; Cards; Games;
Reading groups; Prayer groups; Movies;
Shopping trips; Social/Cultural gatherings.

ELIZABETH

Elizabeth Nursing Home*
1048 Grove St, Elizabeth, NJ, 07202
(201) 354-0002
Admin Zev Fishman.
Licensure Skilled care; Intermediate care. *Beds*
102. *Certified* Medicaid; Medicare.

Plaza Nursing & Convalescent Center
456 Rahway Ave, Elizabeth, NJ, 07202
(201) 354-1300
Admin Nathan Fishman. *Medical Dir/Dir of
Nursing* Robert Solomon MD; Debra
Forman.
Licensure Skilled care; Intermediate care. *Beds*
128. *Certified* Medicaid; Medicare.
Owner Proprietary Corp.
Admissions Requirements Minimum age 60.
Staff Physicians 1 (pt); RNs 4 (ft), 4 (pt);
LPNs 7 (ft), 3 (pt); Nurses aides 18 (ft), 14
(pt); Physical therapists 1 (pt); Recreational
therapists 2 (pt); Activities coordinators 1
(ft); Dietitians 1 (pt); Podiatrists 1 (pt).
Facilities Dining room; Physical therapy
room; Activities room; Chapel; Crafts room;
Laundry room; Barber/Beauty shop; Library;
Patio/Sundeck.
Activities Arts & crafts; Cards; Games;
Reading groups; Prayer groups; Movies;
Shopping trips; Social/Cultural gatherings.

EMERSON

Emerson Convalescent Center
100 Kinderkamack Rd, Emerson, NJ, 07630
(201) 265-3700
Admin Nathan Friedman. *Medical Dir/Dir of
Nursing* J A Perez MD.
Licensure Skilled care; Intermediate care. *Beds*
150. *Certified* Medicaid.
Admissions Requirements Minimum age 50;
Medical examination.
Staff RNs 12 (ft), 4 (pt); LPNs 8 (ft), 7 (pt);
Orderlies 1 (ft); Nurses aides 50 (ft), 7 (pt);
Physical therapists 2 (pt); Recreational
therapists 1 (ft); Occupational therapists 1
(pt); Speech therapists 1 (pt); Activities
coordinators 1 (ft), 4 (pt); Dietitians 1 (pt);
Dentists 1 (pt); Ophthalmologists 1 (pt);
Podiatrists 1 (pt).
Facilities Dining room; Physical therapy
room; Activities room; Crafts room; Laundry
room; Barber/Beauty shop.
Activities Arts & crafts; Cards; Games;
Reading groups; Prayer groups; Movies;
Shopping trips; Social/Cultural gatherings;
Current events; Bowling; Ceramics.

ENGLEWOOD

Inglemoor Nursing Home
333 Grand Ave, Englewood, NJ, 07631
(201) 568-0900
Admin Doris Nelbart. *Medical Dir/Dir of Nursing* Dr Robert Nutt; Rosemary Fernekees DON.
Licensure Skilled care; Intermediate care. *Beds* 62.
Owner Privately owned.
Staff RNs; LPNs; Nurses aides; Physical therapists; Ophthalmologists.
Languages Spanish, Greek, Italian, Hebrew, Yiddish
Facilities Dining room; Physical therapy room; Activities room; Chapel; Crafts room; Laundry room; Barber/Beauty shop; Library.
Activities Arts & crafts; Cards; Games; Reading groups; Prayer groups; Movies; Social/Cultural gatherings.

ENGLEWOOD CLIFFS

Cliff House*
633 Palisade Ave, Englewood Cliffs, NJ, 07632
(201) 567-2626
Admin Richard Heller.
Licensure Skilled care; Intermediate care. *Beds* 36. *Certified* Medicaid; Medicare.

ENGLISHTOWN

Pine Brook Care Center Inc
PO Box 448, Pension Rd, Englishtown, NJ, 07726
(201) 446-3600
Admin Gerald Friederwitzer & Leslie Fisher. *Medical Dir/Dir of Nursing* Dr Rivero; Felicia Brozowski RN.
Licensure Skilled care; Intermediate care; Sheltered care. *Beds* SNF 120; ICF; Sheltered care 60. *Certified* Medicaid; Medicare.
Owner Proprietary Corp.
Admissions Requirements Medical examination.
Staff Physicians 5 (pt); RNs 3 (ft), 6 (pt); LPNs 2 (ft), 5 (pt); Orderlies 2 (ft); Nurses aides 21 (ft), 20 (pt); Activities coordinators 1 (ft), 2 (pt); Dietitians 1 (pt).
Facilities Dining room; Physical therapy room; Activities room; Chapel; Crafts room; Laundry room; Barber/Beauty shop; Library; TV room w/42" projection screen & VCR; Recreation room w/42" projector screen & TV.
Activities Arts & crafts; Cards; Games; Reading groups; Prayer groups; Movies; Shopping trips; Social/Cultural gatherings.

FAIR LAWN

Fair Lawn Manor Nursing Home*
12-15 Saddle River Rd, Fair Lawn, NJ, 07410
(201) 797-9522
Admin B Thelea Fudim.
Licensure Intermediate care. *Beds* 157.

FAR HILLS

Kate Macy Ladd Convalescent Home*
Peapack Rd, Far Hills, NJ, 07931
(201) 234-0860
Admin Barry L Mills.
Licensure Long-Term care. *Beds* 45.

FLORENCE

Florence Nursing Home*
Front & Iron Sts, Florence, NJ, 08518
(609) 499-3224
Admin Paul Rosenthal.
Licensure Long-Term care. *Beds* 15.

FLORHAM PARK

Cheshire Home*
9 Ridgedale Ave, Florham Park, NJ, 07932
(201) 966-1232
Admin Sharon Logan Gronet. *Medical Dir/Dir of Nursing* Charles I Nadel MD.
Licensure Skilled care. *Beds* 35. *Certified* Medicaid.
Owner Nonprofit Corp.
Admissions Requirements Minimum age 18; Medical examination.
Staff Physicians 2 (pt); RNs 3 (ft), 2 (pt); LPNs 2 (ft), 1 (pt); Nurses aides 16 (ft), 5 (pt); Recreational therapists 1 (ft); Activities coordinators 1 (ft); Dietitians 1 (ft), 1 (pt).
Facilities Dining room; Activities room; Crafts room; Laundry room; Library.
Activities Arts & crafts; Games; Movies; Shopping trips; Social/Cultural gatherings.

FRANKLIN PARK

Franklin Convalescent Center
3371 Rte 27, Franklin Park, NJ, 08823
(201) 821-8000
Admin Mary Ann McCarty. *Medical Dir/Dir of Nursing* Dr Lee; Pat Buckelew.
Licensure Skilled care. *Beds* SNF 180; ICF. *Certified* Medicaid; Medicare.
Owner Privately owned.
Admissions Requirements Medical examination.
Staff Physicians; RNs; LPNs; Nurses aides; Physical therapists; Recreational therapists; Occupational therapists; Speech therapists; Activities coordinators; Dietitians; Dentists; Ophthalmologists; Podiatrists.
Facilities Dining room; Physical therapy room; Activities room; Crafts room; Laundry room; Barber/Beauty shop; Library.
Activities Arts & crafts; Cards; Games; Reading groups; Prayer groups; Movies; Shopping trips; Social/Cultural gatherings.

FREEHOLD

Applewood Manor
Rte 537, 689 W Main St, Freehold, NJ, 07728
(201) 431-5200
Admin Michael A DelSordo. *Medical Dir/Dir of Nursing* Dr Howard Schoenfeld; M Martucci DON.
Licensure Skilled care; Intermediate care. *Beds* 120. *Certified* Medicaid; Medicare.
Owner Nonprofit Corp.
Admissions Requirements Minimum age 16.
Staff Physicians; RNs; LPNs; Orderlies; Nurses aides; Physical therapists; Recreational therapists; Occupational therapists; Speech therapists; Activities coordinators; Dietitians; Ophthalmologists; Podiatrists; Dentist.
Facilities Dining room; Physical therapy room; Activities room; Crafts room; Laundry room; Barber/Beauty shop; Library.

John L Montgomery Medical Home
Dutch Lane Rd, Freehold, NJ, 07728
(201) 431-7420
Admin Dora Z Kirby. *Medical Dir/Dir of Nursing* Ross E McRonald MD; Marilyn Schlentz RN DON.
Licensure Skilled care. *Beds* 233. *Certified* Medicaid; Medicare.
Owner Publicly owned.
Admissions Requirements Minimum age 18; Medical examination; Physician's request.
Staff Physicians 2 (pt); RNs 15 (ft), 4 (pt); LPNs 7 (ft), 4 (pt); Nurses aides 108 (ft), 7 (pt); Recreational therapists 5 (ft), 6 (pt); Activities coordinators 2 (ft); Dietitians 1 (ft), 1 (pt).
Facilities Dining room; Physical therapy room; Activities room; Chapel; Crafts room; Laundry room; Barber/Beauty shop; Library; Community room.

Activities Arts & crafts; Cards; Games; Reading groups; Prayer groups; Movies; Shopping trips; Social/Cultural gatherings; Ceramics; Reality orientation; Cooking classes.

Springview Nursing Home
3419 US Hwy 9, Freehold, NJ, 07728
(201) 780-0660
Admin Benjamin Farber. *Medical Dir/Dir of Nursing* Dr Schottlander; Margaret Koury.
Licensure Skilled care. *Beds* 182. *Certified* Medicaid.
Owner Privately owned.
Admissions Requirements Minimum age 50; Medical examination.
Staff Physicians; RNs; LPNs; Orderlies; Nurses aides; Physical therapists; Reality therapists; Recreational therapists; Occupational therapists; Speech therapists; Activities coordinators; Dietitians; Dentists; Ophthalmologists; Podiatrists.
Facilities Dining room; Physical therapy room; Activities room; Crafts room; Laundry room; Barber/Beauty shop; Library.
Activities Arts & crafts; Cards; Games; Reading groups; Prayer groups; Movies; Shopping trips; Social/Cultural gatherings.

FRENCHTOWN

Valley View Manor Inc
Everittstown Rd, Frenchtown, NJ, 08825
(201) 996-4112
Admin Lester Krosskove.
Licensure Intermediate care. *Beds* 45.
Facilities Dining room; Activities room; Laundry room; Barber/Beauty shop.
Activities Arts & crafts; Games; Prayer groups; Social/Cultural gatherings; Church services.

GIBBSBORO

Lakewood of Voorhees
Laurel Oak Rd, Gibbsboro, NJ, 08026
(609) 346-1200
Admin Diane Donnelly. *Medical Dir/Dir of Nursing* J Thornboro DON.
Licensure Skilled care; Intermediate care. *Beds* SNF 60; ICF 180. *Certified* Medicaid; Medicare.
Owner Proprietary Corp (HBA Management Inc).
Staff Physicians 4 (pt); RNs 8 (ft), 4 (pt); LPNs 12 (ft), 5 (pt); Nurses aides 90 (ft), 10 (pt); Physical therapists 1 (ft); Recreational therapists 4 (ft); Occupational therapists 1 (ft); Speech therapists 1 (ft); Activities coordinators 1 (ft); Dietitians 1 (ft); Dentists 1 (pt); Ophthalmologists 1 (pt); Podiatrists 1 (pt).
Languages Tagalog
Facilities Dining room; Physical therapy room; Activities room; Crafts room; Barber/Beauty shop.
Activities Arts & crafts; Cards; Games; Reading groups; Prayer groups; Movies; Shopping trips; Social/Cultural gatherings.

GLEN GARDNER

Hunterdon Hills Nursing Home
R D 1 Box 265 "H", Hill Rd, Glen Gardner, NJ, 08826
(201) 537-2717
Admin Barry Scheier. *Medical Dir/Dir of Nursing* John McGowan.
Licensure Skilled care; Intermediate care. *Beds* 32. *Certified* Medicaid.
Owner Proprietary Corp.
Admissions Requirements Physician's request.
Staff RNs 4 (ft); LPNs 1 (ft); Nurses aides 10 (ft); Physical therapists 1 (pt); Reality therapists 1 (pt); Recreational therapists 1 (pt); Activities coordinators 1 (ft); Dietitians 1 (pt).

Facilities Dining room; Activities room; Laundry room.
Activities Arts & crafts; Cards; Games; Reading groups; Prayer groups; Movies; Shopping trips.

GREENBROOK

Greenbrook Nursing Home*
303 Rock Ave, Greenbrook, NJ, 08812
(201) 968-5500
Admin Herbert Heflich.
Licensure Skilled care; Intermediate care. *Beds* 180. *Certified* Medicaid; Medicare.

GUTTENBERG

Palisade Nursing Home
6819 Boulevard E, Guttenberg, NJ, 07093
(201) 868-3600
Admin Davis Gross. *Medical Dir/Dir of Nursing* Joseph Weisgras MD; Jeanette Bruen RN DON.
Licensure Skilled care. *Beds* SNF 106; Extra bed program 2. *Certified* Medicaid.
Owner Proprietary Corp.
Staff Physicians 2 (ft); RNs 7 (ft), 4 (pt); LPNs 3 (ft); Nurses aides 30 (ft); Physical therapists 1 (ft), 1 (pt); Reality therapists 1 (pt); Recreational therapists 2 (ft), 2 (pt); Occupational therapists 1 (pt); Speech therapists 1 (pt); Activities coordinators 1 (ft); Dietitians 1 (ft); Dentists 1 (pt); Ophthalmologists 1 (pt); Podiatrists 1 (pt).
Languages Spanish, Yiddish, Hebrew
Facilities Dining room; Physical therapy room; Activities room; Chapel; Crafts room; Laundry room; Barber/Beauty shop; Library.
Activities Arts & crafts; Cards; Games; Reading groups; Prayer groups; Movies; Shopping trips; Social/Cultural gatherings.

HACKENSACK

Wellington Hall Nursing Home
301 Union St, Hackensack, NJ, 07601
(201) 487-4900
Admin Bruce H London. *Medical Dir/Dir of Nursing* Arthur Chaney Jr MD; Rosemary Raleigh RN.
Licensure Skilled care; Intermediate care. *Beds* 120. *Certified* Medicaid; Medicare.
Owner Privately owned.
Admissions Requirements Physician's request.
Staff RNs 4 (ft), 3 (pt); LPNs 3 (ft), 1 (pt); Orderlies 1 (ft); Nurses aides 26 (ft), 20 (pt); Physical therapists 1 (ft); Occupational therapists 1 (pt); Speech therapists 1 (pt); Activities coordinators 2 (ft); Dietitians 1 (pt); Dentists 1 (pt); Ophthalmologists 1 (pt).
Facilities Dining room; Physical therapy room; Activities room; Chapel; Crafts room; Laundry room; Barber/Beauty shop; Library.
Activities Arts & crafts; Cards; Games; Reading groups; Prayer groups; Movies; Shopping trips; Social/Cultural gatherings.

HADDONFIELD

Haddonfield Presbyterian Home of Southern New Jersey
132 Warwick Rd, Haddonfield, NJ, 08033
(609) 429-5500
Admin Elizabeth A Gutekunst. *Medical Dir/Dir of Nursing* Dr James Sobel; Judith Slimm RN.
Licensure Intermediate care; Residential care. *Beds* ICF 6; Residential 59.
Owner Nonprofit organization/foundation.
Admissions Requirements Minimum age 62; Medical examination.
Staff Physicians 2 (pt); RNs 1 (ft), 2 (pt); LPNs 6 (pt); Nurses aides 3 (ft), 3 (pt); Activities coordinators 1 (pt); Dietitians 1 (pt); Dentists 1 (pt).
Affiliation Presbyterian

Facilities Dining room; Activities room; Chapel; Crafts room; Laundry room; Barber/Beauty shop; Library; Screened porches; Gazebo.
Activities Arts & crafts; Cards; Games; Reading groups; Prayer groups; Movies; Shopping trips; Social/Cultural gatherings.

HASKELL

Passaic Care Center
25 5th Ave, Haskell, NJ, 07472
(201) 839-6000
Admin Elliott Wiener LNHA. *Medical Dir/Dir of Nursing* Dr Bernard Schwam; Elaine Shapiro.
Licensure Skilled care; Intermediate care. *Beds* 201. *Certified* Medicaid.
Owner Proprietary Corp.
Staff Physicians 4 (ft); RNs 26 (ft), 4 (pt); LPNs 13 (ft), 5 (pt); Nurses aides 40 (ft), 12 (pt); Physical therapists 2 (ft); Recreational therapists 4 (ft); Speech therapists 1 (ft); Activities coordinators 1 (ft); Dietitians 1 (ft); Dentists 1 (ft); Ophthalmologists 1 (ft); Podiatrists 1 (ft).
Languages Spanish, French
Facilities Dining room; Physical therapy room; Activities room; Crafts room; Laundry room; Barber/Beauty shop.
Activities Arts & crafts; Cards; Games; Reading groups; Prayer groups; Movies; Shopping trips; Social/Cultural gatherings.

HAZLET

Arnold Walter Nursing Home*
622 S Laurel Ave, Hazlet, NJ, 07730
(201) 787-6300
Admin Benzion Schachter.
Licensure Skilled care; Intermediate care. *Beds* 132. *Certified* Medicaid; Medicare.

Hazlet Manor Care Center*
3325 Hwy 35, Hazlet, NJ, 07730
(201) 264-5800
Admin Hershel Gottlieb.
Licensure Skilled care; Intermediate care; Residential care. *Beds* ICF 184; Residential 12. *Certified* Medicaid; Medicare.

HIGHTSTOWN

Applegarth Care Center
PO Box 1328, Applegarth Rd, Hightstown, NJ, 08520
(609) 448-7036
Admin Harry C Veale. *Medical Dir/Dir of Nursing* Jeannette McCrory RN.
Licensure Intermediate care. *Beds* ICF 172. *Certified* Medicaid.
Owner Proprietary Corp.
Staff Physicians 10 (pt); RNs 15 (ft), 10 (pt); LPNs 10 (ft), 10 (pt); Orderlies 1 (ft); Nurses aides 30 (ft), 20 (pt); Physical therapists 1 (pt); Recreational therapists 1 (ft), 1 (pt); Activities coordinators 1 (ft); Dietitians 1 (pt); Ophthalmologists 1 (pt).
Facilities Dining room; Activities room; Chapel; Crafts room; Laundry room; Barber/Beauty shop; 4 Resident lounges; Cocktail lounge.
Activities Arts & crafts; Cards; Games; Reading groups; Prayer groups; Movies; Shopping trips; Social/Cultural gatherings.

Sunlawn Nursing Home*
576 Main St, Hightstown, NJ, 08520
(609) 448-0528
Admin Joseph Singer.
Licensure Long-Term care. *Beds* 30.

HOLMDEL

Garden State Manor Nursing Home
16 Van Brackle Rd, Holmdel, NJ, 07733
(201) 264-3548
Admin Helen Dimitrow MD. *Medical Dir/Dir of Nursing* Dr Elias Lehaf.
Licensure Skilled care; Intermediate care. *Beds* SNF 2; ICF 25. *Certified* Medicaid.
Owner Proprietary Corp.
Admissions Requirements Physician's request.
Staff Physicians 1 (pt); RNs 1 (ft), 2 (pt); LPNs 2 (ft), 2 (pt); Nurses aides 17 (ft), 3 (pt); Activities coordinators 1 (pt); Dietitians 1 (pt); Ophthalmologists 1 (pt).
Facilities Dining room; Activities room.
Activities Arts & crafts; Games.

Holmdel Nursing Home
184 Hwy 34, Holmdel, NJ, 07733
(201) 946-4200
Admin Valerie A Kennedy.
Licensure Skilled care. *Beds* SNF 41. *Certified* Medicaid; Medicare.
Owner Privately owned.
Admissions Requirements Minimum age 21.
Staff Physicians; RNs; LPNs; Orderlies; Nurses aides; Physical therapists; Reality therapists; Recreational therapists; Occupational therapists; Speech therapists; Activities coordinators; Dietitians; Dentists; Ophthalmologists; Podiatrists.
Facilities Dining room.
Activities Arts & crafts; Cards; Games; Reading groups; Prayer groups; Movies; Shopping trips; Social/Cultural gatherings; Many other parties.

HOPE

Forest Manor Health Care Center
PO Box 283, State Park Rd, Hope, NJ, 07844
(201) 459-4128
Admin I Joel Foreman. *Medical Dir/Dir of Nursing* M Reddy MD.
Licensure Skilled care; Intermediate care; Residential; Respite. *Beds* SNF 42. *Certified* Medicare.
Owner Proprietary Corp.
Admissions Requirements Minimum age 16.
Staff Physicians 1 (pt); RNs 5 (ft), 2 (pt); LPNs 1 (ft), 3 (pt); Nurses aides 11 (ft), 9 (pt); Physical therapists 1 (pt); Recreational therapists 1 (pt); Occupational therapists 1 (pt); Speech therapists 1 (pt); Activities coordinators 1 (pt), 1 (pt); Dietitians 1 (pt); Ophthalmologists 1 (pt).
Facilities Dining room; Activities room; Laundry room; Barber/Beauty shop; Library.
Activities Arts & crafts; Cards; Games; Reading groups; Movies; Shopping trips; Social/Cultural gatherings; Church service.

JACKSON

Bartley Manor Convalescent Center
20 Bartley Rd, Jackson, NJ, 08527
(201) 370-4700
Admin Patricia de Muro. *Medical Dir/Dir of Nursing* Dr Anthony Christiano.
Licensure Skilled care; Intermediate care. *Beds* 120. *Certified* Medicaid.
Owner Proprietary Corp.
Admissions Requirements Must require 24-hour nursing supervision.
Staff Physicians 413B; LPNs 413E; Occupational therapists; Speech therapists; Activities coordinators 3 (ft).
Languages Italian
Facilities Dining room; Physical therapy room; Activities room; Crafts room; Laundry room; Barber/Beauty shop; Library; Day room on each wing.
Activities Arts & crafts; Cards; Games; Reading groups; Prayer groups; Movies; Shopping trips; Social/Cultural gatherings; Adaptive cooking; Resident council.

JERSEY CITY

Liberty House Nursing Home*
620 Montgomery St, Jersey City, NJ, 07302
(201) 435-0033
Admin Michael Katz. *Medical Dir/Dir of
Nursing* J John DeGoia.
Licensure Skilled care; Intermediate care. *Beds*
180. *Certified* Medicaid; Medicare.
Staff Physicians; RNs; LPNs; Orderlies;
Nurses aides; Physical therapists;
Recreational therapists; Occupational
therapists; Speech therapists; Activities
coordinators; Dietitians; Dentists;
Ophthalmologists; Podiatrists.
Facilities Dining room; Physical therapy
room; Activities room; Crafts room; Laundry
room.
Activities Arts & crafts; Cards; Games;
Reading groups; Prayer groups; Movies;
Social/Cultural gatherings.

Berthold S Pollak Hospital
100 Clifton Pl, Jersey City, NJ, 07304
(201) 432-1000
Admin Dorothea Stovekin. *Medical Dir/Dir of
Nursing* Francis T Molinari MD; Maria
Lapid RN DON.
Licensure Skilled care. *Beds* SNF 460.
Certified Medicaid.
Owner Publicly owned.
Admissions Requirements Minimum age 18;
Physician's request.
Staff Physicians 6 (ft), 10 (pt); RNs 45 (ft), 5
(pt); LPNs 44 (ft), 3 (pt); Orderlies 156 (ft);
Recreational therapists 8 (ft), 1 (pt);
Activities coordinators 1 (ft); Dietitians 3
(ft).
Facilities Dining room; Physical therapy
room; Activities room; Chapel; Crafts room;
Laundry room; Barber/Beauty shop; Library.
Activities Arts & crafts; Cards; Games;
Movies; Shopping trips; Social/Cultural
gatherings; Bus trips; Bowling; Theater;
Sport events.

KEANSBURG

Beachview Rest ICF*
32 Laurel Ave, Keansburg, NJ, 07734
(201) 787-8100
Admin Joseph Cappadona.
Licensure Skilled care; Intermediate care. *Beds*
119. *Certified* Medicaid; Medicare.

KEY POINT

Cliffside Health Care Center
PO Box 54, Key Point, NJ, 07735
(201) 566-8422
Admin Thomas Armour. *Medical Dir/Dir of
Nursing* Dr H O Wiley.
Licensure Intermediate care. *Beds* 109.
Certified Medicaid.
Admissions Requirements Medical
examination.
Staff RNs 3 (ft), 3 (pt); LPNs 6 (ft), 4 (pt);
Orderlies 1 (ft); Nurses aides 27 (ft), 20 (pt);
Recreational therapists 1 (ft), 2 (pt);
Activities coordinators 1 (ft).
Facilities Dining room; Physical therapy
room; Activities room; Crafts room; Barber/
Beauty shop.
Activities Arts & crafts; Cards; Games;
Reading groups; Prayer groups; Movies;
Shopping trips; Social/Cultural gatherings.

LAKEWOOD

King Manor Nursing Home
485 River Ave, Lakewood, NJ, 08701
(201) 774-3500
Admin Laverne Kennedy.
Beds 120.

Leisure Chateau Care Center
962 River Ave, Lakewood, NJ, 08701
(201) 370-8600
Admin Elizabeth E Miller. *Medical Dir/Dir of
Nursing* Dr Roseff; Jean Laverty DON.
Licensure Skilled care; Intermediate care. *Beds*
SNF 242; ICF. *Certified* Medicaid;
Medicare.
Owner Proprietary Corp.
Staff RNs; LPNs; Orderlies; Nurses aides;
Physical therapists; Recreational therapists;
Speech therapists; Activities coordinators;
Dietitians.
Facilities Dining room; Physical therapy
room; Activities room; Crafts room; Laundry
room; Barber/Beauty shop.
Activities Arts & crafts; Cards; Games;
Reading groups; Prayer groups; Movies;
Shopping trips; Social/Cultural gatherings.

Medicenter of Lakewood
685 River Ave, Lakewood, NJ, 08701
(201) 364-8300
Admin William Calvin. *Medical Dir/Dir of
Nursing* Dr James Meehan; Mrs
Henningson.
Licensure Skilled care; Intermediate care. *Beds*
245.
Owner Proprietary Corp (HBA Management
Inc).
Admissions Requirements Minimum age 16.
Staff Physicians 1 (pt); RNs 15 (ft), 3 (pt);
LPNs 15 (ft), 5 (pt); Orderlies 2 (ft); Nurses
aides 63 (ft), 5 (pt); Physical therapists 2 (ft);
Recreational therapists 4 (ft); Occupational
therapists 1 (ft); Speech therapists 1 (ft);
Activities coordinators 1 (ft); Dietitians 1
(pt); Dentists 1 (pt); Ophthalmologists 1 (pt);
Podiatrists 1 (pt).
Facilities Dining room; Physical therapy
room; Activities room; Crafts room; Laundry
room; Barber/Beauty shop; Rolling library.
Activities Arts & crafts; Cards; Games;
Reading groups; Prayer groups; Movies;
Shopping trips; Social/Cultural gatherings.

Newmans Lakewood Nursing Home*
Monmouth Ave & 7th St, Lakewood, NJ,
08701
(201) 363-2659
Admin Felice Newman. *Medical Dir/Dir of
Nursing* Dr Harish Chander.
Licensure Intermediate care. *Beds* 44.
Certified Medicaid.
Admissions Requirements Minimum age 35;
Medical examination; Physician's request.
Staff Physicians 4 (pt); RNs 3 (ft); LPNs 3
(pt); Orderlies 2 (pt); Physical therapists 1
(pt); Reality therapists 1 (ft); Recreational
therapists 1 (ft), 1 (pt); Occupational
therapists 1 (pt); Speech therapists 1 (pt);
Activities coordinators 1 (ft); Dietitians 1
(pt); Dentists 1 (pt); Ophthalmologists 1 (pt);
Podiatrists 1 (pt); Audiologists 1 (pt).
Facilities Dining room; Activities room;
Laundry room.
Activities Arts & crafts; Cards; Games;
Reading groups; Prayer groups; Movies;
Shopping trips.

Ocean Convalescent Center
901 Monmouth Ave, Lakewood, NJ, 08701
(201) 363-0151
Admin Andrew Shawn. *Medical Dir/Dir of
Nursing* Dr Pineles; Mrs Clancy DON.
Licensure Skilled care. *Beds* SNF 61. *Certified*
Medicaid.
Owner Proprietary Corp.
Admissions Requirements Minimum age 50.
Staff RNs 5 (ft); LPNs 2 (ft); Nurses aides 22
(ft); Recreational therapists 1 (ft), 1 (pt).
Facilities Dining room; Activities room;
Laundry room; Barber/Beauty shop.
Activities Arts & crafts; Games; Reading
groups; Prayer groups; Movies; Social/
Cultural gatherings.

Pineland Nursing Home*
Squankum Rd, Lakewood, NJ, 08701
(201) 363-9507
Admin Lucie Zane.
Licensure Skilled care; Intermediate care. *Beds*
18. *Certified* Medicaid.

Summit Convalescent Home*
285 River Ave, Lakewood, NJ, 08701
(201) 363-0400
Admin Anthony Pagliaro.
Licensure Skilled care; Intermediate care. *Beds*
180. *Certified* Medicaid; Medicare.

LAWRENCEVILLE

Lawrenceville Nursing Home
PO Box 6338, 112 Franklin Corner Rd,
Lawrenceville, NJ, 08648
(609) 896-1494
Admin Frank Puzio. *Medical Dir/Dir of
Nursing* Dr S Goldsmith.
Licensure Skilled care. *Beds* SNF 100.
Certified Medicaid; Medicare.
Owner Proprietary Corp.
Staff Physicians 1 (pt); RNs 12 (ft), 4 (pt);
LPNs 4 (ft); Orderlies 2 (ft); Nurses aides 36
(ft), 6 (pt); Physical therapists 1 (pt); Reality
therapists 1 (ft); Recreational therapists 1
(ft); Occupational therapists 1 (pt); Speech
therapists 1 (pt); Activities coordinators 1
(ft); Dietitians 1 (pt); Dentists 1 (pt);
Ophthalmologists 1 (pt); Podiatrists 1 (pt);
Dentist 1 (pt).
Facilities Dining room; Physical therapy
room; Activities room; Chapel; Crafts room;
Laundry room; Barber/Beauty shop; Library.
Activities Arts & crafts; Cards; Games;
Reading groups; Prayer groups; Movies;
Shopping trips; Social/Cultural gatherings.

LINCOLN PARK

Lincoln Park Intermediate Care Center*
499 Pinebrook Rd, Lincoln Park, NJ, 07035
(201) 696-3300
Admin Barbara Ackerman. *Medical Dir/Dir of
Nursing* Pavle Topalovic MD.
Licensure Skilled care; Intermediate care. *Beds*
547. *Certified* Medicaid.
Admissions Requirements Minimum age 21;
Medical examination.
Facilities Dining room; Physical therapy
room; Activities room; Chapel; Crafts room;
Laundry room; Barber/Beauty shop; Library.
Activities Arts & crafts; Cards; Games;
Reading groups; Prayer groups; Movies;
Shopping trips; Social/Cultural gatherings.

Lincoln Park Nursing & Convalescent Home*
521 Pinebrook Rd, Lincoln Park, NJ, 07035
(201) 696-3300
Admin Karen Scienski. *Medical Dir/Dir of
Nursing* Paule Topalovic MD.
Licensure Skilled care. *Beds* 159. *Certified*
Medicaid; Medicare.
Admissions Requirements Medical
examination; Physician's request.
Facilities Dining room; Physical therapy
room; Activities room; Chapel; Crafts room;
Laundry room; Barber/Beauty shop; Library.
Activities Arts & crafts; Games; Reading
groups; Prayer groups; Movies; Shopping
trips; Social/Cultural gatherings.

LINWOOD

Linwood Convalescent Center*
New Rd & Central Ave, Linwood, NJ, 08221
(609) 927-6131
Admin Gary Hand.
Licensure Skilled care; Intermediate care. *Beds*
154. *Certified* Medicaid; Medicare.

LIVINGSTON

Inglemoor West Nursing Home
311 S Livingston Ave, Livingston, NJ, 07039
(201) 994-0221
Admin Georgia S Eitzen RN. *Medical Dir/Dir of Nursing* Dr George Kline Jr MD; Eveline B Hirsch RN.
Licensure Skilled care; Intermediate care. *Beds* 120. *Certified* Medicaid; Medicare.
Owner Proprietary Corp.
Admissions Requirements Physician's request.
Staff RNs 15 (ft), 15 (pt); Nurses aides 41 (ft), 9 (pt); Physical therapists 1 (pt); Occupational therapists 1 (pt); Speech therapists 1 (ft); Activities coordinators 2 (ft); Dietitians 1 (ft); Dentists 1 (pt); Ophthalmologists 1 (pt); Podiatrists 1 (pt).
Facilities Dining room; Physical therapy room; Activities room; Crafts room; Laundry room; Barber/Beauty shop; Library; Diet kitchen.
Activities Arts & crafts; Cards; Games; Reading groups; Prayer groups; Shopping trips; Social/Cultural gatherings; Lunches/dinners.

LONG BRANCH

Monmouth Convalescent Center
229 Bath Ave, Long Branch, NJ, 07740
(201) 229-4300
Admin Jonathan Eigen. *Medical Dir/Dir of Nursing* Dr A Mari; Alleen Jo Williams.
Licensure Skilled care. *Beds* 113. *Certified* Medicaid.
Owner Privately owned.
Admissions Requirements Medical examination.
Staff Physicians 15 (pt); RNs 4 (ft), 8 (pt); LPNs 6 (ft); Orderlies 2 (ft); Nurses aides 18 (ft), 27 (pt); Physical therapists 1 (pt); Recreational therapists 1 (ft); Occupational therapists 1 (pt); Speech therapists 1 (pt); Activities coordinators 1 (ft).
Languages Spanish
Facilities Dining room; Physical therapy room; Activities room; Chapel; Crafts room; Laundry room; Barber/Beauty shop.
Activities Arts & crafts; Cards; Games; Reading groups; Prayer groups; Movies.

Westwood Hall Hebrew Home
281 Bath Ave, Long Branch, NJ, 07740
(201) 222-5277
Admin Joanne E Escovar. *Medical Dir/Dir of Nursing* Dorothy M Sleifer RN.
Licensure Skilled care; Intermediate care. *Beds* SNF 84; ICF. *Certified* Medicaid; Medicare.
Owner Nonprofit Corp.
Admissions Requirements Minimum age 55-60; Physician's request.
Staff RNs 3 (ft), 6 (pt); LPNs 6 (ft), 2 (pt); Nurses aides 35 (ft), 7 (pt); Recreational therapists 1 (ft), 2 (pt); Dietitians 1 (pt).
Affiliation Jewish
Facilities Physical therapy room; Activities room; Laundry room; Barber/Beauty shop.
Activities Arts & crafts; Cards; Games; Reading groups; Prayer groups; Movies; Social/Cultural gatherings.

Witmer House
75 Cooper Ave, Long Branch, NJ, 07753
(201) 229-4352
Admin Mary Washington; Thomas Armour. *Medical Dir/Dir of Nursing* Dr Herman Wiley; Brenda Hodgkiss RN.
Licensure Intermediate care. *Beds* ICF 80; RHCF 34. *Certified* Medicaid.
Owner Proprietary Corp.
Admissions Requirements Medical examination.
Staff Physicians 1 (pt); RNs 3 (ft), 3 (pt); LPNs 1 (ft), 4 (pt); Orderlies 5 (ft), 4 (pt); Nurses aides 8 (ft), 6 (pt); Activities coordinators 1 (ft), 1 (pt); Dietitians 1 (pt).

Languages English, Spanish, Tagalog
Facilities Dining room; Activities room; Laundry room; Barber/Beauty shop.
Activities Arts & crafts; Cards; Games; Reading groups; Prayer groups; Movies; Shopping trips; Social/Cultural gatherings.

MADISON

Pine Acres Nursing Home
51 Madison Ave, Madison, NJ, 07940
(201) 377-2125
Admin Patricia Ledwith.
Licensure Skilled care; Intermediate care. *Beds* 102. *Certified* Medicaid; Medicare.

Royal Oaks*
300 Madison Ave, Madison, NJ, 07940
(201) 377-9762
Admin John Flemming.
Licensure Long-Term care. *Beds* 31.

MANASQUAN

Sunnyside Nursing Home & Convalescent Home
Ramshorn Dr & Lakewood Rd, Manasquan, NJ, 08736
(201) 528-9311
Admin Joseph Singer. *Medical Dir/Dir of Nursing* Colleen Kollogy; RN.
Licensure Skilled care; PCF. *Beds* SNF 45; PCF IV 12.
Owner Proprietary Corp.
Admissions Requirements Medical examination; Physician's request.
Staff RNs 3 (ft), 4 (pt); LPNs 1 (ft), 2 (pt); Nurses aides 20 (ft), 5 (pt); Recreational therapists 1 (ft); Activities coordinators 1 (ft); Dietitians 1 (pt).
Facilities Dining room; Activities room; Barber/Beauty shop; Library.
Activities Arts & crafts; Cards; Games; Reading groups; Prayer groups; Movies; Shopping trips; Social/Cultural gatherings.

MAPLE SHADE

Maple Hill Convalescent Center*
Rte 38 & Mill Rd, Maple Shade, NJ, 08052
(609) 779-1500
Admin Jeffrey Schwartz.
Licensure Skilled care; Intermediate care. *Beds* 162. *Certified* Medicaid; Medicare.

Pinewood Acres Inc
794 N Forklanding Rd, Maple Shade, NJ, 08052
(609) 779-9333
Admin Chaim I Teitelbaum. *Medical Dir/Dir of Nursing* Robert Warden DO; Bernadette Toner RN DON.
Licensure Skilled care. *Beds* 124. *Certified* Medicaid; Medicare.
Owner Proprietary Corp.
Admissions Requirements Medical examination; Physician's request.
Staff Physicians 4 (ft); RNs 6 (ft), 2 (pt); LPNs 9 (ft), 3 (pt); Physical therapists 1 (ft), 1 (pt); Recreational therapists 3 (ft); Occupational therapists 1 (pt); Speech therapists 1 (pt); Dietitians 1 (pt); Ophthalmologists 1 (pt); Podiatrists 1 (pt).
Facilities Dining room; Physical therapy room; Activities room; Laundry room; Barber/Beauty shop.
Activities Arts & crafts; Cards; Games; Reading groups; Prayer groups; Movies; Social/Cultural gatherings.

MARLTON

Care Inn of Voorhees*
Kresson & Evesham Rds, Marlton, NJ, 08053
(609) 424-1222
Admin Craig Donaghy.

Licensure Skilled care; Intermediate care. *Beds* 89. *Certified* Medicaid; Medicare.

MATAWAN

Emery Manor Nursing Home
4 Highway 34, Matawan, NJ, 07747
(201) 566-6400
Admin Barbara A Fyfe. *Medical Dir/Dir of Nursing* Dr A Kubal; Ms E Weigel DON.
Licensure Skilled care. *Beds* SNF 100. *Certified* Medicaid; Medicare.
Owner Proprietary Corp.
Staff Recreational therapists 1 (ft), 3 (pt); Activities coordinators 1 (ft).
Facilities Dining room; Physical therapy room; Activities room; Crafts room; Laundry room; Barber/Beauty shop.
Activities Arts & crafts; Cards; Games; Reading groups; Prayer groups; Movies; Shopping trips; Social/Cultural gatherings; Bowling; Happy hour.

Mt Pleasant Manor*
38 Freneau Ave, Matawan, NJ, 07747
(201) 566-4633
Admin Edward Gann Jr.
Licensure Skilled care; Intermediate care. *Beds* 27. *Certified* Medicaid.

MEDFORD

Medford Convalescent & Nursing Center
185 Tucuerton Rd, Medford, NJ, 08055
(609) 983-8500
Admin David F Gramham LNHA. *Medical Dir/Dir of Nursing* Richard Molino MD; Maureen Cholette RN DON.
Licensure Skilled care. *Beds* SNF 180. *Certified* Medicaid.
Owner Proprietary Corp.
Admissions Requirements Medical examination; Physician's request.
Staff Physicians 8 (pt); RNs 8 (ft), 10 (pt); LPNs 8 (ft), 3 (pt); Orderlies 3 (ft); Nurses aides 46 (ft), 32 (pt); Physical therapists 1 (pt); Reality therapists 1 (pt); Recreational therapists 1 (pt); Occupational therapists 0.1; Speech therapists 1 (pt); Activities coordinators 2 (ft), 3 (pt); Dietitians 1 (ft); Dentists 1 (pt); Ophthalmologists 1 (pt); Podiatrists 1 (pt).
Languages Italian, Sign
Facilities Dining room; Physical therapy room; Activities room; Chapel; Laundry room; Barber/Beauty shop.
Activities Arts & crafts; Cards; Games; Reading groups; Prayer groups; Movies; Shopping trips; Social/Cultural gatherings; Trips to the ballgames.

Medford Leas
PO Box 366, New Freedom Rd, Rte 70, Medford, NJ, 08055
(609) 654-3000
Admin Lois Forrest. *Medical Dir/Dir of Nursing* Benjamin R Paradee MD; Kathleen Gentleman RN.
Licensure Skilled care; Intermediate care. *Beds* SNF 240; ICF. *Certified* Medicare.
Owner Nonprofit Corp.
Admissions Requirements Minimum age 65; Medical examination.
Staff Physicians 1 (ft), 3 (pt); RNs 12 (ft), 22 (pt); LPNs 3 (ft), 9 (pt); Nurses aides 27 (ft), 41 (pt); Physical therapists 1 (pt); Activities coordinators 1 (ft); Dietitians 1 (pt); Dentists 1 (pt).
Affiliation Society of Friends
Facilities Dining room; Physical therapy room; Activities room; Crafts room; Laundry room; Barber/Beauty shop; Library; Shuffle board; Tennis; Greenhouse; Indoor pool; Putting green; Walking trails.
Activities Arts & crafts; Cards; Games; Reading groups; Movies; Shopping trips; Social/Cultural gatherings.

MENDHAM

Holly Manor Nursing Home
84 Cold Hill Rd, Mendham, NJ, 07945
(201) 543-2500, 543-2571
Admin Shirley M Siegel. *Medical Dir/Dir of Nursing* Dr L Schlessinger; Janice Fitzsimmons.
Licensure Skilled care; Intermediate care. *Beds* 114. *Certified* Medicaid; Medicare.
Owner Proprietary Corp.
Admissions Requirements Minimum age 16; Medical examination; Physician's request.
Staff Physicians 12 (pt); RNs 8 (ft), 7 (pt); LPNs 3 (ft), 2 (pt); Orderlies 2 (ft), 1 (pt); Nurses aides 40 (ft), 30 (pt); Physical therapists 1 (ft); Recreational therapists 2 (ft); Occupational therapists 1 (ft); Speech therapists 1 (ft); Activities coordinators 1 (ft); Dietitians 1 (ft).
Facilities Dining room; Physical therapy room; Laundry room; Barber/Beauty shop; 2 enclosed outdoor patios; Private & semi-private rooms; Personal plants; Furniture encouraged.
Activities Arts & crafts; Cards; Games; Reading groups; Prayer groups; Movies; Shopping trips; Social/Cultural gatherings; Gourmet dining; Pet therapy.

MERCERVILLE

Mercerville Nursing & Convalescent Center
2240 White Horse-Mercerville Rd, Mercerville, NJ, 08619
(609) 586-7500
Admin Lois A Mulcahy. *Medical Dir/Dir of Nursing* Dr Robert Keene; Frances Grochala RN.
Licensure Skilled care. *Beds* SNF 104. *Certified* Medicare.
Owner Proprietary Corp (Multicare Management).
Admissions Requirements Minimum age 18; Medical examination.
Staff Physicians; RNs; LPNs; Orderlies; Nurses aides; Physical therapists; Reality therapists; Recreational therapists; Occupational therapists; Speech therapists; Activities coordinators; Dietitians; Dentists; Ophthalmologists.
Languages Italian, Polish, Slavic, German
Facilities Dining room; Physical therapy room; Activities room; Crafts room; Laundry room; Barber/Beauty shop; Library.
Activities Arts & crafts; Cards; Games; Reading groups; Prayer groups; Movies; Social/Cultural gatherings; Concerts; Luncheons; Planetariums.

University Center for Continuing Care
1059 Edinburg Rd, Mercerville, NJ, 08690
(609) 588-0091
Admin Dennis F Molnar. *Medical Dir/Dir of Nursing* Dr B Rivielli; Margaret Neuman RN.
Licensure Skilled care; Intermediate care. *Beds* SNF 180; ICF. *Certified* Medicaid; Medicare.
Owner Privately owned.
Admissions Requirements Medical examination.
Staff Physicians 3 (pt); RNs; LPNs; Nurses aides; Recreational therapists 3 (ft), 1 (pt); Dietitians 1 (pt).
Facilities Dining room; Physical therapy room; Activities room; Barber/Beauty shop; Library.
Activities Arts & crafts; Cards; Games; Prayer groups; Movies; Shopping trips; Social/Cultural gatherings.

MERCHANTVILLE

Maple Lane Inc*
30 W Maple Ave, Merchantville, NJ, 08109
(609) 662-4493

Admin Frank Dumbleton.
Licensure Long-Term care. *Beds* 22.

MIDDLETOWN

Hilltop Private Nursing Home*
Kings Highway, Middletown, NJ, 07748
(201) 671-0177
Admin Ethel Baskin, RN.
Licensure Skilled care; Intermediate care. *Beds* 53. *Certified* Medicaid; Medicare.

New Ivy House*
Kings Hwy, Middletown, NJ, 07748
(201) 671-0169
Admin Paul Seidler. *Medical Dir/Dir of Nursing* Dr D Seigel.
Licensure Skilled care; Intermediate care. *Beds* 88. *Certified* Medicaid.
Staff RNs 4 (ft), 5 (pt); LPNs 3 (ft), 3 (pt); Orderlies 1 (ft); Nurses aides 27 (ft), 3 (pt); Activities coordinators 1 (ft), 1 (pt).

MONTCLAIR

Cherry Nursing Home
111-115 Gates Ave, Montclair, NJ, 07042
(201) 746-4616, 746-4617
Admin Robert B Cherry. *Medical Dir/Dir of Nursing* Dr Pande Josiforski; Ruth Hess DON.
Licensure Skilled care; Intermediate care. *Beds* SNF 58 Private. *Certified* Private.
Owner Proprietary Corp.
Staff RNs; LPNs; Nurses aides; Recreational therapists; Activities coordinators; Dietitians.
Facilities Dining room; Physical therapy room; Activities room; Chapel; Crafts room; Laundry room; Barber/Beauty shop.
Activities Arts & crafts; Cards; Games; Reading groups; Prayer groups; Movies; Shopping trips; Social/Cultural gatherings.

Clover Rest Nursing Home*
16 Madison Ave, Montclair, NJ, 07042
(201) 783-4501
Admin David Austin.
Beds 24.

Little Nursing Home*
71 Christopher St, Montclair, NJ, 07042
(201) 744-5518
Admin R Cumiskey.
Licensure Long-Term care. *Beds* 24.

Madison Nursing Home*
31 Madison Ave, Montclair, NJ, 07042
(201) 783-4502
Admin Eloise Foreman.
Licensure Skilled care; Intermediate care. *Beds* 21. *Certified* Medicaid.

Montcalm Manor*
32 Pleasant Ave, Montclair, NJ, 07042
(201) 744-4560
Admin Eloise Foreman.
Licensure Long-Term care. *Beds* 36.

Montclair Nursing Home*
78 Midland Ave, Montclair, NJ, 07042
(201) 783-4503
Admin David Austin.
Licensure Long-Term care. *Beds* 24.

St Vincent's Nursing Home*
45 Elm St, Montclair, NJ, 07042
(201) 746-4000
Admin Sr Alicia Mullins.
Licensure Intermediate care. *Beds* 135.
Affiliation Roman Catholic

Van Dyk Manor
42 N Mountain Ave, Montclair, NJ, 07042
(201) 783-9400
Admin Robert Brower. *Medical Dir/Dir of Nursing* Dr Bernard Eichler.
Licensure Skilled care. *Beds* SNF 62.

Admissions Requirements Medical examination.
Staff RNs 4 (ft), 4 (pt); LPNs 2 (ft), 3 (pt); Nurses aides 25 (ft), 12 (pt); Physical therapists 1 (pt); Activities coordinators 1 (ft), 2 (pt); Dietitians 1 (ft).
Facilities Dining room; Physical therapy room; Activities room; Chapel; Crafts room; Laundry room; Barber/Beauty shop.
Activities Arts & crafts; Cards; Games; Movies; Shopping trips; Social/Cultural gatherings; Bingo; Bowling; Theater trips; Grandparents Visits; RSVP program.

MOORESTOWN

Greenleaf Extension
28 E Main St, Moorestown, NJ, 08057
(609) 235-4884
Admin Robert Hawthorne. *Medical Dir/Dir of Nursing* Dr Joseph Winston; Eleanor Need RN.
Licensure Skilled care. *Beds* 33.
Owner Nonprofit Corp.
Admissions Requirements Medical examination.
Staff Physicians 1 (pt); RNs 3 (ft), 7 (pt); LPNs 2 (pt); Orderlies; Nurses aides 9 (ft), 11 (pt); Occupational therapists 1 (pt); Activities coordinators 1 (ft); Dietitians 1 (pt).
Facilities Dining room; Activities room; Crafts room; Barber/Beauty shop; Sunroom (glass enclosed heated porch area).
Activities Arts & crafts; Cards; Games; Reading groups; Movies; Social/Cultural gatherings; Picnics.

Moorestown Nursing Home*
2nd & Pantcoast Sts, Moorestown, NJ, 08057
(609) 235-0110
Admin Marc Gelinas.
Licensure Skilled care; Intermediate care. *Beds* 68. *Certified* Medicaid; Medicare.

MORGANVILLE

Queen of Carmel*
Reids Hill Rd, Box 203, Morganville, NJ, 07751
(201) 946-4991
Admin Majorie Morey.
Licensure Skilled care; Intermediate care. *Beds* 31. *Certified* Medicaid.

MORRIS PLAINS

Morris View
PO Box 437, W Hanover Ave, Morris Plains, NJ, 07950
(201) 829-8500
Admin John F Merrigan. *Medical Dir/Dir of Nursing* James H Wolf MD; Elizabeth Belz RN.
Licensure Skilled care. *Beds* SNF 422. *Certified* Medicaid.
Owner Publicly owned.
Admissions Requirements Minimum age 18.
Staff Physicians 8 (pt); RNs 42 (ft), 27 (pt); LPNs 9 (ft), 8 (pt); Nurses aides 167 (ft), 15 (pt); Physical therapists 2 (ft); Occupational therapists 1 (pt); Speech therapists 1 (pt); Activities coordinators 1 (ft); Dietitians 1 (ft); Ophthalmologists 1 (pt); Podiatrists 1 (pt); Dentist 1 (pt); Optometrist 1 (pt); Psychiatrist 1 (pt); Physiatrist 1 (pt); Dermatologist 2 (pt).
Facilities Dining room; Physical therapy room; Activities room; Chapel; Crafts room; Laundry room; Barber/Beauty shop; Library.
Activities Arts & crafts; Cards; Games; Reading groups; Prayer groups; Movies; Shopping trips; Social/Cultural gatherings.

MORRISTOWN

Morris Hills Multicare Center
77 Madison Ave, Morristown, NJ, 07960
(201) 540-9800
Admin Richard Lee. *Medical Dir/Dir of
Nursing* Dr T Angelo; Connie Keller DON.
Licensure Skilled care; Intermediate care. *Beds*
SNF 138; ICF 166. *Certified* Medicaid;
Medicare.
Owner Proprietary Corp (Multicare
Management).
Admissions Requirements Physician's request.
Staff Physicians; RNs; LPNs; Orderlies;
Nurses aides; Physical therapists;
Recreational therapists; Speech therapists;
Activities coordinators; Dietitians; Dentists;
Ophthalmologists; Podiatrists.
Facilities Dining room; Physical therapy
room; Activities room; Chapel; Laundry
room; Barber/Beauty shop.
Activities Arts & crafts; Cards; Games;
Reading groups; Prayer groups; Movies;
Shopping trips; Social/Cultural gatherings.

Morristown Rehabilitation Center
66 Morris St, Morristown, NJ, 07960
(201) 539-3000
Admin Patricia George. *Medical Dir/Dir of
Nursing* Bernard Grabelle MD; Julie Bessler
NS.
Licensure Skilled care; Intermediate care. *Beds*
76. *Certified* Medicaid.
Owner Proprietary Corp.
Admissions Requirements Minimum age 18.
Staff RNs 5 (ft), 4 (pt); LPNs 2 (ft), 1 (pt);
Nurses aides 20 (ft), 5 (pt); Physical
therapists 1 (pt); Recreational therapists 1
(ft), 1 (pt); Speech therapists 1 (pt);
Dietitians 1 (pt); Dentists 1 (pt);
Ophthalmologists 1 (pt).
Facilities Dining room; Physical therapy
room; Activities room; Crafts room; Laundry
room.
Activities Arts & crafts; Cards; Games;
Reading groups; Prayer groups; Movies;
Shopping trips; Social/Cultural gatherings.

MOUNT HOLLY

Mt Holly Center
62 Richmond Ave, Mount Holly, NJ, 08060
(609) 267-8800
Admin Regina H Driesbach. *Medical Dir/Dir
of Nursing* Marvin A Weinar MD; Patricia
Pyne RN DON.
Licensure Skilled care; Intermediate care;
Long-term custodial. *Beds* 120. *Certified*
Medicaid; Medicare.
Owner Nonprofit Corp.
Staff Physicians 23 (pt); RNs 9 (ft), 6 (pt);
LPNs 7 (ft), 10 (pt); Nurses aides 39 (ft), 16
(pt); Physical therapists 2 (pt); Recreational
therapists 1 (pt); Occupational therapists 1
(pt); Speech therapists 1 (pt); Activities
coordinators 1 (pt); Dietitians 1 (pt);
Ophthalmologists 1 (pt); Podiatrists 1 (pt);
Social services 1 (ft).
Languages Spanish
Facilities Dining room; Physical therapy
room; Activities room; Crafts room; Laundry
room; Barber/Beauty shop; Library; Dental;
Podiatrist exam room; Patient day room.
Activities Arts & crafts; Cards; Games;
Reading groups; Prayer groups; Movies;
Shopping trips; Social/Cultural gatherings;
Garden club; Gourmet club; Exercise.

MOUNT LAUREL

Mt Laurel Convalescent Center
Church Rd, Mount Laurel, NJ, 08054
(609) 235-7100
Admin Renee Lake. *Medical Dir/Dir of
Nursing* Dr Frank Pettinelli; Kathleen
MacMillan.

Licensure Skilled care; Intermediate care. *Beds*
SNF 280; ICF. *Certified* Medicaid;
Medicare.
Owner Proprietary Corp (Geriatric & Medical
Centers).
Staff Physicians; RNs; LPNs; Orderlies;
Nurses aides; Physical therapists;
Recreational therapists; Occupational
therapists; Speech therapists; Activities
coordinators; Dietitians; Dentists;
Ophthalmologists; Podiatrists.
Facilities Dining room; Physical therapy
room; Activities room; Crafts room; Laundry
room; Barber/Beauty shop; Enclosed outdoor
courtyard.
Activities Arts & crafts; Cards; Games;
Reading groups; Prayer groups; Movies;
Shopping trips; Social/Cultural gatherings.

NAVESINK

King James Care Center of Middletown*
PO Box R, 400 State Hwy 36, Navesink, NJ,
07752
(201) 291-3400
Admin Herman Black.
Licensure Skilled care; Intermediate care. *Beds*
123. *Certified* Medicaid; Medicare.

NEPTUNE

Conv-A-Center*
101 Walnut St & Hwy 33, Neptune, NJ,
07753
(201) 774-3550
Admin Dean Charles Michals.
Licensure Skilled care; Intermediate care. *Beds*
100. *Certified* Medicaid; Medicare.

The Grove Health Care Center
919 Green Grove Rd, Neptune, NJ, 07753
(201) 922-3400
Admin A David Ornstein. *Medical Dir/Dir of
Nursing* Francis R Dynof MD; Celeste Davis
RN DON.
Licensure Skilled care; Intermediate care. *Beds*
SNF 121; ICF. *Certified* Medicaid;
Medicare.
Owner Nonprofit organization/foundation.
Admissions Requirements Minimum age 16.
Staff Physicians 1 (pt); RNs 7 (ft); LPNs 4
(ft); Nurses aides 43 (ft); Physical therapists
1 (pt); Recreational therapists 2 (pt);
Occupational therapists 1 (pt); Speech
therapists 1 (pt); Activities coordinators 1
(ft); Dietitians 1 (pt); Dentists 1 (pt);
Ophthalmologists 1 (pt); Podiatrists 1 (pt).
Affiliation Presbyterian
Facilities Dining room; Physical therapy
room; Activities room; Laundry room;
Barber/Beauty shop.
Activities Arts & crafts; Cards; Games;
Reading groups; Prayer groups; Movies;
Shopping trips; Social/Cultural gatherings.

The Lodge Intermediate Care Facility*
3510 Rte 66, Neptune, NJ, 07753
(201) 922-1900
Admin Susan Hall-Bruncati. *Medical Dir/Dir
of Nursing* Dr Nathan Troum.
Licensure Intermediate care. *Beds* 167.
Certified Medicaid.
Admissions Requirements Minimum age 16;
Medical examination; Physician's request.
Staff Physicians 1 (pt); RNs 7 (ft); LPNs 5
(ft); Nurses aides 51 (ft); Recreational
therapists 3 (ft); Dietitians 2 (ft).
Affiliation Presbyterian
Facilities Dining room; Physical therapy
room; Activities room; Chapel; Crafts room;
Laundry room; Barber/Beauty shop; Library.
Activities Arts & crafts; Cards; Games;
Reading groups; Prayer groups; Movies;
Shopping trips; Social/Cultural gatherings.

NEPTUNE CITY

Medicenter/Neptune City
2050 6th Ave, Neptune City, NJ, 07753
(201) 774-8300
Admin Carolyn V Larkin.
Licensure Skilled care; Intermediate care. *Beds*
106. *Certified* Medicaid; Medicare.
Staff RNs 7 (ft), 7 (pt); LPNs 2 (ft), 4 (pt);
Orderlies 1 (ft); Nurses aides 33 (ft), 6 (pt);
Physical therapists 1 (pt); Recreational
therapists 2 (ft); Occupational therapists 1
(pt); Speech therapists 1 (pt); Activities
coordinators 1 (ft); Dietitians 1 (pt).
Facilities Dining room; Physical therapy
room; Activities room; Laundry room;
Barber/Beauty shop; Television rooms.
Activities Arts & crafts; Cards; Games;
Reading groups; Prayer groups; Movies;
Shopping trips; Social/Cultural gatherings.

NESHANIC

Foothill Acres Inc
Amwell Rd, Neshanic, NJ, 08853
(201) 369-8711
Admin J R McGavisk. *Medical Dir/Dir of
Nursing* H K Van Duyne MD; Maria
DiMaria RN DON.
Licensure Skilled care. *Beds* 190. *Certified*
Medicaid.
Owner Proprietary Corp.
Admissions Requirements Minimum age 65.
Staff Physicians 1 (pt); RNs 12 (ft), 7 (pt);
LPNs 5 (ft), 7 (pt); Orderlies 4 (ft), 3 (pt);
Nurses aides 32 (ft), 40 (pt); Physical
therapists 1 (pt); Activities coordinators 1
(ft); Dietitians 1 (pt).
Facilities Dining room; Physical therapy
room; Activities room; Chapel; Laundry
room; Barber/Beauty shop.
Activities Arts & crafts; Cards; Games;
Reading groups; Prayer groups; Movies;
Shopping trips; Social/Cultural gatherings.

NEW BRUNSWICK

Brunswick Manor Care Center
US 1 & 18, New Brunswick, NJ, 08901
(201) 828-2400
Admin Neil Kerman. *Medical Dir/Dir of
Nursing* William Allgair MD; Patricia Watts
RN BS DON.
Licensure Skilled care. *Beds* 112. *Certified*
Medicaid; Medicare.
Owner Privately owned.
Facilities Dining room; Physical therapy
room; Activities room; Barber/Beauty shop.
Activities Arts & crafts; Games; Reading
groups; Prayer groups; Movies; Bingo;
Cocktail social hour.

The Francis E Parker Memorial Home
Easton Ave at Landing Ln, New Brunswick,
NJ, 08901
(201) 545-8330
Admin Robert M Piegari. *Medical Dir/Dir of
Nursing* Mrs Nunley.
Licensure Skilled care. *Beds* SNF 51.
Owner Nonprofit Corp.
Staff RNs; LPNs; Nurses aides; Reality
therapists; Recreational therapists; Activities
coordinators; Dietitians.
Facilities Dining room; Physical therapy
room; Activities room; Laundry room;
Barber/Beauty shop; Library.
Activities Arts & crafts; Cards; Games;
Reading groups; Prayer groups; Movies;
Shopping trips; Social/Cultural gatherings.

NEW LISBON

Buttonwood Hospital of Burlington County
Pemberton-Browns Mills Rd, Rte 530, New
Lisbon, NJ, 08064
(609) 726-7000

Admin Lynn O'Connor. *Medical Dir/Dir of Nursing* Andrew Besen MD; Dorothy Santoleri RN.
Licensure Skilled care; Intermediate care; Psychiatric unit. *Beds* SNF; ICF 225; Psychiatric unit 30. *Certified* Medicaid.
Owner Nonprofit Corp.
Admissions Requirements Physician's request.
Staff Physicians 2 (ft); RNs 33 (ft), 12 (pt); LPNs 33 (ft), 6 (pt); Nurses aides 163 (ft), 35 (pt); Recreational therapists; Activities coordinators; Dietitians 1 (ft).
Facilities Dining room; Physical therapy room; Activities room; Chapel; Crafts room; Laundry room; Barber/Beauty shop; Library.
Activities Arts & crafts; Cards; Games; Reading groups; Prayer groups; Movies; Shopping trips; Social/Cultural gatherings.

NEW MILFORD

Woodcrest Center
800 River Rd, New Milford, NJ, 07646
(201) 967-1700
Admin Robert M Hilsen. *Medical Dir/Dir of Nursing* Bernard Greenspan DO; Gail Walsh RN DON.
Licensure Skilled care; Intermediate care. *Beds* 236. *Certified* Medicaid.
Owner Proprietary Corp.
Admissions Requirements Medical examination.
Staff Physicians 67 (pt); RNs 17 (ft), 14 (pt); LPNs 6 (ft), 3 (pt); Nurses aides 64 (ft), 22 (pt); Physical therapists 1 (pt); Recreational therapists 1 (ft); Occupational therapists 1 (pt); Speech therapists 1 (pt); Activities coordinators 1 (ft); Dietitians 1 (pt); Dentists 1 (pt); Ophthalmologists 2 (pt); Podiatrists 1 (pt); Dentist 1 (pt).
Languages Spanish, German, Polish, Italian, Tagalog
Facilities Dining room; Physical therapy room; Activities room; Crafts room; Laundry room; Barber/Beauty shop; Dental clinic.
Activities Arts & crafts; Cards; Games; Reading groups; Prayer groups; Movies; Shopping trips; Social/Cultural gatherings.

NEW PROVIDENCE

Glenside Nursing Center
144 Gales Dr, New Providence, NJ, 07974
(201) 464-8600
Admin Brian Cumiskey. *Medical Dir/Dir of Nursing* Dr Pitoscia; Ms Cochrane.
Licensure Skilled care; Intermediate care. *Beds* 95. *Certified* Medicaid; Medicare.
Owner Proprietary Corp (Health Care & Retirement Corp).
Staff Physicians 2 (ft), 32 (pt); RNs 12 (ft), 6 (pt); LPNs 3 (ft), 3 (pt); Orderlies 1 (ft); Nurses aides 26 (ft), 5 (pt); Physical therapists 1 (pt); Recreational therapists 1 (ft); Occupational therapists 2 (pt); Activities coordinators 1 (ft), 1 (pt); Dietitians 1 (pt); Ophthalmologists 1 (pt); Dentist 1 (pt).
Facilities Dining room; Physical therapy room; Activities room; Crafts room; Laundry room.
Activities Arts & crafts; Cards; Games; Reading groups; Prayer groups; Movies; Shopping trips; Social/Cultural gatherings.

NEWARK

New Community Extended Care Facility
266 S Orange Ave, Newark, NJ, 07103
(201) 624-2020
Admin Sr Mary Pauline Hogan. *Medical Dir/Dir of Nursing* Paul A Kearney MD; Jacqueline Ragin.
Licensure Skilled care; Intermediate care. *Beds* SNF 180; ICF. *Certified* Medicaid.
Owner Nonprofit Corp.

Admissions Requirements Medical examination; Physician's request.
Staff Physicians; RNs 10 (ft), 6 (pt); LPNs 12 (ft), 11 (pt); Orderlies 4 (ft); Nurses aides 48 (ft), 33 (pt); Physical therapists 2 (pt); Recreational therapists 4 (ft); Occupational therapists 1 (pt); Activities coordinators 1 (ft); Dietitians 1 (ft).
Languages Spanish
Facilities Dining room; Physical therapy room; Activities room; Chapel; Laundry room; Barber/Beauty shop; Library.
Activities Arts & crafts; Cards; Games; Reading groups; Prayer groups; Movies; Shopping trips; Social/Cultural gatherings; Womens club.

Newark Health & Extended Care Facility*
65 Jay St, Newark, NJ, 07103
(201) 483-6800
Admin Samuel Paneth.
Licensure Skilled care; Intermediate care. *Beds* 420. *Certified* Medicaid; Medicare.

NEWFIELD

Mater Dei Nursing Home
PO Box 164, RD 3, Newfield, NJ, 08344
(609) 348-2061
Admin Sr Marie de Chantal Roy. *Medical Dir/Dir of Nursing* Dr John Pastore; Sr Laurence.
Licensure Skilled care; Intermediate care. *Beds* 64. *Certified* Medicaid.
Owner Nonprofit organization/foundation.
Staff Physicians 1 (pt); RNs 3 (ft), 10 (pt); LPNs 2 (ft), 2 (pt); Nurses aides 25 (ft), 11 (pt); Physical therapists 1 (pt); Speech therapists 1 (pt); Activities coordinators 1 (ft), 1 (pt); Dietitians 1 (pt); Dentists 1 (pt); Ophthalmologists 1 (pt); Social service 1 (pt).
Affiliation Roman Catholic
Facilities Dining room; Physical therapy room; Activities room; Chapel; Crafts room; Laundry room; Barber/Beauty shop; Library.
Activities Arts & crafts; Cards; Games; Reading groups; Prayer groups; Movies; Social/Cultural gatherings.

NEWTON

Barn Hill Convalescent Center*
High St, Newton, NJ, 07860
(201) 383-5600
Admin Richard Roberto.
Licensure Skilled care; Intermediate care. *Beds* 116. *Certified* Medicaid; Medicare.
Admissions Requirements Minimum age 21; Medical examination; Physician's request.
Staff Physicians 1 (pt); RNs 7 (ft), 2 (pt); LPNs 5 (ft), 2 (pt); Physical therapists 1 (pt); Reality therapists 1 (pt); Recreational therapists 2 (ft); Occupational therapists 1 (pt); Speech therapists 1 (pt); Activities coordinators 1 (ft); Dietitians 2 (pt); Dentists 1 (pt); Podiatrists 1 (pt).
Facilities Dining room; Physical therapy room; Activities room; Chapel; Crafts room; Laundry room; Barber/Beauty shop; Library.
Activities Arts & crafts; Cards; Games; Reading groups; Prayer groups; Movies; Shopping trips; Social/Cultural gatherings.

Newton Nursing Home
1 Summit Ave, Newton, NJ, 07860
(201) 383-1450
Admin Michael Duffy. *Medical Dir/Dir of Nursing* Joyce Faasse RN DON.
Licensure Skilled care. *Beds* SNF 36.
Owner Proprietary Corp.
Admissions Requirements Medical examination; Physician's request.
Staff RNs 2 (ft), 2 (pt); LPNs 1 (ft); Nurses aides 9 (ft), 7 (pt); Recreational therapists 1 (ft); Dietitians 1 (pt).

Facilities Activities room.
Activities Arts & crafts; Cards; Games; Prayer groups; Movies.

Sussex County Homestead
PO Box 78, RD 3, Newton, NJ, 07860
(201) 948-5400
Admin Selma F Rooney. *Medical Dir/Dir of Nursing* D A Hannett MD; Janet Donadio RN.
Licensure Skilled care; Intermediate care. *Beds* 98. *Certified* Medicaid.
Owner Publicly owned.
Admissions Requirements Minimum age 18.
Facilities Dining room; Physical therapy room; Activities room; Barber/Beauty shop.
Activities Arts & crafts; Cards; Games; Movies; Shopping trips; Trips into community.

NORTH BERGEN

Hudson View Care & Rehabilitation Center
9020 Wall St, North Bergen, NJ, 07047
(201) 861-4040
Admin Nicholas Dubner. *Medical Dir/Dir of Nursing* Dr Randolph A London; Mrs Florence Capezzuto.
Licensure Skilled care; Intermediate care. *Beds* 273. *Certified* Medicaid; Medicare.
Owner Proprietary Corp (Health Care Associates Inc).
Admissions Requirements Medical examination; Physician's request.
Staff Physicians 7 (pt); RNs 14 (ft), 3 (pt); LPNs 17 (ft), 2 (pt); Nurses aides 101 (ft), 3 (pt); Physical therapists 1 (pt); Recreational therapists 3 (pt); Occupational therapists 1 (pt); Speech therapists 1 (pt); Activities coordinators 1 (ft); Dietitians 1 (ft); Dentists 1 (pt); Ophthalmologists 1 (pt); Podiatrists 1 (pt).
Languages Spanish
Facilities Dining room; Physical therapy room; Activities room; Chapel; Crafts room; Laundry room; Barber/Beauty shop; Library.
Activities Arts & crafts; Cards; Games; Reading groups; Prayer groups; Movies; Social/Cultural gatherings; Circus.

NORTHFIELD

Atlantic County Nursing Home—Meadowview
235 Dolphin Ave, Northfield, NJ, 08225
(609) 645-7700
Admin Ramon W Lennie. *Medical Dir/Dir of Nursing* Dr Michael S Slotoroff.
Licensure Skilled care. *Beds* SNF 180. *Certified* Medicaid.
Owner Publicly owned.
Staff Physicians 2 (pt); RNs 15 (ft); LPNs 5 (ft); Nurses aides 75 (ft); Physical therapists 1 (pt); Recreational therapists 1 (pt); Occupational therapists 1 (pt); Speech therapists 1 (pt); Dietitians 1 (ft); Dentists 1 (pt); Ophthalmologists 1 (pt); Podiatrists 1 (pt).
Facilities Dining room; Physical therapy room; Activities room; Chapel; Crafts room; Laundry room; Barber/Beauty shop; Library.
Activities Arts & crafts; Cards; Games; Reading groups; Prayer groups; Movies; Shopping trips; Social/Cultural gatherings.

OAKLAND

Oakland Care Center
20 Breakneck Rd, Oakland, NJ, 07436
(201) 337-3300
Admin Susan Lanza. *Medical Dir/Dir of Nursing* Bernard Schwam; Mildred Martyn.
Licensure Skilled care; Intermediate care. *Beds* 252. *Certified* Medicaid; Medicare.
Owner Proprietary Corp.
Admissions Requirements Minimum age 40; Medical examination.

Staff Physicians 1 (ft); RNs 9 (ft), 16 (pt); LPNs 10 (ft), 8 (pt); Orderlies 1 (ft); Nurses aides 63 (ft), 16 (pt); Physical therapists 1 (ft); Recreational therapists 1 (ft); Occupational therapists 1 (ft); Speech therapists 1 (pt); Activities coordinators 3 (ft); Dietitians 1 (ft); Dentists 1 (pt); Ophthalmologists 1 (pt); Podiatrists 1 (pt).
Facilities Dining room; Physical therapy room; Activities room; Crafts room; Laundry room; Barber/Beauty shop; Library.
Activities Arts & crafts; Cards; Games; Reading groups; Prayer groups; Movies; Shopping trips; Social/Cultural gatherings; Church activities; Bible studies.

OCEAN GROVE

Ocean Grove Nursing Home*
63 Clark Ave, Ocean Grove, NJ, 07756
(201) 775-0554
Admin James Handford. *Medical Dir/Dir of Nursing* Y D Kong MD.
Licensure Skilled care; Intermediate care. *Beds* 68. *Certified* Medicaid.
Staff RNs 3 (ft), 2 (pt); LPNs 2 (ft), 4 (pt); Nurses aides 25 (ft), 8 (pt); Physical therapists 1 (ft), 1 (pt); Activities coordinators 2 (ft); Dietitians 1 (pt); Dentists 1 (pt); Podiatrists 1 (pt).
Facilities Dining room; Activities room; Crafts room; Laundry room; Barber/Beauty shop.
Activities Arts & crafts; Games; Movies.

OCEAN VIEW

Lutheran Home at Ocean View*
Rte 9, 184 Shore Rd, Ocean View, NJ, 08230
(609) 263-3881
Admin Jeffrey Kissam.
Licensure Intermediate care; Residential care. *Beds* ICF 63; Residential 64. *Certified* Medicaid.
Owner Nonprofit Corp (Luth Soc Services).
Affiliation Lutheran

OLD BRIDGE

Summer Hill Nursing Home*
111 Rte 516, Old Bridge, NJ, 08857
(201) 254-8200
Admin Melvin Feingenbaum.
Licensure Skilled care; Intermediate care. *Beds* 120. *Certified* Medicaid.

OLD TAPPAN

Ingleside Nursing Home
1016 S Washington Ave, Old Tappan, NJ, 07675
(201) 664-3144
Admin Doris Neibart. *Medical Dir/Dir of Nursing* Mary Lou Knowles DON.
Licensure Skilled care. *Beds* 43.
Owner Proprietary Corp.
Staff RNs 6 (ft), 5 (pt); LPNs 2 (ft), 1 (pt); Nurses aides 8 (ft), 13 (pt); Activities coordinators 1 (pt); Dietitians 1 (ft).
Facilities Dining room; Activities room; Laundry room; Lounge.
Activities Arts & crafts; Cards; Games; Reading groups; Prayer groups; Social/Cultural gatherings.

ORANGE

White House Nursing Home
560 Berkeley Ave, Orange, NJ, 07050
(201) 672-6500
Admin Eliezer M Grossman. *Medical Dir/Dir of Nursing* James Paolino MD.
Licensure Skilled care; Intermediate care. *Beds* SNF 176; ICF. *Certified* Medicaid.
Owner Proprietary Corp.

Admissions Requirements Minimum age 18.
Staff RNs 8 (ft), 4 (pt); LPNs 12 (ft), 4 (pt); Nurses aides 62 (ft), 6 (pt); Recreational therapists 3 (ft); Activities coordinators 1 (ft).
Languages Yiddish, Hebrew, Spanish, Hungarian
Facilities Dining room; Physical therapy room; Activities room; Barber/Beauty shop; Library.
Activities Arts & crafts; Cards; Games; Reading groups; Prayer groups; Movies; Shopping trips; Social/Cultural gatherings.

OXFORD

Warren Haven—The Warren County Nursing Home
RFD 1 Box 306, Oxford, NJ, 07882
(201) 453-2131
Admin Jean Sickles. *Medical Dir/Dir of Nursing* Stanton H Sykes MD; Carmine Quick RN DON.
Licensure Skilled care. *Beds* SNF 180. *Certified* Medicaid.
Owner Publicly owned.
Admissions Requirements Minimum age 18; Medical examination; Physician's request.
Staff Physicians 4 (pt); RNs 15 (ft), 2 (pt); LPNs 11 (ft), 2 (pt); Orderlies 2 (ft); Nurses aides 51 (ft), 9 (pt); Recreational therapists 3 (ft); Activities coordinators 1 (ft); Dietitians 1 (pt); Podiatrists 1 (pt); Social Services 2 (ft); Occupational Therapy Asst 1 (pt).
Facilities Dining room; Physical therapy room; Activities room; Chapel; Crafts room; Laundry room; Barber/Beauty shop.
Activities Arts & crafts; Cards; Games; Reading groups; Prayer groups; Movies; Shopping trips; Social/Cultural gatherings; Volunteer entertainment.

PARAMUS

Dellridge Nursing Home
532 Fairview Ave, Paramus, NJ, 07652
(201) 261-1589
Admin Patricia Volmer. *Medical Dir/Dir of Nursing* Alexander Haseldorn MD; Berniece Dufour RN DON.
Licensure Skilled care. *Beds* SNF 96. *Certified* Medicare.
Owner Proprietary Corp.
Admissions Requirements Medical examination.
Staff Physicians 1 (pt); RNs 6 (ft), 14 (pt); LPNs 2 (ft), 6 (pt); Nurses aides 23 (ft), 29 (pt); Physical therapists 1 (pt); Reality therapists 1 (pt); Recreational therapists 1 (ft), 1 (pt); Occupational therapists 1 (pt); Speech therapists 1 (pt); Activities coordinators 1 (ft); Dietitians 1 (pt); Dentists 1 (pt); Ophthalmologists 1 (pt); Podiatrists 1 (pt); Food Service Supervisor 1 (ft).
Facilities Dining room; Physical therapy room; Activities room; Crafts room; Barber/Beauty shop; Library.
Activities Arts & crafts; Cards; Games; Reading groups; Prayer groups; Movies; International days; Picnics; Family days.

New Jersey Home for Veterans at Paramus
PO Box 546, 1 Veterans Dr, Paramus, NJ, 07653-0546
(201) 967-7676
Admin Joseph Loudermilk. *Medical Dir/Dir of Nursing* A Lantin MD; T Wojekoski RN DON.
Licensure Skilled care. *Beds* SNF.
Owner Publicly owned.
Admissions Requirements Medical examination; Physician's request.
Staff Physicians 2 (ft); RNs 15 (ft); LPNs 3 (ft); Nurses aides 50 (ft); Physical therapists 1 (pt); Recreational therapists 2 (ft); Occupational therapists 1 (pt); Speech

therapists 1 (pt); Activities coordinators 1 (ft); Dietitians 1 (ft); Dentists 2 (pt); Ophthalmologists 2 (pt).
Facilities Dining room; Physical therapy room; Activities room; Chapel; Crafts room; Laundry room; Laundry room; Barber/Beauty shop; Library.
Activities Arts & crafts; Shopping trips.

Paramus Health Care Center*
593 Paramus Rd, Paramus, NJ, 07652
(201) 444-1341
Admin Doris Mangano.
Licensure Skilled care; Intermediate care. *Beds* 35. *Certified* Medicaid.

PARSIPPANY

Beverwyck Nursing Home*
Beverwyck Rd, Parsippany, NJ, 07054
(201) 887-0156
Admin Blanquita Bonafacio.
Licensure Long-Term care. *Beds* 24.

Troy Hills Nursing Center
200 Reynolds Ave, Parsippany, NJ, 07054
(201) 887-8080
Admin Barbara Kaddik. *Medical Dir/Dir of Nursing* Dr T Angelo; Ms C Chapman.
Licensure Skilled care; Intermediate care. *Beds* SNF 31; ICF 97. *Certified* Medicaid; Medicare.
Owner Proprietary Corp (Multicare Management).
Admissions Requirements Minimum age 18.
Staff Physicians 31 (pt); RNs; LPNs; Nurses aides; Physical therapists; Recreational therapists; Occupational therapists; Speech therapists; Activities coordinators; Dietitians; Dentists; Ophthalmologists; Respiratory therapist.
Facilities Dining room; Physical therapy room; Activities room; Laundry room; Barber/Beauty shop; Library.
Activities Arts & crafts; Cards; Games; Reading groups; Prayer groups; Movies; Shopping trips; Social/Cultural gatherings.

PASSAIC

Chestnut Hill Convalescent Center
380 Chestnut St, Passaic, NJ, 07055
(201) 777-7800
Admin Emil Stefanacci. *Medical Dir/Dir of Nursing* Dr Richard G Stefanacci; D Masucci.
Licensure Skilled care. *Beds* SNF 94. *Certified* Medicaid; Medicare.
Owner Proprietary Corp.
Admissions Requirements Medical examination; Physician's request.
Staff Physicians 1 (ft); RNs 4 (ft); LPNs 4 (ft), 6 (pt); Orderlies 2 (ft); Nurses aides 25 (ft), 18 (pt); Physical therapists 1 (pt); Recreational therapists 3 (ft), 2 (pt); Activities coordinators 1 (ft); Dietitians 1 (pt).
Languages Spanish, Polish
Facilities Dining room; Physical therapy room; Activities room; Chapel; Crafts room; Barber/Beauty shop; Library.
Activities Arts & crafts; Cards; Games; Reading groups; Prayer groups; Movies; Social/Cultural gatherings.

Hamilton Plaza Nursing Center
56 Hamilton Ave, Passaic, NJ, 07055
(201) 773-7070
Admin Susan Goldberg. *Medical Dir/Dir of Nursing* Dr Graber, Dr Lintz; Kathleen Diciedue MSN DON.
Licensure Skilled care. *Beds* SNF 120. *Certified* Medicaid; Medicare.
Owner Proprietary Corp (Continental Medical Systems).
Admissions Requirements Minimum age 16; Medical examination.

Staff Physicians 7 (pt); RNs 6 (ft), 3 (pt); LPNs 3 (ft), 2 (pt); Orderlies 2 (ft); Nurses aides 20 (ft), 19 (pt); Physical therapists 1 (pt); Recreational therapists 1 (ft), 2 (pt); Occupational therapists 1 (pt); Speech therapists 1 (pt); Dietitians 1 (pt); Dentists 1 (pt); Ophthalmologists 1 (pt); Podiatrists 1 (pt).
Languages Spanish, Polish, Russian, Italian
Facilities Dining room; Physical therapy room; Activities room; Crafts room; Laundry room; Barber/Beauty shop; Library; Multipurpose; TV room & Occupational therapy room.
Activities Arts & crafts; Cards; Games; Reading groups; Prayer groups; Movies; Shopping trips; Social/Cultural gatherings; Gourmet club; Pet therapy; Picnics; Bingo.

Jefferson Manor Nursing Center*
85 Columbia Ave, Passaic, NJ, 07055
(201) 773-7070
Admin Patrick Meehan.
Licensure Skilled care; Intermediate care. *Beds* 88. *Certified* Medicaid.

Madison Manor Nursing Center*
141 Madison St, Passaic, NJ, 07055
(201) 773-0450
Admin Patrick Meehan.
Licensure Skilled care; Intermediate care. *Beds* 65. *Certified* Medicaid; Medicare.

PATERSON

Preakness Hospital
PO Box V, Valley View Rd, Paterson, NJ, 07509
(201) 942-6800
Admin Victor R Kattak. *Medical Dir/Dir of Nursing* Joseph Lozito MD; Elizabeth Palestis RN MS.
Licensure Skilled care. *Beds* SNF 432. *Certified* Medicaid.
Owner Publicly owned.
Admissions Requirements Minimum age Adult; Physician's request.
Staff Physicians 8 (ft); RNs 58 (ft); LPNs 44 (ft); Nurses aides 175 (ft); Physical therapists 2 (ft); Reality therapists 10 (ft); Recreational therapists 1 (ft); Occupational therapists 1 (ft); Speech therapists 1 (ft); Activities coordinators 1 (ft); Dietitians 5 (ft); Dentists 1 (ft); Ophthalmologists 2 (ft); Podiatrists 2 (pt); Psychologist 1 (pt); Dentist 2 (pt).
Facilities Dining room; Physical therapy room; Activities room; Chapel; Crafts room; Laundry room; Barber/Beauty shop; Library.
Activities Arts & crafts; Cards; Games; Reading groups; Prayer groups; Movies; Shopping trips; Social/Cultural gatherings; Shore trips.

White Birch Nursing Home*
59 Birch St, Paterson, NJ, 07505
(201) 942-8899
Admin Ernest Gianetti. *Medical Dir/Dir of Nursing* P Harami DO.
Licensure Skilled care; Intermediate care. *Beds* 42. *Certified* Medicaid; Medicare.

PENNSAUKEN

Cooper River Convalescent Center
5101 N Park Dr, Pennsauken, NJ, 08109
(609) 665-8844
Admin David Collizzi. *Medical Dir/Dir of Nursing* Alex Makris MD; Joan Baily RN DON.
Licensure Skilled care. *Beds* 393. *Certified* Medicaid; Medicare.
Owner Proprietary Corp (Geriatric & Medical Centers).
Admissions Requirements Medical examination; Physician's request.

Staff Physicians; RNs; LPNs; Nurses aides; Physical therapists; Reality therapists; Recreational therapists; Occupational therapists; Speech therapists; Activities coordinators; Dietitians; Dentists; Ophthalmologists; Podiatrists.
Facilities Dining room; Physical therapy room; Activities room; Laundry room; Barber/Beauty shop.
Activities Arts & crafts; Cards; Games; Reading groups; Prayer groups; Movies; Social/Cultural gatherings; Music groups.

PERTH AMBOY

Amboy Care Center*
Lindberg Ave, Perth Amboy, NJ, 08861
(201) 826-0500
Admin Lori Gabriel.
Licensure Skilled care; Intermediate care. *Beds* 179. *Certified* Medicare.
Owner Proprietary Corp (Beverly Enterprises).

Perth Amboy Nursing Home
303 Elm St, Perth Amboy, NJ, 08861
(201) 442-9540
Admin Berel D Tennenbaum. *Medical Dir/Dir of Nursing* Thaddius Balinski MD; Marianne Pryga RN DON.
Licensure Skilled care; Intermediate care. *Beds* 250. *Certified* Medicaid; Medicare.
Owner Proprietary Corp.
Admissions Requirements Minimum age 52; Medical examination; Physician's request.
Staff Physicians 8 (ft); RNs 54 (ft), 22 (pt); LPNs 73 (ft), 31 (pt); Nurses aides 180 (ft), 73 (pt); Physical therapists 4 (ft), 2 (pt); Reality therapists 7 (ft); Recreational therapists 7 (ft); Occupational therapists 1 (ft); Speech therapists 1 (ft); Activities coordinators 1 (ft); Dietitians 1 (ft); Dentists 1 (ft); Ophthalmologists 1 (ft); Podiatrists 1 (ft).
Facilities Dining room; Physical therapy room; Activities room; Chapel; Crafts room; Laundry room; Barber/Beauty shop; Library.
Activities Arts & crafts; Cards; Games; Reading groups; Prayer groups; Movies; Shopping trips; Social/Cultural gatherings.

PHILLIPSBURG

Care Center of Phillipsburg
843 Wilbur Ave, Phillipsburg, NJ, 08865
(201) 454-2627
Admin Mary Tucker. *Medical Dir/Dir of Nursing* Michael Raab MD; Connie Crouthamel.
Licensure Skilled care. *Beds* SNF 89. *Certified* Medicaid.
Owner Proprietary Corp (Geriatric & Medical Centers).
Admissions Requirements Minimum age 16; Medical examination.
Staff Physicians 17 (pt); RNs 5 (ft), 7 (pt); LPNs 2 (ft), 7 (pt); Nurses aides 27 (ft), 3 (pt); Physical therapists 1 (pt); Recreational therapists 2 (ft), 2 (pt); Occupational therapists 1 (pt); Speech therapists 1 (pt); Activities coordinators; Dietitians 1 (pt); Ophthalmologists 1 (pt); Social worker 1 (ft).
Facilities Dining room; Activities room; Chapel; Crafts room; Laundry room; Barber/Beauty shop; Library; TV room.
Activities Arts & crafts; Cards; Games; Reading groups; Prayer groups; Movies; Shopping trips; Social/Cultural gatherings; Pet care; Plant care.

PINE BROOK

Hilltop Care Center
Hook Mountain Rd, Pine Brook, NJ, 07058
(201) 227-1330

Admin Thomas P Kenney. *Medical Dir/Dir of Nursing* Gilbert Mandel MD; Essie Masci DON.
Licensure Skilled care. *Beds* 114. *Certified* Medicaid; Medicare.
Owner Proprietary Corp.
Admissions Requirements Medical examination.
Staff RNs 10 (ft), 4 (pt); LPNs 10 (ft), 3 (pt); Orderlies 3 (ft), 2 (pt); Nurses aides 40 (ft); Recreational therapists 2 (ft); Activities coordinators 1 (ft); Dietitians 1 (ft).
Facilities Dining room; Activities room; Crafts room; Barber/Beauty shop; Library.
Activities Arts & crafts; Cards; Games; Reading groups; Prayer groups; Social/ Cultural gatherings.

PISCATAWAY

The Francis E Parker Memorial Home
1421 River Rd, Piscataway, NJ, 08854
(201) 545-3110
Admin Robert Piegari. *Medical Dir/Dir of Nursing* Mrs Fedor.
Licensure Skilled care. *Beds* SNF 60.
Owner Nonprofit Corp.
Staff RNs; LPNs; Nurses aides; Reality therapists; Recreational therapists; Activities coordinators; Dietitians.
Facilities Dining room; Physical therapy room; Activities room; Laundry room; Barber/Beauty shop; Library.
Activities Arts & crafts; Cards; Games; Reading groups; Prayer groups; Movies; Shopping trips; Social/Cultural gatherings.

PITTSTOWN

Stone Arch Health Care Center
Rte 1, Box 37, Pittstown, NJ, 08867
(201) 735-6600
Admin Nancy Goczalk. *Medical Dir/Dir of Nursing* Robert Pierce MD; Brenda Demarest RN.
Licensure Skilled care; Intermediate care. *Beds* SNF; ICF 126. *Certified* Medicaid; Medicare.
Owner Proprietary Corp.
Admissions Requirements Minimum age 18; Physician's request.
Staff RNs 6 (ft), 2 (pt); LPNs 4 (ft), 5 (pt); Nurses aides 28 (ft), 16 (pt); Reality therapists 1 (pt); Recreational therapists 2 (ft), 2 (pt); Activities coordinators 1 (ft); Dietitians 7 (ft), 16 (pt); Social services 1 (pt).
Facilities Dining room; Physical therapy room; Activities room; Crafts room; Laundry room; Barber/Beauty shop; Patient lounge.
Activities Arts & crafts; Cards; Games; Reading groups; Prayer groups; Movies; Shopping trips; Social/Cultural gatherings; Bus rides; Theater; Excursions; Picnics.

PLAINFIELD

Abbott Manor Convalescent Center
810 Central Ave, Plainfield, NJ, 07060
(201) 757-0696
Admin Rachel Cobb. *Medical Dir/Dir of Nursing* Joseph Robbins MD; Emma Fisher RN DON.
Licensure Intermediate care. *Beds* ICF 35.
Owner Privately owned.
Admissions Requirements Medical examination.
Staff RNs 3 (ft), 2 (pt); LPNs 3 (ft); Nurses aides 12 (ft), 5 (pt); Recreational therapists 1 (pt); Dietitians 1 (pt).
Facilities Dining room; Activities room; Laundry room.
Activities Arts & crafts; Cards; Games; Reading groups; Prayer groups; Movies; Social/Cultural gatherings.

Hartwyck at Cedar Brook
1340 Park Ave, Plainfield, NJ, 07060
(201) 754-3100
Admin Jane Bernheim. *Medical Dir/Dir of Nursing* Dr Peter Rives; Patricia Stadthaus RN.
Licensure Skilled care; Intermediate care; Medical day care. *Beds* SNF 106; ICF; MDC 20 limited to Alzheimer's clients. *Certified* Medicaid; Medicare.
Owner Nonprofit Corp.
Staff Physicians 1 (pt); RNs 6 (ft), 4 (pt); LPNs 6 (ft), 3 (pt); Orderlies 2 (ft); Nurses aides 34 (ft), 15 (pt); Physical therapists 2 (ft), 2 (pt); Recreational therapists 1 (ft); Occupational therapists 1 (ft), 1 (pt); Activities coordinators 1 (ft).
Facilities Dining room; Physical therapy room; Activities room; Laundry room; Barber/Beauty shop.
Activities Arts & crafts; Cards; Games; Reading groups; Prayer groups; Movies; Shopping trips; Social/Cultural gatherings; Wheelchair exercise; Volunteer work; Gardening; Cooking.

PLEASANTVILLE

Our Lady's Residence
Glendale & Clematis Aves, Pleasantville, NJ, 08232
(609) 646-2450
Admin Sr Mary Aurelia. *Medical Dir/Dir of Nursing* Francesco Pullia MD.
Licensure Skilled care; Intermediate care. *Beds* 214. *Certified* Medicaid.
Owner Nonprofit Corp.
Staff RNs 6 (ft), 17 (pt); LPNs 6 (ft), 4 (pt); Nurses aides 55 (ft), 55 (pt); Physical therapists 1 (pt); Reality therapists 1 (pt); Recreational therapists 1 (ft); Occupational therapists 1 (pt); Speech therapists 1 (pt); Activities coordinators 1 (ft); Dietitians 1 (pt); Dentists 1 (pt); Ophthalmologists 1 (pt); Podiatrists 1 (pt).
Affiliation Roman Catholic

POINT PLEASANT

Claremont Care Center
1550 Hulse Rd, Point Pleasant, NJ, 08742
(201) 295-9300
Admin LaVerne T Kennedy. *Medical Dir/Dir of Nursing* Dolores Phoel RN.
Licensure Skilled care. *Beds* SNF 112. *Certified* Medicaid; Medicare.
Owner Proprietary Corp (Genesis Health Ventures).
Admissions Requirements Physician's request.
Staff RNs 6 (ft), 2 (pt); LPNs 6 (ft), 2 (pt); Nurses aides 24 (ft), 1 (pt); Activities coordinators 1 (ft); Dietitians 1 (ft); 29 (ft), 16 (pt).
Facilities Dining room; Physical therapy room; Activities room; Barber/Beauty shop; TV Room; Patio.
Activities Arts & crafts; Cards; Games; Reading groups; Prayer groups; Movies; Shopping trips; Social/Cultural gatherings.

Point Pleasant Beach Nursing Home*
703 Richmond Ave, Point Pleasant, NJ, 08742
(201) 899-2525
Admin William Graubit.
Licensure Intermediate care. *Beds* 27. *Certified* Medicaid.

PRINCETON

Princeton Nursing Home*
35 Quarry St, Princeton, NJ, 08540
(609) 924-9000
Admin William Bogner.
Licensure Skilled care; Intermediate care. *Beds* 119. *Certified* Medicaid; Medicare.

RAHWAY

Rahway Geriatrics Center Inc
1777 Lawrence St, Rahway, NJ, 07065
(201) 499-7927
Admin Jeffrey S Schwartz. *Medical Dir/Dir of Nursing* Virginia Quintong MD.
Licensure Skilled care. *Beds* SNF 120. *Certified* Medicaid; Medicare.
Owner Nonprofit Corp.
Admissions Requirements Minimum age 18; Medical examination; Physician's request.
Staff RNs 7 (ft); Nurses aides 40 (ft); Physical therapists 1 (pt); Recreational therapists 3 (ft); Activities coordinators 1 (ft); Dietitians 1 (pt).
Languages French, Spanish
Facilities Dining room; Physical therapy room; Activities room; Chapel; Crafts room; Laundry room; Barber/Beauty shop; Library.
Activities Arts & crafts; Cards; Games; Reading groups; Prayer groups; Movies; Shopping trips; Social/Cultural gatherings.

RARITAN

Raritan Health & Extended Care Center*
Rte 28, Raritan, NJ, 08869
(201) 526-8950
Admin Michael Greenberg.
Licensure Skilled care; Intermediate care. *Beds* 128. *Certified* Medicaid; Medicare.

RED BANK

Red Bank Convalescent Center
PO Box 2030, 100 Chapin Ave, Red Bank, NJ, 07701
(201) 741-8811
Admin Ethelyn Leiblich. *Medical Dir/Dir of Nursing* Victor Siegel MD; Wilma Radcliffe RN DON.
Licensure Skilled care; Intermediate care; Respite. *Beds* 180. *Certified* Medicaid.
Owner Proprietary Corp.
Admissions Requirements Minimum age 65; Medical examination.
Staff Physicians 13 (pt); RNs 6 (ft), 9 (pt); LPNs 1 (ft), 4 (pt); Orderlies 3 (ft), 1 (pt); Nurses aides 57 (ft), 20 (pt); Physical therapists 1 (pt); Speech therapists 1 (pt); Activities coordinators 1 (ft); Dietitians 1 (ft); Dentists 1 (pt); Ophthalmologists 1 (pt); Podiatrists 1 (pt); Social worker 1 (ft).
Languages Spanish, French, German
Facilities Dining room; Physical therapy room; Activities room; Chapel; Crafts room; Laundry room; Barber/Beauty shop; Patio & picnic area.
Activities Arts & crafts; Cards; Games; Reading groups; Prayer groups; Movies; Social/Cultural gatherings; Outings; Adopted grandparent programs; Family support groups; Pet therapy; Library visits.

Red Bank Medicenter*
55 W Front St, Red Bank, NJ, 07701
(201) 842-3800
Admin Donald Bisgrove.
Licensure Skilled care; Intermediate care. *Beds* 104. *Certified* Medicaid; Medicare.

RIDGEWOOD

Pine Rest Nursing Home*
PO Box 71, E Ridgewood Ave, Ridgewood, NJ, 07450
(201) 652-1950
Admin William Maloney.
Licensure Long-Term care. *Beds* 50.

Ridgewood Home*
330 Franklin Turnpike, Ridgewood, NJ, 07451
(201) 447-1900

Admin Thomas Sheehy. *Medical Dir/Dir of Nursing* Bernard Sklar MD.
Licensure Skilled care; Intermediate care. *Beds* 90. *Certified* Medicaid; Medicare.
Admissions Requirements Minimum age 18; Physician's request.
Activities Arts & crafts; Cards; Games; Reading groups; Prayer groups; Movies; Shopping trips; Social/Cultural gatherings.

Van Dyk Nursing & Convalescent Home
304 S Van Dien Ave, Ridgewood, NJ, 07450
(201) 445-8200
Admin William & Marvin Van Dyk. *Medical Dir/Dir of Nursing* Dr William Hopewell MD; Ruth Husselman RN DON.
Licensure Skilled care. *Beds* SNF 93.
Owner Proprietary Corp.
Admissions Requirements Minimum age 18.
Staff RNs 4 (ft), 8 (pt); LPNs 1 (ft), 5 (pt); Nurses aides 34 (ft), 24 (pt); Speech therapists 1 (pt); Activities coordinators 2 (ft); Dietitians 1 (ft), 1 (pt); Dentists 1 (pt); Ophthalmologists 2 (pt).
Facilities Dining room; Activities room; Chapel; Crafts room; Laundry room; Barber/Beauty shop; Library.
Activities Arts & crafts; Cards; Games; Reading groups; Movies.

SADDLE BROOK

Brook Wood Convalescent Home
30 Legregni St, Saddle Brook, NJ, 07662
(201) 843-8411
Admin Frederick Soilson. *Medical Dir/Dir of Nursing* Thomas Bellavia MD; Ann Barlas RN DON.
Licensure Skilled care. *Beds* SNF 52. *Certified* Medicaid.
Owner Proprietary Corp.
Admissions Requirements Minimum age 40.
Staff Physicians 6 (pt); RNs 3 (ft), 3 (pt); LPNs 6 (pt); Physical therapists 1 (pt); Activities coordinators 1 (ft), 1 (pt); Dietitians 1 (pt); Dentists 1 (pt); Ophthalmologists 1 (pt); Podiatrists 1 (pt).
Languages Spanish
Facilities Dining room; Barber/Beauty shop.
Activities Arts & crafts; Cards; Games; Reading groups; Prayer groups; Movies; Bingo; Parties.

Saddle Brook Convalescent Home*
15 Caldwell St, Saddle Brook, NJ, 07663
(201) 843-7333
Admin Frederick Soilson. *Medical Dir/Dir of Nursing* Dr Bernard Ross.
Licensure Skilled care; Intermediate care. *Beds* 52. *Certified* Medicaid.
Staff RNs 2 (ft), 3 (pt); LPNs 5 (pt); Nurses aides 9 (ft), 8 (pt); Physical therapists 1 (pt); Recreational therapists 1 (pt); Activities coordinators 1 (pt); Dietitians 1 (pt); Dentists 2 (pt); Podiatrists 2 (pt).
Facilities Dining room; Activities room; Laundry room; Barber/Beauty shop.
Activities Arts & crafts; Cards; Games; Reading groups; Prayer groups; Movies; Shopping trips; Social/Cultural gatherings.

SALEM

Salem County Nursing Home
438 Woodstown Rd, Salem, NJ, 08079
(609) 935-6677
Admin Lee Lanning. *Medical Dir/Dir of Nursing* John S Madara MD.
Licensure Skilled care. *Beds* SNF 110. *Certified* Medicaid; Medicare.
Owner Publicly owned.
Admissions Requirements Minimum age 18; Medical examination; Physician's request.
Staff Physicians 12 (pt); RNs 4 (ft), 4 (pt); LPNs 10 (ft), 2 (pt); Orderlies 3 (ft); Nurses aides 49 (ft); Physical therapists 1 (ft); Recreational therapists 2 (ft); Occupational

therapists 1 (pt); Speech therapists 1 (ft), 1 (pt); Dietitians 1 (pt); Ophthalmologists 3 (pt); Podiatrists 1 (pt); Dentist 1 (pt).
Facilities Dining room; Physical therapy room; Activities room; Crafts room; Laundry room; Barber/Beauty shop.
Activities Arts & crafts; Cards; Games; Reading groups; Prayer groups; Movies; Shopping trips; Social/Cultural gatherings.

SCOTCH PLAINS

Ashbrook Nursing Home
1610 Raritan Rd, Scotch Plains, NJ, 07076
(201) 889-5500
Admin Daniel Moles.
Licensure Skilled care; Intermediate care. *Beds* 120. *Certified* Medicaid; Medicare.

SEWELL

Health Care Center at Washington
PO Box 110A, RR 1, Sewell, NJ, 08080
(609) 582-3170
Admin Anthony Peters. *Medical Dir/Dir of Nursing* Thomas Cavalieri MD; Kathry Hughes RN DON.
Licensure Skilled care; Intermediate care. *Beds* 120. *Certified* Medicaid; Medicare.
Owner Nonprofit Corp.
Admissions Requirements Minimum age 16; Physician's request.
Staff Physicians 11 (pt); RNs 6 (ft), 2 (pt); LPNs 14 (ft), 4 (pt); Nurses aides 36 (ft), 9 (pt); Physical therapists 2 (pt); Recreational therapists 2 (ft), 1 (pt); Occupational therapists 1 (pt); Speech therapists 1 (pt); Dietitians 1 (ft); Dentists 1 (pt); Ophthalmologists 1 (pt); Podiatrists 1 (pt).
Activities Arts & crafts; Cards; Games; Reading groups; Prayer groups; Movies; Shopping trips; Social/Cultural gatherings; Physical ed.

Pinecrest Nursing & Convalescent Home
PO Box 146, Salina & Glassboro-Woodbury Rd, Sewell, NJ, 08080
(609) 468-2500
Admin Ralph Moore. *Medical Dir/Dir of Nursing* Robert Schwartz DO.
Licensure Skilled care; Intermediate care. *Beds* 226. *Certified* Medicaid; Medicare.
Owner Proprietary Corp.
Staff Physicians 12 (ft); RNs 10 (ft), 4 (pt); LPNs 16 (ft), 3 (pt); Orderlies 6 (ft), 2 (pt); Nurses aides 70 (ft), 20 (pt); Physical therapists; Speech therapists; Activities coordinators; Dietitians; Dentists; Ophthalmologists; Podiatrists.
Facilities Dining room; Physical therapy room; Activities room; Laundry room; Barber/Beauty shop; Enclosed patio.
Activities Arts & crafts; Cards; Games; Reading groups; Prayer groups; Movies; Shopping trips; Social/Cultural gatherings.

SHREWSBURY

Shrewsbury Manor Nursing Home
515 Shrewsbury Ave, Shrewsbury, NJ, 07704
(201) 741-2059
Admin Eleanor J Johnson.
Licensure Residential health care facility. *Beds* 35.

SOMERS POINT

Ocean Point Health Care Center*
555 Bay Ave, Somers Point, NJ, 08244
(609) 927-9151
Admin Charle A Wilkins. *Medical Dir/Dir of Nursing* Dr Stanley Edden.
Licensure Skilled care; Intermediate care. *Beds* 145. *Certified* Medicaid; Medicare.

Facilities Dining room; Physical therapy room; Activities room; Chapel; Crafts room; Laundry room; Barber/Beauty shop; Library.
Activities Arts & crafts; Cards; Games; Reading groups; Prayer groups; Movies; Shopping trips; Social/Cultural gatherings.

SOMERSET

Central New Jersey Jewish Home for the Aged
380 DeMott Ln, Somerset, NJ, 08857
(201) 873-2000
Admin Elliott V Solomon. *Medical Dir/Dir of Nursing* Lawrence Gross MD.
Licensure Skilled care. *Beds* 245. *Certified* Medicaid.
Owner Nonprofit organization/foundation; Nonprofit Corp.
Admissions Requirements Minimum age 65; Medical examination.
Staff Physicians 3 (ft); RNs 20 (ft); LPNs 20 (ft); Nurses aides 74 (ft); Physical therapists 1 (ft); Recreational therapists 6 (ft); Speech therapists 1 (pt); Activities coordinators 1 (ft); Dietitians 1 (ft); Dentists 1 (pt); Ophthalmologists 2 (pt).
Languages Yiddish, Hebrew
Affiliation Jewish
Facilities Dining room; Physical therapy room; Activities room; Chapel; Crafts room; Barber/Beauty shop; Library.
Activities Arts & crafts; Cards; Games; Reading groups; Prayer groups; Movies; Shopping trips; Social/Cultural gatherings.

King James Care Center of Somerset*
1165 Easton Ave, Somerset, NJ, 08873
(201) 246-4100
Admin Egon Scheil.
Licensure Skilled care; Intermediate care. *Beds* 180. *Certified* Medicaid; Medicare.

SOUTH AMBOY

Oakview Care Center
Ernston Rd, South Amboy, NJ, 08879
(201) 721-8200
Admin David C Smith. *Medical Dir/Dir of Nursing* Fernando Rodriguez MD; Maxine Kaufman RN.
Licensure Skilled care; Intermediate care. *Beds* SNF 220. *Certified* Medicaid; Medicare.
Owner Proprietary Corp.
Admissions Requirements Minimum age 16; Medical examination; Physician's request.
Staff RNs 10 (ft), 5 (pt); LPNs 10 (ft), 5 (pt); Orderlies 50 (ft), 20 (pt); Physical therapists 1 (ft); Reality therapists 5 (ft); Occupational therapists 1 (pt); Speech therapists 1 (pt); Activities coordinators 1 (pt); Dietitians 1 (pt); Dentists 1 (pt); Ophthalmologists 1 (pt); Podiatrists 1 (pt).
Languages Italian, German
Facilities Dining room; Physical therapy room; Activities room; Chapel; Barber/Beauty shop.
Activities Arts & crafts; Cards; Games; Reading groups; Prayer groups; Movies; Shopping trips; Social/Cultural gatherings.

STRATFORD

Stratford Nursing & Convalescent Center*
Laurel & Warwick Rd, Stratford, NJ, 08084
(609) 784-2400
Admin Anne McNally.
Licensure Skilled care; Intermediate care. *Beds* 104. *Certified* Medicaid; Medicare.

SUCCASUNNA

Merry Heart Nursing Home
200 Rte 10, Succasunna, NJ, 07876
(201) 584-4000
Admin John P Kadimik. *Medical Dir/Dir of Nursing* Muriel Shevac RN DON.

Licensure Skilled care. *Beds* SNF 61. *Certified* Medicaid; Medicare.
Owner Proprietary Corp.
Admissions Requirements Medical examination; Physician's request.
Facilities Dining room; Activities room; Crafts room; Laundry room; Barber/Beauty shop; Library.
Activities Arts & crafts; Cards; Games; Reading groups; Prayer groups; Movies; Shopping trips; Social/Cultural gatherings; Variety; Music; Gourmet club; Resident's council.

TEANECK

Teaneck Nursing Home
1104 Teaneck Rd T, Teaneck, NJ, 07666
(201) 833-2400
Admin Linda Tober. *Medical Dir/Dir of Nursing* Dr Harvey Gross; Toni Krug.
Licensure Skilled care; Intermediate care. *Beds* 107. *Certified* Medicaid; Medicare.
Owner Privately owned.
Admissions Requirements Minimum age 65.
Staff Physicians 1 (ft), 3 (pt); RNs 9 (ft), 2 (pt); LPNs 3 (ft), 7 (pt); Nurses aides 25 (ft), 7 (pt); Physical therapists 1 (ft); Recreational therapists 2 (ft), 1 (pt); Speech therapists 1 (pt); Activities coordinators 1 (ft); Dietitians 1 (pt); Dentists 1 (pt); Ophthalmologists 1 (pt); Podiatrists 1 (pt).
Facilities Dining room; Physical therapy room; Activities room; Crafts room; Laundry room; Barber/Beauty shop; Library.
Activities Arts & crafts; Cards; Games; Reading groups; Prayer groups; Movies; Shopping trips; Social/Cultural gatherings.

TENAFLY

County Manor Nursing Home
133 County Rd, Tenafly, NJ, 07670
(201) 567-7800
Admin Ronald Pearl.
Licensure Skilled care; Intermediate care. *Beds* 64. *Certified* Medicare.
Staff Physicians; RNs; LPNs; Nurses aides; Physical therapists; Recreational therapists; Occupational therapists; Speech therapists; Activities coordinators; Dietitians; Dentists; Ophthalmologists; Podiatrists.
Facilities Dining room; Physical therapy room; Activities room; Chapel; Crafts room; Laundry room; Barber/Beauty shop; Library.
Activities Arts & crafts; Cards; Games; Reading groups; Prayer groups; Movies.

TINTON FALLS

Heritage Hall Nursing Home
524 Wardell Rd, Tinton Falls, NJ, 07753
(201) 922-9330
Admin Elliott Wiener. *Medical Dir/Dir of Nursing* Dr Marshal Silver; Arlene Pollack RN DON.
Licensure Skilled care; Intermediate care. *Beds* 115. *Certified* Medicaid.
Owner Proprietary Corp.
Admissions Requirements Medical examination.
Facilities Dining room; Activities room; Crafts room; Laundry room; Barber/Beauty shop; Library.
Activities Arts & crafts; Cards; Games; Prayer groups; Movies; Social/Cultural gatherings.

TOMS RIVER

Country Manor Nursing Home
16 Whitesville Rd, Toms River, NJ, 08753
(201) 341-1600
Admin Arnold Weiner. *Medical Dir/Dir of Nursing* Dr Jacob Goldstein; Jane Vega.

Licensure Skilled care; Intermediate care;
Coma Treatment. *Beds* SNF 218; ICF;
Coma Treatment. *Certified* Medicaid;
Medicare.
Owner Nonprofit Corp.
Admissions Requirements Physician's request.
Staff Physicians 1 (ft), 20 (pt); RNs 16 (ft), 13
(pt); LPNs 17 (ft), 19 (pt); Orderlies 3 (ft), 1
(pt); Nurses aides 80 (ft), 48 (pt); Physical
therapists 1 (ft); Reality therapists 5 (ft), 2
(pt); Recreational therapists 5 (ft);
Occupational therapists 4 (pt); Speech
therapists 1 (pt); Activities coordinators 1
(ft); Dietitians 1 (pt); Dentists 1 (pt);
Ophthalmologists 1 (pt); Podiatrists 1 (pt).
Facilities Dining room; Physical therapy
room; Activities room; Chapel; Crafts room;
Barber/Beauty shop; Library; Occupational
therapy room.
Activities Arts & crafts; Cards; Games;
Reading groups; Prayer groups; Movies;
Shopping trips; Social/Cultural gatherings;
Wheelchair square dancing; Pet therapy;
Greenhouse.

Toms River Convalescent Center*
Hospital Dr, Toms River, NJ, 08753
(201) 244-3100
Admin Jasper B Phelps. *Medical Dir/Dir of
Nursing* Jeffrey Brustein MD.
Licensure Skilled care; Intermediate care. *Beds*
100. *Certified* Medicaid; Medicare.

TOTOWA BORO

Valley Rest Nursing Home
56 Bogert St, Totowa Boro, NJ, 07512
(201) 942-2534
Admin Marion Henze. *Medical Dir/Dir of
Nursing* Dr Jan Barnes.
Licensure Skilled care; Intermediate care. *Beds*
32. *Certified* Medicaid.
Admissions Requirements Minimum age 65;
Medical examination.
Staff Physicians 1 (pt); RNs 5 (ft), 2 (pt);
LPNs 2 (ft), 3 (pt); Nurses aides 12 (ft), 10
(pt); Physical therapists 1 (pt); Recreational
therapists 1 (ft); Occupational therapists 1
(pt); Speech therapists 1 (pt); Activities
coordinators 1 (ft); Dietitians 1 (pt);
Ophthalmologists 1 (pt).
Languages Italian
Facilities Dining room; Activities room;
Laundry room.
Activities Arts & crafts; Cards; Games;
Reading groups; Prayer groups; Movies;
Shopping trips; Social/Cultural gatherings;
Dining out; Picnics.

TRENTON

Bellevue Care Center*
439 Bellevue Ave, Trenton, NJ, 08618
(609) 396-2646
Admin Mary Ann McCarty. *Medical Dir/Dir
of Nursing* Dr Richard Gordon.
Licensure Skilled care; Intermediate care. *Beds*
100. *Certified* Medicaid; Medicare.
Staff Physicians 4 (pt); RNs 4 (ft), 4 (pt);
LPNs 4 (ft), 6 (pt); Nurses aides 50 (ft), 20
(pt); Physical therapists 1 (pt); Occupational
therapists 1 (pt); Speech therapists 1 (pt);
Activities coordinators 1 (ft); Dietitians 1
(pt); Dentists 1 (pt); Ophthalmologists 1 (pt);
Podiatrists 1 (pt); Audiologists 1 (pt).
Facilities Dining room; Physical therapy
room; Activities room; Crafts room; Laundry
room; Barber/Beauty shop.
Activities Arts & crafts; Cards; Games;
Reading groups; Prayer groups; Movies;
Social/Cultural gatherings.

Ewing Parkway Nursing Home*
1201 Parkway Ave, Trenton, NJ, 08628
(609) 882-6900
Admin Paul Galas.

Licensure Skilled care; Intermediate care. *Beds*
102. *Certified* Medicaid; Medicare.

King James Care Center of Mercer
1501 State Hwy 33, Trenton, NJ, 08690
(609) 586-1114
Admin Lori Gabriel. *Medical Dir/Dir of
Nursing* Dr Albert Valenzuela; Jean
Anderson RN.
Licensure Skilled care; Intermediate care. *Beds*
120. *Certified* Medicaid; Medicare.
Owner Proprietary Corp.
Admissions Requirements Minimum age 16;
Medical examination.
Staff Physicians 13 (ft); RNs 5 (ft), 4 (pt);
LPNs 9 (ft), 2 (pt); Orderlies 3 (ft); Nurses
aides 44 (ft), 4 (pt); Physical therapists 1 (ft),
1 (pt); Reality therapists 1 (ft); Recreational
therapists 2 (ft), 1 (pt); Occupational
therapists 1 (pt); Speech therapists 1 (pt);
Activities coordinators 1 (ft); Dietitians 1
(ft), 1 (pt); Dentists 1 (pt); Ophthalmologists
1 (pt); Podiatrists 1 (pt); Dietary staff 8 (ft),
2 (pt).
Languages Polish, Italian
Facilities Dining room; Physical therapy
room; Activities room; Crafts room; Laundry
room; Barber/Beauty shop; Library.
Activities Arts & crafts; Cards; Games;
Reading groups; Prayer groups; Movies;
Shopping trips; Social/Cultural gatherings;
Barbecue.

**Mercer County Geriatric Center—F W
Donnelly Long-Term Care Facility**
2300 Hamilton Ave, Trenton, NJ, 08619
(609) 588-5859
Admin Steven R Mellion. *Medical Dir/Dir of
Nursing* A Strauss MD.
Licensure Skilled care; Intermediate care. *Beds*
240. *Certified* Medicaid.
Staff Physicians 3 (ft), 1 (pt); RNs 15 (ft), 10
(pt); LPNs 30 (ft), 15 (pt); Nurses aides 91
(ft), 28 (pt); Physical therapists 1 (pt);
Recreational therapists 7 (ft); Occupational
therapists 1 (pt); Speech therapists 1 (pt);
Activities coordinators 1 (ft); Dietitians 1
(ft); Dentists 1 (pt); Ophthalmologists 1 (pt);
Podiatrists 1 (pt); Dentist 1 (pt).

UNION

Cornell Hall Convalescent Center
234 Chestnut St, Union, NJ, 07083
(201) 687-7800
Admin Elizabeth Bataille. *Medical Dir/Dir of
Nursing* Joseph E McDonald MD; Bette
Goodrich DON.
Licensure Skilled care; Intermediate care;
Residential. *Beds* SNF 160; ICF; Residential
20. *Certified* Medicaid; Medicare.
Owner Nonprofit Corp.
Admissions Requirements Minimum age 18;
Medical examination; Physician's request.
Staff Physicians 1 (pt); RNs 8 (ft), 12 (pt);
LPNs 8 (ft), 8 (pt); Nurses aides 54 (ft), 3
(pt); Recreational therapists 3 (ft), 1 (pt);
Dietitians 1 (pt).
Languages Spanish, Polish, Italian
Facilities Dining room; Physical therapy
room; Activities room; Chapel; Crafts room;
Laundry room; Barber/Beauty shop; Library;
Speech therapy; Kosher meal.
Activities Arts & crafts; Cards; Games;
Reading groups; Prayer groups; Movies;
Shopping trips; Social/Cultural gatherings;
Van rides; Picnics; Entertainers.

VINELAND

Bishop McCarthy Residence
1045 E Chestnut Ave, Vineland, NJ, 08360
(609) 692-2850
Admin Sr Mary Elvira. *Medical Dir/Dir of
Nursing* Nicholas Marchione MD.
Licensure Skilled care; Intermediate care. *Beds*
147. *Certified* Medicaid; Medicare.

Owner Nonprofit organization/foundation.
Admissions Requirements Medical
examination; Physician's request.
Staff Physicians 10 (pt); RNs 5 (ft), 4 (pt);
Nurses aides 51 (ft), 18 (pt); Physical
therapists 1 (pt); Occupational therapists 1
(pt) 13J 1 (pt); Activities coordinators 2 (ft),
1 (pt); Dietitians 1 (pt).
Languages Spanish, Italian, Russian
Affiliation Roman Catholic
Facilities Dining room; Physical therapy
room; Activities room; Chapel; Crafts room;
Laundry room; Barber/Beauty shop; Library.
Activities Arts & crafts; Cards; Games; Prayer
groups; Movies; Shopping trips; Social/
Cultural gatherings.

WALL TOWNSHIP

Tower Lodge Nursing Home
1506 Gully Rd, Wall Township, NJ, 07719
(201) 681-1400
Admin William J Seaman. *Medical Dir/Dir of
Nursing* Dr Young Kong; Elizabeth C
Bruton RN.
Licensure Skilled care; Intermediate care. *Beds*
SNF 60; ICF. *Certified* Medicaid; Medicare.
Owner Proprietary Corp.
Admissions Requirements Medical
examination; Physician's request.
Staff Physicians 15 (pt); RNs 3 (ft), 5 (pt);
LPNs 3 (ft), 2 (pt); Nurses aides 18 (ft), 6
(pt); Physical therapists 1 (pt); Recreational
therapists 1 (pt); Occupational therapists 1
(pt); Speech therapists 1 (pt); Activities
coordinators 1 (ft), 1 (pt); Dietitians 1 (pt);
Dentists 1 (pt); Ophthalmologists 1 (pt).
Facilities Dining room; Physical therapy
room; Activities room; Crafts room; Laundry
room.
Activities Arts & crafts; Cards; Games; Prayer
groups; Movies; Bazaars; Picnics; Parties;
Bowling.

WAYNE

Alps Manor Nursing Home*
1120 Alps Rd, Wayne, NJ, 07470
(201) 694-2100
Admin Robert Guggenheim. *Medical Dir/Dir
of Nursing* Paule Topalovic.
Licensure Skilled care; Intermediate care. *Beds*
197. *Certified* Medicaid.
Staff RNs 9 (ft), 4 (pt); LPNs 2 (ft), 1 (pt);
Orderlies 8 (ft); Nurses aides 38 (ft), 2 (pt);
Recreational therapists 2 (ft), 1 (pt);
Activities coordinators 1 (ft); Dietitians 1
(pt).
Facilities Dining room; Physical therapy
room; Activities room; Laundry room;
Barber/Beauty shop.
Activities Arts & crafts; Cards; Games;
Reading groups; Prayer groups; Movies;
Shopping trips; Social/Cultural gatherings;
Picnics.

Lakeview Convalescent Center
130 Terhune Dr, Wayne, NJ, 07470
(201) 839-4500
Admin Richard Grosso Jr. *Medical Dir/Dir of
Nursing* Dr Schlossberg; Margaret Nolan
DON.
Licensure Skilled care; Intermediate care. *Beds*
SNF 108; ICF 108; special care 12. *Certified*
Medicaid; Medicare.
Owner Proprietary Corp.
Staff Physicians 1 (ft), 16 (pt); RNs 11 (ft), 4
(pt); LPNs 4 (ft), 4 (pt); Nurses aides 34 (ft),
18 (pt); Physical therapists 1 (ft); Reality
therapists 1 (pt); Recreational therapists 1
(ft), 2 (pt); Occupational therapists 1 (pt);
Speech therapists 1 (pt); Activities
coordinators 1 (pt); Dietitians 1 (pt); Dentists
1 (pt); Ophthalmologists 1 (pt); Podiatrists 1
(pt); Social workers 1 (pt); Respiratory
therapists 3 (ft), 2 (pt).
Languages Spanish, Hebrew, Yiddish, Italian

Facilities Dining room; Physical therapy room; Activities room; Crafts room; Laundry room; Barber/Beauty shop; Library; Dental office.
Activities Arts & crafts; Cards; Games; Reading groups; Prayer groups; Movies; Shopping trips; Social/Cultural gatherings.

Llanfair House*
1140 Black Oak Ridge Rd, Wayne, NJ, 07470
(201) 835-7443
Admin Adrienne Mayernik.
Licensure Skilled care; Intermediate care. *Beds* 180. *Certified* Medicaid; Medicare.

North Jersey Nursing Center
296 Hamburg Tpke, Wayne, NJ, 07470
(201) 956-8007
Admin Isadore Zuckerman. *Medical Dir/Dir of Nursing* Robert Brabston MD; Thoma Rubino.
Licensure Skilled care. *Beds* 120. *Certified* Medicaid; Medicare.
Owner Proprietary Corp.
Admissions Requirements Medical examination.
Staff Physicians 1 (pt); RNs 8 (ft); LPNs; Nurses aides 16 (ft), 25 (pt); Physical therapists 1 (pt); Recreational therapists; Occupational therapists 1 (pt); Speech therapists; Activities coordinators; Dietitians; Dentists; Ophthalmologists.
Facilities Dining room; Physical therapy room; Activities room; Crafts room; Laundry room; Barber/Beauty shop.
Activities Arts & crafts; Cards; Games; Reading groups; Prayer groups; Movies; Shopping trips; Social/Cultural gatherings.

Oak Ridge Manor Nursing Center
261 Terhune Dr, Wayne, NJ, 07470
(201) 835-3871
Admin Denise Dunlap Ratcliffe. *Medical Dir/Dir of Nursing* Dr Seymour Schlossberg; Monica Koller-Maguire RN DON.
Licensure Skilled care. *Beds* SNF 120. *Certified* Medicaid; Medicare.
Owner Proprietary Corp (Continental Medical Systems).
Admissions Requirements Minimum age 16; Medical examination.
Staff RNs 6 (ft), 8 (pt); LPNs 4 (ft), 5 (pt); Orderlies 1 (ft); Nurses aides 45 (ft), 12 (pt); Physical therapists 1 (pt); Recreational therapists 1 (ft), 2 (pt); Occupational therapists; Speech therapists; Activities coordinators 1 (ft); Dietitians; Dentists; Ophthalmologists; Podiatrists; Respiratory therapist.
Languages Spanish, Polish, Russian, Italian
Facilities Dining room; Physical therapy room; Activities room; Crafts room; Laundry room; Barber/Beauty shop; Occupational therapy room; Visitor lounge.
Activities Arts & crafts; Cards; Games; Reading groups; Prayer groups; Movies; Shopping trips; Shopping trips; Cooking club; Horticulture club.

Wayne Haven Nursing Home
493 Black Oak Ridge Rd, Wayne, NJ, 07470
(201) 694-1842
Admin James Codiroli. *Medical Dir/Dir of Nursing* Mary Zabriskie RN DON.
Licensure Skilled care; Intermediate care. *Beds* 44.
Owner Proprietary Corp.
Admissions Requirements Minimum age 18.
Staff RNs 2 (ft), 2 (pt); LPNs 1 (ft), 1 (pt); Nurses aides 16 (ft), 6 (pt); Activities coordinators 1 (ft); Dietitians 1 (pt).
Facilities Dining room; Activities room; Laundry room; Barber/Beauty shop.
Activities Arts & crafts; Cards; Games; Prayer groups; Movies.

WEST MILFORD

Milford Manor Nursing Home
60 Maple Rd, West Milford, NJ, 07480
(201) 697-5640
Admin Donald Lynch. *Medical Dir/Dir of Nursing* Dr Le.
Licensure New concepts in health care. *Beds* 100.
Admissions Requirements Medical examination; Physician's request.
Staff Physicians; RNs; LPNs; Nurses aides; Physical therapists; Reality therapists; Recreational therapists; Occupational therapists; Activities coordinators; Dietitians; Dentists; Ophthalmologists; Podiatrists.

WEST ORANGE

Daughters of Israel Pleasant Valley Home*
1155 Pleasant Valley Way, West Orange, NJ, 07052
(201) 731-5100
Admin Lawrence Gelfand. *Medical Dir/Dir of Nursing* Raymond Cogan MD.
Licensure Skilled care; Intermediate care. *Certified* Medicaid; Medicare.
Owner Nonprofit Corp.
Admissions Requirements Minimum age 65.
Staff Physicians 1 (ft), 5 (pt); RNs 22 (ft), 16 (pt); LPNs 29 (ft), 5 (pt); Orderlies 9 (ft); Nurses aides 71 (ft), 10 (pt); Physical therapists 2 (pt); Recreational therapists 6 (ft); Occupational therapists 1 (ft); Activities coordinators 1 (ft); Dietitians 1 (ft); Dentists 1 (pt); Podiatrists 1 (pt); Male aides 9 (ft).
Affiliation Jewish
Facilities Dining room; Physical therapy room; Activities room; Chapel; Barber/Beauty shop; Library.
Activities Arts & crafts; Cards; Games; Reading groups; Prayer groups; Movies; Shopping trips; Social/Cultural gatherings.

Theresa Grotta Center for Rehabilitation
20 Summit St, West Orange, NJ, 07052
(201) 736-2000
Admin Robert Meyers. *Medical Dir/Dir of Nursing* Dr S Jaslow; Diane McEvoy DON.
Licensure Skilled care; Intermediate care; Rehabilitation. *Beds* 142. *Certified* Medicaid; Medicare.
Owner Nonprofit Corp.
Admissions Requirements Minimum age 18; Medical examination.
Staff Physicians 6 (pt); RNs 12 (ft), 3 (pt); LPNs 5 (ft), 3 (pt); Nurses aides 44 (ft); Physical therapists 7 (ft); Recreational therapists 3 (ft); Occupational therapists 3 (ft); Speech therapists 2 (ft); Activities coordinators 1 (ft); Dietitians 1 (ft).
Languages Spanish, Polish
Facilities Dining room; Physical therapy room; Activities room; Crafts room; Laundry room; Barber/Beauty shop; Library.
Activities Arts & crafts; Cards; Games; Reading groups; Prayer groups; Movies; Shopping trips; Social/Cultural gatherings.

Northfield Manor Nursing Home
787 Northfield Ave, West Orange, NJ, 07052
(201) 731-4500
Admin William J Rose. *Medical Dir/Dir of Nursing* Dr Joseph Aaron; M J Eicke.
Licensure Skilled care; Intermediate care. *Beds* SNF 131. *Certified* Medicare.
Owner Proprietary Corp.
Staff Physicians 1 (pt); RNs 7 (ft), 5 (pt); LPNs 9 (ft), 5 (pt); Nurses aides 56 (ft), 10 (pt); Physical therapists 2 (pt); Reality therapists 2 (ft), 1 (pt); Recreational therapists 2 (ft), 1 (pt); Occupational therapists 1 (pt); Speech therapists 1 (pt); Activities coordinators 1 (ft); Dietitians 1 (pt); Dentists 1 (pt); Ophthalmologists 1 (pt); Podiatrists 1 (pt).

Facilities Dining room; Physical therapy room; Activities room; Crafts room; Laundry room; Barber/Beauty shop; Library.
Activities Arts & crafts; Cards; Games; Reading groups; Prayer groups; Movies; Shopping trips; Social/Cultural gatherings.

WESTFIELD

Meridian Nursing Center—Westfield*
1515 Lamberts Mill Rd, Westfield, NJ, 07090
(201) 233-9700
Admin Donald Hillegas. *Medical Dir/Dir of Nursing* Dr Howard Lehr.
Licensure Skilled care; Intermediate care. *Beds* 158. *Certified* Medicaid; Medicare.
Owner Proprietary Corp (Meridan Healthcare).
Staff RNs 7 (ft), 5 (pt); LPNs 8 (ft), 5 (pt); Orderlies 1 (ft), 1 (pt); Physical therapists 3 (pt); Recreational therapists 4 (ft), 2 (pt); Occupational therapists 1 (ft); Speech therapists 1 (pt); Activities coordinators 1 (ft); Dietitians 1 (pt); Dentists 1 (pt).
Facilities Dining room; Physical therapy room; Activities room; Crafts room; Laundry room; Barber/Beauty shop.
Activities Arts & crafts; Cards; Games; Reading groups; Prayer groups; Movies; Shopping trips; Social/Cultural gatherings; Bowling; Aerobics; Pet therapy.

WESTWOOD

Valley Nursing Home*
300 Old Hook Rd, Westwood, NJ, 07675
(201) 664-8888
Admin Dorothy Franklin RN. *Medical Dir/Dir of Nursing* H R Hoff MD.
Licensure Long-Term care. *Beds* 120.
Owner Proprietary Corp.
Admissions Requirements Minimum age 17; Medical examination; Physician's request.
Staff RNs; LPNs; Nurses aides; Physical therapists; Occupational therapists; Speech therapists; Activities coordinators; Dietitians; Dentists; Ophthalmologists; Podiatrists; Audiologists.
Facilities Dining room; Physical therapy room; Activities room; Chapel; Crafts room; Laundry room; Barber/Beauty shop; Library.
Activities Arts & crafts; Cards; Games; Reading groups; Prayer groups; Movies; Shopping trips; Social/Cultural gatherings.

WHIPPANY

Crestwood Nursing Home*
101 Whippany Rd, Whippany, NJ, 07981
(201) 887-0311
Admin William Felts RN.
Licensure Long-Term care. *Beds* 75.

WHITING

Logan Manor Health Care Center
23 Schoolhouse Rd, Whiting, NJ, 08759
(201) 849-4300
Admin Kerry Mulvihill. *Medical Dir/Dir of Nursing* Dr Sundhiem; Virginia Zamorski MD.
Licensure Skilled care; Intermediate care. *Beds* 180. *Certified* Medicaid.
Owner Privately owned.
Staff Physicians; RNs; LPNs; Nurses aides; Physical therapists; Recreational therapists; Speech therapists; Activities coordinators; Dietitians; Ophthalmologists; Podiatrists.
Facilities Dining room; Physical therapy room; Activities room; Crafts room; Laundry room; Barber/Beauty shop.
Activities Arts & crafts; Cards; Games; Prayer groups; Movies; Shopping trips; Social/Cultural gatherings.

WOODBURY

Greenbriar Nursing & Convalescent Center*
190 N Evergreen Ave, Woodbury, NJ, 08096
(609) 848-7400
Admin Edward Zirbser Jr.
Licensure Skilled care; Intermediate care. *Beds* 220. *Certified* Medicaid; Medicare.

WOODCLIFF LAKE

Woodcliff Lake Manor Nursing Home
555 Chestnut Ridge Rd, Woodcliff Lake, NJ, 07675
(201) 391-0900
Admin Marsha Z Squires. *Medical Dir/Dir of Nursing* Williams Barnes MD; Ruth Michaelian RN DON.
Licensure Skilled care. *Beds* SNF 104. *Certified* Medicare.
Owner Proprietary Corp.
Admissions Requirements Minimum age 21.
Staff RNs; LPNs; Orderlies; Nurses aides; Physical therapists; Occupational therapists; Speech therapists; Activities coordinators; Dietitians; Dentists; Podiatrists; Dentist.
Facilities Dining room; Physical therapy room; Activities room; Crafts room; Laundry room; Barber/Beauty shop; Library.
Activities Arts & crafts; Cards; Games; Reading groups; Prayer groups; Movies; Shopping trips; Social/Cultural gatherings.

WOODSTOWN

Friends Home at Woodstown
PO Box 249, Friends Dr, Woodstown, NJ, 08098
(609) 769-1500
Admin Robert C Smith. *Medical Dir/Dir of Nursing* Dr Cipolla; Betty Kaminski RN DON.
Licensure Skilled care; Residential care. *Beds* SNF 60; Residential 60. *Certified* Medicaid; Medicare.
Owner Nonprofit organization/foundation.
Admissions Requirements Minimum age 35; Physician's request.
Staff Physicians 8 (ft); RNs 5 (ft), 4 (pt); LPNs 4 (ft), 5 (pt); Nurses aides 23 (ft), 17 (pt); Physical therapists 1 (pt); Recreational therapists 1 (ft), 1 (pt); Occupational therapists 1 (pt); Speech therapists 1 (pt); Dietitians 1 (pt); Dentists 1 (pt); Ophthalmologists 1 (pt); Podiatrists 1 (pt).
Affiliation Society of Friends
Facilities Dining room; Physical therapy room; Activities room; Chapel; Crafts room; Laundry room; Barber/Beauty shop; Library.
Activities Arts & crafts; Cards; Games; Reading groups; Prayer groups; Movies; Shopping trips; Social/Cultural gatherings.

WYCKOFF

Christian Health Care Center
301 Sicomac Ave, Wyckoff, NJ, 07481
(201) 848-0300
Admin Robert Van Dyk. *Medical Dir/Dir of Nursing* Robert J Oehrig MD; Joan P Craper RN DON.
Licensure Skilled care. *Beds* SNF 120. *Certified* Medicaid; Medicare.
Owner Nonprofit Corp.
Admissions Requirements Minimum age 18.
Staff Physicians 1 (ft), 5 (pt); RNs 5 (ft), 11 (pt); LPNs 6 (ft), 3 (pt); Orderlies 3 (ft), 1 (pt); Nurses aides 39 (ft), 20 (pt); Physical therapists 1 (pt); Recreational therapists 1 (ft); Speech therapists 1 (pt); Activities coordinators 2 (ft); Dietitians 1 (ft); Dentists 1 (pt); Ophthalmologists 1 (pt); Podiatrists 2 (pt).
Affiliation Christian Reformed
Facilities Dining room; Physical therapy room; Activities room; Chapel; Crafts room; Laundry room; Barber/Beauty shop.
Activities Arts & crafts; Cards; Games; Reading groups; Prayer groups; Movies; Shopping trips; Social/Cultural gatherings; Ceramics; Painting class; Jewelry class.

NEW MEXICO

ALAMOGORDO

Betty Dare Good Samaritan Center
Box 538, 3101 N Florida, Alamogordo, NM,
88310
(505) 434-0033
Admin Betty Sadler. *Medical Dir/Dir of
Nursing* Marcia Eastlund RN DON.
Licensure Intermediate care. *Beds* ICF 90.
Certified Medicaid.
Owner Nonprofit Corp (Evangelical Lutheran/
Good Samaritan).
Admissions Requirements Medical
examination; Physician's request.
Staff RNs 1 (ft); LPNs 10 (ft); Nurses aides 30
(ft); Activities coordinators 2 (ft); Dietitians
1 (ft).
Affiliation Lutheran
Facilities Dining room; Physical therapy
room; Activities room; Chapel; Crafts room;
Laundry room; Barber/Beauty shop; Library.
Activities Arts & crafts; Games; Prayer groups;
Movies; Shopping trips; Social/Cultural
gatherings.

ALBUQUERQUE

AARC Group Home 2*
5605 Gibson SE, Albuquerque, NM, 87108
(505) 256-1640
Admin Ralph Herrera. *Medical Dir/Dir of
Nursing* Vodra Cox.
Licensure Intermediate care for mentally
retarded. *Beds* 10. *Certified* Medicaid.

AARC Group Home 3*
5609 Gibson SE, Albuquerque, NM, 87108
(505) 256-0846
Admin Ralph Herrera. *Medical Dir/Dir of
Nursing* Vodra Cox.
Licensure Intermediate care for mentally
retarded. *Beds* 8. *Certified* Medicaid.

Americare-Ladera Health Care Center
5901 Ouray Rd NW, Albuquerque, NM,
87120
(505) 836-0023
Admin Julie A Hofland. *Medical Dir/Dir of
Nursing* Gwen Lucy RN.
Licensure Skilled care; Intermediate care. *Beds*
A 24; ICF 96. *Certified* Medicaid; Medicare.
Owner Proprietary Corp.
Admissions Requirements Medical
examination; Physician's request.
Staff Physicians 1 (pt); RNs 2 (ft), 2 (pt);
LPNs 7 (ft), 4 (pt); Nurses aides 40 (ft), 6
(pt); Occupational therapists 1 (pt); Speech
therapists 1 (pt); Activities coordinators 1
(ft), 1 (pt); Dietitians 1 (pt).
Languages Spanish, Navajo
Facilities Dining room; Physical therapy
room; Activities room; Crafts room; Laundry
room; Barber/Beauty shop; Library.
Activities Arts & crafts; Games; Reading
groups; Prayer groups; Movies; Shopping
trips; Social/Cultural gatherings.

Casa Angelica
5629 Isleta Blvd SW, Albuquerque, NM,
87105
(505) 877-5763
Admin Stella Negri. *Medical Dir/Dir of
Nursing* William K Woodard.
Licensure Nursing home for severely retarded
children. *Beds* 25.
Admissions Requirements Minimum age 6
Months; Medical examination; Physician's
request.
Staff Physicians 1 (pt); RNs 3 (ft); LPNs 1
(ft), 1 (pt); Nurses aides 4 (ft), 14 (pt);
Physical therapists 1 (pt); Occupational
therapists 1 (pt); Speech therapists 1 (pt);
Dietitians 1 (pt); Dentist 1 (pt).
Facilities Dining room; Physical therapy
room; Activities room; Chapel; Laundry
room.

El Centro Villa Nursing Center Inc
236 High St NE, Albuquerque, NM, 87102
(505) 243-3561, 243-3562
Admin Beverly Vaughn. *Medical Dir/Dir of
Nursing* Don Hedges; John Jones.
Licensure Intermediate care. *Beds* ICF 105.
Certified Medicaid.
Owner Proprietary Corp.
Admissions Requirements Medical
examination; Physician's request.
Staff RNs 2 (ft); LPNs 7 (ft), 1 (pt); Orderlies
5 (ft); Nurses aides 25 (ft); Reality therapists
2 (ft); Recreational therapists 3 (ft);
Activities coordinators 1 (ft); Dietitians 1
(pt).
Languages Spanish
Facilities Dining room; Physical therapy
room; Activities room; Chapel; Crafts room;
Laundry room; Barber/Beauty shop; Library.
Activities Arts & crafts; Games; Movies;
Shopping trips; Social/Cultural gatherings.

Four Seasons Nursing Center—Camino Vista*
7900 Constitution NE, Albuquerque, NM,
87110
(505) 296-5567
Admin Alan England.
Licensure Intermediate care. *Beds* 108.
Certified Medicaid.
Owner Proprietary Corp (Manor Care).

**Four Seasons Nursing Center—Northeast
Heights**
2216 Lester Dr NE, Albuquerque, NM, 87112
(505) 296-4808
Admin Dianne Moody. *Medical Dir/Dir of
Nursing* Dr Ed Sager.
Licensure Intermediate care. *Beds* 148.
Certified Medicaid.
Owner Proprietary Corp (Manor Care).
Staff Physicians 1 (pt); RNs 9 (ft), 3 (pt);
LPNs 4 (ft), 4 (pt); Orderlies 6 (ft), 2 (pt);
Nurses aides 46 (ft); Physical therapists 1
(pt); Recreational therapists 1 (pt); Activities
coordinators 1 (ft); Dietitians 1 (ft); Dentists
1 (pt).

Facilities Dining room; Physical therapy
room; Activities room; Crafts room; Laundry
room; Barber/Beauty shop; Conference
room.
Activities Arts & crafts; Cards; Games;
Reading groups; Movies; Shopping trips;
Social/Cultural gatherings; Community
programs; Outings.

Four Seasons Nursing Center—Ridgecrest*
2441 Ridgecrest Dr SE, Albuquerque, NM,
87108
(505) 265-8051
Admin Joyce E Stalgren. *Medical Dir/Dir of
Nursing* Marvin D Call MD.
Licensure Skilled care; Intermediate care. *Beds*
SNF 38; ICF 48. *Certified* Medicaid;
Medicare.
Owner Proprietary Corp (Manor Care).
Admissions Requirements Medical
examination; Physician's request.
Staff Physicians 1 (ft); RNs 3 (ft), 2 (pt);
LPNs 11 (ft); Orderlies 5 (ft); Nurses aides
23 (ft), 2 (pt); Physical therapists 1 (ft), 2
(pt); Reality therapists 1 (pt); Recreational
therapists 1 (ft); Occupational therapists 1
(ft), 1 (pt); Speech therapists 1 (ft), 1 (pt);
Activities coordinators 1 (ft); Dietitians 1
(ft), 1 (pt); Dentists 1 (ft); Ophthalmologists
1 (pt); Podiatrists 1 (ft); Audiologists 1 (pt).
Facilities Dining room; Activities room;
Laundry room; Barber/Beauty shop.
Activities Arts & crafts; Cards; Games;
Reading groups; Prayer groups; Movies;
Shopping trips; Social/Cultural gatherings;
Adapted athletics; City-wide outings; Out for
meals; Companions 'N Caring volunteer
program.

La Vida Llena Retirement Center
10501 La Grima de Oro NE, Albuquerque,
NM, 87111
(505) 296-6700
Admin Leon F Adkins. *Medical Dir/Dir of
Nursing* Marvin Call MD; Dorothy Turrieta
DON.
Licensure Skilled care; Intermediate care. *Beds*
SNF 18; ICF 60. *Certified* Medicaid;
Medicare.
Owner Nonprofit organization/foundation.
Admissions Requirements Medical
examination; Physician's request.
Staff RNs 3 (ft), 3 (pt); LPNs 8 (ft), 5 (pt);
Nurses aides 12 (ft), 6 (pt); Recreational
therapists 1 (pt).
Languages Spanish
Facilities Dining room; Physical therapy
room; Activities room; Crafts room; Laundry
room; Barber/Beauty shop; General store; Ice
cream shop.
Activities Arts & crafts; Cards; Games;
Reading groups; Prayer groups; Movies;
Social/Cultural gatherings.

Manzano del Sol Good Samaritan Village
5201 Roma Ave NE, Albuquerque, NM,
87108
(505) 262-2311

Admin Marilyn Goodsell. *Medical Dir/Dir of
Nursing* Dr Jeff Bleakly.
Licensure Intermediate care. *Beds* 120.
Certified Medicaid.
Owner Nonprofit Corp (Evangelical Lutheran/
Good Samaritan).
Admissions Requirements Medical
examination; Physician's request.
Languages Spanish
Affiliation Lutheran
Facilities Dining room; Physical therapy
room; Activities room; Chapel; Crafts room;
Laundry room; Barber/Beauty shop; Library.
Activities Arts & crafts; Cards; Games;
Reading groups; Prayer groups; Movies;
Shopping trips; Social/Cultural gatherings.

Pickard Presbyterian Convalescent
5900 Forest Hills Dr NE, Albuquerque, NM,
87109
(505) 822-6000
Admin Marta Smith. *Medical Dir/Dir of
Nursing* Louis Levin MD; Jerry Mayfield
RN DON.
Licensure Skilled care; Intermediate care. *Beds*
SNF 30; ICF 90. *Certified* Medicaid;
Medicare.
Owner Nonprofit Corp.
Admissions Requirements Medical
examination.
Staff Physicians 1 (pt); Physical therapists 2
(ft), 1 (pt); Occupational therapists 1 (pt);
Speech therapists 2 (pt); Activities
coordinators 2 (ft); Dietitians 1 (pt);
Ophthalmologists 1 (pt).
Languages Spanish
Facilities Dining room; Physical therapy
room; Activities room; Chapel; Laundry
room; Barber/Beauty shop; Library.
Activities Arts & crafts; Cards; Games;
Reading groups; Prayer groups; Movies;
Shopping trips; Social/Cultural gatherings.

St Francis Gardens Inc
904 Las Lomas Rd, NE, Albuquerque, NM,
87102
(505) 842-1410
Admin Marcia Wegmann. *Medical Dir/Dir of
Nursing* Sr Bernadette Silva DON.
Licensure Intermediate care. *Beds* ICF 135.
Certified Medicaid.
Owner Nonprofit Corp.
Admissions Requirements Minimum age 40;
Medical examination; Physician's request.
Staff RNs 3 (ft); LPNs 11 (ft), 2 (pt); Nurses
aides 58 (ft); Recreational therapists 2 (ft), 1
(pt); Activities coordinators 1 (ft); Dietitians
1 (ft); Dentist 1 (pt).
Languages Spanish
Affiliation Roman Catholic
Facilities Dining room; Activities room;
Chapel; Crafts room; Laundry room; Barber/
Beauty shop; Library; On-site child care.
Activities Arts & crafts; Cards; Games;
Reading groups; Prayer groups; Movies;
Shopping trips; Social/Cultural gatherings;
Conversational Spanish; Pet therapy;
Intergenerational programs; Mass; In-room
visits; Bingo; Outings; Exercise; Snack
programs.

Western Eldercare Nursing Center*
1509 University Blvd NE, Albuquerque, NM,
87102
(505) 243-2257
Admin Floyd Gardner.
Licensure Intermediate care. *Beds* 96.
Certified Medicaid.
Owner Proprietary Corp.

ARTESIA

Artesia Good Samaritan Center*
PO Box 620, 1402 Gilchrist, Artesia, NM,
88210
(505) 746-9865
Admin Dennis Beeman. *Medical Dir/Dir of
Nursing* Shirley Sperling.

Licensure Intermediate care. *Beds* 65.
Certified Medicaid.
Owner Nonprofit Corp (Evangelical Lutheran/
Good Samaritan).
Admissions Requirements Medical
examination; Physician's request.
Staff RNs 2 (ft); LPNs 4 (ft), 8 (pt); Orderlies
1 (pt); Nurses aides 5 (ft), 18 (pt); Reality
therapists 1 (pt); Recreational therapists 1
(ft); Activities coordinators 1 (ft); Dietitians
1 (pt).
Facilities Dining room; Physical therapy
room; Activities room; Chapel; Crafts room;
Laundry room; Barber/Beauty shop.
Activities Arts & crafts; Cards; Games;
Reading groups; Prayer groups; Movies;
Shopping trips.

AZTEC

Four Corners Good Samaritan
500 Care Ln, Aztec, NM, 87401
(505) 334-9445
Admin Michael Hinson.
Licensure Intermediate care. *Beds* Apartments
13 Child day care units 30. *Certified*
Medicaid; VA.
Owner Nonprofit Corp (Evangelical Lutheran/
Good Samaritan).
Staff RNs 4 (ft); LPNs 4 (ft), 3 (pt); Orderlies
1 (ft); Nurses aides 23 (ft), 13 (pt); Physical
therapists 1 (ft); Occupational therapists 1
(ft); Activities coordinators 1 (pt); Dietitians
1 (pt).
Affiliation Lutheran
Facilities Dining room; Physical therapy
room; Activities room; Chapel; Crafts room;
Laundry room; Barber/Beauty shop.
Activities Arts & crafts; Cards; Games;
Reading groups; Prayer groups; Movies;
Shopping trips; Social/Cultural gatherings.

CARLSBAD

Lakeview Christian Home—Northgate Unit
1905 W Pierce, Carlsbad, NM, 88220
(505) 885-3161
Admin Joanna Knox. *Medical Dir/Dir of
Nursing* Virgil O McCollum MD; Iris
Wisnoski RN DON.
Licensure Intermediate care. *Beds* ICF 110.
Certified Medicaid.
Owner Nonprofit Corp.
Admissions Requirements Medical
examination.
Staff RNs 7 (ft); LPNs 4 (ft), 3 (pt); Orderlies;
Nurses aides; Physical therapists; Activities
coordinators 1 (ft); Dietitians.
Affiliation Church of Christ
Facilities Dining room; Physical therapy
room; Chapel; Crafts room; Laundry room;
Barber/Beauty shop; Private dining room.
Activities Arts & crafts; Cards; Games; Reading
groups; Prayer groups; Movies; Shopping
trips; Social/Cultural gatherings; Bible class;
Resident council.

Lakeview Christian Home of the Southwest
1300 N Canal St, Carlsbad, NM, 88220
(505) 887-0551
Admin Ray Bailey. *Medical Dir/Dir of Nursing*
Virgil McCollum.
Licensure Intermediate care. *Beds* 118.
Certified Medicaid.
Admissions Requirements Medical
examination; Physician's request.
Staff RNs 3 (ft), 2 (pt); LPNs 11 (ft);
Orderlies 1 (ft); Nurses aides 48 (ft);
Activities coordinators 1 (ft); Dietitians 1
(pt).
Facilities Dining room; Activities room;
Chapel; Crafts room; Laundry room; Barber/
Beauty shop; Library.
Activities Arts & crafts; Cards; Games;
Reading groups; Prayer groups; Movies;
Shopping trips; Social/Cultural gatherings.

Laundsun Homes Inc
1900 Westridge Rd, Carlsbad, NM, 88220
(505) 887-2894
Admin Joe H White. *Medical Dir/Dir of
Nursing* Dr T E Hauser MD; Bobbie Page
RN DON.
Licensure Intermediate care for mentally
retarded. *Beds* ICF 64.
Owner Nonprofit Corp.
Admissions Requirements Medical
examination; Physician's request.
Staff Physicians 1 (ft), 11 (pt); RNs 7 (ft), 1
(pt); LPNs 3 (ft); Nurses aides 29 (ft), 8 (pt);
Physical therapists 2 (pt); Reality therapists
1 (pt); Recreational therapists 1 (pt);
Occupational therapists 1 (pt); Speech
therapists 1 (pt); Activities coordinators 1
(ft); Dietitians 1 (pt); Dentists 2 (pt);
Ophthalmologists 1 (pt); Podiatrists 1 (pt).
Languages Spanish
Affiliation Methodist
Facilities Dining room; Physical therapy
room; Activities room; Chapel; Crafts room;
Laundry room; Barber/Beauty shop; Library.
Activities Arts & crafts; Cards; Games;
Reading groups; Prayer groups; Movies;
Shopping trips; Social/Cultural gatherings.

CLOVIS

Chapparal Nursing Center*
1400 W 21st St, Clovis, NM, 88101
(505) 763-6695
Admin John F Pilger. *Medical Dir/Dir of
Nursing* Susie Small.
Licensure Intermediate care. *Beds* 60.
Certified Medicaid.
Staff LPNs 6 (ft), 1 (pt); Nurses aides 24 (ft);
Activities coordinators 1 (ft).
Facilities Dining room; Activities room;
Laundry room; Barber/Beauty shop.
Activities Arts & crafts; Cards; Games; Prayer
groups; Shopping trips; Social/Cultural
gatherings.

Golden Age Nursing Center*
1201 Norris St, Clovis, NM, 88101
(505) 762-3754
Admin Juandell Dougherty. *Medical Dir/Dir
of Nursing* Mariellen Bonem.
Licensure Intermediate care. *Beds* 60.
Certified Medicaid.
Owner Proprietary Corp (Americare Corp).
Admissions Requirements Medical
examination; Physician's request.
Facilities Dining room; Laundry room;
Barber/Beauty shop.
Activities Arts & crafts; Cards; Games; Prayer
groups; Movies; Shopping trips; Social/
Cultural gatherings.

Retirement Ranch of Clovis
PO Box 1809, 2210 Mabry Dr, Clovis, NM,
88101
(505) 762-4495
Admin William M Kesler. *Medical Dir/Dir of
Nursing* Virginia Dickson.
Licensure Intermediate care; Apartments. *Beds*
ICF 102; Apartments 16. *Certified*
Medicaid.
Owner Nonprofit Corp.
Admissions Requirements Medical
examination; Physician's request.
Staff RNs 1 (ft), 2 (pt); LPNs 9 (ft), 1 (pt);
Orderlies 2 (ft); Nurses aides 43 (ft);
Activities coordinators 1 (ft); Dietitians 1
(ft).
Languages Spanish
Affiliation Presbyterian
Facilities Dining room; Activities room;
Crafts room; Laundry room; Barber/Beauty
shop; Library.
Activities Arts & crafts; Cards; Games;
Reading groups; Prayer groups; Movies;
Shopping trips; Social/Cultural gatherings.

DEMING

Mimbres Memorial Nursing Home
900 W Ash St, Deming, NM, 88030
(505) 546-2761
Admin Roy Rumbaugh. *Medical Dir/Dir of Nursing* Helen McGraw RN.
Licensure Intermediate care. *Beds* ICF 70. *Certified* Medicaid.
Owner Publicly owned.
Admissions Requirements Minimum age 14.
Staff Physicians 10 (pt); RNs 4 (ft); LPNs 3 (ft), 2 (pt); Orderlies 2 (ft), 2 (pt); Nurses aides 22 (ft), 13 (pt); Activities coordinators 1 (pt); Dietitians 1 (pt); Ophthalmologists 1 (pt).
Languages Spanish
Facilities Dining room; Activities room; Chapel; Crafts room; Laundry room; Barber/ Beauty shop.
Activities Arts & crafts; Cards; Games; Reading groups; Prayer groups; Movies; Shopping trips.

FARMINGTON

San Juan Manor
806 W Maple, Farmington, NM, 87401
(505) 325-2910
Admin Ralph W Little. *Medical Dir/Dir of Nursing* Kathy Wright DON.
Licensure Intermediate care. *Beds* ICF 58. *Certified* Medicaid.
Owner Proprietary Corp (Hillhaven Corp).
Staff RNs 2 (ft); LPNs 4 (ft), 3 (pt); Nurses aides 16 (ft), 15 (pt); Activities coordinators 1 (ft).
Languages Navajo
Facilities Dining room; Activities room; Laundry room; Barber/Beauty shop; Lobby.
Activities Arts & crafts; Cards; Games; Reading groups; Prayer groups; Movies; Shopping trips; Social/Cultural gatherings; Cultural events.

FORT BAYARD

Fort Bayard Medical Center—Nurs Home Unit*
PO Box 219, Fort Bayard, NM, 88036
(505) 537-3302
Admin Art Salas. *Medical Dir/Dir of Nursing* Larry Merrett MD.
Licensure Skilled care; Intermediate care. *Beds* 300. *Certified* Medicaid; Medicare.
Admissions Requirements Medical examination; Physician's request.
Staff Physicians 3 (ft); RNs 11 (ft); LPNs 18 (ft); Nurses aides 109 (ft); Physical therapists 1 (ft); Recreational therapists 1 (ft); Activities coordinators 1 (ft); Dietitians 1 (ft); Dentists 1 (pt).
Facilities Dining room; Physical therapy room; Activities room; Crafts room; Barber/ Beauty shop; Library.
Activities Arts & crafts; Cards; Games; Reading groups; Prayer groups; Movies; Shopping trips.

FORT STANTON

Fort Stanton Hospital & Training School
PO Box 8, Fort Stanton, NM, 88323
(505) 354-2211
Admin Ervin T Aldaz. *Medical Dir/Dir of Nursing* Roger A Beechie MD; Joel Lacey RN.
Licensure Intermediate care for mentally retarded. *Beds* 162. *Certified* Medicaid; Medicare.
Owner Publicly owned.
Admissions Requirements Minimum age 14; Medical examination; Physician's request; Court commitment, Guardian request.

Staff Physicians 2 (ft); RNs 5 (ft); LPNs 7 (ft); Nurses aides 75 (ft); Physical therapists 1 (pt); Recreational therapists 3 (ft); Occupational therapists 1 (pt); Speech therapists 1 (ft); Activities coordinators 1 (ft); Dietitians 1 (ft); Podiatrists 1 (pt).
Languages Spanish
Facilities Dining room; Physical therapy room; Activities room; Chapel; Crafts room; Laundry room; Barber/Beauty shop; Library; Gymnasium; Swimming pool; Greenhouse; Farm; Ceramics; Woodshops; Sheltered workshop.
Activities Arts & crafts; Games; Reading groups; Movies; Shopping trips; Social/ Cultural gatherings.

FORT SUMNER

Pecos Valley Nursing Home*
509 N 10th St, PO Box L, Fort Sumner, NM, 88119
(505) 355-2439
Admin Flora Russell. *Medical Dir/Dir of Nursing* E D Fikany MD.
Licensure Intermediate care. *Beds* 44. *Certified* Medicaid.
Owner Proprietary Corp (International Health Care Management).
Admissions Requirements Medical examination; Physician's request.
Staff RNs 1 (ft); LPNs 2 (ft), 3 (pt); Orderlies 1 (ft); Nurses aides 15 (ft), 2 (pt); Activities coordinators 1 (ft); Dietitians 1 (pt).
Facilities Dining room; Laundry room; Barber/Beauty shop.
Activities Arts & crafts; Cards; Games; Reading groups; Prayer groups; Shopping trips; Social/Cultural gatherings; Monthly birthday parties.

GALLUP

Gallup Care Center*
3720 Churchrock Dr, Gallup, NM, 87301
(505) 722-2261
Admin Vickie Carathers.
Licensure Intermediate care. *Beds* 96. *Certified* Medicaid.
Owner Proprietary Corp (Beverly Enterprises).

McKinley Manor
224 Nizhoni Blvd, Gallup, NM, 87301
(505) 863-9551
Admin Ernest R Swanson.
Licensure Intermediate care. *Beds* ICF 62. *Certified* Medicaid.
Owner Proprietary Corp (Hillhaven Corp).
Admissions Requirements Minimum age 21; Medical examination; Physician's request.
Staff RNs 1 (ft), 1 (pt); LPNs 4 (ft), 2 (pt); Nurses aides 20 (ft), 10 (pt); Physical therapists 1 (pt); Activities coordinators 1 (ft); Dietitians 1 (pt).
Languages Navajo, Spanish
Facilities Dining room; Laundry room; Barber/Beauty shop.
Activities Arts & crafts; Games; Reading groups; Prayer groups; Movies; Social/ Cultural gatherings.

GRANTS

Grants Good Samaritan Center
840 Lobo Canyon Rd, Grants, NM, 87020
(505) 287-8868
Admin Cliff Deasy. *Medical Dir/Dir of Nursing* Dr R Avadesian; Donna Graves RN DON.
Licensure Intermediate care; Home health agency. *Beds* ICF 80. *Certified* Medicaid.
Owner Nonprofit Corp (Evangelical Lutheran/ Good Samaritan).

Staff RNs 3 (ft); LPNs 8 (ft); Orderlies 2 (ft); Nurses aides 24 (ft); Physical therapists 1 (ft); Recreational therapists 1 (ft); Activities coordinators 1 (ft).
Affiliation Lutheran

HOBBS

Hobbs Health Care Center
5715 Lovington Hwy, Hobbs, NM, 88240
(505) 392-6845
Admin Richard J Henry Jr. *Medical Dir/Dir of Nursing* Charles R Braun MD; Wilda Moon RN.
Licensure Skilled care; Intermediate care; Residential care. *Beds* SNF 20; ICF 90; Residential 10. *Certified* Medicaid; Medicare.
Owner Proprietary Corp.
Admissions Requirements Medical examination; Physician's request.
Staff RNs; LPNs; Orderlies; Nurses aides; Physical therapists; Speech therapists; Activities coordinators; Dietitians; Podiatrists.
Facilities Dining room; Physical therapy room; Activities room; Crafts room; Laundry room; Barber/Beauty shop; Library.
Activities Arts & crafts; Cards; Games; Reading groups; Prayer groups; Movies; Shopping trips; Social/Cultural gatherings.

La Siesta Retirement Center*
301 Bensing Rd, Hobbs, NM, 88240
(505) 397-1113
Admin Ronnie E Lee.
Licensure Intermediate care. *Beds* 55. *Certified* Medicaid.
Staff RNs 1 (ft); LPNs 5 (ft); Nurses aides 18 (ft); Physical therapists 1 (pt); Activities coordinators 1 (pt); Dietitians 1 (pt).

Lea County Good Samaritan Village*
1701 N Turner, PO Box 2568, Hobbs, NM, 88240
(505) 393-3156
Admin Ken Keller. *Medical Dir/Dir of Nursing* Rita Wade.
Licensure Intermediate care. *Beds* 99. *Certified* Medicaid.
Owner Nonprofit Corp (Evangelical Lutheran/ Good Samaritan).
Admissions Requirements Minimum age 18; Medical examination; Physician's request.
Staff RNs 1 (ft), 1 (pt); LPNs 8 (ft), 2 (pt); Nurses aides 18 (ft), 5 (pt); Physical therapists 1 (pt); Recreational therapists 2 (ft); Activities coordinators 2 (ft); Dietitians 1 (ft).
Facilities Dining room; Physical therapy room; Activities room; Chapel; Crafts room; Laundry room; Barber/Beauty shop; Library.
Activities Arts & crafts; Cards; Games; Reading groups; Prayer groups; Movies; Shopping trips; Social/Cultural gatherings.

LAS CRUCES

Las Cruces Manor*
2905 E Missouri St, Las Cruces, NM, 88001
(505) 522-0404
Admin Jack G Hamlett. *Medical Dir/Dir of Nursing* Adex Cantu MD.
Licensure Intermediate care. *Beds* 62. *Certified* Medicaid.
Owner Proprietary Corp (Hillhaven Corp).
Staff LPNs 5 (ft); Orderlies 3 (ft); Nurses aides 8 (ft); Activities coordinators 1 (ft).
Facilities Dining room; Physical therapy room; Activities room; Crafts room; Laundry room; Barber/Beauty shop; Library.
Activities Arts & crafts; Cards; Games; Reading groups; Prayer groups; Movies; Shopping trips; Social/Cultural gatherings.

Mountain Shadows—Intermediate Care Facility*
1005 Hill Rd, Las Cruces, NM, 88001
(505) 523-4573
Admin Henry Wesley Handy.
Licensure Intermediate care. *Beds* 77.
Certified Medicaid.
Owner Proprietary Corp.

University Terrace Good Samaritan Village
3025 Terrace Dr, Las Cruces, NM, 88001
(505) 522-1362
Admin L Joe Pomplun.
Licensure Intermediate care. *Beds* 60.
Certified Medicaid.
Admissions Requirements Medical
examination.
Staff RNs 4 (ft), 1 (pt); LPNs 4 (ft), 1 (pt);
Orderlies 2 (ft), 1 (pt); Nurses aides 23 (ft),
3 (pt); Activities coordinators 1 (ft);
Dietitians 1 (ft); Social workers 1 (ft).
Affiliation Lutheran
Facilities Dining room; Chapel; Crafts room;
Laundry room; Barber/Beauty shop; Library;
Swimming pool & jacuzzi.
Activities Arts & crafts; Cards; Games;
Reading groups; Prayer groups; Movies;
Shopping trips; Social/Cultural gatherings;
Sing-alongs; Birthday parties.

LAS VEGAS

New Mexico State Hospital Long-Term Care Division*
PO Box 1388, Las Vegas, NM, 87701
(505) 425-6711 ext 5204
Admin Reynaldo Crespin. *Medical Dir/Dir of
Nursing* Raymond Mathewson MD.
Licensure Skilled care; Intermediate care;
Acute care. *Beds* 239. *Certified* Medicaid;
Medicare.
Admissions Requirements Minimum age 16;
Medical examination; Physician's request.
Staff Physicians 3 (ft); RNs 16 (ft); LPNs 21
(ft); Nurses aides 119 (ft); Physical therapists
1 (ft); Recreational therapists 1 (ft);
Occupational therapists 1 (ft); Speech
therapists 2 (ft); Activities coordinators 6
(ft); Dietitians 2 (ft); Dentists 1 (ft);
Podiatrists 1 (pt).
Facilities Dining room; Physical therapy
room; Activities room; Crafts room; Barber/
Beauty shop.
Activities Arts & crafts; Cards; Games;
Reading groups; Prayer groups; Movies;
Shopping trips; Social/Cultural gatherings.

Southwest Senior Care Inc*
2301 Collins Dr, Las Vegas, NM, 87701
(505) 425-9362
Admin Joe C Maestas.
Licensure Intermediate care. *Beds* 102.
Certified Medicaid.
Owner Proprietary Corp.

LORDSBURG

Sunshine Haven*
W Railway Ave, PO Box 340, Lordsburg, NM,
88045
(505) 542-3539
Admin Rose Allen. *Medical Dir/Dir of Nursing*
Lalitha Fernicola MD.
Licensure Intermediate care. *Beds* 82.
Certified Medicaid.
Admissions Requirements Medical
examination.
Staff Physicians 1 (ft); RNs 1 (ft), 4 (pt);
LPNs 5 (ft); Orderlies 5 (ft); Nurses aides 23
(ft), 1 (pt); Physical therapists 1 (ft);
Recreational therapists 1 (ft), 1 (pt);
Activities coordinators 1 (ft); Dietitians 1
(ft); Podiatrists 1 (pt).
Facilities Dining room; Physical therapy
room; Activities room; Crafts room; Laundry
room; Barber/Beauty shop.

Activities Arts & crafts; Cards; Games;
Reading groups; Prayer groups; Movies;
Social/Cultural gatherings.

LOS LUNAS

Los Lunas Hospital & Training School
PO Box 1269, Los Lunas, NM, 87031
(505) 841-5300, 865-9611
Admin Carolyn Klintworth. *Medical Dir/Dir
of Nursing* George Brown MD; Jean Babb
RN DON.
Licensure Intermediate care for mentally
retarded. *Beds* ICF/MR 420. *Certified*
Medicaid; Medicare.
Owner Publicly owned.
Admissions Requirements Physician's request.
Staff Physicians 4 (ft); RNs 19 (ft); LPNs 22
(ft); Nurses aides 59 (ft); Physical therapists
2 (ft); Recreational therapists 12 (ft);
Occupational therapists 2 (ft); Speech
therapists 3 (ft); Dietitians 2 (ft); Podiatrists
1 (ft); Dentist 1 (ft).
Languages Spanish
Facilities Dining room; Physical therapy
room; Activities room; Chapel; Crafts room;
Laundry room; Barber/Beauty shop; Library.
Activities Arts & crafts; Games; Reading
groups; Prayer groups; Movies; Shopping
trips; Social/Cultural gatherings.

LOVINGTON

Lovington Good Samaritan Center*
PO Box 1058, 1600 West Ave I, Lovington,
NM, 88260
(505) 396-5212
Admin Mary Ellen Stroope. *Medical Dir/Dir
of Nursing* Peggy Clayton.
Licensure Intermediate care. *Beds* 62.
Certified Medicaid.
Owner Nonprofit Corp (Evangelical Lutheran/
Good Samaritan).
Affiliation Lutheran

NEW LAGUNA

Laguna Rainbow Nursing & Elderly Care Center
PO Box 236, New Laguna, NM, 87038
(505) 242-2227
Admin Talmage D Smith. *Medical Dir/Dir of
Nursing* Michael Heisler MD; Madalyn
Taylor RN DON.
Licensure Intermediate care. *Beds* ICF 25.
Owner Nonprofit organization/foundation.
Admissions Requirements Minimum age 65;
Medical examination; Physician's request.
Staff Physicians 2 (pt); RNs 1 (ft), 1 (pt);
LPNs 4 (ft), 1 (pt); Orderlies 1 (ft); Nurses
aides 5 (ft), 5 (pt); Physical therapists 1 (pt);
Speech therapists 1 (pt); Activities
coordinators 1 (ft), 1 (pt); Dietitians 1 (pt);
Dentists 1 (pt); Ophthalmologists 1 (pt);
Podiatrists 1 (pt).
Languages Laguna, Acoma
Facilities Dining room; Physical therapy
room; Activities room; Chapel; Crafts room;
Laundry room; Barber/Beauty shop; Living
room.
Activities Arts & crafts; Cards; Games; Prayer
groups; Movies; Shopping trips; Social/
Cultural gatherings; Field trips.

PORTALES

Roosevelt General Hospital—Nurs Home
PO Drawer 60, 1700 S Ave O, Portales, NM,
88130
(505) 356-4411
Admin George McGowan; Bernita Bradshaw.
Medical Dir/Dir of Nursing Dr Charles
Lehman.
Licensure Intermediate care. *Beds* ICF 49.
Certified Medicaid.
Owner Proprietary Corp.

Admissions Requirements Medical
examination; Physician's request.
Staff LPNs 1 (ft), 7 (pt); Orderlies 2 (ft), 4
(pt); Nurses aides 9 (ft), 5 (pt); Activities
coordinators 1 (ft); Dietitians 1 (pt).
Languages Spanish
Facilities Dining room; Physical therapy
room; Activities room; Barber/Beauty shop.
Activities Arts & crafts; Cards; Games;
Reading groups; Prayer groups; Movies;
Social/Cultural gatherings; Local musical
groups; Van rides.

RATON

Hacienda de Salud
1660 Hospital Dr, Raton, NM, 87740
(505) 445-2735
Admin Dawn Mayhan. *Medical Dir/Dir of
Nursing* Byrch Williams MD; Peggy
Shoemaker DON.
Licensure Intermediate care; Residential care.
Beds ICF 70; Residential 10. *Certified*
Medicaid.
Owner Proprietary Corp.
Admissions Requirements Medical
examination; Physician's request.
Staff Physicians 1 (pt); RNs 1 (pt); LPNs 5
(ft), 2 (pt); Orderlies 3 (ft); Nurses aides 9
(ft), 6 (pt); Physical therapists 1 (pt);
Activities coordinators 1 (ft); Dietitians 1
(pt).
Languages Spanish
Facilities Dining room; Physical therapy
room; Activities room; Chapel; Crafts room;
Laundry room; Barber/Beauty shop.
Activities Arts & crafts; Cards; Games;
Reading groups; Prayer groups; Movies;
Shopping trips; Social/Cultural gatherings.

Miners Colfax Medical Center LTC
PO Box 1067, Raton, NM, 87740
(505) 445-2741, 445-3661
Admin Marquita George. *Medical Dir/Dir of
Nursing* O T Bonnett MD; Gloria Garcia
DON.
Licensure Intermediate care; Sheltered care.
Beds ICF 27; Sheltered 27. *Certified*
Medicaid; Miners Trust.
Owner Nonprofit organization/foundation.
Admissions Requirements Males only Priority;
Medical examination; Physician's request.
Staff Physicians 5 (ft); RNs 2 (ft); LPNs 7 (ft),
1 (pt); Orderlies 3 (ft); Nurses aides 7 (ft);
Recreational therapists 1 (ft); Activities
coordinators 1 (ft); Dietitians 1 (pt).
Languages Spanish, Italian, Slavic
Facilities Dining room; Physical therapy
room; Activities room; Chapel; Crafts room;
Laundry room; Respiratory diagnostic; Black
lung testing.
Activities Arts & crafts; Cards; Games;
Reading groups; Prayer groups; Movies;
Shopping trips; Social/Cultural gatherings;
Monthly birthday parties; Ceramics; Picnics;
Outings; Exercise.

RIO RANCHO

Rio Rancho Health Care Center*
4210 Sabana Grande NE, Rio Rancho, NM,
87124
Admin Jim Johnson. *Medical Dir/Dir of
Nursing* James Goodwin MD.
Licensure Skilled care; Intermediate care. *Beds*
SNF 24; ICF 96. *Certified* Medicaid;
Medicare.
Owner Proprietary Corp (Americare Corp).
Admissions Requirements Medical
examination; Physician's request.
Staff RNs; LPNs; Orderlies; Nurses aides;
Physical therapists 1 (pt); Occupational
therapists 1 (pt); Speech therapists 1 (pt);
Activities coordinators 1 (ft); Dietitians 1
(pt); Dentists 1 (pt); Ophthalmologists 1 (pt);
Podiatrists 1 (pt); Audiologists 1 (pt).

Facilities Dining room; Physical therapy
room; Activities room; Crafts room; Laundry
room; Barber/Beauty shop.
Activities Arts & crafts; Cards; Games;
Reading groups; Prayer groups; Movies;
Shopping trips; Social/Cultural gatherings.

ROSWELL

Casa Maria Health Care Centre
PO Box 1938, Roswell, NM, 88201
(505) 623-6008
Admin George S Macko. *Medical Dir/Dir of
Nursing* Charles Fenzi MD; Sr Loretta M
Hall.
Licensure Intermediate care. *Beds* ICF 120.
Certified Medicaid.
Owner Nonprofit organization/foundation.
Staff RNs 6 (ft), 3 (pt); LPNs 15 (ft), 2 (pt);
Orderlies 4 (ft); Nurses aides 50 (ft), 2 (pt);
Recreational therapists 3 (ft); Activities
coordinators 1 (ft); Dietitians 1 (ft); Dentists
1 (ft); Ophthalmologists 1 (ft); Podiatrists 1
(ft).
Languages Spanish
Affiliation Roman Catholic
Facilities Dining room; Physical therapy
room; Activities room; Chapel; Crafts room;
Laundry room; Barber/Beauty shop; Library.
Activities Arts & crafts; Cards; Games;
Reading groups; Prayer groups; Movies;
Shopping trips; Social/Cultural gatherings.

Sunset Villa Care Center
1515 S Sunset Blvd, Roswell, NM, 88201
(505) 623-7097
Admin Kay Rogers. *Medical Dir/Dir of
Nursing* A Stoesser MD; J A Rogers RN.
Licensure Intermediate care. *Beds* ICF 52.
Certified Medicaid.
Owner Proprietary Corp (Americare Corp).
Admissions Requirements Medical
examination; Physician's request.
Staff RNs 2 (ft), 20 (pt); LPNs 2 (ft), 2 (pt);
Nurses aides 17 (ft), 6 (pt).
Facilities Dining room; Activities room;
Laundry room; Barber/Beauty shop.
Activities Arts & crafts; Cards; Games;
Reading groups; Prayer groups; Movies;
Shopping trips; Social/Cultural gatherings.

RUIDOSO

Ruidoso Care Center*
PO Box 2214, 5th & D Sts, Ruidoso, NM,
88345
(505) 257-9071
Licensure Intermediate care. *Beds* 82.
Certified Medicaid.
Owner Proprietary Corp (Beverly Enterprises).

SANTA FE

El Castillo Retirement Residence
250 E Alameda, Santa Fe, NM, 87501
(505) 988-2877
Admin Louis L Padilla. *Medical Dir/Dir of
Nursing* Lois Beene RN.
Licensure Apartments. *Beds* SNF 10; Apts
114.

Owner Nonprofit Corp.
Admissions Requirements Minimum age 62;
Medical examination.
Staff RNs 2 (ft), 4 (pt); LPNs 3 (ft), 1 (pt);
Nurses aides 8 (ft), 5 (pt); Dietitians 1 (ft).
Facilities Dining room; Chapel; Crafts room;
Laundry room; Barber/Beauty shop; Library.
Activities Arts & crafts; Cards; Shopping trips;
Social/Cultural gatherings.

Four Seasons Nursing Center—Santa Fe*
555 Saint Michael's Dr, Santa Fe, NM, 87501
(505) 982-2574
Admin Janice Reynolds.
Licensure Skilled care; Intermediate care. *Beds*
SNF 30; ICF 90. *Certified* Medicaid;
Medicare.
Owner Proprietary Corp (Manor Care).

Granada de Santa Fe*
313 Camino Alire, Santa Fe, NM, 87501
(505) 983-7373
Admin Del Lewis. *Medical Dir/Dir of Nursing*
Dr Matthew Kelly.
Licensure Intermediate care. *Beds* 45.
Certified Medicaid.
Admissions Requirements Medical
examination; Physician's request.
Staff Physicians 1 (pt); Speech therapists 1
(pt); Activities coordinators 1 (ft); Dietitians
1 (pt).
Facilities Dining room.
Activities Arts & crafts; Games; Prayer groups;
Movies; Shopping trips.

La Residencia
PO Box 2327, 820 Paeo de Peralta, Santa Fe,
NM, 87504
(505) 983-2273
Admin John A Malley. *Medical Dir/Dir of
Nursing* Dorothy Aragon LPN DON.
Licensure Intermediate care. *Beds* ICF 135.
Certified Medicaid.
Owner Nonprofit organization/foundation.
Admissions Requirements Minimum age 40;
Medical examination; Physician's request.
Staff RNs 2 (ft), 1 (pt); LPNs 9 (ft), 8 (pt);
Orderlies 3 (ft), 2 (pt); Nurses aides 37 (ft),
11 (pt); Physical therapists 1 (pt);
Occupational therapists 1 (pt); Speech
therapists 1 (pt); Activities coordinators 1
(ft); Dietitians 1 (ft); Social worker 1 (ft).
Languages Spanish, German
Affiliation Presbyterian
Facilities Dining room; Physical therapy
room; Activities room; Chapel; Crafts room;
Laundry room; Barber/Beauty shop.
Activities Arts & crafts; Cards; Games;
Reading groups; Prayer groups; Movies;
Shopping trips; Social/Cultural gatherings.

SOCORRO

Socorro Good Samaritan Village*
Hwy 60 W, PO Box 1279, Socorro, NM,
87801
(505) 835-2724
Admin Tim Faszer. *Medical Dir/Dir of
Nursing* Joan Anderson.
Licensure Intermediate care. *Beds* 62.
Certified Medicaid.

Admissions Requirements Medical
examination.
Staff RNs 2 (ft), 2 (pt); LPNs 2 (ft), 2 (pt);
Nurses aides 20 (ft), 10 (pt); Activities
coordinators 1 (pt).
Affiliation Lutheran
Facilities Dining room; Activities room;
Chapel; Crafts room; Barber/Beauty shop;
Library.
Activities Arts & crafts; Cards; Games;
Reading groups; Prayer groups; Movies;
Shopping trips; Social/Cultural gatherings.

SPRINGER

**Colfax General Hospital—Intermediate Care
Facility***
PO Box 458, 615 Prospect Ave, Springer, NM,
87747
(505) 483-2443
Admin John Saint.
Licensure Intermediate care. *Beds* 18.
Certified Medicaid.

TRUTH OR CONSEQUENCES

Sierra Health Care Center*
1400 Silver St, Truth or Consequences, NM,
87901
(505) 894-7855
Admin Richard J Henry Jr. *Medical Dir/Dir of
Nursing* Ruben Marchisano MD.
Licensure Intermediate care. *Beds* 110.
Certified Medicare.
Owner Nonprofit Corp.
Admissions Requirements Physician's request.
Staff Physicians 1 (ft), 4 (pt); RNs 2 (ft);
LPNs 7 (ft); Orderlies 1 (ft); Nurses aides 23
(ft), 3 (pt); Activities coordinators 1 (ft);
Dietitians 1 (ft).
Facilities Dining room; Physical therapy
room; Activities room; Chapel; Crafts room;
Laundry room; Barber/Beauty shop; Library.
Activities Arts & crafts; Cards; Games;
Reading groups; Prayer groups; Movies;
Shopping trips; Social/Cultural gatherings.

TUCUMCARI

Van Ark Nursing Home*
1005 S Monroe, Tucumcari, NM, 88401
(505) 461-2570
Admin Sarah Haley. *Medical Dir/Dir of
Nursing* Jean Anderson.
Licensure Intermediate care. *Beds* 54.
Certified Medicaid.
Owner Proprietary Corp (Beverly Enterprises).
Admissions Requirements Medical
examination; Physician's request.
Staff RNs 2 (ft), 1 (pt); LPNs 3 (ft); Nurses
aides 13 (ft), 4 (pt); Activities coordinators 1
(ft); Dietitians 1 (ft).
Facilities Dining room; Activities room;
Laundry room; Barber/Beauty shop.
Activities Arts & crafts; Cards; Games;
Reading groups; Prayer groups; Movies;
Shopping trips; Social/Cultural gatherings.

NEW YORK

ALBANY

Albany County Nursing Home*
Albany-Shaker Rd, Albany, NY, 12211
(518) 869-2231
Admin Robert J Lynch. *Medical Dir/Dir of Nursing* George Cuttita MD.
Licensure Skilled care. *Beds* 420. *Certified* Medicaid; Medicare.
Owner Publicly owned.
Staff Physicians 2 (ft), 6 (pt); RNs 55 (ft); LPNs 84 (ft); Orderlies 194 (ft); Physical therapists 5 (ft); Occupational therapists 3 (ft); Speech therapists 1 (ft); Activities coordinators 8 (ft); Dietitians 2 (ft); Dentists 1 (pt); Ophthalmologists 2 (pt); Podiatrists 1 (pt); Audiologists 1 (ft).
Facilities Dining room; Physical therapy room; Activities room; Crafts room; Laundry room; Barber/Beauty shop.
Activities Arts & crafts; Cards; Games; Reading groups; Prayer groups; Movies; Shopping trips; Social/Cultural gatherings.

Childs Nursing Home
25 Hackett Blvd, Albany, NY, 12208
(518) 462-4211
Admin Teresa Gustas. *Medical Dir/Dir of Nursing* Dr Pankin; Joanne Breden RN DON.
Licensure Skilled care. *Beds* SNF 120. *Certified* Medicaid; Medicare.
Owner Nonprofit Corp.
Admissions Requirements Minimum age 16.
Staff RNs; LPNs; Orderlies; Nurses aides; Physical therapists; Recreational therapists; Occupational therapists; Speech therapists; Activities coordinators; Dietitians; Ophthalmologists; Podiatrists.
Facilities Dining room; Physical therapy room; Activities room; Chapel; Crafts room; Barber/Beauty shop.
Activities Arts & crafts; Cards; Games; Reading groups; Prayer groups; Movies; Shopping trips; Social/Cultural gatherings.

Daughters of Sarah Nursing Home Company Inc*
Washington Ave & Rapp Rd, Albany, NY, 12203
(518) 456-7831
Admin Stanley Poskancer.
Licensure Skilled care. *Beds* 200. *Certified* Medicare.
Owner Nonprofit Corp.
Affiliation Jewish

Eden Park Nursing Home
22 Holland Ave, Albany, NY, 12209
(518) 436-8441
Admin Wesley Hale. *Medical Dir/Dir of Nursing* James Pozniakas MD; Marianne Gould RN DON.
Licensure Skilled care. *Beds* SNF 210. *Certified* Medicaid; Medicare.
Owner Proprietary Corp (Eden Park Management).
Admissions Requirements Minimum age 16.

Staff Physicians 6 (pt); RNs 24 (ft), 13 (pt); LPNs 24 (ft), 10 (pt); Nurses aides 73 (ft), 19 (pt); Physical therapists 2 (ft), 1 (pt); Occupational therapists 1 (ft), 1 (pt); Speech therapists 1 (pt); Activities coordinators 1 (ft); Dietitians 1 (ft); Dentists 1 (pt); Ophthalmologists 1 (pt); Podiatrists 1 (pt).
Facilities Dining room; Physical therapy room; Activities room; Laundry room; Barber/Beauty shop; Dental office.
Activities Arts & crafts; Cards; Games; Reading groups; Prayer groups; Movies; Shopping trips; Social/Cultural gatherings.

Ann Lee Home
Albany Shaker Rd, Albany, NY, 12211
(518) 869-5331
Admin Thomas Coffey. *Medical Dir/Dir of Nursing* George Cuttita; Marianne VanDerhyden DON.
Licensure Intermediate care. *Beds* ICF 175. *Certified* Medicaid.
Owner Publicly owned.
Admissions Requirements Medical examination.
Staff Physicians; RNs; LPNs; Orderlies; Nurses aides; Physical therapists; Recreational therapists; Occupational therapists; Speech therapists; Dietitians; Ophthalmologists; Podiatrists.
Facilities Dining room; Physical therapy room; Activities room; Crafts room; Laundry room; Barber/Beauty shop.
Activities Arts & crafts; Cards; Games; Reading groups; Prayer groups; Movies; Shopping trips; Social/Cultural gatherings.

St Margarets House & Hospital for Babies*
27 Hackett Blvd, Albany, NY, 12208
(518) 465-2461
Admin Clinton Lewis.
Licensure Skilled care. *Beds* 58. *Certified* Medicaid.
Owner Nonprofit Corp.

Teresian House Nursing Home Co Inc
Washington Ave Ext, Albany, NY, 12203
(518) 456-2000
Admin Sr Joseph Mary. *Medical Dir/Dir of Nursing* Francis R DeRossi MD; Dorothy M Fitzgerald RN DON.
Licensure Skilled care; Intermediate care; HRF. *Beds* HRF 180; SNF 120. *Certified* Medicaid; Medicare.
Owner Nonprofit Corp.
Admissions Requirements Minimum age 65; Medical examination.
Staff RNs 15 (ft), 13 (pt); LPNs 23 (ft), 11 (pt); Orderlies 3 (ft); Nurses aides 118 (ft), 31 (pt); Physical therapists 1 (ft), 1 (pt); Occupational therapists 1 (ft); Activities coordinators 5 (ft); PT & OT aides 9 (ft).
Languages Spanish
Affiliation Roman Catholic
Facilities Dining room; Physical therapy room; Activities room; Chapel; Crafts room; Laundry room; Barber/Beauty shop; Library.

Activities Arts & crafts; Cards; Games; Reading groups; Prayer groups; Movies; Shopping trips; Social/Cultural gatherings.

University Heights Nursing Home*
325 Northern Blvd, Albany, NY, 12204
(518) 449-1100
Admin Thomas Nicolla.
Licensure Skilled care. *Beds* 200. *Certified* Medicaid; Medicare.
Owner Proprietary Corp.

Villa Mary Immaculate
301 Hackett Blvd, Albany, NY, 12208
(518) 482-3363
Admin James A Reynolds. *Medical Dir/Dir of Nursing* Nicholas Vianna MD; Geneva Kittle DON.
Licensure Skilled care. *Beds* SNF 160. *Certified* Medicaid; Medicare.
Owner Nonprofit Corp.
Admissions Requirements Minimum age 16.
Staff Physicians 4 (pt); RNs 13 (ft), 8 (pt); LPNs 17 (ft), 3 (pt); Orderlies 8 (ft), 1 (pt); Nurses aides 70 (ft), 12 (pt); Physical therapists 1 (ft); Occupational therapists 1 (ft); Speech therapists 1 (pt); Activities coordinators 1 (ft); Dietitians 2 (ft).
Affiliation Roman Catholic
Facilities Dining room; Physical therapy room; Activities room; Chapel; Crafts room; Laundry room; Barber/Beauty shop.
Activities Arts & crafts; Cards; Games; Reading groups; Prayer groups; Movies; Shopping trips.

Westmere Convalescent Home*
5 GippRd, Albany, NY, 12203
(518) 456-8355
Admin Michael Levine.
Licensure Intermediate care. *Beds* 28.
Owner Proprietary Corp.

ALBION

Arnold Gregory Memorial Hospital—Skilled Nursing Facility
243 S Main St, Albion, NY, 14411
(716) 589-4422
Admin William P Gillick. *Medical Dir/Dir of Nursing* Diane L Arsenault MD; Marion Gurzinski RN DON.
Licensure Skilled care. *Beds* SNF 30. *Certified* Medicaid; Medicare.
Owner Nonprofit Corp.
Admissions Requirements Medical examination; Physician's request.
Staff RNs 1 (ft), 1 (pt); LPNs 7 (ft), 5 (pt); Orderlies 1 (ft), 1 (pt); Nurses aides 7 (ft), 5 (pt); Physical therapists 2 (ft); Activities coordinators 1 (ft); Dietitians 1 (pt).
Facilities Dining room; Physical therapy room; Activities room; Crafts room; Laundry room; Barber/Beauty shop; Library.
Activities Arts & crafts; Cards; Games; Prayer groups; Movies; Shopping trips; Social/Cultural gatherings.

Orleans County Nursing Home*
Rte 31, Albion, NY, 14411
(716) 589-7004
Admin Stephen Heard. *Medical Dir/Dir of Nursing* Dr A Nassar.
Licensure Skilled care; Intermediate care; Health related care. *Beds* 132. *Certified* Medicaid; Medicare.
Owner Publicly owned.
Staff Physicians 3 (pt); RNs 8 (ft), 2 (pt); LPNs 11 (ft), 10 (pt); Nurses aides 30 (ft), 36 (pt); Physical therapists 1 (pt); Speech therapists 1 (pt); Activities coordinators 1 (ft); Dietitians 1 (ft); Dentists 1 (pt); Audiologists 1 (pt).
Facilities Dining room; Physical therapy room; Activities room; Crafts room; Laundry room; Barber/Beauty shop.
Activities Arts & crafts; Cards; Games; Reading groups; Prayer groups; Movies; Shopping trips; Social/Cultural gatherings.

ALDEN

Erie County Home & Infirmary
11580 Walden Ave, Alden, NY, 14004
(716) 937-5690
Admin James L Smith. *Medical Dir/Dir of Nursing* Dr John T Gabbey; Margaret Farley.
Licensure Skilled care; Intermediate care. *Beds* SNF 513; ICF 125. *Certified* Medicaid; Medicare.
Owner Publicly owned.
Staff Physicians 1 (ft), 8 (pt); RNs 50 (ft), 7 (pt); LPNs 1 (ft), 18 (pt); Orderlies; Nurses aides 261 (ft); Physical therapists 2 (ft), 2 (pt); Recreational therapists 7 (ft); Occupational therapists 2 (ft); Speech therapists 2 (ft); Activities coordinators 1 (ft); Dietitians 2 (ft); Physical therapy aides 4 (ft); Occupational therapy assts 3 (ft); Diet technicians 5 (ft).
Facilities Dining room; Physical therapy room; Activities room; Chapel; Crafts room; Laundry room; Barber/Beauty shop; Library; Candy shop; Boutique.
Activities Arts & crafts; Cards; Games; Reading groups; Prayer groups; Movies; Shopping trips; Social/Cultural gatherings.

ALEXANDRIA BAY

Edward John Noble Hospital
19 Fuller St, Alexandria Bay, NY, 13607
(315) 482-2511
Admin Joseph Kehoe. *Medical Dir/Dir of Nursing* William Conner RN DON.
Licensure Skilled care. *Beds* SNF 22. *Certified* Medicaid; Medicare.
Owner Nonprofit Corp.
Staff Physicians 1 (pt); RNs 1 (ft), 1 (pt); LPNs 7 (ft), 3 (pt); Nurses aides 4 (ft), 2 (pt); Physical therapists 1 (pt); Occupational therapists 1 (pt); Activities coordinators 1 (ft), 1 (pt); Dietitians 1 (pt); Dentist 1 (pt).
Facilities Dining room; Barber/Beauty shop; Sunroom.
Activities Arts & crafts; Cards; Games; Movies; Social/Cultural gatherings; Sing-alongs; Worship services; Island boat tours.

ALLEGANY

Allegany Nursing Home*
5th & Maple Ave, Allegany, NY, 14706
(716) 373-2238
Admin Gerald Nye.
Licensure Skilled care. *Beds* 37. *Certified* Medicaid; Medicare.
Owner Proprietary Corp.
Admissions Requirements Medical examination.

Staff Physicians 1 (pt); RNs 2 (ft), 1 (pt); LPNs 3 (ft), 4 (pt); Nurses aides 17 (ft), 6 (pt); Physical therapists 1 (pt); Activities coordinators 1 (ft); Dietitians 1 (pt); Dentists 1 (pt); Podiatrists 1 (pt).
Facilities Dining room; Physical therapy room; Activities room; Chapel; Crafts room; Laundry room; Barber/Beauty shop; Library.
Activities Arts & crafts; Cards; Games; Reading groups; Prayer groups; Movies; Shopping trips; Social/Cultural gatherings.

AMHERST

Amherst Nursing & Convalescent Home
4459 Bailey Ave, Amherst, NY, 14226
(716) 655-1544
Medical Dir/Dir of Nursing Howard Lehman MD.
Licensure Skilled care. *Beds* SNF 83. *Certified* Medicaid; Medicare.
Owner Proprietary Corp.
Admissions Requirements Minimum age 17; Medical examination; Physician's request.
Staff Physicians; RNs; LPNs; Orderlies; Nurses aides; Physical therapists; Reality therapists; Recreational therapists; Occupational therapists; Speech therapists; Activities coordinators; Dietitians.
Facilities Dining room; Physical therapy room; Activities room; Crafts room; Laundry room; Barber/Beauty shop.
Activities Arts & crafts; Cards; Games; Reading groups; Prayer groups; Movies; Shopping trips; Social/Cultural gatherings.

AMITYVILLE

Broadlawn Manor Nursing Home and Health Related Facility
399 County Line Rd, Amityville, NY, 11701
(516) 264-0222
Admin Patrick R Martone.
Licensure Skilled care; Intermediate care. *Beds* SNF; ICF 320. *Certified* Medicaid; Medicare.
Owner Proprietary Corp.
Staff Physicians; RNs; LPNs; Orderlies; Nurses aides; Physical therapists; Recreational therapists; Occupational therapists; Speech therapists; Activities coordinators; Dietitians; Dentists; Ophthalmologists; Podiatrists.
Facilities Dining room; Physical therapy room; Activities room; Chapel; Crafts room; Laundry room; Barber/Beauty shop.
Activities Arts & crafts; Cards; Games; Prayer groups; Movies; Shopping trips; Social/ Cultural gatherings.

Brunswick Hospital Center Inc
366 Broadway, Amityville, NY, 11701
(516) 789-7000
Admin John T Digilio Jr. *Medical Dir/Dir of Nursing* Louis Ingrisano MD.
Licensure Skilled care. *Beds* 94. *Certified* Medicaid; Medicare.
Owner Proprietary Corp.
Admissions Requirements Minimum age 21; Medical examination; Physician's request.
Staff Physicians; RNs; LPNs; Orderlies; Nurses aides; Physical therapists; Reality therapists; Recreational therapists; Occupational therapists; Speech therapists; Activities coordinators; Dietitians; Dentists; Ophthalmologists; Podiatrists.
Languages Spanish, Italian
Facilities Dining room; Physical therapy room; Activities room; Crafts room; Laundry room; Barber/Beauty shop; Library.
Activities Arts & crafts; Cards; Games; Reading groups; Prayer groups; Movies; Shopping trips; Social/Cultural gatherings; Ethnic dinners; Dining out; Picnics.

AMSTERDAM

Amsterdam Memorial Hospital—Skilled Nursing Facility
Upper Market St, Amsterdam, NY, 12010
(518) 842-3100
Admin Marjorie Bucknell. *Medical Dir/Dir of Nursing* William Blase MD; Fay Holt RN.
Licensure Skilled care. *Beds* SNF 61. *Certified* Medicaid; Medicare.
Owner Nonprofit Corp.
Admissions Requirements Medical examination; Physician's request.
Staff Physicians; RNs; LPNs; Nurses aides; Physical therapists; Recreational therapists; Occupational therapists; Speech therapists; Activities coordinators; Dietitians; Podiatrists.
Facilities Dining room; Physical therapy room; Activities room; Crafts room; Laundry room; Barber/Beauty shop.
Activities Arts & crafts; Cards; Games; Reading groups; Prayer groups; Movies; Shopping trips; Social/Cultural gatherings.

Montgomery County Infirmary
Sandy Dr, Amsterdam, NY, 12010
(518) 843-3503
Admin John C Quandt. *Medical Dir/Dir of Nursing* Diamond & Achtyl Assoc.
Licensure Skilled care. *Beds* 120. *Certified* Medicaid; Medicare.
Owner Publicly owned.
Admissions Requirements Medical examination.
Staff Physicians 2 (pt); Physical therapists 1 (pt); Occupational therapists 1 (pt); Speech therapists 1 (pt); Activities coordinators 1 (ft); Dietitians 1 (pt); Dentists 1 (pt); Ophthalmologists 1 (pt); Podiatrists 1 (pt).
Languages Polish
Facilities Dining room; Physical therapy room; Activities room; Chapel; Crafts room; Laundry room; Barber/Beauty shop; Solariums.
Activities Arts & crafts; Cards; Games; Reading groups; Prayer groups; Movies; Shopping trips; Social/Cultural gatherings.

Mt Loretto Nursing Home
Rte 3 Swart Hill Rd, Amsterdam, NY, 12010
(518) 842-6790
Admin Sr Mary Gertrude. *Medical Dir/Dir of Nursing* Dr H A Rehman; Virginia Mottolo.
Licensure Skilled care. *Beds* SNF 82. *Certified* Medicaid; Medicare.
Owner Nonprofit Corp.
Staff Physicians 1 (pt); RNs 11 (ft); LPNs 11 (ft), 9 (pt); Nurses aides 36 (ft), 23 (pt); Activities coordinators 1 (ft); Ophthalmologists 1 (pt).
Languages Polish
Affiliation Roman Catholic
Facilities Dining room; Physical therapy room; Activities room; Chapel; Laundry room; Barber/Beauty shop; Sun porches; Outdoor patio.
Activities Arts & crafts; Games; Reading groups; Prayer groups; Movies; Summer outings; In-house shopping.

ARGYLE

Pleasant Valley Infirmary
Rte 40, Argyle, NY, 12809
(518) 638-8274
Admin Frank R Fiske. *Medical Dir/Dir of Nursing* Michael J Lynch MD; Cynthia Canzeri-Labish RN DON.
Licensure Skilled care; Intermediate care. *Beds* SNF 120; ICF. *Certified* Medicaid; Medicare.
Owner Publicly owned.
Admissions Requirements Medical examination; Physician's request.

Staff Physicians 2 (pt); RNs 7 (ft), 6 (pt); LPNs 11 (ft), 3 (pt); Nurses aides 43 (ft), 24 (pt); Physical therapists 1 (pt); Recreational therapists 1 (ft); Occupational therapists 1 (ft); Speech therapists 1 (pt); Activities coordinators 1 (ft); Dietitians 1 (pt); Ophthalmologists 1 (pt); Dentist 1 (pt).
Facilities Dining room; Physical therapy room; Activities room; Crafts room; Laundry room; Barber/Beauty shop; Library; Patio; Fenced-in-yard underneath trees.
Activities Arts & crafts; Cards; Games; Reading groups; Prayer groups; Movies; Shopping trips; Social/Cultural gatherings; Boat trips.

ARVERNE

Lawrence Nursing Home Inc
350 Beach 54th St, Arverne, NY, 11692
(718) 945-0400
Admin Benjamin Levine. *Medical Dir/Dir of Nursing* Dr Tara Saiwi; Karen Thompson RN DOM.
Licensure Skilled care. *Beds* SNF 200. *Certified* Medicaid; Medicare.
Owner Proprietary Corp.
Staff RNs 9 (ft), 6 (pt); LPNs 23 (ft), 6 (pt); Orderlies 3 (ft); Nurses aides 73 (ft), 15 (pt); Physical therapists 2 (pt); Occupational therapists 2 (pt); Speech therapists 1 (pt); Activities coordinators 1 (ft); Dietitians 1 (ft), 1 (pt).
Languages Spanish
Facilities Dining room; Physical therapy room; Activities room; Crafts room; Laundry room; Barber/Beauty shop; Library.
Activities Arts & crafts; Cards; Games; Reading groups; Prayer groups; Movies; Shopping trips; Musical entertainment; Cultural & recreational trips.

Resort Health Related Facility
64-11 Beach Channel Dr, Arverne, NY, 11692
(718) 945-0700
Admin Morris Tenenbaum. *Medical Dir/Dir of Nursing* Gerald Rube MD; Priscilla Brodie DON.
Licensure Intermediate care. *Beds* ICF 280. *Certified* Medicaid.
Owner Privately owned.
Admissions Requirements Minimum age 18; Medical examination; Physician's request.
Staff Physicians 5 (pt); RNs 5 (ft), 3 (pt); LPNs 12 (ft), 3 (pt); Orderlies 9 (ft), 2 (pt); Nurses aides 17 (ft), 1 (pt); Physical therapists 1 (ft), 1 (pt); Recreational therapists 1 (ft); Occupational therapists 2 (pt); Dietitians 3 (ft).
Languages Spanish, Yiddish, Hebrew
Facilities Dining room; Physical therapy room; Activities room; Chapel; Crafts room; Laundry room; Barber/Beauty shop; Library.
Activities Arts & crafts; Cards; Games; Reading groups; Prayer groups; Movies; Shopping trips; Social/Cultural gatherings.

Resort Nursing Home
430 Beach 68th St, Arverne, NY, 11692
(718) 474-5200
Admin Michael Tennebaum.
Licensure Skilled care. *Beds* 280. *Certified* Medicaid; Medicare.
Owner Proprietary Corp.

ASTORIA

Lyden Nursing Home
27-37 27th St, Astoria, NY, 11102
(718) 932-4613
Admin Chaim Sieger. *Medical Dir/Dir of Nursing* Dr Murray Waksman.
Licensure Skilled care. *Beds* 114. *Certified* Medicaid; Medicare.
Owner Proprietary Corp.

Staff Physicians 4 (pt); RNs 7 (ft); LPNs 9 (ft), 3 (pt); Nurses aides 24 (ft), 10 (pt); Physical therapists 1 (pt); Recreational therapists 1 (ft); Occupational therapists 1 (pt); Speech therapists 1 (pt); Activities coordinators 1 (ft); Dietitians 1 (ft); Dentists 1 (pt); Ophthalmologists 1 (pt); Podiatrists 1 (pt).
Affiliation Roman Catholic
Facilities Dining room; Physical therapy room; Activities room; Crafts room; Laundry room; Barber/Beauty shop; Library.
Activities Arts & crafts; Cards; Games; Prayer groups; Movies; Social/Cultural gatherings; Ball game trips.

AUBURN

Auburn Nursing Home
85 Thornton Ave, Auburn, NY, 13021
(315) 253-7351
Admin Martha S MacKay. *Medical Dir/Dir of Nursing* Avanelle P Morgan MD; Monica W Moochler.
Licensure Skilled care. *Beds* 92. *Certified* Medicaid; Medicare.
Owner Privately owned.
Admissions Requirements Minimum age 16; Physician's request; Must meet PRI classifications.
Staff Physicians 1 (pt); RNs 11 (ft), 7 (pt); LPNs 1 (ft), 4 (pt); Nurses aides 42 (ft), 13 (pt); Physical therapists 1 (pt); Recreational therapists 12 (ft); Occupational therapists 1 (pt); Speech therapists 1 (pt); Activities coordinators 1 (ft); Dietitians 1 (pt).
Facilities Dining room; Activities room; Crafts room; Laundry room; Barber/Beauty shop.
Activities Arts & crafts; Cards; Games; Reading groups; Prayer groups; Movies; Shopping trips; Social/Cultural gatherings.

Mercy Health & Rehabilitation Center Nursing Home Inc
100 Thornton Ave, Auburn, NY, 13021
(315) 253-0351
Admin Sr Mary Aquin. *Medical Dir/Dir of Nursing* Robert Kalet DO; Rose Hogan RN DON.
Licensure Skilled care; Intermediate care. *Beds* SNF 252; ICF 45. *Certified* Medicaid; Medicare.
Owner Nonprofit Corp.
Admissions Requirements Minimum age 16; Medical examination; Physician's request.
Staff Physicians; RNs; LPNs; Orderlies; Nurses aides; Physical therapists; Recreational therapists; Occupational therapists; Dietitians.
Affiliation Roman Catholic
Facilities Dining room; Physical therapy room; Activities room; Chapel; Crafts room; Laundry room; Barber/Beauty shop.
Activities Arts & crafts; Cards; Games; Reading groups; Prayer groups; Movies; Shopping trips; Social/Cultural gatherings.

AVON

Avon Nursing Home
Clinton St Extension, Avon, NY, 14414
(716) 226-2225
Admin Richard Baker.
Licensure Skilled care. *Beds* 40. *Certified* Medicaid; Medicare.
Owner Proprietary Corp.

BALDWINSVILLE

Syracuse Home Association
7740 Meigs Rd, Baldwinsville, NY, 13027
(315) 638-2521
Admin Natalie Andreassi. *Medical Dir/Dir of Nursing* John Pipas MD; Kathleen Donovan RN DON.

Licensure Intermediate care. *Beds* ICF 80. *Certified* Medicaid.
Owner Nonprofit Corp.
Admissions Requirements Minimum age 65; Medical examination; Physician's request.
Staff Physicians 1 (pt); RNs 4 (ft), 6 (pt); LPNs 5 (ft), 2 (pt); Nurses aides 11 (ft), 3 (pt); Physical therapists 1 (pt); Dietitians 1 (pt); Ophthalmologists 1 (pt).
Facilities Dining room; Physical therapy room; Activities room; Crafts room; Laundry room; Barber/Beauty shop; Library.
Activities Arts & crafts; Prayer groups; Movies; Shopping trips; Social/Cultural gatherings.

BALLSTON SPA

Saratoga County Infirmary/Health Related Facility
Ballston Ave, Ballston Spa, NY, 12020
(518) 885-4315
Admin Lorraine A Frollo. *Medical Dir/Dir of Nursing* Stephen Strader MD; Laura Benscoter RN DON.
Licensure Skilled care; Health related facility. *Beds* SNF 160; HRF 117. *Certified* Medicaid; Medicare.
Owner Publicly owned.
Admissions Requirements Physician's request.
Staff Physicians; RNs; LPNs; Orderlies; Nurses aides; Physical therapists; Occupational therapists; Speech therapists; Activities coordinators; Dietitians; Dentists; Ophthalmologists; Podiatrists.
Facilities Dining room; Physical therapy room; Activities room; Crafts room; Laundry room; Barber/Beauty shop; Library.
Activities Arts & crafts; Cards; Games; Reading groups; Prayer groups; Movies; Shopping trips; Social/Cultural gatherings.

BATAVIA

Batavia Nursing Home Inc*
257 State St, Batavia, NY, 14020
(716) 343-1300
Admin David A Novak.
Licensure Skilled care. *Beds* 62. *Certified* Medicaid; Medicare.
Owner Proprietary Corp.

Genesee County Nursing Home
278 Bank St, Batavia, NY, 14020
(716) 344-0584
Admin Michael Perry. *Medical Dir/Dir of Nursing* Myron E Williams MD; Jean Zaso RN.
Licensure Skilled care; Intermediate care; Adult home. *Beds* SNF 120; ICF 40; Adult home 80. *Certified* Medicaid; Medicare.
Owner Publicly owned.
Admissions Requirements Minimum age 16.
Staff Physicians 2 (pt); RNs 14 (ft), 9 (pt); LPNs 7 (ft), 12 (pt); Nurses aides 46 (ft), 59 (pt); Physical therapists 1 (pt); Occupational therapists 1 (pt); Speech therapists 1 (pt); Activities coordinators 1 (ft); Dietitians 1 (pt).
Facilities Dining room; Physical therapy room; Activities room; Chapel; Crafts room; Laundry room; Barber/Beauty shop; Library.
Activities Arts & crafts; Cards; Games; Reading groups; Prayer groups; Movies; Social/Cultural gatherings.

St Luke Manor of Batavia
17 Wiard St, Batavia, NY, 14020
(716) 343-4288
Admin Elizabeth Greenman. *Medical Dir/Dir of Nursing* Dr Myron E Williams Jr; Mary Ann Bowen RN.
Licensure Skilled care. *Beds* SNF 20. *Certified* Medicaid; Medicare.
Owner Nonprofit Corp (Catholic Charities).

Staff Physicians 3 (pt); RNs 1 (ft), 5 (pt); LPNs 2 (ft), 2 (pt); Nurses aides 8 (ft), 2 (pt); Physical therapists 1 (pt); Recreational therapists 1 (pt); Dietitians 1 (pt); Podiatrists 1 (pt).
Facilities Dining room; Chapel.
Activities Arts & crafts; Cards; Games; Reading groups; Prayer groups.

BATH

Steuben County Infirmary
County Route 113, Bath, NY, 14810
(607) 776-7651
Admin Terry A Bettis. *Medical Dir/Dir of Nursing* Stephen Schwartz MD; Bonnie Linehan RN.
Licensure Skilled care. *Beds* SNF 105. *Certified* Medicaid; Medicare.
Owner Publicly owned.
Admissions Requirements Minimum age 21.
Staff Physicians 4 (pt); RNs 16 (ft); LPNs 9 (ft); Orderlies 3 (ft); Nurses aides 62 (ft), 1 (pt); Activities coordinators 1 (ft); Dietitians 1 (pt); Dentists 1 (pt); Ophthalmologists 1 (pt); Podiatrists 1 (pt).
Facilities Dining room; Physical therapy room; Activities room; Chapel; Crafts room; Barber/Beauty shop; Library.
Activities Arts & crafts; Cards; Games; Reading groups; Prayer groups; Movies; Shopping trips; Social/Cultural gatherings.

BAY SHORE

Sunrise Manor Nursing Home
PO Box 1330M, 1325 Brentwood Rd, Bay Shore, NY, 117065799
(516) 665-4960
Admin Desmond McManus. *Medical Dir of Nursing* Dr George Raniolo; Ruth Wanzer DON.
Licensure Skilled care. *Beds* SNF 84. *Certified* Medicaid; Medicare.
Owner Privately owned.
Admissions Requirements Minimum age 16.
Staff RNs 5 (ft), 12 (pt); LPNs 5 (ft), 4 (pt); Orderlies 1 (ft), 2 (pt); Nurses aides 23 (ft), 13 (pt); Physical therapists 1 (pt); Recreational therapists 1 (ft), 3 (pt); Occupational therapists; Speech therapists; Activities coordinators 1 (ft), 2 (pt).
Facilities Dining room; Physical therapy room; Activities room; Barber/Beauty shop.
Activities Arts & crafts; Cards; Games; Reading groups; Prayer groups; Movies; Shopping trips; Social/Cultural gatherings.

BAYSIDE

Ozanam Hall of Queens Nursing Home Inc
42-41 201st St, Bayside, NY, 11361
(718) 423-2000
Admin Sr M Joseph Catherine. *Medical Dir/Dir of Nursing* Richard L Bodkin MD; Sr Damian Ann RN.
Licensure Skilled care; Intermediate care. *Beds* SNF 382; ICF 50. *Certified* Medicaid; Medicare.
Owner Nonprofit Corp.
Admissions Requirements Minimum age 65; Medical examination.
Staff Physicians 20 (pt); RNs 25 (ft), 25 (pt); LPNs 15 (ft), 15 (pt); Orderlies 11 (ft), 3 (pt); Nurses aides 150 (ft), 100 (pt); Physical therapists 1 (ft); Recreational therapists 2 (ft); Occupational therapists 1 (ft); Dentist.
Languages Spanish, Italian
Affiliation Roman Catholic
Facilities Dining room; Physical therapy room; Activities room; Chapel; Crafts room; Laundry room; Barber/Beauty shop; Library.
Activities Arts & crafts; Cards; Games; Reading groups; Prayer groups; Movies; Shopping trips; Social/Cultural gatherings.

St Marys Hospital for Children Inc
29-01 216th St, Bayside, NY, 11360
(718) 990-8800
Admin Stuart C Kaplan. *Medical Dir/Dir of Nursing* Neil Lombard MD; Jane McConville RN.
Licensure Skilled care. *Beds* 95. *Certified* Medicaid.
Owner Nonprofit Corp.
Admissions Requirements Medical examination; Physician's request.
Staff RNs 18 (ft), 10 (pt); LPNs 4 (ft), 2 (pt); Nurses aides 5 (ft), 2 (pt); Physical therapists 5 (ft); Recreational therapists 2 (ft); Occupational therapists 3 (ft); Speech therapists 3 (ft); Activities coordinators 1 (ft); Dietitians 1 (ft), 1 (pt); CCTs 48 (ft), 14 (pt).
Languages Spanish, French, Greek
Affiliation Episcopal
Facilities Dining room; Physical therapy room; Activities room; Chapel; Crafts room; Laundry room.
Activities Arts & crafts; Games; Reading groups; Movies.

BEACON

Fishkill Health Related Center Inc*
Dogwood Ln, Beacon, NY, 12508
(914) 831-8704
Licensure Intermediate care. *Beds* 160.
Owner Proprietary Corp.

BINGHAMTON

Chenango Bridge Nursing Home
Box 19, Hospital Hill Rd, Binghamton, NY, 13901-9761
(607) 648-8521
Admin Allen W Carkey. *Medical Dir/Dir of Nursing* F Keith Kennedy MD.
Licensure Skilled care. *Beds* 90. *Certified* Medicaid; Medicare.
Owner Publicly owned.
Admissions Requirements Minimum age 16; Physician's request.
Staff Physicians 1 (pt); RNs 11 (ft), 1 (pt); LPNs 14 (ft), 3 (pt); Orderlies 2 (ft); Nurses aides 37 (ft), 22 (pt); Physical therapists 1 (pt); Occupational therapists 1 (pt); Activities coordinators 1 (ft); Dietitians 1 (pt); Dentists 1 (pt).
Facilities Dining room; Physical therapy room; Activities room; Chapel; Crafts room; Laundry room; Barber/Beauty shop.
Activities Arts & crafts; Cards; Games; Reading groups; Prayer groups; Movies; Shopping trips; Social/Cultural gatherings.

Elizabeth Church Manor*
863 Front St, Binghamton, NY, 13905
(607) 722-3463
Admin Ruth Davis. *Medical Dir/Dir of Nursing* Dr Oscar Astur.
Licensure Skilled care; Intermediate care. *Beds* 105. *Certified* Medicaid; Medicare.
Owner Nonprofit Corp.
Admissions Requirements Physician's request.
Staff Physicians 1 (pt); RNs 7 (ft), 8 (pt); LPNs 4 (ft), 3 (pt); Nurses aides 18 (ft), 21 (pt); Physical therapists 1 (pt); Activities coordinators 1 (ft); Dietitians 1 (pt).
Affiliation Methodist
Facilities Dining room; Physical therapy room; Activities room; Chapel; Crafts room; Laundry room; Barber/Beauty shop; Library.
Activities Arts & crafts; Cards; Games; Reading groups; Prayer groups; Movies; Shopping trips; Social/Cultural gatherings.

Good Shepherd-Fairview Home Inc
80 Fairview Ave, Binghamton, NY, 13904
(607) 724-2477
Admin Eleanor Little. *Medical Dir/Dir of Nursing* Michael J Wasco MD.

Licensure Skilled care; Intermediate care; Domiciliary care. *Beds* SNF 34; ICF 40; Domiciliary care 82. *Certified* Medicaid; Medicare.
Owner Nonprofit Corp.
Admissions Requirements Minimum age 65; Medical examination.
Staff Physicians 1 (pt); RNs 9 (pt); LPNs 4 (pt); Orderlies 2 (pt); Nurses aides 27 (pt); Activities coordinators 1 (ft); Dietitians 1 (pt).
Affiliation Episcopal
Facilities Dining room; Activities room; Crafts room; Laundry room; Barber/Beauty shop; Library.
Activities Arts & crafts; Cards; Games; Reading groups; Prayer groups; Shopping trips; Social/Cultural gatherings.

River Mede Manor*
159-163 Front St, Binghamton, NY, 13902
(607) 722-7225
Admin Elizabeth Slutzker.
Licensure Skilled care; Intermediate care. *Beds* 258. *Certified* Medicaid; Medicare.
Owner Proprietary Corp.

BOONVILLE

Sunset Nursing Home
Academy St, Boonville, NY, 13309
(315) 942-4301
Admin Jerome Britton. *Medical Dir/Dir of Nursing* Robert Smith MD; Jeanne Gaetano RN.
Licensure Skilled care. *Beds* SNF 120. *Certified* Medicaid; Medicare; VA.
Owner Proprietary Corp.
Admissions Requirements Minimum age 16; Physician's request.
Staff Physicians 3 (pt); RNs 8 (ft), 4 (pt); LPNs 12 (ft), 6 (pt); Nurses aides 47 (ft), 19 (pt); Physical therapists 2 (ft), 1 (pt); Recreational therapists 1 (ft), 1 (pt); Occupational therapists 1 (pt); Speech therapists 1 (pt); Activities coordinators 1 (ft); Dietitians 1 (ft), 1 (pt); Ophthalmologists 1 (pt); Podiatrists 1 (pt).
Facilities Dining room; Physical therapy room; Activities room; Chapel; Crafts room; Laundry room; Barber/Beauty shop; Library.
Activities Arts & crafts; Cards; Games; Reading groups; Prayer groups; Movies; Shopping trips; Social/Cultural gatherings.

BRENTWOOD

Ross Nursing Home Inc*
839 Suffolk Ave, Brentwood, NY, 11717
(516) 273-4000
Admin Victor P Russo.
Licensure Skilled care. *Beds* 135. *Certified* Medicaid; Medicare.
Owner Proprietary Corp.

BRIARCLIFF MANOR

Brandywine Nursing Home Inc
620 Sleepy Hollow Rd, Briarcliff Manor, NY, 10510
(914) 941-5100
Admin P Roth. *Medical Dir/Dir of Nursing* Sidney Harvey MD & George Vogel MD.
Licensure Skilled care. *Beds* 120. *Certified* Medicaid; Medicare.
Owner Proprietary Corp.
Admissions Requirements Minimum age 16.
Staff RNs 12 (ft), 5 (pt); LPNs 11 (ft), 4 (pt); Orderlies 5 (ft), 4 (pt); Nurses aides 50 (ft), 13 (pt); Physical therapists 2 (pt); Occupational therapists 1 (pt); Speech therapists 1 (pt); Activities coordinators 1 (ft); Dietitians 1 (pt).
Facilities Dining room; Physical therapy room; Activities room; Crafts room; Laundry room; Barber/Beauty shop; Library.

Activities Arts & crafts; Cards; Games; Reading groups; Prayer groups; Movies; Shopping trips; Social/Cultural gatherings.

BROCKPORT

Cupola Nursing Home*
122 West Ave, Brockport, NY, 14420
(716) 637-4129
Admin Elizabeth Beihirch.
Licensure Skilled care. *Beds* 87. *Certified* Medicaid; Medicare.
Owner Proprietary Corp.

BRONX

Astor Gardens Nursing Home
2316 Bruner Ave, Bronx, NY, 10469
(212) 882-6400
Admin Bruce Rowland. *Medical Dir/Dir of Nursing* Dr Michael DiGiacomo; M Villaneuva DON.
Licensure Skilled care. *Beds* 175. *Certified* Medicaid; Medicare.
Owner Privately owned.
Admissions Requirements Minimum age 16; Medical examination.
Staff Physicians 5 (pt); RNs 7 (ft); LPNs 14 (ft); Orderlies 5 (ft); Nurses aides 55 (ft); Physical therapists 2 (pt); Occupational therapists 3 (ft); Speech therapists 1 (pt); Activities coordinators 1 (ft); Dietitians 1 (ft); Podiatrists; Audiologists.
Languages Spanish, Italian
Facilities Dining room; Physical therapy room; Activities room; Crafts room; Laundry room; Barber/Beauty shop; Library; Garden.
Activities Arts & crafts; Cards; Games; Reading groups; Prayer groups; Movies; Shopping trips; Social/Cultural gatherings.

Bainbridge Nursing Home
3518 Bainbridge Ave, Bronx, NY, 10467
(212) 655-1991
Admin Isaac Goldbrenner. *Medical Dir/Dir of Nursing* Dr Jay Hershkowitz; Teresa Francis RN DON.
Licensure Skilled care. *Beds* SNF 200. *Certified* Medicaid; Medicare.
Owner Privately owned.
Staff Physicians 7 (ft); RNs 10 (ft); LPNs 12 (ft); Orderlies 6 (ft); Nurses aides 54 (ft); Physical therapists 1 (pt); Recreational therapists 3 (ft); Occupational therapists 1 (pt); Speech therapists 1 (pt); Activities coordinators 1 (ft); Dietitians 2 (ft); Dentists 1 (pt); Ophthalmologists 1 (pt); Podiatrists 1 (pt); Dentist 1 (pt).
Languages Spanish, Yiddish, Hebrew
Facilities Dining room; Physical therapy room; Activities room; Crafts room; Laundry room; Barber/Beauty shop; Dental office.
Activities Arts & crafts; Cards; Games; Reading groups; Prayer groups; Movies; Shopping trips; Social/Cultural gatherings; Ceramics; Bowling; BBQs.

Beth Abraham Hospital
612 Allerton Ave, Bronx, NY, 10467
(212) 920-5881
Admin Cecelia C Zuckerman. *Medical Dir/Dir of Nursing* Dr Walter Schwartz; Elsie Blaylock DON.
Licensure Skilled care. *Beds* SNF 520; Hospice. *Certified* Medicaid; Medicare.
Owner Nonprofit organization/foundation.
Admissions Requirements Minimum age 16; Physician's request PRI & screen.
Staff Physicians 5 (ft), 1 (pt); RNs 107 (ft), 4 (pt); Orderlies; Nurses aides 241 (ft), 26 (pt); Physical therapists 6 (ft); Recreational therapists 8 (ft); Occupational therapists 5 (ft); Speech therapists 4 (ft); Activities coordinators 1 (ft); Dietitians 3 (ft), 1 (pt).
Languages Spanish, Yiddish, Hebrew, Russian, Italian
Affiliation Jewish

Facilities Dining room; Physical therapy room; Activities room; Chapel; Crafts room; Laundry room; Barber/Beauty shop; Library; Coffee shop; Outdoor patio; Patient lounge.
Activities Arts & crafts; Cards; Games; Prayer groups; Movies; Shopping trips; Social/Cultural gatherings; Music therapy.

Bruckner Nursing Home
1010 Underhill Ave, Bronx, NY, 10472
(212) 863-6700
Admin Abraham C Grossman. *Medical Dir/Dir of Nursing* Ernst Smith MD; Irene Degnan RN.
Licensure Skilled care. *Beds* SNF 200. *Certified* Medicaid; Medicare.
Owner Privately owned.
Admissions Requirements Medical examination.
Staff Physicians; RNs; LPNs; Orderlies; Nurses aides; Physical therapists; Recreational therapists; Occupational therapists; Speech therapists; Activities coordinators; Dietitians; Dentists; Ophthalmologists; Podiatrists.
Languages Spanish, Hebrew, Yiddish
Facilities Dining room; Physical therapy room; Activities room; Crafts room; Laundry room; Barber/Beauty shop; Library.
Activities Arts & crafts; Cards; Games; Reading groups; Prayer groups; Movies; Shopping trips; Social/Cultural gatherings.

Concourse Nursing Home*
1072 Grand Concourse, Bronx, NY, 10456
(212) 681-4000
Admin Helen Neiman.
Licensure Skilled care. *Beds* 240. *Certified* Medicaid; Medicare.
Owner Proprietary Corp.

Daughters of Jacob Geriatric Center
1160 Teller Ave, Bronx, NY, 10456
(212) 293-1500 Ext 240
Admin Steven J Bernstein. *Medical Dir/Dir of Nursing* Sandra Selikson MD; Jeanne Ward RN.
Licensure Skilled care; Health related facility. *Beds* SNF 347; Health related 168. *Certified* Medicaid; Medicare.
Owner Nonprofit Corp.
Admissions Requirements Minimum age 65; Medical examination.
Staff Physicians 7 (ft); RNs 54 (ft); LPNs 23 (ft); Orderlies 16 (ft); Nurses aides 171 (ft); Physical therapists 4 (ft); Recreational therapists 7 (ft); Occupational therapists 2 (ft), 2 (pt); Speech therapists 1 (ft); Activities coordinators 2 (ft); Dietitians 4 (ft); Dentists 1 (pt); Ophthalmologists 2 (pt); Podiatrists 2 (pt).
Affiliation Jewish
Facilities Dining room; Physical therapy room; Activities room; Chapel; Crafts room; Laundry room; Barber/Beauty shop; Library.
Activities Arts & crafts; Cards; Games; Reading groups; Prayer groups; Movies; Shopping trips; Social/Cultural gatherings; In-house TV station for resident program broadcasting.

East Haven Health Related Facility
2323 Eastchester Rd, Bronx, NY, 10469
(212) 655-2848
Admin Joseph Brachfeld. *Medical Dir/Dir of Nursing* Dr Samuel Kossak MD; Elaine Tucker RN.
Licensure Health related facility. *Beds* Health related 200. *Certified* Medicaid.
Owner Proprietary Corp.
Staff Physicians; RNs; LPNs; Orderlies; Nurses aides; Physical therapists; Occupational therapists; Speech therapists; Activities coordinators; Dietitians; Ophthalmologists.

Facilities Dining room; Physical therapy room; Activities room; Chapel; Crafts room.
Activities Arts & crafts; Cards; Games; Prayer groups; Movies.

Eastchester Park Nursing Home
2700 Eastchester Rd, Bronx, NY, 10469
(212) 231-5550
Admin May Preira. *Medical Dir/Dir of Nursing* Dr Hyman Blume; Lillian Burgess.
Licensure Skilled care. *Beds* SNF 200. *Certified* Medicaid; Medicare.
Owner Privately owned.
Admissions Requirements Medical examination.
Staff RNs 19 (ft); LPNs 21 (ft); Orderlies 9 (ft); Nurses aides 52 (ft); Physical therapists 1 (pt); Recreational therapists 3 (ft); Occupational therapists 1 (pt); Speech therapists 1 (pt); Activities coordinators 1 (ft); Dietitians 2 (ft); Dentists 1 (pt); Ophthalmologists 1 (pt); Podiatrists 1 (pt).
Languages Spanish, French, Yiddish, Italian, German
Facilities Dining room; Physical therapy room; Activities room; Chapel; Crafts room; Laundry room; Barber/Beauty shop; Library; 2 Outdoor sitting areas.
Activities Arts & crafts; Cards; Games; Reading groups; Prayer groups; Movies; Social/Cultural gatherings; Choral group; Adopted grandchildren program.

Fieldston Lodge Nursing Home*
666 Kappock St, Bronx, NY, 10463
(212) 549-1203
Admin Michael Birnbaum. *Medical Dir/Dir of Nursing* Dr Tartaglia.
Licensure Skilled care. *Beds* 200. *Certified* Medicaid; Medicare.
Owner Proprietary Corp.
Staff Physicians 1 (pt); RNs 12 (ft); LPNs 10 (ft); Orderlies 2 (ft); Nurses aides 48 (ft); Physical therapists 1 (ft); Recreational therapists 2 (ft); Occupational therapists 1 (ft); Speech therapists 1 (pt); Activities coordinators 1 (ft); Dietitians 1 (ft).
Facilities Dining room; Physical therapy room; Activities room; Chapel; Crafts room; Laundry room; Barber/Beauty shop.
Activities Arts & crafts; Cards; Games; Reading groups; Prayer groups; Movies; Social/Cultural gatherings.

Grand Manor Health Related Facility*
700 White Plains Rd, Bronx, NY, 10473
(212) 931-5033
Licensure Intermediate care. *Beds* 240.
Owner Proprietary Corp.

Hebrew Home for the Aged/Fairfield Division
3220 Henry Hudson Pkwy, Bronx, NY, 10463
(212) 549-9400
Admin Marie Ferrara. *Medical Dir/Dir of Nursing* Gilbert Cherrick MD.
Licensure Skilled care. *Beds* SNF 167. *Certified* Medicaid; Medicare.
Owner Nonprofit organization/foundation.
Staff Physicians 3 (pt); RNs 14 (ft), 3 (pt); LPNs 12 (ft); Orderlies 2 (ft); Nurses aides 55 (ft); Physical therapists 2 (ft), 2 (pt); Recreational therapists 2 (ft), 1 (pt); Occupational therapists 2 (pt); Speech therapists 1 (pt); Activities coordinators 1 (ft); Dietitians 1 (pt); Dentists 1 (pt); Ophthalmologists 1 (pt); Podiatrists 1 (pt).
Affiliation Jewish
Facilities Dining room; Physical therapy room; Activities room; Crafts room; Barber/Beauty shop; Library; Occupational therapy room; Outdoor roof garden.
Activities Arts & crafts; Cards; Games; Reading groups; Prayer groups; Movies; Shopping trips; Social/Cultural gatherings; Trips to restaurants & cultural events; Sheltered workshop.

Hebrew Hospital for the Chronic Sick*
2200 Givan Ave, Bronx, NY, 10475
(212) 379-5020
Admin Richard Shedlovsky.
Licensure Skilled care; Intermediate care. *Beds*
400. *Certified* Medicaid; Medicare.
Owner Nonprofit Corp.
Affiliation Jewish

House of the Holy Comforter*
2751 Grand Concourse, Bronx, NY, 10468
(212) 867-8100
Admin Luba Mebert.
Licensure Skilled care. *Beds* 151. *Certified*
Medicaid; Medicare.
Owner Nonprofit Corp.

Jeanne Jugan Residence*
3200 Baychester Ave, Bronx, NY, 10475
(212) 671-2120
Medical Dir/Dir of Nursing Dr Giordano.
Owner Nonprofit Corp (Cath Charity/Arch of
NY).
Admissions Requirements Minimum age 60;
Medical examination.
Staff RNs 6 (ft), 10 (pt); LPNs 8 (ft), 6 (pt);
Nurses aides 28 (ft), 37 (pt); Occupational
therapists 1 (pt); Speech therapists 1 (pt);
Activities coordinators 1 (ft); Dietitians 1
(ft), 1 (pt).
Affiliation Roman Catholic
Facilities Dining room; Physical therapy
room; Activities room; Chapel; Crafts room;
Laundry room; Barber/Beauty shop; Library;
Occupational therapy.
Activities Arts & crafts; Cards; Games;
Reading groups; Prayer groups; Movies;
Shopping trips; Social/Cultural gatherings.

**The Jewish Home & Hospital for Aged-
Kingsbridge Center**
100 W Kingsbridge Rd, Bronx, NY, 10468
(212) 579-0500
Admin Harvey Finkelstein. *Medical Dir/Dir of
Nursing* Simon Brandvain MD; Peggy
Barnett RN DON.
Licensure Skilled care; Intermediate care. *Beds*
SNF 540; ICF 272. *Certified* Medicaid;
Medicare.
Owner Nonprofit organization/foundation.
Admissions Requirements Minimum age 60;
Medical examination.
Staff Physicians 11 (ft); RNs 134 (ft); LPNs
38 (ft); Orderlies 61 (ft); Nurses aides 237
(ft); Physical therapists 8 (ft); Recreational
therapists 10 (ft), 1 (pt); Occupational
therapists 8 (ft); Speech therapists 1 (pt);
Activities coordinators 2 (ft); Dietitians 10
(ft).
Languages Yiddish, Hebrew, Russian,
Spanish, Polish, German
Affiliation Jewish
Facilities Dining room; Physical therapy
room; Activities room; Chapel; Crafts room;
Barber/Beauty shop; Library; Occupational
therapy; Enclosed garden space; Clinic;
Geriatric day center; Long Term Health
Care.
Activities Arts & crafts; Cards; Games;
Reading groups; Prayer groups; Movies;
Shopping trips; Social/Cultural gatherings;
College courses; Intergenerational programs;
Guest musicians & speakers; Fashion shows;
Personal history day; BBQs; Poetry groups.

Kings Harbor Care Center*
2000 E Gunhill Rd, Bronx, NY, 10469
(212) 320-0400
Licensure Intermediate care. *Beds* 360.
Owner Proprietary Corp.

Kings Terrace Nursing Home HRF
2678 Kingsbridge Terrace, Bronx, NY, 10463
(212) 796-5800
Admin Lowell S Feldman. *Medical Dir/Dir of
Nursing* Dr Solomon Abbey; Kurt Leggerd
DON.

Licensure Skilled care; Intermediate care. *Beds*
SNF 120; ICF 120. *Certified* Medicaid;
Medicare.
Owner Publicly owned.
Admissions Requirements Minimum age 21;
Medical examination; Physician's request.
Staff Physicians 6 (ft), 5 (pt); RNs 10 (ft), 4
(pt); LPNs 12 (ft), 11 (pt); Nurses aides 47
(ft), 24 (pt); Physical therapists 2 (pt);
Recreational therapists 2 (ft), 1 (pt);
Occupational therapists 2 (pt); Speech
therapists 1 (pt); Activities coordinators 1
(ft); Dietitians 2 (ft); Dentists 1 (pt);
Ophthalmologists 1 (pt); Podiatrists 1 (pt).
Languages Spanish
Facilities Dining room; Physical therapy
room; Activities room; Crafts room; Laundry
room; Barber/Beauty shop.
Activities Arts & crafts; Cards; Games; Prayer
groups; Movies; Shopping trips; Social/
Cultural gatherings; Drama therapy; Adult
education; Sing-alongs; Live entertainment;
Pet therapy.

**Kingsbridge Heights Long-Term Home Health
Care**
3400-3426 Cannon Pl, Bronx, NY, 10463
(212) 796-8100
Admin Rose Boritzer.
Licensure Skilled care; Intermediate care;
Home care. *Beds* SNF 280; ICF 120; Home
care 200. *Certified* Medicaid; Medicare; VA.
Owner Proprietary Corp.

Laconia Nursing Home*
1050 E 230th St, Bronx, NY, 10466
(212) 654-5875
Admin Lawrence J Moshowitz.
Licensure Skilled care. *Beds* 240. *Certified*
Medicaid; Medicare.
Owner Proprietary Corp.

Loeb Center-Montefiore
111 E 210th St, Bronx, NY, 10467
(212) 920-4696
Admin Harvey A Simon. *Medical Dir/Dir of
Nursing* Dr Robert Kennedy; Dora Adom
RN DON.
Licensure Skilled care. *Beds* SNF 80. *Certified*
Medicaid; Medicare.
Owner Nonprofit organization/foundation.
Admissions Requirements Physician's request.
Staff Physicians 4 (pt); RNs 34 (ft), 4 (pt);
Nurses aides 30 (ft); Physical therapists 3
(ft); Recreational therapists 1 (pt);
Occupational therapists 2 (ft); Activities
coordinators 1 (ft); Dietitians 1 (ft).
Facilities Dining room; Physical therapy
room; Activities room; Laundry room;
Library.
Activities Arts & crafts; Cards; Games;
Reading groups; Prayer groups; Movies.

Methodist Church Home for the Aged*
4499 Manhattan College Pkwy, Bronx, NY,
10471
(212) 548-5100
Admin Margaret V Fishburne. *Medical Dir/
Dir of Nursing* Dr Norman Spitzer.
Licensure Skilled care; Intermediate care;
Health related care. *Beds* SNF 80; HRF 33.
Certified Medicaid; Medicare.
Owner Nonprofit Corp.
Admissions Requirements Minimum age 62;
Medical examination; Physician's request.
Staff Physicians 2 (pt); RNs 9 (ft), 7 (pt);
LPNs 5 (ft), 6 (pt); Nurses aides 31 (ft), 8
(pt); Physical therapists 1 (pt); Occupational
therapists 1 (pt); Activities coordinators 2
(ft); Dietitians 1 (pt); Dentists 1 (pt);
Podiatrists 1 (pt).
Affiliation Methodist
Facilities Dining room; Physical therapy
room; Activities room; Chapel; Crafts room;
Barber/Beauty shop; Library; Lounge/day
rooms.

Activities Arts & crafts; Cards; Games;
Reading groups; Prayer groups; Movies;
Shopping trips; Social/Cultural gatherings.

Morningside House Nursing Home Company
1000 Pelham Pkwy S, Bronx, NY, 10461
(212) 863-5800
Admin Cynthia Wallace.
Licensure Skilled care; Intermediate care. *Beds*
SNF 242; ICF 144. *Certified* Medicaid;
Medicare.
Owner Nonprofit Corp.

Morris Park Nursing Home
1235 Pelham Pkwy N, Bronx, NY, 10469
(212) 231-4300
Admin M Berkowitz. *Medical Dir/Dir of
Nursing* Dr Robert Lapin.
Licensure Skilled care. *Beds* 191. *Certified*
Medicaid; Medicare.
Owner Privately owned.
Admissions Requirements Medical
examination; Physician's request.
Staff Physicians; RNs; LPNs; Orderlies;
Nurses aides; Physical therapists; Reality
therapists; Recreational therapists;
Occupational therapists; Speech therapists;
Activities coordinators; Dietitians; Dentists;
Ophthalmologists; Podiatrists.
Languages Italian
Facilities Dining room; Physical therapy
room; Activities room; Crafts room; Barber/
Beauty shop; Library.
Activities Arts & crafts; Cards; Games;
Reading groups; Prayer groups; Movies;
Social/Cultural gatherings.

Mosholu Parkway Nursing Home*
3356 Perry Ave, Bronx, NY, 10467
(212) 655-3568
Admin Issac Shapiro.
Licensure Skilled care. *Beds* 125. *Certified*
Medicaid; Medicare.
Owner Proprietary Corp.

Parkview Nursing Home
6585 Broadway, Bronx, NY, 10471
(212) 549-2200
Admin Joseph Leone. *Medical Dir/Dir of
Nursing* Dr. Argon Atal; Shirley White.
Licensure Skilled care. *Beds* 200. *Certified*
Medicaid; Medicare.
Owner Proprietary Corp.
Admissions Requirements Minimum age 16;
Medical examination; Physician's request.
Staff Physicians 8 (pt); RNs 5 (ft), 11 (pt);
LPNs 17 (ft), 18 (pt); Orderlies 1 (ft); Nurses
aides 49 (ft), 52 (pt); Physical therapists 1
(pt); Occupational therapists 2 (pt); Speech
therapists 1 (pt); Activities coordinators 3
(ft); Dietitians 2 (ft); Dentists 3 (pt);
Ophthalmologists 2 (pt); Podiatrists 1 (pt).
Languages Spanish, Italian, Polish, Hebrew,
Yiddish, French
Facilities Dining room; Physical therapy
room; Activities room; Crafts room; Laundry
room; Barber/Beauty shop.
Activities Arts & crafts; Cards; Games;
Reading groups; Prayer groups; Movies;
Shopping trips; Social/Cultural gatherings;
Dining out; Bowling competition with other
home; Picnics.

Pelham Parkway Nursing Home*
2401 Laconia Ave, Bronx, NY, 10469
(212) 798-8600
Admin Lucy Saskin.
Licensure Skilled care. *Beds* 200. *Certified*
Medicaid; Medicare.
Owner Proprietary Corp.

Providence Rest Home*
3304 Waterbury Ave, Bronx, NY, 10465
(212) 931-3000
Admin S Joanne.
Licensure Skilled care; Intermediate care. *Beds*
149. *Certified* Medicaid; Medicare.
Owner Nonprofit Corp (Cath Charity/Arch of
NY).

Riverdale Nursing Home
641 W 230th St, Bronx, NY, 10463
(212) 796-4800
Admin Michael Kirshner. *Medical Dir/Dir of Nursing* Dr Leslie Walter; Margaret Tencza.
Licensure Skilled care. *Beds* 146. *Certified* Medicaid; Medicare.
Owner Privately owned.
Staff Physicians 12 (pt); RNs 6 (ft), 2 (pt); LPNs 12 (ft), 6 (pt); Orderlies 3 (ft), 2 (pt); Nurses aides 50 (ft), 25 (pt); Physical therapists 2 (ft); Reality therapists 1 (ft); Recreational therapists 2 (ft), 1 (pt); Occupational therapists 1 (ft); Speech therapists 1 (ft); Activities coordinators 1 (ft); Dietitians 1 (ft), 1 (pt); Dentists 1 (pt); Ophthalmologists 2 (pt); Podiatrists 1 (pt).
Languages Spanish, Haitian
Facilities Dining room; Physical therapy room; Activities room; Laundry room; Barber/Beauty shop.
Activities Arts & crafts; Cards; Games; Reading groups; Prayer groups; Movies; Shopping trips; Social/Cultural gatherings.

Rofay Nursing Home
946 E 211th St, Bronx, NY, 10469
(212) 882-1800
Admin Eugene Burger. *Medical Dir/Dir of Nursing* M Teich MD; E Rampino RN DON.
Licensure Skilled care. *Beds* SNF 120. *Certified* Medicaid; Medicare.
Owner Proprietary Corp.
Admissions Requirements Minimum age adult; Medical examination; Physician's request.
Staff Physicians; RNs; LPNs; Orderlies; Nurses aides; Physical therapists; Reality therapists; Recreational therapists; Occupational therapists; Speech therapists; Activities coordinators; Dietitians; Dentists; Ophthalmologists; Podiatrists.
Facilities Dining room; Physical therapy room; Activities room; Chapel; Crafts room; Laundry room; Barber/Beauty shop; Library.
Activities Arts & crafts; Cards; Games; Reading groups; Prayer groups; Movies; Shopping trips; Social/Cultural gatherings.

Sacred Heart Home*
3200 Baychester Ave, Bronx, NY, 10475
(212) 671-2120
Licensure Intermediate care. *Beds* 44.
Owner Nonprofit Corp.
Affiliation Roman Catholic

St Patricks Home for the Aged & Infirm
66 Van Cortlandt Park S, Bronx, NY, 10463
(212) 519-2800
Admin Sr M Patrick Michael. *Medical Dir/Dir of Nursing* Eusebius J Murphy MD; Sr M Veronica DON.
Licensure Skilled care; Intermediate care. *Beds* SNF 162; ICF 63. *Certified* Medicaid; Medicare.
Owner Nonprofit Corp (Cath Charity/Arch of NY).
Admissions Requirements Minimum age 65; Medical examination.
Affiliation Roman Catholic
Facilities Dining room; Physical therapy room; Activities room; Chapel; Crafts room; Laundry room; Barber/Beauty shop.
Activities Arts & crafts; Cards; Games; Prayer groups; Movies; Shopping trips; Social/Cultural gatherings.

Frances Schervier Home & Hospital
2975 Independence Ave, Bronx, NY, 10463-9975
(212) 548-1700
Admin Patricia A Krasnausky. *Medical Dir/Dir of Nursing* Oscar A Palatucci ME; Deborah D Lynch RN DON.
Licensure Skilled care; HRFB. *Beds* SNF 284; HRF 80. *Certified* Medicaid; Medicare.
Owner Nonprofit Corp.

Admissions Requirements Minimum age 65; Medical examination.
Staff Physicians 10 (ft), 3 (pt); RNs 30 (ft), 3 (pt); LPNs 34 (ft), 6 (pt); Nurses aides 116 (ft), 21 (pt); Physical therapists 1 (ft); Recreational therapists 3 (ft); Occupational therapists 2 (ft), 1 (pt); Speech therapists 2 (pt); Activities coordinators 2 (ft), 1 (pt); Dietitians 4 (ft); Dentists 2 (pt); Ophthalmologists 1 (pt); Podiatrists 1 (pt).
Languages Spanish, French, German, Sign
Affiliation Roman Catholic
Facilities Dining room; Physical therapy room; Activities room; Chapel; Crafts room; Laundry room; Barber/Beauty shop; Library; Recreation hall.
Activities Arts & crafts; Cards; Games; Reading groups; Prayer groups; Movies; Shopping trips; Social/Cultural gatherings.

Split Rock Nursing Home*
3525 Baychester Ave, Bronx, NY, 10466
(212) 798-8900
Admin Abe Zelmanowicz.
Licensure Skilled care. *Beds* 240. *Certified* Medicaid; Medicare.
Owner Proprietary Corp.

United Odd Fellow & Rebekah Home
1072 Havemeyer Ave, Bronx, NY, 10462
(212) 863-6200
Admin Alexander D Sajdak. *Medical Dir/Dir of Nursing* Jack Wagner MD.
Licensure Skilled care; Intermediate care. *Beds* 213. *Certified* Medicaid; Medicare.
Owner Nonprofit Corp.
Admissions Requirements Medical examination.
Staff Physicians 1 (ft), 2 (pt); RNs 12 (ft), 3 (pt); LPNs 16 (ft), 3 (pt); Orderlies 4 (ft), 2 (pt); Nurses aides 46 (ft), 10 (pt); Physical therapists 1 (pt); Recreational therapists 1 (ft), 3 (pt); Occupational therapists 1 (pt); Speech therapists 1 (pt); Activities coordinators 1 (pt); Dietitians 1 (ft); Dentists 1 (pt); Ophthalmologists 1 (pt); Podiatrists 1 (pt).
Affiliation Independent Order of Odd Fellows & Rebekahs
Facilities Dining room; Physical therapy room; Activities room; Chapel; Crafts room; Barber/Beauty shop.
Activities Arts & crafts; Cards; Games; Reading groups; Prayer groups; Movies; Shopping trips; Social/Cultural gatherings.

W K Nursing Home Corporation*
2545 University Ave, Bronx, NY, 10468
(212) 579-0500
Licensure Intermediate care. *Beds* 540.
Owner Nonprofit Corp.

Wayne Health Related Facility/Skilled Nursing Facility
3530 Wayne Ave, Bronx, NY, 10467
(212) 655-1700
Admin Alexander Hartman. *Medical Dir/Dir of Nursing* Dr J Hershkowitz.
Licensure Skilled care; Intermediate care. *Beds* SNF; ICF. *Certified* Medicaid; Medicare.
Owner Proprietary Corp.
Admissions Requirements Females only; Medical examination.
Staff Physicians 5 (pt); RNs 10 (ft), 5 (pt); LPNs 10 (ft), 5 (pt); Nurses aides 30 (ft), 10 (pt); Physical therapists 1 (pt); Reality therapists 1 (pt); Recreational therapists 3 (ft); Occupational therapists 1 (pt); Speech therapists 1 (pt); Activities coordinators 2 (ft), 1 (pt); Dietitians 2 (ft); Ophthalmologists 1 (pt); Podiatrists 1 (pt).
Facilities Dining room; Physical therapy room; Activities room; Chapel; Crafts room; Laundry room; Barber/Beauty shop; Library.
Activities Arts & crafts; Cards; Games; Reading groups; Prayer groups; Movies; Shopping trips; Social/Cultural gatherings.

White Plains Nursing Home
3845 Carpenter Ave, Bronx, NY, 10467
(212) 882-4464
Admin Barbara Seidner.
Licensure Skilled care. *Beds* SNF 240. *Certified* Medicaid; Medicare.
Owner Privately owned.
Admissions Requirements Medical examination; Physician's request.
Languages Spanish
Facilities Dining room; Physical therapy room; Activities room; Laundry room; Barber/Beauty shop.
Activities Arts & crafts; Cards; Games; Prayer groups; Movies.

Williamsbridge Manor Nursing Home
1540 Tomlinson Ave, Bronx, NY, 10461
(212) 892-6600
Admin David Paley. *Medical Dir/Dir of Nursing* Dr Ernst Smith; Laurel Skelson.
Licensure Skilled care. *Beds* SNF 77. *Certified* Medicaid; Medicare.
Owner Proprietary Corp.
Admissions Requirements Medical examination; Physician's request.
Staff Physicians; RNs; LPNs; Nurses aides; Physical therapists; Occupational therapists; Speech therapists; Activities coordinators; Dietitians; Dentists; Ophthalmologists; Podiatrists.
Facilities Dining room; Physical therapy room; Activities room; Laundry room.
Activities Arts & crafts; Cards; Games; Reading groups; Prayer groups; Movies.

Workmens Circle Home & Infirmary
3155 Grace Ave, Bronx, NY, 10469
(212) 379-8100
Admin David Londin. *Medical Dir/Dir of Nursing* Dr Edward Isenberg.
Licensure Skilled care; Intermediate care. *Beds* 289. *Certified* Medicaid; Medicare.
Owner Nonprofit Corp.
Staff Physicians 7 (ft), 21 (pt); RNs 36 (ft), 5 (pt); LPNs 38 (ft), 10 (pt); Orderlies 20 (ft), 5 (pt); Nurses aides 170 (ft), 45 (pt); Physical therapists 2 (ft); Recreational therapists 4 (ft), 10 (pt); Occupational therapists 1 (ft), 1 (pt); Speech therapists 1 (pt); Activities coordinators 1 (ft); Dietitians 3 (ft); Dentists 1 (pt); Ophthalmologists 2 (pt); Podiatrists 2 (pt).
Affiliation Jewish
Facilities Dining room; Physical therapy room; Activities room; Chapel; Crafts room; Laundry room; Barber/Beauty shop; Library; Clinics; Pharmacy.
Activities Arts & crafts; Cards; Games; Reading groups; Prayer groups; Movies; Shopping trips; Social/Cultural gatherings; Plays.

BROOKLYN

Aishel Avraham Residential Health Facility Inc*
40 Heyward St, Brooklyn, NY, 11211
(212) 858-6200
Admin David Steinberg.
Licensure Skilled care; Intermediate care. *Beds* 160. *Certified* Medicaid; Medicare.
Owner Nonprofit Corp.
Affiliation Jewish

Augustana Lutheran Home for the Aged
1680 60th St, Brooklyn, NY, 11204
(718) 232-2114
Admin Charles Miller. *Medical Dir/Dir of Nursing* Dr Frank Gulin.
Licensure Skilled care; Intermediate care. *Beds* SNF 55; ICF 35. *Certified* Medicaid; Medicare.
Owner Nonprofit Corp.
Admissions Requirements Medical examination.

Staff Physicians 3 (pt); RNs 14 (ft); LPNs 8 (ft); Nurses aides 45 (ft); Physical therapists 1 (ft); Occupational therapists 1 (pt); Speech therapists 1 (pt); Activities coordinators 1 (ft); Dietitians 1 (ft); Dentists 1 (pt); Ophthalmologists 1 (pt); Podiatrists 1 (pt).
Affiliation Lutheran
Facilities Dining room; Physical therapy room; Activities room; Chapel; Laundry room; Barber/Beauty shop; Outdoor porch.
Activities Arts & crafts; Cards; Games; Prayer groups; Movies; Shopping trips.

Baptist Medical Center Nursing Home
2749 Linden Blvd, Brooklyn, NY, 11208
(718) 277-5100
Admin Anthony A Summers. *Medical Dir/Dir of Nursing* Salvatore F Pisciotto SR DO MD; Geraldine Weber RN.
Licensure Skilled care. *Beds* 140. *Certified* Medicaid; Medicare.
Owner Nonprofit Corp.
Admissions Requirements Physician's request.
Staff Physicians 8 (pt); RNs 13 (ft), 20 (pt); LPNs 20 (ft), 23 (pt); Orderlies 7 (ft), 8 (pt); Nurses aides 38 (ft), 43 (pt); Physical therapists 2 (pt); Recreational therapists 1 (ft); Occupational therapists 1 (pt); Speech therapists 1 (pt); Activities coordinators; Dietitians 3 (ft); Dentists 3 (pt); Ophthalmologists 3 (pt); Podiatrists 1 (pt).
Languages Spanish, Italian
Affiliation Baptist
Facilities Dining room; Physical therapy room; Activities room; Chapel; Crafts room; Laundry room.
Activities Arts & crafts; Cards; Games; Reading groups; Prayer groups; Movies; Social/Cultural gatherings.

Brooklyn United Methodist Church Home*
1485 Dumont Ave, Brooklyn, NY, 11208
(718) 827-4500
Admin H Rober Phillips. *Medical Dir/Dir of Nursing* Dr Babu Jasty.
Licensure Skilled care. *Beds* SNF 120. *Certified* Medicaid; Medicare.
Owner Nonprofit Corp.
Admissions Requirements Minimum age 21; Medical examination.
Staff Physicians 4 (pt); RNs 8 (ft), 14 (pt); LPNs 5 (ft), 3 (pt); Orderlies 6 (ft), 2 (pt); Nurses aides 45 (ft), 10 (pt); Physical therapists 1 (pt); Reality therapists 1 (pt); Recreational therapists 1 (pt); Occupational therapists 1 (pt); Speech therapists 1 (pt); Activities coordinators 1 (ft); Dietitians 1 (ft); Dentists 1 (pt); Ophthalmologists 1 (pt); Podiatrists 1 (pt); Audiologists 1 (pt).
Affiliation Methodist
Facilities Dining room; Physical therapy room; Activities room; Chapel; Crafts room; Laundry room; Barber/Beauty shop; Library; Day rooms.
Activities Arts & crafts; Cards; Games; Reading groups; Prayer groups; Movies; Shopping trips; Social/Cultural gatherings; Pet therapy with adopted cat for patients.

Cabs Nursing Home Company Inc*
270 Nostrand Ave, Brooklyn, NY, 11205
(718) 638-0500
Admin David Wieder. *Medical Dir/Dir of Nursing* Dr Francisco Trilla.
Licensure Skilled care; Intermediate care. *Beds* 157. *Certified* Medicaid; Medicare.
Owner Nonprofit Corp.
Admissions Requirements Minimum age 18.
Staff Physicians 8 (ft), 3 (pt); RNs 11 (ft), 4 (pt); LPNs 5 (ft), 3 (pt); Orderlies 5 (ft), 3 (pt); Nurses aides 35 (ft), 25 (pt); Physical therapists 2 (pt); Recreational therapists 2 (ft); Occupational therapists 1 (pt); Speech therapists 1 (pt); Activities coordinators 1 (ft); Dietitians 1 (ft); Dentists 1 (pt); Ophthalmologists 1 (pt); Podiatrists 1 (pt); Audiologists 1 (pt).

Facilities Dining room; Physical therapy room; Activities room; Crafts room; Laundry room; Barber/Beauty shop.
Activities Arts & crafts; Cards; Games; Reading groups; Prayer groups; Movies; Shopping trips; Social/Cultural gatherings.

Carlton Nursing Home
PO Box 1149, 405 Carlton Ave, Brooklyn, NY, 11238
(718) 789-6262
Licensure Skilled care. *Beds* 148. *Certified* Medicaid; Medicare.
Owner Proprietary Corp.

Caton Park Nursing Home*
1312 Caton Ave, Brooklyn, NY, 11226
(718) 693-7000
Admin J Weiss.
Licensure Skilled care. *Beds* 119. *Certified* Medicaid; Medicare.
Owner Proprietary Corp.

Cobble Hill Nursing Home Inc*
380 Henry St, Brooklyn, NY, 11201
(718) 855-6789
Admin Olga Lipschitz. *Medical Dir/Dir of Nursing* Henry Freedman MD.
Licensure Skilled care. *Beds* 520. *Certified* Medicaid; Medicare.
Owner Nonprofit Corp.
Staff Physicians 1 (ft), 9 (pt); RNs 27 (ft); LPNs 40 (ft); Orderlies 24 (ft), 9 (pt); Nurses aides 143 (ft); Physical therapists 6 (ft), 1 (pt); Recreational therapists 10 (ft), 2 (pt); Occupational therapists 4 (ft); Speech therapists 1 (ft); Dietitians 4 (ft); Dentists 4 (pt); Ophthalmologists 2 (ft); Podiatrists 4 (ft); Audiologists 1 (ft).
Facilities Dining room; Physical therapy room; Activities room; Laundry room; Barber/Beauty shop; Library; General store; Day rooms; Occupational therapy room; Speech/Hearing Room; Dental clinic.
Activities Arts & crafts; Games; Prayer groups; Movies; Shopping trips; Social/Cultural gatherings; Octoberfest; Birthday parties; Christmas party; Yearly "Love is..." party; Horse racing; Lectures; Cooking club; Black history club.

Concord Nursing Home Inc*
300 Madison St, Brooklyn, NY, 11216
(718) 636-7500
Admin James McPherson.
Licensure Skilled care; Intermediate care. *Beds* 82. *Certified* Medicaid; Medicare.
Owner Nonprofit Corp.

Crown Nursing Home*
3457 Nostrand Ave, Brooklyn, NY, 11229
(718) 769-6900
Admin Ann Stillman.
Licensure Skilled care. *Beds* 189. *Certified* Medicaid; Medicare.
Owner Proprietary Corp.

Dover Nursing Home*
1919 Cortelyou Rd, Brooklyn, NY, 11226
(718) 856-4646
Admin Morey Adler.
Licensure Skilled care. *Beds* 41. *Certified* Medicaid; Medicare.
Owner Proprietary Corp.

Flatbush Manor Care Center*
2107 Ditmas Ave, Brooklyn, NY, 11226
(718) 462-8100
Medical Dir/Dir of Nursing Dr Maurice Dunst.
Staff Physicians 5 (pt); RNs 14 (ft); LPNs 12 (ft); Orderlies 4 (ft); Nurses aides 28 (ft); Physical therapists 2 (pt); Recreational therapists 5 (pt); Occupational therapists 1 (pt); Speech therapists 1 (pt); Activities coordinators 1 (ft); Dietitians 2 (pt); Dentists 1 (pt); Ophthalmologists 1 (pt); Podiatrists 1 (pt); Audiologists 1 (pt); Psychiatrists 1 (pt); Urologists 1 (pt); Neurologists 1 (pt).

Facilities Dining room; Physical therapy room; Activities room; Chapel; Crafts room; Laundry room.
Activities Arts & crafts; Cards; Games; Prayer groups; Movies.

Marcus Garvey Nursing Company Inc
810 Saint Marks Ave, Brooklyn, NY, 11213
(718) 467-7300
Admin Ruby Weston. *Medical Dir/Dir of Nursing* Pierre A Brutus.
Licensure Skilled care; Intermediate care. *Beds* SNF 240; ICF 55. *Certified* Medicaid; Medicare.
Owner Nonprofit Corp.
Admissions Requirements Minimum age 40; Medical examination.
Staff RNs 13 (ft); LPNs 23 (ft), 7 (pt); Orderlies 10 (ft), 2 (pt); Nurses aides 84 (ft), 27 (pt); Physical therapists 1 (ft); Occupational therapists 1 (ft); Speech therapists 1 (pt); Activities coordinators 1 (ft); Dietitians 4 (ft); Dentists 1 (pt); Podiatrists 1 (pt).
Facilities Dining room; Physical therapy room; Activities room; Laundry room; Barber/Beauty shop.
Activities Arts & crafts; Cards; Games; Reading groups; Prayer groups; Movies; Shopping trips; Social/Cultural gatherings.

Greenpark Care Center
140 Saint Edwards St, Brooklyn, NY, 11201
(718) 858-6400
Admin Simon Pelman.
Licensure Skilled care; Intermediate care. *Beds* SNF 120; ICF 280. *Certified* Medicaid; Medicare.
Owner Proprietary Corp.

Haym Salomon Home for the Aged*
2300 Cropsey Ave, Brooklyn, NY, 11214
(718) 373-1700
Licensure Skilled care; Intermediate care. *Beds* 110. *Certified* Medicaid; Medicare.
Owner Nonprofit Corp.
Affiliation Jewish

Holy Family Home for the Aged*
1740 84th St, Brooklyn, NY, 11214
(718) 232-3666
Licensure Skilled care; Intermediate care. *Beds* 84. *Certified* Medicaid; Medicare.
Owner Nonprofit Corp.
Affiliation Roman Catholic

JHMCB Center for Nursing & Rehabilitation
520 Prospect Pl, Brooklyn, NY, 11360
(718) 638-1000
Admin George A Miller. *Medical Dir/Dir of Nursing* Bengamin Ross MD.
Licensure Skilled care. *Beds* SNF 320. *Certified* Medicaid; Medicare.
Owner Nonprofit Corp.
Admissions Requirements Minimum age 16; Physician's request.
Staff Physicians 1 (pt); RNs 54 (ft), 5 (pt); LPNs 27 (ft); Orderlies 17 (ft); Nurses aides 150 (ft), 26 (pt); Physical therapists 2 (ft), 1 (pt); Recreational therapists 4 (ft), 1 (pt); Occupational therapists 3 (ft), 1 (pt); Speech therapists 1 (pt); Dietitians 2 (ft); Dentists 1 (pt); Ophthalmologists 3 (pt); Dentist 1 (pt).
Languages French, Creole, Spanish
Affiliation Jewish
Facilities Dining room; Physical therapy room; Activities room; Chapel; Crafts room; Barber/Beauty shop; Library.
Activities Arts & crafts; Cards; Games; Reading groups; Prayer groups; Movies; Shopping trips; Social/Cultural gatherings; Trips to museums, parks, ball games, race track.

Lemberg Home & Geriatric Institute Inc*
8629 Bay Pkwy, Brooklyn, NY, 11214
(718) 266-0900
Admin Rose Clee. *Medical Dir/Dir of Nursing* Anthony Loucella MD.

Licensure Skilled care; Health related care. *Beds* 20. *Certified* Medicaid; Medicare.
Owner Nonprofit Corp.
Admissions Requirements Minimum age 65; Medical examination.
Staff Physicians; RNs 3 (ft), 2 (pt); LPNs 2 (ft), 2 (pt); Orderlies 1 (ft); Physical therapists 1 (pt); Recreational therapists 2 (pt); Occupational therapists 1 (pt); Speech therapists 1 (pt); Activities coordinators 1 (pt); Dietitians 1 (pt); Dentists 1 (pt); Ophthalmologists 1 (pt); Podiatrists 1 (pt); Audiologists 1 (pt).
Facilities Dining room; Physical therapy room; Activities room; Chapel; Laundry room; Library.
Activities Arts & crafts; Cards; Games; Reading groups; Prayer groups; Social/Cultural gatherings; Birthday parties; Holiday parties.

Madonna Residence Inc
1 Prospect Park W, Brooklyn, NY, 11215
(718) 857-1200
Admin Sr Cecilia Regina Murphy. *Medical Dir/Dir of Nursing* Dr Luciano Martinucci MD; Sr Susan William.
Licensure Skilled care; Health related. *Beds* SNF 203; Health related 87. *Certified* Medicaid; Medicare.
Owner Nonprofit Corp.
Admissions Requirements Minimum age 65; Medical examination.
Staff Physicians 50 (pt); RNs 15 (ft), 39 (pt); LPNs 14 (ft), 17 (pt); Orderlies 94 (ft), 53 (pt); Nurses aides; Physical therapists 2 (ft); Occupational therapists 1 (ft), 1 (pt); Speech therapists 1 (pt); Activities coordinators 1 (ft); Dietitians 2 (ft); Dentists 2 (pt); Ophthalmologists 2 (pt); Podiatrists 1 (pt); Social workers 4 (ft).
Languages Spanish, Italian, Polish, Haitian
Affiliation Roman Catholic
Facilities Dining room; Physical therapy room; Activities room; Chapel; Crafts room; Laundry room; Barber/Beauty shop; Library; Coffee shop; Gift shop.
Activities Arts & crafts; Cards; Games; Reading groups; Movies; Shopping trips; Social/Cultural gatherings; Senior Olympics.

Menorah Home & Hospital for the Aged & Infirm
871 Bushwick Ave, Brooklyn, NY, 11221
(718) 443-3000
Admin Shirley Windheim Ex Dir, Jane Rosenthal, Adm. *Medical Dir/Dir of Nursing* Max Kleinmann MD; Enith Lacy RN.
Licensure Skilled care; Intermediate care. *Beds* SNF 233; ICF 40. *Certified* Medicaid; Medicare.
Owner Nonprofit Corp.
Staff Physicians 3 (ft), 3 (pt); RNs 11 (ft), 5 (pt); LPNs 27 (ft), 12 (pt); Orderlies; Nurses aides 132 (ft), 21 (pt); Reality therapists 1 (ft), 2 (pt); Recreational therapists 5 (ft), 4 (pt); Occupational therapists 2 (pt); Speech therapists 1 (pt); Activities coordinators 1 (pt); Dietitians 2 (pt).
Languages Yiddish, Italian, Spanish
Affiliation Jewish
Facilities Dining room; Physical therapy room; Activities room; Chapel; Crafts room; Laundry room; Barber/Beauty shop; Library; Occupational therapy; X-ray; Speech therapy; Audiology.
Activities Arts & crafts; Cards; Games; Reading groups; Prayer groups; Movies; Shopping trips; Social/Cultural gatherings.

Menorah Nursing Home Inc
1516 Oriental Blvd, Brooklyn, NY, 11235
(718) 646-4441
Admin Shirley Windheim. *Medical Dir/Dir of Nursing* Swaminathan Giridharan MD; Suzanne Davis RN DON.

Licensure Skilled care; Intermediate care. *Beds* SNF 180; ICF 73. *Certified* Medicaid; Medicare.
Owner Nonprofit Corp.
Staff Physicians 3 (ft), 3 (pt); RNs 13 (ft), 6 (pt); LPNs 15 (ft), 8 (pt); Orderlies; Nurses aides 106 (ft), 18 (pt); Physical therapists 1 (ft), 3 (pt); Recreational therapists 4 (ft), 4 (pt); Occupational therapists 1 (ft), 2 (pt); Speech therapists 1 (pt); Activities coordinators 1 (pt); Dietitians 1 (ft), 1 (pt).
Languages Yiddish, Hebrew, Italian, Russian
Affiliation Jewish
Facilities Dining room; Physical therapy room; Activities room; Chapel; Crafts room; Laundry room; Barber/Beauty shop; Library; Occupational therapy; X-ray; Speech therapy; Audiology.
Activities Arts & crafts; Cards; Games; Reading groups; Prayer groups; Movies; Shopping trips; Social/Cultural gatherings.

Metropolitan Jewish Genatric Center
Boardwalk & W 29th St, Brooklyn, NY, 11224
(718) 266-5700
Admin Marvin Hochheiser. *Medical Dir/Dir of Nursing* Dr Lila Dogim; Ms Irene Brienza RN DON.
Licensure Skilled care; Intermediate care. *Beds* SNF; ICF 359. *Certified* Medicaid; Medicare.
Owner Nonprofit Corp.
Admissions Requirements Medical examination.
Staff Physicians 6 (ft); RNs 21 (ft); LPNs 47 (ft); Orderlies 131 (ft); Physical therapists 2 (ft); Recreational therapists 7 (ft), 1 (pt); Occupational therapists 2 (ft); Speech therapists 1 (ft); Activities coordinators 1 (ft); Dietitians 2 (ft), 1 (pt); Dentists 1 (ft); Ophthalmologists 1 (ft); Podiatrists 1 (ft); Dentist 1 (ft).
Languages French, Spanish, Italian, Hebrew, Yiddish, Russian
Affiliation Jewish
Facilities Dining room; Physical therapy room; Activities room; Chapel; Crafts room; Barber/Beauty shop; Library; Boardwalk; Activity space.
Activities Arts & crafts; Cards; Games; Reading groups; Prayer groups; Movies; Shopping trips; Social/Cultural gatherings; Field trips; Speakers; BBQs; Religious services.

MJG Nursing Home Company Inc*
4915 10th Ave, Brooklyn, NY, 11219
(718) 851-3710
Licensure Intermediate care. *Beds* 529.
Owner Nonprofit Corp.

New York Congregational Home for the Aged
123 Linden Blvd, Brooklyn, NY, 11226
(718) 284-8256
Admin David F Fielding. *Medical Dir/Dir of Nursing* Dr Glenn Morris.
Licensure Skilled care; Intermediate care. *Beds* SNF 39; ICF 29. *Certified* Medicaid; Medicare.
Owner Nonprofit Corp.
Affiliation Congregational
Facilities Dining room; Physical therapy room; Activities room; Crafts room; Laundry room; Barber/Beauty shop; Library; Solarium garden.
Activities Arts & crafts; Cards; Games; Prayer groups; Movies; Social/Cultural gatherings.

Norwegian Christian Home for the Aged*
1250-70 67th St, Brooklyn, NY, 11219
(718) 232-2322
Licensure Skilled care; Intermediate care. *Beds* 41. *Certified* Medicaid; Medicare.
Owner Nonprofit Corp.

Oxford Nursing Home*
144 S Oxford St, Brooklyn, NY, 11217
(718) 638-0360

Admin Max Goldberg.
Licensure Skilled care. *Beds* 235. *Certified* Medicaid; Medicare.
Owner Proprietary Corp.

Palm Gardens Nursing Home*
615 Ave C, Brooklyn, NY, 11218
(718) 633-3300
Admin Israel Lefkowitz.
Licensure Skilled care. *Beds* 240. *Certified* Medicaid; Medicare.
Owner Proprietary Corp.

Palm Tree Nursing Home
5606 15th Ave, Brooklyn, NY, 11219
(718) 851-1000
Admin Isaac Levy. *Medical Dir/Dir of Nursing* Dr George Jhagroo; Mrs Marie Micara RN DNS.
Licensure Skilled care. *Beds* SNF 79. *Certified* Medicaid; Medicare.
Owner Proprietary Corp.
Admissions Requirements Minimum age 65; Medical examination.
Staff Physicians 2 (ft); RNs 5 (ft); LPNs 7 (ft); Orderlies 2 (ft); Nurses aides 11 (ft); Physical therapists 1 (pt); Occupational therapists 1 (pt); Speech therapists 1 (pt); Activities coordinators 1 (ft); Dietitians 2 (ft), 1 (pt); Dentists 1 (pt); Ophthalmologists 1 (pt); Podiatrists 1 (pt).
Facilities Dining room; Physical therapy room; Activities room; Crafts room; Laundry room; Barber/Beauty shop; Library; Day room.
Activities Arts & crafts; Cards; Games; Reading groups; Prayer groups; Movies; Shopping trips; Social/Cultural gatherings.

Parkshore Manor Health Care Center
1555 Rockaway Pkwy, Brooklyn, NY, 11236
(718) 498-6400
Admin Lawrence Friedman. *Medical Dir/Dir of Nursing* Nazalin Varani MD; Frieda Siegal DON.
Licensure Skilled care; Intermediate care. *Beds* SNF 135; ICF 135. *Certified* Medicaid; Medicare.
Owner Privately owned.
Admissions Requirements Medical examination.
Staff Physicians; RNs; LPNs; Orderlies; Nurses aides; Physical therapists; Reality therapists; Recreational therapists; Occupational therapists; Speech therapists; Activities coordinators; Dietitians; Dentists; Ophthalmologists; Podiatrists.
Languages Yiddish, Hebrew, Italian
Facilities Dining room; Physical therapy room; Activities room; Chapel; Barber/Beauty shop; Library.
Activities Arts & crafts; Cards; Games; Reading groups; Prayer groups; Movies; Shopping trips; Social/Cultural gatherings.

Prospect Park Nursing Home Inc
1455 Coney Island Ave, Brooklyn, NY, 11230
(718) 252-9800
Admin Shirley Kurzman. *Medical Dir/Dir of Nursing* Lawrence Sher; Evelyn Power RN DON.
Licensure Skilled care. *Beds* SNF 215. *Certified* Medicaid; Medicare.
Owner Nonprofit Corp.
Admissions Requirements Minimum age 50; Medical examination.
Staff Physicians 2 (ft); RNs 7 (ft), 5 (pt); LPNs 21 (ft), 4 (pt); Orderlies 9 (ft), 6 (pt); Nurses aides 18 (ft), 12 (pt); Physical therapists 2 (ft), 1 (pt); Recreational therapists 1 (ft), 6 (pt); Occupational therapists 1 (pt); Speech therapists 1 (pt); Activities coordinators 1 (ft); Dietitians 3 (ft), 1 (pt); Dentists 1 (pt); Ophthalmologists 2 (pt); Podiatrists 2 (pt); Dentist 1 (pt).
Languages Spanish, Yiddish, Hebrew, Russian, Italian, French, German, Hungarian
Affiliation Jewish

Facilities Dining room; Physical therapy room; Activities room; Crafts room; Laundry room; Barber/Beauty shop; Library; Dental office.
Activities Arts & crafts; Cards; Games; Reading groups; Prayer groups; Movies; Shopping trips; Social/Cultural gatherings.

River Manor HRF*
630 E 104th St, Brooklyn, NY, 11236
(718) 272-1050
Licensure Intermediate care. *Beds* 380.
Owner Proprietary Corp.

Rutland Nursing Home Co Inc*
585 Schenectady Ave, Brooklyn, NY, 11203
(718) 604-5000
Admin Harris Brodsky. *Medical Dir/Dir of Nursing* Morris Mienfeld MD.
Licensure Skilled care. *Beds* 538. *Certified* Medicaid; Medicare.
Owner Nonprofit Corp.
Staff Physicians; RNs; LPNs; Orderlies; Nurses aides; Physical therapists; Reality therapists; Recreational therapists; Occupational therapists; Speech therapists; Activities coordinators; Dietitians; Dentists; Ophthalmologists; Podiatrists; Audiologists.
Affiliation Jewish
Facilities Dining room; Physical therapy room; Activities room; Chapel; Crafts room; Laundry room; Barber/Beauty shop; Library.
Activities Arts & crafts; Cards; Games; Reading groups; Prayer groups; Movies; Shopping trips; Social/Cultural gatherings.

St Johns Episcopal Homes for the Aged & the Blind
452 Herkimer St, Brooklyn, NY, 11213
(718) 467-1885
Admin Roberta Don Diego. *Medical Dir/Dir of Nursing* Dr Rasikal Amin; Cynthia Reid.
Licensure Skilled care; Intermediate care. *Beds* SNF 43; ICF 54. *Certified* Medicaid; Medicare.
Owner Nonprofit organization/foundation.
Admissions Requirements Minimum age 62 (blind), 65 (aged); PRI & Screen.
Staff Physicians 8 (pt); RNs 10 (ft), 3 (pt); LPNs 3 (ft); Orderlies 1 (ft); Nurses aides 22 (ft), 6 (pt); Physical therapists 1 (pt); Recreational therapists 1 (ft), 1 (pt); Occupational therapists 1 (pt); Speech therapists 1 (pt); Activities coordinators 1 (ft); Dietitians 2 (pt); Dentists 1 (pt); Ophthalmologists 1 (pt); Podiatrists 1 (pt); Dentist 1 (pt).
Languages Spanish
Affiliation Episcopal
Facilities Dining room; Physical therapy room; Activities room; Chapel; Crafts room; Barber/Beauty shop; Living room.
Activities Arts & crafts; Cards; Games; Reading groups; Prayer groups; Movies; Shopping trips; Social/Cultural gatherings.

The Samuel Schulman Institute for Nursing & Rehabilitation
555 Rockaway Pkwy, Brooklyn, NY, 11212
(718) 240-5101
Admin Marcel Baruch. *Medical Dir/Dir of Nursing* Dr E P Dooley Medical Director.
Licensure Skilled care. *Beds* SNF 220. *Certified* Medicaid; Medicare.
Owner Nonprofit Corp.
Admissions Requirements Medical examination; Physician's request.
Staff Physicians; RNs; LPNs; Orderlies; Nurses aides; Physical therapists; Recreational therapists; Occupational therapists; Speech therapists; Activities coordinators; Dietitians; Dentists; Ophthalmologists; Podiatrists.
Facilities Dining room; Physical therapy room; Activities room; Chapel; Crafts room; Laundry room; Barber/Beauty shop; Library.

Activities Arts & crafts; Cards; Games; Reading groups; Prayer groups; Movies; Shopping trips; Social/Cultural gatherings.

Sea Crest Health Care Center
3035 W 24th St, Brooklyn, NY, 11224
(718) 372-4500
Admin A L Urbach. *Medical Dir/Dir of Nursing* Dr Indravadan Shah; Myra Levine RN DON.
Licensure Skilled care. *Beds* SNF 231; Health related 89. *Certified* Medicaid; Medicare.
Owner Proprietary Corp.
Admissions Requirements Minimum age 16; Medical examination; Physician's request.
Staff RNs 21 (ft), 15 (pt); LPNs 20 (ft), 16 (pt); Orderlies 18 (ft), 2 (pt); Nurses aides 86 (ft), 27 (pt); Recreational therapists 4 (ft); Activities coordinators 1 (ft); Dietitians 2 (ft); Social worker 4 (ft).
Languages Yiddish, Hebrew, Spanish, Italian
Facilities Dining room; Physical therapy room; Activities room; Crafts room; Laundry room; Barber/Beauty shop; Library; Occupational therapy room; Speech therapy room.
Activities Arts & crafts; Cards; Games; Reading groups; Prayer groups; Movies; Social/Cultural gatherings; BBQs; Outings.

Sephardic Home for the Aged Inc
2266 Cropsey Ave, Brooklyn, NY, 11214
(718) 266-6100
Admin Herbert Freeman. *Medical Dir/Dir of Nursing* Augusta Miyashiro MD; Josephine Mittelmark RN.
Licensure Skilled care; Health related facility. *Beds* SNF 182; Health related 87. *Certified* Medicaid; Medicare.
Owner Nonprofit Corp.
Admissions Requirements Medical examination; Physician's request.
Staff Physicians; RNs; LPNs; Orderlies; Nurses aides; Physical therapists; Reality therapists; Recreational therapists; Occupational therapists; Speech therapists; Activities coordinators; Dietitians; Dentists; Ophthalmologists; Podiatrists; Social workers.
Languages Spanish, Greek, Turkish, Arabic, Hebrew, Yiddish
Affiliation Jewish
Facilities Dining room; Physical therapy room; Activities room; Chapel; Crafts room; Laundry room; Barber/Beauty shop; Library.
Activities Arts & crafts; Cards; Games; Reading groups; Prayer groups; Movies; Shopping trips; Social/Cultural gatherings.

Sheepshead Nursing Home*
2840 Knapp St, Brooklyn, NY, 11235
(718) 646-5700
Admin Theresa Holzer.
Licensure Skilled care. *Beds* 200. *Certified* Medicaid; Medicare.
Owner Proprietary Corp.

Shore View Nursing Home
2865 Brighton 3rd St, Brooklyn, NY, 11235
(718) 891-4400
Admin Mr Eric Kalt. *Medical Dir/Dir of Nursing* Dr I Shah; Ms P Pyle RN.
Licensure Skilled care. *Beds* SNF 320. *Certified* Medicaid; Medicare.
Owner Proprietary Corp.
Admissions Requirements Medical examination; Physician's request.
Staff Physicians; RNs; LPNs; Orderlies; Nurses aides; Physical therapists; Reality therapists; Recreational therapists; Occupational therapists; Speech therapists; Activities coordinators; Dietitians; Dentists; Ophthalmologists; Podiatrists.
Facilities Dining room; Physical therapy room; Activities room; Crafts room; Laundry room; Barber/Beauty shop; Library.

Activities Arts & crafts; Cards; Games; Reading groups; Prayer groups; Movies; Shopping trips; Social/Cultural gatherings.

Wartburg Lutheran Home for the Aging
2598 Fulton St, Brooklyn, NY, 11207
(718) 345-2273
Admin Ronald B Stuckey. *Medical Dir/Dir of Nursing* Dr S Y Gowd; Mildred David.
Licensure Skilled care; Intermediate care. *Beds* SNF 183; ICF 41. *Certified* Medicaid; Medicare.
Owner Nonprofit Corp.
Admissions Requirements Minimum age 18.
Staff Physicians 1 (pt); RNs 17 (ft); LPNs 32 (ft); Orderlies 8 (ft); Nurses aides 78 (ft); Physical therapists 1 (ft); Recreational therapists 3 (ft), 1 (pt); Occupational therapists 1 (ft); Speech therapists 1 (pt); Activities coordinators 1 (ft); Dietitians 2 (ft), 1 (pt); Dentists 1 (pt); Ophthalmologists 1 (pt); Podiatrists 1 (pt).
Languages German, Spanish, Italian
Affiliation Lutheran
Facilities Dining room; Physical therapy room; Activities room; Chapel; Laundry room; Barber/Beauty shop; Library.
Activities Arts & crafts; Cards; Games; Reading groups; Prayer groups; Movies; Shopping trips; Social/Cultural gatherings.

Willoughby Nursing Home*
949 Willoughby Ave, Brooklyn, NY, 11221
(718) 443-1600
Admin Jerome Mann.
Licensure Skilled care. *Beds* 161. *Certified* Medicaid; Medicare.
Owner Proprietary Corp.

BUFFALO

Rosa Coplon Jewish Home & Infirmary
10 Symphony Circle, Buffalo, NY, 14201
(716) 885-3311
Admin David M Dunkelman.
Licensure Skilled care; Intermediate care. *Beds* 111. *Certified* Medicaid; Medicare.
Owner Nonprofit Corp.
Affiliation Jewish

Downtown Nursing Home Inc
200 7th St, Buffalo, NY, 14201
(716) 847-2500
Admin Betty D'Arcy. *Medical Dir/Dir of Nursing* Dr Cheng Shung Fu; Roberta Courtade.
Licensure Skilled care. *Beds* SNF 80. *Certified* Medicaid; Medicare; VA.
Owner Nonprofit Corp.
Admissions Requirements Minimum age 16; Medical examination; Physician's request.
Staff Physicians 3 (pt); RNs 8 (ft), 10 (pt); LPNs 6 (ft), 11 (pt); Nurses aides 22 (ft), 15 (pt); Physical therapists 1 (pt); Occupational therapists 1 (ft); Speech therapists 1 (pt); Activities coordinators 1 (ft); Dietitians 1 (pt); Ophthalmologists 2 (pt).
Facilities Dining room; Physical therapy room; Activities room; Barber/Beauty shop.
Activities Arts & crafts; Cards; Games; Reading groups; Prayer groups; Movies; Shopping trips; Social/Cultural gatherings.

Georgian Court Nursing Home of Buffalo Inc*
1040 Delaware Ave, Buffalo, NY, 14209
(716) 886-7740
Admin J Hall.
Licensure Skilled care. *Beds* 134. *Certified* Medicaid; Medicare.
Owner Proprietary Corp.

Hamlin Terrace Health Care Center
1014 Delaware Ave, Buffalo, NY, 14209
(716) 882-8221
Admin Sharon Carlo. *Medical Dir/Dir of Nursing* Dr Edwin Lenahan; Joyce Lienert RN.

Licensure Skilled care; Intermediate care. *Beds* SNF 140; ICF 60. *Certified* Medicaid; Medicare.
Owner Proprietary Corp.
Admissions Requirements Minimum age 16; Medical examination; Physician's request.
Staff Physicians 2 (pt); RNs 14 (ft); LPNs 19 (ft); Nurses aides 70 (ft); Physical therapists 1 (pt); Occupational therapists 1 (ft), 1 (pt); Speech therapists 1 (pt); Activities coordinators 4 (ft); Dietitians 1 (ft); Dentists 1 (pt); Ophthalmologists 1 (pt); Podiatrists 1 (pt); Dentist 1 (pt).
Facilities Dining room; Physical therapy room; Activities room; Chapel; Crafts room; Laundry room; Barber/Beauty shop; Library.
Activities Arts & crafts; Cards; Games; Reading groups; Prayer groups; Movies; Shopping trips; Social/Cultural gatherings.

Manhattan Manor Nursing Home
300 Manhattan Ave, Buffalo, NY, 14214
(716) 838-5460
Admin Lorraine Kramer. *Medical Dir/Dir of Nursing* Dr Painton; Jean Bucholtz.
Licensure Skilled care; Intermediate care. *Beds* SNF 44; ICF 81. *Certified* Medicaid; Medicare.
Owner Proprietary Corp.
Admissions Requirements Minimum age 65; Medical examination; Physician's request.
Staff RNs 3 (ft), 4 (pt); LPNs 2 (ft), 6 (pt); Nurses aides 29 (ft), 1 (pt); Physical therapists 1 (pt); Occupational therapists 1 (pt); Speech therapists 1 (pt); Activities coordinators 1 (ft); Dietitians 1 (ft); Ophthalmologists 1 (pt); Podiatrists 1 (pt).
Languages German, Ukranian, Polish, Italian, Greek
Facilities Dining room; Physical therapy room; Activities room; Chapel; Crafts room; Laundry room; Barber/Beauty shop; Library.
Activities Arts & crafts; Cards; Games; Reading groups; Prayer groups; Movies; Shopping trips; Social/Cultural gatherings; Dinners.

Mercy Hospital—Skilled Nursing Facility
565 Abbott Rd, Buffalo, NY, 14220
(716) 826-7000
Admin Sr Sheila Marie Walsh.
Licensure Skilled care. *Beds* 60. *Certified* Medicaid; Medicare.
Owner Nonprofit Corp.
Admissions Requirements Physician's request.
Facilities Dining room; Physical therapy room; Activities room; Chapel; Crafts room; Laundry room; Barber/Beauty shop; Library.
Activities Arts & crafts; Cards; Games; Prayer groups; Movies; Shopping trips.

Millard Fillmore Skilled Nursing Facility
3 Gates Circle, Buffalo, NY, 14209
(716) 887-4012
Admin Joanne L Zink. *Medical Dir/Dir of Nursing* Dr Jack Freer.
Licensure Skilled care. *Beds* SNF 75. *Certified* Medicaid; Medicare.
Owner Nonprofit Corp.
Admissions Requirements Minimum age 16.
Staff Physicians 2 (pt); RNs 7 (ft), 12 (pt); LPNs 7 (ft), 10 (pt); Orderlies 3 (ft), 2 (pt); Nurses aides 20 (ft), 22 (pt); Physical therapists 1 (ft); Recreational therapists 1 (pt); Occupational therapists 1 (pt); Speech therapists 1 (pt); Activities coordinators 1 (ft); Dietitians 2 (pt); Ophthalmologists 1 (pt); Podiatrists 1 (pt).
Languages Polish
Facilities Dining room; Physical therapy room; Activities room; Laundry room; Barber/Beauty shop.
Activities Arts & crafts; Cards; Games; Reading groups; Prayer groups; Movies; Shopping trips; Social/Cultural gatherings.

Nazareth Health Related Facility
291 W North St, Buffalo, NY, 14201
(716) 881-2323
Admin Austin J Barrett. *Medical Dir/Dir of Nursing* Donald M Wilson MD.
Licensure Skilled care; Intermediate care. *Beds* SNF 95; ICF 30. *Certified* Medicaid; Medicare.
Owner Nonprofit Corp.
Admissions Requirements Minimum age 16; Females only; Medical examination; Physician's request.
Staff Physicians 1 (pt); RNs 5 (ft), 6 (pt); LPNs 12 (ft), 7 (pt); Nurses aides 40 (ft), 9 (pt); Physical therapists 2 (pt); Occupational therapists 1 (pt); Speech therapists 1 (pt); Activities coordinators 1 (ft); Dietitians 1 (pt); Dentists 1 (pt); Ophthalmologists 2 (pt); Podiatrists 1 (pt).
Affiliation Roman Catholic
Facilities Dining room; Physical therapy room; Activities room; Chapel; Crafts room; Laundry room; Barber/Beauty shop; Library.
Activities Arts & crafts; Cards; Games; Reading groups; Prayer groups; Movies; Shopping trips; Social/Cultural gatherings.

Niagara Lutheran Home Inc
64 Hager St, Buffalo, NY, 14208
(716) 886-4377
Admin Donald L Broecker. *Medical Dir/Dir of Nursing* Donald M Wilson MD.
Licensure Skilled care. *Beds* SNF 169. *Certified* Medicaid; Medicare.
Owner Nonprofit organization/foundation.
Admissions Requirements Minimum age 21; Medical examination; Physician's request.
Staff Physicians 1 (pt); RNs 14 (ft), 7 (pt); LPNs 12 (ft), 3 (pt); Orderlies 10 (ft), 1 (pt); Nurses aides 48 (ft), 29 (pt); Physical therapists 2 (pt); Occupational therapists 1 (pt); Speech therapists 1 (pt); Activities coordinators 1 (ft); Dietitians 1 (ft).
Affiliation Lutheran
Facilities Dining room; Physical therapy room; Activities room; Chapel; Crafts room; Laundry room; Barber/Beauty shop; Library; X-ray room; Occupational therapy room; Speech pathology room; Sitting rooms; Treatment room; Podiatry room.
Activities Arts & crafts; Cards; Games; Reading groups; Movies; Shopping trips; Social/Cultural gatherings; Church services & Catholic Mass; Picnics; Weekly Sing-alongs; Luncheons; Discussion groups; Trips to area parks & the Buffalo Zoo; Holiday & birthday celebrations.

Ridge View Manor Nursing Home
300 Dorrance Ave, Buffalo, NY, 14220
(716) 825-4884
Admin Alice Breyer. *Medical Dir/Dir of Nursing* Dr Vincent Cotroneo.
Licensure Skilled care; Intermediate care. *Beds* SNF 80; ICF 40. *Certified* Medicaid; Medicare.
Owner Privately owned.
Admissions Requirements Minimum age 17; Medical examination; Physician's request.
Staff Physicians 14 (pt); RNs 7 (ft), 5 (pt); LPNs 11 (ft), 7 (pt); Orderlies 4 (ft), 4 (pt); Nurses aides 35 (ft), 50 (pt); Physical therapists 1 (pt); Occupational therapists 1 (pt); Speech therapists 1 (pt); Activities coordinators 1 (ft); Dietitians 1 (ft); Dentists 1 (pt); Ophthalmologists 1 (pt); Podiatrists 1 (pt).
Facilities Dining room; Physical therapy room; Activities room; Crafts room; Laundry room; Barber/Beauty shop.
Activities Arts & crafts; Cards; Games; Reading groups; Prayer groups; Movies; Shopping trips; Social/Cultural gatherings.

St Lukes Presbyterian Nursing Center
1175 Delaware Ave, Buffalo, NY, 14221
(716) 885-6733

Admin Randy A Muenzner. *Medical Dir/Dir of Nursing* Dr Matthew O'Brien; Mary Klink.
Licensure Skilled care; Intermediate care. *Beds* 120. *Certified* Medicaid 16B.
Owner Nonprofit Corp.
Admissions Requirements Minimum age 16.
Staff RNs; LPNs; Orderlies; Nurses aides; Physical therapists 1 (pt); Recreational therapists 2 (ft); Occupational therapists 1 (ft); Speech therapists 1 (pt); Activities coordinators 1 (ft); Dietitians 1 (pt); Ophthalmologists 1 (pt); Podiatrists 1 (pt).
Affiliation Presbyterian
Facilities Dining room; Physical therapy room; Activities room; Chapel; Crafts room; Laundry room; Barber/Beauty shop; Library.
Activities Arts & crafts; Cards; Games; Reading groups; Prayer groups; Movies; Shopping trips; Social/Cultural gatherings.

Sisters of Charity Hospital—Skilled Nursing Facility
2157 Main St, Buffalo, NY, 14214
(716) 862-2000
Admin Leonard Sicurella. *Medical Dir/Dir of Nursing* Young Paik MD; Ruth Balkin RN DNS.
Licensure Skilled care. *Beds* SNF 80. *Certified* Medicaid; Medicare.
Owner Nonprofit Corp.
Admissions Requirements Minimum age 16; Medical examination; Physician's request.
Staff Physicians 1 (pt); RNs 6 (ft), 6 (pt); LPNs 16 (ft), 6 (pt); Nurses aides 14 (ft), 14 (pt); Physical therapists 1 (ft), 1 (pt); Recreational therapists 1 (ft), 1 (pt); Occupational therapists 1 (ft), 1 (pt); Speech therapists 1 (pt); Dietitians 1 (ft), 1 (pt); Dentists 1 (pt); Ophthalmologists 1 (pt); Podiatrists 1 (pt); Dentist 1 (pt).
Languages Polish, Italian, Spanish
Affiliation Roman Catholic
Facilities Dining room; Physical therapy room; Chapel; Crafts room; Laundry room; Barber/Beauty shop.
Activities Arts & crafts; Cards; Games; Reading groups; Prayer groups; Movies; Shopping trips; Social/Cultural gatherings; Sporting events.

24 Rhode Island Street Nursing Home Company Inc
24 Rhode Island St, Buffalo, NY, 14213
(716) 884-6500
Admin Darlene Jones Crispell. *Medical Dir/ Dir of Nursing* John Edwards MD; Merle Malone RN DON.
Licensure Skilled care; Intermediate care. *Beds* 128. *Certified* Medicaid; Medicare.
Owner Nonprofit Corp.
Admissions Requirements Minimum age 16; Medical examination; Physician's request.
Staff RNs 10 (ft), 5 (pt); LPNs 11 (ft), 8 (pt); Nurses aides 22 (ft), 22 (pt); Occupational therapists 1 (ft); Activities coordinators 1 (ft); Dietitians 1 (ft).
Facilities Dining room; Physical therapy room; Activities room; Chapel; Crafts room; Laundry room; Barber/Beauty shop; Library.
Activities Arts & crafts; Cards; Games; Reading groups; Prayer groups; Movies; Shopping trips; Social/Cultural gatherings; Camping.

CAMBRIDGE

Mary McClellan Skilled Nursing Facility
Cambridge, NY, 12816
(518) 677-2611
Admin John Remillard. *Medical Dir/Dir of Nursing* Newton Krumdieck MD; Kathleen Lacasse RN Asst Admin, Nursing.
Licensure Skilled care. *Beds* SNF 39. *Certified* Medicaid; Medicare.
Owner Nonprofit Corp.

Admissions Requirements Minimum age 16;
Medical examination; Physician's request.
Staff Physicians 1 (pt); RNs 4 (ft), 2 (pt);
LPNs 4 (ft), 4 (pt); Nurses aides 8 (ft), 12
(pt); Physical therapists 1 (pt); Occupational
therapists 1 (pt); Activities coordinators 1
(ft); Dietitians 1 (pt).
Facilities Dining room; Physical therapy
room; Activities room; Chapel; Barber/
Beauty shop.
Activities Arts & crafts; Cards; Games;
Reading groups; Prayer groups; Movies;
Social/Cultural gatherings; Resident council.

CAMPBELL HALL

Doanes Nursing Home
RD 2, Box 291, Campbell Hall, NY, 10916
(914) 294-8154
Admin Joseph Cornetta. *Medical Dir/Dir of
Nursing* Dr Francis Imbarrato; Judith Lyons
DON.
Licensure Intermediate care; Health related
facility. *Beds* SNF 80; HRF 40. *Certified*
Medicaid; Medicare.
Owner Proprietary Corp.
Admissions Requirements Minimum age 16;
Medical examination; Physician's request.
Staff Physicians; RNs; LPNs; Orderlies;
Nurses aides; Physical therapists; Reality
therapists; Recreational therapists;
Occupational therapists; Speech therapists;
Activities coordinators; Dietitians; Dentists;
Ophthalmologists; Podiatrists.
Facilities Dining room; Physical therapy
room; Activities room; Chapel; Crafts room;
Laundry room; Barber/Beauty shop.
Activities Arts & crafts; Cards; Games;
Reading groups; Prayer groups; Movies;
Social/Cultural gatherings.

CANANDAIGUA

Elm Manor Nursing Home
210 N Main St, Canandaigua, NY, 14424
(716) 394-3883
Admin Thomas Madigan. *Medical Dir/Dir of
Nursing* Dr Gerald Duffner; Carman Coons
DON.
Licensure Skilled care. *Beds* SNF 46. *Certified*
Medicaid; Medicare.
Owner Privately owned.
Admissions Requirements Minimum age 16;
Medical examination; Physician's request.
Staff Physicians 13 (pt); RNs 6 (ft), 1 (pt);
LPNs 7 (ft), 3 (pt); Orderlies 1 (pt); Nurses
aides 25 (ft), 7 (pt); Physical therapists 1
(pt); Occupational therapists 1 (pt); Speech
therapists 1 (pt); Activities coordinators 1
(ft); Dietitians 1 (pt); Podiatrists 1 (pt).
Facilities Dining room; Activities room;
Laundry room; Barber/Beauty shop.
Activities Arts & crafts; Cards; Games;
Reading groups; Movies; Shopping trips.

Ontario County Health Facility*
Rte 2, Canandaigua, NY, 14424
(716) 394-2100
Admin Gerald B Cole. *Medical Dir/Dir of
Nursing* Charles Bathrick MD.
Licensure Skilled care; Health related care.
Beds SNF 48; HRC 50. *Certified* Medicaid;
Medicare.
Owner Publicly owned.
Admissions Requirements Minimum age 18;
Medical examination; Physician's request.
Staff Physicians 1 (pt); RNs 6 (ft), 3 (pt);
LPNs 10 (ft), 1 (pt); Nurses aides 30 (ft), 5
(pt); Physical therapists 1 (pt); Recreational
therapists 1 (ft); Speech therapists 1 (pt);
Activities coordinators 1 (ft), 1 (pt);
Dietitians 1 (ft); Dentists 1 (pt); Podiatrists
1 (pt); Audiologists 1 (pt).
Facilities Dining room; Physical therapy
room; Activities room; Crafts room; Laundry
room; Barber/Beauty shop; Library.

Activities Arts & crafts; Cards; Games;
Reading groups; Prayer groups; Movies;
Shopping trips; Social/Cultural gatherings.

Thompson Nursing Home Inc
350 Parrish St, Canandaigua, NY, 14424
(716) 394-1100
Admin Fred M Thomas. *Medical Dir/Dir
of Nursing* George Allen MD; Susan M Sikes
RN DON.
Licensure Skilled care; Intermediate care. *Beds*
SNF 68; ICF 40. *Certified* Medicaid;
Medicare.
Owner Nonprofit Corp.
Admissions Requirements Minimum age 16;
Medical examination; Physician's request.
Staff Physicians 2 (pt); RNs 4 (ft), 4 (pt);
LPNs 17 (ft), 2 (pt); Orderlies 2 (ft), 1 (pt);
Nurses aides 24 (ft), 22 (pt); Reality
therapists 1 (pt); Recreational therapists 1
(ft), 2 (pt); Occupational therapists 2 (ft);
Speech therapists 1 (pt); Activities
coordinators 1 (pt); Dietitians 1 (ft).
Facilities Dining room; Physical therapy
room; Activities room; Chapel; Crafts room;
Laundry room; Barber/Beauty shop.
Activities Arts & crafts; Cards; Games;
Reading groups; Prayer groups; Movies;
Shopping trips; Social/Cultural gatherings.

CANTON

United Helpers Canton Nursing Home Inc*
W Main St, Canton, NY, 13617
(315) 386-4541
Admin Wheeler D Maynard Jr.
Licensure Skilled care; Intermediate care. *Beds*
80. *Certified* Medicaid; Medicare.
Owner Nonprofit Corp.

CARTHAGE

**Carthage Area Hospital Skilled Nursing
Facility**
West Street Rd, Carthage, NY, 13619
(315) 493-1000
Admin Jeffrey S Drop. *Medical Dir/Dir of
Nursing* Anthony H Doldo RN.
Licensure Skilled care. *Beds* SNF 30.
Owner Nonprofit Corp.
Admissions Requirements Minimum age 16;
Medical examination; Physician's request.
Staff Physicians 4 (ft); RNs 1 (ft), 2 (pt);
LPNs 3 (ft), 3 (pt); Nurses aides 8 (ft), 9
(pt); Physical therapists 1 (ft); Occupational
therapists 1 (pt); Speech therapists 1 (pt);
Activities coordinators 1 (pt); Dietitians 1
(pt); Podiatrists 1 (pt).
Languages Spanish
Facilities Dining room; Physical therapy
room; Laundry room; Barber/Beauty shop.
Activities Arts & crafts; Cards; Games;
Reading groups; Prayer groups; Movies;
Shopping trips; Social/Cultural gatherings;
Pet program; barbecues.

Greenbriar Nursing Home*
West Street Rd, Carthage, NY, 13619
(315) 493-3220
Admin James Sligar.
Licensure Skilled care. *Beds* 40. *Certified*
Medicaid; Medicare.
Owner Proprietary Corp.

CASTLETON-ON-HUDSON

Resurrection Rest Home*
Castleton-on-Hudson, NY, 12033
(518) 732-7617
Admin S Therese.
Licensure Skilled care; Intermediate care. *Beds*
36. *Certified* Medicaid; Medicare.
Owner Nonprofit Corp.

CATSKILL

**Eden Park Nursing Home & Health Related
Facility**
154 Jefferson Heights, Catskill, NY, 12414
(518) 943-5151
Admin Leitha B Boice.
Licensure Skilled care; Intermediate care. *Beds*
SNF 86; ICF 47. *Certified* Medicaid;
Medicare.
Owner Proprietary Corp (Eden Park
Management).
Staff Physicians; RNs; LPNs; Orderlies;
Nurses aides; Physical therapists; Reality
therapists; Recreational therapists;
Occupational therapists; Speech therapists;
Activities coordinators; Dietitians; Dentists;
Ophthalmologists; Podiatrists.
Facilities Dining room; Physical therapy
room; Activities room; Chapel; Crafts room;
Laundry room; Barber/Beauty shop; Library.
Activities Arts & crafts; Cards; Games;
Reading groups; Prayer groups; Movies;
Shopping trips; Social/Cultural gatherings.

**Memorial Hospital & Nursing Home of Greene
County**
161 Jefferson Heights, Catskill, NY, 12414
(518) 943-9380
Admin Garret A Falcone. *Medical Dir/Dir of
Nursing* Dr John Y Tsou; Greta M
Hutchinson.
Licensure Skilled care; Intermediate care. *Beds*
SNF 80; ICF 40. *Certified* Medicaid;
Medicare.
Owner Publicly owned.
Admissions Requirements Minimum age 14;
Medical examination; Physician's request.
Staff Physicians 1 (ft), 9 (pt); RNs 11 (ft), 4
(pt); LPNs 8 (ft), 5 (pt); Nurses aides 41 (ft),
6 (pt); Physical therapists 1 (pt); Reality
therapists 2 (ft) 13H 2 (ft); Occupational
therapists 1 (ft), 1 (pt); Speech therapists 1
(pt); Activities coordinators 1 (ft); Dietitians
3 (pt); Ophthalmologists 1 (pt).
Facilities Dining room; Physical therapy
room; Activities room; Laundry room;
Barber/Beauty shop.
Activities Arts & crafts; Cards; Games;
Reading groups; Prayer groups; Movies;
Shopping trips; Social/Cultural gatherings;
Resident council; Limber up; German group;
Pet therapy; Floor games; Music & art
appreciation; Programs with children.

CENTER MORICHES

Cedar Lodge Nursing Home
PO Box 667, 6 Frowein Rd, Center Moriches,
NY, 11934
(516) 878-4400
Admin Muriel Corcoran.
Licensure Skilled care. *Beds* 100. *Certified*
Medicaid; Medicare.
Owner Proprietary Corp.

CHEEKTOWAGA

Garden Gate Manor
2365 Union Rd, Cheektowaga, NY, 14227
(716) 668-8100
Admin Eugene L Urban. *Medical Dir/Dir of
Nursing* Dr Douglas Moffat; Cynthia
McNally.
Licensure Skilled care; Health related. *Beds*
SNF 120; Health related 40. *Certified*
Medicaid; Medicare.
Owner Proprietary Corp.
Admissions Requirements Medical
examination; Physician's request.
Staff RNs 11 (ft); LPNs 18 (ft); Nurses aides
61 (ft); Physical therapists 1 (ft);
Occupational therapists 1 (ft); Activities
coordinators 1 (ft); Dietitians 1 (ft).
Facilities Dining room; Physical therapy
room; Activities room; Crafts room; Laundry
room; Barber/Beauty shop; Indoor solarium.

Activities Arts & crafts; Games; Prayer groups; Movies; Shopping trips; Social/Cultural gatherings.

Manor Oak Skilled Nursing Facilities Inc*
3600 Harlem Rd, Cheektowaga, NY, 14215
(716) 837-3880
Admin Randy Muenzner.
Licensure Skilled care. *Beds* 158. *Certified* Medicaid; Medicare.
Owner Proprietary Corp.

CHITTENANGO

Stonehedge-Chittenango Nursing Home*
331 Russell St, Chittenango, NY, 13037
(315) 687-7255
Admin Gloria Coughlin. *Medical Dir/Dir of Nursing* Juaquin Solar MD.
Licensure Skilled care. *Beds* 40. *Certified* Medicaid; Medicare.
Owner Proprietary Corp.
Admissions Requirements Medical examination; Physician's request.
Staff Physicians 1 (pt); RNs 3 (ft), 3 (pt); LPNs 4 (ft), 4 (pt); Nurses aides 19 (ft), 15 (pt); Physical therapists 1 (pt); Activities coordinators 1 (ft); Dietitians 1 (pt); Dentists 1 (pt).
Facilities Dining room; Physical therapy room; Activities room; Laundry room; Barber/Beauty shop.
Activities Arts & crafts; Cards; Games; Reading groups; Prayer groups; Movies; Shopping trips; Social/Cultural gatherings.

CLARENCE

Brothers of Mercy Nursing & Rehabilitation Center
10570 Bergtold Rd, Clarence, NY, 14031-2198
(716) 759-6985
Admin Daniel J Kenny. *Medical Dir/Dir of Nursing* Ferdinand A Paolini MD; Mildred Kody DON.
Licensure Skilled care; Health related care rehabilitation. *Beds* SNF 200; HRC 40. *Certified* Medicaid; Medicare.
Owner Nonprofit Corp.
Admissions Requirements Minimum age 16; Medical examination; Physician's request.
Staff Physicians 1 (ft), 1 (pt); RNs 38 (ft), 4 (pt); LPNs 25 (ft); Orderlies 2 (ft); Nurses aides 122 (ft), 3 (pt); Physical therapists 9 (ft); Reality therapists 5 (ft); Recreational therapists 5 (ft); Occupational therapists 5 (ft), 3 (pt); Speech therapists 1 (ft), 1 (pt); Activities coordinators 1 (ft); Dietitians 3 (ft); Ophthalmologists 1 (pt); Podiatrists 1 (ft), 1 (pt).
Affiliation Roman Catholic
Facilities Dining room; Physical therapy room; Activities room; Chapel; Crafts room; Laundry room; Barber/Beauty shop; Library; Gift shop; Occupational therapy clinic; Patios.
Activities Arts & crafts; Cards; Games; Reading groups; Prayer groups; Movies; Shopping trips; Social/Cultural gatherings; Walks; Birthday parties; Spouse program; Special meals.

CLIFTON SPRINGS

Clifton Springs Hospital & Clinic Extended Care
2 Coulter Rd, Clifton Springs, NY, 14432
(315) 462-9561
Admin M J Romeiser, Acting Admin. *Medical Dir/Dir of Nursing* Karen Miller.
Licensure Skilled care. *Beds* SNF 40. *Certified* Medicaid; Medicare.
Owner Nonprofit Corp.
Admissions Requirements Medical examination.

Languages Spanish
Facilities Dining room; Physical therapy room; Activities room; Chapel; Laundry room; Barber/Beauty shop.

CLINTON

The Martin Luther Nursing Home Inc
110 Utica Rd, Clinton, NY, 13323
(315) 853-5515
Admin Rev Hans J R Irmer; Rev S Kenneth Arntsen Exec Dir. *Medical Dir/Dir of Nursing* Dr Gerald C Gant; Elaine Cain RN.
Licensure Skilled care; Intermediate care. *Beds* SNF 80; ICF 80. *Certified* Medicaid; Medicare.
Owner Nonprofit Corp.
Admissions Requirements Minimum age 17.
Staff Physicians 2 (pt); RNs 4 (ft), 13 (pt); LPNs 9 (ft), 8 (pt); Orderlies 5 (ft), 4 (pt); Nurses aides 48 (ft), 24 (pt); Activities coordinators 3 (ft); Dietitians 2 (pt).
Affiliation Lutheran
Facilities Dining room; Physical therapy room; Activities room; Chapel; Crafts room; Laundry room; Barber/Beauty shop; Library.
Activities Arts & crafts; Cards; Games; Reading groups; Prayer groups; Movies; Shopping trips; Social/Cultural gatherings.

COBLESKILL

Eden Park Health Services Inc
Parkway Dr, Cobleskill, NY, 12043
(518) 234-3557
Admin A Edel Groski. *Medical Dir/Dir of Nursing* Dr J Vrolijk; Nancy DeSando.
Licensure Skilled care; Health related care. *Beds* SNF 90; Health related 35. *Certified* Medicaid; Medicare.
Owner Proprietary Corp (Eden Park Management).
Admissions Requirements Minimum age 18; Medical examination; Physician's request.
Staff Physicians; RNs; LPNs; Orderlies; Nurses aides; Physical therapists; Occupational therapists; Activities coordinators; Dietitians.
Facilities Dining room; Physical therapy room; Activities room; Crafts room; Barber/Beauty shop; Occupational therapy room.
Activities Arts & crafts; Cards; Games; Reading groups; Prayer groups; Movies; Shopping trips; Social/Cultural gatherings.

COHOES

Capital Region Ford Nursing Home
W Columbia St, Cohoes, NY, 12047
(518) 237-5630
Admin Mark R Jantzi. *Medical Dir/Dir of Nursing* James H Mitchell MD; Deborah Bolognino RN DON.
Licensure Skilled care. *Beds* SNF 80. *Certified* Medicaid; Medicare.
Owner Nonprofit organization/foundation.
Admissions Requirements Minimum age 18.
Staff Physicians 1 (pt); RNs 9 (ft), 3 (pt); LPNs 5 (ft), 7 (pt); Orderlies 3 (ft), 4 (pt); Nurses aides 20 (ft), 22 (pt); Physical therapists 1 (pt); Recreational therapists 1 (ft); Occupational therapists 1 (pt); Speech therapists 1 (pt); Activities coordinators 1 (ft); Dietitians 1 (ft); Dentists 1 (pt); Podiatrists 1 (pt).
Facilities Dining room; Physical therapy room; Activities room; Crafts room; Laundry room; Barber/Beauty shop.
Activities Arts & crafts; Cards; Games; Reading groups; Prayer groups; Movies; Shopping trips; Social/Cultural gatherings.

COMMACK

The Rosaline & Joseph Gurwin Jewish Geriatric Center of Long Island
74 Hauppauge Rd, Commack, NY, 11725
(516) 462-9886
Admin Herbert H Friedman Exec Dir.
Licensure Skilled care; Intermediate care. *Beds* SNF 240; ICF 60. *Certified* Medicaid; Medicare.
Owner Nonprofit Corp.
Affiliation Jewish
Facilities Dining room; Physical therapy room; Activities room; Chapel; Crafts room; Laundry room; Barber/Beauty shop; Library.

COOPERSTOWN

The Meadows
Rte 3, Box 89A, Cooperstown, NY, 13326
(607) 547-2579
Admin Pamela Tritten. *Medical Dir/Dir of Nursing* Donald Pollock MD; Eleanor Sosnowski DON.
Licensure Skilled care; Intermediate care. *Beds* SNF 136; ICF 38. *Certified* Medicaid; Medicare.
Owner Publicly owned.
Admissions Requirements Physician's request.
Staff Physicians 4 (pt); RNs; LPNs; Nurses aides; Physical therapists 1 (pt); Occupational therapists 1 (ft), 1 (pt); Activities coordinators; Dietitians 1 (ft).
Facilities Dining room; Physical therapy room; Activities room; Chapel; Laundry room; Barber/Beauty shop.
Activities Arts & crafts; Cards; Reading groups; Prayer groups; Movies; Shopping trips.

CORNING

Corning Hospital—Founders Pavilion
205 E 1st St, Corning, NY, 14830
(607) 937-7500
Admin Linda L Patrick. *Medical Dir/Dir of Nursing* Norman C Walton MD; Terry Bushnell RN DON.
Licensure Skilled care. *Beds* SNF 120. *Certified* Medicaid; Medicare.
Owner Nonprofit Corp.
Admissions Requirements Minimum age 16; Physician's request.
Staff RNs 8 (ft), 2 (pt); LPNs 20 (ft), 3 (pt); Orderlies 4 (ft); Nurses aides 53 (ft), 5 (pt); Activities coordinators 1 (ft).
Facilities Dining room; Physical therapy room; Activities room; Laundry room; Barber/Beauty shop.
Activities Arts & crafts; Cards; Games; Reading groups; Prayer groups; Movies; Shopping trips; Social/Cultural gatherings; Entertainment.

CORTLAND

Cortland Nursing Home
193 Clinton Ave, Cortland, NY, 13045
(607) 756-9921
Admin Michael Sweeney. *Medical Dir/Dir of Nursing* Patrick Hayes MD; Diane Abdallah RN.
Licensure Skilled care. *Beds* SNF 80. *Certified* Medicaid; Medicare.
Owner Proprietary Corp.
Admissions Requirements Minimum age 16; Medical examination.
Staff RNs 7 (ft), 3 (pt); LPNs 10 (ft), 2 (pt); Orderlies 3 (ft), 1 (pt); Nurses aides 40 (ft), 20 (pt); Physical therapists 1 (pt); Occupational therapists 1 (pt); Speech therapists 1 (pt); Activities coordinators 1 (ft), 1 (pt); Dietitians 1 (pt); Dentists 1 (pt); Ophthalmologists 1 (pt); Podiatrists 1 (pt); Dentist 1 (pt).

Facilities Dining room; Physical therapy
room; Activities room; Crafts room; Laundry
room; Barber/Beauty shop; Library.
Activities Arts & crafts; Cards; Games;
Reading groups; Prayer groups; Movies;
Shopping trips; Social/Cultural gatherings.

Highgate Manor of Cortland
28 Kellog Rd, Cortland, NY, 13045
(607) 753-9443
Admin Mitchell S Marsh. *Medical Dir/Dir of
Nursing* John E Eckel MD; Sandra Russell
RN.
Licensure Skilled care; Intermediate care;
Head injury rehabilitation. *Beds* SNF 200.
Certified Medicaid; Medicare.
Owner Proprietary Corp (New Medico Assoc).
Admissions Requirements Minimum age 16.
Staff Physicians 1 (ft), 13 (pt); RNs 24 (ft), 11
(pt); LPNs 26 (ft), 13 (pt); Orderlies 15 (ft),
7 (pt); Nurses aides 84 (ft), 41 (pt); Physical
therapists 6 (ft), 1 (pt); Recreational
therapists 5 (ft); Occupational therapists 5
(ft); Speech therapists 4 (ft); Activities
coordinators 1 (ft); Dietitians 1 (ft); Dentists
1 (ft); Ophthalmologists 1 (pt); Podiatrists 1
(pt); Dentist 1 (pt); Music therapists 2 (ft);
Psychologists 4 (ft); Respiratory therapist 2
(ft); Cognitive therapist 2 (ft).
Facilities Dining room; Physical therapy
room; Activities room; Chapel; Crafts room;
Laundry room; Barber/Beauty shop; Library.
Activities Arts & crafts; Cards; Games;
Reading groups; Prayer groups; Movies;
Shopping trips; Social/Cultural gatherings;
American Legion Post.

CROTON-ON-HUDSON

Sky View Haven Nursing Home*
Albany Post Rd, Croton-on-Hudson, NY,
10520
(914) 271-5151
Admin Kurt Oppemheim. *Medical Dir/Dir of
Nursing* Leonard Kaufman MD.
Licensure Skilled care; Intermediate care. *Beds*
SNF 130; HRF 30. *Certified* Medicaid;
Medicare.
Owner Proprietary Corp.
Admissions Requirements Minimum age 16;
Medical examination.
Staff RNs 9 (ft), 2 (pt); LPNs 17 (ft), 4 (pt);
Orderlies 2 (ft); Nurses aides 65 (ft);
Physical therapists 2 (pt); Activities
coordinators 1 (ft); Dietitians 1 (ft); Activity
workers 2 (ft), 2 (pt).
Facilities Dining room; Physical therapy
room; Activities room; Laundry room;
Barber/Beauty shop; Sitting rooms.
Activities Arts & crafts; Cards; Games;
Reading groups; Prayer groups; Movies;
Shopping trips; Social/Cultural gatherings;
House newspaper.

CUBA

**Cuba Memorial Hospital Inc—Skilled Nursing
Facility**
140 W Main St, Cuba, NY, 14727
(716) 968-2000
Admin Marc A Subject. *Medical Dir/Dir of
Nursing* Rajan Gulati MD; Earletta Swift
RN.
Licensure Skilled care. *Beds* 46. *Certified*
Medicaid; Medicare.
Owner Nonprofit Corp.
Admissions Requirements Minimum age 17;
Medical examination; Physician's request.
Staff RNs 2 (ft), 1 (pt); LPNs 1 (ft), 3 (pt);
Nurses aides 20 (ft), 8 (pt); Physical
therapists 1 (ft); Recreational therapists 1
(ft); Dietitians 1 (ft); Ophthalmologists 1
(pt).
Facilities Dining room; Physical therapy
room; Activities room; Chapel; Laundry
room; Barber/Beauty shop; Library.

Activities Arts & crafts; Cards; Games;
Reading groups; Prayer groups; Movies;
Shopping trips; Social/Cultural gatherings.

DELHI

Delaware County Home & Infirmary
Rd 1, Box 417, Delhi, NY, 13753
(607) 746-2331
Admin Matthew Luger. *Medical Dir/Dir of
Nursing* Fredrick Heinegg MD.
Licensure Skilled care; Intermediate care. *Beds*
SNF 100; ICF 99. *Certified* Medicaid;
Medicare.
Owner Publicly owned.
Admissions Requirements Minimum age 16;
Medical examination.
Staff Physicians 3 (pt); RNs 18 (ft), 9 (pt);
LPNs 35 (ft), 10 (pt); Nurses aides 70 (ft),
40 (pt); Physical therapists 1 (ft);
Occupational therapists 1 (ft); Speech
therapists 1 (pt); Activities coordinators 1
(ft); Dietitians 1 (pt); Dentists 1 (pt).
Facilities Dining room; Physical therapy
room; Activities room; Crafts room; Barber/
Beauty shop.
Activities Arts & crafts; Cards; Games; Prayer
groups; Movies; Shopping trips; Social/
Cultural gatherings.

DELMAR

Good Samaritan Nursing Home
125 Rockefeller Rd, Delmar, NY, 12054
(518) 439-8116
Admin Robert W Snow. *Medical Dir/Dir of
Nursing* Roger Drew MD; Lois Quick RN
DON.
Licensure Intermediate care. *Beds* ICF 100.
Certified Medicaid.
Owner Nonprofit Corp.
Admissions Requirements Medical
examination.
Staff Physicians 3 (pt); RNs 3 (ft), 3 (pt);
LPNs 4 (ft), 4 (pt); Nurses aides 10 (ft), 6
(pt); Physical therapists 1 (pt); Activities
coordinators 1 (ft); Dietitians 1 (pt).
Affiliation Lutheran
Facilities Dining room; Physical therapy
room; Activities room; Crafts room; Laundry
room; Library.
Activities Arts & crafts; Cards; Games;
Reading groups; Prayer groups; Movies;
Shopping trips; Social/Cultural gatherings.

DOBBS FERRY

St Cabrini Nursing Home Inc
115 Broadway, Dobbs Ferry, NY, 10522
(914) 693-6800
Admin William T Smith. *Medical Dir/Dir of
Nursing* Frank Quattromani MD.
Licensure Skilled care. *Beds* 200. *Certified*
Medicaid; Medicare.
Owner Nonprofit Corp (Cath Charity/Arch of
NY).
Admissions Requirements Minimum age 65;
Medical examination; Physician's request.
Staff Physicians 6 (pt); RNs 29 (ft), 14 (pt);
LPNs 7 (ft), 15 (pt); Nurses aides 63 (ft);
Physical therapists 1 (ft), 1 (pt); Recreational
therapists 2 (ft), 2 (pt); Occupational
therapists 1 (ft), 2 (pt); Speech therapists 1
(pt); Activities coordinators 1 (ft).
Affiliation Roman Catholic
Facilities Dining room; Physical therapy
room; Activities room; Chapel; Crafts room;
Laundry room; Barber/Beauty shop; Library.
Activities Arts & crafts; Cards; Games; Prayer
groups; Movies; Social/Cultural gatherings;
BBQs; Picnics.

DUNKIRK

Chautauqua County Home
Temple Rd, Dunkirk, NY, 14048
(716) 366-6400
Admin Christopher L Carlson. *Medical Dir/
Dir of Nursing* Dr Yi Yung Ting MD; Gail
Riforgiat RN DON.
Licensure Skilled care; Health related facility.
Beds SNF 197; Health related 19. *Certified*
Medicaid; Medicare.
Owner Publicly owned.
Admissions Requirements Minimum age 16;
Medical examination; Physician's request.
Staff Physicians 1 (ft); RNs 9 (ft), 3 (pt);
LPNs 23 (ft), 1 (pt); Nurses aides 59 (ft), 20
(pt); Physical therapists 1 (pt); Occupational
therapists 1 (pt); Speech therapists 1 (pt);
Activities coordinators 1 (ft); Dietitians 1
(ft); Dentist 1 (pt).
Facilities Dining room; Physical therapy
room; Activities room; Chapel; Crafts room;
Laundry room; Barber/Beauty shop; Library.
Activities Arts & crafts; Cards; Games;
Reading groups; Prayer groups; Movies;
Shopping trips; Social/Cultural gatherings.

Margaret-Anthony Nursing Home
447-449 Lake Shore Dr W, Dunkirk, NY,
14048
(716) 366-6710
Admin Casimier T Czamara.
Licensure Skilled care. *Beds* 40. *Certified*
Medicaid; Medicare.
Owner Proprietary Corp.

EAST AURORA

Aurora Park Health Care Center Inc*
292 Main St, East Aurora, NY, 14052
(716) 652-1560
Admin Neil Chur.
Licensure Skilled care; Intermediate care. *Beds*
320. *Certified* Medicaid; Medicare.
Owner Proprietary Corp.

EAST ISLIP

Little Flower Nursing Home & HRF*
340 E Montauk Hwy, East Islip, NY, 11730
(516) 581-6400
Admin Theresa M Santmann.
Licensure Skilled care; Intermediate care. *Beds*
80. *Certified* Medicaid; Medicare.
Owner Proprietary Corp.

EAST SYRACUSE

Sunnyside Nursing Home
7000 Collamer Rd, East Syracuse, NY, 13057
(315) 656-7218
Admin Burnell Carney. *Medical Dir/Dir of
Nursing* Robert Weilt; Alice E Carney DON.
Licensure Skilled care. *Beds* 80. *Certified*
Medicaid; Medicare.
Owner Privately owned.
Admissions Requirements Medical
examination; Physician's request.
Staff Physicians 1 (pt); RNs 7 (ft), 5 (pt);
LPNs 6 (ft), 7 (pt); Orderlies 4 (ft), 1 (pt);
Nurses aides 27 (ft), 17 (pt); Physical
therapists 1 (pt); Recreational therapists 1
(ft); Occupational therapists 1 (pt); Speech
therapists 1 (pt); Activities coordinators 1
(ft); Dietitians 1 (pt); Ophthalmologists 1
(pt); Podiatrists 1 (pt).
Facilities Dining room; Physical therapy
room; Activities room; Chapel; Crafts room;
Laundry room; Barber/Beauty shop.
Activities Arts & crafts; Cards; Games;
Reading groups; Prayer groups; Movies;
Shopping trips; Social/Cultural gatherings.

EATON

Gerrit Smith Memorial Infirmary
River Rd, Box 111, Eaton, NY, 13334-0111
(315) 684-3951
Admin David W Felton. *Medical Dir/Dir of Nursing* Howard Amann; Julie Hotaling.
Licensure Skilled care. *Beds* SNF 95. *Certified* Medicaid; Medicare.
Owner Publicly owned.
Admissions Requirements Minimum age 16; Medical examination; Physician's request.
Staff RNs 8 (ft), 4 (pt); LPNs 11 (ft), 11 (pt); Nurses aides 33 (ft), 30 (pt); Physical therapists 1 (pt); Occupational therapists 1 (pt); Speech therapists 1 (pt); Activities coordinators 1 (ft); Dietitians 1 (pt).
Languages Italian
Facilities Dining room; Physical therapy room; Activities room; Barber/Beauty shop; Library.
Activities Arts & crafts; Cards; Games; Reading groups; Movies; Shopping trips; Social/Cultural gatherings.

EDEN

St George Nursing Home*
2806 George St, Eden, NY, 14057
(716) 992-3987
Admin Anthony St George Jr.
Licensure Skilled care. *Beds* 40. *Certified* Medicaid; Medicare.
Owner Proprietary Corp.

EDGEMERE

Rockaway Care Center*
353 Beach 48th St, Edgemere, NY, 11691
(718) 471-5000
Admin Mark Stenzler.
Licensure Skilled care; Intermediate care. *Beds* 80. *Certified* Medicaid; Medicare.
Owner Proprietary Corp.

ELIZABETHTOWN

Horace Nye Home*
Park St, Elizabethtown, NY, 12932
(518) 873-6301
Admin Chester W Arthur.
Licensure Skilled care; Intermediate care. *Beds* 60. *Certified* Medicaid; Medicare.
Owner Publicly owned.

ELMIRA

Arnot-Ogden Memorial Hospital—Skilled Nursing Unit
Roe Ave, Elmira, NY, 14905
(607) 737-4100
Admin Helen G Scollon. *Medical Dir/Dir of Nursing* Otto Lederer MD; Gaynelle Bowen.
Licensure Skilled care. *Beds* 40. *Certified* Medicaid; Medicare.
Owner Nonprofit organization/foundation.
Admissions Requirements Minimum age 18.
Staff Physicians 1 (pt); RNs 5 (ft), 5 (pt); LPNs 2 (ft); Nurses aides 22 (ft); Physical therapists 1 (pt); Recreational therapists 1 (pt); Occupational therapists 1 (pt); Speech therapists 1 (pt); Activities coordinators 1 (ft); Dietitians 1 (pt); Dentists 1 (pt); Ophthalmologists 1 (pt); Podiatrists 1 (pt); Dentist 1 (pt).
Facilities Dining room; Physical therapy room; Activities room; Crafts room; Laundry room; Barber/Beauty shop; Library.
Activities Arts & crafts; Cards; Games; Reading groups; Prayer groups; Movies; Shopping trips.

Chemung County Health Center—Nurs Facility*
Heritage Park, Elmira, NY, 14901
(607) 737-2001

Admin Warren L Tessier.
Licensure Skilled care. *Beds* 200. *Certified* Medicaid; Medicare.
Owner Publicly owned.

St Josephs Hospital—Skilled Nursing Facility
555 E Market St, Elmira, NY, 14902
(607) 733-6541
Admin Sr Marie Michael Miller. *Medical Dir/Dir of Nursing* Dr A D Smith.
Licensure Skilled care. *Beds* SNF 31. *Certified* Medicaid; Medicare.
Owner Nonprofit Corp.
Admissions Requirements Minimum age 16; Physician's request.
Activities Arts & crafts; Cards; Games; Reading groups; Prayer groups; Movies; Shopping trips.

ENDICOTT

Sullivan Park Health Care Center Inc
Nantucket Dr, Endicott, NY, 13760
(607) 754-2705
Admin Charles Yannett.
Licensure Skilled care; Intermediate care. *Beds* 80. *Certified* Medicaid; Medicare.
Owner Proprietary Corp.

FAIRPORT

Crest Manor Nursing Home
6745 Pittsford-Palmyra Rd, Fairport, NY, 14450
(716) 223-3633
Admin A John Bartholomew. *Medical Dir/Dir of Nursing* Mary C Dryer DON.
Licensure Skilled care. *Beds* SNF 80. *Certified* Medicaid; Medicare.
Owner Privately owned Partnership.
Admissions Requirements Minimum age 16.
Staff RNs; LPNs; Nurses aides.
Facilities Dining room; Physical therapy room; Activities room; Chapel; Crafts room; Laundry room; Barber/Beauty shop.
Activities Arts & crafts; Cards; Games; Reading groups; Prayer groups; Movies; Shopping trips.

Fairport Baptist Home
4646 9 Mile Point Rd, Fairport, NY, 14450
(716) 377-0350
Admin Alvin C Foster.
Licensure Skilled care; Intermediate care. *Beds* 196. *Certified* Medicaid; Medicare.
Owner Nonprofit Corp.
Affiliation Baptist
Facilities Dining room; Physical therapy room; Activities room; Chapel; Crafts room; Laundry room; Barber/Beauty shop; Library.

FAR ROCKAWAY

Bezalel Nursing Home Company
29-38 Far Rockaway Blvd, Far Rockaway, NY, 11691
(718) 471-2600
Admin Solomon B Reifman. *Medical Dir/Dir of Nursing* Anthony Tavormina MD; Rochelle Stern RN DON.
Licensure Skilled care; Intermediate care. *Beds* 120. *Certified* Medicaid; Medicare.
Owner Nonprofit Corp.
Admissions Requirements Minimum age 21; Medical examination.
Staff Physicians; RNs; LPNs; Orderlies; Nurses aides; Physical therapists; Occupational therapists; Speech therapists; Activities coordinators; Dietitians.
Languages Spanish, Hebrew, Yiddish, Russian
Affiliation Jewish
Facilities Dining room; Physical therapy room; Activities room; Chapel; Laundry room; Barber/Beauty shop.

Activities Arts & crafts; Cards; Games; Reading groups; Prayer groups; Movies; Shopping trips; Social/Cultural gatherings; Birthday celebrations.

Brookhaven Beach Health Related Facility*
250 Beach 17th St, Far Rockaway, NY, 11691
(718) 471-7500
Admin Herbert Rothman.
Licensure Skilled care; Intermediate care. *Beds* 58. *Certified* Medicaid; Medicare.
Owner Proprietary Corp.

Far Rockaway Nursing Home*
13-11 Virginia St, Far Rockaway, NY, 11691
(718) 327-2909
Admin Aaron Feuereisen.
Licensure Skilled care. *Beds* 100. *Certified* Medicaid; Medicare.
Owner Proprietary Corp.

Haven Manor Health Care Center
1441 Gateway Boulevard, Far Rockaway, NY, 11691
(718) 471-1500
Admin Aron Cytryn. *Medical Dir/Dir of Nursing* Dr Marc S Kaufman; Ella Klug RN DON.
Licensure Skilled care; Intermediate care. *Beds* SNF 48; ICF 192. *Certified* Medicaid; Medicare.
Owner Privately owned.
Admissions Requirements Medical examination.
Staff Physicians; RNs; LPNs; Orderlies; Nurses aides; Physical therapists; Reality therapists; Recreational therapists; Occupational therapists; Speech therapists; Activities coordinators; Dietitians; Dentists; Ophthalmologists; Podiatrists.
Languages Spanish, Yiddish, Hebrew, French
Facilities Dining room; Physical therapy room; Activities room; Crafts room; Laundry room; Barber/Beauty shop; Library.
Activities Arts & crafts; Cards; Games; Reading groups; Prayer groups; Movies; Shopping trips; Social/Cultural gatherings.

Oceanview Nursing Home*
315 Beach 9th St, Far Rockaway, NY, 11691
(718) 471-6000
Admin Alex Weiss. *Medical Dir/Dir of Nursing* Dr John Timothy.
Licensure Skilled care. *Beds* 102. *Certified* Medicaid; Medicare.
Owner Proprietary Corp.
Admissions Requirements Minimum age 26; Medical examination; Physician's request.
Staff RNs 6 (ft); LPNs 30 (ft); Orderlies 5 (ft); Nurses aides 30 (ft); Physical therapists 1 (pt); Recreational therapists 1 (pt); Occupational therapists 1 (pt); Speech therapists 1 (pt); Activities coordinators 1 (ft); Dietitians 1 (pt).
Facilities Dining room; Physical therapy room; Activities room; Chapel; Crafts room; Laundry room; Barber/Beauty shop; Library.
Activities Arts & crafts; Cards; Games; Reading groups; Prayer groups; Movies; Social/Cultural gatherings.

Peninsula General Nursing Home
50-15 Beach Channel Dr, Far Rockaway, NY, 11691
(718) 945-7100
Admin Bernard Satin. *Medical Dir/Dir of Nursing* Alfred Fleischman MD; Rita Davidson RN DON.
Licensure Skilled care; Rehabilitation. *Beds* SNF 200. *Certified* Medicaid; Medicare.
Owner Nonprofit Corp.
Admissions Requirements Minimum age 16.
Staff Physicians 5 (ft); RNs 23 (ft); LPNs 26 (ft); Orderlies 2 (ft); Nurses aides 69 (ft); Physical therapists 9 (ft); Recreational therapists 3 (ft); Occupational therapists 5 (ft); Speech therapists 4 (ft); Activities

coordinators 1 (ft); Dietitians 1 (ft); Podiatrists 2 (ft); Recreation aides 1 (ft), 1 (pt).
Languages Spanish, French, Yiddish, Haitian, Russian, Chinese, Indian dialects
Facilities Dining room; Physical therapy room; Activities room; Chapel; Crafts room; Laundry room; Barber/Beauty shop; Library; Ground floor outdoor garden; Large second floor terrace.
Activities Arts & crafts; Cards; Games; Reading groups; Prayer groups; Movies; Shopping trips; Social/Cultural gatherings; Resident council; Large print library; Art therapy; Sports; BBQs.

Queens Nassau Nursing Home
520 Beach 19th St, Far Rockaway, NY, 11691
(718) 471-7400
Admin I Sherman. *Medical Dir/Dir of Nursing* Dr D Beer; Barbara Porcano.
Licensure Skilled care. *Beds* 200. *Certified* Medicaid; Medicare.
Owner Proprietary Corp.
Facilities Dining room; Physical therapy room; Activities room; Laundry room; Barber/Beauty shop.
Activities Arts & crafts; Cards; Games; Reading groups; Prayer groups; Movies; Shopping trips; Social/Cultural gatherings.

Seagirt Health Related Facility
1410 S Seagirt Blvd, Far Rockaway, NY, 11691
(718) 471-7000
Admin Maurice H Radzik. *Medical Dir/Dir of Nursing* Tara Saini MD; Phyllis Siboney RN DON.
Licensure Intermediate care. *Beds* ICF 210. *Certified* Medicaid.
Owner Proprietary Corp.
Admissions Requirements Minimum age 60; Medical examination.
Staff Physicians 6 (pt); RNs 10 (ft), 1 (pt); LPNs 30 (ft); Orderlies 20 (ft); Nurses aides 20 (ft); Physical therapists 2 (ft), 1 (pt); Recreational therapists 1 (ft), 1 (pt); Occupational therapists 2 (pt); Speech therapists 1 (pt); Activities coordinators 1 (ft); Dietitians 1 (ft), 1 (pt).
Languages Yiddish, Spanish, Haitian, French, Hebrew, Greek
Facilities Dining room; Physical therapy room; Activities room; Chapel; Crafts room; Laundry room; Barber/Beauty shop; Library.
Activities Arts & crafts; Cards; Games; Reading groups; Prayer groups; Movies; Shopping trips; Social/Cultural gatherings.

Surfside Nursing Home
22-41 Newhaven Ave, Far Rockaway, NY, 11691
(718) 471-3400
Admin Dorothy Galasso. *Medical Dir/Dir of Nursing* Gail Holtz DON.
Licensure Skilled care. *Beds* SNF 175. *Certified* Medicaid; Medicare.
Owner Proprietary Corp.
Staff Physicians; RNs; LPNs; Orderlies; Nurses aides; Physical therapists; Recreational therapists; Occupational therapists; Speech therapists; Activities coordinators; Dietitians; Dentists; Ophthalmologists; Podiatrists.
Facilities Dining room; Physical therapy room; Activities room; Chapel; Crafts room; Barber/Beauty shop; Library.
Activities Arts & crafts; Cards; Games; Reading groups; Prayer groups; Movies.

FARMINGDALE

Daleview Nursing Home & Manor
574 & 530 Fulton St, Farmingdale, NY, 11735
(516) 694-6242
Admin Paul J Dioguardi. *Medical Dir/Dir of Nursing* Armando Deschamps MD.

Licensure Skilled care; Intermediate care. *Beds* SNF 86; ICF 56. *Certified* Medicaid; Medicare.
Owner Privately owned.
Admissions Requirements Minimum age 16; Physician's request.
Staff Physicians 17 (pt); RNs 5 (ft), 9 (pt); LPNs 8 (ft), 6 (pt); Orderlies 1 (ft), 1 (pt); Nurses aides 25 (ft), 15 (pt); Physical therapists 1 (pt); Occupational therapists 1 (pt); Speech therapists 1 (pt); Activities coordinators 2 (ft), 2 (pt); Dietitians 1 (ft); Dentists 1 (pt); Ophthalmologists 3 (pt); Podiatrists 1 (pt).
Facilities Dining room; Physical therapy room; Activities room; Laundry room; Barber/Beauty shop.
Activities Arts & crafts; Cards; Games; Reading groups; Prayer groups; Movies; Shopping trips; Social/Cultural gatherings; Musical entertainment.

FLUSHING

Cliffside Nursing Home
119-19 Graham Ct, Flushing, NY, 11354
(718) 886-0700
Admin Jack Deutsch. *Medical Dir/Dir of Nursing* Gerald Kreitman MD; Diane Reeder RNN.
Licensure Skilled care. *Beds* SNF 220. *Certified* Medicaid; Medicare.
Owner Privately owned.
Admissions Requirements Physician's request.
Staff Physicians 1 (pt); RNs 10 (ft), 5 (pt); LPNs 22 (ft), 12 (pt); Orderlies 1 (ft), 1 (pt); Nurses aides 65 (ft), 35 (pt); Physical therapists 1 (pt); Recreational therapists 2 (ft), 2 (pt); Occupational therapists 2 (pt); Speech therapists 1 (pt); Activities coordinators 1 (ft), 1 (pt); Dietitians 2 (ft).
Languages Yiddish, Hebrew, Spanish, Russian, German, Hungarian, French
Facilities Dining room; Physical therapy room; Activities room; Barber/Beauty shop; Library; Outside sitting area.
Activities Arts & crafts; Cards; Games; Reading groups; Prayer groups; Movies; Social/Cultural gatherings; Discussion groups; Cooking; Baking.

Flushing Manor Nursing Home & Flushing Manor Care Center
35-15 Parsons Blvd, Flushing, NY, 11354
(718) 961-3500
Admin Esther Benenson. *Medical Dir/Dir of Nursing* W Benenson MD; Vivian Smith RN.
Licensure Skilled care; Intermediate care. *Beds* SNF 327; ICF 100. *Certified* Medicaid; Medicare.
Owner Privately owned.
Admissions Requirements Medical examination; Physician's request.
Staff Physicians 23 (pt); RNs 9 (ft), 12 (pt); LPNs 7 (ft), 11 (pt); Orderlies 17 (ft); Nurses aides 130 (ft); Physical therapists 6 (ft); Recreational therapists 3 (ft); Occupational therapists 7 (ft); Speech therapists 2 (ft); Dietitians 6 (ft); Dentists 2 (pt); Ophthalmologists 4 (pt); Podiatrists 2 (pt).
Languages Spanish, Korean
Facilities Dining room; Physical therapy room; Activities room; Chapel; Crafts room; Laundry room; Barber/Beauty shop; Library.
Activities Arts & crafts; Cards; Games; Reading groups; Prayer groups; Movies; Shopping trips; Social/Cultural gatherings.

Franklin Nursing Home
142-27 Franklin Ave, Flushing, NY, 11355
(718) 463-8200
Admin Sylvia Stern. *Medical Dir/Dir of Nursing* Dr George Martin MD; Diana Gross RN.
Licensure Skilled care. *Beds* SNF 320. *Certified* Medicaid; Medicare.

Owner Proprietary Corp.
Admissions Requirements Medical examination.
Staff Physicians 10 (pt); RNs 18 (ft), 8 (pt); LPNs 23 (ft), 9 (pt); Orderlies 1 (ft); Nurses aides 95 (ft), 13 (pt); Physical therapists 2 (ft); Occupational therapists 2 (pt); Speech therapists 1 (pt); Activities coordinators 1 (ft); Dietitians 4 (ft).
Affiliation Jewish
Facilities Dining room; Physical therapy room; Activities room; Crafts room; Barber/Beauty shop; Library.
Activities Arts & crafts; Cards; Games; Reading groups; Prayer groups; Movies; Social/Cultural gatherings.

Long Island Nursing Home
144-61 38th Ave, Flushing, NY, 11354
(718) 939-7500
Admin Phyllis Schindler. *Medical Dir/Dir of Nursing* Dr Michael Shechtman.
Licensure Skilled care. *Beds* 200. *Certified* Medicaid; Medicare.
Owner Privately owned.
Admissions Requirements Minimum age 21.
Staff Physicians; RNs; LPNs; Orderlies; Nurses aides; Physical therapists; Reality therapists; Recreational therapists; Occupational therapists; Speech therapists; Activities coordinators; Dietitians; Podiatrists.
Languages Spanish, Hungarian, Korean, Tagalog, Chinese, Italian, Yiddish, Hebrew
Facilities Dining room; Physical therapy room; Activities room; Chapel; Crafts room; Barber/Beauty shop; Library (mobile); Social Services.
Activities Arts & crafts; Cards; Games; Reading groups; Prayer groups; Movies; Shopping trips; Social/Cultural gatherings.

Meadow Park Nursing Home
78-10 164th St, Flushing, NY, 11366
(718) 591-8300
Admin Abraham Schlafrig. *Medical Dir/Dir of Nursing* Dr Richard Falivena; Louise Scaparro RN DON.
Licensure Skilled care. *Beds* SNF 143. *Certified* Medicaid; Medicare.
Owner Proprietary Corp.
Admissions Requirements Minimum age 21.
Staff RNs 6 (ft); LPNs 9 (ft); Orderlies 2 (ft), 1 (pt); Nurses aides 8 (ft), 5 (pt); Recreational therapists 2 (ft); Speech therapists 1 (ft); Dietitians 1 (ft).
Facilities Dining room; Physical therapy room; Activities room.
Activities Arts & crafts; Cards; Games; Reading groups; Prayer groups; Movies; Shopping trips; Social/Cultural gatherings.

Rego Park Nursing Home
111-26 Corona Ave, Flushing, NY, 11368
(718) 592-6400
Admin Arnold Klein. *Medical Dir/Dir of Nursing* Dr Casear Strong; Anna Morawski.
Licensure Skilled care. *Beds* SNF 200. *Certified* Medicaid; Medicare.
Owner Proprietary Corp.
Admissions Requirements Medical examination.
Staff Physicians 6 (pt); RNs 9 (ft), 2 (pt); LPNs 15 (ft), 10 (pt); Orderlies 9 (ft), 2 (pt); Nurses aides 53 (ft), 17 (pt); Physical therapists 2 (ft); Recreational therapists 3 (ft), 1 (pt); Occupational therapists 2 (ft); Speech therapists 1 (pt); Activities coordinators 1 (pt); Dietitians 2 (pt); Dentists 1 (pt); Ophthalmologists 1 (pt); Podiatrists 1 (pt).
Languages Spanish, Yiddish, Hebrew, Russian
Facilities Dining room; Physical therapy room; Activities room; Chapel; Crafts room; Laundry room; Barber/Beauty shop; Library.

Activities Arts & crafts; Cards; Games; Reading groups; Prayer groups; Movies; Shopping trips; Social/Cultural gatherings; International programs; Dance therapy; BBQ's; Family activities.

Waterview Nursing Care Center
119-15 27th Ave, Flushing, NY, 11354
(718) 461-5000
Admin Larry I Slatky. *Medical Dir/Dir of Nursing* Dr Chenna Reddy; Delores Belizaire DON.
Licensure Skilled care. *Beds* SNF 200. *Certified* Medicaid; Medicare.
Owner Privately owned.
Staff Physicians 1 (pt); RNs 12 (ft), 2 (pt); LPNs 20 (ft), 8 (pt); Orderlies 5 (ft), 2 (pt); Nurses aides 80 (ft), 30 (pt); Physical therapists 1 (pt); Recreational therapists 4 (ft); Occupational therapists 1 (pt); Speech therapists 1 (pt); Activities coordinators 1 (ft); Dietitians 2 (ft), 2 (pt); Dentists 1 (pt); Ophthalmologists 1 (pt); Podiatrists 1 (pt).
Languages Hebrew, Yiddish, Polish, Italian, Indian, Spanish
Facilities Dining room; Physical therapy room; Activities room; Chapel; Crafts room; Laundry room; Barber/Beauty shop; Library.
Activities Arts & crafts; Cards; Games; Reading groups; Prayer groups; Movies; Shopping trips; Social/Cultural gatherings.

Woodcrest Nursing Home
110-09 26th Ave, Flushing, NY, 11354
(718) 762-6100
Admin Josef Hirsch. *Medical Dir/Dir of Nursing* Gerald Kreitman; Elma Gonzales.
Licensure Skilled care. *Beds* SNF 200. *Certified* Medicaid; Medicare.
Owner Privately owned.
Admissions Requirements Minimum age 21; Medical examination.
Staff RNs 7 (ft), 8 (pt); LPNs 14 (ft), 8 (pt); Orderlies 8 (ft), 1 (pt); Nurses aides 40 (ft), 22 (pt); Physical therapists 2 (ft), 1 (pt); Recreational therapists 1 (ft), 1 (pt); Occupational therapists 1 (pt); Speech therapists 1 (pt); Activities coordinators 1 (ft); Dietitians 1 (ft); Dentists 1 (pt); Ophthalmologists 2 (pt); Podiatrists 1 (pt).
Languages Spanish, Yiddish, Hebrew, Hungarian
Facilities Dining room; Physical therapy room; Activities room; Crafts room; Laundry room; Barber/Beauty shop; Library.
Activities Arts & crafts; Cards; Games; Prayer groups; Movies; Social/Cultural gatherings.

FOREST HILLS

Fairview Nursing Home
69-70 Grand Central Pkwy, Forest Hills, NY, 11375
(718) 263-4600
Admin Abraham N Klein. *Medical Dir/Dir of Nursing* Dr Elias; Stephanie Manor DON.
Licensure Skilled care. *Beds* SNF 200. *Certified* Medicaid; Medicare.
Owner Privately owned.
Staff Physicians 5 (pt); RNs 10 (ft), 3 (pt); LPNs 15 (ft), 10 (pt); Nurses aides 55 (ft), 20 (pt); Physical therapists 1 (ft); Recreational therapists 1 (ft), 3 (pt); Occupational therapists 1 (ft); Speech therapists 1 (pt); Activities coordinators 1 (ft); Dietitians 2 (ft); Dentists 1 (pt); Ophthalmologists 1 (pt); Podiatrists 1 (pt).
Languages French, Spanish, German, Polish, Yiddish, Hebrew
Facilities Dining room; Physical therapy room; Activities room; Chapel; Crafts room; Laundry room; Barber/Beauty shop; Library.
Activities Arts & crafts; Cards; Games; Reading groups; Prayer groups; Movies; Shopping trips; Social/Cultural gatherings; Trips to cultural events.

Forest Hills Nursing Home*
71-44 Yellowstone Blvd, Forest Hills, NY, 11375
(718) 544-4300
Admin Cathrine Powers.
Licensure Skilled care. *Beds* 100. *Certified* Medicaid; Medicare.
Owner Proprietary Corp.

Forest View Nursing Home
71-20 110th St, Forest Hills, NY, 11375
(718) 793-3200
Admin Joseph L Bloch. *Medical Dir/Dir of Nursing* Hiralal Patel.
Licensure Skilled care. *Beds* 159. *Certified* Medicaid; Medicare.
Owner Proprietary Corp.
Admissions Requirements Medical examination; Physician's request.
Staff Physicians 6 (pt); RNs 4 (ft), 3 (pt); LPNs 18 (ft), 12 (pt); Nurses aides 43 (ft), 28 (pt); Physical therapists 1 (ft), 1 (pt); Recreational therapists 1 (ft), 3 (pt); Occupational therapists 1 (pt); Speech therapists 1 (pt); Activities coordinators 1 (ft); Dietitians 1 (ft).
Facilities Dining room; Physical therapy room; Activities room; Laundry room; Barber/Beauty shop; Library.
Activities Arts & crafts; Cards; Games; Reading groups; Movies; Social/Cultural gatherings; BBQs; Trips to museums & race track.

FORT EDWARD

Fort Hudson Nursing Home Inc
Upper Broadway, Fort Edward, NY, 12828
(518) 747-2811
Admin Dorothy S Kubricky. *Medical Dir/Dir of Nursing* Philip J Gara Jr MD; Donna Wassel RN DON.
Licensure Skilled care; Intermediate care; Health related facility. *Beds* SNF 80; ICF; Health related 80. *Certified* Medicaid; Medicare.
Owner Nonprofit Corp.
Admissions Requirements Minimum age 16; Medical examination.
Staff Physicians 1 (pt); RNs 9 (ft), 6 (pt); LPNs 15 (ft), 10 (pt); Orderlies 2 (ft), 3 (pt); Nurses aides 34 (ft), 23 (pt); Physical therapists 1 (pt); Occupational therapists 1 (pt); Speech therapists 1 (pt); Activities coordinators 1 (ft); Dietitians 1 (pt).
Facilities Dining room; Physical therapy room; Activities room; Crafts room; Laundry room; Barber/Beauty shop; Movie/Theater room; Quiet room.
Activities Arts & crafts; Cards; Games; Reading groups; Prayer groups; Movies; Shopping trips; Social/Cultural gatherings.

FRANKLIN SQUARE

Franklin Park Nursing Home
135 Franklin Ave, Franklin Square, NY, 11010
(516) 488-1600
Admin Clifford Schein. *Medical Dir/Dir of Nursing* Dr Harold Langs.
Licensure Skilled care. *Beds* 150. *Certified* Medicaid; Medicare.
Owner Proprietary Corp.
Admissions Requirements Minimum age 17; Medical examination.

FREEPORT

South Shore Nursing Home Inc
275 W Merrick Rd, Freeport, NY, 11520
(516) 623-4000
Admin Marylynne Geraghty. *Medical Dir/Dir of Nursing* T Walker MD; R Donges RN.
Licensure Skilled care. *Beds* SNF 100. *Certified* Medicaid; Medicare.

Owner Proprietary Corp.
Admissions Requirements Minimum age 16.
Staff RNs 13 (ft); LPNs 12 (ft); Nurses aides 46 (ft); Physical therapists 1 (pt); Occupational therapists 1 (pt); Activities coordinators 1 (ft); Dietitians 1 (pt).
Facilities Dining room; Physical therapy room; Activities room; Laundry room; Barber/Beauty shop.
Activities Arts & crafts; Cards; Games; Reading groups; Prayer groups; Movies; Shopping trips; Social/Cultural gatherings.

FULTON

Andrew Michaud Nursing Home*
450 S 4th St, Fulton, NY, 13069
(315) 592-9521
Admin Fred Blackwood.
Licensure Skilled care. *Beds* 89. *Certified* Medicaid; Medicare.
Owner Publicly owned.

GASPORT

United Church Colony Homes Inc*
4540 Lincoln Dr, Gasport, NY, 14067
(716) 772-2631
Admin James Surridge.
Licensure Skilled care. *Beds* 83. *Certified* Medicaid; Medicare.
Owner Nonprofit Corp.

GENESEO

Livingston County Skilled Nursing Facility
4223 Lakeville Rd, Geneseo, NY, 14454
(716) 243-3340
Admin Greg Miller. *Medical Dir/Dir of Nursing* Dr Sweeney; Jane Hill.
Licensure Skilled care. *Beds* SNF 126. *Certified* Medicaid; Medicare.
Owner Publicly owned.
Admissions Requirements Minimum age 16.
Staff Physicians 2 (pt); RNs 13 (ft), 1 (pt); LPNs 16 (ft), 1 (pt); Nurses aides 51 (ft), 22 (pt); Physical therapists 1 (ft); Speech therapists 1 (pt); Activities coordinators 1 (ft); Dietitians 1 (pt); Ophthalmologists 1 (pt); Physician assistant 1 (pt).
Facilities Dining room; Physical therapy room; Activities room; Chapel; Laundry room; Barber/Beauty shop; Auditorium.
Activities Arts & crafts; Cards; Games; Reading groups; Prayer groups; Movies; Shopping trips; Social/Cultural gatherings.

GENEVA

Geneva General Hospital Nursing Home Co Inc*
196-198 North St, Geneva, NY, 14456
(315) 789-4222
Admin James Dooley.
Licensure Skilled care; Intermediate care. *Beds* 67. *Certified* Medicaid; Medicare.
Owner Nonprofit Corp.

GERRY

Gerry Nursing Home Co Inc
Rte 60, Gerry, NY, 14740
(716) 985-4612
Admin Vivian J DiNardo. *Medical Dir/Dir of Nursing* George Lewis MD; Lois Farro RN DON.
Licensure Skilled care; Intermediate care. *Beds* SNF 80; ICF 40. *Certified* Medicaid; Medicare.
Owner Nonprofit Corp.
Admissions Requirements Minimum age 16; Physician's request.
Staff Physicians; RNs; LPNs; Orderlies; Nurses aides; Physical therapists; Recreational therapists; Occupational

therapists; Speech therapists; Activities coordinators; Dietitians; Ophthalmologists; Podiatrists.
Affiliation Methodist
Facilities Dining room; Physical therapy room; Activities room; Chapel; Crafts room; Laundry room; Barber/Beauty shop; Library.
Activities Arts & crafts; Games; Reading groups; Prayer groups; Movies; Shopping trips; Social/Cultural gatherings.

GETZVILLE

Niagara Frontier Nursing Home Co Inc*
100 Stahl Rd, Getzville, NY, 14068
(716) 688-8822
Admin Arthur Shade.
Licensure Skilled care. *Beds* 120. *Certified* Medicaid; Medicare.
Owner Nonprofit Corp.

Niagra Frontier Methodist Home Inc Health Related Facility*
2235 Millersport Hwy, Getzville, NY, 14068
(716) 688-8822
Licensure Intermediate care. *Beds* 157.
Owner Nonprofit Corp.
Affiliation Methodist

GLEN COVE

Forest Manor Health Related Facility*
6 Medical Plaza, Glen Cove, NY, 11542
(516) 671-9010
Licensure Intermediate care. *Beds* 148.
Owner Proprietary Corp.

The Glengariff Health Care Center
Dosoris Ln, Glen Cove, NY, 11542
(516) 676-1100
Admin Kenneth Winston. *Medical Dir/Dir of Nursing* Ferdinand Kann MD; Joan Kelly RN DON.
Licensure Skilled care; Intermediate care. *Beds* SNF 202; ICF 60. *Certified* Medicaid; Medicare.
Owner Proprietary Corp.
Admissions Requirements Minimum age 16; Medical examination; Physician's request.
Staff Physicians 4 (pt); RNs 15 (ft), 5 (pt); LPNs 20 (ft), 5 (pt); Orderlies 1 (ft); Nurses aides 60 (ft), 15 (pt); Physical therapists 1 (pt); Recreational therapists 4 (ft); Occupational therapists 1 (pt); Speech therapists 1 (pt); Activities coordinators 1 (ft); Dietitians 2 (pt); Dentists 1 (pt); Ophthalmologists 1 (pt); Podiatrists 1 (pt).
Facilities Dining room; Physical therapy room; Activities room; Crafts room; Laundry room; Barber/Beauty shop; Library.
Activities Arts & crafts; Cards; Games; Reading groups; Prayer groups; Movies; Shopping trips; Social/Cultural gatherings.

Montclair Nursing Home*
2 Medical Plaza, Glen Cove, NY, 11542
(516) 671-0858
Admin Joseph Kane. *Medical Dir/Dir of Nursing* Gabriella Wasserman.
Licensure Skilled care. *Beds* 102. *Certified* Medicaid; Medicare.
Owner Proprietary Corp.
Staff RNs 8 (ft), 4 (pt); LPNs 5 (ft), 4 (pt); Orderlies 1 (ft); Nurses aides 30 (ft), 11 (pt).
Facilities Dining room; Activities room; Barber/Beauty shop.
Activities Arts & crafts; Cards; Games; Reading groups; Prayer groups; Movies; Shopping trips; Social/Cultural gatherings.

GLEN OAKS

New Glen Oaks Nursing Home*
260-01 79th Ave, Glen Oaks, NY, 11004
(718) 343-0770
Admin Caroline Snigur.

Licensure Skilled care. *Beds* 60. *Certified* Medicaid; Medicare.
Owner Proprietary Corp.

GLENS FALLS

Eden Park Nursing Home & Health Related Facility*
170 Warren St, Glens Falls, NY, 12801
(518) 793-5163
Admin Lloyd Cote. *Medical Dir/Dir of Nursing* Dr Allen Kauffman MD.
Licensure Skilled care; Intermediate care. *Certified* Medicaid; Medicare.
Owner Proprietary Corp (Eden Park Management).
Admissions Requirements Minimum age 16; Medical examination; Physician's request.
Staff RNs 10 (ft), 10 (pt); LPNs 8 (ft), 2 (pt); Nurses aides 35 (ft), 26 (pt); Physical therapists 1 (pt); Recreational therapists 1 (ft); Occupational therapists 1 (ft), 1 (pt); Speech therapists 1 (pt); Activities coordinators 1 (ft); Dietitians 1 (pt); Dentists 1 (pt).
Facilities Dining room; Physical therapy room; Activities room; Crafts room; Barber/Beauty shop; Library; Wheelchair garden.
Activities Arts & crafts; Games; Reading groups; Prayer groups; Movies; Shopping trips; Social/Cultural gatherings; Music, video, and drama programs.

Hallmark Nursing Centre*
152 Sherman Ave, Glens Falls, NY, 12801
(518) 793-2575
Admin M R Kubricky.
Licensure Skilled care. *Beds* 80. *Certified* Medicaid; Medicare.
Owner Proprietary Corp.

Westmount Health Facility*
Rte 2, Gurney Ln, Glens Falls, NY, 12801
(518) 761-6540
Admin James Shoemaker. *Medical Dir/Dir of Nursing* Dr John E Cunnigham Jr.
Licensure Skilled care. *Beds* 80. *Certified* Medicaid; Medicare.
Owner Publicly owned.
Admissions Requirements Minimum age 16; Medical examination; Physician's request.
Staff Physicians 3 (pt); RNs 9 (ft); LPNs 9 (ft); Nurses aides 39 (ft); Physical therapists 1 (ft), 1 (pt); Recreational therapists 2 (ft); Occupational therapists; Speech therapists; Activities coordinators 1 (pt); Dietitians 1 (pt); Dentists 1 (pt); Audiologists.
Facilities Dining room; Physical therapy room; Activities room; Crafts room; Laundry room; Barber/Beauty shop.
Activities Arts & crafts; Cards; Reading groups; Prayer groups; Movies; Shopping trips; Social/Cultural gatherings.

GLOVERSVILLE

Fulton County Infirmary
Ext Phelps St Rd, Gloversville, NY, 12078
(518) 725-8631
Admin Cynthia Dodge. *Medical Dir/Dir of Nursing* Dr Curtis Mills; Shirley Wands RN.
Licensure Skilled care; Health related care. *Beds* SNF 134; HRF 42. *Certified* Medicaid; Medicare.
Owner Publicly owned.
Admissions Requirements Minimum age 16; Medical examination.
Staff Physicians 5 (pt); RNs 11 (ft); LPNs 20 (ft), 2 (pt); Nurses aides 61 (ft), 37 (pt); Physical therapists 1 (pt); Occupational therapists 1 (pt); Activities coordinators 1 (ft); Dietitians 1 (pt); Ophthalmologists 1 (pt).
Facilities Dining room; Physical therapy room; Activities room; Laundry room; Barber/Beauty shop.

Activities Arts & crafts; Cards; Games; Reading groups; Prayer groups; Movies; Shopping trips; Social/Cultural gatherings; Ceramics.

Gloversville Extended Care & Nursing Home Co Inc
99 E State St, Gloversville, NY, 12078
(518) 725-8611
Admin Daniel Governanti. *Medical Dir/Dir of Nursing* Julia Ferrara RN DON.
Licensure Skilled care. *Beds* SNF 84. *Certified* Medicaid; Medicare.
Owner Nonprofit Corp.
Admissions Requirements Minimum age 16; Physician's request.
Staff Physicians; RNs; LPNs; Orderlies; Nurses aides; Physical therapists; Activities coordinators; Dietitians.
Facilities Dining room; Physical therapy room; Activities room; Laundry room; Barber/Beauty shop.
Activities Arts & crafts; Cards; Games; Reading groups; Prayer groups; Movies; Social/Cultural gatherings.

GOSHEN

Orange County Home & Infirmary
PO Box 59, Goshen, NY, 10924
(914) 294-7971
Admin John Watson.
Licensure Skilled care; Intermediate care. *Beds* 340. *Certified* Medicaid; Medicare.
Owner Publicly owned.

GOUVERNEUR

Kinney Nursing Home
57 W Barney St, Gouverneur, NY, 13642
(315) 287-1400
Admin Byron Quinton.
Licensure Skilled care. *Beds* SNF 40. *Certified* Medicaid; Medicare.
Owner Nonprofit Corp.
Staff RNs; LPNs; Nurses aides; Physical therapists; Activities coordinators; Dietitians.
Facilities Dining room; Physical therapy room; Activities room; Crafts room; Laundry room; Barber/Beauty shop.
Activities Arts & crafts; Cards; Games; Reading groups; Prayer groups; Movies; Shopping trips; Social/Cultural gatherings.

GOWANDA

Gowanda Nursing Home
100 Miller St, Gowanda, NY, 14070
(716) 532-5700
Admin Celin C Hart. *Medical Dir/Dir of Nursing* C Frederick Kurtz MD; Cindy Wilkins RN DON.
Licensure Skilled care; Intermediate care. *Beds* SNF 80; ICF 40. *Certified* Medicaid; Medicare.
Owner Proprietary Corp.
Admissions Requirements Minimum age 16; Medical examination; Physician's request.
Staff RNs 6 (ft), 4 (pt); LPNs 4 (ft), 6 (pt); Orderlies 2 (ft); Nurses aides 30 (ft), 15 (pt); Physical therapists 1 (pt); Speech therapists 1 (pt); Activities coordinators 1 (ft), 2 (pt).
Facilities Dining room; Physical therapy room; Activities room; Crafts room; Laundry room; Barber/Beauty shop; Treatment room.
Activities Arts & crafts; Cards; Games; Reading groups; Prayer groups; Movies; Shopping trips; Social/Cultural gatherings; Ceramics; Dinner club.

GRAND ISLAND

Grand Island Manor Nursing Home*
2850 Grand Island Blvd, Grand Island, NY, 14072
(716) 773-5900

Admin Sam W Ware Jr. *Medical Dir/Dir of Nursing* Ida Levine MD.
Licensure Skilled care. *Beds* 80. *Certified* Medicaid; Medicare.
Owner Proprietary Corp.
Admissions Requirements Minimum age 16.
Staff Physicians 1 (pt); RNs 5 (ft), 5 (pt); LPNs 10 (ft), 4 (pt); Nurses aides 16 (ft), 24 (pt); Physical therapists 1 (pt); Recreational therapists 1 (ft), 1 (pt); Occupational therapists 1 (pt); Speech therapists 1 (pt); Dietitians 1 (pt); Dentists 1 (pt); Ophthalmologists 1 (pt); Podiatrists 1 (pt); Audiologists 1 (pt).
Facilities Dining room; Physical therapy room; Activities room; Crafts room; Laundry room; Barber/Beauty shop.
Activities Arts & crafts; Cards; Games; Reading groups; Prayer groups; Movies; Shopping trips; Social/Cultural gatherings.

GRANVILLE

Indian River Nursing Home & Health Related Facility Inc
17 Madison St, Granville, NY, 12832
(518) 642-2710
Admin Daniel L Morris. *Medical Dir/Dir of Nursing* Dr John Glennon.
Licensure Skilled care; Intermediate care. *Beds* SNF 40; HRF 40. *Certified* Medicaid; Medicare.
Owner Proprietary Corp.
Admissions Requirements Medical examination.
Staff Physicians 2 (pt); RNs 3 (ft), 2 (pt); LPNs 3 (ft), 4 (pt); Nurses aides 23 (ft), 8 (pt); Physical therapists 1 (ft), 1 (pt); Recreational therapists 1 (ft); Speech therapists 1 (pt); Activities coordinators 1 (ft); Dietitians 1 (ft); Dentists 1 (pt); Podiatrists 1 (pt).
Facilities Dining room; Physical therapy room; Activities room; Laundry room; Barber/Beauty shop; Library.
Activities Arts & crafts; Games; Reading groups; Movies; Shopping trips; Social/Cultural gatherings.

GREAT NECK

Grace Plaza of Great Neck Inc
15 Saint Pauls Pl, Great Neck, NY, 11021
(516) 466-3001
Admin Celia Strow. *Medical Dir/Dir of Nursing* Lester Corn MD; Jo Wolfson DNS.
Licensure Skilled care; Intermediate care. *Beds* SNF 165; ICF 49. *Certified* Medicaid; Medicare.
Owner Proprietary Corp.
Admissions Requirements Minimum age 16; Medical examination; Physician's request.
Staff RNs 20 (ft), 10 (pt); LPNs 20 (ft), 12 (pt); Orderlies; Nurses aides 85 (ft), 30 (pt); Physical therapists 1 (pt); Recreational therapists 4 (ft), 2 (pt); Occupational therapists 1 (pt); Speech therapists 1 (pt); Activities coordinators 1 (ft); Dietitians 2 (ft).
Facilities Dining room; Physical therapy room; Activities room; Crafts room; Laundry room; Barber/Beauty shop.
Activities Arts & crafts; Cards; Games; Reading groups; Prayer groups; Movies; Social/Cultural gatherings.

Wedgewood Nursing Home*
199 Community Dr, Great Neck, NY, 11021
(516) 365-9229
Admin Fred White.
Licensure Skilled care. *Beds* 200. *Certified* Medicaid; Medicare.
Owner Proprietary Corp.

GREENHURST

Fenton Park Health Related Facility
Rte 430, Greenhurst, NY, 14742
(716) 483-5000
Admin Frederick J Landy. *Medical Dir/Dir of Nursing* Dr Charles Sinatra; Sally Field RN.
Licensure Intermediate care. *Beds* ICF 100. *Certified* Medicaid; Medicare.
Owner Privately owned.
Admissions Requirements Minimum age 18; Medical examination; Physician's request.
Staff Physicians 1 (pt); RNs 3 (ft), 2 (pt); LPNs 7 (ft), 4 (pt); Orderlies 2 (ft); Nurses aides 17 (ft), 6 (pt); Physical therapists 1 (pt); Recreational therapists 1 (ft); Occupational therapists 1 (pt); Speech therapists 1 (pt); Activities coordinators 1 (ft); Dietitians 1 (ft); Dentists 1 (pt); Ophthalmologists 1 (pt); Podiatrists 1 (pt); Dentist; Social worker; Medical records; Business office; Maintenance supervisor; Housekeeping; Laundry supervisor.
Facilities Dining room; Physical therapy room; Activities room; Chapel; Crafts room; Laundry room; Barber/Beauty shop; Library; Atrium room; TV lounges; Lake access; Picnic areas; Courtyards.
Activities Arts & crafts; Cards; Games; Reading groups; Prayer groups; Movies; Shopping trips; Social/Cultural gatherings; Baking club; Bake sales; Rummage sales.

GREENPORT

San Simeon by the Sound —Skilled Nursing Facility*
North Rd, Greenport, NY, 11944
(516) 477-2110
Admin Arthur Loeffler.
Licensure Skilled care. *Beds* 70. *Certified* Medicaid; Medicare.
Owner Nonprofit Corp.

GROTON

Groton Residential Care Facility
120 Sykes St, Groton, NY, 13073
(607) 898-5876
Admin James X Kennedy. *Medical Dir/Dir of Nursing* David Newman MD; Margaret Proulx DON.
Licensure Skilled care; Intermediate care. *Beds* SNF 40; ICF 40. *Certified* Medicaid; Medicare.
Owner Nonprofit Corp.
Admissions Requirements Minimum age 16.
Staff RNs 4 (ft), 1 (pt); LPNs 7 (ft), 4 (pt); Nurses aides 11 (ft), 26 (pt); Activities coordinators 1 (ft); Dietitians 2 (ft).
Facilities Dining room; Physical therapy room; Activities room; Laundry room; Barber/Beauty shop.
Activities Arts & crafts; Cards; Games; Prayer groups; Movies; Shopping trips; Social/Cultural gatherings; Intergenerational gatherings.

GUILDERLAND CENTER

Guilderland Center Nursing Home Inc*
127 Main St, Guilderland Center, NY, 12085
(518) 861-5141
Admin James Reed & Hazel Reed.
Licensure Skilled care. *Beds* 127. *Certified* Medicaid; Medicare.
Owner Proprietary Corp.

HAMBURG

Autumn View Manor
4650 Southwestern Blvd, Hamburg, NY, 14052
(716) 648-2450
Admin Suzette Wilson. *Medical Dir/Dir of Nursing* Douglas Moffat.

Licensure Skilled care; Intermediate care. *Beds* SNF 122; ICF 38. *Certified* Medicaid; Medicare.
Owner Privately owned.
Admissions Requirements Minimum age 18; Physician's request.
Staff RNs 20 (ft); LPNs 25 (ft); Nurses aides 80 (ft); Physical therapists 1 (ft); Recreational therapists 2 (ft), 1 (pt); Occupational therapists 1 (ft); Speech therapists 1 (ft); Activities coordinators 1 (ft); Dietitians 1 (ft); Dentists 1 (ft); Ophthalmologists 1 (ft); Podiatrists 1 (ft); Social workers; Business office personnel; Housekeeping; Laundry; Dietary.
Facilities Dining room; Physical therapy room; Activities room; Crafts room; Laundry room; Barber/Beauty shop.
Activities Arts & crafts; Cards; Games; Reading groups; Prayer groups; Movies; Shopping trips; Social/Cultural gatherings; Religious services for all faiths.

Hamburg Health Care Center Inc
5775 Maelou Dr, Hamburg, NY, 14075
(716) 648-2820
Admin Margaret Mary Wagner. *Medical Dir/Dir of Nursing* Charlotte Torres DON; Eric Goodwin MD.
Licensure Skilled care. *Beds* 160.
Owner Proprietary Corp.
Admissions Requirements Minimum age 16; Medical examination; Physician's request.
Staff Physicians 1 (pt); RNs 14 (ft), 10 (pt); LPNs 16 (ft), 8 (pt); Nurses aides 55 (ft), 32 (pt); Physical therapists 3 (pt); Occupational therapists 1 (ft); Speech therapists 1 (pt); Activities coordinators 1 (ft); Dietitians 1 (ft).
Facilities Dining room; Physical therapy room; Activities room; Chapel; Crafts room; Laundry room; Barber/Beauty shop; Occupational therapy room; Speech therapy room; Large front porch.
Activities Arts & crafts; Cards; Games; Reading groups; Prayer groups; Movies; Shopping trips; Social/Cultural gatherings; Current events; Cooking; Gardening; Exercise groups; Residents' council; Community outings; Ceramics; Ecumenical worship services; Reminiscence groups.

HAMILTON

Community Memorial Hospital Inc—Nurs Home Unit*
150 Broad St, Hamilton, NY, 13346
(315) 824-1100
Admin David Felton.
Licensure Skilled care. *Beds* 40. *Certified* Medicaid; Medicare.
Owner Nonprofit Corp.

HARRIS

Community General Hospital of Sullivan County
PO Box 800, Bushville Rd, Harris, NY, 12742
(914) 794-3300
Admin Barbara Hallenbeck. *Medical Dir/Dir of Nursing* Dr Alan Greenbaum; Mary Ann Burlingame.
Licensure Skilled care. *Beds* 60. *Certified* Medicaid; Medicare.
Owner Nonprofit organization/foundation.
Admissions Requirements Medical examination.
Staff Physicians 60 (pt); RNs 5 (ft); LPNs 6 (ft), 1 (pt); Orderlies 13 (ft), 1 (pt); Nurses aides 13 (ft), 1 (pt); Physical therapists 1 (pt); Occupational therapists 1 (pt); Speech therapists 1 (pt); Activities coordinators 1 (ft); Dietitians 1 (pt); Podiatrists 1 (pt).

Facilities Dining room; Physical therapy room; Activities room; Chapel; Crafts room.
Activities Arts & crafts; Cards; Games; Prayer groups; Movies; Shopping trips; Social/ Cultural gatherings.

HASTINGS

Andrus Retirement Community
185 Old Broadway, Hastings, NY, 10706
(914) 478-3700
Admin James J Lindes. *Medical Dir/Dir of Nursing* James Jones MD; Jeanne Brimigion RN DNS.
Licensure Skilled care; Intermediate care; Adult home. *Beds* 247.
Owner Nonprofit organization/foundation.
Admissions Requirements Minimum age 65; Medical examination.
Staff Physicians 2 (pt); RNs 11 (ft); LPNs 9 (ft); Orderlies 1 (ft); Nurses aides 27 (ft); Physical therapists 1 (pt); Recreational therapists 4 (ft); Dietitians 2 (ft).
Facilities Dining room; Physical therapy room; Activities room; Chapel; Crafts room; Laundry room; Barber/Beauty shop; Library.
Activities Arts & crafts; Cards; Games; Reading groups; Prayer groups; Movies; Shopping trips; Social/Cultural gatherings.

HASTINGS ON HUDSON

Andrys Retirement Community
185 Old Broadway, Hastings on Hudson, NY, 10706
(914) 478-3700
Admin James J Lindes. *Medical Dir/Dir of Nursing* J J Jones MD; J Brimigion DNS.
Licensure Skilled care; Intermediate care. *Beds* SNF 52; ICF 195.
Owner Nonprofit Corp.
Admissions Requirements Minimum age 65.
Staff Physicians 3 (pt); RNs 7 (ft), 7 (pt); LPNs 7 (ft), 4 (pt); Orderlies 2 (ft); Nurses aides 17 (ft), 18 (pt); Physical therapists 1 (ft), 1 (pt); Occupational therapists 1 (pt); Speech therapists 1 (pt); Dietitians 1 (ft).
Facilities Dining room; Physical therapy room; Activities room; Crafts room; Laundry room; Barber/Beauty shop; Library; Game room; Auditorium.
Activities Arts & crafts; Cards; Games; Reading groups; Prayer groups; Movies; Shopping trips; Social/Cultural gatherings; Swimming; Golf; Exercise groups.

HAVERSTRAW

Riverside Nursing Home*
87 S Rte 9W, Haverstraw, NY, 10927
(914) 429-5381
Admin Sarah Muschel.
Licensure Skilled care. *Beds* 100. *Certified* Medicaid; Medicare.
Owner Proprietary Corp.

HAWTHORNE

Ruth Taylor Geriatric & Rehabilitation Institute/Weschester County Medical Center
25 Bradhurst Ave, Hawthorne, NY, 10532
(914) 285-7762
Admin James Davis. *Medical Dir/Dir of Nursing* Steven R Gambert MD.
Licensure Skilled care; Intermediate care; Health related care. *Beds* 400. *Certified* Medicaid; Medicare.
Owner Publicly owned.
Staff Physicians 2 (ft), 5 (pt); RNs 36 (ft); LPNs 48 (ft), 1 (pt); Nurses aides 155 (ft); Physical therapists 1 (ft); Recreational therapists 8 (ft), 1 (pt); Occupational therapists 1 (ft); Speech therapists 1 (pt); Activities coordinators 1 (ft); Dietitians 4 (ft); Dentists 1 (pt); Podiatrists 1 (pt).

Facilities Dining room; Physical therapy room; Activities room; Chapel; Crafts room; Laundry room; Barber/Beauty shop; Library; Speech therapy; Occupational therapy room; Patient lounge; Patient private rooms; John E Kule Park; Coffee shop; Patient property rooms; Sewing room; Clothing shop.
Activities Arts & crafts; Cards; Games; Reading groups; Prayer groups; Movies; Shopping trips; Social/Cultural gatherings; Newcomers club; Sunshine club; Resident incentive work programs; Tasting time; RSVP; Resident newspaper; Garden club.

HEMPSTEAD

Hempstead Park Nursing Home
800 Front St, Hempstead, NY, 11551
(516) 560-1422
Admin Sol Forman. *Medical Dir/Dir of Nursing* Harold Levy MD; JoAnn Bianco DON.
Licensure Skilled care. *Beds* SNF 240. *Certified* Medicaid; Medicare.
Owner Privately owned.

Mayfair Nursing Home
100 Baldwin Rd, Hempstead, NY, 11550
(516) 538-7171
Admin John Ryan.
Licensure Skilled care. *Beds* 200. *Certified* Medicaid; Medicare.
Owner Proprietary Corp.

HERKIMER

Folts Home
104 N Washington St, Herkimer, NY, 13350
(315) 866-6964
Admin Virginia Sheehan. *Medical Dir/Dir of Nursing* Stephen P Martell MD.
Licensure Skilled care; Health related care. *Beds* SNF 79; HRC 45. *Certified* Medicaid; Medicare.
Owner Nonprofit Corp.
Admissions Requirements Minimum age 16; Medical examination.
Staff RNs 10 (ft); LPNs 19 (ft), 6 (pt); Orderlies 1 (ft), 1 (pt); Nurses aides 58 (ft); Physical therapists; Occupational therapists; Activities coordinators; Dietitians; Dentists; Podiatrists; Dentist.
Affiliation Methodist
Facilities Dining room; Physical therapy room; Activities room; Chapel; Crafts room; Laundry room; Barber/Beauty shop.
Activities Arts & crafts; Cards; Games; Reading groups; Prayer groups; Movies; Shopping trips; Social/Cultural gatherings.

Valley Health Services Inc
690 W German St, Herkimer, NY, 13350
(315) 866-3330
Admin Carmen C Paone. *Medical Dir/Dir of Nursing* Dr Richard Trimble; Charlotte Szarjeko DON.
Licensure Skilled care. *Beds* SNF 128. *Certified* Medicaid; Medicare.
Owner Nonprofit Corp.
Admissions Requirements Physician's request.
Staff RNs 11 (ft), 4 (pt); LPNs 24 (ft), 14 (pt); Nurses aides 31 (ft), 32 (pt); Physical therapists 1 (ft); Recreational therapists 1 (ft); Occupational therapists 1 (ft); Activities coordinators 1 (ft).
Facilities Dining room; Physical therapy room; Crafts room; Barber/Beauty shop.
Activities Arts & crafts; Cards; Games; Reading groups; Prayer groups; Movies; Shopping trips; Social/Cultural gatherings.

HIGHLAND

Hudson Valley Nursing Center*
Vineyard Ave, Highland, NY, 12528
(914) 691-7201
Admin Alan Porter.

Licensure Skilled care. *Beds* 120. *Certified* Medicaid; Medicare.
Owner Proprietary Corp.

HOLLIS

Hollis Park Manor Nursing Home
191-06 Hillside Ave, Hollis, NY, 11423
(718) 479-1010
Admin Marianne Giacolone. *Medical Dir/Dir of Nursing* Dr Peter Barra; Yvonne Grant DON.
Licensure Skilled care. *Beds* SNF 80. *Certified* Medicaid; Medicare.
Owner Privately owned.
Admissions Requirements Minimum age 16; Medical examination.
Staff Physicians; RNs; LPNs; Orderlies; Nurses aides; Physical therapists; Occupational therapists; Speech therapists; Activities coordinators; Dietitians; Ophthalmologists; Podiatrists; Social service.
Facilities Dining room; Physical therapy room; Activities room; Crafts room; Laundry room; Barber/Beauty shop.
Activities Arts & crafts; Cards; Games; Reading groups; Prayer groups; Movies; Social/Cultural gatherings.

Holliswood Care Center Inc*
195-44 Woodhull Ave, Hollis, NY, 11423
(718) 740-3500
Admin Hal Schifter.
Licensure Skilled care; Intermediate care. *Beds* 58. *Certified* Medicaid; Medicare.
Owner Proprietary Corp.

HOLMES

Kent Nursing Home
RR 1 Box 85, Holmes, NY, 12531
(914) 878-3241
Admin Joan Kean. *Medical Dir/Dir of Nursing* Richard Gang MD; Barbara Parlatore RN DON.
Licensure Skilled care. *Beds* SNF 160. *Certified* Medicaid; Medicare.
Owner Proprietary Corp.
Admissions Requirements Minimum age 16.
Staff Physicians 12 (pt); RNs 9 (ft), 7 (pt); LPNs 9 (ft), 4 (pt); Nurses aides 37 (ft), 29 (pt); Physical therapists 1 (pt); Recreational therapists 3 (ft); Occupational therapists 1 (pt); Speech therapists 1 (pt); Activities coordinators 1 (ft); Dietitians 1 (ft); Dentists 1 (pt); Ophthalmologists 1 (pt); Podiatrists 1 (pt); Social services 1 (ft), 1 (pt).
Facilities Dining room; Physical therapy room; Activities room; Crafts room; Laundry room; Barber/Beauty shop.
Activities Arts & crafts; Cards; Games; Reading groups; Prayer groups; Movies; Social/Cultural gatherings.

HOOSICK FALLS

Hoosick Falls Health Center
PO Box 100, 21 Danforth St, Hoosick Falls, NY, 12090
(518) 686-4371
Admin Leslie Beadle. *Medical Dir/Dir of Nursing* Dr Newton Krumdieck; Mildred C Lewis RN DON.
Licensure Skilled care. *Beds* SNF 41. *Certified* Medicaid; Medicare.
Owner Nonprofit Corp.
Staff RNs 2 (ft), 4 (pt); LPNs 4 (ft); Nurses aides 11 (ft), 8 (pt); Physical therapists 1 (pt); Occupational therapists 1 (pt); Speech therapists 1 (pt); Activities coordinators 1 (ft); Dietitians 1 (pt); PT Aide 1 (ft).
Facilities Dining room; Physical therapy room; Activities room; Laundry room; Barber/Beauty shop.

Activities Arts & crafts; Games; Reading groups; Prayer groups; Movies; Shopping trips; Social/Cultural gatherings.

HORNELL

Hornell Nursing Home & HRF*
434 Monroe Ave, Hornell, NY, 14843
(607) 324-7740
Admin James Bicker.
Licensure Skilled care; Intermediate care. *Beds* 60. *Certified* Medicaid; Medicare.
Owner Proprietary Corp.

HORSEHEADS

Bethany Nursing Home & Health Related Facility Inc
751 Watkins Rd, Horseheads, NY, 14845
(607) 739-8711
Admin Sharon M Pepper. *Medical Dir/Dir of Nursing* Dr Joseph Calderone; Stephanie Mitchell RN DON.
Licensure Skilled care. *Beds* SNF 80. *Certified* Medicaid; Medicare.
Owner Nonprofit Corp.
Admissions Requirements Minimum age 16; Physician's request.
Staff RNs 12 (ft), 3 (pt); LPNs 16 (ft), 2 (pt); Nurses aides 47 (ft), 4 (pt); Activities coordinators 1 (ft), 1 (pt); Dietitians 1 (ft); Social worker 1 (ft), 1 (pt).
Affiliation Methodist
Facilities Dining room; Physical therapy room; Activities room; Crafts room; Laundry room; Barber/Beauty shop; Library.
Activities Arts & crafts; Cards; Games; Reading groups; Prayer groups; Movies; Shopping trips; Social/Cultural gatherings.

Elcor Health Services
108-110 Colonial Dr, Horseheads, NY, 14845
(607) 739-0304
Admin Richard Poes. *Medical Dir/Dir of Nursing* Dr John Roemmelt.
Licensure Skilled care; Intermediate care; Day care. *Beds* SNF 105; ICF 120; Day care 42. *Certified* Medicaid; Medicare.
Owner Proprietary Corp.
Staff RNs 3 (ft), 9 (pt); LPNs 10 (ft), 5 (pt); Nurses aides 46 (ft), 21 (pt); Activities coordinators 1 (ft).
Facilities Dining room; Physical therapy room; Activities room; Crafts room; Laundry room; Barber/Beauty shop; Dental room.
Activities Arts & crafts; Cards; Games; Reading groups; Prayer groups; Movies; Shopping trips; Social/Cultural gatherings.

Elcor's Marriott Manor
108 Colonial Dr, Horseheads, NY, 14845
(607) 739-0304
Admin Richard Poes. *Medical Dir/Dir of Nursing* John Roemmelt MD.
Licensure Intermediate care. *Beds* ICF 120. *Certified* Medicaid.
Owner Proprietary Corp.
Admissions Requirements Medical examination.
Staff Physicians 1 (pt); RNs 2 (ft), 2 (pt); LPNs 6 (ft), 8 (pt); Nurses aides 17 (ft), 13 (pt); Activities coordinators 2 (ft), 1 (pt); Dietitians 1 (pt).
Facilities Dining room; Physical therapy room; Activities room; Crafts room; Laundry room; Barber/Beauty shop; Library.
Activities Arts & crafts; Cards; Games; Reading groups; Prayer groups; Movies; Shopping trips; Social/Cultural gatherings.

HOUGHTON

Houghton Nursing Care Center Inc
PO Box G-12, RD 1, Houghton, NY, 14744
(716) 567-2207
Admin Harold McIntire. *Medical Dir/Dir of Nursing* Storer Emmett MD.

Licensure Skilled care; Intermediate care. *Beds* SNF 40; ICF 40. *Certified* Medicaid; Medicare.
Owner Proprietary Corp.
Admissions Requirements Minimum age 16; Medical examination.
Staff Physicians 3 (pt); RNs 5 (ft), 3 (pt); LPNs 4 (ft), 6 (pt); Orderlies 1 (ft), 1 (pt); Nurses aides 28 (ft), 15 (pt); Activities coordinators 1 (ft), 1 (pt); Dietitians 1 (ft).
Facilities Dining room; Physical therapy room; Activities room; Crafts room; Laundry room; Barber/Beauty shop; Library.
Activities Arts & crafts; Cards; Games; Reading groups; Prayer groups; Movies; Shopping trips.

HUDSON

Eden Park Nursing Home*
30 Prospect Ave, Hudson, NY, 12534
(518) 828-9439
Admin Michael A Palmieri. *Medical Dir/Dir of Nursing* Dr Rosewall Shaw.
Licensure Skilled care. *Beds* 78. *Certified* Medicaid; Medicare.
Owner Proprietary Corp (Eden Park Management).
Admissions Requirements Minimum age 16; Medical examination; Physician's request.
Staff Physicians 1 (pt); Physical therapists 1 (ft); Occupational therapists 1 (pt); Speech therapists 1 (pt); Activities coordinators 1 (ft), 1 (pt); Dietitians 1 (pt); Dentists 1 (pt); Ophthalmologists 1 (pt); Podiatrists 1 (pt); Audiologists 1 (pt).
Facilities Dining room; Physical therapy room; Activities room; Crafts room; Laundry room; Barber/Beauty shop.
Activities Arts & crafts; Cards; Games; Reading groups; Prayer groups; Movies; Shopping trips; Social/Cultural gatherings.

Firemans Home of the State of New York Volunteer Firemens Assoc
Harry-Howard Ave, Hudson, NY, 12534
(518) 828-7695
Admin David C Gluck. *Medical Dir/Dir of Nursing* Susan Neer RN DON.
Licensure Skilled care; Intermediate care. *Beds* SNF 90; ICF 50.
Owner Nonprofit Corp.
Admissions Requirements Minimum age 21; Males only.
Staff RNs 25 (ft), 4 (pt); LPNs 5 (ft), 1 (pt); Orderlies 3 (ft), 1 (pt); Nurses aides 32 (ft), 6 (pt); Physical therapists 1 (pt); Recreational therapists 1 (ft), 1 (pt); Occupational therapists 1 (pt); Activities coordinators 1 (pt); Dietitians 1 (pt); Ophthalmologists 1 (pt).
Affiliation Volunteer Firefighting Service
Facilities Dining room; Physical therapy room; Activities room; Chapel; Crafts room; Laundry room; Barber/Beauty shop; Library; TV room.
Activities Arts & crafts; Cards; Games; Reading groups; Prayer groups; Movies; Shopping trips; Social/Cultural gatherings; Parades; Trips; Conventions.

HUNTINGTON

Carillon House Nursing Home*
830 Park Ave, Huntington, NY, 11743
(516) 271-5800
Admin Joseph Alfano.
Licensure Skilled care; Intermediate care. *Beds* 142. *Certified* Medicaid; Medicare.
Owner Proprietary Corp.

Hilaire Farm Nursing Home
Hilaire Dr, Huntington, NY, 11743
(516) 427-0254
Admin Michael M Gottsegen.

Licensure Skilled care. *Beds* 76. *Certified* Medicaid; Medicare.
Owner Proprietary Corp.

HUNTINGTON STATION

Birchwood Nursing Home
78 Birchwood Dr, Huntington Station, NY, 11746
(516) 423-3673
Admin Dr Timothy P Steffens. *Medical Dir/Dir of Nursing* Dr Frederick R Long; Monna Rockefeller RN.
Licensure Skilled care; Intermediate care. *Beds* SNF 120; ICF 75. *Certified* Medicaid; Medicare.
Owner Proprietary Corp.
Admissions Requirements Minimum age 18; Medical examination; Physician's request.
Staff Physicians 32 (pt); RNs 3 (ft), 13 (pt); LPNs 8 (ft), 24 (pt); Orderlies 1 (ft); Nurses aides 52 (ft), 34 (pt); Physical therapists 2 (ft); Recreational therapists 3 (ft); Occupational therapists 1 (pt); Speech therapists 1 (pt); Activities coordinators 1 (ft); Dietitians 1 (ft); Ophthalmologists 1 (pt); Podiatrists 1 (pt).
Facilities Dining room; Physical therapy room; Activities room; Chapel; Crafts room; Laundry room; Barber/Beauty shop; Library.
Activities Arts & crafts; Cards; Games; Reading groups; Prayer groups; Movies; Shopping trips; Social/Cultural gatherings.

HYDE PARK

Victory Lake Nursing Center*
101 N Quaker Ln, Hyde Park, NY, 12538
(914) 229-9177
Admin George H Pelote.
Licensure Skilled care. *Beds* 120. *Certified* Medicaid; Medicare.
Owner Nonprofit Corp.
Admissions Requirements Minimum age 16; Medical examination; Physician's request.
Staff Physicians 1 (ft), 8 (pt); RNs 16 (ft), 6 (pt); LPNs 12 (ft), 8 (pt); Orderlies 2 (ft); Nurses aides 46 (ft), 12 (pt); Physical therapists 1 (pt); Reality therapists 2 (ft); Recreational therapists 2 (ft); Occupational therapists 1 (pt); Speech therapists 1 (pt); Activities coordinators 1 (ft); Dietitians 2 (ft); Dentists 1 (pt); Ophthalmologists 1 (pt); Podiatrists 1 (pt); Audiologists 1 (pt).
Facilities Dining room; Physical therapy room; Activities room; Chapel; Crafts room; Laundry room; Barber/Beauty shop; Library.
Activities Arts & crafts; Cards; Games; Reading groups; Prayer groups; Movies; Shopping trips; Social/Cultural gatherings.

ILION

Mohawk Valley Nursing Home
295 W Main St, Ilion, NY, 13357
(315) 895-7474
Admin Marjorie Dolch. *Medical Dir/Dir of Nursing* Richard Brown DO.
Licensure Skilled care. *Beds* 120. *Certified* Medicaid; Medicare.
Owner Nonprofit Corp.
Admissions Requirements Minimum age 16; Medical examination; Physician's request.
Staff RNs 7 (ft), 9 (pt); LPNs 13 (ft), 13 (pt); Nurses aides 49 (ft), 50 (pt); Physical therapists 1 (ft), 1 (pt); Occupational therapists 1 (ft); Activities coordinators 1 (ft); Dentists 1 (pt).
Facilities Dining room; Activities room; Chapel; Crafts room; Barber/Beauty shop.
Activities Arts & crafts; Cards; Games; Reading groups; Prayer groups; Movies; Social/Cultural gatherings.

IRVING

Lake Shore Hospital Inc HRF
845 Rts 5 & 20, Irving, NY, 14081
(716) 934-2654
Admin Ivan Tarnopoll. *Medical Dir/Dir of
Nursing* Russell J Joy DO; Starlene Luther
RN DON.
Licensure Skilled care; Intermediate care. *Beds*
120. *Certified* Medicaid.
Owner Nonprofit Corp.
Admissions Requirements Minimum age 16;
Physician's request.
Staff Physicians 1 (pt); RNs 1 (ft), 1 (pt);
LPNs 6 (ft), 5 (pt); Nurses aides 12 (ft), 13
(pt); Physical therapists 1 (pt); Recreational
therapists 1 (ft), 2 (pt); Occupational
therapists 1 (pt); Activities coordinators 1
(ft), 5 (pt); Dietitians 1 (ft).
Facilities Dining room; Physical therapy
room; Activities room; Crafts room; Barber/
Beauty shop.
Activities Arts & crafts; Cards; Games;
Reading groups; Prayer groups; Movies;
Shopping trips; Social/Cultural gatherings;
Cooking.

ISLAND PARK

Bayview Nursing Home*
1 Long Beach Rd, Island Park, NY, 11558
(516) 432-0300
Admin Richard Lap.
Licensure Skilled care. *Beds* 185. *Certified*
Medicaid; Medicare.
Owner Proprietary Corp.

ITHACA

Lakeside Nursing Home Inc
1229 Trumansburg Rd, Ithaca, NY, 14850
(607) 273-8072
Admin Jeffery Earle. *Medical Dir/Dir of
Nursing* Jerry Hersh MD; Mary Ellen
Schreher DON.
Licensure Skilled care; Intermediate care. *Beds*
SNF 160; ICF 100. *Certified* Medicaid;
Medicare.
Owner Proprietary Corp.
Admissions Requirements Minimum age 16;
Medical examination; Physician's request.
Staff Physicians 1 (pt); RNs 20 (ft), 10 (pt);
LPNs 10 (ft), 5 (pt); Nurses aides 100 (ft),
20 (pt); Physical therapists 1 (ft);
Recreational therapists 2 (ft), 1 (pt);
Occupational therapists 1 (pt); Speech
therapists 1 (pt); Activities coordinators 1
(ft); Dietitians 1 (ft); Dentists 1 (pt);
Ophthalmologists 1 (pt); Podiatrists 1 (pt).
Facilities Dining room; Physical therapy
room; Activities room; Chapel; Crafts room;
Laundry room; Barber/Beauty shop; Library.
Activities Arts & crafts; Cards; Games;
Reading groups; Prayer groups; Movies;
Shopping trips; Social/Cultural gatherings.

Oak Hill Manor Nursing Home
602 Hudson St, Ithaca, NY, 14850
(607) 272-8282
Admin Eugene Battaglini. *Medical Dir/Dir of
Nursing* Thomas Mosher MD.
Licensure Skilled care. *Beds* 60. *Certified*
Medicaid; Medicare.
Owner Proprietary Corp.
Admissions Requirements Minimum age 16.
Staff RNs 6 (ft), 4 (pt); LPNs 3 (ft), 4 (pt);
Nurses aides 25 (ft), 7 (pt); Physical
therapists 1 (ft); Recreational therapists 1
(ft), 1 (pt); Speech therapists 1 (pt);
Dietitians 1 (pt).
Facilities Dining room; Physical therapy
room; Activities room; Laundry room;
Barber/Beauty shop.
Activities Arts & crafts; Cards; Games;
Reading groups; Prayer groups; Movies;
Shopping trips; Social/Cultural gatherings.

Reconstruction Home Inc*
318 S Albany St, Ithaca, NY, 14850
(607) 273-4166
Admin Jero ne Lutherhouse.
Licensure Skilled care. *Beds* 72. *Certified*
Medicaid; Medicare.
Owner Nonprofit Corp.

JAMAICA

Chapin Home for the Aging
165-01 Chapin Pkwy, Jamaica, NY, 11432
(718) 739-2523
Admin Joanne Buccellato. *Medical Dir/Dir of
Nursing* Arthur T Risbrook MD; Evelyn
McPherson RN DON.
Licensure Skilled care; Intermediate care. *Beds*
SNF 49; ICF 29. *Certified* Medicaid;
Medicare.
Owner Nonprofit Corp.
Admissions Requirements Medical
examination.
Staff Physicians 4 (pt); RNs 6 (ft), 2 (pt);
LPNs 8 (ft), 4 (pt); Nurses aides 23 (ft), 6
(pt); Recreational therapists 1 (ft), 1 (pt);
Occupational therapists 1 (pt); Speech
therapists 1 (pt); Dietitians 1 (ft), 1 (pt);
Podiatrists 1 (pt); COTA 1 (pt).
Languages Chinese, French, Spanish, Greek,
Hindi, Italian, German, Hungarian, Tagalog
Facilities Dining room; Physical therapy
room; Activities room; Chapel; Crafts room;
Laundry room; Barber/Beauty shop; Library;
General store.
Activities Arts & crafts; Games; Reading
groups; Movies; Social/Cultural gatherings;
Exercise group; Piano music; Pet/child
therapy; Trips.

Highland Care Center*
91-31 175th St, Jamaica, NY, 11432
(212) 657-6363
Admin Chiam Kaminetsky.
Licensure Skilled care; Intermediate care. *Beds*
120. *Certified* Medicaid; Medicare.
Owner Proprietary Corp.

Jamaica Hospital Nursing Home Company Inc
90-28 Van Wyck Expwy, Jamaica, NY, 11418
(718) 291-5300
Admin Joseph S Kane. *Medical Dir/Dir of
Nursing* Charles Huey MD; Ann Bonadio.
Licensure Skilled care. *Beds* SNF 200.
Certified Medicaid; Medicare.
Owner Nonprofit Corp.
Staff Physicians 5 (pt); RNs 20 (ft); LPNs 17
(ft); Orderlies 70 (ft); Nurses aides; Physical
therapists 2 (ft), 1 (pt); Recreational
therapists 1 (ft); Occupational therapists 2
(ft); Speech therapists 1 (pt); Activities
coordinators 1 (ft); Dietitians 1 (ft); Dentists
1 (pt); Ophthalmologists 1 (pt); Podiatrists 1
(pt).
Facilities Dining room; Physical therapy
room; Activities room; Laundry room;
Barber/Beauty shop; Library.
Activities Arts & crafts; Cards; Games;
Reading groups; Movies; Shopping trips;
Social/Cultural gatherings.

Margaret Tietz Center for Nursing Care
164-11 Chapin Pkwy, Jamaica, NY, 11432
(718) 523-6400
Admin Kenneth M Brown. *Medical Dir/Dir of
Nursing* Gail Lowenstein MD; Carol
McNally DON.
Licensure Skilled care; Intermediate care. *Beds*
200. *Certified* Medicaid; Medicare.
Owner Nonprofit Corp.
Admissions Requirements Minimum age 18;
Medical examination; Physician's request.
Staff Physicians 1 (ft), 5 (pt); Physical
therapists 2 (pt); Recreational therapists 2
(ft), 2 (pt); Occupational therapists 2 (ft);
Speech therapists 1 (pt); Activities
coordinators 1 (ft); Dietitians 1 (ft), 1 (pt);
Dentists 1 (pt); Ophthalmologists 1 (pt);
Podiatrists 1 (pt).

Facilities Dining room; Physical therapy
room; Activities room; Chapel; Crafts room;
Laundry room; Barber/Beauty shop; Library;
Garden; Terraces on each floor.
Activities Arts & crafts; Cards; Games;
Reading groups; Prayer groups; Movies;
Shopping trips; Social/Cultural gatherings.

JAMAICA ESTATES

Hillside Manor Health Related Facility*
182-15 Hillside Ave, Jamaica Estates, NY,
11432
(718) 291-8200
Admin Bengt Barbaccia.
Licensure Skilled care; Intermediate care. *Beds*
205. *Certified* Medicaid; Medicare.
Owner Proprietary Corp.

JAMESTOWN

Fenton Park Nursing Home
150 Prather Ave, Jamestown, NY, 14701
(716) 488-1921
Admin Charlotte M Albano. *Medical Dir/Dir
of Nursing* Charles Sinatra MD; Joan Kuell
RN.
Licensure Skilled care. *Beds* SNF 200.
Certified Medicaid; Medicare.
Owner Privately owned.
Admissions Requirements Physician's request.
Staff Physicians; RNs; LPNs; Orderlies;
Nurses aides; Physical therapists;
Recreational therapists; Occupational
therapists; Speech therapists; Activities
coordinators; Dietitians; Ophthalmologists;
Podiatrists; Dentist.
Facilities Dining room; Physical therapy
room; Activities room; Crafts room; Laundry
room; Barber/Beauty shop.
Activities Arts & crafts; Cards; Games;
Reading groups; Prayer groups; Movies;
Shopping trips; Social/Cultural gatherings.

Lutheran Retirement Home*
715 Falconer St, Jamestown, NY, 14701
(716) 665-4905
Admin Floyd Addison. *Medical Dir/Dir of
Nursing* John D Voltmann MD.
Licensure Skilled care; Intermediate care. *Beds*
124. *Certified* Medicaid; Medicare.
Owner Nonprofit Corp.
Staff RNs 12 (ft); LPNs 16 (ft); Orderlies 5
(ft); Nurses aides 65 (ft); Physical therapists
1 (pt); Recreational therapists 4 (ft), 1 (pt);
Occupational therapists 1 (pt); Speech
therapists 1 (pt); Activities coordinators 1
(ft); Dietitians 3 (ft), 1 (pt); Dentists 1 (pt);
Podiatrists 1 (pt).
Affiliation Lutheran
Facilities Dining room; Physical therapy
room; Activities room; Chapel; Laundry
room; Barber/Beauty shop.
Activities Arts & crafts; Cards; Games;
Reading groups; Prayer groups; Movies;
Shopping trips; Social/Cultural gatherings.

Manor Oak Skilled Nursing Facilities Inc
423 Baker St, Jamestown, NY, 14701
(716) 484-9181
Admin James E Bottomley. *Medical Dir/Dir of
Nursing* Dr Alina Wiecha Med Dir; Rosanna
Nocero DON.
Licensure Skilled care. *Beds* 104. *Certified*
Medicaid; Medicare.
Owner Privately owned.
Admissions Requirements Minimum age 16;
Medical examination; Physician's request.
Staff RNs 7 (ft), 3 (pt); LPNs 8 (ft), 8 (pt);
Nurses aides 26 (ft), 34 (pt); Physical
therapists 1 (ft); Occupational therapists;
Speech therapists; Activities coordinators 2
(ft); Dietitians; Ophthalmologists;
Podiatrists.
Facilities Dining room; Physical therapy
room; Activities room; Chapel; Crafts room;
Laundry room; Barber/Beauty shop.

Activities Arts & crafts; Cards; Games;
Reading groups; Prayer groups; Movies;
Shopping trips; Social/Cultural gatherings;
Music therapy.

Presbyterian Homes of Western New York Inc*
715 Falconer St, Jamestown, NY, 14701
(716) 665-5214
Admin Ruthie L Hunt.
Licensure Skilled care. *Beds* 86. *Certified*
Medicaid; Medicare.
Owner Nonprofit Corp.
Affiliation Presbyterian

JOHNSON CITY

**Susquehanna Nursing Home & Health Related
Facility**
282 Riverside Dr, Johnson City, NY, 13790
(607) 729-9206
Admin Paul Sadlon.
Licensure Skilled care; Intermediate care. *Beds*
100. *Certified* Medicaid; Medicare.
Owner Proprietary Corp.

Wilson Hospital Skilled Nursing Facility*
33-57 Harrison St, Johnson City, NY, 13790
(607) 773-6289
Admin Alan Kopman. *Medical Dir/Dir of
Nursing* Louis R Borelli MD.
Licensure Skilled care. *Beds* 100. *Certified*
Medicaid; Medicare.
Owner Nonprofit Corp.
Admissions Requirements Minimum age 16;
Medical examination; Physician's request.
Staff RNs 15 (ft), 8 (pt); LPNs 13 (ft), 7 (pt);
Nurses aides 24 (ft), 14 (pt); Physical
therapists 3 (ft), 3 (pt); Occupational
therapists 2 (ft); Speech therapists 1 (ft);
Activities coordinators 2 (ft); Dietitians 1
(pt); Dentists 1 (pt); Audiologists 1 (ft).
Facilities Dining room; Physical therapy
room; Laundry room; Barber/Beauty shop.
Activities Arts & crafts; Games; Reading
groups; Prayer groups; Movies; Shopping
trips; Social/Cultural gatherings.

JOHNSTOWN

Wells Nursing Home
201 W Madison Ave, Johnstown, NY, 12095
(518) 762-4546
Admin Joyce Brower. *Medical Dir/Dir of
Nursing* Vincent Leonti MD; Nita Bell RN.
Licensure Skilled care. *Beds* SNF 60. *Certified*
Medicaid; Medicare.
Owner Nonprofit organization/foundation.
Admissions Requirements Medical
examination; Physician's request.
Staff Physicians 2 (pt); RNs 4 (ft), 3 (pt);
LPNs 2 (ft), 2 (pt); Nurses aides 18 (ft), 20
(pt); Physical therapists 1 (ft); Activities
coordinators 1 (ft), 1 (pt); Dietitians 1 (pt).
Facilities Dining room; Physical therapy
room; Activities room; Crafts room; Laundry
room; Barber/Beauty shop.
Activities Arts & crafts; Cards; Games;
Reading groups; Prayer groups; Movies;
Shopping trips; Social/Cultural gatherings.

KENMORE

Abbey Nursing Home*
2865 Elmwood Ave, Kenmore, NY, 14217
(716) 876-5900
Admin Frances Larson. *Medical Dir/Dir of
Nursing* Dr C T Yu.
Licensure Skilled care. *Beds* 79. *Certified*
Medicaid; Medicare.
Owner Proprietary Corp.
Admissions Requirements Minimum age 60;
Medical examination.
Staff Physicians 5 (pt); RNs 4 (ft), 8 (pt);
LPNs 5 (ft), 4 (pt); Orderlies 5 (ft), 2 (pt);
Nurses aides 21 (ft), 20 (pt); Physical
therapists 1 (pt); Recreational therapists 1
(ft); Occupational therapists 1 (pt); Speech

therapists 1 (pt); Activities coordinators 1
(ft); Dietitians 1 (ft); Dentists 1 (pt);
Podiatrists 1 (pt); Audiologists 1 (pt).
Facilities Dining room; Physical therapy
room; Activities room; Laundry room.
Activities Arts & crafts; Cards; Games;
Reading groups; Prayer groups; Movies;
Social/Cultural gatherings; Picnics.

Kenmore Mercy Skilled Nursing Facility
2950 Elmwood Ave, Kenmore, NY, 14217
(716) 879-6100
Admin Francis J Redding, Director; Shari
Borner, Assistant Director. *Medical Dir/Dir
of Nursing* Dr Joseph C Tutton; Jacqueline
M Pellien RN DON.
Licensure Skilled care. *Beds* 80. *Certified*
Medicaid; Medicare.
Owner Nonprofit Corp.
Admissions Requirements Medical
examination.
Staff Physicians 1 (ft); RNs 8 (ft), 7 (pt);
LPNs 10 (ft), 9 (pt); Orderlies 19 (ft), 29
(pt); Physical therapists 4 (pt); Occupational
therapists 1 (pt); Speech therapists 1 (pt);
Activities coordinators 1 (ft); Dietitians 1
(pt); Dentists 1 (pt); Podiatrists 1 (pt).
Affiliation Roman Catholic
Facilities Dining room; Physical therapy
room; Activities room; Chapel; Barber/
Beauty shop.
Activities Arts & crafts; Games; Prayer groups;
Movies; Social/Cultural gatherings; Baking;
Sing-alongs; Exercise class; Music therapy;
Field trips.

Schofield Residence*
3333 Elmwood, Kenmore, NY, 14217
(716) 874-1566
Admin Edward Gray.
Licensure Skilled care; Intermediate care. *Beds*
80. *Certified* Medicaid; Medicare.
Owner Nonprofit Corp.

KINGS PARK

St Johnland Nursing Home Inc*
Sunken Meadow Rd, Kings Park, NY, 11754
(516) 269-5800
Admin Joan Wood.
Licensure Skilled care. *Beds* 160. *Certified*
Medicaid; Medicare.
Owner Nonprofit Corp.

KINGSTON

Albany Avenue Nursing Home Inc
166 Albany Ave, Kingston, NY, 12401
(914) 338-1780
Admin Charlotte Shuler. *Medical Dir/Dir of
Nursing* Johannes Weltin MD; Elnora
McSpirit RN.
Licensure Skilled care. *Beds* SNF 22.
Owner Proprietary Corp.
Admissions Requirements Minimum age 21.
Staff RNs 5 (ft), 9 (pt); LPNs 3 (ft), 5 (pt);
Nurses aides 4 (ft), 8 (pt); Physical therapists
1 (pt); Activities coordinators 1 (ft).
Facilities Activities room; Laundry room.
Activities Arts & crafts; Cards; Games;
Reading groups; Prayer groups; Movies;
Music.

Hutton Nursing Home*
346-364 Washington Ave, Kingston, NY,
12401
(914) 331-6327
Admin Nancy A Maxwell. *Medical Dir/Dir of
Nursing* Chester Robbins.
Licensure Skilled care. *Beds* 80. *Certified*
Medicaid; Medicare.
Owner Proprietary Corp.
Admissions Requirements Minimum age 19.
Staff RNs 5 (ft), 6 (pt); LPNs 6 (ft), 5 (pt);
Orderlies 3 (ft), 2 (pt); Nurses aides 33 (ft),
11 (pt); Physical therapists 2 (ft); Activities
coordinators 2 (ft).

Facilities Dining room; Physical therapy
room; Activities room; Laundry room;
Barber/Beauty shop.
Activities Arts & crafts; Cards; Games; Prayer
groups; Movies; Shopping trips; Social/
Cultural gatherings.

**Ulster County Infirmary Health Related
Facility***
Golden Hill Dr, Kingston, NY, 12401
(914) 339-4540
Admin Elnora McSpirit. *Medical Dir/Dir of
Nursing* Dr Arthur Carr.
Licensure Skilled care; Intermediate care. *Beds*
280. *Certified* Medicaid; Medicare.
Owner Publicly owned.
Staff Physicians 7 (pt); RNs 28 (ft); LPNs 24
(ft); Nurses aides 106 (ft); Physical therapists
1 (pt); Occupational therapists 1 (pt);
Activities coordinators 2 (ft); Dietitians 1
(ft); Dentists 1 (pt).
Facilities Dining room; Physical therapy
room; Activities room; Chapel; Crafts room;
Laundry room; Barber/Beauty shop; Library.
Activities Arts & crafts; Cards; Games;
Reading groups; Prayer groups; Movies;
Shopping trips; Social/Cultural gatherings.

LAKE PLACID

Uihlein Mercy Center
420 Old Military Rd, Lake Placid, NY, 12946
(518) 523-2464
Admin Sr Mary Camillus. *Medical Dir/Dir of
Nursing* H Douglas Wilson MD; Eileen
McEneany RN DON.
Licensure Skilled care. *Beds* SNF 156.
Certified Medicaid; Medicare.
Owner Nonprofit Corp.
Admissions Requirements Medical
examination; Physician's request.
Staff Physicians 1 (ft), 3 (pt); RNs 8 (ft), 5
(pt); LPNs 12 (ft), 4 (pt); Orderlies 1 (ft);
Nurses aides 84 (ft), 16 (pt); Physical
therapists 1 (ft); Recreational therapists 1
(ft); Occupational therapists 1 (pt); Speech
therapists 1 (pt); Activities coordinators 1
(ft); Dietitians 1 (ft); Dentists 1 (pt);
Ophthalmologists 1 (pt) 13O 1 (pt).
Affiliation Roman Catholic
Facilities Dining room; Physical therapy
room; Activities room; Chapel; Crafts room;
Laundry room; Barber/Beauty shop; Library.
Activities Arts & crafts; Cards; Games;
Reading groups; Prayer groups; Movies;
Shopping trips; Social/Cultural gatherings.

LANCASTER

Furgala Nursing Home
1818 Como Park Blvd, Lancaster, NY, 14086
(716) 683-6165
Admin Chester J Furgala. *Medical Dir/Dir of
Nursing* Dr Albert Addesa.
Licensure Skilled care. *Beds* 89. *Certified*
Medicaid; Medicare.
Owner Proprietary Corp.
Admissions Requirements Minimum age 18;
Physician's request.
Staff RNs 14 (ft); LPNs 4 (ft); Nurses aides 76
(ft); Physical therapists 1 (pt); Reality
therapists 1 (pt); Recreational therapists 1
(ft); Occupational therapists 1 (ft); Speech
therapists 1 (pt); Activities coordinators 1
(ft); Dietitians 1 (pt); Dentists 1 (pt);
Ophthalmologists 1 (pt); Podiatrists 1 (pt).
Facilities Dining room; Physical therapy
room; Activities room; Chapel; Crafts room;
Laundry room; Barber/Beauty shop; Library.
Activities Arts & crafts; Cards; Games;
Reading groups; Prayer groups; Movies;
Shopping trips; Social/Cultural gatherings.

LATHAM

Our Lady of Hope Residence-Little Sisters of the Poor*
1 Jeanne Jugan Ln, Latham, NY, 12110
(518) 785-4551
Admin M Mary Vincent.
Licensure Skilled care; Intermediate care. *Beds* 80. *Certified* Medicaid; Medicare.
Owner Nonprofit Corp.
Affiliation Roman Catholic

LEROY

Leroy Village Green Nursing Home & Health Related Facility Inc
10 Munson St, Leroy, NY, 14482
(716) 768-2561
Admin Robert Harrington. *Medical Dir/Dir of Nursing* Nayan Kumar MD.
Licensure Skilled care; Intermediate care. *Beds* SNF 80; ICF 60. *Certified* Medicaid; Medicare.
Owner Proprietary Corp.
Admissions Requirements Minimum age 16.
Staff Physicians 1 (pt); RNs 12 (ft); LPNs 13 (ft); Nurses aides 46 (ft); Physical therapists 1 (pt); Occupational therapists 1 (pt); Speech therapists 1 (pt); Activities coordinators 1 (ft); Dietitians 1 (pt); Ophthalmologists 1 (pt); Dentist 1 (pt).
Facilities Dining room; Physical therapy room; Activities room; Laundry room; Barber/Beauty shop.
Activities Arts & crafts; Cards; Games; Reading groups; Prayer groups; Movies; Social/Cultural gatherings.

LEWISTON

Fairchild Manor Nursing Home*
765 Fairchild Pl, Lewiston, NY, 14092
(716) 754-4322
Admin Henry M Sloma. *Medical Dir/Dir of Nursing* Anthony B Schiam MD.
Licensure Skilled care. *Beds* 100. *Certified* Medicaid; Medicare.
Owner Proprietary Corp.
Staff Physicians 17 (pt); RNs 6 (ft), 5 (pt); LPNs 12 (ft), 13 (pt); Nurses aides 31 (ft), 22 (pt); Physical therapists 1 (pt); Speech therapists 1 (pt); Activities coordinators 1 (ft); Dietitians 1 (ft), 1 (pt); Dentists 1 (pt); Ophthalmologists 1 (pt); Podiatrists 1 (pt); Audiologists 1 (pt).
Facilities Dining room; Physical therapy room; Activities room; Crafts room; Barber/Beauty shop; Library.
Activities Arts & crafts; Cards; Games; Reading groups; Prayer groups; Movies; Shopping trips; Social/Cultural gatherings.

LIBERTY

Sullivan County Home & Infirmary
PO Box 231, Liberty, NY, 12754
(914) 292-8640
Admin George H Lane. *Medical Dir/Dir of Nursing* A Hauser.
Licensure Skilled care; Intermediate care. *Beds* SNF 46; ICF 30. *Certified* Medicaid; Medicare.
Owner Publicly owned.
Admissions Requirements Medical examination; Physician's request.
Staff Physicians 1 (ft), 1 (pt); Recreational therapists 2 (ft); Dietitians 1 (ft).
Facilities Dining room; Physical therapy room; Activities room; Chapel; Laundry room; Library.
Activities Arts & crafts; Cards; Games; Movies.

Walnut Mountain Nursing Home
Lake St, Liberty, NY, 12754
(914) 292-4200

Admin John J Rada. *Medical Dir/Dir of Nursing* Walter Dobushak MD.
Licensure Skilled care; Intermediate care. *Beds* SNF 104; ICF 74. *Certified* Medicaid; Medicare.
Owner Proprietary Corp.
Admissions Requirements Minimum age 16; Medical examination; Physician's request.
Staff RNs; LPNs; Orderlies; Nurses aides; Physical therapists; Occupational therapists; Speech therapists; Activities coordinators; Dietitians; Dentists; Ophthalmologists; Podiatrists.
Facilities Dining room; Physical therapy room; Activities room; Chapel; Crafts room; Barber/Beauty shop.
Activities Arts & crafts; Cards; Games; Reading groups; Movies.

LITTLE FALLS

Little Falls Hospital
140 Burwell St, Little Falls, NY, 13365
(315) 823-1000
Admin David S Armstrong Jr. *Medical Dir/Dir of Nursing* Oscar Muller MD.
Licensure Skilled care. *Beds* SNF 34. *Certified* Medicaid; Medicare.
Owner Nonprofit organization/foundation.
Admissions Requirements Minimum age 16; Physician's request.
Staff Physicians 20 (ft); RNs 3 (ft), 3 (pt); LPNs 5 (ft), 2 (pt); Nurses aides 12 (ft), 9 (pt); Physical therapists 3 (pt); Recreational therapists 1 (pt); Occupational therapists 1 (pt); Speech therapists 1 (pt); Activities coordinators 1 (pt); Dietitians 1 (pt); Dentists 1 (ft); Ophthalmologists 2 (pt).
Facilities Dining room; Physical therapy room; Activities room; Chapel; Crafts room; Laundry room; Barber/Beauty shop; Library.
Activities Arts & crafts; Cards; Games; Reading groups; Prayer groups; Movies; Shopping trips; Resident council.

Van Allen Nursing Home
755 E Monroe St, Little Falls, NY, 13365
(315) 823-0973
Admin William Van Allen. *Medical Dir/Dir of Nursing* Dr Oscar Stivala.
Licensure Skilled care. *Beds* 42. *Certified* Medicaid; Medicare.
Owner Proprietary Corp.
Admissions Requirements Physician's request.
Staff Physicians 7 (pt); RNs 6 (ft), 6 (pt); LPNs 5 (ft), 6 (pt); Activities coordinators 1 (ft).
Facilities Dining room; Physical therapy room; Activities room; Chapel; Laundry room; Barber/Beauty shop.
Activities Arts & crafts; Cards; Games; Reading groups; Prayer groups; Movies; Shopping trips; Social/Cultural gatherings.

LITTLE NECK

Little Neck Nursing Home
260-19 Nassau Blvd, Little Neck, NY, 11362
(718) 423-6400
Admin Frank Misiano. *Medical Dir/Dir of Nursing* Louis Orens MD Medical Director; Galia Kahane DNS.
Licensure Skilled care. *Beds* SNF 120. *Certified* Medicaid; Medicare.
Owner Proprietary Corp.
Admissions Requirements Medical examination.
Staff Physicians; RNs; LPNs; Orderlies; Nurses aides; Physical therapists; Recreational therapists; Occupational therapists; Speech therapists; Activities coordinators; Dietitians; Dentists; Ophthalmologists; Podiatrists.
Facilities Dining room; Physical therapy room; Activities room; Crafts room; Laundry room; Barber/Beauty shop; Library.

Activities Arts & crafts; Cards; Games; Reading groups; Prayer groups; Movies; Social/Cultural gatherings.

LIVERPOOL

Birchwood Health Care Center Inc
4800 Bear Rd, Liverpool, NY, 13088
(315) 423-5505
Admin Robert M Chur. *Medical Dir/Dir of Nursing* Marty Coburn DON; David Wrisley MD.
Licensure Skilled care. *Beds* 160.
Owner Proprietary Corp.
Admissions Requirements Minimum age 16; Medical examination; Physician's request.
Staff Physicians 1 (pt); RNs 9 (ft), 7 (pt); LPNs 20 (ft), 18 (pt); Nurses aides 54 (ft), 40 (pt); Physical therapists 3 (pt); Occupational therapists 1 (ft); Speech therapists 1 (pt); Activities coordinators 1 (ft); Dietitians 2 (ft).
Facilities Dining room; Physical therapy room; Activities room; Chapel; Crafts room; Laundry room; Barber/Beauty shop; Occupational therapy room; Speech therapy room; Large front porch.
Activities Arts & crafts; Cards; Games; Reading groups; Prayer groups; Movies; Shopping trips; Social/Cultural gatherings; Current events; Cooking; Gardening; Exercise groups; Resident council; Community outings; Ceramics; Ecuemenical worship services; Reminiscence groups.

LIVINGSTON

Adventist Nursing Home Inc
Rte 9, Box 95, Livingston, NY, 12541
(518) 851-3041
Admin Joseph H Newcomb. *Medical Dir/Dir of Nursing* Joseph Fusco MD.
Licensure Skilled care; Intermediate care. *Beds* SNF 80; ICF 40. *Certified* Medicaid; Medicare.
Owner Nonprofit Corp (Adventist Health Sys-USA).
Admissions Requirements Minimum age 18; Medical examination.
Staff RNs 21 (ft); LPNs 13 (ft); Orderlies 1 (ft); Nurses aides 80 (ft); Physical therapists 1 (ft); Recreational therapists 1 (ft); Occupational therapists 1 (pt); Speech therapists 1 (pt); Activities coordinators 1 (ft); Dietitians 1 (pt); Ophthalmologists 1 (pt); Podiatrists 1 (pt); Physical therapy aides 2 (ft), Dentist 1 (pt).
Affiliation Seventh-Day Adventist
Facilities Dining room; Physical therapy room; Activities room; Crafts room; Barber/Beauty shop.
Activities Arts & crafts; Cards; Games; Reading groups; Prayer groups; Movies; Shopping trips; Social/Cultural gatherings; Day care center 2 days per week.

LIVONIA

Conesus Lake Nursing Home*
Rte 15, Livonia, NY, 14487
(716) 346-3001
Admin Gail West.
Licensure Skilled care. *Beds* 48. *Certified* Medicaid; Medicare.
Owner Proprietary Corp.

LOCKPORT

Briody Nursing Home
909 Lincoln Ave, Lockport, NY, 14094
(716) 434-6361
Admin Joan Briody. *Medical Dir/Dir of Nursing* Berjenda Goupta MD.
Licensure Skilled care. *Beds* SNF 82. *Certified* Medicaid; Medicare.
Owner Privately owned Partnership.

Admissions Requirements Minimum age 16.
Staff Physicians 1 (pt); RNs 5 (ft), 6 (pt);
LPNs 6 (ft), 7 (pt); Nurses aides 45 (ft), 15
(pt); Occupational therapists 1 (pt); Speech
therapists 1 (pt); Activities coordinators 2
(ft); Dietitians 1 (pt); Ophthalmologists 1
(pt); Podiatrists 1 (pt).
Activities Arts & crafts; Cards; Games;
Reading groups; Prayer groups; Movies;
Shopping trips; Social/Cultural gatherings.

Mt View Health Facility*
5465 Upper Mountain Rd, Lockport, NY,
14094
(716) 439-6003
Admin Richard Majlea.
Licensure Skilled care. *Beds* 172. *Certified*
Medicaid; Medicare.
Owner Publicly owned.

Odd Fellow & Rebekah Nursing Home Inc*
104 Old Niagara Rd, Lockport, NY, 14094
(716) 434-6324
Admin Bonnie Cunningham.
Licensure Skilled care; Intermediate care. *Beds*
40. *Certified* Medicaid; Medicare.
Owner Nonprofit Corp.
Affiliation Independent Order of Odd Fellows
& Rebekahs

St Clare Manor
543 Locust St, Lockport, NY, 14094
(716) 434-4718
Admin Sr Mary Christopher. *Medical Dir/Dir
of Nursing* William C Stein MD; Marjorie
Hicks DON.
Licensure Skilled care. *Beds* SNF 28. *Certified*
Medicaid; Medicare.
Owner Nonprofit Corp (Catholic Charities).
Admissions Requirements Minimum age 16;
Medical examination; Physician's request.
Staff Physicians 4 (pt); RNs 1 (ft), 4 (pt);
LPNs 2 (ft), 3 (pt); Nurses aides 9 (ft), 10
(pt); Physical therapists 1 (pt); Activities
coordinators 1 (pt); Dietitians 1 (ft).
Languages Polish
Affiliation Roman Catholic
Facilities Dining room; Physical therapy
room; Activities room; Chapel; Laundry
room; Barber/Beauty shop.
Activities Arts & crafts; Cards; Games;
Reading groups; Prayer groups; Movies;
Shopping trips.

LONG BEACH

Long Beach Grandell Co*
645 W Broadway, Long Beach, NY, 11561
(516) 889-1100
Admin Vernon Rossner.
Licensure Skilled care; Intermediate care. *Beds*
54. *Certified* Medicaid; Medicare.
Owner Proprietary Corp.

Long Beach Memorial Nursing Home Inc
375 E Bay Dr, Long Beach, NY, 11561
(516) 432-8000
Admin Douglas L Melzer. *Medical Dir/Dir of
Nursing* Munagala J Reddy MD; Catherine
C Cox RN.
Licensure Skilled care; Intermediate care. *Beds*
SNF 150; ICF 50. *Certified* Medicaid;
Medicare.
Owner Nonprofit Corp.
Admissions Requirements Medical
examination; Physician's request.
Staff Physicians 1 (pt); RNs 18 (ft), 15 (pt);
LPNs 20 (ft), 13 (pt); Nurses aides 51 (ft),
19 (pt); Physical therapists 1 (pt);
Recreational therapists 1 (ft); Occupational
therapists 2 (ft); Speech therapists 1 (pt);
Activities coordinators 3 (ft), 1 (pt);
Dietitians 2 (ft); Dentists 1 (pt);
Ophthalmologists 1 (pt); Podiatrists 1 (pt).
Facilities Dining room; Physical therapy
room; Activities room; Crafts room; Laundry
room; Barber/Beauty shop; Occupational
therapy room.

Activities Arts & crafts; Cards; Games;
Reading groups; Prayer groups; Shopping
trips; Social/Cultural gatherings; Dinner
trips; Sports trips.

Long Island Tides Nursing Home
640 W Broadway, Long Beach, NY, 11561
(516) 431-4400
Admin Lucille Pagones. *Medical Dir/Dir of
Nursing* Dr R Tizes; L Zelaya DON.
Licensure Skilled care. *Beds* SNF 182.
Certified Medicaid; Medicare.
Owner Privately owned.
Activities Arts & crafts; Cards; Games;
Reading groups; Prayer groups; Movies.

LOWVILLE

**Lewis County General Hospital—Nurs Home
Unit**
7785 N State St, Lowville, NY, 13367
(315) 376-5200
Admin Allan Raymond. *Medical Dir/Dir of
Nursing* Howard Meny MD; Margaret
Shunk RN.
Licensure Skilled care; Health related care.
Beds SNF 98; ICF 40. *Certified* Medicaid;
Medicare.
Owner Publicly owned.
Admissions Requirements Minimum age 16;
Medical examination; Physician's request.
Staff Physicians 5 (ft); RNs 7 (ft), 2 (pt);
LPNs 17 (ft), 9 (pt); Orderlies 3 (ft); Nurses
aides 38 (ft), 16 (pt); Occupational therapists
1 (pt); Activities coordinators 1 (ft);
Dietitians 1 (ft); Ophthalmologists 1 (pt).
Facilities Dining room; Physical therapy
room; Activities room; Chapel; Crafts room;
Laundry room; Barber/Beauty shop; Library.
Activities Arts & crafts; Cards; Games;
Reading groups; Prayer groups; Movies;
Social/Cultural gatherings.

LYNBROOK

East Rockaway Nursing Home
243 Atlantic Ave, Lynbrook, NY, 11563
(516) 599-2744
Admin Robert Keon. *Medical Dir/Dir of
Nursing* Dr Florenzio Gomez.
Licensure Skilled care. *Beds* 100. *Certified*
Medicaid; Medicare.
Owner Proprietary Corp.
Admissions Requirements Minimum age 16;
Medical examination; Physician's request.
Staff Physicians 30 (pt); RNs 7 (ft), 15 (pt);
LPNs 8 (ft), 15 (pt); Orderlies 1 (ft), 2 (pt);
Nurses aides 28 (ft), 52 (pt); Physical
therapists 1 (pt); Occupational therapists 1
(pt); Speech therapists 1 (pt); Activities
coordinators 1 (ft), 3 (pt); Dietitians 1 (pt);
Dentists 1 (pt); Ophthalmologists 1 (pt);
Podiatrists 3 (pt).
Facilities Dining room; Physical therapy
room; Activities room; Crafts room; Barber/
Beauty shop; Library.
Activities Arts & crafts; Cards; Games;
Reading groups; Prayer groups; Movies;
Shopping trips.

LYONS

**Wayne County Nursing Home & Health
Related Facility**
7376 Rte 31, Lyons, NY, 14489
(315) 946-4817
Admin John F Demske. *Medical Dir/Dir of
Nursing* Dr David Blaszok; Helene Scribner
DON.
Licensure Skilled care; Intermediate care. *Beds*
SNF 99; ICF 40. *Certified* Medicaid;
Medicare.
Owner Publicly owned.
Admissions Requirements Minimum age 16.

Staff Physicians 1 (pt); RNs 4 (ft); LPNs 12
(ft), 5 (pt); Nurses aides 53 (ft), 21 (pt);
Occupational therapists 1 (pt); Speech
therapists 1 (pt); Activities coordinators 1
(ft); Dietitians 1 (ft); Ophthalmologists 1
(pt); Podiatrists 1 (pt).
Facilities Dining room; Physical therapy
room; Activities room; Crafts room; Laundry
room; Barber/Beauty shop; Library.
Activities Arts & crafts; Cards; Games;
Reading groups; Prayer groups; Movies;
Shopping trips; Social/Cultural gatherings.

MACHIAS

Cattaraugus County Home & Infirmary*
Rte 16, Machias, NY, 14101
(716) 353-8516
Admin Margaret Mary Wagner.
Licensure Skilled care; Intermediate care. *Beds*
79. *Certified* Medicaid; Medicare.
Owner Publicly owned.

MALONE

Franklin County Nursing Home*
Rte 30, Finney Blvd, Malone, NY, 12953
(518) 483-3300
Admin William O'Reilly. *Medical Dir/Dir of
Nursing* Alfred A Hartmann Sr MD.
Licensure Skilled care. *Beds* 80.
Owner Publicly owned.
Admissions Requirements Minimum age 16;
Physician's request.
Facilities Dining room; Physical therapy
room; Activities room; Crafts room; Laundry
room; Barber/Beauty shop.
Activities Arts & crafts; Cards; Games;
Reading groups; Prayer groups; Movies;
Shopping trips; Social/Cultural gatherings.

Alice Hyde Nursing Home
115 Park St, Malone, NY, 12953
(518) 483-3000
Admin Paul LaVine. *Medical Dir/Dir of
Nursing* Dr John T St Mary; Florence King
RN DON.
Licensure Skilled care. *Beds* SNF 75. *Certified*
Medicaid; Medicare.
Owner Nonprofit Corp.
Admissions Requirements Physician's request.
Staff Physicians; RNs; LPNs; Orderlies;
Nurses aides; Physical therapists; Activities
coordinators; Dietitians.
Facilities Dining room; Activities room;
Crafts room; Crafts room; Barber/Beauty
shop; Library.
Activities Arts & crafts; Cards; Games;
Reading groups; Prayer groups; Movies;
Shopping trips.

MAMARONECK

Sarah R Neuman Nursing Home
845 Palmer Ave, Mamaroneck, NY, 10543
(914) 698-6005
Admin Jean M Wetstine. *Medical Dir/Dir of
Nursing* Dr E Bevon Miele.
Licensure Skilled care; Intermediate care. *Beds*
SNF 180; ICF 90.
Owner Proprietary Corp.
Staff Physicians 4 (ft); RNs 10 (ft), 6 (pt);
LPNs 11 (ft), 3 (pt); Orderlies 5 (ft), 1 (pt);
Nurses aides 66 (ft), 14 (pt); Physical
therapists 1 (ft); Recreational therapists 2
(ft); Occupational therapists 1 (ft); Speech
therapists 1 (pt); Activities coordinators 1
(ft), 2 (pt); Dietitians 2 (ft), 1 (pt);
Ophthalmologists 1 (pt).
Facilities Dining room; Physical therapy
room; Activities room; Crafts room; Laundry
room; Barber/Beauty shop.
Activities Arts & crafts; Cards; Games;
Reading groups; Prayer groups; Movies;
Shopping trips; Social/Cultural gatherings.

MARGARETVILLE

Margaretville Memorial Hospital Nursing Home*
Rte 28, Margaretville, NY, 12455
(914) 586-2631
Admin Joseph Kehoe.
Licensure Skilled care; Intermediate care. *Beds*
31. *Certified* Medicaid; Medicare.
Owner Nonprofit Corp.

MASPETH

Midway Nursing Home*
69-95 Queens Midtown Expwy, Maspeth, NY,
11378
(718) 429-2200
Admin Sam Gottlieb.
Licensure Skilled care. *Beds* 200. *Certified*
Medicaid; Medicare.
Owner Proprietary Corp.

MASSAPEQUA

Park View Nursing Home Inc*
5353 Merrick Rd, Massapequa, NY, 11758
(516) 798-1800
Admin Owen Kaye.
Licensure Skilled care. *Beds* 164. *Certified*
Medicaid; Medicare.
Owner Proprietary Corp.

MASSENA

Highland Nursing Home Inc
PO Box 86, Rte 2 Highland Rd, Massena,
NY, 13662
(315) 769-9956
Admin Edward J Kaneb. *Medical Dir/Dir of
Nursing* Dr S Goswami.
Licensure Skilled care. *Beds* SNF 140.
Certified Medicaid; Medicare.
Owner Proprietary Corp.
Admissions Requirements Minimum age 16;
Physician's request.
Staff Physicians 20 (pt); RNs 6 (ft), 4 (pt);
LPNs 16 (ft), 4 (pt); Orderlies 2 (ft); Nurses
aides 45 (ft), 25 (pt); Physical therapists 1
(ft); Occupational therapists 1 (pt); Speech
therapists 1 (pt); Activities coordinators 1
(ft); Dietitians 1 (pt).
Facilities Dining room; Physical therapy
room; Activities room; Chapel; Crafts room;
Laundry room; Barber/Beauty shop.
Activities Arts & crafts; Cards; Games;
Reading groups; Prayer groups; Movies;
Shopping trips; Social/Cultural gatherings.

**St Regis Nursing Home & Health Related
Facility Inc**
Saint Regis Blvd, Massena, NY, 13662
(315) 769-2494
Admin John Bogosian. *Medical Dir/Dir of
Nursing* Henry Dobies MD.
Licensure Skilled care; Intermediate care. *Beds*
SNF 44; ICF 108. *Certified* Medicaid;
Medicare.
Owner Proprietary Corp.
Admissions Requirements Physician's request.
Staff RNs 13 (ft); LPNs 15 (ft); Nurses aides
53 (ft), 2 (pt); Physical therapists 1 (pt);
Recreational therapists 1 (pt); Occupational
therapists 1 (pt); Speech therapists 1 (pt);
Activities coordinators 2 (ft); Dietitians 1
(ft).
Facilities Dining room; Physical therapy
room; Activities room; Crafts room; Laundry
room; Barber/Beauty shop.
Activities Arts & crafts; Cards; Games;
Reading groups; Prayer groups; Movies;
Shopping trips; Social/Cultural gatherings.

MEDINA

**Medina Memorial Hospital—Skilled Nursing
Facility***
500 Ohio St, Medina, NY, 14103
(716) 798-2000
Admin James Morey.
Licensure Skilled care. *Beds* 30. *Certified*
Medicaid; Medicare.
Owner Nonprofit Corp.

**Orchard Manor Nursing Home & Health
Related Facility**
600 Bates Rd, Medina, NY, 14103
(716) 798-4100
Admin Thomas Morien. *Medical Dir/Dir of
Nursing* Dr Harvey J Blanchet Jr MD;
Patricia Dool RN DON.
Licensure Skilled care; Intermediate care. *Beds*
SNF 120; ICF. *Certified* Medicaid;
Medicare.
Owner Proprietary Corp.
Admissions Requirements Minimum age 16.
Staff RNs 4 (ft), 6 (pt); LPNs 9 (ft), 10 (pt);
Nurses aides 20 (ft), 33 (pt); Physical
therapists 1 (pt); Occupational therapists 1
(pt); Speech therapists 1 (pt); Activities
coordinators 2 (ft); Dietitians 1 (ft);
Ophthalmologists 1 (pt); Podiatrists 1 (pt).
Facilities Dining room; Physical therapy
room; Activities room; Chapel; Crafts room;
Laundry room; Barber/Beauty shop; Library;
TV lounges.
Activities Arts & crafts; Cards; Games;
Reading groups; Prayer groups; Movies;
Shopping trips; Social/Cultural gatherings;
Parties; Outings; Musical entertainment.

MIDDLE ISLAND

Crest Hall Health Related Facility
Oakcrest Ave & Church Lane, Middle Island,
NY, 11953
(516) 924-8830
Admin Dwight T Worthy. *Medical Dir/Dir of
Nursing* Mark Steinberg MD; Elizabeth
Frattuna.
Licensure Intermediate care. *Beds* 120.
Certified Medicaid.
Owner Proprietary Corp.
Admissions Requirements Minimum age 18;
Physician's request.
Staff Physicians 1 (ft); RNs 1 (ft); LPNs 20
(ft); Nurses aides 20 (ft), 7 (pt); Physical
therapists 1 (ft); Reality therapists 4 (pt);
Recreational therapists 1 (ft), 4 (pt);
Occupational therapists 1 (ft); Speech
therapists 1 (ft); Dietitians 1 (ft);
Ophthalmologists 1 (ft); Podiatrists 2 (ft).
Facilities Dining room; Physical therapy
room; Activities room; Crafts room; Laundry
room; Barber/Beauty shop.
Activities Arts & crafts; Cards; Games;
Reading groups; Prayer groups; Movies;
Shopping trips; Social/Cultural gatherings.

Oak Hollow Nursing Center
PO Box 488, Church Ln & Oak Crest Ave,
Middle Island, NY, 11953
(516) 924-8824
Admin Joan Portnoy. *Medical Dir/Dir of
Nursing* Dr Robert Mullaney; Constance
Nadig DON.
Licensure Skilled care. *Beds* SNF 164.
Certified Medicaid; Medicare.
Owner Privately owned.
Admissions Requirements Minimum age 18;
Medical examination.
Staff RNs 8 (ft), 9 (pt); LPNs 17 (ft), 10 (pt);
Orderlies; Nurses aides 46 (ft), 24 (pt);
Physical therapists 1 (pt); Occupational
therapists 1 (pt); Speech therapists 1 (pt);
Activities coordinators 1 (ft); Dietitians 1
(pt); Ophthalmologists 2 (pt); Podiatrists 1
(pt).

Facilities Dining room; Physical therapy
room; Activities room; Crafts room; Laundry
room; Barber/Beauty shop; Book cart.
Activities Arts & crafts; Cards; Games;
Reading groups; Prayer groups; Movies;
Shopping trips; Social/Cultural gatherings;
Special events.

MIDDLE VILLAGE

Dry Harbor Nursing Home*
61-35 Dry Harbor Rd, Middle Village, NY,
11379
(718) 446-3600
Admin Robert Friedman. *Medical Dir/Dir of
Nursing* Dr Crusco.
Licensure Skilled care; Intermediate care. *Beds*
360. *Certified* Medicaid; Medicare.
Owner Proprietary Corp.
Admissions Requirements Medical
examination.
Staff Physicians 1 (ft), 5 (pt); RNs 8 (ft);
LPNs 25 (ft); Nurses aides 76 (ft); Physical
therapists 3 (ft); Recreational therapists 1
(ft); Occupational therapists 1 (pt); Speech
therapists 1 (pt); Activities coordinators 6
(ft); Dietitians 1 (ft); Dentists 1 (pt);
Podiatrists 1 (pt); Audiologists 1 (pt).
Facilities Dining room; Physical therapy
room; Activities room; Crafts room; Laundry
room; Barber/Beauty shop; Library.
Activities Arts & crafts; Cards; Games;
Reading groups; Prayer groups; Movies;
Shopping trips; Social/Cultural gatherings.

MIDDLETOWN

Middletown Park Manor Health Facility
105 Dunning Rd, Middletown, NY, 10940
(914) 343-0801
Admin Audrey E Martin. *Medical Dir/Dir of
Nursing* Margaret McKenna DON.
Licensure Skilled care; Intermediate care. *Beds*
85 SNF; 45 HRF. *Certified* Medicaid;
Medicare.
Owner Privately owned.
Admissions Requirements Medical
examination; Physician's request.
Staff Physicians; RNs; LPNs; Orderlies;
Nurses aides; Physical therapists; Reality
therapists; Recreational therapists;
Occupational therapists; Speech therapists;
Activities coordinators; Dietitians; Dentists;
Ophthalmologists; Podiatrists.
Facilities Dining room; Physical therapy
room; Activities room; Crafts room; Laundry
room; Barber/Beauty shop.
Activities Arts & crafts; Cards; Games;
Reading groups; Prayer groups; Movies;
Shopping trips; Social/Cultural gatherings.

St Teresas Nursing Home Inc
120 Highland Ave, Middletown, NY, 10940
(914) 342-1033
Admin Sr Mary Grace. *Medical Dir/Dir of
Nursing* Samuel Mills MD; Sr Mary Ann
RN DON.
Licensure Skilled care. *Beds* SNF 92. *Certified*
Medicaid; Medicare.
Owner Nonprofit Corp (Cath Charity/Arch of
NY).
Admissions Requirements Minimum age 65;
Medical examination; Physician's request.
Staff Physicians 1 (pt); RNs 12 (ft), 2 (pt);
LPNs 4 (ft); Orderlies 1 (ft); Nurses aides 49
(ft), 4 (pt); Physical therapists 2 (pt);
Recreational therapists 1 (ft), 2 (pt);
Occupational therapists 1 (pt); Speech
therapists 1 (pt); Activities coordinators 1
(ft); Dietitians 1 (pt); Ophthalmologists 1
(pt); Podiatrists 1 (pt).
Languages Spanish
Affiliation Roman Catholic
Facilities Dining room; Physical therapy
room; Activities room; Chapel; Crafts room;
Laundry room; Barber/Beauty shop; Library.

Activities Arts & crafts; Cards; Games;
Reading groups; Prayer groups; Movies;
Shopping trips.

MILLBROOK

Dutchess County Health Care Facility*
Oak Summit Rd, Millbrook, NY, 12545
(914) 677-3925
Licensure Skilled care. *Beds* 62. *Certified*
Medicaid; Medicare.
Owner Publicly owned.
Admissions Requirements Minimum age 16;
Medical examination; Physician's request.
Facilities Dining room; Physical therapy
room; Activities room; Crafts room; Laundry
room; Barber/Beauty shop; Library.
Activities Arts & crafts; Cards; Games;
Reading groups; Prayer groups; Movies;
Shopping trips; Social/Cultural gatherings.

MINOA

Hallmark Nursing Centre Inc
217 East Ave, Minoa, NY, 13116
(315) 656-7277
Admin Raymond Klocek. *Medical Dir/Dir of
Nursing* David Saunders MD.
Licensure Skilled care. *Beds* 82. *Certified*
Medicaid; Medicare.
Owner Proprietary Corp.
Staff Physicians 5 (pt); RNs 7 (ft), 3 (pt);
LPNs 10 (ft), 4 (pt); Orderlies 1 (ft), 2 (pt);
Nurses aides 30 (ft), 19 (pt); Physical
therapists 1 (pt); Recreational therapists 1
(ft); Occupational therapists 1 (pt); Speech
therapists 1 (pt); Activities coordinators 1
(ft); Dietitians 1 (pt); Dentists 1 (pt);
Ophthalmologists 1 (pt); Podiatrists 1 (pt).
Facilities Dining room; Physical therapy
room; Activities room; Chapel; Crafts room;
Laundry room; Barber/Beauty shop; Library.
Activities Arts & crafts; Cards; Games;
Reading groups; Prayer groups; Movies;
Shopping trips; Social/Cultural gatherings.

MOHEGAN LAKE

Marrs Nursing Home
3550 Lexington Ave, Mohegan Lake, NY,
10547
(914) 528-2000
Admin Roslyn A Hurwitz. *Medical Dir/Dir of
Nursing* Dr John Vesce; Constance Daniels
RN.
Licensure Skilled care. *Beds* 120. *Certified*
Medicaid; Medicare.
Owner Privately owned.
Admissions Requirements Minimum age 16;
Medical examination.
Staff Physicians; RNs; LPNs; Orderlies;
Nurses aides; Physical therapists;
Recreational therapists; Occupational
therapists; Speech therapists; Activities
coordinators; Dietitians; Dentists;
Ophthalmologists; Podiatrists.
Languages Italian, Spanish
Facilities Dining room; Physical therapy
room; Activities room; Crafts room; Laundry
room; Barber/Beauty shop.
Activities Arts & crafts; Games; Reading
groups; Prayer groups; Movies; Social/
Cultural gatherings; Music therapy.

MONSEY

**Northern Metropolitan Residential Health Care
Facility Inc**
125 Maple Ave, Monsey, NY, 10952
(914) 352-9000
Admin Donna Mack. *Medical Dir/Dir of
Nursing* Stanley Greenbaum MD: Federica
Guerrero RN DON.
Licensure Skilled care. *Beds* SNF 120.
Certified Medicaid; Medicare.
Owner Nonprofit Corp.

Admissions Requirements Minimum age 16;
Medical examination.
Staff Physicians 9 (pt); RNs 10 (ft), 9 (pt);
LPNs 8 (ft), 2 (pt); Nurses aides 45 (ft), 10
(pt); Physical therapists 1 (pt); Recreational
therapists 2 (ft); Occupational therapists 1
(pt); Speech therapists 1 (pt); Activities
coordinators 1 (ft); Dietitians 1 (ft).
Languages Yiddish, Hebrew
Facilities Dining room; Physical therapy
room; Activities room; Chapel; Crafts room;
Laundry room; Barber/Beauty shop; Library.
Activities Arts & crafts; Cards; Games;
Reading groups; Prayer groups; Movies;
Social/Cultural gatherings.

MONTGOMERY

Montgomery Nursing Home*
Albany Post Rd, PO Box 158, Montgomery,
NY, 12549
(914) 457-3155
Admin Matthew Marciano. *Medical Dir/Dir of
Nursing* Dr Sung J Sohn.
Licensure Skilled care. *Beds* 100. *Certified*
Medicaid; Medicare.
Owner Proprietary Corp.
Admissions Requirements Medical
examination.
Staff RNs 3 (ft), 8 (pt); LPNs 5 (ft), 10 (pt);
Orderlies 1 (ft); Nurses aides 33 (ft), 17 (pt);
Physical therapists 1 (pt); Recreational
therapists 1 (pt); Occupational therapists 1
(pt); Speech therapists 1 (pt); Activities
coordinators 1 (ft); Dietitians 1 (ft); Dentists
1 (pt); Ophthalmologists 1 (pt); Podiatrists 1
(pt); Audiologists 1 (pt).
Facilities Dining room; Physical therapy
room; Activities room; Chapel; Crafts room;
Laundry room; Barber/Beauty shop.
Activities Arts & crafts; Cards; Games;
Reading groups; Prayer groups; Movies;
Shopping trips; Social/Cultural gatherings.

MONTOUR FALLS

Schuyler Hospital Long-Term Care
Montour-Townsend Rd, Montour Falls, NY,
14865
(607) 535-7121
Admin Frank S Alo. *Medical Dir/Dir of
Nursing* William F Tague MD; Roseleah
Lodge RN DON.
Licensure Skilled care. *Beds* SNF 40. *Certified*
Medicaid; Medicare.
Owner Nonprofit organization/foundation.
Admissions Requirements Minimum age 16;
Medical examination; Physician's request.
Staff Physicians 9 (pt); RNs 2 (ft), 2 (pt);
LPNs 2 (ft), 3 (pt); Nurses aides 7 (ft), 20
(pt); Physical therapists 1 (pt); Occupational
therapists 1 (pt); Speech therapists 1 (pt);
Activities coordinators 1 (pt); Dietitians 1
(pt); Dentists 1 (pt); Ophthalmologists 1 (pt);
Podiatrists 1 (pt); Activities aide 1 (pt);
COTA 1 (pt); PT aide 1 (pt); Rehab aide 1
(pt).
Facilities Dining room; Physical therapy
room; Activities room; Crafts room; Laundry
room; Barber/Beauty shop.
Activities Arts & crafts; Cards; Games;
Reading groups; Prayer groups; Movies;
Shopping trips.

MORAVIA

Howd Nursing Home
7 Keeler Ave, Moravia, NY, 13118
(315) 497-0440
Admin Jack Pease. *Medical Dir/Dir of Nursing*
Laura McLaughlin.
Licensure Skilled care. *Beds* 40. *Certified*
Medicaid; Medicare.
Owner Privately owned.
Admissions Requirements Minimum age 16;
Medical examination; Physician's request.

Staff Physicians 3 (pt); RNs 3 (pt); LPNs 10
(pt); Nurses aides 25 (pt); Physical
therapists; Occupational therapists; Activities
coordinators; Dietitians; Ophthalmologists.
Facilities Dining room; Physical therapy
room; Activities room; Chapel; Crafts room;
Laundry room; Barber/Beauty shop.
Activities Arts & crafts; Cards; Games;
Reading groups; Prayer groups; Movies;
Shopping trips; Social/Cultural gatherings.

MOUNT KISCO

Swiss Home Health Related Facility
53 Mountain Ave, Mount Kisco, NY, 10549
(914) 666-4587
Medical Dir/Dir of Nursing J L Stewart.
Licensure Intermediate care. *Beds* ICF 28.
Certified Medicaid.
Owner Nonprofit organization/foundation.
Admissions Requirements Medical
examination.
Staff RNs 1 (ft), 2 (pt); LPNs 3 (ft), 3 (pt);
Nurses aides 3 (ft), 2 (pt); Recreational
therapists 1 (pt); Activities coordinators 1
(pt); Dietitians 1 (pt).
Facilities Dining room; Activities room;
Laundry room; Barber/Beauty shop; Library.
Activities Arts & crafts; Cards; Games; Prayer
groups; Movies; Shopping trips; Social/
Cultural gatherings.

MOUNT MORRIS

Livingston County HRF & Campus SNF
Livingston County Campus Bldg 1, Mount
Morris, NY, 14510
(716) 658-2881
Admin James B West.
Licensure Skilled care; Intermediate care; Day
care for adults. *Beds* SNF 42; ICF 142; Day
care for adults 40. *Certified* Medicaid;
Medicare.
Owner Publicly owned.
Admissions Requirements Minimum age 18.
Staff Physicians 2 (pt); Physical therapists 2
(pt); Recreational therapists 2 (ft);
Occupational therapists 1 (pt); Speech
therapists 1 (pt); Activities coordinators 1
(ft); Dietitians 2 (pt); Dentists 1 (pt);
Ophthalmologists 1 (pt); Podiatrists 1 (pt).
Facilities Dining room; Physical therapy
room; Activities room; Chapel; Crafts room;
Laundry room; Barber/Beauty shop; Library;
Theater; Auditorium.
Activities Arts & crafts; Cards; Games;
Reading groups; Prayer groups; Movies;
Shopping trips; Social/Cultural gatherings.

MOUNT VERNON

Shalom Nursing Home*
10 Claremont Ave, Mount Vernon, NY, 10550
(914) 699-1600
Admin Howard Wolf.
Licensure Skilled care. *Beds* 240. *Certified*
Medicaid; Medicare.
Owner Nonprofit Corp.

**The Wartburg Home of the Evangelical
Lutheran Church**
Bradley Ave, Mount Vernon, NY, 10552
(914) 699-0800
Admin Reverend Donald A Kraft. *Medical
Dir/Dir of Nursing* Dr Debabrata Dutta.
Licensure Skilled care; Intermediate care. *Beds*
SNF 80; ICF 48. *Certified* Medicaid;
Medicare.
Owner Nonprofit organization/foundation.
Admissions Requirements Minimum age 65.
Staff Physicians; RNs; LPNs; Orderlies;
Nurses aides; Physical therapists;
Recreational therapists; Occupational
therapists; Speech therapists; Activities
coordinators; Dietitians; Dentists;
Ophthalmologists; Podiatrists; Dentist.

Affiliation Lutheran
Facilities Dining room; Physical therapy room; Activities room; Chapel; Laundry room; Barber/Beauty shop.
Activities Arts & crafts; Cards; Games; Prayer groups; Movies; Shopping trips.

NANUET

Elmwood Manor Nursing Home Inc*
199 N Middletown Rd, Nanuet, NY, 10954
(914) 623-3904
Admin Daniel Harfenist.
Licensure Skilled care. *Beds* 228. *Certified* Medicaid; Medicare.
Owner Proprietary Corp.

NEW BERLIN

Chase Memorial Nursing Home Co Inc*
1 Terrace Heights, New Berlin, NY, 13411
(607) 847-6117
Admin Merritt C Meyers.
Licensure Skilled care; Intermediate care. *Beds* 41. *Certified* Medicaid; Medicare.
Owner Nonprofit Corp.

NEW CITY

Friedwald House
475 New Hempstead Rd, New City, NY, 10956
(914) 354-7000
Admin Stephen J Epstein. *Medical Dir/Dir of Nursing* Vincent Garofalo MD; Janet Allen RN DON.
Licensure Intermediate care. *Beds* ICF 180. *Certified* Medicaid.
Owner Privately owned.
Admissions Requirements Minimum age 16; Medical examination; Physician's request.
Staff Physicians 1 (ft), 9 (pt); RNs 10 (ft); LPNs 6 (ft); Orderlies 1 (ft); Nurses aides 20 (ft), 5 (pt); Physical therapists 1 (ft); Recreational therapists 2 (ft); Occupational therapists 1 (pt); Speech therapists 1 (pt); Activities coordinators 1 (ft); Dietitians 1 (ft); Dentists 1 (pt); Ophthalmologists 1 (pt); Podiatrists 1 (pt).
Languages Yiddish, Hebrew, Italian
Facilities Dining room; Physical therapy room; Activities room; Chapel; Crafts room; Laundry room; Barber/Beauty shop; Library.
Activities Arts & crafts; Cards; Games; Reading groups; Prayer groups; Movies; Shopping trips; Social/Cultural gatherings.

NEW HARTFORD

Presbyterian Home for Central New York Inc
PO Box 1144, Middle Settlement Rd, New Hartford, NY, 13413-1144
(315) 797-7500
Admin Raymond L Garrett. *Medical Dir/Dir of Nursing* William F Krause MD.
Licensure Skilled care; Intermediate care. *Beds* SNF 162; ICF 80. *Certified* Medicaid; Medicare.
Owner Nonprofit Corp.
Admissions Requirements Minimum age 16; Medical examination.
Staff RNs 15 (ft), 3 (pt); LPNs 22 (ft), 2 (pt); Orderlies 5 (ft); Nurses aides 85 (ft), 34 (pt); Physical therapists 1 (pt); Recreational therapists 1 (ft); Occupational therapists 1 (pt); Speech therapists 1 (pt); Activities coordinators 1 (ft); Dietitians 1 (ft).
Affiliation Presbyterian
Facilities Dining room; Physical therapy room; Activities room; Chapel; Crafts room; Laundry room; Barber/Beauty shop; Library.
Activities Arts & crafts; Cards; Games; Reading groups; Prayer groups; Movies; Shopping trips; Social/Cultural gatherings; Walk groups; Grooming groups.

Charles T Sitrin Nursing Home Company Inc
PO Box 1000, Tilden Ave, New Hartford, NY, 13413
(315) 797-3114
Admin Richard A Wilson. *Medical Dir/Dir of Nursing* Irving Cramer MD; Patricia A Barr DON.
Licensure Skilled care; Intermediate care; Day care. *Beds* SNF 71; ICF 40; Day care 20. *Certified* Medicaid; Medicare.
Owner Nonprofit Corp.
Admissions Requirements Minimum age 16; Medical examination.
Staff Physicians 2 (pt); RNs 9 (ft), 6 (pt); LPNs 9 (ft), 7 (pt); Orderlies 2 (ft); Nurses aides 32 (ft), 27 (pt); Physical therapists 1 (pt); Recreational therapists 1 (ft), 1 (pt); Occupational therapists 1 (pt); Speech therapists 1 (pt); Dietitians 2 (ft); Ophthalmologists 1 (pt).
Affiliation Jewish
Facilities Dining room; Physical therapy room; Activities room; Chapel; Crafts room; Laundry room; Barber/Beauty shop; Library.
Activities Arts & crafts; Cards; Games; Reading groups; Prayer groups; Movies; Shopping trips; Social/Cultural gatherings.

NEW HYDE PARK

Jewish Institute for Geriatric Care Nursing Home Co Inc
271-11 76th Ave, New Hyde Park, NY, 11042
(718) 343-2100; 437-0090
Admin David Glaser, Exec VP. *Medical Dir/Dir of Nursing* Conn Foley MD; Ethel Mitty PhD DON.
Licensure Skilled care. *Beds* SNF 527. *Certified* Medicaid; Medicare.
Owner Nonprofit Corp.
Admissions Requirements Minimum age 65; Medical examination.
Staff Physicians 13 (ft), 6 (pt); RNs 74 (ft), 22 (pt); LPNs 40 (ft), 6 (pt); Orderlies 25 (ft), 9 (pt); Nurses aides 202 (ft), 78 (pt); Physical therapists 12 (ft), 2 (pt); Recreational therapists 7 (ft), 3 (pt); Occupational therapists 5 (ft); Speech therapists 1 (ft); Activities coordinators 1 (ft); Dietitians 8 (ft), 1 (pt); Podiatrists 1 (ft); 651 (ft).
Languages Yiddish, Hebrew, Spanish, Italian
Affiliation Jewish
Facilities Dining room; Physical therapy room; Activities room; Chapel; Crafts room; Laundry room; Barber/Beauty shop; Library; Two patios.
Activities Arts & crafts; Cards; Games; Reading groups; Prayer groups; Movies; Shopping trips; Social/Cultural gatherings.

NEW PALTZ

New Paltz Nursing Home*
1 Jansen Rd, New Paltz, NY, 12561
(914) 255-0830
Admin Norton Blue.
Licensure Skilled care. *Beds* 79. *Certified* Medicaid; Medicare.
Owner Proprietary Corp.

NEW ROCHELLE

Bayberry Nursing Home
40 Keogh Ln, New Rochelle, NY, 10805
(914) 636-3947
Admin Leonard Russ. *Medical Dir/Dir of Nursing* A V Clement; Carole Coviello RN.
Licensure Skilled care. *Beds* 60. *Certified* Medicaid; Medicare.
Owner Privately owned.
Staff Physicians 15 (pt); RNs 6 (ft), 10 (pt); LPNs 2 (ft), 6 (pt); Orderlies 1 (ft); Nurses aides 19 (ft), 8 (pt); Physical therapists 1 (pt); Reality therapists 1 (pt); Recreational therapists 2 (pt); Occupational therapists 1

(pt); Activities coordinators 1 (ft); Dietitians 1 (pt); Dentists 1 (pt); Ophthalmologists 1 (pt); Podiatrists 1 (pt).
Languages Italian, German, French, Spanish
Facilities Dining room; Physical therapy room; Activities room; Chapel; Crafts room; Laundry room; Barber/Beauty shop; Library.
Activities Arts & crafts; Cards; Games; Reading groups; Prayer groups; Movies; Shopping trips; Social/Cultural gatherings; Exercise sessions.

German Masonic Home Corp*
676 Pelham Rd, New Rochelle, NY, 10805
(914) 632-9600
Admin Pearl Sherman.
Licensure Skilled care. *Beds* 120. *Certified* Medicaid; Medicare.
Owner Nonprofit Corp.
Affiliation Masons

Howe Avenue Nursing Home Inc
16 Guion Pl, New Rochelle, NY, 10802
(914) 632-5000
Admin Carol Ann Zeidler. *Medical Dir/Dir of Nursing* Richard P Barone MD; Audrey Berkeley RN.
Licensure Skilled care. *Beds* 150. *Certified* Medicaid; Medicare.
Owner Nonprofit Corp.
Admissions Requirements Minimum age 16.
Staff Physicians 2 (pt); RNs 25 (ft); LPNs 15 (ft); Orderlies 3 (ft); Nurses aides 60 (ft); Physical therapists 5 (ft); Recreational therapists 4 (ft); Occupational therapists 2 (ft); Speech therapists 1 (ft); Dietitians 1 (ft); Podiatrists 1 (ft).
Languages Spanish, French, German
Facilities Dining room; Physical therapy room; Activities room; Crafts room; Laundry room; Library; Beauty shop.
Activities Arts & crafts; Cards; Games; Reading groups; Prayer groups; Movies; Social/Cultural gatherings; Ceramics; Baking.

New Rochelle Nursing Home & Adult Day Care Program
31 Lockwood Ave, New Rochelle, NY, 10801
(914) 576-0600
Admin Gilbert Preira. *Medical Dir/Dir of Nursing* Dr J Kaltchthaler; M Vlymen RN.
Licensure Skilled care; Adult day care; Long-term care. *Beds* SNF 160; Adult day care 50; Long-term care 75. *Certified* Medicaid; Medicare.
Owner Privately owned.
Admissions Requirements Minimum age 45; Medical examination; Physician's request.
Staff Physicians 1 (pt); RNs 12 (ft), 10 (pt); LPNs 12 (ft), 12 (pt); Orderlies 3 (ft), 5 (pt); Nurses aides 40 (ft), 40 (pt); Physical therapists 1 (ft); Recreational therapists 3 (ft), 2 (pt); Occupational therapists 1 (pt); Speech therapists 1 (pt); Activities coordinators 1 (ft); Dietitians 1 (ft).
Languages Spanish, French, Italian
Facilities Dining room; Physical therapy room; Activities room; Crafts room; Laundry room; Barber/Beauty shop.
Activities Arts & crafts; Cards; Games; Reading groups; Prayer groups; Movies; Shopping trips; Social/Cultural gatherings.

United Home for Aged Hebrews
60 Willow Dr, New Rochelle, NY, 10538
(914) 632-2804
Admin Saunders T Preiss. *Medical Dir/Dir of Nursing* Frank A Napolitano MD.
Licensure Skilled care; Intermediate care. *Beds* SNF 46; ICF 104. *Certified* Medicaid; Medicare.
Owner Nonprofit organization/foundation.
Admissions Requirements Medical examination.
Affiliation Jewish
Facilities Dining room; Physical therapy room; Activities room; Chapel; Crafts room; Laundry room; Library.

Activities Arts & crafts; Cards; Games;
Reading groups; Prayer groups; Movies;
Social/Cultural gatherings.

United Nursing Home for the Aged Inc
391 Pelham Rd, New Rochelle, NY, 10805
(914) 632-2804
Admin Saunders T Preiss. Medical Dir/Dir of
Nursing Frank A Napolitain MD.
Licensure Skilled care. Beds SNF 120.
Certified Medicaid; Medicare.
Owner Nonprofit organization/foundation.
Admissions Requirements Medical
examination.
Affiliation Jewish
Facilities Dining room; Physical therapy
room; Activities room; Chapel; Crafts room;
Laundry room; Barber/Beauty shop; Library.
Activities Arts & crafts; Cards; Games;
Reading groups; Prayer groups; Movies;
Social/Cultural gatherings.

Woodland Nursing Home
490 Pelham Rd, New Rochelle, NY, 10805
(914) 636-2800
Admin Irene Ross. Medical Dir/Dir of Nursing
Alan Jaffe; Bernadette Costagliola.
Licensure Skilled care. Beds 182. Certified
Medicaid; Medicare.
Owner Proprietary Corp.
Admissions Requirements Medical
examination; Physician's request.
Staff Physicians 21 (pt); RNs 14 (ft); LPNs 29
(ft); Orderlies 4 (ft); Nurses aides 93 (ft);
Physical therapists 2 (pt); Occupational
therapists 1 (pt); Speech therapists 1 (pt);
Activities coordinators 1 (ft); Dietitians 1
(ft); Dentists 1 (pt); Ophthalmologists 1 (pt);
Podiatrists 1 (pt).
Languages Italian, Spanish
Facilities Dining room; Physical therapy
room; Activities room; Laundry room;
Barber/Beauty shop; Library.
Activities Arts & crafts; Cards; Games;
Reading groups; Prayer groups; Movies;
Social/Cultural gatherings.

NEW YORK

American Nursing Home*
62 Ave B, New York, NY, 10009
(212) 677-4161
Admin Moses Unger. Medical Dir/Dir of
Nursing Joseph J Kelter.
Licensure Skilled care. Beds 240. Certified
Medicaid; Medicare.
Owner Proprietary Corp.

Amsterdam House Nursing Home*
1060 Amsterdam Ave, New York, NY, 10025
(212) 678-2600
Admin Robert C Bryan.
Licensure Skilled care; Intermediate care. Beds
54. Certified Medicaid; Medicare.
Owner Nonprofit Corp.

Bialystoker Home for the Aged*
228 E Broadway, New York, NY, 10002
(212) 475-7755
Medical Dir/Dir of Nursing Dr Albert Khaski.
Licensure Skilled care; Intermediate care. Beds
95. Certified Medicaid; Medicare.
Owner Nonprofit Corp.
Admissions Requirements Minimum age 65;
Medical examination.
Affiliation Jewish
Facilities Dining room; Physical therapy
room; Activities room; Chapel; Crafts room;
Laundry room; Barber/Beauty shop; Library.
Activities Arts & crafts; Prayer groups;
Movies.

**Coler Memorial Hospital—Skilled Nursing
Facility**
Roosevelt Island, New York, NY, 10044
(212) 688-9400

Licensure Skilled care. Beds 976. Certified
Medicaid; Medicare.
Owner Publicly owned.

Dewitt Nursing Home*
211 E 79th St, New York, NY, 10021
(212) 879-1600
Admin Marilyn Lichtman.
Licensure Skilled care. Beds 499. Certified
Medicaid; Medicare.
Owner Proprietary Corp.

Florence Nightingale Nursing Home
1760 Third Ave, New York, NY, 10029
(212) 410-8700
Admin Georgine McCabe. Medical Dir/Dir of
Nursing Dr Mitchel Kaplan MD; Dr
Mitchell Wolfson MD; Barbara Russo DON.
Licensure Skilled care. Beds 561. Certified
Medicaid; Medicare.
Owner Privately owned.
Staff Physicians; RNs; LPNs; Orderlies;
Nurses aides; Physical therapists;
Recreational therapists; Occupational
therapists; Speech therapists; Activities
coordinators; Dietitians; Dentists;
Ophthalmologists; Podiatrists.
Languages Spanish, Yiddish, German,
Russian, Hebrew, Italian
Facilities Dining room; Physical therapy
room; Activities room; Crafts room; Laundry
room; Barber/Beauty shop; Library.
Activities Arts & crafts; Cards; Games;
Reading groups; Prayer groups; Movies;
Social/Cultural gatherings; Outside trips to
museums, ball games, zoos.

Fort Tryon Nursing Home*
801 W 190th St, New York, NY, 10040
(212) 923-2530
Admin Israel Sherman. Medical Dir/Dir of
Nursing Dr Ben W Aberman.
Licensure Skilled care. Beds 205. Certified
Medicaid; Medicare.
Owner Proprietary Corp.
Staff RNs 15 (ft), 8 (pt); LPNs 6 (ft), 16 (pt);
Orderlies 4 (ft), 4 (pt); Nurses aides 52 (ft),
27 (pt); Physical therapists 3 (pt);
Occupational therapists 1 (pt); Speech
therapists 1 (pt); Activities coordinators 1
(ft); Dietitians 1 (ft); Dentists 1 (pt);
Ophthalmologists 1 (pt); Podiatrists 1 (pt);
Audiologists 1 (pt).
Affiliation Jewish
Facilities Dining room; Physical therapy
room; Activities room; Chapel; Crafts room;
Barber/Beauty shop.
Activities Arts & crafts; Cards; Games;
Movies; Social/Cultural gatherings; Birthday
parties; Masquerades.

**Goldwater Memorial Hospital—Extended Care
Facility**
Franklin D. Roosevelt Island, New York, NY,
10044
(212) 750-6800
Admin I Bernard Hirsch. Medical Dir/Dir of
Nursing Mathew H M Lee MD; Howard
Garrison RN.
Licensure Skilled care. Beds SNF 412.
Certified Medicaid; Medicare.
Owner Publicly owned.
Admissions Requirements Minimum age 18;
Medical examination.
Staff Physicians 5 (ft), 4 (pt); RNs 65 (ft);
LPNs 50 (ft); Nurses aides 169 (ft); Physical
therapists 23 (ft); Reality therapists 5 (ft);
Recreational therapists 13 (ft), 2 (pt);
Occupational therapists 17 (ft); Speech
therapists 7 (ft); Dietitians 3 (ft); Dentists 2
(pt); Ophthalmologists 2 (pt); Podiatrists 3
(ft).
Facilities Dining room; Physical therapy
room; Activities room; Chapel; Crafts room;
Laundry room; Barber/Beauty shop; Library;
Occupational therapy room; Speech therapy
room; Audiology center; Language bank.

Activities Arts & crafts; Cards; Games;
Reading groups; Prayer groups; Movies;
Shopping trips; Social/Cultural gatherings;
Creative writing; Music groups.

Greater Harlem Nursing Home Co Inc
30 W 138th St, New York, NY, 10037
(212) 690-7400
Admin Marshall Seiden. Medical Dir/Dir of
Nursing Serge Moise MD; Louise Bedford
RN DON.
Licensure Skilled care. Beds SNF 200.
Certified Medicaid; Medicare.
Owner Nonprofit Corp.
Admissions Requirements Minimum age 17;
Medical examination.
Staff Physicians 2 (ft), 10 (pt); RNs 14 (ft);
LPNs 25 (ft); Nurses aides 83 (ft); Physical
therapists 1 (ft), 1 (pt); Recreational
therapists 2 (ft), 2 (pt); Occupational
therapists 1 (ft), 1 (pt); Speech therapists 1
(pt); Activities coordinators 1 (ft); Dietitians
2 (ft), 1 (pt); Dentists 1 (pt);
Ophthalmologists 1 (pt).
Facilities Dining room; Physical therapy
room; Activities room; Barber/Beauty shop.
Activities Arts & crafts; Cards; Games;
Reading groups; Prayer groups; Shopping
trips; Social/Cultural gatherings; Sports
events; Trips; Music.

The Hebrew Home for the Aged at Riverdale
5901 Palisade Ave, New York, NY, 10471
(212) 549-8700
Admin Jacob Reingold. Medical Dir/Dir of
Nursing Harrison G Bloom MD; Jeanette
Seggebruch DON.
Licensure Skilled care; Intermediate care. Beds
SNF 486; ICF 298. Certified Medicaid;
Medicare.
Owner Nonprofit Corp.
Admissions Requirements Medical
examination.
Staff Physicians 8 (ft), 2 (pt); RNs 60 (ft), 10
(pt); LPNs 36 (ft), 8 (pt); Orderlies 7 (ft);
Nurses aides 217 (ft); Physical therapists 2
(ft), 2 (pt); Occupational therapists 2 (ft), 1
(pt); Speech therapists 1 (ft); Activities
coordinators 7 (ft), 14 (pt); Dietitians 5 (ft);
Dentists 3 (pt); Ophthalmologists 4 (pt);
Podiatrists 4 (pt).
Languages Yiddish, Hebrew
Affiliation Jewish
Facilities Dining room; Physical therapy
room; Activities room; Chapel; Crafts room;
Laundry room; Barber/Beauty shop;
Occupational therapy room; Laboratory;
Pharmacy; Radiology; Audiology suite.
Activities Arts & crafts; Cards; Games;
Reading groups; Prayer groups; Movies;
Shopping trips; Social/Cultural gatherings.

Home of the Sages of Isreal Inc
25 Bialystoker Place, New York, NY, 10002
(212) 673-8500
Admin Hersh Fluss. Medical Dir/Dir of
Nursing Dr Albert Khaski.
Licensure Skilled care. Beds 58. Certified
Medicaid; Medicare.
Owner Nonprofit organization/foundation.
Admissions Requirements Minimum age 62;
Medical examination.
Staff Physicians 3 (pt); RNs 8 (ft), 4 (pt);
LPNs 4 (ft), 2 (pt); Orderlies 8 (ft), 1 (pt);
Nurses aides 16 (ft), 4 (pt); Physical
therapists 1 (pt); Recreational therapists 2
(ft); Occupational therapists 1 (ft), 1 (pt);
Speech therapists 1 (pt); Dietitians 1 (ft), 1
(pt); Dentists 1 (pt); Ophthalmologists 1 (pt);
Podiatrists 1 (pt).
Facilities Dining room; Physical therapy
room; Activities room; Chapel; Crafts room;
Laundry room; Library.
Activities Arts & crafts; Cards; Games;
Reading groups; Prayer groups; Movies;
Social/Cultural gatherings.

Isabella Home Nursing Home Company Inc*
515 Audubon Ave, New York, NY, 10040
(212) 781-9800
Admin Thomas F Coughlin.
Licensure Intermediate care. *Beds* 315.
Certified Medicaid.
Owner Nonprofit Corp.

Jewish Home & Hospital for the Aged
120 W 106th St, New York, NY, 10025
(212) 870-5000
Admin Kenneth Sherman. *Medical Dir/Dir of Nursing* Richard Neufeld MD; Sheldon Ornstein RN DON.
Licensure Skilled care; Intermediate care. *Beds* SNF 476; ICF 38. *Certified* Medicaid; Medicare.
Owner Nonprofit organization/foundation.
Admissions Requirements Minimum age 60; Medical examination.
Staff Physicians 7 (ft), 50 (pt); RNs 76 (ft); LPNs 29 (ft); Nurses aides 227 (ft); Physical therapists 3 (ft), 4 (pt); Recreational therapists 8 (ft); Occupational therapists 3 (ft); Activities coordinators 1 (ft); Dietitians 5 (ft); Ophthalmologists 3 (ft); Podiatrists 1 (pt); Dentist 2 (ft) Nursing supervisors 11 (ft) Occupational therapy assistants 2 (ft) Speech pathologist 1 (pt).
Languages Spanish, Yiddish, Hebrew, Russian, German, Polish
Affiliation Jewish
Facilities Physical therapy room; Chapel; Crafts room; Barber/Beauty shop; Library; Garden; Occupational therapy room; Medical clinics.
Activities Arts & crafts; Cards; Games; Reading groups; Prayer groups; Movies; Shopping trips; Social/Cultural gatherings; College courses; Resident council; Drama group; Inter-generational programs.

Kateri Residence
150 Riverside Dr, New York, NY, 10024
(212) 769-0744
Admin James D Cameron. *Medical Dir/Dir of Nursing* Anthony Lechich MD; Margaret Taylor RN.
Licensure Skilled care. *Beds* SNF 520.
Certified Medicaid; Medicare.
Owner Nonprofit Corp (Cath Charity/Arch of NY).
Admissions Requirements Minimum age 65; Medical examination; Physician's request.
Staff Physicians 9 (pt); RNs 41 (ft); LPNs 85 (ft); Orderlies 15 (ft); Nurses aides 232 (ft); Physical therapists 2 (ft); Recreational therapists 6 (ft); Occupational therapists 1 (ft); Speech therapists 1 (ft); Activities coordinators 1 (ft); Dietitians 70 (ft); Dentists 1 (pt); Ophthalmologists 1 (pt); Podiatrists 1 (pt); Social workers 5 (ft), 2 (pt).
Languages Spanish, Yiddish, Hebrew
Affiliation Roman Catholic
Facilities Dining room; Physical therapy room; Activities room; Chapel; Crafts room; Laundry room; Barber/Beauty shop; Library.
Activities Arts & crafts; Cards; Games; Reading groups; Prayer groups; Movies; Shopping trips; Social/Cultural gatherings.

Kingsbridge Heights Nursing Home
3426 Cannon Pl, New York, NY, 10463
(217) 796-8100
Admin Rose Boritzer. *Medical Dir/Dir of Nursing* Leonard Essman MD; Charmaine Taylor.
Licensure Skilled care; HRF; LTHHCP. *Beds* 600. *Certified* Medicaid; Medicare.
Owner Privately owned.
Admissions Requirements Minimum age 18.
Staff Physicians 6 (pt); RNs 15 (ft); LPNs 50 (ft); Orderlies 20 (ft); Nurses aides 180 (ft); Physical therapists 4 (ft); Recreational therapists 8 (ft); Occupational therapists 3

(pt); Speech therapists 2 (pt); Activities coordinators 2 (ft); Dietitians 5 (ft); Ophthalmologists 3 (pt); Podiatrists 2 (pt).
Languages Hebrew, Spanish, Italian
Facilities Dining room; Physical therapy room; Activities room; Chapel; Crafts room; Laundry room; Barber/Beauty shop; Library.
Activities Arts & crafts; Games; Reading groups; Prayer groups; Movies; Shopping trips; Social/Cultural gatherings.

Lily Pond Nursing Home
150 Lily Pond Ave, New York, NY, 10305
(718) 981-5300
Admin Miriam Rozenberg. *Medical Dir/Dir of Nursing* D Hepkins RN DON.
Licensure Skilled care. *Beds* SNF 35. *Certified* Medicaid; Medicare.
Owner Privately owned.
Admissions Requirements Minimum age 62; Medical examination; Physician's request.
Staff Physicians 2 (pt); RNs 1 (ft), 3 (pt); LPNs 3 (ft), 2 (pt); Orderlies 2 (ft), 1 (pt); Nurses aides 10 (ft), 3 (pt); Physical therapists 1 (pt); Recreational therapists 1 (ft), 3 (pt); Occupational therapists 1 (pt); Speech therapists 1 (pt); Activities coordinators 1 (ft), 3 (pt); Dietitians 1 (pt); Dentists 1 (pt); Ophthalmologists 1 (pt); Podiatrists 1 (pt); Pharmacist 1 (pt).
Languages Italian, Spanish
Facilities Dining room; Physical therapy room; Activities room; Crafts room; Laundry room; Barber/Beauty shop.
Activities Arts & crafts; Cards; Games; Prayer groups; Movies; Social/Cultural gatherings; Outings to the circus; Plays.

Neponsit Health Care Center
149-25 Rockway Beach Blvd, New York, NY, 11694
(718) 474-1900
Admin Moshe Bain. *Medical Dir/Dir of Nursing* Estella Gonzales MD; Christine McGrath RN.
Licensure Intermediate care. *Beds* 231. *Certified* Medicaid; Medicare.
Owner Publicly owned.
Admissions Requirements Minimum age 17; Medical examination; Physician's request.
Staff Physicians 1 (ft), 4 (pt); RNs 12 (ft); LPNs 18 (ft); Nurses aides 58 (ft); Physical therapists 1 (pt); Recreational therapists 2 (ft); Occupational therapists 1 (pt); Activities coordinators 1 (ft); Dietitians 3 (ft); Dentists 2 (pt); Ophthalmologists 2 (pt); Social workers 4 (ft), 1 (pt); Psychologist 1 (pt).
Facilities Dining room; Physical therapy room; Activities room; Chapel; Crafts room; Laundry room; Barber/Beauty shop; Library; Game room; Social hall; Theater; Boutique.
Activities Arts & crafts; Cards; Games; Reading groups; Prayer groups; Movies; Shopping trips; Social/Cultural gatherings; Drama groups; Literary groups; Trips to cultural events.

New Gouverneur Hospital—Skilled Nursing Facility
227 Madison St, New York, NY, 10002
(212) 374-4000
Admin Alan H Rosenblut.
Licensure Skilled care. *Beds* 196. *Certified* Medicaid; Medicare.
Owner Publicly owned.

St Roses Home
71 Jackson St, New York, NY, 10002
(212) 677-8132
Admin Sr M Rosaria OP. *Medical Dir/Dir of Nursing* Arthur Larkin MD; Sr M Edwin RN.
Licensure Skilled care. *Beds* SNF 60.
Owner Nonprofit Corp (Cath Charity/Arch of NY).
Admissions Requirements Medical examination; Physician's request.

Staff RNs 5 (ft); LPNs 4 (ft); Orderlies 18 (ft); Nurses aides 5 (ft); Activities coordinators 1 (ft); Dietitians 1 (ft); Ophthalmologists 1 (ft).
Languages Spanish
Facilities Activities room; Chapel; Laundry room.
Activities Arts & crafts; Cards; Games; Prayer groups; Movies.

University Nursing Home
2505 Grand Ave, New York, NY, 10468
(212) 295-1400
Admin Eva Spiegel. *Medical Dir/Dir of Nursing* Zoila Mahbee.
Licensure Skilled care. *Beds* 46. *Certified* Medicaid; Medicare.
Owner Proprietary Corp.

Village Nursing Home Inc*
607 Hudson St, New York, NY, 10014
(212) 255-3003
Admin John J Issowits.
Licensure Skilled care. *Beds* 201. *Certified* Medicaid; Medicare.
Owner Nonprofit Corp.

Mary Manning Walsh Nursing Home Company Inc
1339 York Ave, New York, NY, 10021
(212) 628-2800
Admin Sr M Kevin Patricia.
Licensure Skilled care; Intermediate care. *Beds* 362. *Certified* Medicaid; Medicare.
Owner Nonprofit Corp (Cath Charity/Arch of NY).

NEWARK

Newark Manor Nursing Home*
222 W Pearl St, Newark, NY, 14513
(315) 331-4690
Admin Janis Sharrow.
Licensure Skilled care. *Beds* 60. *Certified* Medicaid; Medicare.
Owner Proprietary Corp.

Newark-Wayne Community Hospital Inc—Skilled Nursing Facility
Box 111, Driving Park Ave, Newark, NY, 14513
(315) 332-2022
Admin Sylvia Courtney. *Medical Dir/Dir of Nursing* Gerald Duffner MD; Donna Smith RN DON.
Licensure Skilled care. *Beds* SNF 44. *Certified* Medicaid; Medicare.
Owner Nonprofit Corp.
Admissions Requirements Minimum age 16; Physician's request.
Staff Physicians 14 (pt); RNs 3 (ft), 1 (pt); LPNs 6 (ft), 5 (pt); Nurses aides 9 (ft), 9 (pt); Physical therapists 3 (pt); Occupational therapists 1 (pt); Speech therapists 2 (pt); Activities coordinators 1 (ft); Dietitians 1 (pt); Dentists 2 (pt); Ophthalmologists 1 (pt); Rehabilitation Aide 1 (ft); Activities Aide 1 (pt).
Facilities Dining room; Physical therapy room; Activities room; Laundry room; Barber/Beauty shop.
Activities Arts & crafts; Cards; Games; Reading groups; Movies; Shopping trips; Social/Cultural gatherings; Church services; Family dinners.

NEWBURGH

Sylcox Nursing Home & Health Related Facility*
56 Meadow Hill Rd, Newburgh, NY, 12550
(914) 564-1700
Admin Edward Sylcox Sr.
Licensure Skilled care; Intermediate care. *Beds* 100. *Certified* Medicaid; Medicare.
Owner Proprietary Corp.

NEWFANE

Newfane Health Facility
2709 Transit Rd, Newfane, NY, 14108
(716) 778-7111
Admin Joan M McAndrew. *Medical Dir/Dir of Nursing* Dr Walter Altbach; Donna Haley RN DON.
Licensure Skilled care; Intermediate care. *Beds* SNF 124; ICF 51. *Certified* Medicaid; Medicare.
Owner Privately owned.
Admissions Requirements Medical examination; Physician's request.
Staff Physicians 1 (pt); RNs 10 (ft), 6 (pt); LPNs 10 (ft), 9 (pt); Orderlies 7 (ft), 6 (pt); Nurses aides 29 (ft), 48 (pt); Physical therapists 1 (pt); Occupational therapists 2 (pt); Speech therapists 1 (pt); Activities coordinators 1 (ft); Dietitians 1 (pt); Podiatrists 1 (pt).
Facilities Dining room; Physical therapy room; Activities room; Crafts room; Laundry room; Barber/Beauty shop; Library.
Activities Arts & crafts; Cards; Games; Reading groups; Prayer groups; Movies; Shopping trips; Social/Cultural gatherings.

NIAGARA FALLS

Deveaux Manor Nursing Home
2600 Main St, Niagara Falls, NY, 14305
(716) 285-9155
Admin Francis T Stolte. *Medical Dir/Dir of Nursing* Christian Kivi MD; Maureen Carvana RN.
Licensure Skilled care. *Beds* SNF 129. *Certified* Medicaid; Medicare.
Owner Nonprofit Corp.
Admissions Requirements Minimum age 21; Medical examination; Physician's request.
Staff Physicians 1 (pt); RNs 10 (ft); LPNs 18 (ft), 4 (pt); Orderlies 2 (ft); Nurses aides 42 (ft), 3 (pt); Physical therapists 1 (ft), 1 (pt); Recreational therapists 2 (ft); Speech therapists 1 (pt); Activities coordinators 1 (ft); Dietitians 1 (ft), 1 (pt); Ophthalmologists 1 (pt); Podiatrists 1 (pt).
Facilities Dining room; Physical therapy room; Activities room; Chapel; Crafts room; Barber/Beauty shop.
Activities Arts & crafts; Games; Prayer groups; Movies; Shopping trips; Social/Cultural gatherings; Outings; Picnics; Circus; Shrines.

Niagara Falls Memorial Nursing Home Co Inc
621 10th St, Niagara Falls, NY, 14302
(716) 278-4578
Admin John Ferguson. *Medical Dir/Dir of Nursing* Dr William Henderson MD; J Salerno DON.
Licensure Skilled care. *Beds* SNF 120. *Certified* Medicaid; Medicare.
Owner Nonprofit Corp.
Admissions Requirements Physician's request.
Staff Physicians 124 (ft); RNs 11 (ft); LPNs 13 (ft), 9 (pt); Nurses aides 44 (ft), 20 (pt); Physical therapists 1 (ft); Recreational therapists 1 (ft); Occupational therapists 1 (ft); Speech therapists 1 (pt); Activities coordinators 2 (ft); Dietitians 1 (ft), 1 (pt); Dentists 1 (pt); Ophthalmologists 1 (pt).
Facilities Dining room; Activities room; Crafts room; Laundry room; Barber/Beauty shop.
Activities Arts & crafts; Cards; Games; Reading groups; Prayer groups; Movies; Shopping trips; Social/Cultural gatherings.

Niagara Geriatric Center
822 Cedar Ave, Niagara Falls, NY, 14301
(716) 282-1207
Admin James G Marrione. *Medical Dir/Dir of Nursing* William Sullivan.
Licensure Intermediate care. *Beds* ICF 160. *Certified* Medicaid.
Owner Privately owned.

Admissions Requirements Minimum age 16; Medical examination.
Staff RNs 2 (ft), 3 (pt); LPNs 8 (ft), 10 (pt); Nurses aides 11 (ft), 16 (pt); Activities coordinators 1 (ft); Dietitians 1 (ft), 1 (pt).
Languages Polish, Italian, Sign
Facilities Dining room; Activities room; Laundry room; Barber/Beauty shop; Library.
Activities Arts & crafts; Cards; Games; Reading groups; Prayer groups; Movies; Shopping trips; Social/Cultural gatherings; Field trips; Fishing.

St Mary's Manor*
515 6th St, Niagara Falls, NY, 14301
(716) 285-3236
Admin Sr M Joseph Clare. *Medical Dir/Dir of Nursing* Melvin B Dyster MD.
Licensure Skilled care. *Beds* 119. *Certified* Medicaid; Medicare.
Owner Nonprofit Corp (Catholic Charities).
Admissions Requirements Minimum age 17; Medical examination; Physician's request.
Staff RNs 10 (ft), 6 (pt); LPNs 13 (ft), 4 (pt); Orderlies 5 (ft), 3 (pt); Nurses aides 49 (ft), 16 (pt); Physical therapists 2 (pt); Occupational therapists 1 (pt); Speech therapists 1 (pt); Activities coordinators 2 (ft); Dietitians 1 (ft); Dentists 1 (pt).
Facilities Dining room; Physical therapy room; Activities room; Chapel; Crafts room; Laundry room; Barber/Beauty shop.
Activities Arts & crafts; Cards; Games; Reading groups; Prayer groups; Movies; Shopping trips; Social/Cultural gatherings.

NORTH BELLMORE

Belair Nursing Home
2478 Jerusalem Ave, North Bellmore, NY, 11710
(516) 826-1160
Admin Mildred Greenberg.
Licensure Skilled care. *Beds* 102. *Certified* Medicaid; Medicare.
Owner Proprietary Corp.

NORTH CREEK

Adirondack Tri-County Nursing Home Inc
PO Box 500, North Creek, NY, 12853
(518) 251-2447
Admin Sandra MacWilliam. *Medical Dir/Dir of Nursing* John Rugge MD; Nancy Tucker RN.
Licensure Skilled care. *Beds* SNF 30. *Certified* Medicaid; Medicare.
Owner Nonprofit Corp.
Admissions Requirements Minimum age 21; Medical examination; Physician's request.
Staff RNs 5 (ft), 3 (pt); LPNs 4 (ft), 4 (pt); Nurses aides 24 (ft), 12 (pt); Activities coordinators 1 (ft).
Facilities Dining room; Physical therapy room; Activities room; Laundry room; Barber/Beauty shop; Adult day care.
Activities Arts & crafts; Cards; Games; Reading groups; Prayer groups; Movies; Shopping trips; Social/Cultural gatherings.

NORTH TONAWANDA

Degraff Memorial Hospital—Skilled Nursing Facility*
445 Tremont St, North Tonawanda, NY, 14120
(716) 694-4500
Admin Mark E Celmer. *Medical Dir/Dir of Nursing* Dr H Chang.
Licensure Skilled care. *Beds* 44. *Certified* Medicaid; Medicare.
Owner Nonprofit Corp.
Admissions Requirements Minimum age 16; Medical examination; Physician's request.

Staff RNs 5 (ft), 5 (pt); LPNs 7 (ft), 7 (pt); Orderlies 2 (ft), 1 (pt); Nurses aides 8 (ft), 7 (pt); Physical therapists 1 (pt); Occupational therapists 1 (pt); Speech therapists 1 (pt); Activities coordinators 1 (ft); Dietitians 1 (ft); Dentists 1 (pt); Podiatrists 1 (pt).
Facilities Dining room; Physical therapy room; Activities room; Barber/Beauty shop; Library.
Activities Arts & crafts; Cards; Games; Movies.

Northgate Manor
7264 Nash Rd, North Tonawanda, NY, 14120
(716) 694-7700
Admin Dennis M Piatz. *Medical Dir/Dir of Nursing* Richard Carlson MD.
Licensure Skilled care; Intermediate care. *Beds* SNF 122; ICF 38. *Certified* Medicaid; Medicare.
Owner Privately owned.
Admissions Requirements Minimum age 16; Medical examination; Physician's request.
Staff RNs 9 (ft), 5 (pt); LPNs 12 (ft), 14 (pt); Orderlies 9 (ft), 1 (pt); Nurses aides 36 (ft), 44 (pt); Physical therapists 1 (pt); Recreational therapists 1 (ft), 1 (pt).
Facilities Dining room; Physical therapy room; Activities room; Crafts room; Laundry room; Barber/Beauty shop.
Activities Arts & crafts; Cards; Games; Reading groups; Prayer groups; Movies; Shopping trips; Social/Cultural gatherings; Annual boat ride.

NORWICH

Chenango Memorial Hospital Inc—Skilled Nursing Facility
179 N Broad St, Norwich, NY, 13815
(607) 335-4114
Admin Dorothy C Zegarelli.
Licensure Skilled care. *Beds* 54. *Certified* Medicaid; Medicare.
Owner Nonprofit Corp.

Valley View Manor Nursing Home
Park St, Norwich, NY, 13815
(607) 334-9931
Admin Stephanie J Benner. *Medical Dir/Dir of Nursing* Dr Robert Frank; Maureen Laughren RN DON.
Licensure Skilled care. *Beds* SNF 82. *Certified* Medicaid; Medicare.
Owner Privately owned.
Staff RNs 10 (ft), 4 (pt); LPNs 9 (ft), 4 (pt); Orderlies 3 (ft); Nurses aides 35 (ft), 16 (pt); Physical therapists 1 (pt); Occupational therapists 1 (pt); Speech therapists 1 (pt); Activities coordinators 1 (ft); Dietitians 1 (pt).
Facilities Dining room; Barber/Beauty shop; 2 dining rooms.
Activities Arts & crafts; Cards; Games; Reading groups; Prayer groups; Movies; Shopping trips; Social/Cultural gatherings; Weekly pet therapy.

OCEANSIDE

Nassau Nursing Home*
2914 Lincoln Ave, Oceanside, NY, 11572
(516) 536-2300
Admin Alex Sreter. *Medical Dir/Dir of Nursing* Frances Kapp MD.
Licensure Skilled care. *Beds* 100. *Certified* Medicaid; Medicare.
Owner Proprietary Corp.
Admissions Requirements Minimum age 21; Physician's request.
Facilities Dining room; Physical therapy room; Activities room; Chapel; Crafts room; Laundry room; Barber/Beauty shop.
Activities Arts & crafts; Cards; Games; Reading groups; Prayer groups; Movies; Shopping trips; Social/Cultural gatherings.

OGDENSBURG

A Barton Hepburn Hospital Skilled Nursing Facility
214 King St, Ogdensburg, NY, 13669
(315) 393-3600
Admin Donald C Lewis. *Medical Dir/Dir of Nursing* Mark Chalom MD; Sr Mary Brennan DON.
Licensure Skilled care. *Beds* 29. *Certified* Medicaid; Medicare.
Owner Nonprofit Corp.
Admissions Requirements Minimum age 16; Medical examination; Physician's request.
Staff Physicians 8 (ft); RNs 1 (ft); LPNs 3 (ft), 3 (pt); Nurses aides 11 (ft), 6 (pt); Physical therapists 1 (ft); Occupational therapists 1 (ft); Activities coordinators 1 (ft); Dietitians 1 (ft).
Affiliation Roman Catholic
Facilities Dining room.
Activities Arts & crafts; Cards; Games; Reading groups; Prayer groups; Movies; Shopping trips; Social/Cultural gatherings.

St Josephs Home
420 Lafayette St, Ogdensburg, NY, 13669
(315) 393-3780
Admin Kathleen Sholette. *Medical Dir/Dir of Nursing* Dr Michael Schuler; Ms Barbara Colbert.
Licensure Skilled care. *Beds* SNF 82. *Certified* Medicaid; Medicare.
Owner Nonprofit Corp.
Admissions Requirements Minimum age 16; Medical examination.
Staff RNs 6 (ft), 5 (pt); LPNs 10 (ft), 3 (pt); Nurses aides 24 (ft), 13 (pt); Activities coordinators 2 (ft), 1 (pt); Dietitians 1 (pt).
Affiliation Roman Catholic
Facilities Dining room; Physical therapy room; Activities room; Chapel; Laundry room; Barber/Beauty shop.
Activities Arts & crafts; Games; Prayer groups; Movies; Social/Cultural gatherings.

United Helpers Cedars Nursing Home Inc
Riverside Dr, RD 4, Ogdensburg, NY, 13669
(315) 393-4810
Admin Cynthia L Barlow. *Medical Dir/Dir of Nursing* Mark Chalom MD.
Licensure Skilled care. *Beds* 82. *Certified* Medicaid; Medicare.
Owner Nonprofit Corp.
Admissions Requirements Minimum age 16; Medical examination; Physician's request.
Staff Physicians 1 (pt); RNs 8 (ft), 5 (pt); LPNs 6 (ft), 3 (pt); Orderlies 2 (ft), 3 (pt); Nurses aides 22 (ft), 15 (pt); Physical therapists 1 (pt); Occupational therapists 1 (pt); Activities coordinators 1 (ft); Dietitians 1 (pt).
Facilities Dining room; Physical therapy room; Laundry room; Barber/Beauty shop.
Activities Arts & crafts; Cards; Games; Prayer groups; Movies; Shopping trips; Social/Cultural gatherings.

United Helpers Nursing Home Inc*
Riverside Dr, Ogdensburg, NY, 13669
(315) 393-0730
Admin Robert Russell.
Licensure Skilled care; Intermediate care. *Beds* 40. *Certified* Medicaid; Medicare.
Owner Nonprofit Corp.

OLEAN

Cattaraugus County Public Nursing Home
2245 W State St, Olean, NY, 14760
(716) 373-1910
Admin Maureen Mooney-Myers. *Medical Dir/Dir of Nursing* Duncan C Wormer MD; Patricia K Drake RN DON.
Licensure Skilled care. *Beds* 120. *Certified* Medicaid; Medicare.
Owner Publicly owned.

Admissions Requirements Minimum age 16; Medical examination; Physician's request.
Staff Physicians 45 (pt); RNs 7 (ft), 10 (pt); LPNs 16 (ft), 9 (pt); Orderlies 2 (ft); Nurses aides 44 (ft), 21 (pt); Physical therapists 1 (ft); Occupational therapists 1 (pt); Speech therapists 1 (pt); Activities coordinators 1 (ft); Dietitians 1 (pt); Dentists 1 (pt); Podiatrists 1 (pt); Dentist 1 (pt).
Facilities Dining room; Physical therapy room; Activities room; Chapel; Crafts room; Laundry room; Barber/Beauty shop; Library; Atrium; Patient lounges.
Activities Arts & crafts; Cards; Games; Reading groups; Prayer groups; Movies; Shopping trips; Social/Cultural gatherings; Cooking; Trading post; Gardening; Makeup; Bowling; Resident council; Baking services.

St Josephs Manor
W State St, Olean, NY, 14727
(716) 372-7810
Admin Margaret McIntire. *Medical Dir/Dir of Nursing* Dr Ben M L Hwang; Michael Paar.
Licensure Skilled care. *Beds* SNF 22. *Certified* Medicaid; Medicare.
Owner Nonprofit organization/foundation.
Admissions Requirements Minimum age 21; Physician's request.
Staff RNs 2 (ft), 3 (pt); LPNs 3 (ft), 2 (pt); Nurses aides 8 (ft), 8 (pt); Physical therapists 1 (pt); Activities coordinators 1 (pt); Dietitians 1 (pt).
Affiliation Roman Catholic
Facilities Dining room; Activities room; Chapel; Crafts room; Laundry room.
Activities Arts & crafts; Games; Reading groups; Prayer groups; Movies.

ONEIDA

Oneida City Hospital—Extended Care Facility
221 Broad St, Oneida, NY, 13421
(315) 363-6000 ext 17
Admin Christine D Giamporcaro. *Medical Dir/Dir of Nursing* Waldo Zeun MD; Gail Hood DON.
Licensure Skilled care 10B. *Beds* SNF 77; ICF 31. *Certified* Medicaid; Medicare.
Owner Publicly owned.
Admissions Requirements Minimum age 16; Medical examination; Physician's request.
Staff RNs 10 (ft), 4 (pt); LPNs 15 (ft), 12 (pt); Orderlies 1 (pt); Nurses aides 45 (ft), 29 (pt); Physical therapists 4 (ft); Activities coordinators 1 (ft); Dietitians 1 (ft); Social worker 1 (ft).
Facilities Dining room; Physical therapy room; Activities room; Crafts room; Laundry room; Barber/Beauty shop.
Activities Arts & crafts; Cards; Games; Reading groups; Prayer groups; Movies; Shopping trips; Social/Cultural gatherings.

ONEONTA

Aurelia Osborn Fox Memorial Hospital Nursing Home
1 Norton Ave, Oneonta, NY, 13820
(607) 432-2000
Admin Gary M Smith. *Medical Dir/Dir of Nursing* Mohammed Egal; Raenell K Birdsall.
Licensure Skilled care; Intermediate care. *Beds* SNF 85; ICF 45. *Certified* Medicaid; Medicare.
Owner Nonprofit organization/foundation.
Admissions Requirements Minimum age 17; Physician's request.
Staff Physicians 1 (pt); RNs 7 (ft), 6 (pt); LPNs 9 (ft), 12 (pt); Nurses aides 30 (ft), 24 (pt); Physical therapists 1 (pt); Speech therapists 1 (pt); Activities coordinators 1 (ft), 2 (pt); Dietitians 1 (ft).
Facilities Dining room; Physical therapy room; Activities room; Crafts room; Laundry room; Barber/Beauty shop; Library.

Activities Arts & crafts; Cards; Games; Reading groups; Prayer groups; Movies; Shopping trips; Social/Cultural gatherings; Outings.

Oneonta-Richmond Inc*
330 Chestnut St, Oneonta, NY, 13820
(607) 432-8501
Medical Dir/Dir of Nursing Reade Sisson MD.
Licensure Skilled care. *Beds* 80. *Certified* Medicaid; Medicare.
Owner Proprietary Corp.
Admissions Requirements Minimum age 18; Physician's request.
Staff Physicians 1 (pt); RNs 6 (ft), 4 (pt); LPNs 8 (ft), 6 (pt); Orderlies 4 (ft); Nurses aides 25 (ft), 32 (pt); Physical therapists 1 (pt); Speech therapists 1 (pt); Activities coordinators 1 (ft), 1 (pt); Dietitians 1 (pt); Dentists 1 (pt); Podiatrists 1 (pt).
Facilities Dining room; Physical therapy room; Activities room; Crafts room; Barber/Beauty shop.
Activities Arts & crafts; Cards; Games; Reading groups; Prayer groups; Movies; Shopping trips.

ORCHARD PARK

Orchard Park Health Care Center Inc
6060 Armor Rd, Orchard Park, NY, 14127
(716) 662-4433
Admin Mary Tribuzzi. *Medical Dir/Dir of Nursing* Dr James Norton; Ann Cornish DNS.
Licensure Skilled care; Intermediate care. *Beds* SNF 86; ICF 80. *Certified* Medicaid; Medicare.
Owner Proprietary Corp.
Admissions Requirements Minimum age 16; Medical examination; Physician's request.
Staff Physicians; RNs; LPNs; Orderlies; Nurses aides; Physical therapists; Recreational therapists; Occupational therapists; Speech therapists; Activities coordinators; Dietitians; Ophthalmologists; Podiatrists; Audiologists; Social workers.
Facilities Dining room; Physical therapy room; Activities room; Crafts room; Laundry room; Barber/Beauty shop.
Activities Arts & crafts; Cards; Games; Reading groups; Prayer groups; Movies; Shopping trips; Social/Cultural gatherings; Van rides; Senior Olympics.

ORISKANY

Eastern Star Home & Infirmary
Utica St, Oriskany, NY, 13424
(315) 736-9311
Admin Unamae Ferguson. *Medical Dir/Dir of Nursing* Dr A Jabhon; Mrs Karen Wentrick DON.
Licensure Skilled care; Health related care. *Beds* SNF 54; HRF 28. *Certified* Medicaid; Medicare.
Owner Nonprofit Corp.
Admissions Requirements Medical examination; Physician's request.
Staff Physicians; RNs; LPNs; Nurses aides; Physical therapists; Recreational therapists; Occupational therapists; Activities coordinators; Dietitians; Ophthalmologists.
Affiliation Order of Eastern Star
Facilities Dining room; Physical therapy room; Activities room; Chapel; Crafts room; Laundry room; Barber/Beauty shop; Library.
Activities Arts & crafts; Cards; Games; Reading groups; Prayer groups; Movies; Shopping trips; Social/Cultural gatherings; Chapter meetings; Luncheon & dinner outings; Picnics.

OSSINING

Asthmatic Childrens Foundation of New York Inc
Spring Valley Rd, Ossining, NY, 10562
(914) 762-2110
Admin Raphael Cubisino. *Medical Dir/Dir of Nursing* Dr Armond V Mascia; John Greenwood RN.
Licensure Skilled care. *Beds* SNF 36. *Certified* Medicaid.
Owner Nonprofit organization/foundation.
Admissions Requirements Minimum age 5.
Staff Physicians; RNs; Nurses aides; Activities coordinators; Dietitians; Dentists.
Facilities Dining room; Activities room; Crafts room; Laundry room; Library; Gym.
Activities Arts & crafts; Games; Reading groups; Prayer groups; Movies; Shopping trips; Social/Cultural gatherings.

Bethel Nursing Home Company Inc
19 Narragansett Ave, Ossining, NY, 10530
(914) 941-7300
Admin Janet M Beard.
Licensure Skilled care. *Beds* SNF 78. *Certified* Medicaid; Medicare.
Owner Nonprofit Corp.
Staff Physicians; RNs; LPNs; Orderlies; Nurses aides; Physical therapists; Recreational therapists; Occupational therapists; Speech therapists; Dietitians.
Languages Spanish
Affiliation Methodist
Facilities Dining room; Physical therapy room; Activities room; Chapel; Crafts room; Laundry room; Barber/Beauty shop; Library; Swimming pool at retirement facility.
Activities Arts & crafts; Cards; Games; Reading groups; Movies; Social/Cultural gatherings.

Briar Crest Nursing Home
31 Overton Rd, Ossining, NY, 10562
(914) 941-4047
Admin Peter T Gendron. *Medical Dir/Dir of Nursing* Dr M G Giatzis; Linda Karl RN.
Licensure Skilled care. *Beds* SNF 86. *Certified* Medicaid; Medicare.
Owner Proprietary Corp.
Admissions Requirements Minimum age 18; Medical examination; Physician's request.
Staff Physicians 1 (pt); RNs 12 (ft), 3 (pt); LPNs 5 (ft), 6 (pt); Nurses aides 43 (ft), 3 (pt); Physical therapists 2 (pt); Recreational therapists 2 (ft); Occupational therapists 1 (pt); Activities coordinators 3 (pt); Dietitians 1 (pt).
Languages Spanish, German
Facilities Dining room; Physical therapy room; Activities room; Laundry room; Barber/Beauty shop.
Activities Arts & crafts; Cards; Games; Prayer groups; Movies; Social/Cultural gatherings; Discussion groups; Pet therapy; BBQs; Picnics.

Cedar Manor Nursing Home
PO Box 928, Cedar Ln, Ossining, NY, 10562
(914) 762-1600
Admin Ms J M Myshrall. *Medical Dir/Dir of Nursing* Stuart Pines MD; Debra A Sabato RN BSN DON.
Licensure Skilled care. *Beds* SNF 153. *Certified* Medicaid; Medicare.
Owner Privately owned.
Admissions Requirements Minimum age 21; Medical examination.
Languages Spanish
Facilities Dining room; Physical therapy room; Activities room; Laundry room; Barber/Beauty shop.
Activities Arts & crafts; Cards; Games; Prayer groups; Movies; Social/Cultural gatherings.

Victoria Home for Retired Men & Women
N Malcolm St, Ossining, NY, 10562
(914) 941-2450

Admin Madeline Callahan. *Medical Dir/Dir of Nursing* Dr E Argenziano; Patricia Draper.
Licensure HRF. *Beds* 49. *Certified* Medicaid.
Owner Nonprofit Corp.
Admissions Requirements Medical examination.
Staff Physicians 1 (pt); RNs 1 (ft), 1 (pt); LPNs 2 (ft), 5 (pt); Nurses aides 5 (ft), 4 (pt); Physical therapists 1 (pt); Activities coordinators 1 (ft); Dietitians 1 (pt); Social services 1 (pt).
Facilities Dining room; Activities room; Laundry room; Barber/Beauty shop; Library Living rooms.
Activities Arts & crafts; Cards; Games; Reading groups; Prayer groups; Movies; Shopping trips.

OSWEGO

Harr-Wood Nursing Home
17 Sunrise Dr, Oswego, NY, 13126
(315) 342-4790
Admin Martin D Miller.
Licensure Skilled care. *Beds* 120. *Certified* Medicaid; Medicare.
Owner Proprietary Corp.

Hillcrest Nursing Home
132 Ellen St, Oswego, NY, 13126
(315) 342-2440
Admin Stanley J Wojciechowski. *Medical Dir/Dir of Nursing* Roger Cook MD Med Dir; Joyce Boronkay RN DON.
Licensure SNF/HRF. *Beds* SNF/HRF 120. *Certified* Medicaid; Medicare.
Owner Proprietary Corp.
Staff Physicians 6 (pt); RNs 7 (ft), 3 (pt); LPNs 11 (ft), 4 (pt); Nurses aides 38 (ft), 4 (pt); Physical therapists 1 (pt); Speech therapists 1 (pt); Activities coordinators 1 (ft); Dietitians 1 (ft); Ophthalmologists 1 (pt).
Languages Polish, Italian, Hindi
Facilities Dining room; Physical therapy room; Activities room; Chapel; Crafts room; Laundry room; Barber/Beauty shop.
Activities Arts & crafts; Cards; Games; Reading groups; Prayer groups; Movies.

Oswego Hospital Extended Care Facility
110 W 6th St, Oswego, NY, 13126
(315) 349-5511
Admin Corte J Spencer. *Medical Dir/Dir of Nursing* Bipin Parekh MD; Eugenia Bowman DON.
Licensure Skilled care. *Beds* SNF 38. *Certified* Medicaid; Medicare.
Owner Nonprofit Corp.
Admissions Requirements Minimum age 16.
Staff Physicians 1 (pt); RNs 4 (ft), 1 (pt); LPNs 6 (ft), 1 (pt); Orderlies 1 (pt); Nurses aides 15 (ft), 6 (pt); Physical therapists 1 (pt); Activities coordinators 1 (ft).
Facilities Dining room; Physical therapy room; Activities room; Chapel; Barber/Beauty shop; Library.
Activities Arts & crafts; Cards; Games; Prayer groups; Movies; Sing-along; Trips to farm; Circuses; Band concerts.

Pontiac Nursing Home
E River Rd, Oswego, NY, 13126
(315) 343-1800
Admin John Vivenzio.
Licensure Skilled care. *Beds* 80. *Certified* Medicaid; Medicare.
Owner Proprietary Corp.

St Luke Nursing Home Company Inc
Rd 4, East River Rd, Oswego, NY, 13126
(315) 342-3166
Admin Francis A Boyce. *Medical Dir/Dir of Nursing* Dr David D O'Brien Jr.
Licensure Intermediate care. *Beds* ICF 120. *Certified* Medicaid.
Owner Nonprofit Corp.

Admissions Requirements Minimum age 16; Medical examination.
Staff RNs 4 (ft), 2 (pt); LPNs 10 (ft), 9 (pt); Orderlies 2 (ft), 1 (pt); Nurses aides 22 (ft), 18 (pt); Physical therapists 1 (pt); Speech therapists 1 (pt); Activities coordinators 2 (ft); Dietitians 1 (pt).
Languages Polish
Affiliation Roman Catholic
Facilities Dining room; Physical therapy room; Activities room; Crafts room; Barber/Beauty shop; Library.
Activities Arts & crafts; Cards; Games; Reading groups; Prayer groups; Movies; Shopping trips; Social/Cultural gatherings.

OWEGO

Riverview Manor Nursing Home
510 5th Ave, Owego, NY, 13827
(607) 687-2594
Admin Larry M Ramsay. *Medical Dir/Dir of Nursing* W R Schmits MD; Birdie Abrams RN.
Licensure Skilled care. *Beds* SNF 77. *Certified* Medicaid; Medicare.
Owner Proprietary Corp.
Admissions Requirements Minimum age 16; Medical examination; Physician's request.
Staff Physicians 7 (pt); RNs 7 (ft), 5 (pt); LPNs 4 (ft), 2 (pt); Nurses aides 30 (ft), 21 (pt); Physical therapists 1 (pt); Reality therapists 1 (pt); Recreational therapists 1 (ft), 1 (pt); Occupational therapists 1 (pt); Speech therapists 1 (pt); Activities coordinators 1 (pt); Dietitians 1 (pt); Dentists 1 (pt); Ophthalmologists 1 (pt); Podiatrists 1 (pt); Social worker 1 (ft), 1 (pt).
Facilities Dining room; Physical therapy room; Activities room; Crafts room; Laundry room; Barber/Beauty shop; Library; Solarium.
Activities Arts & crafts; Cards; Games; Reading groups; Prayer groups; Movies; Shopping trips; Social/Cultural gatherings; Picnics.

OXFORD

New York State Veterans Home
Rte 220, E River Rd, Oxford, NY, 13830
(607) 843-6991
Admin Mary J Brown. *Medical Dir/Dir of Nursing* Raymond Vickers MD; Shirley Panlauskas RN.
Licensure Skilled care; Intermediate care. *Beds* SNF 124; ICF 118. *Certified* Medicaid; Medicare.
Owner Publicly owned.
Admissions Requirements Medical examination; Physician's request.
Staff Physicians 1 (ft), 2 (pt); RNs 20 (ft); LPNs 39 (ft); Nurses aides 74 (ft); Physical therapists 1 (ft); Recreational therapists 4 (ft); Occupational therapists 1 (ft); Speech therapists 1 (pt); Dietitians 1 (ft); Dentists 1 (pt); Ophthalmologists 1 (pt).
Facilities Dining room; Physical therapy room; Activities room; Chapel; Crafts room; Barber/Beauty shop; Library.
Activities Arts & crafts; Cards; Games; Reading groups; Prayer groups; Movies; Shopping trips; Social/Cultural gatherings; Pet therapy program twice monthly.

PAINTED POST

Three Rivers Health Care Center Inc*
101 Creekside Dr, Painted Post, NY, 14870
(607) 936-4108
Licensure Intermediate care. *Beds* 80.
Owner Proprietary Corp.

PALATINE BRIDGE

Palatine Nursing Home*
Upper Lafayette St, Palatine Bridge, NY, 13428
(518) 673-5212
Admin Laverne A Bouton III. *Medical Dir/Dir of Nursing* Dr Benjamin Button.
Licensure Skilled care. *Beds* 50.
Owner Nonprofit Corp.
Staff Physicians 1 (pt); RNs 4 (ft), 2 (pt); LPNs 5 (ft), 1 (pt); Nurses aides 18 (ft), 9 (pt); Physical therapists 1 (pt); Reality therapists 2 (ft); Recreational therapists 1 (ft); Occupational therapists 1 (pt); Speech therapists 1 (pt); Activities coordinators 1 (ft); Dietitians 1 (pt); Dentists 1 (pt); Podiatrists 1 (pt); Audiologists 1 (pt).
Facilities Dining room; Physical therapy room; Activities room; Chapel; Laundry room; Barber/Beauty shop.
Activities Arts & crafts; Cards; Games; Reading groups; Prayer groups; Movies; Shopping trips.

PATCHOGUE

Patchogue Nursing Center
25 Schoenfeld Blvd, Patchogue, NY, 11772
(516) 289-7700
Admin Paul C Maggio. *Medical Dir/Dir of Nursing* Jack R Muth MD.
Licensure Skilled care. *Beds* 120. *Certified* Medicaid; Medicare.
Owner Proprietary Corp.
Staff Physicians 1 (ft); RNs 13 (ft); LPNs 18 (ft); Orderlies 6 (ft); Nurses aides 72 (ft); Physical therapists 1 (ft); Reality therapists 1 (ft); Recreational therapists 1 (ft); Occupational therapists 1 (ft); Speech therapists 1 (pt); Activities coordinators 1 (ft); Dietitians 1 (pt); Dentists 1 (pt); Ophthalmologists 1 (pt); Podiatrists 1 (pt); Dentist 1 (pt).
Facilities Dining room; Physical therapy room; Activities room; Chapel; Crafts room; Laundry room; Barber/Beauty shop; Library; Dental treatment room.
Activities Arts & crafts; Cards; Games; Reading groups; Prayer groups; Movies; Shopping trips; Social/Cultural gatherings; Picnics; Fishing trips.

PAWLING

Lovely Hill Nursing Home
Rte 22 & S Reservoir Rd, Pawling, NY, 12564
(914) 855-5700
Admin Clayton M Harbby. *Medical Dir/Dir of Nursing* Jeffrey Carr MD; Mary E Fay DON.
Licensure Skilled care; Intermediate care. *Beds* SNF 80; ICF 40. *Certified* Medicaid; Medicare.
Owner Privately owned.
Admissions Requirements Minimum age 16; Medical examination.
Staff Physicians; RNs; LPNs; Orderlies; Nurses aides; Physical therapists; Recreational therapists; Occupational therapists; Speech therapists; Activities coordinators; Dietitians; Dentists; Ophthalmologists; Podiatrists.
Facilities Dining room; Physical therapy room; Activities room; Chapel; Crafts room; Barber/Beauty shop; Library.
Activities Arts & crafts; Cards; Games; Reading groups; Prayer groups; Movies; Shopping trips; Social/Cultural gatherings.

PEEKSKILL

Cortlandt Nursing Care Center Inc
110 Oregon Rd, Peekskill, NY, 10566
(914) 739-9150
Admin Joel Garson. *Medical Dir/Dir of Nursing* Stuart Pines MD; Kathleen Tangorra RN.
Licensure Skilled care; Intermediate care. *Beds* SNF 40; ICF 80. *Certified* Medicaid; Medicare.
Owner Proprietary Corp.
Staff RNs 7 (ft), 1 (pt); LPNs 9 (ft), 1 (pt); Nurses aides 25 (ft), 15 (pt); Physical therapists 1 (pt); Recreational therapists 1 (ft); Occupational therapists 1 (pt); Speech therapists 1 (pt); Activities coordinators 2 (ft); Dietitians 1 (ft); Social worker 1 (ft).
Languages Italian, Spanish, Yiddish, Hebrew
Facilities Dining room; Physical therapy room; Activities room; Crafts room; Laundry room; Barber/Beauty shop; 5 balconies on patient floors; Enclosed outdoor courtyard; 5 acres of grounds.
Activities Arts & crafts; Cards; Games; Reading groups; Prayer groups; Movies; Shopping trips; Social/Cultural gatherings.

Westledge Nursing Home
2100 E Main St, Peekskill, NY, 10566
(914) 737-8400
Admin Helen R Brown. *Medical Dir/Dir of Nursing* Stuart L Pines MD; Mrs A Bobay DON.
Licensure Skilled care. *Beds* SNF 100. *Certified* Medicaid; Medicare.
Owner Privately owned.
Admissions Requirements Medical examination; Physician's request.
Staff RNs 7 (ft), 6 (pt); LPNs 8 (ft), 7 (pt); Nurses aides 39 (ft), 13 (pt); Physical therapists 1 (pt); Activities coordinators 2 (ft); Dietitians 1 (ft), 1 (pt).
Facilities Dining room; Physical therapy room; Activities room; Laundry room; Barber/Beauty shop; Library; Day rooms; Patios; Lounges.
Activities Arts & crafts; Games; Prayer groups; Movies; Social/Cultural gatherings; Residents council; Music; Dance; Holiday programs.

PENFIELD

Penfield Nursing Home
1700 Penfield Rd, Penfield, NY, 14526
(716) 586-7433
Admin Diedre L Murphy. *Medical Dir/Dir of Nursing* Kenneth S Thomson MD.
Licensure Skilled care. *Beds* SNF 48. *Certified* Medicaid; Medicare.
Owner Proprietary Corp.
Admissions Requirements Minimum age 16; Medical examination.
Staff Physicians 1 (pt); RNs 2 (ft), 6 (pt); LPNs 2 (ft), 5 (pt); Nurses aides 12 (ft), 14 (pt); Physical therapists 1 (pt); Occupational therapists 1 (pt); Activities coordinators 1 (ft); Dietitians 1 (pt); Dentists 1 (pt); Ophthalmologists 1 (pt); Podiatrists 1 (pt); Social workers 2 (pt); Rehabilitation aides 1 (ft).
Facilities Dining room; Physical therapy room; Activities room; Laundry room; Barber/Beauty shop; Living room/TV room; Patio.
Activities Arts & crafts; Cards; Games; Reading groups; Prayer groups; Movies; Shopping trips; Social/Cultural gatherings; Field trips; Performances.

PENN YAN

Penn Yan Manor Nursing Home Inc
655 N Liberty St, Penn Yan, NY, 14527
(315) 536-2311
Admin Noreen B Curtis. *Medical Dir/Dir of Nursing* Dr Norman W Lindenmuth; Ruth B Dorrough RN.
Licensure Skilled care. *Beds* SNF 46. *Certified* Medicaid; Medicare.
Owner Nonprofit Corp.

Admissions Requirements Minimum age 16; Medical examination; Physician's request.
Staff Physicians 1 (pt); RNs 3 (ft), 1 (pt); LPNs 4 (ft), 4 (pt); Nurses aides 21 (ft), 16 (pt); Physical therapists 1 (pt); Occupational therapists 1 (pt); Speech therapists 1 (pt); Activities coordinators 1 (pt); Dietitians 1 (pt); Dentists 1 (pt); Ophthalmologists 1 (pt); Podiatrists 1 (pt); 7 (ft), 6 (pt) Maintenance; Housekeeping; Office; SW.
Facilities Dining room; Physical therapy room; Activities room; Chapel; Crafts room; Laundry room; Barber/Beauty shop; Library.
Activities Arts & crafts; Cards; Games; Reading groups; Prayer groups; Movies; Social/Cultural gatherings.

Soldiers & Sailors Memorial Hospital Health Related Facility*
418 N Main St, Penn Yan, NY, 14527
(315) 536-4431
Admin James Krembs.
Licensure Skilled care. *Beds* 24. *Certified* Medicaid; Medicare.
Owner Nonprofit Corp.

PHILMONT

Pine Haven Home
Rte 217, Philmont, NY, 12565
(518) 672-4021
Admin Alice M Blaauw. *Medical Dir/Dir of Nursing* Irma Waldo MD; Nancy DeLaurentis RN DON.
Licensure Skilled care; Intermediate care. *Beds* SNF 80; ICF 40. *Certified* Medicaid; Medicare.
Owner Publicly owned.
Admissions Requirements Minimum age 18 & Columbia County resident.
Staff Physicians 3 (pt); RNs 13 (ft), 6 (pt); LPNs 7 (ft), 8 (pt); Nurses aides 44 (ft), 21 (pt); Physical therapists 1 (pt); Occupational therapists 1 (pt); Speech therapists 1 (pt); Activities coordinators 1 (ft); Dietitians 1 (pt).
Facilities Dining room; Physical therapy room; Activities room; Chapel; Laundry room; Barber/Beauty shop.
Activities Arts & crafts; Cards; Games; Reading groups; Prayer groups; Movies; Shopping trips.

PLAINVIEW

Central Island Nursing Home Inc
825 Old Country Rd, Plainview, NY, 11803
(516) 433-0600
Admin Martha Sweet Fachca. *Medical Dir/Dir of Nursing* Donald Orofino MD; Chiaramomte RN DON.
Licensure Skilled care. *Beds* SNF 202. *Certified* Medicaid; Medicare.
Owner Proprietary Corp.
Facilities Dining room; Physical therapy room; Activities room; Chapel; Crafts room; Laundry room; Barber/Beauty shop; Library; Patio.
Activities Arts & crafts; Cards; Games; Reading groups; Prayer groups; Movies; Social/Cultural gatherings.

PLATTSBURGH

Champlain Valley Physicians Hospital Medical Center—Skilled Nursing Facility*
100 Beekman St, Plattsburgh, NY, 12901
(518) 561-2000
Admin Marilyn O'Connor.
Licensure Skilled care; Intermediate care. *Beds* 54. *Certified* Medicaid; Medicare.
Owner Nonprofit Corp.

Clinton County Nursing Home & Health Related Facility
3 Flynn Ave, Plattsburgh, NY, 12901
(518) 563-0950

Admin Barbara A Thompson. *Medical Dir/Dir of Nursing* Dr William LaDue; Elizabeth Brown RN.
Licensure Skilled care; Intermediate care. *Beds* SNF 55; ICF 25. *Certified* Medicaid; Medicare.
Owner Publicly owned.
Admissions Requirements Minimum age 16; Medical examination; Physician's request.
Staff Physicians 1 (pt); RNs 6 (ft), 7 (pt); LPNs 8 (ft), 7 (pt); Nurses aides 20 (ft), 22 (pt); Physical therapists 1 (pt); Recreational therapists 1 (pt); Speech therapists 1 (pt); Activities coordinators 2 (pt); Dietitians 1 (pt).
Facilities Dining room; Physical therapy room; Activities room; Laundry room; Barber/Beauty shop; Central courtyard-patio.
Activities Games; Prayer groups; Movies; Shopping trips; Social/Cultural gatherings; Monthly theme culminating in a special event each month.

Meadowbrook Nursing Home*
80 N Prospect Ave, Plattsburgh, NY, 12901
(518) 563-5440
Admin Hobbie Hyatt.
Licensure Skilled care; Intermediate care. *Beds* 80. *Certified* Medicaid; Medicare.
Owner Proprietary Corp.

Sacred Heart Home Inc
8 Mickle St, Plattsburgh, NY, 12901
(518) 563-3261
Admin William J Dooley. *Medical Dir/Dir of Nursing* John P Dickard MD; Sr Caroline M Stoltz RN DON.
Licensure Skilled care. *Beds* SNF 89. *Certified* Medicaid; Medicare.
Owner Nonprofit Corp.
Admissions Requirements Minimum age 21.
Staff Physicians 1 (pt); RNs 9 (ft), 6 (pt); LPNs 6 (ft), 5 (pt); Orderlies 1 (ft), 1 (pt); Nurses aides 33 (ft), 31 (pt); Physical therapists 2 (ft); Activities coordinators 1 (ft); Dietitians 1 (ft).
Affiliation Roman Catholic
Facilities Dining room; Physical therapy room; Activities room; Chapel; Crafts room; Laundry room; Barber/Beauty shop; Library.
Activities Arts & crafts; Cards; Games; Reading groups; Prayer groups; Movies; Shopping trips; Lovely lady/Handsome gent contest; Spelling contest; Bingo.

POMANA

Summit Park Hospital—Rockland County Infirmary*
Sanatorium Rd, Pomana, NY, 10970
(914) 354-0200
Admin George T Giacobbe.
Licensure Skilled care. *Beds* 300. *Certified* Medicaid; Medicare.
Owner Publicly owned.

PORT CHESTER

Port Chester Nursing Home
1000 High St, Port Chester, NY, 10573
(914) 937-1200
Medical Dir/Dir of Nursing Joseph Silberstein MD.
Licensure Skilled care. *Beds* 160. *Certified* Medicaid; Medicare.
Owner Nonprofit Corp.
Staff Physicians 1 (pt); RNs 8 (ft); LPNs 11 (ft); Orderlies 8 (ft); Nurses aides 41 (ft); Physical therapists 1 (pt); Occupational therapists 1 (pt); Speech therapists 1 (pt); Activities coordinators 3 (ft).
Affiliation Jewish
Facilities Dining room; Physical therapy room; Activities room; Laundry room; Barber/Beauty shop; Library.

Activities Arts & crafts; Cards; Games; Reading groups; Prayer groups; Movies; Shopping trips.

PORT JEFFERSON

Port Jefferson Nursing Home & Health Related Facility*
Dark Hollow Rd, Box 637, Port Jefferson, NY, 11777
(516) 473-5400
Admin Gail M Miranda. *Medical Dir/Dir of Nursing* Jerome Feldstein MD.
Licensure Skilled care; Intermediate care. *Beds* 60. *Certified* Medicaid; Medicare.
Owner Proprietary Corp.
Staff RNs 5 (ft), 5 (pt); LPNs 7 (ft), 7 (pt); Orderlies 1 (ft), 1 (pt); Nurses aides 27 (ft), 18 (pt); Physical therapists 1 (pt); Occupational therapists 1 (pt); Speech therapists 1 (pt); Activities coordinators 1 (ft), 3 (pt); Dietitians 1 (ft); Dentists 1 (pt); Podiatrists 1 (pt).
Facilities Dining room; Physical therapy room; Activities room; Laundry room; Barber/Beauty shop.
Activities Arts & crafts; Cards; Games; Reading groups; Prayer groups; Movies; Shopping trips; Social/Cultural gatherings.

Sunrest Health Facilities Inc
70 N Country Rd, Port Jefferson, NY, 11777
(516) 928-2000
Admin Paul Dioguardi.
Licensure Skilled care. *Beds* 138. *Certified* Medicaid; Medicare.
Owner Proprietary Corp.

PORT JEFFERSON STATION

Woodhaven Nursing Home
1360 Rte 112, Port Jefferson Station, NY, 11776
(516) 473-7100
Admin Eurydice Loucopoulos.
Licensure Skilled care. *Beds* 143. *Certified* Medicaid; Medicare.
Owner Proprietary Corp.

PORT WASHINGTON

Sands Point Nursing Home
1440 Port Washington Blvd, Port Washington, NY, 11050
(516) 767-2320
Admin Chana Zlotnick. *Medical Dir/Dir of Nursing* Dr J Rawlings.
Licensure Skilled care. *Beds* SNF 130. *Certified* Medicaid; Medicare.
Owner Proprietary Corp.
Admissions Requirements Medical examination; Physician's request.
Staff RNs 5 (ft), 9 (pt); LPNs 13 (ft), 5 (pt); Orderlies 8 (ft), 3 (pt); Nurses aides 41 (ft), 13 (pt); Activities coordinators 1 (ft); Dietitians 1 (pt).
Facilities Dining room; Physical therapy room; Activities room; Laundry room; Barber/Beauty shop; Library.
Activities Arts & crafts; Cards; Games; Reading groups; Prayer groups; Movies; Shopping trips; Social/Cultural gatherings; Nursery group visits; Bible study.

POTSDAM

Potsdam Nursing Home*
Cottage Grove, Potsdam, NY, 13676
(315) 265-6330
Admin Norma Secours.
Licensure Skilled care. *Beds* 80. *Certified* Medicaid; Medicare.
Owner Proprietary Corp.

POUGHKEEPSIE

Eden Park Nursing Home*
100 Franklin St, Poughkeepsie, NY, 12601
(914) 454-4100
Licensure Skilled care; Intermediate care. *Beds* 120. *Certified* Medicaid; Medicare.
Owner Proprietary Corp (Eden Park Management).

PURDYS

Salem Hills Health Care Center
PO Box 66, Rte 22, Purdys, NY, 10578-0066
(914) 277-3626
Admin Martha M Habermann. *Medical Dir/Dir of Nursing* Charles Block MD.
Licensure Skilled care; Intermediate care. *Beds* SNF 63; ICF 63. *Certified* Medicaid; Medicare.
Owner Privately owned.
Admissions Requirements Minimum age 16; Physician's request.
Staff RNs; LPNs; Orderlies; Nurses aides; Physical therapists; Occupational therapists; Speech therapists; Activities coordinators; Dietitians.
Facilities Dining room; Physical therapy room; Activities room; Laundry room; Barber/Beauty shop; Multi-purpose room.
Activities Arts & crafts; Cards; Games; Reading groups; Prayer groups; Movies; Shopping trips; Social/Cultural gatherings.

Waterview Hills Nursing Center Inc
PO Box 257, Old Rte 22, Purdys, NY, 10578
(914) 277-3691
Admin Barry F Reisler. *Medical Dir/Dir of Nursing* Dhimant Pandya MD; Patricia Mackin RN DON.
Licensure Skilled care. *Beds* SNF 126. *Certified* Medicaid; Medicare.
Owner Proprietary Corp.
Admissions Requirements Minimum age 21; Medical examination.
Staff RNs; LPNs; Orderlies; Nurses aides; Physical therapists; Occupational therapists; Speech therapists; Activities coordinators; Dietitians.
Facilities Dining room; Physical therapy room; Activities room; Crafts room; Laundry room; Barber/Beauty shop; Library; Century tub; Kitchenettes; Garden room; Treatment rooms.
Activities Arts & crafts; Cards; Games; Reading groups; Prayer groups; Movies; Social/Cultural gatherings; Art therapy; Pet therapy; Horticulture groups.

QUEENS VILLAGE

Queen of Peace Residence*
110-30 221st St, Queens Village, NY, 11429
(718) 464-1800
Admin Christine de la Trinite.
Licensure Skilled care; Intermediate care. *Beds* 70. *Certified* Medicaid; Medicare.
Owner Nonprofit Corp.

Windsor Park Nursing Home Inc
212-40 Hillside Ave, Queens Village, NY, 11427
(718) 468-0800
Admin Elizabeth Rothchild. *Medical Dir/Dir of Nursing* Michael Sheehtman MD; Vna Johnson RN DON.
Licensure Skilled care. *Beds* SNF 70. *Certified* Medicaid; Medicare.
Owner Proprietary Corp.
Admissions Requirements Minimum age 80; Medical examination; Physician's request.
Staff Physicians; RNs; LPNs; Orderlies; Nurses aides; Physical therapists; Reality therapists; Recreational therapists; Occupational therapists; Speech therapists; Activities coordinators; Dietitians; Dentists; Ophthalmologists; Podiatrists.

Facilities Dining room; Physical therapy room; Activities room; Chapel; Crafts room; Laundry room; Barber/Beauty shop; Library.
Activities Arts & crafts; Cards; Games; Prayer groups; Movies; Shopping trips; Social/Cultural gatherings; Field trips.

REGO PARK

Van Doren Nursing Home*
59-20 Van Doren St, Rego Park, NY, 11368
(718) 592-9200
Admin A Sreter.
Licensure Skilled care. *Beds* 200. *Certified* Medicaid; Medicare.
Owner Proprietary Corp.

RENSSELAER

Rosewood Gardens Health Related Facility
Rts 4 & 40, RD 2, Rensselaer, NY, 12144
(518) 286-1621
Admin Beverly R Benno. *Medical Dir/Dir of Nursing* A Farol MD; Shirley Sheridan DON.
Licensure Intermediate care for mentally retarded. *Beds* ICF/MR 80.
Owner Proprietary Corp (New Medico Assoc).
Staff RNs; LPNs; Nurses aides; Physical therapists; Recreational therapists; Occupational therapists; Speech therapists; Activities coordinators; Dietitians; Ophthalmologists.

RHINEBECK

Baptist Home of Brooklyn New York
Rte 308, Box 129, Rhinebeck, NY, 12572
(914) 876-2071
Admin Adele Jansson. *Medical Dir/Dir of Nursing* Irma Waldo MD; Mary DeWitt RN DON.
Licensure Skilled care; Health related care. *Beds* SNF 80; HRC 40. *Certified* Medicaid.
Owner Nonprofit Corp.
Admissions Requirements Medical examination; Physician's request.
Staff Physicians 3 (pt); RNs 5 (ft), 8 (pt); LPNs 5 (ft), 10 (pt); Nurses aides 35 (ft), 27 (pt); Occupational therapists 1 (pt); Speech therapists 1 (pt); Activities coordinators 1 (ft); Dietitians 1 (pt); Dentists 1 (pt); Ophthalmologists 1 (pt); Podiatrists 1 (pt); Dentist 1 (pt).
Affiliation Baptist
Facilities Dining room; Physical therapy room; Activities room; Chapel; Crafts room; Laundry room; Barber/Beauty shop; Library; Solarium; Coffee shop.
Activities Arts & crafts; Cards; Games; Reading groups; Prayer groups; Movies; Shopping trips; Social/Cultural gatherings.

Ferncliff Nursing Home Co Inc
PO Box 386, River Rd, Rhinebeck, NY, 12572
(914) 876-2011
Admin Sr Robert Walsh. *Medical Dir/Dir of Nursing* George Verrilli MD.
Licensure Skilled care; Health related care. *Beds* SNF 240; HRC 80. *Certified* Medicaid; Medicare.
Owner Nonprofit Corp.
Admissions Requirements Medical examination.
Staff Physicians 8 (pt); RNs 14 (ft), 12 (pt); LPNs 18 (ft), 20 (pt); Nurses aides 104 (ft), 49 (pt); Physical therapists 1 (ft); Occupational therapists 1 (pt); Speech therapists 1 (pt); Activities coordinators 1 (ft); Dietitians 1 (ft); Dentists 4 (pt); Ophthalmologists 1 (pt); Podiatrists 1 (pt).
Affiliation Roman Catholic

Facilities Dining room; Physical therapy room; Activities room; Chapel; Crafts room; Laundry room; Barber/Beauty shop; Library; Lounge; Gift shop.
Activities Arts & crafts; Cards; Games; Reading groups; Movies; Shopping trips; Social/Cultural gatherings; Grooming; Cooking.

Northern Dutchess Hospital Skilled Nursing Facility
Springbrook Ave, Rhinebeck, NY, 12572
(914) 876-3001
Admin Michael C Mazzarella. *Medical Dir/Dir of Nursing* William G Thompson MD; Laura Tilipko RN DON.
Licensure Skilled care. *Beds* SNF 50. *Certified* Medicaid; Medicare.
Owner Nonprofit Corp.
Staff RNs 3 (ft), 3 (pt); LPNs 4 (ft), 3 (pt); Nurses aides 19 (ft), 10 (pt); Physical therapists 1 (ft), 2 (pt); Recreational therapists 1 (ft), 2 (pt); Occupational therapists 1 (pt); Speech therapists 1 (pt); Activities coordinators 1 (ft); Dietitians 1 (pt); Dentists 1 (pt); Ophthalmologists 1 (pt); Podiatrists 1 (pt).
Facilities Dining room; Physical therapy room; Activities room; Chapel; Crafts room; Barber/Beauty shop.
Activities Arts & crafts; Cards; Games; Reading groups; Prayer groups; Movies; Shopping trips; Social/Cultural gatherings.

RIVERHEAD

Riverhead Nursing Home/Health Related Facility
1146 Woodcrest Ave, Riverhead, NY, 11901
(516) 727-7744
Admin Madeline C Butler. *Medical Dir/Dir of Nursing* I F Frankel MD; Mrs Zepmeisel RN DON.
Licensure Skilled care; Intermediate care. *Beds* SNF 121; ICF 60. *Certified* Medicaid; Medicare.
Owner Privately owned.
Admissions Requirements Medical examination; Physician's request.
Staff RNs; LPNs; Orderlies; Nurses aides; Physical therapists; Reality therapists; Occupational therapists; Speech therapists; Activities coordinators; Dietitians.
Languages Polish
Facilities Dining room; Physical therapy room; Activities room; Chapel; Crafts room; Laundry room; Barber/Beauty shop; Library.
Activities Arts & crafts; Cards; Games; Reading groups; Movies; Shopping trips; Social/Cultural gatherings; Bingo; Resident council; Food service committee; Welcoming committee.

ROCHESTER

Aberdeen Nursing Home
1290 Lake Ave, Rochester, NY, 14613
(716) 254-1593
Admin Joseph B Dilal III. *Medical Dir/Dir of Nursing* Rose Samentello RN DON.
Licensure Skilled care. *Beds* SNF 98. *Certified* Medicaid; Medicare.
Owner Proprietary Corp.
Admissions Requirements Minimum age 18; Physician's request.
Staff RNs; LPNs; Orderlies; Nurses aides; Physical therapists; Recreational therapists; Speech therapists; Activities coordinators; Dietitians; Ophthalmologists.
Facilities Dining room; Physical therapy room; Activities room; Laundry room; Barber/Beauty shop; Library.
Activities Arts & crafts; Cards; Games; Reading groups; Prayer groups; Movies; Shopping trips; Social/Cultural gatherings.

Alaimo Nursing Home
1140 Norton St, Rochester, NY, 14621
(716) 467-2100
Admin Claudia Spindelman. *Medical Dir/Dir of Nursing* Caroline Christ.
Licensure Skilled care. *Beds* 42. *Certified* Medicaid; Medicare.
Owner Proprietary Corp.
Staff Physicians; RNs; LPNs; Orderlies; Nurses aides; Physical therapists; Recreational therapists; Speech therapists; Activities coordinators; Dietitians; Ophthalmologists.
Facilities Dining room; Laundry room.
Activities Arts & crafts; Cards; Games; Reading groups; Prayer groups; Movies; Shopping trips; Social/Cultural gatherings.

Baird Nursing Home
2150 Saint Paul St, Rochester, NY, 14621
(716) 342-5540
Admin Norine B Nickason. *Medical Dir/Dir of Nursing* Dr John Burkhardt; Katherine Sweeney RN DON.
Licensure Skilled care. *Beds* SNF 28.
Owner Privately owned.
Admissions Requirements Minimum age 16; Physician's request.
Staff Physicians 9 (pt); RNs 2 (ft), 4 (pt); LPNs 1 (ft), 2 (pt); Nurses aides 4 (ft), 13 (pt); Physical therapists 1 (pt); Recreational therapists 1 (pt); Activities coordinators 1 (pt); Dietitians 1 (ft), 1 (pt).
Facilities Dining room; Physical therapy room; Activities room; Laundry room; Barber/Beauty shop.
Activities Arts & crafts; Cards; Games; Prayer groups; Movies; Shopping trips; Social/Cultural gatherings.

Beechwood Sanitarium
900 Culver Rd, Rochester, NY, 14609
(716) 288-3335
Admin Herbert Chambery. *Medical Dir/Dir of Nursing* Louis Siegel.
Licensure Skilled care. *Beds* 80. *Certified* Medicaid; Medicare.
Owner Proprietary Corp.
Admissions Requirements Medical examination; Physician's request.
Staff Physicians 1 (pt); RNs 5 (ft), 4 (pt); LPNs 12 (ft), 3 (pt); Nurses aides 31 (ft), 14 (pt); Physical therapists 1 (pt); Occupational therapists 1 (pt); Speech therapists 1 (pt); Activities coordinators 1 (ft); Dietitians 1 (pt); Dentists 1 (pt); Podiatrists 1 (pt).
Facilities Dining room; Physical therapy room; Activities room; Crafts room; Laundry room; Barber/Beauty shop; Library.
Activities Arts & crafts; Cards; Games; Reading groups; Shopping trips; Social/Cultural gatherings.

Blossom Nursing Home
989 Blossom Rd, Rochester, NY, 14610
(716) 482-3500
Admin Barbara Kitanik. *Medical Dir/Dir of Nursing* Ernest T Anderson MD.
Licensure Skilled care. *Beds* 80. *Certified* Medicaid; Medicare.
Owner Proprietary Corp.
Admissions Requirements Physician's request.
Staff Physicians 1 (pt); RNs 9 (ft), 6 (pt); LPNs 7 (ft), 1 (pt); Nurses aides 34 (ft), 7 (pt); Physical therapists 1 (pt); Recreational therapists 1 (ft); Occupational therapists 1 (pt); Speech therapists 1 (pt); Activities coordinators 1 (ft); Dietitians 1 (ft).
Facilities Dining room; Physical therapy room; Activities room; Crafts room; Laundry room; Barber/Beauty shop.
Activities Arts & crafts; Cards; Games; Reading groups; Movies.

Brightonian Nursing Home
1919 Elmwood Ave, Rochester, NY, 14620
(716) 271-8700

Admin Stephen Sclamo. *Medical Dir/Dir of Nursing* Ernest T Anderson MD.
Licensure Skilled care. *Beds* 54. *Certified* Medicaid; Medicare.
Owner Proprietary Corp.
Admissions Requirements Minimum age 16; Medical examination; Physician's request.
Staff Physicians 1 (pt); RNs 15 (ft); LPNs 4 (ft); Orderlies 2 (ft); Nurses aides 24 (ft), 1 (pt); Physical therapists 1 (pt); Occupational therapists 1 (pt); Speech therapists 1 (pt); Activities coordinators 2 (ft); Dietitians 1 (pt); Ophthalmologists 1 (pt); Podiatrists 1 (pt); Audiologists 1 (pt).
Facilities Dining room; Physical therapy room; Activities room; Crafts room; Laundry room; Barber/Beauty shop.
Activities Arts & crafts; Games; Reading groups; Movies; Social/Cultural gatherings.

Episcopal Church Home
505 Mount Hope Ave, Rochester, NY, 14620
(716) 546-8400
Admin Loren J Ranaletta. *Medical Dir/Dir of Nursing* Dr P Bomba; Karen Ekiert RN DON.
Licensure Skilled care; Intermediate care. *Beds* SNF 80 11B 62. *Certified* Medicaid; Medicare.
Owner Nonprofit Corp.
Admissions Requirements Minimum age 62; Medical examination.
Staff RNs 7 (ft), 4 (pt); LPNs 11 (ft), 5 (pt); Nurses aides 43 (ft), 14 (pt); Physical therapists 1 (pt); Physical therapy aides 4 (ft).
Facilities Dining room; Physical therapy room; Activities room; Chapel; Crafts room; Barber/Beauty shop; Library; Music room.
Activities Arts & crafts; Cards; Games; Reading groups; Prayer groups; Movies; Shopping trips; Social/Cultural gatherings; Exercise; Discussion groups; Literature readings; Music.

Genesee Hospital—Extended Care Facility
224 Alexander St, Rochester, NY, 14607
(716) 263-6000
Admin John D Hellems. *Medical Dir/Dir of Nursing* Neal McNabb MD; Shirley Reber RN.
Licensure Skilled care. *Beds* SNF 40. *Certified* Medicaid; Medicare.
Owner Nonprofit Corp.
Admissions Requirements Medical examination; Physician's request.
Staff Physicians 30 (ft); RNs 4 (ft), 1 (pt); LPNs 4 (ft), 1 (pt); Orderlies 1 (ft); Nurses aides 17 (ft), 3 (pt); Physical therapists 1 (ft); Activities coordinators 1 (pt); Dietitians 1 (ft).
Languages Italian, Spanish
Facilities Dining room; Physical therapy room; Activities room; Chapel; Laundry room; Barber/Beauty shop.
Activities Arts & crafts; Games; Reading groups; Prayer groups; Movies; Music therapy; Broadcasting within facility; Pet visitations.

Goodman Gardens Nursing Home Co Inc
8 N Goodman St, Rochester, NY, 14607
(716) 473-1970
Admin Jon R Zemans. *Medical Dir/Dir of Nursing* Donald Symer MD; Susan Reynolds.
Licensure Skilled care; Intermediate care. *Beds* SNF 105; ICF 47. *Certified* Medicaid; Medicare.
Owner Nonprofit Corp.
Admissions Requirements Minimum age 65; Medical examination; Physician's request.
Staff Physicians 2 (pt); RNs 7 (ft); LPNs 15 (ft); Nurses aides 40 (ft); Physical therapists 1 (pt); Recreational therapists 1 (ft); Occupational therapists 1 (pt); Speech therapists 1 (pt); Activities coordinators 3

(ft); Dietitians 1 (ft); Dentists 1 (pt); Ophthalmologists 1 (pt); Podiatrists 1 (pt); Dentist 1 (pt).
Facilities Dining room; Physical therapy room; Activities room; Crafts room; Barber/Beauty shop.
Activities Arts & crafts; Cards; Games; Reading groups; Prayer groups; Movies; Shopping trips; Social/Cultural gatherings.

Hamilton Manor Nursing Home
1172 Long Pond Rd, Rochester, NY, 14626
(716) 225-0450
Admin Morris F Richardson. *Medical Dir/Dir of Nursing* Russell Barton MD; Pheebe Dutille RN DON.
Licensure Skilled care. *Beds* SNF 40. *Certified* Medicaid; Medicare.
Owner Privately owned.
Staff RNs 2 (ft), 2 (pt); LPNs 2 (ft), 5 (pt); Nurses aides 10 (ft), 11 (pt); Physical therapists 1 (pt); Occupational therapists 1 (pt); Speech therapists 1 (pt); Activities coordinators 1 (pt); Ophthalmologists; Podiatrists 1 (pt).
Facilities Dining room; Activities room; Crafts room; Laundry room; Barber/Beauty shop.
Activities Arts & crafts; Cards; Games; Reading groups; Prayer groups; Movies; Shopping trips.

Hurlbut Nursing Home*
1177 E Henrietta Rd, Rochester, NY, 14623
(716) 424-4770
Admin Vincent F Distefano. *Medical Dir/Dir of Nursing* Kenneth Nudo MD.
Licensure Skilled care. *Beds* 160. *Certified* Medicaid; Medicare.
Owner Proprietary Corp.
Staff Physicians; RNs; LPNs.
Facilities Dining room; Physical therapy room; Activities room; Chapel; Crafts room; Laundry room; Barber/Beauty shop; Library.
Activities Arts & crafts; Cards; Games; Reading groups; Prayer groups.

Jewish Home of Rochester
2021 Winton Rd S, Rochester, NY, 14618
(716) 427-7760
Admin Arnold S Gissin. *Medical Dir/Dir of Nursing* Bernard Shore MD; Mercelle Grant RN.
Licensure Skilled care; Intermediate care. *Beds* 362. *Certified* Medicaid; Medicare.
Owner Nonprofit Corp.
Admissions Requirements Minimum age 65 (with exceptions).
Staff Physicians 1 (ft), 5 (pt); RNs 22 (ft); Nurses aides 113 (ft); Physical therapists 3 (ft); Recreational therapists 5 (ft); Occupational therapists 1 (ft); Dietitians 3 (ft); Dentists 1 (pt); Ophthalmologists 1 (pt); Podiatrists 1 (pt); Audiologists 1 (pt).
Affiliation Jewish
Facilities Dining room; Physical therapy room; Activities room; Chapel; Crafts room; Laundry room; Barber/Beauty shop; Library; Training kitchen; Occupational therapy room.
Activities Arts & crafts; Games; Reading groups; Prayer groups; Movies; Shopping trips; Social/Cultural gatherings.

Lakeshore Nursing Home
425 Beach Ave, Rochester, NY, 14612
(716) 663-0930
Admin Claude B Flack. *Medical Dir/Dir of Nursing* Cheryl O'Brien RN.
Licensure Skilled care. *Beds* SNF 229. *Certified* Medicaid; Medicare.
Owner Proprietary Corp.
Admissions Requirements Minimum age 16; Medical examination; Physician's request.
Staff Physicians; RNs; LPNs; Orderlies; Nurses aides; Physical therapists; Recreational therapists; Occupational

therapists; Speech therapists; Activities coordinators; Dietitians; Audiologists Dentist; Clerk.
Facilities Dining room; Physical therapy room; Activities room; Crafts room; Laundry room; Barber/Beauty shop; Library.
Activities Arts & crafts; Cards; Games; Reading groups; Prayer groups; Movies.

Latta Road Nursing Home
2100 Latta Rd, Rochester, NY, 14612
(716) 225-0910
Admin Eleanor Richardson.
Licensure Skilled care. *Beds* 40. *Certified* Medicaid; Medicare.
Owner Proprietary Corp.

Latta Road Nursing Home A
2102 Latta Rd, Rochester, NY, 14612
(716) 225-0920
Admin Daniel E Richardson.
Licensure Skilled care. *Beds* SNF 40. *Certified* Medicaid; Medicare.
Owner Proprietary Corp.

Monroe Community Hospital—Extended Care Facility
435 E Henrietta Rd, Rochester, NY, 14603
(716) 473-4080
Admin J Raymond Diehl Jr. *Medical Dir/Dir of Nursing* (Acting) Anthony J Izzo MD.
Licensure Skilled care; Intermediate care. *Beds* 354. *Certified* Medicaid; Medicare.
Owner Publicly owned.
Staff Physicians 19 (ft), 75 (pt); RNs 83 (ft), 22 (pt); LPNs 135 (ft), 16 (pt); Nurses aides 131 (ft), 17 (pt); Physical therapists 11 (ft); Recreational therapists 9 (ft); Occupational therapists 5 (ft); Speech therapists 1 (ft); Activities coordinators 4 (ft); Dietitians 4 (ft); Dentists 1 (ft); Ophthalmologists 3 (pt); Podiatrists 1 (pt); Dentist 1 (pt).
Facilities Dining room; Physical therapy room; Activities room; Chapel; Crafts room; Laundry room; Barber/Beauty shop; Library.
Activities Arts & crafts; Cards; Games; Reading groups; Prayer groups; Movies; Shopping trips; Social/Cultural gatherings.

Nortonian Nursing Home*
1335 Portland Ave, Rochester, NY, 14621
(716) 544-4000
Admin John Hansen.
Licensure Skilled care. *Beds* 120. *Certified* Medicaid; Medicare.
Owner Proprietary Corp.

Park Home Nursing Home*
1556 Mount Hope Ave, Rochester, NY, 14620
(716) 473-2444
Admin Kathryn S Brady.
Licensure Skilled care. *Beds* 120. *Certified* Medicaid; Medicare.
Owner Proprietary Corp.

Park Ridge Nursing Home
1555 Long Pond Rd, Rochester, NY, 14626
(716) 723-7200
Admin Frank R Tripodi. *Medical Dir/Dir of Nursing* Nathaniel J Hurst MD.
Licensure Skilled care. *Beds* 120. *Certified* Medicaid; Medicare.
Owner Nonprofit Corp.
Admissions Requirements Minimum age 16; Medical examination; Physician's request.
Staff RNs; LPNs; Nurses aides; Physical therapists; Recreational therapists 1 (ft); Occupational therapists 1 (ft); Speech therapists 1 (pt); Activities coordinators 1 (pt); Dietitians 1 (ft); Podiatrists 1 (pt).
Facilities Dining room; Physical therapy room; Activities room; Crafts room; Laundry room; Barber/Beauty shop.
Activities Arts & crafts; Cards; Games; Reading groups; Prayer groups; Movies; Shopping trips; Social/Cultural gatherings; Gift cart; Gardening; Mom & tots visit.

Pinnacle Nursing Home
1175 Monroe Ave, Rochester, NY, 14620
(716) 442-0450
Admin Renee P Cassano. *Medical Dir/Dir of
Nursing* Joel Shamaskin MD; Donna M
Giorgini RN.
Licensure Skilled care. *Beds* SNF 161.
Certified Medicaid; Medicare.
Owner Proprietary Corp.
Admissions Requirements Minimum age 21;
Medical examination.
Staff RNs 6 (ft), 3 (pt); LPNs 19 (ft), 5 (pt);
Nurses aides 68 (ft), 15 (pt); Physical
therapists 1 (pt); Occupational therapists 1
(pt); Activities coordinators 3 (ft); Dietitians
1 (pt).
Facilities Dining room; Physical therapy
room; Activities room; Crafts room; Laundry
room; Barber/Beauty shop; Library.
Activities Arts & crafts; Cards; Games;
Reading groups; Prayer groups; Movies;
Shopping trips; Social/Cultural gatherings;
Garden club; Veterans club; Cooking class.

Rochester Friendly Home
3156 East Ave, Rochester, NY, 14618
(716) 381-1600
Admin James E Tewhirst.
Licensure Skilled care; Intermediate care. *Beds*
SNF 80; ICF 124. *Certified* Medicaid;
Medicare.
Owner Nonprofit Corp.
Admissions Requirements Minimum age 55;
Medical examination; Physician's request.
Staff Physicians 3 (pt); RNs 6 (ft), 19 (pt);
LPNs 8 (ft), 22 (pt); Nurses aides 40 (ft), 42
(pt); Physical therapists 2 (ft); Occupational
therapists 1 (pt); Speech therapists 1 (pt);
Activities coordinators 1 (ft); Dietitians 1
(ft); Dentists 1 (pt); Ophthalmologists 1 (pt);
Podiatrists 1 (pt); Medical director 1 (pt);
Assistant director of nursing 1 (pt); Social
workers 3 (ft); Pharmacist 1 (pt); Dentist 1
(pt); Volunteer coordinator 1 (pt); Director
of nursing 1 (ft).
Facilities Dining room; Physical therapy
room; Activities room; Crafts room; Laundry
room; Barber/Beauty shop; Library.
Activities Arts & crafts; Cards; Games;
Reading groups; Movies; Shopping trips;
Social/Cultural gatherings.

**St Ann's Home for the Aged Inc—The
Heritage***
1500 Portland Ave, Rochester, NY, 14621
(716) 342-1700
Admin Marie Michelle.
Licensure Skilled care; Intermediate care. *Beds*
354. *Certified* Medicaid; Medicare.
Owner Nonprofit Corp.
Affiliation Roman Catholic

St John's Nursing Home Inc
150 Highland Ave, Rochester, NY, 14620
(716) 271-5413
Admin Vincent Parks. *Medical Dir/Dir of
Nursing* R Paul Miller MD.
Licensure Skilled care. *Beds* 230. *Certified*
Medicaid; Medicare.
Owner Nonprofit Corp.
Admissions Requirements Medical
examination.
Staff Physicians 3 (ft), 2 (pt); RNs 23 (ft), 14
(pt); LPNs 29 (ft), 16 (pt); Nurses aides 109
(ft), 24 (pt); Physical therapists 4 (ft);
Recreational therapists 4 (ft); Occupational
therapists 1 (pt); Speech therapists 2 (ft), 1
(pt); Activities coordinators 1 (ft); Dietitians
2 (ft), 1 (pt); Dentists 1 (pt);
Ophthalmologists 1 (pt); Podiatrists 1 (pt);
Dentist 1 (pt).
Facilities Dining room; Physical therapy
room; Activities room; Chapel; Crafts room;
Laundry room; Barber/Beauty shop; Library.

Activities Arts & crafts; Cards; Games;
Reading groups; Prayer groups; Movies;
Shopping trips; Social/Cultural gatherings;
Performing arts troupe for residents;
Sunshine olympics; Recreational outings.

**Strong Memorial Hospital Skilled Nursing
Facility**
601 Elmwood Ave, Rochester, NY, 14642
(716) 275-2644
Admin Fran Carlin-Rogers. *Medical Dir/Dir of
Nursing* A Izzo MD; Margaret Smith RN
DON.
Licensure Skilled care. *Beds* SNF 40. *Certified*
Medicaid; Medicare.
Owner Nonprofit organization/foundation.
Admissions Requirements Physician's request.
Staff Physicians 1 (pt); RNs; LPNs; Physical
therapists 1 (ft); Recreational therapists 1
(ft); Occupational therapists 1 (pt); Speech
therapists 1 (pt); Dietitians 1 (pt); Podiatrists
1 (pt).
Facilities Dining room; Physical therapy
room; Activities room; Chapel; Laundry
room; Use of all hospital facilities.
Activities Arts & crafts; Group & individual
activities.

Wesley-on-East Ltd*
630 East Ave, Rochester, NY, 14607-2194
(716) 473-1970
Admin Jon R Zemans. *Medical Dir/Dir of
Nursing* Donald Symer MD; Susan
Reynolds.
Owner Nonprofit Corp.
Admissions Requirements Minimum age 65;
Medical examination; Physician's request.
Staff RNs 7 (ft), 6 (pt); LPNs 15 (ft), 5 (pt);
Nurses aides 38 (ft), 12 (pt); Physical
therapists 1 (ft); Recreational therapists 2
(ft), 1 (pt); Occupational therapists 1 (pt);
Speech therapists 1 (pt); Activities
coordinators 1 (pt); Dietitians 3 (ft);
Ophthalmologists 1 (pt).
Affiliation Methodist
Facilities Dining room; Physical therapy
room; Activities room; Chapel; Crafts room;
Laundry room; Barber/Beauty shop; Library.
Activities Arts & crafts; Cards; Games;
Reading groups; Prayer groups; Movies;
Shopping trips; Social/Cultural gatherings;
Exercise sessions; Humanities; Remotivation;
Trips; Sing-alongs.

Westgate Nursing Home
525 Beahan Rd, Rochester, NY, 14624
(716) 247-7880
Admin David Giunta. *Medical Dir/Dir of
Nursing* Agnes Gaulin DON.
Licensure Skilled care. *Beds* 124. *Certified*
Medicaid; Medicare.
Owner Privately owned.
Admissions Requirements Minimum age 16;
Medical examination; Physician's request.
Staff RNs; LPNs; Orderlies; Nurses aides;
Physical therapists; Reality therapists;
Recreational therapists; Occupational
therapists; Activities coordinators; Dietitians;
Dentists; Ophthalmologists.
Facilities Dining room; Physical therapy
room; Activities room; Chapel; Crafts room;
Laundry room; Barber/Beauty shop; Library.
Activities Arts & crafts; Cards; Games;
Reading groups; Prayer groups; Movies;
Shopping trips; Social/Cultural gatherings;
Wheelchair accesible van.

Woodside Manor Nursing Home Inc*
2425 Clinton Ave S, Rochester, NY, 14618
(716) 275-0370
Admin Margaret Gallagher.
Licensure Skilled care. *Beds* 44. *Certified*
Medicaid; Medicare.
Owner Proprietary Corp.

ROCKAWAY PARK

Park Nursing Home*
128 Beach 115th St, Rockaway Park, NY,
11694
(718) 474-6400
Admin Ralph Newman.
Licensure Skilled care. *Beds* 196. *Certified*
Medicaid; Medicare.
Owner Proprietary Corp.

Promenade Nursing Home
140 Beach 114th St, Rockaway Park, NY,
11694
(718) 945-4600
Admin Moses Vogel. *Medical Dir/Dir of
Nursing* Reuben Tizes MD; Jodee Berkowitz
RN DON.
Licensure Skilled care. *Beds* SNF 240.
Certified Medicaid; Medicare.
Owner Proprietary Corp.
Admissions Requirements Medical
examination; Physician's request.
Staff Physicians 4 (pt); RNs 8 (ft), 4 (pt);
LPNs 21 (ft), 6 (pt); Orderlies 5 (ft), 3 (pt);
Nurses aides 77 (ft), 12 (pt); Physical
therapists 1 (ft); Occupational therapists 1
(ft); Speech therapists 1 (pt); Activities
coordinators 1 (ft); Dietitians 1 (ft);
Ophthalmologists 2 (ft).
Languages Yiddish, Hebrew, Italian, French
Facilities Dining room; Physical therapy
room; Activities room; Chapel; Crafts room;
Laundry room; Barber/Beauty shop; Library.
Activities Arts & crafts; Cards; Games;
Reading groups; Prayer groups; Movies;
Shopping trips; Social/Cultural gatherings.

ROCKVILLE CENTRE

Rockville Nursing Center Inc
41 Maine Ave, Rockville Centre, NY, 11570
(516) 536-7730
Admin Siegmundo Hirsch. *Medical Dir/Dir of
Nursing* Harvey Kuschner MD; Barbara
Silver RN DNS.
Licensure Skilled care. *Beds* SNF 152.
Certified Medicaid; Medicare.
Owner Proprietary Corp.
Admissions Requirements Minimum age 16;
Physician's request.
Staff RNs 12 (ft), 5 (pt); LPNs 14 (ft), 2 (pt);
Orderlies 1 (ft); Nurses aides 47 (ft), 22 (pt);
Physical therapists 1 (pt); Recreational
therapists 2 (ft); Activities coordinators 1
(ft); Dietitians 1 (ft), 1 (pt).
Languages Spanish, German, Hebrew,
Yiddish, Italian, French, Creole, Cantonese,
Japanese
Facilities Dining room; Physical therapy
room; Activities room; Crafts room; Laundry
room; Barber/Beauty shop.
Activities Arts & crafts; Cards; Games;
Reading groups; Prayer groups; Movies;
Social/Cultural gatherings; Excursions.

Rockville Residence Manor*
50 Maine Ave, Rockville Centre, NY, 11570
(516) 536-8000
Licensure Intermediate care. *Beds* 66.
Owner Proprietary Corp.

ROME

Betsy Ross Health Related Facility*
Elsie St-Cedarbrook Ln, Rome, NY, 13440
(315) 339-2220
Licensure Intermediate care. *Beds* 120.
Owner Proprietary Corp.

**Health Related Facility & Nursing Home
Company of Rome Inc**
800 W Chestnut St, Rome, NY, 13440
(315) 339-3210
Admin H Priscilla Emmans. *Medical Dir/Dir
of Nursing* Dr S V Ramineni; Mrs Mary
Marlar.

Licensure Intermediate care. *Beds* ICF 100.
Owner Nonprofit Corp.
Admissions Requirements Minimum age;
Medical examination; Physician's request.
Staff Physicians 1 (pt); RNs 3 (ft), 4 (pt);
LPNs 2 (ft), 5 (pt); Nurses aides 12 (ft), 20
(pt); Physical therapists 1 (pt); Occupational
therapists 1 (pt); Speech therapists 1 (pt);
Activities coordinators 1 (ft), 1 (pt);
Dietitians 1 (pt).
Facilities Dining room; Physical therapy
room; Activities room; Laundry room;
Barber/Beauty shop.
Activities Arts & crafts; Cards; Games; Prayer
groups; Movies; Shopping trips; Social/
Cultural gatherings.

Rome & Murphy Memorial Hospital
1500 N James St, Rome, NY, 13440
(315) 338-7000
Admin Kent Longnecker. *Medical Dir/Dir of
Nursing* Dr Neville Harper.
Licensure Skilled care. *Beds* SNF 40. *Certified*
Medicaid; Medicare.
Owner Nonprofit organization/foundation.
Admissions Requirements Minimum age 16;
Medical examination; Physician's request.
Staff Physicians 1 (pt); RNs 2 (ft), 1 (pt);
LPNs 3 (ft), 3 (pt); Orderlies 4 (ft); Nurses
aides 15 (ft); Physical therapists 1 (pt);
Occupational therapists 1 (pt); Activities
coordinators 1 (ft); Dietitians 1 (pt);
Ophthalmologists 1 (pt).
Languages Italian, Polish, Spanish
Facilities Dining room; Physical therapy
room; Activities room; Chapel; Crafts room;
Laundry room; Barber/Beauty shop.
Activities Arts & crafts; Cards; Games;
Reading groups; Prayer groups; Movies;
Shopping trips; Social/Cultural gatherings;
Picnics.

Rome-Parkway Inc
950 Floyd Ave, Rome, NY, 13440
(315) 336-5400
Admin Joseph Corradino. *Medical Dir/Dir of
Nursing* Dr Gary Wakeman; Karen Smith
RN.
Licensure Skilled care. *Beds* SNF 80.
Owner Proprietary Corp.
Admissions Requirements Minimum age 21;
Medical examination; Physician's request.
Staff Physicians 1 (pt); RNs 6 (ft), 2 (pt);
LPNs 9 (ft), 6 (pt); Orderlies 1 (ft); Nurses
aides 28 (ft), 25 (pt); Physical therapists 2
(ft), 1 (pt); Recreational therapists 2 (ft);
Occupational therapists 1 (ft), 1 (pt); Speech
therapists 1 (pt); Dietitians 1 (ft), 1 (pt).
Facilities Dining room; Physical therapy
room; Activities room; Crafts room; Laundry
room; Barber/Beauty shop.
Activities Arts & crafts; Cards; Games;
Reading groups; Prayer groups; Movies;
Shopping trips; Social/Cultural gatherings.

Stonehedge Nursing Home*
801 N James St, Rome, NY, 13440
(315) 337-0550
Admin Brian Jordan. *Medical Dir/Dir of
Nursing* Dr James J DiCastro.
Licensure Skilled care. *Beds* 160. *Certified*
Medicaid; Medicare.
Owner Proprietary Corp.
Admissions Requirements Minimum age 16.
Staff RNs 9 (ft), 4 (pt); LPNs 18 (ft), 10 (pt);
Orderlies 2 (ft); Nurses aides 70 (ft), 35 (pt);
Physical therapists 1 (pt); Reality therapists
1 (ft); Recreational therapists 1 (ft);
Occupational therapists 1 (pt); Speech
therapists 1 (pt); Activities coordinators 1
(ft); Dietitians 2 (ft), 6 (pt); Dentists 1 (pt).
Facilities Dining room; Physical therapy
room; Activities room; Chapel; Crafts room;
Laundry room; Barber/Beauty shop.
Activities Arts & crafts; Cards; Games;
Reading groups; Prayer groups; Movies;
Shopping trips; Social/Cultural gatherings.

ROSCOE

Roscoe Community Nursing Home
Rockland Rd, Roscoe, NY, 12776
(607) 498-4121, (914) 439-4350
Admin Richard D Sherman. *Medical Dir/Dir
of Nursing* Alan Fried MD.
Licensure Skilled care. *Beds* 85. *Certified*
Medicaid; Medicare.
Owner Nonprofit Corp.
Admissions Requirements Minimum age 16;
Medical examination; Physician's request.
Staff Physicians 2 (pt); RNs 6 (ft), 4 (pt);
LPNs 6 (ft), 1 (pt); Nurses aides 50 (ft), 2
(pt); Physical therapists 1 (pt); Occupational
therapists 1 (pt); Speech therapists 1 (pt);
Activities coordinators 1 (ft); Dietitians 1
(pt); Ophthalmologists 1 (pt).
Facilities Dining room; Physical therapy
room; Activities room; Crafts room; Laundry
room; Barber/Beauty shop; Library.
Activities Arts & crafts; Cards; Games;
Reading groups; Prayer groups; Movies;
Shopping trips; Social/Cultural gatherings.

ROSLYN HEIGHTS

Sunharbor Manor
255 Warner Ave, Roslyn Heights, NY, 11577
(516) 621-5400
Admin Clifford R Osinoff. *Medical Dir/Dir of
Nursing* Dr J Cohen.
Licensure Skilled care; Health related care.
Beds SNF 112; HRF 54. *Certified* Medicaid.
Owner Proprietary Corp.
Facilities Dining room; Physical therapy
room; Activities room; Crafts room; Laundry
room; Barber/Beauty shop; Library.
Activities Arts & crafts; Cards; Games;
Reading groups; Prayer groups; Movies;
Shopping trips; Social/Cultural gatherings.

ROUSES POINT

Cedar Hedge Nursing Home
260 Lake St, Rouses Point, NY, 12979-1598
(518) 297-5190
Admin William H Pollock. *Medical Dir/Dir of
Nursing* Dawn L Pollock RN DON.
Licensure Skilled care. *Beds* SNF 60. *Certified*
Medicaid; Medicare.
Owner Privately owned.
Admissions Requirements Minimum age 18;
Medical examination; Physician's request.
Staff Physicians 1 (pt); RNs 4 (ft), 2 (pt);
LPNs 5 (ft), 2 (pt); Nurses aides 24 (ft), 6
(pt); Physical therapists 1 (pt); Speech
therapists 1 (pt); Activities coordinators 1
(ft); Dietitians 1 (pt); Dentists 1 (pt);
Podiatrists 1 (pt).
Languages French
Facilities Dining room; Physical therapy
room; Activities room; Laundry room;
Barber/Beauty shop; Leisure areas.
Activities Arts & crafts; Cards; Games;
Reading groups; Prayer groups; Movies;
Shopping trips; Social/Cultural gatherings.

RYE BROOK

King Street Nursing Home
787 King St, Rye Brook, NY, 10573
(914) 937-5800
Admin Yale Wilner.
Licensure Skilled care; Intermediate care. *Beds*
SNF 80; ICF 40. *Certified* Medicaid;
Medicare.
Owner Proprietary Corp.
Admissions Requirements Minimum age 55;
Medical examination; Physician's request.
Staff Physicians; RNs; LPNs; Orderlies;
Nurses aides; Physical therapists;
Recreational therapists; Occupational
therapists; Speech therapists; Activities
coordinators; Dietitians; Dentists;
Ophthalmologists; Podiatrists.

Facilities Dining room; Physical therapy
room; Activities room; Chapel; Crafts room;
Laundry room; Barber/Beauty shop; Library;
On 10 landscaped acres; 8 outdoor terraces;
Outdoor walks.
Activities Arts & crafts; Cards; Games;
Reading groups; Prayer groups; Movies;
Shopping trips; Social/Cultural gatherings.

SAINT JAMES

St James Nursing Home Skilled
275 Moriches Rd, Saint James, NY, 11780
(516) 862-8000
Admin Hal Jame Schifter. *Medical Dir/Dir of
Nursing* R Anthony Martino MD; B R
Foray DNS.
Licensure Skilled care. *Beds* SNF 230.
Certified Medicaid; Medicare.
Owner Proprietary Corp.
Admissions Requirements Minimum age 14;
Physician's request.
Staff Physicians; RNs; LPNs; Orderlies;
Nurses aides; Physical therapists;
Recreational therapists; Occupational
therapists; Speech therapists; Activities
coordinators; Dietitians; Dentists;
Ophthalmologists; Podiatrists.
Languages Spanish, Italian, French, German
Facilities Dining room; Physical therapy
room; Activities room; Chapel; Crafts room;
Laundry room; Barber/Beauty shop; Library.
Activities Arts & crafts; Cards; Games;
Reading groups; Prayer groups; Movies;
Shopping trips; Social/Cultural gatherings.

SALAMANCA

Salamanca Nursing Home Inc
451 Broad St, Salamanca, NY, 14779
(716) 945-1800
Admin Doris Ann Brown. *Medical Dir/Dir of
Nursing* Dr Paul Sum.
Licensure Skilled care; Intermediate care. *Beds*
120. *Certified* Medicaid; Medicare.
Owner Proprietary Corp.
Admissions Requirements Minimum age 16;
Medical examination; Physician's request.
Staff Physicians 13 (pt); RNs 6 (ft), 4 (pt);
LPNs 5 (ft), 12 (pt); Orderlies 5 (pt); Nurses
aides 32 (ft), 17 (pt); Physical therapists 1
(pt); Recreational therapists 2 (ft);
Occupational therapists 1 (pt); Speech
therapists 1 (pt); Activities coordinators 2
(ft); Dietitians 1 (ft); Dentists 1 (pt);
Podiatrists 1 (pt).
Facilities Dining room; Physical therapy
room; Activities room; Laundry room;
Barber/Beauty shop; Library.
Activities Arts & crafts; Cards; Games;
Reading groups; Prayer groups; Movies;
Shopping trips; Social/Cultural gatherings.

SARATOGA SPRINGS

Saratoga Hospital Nursing Home
211 Church St, Saratoga Springs, NY, 12866
(518) 584-6000
Admin James E Shoemaker. *Medical Dir/Dir
of Nursing* Dr Warren Letts.
Licensure Skilled care. *Beds* 72. *Certified*
Medicaid; Medicare.
Owner Nonprofit Corp.
Staff RNs; LPNs; Nurses aides; Physical
therapists; Speech therapists; Activities
coordinators; Dietitians; Dentists;
Podiatrists.
Facilities Dining room; Physical therapy
room; Activities room; Barber/Beauty shop.
Activities Arts & crafts; Games; Reading
groups; Prayer groups; Movies; Shopping
trips; Social/Cultural gatherings.

Wesley Health Care Center Inc
Lawrence St, Saratoga Springs, NY, 12866
(518) 587-3600

Admin Ralph J Barron Jr. *Medical Dir/Dir of Nursing* Fred A Phillips Jr MD.
Licensure Skilled care; Intermediate care. *Beds* SNF 194; ICF 70. *Certified* Medicaid; Medicare.
Owner Nonprofit Corp.
Admissions Requirements Minimum age 16; Medical examination; Physician's request.
Affiliation Methodist
Facilities Dining room; Physical therapy room; Activities room; Chapel; Crafts room; Laundry room; Barber/Beauty shop; Library.
Activities Arts & crafts; Cards; Games; Reading groups; Prayer groups; Movies; Shopping trips; Social/Cultural gatherings.

SAYVILLE

Good Samaritan Nursing Home
101 Elm St, Sayville, NY, 11782
(516) 567-6600
Admin Kenneth B Knutsen. *Medical Dir/Dir of Nursing* John Canning MD; Susan Bowes RN.
Licensure Skilled care. *Beds* SNF 100. *Certified* Medicaid; Medicare.
Owner Nonprofit Corp.
Staff RNs 6 (ft), 7 (pt); LPNs 4 (ft), 6 (pt); Orderlies 1 (pt); Nurses aides 30 (ft), 20 (pt); Physical therapists 1 (pt); Recreational therapists 1 (ft), 4 (pt); Occupational therapists 1 (pt); Activities coordinators 1 (ft); Dietitians 1 (ft).
Languages Italian
Affiliation Roman Catholic
Facilities Dining room; Physical therapy room; Activities room; Chapel; Crafts room; Barber/Beauty shop.
Activities Arts & crafts; Cards; Games; Reading groups; Prayer groups; Movies; Social/Cultural gatherings; Pet visits; Special meals.

SCARSDALE

Sprain Brook Manor Nursing Home
77 Jackson Ave, Scarsdale, NY, 10583
(914) 472-3200
Admin Henry Book. *Medical Dir/Dir of Nursing* John F Salimbene MD; Mary Grace RN.
Licensure Skilled care. *Beds* SNF 121. *Certified* Medicaid; Medicare.
Owner Privately owned.
Staff RNs 20 (ft); LPNs 5 (ft); Nurses aides 50 (ft); Physical therapists; Recreational therapists 2 (ft); Occupational therapists 1 (pt); Speech therapists 1 (pt); Activities coordinators 1 (ft); Dietitians 1 (ft); Dentists; Ophthalmologists; Podiatrists.
Languages Spanish, Italian, Yiddish, Hebrew, German, Portuguese
Activities Arts & crafts; Cards; Games; Reading groups; Prayer groups; Movies; Shopping trips; Social/Cultural gatherings.

SCHENECTADY

Hallmark Nursing Centre Inc
526 Altamont Ave, Schenectady, NY, 12303
(518) 346-6121
Admin Raymond Klocek.
Licensure Skilled care. *Beds* SNF 224. *Certified* Medicaid; Medicare.
Owner Proprietary Corp.
Admissions Requirements Minimum age 16; Medical examination; Physician's request.
Staff Physicians 14 (pt); RNs 12 (ft), 11 (pt); LPNs 15 (ft), 12 (pt); Nurses aides 84 (ft), 29 (pt); Physical therapists 1 (ft), 1 (pt); Recreational therapists 5 (pt); Occupational therapists 2 (ft); Speech therapists 1 (pt); Activities coordinators 1 (ft); Dietitians 1 (ft); Dentists 1 (pt); Ophthalmologists 1 (pt); Podiatrists 1 (pt).
Languages Spanish, Polish

Facilities Dining room; Physical therapy room; Activities room; Chapel; Crafts room; Laundry room; Barber/Beauty shop; Library.
Activities Arts & crafts; Cards; Games; Reading groups; Prayer groups; Movies; Shopping trips; Social/Cultural gatherings.

Kingsway Arms Nursing Center Inc
Kings Rd, Schenectady, NY, 12304
(518) 393-4117
Admin Robert DeAngelis.
Licensure Skilled care; Intermediate care. *Beds* 160. *Certified* Medicaid; Medicare.
Owner Proprietary Corp.

Silver Haven Nursing Home
1940 Hamburg St, Schenectady, NY, 12304
(518) 370-5051
Admin Jean E Duket. *Medical Dir/Dir of Nursing* A J Arony MD; Dorothy Kenny RN.
Licensure Skilled care. *Beds* SNF 86. *Certified* Medicaid; Medicare.
Owner Privately owned.
Staff Physicians 3 (pt); RNs 7 (ft), 8 (pt); LPNs 5 (ft), 11 (pt); Nurses aides 28 (ft), 16 (pt); Activities coordinators 1 (ft); Physical therapy assistants 1 (ft).
Facilities Dining room; Physical therapy room; Barber/Beauty shop.
Activities Arts & crafts; Cards; Games; Reading groups; Prayer groups; Movies; Shopping trips; Social/Cultural gatherings; Pet therapy.

SCOTIA

Baptist Retirement Center
297 N Ballston Ave, Scotia, NY, 12302
(518) 370-4700
Admin Timothy W Bartos. *Medical Dir/Dir of Nursing* Robert J Halbig MD; Jeffrey J Holmstrom.
Licensure Skilled care; Intermediate care. *Beds* SNF 100; ICF 80. *Certified* Medicaid; Medicare.
Owner Nonprofit Corp.
Admissions Requirements Minimum age 16; Medical examination.
Staff RNs 12 (ft), 24 (pt); LPNs 15 (ft), 21 (pt); Nurses aides 44 (ft), 40 (pt); Physical therapists 1 (ft); Occupational therapists 1 (ft); Activities coordinators 1 (ft); Dietitians 1 (pt).
Affiliation Baptist
Facilities Dining room; Physical therapy room; Activities room; Chapel; Crafts room; Laundry room; Barber/Beauty shop; Library; Occupational therapy room.
Activities Arts & crafts; Cards; Games; Reading groups; Prayer groups; Movies; Shopping trips; Social/Cultural gatherings.

Glendale Nursing Home
Hetcheltown Rd, Scotia, NY, 12302
(518) 384-3602
Admin John T McGrath. *Medical Dir/Dir of Nursing* Jung-Wen Chen MD; Anne O'Brien RN DON.
Licensure Skilled care; Intermediate care. *Beds* SNF 378; ICF 150. *Certified* Medicaid; Medicare.
Owner Publicly owned.
Staff Physicians 1 (ft), 5 (pt); RNs 45 (ft), 25 (pt); LPNs 38 (ft), 8 (pt); Nurses aides 181 (ft), 5 (pt); Physical therapists 1 (ft); Recreational therapists 5 (pt); Occupational therapists 2 (pt); Speech therapists 1 (pt); Activities coordinators 1 (ft); Dietitians 1 (ft); Dentists 1 (pt); Ophthalmologists 1 (pt); Podiatrists 1 (pt).
Facilities Dining room; Physical therapy room; Activities room; Chapel; Crafts room; Laundry room; Barber/Beauty shop; Bookmobile.

Activities Arts & crafts; Cards; Games; Reading groups; Prayer groups; Movies; Shopping trips; Social/Cultural gatherings; Picnics.

SIDNEY

The Hospital—Skilled Nursing Facility
Pearl St, Sidney, NY, 13838
(607) 563-3512
Admin Betty Ebert. *Medical Dir/Dir of Nursing* Dr R Hust; Winifred Armitage DON.
Licensure Skilled care. *Beds* 30. *Certified* Medicaid; Medicare.
Owner Publicly owned.
Admissions Requirements Minimum age 16; Physician's request.
Staff Physicians 15 (ft); RNs 1 (ft), 1 (pt); LPNs 5 (ft), 2 (pt); Nurses aides 8 (ft), 8 (pt); Physical therapists 1 (ft); Speech therapists 1 (pt); Activities coordinators 1 (pt); Dietitians 1 (pt); Dentists 1 (pt); Podiatrists 1 (pt).
Facilities Dining room; Physical therapy room; Activities room; Chapel; Crafts room; Barber/Beauty shop; Patio.
Activities Arts & crafts; Cards; Games; Reading groups; Prayer groups; Movies; Social/Cultural gatherings.

SMITHTOWN

Lutheran Center for the Aging
Rte 25A, Smithtown, NY, 11787
(516) 724-2200
Admin David Weinstein. *Medical Dir/Dir of Nursing* Dr Cruz; Elizabeth Dawling RN DON.
Licensure Skilled care; Intermediate care. *Beds* 353. *Certified* Medicaid; Medicare.
Owner Nonprofit Corp.
Admissions Requirements Minimum age 62; Medical examination; Physician's request.
Staff Physical therapists 2 (ft); Occupational therapists 1 (pt); Dentists 1 (pt); Podiatrists 1 (pt).
Languages Italian, Spanish, German
Affiliation Lutheran
Facilities Dining room; Physical therapy room; Activities room; Crafts room; Laundry room; Barber/Beauty shop; Library.
Activities Arts & crafts; Cards; Games; Reading groups; Prayer groups; Movies; Shopping trips; Social/Cultural gatherings.

SODUS

Blossom View Nursing Home*
6884 Maple Ave, Sodus, NY, 14551
(315) 483-9118
Admin Donna M Brown. *Medical Dir/Dir of Nursing* John L Ghertner MD.
Licensure Skilled care. *Beds* 60. *Certified* Medicaid; Medicare.
Owner Proprietary Corp.
Facilities Dining room; Physical therapy room; Activities room; Barber/Beauty shop.
Activities Arts & crafts; Games; Reading groups; Prayer groups; Shopping trips; Social/Cultural gatherings.

SOMERS

Somers Manor Nursing Home Inc
PO Box 445, Rte 100, Somers, NY, 10589
(914) 232-5101
Admin Janice C Depp. *Medical Dir/Dir of Nursing* James L Koo MD; Mary Joy Bloomer RN.
Licensure Skilled care; Health related. *Beds* SNF 123; Health related 101. *Certified* Medicaid; Medicare.
Owner Proprietary Corp.
Admissions Requirements Minimum age 17; Medical examination; Physician's request.

Staff RNs; LPNs; Nurses aides; Physical therapists 2 (pt); Occupational therapists 1 (pt); Activities coordinators 1 (ft); Dietitians 1 (ft).
Facilities Dining room; Physical therapy room; Activities room; Crafts room; Laundry room; Barber/Beauty shop.
Activities Arts & crafts; Cards; Games; Reading groups; Prayer groups; Movies; Shopping trips; Social/Cultural gatherings.

SOUTHAMPTON

Southampton Nursing Home Inc
330 Meeting House Ln, Southampton, NY, 11968
(516) 283-2134
Admin Maureen O Mahoney. Medical Dir/Dir of Nursing Dean Monaco MD; Margaret Schultz DON.
Licensure Skilled care. Beds SNF 62. Certified Medicaid; Medicare.
Owner Nonprofit Corp.
Admissions Requirements Minimum age 16.
Staff Activities coordinators 2 (ft); Dietitians 1 (ft).
Facilities Dining room; Physical therapy room; Activities room; Crafts room; Barber/Beauty shop; Library.
Activities Arts & crafts; Cards; Games; Reading groups; Prayer groups; Movies; Social/Cultural gatherings.

SPENCERPORT

Wedgewood Nursing Home
5 Church St, Spencerport, NY, 14559
(716) 352-4810
Admin Ann M Chupay. Medical Dir/Dir of Nursing Paul Rapoza MD; Ellen Hopkins DON.
Licensure Skilled care. Beds SNF 29. Certified Medicaid; Medicare.
Owner Proprietary Corp.
Admissions Requirements Minimum age 14; Medical examination; Physician's request.
Staff RNs 2 (ft), 4 (pt); LPNs 3 (ft), 6 (pt); Orderlies 1 (ft); Nurses aides 6 (ft), 20 (pt); Activities coordinators 1 (pt); Dietitians 1 (ft), 1 (pt).
Languages Italian
Facilities Dining room; Physical therapy room; Activities room; Chapel; Crafts room; Laundry room; Barber/Beauty shop; Library.
Activities Arts & crafts; Cards; Games; Reading groups; Prayer groups; Movies; Shopping trips; Social/Cultural gatherings.

SPRING VALLEY

Hillcrest Nursing Home*
661 N Main St, Spring Valley, NY, 10977
(914) 356-0567
Admin Harry Satin.
Licensure Skilled care. Beds 200. Certified Medicaid; Medicare.
Owner Proprietary Corp.

SPRINGVILLE

Fiddlers Green Manor Nursing Home
168 W Main St, Springville, NY, 14141
(716) 592-4781
Admin Thomas DuPont. Medical Dir/Dir of Nursing Mary Eileen Beland.
Licensure Skilled care. Beds SNF 82. Certified Medicaid; Medicare.
Owner Privately owned.
Admissions Requirements Medical examination.
Staff Physicians 5 (pt); RNs 4 (ft), 9 (pt); LPNs 8 (ft), 4 (pt); Orderlies 3 (ft); Nurses aides 24 (ft), 28 (pt); Occupational therapists 1 (ft), 1 (pt); Speech therapists 1 (pt); Activities coordinators 1 (ft), 1 (pt); Ophthalmologists 1 (pt).

Facilities Dining room; Physical therapy room; Activities room; Laundry room; Barber/Beauty shop.
Activities Arts & crafts; Games; Prayer groups; Movies; Shopping trips.

Jennie B Richmond Chaffee Nursing Home
222 E Main St, Springville, NY, 14141
(716) 592-2871
Admin Roger Ford. Medical Dir/Dir of Nursing Wade Stearns RN DNS.
Licensure Skilled care; HRF. Beds SNF 40; HRF 40. Certified Medicaid; Medicare.
Owner Nonprofit Corp.
Admissions Requirements Medical examination.
Staff RNs 3 (ft), 4 (pt); LPNs 8 (ft), 10 (pt); Nurses aides 13 (ft), 24 (pt); Physical therapists 2 (ft), 2 (pt); Recreational therapists 2 (ft), 1 (pt); Occupational therapists 2 (ft); Speech therapists 1 (pt); Dietitians 2 (ft).
Facilities Dining room; Physical therapy room; Activities room; Laundry room; Barber/Beauty shop.
Activities Arts & crafts; Cards; Games; Reading groups; Prayer groups; Movies; Social/Cultural gatherings.

STAATSBURG

Hyde Park Nursing Home
Rte 9 & Anderson School Rd, Staatsburg, NY, 12580
(914) 889-4500
Admin Raphael Yenowitz. Medical Dir/Dir of Nursing Pinaki Ray MD; Patricia McDermott RN DON.
Licensure Skilled care. Beds SNF 120. Certified Medicaid; Medicare.
Owner Proprietary Corp.
Staff Physicians 5 (pt); RNs 18 (ft), 8 (pt); LPNs 12 (ft), 6 (pt); Orderlies 10 (ft), 10 (pt); Nurses aides 40 (ft), 15 (pt); Physical therapists 1 (pt); Recreational therapists 1 (ft); Occupational therapists 1 (pt); Speech therapists 1 (pt); Activities coordinators 1 (ft); Dietitians 1 (ft); Dentists 1 (pt); Ophthalmologists 1 (pt).
Facilities Dining room; Physical therapy room; Activities room; Crafts room; Laundry room; Barber/Beauty shop; Library.
Activities Arts & crafts; Cards; Games; Reading groups; Prayer groups; Movies; Shopping trips; Social/Cultural gatherings.

STAMFORD

Community Hospital Skilled Nursing Facility
Harper St, Stamford, NY, 12167
(607) 652-7521
Admin Eleanor Fieldhouse. Medical Dir/Dir of Nursing Glen Joshpe MD; June Egan RN DON.
Licensure Skilled care. Beds SNF 40. Certified Medicaid; Medicare.
Owner Nonprofit Corp.
Admissions Requirements Minimum age 16.
Staff RNs 3 (ft), 1 (pt); LPNs 3 (ft), 2 (pt); Nurses aides 12 (ft), 10 (pt); Physical therapists 1 (ft); Occupational therapists 1 (pt); Speech therapists 1 (pt); Activities coordinators 1 (ft), 1 (pt); Dietitians 1 (ft); Ophthalmologists 1 (pt).
Facilities Dining room; Physical therapy room; Activities room; Barber/Beauty shop.
Activities Arts & crafts; Cards; Games; Reading groups; Movies.

STATEN ISLAND

Beth Rifka Nursing Home*
1000 Targee St, Staten Island, NY, 10304
(212) 720-7800
Licensure Intermediate care. Beds 200.
Owner Nonprofit Corp.

Carmel Richmond Nursing Home Inc*
88 Old Town Rd, Staten Island, NY, 10304
(718) 979-5000
Licensure Skilled care; Intermediate care. Beds 270. Certified Medicaid; Medicare.
Owner Nonprofit Corp (Cath Charity/Arch of NY).

Clove Lakes Nursing Home & Health Related Facility
25 Fanning St, Staten Island, NY, 10314-0023
(718) 761-2100
Admin Nicholas Demisay. Medical Dir/Dir of Nursing Jacob Dimant MD; Anna Fredericksen RN DON.
Licensure Skilled care; Intermediate care. Beds SNF 326; ICF 250. Certified Medicaid; Medicare.
Owner Privately owned.
Admissions Requirements Minimum age 16; Medical examination; Physician's request.
Staff Physicians 1 (pt); RNs 26 (ft), 7 (pt); LPNs 43 (ft), 11 (pt); Orderlies 35 (ft), 1 (pt); Nurses aides 145 (ft), 13 (pt); Physical therapists 3 (pt); Recreational therapists 9 (ft), 5 (pt); Occupational therapists 2 (ft), 2 (pt); Speech therapists 1 (pt); Activities coordinators 1 (ft); Dietitians 8 (ft).
Languages French, German, Italian, Spanish, Sign
Facilities Dining room; Physical therapy room; Activities room; Chapel; Crafts room; Laundry room; Barber/Beauty shop; Library; Greenhouse.
Activities Arts & crafts; Cards; Games; Reading groups; Prayer groups; Movies; Shopping trips; Social/Cultural gatherings; Horticultural program.

Eger Nursing Home Inc
140 Meisner Ave, Staten Island, NY, 10306
(718) 979-1800
Admin Paul K Jensen. Medical Dir/Dir of Nursing Frank Tellefsen MD.
Licensure Skilled care; Intermediate care. Beds 378. Certified Medicaid.
Owner Nonprofit Corp.
Admissions Requirements Minimum age 16; Medical examination; Physician's request.
Staff Physicians 11 (pt); RNs 31 (ft), 40 (pt); LPNs 12 (ft), 19 (pt); Nurses aides 131 (ft), 95 (pt); Physical therapists 3 (ft); Occupational therapists 2 (ft); Speech therapists 1 (pt); Activities coordinators 1 (ft); Dietitians 4 (ft); Dentists 1 (pt); Ophthalmologists 2 (pt); Podiatrists 1 (pt).
Affiliation Lutheran
Facilities Dining room; Physical therapy room; Activities room; Chapel; Crafts room; Laundry room; Barber/Beauty shop; Library; Speech pathology room; Occupational therapy room; Pharmacy.
Activities Arts & crafts; Cards; Games; Reading groups; Prayer groups; Movies; Shopping trips; Social/Cultural gatherings.

Golden Gate Health Care Center
191 Bradley Ave, Staten Island, NY, 10314
(718) 698-8800
Admin Alan Chopp. Medical Dir/Dir of Nursing Dr Morton Kliener; Christine Tacardan.
Licensure Skilled care; HRF. Beds SNF 118; HRF 120. Certified Medicaid; Medicare.
Owner Privately owned.
Admissions Requirements Minimum age 21; Physician's request.
Staff RNs 14 (ft), 14 (pt); LPNs 10 (ft), 9 (pt); Orderlies 18 (ft), 1 (pt); Nurses aides 46 (ft), 5 (pt); Physical therapists 1 (ft), 1 (pt); Recreational therapists 4 (ft), 1 (pt); Occupational therapists 1 (ft); Speech therapists 1 (pt); Activities coordinators 1 (ft); Dietitians 2 (ft).
Facilities Dining room; Physical therapy room; Activities room; Chapel; Crafts room; Laundry room; Barber/Beauty shop; Library.

Activities Arts & crafts; Cards; Games; Reading groups; Prayer groups; Movies; Shopping trips; Social/Cultural gatherings.

New Brighton Manor Care Center
200 Lafayette Ave, Staten Island, NY, 10301
(718) 448-9000
Admin Joshuah Levy.
Licensure Skilled care; Intermediate care. *Beds* 80. *Certified* Medicaid; Medicare.
Owner Proprietary Corp.

New Vanderbilt Nursing Home
135 Vanderbilt Ave, Staten Island, NY, 10304
(718) 447-0701
Admin Henry A Schon. *Medical Dir/Dir of Nursing* Dr Howard Guterman; Josephine Choe DON.
Licensure Skilled care. *Beds* SNF 320. *Certified* Medicaid; Medicare.
Owner Privately owned.
Admissions Requirements Minimum age 35; Medical examination.
Staff Physicians 5 (pt); RNs 26 (ft), 6 (pt); LPNs 22 (ft), 8 (pt); Orderlies 10 (ft), 3 (pt); Nurses aides 80 (ft), 20 (pt); Physical therapists 2 (ft), 1 (pt); Recreational therapists 4 (ft), 3 (pt); Occupational therapists 1 (ft); Speech therapists 1 (pt); Activities coordinators 1 (ft); Dietitians 4 (ft); Dentists 1 (pt); Ophthalmologists 2 (pt); Podiatrists 1 (pt).
Languages Italian, Spanish
Facilities Dining room; Physical therapy room; Activities room; Crafts room; Laundry room; Barber/Beauty shop.
Activities Arts & crafts; Cards; Games; Reading groups; Prayer groups; Movies; Social/Cultural gatherings.

Sea View Hospital & Home*
460 Brielle Ave, Staten Island, NY, 10314
(718) 390-8181
Admin Michael Cantatore.
Licensure Skilled care. *Beds* 304. *Certified* Medicaid; Medicare.
Owner Publicly owned.

Silver Lake Nursing Home
275 Castleton Ave, Staten Island, NY, 10301
(718) 447-7800
Admin Otto Weingarten. *Medical Dir/Dir of Nursing* Dr Barbara Malach.
Licensure Skilled care. *Beds* SNF 278. *Certified* Medicaid; Medicare.
Owner Privately owned.
Admissions Requirements Minimum age 18; Medical examination; Physician's request.
Staff Physicians; RNs; LPNs; Orderlies; Nurses aides; Physical therapists; Reality therapists; Recreational therapists; Occupational therapists; Speech therapists; Activities coordinators; Dietitians; Dentists; Ophthalmologists; Podiatrists.
Languages Hebrew, Yiddish, Italian, Spanish, Chinese
Facilities Dining room; Physical therapy room; Activities room; Chapel; Crafts room; Barber/Beauty shop; Library.
Activities Arts & crafts; Cards; Games; Reading groups; Prayer groups; Movies; Shopping trips; Social/Cultural gatherings.

Verrazano Nursing Home
100 Castleton Ave, Staten Island, NY, 10301
(718) 273-1300
Admin Israel Weingarten. *Medical Dir/Dir of Nursing* L Sasso MD.
Licensure Skilled care. *Beds* SNF 120. *Certified* Medicaid; Medicare.
Owner Proprietary Corp.
Admissions Requirements Minimum age 16; Medical examination; Physician's request.
Staff Physicians 3 (pt); RNs 4 (ft), 4 (pt); LPNs 9 (ft), 6 (pt); Orderlies 4 (ft), 3 (pt); Nurses aides 26 (ft), 4 (pt); Physical therapists 1 (ft), 2 (pt); Occupational therapists 1 (pt);

Speech therapists 1 (pt); Activities coordinators 1 (ft); Dietitians 1 (ft), 1 (pt); Dentists 1 (pt); Ophthalmologists 1 (pt).
Languages Spanish, Italian, Yiddish, Hebrew, Hungarian
Facilities Dining room; Physical therapy room; Activities room; Barber/Beauty shop.
Activities Arts & crafts; Cards; Games; Reading groups; Prayer groups; Movies; Shopping trips; Social/Cultural gatherings.

SUFFERN

Ramapo Manor Nursing Center, Inc
Cragmere Rd, Suffern, NY, 10901
(914) 357-1230
Admin Sanford Rexon. *Medical Dir/Dir of Nursing* George Cox MD; Ruth Avrin BSN DON.
Licensure Skilled care; Intermediate care. *Beds* SNF 122; ICF 41. *Certified* Medicaid; Medicare.
Owner Proprietary Corp.
Admissions Requirements Minimum age 16; Medical examination.
Staff RNs 30 (ft); LPNs 6 (ft); Orderlies 1 (ft); Nurses aides 64 (ft); Physical therapists 3 (pt); Recreational therapists 2 (ft), 2 (pt); Occupational therapists 1 (pt); Speech therapists 1 (pt); Activities coordinators 1 (ft); Dietitians 1 (ft).
Languages French, Spanish, Russian, Hebrew, Yiddish, Italian
Facilities Dining room; Activities room; Crafts room; Laundry room; Barber/Beauty shop; Library; Gift shop.
Activities Arts & crafts; Cards; Games; Reading groups; Prayer groups; Movies; Shopping trips; Social/Cultural gatherings; Music therapy; Stroke group; Resident chorus; Intergenerational programs.

SYRACUSE

Castle Rest Nursing Home
116 E Castle St, Syracuse, NY, 13205
(315) 475-1641
Admin Thomas Fahey.
Licensure Skilled care. *Beds* 140. *Certified* Medicaid; Medicare.
Owner Proprietary Corp.
Admissions Requirements Minimum age 65.
Facilities Dining room; Physical therapy room; Activities room; Crafts room; Barber/Beauty shop; Library.
Activities Arts & crafts; Cards; Games; Reading groups; Prayer groups; Movies; Shopping trips; Social/Cultural gatherings; Picnics; Fishing trips; Luncheon outings.

Hill Haven Nursing Home*
4001 E Genesee St, Syracuse, NY, 13214
(315) 446-8310
Admin Gladys Stanton.
Licensure Skilled care. *Beds* 121. *Certified* Medicaid; Medicare.
Owner Proprietary Corp.

James Square Nursing Home
918 James St, Syracuse, NY, 13203
(315) 474-1561
Admin Edward Leffler. *Medical Dir/Dir of Nursing* Helmam J Rubinson MD; Joan Roen Beck RN.
Licensure Skilled care; Health related care. *Beds* SNF 415; HRC 40. *Certified* Medicaid; Medicare.
Owner Proprietary Corp.
Staff Physicians 7 (ft); RNs 30 (ft), 15 (pt); LPNs 55 (ft), 23 (pt); Orderlies 5 (ft), 2 (pt); Nurses aides 180 (ft), 55 (pt); Physical therapists 2 (ft), 1 (pt); Reality therapists 1 (ft); Recreational therapists 7 (ft); Occupational therapists 2 (ft); Speech therapists 1 (ft); Activities coordinators 1 (ft); Dietitians 3 (ft); RRt 1 (ft); Volunteer coord 1 (ft).

Languages Italian, Polish
Facilities Dining room; Physical therapy room; Activities room; Crafts room; Laundry room; Barber/Beauty shop; Occupational therapy room; Speech therapy room; Venilator-dependent pulmonary rehabilitation unit.
Activities Arts & crafts; Cards; Games; Reading groups; Prayer groups; Movies; Shopping trips; Social/Cultural gatherings; Pet therapy.

Jewish Home of Central New York
4101 E Genesee St, Syracuse, NY, 13214
(315) 446-9111
Admin Harvey N Finkelstein. *Medical Dir/Dir of Nursing* Dr Albert Tripodi.
Licensure Skilled care. *Beds* 145. *Certified* Medicaid; Medicare.
Owner Nonprofit Corp.
Admissions Requirements Minimum age 62; Medical examination; Physician's request.
Staff Physicians 2 (pt); RNs 16 (ft), 5 (pt); LPNs 26 (ft), 3 (pt); Orderlies 4 (ft); Nurses aides 59 (ft), 6 (pt); Physical therapists 2 (pt); Occupational therapists 1 (pt); Speech therapists 1 (pt); Activities coordinators 1 (ft); Dietitians 1 (pt); Dentists 1 (pt); Podiatrists 1 (pt).
Affiliation Jewish
Facilities Dining room; Physical therapy room; Activities room; Chapel; Crafts room; Laundry room; Barber/Beauty shop; Library.
Activities Arts & crafts; Cards; Games; Reading groups; Prayer groups; Movies; Shopping trips; Social/Cultural gatherings.

Loretto Geriatric Center
700 E Brighton Ave, Syracuse, NY, 13205
(315) 469-5561
Admin Patrick M Deptula MS. *Medical Dir/Dir of Nursing* Frank Brand MD.
Licensure Skilled care; Intermediate care. *Beds* 520. *Certified* Medicaid; Medicare.
Owner Nonprofit Corp.
Admissions Requirements Minimum age 62.
Staff Physicians 1 (ft); RNs 29 (ft), 12 (pt); LPNs 41 (ft), 15 (pt); Nurses aides 113 (ft), 49 (pt); Physical therapists 2 (ft); Recreational therapists 7 (ft); Occupational therapists 1 (ft); Speech therapists 1 (pt); Activities coordinators 1 (ft); Dietitians 1 (ft); Dentists 01; Ophthalmologists 1 (pt); Podiatrists 2 (pt).
Facilities Dining room; Physical therapy room; Activities room; Chapel; Crafts room; Laundry room; Barber/Beauty shop; Library.
Activities Arts & crafts; Cards; Games; Reading groups; Prayer groups; Movies; Shopping trips; Social/Cultural gatherings.

Plaza Nursing Home Company Inc
614 S Crouse Ave, Syracuse, NY, 13210
(315) 474-4431
Admin Edward A Leone. *Medical Dir/Dir of Nursing* Leo Jivoff MD; Esther LeVine RN DON.
Licensure Skilled care. *Beds* SNF 242. *Certified* Medicaid; Medicare.
Owner Nonprofit Corp.
Admissions Requirements Minimum age 16; Physician's request.
Staff Physicians 4 (pt); RNs 46 (ft), 9 (pt); LPNs 28 (ft), 3 (pt); Nurses aides 79 (ft), 26 (pt); Physical therapists 4 (ft); Recreational therapists 3 (ft); Occupational therapists 4 (ft); Speech therapists 1 (pt); Activities coordinators 1 (ft); Dietitians 1 (ft); Podiatrists 1 (pt); Dentist 1 (pt).
Facilities Dining room; Physical therapy room; Activities room; Chapel; Crafts room; Laundry room; Barber/Beauty shop.
Activities Arts & crafts; Cards; Games; Reading groups; Prayer groups; Movies; Shopping trips; Social/Cultural gatherings; Cooking groups; Horticulture therapy.

St Camillus Residential Health Care Facility*
813 Fay Rd, Syracuse, NY, 13219
(315) 488-2951
Admin Robert Mack. *Medical Dir/Dir of Nursing* Dr John O'Brien.
Licensure Skilled care; Health related care. *Beds* 250. *Certified* Medicaid; Medicare.
Owner Nonprofit Corp.
Admissions Requirements Physician's request.
Staff Physicians 1 (ft), 9 (pt); RNs 18 (ft), 5 (pt); LPNs 17 (ft), 10 (pt); Nurses aides 45 (ft), 20 (pt); Physical therapists 8 (ft); Recreational therapists 6 (ft); Occupational therapists 3 (ft); Speech therapists 6 (ft), 1 (pt); Activities coordinators 1 (ft); Dietitians 3 (ft); Dentists 5 (pt); Podiatrists 2 (pt); Audiologists 1 (ft).
Affiliation Roman Catholic
Facilities Dining room; Physical therapy room; Activities room; Chapel; Crafts room; Laundry room; Barber/Beauty shop; Library.
Activities Arts & crafts; Cards; Games; Reading groups; Prayer groups; Movies; Shopping trips; Social/Cultural gatherings.

Van Duyn Home & Hospital
W Seneca Turnpike, Syracuse, NY, 13215
(315) 469-5511
Admin Raymond J Schumacher. *Medical Dir/ Dir of Nursing* Arthur H Dube MD; Shirley Lewis.
Licensure Skilled care; Intermediate care. *Beds* SNF 418; ICF 108. *Certified* Medicaid; Medicare.
Owner Publicly owned.
Admissions Requirements Minimum age 18 mos; Physician's request.
Staff Physicians 1 (ft), 17 (pt); RNs 84 (ft), 4 (pt); LPNs 121 (ft); Nurses aides 190 (ft); Physical therapists 2 (ft); Recreational therapists 7 (ft); Occupational therapists 2 (ft); Activities coordinators 1 (ft); Dietitians 2 (ft); Dentists 1 (pt); Ophthalmologists 2 (pt); Radiologic tech 1 (ft), 1 (pt) Social service 7 (ft) Inhalation therapy 1 (ft) Dentist 2 (pt).
Facilities Dining room; Physical therapy room; Activities room; Chapel; Crafts room; Laundry room; Barber/Beauty shop; Library; Radiology lab; Occupational therapy room; Library; Pharmacy; Clinic; Inhalation therapy.
Activities Arts & crafts; Cards; Games; Reading groups; Prayer groups; Movies; Shopping trips; Social/Cultural gatherings; Beach parties; Picnics; Gardening; Aerobics; Wheelchair volley ball.

TARRYTOWN

Tarrytown Hall Nursing Home*
Wood Ct, Tarrytown, NY, 10591
(914) 631-2600
Admin Leslie Kaye.
Licensure Skilled care; Intermediate care. *Beds* 80. *Certified* Medicaid; Medicare.
Owner Proprietary Corp.

TICONDEROGA

Moses-Ludington Nursing Home Company Inc
Wicker St, Ticonderoga, NY, 12883
(518) 585-6771
Admin Margaret Haroff. *Medical Dir/Dir of Nursing* Michael Beehner MD; Regina Muscatello RN DON.
Licensure Skilled care; Intermediate care. *Beds* 40. *Certified* Medicaid; Medicare.
Owner Nonprofit Corp.
Staff Physicians 1 (ft); RNs 5 (ft), 1 (pt); LPNs 4 (ft); Orderlies 1 (ft); Nurses aides 14 (ft), 10 (pt); Physical therapists 1 (pt); Recreational therapists 2 (ft); Activities coordinators 1 (ft); Dietitians 1 (pt); Dentists 1 (pt).

Facilities Dining room; Physical therapy room; Activities room; Barber/Beauty shop.
Activities Arts & crafts; Cards; Games; Reading groups; Prayer groups; Movies; Shopping trips; Social/Cultural gatherings; Cooking club.

TONAWANDA

Sheridan Manor Nursing Home Inc*
2799 Sheridan Dr, Tonawanda, NY, 14150
(716) 837-4466
Admin Geraldine Sufrane.
Licensure Skilled care. *Beds* 100. *Certified* Medicaid; Medicare.
Owner Proprietary Corp.

TROY

James A Eddy Memorial Geriatric Center
2256 Burdett Ave, Troy, NY, 12180
(518) 274-9890
Admin Peter G Young. *Medical Dir/Dir of Nursing* Arsenio Agopovich MD; Gayleen Kelsey DON.
Licensure Skilled care; Intermediate care; DOM. *Beds* SNF 30; ICF 30; DOM 40. *Certified* Medicaid; Medicare.
Owner Nonprofit organization/foundation.
Admissions Requirements Minimum age 16; Medical examination.
Staff RNs 4 (ft), 4 (pt); LPNs 3 (ft), 6 (pt); Nurses aides 12 (ft), 19 (pt); Physical therapists 1 (pt); Occupational therapists 1 (pt); Activities coordinators 1 (ft).
Facilities Dining room; Physical therapy room; Activities room; Laundry room; Barber/Beauty shop; Library.
Activities Arts & crafts; Cards; Games; Reading groups; Prayer groups; Movies; Shopping trips; Social/Cultural gatherings; Baking clubs; Men's clubs; Gardening; Stimulation program.

Eden Park Health Services Inc*
2417 15th St, Troy, NY, 12180
(518) 272-0404
Admin Eugene Evans.
Licensure Skilled care. *Beds* 130. *Certified* Medicaid; Medicare.
Owner Proprietary Corp (Eden Park Management).

Hallmark Nursing Centre
49 Marvin Ave, Troy, NY, 12180
(518) 273-6646
Admin Mark D Petell.
Licensure Skilled care. *Beds* 80. *Certified* Medicaid; Medicare.
Owner Proprietary Corp.
Facilities Dining room; Physical therapy room; Activities room; Barber/Beauty shop.
Activities Arts & crafts; Cards; Games; Reading groups; Prayer groups; Movies; Shopping trips; Social/Cultural gatherings.

Highgate Manor of Rensselaer
100 New Turnpike Rd, Troy, NY, 12182
(518) 235-1410
Admin Gregory J Zucco. *Medical Dir/Dir of Nursing* Antonio Farol MD, Lucilo Roman MD; Mary Calabrese RN.
Licensure Skilled care; Intermediate care. *Beds* SNF 80; ICF 40. *Certified* Medicaid; Medicare.
Owner Proprietary Corp (New Medico Assoc).
Admissions Requirements Minimum age 16; Medical examination; Physician's request.
Staff Physicians 1 (ft), 2 (pt); RNs 14 (ft), 4 (pt); LPNs 14 (ft), 17 (pt); Nurses aides 38 (ft), 32 (pt); Physical therapists 4 (ft); Recreational therapists 4 (ft); Occupational therapists 4 (ft); Speech therapists 4 (ft); Activities coordinators 1 (ft); Dietitians 1 (ft).

Facilities Dining room; Physical therapy room; Activities room; Crafts room; Barber/ Beauty shop; Dayroom; Dining room.
Activities Arts & crafts; Cards; Games; Reading groups; Prayer groups; Movies; Shopping trips; Social/Cultural gatherings.

Leisure Arms Health Related Facility
2405 15th St, Troy, NY, 12180
(518) 271-7665
Admin Rebecca Smith. *Medical Dir/Dir of Nursing* Dr Myron Fribush; Susan Dyer DON.
Licensure Intermediate care. *Beds* ICF 88. *Certified* Medicaid.
Owner Proprietary Corp.
Admissions Requirements Minimum age 16; Medical examination.
Staff RNs 2 (ft); LPNs 4 (ft), 6 (pt); Orderlies 1 (ft), 2 (pt); Nurses aides 10 (ft), 6 (pt); Activities coordinators 1 (ft).
Facilities Dining room; Activities room; Laundry room; Barber/Beauty shop.
Activities Arts & crafts; Cards; Games; Prayer groups; Movies; Shopping trips; Social/ Cultural gatherings.

Van Rensselaer Manor*
133 Bloomingrove Dr, Troy, NY, 12181
(518) 283-2000
Admin Bob Beaudion.
Licensure Skilled care; Intermediate care. *Beds* 194. *Certified* Medicaid; Medicare.
Owner Publicly owned.

TUPPER LAKE

Mercy Healthcare Center
114 Wawbeek Ave, Tupper Lake, NY, 12986
(518) 359-3355
Admin Sr Mary Paschal Hill RSM. *Medical Dir/Dir of Nursing* H Douglas Wilson MD; Mary Rogers RN DON.
Licensure Skilled care. *Beds* SNF 54. *Certified* Medicaid; Medicare.
Owner Nonprofit Corp.
Admissions Requirements Minimum age 16.
Staff Physicians 4 (pt); RNs 3 (ft), 4 (pt); LPNs 4 (ft), 2 (pt); Orderlies 2 (ft); Nurses aides 26 (ft), 10 (pt); Physical therapists 1 (pt); Activities coordinators 1 (ft); Dietitians 1 (pt); Ophthalmologists 1 (pt).
Languages French
Affiliation Roman Catholic
Facilities Dining room; Physical therapy room; Activities room; Chapel; Laundry room; Barber/Beauty shop.
Activities Arts & crafts; Cards; Games; Prayer groups; Movies; Shopping trips; Social/ Cultural gatherings.

UNIONDALE

A Holly Patterson Home
875 Jerusalem Ave, Uniondale, NY, 11553
(516) 663-5700
Admin William J St George. *Medical Dir/Dir of Nursing* Terrance O'Flanagan MD; Ann Bowker RN DON.
Licensure Skilled care. *Beds* 889. *Certified* Medicaid; Medicare.
Owner Publicly owned.
Admissions Requirements Minimum age 16; Medical examination; Physician's request.
Staff Physicians 3 (ft), 14 (pt); RNs 99 (ft), 34 (pt); LPNs 92 (ft), 43 (pt); Nurses aides 366 (ft), 149 (pt); Physical therapists 4 (ft); Recreational therapists 17 (ft); Occupational therapists 1 (ft); Speech therapists 1 (ft); Activities coordinators 1 (ft); Dietitians 5 (ft), 1 (pt); Dentists 2 (pt); Ophthalmologists 2 (pt); Podiatrists 2 (pt).
Facilities Dining room; Physical therapy room; Activities room; Chapel; Crafts room; Laundry room; Barber/Beauty shop; Library.

Activities Arts & crafts; Cards; Games;
Reading groups; Prayer groups; Movies;
Shopping trips; Social/Cultural gatherings;
Clubs; Gardening; Workshops; Crafts;
Musical concerts; Exercise program; Cooking
programs; Community group.

UTICA

Broadacres
Walker Rd, Utica, NY, 13502
(315) 798-9200
Admin Richard DuRose. *Medical Dir/Dir of
Nursing* Dr Jeanne F Arnold.
Licensure Skilled care. *Beds* SNF 168.
Certified Medicaid; Medicare.
Owner Publicly owned.
Staff Physicians 17 (pt); RNs 16 (ft), 7 (pt);
LPNs 34 (ft), 7 (pt); Nurses aides 93 (ft), 36
(pt); Physical therapists 1 (pt); Occupational
therapists 1 (pt); Speech therapists 1 (pt);
Activities coordinators 1 (pt); Dietitians 1
(pt); Dentists 1 (pt); Podiatrists Dentist 1
(pt).
Facilities Dining room; Physical therapy
room; Activities room; Crafts room; Laundry
room; Barber/Beauty shop; Library.
Activities Arts & crafts; Cards; Games;
Reading groups; Prayer groups; Movies;
Shopping trips; Social/Cultural gatherings.

**Allen Calder Skilled Nursing Facility—St
Lukes Memorial Hospital Center**
Box 479, Utica, NY, 13503
(315) 798-6093
Admin Grace Steppello RN. *Medical Dir/Dir
of Nursing* Guy Wilcox MD; Kathleen
DeSimone Galindo RN DON.
Licensure Skilled care. *Beds* SNF 76. *Certified*
Medicaid; Medicare.
Owner Nonprofit Corp.
Admissions Requirements Medical
examination; Physician's request.
Staff RNs 7 (ft), 4 (pt); LPNs 7 (ft), 16 (pt);
Orderlies 3 (ft); Nurses aides 17 (ft), 39 (pt);
Physical therapists 4 (ft), 1 (pt);
Occupational therapists 2 (ft); Speech
therapists 1 (pt); Activities coordinators 1
(ft), 1 (pt); Dietitians 1 (pt).
Facilities Dining room; Physical therapy
room; Activities room; Chapel; Crafts room.
Activities Arts & crafts; Cards; Games;
Movies; Shopping trips; Social/Cultural
gatherings.

Eden Park Nursing Home & HRF*
1800 E Butterfield Ave, Utica, NY, 13501
(315) 797-3570
Admin Clara Mae Durant. *Medical Dir/Dir of
Nursing* Esther Johnston MD.
Licensure Skilled care; Intermediate care. *Beds*
80. *Certified* Medicaid; Medicare.
Owner Proprietary Corp (Eden Park
Mngmnt).
Admissions Requirements Minimum age 16;
Medical examination; Physician's request.
Staff Physicians 17 (pt); RNs 9 (ft), 4 (pt);
LPNs 13 (ft), 6 (pt); Nurses aides 44 (ft), 15
(pt); Physical therapists 1 (pt); Occupational
therapists 1 (pt); Speech therapists 1 (pt);
Activities coordinators 1 (ft); Dietitians 1
(pt); Dentists 1 (pt); Podiatrists 1 (pt).
Facilities Dining room; Physical therapy
room; Activities room; Crafts room; Laundry
room; Barber/Beauty shop.
Activities Arts & crafts; Cards; Games;
Reading groups; Prayer groups; Movies;
Shopping trips; Social/Cultural gatherings.

Genesee Nursing Home
1634 Genesee St, Utica, NY, 13502
(315) 724-2151
Admin Stephen A Ross. *Medical Dir/Dir of
Nursing* Ada Buffington RN.
Licensure Skilled care. *Beds* SNF 100.
Certified Medicaid; Medicare.
Owner Proprietary Corp.

Admissions Requirements Minimum age 18;
Medical examination.
Staff Physicians 2 (ft); RNs 5 (ft), 3 (pt);
LPNs 8 (ft), 5 (pt); Orderlies 5 (ft), 1 (pt);
Nurses aides 40 (ft), 10 (pt); Physical
therapists 2 (ft); Reality therapists 1 (ft);
Recreational therapists 3 (ft); Occupational
therapists 1 (ft); Activities coordinators 1
(ft); Dietitians 1 (ft); Dentists 1 (pt);
Ophthalmologists 1 (pt).
Languages French
Facilities Physical therapy room; Activities
room; Crafts room; Laundry room; Barber/
Beauty shop.
Activities Arts & crafts; Games; Reading
groups; Prayer groups; Movies; Shopping
trips.

Masonic Home & Health Facility
2150 Bleecker St, Utica, NY, 13501-1788
(315) 798-4833
Admin Richard M Dowe. *Medical Dir/Dir of
Nursing* Edward Bradley MD; Bernadette
Millett.
Licensure Skilled care; Intermediate care;
DCF; Independent living apartments. *Beds*
SNF 458; ICF. *Certified* Medicaid;
Medicare.
Owner Nonprofit organization/foundation.
Staff Physicians 2 (ft); RNs 20 (ft), 7 (pt);
LPNs 27 (ft), 28 (pt); Orderlies 25 (ft);
Nurses aides 114 (ft), 74 (pt); Physical
therapists 3 (ft); Occupational therapists 1
(ft), 1 (pt); Speech therapists 1 (ft); Activities
coordinators 6 (ft), 2 (pt); Dietitians 3 (ft);
Dentists 1 (ft); Ophthalmologists 1 (ft);
Podiatrists 1 (ft).
Affiliation Masons
Facilities Dining room; Physical therapy
room; Activities room; Chapel; Crafts room;
Laundry room; Barber/Beauty shop; Library.
Activities Arts & crafts; Cards; Games;
Reading groups; Prayer groups; Movies;
Shopping trips; Social/Cultural gatherings.

**Faxton Sunset St Luke's Health Related
Facility & Nursing Home Inc**
1657 Sunset Ave, Utica, NY, 13502
(315) 797-7392
Admin Ronald T Cerow. *Medical Dir/Dir of
Nursing* Clarke Case MD; Johann Varieur
RN DON.
Licensure Skilled care; Intermediate care. *Beds*
SNF 199; ICF. *Certified* Medicaid;
Medicare.
Owner Nonprofit Corp.
Admissions Requirements Minimum age 16;
Medical examination; Physician's request.
Staff RNs 7 (ft), 6 (pt); LPNs 16 (ft), 16 (pt);
Nurses aides 40 (ft), 34 (pt); Activities
coordinators 1 (ft); Dietitians 1 (pt).
Facilities Dining room; Physical therapy
room; Activities room; Crafts room; Laundry
room; Barber/Beauty shop; Library; Resident
lounges.
Activities Arts & crafts; Cards; Games;
Reading groups; Prayer groups; Movies;
Shopping trips; Social/Cultural gatherings;
Horse racing; Camping; Opera; Fishing.

St Joseph Nursing Home
2535 Genesee St, Utica, NY, 13501
(315) 797-1230
Admin Sr M Zavier. *Medical Dir/Dir of
Nursing* Theodore C Mehalic MD.
Licensure Skilled care. *Beds* SNF 120.
Certified Medicaid; Medicare.
Owner Nonprofit Corp.
Staff RNs 7 (ft), 11 (pt); LPNs 13 (ft), 5 (pt);
Nurses aides 50 (ft), 32 (pt); Physical
therapists 1 (pt); Occupational therapists 1
(pt); Activities coordinators 1 (ft); Dietitians
1 (pt).
Facilities Dining room; Physical therapy
room; Activities room; Chapel; Laundry
room; Barber/Beauty shop; Occupational
therapy room; Library cart.

Activities Arts & crafts; Cards; Games;
Reading groups; Prayer groups; Movies;
Shopping trips; Pen pal club with 7th & 8th
graders; Pre-nursery school activity weekly;
Fund raising.

VALATIE

**Barnwell Nursing Home & Health Facilities
Inc**
Church St, Valatie, NY, 12184
(518) 758-6222
Admin Greta M Hutchinson. *Medical Dir/Dir
of Nursing* Dr Carl Whitbeck; M Katherine
Logan RN.
Licensure Skilled care; Intermediate care. *Beds*
228. *Certified* Medicaid; Medicare.
Owner Proprietary Corp.
Admissions Requirements Medical
examination; Physician's request.
Staff RNs; LPNs; Orderlies; Nurses aides;
Physical therapists; Reality therapists;
Recreational therapists; Occupational
therapists; Activities coordinators; Dietitians.
Facilities Dining room; Physical therapy
room; Activities room; Chapel; Crafts room;
Laundry room; Barber/Beauty shop; Library;
Greenhouse; Spacious grounds; Gazebo;
Wheelchair equipped bus.
Activities Arts & crafts; Cards; Games;
Reading groups; Prayer groups; Movies;
Shopping trips; Social/Cultural gatherings.

VALLEY COTTAGE

Nyack Manor Nursing Home*
Christian Herald Rd, Valley Cottage, NY,
10989
(914) 268-6861
Admin Herbert A Rothman. *Medical Dir/Dir
of Nursing* Norman Rubinstein MD.
Licensure Skilled care. *Beds* 160. *Certified*
Medicaid; Medicare.
Owner Proprietary Corp.

**Tolstoy Foundation Nursing Home Company
Inc**
Lake Rd, Valley Cottage, NY, 10989
(914) 268-6813
Admin Vladimir Grigoriev.
Licensure Skilled care. *Beds* 96. *Certified*
Medicaid; Medicare.
Owner Nonprofit Corp.
Admissions Requirements Minimum age 65;
Medical examination.
Staff Physicians 1 (pt); RNs 12 (ft); LPNs 4
(ft); Orderlies 6 (ft); Nurses aides 40 (ft);
Physical therapists 1 (pt); Reality therapists
1 (pt); Occupational therapists 1 (pt); Speech
therapists 1 (pt); Activities coordinators 1
(ft); Dietitians 1 (pt); Dentists 1 (pt);
Ophthalmologists 2 (pt); Podiatrists 2 (pt).
Facilities Dining room; Physical therapy
room; Activities room; Chapel; Laundry
room; Barber/Beauty shop; Library.
Activities Arts & crafts; Cards; Games;
Reading groups; Prayer groups; Movies;
Shopping trips.

VESTAL

Vestal Nursing Center
860 Old Vestal Rd, Vestal, NY, 13850
(607) 754-4105
Admin Denise B Johnson. *Medical Dir/Dir of
Nursing* Edmund Goldenberg; Carol Scerry.
Licensure Skilled care; Intermediate care. *Beds*
SNF 120; ICF 60. *Certified* Medicaid;
Medicare.
Owner Proprietary Corp.

**Willow Point Nursing Home & Health Related
Facility**
3700 Old Vestal Rd, Vestal, NY, 13850
(607) 729-8000

Admin Walter Stroly. *Medical Dir/Dir of Nursing* F Keith Kennedy MD; Judy Franklin RN DON.
Licensure Skilled care; Intermediate care. *Beds* SNF 222; 120. *Certified* Medicaid; Medicare.
Owner Publicly owned.
Admissions Requirements Minimum age 16; Physician's request.
Staff Physicians 1 (pt); RNs 27 (ft), 20 (pt); LPNs 20 (ft), 14 (pt); Nurses aides 113 (ft), 78 (pt); Physical therapists 4 (ft); Reality therapists 1 (ft); Recreational therapists 1 (ft), 1 (pt); Occupational therapists 1 (ft); Speech therapists 1 (pt); Activities coordinators 1 (ft); Dietitians 1 (ft); Dentists 1 (pt); Ophthalmologists 1 (pt); Podiatrists 1 (pt); Dentist 1 (pt); Occupational therapy aide 1 (pt); Physical therapy aides 2 (ft).
Facilities Dining room; Physical therapy room; Activities room; Chapel; Crafts room; Laundry room; Barber/Beauty shop; Library.
Activities Arts & crafts; Cards; Games; Reading groups; Prayer groups; Movies; Shopping trips; Social/Cultural gatherings.

WAPPINGERS FALLS

Central Dutchess Nursing Home Inc
37 Mesier Ave, Wappingers Falls, NY, 12590
(914) 297-3793
Admin Everett Alexander. *Medical Dir/Dir of Nursing* Subhash Kulkarni; Marguerite Ippolito DON.
Licensure Skilled care. *Beds* 62. *Certified* Medicaid; Medicare.
Owner Proprietary Corp.
Admissions Requirements Minimum age 16; Physician's request.
Staff Physicians 4 (pt); RNs 6 (ft), 6 (pt); LPNs 4 (ft), 2 (pt); Orderlies 1 (ft); Nurses aides 20 (ft), 15 (pt); Physical therapists 1 (pt); Recreational therapists 1 (ft), 1 (pt); Occupational therapists 1 (pt); Speech therapists 1 (pt); Dietitians 1 (pt); Dentists 1 (pt); Ophthalmologists 1 (pt); Podiatrists 1 (pt).
Facilities Dining room; Physical therapy room; Activities room; Chapel; Laundry room; Barber/Beauty shop; Library.
Activities Arts & crafts; Cards; Games; Reading groups; Prayer groups; Movies; Inhouse shopping.

WARSAW

East Side Nursing Home
62 Prospect St, Warsaw, NY, 14569
(716) 786-8151
Admin Sophia Hayes. *Medical Dir/Dir of Nursing* Dr J Thomas Reagan.
Licensure Skilled care. *Beds* SNF 80. *Certified* Medicaid; Medicare.
Owner Proprietary Corp.
Staff Physicians 10 (pt); RNs 6 (ft), 5 (pt); LPNs 9 (ft), 6 (pt); Orderlies 1 (ft); Nurses aides 30 (ft), 21 (pt); Physical therapists 1 (pt); Occupational therapists 1 (pt); Speech therapists 1 (pt); Activities coordinators 1 (ft); Dietitians 1 (pt); Ophthalmologists 1 (pt).
Facilities Dining room; Physical therapy room; Laundry room; Barber/Beauty shop.
Activities Arts & crafts; Games; Prayer groups; Movies; Social/Cultural gatherings.

Manor Oak Skilled Nursing Facilities Inc*
283 N Main St, Warsaw, NY, 14569
(716) 786-2211
Admin Peter Young. *Medical Dir/Dir of Nursing* Frederich Downs MD.
Licensure Skilled care. *Beds* 100. *Certified* Medicaid; Medicare.
Owner Proprietary Corp.
Admissions Requirements Minimum age 16; Medical examination; Physician's request.

Staff RNs 5 (ft), 5 (pt); LPNs 8 (ft), 7 (pt); Orderlies 6 (ft); Nurses aides 31 (ft), 40 (pt); Physical therapists 1 (ft); Speech therapists 1 (pt); Activities coordinators 1 (ft); Dietitians 1 (ft); Dentists 1 (pt); Ophthalmologists 1 (pt); Podiatrists 1 (pt); Audiologists 1 (pt).
Facilities Dining room; Physical therapy room; Activities room; Crafts room; Laundry room; Barber/Beauty shop.
Activities Arts & crafts; Cards; Games; Reading groups; Prayer groups; Movies; Shopping trips; Social/Cultural gatherings; Adopt-a-grandparent; Fitness classes; Special dinners; Trips to parks, zoo, racetrack, & restaurants.

Wyoming County Community Hospital, Skilled Nursing Facility
400 N Main St, Warsaw, NY, 14569
(716) 786-2233
Admin William E Holt. *Medical Dir/Dir of Nursing* Douglas Mayhle MD; Carole Butler RN DON.
Licensure Skilled care. *Beds* SNF 72. *Certified* Medicaid; Medicare.
Owner Publicly owned.
Staff Physicians 11 (pt); RNs 6 (ft), 3 (pt); LPNs 11 (ft), 7 (pt); Orderlies 4 (ft); Nurses aides 26 (ft), 10 (pt); Physical therapists 2 (ft); Recreational therapists 1 (ft); Occupational therapists 1 (pt); Speech therapists 1 (pt); Activities coordinators 1 (pt); Dietitians 2 (ft); Dentists 1 (pt); Ophthalmologists 1 (pt); Podiatrists 1 (pt).
Facilities Dining room; Physical therapy room; Activities room; Chapel; Crafts room; Barber/Beauty shop.
Activities Arts & crafts; Cards; Games; Reading groups; Prayer groups; Movies; Shopping trips; Social/Cultural gatherings; Restaurant visits; Gardening; Community functions.

WATERLOO

Seneca Nursing Home & HRF
200 Douglas Dr, Waterloo, NY, 13165
(315) 539-9202
Admin Warren Elston. *Medical Dir/Dir of Nursing* Mary Lou Maguire RN DON.
Licensure Skilled care; Intermediate care. *Beds* SNF 80; ICF 40; Adult day health care 10. *Certified* Medicaid; Medicare.
Owner Privately owned.
Admissions Requirements Physician's request.
Staff RNs; LPNs; Orderlies; Nurses aides; Physical therapists; Occupational therapists; Activities coordinators; Dietitians; Ophthalmologists.
Facilities Dining room; Physical therapy room; Activities room; Chapel; Crafts room; Laundry room; Barber/Beauty shop; Library.
Activities Arts & crafts; Cards; Games; Reading groups; Prayer groups; Movies; Shopping trips; Social/Cultural gatherings.

Taylor/Brown Memorial Hospital Nursing Home*
369 E Main St, Waterloo, NY, 13165
(315) 539-9204
Licensure Intermediate care. *Beds* 53.
Owner Nonprofit Corp.

WATERTOWN

Madonna Home of Mercy Hospital of Watertown
218 Stone St, Watertown, NY, 13601
(315) 782-7400
Admin Sr Mary Pierre Seguin. *Medical Dir/Dir of Nursing* Warren Daub MD; Anna Guyette RN.
Licensure Skilled care; Intermediate care. *Beds* 204. *Certified* Medicaid; Medicare.
Owner Nonprofit Corp.
Admissions Requirements Minimum age 16; Medical examination; Physician's request.

Staff Physicians 1 (pt); RNs 19 (ft); LPNs 32 (ft); Orderlies 4 (ft); Nurses aides 68 (ft); Physical therapists 1 (pt); Occupational therapists 1 (pt); Speech therapists 1 (pt); Activities coordinators 5 (ft); Dietitians 1 (ft), 1 (pt); Ophthalmologists 1 (pt); Podiatrists 1 (pt).
Affiliation Roman Catholic
Facilities Dining room; Activities room; Chapel; Crafts room; Laundry room; Barber/Beauty shop; Library; Handicap van.
Activities Arts & crafts; Cards; Games; Reading groups; Prayer groups; Movies; Shopping trips; Social/Cultural gatherings; Community programs; Motor trips.

Samaritan-Keep Nursing Home Inc
133 Pratt St, Watertown, NY, 13601
(315) 785-4400
Admin Gordon Paul Jeffery II. *Medical Dir/Dir of Nursing* William Heady MD; Pamela Puccia RN DON.
Licensure Skilled care; Intermediate care; Adult day care. *Beds* SNF 196; ICF 76; Adult day care 45. *Certified* Medicaid; Medicare; NYS; VA.
Owner Nonprofit Corp.
Admissions Requirements Minimum age 16; Medical examination; Physician's request.
Staff Physicians 1 (ft); RNs 14 (ft), 6 (pt); LPNs 27 (ft), 13 (pt); Nurses aides 81 (ft), 33 (pt); Physical therapists 1 (pt); Occupational therapists 2 (ft); Speech therapists 1 (ft); Activities coordinators 1 (ft); Dietitians 1 (ft); Dentists 1 (pt); Ophthalmologists 1 (ft); Podiatrists 1 (ft); Dentist 1 (pt).
Facilities Dining room; Physical therapy room; Activities room; Crafts room; Laundry room; Barber/Beauty shop; Library; Multipurpose auditorium; Adult day care; Medical office building; Transportation program.
Activities Arts & crafts; Cards; Games; Reading groups; Prayer groups; Movies; Shopping trips; Social/Cultural gatherings; Transportation to community events.

WATERVILLE

Harding Nursing Home
220 Tower St, Waterville, NY, 13480
(315) 841-4156
Admin Louise S Harding. *Medical Dir/Dir of Nursing* Robert Delorme MD; Anna Mae Williams RN DON.
Licensure Skilled care; Intermediate care. *Beds* SNF 62; ICF 30. *Certified* Medicaid; Medicare.
Owner Privately owned.
Facilities Dining room; Physical therapy room; Activities room; Laundry room; Barber/Beauty shop.
Activities Arts & crafts; Cards; Games; Reading groups; Prayer groups; Movies; Shopping trips; Social/Cultural gatherings.

WAVERLY

Tioga General Hospital Health Related Facility*
32 Ithica St, Waverly, NY, 14892
(607) 565-2861
Licensure Intermediate care. *Beds* 51.
Owner Nonprofit Corp.

Tioga Nursing Home Inc*
37 N Chemung St, Waverly, NY, 14892
(607) 565-2861
Admin Fred Kauffman.
Licensure Skilled care. *Beds* 80. *Certified* Medicaid; Medicare.
Owner Nonprofit Corp.

WEBSTER

Hill Haven Nursing Home of Rochester Co
1550 Empire Blvd, Webster, NY, 14580
(716) 671-4300
Admin Robert Goldstein. *Medical Dir/Dir of Nursing* Dr Zsolt de Papp MD; Mavis Usselman RN.
Licensure Skilled care; Intermediate care; Rehabilitation. *Beds* SNF 170; ICF 168; Rehab 17. *Certified* Medicaid; Medicare.
Owner Privately owned.
Admissions Requirements Minimum age 17.
Staff Physicians 2 (ft), 1 (pt); LPNs 21 (ft), 14 (pt); Nurses aides 65 (ft), 67 (pt); Physical therapists 1 (ft); Occupational therapists 1 (pt); Activities coordinators 2 (ft).
Facilities Dining room; Physical therapy room; Activities room; Crafts room; Laundry room; Barber/Beauty shop; Library.
Activities Arts & crafts; Cards; Games; Reading groups; Prayer groups; Movies; Shopping trips; Social/Cultural gatherings; Trips to community events; Live entertainment.

Maplewood Nursing Home Inc
100 Daniel Dr, Webster, NY, 14580
(716) 872-1800
Admin James H Chambery. *Medical Dir/Dir of Nursing* Stephan Cohen; Judith A Chambery.
Licensure Skilled care. *Beds* SNF 72. *Certified* Medicaid; Medicare.
Owner Proprietary Corp.
Admissions Requirements Medical examination; Physician's request.
Staff Physicians 1 (pt); RNs 6 (ft), 12 (pt); LPNs 4 (ft), 2 (pt); Nurses aides 23 (ft), 48 (pt); Physical therapists 1 (pt); Occupational therapists 1 (pt); Speech therapists 1 (pt); Activities coordinators 1 (ft), 1 (pt); Dietitians 1 (pt); Ophthalmologists 1 (pt).
Facilities Dining room; Physical therapy room; Activities room; Crafts room; Barber/Beauty shop.
Activities Arts & crafts; Cards; Games; Prayer groups; Movies; Shopping trips; Social/Cultural gatherings.

WELLSVILLE

Wellsville Highland Inc
PO Box 112, 160 Seneca St, Wellsville, NY, 14895-0112
(716) 593-3750
Admin Beverly R Rahr. *Medical Dir/Dir of Nursing* Dr Coch.
Licensure Skilled care. *Beds* 80. *Certified* Medicaid; Medicare.
Owner Proprietary Corp.
Admissions Requirements Minimum age 21.
Staff Physicians; RNs 7 (ft); LPNs 9 (ft), 5 (pt); Orderlies 2 (ft), 1 (pt); Nurses aides 22 (ft), 21 (pt); Physical therapists 1 (pt); Occupational therapists; Speech therapists; Activities coordinators 1 (ft), 1 (pt); Dietitians 1 (pt); Ophthalmologists; Podiatrists.
Facilities Dining room; Physical therapy room; Activities room; Crafts room; Laundry room; Barber/Beauty shop.
Activities Arts & crafts; Cards; Games; Reading groups; Prayer groups; Movies.

WEST BABYLON

Berkshire Nursing Center Inc*
10 Berkshire Rd, West Babylon, NY, 11704
(516) 587-0600
Admin Stuart Goldberg.
Licensure Skilled care. *Beds* 175. *Certified* Medicaid; Medicare.
Owner Proprietary Corp.

WEST ISLIP

Consolation Nursing Home Inc
111 Beach Dr, West Islip, NY, 11795
(516) 587-1600
Admin Sr Audrey Hansen. *Medical Dir/Dir of Nursing* Dr Martin D Podgainy; Gloria Payne DON.
Licensure Skilled care; Intermediate care; Long-term home health care. *Beds* SNF; ICF. *Certified* Medicaid; Medicare.
Owner Nonprofit Corp.
Admissions Requirements Minimum age 65; Medical examination; Physician's request.
Staff Physicians 1 (pt); RNs 22 (ft), 13 (pt); LPNs 14 (ft), 15 (pt); Nurses aides 58 (ft), 38 (pt); Physical therapists 1 (ft); Recreational therapists 2 (ft), 2 (pt); Occupational therapists 1 (pt); Activities coordinators 1 (ft); Dietitians 1 (ft).
Languages Spanish, Italian
Affiliation Roman Catholic
Facilities Dining room; Physical therapy room; Activities room; Chapel; Crafts room; Laundry room; Barber/Beauty shop; Library; Auditorium; Day rooms; Gift shop; Cafeteria.
Activities Arts & crafts; Cards; Games; Reading groups; Prayer groups; Movies; Shopping trips; Social/Cultural gatherings; Discussion groups; Sing-alongs; Creative writing.

WEST SENECA

Seneca Manor Health Care Facility
2987 Seneca St, West Seneca, NY, 14224
(716) 828-0500
Admin Matthew J Hriczko. *Medical Dir/Dir of Nursing* Dr Herle; Carol Nowinski.
Licensure Skilled care; Intermediate care. *Beds* SNF 120; ICF 40. *Certified* Medicaid; Medicare.
Owner Proprietary Corp.
Admissions Requirements Minimum age 16.
Staff Physicians; RNs; LPNs; Orderlies; Nurses aides; Physical therapists 1 (pt); Occupational therapists 1 (pt); Speech therapists 1 (pt); Activities coordinators 2 (ft); Dietitians 1 (pt); Dentists 1 (pt); Ophthalmologists 1 (pt); Podiatrists 1 (pt).
Facilities Dining room; Physical therapy room; Activities room; Crafts room; Laundry room; Barber/Beauty shop.
Activities Arts & crafts; Cards; Games; Reading groups; Prayer groups; Movies; Shopping trips; Social/Cultural gatherings.

WESTFIELD

Westfield Health Care Center Inc
26 Cass St, Westfield, NY, 14787
(716) 326-4646
Admin James E Pratt. *Medical Dir/Dir of Nursing* Robert Berke; Deborah Mackmer DON.
Licensure Skilled care; Intermediate care. *Beds* SNF 80; ICF 40. *Certified* Medicaid; Medicare.
Owner Privately owned.
Admissions Requirements Minimum age 17; Physician's request.
Facilities Dining room; Physical therapy room; Activities room; Chapel; Laundry room; Barber/Beauty shop.
Activities Arts & crafts; Cards; Games; Reading groups; Prayer groups; Movies; Shopping trips; Social/Cultural gatherings.

WHITE PLAINS

Nathan Miller Center for Nursing Care, Inc
220 West Post Rd, White Plains, NY, 10606
(914) 686-8880
Admin Dulcy B Miller. *Medical Dir/Dir of Nursing* Michael B Miller MD.

Licensure Skilled nursing companion/homemaker apt setting. *Beds* Apts 7. *Certified* Medicaid.
Owner Proprietary Corp.
Staff Physicians 1 (pt); RNs 2 (ft), 1 (pt); Physical therapists 2 (pt); Occupational therapists 2 (pt); Speech therapists 2 (pt); Podiatrists 1 (pt); Audiologists 1 (pt); MSW 2 (pt); Nutritionist 1 (pt).
Activities Arts & crafts; Cards; Games; Reading groups; Prayer groups; Movies; Social/Cultural gatherings.

Tibbits Health Care Facility
12 Tibbits Ave, White Plains, NY, 10606
(914) 428-0910
Admin James Marmon. *Medical Dir/Dir of Nursing* Dr Frederick Saunders; Janet Yuscak RN.
Licensure Skilled care; Intermediate care. *Beds* SNF 102; ICF 128. *Certified* Medicaid; Medicare.
Owner Privately owned.
Staff RNs 11 (ft), 5 (pt); LPNs 14 (ft), 13 (pt); Nurses aides 37 (ft), 22 (pt); Physical therapists 1 (ft); Occupational therapists 1 (pt); Speech therapists 1 (pt); Activities coordinators 4 (ft); Dietitians 1 (ft).
Affiliation Roman Catholic
Facilities Dining room; Physical therapy room; Activities room; Chapel; Barber/Beauty shop; Library.
Activities Arts & crafts; Cards; Games; Reading groups; Prayer groups; Movies; Shopping trips; Social/Cultural gatherings.

WHITESTONE

Bridge View Nursing Home*
143-10 20th Ave, Whitestone, NY, 11357
(718) 961-1212
Admin Henry Jacoby. *Medical Dir/Dir of Nursing* Alexander Sebo MD.
Licensure Skilled care. *Beds* 200. *Certified* Medicaid; Medicare.
Owner Proprietary Corp.
Admissions Requirements Medical examination; Physician's request.
Staff Physicians 3 (pt); RNs 4 (ft); LPNs 15 (ft); Orderlies 6 (ft); Nurses aides 34 (ft); Physical therapists 1 (ft); Recreational therapists 3 (ft); Occupational therapists 1 (pt); Speech therapists 1 (pt); Dietitians 1 (ft); Dentists 1 (pt); Ophthalmologists 1 (pt); Podiatrists 1 (pt); Audiologists 1 (pt).

Clearview Nursing Home*
157-15 19th Ave, Whitestone, NY, 11357
(718) 746-0400
Admin Raymond Small.
Licensure Skilled care. *Beds* 179. *Certified* Medicaid; Medicare.
Owner Proprietary Corp.

WILLIAMSVILLE

Amherst Presbyterian Nursing Center
200 Bassett Rd, Williamsville, NY, 14221
(716) 689-6681
Admin Eugene Urban. *Medical Dir/Dir of Nursing* Mary T Perrone.
Licensure Skilled care; Intermediate care; Rehabilitation; Special care. *Beds* SNF 120; ICF 80. *Certified* Medicaid; Medicare.
Owner Nonprofit Corp (Presbyterian Homes of Western).
Admissions Requirements Minimum age 16; Medical examination.
Staff Physicians 4 (pt); RNs 12 (ft), 12 (pt); LPNs 22 (ft), 7 (pt); Nurses aides 65 (ft), 19 (pt); Physical therapists 1 (ft), 1 (pt); Occupational therapists 1 (pt); Speech therapists 1 (pt); Activities coordinators 1 (ft); Dietitians 1 (pt); Ophthalmologists 1 (pt); Podiatrists 1 (pt).
Affiliation Presbyterian

Facilities Dining room; Physical therapy
room; Activities room; Chapel; Crafts room;
Laundry room; Barber/Beauty shop; Library.
Activities Arts & crafts; Cards; Games;
Reading groups; Prayer groups; Movies;
Shopping trips; Social/Cultural gatherings.

Heathwood Health Care Center Inc
815 Hopkins Rd, Williamsville, NY, 14221
(716) 688-0217
Admin Barbara Bernardis. *Medical Dir/Dir of
Nursing* Dr Ida Levine, Medical Director;
Joan Wells, DON.
Licensure Skilled care. *Beds* 160. *Certified*
Medicaid; Medicare.
Owner Proprietary Corp.
Admissions Requirements Minimum age 16;
Medical examination; Physician's request.
Staff Physicians 1 (pt); RNs 8 (ft), 14 (pt);
LPNs 22 (ft), 16 (pt); Nurses aides 42 (ft),
34 (pt); Physical therapists 2 (pt);
Occupational therapists 3 (pt); Speech
therapists 1 (pt); Activities coordinators 1
(ft); Dietitians 2 (pt).
Facilities Dining room; Physical therapy
room; Activities room; Chapel; Crafts room;
Laundry room; Barber/Beauty shop;
Occupational therapy room; Speech therapy
room; Large front porch.
Activities Arts & crafts; Cards; Games;
Reading groups; Prayer groups; Movies;
Shopping trips; Social/Cultural gatherings;
Current events; Cooking; Gardening;
Exercise groups; Resident council; Ceramics;
Community outings; Reminiscense groups;
Ecumenical worship services.

St Francis Home of Williamsville*
147 Reist St, Williamsville, NY, 14221
(716) 633-5400
Admin Daniel Kenny.
Licensure Skilled care; Intermediate care. *Beds*
50. *Certified* Medicaid; Medicare.
Owner Nonprofit Corp (Catholic Charities).

Williamsville Suburban Nursing Home*
193 S Union Rd, Williamsville, NY, 14221
(716) 632-6152
Licensure Intermediate care. *Beds* 80.
Owner Proprietary Corp.

Williamsville View Manor
165 S Union Rd, Williamsville, NY, 14221
(716) 633-9610
Admin Sam W Ware Jr. *Medical Dir/Dir of
Nursing* Joseph Gentile MD; Louise
Theriault RN DON.
Licensure Intermediate care. *Beds* ICF 140.
Certified Medicaid.
Owner Privately owned.
Admissions Requirements Minimum age 16.
Staff RNs 4 (ft), 4 (pt); LPNs 6 (ft), 24 (pt);
Nurses aides 16 (ft), 40 (pt); Physical
therapists 1 (pt); Recreational therapists 1
(ft); Occupational therapists 1 (pt); Activities
coordinators 1 (ft); Dietitians 1 (ft).
Facilities Dining room; Physical therapy
room; Activities room; Chapel; Crafts room;
Laundry room; Barber/Beauty shop; Library.
Activities Arts & crafts; Cards; Games;
Reading groups; Prayer groups; Movies;
Shopping trips; Social/Cultural gatherings;
Special dinners.

WOODBURY

United Presbyterian Home at Syosset Inc
378 Syosset-Woodbury Rd, Woodbury, NY,
11797
(516) 921-3900
Admin Alfred S Heim. *Medical Dir/Dir of
Nursing* Mr Trousdell MD DON.
Licensure Skilled care 10D Health related.
Beds 602. *Certified* Medicaid; Medicare.

Owner Nonprofit Corp.
Admissions Requirements Minimum age 16;
Medical examination.
Staff Physicians 6 (ft); RNs 50 (ft); LPNs 60
(ft); Dietitians; Rehabilitation therapist.
Facilities Dining room; Physical therapy
room; Activities room; Chapel; Crafts room;
Laundry room; Barber/Beauty shop; Library;
Game room; Music room; Bank branch;
Community outreach programs; Long-term
home health care; United lifeline; Personal
emergency response system.
Activities Arts & crafts; Cards; Games;
Reading groups; Movies; Shopping trips;
Social/Cultural gatherings; May festival;
Candlelight dinner; Variety shows; BBQs.

**Woodbury East Skilled Nursing & Health
Related Facility**
8565 Jericho Tpke, Woodbury, NY, 11561
(516) 367-3400
Admin Mitchell B Teller. *Medical Dir/Dir of
Nursing* Kathleen Gill.
Licensure SNF; HRF. *Beds* SNF 100; HRF
100. *Certified* Medicaid; Medicare.
Owner Privately owned.
Admissions Requirements Medical
examination; Physician's request.
Staff RNs; LPNs; Orderlies; Nurses aides;
Physical therapists; Recreational therapists;
Dietitians.
Facilities Dining room; Physical therapy
room; Activities room; Crafts room; Barber/
Beauty shop; Library; 11 acres with pond.
Activities Arts & crafts; Cards; Games;
Reading groups; Prayer groups; Movies;
Shopping trips; Social/Cultural gatherings.

Woodbury Nursing Home*
8533 Jericho Turnpike, Woodbury, NY, 11797
(516) 692-4100
Admin Maxwell White.
Licensure Skilled care. *Beds* 123. *Certified*
Medicaid; Medicare.
Owner Proprietary Corp.

WOODMERE

Woodmere Health Care Center Inc*
130 Irving Pl, Woodmere, NY, 11598
(516) 374-9300
Admin Miriam Feldman. *Medical Dir/Dir of
Nursing* Dr Harold Langs.
Licensure Skilled care. *Beds* 186. *Certified*
Medicaid; Medicare.
Owner Proprietary Corp.
Admissions Requirements Minimum age 18.
Staff Physicians; RNs; LPNs; Orderlies;
Nurses aides; Physical therapists; Reality
therapists; Recreational therapists;
Occupational therapists; Speech therapists;
Activities coordinators; Dietitians; Dentists;
Ophthalmologists; Podiatrists; Audiologists;
Nursing care coord.
Facilities Dining room; Physical therapy
room; Activities room; Crafts room; Laundry
room; Barber/Beauty shop; Library.
Activities Arts & crafts; Cards; Games;
Reading groups; Prayer groups; Movies;
Shopping trips; Social/Cultural gatherings;
Various outdoor trips; Picnics.

YAPHANK

Suffolk Infirmary
Yaphank Ave, Yaphank, NY, 11980
(516) 924-4300
Admin Kenneth E Gaul.
Licensure Skilled care. *Beds* 215. *Certified*
Medicaid; Medicare.
Owner Publicly owned.

Staff Physicians 1 (ft), 2 (pt); RNs 17 (ft);
LPNs 65 (ft); Physical therapists 1 (ft), 1
(pt); Recreational therapists 8 (ft);
Occupational therapists 1 (pt); Speech
therapists 1 (pt); Activities coordinators 1
(ft); Dietitians 1 (ft); Podiatrists 1 (pt).
Facilities Dining room; Physical therapy
room; Activities room; Barber/Beauty shop.
Activities Games; Reading groups; Prayer
groups; Movies.

YONKERS

Home for the Aged Blind
75 Stratton St S, Yonkers, NY, 10701
(212) (914) 963-4661
Licensure Skilled care; Health related care.
Beds SNF 47; HRF 125. *Certified* Medicaid;
Medicare.
Owner Nonprofit Corp.
Admissions Requirements Medical
examination.
Affiliation Jewish
Facilities Dining room; Physical therapy
room; Activities room; Crafts room; Barber/
Beauty shop.

Hudson View Nursing Home Inc*
65 Ashburton Ave, Yonkers, NY, 10701
(914) 963-4000
Admin Scott Sandford.
Licensure Skilled care. *Beds* 300. *Certified*
Medicaid; Medicare.
Owner Proprietary Corp.

New Sans Souci Nursing Home
115 Park Ave, Yonkers, NY, 10703
(914) 423-9800
Admin Marilyn Mittman. *Medical Dir/Dir of
Nursing* Dr Reddy; J DiScenza RN.
Licensure Skilled care. *Beds* SNF 120.
Certified Medicaid; Medicare.
Owner Privately owned.
Staff Physicians 1 (pt); RNs 10 (ft), 9 (pt);
LPNs 12 (ft), 5 (pt); Orderlies 1 (ft); Nurses
aides 30 (ft), 21 (pt); Physical therapists 2
(pt); Recreational therapists 1 (ft), 2 (pt);
Occupational therapists 1 (pt); Speech
therapists 1 (pt); Dietitians 1 (pt).
Facilities Dining room; Physical therapy
room; Activities room; Crafts room; Barber/
Beauty shop.
Activities Arts & crafts; Cards; Games;
Reading groups; Prayer groups; Movies;
Social/Cultural gatherings; Boat trips; BBQs.

**St Josephs Hospital Nursing Home of Yonkers
New York Inc**
127 S Broadway, Yonkers, NY, 10701
(914) 965-6700
Admin Dennis J Verzi. *Medical Dir/Dir of
Nursing* Dr Thomas Kalchthaler; Rosalie
Schiel RN DON.
Licensure Skilled care; HRF. *Beds* SNF 160;
HRF 40. *Certified* Medicaid; Medicare.
Owner Nonprofit Corp.
Admissions Requirements Minimum age 16;
Medical examination; Physician's request.
Staff Physicians 3 (ft); RNs 33 (ft); LPNs 34
(ft); Nurses aides 91 (ft); Physical therapists
1 (ft); Reality therapists 1 (ft); Recreational
therapists 3 (ft); Occupational therapists 2
(ft); Activities coordinators 1 (ft); Dietitians
2 (ft).
Languages Spanish, Portuguese, Arabic,
Italian, Russian, German, French
Affiliation Roman Catholic
Facilities Dining room; Physical therapy
room; Activities room; Chapel; Barber/
Beauty shop; Non-occupant day program for
adults; Long-term home health care program.
Activities Arts & crafts; Cards; Games;
Reading groups; Prayer groups; Movies;
Social/Cultural gatherings.

NORTH CAROLINA

AHOSKIE

Guardian Care Nursing Home
604 E Stokes St, Ahoskie, NC, 27910
(919) 332-2126
Admin Yvonne F Jernigan. *Medical Dir/Dir of Nursing* Rebecca E Carter RN.
Licensure Intermediate care. *Beds* 131. *Certified* Medicaid.
Owner Proprietary Corp (Hillhaven Corp).
Admissions Requirements Medical examination.
Staff RNs 2 (ft), 1 (pt); LPNs 11 (ft), 4 (pt); Orderlies 4 (ft), 2 (pt); Nurses aides 30 (ft), 12 (pt); Activities coordinators 1 (ft); Dietitians 1 (ft).
Facilities Dining room; Activities room; Crafts room; Laundry room; Barber/Beauty shop.
Activities Arts & crafts; Games; Reading groups; Prayer groups; Movies; Shopping trips; Social/Cultural gatherings.

ALBEMARLE

Britthaven of Piedmont
PO Box 1250, 33426 Old Salisbury Rd, Albemarle, NC, 28002
(704) 983-1195
Admin Paula T Smith. *Medical Dir/Dir of Nursing* Dr Eric M Johnsen; Sharom M Scheble.
Licensure Skilled care; Intermediate care. *Beds* SNF 60; ICF 60. *Certified* Medicaid; Medicare.
Admissions Requirements Minimum age 18; Medical examination.
Facilities Dining room; Physical therapy room; Activities room; Crafts room; Laundry room; Barber/Beauty shop.
Activities Arts & crafts; Cards; Games; Reading groups; Prayer groups; Movies; Shopping trips; Social/Cultural gatherings.

Lutheran Nursing Homes Inc—Albemarle Unit
Rte 1, Box 273, Albemarle, NC, 28001
(704) 982-8191
Admin J D Lawson. *Medical Dir/Dir of Nursing* Thomas F Kelley MD; Mrs Ethel Plyler.
Licensure Skilled care; Intermediate care; Home for aged. *Beds* SNF 54; ICF 10; Home for aged 11. *Certified* Medicaid; Medicare.
Owner Nonprofit Corp (NC Lutheran Homes).
Admissions Requirements Minimum age 60; Medical examination; Physician's request.
Staff Physicians; RNs; LPNs; Orderlies; Nurses aides; Activities coordinators; Dietitians; Dentists.
Affiliation Lutheran
Facilities Dining room; Physical therapy room; Activities room; Chapel; Crafts room; Laundry room; Barber/Beauty shop; Library; Livng room; Sitting room.
Activities Arts & crafts; Cards; Games; Reading groups; Prayer groups; Movies; Shopping trips; Social/Cultural gatherings.

ASHEBORO

Brian Center—Asheboro*
230 E Presnell St, PO Drawer 1928, Asheboro, NC, 27203
(919) 629-1447
Admin Leonard P Smith. *Medical Dir/Dir of Nursing* Ken Gobel MD.
Licensure Skilled care; Intermediate care. *Beds* SNF 90; ICF 124. *Certified* Medicaid; Medicare.
Owner Proprietary Corp (Brian Center Management Corp).
Admissions Requirements Minimum age 18.
Staff Physicians 22 (pt); RNs 10 (ft), 4 (pt); LPNs 20 (ft), 10 (pt); Orderlies 4 (ft), 1 (pt); Nurses aides 65 (ft), 15 (pt); Physical therapists 2 (pt); Speech therapists 1 (pt); Activities coordinators 3 (ft); Dietitians 1 (pt); Dentists 1 (pt); Ophthalmologists 3 (pt); Podiatrists 1 (pt); Audiologists 1 (pt).
Facilities Dining room; Physical therapy room; Activities room; Crafts room; Laundry room; Barber/Beauty shop; Library.
Activities Arts & crafts; Cards; Games; Prayer groups; Movies; Shopping trips; Social/Cultural gatherings.

Clapp's Convalescent Nursing Home Inc*
Rte 1, Box 395, Coleridge Rd, Asheboro, NC, 27203
(919) 625-2074
Admin George Donald Clapp.
Licensure Skilled care. *Beds* 26. *Certified* Medicaid; Medicare.

ASHEVILLE

Aston Park Health Care Center Inc
380 Brevard Rd, Asheville, NC, 28806
(704) 253-4437
Admin Martha M Smart. *Medical Dir/Dir of Nursing* Dr Kenneth Kubitschek; Louise R Carter.
Licensure Skilled care; Intermediate care. *Beds* SNF 54; ICF 66. *Certified* Medicaid; Medicare; VA.
Admissions Requirements Medical examination; Physician's request.
Staff RNs 8 (ft); LPNs 15 (ft); Orderlies 8 (ft); Nurses aides 46 (ft); Physical therapists 1 (pt); Speech therapists 1 (pt); Activities coordinators 1 (ft), 1 (pt); Dietitians 1 (ft); Ophthalmologists 1 (pt); Dentist 1 (pt).
Facilities Dining room; Physical therapy room; Activities room; Crafts room; Barber/Beauty shop; Day room.
Activities Arts & crafts; Cards; Games; Reading groups; Prayer groups; Movies; Shopping trips; Social/Cultural gatherings.

Biltmore Manor*
PO Box 15073, 14 All Souls Crescent, Asheville, NC, 28813
(704) 274-2336
Admin Robert C Brady.

Licensure Skilled care; Intermediate care; Home for aged. *Beds* SNF 53; ICF 26; Home for aged 21. *Certified* Medicaid; Medicare.

Brentwood Hills Nursing Center
500 Beaverdam Rd, Asheville, NC, 28804
(704) 254-8833
Admin Wayne Adams. *Medical Dir/Dir of Nursing* Mary Burgess.
Licensure Skilled care. *Beds* 77. *Certified* Medicaid; Medicare.
Owner Proprietary Corp (Beverly Enterprises).
Admissions Requirements Minimum age 21.
Staff Physicians 1 (ft); RNs 5 (ft); LPNs 15 (ft); Orderlies 6 (ft); Nurses aides 15 (ft); Physical therapists 2 (ft); Recreational therapists 1 (ft); Occupational therapists 1 (pt); Speech therapists 1 (pt); Activities coordinators 1 (ft); Dietitians 1 (ft); Ophthalmologists 1 (pt); Podiatrists 1 (pt).
Facilities Dining room; Physical therapy room; Activities room; Crafts room; Laundry room; Barber/Beauty shop.
Activities Arts & crafts; Cards; Games; Reading groups; Prayer groups; Movies; Shopping trips; Social/Cultural gatherings.

Brian Center Health & Retirement—Asheville
67 Mountainbrook Rd, Asheville, NC, 28805
(704) 258-8787
Admin Rita Van Nuys. *Medical Dir/Dir of Nursing* Dr Ricard Olson.
Licensure Skilled care; Intermediate care; Home for aged. *Beds* SNF 42; ICF 18; Home for aged 12. *Certified* Medicaid; Medicare.
Owner Proprietary Corp (Brian Center Management Corp).
Admissions Requirements Minimum age 21; Physician's request.
Staff Physicians 16 (pt); RNs 3 (ft), 1 (pt); LPNs 5 (ft), 2 (pt); Orderlies 1 (ft); Nurses aides 23 (ft), 6 (pt); Physical therapists 1 (pt); Speech therapists 1 (pt); Activities coordinators 1 (ft), 1 (pt); Dietitians 1 (ft); Dentists; Ophthalmologists 1 (pt).
Facilities Dining room; Physical therapy room; Laundry room; Barber/Beauty shop.
Activities Arts & crafts; Cards; Games; Reading groups; Prayer groups; Movies; Shopping trips; Social/Cultural gatherings; Supper club; Exercise class.

Brooks-Howell Home*
29 Spears Ave, Asheville, NC, 28801
(704) 253-6712
Admin Vivian McGraw.
Licensure Skilled care; Intermediate care. *Beds* SNF 40; ICF 18.
Affiliation Methodist
Facilities Dining room; Physical therapy room; Activities room; Chapel; Crafts room; Laundry room; Barber/Beauty shop; Library.
Activities Arts & crafts; Games; Reading groups; Prayer groups; Movies; Shopping trips; Social/Cultural gatherings.

Deerfield Episcopal Retirement Community Inc
1617 Hendersonville Rd, Asheville, NC, 28803
(704) 274-1531
Admin John D Olofson. *Medical Dir/Dir of Nursing* Dr Fuller Shuford; Nyla Sailor RN DON.
Licensure Skilled care; Home for aged. *Beds* SNF 31; Home for aged 8.
Admissions Requirements Minimum age 62; Medical examination.
Staff RNs 5 (ft), 6 (pt); LPNs 1 (ft), 2 (pt); Nurses aides 14 (ft), 16 (pt); Activities coordinators 1 (ft), 1 (pt).
Affiliation Episcopal
Facilities Dining room; Activities room; Chapel; Crafts room; Laundry room; Barber/Beauty shop; Library.
Activities Arts & crafts; Cards; Games; Reading groups; Prayer groups; Movies; Shopping trips; Social/Cultural gatherings.

Hillhaven Rehabilitation & Conv Center—Asheville
91 Victoria Rd, Asheville, NC, 28801
(704) 255-0076
Admin Glenn T Pierce. *Medical Dir/Dir of Nursing* Robert Reynolds MD; Susan Latta RN DON.
Licensure Skilled care; Intermediate care. *Beds* SNF 60; ICF 60. *Certified* Medicaid; Medicare.
Owner Proprietary Corp (Hillhaven Corp).
Admissions Requirements Minimum age 18; Medical examination; Physician's request.
Staff RNs; LPNs; Orderlies; Nurses aides; Physical therapists; Recreational therapists; Occupational therapists; Speech therapists.
Facilities Dining room; Physical therapy room; Activities room; Barber/Beauty shop.
Activities Arts & crafts; Cards; Games; Reading groups; Prayer groups; Movies; Shopping trips; Social/Cultural gatherings.

Hillside Nursing Home Inc*
PO Box 1530, Asheville, NC, 28802
(704) 254-2151
Admin Harry W Tolley. *Medical Dir/Dir of Nursing* Dr Everett Smith MD.
Licensure Intermediate care; Home for aged. *Beds* ICF 18; Home for aged 25. *Certified* Medicaid.
Admissions Requirements Medical examination; Physician's request.
Staff Physicians 5 (ft); RNs 2 (ft); LPNs 3 (ft); Orderlies 2 (ft); Nurses aides 10 (ft), 8 (pt); Physical therapists 3 (pt); Activities coordinators 1 (ft); Dietitians 1 (ft); Dentists 2 (pt); Podiatrists 1 (pt).
Facilities Dining room; Activities room; Laundry room.
Activities Arts & crafts; Cards; Games; Reading groups; Shopping trips; Social/Cultural gatherings.

Victoria Health Care Center*
455 Victoria Rd, Asheville, NC, 28801
(704) 252-0099
Admin Debra Koontz. *Medical Dir/Dir of Nursing* John Kelly MD.
Licensure Skilled care; Intermediate care. *Beds* SNF 60; ICF 60. *Certified* Medicaid; Medicare.
Admissions Requirements Medical examination; Physician's request.
Staff RNs 5 (ft); LPNs 12 (ft); Orderlies 2 (ft); Physical therapists 3 (ft); Recreational therapists 1 (ft); Speech therapists 1 (pt); Activities coordinators 1 (ft); Dietitians 1 (ft); Dentists 1 (pt).
Facilities Dining room; Physical therapy room; Activities room; Laundry room; Barber/Beauty shop.
Activities Arts & crafts; Cards; Games; Reading groups; Movies; Social/Cultural gatherings.

BANNER ELK

Heritage Manor of Banner Elk
PO Box 187, Norwood Hollow Rd, Banner Elk, NC, 28604
(704) 898-5136
Admin Pete Falkowski. *Medical Dir/Dir of Nursing* Dr Cathy Messick; Donna Cooke RN DON.
Licensure Skilled care; Intermediate care. *Beds* SNF 88; ICF 32. *Certified* Medicaid; Medicare.
Owner Proprietary Corp (National Heritage).
Admissions Requirements Physician's request.
Staff Physicians 1 (pt); RNs 5 (ft), 7 (pt); LPNs 8 (ft), 5 (pt); Orderlies 2 (ft), 1 (pt); Nurses aides 41 (ft), 11 (pt); Physical therapists 1 (pt); Speech therapists 1 (pt); Activities coordinators 1 (ft); Dietitians 1 (pt); Dentists 1 (pt); Ophthalmologists 1 (pt); Dentist 1 (pt).
Facilities Dining room; Physical therapy room; Activities room; Crafts room; Laundry room; Barber/Beauty shop; Family meeting room.
Activities Arts & crafts; Cards; Games; Reading groups; Prayer groups; Movies.

BISCOE

Montgomery Nursing Home*
Lambert Rd, Box 708, Biscoe, NC, 27209
(919) 428-2117
Admin Jean Allen. *Medical Dir/Dir of Nursing* Dr C N Eckerson.
Licensure Skilled care. *Beds* 57. *Certified* Medicaid; Medicare.
Admissions Requirements Medical examination.
Staff RNs 2 (ft), 1 (pt); LPNs 6 (ft), 1 (pt); Orderlies 1 (ft); Nurses aides 14 (ft), 4 (pt); Activities coordinators 1 (ft); Dietitians 1 (ft).
Facilities Dining room; Activities room; Chapel; Crafts room; Barber/Beauty shop.
Activities Arts & crafts; Games; Prayer groups; Movies; Social/Cultural gatherings.

BLACK MOUNTAIN

Black Mountain Center
Old Hwy 70, Black Mountain, NC, 28711
(704) 669-3100
Admin Dr Jack St Clair. *Medical Dir/Dir of Nursing* Dr Rasheeda Ahsanuddin.
Licensure Intermediate care for mentally retarded. *Beds* 120. *Certified* Medicaid.
Owner Publicly owned.
Admissions Requirements Medical examination.
Staff Physicians 2 (ft); RNs 11 (ft); LPNs 4 (ft); Nurses aides 99 (ft); Physical therapists 1 (ft); Recreational therapists 3 (ft); Occupational therapists 1 (ft); Speech therapists 2 (ft); Dietitians 2 (ft).
Facilities Dining room; Physical therapy room; Activities room; Chapel; Laundry room; Barber/Beauty shop; Library.
Activities Arts & crafts; Cards; Games; Reading groups; Prayer groups; Movies; Shopping trips; Social/Cultural gatherings; Individual training in self-help; Community living; Vocational skills, etc.

Highland Farms Inc*
Tabernacle Rd, Black Mountain, NC, 28711
(704) 669-6473
Admin Sheila Morse.
Licensure Skilled care. *Beds* 60. *Certified* Medicaid; Medicare.

BLOWING ROCK

Blowing Rock Hospital—SNF/ICF
PO Box 148, Chestnut Ave, Blowing Rock, NC, 28605
(704) 295-3136
Admin James P White. *Medical Dir/Dir of Nursing* Charles Davant Jr MD; Venn A Long DON.
Licensure Skilled care; Intermediate care. *Beds* 100. *Certified* Medicaid; Medicare; VA.
Owner Nonprofit Corp.
Admissions Requirements Medical examination; Physician's request.
Staff Physical therapists 2 (pt); Activities coordinators 1 (ft), 1 (pt).
Facilities Dining room; Physical therapy room; Activities room; Chapel; Crafts room; Laundry room; Barber/Beauty shop.
Activities Arts & crafts; Cards; Games; Reading groups; Prayer groups; Movies; Shopping trips; Social/Cultural gatherings; Ceramics; Exercise.

BOONE

Watauga Nursing Care Center
PO Box 2150, 535-A Elizabeth Dr, Boone, NC, 28607
(704) 264-6720
Admin Valerie J Keck. *Medical Dir/Dir of Nursing* Mark R Harter MD; Marion Young RN DON.
Licensure Skilled care; Intermediate care. *Beds* SNF 50; ICF 54. *Certified* Medicaid; Medicare; VA; Champus.
Owner Proprietary Corp (Tullock Management).
Admissions Requirements Minimum age 16; Physician's request.
Staff Physicians 15 (pt); RNs 5 (ft), 3 (pt); LPNs 7 (ft), 2 (pt); Orderlies 5 (ft), 1 (pt); Nurses aides 33 (ft), 12 (pt); Physical therapists 1 (ft); Recreational therapists 1 (pt); Occupational therapists 1 (ft), 1 (pt); Speech therapists 1 (pt); Activities coordinators 1 (ft); Dietitians 1 (pt); Ophthalmologists 1 (pt); Podiatrists 1 (pt).
Facilities Dining room; Physical therapy room; Activities room; Laundry room; Barber/Beauty shop; Covered patio area.
Activities Arts & crafts; Cards; Games; Reading groups; Prayer groups; Movies; Shopping trips; Social/Cultural gatherings.

BOSTIC

Haven In The Hills
Rte 2, Bostic, NC, 28018
(704) 245-2998
Admin Olive J Hunt. *Medical Dir/Dir of Nursing* Wanda Robinson.
Licensure Intermediate care; Rest home. *Beds* ICF 22; Rest home 28.
Owner Proprietary Corp.
Admissions Requirements Medical examination; Physician's request.
Staff Physicians 2 (pt); RNs 3 (pt); LPNs 1 (ft); Orderlies 1 (ft), 2 (pt); Nurses aides 12 (ft), 8 (pt); Activities coordinators 1 (pt); Dietitians 1 (pt).
Facilities Dining room; Activities room; Chapel; Laundry room; Barber/Beauty shop.
Activities Games; Prayer groups; Movies; Social/Cultural gatherings.

BREVARD

Brian Center Health & Retirement—Brevard*
PO Box 1096, 531 Country Club Rd, Brevard, NC, 28712
(704) 884-2031
Admin Patricia F Woody.

Licensure Skilled care; Intermediate care;
Home for aged. *Beds* SNF 54; ICF 53;
Home for aged 34. *Certified* Medicaid;
Medicare.
Owner Proprietary Corp (Brian Center
Management Corp).

BRYSON CITY

Mountain View Manor Nursing Center*
PO Drawer Y, Buckner Branch Rd, Bryson
City, NC, 28713
(704) 488-2101
Admin Christine Woolfenden.
Licensure Skilled care; Intermediate care. *Beds*
SNF 41; ICF 79. *Certified* Medicaid;
Medicare.

BURGAW

Guardian Care of Burgaw*
PO Box 874, Hwy 117-A S, Burgaw, NC,
28425
(919) 259-2149
Admin Bridget S Becher.
Licensure Intermediate care. *Beds* 72.
Certified Medicaid.
Owner Proprietary Corp (Hillhaven Corp).
Admissions Requirements Medical
examination.
Staff Physicians 4 (pt); RNs 1 (ft), 2 (pt);
LPNs 6 (ft), 4 (pt); Orderlies 3 (ft); Nurses
aides 16 (ft), 7 (pt); Activities coordinators 1
(ft); Dietitians 1 (ft); Dentists 2 (pt);
Podiatrists 2 (pt).
Facilities Dining room; Activities room;
Laundry room; Barber/Beauty shop.
Activities Arts & crafts; Cards; Games; Prayer
groups; Movies; Shopping trips.

BURLINGTON

**Alamance Memorial Hospital Skilled Nursing
Division**
PO Box 4008, 730 Hermitage Rd, Burlington,
NC, 27215
(919) 229-2600
Admin Robert E Byrd. *Medical Dir/Dir of
Nursing* Robert A Watson MD; Joan Severa
RN DON.
Licensure Skilled care. *Beds* SNF 81. *Certified*
Medicaid; Medicare.
Owner Nonprofit Corp.
Admissions Requirements Medical
examination; Physician's request.
Staff Physicians 35 (pt); RNs 9 (ft), 2 (pt);
LPNs 6 (ft), 1 (pt); Orderlies 3 (ft), 1 (pt);
Nurses aides 26 (ft), 11 (pt); Physical
therapists 1 (ft); Occupational therapists 1
(pt); Speech therapists 1 (pt); Activities
coordinators 2 (ft), 2 (pt); Dietitians 1 (ft);
Dentists 4 (pt); Ophthalmologists 2 (pt).
Facilities Dining room; Physical therapy
room; Activities room; Crafts room; Barber/
Beauty shop; Library.
Activities Arts & crafts; Cards; Games;
Reading groups; Prayer groups; Movies; Pet
therapy; Music programs; Hymn singing.

Central Piedmont Nursing Center
323 Baldwin Rd, PO Box 3427, Burlington,
NC, 27217
(919) 229-5571
Admin Jeanne K Hutcheson. *Medical Dir/Dir
of Nursing* James Hawkins Jr.
Licensure Intermediate care. *Beds* 100.
Certified Medicaid.
Admissions Requirements Minimum age 18;
Medical examination; Physician's request.
Staff RNs 3 (ft), 1 (pt); LPNs 5 (ft), 3 (pt);
Orderlies 5 (ft), 2 (pt); Nurses aides 35 (ft),
20 (pt); Physical therapists 1 (ft); Activities
coordinators 1 (ft), 4 (pt); Dietitians 1 (pt);
Dentists 1 (pt).

Facilities Dining room; Physical therapy
room; Activities room; Crafts room; Laundry
room; Barber/Beauty shop.
Activities Arts & crafts; Cards; Games;
Reading groups; Prayer groups; Movies;
Shopping trips; Social/Cultural gatherings.

Twin Lakes Care Center
100 Wade Coble Dr, Burlington, NC, 27215
(919) 584-7724
Admin Dr Clyde J Christmas III. *Medical Dir/
Dir of Nursing* Dr John B Walker III; Judith
A Holsinger DON.
Licensure Skilled care; Intermediate care;
Assisted living. *Beds* SNF 36; ICF 37;
Assisted living 30. *Certified* Medicaid;
Medicare.
Owner Nonprofit Corp.
Admissions Requirements Physician's request.
Staff RNs 5 (ft), 4 (pt); LPNs 8 (ft), 2 (pt);
Orderlies 4 (ft); Nurses aides 27 (ft), 6 (pt);
Physical therapists 1 (pt); Reality therapists
1 (pt); Occupational therapists 1 (pt); Speech
therapists 1 (pt); Activities coordinators 2
(ft); Dietitians 1 (pt); Ophthalmologists 1
(pt).
Affiliation Lutheran
Facilities Dining room; Physical therapy
room; Activities room; Chapel; Crafts room;
Laundry room; Barber/Beauty shop; Library.
Activities Arts & crafts; Cards; Games;
Reading groups; Prayer groups; Movies;
Shopping trips.

BUTNER

Murdoch Center*
C St, Butner, NC, 27509
(919) 575-7734
Admin J Michael Hennike.
Licensure Intermediate care for mentally
retarded. *Beds* 394. *Certified* Medicaid.

John Umstead Hospital—ICF
12th St, Butner, NC, 27509
(919) 575-7211
Admin M F Hall Jr.
Licensure Intermediate care. *Beds* 32.
Certified Medicaid.

CANDLER

Pisgah Manor Inc*
PO Box 1000, Holcombe Cove Rd, Candler,
NC, 28715
(704) 667-9851
Admin Dan Kidder. *Medical Dir/Dir of
Nursing* Dr Everett Smith.
Licensure Intermediate care. *Beds* 118.
Certified Medicaid.
Admissions Requirements Minimum age 18;
Medical examination; Physician's request.
Staff Physicians 1 (pt); RNs 1 (ft), 1 (pt);
LPNs 9 (ft), 7 (pt); Orderlies 3 (ft), 5 (pt);
Nurses aides 12 (ft), 53 (pt); Activities
coordinators 1 (ft), 4 (pt); Dietitians 1 (pt).
Affiliation Seventh-Day Adventist
Facilities Dining room; Activities room;
Crafts room; Laundry room; Barber/Beauty
shop; Library; TV room.
Activities Arts & crafts; Cards; Games;
Reading groups; Prayer groups; Movies;
Shopping trips; Social/Cultural gatherings.

CANTON

Canton Health Care Center*
PO Box 1449, 27 N Main St, Canton, NC,
28716
(704) 648-3551
Admin Edward L "Matt" Dillon. *Medical Dir/
Dir of Nursing* F C Morrison MD.
Licensure Skilled care; Intermediate care. *Beds*
SNF 60; ICF 54. *Certified* Medicaid;
Medicare.
Owner Proprietary Corp (National Health
Corp).

Admissions Requirements Medical
examination.
Staff Physicians 8 (pt); RNs 3 (ft), 5 (pt);
LPNs 15 (ft), 8 (pt); Nurses aides 28 (ft), 12
(pt); Physical therapists 1 (ft); Speech
therapists 1 (pt); Activities coordinators 1
(ft), 2 (pt); Dietitians 1 (pt); Dentists 1 (pt).
Facilities Dining room; Physical therapy
room; Activities room; Crafts room; Laundry
room; Barber/Beauty shop.
Activities Arts & crafts; Cards; Games;
Reading groups; Prayer groups; Movies;
Shopping trips; Social/Cultural gatherings.

CHAPEL HILL

Carol Woods
750 Weaver Dairy Rd, Chapel Hill, NC,
27514
(919) 968-4511
Admin John Diffey. *Medical Dir/Dir of
Nursing* Robert J Sullivan.
Licensure Skilled care; Home for aged. *Beds*
SNF 30; Home for aged 30.
Owner Nonprofit Corp.
Admissions Requirements Minimum age 65;
Medical examination; Physician's request.
Staff Physicians 1 (pt); RNs 6 (ft), 10 (pt);
LPNs 6 (ft), 10 (pt); Nurses aides 15 (ft), 10
(pt); Physical therapists 1 (pt); Recreational
therapists 1 (ft); Occupational therapists 1
(pt); Speech therapists 1 (pt); Dietitians 1
(ft); Dentists 1 (pt); Ophthalmologists 1 (pt);
Dentist 1 (pt).
Facilities Dining room; Physical therapy
room; Activities room; Crafts room; Laundry
room; Barber/Beauty shop; Library.
Activities Arts & crafts; Cards; Games;
Reading groups; Shopping trips; Social/
Cultural gatherings.

Hillhaven Conv Center of Chapel Hill*
1602 E Franklin St, Chapel Hill, NC, 27514
(919) 967-1418
Admin Vicki Jones. *Medical Dir/Dir of
Nursing* Dr Glen Pickard.
Licensure Skilled care; Intermediate care. *Beds*
120. *Certified* Medicaid; Medicare.
Owner Proprietary Corp (Hillhaven Corp).
Admissions Requirements Medical
examination.
Staff RNs 5 (ft), 2 (pt); LPNs 8 (ft), 5 (pt);
Nurses aides 33 (ft), 6 (pt); Physical
therapists 2 (ft); Recreational therapists 1
(ft); Occupational therapists 1 (pt); Speech
therapists 1 (pt); Activities coordinators 1
(pt); Dietitians 1 (ft).
Facilities Dining room; Physical therapy
room; Activities room; Laundry room;
Barber/Beauty shop.
Activities Arts & crafts; Cards; Games;
Reading groups; Prayer groups; Movies;
Shopping trips; Social/Cultural gatherings.

Lakeview Manor
1716 Legion Rd, Chapel Hill, NC, 27514
(919) 929-7146
Admin Mary Lou James.
Licensure Skilled care. *Beds* 58. *Certified*
Medicaid.
Owner Proprietary Corp (Hillhaven Corp).

CHARLOTTE

Beverly Manor-Charlotte
2616 E 5th St, Charlotte, NC, 28204
(704) 333-5165
Admin Paul T Babinski. *Medical Dir/Dir of
Nursing* Alex Sanchez MD; Caroline
McCrain RN DON.
Licensure Skilled care; Intermediate care. *Beds*
SNF 88; ICF 32. *Certified* Medicaid;
Medicare.
Owner Proprietary Corp (Beverly Enterprises).
Admissions Requirements Medical
examination.

Staff Physicians 4 (pt); RNs 6 (ft); LPNs 11 (ft); Orderlies 4 (ft), 1 (pt); Nurses aides 75 (ft), 5 (pt); Physical therapists 1 (pt); Occupational therapists 1 (pt); Speech therapists 1 (pt); Activities coordinators 1 (ft); Dietitians 1 (pt); Dentists 1 (pt); Ophthalmologists 1 (pt); Podiatrists 1 (pt).
Facilities Dining room; Physical therapy room; Activities room; Crafts room; Laundry room; Barber/Beauty shop; Library; Enclosed courtyard with front porch.
Activities Arts & crafts; Cards; Games; Reading groups; Prayer groups; Movies; Shopping trips; Social/Cultural gatherings; Bingo; Exercise; Resident council.

Hawthorne Nursing Center
333 Hawthorne Ln, Charlotte, NC, 28204
(704) 372-1270
Admin James F Leach. *Medical Dir/Dir of Nursing* Donald Goodman MD.
Licensure Skilled care; Intermediate care. *Beds* SNF 126; ICF 16. *Certified* Medicaid; Medicare.
Owner Proprietary Corp (Life Care Centers of America).
Admissions Requirements Physician's request.
Staff RNs 7 (ft), 4 (pt); LPNs 12 (ft), 6 (pt); Orderlies 5 (ft), 2 (pt); Nurses aides 40 (ft), 10 (pt); Physical therapists 1 (ft); Speech therapists 2 (pt); Activities coordinators 2 (ft); Dietitians 1 (pt).
Facilities Dining room; Physical therapy room; Activities room; Chapel; Laundry room; Barber/Beauty shop.
Activities Arts & crafts; Cards; Games; Reading groups; Prayer groups; Movies; Shopping trips; Social/Cultural gatherings.

Hillcrest Manor Nursing Home*
2435 Sharon Rd, Charlotte, NC, 28211
(704) 366-1511
Admin W B O'Neal. *Medical Dir/Dir of Nursing* Dr Charles L Stuckey.
Licensure Intermediate care. *Beds* 24.
Admissions Requirements Medical examination.
Staff RNs 1 (ft), 2 (pt); LPNs 6 (ft); Orderlies 2 (ft); Nurses aides 6 (ft); Activities coordinators 1 (pt); Dietitians 1 (pt).

Hospitality Care Center of Charlotte*
4801 Randolph Rd, Charlotte, NC, 28211
(704) 364-8363
Admin Douglas Shuman.
Licensure Skilled care; Intermediate care. *Beds* SNF 62; ICF 38. *Certified* Medicaid; Medicare.

Mecklenburg Autistic Group Homes Inc
3201 Park Rd, Charlotte, NC, 28209
(704) 527-5366
Admin J Michael Dyson. *Medical Dir/Dir of Nursing* Dr Joal Fischer.
Licensure Intermediate care for mentally retarded. *Beds* 10. *Certified* Medicaid.
Owner Nonprofit Corp.
Admissions Requirements Minimum age 18; Medical examination.
Staff Physicians 1 (pt); RNs 1 (pt); Nurses aides 5 (ft); Speech therapists 1 (pt); Dietitians 1 (pt).
Facilities Dining room; Activities room; Crafts room; Laundry room.
Activities Arts & crafts; Cards; Games; Reading groups; Movies; Shopping trips; Social/Cultural gatherings.

The Presbyterian Home at Charlotte Inc
5100 Sharon Rd, Charlotte, NC, 28212
(704) 553-1670
Admin Paul A Craig Jr. *Medical Dir/Dir of Nursing* Dr Jack Hobson; Betty W Mauney RN DON.
Licensure Skilled care; Retirement/residential. *Beds* 330.
Owner Nonprofit Corp.

Admissions Requirements Minimum age 65; Medical examination.
Staff RNs 16 (ft), 6 (pt); LPNs 12 (ft), 4 (pt); Nurses aides 30 (ft), 18 (pt); Activities coordinators 1 (ft); Dietitians 1 (ft).
Affiliation Presbyterian
Facilities Dining room; Physical therapy room; Activities room; Chapel; Crafts room; Laundry room; Barber/Beauty shop; Library; Pool table area; Sewing room; Art room.
Activities Arts & crafts; Cards; Games; Reading groups; Prayer groups; Movies; Shopping trips; Social/Cultural gatherings; Exercise classes.

Providence Convalescent Residence Inc*
300 Providence Rd, Charlotte, NC, 28207
(704) 334-1671
Admin William S Bradley Jr. *Medical Dir/Dir of Nursing* Dr Henry Stuckey.
Licensure Skilled care; Home for aged. *Beds* SNF 125; Home for aged 25. *Certified* Medicaid; Medicare.
Admissions Requirements Minimum age 55; Medical examination; Physician's request.
Staff Physicians 26 (pt); RNs 9 (ft), 2 (pt); LPNs 10 (ft), 2 (pt); Orderlies 4 (ft), 4 (pt); Nurses aides 46 (ft), 16 (pt); Physical therapists 2 (pt); Speech therapists 1 (pt); Activities coordinators 1 (pt); Dietitians 1 (pt); Dentists 1 (pt); Podiatrists 1 (pt).
Facilities Dining room; Physical therapy room; Activities room; Chapel; Crafts room; Laundry room; Barber/Beauty shop.
Activities Arts & crafts; Games; Reading groups; Movies; Shopping trips; Social/Cultural gatherings.

Randolph Manor*
2623 Cranbrook Ln, Charlotte, NC, 28207
(704) 332-1161
Admin Carolyn H Sherrill. *Medical Dir/Dir of Nursing* Russell Long MD.
Licensure Skilled care; Intermediate care; Retirement & Rest home. *Beds* SNF 56; ICF 52; Retirement home 30; Rest home 25. *Certified* Medicaid; Medicare.
Owner Proprietary Corp (Hillhaven Corp).
Admissions Requirements Minimum age 18; Medical examination; Physician's request.
Staff RNs 8 (ft), 2 (pt); LPNs 10 (ft), 4 (pt); Orderlies 4 (ft), 2 (pt); Nurses aides 42 (ft), 10 (pt); Physical therapists 1 (ft); Activities coordinators 1 (ft).
Facilities Dining room; Physical therapy room; Activities room; Crafts room; Laundry room; Barber/Beauty shop.
Activities Arts & crafts; Cards; Games; Reading groups; Prayer groups; Movies; Shopping trips; Social/Cultural gatherings.

Sharon Village
PO Box 220130, 4009 Craig Ave, Charlotte, NC, 28222
(704) 365-2620
Admin Stephen Reynolds.
Licensure Intermediate care. *Beds* 60.

Wesleyan Nursing Home Inc*
2623 Cranbrook Ln, Charlotte, NC, 28207
(704) 332-1161
Admin Carolyn Sherrill. *Medical Dir/Dir of Nursing* Russell Long MD.
Licensure Skilled care; Intermediate care; Home for aged; Retirement. *Beds* SNF 56; ICF 52; Home for aged 25; Retirement 30. *Certified* Medicaid; Medicare.
Admissions Requirements Minimum age 18; Medical examination; Physician's request.
Staff RNs 7 (ft), 2 (pt); LPNs 8 (ft), 3 (pt); Orderlies 1 (ft); Nurses aides 40 (ft), 13 (pt); Physical therapists; Occupational therapists; Speech therapists; Activities coordinators 2 (ft), 1 (pt); Dietitians; Dentists; Podiatrists.
Facilities Dining room; Physical therapy room; Activities room; Crafts room; Laundry room; Barber/Beauty shop.

Activities Arts & crafts; Cards; Games; Reading groups; Prayer groups; Movies; Shopping trips; Social/Cultural gatherings.

Wessel's Nursing Home Inc
515 Templeton Ave, Charlotte, NC, 28203
(704) 332-2354
Admin Sonja Kaminin. *Medical Dir/Dir of Nursing* W Tyson Bennett MD.
Licensure Skilled care. *Beds* SNF 26. *Certified* Medicaid; Medicare.
Owner Proprietary Corp.
Admissions Requirements Medical examination; Physician's request.
Staff Physicians 2 (pt); RNs 1 (ft), 1 (pt); LPNs 3 (ft); Nurses aides 7 (ft), 4 (pt); Physical therapists 1 (pt); Activities coordinators 1 (pt); Dietitians 1 (pt); Dentists 1 (pt); Ophthalmologists 1 (pt); Podiatrists dentist 1 (pt).
Facilities Activities room; Laundry room.
Activities Arts & crafts; Games; Reading groups; Prayer groups; Movies.

CHERRYVILLE

Carolina Care Center of Cherryville
PO Box 580, Hwy 274 N, Cherryville, NC, 28021
(704) 435-4161
Admin Judy B Beam. *Medical Dir/Dir of Nursing* Marjorie Humphrey.
Licensure Skilled care; Intermediate care; Rest home. *Beds* SNF 21; ICF 86; Rest home 12. *Certified* Medicaid; Medicare.
Owner Privately owned.
Admissions Requirements Medical examination.
Staff RNs 6 (ft), 1 (pt); LPNs 7 (ft), 1 (pt); Nurses aides 31 (ft), 2 (pt); Activities coordinators 1 (ft); Dietitians 1 (ft).
Facilities Dining room; Activities room; Crafts room; Laundry room; Barber/Beauty shop.
Activities Arts & crafts; Cards; Games; Prayer groups; Movies; Shopping trips; Social/Cultural gatherings.

Meadowbrook Manor of Cherryville
PO Box 638, 700 Self St, Cherryville, NC, 28021
(704) 435-6029
Admin Edwin L Ware. *Medical Dir/Dir of Nursing* Dr M E Agner; Chris McCall RN.
Licensure Intermediate care; Home for aged. *Beds* ICF 54; Home for aged 57. *Certified* Medicaid.
Owner Proprietary Corp (Tullock Management).
Admissions Requirements Minimum age 18; Medical examination; Physician's request.
Staff Physicians 3 (pt); RNs 2 (ft); LPNs 5 (ft), 5 (pt); Nurses aides 18 (ft), 25 (pt); Physical therapists 1 (pt); Activities coordinators 1 (ft); Dietitians 1 (pt); Ophthalmologists 1 (pt).
Facilities Dining room; Activities room; Chapel; Crafts room; Laundry room; Barber/Beauty shop.
Activities Arts & crafts; Games; Prayer groups; Movies; Shopping trips; Social/Cultural gatherings.

CLEMMONS

The Bluementhal Jewish Home for the Aged Inc
PO Box 38, 7870 Fair Oaks Dr, Clemmons, NC, 27012-0038
(919) 766-6401
Admin Donald J Morris. *Medical Dir/Dir of Nursing* William C Sugg MD; Patsy Petree RN DON.
Licensure Skilled care; Intermediate care; Personal care. *Beds* SNF 90; ICF 44; Personal 46. *Certified* Medicaid; Medicare.
Owner Nonprofit organization/foundation.

Admissions Requirements Minimum age 65; Medical examination; Physician's request.
Staff Physicians 3 (pt); RNs 18 (ft); LPNs 10 (ft); Orderlies 2 (ft), 4 (pt); Nurses aides 46 (ft), 10 (pt); Physical therapists 1 (pt); Recreational therapists 3 (ft); Occupational therapists 2 (pt); Speech therapists 1 (pt); Activities coordinators 1 (ft); Dietitians 1 (ft), 1 (pt); Dentists 1 (pt); Ophthalmologists 3 (pt); Podiatrists 1 (pt); Social worker 2 (ft).
Languages Yiddish, Hebrew, German
Affiliation Jewish
Facilities Dining room; Physical therapy room; Activities room; Chapel; Crafts room; Barber/Beauty shop; Library; Gardens; Large terrace; Wooded area.
Activities Arts & crafts; Cards; Games; Reading groups; Prayer groups; Movies; Shopping trips; Social/Cultural gatherings; Religious services & celebrations; Discussion groups; Holidays; Concert & lecture series; Volunteer programs; Resident council.

Meadowbrook Manor
PO Box 249, Hwy 158, Clemmons, NC, 27012
(919) 766-9158
Admin C Jean Small. *Medical Dir/Dir of Nursing* Dr Robert Eberle.
Licensure Skilled care; Intermediate care. *Beds* SNF 60; ICF 60. *Certified* Medicaid; Medicare.
Owner Proprietary Corp (Angell Group).
Admissions Requirements Medical examination; Physician's request.
Staff Physicians; RNs; LPNs; Orderlies; Nurses aides; Physical therapists; Reality therapists; Recreational therapists; Occupational therapists; Speech therapists; Activities coordinators; Dietitians; Dentists; Ophthalmologists; Podiatrists.
Facilities Dining room; Physical therapy room; Activities room; Chapel; Crafts room; Barber/Beauty shop.
Activities Arts & crafts; Cards; Games; Reading groups; Prayer groups; Movies; Shopping trips; Social/Cultural gatherings.

CLINTON

Mary-Gran Nursing Center*
PO Box 379, 120 Southwood Dr, Clinton, NC, 28328
(919) 592-7981
Admin Garland Slate.
Licensure Skilled care; Intermediate care; Home for aged. *Beds* SNF 90; ICF 30; Home for aged 5. *Certified* Medicaid; Medicare.

CLYDE

Britthaven of Clyde*
PO Box 504, 30 Morgan St, Clyde, NC, 28721-0504
(704) 627-2789
Admin Jerry Rogers. *Medical Dir/Dir of Nursing* Dr E B Goodwin Jr.
Licensure Intermediate care. *Beds* 50. *Certified* Medicaid.
Owner Proprietary Corp (Britthaven Inc).
Admissions Requirements Medical examination.
Staff LPNs 5 (ft); Orderlies 1 (ft); Nurses aides 17 (ft); Activities coordinators 1 (ft).
Facilities Dining room; Activities room; Laundry room; Barber/Beauty shop.
Activities Arts & crafts; Games; Reading groups; Prayer groups; Movies; Social/Cultural gatherings.

CONCORD

Cabarrus Nursing Center Inc
PO Box 748, 515 Concord Lake Rd, Concord, NC, 28026-0748
(704) 786-9151
Admin Rebecca Pullin. *Medical Dir/Dir of Nursing* Dr Robert E Hammonds; Melania Eaves RN DON.
Licensure Skilled care; Intermediate care. *Beds* SNF 88; ICF 32. *Certified* Medicaid; Medicare.
Admissions Requirements Medical examination; Physician's request.
Staff RNs 5 (ft), 4 (pt); LPNs 7 (ft), 2 (pt); Nurses aides 31 (ft), 21 (pt); Physical therapists 1 (ft); Activities coordinators 1 (ft); Dietitians 1 (ft); Ophthalmologists 1 (ft); Dentist 1 (ft).
Facilities Dining room; Physical therapy room; Activities room; Chapel; Crafts room; Laundry room; Barber/Beauty shop; Reading Room; TV Room.
Activities Arts & crafts; Cards; Games; Reading groups; Prayer groups; Movies; Shopping trips; Social/Cultural gatherings.

Concord Nursing Center
PO Box 748, 430 Brookwood Ave NE, Concord, NC, 28026-0748
(704) 788-4115
Admin Shirley S Rogers. *Medical Dir/Dir of Nursing* Robert E Hammonds MD.
Licensure Skilled care; Intermediate care. *Beds* SNF 90; ICF 30. *Certified* Medicaid; Medicare.
Owner Proprietary Corp.
Admissions Requirements Medical examination; Physician's request.
Staff Physicians 4 (pt); RNs 6 (ft), 2 (pt); LPNs 5 (ft), 4 (pt); Nurses aides 39 (ft), 8 (pt); Physical therapists 1 (ft); Recreational therapists 1 (ft); Activities coordinators 1 (ft); Dietitians 1 (ft); Dentists 1 (pt); Ophthalmologists 1 (pt); Dentist 1 (pt).
Facilities Dining room; Physical therapy room; Activities room; Chapel; Crafts room; Laundry room; Barber/Beauty shop; Library.
Activities Arts & crafts; Cards; Games; Reading groups; Prayer groups; Movies; Shopping trips; Social/Cultural gatherings; Video recorder & video movies; Rowan Technical College classes.

Five Oaks Nursing Center
PO Box 384, 413 Winecoff School Rd, Concord, NC, 28026-0384
(704) 788-2131
Admin Dorothy M Critz. *Medical Dir/Dir of Nursing* Dr Vincent Keipper; Nancy Bust.
Licensure Skilled care; Intermediate care; Home for aged. *Beds* SNF 63; ICF 60; Home for aged 12. *Certified* Medicaid; Medicare.
Owner Privately owned.
Admissions Requirements Medical examination.
Staff Physicians 2 (pt); RNs 8 (ft), 4 (pt); LPNs 5 (ft), 1 (pt); Nurses aides 37 (ft), 16 (pt); Physical therapists 1 (pt); Activities coordinators 2 (ft); Dietitians 1 (pt); Ophthalmologists 1 (pt); Dentist 1 (pt).
Facilities Dining room; Physical therapy room; Activities room; Crafts room; Laundry room; Barber/Beauty shop.
Activities Arts & crafts; Cards; Games; Reading groups; Prayer groups; Movies; Shopping trips; Social/Cultural gatherings.

Odell Nursing Center
2339 Odell School Rd, Concord, NC, 28025
(704) 782-9770
Admin Ben Setzer Jr. *Medical Dir/Dir of Nursing* Sandra Freeze RN DON.
Licensure Skilled care; Intermediate care. *Beds* SNF 22; ICF 25. *Certified* Medicaid; Medicare.
Owner Proprietary Corp.
Admissions Requirements Medical examination; Physician's request.
Staff Physicians 1 (pt); RNs 2 (ft), 1 (pt); LPNs 4 (ft), 2 (pt); Orderlies 3 (ft), 2 (pt); Nurses aides 10 (ft), 4 (pt); Physical

therapists 2 (pt); Recreational therapists 1 (ft); Occupational therapists 1 (pt); Speech therapists 1 (pt); Activities coordinators 1 (ft); Dietitians 1 (ft); Ophthalmologists 1 (pt).
Facilities Dining room; Physical therapy room; Activities room; Chapel; Crafts room; Laundry room; Barber/Beauty shop.
Activities Arts & crafts; Cards; Games; Reading groups; Prayer groups; Movies.

Piedmont Residential Developmental Center*
PO Box 909, Concord, NC, 28025
(704) 788-2304
Admin Paul Caldwell.
Licensure Intermediate care for mentally retarded. *Beds* 10. *Certified* Medicaid.

DANBURY

Stokes-Reynolds Memorial Hospital—SNF*
PO Box 10, Danbury, NC, 27016
(919) 593-2831
Admin Sandra D Priddy. *Medical Dir/Dir of Nursing* Dr Renato Zarate.
Licensure Skilled care. *Beds* 40. *Certified* Medicaid; Medicare.
Owner Nonprofit Corp.
Staff Physicians 5 (ft); RNs 1 (ft); LPNs 8 (ft); Orderlies 2 (ft); Nurses aides 22 (ft); Physical therapists 1 (ft); Activities coordinators 1 (ft); Dietitians 1 (ft); Dentists 1 (ft).

DENTON

Mountain Vista Health Park
PO Box 458, Jackson Hill Rd, Denton, NC, 27239
(704) 869-2181
Admin Wanda Stone. *Medical Dir/Dir of Nursing* Drs FH & FC Mangundayao; Kathy McDonald RN DON.
Licensure Skilled care; Intermediate care; Rest home. *Beds* SNF 24; ICF 36; Rest home 60. *Certified* Medicaid; Medicare.
Owner Proprietary Corp (White Oak Manor).
Admissions Requirements Minimum age 18; Medical examination; Physician's request.
Staff RNs 4 (ft), 1 (pt); LPNs 7 (ft), 1 (pt); Orderlies 2 (ft); Nurses aides 23 (ft), 6 (pt); Activities coordinators 2 (ft).
Facilities Dining room; Physical therapy room; Activities room; Chapel; Crafts room; Laundry room; Barber/Beauty shop.
Activities Arts & crafts; Cards; Games; Reading groups; Prayer groups; Movies; Shopping trips; Social/Cultural gatherings.

DREXEL

Autumn Care of Drexel
307 Oakland Ave, Drexel, NC, 28619
(704) 433-6180
Admin Mary G Taychert. *Medical Dir/Dir of Nursing* C J Dellinger MD; Frances Burns RN.
Licensure Skilled care; Intermediate care; Home for aged. *Beds* SNF 50; ICF 50; Home for aged 20. *Certified* Medicaid; Medicare.
Owner Proprietary Corp (Autumn Corp).
Admissions Requirements Minimum age 21; Medical examination; Physician's request.
Staff Physicians; RNs 8 (ft), 6 (pt); LPNs 7 (ft), 5 (pt); Nurses aides 45 (ft); Physical therapists 1 (pt); Speech therapists 1 (pt); Activities coordinators 1 (ft), 3 (pt); Dietitians 1 (pt).
Facilities Dining room; Physical therapy room; Activities room; Chapel; Crafts room; Laundry room; Barber/Beauty shop.
Activities Arts & crafts; Cards; Games; Reading groups; Prayer groups; Movies; Social/Cultural gatherings.

DUNN

Charles Parrish Memorial Nursing Center*
201 N Ellis Ave, PO Box 1707, Dunn, NC, 28334
(919) 892-4021
Admin Joy Strickland. *Medical Dir/Dir of Nursing* L R Doffermyre MD.
Licensure Skilled care; Intermediate care. *Beds* SNF 63; ICF 39. *Certified* Medicaid; Medicare.
Admissions Requirements Medical examination.
Staff RNs 6 (ft); LPNs 9 (ft), 2 (pt); Orderlies 4 (ft), 2 (pt); Nurses aides 36 (ft), 5 (pt); Physical therapists 1 (ft).
Facilities Dining room; Laundry room.
Activities Arts & crafts; Cards; Games; Reading groups; Prayer groups; Movies; Social/Cultural gatherings; Exercise classes.

DURHAM

Greenery Rehabilitation Center
3100 Erwin Rd, Durham, NC, 27705
(919) 383-1546
Admin Soultana Rouses. *Medical Dir/Dir of Nursing* Arnett Coleman MD; Gwen Cobb RN DON.
Licensure Skilled care; Intermediate care. *Beds* SNF 109; ICF 36. *Certified* Medicaid; Medicare.
Owner Proprietary Corp (Greenery Rehab Grp).
Admissions Requirements Medical examination; Physician's request.
Staff RNs 10 (ft), 3 (pt); LPNs 20 (ft), 2 (pt); Orderlies 6 (ft); Nurses aides 60 (ft), 8 (pt); Recreational therapists 1 (ft); Activities coordinators 1 (ft); Dietitians 1 (ft).
Facilities Dining room; Physical therapy room; Activities room; Chapel; Crafts room; Laundry room; Barber/Beauty shop.
Activities Arts & crafts; Cards; Games; Reading groups; Prayer groups; Movies; Shopping trips; Social/Cultural gatherings; Local activities.

Hillcrest Convalescent Center Inc*
1417 W Pettigrew St, PO Box 2816, Durham, NC, 27705
(919) 286-7705
Admin J R Garrett Jr. *Medical Dir/Dir of Nursing* Lewis M McKee MD.
Licensure Skilled care. *Beds* 120. *Certified* Medicaid; Medicare.
Admissions Requirements Medical examination; Physician's request.
Staff RNs 5 (ft), 2 (pt); LPNs 10 (ft), 5 (pt); Orderlies 3 (ft), 2 (pt); Nurses aides 37 (ft), 10 (pt); Physical therapists 1 (ft), 1 (pt); Reality therapists 1 (pt); Recreational therapists 2 (ft); Occupational therapists 1 (pt); Speech therapists 1 (pt); Activities coordinators 1 (ft); Dietitians 1 (ft), 1 (pt); Dentists 1 (pt); Ophthalmologists 1 (pt); Podiatrists 1 (pt); Audiologists 1 (pt).
Facilities Dining room; Physical therapy room; Activities room; Chapel; Crafts room; Laundry room; Barber/Beauty shop; Library.
Activities Arts & crafts; Cards; Games; Reading groups; Prayer groups; Movies; Shopping trips; Social/Cultural gatherings; Current events; Music appreciation.

Hillhaven LaSalle Nursing Center
411 S LaSalle St, Durham, NC, 27705
(919) 383-5521
Admin Mary Lou James. *Medical Dir/Dir of Nursing* Noel List MD.
Licensure Skilled care; Intermediate care. *Beds* SNF 46; ICF 80. *Certified* Medicaid; Medicare; VA.
Owner Proprietary Corp (Hillhaven Corp).
Admissions Requirements Medical examination; Physician's request.

Staff RNs 3 (ft); LPNs 10 (ft); Orderlies 3 (ft); Nurses aides 20 (ft); Physical therapists 1 (ft); Recreational therapists 2 (ft); Occupational therapists 1 (pt); Speech therapists 1 (pt); Dietitians 1 (ft), 1 (pt).
Facilities Dining room; Physical therapy room; Activities room; Chapel; Barber/Beauty shop; TV Room; Courtyard.
Activities Arts & crafts; Games; Reading groups; Prayer groups; Movies; Shopping trips; Social/Cultural gatherings; Educational classes.

Hillhaven Orange Nursing Center*
Rte 1, Box 155, Mt Sinai Rd, Durham, NC, 27705
(919) 489-2361
Admin Virginia L Smith. *Medical Dir/Dir of Nursing* Dr Byron Cole.
Licensure Skilled care; Intermediate care. *Beds* SNF 42; ICF 74. *Certified* Medicaid; Medicare.
Owner Proprietary Corp (Hillhaven Corp).
Admissions Requirements Medical examination.
Staff Physicians 1 (ft); RNs 5 (ft); LPNs 12 (ft), 4 (pt); Nurses aides 40 (ft), 15 (pt); Physical therapists 1 (pt); Reality therapists 1 (pt); Recreational therapists 1 (ft), 1 (pt); Speech therapists 1 (pt); Activities coordinators 1 (ft); Dietitians 1 (ft); Dentists; Ophthalmologists; Podiatrists; Audiologists.
Facilities Dining room; Physical therapy room; Activities room; Barber/Beauty shop.
Activities Arts & crafts; Cards; Games; Reading groups; Prayer groups; Movies; Shopping trips; Social/Cultural gatherings.

Hillhaven Rehabilitation & Convalescent Center
1515 W Pettigrew St, Durham, NC, 27705
(919) 286-0751
Admin Christine Coley. *Medical Dir/Dir of Nursing* Richard Bruch; Jacqueline Roberts.
Licensure Skilled care. *Beds* 107. *Certified* Medicaid; Medicare.
Owner Proprietary Corp (Hillhaven Corp).
Admissions Requirements Physician's request.
Staff RNs; LPNs; Orderlies; Nurses aides 21 (ft), 7 (pt); Physical therapists 1 (ft), 2 (pt); Recreational therapists 1 (pt); Speech therapists; Activities coordinators 1 (ft); Dietitians 1 (ft).
Facilities Dining room; Physical therapy room; Activities room; Chapel; Crafts room; Laundry room; Barber/Beauty shop.
Activities Arts & crafts; Cards; Games; Reading groups; Prayer groups; Movies; Shopping trips; Social/Cultural gatherings.

Hillhaven Rose Manor
4230 N Roxboro Rd, Durham, NC, 27704
(919) 477-9805
Admin Mary Lynn Williams. *Medical Dir/Dir of Nursing* Donald Neish MD; Lois Finestone DON.
Licensure Skilled care; Intermediate care; Alzheimer's unit. *Beds* SNF 58; ICF 45; Special care unit 20. *Certified* Medicaid; Medicare.
Owner Proprietary Corp (Hillhaven Corp).
Admissions Requirements Medical examination; Physician's request.
Staff RNs; LPNs; Nurses aides; Physical therapists; Recreational therapists; Occupational therapists; Speech therapists; Activities coordinators; Dietitians; Dentists; Ophthalmologists.
Facilities Dining room; Physical therapy room; Activities room; Chapel; Crafts room; Laundry room; Barber/Beauty shop.
Activities Arts & crafts; Games; Reading groups; Prayer groups; Movies; Social/Cultural gatherings.

Methodist Retirement Homes Inc*
2616 Erwin Rd, Durham, NC, 27705
(919) 383-2567

Admin Wayne Powers. *Medical Dir/Dir of Nursing* Dr Donald Neish.
Licensure Skilled care; Intermediate care; Home for aged. *Beds* SNF 46; ICF 77; Home for aged 40. *Certified* Medicaid; Medicare.
Owner Proprietary Corp (Pinnacle Care Corp).
Admissions Requirements Medical examination.
Staff Physicians 1 (pt); RNs 10 (ft), 3 (pt); LPNs 21 (ft), 7 (pt); Orderlies 12 (ft), 4 (pt); Nurses aides 51 (ft), 13 (pt); Physical therapists 2 (pt); Recreational therapists 4 (ft); Speech therapists 1 (pt); Activities coordinators 1 (ft), 1 (pt); Dietitians 1 (ft); Dentists 1 (pt).
Affiliation Methodist
Facilities Dining room; Physical therapy room; Activities room; Chapel; Crafts room; Laundry room; Barber/Beauty shop; Library; Store operated by patients.
Activities Arts & crafts; Cards; Games; Reading groups; Prayer groups; Movies; Shopping trips; Social/Cultural gatherings; Music & singing; Talent shows; Horticulture; Science; Community service projects; Exercise groups; Cooking.

EDENTON

Britthaven of Edenton
PO Box 566, Paradise Rd, Edenton, NC, 27932
(919) 482-7481
Admin Craig Miller. *Medical Dir/Dir of Nursing* Archie Walker MD, James Slade MD; DeAnna Darnell RN.
Licensure Skilled care; Intermediate care; Rest home. *Beds* SNF 32; ICF 98; Rest home 30. *Certified* Medicaid; Medicare; VA.
Owner Proprietary Corp (Britthaven Inc).
Admissions Requirements Minimum age 18; Medical examination.
Staff RNs 5 (ft), 3 (pt); LPNs 12 (ft), 6 (pt); Orderlies 1 (ft); Nurses aides 37 (ft), 15 (pt); Activities coordinators 1 (ft), 1 (pt); Dietitians 1 (ft); Dentists; Dentist 1 (pt).
Facilities Dining room; Physical therapy room; Activities room; Crafts room; Laundry room; Barber/Beauty shop.
Activities Arts & crafts; Cards; Games; Reading groups; Prayer groups; Movies; Shopping trips; Social/Cultural gatherings.

Chowan Hospital Inc-Skilled Nursing Facility
PO Box 629, Virginia Rd, Edenton, NC, 27932
(919) 482-8451
Admin Marvin A Bryan. *Medical Dir/Dir of Nursing* Lance Potocki MD; Judy A Peele RN DON.
Licensure Skilled care. *Beds* SNF 56. *Certified* Medicaid; Medicare.
Owner Nonprofit Corp.
Admissions Requirements Physician's request.
Staff Physicians; RNs 5 (ft); LPNs 6 (ft), 2 (pt); Orderlies 5 (ft); Nurses aides 16 (ft), 4 (pt); Physical therapists 1 (ft); Activities coordinators 1 (ft); Dietitians 1 (ft); Rehab nurse 1 (ft).
Facilities Dining room; Physical therapy room; Activities room; Crafts room; Laundry room; Barber/Beauty shop.
Activities Arts & crafts; Cards; Games; Reading groups; Prayer groups; Movies; Social/Cultural gatherings.

ELIZABETH CITY

Guardian Care
901 S Halstead Blvd, Elizabeth City, NC, 27909-9998
(919) 338-0137
Admin Mary Ann Crocker. *Medical Dir/Dir of Nursing* Dr Wm Wassink; Sarah Hall RN DON.

Licensure Skilled care; Intermediate care. *Beds* SNF 31; ICF 89. *Certified* Medicaid; Medicare.
Owner Proprietary Corp (Hillhaven Corp).
Admissions Requirements Minimum age 21; Medical examination.
Staff RNs 2 (ft), 5 (pt); LPNs 6 (ft), 5 (pt); Nurses aides 45 (ft), 7 (pt); Recreational therapists 1 (ft); Activities coordinators 1 (pt); Dietitians 1 (ft).
Facilities Dining room; Physical therapy room; Activities room; Chapel; Crafts room; Laundry room; Barber/Beauty shop.
Activities Arts & crafts; Cards; Games; Reading groups; Prayer groups; Movies; Shopping trips; Social/Cultural gatherings.

W R Winslow Memorial Home Inc*
1700 W Ehringhaus St, Elizabeth City, NC, 27909
(919) 338-3975
Admin David L Fardulis.
Licensure Skilled care; Intermediate care. *Beds* SNF 34; ICF 87. *Certified* Medicaid; Medicare.

ELIZABETHTOWN

Elizabethtown Nursing Center
PO Box 1447, Elizabethtown, NC, 28337
(919) 862-8181
Admin Janet R Tennant. *Medical Dir/Dir of Nursing* Barbara Nobles RN.
Licensure Skilled care; Intermediate care. *Beds* SNF 44; ICF 40. *Certified* Medicaid; Medicare.
Owner Privately owned.
Admissions Requirements Medical examination; Physician's request.
Staff RNs 3 (ft), 4 (pt); LPNs 5 (ft), 6 (pt); Nurses aides 26 (ft), 10 (pt); Activities coordinators 1 (ft), 1 (pt).
Facilities Dining room; Activities room; Crafts room; Laundry room; Barber/Beauty shop.
Activities Arts & crafts; Games; Prayer groups; Movies; Shopping trips; Social/Cultural gatherings.

ELKIN

Hugh Chatham Memorial Hospital—SNF*
230 Hawthorne Rd, Elkin, NC, 28621
(919) 835-3722
Admin William S Clark.
Licensure Skilled care. *Beds* 64. *Certified* Medicaid; Medicare.

Guardian Care of Elkin
560 Johnson Ridge Rd, Elkin, NC, 28621
(919) 835-7802
Admin Marilyn Gardner. *Medical Dir/Dir of Nursing* Dr Hal Stuart; Debi Westbrook.
Licensure Skilled care; Intermediate care. *Beds* SNF 50; ICF 50. *Certified* Medicaid; Medicare.
Owner Proprietary Corp (Hillhaven Corp).
Staff RNs; LPNs; Nurses aides; Physical therapists; Recreational therapists; Occupational therapists; Speech therapists; Activities coordinators; Dietitians.
Facilities Dining room; Physical therapy room; Activities room; Crafts room; Laundry room; Barber/Beauty shop.
Activities Arts & crafts; Cards; Games; Reading groups; Prayer groups; Movies; Shopping trips; Social/Cultural gatherings.

ENFIELD

Conv Care of Enfield Inc
PO Box 456, 208 Cary St,, Enfield, NC, 27823
(919) 445-2111
Admin Donald L Williams. *Medical Dir/Dir of Nursing* Dr Alton Anderson.

Licensure Skilled care. *Beds* 63. *Certified* Medicaid; Medicare.
Admissions Requirements Medical examinatio 1; Physician's request.
Staff Physicians 3 (pt); RNs 6 (ft), 1 (pt); LPNs 5 (ft); Orderlies 3 (ft), 2 (pt); Nurses aides 21 (ft), 3 (pt); Physical therapists 1 (pt); Reality therapists 1 (ft); Recreational therapists 1 (ft); Occupational therapists 1 (pt); Speech therapists 1 (pt); Activities coordinators 1 (ft); Dietitians 1 (ft), 1 (pt); Dentists 1 (pt); Ophthalmologists 1 (pt); Podiatrists 1 (pt).
Facilities Dining room; Physical therapy room; Activities room; Laundry room; Barber/Beauty shop.
Activities Arts & crafts; Cards; Games; Reading groups; Prayer groups; Movies; Shopping trips.

FALCON

Golden Years Nursing Home
PO Box 40, Hwy 82, West St, Falcon, NC, 28342
(919) 892-6048
Admin Wilma Honeycutt. *Medical Dir/Dir of Nursing* Dr Andrew G Misulia; Jane Slate RN DON.
Licensure Intermediate care. *Beds* ICF 58. *Certified* Medicaid.
Owner Proprietary Corp.
Admissions Requirements Minimum age 55.
Staff Physicians 1 (ft); RNs 2 (ft); LPNs 4 (ft), 4 (pt); Orderlies 2 (ft), 1 (pt); Nurses aides 15 (ft), 7 (pt); Activities coordinators 1 (ft); Dietitians 1 (pt).
Facilities Dining room; Physical therapy room; Activities room; Laundry room; Barber/Beauty shop.
Activities Arts & crafts; Games; Reading groups; Prayer groups; Movies.

FARMVILLE

Guardian Care of Farmville*
Rte 1, Box 96, Farmville, NC, 27828
(919) 753-5547
Admin Alawoise S Flanagan.
Licensure Intermediate care. *Beds* 56. *Certified* Medicaid.
Owner Proprietary Corp (Hillhaven Corp).

FAYETTEVILLE

Bethesda Health Care Facility
Rte 1, Box 118-A, Fayetteville, NC, 28301
(919) 323-3223
Admin Barbara Broome. *Medical Dir/Dir of Nursing* Christian F Siewers MD; Cathy Williams DON.
Licensure Skilled care; Intermediate care. *Beds* SNF 16; ICF 44. *Certified* Medicaid; Medicare.
Owner Nonprofit organization/foundation.
Admissions Requirements Medical examination; Physician's request.
Staff Physicians 3 (ft); RNs 4 (ft); LPNs 7 (ft); Nurses aides 25 (ft); Physical therapists 1 (ft); Speech therapists 1 (ft); Activities coordinators 1 (ft); Dietitians 1 (ft).
Facilities Dining room; Physical therapy room; Activities room; Chapel; Crafts room; Laundry room; Barber/Beauty shop.
Activities Arts & crafts; Cards; Games; Reading groups; Prayer groups; Movies; Shopping trips; Social/Cultural gatherings.

Elderlodge of Fayetteville
PO Box 1803, 707 Murchison Rd, Fayetteville, NC, 28301
(919) 483-3400
Admin Harold A Breitt. *Medical Dir/Dir of Nursing* Mildred P Hunt.

Licensure Skilled care; Intermediate care; Rest home. *Beds* SNF 70; ICF 58; Rest home 40. *Certified* Medicaid; Medicare.
Owner Proprietary Corp.
Admissions Requirements Medical examination.
Staff RNs 8 (ft); LPNs 14 (ft); Orderlies 6 (ft); Nurses aides 32 (ft); Activities coordinators.
Facilities Dining room; Activities room; Crafts room; Laundry room; Barber/Beauty shop.
Activities Arts & crafts; Cards; Games; Reading groups; Prayer groups; Movies; Shopping trips; Social/Cultural gatherings.

Highland House of Fayetteville Inc*
PO Box 35887, 1700 Pamalee Dr, Fayetteville, NC, 28303
(919) 488-2295
Admin Allyson M Wherren.
Licensure Intermediate care; Home for aged. *Beds* ICF 62; Home for aged 37. *Certified* Medicaid.
Admissions Requirements Minimum age 18; Medical examination.
Staff RNs 1 (ft); LPNs 7 (ft); Nurses aides 28 (ft); Physical therapists 2 (ft); Speech therapists 1 (pt); Activities coordinators 2 (ft), 1 (pt); Dentists 1 (pt); Podiatrists 1 (pt).
Facilities Dining room; Activities room; Chapel; Crafts room; Laundry room; Barber/Beauty shop.
Activities Arts & crafts; Cards; Games; Reading groups; Prayer groups; Movies; Shopping trips; Social/Cultural gatherings.

Rest Haven Nursing Home
1769 Dunn Rd, Fayetteville, NC, 28301
(919) 483-5027
Admin Charlotte C Fitch. *Medical Dir/Dir of Nursing* Resa Edge RN.
Licensure Intermediate care. *Beds* ICF 46. *Certified* Medicaid.
Owner Privately owned.
Admissions Requirements Medical examination; Physician's request.
Staff RNs 1 (ft); LPNs 4 (ft), 3 (pt); Orderlies 1 (ft); Nurses aides 12 (ft), 4 (pt); Recreational therapists 1 (ft); Activities coordinators 1 (ft); Dietitians 1 (ft).
Facilities Dining room; Laundry room.
Activities Arts & crafts; Games; Reading groups; Prayer groups; Movies.

Whispering Pines Nursing Home*
523 Country Club Dr, Fayetteville, NC, 28301
(910) 488-0711
Admin Jeanne A Novello.
Licensure Intermediate care; Rest home. *Beds* ICF 58; Rest home 2. *Certified* Medicaid.
Admissions Requirements Medical examination; Physician's request.
Staff Physicians 9 (pt); RNs 1 (ft), 1 (pt); LPNs 3 (ft), 4 (pt); Orderlies 1 (ft); Nurses aides 17 (ft), 6 (pt); Physical therapists 1 (pt); Recreational therapists 1 (ft); Dietitians 1 (pt).
Facilities Activities room; Barber/Beauty shop; Library.
Activities Arts & crafts; Cards; Games; Reading groups; Prayer groups; Movies; Shopping trips; Social/Cultural gatherings.

FUQUAY-VARINA

Kinton Nursing Home
PO Box 519, 415 Sunset Dr, Fuquay-Varina, NC, 27526
(919) 552-5609
Admin Ruth C Kinton. *Medical Dir/Dir of Nursing* Karen Reid DON.
Licensure Intermediate care; Home for aged. *Beds* ICF 49; Home for aged 31. *Certified* Medicaid.
Owner Privately owned.
Admissions Requirements Medical examination.

Staff RNs 2 (ft); LPNs 4 (ft), 5 (pt); Orderlies 1 (ft); Nurses aides 20 (ft), 5 (pt); Activities coordinators 2 (ft), 1 (pt); Dietitians 7 (ft), 1 (pt).
Facilities Dining room; Activities room; Laundry room; Barber/Beauty shop.
Activities Arts & crafts; Games; Movies; Shopping trips.

GASTONIA

Autumnfield Inc of Lowell*
398 Wilkinson Blvd, Gastonia, NC, 28054
(704) 824-4316
Admin Brenda H Parris. *Medical Dir/Dir of Nursing* Dr W H Hammond Jr.
Licensure Skilled care. *Beds* 50. *Certified* Medicaid; Medicare.
Admissions Requirements Minimum age 18.
Staff RNs 3 (ft), 1 (pt); LPNs 3 (ft), 2 (pt); Nurses aides 15 (ft), 3 (pt); Physical therapists; Speech therapists; Activities coordinators 1 (ft); Dietitians 1 (ft); Dentists; Ophthalmologists; Podiatrists.
Facilities Dining room; Activities room; Barber/Beauty shop.
Activities Arts & crafts; Cards; Games; Reading groups; Prayer groups; Movies; Shopping trips; Social/Cultural gatherings.

Brian Center Nursing Care—Gastonia Inc*
969 Cox Rd, Gastonia, NC, 28054
(704) 866-8596
Admin Doris Powell. *Medical Dir/Dir of Nursing* Dr James S Forrester.
Licensure Skilled care; Intermediate care. *Beds* SNF 90; ICF 30. *Certified* Medicaid; Medicare.
Owner Proprietary Corp (Brian Center Management Corp).
Staff RNs 8 (ft), 1 (pt); LPNs 9 (ft), 7 (pt); Nurses aides 41 (ft), 10 (pt); Physical therapists 1 (pt); Activities coordinators 1 (ft); Dietitians 2 (ft).
Facilities Dining room; Physical therapy room; Activities room; Laundry room; Barber/Beauty shop.
Activities Arts & crafts; Games; Reading groups; Prayer groups; Movies; Social/ Cultural gatherings.

Covenant Village*
1351 Robinwood Rd, Gastonia, NC, 28054
(704) 867-2319
Admin Thomas P Hauer. *Medical Dir/Dir of Nursing* Dr Thomason.
Licensure Skilled care; Intermediate care. *Beds* 40.
Owner Nonprofit Corp.
Admissions Requirements Minimum age 65; Medical examination; Physician's request.
Staff RNs 7 (ft); LPNs 3 (ft); Nurses aides 20 (ft); Physical therapists; Activities coordinators 1 (ft); Dietitians 1 (ft).
Affiliation Presbyterian
Facilities Dining room; Activities room; Chapel; Crafts room; Laundry room; Barber/Beauty shop; Library.
Activities Arts & crafts; Cards; Games; Reading groups; Prayer groups; Movies; Shopping trips; Social/Cultural gatherings.

Guardian Care of Gastonia
416 N Highland St, Gastonia, NC, 28052-2199
(704) 864-0371
Admin Kathy F Putnam. *Medical Dir/Dir of Nursing* Gena H Avery DON.
Licensure Skilled care; Intermediate care. *Beds* SNF 61; ICF 57. *Certified* Medicaid; Medicare.
Owner Proprietary Corp (Hillhaven Corp).
Admissions Requirements Minimum age 18; Medical examination.
Staff RNs 7 (ft), 2 (pt); LPNs 11 (ft), 2 (pt); Orderlies 3 (ft); Nurses aides 47 (ft), 3 (pt); Activities coordinators 1 (ft); Dietitians 1 (ft), 1 (pt); Social worker 1 (ft), 1 (pt).

Facilities Dining room; Physical therapy room; Activities room; Crafts room; Laundry room; Barber/Beauty shop.
Activities Arts & crafts; Cards; Games; Reading groups; Prayer groups; Movies; Shopping trips; Social/Cultural gatherings.

Meadowbrook Manor of Gastonia*
PO Box 1375, 960 X-Ray Dr, Gastonia, NC, 28053
(704) 861-0981
Admin Sharon Stiles.
Licensure Skilled care; Intermediate care. *Beds* SNF 60; ICF 60. *Certified* Medicaid; Medicare.
Owner Proprietary Corp (Tullock Management).

GOLDSBORO

Caswell Annex*
Hwy 581, Goldsboro, NC, 27530
(919) 731-3470
Admin Richard Zaharia.
Licensure Intermediate care for mentally retarded. *Beds* 100. *Certified* Medicaid.

Cherry Hospital—ICF*
Caller Box 8000, Hwy 581, Goldsboro, NC, 27530
(919) 731-3202
Admin J Field Montgomery, Jr.
Licensure Intermediate care. *Beds* 66. *Certified* Medicaid.

Guardian Care of Goldsboro
501 Forest Hill Dr, Goldsboro, NC, 27530
(919) 735-4427
Admin Juanita M Mansour. *Medical Dir/Dir of Nursing* Juanita M Mansour RN DON.
Licensure Skilled care. *Beds* SNF 49.
Owner Proprietary Corp (Hillhaven Corp).
Admissions Requirements Minimum age 20; Medical examination.
Staff Physicians; RNs; LPNs; Orderlies; Nurses aides; Physical therapists; Recreational therapists; Occupational therapists; Activities coordinators; Dietitians.
Activities Arts & crafts; Cards; Games; Reading groups; Prayer groups; Movies; Shopping trips.

Howell's Child Care Center—Walnut Creek*
Rte 9, Box 246, Goldsboro, NC, 27530
(919) 778-3524
Admin Valentine H Gray.
Licensure Intermediate care. *Beds* 37. *Certified* Medicaid.

O'Berry Center
PO Box 247, Goldsboro, NC, 27533-0247
(919) 731-3545
Admin Dr Jerry H Lyall. *Medical Dir/Dir of Nursing* James Hughs MD; Linda Fish Nurs Coord.
Licensure Skilled care; Intermediate care for mentally retarded. *Beds* SNF 35; ICF/MR 485. *Certified* Medicaid; Medicare; Medi-Cal.
Owner Publicly owned.
Admissions Requirements Minimum age 7.
Staff Physicians 8 (ft); RNs 40 (ft); LPNs 28 (ft); Nurses aides 444 (ft); Physical therapists 2 (ft); Recreational therapists 31 (ft); Occupational therapists 7 (ft); Speech therapists 10 (ft); Activities coordinators 24 (ft).
Facilities Dining room; Physical therapy room; Activities room; Chapel; Crafts room; Laundry room; Barber/Beauty shop; Library; Training areas.
Activities Arts & crafts; Prayer groups; Movies; Shopping trips; Social/Cultural gatherings; Developmental skills for severely/ profoundly MR with multiple handicaps.

GRAHAM

Hillhaven of Alamance
779 Woody Dr, Graham, NC, 27253
(919) 228-8394
Admin Stephen M Harrison. *Medical Dir/Dir of Nursing* Lynne Lavasque.
Licensure Intermediate care. *Beds* ICF 120. *Certified* Medicaid.
Owner Proprietary Corp (Hillhaven Corp).
Staff RNs; LPNs; Orderlies; Nurses aides; Physical therapists; Recreational therapists; Speech therapists; Dietitians; Dentists; Ophthalmologists; Podiatrists.
Facilities Dining room; Physical therapy room; Activities room; Laundry room; Barber/Beauty shop.
Activities Arts & crafts; Cards; Games; Reading groups; Prayer groups; Movies; Shopping trips; Social/Cultural gatherings.

GREENSBORO

Clarence Johnson Care Center
512 Pisgah Church Rd, Greensboro, NC, 27405
(919) 288-0788
Admin Mary Ruth McDuffie. *Medical Dir/Dir of Nursing* Mrs Essie P Haynes DON.
Licensure Intermediate care. *Beds* ICF 29. *Certified* Medicaid.
Owner Privately owned.
Admissions Requirements Minimum age 18; Medical examination; Physician's request.
Staff Physicians 1 (pt); RNs 1 (ft), 2 (pt); LPNs 1 (ft), 5 (pt); Nurses aides 5 (ft), 6 (pt); Recreational therapists 1 (pt); Speech therapists 1 (ft); Dietitians 1 (ft).
Facilities Dining room; Activities room; Crafts room; Laundry room; Living room.
Activities Arts & crafts; Cards; Games; Reading groups; Prayer groups; Movies; Shopping trips; Social/Cultural gatherings.

The Evergreens Inc—Greensboro
4007 W Wendover Ave, Greensboro, NC, 27407
(919) 292-8620
Admin Su James RN; Dennis W Streets MPH Executive Director. *Medical Dir/Dir of Nursing* William B Herring MD; Gladys McNew RN.
Licensure Skilled care; Intermediate care; Home for Aged & Disabled (rest home); Adult Day Health Program (certified for 25 day participants). *Beds* SNF 94; ICF 172; Rest home 94. *Certified* Medicaid; Medicare.
Owner Nonprofit Corp.
Admissions Requirements Minimum age 21; Medical examination; Physician's request.
Staff Physicians 1 (pt); RNs 16 (ft); LPNs 11 (ft), 3 (pt); Nurses aides 137 (ft), 4 (pt); Physical therapists 2 (pt); Recreational therapists 3 (ft), 3 (pt); Speech therapists 1 (pt); Dietitians 2 (ft), 2 (pt).
Facilities Dining room; Physical therapy room; Activities room; Chapel; Crafts room; Laundry room; Barber/Beauty shop; Library.
Activities Arts & crafts; Cards; Games; Reading groups; Prayer groups; Movies; Shopping trips; Social/Cultural gatherings; Grooming; Music; Pet program; Community exchange program; Exercise; Bowling; Swimming.

Friends Home Inc
925 New Garden Rd, Greensboro, NC, 27410
(919) 292-8187
Admin Wilson M Sheldon. *Medical Dir/Dir of Nursing* Dr Robert Thacker; Ms Patricia Kiuett.
Licensure Skilled care; Intermediate care; Home for aged; Apartments. *Beds* SNF 32; ICF 37; HFA 60 Apartments 180. *Certified* Medicaid; Medicare.
Owner Nonprofit Corp.

Admissions Requirements Minimum age 60; Medical examination.
Staff RNs 9 (ft), 5 (pt); LPNs 4 (ft), 2 (pt); Orderlies 1 (ft); Nurses aides 45 (ft), 10 (pt); Physical therapists 1 (pt); Recreational therapists 2 (ft); Activities coordinators 4 (ft); Dietitians 2 (ft).
Affiliation Society of Friends
Facilities Dining room; Physical therapy room; Activities room; Crafts room; Laundry room; Barber/Beauty shop; Library; Living rooms.
Activities Arts & crafts; Cards; Games; Reading groups; Prayer groups; Movies; Shopping trips; Social/Cultural gatherings; Interest groups.

Greensboro Health Care Center
1201 Carolina St, Greensboro, NC, 27401
(919) 275-0751
Admin Larry M Parrish. *Medical Dir/Dir of Nursing* Dr William McKeown.
Licensure Skilled care; Intermediate care. *Beds* SNF 35; ICF 70. *Certified* Medicaid; Medicare.
Facilities Dining room; Physical therapy room; Activities room; Crafts room; Laundry room; Barber/Beauty shop.
Activities Arts & crafts; Games; Movies; Shopping trips.

Healthhaven Nursing Center*
801 Greenhaven Dr, Greensboro, NC, 27406-7199
(919) 292-8371
Admin Ruth M Quate.
Licensure Skilled care; Intermediate care. *Beds* SNF 60; ICF 60. *Certified* Medicaid; Medicare.
Owner Proprietary Corp (Angell Group).

Masonic & Eastern Star Home of North Carolina Inc
700 S Holden Rd, Greensboro, NC, 27420
(919) 299-0031
Admin Tommy L Jones. *Medical Dir/Dir of Nursing* Rebecca Burton RN.
Licensure Skilled care; Intermediate care. *Beds* SNF 32; ICF 56.
Admissions Requirements Minimum age 60; Medical examination.
Staff Physicians 1 (pt); RNs 10 (ft), 3 (pt); LPNs 4 (ft), 1 (pt); Nurses aides 28 (ft), 13 (pt); Physical therapists 2 (pt); Recreational therapists 1 (ft); Activities coordinators 1 (ft); Dentists 1 (pt); Dentist 1 (pt); Dermatologist 1 (pt).
Affiliation Masons
Facilities Dining room; Physical therapy room; Activities room; Chapel; Crafts room; Laundry room; Barber/Beauty shop; Library.
Activities Arts & crafts; Games; Prayer groups; Movies; Shopping trips; Social/Cultural gatherings.

St James Nursing Center Inc*
PO Box 20946, 603 S Benbow Rd, Greensboro, NC, 27420
(919) 275-9941
Admin Ann Griffin.
Licensure Skilled care. *Beds* 100. *Certified* Medicaid; Medicare.

Starmount Villa
109 S Holden Rd, Greensboro, NC, 27407
(919) 292-5390
Admin Michael L Kelly. *Medical Dir/Dir of Nursing* William D McKeown.
Licensure Skilled care; Intermediate care. *Beds* SNF 64; ICF 62. *Certified* Medicaid; Medicare.
Owner Proprietary Corp (Beverly Enterprises).
Staff RNs 4 (ft), 1 (pt); LPNs 15 (ft), 4 (pt); Orderlies 7 (ft), 2 (pt); Nurses aides 30 (ft), 6 (pt); Physical therapists 1 (pt); Reality therapists 1 (pt); Speech therapists 1 (pt); Activities coordinators 2 (ft); Dietitians 1 (ft); Ophthalmologists; Podiatrists.

Facilities Dining room; Physical therapy room; Activities room; Chapel; Crafts room; Laundry room; Barber/Beauty shop; Library.
Activities Arts & crafts; Cards; Games; Reading groups; Prayer groups; Movies; Shopping trips; Social/Cultural gatherings.

GREENVILLE

Greenville Villa*
PO Box 5046, Moye Blvd, Greenville, NC, 27834
(919) 758-4121
Admin R Lee Crabill.
Licensure Skilled care; Intermediate care. *Beds* SNF 40; ICF 112. *Certified* Medicaid; Medicare.

University Nursing Center*
Rte 1, Box 21, Greenville, NC, 27834
(919) 758-7100
Admin Kyle Dilday. *Medical Dir/Dir of Nursing* Joseph Ward MD.
Licensure Skilled care; Intermediate care. *Beds* SNF 51; ICF 69. *Certified* Medicaid; Medicare.
Owner Proprietary Corp (Hillhaven Corp).
Admissions Requirements Medical examination.
Staff Physicians 21 (pt); RNs 6 (ft), 2 (pt); LPNs 7 (ft), 4 (pt); Orderlies 7 (ft), 1 (pt); Nurses aides 28 (ft), 19 (pt); Physical therapists 2 (pt); Speech therapists 1 (pt); Activities coordinators 1 (ft), 1 (pt); Dietitians 1 (ft); Social workers 1 (ft).

HENDERSON

Guardian Care of Henderson
PO Box 1616, 519 Roanoke Ave, Henderson, NC, 27536
(919) 438-6141
Admin Helen O Brame.
Licensure Intermediate care. *Beds* 80. *Certified* Medicaid.
Owner Proprietary Corp (Hillhaven Corp).

Pine Haven Conv Center of Henderson Inc*
PO Box 1098, 1245 Park Ave, Henderson, NC, 27536
(919) 492-1088
Admin Dianne Walker.
Licensure Intermediate care; Home for aged. *Beds* ICF 52; Home for aged 23. *Certified* Medicaid.

HENDERSONVILLE

Carolina Village Inc*
600 Carolina Village Rd, Hendersonville, NC, 28739
(704) 692-6275
Admin Doley S Bell.
Licensure Skilled care. *Beds* 58. *Certified* Medicaid; Medicare.

Lakewood Manor Nursing Center*
1510 Hebron St, Hendersonville, NC, 28739
(704) 693-8461
Admin Jane Kinard.
Licensure Skilled care; Intermediate care. *Beds* SNF 30; ICF 120. *Certified* Medicaid; Medicare.
Owner Proprietary Corp (Beverly Enterprises).

Margaret R Pardee Memorial Skilled Nursing Facility
715 Flemming St, Hendersonville, NC, 28742
(704) 693-6522
Admin Frank J Aaron Jr. *Medical Dir/Dir of Nursing* Howard B Norton MD; Elizabeth Taylor DON.
Licensure Skilled care. *Beds* SNF 40. *Certified* Medicaid; Medicare.
Owner Publicly owned.

Staff Physicians 87 (ft); RNs 3 (ft), 4 (pt); LPNs 5 (ft), 3 (pt); Orderlies 3 (pt); Nurses aides 13 (ft), 4 (pt); Physical therapists 2 (ft); Speech therapists 1 (ft); Activities coordinators 1 (ft); Dietitians 3 (ft); Dentists 4 (ft).
Facilities Activities room.

HICKORY

Brian Center Nursing Care—Catawba County*
Rte 11, Box 355, Hickory, NC, 28601
(704) 322-3343
Admin William N Mitchell.
Licensure Skilled care; Intermediate care. *Beds* SNF 30; ICF 80. *Certified* Medicaid; Medicare.
Owner Proprietary Corp (Brian Center Management Corp).

Brian Center of Hickory
220 13th Ave Pl NW, Hickory, NC, 28601
(704) 382-5646
Admin Jo Ann S Kessler. *Medical Dir/Dir of Nursing* Dr John Earl; Donna Price RN DON.
Licensure Skilled care; Intermediate care. *Beds* SNF 63; ICF 41. *Certified* Medicaid; Medicare.
Owner Proprietary Corp (Brian Center Management Corp).
Admissions Requirements Minimum age 18; Medical examination.
Facilities Dining room; Physical therapy room; Activities room; Crafts room; Laundry room; Barber/Beauty shop; Social Service Department.
Activities Arts & crafts; Cards; Games; Reading groups; Prayer groups; Movies; Shopping trips; Social/Cultural gatherings.

Lutheran Nursing Homes Inc—Hickory Unit
1265 21st St NE, Hickory, NC, 28601
(704) 328-2006
Admin Rev Floyd Addison Jr. *Medical Dir/Dir of Nursing* Dr George Tolhurst; Mrs Irene Everett RN.
Licensure Skilled care; Intermediate care; Rest home. *Beds* SNF 48; ICF 16; Rest home 76. *Certified* Medicaid; Medicare.
Owner Nonprofit Corp (NC Lutheran Homes).
Staff RNs 8 (ft), 2 (pt); LPNs 8 (ft); Orderlies 4 (ft); Nurses aides 17 (ft), 8 (pt); Activities coordinators 1 (ft).
Affiliation Lutheran
Facilities Dining room; Activities room; Chapel; Crafts room; Laundry room; Barber/Beauty shop; Library; Day room.
Activities Arts & crafts; Cards; Games; Reading groups; Prayer groups; Movies; Shopping trips; Social/Cultural gatherings.

Pellcare Nursing Home
1125 10th St Blvd NW, Hickory, NC, 28601
(704) 322-6995
Admin Connie L Wright. *Medical Dir/Dir of Nursing* John K Earl MD; Christopher N Propst RN DON.
Licensure Skilled care; Intermediate care. *Beds* SNF 60; ICF 60. *Certified* Medicaid; Medicare.
Owner Proprietary Corp.
Admissions Requirements Minimum age 18; Medical examination; Physician's request.
Staff Physicians 1 (ft); RNs 3 (ft), 4 (pt); LPNs 8 (ft), 2 (pt); Nurses aides 38 (ft), 12 (pt); Physical therapists 1 (pt); Occupational therapists 1 (pt); Speech therapists 1 (pt); Activities coordinators 2 (ft); Dietitians 1 (pt); Dentists 1 (pt); Ophthalmologists 1 (pt).
Facilities Dining room; Physical therapy room; Activities room; Crafts room; Laundry room; Barber/Beauty shop.
Activities Arts & crafts; Games; Prayer groups; Movies; Shopping trips; Social/Cultural gatherings; Birthday parties; Special church services at Easter, Thanksgiving, & Christmas.

HIGH POINT

The Evergreens—High Point
206 Greensboro Rd, High Point, NC, 27260
(919) 886-4121
Admin Felton Wooten; Dennis W Streets
Executive Director. *Medical Dir/Dir of
Nursing* Dr Eldora Terrell; Martha
Hayworth RN.
Licensure Skilled care; Intermediate care; Rest
home. *Beds* SNF 27; ICF 66; Rest home 27.
Certified Medicaid; Medicare.
Owner Nonprofit Corp.
Admissions Requirements Minimum age 21;
Medical examination; Physician's request.
Staff Physicians 1 (pt); RNs 5 (ft), 7 (pt);
LPNs 6 (ft), 5 (pt); Orderlies 3 (ft); Nurses
aides 30 (ft), 22 (pt); Speech therapists 1
(pt); Activities coordinators 1 (ft); Dietitians
1 (pt).
Facilities Dining room; Physical therapy
room; Activities room; Chapel; Crafts room;
Laundry room; Barber/Beauty shop; Library.
Activities Arts & crafts; Games; Movies;
Social/Cultural gatherings.

Lambs Nursing Home
3830 N Main St, High Point, NC, 27260
(919) 869-3752
Admin Dan Tullock. *Medical Dir/Dir of
Nursing* Bansi P Shah MD; Esther Sykes RN
DON.
Licensure Skilled care; Intermediate care. *Beds*
SNF 40; ICF 60. *Certified* Medicaid;
Medicare.
Owner Proprietary Corp.
Admissions Requirements Medical
examination.
Staff Physicians 2 (pt); RNs 3 (ft), 1 (pt);
LPNs 6 (ft), 2 (pt); Orderlies 1 (ft); Nurses
aides 27 (ft), 20 (pt); Activities coordinators
1 (ft); Dietitians 1 (ft).
Facilities Dining room; Activities room;
Chapel; Crafts room; Laundry room; Barber/
Beauty shop.
Activities Arts & crafts; Cards; Games;
Reading groups; Prayer groups; Movies;
Shopping trips.

Maryfield Nursing Home
1315 Greensboro Rd, High Point, NC, 27260
(919) 454-5313
Admin Sr Lucy Hennessy. *Medical Dir/Dir of
Nursing* W H Flythe MD; Marge Myers RN
DON.
Licensure Skilled care; Intermediate care. *Beds*
SNF 111; ICF 4. *Certified* Medicaid;
Medicare.
Owner Nonprofit Corp.
Admissions Requirements Medical
examination; Physician's request.
Staff Physicians 1 (pt); RNs 9 (ft), 6 (pt);
LPNs 6 (ft), 3 (pt); Orderlies 1 (ft); Nurses
aides 40 (ft), 10 (pt); Physical therapists 1
(pt); Recreational therapists 2 (ft); Speech
therapists 1 (pt); Activities coordinators 1
(ft); Dietitians 1 (pt); Ophthalmologists 1
(pt).
Affiliation Roman Catholic
Facilities Dining room; Physical therapy
room; Activities room; Chapel; Crafts room;
Laundry room; Barber/Beauty shop; Library.
Activities Arts & crafts; Cards; Games;
Reading groups; Prayer groups; Movies;
Shopping trips; Social/Cultural gatherings;
Picnics; Fishing trips; Trips to zoo.

Medical Park Nursing Center*
707 N Elm St, High Point, NC, 27262
(919) 885-0141
Admin Lonnie Hoffpauir. *Medical Dir/Dir of
Nursing* Sam T Bickley MD.
Licensure Skilled care; Intermediate care. *Beds*
SNF 93; ICF 106. *Certified* Medicaid;
Medicare.
Admissions Requirements Medical
examination; Physician's request.

Staff Physicians 4 (pt); RNs 20 (ft); LPNs 30
(ft); Orderlies 8 (ft); Nurses aides 60 (ft);
Physical therapists 2 (ft); Reality therapists 2
(ft); Recreational therapists 3 (ft); Speech
therapists 1 (ft); Activities coordinators 1
(ft); Dietitians 1 (ft); Dentists 1 (pt);
Podiatrists 1 (pt).
Facilities Dining room; Physical therapy
room; Activities room; Crafts room; Laundry
room; Barber/Beauty shop.
Activities Arts & crafts; Cards; Games;
Reading groups; Prayer groups; Movies;
Shopping trips; Social/Cultural gatherings.

The Presbyterian Home of High Point
PO Box 2007, 201 Greensboro Rd, High
Point, NC, 27261
(919) 883-9111
Admin Betty Hayes.
Licensure Skilled care; Intermediate care;
Home for aged. *Beds* SNF 68; ICF 10;
Home for aged 75. *Certified* Medicaid;
Medicare.
Admissions Requirements Minimum age 62;
Medical examination.
Staff Physicians 1 (pt); RNs 12 (ft), 12 (pt);
LPNs 2 (ft), 4 (pt); Orderlies 3 (ft), 2 (pt);
Nurses aides 33 (ft), 24 (pt); Activities
coordinators 3 (ft), 1 (pt); Dietitians 1 (ft).
Affiliation Presbyterian
Facilities Dining room; Physical therapy
room; Activities room; Chapel; Crafts room;
Laundry room; Barber/Beauty shop; Library.
Activities Arts & crafts; Games; Reading
groups; Movies; Shopping trips; Social/
Cultural gatherings.

Wesleyan Arms Inc
1901 N Centennial St, High Point, NC,
27260-3199
(919) 884-2222
Admin Frances P Kiser. *Medical Dir/Dir of
Nursing* Alton A Reeder MD; Lu Jackson
DON.
Licensure Skilled care; Intermediate care;
Home for aged. *Beds* SNF 50; ICF 50;
Home for aged 100. *Certified* Medicaid;
Medicare.
Owner Nonprofit Corp.
Admissions Requirements Medical
examination; Financial certification.
Staff Physicians 15 (pt); RNs 11 (ft); LPNs 8
(ft), 1 (pt); Orderlies 1 (pt); Nurses aides 56
(ft), 10 (pt); Activities coordinators 3 (ft), 1
(pt).
Affiliation First Wesleyan Church
Facilities Dining room; Physical therapy
room; Activities room; Chapel; Crafts room;
Laundry room; Barber/Beauty shop; Library;
Treatment room.
Activities Arts & crafts; Games; Prayer groups;
Movies; Shopping trips.

HUNTERSVILLE

Huntersville Oaks Nursing Home*
Rte 1, Hwy 115, Box 390, Huntersville, NC,
28078
(704) 875-7400
Admin Phillip Evans. *Medical Dir/Dir of
Nursing* William T Williams Jr.
Licensure Skilled care; Intermediate care. *Beds*
274. *Certified* Medicaid; Medicare.
Owner Nonprofit Corp.
Admissions Requirements Medical
examination; Physician's request.
Staff Physicians 8 (ft); RNs 25 (ft), 25 (pt);
LPNs 22 (ft), 4 (pt); Orderlies 2 (ft), 3 (pt);
Nurses aides 115 (ft), 42 (pt); Physical
therapists 1 (ft); Recreational therapists 3
(ft); Speech therapists 1 (pt); Activities
coordinators 1 (ft); Dietitians 1 (ft); Dentists
1 (pt); Ophthalmologists 1 (pt); Podiatrists 1
(pt).
Facilities Dining room; Physical therapy
room; Activities room; Chapel; Crafts room;
Laundry room; Barber/Beauty shop; Library.

Activities Arts & crafts; Cards; Games;
Reading groups; Prayer groups; Movies;
Shopping trips; Social/Cultural gatherings.

JACKSONVILLE

Britthaven of Jacksonville*
225 White St, Jacksonville, NC, 28540
(919) 353-7222
Admin Troy C Hefner. *Medical Dir/Dir of
Nursing* Dr Wesley Murfin.
Owner Proprietary Corp (Britthaven Inc).
Admissions Requirements Minimum age 18;
Medical examination; Physician's request.
Staff RNs 9 (ft), 4 (pt); LPNs 25 (ft), 6 (pt);
Orderlies 4 (ft); Nurses aides 75 (ft), 40 (pt);
Activities coordinators 2 (ft); Dietitians 1
(ft); Dentists 1 (pt); Ophthalmologists 1 (pt);
Podiatrists 1 (pt).
Facilities Dining room; Activities room;
Chapel; Crafts room; Laundry room; Barber/
Beauty shop; Library.
Activities Arts & crafts; Cards; Games; Prayer
groups; Movies; Shopping trips; Social/
Cultural gatherings.

Britthaven of Onslow
PO Box 5021, 1839 Onslow Dr, Jacksonville,
NC, 28540
(919) 455-3610
Admin Maxwell Hodges. *Medical Dir/Dir of
Nursing* Dr Gregory Streeter.
Licensure Skilled care. *Beds* SNF 80. *Certified*
Medicaid; Medicare.
Owner Proprietary Corp (Britthaven Inc).
Admissions Requirements Minimum age 18;
Medical examination.
Staff Physicians 2 (ft); RNs 3 (ft), 4 (pt);
LPNs 8 (ft), 1 (pt); Nurses aides 25 (ft), 32
(pt); Physical therapists 1 (pt); Speech
therapists 1 (pt); Activities coordinators 1
(ft); Dietitians 1 (ft); Dentists 1 (pt);
Ophthalmologists 1 (pt).
Facilities Dining room; Physical therapy
room; Activities room; Crafts room; Laundry
room; Barber/Beauty shop.
Activities Arts & crafts; Cards; Games;
Reading groups; Prayer groups; Movies;
Shopping trips; Social/Cultural gatherings;
Picnics.

KENANSVILLE

Guardian Care of Kenansville
PO Box 478, Beasley St, Kenansville, NC,
28349
(919) 296-1561
Admin Elizabeth Rogers. *Medical Dir/Dir of
Nursing* Corazon Ngo MD; Elsie Pitts RN
DON.
Licensure Skilled care; Intermediate care. *Beds*
SNF 28; ICF 64. *Certified* Medicaid;
Medicare.
Owner Proprietary Corp (Hillhaven Corp).
Admissions Requirements Physician's request.
Staff Physicians 8 (ft); RNs 5 (ft), 2 (pt);
LPNs 3 (ft), 1 (pt); Orderlies 2 (ft), 1 (pt);
Nurses aides 27 (ft), 5 (pt); Speech therapists
1 (ft); Activities coordinators 1 (ft);
Dietitians 1 (ft); Social worker 1 (ft).
Facilities Dining room; Physical therapy
room; Activities room; Laundry room;
Barber/Beauty shop.
Activities Arts & crafts; Games; Prayer groups;
Movies; Social/Cultural gatherings; Music
performances; Birthday parties; Special
parties.

KERNERSVILLE

Oakwood Knoll Nursing Home
2680 Hwy 66 S, Kernersville, NC, 27284
(919) 869-4114
Admin Rachel Gordon. *Medical Dir/Dir of
Nursing* Sam Bickley MD; Gay Wyche
DON.

Licensure Intermediate care. *Beds* ICF 32. *Certified* Medicaid.
Owner Privately owned.
Admissions Requirements Medical examination.
Staff Physicians 1 (ft); RNs 1 (ft); LPNs 3 (ft); Nurses aides 5 (ft), 8 (pt); Speech therapists 1 (ft); Activities coordinators 1 (ft); Dietitians 1 (ft); Social worker 1 (ft).
Facilities Dining room; Activities room; Crafts room; Laundry room; Barber/Beauty shop.
Activities Arts & crafts; Games; Reading groups; Prayer groups; Movies; Shopping trips; Social/Cultural gatherings.

Willowbrook Care Center*
PO Box 947, 730 Piney Grove Rd, Kernersville, NC, 27285
(919) 996-4038
Admin Rodney Worley. *Medical Dir/Dir of Nursing* Dr Wesley Phillips.
Licensure Intermediate care. *Beds* 60. *Certified* Medicaid.
Owner Proprietary Corp (Hillhaven Corp).
Admissions Requirements Minimum age 18; Medical examination.
Staff RNs 2 (ft); LPNs 6 (ft); Nurses aides 25 (ft), 10 (pt); Recreational therapists 1 (pt); Activities coordinators 1 (ft).
Facilities Dining room; Activities room; Laundry room; Barber/Beauty shop.
Activities Arts & crafts; Cards; Games; Reading groups; Prayer groups; Movies; Shopping trips; Social/Cultural gatherings.

KINGS MOUNTAIN

Kings Mountain Convalescent Center
PO Box 578, 716 Sipes St, Kings Mountain, NC, 28086
(704) 739-8132
Admin Karen Greene Radford. *Medical Dir/Dir of Nursing* Dr Joseph Lee; Margaret Black.
Licensure Skilled care; Intermediate care. *Beds* SNF 62; ICF 62. *Certified* Medicaid; Medicare.
Owner Proprietary Corp (White Oak Manor Inc).
Admissions Requirements Medical examination; Physician's request.
Staff Physicians 1 (ft); RNs 5 (ft), 1 (pt); LPNs 8 (ft), 1 (pt); Orderlies 5 (ft); Nurses aides 50 (ft), 3 (pt); Physical therapists 1 (pt); Recreational therapists 1 (pt); Speech therapists 1 (pt); Activities coordinators 1 (ft), 2 (pt); Dietitians 1 (pt); Ophthalmologists 1 (pt).
Facilities Dining room; Physical therapy room; Activities room; Crafts room; Laundry room; Barber/Beauty shop; Library; 2 dayrooms.
Activities Arts & crafts; Cards; Games; Reading groups; Prayer groups; Movies; Shopping trips; Social/Cultural gatherings.

KINSTON

Britthaven of Kinston*
317 Rhodes Ave, Kinston, NC, 28501
(919) 523-0082
Admin Carolyn Harrell.
Licensure Skilled care; Intermediate care. *Beds* SNF 83; ICF 99. *Certified* Medicaid; Medicare.
Owner Proprietary Corp (Britthaven Inc).

Caswell Center
2415 W Vernon Ave, Kinston, NC, 28501
(919) 522-1261
Admin Jimmie S Woodall. *Medical Dir/Dir of Nursing* Dr K S Salameh.
Licensure Intermediate care for mentally retarded. *Beds* ICF/MR 752; Regular mentally retarded 295. *Certified* Medicaid.
Owner Publicly owned.

Admissions Requirements Minimum age 8; Medical examination.
Staff Physicians 9 (ft); RNs 40 (ft); LPNs 60 (ft); Physical therapists 9 (ft); Recreational therapists 5 (ft); Occupational therapists 5 (ft); Speech therapists 4 (ft); Activities coordinators 9 (ft); Dietitians 12 (ft); Podiatrists 4 (ft).
Facilities Dining room; Physical therapy room; Activities room; Chapel; Crafts room; Laundry room; Barber/Beauty shop; Library.
Activities Arts & crafts; Games; Reading groups; Prayer groups; Movies; Shopping trips; Social/Cultural gatherings.

Guardian Care of Kinston
PO Box 1438, Cunningham Rd, Kinston, NC, 28501
(919) 527-5146
Admin Charles Sharpe Jr. *Medical Dir/Dir of Nursing* Jennifer Adams DON.
Licensure Intermediate care. *Beds* ICF/MR 114. *Certified* Medicaid.
Owner Proprietary Corp (Hillhaven Corp).
Admissions Requirements Minimum age 18; Medical examination; Physician's request.
Staff RNs 3 (ft), 1 (pt); LPNs 7 (ft), 4 (pt); Orderlies 2 (ft); Nurses aides 34 (ft), 9 (pt); Speech therapists 1 (pt); Activities coordinators 1 (ft); Dietitians 1 (ft).
Facilities Dining room; Physical therapy room; Activities room; Crafts room; Laundry room; Barber/Beauty shop.
Activities Arts & crafts; Cards; Games; Reading groups; Prayer groups; Movies; Shopping trips; Social/Cultural gatherings.

LAGRANGE

Howell's Child Care Center, Inc/Bear Creek
100 Howell Drive, LaGrange, NC, 28551
(919) 778-3067
Admin Tina Howell. *Medical Dir/Dir of Nursing* Janice M Boyd.
Licensure Intermediate care for mentally retarded. *Beds* ICF/MR 120. *Certified* Medicaid.
Owner Nonprofit Corp.
Staff Physicians 1 (pt); RNs 8 (ft), 4 (pt); LPNs 8 (ft), 2 (pt); Nurses aides 161 (ft), 40 (pt); Physical therapists 1 (ft); Recreational therapists 4 (ft); Occupational therapists 1 (ft); Speech therapists 1 (ft); Dietitians 1 (ft).
Facilities Dining room; Physical therapy room; Activities room; Chapel; Barber/Beauty shop.

LAKE WACCAMAW

Lake Waccamaw Convalescent Center Inc
PO Box 196, Cameron St, Lake Waccamaw, NC, 28450
(919) 646-3144
Admin Margaret E Marley. *Medical Dir/Dir of Nursing* John Munroe MD; Sherry Grainger.
Licensure Skilled care; Intermediate care; Home for aged. *Beds* SNF 29; ICF 48; Home for aged 65. *Certified* Medicaid; Medicare.
Owner Proprietary Corp.
Admissions Requirements Medical examination; Physician's request.
Staff RNs 5 (ft); LPNs 10 (ft), 1 (pt); Orderlies 6 (ft); Physical therapists 1 (ft); Activities coordinators 2 (ft); Ophthalmologists 1 (pt); Ward clerks 3 (ft) Dentist 1 (pt).
Facilities Dining room; Physical therapy room; Activities room; Chapel; Crafts room; Laundry room; Barber/Beauty shop.
Activities Arts & crafts; Games; Reading groups; Prayer groups; Movies; Shopping trips; Social/Cultural gatherings.

LAURINBURG

Century Care of Laurinburg*
Rte 3, Box 95, Hasty Rd, Laurinburg, NC, 28352
(919) 276-8400
Admin Noah Kinlaw Duncan.
Licensure Intermediate care. *Beds* 43. *Certified* Medicaid.

Edwin Morgan Center Scotland Memorial Hospital—SNF*
Peden St, Laurinburg, NC, 28352
(919) 276-0016
Admin Robert R Martin.
Licensure Skilled care. *Beds* 40. *Certified* Medicaid; Medicare.

LENOIR

Brian Center Nursing Care—Lenoir*
322 Nu-Way Circle, Lenoir, NC, 28645
(704) 758-7326
Admin Ronald Vaughan.
Licensure Skilled care; Intermediate care. *Beds* SNF 68; ICF 52. *Certified* Medicaid; Medicare.
Owner Proprietary Corp (Brian Center Management Corp).

LEXINGTON

Brian Center Nursing Care—Lexington Inc
Rte 17, Box 58A, Lexington, NC, 27292
(704) 249-7521
Admin Annie L Tilley. *Medical Dir/Dir of Nursing* Michael Garrison MD; Diane Roseberry.
Licensure Skilled care; Intermediate care. *Beds* SNF 38; ICF 18. *Certified* Medicaid; Medicare.
Owner Proprietary Corp (Brian Center Management Corp).
Admissions Requirements Medical examination; Physician's request.
Staff Physicians 1 (pt); RNs 3 (ft), 4 (pt); LPNs; Nurses aides 21 (ft), 2 (pt); Activities coordinators 2 (pt); Dietitians 1 (ft).
Facilities Dining room; Activities room; Laundry room; Barber/Beauty shop.
Activities Arts & crafts; Cards; Games; Reading groups; Prayer groups; Movies; Shopping trips.

Buena Vista Nursing Center Inc
PO Box 419, Everhart Rd, Lexington, NC, 27292
(704) 246-6644
Admin Thurman L Fritts. *Medical Dir/Dir of Nursing* Lillian B Fritts DON.
Licensure Intermediate care; Home for aged. *Beds* ICF 36; Home for aged 9. *Certified* Medicaid.
Owner Proprietary Corp.
Staff RNs 2 (ft), 2 (pt); LPNs 3 (ft), 1 (pt); Orderlies 1 (ft), 1 (pt); Nurses aides 14 (ft), 6 (pt); Activities coordinators 1 (ft), 1 (pt); Dentist 1 (pt).
Facilities Dining room; Activities room; Crafts room; Laundry room; Barber/Beauty shop; Library.
Activities Arts & crafts; Cards; Games; Reading groups; Prayer groups; Movies.

Centerclair Inc
Rte 2, Box 23, Lexington, NC, 27292
(704) 249-7057
Admin Geneva F Williams. *Medical Dir/Dir of Nursing* Gerald P Briggs MD; Olga James RN.
Licensure Intermediate care. *Beds* ICF 60. *Certified* Medicaid.
Owner Proprietary Corp.
Admissions Requirements Medical examination.

Staff Physicians 6 (pt); RNs 1 (ft); LPNs 3 (ft); Orderlies 1 (ft); Nurses aides 13 (ft), 9 (pt); Activities coordinators 1 (ft); Dietitians 1 (pt); Social director 1 (ft).
Facilities Dining room; Activities room; Crafts room; Laundry room; Barber/Beauty shop; Courtyard.
Activities Arts & crafts; Cards; Games; Prayer groups; Movies; Shopping trips; Social/Cultural gatherings; Elegant, in-house dinners; Child day care center; Dining out; Fair.

Golden Age Inc*
Rte 15, Box 216, Cowplace Rd, Lexington, NC, 27292
(704) 956-6219
Admin Samuel E McBride.
Licensure Skilled care; Home for aged. *Beds* SNF 50; Home for aged 14. *Certified* Medicaid; Medicare.

LILLINGTON

Adams & Kinton Nursing Home Inc*
PO Box 789, Hwy 421, Lillington, NC, 27546
(919) 893-5141
Admin John H Kinton.
Licensure Skilled care; Intermediate care. *Beds* SNF 40; ICF 89. *Certified* Medicaid; Medicare.

LINCOLNTON

Lincoln Nursing Center Inc
PO Box 898, 1410 Gaston St Extension, Lincolnton, NC, 28093
(704) 732-1138
Admin Susie H Martin.
Licensure Skilled care; Intermediate care; Home for aged. *Beds* SNF 60; ICF 50; Home for aged 10. *Certified* Medicaid; Medicare.
Owner Proprietary Corp (Hillhaven Corp).

LOUISBURG

Louisburg Nursing Center Inc*
PO Box 759, Smoke Tree Way, Louisburg, NC, 27549
(919) 496-2188
Admin Anne Hutchinson. *Medical Dir/Dir of Nursing* B L Patterson MD.
Licensure Intermediate care. *Beds* 92. *Certified* Medicaid.
Owner Proprietary Corp (Angell Group).
Admissions Requirements Medical examination; Physician's request.
Staff RNs 1 (ft), 2 (pt); LPNs 8 (ft), 6 (pt); Orderlies 5 (ft), 2 (pt); Nurses aides 32 (ft), 8 (pt); Activities coordinators 1 (ft); Dietitians 1 (pt).
Facilities Dining room; Physical therapy room; Activities room; Crafts room; Laundry room; Barber/Beauty shop.
Activities Arts & crafts; Cards; Games; Reading groups; Prayer groups; Movies; Shopping trips.

LUMBERTON

Kingsdale Manor
PO Box 1675, 1555 Willis Ave, Lumberton, NC, 28358
(919) 739-6048
Admin Larris Mullins. *Medical Dir/Dir of Nursing* Rudine K Smith.
Licensure Skilled care; Intermediate care. *Beds* 125. *Certified* Medicaid; Medicare.
Owner Proprietary Corp (Beverly Enterprises).
Admissions Requirements Medical examination; Physician's request.
Staff Physicians 1 (ft); RNs 4 (ft); LPNs 13 (ft), 2 (pt); Orderlies 8 (ft), 1 (pt); Nurses aides 23 (ft), 8 (pt); Physical therapists 1

(pt); Speech therapists 1 (pt); Activities coordinators 1 (ft); Dietitians 1 (ft); Dentists 1 (pt).
Facilities Dining room; Physical therapy room; Activities room; Barber/Beauty shop.
Activities Arts & crafts; Games; Prayer groups; Social/Cultural gatherings.

Methodist Retirement Home—Wesley Pines
100 Wesley Pine Rd, Lumberton, NC, 28358
(919) 738-9691
Admin Paul G Bunn. *Medical Dir/Dir of Nursing* Kathy Freeman.
Licensure Skilled care; Intermediate care; Independent living. *Beds* SNF 18; ICF 23; Home for aged 15. *Certified* Medicaid; Medicare.
Owner Nonprofit Corp.
Admissions Requirements Minimum age 62; Medical examination.
Staff Physicians 1 (pt); RNs 3 (ft), 2 (pt); LPNs 3 (ft), 1 (pt); Orderlies 4 (ft), 2 (pt); Nurses aides 7 (ft), 8 (pt); Physical therapists 2 (pt); Speech therapists 1 (pt); Activities coordinators 1 (ft); Dietitians 1 (pt); Ophthalmologists 2 (pt).
Affiliation Methodist
Facilities Dining room; Physical therapy room; Activities room; Chapel; Crafts room; Laundry room; Barber/Beauty shop; Library; Family rooms.
Activities Arts & crafts; Cards; Games; Reading groups; Prayer groups; Shopping trips; Social/Cultural gatherings; Worship; Fashion shows; Swimming.

North Carolina Cancer Institute Inc
PO Box 1445, Hwy 711 & Hwy 72, Lumberton, NC, 28359-1445
(919) 739-2821
Admin Kenneth Jackson. *Medical Dir/Dir of Nursing* W C Hedgpeth MD; Peggy Hughes RN.
Licensure Skilled care; Long-term hospital. *Beds* SNF 52 11D 4 Long-term hospital. *Certified* Medicaid; Medicare.
Owner Nonprofit Corp.
Admissions Requirements Physician's request.
Staff Physicians 1 (ft); RNs 5 (ft); LPNs 5 (ft), 1 (pt); Orderlies 4 (ft); Nurses aides 22 (ft), 2 (pt); Activities coordinators 1 (pt); Dietitians 1 (pt); 20 (ft), 2 (pt).
Facilities Dining room; Activities room; Chapel; Crafts room; Laundry room; Barber/Beauty shop.
Activities Arts & crafts; Cards; Games; Prayer groups.

Southeastern General Hospital SNC/ICF
PO Box 1408, 300 W 27th St, Lumberton, NC, 28358
(919) 738-6441
Admin Donald C Hiscott. *Medical Dir/Dir of Nursing* George S Nettles MD; Betty C Edens VP DON.
Licensure Skilled care; Intermediate care. *Beds* SNF 40; ICF 40. *Certified* Medicaid; Medicare.
Owner Nonprofit Corp.
Staff Physicians 1 (ft); RNs 9 (ft); LPNs 13 (ft); Orderlies 6 (ft); Nurses aides 32 (ft); Physical therapists 1 (pt); Activities coordinators 1 (ft); Dietitians 1 (ft); Ophthalmologists 1 (pt); Podiatrists 1 (pt); Social worker 1 (ft); Ward secretary 2 (ft).

MADISON

Britthaven of Madison
Rte 2, Box 886, Madison, NC, 27025
(919) 548-9658
Admin P J Minton. *Medical Dir/Dir of Nursing* Dr C W Joyce MD; Tina Hesser DON.
Licensure Skilled care; Intermediate care. *Beds* SNF 22; ICF 78. *Certified* Medicaid; Medicare.
Owner Proprietary Corp (Britthaven Inc).

Admissions Requirements Medical examination.
Staff Physicians 3 (ft); RNs 6 (ft), 5 (pt); LPNs 3 (ft), 4 (pt); Orderlies 1 (ft); Nurses aides 29 (ft), 5 (pt); Recreational therapists 1 (ft); Speech therapists 1 (pt); Activities coordinators 1 (ft); Dietitians 1 (pt); Ophthalmologists 1 (pt).
Facilities Dining room; Physical therapy room; Activities room; Crafts room; Laundry room; Barber/Beauty shop.
Activities Arts & crafts; Cards; Games; Reading groups; Prayer groups; Movies; Social/Cultural gatherings.

MARION

Autumn Care of Marion*
PO Box 339, 610 Airport Rd, Marion, NC, 28752
(704) 652-6701
Admin Thomas G Koontz. *Medical Dir/Dir of Nursing* Dr Michael McCall.
Licensure Skilled care; Intermediate care. *Beds* SNF 50; ICF 30. *Certified* Medicaid; Medicare.
Owner Proprietary Corp (Autumn Corp).
Admissions Requirements Minimum age 21; Medical examination.
Staff Physicians 8 (pt); RNs 7 (ft), 5 (pt); LPNs 6 (ft), 3 (pt); Orderlies 2 (ft); Nurses aides 35 (ft), 15 (pt); Physical therapists 2 (pt); Speech therapists 1 (pt); Activities coordinators 1 (ft); Dietitians 1 (pt); Dentists 1 (pt); Ophthalmologists 1 (pt); Podiatrists 1 (pt).
Facilities Dining room; Physical therapy room; Activities room; Crafts room; Laundry room; Barber/Beauty shop.
Activities Arts & crafts; Cards; Games; Reading groups; Prayer groups; Movies; Shopping trips; Social/Cultural gatherings.

MARS HILL

Madison Manor Nursing Center
50 Manor Rd, Mars Hill, NC, 28754
(704) 689-5200
Admin Mary J Lance. *Medical Dir/Dir of Nursing* Dr Otis Duck; Cindy Kroksh DON.
Licensure Skilled care; Intermediate care. *Beds* SNF 51; ICF 49. *Certified* Medicaid; Medicare; VA.
Owner Proprietary Corp (Beverly Enterprises).
Admissions Requirements Minimum age 18.
Staff Physicians 3 (pt); RNs 3 (ft), 2 (pt); LPNs 12 (ft), 3 (pt); Nurses aides 32 (ft), 3 (pt); Physical therapists 2 (ft); Occupational therapists 1 (pt); Speech therapists 1 (pt); Activities coordinators 1 (ft), 1 (pt); Ophthalmologists 1 (pt); Social worker 1 (ft), 1 (pt).
Facilities Dining room; Physical therapy room; Activities room; Laundry room; Barber/Beauty shop; Courtyard.
Activities Arts & crafts; Cards; Games; Reading groups; Prayer groups; Movies; Social/Cultural gatherings; Exercise; Cooking; Singing; Music therapy; Sensory stimulation; Worship service; Gardening.

MEBANE

The Presbyterian Home of Hawfields, Inc
PO Box 193, Rte 1, Mebane, NC, 27302
(919) 578-4701
Admin Marvin E Yount Jr. *Medical Dir/Dir of Nursing* Danette Shanklin RN DON.
Licensure Intermediate care; Rest home; Independent living. *Beds* ICF 68; Rest home 46; Independent living. *Certified* Medicaid.
Owner Nonprofit Corp.
Admissions Requirements Medical examination; Physician's request.

Staff RNs 3 (ft), 1 (pt); LPNs 6 (ft), 3 (pt); Nurses aides 21 (ft), 15 (pt); Physical therapists 2 (pt); Occupational therapists 1 (pt); Speech therapists 1 (pt); Activities coordinators 1 (ft); Dietitians 1 (ft); Ophthalmologists 1 (pt).
Affiliation Presbyterian
Facilities Dining room; Physical therapy room; Activities room; Crafts room; Laundry room; Barber/Beauty shop; Living room; Lounge.
Activities Arts & crafts; Cards; Games; Reading groups; Prayer groups; Movies; Shopping trips; Social/Cultural gatherings.

MOCKSVILLE

Autumn Care of Mocksville
PO Box 527, 1007 Howard St, Mocksville, NC, 27028
(704) 634-3535
Admin Nettie D Groce. *Medical Dir/Dir of Nursing* Dr George Kimberly.
Licensure Skilled care; Intermediate care; Rest home. *Beds* SNF 85; ICF; Rest home. *Certified* Medicaid; Medicare.
Owner Proprietary Corp (Autumn Corp).
Admissions Requirements Minimum age 18; Medical examination; Physician's request.
Staff RNs 4 (ft), 2 (pt); LPNs 9 (ft), 5 (pt); Orderlies 3 (ft), 1 (pt); Nurses aides 25 (ft), 10 (pt); Physical therapists 1 (pt); Speech therapists 1 (ft), 1 (pt); Dietitians 1 (pt); Dentists 1 (pt); Ophthalmologists 1 (pt).
Facilities Dining room; Physical therapy room; Activities room; Crafts room; Laundry room; Barber/Beauty shop.
Activities Arts & crafts; Games; Reading groups; Movies; Social/Cultural gatherings.

MONROE

Guardian Care of Monroe
PO Box 1189, 1212 Sunset Dr, Monroe, NC, 28110
(704) 283-8548
Admin Mary M Carter. *Medical Dir/Dir of Nursing* Dr B W Springs; Barbara Owens RN.
Licensure Skilled care; Intermediate care; Retirement. *Beds* SNF 20; ICF 114; Retirement 40. *Certified* Medicaid; Medicare.
Owner Proprietary Corp (Hillhaven Corp).
Staff Physicians 18 (ft), 5 (pt); RNs 6 (ft), 2 (pt); LPNs 12 (ft), 5 (pt); Orderlies 2 (ft); Nurses aides 40 (ft), 8 (pt); Physical therapists 2 (ft); Speech therapists 1 (ft); Activities coordinators 1 (ft); Dietitians 1 (ft), 1 (pt).
Facilities Dining room; Physical therapy room; Activities room; Crafts room; Laundry room; Barber/Beauty shop.
Activities Arts & crafts; Cards; Games; Reading groups; Prayer groups; Movies; Shopping trips; Social/Cultural gatherings.

Union Memorial Hospital
PO Box 5003, 600 Hospital Dr, Monroe, NC, 28110
(704) 283-2111
Admin J Larry Bishop. *Medical Dir/Dir of Nursing* Carol Williams RN DON.
Licensure Skilled care; Intermediate care. *Beds* SNF 34; ICF 32. *Certified* Medicaid; Medicare.
Owner Nonprofit Corp.
Admissions Requirements Medical examination.
Staff RNs 6 (ft), 1 (pt); LPNs 6 (ft), 2 (pt); LPNs 6 (ft); Nurses aides 29 (ft), 6 (pt); Physical therapists 1 (pt); Speech therapists; Activities coordinators 1 (ft); Dietitians 1 (ft); Social service 1 (ft); Ward secretary 1 (ft).

Facilities Dining room; Physical therapy room; Activities room; Crafts room; Laundry room; Barber/Beauty shop.
Activities Arts & crafts; Games; Prayer groups; Movies; Exercise.

MOORESVILLE

Brian Center Nursing Care—Mooresville
752 E Center Ave, Mooresville, NC, 28115
(704) 663-3448
Admin Patsy B Sherrill. *Medical Dir/Dir of Nursing* William W Skeen MD; Mary S Johnston RN.
Licensure Skilled care; Intermediate care. *Beds* SNF 55; ICF 45. *Certified* Medicaid; Medicare.
Owner Proprietary Corp (Brian Center Management Corp).
Admissions Requirements Medical examination; Physician's request.
Staff Physicians 6 (pt); RNs 7 (ft), 6 (pt); LPNs 5 (ft), 4 (pt); Nurses aides 27 (ft), 25 (pt); Physical therapists 1 (ft); Speech therapists 1 (pt); Activities coordinators 1 (ft); Dietitians 1 (ft); Dentists 1 (pt); Ophthalmologists 1 (pt).
Facilities Dining room; Physical therapy room; Activities room; Crafts room; Laundry room; Barber/Beauty shop.
Activities Arts & crafts; Cards; Games; Reading groups; Prayer groups; Movies; Shopping trips.

MOREHEAD CITY

Harborview Nursing Home
812 Shepard St, Morehead City, NC, 28557
(919) 726-6855
Admin Doris B Jernigan. *Medical Dir/Dir of Nursing* William M Brady MD; Bonnie Higgins RN DON.
Licensure Skilled care; Intermediate care; Home for aged. *Beds* SNF 20; ICF 42; Home for aged 13. *Certified* Medicaid; Medicare.
Owner Proprietary Corp.
Admissions Requirements Physician's request.
Staff RNs; LPNs; Orderlies; Nurses aides; Activities coordinators; Dietitians.
Facilities Dining room; Activities room; Chapel; Crafts room; Laundry room; Barber/Beauty shop; Library.
Activities Arts & crafts; Cards; Games; Reading groups; Prayer groups; Movies; Shopping trips; Social/Cultural gatherings.

Morehead Nursing Center
PO Box 728, Penny Ln, Morehead City, NC, 28557
(919) 726-0031
Admin Beverly Jorgenson. *Medical Dir/Dir of Nursing* Dr Donald Reece; Kathy Glussman RN DON.
Licensure Skilled care; Intermediate care. *Beds* SNF 31; ICF 61. *Certified* Medicaid; Medicare.
Owner Proprietary Corp (Tullock Management).
Admissions Requirements Medical examination; Physician's request.
Staff RNs 3 (ft), 1 (pt); LPNs 7 (ft), 5 (pt); Orderlies 1 (ft); Nurses aides 32 (ft), 3 (pt); Physical therapists 1 (pt); Occupational therapists 1 (pt); Speech therapists 1 (pt); Activities coordinators 1 (ft); Dietitians 1 (ft).
Languages German
Facilities Dining room; Physical therapy room; Activities room; Crafts room; Laundry room; Barber/Beauty shop.
Activities Arts & crafts; Cards; Games; Movies; Social/Cultural gatherings.

MORGANTON

Britthaven of Morganton*
107 Magnolia Dr, Morganton, NC, 28655
(704) 437-8760
Admin Nancy N Hipps.
Licensure Skilled care; Intermediate care. *Beds* SNF 31; ICF 60. *Certified* Medicaid; Medicare.
Owner Proprietary Corp (Britthaven Inc).

Broughton Hospital
1000 S Sterling St, Morganton, NC, 28755
(704) 433-2324, 433-2111
Admin Arthur J Robarge. *Medical Dir/Dir of Nursing* Dr Ludwik Tramer; Juanita Long RN DON.
Licensure Intermediate care; Intermediate care for mentally retarded; State psychiatric facility. *Beds* ICF 30; ICF/MR 78; Med/Sur 44; Psychiatric 757. *Certified* Medicaid; Medicare.
Owner Publicly owned.
Admissions Requirements Psychiatric determination according to NC law.
Staff RNs 156 (ft); LPNs 54 (ft); Physical therapists 1 (ft); Recreational therapists 19 (ft); Occupational therapists 12 (ft); Speech therapists 2 (ft); Activities coordinators 1 (ft); Dietitians 4 (ft).
Facilities Dining room; Physical therapy room; Activities room; Chapel; Crafts room; Laundry room; Barber/Beauty shop; Library.

Foothills ICF/MR Group Home*
309 E View St, Morganton, NC, 28655
(704) 433-6488
Admin Janie Cloer.
Licensure Intermediate care; Intermediate care for mentally retarded. *Beds* 5. *Certified* Medicaid.

Pinnacle Care Center
109 Foothills Dr, Morganton, NC, 28655
(704) 433-7160
Admin Amy G Hughes. *Medical Dir/Dir of Nursing* Dr Luther Clontz.
Licensure Skilled care; Intermediate care. *Beds* SNF 70; ICF 50. *Certified* Medicaid; Medicare; VA.
Owner Proprietary Corp.
Admissions Requirements Minimum age 18.
Staff Physicians 1 (pt); RNs 5 (ft), 1 (pt); LPNs 14 (ft), 4 (pt); Nurses aides 45 (ft), 9 (pt); Physical therapists 1 (ft), 1 (pt); Recreational therapists 1 (pt); Occupational therapists 1 (pt); Speech therapists 1 (pt); Activities coordinators 2 (ft); Dietitians 1 (pt); Ophthalmologists 1 (pt); Rehabilitation Aides 2 (ft).
Facilities Dining room; Physical therapy room; Activities room; Crafts room; Laundry room; Barber/Beauty shop.
Activities Arts & crafts; Cards; Games; Reading groups; Prayer groups; Movies; Shopping trips; Social/Cultural gatherings.

Western Carolina Center
200 Enola Rd, Morganton, NC, 28655
(704) 433-2711
Admin J Iverson Riddle. *Medical Dir/Dir of Nursing* Luther H Clontz MD; Helen C Wilson RN DON.
Licensure Intermediate care for mentally retarded. *Beds* ICF/MR 498. *Certified* Medicaid.
Owner Publicly owned.
Staff Physicians 7 (ft), 1 (pt); RNs 38 (ft); LPNs 31 (ft), 3 (pt); Physical therapists 2 (ft); Recreational therapists 10 (ft); Occupational therapists 6 (ft); Speech therapists 9 (ft); Dietitians 3 (ft); Podiatrists 2 (ft).
Facilities Dining room; Physical therapy room; Chapel; Crafts room; Laundry room; Barber/Beauty shop; Library.

MOUNT AIRY

Surry Community Nursing Center
942 Allred Mill Rd, Mount Airy, NC, 27030
(919) 789-5076
Admin Rebecca M Phillips. *Medical Dir/Dir of Nursing* J Gillum Burke MD; Wanda Jackson DON.
Licensure Skilled care; Intermediate care. *Beds* SNF 60; ICF 60. *Certified* Medicaid; Medicare.
Owner Proprietary Corp (Beverly Enterprises).
Admissions Requirements Minimum age 18; Medical examination; Physician's request.
Staff RNs 1 (ft), 9 (pt); LPNs 4 (ft), 9 (pt); Nurses aides 30 (ft), 6 (pt); Physical therapists 1 (ft); Recreational therapists 1 (ft); Speech therapists 1 (ft); Activities coordinators 1 (ft); Dietitians 1 (ft); Dentists 1 (ft); Ophthalmologists 1 (ft); Podiatrists 1 (ft).
Facilities Dining room; Physical therapy room; Activities room; Crafts room; Laundry room; Barber/Beauty shop; Library.
Activities Arts & crafts; Cards; Games; Reading groups; Prayer groups; Movies; Shopping trips; Social/Cultural gatherings.

MOUNT OLIVE

Medical Park Nursing Center*
PO Box 329, 228 Smith Chapel Rd, Mount Olive, NC, 28365
(919) 658-9522
Admin Walter Singleton. *Medical Dir/Dir of Nursing* Dr Hervy B Kornegay.
Licensure Skilled care; Intermediate care; Home for aged. *Beds* SNF 75; ICF 75. *Certified* Medicaid; Medicare.
Owner Proprietary Corp (Tullock Management).
Admissions Requirements Minimum age 18; Medical examination; Physician's request.
Staff Physicians 5 (pt); RNs 4 (ft), 2 (pt); LPNs 10 (ft), 4 (pt); Orderlies 4 (ft), 2 (pt); Nurses aides 59 (ft), 16 (pt); Physical therapists 1 (ft); Recreational therapists 1 (pt); Speech therapists 1 (pt); Activities coordinators 1 (ft); Dietitians 1 (ft); Dentists 1 (pt).
Facilities Dining room; Physical therapy room; Activities room; Chapel; Crafts room; Laundry room; Barber/Beauty shop.
Activities Arts & crafts; Games; Reading groups; Prayer groups; Movies; Shopping trips.

MURPHY

Murphy Medical Center
2002 US Hwy 64 E, Murphy, NC, 28906
(704) 837-8161
Admin J Michael Stevenson. *Medical Dir/Dir of Nursing* John R Hagre MD; Joan Archambault DON.
Licensure Skilled care; Intermediate care. *Beds* 120. *Certified* Medicaid; Medicare.
Owner Publicly owned.
Admissions Requirements Physician's request.
Staff Physicians 18 (ft); Physical therapists 1 (ft), 1 (pt); Reality therapists 1 (ft); Occupational therapists 1 (pt); Speech therapists 1 (pt); Activities coordinators 1 (ft); Dietitians 1 (ft); Dentists 1 (ft).
Facilities Dining room; Physical therapy room; Activities room; Chapel; Crafts room; Laundry room; Barber/Beauty shop.
Activities Arts & crafts; Games; Reading groups; Prayer groups; Shopping trips; Social/Cultural gatherings.

NAGS HEAD

Britthaven of Outer Banks
430 W Health Ctr Dr, Nags Head, NC, 27959
(919) 441-3116

Admin Don Phelps RN. *Medical Dir/Dir of Nursing* Dr Grayson Waldrom MD; Maxine Sawyer RN DON.
Licensure Skilled care; Intermediate care; Home for aged. *Beds* SNF 32; ICF 64; Home for aged 24. *Certified* Medicaid; Medicare.
Owner Proprietary Corp (Britthaven Inc).
Admissions Requirements Medical examination; Physician's request.
Staff Physicians; RNs; LPNs; Orderlies; Nurses aides; Physical therapists; Speech therapists; Activities coordinators; Dietitians.
Facilities Dining room; Physical therapy room; Activities room; Crafts room; Laundry room; Barber/Beauty shop.
Activities Arts & crafts; Cards; Games; Prayer groups; Movies; Social/Cultural gatherings.

NEBO

McDowell Nursing Center*
Rte 3, Box 270, Nebo, NC, 28761
(704) 652-3032
Admin Juanita C Fickling.
Licensure Skilled care; Intermediate care. *Beds* 100. *Certified* Medicaid; Medicare.
Staff Physicians 2 (pt); RNs 5 (ft), 1 (pt); LPNs 9 (ft), 1 (pt); Nurses aides 43 (ft); Physical therapists 1 (pt); Activities coordinators 2 (ft); Dietitians 1 (pt); Dentists 1 (pt); Podiatrists 1 (pt).
Facilities Dining room; Activities room; Crafts room; Laundry room; Barber/Beauty shop.
Activities Arts & crafts; Cards; Games; Reading groups; Prayer groups; Movies; Shopping trips; Social/Cultural gatherings.

NEW BERN

Britthaven of New Bern
PO Box 3397, 2600 Old Cherry Point Rd, New Bern, NC, 28560
(919) 637-4730
Admin Dean Picot. *Medical Dir/Dir of Nursing* Dottie Conlan.
Licensure Skilled care. *Beds* 73. *Certified* Medicaid; Medicare.
Owner Proprietary Corp (Britthaven Inc).
Staff RNs 2 (ft), 3 (pt); LPNs 8 (ft), 2 (pt); Nurses aides 25 (ft), 5 (pt).
Activities Arts & crafts; Cards; Games; Reading groups; Prayer groups; Movies; Shopping trips; Social/Cultural gatherings.

Guardian Care of New Bern
PO Box 2037, 836 Hospital Dr, New Bern, NC, 28560
(919) 638-6001
Admin Stephen Harrison.
Licensure Intermediate care. *Beds* 116. *Certified* Medicaid.
Owner Proprietary Corp (Hillhaven Corp).

Howell's Child Care Center Inc (Riverbend)
PO Box 2159, New Bern, NC, 28561
(919) 638-6519
Admin Joseph A Howell. *Medical Dir/Dir of Nursing* Dr Ron May.
Licensure Intermediate care for mentally retarded. *Beds* 125. *Certified* Medicaid.
Owner Nonprofit Corp.
Admissions Requirements Minimum age Birth.
Staff Physicians 1 (ft), 4 (pt); RNs; Nurses aides 157 (ft); Physical therapists 1 (ft); Recreational therapists 1 (ft); Occupational therapists 1 (ft); Speech therapists 1 (ft); Activities coordinators 1 (ft); Dietitians 1 (ft).
Facilities Dining room; Physical therapy room; Activities room; Chapel; Crafts room; Laundry room; Barber/Beauty shop; Classrooms; Gymnasium; Swimming pool; Water therapy room.

Activities Arts & crafts; Cards; Games; Movies; Shopping trips; Social/Cultural gatherings.

NEWTON

J W Abernethy Center—United Church Retirement Homes Inc
102 Leonard Ave, Newton, NC, 28658
(704) 464-8260
Admin Van D Grimes. *Medical Dir/Dir of Nursing* Dr William Long; W Larry Sink.
Licensure Skilled care; Intermediate care; Independent living; Home for aged. *Beds* SNF 31; ICF 67; Home for aged 33; Independent living 90. *Certified* Medicaid; Medicare.
Owner Nonprofit Corp.
Admissions Requirements Minimum age 62; Medical examination.
Staff Physicians 4 (pt); RNs 7 (ft), 3 (pt); LPNs 10 (ft), 3 (pt); Nurses aides 32 (ft), 13 (pt); Physical therapists 1 (ft); Recreational therapists 1 (ft); Activities coordinators 1 (ft); Dietitians 1 (ft).
Affiliation Church of Christ
Facilities Dining room; Physical therapy room; Activities room; Chapel; Crafts room; Laundry room; Barber/Beauty shop; Library.
Activities Arts & crafts; Cards; Games; Reading groups; Prayer groups; Movies; Shopping trips; Social/Cultural gatherings; Personalized activities & programs.

OXFORD

Granville County Group Home*
Rte 3, Box 193, Oxford, NC, 27565
(919) 693-4610
Admin Ruth E Gierisch.
Licensure Intermediate care for mentally retarded. *Beds* 5. *Certified* Medicaid.

Louise Parham Health Care Complex
PO Box 986, Prospect Ave, Oxford, NC, 27565
(919) 693-1531
Admin Louise B Parham. *Medical Dir/Dir of Nursing* Joy W Moss.
Licensure Skilled care; Intermediate care. *Beds* SNF 20; ICF 100. *Certified* Medicaid.
Owner Privately owned.
Admissions Requirements Medical examination.
Staff RNs 1 (ft); LPNs 9 (ft), 4 (pt); Orderlies 4 (ft); Nurses aides 42 (ft); Activities coordinators 1 (ft); Dietitians 1 (ft).
Facilities Dining room; Physical therapy room; Activities room; Crafts room; Laundry room; Barber/Beauty shop.
Activities Arts & crafts; Cards; Games; Reading groups; Prayer groups; Movies; Social/Cultural gatherings; Music.

PINEHURST

Manor Care of Pinehurst
PO Box 1667, Pinehurst, NC, 28374
(919) 295-1781
Admin Jacqueline R Rio. *Medical Dir/Dir of Nursing* Dr. Ward Patrick, MD; Willavene Bradham, RN.
Licensure Skilled care; Intermediate care. *Beds* SNF 59; ICF 61. *Certified* Medicaid; Medicare; VA.
Owner Proprietary Corp (Manor Care).
Admissions Requirements Minimum age 18; Medical examination; Physician's request.
Staff Physicians 1 (pt); RNs 7 (ft), 4 (pt); LPNs 9 (ft), 4 (pt); Orderlies; Nurses aides 35 (ft), 11 (pt); Physical therapists 1 (ft); Recreational therapists 1 (ft); Activities coordinators 1 (ft); Dietitians 1 (ft); 1 (pt) Chaplain.

Facilities Dining room; Physical therapy
room; Activities room; Chapel; Crafts room;
Laundry room; Barber/Beauty shop.
Activities Arts & crafts; Cards; Games;
Reading groups; Prayer groups; Movies;
Shopping trips; Social/Cultural gatherings.

Pinehurst Nursing Center*
PO Box 1179, Hwy 5, Pinehurst, NC, 28374
(919) 295-6158
Admin Sandra Edwards. *Medical Dir/Dir of
Nursing* Dr F Owens.
Licensure Intermediate care; Home for aged.
Beds ICF 64; Home for aged 17. *Certified*
Medicaid.
Staff RNs 1 (ft); LPNs 5 (ft), 6 (pt); Nurses
aides 25 (ft), 4 (pt); Activities coordinators 1
(ft).
Facilities Dining room; Activities room;
Chapel; Laundry room; Barber/Beauty shop;
Library.
Activities Arts & crafts; Cards; Games;
Movies.

PLEASANT GARDEN

Clapp's Nursing Center Inc
PO Box 249, 4558 Pleasant Garden Rd,
Pleasant Garden, NC, 27313
(919) 674-2252
Admin Riley W Clapp. *Medical Dir/Dir of
Nursing* Dr W O Elkins.
Licensure Skilled care; Home for aged. *Beds*
SNF 28; Home for aged 5. *Certified*
Medicaid; Medicare.
Admissions Requirements Minimum age 18;
Medical examination; Physician's request.
Staff RNs 2 (ft), 1 (pt); LPNs 4 (ft), 2 (pt);
Orderlies 1 (ft); Nurses aides 10 (ft), 6 (pt);
Physical therapists 1 (pt); Recreational
therapists 1 (pt); Speech therapists 1 (pt);
Activities coordinators 1 (pt); Dietitians 1
(pt); Dentists 1 (pt).

RALEIGH

Brian Center Nursing Care—Raleigh*
3000 Holston Ln, Raleigh, NC, 27610
(919) 828-3904
Admin Susan Hyland.
Licensure Skilled care; Intermediate care. *Beds*
SNF 60; ICF 65. *Certified* Medicaid;
Medicare.
Owner Proprietary Corp (Brian Center
Management Corp).

Glenwood Hills Intermediate Care Facility*
3910 Blue Ridge Rd, Raleigh, NC, 27612
(919) 787-4747
Admin Rachel Brantley.
Licensure Intermediate care. *Beds* 30.
Certified Medicaid.

Hillhaven Conv Center
616 Wade Ave, Raleigh, NC, 27605
(919) 828-6251
Admin Vicki Jones. *Medical Dir/Dir of
Nursing* Sallie Rascoe RN.
Licensure Skilled care; Intermediate care. *Beds*
SNF 116; ICF 58. *Certified* Medicaid;
Medicare.
Owner Proprietary Corp (Hillhaven Corp).
Staff RNs 9 (ft), 17 (pt); LPNs 8 (ft), 14 (pt);
Nurses aides 59 (ft), 6 (pt); Physical
therapists 1 (ft); Occupational therapists 1
(ft); Speech therapists 1 (ft); Activities
coordinators 1 (ft); Dietitians 2 (pt).
Facilities Dining room; Physical therapy
room; Activities room; Crafts room; Laundry
room; Barber/Beauty shop.
Activities Arts & crafts; Cards; Games;
Reading groups; Prayer groups; Movies;
Shopping trips; Social/Cultural gatherings.

Hillhaven Sunnybrook Conv Center*
25 Sunnybrook Rd, Raleigh, NC, 27610
(919) 828-0747

Admin Keith L Avant.
Licensure Skilled care; Intermediate care. *Beds*
SNF 51; ICF 75. *Certified* Medicaid;
Medicare.
Owner Proprietary Corp (Hillhaven Corp).

Knollwood Manor Intermediate Care Facility*
4809 North Blvd, Raleigh, NC, 27604
(919) 876-4613
Admin Rachel A Brantley.
Licensure Intermediate care. *Beds* 108.
Certified Medicaid.

Mayview Convelescent Center
513 E Whitaker Mill Rd, Raleigh, NC, 27608
(919) 828-2348
Admin Travis H Tomlinson Jr. *Medical Dir/
Dir of Nursing* Dr James S Parsons.
Licensure Skilled care. *Beds* 139. *Certified*
Medicaid; Medicare.
Admissions Requirements Physician's request.
Facilities Dining room; Physical therapy
room; Activities room; Crafts room; Laundry
room; Barber/Beauty shop.
Activities Arts & crafts; Cards; Games;
Reading groups; Prayer groups; Movies;
Social/Cultural gatherings.

Stewart Health Center
1500 Sawmill Rd, Raleigh, NC, 27615
(919) 848-7013
Admin Kyle Dilday. *Medical Dir/Dir of
Nursing* Dr Wells Edmundson; Louise
Mauney RN DON.
Licensure Skilled care; Intermediate care; Rest
home. *Beds* SNF 24; ICF 8; Rest home 68.
Owner Nonprofit Corp.
Admissions Requirements Minimum age 18;
Medical examination; Physician's request.
Staff Physicians 2 (pt); RNs 14 (ft), 6 (pt);
LPNs 26 (ft), 11 (pt); Orderlies 6 (ft), 2 (pt);
Nurses aides 58 (ft), 21 (pt); Physical
therapists 1 (ft), 2 (pt); Reality therapists 1
(ft); Recreational therapists 1 (ft);
Occupational therapists 1 (pt); Speech
therapists 1 (pt); Activities coordinators 1
(ft); Dietitians 1 (ft); Dentists 1 (pt);
Ophthalmologists 1 (pt); Podiatrists 1 (pt);
Dentist 1 (pt).
Facilities Dining room; Physical therapy
room; Activities room; Chapel; Crafts room;
Laundry room; Barber/Beauty shop; Library;
Pool rooms; Swimming pool.
Activities Arts & crafts; Cards; Games;
Reading groups; Prayer groups; Movies;
Shopping trips; Social/Cultural gatherings.

REIDSVILLE

Maplewood Nursing Center
543 Maple Ave, Reidsville, NC, 27320
(919) 342-1382
Admin J C Cowan. *Medical Dir/Dir of
Nursing* Dr George Lothian; Linda Smith
DON.
Licensure Skilled care; Intermediate care. *Beds*
SNF 44; ICF 66. *Certified* Medicaid;
Medicare.
Owner Proprietary Corp (Beverly Enterprises).
Admissions Requirements Minimum age 18;
Medical examination; Physician's request.
Staff Physicians 1 (pt); RNs 8 (ft), 1 (pt);
LPNs 4 (ft); Orderlies 2 (ft); Nurses aides 40
(ft), 20 (pt); Physical therapists 1 (pt);
Speech therapists 1 (pt); Activities
coordinators 2 (ft); Dietitians 1 (pt); Dentists
1 (pt); Ophthalmologists 1 (pt); Podiatrists 1
(pt).
Facilities Dining room; Physical therapy
room; Activities room; Crafts room; Laundry
room; Barber/Beauty shop.
Activities Arts & crafts; Reading groups;
Prayer groups; Shopping trips; Social/
Cultural gatherings.

RICH SQUARE

Roanoke Valley Nursing Home
PO Box 560, Rich Square, NC, 27869
(919) 539-4161
Admin James T Johnson. *Medical Dir/Dir of
Nursing* Peggy A Futrell DON.
Licensure Intermediate care. *Beds* ICF 69.
Certified Medicaid.
Owner Privately owned.
Admissions Requirements Medical
examination.
Staff RNs 2 (ft); LPNs 5 (ft); Orderlies 1 (ft),
1 (pt); Nurses aides 29 (ft); Activities
coordinators 1 (ft); Dietitians 1 (ft).
Facilities Dining room; Physical therapy
room; Activities room; Chapel; Crafts room;
Laundry room; Barber/Beauty shop.
Activities Arts & crafts; Cards; Games; Prayer
groups; Social/Cultural gatherings.

ROANOKE RAPIDS

Guardian Care
305 14th St, Roanoke Rapids, NC, 27870
(919) 537-6181
Admin Joan D Garvey. *Medical Dir/Dir of
Nursing* Dr William Brown; Judy Glisan.
Licensure Intermediate care. *Beds* ICF 110.
Certified Medicaid.
Owner Proprietary Corp (Hillhaven Corp).
Admissions Requirements Medical
examination.
Staff RNs 5 (ft), 2 (pt); LPNs 8 (ft), 3 (pt);
Orderlies 2 (ft); Nurses aides 40 (ft), 10 (pt);
Recreational therapists 1 (ft); Activities
coordinators 1 (ft); Dietitians 1 (pt).
Facilities Dining room; Activities room;
Chapel; Crafts room; Laundry room; Barber/
Beauty shop.
Activities Arts & crafts; Cards; Games;
Reading groups; Prayer groups; Movies;
Shopping trips; Social/Cultural gatherings.

ROCKINGHAM

Care Inn—Rockingham*
804 Long Dr, PO Box 1237, Rockingham,
NC, 28379
(919) 997-4493
Admin Michael W Whitecomb.
Licensure Intermediate care. *Beds* 120.
Certified Medicaid.
Admissions Requirements Medical
examination.
Staff RNs 3 (ft), 1 (pt); LPNs 7 (ft), 1 (pt);
Nurses aides 39 (ft), 2 (pt); Physical
therapists 1 (pt).
Facilities Dining room; Physical therapy
room; Activities room; Laundry room;
Barber/Beauty shop.
Activities Arts & crafts; Cards; Games;
Reading groups; Prayer groups; Movies;
Shopping trips; Social/Cultural gatherings;
Bazaars; Heart fund & drive.

ROCKY MOUNT

Guardian Care of Rocky Mount
160 Winstead Ave, Rocky Mount, NC, 27804
(919) 443-7666
Admin Robin J Suddreth. *Medical Dir/Dir of
Nursing* Lewis Thorp MD.
Licensure Skilled care; Intermediate care. *Beds*
SNF 20; ICF 98. *Certified* Medicaid;
Medicare.
Owner Proprietary Corp (Hillhaven Corp).
Admissions Requirements Minimum age 18;
Medical examination; Physician's request.
Staff RNs; LPNs; Orderlies; Nurses aides;
Recreational therapists; Speech therapists;
Activities coordinators.
Facilities Dining room; Activities room;
Chapel; Crafts room; Laundry room; Barber/
Beauty shop.

Activities Arts & crafts; Cards; Games; Reading groups; Prayer groups; Movies; Social/Cultural gatherings.

Westgate Nursing Center*
2221 Raleigh Rd, Rocky Mount, NC, 27801
(919) 442-4156
Admin Carrol S Roberson.
Licensure Skilled care; Intermediate care. *Beds* SNF 36; ICF 50. *Certified* Medicaid; Medicare.

ROXBORO

Person County Memorial Hospital—SNF*
Reginald L Harris Annex, 615 Ridge Rd, Roxboro, NC, 27573
(919) 599-2121
Admin S Grant Boone Jr.
Licensure Skilled care. *Beds* 23. *Certified* Medicaid; Medicare.

Roxboro Nursing Center
PO Box 3070, 901 Ridge Rd, Roxboro, NC, 27573
(919) 599-0106
Admin Kenneth O Stone. *Medical Dir/Dir of Nursing* Dr Thomas D Long.
Licensure Intermediate care; Home Health Agency located in facility. *Beds* ICF 92. *Certified* Medicaid.
Owner Proprietary Corp (Angell Group).
Admissions Requirements Medical examination; Physician's request.
Staff Physicians; RNs; LPNs; Orderlies; Nurses aides; Physical therapists; Reality therapists; Recreational therapists; Occupational therapists; Speech therapists; Activities coordinators; Dietitians; Ophthalmologists; Podiatrists; MSW.
Facilities Dining room; Physical therapy room; Activities room; Chapel; Crafts room; Laundry room; Barber/Beauty shop; Library.
Activities Arts & crafts; Cards; Games; Reading groups; Prayer groups; Movies; Shopping trips; Social/Cultural gatherings.

RUTHERFORDTON

Rutherford County Convalescent Center
PO Box 39-A, Ocar Justice Rd, Rte 2, Rutherfordton, NC, 28139
(704) 286-9001
Admin Brenda S Price. *Medical Dir/Dir of Nursing* Dr Landis P Mitchell; Barbara Martin RN DON.
Licensure Skilled care. *Beds* 50. *Certified* Medicaid; Medicare.
Owner Proprietary Corp (White Oak Manor Inc).
Staff Physicians 1 (pt); RNs 5 (ft), 2 (pt); LPNs 2 (ft), 2 (pt); Nurses aides 18 (ft), 6 (pt); Physical therapists 1 (pt); Speech therapists 1 (pt); Activities coordinators 1 (ft); Dietitians 1 (ft); Ophthalmologists 1 (pt).
Facilities Dining room; Activities room; Crafts room; Laundry room; Barber/Beauty shop.
Activities Arts & crafts; Cards; Games; Reading groups; Prayer groups; Movies; Shopping trips; Social/Cultural gatherings.

Rutherford Nursing Center
PO Drawer 1000, Clubhouse Rd, Rutherfordton, NC, 28139
(704) 287-2169
Admin Michael F Vicario. *Medical Dir/Dir of Nursing* H V Hendrick; Janet Hoover DON.
Licensure Skilled care; Intermediate care. *Beds* SNF 108; ICF 42. *Certified* Medicaid; Medicare.
Owner Proprietary Corp (Brian Center Management Corp).
Admissions Requirements Medical examination; Physician's request.

Staff Physicians 2 (pt); RNs 7 (ft), 3 (pt); LPNs 11 (ft), 4 (pt); Nurses aides 45 (ft), 25 (pt); Physical therapists 1 (ft), 1 (pt); Recreational therapists 1 (ft); Speech therapists 1 (ft); Activities coordinators 1 (ft); Dietitians 1 (ft), 1 (pt); Dentists 1 (pt); Ophthalmologists 1 (pt).
Facilities Dining room; Physical therapy room; Activities room; Laundry room; Barber/Beauty shop; Day room; kitchen; offices.
Activities Arts & crafts; Cards; Games; Reading groups; Prayer groups; Movies; Shopping trips; Social/Cultural gatherings Manicures; Sing-a-longs; Cooking; Residents council; Bingo.

SALISBURY

Jo Lene's Nursing Home*
PO Box 2167, 615 W Innes St, Salisbury, NC, 28144
(704) 633-2781
Admin Cherrathee Y Hager.
Licensure Skilled care; Home for aged. *Beds* SNF 41; Home for aged 25. *Certified* Medicaid; Medicare.

Lutheran Nursing Homes Inc—Salisbury Unit
820 Klumac Rd, Salisbury, NC, 28144
(704) 637-3784
Admin William Beilfuss. *Medical Dir/Dir of Nursing* Cecil Farrington MD; Donna Stepanian RN DON.
Licensure Skilled care; Intermediate care; Rest home. *Beds* SNF 60; ICF 25; Rest home 25. *Certified* Medicaid; Medicare.
Owner Nonprofit Corp (NC Lutheran Homes).
Admissions Requirements Minimum age 60; Medical examination.
Staff RNs 10 (ft), 8 (pt); LPNs 9 (ft), 6 (pt); Orderlies; Nurses aides; Physical therapists; Activities coordinators; Dietitians.
Affiliation Lutheran
Facilities Dining room; Physical therapy room; Activities room; Chapel; Crafts room; Laundry room; Barber/Beauty shop; Library.
Activities Arts & crafts; Cards; Games; Reading groups; Prayer groups; Movies; Shopping trips; Social/Cultural gatherings; Church services; Bible study.

Rowan Manor Nursing Center*
PO Box 2105, 635 Statesville Blvd, Salisbury, NC, 28144
(704) 633-7390
Admin Glenn R Terry.
Licensure Skilled care; Intermediate care. *Beds* SNF 116; ICF 69. *Certified* Medicaid; Medicare.
Owner Proprietary Corp (Brian Center Management Corp).

SALUDA

Saluda Nursing & Convalescent Center*
PO Box 488, Esseola Circle, Saluda, NC, 28773
(704) 749-2261
Admin Mary F Adkins.
Licensure Intermediate care. *Beds* 59. *Certified* Medicaid.

SANFORD

Conv Center of Sanford Inc
4000 Farrell Rd, Sanford, NC, 27330
(919) 775-7207
Admin Frances H Hall. *Medical Dir/Dir of Nursing* John F Blue MD; Joyce F Smith RN.
Licensure Skilled care; Intermediate care. *Beds* SNF 55; ICF 46. *Certified* Medicaid; Medicare.
Owner Proprietary Corp.
Admissions Requirements Minimum age 18; Medical examination.

Staff Physicians 8 (pt); RNs 3 (ft), 1 (pt); LPNs 11 (ft); Orderlies 1 (ft); Nurses aides 43 (ft), 4 (pt); Physical therapists 1 (pt); Occupational therapists 1 (pt); Speech therapists 1 (pt); Activities coordinators 2 (ft); Dietitians 1 (pt); Dentists 1 (pt); Ophthalmologists 1 (pt).
Facilities Dining room; Laundry room; Barber/Beauty shop.
Activities Arts & crafts; Games; Reading groups; Prayer groups; Movies; Shopping trips; Social/Cultural gatherings.

Convalescent Center of Lee County Inc
PO Box 1346, 714 Westover Dr, Sanford, NC, 27330
(919) 775-5404
Admin Norma Jean Stone. *Medical Dir/Dir of Nursing* John Dotterer; Ethel McLean.
Licensure Skilled care; Intermediate care. *Beds* SNF 26; ICF 77. *Certified* Medicaid; Medicare.
Owner Proprietary Corp.
Staff RNs 2 (ft), 2 (pt); LPNs 10 (ft), 3 (pt); Nurses aides 40 (ft), 11 (pt); Activities coordinators 2 (ft); Social worker 1 (ft).

SCOTLAND NECK

Guardian Care of Scotland Neck
1400 Junior High School Rd, Scotland Neck, NC, 27874
(919) 826-5146
Admin Elizabeth Rogers. *Medical Dir/Dir of Nursing* Claudia Sanford.
Licensure Intermediate care. *Beds* ICF 62. *Certified* Medicaid.
Owner Proprietary Corp (Hillhaven Corp).
Admissions Requirements Medical examination 18E.
Staff RNs 1 (ft), 1 (pt); LPNs 5 (ft), 1 (pt); Nurses aides 19 (ft), 5 (pt); Activities coordinators 1 (ft); Dietitians 1 (pt); Ophthalmologists 1 (pt).
Facilities Dining room; Activities room; Laundry room; Barber/Beauty shop.
Activities Cards; Games; Reading groups; Prayer groups; Movies; Shopping trips; Social/Cultural gatherings.

SEA LEVEL

The Sailors' Snug Harbor
PO Box 150, Rte 70, Sea Level, NC, 28577
(919) 225-4411
Admin Leo Kraszeski. *Medical Dir/Dir of Nursing* Dr James T Best; Marjorie Best DON.
Licensure Skilled care; Intermediate care; Retirement home. *Beds* SNF 22; ICF 20; Retirement home 80.
Owner Nonprofit Corp.
Admissions Requirements Medical examination.
Staff Physicians 3 (pt); RNs 4 (ft), 2 (pt); LPNs 5 (ft), 1 (pt); Nurses aides 11 (ft), 6 (pt); Physical therapists 1 (pt); Recreational therapists 2 (ft); Activities coordinators 3 (ft); Dietitians 1 (ft).
Facilities Dining room; Physical therapy room; Activities room; Chapel; Crafts room; Laundry room; Barber/Beauty shop; Library.
Activities Arts & crafts; Cards; Games; Movies; Shopping trips; Social/Cultural gatherings.

Sea Level Hospital—SNF/ICF
Hwy 70E, Sea Level, NC, 28577
(919) 225-4611
Admin Bea Vaughan. *Medical Dir/Dir of Nursing* Jean D Long.
Licensure Skilled care; Intermediate care. *Beds* SNF 40; ICF 20. *Certified* Medicaid; Medicare.
Owner Nonprofit Corp.

Staff Physicians 3 (ft); RNs; LPNs; Nurses aides; Physical therapists 1 (pt); Speech therapists 1 (pt); Activities coordinators 1 (ft); Dietitians 1 (pt).
Facilities Dining room; Physical therapy room; Activities room; Chapel; Crafts room; Laundry room; Barber/Beauty shop.
Activities Arts & crafts; Games; Prayer groups; Movies; Shopping trips; Social/Cultural gatherings.

SHELBY

Meadowbrook Manor of Shelby
PO Box 2287, 1101 N Morgan St, Shelby, NC, 28150
(704) 482-5396
Admin Judy W Beam. Medical Dir/Dir of Nursing John B Crow MD; Marie Graham DON.
Licensure Skilled care; Intermediate care. Beds SNF 35; ICF 65. Certified Medicaid; Medicare; VA.
Owner Proprietary Corp (Angell Group).
Admissions Requirements Medical examination; Physician's request.
Staff RNs 5 (ft), 1 (pt); LPNs 6 (ft), 1 (pt); Orderlies 3 (ft), 1 (pt); Nurses aides 40 (ft), 6 (pt); Physical therapists 1 (pt); Speech therapists 1 (pt); Activities coordinators 1 (ft); Dietitians 1 (ft).
Facilities Dining room; Physical therapy room; Activities room; Chapel; Crafts room; Laundry room; Barber/Beauty shop.
Activities Arts & crafts; Cards; Games; Reading groups; Prayer groups; Movies; Shopping trips; Social/Cultural gatherings.

Shelby Convalescent Center*
401 N Morgan St, PO Box 790, Shelby, NC, 28150
(704) 482-7326
Admin Gwen Butler. Medical Dir/Dir of Nursing Dr Richard Maybin.
Licensure Skilled care; Intermediate care. Beds SNF 60; ICF 100. Certified Medicaid; Medicare.
Admissions Requirements Medical examination; Physician's request.
Staff RNs 5 (ft), 1 (pt); LPNs 14 (ft), 5 (pt); Orderlies 6 (ft), 3 (pt); Nurses aides 52 (ft), 18 (pt); Physical therapists 1 (ft); Activities coordinators 1 (ft); Dietitians 1 (pt).
Facilities Dining room; Physical therapy room; Activities room; Crafts room; Laundry room; Barber/Beauty shop; Resident lounge.
Activities Arts & crafts; Games; Reading groups; Prayer groups; Movies; Shopping trips; Social/Cultural gatherings; Birthday parties; Exercise class.

SILER CITY

Meadowbrook Manor of Siler City
900 W Dolphin St, Siler City, NC, 27344
(919) 663-3431
Admin Christine P Caviness. Medical Dir/Dir of Nursing John Dykers MD; Linda Emerson RN DON.
Licensure Skilled care; Intermediate care; Personal care. Beds SNF 98; ICF 52; 10 Personal. Certified Medicaid; Medicare.
Owner Proprietary Corp.
Admissions Requirements Medical examination; Physician's request.
Staff Physicians 1 (pt); RNs 6 (ft), 4 (pt); LPNs 5 (ft), 6 (pt); Orderlies 5 (ft), 1 (pt); Nurses aides 44 (ft), 15 (pt); Physical therapists 2 (ft); Speech therapists 1 (pt); Activities coordinators 2 (ft); Dietitians 1 (pt); Social worker; Certified food service 2 (ft).
Facilities Dining room; Physical therapy room; Activities room; Chapel; Crafts room; Laundry room; Barber/Beauty shop; Library; Family room.

Activities Arts & crafts; Cards; Games; Reading groups; Prayer groups; Movies; Shopping trips; Social/Cultural gatherings; Education; Current events; Therapy groups; Resident council.

SMITHFIELD

Johnston County Memorial Nursing Center Inc
PO Box 1940, 902 Berkshire Rd, Smithfield, NC, 27577
(919) 934-3171
Admin David F Arnn. Medical Dir/Dir of Nursing Woodrow Batten MD.
Licensure Skilled care; Intermediate care. Beds SNF 84; ICF 36. Certified Medicaid; Medicare.
Owner Privately owned.
Admissions Requirements Medical examination; Physician's request.
Staff Physicians 9 (pt); RNs 6 (ft), 1 (pt); LPNs 12 (ft), 6 (pt); Orderlies 3 (ft); Nurses aides 47 (ft), 4 (pt); Physical therapists 1 (pt); Speech therapists 1 (pt); Activities coordinators 1 (ft); Dietitians 1 (pt); Ophthalmologists 01.
Facilities Dining room; Physical therapy room; Activities room; Crafts room; Laundry room; Barber/Beauty shop.
Activities Arts & crafts; Cards; Games; Prayer groups; Movies; Shopping trips; Social/Cultural gatherings.

SNOW HILL

Britthaven of Snow Hill*
PO Box 157, 1304 SE 2nd St, Snow Hill, NC, 28580
(919) 747-8126
Admin Faye Jones.
Licensure Intermediate care. Beds ICF 75. Certified Medicaid.
Owner Proprietary Corp (Britthaven Inc).

SOUTHERN PINES

Penick Memorial Home
PO Box 2001, E Rhode Island Ave Ext, Southern Pines, NC, 28387
(919) 692-0300
Admin Philip S Brown. Medical Dir/Dir of Nursing Joseph Hiatt Jr; Sylvia F Andrews.
Licensure Skilled care; Intermediate care; Retirement; Rest home. Beds SNF 37; ICF 13; Retirement 150; Rest home 29. Certified Medicaid; Medicare.
Owner Nonprofit Corp.
Admissions Requirements Minimum age 60; Medical examination.
Staff Physicians 1 (pt); RNs 6 (ft), 3 (pt); LPNs 7 (ft), 3 (pt); Nurses aides 25 (ft), 10 (pt); Physical therapists 1 (pt); Activities coordinators 2 (ft); Dietitians 1 (pt).
Facilities Dining room; Physical therapy room; Activities room; Chapel; Crafts room; Laundry room; Barber/Beauty shop; Library.
Activities Arts & crafts; Cards; Games; Reading groups; Prayer groups; Movies; Shopping trips; Social/Cultural gatherings.

St Joseph of the Pines Hospital—SNF*
590 Central Dr, Southern Pines, NC, 28387
(919) 692-2212
Admin George Kecatos.
Licensure Skilled care. Beds 84. Certified Medicaid; Medicare.

SOUTHPORT

Ocean Trail Convalescent Center Inc
430 Fodale Ave, Southport, NC, 28461
(919) 457-9581
Admin Danny W Moss. Medical Dir/Dir of Nursing Dr Gene A Wallin.
Licensure Intermediate care; Rest home. Beds ICF 64; Rest home 42. Certified Medicaid.

Owner Privately owned.
Admissions Requirements Medical examination.
Staff Physicians 7 (ft); RNs 1 (pt); LPNs 8 (ft); Orderlies 3 (ft); Nurses aides 30 (ft); Reality therapists 1 (ft); Recreational therapists 1 (ft); Dietitians 1 (ft).
Facilities Dining room; Activities room; Laundry room; Barber/Beauty shop.
Activities Arts & crafts; Cards; Games; Reading groups; Prayer groups; Movies; Shopping trips; Social/Cultural gatherings; Exercise classes; VCR; Activities for visual & hearing impaired available.

STATESVILLE

Brian Center Nursing Care—Statesville Inc
520 Valley St, Statesville, NC, 28677
(704) 873-0517
Admin Isaac Kuhn.
Licensure Skilled care; Intermediate care. Beds SNF 60; ICF 60. Certified Medicaid; Medicare.
Owner Proprietary Corp (Brian Center Management Corp).

Hill Haven Skilled Nursing Home & Rest Home*
Rte 10, Box 401, Statesville, NC, 28677
(704) 872-7601
Admin Dorothy S Edwards.
Licensure Skilled care; Home for aged. Beds SNF 30; Home for aged 77.
Owner Proprietary Corp (Hillhaven Corp).

STOKESDALE

Countryside Manor
7700 US 158, Stokesdale, NC, 27357
(919) 643-6301
Admin Mary Stuart Mizelle. Medical Dir/Dir of Nursing Dr David M Kaplan; Kathy Hawkins DON.
Licensure Intermediate care. Beds ICF 60. Certified Medicaid.
Owner Privately owned.
Admissions Requirements Medical examination; Physician's request.
Staff RNs 4 (ft); LPNs 1 (ft), 2 (pt); Nurses aides 15 (ft), 6 (pt); Activities coordinators 1 (ft); Dietitians 1 (pt).
Facilities Dining room; Activities room; Crafts room; Laundry room; Barber/Beauty shop; Library.
Activities Arts & crafts; Cards; Games; Reading groups; Prayer groups; Movies; Shopping trips; Social/Cultural gatherings.

SYLVA

Skyland Care Center Inc*
21 Skyland Dr, Sylva, NC, 28779
(704) 586-8935
Admin Mildred M Sloan. Medical Dir/Dir of Nursing E H Henning MD.
Licensure Intermediate care. Beds 94. Certified Medicaid.
Admissions Requirements Minimum age 18.
Staff RNs 1 (ft); LPNs 9 (ft); Orderlies 1 (ft); Nurses aides 22 (ft); Recreational therapists 1 (ft); Activities coordinators 1 (ft); Dietitians 1 (pt); Dentists 1 (pt).
Facilities Dining room; Activities room; Laundry room; Barber/Beauty shop.
Activities Arts & crafts; Games; Reading groups; Prayer groups; Movies; Shopping trips.

TARBORO

Beverly Health Care Center*
1000 Western Blvd, Box 7008, Tarboro, NC, 27886
(919) 823-0401

Admin Effie Webb. *Medical Dir/Dir of Nursing* Dr L M Cutchin.
Licensure Skilled care; Intermediate care. *Beds* SNF 48; ICF 111. *Certified* Medicaid; Medicare.
Owner Proprietary Corp (Beverly Enterprises).
Admissions Requirements Medical examination.
Staff Physicians 10 (ft); RNs 6 (ft), 1 (pt); LPNs 11 (ft), 5 (pt); Nurses aides 56 (ft), 15 (pt); Physical therapists 1 (pt); Speech therapists 1 (pt); Activities coordinators 2 (ft); Dietitians 1 (ft); Dentists 1 (pt); Ophthalmologists 1 (pt); Podiatrists 1 (pt).
Facilities Dining room; Physical therapy room; Activities room; Chapel; Crafts room; Laundry room; Barber/Beauty shop.
Activities Arts & crafts; Cards; Games; Reading groups; Prayer groups; Movies; Shopping trips; Social/Cultural gatherings; Adult basic education class.

Westgate of Tarboro
Hwy 64 By Pass, Tarboro, NC, 27886
(919) 823-2041
Admin Hobson Lewis.
Licensure Intermediate care. *Beds* 58. *Certified* Medicaid.
Staff RNs 3 (ft); LPNs 4 (ft); Orderlies 3 (ft); Nurses aides 30 (ft); Physical therapists 1 (pt); Reality therapists 1 (pt); Recreational therapists 1 (pt); Occupational therapists 1 (pt); Speech therapists 1 (pt); Activities coordinators 1 (ft); Dietitians 1 (ft); Dentists 1 (pt); Podiatrists 1 (pt).
Facilities Dining room; Activities room; Crafts room; Laundry room; Barber/Beauty shop.
Activities Arts & crafts; Cards; Games; Reading groups; Prayer groups; Movies; Shopping trips; Social/Cultural gatherings.

THOMASVILLE

Davidson Nursing Center
706 Pineywood Rd, Thomasville, NC, 27360
(919) 475-9116
Admin Linda K Morrison. *Medical Dir/Dir of Nursing* Dr Harold C Burchel.
Licensure Skilled care; Intermediate care. *Beds* SNF 60; ICF 52. *Certified* Medicaid; Medicare.
Owner Proprietary Corp (Britthaven Inc).
Admissions Requirements Medical examination; Physician's request.
Staff Physicians 1 (pt); RNs 4 (ft), 5 (pt); LPNs 6 (ft), 4 (pt); Orderlies 1 (pt); Nurses aides 60 (ft); Physical therapists 1 (ft); Speech therapists 1 (pt); Activities coordinators 1 (ft); Dietitians 1 (ft); Ophthalmologists 1 (pt); Podiatrists 1 (pt).
Facilities Dining room; Physical therapy room; Activities room; Chapel; Crafts room; Laundry room; Barber/Beauty shop.
Activities Arts & crafts; Cards; Games; Reading groups; Prayer groups; Movies; Social/Cultural gatherings.

Liberty House Nursing Home
PO Box 1168, 1028 Blair St, Thomasville, NC, 27360
(919) 472-7771
Admin Jane M Stearns. *Medical Dir/Dir of Nursing* Dr Thomas Futrell; Maldia Hart.
Licensure Skilled care; Intermediate care. *Beds* SNF 61; ICF 59. *Certified* Medicaid; Medicare.
Owner Proprietary Corp (Beverly Enterprises).
Admissions Requirements Minimum age 18; Medical examination; Physician's request.
Facilities Dining room; Physical therapy room; Activities room; Chapel; Crafts room; Laundry room; Barber/Beauty shop.
Activities Arts & crafts; Cards; Games; Reading groups; Prayer groups; Movies; Shopping trips; Social/Cultural gatherings.

Piedmont Center-United Church Retirement Homes Inc
100 Hedrick Dr, Thomasville, NC, 27360
(919) 472-2017
Admin D Russell Myers. *Medical Dir/Dir of Nursing* Margaret Joye.
Licensure Skilled care; Intermediate care; Residential; Independent living. *Beds* SNF 24; ICF 24; Residential 24; Independent living 40.
Owner Nonprofit Corp.
Admissions Requirements Minimum age 62; Medical examination.
Staff Physicians 5 (pt); RNs 4 (ft), 3 (pt); LPNs 4 (ft), 2 (pt); Nurses aides 12 (ft), 6 (pt); Physical therapists 1 (pt); Activities coordinators 1 (ft); Dietitians 1 (ft).
Affiliation Church of Christ
Facilities Dining room; Physical therapy room; Activities room; Chapel; Crafts room; Laundry room; Barber/Beauty shop; Library.
Activities Arts & crafts; Cards; Games; Reading groups; Prayer groups; Movies; Shopping trips; Social/Cultural gatherings.

TRYON

White Oak Terrace*
200 Oak St, PO Box 1535, Tryon, NC, 28782
(704) 859-9161
Admin Doris G Cole.
Licensure Skilled care. *Beds* 60. *Certified* Medicaid; Medicare.
Facilities Dining room; Physical therapy room; Activities room; Crafts room; Laundry room; Barber/Beauty shop.
Activities Arts & crafts; Cards; Games; Reading groups; Prayer groups; Movies; Shopping trips; Social/Cultural gatherings.

WADESBORO

Anson County Hospital-SNF
500 Morven Rd, Wadesboro, NC, 28170
(704) 694-5131
Admin Thomas W Northrop. *Medical Dir/Dir of Nursing* Beth Swink RN.
Licensure Skilled care. *Beds* SNF 45. *Certified* Medicaid; Medicare.
Owner Publicly owned.
Admissions Requirements Medical examination; Physician's request.
Staff Physicians; RNs; LPNs; Orderlies; Nurses aides; Physical therapists; Activities coordinators; Dietitians.
Languages Spanish
Facilities Dining room; Activities room; Laundry room; Barber/Beauty shop.
Activities Arts & crafts; Cards; Games; Reading groups; Prayer groups; Movies; Social/Cultural gatherings.

Wadesboro Nursing Home
PO Box 658, 2000 Country Club Rd, Wadesboro, NC, 28170
(704) 694-4106
Admin Violet U Lee. *Medical Dir/Dir of Nursing* Elaine P Cooke RN.
Licensure Intermediate care; Home for aged. *Beds* ICF 66; Home for aged 53. *Certified* Medicaid.
Owner Proprietary Corp.
Admissions Requirements Medical examination; Physician's request.
Staff RNs 1 (ft); LPNs 8 (ft), 1 (pt); Orderlies 4 (ft), 1 (pt); Activities coordinators 1 (ft); Dietitians 1 (pt).
Facilities Dining room; Activities room; Laundry room; Barber/Beauty shop.
Activities Arts & crafts; Cards; Games; Reading groups; Prayer groups; Shopping trips; Social/Cultural gatherings.

WALNUT COVE

Guardian Care of Walnut Cove*
PO Box 158, 508 Windmill St, Walnut Cove, NC, 27052
(919) 591-4353
Admin Joan H Smith. *Medical Dir/Dir of Nursing* H W Hollingsworth MD.
Licensure Skilled care. *Beds* 60. *Certified* Medicaid; Medicare.
Owner Proprietary Corp (Hillhaven Corp).
Admissions Requirements Medical examination.
Staff Physicians 3 (pt); RNs 4 (ft), 7 (pt); LPNs 3 (ft), 3 (pt); Nurses aides 20 (ft), 9 (pt); Physical therapists 1 (ft), 1 (pt); Occupational therapists 1 (pt); Speech therapists 1 (pt); Activities coordinators 1 (ft); Dietitians 1 (ft), 1 (pt); Dentists 1 (pt); Podiatrists 1 (pt).
Facilities Dining room; Physical therapy room; Activities room; Chapel; Laundry room; Barber/Beauty shop.
Activities Arts & crafts; Cards; Games; Reading groups; Prayer groups; Movies; Shopping trips; Social/Cultural gatherings; Therapeutic activities relating to exercise/strengthening.

WASHINGTON

Britthaven of Washington*
120 Washington St, Washington, NC, 27889
(919) 946-7141
Admin Leigh Norman. *Medical Dir/Dir of Nursing* Dr Frank Sheldon.
Licensure Skilled care; Intermediate care. *Beds* 60. *Certified* Medicaid; Medicare.
Owner Proprietary Corp (Britthaven Inc).
Admissions Requirements Medical examination.
Staff Physicians 15 (pt); RNs 4 (ft), 3 (pt); LPNs 9 (ft), 4 (pt); Orderlies 4 (ft), 2 (pt); Nurses aides 40 (ft), 8 (pt); Physical therapists 1 (pt); Speech therapists 1 (pt); Activities coordinators 1 (ft); Dietitians 1 (pt); Dentists 1 (pt); Podiatrists 1 (pt).
Facilities Dining room; Activities room; Crafts room; Laundry room; Barber/Beauty shop.
Activities Arts & crafts; Cards; Games; Reading groups; Prayer groups; Movies; Shopping trips; Social/Cultural gatherings.

Ridgewood Manor
PO Box 1868, 1604 Highland Dr, Washington, NC, 27889
(919) 946-9570
Admin Shirley W Clark. *Medical Dir/Dir of Nursing* Dr Ray G Silverthorne.
Licensure Skilled care; Intermediate care. *Beds* SNF 96; ICF 24. *Certified* Medicaid; Medicare.
Owner Proprietary Corp.
Admissions Requirements Minimum age 21; Medical examination; Physician's request.
Staff Physicians 2 (pt); RNs 14 (ft), 4 (pt); LPNs 10 (ft), 5 (pt); Orderlies 10 (ft), 4 (pt); Nurses aides 80 (ft), 12 (pt); Physical therapists 1 (pt); Recreational therapists 1 (ft); Speech therapists 1 (pt); Activities coordinators 2 (pt); Dietitians 1 (ft), 1 (pt); Podiatrists 1 (pt).
Languages Spanish
Facilities Dining room; Physical therapy room; Activities room; Chapel; Crafts room; Laundry room; Barber/Beauty shop; Library.
Activities Arts & crafts; Cards; Games; Reading groups; Prayer groups; Movies; Shopping trips; Social/Cultural gatherings.

WAYNESVILLE

Autumn Care of Waynesville*
PO Box 783, Timberlane Rd, Waynesville, NC, 28786
(704) 456-7381

Admin Christine Henson. *Medical Dir/Dir of Nursing* Dr James B Milling.
Licensure Skilled care. *Beds* 56. *Certified* Medicaid; Medicare.
Owner Proprietary Corp (Autumn Corp).
Admissions Requirements Medical examination; Physician's request.
Staff Physicians 5 (pt); RNs 4 (ft); LPNs 5 (ft), 3 (pt); Orderlies 5 (ft); Nurses aides 15 (ft), 3 (pt); Physical therapists 1 (pt); Recreational therapists 1 (ft); Speech therapists 1 (pt); Activities coordinators 1 (ft); Dietitians 1 (ft), 1 (pt); Dentists 1 (pt); Audiologists 1 (pt).
Facilities Dining room; Activities room; Crafts room; Laundry room; Barber/Beauty shop.
Activities Arts & crafts; Games; Reading groups; Prayer groups; Movies; Social/Cultural gatherings.

WHITEVILLE

Century Care Center Inc
PO Box 1217, 316 W Burkhead St, Whiteville, NC, 28472
(919) 642-7139
Admin O Wade Avant Jr. *Medical Dir/Dir of Nursing* Dr F M Carroll.
Licensure Skilled care; Intermediate care. *Beds* SNF 32; ICF 74. *Certified* Medicaid; Medicare.
Admissions Requirements Minimum age 18.
Staff Physicians 1 (pt); RNs 10 (ft), 2 (pt); LPNs 6 (ft), 1 (pt); Orderlies 2 (ft); Nurses aides 40 (ft), 2 (pt); Physical therapists 1 (pt); Speech therapists 1 (pt); Activities coordinators 1 (ft); Dietitians 1 (pt); Ophthalmologists 1 (pt); Dentist 1 (pt).

WILKESBORO

Britthaven of Wilkesboro*
1016 Fletcher St, Wilkesboro, NC, 28697
(919) 667-9261
Admin Juanita Harvey.
Licensure Skilled care; Intermediate care. *Beds* SNF 68; ICF 58. *Certified* Medicaid; Medicare.
Owner Proprietary Corp (Britthaven Inc).
Admissions Requirements Medical examination.
Staff Physicians 5 (ft); RNs 4 (ft), 2 (pt); LPNs 9 (ft), 10 (pt); Orderlies 6 (ft), 2 (pt); Nurses aides 39 (ft), 30 (pt); Physical therapists 1 (ft); Speech therapists 1 (ft); Activities coordinators 2 (ft); Dietitians 1 (ft); Dentists 1 (pt); Podiatrists 1 (pt).
Facilities Dining room; Physical therapy room; Activities room; Laundry room; Barber/Beauty shop; Library.
Activities Arts & crafts; Games; Prayer groups; Movies; Shopping trips; Social/Cultural gatherings.

Vespers Nursing Home*
1000 College St, Wilkesboro, NC, 28697
(919) 838-4141
Admin Deborah Ann Sheffield. *Medical Dir/Dir of Nursing* Larry R Kilby MD.
Licensure Skilled care; Intermediate care. *Beds* SNF 58; ICF 62. *Certified* Medicaid; Medicare.
Owner Proprietary Corp (Brian Center Management Corp).
Admissions Requirements Minimum age 65; Medical examination; Physician's request.
Staff Physicians 3 (pt); RNs 8 (ft), 2 (pt); LPNs 8 (ft), 3 (pt); Nurses aides 33 (ft), 9 (pt); Physical therapists 1 (pt); Speech therapists 1 (pt); Activities coordinators 1 (ft); Dietitians 1 (pt); Dentists 1 (pt); Ophthalmologists 1 (pt); Podiatrists 1 (pt); 48 (ft), 8 (pt).
Facilities Dining room; Physical therapy room; Activities room; Chapel; Crafts room; Laundry room; Barber/Beauty shop.

Activities Arts & crafts; Cards; Games; Prayer groups; Movies.

WILLIAMSTON

Albemarle Villa*
PO Box 1068, 119 Gatlin St, Williamston, NC, 27892
(919) 792-1616
Admin Al Woodring.
Licensure Skilled care; Intermediate care. *Beds* SNF 36; ICF 88. *Certified* Medicaid; Medicare.
Owner Proprietary Corp (Beverly Enterprises).

WILMINGTON

Bowden Nursing Home
221 Summer Rest Rd, Wilmington, NC, 28403
(919) 256-3733
Admin Jane C Pendergrass. *Medical Dir/Dir of Nursing* Gerald Points MD; Cathy B Williams RN DON.
Licensure Intermediate care. *Beds* ICF 80. *Certified* Medicaid.
Owner Proprietary Corp.
Admissions Requirements Medical examination; Physician's request.
Staff RNs 4 (ft); LPNs 6 (ft), 1 (pt); Nurses aides 32 (ft); Activities coordinators 1 (ft), 1 (pt); Dietitians 1 (pt).
Facilities Dining room; Laundry room; Barber/Beauty shop.
Activities Arts & crafts; Games; Reading groups; Prayer groups; Movies; Social/Cultural gatherings.

Cornelia Nixon Davis Health Care Center*
Rte 1, Box 644, Wilmington, NC, 28405
(919) 686-7195
Admin John Paluck.
Licensure Skilled care; Intermediate care. *Beds* SNF 155; ICF 44. *Certified* Medicaid; Medicare.

Grotgen Nursing Home*
5429 Oleander Dr, PO Box 4699, Wilmington, NC, 28406
(919) 791-3451
Admin Faye K Bell. *Medical Dir/Dir of Nursing* Dr James Pence Jr.
Licensure Skilled care. *Beds* 50. *Certified* Medicaid; Medicare.
Admissions Requirements Minimum age 18; Medical examination; Physician's request.
Staff RNs 2 (ft), 4 (pt); LPNs 5 (ft), 4 (pt); Nurses aides 25 (ft), 5 (pt); Recreational therapists 1 (ft); Activities coordinators 1 (ft); Dietitians 1 (pt); Podiatrists 1 (pt).
Facilities Dining room; Activities room; Laundry room; Barber/Beauty shop.
Activities Arts & crafts; Cards; Games; Reading groups; Prayer groups; Movies; Social/Cultural gatherings.

Hillhaven Rehabilitation & Conv Center*
2006 S 16th St, Wilmington, NC, 28401
(919) 763-6271
Admin Faye Kennedy. *Medical Dir/Dir of Nursing* H L Armistead Jr MD.
Licensure Skilled care; Intermediate care. *Beds* SNF 56; ICF 44. *Certified* Medicaid; Medicare.
Owner Proprietary Corp (Hillhaven Corp).
Admissions Requirements Medical examination; Physician's request.
Staff RNs 6 (ft), 3 (pt); LPNs 4 (ft), 3 (pt); Nurses aides 26 (ft), 6 (pt); Physical therapists 2 (ft); Recreational therapists 1 (ft), 1 (pt); Dietitians 1 (ft).
Facilities Dining room; Physical therapy room; Activities room; Crafts room; Laundry room; Barber/Beauty shop.
Activities Arts & crafts; Cards; Games; Reading groups; Prayer groups; Movies; Shopping trips; Social/Cultural gatherings.

WILSON

North Carolina Special Care Center
Ward Blvd, Wilson, NC, 27893
(919) 237-1121
Admin Joseph G Doby. *Medical Dir/Dir of Nursing* Thomas R Maloney MD.
Licensure Skilled care; Intermediate care. *Beds* SNF 109; ICF 99. *Certified* Medicaid; Medicare.
Staff Physicians 2 (ft); RNs 23 (ft); LPNs 20 (ft); Nurses aides 129 (ft); Physical therapists 1 (pt); Recreational therapists 1 (ft); Activities coordinators 1 (ft); Dietitians 2 (ft); Ophthalmologists 1 (pt); Dentist 1 (pt).
Facilities Dining room; Physical therapy room; Activities room; Chapel; Crafts room; Barber/Beauty shop; Library.
Activities Arts & crafts; Games; Reading groups; Movies; Shopping trips; Social/Cultural gatherings.

Westwood Manor Nursing Home
1804 Forest Hills Rd, Wilson, NC, 27895-7156
(919) 237-8161
Medical Dir/Dir of Nursing John McCain MD; Myrtle Necci RN.
Licensure Skilled care; Intermediate care. *Beds* SNF 60; ICF 50. *Certified* Medicaid; Medicare; VA.
Owner Proprietary Corp (Beverly Enterprises).
Admissions Requirements Medical examination; Physician's request.
Staff RNs 6 (ft), 4 (pt); LPNs 9 (ft), 6 (pt); Orderlies 1 (ft), 1 (pt); Nurses aides 28 (ft), 18 (pt); Recreational therapists 1 (ft); Speech therapists 1 (ft); Dietitians 1 (ft); Social worker 1 (ft).
Facilities Dining room; Physical therapy room; Activities room; Laundry room; Barber/Beauty shop; Family room w/ fireplace.
Activities Arts & crafts; Cards; Games; Prayer groups; Movies; Shopping trips; Social/Cultural gatherings; RO; Current events; Exercise; Education classes.

Wilson Convalescent Center
403 Crestview Ave, Wilson, NC, 27893
(919) 237-0724
Admin Richard L Blackmon. *Medical Dir/Dir of Nursing* Dr Lawrence Krabill; Brenda Simpson DON.
Licensure Skilled care. *Beds* SNF 46.
Owner Proprietary Corp (Britthaven Inc).
Admissions Requirements Medical examination; Physician's request.
Staff Physicians 1 (pt); RNs 2 (ft); LPNs 4 (ft), 2 (pt); Nurses aides 18 (ft), 2 (pt); Physical therapists 1 (pt); Occupational therapists 1 (pt); Speech therapists 1 (pt); Activities coordinators 1 (ft); Dietitians 1 (pt); Dentists 1 (pt); Ophthalmologists 1 (pt).
Facilities Dining room; Laundry room; Barber/Beauty shop.
Activities Arts & crafts; Cards; Games; Reading groups; Prayer groups; Movies; Social/Cultural gatherings.

WINSTON-SALEM

Frances J Anthony
3350 Silas Creek Pkwy, Winston-Salem, NC, 27103
(919) 765-0550
Admin Frances J Anthony. *Medical Dir/Dir of Nursing* Dr Story; Maureen Huey RN.
Licensure Skilled care; Intermediate care. *Beds* SNF 69; ICF 30. *Certified* Medicaid; Medicare.
Owner Proprietary Corp.
Admissions Requirements Medical examination; Physician's request.

Staff RNs 8 (ft), 4 (pt); LPNs 5 (ft), 5 (pt); Nurses aides 32 (ft), 5 (pt); Physical therapists; Occupational therapists; Speech therapists; Activities coordinators; Dietitians.
Facilities Dining room; Physical therapy room; Activities room; Crafts room; Laundry room; Barber/Beauty shop.
Activities Arts & crafts; Cards; Games; Reading groups; Prayer groups; Movies; Shopping trips; Social/Cultural gatherings.

Baptist Retirement Homes of North Carolina Inc
2900 Reynolds Park Rd, Winston-Salem, NC, 27107
(919) 788-2441
Admin Jackson S Hoyle. *Medical Dir/Dir of Nursing* Dr Norman Adair; Kathy Siegle.
Licensure Skilled care; Intermediate care; Personal care; Apartments. *Beds* SNF 27; ICF 58; Personal 36; Apt units 21. *Certified* Medicaid; Medicare.
Owner Nonprofit Corp.
Admissions Requirements Minimum age 65; Medical examination; Physician's request.
Staff Physicians 3 (pt); RNs 7 (ft); LPNs 12 (ft), 5 (pt); Orderlies 2 (ft); Nurses aides 40 (ft), 12 (pt); Physical therapists 1 (pt); Reality therapists 1 (pt); Recreational therapists 3 (ft), 1 (pt); Occupational therapists 1 (pt); Speech therapists 1 (pt); Activities coordinators 1 (ft); Dietitians 1 (ft); Dentists 1 (pt); Ophthalmologists 1 (pt); Podiatrists 1 (pt); Dentist 1 (pt).
Affiliation Baptist
Facilities Dining room; Activities room; Chapel; Crafts room; Laundry room; Barber/Beauty shop; Library.
Activities Arts & crafts; Cards; Games; Reading groups; Prayer groups; Movies; Shopping trips; Social/Cultural gatherings.

Moravian Home Inc*
5401 Indiana Ave, Winston-Salem, NC, 27106
(919) 767-8130
Admin Sadie Blalock. *Medical Dir/Dir of Nursing* Clementine Shaw.
Licensure Skilled care; Intermediate care; Home for aged. *Beds* SNF 20; ICF 40; 106.
Admissions Requirements Minimum age 65.
Affiliation Moravian
Facilities Dining room; Activities room; Chapel; Crafts room; Laundry room; Barber/Beauty shop; Library.

Pellcare*
Rte 3, Box 315, Winston-Salem, NC, 27105
(919) 595-2166
Admin Norma M Guthrie. *Medical Dir/Dir of Nursing* Dr Sam Imamura.

Licensure Skilled care; Intermediate care. *Beds* SNF 60; ICF 158. *Certified* Medicaid; Medicare.
Admissions Requirements Minimum age 18; Medical examination.
Staff Physicians 1 (ft); RNs 7 (ft), 3 (pt); LPNs 14 (ft), 6 (pt); Orderlies 4 (ft); Nurses aides 75 (ft), 2 (pt); Physical therapists 1 (ft); Recreational therapists 1 (ft); Speech therapists 1 (ft); Activities coordinators 3 (ft); Dietitians 2 (ft); Podiatrists 1 (pt).
Facilities Dining room; Physical therapy room; Activities room; Chapel; Crafts room; Laundry room; Barber/Beauty shop; Library.
Activities Arts & crafts; Cards; Games; Reading groups; Prayer groups; Movies; Shopping trips; Social/Cultural gatherings.

Regency Knollwood Hall*
PO Box 11907, 5755 Shattalon Dr, Winston-Salem, NC, 27116
(919) 767-2750
Admin Donna Rae McMillan.
Licensure Skilled care; Intermediate care. *Beds* SNF 100; ICF 100. *Certified* Medicaid; Medicare.
Owner Proprietary Corp (Regency Health Care Centers).
Facilities Dining room; Physical therapy room; Activities room; Crafts room; Barber/Beauty shop.
Activities Arts & crafts; Cards; Games; Reading groups; Prayer groups; Movies; Shopping trips; Social/Cultural gatherings.

Triad Rehabilitation Center
5581 University Pkwy, Winston-Salem, NC, 27105
(919) 767-2815
Admin Annie L Tilley. *Medical Dir/Dir of Nursing* Dr James Minick; Beulah Wade RN DON.
Licensure Skilled care. *Beds* SNF 40. *Certified* Medicaid; Medicare.
Owner Proprietary Corp (Brian Center Management Corp).
Admissions Requirements Medical examination.
Staff Physicians 2 (pt); RNs 2 (ft), 2 (pt); LPNs 3 (ft), 6 (pt); Orderlies 1 (pt); Nurses aides; Activities coordinators 1 (pt); Dietitians 1 (ft).
Facilities Dining room; Activities room; Laundry room; Barber/Beauty shop.
Activities Arts & crafts; Cards; Games; Reading groups; Prayer groups; Movies; Patient, families, staff picnics; cookouts.

Winston-Salem Convalescent Center
1900 W 1st St, Winston-Salem, NC, 27104
(919) 724-2821

Admin Bernadette Murphy. *Medical Dir/Dir of Nursing* Lloyd J Story MD.
Licensure Skilled care; Intermediate care. *Beds* SNF 114; ICF 116. *Certified* Medicaid; Medicare.
Owner Proprietary Corp (Hillhaven Corp).
Admissions Requirements Minimum age 18; Medical examination; Physician's request.
Staff RNs; LPNs; Orderlies; Nurses aides; Physical therapists; Activities coordinators; Dietitians.
Facilities Dining room; Physical therapy room; Activities room; Crafts room; Laundry room; Barber/Beauty shop; Day rooms.
Activities Arts & crafts; Cards; Games; Reading groups; Prayer groups; Movies; Shopping trips; Social/Cultural gatherings; Regular special events; Birthday parties.

YADKINVILLE

Yadkin Nursing Care Center*
PO Box 879, 903 W Main St, Yadkinville, NC, 27055
(919) 679-8863
Admin Nolan G Brown. *Medical Dir/Dir of Nursing* Sam J Crawley MD.
Licensure Skilled care; Intermediate care. *Beds* SNF 30; ICF 54. *Certified* Medicaid; Medicare.
Owner Proprietary Corp (Angell Group).
Admissions Requirements Medical examination; Physician's request.
Staff Physicians 5 (pt); RNs 3 (ft); LPNs 9 (ft); Nurses aides 22 (ft); Physical therapists 1 (pt); Reality therapists 1 (pt); Recreational therapists 2 (ft), 1 (pt); Occupational therapists 1 (pt); Activities coordinators 2 (ft), 1 (pt); Dietitians 1 (ft), 1 (pt); Dentists 1 (pt); Ophthalmologists 1 (pt); Podiatrists 1 (pt).
Facilities Dining room; Physical therapy room; Activities room; Chapel; Crafts room; Laundry room; Barber/Beauty shop; Library.
Activities Arts & crafts; Cards; Games; Reading groups; Prayer groups; Movies; Shopping trips; Social/Cultural gatherings.

ZEBULON

Guardian Care of Zebulon*
PO Box 1157, 509 Gannon Ave, Zebulon, NC, 27597
(919) 269-9621
Admin Teresa Head.
Licensure Skilled care. *Beds* 60. *Certified* Medicaid; Medicare.
Owner Proprietary Corp (Hillhaven Corp).

NORTH DAKOTA

ANETA

Aneta Good Samaritan Center
Box 287, Aneta, ND, 58212
(701) 326-4234
Admin Jane M Strommen. *Medical Dir/Dir of Nursing* Dr Robert DeLano.
Licensure Intermediate care. *Beds* ICF 51.
Certified Medicaid.
Owner Nonprofit Corp (Evangelical Lutheran/ Good Samaritan).
Admissions Requirements Medical examination.
Staff Physicians 1 (ft); LPNs 1 (ft), 5 (pt); Nurses aides 15 (pt); Activities coordinators 1 (ft), 2 (pt).
Facilities Dining room; Activities room; Crafts room; Laundry room; Barber/Beauty shop.
Activities Arts & crafts; Cards; Games; Reading groups; Prayer groups; Movies; Shopping trips; Social/Cultural gatherings.

ARTHUR

Arthur Good Samaritan Center*
Box 16, Arthur, ND, 58006
(701) 967-8316
Admin Henry Reith. *Medical Dir/Dir of Nursing* Laurel Maker.
Licensure Intermediate care. *Beds* 96.
Certified Medicaid.
Admissions Requirements Medical examination; Physician's request.
Staff RNs 1 (ft), 5 (pt); LPNs 2 (pt); Nurses aides 20 (ft), 5 (pt); Activities coordinators 2 (ft), 2 (pt).
Affiliation Lutheran
Facilities Dining room; Activities room; Chapel; Crafts room; Laundry room; Barber/ Beauty shop; Library.
Activities Arts & crafts; Cards; Games; Reading groups; Prayer groups; Movies; Shopping trips; Social/Cultural gatherings.

ASHLEY

Ashley Medical Center SNF
612 Center Ave N, Ashley, ND, 58413
(701) 288-3433
Admin Leo Geiger. *Medical Dir/Dir of Nursing* Gordon Roget MD; Faye Salzer.
Licensure Skilled care. *Beds* 30. *Certified* Medicaid; Medicare.
Owner Nonprofit Corp.
Admissions Requirements Medical examination; Physician's request.
Staff Physicians 2 (ft); RNs 1 (ft), 3 (pt); LPNs 2 (ft), 3 (pt); Nurses aides 9 (ft), 5 (pt); Physical therapists 1 (pt); Activities coordinators 1 (ft); Dietitians 1 (pt).
Languages German
Facilities Dining room; Physical therapy room; Activities room; Chapel; Crafts room; Laundry room; Barber/Beauty shop; Library.
Activities Arts & crafts; Games; Reading groups; Prayer groups; Movies.

BEULAH

Beulah Community Nursing Home*
106 4th St NW, Beulah, ND, 58523
(701) 873-4322
Admin David Almen.
Licensure Skilled care; Intermediate care. *Beds* SNF 50; ICF 20. *Certified* Medicaid; Medicare.

BISMARCK

Baptist Home Inc
1100 Blvd Ave, Bismarck, ND, 58501
(701) 223-3040
Admin Alvin Haas. *Medical Dir/Dir of Nursing* Renee Schaff RN.
Licensure Skilled care; Intermediate care; Custodial care; Independent living units. *Beds* SNF 124; ICF; Custodial care 16; Independent living units 8. *Certified* Medicaid; Medicare.
Owner Nonprofit Corp.
Admissions Requirements Medical examination; Physician's request.
Staff RNs; LPNs; Nurses aides; Physical therapists; Activities coordinators; Dietitians; Employees 130.
Affiliation Baptist
Facilities Dining room; Physical therapy room; Activities room; Chapel; Crafts room; Laundry room; Barber/Beauty shop.
Activities Arts & crafts; Games; Reading groups; Prayer groups; Movies; Shopping trips.

Missouri Slope Lutheran Home Inc
2425 Hillview Ave, Bismarck, ND, 58501
(701) 223-9407
Admin Robert Thompson. *Medical Dir/Dir of Nursing* Dr Steven Miller; Anita J Wilkens RN BS DON.
Licensure Skilled care; Apartmens. *Beds* SNF 221; Apts 13. *Certified* Medicaid; Medicare.
Owner Nonprofit Corp.
Admissions Requirements Medical examination; Physician's request.
Staff RNs 18 (ft), 9 (pt); LPNs 7 (ft), 3 (pt); Orderlies 3 (ft); Nurses aides 81 (ft), 20 (pt); Physical therapists 1 (pt); Recreational therapists 5 (ft); Speech therapists 1 (pt); Activities coordinators 1 (ft); Dietitians 1 (ft).
Languages German, Norwegian
Affiliation Lutheran
Facilities Dining room; Physical therapy room; Activities room; Chapel; Crafts room; Laundry room; Barber/Beauty shop; Library.
Activities Arts & crafts; Cards; Games; Reading groups; Prayer groups; Movies; Shopping trips; Social/Cultural gatherings.

St Vincent's Nursing Home
1021 26th St N, Bismarck, ND, 58501
(701) 223-6888
Admin Keith Gendreau. *Medical Dir/Dir of Nursing* Dr Rudolfo Carriedo.
Licensure Skilled care; Intermediate care. *Beds* 94. *Certified* Medicaid; Medicare.
Admissions Requirements Medical examination; Physician's request.
Staff Physicians 8 (pt); RNs 10 (ft), 6 (pt); LPNs 10 (ft), 6 (pt); Orderlies 8 (ft), 3 (pt); Nurses aides 70 (ft), 16 (pt); Physical therapists 1 (pt); Recreational therapists 4 (ft), 1 (pt); Occupational therapists 1 (pt); Speech therapists 1 (pt); Activities coordinators 1 (ft); Dietitians 1 (pt); Dentists 1 (pt); Ophthalmologists 1 (pt); Podiatrists 1 (pt); Dentist 1 (pt).
Affiliation Roman Catholic
Facilities Dining room; Physical therapy room; Activities room; Chapel; Crafts room; Laundry room; Barber/Beauty shop; Library.
Activities Arts & crafts; Cards; Games; Reading groups; Prayer groups; Movies; Shopping trips; Social/Cultural gatherings; Senior Olympics.

BOTTINEAU

Bottineau Good Samaritan Center*
725 E 10th, Bottineau, ND, 58318
(701) 228-3601
Admin Richard Hunt.
Licensure Intermediate care. *Beds* 81.
Certified Medicaid.
Owner Nonprofit Corp (Evangelical Lutheran/ Good Samaritan).

St Andrew's Hospital & Nursing Home
316 Ohmer, Bottineau, ND, 58318
(701) 228-2255
Admin Keith Korman. *Medical Dir/Dir of Nursing* K W Kihle MD; Gwen Wall RN DON.
Licensure Skilled care. *Beds* 26. *Certified* Medicaid; Medicare.
Owner Nonprofit Corp.
Affiliation Roman Catholic
Facilities Dining room; Physical therapy room; Activities room; Chapel; Crafts room; Laundry room; Barber/Beauty shop.
Activities Arts & crafts; Cards; Games; Reading groups; Prayer groups; Movies; Shopping trips; Social/Cultural gatherings.

BOWMAN

Sunset Home Inc
802 NW Dover, Bowman, ND, 58623
(701) 523-3214
Admin Tony Hanson. *Medical Dir/Dir of Nursing* Dr Robert Thom MD; Naomi Kraiger RN DON.
Licensure Skilled care; Intermediate care; Basic care; Independent living. *Beds* SNF 63; Basic care 7; Independent living 16. *Certified* Medicaid; Medicare.
Owner Nonprofit Corp.
Admissions Requirements Medical examination; Physician's request.

Staff RNs 6 (ft), 5 (pt); LPNs 2 (ft), 6 (pt); Nurses aides 30 (ft), 10 (pt); Activities coordinators 1 (ft), 2 (pt).
Affiliation Lutheran
Facilities Dining room; Physical therapy room; Activities room; Chapel; Crafts room; Laundry room; Barber/Beauty shop; Day care.
Activities Arts & crafts; Cards; Games; Reading groups; Prayer groups; Movies; Shopping trips; Social/Cultural gatherings.

CANDO

Rest Haven Manor Nursing Center
701 11th St, Cando, ND, 58324
(701) 968-3351
Admin William Amundson. *Medical Dir/Dir of Nursing* G H Hitts MD & P W Marsh MD; Eileen Heardt RN DON.
Licensure Skilled care. *Beds* 74. *Certified* Medicaid; Medicare.
Owner Proprietary Corp.
Admissions Requirements Medical examination.
Staff RNs 1 (ft), 10 (pt); LPNs 5 (pt); Orderlies 1 (pt); Nurses aides 17 (ft), 14 (pt); Physical therapists 1 (pt); Activities coordinators 1 (ft), 2 (pt); Dietitians 1 (pt).
Facilities Dining room; Physical therapy room; Activities room; Chapel; Crafts room; Laundry room; Barber/Beauty shop.
Activities Arts & crafts; Games; Reading groups; Prayer groups; Movies; Shopping trips; Social/Cultural gatherings.

CARRINGTON

Carrington Health Care LTC
800 N 4th, Carrington, ND, 58421
(701) 652-3141
Admin Duane Jerde. *Medical Dir/Dir of Nursing* Dorothy Schaffer RN.
Licensure Skilled care; Intermediate care. *Beds* 38. *Certified* Medicaid; Medicare.
Owner Nonprofit Corp.
Staff Physicians 3 (ft); RNs 1 (ft), 2 (pt); LPNs 2 (ft), 5 (pt); Orderlies 2 (pt); Nurses aides 6 (ft), 10 (pt); Physical therapists 1 (ft); Activities coordinators 2 (ft); Dietitians 1 (pt).
Affiliation Roman Catholic
Facilities Dining room; Physical therapy room; Activities room; Chapel; Crafts room; Laundry room; Barber/Beauty shop.
Activities Arts & crafts; Cards; Games; Reading groups; Prayer groups; Movies; Shopping trips; Social/Cultural gatherings.

Golden Acres Manor*
No 1 E Main St, Carrington, ND, 58421
(701) 652-3117
Admin Allan Metzger.
Licensure Skilled care. *Beds* 60. *Certified* Medicaid; Medicare.

CAVALIER

Pembina County Memorial Nursing Home*
Hwy 5, Box 597A, Cavalier, ND, 58220
(701) 265-8453
Admin Helen Frampton. *Medical Dir/Dir of Nursing* E J Larson MD.
Licensure Skilled care. *Certified* Medicaid; Medicare.
Owner Nonprofit Corp (Luth Hosp & Homes Socty).
Admissions Requirements Medical examination; Physician's request.
Staff RNs 2 (ft), 2 (pt); LPNs 4 (ft), 4 (pt); Nurses aides 22 (ft), 16 (pt); Physical therapists 1 (pt); Activities coordinators 1 (ft), 1 (pt); Dietitians 1 (pt).
Affiliation Lutheran

Facilities Dining room; Physical therapy room; Activities room; Crafts room; Barber/Beauty shop.
Activities Arts & crafts; Cards; Games; Reading groups; Prayer groups; Movies; Shopping trips.

COOPERSTOWN

Griggs County Nursing Home
1300 Roberts Ave, Cooperstown, ND, 58425
(701) 797-3212
Admin Joan Bachman. *Medical Dir/Dir of Nursing* Paul Davis MD; Merle Haerter RN.
Licensure Skilled care. *Beds* SNF 50. *Certified* Medicaid; Medicare.
Owner Nonprofit Corp.
Admissions Requirements Physician's request.
Staff RNs 1 (ft), 2 (pt); LPNs 2 (ft), 5 (pt); Nurses aides 9 (ft), 14 (pt); Activities coordinators 1 (ft); Dietitians 1 (pt).
Facilities Dining room; Activities room; Barber/Beauty shop.
Activities Arts & crafts; Cards; Games; Reading groups; Prayer groups; Movies; Shopping trips; Social/Cultural gatherings.

CROSBY

Crosby Good Samaritan Center*
705 SE 4th, Box 187, Crosby, ND, 58730
(701) 965-6086
Admin Louis Huff.
Licensure Intermediate care. *Beds* 81. *Certified* Medicaid.

DEVILS LAKE

Good Samaritan Center
302 7th Ave, Devils Lake, ND, 58301
(701) 662-7525
Admin Sandra K Bentley. *Medical Dir/Dir of Nursing* Donna Rook DON.
Licensure Intermediate care. *Beds* ICF 104. *Certified* Medicaid.
Owner Nonprofit Corp (Evangelical Lutheran/ Good Samaritan).
Admissions Requirements Medical examination.
Staff RNs 1 (ft); LPNs 4 (ft), 10 (pt); Nurses aides 8 (ft), 20 (pt); Physical therapists 1 (pt); Activities coordinators 1 (ft); Dietitians 1 (pt).
Facilities Dining room; Activities room; Chapel; Laundry room; Barber/Beauty shop; Day rooms.
Activities Arts & crafts; Cards; Games; Reading groups; Movies; Shopping trips; Social/Cultural gatherings.

Lake Region Lutheran Home*
E 14th Ave, Devils Lake, ND, 58301
(701) 662-4905
Admin Al Holte.
Licensure Skilled care. *Beds* 104. *Certified* Medicaid; Medicare.
Affiliation Lutheran

DICKINSON

Dickinson Nursing Center
851 4th Ave E, Dickinson, ND, 58601
(701) 225-5138
Admin Lee Stickland. *Medical Dir/Dir of Nursing* Dr. Laslo Kolta.
Licensure Skilled care; Intermediate care. *Beds* SNF 110; ICF 75. *Certified* Medicaid; Medicare.
Owner Proprietary Corp (Beverly Enterprises).
Admissions Requirements Medical examination; Physician's request.
Staff RNs 6 (ft), 5 (pt); LPNs 5 (ft), 6 (pt); Orderlies 3 (ft), 1 (pt); Nurses aides 40 (ft), 38 (pt); Activities coordinators 1 (ft).

Facilities Dining room; Physical therapy room; Activities room; Chapel; Crafts room; Laundry room; Barber/Beauty shop.
Activities Arts & crafts; Cards; Games; Reading groups; Prayer groups; Movies; Shopping trips; Social/Cultural gatherings.

St Luke's Home
242 W 10th St, Dickinson, ND, 58601
(701) 225-6026
Admin Lyle D Brudvig. *Medical Dir/Dir of Nursing* Dr Dennis Wolf; Judith Hicks RN.
Licensure Skilled care. *Beds* 83. *Certified* Medicaid; Medicare.
Owner Nonprofit organization/foundation.
Admissions Requirements Physician's request.
Staff RNs 5 (ft), 7 (pt); LPNs 3 (ft), 3 (pt); Nurses aides 26 (ft), 28 (pt); Physical therapists 3 (ft); Reality therapists 1 (pt); Recreational therapists 2 (ft), 3 (pt); Activities coordinators 1 (ft).
Affiliation Lutheran
Facilities Dining room; Physical therapy room; Activities room; Chapel; Crafts room; Laundry room; Barber/Beauty shop; Library.
Activities Arts & crafts; Cards; Games; Reading groups; Prayer groups; Movies; Shopping trips; Social/Cultural gatherings.

DUNSEITH

Dunseith Community Nursing Home*
Peace Garden Ave, Box 220, Dunseith, ND, 58329
(701) 244-5495
Admin Cliff Tuttle. *Medical Dir/Dir of Nursing* Dr Dave Crozier.
Licensure Skilled care; Intermediate care. *Beds* 40. *Certified* Medicaid; Medicare.
Admissions Requirements Medical examination.
Staff Physicians 2 (pt); RNs 2 (ft), 1 (pt); LPNs 3 (ft), 2 (pt); Orderlies 4 (ft), 2 (pt); Nurses aides 9 (ft), 2 (pt); Physical therapists 1 (pt); Activities coordinators 1 (ft), 1 (pt); Dietitians 1 (pt).
Facilities Dining room; Physical therapy room; Activities room; Crafts room; Laundry room; Barber/Beauty shop.
Activities Arts & crafts; Cards; Games; Reading groups; Prayer groups; Movies; Shopping trips; Social/Cultural gatherings.

ELGIN

Jacobson Memorial Hospital Care Center
601 N East, Box 367, Elgin, ND, 58533
(701) 584-2792
Admin Jackie Seibel. *Medical Dir/Dir of Nursing* S K Patel MD; Cathy Green RN.
Licensure Skilled care. *Beds* SNF 25. *Certified* Medicaid; Medicare.
Owner Nonprofit Corp.
Admissions Requirements Physician's request.
Staff Physicians 2 (ft); RNs 1 (ft), 2 (pt); LPNs 1 (ft), 3 (pt); Nurses aides 2 (ft), 12 (pt); Physical therapists 1 (pt); Activities coordinators 1 (ft); Dietitians 1 (pt).
Languages German
Facilities Dining room; Physical therapy room; Activities room; Chapel; Crafts room; Barber/Beauty shop.
Activities Arts & crafts; Cards; Games; Reading groups; Movies; Social/Cultural gatherings.

ELLENDALE

Ellendale Nursing Center
N Hwy 281, Ellendale, ND, 58436
(701) 349-3312
Admin Mark Kealy. *Medical Dir/Dir of Nursing* Brian Bonte MD; Vicki Hack RN.
Licensure Skilled care. *Beds* SNF 84. *Certified* Medicaid; Medicare.
Owner Proprietary Corp (Beverly Enterprises).

Admissions Requirements Medical
examination; Physician's request.
Staff Physicians 2 (pt); RNs 7 (ft), 5 (pt);
LPNs 1 (pt); Orderlies 3 (ft); Nurses aides
22 (ft), 17 (pt); Physical therapists 1 (pt);
Activities coordinators 1 (ft); Dietitians 1
(pt); Dentists 1 (pt).
Facilities Dining room; Physical therapy
room; Activities room; Laundry room;
Barber/Beauty shop.
Activities Arts & crafts; Cards; Games;
Reading groups; Prayer groups; Movies;
Shopping trips; Social/Cultural gatherings.

ENDERLIN

Enderlin Hillcrest Manor Ltd
110 Hillcrest Dr, Enderlin, ND, 58027
(701) 437-3544
Admin Mark Bertilrud. *Medical Dir/Dir of
Nursing* Dr James Buhr; Alana Cavett.
Licensure Intermediate care. *Beds* 62.
Certified Medicaid.
Owner Nonprofit Corp (Luth Hosp & Homes
Socty).
Admissions Requirements Medical
examination; Physician's request.
Staff RNs 1 (ft), 1 (pt); LPNs 1 (ft), 5 (pt);
Nurses aides 3 (ft), 17 (pt); Activities
coordinators 1 (ft).
Affiliation Lutheran
Facilities Dining room; Activities room;
Crafts room; Laundry room; Barber/Beauty
shop.
Activities Arts & crafts; Cards; Games;
Reading groups; Prayer groups; Movies;
Shopping trips; Social/Cultural gatherings.

FARGO

Americana Healthcare Center—Fargo
1315 S University Dr, Fargo, ND, 58103
(701) 237-3030
Admin Arlene Payne. *Medical Dir/Dir of
Nursing* Dr J Talbot; Linda Kennedy BSN.
Licensure Skilled care. *Beds* 104. *Certified*
Medicaid; Medicare.
Owner Proprietary Corp (Manor Care).
Admissions Requirements Medical
examination; Physician's request.
Staff RNs; LPNs; Orderlies; Nurses aides;
Physical therapists; Occupational therapists;
Speech therapists; Activities coordinators.
Facilities Dining room; Physical therapy
room; Activities room; Crafts room; Laundry
room; Barber/Beauty shop; Library.
Activities Arts & crafts; Cards; Games;
Reading groups; Prayer groups; Movies;
Shopping trips; Social/Cultural gatherings.

Bethany Homes
201 S University Dr, Fargo, ND, 58103
(701) 237-0720
Admin John Thompson. *Medical Dir/Dir of
Nursing* G J Kavanaugh MD.
Licensure Skilled care; Intermediate care;
Retirement. *Beds* SNF 96; ICF 96;
Retirement 158. *Certified* Medicaid;
Medicare.
Owner Nonprofit Corp.
Staff Physicians 1 (ft); RNs 7 (ft), 8 (pt);
LPNs 8 (ft), 8 (pt); Nurses aides 38 (ft), 62
(pt); Physical therapists 1 (pt); Reality
therapists 2 (ft); Occupational therapists 1
(pt); Speech therapists 1 (pt); Activities
coordinators 1 (ft); Dietitians 2 (ft).
Facilities Dining room; Physical therapy
room; Activities room; Chapel; Crafts room;
Laundry room; Barber/Beauty shop; Library;
Coffee shop.
Activities Arts & crafts; Cards; Games;
Reading groups; Prayer groups; Movies;
Shopping trips; Social/Cultural gatherings.

Elim Home
3534 S University Dr, Fargo, ND, 58103
(701) 237-4392

Admin Steve Karnes. *Medical Dir/Dir of
Nursing* Dr Henry Wiers; Karen Pallanseh
DON.
Licensure Skilled care. *Beds* SNF 125.
Certified Medicaid; Medicare.
Owner Nonprofit Corp.
Admissions Requirements Minimum age 18;
Medical examination; Physician's request.
Staff RNs 7 (ft), 8 (pt); LPNs 2 (ft), 2 (pt);
Nurses aides 25 (ft), 44 (pt); Recreational
therapists 1 (ft), 3 (pt); Activities
coordinators 1 (ft).
Affiliation Evangelical Free Church
Facilities Dining room; Physical therapy
room; Activities room; Chapel; Crafts room;
Laundry room; Barber/Beauty shop.
Activities Arts & crafts; Cards; Games;
Reading groups; Prayer groups; Movies;
Shopping trips; Social/Cultural gatherings.

Fargo Nursing Home
1351 Broadway, Fargo, ND, 58102
(701) 235-7597
Admin Rick Wittmeier. *Medical Dir/Dir of
Nursing* Janelle Sanda/Edith Jamieson.
Licensure Skilled care. *Beds* SNF 102.
Certified Medicaid; Medicare.
Owner Nonprofit Corp (Luth Hosp & Homes
Socty).
Admissions Requirements Medical
examination; Physician's request.
Staff RNs 2 (ft), 6 (pt); LPNs 7 (ft), 3 (pt);
Orderlies 1 (ft), 5 (pt); Nurses aides 32 (ft),
30 (pt); Activities coordinators 1 (ft);
Dietitians 1 (pt).
Facilities Dining room; Physical therapy
room; Activities room; Chapel; Crafts room;
Laundry room; Barber/Beauty shop.
Activities Arts & crafts; Cards; Games;
Reading groups; Prayer groups; Movies;
Shopping trips; Social/Cultural gatherings.

Villa Maria Healthcare Ltd
3102 S University Dr, Fargo, ND, 58103
(701) 293-7750
Admin Bruce Johnson. *Medical Dir/Dir of
Nursing* Manette Durand.
Licensure Skilled care; Intermediate care. *Beds*
132. *Certified* Medicaid; Medicare.

FORMAN

Sargent Manor Health Care Center
Box 196, 575 5th St, Forman, ND, 58032
(701) 724-6211
Admin De De Diegel Cookson. *Medical Dir/
Dir of Nursing* Dr Matt Kidd; Annette
Stevens DON.
Licensure Intermediate care. *Beds* ICF 62.
Certified Medicaid.
Owner Privately owned.
Staff RNs 1 (ft); LPNs 6 (pt); Nurses aides 16
(pt); Activities coordinators 1 (ft), 1 (pt).
Facilities Dining room; Physical therapy
room; Activities room; Chapel; Crafts room;
Laundry room; Barber/Beauty shop; Library.
Activities Arts & crafts; Cards; Games;
Reading groups; Prayer groups; Movies;
Shopping trips; Social/Cultural gatherings.

GARRISON

Garrison Memorial Hospital—ICF
407 3rd Ave SE, Box 39, Garrison, ND,
58540
(701) 463-2275
Admin Sr Madonna Wagendorf. *Medical Dir/
Dir of Nursing* John T Boyle MD; Rosalie
Yahnke RN DON.
Licensure Intermediate care. *Beds* 24.
Certified Medicaid.
Admissions Requirements Medical
examination.

Staff Physicians 1 (pt); RNs 3 (pt); LPNs 1
(ft), 6 (pt); Orderlies 1 (pt); Nurses aides 3
(ft), 6 (pt); Physical therapists 1 (pt);
Activities coordinators 1 (ft); Dietitians 1
(pt); Dentist 1 (pt).
Affiliation Roman Catholic
Facilities Dining room; Physical therapy
room; Activities room; Chapel; Crafts room;
Laundry room; Barber/Beauty shop.
Activities Arts & crafts; Cards; Games; Prayer
groups; Movies; Shopping trips; Social/
Cultural gatherings.

Garrison Nursing Home Inc*
Eastern Acres, Garrison, ND, 58540
(701) 463-2226
Admin Jeanne Stout.
Licensure Skilled care. *Beds* 71. *Certified*
Medicaid; Medicare.
Owner Proprietary Corp (Beverly Enterprises).

GLEN ULLIN

Marian Manor Nursing Home
Box 528, 604 Ash Ave E, Glen Ullin, ND,
58631
(701) 348-3107
Admin Rodney Auer. *Medical Dir/Dir of
Nursing* Dr Walter Skwaruk; Barbara Ding
DON.
Licensure Skilled care. *Beds* SNF 80. *Certified*
Medicaid; Medicare.
Owner Nonprofit Corp.
Staff RNs; LPNs; Orderlies; Nurses aides.
Facilities Dining room; Physical therapy
room; Activities room; Chapel; Crafts room;
Laundry room; Barber/Beauty shop.
Activities Arts & crafts; Cards; Games;
Reading groups; Prayer groups; Movies;
Social/Cultural gatherings.

GRAFTON

Lutheran Sunset Home*
333 Eastern Ave, Grafton, ND, 58237
(701) 352-1901
Admin Rodney Alme.
Licensure Skilled care. *Beds* 119. *Certified*
Medicaid; Medicare.
Affiliation Lutheran

GRAND FORKS

Valley Memorial Home—Almonte
1023 Almonte Ave, Grand Forks, ND, 58201
(701) 772-4815
Admin James Opdahl. *Medical Dir/Dir of
Nursing* Keith Vandergon MD.
Licensure Intermediate care; Basic care. *Beds*
ICF 118; Basic care 68. *Certified* Medicaid.
Owner Nonprofit Corp.
Admissions Requirements Medical
examination.
Staff Physicians 1 (pt); RNs 2 (ft), 9 (pt);
LPNs 1 (ft), 10 (pt); Orderlies 1 (ft), 5 (pt);
Nurses aides 16 (ft), 49 (pt); Physical
therapists 2 (pt); Activities coordinators 1
(ft), 5 (pt); Dietitians 1 (ft); Chaplain 1 (ft).
Affiliation Lutheran
Facilities Dining room; Physical therapy
room; Activities room; Chapel; Crafts room;
Laundry room; Barber/Beauty shop.
Activities Arts & crafts; Cards; Games;
Reading groups; Movies; Shopping trips;
Social/Cultural gatherings.

Valley Memorial Home—Medical Park
2900 14th Ave S, Grand Forks, ND, 58201
(701) 780-5500
Admin James Opdahl. *Medical Dir/Dir of
Nursing* Keith Vandergon MD; Bruce
Johnson.
Licensure Skilled care. *Beds* SNF 160.
Certified Medicaid; Medicare.
Owner Nonprofit Corp.
Admissions Requirements Medical
examination.

Staff Physicians 1 (pt); RNs 7 (ft), 2 (pt);
LPNs 10 (ft), 23 (pt); Orderlies 2 (ft), 7 (pt);
Nurses aides 51 (ft), 75 (pt); Physical
therapists 1 (ft), 5 (pt); Occupational
therapists 1 (ft); Activities coordinators 1
(ft), 3 (pt); Dietitians 1 (ft); Chaplain 1 (ft).
Affiliation Lutheran
Facilities Dining room; Physical therapy
room; Activities room; Chapel; Crafts room;
Laundry room; Barber/Beauty shop.
Activities Arts & crafts; Cards; Games;
Reading groups; Prayer groups; Movies;
Shopping trips; Social/Cultural gatherings.

HANKINSON

St Gerard's Nursing Home*
Box 279, 613 1st Ave SW, Hankinson, ND,
58041
(701) 242-7891
Admin Gene Hoefs.
Licensure Skilled care. *Beds* 23. *Certified*
Medicaid; Medicare.

HARVEY

St Aloisius Skilled Nursing Home*
325 E Brewster, Harvey, ND, 58341
(701) 324-4651
Admin Ron Torkelson. *Medical Dir/Dir of*
Nursing Dr Charles Nyhys.
Licensure Skilled care. *Beds* 116. *Certified*
Medicaid; Medicare.
Admissions Requirements Medical
examination; Physician's request.
Staff Physicians 4 (pt); RNs 2 (ft), 2 (pt);
LPNs 8 (ft), 3 (pt); Nurses aides 45 (ft), 20
(pt); Physical therapists 1 (pt); Recreational
therapists 2 (ft), 2 (pt); Speech therapists 1
(pt); Activities coordinators 1 (ft); Dietitians
1 (pt); Dentists 2 (pt).
Affiliation Roman Catholic
Facilities Dining room; Activities room;
Chapel; Crafts room; Laundry room; Barber/
Beauty shop.
Activities Arts & crafts; Cards; Games;
Reading groups; Prayer groups; Movies;
Shopping trips; Social/Cultural gatherings.

HATTON

Tri-County Retirement & Nursing Home
930 Dakota Ave, Hatton, ND, 58240
(701) 543-3102
Admin Lorraine Quie. *Medical Dir/Dir of*
Nursing Dr D J Hlavinka; Nancy Karlstad
DON.
Licensure Skilled care; Intermediate care. *Beds*
60. *Certified* Medicaid; Medicare.
Owner Nonprofit organization/foundation.
Staff RNs 6 (ft); LPNs 2 (ft); Orderlies 1 (ft);
Nurses aides 35 (ft); Physical therapists 1
(ft); Activities coordinators 3 (ft); Dietitians
1 (ft).
Languages Norweigen
Affiliation Lutheran
Facilities Dining room; Physical therapy
room; Activities room; Chapel; Crafts room;
Laundry room; Barber/Beauty shop.
Activities Arts & crafts; Cards; Games;
Reading groups; Movies; Birthday parties.

HETTINGER

Hillcrest Care Center Inc
E Hwy 12, Hettinger, ND, 58639
(701) 567-2401
Admin Bob Owens.
Licensure Skilled care; Intermediate care. *Beds*
88. *Certified* Medicaid; Medicare.
Staff RNs 2 (ft), 2 (pt); LPNs 4 (ft), 2 (pt);
Nurses aides 16 (ft), 6 (pt); Physical
therapists 1 (pt); Activities coordinators 1
(ft); Dietitians 1 (pt); Dentists 1 (pt).

Facilities Dining room; Physical therapy
room; Activities room; Laundry room;
Barber/Beauty shop.
Activities Arts & crafts; Cards; Games;
Reading groups; Movies; Social/Cultural
gatherings.

HILLSBORO

Hillsboro Community Nursing Home
Box 48, 320 1st Ave SE, Hillsboro, ND,
58045
(701) 436-5755
Admin Bruce Bowersox. *Medical Dir/Dir of*
Nursing Dr Breen; Elaine Evenson.
Licensure Skilled care; Intermediate care. *Beds*
SNF 50. *Certified* Medicaid; Medicare.
Owner Nonprofit Corp.
Admissions Requirements Minimum age 18;
Medical examination.
Staff RNs 4 (ft), 3 (pt); LPNs 1 (ft); Nurses
aides 12 (ft), 5 (pt); Physical therapists 1
(pt); Activities coordinators 1 (ft), 1 (pt);
Dietitians 1 (pt); 10 (ft), 5 (pt).
Languages Norweigian
Facilities Dining room; Physical therapy
room; Activities room; Chapel; Crafts room;
Laundry room; Barber/Beauty shop.
Activities Arts & crafts; Cards; Games;
Reading groups; Prayer groups; Movies;
Shopping trips; Social/Cultural gatherings.

JAMESTOWN

Central Dakota Nursing Home
501 19th St NE, Jamestown, ND, 58401
(701) 252-5660
Admin Alex C Schweitzer. *Medical Dir/Dir of*
Nursing William Stewart MD; Beverly
Owens RN DON.
Licensure Skilled care. *Beds* SNF 100.
Certified Medicaid; Medicare.
Owner Nonprofit Corp (Luth Hosp & Homes
Socty).
Staff RNs 5 (ft), 5 (pt); LPNs 2 (ft), 2 (pt);
Orderlies 1 (ft), 2 (pt); Nurses aides 20 (ft),
34 (pt); Physical therapists 1 (ft);
Recreational therapists 1 (ft), 1 (pt);
Occupational therapists 1 (ft); Activities
coordinators 1 (ft); Social worker 1 (ft).
Facilities Dining room; Physical therapy
room; Activities room; Chapel; Crafts room;
Laundry room; Barber/Beauty shop.
Activities Arts & crafts; Cards; Games;
Reading groups; Prayer groups; Movies;
Shopping trips; Social/Cultural gatherings;
Aerobics; Work therapy; Bingo.

Hi Acres Manor Nursing Center
1300 2nd Place NE, Jamestown, ND, 58401
(701) 252-5881
Admin Gary M Riffe. *Medical Dir/Dir of*
Nursing Scott Rowe MD; Shar La Qua RN
DON.
Licensure Skilled care; Intermediate care. *Beds*
SNF 116; ICF 26. *Certified* Medicaid;
Medicare; VA.
Owner Proprietary Corp.
Admissions Requirements Medical
examination.
Staff RNs 4 (ft), 3 (pt); LPNs 14 (ft), 5 (pt);
Orderlies 4 (pt); Nurses aides 45 (ft), 27 (pt);
Recreational therapists 1 (ft); Activities
coordinators 1 (ft), 3 (pt).
Facilities Dining room; Physical therapy
room; Activities room; Chapel; Crafts room;
Laundry room; Barber/Beauty shop.
Activities Arts & crafts; Games; Reading
groups; Prayer groups; Movies; Shopping
trips; Social/Cultural gatherings.

KENMARE

Kenmare Community Health Care Corporation
317 1st Ave NW, Kenmare, ND, 58746
(701) 385-4296

Admin Ella Gutzke. *Medical Dir/Dir of*
Nursing Connie Schmit.
Licensure Skilled care. *Beds* SNF 12. *Certified*
Medicaid; Medicare.
Owner Nonprofit Corp.
Admissions Requirements Physician's request.
Staff RNs 1 (ft), 3 (pt); LPNs 3 (ft), 2 (pt);
Nurses aides 5 (ft), 3 (pt); Physical therapists
1 (pt); Activities coordinators 2 (ft);
Dietitians 1 (pt).
Facilities Dining room; Physical therapy
room; Activities room; Chapel; Crafts room;
Laundry room; Barber/Beauty shop.
Activities Arts & crafts; Cards; Games;
Reading groups; Prayer groups; Movies;
Shopping trips; Social/Cultural gatherings.

LAKOTA

Gronna Good Samaritan Center
116 E "C" Ave, Lakota, ND, 58344
(701) 247-2902
Admin David Holmberg. *Medical Dir/Dir of*
Nursing Debby Anderson.
Licensure Intermediate care. *Beds* ICF 58.
Certified Medicaid.
Owner Nonprofit Corp (Evangelical Lutheran/
Good Samaritan).
Admissions Requirements Medical
examination.
Staff Physicians 1 (pt); RNs 1 (ft), 1 (pt);
LPNs 3 (ft), 3 (pt); Orderlies 1 (pt); Nurses
aides 6 (ft), 16 (pt); Physical therapists 1
(pt); Activities coordinators 1 (ft); Dietitians
1 (pt).
Affiliation Lutheran
Facilities Dining room; Activities room;
Crafts room; Laundry room; Barber/Beauty
shop.
Activities Arts & crafts; Cards; Games;
Reading groups; Prayer groups; Movies;
Shopping trips; Social/Cultural gatherings.

LAMOURE

Colonial Manor of LaMoure*
Box 627, LaMoure, ND, 58458
(701) 883-5363
Admin Adele Spicer.
Licensure Intermediate care. *Beds* 60.
Certified Medicaid.
Owner Proprietary Corp (Beverly Enterprises).

LANGDON

Maple Manor Nursing Home
Hwy 5 W, Langdon, ND, 58249
(701) 256-2987
Admin Charles Shortridge. *Medical Dir/Dir of*
Nursing N J Kaluzniak MD; Gail Melland
RN DON.
Licensure Skilled care. *Beds* SNF 63. *Certified*
Medicaid; Medicare.
Owner Proprietary Corp.
Admissions Requirements Minimum age 21;
Medical examination; Physician's request.
Staff Physicians 2 (pt); RNs 1 (ft), 7 (pt);
LPNs 1 (ft), 3 (pt); Nurses aides 14 (ft), 25
(pt); Physical therapists 1 (pt); Activities
coordinators 1 (ft), 1 (pt); Dietitians 1 (ft), 1
(pt).
Facilities Dining room; Activities room;
Chapel; Crafts room; Laundry room; Barber/
Beauty shop.
Activities Arts & crafts; Cards; Games;
Reading groups; Prayer groups; Movies;
Shopping trips; Social/Cultural gatherings.

LARIMORE

Larimore Good Samaritan Center
PO Box 637, 501 E Front St, Larimore, ND,
58251
(701) 343-6244
Admin Robert P Nixon. *Medical Dir/Dir of*
Nursing Dr Jon Rice; Kathy Finn RN.

Licensure Intermediate care. *Beds* ICF 68.
  Certified Medicaid.
Owner Nonprofit Corp (Evangelical Lutheran/
  Good Samaritan).
Admissions Requirements Medical
  examination; Physician's request.
Staff Physicians 1 (pt); RNs 1 (ft), 1 (pt);
  LPNs 1 (ft), 7 (pt); Nurses aides 10 (ft), 12
  (pt); Physical therapists 1 (pt); Activities
  coordinators 1 (ft); Dietitians 1 (ft).
Affiliation Lutheran
Facilities Dining room; Physical therapy
  room; Activities room; Crafts room; Laundry
  room; Barber/Beauty shop.
Activities Arts & crafts; Cards; Games;
  Reading groups; Prayer groups; Movies;
  Shopping trips; Social/Cultural gatherings;
  Picnics; Manicures; Hiking; Worship service;
  Mind bending; Outings & fieldtrips; Music
  appreciation; Resident volunteer program.

LISBON

Community Memorial Nursing Home
905 Main St, Lisbon, ND, 58054
(701) 683-5241
Admin Wendell Rawlings. *Medical Dir/Dir of
  Nursing* Dr A K Lewis MD; Betty Nelson
  RN DON.
Licensure Skilled care; Intermediate care. *Beds*
  45. *Certified* Medicaid; Medicare.
Owner Nonprofit Corp (Luth Hosp & Homes
  Socty).
Admissions Requirements Medical
  examination; Physician's request.
Staff Physicians 4 (pt); RNs 3 (pt); LPNs 2
  (ft), 9 (pt); Nurses aides 10 (ft), 21 (pt);
  Physical therapists 1 (ft); Activities
  coordinators 1 (ft); Dietitians 1 (ft); Social
  worker 1 (ft).
Facilities Dining room; Physical therapy
  room; Activities room; Chapel; Crafts room;
  Barber/Beauty shop; Library.
Activities Arts & crafts; Cards; Games;
  Reading groups; Prayer groups; Movies;
  Shopping trips; Social/Cultural gatherings.

Parkside Lutheran Home*
Prospect St, Box 153, Lisbon, ND, 58054
(701) 683-5239
Admin Arlys Carter.
Licensure Intermediate care. *Beds* 40.
  Certified Medicaid.
Affiliation Lutheran

MANDAN

Dacotah Alpha
1007 18th St NW, Mandan, ND, 58554
(701) 663-0376
Admin Dorothy Fisher. *Medical Dir/Dir of
  Nursing* Paul Knudson MD.
Licensure Intermediate care Extended
  rehabilitation for physically disabled & head
  injuries. *Beds* 9. *Certified* Medicaid.
Owner Nonprofit Corp.
Admissions Requirements Minimum age 18;
  Medical examination; Physician's request.
Staff RNs 1 (ft); LPNs 3 (ft); Personal care
  attendants 7 (ft).
Facilities Dining room; Physical therapy
  room; Activities room; Crafts room; Laundry
  room; Living room; Visitation room.
Activities Arts & crafts; Cards; Games;
  Reading groups; Movies; Shopping trips;
  Social/Cultural gatherings.

Mandan Villa
201 14th St NW, Mandan, ND, 58554
(701) 663-4267
Admin Layne Gross. *Medical Dir/Dir of
  Nursing* Arthur Van Vranken MD.
Licensure Skilled care; Intermediate care. *Beds*
  SNF 92; ICF 28. *Certified* Medicaid;
  Medicare.
Owner Proprietary Corp (Beverly Enterprises).

Admissions Requirements Medical
  examination.
Staff RNs 7 (ft); LPNs 8 (ft); Orderlies 2 (ft);
  Nurses aides 20 (ft), 15 (pt); Physical
  therapists 1 (pt); Activities coordinators 3
  (ft), 2 (pt); Dietitians 1 (pt).
Facilities Dining room; Physical therapy
  room; Activities room; Crafts room; Laundry
  room; Barber/Beauty shop.
Activities Arts & crafts; Cards; Games;
  Reading groups; Prayer groups; Movies;
  Shopping trips; Social/Cultural gatherings.

MAYVILLE

Luther Memorial Home*
750 Main St E, Mayville, ND, 58257
(701) 786-3401
Admin Adrian Knudsvig.
Licensure Skilled care; Intermediate care. *Beds*
  SNF 69; ICF 30. *Certified* Medicaid;
  Medicare.
Affiliation Lutheran

MCVILLE

Friendship Manor*
Nyhus St, McVille, ND, 58254
(701) 322-4413
Admin Brian Huso.
Licensure Skilled care. *Beds* 52. *Certified*
  Medicaid; Medicare.

MINOT

Americana Healthcare Center—Minot
600 S Main, Minot, ND, 58701
(701) 852-1255
Admin Tony Stork. *Medical Dir/Dir of
  Nursing* Dr Richard Larson; Mary Kraljic.
Licensure Skilled care; Intermediate care. *Beds*
  106. *Certified* Medicaid; Medicare.
Owner Proprietary Corp (Manor Care).
Admissions Requirements Medical
  examination.
Staff RNs 7 (ft), 5 (pt); LPNs 4 (ft), 2 (pt);
  Nurses aides 30 (ft), 22 (pt); Physical
  therapists 1 (pt); Recreational therapists;
  Occupational therapists 1 (pt); Speech
  therapists 1 (pt); Activities coordinators 1
  (ft); Dietitians 1 (pt).
Facilities Dining room; Physical therapy
  room; Activities room; Chapel; Crafts room;
  Crafts room; Laundry room; Barber/Beauty
  shop.
Activities Arts & crafts; Cards; Games;
  Reading groups; Prayer groups; Movies;
  Shopping trips; Social/Cultural gatherings.

Trinity Nursing Unit
305 8th Ave NE, Minot, ND, 58701
(701) 857-5000
Admin Terry G Hoff. *Medical Dir/Dir of
  Nursing* Margaret Shawn Smothers RN
  DON.
Licensure Skilled care; Intermediate care. *Beds*
  329. *Certified* Medicaid; Medicare.
Owner Nonprofit Corp.
Admissions Requirements Medical
  examination; Physician's request.
Staff Physicians 1 (pt); RNs 13 (ft), 12 (pt);
  LPNs 17 (ft), 15 (pt); Orderlies 1 (ft), 3 (pt);
  Nurses aides 67 (ft), 65 (pt); Physical
  therapists 1 (ft); Recreational therapists 7
  (ft); Occupational therapists 1 (pt); Speech
  therapists 1 (pt); Activities coordinators 1
  (ft); Dietitians 1 (ft); Ophthalmologists 1
  (pt).
Languages Norwegian
Facilities Dining room; Physical therapy
  room; Activities room; Chapel; Crafts room;
  Laundry room; Barber/Beauty shop; Sewing
  room.
Activities Arts & crafts; Cards; Games;
  Reading groups; Prayer groups; Movies;
  Shopping trips; Social/Cultural gatherings.

MOHALL

North Central Good Samaritan Center*
602 E Main St, Mohall, ND, 58761
(701) 756-6831
Admin Paul Schroeder.
Licensure Intermediate care. *Beds* 59.
  Certified Medicaid.
Owner Nonprofit Corp (Evangelical Lutheran/
  Good Samaritan).

MOTT

Mott Good Samaritan Nursing Center
401 Millionaire Ave, Mott, ND, 58646
(701) 824-3222
Admin Mildred Waddell. *Medical Dir/Dir of
  Nursing* Katheryn Greff.
Licensure Intermediate care. *Beds* 60.
  Certified Medicaid.
Owner Nonprofit Corp (Evangelical Lutheran/
  Good Samaritan).
Admissions Requirements Medical
  examination.
Affiliation Lutheran
Facilities Dining room; Activities room;
  Chapel; Crafts room; Laundry room; Barber/
  Beauty shop; Library.
Activities Arts & crafts; Cards; Games;
  Reading groups; Prayer groups; Movies;
  Shopping trips; Social/Cultural gatherings.

NAPOLEON

Logan County Home for the Aged
311 E 4th, Napoleon, ND, 58561
(701) 754-2662
Admin Paulette Wentz.
Licensure Intermediate care. *Beds* 44.
  Certified Medicaid.
Staff RNs 3 (pt); LPNs 2 (pt); Nurses aides 5
  (ft), 7 (pt); Activities coordinators 1 (ft);
  Dietitians 1 (pt).
Facilities Dining room; Activities room;
  Chapel; Crafts room; Laundry room; Barber/
  Beauty shop.
Activities Arts & crafts; Cards; Games;
  Reading groups; Prayer groups; Movies;
  Shopping trips; Social/Cultural gatherings.

NEW ROCKFORD

Lutheran Home of the Good Shepherd Inc*
1226 1st Ave N, New Rockford, ND, 58536
(701) 947-2944
Admin James Opdahl. *Medical Dir/Dir of
  Nursing* Dr E J Schwinghamer.
Licensure Skilled care; Intermediate care. *Beds*
  SNF 58; ICF 28. *Certified* Medicaid;
  Medicare.
Admissions Requirements Medical
  examination.
Affiliation Lutheran
Facilities Dining room; Activities room;
  Crafts room; Laundry room; Barber/Beauty
  shop.
Activities Arts & crafts; Cards; Games;
  Reading groups; Prayer groups; Movies;
  Shopping trips; Social/Cultural gatherings.

NEW SALEM

Elm Crest Manor
100 Elm Ave, Box 396, New Salem, ND,
  58563
(701) 843-7526
Admin Gary Kreidt. *Medical Dir/Dir of
  Nursing* Steve Miller.
Licensure Intermediate care. *Beds* 60.
  Certified Medicaid.
Owner Nonprofit Corp.
Admissions Requirements Medical
  examination; Physician's request.

Staff Physicians 1 (pt); RNs 1 (ft), 3 (pt);
LPNs 1 (ft), 2 (pt); Nurses aides 6 (ft), 10
(pt); Physical therapists 1 (pt); Activities
coordinators 1 (ft), 2 (pt); Dietitians 1 (pt).
Affiliation Church of Christ
Facilities Dining room; Physical therapy
room; Activities room; Chapel; Crafts room;
Laundry room; Barber/Beauty shop.
Activities Arts & crafts; Cards; Games;
Reading groups; Prayer groups; Movies;
Shopping trips; Social/Cultural gatherings.

NEW TOWN

New Town Nursing Home
PO Box 399, New Town, ND, 58763
(701) 627-4711
Admin Lorraine Quie. *Medical Dir/Dir of
Nursing* Herbert J Wilson MD; Collette
Garcia RN DON.
Licensure Skilled care. *Beds* 67. *Certified*
Medicaid; Medicare.
Owner Proprietary Corp.
Admissions Requirements Medical
examination; Physician's request.
Staff Physicians; RNs; LPNs; Orderlies;
Nurses aides; Physical therapists;
Recreational therapists; Occupational
therapists; Activities coordinators; Dietitians.
Facilities Dining room; Physical therapy
room; Activities room; Chapel; Crafts room;
Laundry room; Barber/Beauty shop.
Activities Arts & crafts; Cards; Games;
Reading groups; Prayer groups; Movies;
Shopping trips; Social/Cultural gatherings.

NORTHWOOD

Northwood Deaconess Nursing Home
Box 190, 4 N Park St, Northwood, ND, 58267
(701) 587-6060
Admin Larry Feickert.
Licensure Skilled care; Intermediate care. *Beds*
SNF 90. *Certified* Medicaid; Medicare.

OAKES

Oakes Manor Good Samaritan Center
213 N 9th, Oakes, ND, 58474
(701) 742-3274
Admin Marlyn Tande. *Medical Dir/Dir of
Nursing* Marilyn Folkestad.
Licensure Intermediate care. *Beds* ICF 142.
Certified Medicaid.
Owner Nonprofit Corp (Evangelical Lutheran/
Good Samaritan).
Staff RNs 2 (ft), 3 (pt); LPNs 2 (ft), 5 (pt);
Orderlies 1 (ft); Nurses aides 23 (ft), 34 (pt);
Activities coordinators 1 (ft).
Languages German
Affiliation Lutheran
Facilities Dining room; Physical therapy
room; Activities room; Chapel; Crafts room;
Laundry room; Barber/Beauty shop.
Activities Arts & crafts; Cards; Games;
Reading groups; Prayer groups; Movies;
Shopping trips; Social/Cultural gatherings.

OSNABROCK

Osnabrock Good Samaritan Center
PO Box 4, Rte 1, Osnabrock, ND, 58269
(701) 496-3131
Admin G M Nelson. *Medical Dir/Dir of
Nursing* Mary Freyholtz.
Licensure Intermediate care. *Beds* 41.
Certified Medicaid.
Owner Nonprofit Corp (Evangelical Lutheran/
Good Samaritan).
Staff RNs 2 (ft); LPNs 4 (ft); Orderlies 1 (ft);
Nurses aides 10 (ft), 5 (pt); Activities
coordinators 1 (ft); Dietitians 1 (ft).
Facilities Dining room; Physical therapy
room; Activities room; Laundry room;
Barber/Beauty shop; Family room.

Activities Arts & crafts; Cards; Games;
Reading groups; Prayer groups; Movies;
Shopping trips; Social/Cultural gatherings.

PARK RIVER

Park River Good Samaritan Center
PO Box 659, 301 S Hwy 12B, Park River,
ND, 58270
(701) 284-7115
Admin Jerome Swanson. *Medical Dir/Dir of
Nursing* Dr M J Lewis.
Licensure Skilled care. *Beds* 80. *Certified*
Medicaid; Medicare.
Owner Nonprofit Corp (Evangelical Lutheran/
Good Samaritan).
Admissions Requirements Medical
examination.
Staff RNs 6 (ft); LPNs 4 (ft), 4 (pt); Nurses
aides 2 (ft), 1 (pt); Nurses aides 8 (ft), 18
(pt); Physical therapists 2 (pt); Activities
coordinators 1 (ft).
Facilities Dining room; Physical therapy
room; Activities room; Laundry room;
Barber/Beauty shop; Non-denominational
chapel; Crafts room; Library room.
Activities Arts & crafts; Cards; Games;
Reading groups; Prayer groups; Movies;
Shopping trips; Social/Cultural gatherings.

PARSHALL

Rock View Good Samaritan Center*
Parshall, ND, 58770
(701) 862-3611
Admin Mary Brendle.
Licensure Intermediate care. *Beds* 60.
Certified Medicaid.

ROLLA

Rolla Community Hospital—SNF*
213 3rd St NE, Rolla, ND, 58367
(701) 477-3161
Admin Michael Baumgartner. *Medical Dir/Dir
of Nursing* Arnold Overland.
Licensure Skilled care; Intermediate care. *Beds*
SNF 26; ICF 22. *Certified* Medicaid;
Medicare.
Owner Publicly owned.
Staff RNs 2 (ft), 1 (pt); LPNs 4 (ft), 3 (pt);
Nurses aides 15 (ft), 7 (pt); Physical
therapists 1 (ft); Occupational therapists 1
(ft); Activities coordinators 1 (ft), 1 (pt).
Facilities Dining room; Physical therapy
room; Activities room; Chapel; Crafts room;
Laundry room; Barber/Beauty shop; Library.
Activities Arts & crafts; Cards; Games;
Reading groups; Prayer groups; Movies;
Shopping trips; Social/Cultural gatherings.

RUGBY

Good Samaritan—LTC*
Rugby, ND, 58368
(701) 776-5261
Admin Charles Schulz. *Medical Dir/Dir of
Nursing* Dr Lee Potter.
Licensure Skilled care; Intermediate care. *Beds*
SNF 74; ICF 30. *Certified* Medicaid;
Medicare.
Affiliation Lutheran
Facilities Dining room; Activities room;
Chapel; Crafts room; Laundry room; Barber/
Beauty shop; Library; Family room.
Activities Arts & crafts; Cards; Games;
Reading groups; Prayer groups; Movies;
Shopping trips; Social/Cultural gatherings.

Harold S Haaland Home
1025 3rd Ave S, Rugby, ND, 58368
(701) 776-6839
Admin Chuck Schultz. *Medical Dir/Dir of
Nursing* Kay Hovland.
Licensure Basic/custodial. *Beds* Basic/
custodial 80. *Certified* Medicaid; Medicare.

Owner Nonprofit organization/foundation.
Admissions Requirements Medical
examination; Physician's request.
Staff Physicians referral 12 (ft); RNs 1 (ft);
LPNs 2 (ft), 3 (pt); Nurses aides 3 (ft), 6
(pt); Dietitians 1 (pt).
Languages Norwegian German, French
Facilities Dining room; Activities room;
Chapel; Crafts room; Laundry room; Barber/
Beauty shop; Library; Greenhouse;
Carpenter Shop; Exercise course.
Activities Arts & crafts; Cards; Games;
Reading groups; Prayer groups; Movies;
Shopping trips; Social/Cultural gatherings;
Bus trips; Bingo; Exercises; Cooking; Baking;
Fishing; Gardening; Recitals.

STANLEY

Mountrail Bethel Home
Box 700, Stanley, ND, 58784
(701) 628-2442
Admin Fern Wittmayer.
Licensure Skilled care; Intermediate care. *Beds*
SNF 41; ICF 16. *Certified* Medicaid;
Medicare.

STEELE

Golden Manor Inc
215 4th St NW, Steele, ND, 58482-9701
(701) 475-2251
Admin James B Olson. *Medical Dir/Dir of
Nursing* Ron Tello MD; Alice Olson RN
DON.
Licensure Intermediate care. *Beds* ICF 42.
Certified Medicaid.
Owner Proprietary Corp.
Admissions Requirements Medical
examination.
Staff RNs; LPNs; Orderlies; Nurses aides;
Physical therapists; Recreational therapists;
Activities coordinators; Dietitians.
Activities Arts & crafts; Cards; Games;
Reading groups; Prayer groups; Movies;
Shopping trips.

STRASBURG

Strasburg Nursing Home
Rte 1, Box 220, Strasburg, ND, 58573
(701) 336-2651
Admin Andrew J Reis. *Medical Dir/Dir of
Nursing* H P Janssen MD; Judy Reierson
DON.
Licensure Skilled care. *Beds* SNF 80. *Certified*
Medicaid; Medicare.
Owner Nonprofit Corp.
Admissions Requirements Medical
examination; Physician's request.
Staff RNs 5 (ft), 4 (pt); LPNs 2 (ft), 2 (pt);
Nurses aides 16 (ft), 13 (pt); Activities
coordinators 1 (ft); Dietitians 1 (pt).
Languages German
Facilities Dining room; Physical therapy
room; Activities room; Chapel; Laundry
room; Barber/Beauty shop.
Activities Arts & crafts; Cards; Games;
Reading groups; Prayer groups; Movies.

TIOGA

Tioga Community Nursing Home
PO Box 159, 810 W Welo St, Tioga, ND,
58852
(701) 664-3313
Admin Lowell D Herfindahl. *Medical Dir/Dir
of Nursing* Dr Mukesh U Patel.
Licensure Skilled care. *Beds* SNF 30. *Certified*
Medicaid; Medicare.
Owner Nonprofit Corp.
Admissions Requirements Medical
examination; Physician's request.

Staff Physicians 2 (pt); RNs 1 (ft), 3 (pt);
LPNs 3 (ft), 10 (pt); Nurses aides 5 (ft), 11
(pt); Physical therapists 1 (pt); Activities
coordinators 1 (pt); Dietitians 1 (pt).
Facilities Dining room; Activities room;
Chapel; Crafts room; Barber/Beauty shop.
Activities Arts & crafts; Cards; Games;
Reading groups; Prayer groups; Movies;
Shopping trips; Social/Cultural gatherings.

UNDERWOOD

Prairieview Homes Inc
83 Lincoln Ave, Box 10, Underwood, ND,
58576
(701) 442-3222
Admin Randal Albrecht. *Medical Dir/Dir of
Nursing* Dr John T Boyle; Coleen Schulz
DON.
Licensure Skilled care. *Beds* SNF 64. *Certified*
Medicaid; Medicare.
Owner Proprietary Corp.
Admissions Requirements Medical
examination; Physician's request.
Staff RNs 2 (ft), 8 (pt); LPNs 3 (pt); Orderlies
3 (pt); Nurses aides 3 (ft), 23 (pt); Activities
coordinators 1 (ft), 1 (pt).
Facilities Dining room; Physical therapy
room; Activities room; Chapel; Laundry
room; Barber/Beauty shop.
Activities Arts & crafts; Cards; Games;
Reading groups; Prayer groups; Movies.

VALLEY CITY

Sheyenne Care Center—SNF*
1030 2nd Ave NW, Valley City, ND, 58072
(701) 845-2320
Admin James Tourville. *Medical Dir/Dir of
Nursing* Dr R E Wiisanen.
Licensure Skilled care; Intermediate care. *Beds*
SNF 78; ICF 80. *Certified* Medicaid;
Medicare.
Admissions Requirements Medical
examination; Physician's request.
Facilities Dining room; Physical therapy
room; Activities room; Chapel; Crafts room;
Laundry room; Barber/Beauty shop.
Activities Arts & crafts; Cards; Games; Prayer
groups; Movies; Shopping trips; Social/
Cultural gatherings.

VELVA

Souris Valley Care Center
Box 66E, Hwy 41 S, Velva, ND, 58790
(701) 338-2072
Admin Stephen Miles.
Licensure Intermediate care. *Beds* ICF 48.
Owner Nonprofit Corp.
Admissions Requirements Minimum age 55;
Medical examination; Physician's request.
Staff RNs 2 (pt); LPNs 7 (pt); Nurses aides 25
(pt); Activities coordinators 1 (pt).

Affiliation Lutheran
Facilities Dining room; Physical therapy
room; Activities room; Chapel; Crafts room;
Laundry room; Barber/Beauty shop; Library.
Activities Arts & crafts; Cards; Games;
Reading groups; Prayer groups; Movies;
Shopping trips; Social/Cultural gatherings.

WAHPETON

Wahpeton Nursing Center*
1307 N 7th St, Wahpeton, ND, 58075
(701) 642-6667
Admin Kathy Hoeft.
Licensure Skilled care; Intermediate care. *Beds*
110. *Certified* Medicaid; Medicare.
Owner Proprietary Corp (Beverly Enterprises).

WALHALLA

Walhalla Community Hospital Assoc
500 Delano, Box 467, Walhalla, ND, 58282
(701) 549-3831
Admin Brett Ulrich. *Medical Dir/Dir of
Nursing* Dr Warren Jensen.
Licensure Skilled care; Intermediate care. *Beds*
60. *Certified* Medicaid; Medicare; VA.
Staff Physicians 3 (pt); RNs 4 (ft); LPNs 3
(ft), 3 (pt); Orderlies 1 (pt); Nurses aides 20
(ft), 14 (pt); Physical therapists 1 (ft), 1 (pt);
Activities coordinators 1 (ft), 2 (pt);
Dietitians 1 (pt).
Facilities Dining room; Physical therapy
room; Activities room; Chapel; Crafts room;
Laundry room; Barber/Beauty shop.
Activities Arts & crafts; Cards; Games;
Reading groups; Prayer groups; Movies;
Shopping trips; Social/Cultural gatherings.

WATFORD CITY

The Good Shepherd Home
Box 564, Hwy 23 E, Watford City, ND, 58854
(701) 842-2331
Admin Nyla J Dahl. *Medical Dir/Dir of
Nursing* G D Ebel MD; Rebecca Heringer.
Licensure Skilled care. *Beds* SNF 49. *Certified*
Medicaid; Medicare.
Owner Nonprofit Corp.
Admissions Requirements Physician's request.
Staff Physicians 2 (pt); RNs 2 (ft), 3 (pt);
LPNs 1 (ft), 6 (pt); Nurses aides 5 (ft), 20
(pt); Physical therapists 1 (pt); Activities
coordinators 1 (ft), 1 (pt); Dietitians 1 (pt);
Ophthalmologists 1 (pt).
Languages Norweigan
Affiliation Lutheran
Facilities Dining room; Physical therapy
room; Activities room; Chapel; Crafts room;
Laundry room; Barber/Beauty shop; Library.
Activities Arts & crafts; Cards; Games;
Reading groups; Prayer groups; Movies;
Shopping trips; Social/Cultural gatherings.

WESTHOPE

Westhope Home
PO Box 366, 201 3rd St E, Westhope, ND,
58793
(701) 245-6167
Admin Darwin M Lee. *Medical Dir/Dir of
Nursing* Dr Kenneth Kihle; Arles Hatlestad
DON.
Licensure Skilled care; Intermediate care. *Beds*
SNF 59; ICF. *Certified* Medicaid; Medicare.
Owner Nonprofit Corp.
Admissions Requirements Minimum age 16;
Medical examination; Physician's request.
Staff Physicians 4 (ft); RNs 5 (ft); LPNs 3 (ft);
Nurses aides 21 (ft); Physical therapists 2
(ft); Activities coordinators 1 (ft); Dietitians
1 (ft).
Affiliation Lutheran
Facilities Dining room; Physical therapy
room; Activities room; Chapel; Crafts room;
Laundry room; Barber/Beauty shop; Library;
Clinic attached.
Activities Arts & crafts; Cards; Games;
Reading groups; Prayer groups; Movies;
Social/Cultural gatherings.

WILLISTON

Bethel Lutheran Home*
Box 1828, 1515 2nd Ave W, Williston, ND,
58801
(701) 572-6766
Admin Wayne L Hansen.
Licensure Skilled care; Intermediate care. *Beds*
SNF 118; ICF 55. *Certified* Medicaid;
Medicare.

WISHEK

Wishek Home for the Aged
PO Box 187, 4th St and 4th Ave S, Wishek,
ND, 58495
(701) 452-2333
Admin Harvey Schanzenbach. *Medical Dir/Dir
of Nursing* Dr Kosiak.
Licensure Skilled care. *Beds* SNF 95. *Certified*
Medicaid; Medicare.
Owner Nonprofit Corp.
Admissions Requirements Medical
examination; Physician's request.
Staff Physicians 2 (pt); RNs 3 (ft); LPNs 5
(ft), 3 (pt); Orderlies 3 (ft), 1 (pt); Nurses
aides 20 (ft), 10 (pt); Physical therapists 2
(pt); Dietitians 1 (ft).
Languages German
Affiliation Church of Christ
Facilities Dining room; Physical therapy
room; Activities room; Chapel; Crafts room;
Laundry room; Barber/Beauty shop; Library.
Activities Arts & crafts; Cards; Games;
Reading groups; Prayer groups; Movies;
Shopping trips; Social/Cultural gatherings.

OHIO

ADENA

McGraw Nursing Home Inc*
Rte 2, 73841 Pleasant Grove, Adena, OH, 43901
(614) 546-3013
Beds 43.
Owner Proprietary Corp.

Reynolds Nursing Home Inc*
Rte 1, Adena, OH, 43901
(614) 546-3620
Licensure Intermediate care. *Beds* 50.
Certified Medicaid.
Owner Proprietary Corp.

Valley View Nursing Home
56143 Colerain Pike, Adena, OH, 43935
(614) 633-9637
Admin Alice Callarik.
Licensure Intermediate care. *Beds* ICF 25.
Certified Medicaid.
Owner Privately owned.
Admissions Requirements Minimum age 18;
Medical examination; Physician's request.
Staff Physicians 1 (ft); RNs 1 (ft); LPNs 6 (ft);
Orderlies 1 (ft); Nurses aides 8 (ft); Physical
therapists 1 (ft); Reality therapists 1 (ft);
Recreational therapists 1 (ft); Activities
coordinators 1 (ft); Dietitians 1 (ft);
Ophthalmologists 1 (ft); Podiatrists 1 (ft).
Facilities Dining room; Laundry room;
Multipurpose room.
Activities Arts & crafts; Cards; Games;
Reading groups; Prayer groups; Movies;
Shopping trips; Social/Cultural gatherings.

AKRON

Dee-Maret Nursing Home*
1140 S Hawkins Ave, Akron, OH, 44320
(216) 836-2310
Licensure Nursing home. *Beds* 13.
Owner Proprietary Corp.

Ellet Manor
2755 Ellet Ave, Akron, OH, 44312
(216) 733-3623
Admin Mariann Riley. *Medical Dir/Dir of
Nursing* George Tabakov MD; Lisa Cohen
RN.
Licensure Intermediate care. *Beds* 16.
Certified Medicaid.
Owner Proprietary Corp.
Admissions Requirements Medical
examination.
Staff LPNs 3 (ft), 1 (pt); Nurses aides 6 (ft), 3
(pt); Recreational therapists 1 (pt); Activities
coordinators 1 (ft); Dietitians 1 (pt);
Podiatrists 1 (pt).
Facilities Dining room; Activities room;
Crafts room; Laundry room.
Activities Arts & crafts; Cards; Games;
Reading groups; Prayer groups; Movies;
Shopping trips; Social/Cultural gatherings.

Healthaven Nursing Home
615 Latham Ln, Akron, OH, 44319
(216) 644-3914
Medical Dir/Dir of Nursing Dr John M Kim.
Licensure Intermediate care. *Beds* 56.
Certified Medicaid.
Owner Nonprofit Corp.
Admissions Requirements Minimum age 60;
Medical examination.
Staff Physicians 1 (ft); RNs 1 (ft), 1 (pt);
LPNs 6 (ft), 4 (pt); Nurses aides 16 (ft), 9
(pt); Activities coordinators 1 (pt); Dietitians
1 (pt).
Affiliation Methodist
Facilities Dining room; Activities room;
Crafts room; Laundry room; Library.
Activities Arts & crafts; Cards; Games; Prayer
groups; Movies; Shopping trips.

Hillhaven Convalescent Center
145 Olive St, Akron, OH, 44310
(216) 762-0901
Admin A Wayne Davis. *Medical Dir/Dir of
Nursing* Walter R Hoffman DO; Lois
Douglas RN DON.
Licensure Skilled care; Intermediate care. *Beds*
SNF 30; ICF 144. *Certified* Medicaid;
Medicare.
Owner Proprietary Corp (Hillhaven Corp).
Admissions Requirements Medical
examination; Physician's request.
Staff Physicians 40 (pt); RNs 6 (ft), 3 (pt);
LPNs 10 (ft), 15 (pt); Nurses aides 48 (ft), 9
(pt); Physical therapists 1 (ft); Recreational
therapists 1 (ft); Occupational therapists 1
(pt); Speech therapists 1 (pt); Activities
coordinators 2 (ft); Dietitians 1 (pt); Dentists
1 (pt); Ophthalmologists 1 (pt); Podiatrists 1
(pt).
Facilities Dining room; Physical therapy
room; Activities room; Chapel; Crafts room;
Laundry room; Barber/Beauty shop.
Activities Arts & crafts; Cards; Games;
Reading groups; Prayer groups; Movies;
Shopping trips.

Little Forest Medical Center*
797 E Market St, Akron, OH, 44305
(216) 434-4514
Licensure Skilled care; Intermediate care. *Beds*
256. *Certified* Medicaid; Medicare.
Owner Proprietary Corp.

Lorantffy Care Center Inc
2631 Copley Rd, Akron, OH, 44321
(216) 666-2631, 666-2611
Admin Rev Tibor Domotor. *Medical Dir/Dir
of Nursing* Arpad Batizy MD; Clara Brown
RN DON.
Licensure Skilled care; Intermediate care. *Beds*
ICF 74; ICF 27. *Certified* Medicaid;
Medicare.
Owner Nonprofit Corp.
Admissions Requirements Medical
examination.
Staff Physicians; RNs; LPNs; Orderlies;
Nurses aides; Physical therapists; Speech
therapists; Activities coordinators; Dietitians.
Languages Hungarian

Affiliation Christian Reformed Hungarian
Church
Facilities Dining room; Physical therapy
room; Activities room; Chapel; Crafts room;
Laundry room; Barber/Beauty shop.
Activities Arts & crafts; Cards; Games; Prayer
groups; Movies; Social/Cultural gatherings;
Church services.

Manor Care of Akron Inc
1211 W Market St, Akron, OH, 44313
(216) 867-8530
Admin Elizabeth Carter. *Medical Dir/Dir of
Nursing* Dr S Cochran; Donna Malloy RN
DON.
Licensure Skilled care; Intermediate care. *Beds*
SNF 109. *Certified* Medicare.
Owner Proprietary Corp (Manor Care).
Admissions Requirements Minimum age 16;
Medical examination; Physician's request.
Staff Physicians; RNs; LPNs; Nurses aides;
Physical therapists; Recreational therapists;
Occupational therapists; Speech therapists;
Activities coordinators; Dietitians.
Languages Sign
Facilities Dining room; Physical therapy
room; Activities room; Crafts room; Laundry
room; Barber/Beauty shop; Library; Multi-
purpose room.
Activities Arts & crafts; Cards; Games;
Reading groups; Prayer groups; Movies;
Shopping trips; Social/Cultural gatherings;
Happy hour; Outside trips.

**Middlebury Manor Nursing & Convalescent
Home***
974 E Market St, Akron, OH, 44305
(216) 762-9066
Licensure Skilled care; Intermediate care. *Beds*
141. *Certified* Medicaid; Medicare.
Owner Proprietary Corp.

Pearlview Extended Care & Nursing Home
3558 Ridgewood Rd, Akron, OH, 44313
(216) 666-3776
Admin John Durkin. *Medical Dir/Dir of
Nursing* Barbara Capron DON.
Licensure Skilled care; Intermediate care. *Beds*
139. *Certified* Medicaid; Medicare.
Owner Privately owned.
Admissions Requirements Medical
examination; Physician's request.
Staff RNs; LPNs; Orderlies; Nurses aides;
Physical therapists; Speech therapists;
Activities coordinators; Dietitians.
Facilities Dining room; Physical therapy
room; Activities room; Laundry room;
Barber/Beauty shop.
Activities Arts & crafts; Games; Prayer groups;
Movies; Social/Cultural gatherings.

Rockynol Retirement Community
1150 W Market St, Akron, OH, 44224
(216) 867-2150
Admin Mary Johnson. *Medical Dir/Dir of
Nursing* Steve Cochran MD; Mary Cochran
DON.
Licensure Skilled care; Intermediate care. *Beds*
SNF 72; ICF. *Certified* Medicaid; Medicare.

Owner Nonprofit Corp (OH Presbyterian
Homes).
Admissions Requirements Minimum age 60.
Staff RNs 4 (ft), 3 (pt); LPNs 5 (ft), 5 (pt);
Nurses aides 24 (ft), 10 (pt); Activities
coordinators 1 (ft), 1 (pt); Dietitians 1 (ft);
Chaplain 1 (ft).
Facilities Dining room; Activities room;
Chapel; Crafts room; Barber/Beauty shop;
Library; Laundry services provided.
Activities Arts & crafts; Cards; Games;
Reading groups; Prayer groups; Movies;
Shopping trips; Social/Cultural gatherings;
Baking; Special lunches; Pets.

St Edward Home
3131 Smith Rd, Akron, OH, 44313
(216) 666-1183
Admin John J Hennelly. *Medical Dir/Dir of
Nursing* Donna Bender RN.
Licensure Intermediate care. *Beds* ICF 100.
Certified Medicaid.
Owner Nonprofit Corp.
Admissions Requirements Medical
examination.
Staff RNs 4 (ft), 8 (pt); LPNs 2 (ft), 4 (pt);
Nurses aides 28 (ft), 19 (pt); Activities
coordinators 1 (ft); Dietitians 1 (ft).
Affiliation Roman Catholic
Facilities Dining room; Physical therapy
room; Activities room; Chapel; Crafts room;
Laundry room.
Activities Arts & crafts; Cards; Games;
Reading groups; Prayer groups; Movies;
Shopping trips; Social/Cultural gatherings;
Religious services; Secluded walkway with
terraces; Picnic pavillion.

Sumner Home
209 Merriman Rd, Akron, OH, 44303
(216) 762-9341
Admin Christine Hunter. *Medical Dir/Dir of
Nursing* Marie Fatur DON.
Licensure Skilled care; Intermediate care;
Assisted living. *Beds* SNF 14; ICF 30;
Assisted living 70.
Owner Nonprofit Corp.
Admissions Requirements Minimum age 65;
Medical examination.
Staff RNs 1 (ft), 2 (pt); LPNs 6 (ft), 6 (pt);
Nurses aides 12 (ft), 6 (pt); Physical
therapists; Recreational therapists 1 (ft);
Activities coordinators 1 (ft); Dietitians;
Dentists; Ophthalmologists.
Facilities Dining room; Physical therapy
room; Activities room; Chapel; Crafts room;
Laundry room; Barber/Beauty shop; Library.
Activities Arts & crafts; Cards; Games;
Reading groups; Prayer groups; Movies;
Shopping trips; Social/Cultural gatherings.

Valley View Nursing Home
721 Hickory St, Akron, OH, 44303
(216) 762-6486
Admin James Wilson. *Medical Dir/Dir of
Nursing* Dr John McFadden; Linda Postich.
Licensure Skilled care; Intermediate care. *Beds*
234. *Certified* Medicaid; Medicare.
Owner Proprietary Corp (Beverly Enterprises).
Admissions Requirements Minimum age 14;
Medical examination.
Staff Physicians; RNs; LPNs; Orderlies;
Nurses aides; Physical therapists;
Occupational therapists; Speech therapists;
Activities coordinators; Dietitians;
Ophthalmologists; Podiatrists.
Facilities Dining room; Physical therapy
room; Activities room; Laundry room;
Barber/Beauty shop.
Activities Arts & crafts; Cards; Games;
Reading groups; Prayer groups; Movies;
Shopping trips; Social/Cultural gatherings.

ALBANY

Russell Nursing Home
PO Box 37, 101 Washington St, Albany, OH,
45710
(614) 698-3631
Admin Helen Kaylor. *Medical Dir/Dir of
Nursing* Marie McVey.
Licensure Intermediate care. *Beds* ICF 25.
Certified Medicaid.
Owner Proprietary Corp.
Admissions Requirements Minimum age 21;
Medical examination; Physician's request.
Staff Physicians; RNs; LPNs; Nurses aides;
Physical therapists; Reality therapists;
Activities coordinators; Dietitians;
Ophthalmologists; Podiatrists.
Facilities Dining room; Physical therapy
room; Activities room; Chapel; Crafts room;
Laundry room; Library.
Activities Arts & crafts; Cards; Games;
Reading groups; Prayer groups; Shopping
trips; Social/Cultural gatherings.

ALLIANCE

Alliance Nursing Home Inc*
11677 N Rockhill Rd, Alliance, OH, 44601
(216) 821-0071
Licensure Intermediate care. *Beds* 75.
Certified Medicaid.
Owner Proprietary Corp.

**Americare Nursing & Rehabilitation Center of
Alliance**
2040 McCrea St, Alliance, OH, 44601
(216) 823-9005
Admin Donna Lane. *Medical Dir/Dir of
Nursing* Dr Duane Kuentz; Anita Peffer RN
DON.
Licensure Skilled care; Intermediate care. *Beds*
SNF 24; ICF 76. *Certified* Medicaid;
Medicare.
Owner Proprietary Corp (Care Enterprises).
Admissions Requirements Medical
examination.
Staff Physicians; RNs; LPNs; Orderlies;
Nurses aides; Speech therapists; Activities
coordinators.
Facilities Dining room; Physical therapy
room; Activities room; Crafts room; Laundry
room; Barber/Beauty shop.
Activities Arts & crafts; Cards; Games;
Reading groups; Prayer groups; Movies;
Shopping trips; Social/Cultural gatherings.

Bel-Air Convalescent Center*
2350 S Cherry Ave, Alliance, OH, 44601
Licensure Nursing home. *Beds* 54.
Owner Proprietary Corp.
Staff Physicians; RNs 1 (pt); LPNs 4 (ft), 3
(pt); Nurses aides 8 (ft), 6 (pt); Physical
therapists; Recreational therapists 1 (ft), 1
(pt); Activities coordinators 1 (ft), 1 (pt);
Dietitians 1 (pt); Dentists; Ophthalmologists;
Podiatrists.
Facilities Dining room; Activities room.
Activities Arts & crafts; Cards; Games;
Reading groups; Prayer groups; Movies;
Shopping trips; Social/Cultural gatherings.

Blossom Nursing Center
11750 Klinger Ave, Alliance, OH, 44601
(216) 823-8263
Admin Michele L Yarde. *Medical Dir/Dir of
Nursing* Dr Michael McGrady; Thelma
Yoho RN.
Licensure Skilled care; Intermediate care. *Beds*
100. *Certified* Medicaid; Medicare.
Owner Proprietary Corp (Altercare Inc).
Admissions Requirements Medical
examination; Physician's request.
Staff RNs 10 (pt); LPNs 7 (pt); Nurses aides
15 (ft), 30 (pt); Physical therapists 1 (pt);
Speech therapists 1 (pt); Activities
coordinators 1 (ft), 1 (pt); Dietitians 1 (pt);
Ophthalmologists 1 (pt).

Facilities Dining room; Physical therapy
room; Activities room; Crafts room; Laundry
room; Barber/Beauty shop; Lounges; Outside
patios.
Activities Arts & crafts; Cards; Games; Prayer
groups; Movies; Shopping trips; Social/
Cultural gatherings; Bingo; Bowling; Lunch
outings.

Canterbury Villa of Alliance
1785 S Freshley Ave, Alliance, OH, 44601
(216) 821-4000
Admin James C Egli. *Medical Dir/Dir of
Nursing* Donald Carter MD; Beverly
Lockhart DON.
Licensure Skilled care; Intermediate care. *Beds*
SNF 100; ICF. *Certified* Medicaid;
Medicare.
Owner Proprietary Corp (Health Enter of
America).
Admissions Requirements Medical
examination; Physician's request.
Staff Physicians 3 (pt); RNs 4 (ft), 3 (pt);
LPNs 5 (ft), 3 (pt); Nurses aides 20 (ft), 10
(pt); Physical therapists 1 (pt); Occupational
therapists 1 (pt); Speech therapists 1 (pt);
Activities coordinators 1 (ft), 2 (pt);
Dietitians 1 (pt); Dentists 1 (pt);
Ophthalmologists 1 (pt); Podiatrists 1 (pt).
Facilities Dining room; Physical therapy
room; Activities room; Chapel; Laundry
room; Barber/Beauty shop; Library.
Activities Arts & crafts; Cards; Games;
Reading groups; Prayer groups; Movies;
Shopping trips; Social/Cultural gatherings.

Health Center Inc
145 E College St, Alliance, OH, 44601
(216) 823-2333
Admin Joseph R Ketchaver. *Medical Dir/Dir
of Nursing* Dr Anthony Lee; Betty
Starkweather RN, Gloria Woods RN.
Licensure Intermediate care 10C. *Beds* ICF
58; ICF/MR 20. *Certified* Medicaid.
Owner Proprietary Corp.
Admissions Requirements Medical
examination; Physician's request.
Staff Physicians; RNs; LPNs; Orderlies;
Nurses aides; Physical therapists;
Occupational therapists; Speech therapists;
Activities coordinators; Dietitians;
Ophthalmologists; Podiatrists; Dentist.
Facilities Dining room; Physical therapy
room; Activities room; Laundry room;
Barber/Beauty shop.
Activities Arts & crafts; Cards; Games; Prayer
groups; Movies; Shopping trips.

Ro-Ker Nursing Home
1495 S Freshley Ave, Alliance, OH, 44601
(216) 823-1097
Admin Mary E O'Reilly. *Medical Dir/Dir of
Nursing* Iris Baddeley LPN DNS.
Licensure Intermediate care. *Beds* ICF 78.
Certified Medicaid.
Owner Proprietary Corp (Horizon Healthcare
Corp).
Admissions Requirements Medical
examination.
Staff RNs; LPNs; Orderlies; Nurses aides;
Activities coordinators.
Facilities Dining room; Laundry room;
Barber/Beauty shop.
Activities Arts & crafts; Cards; Games;
Reading groups; Prayer groups; Movies;
Shopping trips.

Rose Lawn Geriatric Center*
11999 Klinger Ave NE, Alliance, OH, 44601
(216) 823-0618
Licensure Nursing home. *Beds* 15.
Owner Proprietary Corp.

Sun Valley Nursing Home*
1850 Electric Blvd, Alliance, OH, 44601
(216) 823-4287

Licensure Intermediate care. *Beds* 37.
Certified Medicaid.
Owner Proprietary Corp.

ALVORDTON

Evergreen North Nursing Home
PO Box 182, Alvordton, OH, 43501
(419) 924-2898
Admin Iris Shook. *Medical Dir/Dir of Nursing*
Clarence Bell MD.
Licensure Intermediate care. *Beds* ICF 23.
Certified Medicaid.
Owner Proprietary Corp (American Health
Care Centers).
Staff Physicians; RNs; LPNs 4 (ft), 2 (pt);
Nurses aides 6 (ft), 3 (pt); Activities
coordinators 1 (ft); Dietitians.
Facilities Dining room; Crafts room; Laundry
room.
Activities Arts & crafts; Cards; Games;
Reading groups; Prayer groups; Shopping
trips; Social/Cultural gatherings.

AMELIA

Sunrise Manor & Convalescent Center Inc
PO Box 3434, State Rte 132, Amelia, OH,
45102
(513) 797-5144
Admin Florel Meeker. *Medical Dir/Dir of
Nursing* Patricia Jones DON.
Licensure Intermediate care. *Beds* ICF.
Certified Medicaid.
Owner Proprietary Corp.
Admissions Requirements Medical
examination.
Staff Physicians 8 (ft); RNs 1 (ft); LPNs 8 (ft);
Nurses aides 20 (ft); Physical therapists 1
(ft); Dietitians 1 (ft).
Facilities Dining room; Physical therapy
room; Activities room; Chapel; Crafts room;
Laundry room.
Activities Arts & crafts; Cards; Games;
Reading groups; Prayer groups; Movies;
Shopping trips; Social/Cultural gatherings.

AMHERST

Amherst Manor*
175 N Lake Dr, Amherst, OH, 44001
(216) 988-4415
Licensure Intermediate care. *Beds* 102.
Certified Medicaid.
Owner Proprietary Corp.

ANDOVER

Miller Memorial Nursing Center
486 S Main St, Andover, OH, 44003
(216) 293-5416
Admin Carol J Duva RN. *Medical Dir/Dir of
Nursing* Dr Randall Tharp; Nancy Bowker
RN DON.
Licensure Skilled care; Intermediate care. *Beds*
SNF; ICF 200. *Certified* Medicaid.
Owner Proprietary Corp.
Admissions Requirements Medical
examination.
Staff Physicians 2 (pt); RNs 5 (ft), 4 (pt);
LPNs 12 (ft), 4 (pt); Orderlies 1 (ft); Nurses
aides 35 (ft), 20 (pt); Activities coordinators
3 (ft); Ophthalmologists 1 (pt).
Languages Sign
Facilities Dining room; Physical therapy
room; Activities room; Chapel; Crafts room;
Laundry room; Barber/Beauty shop; Library.
Activities Arts & crafts; Cards; Games;
Reading groups; Prayer groups; Movies;
Shopping trips; Social/Cultural gatherings.

APPLE CREEK

Apple Creek Developmental Center*
County Rd 44, Apple Creek, OH, 44606
(216) 698-2411
Licensure Intermediate care for mentally
retarded. *Beds* 316. *Certified* Medicaid.
Owner Publicly owned.

ARCHBOLD

Fairlawn Haven
E Lutz Rd, Archbold, OH, 43502
(419) 445-3075
Medical Dir/Dir of Nursing Robert A
Ebersole.
Licensure Intermediate care. *Beds* 100.
Certified Medicaid.
Owner Nonprofit Corp.
Admissions Requirements Minimum age;
Medical examination.
Staff RNs 2 (ft), 10 (pt); LPNs 4 (ft), 5 (pt);
Orderlies 2 (ft); Nurses aides 24 (ft), 34 (pt);
Physical therapists 1 (pt); Activities
coordinators 1 (ft), 2 (pt); Dietitians 1 (pt);
Dentists 1 (pt); Podiatrists 1 (pt); Dentist 1
(pt).
Affiliation Mennonite
Facilities Dining room; Physical therapy
room; Activities room; Crafts room; Laundry
room; Barber/Beauty shop; Library.
Activities Arts & crafts; Cards; Games;
Reading groups; Prayer groups; Movies;
Shopping trips; Social/Cultural gatherings.

ARLINGTON

Arlington Good Samaritan Center*
PO Box 200, State Rte 103, Arlington, OH,
45814
(419) 365-5115
Licensure Intermediate care. *Beds* 50.
Certified Medicaid.
Owner Nonprofit Corp.

ASHLAND

Brethren Care Inc
2000 Center St, Ashland, OH, 44805
(419) 289-1585
Admin Darrel Barnes. *Medical Dir/Dir of
Nursing* Dr Charles Slagle; Regina Smeltzer
RN DON.
Licensure Intermediate care. *Beds* ICF 91.
Certified Medicaid.
Owner Nonprofit Corp.
Admissions Requirements Medical
examination; Physician's request.
Staff RNs 1 (ft), 6 (pt); LPNs 4 (ft), 6 (pt);
Orderlies 2 (ft); Nurses aides 17 (ft), 38 (pt);
Activities coordinators 1 (ft), 1 (pt).
Affiliation Church of the Brethren
Facilities Dining room; Activities room;
Laundry room; Barber/Beauty shop;
Conference room.
Activities Cards; Games; Reading groups;
Prayer groups; Movies.

Good Shepherd Home for the Aged*
622 S Center St, Ashland, OH, 44805
(419) 289-3523
Licensure Skilled care; Intermediate care. *Beds*
130. *Certified* Medicaid; Medicare.
Owner Nonprofit Corp.

Griffeth Nursing Home
PO Box 382, 1251 Wooster Rd, Ashland, OH,
44805
(419) 322-9595
Licensure Intermediate care. *Beds* 50.
Certified Medicaid.
Owner Proprietary Corp.
Admissions Requirements Medical
examination; Physician's request.

Staff RNs 1 (pt); LPNs 3 (ft), 4 (pt); Nurses
aides 10 (ft), 4 (pt); Recreational therapists 2
(ft), 1 (pt); Activities coordinators 1 (ft);
Dietitians 1 (pt).
Facilities Dining room; Activities room;
Crafts room; Laundry room.
Activities Arts & crafts; Cards; Games;
Reading groups; Prayer groups; Movies;
Shopping trips; Social/Cultural gatherings.

ASHTABULA

Ashtabula Medicare Nursing Center*
2217 West Ave, Ashtabula, OH, 44004
(216) 964-8446
Licensure Skilled care; Intermediate care. *Beds*
200. *Certified* Medicaid; Medicare.
Owner Proprietary Corp.

Country Club Retirement Center
925 E 26th St, Ashtabula, OH, 44004
(216) 992-0022
Admin Wallace Warren. *Medical Dir/Dir of
Nursing* Dolly Waddle DON.
Licensure Skilled care; Intermediate care. *Beds*
SNF 65; ICF. *Certified* Medicaid; Medicare.
Owner Proprietary Corp (Je Holland Assoc).
Admissions Requirements Medical
examination; Physician's request.
Staff Physicians 2 (pt); RNs 2 (ft), 1 (pt);
LPNs 5 (ft), 5 (pt); Nurses aides 16 (ft), 12
(pt); Physical therapists 2 (pt); Speech
therapists 1 (pt); Activities coordinators 1
(ft); Dietitians 1 (pt); Ophthalmologists 1
(pt); Podiatrists 1 (pt).
Facilities Dining room; Physical therapy
room; Activities room; Chapel; Crafts room;
Laundry room; Barber/Beauty shop.
Activities Arts & crafts; Cards; Games;
Reading groups; Prayer groups; Movies;
Shopping trips.

Smith Home for Aged Women*
4533 Park Ave, Ashtabula, OH, 44004
(216) 992-9441
Admin Leonard Kroner. *Medical Dir/Dir of
Nursing* Dr Hassain.
Licensure Home for aged. *Beds* 30.
Owner Nonprofit Corp.
Admissions Requirements Minimum age 65;
Females only; Medical examination.
Staff Physicians 1 (pt); RNs 3 (pt); LPNs 3
(pt); Nurses aides 9 (pt).
Facilities Dining room; Activities room;
Chapel; Crafts room; Laundry room; Barber/
Beauty shop; Library.
Activities Cards; Games; Prayer groups;
Shopping trips.

ATHENS

Echoing Meadows Residential Center
319 W Union St, Athens, OH, 45701
(614) 594-3541
Admin Thomas E O'Brien. *Medical Dir/Dir of
Nursing* Denise Smith RN.
Licensure Intermediate care; Intermediate care
for mentally retarded; Nursing home. *Beds*
ICF/MR 36. *Certified* Medicaid.
Owner Nonprofit Corp.
Admissions Requirements Minimum age 18;
Medical examination.
Staff Physicians 1 (pt); RNs 2 (ft), 1 (pt);
LPNs 3 (ft), 3 (pt); Orderlies 4 (ft); Nurses
aides 20 (ft), 6 (pt); Physical therapists 1
(pt); Occupational therapists 1 (pt); Speech
therapists 1 (pt); Activities coordinators 1
(ft); Dietitians 1 (pt); Dentists 2 (pt);
Program Director 1 (ft); Food Service Sup 1
(ft); Maintenance Dir 1 (ft); Drivers 2 (ft);
Habilitation Assist 2 (ft); Cooks 3 (ft), 1 (pt).
Facilities Dining room; Physical therapy
room; Activities room; Crafts room; Laundry
room; Swimming pool; Patio.

Activities Arts & crafts; Cards; Games;
Reading groups; Prayer groups; Movies;
Shopping trips; Social/Cultural gatherings;
Picnics; Camp; Special Olympics; Church in
community.

Kimes Convalescent Center
Albany Rd, Athens, OH, 45701
(614) 593-3391
Admin Mrs Harold R Kimes. *Medical Dir/Dir
of Nursing* W Baumgaertel MD.
Licensure Skilled care. *Beds* 61.
Owner Privately owned.
Admissions Requirements Medical
examination.
Staff Physicians 7 (pt); RNs 2 (ft); LPNs 8
(ft); Nurses aides 18 (ft), 5 (pt); Physical
therapists 1 (pt); Speech therapists 1 (pt);
Dentists 1 (pt); Ophthalmologists 1 (pt).
Facilities Dining room; Chapel; Laundry
room; Barber/Beauty shop; Library.
Activities Cards; Games; Reading groups;
Senior citizen band appearances; Religious
services by 5 groups.

AURORA

Anna Maria of Aurora Inc
889 N Aurora Rd, Aurora, OH, 44202
(216) 562-6171
Admin George J Norton. *Medical Dir/Dir of
Nursing* Willard E Stoner MD; Marlene
Peoples RN.
Licensure Skilled care; Intermediate care;
Alzheimer's Wing. *Beds* SNF 43; ICF 84.
Certified Medicare.
Owner Proprietary Corp.
Admissions Requirements Medical
examination; Physician's request.
Facilities Dining room; Physical therapy
room; Activities room; Chapel; Crafts room;
Laundry room; Barber/Beauty shop; Library.
Activities Arts & crafts; Cards; Games;
Reading groups; Prayer groups; Movies;
Shopping trips; Social/Cultural gatherings.

AUSTINTOWN

Austin Woods Nursing Center Inc
4780 Kirk Rd, Austintown, OH, 44515
(216) 792-7681
Admin Norman Reuven. *Medical Dir/Dir of
Nursing* Dr Wilkens.
Licensure Skilled care; Intermediate care. *Beds*
230. *Certified* Medicaid; Medicare.
Owner Proprietary Corp.
Admissions Requirements Minimum age 18.
Staff Physicians; RNs; LPNs; Orderlies;
Nurses aides; Physical therapists;
Recreational therapists; Speech therapists;
Activities coordinators; Dietitians; Dentists;
Podiatrists.
Facilities Dining room; Physical therapy
room; Activities room; Chapel; Crafts room;
Laundry room; Barber/Beauty shop; Library;
Auditorium.
Activities Arts & crafts; Cards; Games;
Reading groups; Prayer groups; Movies;
Shopping trips; Social/Cultural gatherings.

AVON

Avon Oaks Nursing Home
37800 French Creek Rd, Avon, OH, 44011
(216) 934-5204
Admin Joan Reidy Zemanek. *Medical Dir/Dir
of Nursing* Laura Englehart RN.
Licensure Intermediate care. *Beds* ICF 105.
Certified Medicaid.
Owner Privately owned.
Admissions Requirements Medical
examination.

Staff Physicians 5 (pt); RNs 4 (ft), 1 (pt);
LPNs 11 (ft), 2 (pt); Nurses aides 37 (ft);
Physical therapists 1 (pt); Activities
coordinators 2 (ft); Dietitians 1 (pt); Dentists
1 (pt); Ophthalmologists 1 (pt).
Languages Spanish, Hungarian
Facilities Dining room; Physical therapy
room; Activities room; Barber/Beauty shop;
Kitchen for cooking class; Child care center.
Activities Arts & crafts; Cards; Games;
Reading groups; Prayer groups; Movies;
Shopping trips; Social/Cultural gatherings;
Cooking; International program.

Good Samaritan Nursing Home
32900 Detroit Rd, Avon, OH, 44011
(216) 937-6201
Admin Gail Bash. *Medical Dir/Dir of Nursing*
Fanous.
Licensure Skilled care; Intermediate care. *Beds*
SNF 20; ICF 192. *Certified* Medicaid;
Medicare.
Owner Proprietary Corp.
Admissions Requirements Medical
examination.
Staff Physicians 7 (pt); RNs 11 (ft); LPNs 36
(ft), 1 (pt); Nurses aides 95 (ft), 6 (pt);
Physical therapists 2 (ft), 1 (pt); Recreational
therapists 1 (ft); Occupational therapists 1
(ft), 1 (pt); Speech therapists 1 (pt);
Activities coordinators 1 (ft); Dietitians 1
(ft); Dentists 1 (pt); Podiatrists 1 (pt).
Facilities Dining room; Physical therapy
room; Activities room; Chapel; Crafts room;
Laundry room; Barber/Beauty shop; Library.
Activities Arts & crafts; Cards; Games;
Reading groups; Prayer groups; Movies;
Shopping trips; Social/Cultural gatherings;
Camping trips; Gardening.

BAINBRIDGE

Maple View Manor*
Box 613, 430 S Maple St, Bainbridge, OH,
45612
(614) 634-3301
Licensure Intermediate care. *Beds* 20.
Certified Medicaid.
Owner Proprietary Corp.

BALTIC

Baltic Country Manor
130 Buena Vista St, Baltic, OH, 43804
(216) 897-4311
Admin Mark J Morley. *Medical Dir/Dir of
Nursing* Dr Maurice Stutzman; Barbara
Sparr.
Licensure Skilled care; Intermediate care;
Alzheimer's unit. *Beds* SNF 8; ICF 92.
Certified Medicaid; Medicare.
Owner Proprietary Corp (Health Enter of
America).
Admissions Requirements Minimum age 18;
Medical examination.
Staff Physicians 1 (ft), 1 (pt); RNs 4 (ft), 1
(pt); LPNs 8 (ft), 2 (pt); Orderlies 2 (ft), 2
(pt); Nurses aides 15 (ft), 13 (pt); Physical
therapists 3 (pt); Recreational therapists 1
(ft); Speech therapists 1 (pt); Activities
coordinators 1 (ft); Dietitians 2 (pt);
Ophthalmologists 1 (pt).
Languages Pennsylvania Dutch
Facilities Dining room; Physical therapy
room; Activities room; Laundry room;
Barber/Beauty shop; Outdoor patio.
Activities Arts & crafts; Cards; Prayer groups;
Movies; Shopping trips; Social/Cultural
gatherings; Picnics; Community choirs &
quartet.

BALTIMORE

Gaulden Manor
225 Hansberger St, Baltimore, OH, 43105
(614) 862-8093

Admin April Cross. *Medical Dir/Dir of
Nursing* Anna Whetstone; Dana Keller.
Licensure Intermediate care. *Beds* ICF 45.
Certified Medicaid.
Owner Proprietary Corp.
Admissions Requirements Medical
examination; Physician's request.
Staff Physicians; RNs; LPNs; Nurses aides;
Activities coordinators; Dietitians.
Facilities Dining room; Activities room;
Crafts room; Laundry room; Barber/Beauty
shop.
Activities Arts & crafts; Cards; Games;
Reading groups; Prayer groups; Movies;
Shopping trips; Social/Cultural gatherings.

BARBERTON

Manor Care Nursing Center
85 3rd St SE, Barberton, OH, 44203
(216) 753-5005
Admin Jerry Smith. *Medical Dir/Dir of
Nursing* Dr Robert Littlejohn; Monia Miller
RN DON.
Licensure Skilled care; Intermediate care. *Beds*
SNF 120; ICF. *Certified* Medicaid;
Medicare.
Owner Proprietary Corp (Manor Care).
Admissions Requirements Medical
examination; Physician's request.
Staff Physicians 2 (pt); RNs 4 (ft), 3 (pt);
LPNs 10 (ft), 10 (pt); Orderlies 4 (ft); Nurses
aides 7 (ft), 13 (pt); Physical therapists 1 (ft);
Recreational therapists; Occupational
therapists 1 (pt); Speech therapists 1 (pt);
Activities coordinators 1 (ft); Dietitians 1
(ft); Ophthalmologists 1 (pt); Podiatrists 1
(pt); Dentist 1 (pt).
Facilities Dining room; Physical therapy
room; Activities room; Crafts room; Laundry
room; Barber/Beauty shop.
Activities Arts & crafts; Cards; Games;
Reading groups; Prayer groups; Movies;
Shopping trips; Social/Cultural gatherings.

Pleasant View Health Care Center
401 Snyder Ave, Barberton, OH, 44203
(216) 745-6028
Admin Kenneth Morris. *Medical Dir/Dir of
Nursing* Phillip N Gilcrest MD; Diane
Boyle.
Licensure Skilled care; Intermediate care. *Beds*
48. *Certified* Medicaid; Medicare.
Owner Privately owned.
Admissions Requirements Minimum age 18;
Medical examination; Physician's request.
Staff Physicians 5 (pt); RNs 3 (ft), 1 (pt);
LPNs 3 (ft), 2 (pt); Nurses aides 15 (ft), 9
(pt); Physical therapists 1 (pt); Activities
coordinators 1 (ft); Dietitians 1 (ft); Laundry
2 (ft), 2 (pt); Dietary 6 (ft), 4 (pt);
Housekeeping 2 (ft), 1 (pt).
Facilities Dining room; Physical therapy
room; Laundry room; Barber/Beauty shop.
Activities Arts & crafts; Cards; Games;
Reading groups; Prayer groups; Movies;
Social/Cultural gatherings.

Toth's Rest Home*
42 1st St SE, Barberton, OH, 44203
(216) 745-5786
Licensure Rest home. *Beds* 9.
Owner Proprietary Corp.

BARNESVILLE

Barnesville Health Care Center*
400 Carrie Ave, Barnesville, OH, 43713
(614) 425-3648
Licensure Intermediate care. *Beds* 100.
Certified Medicaid.
Owner Proprietary Corp.

Walton Retirement Home
61675 Roosevelt Rd, Barnesville, OH, 43713
(614) 425-1014, 425-2635
Admin Raymond W Stanley.

Licensure Retirement/Rest home. *Beds* 33.
Owner Nonprofit organization/foundation.
Admissions Requirements Medical
examination; Ambulatory status.
Staff RNs 1 (pt); Nurses aides 6 (ft); Activities
coordinators 1 (pt); Dietitians 1 (ft); Cooks 4
(ft).
Affiliation Society of Friends
Facilities Dining room; Activities room;
Chapel; Crafts room; Laundry room; Barber/
Beauty shop; Library; Parlor; Sun porch;
Separate apartments & cottages available.
Activities Arts & crafts; Cards; Games;
Reading groups; Prayer groups; Movies;
Shopping trips; Crafts.

BATAVIA

Batavia Nursing & Convalescent Inn*
4000 Golden Age Dr, Batavia, OH, 45103
(513) 732-6500
Medical Dir/Dir of Nursing Dr Jonathan
Head.
Licensure Skilled care; Intermediate care. *Beds*
216. *Certified* Medicaid; Medicare.
Owner Proprietary Corp.
Admissions Requirements Medical
examination.
Facilities Dining room; Physical therapy
room; Activities room; Crafts room; Laundry
room; Barber/Beauty shop; Library.
Activities Arts & crafts; Cards; Games;
Reading groups; Movies; Shopping trips;
Social/Cultural gatherings.

Batavia Nursing Home Inc*
Box 93, S 4th St, Batavia, OH, 45103
(513) 732-1535
Licensure Intermediate care. *Beds* 34.
Certified Medicaid.
Owner Proprietary Corp.

BAY VILLAGE

Bradley Road Nursing Home
605 Bradley Rd, Bay Village, OH, 44140
(216) 871-3474
Medical Dir/Dir of Nursing James Rush MD.
Licensure Skilled care. *Beds* 109. *Certified*
Medicare.
Owner Proprietary Corp.
Staff Physicians 18 (pt); RNs 3 (ft), 3 (pt);
LPNs 7 (ft), 7 (pt); Nurses aides 31 (ft), 6
(pt); Physical therapists 1 (pt); Occupational
therapists 1 (pt); Speech therapists 1 (pt);
Activities coordinators 1 (ft); Dietitians 1
(pt); Dentists 1 (pt); Ophthalmologists 1 (pt);
Podiatrists 1 (pt); Dentist 1 (pt).
Facilities Dining room; Physical therapy
room; Activities room; Crafts room; Laundry
room; Barber/Beauty shop; Private rooms.
Activities Arts & crafts; Cards; Games;
Reading groups; Prayer groups; Movies;
Shopping trips; Social/Cultural gatherings.

BEACHWOOD

Beach Haven Health Care Center
23900 Chagrin Blvd, Beachwood, OH, 44122
(216) 464-1000
Admin Sam Zimerman. *Medical Dir/Dir of
Nursing* Dusan Naunovich MD.
Licensure Skilled care; Intermediate care. *Beds*
210. *Certified* Medicaid; Medicare.
Owner Proprietary Corp.
Admissions Requirements Minimum age 18;
Medical examination.
Staff RNs 10 (ft), 4 (pt); LPNs 30 (ft), 11 (pt);
Nurses aides 97 (ft), 21 (pt); Physical
therapists 1 (ft); Speech therapists 1 (pt);
Activities coordinators 2 (ft), 1 (pt);
Dietitians 1 (ft).
Facilities Dining room; Physical therapy
room; Activities room; Crafts room; Laundry
room; Barber/Beauty shop.

Activities Arts & crafts; Cards; Games;
Reading groups; Games; Movies;
Shopping trips; Social/Cultural gatherings.

Menorah Park Center for the Aging
27100 Cedar Rd, Beachwood, OH, 44122
(216) 831-6500
Admin Howard B Bram. *Medical Dir/Dir of
Nursing* Julius Fishman MD; Dolly
Bheemaswarroop RN.
Licensure Skilled care; Intermediate care. *Beds*
SNF; ICF 352. *Certified* Medicaid;
Medicare.
Owner Nonprofit organization/foundation.
Admissions Requirements Medical
examination.
Staff Physicians 1 (ft), 21 (pt); RNs 19 (ft), 18
(pt); LPNs 28 (ft), 37 (pt); Orderlies 12 (ft);
Nurses aides 125 (ft), 12 (pt); Physical
therapists 1 (ft), 1 (pt); Recreational
therapists 5 (ft), 3 (pt); Occupational
therapists 2 (pt); Speech therapists 1 (pt);
Activities coordinators 1 (ft); Dietitians 2
(pt); Dentists 1 (pt); Ophthalmologists 1 (pt);
Podiatrists 1 (pt).
Affiliation Jewish
Facilities Dining room; Physical therapy
room; Activities room; Chapel; Crafts room;
Laundry room; Barber/Beauty shop; Library;
Sheltered workshop; Day care center;
Volunteer office; In-service training.
Activities Arts & crafts; Cards; Games;
Reading groups; Prayer groups; Movies;
Shopping trips; Social/Cultural gatherings;
Pet therapy; Horticulture therapy; Music &
art therapy.

BEAVER

Pineview Manor Inc
4136 German Rd, Beaver, OH, 45613
(614) 226-3074
Admin Linda Fisher. *Medical Dir/Dir of
Nursing* Sherry Leach RN.
Licensure Intermediate care. *Beds* ICF 50.
Certified Medicaid.
Owner Proprietary Corp.
Staff Physicians 1 (pt); RNs 1 (pt); LPNs 4
(ft), 1 (pt); Nurses aides 30 (ft), 5 (pt);
Recreational therapists 1 (ft); Activities
coordinators 1 (ft); Dietitians 1 (pt);
Ophthalmologists 1 (pt).
Facilities Dining room; Activities room;
Laundry room.
Activities Arts & crafts; Cards; Games; Prayer
groups; Movies; Shopping trips; Social/
Cultural gatherings.

BELLBROOK

Carriage-by-the-Lake Nursing Center
1957 N Lakeman Dr, Bellbrook, OH, 45305
(513) 848-8421
Admin Jeanne Palcic. *Medical Dir/Dir of
Nursing* Dr Charles Moody; Sue Jones.
Licensure Skilled care; Intermediate care. *Beds*
SNF 78; ICF 78. *Certified* Medicaid;
Medicare.
Owner Proprietary Corp (Health Care
Management).
Admissions Requirements Medical
examination.
Staff RNs 7 (ft), 6 (pt); LPNs 4 (ft), 2 (pt);
Orderlies 2 (ft), 2 (pt); Nurses aides 16 (ft),
17 (pt); Activities coordinators 1 (ft);
Dietitians 1 (pt); Restorative Aide 1 (ft).
Facilities Dining room; Activities room;
Crafts room; Laundry room; Barber/Beauty
shop; Courtyard; Van for resident
transportation.
Activities Arts & crafts; Cards; Games;
Reading groups; Prayer groups; Movies;
Shopping trips; Social/Cultural gatherings.

BELLEFONTAINE

Heartland of Bellefontaine
221 N School St, Bellefontaine, OH, 43311
(513) 599-5123
Admin Charles George. *Medical Dir/Dir of
Nursing* Dr David Eubanks.
Licensure Skilled care; Intermediate care; Rest
home. *Beds* SNF 75; ICF; Rest home 25.
Certified Medicaid; Medicare.
Owner Proprietary Corp (Health Care &
Retirement Corp).
Admissions Requirements Minimum age 40;
Medical examination.
Staff Physicians; RNs; LPNs; Orderlies;
Nurses aides; Physical therapists;
Occupational therapists; Speech therapists;
Activities coordinators; Dietitians;
Ophthalmologists; Podiatrists.
Facilities Dining room; Physical therapy
room; Activities room; Laundry room;
Barber/Beauty shop.
Activities Arts & crafts; Cards; Games;
Reading groups; Prayer groups; Movies;
Shopping trips; Social/Cultural gatherings.

Logan Acres
9123 County Rd 91, Bellefontaine, OH, 43311
(513) 592-2901
Admin Sue Crawfis. *Medical Dir/Dir of
Nursing* Dr A Roldan; Sue Allen.
Licensure Intermediate care. *Beds* ICF 95.
Certified Medicaid.
Owner Publicly owned.
Admissions Requirements Medical
examination.
Staff Physicians 1 (pt); RNs 2 (ft), 2 (pt);
LPNs 7 (ft), 3 (pt); Nurses aides 21 (ft), 18
(pt); Activities coordinators 1 (ft), 1 (pt).
Facilities Dining room; Crafts room; Barber/
Beauty shop; Library.
Activities Arts & crafts; Cards; Games;
Reading groups; Prayer groups; Movies;
Shopping trips; Social/Cultural gatherings.

BELLEVUE

Bellevue Nursing Home
1 Audrich Sq, Bellevue, OH, 44811
(419) 483-6225
Licensure Nursing home. *Beds* 24.
Owner Proprietary Corp.

BELLVILLE

Overlook Nursing Home*
Rte 2, Algire Rd, Bellville, OH, 44813
(419) 886-3922
Licensure Intermediate care. *Beds* 27.
Certified Medicaid.
Owner Proprietary Corp.

BELMONT

Bell Nursing Home Inc
42350 National Rd, Belmont, OH, 43718
(614) 782-1561
Admin Michael G Maistros. *Medical Dir/Dir
of Nursing* Dr Matt Kirkland; Rose
Pittenger.
Licensure Skilled care. *Beds* SNF; ICF 52.
Certified Medicaid; Medicare.
Owner Proprietary Corp.
Staff Physicians; RNs; LPNs; Nurses aides;
Physical therapists; Occupational therapists;
Activities coordinators; Dietitians; Dentists;
Ophthalmologists.
Facilities Dining room; Physical therapy
room; Activities room; Chapel; Laundry
room; Barber/Beauty shop.

BEREA

Berea North Quality Care Nursing Center*
49 Sheldon Rd, Berea, OH, 44017
(216) 234-0454

Licensure Nursing home. *Beds* 50.
Owner Proprietary Corp.

Berea Quality Care Nursing Center
570 N Rocky River Dr, Berea, OH, 44017
(216) 234-2294
Admin Mr C E Rogerson. *Medical Dir/Dir of Nursing* William Bond MD; Kathy Lazroff LPN.
Licensure Intermediate care. *Beds* ICF 50. *Certified* Medicaid.
Owner Proprietary Corp (Northwestern Service Corp).
Admissions Requirements Medical examination.
Staff Physicians 1 (ft); RNs 1 (pt); LPNs 6 (ft); Orderlies 1 (ft); Nurses aides 19 (ft), 2 (pt); Physical therapists 1 (ft); Activities coordinators 2 (ft); Dietitians 1 (ft); Dentists 1 (pt); Ophthalmologists 1 (pt).
Facilities Dining room; Physical therapy room; Activities room; Chapel; Laundry room; Barber/Beauty shop; Living room.
Activities Arts & crafts; Cards; Games; Prayer groups; Movies; Van outings.

BETHEL

Morris Nursing Home*
322 S Charity St, Bethel, OH, 45106
(513) 734-7401
Licensure Intermediate care. *Beds* 18. *Certified* Medicaid.
Owner Proprietary Corp.

BETHESDA

Star Nursing Home
40060 National Rd-Morristown, Bethesda, OH, 43719
(614) 782-1944
Admin Tino Agostini. *Medical Dir/Dir of Nursing* Pam Chase DON.
Licensure Intermediate care. *Beds* ICF 50. *Certified* Medicaid.
Owner Proprietary Corp.
Staff Physicians 1 (ft); RNs 2 (ft); LPNs 4 (ft), 7 (pt); Orderlies 1 (pt); Nurses aides 11 (ft), 11 (pt); Physical therapists 1 (pt); Activities coordinators 1 (ft); Dietitians 1 (pt); Ophthalmologists 1 (pt).

BEVERLY

Fairview Manor Nursing Home Inc*
501 Pinecrest Dr, Box 458, Beverly, OH, 45715
(614) 984-4262
Admin Pansy Pickenpaugh. *Medical Dir/Dir of Nursing* Victor Whitacre MD.
Licensure Skilled care; Intermediate care. *Beds* 76. *Certified* Medicaid; Medicare.
Owner Proprietary Corp.
Admissions Requirements Minimum age 18.
Staff Physicians 3 (pt); RNs 4 (ft), 3 (pt); LPNs 6 (ft), 3 (pt); Nurses aides 22 (ft), 7 (pt); Physical therapists 1 (pt); Activities coordinators 1 (ft); Dietitians 1 (pt); Rehabilitation aides 1 (ft).
Facilities Dining room; Activities room; Crafts room; Laundry room; Barber/Beauty shop; Library; TV lounges.
Activities Arts & crafts; Cards; Games; Reading groups; Prayer groups; Movies; Shopping trips; Social/Cultural gatherings.

BIDWELL

Buckeye Community Services—Bidwell Home*
Box 398, Rte 1, Bidwell, OH, 45614
Licensure Intermediate care for mentally retarded. *Beds* 5. *Certified* Medicaid.
Owner Nonprofit Corp.

Scenic Hills Nursing Center
RR 2, Bidwell, OH, 45614

Licensure Skilled care; Intermediate care. *Beds* SNF 100; ICF 100. *Certified* Medicaid; Medicare.
Owner Proprietary Corp (Health Care Management).

BLANCHESTER

Blanchester Care Center
839 E Cherry St, Blanchester, OH, 45107
(513) 783-4911
Admin Joetta Meyer. *Medical Dir/Dir of Nursing* Bruce Staley MD; Carol Weber RN.
Licensure Skilled care; Intermediate care. *Beds* 50. *Certified* Medicaid; Medicare.
Owner Proprietary Corp (Southmark Heritage Corp).
Admissions Requirements Medical examination; Physician's request.
Staff Physicians 7 (pt); RNs 2 (ft), 2 (pt); LPNs 5 (ft), 1 (pt); Nurses aides 17 (ft), 3 (pt); Physical therapists 1 (pt); Recreational therapists 1 (ft); Occupational therapists 1 (pt); Speech therapists 1 (pt); Activities coordinators 1 (ft); Dietitians 1 (pt); Ophthalmologists 1 (pt); Social Service 1 (ft).
Facilities Dining room; Physical therapy room; Activities room; Laundry room; Barber/Beauty shop.
Activities Arts & crafts; Cards; Games; Reading groups; Prayer groups; Movies; Shopping trips; Social/Cultural gatherings.

Continental Manor Nursing & Rehabilitation Center
820 E Center St, Blanchester, OH, 45107
(513) 783-4949
Admin Robert B Snader. *Medical Dir/Dir of Nursing* Dr Thomas Neville; Gladys M Fuller DON.
Licensure Skilled care; Intermediate care. *Beds* 74. *Certified* Medicaid; Medicare.
Owner Privately owned.
Admissions Requirements Medical examination; Physician's request.
Languages Spanish
Facilities Dining room; Physical therapy room; Crafts room; Laundry room; Barber/Beauty shop.
Activities Arts & crafts; Cards; Games; Reading groups; Prayer groups; Movies; Shopping trips; Social/Cultural gatherings.

BLOOMVILLE

Bloomville Nursing Care Center*
22 Clinton St, Bloomville, OH, 44818
(419) 983-2021
Medical Dir/Dir of Nursing Dr Olgierd Garlo.
Licensure Intermediate care. *Beds* 30. *Certified* Medicaid.
Owner Proprietary Corp.
Staff Physicians 1 (ft); RNs 2 (ft), 2 (pt); LPNs 1 (ft), 2 (pt); Nurses aides 6 (ft), 8 (pt); Activities coordinators 1 (ft); Dietitians 1 (pt).
Facilities Dining room; Activities room; Chapel; Crafts room; Laundry room; Barber/Beauty shop.
Activities Arts & crafts; Cards; Games; Reading groups; Prayer groups; Movies; Shopping trips; Social/Cultural gatherings.

BLUE ASH

Blue Ash Nursing & Convalescent Home Inc*
4900 Cooper Rd, Blue Ash, OH, 45242
(513) 793-3362
Licensure Skilled care; Intermediate care. *Beds* 114. *Certified* Medicaid; Medicare.
Owner Proprietary Corp.

BLUFFTON

Mennonite Memorial Home
410 W Elm St, Bluffton, OH, 45817
(419) 358-1015
Admin Paul I Dyck. *Medical Dir/Dir of Nursing* O Lugibihl MD; Mary Weaver DON.
Licensure Intermediate care. *Beds* ICF 92. *Certified* Medicaid.
Owner Nonprofit organization/foundation.
Admissions Requirements Minimum age 62.
Staff RNs 6 (ft), 3 (pt); LPNs 4 (ft), 4 (pt); Nurses aides 22 (ft), 29 (pt); Occupational therapists 2 (ft); Activities coordinators 1 (ft); Social workers 1 (ft).
Affiliation Mennonite
Facilities Dining room; Activities room; Chapel; Crafts room; Laundry room; Barber/Beauty shop; Library.
Activities Arts & crafts; Games; Reading groups; Prayer groups; Movies; Shopping trips; Social/Cultural gatherings.

Richland Manor Nursing Home*
7400 Swaney Rd, Bluffton, OH, 45817
(419) 643-3161, 4511
Licensure Skilled care; Intermediate care. *Beds* 100. *Certified* Medicaid; Medicare.
Owner Proprietary Corp.

BOARDMAN

Ron Joy Nursing Home Inc
830 BoardmanCanfield Rd, Boardman, OH, 44512
(216) 758-8106
Admin Felix Savon. *Medical Dir/Dir of Nursing* Dr Ho; Regina Graygo RN.
Licensure Intermediate care. *Beds* ICF 87. *Certified* Medicaid.
Owner Proprietary Corp.
Admissions Requirements Medical examination.
Staff RNs 4 (ft); LPNs 10 (ft), 3 (pt); Orderlies 6 (ft); Nurses aides 17 (ft), 7 (pt); Activities coordinators 1 (ft).
Languages Greek, Italian
Facilities Dining room; Physical therapy room; Activities room; Chapel; Crafts room; Laundry room; Barber/Beauty shop.
Activities Arts & crafts; Cards; Games; Reading groups; Prayer groups; Movies; Social/Cultural gatherings.

Westwood Rehabilitation Medical Center
7148 West Blvd, Boardman, OH, 44512
(216) 726-9061
Admin William Heckman. *Medical Dir/Dir of Nursing* Anthony Pannozzo MD; Patricia A Holmes RN DON.
Licensure Skilled care; Intermediate care. *Beds* 149. *Certified* Medicaid; Medicare.
Owner Proprietary Corp.
Admissions Requirements Medical examination; Physician's request.
Staff Physicians 1 (ft), 3 (pt); RNs 7 (ft), 1 (pt); LPNs 24 (ft), 6 (pt); Orderlies; Nurses aides; Physical therapists 1 (ft), 1 (pt); Occupational therapists 1 (pt); Speech therapists 1 (pt); Activities coordinators 3 (ft); Dietitians 1 (ft), 1 (pt); Ophthalmologists 1 (pt); Podiatrists 1 (pt); Psychologist 1 (pt); Rehab Nursing 1 (ft); Rehab NAs 2 (ft), 1 (pt); Dentist 1 (pt).
Facilities Dining room; Physical therapy room; Activities room; Crafts room; Laundry room; Barber/Beauty shop.
Activities Arts & crafts; Cards; Games; Reading groups; Prayer groups; Movies; Shopping trips; Social/Cultural gatherings.

BOWERSTON

Bowerston Health Care Center*
9076 Cumberland Rd, Bowerston, OH, 44695
(614) 269-8393

Licensure Intermediate care. *Beds* 25.
Certified Medicaid.
Owner Nonprofit Corp.

Sunnyslope Nursing Home
102 Boyce Dr, Bowerston, OH, 44695
(614) 269-8001
Admin Glenn W Roth. *Medical Dir/Dir of
Nursing* Wandalee Brannon LPN DON.
Licensure Intermediate care. *Beds* ICF 48.
Owner Nonprofit Corp.
Admissions Requirements Medical
examination.
Staff LPNs 6 (ft), 1 (pt); Nurses aides 11 (ft),
6 (pt); Activities coordinators 1 (ft);
Dietitians 1 (ft).
Facilities Dining room; Laundry room;
Barber/Beauty shop; Library.
Activities Cards; Games; Reading groups;
Prayer groups; Movies; Shopping trips;
Picnics; Van rides.

BOWLING GREEN

Bowling Green Manor
1021 Poe Rd, Bowling Green, OH, 43402
(419) 352-4684
Admin Rhoda Terlizzi. *Medical Dir/Dir of
Nursing* Thomas W Watson MD.
Licensure Skilled care; Intermediate care. *Beds*
100. *Certified* Medicaid; Medicare.
Owner Proprietary Corp (Health Care
Facilities Inc).
Admissions Requirements Medical
examination.
Staff Physicians 1 (ft); RNs 5 (ft); LPNs 10
(ft), 1 (pt); Nurses aides 36 (ft); Physical
therapists 1 (pt); Reality therapists 1 (ft);
Recreational therapists 1 (ft); Speech
therapists 1 (pt); Activities coordinators 1
(ft), 1 (pt); Dietitians 1 (ft).
Facilities Dining room; Physical therapy
room; Activities room; Crafts room; Laundry
room; Barber/Beauty shop.
Activities Arts & crafts; Cards; Games;
Reading groups; Prayer groups; Movies;
Shopping trips; Social/Cultural gatherings.

Community Nursing Home
850 W Poe Rd, Bowling Green, OH, 43402
(419) 352-7558
Admin Renee L Sessi. *Medical Dir/Dir of
Nursing* Marjorie Conrad MD; Karen Bell
RN.
Licensure Skilled care; Intermediate care. *Beds*
SNF 24; ICF 76. *Certified* Medicare.
Owner Proprietary Corp (Beverly Enterprises).
Admissions Requirements Minimum age 18;
Medical examination.
Facilities Dining room; Physical therapy
room; Activities room; Crafts room; Laundry
room; Barber/Beauty shop.
Activities Arts & crafts; Games; Reading
groups; Prayer groups; Movies; Shopping
trips; Social/Cultural gatherings; Lunch-out
group; Adopt-a-grandparent.

Maria Care Center
308 W Wooster St, Bowling Green, OH,
43402
(419) 353-7651
Admin Marcus Kim. *Medical Dir/Dir of
Nursing* Dr William Feeman.
Licensure Intermediate care. *Beds* ICF 24.
Certified Medicaid; Medicare.
Owner Proprietary Corp.
Admissions Requirements Medical
examination.
Staff Physicians 1 (pt); RNs 1 (pt); LPNs 2
(ft), 3 (pt); Orderlies 1 (ft); Nurses aides 1
(ft), 7 (pt); Recreational therapists 1 (ft);
Activities coordinators 1 (pt); Dietitians 1
(pt).
Affiliation Roman Catholic

Facilities Dining room; Activities room;
Crafts room; Laundry room.
Activities Arts & crafts; Cards; Games;
Reading groups; Prayer groups; Movies;
Shopping trips; Social/Cultural gatherings.

Wood County Nursing Home
11080 E Gypsy Lane Rd, Bowling Green, OH,
43402
(419) 353-8411
Admin Martin Jan. *Medical Dir/Dir of
Nursing* Dr Roger A Peatee; Susan E Coker
RN DON.
Licensure Skilled care; Intermediate care. *Beds*
SNF 127; ICF. *Certified* Medicaid;
Medicare.
Owner Publicly owned.
Admissions Requirements Minimum age Aged
given priority; Medical examination.
Staff Physicians 1 (pt); RNs 5 (ft), 2 (pt);
LPNs 8 (ft), 2 (pt); Orderlies 2 (pt); Nurses
aides 38 (ft); Speech therapists 1 (pt);
Activities coordinators 1 (ft); Dietitians 1
(ft); Social workers 2 (ft).
Facilities Dining room; Physical therapy
room; Activities room; Chapel; Crafts room;
Laundry room; Barber/Beauty shop; Library;
Mobile library.
Activities Arts & crafts; Cards; Games;
Reading groups; Prayer groups; Movies;
Shopping trips; Social/Cultural gatherings.

Wooster Nursing Home
PO Box 1102, 416 W Wooster St, Bowling
Green, OH, 43402
(419) 352-6414
Admin Ernest R Tebeau. *Medical Dir/Dir of
Nursing* Dr Mohammad Sidiq.
Licensure Intermediate care. *Beds*
Intermediate care-Mild Mental 21. *Certified*
Medicaid.
Owner Privately owned.
Staff Physicians 1 (pt); RNs 1 (pt); LPNs 2
(ft), 2 (pt); Orderlies 1 (ft); Nurses aides 5
(ft), 4 (pt); Activities coordinators 1 (ft), 1
(pt); Dietitians 1 (pt); Psychologist 1 (pt).
Facilities Dining room.
Activities Arts & crafts; Cards; Games;
Reading groups; Movies.

BRADFORD

Bradford Living Care Center
325 S Miami Ave, Bradford, OH, 45308
(513) 448-2259
Admin Joyce Helman.
Licensure Intermediate care. *Beds* 17.
Certified Medicaid.
Owner Proprietary Corp.
Staff Physicians; LPNs; Nurses aides;
Activities coordinators.
Facilities Dining room; Laundry room;
Barber/Beauty shop.
Activities Arts & crafts; Games; Reading
groups; Prayer groups; Shopping trips;
Social/Cultural gatherings; Beauty shop; Van
rides.

BRATENAHL

Bolton Convalescent Home
13802 Lake Shore Blvd, Bratenahl, OH, 44110
(216) 457-3334
Admin Lenore Finerman. *Medical Dir/Dir of
Nursing* Dr Javier Clemente; Denise
Freeman DON.
Licensure Intermediate care. *Beds* ICF 16.
Certified Medicaid.
Owner Proprietary Corp.
Admissions Requirements Minimum age 21;
Females only.
Staff Physicians 1 (pt); RNs 1 (pt); LPNs 2
(ft), 1 (pt); Nurses aides 5 (ft), 5 (pt);
Occupational therapists 1 (pt); Activities
coordinators 1 (pt); Dentists 1 (pt);
Ophthalmologists 1 (pt); Dentist 1 (pt).

Facilities Dining room; Activities room;
Laundry room.
Activities Arts & crafts; Cards; Games; Prayer
groups; Movies; Shopping trips.

BRECKSVILLE

Haven Hill Home
4400 Oakes Rd Cottage 1, Brecksville, OH,
44141
(216) 526-6515
Admin Joyce A Swaisgood. *Medical Dir/Dir of
Nursing* Dr Barry Brooks.
Licensure Intermediate care for mentally
retarded. *Beds* ICF/MR 13. *Certified*
Medicaid.
Owner Nonprofit Corp.
Admissions Requirements Minimum age 18;
Medical examination.
Staff RNs 4 (pt); LPNs 3 (ft), 2 (pt); Orderlies
2 (ft), 2 (pt); Nurses aides 4 (ft), 4 (pt);
Recreational therapists 1 (pt).
Facilities Dining room; Activities room;
Laundry room.
Activities Arts & crafts; Games; Movies;
Shopping trips; Social/Cultural gatherings.

BREWSTER

Brewster Parke Convalescent Center
264 Mohican St, Brewster, OH, 44613
(216) 832-2171, 767-4179
Admin Cheryl Childs. *Medical Dir/Dir of
Nursing* Philip R Nicol MD; Virginia Kula
RN.
Licensure Intermediate care. *Beds* ICF 51.
Certified Medicaid.
Owner Proprietary Corp.
Admissions Requirements Minimum age 55.
Staff Physicians; RNs 1 (ft), 1 (pt); LPNs 4
(ft), 2 (pt); Nurses aides 9 (ft), 7 (pt);
Physical therapists; Activities coordinators 1
(ft); Dietitians 1 (ft); Ophthalmologists;
Dentist.
Facilities Dining room; Activities room;
Chapel; Laundry room; Barber/Beauty shop;
Library.
Activities Arts & crafts; Cards; Games; Prayer
groups; Shopping trips.

BROADVIEW HEIGHTS

Broadview Developmental Center
9543 Broadview Rd, Broadview Heights, OH,
44147
(216) 526-5000
Admin Purcell Taylor Jr Ed D. *Medical Dir/
Dir of Nursing* Chu Ho Chung MD.
Licensure Intermediate care for mentally
retarded. *Beds* Licensed beds 192. *Certified*
Medicaid.
Owner Publicly owned State of Ohio.
Admissions Requirements Medical
examination.
Staff Physicians 2 (ft); RNs 5 (ft), 2 (pt);
LPNs 7 (ft); Nurses aides 180 (ft), 10 (pt);
Physical therapists 1 (ft), 3 (pt); Recreational
therapists 12 (ft), 1 (pt); Occupational
therapists 1 (ft), 1 (pt); Speech therapists 1
(ft); Dietitians 1 (ft); Ophthalmologists 1 (ft);
Podiatrists 1 (pt).
Facilities Dining room; Physical therapy
room; Activities room; Chapel; Crafts room;
Laundry room; Barber/Beauty shop; Library;
Residential units; Pre-vocational class
rooms; Gymnasium; Swimming pool;
Bowling alley.
Activities Arts & crafts; Games; Reading
groups; Prayer groups; Movies; Shopping
trips; Social/Cultural gatherings.

Ohio Residential Services*
9571 Broadview Rd, Broadview Heights, OH,
44147

Licensure Skilled care. *Beds* 8. *Certified*
Medicaid.
Owner Nonprofit Corp.

BROOK PARK

The Lamp*
6034 Engle Rd, Brook Park, OH, 44142
(216) 433-4446
Licensure Nursing home. *Beds* 34.
Owner Proprietary Corp.

BROOKVILLE

Brookhaven Nursing Care Center*
770 N Albert Rd, Brookville, OH, 45309
(513) 833-2133
Admin Ruby J Ferrier. *Medical Dir/Dir of
Nursing* Vinton Young MD.
Licensure Skilled care; Intermediate care. *Beds*
100. *Certified* Medicaid; Medicare.
Owner Proprietary Corp.
Admissions Requirements Medical
examination.
Staff Physicians 8 (pt); RNs 4 (ft), 4 (pt);
LPNs 4 (ft), 3 (pt); Orderlies 2 (ft), 1 (pt);
Nurses aides 27 (ft), 19 (pt); Physical
therapists 2 (pt); Occupational therapists 1
(pt); Speech therapists 1 (pt); Activities
coordinators 1 (ft), 1 (pt); Dietitians 1 (pt);
Dentists 1 (pt); Ophthalmologists 1 (pt);
Podiatrists 1 (pt); Audiologists 1 (pt).
Facilities Dining room; Physical therapy
room; Activities room; Chapel; Crafts room;
Laundry room; Barber/Beauty shop; Library.
Activities Arts & crafts; Cards; Games;
Reading groups; Prayer groups; Movies;
Shopping trips; Social/Cultural gatherings.

BRUNSWICK

Pearlview Nursing Home
PO Box 0070, 4426 Homestead Dr,
Brunswick, OH, 44212
(216) 225-9121
Admin Basil Gaitanoros. *Medical Dir/Dir of
Nursing* Dr T Gaitanoros; Ellen Raley RN.
Licensure Skilled care; Intermediate care. *Beds*
SNF 127; ICF. *Certified* Medicaid;
Medicare.
Owner Proprietary Corp.
Admissions Requirements Minimum age 62.
Staff Physicians 4 (pt); RNs 6 (ft), 6 (pt);
LPNs 4 (ft), 6 (pt); Nurses aides 34 (ft), 34
(pt); Physical therapists 1 (pt); Speech
therapists 1 (pt); Activities coordinators 1
(ft); Dietitians 1 (pt); Dentists 1 (pt);
Ophthalmologists 1 (pt); Podiatrists 1 (pt); 1
(pt) Dentist 1 (pt).
Facilities Dining room; Physical therapy
room; Activities room; Chapel; Crafts room;
Laundry room; Barber/Beauty shop.
Activities Arts & crafts; Cards; Games;
Movies; Social/Cultural gatherings; Patio &
bake sales.

Willowood Nursing Home Inc
PO Box 810, 1186 Hadcock Rd, Brunswick,
OH, 44212
(216) 225-3156
Admin Patrick M Pozderac, Denis T
Pozderac. *Medical Dir/Dir of Nursing* Dr B
H Ferrer; Rosie Bland.
Licensure Intermediate care for mentally
retarded. *Beds* ICF 100; ICF/MR 96.
Certified Medicaid.
Owner Proprietary Corp.
Admissions Requirements Medical
examination.
Staff Physicians 2 (pt); RNs 6 (ft), 6 (pt);
LPNs 24 (ft), 14 (pt); Orderlies 5 (ft), 12
(pt); Nurses aides 85 (ft), 35 (pt); Physical
therapists 2 (pt); Occupational therapists 2
(pt); Speech therapists 1 (pt); Activities
coordinators 2 (ft); Dietitians 1 (pt); Dentists
1 (pt); Ophthalmologists 1 (pt).

Facilities Dining room; Physical therapy
room; Activities room; Chapel; Crafts room;
Laundry room; Barber/Beauty shop.
Activities Arts & crafts; Cards; Games;
Reading groups; Prayer groups; Movies;
Shopping trips; Social/Cultural gatherings.

BRYAN

Bryan Nursing Care Center*
1104 Wesley Avenue, PO Box 647, Bryan,
OH, 43506
(419) 636-5071
Medical Dir/Dir of Nursing R K Meyer.
Licensure Skilled care; Intermediate care. *Beds*
189. *Certified* Medicaid.
Owner Proprietary Corp.
Staff Physicians; RNs 5 (ft), 7 (pt); LPNs 8
(ft), 8 (pt); Orderlies 3 (ft); Nurses aides 49
(ft), 24 (pt); Physical therapists; Speech
therapists; Activities coordinators.
Facilities Dining room; Physical therapy
room; Activities room; Crafts room; Laundry
room; Barber/Beauty shop; Library; Isolation
room.
Activities Arts & crafts; Cards; Games;
Reading groups; Prayer groups; Movies;
Shopping trips; Social/Cultural gatherings.

Williams County Hillside Nursing Home*
Rte 3, Box 234, Bryan, OH, 43506
(419) 636-4508
Licensure Intermediate care. *Beds* 71.
Certified Medicaid.
Owner Publicly owned.

BUCYRUS

Belle Hoffman Michael Home
518 E Rensselaer St, Bucyrus, OH, 44820
(419) 562-0168
Admin Mrs J B Wert.
Licensure Rest home for aged christian
women. *Beds* Rest home 12.
Owner Nonprofit Corp.
Admissions Requirements Females only;
Medical examination.
Staff Nurses aides.
Affiliation King's Daughters & Sons
Facilities Dining room; Laundry room.
Activities Cards; Games; Sunday worship.

Heartland of Bucyrus HCR Inc
1170 W Mansfield St, Bucyrus, OH, 44820
(419) 562-9907
Admin Ann Stover Wyatt. *Medical Dir/Dir of
Nursing* Dr Ralph Lyon; Geri Sullivan
DON.
Licensure Skilled care; Intermediate care. *Beds*
100. *Certified* Medicaid; Medicare.
Owner Proprietary Corp (Health Care &
Retirement Corp).
Admissions Requirements Medical
examination; Physician's request.
Staff Physicians 5 (ft); RNs 4 (ft); LPNs 5 (ft),
2 (pt); Orderlies 1 (ft); Nurses aides 28 (ft),
8 (pt); Physical therapists 1 (ft);
Occupational therapists 1 (ft); Speech
therapists 1 (ft); Activities coordinators 1
(ft), 1 (pt); Dietitians 1 (ft); Dentists 1 (ft);
Ophthalmologists 1 (ft); Podiatrists 1 (ft).
Facilities Dining room; Physical therapy
room; Activities room; Laundry room;
Barber/Beauty shop; Lounges; Glassed-in
porch; Gazebo.
Activities Arts & crafts; Cards; Games;
Reading groups; Prayer groups; Movies;
Shopping trips; Social/Cultural gatherings;
Bingo; Sing-alongs; Swimming; Country
rides.

Maplecrest Home*
717 Rogers St, Bucyrus, OH, 44820
(419) 562-4988
Licensure Rest home. *Beds* 25.
Owner Nonprofit Corp.

Oakwood Manor
1929 Whetstone St, Bucyrus, OH, 44820
(419) 562-7644
Admin Catherine M Carter. *Medical Dir/Dir
of Nursing* Dr Skinner; Jan Strouse DON.
Licensure Skilled care; Intermediate care. *Beds*
SNF 98; ICF. *Certified* Medicaid; Medicare.
Owner Privately owned.
Staff Physicians 1 (pt); RNs 5 (ft); LPNs 15
(ft), 5 (pt); Orderlies 6 (ft), 2 (pt); Nurses
aides 40 (ft), 10 (pt); Physical therapists 1
(ft), 1 (pt); Reality therapists 1 (ft);
Recreational therapists 1 (ft); Occupational
therapists 1 (pt); Speech therapists 1 (pt);
Activities coordinators 1 (ft); Dietitians 1
(pt); Dentists 1 (pt); Ophthalmologists 2 (pt);
Podiatrists 1 (pt).
Facilities Dining room; Physical therapy
room; Activities room; Crafts room; Laundry
room; Barber/Beauty shop.
Activities Arts & crafts; Cards; Games;
Reading groups; Prayer groups; Movies;
Shopping trips; Social/Cultural gatherings.

Westfall Nursing Home*
320 E Warren St, Bucyrus, OH, 44820
(419) 562-6986
Licensure Nursing home. *Beds* 17.
Owner Proprietary Corp.

CADIZ

Alternative Residence 44-Cadiz Group Home
215 Burton Ave, Cadiz, OH, 43907
(614) 942-4931
Admin Bob Connell. *Medical Dir/Dir of
Nursing* Janet Ruckman.
Licensure Intermediate care for mentally
retarded. *Beds* ICF/MR 10.
Owner Nonprofit Corp.
Staff Physicians 1 (pt); RNs 1 (pt); LPNs 1
(ft), 3 (pt); Orderlies 4 (ft), 9 (pt); Physical
therapists 1 (pt); Occupational therapists 1
(pt); Speech therapists 1 (pt); Dietitians 1
(pt); Dentists 1 (pt); Ophthalmologists 1 (pt);
Podiatrists 1 (pt).

Carriage Inn of Cadiz Inc*
259 Jamison Ave, Cadiz, OH, 43907
(614) 942-3079
Licensure Skilled care; Intermediate care. *Beds*
140. *Certified* Medicaid; Medicare.
Owner Proprietary Corp.

CALDWELL

Summit Acres Nursing Home
PO Box 140, Rte 1, Caldwell, OH, 43724
(614) 732-2364
Admin Donald J Crock. *Medical Dir/Dir of
Nursing* Dr Fredrick Cox; Nancy Morris
DON.
Licensure Skilled care; Intermediate care. *Beds*
SNF 11; ICF 139. *Certified* Medicaid;
Medicare.
Owner Proprietary Corp.
Staff Physicians 3 (pt); RNs 9 (ft), 1 (pt);
LPNs 16 (ft), 2 (pt); Nurses aides 52 (ft), 7
(pt); Physical therapists 1 (pt); Recreational
therapists 2 (pt); Speech therapists 1 (pt);
Activities coordinators 4 (ft); Dietitians 1
(pt); Dentists 1 (pt); Ophthalmologists 1 (pt);
Podiatrists 1 (pt).
Facilities Dining room; Physical therapy
room; Activities room; Chapel; Crafts room;
Laundry room; Barber/Beauty shop; Library.
Activities Arts & crafts; Cards; Games;
Reading groups; Prayer groups; Movies;
Shopping trips; Social/Cultural gatherings.

Summit Acres Nursing Home Inc—Home B
Rte 1, Box 140, Caldwell, OH, 43724
(614) 732-2364
Admin Donald J Crock. *Medical Dir/Dir of
Nursing* Dr Cox; Nancy Morris DON.

Licensure Skilled care; Intermediate care. *Beds* SNF 11; ICF 139. *Certified* Medicaid; Medicare.
Owner Proprietary Corp.
Staff Physicians 2 (pt); RNs 8 (ft), 2 (pt); LPNs 13 (ft), 4 (pt); Nurses aides 52 (ft), 2 (pt); Physical therapists 1 (pt); Recreational therapists 2 (pt); Speech therapists 1 (pt); Activities coordinators 4 (ft); Dietitians & Aides 11 (ft); Ophthalmologists 1 (pt).
Facilities Dining room; Physical therapy room; Activities room; Chapel; Laundry room; Barber/Beauty shop; Library.
Activities Arts & crafts; Cards; Games; Reading groups; Prayer groups; Movies; Shopping trips; Social/Cultural gatherings.

CAMBRIDGE

Cambridge Developmental Center
County Rd 35, Cambridge, OH, 43725
(614) 439-1371
Admin William N Spradley. *Medical Dir/Dir of Nursing* Clarence R Apel MD; Ralph Ray RN.
Licensure Intermediate care for mentally retarded. *Beds* ICF/MR 159. *Certified* Medicaid.
Owner Publicly owned.
Admissions Requirements Minimum age 18.
Staff Physicians 2 (pt); RNs 12 (ft), 1 (pt); LPNs 13 (ft); Nurses aides 117 (ft), 7 (pt); Physical therapists 1 (pt); Recreational therapists 3 (ft); Podiatrists 1 (ft).
Facilities Dining room; Physical therapy room; Activities room; Chapel; Crafts room; Laundry room; Barber/Beauty shop; Library; Cottage/habilitation areas.
Activities Arts & crafts; Cards; Games; Reading groups; Prayer groups; Movies; Shopping trips; Social/Cultural gatherings; All activity/program services consistent with ICF/MR standards.

Cambridge Health Care Center*
1471 Wills Creek Valley Dr, Cambridge, OH, 43725
(614) 439-4437
Admin Betty Bell. *Medical Dir/Dir of Nursing* John Haun MD; Pat Snader DON.
Licensure Intermediate care. *Beds* ICF 159. *Certified* Medicaid.
Owner Proprietary Corp.
Staff Physicians 1 (pt); RNs 10 (ft), 4 (pt); LPNs 12 (ft), 6 (pt); Nurses aides 60 (ft), 25 (pt); Physical therapists 1 (pt); Speech therapists 1 (pt); Activities coordinators 3 (ft), 1 (pt).
Facilities Dining room; Physical therapy room; Activities room; Chapel; Crafts room; Laundry room; Barber/Beauty shop; Library.
Activities Arts & crafts; Cards; Games; Reading groups; Prayer groups; Movies; Shopping trips; Social/Cultural gatherings.

Red Carpet Health Care Center
PO Box 1489, 8420 Georgetown Rd, Cambridge, OH, 43725
(614) 439-4401
Admin Vern Beynon. *Medical Dir/Dir of Nursing* Dorothy Diment DON.
Licensure Intermediate care; Rest home. *Beds* ICF 78; Rest home 84. *Certified* Medicaid.
Owner Proprietary Corp.
Admissions Requirements Medical examination.
Staff RNs; LPNs; Nurses aides; Activities coordinators.
Facilities Dining room; Activities room; Crafts room; Laundry room; Barber/Beauty shop.
Activities Arts & crafts; Cards; Games; Prayer groups; Movies; Shopping trips; Social/Cultural gatherings.

CANAL FULTON

Chapel Hill Home
12200 Strasser Rd, Canal Fulton, OH, 44614
(216) 854-4177
Admin Gloria J Prose. *Medical Dir/Dir of Nursing* Dr Jeffery Duffy.
Licensure Skilled care; Intermediate care; Rest home. *Beds* 152. *Certified* Medicaid; Medicare.
Owner Nonprofit Corp (United Church Homes).
Admissions Requirements Medical examination.
Affiliation Church of Christ
Facilities Dining room; Physical therapy room; Activities room; Chapel; Crafts room; Laundry room; Barber/Beauty shop; Library.
Activities Arts & crafts; Cards; Games; Reading groups; Prayer groups; Movies; Shopping trips; Social/Cultural gatherings; Community events; Crafts for kids; Pumpkin festival.

Echoing Ridge Residential Center
643 Beverly Ave, Canal Fulton, OH, 44614
(216) 854-6621
Admin Bill Hall. *Medical Dir/Dir of Nursing* Mary Ann Hearn.
Licensure Intermediate care for mentally retarded. *Beds* ICF/MR 50. *Certified* Medicaid.
Owner Nonprofit Corp.
Admissions Requirements Minimum age 17; Medical examination; Physician's request.
Staff Physicians 1 (pt); RNs 2 (ft), 1 (pt); LPNs 4 (ft), 3 (pt); Orderlies 6 (ft), 1 (pt); Nurses aides 21 (ft), 5 (pt); Physical therapists 1 (pt); Occupational therapists 1 (pt); Speech therapists 1 (pt); Activities coordinators 1 (ft); Dietitians 1 (pt); Ophthalmologists 1 (pt); Podiatrists 1 (pt); Psychologist 1 (pt).
Facilities Dining room; Physical therapy room; Activities room; Crafts room; Laundry room; Library.
Activities Arts & crafts; Games; Reading groups; Prayer groups; Movies; Shopping trips; Church; Camping; Outings; Special Olympics.

Gaslite Villa Convalescent Center Inc
7055 High Mill Ave NW, Canal Fulton, OH, 44614
(216) 854-4545
Admin Corita C Maxson. *Medical Dir/Dir of Nursing* Patrick D McFeely MD; Susan E Diamond.
Licensure Intermediate care. *Beds* ICF 98. *Certified* Medicaid.
Owner Proprietary Corp.
Admissions Requirements Minimum age 55; Medical examination.
Staff Physicians 1 (ft); RNs 2 (ft), 1 (pt); LPNs 4 (ft), 4 (pt); Nurses aides 29 (ft), 9 (pt); Physical therapists 1 (pt); Activities coordinators 1 (ft); Dietitians 1 (pt); Ophthalmologists 1 (pt).
Facilities Dining room; Activities room; Chapel; Crafts room; Laundry room; Barber/Beauty shop.
Activities Arts & crafts; Cards; Games; Prayer groups; Movies; Shopping trips; Social/Cultural gatherings; Catholic & Protestant Church services; Bus trips; Baking.

CANAL WINCHESTER

Winchester Place
36 Lehman Dr, Canal Winchester, OH, 43110
(614) 837-9666
Admin Stephen C Wise. *Medical Dir/Dir of Nursing* Dr Gail Burrien; Carol Meyer.
Licensure Skilled care; Intermediate care. *Beds* SNF 10; ICF 191. *Certified* Medicaid; Medicare.
Owner Proprietary Corp (Hillhaven Corp).

Admissions Requirements Medical examination.
Staff Physicians 2 (ft), 4 (pt); RNs 8 (ft), 2 (pt); LPNs 10 (ft), 2 (pt); Orderlies 4 (ft); Nurses aides 75 (ft), 4 (pt); Physical therapists 1 (ft); Occupational therapists 1 (ft); Speech therapists 1 (ft); Activities coordinators 1 (ft); Dietitians 1 (ft); Dentists 1 (pt); Ophthalmologists 1 (ft); Podiatrists 1 (pt); Dentist 1 (pt).
Facilities Dining room; Physical therapy room; Activities room; Crafts room; Laundry room; Barber/Beauty shop; Library; Multi-purpose room.
Activities Arts & crafts; Cards; Games; Reading groups; Prayer groups; Movies; Shopping trips; Social/Cultural gatherings.

CANTON

Baker-Sumser Retirement Village*
836 34th St, Canton, OH, 44709
(216) 492-7131
Medical Dir/Dir of Nursing Dr Aziz Alasayli.
Licensure Health care Center; Rest home. *Beds* 172. *Certified* Medicaid.
Owner Proprietary Corp.
Admissions Requirements Minimum age 55; Medical examination; Physician's request.
Staff RNs 2 (ft), 8 (pt); LPNs 3 (ft), 3 (pt); Nurses aides 18 (ft), 29 (pt); Activities coordinators 1 (ft); Dietitians 1 (ft).
Facilities Dining room; Physical therapy room; Activities room; Chapel; Crafts room; Laundry room; Barber/Beauty shop; Library; Community rooms.
Activities Arts & crafts; Cards; Games; Prayer groups; Movies; Shopping trips; Social/Cultural gatherings.

Bethany Nursing Home
626 34th St, NW, Canton, OH, 44709
(216) 492-7171
Admin John F Baum. *Medical Dir/Dir of Nursing* Dr Elizabeth E Baum MD; Mildred Downerd RN.
Licensure Intermediate care; Nursing home. *Beds* 32.
Owner Proprietary Corp.
Admissions Requirements Minimum age 18; Medical examination; Physician's request.
Staff Physicians 1 (ft); RNs 4 (ft); LPNs 3 (ft); Nurses aides 12 (ft), 16 (pt); Activities coordinators 1 (pt); Dietitians 1 (pt).
Facilities Dining room; Activities room; Laundry room; Barber/Beauty shop.
Activities Arts & crafts; Cards; Games; Reading groups; Prayer groups; Movies; Shopping trips; Musical programs; Sing-alongs; Social activities; Teas & dinners.

Canton Christian Home
2550 Cleveland Ave N, Canton, OH, 44709
(216) 456-0004
Admin Paul E Wiener. *Medical Dir/Dir of Nursing* Dr A J Gilbert; Betheen Grubaugh RN DON.
Licensure Intermediate care; Rest home; Independent living. *Beds* ICF 53; Rest home 22; Independent living units 115.
Owner Nonprofit organization/foundation.
Admissions Requirements Minimum age 62; Medical examination.
Staff Physicians 1 (ft); RNs 6 (ft), 5 (pt); LPNs 6 (ft), 7 (pt); Nurses aides 35 (ft), 11 (pt); Activities coordinators 2 (ft), 1 (pt); Dietitians 1 (ft); Social service 2 (ft).
Languages German
Affiliation Church of Christ
Facilities Dining room; Physical therapy room; Activities room; Chapel; Crafts room; Laundry room; Barber/Beauty shop; Library; Patio; Outdoor shuffle board; Putting green.
Activities Arts & crafts; Cards; Games; Reading groups; Prayer groups; Movies; Shopping trips; Social/Cultural gatherings.

Canton Health Care Center
1223 Market Ave N, Canton, OH, 44714
(216) 454-2152
Admin Michele Joiner. *Medical Dir/Dir of Nursing* Nancy Allen DON.
Licensure Intermediate care; Intermediate care for mentally retarded. *Beds* ICF 166; ICF/MR 34. *Certified* Medicaid.
Owner Proprietary Corp (American Health Care Centers).
Admissions Requirements Minimum age 18; Medical examination; Physician's request.
Staff RNs 8 (ft), 2 (pt); LPNs 34 (ft), 1 (pt); Orderlies 10 (ft), 9 (pt); Nurses aides 58 (ft), 19 (pt); Physical therapists; Recreational therapists; Occupational therapists; Speech therapists; Activities coordinators 2 (ft); Dietitians; Ophthalmologists; Podiatrists; Social Service 3 (ft).
Facilities Dining room; Physical therapy room; Activities room; Crafts room; Laundry room; Barber/Beauty shop.
Activities Arts & crafts; Cards; Games; Reading groups; Prayer groups; Movies; Shopping trips; Social/Cultural gatherings.

Colonial Nursing Center
1528 Market Ave N, Canton, OH, 44714
(216) 453-8456
Admin John E Reiser. *Medical Dir/Dir of Nursing* Dr Sandra Beichler.
Licensure Intermediate care. *Beds* ICF 70. *Certified* Medicaid.
Owner Proprietary Corp.
Admissions Requirements Minimum age 40; Medical examination.
Staff Physicians 1 (ft), 1 (pt); RNs 3 (ft), 1 (pt); LPNs 7 (ft), 2 (pt); Nurses aides 20 (ft), 9 (pt); Physical therapists 1 (pt); Activities coordinators 1 (pt); Dietitians 1 (pt); Dentists 1 (ft); Ophthalmologists 1 (ft); Podiatrists 1 (pt).
Facilities Dining room; Activities room; Laundry room.
Activities Arts & crafts; Cards; Games; Reading groups; Prayer groups; Movies; Shopping trips; Social/Cultural gatherings.

Convalescent Care*
315 McKinley Ave NW, Canton, OH, 44702
(216) 453-4010
Licensure Intermediate care. *Beds* 90. *Certified* Medicaid.
Owner Proprietary Corp.

Cormon Health Care
1435 Market Ave NW, Canton, OH, 44714
453-0831
Admin Cleme As-Samad. *Medical Dir/Dir of Nursing* Farakana As-Samad RN DON.
Licensure Intermediate care. *Beds* ICF 33. *Certified* Medicaid; Medicare.
Owner Privately owned.
Admissions Requirements Minimum age 18; Medical examination.
Staff RNs 1 (pt); LPNs 3 (ft), 1 (pt); Orderlies 1 (ft); Nurses aides 4 (ft), 2 (pt); Activities coordinators 1 (ft); Dietitians 1 (ft), 1 (pt); Ophthalmologists 1 (pt).
Facilities Dining room; Activities room; Laundry room.
Activities Arts & crafts; Cards; Games; Reading groups; Prayer groups; Movies; Shopping trips; Social/Cultural gatherings.

House of Loreto*
2812 Harvard Ave NW, Canton, OH, 44709
(216) 453-8137
Licensure Nursing home. *Beds* 98.
Owner Nonprofit Corp.

Jean Carol's Nursing Home Inc
1432 Tuscarawas E, Canton, OH, 44707-3193
(216) 453-2196
Admin Judith K Bendick. *Medical Dir/Dir of Nursing* Dr Saroj Kothari MD; Ina Jones LPN.

Licensure Intermediate care; Intermediate care for mentally retarded. *Beds* ICF 29; ICF/MR 21. *Certified* Medicaid.
Owner Proprietary Corp.
Admissions Requirements Minimum age 18; Medical examination.
Staff Physicians 1 (pt); RNs 2 (pt); LPNs 3 (ft), 2 (pt); Orderlies 1 (pt); Nurses aides 26 (ft); Activities coordinators 1 (ft); Dietitians 1 (pt); Psychologist 1 (pt); QMRP 1 (pt).
Facilities Dining room; Activities room; Crafts room; Laundry room; Barber/Beauty shop.
Activities Arts & crafts; Cards; Games; Reading groups; Prayer groups; Movies; Shopping trips; Social/Cultural gatherings; In-house fashion shows; Talking books; Exercise to music program; Coffee/social hour; Community outings.

Lyon Nursing Home*
1612 Harrisburg Rd NE, Canton, OH, 44705
(216) 453-6686
Licensure Intermediate care. *Beds* 50. *Certified* Medicaid.
Owner Proprietary Corp.

Manor Care Belden Village
5005 Higbee Ave NW, Canton, OH, 44718
(216) 492-7835
Admin Patricia Tyler. *Medical Dir/Dir of Nursing* Dr Daniel Cannone; Jacqueline Hibbard.
Licensure Skilled care; Intermediate care. *Beds* SNF 44; ICF 103. *Certified* Medicaid; Medicare.
Owner Proprietary Corp (Manor Care).
Admissions Requirements Medical Examination, Chest X-Ray.
Staff RNs; LPNs; Nurses aides; Recreational therapists; Activities coordinators.
Facilities Dining room; Physical therapy room; Activities room; Laundry room; Barber/Beauty shop.
Activities Arts & crafts; Cards; Games; Reading groups; Prayer groups; Movies; Shopping trips; Social/Cultural gatherings.

McKinley Life Care Centre
800 Market Ave N, Canton, OH, 44702
(216) 456-1014
Admin LeRoy J Wilson. *Medical Dir/Dir of Nursing* John Jeverette MD; Mrs P Huprich RN.
Licensure Skilled care. *Beds* 214. *Certified* Medicaid; Medicare.
Owner Proprietary Corp.
Admissions Requirements Medical examination; Physician's request.
Staff Physicians 2 (pt); RNs 10 (ft); LPNs 31 (ft); Nurses aides 90 (ft); Physical therapists 1 (pt); Occupational therapists 1 (pt); Speech therapists 1 (pt); Activities coordinators 1 (ft); Dietitians 1 (pt); Ophthalmologists 1 (pt); Podiatrists 1 (pt).
Facilities Dining room; Physical therapy room; Activities room; Crafts room; Laundry room; Barber/Beauty shop; Library; Lower court yard.
Activities Arts & crafts; Cards; Games; Reading groups; Prayer groups; Movies; Shopping trips; Social/Cultural gatherings.

Smith Nursing Home Inc
2330 Penn Pl NE, Canton, OH, 44704-2298
(216) 456-9070
Admin Abraham Smith. *Medical Dir/Dir of Nursing* Arlene Logan.
Licensure Intermediate care. *Beds* ICF 50. *Certified* Medicaid.
Owner Proprietary Corp.
Admissions Requirements Medical examination.
Staff Physicians 1 (pt); RNs 2 (ft), 1 (pt); LPNs 3 (ft); Orderlies 2 (ft); Nurses aides 14 (ft), 2 (pt); Physical therapists 1 (pt); Recreational therapists 1 (pt); Occupational therapists 1 (pt); Speech therapists 1 (pt);

Activities coordinators 2 (ft); Dietitians 1 (pt); Dentists 1 (pt); Ophthalmologists 1 (pt); Podiatrists 1 (pt).
Facilities Dining room; Activities room; Chapel; Crafts room; Laundry room; Barber/Beauty shop; Lounge or Reading room.
Activities Arts & crafts; Cards; Games; Reading groups; Prayer groups; Movies; Shopping trips; Social/Cultural gatherings.

Twin-M Nursing Home
1722 Homedale Ave NW, Canton, OH, 44708
(216) 454-6508
Admin Deborah Leffel. *Medical Dir/Dir of Nursing* Gert Curran DON.
Licensure Intermediate care. *Beds* ICF 23.
Owner Proprietary Corp (American Health Care Centers).
Admissions Requirements Medical examination; Physician's request.
Staff RNs 2 (ft), 1 (pt); LPNs 2 (ft); Nurses aides 5 (ft), 8 (pt); Activities coordinators 1 (ft); Social Service 1 (pt).
Facilities Dining room; Activities room; Laundry room.
Activities Cards; Games; Reading groups; Prayer groups; Movies; Shopping trips; Social/Cultural gatherings.

Westbrook Park Nursing Center
2714 13th St NW, Canton, OH, 44708
(216) 456-2842
Admin William R Watson II. *Medical Dir/Dir of Nursing* Paul B Bartos MD; Michele M Donnelly RN.
Licensure Skilled care. *Beds* SNF 22; ICF 105. *Certified* Medicaid; Medicare.
Owner Proprietary Corp (Arbor Health Care).
Admissions Requirements Minimum age 18; Medical examination; Physician's request.
Staff Physicians 12 (pt); RNs 4 (ft), 3 (pt); LPNs 6 (ft), 12 (pt); Nurses aides 16 (ft), 27 (pt); Physical therapists 1 (pt); Recreational therapists 1 (ft); Occupational therapists 2 (pt); Speech therapists 1 (pt); Dietitians 1 (pt); Ophthalmologists 1 (pt); Podiatrists 1 (pt).
Activities Arts & crafts; Cards; Games; Reading groups; Prayer groups; Movies; Shopping trips; Social/Cultural gatherings.

White Oak Convalescent Home*
3516 White Oak Dr SW, Canton, OH, 44710
(216) 452-3035
Licensure Intermediate care. *Beds* 40. *Certified* Medicaid.
Owner Proprietary Corp.

CAREY

Carey Nursing Home
127 Brayton St, Carey, OH, 43316
(419) 396-7488
Admin Donald L Lynch. *Medical Dir/Dir of Nursing* Dr William Kose; Juanita F Lynch DON.
Licensure Intermediate care. *Beds* ICF 16. *Certified* Medicaid.
Owner Privately owned.
Admissions Requirements Medical examination; Physician's request.
Staff RNs 1 (pt); LPNs 3 (pt); Nurses aides 6 (ft), 1 (pt); Activities coordinators 1 (ft).
Facilities Dining room; Activities room; Laundry room.
Activities Arts & crafts; Cards; Games; Reading groups; Prayer groups; Movies; Shopping trips; Picnics; Zoo trips.

Indian Trail Nursing Home Inc
PO Box 67, 821 E Findlay St, Carey, OH, 43316
(419) 396-6344
Admin Cindy Weatherholtz. *Medical Dir/Dir of Nursing* Dr William Kose; Rose McCloud RN.
Licensure Intermediate care. *Beds* ICF 51. *Certified* Medicaid.

Owner Proprietary Corp.
Staff Physicians 1 (pt); RNs 1 (ft); LPNs 5 (ft); Orderlies 2 (ft); Nurses aides 30 (ft); Activities coordinators 1 (ft); Dietitians 1 (pt); Dentists 1 (pt); Podiatrists 1 (pt).
Facilities Dining room; Activities room; Crafts room; Laundry room; Barber/Beauty shop.
Activities Arts & crafts; Cards; Games; Reading groups; Prayer groups; Movies; Shopping trips; Social/Cultural gatherings; Cooking; Make-up days; Bingo.

CARROLLTON

Carroll Healthcare Center
648 Long St, Carrollton, OH, 44615
(216) 627-5501
Admin Alan Miller. *Medical Dir/Dir of Nursing* Dr Donald Wingard; Cheryl Grimes RN DON.
Licensure Skilled care; Intermediate care. *Beds* SNF 50; ICF 101. *Certified* Medicaid; Medicare.
Owner Proprietary Corp.
Admissions Requirements Minimum age 18; Medical examination.
Staff Physicians 4 (pt); RNs 3 (ft), 4 (pt); LPNs 9 (ft), 5 (pt); Nurses aides 28 (ft), 35 (pt); Physical therapists 1 (pt); Occupational therapists 1 (pt); Speech therapists 1 (pt); Activities coordinators 2 (ft); Dietitians 1 (ft), 1 (pt); Ophthalmologists 1 (pt); Podiatrists 1 (pt).
Facilities Dining room; Physical therapy room; Activities room; Chapel; Crafts room; Laundry room; Barber/Beauty shop; Library.
Activities Arts & crafts; Cards; Games; Reading groups; Prayer groups; Movies; Shopping trips; Social/Cultural gatherings.

Carroll Nursing Home
PO Box 397, 347 Steubenville Rd SE, Carrollton, OH, 44615
(216) 627-4233
Medical Dir/Dir of Nursing T J Atchison MD.
Licensure Intermediate care. *Beds* 18. *Certified* Medicaid.
Owner Proprietary Corp.
Admissions Requirements Minimum age 18.
Staff Physicians 1 (pt); RNs 1 (ft), 2 (pt); LPNs 2 (ft), 1 (pt); Nurses aides 8 (ft), 8 (pt); Physical therapists 1 (pt); Reality therapists 1 (ft); Recreational therapists 1 (ft); Occupational therapists 1 (pt); Speech therapists 1 (pt); Activities coordinators 1 (ft); Dietitians 1 (ft); Dentists 1 (pt); Podiatrists 1 (pt).
Facilities Dining room; Activities room; Crafts room; Laundry room.
Activities Arts & crafts; Cards; Games; Reading groups; Prayer groups; Movies; Shopping trips; Social/Cultural gatherings.

CELINA

Celina Manor
1001 Myers Rd, Celina, OH, 45822
(419) 586-6645
Admin Glenn V Propst. *Medical Dir/Dir of Nursing* Donald R Fox MD; Marianne Roether DON.
Licensure Skilled care; Intermediate care. *Beds* SNF 101; ICF. *Certified* Medicaid; Medicare.
Owner Proprietary Corp (Health Care Facilities Inc).
Admissions Requirements Medical examination.
Staff Physicians; RNs 6 (ft), 3 (pt); LPNs 7 (ft), 4 (pt); Orderlies 1 (ft); Nurses aides 32 (ft), 20 (pt); Physical therapists 1 (ft); Activities coordinators 1 (ft), 1 (pt); Dietitians 1 (ft).
Facilities Dining room; Physical therapy room; Activities room; Chapel; Laundry room; Barber/Beauty shop; Library; Patios.

Activities Arts & crafts; Games; Movies; Social/Cultural gatherings; Field trips.

Hometown Nursing Home
401 E Myers, Celina, OH, 45822
(419) 586-3016
Admin Jerry Robertson. *Medical Dir/Dir of Nursing* Phillip Masser; Betty Patton.
Licensure Intermediate care. *Beds* ICF 50. *Certified* Medicaid.
Owner Proprietary Corp.
Admissions Requirements Medical examination; Physician's request.
Staff Physicians 1 (pt); RNs 1 (ft), 3 (pt); LPNs 4 (ft), 2 (pt); Orderlies 1 (ft), 1 (pt); Nurses aides 10 (ft), 22 (pt); Physical therapists 1 (pt); Activities coordinators 1 (ft); Dietitians 1 (pt); Dentists 1 (pt); Ophthalmologists 1 (pt); Social service; 1 (pt) Dentist 1 (pt).
Facilities Dining room; Activities room; Laundry room; Barber/Beauty shop.
Activities Arts & crafts; Cards; Games; Prayer groups; Movies; Shopping trips; Social/Cultural gatherings; Bingo.

Mercer County Residential Homes Inc
4784 Mud Pike, Celina, OH, 45822
(513) 586-1432
Admin Garry B Mosier BA QMRP. *Medical Dir/Dir of Nursing* Ruth Hanna RN.
Licensure Intermediate care for mentally retarded. *Beds* ICF/MR 8. *Certified* Medicaid.
Owner Nonprofit Corp.
Admissions Requirements Minimum age 18; Medical examination.
Staff Physicians 1 (pt); RNs 1 (pt); Occupational therapists 1 (pt); Activities coordinators 1 (ft); Dietitians 1 (pt); Podiatrists 1 (pt); Habilitation specialist 1 (ft).
Facilities Dining room; Activities room; Laundry room.
Activities Games; Movies; Shopping trips; Social/Cultural gatherings.

CENTERBURG

Canterbury Villa of Centerburg
80 Miller St, Centerburg, OH, 43011
(614) 625-6873
Admin Susan Mehr. *Medical Dir/Dir of Nursing* Dr Posada; Laura Segraves.
Licensure Intermediate care. *Beds* 50. *Certified* Medicaid; Medicare.
Owner Proprietary Corp (Horizon Healthcare Corp).
Admissions Requirements Medical examination.
Staff RNs 1 (pt); LPNs 4 (ft), 2 (pt); Nurses aides 15 (ft); Activities coordinators 1 (ft); Dietitians 2 (ft); Ophthalmologists 1 (pt).
Facilities Dining room; Activities room; Crafts room; Laundry room.
Activities Arts & crafts; Cards; Games; Reading groups; Prayer groups; Movies; Shopping trips; Social/Cultural gatherings.

Harrod Nursing Home*
26 N Hartford Ave, Centerburg, OH, 43011
(614) 625-5049
Licensure Nursing home. *Beds* 28.
Owner Proprietary Corp.

Morning View Care Center 1
4531 Columbus Rd, Centerburg, OH, 43011
(614) 625-5401
Licensure Intermediate care. *Beds* 34. *Certified* Medicaid.
Owner Proprietary Corp (Morning View Care Center).

Salyer Nursing Home Inc*
218 Clayton St, Centerburg, OH, 43011
(614) 625-5774
Medical Dir/Dir of Nursing Hernando Posado MD.

Licensure Skilled care; Intermediate care. *Beds* 83. *Certified* Medicaid; Medicare.
Owner Proprietary Corp.
Staff Physicians 1 (pt); RNs 2 (ft), 3 (pt); LPNs 14 (ft), 5 (pt); Orderlies 4 (ft); Nurses aides 30 (ft); Physical therapists 1 (pt); Occupational therapists 1 (pt); Speech therapists 1 (pt); Activities coordinators 1 (ft); Dietitians 1 (pt); Dentists 1 (pt); Podiatrists 1 (pt).
Facilities Dining room; Laundry room; Barber/Beauty shop.
Activities Arts & crafts; Cards; Games; Reading groups; Prayer groups; Movies; Shopping trips; Social/Cultural gatherings.

CHAGRIN FALLS

Hamlet Manor*
150 Cleveland St, Chagrin Falls, OH, 44022
(216) 247-4200
Medical Dir/Dir of Nursing Helena Hoelscher.
Licensure Nursing home. *Beds* 98.
Owner Proprietary Corp (Beverly Enterprises).
Admissions Requirements Medical examination.
Staff RNs 5 (ft), 12 (pt); LPNs 6 (ft), 1 (pt); Orderlies 2 (ft), 1 (pt); Nurses aides 28 (ft), 15 (pt); Physical therapists; Speech therapists 1 (pt); Activities coordinators 2 (ft), 1 (pt); Dietitians 1 (pt); Podiatrists 2 (ft); Audiologists 1 (ft).
Facilities Dining room; Physical therapy room; Activities room; Crafts room; Laundry room; Barber/Beauty shop; Library.
Activities Arts & crafts; Cards; Games; Reading groups; Prayer groups; Movies; Shopping trips; Social/Cultural gatherings.

CHARDON

Heather Hill Inc
12340 Bass Lake Rd, Chardon, OH, 44024
(216) 285-9151
Admin Robert G Hare. *Medical Dir/Dir of Nursing* Martha Hackett MD; Shirley French RN DON.
Licensure Skilled care; Intermediate care. *Beds* SNF 210; ICF. *Certified* Medicaid; Medicare.
Owner Nonprofit organization/foundation.
Admissions Requirements Minimum age 18; Medical examination.
Staff Physicians; RNs; LPNs; Orderlies; Nurses aides; Physical therapists; Occupational therapists; Speech therapists; Activities coordinators; Dietitians; Ophthalmologists; Podiatrists.
Facilities Dining room; Physical therapy room; Activities room; Chapel; Crafts room; Laundry room; Barber/Beauty shop; Library; Occupational therapy rooms.
Activities Arts & crafts; Cards; Games; Reading groups; Prayer groups; Movies; Shopping trips; Social/Cultural gatherings.

CHESTERLAND

Maple Nursing Home
13417 Rockhaven Rd, Chesterland, OH, 44026
(216) 286-6180
Admin Vera Light. *Medical Dir/Dir of Nursing* Dr W Larrick; Nancy Batteiger DON.
Licensure Intermediate care. *Beds* ICF 21. *Certified* Medicaid.
Owner Proprietary Corp.
Admissions Requirements Medical examination.
Staff Physicians 1 (ft); RNs 1 (pt); LPNs 2 (ft), 1 (pt); Nurses aides 5 (ft), 3 (pt); Activities coordinators 1 (pt); Dietitians 1 (pt); Ophthalmologists 1 (pt); Social Service 1 (pt).

Facilities Dining room.
Activities Arts & crafts; Cards; Games; Reading groups; Prayer groups; Movies; Shopping trips.

Metzenbaum Residence*
8132 Cedar Rd, Chesterland, OH, 44026
(216) 729-9409
Licensure Intermediate care for mentally retarded. *Beds* 36.
Owner Publicly owned.

CHESTERVILLE

Morrow Manor Nursing Center
PO Box 44, State Rte 95 & 314, Chesterville, OH, 43338
(419) 768-2401
Admin Darlene K Kunze. *Medical Dir/Dir of Nursing* Edward D Blackburn; Alice A Cole.
Licensure Intermediate care. *Beds* ICF 50. *Certified* Medicaid.
Owner Proprietary Corp.
Admissions Requirements Minimum age 18; Medical examination.
Staff RNs 1 (ft), 1 (pt); LPNs 5 (ft); Nurses aides 16 (ft), 2 (pt); Activities coordinators 1 (ft).
Facilities Dining room; Laundry room; Barber/Beauty shop.
Activities Arts & crafts; Cards; Games; Reading groups; Prayer groups; Movies; Shopping trips; Social/Cultural gatherings.

CHEVIOT

Hillebrand Nursing Center
4307 Bridgetown Rd, Cheviot, OH, 45211
(513) 574-4550
Medical Dir/Dir of Nursing Dr Gene Simon.
Licensure Skilled care; Intermediate care. *Beds* SNF 52; ICF 58. *Certified* Medicaid; Medicare.
Owner Proprietary Corp.
Staff Physicians; RNs 6 (ft), 12 (pt); LPNs 2 (ft), 10 (pt); Nurses aides 25 (ft), 28 (pt); Physical therapists 2 (ft); Recreational therapists 2 (ft), 1 (pt); Speech therapists 1 (ft); Activities coordinators 2 (ft); Dietitians 1 (pt); Podiatrists 1 (pt).
Facilities Dining room; Physical therapy room; Activities room; Chapel; Barber/Beauty shop; Library.
Activities Arts & crafts; Cards; Games; Reading groups; Prayer groups; Movies; Social/Cultural gatherings.

CHILLICOTHE

Heartland of Chillicothe
1058 Columbus St, Chillicothe, OH, 45601
(614) 773-5000
Admin Laura L Minner. *Medical Dir/Dir of Nursing* Daniel Colopy MD; Kathy Corcoran RN DON.
Licensure Skilled care; Intermediate care. *Beds* 101. *Certified* Medicaid; Medicare.
Owner Proprietary Corp (Health Care & Retirement Corp).
Admissions Requirements Medical examination.
Staff Physicians 1 (pt); RNs; LPNs; Nurses aides; Activities coordinators; Social workers 1 (ft); Restorative CNA 1 (ft).
Facilities Dining room; Physical therapy room; Activities room; Laundry room; Barber/Beauty shop.
Activities Arts & crafts; Cards; Games; Reading groups; Prayer groups; Movies; Shopping trips; Social/Cultural gatherings.

Marietta Place*
10 Marietta Pike, Chillicothe, OH, 45601
(614) 772-5900
Licensure Intermediate care. *Beds* 100. *Certified* Medicaid.
Owner Proprietary Corp (Hillhaven Corp).

Admissions Requirements Medical examination; Physician's request.
Staff RNs 12 (ft); LPNs 4 (ft); Orderlies 2 (ft); Nurses aides 30 (ft), 2 (pt); Physical therapists 1 (pt); Speech therapists 1 (pt); Activities coordinators 1 (ft), 1 (pt); Dietitians 1 (pt); Dentists; Ophthalmologists; Podiatrists.
Facilities Dining room; Activities room; Laundry room; Barber/Beauty shop; Library.
Activities Arts & crafts; Cards; Games; Reading groups; Prayer groups; Movies; Shopping trips; Social/Cultural gatherings.

Westmoreland Place Nursing Home*
230 Cherry St, Chillicothe, OH, 45601
(614) 773-6470
Licensure Skilled care; Intermediate care. *Beds* 150. *Certified* Medicaid; Medicare.
Owner Proprietary Corp.

CINCINNATI

Able Manor Nursing Home*
2927 Douglas Terrace, Cincinnati, OH, 45212
(513) 531-6676
Licensure Intermediate care. *Beds* 33. *Certified* Medicaid.
Owner Proprietary Corp.

Alaska Nursing Home*
3584 Alaska Ave, Cincinnati, OH, 45229
(513) 281-7782
Licensure Intermediate care. *Beds* 43. *Certified* Medicaid.
Owner Proprietary Corp.

The Alois Alzheimer Center
70 Damon Rd, Cincinnati, OH, 45218
(513) 825-2255
Admin Michael Levenson.
Licensure Skilled care; Intermediate care. *Beds* SNF 82; ICF.
Owner Proprietary Corp.
Admissions Requirements Medical examination.
Staff Physicians; RNs; LPNs; Orderlies; Nurses aides; Physical therapists; Occupational therapists; Speech therapists; Activities coordinators; Dietitians.
Facilities Dining room; Physical therapy room; Activities room; Chapel; Crafts room; Laundry room; Barber/Beauty shop; Library.
Activities Arts & crafts; Cards; Games; Reading groups; Prayer groups; Movies; Shopping trips; Social/Cultural gatherings; Gardening; Reality therapy.

Ambassador North*
5501 Verulam St, Cincinnati, OH, 45213
(513) 531-3654
Licensure Skilled care; Intermediate care. *Beds* 50. *Certified* Medicaid; Medicare.
Owner Proprietary Corp.

Ambassador South*
3030 Carpathia, Cincinnati, OH, 45213
(513) 631-1310
Licensure Skilled care; Intermediate care. *Beds* 50. *Certified* Medicaid; Medicare.
Owner Proprietary Corp.

Arcadia Manor*
5500 Verulam Ave, Cincinnati, OH, 45213
(513) 631-0003
Licensure Skilled care; Intermediate care. *Beds* 121. *Certified* Medicaid; Medicare.
Owner Proprietary Corp.

Archbishop Leibold Home
476 Riddle Rd, Cincinnati, OH, 45220
(513) 281-8001
Admin Sr Andrea Munarriz. *Medical Dir/Dir of Nursing* Sr Mildred Ryan.
Licensure Intermediate care; Rest home. *Beds* ICF 75; Rest home 50. *Certified* Medicaid.
Owner Nonprofit Corp.
Affiliation Roman Catholic

Facilities Dining room; Physical therapy room; Activities room; Chapel; Crafts room; Laundry room; Barber/Beauty shop; Library.
Activities Arts & crafts; Cards; Games; Reading groups; Prayer groups; Movies; Shopping trips; Social/Cultural gatherings.

Beechknoll Centers
6550 Hamilton Ave, Cincinnati, OH, 45224
(513) 522-5516
Admin Mark Wellinghoff. *Medical Dir/Dir of Nursing* Richard Longshore MD; Wilma McGlasson RNC.
Licensure Skilled care; Rest home; Independent. *Beds* SNF 100; Rest home 104; Independent units 98. *Certified* Medicare.
Owner Proprietary Corp.
Admissions Requirements Minimum age 16; Medical examination.
Staff Physicians 1 (pt); RNs 8 (ft), 9 (pt); LPNs 9 (ft), 9 (pt); Nurses aides 37 (ft), 23 (pt); Activities coordinators 4 (ft); Dentist 1 (pt).
Facilities Dining room; Physical therapy room; Activities room; Crafts room; Laundry room; Barber/Beauty shop; Library.
Activities Arts & crafts; Cards; Games; Reading groups; Prayer groups; Movies; Shopping trips; Social/Cultural gatherings.

Beechwood Home for Incurables Inc*
2140 Pogue Ave, Cincinnati, OH, 45208
(513) 321-9294
Licensure Skilled care; Intermediate care. *Beds* 70. *Certified* Medicaid; Medicare.
Owner Nonprofit Corp.

Bethesda Montgomery Care Center
7777 Cooper Rd, Cincinnati, OH, 45242
(513) 793-5092
Admin Michael J Bradford. *Medical Dir/Dir of Nursing* S Berg; I Morgan.
Licensure Skilled care. *Beds* 102. *Certified* Medicaid; Medicare.
Owner Nonprofit organization/foundation.
Staff RNs; LPNs; Nurses aides; Physical therapists; Recreational therapists; Occupational therapists; Speech therapists; Activities coordinators.
Facilities Dining room; Physical therapy room; Activities room; Chapel; Laundry room; Barber/Beauty shop.
Activities Arts & crafts; Cards; Games; Reading groups; Prayer groups; Movies; Social/Cultural gatherings; Dinning out; Ethnic & special theme dinners.

Bethesda Scarlet Oaks Retirement Community
440 Lafayette Ave, Cincinnati, OH, 45220
(513) 861-0400
Medical Dir/Dir of Nursing John Spaccarelli MD.
Licensure Nursing home. *Beds* 70.
Owner Nonprofit Corp.
Admissions Requirements Medical examination.
Staff Physicians 2 (pt); RNs 12 (ft); LPNs 8 (ft); Nurses aides 19 (ft); Physical therapists 1 (ft); Reality therapists 1 (ft); Recreational therapists 1 (ft); Occupational therapists 1 (ft); Speech therapists 1 (pt); Activities coordinators 1 (ft); Dietitians 1 (ft); Dentists 1 (pt); Ophthalmologists 1 (pt); Podiatrists 1 (pt).
Facilities Dining room; Physical therapy room; Activities room; Chapel; Crafts room; Laundry room; Barber/Beauty shop; Library.
Activities Arts & crafts; Cards; Games; Reading groups; Prayer groups; Movies; Shopping trips; Social/Cultural gatherings.

Briarwood Terrace Nursing Home*
3103 Fairfield Ave, Cincinnati, OH, 45207
Licensure Nursing home. *Beds* 25.
Owner Proprietary Corp.

Byrnes Convalescent Center
2203 Fulton Ave, Cincinnati, OH, 45206
(513) 751-1752
Admin Ron Jimmar. *Medical Dir/Dir of Nursing* Kyu H Kim; Denise Tartaglia.
Licensure Intermediate care. *Beds* ICF 64. *Certified* Medicaid.
Owner Proprietary Corp.
Staff RNs 1 (ft), 1 (pt); LPNs 7 (ft), 3 (pt); Orderlies 2 (ft), 2 (pt); Nurses aides 10 (ft), 8 (pt); Activities coordinators 1 (ft), 1 (pt); Dietitians 1 (ft).
Facilities Dining room; Activities room; Crafts room; Barber/Beauty shop.
Activities Arts & crafts; Cards; Games; Reading groups; Prayer groups; Movies; Social/Cultural gatherings.

Camargo Manor Nursing Home
7625 Camargo Rd, Cincinnati, OH, 45243
(513) 561-6210
Admin Franklin Nathan. *Medical Dir/Dir of Nursing* Nolan Weinberg MD; Peggy Kelch RN DON.
Licensure Skilled care; Intermediate care. *Beds* 53.
Owner Proprietary Corp.
Admissions Requirements Medical examination.
Staff RNs; LPNs; Nurses aides; Physical therapists; Recreational therapists; Occupational therapists; Activities coordinators; Dietitians; Ophthalmologists; Podiatrists.
Facilities Dining room; Activities room; Laundry room; Barber/Beauty shop.
Activities Arts & crafts; Cards; Games; Reading groups; Prayer groups; Movies; Shopping trips; Social/Cultural gatherings; Therapy groups.

Christian Care of Cincinnati Inc*
1067 Compton Rd, Cincinnati, OH, 45231
(513) 522-5533
Medical Dir/Dir of Nursing Dr Longshore.
Licensure Intermediate care. *Beds* 33. *Certified* Medicaid.
Owner Proprietary Corp.
Admissions Requirements Minimum age 21; Medical examination; Physician's request.
Staff Physicians 1 (pt); RNs 1 (pt); LPNs 2 (ft), 3 (pt); Nurses aides 7 (ft), 4 (pt); Activities coordinators 1 (ft); Dietitians 1 (ft); Dentists; Ophthalmologists; Podiatrists.

Clifton Care Center Inc
625 Probasco Ave, Cincinnati, OH, 45220
(513) 281-2464
Licensure Skilled care; Intermediate care. *Beds* 142. *Certified* Medicaid; Medicare.
Owner Proprietary Corp.

Clifton Villa Inc
515 Melish Ave, Cincinnati, OH, 45229
(513) 961-2853
Admin Mona Jo Trowbridge. *Medical Dir/Dir of Nursing* Dr Kyu Kim.
Licensure Intermediate care; Rest home. *Beds* ICF 100; Rest home 50.
Owner Proprietary Corp.
Admissions Requirements Physician's request.
Facilities Dining room; Physical therapy room; Activities room; Crafts room; Barber/Beauty shop; Library.
Activities Arts & crafts; Cards; Games; Prayer groups; Movies; Shopping trips; Social/Cultural gatherings.

Crestview Parke Nursing Home
2420 Harrison Ave, Cincinnati, OH, 45211
(513) 481-1100
Admin Ron Jemmar. *Medical Dir/Dir of Nursing* Dr Luid Ouiroga; Mary Jo Betz.
Licensure Skilled care; Intermediate care. *Beds* SNF 131; ICF. *Certified* Medicaid; Medicare.
Owner Proprietary Corp (Parke Care Inc).

Admissions Requirements Medical examination.
Staff RNs 5 (ft); Orderlies 3 (ft); Nurses aides 46 (ft), 18 (pt); Physical therapists 1 (pt); Speech therapists 1 (pt); Activities coordinators 1 (ft); Dietitians 1 (pt).
Facilities Dining room; Activities room; Barber/Beauty shop.
Activities Arts & crafts; Cards; Games; Reading groups; Prayer groups; Movies; Shopping trips; Social/Cultural gatherings; Bowling.

Daly Parke Nursing Home
6300 Daly Rd, Cincinnati, OH, 45224
(513) 542-6800
Admin Shirley Trieschman. *Medical Dir/Dir of Nursing* Dr Charles Armstrong MD; Shelley McDowell DON.
Licensure Skilled care; Intermediate care. *Beds* 132. *Certified* Medicaid; Medicare.
Owner Proprietary Corp (Parke Care Inc).
Admissions Requirements Minimum age 21.
Staff RNs 4 (ft), 3 (pt); LPNs 8 (ft), 6 (pt); Orderlies 3 (ft); Nurses aides 39 (ft), 15 (pt); Physical therapists 1 (pt); Recreational therapists 1 (pt); Occupational therapists 1 (pt); Speech therapists 1 (pt); Activities coordinators 2 (pt); Dietitians 1 (pt); Dentists 1 (pt); Ophthalmologists 1 (pt); Podiatrists 1 (pt).
Facilities Dining room; Physical therapy room; Activities room; Chapel; Crafts room; Barber/Beauty shop; Library.
Activities Arts & crafts; Cards; Games; Reading groups; Prayer groups; Movies; Shopping trips; Social/Cultural gatherings.

Deer Parke Nursing Home
6922 Ohio Ave, Cincinnati, OH, 45236
(513) 793-2090
Admin Patricia Troehler. *Medical Dir/Dir of Nursing* Stephen Berg; Judy Lyons.
Licensure Skilled care; Intermediate care. *Beds* SNF 136; ICF. *Certified* Medicaid; Medicare.
Owner Proprietary Corp (Parke Care Inc).
Admissions Requirements Medical examination; Physician's request.
Staff RNs 5 (ft); LPNs 9 (ft); Nurses aides 38 (ft); Physical therapists 1 (pt); Recreational therapists 1 (pt); Occupational therapists 1 (pt); Activities coordinators 3 (ft); Dietitians 1 (ft).
Facilities Dining room; Activities room; Laundry room; Barber/Beauty shop.
Activities Cards; Games; Prayer groups.

Daniel Drake Memorial Hospital
151 W Galbraith Rd, Cincinnati, OH, 45216
(513) 761-3440
Admin Jan C Taylor. *Medical Dir/Dir of Nursing* Walter E Matern; Marie Moore.
Licensure Skilled care; Intermediate care; Rehabilitation. *Beds* SNF 256; ICF; Rehab Hosp 116. *Certified* Medicaid; Medicare.
Owner Nonprofit organization/foundation.
Admissions Requirements Medical examination.
Staff Physicians 9 (ft), 41 (pt); RNs 87 (ft); LPNs 82 (ft); Nurses aides 145 (ft); Physical therapists 6 (ft); Recreational therapists 8 (ft); Occupational therapists 6 (ft); Speech therapists 3 (ft); Dietitians 3 (ft); Dentists 1 (pt); Ophthalmologists 2 (pt); Podiatrists 1 (pt).
Facilities Dining room; Physical therapy room; Activities room; Chapel; Crafts room; Laundry room; Barber/Beauty shop; Library; Occupational therapy room; Speech room; Audiology test room; Auditorium; Patient lounge.
Activities Arts & crafts; Cards; Games; Reading groups; Prayer groups; Movies; Shopping trips; Social/Cultural gatherings; Outings.

East Galbraith Health Care Center
3889 E Galbraith Rd, Cincinnati, OH, 45236
(513) 793-5220 & 791-9669
Admin Frank Nathan. *Medical Dir/Dir of Nursing* Dr Loraine Glaser; Sharon Strunk RN.
Licensure Skilled care; Intermediate care. *Beds* SNF; ICF 145. *Certified* Medicaid.
Owner Proprietary Corp.
Staff Physicians 1 (pt); RNs 5 (ft), 2 (pt); LPNs 14 (ft), 4 (pt); Orderlies 5 (ft), 1 (pt); Nurses aides 25 (ft), 4 (pt); Physical therapists 1 (ft), 1 (pt); Occupational therapists 1 (pt); Speech therapists 1 (pt); Activities coordinators 3 (ft); Dietitians 1 (pt); Dentists 1 (pt); Ophthalmologists 1 (pt); Podiatrists 1 (pt).
Facilities Dining room; Physical therapy room; Activities room; Chapel; Crafts room; Laundry room; Barber/Beauty shop; Multi purpose rooms.
Activities Arts & crafts; Cards; Games; Reading groups; Prayer groups; Movies; Shopping trips; Social/Cultural gatherings.

East Galbraith Nursing Home
3875 E Galbraith Rd, Cincinnati, OH, 45236
(513) 793-5220
Admin Frank Nathan. *Medical Dir/Dir of Nursing* Dr Stuart Zakem; Sharon Strunk RN.
Licensure Skilled care; Intermediate care. *Beds* SNF; ICF 91. *Certified* Medicaid; Medicare.
Owner Proprietary Corp.
Staff Physicians 1 (pt); RNs 2 (ft), 1 (pt); LPNs 6 (ft), 2 (pt); Orderlies 5 (ft), 1 (pt); Nurses aides 15 (ft), 4 (pt); Physical therapists 1 (ft), 1 (pt); Occupational therapists 1 (pt); Speech therapists 1 (pt); Activities coordinators 3 (ft); Dietitians 1 (pt); Dentists 1 (pt); Ophthalmologists 1 (pt); Podiatrists 1 (pt).
Facilities Dining room; Physical therapy room; Activities room; Chapel; Crafts room; Laundry room; Barber/Beauty shop; Multipurpose rooms.
Activities Arts & crafts; Cards; Games; Reading groups; Prayer groups; Movies; Shopping trips; Social/Cultural gatherings.

Elite Rest & Nursing Home*
965 Burton Ave, Cincinnati, OH, 45229
(513) 221-3900
Licensure Intermediate care. *Beds* 50. *Certified* Medicaid.
Owner Proprietary Corp.

Empress Convalescent Home—1
PO Box 6276, 2321 Upland Pl, Cincinnati, OH, 45206-0276
(513) 281-7700
Admin Hugo G Eichelberg. *Medical Dir/Dir of Nursing* Lenzy G Southall MD; M Compuber RN.
Licensure Intermediate care. *Beds* ICF 45. *Certified* Medicaid.
Owner Proprietary Corp.
Admissions Requirements Medical examination.
Staff Physicians 4 (pt); RNs 5 (ft); LPNs 2 (ft); Orderlies; Nurses aides 11 (ft), 3 (pt); Physical therapists 1 (pt); Activities coordinators 1 (ft); Dietitians 1 (pt); Dentists 1 (pt); Ophthalmologists 1 (pt); Podiatrists 1 (pt).
Languages German
Facilities Dining room; Activities room; Chapel; Crafts room; Laundry room; Library.
Activities Arts & crafts; Cards; Games; Reading groups; Prayer groups; Movies; Shopping trips; Social/Cultural gatherings; Picnics; Outings.

Empress Convalescent Home—2
PO Box 6276, 2327 Upland Pl, Cincinnati, OH, 45206-0276
(513) 281-7700

Admin Hugo G Eichelberg. *Medical Dir/Dir of Nursing* Dr Lenzy Southall; M Capuber RN DON.
Licensure Intermediate care. *Beds* ICF 25. *Certified* Medicaid.
Owner Proprietary Corp.
Admissions Requirements Females only; Medical examination; Physician's request.
Staff Physicians 4 (pt); RNs 1 (ft); LPNs 4 (ft), 2 (pt); Orderlies; Nurses aides 8 (ft), 3 (pt); Physical therapists; Reality therapists; Speech therapists; Activities coordinators 1 (ft); Dietitians 1 (pt); Dentists 1 (pt); Ophthalmologists 1 (pt); Podiatrists 1 (pt); Dentist 1 (pt).
Languages German
Facilities Dining room; Activities room; Chapel; Crafts room; Laundry room.
Activities Arts & crafts; Cards; Games; Reading groups; Prayer groups; Movies; Social/Cultural gatherings; Picnics; Outings.

Fairview Nursing Home
1804 Kinney Ave, Cincinnati, OH, 45207
(513) 221-0433
Licensure Intermediate care. *Beds* 50. *Certified* Medicaid.
Owner Proprietary Corp.

Forestview Nursing Home
610 Forest Ave, Cincinnati, OH, 45229
(503) 751-1602
Licensure Intermediate care. *Beds* 28. *Certified* Medicaid.
Owner Proprietary Corp.

Franciscan Terrace at St Clare Center
100 Compton Rd, Cincinnati, OH, 45215
(513) 761-9036
Medical Dir/Dir of Nursing Richard G Klopp MD; Letitia R Mundew RN C.
Licensure Home for aged; Rest home. *Beds* Rest home 50 Nursing home 110.
Owner Nonprofit Corp.
Admissions Requirements Medical examination; Physician's request.
Staff Physicians 1 (pt); RNs 6 (ft), 7 (pt); LPNs 12 (ft), 12 (pt); Nurses aides 34 (ft), 19 (pt); Activities coordinators 3 (ft); Dietitians 1 (ft); Ophthalmologists 1 (pt).
Languages German
Affiliation Roman Catholic
Facilities Dining room; Physical therapy room; Activities room; Chapel; Crafts room; Laundry room; Barber/Beauty shop; Library; Indoor swimming pool & whirlpool.
Activities Arts & crafts; Cards; Games; Reading groups; Prayer groups; Movies; Shopping trips; Social/Cultural gatherings.

Gardenview Nursing Home
3544 Washington Ave, Cincinnati, OH, 45229
(513) 751-2241
Licensure Skilled care; Intermediate care. *Beds* 45. *Certified* Medicaid; Medicare.
Owner Proprietary Corp.

Glen Manor Home for Jewish Aged
6969 Glenmeadow Ln, Cincinnati, OH, 45237
(513) 351-7007
Admin Ann E Clabaugh. *Medical Dir/Dir of Nursing* Stanley Wacksman MD; Mary Basnight RN DON.
Licensure Skilled care; Intermediate care. *Beds* 118. *Certified* Medicaid; Medicare.
Owner Nonprofit Corp.
Admissions Requirements Minimum age 65; Medical examination.
Staff Physicians 1 (pt); RNs 8 (ft), 5 (pt); LPNs 12 (ft), 5 (pt); Orderlies 8 (ft), 3 (pt); Nurses aides 34 (ft), 7 (pt); Physical therapists 1 (pt); Recreational therapists 2 (ft); Occupational therapists 1 (ft), 1 (pt); Speech therapists 1 (pt); Activities coordinators 1 (ft); Dietitians 1 (pt); Ophthalmologists 1 (pt).
Affiliation Jewish

Facilities Dining room; Physical therapy room; Activities room; Chapel; Crafts room; Laundry room; Barber/Beauty shop; Library.
Activities Arts & crafts; Cards; Games; Reading groups; Movies; Shopping trips; Social/Cultural gatherings.

Glen Parke Nursing Home
548 Glenwood Ave, Cincinnati, OH, 45229
(513) 961-8881
Admin Helen E Martin. *Medical Dir/Dir of Nursing* Dr Mediodia; Laurie Westermeyer RN.
Licensure Intermediate care. *Beds* ICF 105; ICF/MR 50. *Certified* Medicaid.
Owner Proprietary Corp.
Staff Physicians 4 (pt); RNs 7 (ft); LPNs 17 (ft); Orderlies 5 (ft); Nurses aides 60 (ft); Physical therapists 2 (pt); Recreational therapists 4 (ft), 1 (pt); Occupational therapists 2 (ft); Speech therapists 1 (pt); Activities coordinators 2 (ft); Dietitians 1 (ft); Dentists 1 (pt); Ophthalmologists 1 (pt); Podiatrists 1 (pt).
Facilities Dining room; Physical therapy room; Activities room; Crafts room; Barber/Beauty shop.
Activities Arts & crafts; Cards; Games; Reading groups; Prayer groups; Movies; Shopping trips; Social/Cultural gatherings.

Gold Crest Nursing Home
3663 Reading Rd, Cincinnati, OH, 45229
(513) 961-8176
Admin Vandadean R Fulton. *Medical Dir of Nursing* Dr Morris Plotnick.
Licensure Intermediate care. *Beds* 50. *Certified* Medicaid; Medicare.
Owner Privately owned.
Admissions Requirements Medical examination.
Staff Physicians; RNs; LPNs; Nurses aides; Activities coordinators; Dietitians; Dentists; Ophthalmologists.
Facilities Dining room; Activities room; Crafts room; Laundry room.
Activities Arts & crafts; Cards; Games; Reading groups; Prayer groups; Movies; Shopping trips; Social/Cultural gatherings National Nursing Home Week.

Golden Age Retirement Home
3635 Reading Rd, Cincinnati, OH, 45229
(513) 281-1922
Admin Henrietta DePuccio. *Medical Dir of Nursing* Dr Morris Plotnick MD; Marie Willingham DON.
Licensure Skilled care; Intermediate care. *Beds* SNF 50; ICF. *Certified* Medicaid; Medicare.
Owner Proprietary Corp.
Admissions Requirements Medical examination; Physician's request.
Staff Physicians; RNs; LPNs; Orderlies; Nurses aides; Physical therapists; Reality therapists; Recreational therapists; Speech therapists; Activities coordinators; Dietitians.
Facilities Dining room; Physical therapy room; Laundry room.
Activities Arts & crafts; Cards; Games; Reading groups; Prayer groups; Movies; Shopping trips; Social/Cultural gatherings.

Grace Manor Nursing Home
PO Box 6276, 2404 Grandview, Cincinnati, OH, 45206-0276
(513) 281-8900
Admin Hugo G Eichelberg. *Medical Dir/Dir of Nursing* Lenzy G Southall MD; Debbie Eckart.
Licensure Intermediate care. *Beds* 30. *Certified* Medicaid.
Owner Proprietary Corp.
Admissions Requirements Females only; Medical examination.
Staff Physicians 5 (pt); RNs 1 (ft); LPNs 4 (ft); Orderlies; Nurses aides 9 (ft); Physical therapists 1 (pt); Reality therapists 1 (pt); Recreational therapists 1 (pt); Speech

therapists; Activities coordinators 1 (ft); Dietitians 1 (pt); Ophthalmologists 1 (pt); Podiatrists 1 (pt).
Languages German
Facilities Dining room; Activities room; Crafts room; Laundry room.
Activities Arts & crafts; Cards; Games; Reading groups; Prayer groups; Movies; Social/Cultural gatherings.

Hamilton County Eastern Star Home Inc*
1630 W North Bend Rd, Cincinnati, OH, 45224
(513) 542-6464
Licensure Nursing home; Rest home. *Beds* Nursing home 36; Rest home 34.
Owner Nonprofit Corp.
Affiliation Order of Eastern Star

Harrison House Inc
2171 Harrison Ave, Cincinnati, OH, 45211
(513) 662-5800
Medical Dir/Dir of Nursing Margaret Schneider MD.
Licensure Skilled care; Intermediate care. *Beds* 101. *Certified* Medicaid; Medicare.
Owner Proprietary Corp.
Admissions Requirements Minimum age 18; Medical examination.
Staff Physicians 26 (pt); RNs 2 (ft), 6 (pt); LPNs 5 (ft), 5 (pt); Nurses aides 22 (ft), 23 (pt); Physical therapists 1 (pt); Recreational therapists 1 (ft); Occupational therapists 1 (pt); Speech therapists 1 (pt); Activities coordinators 1 (ft); Dietitians 1 (pt); Ophthalmologists 1 (pt); Podiatrists 1 (pt).
Facilities Dining room; Physical therapy room; Activities room; Chapel; Barber/Beauty shop; Library.
Activities Arts & crafts; Cards; Games; Reading groups; Prayer groups; Movies; Shopping trips; Social/Cultural gatherings.

Hillside Manor Health Care Facility Inc*
3539 Eden Ave, Cincinnati, OH, 45229
(216) 861-1482
Admin Karen L Williams. *Medical Dir/Dir of Nursing* James J Alikonis MD.
Licensure Intermediate care. *Beds* 67. *Certified* Medicaid.
Owner Proprietary Corp (Blackeye Fam & Nursing Hm).
Admissions Requirements Minimum age 18; Medical examination.
Staff RNs 1 (ft); LPNs 6 (ft), 6 (pt); Orderlies 3 (ft), 4 (pt); Nurses aides 11 (ft), 7 (pt); Speech therapists; Activities coordinators 1 (ft); Dietitians 1 (pt); Dentists; Ophthalmologists; Podiatrists; Audiologists.
Facilities Dining room; Activities room; Laundry room; Library.
Activities Arts & crafts; Cards; Games; Prayer groups; Movies; Shopping trips; Social/Cultural gatherings; Discussion groups; Exercise classes.

Hilltop Nursing & Retirement Home Inc
2586 LaFeuille Ave, Cincinnati, OH, 45211
(513) 662-2444
Admin Frances R Glaser. *Medical Dir/Dir of Nursing* Manual Mediodia MD; Mary Nau DON.
Licensure Skilled care; Intermediate care. *Beds* SNF 24; ICF 30. *Certified* Medicare.
Owner Proprietary Corp.
Admissions Requirements Minimum age 40; Females only.
Staff RNs 4 (ft), 1 (pt); LPNs 9 (ft), 4 (pt); Nurses aides 22 (ft), 6 (pt); Physical therapists 1 (pt); Recreational therapists 1 (ft), 1 (pt); Activities coordinators 1 (ft); Dietitians 1 (ft); Music therapist 1 (ft).
Facilities Dining room; Physical therapy room; Activities room; Chapel; Crafts room; Barber/Beauty shop; Library.

Activities Arts & crafts; Cards; Games; Reading groups; Prayer groups; Movies; Shopping trips; Social/Cultural gatherings; Music therapy.

Hillview Nursing Home*
2025 Wyoming Ave, Cincinnati, OH, 45214
(513) 251-2557
Licensure Skilled care; Intermediate care. *Beds* SNF 50; ICF 50. *Certified* Medicaid; Medicare.
Owner Proprietary Corp.
Admissions Requirements Medical examination; Physician's request.
Staff Physicians 2 (pt); RNs 4 (ft), 1 (pt); LPNs 6 (ft); Orderlies 2 (ft), 6 (pt); Nurses aides 26 (ft); Physical therapists 1 (ft), 1 (pt); Reality therapists 1 (ft); Recreational therapists 1 (ft), 1 (pt); Activities coordinators; Dietitians.
Facilities Dining room; Physical therapy room; Activities room; Crafts room; Laundry room; Barber/Beauty shop; Library.
Activities Arts & crafts; Cards; Games; Reading groups; Prayer groups; Movies; Shopping trips; Social/Cultural gatherings; Picnics.

Hyde Park Villa Inc
PO Box 11327, 4015 Red Villa Ct, Cincinnati, OH, 45211-0327
(513) 272-0600
Medical Dir/Dir of Nursing August Lambers MD.
Licensure Skilled care; Intermediate care. *Beds* 150. *Certified* Medicaid; Medicare.
Owner Proprietary Corp.
Admissions Requirements Minimum age 18.
Staff RNs 4 (ft), 11 (pt); LPNs 10 (ft), 6 (pt); Nurses aides 34 (ft), 20 (pt); Physical therapists 1 (pt); Occupational therapists 1 (pt); Speech therapists 1 (pt); Activities coordinators 2 (ft); Dietitians 1 (ft); Dentists 1 (pt); Ophthalmologists 1 (pt); Podiatrists 1 (pt).
Facilities Dining room; Physical therapy room; Activities room; Chapel; Barber/ Beauty shop; Gift shop; Lounges.
Activities Arts & crafts; Cards; Games; Reading groups; Prayer groups; Movies; Shopping trips; Social/Cultural gatherings; Cooking; Baking; Field trips; Exercise groups.

Judson Village
2373 Harrison Ave, Cincinnati, OH, 45211
(513) 662-5880
Admin James Piepenbrink. *Medical Dir/Dir of Nursing* William Rudemiller MD; Grova Vaughn RN DON.
Licensure Intermediate care; Rest home. *Beds* ICF 50; Rest Home 50. *Certified* Medicaid.
Owner Nonprofit Corp.
Admissions Requirements Minimum age 62; Medical examination.
Affiliation Baptist
Facilities Dining room; Activities room; Chapel; Crafts room; Laundry room; Barber/ Beauty shop; Library.
Activities Arts & crafts; Cards; Games; Reading groups; Prayer groups; Movies; Shopping trips; Social/Cultural gatherings; Religious services.

Kenwood Terrace Nursing Center Inc
8440 Montgomery Rd, Cincinnati, OH, 45236
(513) 793-2255
Admin Ann Glass Block. *Medical Dir/Dir of Nursing* Dr Robert Burt.
Licensure Skilled care; Intermediate care. *Beds* SNF 48; ICF 78. *Certified* Medicaid; Medicare.
Owner Proprietary Corp.
Staff RNs; LPNs; Nurses aides; Physical therapists; Reality therapists; Recreational therapists; Occupational therapists; Speech therapists; Activities coordinators; Dietitians; Ophthalmologists.

Facilities Dining room; Physical therapy room; Activities room; Barber/Beauty shop.
Activities Arts & crafts; Cards; Games; Reading groups; Prayer groups; Movies; Shopping trips; Social/Cultural gatherings.

Lebraun Convalescent Home*
2125 Alpine Pl, Cincinnati, OH, 45206
(513) 281-1890
Medical Dir/Dir of Nursing Albert I Aronoff MD.
Licensure Intermediate care. *Beds* 34. *Certified* Medicaid.
Owner Proprietary Corp.
Staff RNs 1 (ft); LPNs 4 (ft), 1 (pt); Nurses aides 8 (ft), 1 (pt); Physical therapists 1 (pt); Activities coordinators 1 (pt); Dietitians 1 (pt).
Facilities Dining room; Activities room; Laundry room.
Activities Arts & crafts; Cards; Games; Reading groups; Prayer groups; Shopping trips; Social/Cultural gatherings.

Marjorie P Lee Retirement Community
3550 Shaw Ave, Cincinnati, OH, 45208
(513) 871-2090
Admin Adrienne Walsh. *Medical Dir/Dir of Nursing* Donald Nunlist Young; Suzanne Murphy.
Licensure Intermediate care; Assisted living. *Beds* ICF 72; Assisted living 50. *Certified* Medicaid.
Owner Nonprofit Corp.
Admissions Requirements Medical examination; Physician's request.
Staff Physicians 5 (pt); RNs 3 (ft), 1 (pt); LPNs 10 (ft), 2 (pt); Orderlies 1 (ft); Nurses aides 27 (ft), 10 (pt); Physical therapists 1 (pt); Activities coordinators 3 (ft); Dietitians 1 (ft); Dentists 1 (pt); Ophthalmologists 1 (pt).
Affiliation Episcopal
Facilities Dining room; Physical therapy room; Activities room; Chapel; Crafts room; Laundry room; Barber/Beauty shop; Library; Corner store; Game area.
Activities Arts & crafts; Cards; Games; Reading groups; Prayer groups; Movies; Shopping trips; Social/Cultural gatherings.

Lincoln Avenue & Crawford's Home for the Aged*
1346 Lincoln Ave, Cincinnati, OH, 45206
(513) 861-2044 & 559-1494
Licensure Skilled care; Intermediate care. *Beds* 100. *Certified* Medicaid; Medicare.
Owner Nonprofit Corp.

Llanfair Terrace*
1701 Llanfair Ave, Cincinnati, OH, 45224
(513) 681-4230
Licensure Skilled care; Intermediate care; Rest home. *Beds* ICF 75; Rest home 25. *Certified* Medicaid; Medicare.
Owner Nonprofit Corp (OH Presbyterian Homes).

Longview Unit 22 Group Home*
6600 Paddock Rd, Cincinnati, OH, 45216
Licensure Intermediate care for mentally retarded. *Beds* 12. *Certified* Medicaid.
Owner Publicly owned.

Madison Nursing Home
PO Box 27166, 6845 Indian Hill Rd, Cincinnati, OH, 45227-0166
(613) 271-0429
Licensure Intermediate care. *Beds* 27. *Certified* Medicaid.
Owner Proprietary Corp.

Manor Care Nursing Home
2250 Banning Rd, Cincinnati, OH, 45239
(513) 591-0400
Licensure Skilled care; Intermediate care. *Beds* 151. *Certified* Medicaid; Medicare.
Owner Proprietary Corp (Manor Care).

Manor Care—Woodside Nursing Facility*
5970 Kenwood Rd, Cincinnati, OH, 45243
(513) 561-4111
Medical Dir/Dir of Nursing Jack Rhodes MD.
Licensure Skilled care. *Beds* SNF 156. *Certified* Medicare.
Owner Proprietary Corp.
Staff Physicians 1 (pt); RNs 11 (ft), 5 (pt); LPNs 14 (ft), 4 (pt); Nurses aides 54 (ft), 27 (pt); Physical therapists 1 (ft); Occupational therapists 1 (pt); Speech therapists 1 (pt); Activities coordinators 2 (ft); Dietitians 1 (ft); Dentists 1 (pt); Ophthalmologists 1 (pt); Podiatrists 1 (pt); Audiologists 1 (pt).
Facilities Dining room; Physical therapy room; Activities room; Laundry room; Barber/Beauty shop.
Activities Arts & crafts; Cards; Games; Reading groups; Prayer groups; Movies; Shopping trips; Social/Cultural gatherings.

Maple Knoll Village*
11100 Springfield Pike, Cincinnati, OH, 45246
(513) 785-2400
Licensure Skilled care; Intermediate care. *Beds* 174. *Certified* Medicaid; Medicare.
Owner Nonprofit Corp.

George A Martin Gerontology Center*
3603 Washington Ave, Cincinnati, OH, 45229
(513) 961-0144
Medical Dir/Dir of Nursing John Falk MD.
Licensure Intermediate care. *Beds* 25. *Certified* Medicaid.
Owner Nonprofit Corp.
Admissions Requirements Minimum age 21; Medical examination; Physician's request.
Staff Physicians; RNs; LPNs; Orderlies; Nurses aides; Physical therapists; Reality therapists; Recreational therapists; Occupational therapists; Speech therapists; Activities coordinators; Dietitians; Dentists; Ophthalmologists.
Facilities Dining room; Activities room; Laundry room.
Activities Arts & crafts; Cards; Games; Reading groups; Prayer groups; Movies; Shopping trips; Social/Cultural gatherings.

Mt Healthy Christian Home
8097 Hamilton Ave, Cincinnati, OH, 45231
(513) 931-5000
Admin J Donald Sams. *Medical Dir/Dir of Nursing* Dr Janice Singerman & Dr Stephen Berg; Arlene Windhorst DON.
Licensure Intermediate care; Home for aged. *Beds* ICF 64; Home for aged 32. *Certified* Medicaid.
Owner Nonprofit Corp.
Admissions Requirements Minimum age 62; Medical examination.
Staff Physicians 2 (pt); RNs 3 (ft), 5 (pt); LPNs 9 (ft), 3 (pt); Nurses aides 34 (ft), 4 (pt); Physical therapists 1 (pt); Recreational therapists 1 (pt); Activities coordinators 1 (ft); Dietitians 1 (pt); Ophthalmologists 1 (pt).
Languages German
Affiliation Church of Christ
Facilities Dining room; Physical therapy room; Activities room; Chapel; Crafts room; Laundry room; Barber/Beauty shop; Library; Multipurpose room.
Activities Arts & crafts; Cards; Games; Reading groups; Prayer groups; Movies; Shopping trips.

Mt Washington Care Center
6900 Beechmont Ave, Cincinnati, OH, 45230
(513) 231-4561
Admin Daniel J Suer. *Medical Dir/Dir of Nursing* Drs Tom Popa; Art Gendelmen; Janet Boblenz.
Licensure Skilled care; Intermediate care. *Beds* SNF 18; ICF 145. *Certified* Medicaid; Medicare.
Owner Proprietary Corp.

Staff Physicians 1 (pt); RNs 6 (ft); LPNs 30 (ft); Orderlies 35 (ft); Physical therapists 1 (pt); Reality therapists 1 (pt); Recreational therapists 1 (pt); Occupational therapists 1 (pt); Speech therapists 1 (pt); Activities coordinators 3 (ft); Dietitians 1 (pt); Dentists 1 (pt); Ophthalmologists 1 (pt); Podiatrists 1 (pt); Dentist 1 (pt).
Facilities Dining room; Physical therapy room; Activities room; Chapel; Crafts room; Laundry room; Barber/Beauty shop; Library.
Activities Arts & crafts; Cards; Games; Reading groups; Prayer groups; Movies; Shopping trips; Social/Cultural gatherings; Outpatient physical therapy.

Oak Pavilion Nursing Center
510 Oak St, Cincinnati, OH, 45819
(513) 751-0880
Admin Mavis Phipps. *Medical Dir/Dir of Nursing* Dr Edmund Rothchild; Margaret Bradshaw.
Licensure Skilled care; Intermediate care. *Beds* SNF 50; ICF 100. *Certified* Medicaid; Medicare.
Owner Proprietary Corp (Health Care & Retirement Corp).
Admissions Requirements Minimum age 21.
Staff RNs; LPNs; Orderlies; Nurses aides; Physical therapists; Speech therapists; Activities coordinators; Dietitians; Dentist.
Facilities Dining room; Physical therapy room; Activities room; Laundry room; Barber/Beauty shop.
Activities Arts & crafts; Cards; Games; Reading groups; Prayer groups; Movies; Shopping trips; Social/Cultural gatherings.

Oak Tree Convalescent Center Inc*
3545 Eden Ave, Cincinnati, OH, 45229
(216) 861-1483
Admin Karen L Williams. *Medical Dir/Dir of Nursing* James J Alikonis MD.
Licensure Intermediate care. *Beds* 50. *Certified* Medicaid.
Owner Proprietary Corp.
Admissions Requirements Minimum age 18; Medical examination.
Staff RNs 1 (ft); LPNs 3 (ft), 3 (pt); Orderlies 3 (ft), 4 (pt); Nurses aides 6 (ft), 3 (pt); Speech therapists; Activities coordinators 1 (ft); Dietitians 1 (pt); Dentists; Ophthalmologists; Podiatrists; Audiologists.
Facilities Dining room; Activities room; Laundry room; Library.
Activities Arts & crafts; Cards; Games; Prayer groups; Movies; Shopping trips; Social/Cultural gatherings; Discussion groups; Exercise classes.

Oakview Nursing Home
618 Forest Ave, Cincinnati, OH, 45229
(513) 751-2062
Licensure Intermediate care. *Beds* 27. *Certified* Medicaid.
Owner Proprietary Corp (Blackeye Fam & Nursing Hm).

Orthodox Jewish Home for the Aged
1171 Towne St, Cincinnati, OH, 45216
(513) 242-1360
Admin Leonard Sternberg ACSW. *Medical Dir/Dir of Nursing* Dr Walter Schur; Leah Satzber.
Licensure Skilled care; Intermediate care. *Beds* 172. *Certified* Medicaid; Medicare.
Owner Nonprofit Corp.
Admissions Requirements Minimum age 65; Medical examination.
Staff RNs; LPNs; Orderlies; Nurses aides; Physical therapists; Reality therapists; Recreational therapists; Activities coordinators; Podiatrists.
Affiliation Jewish
Facilities Dining room; Physical therapy room; Activities room; Chapel; Crafts room; Laundry room; Barber/Beauty shop; Library.

Activities Arts & crafts; Cards; Games; Reading groups; Prayer groups; Movies; Shopping trips; Social/Cultural gatherings.

Price Hill Nursing Home*
584 Elberon Ave, Cincinnati, OH, 45205
(513) 251-0367
Medical Dir/Dir of Nursing Morris Plotnick MD.
Licensure Skilled care; Intermediate care. *Beds* 48. *Certified* Medicaid; Medicare.
Owner Proprietary Corp.
Admissions Requirements Minimum age 18; Medical examination.
Staff Physicians 6 (pt); RNs 5 (ft); LPNs 1 (ft), 3 (pt); Nurses aides 11 (ft), 3 (pt); Physical therapists 1 (pt); Occupational therapists; Speech therapists; Activities coordinators; Dietitians; Dentists; Ophthalmologists; Podiatrists; Audiologists.
Facilities Dining room; Activities room; Laundry room; Barber/Beauty shop.
Activities Cards; Games; Reading groups; Prayer groups; Movies; Social/Cultural gatherings.

Queen City Nursing Home*
400 Forest Ave, Cincinnati, OH, 45229
(513) 961-6452
Licensure Intermediate care. *Beds* 37. *Certified* Medicaid.
Owner Proprietary Corp.

Red Haven Nursing Home Inc*
751 Greenwood Ave, Cincinnati, OH, 45229
(513) 751-1157
Licensure Skilled care; Intermediate care. *Beds* 31. *Certified* Medicaid; Medicare.
Owner Proprietary Corp.

Restview Nursing Home
3550 Washington Ave, Cincinnati, OH, 45229
(513) 751-1308
Licensure Intermediate care. *Beds* 44. *Certified* Medicaid.
Owner Proprietary Corp.

Riverview Home*
5999 Bender Rd, Cincinnati, OH, 45233
(513) 922-1440
Licensure Skilled care; Intermediate care; Rest home. *Beds* 146. *Certified* Medicaid; Medicare.
Owner Nonprofit Corp (United Church Homes).

St Joseph Infant Home*
10722 Wyscarver Rd, Cincinnati, OH, 45241
Licensure Intermediate care for mentally retarded. *Beds* 32. *Certified* Medicaid.
Owner Nonprofit Corp.

St Margaret Hall
1960 Madison Rd, Cincinnati, OH, 45206
(513) 751-5880
Licensure Nursing home; Rest home. *Beds* Nursing home 99; Rest home 45.
Owner Nonprofit Corp.

St Theresa Home
6760 Belkenton Pl, Cincinnati, OH, 45236
(513) 891-1090, 891-1094
Admin Sr Brenda Hilger. *Medical Dir/Dir of Nursing* Sandra Frommeyer.
Licensure Intermediate care; Nursing home; Rest home. *Beds* ICF 37; Rest home 63. *Certified* Medicare.
Owner Nonprofit organization/foundation.
Admissions Requirements Medical examination.
Staff RNs 1 (ft); LPNs 6 (ft); Nurses aides 18 (ft), 20 (pt); Activities coordinators 2 (ft); Dietitians 1 (ft).
Affiliation Roman Catholic
Facilities Dining room; Activities room; Chapel; Crafts room; Laundry room; Barber/Beauty shop.

Activities Arts & crafts; Cards; Games; Reading groups; Prayer groups; Movies; Shopping trips; Social/Cultural gatherings.

Salem Parke Nursing Home
6128 Salem Rd, Cincinnati, OH, 45230
(513) 231-8292
Admin Barbara Wolf. *Medical Dir/Dir of Nursing* John Cardosi MD; Helen Bishop RNC.
Licensure Skilled care; Intermediate care. *Beds* 107. *Certified* Medicaid; Medicare.
Owner Proprietary Corp (Parke Care Inc).
Staff RNs 8 (ft), 7 (pt); LPNs 3 (ft), 2 (pt); Orderlies 2 (ft); Nurses aides 25 (ft), 20 (pt); Physical therapists 1 (pt); Occupational therapists 1 (pt); Speech therapists 1 (pt); Activities coordinators 1 (ft); Dietitians 2 (pt); Dentists 1 (pt); Ophthalmologists 1 (pt); Podiatrists 1 (pt).
Facilities Dining room; Physical therapy room; Activities room; Crafts room; Laundry room; Barber/Beauty shop.
Activities Arts & crafts; Cards; Games; Reading groups; Prayer groups; Movies; Shopping trips; Social/Cultural gatherings; Dinners; Exercises; Current events; Happy hour; Parties.

Summit Nursing & Convalescent Home Inc
2586 La Feuille Ave, Cincinnati, OH, 45211
(513) 662-2445
Admin Frances R Glaser. *Medical Dir/Dir of Nursing* Manuel Mediodia MD; Mary Noll DON.
Licensure Skilled care; Intermediate care. *Beds* SNF 50; ICF 115. *Certified* Medicaid; Medicare.
Owner Proprietary Corp.
Admissions Requirements Minimum age 40; Medical examination.
Facilities Dining room; Physical therapy room; Activities room; Chapel; Crafts room; Laundry room; Barber/Beauty shop; Library.
Activities Arts & crafts; Cards; Games; Reading groups; Prayer groups; Movies; Shopping trips; Social/Cultural gatherings; Outside recreational sports.

Three Rivers Convalescent Center
7800 Jandaracres Dr, Cincinnati, OH, 45248-2097
(513) 941-0787
Admin David P Walsh. *Medical Dir/Dir of Nursing* Dr George Shields; Dorothy Daughters.
Licensure Skilled care; Intermediate care. *Beds* SNF 169; ICF. *Certified* Medicaid; Medicare.
Owner Proprietary Corp.
Admissions Requirements Minimum age Geriatrics; Medical examination; Physician's request.
Staff Physicians 1 (pt); RNs 10 (ft), 2 (pt); LPNs 19 (ft), 4 (pt); Nurses aides 45 (ft), 10 (pt); Physical therapists 1 (pt); Recreational therapists 3 (ft); Speech therapists 1 (pt); Activities coordinators 1 (ft); Dietitians 1 (pt); Dentists 1 (pt); Ophthalmologists 1 (pt); Podiatrists 1 (pt).
Languages Italian, German
Facilities Dining room; Physical therapy room; Activities room; Chapel; Crafts room; Laundry room; Barber/Beauty shop; Library.
Activities Arts & crafts; Cards; Games; Reading groups; Prayer groups; Movies; Shopping trips; Social/Cultural gatherings.

Turner Nursing Home
1550 Glen Parker, Cincinnati, OH, 45223-1602
(513) 554-4060
Licensure Intermediate care. *Beds* 17. *Certified* Medicaid.
Owner Proprietary Corp.

Twin Towers
5343 Hamilton Ave, Cincinnati, OH, 45224
(513) 853-2000
Admin Joseph R Graham. *Medical Dir/Dir of Nursing* Kenneth A Frederick MD.
Licensure Intermediate care; Retirement Community. *Beds* 136. *Certified* Medicaid.
Owner Nonprofit Corp.
Admissions Requirements Minimum age 62; Medical examination.
Staff Physicians 2 (pt); RNs 10 (ft), 4 (pt); LPNs 13 (ft), 6 (pt); Orderlies 4 (ft), 1 (pt); Nurses aides 29 (ft), 20 (pt); Physical therapists 1 (pt); Occupational therapists 1 (pt); Speech therapists; Activities coordinators 1 (ft); Dietitians 1 (ft); Dentists; Podiatrists.
Affiliation Methodist
Facilities Dining room; Physical therapy room; Activities room; Chapel; Crafts room; Laundry room; Barber/Beauty shop; Library; Post office.
Activities Arts & crafts; Cards; Games; Reading groups; Prayer groups; Movies; Shopping trips; Social/Cultural gatherings; Chapel.

The Washington
3615 Washington Ave, Cincinnati, OH, 45229
(513) 751-5223
Licensure Skilled care; Intermediate care. *Beds* 55. *Certified* Medicaid; Medicare.
Owner Proprietary Corp.
Staff Physicians; RNs; LPNs; Nurses aides; Physical therapists; Activities coordinators; Dietitians; Ophthalmologists.
Facilities Dining room; Activities room.
Activities Arts & crafts; Cards; Games; Reading groups; Prayer groups; Movies; Shopping trips; Social/Cultural gatherings.

Wesley Hall Inc*
315 Lilienthal St, Cincinnati, OH, 45204
(513) 471-8667
Medical Dir/Dir of Nursing Dr George Shields.
Licensure Intermediate care. *Beds* 128. *Certified* Medicaid.
Owner Nonprofit Corp.
Staff Physicians 1 (pt); RNs 5 (ft); LPNs 15 (ft); Orderlies 1 (ft); Nurses aides 56 (ft); Physical therapists 2 (ft); Occupational therapists 1 (pt); Activities coordinators 3 (ft); Dietitians 19 (ft); Podiatrists 1 (pt).
Affiliation Methodist
Facilities Dining room; Physical therapy room; Activities room; Chapel; Crafts room; Laundry room; Barber/Beauty shop.
Activities Arts & crafts; Cards; Games; Prayer groups; Social/Cultural gatherings.

West Hills Nursing Home Inc*
2841 Harrison Ave, Cincinnati, OH, 45211
(513) 481-4555
Licensure Skilled care; Intermediate care. *Beds* 46. *Certified* Medicaid; Medicare.
Owner Nonprofit Corp.

West Park Villa Health Care Center
One Hegry Court, Cincinnati, OH, 45238
Licensure Skilled care; Intermediate care. *Beds* 100. *Certified* Medicaid; Medicare.
Owner Proprietary Corp.

West Side Health Care Center*
1857 Grand Ave, Cincinnati, OH, 45214
(513) 921-4281
Licensure Skilled care; Intermediate care. *Beds* 69. *Certified* Medicaid; Medicare.
Owner Proprietary Corp.

Windsor Park Nursing Home Inc*
2245 Park Ave, Cincinnati, OH, 45206
(513) 861-1300
Licensure Skilled care; Intermediate care. *Beds* 49. *Certified* Medicaid; Medicare.
Owner Proprietary Corp.

Zion Nursing Home Inc*
3610 Washington Ave, Cincinnati, OH, 45229
(513) 221-2775
Licensure Intermediate care. *Beds* 50. *Certified* Medicaid.
Owner Nonprofit Corp.

CIRCLEVILLE

Americare Circleville Nursing & Rehabilitation Center
1155 Atwater Ave, Circleville, OH, 43113
(614) 477-1695
Admin David M Dixon. *Medical Dir/Dir of Nursing* Dr Bolendar; Gary Miller DON.
Licensure Skilled care; Intermediate care. *Beds* SNF 20; ICF 100. *Certified* Medicaid; Medicare.
Owner Proprietary Corp (Care Enterprises).
Admissions Requirements Medical examination; Physician's request.
Staff Physicians; RNs; LPNs; Nurses aides; Physical therapists; Occupational therapists; Speech therapists; Activities coordinators; Dietitians.
Facilities Dining room; Physical therapy room; Activities room; Crafts room; Laundry room; Barber/Beauty shop; Library.
Activities Arts & crafts; Cards; Games; Reading groups; Prayer groups; Movies; Shopping trips; Social/Cultural gatherings.

Brown Memorial Home Inc
158 E Mound St, Circleville, OH, 43113
(614) 474-6065
Licensure Intermediate care. *Beds* 35. *Certified* Medicaid.
Owner Nonprofit Corp.
Admissions Requirements Medical examination.
Staff RNs 1 (ft), 2 (pt); LPNs 5 (ft), 3 (pt); Nurses aides 18 (ft), 8 (pt); Activities coordinators 1 (ft).
Facilities Dining room; Activities room; Laundry room.
Activities Arts & crafts; Cards; Games; Reading groups; Prayer groups; Movies; Shopping trips; Social/Cultural gatherings.

Logan Elm Health Care Center
370 Tarlton Rd, Circleville, OH, 43113
(614) 474-3121
Admin Jerry Kuyoth. *Medical Dir/Dir of Nursing* Dr Lynn Chrismer, Dr Andrew Smith; Esther Boyer.
Licensure Skilled care; Intermediate care. *Beds* SNF 27; ICF 74. *Certified* Medicaid; Medicare.
Owner Proprietary Corp.
Admissions Requirements Medical examination.
Staff Physicians 2 (pt); RNs 8 (ft); LPNs 10 (ft); Orderlies 1 (ft); Nurses aides 40 (ft), 13 (pt); Physical therapists 1 (pt); Recreational therapists 2 (ft); Occupational therapists 1 (pt); Speech therapists 1 (pt); Activities coordinators 1 (ft); Dietitians 1 (pt); Dentists 1 (pt); Ophthalmologists 1 (pt); Podiatrists 1 (pt).
Facilities Dining room; Physical therapy room; Activities room; Crafts room; Laundry room; Barber/Beauty shop; 2 television rooms; 2 consultation rooms.
Activities Arts & crafts; Cards; Games; Reading groups; Prayer groups; Movies; Shopping trips; Social/Cultural gatherings.

Pickaway Manor Care Center
391 Clark Dr, Circleville, OH, 43113
(614) 474-6036
Admin Charles P Bradley. *Medical Dir/Dir of Nursing* Carlos Alvarez MD; Virginia Davis DON.
Licensure Skilled care; Intermediate care. *Beds* 100. *Certified* Medicaid; Medicare.
Owner Proprietary Corp (Southmark Heritage Corp).

Admissions Requirements Medical examination; Physician's request.
Staff RNs 8 (ft), 5 (pt); LPNs 9 (ft), 2 (pt); Orderlies 1 (ft), 1 (pt); Nurses aides 27 (ft); Physical therapists 1 (pt); Reality therapists 1 (ft); Recreational therapists 1 (ft); Occupational therapists 1 (pt); Speech therapists 1 (pt); Activities coordinators 1 (ft); Dietitians 1 (pt); Dentists 1 (pt); Ophthalmologists 1 (pt); Podiatrists 1 (pt).
Facilities Dining room; Physical therapy room; Activities room; Crafts room; Laundry room; Barber/Beauty shop.
Activities Arts & crafts; Cards; Games; Reading groups; Prayer groups; Movies; Shopping trips; Social/Cultural gatherings.

CLARKSBURG

Walnut Manor Care Center*
PO Box 158, 11017 Main St, Clarksburg, OH, 43115
(614) 893-4201
Licensure Intermediate care. *Beds* 22. *Certified* Medicaid.
Owner Proprietary Corp.

CLEVELAND

Algart Health Care Inc*
8902 Detroit Ave, Cleveland, OH, 44102
(216) 631-1550
Licensure Intermediate care. *Beds* 50. *Certified* Medicaid.
Owner Proprietary Corp.

Amasa Stone House Inc
975 East Blvd, Cleveland, OH, 44108
(216) 451-1884
Admin John L Prose. *Medical Dir/Dir of Nursing* Dr Kevin Geraci; Cartha Ohanessian.
Licensure Intermediate care. *Beds* ICF 50. *Certified* Medicaid.
Owner Nonprofit Corp.
Admissions Requirements Minimum age 65; Females only; Medical examination.
Staff RNs 2 (ft); LPNs 3 (ft), 3 (pt); Nurses aides 16 (ft), 10 (pt); Activities coordinators 1 (ft).
Facilities Dining room; Physical therapy room; Activities room; Crafts room; Laundry room; Barber/Beauty shop; Library.
Activities Arts & crafts; Games; Reading groups; Prayer groups; Movies; Shopping trips; Social/Cultural gatherings.

Aristocrat West Skilled Nursing Facility
4387 W 150th St, Cleveland, OH, 44135
(216) 252-7730
Admin Daniel Zawadzki. *Medical Dir/Dir of Nursing* Dr J Cua; Rose Marie Kelly RN.
Licensure Skilled care; Intermediate care. *Beds* 124. *Certified* Medicaid; Medicare.
Owner Proprietary Corp.
Admissions Requirements Minimum age 14; Medical examination; Physician's request.
Staff Physicians 2 (pt); RNs 5 (ft), 3 (pt); LPNs 11 (ft), 4 (pt); Nurses aides 31 (ft), 14 (pt); Physical therapists 1 (ft), 1 (pt); Occupational therapists 2 (pt); Activities coordinators 1 (ft); Dietitians 1 (pt); Music therapist 1 (pt).
Languages Spanish, Slavic
Facilities Dining room; Physical therapy room; Activities room; Crafts room; Laundry room; Barber/Beauty shop; Library.
Activities Arts & crafts; Cards; Games; Reading groups; Prayer groups; Movies; Shopping trips; Social/Cultural gatherings; Horticulture club; Choir; Visiting pets.

Baldwin Manor Nursing Home Inc
2437 Baldwin Rd, Cleveland, OH, 44104
(216) 229-4800

Admin David Newman. *Medical Dir/Dir of Nursing* A Aronshteyn MD; Julie Gross RN DON.
Licensure Skilled care; Intermediate care. *Beds* SNF 50; ICF. *Certified* Medicaid.
Owner Proprietary Corp.
Admissions Requirements Medical examination.
Staff Physicians 1 (pt); RNs 2 (ft); LPNs 3 (ft); Nurses aides 16 (ft), 1 (pt); Physical therapists 1 (ft); Occupational therapists 1 (ft), 1 (pt); Speech therapists 1 (pt); Activities coordinators 1 (ft); Dietitians 1 (pt); Dentists 1 (pt); Ophthalmologists 1 (pt); Podiatrists 1 (pt); Speech therapist 1 (pt).
Facilities Dining room; Physical therapy room; Activities room; Chapel; Crafts room; Laundry room; Library.
Activities Arts & crafts; Cards; Games; Reading groups; Prayer groups; Movies; Shopping trips.

Carnegie Care Center*
8800 Carnegie Ave, Cleveland, OH, 44106
Licensure Intermediate care. *Beds* 211.
Certified Medicaid.
Owner Proprietary Corp.

Cleveland Golden Age Nursing Home*
928 E 152nd St, Cleveland, OH, 44110
(216) 761-3000
Licensure Intermediate care. *Beds* 100.
Certified Medicaid.
Owner Proprietary Corp.

Concord Manor Nursing Home*
1877 E 82nd St, Cleveland, OH, 44103
(216) 795-6110
Medical Dir/Dir of Nursing Dr Navnvich.
Licensure Intermediate care. *Beds* 34.
Certified Medicaid.
Owner Proprietary Corp.
Admissions Requirements Medical examination; Physician's request.
Staff Physicians 1 (pt); RNs 1 (pt); LPNs 2 (ft), 2 (pt); Orderlies 1 (ft); Nurses aides 11 (ft); Activities coordinators 1 (pt); Dietitians 1 (pt); Dentists 1 (pt); Ophthalmologists 1 (pt); Podiatrists 1 (pt).
Facilities Dining room; Activities room; Laundry room.
Activities Arts & crafts; Cards; Games; Prayer groups; Movies; Shopping trips.

Cuyahoga County Nursing Home
3305 Franklin Blvd, Cleveland, OH, 44105
(216) 961-4344
Admin Jerome M Weissfeld. *Medical Dir/Dir of Nursing* Alicia Tupaz RN.
Licensure Intermediate care. *Beds* ICF 177.
Certified Medicaid.
Owner Publicly owned.
Admissions Requirements Minimum age 21.
Languages Spanish
Facilities Dining room; Physical therapy room; Activities room; Crafts room; Laundry room; Barber/Beauty shop; Library.
Activities Arts & crafts; Games; Reading groups; Prayer groups; Movies; Shopping trips; Social/Cultural gatherings; Gardening; Concerts; Athletic events.

Dunbar Nursing Home*
2415 E 55th St, Cleveland, OH, 44104
(216) 391-7100
Licensure Skilled care; Intermediate care. *Beds* 155. *Certified* Medicaid; Medicare.
Owner Proprietary Corp.

Eliza Bryant Center
7201 Wade Park Ave, Cleveland, OH, 44103
(216) 361-6141
Admin Shirley Hrovatt; Ronald Winbush Ex Dir.
Licensure Intermediate care. *Beds* 100.
Certified Medicaid.
Owner Nonprofit Corp.

Staff Physicians 4 (pt); RNs 4 (pt); LPNs 12 (ft); Orderlies 10 (ft); Nurses aides 25 (ft); Physical therapists 1 (pt); Activities coordinators 1 (ft), 1 (pt); Dietitians 1 (pt); Ophthalmologists 1 (pt); Social worker 1 (ft).
Facilities Dining room; Physical therapy room; Activities room; Crafts room; Laundry room; Barber/Beauty shop; Library.
Activities Arts & crafts; Cards; Games; Reading groups; Prayer groups; Movies; Shopping trips; Social/Cultural gatherings.

Euclid Manor Nursing Home*
17322 Euclid Ave, Cleveland, OH, 44112
(216) 486-2280
Medical Dir/Dir of Nursing Nachman Kacen MD.
Licensure Skilled care; Intermediate care. *Beds* 174. *Certified* Medicaid; Medicare.
Owner Proprietary Corp.
Staff Physicians; RNs; LPNs; Orderlies; Nurses aides; Physical therapists; Occupational therapists; Activities coordinators; Dietitians; Dentists; Podiatrists.
Facilities Dining room; Physical therapy room; Activities room; Crafts room; Laundry room; Barber/Beauty shop; Library.
Activities Arts & crafts; Cards; Games; Reading groups; Prayer groups; Movies; Shopping trips.

Forest Hills Nursing Home Inc*
736 Lakeview Rd, Cleveland, OH, 44108
(216) 268-3800
Licensure Skilled care; Intermediate care. *Beds* 252. *Certified* Medicaid; Medicare.
Owner Proprietary Corp.

Franklin Plaza
3600 Franklin Blvd, Cleveland, OH, 44113
(216) 651-1600
Admin Edith Rock. *Medical Dir/Dir of Nursing* Dr Jarawal Jephtva.
Licensure Skilled care; Intermediate care. *Beds* SNF 36; ICF 191. *Certified* Medicaid; Medicare.
Owner Proprietary Corp.
Admissions Requirements Medical examination.
Staff Physicians 35 (pt); RNs 12 (ft); LPNs 33 (ft); Orderlies 8 (ft); Nurses aides 70 (ft); Physical therapists 1 (ft); Reality therapists 1 (ft); Recreational therapists 1 (ft); Occupational therapists 1 (ft); Speech therapists 1 (ft); Activities coordinators 2 (ft); Dietitians 1 (pt); Dentists 1 (pt); Ophthalmologists 1 (pt); Podiatrists 1 (pt).
Facilities Dining room; Physical therapy room; Activities room; Laundry room; Barber/Beauty shop.
Activities Arts & crafts; Cards; Games; Reading groups; Prayer groups; Movies; Shopping trips; Social/Cultural gatherings.

Geri-Care Inc
2438 Mapleside Rd, Cleveland, OH, 44104
(216) 229-9600
Admin David Neuman. *Medical Dir/Dir of Nursing* A Aronshteyn MD; Julie Gross RN DON.
Licensure Intermediate care. *Beds* ICF 36.
Certified Medicaid.
Owner Proprietary Corp.
Admissions Requirements Medical examination.
Staff Physicians 1 (pt); RNs 2 (pt); LPNs 4 (ft), 1 (pt); Nurses aides 10 (ft); Physical therapists 1 (pt); Occupational therapists 1 (pt); Speech therapists 1 (pt); Activities coordinators 1 (ft); Dietitians 1 (pt); Dentists 1 (pt); Ophthalmologists 1 (pt); Podiatrists 1 (pt).
Facilities Dining room; Physical therapy room; Activities room; Crafts room; Laundry room; Library.

Activities Arts & crafts; Cards; Games; Reading groups; Prayer groups; Movies; Shopping trips.

Inner City Nursing Home Inc
9014 Cedar Ave, Cleveland, OH, 44106
(216) 795-1363
Admin Ethel L Pye. *Medical Dir/Dir of Nursing* Billy Brown MD.
Licensure Intermediate care. *Beds* ICF 50.
Certified Medicaid.
Owner Privately owned.
Admissions Requirements Minimum age 18; Medical examination.
Staff Physicians; RNs; LPNs; Orderlies; Nurses aides; Activities coordinators; Dietitians; Dentists; Ophthalmologists.
Facilities Dining room; Laundry room; Barber/Beauty shop.
Activities Arts & crafts; Games; Reading groups; Prayer groups; Social/Cultural gatherings.

Eliza Jennings Home
10603 Detroit Ave, Cleveland, OH, 44102
(216) 226-0282
Licensure Rest home. *Beds* 58.
Owner Nonprofit Corp.

Laub Pavillion of Cleveland Ohio
10603 Detroit Ave, Cleveland, OH, 44102
(216) 226-0282
Licensure Skilled care; Intermediate care. *Beds* 131. *Certified* Medicaid.
Owner Nonprofit Corp.

Little Sisters of the Poor
4291 Richmond Rd, Cleveland, OH, 44122
(216) 464-1222
Admin Sr Paul. *Medical Dir/Dir of Nursing* Dr Yalcin Dinceman.
Licensure Intermediate care; Rest home; Independent living. *Beds* ICF 99; Rest home 31; Independent living 21. *Certified* Medicaid.
Owner Nonprofit Corp.
Admissions Requirements Medical examination.
Staff RNs 5 (ft), 11 (pt); LPNs 7 (ft), 6 (pt); Nurses aides 36 (ft), 11 (pt); Physical therapists 1 (pt); Activities coordinators 1 (ft); Dietitians 1 (pt).
Affiliation Roman Catholic
Facilities Dining room; Physical therapy room; Activities room; Chapel; Crafts room; Laundry room; Barber/Beauty shop; Library.
Activities Arts & crafts; Cards; Games; Reading groups; Prayer groups; Movies; Shopping trips; Social/Cultural gatherings; Social service counseling.

Madonna Hall*
1906 E 82nd St, Cleveland, OH, 44103
(216) 421-5660
Admin Howard B Bram. *Medical Dir/Dir of Nursing* Pamala Murphy MD.
Licensure Intermediate care. *Beds* 99.
Certified Medicaid.
Owner Nonprofit Corp.
Admissions Requirements Minimum age 60; Medical examination.
Staff RNs 1 (ft), 1 (pt); LPNs 6 (ft), 4 (pt); Orderlies 2 (ft); Nurses aides 23 (ft); Activities coordinators 2 (pt).
Affiliation Roman Catholic
Facilities Dining room; Physical therapy room; Activities room; Chapel; Crafts room; Laundry room.
Activities Arts & crafts; Cards; Games; Movies; Shopping trips; Social/Cultural gatherings.

Manor Care Lakeshore Nursing Center
16101 Lake Shore Blvd, Cleveland, OH, 44110
(216) 486-2300
Admin Michael A Scocos. *Medical Dir/Dir of Nursing* William L George; Beth Conklin RN DON.

Licensure Skilled care; Intermediate care. *Beds* SNF 20; ICF 182. *Certified* Medicaid; Medicare.
Owner Proprietary Corp (Manor Care).
Admissions Requirements Medical examination.
Staff Physicians 3 (pt); RNs 6 (ft), 6 (pt); LPNs 21 (ft), 16 (pt); Nurses aides 40 (ft), 20 (pt); Physical therapists 1 (ft); Recreational therapists 1 (ft); Occupational therapists 1 (pt); Speech therapists 1 (pt); Activities coordinators 1 (ft); Dietitians 1 (ft); Dentists 1 (pt); Ophthalmologists 1 (pt); Podiatrists 1 (pt).
Languages Slavic, Croatian, Italian, German, Lithuanian
Facilities Dining room; Physical therapy room; Activities room; Crafts room; Laundry room; Barber/Beauty shop; Library.
Activities Arts & crafts; Cards; Games; Reading groups; Prayer groups; Movies; Shopping trips; Social/Cultural gatherings.

Manor Care Nursing Center—Rocky River*
4102 Rocky River Dr, Cleveland, OH, 44135
(216) 251-3300
Admin Thomas A Armagno. *Medical Dir/Dir of Nursing* Javier Clemente MD.
Licensure Skilled care; Intermediate care. *Beds* 210. *Certified* Medicaid; Medicare.
Owner Proprietary Corp.
Admissions Requirements Medical examination.
Staff Physicians 2 (pt); RNs 8 (ft), 9 (pt); LPNs 13 (ft), 11 (pt); Orderlies 3 (ft), 2 (pt); Nurses aides 50 (ft), 32 (pt); Physical therapists 1 (ft), 3 (pt); Reality therapists 1 (ft); Recreational therapists 1 (ft); Occupational therapists 2 (ft), 1 (pt); Speech therapists 1 (pt); Activities coordinators 1 (ft); Dietitians 1 (pt); Dentists 1 (pt); Ophthalmologists 1 (pt); Podiatrists 1 (pt); Audiologists 1 (pt).
Facilities Dining room; Physical therapy room; Activities room; Chapel; Crafts room; Laundry room; Barber/Beauty shop; Library; Patio.
Activities Arts & crafts; Cards; Games; Reading groups; Prayer groups; Movies; Shopping trips; Social/Cultural gatherings; Field trips.

Marietta Manor*
694 E 109th St, Cleveland, OH, 44108
(216) 851-7100
Medical Dir/Dir of Nursing Dr Naunovich.
Licensure Nursing home. *Beds* 15.
Owner Proprietary Corp.
Admissions Requirements Females only.
Staff Physicians 1 (ft); RNs 1 (ft); LPNs 4 (ft), 2 (pt); Orderlies 1 (ft); Nurses aides 8 (ft), 2 (pt); Activities coordinators 1 (ft); Dietitians 1 (ft); Dentists 1 (ft); Podiatrists 1 (ft).
Affiliation Presbyterian
Facilities Dining room; Activities room; Laundry room.
Activities Arts & crafts; Games; Prayer groups; Shopping trips.

Mary Louise Nursing Home*
670 Lakeview Rd, Cleveland, OH, 44108
Licensure Intermediate care. *Beds* 11.
Certified Medicaid.
Owner Proprietary Corp.

Medicare Nursing Homes Inc
18220 Euclid Ave, Cleveland, OH, 44112
(216) 486-6300
Admin Delbert S Cohon. *Medical Dir/Dir of Nursing* Leonard Lewin MD; Don & Linda Lane RN.
Licensure Skilled care; Intermediate care. *Beds* 50. *Certified* Medicaid; Medicare.
Owner Proprietary Corp.
Admissions Requirements Medical examination.

Facilities Dining room; Physical therapy room; Activities room; Laundry room.
Activities Arts & crafts; Cards; Games; Reading groups; Prayer groups; Movies; Shopping trips; Social/Cultural gatherings.

Mt Pleasant Nursing Home*
10406 Kinsman Rd, Cleveland, OH, 44104
(216) 271-0073
Medical Dir/Dir of Nursing Dr Naunovich.
Licensure Intermediate care. *Beds* 33.
Certified Medicaid.
Owner Proprietary Corp.
Staff Physicians 1 (ft); RNs 1 (ft); LPNs 5 (ft), 4 (pt); Orderlies 1 (ft); Nurses aides 10 (ft), 5 (pt); Activities coordinators 1 (ft); Dietitians 1 (ft); Dentists 1 (ft); Podiatrists 1 (ft).
Affiliation Presbyterian
Facilities Dining room; Activities room; Laundry room.
Activities Arts & crafts; Cards; Games; Prayer groups; Shopping trips.

Northeast Ohio Development Center*
4445 Turney Rd, Cleveland, OH, 44105
(216) 441-6200
Licensure Intermediate care for mentally retarded. *Beds* 142.
Owner Publicly owned.

Overlook House*
2187 Overlook Rd, Cleveland, OH, 44106
(216) 795-3550
Licensure Nursing home. *Beds* 33.
Owner Nonprofit Corp.
Affiliation Christian Science
Facilities Dining room; Activities room; Chapel; Laundry room; Barber/Beauty shop; Library.
Activities Reading groups; Prayer groups; Movies; Social/Cultural gatherings.

Palm Crest Bellaire Nursing Home
12709 Bellaire Rd, Cleveland, OH, 44135
(216) 941-4545
Licensure Intermediate care. *Beds* 28.
Certified Medicaid.
Owner Proprietary Corp.

Parent's Volunteer Association*
17608 Euclid Ave, Cleveland, OH, 44112
(216) 481-1907
Licensure Intermediate care for mentally retarded. *Beds* 72.
Owner Nonprofit Corp.

Prospect Manor*
3912 Prospect Ave, Cleveland, OH, 44115
(216) 361-6655
Licensure Intermediate care. *Beds* 50.
Certified Medicaid.
Owner Proprietary Corp.

Rae-Ann Nursing Center*
18223 Rockland Ave, Cleveland, OH, 44135
(216) 267-5445
Licensure Intermediate care. *Beds* 28.
Certified Medicaid.
Owner Proprietary Corp.

Rose Park Convalescent & Rehabilitation Center*
18810 Harvard Ave, Cleveland, OH, 44122
(216) 752-3600
Licensure Skilled care; Intermediate care. *Beds* 84. *Certified* Medicaid; Medicare.
Owner Proprietary Corp.

St Augustine Manor
7800 Detroit Ave, Cleveland, OH, 44102
(216) 651-3680
Licensure Skilled care; Intermediate care. *Beds* 194. *Certified* Medicaid; Medicare.
Owner Nonprofit Corp.

Singleton Health Care Center*
1867 E 82nd St, Cleveland, OH, 44103
(216) 231-8467

Licensure Intermediate care. *Beds* 50.
Certified Medicaid.
Owner Proprietary Corp.

Sunset Nursing Home
1802 Crawford Rd, Cleveland, OH, 44106
(216) 795-5710
Admin Ms M Dinkes. *Medical Dir/Dir of Nursing* Ms Mosby.
Licensure Intermediate care. *Beds* ICF 15.
Certified Medicaid.
Owner Proprietary Corp.
Admissions Requirements Females only.
Staff Physicians 1 (pt); RNs 1 (pt); LPNs 2 (ft), 2 (pt); Nurses aides 9 (ft), 2 (pt); Physical therapists 1 (pt); Reality therapists 1 (pt); Recreational therapists 1 (pt); Occupational therapists 1 (pt); Speech therapists 1 (pt); Activities coordinators 1 (pt); Dietitians 1 (pt); Dentists 1 (pt); Ophthalmologists 1 (pt); Podiatrists 1 (pt).
Facilities Dining room; Crafts room.
Activities Arts & crafts; Games; Prayer groups.

United Cerebral Palsy Association Home of Cuyahoga County
2803 Martin Luther King, Cleveland, OH, 44104
(216) 721-1620
Admin Patricia Hurley. *Medical Dir/Dir of Nursing* Virgene Nowacek MD; Marleen Gross RN.
Licensure Intermediate care for mentally retarded. *Beds* ICF/MR 10. *Certified* Medicaid.
Owner Nonprofit Corp.
Admissions Requirements Minimum age 18; Medical examination.
Staff Physicians 1 (pt); RNs 2 (pt); Nurses aides 4 (ft), 5 (pt); Physical therapists 1 (pt); Recreational therapists 1 (pt); Occupational therapists 1 (pt); Speech therapists 1 (pt); Activities coordinators 1 (pt); Dietitians 1 (pt).
Languages Sign
Facilities Activities room; Laundry room; Each apartment has dining room, kitchen, bedroom, & bathroom.
Activities Arts & crafts; Cards; Games; Reading groups; Movies; Shopping trips; Social/Cultural gatherings.

Villa Care Center
4835 Broadview Rd, Cleveland, OH, 44109
(216) 749-3939
Admin Mary Lou Fleck. *Medical Dir/Dir of Nursing* M T Sheth MD.
Licensure Intermediate care. *Beds* ICF 50.
Certified Medicaid.
Owner Proprietary Corp.
Admissions Requirements Minimum age 30.
Staff RNs 3 (ft), 5 (pt); LPNs 1 (ft), 2 (pt); Orderlies 2 (ft); Nurses aides 16 (ft), 2 (pt); Physical therapists 1 (pt); Activities coordinators 2 (ft); Dietitians 1 (pt); Dentists 1 (pt); Ophthalmologists 1 (pt); Podiatrists 1 (pt).
Facilities Dining room; Activities room; Crafts room; Laundry room.
Activities Arts & crafts; Cards; Games; Reading groups; Prayer groups; Movies; Shopping trips; Social/Cultural gatherings.

Villa Sancta Anna Home for the Aged Inc
25000 Chagrin Blvd, Cleveland, OH, 44122
(216) 464-9250
Admin Sr Mary Elizabeth Ann Rechka. *Medical Dir/Dir of Nursing* Dr Sylvia Marshall; Anna Woodside.
Licensure Intermediate care. *Beds* 68.
Certified Medicaid.
Owner Nonprofit organization/foundation.
Admissions Requirements Medical examination.
Staff Physicians 3 (pt); RNs 2 (ft), 2 (pt); LPNs 4 (pt), 2 (pt); Nurses aides 16 (ft), 8 (pt); Physical therapists 1 (pt); Recreational

therapists 1 (ft); Activities coordinators 1
(ft); Dietitians 1 (pt); Ophthalmologists 2
(pt).
Languages Slavic
Facilities Dining room; Physical therapy
room; Activities room; Chapel; Crafts room;
Laundry room; Laundry room; Library;
Solariums; TV Room; Recreation Room.
Activities Arts & crafts; Games; Prayer groups;
Movies; Social/Cultural gatherings.

CLEVELAND HEIGHTS

Judson Park
1801 Chestnut Hills Dr, Cleveland Heights,
OH, 44106
(216) 721-1234
Admin Cynthia H Dunn. *Medical Dir/Dir of
Nursing* Diane McCarty.
Licensure Intermediate care; Retirement
community. *Beds* 93. *Certified* Medicaid.
Owner Nonprofit Corp.
Admissions Requirements Minimum age 62;
Medical examination.
Staff Physicians 1 (pt); RNs 16 (ft); LPNs 12
(ft), 2 (pt); Nurses aides 46 (ft), 8 (pt);
Physical therapists 3 (pt); Reality therapists
1 (pt); Recreational therapists 3 (ft), 3 (pt);
Occupational therapists 1 (ft); Speech
therapists 1 (pt); Activities coordinators 3
(ft); Dietitians 2 (ft); Dentists 1 (pt);
Ophthalmologists 1 (pt); Podiatrists 1 (pt).
Facilities Dining room; Physical therapy
room; Activities room; Chapel; Crafts room;
Laundry room; Barber/Beauty shop; Library.
Activities Arts & crafts; Games; Reading
groups; Prayer groups; Movies; Shopping
trips; Social/Cultural gatherings.

Montefiore Home
3151 Mayfield Rd, Cleveland Heights, OH,
44118
(216) 371-5500
Admin Ira C Robbins. *Medical Dir/Dir of
Nursing* Dr Morton Rosenthal; Gloria
Goodman DON.
Licensure Skilled care; Intermediate care. *Beds*
SNF 174; ICF. *Certified* Medicaid;
Medicare.
Owner Nonprofit Corp.
Staff RNs 16 (ft); LPNs 25 (ft), 2 (pt); Nurses
aides 61 (ft), 2 (pt); Physical therapists 3 (ft),
1 (pt); Reality therapists 1 (ft); Recreational
therapists 2 (ft), 5 (pt); Occupational
therapists 6 (pt); Activities coordinators 1
(ft); Dietitians 1 (ft); Dentists 1 (pt);
Ophthalmologists 1 (pt).

Rose Nursing Home
2435 W St James Pkwy, Cleveland Heights,
OH, 44106
(216) 229-2984
Admin Robert Gelender. *Medical Dir/Dir of
Nursing* Evelyn Brock DON.
Licensure Nursing home. *Beds* Nursing home
22.
Owner Privately owned.
Admissions Requirements Medical
examination.
Staff LPNs 3 (ft); Nurses aides 5 (ft);
Dietitians 1 (ft); Ophthalmologists 1 (ft).
Facilities Laundry room.

Margaret Wagner House*
2373 Euclid Hgts Blvd, Cleveland Heights,
OH, 44104
(216) 795-5450
Medical Dir/Dir of Nursing George Gelehrter
MD.
Licensure Skilled care; Intermediate care. *Beds*
175. *Certified* Medicaid; Medicare.
Owner Nonprofit Corp.
Admissions Requirements Minimum age 60;
Medical examination; Physician's request.
Staff Physicians; RNs; LPNs; Nurses aides;
Physical therapists; Reality therapists;
Recreational therapists; Occupational
therapists; Activities coordinators; Dietitians.

Facilities Dining room; Physical therapy
room; Activities room; Chapel; Crafts room;
Laundry room; Barber/Beauty shop; Dentist
& podiatrist offices.
Activities Arts & crafts; Cards; Games;
Reading groups; Prayer groups; Movies;
Shopping trips; Social/Cultural gatherings.

Whitecliff Manor Nursing Home
12504 Cedar Rd, Cleveland Heights, OH,
44106
(216) 371-3600
Licensure Skilled care; Intermediate care. *Beds*
116. *Certified* Medicaid; Medicare.
Owner Proprietary Corp.

CLEVES

Miami Haven Nursing Home
5485 State Rte 128, Cleves, OH, 45002
(513) 353-2900
Admin Bertha B Hobbs NHA. *Medical Dir/
Dir of Nursing* Bertha B Hobbs RN.
Licensure Intermediate care. *Beds* ICF 29.
Certified Medicare.
Owner Proprietary Corp.
Admissions Requirements Medical
examination.
Staff RNs 2; LPNs 6; Orderlies 2; Nurses
aides 20; Activities coordinators; Dietitians.
Languages Spanish, Japanese, Latin
Facilities Dining room; Activities room;
Crafts room; Laundry room; Library.
Activities Arts & crafts; Cards; Games;
Reading groups; Prayer groups; Movies;
Shopping trips; Social/Cultural gatherings.

CLINTON

Rafferty's Nursing Home*
7055 S Cleveland-Massillon Rd, Clinton, OH,
44216
(216) 882-6349
Licensure Intermediate care. *Beds* 30.
Certified Medicaid.
Owner Proprietary Corp.

CLOVERDALE

Paradise Oaks Quality Care Nursing Center
98 Main St, Cloverdale, OH, 45827
(419) 488-3911
Admin Randall L Cox. *Medical Dir/Dir of
Nursing* Rosalie Wright.
Licensure Skilled care; Intermediate care. *Beds*
SNF 50; ICF 50. *Certified* Medicaid;
Medicare.
Owner Proprietary Corp (Northwestern
Service Corp).
Admissions Requirements Medical
examination.
Staff Physicians; RNs; LPNs; Orderlies;
Nurses aides.
Facilities Dining room; Physical therapy
room; Activities room; Chapel; Crafts room;
Laundry room; Barber/Beauty shop.
Activities Arts & crafts; Cards; Games;
Reading groups; Prayer groups; Movies;
Shopping trips.

CLYDE

Buckeye Nursing Home
234 W Buckeye St, Clyde, OH, 43410
(419) 483-6225
Admin Larry F Tebeau.
Licensure Intermediate care. *Beds* ICF 35.
Certified Medicaid.
Owner Proprietary Corp.
Admissions Requirements Medical
examination.
Staff RNs 2 (pt); LPNs 9 (ft), 2 (pt); Nurses
aides 12 (ft), 4 (pt); Recreational therapists 1
(pt); Activities coordinators 1 (pt); Dietitians
1 (pt).

Facilities Dining room; Activities room;
Laundry room; Barber/Beauty shop.
Activities Arts & crafts; Cards; Games;
Reading groups; Prayer groups; Movies;
Shopping trips; Social/Cultural gatherings;
Numerous other activities.

Eshelman Nursing Home Inc*
700 Helen St, Clyde, OH, 43410
(419) 547-9595
Licensure Intermediate care. *Beds* 100.
Certified Medicaid.
Owner Proprietary Corp.

Hospitality Nursing Home*
167 E Forest St, Clyde, OH, 43410
(419) 547-0764
Licensure Intermediate care. *Beds* 21.
Certified Medicaid.
Owner Proprietary Corp.

COLDWATER

HCF Inc Briarwood Manor
830 W Main St, Coldwater, OH, 45828
(419) 678-2311
Admin Brenda Hebden. *Medical Dir/Dir of
Nursing* Rosemary Schmit.
Licensure Skilled care; Intermediate care. *Beds*
100. *Certified* Medicaid; Medicare.
Owner Proprietary Corp (Health Care
Facilities Inc).
Admissions Requirements Medical
examination; Physician's request.
Staff Physicians 2 (pt); RNs 5 (ft), 9 (pt);
LPNs 6 (ft), 1 (pt); Nurses aides 33 (ft), 38
(pt); Physical therapists 2 (pt); Speech
therapists 1 (pt); Activities coordinators 1
(ft); Dietitians 1 (ft); Ophthalmologists 1
(pt).
Facilities Dining room; Physical therapy
room; Activities room; Chapel; Laundry
room; Barber/Beauty shop.
Activities Arts & crafts; Cards; Games;
Reading groups; Prayer groups; Movies;
Shopping trips; Social/Cultural gatherings;
Gardening.

COLUMBIA STATION

The Villa Camillus
10515 E River Rd, Columbia Station, OH,
44028
(216) 236-5091
Admin Bruce Schirhart. *Medical Dir/Dir of
Nursing* V R Mankad MD.
Licensure Skilled care; Intermediate care. *Beds*
50.
Owner Proprietary Corp.
Admissions Requirements Minimum age 18;
Females only; Medical examination.
Staff Physicians 1 (pt); RNs 1 (ft), 4 (pt);
LPNs 1 (ft), 4 (pt); Nurses aides 21 (pt);
Physical therapists 1 (pt); Recreational
therapists 1 (pt); Speech therapists 1 (pt);
Activities coordinators 1 (pt); Dietitians 1
(pt); Ophthalmologists 1 (pt); Podiatrists 1
(pt).
Facilities Dining room; Physical therapy
room; Activities room; Chapel; Crafts room;
Laundry room; Barber/Beauty shop; Library.
Activities Arts & crafts; Cards; Games; Prayer
groups; Movies; Social/Cultural gatherings.

COLUMBUS

Alum Crest
1599 Alum Creek Dr, Columbus, OH, 43207
(614) 445-8261
Admin David Colburn. *Medical Dir/Dir of
Nursing* Dr Harry Topolosky; Marian
Gresham RN.
Licensure Skilled care; Intermediate care. *Beds*
SNF 192; ICF 83. *Certified* Medicaid;
Medicare.
Owner Publicly owned.

Staff Physicians 1 (ft), 4 (pt); RNs 10 (ft); LPNs 31 (ft), 2 (pt); Orderlies 16 (ft); Nurses aides 127 (ft), 2 (pt); Physical therapists 1 (pt); Recreational therapists 1 (ft); Occupational therapists 1 (pt); Speech therapists 1 (pt); Activities coordinators 1 (ft); Dietitians 1 (ft); Ophthalmologists 1 (pt).
Facilities Dining room; Physical therapy room; Activities room; Chapel; Crafts room; Laundry room; Barber/Beauty shop; Library; Resident telephone lounge; Large screen TV connected to satellite dish network.
Activities Arts & crafts; Cards; Games; Reading groups; Prayer groups; Movies; Shopping trips; Social/Cultural gatherings.

Alvis House-Wittwer Hall
624 S Ohio Ave, Columbus, OH, 43205
(614) 252-6196
Admin Denise M Robinson. *Medical Dir/Dir of Nursing* Beth O Tranen DO; Mary Waterfield RN DON.
Licensure Intermediate care for mentally retarded. *Beds* 15. *Certified* Medicaid.
Owner Nonprofit organization/foundation.
Admissions Requirements Minimum age 18; Males only; Medical examination.
Staff Physicians 1 (pt); RNs 1 (ft); LPNs 2 (pt); Nurses aides 8 (ft), 5 (pt); Occupational therapists 1 (pt); Speech therapists 1 (pt); Activities coordinators 1 (ft); Dietitians 1 (pt); Podiatrists 1 (pt).
Facilities Dining room; Activities room; Laundry room; TV lounge; Upstairs lounge.
Activities Arts & crafts; Cards; Games; Movies; Shopping trips; Housekeeping; Laundry; Cooking; Money management.

Amber Health Care Center
813 Bryden Rd, Columbus, OH, 43205
(614) 252-4893 & 252-2535
Admin Larry Rosenberg. *Medical Dir/Dir of Nursing* E Harris; Judith M Tracey RNC DON.
Licensure Skilled care; Intermediate care. *Beds* SNF 133; ICF. *Certified* Medicaid; Medicare; VA.
Owner Proprietary Corp.
Admissions Requirements Medical examination; Physician's request.
Staff Physicians 6 (pt); RNs 8 (ft) 13C 14 (ft); Orderlies 6 (ft); Nurses aides 42 (ft); Physical therapists 2 (pt); Recreational therapists 3 (ft); Occupational therapists 1 (pt); Speech therapists 1 (pt); Activities coordinators 1 (ft); Dietitians 1 (ft); Dentists 1 (pt); Ophthalmologists 1 (pt); Podiatrists 1 (pt); Dentist 2 (pt);; Social service 1 (ft); Optometrists 1 (pt); Medical records 2 (ft); QMRP 1 (pt); Psychologist 1 (pt).
Facilities Dining room; Physical therapy room; Activities room; Crafts room; Laundry room; Barber/Beauty shop; Library; 5 TV lounges.
Activities Arts & crafts; Cards; Games; Reading groups; Prayer groups; Movies; Shopping trips; Social/Cultural gatherings; Discussion groups; Exercise class.

Americare Columbus Nursing & Rehabilitation Center
1700 Heinzerling Dr, Columbus, OH, 43223
(614) 274-4222
Admin Carol J Keene. *Medical Dir/Dir of Nursing* Dr Michael Downy/Bonnie Phillips RN-DON.
Licensure Skilled care; Intermediate care; Alzheimer's. *Beds* SNF 22; ICF 78; ICF/Alzheimer's 28. *Certified* Medicaid; Medicare.
Owner Proprietary Corp (Americare Corp).
Admissions Requirements Medical examination; Physician's request.
Staff Physicians 1 (pt); RNs 4 (ft), 1 (pt); LPNs 6 (ft), 1 (pt); Nurses aides; Physical therapists 1 (ft); Activities coordinators 2 (ft), 1 (pt); Dietitians 1 (ft), 1 (pt).

Facilities Dining room; Physical therapy room; Activities room; Crafts room; Laundry room; Barber/Beauty shop; Private dining room; Rehabilitation dining; Physician's exam rooms; Dental chair.
Activities Arts & crafts; Cards; Games; Reading groups; Prayer groups; Movies; Shopping trips; Social/Cultural gatherings; Exercises; Cooking club.

Arlington Court Nursing Home
1605 NW Professional Plaza, Columbus, OH, 43220
(614) 451-5677
Admin James D Herron. *Medical Dir/Dir of Nursing* Michael Moftah MD; Barbara Rattan RN DON.
Licensure Skilled care. *Beds* SNF 120.
Owner Proprietary Corp.
Staff RNs 4 (ft), 6 (pt); LPNs 3 (ft), 7 (pt); Orderlies 3 (ft); Nurses aides 15 (ft), 15 (pt); Physical therapists 1 (pt); Recreational therapists 1 (ft); Activities coordinators 1 (ft); Dietitians 1 (pt).
Facilities Dining room; Physical therapy room; Activities room; Chapel; Crafts room; Barber/Beauty shop; Library.
Activities Arts & crafts; Cards; Games; Reading groups; Prayer groups; Movies; Social/Cultural gatherings.

Bescare Nursing Home
1288 Bryden Rd, Columbus, OH, 43205
(614) 258-6371
Admin H Thomas Wilson. *Medical Dir/Dir of Nursing* Dr Sergio Payuyo; Mrs Arteen Glenn DON.
Licensure Intermediate care. *Beds* ICF 17. *Certified* Medicaid.
Owner Proprietary Corp.
Staff Physicians 1 (pt); LPNs 3 (ft); Nurses aides 3 (ft), 2 (pt); Activities coordinators 1 (ft).
Facilities Dining room; Activities room; Crafts room; Laundry room.
Activities Arts & crafts; Cards; Games; Prayer groups; Movies; Shopping trips.

Bon-Ing Inc*
173 Woodland Ave, Columbus, OH, 43203
(614) 475-2222
Licensure Intermediate care. *Beds* 26. *Certified* Medicaid.
Owner Proprietary Corp.

Bryden Manor*
1138 Bryden Rd, Columbus, OH, 43205
(614) 252-4727
Licensure Intermediate care. *Beds* 34. *Certified* Medicaid.
Owner Proprietary Corp.

Christian Home for the Aged*
PO Box 03605, 1454 Eastwood Ave, Columbus, OH, 43203
(614) 258-2769
Licensure Intermediate care. *Beds* 14. *Certified* Medicaid.
Owner Proprietary Corp.

Clearview Convalescent Center*
2120 E 5th Ave, Columbus, OH, 43219
(614) 258-8437
Licensure Skilled care; Intermediate care. *Beds* 93. *Certified* Medicaid; Medicare.
Owner Proprietary Corp.

Columbus Developmental Center
1601 W Broad St, Columbus, OH, 43223
(614) 272-0509
Admin Susan Arnoczky PhD Supt. *Medical Dir/Dir of Nursing* Ruth Ann Holzhauser MD.
Licensure Intermediate care for mentally retarded. *Beds* ICF/MR 393. *Certified* Medicaid.
Owner Publicly owned.
Admissions Requirements Minimum age 6.

Staff Physicians 3 (ft), 3 (pt); RNs 16 (ft); LPNs 29 (ft); Orderlies; Nurses aides 348 (ft), 13 (pt); Physical therapists 2 (ft); Recreational therapists 10 (ft); Occupational therapists 2 (ft); Speech therapists 2 (ft); Activities coordinators 2 (ft); Dietitians 3 (ft).
Languages Sign
Facilities Dining room; Physical therapy room; Activities room; Chapel; Crafts room; Laundry room.
Activities Arts & crafts; Cards; Games; Movies; Shopping trips; Social/Cultural gatherings.

Columbus Nursing Homes Inc*
1169 Bryden Rd, Columbus, OH, 43205
(614) 258-6623
Licensure Skilled care; Intermediate care. *Beds* 147. *Certified* Medicaid; Medicare.
Owner Proprietary Corp.

Derrer Road ICF/MR*
340 Derrer Rd, Columbus, OH, 43223
Licensure Intermediate care for mentally retarded. *Beds* 8. *Certified* Medicaid.
Owner Nonprofit Corp.

East Broad Manor
1243 Broad St, Columbus, OH, 43205
(614) 252-3836
Admin Edward J Powell. *Medical Dir/Dir of Nursing* William Conway MD; Jane C Belt, RN DON.
Licensure Intermediate care. *Beds* 29. *Certified* Medicaid.
Owner Proprietary Corp.
Admissions Requirements Minimum age 18; Females only; Medical examination.
Staff Physicians 1 (pt); RNs 1 (ft); LPNs 3 (ft), 5 (pt); Nurses aides 7 (ft), 3 (pt); Physical therapists 1 (pt); Speech therapists 1 (pt); Activities coordinators 1 (pt); Dietitians 1 (pt); Dentists 1 (pt); Ophthalmologists 1 (pt); Podiatrists 1 (pt).
Facilities Dining room; Activities room.
Activities Arts & crafts; Cards; Games; Prayer groups; Movies; Shopping trips; Social/Cultural gatherings; Camping trips.

Eastland Care Center
2425 Kimberly Pkwy E, Columbus, OH, 43232
(614) 868-9306
Admin Richard M Tobin. *Medical Dir/Dir of Nursing* Richard N McCarty MD; Carolyn C Vacca RN DON.
Licensure Skilled care; Intermediate care. *Beds* 100. *Certified* Medicaid; Medicare.
Owner Nonprofit Corp (Volunteers of America Care).
Admissions Requirements Medical examination; Physician's request.
Staff Physicians 1 (pt); RNs 4 (ft), 2 (pt); LPNs 7 (ft), 4 (pt); Orderlies 4 (ft); Nurses aides 28 (ft), 11 (pt); Physical therapists 1 (pt); Occupational therapists 1 (pt); Speech therapists 1 (pt); Activities coordinators 2 (ft); Dietitians 1 (pt); Dentists 1 (pt); Ophthalmologists 1 (pt); Podiatrists 1 (pt).
Facilities Dining room; Physical therapy room; Activities room; Chapel; Crafts room; Laundry room; Barber/Beauty shop; Patio; Front living room.
Activities Arts & crafts; Cards; Games; Reading groups; Prayer groups; Movies; Shopping trips; Social/Cultural gatherings.

First Community Village Healthcare Center
1800 Riverside Dr, Columbus, OH, 43212
(614) 486-9511
Admin Nancy Billings RN NHA. *Medical Dir/Dir of Nursing* Steven Lichtblau MD; Jean Leyde RN.
Licensure Skilled care; Intermediate care. *Beds* SNF 175; ICF. *Certified* Medicaid; Medicare.
Owner Nonprofit organization/foundation.

Admissions Requirements Minimum age 55; Medical examination.
Staff Physicians 4 (pt); RNs 11 (ft), 18 (pt); LPNs 8 (ft), 7 (pt); Nurses aides 48 (ft), 28 (pt); Physical therapists 1 (ft), 1 (pt); Recreational therapists 1 (ft); Occupational therapists 1 (pt); Speech therapists 1 (pt); Activities coordinators 3 (ft); Dietitians 1 (ft); Ophthalmologists 1 (pt).
Affiliation First Community Church
Facilities Dining room; Physical therapy room; Activities room; Chapel; Crafts room; Laundry room; Barber/Beauty shop; Library.
Activities Arts & crafts; Cards; Games; Reading groups; Prayer groups; Movies; Shopping trips; Social/Cultural gatherings; Sing-alongs; Music therapy; Chaplain; Clinical site for academic healthcare programs.

Friendship Village of Columbus Health Care Center
5800 Forest Hills Blvd, Columbus, OH, 43229
(614) 890-8287
Admin Pat Zoerner. *Medical Dir/Dir of Nursing* John B Krupko MD; Donna Shipka.
Licensure Skilled care; Intermediate care. *Beds* 90. *Certified* Medicaid; Medicare.
Owner Nonprofit Corp (Life Care Services Corp).
Admissions Requirements Minimum age 62.
Staff Physicians 1 (pt); RNs 8 (ft), 4 (pt); LPNs 5 (ft), 2 (pt); Nurses aides 35 (ft), 12 (pt); Physical therapists 1 (ft); Occupational therapists 1 (pt); Speech therapists 1 (pt); Activities coordinators 1 (ft); Dietitians 1 (pt); Ophthalmologists 1 (pt).
Facilities Dining room; Physical therapy room; Activities room; Crafts room; Laundry room; Barber/Beauty shop; Library.
Activities Arts & crafts; Games; Prayer groups; Movies; Shopping trips.

Genesis*
4133 Karl Rd, Columbus, OH, 43224
Licensure Intermediate care for mentally retarded. *Beds* 24. *Certified* Medicaid.
Owner Nonprofit Corp.

Heartland Thurber Village
920 Thurber Dr W, Columbus, OH, 43215
(614) 464-2273
Admin Brenda Ferguson Stabile. *Medical Dir/Dir of Nursing* Raymond Pongonis DO; Donna Taylor Stevenson.
Licensure Skilled care; Intermediate care. *Beds* SNF 148; ICF. *Certified* Medicaid; Medicare.
Owner Proprietary Corp (Southmark Heritage Corp).
Admissions Requirements Medical examination; Physician's request.
Staff Physicians 2 (ft); RNs 5 (ft); LPNs 12 (ft), 1 (pt); Physical therapists 1 (ft); Occupational therapists 1 (pt); Speech therapists 1 (pt); Activities coordinators 1 (ft); Dietitians 1 (pt); Dentists 1 (pt); Ophthalmologists 1 (pt); Podiatrists 1 (pt).
Facilities Dining room; Physical therapy room; Activities room; Laundry room; Barber/Beauty shop; General Store.
Activities Arts & crafts; Cards; Games; Reading groups; Prayer groups; Movies; Shopping trips; Social/Cultural gatherings.

Heinzerling Developmental Center*
1755 Heinzerling Drive, Columbus, OH, 43223
(614) 272-2000
Licensure Intermediate care for mentally retarded. *Beds* 104.
Owner Nonprofit Corp; Proprietary Corp.
Admissions Requirements Minimum age 21.

Heritage House-Columbus Jewish Home for the Aged*
1151 College Ave, Columbus, OH, 43209
(614) 237-7417

Licensure Skilled care; Intermediate care. *Beds* 146. *Certified* Medicaid; Medicare.
Owner Nonprofit Corp.
Affiliation Jewish

Lutheran Senior City
935 N Cassady Ave, Columbus, OH, 43219
(614) 252-4987
Admin Caryl A Kemper. *Medical Dir/Dir of Nursing* Dr Patrick Dineen MD; Martha Maite DON.
Licensure Long-term care facility. *Beds* SNF 136; ICF; Rest home 25; Assisted living 50; Congregate 92. *Certified* Medicaid; Medicare.
Owner Nonprofit Corp.
Admissions Requirements Minimum age 65; Medical examination.
Staff Physicians 6 (pt); RNs 14 (ft), 5 (pt); LPNs 14 (ft), 4 (pt); Nurses aides 64 (ft), 4 (pt); Physical therapists 1 (ft); Recreational therapists 1 (ft); Occupational therapists 4 (ft); Activities coordinators 1 (ft); Dietitians 1 (ft).
Affiliation Lutheran
Facilities Dining room; Physical therapy room; Activities room; Chapel; Crafts room; Laundry room; Barber/Beauty shop; Library.
Activities Arts & crafts; Cards; Games; Reading groups; Prayer groups; Movies; Shopping trips; Social/Cultural gatherings; Outings.

Mayfair Nursing Care Center*
3000 Bethel Rd, Columbus, OH, 43220
(614) 889-6920
Admin Sharon L Reynolds. *Medical Dir/Dir of Nursing* Charles Twul MD.
Licensure Skilled care; Intermediate care. *Beds* 100. *Certified* Medicaid; Medicare.
Owner Proprietary Corp (Life Care Centers of America).
Admissions Requirements Minimum age 18; Medical examination; Physician's request.
Staff Physicians 1 (pt); RNs 6 (ft), 13 (pt); LPNs 4 (ft); Nurses aides 26 (ft), 12 (pt); Physical therapists 1 (pt); Reality therapists 1 (ft); Recreational therapists 1 (ft); Occupational therapists 1 (pt); Speech therapists 1 (pt); Dietitians 1 (pt); Dentists 1 (pt); Ophthalmologists 1 (pt); Podiatrists 1 (pt); Audiologists 1 (pt).
Facilities Dining room; Physical therapy room; Activities room; Crafts room; Laundry room; Barber/Beauty shop; Library.
Activities Arts & crafts; Cards; Games; Reading groups; Prayer groups; Movies; Shopping trips; Social/Cultural gatherings.

Minerva Park Place
5460 Cleveland Ave, Columbus, OH, 43229
(614) 882-2490
Admin Michael Fannin. *Medical Dir/Dir of Nursing* Dr H T Villavecer.
Licensure Intermediate care. *Beds* ICF 101. *Certified* Medicaid.
Owner Proprietary Corp (Hillhaven Corp).
Admissions Requirements Medical examination; Physician's request.
Staff RNs 6 (ft); LPNs 8 (ft); Nurses aides 33 (ft); Physical therapists 1 (pt); Recreational therapists 1 (ft); Occupational therapists 1 (pt); Speech therapists 1 (pt); Activities coordinators 1 (ft), 2 (pt); Dietitians 1 (pt); Ophthalmologists 1 (pt).
Facilities Dining room; Activities room; Crafts room; Laundry room; Barber/Beauty shop; Library; TV lounges.
Activities Arts & crafts; Cards; Games; Prayer groups; Movies; Shopping trips; Social/Cultural gatherings; Exercise; Garden; Pet visits.

Mohun Hall Infirmary*
Saint Mary of the Springs, Columbus, OH, 43219
Licensure Nursing home. *Beds* 48.
Owner Nonprofit Corp.

Northland Terrace Nursing & Rehabilitation Center
5700 Karl Rd, Columbus, OH, 43229
(614) 846-5420
Admin Sharon L Reynolds. *Medical Dir/Dir of Nursing* Stephen D Shell MD; Sue Longhenry RN.
Licensure Skilled care; Intermediate care; Childrens unit; Ventilator unit. *Beds* SNF 104; ICF 156. *Certified* Medicaid; Medicare; JCAH approved.
Owner Privately owned.
Admissions Requirements Minimum age 2 months; Physician's request.
Staff Physicians 1 (pt); RNs 25 (ft), 14 (pt); LPNs 45 (ft), 11 (pt); Nurses aides 85 (ft), 23 (pt); Physical therapists 2 (ft); Recreational therapists 5 (ft); Occupational therapists 1 (ft); Speech therapists 3 (pt); Dietitians 1 (ft); Dentists 1 (pt); Ophthalmologists 1 (pt); Podiatrists 1 (pt); Physical therapy aides 2 (ft); Certified occupational therapy asst 2 (ft).
Facilities Dining room; Physical therapy room; Activities room; Crafts room; Barber/Beauty shop; Library; Shaded patio.
Activities Arts & crafts; Cards; Games; Reading groups; Prayer groups; Movies; Shopping trips; Social/Cultural gatherings.

Margaret Clark Oakfield Convalescent Center—Columbus
500 N Nelson Rd, Columbus, OH, 43219
(614) 252-5244
Admin Harriett A White. *Medical Dir/Dir of Nursing* Marina Pilic.
Licensure Intermediate care. *Beds* 152. *Certified* Medicaid.
Owner Proprietary Corp.
Admissions Requirements Medical examination; Physician's request.
Staff Physicians 6 (pt); RNs 6 (ft), 5 (pt); LPNs 10 (ft), 1 (pt); Orderlies 1 (ft); Nurses aides 37 (ft), 3 (pt); Reality therapists 2 (ft), 1 (pt); Recreational therapists 2 (ft); Activities coordinators 2 (ft), 1 (pt).
Facilities Dining room; Activities room; Laundry room; Barber/Beauty shop.
Activities Arts & crafts; Cards; Games; Reading groups; Prayer groups; Movies; Shopping trips; Social/Cultural gatherings.

Parkwood Nursing Home
32 Parkwood Ave, Columbus, OH, 43203
(614) 258-3088
Admin Edward J Powell. *Medical Dir/Dir of Nursing* William F Conway MD; Jane C Belt RN.
Licensure Intermediate care. *Beds* 25. *Certified* Medicaid.
Owner Proprietary Corp.
Admissions Requirements Minimum age 18; Females only.
Staff Physicians 1 (pt); RNs 1 (ft); LPNs 2 (ft), 3 (pt); Nurses aides 7 (ft), 4 (pt); Activities coordinators 1 (ft); Dietitians 1 (ft); Dentists 1 (pt); Ophthalmologists 1 (pt); Podiatrists 1 (pt).
Facilities Dining room; Activities room; Laundry room.
Activities Arts & crafts; Cards; Games; Reading groups; Prayer groups; Movies; Shopping trips; Social/Cultural gatherings.

Patterson Health Center
71 Woodland Ave, Columbus, OH, 43203
(614) 258-7424
Admin Esther R Chapman.
Licensure Intermediate care. *Beds* ICF 43. *Certified* Medicaid.
Owner Proprietary Corp (Omnilife Systems Inc).

Pauline Home for the Aged
1303 E Main St, Columbus, OH, 43205
(614) 258-4822
Admin Linda L Lehrer. *Medical Dir/Dir of Nursing* Dr Gallagher.

Licensure Home for aged. *Beds* 35.
Owner Privately owned.
Admissions Requirements Minimum age 70;
Females only.
Staff LPNs 2 (ft), 2 (pt); Nurses aides 4 (ft).
Facilities Dining room; Activities room;
Barber/Beauty shop.
Activities Cards; Religious services.

Isabelle Ridgway Nursing Center
1520 Hawthorne Ave, Columbus, OH, 43203
(614) 252-4931
Admin Russell Boyce. *Medical Dir/Dir of
Nursing* Dr George Barnett Jr MD; Donna
Angelo, DON.
Licensure Skilled care; Intermediate care. *Beds*
SNF 100; ICF. *Certified* Medicaid;
Medicare.
Owner Nonprofit Corp.
Admissions Requirements Minimum age 21;
Medical examination; Physician's request.
Staff Physicians 5 (pt); RNs 3 (ft); LPNs 14
(ft); Orderlies 35 (ft); Physical therapists 1
(pt); Occupational therapists 1 (pt); Speech
therapists 1 (pt); Activities coordinators 1
(ft); Dietitians 1 (pt); Dentists 1 (pt);
Ophthalmologists 1 (pt); Podiatrists 1 (pt).
Facilities Dining room; Physical therapy
room; Activities room; Chapel; Laundry
room; Barber/Beauty shop; Senior activity
room.
Activities Arts & crafts; Games; Reading
groups; Prayer groups; Movies; Shopping
trips; Social/Cultural gatherings; One-on-one
companion programs.

**Riverside Methodist Hospital's Extended Care
Unit**
3535 Olentangy River Rd, Columbus, OH,
43214
(614) 261-5000
Admin Erie Chapman III. *Medical Dir/Dir of
Nursing* Dr John Burkhart; Claudia Wilder
DON.
Licensure Skilled care. *Beds* SNF 48. *Certified*
Medicare.
Owner Nonprofit organization/foundation.
Admissions Requirements Minimum age 16;
Physician's request.
Staff Physicians 1 (pt); RNs 18 (ft), 6 (pt);
LPNs 6 (ft), 1 (pt); Nurses aides 8 (ft);
Physical therapists 15 (ft); Occupational
therapists 5 (ft); Speech therapists 4 (ft);
Activities coordinators 1 (ft); Dietitians 1
(ft); Dentists; Ophthalmologists; Podiatrists.
Affiliation Methodist
Facilities Dining room; Physical therapy
room; Activities room; Chapel; Barber/
Beauty shop; Library.
Activities Arts & crafts; Cards; Games;
Reading groups; Movies; Holiday parties.

Rosegate Care Center
1850 Crown Park Ct, Columbus, OH, 43220
(614) 459-7293
Admin Roy Miller. *Medical Dir/Dir of Nursing*
Link Murphy MD; Ann Evans DON.
Licensure Skilled care; Intermediate care. *Beds*
100. *Certified* Medicaid; Medicare.
Owner Proprietary Corp (National Heritage).
Admissions Requirements Minimum age 65;
Medical examination.
Staff Physicians 25 (pt); RNs 4 (ft), 3 (pt);
LPNs 5 (ft), 3 (pt); Nurses aides 23 (ft), 8
(pt); Physical therapists 1 (pt); Reality
therapists 1 (pt); Occupational therapists 1
(pt); Speech therapists 1 (pt); Activities
coordinators 2 (ft); Dietitians 1 (pt);
Ophthalmologists 1 (pt); Podiatrists 1 (pt).
Facilities Dining room; Physical therapy
room; Activities room; Crafts room; Laundry
room; Barber/Beauty shop; TV lounge;
Sidewalk cafe.
Activities Arts & crafts; Cards; Games;
Reading groups; Prayer groups; Movies;
Shopping trips; Social/Cultural gatherings.

St Luke Convalescent Center
44 S Souder Ave, Columbus, OH, 43222
(614) 228-5900
Admin J M Boyd. *Medical Dir/Dir of Nursing*
John Raabe MD.
Licensure Skilled care. *Beds* 120. *Certified*
Medicaid; Medicare.
Owner Proprietary Corp.
Facilities Dining room; Physical therapy
room; Activities room; Chapel; Crafts room;
Laundry room; Barber/Beauty shop; Library.
Activities Arts & crafts; Cards; Games;
Reading groups; Prayer groups; Movies;
Shopping trips; Social/Cultural gatherings.

St Luke-East Convalescent Center
5500 E Broad St, Columbus, OH, 43213
(614) 868-0888
Admin William A Wershing. *Medical Dir/Dir
of Nursing* John P Hanyak MD; Sandra
Hirsch RN DON.
Licensure Intermediate care. *Beds* ICF 100.
Certified Medicaid.
Owner Privately owned.
Admissions Requirements Medical
examination; Physician's request.
Staff Physicians 1 (ft); RNs 7 (ft); LPNs 6 (ft);
Nurses aides 30 (ft); Activities coordinators
1 (ft).
Facilities Dining room; Physical therapy
room; Activities room; Barber/Beauty shop;
Solariums.
Activities Arts & crafts; Cards; Games;
Reading groups; Movies; Social/Cultural
gatherings.

St Raphaels Home for the Aged
1550 Roxbury Rd, Columbus, OH, 43212
(614) 486-0436
Admin Sr Maureen Hughes. *Medical Dir/Dir
of Nursing* Haushong Ma'ani MD.
Licensure Skilled care. *Beds* 78. *Certified*
Medicaid; Medicare.
Owner Nonprofit Corp.
Admissions Requirements Medical
examination.
Staff Physicians 1 (pt); RNs 6 (ft); LPNs 4
(ft); Physical therapists 1 (pt); Occupational
therapists 1 (pt); Speech therapists 1 (pt);
Activities coordinators 1 (ft), 1 (pt);
Dietitians 1 (pt); Dentists 1 (pt);
Ophthalmologists 1 (pt).
Affiliation Roman Catholic
Facilities Dining room; Physical therapy
room; Activities room; Chapel; Crafts room;
Laundry room; Barber/Beauty shop; Library.
Activities Arts & crafts; Cards; Games;
Reading groups; Prayer groups; Movies;
Shopping trips; Social/Cultural gatherings;
Pet therapy.

St Rita's Home for the Aged Inc
880 Greenlawn Ave, Columbus, OH, 43223
(614) 443-9433
Admin Sr M Veronica. *Medical Dir/Dir of
Nursing* Mina Mokhtari MD; Phyllis Wright
RN DON.
Licensure Skilled care; Intermediate care. *Beds*
100. *Certified* Medicaid; Medicare.
Owner Nonprofit Corp.
Admissions Requirements Minimum age 65;
Medical examination; Physician's request.
Staff Physicians 1 (ft); RNs 6 (ft), 1 (pt);
LPNs 10 (ft), 3 (pt); Nurses aides 47 (ft), 8
(pt); Physical therapists 1 (ft); Occupational
therapists 1 (pt); Activities coordinators 2
(ft); Dietitians 1 (pt); Dentists 1 (pt);
Ophthalmologists 1 (pt); Podiatrists 1 (pt);
Food service manager 1 (pt) Dentist 1 (pt).
Affiliation Roman Catholic
Facilities Dining room; Physical therapy
room; Activities room; Chapel; Crafts room;
Laundry room; Barber/Beauty shop; Library;
Ancillary services room.

Activities Arts & crafts; Cards; Games;
Reading groups; Prayer groups; Movies;
Shopping trips; Social/Cultural gatherings;
Cooking; Music therapy; One-on-one
projects; Bowling.

Shasta Avenue
3273 Shasta Ave, Columbus, OH, 43229
(614) 890-6370
Admin Nancy West. *Medical Dir/Dir of
Nursing* Mary Berry RN.
Licensure Intermediate care for mentally
retarded. *Beds* ICF/MR 11. *Certified*
Medicaid.
Owner Privately owned.
Admissions Requirements Minimum age 21;
Medical examination; Physician's request.
Staff LPNs 2 (ft), 2 (pt); Physical therapists 1
(pt); Occupational therapists 1 (pt); Speech
therapists 1 (pt); Dietitians 1 (pt);
Ophthalmologists 1 (pt); Podiatrists 1 (pt).
Facilities Dining room; Laundry room.
Activities Arts & crafts; Cards; Games;
Movies; Shopping trips; Social/Cultural
gatherings; Sheltered workshop;
Employment.

**United Cerebral Palsy of Columbus & Franklin
County Inc Genesis Facility**
4133 Karl Rd, Columbus, OH, 43224
(614) 263-5971
Admin D Hilty. *Medical Dir/Dir of Nursing* J
Guerrero; D Obrosky DON.
Licensure Intermediate care for mentally
retarded. *Beds* ICF/MR 24. *Certified*
Medicaid.
Owner Publicly owned.
Admissions Requirements Minimum age 18.
Staff Physicians 1 (pt); RNs 1 (pt); LPNs 2
(ft); Nurses aides 30 (ft), 10 (pt); Physical
therapists 1 (pt); Recreational therapists 1
(pt); Occupational therapists 1 (pt); Speech
therapists 1 (pt); Dietitians 1 (pt).
Facilities Dining room; Physical therapy
room; Laundry room.
Activities Arts & crafts; Cards; Games;
Reading groups; Movies; Shopping trips;
Social/Cultural gatherings.

We Care Health Facility
740 Canonby Pl, Columbus, OH, 43223
(614) 224-5738
Admin John Reynolds. *Medical Dir/Dir of
Nursing* Mark Williamson.
Licensure Intermediate care. *Beds* ICF 101.
Certified Medicaid.
Owner Proprietary Corp.
Staff RNs 2 (ft), 1 (pt); LPNs 11 (ft), 1 (pt);
Orderlies 6 (ft); Nurses aides 31 (ft), 9 (pt);
Physical therapists 1 (pt); Activities
coordinators 5 (ft); Dietitians 1 (pt); Dentists
1 (pt); Ophthalmologists 1 (pt).

Wesley Glen Inc
5155 N High St, Columbus, OH, 43214
(614) 888-7492
Admin Wesley Clarke. *Medical Dir/Dir of
Nursing* Ronald C Van Buren MD; Dorothy
Pfefferle DON.
Licensure Skilled care; Intermediate care. *Beds*
SNF 83; ICF. *Certified* Medicaid; Medicare.
Owner Nonprofit Corp.
Admissions Requirements Minimum age 65;
Medical examination; Physician's request.
Staff Physicians 1 (pt); RNs 2 (ft), 8 (pt);
LPNs 1 (ft), 2 (pt); Nurses aides 37 (ft), 10
(pt); Physical therapists 1 (pt); Speech
therapists 1 (pt); Activities coordinators 2
(ft); Dietitians 1 (ft); Dentists 1 (pt);
Podiatrists 1 (pt).
Affiliation Methodist
Facilities Dining room; Physical therapy
room; Activities room; Chapel; Crafts room;
Laundry room; Barber/Beauty shop; Library.
Activities Arts & crafts; Cards; Games;
Reading groups; Prayer groups; Movies;
Shopping trips; Social/Cultural gatherings.

Westminster Thurber Community
717 Neil Ave, Columbus, OH, 43215
(614) 228-8888
Admin Patricia B Mullins. *Medical Dir/Dir of Nursing* Roy L Donnerberg MD; Terry Halsey DON.
Licensure Skilled care; Intermediate care; Rest home. *Beds* 144. *Certified* Medicaid; Medicare.
Owner Nonprofit Corp (OH Presbyterian Homes).
Admissions Requirements Minimum age 60; Medical examination.
Staff Physicians 1 (pt); RNs 4 (ft), 1 (pt); LPNs 8 (ft), 1 (pt); Nurses aides 41 (ft), 6 (pt); Physical therapists 1 (pt); Recreational therapists 2 (ft); Occupational therapists 1 (pt); Activities coordinators 1 (ft); Dietitians 2 (pt); Ophthalmologists 1 (pt).
Affiliation Presbyterian
Facilities Dining room; Physical therapy room; Activities room; Chapel; Crafts room; Laundry room; Barber/Beauty shop; Library.
Activities Arts & crafts; Cards; Games; Reading groups; Prayer groups; Movies; Shopping trips; Social/Cultural gatherings; Van & bus.

Whetstone Convalescent Center
3700 Olentangy River Rd, Columbus, OH, 43214
(614) 457-1100
Admin R Douglas Spitler. *Medical Dir/Dir of Nursing* Dr William T Paul; Mary Monahan.
Licensure Skilled care; Intermediate care. *Beds* 200. *Certified* Medicaid; Medicare.
Owner Nonprofit organization/foundation.
Admissions Requirements Medical examination; Physician's request.
Staff Physicians 1 (pt); RNs 25 (ft), 2 (pt); LPNs 13 (ft); Orderlies 8 (ft), 2 (pt); Nurses aides 69 (ft), 27 (pt); Physical therapists 1 (ft), 1 (pt); Recreational therapists 2 (ft), 2 (pt); Occupational therapists 1 (ft); Activities coordinators 1 (ft); Dietitians 1 (pt); Food Service Managers 2 (ft).
Affiliation Episcopal
Facilities Dining room; Physical therapy room; Activities room; Chapel; Crafts room; Laundry room; Barber/Beauty shop; Library; Social services conference room; 6 lounges; Courtyard.
Activities Arts & crafts; Cards; Games; Reading groups; Prayer groups; Movies; Shopping trips; Social/Cultural gatherings; Continuing education; Music appreciation; Ceramics; Current events; One-on-one; Exercise.

Woodland Manor
81 Woodland Ave, Columbus, OH, 43203
(614) 258-8688
Admin Edward J Powell. *Medical Dir/Dir of Nursing* William F Conway MD; Jane Belt RN DON.
Licensure Intermediate care. *Beds* 29. *Certified* Medicaid.
Owner Proprietary Corp.
Admissions Requirements Minimum age 18.
Staff Physicians 1 (pt); RNs 1 (ft); LPNs 3 (ft), 5 (pt); Orderlies 3 (ft); Nurses aides 3 (ft), 3 (pt); Physical therapists 1 (pt); Speech therapists 1 (pt); Activities coordinators 1 (ft); Dietitians 1 (pt); Dentists 1 (pt); Ophthalmologists 1 (pt); Podiatrists 1 (pt).
Facilities Dining room; Activities room; Laundry room.
Activities Arts & crafts; Cards; Games; Prayer groups; Movies; Shopping trips; Social/Cultural gatherings.

Yorkshire Health Care Center
1425 Yorkland Rd, Columbus, OH, 43232
(614) 861-6666
Admin Fran Richardson. *Medical Dir/Dir of Nursing* S L Richardson MD; Margaret Louthen RN DON.

Licensure Skilled care. *Beds* 200. *Certified* Medicaid; Medicare.
Owner Proprietary Corp (Beverly Enterprises).
Admissions Requirements Minimum age 18; Medical examination; Physician's request.
Staff Physicians 1 (pt); RNs 28 (ft); LPNs 12 (ft); Nurses aides 70 (ft), 20 (pt); Physical therapists 1 (pt); Occupational therapists 1 (pt); Speech therapists 1 (ft); Activities coordinators 3 (ft); Dietitians 1 (pt); Dentists 1 (pt); Ophthalmologists 1 (pt); Podiatrists 1 (pt).
Facilities Dining room; Physical therapy room; Activities room; Crafts room; Laundry room; Barber/Beauty shop.
Activities Arts & crafts; Cards; Games; Reading groups; Prayer groups; Movies; Shopping trips; Social/Cultural gatherings.

CONNEAUT

Ashtabula County Residential Services Corp Maples 2
27 Parrish Rd, Conneaut, OH, 44030
(216) 998-3334 or 593-6404
Admin Gregory J Arcaro.
Licensure Intermediate care for mentally retarded. *Beds* ICF/MR 8. *Certified* Medicaid.
Owner Nonprofit Corp.
Admissions Requirements Minimum age 18; Females only.
Activities Arts & crafts; Games; Movies; Shopping trips; Social/Cultural gatherings.

Inn-Conneaut Health Center*
22 Parrish Rd, Conneaut, OH, 44030
(216) 593-6266
Admin Richard D Van Allen. *Medical Dir/Dir of Nursing* William Anderson Jr MD.
Licensure Skilled care; Intermediate care. *Beds* 100. *Certified* Medicaid; Medicare.
Owner Proprietary Corp.
Admissions Requirements Minimum age 21; Medical examination.
Staff Physicians 8 (pt); RNs 6 (ft), 4 (pt); LPNs 5 (ft), 3 (pt); Nurses aides 27 (ft), 5 (pt); Physical therapists 1 (pt); Reality therapists 1 (pt); Recreational therapists 1 (ft); Occupational therapists 1 (pt); Speech therapists 1 (pt); Activities coordinators 1 (ft); Dietitians 1 (pt); Dentists 1 (pt); Podiatrists 2 (pt).
Facilities Dining room; Physical therapy room; Activities room; Crafts room; Laundry room; Barber/Beauty shop; Library.
Activities Arts & crafts; Cards; Games; Reading groups; Prayer groups; Movies; Shopping trips; Social/Cultural gatherings.

CONVOY

Convoy Care Center
127 Mentzer Dr, Convoy, OH, 45832
(419) 749-2194
Admin Peg Zeis. *Medical Dir/Dir of Nursing* Sharon Geyer RN.
Licensure Intermediate care. *Beds* ICF 50. *Certified* Medicaid.
Owner Proprietary Corp.
Staff RNs 1 (ft), 1 (pt); LPNs 1 (ft), 5 (pt); Nurses aides 8 (ft), 12 (pt); Activities coordinators 1 (pt); Dietitians 1 (ft).
Facilities Dining room; Physical therapy room; Activities room; Crafts room; Laundry room; Barber/Beauty shop.
Activities Arts & crafts; Games; Reading groups; Prayer groups; Shopping trips; Social activities which include families.

COOLVILLE

Arcadia Nursing Center
PO Box A, E Main St, Coolville, OH, 45723
(614) 667-3156

Licensure Skilled care; Intermediate care. *Beds* 75. *Certified* Medicaid; Medicare.
Owner Proprietary Corp (Health Care Management).

CORTLAND

Cortland Quality Care Nursing Center*
369 N High St, Cortland, OH, 44410
(216) 638-4015
Medical Dir/Dir of Nursing Dr Anthony M Dominic.
Licensure Nursing home. *Beds* 50.
Owner Nonprofit Corp.
Admissions Requirements Medical examination.
Staff Physicians 5 (pt); RNs 1 (ft), 1 (pt); LPNs 4 (ft), 1 (pt); Nurses aides 11 (ft), 6 (pt); Physical therapists 1 (pt); Activities coordinators 1 (ft); Dietitians 1 (pt); Dentists 1 (pt); Podiatrists 1 (pt).
Facilities Dining room; Activities room; Crafts room; Laundry room; Barber/Beauty shop; Library.
Activities Arts & crafts; Cards; Games; Prayer groups; Movies; Shopping trips; Social/Cultural gatherings.

Faber Nursing Home Inc
4250 Sodom-Hutchings Rd NE, Cortland, OH, 44410
(216) 637-7906
Admin Lynn Meyers. *Medical Dir/Dir of Nursing* Dr John W Dowswell; Martha Richards LPN.
Licensure Intermediate care. *Beds* ICF 38. *Certified* Medicaid.
Owner Proprietary Corp.
Staff Physicians 1 (ft), 3 (pt); RNs 1 (pt); LPNs 3 (ft), 4 (pt); Nurses aides 11 (ft), 4 (pt); Speech therapists 1 (pt); Activities coordinators 1 (ft); Dietitians 1 (pt); Dentists 1 (pt); Ophthalmologists 1 (pt); Podiatrists 1 (pt).

COSHOCTON

Coshocton County Home*
Rte 4, Box 53, Coshocton, OH, 43812
(614) 622-2074
Medical Dir/Dir of Nursing G W Stelzner MD.
Licensure Intermediate care. *Beds* 74. *Certified* Medicaid.
Owner Publicly owned.
Admissions Requirements Minimum age 18; Medical examination.
Staff RNs 2 (ft), 1 (pt); LPNs 8 (ft), 2 (pt); Orderlies 2 (ft), 1 (pt); Nurses aides 15 (ft), 3 (pt); Activities coordinators 2 (ft).
Facilities Dining room; Physical therapy room; Activities room; Chapel; Crafts room; Laundry room; Barber/Beauty shop; TV lounges.
Activities Arts & crafts; Cards; Games; Reading groups; Prayer groups; Movies; Shopping trips; Social/Cultural gatherings.

Coshocton County Memorial Hospital
1460 Orange St, Coshocton, OH, 43812
(614) 622-6411
Licensure Skilled care; Intermediate care. *Beds* 61. *Certified* Medicaid; Medicare.
Owner Publicly owned.

Coshocton Health Care Center
100 S Whitewoman St, Coshocton, OH, 43812
(614) 622-1220
Admin Wayne E Derr. *Medical Dir/Dir of Nursing* Kaye Burch RN.
Licensure Intermediate care. *Beds* ICF 110. *Certified* Medicaid.
Owner Proprietary Corp.
Admissions Requirements Minimum age 18; Medical examination; Physician's request.

Staff RNs 6 (ft), 7 (pt); LPNs 4 (ft), 3 (pt); Nurses aides 23 (ft), 14 (pt); Activities coordinators 2 (ft), 2 (pt); Dietitians 1 (pt); Dentist 1 (pt).
Languages French, Spanish, German
Facilities Dining room; Physical therapy room; Activities room; Chapel; Crafts room; Laundry room; Barber/Beauty shop; Library; Two private lounges; Whirlpool room.
Activities Arts & crafts; Cards; Games; Reading groups; Prayer groups; Movies; Shopping trips; Social/Cultural gatherings.

Jacob's Dwelling*
25645 T.R. 36, Coshocton, OH, 43812
(614) 824-3635
Licensure Intermediate care. *Beds* 24. *Certified* Medicaid.
Owner Nonprofit Corp.

COVINGTON

Covington Community Care Center*
75 Mote Dr, Covington, OH, 45318
(513) 473-2075
Licensure Skilled care; Intermediate care. *Beds* 101. *Certified* Medicaid; Medicare.
Owner Proprietary Corp.

Sunny Acres*
8615 W US Rte 36, Covington, OH, 45318
(513) 473-3017
Licensure Intermediate care. *Beds* 16. *Certified* Medicaid.
Owner Proprietary Corp.

CRESTLINE

Crestline Nursing Home
327 W Main St, Crestline, OH, 44827
(419) 683-3255
Licensure Skilled care. *Beds* SNF 30.
Owner Proprietary Corp.
Admissions Requirements Medical examination.
Staff RNs 2 (ft), 1 (pt); LPNs 2 (ft), 1 (pt); Nurses aides 6 (ft), 3 (pt); Recreational therapists 1 (ft).
Facilities Dining room; Activities room.
Activities Arts & crafts; Cards; Games; Reading groups; Prayer groups; Movies; Shopping trips; Social/Cultural gatherings.

CRIDERSVILLE

Cridersville Nursing Home
603 E Main St, Cridersville, OH, 45806
(419) 645-4468
Admin Wilma A Springer. *Medical Dir/Dir of Nursing* Evelyn M Steere MD; Melinda Smith RN DON.
Licensure Intermediate care. *Beds* 50. *Certified* Medicaid.
Owner Proprietary Corp.
Admissions Requirements Medical examination; Physician's request.
Facilities Dining room; Activities room; Chapel; Crafts room; Laundry room; Barber/Beauty shop; Library.
Activities Arts & crafts; Cards; Games; Reading groups; Prayer groups; Movies; Shopping trips.

CROOKSVILLE

Ketcham's Nursing Home*
Rte 2, 14063 State Rte 37 E, Crooksville, OH, 43731
(614) 342-2877
Licensure Intermediate care. *Beds* 30. *Certified* Medicaid.
Owner Proprietary Corp.

CUYAHOGA FALLS

Bethel Rest Home*
2107 4th St, Cuyahoga Falls, OH, 44221
(216) 928-5757
Licensure Rest home. *Beds* 18.
Owner Proprietary Corp.

Cuyahoga Falls Country Place*
2728 Bailey Rd, Cuyahoga Falls, OH, 44221
(216) 929-4231
Medical Dir/Dir of Nursing Walter R Hoffman DO.
Licensure Skilled care. *Beds* 107. *Certified* Medicare.
Owner Proprietary Corp.
Admissions Requirements Minimum age 21; Medical examination; Physician's request.
Staff Physicians 3 (pt); RNs 2 (ft), 10 (pt); LPNs 9 (ft), 3 (pt); Orderlies 1 (ft); Nurses aides 29 (ft), 10 (pt); Physical therapists 1 (ft), 1 (pt); Recreational therapists 1 (ft); Speech therapists 1 (pt); Activities coordinators 1 (ft); Dietitians 1 (ft), 1 (pt); Dentists 1 (pt); Ophthalmologists 1 (pt); Podiatrists 1 (pt).
Facilities Dining room; Physical therapy room; Activities room; Crafts room; Laundry room; Barber/Beauty shop; Library.
Activities Arts & crafts; Cards; Games; Reading groups; Prayer groups; Movies; Shopping trips; Social/Cultural gatherings.

Twin Pines Retreat*
456 Seasons Rd, Cuyahoga Falls, OH, 44224
(216) 688-5553
Licensure Intermediate care. *Beds* 50. *Certified* Medicaid.
Owner Proprietary Corp.

DALTON

Shady Lawn Home Inc*
Rte 1, Dalton, OH, 44618
(216) 828-2278
Medical Dir/Dir of Nursing Dr Robert Cananne.
Licensure Intermediate care. *Beds* 151. *Certified* Medicaid; Medicare.
Owner Proprietary Corp.
Admissions Requirements Medical examination.
Staff Physicians; RNs; LPNs; Nurses aides; Physical therapists; Reality therapists; Recreational therapists; Speech therapists; Activities coordinators; Dietitians; Dentists; Podiatrists.
Facilities Dining room; Physical therapy room; Activities room; Crafts room; Laundry room; Barber/Beauty shop.
Activities Arts & crafts; Cards; Games; Reading groups; Prayer groups; Movies; Social/Cultural gatherings.

DANVILLE

Morning View Care Center
25326 Snively Rd, Danville, OH, 43014
(614) 599-6357
Admin Dixie Waite. *Medical Dir/Dir of Nursing* Nancy George RN, Judy Miller RN.
Licensure Intermediate care. *Beds* ICF 42. *Certified* Medicaid.
Owner Proprietary Corp (Morning View Care Center).
Staff RNs 2 (ft); LPNs 4 (ft), 1 (pt); Nurses aides 9 (ft), 6 (pt); Activities coordinators 1 (ft); Dietitians 1 (ft).
Facilities Dining room; Activities room; Laundry room; Barber/Beauty shop; 2 sitting rooms.
Activities Arts & crafts; Cards; Games; Reading groups; Prayer groups; Movies; Shopping trips; Social/Cultural gatherings; Parties; Exercise groups.

DAYTON

Alta Nursing Home Inc
PO Box 1336, 20 Livingston, Dayton, OH, 45401
(513) 253-4673
Admin Sol Augenbraun. *Medical Dir/Dir of Nursing* James Nagle MD.
Licensure Skilled care; Intermediate care. *Beds* SNF 50; ICF 50. *Certified* Medicaid; Medicare.
Owner Proprietary Corp.
Admissions Requirements Medical examination; Physician's request.
Staff Physicians 3 (ft); RNs 4 (ft); LPNs 9 (ft); Nurses aides 35 (ft); Physical therapists 1 (ft); Reality therapists 1 (ft); Recreational therapists 2 (ft); Activities coordinators 1 (ft); Dietitians 1 (ft).
Facilities Dining room; Physical therapy room; Activities room; Crafts room; Laundry room.
Activities Arts & crafts; Cards; Games; Reading groups; Prayer groups; Movies; Shopping trips.

Barnett Stilhaven Nursing Home
201 Central Ave, Dayton, OH, 45406
(513) 223-2835
Admin Joe Barnett. *Medical Dir/Dir of Nursing* Vivek Agarwal MD.
Licensure Intermediate care. *Beds* 50. *Certified* Medicaid.
Owner Privately owned.
Admissions Requirements Minimum age 18; Medical examination.
Staff Physicians 1 (pt); RNs 1 (pt); LPNs 5 (ft), 2 (pt); Orderlies 1 (ft); Nurses aides 20 (ft), 5 (pt); Activities coordinators 2 (ft), 2 (pt); Dietitians 1 (pt).
Facilities Dining room; Activities room; Chapel; Crafts room; Laundry room; Barber/Beauty shop; Enclosed patio with partial covered roof.
Activities Arts & crafts; Cards; Games; Reading groups; Prayer groups; Movies; Shopping trips; Social/Cultural gatherings.

Bethany Lutheran Village
6451 Far Hills Ave, Dayton, OH, 45459
(513) 433-2110
Admin Donald E Claggett. *Medical Dir/Dir of Nursing* Fernando N Perez MD; Mary Jo Gunn RN DON.
Licensure Skilled care; Intermediate care. *Beds* SNF 232. *Certified* Medicaid; Medicare.
Owner Nonprofit Corp.
Admissions Requirements Minimum age 60; Medical examination.
Staff RNs 13 (ft), 5 (pt); LPNs 9 (ft), 3 (pt); Nurses aides 52 (ft), 22 (pt); Activities coordinators 1 (ft); Dietitians 1 (ft).
Affiliation Lutheran
Facilities Dining room; Physical therapy room; Activities room; Chapel; Crafts room; Barber/Beauty shop; Library; Laundry done in-house.
Activities Arts & crafts; Cards; Games; Reading groups; Prayer groups; Movies; Shopping trips; Social/Cultural gatherings.

Catalpa Manor
3650 Klepinger Rd, Dayton, OH, 45377
(513) 278-0663
Admin Florence Julian. *Medical Dir/Dir of Nursing* Dr Sugumaran.
Licensure Skilled care. *Beds* SNF 201. *Certified* Medicaid; Medicare.
Owner Proprietary Corp (Unicare).
Admissions Requirements Minimum age None; Medical examination.
Staff Physicians o 20 (pt); RNs 6 (ft), 4 (pt); LPNs 15 (ft), 2 (pt); Orderlies 1 (ft); Nurses aides 47 (ft), 24 (pt); Physical therapists 1 (pt); Speech therapists 1 (pt); Activities coordinators 3 (ft); Dietitians 1 (ft); Dentists 1 (pt); Ophthalmologists 1 (pt); Podiatrists 1 (pt); Rehabilitation aide 1 (ft).

Languages German
Facilities Dining room; Physical therapy
room; Activities room; Crafts room; Laundry
room; Barber/Beauty shop.
Activities Arts & crafts; Cards; Games;
Reading groups; Prayer groups; Movies;
Shopping trips; Social/Cultural gatherings.

Covenant House—Jewish Home for Aged
4911 Covenant House Dr, Dayton, OH, 45426
(513) 837-2651
Licensure Skilled care; Intermediate care. *Beds*
46. *Certified* Medicaid; Medicare.
Owner Nonprofit Corp.
Affiliation Jewish
Facilities Dining room; Physical therapy
room; Activities room; Chapel; Crafts room;
Barber/Beauty shop.
Activities Arts & crafts; Cards; Games;
Reading groups; Movies; Shopping trips;
Social/Cultural gatherings.

Crawford Convalescent Center Inc
806 W 5th St, Dayton, OH, 45407
(513) 223-3581
Admin Lillian A Shaw-Arrington. *Medical Dir/
Dir of Nursing* Edward J Kinkopf Jr OD;
Jeanne Wagner DON.
Licensure Intermediate care. *Beds* 58.
Owner Proprietary Corp.
Admissions Requirements Minimum age 18;
Medical examination.
Staff Physicians 2 (pt); RNs 2 (ft), 1 (pt);
LPNs 2 (ft), 4 (pt); Orderlies 4 (ft); Nurses
aides 8 (ft); Recreational therapists 1 (pt);
Activities coordinators 1 (ft).
Facilities Dining room; Physical therapy
room; Activities room; Crafts room; Laundry
room; Barber/Beauty shop; Library.
Activities Arts & crafts; Cards; Games;
Reading groups; Prayer groups; Movies;
Shopping trips; Social/Cultural gatherings;
Trips to baseball games, zoo, Air Force
museum, amusement park.

Crestview Nursing Home II
4381 Tonawanda Trail, Dayton, OH, 45430
(513) 426-5033
Admin Esther L Hofferbert. *Medical Dir/Dir
of Nursing* Douglas Romer MD; Kay Llacera
RN DON.
Licensure Skilled care; Intermediate care. *Beds*
102. *Certified* Medicaid; Medicare.
Owner Proprietary Corp.
Admissions Requirements Medical
examination.
Staff Physicians 2 (pt); RNs 5 (ft), 9 (pt);
LPNs 1 (ft), 2 (pt); Orderlies 1 (ft); Nurses
aides 46 (ft), 5 (pt); Physical therapists 1
(pt); Recreational therapists 1 (pt); Speech
therapists 1 (pt); Activities coordinators 1
(ft); Dietitians 1 (pt); Dentists 1 (pt);
Ophthalmologists 1 (pt); Podiatrists 1 (pt).
Facilities Dining room; Physical therapy
room; Activities room; Barber/Beauty shop.
Activities Arts & crafts; Cards; Games;
Reading groups; Prayer groups; Social/
Cultural gatherings; Bingo; Outings; Bowling;
Religious services; Bible study; Special
dinners; Exercise; Ceramics; Poetry group.

Echoing Valley Residential Center
7040 Union School House Rd, Dayton, OH,
45424
(513) 237-7881
Admin Kent Dyer. *Medical Dir/Dir of Nursing*
Phyllis Lane.
Licensure Intermediate care for mentally
retarded. *Beds* ICF/MR 36. *Certified*
Medicaid; Medicare.
Owner Nonprofit Corp.
Admissions Requirements Minimum age 18;
Medical examination.
Staff Physicians 1 (pt); RNs 1 (ft); LPNs 6
(ft); Physical therapists 1 (pt); Recreational
therapists 1 (ft); Occupational therapists 1

(pt); Speech therapists 1 (pt); Dietitians 1
(pt); Ophthalmologists 1 (pt); Podiatrists 1
(pt).
Facilities Dining room; Physical therapy
room; Activities room; Crafts room; Laundry
room.
Activities Arts & crafts; Cards; Games;
Reading groups; Prayer groups; Movies;
Shopping trips; Social/Cultural gatherings.

Echoing Woods Residential Center
5455 Salem Bend Dr, Dayton, OH, 45426
(513) 854-5151
Admin Kent Dyer. *Medical Dir/Dir of Nursing*
Phyllis Lane.
Licensure Intermediate care for mentally
retarded. *Beds* ICF/MR 36. *Certified*
Medicaid; Medicare.
Owner Nonprofit Corp.
Admissions Requirements Minimum age 18;
Medical examination; Physician's request.
Staff Physicians 1 (pt); LPNs 3 (ft), 3 (pt);
Recreational therapists 1 (ft); Occupational
therapists 1 (pt); Speech therapists 1 (pt);
Dietitians 1 (pt); Ophthalmologists 1 (pt);
Podiatrists 1 (pt).
Facilities Dining room; Physical therapy
room; Activities room; Crafts room; Laundry
room.
Activities Arts & crafts; Cards; Games;
Reading groups; Prayer groups; Movies;
Shopping trips; Social/Cultural gatherings.

Franklin Nursing Home of Dayton*
652 Superior Ave, Dayton, OH, 45407
(513) 228-7216
Licensure Intermediate care. *Beds* 38.
Certified Medicaid.
Owner Proprietary Corp.

Friendship Village*
5790 Denlinger Rd, Dayton, OH, 45426
(513) 837-5581
Licensure Skilled care; Intermediate care. *Beds*
57. *Certified* Medicaid; Medicare.
Owner Nonprofit Corp.

Glenn Haven Nursing Home
5205 N Main St, Dayton, OH, 45415
(513) 275-0791
Admin Deborah Hardy. *Medical Dir/Dir of
Nursing* Dr Kasimir Oganowski; Brenda
Mosley DON.
Licensure Intermediate care. *Beds* ICF 34.
Certified Medicaid.
Owner Privately owned.
Admissions Requirements Medical
examination; Physician's request.
Staff RNs 1 (ft), 1 (pt); LPNs 3 (ft); Nurses
aides 10 (ft); Physical therapists 1 (pt);
Activities coordinators 1 (ft); Dietitians 1
(pt); Dentist 1 (pt).
Facilities Dining room; Activities room.
Activities Arts & crafts; Cards; Games;
Reading groups; Prayer groups; Movies;
Shopping trips; Social/Cultural gatherings.

Grandview Manor Nursing Home Inc
405 Grafton Ave, Dayton, OH, 45406
(513) 276-4040
Admin Annette Smith. *Medical Dir/Dir of
Nursing* James Nagle MD; Paulette Lewis
DON.
Licensure Intermediate care. *Beds* ICF 29.
Certified Medicaid.
Owner Privately owned.
Admissions Requirements Minimum age 18.
Staff Physicians 1 (ft), 1 (pt); RNs 1 (pt);
LPNs 4 (ft); Nurses aides 12 (ft), 2 (pt);
Activities coordinators 1 (ft); Dietitians 1
(pt); Ophthalmologists 1 (pt); Social worker.
Facilities Activities room; Laundry room.
Activities Arts & crafts; Cards; Games;
Reading groups; Prayer groups; Movies;
Shopping trips; Social/Cultural gatherings.

Grandview Quality Care Center*
923 Grand Ave, Dayton, OH, 45407
(513) 278-6597

Medical Dir/Dir of Nursing Dr O'Samkari.
Licensure Intermediate care. *Beds* 24.
Certified Medicaid.
Owner Proprietary Corp.
Admissions Requirements Females only;
Medical examination.
Staff Physicians 2 (pt); RNs 1 (ft), 2 (pt);
LPNs 3 (ft); Orderlies 1 (ft); Nurses aides 8
(ft), 2 (pt); Physical therapists 1 (pt); Reality
therapists 1 (pt); Recreational therapists 1
(pt); Activities coordinators 1 (pt); Dietitians
1 (pt); Dentists 1 (pt); Ophthalmologists 1
(pt); Podiatrists 1 (pt); Audiologists 1 (pt).
Facilities Dining room; Activities room;
Laundry room.
Activities Arts & crafts; Cards; Games;
Reading groups; Prayer groups; Movies;
Shopping trips; Social/Cultural gatherings.

Heartland—Beavercreek*
1974 N Fairfield Rd, Dayton, OH, 45432
(513) 429-1106
Licensure Skilled care; Intermediate care. *Beds*
100. *Certified* Medicaid; Medicare.
Owner Proprietary Corp (Southmark Heritage
Corp).

Hester Memorial Nursing Home*
322 Park Dr, Dayton, OH, 45410
(513) 223-5453
Admin Jim McPherson. *Medical Dir/Dir of
Nursing* Dr James B Nogle.
Licensure Intermediate care. *Beds* 45.
Certified Medicaid.
Owner Nonprofit Corp.
Admissions Requirements Medical
examination.
Affiliation Church of God
Facilities Dining room; Activities room;
Laundry room.
Activities Arts & crafts; Cards; Games;
Reading groups; Prayer groups; Movies;
Shopping trips; Social/Cultural gatherings.

Hickory Creek Nursing Home Inc
4231 Pinnacle Rd, Dayton, OH, 45418
(513) 268-3488
Admin Robert L Briley. *Medical Dir/Dir of
Nursing* Dr Rhee; Patricia Miller RN.
Licensure Skilled care. *Beds* SNF 150.
Certified Medicaid; Medicare.
Owner Proprietary Corp (Health Care
Management).
Admissions Requirements Medical
examination.
Staff Physicians 1 (pt); RNs 7 (ft), 2 (pt);
LPNs 8 (ft), 3 (pt); Orderlies 4 (ft), 2 (pt);
Nurses aides 18 (ft), 24 (pt); Physical
therapists 2 (pt); Reality therapists 1 (ft);
Occupational therapists 2 (pt); Speech
therapists 2 (pt); Activities coordinators 2
(ft); Dietitians 1 (pt); Dentists 1 (pt);
Ophthalmologists 1 (pt); Podiatrists 1 (pt).
Languages German
Facilities Dining room; Physical therapy
room; Activities room; Chapel; Crafts room;
Laundry room; Barber/Beauty shop; Library.
Activities Arts & crafts; Cards; Games;
Reading groups; Prayer groups; Movies;
Shopping trips; Social/Cultural gatherings.

Hill Top House Nursing Home Inc*
437 Blackwood Ave, Dayton, OH, 45403
(513) 253-8944
Licensure Skilled care. *Beds* 63. *Certified*
Medicare.
Owner Proprietary Corp.

Jones Nursing & Convalescent Home*
1033 Grand Ave, Dayton, OH, 45407
(513) 277-1281
Licensure Intermediate care. *Beds* 22.
Certified Medicaid.
Owner Proprietary Corp.

Josephine Nursing Home*
519 McLain St, Dayton, OH, 45403
(513) 222-0823

Licensure Intermediate care. *Beds* 24.
Certified Medicaid.
Owner Proprietary Corp.

King Tree Center
1390 King Tree Dr, Dayton, OH, 45405
(513) 278-0723
Admin Donald C Leine. *Medical Dir/Dir of
Nursing* R Chunduri MD; Darlene Hartley
RN.
Licensure Skilled care. *Beds* SNF 50; ICF
150. *Certified* Medicaid; Medicare.
Owner Proprietary Corp.
Admissions Requirements Minimum age 16;
Medical examination; Physician's request.
Staff Physicians 20 (pt); RNs 16 (ft); LPNs 10
(ft), 4 (pt); Orderlies 4 (ft); Nurses aides 67
(ft); Physical therapists 1 (ft); Occupational
therapists 1 (pt); Speech therapists 1 (pt);
Activities coordinators 3 (ft); Dietitians 1
(pt); Dentists 1 (pt); Ophthalmologists 1 (pt).
Facilities Dining room; Physical therapy
room; Activities room; Chapel; Crafts room;
Laundry room; Barber/Beauty shop; Library.
Activities Arts & crafts; Cards; Games;
Reading groups; Prayer groups; Movies;
Shopping trips; Social/Cultural gatherings.

Linden Health Care Center*
42 Linden Ave, Dayton, OH, 45403
(513) 252-4711
Licensure Intermediate care. *Beds* 25.
Certified Medicaid.
Owner Proprietary Corp.
Admissions Requirements Medical
examination.
Staff Physicians 1 (pt); RNs 1 (pt); LPNs 2
(ft), 3 (pt); Nurses aides 7 (ft), 3 (pt);
Activities coordinators 1 (ft); Dietitians 1
(pt); Dentists 1 (pt); Ophthalmologists 1 (pt);
Podiatrists 1 (pt).
Facilities Dining room; Laundry room.
Activities Arts & crafts; Cards; Games; Prayer
groups; Movies; Shopping trips.

The Maria-Joseph Center
4830 Salem Ave, Dayton, OH, 45416
(513) 278-2692
Admin Mr Magdi R Kamil. *Medical Dir/Dir
of Nursing* Joseph Premanandan MD; Penny
Kenley RN DON.
Licensure Skilled care; Intermediate care;
Independent living. *Beds* SNF 124; ICF 260;
Independent living 56. *Certified* Medicaid;
Medicare.
Owner Nonprofit Corp.
Admissions Requirements Medical
examination.
Staff Physicians 1 (ft), 2 (pt); RNs 15 (ft), 25
(pt); LPNs 16 (ft), 27 (pt); Nurses aides 100
(ft), 100 (pt); Physical therapists 1 (ft);
Occupational therapists 2 (ft); Speech
therapists 1 (pt); Activities coordinators 5
(ft), 2 (pt); Dietitians 2 (ft); Dentists 1 (pt);
Ophthalmologists 1 (pt); Podiatrists 1 (pt).
Affiliation Roman Catholic
Facilities Dining room; Physical therapy
room; Activities room; Chapel; Crafts room;
Laundry room; Barber/Beauty shop; Library.
Activities Arts & crafts; Cards; Games;
Reading groups; Prayer groups; Movies;
Shopping trips; Social/Cultural gatherings.

McGills Nursing Home—South*
15 Arnold Pl, Dayton, OH, 45407
(513) 274-2447
Licensure Intermediate care. *Beds* 30.
Certified Medicaid.
Owner Proprietary Corp.

Oxford Manor Nursing Home
601 Oxford Ave, Dayton, OH, 45407
(513) 275-3288
Admin Imogene Jackson. *Medical Dir/Dir of
Nursing* Imogene Hacker.
Licensure Intermediate care. *Certified*
Medicaid.

Admissions Requirements Medical
examination.
Staff RNs 1 (pt); LPNs 3 (ft), 2 (pt); Nurses
aides 9 (ft); Activities coordinators 1 (ft);
Dietitians 1 (pt); Podiatrists 1 (pt).
Facilities Dining room; Laundry room;
Barber/Beauty shop.
Activities Arts & crafts; Cards; Games;
Reading groups; Prayer groups; Movies;
Shopping trips; Social/Cultural gatherings;
Cook outs.

Parkview Manor Nursing Home
250 Park Dr, Dayton, OH, 45410
(513) 224-0609
Admin James Lauricella Jr. *Medical Dir/Dir of
Nursing* James Nagle MD; Judy McCullough
RN.
Licensure Intermediate care. *Beds* ICF 50.
Certified Medicaid.
Owner Proprietary Corp.
Admissions Requirements Physician's request.
Staff RNs 1 (ft); LPNs 3 (ft), 2 (pt); Nurses
aides 21 (ft), 5 (pt); Physical therapists 1
(pt); Activities coordinators 1 (pt); Dietitians
1 (pt).
Facilities Dining room; Activities room;
Laundry room; Barber/Beauty shop.
Activities Arts & crafts; Games; Reading
groups; Prayer groups; Movies; Shopping
trips; Exercise.

Rest Haven*
34 Arnold Pl, Dayton, OH, 45407
(513) 275-6033
Licensure Intermediate care. *Beds* 19.
Certified Medicaid.
Owner Proprietary Corp.

Schulze Nursing Home
409 Forest Ave, Dayton, OH, 45405
(513) 228-7143
Admin Robert Huff. *Medical Dir/Dir of
Nursing* Lynne J Huff; Gary Collier.
Licensure Intermediate care. *Beds* ICF 35.
Certified Medicaid.
Owner Privately owned.
Admissions Requirements Females only.
Staff RNs; LPNs; Nurses aides; Activities
coordinators.
Facilities Dining room; Barber/Beauty shop.
Activities Arts & crafts; Cards; Games;
Reading groups; Prayer groups; Movies;
Shopping trips; Social/Cultural gatherings.

Mary Scott Nursing Center*
3109 Campus Dr, Dayton, OH, 45406
(513) 278-0761
Medical Dir/Dir of Nursing Dr Robert
McConnell.
Licensure Skilled care; Intermediate care. *Beds*
130. *Certified* Medicaid; Medicare.
Owner Proprietary Corp (Health Care
Management).
Admissions Requirements Medical
examination.
Staff Physicians 1 (pt); RNs 4 (ft), 1 (pt);
LPNs 12 (ft), 1 (pt); Nurses aides 40 (ft), 6
(pt); Activities coordinators 1 (ft); Dietitians
1 (ft).
Facilities Dining room; Physical therapy
room; Activities room; Crafts room; Laundry
room; Barber/Beauty shop; Library.
Activities Arts & crafts; Cards; Games;
Reading groups; Prayer groups; Movies;
Shopping trips; Social/Cultural gatherings.

The Siena Home
235 W Orchard Springs Dr, Dayton, OH,
45415-3195
(513) 278-8211
Admin Sr Mary Andrea Simpson. *Medical
Dir/Dir of Nursing* Bernard Liddy MD;
Cheryl Bombok DON.
Licensure Intermediate care. *Certified*
Medicaid.
Owner Nonprofit Corp.
Admissions Requirements Minimum age 65.

Staff Physicians 1 (pt); RNs 8 (ft), 5 (pt);
Orderlies 3 (ft); Nurses aides 32 (ft), 15 (pt);
Physical therapists 1 (pt); Activities
coordinators 1 (ft); Dietitians 1 (pt);
Ophthalmologists 1 (pt).
Facilities Dining room; Activities room;
Chapel; Crafts room; Laundry room; Barber/
Beauty shop.
Activities Arts & crafts; Cards; Reading
groups; Prayer groups; Movies; Social/
Cultural gatherings.

Stillwater Health Center
8100 N Main St, Dayton, OH, 45415
(513) 890-0646
Admin Benton Wahl. *Medical Dir/Dir of
Nursing* Dr Jose A Aceituno MD; Joanne
Hale DON.
Licensure Skilled care; Intermediate care. *Beds*
SNF; ICF 140. *Certified* Medicaid.
Owner Publicly owned.
Admissions Requirements Medical
examination.
Staff Physicians 1 (pt); RNs 12 (ft), 10 (pt);
LPNs 16 (ft), 4 (pt); Nurses aides 46 (ft), 7
(pt); Physical therapists 1 (pt); Recreational
therapists 1 (ft); Occupational therapists 1
(pt); Speech therapists 2 (pt); Activities
coordinators 1 (ft); Dietitians 1 (ft);
Ophthalmologists 1 (pt).
Facilities Dining room; Physical therapy
room; Activities room; Crafts room; Library;
Residents lounge.
Activities Arts & crafts; Cards; Games;
Reading groups; Prayer groups; Movies;
Shopping trips; Social/Cultural gatherings.

Stillwater Health Center/ICFMR
8100 N Main St, Dayton, OH, 45415
(513) 890-0646
Admin Benton Wahl. *Medical Dir/Dir of
Nursing* Ceferino Cata MD; Janet Zykoski
DON.
Licensure Intermediate care for mentally
retarded. *Beds* ICF/MR 34. *Certified*
Medicaid.
Owner Publicly owned.
Admissions Requirements Minimum age 0-18;
Medical examination.
Staff Physicians 1 (pt); RNs 4 (ft), 1 (pt);
LPNs 3 (ft); Nurses aides 15 (ft), 9 (pt);
Physical therapists 1 (pt); Recreational
therapists 1 (ft); Occupational therapists 1
(pt); Speech therapists 2 (pt); Activities
coordinators 1 (ft); Dietitians 1 (ft).
Facilities Dining room; Physical therapy
room; Activities room; Laundry room.
Activities Arts & crafts; Cards; Games;
Reading groups; Prayer groups; Movies;
Shopping trips; Social/Cultural gatherings;
Exercise groups; Daily outside activities.

Trinity Retirement Community
3218 Indian Ripple Rd, Dayton, OH, 45440
(513) 426-8481
Medical Dir/Dir of Nursing Sherry Stanley
MD; Charlotte Lynch RN.
Licensure Skilled care; Intermediate care;
Retirement Community. *Beds* SNF 175.
Certified Medicaid; Medicare.
Owner Nonprofit Corp (United Church
Homes).
Admissions Requirements Minimum age 65;
Medical examination.
Staff Physicians; RNs; LPNs; Nurses aides;
Physical therapists; Occupational therapists;
Speech therapists; Activities coordinators;
Dietitians.
Affiliation Church of Christ
Facilities Dining room; Physical therapy
room; Activities room; Chapel; Crafts room;
Laundry room; Barber/Beauty shop; Library.
Activities Arts & crafts; Cards; Games;
Reading groups; Prayer groups; Movies;
Shopping trips; Social/Cultural gatherings;
Seasonal programs.

Washington Manor
7300 McEwen Rd, Dayton, OH, 45459
(513) 433-3441
Licensure Skilled care; Intermediate care. *Beds* SNF 178; ICF. *Certified* Medicaid; Medicare.
Owner Proprietary Corp.
Admissions Requirements Medical examination; Physician's request.
Staff Physicians; RNs; LPNs; Orderlies; Nurses aides; Physical therapists; Occupational therapists; Speech therapists; Activities coordinators; Dietitians; Dentists; Ophthalmologists.
Facilities Dining room; Physical therapy room; Activities room; Chapel; Crafts room; Laundry room; Barber/Beauty shop; 2 lounges.
Activities Arts & crafts; Cards; Games; Prayer groups; Movies; Social/Cultural gatherings; Exercises; Bingo; Current events; Music.

Widows Home of Dayton
50 S Findlay St, Dayton, OH, 45403
(513) 252-1661, 252-7280
Admin Harvey S Klein Jr. *Medical Dir/Dir of Nursing* Dorothy Creekmore DON.
Licensure Skilled care; Home for aged. *Beds* SNF 14; Home for aged 30.
Owner Nonprofit Corp.
Admissions Requirements Minimum age 65; Females only; Medical examination.
Staff LPNs 3 (ft), 3 (pt); Orderlies 1 (ft); Nurses aides 8 (ft), 9 (pt); Dietitians 1 (pt).
Facilities Dining room; Activities room; Chapel; Crafts room; Laundry room; Barber/Beauty shop; Library.
Activities Arts & crafts; Cards; Games; Prayer groups; Shopping trips; Social/Cultural gatherings.

Yale Manor Inc*
35 Yale Ave, Dayton, OH, 45406
(513) 276-5237
Licensure Intermediate care. *Beds* 42. *Certified* Medicaid.
Owner Proprietary Corp.

DEFIANCE

Defiance Health Care Center
1701 S Jefferson, Defiance, OH, 43512
(419) 782-7879
Admin M Wendy Hockley. *Medical Dir/Dir of Nursing* Dr William Busteed.
Licensure Skilled care. *Beds* SNF 51. *Certified* Medicaid; Medicare.
Owner Proprietary Corp (Health Resources Dev).
Admissions Requirements Minimum age 18; Medical examination.
Staff Physicians 1 (pt); RNs 1 (ft), 3 (pt); LPNs 3 (ft), 6 (pt); Nurses aides 12 (ft), 12 (pt); Physical therapists 1 (pt); Speech therapists 1 (pt); Activities coordinators 1 (ft); Dietitians 1 (pt); Ophthalmologists 1 (pt).
Facilities Dining room; Physical therapy room; Activities room; Chapel; Crafts room; Laundry room; Barber/Beauty shop; Library; Gazebo.
Activities Arts & crafts; Cards; Games; Reading groups; Prayer groups; Movies; Shopping trips; Social/Cultural gatherings; Outtings in the van.

Glenwood Care Center*
301 Glenwood Dr, Defiance, OH, 43512
(419) 782-9761
Medical Dir/Dir of Nursing Dr George Boomer.
Licensure Intermediate care. *Beds* 50. *Certified* Medicaid.
Owner Proprietary Corp (Health Resources Dev).
Admissions Requirements Medical examination.

Staff Physicians 5 (pt); RNs 1 (pt); LPNs 3 (ft), 4 (pt); Orderlies 1 (ft), 2 (pt); Nurses aides 2 (ft), 13 (pt); Activities coordinators 1 (ft); Dietitians 1 (pt); Podiatrists 1 (pt).
Facilities Dining room; Activities room; Crafts room; Laundry room; Barber/Beauty shop.
Activities Arts & crafts; Games; Movies; Shopping trips.

Leisure Oaks Convalescent Center*
214 Harding St, Defiance, OH, 43512
(419) 784-1014
Medical Dir/Dir of Nursing John Forester Jr MD.
Licensure Skilled care; Intermediate care. *Beds* 93. *Certified* Medicaid; Medicare.
Owner Nonprofit Corp (Volunteers of America Care).
Admissions Requirements Medical examination; Physician's request.
Staff RNs 3 (ft), 8 (pt); LPNs 2 (ft), 8 (pt); Nurses aides 20 (ft), 20 (pt); Physical therapists 1 (pt); Speech therapists 1 (pt); Activities coordinators 1 (ft); Dietitians 1 (pt); Dentists 1 (pt); Podiatrists 1 (pt); Audiologists 1 (pt).
Affiliation Volunteers of America
Facilities Dining room; Physical therapy room; Activities room; Chapel; Crafts room; Laundry room; Barber/Beauty shop; Library.
Activities Arts & crafts; Cards; Games; Reading groups; Prayer groups; Movies; Shopping trips; Social/Cultural gatherings; Pet therapy.

Twin Rivers Nursing Care Center*
395 Harding St, Defiance, OH, 43512
(419) 784-1450
Medical Dir/Dir of Nursing Dr John Fauster.
Licensure Skilled care; Intermediate care. *Beds* 100. *Certified* Medicaid; Medicare.
Owner Proprietary Corp.
Admissions Requirements Medical examination.
Staff Physicians 1 (pt); RNs 2 (ft), 3 (pt); LPNs 2 (ft), 11 (pt); Orderlies 1 (ft), 1 (pt); Nurses aides 15 (ft), 29 (pt); Physical therapists 1 (pt); Speech therapists 1 (pt); Activities coordinators 1 (ft), 1 (pt); Dietitians 1 (ft); Dentists 1 (pt); Podiatrists 1 (pt).
Facilities Dining room; Physical therapy room; Activities room; Laundry room; Barber/Beauty shop; Library.
Activities Arts & crafts; Cards; Games; Reading groups; Movies; Shopping trips; Social/Cultural gatherings.

DELAWARE

Delaware Park Care Center
2270 Warrensburg Rd, Delaware, OH, 43015
(614) 369-9614
Admin W Robert Huffman. *Medical Dir/Dir of Nursing* Dr Robert Gnade MD; Rosanna Crim RN.
Licensure Skilled care; Intermediate care. *Beds* SNF 117; ICF. *Certified* Medicaid; Medicare.
Owner Proprietary Corp.
Admissions Requirements Medical examination.
Staff Physicians; RNs; LPNs; Orderlies; Nurses aides; Physical therapists; Recreational therapists; Occupational therapists; Speech therapists; Activities coordinators; Ophthalmologists.
Facilities Dining room; Physical therapy room; Activities room; Laundry room; Barber/Beauty shop; Private dining room; Rehab dining room.
Activities Arts & crafts; Cards; Games; Reading groups; Prayer groups; Movies; Shopping trips; Social/Cultural gatherings.

Evergreen Manor
36 Griswold St, Delaware, OH, 43015
(614) 362-6031
Admin April Cross MSN. *Medical Dir/Dir of Nursing* Dr Shivashanker; Marsha Staliano.
Licensure Intermediate care. *Beds* ICF 34. *Certified* Medicaid.
Owner Proprietary Corp.
Admissions Requirements Medical examination; Physician's request.
Facilities Dining room; Activities room; Crafts room; Laundry room.
Activities Arts & crafts; Cards; Games; Reading groups; Prayer groups; Movies; Shopping trips; Social/Cultural gatherings.

Sarah Moore Home Inc*
47 E William St, Delaware, OH, 43015
(614) 362-9641
Licensure Intermediate care. *Beds* 31. *Certified* Medicaid.
Owner Nonprofit Corp.

Sunny Vee Nursing Home Inc*
54 W Lincoln Ave, Delaware, OH, 43015
(614) 363-1587
Licensure Skilled care; Intermediate care. *Beds* 56. *Certified* Medicaid; Medicare.
Owner Proprietary Corp.

Wintersong Village of Delaware
478 S Sandusky St, Delaware, OH, 43015
(614) 369-8741
Admin Michael L Daffin. *Medical Dir/Dir of Nursing* Linda Hinos.
Licensure Intermediate care. *Beds* 50. *Certified* Medicaid.
Owner Proprietary Corp.
Staff Physicians; RNs; LPNs; Orderlies; Nurses aides; Activities coordinators; Dietitians.
Facilities Dining room; Activities room; Laundry room; Barber/Beauty shop.
Activities Arts & crafts; Cards; Games; Reading groups; Movies; Social/Cultural gatherings.

DELPHOS

Sarah Jane E Chambers Geriatric Center
328 W 2nd St, Delphos, OH, 45833
(419) 695-1921
Admin Virginia Christen. *Medical Dir/Dir of Nursing* Walter W Wolery MD; Ruth Michael RN.
Licensure Intermediate care. *Beds* ICF 50. *Certified* Medicaid; Medicare.
Owner Nonprofit Corp.
Admissions Requirements Minimum age 18.
Staff RNs 1 (ft), 9 (pt); LPNs 1 (pt); Nurses aides 8 (ft), 18 (pt); Activities coordinators 1 (ft), 1 (pt).
Facilities Dining room; Activities room; Laundry room; Barber/Beauty shop.
Activities Arts & crafts; Cards; Games; Reading groups; Prayer groups; Movies.

Delphos Memorial Home
PO Box 334, 1425 E Fifth St, Delphos, OH, 45833
(419) 695-2871 & 692-4242
Admin Virginia Christen. *Medical Dir/Dir of Nursing* Walter W Wolery MD; Sharon Gengler RN.
Licensure Intermediate care. *Beds* ICF 100. *Certified* Medicaid.
Owner Nonprofit organization/foundation.
Admissions Requirements Minimum age 18.
Staff RNs 4 (ft), 9 (pt); LPNs 2 (ft), 7 (pt); Nurses aides 25 (ft), 26 (pt); Activities coordinators 1 (ft), 3 (pt).
Facilities Dining room; Activities room; Laundry room; Barber/Beauty shop.
Activities Arts & crafts; Cards; Games; Reading groups; Prayer groups; Movies.

DENNISON

Charity Nursing Facility*
509 Grant St, Dennison, OH, 44621
(614) 922-2036
Licensure Intermediate care. *Beds* 18.
  Certified Medicaid.
Owner Proprietary Corp.

DESHLER

Oak Grove Quality Care Nursing Center
620 E Water St, Deshler, OH, 43516
(419) 278-6921
Admin Sally Hurles. *Medical Dir/Dir of
  Nursing* R J Blough MD; Barbara Wilhelm
  RN DON.
Licensure Intermediate care. *Beds* ICF 66.
  Certified Medicaid.
Owner Proprietary Corp (Northwestern
  Service Corp).
Staff RNs; LPNs; Orderlies; Nurses aides;
  Activities coordinators.
Facilities Dining room; Activities room;
  Chapel; Laundry room; Barber/Beauty shop.
Activities Arts & crafts; Cards; Games;
  Reading groups; Prayer groups; Movies;
  Shopping trips; Social/Cultural gatherings.

DOVER

Country Club Center
860 Iron Ave, Dover, OH, 44663
(216) 343-5568
Admin Richard L Morris. *Medical Dir/Dir of
  Nursing* Dr Phillip Doughten; Constance
  Ivan RN DON.
Licensure Skilled care. *Beds* 72. *Certified*
  Medicaid; Medicare.
Owner Proprietary Corp (Je Holland Assoc).
Admissions Requirements Minimum age 18;
  Medical examination; Physician's request.
Staff Physicians 1 (pt); RNs 2 (ft), 4 (pt);
  LPNs 9 (pt); Nurses aides 11 (ft), 13 (pt);
  Physical therapists 1 (pt); Speech therapists
  1 (pt); Activities coordinators 1 (ft);
  Dietitians 1 (pt); Podiatrists 1 (pt).
Facilities Dining room; Physical therapy
  room; Activities room; Crafts room; Laundry
  room; Barber/Beauty shop.
Activities Arts & crafts; Cards; Games;
  Reading groups; Prayer groups; Movies;
  Shopping trips; Social/Cultural gatherings;
  Bingo; "Out-to-lunch" group.

Hennis Care Center*
1720 Cross St, Dover, OH, 44622
(216) 364-8849
Licensure Intermediate care. *Beds* 52.
  Certified Medicaid.
Owner Proprietary Corp.

New Dawn Health Care & Retirement Center
865 E Iron Ave, Dover, OH, 44622
(216) 343-5521
Admin Dan Hershberger. *Medical Dir/Dir of
  Nursing* Dr Paul McFadden; Mildred
  Weston RN.
Licensure Intermediate care. *Beds* ICF 101.
  Certified Medicaid.
Owner Proprietary Corp.
Admissions Requirements Medical
  examination.
Staff Physicians 1 (pt); RNs 2 (ft), 8 (pt);
  LPNs 1 (ft), 5 (pt); Nurses aides 6 (ft), 42
  (pt); Activities coordinators 1 (ft), 1 (pt);
  Medical Records 1 (pt).
Facilities Dining room; Physical therapy
  room; Activities room; Chapel; Crafts room;
  Laundry room; Barber/Beauty shop; In-
  service room.
Activities Arts & crafts; Cards; Games;
  Reading groups; Prayer groups; Movies;
  Shopping trips; Social/Cultural gatherings.

Park Village Health Care Center
1525 Crater Ave, Dover, OH, 44622
(216) 364-4436
Admin Robert O'Donnell.
Licensure Intermediate care. *Beds* ICF 100.
  Certified Medicaid.
Owner Privately owned.
Admissions Requirements Minimum age 18;
  Physician's request.
Facilities Dining room; Activities room;
  Crafts room; Laundry room; Barber/Beauty
  shop.
Activities Arts & crafts; Cards; Games;
  Reading groups; Prayer groups; Movies;
  Shopping trips; Social/Cultural gatherings.

DOYLESTOWN

Sara Lee Nursing Home
Rte 1, 140 Wall Rd, Doylestown, OH, 44230
(216) 334-4184
Admin Roger Myers. *Medical Dir/Dir of
  Nursing* P L Gilcrest MD; Amy Steele DON.
Licensure Intermediate care. *Beds* ICF 48.
  Certified Medicaid.
Owner Proprietary Corp.
Admissions Requirements Minimum age 18.
Staff Physicians; RNs; LPNs; Nurses aides;
  Recreational therapists; Activities
  coordinators; Dietitians; Ophthalmologists;
  Podiatrists.
Facilities Dining room; Activities room;
  Crafts room; Laundry room; Barber/Beauty
  shop.
Activities Arts & crafts; Cards; Games;
  Reading groups; Prayer groups; Movies;
  Shopping trips; Social/Cultural gatherings.

DUBLIN

Friendship Village of Dublin Health Center*
6000 Riverside Dr, Dublin, OH, 43017
Licensure Skilled care; Intermediate care. *Beds*
  SNF 60; ICF 60. *Certified* Medicaid;
  Medicare.
Owner Nonprofit Corp.

EAST CLEVELAND

Ambassador Nursing Center*
1835 Belmore Ave, East Cleveland, OH,
44112
(216) 268-3600
Medical Dir/Dir of Nursing Dr Charles
  Barnes.
Licensure Skilled care; Intermediate care. *Beds*
  159. *Certified* Medicaid; Medicare.
Owner Proprietary Corp.
Admissions Requirements Minimum age 30.
Staff Physicians; RNs; LPNs; Orderlies;
  Nurses aides; Physical therapists;
  Recreational therapists; Occupational
  therapists; Speech therapists; Activities
  coordinators; Dietitians; Dentists;
  Ophthalmologists; Podiatrists.
Facilities Dining room; Physical therapy
  room; Activities room; Chapel; Crafts room;
  Laundry room; Barber/Beauty shop; Library.
Activities Arts & crafts; Cards; Games;
  Reading groups; Prayer groups; Movies;
  Shopping trips; Social/Cultural gatherings.

Eastern Star Home of Cuyahoga County*
2114 Noble Rd, East Cleveland, OH, 44112
Licensure Intermediate care. *Beds* 81.
  Certified Medicaid.
Owner Nonprofit Corp.
Affiliation Order of Eastern Star

A M McGregor Home
14900 Terrace Rd, East Cleveland, OH, 44112
(216) 851-8200
Admin Carol A Marks. *Medical Dir/Dir of
  Nursing* Barry Siegel MD, Ralph Wieland
  MD; Shirley Baker DON.
Licensure Intermediate care. *Beds* ICF 100.
Owner Nonprofit organization/foundation.

Admissions Requirements Minimum age 65;
  Medical examination.
Staff Physicians 2 (pt); RNs 7 (ft); LPNs 4
  (ft), 4 (pt); Nurses aides 21 (ft), 3 (pt);
  Physical therapists 1 (pt); Recreational
  therapists 1 (ft); Activities coordinators 1
  (ft); Dietitians 1 (pt); Dentists 1 (pt);
  Ophthalmologists 1 (pt).
Facilities Dining room; Physical therapy
  room; Activities room; Crafts room; Laundry
  room; Barber/Beauty shop; Library.
Activities Arts & crafts; Cards; Games;
  Reading groups; Prayer groups; Movies;
  Shopping trips; Social/Cultural gatherings.

EAST LIVERPOOL

Convalescent Center 2*
701 Armstrong Ln, East Liverpool, OH, 43920
(216) 385-5212
Licensure Intermediate care. *Beds* 50.
  Certified Medicaid.
Owner Proprietary Corp.

East Liverpool Convalescent Center*
709 Armstrong Ln, East Liverpool, OH, 43920
(216) 385-3600
Licensure Intermediate care. *Beds* 60.
  Certified Medicaid.
Owner Proprietary Corp.

East Liverpool Extended Care Center
430 W 5th St, East Liverpool, OH, 43920
(216) 385-9500
Admin Peter Visnic. *Medical Dir/Dir of
  Nursing* Janis Lauva MD; Sharen Ault RN
  DON.
Licensure Intermediate care. *Beds* ICF 50.
  Certified Medicaid.
Owner Proprietary Corp.
Admissions Requirements Minimum age 14;
  Medical examination; Physician's request.
Staff Physicians 1 (pt); RNs 3 (ft), 2 (pt);
  LPNs 4 (ft); Nurses aides 11 (ft), 9 (pt);
  Physical therapists 1 (pt); Occupational
  therapists 1 (pt); Speech therapists 1 (pt);
  Activities coordinators 1 (ft); Dietitians 1
  (pt); Dentist 1 (pt).
Facilities Dining room; Physical therapy
  room; Activities room; Laundry room;
  Barber/Beauty shop; TV lounge; Patio.
Activities Arts & crafts; Cards; Games;
  Reading groups; Prayer groups; Movies;
  Social/Cultural gatherings; Bingo.

Nentwick Convalescent Home Inc*
500 Seltridge St, East Liverpool, OH, 43920
(216) 385-5001
Medical Dir/Dir of Nursing Dr William
  Sarger.
Licensure Intermediate care. *Beds* 100.
  Certified Medicaid.
Owner Proprietary Corp.
Admissions Requirements Medical
  examination.
Staff Physicians 1 (pt); RNs 6 (ft); LPNs 4
  (ft); Orderlies 2 (ft), 1 (pt); Nurses aides 35
  (ft), 4 (pt); Physical therapists 1 (pt);
  Occupational therapists 1 (pt); Speech
  therapists 1 (pt); Activities coordinators 3
  (ft); Dietitians 1 (pt); Dentists 1 (pt);
  Podiatrists 1 (pt); Audiologists 1 (pt).
Facilities Dining room; Physical therapy
  room; Activities room; Chapel; Crafts room;
  Laundry room; Barber/Beauty shop; Library;
  Courtyard; Whirlpool baths.
Activities Arts & crafts; Cards; Games;
  Reading groups; Prayer groups; Movies;
  Shopping trips; Social/Cultural gatherings;
  Ceramics; Newspaper; Leathercraft; Exercise
  groups; Resident council; Resident dietary
  support group.

Ross Nursing Home*
941-949 Ambrose Ave, East Liverpool, OH,
43920
(216) 385-6623

Medical Dir/Dir of Nursing Dr William Horger.
Licensure Intermediate care. *Beds* 50. *Certified* Medicaid.
Owner Nonprofit Corp.
Admissions Requirements Medical examination; Physician's request.
Staff Physicians 1 (ft), 3 (pt); RNs 1 (ft), 1 (pt); LPNs 7 (ft); Nurses aides 20 (ft), 6 (pt); Recreational therapists 1 (ft); Activities coordinators 1 (ft); Dietitians 2 (pt).
Facilities Dining room; Activities room; Laundry room.
Activities Arts & crafts; Games; Prayer groups; Shopping trips.

EATON

Governor Harris Homestead
PO Box 147, 310 N Cherry St, Eaton, OH, 45320
(513) 456-5120
Admin Richard Heath. *Medical Dir/Dir of Nursing* Mark Vosler DO; Linda Blount LPN.
Licensure Intermediate care. *Beds* ICF 27. *Certified* Medicaid.
Owner Proprietary Corp.
Admissions Requirements Minimum age 60; Medical examination; Physician's request.
Staff RNs 1 (pt); LPNs 4 (ft), 2 (pt); Nurses aides 9 (ft), 3 (pt); Activities coordinators 2 (pt).
Facilities Dining room; Barber/Beauty shop.
Activities Arts & crafts; Cards; Games; Reading groups; Prayer groups; Movies; Shopping trips; Social/Cultural gatherings; Pets.

Heartland of Eaton
515 S Maple St, Eaton, OH, 45320
(513) 456-5537
Admin David Gray. *Medical Dir/Dir of Nursing* Richard Siehl DO.
Licensure Skilled care. *Beds* 100. *Certified* Medicaid; Medicare.
Owner Proprietary Corp (Health Care & Retirement Corp).
Admissions Requirements Minimum age 35; Medical examination; Physician's request.
Staff Physicians 1 (pt); RNs 3 (ft), 3 (pt); LPNs 3 (ft), 8 (pt); Nurses aides 29 (ft), 11 (pt); Physical therapists 1 (pt); Occupational therapists 1 (pt); Speech therapists 1 (pt); Activities coordinators 2 (ft); Dietitians 1 (ft).
Facilities Dining room; Physical therapy room; Activities room; Barber/Beauty shop.
Activities Arts & crafts; Cards; Games; Reading groups; Shopping trips; Social/Cultural gatherings; Fair; Pork festival; Picnics; Rock 'n roll jamboree; Flower arranging; Bible study; Worship services.

Morris Oak Lawn Nursing Home*
120 N Cherry St, Eaton, OH, 45320
(513) 456-7167
Licensure Intermediate care. *Beds* 34. *Certified* Medicaid.
Owner Proprietary Corp.
Staff RNs 1 (pt); LPNs 3 (ft), 3 (pt); Nurses aides 6 (ft), 4 (pt); Activities coordinators 1 (pt).
Facilities Dining room; Activities room; Crafts room; Laundry room.
Activities Arts & crafts; Cards; Games; Reading groups; Prayer groups; Movies; Shopping trips; Social/Cultural gatherings.

Rust-McGills Nursing Center
119 W Somers St, Eaton, OH, 45320-1799
(513) 456-3640
Admin Flossie E McGill. *Medical Dir/Dir of Nursing* Flossie E McGill.
Licensure Skilled care; Intermediate care. *Beds* SNF 10; ICF 13. *Certified* Medicaid.
Owner Privately owned.

Staff RNs 1 (pt); LPNs 3 (ft); Orderlies 1 (ft); Nurses aides 8 (ft); Activities coordinators 1 (pt); Dietitians 1 (pt); Dentists 1 (pt); Ophthalmologists 1 (pt).
Facilities Dining room; Activities room; Crafts room; Laundry room; Barber/Beauty shop.
Activities Arts & crafts; Cards; Games; Reading groups; Prayer groups; Shopping trips.

EDGERTON

Park View Nursing Center
US Rte 6 W, Edgerton, OH, 43517
(419) 298-2321
Medical Dir/Dir of Nursing Dr R Meyer.
Licensure Skilled care; Intermediate care. *Beds* 100. *Certified* Medicaid; Medicare.
Owner Proprietary Corp.
Admissions Requirements Medical examination.
Staff RNs 3 (ft), 1 (pt); LPNs 3 (ft), 6 (pt); Nurses aides 24 (ft), 2 (pt); Physical therapists 1 (pt); Activities coordinators 2 (ft); Dietitians 1 (pt); Podiatrists 1 (pt).
Facilities Dining room; Physical therapy room; Activities room; Laundry room; Barber/Beauty shop.
Activities Arts & crafts; Cards; Games; Reading groups; Prayer groups; Movies; Shopping trips; Social/Cultural gatherings.

ELYRA

Ferry Nursing Home
1015 Middle Ave, Elyra, OH, 44035
(216) 323-2892
Admin Nancy A Comer. *Medical Dir/Dir of Nursing* Dr McGowan.
Licensure Intermediate care. *Beds* ICF 26. *Certified* Medicaid.
Owner Proprietary Corp.
Admissions Requirements Physician's request.
Staff LPNs 3 (ft), 3 (pt); Nurses aides 5 (ft), 5 (pt); Physical therapists O 1 (pt); Activities coordinators 1 (pt); Ophthalmologists 1 (pt).
Facilities Dining room; Activities room.
Activities Arts & crafts; Cards; Games; Reading groups.

ELYRIA

The Elyria United Methodist Home
807 West Ave, Elyria, OH, 44035
(216) 323-3395
Admin Roger W Turnau. *Medical Dir/Dir of Nursing* Roger L Baldoza MD; Mary Tompos DON.
Licensure Skilled care; Intermediate care; Retirement home. *Beds* 209. *Certified* Medicaid; Medicare.
Owner Nonprofit organization/foundation.
Admissions Requirements Minimum age 65; Medical examination.
Staff Physicians 6 (pt); RNs 7 (ft), 7 (pt); LPNs 27 (ft), 19 (pt); Nurses aides 80 (ft), 14 (pt); Physical therapists 1 (pt); Recreational therapists 1 (pt); Occupational therapists 1 (pt); Speech therapists 1 (pt); Activities coordinators 3 (ft); Dietitians 1 (ft); Dentists 1 (pt); Ophthalmologists 1 (pt).
Affiliation Methodist
Facilities Dining room; Physical therapy room; Activities room; Chapel; Crafts room; Laundry room; Barber/Beauty shop; Library; Kitchen/lounge; Store.
Activities Arts & crafts; Cards; Games; Reading groups; Prayer groups; Movies; Shopping trips; Social/Cultural gatherings; Support groups; Cooking & baking; Mens club.

J Ferry Nursing Home*
1015 Middle Ave, Elyria, OH, 44035
(216) 323-2892

Licensure Intermediate care. *Beds* 26. *Certified* Medicaid.
Owner Proprietary Corp.

Palm Crest East Nursing Home
1251 East Ave, Elyria, OH, 44035
(216) 322-0726
Admin Abraham Schwartz. *Medical Dir/Dir of Nursing* June H Cole RN.
Licensure Intermediate care; Intermediate care for mentally retarded. *Beds* ICF 30; ICF/MR 20. *Certified* Medicaid.
Owner Proprietary Corp.
Staff RNs 1 (ft), 1 (pt); LPNs 5 (pt); Nurses aides 23 (pt); Recreational therapists 1 (pt); Activities coordinators 1 (pt).

Palm Crest West Nursing Home Inc
221 West Ave, Elyria, OH, 44035
(216) 322-2525
Admin Abraham Schwartz. *Medical Dir/Dir of Nursing* June H Cole RN.
Licensure Intermediate care. *Beds* ICF 50. *Certified* Medicaid.
Owner Proprietary Corp.
Staff RNs 1 (pt); LPNs 7 (pt); Nurses aides 18 (pt); Recreational therapists 1 (pt); Activities coordinators 1 (pt).

ENGLEWOOD

Englewood Manor Nursing Home
20 Union Blvd, Englewood, OH, 45322
(513) 836-5143
Admin James A Lauricella Sr. *Medical Dir/Dir of Nursing* Dr W C Clark Jr; Geneva Brunk RN DON.
Licensure Skilled care; Intermediate care. *Beds* 80. *Certified* Medicaid; Medicare.
Owner Proprietary Corp.
Admissions Requirements Medical examination.
Staff RNs 2 (ft), 4 (pt); LPNs 8 (ft), 2 (pt); Nurses aides 37 (ft); Physical therapists 1 (pt); Activities coordinators 2 (ft); Dietitians 1 (pt); Ophthalmologists 1 (pt).
Languages Italian
Facilities Dining room; Physical therapy room; Activities room; Crafts room; Laundry room; Barber/Beauty shop; Library.
Activities Arts & crafts; Cards; Games; Reading groups; Prayer groups; Movies; Shopping trips; Social/Cultural gatherings; Fishing trips; Picnics.

Grace Brethren Village
1010 Taywood Rd, Englewood, OH, 45322
(513) 836-4011
Admin Joseph Lefkoritz. *Medical Dir/Dir of Nursing* Pam Jones.
Licensure Intermediate care. *Beds* ICF 50. *Certified* Medicare.
Owner Nonprofit Corp.
Admissions Requirements Minimum age 60; Medical examination.
Staff LPNs 8 (ft); Nurses aides 14 (ft), 3 (pt); Physical therapists 1 (pt); Activities coordinators 1 (pt).
Facilities Dining room; Activities room; Chapel; Crafts room; Barber/Beauty shop; Library.
Activities Arts & crafts; Cards; Games; Prayer groups; Movies; Social/Cultural gatherings.

EUCLID

Cuy-La Home
1691 Hillandale Dr, Euclid, OH, 44132
(216) 731-2690
Licensure Intermediate care. *Beds* 30. *Certified* Medicaid.
Owner Proprietary Corp.

Mt St Joseph*
21800 Chardon Rd, Euclid, OH, 44117

Licensure Skilled care; Intermediate care. *Beds* 100. *Certified* Medicaid; Medicare. *Owner* Nonprofit Corp.

Park Rehabilitation Center*
20611 Euclid Ave, Euclid, OH, 44117
(216) 486-9300
Licensure Skilled care; Intermediate care. *Beds* 237. *Certified* Medicaid; Medicare.
Owner Proprietary Corp.

Rose-Mary, The Grasselli Rehabilitation & Education Center*
19350 Euclid Ave, Euclid, OH, 44117
Licensure Intermediate care for mentally retarded. *Beds* 40. *Certified* Medicaid.
Owner Nonprofit Corp.

FAIRBORN

Christel Manor Nursing Home*
789 Stoneybrook Trail, Fairborn, OH, 45324
(513) 878-0262
Licensure Intermediate care. *Beds* 100. *Certified* Medicaid.
Owner Proprietary Corp.

Heritage Inn Nursing Home
201 W Dayton Dr, Fairborn, OH, 45324
(513) 878-6153
Licensure Intermediate care. *Beds* 34. *Certified* Medicaid.
Owner Proprietary Corp.

FAIRFIELD

Community Multicare Center*
908 Symmes Rd, Fairfield, OH, 45014
(513) 868-6500
Medical Dir/Dir of Nursing Kurt Landel MD.
Licensure Skilled care; Intermediate care. *Beds* 101. *Certified* Medicaid; Medicare.
Owner Proprietary Corp.
Staff Physicians 1 (pt); Physical therapists 1 (ft), 1 (pt); Occupational therapists 2 (pt); Speech therapists 1 (pt); Activities coordinators 1 (ft); Dietitians 1 (ft).
Facilities Dining room; Physical therapy room; Activities room; Laundry room; Barber/Beauty shop.
Activities Arts & crafts; Cards; Games; Reading groups; Prayer groups; Movies; Shopping trips; Social/Cultural gatherings.

Crestwood Care Center Inc
6200 Pleasant Ave, Fairfield, OH, 45014
(513) 829-5349
Admin Mildred P Wilson, Sr Mary Antonita. *Medical Dir/Dir of Nursing* Howard Hunter MD; Verna Eilers RN.
Licensure Skilled care; Intermediate care. *Beds* 60. *Certified* Medicaid; Medicare.
Owner Privately owned.
Admissions Requirements Minimum age 50; Physician's request.
Staff Physicians 6 (pt); RNs 3 (ft), 2 (pt); LPNs 7 (ft), 1 (pt); Nurses aides 17 (ft), 2 (pt); Activities coordinators 1 (ft), 1 (pt); Dietitians 1 (pt).
Facilities Dining room; Activities room; Barber/Beauty shop; Library.
Activities Arts & crafts; Cards; Games; Reading groups; Prayer groups; Movies; Shopping trips; Social/Cultural gatherings; Dine-out; Bingo; Yard sales; Charity fairs.

Tri-County Extended Care Center
5200 Camelot Dr, Fairfield, OH, 45014
(513) 839-8100
Admin Barry A Kohn. *Medical Dir/Dir of Nursing* Elmer Wahl MD; Mary Morris RN DON.
Licensure Skilled care; Intermediate care. *Beds* SNF 217; ICF 258. *Certified* Medicaid; Medicare.
Owner Proprietary Corp.
Admissions Requirements Medical examination.

Staff RNs 9 (ft), 4 (pt); LPNs 33 (ft), 5 (pt); Orderlies 2 (pt); Nurses aides 130 (ft), 4 (pt); Physical therapists 1 (ft); Recreational therapists 3 (ft); Occupational therapists 1 (pt); Speech therapists 1 (pt); Activities coordinators 1 (ft); Dietitians 1 (pt); Dentists 1 (pt); Ophthalmologists 1 (pt); Podiatrists 1 (pt).
Facilities Dining room; Physical therapy room; Activities room; Chapel; Crafts room; Laundry room; Barber/Beauty shop.
Activities Arts & crafts; Cards; Games; Reading groups; Prayer groups; Movies; Social/Cultural gatherings.

FAIRLAWN

Fairlawn Chateau*
200 Wyant Rd, Fairlawn, OH, 44313
(216) 836-7953
Medical Dir/Dir of Nursing Robert Norman MD.
Licensure Intermediate care. *Beds* 200. *Certified* Medicaid.
Owner Proprietary Corp.
Admissions Requirements Medical examination.
Staff Physicians 20 (ft); RNs 5 (ft), 3 (pt); LPNs 18 (ft), 5 (pt); Orderlies 10 (ft); Nurses aides 34 (ft), 10 (pt); Activities coordinators 1 (ft), 1 (pt); Dietitians 1 (ft); Social workers 1 (ft).
Facilities Dining room; Physical therapy room; Activities room; Chapel; Crafts room; Laundry room; Barber/Beauty shop.
Activities Arts & crafts; Cards; Games; Reading groups; Prayer groups; Movies; Shopping trips; Social/Cultural gatherings.

FELICITY

Longworth Manor
305 W Main St, Felicity, OH, 45120
(513) 876-3261, 876-3360
Admin Sharon Arnett. *Medical Dir/Dir of Nursing* Blair Chick MD; Helen Seal DON.
Licensure Intermediate care for mentally retarded. *Beds* ICF/MR 30. *Certified* Medicaid.
Owner Proprietary Corp.
Admissions Requirements Minimum age 18.
Staff Physicians 1 (pt); RNs 1 (ft); LPNs 3 (ft), 3 (pt); Nurses aides 9 (ft), 14 (pt); Physical therapists 1 (pt); Occupational therapists 1 (pt); Speech therapists 1 (pt); Activities coordinators 1 (ft); Dietitians 1 (pt); Dentists 1 (pt); Ophthalmologists 1 (pt); Podiatrists 1 (pt).
Facilities Dining room; Activities room; Crafts room; Laundry room.
Activities Arts & crafts; Cards; Games; Movies; Shopping trips; Social/Cultural gatherings.

FINDLAY

Fox Run Manor
2101 Greendale Blvd, Findlay, OH, 45840
(419) 424-0832
Admin Phil Crawford. *Medical Dir/Dir of Nursing* Dr B A Mick; Donna Ewing.
Licensure Skilled care; Intermediate care. *Beds* SNF 100; ICF. *Certified* Medicaid; Medicare.
Owner Proprietary Corp (Health Care Facilities Inc).
Admissions Requirements Minimum age 12; Medical examination; Physician's request.
Staff RNs 7 (ft), 1 (pt); LPNs 7 (ft), 4 (pt); Orderlies 2 (ft); Nurses aides 30 (ft), 20 (pt); Activities coordinators 1 (ft), 1 (pt); Dietitians 1 (ft).
Facilities Dining room; Physical therapy room; Activities room; Crafts room; Laundry room; Barber/Beauty shop; Library; TV room.

Activities Arts & crafts; Cards; Games; Reading groups; Prayer groups; Movies; Shopping trips; Social/Cultural gatherings.

The Heritage
2820 Green Acre Dr, Findlay, OH, 45840
(419) 424-1808
Admin L Don Manley. *Medical Dir/Dir of Nursing* William Kose; Susan Hackworth.
Licensure Skilled care. *Beds* SNF 150. *Certified* Medicaid; Medicare.
Owner Proprietary Corp.
Staff RNs 7 (ft); LPNs 6 (ft); Nurses aides 30 (ft), 17 (pt); Physical therapists 1 (ft); Reality therapists 1 (ft); Recreational therapists 2 (ft); Occupational therapists 1 (pt); Speech therapists 1 (pt); Activities coordinators 2 (ft); Dietitians 1 (pt).
Facilities Dining room; Physical therapy room; Activities room; Barber/Beauty shop.
Activities Arts & crafts; Cards; Games; Reading groups; Prayer groups; Movies; Shopping trips; Social/Cultural gatherings.

Judson Palmer Home
PO Box 119, Findlay, OH, 45840
(419) 422-9599
Admin Lester B Moss. *Medical Dir/Dir of Nursing* Dr T Shoupe.
Licensure Rest home. *Beds* 18.
Owner Nonprofit Corp.
Admissions Requirements Minimum age 55; Medical examination.
Staff Physicians 1 (pt); RNs 1 (ft); Nurses aides 4 (ft), 7 (pt); Dietitians 2 (pt).
Facilities Dining room; Laundry room; Barber/Beauty shop.
Activities Cards; Prayer groups.

Manley's Manor Nursing Home Inc*
1918 N Main St, Findlay, OH, 45840
Licensure Nursing home. *Beds* 50.
Owner Proprietary Corp.

Marlesta 1
401 Infirmary Rd, Findlay, OH, 45840
(419) 423-9183
Admin Gail Fisher. *Medical Dir/Dir of Nursing* Drs Blake, Elderbrock, Miller; Jill Combs.
Licensure Intermediate care. *Beds* ICF 40. *Certified* Medicaid.
Owner Proprietary Corp.
Admissions Requirements Medical examination.
Staff RNs 1 (pt); LPNs 4 (ft), 2 (pt); Nurses aides 13 (ft), 3 (pt); Activities coordinators 1 (ft).
Facilities Dining room; Activities room; Laundry room.
Activities Arts & crafts; Cards; Games; Reading groups; Prayer groups; Movies; Social/Cultural gatherings.

Marlesta 2
401 Infirmary Rd, Findlay, OH, 45840
(419) 422-3978
Admin Gail Fisher. *Medical Dir/Dir of Nursing* Drs Blake, Elderbrock, Miller; Diane Radabaugh.
Licensure Intermediate care. *Beds* ICF 60. *Certified* Medicaid.
Owner Proprietary Corp.
Admissions Requirements Medical examination.
Staff RNs 1 (pt); LPNs 4 (ft), 4 (pt); Nurses aides 13 (ft), 3 (pt); Activities coordinators 1 (ft).
Facilities Dining room; Activities room; Laundry room; Barber/Beauty shop; Examination room.
Activities Arts & crafts; Cards; Games; Reading groups; Prayer groups; Movies; Social/Cultural gatherings.

Winebrenner Extended Care Facility*
425 Frazer St, Findlay, OH, 45840
(419) 424-9591

Medical Dir/Dir of Nursing C L Samuelson
MD.
Licensure Intermediate care. *Beds* 150.
Certified Medicaid.
Owner Nonprofit Corp.
Admissions Requirements Medical
examination.
Staff Physicians 1 (pt); RNs 4 (ft), 6 (pt);
LPNs 9 (ft), 6 (pt); Physical therapists 1 (pt);
Activities coordinators 2 (ft); Dietitians 1
(ft).
Affiliation Church of God
Facilities Dining room; Chapel; Laundry
room; Barber/Beauty shop; Solarium; Gift
shop.
Activities Arts & crafts; Games; Reading
groups; Prayer groups; Movies; Shopping
trips.

Winebrenner Haven*
425 Frazer St, Findlay, OH, 45840
(419) 422-2773
Medical Dir/Dir of Nursing C L Samuelson
MD.
Licensure Intermediate care. *Beds* 24.
Certified Medicaid.
Owner Nonprofit Corp.
Admissions Requirements Medical
examination.
Staff Physicians 1 (pt); LPNs 3 (ft), 2 (pt);
Nurses aides 2 (pt); Activities coordinators 1
(ft).
Affiliation Church of God
Facilities Dining room; Activities room;
Chapel; Laundry room; Barber/Beauty shop;
Library.
Activities Arts & crafts; Cards; Games;
Reading groups; Prayer groups; Movies;
Shopping trips.

FLAT ROCK

Flat Rock Care Center
PO Box 1, Flat Rock, OH, 44828
(419) 483-7330
Admin Donald C Bable. *Medical Dir/Dir of
Nursing* Jeanine Purdum RN DON.
Licensure Intermediate care for mentally
retarded. *Beds* ICF/MR 34. *Certified*
Medicaid.
Owner Nonprofit Corp.
Admissions Requirements Minimum age 6;
Medical examination; Physician's request.
Staff Physicians 1 (pt); RNs 1 (ft); LPNs 2
(ft), 1 (pt); Nurses aides 30 (ft); Physical
therapists 1 (pt); Recreational therapists 1
(ft); Occupational therapists 2 (pt); Speech
therapists 1 (pt); Activities coordinators 1
(ft); Dietitians 1 (pt).
Affiliation Methodist
Facilities Dining room; Physical therapy
room; Activities room; Chapel; Crafts room;
Laundry room.

FLUSHING

Hillview Nursing Home*
E High St, Box 33, Flushing, OH, 43977
(614) 968-3113
Medical Dir/Dir of Nursing Dr Modi.
Licensure Intermediate care. *Beds* 23.
Certified Medicaid.
Owner Proprietary Corp.
Admissions Requirements Medical
examination.
Staff Physicians 1 (ft); RNs 1 (ft); LPNs 2 (ft),
3 (pt); Nurses aides 4 (ft), 4 (pt); Dietitians 1
(pt).
Facilities Dining room; Laundry room.
Activities Arts & crafts; Cards; Games; Prayer
groups.

FOSTORIA

Edgewood Manor of Fostoria Inc
25 Christopher Dr, Fostoria, OH, 44830
(419) 435-8112
Admin Robert A Groh. *Medical Dir/Dir of
Nursing* Dr R Gibbs; Jo Ann Goddard RN.
Licensure Skilled care; Intermediate care; Rest
home. *Beds* 102. *Certified* Medicaid;
Medicare.
Owner Proprietary Corp (Cloverleaf
Enterprises).
Admissions Requirements Medical
examination; Physician's request.
Staff RNs; LPNs; Orderlies; Nurses aides;
Activities coordinators.
Facilities Dining room; Activities room;
Crafts room; Laundry room; Barber/Beauty
shop; Lounge.
Activities Arts & crafts; Cards; Games;
Reading groups; Prayer groups; Movies;
Shopping trips; Social/Cultural gatherings;
Community entertainment.

Good Shepherd Home*
725 Columbus Ave, PO Box G, Fostoria, OH,
44830
(419) 435-1801
Licensure Intermediate care. *Beds* 100.
Certified Medicaid.
Owner Nonprofit Corp.
Admissions Requirements Medical
examination.
Staff RNs 3 (ft), 2 (pt); LPNs 10 (ft), 3 (pt);
Orderlies 3 (ft), 3 (pt); Nurses aides 38 (ft),
17 (pt); Physical therapists 1 (pt);
Recreational therapists 2 (ft); Speech
therapists 1 (pt); Activities coordinators 1
(ft).
Affiliation Church of the Brethren

FOWLER

Meadowbrook Manor of Hartford
3090 Five Pts-Hartford Rd, Fowler, OH,
44418
(216) 772-5253
Admin John Patrick. *Medical Dir/Dir of
Nursing* Laurie Horig.
Licensure Intermediate care. *Beds* ICF 54.
Certified Medicaid.
Owner Privately owned.
Admissions Requirements Physician's request.
Staff RNs 4 (ft); LPNs 3 (ft), 6 (pt); Nurses
aides 15 (ft), 10 (pt).
Facilities Dining room; Activities room;
Laundry room; Barber/Beauty shop.
Activities Arts & crafts; Cards; Games;
Reading groups; Prayer groups; Movies;
Shopping trips; Social/Cultural gatherings.

FRANKFORT

Valley View Manor*
3363 Ragged Ridge Rd, Frankfort, OH, 45628
(614) 998-2948
Medical Dir/Dir of Nursing Dr Patrick J
McKibben.
Licensure Intermediate care. *Beds* 44.
Certified Medicaid.
Owner Proprietary Corp.
Admissions Requirements Medical
examination.
Staff Physicians 2 (ft); RNs 1 (ft); LPNs 3 (ft),
2 (pt); Nurses aides 2 (ft), 7 (pt); Activities
coordinators 2 (ft); Dietitians 1 (pt).
Facilities Dining room; Activities room;
Crafts room; Laundry room; Barber/Beauty
shop; Library.
Activities Arts & crafts; Cards; Games;
Movies; Shopping trips.

FRANKLIN

Carlisle Manor
730 Hillcrest Ave, Franklin, OH, 45005
(513) 746-2662
Admin Terri L Dickey. *Medical Dir/Dir of
Nursing* Scott Zollett MD.
Licensure Intermediate care. *Beds* 48.
Certified Medicaid.
Owner Proprietary Corp.
Staff Physicians 4 (ft); RNs 3 (ft); LPNs 5 (ft);
Nurses aides 9 (ft), 2 (pt); Physical therapists
1 (pt); Occupational therapists 1 (pt);
Activities coordinators 1 (ft); Dietitians 1
(pt); Dentists 1 (pt); Ophthalmologists 1 (pt);
Podiatrists 1 (pt).
Facilities Dining room; Activities room;
Laundry room.
Activities Arts & crafts; Cards; Games;
Reading groups; Prayer groups; Movies;
Shopping trips; Social/Cultural gatherings.

Franklin Nursing Home of Franklin
422 Mission Lane, Franklin, OH, 45005
(513) 746-3943
Admin Mildred R Gilliam. *Medical Dir/Dir of
Nursing* Scott Swope DO; Norma Glosser
RN DON.
Licensure Skilled care; Intermediate care. *Beds*
SNF 99; ICF. *Certified* Medicaid; Medicare.
Owner Proprietary Corp.
Admissions Requirements Minimum age 18;
Medical examination.
Staff Physicians 2 (ft), 3 (pt); RNs 4 (ft), 1
(pt); LPNs 10 (ft), 4 (pt); Nurses aides 39
(ft), 4 (pt); Physical therapists 1 (pt);
Occupational therapists 1 (pt); Speech
therapists 1 (pt); Activities coordinators 2
(ft); Dietitians 1 (pt); Dentists 1 (pt);
Ophthalmologists 1 (pt); Podiatrists 1 (pt);
Social worker 1 (ft) Dentist 1 (pt).
Facilities Dining room; Physical therapy
room; Activities room; Laundry room;
Barber/Beauty shop; Patient lounges; Formal
living room.
Activities Arts & crafts; Cards; Games;
Reading groups; Prayer groups; Movies;
Shopping trips; Social/Cultural gatherings.

Zartman Nursing Home*
120 S Main St, Franklin, OH, 45005
(513) 746-9588
Licensure Nursing home. *Beds* 10.
Owner Nonprofit Corp.

FRANKLIN FURNACE

Fountainhead Nursing Home*
PO Box 36, Old Rte 52, Franklin Furnace,
OH, 45629
(614) 574-6200
Licensure Intermediate care. *Beds* 30.
Certified Medicaid.
Owner Proprietary Corp.

FREDERICKTOWN

Hillcrest Nursing Center Inc
1765 Paintes Rd, Fredericktown, OH, 43019
(419) 886-3931
Admin Doan Levering. *Medical Dir/Dir of
Nursing* Linda Lamson.
Licensure Skilled care; Intermediate care. *Beds*
50. *Certified* Medicaid; Medicare.
Owner Proprietary Corp.
Admissions Requirements Medical
examination.
Staff Physicians; RNs; LPNs; Nurses aides;
Physical therapists; Recreational therapists;
Occupational therapists; Speech therapists;
Activities coordinators; Dietitians.
Facilities Dining room; Activities room;
Crafts room; Laundry room; Barber/Beauty
shop; Whirlpool room.
Activities Arts & crafts; Cards; Games;
Reading groups; Prayer groups; Movies;
Volleyball.

FREMONT

Bethesda Care Center
600 N Brush St, Fremont, OH, 43420
(419) 334-9521
Admin Mr H L Dunn. *Medical Dir/Dir of
Nursing* Dr Daniel Kelderhouse; Mrs Eileen
Gill DON.
Licensure Skilled care; Intermediate care. *Beds*
108. *Certified* Medicaid; Medicare.
Owner Nonprofit Corp (Volunteers of
America Care).
Staff Physicians; RNs; LPNs; Nurses aides;
Physical therapists; Occupational therapists;
Speech therapists; Activities coordinators;
Dietitians; Dentists; Ophthalmologists.
Facilities Dining room; Physical therapy
room; Activities room; Chapel; Laundry
room; Barber/Beauty shop; Library.
Activities Arts & crafts; Cards; Games;
Reading groups; Prayer groups; Movies;
Social/Cultural gatherings.

Countryside Continuing Care Center
1865 Countryside Dr, Fremont, OH, 43420
(419) 334-2602
Admin Gregory T Storer. *Medical Dir/Dir of
Nursing* Michael J Hazlett MD.
Licensure Skilled care; Intermediate care. *Beds*
119. *Certified* Medicaid; Medicare.
Owner Publicly owned.
Admissions Requirements Medical
examination; Physician's request.
Staff Physicians 1 (pt); RNs 3 (ft), 4 (pt);
LPNs 8 (ft), 4 (pt); Nurses aides 31 (ft), 31
(pt); Physical therapists 1 (pt); Occupational
therapists 1 (pt); Speech therapists 1 (ft), 1
(pt); Dietitians 1 (pt); Dentists 1 (pt);
Ophthalmologists 1 (pt); Dentist 1 (pt).
Facilities Dining room; Physical therapy
room; Activities room; Chapel; Crafts room;
Laundry room; Barber/Beauty shop.
Activities Arts & crafts; Cards; Games; Prayer
groups; Movies; Shopping trips; Social/
Cultural gatherings.

Parkview Care Center
PO Box 1108, 1406 Oak Harbor Rd, Fremont,
OH, 43420
(419) 332-2589
Admin James L Oedy. *Medical Dir/Dir of
Nursing* Dr Sam Lowery; Martha McCoy.
Licensure Intermediate care. *Beds* ICF 50.
Certified Medicaid.
Owner Proprietary Corp.
Admissions Requirements Minimum age 65;
Medical examination.
Staff Physicians 1 (pt); RNs 1 (pt); LPNs 6
(ft), 1 (pt); Nurses aides 23 (ft), 10 (pt);
Physical therapists 1 (pt); Reality therapists
1 (pt); Recreational therapists 1 (pt);
Occupational therapists 1 (pt); Activities
coordinators 1 (ft); Dietitians 1 (pt);
Ophthalmologists 1 (pt).
Facilities Dining room; Physical therapy
room; Activities room; Chapel; Crafts room;
Laundry room; Barber/Beauty shop; Library;
3 lounges; Reading rooms.
Activities Arts & crafts; Cards; Games;
Reading groups; Prayer groups; Movies;
Shopping trips; Social/Cultural gatherings.

Quality Care Nursing Facility
825 June St, Fremont, OH, 43420
(419) 332-0103
Admin Dale Cuthbertson. *Medical Dir/Dir of
Nursing* Dr Daniel Kelderhouse; Peggy
Snyder RN.
Licensure Intermediate care. *Beds* ICF 100.
Certified Medicaid.
Owner Proprietary Corp (Northwestern
Service Corp).
Admissions Requirements Medical
examination.
Staff Physicians 2 (pt); RNs 1 (ft), 3 (pt);
LPNs 6 (ft), 5 (pt); Orderlies 1 (ft); Nurses
aides 24 (ft), 17 (pt); Activities coordinators
1 (ft), 2 (pt); Dietitians 1 (pt).

Languages Spanish
Facilities Dining room; Activities room;
Laundry room; Barber/Beauty shop; New
wheelchair van.
Activities Arts & crafts; Cards; Games.

FULTON

Morning View Care Center 2
PO Box 38, 101 W Main St, Fulton, OH,
43321
(419) 864-6941
Admin Jane Smith. *Medical Dir/Dir of
Nursing* Dr Hickson; Charlotte Stember
DON.
Licensure Intermediate care; Intermediate care
for mentally retarded. *Beds* ICF 34; ICF/MR
31. *Certified* Medicaid.
Owner Proprietary Corp (Morning View Care
Center).
Admissions Requirements Medical
examination; Physician's request.
Staff Physicians 1 (pt); RNs 1 (pt); LPNs 9
(ft); Orderlies 2 (ft); Nurses aides 28 (ft), 8
(pt); Physical therapists 2 (pt); Reality
therapists 4 (pt); Recreational therapists 1
(pt); Occupational therapists 4 (pt); Speech
therapists 1 (pt); Activities coordinators 2
(ft); Dietitians 1 (pt); Ophthalmologists 1
(pt); Podiatrists 2 (pt); Social service 1 (ft).
Facilities Dining room; Physical therapy
room; Activities room; Crafts room; Laundry
room; Barber/Beauty shop; Library.
Activities Arts & crafts; Cards; Games;
Reading groups; Prayer groups; Movies;
Shopping trips; Social/Cultural gatherings.

Morning View Care Center 2 Annex
PO Box 38, 101 W Main St, Fulton, OH,
43321
(419) 864-6941
Admin Jane Smith. *Medical Dir/Dir of
Nursing* Dr Hickson; Charlotte Stember
DON.
Licensure Intermediate care; Intermediate care
for mentally retarded. *Beds* ICF 34; ICF/MR
31. *Certified* Medicaid.
Owner Proprietary Corp.
Admissions Requirements Medical
examination; Physician's request.
Staff Physicians 1 (pt); RNs 1 (pt); LPNs 9
(ft); Orderlies 2 (ft); Nurses aides 28 (ft), 8
(pt); Physical therapists 2 (pt); Reality
therapists 4 (pt); Recreational therapists 1
(pt); Occupational therapists 4 (pt); Speech
therapists 1 (pt); Activities coordinators 2
(ft); Dietitians 1 (pt); Ophthalmologists 1
(pt); Podiatrists 2 (pt); Social service 1 (ft).
Facilities Dining room; Physical therapy
room; Activities room; Crafts room; Laundry
room; Barber/Beauty shop; Library.
Activities Arts & crafts; Cards; Games;
Reading groups; Prayer groups; Movies;
Shopping trips; Social/Cultural gatherings.

FURNACE

New Dawn Convalescent Center
PO Box 36, Furnace, OH, 45505
(513) 324-5709 & 324-5700
Medical Dir/Dir of Nursing Dr Kneisley.
Licensure Intermediate care. *Beds* 21.
Certified Medicaid.
Owner Nonprofit Corp.
Admissions Requirements Females only.
Staff RNs 1 (pt); LPNs 4 (ft); Nurses aides 10
(ft); Activities coordinators 1 (ft).
Affiliation Swedenborgian

GAHANNA

Bon-Ing Care Center
121 James Rd, Gahanna, OH, 43230
(614) 475-7222
Admin Jennie E Ingram. *Medical Dir/Dir of
Nursing* Vera Leonard RN.

Licensure Intermediate care. *Beds* 100.
Certified Medicaid.
Owner Proprietary Corp.
Staff RNs 3 (ft), 2 (pt); LPNs 3 (ft), 3 (pt);
Orderlies 4 (ft); Nurses aides 19 (ft), 1 (pt);
Activities coordinators 1 (ft); Dietitians 1
(pt).
Facilities Dining room; Physical therapy
room; Activities room; Laundry room;
Barber/Beauty shop.
Activities Arts & crafts; Games; Prayer groups;
Movies; Shopping trips; Social/Cultural
gatherings.

GALION

Atwood Manor
347 W Atwood St, Galion, OH, 44833
(419) 468-1893
Admin Susan K Rodabaugh. *Medical Dir/Dir
of Nursing* Dr Skinner; Nancy Triplett RN
DON.
Licensure Intermediate care. *Beds* ICF 50.
Certified Medicaid.
Owner Proprietary Corp.
Admissions Requirements Medical
examination.
Staff Physicians 1 (pt); RNs 1 (ft); LPNs 5
(ft), 2 (pt); Nurses aides 8 (ft), 6 (pt);
Physical therapists 1 (pt); Reality therapists
1 (pt); Recreational therapists 1 (ft);
Dietitians 1 (pt); Ophthalmologists 1 (pt).
Facilities Dining room; Activities room;
Crafts room; Laundry room; Barber/Beauty
shop; Library.
Activities Arts & crafts; Cards; Games;
Reading groups; Prayer groups; Movies;
Shopping trips; Social/Cultural gatherings.

Rosewood Manor
935 Rosewood Dr, Galion, OH, 44833
(419) 468-7544
Admin Helen J Landon. *Medical Dir/Dir of
Nursing* Dr B Mansfield; Mary Victoria
Carter.
Licensure Skilled care. *Beds* SNF 90. *Certified*
Medicaid; Medicare.
Owner Proprietary Corp.
Admissions Requirements Medical
examination; Physician's request.
Staff Physicians 1 (ft); RNs 9 (ft), 4 (pt);
LPNs 5 (ft), 3 (pt); Nurses aides 37 (ft), 14
(pt); Physical therapists 1 (pt); Reality
therapists 1 (pt); Recreational therapists 1
(ft), 1 (pt); Occupational therapists 1 (pt);
Speech therapists 1 (pt); Activities
coordinators 1 (ft), 1 (pt); Dietitians 1 (pt);
Dentists 1 (pt); Ophthalmologists 1 (pt);
Dentist 1 (pt).
Facilities Dining room; Physical therapy
room; Activities room; Chapel; Crafts room;
Laundry room; Barber/Beauty shop; Library.
Activities Arts & crafts; Cards; Games;
Reading groups; Prayer groups; Movies;
Shopping trips; Social/Cultural gatherings.

Village Care Center*
925 Wagner Ave, Galion, OH, 44833
(419) 468-1090
Admin Helen J Lundon. *Medical Dir/Dir of
Nursing* Dr William Mantley & Dr Warren
Sawyer.
Licensure Skilled care; Intermediate care. *Beds*
58. *Certified* Medicaid; Medicare.
Owner Nonprofit Corp.
Admissions Requirements Medical
examination.
Staff Physicians 2 (pt); RNs 8 (ft), 4 (pt);
LPNs 3 (ft), 9 (pt); Nurses aides 11 (ft), 22
(pt); Physical therapists 1 (pt); Reality
therapists 1 (pt); Recreational therapists 1
(pt); Occupational therapists 1 (pt); Speech
therapists 1 (pt); Activities coordinators 1
(ft), 1 (pt); Dietitians 1 (ft), 1 (pt); Dentists 1
(pt); Ophthalmologists 1 (pt); Podiatrists 1
(pt); Audiologists 1 (pt).

Facilities Dining room; Physical therapy room; Activities room; Crafts room; Laundry room; Barber/Beauty shop; Library; Greenhouse.
Activities Arts & crafts; Cards; Games; Reading groups; Prayer groups; Movies; Shopping trips; Social/Cultural gatherings.

GALLIPOLIS

Alternative Residence Two Inc—Middleton Estates*
Rte 1, Gallipolis, OH, 45631
Licensure Intermediate care for mentally retarded. *Beds* 32. *Certified* Medicaid.
Owner Nonprofit Corp.

Buckeye Community Services—Transitional Facility*
PO Box 906, Gallipolis, OH, 45631
Licensure Intermediate care for mentally retarded. *Beds* 8. *Certified* Medicaid.
Owner Nonprofit Corp.

Gallipolis State Institute*
2500 Ohio Ave, Gallipolis, OH, 45631
(614) 446-1642
Licensure Intermediate care for mentally retarded. *Beds* 320.
Owner Publicly owned.

Pinecrest Care Center*
555 Jackson Pike, Gallipolis, OH, 45631
(614) 446-7112
Medical Dir/Dir of Nursing Dr Balusamy Subbiah.
Licensure Skilled care; Intermediate care. *Beds* 116. *Certified* Medicaid; Medicare.
Owner Proprietary Corp.
Admissions Requirements Physician's request.
Facilities Dining room; Physical therapy room; Activities room; Laundry room; Barber/Beauty shop.
Activities Arts & crafts; Games; Reading groups; Prayer groups; Movies; Shopping trips.

GARFIELD HEIGHTS

Jennings Hall Inc
10204 Granger Rd, Garfield Heights, OH, 44125
(216) 581-2900
Admin Sr Mary Loretta. *Medical Dir/Dir of Nursing* Dr Sylvia Marshall.
Licensure Intermediate care. *Beds* ICF 100. *Certified* Medicaid.
Owner Nonprofit Corp.
Admissions Requirements Minimum age 65; Medical examination.
Staff Physicians 5 (ft); RNs 7 (ft); LPNs 11 (ft); Nurses aides 40 (ft); Physical therapists 5 (ft); Recreational therapists 1 (ft); Activities coordinators 1 (ft); Dietitians 1 (ft); Dentists 1 (ft); Ophthalmologists 1 (ft).
Affiliation Roman Catholic
Facilities Dining room; Physical therapy room; Activities room; Chapel; Crafts room; Laundry room; Barber/Beauty shop.
Activities Arts & crafts; Cards; Games; Reading groups; Prayer groups; Movies; Shopping trips; Social/Cultural gatherings.

GENEVA

Broadway Nursing Home
162 S Broadway, Geneva, OH, 44041
(216) 466-4843
Admin Bruce M Radman. *Medical Dir/Dir of Nursing* Dr Kavur; Pat Creighton RN DON.
Licensure Intermediate care. *Beds* ICF 85. *Certified* Medicaid.
Owner Proprietary Corp.
Admissions Requirements Minimum age 18; Medical examination.

Staff RNs 2 (ft), 2 (pt); LPNs 6 (ft), 4 (pt); Orderlies 1 (ft), 2 (pt); Nurses aides 15 (ft), 10 (pt); Activities coordinators 2 (ft).
Facilities Dining room; Activities room; Crafts room; Laundry room; Barber/Beauty shop.
Activities Arts & crafts; Cards; Games; Reading groups; Prayer groups; Movies; Shopping trips; Social/Cultural gatherings.

Catherine Ellen Convalescent Home*
750 Eastlawn Ave, Geneva, OH, 44041
(216) 466-3942
Medical Dir/Dir of Nursing Miroslav Kavur DO.
Licensure Intermediate care. *Beds* 16. *Certified* Medicaid.
Owner Proprietary Corp.
Admissions Requirements Minimum age 25; Medical examination; Physician's request.
Staff RNs 1 (pt); LPNs 4 (ft), 1 (pt); Nurses aides 8 (ft); Activities coordinators 1 (ft).
Facilities Dining room; Laundry room.
Activities Arts & crafts; Cards; Games; Prayer groups; Shopping trips.

Con Lea Nursing Home
388 S Broadway, Geneva, OH, 44041
(216) 466-3512
Admin Paul Wadowick LSW NHA. *Medical Dir/Dir of Nursing* Carol Saylor RN DON.
Licensure Intermediate care. *Beds* ICF 42. *Certified* Medicaid.
Owner Proprietary Corp.
Admissions Requirements Females only; Medical examination.
Staff RNs 1 (ft), 1 (pt); LPNs 2 (ft), 4 (pt); Nurses aides 11 (ft), 4 (pt); Activities coordinators 1 (ft).
Facilities Dining room.
Activities Arts & crafts; Cards; Games; Reading groups; Prayer groups; Movies; Shopping trips; Social/Cultural gatherings.

Esther Marie Nursing Center*
60 West St, Geneva, OH, 44041
(216) 466-1181
Licensure Intermediate care. *Beds* 53. *Certified* Medicaid.
Owner Proprietary Corp.

Geneva Health Care
840 Sherman St, Geneva, OH, 44004
(216) 466-4881
Admin Donna Colvui. *Medical Dir/Dir of Nursing* Cheng-Nan Huang MD; M Kerestman RN.
Licensure Skilled care; Intermediate care. *Beds* 106. *Certified* Medicaid; Medicare.
Owner Proprietary Corp.
Admissions Requirements Minimum age 16; Medical examination; Physician's request.
Staff RNs; LPNs; Orderlies; Nurses aides; Physical therapists; Speech therapists; Activities coordinators; Dietitians; Ophthalmologists.
Facilities Dining room; Physical therapy room; Activities room; Crafts room; Laundry room; Barber/Beauty shop.
Activities Arts & crafts; Cards; Games; Reading groups; Prayer groups; Movies; Shopping trips; Social/Cultural gatherings.

Homestead Nursing Home*
599 W Main St, Geneva, OH, 44041
(216) 466-1079
Licensure Intermediate care for mentally retarded. *Beds* 50. *Certified* Medicaid.
Owner Proprietary Corp.

Lakeland Nursing Home
PO Box 271, 3142 So Coty Line Rd, Geneva, OH, 44041
(216) 466-1678
Admin James F Clark. *Medical Dir/Dir of Nursing* John Popovick MD.
Licensure Intermediate care for mentally retarded. *Beds* ICF/MR 25. *Certified* Medicaid.

Owner Proprietary Corp.
Admissions Requirements Minimum age 18; Females only; Medical examination.
Staff Physicians 1 (pt); RNs 1 (ft); LPNs 3 (ft), 1 (pt); Nurses aides 10 (ft), 3 (pt); Occupational therapists 1 (pt); Activities coordinators 1 (ft), 1 (pt); Dietitians 1 (pt).
Facilities Dining room; Activities room; Crafts room; Laundry room.
Activities Arts & crafts; Cards; Games; Reading groups; Prayer groups; Movies; Shopping trips; Social/Cultural gatherings.

Manor Home Management Inc
PO Box 640, 246 N Broadway, Geneva, OH, 44041
(216) 466-1808
Admin Gary A Toth. *Medical Dir/Dir of Nursing* Ron Newsome.
Licensure Intermediate care for mentally retarded. *Beds* ICF/MR 54. *Certified* Medicaid.
Owner Privately owned.
Admissions Requirements Minimum age 18; Males only.
Staff RNs 1 (ft); LPNs 6 (ft), 1 (pt); Nurses aides 39 (ft), 2 (pt); Physical therapists 1 (pt); Recreational therapists 4 (pt); Occupational therapists 1 (pt); Speech therapists 1 (pt); Activities coordinators 1 (ft); Dietitians 1 (pt); Dentists 1 (pt); Ophthalmologists 1 (pt); Podiatrists 1 (pt).
Facilities Dining room; Physical therapy room; Activities room; Crafts room; Laundry room; Barber/Beauty shop; Library.
Activities Arts & crafts; Cards; Games; Reading groups; Prayer groups; Movies; Shopping trips; Social/Cultural gatherings.

Rae-Ann Geneva*
PO Box 653, 839 W Main St, Geneva, OH, 44041
(216) 466-5733
Licensure Intermediate care. *Beds* 77. *Certified* Medicaid.
Owner Proprietary Corp.

GENOA

Genoa Care Center
300 Cherry St, Genoa, OH, 43430
(419) 855-7755
Admin William J McClellan. *Medical Dir/Dir of Nursing* Dr Mark Nadaud, Dr Mitcheal Bowen DO; Jane Tank RN BSN DON.
Licensure Skilled care; Intermediate care. *Beds* SNF 100; ICF. *Certified* Medicaid; Medicare.
Owner Privately owned.
Admissions Requirements Medical examination; Physician's request.
Staff RNs; LPNs; Nurses aides; Physical therapists; Occupational therapists; Speech therapists; Activities coordinators; Dietitians.
Facilities Dining room; Physical therapy room; Activities room; Crafts room; Laundry room; Barber/Beauty shop; 2 lounges.
Activities Arts & crafts; Cards; Games; Reading groups; Prayer groups; Movies; Shopping trips; Social/Cultural gatherings.

GEORGETOWN

Georgetown Nursing Home Inc
312 W State St, Georgetown, OH, 45121
(513) 378-6616
Admin Connie Fenton. *Medical Dir/Dir of Nursing* Dr James Kaya.
Licensure Intermediate care. *Beds* ICF 33. *Certified* Medicaid.
Owner Proprietary Corp.
Admissions Requirements Medical examination.
Staff RNs 1 (pt); LPNs 3 (ft), 3 (pt); Nurses aides 10 (ft), 1 (pt); Activities coordinators 1 (ft).

Facilities Dining room; Activities room; Laundry room; Barber/Beauty shop.
Activities Arts & crafts; Cards; Games; Reading groups; Prayer groups; Movies; Shopping trips; Social/Cultural gatherings.

Meadow Wood Nursing Home Inc*
Stephens Ave, Georgetown, OH, 45121
(513) 378-3727
Admin Jack Crout. *Medical Dir/Dir of Nursing* Leslie Hampton MD.
Licensure Skilled care; Intermediate care. *Beds* 49. *Certified* Medicaid; Medicare.
Owner Proprietary Corp.
Admissions Requirements Medical examination.
Staff Physicians 6 (pt); RNs 2 (ft), 2 (pt); LPNs 4 (ft), 3 (pt); Orderlies 3 (ft), 4 (pt); Nurses aides 11 (ft), 18 (pt); Physical therapists 1 (pt); Speech therapists 1 (pt); Activities coordinators 1 (pt); Dietitians 1 (pt); Dentists 1 (pt); Podiatrists 1 (pt); Audiologists 1 (pt).
Facilities Dining room; Physical therapy room; Activities room.
Activities Arts & crafts; Cards; Games; Movies; Social/Cultural gatherings.

GLENDALE

St Mary's Memorial Home*
469 Albion Ave, Glendale, OH, 45246
(513) 771-2170
Licensure Nursing home. *Beds* 21.
Owner Nonprofit Corp.

GRAND RAPIDS

Rapids Nursing Home*
24305 3rd St, Grand Rapids, OH, 43522
(419) 832-5195
Licensure Intermediate care. *Beds* 25. *Certified* Medicaid.
Owner Proprietary Corp.
Admissions Requirements Medical examination.
Staff RNs 1 (ft), 1 (pt); LPNs 2 (ft), 2 (pt); Nurses aides 8 (ft), 2 (pt); Activities coordinators 1 (ft); Dietitians 1 (pt).
Facilities Dining room; Crafts room; Laundry room; Barber/Beauty shop.
Activities Arts & crafts; Cards; Games; Prayer groups; Movies; Shopping trips; Social/Cultural gatherings.

GREEN SPRINGS

Elmwood Nursing Home
N 430 Broadway St, Green Springs, OH, 44836
(419) 639-2581
Admin Kathy Luhring LNHA. *Medical Dir/Dir of Nursing* Douglas Smith MD; Jeanette Swartzlander DON.
Licensure Intermediate care; Intermediate care for mentally retarded. *Beds* ICF 16; ICF/MR 15. *Certified* Medicaid.
Owner Proprietary Corp.
Admissions Requirements Minimum age 18; Medical examination TB test; Physician's request.
Staff Physicians 1 (pt); RNs 1 (pt); LPNs 4 (ft), 1 (pt); Nurses aides 15 (ft), 5 (pt); Physical therapists 1 (pt); Reality therapists 2 (ft); Recreational therapists 2 (ft); Occupational therapists 1 (pt); Speech therapists 1 (pt); Activities coordinators 2 (ft); Dietitians 1 (pt); Ophthalmologists 1 (pt); Podiatrists 1 (pt); OMRP 1 (ft), 1 (pt).
Facilities Dining room; Activities room; Crafts room; Laundry room; Barber/Beauty shop; Living room.

Activities Arts & crafts; Cards; Games; Reading groups; Prayer groups; Movies; Shopping trips; Social/Cultural gatherings; Happy hour; Diners' club; Camping trips; Devotions; Sunday drives; Ice cream socials.

St Francis Rehabilitation Hospital & Nursing Home
401 N Boadway St, Green Springs, OH, 44836
(419) 639-2626
Admin Sr Michael Marie Wiesen. *Medical Dir/Dir of Nursing* Robert Gosling MD; Cathy Benninghoff RN.
Licensure Skilled care; Intermediate care; Physical Rehabilitation. *Beds* SNF 40; ICF 110; Physical Rehabilitation 36. *Certified* Medicaid; Medicare.
Owner Nonprofit Corp.
Admissions Requirements Minimum age 13; Physician's request.
Staff Physicians 29 (pt); RNs; LPNs; Orderlies; Nurses aides; Physical therapists 15 (ft); Recreational therapists 5 (ft); Occupational therapists 8 (ft); Speech therapists 3 (ft); Dietitians 2 (ft); Dentists 1 (pt); Ophthalmologists 1 (pt); Podiatrists 1 (pt); Dentist 1 (pt).
Affiliation Roman Catholic
Facilities Dining room; Physical therapy room; Activities room; Chapel; Laundry room; Barber/Beauty shop; Occupational therapy room; Cafeteria; Student dormitory; Medical building; Bus; Van; Meeting rooms; Laboratory.
Activities Arts & crafts; Cards; Games; Reading groups; Prayer groups; Movies; Shopping trips; Social/Cultural gatherings; Camping; Swimming; Fishing.

GREENFIELD

Buckingham Nursing Home*
238 S Washington St, Greenfield, OH, 45123
(513) 981-3349
Licensure Intermediate care. *Beds* 22. *Certified* Medicaid.
Owner Proprietary Corp.

Edgewood Manor
850 Nellie St, Greenfield, OH, 45123
(513) 981-2165
Admin Jerry Bland. *Medical Dir/Dir of Nursing* Dr Michele Morris; Freda Boggs DON.
Licensure Skilled care. *Beds* SNF 63. *Certified* Medicaid; Medicare.
Owner Proprietary Corp.
Admissions Requirements Medical examination; Physician's request.
Staff RNs 2 (ft); Orderlies 2 (ft); Nurses aides 20 (ft), 10 (pt); Physical therapists 1 (pt); Activities coordinators 1 (ft); Dietitians 1 (ft); Dentists 1 (pt); Ophthalmologists 1 (pt); Podiatrists 1 (pt).
Facilities Dining room; Physical therapy room; Activities room; Crafts room; Laundry room; Barber/Beauty shop; Library.
Activities Arts & crafts; Cards; Games; Reading groups; Prayer groups; Movies; Shopping trips; Social/Cultural gatherings.

GREENVILLE

The Brethren's Home
750 Chestnut St, Greenville, OH, 45331
(513) 547-8000
Admin Robert D Cain Jr. *Medical Dir/Dir of Nursing* Alvan Thuma MD.
Licensure Skilled care; Intermediate care; Independent. *Beds* SNF 160; ICF 102; Independent 250. *Certified* Medicaid; Medicare.
Owner Nonprofit Corp.
Admissions Requirements Minimum age 65; Medical examination.
Affiliation Church of the Brethren

Facilities Dining room; Physical therapy room; Activities room; Chapel; Crafts room; Laundry room; Barber/Beauty shop; Library.
Activities Arts & crafts; Cards; Games; Reading groups; Prayer groups; Movies; Shopping trips; Social/Cultural gatherings.

Gade Nursing Home Inc
405 Chestnut St, Greenville, OH, 45331
(513) 548-1993
Admin Tim Gade. *Medical Dir/Dir of Nursing* Dr Alvin Heise; Robin Haney.
Licensure Skilled care; Intermediate care. *Beds* SNF 51; ICF. *Certified* Medicaid; Medicare.
Owner Proprietary Corp.
Admissions Requirements Medical examination; Physician's request.
Staff Physicians 1 (ft), 8 (pt); RNs 1 (ft), 1 (pt); LPNs 3 (ft), 2 (pt); Nurses aides 10 (ft), 6 (pt); Physical therapists 1 (pt); Occupational therapists 1 (pt); Speech therapists 1 (pt); Activities coordinators 2 (ft); Dietitians 1 (pt).
Facilities Dining room; Physical therapy room; Activities room; Laundry room; Barber/Beauty shop.
Activities Arts & crafts; Games; Reading groups; Movies; Shopping trips.

Gade Nursing Home Inc 1
208 Sweitzer St, Greenville, OH, 45331
(513) 548-1993
Admin Tim Gade. *Medical Dir/Dir of Nursing* Dr Alvin Heise; Robin Haney.
Licensure Intermediate care. *Beds* ICF 19. *Certified* Medicaid.
Owner Proprietary Corp.
Admissions Requirements Medical examination; Physician's request.
Staff Physicians 1 (ft), 3 (pt); LPNs 2 (ft), 2 (pt); Nurses aides 2 (ft), 4 (pt); Activities coordinators 1 (ft).
Facilities Dining room; Laundry room; Library.
Activities Arts & crafts; Games; Reading groups; Movies; Shopping trips.

Heartland of Greenville*
130 Marion Dr, Greenville, OH, 45331
(513) 548-3141, 3142
Licensure Skilled care; Intermediate care. *Beds* 70. *Certified* Medicaid; Medicare.
Owner Proprietary Corp (Health Care & Retirement Corp).

Rest Haven Nursing Home Inc
1096 N Ohio St, Greenville, OH, 45331
(513) 548-1138
Admin Elma L Moss. *Medical Dir/Dir of Nursing* Dr Alvin Heise; LaRose Boyer RN.
Licensure Skilled care; Intermediate care. *Beds* 68. *Certified* Medicaid; Medicare.
Owner Proprietary Corp.
Admissions Requirements Minimum age 20; Medical examination.
Staff RNs 4 (ft), 3 (pt); LPNs 4 (ft), 3 (pt); Nurses aides 24 (ft), 14 (pt); Physical therapists 1 (pt); Speech therapists 1 (pt); Activities coordinators 1 (ft); Dietitians 1 (pt); Social services 1 (ft).
Facilities Dining room; Physical therapy room; Chapel; Laundry room; Barber/Beauty shop.
Activities Arts & crafts; Cards; Games; Prayer groups; Shopping trips; Social/Cultural gatherings; Trips to fairs, parades, & more.

GROVE CITY

Monterey Nursing Inn*
3929 Hoover Rd, Grove City, OH, 43123
(614) 875-7700
Licensure Skilled care; Intermediate care. *Beds* 200. *Certified* Medicaid; Medicare.
Owner Proprietary Corp (Beverly Enterprises).

HAMDEN

Huston Nursing Home Inc
PO Box 182, Rte 1, Hamden, OH, 45634
(614) 384-3485
Admin Marjorie Huston. *Medical Dir/Dir of Nursing* Linda L Burns DON.
Licensure Skilled care; Intermediate care. *Beds* 77. *Certified* Medicaid; Medicare.
Owner Privately owned.
Admissions Requirements Medical examination.
Staff Physicians; RNs; LPNs; Nurses aides; Physical therapists; Reality therapists; Recreational therapists; Speech therapists; Activities coordinators; Dietitians; Ophthalmologists.
Facilities Dining room; Physical therapy room; Laundry room; Barber/Beauty shop.
Activities Arts & crafts; Games; Reading groups; Prayer groups; Movies; Shopping trips; Social/Cultural gatherings.

HAMILTON

Butler County Home*
1800 Princeton Rd, Hamilton, OH, 45011
(513) 837-5721
Licensure Intermediate care. *Beds* 101. *Certified* Medicaid.
Owner Publicly owned.

Center Haven Health Center Inc
422 N 2nd St, Hamilton, OH, 45011
(513) 868-9600
Admin Stephen P Plouck. *Medical Dir/Dir of Nursing* Dr Erich Ringel; Joann Miranda DON.
Licensure Intermediate care. *Beds* ICF 29. *Certified* Medicaid.
Owner Proprietary Corp (Omnilife Systems Inc).
Admissions Requirements Medical examination; Physician's request.
Staff Physicians 4 (pt); RNs 1 (ft); LPNs 3 (ft), 2 (pt); Nurses aides 8 (ft), 1 (pt); Physical therapists 1 (pt); Activities coordinators 1 (pt); Dietitians 1 (pt); Dentists 1 (pt); Ophthalmologists 1 (pt).
Facilities Dining room; Activities room; Laundry room.
Activities Arts & crafts; Cards; Games; Prayer groups; Social/Cultural gatherings.

Glenward Health Care Center
3472 Hamilton-Mason Rd, Hamilton, OH, 45011
(513) 863-3100
Admin Glyndon Powell. *Medical Dir/Dir of Nursing* Edward P Drohan MD; Susan Castor RN.
Licensure Skilled care; Intermediate care. *Beds* SNF 22; ICF 95. *Certified* Medicaid; Medicare.
Owner Proprietary Corp.
Admissions Requirements Minimum age 18.
Staff Physicians 11 (pt); RNs 8 (ft), 3 (pt); LPNs 13 (ft), 3 (pt); Nurses aides 44 (ft), 3 (pt); Physical therapists 2 (pt); Occupational therapists 1 (pt); Speech therapists 1 (pt); Activities coordinators 2 (ft); Dietitians 1 (pt); Dentists 1 (pt); Ophthalmologists 1 (pt); Podiatrists 1 (pt); Dentist 1 (pt).
Facilities Dining room; Physical therapy room; Activities room; Crafts room; Laundry room; Barber/Beauty shop.
Activities Arts & crafts; Cards; Games; Reading groups; Prayer groups; Movies; Shopping trips; Social/Cultural gatherings.

Golden Years Healthcare*
2436 Old Oxford Rd, Hamilton, OH, 45013
(513) 893-0471
Medical Dir/Dir of Nursing Harry Davin MD.
Licensure Intermediate care. *Beds* 50. *Certified* Medicaid.
Owner Proprietary Corp.

Staff RNs 2 (pt); LPNs 3 (ft), 3 (pt); Nurses aides 9 (ft), 5 (pt); Activities coordinators 1 (ft); Dietitians 1 (pt).
Facilities Dining room; Laundry room; Barber/Beauty shop.
Activities Arts & crafts; Cards; Games; Social/Cultural gatherings.

Greenwood Quality Care Center*
925 Greenwood Ave, Hamilton, OH, 45011
(513) 867-8334
Admin M O'Reilly. *Medical Dir/Dir of Nursing* Dr E Ringel.
Licensure Intermediate care. *Beds* 27. *Certified* Medicaid.
Owner Proprietary Corp.
Admissions Requirements Medical examination.
Staff Physicians; LPNs; Orderlies; Nurses aides; Physical therapists; Recreational therapists; Occupational therapists; Speech therapists; Activities coordinators; Dietitians; Dentists; Podiatrists.
Facilities Dining room; Activities room; Laundry room.
Activities Arts & crafts; Cards; Games; Shopping trips.

Helton Health Center Inc
819 Buckeye St, Hamilton, OH, 45011
(513) 868-8842
Admin Stephen P Plouck. *Medical Dir/Dir of Nursing* Dr Erich Ringel; Joann Miranda DON.
Licensure Intermediate care. *Beds* ICF 24. *Certified* Medicaid.
Owner Proprietary Corp (Omnilife Systems Inc).
Admissions Requirements Medical examination; Physician's request.
Staff Physicians 3 (pt); RNs 1 (ft); LPNs 4 (ft); Nurses aides 6 (ft); Physical therapists 1 (pt); Activities coordinators 1 (pt); Dietitians 1 (pt); Dentists 1 (pt); Ophthalmologists 1 (pt).
Facilities Dining room; Activities room; Laundry room.
Activities Arts & crafts; Cards; Games; Reading groups; Prayer groups.

Hillandale Nursing Home*
4195 Hamilton-Mason Rd, Hamilton, OH, 45011
(513) 868-2266
Licensure Nursing home. *Beds* 53.
Owner Proprietary Corp.

Parkway Parke Nursing Home
4070 Hamilton-Mason Rd, Hamilton, OH, 45011
(513) 868-3300, 868-3318, 868-3326
Admin Beth Braunecker. *Medical Dir/Dir of Nursing* Marlene Kunz.
Licensure Intermediate care. *Beds* ICF 75. *Certified* Medicaid.
Owner Proprietary Corp (Parke Care Inc).
Staff RNs 1 (ft); LPNs 7 (ft), 2 (pt); Orderlies 5 (pt); Nurses aides 15 (ft), 5 (pt); Activities coordinators 1 (ft); Social worker 1 (ft).
Facilities Dining room; Activities room; Laundry room.
Activities Arts & crafts; Cards; Games; Reading groups; Prayer groups; Movies; Shopping trips; Social/Cultural gatherings; Church; Cooking classes; Senior Olympics; Performers; Birthday parties.

Powell's Convalescent Home*
PO Box 845, 2923 Hamilton-Mason Rd, Hamilton, OH, 45011
(513) 863-0360
Licensure Skilled care; Intermediate care. *Beds* 99. *Certified* Medicaid; Medicare.
Owner Proprietary Corp.

Schroder Manor
1302 Millville Ave, Hamilton, OH, 45013
(513) 867-1300

Admin Sr M Pascaline Colling. *Medical Dir/Dir of Nursing* Kurt Lande MD; Sr Karen Hartman RN DON.
Licensure Skilled care; Intermediate care; Rest home. *Beds* SNF 23; ICF 18; Rest home 59. *Certified* Medicare.
Owner Nonprofit Corp.
Admissions Requirements Medical examination; Physician's request.
Staff Physicians 1 (pt); RNs 2 (ft), 3 (pt); LPNs 4 (ft), 3 (pt); Nurses aides 13 (ft), 6 (pt); Physical therapists 1 (pt); Recreational therapists 2 (pt); Occupational therapists 1 (pt); Speech therapists 1 (pt); Activities coordinators 1 (ft); Dietitians 1 (pt); Podiatrists 1 (pt).
Languages Spanish
Affiliation Roman Catholic
Facilities Dining room; Physical therapy room; Activities room; Chapel; Crafts room; Laundry room; Barber/Beauty shop; Library; Outdoor shelter; Fishing pond.
Activities Arts & crafts; Cards; Games; Reading groups; Prayer groups; Movies; Shopping trips; Social/Cultural gatherings; Shuffleboard.

Sunnybreeze Health Care Inc
350 Hancock Ave, Hamilton, OH, 45011
(513) 863-4218
Admin Mildred Ross. *Medical Dir/Dir of Nursing* Harry Davin MD; Patty Yeary DON.
Licensure Intermediate care. *Beds* ICF 81.
Owner Proprietary Corp.
Admissions Requirements Medical examination; Physician's request.
Staff Physicians 6 (pt); RNs 1 (ft), 2 (pt); LPNs 8 (ft), 4 (pt); Nurses aides 25 (ft), 14 (pt); Physical therapists 1 (pt); Reality therapists 1 (pt); Recreational therapists 1 (pt); Occupational therapists 1 (pt); Speech therapists 1 (pt); Activities coordinators 1 (ft), 1 (pt); Dietitians 1 (pt); Dentists 1 (pt); Ophthalmologists 1 (pt); Podiatrists 1 (pt).
Facilities Dining room; Activities room; Laundry room; Barber/Beauty shop.
Activities Arts & crafts; Cards; Games; Reading groups; Movies; Shopping trips; Social/Cultural gatherings.

Westhaven Quality Care Center
215 N "C" St, Hamilton, OH, 45013
(513) 863-5511
Admin J Gentry. *Medical Dir/Dir of Nursing* Dr E Ringel.
Licensure Intermediate care. *Beds* 23. *Certified* Medicaid.
Owner Proprietary Corp (Blackeye Fam & Nursing Hm).
Admissions Requirements Females only; Medical examination.
Staff Physicians; LPNs; Nurses aides; Recreational therapists; Occupational therapists; Speech therapists; Activities coordinators; Dietitians; Dentists; Podiatrists.
Facilities Dining room; Activities room; Laundry room.
Activities Cards; Games; Shopping trips.

Westover Retirement Community
855 Stahlheber Rd, Hamilton, OH, 45013
(513) 895-9539
Admin Jeffrey P Thurman. *Medical Dir/Dir of Nursing* Daniel Niehaus MD; Marion Mier RN DON.
Licensure Intermediate care; Rest home; Independent living. *Beds* ICF 50; Rest home 50 Independent living 40.
Owner Nonprofit Corp.
Admissions Requirements Minimum age 55; Medical examination; Physician's request.
Staff Physicians 1 (pt); RNs 2 (ft); LPNs 4 (ft), 3 (pt); Nurses aides 24 (ft), 6 (pt); Physical therapists 1 (pt); Activities coordinators 2 (ft); Dietitians 1 (pt); Ophthalmologists 1 (pt).

Facilities Dining room; Physical therapy room; Activities room; Chapel; Crafts room; Laundry room; Barber/Beauty shop; Library; Pre-school.
Activities Arts & crafts; Cards; Reading groups; Prayer groups; Movies; Shopping trips; Social/Cultural gatherings; Various outings with 25-passenger bus & van.

HARTVILLE

Hartville Healthcare Center
1420 Smith Kramer Rd, Hartville, OH, 44632
(216) 877-2666
Admin James Alexander. *Medical Dir/Dir of Nursing* Gertrude Stilts RN.
Licensure Intermediate care. *Beds* ICF 66. *Certified* Medicaid.
Owner Privately owned.
Admissions Requirements Minimum age 60.
Facilities Dining room; Activities room; Laundry room; Barber/Beauty shop; Library.
Activities Arts & crafts; Cards; Games; Reading groups; Prayer groups; Movies; Social/Cultural gatherings.

Hartville Meadows*
844 W Orange, Hartville, OH, 44632
Licensure Intermediate care for mentally retarded. *Beds* 32. *Certified* Medicaid.
Owner Nonprofit Corp.

HAYESVILLE

Wintersong Village of Hayesville Inc
PO Box 204, 82 S Mechanic St, Hayesville, OH, 44838
(419) 368-4381
Admin Robert H Rice. *Medical Dir/Dir of Nursing* Jessie Van Auker RN; Pat Abrams DON.
Licensure Intermediate care. *Beds* ICF 22. *Certified* Medicaid.
Owner Proprietary Corp.
Admissions Requirements Medical examination; Physician's request.
Staff Physicians 2 (ft); RNs 1 (ft); LPNs 3 (ft); Orderlies 1 (ft); Nurses aides 9 (ft); Activities coordinators 1 (ft); Dietitians 1 (pt).
Facilities Dining room; Activities room; Crafts room; Laundry room.
Activities Arts & crafts; Cards; Games; Reading groups; Movies; Shopping trips; Social/Cultural gatherings.

HICKSVILLE

Fountain Manor
401 Fountain St, Hicksville, OH, 43526
(419) 542-7795
Admin Earl E Brinsfield. *Medical Dir/Dir of Nursing* Laverne Miller MD; Irene Dalton RN DON.
Licensure Skilled care. *Beds* SNF 64. *Certified* Medicaid; Medicare.
Owner Proprietary Corp.
Admissions Requirements Minimum age 18; Medical examination; Physician's request.
Staff Physicians 3 (pt); RNs 2 (ft), 1 (pt); LPNs 6 (ft), 5 (pt); Nurses aides 15 (ft), 7 (pt); Physical therapists 1 (pt); Speech therapists 1 (pt); Activities coordinators 1 (ft), 1 (pt); Dietitians 1 (pt); Ophthalmologists 1 (pt).
Facilities Dining room; Activities room; Crafts room; Laundry room; Barber/Beauty shop.
Activities Arts & crafts; Cards; Games; Reading groups; Prayer groups; Movies; Shopping trips; Social/Cultural gatherings.

HILLIARD

The Arbors at Hilliard
5471 Scioto Darby Rd, Hilliard, OH, 43026
(614) 876-7356
Admin Jan S Goldhardt. *Medical Dir/Dir of Nursing* Michael Kirwin MD; Lynn Temple RN.
Licensure Skilled care; Intermediate care. *Beds* 122. *Certified* Medicaid; Medicare.
Owner Proprietary Corp.
Admissions Requirements Medical examination.
Staff RNs 3 (ft), 8 (pt); LPNs 5 (ft), 1 (pt); Nurses aides 28 (ft), 8 (pt); Activities coordinators 1 (ft).
Facilities Dining room; Physical therapy room; Activities room; Crafts room; Laundry room; Barber/Beauty shop.
Activities Arts & crafts; Cards; Games; Prayer groups; Movies; Shopping trips; Social/Cultural gatherings.

HILLSBORO

Oakland Nursing Center*
175 Chillicothe Ave, Hillsboro, OH, 45133
(513) 393-1925
Admin George Oney.
Licensure Intermediate care. *Beds* 101. *Certified* Medicaid.
Owner Proprietary Corp.
Admissions Requirements Medical examination; Physician's request.
Staff RNs 3 (ft), 1 (pt); LPNs 5 (ft), 7 (pt); Nurses aides 27 (ft), 13 (pt); Activities coordinators 3 (ft), 2 (pt); Dietitians 1 (pt).
Facilities Dining room; Physical therapy room; Activities room; Laundry room; Barber/Beauty shop.
Activities Arts & crafts; Cards; Games; Reading groups; Prayer groups; Movies; Shopping trips; Social/Cultural gatherings.

Whitehouse Health Care Center*
410 E Main St, Hillsboro, OH, 45133
(513) 393-1012
Licensure Intermediate care. *Beds* 46. *Certified* Medicaid.
Owner Proprietary Corp.

HUBER HEIGHTS

Montgomery Developmental Center
7650 Timbercrest Dr, Huber Heights, OH, 45424
(513) 233-8108
Admin Fred L Williams. *Medical Dir/Dir of Nursing* Maggie S Russell RN.
Licensure Intermediate care for mentally retarded. *Beds* 104. *Certified* Medicaid; Medicare.
Owner Publicly owned.
Admissions Requirements Minimum age 18.
Staff Physicians 2 (pt); RNs 3 (ft), 3 (pt); LPNs 6 (ft), 2 (pt); Recreational therapists 5 (pt); Speech therapists 1 (pt); Activities coordinators 1 (ft); Podiatrists 1 (pt).
Languages Sign
Facilities Activities room; Laundry room; Library.
Activities Arts & crafts; Cards; Games; Movies; Shopping trips; Social/Cultural gatherings.

HUDSON

Hudson Elms Inc
597 E Streetsboro Rd, Hudson, OH, 44236
(216) 650-0436
Licensure Intermediate care. *Beds* 50. *Certified* Medicaid.
Owner Proprietary Corp.

HUNTSBURG

Blossom Hill Nursing Home*
12496 Princeton Rd, Huntsburg, OH, 44046
(216) 635-5567
Licensure Intermediate care. *Beds* 30. *Certified* Medicaid.
Owner Proprietary Corp.

HURON

Erie County Care Facility
3916 E Perkins Ave, Huron, OH, 44839
(419) 627-8733
Admin William J Hart. *Medical Dir/Dir of Nursing* Sidhaiyan Aiyappasamy MD, C S Ahluwalia MD; Mary J Slusher DON.
Licensure Intermediate care. *Beds* 160. *Certified* Medicaid.
Owner Publicly owned.
Admissions Requirements Medical examination.
Staff Physicians 2 (ft), 14 (pt); RNs 4 (ft), 2 (pt); LPNs 19 (ft), 4 (pt); Nurses aides 51 (ft), 15 (pt); Physical therapists 2 (pt); Recreational therapists 1 (ft); Speech therapists 1 (pt); Activities coordinators 1 (ft); Dietitians 1 (pt); Ophthalmologists 2 (pt); Podiatrists 1 (pt).
Facilities Dining room; Activities room; Chapel; Crafts room; Laundry room; Barber/Beauty shop.
Activities Arts & crafts; Cards; Games; Prayer groups; Movies; Shopping trips; Social/Cultural gatherings.

INDIAN LAKE

Heartland of Indian Lake
1442 St Rte 33 W, Indian Lake, OH, 43331
(513) 843-4929
Admin Charles T George. *Medical Dir/Dir of Nursing* Sue Evans.
Licensure Skilled care; Intermediate care. *Beds* SNF 50; ICF 78; ICF/MR 18. *Certified* Medicaid; Medicare.
Owner Proprietary Corp.
Admissions Requirements Minimum age 18; Medical examination; Physician's request.
Staff Physicians 1 (pt); RNs 5 (ft), 1 (pt); LPNs 14 (ft), 2 (pt); Nurses aides 61 (ft), 4 (pt); Physical therapists 1 (ft); Recreational therapists 1 (ft); Occupational therapists 1 (ft); Speech therapists 1 (ft); Dietitians 1 (pt); Ophthalmologists 1 (pt); Podiatrists 1 (pt).
Facilities Dining room; Physical therapy room; Activities room; Barber/Beauty shop.
Activities Arts & crafts; Cards; Games; Reading groups; Movies; Shopping trips; Social/Cultural gatherings.

IRONTON

Dalton Health Center*
5th & Clinton Sts, Ironton, OH, 45638
(614) 532-6188
Licensure Intermediate care. *Beds* 91. *Certified* Medicaid.
Owner Proprietary Corp.

Jo-Lin Health Center Inc*
1050 Clinton St, Ironton, OH, 45638
(614) 532-6096
Licensure Intermediate care. *Beds* 112. *Certified* Medicaid.
Owner Nonprofit Corp.

Sunset Nursing Home Inc*
813 1/2 Marion Pike, Ironton, OH, 45638
(614) 532-0449
Medical Dir/Dir of Nursing Dr A B Payne.
Licensure Intermediate care. *Beds* 50. *Certified* Medic
Owner Proprietar Corp.

Facilities Dining room; Physical therapy room; Activities room; Chapel; Crafts room; Laundry room; Barber/Beauty shop; Library.
Activities Arts & crafts; Cards; Games; Reading groups; Prayer groups; Movies; Shopping trips; Social/Cultural gatherings.

JACKSON

Buckeye Community Services—South Street Home*
6 South St, Jackson, OH, 45640
Licensure Intermediate care. *Beds* 8. *Certified* Medicaid.
Owner Nonprofit Corp.

Heartland of Jackson
PO Box 8668, SR 93, Jackson, OH, 45640
(614) 286-5026
Admin Jeff Hunter. *Medical Dir/Dir of Nursing* Dr Louis J Jindra; Diana Gail Rawlins.
Licensure Skilled care; Intermediate care. *Beds* SNF 100; ICF. *Certified* Medicaid; Medicare.
Owner Proprietary Corp (Health Care & Retirement Corp).
Admissions Requirements Medical examination.
Staff Physicians 2 (pt); RNs 4 (ft); LPNs 8 (ft), 2 (pt); Orderlies 1 (ft); Nurses aides; Physical therapists 1 (ft); Occupational therapists 1 (ft); Speech therapists 1 (ft); Activities coordinators 1 (ft); Dietitians 1 (ft); Dentists 1 (ft); Ophthalmologists 1 (ft); Podiatrists 1 (ft); Dentist 1 (pt).
Facilities Dining room; Physical therapy room; Activities room; Laundry room; Barber/Beauty shop.
Activities Arts & crafts; Cards; Games; Reading groups; Prayer groups; Movies; Shopping trips; Social/Cultural gatherings.

JAMESTOWN

Heathergreen II Inc*
4960 US Rte 35 E, Jamestown, OH, 45335
(513) 675-3311
Licensure Skilled care; Intermediate care. *Beds* 100. *Certified* Medicaid; Medicare.
Owner Proprietary Corp.

JOHNSTOWN

Northview Nursing Home
267 N Main, Johnstown, OH, 43031
(614) 967-7896
Medical Dir/Dir of Nursing Robert Young MD.
Licensure Intermediate care. *Beds* 36. *Certified* Medicaid.
Owner Proprietary Corp.
Staff Physicians 2 (pt); RNs 1 (ft), 2 (pt); LPNs 1 (ft), 3 (pt); Nurses aides 8 (ft), 5 (pt); Activities coordinators 1 (ft); Dietitians 1 (pt); Dentists 1 (pt); Ophthalmologists 1 (pt); Podiatrists 1 (pt).
Facilities Dining room; Activities room; Chapel; Crafts room; Laundry room; Barber/ Beauty shop.
Activities Arts & crafts; Cards; Games; Reading groups; Prayer groups; Movies; Social/Cultural gatherings.

KENSINGTON

East Carroll Nursing Home Inc
7233 Apollo Rd NE, Kensington, OH, 44427
(216) 223-1536
Admin Jean Miller. *Medical Dir/Dir of Nursing* Donald Wingard DO; Lois Slentz LPN.
Licensure Intermediate care for mentally retarded. *Beds* ICF/MR 26. *Certified* Medicaid.
Owner Proprietary Corp.

Admissions Requirements Medical examination.
Staff LPNs; Nurses aides; Activities coordinators.
Facilities Dining room; Activities room; Crafts room; Laundry room.
Activities Arts & crafts; Cards; Games; Reading groups; Movies; Shopping trips; Social/Cultural gatherings; Sunday School.

KENT

Kent Quality Care Nursing Center
1290 Fairchild Rd, Kent, OH, 44240
(216) 678-4912
Admin Christine M Joseph. *Medical Dir/Dir of Nursing* James Mottice MD; Pat Harriger DON.
Licensure Intermediate care. *Beds* ICF 100. *Certified* Medicaid.
Owner Proprietary Corp (Northwestern Service Corp).
Staff Physicians 1 (pt); RNs 1 (ft), 2 (pt); LPNs 6 (ft), 5 (pt); Nurses aides 28 (ft), 12 (pt); Physical therapists 1 (pt); Activities coordinators 1 (ft), 3 (pt); Dietitians 3 (ft), 4 (pt).
Facilities Dining room; Physical therapy room; Activities room; Chapel; Crafts room; Laundry room; Barber/Beauty shop; Library.
Activities Arts & crafts; Cards; Games; Reading groups; Prayer groups; Movies; Shopping trips; Social/Cultural gatherings.

Longmeadow Care Center
565 Bryn Mawr, Kent, OH, 44266
(216) 297-5781
Admin Mary Ellen Thornton. *Medical Dir/Dir of Nursing* Louis Castaldi MD; Patricia Gregory RN DON.
Licensure Skilled care; Intermediate care. *Beds* 120. *Certified* Medicaid; Medicare.
Owner Proprietary Corp (Beverly Enterprises).
Admissions Requirements Minimum age 18.
Staff RNs 6 (ft), 3 (pt); LPNs 5 (ft), 5 (pt); Nurses aides 35 (ft), 15 (pt); Activities coordinators 1 (ft), 1 (pt).
Facilities Dining room; Physical therapy room; Activities room; Crafts room; Laundry room; Barber/Beauty shop.
Activities Arts & crafts; Cards; Games; Reading groups; Prayer groups; Movies; Shopping trips; Social/Cultural gatherings.

KENTON

The Corinthian Nursing Facility
320 N Wayne St, Kenton, OH, 43326
(419) 673-1295
Medical Dir/Dir of Nursing Dr J Sanders.
Licensure Intermediate care. *Beds* 82. *Certified* Medicaid.
Owner Privately owned.
Admissions Requirements Minimum age 18; Medical examination; Physician's request.
Staff Physicians 10 (pt); RNs 3 (ft), 1 (pt); LPNs 3 (ft), 6 (pt); Nurses aides 21 (ft), 13 (pt); Physical therapists 1 (pt); Reality therapists 1 (pt); Recreational therapists 1 (pt); Occupational therapists 1 (pt); Speech therapists 1 (pt); Activities coordinators 1 (ft), 2 (pt); Dietitians 1 (pt); Dentists 1 (pt); Ophthalmologists 1 (pt); Podiatrists 1 (pt).
Languages Sign
Facilities Dining room; Activities room; Crafts room; Laundry room; Barber/Beauty shop; Library.
Activities Arts & crafts; Cards; Games; Reading groups; Prayer groups; Movies; Shopping trips; Social/Cultural gatherings; Van outings.

Country Manor of Kenton Inc
911 W Pattison Ave, Kenton, OH, 43326
(419) 675-6193, 675-3168
Admin Cindy Weatherholtz. *Medical Dir/Dir of Nursing* Susan Jarvis.

Licensure Intermediate care. *Beds* ICF 50. *Certified* Medicaid.
Owner Proprietary Corp.
Staff Physicians 1 (pt); RNs 1 (ft); LPNs 3 (ft), 2 (pt); Orderlies 1 (ft); Activities coordinators 1 (ft); Dietitians 1 (ft).
Facilities Dining room; Activities room; Laundry room; Barber/Beauty shop.
Activities Arts & crafts; Cards; Games; Reading groups; Prayer groups; Movies; Shopping trips; Social/Cultural gatherings.

Green Acres Nursing Home Inc
117 Cemetery Rd, Kenton, OH, 43326
(419) 674-4197
Admin Doris A Baldwin. *Medical Dir/Dir of Nursing* Dr Jim Sanders; Sandra E Kahler RN DON.
Licensure Intermediate care. *Beds* ICF 101. *Certified* Medicaid.
Owner Privately owned.
Admissions Requirements Medical examination.
Staff RNs 1 (ft), 1 (pt); LPNs 8 (ft), 1 (pt); Nurses aides 25 (ft), 16 (pt); Physical therapists 1 (pt); Activities coordinators 2 (ft), 1 (pt); Dietitians 1 (ft).
Facilities Dining room; Activities room; Laundry room; Barber/Beauty shop.
Activities Arts & crafts; Cards; Games; Reading groups; Prayer groups; Movies; Shopping trips; Social/Cultural gatherings; Kitchen corner.

Hardin County Home*
Rte 2, Kenton, OH, 43326
(419) 673-5251
Licensure Intermediate care. *Beds* 51. *Certified* Medicaid.
Owner Publicly owned.

KETTERING

Heartland of Kettering
3313 Wilmington Pike, Kettering, OH, 45429
(513) 298-8084
Admin William G Shannon. *Medical Dir/Dir of Nursing* Cal Kogut RN.
Licensure Skilled care; Intermediate care. *Beds* SNF 100; ICF. *Certified* Medicaid; Medicare.
Owner Proprietary Corp (Health Care & Retirement Corp).
Admissions Requirements Minimum age 55; Medical examination.
Staff RNs 6 (ft); LPNs 7 (ft); Nurses aides 65 (ft); Physical therapists 3 (pt); Occupational therapists 1 (pt); Speech therapists 1 (pt); Activities coordinators 1 (ft); Dietitians 1 (ft); Dentists 1 (pt); Ophthalmologists 1 (pt); Dentist 1 (pt); Social worker 1 (ft).
Facilities Dining room; Physical therapy room; Activities room; Laundry room; Barber/Beauty shop; 5 Lounges (4 w/TVs); 2 large porches/patios.
Activities Arts & crafts; Cards; Games; Prayer groups; Movies; Social/Cultural gatherings; Lunches out & other outings on facility bus.

Kettering Convalescent Center
1150 W Dorothy Ln, Kettering, OH, 45409
(513) 293-1152
Admin T E Westervelt. *Medical Dir/Dir of Nursing* William A Romer MD; Catherine L Hoffman RN.
Licensure Skilled care; Intermediate care. *Beds* SNF 168; ICF. *Certified* Medicaid; Medicare.
Owner Nonprofit Corp (Volunteers of America Care).
Admissions Requirements Medical examination; Physician's request.
Staff RNs 10 (ft), 13 (pt); LPNs 3 (ft), 12 (pt); Nurses aides 50 (ft), 47 (pt); Physical therapists 2 (ft); Recreational therapists 3 (pt); Activities coordinators 1 (ft).
Affiliation Volunteers of America

Facilities Dining room; Physical therapy
  room; Activities room; Chapel; Laundry
  room; Barber/Beauty shop.
Activities Arts & crafts; Cards; Games;
  Reading groups; Prayer groups; Movies;
  Shopping trips; Social/Cultural gatherings.

KIMBOLTON

Bell Health Care Inc
PO Box 51, Main St, Kimbolton, OH, 43749
(614) 432-7717
Admin James Romig. *Medical Dir/Dir of
  Nursing* Kamelia Childs.
Licensure Intermediate care. *Beds* ICF 50.
  Certified Medicaid.
Owner Proprietary Corp.
Staff RNs; LPNs; Orderlies; Nurses aides;
  Physical therapists; Activities coordinators;
  Dietitians.
Facilities Dining room; Activities room;
  Laundry room.
Activities Arts & crafts; Cards; Games;
  Reading groups; Prayer groups; Movies;
  Shopping trips; Social/Cultural gatherings.

KINGSTON

Gospel Light Nursing Home
PO Box 238, 3rd St, Kingston, OH, 45644
(614) 642-2503
Admin Helen M Davis. *Medical Dir/Dir of
  Nursing* Dr Nissimor.
Licensure Intermediate care. *Beds* 50.
  Certified Medicaid.
Owner Proprietary Corp.
Admissions Requirements Medical
  examination.
Staff Physicians 1 (ft), 1 (pt); RNs 1 (ft);
  LPNs 4 (ft); Orderlies 2 (ft); Nurses aides 25
  (ft); Recreational therapists 1 (ft); Activities
  coordinators 1 (ft); Dietitians 1 (pt);
  Podiatrists 1 (ft).
Facilities Dining room; Activities room;
  Laundry room; Barber/Beauty shop.
Activities Arts & crafts; Cards; Games;
  Reading groups; Prayer groups; Movies;
  Shopping trips; Social/Cultural gatherings.

KINGSVILLE

Ashtabula County Nursing Home
Dibble Rd, Kingsville, OH, 44048
(216) 224-2161
Admin Carolyn Constiner. *Medical Dir/Dir of
  Nursing* Pat Hunter.
Licensure Intermediate care. *Beds* ICF 310.
  Certified Medicaid.
Owner Publicly owned.
Admissions Requirements Minimum age 18.
Staff Physicians 2 (pt); RNs 14 (ft), 2 (pt);
  LPNs 28 (ft); Orderlies 3 (ft); Nurses aides
  98 (ft), 6 (pt); Physical therapists 1 (pt);
  Recreational therapists 5 (ft); Speech
  therapists 1 (pt); Activities coordinators 1
  (ft); Dietitians 1 (pt); Ophthalmologists 1
  (pt); Podiatrists 1 (pt).
Facilities Dining room; Physical therapy
  room; Activities room; Chapel; Crafts room;
  Laundry room; Barber/Beauty shop; Library.
Activities Arts & crafts; Cards; Games;
  Reading groups; Prayer groups; Movies;
  Shopping trips; Social/Cultural gatherings.

KINSMAN

Boyd's Kinsman Home
PO Box 315, Rte 5, Kinsman, OH, 44428
(216) 876-5581
Admin Paula L Ruley. *Medical Dir/Dir of
  Nursing* Carlene Jones DON.
Licensure Intermediate care for mentally
  retarded. *Beds* ICF/MR 47. *Certified*
  Medicaid.
Owner Nonprofit Corp.
Admissions Requirements Minimum age 18.

Staff RNs 1 (ft), 2 (pt); LPNs 2 (pt); Nurses
  aides 2 (ft), 7 (pt); Speech therapists 1 (pt);
  Activities coordinators 1 (ft).
Facilities Dining room; Activities room;
  Crafts room; Laundry room.
Activities Arts & crafts; Cards; Games;
  Movies; Shopping trips; Social/Cultural
  gatherings; Church; Bowling; Library.

KIRKERSVILLE

Pine Kirk Nursing Home Inc
205 E Main St, Kirkersville, OH, 43033
(614) 927-3209
Admin Karen Rosser. *Medical Dir/Dir of
  Nursing* Dr J I Fast DO; Beverly Bradley
  DON.
Licensure Intermediate care. *Beds* ICF 39.
  Certified Medicaid.
Owner Proprietary Corp.
Admissions Requirements Medical
  examination; Physician's request.
Staff Physicians 1 (ft); RNs 2 (ft); LPNs 4 (ft);
  Nurses aides 9 (ft); Activities coordinators 1
  (ft); Dietitians 1 (ft); Ophthalmologists 1 (ft).
Facilities Dining room; Laundry room.
Activities Arts & crafts; Cards; Games;
  Reading groups; Prayer groups; Movies;
  Shopping trips; Social/Cultural gatherings.

KIRTLAND

Western Reserve Convalescent Homes Inc*
9769 Chillicothe Rd, Kirtland, OH, 44094
(216) 946-7858
Admin William E Rabe. *Medical Dir/Dir of
  Nursing* Donald Patchin MD.
Licensure Nursing home. *Beds* 150.
Owner Proprietary Corp (Beverly Enterprises).
Admissions Requirements Minimum age 18;
  Medical examination; Physician's request.
Staff Physicians 5 (pt); RNs 5 (ft), 2 (pt);
  LPNs 5 (ft), 5 (pt); Nurses aides 40 (ft);
  Physical therapists 2 (ft); Occupational
  therapists 1 (pt); Speech therapists 1 (ft);
  Activities coordinators 1 (ft), 1 (pt);
  Dietitians 1 (ft); Dentists 1 (pt);
  Ophthalmologists 1 (pt); Podiatrists 1 (pt);
  Audiologists 1 (pt).
Facilities Dining room; Physical therapy
  room; Activities room; Chapel; Crafts room;
  Laundry room; Barber/Beauty shop; Library.
Activities Arts & crafts; Cards; Games;
  Reading groups; Prayer groups; Movies;
  Shopping trips; Social/Cultural gatherings.

Western Reserve Extended Care Inc
9685 Chillicothe Rd, Kirtland, OH, 44094
(216) 951-7272
Admin Frances C Horton. *Medical Dir/Dir of
  Nursing* Armin Green MD; Donna Higgins
  DON.
Licensure Skilled care; Intermediate care. *Beds*
  52. *Certified* Medicare.
Owner Proprietary Corp (Beverly Enterprises).
Admissions Requirements Minimum age 18;
  Medical examination; Physician's request.
Staff RNs 8 (ft), 3 (pt); LPNs 10 (ft); Nurses
  aides 13 (ft), 1 (pt); Physical therapists 1 (ft);
  Recreational therapists 1 (ft); Activities
  coordinators 1 (ft); Dietitians 1 (ft);
  Podiatrists 1 (pt).
Facilities Dining room; Physical therapy
  room; Activities room; Laundry room;
  Barber/Beauty shop; Library.
Activities Arts & crafts; Cards; Games; Prayer
  groups; Movies; Social/Cultural gatherings.

LAKE MILTON

Edgewater Quality Care Nursing Center
1930 Craig Dr, Lake Milton, OH, 44429
(216) 654-3700
Admin Michael J Anthony. *Medical Dir/Dir of
  Nursing* Diane Prentice.

Licensure Intermediate care. *Beds* ICF 75.
  Certified Medicaid.
Owner Proprietary Corp (Northwestern
  Service Corp).
Admissions Requirements Medical
  examination.
Staff RNs 1 (ft), 1 (pt); LPNs 8 (ft); Nurses
  aides 14 (ft), 8 (pt); Activities coordinators 1
  (ft), 1 (pt); Dietitians 1 (ft); 8 (ft), 3 (pt).
Facilities Dining room; Activities room;
  Laundry room; Barber/Beauty shop.
Activities Arts & crafts; Cards; Games;
  Reading groups; Prayer groups; Movies;
  Shopping trips.

Milton Manor Nursing Home
Box 98, 1574 Jersey St, Lake Milton, OH,
44429
(216) 654-5555 or 747-6940
Admin Joan Miller.
Licensure Private pay. *Beds* 45. *Certified*
  Private pay.
Owner Proprietary Corp.
Admissions Requirements Medical
  examination; Physician's request.
Staff RNs 1 (ft); LPNs 4 (ft), 2 (pt); Nurses
  aides 8 (ft), 4 (pt); Activities coordinators 1
  (ft), 1 (pt).
Facilities Dining room; Activities room;
  Crafts room; Laundry room.
Activities Arts & crafts; Cards; Games;
  Reading groups; Prayer groups; Movies;
  Shopping trips; Social/Cultural gatherings;
  Dinner out; Fairs.

LAKEWOOD

Aristocrat Lakewood
13900 Detroit Ave, Lakewood, OH, 44107
(216) 228-7650
Admin Timothy M Coury. *Medical Dir/Dir of
  Nursing* Dr James Tsai Med Dir; Nancy
  Smitley DON.
Licensure Skilled care; Intermediate care. *Beds*
  SNF; ICF 132. *Certified* Medicaid;
  Medicare.
Owner Proprietary Corp.
Admissions Requirements Minimum age 18;
  Medical examination; Physician's request.
Staff Physicians; RNs; LPNs; Orderlies;
  Nurses aides; Physical therapists;
  Recreational therapists; Occupational
  therapists; Speech therapists; Activities
  coordinators; Dietitians; Dentists;
  Ophthalmologists; Podiatrists.
Facilities Dining room; Physical therapy
  room; Activities room; Crafts room; Laundry
  room; Barber/Beauty shop; Library.
Activities Arts & crafts; Cards; Games;
  Reading groups; Prayer groups; Movies;
  Shopping trips; Social/Cultural gatherings.

Crestmont Nursing Home North Inc*
13330 Detroit Ave, Lakewood, OH, 44107
(216) 228-9550
Licensure Intermediate care; Rest home. *Beds*
  ICF 73; Rest home 19. *Certified* Medicaid.
Owner Proprietary Corp.

Wright Nursing Center*
13315 Detroit Ave, Lakewood, OH, 44107
(216) 226-3858
Licensure Intermediate care. *Beds* 50.
  Certified Medicaid.
Owner Proprietary Corp.

LANCASTER

**Americare-Homestead Nursing &
Rehabilitation Center**
1900 E Main St, Lancaster, OH, 43130
(614) 653-8630
Admin Andrea Korody. *Medical Dir/Dir of
  Nursing* Dr John Lloyd, Dr Robert Sprouse;
  Sandy O'Brien DON.

Licensure Skilled care; Intermediate care. *Beds* SNF 28; ICF 72. *Certified* Medicaid; Medicare.
Owner Proprietary Corp (Care Enterprises).
Admissions Requirements Medical examination.
Staff Physicians 2 (pt); RNs 8 (ft); LPNs 6 (ft), 1 (pt); Nurses aides 55 (ft), 4 (pt); Physical therapists 1 (pt); Activities coordinators 1 (ft), 1 (pt).
Languages Hungarian
Facilities Dining room; Physical therapy room; Activities room; Crafts room; Laundry room; Barber/Beauty shop.
Activities Arts & crafts; Cards; Games; Reading groups; Prayer groups; Movies; Shopping trips; Social/Cultural gatherings.

Crestview Manor Nursing Home I
925 Becks Knob Rd, Lancaster, OH, 43130
(614) 654-2634
Admin Winfield S Eckert. *Medical Dir/Dir of Nursing* Richard E Hartle MD; Nancy Tillinghest RN DON.
Licensure Skilled care; Intermediate care. *Beds* 101. *Certified* Medicaid; Medicare.
Owner Proprietary Corp.
Admissions Requirements Minimum age 18; Medical examination.
Staff Physicians 3 (pt); RNs 6 (ft), 2 (pt); LPNs 8 (ft), 2 (pt); Orderlies 6 (ft), 2 (pt); Nurses aides 58 (ft), 4 (pt); Physical therapists 1 (pt); Recreational therapists 1 (pt); Activities coordinators 1 (pt); Dietitians 1 (pt); Dentists 1 (pt); Podiatrists 1 (pt).
Facilities Dining room; Physical therapy room; Activities room; Crafts room; Laundry room; Barber/Beauty shop.
Activities Arts & crafts; Cards; Games; Reading groups; Prayer groups; Movies.

Crestview Manor Nursing Home II
957 Becks Knob Rd, Lancaster, OH, 43130
(614) 654-2634
Admin Winfield S Eckert. *Medical Dir/Dir of Nursing* Richard E Hartle MD; Debra Skaggs RN DON.
Licensure Skilled care; Intermediate care. *Beds* 101. *Certified* Medicaid; Medicare.
Owner Proprietary Corp.
Admissions Requirements Minimum age 18; Medical examination.
Staff Physicians 3 (pt); RNs 5 (ft), 2 (pt); LPNs 7 (ft), 2 (pt); Orderlies 8 (ft), 2 (pt); Nurses aides 56 (ft), 2 (pt); Physical therapists 1 (pt); Recreational therapists 1 (pt); Activities coordinators 1 (pt); Dietitians 1 (pt); Ophthalmologists 1 (pt); Podiatrists 1 (pt).
Facilities Dining room; Physical therapy room; Activities room; Crafts room; Laundry room; Barber/Beauty shop.
Activities Arts & crafts; Cards; Games; Reading groups; Prayer groups; Movies; Social/Cultural gatherings.

Crites Nursing Home
1318 E Main St, Lancaster, OH, 43130
(614) 653-3431
Admin Randall Crites. *Medical Dir/Dir of Nursing* Galen Durose DO; Shirley Tipple RN.
Licensure Intermediate care. *Beds* ICF 60. *Certified* Medicaid.
Owner Privately owned.
Staff RNs 2 (ft), 5 (pt); LPNs 8 (ft), 6 (pt); Nurses aides 20 (ft), 8 (pt); Activities coordinators 2 (ft), 2 (pt); Dietitians 1 (ft).
Facilities Dining room; Activities room; Crafts room; Laundry room.
Activities Arts & crafts; Cards; Games; Reading groups; Movies; Shopping trips; Social/Cultural gatherings.

Johnston Nursing Home
1246 E Main St, Lancaster, OH, 43130
(614) 653-1410

Admin Randall Crites. *Medical Dir/Dir of Nursing* Galen G Durose DO; Linda Godenschwager DON.
Licensure Intermediate care. *Beds* SNF. *Certified* Medicaid.
Owner Privately owned.
Staff RNs 2 (ft), 2 (pt); LPNs 8 (ft), 4 (pt); Nurses aides 12 (ft), 6 (pt); Activities coordinators 1 (ft), 2 (pt); Dietitians 1 (ft).
Facilities Dining room; Activities room; Crafts room; Laundry room.
Activities Arts & crafts; Cards; Games; Reading groups; Movies; Shopping trips.

Lancaster Health Care Center
PO Box 786, Dolson Ct NW, Lancaster, OH, 43130
(614) 654-0641
Medical Dir/Dir of Nursing Dr John Bowling.
Licensure Skilled care; Intermediate care. *Beds* 100. *Certified* Medicaid; Medicare.
Owner Proprietary Corp (Americare Corp).
Staff Physicians 1 (pt); RNs 5 (ft), 3 (pt); LPNs 5 (ft), 2 (pt); Nurses aides 29 (ft), 18 (pt); Physical therapists 2 (pt); Occupational therapists 1 (pt); Speech therapists 1 (pt); Activities coordinators 1 (ft); Dietitians 1 (pt); Podiatrists 1 (pt).
Facilities Dining room; Physical therapy room; Activities room; Crafts room; Laundry room; Barber/Beauty shop.
Activities Arts & crafts; Cards; Games; Reading groups; Prayer groups; Movies; Shopping trips; Social/Cultural gatherings.

Valley View Nursing Home
5185 Lithopolis Rd, Lancaster, OH, 43130
(614) 687-0566
Medical Dir/Dir of Nursing Dr Ralph R Romaker.
Licensure Intermediate care. *Beds* 25. *Certified* Medicaid.
Owner Proprietary Corp.
Admissions Requirements Minimum age 18; Medical examination.
Staff Physicians 1 (pt); RNs 2 (ft), 2 (pt); LPNs 2 (pt); Nurses aides 5 (ft), 3 (pt); Physical therapists 1 (pt); Activities coordinators 1 (pt); Dietitians 1 (pt).
Facilities Dining room; Activities room; Laundry room.
Activities Arts & crafts; Cards; Games; Reading groups; Prayer groups; Movies; Shopping trips; Social/Cultural gatherings.

LANSING

Heartland-Lansing*
300 Commercial Dr, Lansing, OH, 43934
Licensure Skilled care; Intermediate care. *Beds* SNF 100; ICF 100. *Certified* Medicaid; Medicare.
Owner Proprietary Corp.

LAURELVILLE

Wintersong Village of Laurelvillle
PO Box 128, 16128 Pike St, Laurelville, OH, 43135
(614) 332-3221
Admin Michael Daffin. *Medical Dir/Dir of Nursing* Joyce Hoover.
Licensure Intermediate care. *Beds* ICF 18. *Certified* Medicaid.
Owner Proprietary Corp.
Admissions Requirements Medical examination.
Staff Physicians 2 (pt); RNs 2 (pt); LPNs 2 (ft), 1 (pt); Nurses aides 7 (ft), 3 (pt); Recreational therapists; Activities coordinators 1 (pt); Dietitians 1 (pt); Ophthalmologists.
Facilities Dining room; Activities room; Laundry room; Barber/Beauty shop.
Activities Arts & crafts; Cards; Games; Reading groups; Prayer groups; Movies; Shopping trips.

LEBANON

Lebanon Health Care Center*
115 Oregonia Rd, Lebanon, OH, 45036
(513) 932-1121
Licensure Skilled care; Intermediate care. *Beds* 57. *Certified* Medicaid; Medicare.
Owner Proprietary Corp.

Lebanon Nursing Home*
220 S Mechanic St, Lebanon, OH, 45036
(513) 932-4861
Medical Dir/Dir of Nursing Ralph Young DO.
Licensure Intermediate care. *Beds* 36. *Certified* Medicaid.
Owner Proprietary Corp.
Staff Physicians 1 (ft); RNs 1 (ft); LPNs 4 (ft), 5 (pt); Nurses aides 12 (ft), 5 (pt); Physical therapists 1 (pt); Recreational therapists 1 (ft); Activities coordinators 1 (ft); Dietitians 1 (ft).
Facilities Dining room; Activities room; Laundry room.
Activities Arts & crafts; Games; Reading groups; Prayer groups; Movies; Shopping trips; Social/Cultural gatherings.

Otterbein Home*
585 N State Rte 741, Lebanon, OH, 45036
(513) 932-2020
Medical Dir/Dir of Nursing James Barry.
Licensure Skilled care; Intermediate care. *Beds* SNF 132; ICF 224. *Certified* Medicaid; Medicare.
Owner Nonprofit Corp.
Admissions Requirements Minimum age 62; Medical examination.
Staff Physicians 1 (ft), 1 (pt); RNs 19 (ft), 13 (pt); LPNs 23 (ft), 4 (pt); Nurses aides 92 (ft), 9 (pt); Physical therapists 1 (ft); Recreational therapists 1 (ft); Occupational therapists 1 (ft); Speech therapists 1 (pt); Activities coordinators 3 (ft), 2 (pt); Dietitians 1 (pt); Dentists 1 (pt); Ophthalmologists 1 (pt); Podiatrists 1 (pt); Audiologists 1 (pt).
Affiliation Methodist
Facilities Dining room; Physical therapy room; Activities room; Chapel; Crafts room; Laundry room; Barber/Beauty shop; Library.
Activities Arts & crafts; Cards; Games; Reading groups; Prayer groups; Movies; Shopping trips; Social/Cultural gatherings.

LEXINGTON

Griffeth Nursing Home*
Rte 7, Vanderbilt Rd, PO Box 3167, Lexington, CH, 44404
(419) 756-3623
Licensure Intermediate care. *Beds* 50. *Certified* Medicaid.
Owner Proprietary Corp.
Admissions Requirements Medical examination; Physician's request.
Staff RNs 1 (pt); LPNs 3 (ft), 4 (pt); Nurses aides 10 (ft), 4 (pt); Recreational therapists 2 (ft), 1 (pt); Activities coordinators 1 (ft); Dietitians 1 (pt).
Facilities Dining room; Activities room; Crafts room; Laundry room.
Activities Arts & crafts; Cards; Games; Reading groups; Prayer groups; Movies; Shopping trips; Social/Cultural gatherings.

LIMA

Allen County Inn for the Aged
3125 Ada Rd, Lima, OH, 45801
(419) 228-2346
Admin Jerome J O'Neal. *Medical Dir/Dir of Nursing* Dwight Becker MD; Nancy Sidey DON.
Licensure Intermediate care. *Beds* ICF 134. *Certified* Medicaid.
Owner Nonprofit organization/foundation.

Admissions Requirements Medical examination; Physician's request.
Staff Physicians 1 (pt); RNs 3 (ft), 1 (pt); LPNs 7 (ft), 4 (pt); Orderlies 2 (ft), 1 (pt); Nurses aides 22 (ft), 3 (pt); Activities coordinators 1 (ft); Dietitians 1 (pt).
Facilities Dining room; Activities room; Chapel; Crafts room; Laundry room; Barber/Beauty shop; Library.
Activities Arts & crafts; Cards; Games; Reading groups; Prayer groups; Movies; Shopping trips; Social/Cultural gatherings.

Columbia Care Center
651 Columbia Dr, Lima, OH, 45805
(419) 227-2441
Admin Patricia Ann Parton. *Medical Dir/Dir of Nursing* Dr James Bowlus; Iris Jay RN.
Licensure Skilled care. *Beds* 50. *Certified* Medicaid; Medicare.
Owner Proprietary Corp (Beverly Enterprises).
Admissions Requirements Medical examination; Physician's request.
Staff Physicians 1 (pt); RNs 5 (ft), 3 (pt); LPNs 3 (pt); Nurses aides 13 (ft), 5 (pt); Physical therapists 1 (pt); Recreational therapists 1 (pt); Occupational therapists 1 (pt); Speech therapists 1 (pt); Activities coordinators; Dietitians 1 (pt); Podiatrists 1 (pt).
Facilities Dining room; Laundry room; Barber/Beauty shop.
Activities Arts & crafts; Cards; Games; Reading groups; Prayer groups; Movies; Shopping trips; Social/Cultural gatherings.

Lima Convalescent Home
1650 W Allentown Rd, Lima, OH, 45805
(419) 224-9741
Beds 100.
Owner Nonprofit Corp.

Lima Manor
750 Brower Rd, Lima, OH, 45801
(419) 227-2611
Admin Joyce A Emrick. *Medical Dir/Dir of Nursing* J S Sanoy MD; Mary Davis DON.
Licensure Skilled care; Intermediate care. *Beds* SNF; ICF 100. *Certified* Medicaid; Medicare.
Owner Proprietary Corp (Health Care Facilities Inc).
Admissions Requirements Medical examination; Physician's request.
Staff RNs 6 (ft), 6 (pt); RNs 8 (ft), 6 (pt); LPNs 2 (ft); Nurses aides 46 (ft), 20 (pt); Physical therapists 2 (pt); Occupational therapists 1 (pt); Speech therapists 1 (pt); Activities coordinators 1 (ft); Dietitians 1 (ft).
Facilities Dining room; Physical therapy room; Activities room; Chapel; Crafts room; Laundry room; Barber/Beauty shop.
Activities Arts & crafts; Cards; Games; Reading groups; Prayer groups; Movies; Shopping trips; Social/Cultural gatherings.

Lost Creek Care Center
804 S Mumaugh Rd, Lima, OH, 45804
(419) 225-9040
Admin Albert C Parton Jr. *Medical Dir/Dir of Nursing* Melvin Monroe MD; Frances Reese DON.
Licensure Skilled care; Intermediate care. *Beds* 100. *Certified* Medicaid; Medicare; VA.
Owner Nonprofit Corp (Volunteers of America Care).
Admissions Requirements Medical examination; Physician's request.
Staff Physicians 30 (pt); RNs 8 (ft); LPNs 10 (ft); Nurses aides 72 (pt); Physical therapists 3 (ft); Recreational therapists 1 (ft); Occupational therapists 1 (ft); Speech therapists 1 (ft); Activities coordinators 1 (ft); Dietitians 1 (ft); Ophthalmologists 1 (pt).

Facilities Dining room; Physical therapy room; Activities room; Chapel; Crafts room; Laundry room; Barber/Beauty shop; Library.
Activities Arts & crafts; Cards; Games; Reading groups; Prayer groups; Movies; Shopping trips; Social/Cultural gatherings.

Oaks Convalescent Center
599 S Shawnee St, Lima, OH, 45804
(419) 227-2154
Admin Mary Ellen Thornton. *Medical Dir/Dir of Nursing* Dr Thompson; Ginny Rainsburg RN DON.
Licensure Skilled care; Intermediate care. *Beds* SNF 19; ICF 81. *Certified* Medicaid; Medicare.
Owner Proprietary Corp (Beverly Enterprises).
Admissions Requirements Minimum age 18; Medical examination; Physician's request.
Staff RNs 4 (ft), 4 (pt); LPNs 7 (ft), 3 (pt); Nurses aides 30 (ft), 18 (pt); Activities coordinators 1 (ft); Dietitians 1 (ft).
Facilities Dining room; Physical therapy room; Activities room; Crafts room; Laundry room; Barber/Beauty shop.
Activities Arts & crafts; Cards; Games; Reading groups; Prayer groups; Movies; Shopping trips; Social/Cultural gatherings.

Shawnee Manor*
2535 Fort Amanda Rd, Lima, OH, 45804
(419) 999-2055
Licensure Skilled care; Intermediate care. *Beds* 100. *Certified* Medicaid; Medicare.
Owner Proprietary Corp (Health Care Facilities Inc).

Springview Manor*
883 W Spring St, Lima, OH, 45805
(419) 227-3661
Licensure Intermediate care. *Beds* 43. *Certified* Medicaid.
Owner Proprietary Corp.
Staff Physicians 1 (ft), 1 (pt); RNs 3 (ft), 1 (pt); LPNs 3 (ft); Orderlies 1 (ft); Nurses aides 15 (ft), 2 (pt); Physical therapists 1 (ft); Recreational therapists 1 (ft); Occupational therapists 1 (ft); Speech therapists 1 (ft); Activities coordinators 1 (ft); Dietitians 1 (ft); Podiatrists 1 (ft).
Facilities Dining room; Physical therapy room; Activities room; Crafts room; Laundry room; Barber/Beauty shop; Library.
Activities Arts & crafts; Cards; Games; Reading groups; Prayer groups; Movies; Shopping trips; Social/Cultural gatherings.

LINCOLN HEIGHTS

Brown's Nursing Home*
PO Box 15488, 1153 Lindy St, Lincoln Heights, OH, 45215
(513) 733-4240
Licensure Intermediate care. *Beds* 70. *Certified* Medicaid.
Owner Proprietary Corp.

LISBON

Opportunity Homes Inc
7891 State Rte 45, Lisbon, OH, 44432
(216) 424-1411
Admin Mary Jane Jones. *Medical Dir/Dir of Nursing* William Stevenson; Marilyn Robb DON.
Licensure Intermediate care for mentally retarded. *Beds* ICF/MR 22. *Certified* Medicaid; Dept of Health funding.
Owner Nonprofit Corp.
Admissions Requirements Medical examination.
Staff LPNs 6 (ft), 1 (pt); Orderlies 4 (ft), 5 (pt); Nurses aides 6 (ft), 11 (pt); Activities coordinators 1 (pt); Dietitians 1 (ft); Social Service 2 (ft); QMRPs 2 (ft); Therapy Aides 3 (ft).

Facilities Dining room; Physical therapy room; Activities room; Crafts room; Laundry room.
Activities Arts & crafts; Games; Movies; Shopping trips; Social/Cultural gatherings; Pet therapy; Special Olympics; Community awareness.

Pleasant View Nursing Home
7451 Pleasant View Dr, Lisbon, OH, 44432
(216) 424-3721
Admin Iva G Myers. *Medical Dir/Dir of Nursing* Dr Walter Dombroski.
Licensure Intermediate care. *Beds* ICF 50. *Certified* Medicaid.
Owner Proprietary Corp.
Staff RNs 1 (pt); LPNs 3 (ft), 4 (pt); Orderlies 2 (ft); Nurses aides 12 (ft), 7 (pt); Activities coordinators 1 (ft).
Facilities Dining room; Activities room; Crafts room; Laundry room.
Activities Arts & crafts; Cards; Games; Reading groups; Prayer groups; Movies; Shopping trips; Social/Cultural gatherings.

Windsor Manor Nursing Home
8473 County Home Rd, Lisbon, OH, 44432
(216) 424-7203
Admin Sally A Beil NHA. *Medical Dir/Dir of Nursing* Dr William Stevenson; Maureen Bezon RN DON.
Licensure Skilled care. *Beds* SNF 50. *Certified* Medicaid; Medicare.
Owner Proprietary Corp.
Admissions Requirements Medical examination.
Staff Physicians 1 (pt); RNs 1 (ft), 3 (pt); LPNs 4 (ft), 10 (pt); Orderlies 3 (pt); Nurses aides 20 (ft), 6 (pt); Physical therapists 1 (pt); Occupational therapists 1 (pt); Speech therapists 1 (pt); Activities coordinators 1 (pt); Dietitians 1 (pt); Dentists 1 (pt); Podiatrists 1 (pt).
Facilities Dining room; Physical therapy room; Activities room; Crafts room; Laundry room; Barber/Beauty shop.
Activities Arts & crafts; Cards; Games; Reading groups; Prayer groups; Movies; Shopping trips; Social/Cultural gatherings; Fashion shows.

LOGAN

Arcadia Acres*
20017 State Rte 93 S, Logan, OH, 43138
(614) 385-2461
Licensure Intermediate care. *Beds* 50. *Certified* Medicaid.
Owner Proprietary Corp.

Buckeye Community Services—Culver Street Home*
30 N Culver St, Logan, OH, 43138
(614) 385-7261
Licensure Skilled care. *Beds* 8. *Certified* Medicaid.
Owner Nonprofit Corp.

Buckeye Community Services—Hunter Street Home
412 W Hunter St, Logan, OH, 43138
(614) 385-5787
Admin Pamela S Pauley. *Medical Dir/Dir of Nursing* Jennifer VanSickle RN.
Licensure Intermediate care for mentally retarded. *Beds* ICF/MR 5. *Certified* Medicaid.
Owner Nonprofit organization/foundation.
Admissions Requirements Minimum age Legal adult; Males only.
Staff RNs 1 (pt); LPNs 3 (pt); Orderlies 2 (ft), 3 (pt); Physical therapists 1 (pt); Occupational therapists 1 (pt); Speech therapists 1 (pt); Activities coordinators 1 (pt).
Activities Arts & crafts; Cards; Games; Reading groups; Movies; Shopping trips; Social/Cultural gatherings.

Buckeye Community Services—Walnut Street Home*
823 Walnut-Dowler Rd, Logan, OH, 43138
Licensure Intermediate care for mentally retarded. *Beds* 10. *Certified* Medicaid.
Owner Nonprofit Corp.

Hocking Valley Community Hospital
PO Box 966, Logan, OH, 43138-0966
(614) 385-5631
Licensure Skilled care; Intermediate care. *Beds* SNF 30; ICF 30. *Certified* Medicaid; Medicare.
Owner Publicly owned.

Logan Health Care Center
300 Arlington Ave, Logan, OH, 43138
(614) 385-2155
Admin Shirley A. Campbell. *Medical Dir/Dir of Nursing* Dr Teresa Ouinlin, Medical Director; Millie Price RN.
Licensure Skilled care; Intermediate care. *Beds* SNF 8; ICF 151. *Certified* Medicaid; Medicare.
Owner Proprietary Corp (Hillhaven Corp).
Admissions Requirements Medical examination; Physician's request.
Staff RNs 6 (ft), 3 (pt); LPNs 10 (ft), 16 (pt); Nurses aides 20 (ft), 17 (pt); Activities coordinators 2 (ft).
Facilities Dining room; Physical therapy room; Activities room; Laundry room; Barber/Beauty shop.
Activities Arts & crafts; Cards; Games; Reading groups; Prayer groups; Movies; Shopping trips; Social/Cultural gatherings.

LONDON

Madison Elms Nursing Center
218 Elm St, London, OH, 43140
(614) 852-3100
Admin Gary Brand. *Medical Dir/Dir of Nursing* William T Bacon MD; Sharon Ellis RN.
Licensure Skilled care; Intermediate care. *Beds* SNF 100; ICF. *Certified* Medicaid; Medicare.
Owner Proprietary Corp (Arbor Health Care).
Admissions Requirements Medical examination.
Staff RNs 5 (ft), 1 (pt); LPNs 4 (ft), 1 (pt); Nurses aides 26 (ft), 3 (pt); Physical therapists 1 (ft); Occupational therapists 1 (ft); Speech therapists 1 (ft); Activities coordinators 1 (ft); Dietitians 1 (pt); Dentists; Ophthalmologists.
Facilities Dining room; Physical therapy room; Chapel; Laundry room; Barber/Beauty shop.
Activities Arts & crafts; Cards; Games; Reading groups; Prayer groups; Movies; Shopping trips; Social/Cultural gatherings.

LORAIN

Anchor Lodge Nursing Home
3756 W Erie Ave, Lorain, OH, 44053
(216) 244-2019
Admin Marenia G Davis. *Medical Dir/Dir of Nursing* Dr I A Eren.
Licensure Intermediate care. *Beds* 103. *Certified* Medicaid.
Owner Proprietary Corp.
Admissions Requirements Medical examination.
Staff RNs 2 (ft), 2 (pt); LPNs 6 (ft), 8 (pt); Nurses aides 28 (ft), 12 (pt); Physical therapists 1 (ft), 1 (pt); Recreational therapists 1 (ft); Activities coordinators 1 (ft); Dietitians 1 (ft); Dentists 1 (ft); Ophthalmologists 1 (ft); Podiatrists 1 (ft).
Languages Spanish, Hungarian
Facilities Dining room; Physical therapy room; Activities room; Crafts room; Laundry room; Barber/Beauty shop; Library.

Activities Arts & crafts; Cards; Games; Reading groups; Prayer groups; Movies; Shopping trips; Social/Cultural gatherings.

Autumn Aegis Nursing Home
3905 Oberlin Ave, Lorain, OH, 44053
(216) 292-6768
Licensure Intermediate care. *Beds* 100. *Certified* Medicaid.
Owner Proprietary Corp.

Lorain Manor Nursing Home*
1882 E 32nd St, Lorain, OH, 44055
Licensure Intermediate care. *Beds* 76. *Certified* Medicaid.
Owner Proprietary Corp.

Meister Road Home
4609 Meister Rd, Lorain, OH, 44053
(216) 282-3074
Admin Dr Ellen L Payner. *Medical Dir/Dir of Nursing* Patricia Paul RN.
Licensure Intermediate care for mentally retarded. *Beds* ICF/MR 18. *Certified* Medicaid.
Owner Publicly owned.
Admissions Requirements Minimum age 7.
Staff RNs 2 (ft); LPNs 2 (ft), 4 (pt); Nurses aides 8 (ft), 20 (pt); Recreational therapists 1 (ft); Dietitians 1 (ft).
Facilities Dining room; Laundry room.
Activities Arts & crafts; Games; Reading groups; Movies; Shopping trips; Social/Cultural gatherings; County ARC activities; School & community functions.

Oak Hills Nursing Home
3650 Beavercrest Dr, Lorain, OH, 44053
(216) 282-9171
Admin Helen Landen. *Medical Dir/Dir of Nursing* Dr John Gray; Joann Buck RN DON.
Licensure Skilled care; Intermediate care. *Beds* 100. *Certified* Medicaid; Medicare.
Owner Proprietary Corp (Unicare).
Admissions Requirements Medical examination; Physician's request.
Staff Physicians; RNs; LPNs; Nurses aides; Physical therapists; Recreational therapists; Speech therapists; Activities coordinators; Dietitians; Ophthalmologists; Podiatrists.
Facilities Dining room; Physical therapy room; Activities room; Laundry room; Barber/Beauty shop.
Activities Arts & crafts; Cards; Games; Reading groups; Prayer groups; Movies; Shopping trips; Social/Cultural gatherings.

Ohio Extended Care Center*
3364 Kolbe Rd, Lorain, OH, 44053
(216) 282-2244
Licensure Intermediate care. *Beds* 203. *Certified* Medicaid.
Owner Proprietary Corp.

LOUDONVILLE

Colonial Manor Health Care Center Inc
747 S Mount Vernon Ave, Loudonville, OH, 44842
(419) 994-4191
Admin Linda Snowbarger. *Medical Dir/Dir of Nursing* Dr Jon Cooperrider; Pat Shireman DON.
Licensure Intermediate care. *Beds* ICF 80. *Certified* Medicaid.
Owner Privately owned.
Admissions Requirements Minimum age 18; Medical examination; Physician's request.
Staff RNs 3 (ft), 1 (pt); LPNs 4 (ft), 5 (pt); Nurses aides 8 (ft), 18 (pt); Physical therapists 1 (ft), 1 (pt); Recreational therapists 1 (ft); Activities coordinators 1 (ft); Dietitians 1 (pt).
Facilities Dining room; Physical therapy room; Activities room; Crafts room; Laundry room; Barber/Beauty shop.

Activities Arts & crafts; Cards; Games; Reading groups; Prayer groups; Movies; Shopping trips; Social/Cultural gatherings.

Colonial Manor Health Care Center Inc II*
Rte 1, Box 4-A, Loudonville, OH, 44842
(419) 994-3148
Licensure Intermediate care. *Beds* 36. *Certified* Medicaid.
Owner Proprietary Corp.

Loudonville Nursing Home, Inc
205 N Water St, Loudonville, OH, 44842
(419) 994-4250
Admin Walter E Lang. *Medical Dir/Dir of Nursing* John L McMullen.
Licensure Intermediate care. *Beds* ICF 25. *Certified* Medicaid.
Owner Privately owned.
Admissions Requirements Medical examination.
Staff RNs 1 (pt); LPNs 3 (ft), 1 (pt); Nurses aides 6 (ft), 3 (pt); Activities coordinators 2 (pt); Dietitians 1 (pt).
Facilities Dining room; Activities room; Crafts room; Laundry room; Barber/Beauty shop.
Activities Arts & crafts; Cards; Games; Reading groups; Prayer groups; Movies; Shopping trips; Social/Cultural gatherings; School children's visitation; Exercise.

LOUISVILLE

Mapleview Care Center Inc*
4466 Lynnhaven Ave NE, Louisville, OH, 44641
(216) 875-5060
Licensure Intermediate care. *Beds* 50. *Certified* Medicaid.
Owner Proprietary Corp.

The Marcelle Home*
7121 W Saint Francis St, Louisville, OH, 44641
(216) 875-4224
Licensure Intermediate care. *Beds* 50. *Certified* Medicaid.
Owner Proprietary Corp (Altercare Inc).

Miller Care Center Inc*
11701 Louisville St NE, Louisville, OH, 44641
(216) 875-8444
Licensure Intermediate care. *Beds* 50. *Certified* Medicaid.
Owner Proprietary Corp.

Joseph T Nist Nursing Home
7770 Columbus Rd NE, Louisville, OH, 44614
(216) 875-1456 Ext 5327
Admin John E Reiser. *Medical Dir/Dir of Nursing* Eugene Pogorelec DO; Donna Craig RN.
Licensure Skilled care; Intermediate care. *Beds* SNF 248; ICF. *Certified* Medicaid; Medicare.
Owner Publicly owned.
Admissions Requirements Medical examination.
Staff RNs 8 (ft), 4 (pt); LPNs 18 (ft), 12 (pt); Nurses aides 70 (ft), 30 (pt); Activities coordinators 2 (ft).
Facilities Dining room; Physical therapy room; Activities room; Crafts room; Laundry room; Barber/Beauty shop; Library.
Activities Arts & crafts; Cards; Games; Reading groups; Prayer groups; Movies; Shopping trips; Social/Cultural gatherings.

St Joseph Hospice Home for the Aged
2308 Reno Dr NE, Louisville, OH, 44641
(216) 875-5562
Admin Sr Monica Bellinger. *Medical Dir/Dir of Nursing* Dr Joseph Kolp; Marilyn May DOA.
Licensure Intermediate care. *Beds* 100. *Certified* Medicaid.

Owner Nonprofit Corp.
Admissions Requirements Minimum age 60;
Medical examination; Physician's request.
Staff Physicians 4 (ft), 10 (pt); RNs 6 (ft), 10
(pt); LPNs 5 (ft), 5 (pt); Nurses aides 20 (ft),
29 (pt); Activities coordinators 1 (ft), 2 (pt);
Physical therapist aides 2 (ft).
Affiliation Roman Catholic
Facilities Dining room; Activities room;
Chapel; Crafts room; Laundry room; Barber/
Beauty shop.
Activities Arts & crafts; Cards; Games;
Reading groups; Prayer groups; Movies;
Shopping trips; Social/Cultural gatherings.

Molly Stark Hospital
7900 Columbus Rd NE, Louisville, OH,
44641
(216) 875-5531
Admin Donald T McKenna. *Medical Dir/Dir
of Nursing* Eugene Pogorelec; Roberta Wolf
RN.
Licensure Skilled care; Intermediate care for
mentally retarded; Chemical dependency
detox Rehab; Chronic. *Beds* SNF 30; ICF/
MR 76; Chemical dependency 24 Chronic
18. *Certified* Medicaid; Medicare.
Owner Publicly owned.
Admissions Requirements Physician's request.
Staff Physicians 4 (pt); RNs 9 (ft), 9 (pt);
LPNs 24 (ft), 9 (pt); Nurses aides 50 (ft), 9
(pt); Physical therapists 1 (pt); Recreational
therapists 1 (ft); Occupational therapists 1
(pt); Speech therapists 1 (pt); Activities
coordinators 1 (ft); Dietitians 1 (ft); Dentists
3 (pt); Ophthalmologists 1 (pt).
Facilities Dining room; Physical therapy
room; Activities room; Chapel; Crafts room;
Laundry room; Barber/Beauty shop.
Activities Arts & crafts; Cards; Games;
Reading groups; Prayer groups; Movies;
Shopping trips; Social/Cultural gatherings.

LOVELAND

Colonial Acres Nursing Home*
11887 Lebanon Rd, Loveland, OH, 45140
Licensure Nursing home. *Beds* 10.
Owner Proprietary Corp.

Loveland Health Care Center*
State Rte 48, 501 N 2nd St, Loveland, OH,
45140
(513) 683-0010
Admin Donald J Benson. *Medical Dir/Dir of
Nursing* William Blake Selnick DO.
Licensure Skilled care; Intermediate care. *Beds*
100. *Certified* Medicaid; Medicare.
Owner Proprietary Corp.
Admissions Requirements Minimum age 18;
Medical examination; Physician's request.
Staff RNs 5 (ft), 9 (pt); LPNs 4 (ft), 5 (pt);
Nurses aides 27 (ft), 17 (pt); Physical
therapists 1 (pt); Activities coordinators 1
(ft).
Facilities Dining room; Physical therapy
room; Activities room; Laundry room;
Barber/Beauty shop.
Activities Arts & crafts; Cards; Games;
Reading groups; Prayer groups; Movies;
Shopping trips; Social/Cultural gatherings.

LUCASVILLE

Taylor's Health Care Inc—Riverview*
PO Box 785, Rte 5, Lucasville, OH, 45648
(614) 259-5536
Licensure Mental Nursing home. *Beds* 100.
Owner Proprietary Corp.

MADEIRA

Madeira Nursing Inc
6940 Stiegler Ln, Madeira, OH, 45243
(513) 561-6400
Admin Lisa G Weber. *Medical Dir/Dir of
Nursing* David S Norris MD.

Licensure Skilled care; Intermediate care. *Beds*
SNF; ICF 100. *Certified* Medicaid;
Medicare.
Owner Privately owned.
Admissions Requirements Minimum age 18;
Medical examination.
Staff RNs 5 (ft), 2 (pt); LPNs 5 (ft), 1 (pt);
Nurses aides 30 (ft), 2 (pt); Physical
therapists 1 (pt); Speech therapists 1 (pt);
Activities coordinators 1 (ft); Dietitians 1
(pt); Dentists 1 (pt); Ophthalmologists 1 (pt);
Podiatrists 1 (pt); Dentist 1 (pt).
Facilities Dining room; Activities room;
Barber/Beauty shop.
Activities Arts & crafts; Cards; Games;
Reading groups; Prayer groups; Movies;
Social/Cultural gatherings.

MADISON

**Broadfield Manor Nursing & Convalescent
Home***
7927 Middle Ridge, Madison, OH, 44057
(216) 466-3702
Admin Torild Barbins. *Medical Dir/Dir of
Nursing* Janis Zemzars MD.
Licensure Skilled care; Intermediate care;
Intermediate care for mentally retarded.
Beds ICF 133. *Certified* Medicaid;
Medicare.
Owner Proprietary Corp.
Admissions Requirements Medical
examination.
Staff Physicians 4 (pt); Physical therapists 1
(pt); Occupational therapists 1 (pt); Speech
therapists 1 (pt); Activities coordinators 2
(ft); Dietitians 1 (pt); Dentists 1 (pt);
Podiatrists 1 (pt).
Facilities Dining room; Physical therapy
room; Activities room; Crafts room; Laundry
room; Barber/Beauty shop.
Activities Arts & crafts; Cards; Games;
Reading groups; Prayer groups; Movies;
Shopping trips; Social/Cultural gatherings;
Organ music at mealtime 3 times a week.

Gables Nursing Home*
PO Box 272, 731 Lake St, Madison, OH,
44057
(216) 428-1519
Licensure Intermediate care for mentally
retarded. *Beds* 20.
Owner Proprietary Corp.

Madison Health Care
7600 S Ridge Rd, Madison, OH, 44057
(216) 428-1492, 428-1116, 951-9299
Admin Mr Jon Hall. *Medical Dir/Dir of
Nursing* Dr Moschkovich; Jean Dollar.
Licensure Skilled care; Intermediate care. *Beds*
130. *Certified* Medicaid; Medicare.
Owner Proprietary Corp.
Admissions Requirements Medical
examination.
Staff Physicians 4 (ft); RNs 5 (ft), 3 (pt);
LPNs 14 (ft); Orderlies 3 (ft); Nurses aides
48 (ft), 2 (pt); Physical therapists 1 (pt);
Reality therapists 1 (pt); Speech therapists 1
(pt); Activities coordinators 2 (ft); Dietitians
1 (pt); Ophthalmologists 2 (pt); Podiatrists 1
(pt); Social service 1 (pt).
Facilities Dining room; Physical therapy
room; Activities room; Crafts room; Laundry
room; Barber/Beauty shop; Library.
Activities Arts & crafts; Cards; Games;
Reading groups; Prayer groups; Movies;
Shopping trips; Social/Cultural gatherings;
Community service projects; Fund raisers
for Heart & Arthritis Associations.

Madison Village Nursing Home*
148 E Main St, Madison, OH, 44057
(216) 428-4322
Licensure Intermediate care. *Beds* 12.
Certified Medicaid.
Owner Proprietary Corp.

Stewart Lodge*
7774 Warner Rd, Madison, OH, 44057
(216) 428-7121
Licensure Intermediate care for mentally
retarded. *Beds* 50. *Certified* Medicaid.
Owner Proprietary Corp.

MALTA

Parmiter Nursing Home*
300 N Main St, Malta, OH, 43758
(614) 962-4861
Licensure Intermediate care. *Beds* 30.
Certified Medicaid.
Owner Proprietary Corp (Community Care
Centers).

MANSFIELD

Chenita Nursing Home 1
245 W 4th St, Mansfield, OH, 44903
(419) 524-2335
Admin Anthony L Wheaton. *Medical Dir/Dir
of Nursing* Jessie Van Aucker RN DON.
Licensure Intermediate care. *Beds* ICF 13.
Certified Medicaid.
Owner Proprietary Corp.
Admissions Requirements Medical
examination.
Staff LPNs 3 (ft); Nurses aides 3 (ft), 2 (pt).
Facilities Dining room; Activities room;
Crafts room; Laundry room.
Activities Arts & crafts; Cards; Games;
Reading groups; Movies; Shopping trips;
Social/Cultural gatherings.

Chenita Nursing Home 2
111 S Diamond St, Mansfield, OH, 44903
(419) 524-4149
Admin Anthony L Wheaton. *Medical Dir/Dir
of Nursing* Gordon Morkel MD.
Licensure Intermediate care. *Beds* ICF 50.
Certified Medicaid.
Owner Proprietary Corp.
Admissions Requirements Minimum age 16;
Medical examination.
Staff Physicians 1 (pt); RNs 2 (ft); LPNs 4
(ft), 1 (pt); Orderlies 1 (ft); Nurses aides 14
(ft); Physical therapists 1 (pt); Reality
therapists 1 (pt); Recreational therapists 1
(ft); Occupational therapists 1 (pt); Speech
therapists 1 (pt); Activities coordinators 1
(ft); Dietitians 1 (pt); Dentists 1 (pt);
Ophthalmologists 1 (pt); Podiatrists 1 (pt).
Facilities Dining room; Physical therapy
room; Activities room; Crafts room; Laundry
room; Library.
Activities Arts & crafts; Cards; Games;
Reading groups; Prayer groups; Movies;
Shopping trips; Social/Cultural gatherings.

Crestwood Care Center—Mansfield*
Rock Rd, Mansfield, OH, 44903
(419) 529-9855
Licensure Nursing home. *Beds* 25.
Owner Proprietary Corp.

Geriatric Center-Mansfield Memorial Homes*
50 Blymyer Ave, PO Box 966, Mansfield, OH,
44901
(419) 524-4178
Medical Dir/Dir of Nursing Charles G Young
MD.
Licensure Skilled care; Intermediate care. *Beds*
99. *Certified* Medicaid; Medicare.
Owner Nonprofit Corp.
Admissions Requirements Minimum age;
Medical examination; Physician's request.
Staff RNs 7 (ft), 8 (pt); LPNs 5 (ft), 7 (pt);
Nurses aides 25 (ft), 15 (pt); Physical
therapists 1 (ft); Reality therapists 1 (ft);
Recreational therapists 1 (ft); Occupational
therapists 1 (ft), 1 (pt); Speech therapists 1
(pt); Activities coordinators 1 (ft); Dietitians
1 (pt).

Facilities Dining room; Physical therapy
room; Activities room; Chapel; Crafts room;
Laundry room; Barber/Beauty shop; Library.
Activities Arts & crafts; Cards; Games;
Reading groups; Prayer groups; Movies;
Shopping trips; Social/Cultural gatherings;
Occupational therapy; Speech therapy.

The Glendale Home*
624 Glendale Blvd, Mansfield, OH, 44907
Licensure Intermediate care for mentally
retarded. *Beds* 12. *Certified* Medicaid.
Owner Publicly owned.

McCaulley Care Center
1670 Crider Rd, Mansfield, OH, 44903
(419) 589-6222
Admin Dr James A McCaulley. *Medical Dir/
Dir of Nursing* Jessie VanAuker.
Licensure Intermediate care; Intermediate care
for mentally retarded. *Beds* ICF 75; ICF/MR
25. *Certified* Medicaid.
Owner Proprietary Corp.
Admissions Requirements Minimum age
Teenage; Medical examination.
Staff RNs 4 (ft), 1 (pt); LPNs 9 (ft), 8 (pt);
Nurses aides 23 (ft), 7 (pt); Activities
coordinators 1 (ft); Dietitians 1 (ft).
Facilities Dining room; Physical therapy
room; Activities room; Crafts room; Laundry
room.
Activities Arts & crafts; Cards; Games;
Reading groups; Movies; Shopping trips;
Social/Cultural gatherings.

The Raintree
721 Scholl Rd, Mansfield, OH, 44907
(419) 756-0650
Admin Robert R Ling. *Medical Dir/Dir of
Nursing* Dr T Polevoy; Dorothy Morales
RN.
Licensure Intermediate care for mentally
retarded. *Beds* 48. *Certified* Medicaid.
Owner Publicly owned.
Staff Physicians 1 (pt); RNs; LPNs; Nurses
aides; Physical therapists; Recreational
therapists; Occupational therapists; Speech
therapists; Dietitians.
Facilities Dining room; Physical therapy
room; Activities room; Laundry room.
Activities Movies; Shopping trips.

Rosemont Nursing Home*
1159 Wyandotte Ave, Mansfield, OH, 44906
(419) 747-2666
Licensure Intermediate care. *Beds* 24.
Certified Medicaid.
Owner Proprietary Corp.

Sturges Convalescent Home*
81 Sturges Ave, Mansfield, OH, 44902
(419) 522-3651
Licensure Intermediate care. *Beds* 29.
Certified Medicaid.
Owner Proprietary Corp.

Twin Oaks
73 Madison Rd, Mansfield, OH, 44905
(419) 526-0124
Admin Robert H Rice. *Medical Dir/Dir of
Nursing* Dr P K Athmaram; Barbara
Dunham DON.
Licensure Intermediate care; Intermediate care
for mentally retarded. *Beds* ICF 18; ICF/MR
32. *Certified* Medicaid.
Owner Proprietary Corp.
Admissions Requirements Minimum age 16;
Medical examination.
Staff Physicians 1 (pt); RNs 1 (ft); LPNs 6
(ft); Nurses aides 14 (ft); Physical therapists
1 (pt); Recreational therapists 2 (ft);
Occupational therapists 1 (pt); Speech
therapists 1 (pt); Activities coordinators 1
(ft); Dietitians 1 (pt); Dentists 1 (pt);
Ophthalmologists 1 (pt); Podiatrists 1 (pt).
Facilities Dining room; Physical therapy
room; Activities room; Crafts room; Laundry
room; Library.

Activities Arts & crafts; Cards; Games;
Reading groups; Prayer groups; Movies;
Shopping trips; Social/Cultural gatherings.

Winchester Terrace Inc
70 Winchester Rd, Mansfield, OH, 44907
(419) 756-4747
Admin Linn Dunn. *Medical Dir/Dir of
Nursing* Donald Beddard MD; Ann Kinstle
RN DON.
Licensure Skilled care. *Beds* SNF 63.
Owner Proprietary Corp.
Admissions Requirements Medical
examination.
Staff RNs 4 (ft); LPNs 6 (ft); Nurses aides 20
(ft); Activities coordinators 1 (ft).
Facilities Dining room; Activities room;
Crafts room; Laundry room; Barber/Beauty
shop; Library.
Activities Arts & crafts; Cards; Games;
Reading groups; Prayer groups; Movies;
Shopping trips; Social/Cultural gatherings.

Woodlawn Nursing Home
535 Lexington Ave, Mansfield, OH, 44907
(419) 756-7111
Admin Douglas C Dotson. *Medical Dir/Dir of
Nursing* Dr Sawyer; Cathy Wiltanger.
Licensure Skilled care; Intermediate care; Rest
home. *Beds* SNF 155; ICF; Rest home 9.
Certified Medicaid; Medicare.
Owner Proprietary Corp.
Facilities Dining room; Physical therapy
room; Activities room; Crafts room; Laundry
room; Barber/Beauty shop.
Activities Arts & crafts; Cards; Games;
Reading groups; Prayer groups; Movies;
Shopping trips; Social/Cultural gatherings;
Recreational therapy.

MANTUA

Hattie Larlham Foundation*
9772 Diagonal Rd, Mantua, OH, 44255
(216) 274-2272
Medical Dir/Dir of Nursing Mary Marsick
MD.
Licensure Intermediate care for mentally
retarded. *Beds* 130.
Owner Nonprofit Corp.
Admissions Requirements Medical
examination.
Staff Physicians 1 (ft); RNs 9 (ft); LPNs 17
(ft); Nurses aides 94 (ft); Physical therapists
3 (ft); Recreational therapists 1 (ft);
Occupational therapists 4 (ft); Speech
therapists 1 (ft); Dietitians 1 (ft); Dentists 1
(pt); Audiologists 1 (pt).
Facilities Physical therapy room; Activities
room; Chapel; Laundry room.

MAPLE HEIGHTS

Maple Care Center
PO Box 37191, 16231 Broadway Ave, Maple
Heights, OH, 44105
(216) 662-0551
Medical Dir/Dir of Nursing M Reddy MD.
Licensure Skilled care; Intermediate care. *Beds*
100. *Certified* Medicaid; Medicare.
Owner Proprietary Corp.
Admissions Requirements Medical
examination.
Staff RNs 3 (ft); LPNs 6 (ft); Nurses aides 28
(ft); Physical therapists 1 (pt); Activities
coordinators 1 (ft), 1 (pt).
Facilities Dining room; Physical therapy
room; Activities room; Chapel; Crafts room;
Library; Occupational therapy room; Exam
room; Shampoo room; Patio.
Activities Arts & crafts; Cards; Games;
Reading groups; Prayer groups; Movies;
Social/Cultural gatherings; Entertainment
and shows.

Pedone Nursing Center*
19900 Clare Ave, Maple Heights, OH, 44137
(216) 662-3343
Licensure Skilled care; Intermediate care. *Beds*
100. *Certified* Medicaid; Medicare.
Owner Proprietary Corp.
Admissions Requirements Medical
examination.
Facilities Dining room; Physical therapy
room; Activities room; Chapel; Crafts room;
Laundry room; Barber/Beauty shop; Library.
Activities Arts & crafts; Cards; Games;
Reading groups; Prayer groups; Movies;
Shopping trips.

MARIETTA

Christian Anchorage Retirement Home Inc*
355 Putnam Ave, Marietta, OH, 45715
Licensure Intermediate care. *Beds* 48.
Certified Medicaid.

Heartland of Marietta*
Rte 60, Devola, Marietta, OH, 45750
(614) 373-8920
Licensure Intermediate care. *Beds* 101.
Certified Medicaid.
Owner Proprietary Corp (Health Care &
Retirement Corp).

The Marie Antoinette Pavilion
PO Box 756, 355 Putnam Ave, Marietta, OH,
45750
(614) 373-4066
Admin H A Kolshorn. *Medical Dir/Dir of
Nursing* C Dehmlow MD.
Licensure Intermediate care. *Beds* ICF 50.
Certified Medicaid.
Owner Proprietary Corp.
Admissions Requirements Medical
examination.
Staff Physicians 1 (pt); RNs 2 (ft); LPNs 11
(ft), 4 (pt); Nurses aides 18 (ft), 4 (pt);
Physical therapists 2 (pt); Occupational
therapists 1 (pt); Speech therapists 1 (pt);
Activities coordinators 2 (ft), 1 (pt);
Dietitians 1 (pt); Dentists 1 (pt);
Ophthalmologists 1 (pt); Podiatrists 1 (pt).
Languages German, French, Arabic
Facilities Dining room; Activities room;
Crafts room; Laundry room; Barber/Beauty
shop; Library.
Activities Arts & crafts; Cards; Games;
Reading groups; Prayer groups; Movies;
Shopping trips; Social/Cultural gatherings.

Marietta Convalescent Center
117 Barlett St, Marietta, OH, 45750
(614) 373-1867
Admin Gary Wickham. *Medical Dir/Dir of
Nursing* Kenneth E Bennett MD; Lillie
Varner.
Licensure Intermediate care. *Beds* ICF 120.
Certified Medicaid.
Owner Proprietary Corp.
Admissions Requirements Medical
examination; Physician's request.
Staff Physicians 1 (ft), 10 (pt); RNs 6 (ft), 3
(pt); LPNs 9 (ft), 5 (pt); Nurses aides 30 (ft),
5 (pt); Physical therapists 1 (pt); Activities
coordinators 2 (ft), 2 (pt); Dietitians 1 (pt);
Ophthalmologists 1 (pt); Podiatrists 1 (pt).
Facilities Dining room; Activities room;
Chapel; Crafts room; Laundry room; Barber/
Beauty shop; 2 Lounges.
Activities Arts & crafts; Cards; Games;
Reading groups; Prayer groups; Movies;
Shopping trips; Social/Cultural gatherings;
Van outings; Family programs.

Washington County Woman's Home
812 3rd St, Marietta, OH, 45750
(614) 373-2329
Admin Joan Allphin.
Licensure Rest home; Assisted living. *Beds*
22.
Owner Nonprofit Corp.

Admissions Requirements Females only;
Medical examination.
Staff LPNs 1 (ft); Nurses aides 8 (ft).
Facilities Dining room; Laundry room;
Barber/Beauty shop.
Activities Arts & crafts; Games; Reading
groups; Prayer groups; Movies; Shopping
trips.

MARION

**American Marion Nursing & Rehabilitation
Center**
524 Jamesway, Marion, OH, 43302
(614) 389-6306
Admin Michael Campbell. *Medical Dir/Dir of
Nursing* Dr Landefeld; Sara Bader DON.
Licensure Skilled care; Intermediate care. *Beds*
SNF 25; ICF 75. *Certified* Medicaid;
Medicare.
Owner Proprietary Corp (Care Enterprises).
Admissions Requirements Physician's request.
Staff RNs 5 (ft); LPNs 8 (ft); Orderlies 25 (ft);
Nurses aides 5 (ft); Recreational therapists 1
(ft); Dietitians 1 (ft).
Facilities Dining room; Physical therapy
room; Activities room; Crafts room; Laundry
room; Barber/Beauty shop.
Activities Arts & crafts; Cards; Games;
Reading groups; Prayer groups; Movies;
Shopping trips.

Community Nursing Center
175 Community Dr, Marion, OH, 43302
(614) 387-7537
Admin Michael J Rau. *Medical Dir/Dir of
Nursing* Carol Buchanan DON.
Licensure Skilled care; Intermediate care. *Beds*
SNF 109; ICF. *Certified* Medicaid;
Medicare.
Owner Proprietary Corp (Hillhaven Corp).
Admissions Requirements Minimum age 18;
Medical examination.
Staff RNs 4 (ft), 1 (pt); LPNs 7 (ft), 2 (pt);
Nurses aides 35 (ft), 15 (pt); Physical
therapists 1 (pt); Recreational therapists 1
(ft); Occupational therapists 1 (pt); Speech
therapists 1 (pt); Activities coordinators 2
(ft); Dietitians 1 (pt).
Facilities Dining room; Physical therapy
room; Activities room; Crafts room; Laundry
room; Barber/Beauty shop.
Activities Arts & crafts; Cards; Games;
Reading groups; Prayer groups; Movies;
Shopping trips; Social/Cultural gatherings.

East Lawn Manor
1422 Mt Vernon Ave, Marion, OH, 43302
(614) 389-4624
Admin Larry M Marburger. *Medical Dir/Dir
of Nursing* Dr Ronald Landefeld.
Licensure Skilled care. *Beds* SNF ICF/SNF
26; ICF ICF 113. *Certified* Medicaid;
Medicare.
Owner Publicly owned.
Admissions Requirements Physician's request.
Staff RNs 9 (ft), 3 (pt); LPNs 12 (ft), 6 (pt);
Orderlies 2 (ft), 1 (pt); Nurses aides 41 (ft),
12 (ft); Physical therapists 4 (ft); Activities
coordinators 2 (ft), 1 (pt).
Facilities Dining room; Physical therapy
room; Activities room; Chapel; Crafts room;
Laundry room; Barber/Beauty shop; Library.
Activities Arts & crafts; Cards; Games;
Reading groups; Prayer groups; Movies;
Shopping trips; Social/Cultural gatherings.

Hillside Nursing Home
333 N Prospect Ave, Marion, OH, 43302
(614) 382-5042
Admin George Davis. *Medical Dir/Dir of
Nursing* Colleen Place.
Licensure Intermediate care. *Beds* ICF 24.
Certified Medicaid; Medicare.
Owner Proprietary Corp.
Admissions Requirements Medical
examination.

Staff RNs 1 (pt); LPNs 3 (ft), 2 (pt); Orderlies
2 (ft), 1 (pt); Nurses aides 7 (ft), 3 (pt);
Activities coordinators 1 (ft); Dietitians 1
(pt); Ophthalmologists 1 (pt); Cooks 3 (ft).
Facilities Dining room; Laundry room.
Activities Arts & crafts; Cards; Games;
Reading groups; Prayer groups; Movies;
Shopping trips.

Maplewood Nursing Center Inc
409 Bellefontaine Ave, Marion, OH, 43302
(614) 383-2126
Medical Dir/Dir of Nursing Dr Warren
Sawyer.
Licensure Skilled care; Intermediate care. *Beds*
50. *Certified* Medicaid; Medicare.
Owner Proprietary Corp.
Admissions Requirements Minimum age 21.
Staff Physicians 1 (pt); RNs 5 (ft); LPNs 4
(ft); Nurses aides 25 (ft); Physical therapists
1 (ft); Occupational therapists 1 (pt); Speech
therapists 1 (pt); Activities coordinators 1
(ft); Dietitians 1 (pt); Dentists 1 (pt);
Ophthalmologists 1 (pt); Podiatrists 1 (pt);
Dentist 1 (pt).
Facilities Dining room; Physical therapy
room; Activities room; Chapel; Laundry
room; Barber/Beauty shop.
Activities Arts & crafts; Cards; Prayer groups;
Movies.

Marion Manor Nursing Home Inc*
195 Executive Dr, Marion, OH, 43302
(614) 387-9545
Licensure Skilled care; Intermediate care. *Beds*
100. *Certified* Medicaid; Medicare.

Morning View Care Center
PO Box 656, Marion-Cardington Rd, Marion,
OH, 43302
(614) 389-1214
Admin Glen Dearth. *Medical Dir/Dir of
Nursing* Pat Heffernan.
Licensure Intermediate care. *Beds* 30.
Certified Medicaid.
Owner Proprietary Corp (Morning View Care
Center).
Admissions Requirements Medical
examination; Physician's request.
Staff Physicians; LPNs; Nurses aides;
Activities coordinators; Dietitians;
Ophthalmologists.
Facilities Dining room; Laundry room;
Barber/Beauty shop; Library.
Activities Arts & crafts; Cards; Games;
Reading groups; Prayer groups; Movies;
Shopping trips; Social/Cultural gatherings.

MARTINS FERRY

**East Ohio Regional Hospital Long-Term Care
Unit**
90 N 4th St, Martins Ferry, OH, 43935
(614) 633-1100
Admin Angelo Calbone. *Medical Dir/Dir of
Nursing* Dr F W Cook; J Loccisano RN.
Licensure Skilled care; Intermediate care. *Beds*
SNF 75; ICF. *Certified* Medicaid; Medicare;
JCAH.
Owner Nonprofit Corp.
Admissions Requirements Medical
examination; Physician's request.
Staff RNs; LPNs; Orderlies; Nurses aides;
Physical therapists; Activities coordinators;
Dietitians.
Facilities Dining room; Physical therapy
room; Activities room; Chapel; Crafts room;
Barber/Beauty shop.
Activities Arts & crafts; Cards; Games;
Reading groups; Prayer groups; Movies;
Shopping trips; Social/Cultural gatherings.

MARYSVILLE

Heartland of Marysville*
755 Plum St, Marysville, OH, 43040
Licensure Skilled care; Intermediate care. *Beds*
SNF 100; ICF 100. *Certified* Medicaid;
Medicare.
Owner Proprietary Corp (Southmark Heritage
Corp).

Milcrest Nursing Center
730 Milcrest Dr, Marysville, OH, 43040
(513) 642-1026
Admin Donna Crawford. *Medical Dir/Dir of
Nursing* Malcolm MacIvor MD; Maxine
Gregg.
Licensure Skilled care; Intermediate care. *Beds*
50. *Certified* Medicaid; Medicare.
Owner Proprietary Corp.
Admissions Requirements Minimum age 40.
Staff RNs 2 (ft), 1 (pt); LPNs 3 (ft), 3 (pt);
Nurses aides 16 (ft), 3 (pt); Physical
therapists 1 (pt); Recreational therapists 1
(ft), 1 (pt); Activities coordinators 1 (pt);
Dietitians 1 (pt); Podiatrists 1 (pt).
Facilities Dining room; Physical therapy
room; Laundry room; Barber/Beauty shop.
Activities Arts & crafts; Cards; Games;
Reading groups; Prayer groups; Movies;
Shopping trips; Social/Cultural gatherings;
Current events; Adopt-a-grandparent
program; Children's hour; Pet visiting; Out-
to-lunch group.

Union Manor*
18000 State Rte 4, Marysville, OH, 43040
(513) 642-3893
Licensure Intermediate care. *Beds* 112.
Certified Medicaid.
Owner Publicly owned.

MASON

Brookside Extended Care Center
780 Snider Rd, Mason, OH, 45040
Licensure Intermediate care for mentally
retarded. *Beds* ICF/MR 104. *Certified*
Medicaid.
Owner Proprietary Corp.
Staff Physicians; RNs; LPNs; Nurses aides;
Physical therapists; Recreational therapists;
Occupational therapists; Speech therapists;
Activities coordinators; Dietitians.
Languages Sign
Facilities Dining room; Physical therapy
room; Activities room; Crafts room; Laundry
room; Barber/Beauty shop.
Activities Arts & crafts; Cards; Games;
Reading groups; Prayer groups; Movies;
Shopping trips; Social/Cultural gatherings.

Edgewood Manor of Mason
5640 Cox-Smith Rd, Mason, OH, 45040
(513) 398-2881
Admin C Michael Filburn. *Medical Dir/Dir of
Nursing* Dr Martin Lehenbauer; Bonnie
Jones.
Licensure Intermediate care. *Beds* ICF 50.
Certified Medicaid.
Owner Proprietary Corp.
Admissions Requirements Medical
examination; Physician's request.
Staff Physicians 4 (pt); RNs 1 (pt); LPNs 10
(ft); Nurses aides 18 (ft); Activities
coordinators 1 (ft); Dietitians 1 (ft).
Facilities Dining room; Activities room;
Laundry room; Barber/Beauty shop.
Activities Arts & crafts; Cards; Games;
Reading groups; Prayer groups; Movies;
Shopping trips; Social/Cultural gatherings.

MASSILLON

Eventide Nursing Home*
200 Stewart Ave NW, Massillon, OH, 44646
(216) 477-4686

Licensure Nursing home. *Beds* 14.
Owner Proprietary Corp.

Hanover House Inc
435 Avis Ave NW, Massillon, OH, 44646
(216) 837-1741
Admin Amy J Francis. *Medical Dir/Dir of Nursing* M Kamel MD.
Licensure Skilled care; Intermediate care. *Beds* SNF 49; ICF 151. *Certified* Medicaid; Medicare.
Owner Proprietary Corp.
Staff Physicians 4 (pt); RNs 7 (ft), 6 (pt); LPNs 16 (ft), 7 (pt); Orderlies 1 (pt); Nurses aides 55 (ft), 12 (pt); Physical therapists 1 (ft); Occupational therapists 1 (pt); Speech therapists 1 (pt); Activities coordinators 1 (ft); Dietitians 1 (pt); Ophthalmologists 1 (pt).
Facilities Dining room; Physical therapy room; Activities room; Chapel; Laundry room; Barber/Beauty shop.
Activities Arts & crafts; Cards; Games; Reading groups; Prayer groups; Movies; Shopping trips.

Hospitality House*
205 Rohr Ave, Massillon, OH, 44646
(216) 837-2100
Medical Dir/Dir of Nursing Dr Wayne Lutzke.
Licensure Intermediate care. *Beds* 28. *Certified* Medicaid.
Owner Proprietary Corp.
Admissions Requirements Minimum age 60; Medical examination.
Staff RNs 1 (pt); LPNs 3 (ft), 4 (pt); Nurses aides 5 (ft), 10 (pt); Activities coordinators 1 (pt).
Facilities Dining room; Activities room; Crafts room; Laundry room; Barber/Beauty shop.
Activities Arts & crafts; Cards; Games; Movies; Shopping trips.

Massillon State Hospital
3000 S Erie St, Massillon, OH, 44646
(216) 833-3135
Admin Kenneth W Thomas. *Medical Dir/Dir of Nursing* Nathanael Sidharta MD; Delores Simms RN DON.
Licensure Intermediate care for mentally retarded. *Beds* ICF/MR 15. *Certified* Medicaid.
Owner Publicly owned.
Admissions Requirements Minimum age 18; Males only.
Staff Physicians 2 (pt); RNs 1 (ft); LPNs 2 (ft); Nurses aides 10 (ft); Physical therapists 1 (pt); Recreational therapists 1 (pt); Occupational therapists 2 (pt); Dietitians 1 (pt).
Facilities Dining room; Activities room; Chapel; Laundry room; Barber/Beauty shop; Library.
Activities Arts & crafts; Games; Movies; Shopping trips; Social/Cultural gatherings.

Park View Manor Inc*
54 Pine St NE, Massillon, OH, 44646
(216) 833-8352
Medical Dir/Dir of Nursing Dr H J Gashash.
Licensure Intermediate care. *Beds* 23. *Certified* Medicaid.
Owner Proprietary Corp.
Admissions Requirements Females only.
Staff Physicians 1 (pt); LPNs 2 (ft), 2 (pt); Nurses aides 6 (ft), 3 (pt); Activities coordinators 1 (pt); Dietitians 1 (pt); Dentists 1 (pt); Ophthalmologists 1 (pt); Podiatrists 1 (pt).
Facilities Dining room; Activities room; Crafts room.
Activities Arts & crafts; Cards; Games; Reading groups; Prayer groups; Movies; Shopping trips; Social/Cultural gatherings.

Rose Lane Health Center
5425 High Mill Ave NW, Massillon, OH, 44646
(216) 833-3174, 376-8527
Admin Dennis Potts. *Medical Dir/Dir of Nursing* Donald Zimmerman MD; Carol Richards RN DON.
Licensure Skilled care; Intermediate care. *Beds* SNF 66; ICF 121. *Certified* Medicaid; Medicare; VA.
Owner Proprietary Corp.
Admissions Requirements Minimum age 16; Medical examination; Physician's request.
Staff Physicians 28 (pt); RNs 8 (ft), 2 (pt); LPNs 19 (ft), 6 (pt); Orderlies 1 (ft), 2 (pt); Nurses aides 52 (ft), 24 (pt); Physical therapists 2 (ft); Occupational therapists 1 (ft); Speech therapists 1 (pt); Activities coordinators 1 (ft); Dietitians 1 (ft); Dentists 1 (pt); Ophthalmologists 1 (pt); Podiatrists 1 (pt).
Facilities Dining room; Physical therapy room; Activities room; Crafts room; Laundry room; Barber/Beauty shop; Multi-purpose room.
Activities Arts & crafts; Cards; Games; Reading groups; Prayer groups; Movies; Shopping trips; Social/Cultural gatherings; Quilting; Gardening; Cooking.

Shalem Rest Nursing Home*
906 16th St SE, Massillon, OH, 44646
(216) 832-0403
Medical Dir/Dir of Nursing A Alasyali MD.
Licensure Intermediate care. *Beds* 19. *Certified* Medicaid.
Owner Proprietary Corp.
Admissions Requirements Minimum age; Medical examination.
Staff Physicians; RNs; LPNs; Nurses aides; Physical therapists; Reality therapists; Recreational therapists; Occupational therapists; Speech therapists; Activities coordinators; Dietitians; Dentists; Ophthalmologists; Podiatrists; Audiologists.
Facilities Dining room; Activities room; Crafts room; Laundry room.
Activities Arts & crafts; Cards; Games; Reading groups; Prayer groups; Movies; Social/Cultural gatherings.

Walnut Hills Pavillion
1236 Huron Rd SE, Massillon, OH, 44646
(216) 832-5252
Admin Abraham Smith. *Medical Dir/Dir of Nursing* Dr Joseph Urabel DO; Sally Bredenberg DON.
Licensure Intermediate care. *Beds* ICF 23. *Certified* Medicaid.
Owner Proprietary Corp.
Admissions Requirements Minimum age 18; Medical examination.
Staff Physicians; LPNs 3 (ft), 4 (pt); Nurses aides 8 (ft), 2 (pt); Activities coordinators 1 (ft); Dietitians 2 (ft), 2 (pt).
Facilities Dining room; Activities room; Crafts room; Laundry room.
Activities Arts & crafts; Cards; Games; Reading groups; Prayer groups; Shopping trips; Out for breakfast.

MASURY

O'Brien Memorial Nursing Home
563 Brookfield Ave, SE, Masury, OH, 44438
(216) 448-2557
Admin Peter M Ghiates. *Medical Dir/Dir of Nursing* Dr Samuel J Pipes; Margaret Miller RN.
Licensure Skilled care; Intermediate care. *Beds* SNF 159; ICF. *Certified* Medicaid; Medicare.
Owner Proprietary Corp.
Admissions Requirements Medical examination; Physician's request.

Staff Physicians 1 (pt); RNs 7 (ft), 6 (pt); LPNs 17 (ft), 12 (pt); Orderlies 11 (ft), 5 (pt); Nurses aides 40 (ft), 25 (pt); Occupational therapists 1 (pt); Speech therapists 1 (pt); Activities coordinators 1 (ft); Dietitians 1 (pt); Ophthalmologists 1 (pt); Podiatrists 1 (pt).
Facilities Dining room; Physical therapy room; Activities room; Chapel; Crafts room; Laundry room; Barber/Beauty shop; Living room.
Activities Arts & crafts; Cards; Games; Reading groups; Prayer groups; Movies; Shopping trips; Social/Cultural gatherings; Diners club.

Orange Village Care Center Inc
8055 Addison Rd SE, Masury, OH, 44438
(216) 448-2547
Admin John T Banks. *Medical Dir/Dir of Nursing* Pat DiTommaso DO; Dorothy Tomorie RN.
Licensure Intermediate care; Intermediate care for mentally retarded. *Beds* ICF 76; ICF/MR 40. *Certified* Medicaid.
Owner Proprietary Corp (American Health Care Centers).
Admissions Requirements Minimum age 6 (for MR); Medical examination; Physician's request.
Staff Physicians 1 (pt); RNs 7 (ft), 1 (pt); LPNs 12 (ft), 3 (pt); Orderlies 3 (ft); Nurses aides 60 (ft), 3 (pt); Physical therapists 1 (pt); Occupational therapists 1 (pt); Speech therapists 1 (pt); Activities coordinators 3 (ft); Dietitians 1 (pt).
Facilities Dining room; Physical therapy room; Activities room; Chapel; Crafts room; Laundry room; Barber/Beauty shop.
Activities Arts & crafts; Cards; Games; Reading groups; Prayer groups; Movies; Shopping trips; Social/Cultural gatherings.

MAUMEE

Lucas County Children Services-Extended Care Unit
2500 River Rd, Maumee, OH, 43537
(419) 891-3343
Admin Faith E Marcinek. *Medical Dir/Dir of Nursing* Debra Osborn DON.
Licensure Intermediate care for mentally retarded. *Beds* ICF/MR 32. *Certified* Medicaid.
Owner Publicly owned.
Admissions Requirements Medical examination.
Staff Physicians 1 (pt); RNs 3 (ft), 1 (pt); LPNs 4 (ft), 4 (pt); Nurses aides 8 (ft), 23 (pt); Physical therapists 2 (pt); Recreational therapists 1 (ft); Occupational therapists 2 (pt); Speech therapists 1 (pt); Dietitians 1 (pt); Program Managers 3 (ft), 3 (pt).
Facilities Dining room; Physical therapy room; Activities room; Crafts room; Laundry room.
Activities Arts & crafts; Games; Movies; Shopping trips.

Elizabeth Scott Memorial Care Center
2720 Albon Rd, Maumee, OH, 43537
(419) 865-7321
Admin Philip E Witker. *Medical Dir/Dir of Nursing* Nancy Johnson RN DON.
Licensure Intermediate care. *Beds* ICF 50. *Certified* Medicaid.
Owner Proprietary Corp.
Admissions Requirements Medical examination; Physician's request.
Staff RNs 6 (ft); LPNs 2 (ft); Nurses aides 28 (ft); Activities coordinators 1 (ft); Dietitians 1 (pt).
Facilities Dining room; Activities room; Crafts room; Laundry room; Barber/Beauty shop.

Activities Arts & crafts; Cards; Games;
Reading groups; Prayer groups; Movies;
Shopping trips; Social/Cultural gatherings.

MAYFIELD HEIGHTS

Manor Care
6757 Mayfield Rd, Mayfield Heights, OH,
44124
(216) 473-0090
Admin Sally B Hahn. *Medical Dir/Dir of
Nursing* T Isakov MD; Jane E Bibb RN
DON.
Licensure Skilled care; Intermediate care. *Beds*
SNF 38; ICF 112. *Certified* Medicare.
Owner Proprietary Corp (Manor Care).
Admissions Requirements Minimum age 18.
Staff Physicians 1 (pt); RNs 11 (ft), 9 (pt);
LPNs 10 (ft), 8 (pt); Orderlies 4 (ft), 1 (pt);
Nurses aides 32 (ft), 16 (pt); Physical
therapists 2 (ft), 1 (pt); Recreational
therapists 2 (ft); Occupational therapists 1
(pt); Speech therapists 1 (pt); Dietitians 1
(pt); Dentists 1 (pt); Ophthalmologists 1 (pt).
Facilities Dining room; Physical therapy
room; Activities room; Laundry room;
Barber/Beauty shop.
Activities Arts & crafts; Cards; Games;
Reading groups; Prayer groups; Movies;
Shopping trips; Social/Cultural gatherings;
Exercise group; Shopping cart.

MCARTHUR

Twin Maples Nursing Home*
Rte 1, McArthur, OH, 45651
(614) 596-5955
Medical Dir/Dir of Nursing Dr Susan Crapes.
Licensure Intermediate care. *Beds* 42.
Certified Medicaid.
Owner Proprietary Corp.
Admissions Requirements Medical
examination; Physician's request.
Staff RNs 3 (pt); LPNs 4 (ft), 3 (pt); Nurses
aides 11 (ft), 4 (pt); Physical therapists 1
(pt); Activities coordinators 1 (ft), 1 (pt);
Dietitians 1 (pt); Dentists 1 (pt); Podiatrists
1 (pt).
Facilities Dining room; Activities room;
Laundry room.
Activities Cards; Games; Reading groups;
Shopping trips.

MCCONNELSVILLE

Mark Rest Center
4114 "N" St, Rte 376 NW, McConnelsville,
OH, 43756-9702
(614) 962-3761 or 962-2122
Admin David D Bankes. *Medical Dir/Dir of
Nursing* John Shaner MD; Harriet Huck RN
DON.
Licensure Skilled care; Intermediate care. *Beds*
151. *Certified* Medicaid; Medicare.
Owner Nonprofit Corp.
Admissions Requirements Minimum age 18;
Medical examination; Physician's request.
Staff Physicians 1 (pt); RNs 9 (ft), 3 (pt);
LPNs 15 (ft), 10 (pt); Orderlies 5 (ft); Nurses
aides 41 (ft), 22 (pt); Physical therapists 2
(pt); Occupational therapists 1 (pt); Speech
therapists 1 (pt); Activities coordinators 2
(ft); Dietitians 1 (pt); Therapist aides 2 (ft),
2 (pt).
Facilities Dining room; Physical therapy
room; Activities room; Laundry room;
Barber/Beauty shop.
Activities Arts & crafts; Cards; Games;
Reading groups; Movies; Shopping trips;
Bible study; Music; Picnics; Home meals.

Morgan County Care Center*
856 S Riverside Dr NE, McConnelsville, OH,
43756
(614) 962-6141

Licensure Intermediate care. *Beds* 50.
Certified Medicaid.
Owner Proprietary Corp (Community Care
Centers).

MCDERMOTT

Rendezvous Medi-Home*
Rte 2, Box 135, McDermott, OH, 45652
(614) 858-4546
Licensure Intermediate care. *Beds* 46.
Certified Medicaid.
Owner Proprietary Corp.

Rest Haven Nursing Home*
Baker St, McDermott, OH, 45652
(614) 259-2838
Licensure Intermediate care. *Beds* 23.
Certified Medicaid.
Owner Proprietary Corp.

MEDINA

Care House
809 E Washington St, Medina, OH, 44256
(216) 725-4123
Licensure Rest home. *Beds* 50.
Owner Proprietary Corp.
Admissions Requirements Medical
examination.
Facilities Dining room; Activities room;
Crafts room; Barber/Beauty shop; Library.
Activities Arts & crafts; Cards; Games;
Reading groups; Prayer groups; Movies;
Shopping trips.

Crestview Nursing Home
806 E Washington St, Medina, OH, 44256
(216) 725-4123
Admin Gary L DeHass.
Licensure Nursing home; Rest home. *Beds*
Nursing home 49; Rest home 81.
Owner Proprietary Corp.
Admissions Requirements Medical
examination.
Facilities Dining room; Physical therapy
room; Activities room; Barber/Beauty shop.
Activities Arts & crafts; Cards; Games;
Reading groups; Prayer groups; Movies.

Eckfield Rest Home*
1530 Remsen Rd, Medina, OH, 44256
(216) 239-1717
Licensure Rest home. *Beds* 22.
Owner Proprietary Corp.

Ohio Pythian Sisters Home of Medina
550 Miner Dr, Medina, OH, 44256
(216) 725-1550
Admin Irvin S Bayer. *Medical Dir/Dir of
Nursing* Dr Irene Leszkiewicz; Martha
Grannis RN DON.
Licensure Intermediate care. *Beds* ICF 50.
Certified Medicaid.
Owner Nonprofit organization/foundation.
Admissions Requirements Minimum age 65;
Medical examination; Physician's request.
Staff Physicians 1 (pt); RNs 1 (ft), 1 (pt);
LPNs 5 (ft), 2 (pt); Nurses aides 19 (ft), 4
(pt); Activities coordinators 1 (ft); Dietitians
1 (pt).
Facilities Dining room; Activities room;
Crafts room; Laundry room; Barber/Beauty
shop.
Activities Arts & crafts; Cards; Games;
Reading groups; Prayer groups; Movies;
Shopping trips.

Paradise Village*
PO Box 481, 4281 Paradise Rd, Medina, OH,
44256
(216) 722-2100
Licensure Intermediate care for mentally
retarded. *Beds* 24.
Owner Nonprofit Corp.

Sophia Huntington Parker Home
635 N Huntington St, Medina, OH, 44256
(216) 722-4672
Admin Irvin S Bayer. *Medical Dir/Dir of
Nursing* Dr Irene Leszkiewicz; Martha
Grannis RN DON.
Licensure Intermediate care. *Beds* ICF 34.
Owner Nonprofit organization/foundation.
Admissions Requirements Minimum age 62;
Females only; Medical examination;
Physician's request.
Staff Physicians 1 (pt); RNs 1 (pt); LPNs 3
(ft), 4 (pt); Nurses aides 9 (ft), 6 (pt);
Activities coordinators 1 (ft); Dietitians 1
(pt).
Affiliation Knights of Pythias
Facilities Dining room; Activities room;
Chapel; Crafts room; Laundry room; Barber/
Beauty shop.
Activities Arts & crafts; Cards; Games;
Reading groups; Prayer groups; Movies;
Shopping trips.

Shangri-La Health Care Center
2400 Columbia Rd, Medina, OH, 44256
(216) 483-3131; 225-9171; 336-4747
Admin Linda L Ferguson RN MSN NHA.
Medical Dir/Dir of Nursing Judith F
Gooding MD; Pat Reynolds RN MEd.
Licensure Skilled care; Intermediate care; Rest
home. *Beds* SNF 200; ICF 200; Rest home
38. *Certified* Medicaid; Medicare.
Owner Proprietary Corp.
Staff Physicians 1 (pt); RNs 7 (ft); LPNs 19
(ft); Nurses aides 64 (ft), 24 (pt); Physical
therapists 1 (pt); Speech therapists 1 (pt);
Activities coordinators 1 (ft); Dietitians 1
(pt); Dentists 1 (pt); Ophthalmologists 1 (pt).
Facilities Dining room; Physical therapy
room; Activities room; Crafts room; Laundry
room; Barber/Beauty shop.
Activities Arts & crafts; Cards; Games; Prayer
groups; Movies; Social/Cultural gatherings.

MEDWAY

Med Rest Center
10917 Gerlaugh Rd, Medway, OH, 45341
(513) 849-1353
Admin Dave Bennett.
Licensure Rest home. *Beds* Rest home 37.
Owner Proprietary Corp.
Admissions Requirements Medical
examination.
Staff Physicians 1 (pt); LPNs 2 (pt); Orderlies
1 (pt); Nurses aides 11 (pt); Activities
coordinators 1 (pt); Dietitians 1 (pt).
Facilities Dining room; Laundry room; Living
room.
Activities Games; Prayer groups; Social/
Cultural gatherings; Parties.

MENTOR

Greenlawn Health Care Center
PO Box 119, 9901 Johnnycake Ridge Rd,
Mentor, OH, 44061
(216) 357-7900
Licensure Intermediate care. *Beds* ICF 71.
Certified Medicaid.
Owner Proprietary Corp.
Admissions Requirements Medical
examination.
Staff Physicians 1 (pt); RNs 1 (ft), 2 (pt);
LPNs 6 (ft), 3 (pt); Nurses aides 25 (ft);
Activities coordinators 1 (ft), 2 (pt);
Dietitians 1 (pt); Ophthalmologists 1 (pt).
Facilities Dining room; Activities room;
Laundry room; Barber/Beauty shop.
Activities Arts & crafts; Cards; Games;
Reading groups; Prayer groups; Movies;
Shopping trips.

Lake County Adult Resident Center*
8211 Deepwood Blvd, Mentor, OH, 44060

Licensure Intermediate care for mentally retarded. *Beds* 64.
Owner Publicly owned.

Lake County Child Development Center*
8121 Deepwood Blvd, Mentor, OH, 44060
Licensure Intermediate care for mentally retarded. *Beds* 26.
Owner Publicly owned.

Mentor Way Villa Nursing Home*
Mentor Ave & 8903 Schaefer St, Mentor, OH, 44060
(216) 255-9309
Licensure Intermediate care. *Beds* 79.
Certified Medicaid.
Owner Proprietary Corp.

MIAMISBURG

Friendly Nursing Home Inc*
542 E Linden Ave, Miamisburg, OH, 45342
(513) 866-4051
Licensure Intermediate care. *Beds* 36.
Certified Medicaid.
Owner Proprietary Corp.

Miami Christel Manor Inc*
1120 S Dunaway St, Miamisburg, OH, 45342
(513) 866-9089
Licensure Intermediate care. *Beds* 101.
Certified Medicaid.
Owner Proprietary Corp.

MIDDLEFIELD

Briar Hill Nursing Home*
PO Box 277, Middlefield, OH, 44062
(216) 632-5241
Licensure Intermediate care. *Beds* 39.
Certified Medicaid.
Owner Proprietary Corp.

MIDDLETOWN

Colonial Manor Corporation
508 S Main St, Middletown, OH, 45044
(513) 423-3882
Admin Bob Sisson. *Medical Dir/Dir of Nursing* Dr Jeff Zollett.
Licensure Nursing home. *Beds* ICF 29.
Owner Proprietary Corp.
Admissions Requirements Minimum age 18; Medical examination; Physician's request.
Staff RNs 1 (ft); LPNs 4 (ft), 3 (pt); Nurses aides 12 (ft), 4 (pt); Physical therapists 1 (pt); Recreational therapists 1 (ft); Occupational therapists 1 (pt); Speech therapists 1 (pt); Activities coordinators 1 (ft); Dietitians 1 (pt); Dentists 1 (pt); Ophthalmologists 1 (pt); Podiatrists 1 (pt).
Facilities Dining room; Laundry room.
Activities Arts & crafts; Cards; Games; Reading groups; Prayer groups; Movies; Shopping trips; Social/Cultural gatherings.

Garden Manor Extended Care Center Inc*
6898 Hamilton-Middletown Rd, Middletown, OH, 45042
(513) 424-5321
Medical Dir/Dir of Nursing Jeffery Zollett MD.
Licensure Skilled care; Intermediate care. *Beds* 202. *Certified* Medicaid; Medicare.
Owner Nonprofit Corp.

Middletown Quality Care Center*
3100 S Main St, Middletown, OH, 45042
(513) 423-9621
Licensure Intermediate care. *Beds* 24.
Certified Medicaid.
Owner Proprietary Corp (Blackeye Fam/ Nursing Hm).

Barbara Park Convalescent Center
751 Kensington St, Middletown, OH, 45044
(513) 424-3511

Admin Larry N Steele. *Medical Dir/Dir of Nursing* Judith A Fadden DON.
Licensure Skilled care; Intermediate care. *Beds* SNF 208; ICF. *Certified* Medicaid; Medicare.
Owner Proprietary Corp (Parke Care Inc).
Staff RNs 7 (ft); LPNs 23 (ft); Orderlies 2 (ft); Nurses aides 87 (ft); Physical therapists 1 (pt); Occupational therapists 1 (pt); Speech therapists 1 (pt); Activities coordinators 3 (ft); Dietitians 1 (pt); Ophthalmologists 1 (pt).
Facilities Dining room; Physical therapy room; Activities room; Chapel; Crafts room; Laundry room; Barber/Beauty shop.
Activities Arts & crafts; Cards; Games; Reading groups; Prayer groups; Movies; Shopping trips; Social/Cultural gatherings.

MILAN

Canterbury Villa of Milan*
185 S Main St, PO Box 479, Milan, OH, 44846-0479
(419) 499-2576
Medical Dir/Dir of Nursing R L Blackann DO.
Licensure Intermediate care. *Beds* 96.
Certified Medicaid.
Owner Proprietary Corp.
Admissions Requirements Medical examination; Physician's request.
Staff RNs 1 (ft), 2 (pt); LPNs 8 (ft), 5 (pt); Nurses aides 25 (ft), 13 (pt); Activities coordinators 1 (pt); Dietitians 1 (pt); Social workers.
Facilities Dining room; Barber/Beauty shop.
Activities Arts & crafts; Games; Prayer groups; Movies; Shopping trips.

MILFORD

Clermont Nursing & Convalescent Center*
934 Star Rte 28, Milford, OH, 45150
(513) 831-1770
Licensure Skilled care; Intermediate care. *Beds* 206. *Certified* Medicaid; Medicare.
Owner Proprietary Corp.

SEM Haven Health Care Center
225 Cleveland Ave, Milford, OH, 45150
(513) 248-1270
Admin Alice D Lamping. *Medical Dir/Dir of Nursing* Dr Jonathan Head; Helen Canfield.
Licensure Skilled care; Intermediate care. *Beds* 100. *Certified* Medicaid 16B.
Owner Nonprofit Corp.
Admissions Requirements Medical examination; Physician's request.
Staff Physicians 1 (pt); RNs 6 (ft), 4 (pt); LPNs 8 (ft), 2 (pt); Nurses aides 39 (ft), 8 (pt); Physical therapists 1 (pt); Occupational therapists 1 (pt); Speech therapists 1 (pt); Activities coordinators 2 (ft); Dietitians 1 (pt); Dentists 1 (pt); Ophthalmologists 1 (pt); Podiatrists O 1 (pt); Psychologist 1 (pt).
Facilities Dining room; Physical therapy room; Activities room; Crafts room; Laundry room; Barber/Beauty shop.
Activities Arts & crafts; Games; Reading groups; Prayer groups; Movies; Shopping trips; Social/Cultural gatherings; Bowling; Horse races; Basketball; Weekly gentleman's luncheon.

MILLERSBURG

Fairview Castle Nursing Home*
W Jackson St, Millersburg, OH, 44654
Licensure Intermediate care. *Beds* 34.
Certified Medicaid.
Owner Proprietary Corp.

Overlook Castle Nursing Home*
Hebron St, Millersburg, OH, 44654
Licensure Intermediate care. *Beds* 35.
Certified Medicaid.
Owner Proprietary Corp.

Scenic View Nursing Home*
Twp Rd 190, Millersburg, OH, 44654
Licensure Intermediate care. *Beds* 164.
Certified Medicaid.
Owner Proprietary Corp.

Sunset View*
Rte 5, Millersburg, OH, 44654
Licensure Intermediate care. *Beds* 75.
Certified Medicaid.
Owner Proprietary Corp.

Terrace View Castle Nursing Home*
Hebron St, Millersburg, OH, 44654
Licensure Intermediate care. *Beds* 120.
Certified Medicaid.
Owner Proprietary Corp.

Valley View Castle Nursing Home*
Rte 1, Millersburg, OH, 44654
Licensure Intermediate care. *Beds* 42.
Certified Medicaid.
Owner Proprietary Corp.

MINERAL RIDGE

Glenn View Manor
3379 Main St, Mineral Ridge, OH, 44440
(216) 652-9901, 743-2242
Admin Richard J Chasko. *Medical Dir/Dir of Nursing* Dr J Enyeart; Nancy Gray DON.
Licensure Intermediate care; Assisted living. *Beds* ICF 116; Assisted living 52. *Certified* Medicaid.
Owner Proprietary Corp.
Admissions Requirements Minimum age 50.
Staff Physicians 2 (ft); RNs 12 (ft); LPNs 21 (ft); Nurses aides 73 (ft); Physical therapists 1 (ft); Occupational therapists 1 (ft); Activities coordinators 3 (ft); Dietitians 1 (ft); Ophthalmologists 1 (ft); Podiatrists 1 (ft).
Facilities Dining room; Physical therapy room; Activities room; Chapel; Crafts room; Laundry room; Barber/Beauty shop; Library; Pool; Sunroom; Gift shop; Putting green.
Activities Arts & crafts; Games; Reading groups; Prayer groups; Movies; Shopping trips; Social/Cultural gatherings.

Youngstown Developmental Center*
4891 E County Line Rd, Mineral Ridge, OH, 44440
Licensure Intermediate care for mentally retarded. *Beds* 117. *Certified* Medicaid; Medicare.
Owner Publicly owned.

MINERVA

Great Trail Care Center Inc
400 Carolyn Ct, Minerva, OH, 44657
(216) 868-4104
Admin Patrick D Martell. *Medical Dir/Dir of Nursing* Dr Robert Hinks; Donna Wey RN.
Licensure Skilled care; Intermediate care. *Beds* SNF 25; ICF 75. *Certified* Medicaid; Medicare.
Owner Proprietary Corp.
Admissions Requirements Medical examination.
Staff RNs 2 (ft), 4 (pt); LPNs 2 (ft), 5 (pt); Nurses aides 15 (ft), 14 (pt); Physical therapists; Reality therapists; Recreational therapists; Occupational therapists; Speech therapists; Activities coordinators; Dietitians; Dentists; Ophthalmologists; Podiatrists.
Facilities Dining room; Physical therapy room; Activities room; Crafts room; Laundry room; Barber/Beauty shop; Library.
Activities Arts & crafts; Cards; Games; Reading groups; Prayer groups; Movies; Shopping trips; Social/Cultural gatherings.

Minerva Convalescent Center Inc
1035 E Lincoln Way, Minerva, OH, 44657
(216) 868-4147

Admin Michael A Martell. *Medical Dir/Dir of Nursing* Dr Robert Hines; JoAnne Simms RN DON.
Licensure Intermediate care. *Beds* ICF 57. *Certified* Medicaid.
Owner Proprietary Corp.
Admissions Requirements Medical examination.
Staff Physicians 1 (pt); RNs 2 (ft); LPNs 3 (ft), 3 (pt); Nurses aides 8 (ft), 9 (pt); Activities coordinators 1 (ft); Dietitians 1 (pt); Ophthalmologists 1 (pt).
Facilities Dining room; Laundry room; Barber/Beauty shop.
Activities Arts & crafts; Cards; Games; Movies; Shopping trips; Social/Cultural gatherings.

Minerva Nursing Home
301 W Lincoln Way, Minerva, OH, 44657
(216) 868-5666
Admin Lorraine Smith RN LNHA. *Medical Dir/Dir of Nursing* Lorraine Smith RN LNHA.
Licensure Private Pay. *Beds* 15.
Owner Privately owned.
Admissions Requirements Females only; Medical examination; Physician's request.
Staff RNs 1 (ft); LPNs 1 (pt); Nurses aides 9 (ft); Cooks 1 (ft), 1 (pt); Housekeeping 1 (pt).
Facilities Dining room; Laundry room; 2 sitting rooms.
Activities Games; Community groups; Communion every Sunday evening.

MINSTER

Heritage Manor Nursing Center*
24 N Hamilton St, Minster, OH, 45865
(419) 628-2396
Admin Donald J Crock. *Medical Dir/Dir of Nursing* Joseph Steurnagel MC.
Licensure Skilled care. *Beds* 100. *Certified* Medicaid; Medicare.
Owner Proprietary Corp.
Admissions Requirements Medical examination; Physician's request.
Staff RNs 7 (ft), 7 (pt); LPNs 8 (ft), 1 (pt); Nurses aides 31 (ft), 31 (pt); Physical therapists 2 (pt); Occupational therapists 1 (pt); Speech therapists 1 (pt); Activities coordinators 2 (ft); Dietitians 1 (pt).
Facilities Dining room; Physical therapy room; Activities room; Chapel; Laundry room; Barber/Beauty shop.
Activities Arts & crafts; Cards; Games; Prayer groups; Movies; Shopping trips; Social/Cultural gatherings; Remotivation.

MONCLOVA

Monclova Care Center
9831 Garden Rd, Monclova, OH, 43542
(419) 865-6241
Licensure Intermediate care. *Beds* 100. *Certified* Medicaid.
Owner Proprietary Corp.

Villa Homes West Inc*
10005 Garden Rd, Monclova, OH, 43542
(419) 865-1248
Licensure Intermediate care. *Beds* ICF 100. *Certified* Medicaid.
Owner Proprietary Corp.
Staff Physicians 5 (pt); RNs 5 (ft); LPNs 9 (ft); Orderlies 2 (ft); Nurses aides 24 (ft); Physical therapists 1 (pt); Recreational therapists 2 (ft); Activities coordinators 1 (ft); Dietitians 1 (pt).
Facilities Dining room; Physical therapy room; Activities room; Crafts room; Laundry room; Barber/Beauty shop; Library.
Activities Arts & crafts; Cards; Games; Reading groups; Prayer groups; Movies; Shopping trips; Social/Cultural gatherings.

MONROE

Mt Pleasant Village
225 Britton Lane, Monroe, OH, 45050
(513) 539-7391
Admin David A Loop. *Medical Dir/Dir of Nursing* Dr Gordon F Smith; Fran Giltrow RN.
Licensure Skilled care; Intermediate care; CCRC. *Beds* SNF 70; ICF 29; Rest home 32; Congregate 20; Duplexes 35; Cottages 74. *Certified* Medicaid; Medicare.
Owner Nonprofit Corp (OH Presbyterian Homes).
Admissions Requirements Minimum age 60; Medical examination.
Staff Physicians 1 (ft); RNs 7 (ft), 3 (pt); LPNs 10 (ft), 5 (pt); Orderlies 1 (pt); Nurses aides 18 (ft), 9 (pt); Physical therapists 2 (ft); Recreational therapists 1 (ft); Occupational therapists 1 (ft); Speech therapists 1 (ft); Activities coordinators 3 (ft); Dietitians 1 (ft); Dentists 1 (ft); Ophthalmologists 1 (ft); Podiatrists 1 (ft).
Affiliation Presbyterian
Facilities Dining room; Physical therapy room; Activities room; Chapel; Crafts room; Laundry room; Barber/Beauty shop; Library.
Activities Arts & crafts; Cards; Games; Reading groups; Prayer groups; Movies; Shopping trips; Social/Cultural gatherings.

MONTGOMERY

Meadowbrook Living Center
8211 Weller Rd, Montgomery, OH, 45242
(513) 489-2444
Admin Frank Philbin. *Medical Dir/Dir of Nursing* Dr Jo Donovan.
Licensure Skilled care; Intermediate care. *Beds* SNF 156; ICF. *Certified* Medicaid; Medicare.
Owner Nonprofit Corp (Adventist Health Sys-USA).
Admissions Requirements Minimum age 18; Medical examination.
Staff Physicians 2 (pt); RNs 12 (ft), 9 (pt); LPNs 7 (ft), 5 (pt); Orderlies 9 (ft), 2 (pt); Nurses aides 60 (ft), 26 (pt); Physical therapists 1 (pt); Reality therapists 1 (pt); Recreational therapists 1 (pt); Occupational therapists 1 (pt); Speech therapists 1 (pt); Activities coordinators 2 (ft); Dietitians 1 (pt); Dentists 1 (pt); Ophthalmologists 1 (pt); Podiatrists 1 (pt); Social service 1 (ft); Treatment nurse 1 (ft); In-service 1 (ft).
Languages German, French
Affiliation Seventh-Day Adventist
Facilities Dining room; Physical therapy room; Activities room; Crafts room; Laundry room; Barber/Beauty shop; Library; Montessori school; Lounge.
Activities Arts & crafts; Cards; Games; Reading groups; Prayer groups; Movies; Shopping trips; Social/Cultural gatherings.

MONTPELIER

Evergreen Manor Nursing Home
924 Robinair Way, Montpelier, OH, 43543
(419) 485-3416
Admin Iris Shook. *Medical Dir/Dir of Nursing* Clarence A Bell MD.
Licensure Skilled care; Intermediate care. *Beds* 50. *Certified* Medicaid; Medicare.
Owner Proprietary Corp (American Health Care Centers).
Staff Physicians; RNs 5 (ft); LPNs 3 (ft), 2 (pt); Nurses aides 21 (ft); Activities coordinators 2 (ft); Dietitians 1 (ft); Dentists; Ophthalmologists.
Facilities Dining room; Physical therapy room; Activities room; Chapel; Crafts room; Laundry room; Barber/Beauty shop.

Activities Arts & crafts; Cards; Games; Reading groups; Prayer groups; Movies; Shopping trips; Social/Cultural gatherings.

MORROW

Pine Crest Nursing Center
463 E Pike St, Morrow, OH, 45152
(513) 899-2801
Admin Freda Kilburn. *Medical Dir/Dir of Nursing* Carl Durning MD.
Licensure Intermediate care. *Beds* ICF 50. *Certified* Medicaid.
Owner Proprietary Corp (Congregate Living of America).
Admissions Requirements Medical examination.
Staff RNs 1 (ft); LPNs 5 (ft), 5 (pt); Nurses aides 14 (ft), 6 (pt); Activities coordinators 1 (ft); Dietitians 1 (pt).
Facilities Dining room; Activities room; Crafts room; Barber/Beauty shop.
Activities Arts & crafts; Cards; Games; Reading groups; Prayer groups; Movies; Shopping trips.

MOUNT GILEAD

Morrow County Extended Care Facility
651 W Marion Rd, Mount Gilead, OH, 43338
(419) 946-5015
Admin Randal M Arnett. *Medical Dir/Dir of Nursing* L Bruce Hensley DO; Terry Weber RN.
Licensure Skilled care 10B. *Beds* 10.
Owner Publicly owned.
Admissions Requirements Medical examination; Physician's request.
Staff Physicians; RNs; LPNs; Nurses aides; Physical therapists; Speech therapists; Activities coordinators; Dietitians; Ophthalmologists; Podiatrists.
Facilities Dining room; Physical therapy room; Activities room; Chapel; Barber/Beauty shop; Library.
Activities Arts & crafts; Cards; Games; Reading groups; Movies; Social/Cultural gatherings Birthday/holiday parties; Family events.

Woodside Village Care Center Ltd*
W Marion Rd, Mount Gilead, OH, 43338
(419) 947-2015
Licensure Intermediate care. *Beds* 100. *Certified* Medicaid.
Owner Proprietary Corp.

MOUNT ORAB

Mt Orab Nursing Care Center
Farley Lane, Mount Orab, OH, 45154
(513) 444-3511
Licensure Intermediate care. *Beds* 25. *Certified* Medicaid.
Owner Nonprofit Corp.
Staff RNs 1 (pt); LPNs 4 (ft), 1 (pt); Nurses aides 8 (ft), 2 (pt); Activities coordinators 1 (ft).
Facilities Dining room; Activities room; Laundry room; TV area.
Activities Arts & crafts; Cards; Games; Reading groups; Prayer groups; Shopping trips; Bingo.

MOUNT SAINT JOSEPH

Mother Margaret Hall*
Delhi Pike, Mount Saint Joseph, OH, 45051
(513) 244-4692
Admin Sr Agnes Celestia. *Medical Dir/Dir of Nursing* Ronald Gall MD.
Licensure Skilled care; Intermediate care. *Beds* 132. *Certified* Medicaid; Medicare.
Owner Nonprofit Corp.
Admissions Requirements Medical examination; Physician's request.

Staff Physicians 2 (pt); Physical therapists 2 (pt); Recreational therapists 1 (ft); Occupational therapists 1 (pt); Speech therapists 1 (pt); Activities coordinators 1 (ft); Dietitians 1 (ft), 1 (pt); Dentists 1 (pt); Podiatrists 1 (pt).
Affiliation Roman Catholic
Facilities Dining room; Physical therapy room; Activities room; Chapel; Crafts room; Laundry room; Barber/Beauty shop; Library; Speech therapists room.
Activities Arts & crafts; Cards; Games; Reading groups; Prayer groups; Movies; Shopping trips; Social/Cultural gatherings.

MOUNT VERNON

The Hannah Browning Home
7 E Sugar St, Mount Vernon, OH, 43050
(614) 392-7111
Medical Dir/Dir of Nursing Kay Hall.
Licensure Life care. *Beds* 9. *Certified* Medicare.
Owner Nonprofit Corp.
Admissions Requirements Females only; Medical examination.
Staff Nurses aides.
Facilities Dining room; Laundry room.

Country Club Center II
1350 Yauger Rd, Mount Vernon, OH, 43050
(614) 397-2350
Admin Tanya Ressing. *Medical Dir/Dir of Nursing* Dr W Elder; Kristina R Leiter RN DON.
Licensure Skilled care; Intermediate care; Intermediate care for mentally retarded. *Beds* 76. *Certified* Medicaid; Medicare.
Owner Proprietary Corp (Je Holland Assoc).
Admissions Requirements Medical examination; Physician's request.
Staff Physicians 1 (pt); RNs 6 (ft); LPNs 9 (ft); Orderlies 3 (ft); Physical therapists 1 (ft); Reality therapists 1 (ft); Recreational therapists 1 (ft); Occupational therapists 1 (ft); Speech therapists 1 (ft); Activities coordinators 1 (ft), 2 (pt); Dietitians 1 (ft); Dentists 1 (ft); Ophthalmologists 1 (ft); Podiatrists 1 (ft).
Facilities Dining room; Physical therapy room; Activities room; Chapel; Crafts room; Laundry room; Barber/Beauty shop; Library.
Activities Arts & crafts; Cards; Games; Reading groups; Prayer groups; Movies; Shopping trips; Social/Cultural gatherings; Choral group travels to other facilities; Out to lunch bunch.

Country Court*
1076 Coshocton Ave, Mount Vernon, OH, 43050
(614) 397-4125
Licensure Skilled care; Intermediate care. *Beds* 122. *Certified* Medicaid; Medicare.
Owner Proprietary Corp.

Mt Vernon Developmental Center
PO Box 762, Mount Vernon, OH, 43050
(614) 397-1010
Admin Ronald C Boley. *Medical Dir/Dir of Nursing* Raymond L Sheets MD.
Licensure Intermediate care for mentally retarded. *Beds* ICF/MR 367. *Certified* Medicaid.
Owner Publicly owned.
Admissions Requirements Minimum age 6.
Staff Physicians 3 (ft); RNs 26 (ft); LPNs 38 (ft), 2 (pt); Nurses aides 208 (ft); Physical therapists 1 (ft); Recreational therapists 1 (ft); Occupational therapists 1 (ft); Speech therapists 3 (ft); Activities coordinators 1 (ft); Dietitians 1 (ft); Teachers 23 (ft); Psychologists 3 (ft).
Facilities Dining room; Physical therapy room; Activities room; Chapel; Crafts room; Laundry room; Barber/Beauty shop; Library;

Occupational therapy room; Educational classrooms; Workshop; Greenhouse; Gymnasium; Swimming pool.
Activities Arts & crafts; Cards; Games; Reading groups; Prayer groups; Movies; Shopping trips; Social/Cultural gatherings; Special Olympics; Scouting.

Mt Vernon Nursing Home*
PO Box 790, 414 Wooster Rd, Mount Vernon, OH, 43050
(614) 397-9626
Licensure Intermediate care. *Beds* 44. *Certified* Medicaid.
Owner Proprietary Corp.

Northside Manor Living Center
13 Avalon Rd, Mount Vernon, OH, 43050
(614) 397-3200
Admin Lee Mitchell. *Medical Dir/Dir of Nursing* Helen Dove DON.
Licensure Skilled care; Intermediate care. *Beds* SNF 50; ICF 59. *Certified* Medicaid; Medicare.
Owner Nonprofit Corp (Adventist Health Sys-USA).
Admissions Requirements Minimum age 30; Medical examination.
Staff Physicians 1 (pt); RNs 5 (ft), 2 (pt); LPNs 4 (ft), 3 (pt); Orderlies 1 (ft); Nurses aides 23 (ft), 20 (pt); Physical therapists 1 (pt); Recreational therapists 1 (pt); Occupational therapists 1 (pt); Speech therapists 1 (pt); Activities coordinators 1 (ft); Dietitians 1 (pt); Dentists 1 (pt); Ophthalmologists 1 (pt); Podiatrists 1 (pt).
Affiliation Seventh-Day Adventist
Facilities Dining room; Physical therapy room; Activities room; Laundry room; Barber/Beauty shop.
Activities Arts & crafts; Cards; Games; Reading groups; Prayer groups; Movies; Shopping trips; Social/Cultural gatherings.

Ohio Eastern Star Home
1451 E Gambier Rd, Mount Vernon, OH, 43050
(614) 397-1706
Admin Andrew Beyers. *Medical Dir/Dir of Nursing* Henry Lapp MD; Louise LaBenne RN.
Licensure Intermediate care. *Beds* 86.
Owner Nonprofit Corp.
Staff Physicians 1 (pt); RNs 3 (ft), 2 (pt); LPNs 2 (ft), 2 (pt); Nurses aides 19 (ft), 7 (pt); Activities coordinators 1 (ft), 1 (pt).
Affiliation Order of Eastern Star
Activities Arts & crafts; Cards; Games; Reading groups; Prayer groups; Movies; Shopping trips; Social/Cultural gatherings; Field trips.

Rose Garden Nursing Home
303 N Main St, Mount Vernon, OH, 43050
(614) 393-2046
Admin Eleanor Burke. *Medical Dir/Dir of Nursing* Carol Hanger.
Licensure Intermediate care. *Beds* ICF 30. *Certified* Medicaid.
Owner Privately owned.
Admissions Requirements Medical examination; Physician's request.
Staff RNs 1 (ft); LPNs 4 (ft); Nurses aides 10 (ft); Activities coordinators 1 (ft); Dietitians 1 (ft).
Facilities Dining room; Activities room; Laundry room.
Activities Arts & crafts; Cards; Games; Prayer groups; Movies; Shopping trips; Exercise daily.

NAPOLEON

Filling Memorial Home of Mercy Inc
Rte 5 N-160 SR 108, Napoleon, OH, 43545
(419) 592-6451
Admin Paul E Oehrtman. *Medical Dir/Dir of Nursing* Carol A Nachtrab DON.

Licensure Intermediate care for mentally retarded. *Beds* 53. *Certified* Medicaid.
Owner Nonprofit Corp.
Admissions Requirements Medical examination.
Staff RNs 3 (ft), 2 (pt); LPNs 2 (ft), 7 (pt); Recreational therapists 2 (ft); Occupational therapists 2 (ft); Activities coordinators 1 (ft); Dietitians 1 (pt).
Affiliation Lutheran
Facilities Dining room; Physical therapy room; Activities room; Chapel; Laundry room.
Activities Arts & crafts; Games; Movies; Shopping trips; Social/Cultural gatherings.

Northcrest Nursing Home
Northcrest Dr, Rte 6, Napoleon, OH, 43545
(419) 599-4070
Admin Mary Anne Moomaw. *Medical Dir/Dir of Nursing* Dr Busteed; Colleen Wiley.
Licensure Skilled care; Intermediate care. *Beds* SNF 16; ICF 84. *Certified* Medicaid; Medicare.
Owner Proprietary Corp (Beverly Enterprises).
Admissions Requirements Minimum age 12; Medical examination; Physician's request.
Staff RNs 2 (ft); LPNs 15 (ft); Nurses aides 86 (ft); Physical therapists 1 (pt); Speech therapists 1 (pt); Activities coordinators 1 (ft); Dietitians 1 (pt); Ophthalmologists 1 (pt); Podiatrists 1 (pt).
Facilities Dining room; Physical therapy room; Activities room; Laundry room; Barber/Beauty shop.
Activities Arts & crafts; Cards; Games; Reading groups; Prayer groups; Movies; Shopping trips; Social/Cultural gatherings.

NAVARRE

Country Lawn Nursing Home*
Rte 3, 10608 Navarre Rd S, Navarre, OH, 44662
(216) 767-3455
Licensure Intermediate care. *Beds* 126. *Certified* Medicaid.
Owner Proprietary Corp (Altercare Inc).

Lodge Nursing Home*
23 Ohio St, Navarre, OH, 44662
(216) 879-5930
Licensure Intermediate care. *Beds* 30. *Certified* Medicaid.
Owner Proprietary Corp.

Navarre Community Health Center
517 Park St W, Navarre, OH, 44662
(216) 879-2765
Admin Gregory R Colaner. *Medical Dir/Dir of Nursing* Eugene Pogorelec DO; Jeannie Janson RN DON.
Licensure Skilled care; Intermediate care. *Beds* SNF 17; ICF 61. *Certified* Medicaid; Medicare.
Owner Proprietary Corp (Altercare Inc).
Admissions Requirements Medical examination.
Staff Physicians 4 (pt); RNs 4 (ft), 4 (pt); LPNs 7 (ft), 2 (pt); Nurses aides 10 (ft), 23 (pt); Physical therapists 1 (pt); Speech therapists 1 (pt); Activities coordinators 1 (ft); Dietitians 1 (pt); Dentists 1 (pt); Ophthalmologists 1 (pt); Podiatrists 1 (pt).
Facilities Dining room; Physical therapy room; Activities room; Chapel; Crafts room; Laundry room; Barber/Beauty shop; Library.
Activities Arts & crafts; Cards; Games; Reading groups; Prayer groups; Movies; Shopping trips; Social/Cultural gatherings.

NEW BREMEN

Lone Pine Nursing Home Inc*
403 N Main St, New Bremen, OH, 45869
(419) 629-2793
Medical Dir/Dir of Nursing Dr Harbard.

Licensure Intermediate care. *Beds* 19.
Certified Medicaid.
Owner Proprietary Corp.
Admissions Requirements Medical
examination.
Staff RNs 1 (ft); LPNs 2 (ft), 1 (pt); Nurses
aides 10 (ft), 2 (pt); Recreational therapists 1
(pt); Activities coordinators 1 (ft); Dentists 1
(pt); Ophthalmologists 1 (pt); Podiatrists 1
(pt).
Facilities Dining room; Activities room;
Laundry room.
Activities Arts & crafts; Cards; Games;
Reading groups; Prayer groups; Movies;
Shopping trips; Social/Cultural gatherings.

NEW CARLISLE

Belle Manor Nursing Home
107 N Pike St, New Carlisle, OH, 45344
(513) 845-3561
Admin Sanford R Gerber. *Medical Dir/Dir of
Nursing* Thomas Honningford DO; Janet
Addeo DON.
Licensure Skilled care; Intermediate care. *Beds*
SNF 123; ICF. *Certified* Medicaid;
Medicare.
Owner Proprietary Corp.
Admissions Requirements Medical
examination.
Staff Physicians 1 (pt); RNs 6 (ft), 2 (pt);
LPNs 4 (ft), 3 (pt); Nurses aides 40 (ft), 12
(pt); Physical therapists 2 (ft); Reality
therapists 1 (pt); Recreational therapists 1
(ft); Occupational therapists 1 (pt); Speech
therapists 1 (pt); Activities coordinators 1
(ft); Dietitians 1 (pt); Dentists 1 (pt);
Ophthalmologists 1 (pt); Podiatrists 1 (pt).
Facilities Dining room; Physical therapy
room; Activities room; Chapel; Crafts room;
Laundry room; Barber/Beauty shop; Library.
Activities Arts & crafts; Cards; Games;
Reading groups; Prayer groups; Movies;
Shopping trips; Social/Cultural gatherings.

Dayview Care Center
1885 N Dayton-Lakeview Rd, New Carlisle,
OH, 45344
(513) 845-8219
Admin Jim Snyder. *Medical Dir/Dir of
Nursing* Janice Doll DON.
Licensure Intermediate care. *Beds* ICF 50.
Certified Medicaid.
Owner Nonprofit Corp.
Admissions Requirements Medical
examination.
Staff Physicians 1 (pt); RNs 2 (ft), 1 (pt);
LPNs 2 (ft); Orderlies 1 (pt); Nurses aides
15 (ft), 11 (pt); Physical therapists 1 (pt);
Activities coordinators 1 (ft); Dietitians 1
(pt).
Facilities Dining room; Laundry room;
Barber/Beauty shop.
Activities Arts & crafts; Cards; Games;
Reading groups; Prayer groups; Movies;
Shopping trips; Social/Cultural gatherings.

NEW CONCORD

New Concord Nursing Center
Rte 3, 75 Fox Creek Rd, New Concord, OH,
43762
(614) 826-7649
Admin Barbara Noland. *Medical Dir/Dir of
Nursing* Carl Spragg MD; Georgia Shepard
RN.
Licensure Intermediate care. *Beds* ICF 50.
Certified Medicaid.
Owner Proprietary Corp.
Admissions Requirements Minimum age 45;
Medical examination.
Staff RNs 1 (ft), 1 (pt); LPNs 3 (ft), 3 (pt);
Orderlies 1 (ft); Nurses aides 12 (ft), 7 (pt);
Activities coordinators 1 (ft).
Facilities Dining room; Activities room;
Laundry room; Barber/Beauty shop;
Solarium.

Activities Arts & crafts; Cards; Games;
Reading groups; Prayer groups; Movies;
Coffee hour; Current events.

NEW LEBANON

Canterbury Care Center
101 Mills Pl, New Lebanon, OH, 45345
(513) 687-1311
Medical Dir/Dir of Nursing Michael O Phillips
MD.
Licensure Intermediate care. *Beds* 101.
Certified Medicaid; Medicare.
Owner Proprietary Corp.
Admissions Requirements Medical
examination.
Staff Physicians 2 (pt); RNs 3 (ft); LPNs 7
(ft), 3 (pt); Nurses aides 28 (ft), 20 (pt);
Physical therapists 1 (pt); Recreational
therapists 1 (ft), 2 (pt); Occupational
therapists 1 (pt); Speech therapists 1 (pt);
Activities coordinators 1 (ft); Dietitians 1
(pt); Dentists 1 (pt); Ophthalmologists 1 (pt);
Podiatrists 1 (pt); Dentist 1 (pt).
Facilities Dining room; Physical therapy
room; Activities room; Chapel; Crafts room;
Laundry room; Barber/Beauty shop; Library.
Activities Arts & crafts; Cards; Games;
Reading groups; Prayer groups; Movies;
Shopping trips; Social/Cultural gatherings.

NEW LEXINGTON

Americare of New Lexington
920 S Main St, New Lexington, OH, 43764
(614) 342-5161
Admin Robert C Wells. *Medical Dir/Dir of
Nursing* Dr Ralph E Herendeen; Debra D
Wilson DON.
Licensure Skilled care; Intermediate care. *Beds*
100. *Certified* Medicaid; Medicare.
Owner Proprietary Corp (Americare Corp).

NEW LONDON

Firelands Nursing Center
8204 W Main St, New London, OH, 44851
(419) 929-1563
Admin Paul Kocsis. *Medical Dir/Dir of
Nursing* Dr Erlenbach; Ann Holland.
Licensure Skilled care; Intermediate care. *Beds*
50. *Certified* Medicaid; Medicare.
Owner Proprietary Corp (Health Care
Management).
Admissions Requirements Medical
examination; Physician's request.
Staff Physicians 7 (pt); RNs 3 (ft); LPNs 3
(ft), 2 (pt); Nurses aides 15 (ft), 5 (pt);
Physical therapists 1 (pt); Occupational
therapists 1 (pt); Speech therapists 1 (pt);
Activities coordinators 1 (ft); Dietitians 1
(ft), 1 (pt); Dentists 1 (pt); Ophthalmologists
1 (pt); Podiatrists 1 (pt).
Facilities Dining room; Physical therapy
room; Activities room; Laundry room;
Barber/Beauty shop.
Activities Arts & crafts; Cards; Games;
Reading groups; Prayer groups; Movies;
Shopping trips; Social/Cultural gatherings;
Outings; Cheese socials; Ice cream socials.

NEW PARIS

Heartland of Cedar Springs
7739 Rte 40, New Paris, OH, 45347
(513) 437-0580
Admin James V Kyle. *Medical Dir/Dir of
Nursing* Jeung W Ahn MD; Susan Melzer
RN DON.
Licensure Intermediate care for mentally
retarded. *Beds* ICF/MR 66. *Certified*
Medicaid.
Owner Proprietary Corp (Health Care &
Retirement Corp).
Admissions Requirements Minimum age 45;
Medical examination.

Staff Physicians 1 (pt); RNs 4 (ft), 2 (pt);
LPNs 4 (ft); Nurses aides 39 (ft), 4 (pt);
Physical therapists 1 (pt); Reality therapists
1 (pt); Recreational therapists 1 (pt);
Occupational therapists 1 (pt); Speech
therapists 1 (pt); Activities coordinators 1
(ft); Dietitians 1 (pt); Dentists 1 (pt);
Ophthalmologists 1 (pt); Podiatrists 1 (pt);
QMRPs 4 (ft); Dentist.
Facilities Dining room; Physical therapy
room; Activities room; Crafts room; Laundry
room; Barber/Beauty shop.
Activities Arts & crafts; Cards; Games;
Reading groups; Prayer groups; Movies;
Shopping trips; Social/Cultural gatherings;
Exercise groups; Boy/Girl Scouts; Swimming;
Bowling.

NEW PHILADELPHIA

Horizons of Tuscarawas & Carroll Counties Inc
158 1/2 N Broadway, New Philadelphia, OH,
44663
(216) 364-5415
Admin Janet E Watts. *Medical Dir/Dir of
Nursing* Brenda Gallion.
Licensure Intermediate care for mentally
retarded. *Beds* ICF/MR 12. *Certified*
Medicaid.
Owner Nonprofit Corp.
Admissions Requirements Minimum age 18;
Medical examination.
Staff RNs 1 (pt); LPNs 3 (pt); Nurses aides 5
(ft), 25 (pt); Physical therapists 1 (pt);
Recreational therapists 1 (pt); Occupational
therapists 1 (pt); Speech therapists 1 (pt);
Activities coordinators 1 (ft); Dietitians 1
(pt); Podiatrists 1 (pt).
Facilities Dining room; Activities room;
Laundry room.
Activities Arts & crafts; Cards; Games;
Reading groups; Prayer groups; Movies;
Shopping trips; Social/Cultural gatherings;
Dinning out.

South Broadway Nursing Home Inc
245-251 S Broadway, New Philadelphia, OH,
44663
(216) 339-2151
Admin Gloria Sentz. *Medical Dir/Dir of
Nursing* Joan Butler.
Licensure Intermediate care. *Beds* 99.
Certified Medicaid.
Owner Proprietary Corp.
Admissions Requirements Medical
examination; Physician's request.
Staff Physicians; RNs; LPNs; Nurses aides;
Activities coordinators; Dietitians.
Facilities Dining room; Activities room;
Laundry room.
Activities Arts & crafts; Cards; Games;
Reading groups; Prayer groups; Shopping
trips.

Valley Manor Nursing Home
Rte 4, Box 4348, New Philadelphia, OH,
44663
(216) 339-3595
Admin Shirley G Hebb. *Medical Dir/Dir of
Nursing* Rita Goth DON.
Licensure Skilled care; Intermediate care. *Beds*
SNF 219; ICF. *Certified* Medicaid;
Medicare.
Owner Proprietary Corp.
Admissions Requirements Minimum age 16;
Medical examination.
Staff RNs 10 (ft); LPNs 20 (ft); Orderlies 4
(ft); Nurses aides 160 (ft); Activities
coordinators 1 (ft); Dietitians 1 (ft).
Facilities Dining room; Physical therapy
room; Activities room; Crafts room; Laundry
room; Barber/Beauty shop.
Activities Arts & crafts; Cards; Games;
Reading groups; Prayer groups; Movies;
Shopping trips; Social/Cultural gatherings.

NEW RICHMOND

Dobbins Nursing Home Inc*
400 Main St, New Richmond, OH, 45157
(513) 553-4139
Admin Patricia Meeker. *Medical Dir/Dir of Nursing* John Wehby MD.
Licensure Intermediate care. *Beds* 22. *Certified* Medicaid.
Owner Nonprofit Corp.
Admissions Requirements Females only.
Staff RNs 1 (pt); LPNs 3 (ft), 2 (pt); Nurses aides 12 (ft); Physical therapists 1 (pt); Recreational therapists 1 (pt); Activities coordinators 1 (ft); Dietitians 1 (pt); Dentists 1 (pt); Podiatrists 1 (pt).
Facilities Dining room; Activities room; Crafts room; Laundry room; Barber/Beauty shop.
Activities Arts & crafts; Cards; Games; Reading groups; Prayer groups; Movies; Shopping trips; Social/Cultural gatherings; Fund raisers.

NEWARK

Arlington Nursing Home Inc
98 S 30th St, Newark, OH, 43055
(614) 344-0303
Admin Roy Hodges. *Medical Dir/Dir of Nursing* Dr T T Mills.
Licensure Skilled care; Intermediate care. *Beds* 200. *Certified* Medicaid; Medicare.
Owner Proprietary Corp.
Staff Physicians; RNs; LPNs; Orderlies; Nurses aides; Physical therapists; Reality therapists; Recreational therapists; Occupational therapists; Speech therapists; Activities coordinators; Dietitians; Dentists; Ophthalmologists; Podiatrists.
Facilities Dining room; Physical therapy room; Activities room; Crafts room; Laundry room; Barber/Beauty shop; Library; Hydrotherapy room; Occupational therapy room.
Activities Arts & crafts; Cards; Games; Reading groups; Prayer groups; Movies; Shopping trips; Social/Cultural gatherings.

Athena Manor, Inc
17 Forry St, Newark, OH, 43055
(614) 349-8175
Admin April Cross. *Medical Dir/Dir of Nursing* Dr Donald Adams; Sue Miller DON.
Licensure Intermediate care. *Beds* ICF 48. *Certified* Medicaid.
Owner Proprietary Corp.
Admissions Requirements Medical examination; Physician's request.
Staff Physicians; RNs; LPNs; Nurses aides; Recreational therapists; Activities coordinators; Dietitians; Dentists; Ophthalmologists.
Facilities Dining room; Activities room; Crafts room; Laundry room.
Activities Cards; Games; Reading groups; Prayer groups; Movies; Shopping trips; Social/Cultural gatherings.

Heath Nursing & Convalescent Center*
717 S 30th St, Newark, OH, 43055
(614) 522-1171
Licensure Skilled care; Intermediate care. *Beds* 216. *Certified* Medicaid; Medicare.
Owner Nonprofit Corp.

LPN Geriatric Nursing Center Inc
1450 W Main St, Newark, OH, 43055
(614) 344-9465
Admin Sara F Johnson. *Medical Dir/Dir of Nursing* Patty E Whisman MD; Opal Yost RN DON.
Licensure Skilled care; Intermediate care. *Beds* SNF 101; ICF. *Certified* Medicaid; Medicare.
Owner Proprietary Corp.

Admissions Requirements Medical examination.
Staff Physicians 22 (pt); RNs 4 (ft), 2 (pt); LPNs 4 (ft), 4 (pt); Nurses aides 18 (ft), 18 (pt); Physical therapists 2 (pt); Reality therapists 1 (pt); Recreational therapists 1 (pt); Occupational therapists 1 (pt); Speech therapists 1 (pt); Activities coordinators 1 (ft), 1 (pt); Dietitians 1 (pt); Dentists 1 (pt); Ophthalmologists 1 (pt); Podiatrists 1 (pt); Social services 1 (pt); Pastoral services 1 (pt).
Facilities Dining room; Physical therapy room; Activities room; Chapel; Crafts room; Laundry room; Barber/Beauty shop; Library.
Activities Arts & crafts; Cards; Games; Reading groups; Prayer groups; Movies; Shopping trips; Social/Cultural gatherings; Bingo; Dancercise; Pet therapy; Grandparent program; Political participation; Community services; Fishing trips; Special therapies; Outings.

LPN Health Care Facility
151 Price Rd, Newark, OH, 43055
(614) 366-2321
Medical Dir/Dir of Nursing Charles F Sinsabaugh MD.
Licensure Skilled care; Intermediate care. *Beds* 101. *Certified* Medicaid; Medicare.
Owner Proprietary Corp.
Admissions Requirements Minimum age 55; Physician's request.
Staff RNs 8 (ft), 2 (pt); LPNs 9 (ft), 3 (pt); Nurses aides 26 (ft), 8 (pt); Physical therapists 2 (ft); Speech therapists 1 (pt); Activities coordinators 1 (ft); Dietitians 1 (pt).
Facilities Dining room; Physical therapy room; Activities room; Chapel; Laundry room; Barber/Beauty shop.
Activities Arts & crafts; Cards; Games; Prayer groups; Movies; Shopping trips; Social/Cultural gatherings.

Newark Healthcare Centre
75 McMillen Dr, Newark, OH, 43055
(614) 344-0357
Admin Paul L Massa. *Medical Dir/Dir of Nursing* Fred N Karaffa MD; Lucinda Swank RN DON.
Licensure Skilled care; Intermediate care. *Beds* SNF 22; ICF 278. *Certified* Medicaid; Medicare.
Owner Proprietary Corp (Hillhaven Corp).
Admissions Requirements Minimum age 18; Physician's request.
Staff Physicians 1 (pt); RNs 25 (ft); LPNs 25 (ft); Nurses aides 80 (ft), 30 (pt); Physical therapists 1 (ft), 1 (pt); Occupational therapists 1 (ft), 1 (pt); Speech therapists 1 (pt); Activities coordinators 1 (ft); Dietitians 1 (pt); Ophthalmologists 1 (pt); Podiatrists 1 (pt).
Facilities Dining room; Physical therapy room; Activities room; Chapel; Crafts room; Laundry room; Barber/Beauty shop.
Activities Arts & crafts; Cards; Games; Reading groups; Prayer groups; Movies; Shopping trips; Social/Cultural gatherings.

NEWBURY

Holly Hills Farms*
10190 Fairmount Rd, Newbury, OH, 44065
(216) 564-2209
Medical Dir/Dir of Nursing Dr Jay Polinar & Dr Barry Polinar.
Licensure Intermediate care. *Beds* 33. *Certified* Medicaid.
Owner Proprietary Corp.
Admissions Requirements Medical examination; Physician's request.

Staff Physicians; RNs 3 (ft), 2 (pt); LPNs 2 (ft), 4 (pt); Nurses aides 15 (ft), 20 (pt); Physical therapists; Speech therapists; Activities coordinators 1 (ft); Dietitians 1 (pt); Dentists; Podiatrists; 1 (pt).
Facilities Dining room; Activities room; Crafts room; Laundry room; TV lounges.
Activities Arts & crafts; Cards; Games; Reading groups; Prayer groups; Movies; Formal tea party monthly; Birthday party monthly.

NEWCOMERSTOWN

Riverside Manor Nursing & Rehabilitation Center
1100 E State Rd, Newcomerstown, OH, 43832
(614) 498-5165
Admin Stanley H Richards. *Medical Dir/Dir of Nursing* Dr Terry Overholser DO; Judy Mizer RN DON.
Licensure Skilled care. *Beds* SNF 100. *Certified* Medicaid; Medicare.
Owner Proprietary Corp.
Admissions Requirements Medical examination; Physician's request.
Staff RNs 7 (ft), 4 (pt); LPNs 6 (ft), 3 (pt); Orderlies 1 (ft); Nurses aides 36 (ft), 20 (pt); Physical therapists 1 (ft); Occupational therapists 1 (ft); Speech therapists 1 (pt); Activities coordinators 2 (ft).
Facilities Dining room; Physical therapy room; Activities room; Crafts room; Laundry room; Barber/Beauty shop.
Activities Arts & crafts; Cards; Games; Reading groups; Prayer groups; Movies; Shopping trips; Social/Cultural gatherings.

NEWTON FALLS

Colvin Nursing Home*
150 Charles Court, Newton Falls, OH, 44444
(216) 872-1987
Medical Dir/Dir of Nursing Ellis List Jr MD.
Licensure Nursing home. *Beds* 25.
Owner Proprietary Corp.
Admissions Requirements Females only; Medical examination.
Staff RNs 1 (pt); LPNs 4 (ft); Nurses aides 6 (ft), 5 (pt).
Facilities Laundry room.
Activities Arts & crafts; Cards; Games; Prayer groups.

NILES

Shepherd of the Valley Nursing Home
1500 McKinley Ave, Niles, OH, 44446
(216) 544-0771
Admin Donald Kacmar. *Medical Dir/Dir of Nursing* Mary Beth Williams; Susan Bendel RN DON.
Licensure Skilled care; Intermediate care; Assisted living apartments; Independent apartments; Residential beds. *Beds* SNF 100; ICF 40; Assisted living 16; Independent 54; Residential 32. *Certified* Medicaid; Medicare.
Owner Nonprofit Corp.
Admissions Requirements Medical examination; Physician's request.
Staff RNs 3 (ft), 10 (pt); LPNs 10 (ft), 8 (pt); Nurses aides 42 (ft), 35 (pt); Activities coordinators 1 (ft), 1 (pt); Dietitians 1 (ft).
Affiliation Lutheran
Activities Arts & crafts; Games; Reading groups; Prayer groups; Movies; Shopping trips.

NORTH BALTIMORE

Blakely Care Center
600 Sterling Dr, North Baltimore, OH, 45872
(419) 257-2421
Admin Thomas Blakely. *Medical Dir/Dir of Nursing* Douglas Blakely DON.

Licensure Skilled care; Intermediate care. *Beds* SNF 53; ICF. *Certified* Medicaid; Medicare.
Owner Proprietary Corp.
Admissions Requirements Medical examination.
Staff Physicians 3 (pt); RNs 2 (ft), 1 (pt); LPNs 5 (ft), 5 (pt); Orderlies 1 (pt); Nurses aides 14 (ft), 16 (pt); Physical therapists 1 (pt); Reality therapists 3 (pt); Recreational therapists 1 (pt); Occupational therapists 1 (pt); Speech therapists 1 (pt); Activities coordinators 2 (ft); Dietitians 1 (pt); Dentists 1 (pt); Ophthalmologists 1 (pt); Podiatrists 1 (pt).
Facilities Dining room; Activities room; Laundry room; Barber/Beauty shop.
Activities Arts & crafts; Cards; Games; Reading groups; Prayer groups; Movies; Shopping trips; Social/Cultural gatherings.

NORTH CANTON

St Luke Lutheran Home for the Aging
220 Applegrove St NE, North Canton, OH, 44720
(216) 499-8341
Admin Rev Luther W Lautenschlager. *Medical Dir/Dir of Nursing* Dr Meade Perlman; Linda Scherger RN MSN.
Licensure Skilled care; Intermediate care; Rest home. *Beds* SNF 52; ICF 150; Rest home 32. *Certified* Medicaid; Medicare.
Owner Nonprofit Corp.
Admissions Requirements Medical examination.
Staff Physicians; RNs 19 (ft); LPNs 31 (ft); Nurses aides 125 (ft); Physical therapists; Speech therapists 1 (pt); Activities coordinators 3 (ft); Dietitians 1 (pt); Ophthalmologists 1 (pt).
Affiliation Lutheran
Facilities Dining room; Physical therapy room; Activities room; Chapel; Crafts room; Laundry room; Barber/Beauty shop; Library.
Activities Arts & crafts; Cards; Games; Reading groups; Prayer groups; Movies; Shopping trips; Social/Cultural gatherings.

Windsor Medical Center Inc
1454 Easton St NW, North Canton, OH, 44720
(216) 499-8300
Licensure Skilled care. *Beds* 41.
Owner Proprietary Corp.
Facilities Dining room; Physical therapy room; Activities room; Chapel; Crafts room; Laundry room; Barber/Beauty shop; Library.
Activities Arts & crafts; Cards; Games; Reading groups; Prayer groups; Movies; Shopping trips; Social/Cultural gatherings; Special events.

NORTH LIMA

Diamondhead Extended Care Center
9184 Market St, North Lima, OH, 44452
(216) 758-5743
Admin Jacqueline O Diamond. *Medical Dir/ Dir of Nursing* Anthony Dominic DO; Patricia Hatala, RN DON.
Licensure Intermediate care. *Beds* ICF 106. *Certified* Medicaid.
Owner Privately owned.
Admissions Requirements Medical examination.
Staff RNs 5 (ft), 3 (pt); LPNs 8 (ft), 5 (pt); Orderlies 7 (ft); Nurses aides 37 (ft), 12 (pt); Physical therapists 1 (ft); Speech therapists 3 (pt); Activities coordinators 2 (ft); Dietitians 1 (ft); Ophthalmologists 1 (pt).
Languages Spanish, Italian, Slavic
Facilities Dining room; Physical therapy room; Activities room; Crafts room; Laundry room; Barber/Beauty shop; Patio with gliders, picnic tables & umbrellas.

Activities Arts & crafts; Cards; Games; Prayer groups; Movies; Shopping trips; Social/ Cultural gatherings; Exercise programs; Ice cream on wheels.

Diamondhead Extended Care Center 1*
9174 Market St, North Lima, OH, 44452
(216) 758-5743
Licensure Skilled care; Intermediate care. *Beds* 130. *Certified* Medicaid; Medicare.
Owner Proprietary Corp.

Rolling Acres Care Center
9625 Market Street Ext, North Lima, OH, 44452
(216) 549-3939
Admin Edward G Martell. *Medical Dir/Dir of Nursing* Dr Joseph Mersol.
Licensure Skilled care; Intermediate care. *Beds* SNF 101; ICF. *Certified* Medicaid; Medicare.
Owner Proprietary Corp.
Staff Physicians 1 (pt); RNs 5 (ft), 2 (pt); LPNs 8 (ft), 5 (pt); Orderlies 4 (ft), 1 (pt); Nurses aides 22 (ft), 5 (pt); Physical therapists 1 (pt); Reality therapists 1 (pt); Recreational therapists 1 (pt); Occupational therapists 1 (pt); Speech therapists 1 (ft); Activities coordinators 2 (ft); Dietitians 2 (ft); Dentists 1 (pt); Ophthalmologists 1 (pt).
Languages French
Facilities Dining room; Physical therapy room; Activities room; Crafts room; Laundry room; Barber/Beauty shop; Library; Classroom; Family dining room; Courtyard.
Activities Arts & crafts; Cards; Games; Prayer groups; Movies; Social/Cultural gatherings.

NORTH OLMSTED

Manor Care of North Olmsted Inc
23225 Lorain Rd, North Olmsted, OH, 44070
(216) 779-6900
Admin Joanne Ryder. *Medical Dir/Dir of Nursing* Klaus Neumann MD; Delice Feretti.
Licensure Skilled care; Intermediate care. *Beds* 198. *Certified* Medicaid; Medicare.
Owner Proprietary Corp (Manor Care).
Admissions Requirements Medical examination.
Staff Physical therapists 1 (pt); Recreational therapists 3 (pt); Occupational therapists 1 (pt); Speech therapists 1 (pt); Activities coordinators 1 (pt); Dietitians 1 (pt); Dentists 1 (pt); Ophthalmologists 1 (pt); Podiatrists 1 (pt).
Facilities Dining room; Physical therapy room; Activities room; Crafts room; Barber/ Beauty shop; Library.
Activities Arts & crafts; Cards; Games; Reading groups; Prayer groups; Movies; Shopping trips; Social/Cultural gatherings.

Margies Nursing Home*
27048 Lorain Rd, North Olmsted, OH, 44070
(216) 777-4811
Medical Dir/Dir of Nursing Dr Louis La Riccia.
Licensure Intermediate care. *Beds* 35. *Certified* Medicaid.
Owner Proprietary Corp.
Admissions Requirements Medical examination; Physician's request.
Staff Physicians 1 (ft); RNs 1 (pt); LPNs 3 (ft), 2 (pt); Nurses aides 9 (ft); Recreational therapists 1 (pt); Activities coordinators 1 (ft); Dietitians 1 (pt); Dentists 1 (pt); Ophthalmologists 1 (pt); Podiatrists 1 (pt).

Olmsted Manor Skilled Nursing Center
27500 Mill Rd, North Olmsted, OH, 44070
(216) 777-8444
Admin Deborah L Lontor. *Medical Dir/Dir of Nursing* Dr Walter Wozniak; Dorothy Fricke.
Licensure Skilled care; Intermediate care. *Beds* SNF 99; ICF. *Certified* Medicaid; Medicare.

Owner Proprietary Corp.
Admissions Requirements Minimum age No children.
Staff Physicians 1 (ft), 13 (pt); RNs 7 (ft), 5 (pt); LPNs 7 (ft), 3 (pt); Orderlies 5 (ft), 2 (pt); Nurses aides 18 (ft), 4 (pt); Physical therapists 1 (ft), 1 (pt); Reality therapists 1 (ft); Recreational therapists 1 (ft); Occupational therapists 1 (ft); Speech therapists 1 (ft); Activities coordinators 2 (ft), 1 (pt); Dietitians 1 (ft); Dentists 1 (pt); Ophthalmologists 1 (ft); Podiatrists 1 (ft); Dentist 1 (ft).
Languages German, Italian, Ukranian, Polish, Spanish, Japanese
Facilities Dining room; Physical therapy room; Activities room; Chapel; Crafts room; Laundry room; Barber/Beauty shop; Library Gift shop.
Activities Arts & crafts; Cards; Games; Reading groups; Prayer groups; Movies; Shopping trips; Social/Cultural gatherings; Indoor & outdoor community programs.

NORTH RANDALL

Suburban Pavillion Inc*
20265 Emery Rd, North Randall, OH, 44128
(216) 475-8880
Medical Dir/Dir of Nursing Alan Kravitz MD.
Licensure Skilled care; Intermediate care. *Beds* 98. *Certified* Medicaid; Medicare.
Owner Proprietary Corp.
Admissions Requirements Medical examination; Physician's request.
Staff RNs 7 (ft), 2 (pt); LPNs 10 (ft), 2 (pt); Nurses aides 35 (ft), 5 (pt); Physical therapists 1 (ft); Recreational therapists 1 (ft); Occupational therapists 1 (pt); Speech therapists 1 (pt); Activities coordinators 1 (ft); Dietitians 1 (pt); Dentists 1 (pt); Podiatrists 1 (pt); Audiologists 1 (pt).
Facilities Dining room; Physical therapy room; Activities room; Crafts room; Barber/ Beauty shop.
Activities Arts & crafts; Cards; Games; Reading groups; Prayer groups; Movies; Social/Cultural gatherings.

NORTH RIDGEVILLE

Altercare of North Ridgeville
35990 Westmeinister Ave, North Ridgeville, OH, 44039
(216) 327-8511
Admin Nancy A Comer. *Medical Dir/Dir of Nursing* Dr Clemente; Bernadene Ulichney DON.
Licensure Skilled care; Intermediate care. *Certified* Medicaid; Medicare.
Owner Proprietary Corp (Altercare Inc).
Admissions Requirements Medical examination.
Staff Physicians 5 (pt); RNs 8 (ft); LPNs 10 (ft), 5 (pt); Nurses aides 40 (ft); Physical therapists 1 (pt); Occupational therapists 1 (pt); Speech therapists 1 (pt); Activities coordinators 1 (ft), 1 (pt); Dietitians 1 (pt); Dentists 1 (pt); Ophthalmologists 1 (pt); Podiatrists 1 (pt).
Facilities Dining room; Physical therapy room; Activities room; Crafts room; Laundry room; Barber/Beauty shop.
Activities Arts & crafts; Cards; Games; Prayer groups; Movies; Shopping trips; Social/ Cultural gatherings.

Center Ridge Nursing Home
38600 Center Ridge Rd, North Ridgeville, OH, 44039
327-1295, 777-2186
Admin John T O'Neill. *Medical Dir/Dir of Nursing* Dr Rudy Moe; Barbara McGrady.
Licensure Skilled care; Intermediate care. *Beds* SNF 100; ICF. *Certified* Medicaid; Medicare.
Owner Privately owned.

Admissions Requirements Minimum age 50; Medical examination.
Staff Physicians 10 (pt); RNs 5 (ft); LPNs 10 (ft); Orderlies 3 (ft); Nurses aides 47 (ft); Physical therapists 1 (pt); Occupational therapists 1 (pt); Speech therapists 1 (pt); Activities coordinators 1 (ft); Dietitians 2 (pt); Dentists 1 (pt); Ophthalmologists 1 (pt); Podiatrists 1 (pt).
Languages Spanish
Facilities Dining room; Physical therapy room; Activities room; Crafts room; Laundry room; Barber/Beauty shop.
Activities Arts & crafts; Cards; Games; Reading groups; Prayer groups; Movies; Shopping trips; Social/Cultural gatherings.

Holly Terrace Nursing Home
32415 Center Ridge Rd, North Ridgeville, OH, 44039
(216) 327-8370
Admin Ruth M Jackson. *Medical Dir/Dir of Nursing* Firas Atassi MD; Patricia Cook RN NHA.
Licensure Intermediate care. *Beds* ICF 18. *Certified* Medicaid.
Owner Privately owned.
Admissions Requirements Medical examination.
Staff Physicians 1 (pt); RNs 1 (ft), 2 (pt); LPNs 4 (ft), 2 (pt); Nurses aides 5 (ft), 4 (pt); Activities coordinators 1 (ft), 1 (pt); Dietitians 1 (pt); Ophthalmologists 1 (pt); Social worker 1 (pt).
Facilities Dining room; Activities room; Laundry room; Sitting room; Large porch.
Activities Arts & crafts; Cards; Games; Reading groups; Prayer groups.

NORTH ROYALTON

Mt Royal Villa*
13900 Bennett Rd, North Royalton, OH, 44133
(216) 237-7966
Licensure Nursing home; Rest home. *Beds* Nursing home 43; Rest home 63.
Owner Proprietary Corp.

Patrician Nursing Center Inc
9001 W 130th St, North Royalton, OH, 44133
(216) 237-3104
Licensure Skilled care; Intermediate care. *Beds* ICF 225. *Certified* Medicaid; Medicare.
Owner Proprietary Corp.
Staff Physicians 1 (pt); RNs 11 (ft), 11 (pt); LPNs 11 (ft), 11 (pt); Orderlies 7 (ft); Nurses aides 56 (ft), 32 (pt); Physical therapists 1 (ft); Reality therapists 1 (ft); Recreational therapists 1 (ft); Occupational therapists 1 (pt); Speech therapists 1 (pt); Activities coordinators 3 (ft); Dietitians 1 (pt); Dentists 1 (pt); Ophthalmologists 1 (pt); Podiatrists 1 (pt); Dentist 1 (pt).
Facilities Dining room; Physical therapy room; Activities room; Chapel; Crafts room; Barber/Beauty shop; Library.
Activities Arts & crafts; Cards; Games; Reading groups; Prayer groups; Movies; Social/Cultural gatherings.

NORTON

Ideal Nursing Home Inc*
5671 Wooster Rd W, Norton, OH, 44203
(216) 825-2525
Licensure Intermediate care. *Beds* 20. *Certified* Medicaid.
Owner Proprietary Corp.

NORWALK

Gaymont Nursing Center
66 Norwood Ave, Norwalk, OH, 44857
(419) 668-8258
Admin William C. Dotson. *Medical Dir/Dir of Nursing* Warren Sawyer MD.

Licensure Skilled care; Intermediate care. *Beds* SNF; ICF 100. *Certified* Medicaid; Medicare.
Owner Privately owned.
Admissions Requirements Medical examination; Physician's request.
Staff Physicians; RNs; LPNs; Nurses aides; Physical therapists; Occupational therapists; Speech therapists; Activities coordinators; Dietitians; Ophthalmologists.
Facilities Dining room; Physical therapy room; Activities room; Chapel; Crafts room; Laundry room; Barber/Beauty shop.
Activities Arts & crafts; Games; Reading groups; Prayer groups; Movies; Shopping trips; Social/Cultural gatherings.

Norwalk Memorial Home
272 Benedict Avenue, Norwalk, OH, 44857
(419) 668-5162
Admin Richard C Westhofen. *Medical Dir/Dir of Nursing* Harold D Erlenbach MD; Sharen Hochsedler RN.
Licensure Skilled care; Intermediate care. *Beds* SNF; ICF dual certified 50. *Certified* Medicaid; Medicare.
Owner Nonprofit Corp.
Admissions Requirements Medical examination; Physician's request.
Staff RNs 1 (ft), 1 (pt); LPNs 1 (ft), 7 (pt); Nurses aides 9 (ft), 13 (pt); Activities coordinators 1 (pt); Housekeeping 3 (ft), 2 (pt).
Facilities Dining room; Physical therapy room; Activities room; Crafts room; Laundry room; Barber/Beauty shop.
Activities Arts & crafts; Cards; Games; Reading groups; Prayer groups; Movies; Shopping trips; Social/Cultural gatherings.

Twilight Gardens Home Inc
196 W Main St, Norwalk, OH, 44857
(419) 668-2086
Admin Carol Starkey. *Medical Dir/Dir of Nursing* Ronald D Winland.
Licensure Skilled care; Intermediate care. *Beds* 100. *Certified* Medicaid; Medicare.
Owner Proprietary Corp.
Admissions Requirements Medical examination; Physician's request.
Staff RNs 2 (ft), 1 (pt); LPNs 9 (ft), 12 (pt); Nurses aides 36 (ft), 11 (pt); Physical therapists; Recreational therapists; Occupational therapists; Speech therapists; Activities coordinators 1 (pt); Dietitians; Dentists; Podiatrists; Ophthalmologists; Dentist.
Facilities Dining room; Physical therapy room; Activities room; Crafts room; Laundry room; Barber/Beauty shop; Library; Sunroom; Meditation room; TV room.
Activities Arts & crafts; Cards; Games; Reading groups; Prayer groups; Movies; Shopping trips; Social/Cultural gatherings.

NORWOOD

Victory Park Nursing Home Inc
1578 Sherman Ave, Norwood, OH, 45212
(513) 351-0153
Admin Herb Seidner. *Medical Dir/Dir of Nursing* Dr Manuel Mediodia Jr.
Licensure Skilled care; Intermediate care; Independent living. *Beds* SNF 56; ICF 46. *Certified* Medicaid; Medicare.
Owner Privately owned.
Admissions Requirements Medical examination; Physician's request.
Staff Physicians; RNs; LPNs; Nurses aides; Activities coordinators; Dietitians; Ophthalmologists.
Facilities Dining room; Activities room; Chapel; Laundry room; Barber/Beauty shop; TV room.
Activities Arts & crafts; Cards; Games; Reading groups; Prayer groups; Movies; Social/Cultural gatherings.

OAK HARBOR

Ottawa County Riverview Nursing Home
PO Box 188, St Rte 163, Oak Harbor, OH, 43449
(419) 898-2851
Admin John Moore. *Medical Dir/Dir of Nursing* Robert W Minick MD; Lois Karshuk RN.
Licensure Skilled care; Intermediate care. *Beds* 166. *Certified* Medicaid; Medicare.
Owner Publicly owned.
Admissions Requirements Medical examination; Physician's request.
Staff Physicians 8 (pt); RNs 9 (ft), 8 (pt); LPNs 7 (ft), 14 (pt); Nurses aides 51 (ft), 25 (pt); Physical therapists 1 (pt); Reality therapists 2 (pt); Occupational therapists 1 (pt); Speech therapists 1 (pt); Activities coordinators 1 (ft); Dietitians 1 (pt); Dentists 1 (pt); Ophthalmologists 1 (pt); Podiatrists 1 (pt).
Facilities Dining room; Activities room; Crafts room; Barber/Beauty shop.
Activities Arts & crafts; Cards; Games; Prayer groups; Movies; Shopping trips; Social/Cultural gatherings; Wine & cheese parties; Birthday parties; Bingo; Picnics; "Make your own sundae" parties.

OAK HILL

Davis Home for the Aged
315 Washington St, Oak Hill, OH, 45656
(614) 682-7585
Admin Theresa Stout.
Licensure Rest home. *Beds* Rest home 32.
Owner Nonprofit organization/foundation.
Admissions Requirements Minimum age 50; Females only; Medical examination.
Staff LPNs 1 (ft).
Facilities Dining room; Laundry room; Barber/Beauty shop.
Activities Arts & crafts; Cards; Reading groups; Shopping trips; Bible study; Visiting groups.

OAKWOOD VILLAGE

Oak Park*
24613 Broadway, Oakwood Village, OH, 44146
(216) 439-1448
Licensure Skilled care; Intermediate care. *Beds* 125. *Certified* Medicaid; Medicare.
Owner Proprietary Corp.

OBERLIN

Carter's Nursing Home
PO Box 276, 284 E Lorain St, Oberlin, OH, 44074
(216) 774-7202
Admin Wanda L Carter. *Medical Dir/Dir of Nursing* Dorothy Stephens DON.
Licensure Intermediate care. *Beds* ICF 50. *Certified* Medicaid.
Owner Proprietary Corp.
Admissions Requirements Medical examination.
Staff Physicians 5 (ft); RNs 1 (ft), 1 (pt); LPNs 4 (ft), 2 (pt); Orderlies 1 (ft); Nurses aides 9 (ft), 4 (pt); Activities coordinators 1 (ft), 1 (pt); Dietitians 1 (pt); Ophthalmologists 1 (pt).
Facilities Dining room; Activities room; Crafts room; Laundry room.
Activities Arts & crafts; Cards; Games; Prayer groups; Shopping trips; Social/Cultural gatherings.

Tressie's Nursing Home
277 N Professor St, Oberlin, OH, 44074
(216) 774-1255
Admin Don H Wessell. *Medical Dir/Dir of Nursing* Marlene Freshwater RN RSD.

Licensure Intermediate care. *Beds* ICF 19.
Certified Medicaid.
Owner Proprietary Corp.
Admissions Requirements Females only;
Medical examination; Physician's request.
Staff RNs 1 (ft); LPNs 2 (ft), 3 (pt); Nurses
aides 5 (ft), 4 (pt); Activities coordinators 1
(pt); Dietitians 1 (pt).
Facilities Dining room; Activities room.
Activities Arts & crafts; Cards; Games;
Reading groups; Prayer groups; Movies;
Shopping trips; Social/Cultural gatherings.

Welcome Nursing Home Inc
54 E Hamilton St, Oberlin, OH, 44074
(216) 775-1491
Admin Don H Wessell NHA. *Medical Dir/Dir
of Nursing* Theo M Wessell RN NHA.
Licensure Skilled care; Intermediate care. *Beds*
SNF 53; ICF 53. *Certified* Medicaid;
Medicare.
Owner Proprietary Corp.
Admissions Requirements Medical
examination; Physician's request.
Staff RNs 2 (ft), 2 (pt); LPNs 5 (ft), 4 (pt);
Nurses aides 11 (ft), 11 (pt); Physical
therapists 1 (pt); Reality therapists 1 (ft);
Activities coordinators 1 (ft); Dietitians 1
(ft); Activities coordinators 1 (ft); Dietitians
1 (ft); Ophthalmologists 1 (pt).
Facilities Dining room; Physical therapy
room; Activities room; Barber/Beauty shop;
Library.
Activities Arts & crafts; Cards; Games;
Reading groups; Prayer groups; Movies;
Shopping trips; Social/Cultural gatherings.

Will-O-Lee Nursing Home No 1 Inc
PO Box 149, Rte 58 N, Oberlin, OH, 44074
(216) 775-3639
Admin William McKinney. *Medical Dir/Dir of
Nursing* John Jonesco DON.
Licensure Intermediate care. *Beds* ICF 45.
Certified Medicaid.
Owner Proprietary Corp.
Admissions Requirements Medical
examination.
Staff Physicians 1 (pt); RNs 2 (ft), 2 (pt);
LPNs 9 (ft); Orderlies 3 (ft); Nurses aides 17
(ft); Activities coordinators 1 (ft); Dietitians
1 (ft); Ophthalmologists 1 (pt); Activities
aides 3 (ft).
Facilities Dining room; Activities room;
Chapel; Laundry room.
Activities Arts & crafts; Cards; Games;
Reading groups; Prayer groups; Movies;
Shopping trips; Social/Cultural gatherings.

Will-O-Lee Nursing Home 2
345 N Professor St, Oberlin, OH, 44074
(216) 775-3639
Medical Dir/Dir of Nursing George Hoover.
Licensure Intermediate care for mentally
retarded. *Beds* 25. *Certified* Medicaid.
Owner Proprietary Corp.
Admissions Requirements Medical
examination.
Staff Physicians 2 (pt); RNs 1 (ft), 1 (pt);
LPNs 10 (ft); Nurses aides 9 (ft);
Recreational therapists 1 (pt); Activities
coordinators 1 (ft); Dietitians 1 (ft); Dentists
1 (pt); Podiatrists 1 (pt).
Facilities Dining room; Activities room;
Crafts room; Laundry room.
Activities Arts & crafts; Cards; Games;
Reading groups; Prayer groups; Movies;
Shopping trips; Social/Cultural gatherings.

OREGON

**Americare-Oregon Nursing & Rehabilitation
Center**
904 Isaac St, Oregon, OH, 43616
(419) 691-2483
Admin Joyce Arend. *Medical Dir/Dir of
Nursing* Marty Agha.
Licensure Skilled care; Intermediate care. *Beds*
100. *Certified* Medicaid; Medicare.

Owner Proprietary Corp (Americare Corp).
Admissions Requirements Medical
examination; Physician's request.
Staff RNs; LPNs; Orderlies; Nurses aides;
Recreational therapists; Activities
coordinators; Dietitians.
Facilities Dining room; Physical therapy
room; Activities room; Crafts room; Laundry
room; Barber/Beauty shop.
Activities Arts & crafts; Cards; Games;
Reading groups; Prayer groups; Movies;
Shopping trips; Social/Cultural gatherings;
Happy hour.

Family Tree Care Center*
3952 Navarre Ave, Oregon, OH, 43616
(419) 698-4521
Licensure Skilled care; Intermediate care. *Beds*
SNF 43; ICF 58. *Certified* Medicaid;
Medicare.
Owner Proprietary Corp.

**Sacred Heart Home for Aged—Little Sisters of
the Poor**
4900 Navarre Ave, Oregon, OH, 43616
(419) 698-4331
Admin Sr Gertrude McConnell. *Medical Dir/
Dir of Nursing* F Abbati MD; Sr Mary
Elizabeth Anderson RN.
Licensure Intermediate care; Rest home;
Independent living apartments. *Beds* ICF 86;
Rest home 40; Independent living 20.
Certified Medicaid.
Owner Nonprofit Corp.
Admissions Requirements Minimum age 60;
Medical examination.
Staff RNs 2 (ft); Reality therapists 1 (pt);
Speech therapists 1 (pt); Activities
coordinators 1 (ft); Dietitians 1 (pt); Dentists
1 (pt); Ophthalmologists 1 (pt); Podiatrists 1
(pt).
Affiliation Roman Catholic
Facilities Dining room; Physical therapy
room; Activities room; Chapel; Crafts room;
Laundry room; Barber/Beauty shop; Library.
Activities Arts & crafts; Cards; Games;
Reading groups; Prayer groups; Movies;
Shopping trips; Social/Cultural gatherings.

ORRVILLE

Brenn Field Nursing Center
1980 Lynn Dr, Orrville, OH, 44667
(216) 683-4075
Admin Richard Brenneman. *Medical Dir/Dir
of Nursing* Dorothy Brenneman DON.
Licensure Intermediate care. *Beds* ICF 100.
Certified Medicaid.
Owner Proprietary Corp.
Admissions Requirements Medical
examination.
Staff RNs 2 (ft), 3 (pt); LPNs 6 (ft), 5 (pt);
Orderlies 1 (ft); Nurses aides 15 (ft), 25 (pt);
Physical therapists 1 (pt); Recreational
therapists 1 (pt); Activities coordinators 1
(ft); Dietitians 1 (ft).
Languages Italian
Facilities Dining room; Physical therapy
room; Activities room; Crafts room; Laundry
room; Barber/Beauty shop; Library.
Activities Arts & crafts; Cards; Games;
Reading groups; Prayer groups; Movies;
Shopping trips.

ORWELL

Village Square Nursing Center
7787 Staley Rd, Orwell, OH, 44076
(216) 437-6611
Admin Mary Brown. *Medical Dir/Dir of
Nursing* Dr L A Loria; Darlene Peterson RN
DON.
Licensure Intermediate care. *Beds* ICF 50.
Certified Medicaid.
Owner Proprietary Corp (Horizon Healthcare
Corp).

Admissions Requirements Medical
examination.
Staff RNs; LPNs; Orderlies; Nurses aides;
Physical therapists; Activities coordinators;
Dietitians; Ophthalmologists; Podiatrists.
Facilities Dining room; Activities room;
Crafts room; Laundry room.
Activities Arts & crafts; Cards; Games;
Reading groups; Prayer groups; Movies;
Shopping trips; Social/Cultural gatherings.

OTTAWA

Calvary Manor Nursing Home
Glandorf Rd, RR 4, Ottawa, OH, 45875
(419) 538-6529
Admin Larry Schroeder. *Medical Dir/Dir of
Nursing* Dr Biery; J Ogle.
Licensure Intermediate care. *Beds* ICF 78.
Certified Medicaid.
Owner Proprietary Corp.
Admissions Requirements Medical
examination.
Staff RNs 3 (ft), 4 (pt); LPNs 3 (ft), 4 (pt);
Nurses aides 8 (ft), 29 (pt); Activities
coordinators 1 (ft), 1 (pt).
Facilities Dining room; Physical therapy
room; Activities room; Chapel; Laundry
room; Barber/Beauty shop.
Activities Arts & crafts; Cards; Games;
Reading groups; Prayer groups; Movies;
Shopping trips; Social/Cultural gatherings.

Putnam Acres Care Center
10170 Rd 5-H, Ottawa, OH, 45825
(419) 523-4092
Admin Anita S Warden. *Medical Dir/Dir of
Nursing* James Overmier MD; Natalie
Saloum RN DON.
Licensure Intermediate care. *Beds* ICF 88.
Certified Medicaid.
Owner Publicly owned.
Admissions Requirements Minimum age 16.
Staff Physicians 1 (pt); RNs 4 (ft), 3 (pt);
LPNs 2 (ft), 5 (pt); Nurses aides 23 (ft), 17
(pt); Physical therapists 1 (pt); Occupational
therapists 1 (pt); Speech therapists 1 (pt);
Activities coordinators 2 (ft); Dietitians 1
(pt); Dentists 1 (pt); Ophthalmologists 1 (pt);
Podiatrists 1 (pt).
Facilities Dining room; Physical therapy
room; Activities room; Chapel; Crafts room;
Laundry room; Barber/Beauty shop; Library.
Activities Arts & crafts; Cards; Games;
Reading groups; Prayer groups; Movies;
Shopping trips; Social/Cultural gatherings.

Total Care of Ottawa*
1925 E 4th St, Ottawa, OH, 45875
(419) 523-4370
Medical Dir/Dir of Nursing Dr James
Overmier.
Licensure Intermediate care. *Beds* 50.
Certified Medicaid.
Owner Proprietary Corp.
Admissions Requirements Minimum age 18;
Medical examination.
Staff RNs 3 (ft); LPNs 1 (ft), 4 (pt); Nurses
aides 8 (ft), 14 (pt); Physical therapists 1
(pt); Reality therapists 1 (pt); Recreational
therapists 1 (pt); Occupational therapists 1
(pt); Speech therapists 1 (pt); Activities
coordinators 1 (ft), 1 (pt); Dietitians 1 (pt);
Dentists 1 (pt); Ophthalmologists 1 (pt);
Podiatrists 1 (pt); Audiologists 1 (pt).
Facilities Dining room; Activities room;
Chapel; Crafts room; Laundry room; Barber/
Beauty shop; Library.
Activities Arts & crafts; Cards; Games;
Reading groups; Prayer groups; Movies;
Shopping trips; Social/Cultural gatherings.

OXFORD

Oxford View Nursing Center
6099 Fairfield Rd, Oxford, OH, 45056
(513) 523-6353

Admin Mark E Johnson. *Medical Dir/Dir of Nursing* Dr Robert Prots MD; Jan Kirkpatrick RN.
Licensure Skilled care; Intermediate care. *Beds* SNF 12; ICF 148. *Certified* Medicaid; Medicare.
Owner Proprietary Corp.
Admissions Requirements Medical examination; Physician's request.
Staff Physicians 1 (pt); RNs 6 (ft), 2 (pt); LPNs 13 (ft), 5 (pt); Nurses aides 39 (ft), 43 (pt); Recreational therapists 2 (ft); Activities coordinators 1 (ft).
Facilities Dining room; Physical therapy room; Activities room; Laundry room; Barber/Beauty shop; Courtyard; Cooperative exchange with local university services.
Activities Arts & crafts; Games; Prayer groups; Movies; Social/Cultural gatherings; Exercise groups; Weekly bus outings; Music appreciation; Adopt-a-grandparent program.

Woodland Manor Nursing Home
4166 Somerville Rd, Oxford, OH, 45064
(513) 523-4449 & 523-7486
Admin Dora Webb. *Medical Dir/Dir of Nursing* Gayneil Browning.
Licensure Intermediate care. *Beds* ICF 50. *Certified* Medicaid.
Owner Privately owned.
Admissions Requirements Medical examination.
Staff Physicians 8 (pt); RNs 1 (ft), 1 (pt); LPNs 3 (ft), 2 (pt); Nurses aides 16 (ft), 1 (pt); Activities coordinators 2 (pt); Dietitians 1 (pt).
Facilities Dining room; Physical therapy room; Activities room; Laundry room.
Activities Arts & crafts; Cards; Games; Reading groups; Prayer groups; Movies; Shopping trips; Social/Cultural gatherings.

PAINESVILLE

Cerri Painesville Nursing Home
252 W Jackson St, Painesville, OH, 44077
(216) 354-5300
Admin L J O'Donnell. *Medical Dir/Dir of Nursing* Sharon Schultz.
Licensure Intermediate care. *Beds* ICF 18. *Certified* Medicaid.
Owner Proprietary Corp.
Admissions Requirements Minimum age 20; Females only; Medical examination; Physician's request.
Staff RNs 1 (pt); LPNs 6 (ft); Nurses aides 15 (ft); Dietitians 1 (pt).
Facilities Dining room; Crafts room; Laundry room; Yard; Patio; Garden.
Activities Arts & crafts; Cards; Games; Reading groups; Prayer groups; Movies; Shopping trips; Social/Cultural gatherings; Camping.

Homestead II Nursing Home
60 Wood St, Painesville, OH, 44077
(216) 352-0788, 951-0964
Admin Myra Shinas. *Medical Dir/Dir of Nursing* Dr Robert Whitehouse; Elaine Gallovic RN.
Licensure Skilled care; Intermediate care. *Beds* SNF 52; ICF 52. *Certified* Medicaid; Medicare.
Owner Proprietary Corp (Multicare Management).
Staff Physicians 6 (pt); RNs 3 (ft), 1 (pt); LPNs 4 (ft), 3 (pt); Nurses aides 21 (ft), 6 (pt); Physical therapists 1 (pt); Speech therapists 1 (pt); Activities coordinators 1 (ft); Dietitians 1 (pt); Dentists 1 (pt); Ophthalmologists 1 (pt); Podiatrists 1 (pt).
Facilities Dining room; Physical therapy room; Activities room; Crafts room; Laundry room; Barber/Beauty shop.
Activities Arts & crafts; Cards; Games; Reading groups; Prayer groups; Movies; Shopping trips; Social/Cultural gatherings.

Homestead Nursing Home 1*
164 Liberty St, Painesville, OH, 44077
(216) 357-6181
Licensure Intermediate care. *Beds* 53. *Certified* Medicaid.
Owner Proprietary Corp.

Ivy House*
308 S State St, Painesville, OH, 44077
(216) 354-2131
Admin Marie Swaim. *Medical Dir/Dir of Nursing* Dr F Veroni.
Licensure Intermediate care. *Beds* 50. *Certified* Medicaid.
Owner Proprietary Corp.
Admissions Requirements Minimum age 60; Medical examination.
Staff Physicians 1 (pt); RNs 1 (ft); LPNs 4 (ft); Recreational therapists 1 (ft), 1 (pt); Activities coordinators 1 (ft), 1 (pt); Dietitians 1 (pt).
Facilities Dining room; Activities room; Chapel; Crafts room; Laundry room; Barber/Beauty shop; Library.
Activities Arts & crafts; Cards; Games; Reading groups; Prayer groups; Movies; Shopping trips; Social/Cultural gatherings.

PANDORA

Hilty Memorial Home*
Rte 12, Pandora, OH, 45877
(419) 384-3218
Medical Dir/Dir of Nursing Dr Oliver Lugibihl.
Licensure Intermediate care. *Beds* 61. *Certified* Medicaid.
Owner Nonprofit Corp.
Admissions Requirements Medical examination.
Staff RNs; LPNs; Nurses aides.
Facilities Dining room; Physical therapy room; Activities room; Chapel; Laundry room; Barber/Beauty shop.
Activities Arts & crafts; Cards; Reading groups; Movies; Bible study; Sunshine rhythm band; Current events discussion.

PARMA

Broadview Nursing Home*
5520 Broadview Rd, Parma, OH, 44134
(216) 749-4010
Licensure Skilled care; Intermediate care. *Beds* 198. *Certified* Medicaid; Medicare.
Owner Proprietary Corp.

Holy Family Home
6707 State Rd, Parma, OH, 44134
(216) 885-3100
Licensure Skilled care. *Beds* 50.
Owner Nonprofit Corp.
Staff Physicians 1 (pt); RNs 2 (ft), 2 (pt); LPNs 7 (ft); Orderlies 6 (ft), 6 (pt); Dietitians 1 (pt); Podiatrists 1 (pt); Dentist 2 (pt).
Affiliation Roman Catholic
Facilities Chapel; Crafts room; Laundry room; Barber/Beauty shop.
Activities Arts & crafts; Movies.

Mt Alverna Home*
6765 State Rd, Parma, OH, 44134
(216) 843-7800
Medical Dir/Dir of Nursing Dr Wiliam Dowdell.
Licensure Intermediate care. *Beds* 200. *Certified* Medicaid.
Owner Nonprofit Corp (Franciscan Sisters).
Staff Physicians 3 (pt); RNs 9 (ft), 7 (pt); LPNs 9 (ft), 6 (pt); Orderlies 4 (ft), 1 (pt); Nurses aides 45 (ft), 18 (pt); Physical therapists 2 (pt); Recreational therapists 1 (pt); Speech therapists 1 (pt); Activities coordinators 2 (ft); Dietitians 2 (pt); Dentists 1 (pt); Ophthalmologists 1 (pt); Podiatrists 1 (pt); Audiologists 1 (pt).

Affiliation Roman Catholic
Facilities Dining room; Physical therapy room; Activities room; Chapel; Crafts room; Laundry room; Barber/Beauty shop; Library.
Activities Arts & crafts; Cards; Games; Reading groups; Prayer groups; Movies; Social/Cultural gatherings.

Nelson Broadview Nursing Home*
5520 Broadview Rd, Parma, OH, 44134
(216) 749-4010
Licensure Intermediate care. *Beds* 27. *Certified* Medicaid.
Owner Proprietary Corp.

Parma Care Center
5553 Broadview Rd, Parma, OH, 44134
(216) 741-7195
Admin Louis Schonfeld. *Medical Dir/Dir of Nursing* Charlotte A Bull DON.
Licensure Skilled care; Intermediate care; Rest home. *Beds* 100. *Certified* Medicaid; Medicare.
Owner Proprietary Corp.
Admissions Requirements Medical examination.
Staff Physicians 3 (ft); RNs 1 (ft); LPNs 10 (ft); Nurses aides 28 (ft); Physical therapists 4 (ft); Reality therapists 2 (ft); Recreational therapists 5 (ft); Occupational therapists 1 (ft); Speech therapists 2 (ft); Activities coordinators 2 (ft); Dietitians 2 (ft); Dentists 1 (ft); Ophthalmologists 3 (ft); Podiatrists 1 (ft).
Languages Hungarian, Slavic, Polish
Facilities Dining room; Physical therapy room; Activities room; Chapel; Laundry room; Barber/Beauty shop; Library; Occupational therapy room; Lounge areas; Public sitting areas.
Activities Arts & crafts; Cards; Games; Reading groups; Prayer groups; Movies; Shopping trips; Social/Cultural gatherings.

Pleasantview Nursing Home
7377 Ridge Rd, Parma, OH, 44129
(216) 845-0200
Medical Dir/Dir of Nursing Dr T Burney.
Licensure Skilled care; Intermediate care. *Beds* 187. *Certified* Medicaid; Medicare.
Owner Proprietary Corp.
Admissions Requirements Medical examination.
Staff RNs 7 (ft), 5 (pt); LPNs 11 (ft), 12 (pt); Orderlies 7 (ft), 2 (pt); Nurses aides 43 (ft), 35 (pt); Physical therapists 1 (ft), 1 (pt); Recreational therapists 1 (ft); Speech therapists 1 (pt); Activities coordinators 1 (pt); Dietitians 1 (pt); Dentists 1 (pt); Ophthalmologists 2 (pt); Dentist 1 (pt).
Facilities Dining room; Physical therapy room; Activities room; Chapel; Crafts room; Laundry room; Barber/Beauty shop; Library.
Activities Arts & crafts; Games; Reading groups; Prayer groups; Movies; Social/Cultural gatherings.

PARMA HEIGHTS

Aristocrat South
6455 Pearl Rd, Parma Heights, OH, 44130
(216) 888-5900
Admin Tom Coury.
Licensure Skilled care; Intermediate care; Intermediate care for mentally retarded. *Beds* 199. *Certified* Medicaid; Medicare.
Owner Proprietary Corp.
Admissions Requirements Minimum age 15; Medical examination.
Staff RNs; LPNs; Orderlies; Nurses aides; Physical therapists; Reality therapists; Occupational therapists; Speech therapists; Activities coordinators; Dietitians; Ophthalmologists; Podiatrists.
Facilities Dining room; Physical therapy room; Activities room; Crafts room; Laundry room; Barber/Beauty shop; Library.

Activities Arts & crafts; Cards; Games;
Reading groups; Prayer groups; Social/
Cultural gatherings.

PAULDING

Hometown Nursing Home
PO Box 157, S R 111 West, Paulding, OH,
45879
(419) 399-4940
Admin Nancy J Coughlan. *Medical Dir/Dir of
Nursing* Linda Eifrid DON.
Licensure Intermediate care. *Beds* ICF 50.
Certified Medicaid.
Owner Proprietary Corp.
Admissions Requirements Medical
examination; Physician's request.
Staff RNs; LPNs; Nurses aides; Activities
coordinators; Dietitians; Ophthalmologists.
Languages Spanish
Facilities Dining room; Activities room;
Crafts room; Laundry room; Barber/Beauty
shop.
Activities Arts & crafts; Cards; Games;
Reading groups; Prayer groups; Movies;
Shopping trips; Social/Cultural gatherings.

PAYNE

Dallas Lamb Foundation Home*
PO Box 56, 650 N Main, Payne, OH, 45880
(419) 263-2334
Licensure Intermediate care. *Beds* 50.
Certified Medicaid.
Owner Nonprofit Corp.

PEEBLES

Hillcrest Nursing Home
3564 Lawshe Rd, Peebles, OH, 45660
(513) 386-2522
Admin Oscar Jarnicki. *Medical Dir/Dir of
Nursing* Dr K Lim; Connie Fenton RN.
Licensure Intermediate care. *Beds* ICF 50.
Certified Medicaid.
Owner Proprietary Corp (Congregate Living of
America).
Staff RNs 2 (ft); LPNs 6 (ft), 3 (pt); Nurses
aides 25 (ft); Recreational therapists 1 (ft);
Dietitians 1 (pt).
Facilities Dining room; Activities room;
Crafts room; Laundry room; Barber/Beauty
shop; Library.
Activities Arts & crafts; Cards; Games;
Reading groups; Prayer groups; Movies;
Shopping trips; Social/Cultural gatherings.

PEMBERVILLE

Otterbein Portage Valley
20311 Pemberville Rd, Pemberville, OH,
43450
(419) 833-7000
Admin Brian R Tansey. *Medical Dir/Dir of
Nursing* Gustave Link MD; Elsie Street RN
DON.
Licensure Skilled care; Intermediate care. *Beds*
100. *Certified* Medicaid; Medicare.
Owner Nonprofit Corp.
Admissions Requirements Medical
examination; Physician's request.
Staff Physicians 1 (pt); RNs 3 (ft), 3 (pt);
LPNs 6 (ft), 8 (pt); Nurses aides 18 (ft), 28
(pt); Activities coordinators 1 (ft); Dietitians
1 (ft).
Affiliation Methodist
Facilities Dining room; Physical therapy
room; Activities room; Laundry room;
Barber/Beauty shop.
Activities Arts & crafts; Cards; Games;
Reading groups; Prayer groups; Movies;
Shopping trips; Social/Cultural gatherings.

PENINSULA

Wayside Farm Inc
4557 Quick Rd, Peninsula, OH, 44264
(216)
Licensure Intermediate care for mentally
retarded. *Beds* 95. *Certified* Medicaid.
Owner Proprietary Corp.

PERRY

Perry Ridge Nursing Home Inc*
5051 S Ridge Rd, Perry, OH, 44081
(216) 259-4300
Licensure Intermediate care. *Beds* 39.
Certified Medicaid.
Owner Proprietary Corp.

PERRYSBURG

Heartland of Perrysburg
10540 Fremont Pike, Perrysburg, OH, 43551
(419) 874-3578
Admin Jean Wolfe. *Medical Dir/Dir of
Nursing* S R Torres MD.
Licensure Skilled care; Intermediate care. *Beds*
131. *Certified* Medicare.
Owner Proprietary Corp (Health Care &
Retirement Corp).
Staff RNs 6 (ft), 9 (pt); LPNs 12 (ft), 3 (pt);
Nurses aides 34 (ft), 21 (pt); Physical
therapists 1 (ft); Recreational therapists 1
(ft); Speech therapists 1 (ft); Activities
coordinators 1 (ft); Dietitians 1 (ft); Dentists
1 (pt); Ophthalmologists 1 (pt); Podiatrists 1
(pt).
Facilities Dining room; Physical therapy
room; Activities room; Crafts room; Laundry
room; Barber/Beauty shop.
Activities Arts & crafts; Cards; Games;
Reading groups; Prayer groups; Movies;
Shopping trips; Social/Cultural gatherings.

PICKERINGTON

Echo Manor Extended Care Center*
10270 Blacklick Eastern Rd NW,
Pickerington, OH, 43147
Licensure Skilled care; Intermediate care. *Beds*
100. *Certified* Medicaid; Medicare.
Owner Nonprofit Corp.

PIKETON

Casey Nursing Home
2386 Wakefield Mound Rd, Piketon, OH,
45661
(614) 289-2137
Admin Erma Jewett. *Medical Dir/Dir of
Nursing* K A Wilkinson MD.
Licensure Intermediate care. *Beds* 38.
Certified Medicaid.
Owner Proprietary Corp.
Admissions Requirements Medical
examination; Physician's request.
Staff RNs 1 (pt); LPNs 4 (ft), 1 (pt); Nurses
aides 9 (ft); Recreational therapists 1 (ft);
Activities coordinators 1 (ft).
Facilities Dining room; Activities room;
Crafts room; Laundry room.
Activities Arts & crafts; Games; Reading
groups; Prayer groups; Movies; Shopping
trips; Social/Cultural gatherings.

Gayhart's Nursing Home*
2582 Wakefield Mound Rd, Piketon, OH,
45661
(614) 289-4024
Licensure Intermediate care. *Beds* 32.
Certified Medicaid.
Owner Proprietary Corp.

Mullins Nursing Home*
2266 Wakefield Mound Rd, Piketon, OH,
45661
(614) 289-4360

Licensure Intermediate care. *Beds* 32.
Certified Medicaid.
Owner Proprietary Corp.

Pike Manor Nursing Home*
PO Box 308, 214 E Main St, Piketon, OH,
45661
(614) 289-2129
Licensure Intermediate care. *Beds* 25.
Certified Medicaid.
Owner Nonprofit Corp.

Pleasant Hill Convalescent Center*
Box 334, Piketon, OH, 45661
(614) 289-2394
Licensure Skilled care; Intermediate care. *Beds*
101. *Certified* Medicaid; Medicare.
Owner Proprietary Corp.

Spears & Spears Nursing Home*
300 Overlook Dr, Piketon, OH, 45661
(614) 289-4074
Licensure Intermediate care. *Beds* 25.
Certified Medicaid.
Owner Proprietary Corp.

PIQUA

Piqua Manor
PO Box 1137, W High St, Piqua, OH, 45356
(513) 773-0040
Medical Dir/Dir of Nursing Jack P Steinhilben
MD.
Licensure Skilled care; Intermediate care. *Beds*
100. *Certified* Medicaid; Medicare.
Owner Proprietary Corp (Health Care
Facilities Inc).
Admissions Requirements Medical
examination; Physician's request.
Staff RNs 2 (ft), 5 (pt); LPNs 7 (ft), 5 (pt);
Orderlies 3 (ft), 6 (pt); Nurses aides 13 (ft),
20 (pt); Physical therapists 1 (ft); Activities
coordinators 2 (ft).
Facilities Dining room; Physical therapy
room; Activities room; Crafts room; Laundry
room; Barber/Beauty shop.
Activities Arts & crafts; Cards; Games;
Reading groups; Prayer groups; Movies;
Shopping trips; Social/Cultural gatherings.

PLAINS

**Buckeye Community Services-Childrens
Transitional Facility***
33 Hartman Rd, The Plains, OH, 45780
Licensure Intermediate care for mentally
retarded. *Beds* 10. *Certified* Medicaid.
Owner Nonprofit Corp.

Hickory Creek of Athens
51 E 4th St, The Plains, OH, 45780
(614) 797-4561
Admin David Lucid. *Medical Dir/Dir of
Nursing* Edward A Sprague MD; Carol
McQuate RN DON.
Licensure Skilled care; Intermediate care. *Beds*
132. *Certified* Medicaid; Medicare.
Owner Proprietary Corp (Health Care
Management).
Admissions Requirements Medical
examination; Physician's request.
Staff Physicians 9 (ft); RNs 7 (ft), 3 (pt);
LPNs 12 (ft), 5 (pt); Nurses aides 46 (ft), 16
(pt); Physical therapists 1 (pt); Occupational
therapists 1 (pt); Speech therapists 1 (pt);
Activities coordinators 1 (pt); Dietitians 1
(ft); Dentists 2 (pt); Ophthalmologists 1 (pt);
Podiatrists 1 (pt); Psychologist 1 (pt).
Facilities Dining room; Physical therapy
room; Activities room; Laundry room;
Barber/Beauty shop.
Activities Arts & crafts; Cards; Games;
Reading groups; Prayer groups; Shopping
trips; Social/Cultural gatherings.

POMEROY

Americare Pomeroy Nursing & Rehabilitation Center
36759 Rocksprings Rd, Pomeroy, OH, 45769
(614) 992-6606
Admin Roger Covert. *Medical Dir/Dir of Nursing* Wilma Mansfield MD; Nancy K Van Meter RN.
Licensure Skilled care; Intermediate care. *Beds* SNF 20; ICF 80. *Certified* Medicaid; Medicare.
Owner Proprietary Corp (Americare Corp).
Admissions Requirements Physician's request.
Staff RNs 3 (ft), 3 (pt); LPNs 8 (ft), 6 (pt); Orderlies 3 (ft), 2 (pt); Nurses aides 32 (ft), 5 (pt); Activities coordinators 1 (ft), 1 (pt).
Facilities Dining room; Physical therapy room; Activities room; Laundry room; Barber/Beauty shop.
Activities Arts & crafts; Cards; Games; Reading groups; Prayer groups; Movies; Shopping trips; Social/Cultural gatherings.

PORT CLINTON

Edgewood Manor Nursing Center*
1330 S Fulton, Port Clinton, OH, 43452
(419) 734-5506
Medical Dir/Dir of Nursing R W Minick MD.
Licensure Skilled care; Intermediate care. *Beds* 100. *Certified* Medicaid; Medicare.
Owner Proprietary Corp (Shive Nursing Centers).
Admissions Requirements Medical examination.
Staff Physicians 7 (pt); RNs 6 (ft); LPNs 3 (ft), 6 (pt); Nurses aides 44 (ft); Physical therapists; Recreational therapists; Occupational therapists; Speech therapists; Activities coordinators 1 (ft); Dietitians 1 (pt); Dentists; Podiatrists 1 (pt); Audiologists.
Facilities Dining room; Physical therapy room; Activities room; Chapel; Laundry room; Barber/Beauty shop; Library; Living room.
Activities Arts & crafts; Cards; Games; Prayer groups; Movies; Shopping trips; Social/Cultural gatherings; Exercises.

PORTAGE

Nichols Home
355 W Main St, Portage, OH, 43451
(419) 352-5115
Admin Gregory A Bair. *Medical Dir/Dir of Nursing* Judy Yackee.
Licensure Intermediate care for mentally retarded. *Beds* ICF/MR 8. *Certified* Medicaid.
Owner Nonprofit organization/foundation.
Admissions Requirements Minimum age 18.
Staff Physicians 1 (pt); RNs 3 (ft); LPNs 2 (ft); Nurses aides 10 (ft); Recreational therapists 1 (pt); Occupational therapists 1 (pt); Speech therapists 1 (pt); Activities coordinators 1 (pt); Dietitians 1 (pt).
Activities Arts & crafts; Cards; Games; Reading groups; Prayer groups; Movies; Shopping trips; Social/Cultural gatherings.

Restle Home
353 W Main St, Portage, OH, 43451
(419) 352-5115
Admin Gregory A Bair. *Medical Dir/Dir of Nursing* Judy Yackee.
Licensure Intermediate care for mentally retarded. *Beds* ICF/MR 8. *Certified* Medicaid.
Owner Nonprofit organization/foundation.
Admissions Requirements Minimum age 18.
Staff Physicians 1 (pt); RNs 3 (ft); LPNs 2 (ft); Nurses aides 10 (ft); Recreational therapists 1 (pt); Occupational therapists 1 (pt); Speech therapists 1 (pt); Activities coordinators 1 (pt); Dietitians 1 (pt).
Activities Arts & crafts; Cards; Games; Reading groups; Prayer groups; Movies; Shopping trips; Social/Cultural gatherings.

Werner Home
351 W Main St, Portage, OH, 43451
(419) 352-5115
Admin Gregory A Bair. *Medical Dir/Dir of Nursing* Judy Yackee.
Licensure Intermediate care for mentally retarded. *Beds* ICF/MR 10. *Certified* Medicaid.
Owner Nonprofit organization/foundation.
Admissions Requirements Minimum age 18.
Staff Physicians 1 (pt); RNs 3 (ft); LPNs 2 (ft); Nurses aides 10 (ft); Recreational therapists 1 (pt); Occupational therapists 1 (pt); Speech therapists 1 (pt); Activities coordinators 1 (pt); Dietitians 1 (pt).
Activities Arts & crafts; Cards; Games; Reading groups; Prayer groups; Movies; Shopping trips; Social/Cultural gatherings.

PORTSMOUTH

Elmwood Village*
2001 Scioto Trail, Portsmouth, OH, 45662
(614) 354-8631
Licensure Intermediate care. *Beds* 110. *Certified* Medicaid.
Owner Proprietary Corp.

Flannery's Health Care Center
605 Front St, Portsmouth, OH, 45662
(614) 353-5535
Admin Karen Bryan. *Medical Dir/Dir of Nursing* Barbara Rowe DON.
Licensure Intermediate care. *Beds* ICF 29. *Certified* Medicaid.
Owner Proprietary Corp.
Admissions Requirements Minimum age 21; Medical examination; Physician's request.
Staff Physicians 2 (pt); RNs 1 (ft); LPNs 6 (ft); Nurses aides 14 (ft); Activities coordinators 1 (ft).
Facilities Dining room; Physical therapy room; Activities room; Crafts room; Laundry room; Barber/Beauty shop; Library.
Activities Arts & crafts; Cards; Games; Reading groups; Prayer groups; Shopping trips; Social/Cultural gatherings.

Golden Years Convalescent Center
2125 Royce St, PO Box 1148, Portsmouth, OH, 45662
(614) 354-6635
Medical Dir/Dir of Nursing Wayne Young MD.
Licensure Skilled care; Intermediate care. *Beds* 100. *Certified* Medicaid; Medicare.
Owner Proprietary Corp.
Admissions Requirements Medical examination.
Staff Physicians 8 (pt); RNs 6 (ft); LPNs 12 (ft); Nurses aides 43 (ft), 4 (pt); Physical therapists 1 (pt); Reality therapists 2 (pt); Recreational therapists 2 (pt); Speech therapists 1 (pt); Activities coordinators 1 (ft); Dietitians 1 (ft); Dentists 1 (pt); Ophthalmologists 1 (pt); Podiatrists 1 (pt); Dentist 1 (pt); Occupational therapist 1 (ft); Occupational therapy assistant 1 (ft).
Facilities Dining room; Physical therapy room; Activities room; Chapel; Crafts room; Laundry room; Barber/Beauty shop.
Activities Arts & crafts; Cards; Games; Reading groups; Prayer groups; Movies; Shopping trips; Social/Cultural gatherings.

Heartland of Portsmouth
Box 10, Rte 6, Feurt Hill Rd, Portsmouth, OH, 45662
(614) 354-4505
Admin Jeffrey C Hunter. *Medical Dir/Dir of Nursing* Aaron Adams DO; Lois Zuhars RN DON.
Licensure Skilled care; Intermediate care. *Beds* 100. *Certified* Medicaid; Medicare.

Owner Proprietary Corp (Health Care & Retirement Corp).
Staff RNs 3 (ft), 2 (pt); LPNs 8 (ft), 2 (pt); Orderlies 1 (ft), 1 (pt); Nurses aides 30 (ft), 15 (pt); Physical therapists 1 (ft); Activities coordinators 1 (ft); Dietitians 1 (ft).
Facilities Dining room; Physical therapy room; Activities room; Laundry room; Barber/Beauty shop.
Activities Arts & crafts; Cards; Games; Reading groups; Prayer groups; Movies; Shopping trips; Social/Cultural gatherings.

Hill View Health Center
1610 28th St, Portsmouth, OH, 45662
(614) 353-2746
Admin John E Zinsmeister NHA; Calvin Rodhetter Exec Dir. *Medical Dir/Dir of Nursing* Thomas K Swope DO; Bernardine Hartley DON.
Licensure Skilled care; Intermediate care. *Beds* SNF 55; ICF. *Certified* Medicaid; Medicare.
Owner Nonprofit organization/foundation.
Admissions Requirements Medical examination; Physician's request.
Staff Physicians 1 (ft), 4 (pt); RNs 8 (ft); LPNs 8 (ft); Orderlies 1 (ft); Nurses aides 21 (ft); Activities coordinators 3 (ft); Dietitians 1 (ft).
Affiliation Methodist
Facilities Dining room; Physical therapy room; Activities room; Crafts room; Laundry room; Barber/Beauty shop; Library; Multi-purpose room.
Activities Arts & crafts; Cards; Games; Reading groups; Prayer groups; Movies; Shopping trips; Social/Cultural gatherings.

Hilltop Nursing Home*
1319 Spring St, Portsmouth, OH, 45662
(614) 354-6619
Licensure Intermediate care. *Beds* 25. *Certified* Medicaid.
Owner Proprietary Corp.

RAVENNA

Jane Francis Nursing Home*
245 New Milford Rd, Ravenna, OH, 44266
(216) 296-6415
Licensure Skilled care; Intermediate care. *Beds* 99. *Certified* Medicaid; Medicare.
Owner Proprietary Corp.

Portage County Nursing Home*
7988 Infirmary Rd, Ravenna, OH, 44266
(216) 296-9977
Medical Dir/Dir of Nursing Albert Tsai MD.
Licensure Intermediate care. *Beds* 99. *Certified* Medicaid.
Owner Publicly owned.
Admissions Requirements Medical examination.
Staff Physicians 1 (pt); RNs 4 (ft); LPNs 5 (ft), 5 (pt); Nurses aides 21 (ft), 14 (pt); Physical therapists 1 (pt); Activities coordinators 1 (ft); Dietitians 1 (pt); Dentists 1 (pt); Ophthalmologists 1 (pt); Podiatrists 1 (pt).
Facilities Dining room; Physical therapy room; Activities room; Chapel; Crafts room; Barber/Beauty shop.
Activities Arts & crafts; Cards; Games; Reading groups; Prayer groups; Movies; Shopping trips; Social/Cultural gatherings.

READING

Aaron Convalescent Home
21 W Columbia St, Reading, OH, 45215
(513) 554-1141
Admin Patricia E Vogel. *Medical Dir/Dir of Nursing* Dr George Shields MD; Rae M Smith DON.
Licensure Intermediate care. *Beds* 142. *Certified* Medicaid.
Owner Proprietary Corp.

Staff Physicians; RNs; LPNs; Orderlies;
Nurses aides; Physical therapists; Speech
therapists; Activities coordinators; Dietitians;
Ophthalmologists.
Facilities Dining room; Physical therapy
room; Activities room; Chapel; Crafts room;
Laundry room; Barber/Beauty shop.
Activities Arts & crafts; Cards; Games;
Reading groups; Prayer groups; Movies;
Shopping trips; Social/Cultural gatherings.

RICHFIELD

Pine Valley Nursing Center
4360 Brecksville Rd, Richfield, OH, 44286
(216) 659-6166
Admin Dr Sheth.
Licensure Skilled care; Intermediate care. *Beds*
95. *Certified* Medicaid; Medicare.
Owner Proprietary Corp.
Admissions Requirements Minimum age 14;
Medical examination.
Staff Physicians 4 (pt); RNs 4 (ft), 3 (pt);
LPNs 10 (ft), 1 (pt); Orderlies 2 (ft), 2 (pt);
Nurses aides 30 (ft), 17 (pt); Physical
therapists 1 (pt); Activities coordinators 1
(ft); Dietitians 1 (pt).
Facilities Dining room; Activities room;
Laundry room; Barber/Beauty shop.
Activities Arts & crafts; Cards; Games; Prayer
groups; Movies; Shopping trips; Social/
Cultural gatherings.

RIPLEY

Ohio Valley Manor Convalescent Center
5280 Rtes 62 & 68, Ripley, OH, 45167
(513) 392-4318
Admin George W Balz. *Medical Dir/Dir of
Nursing* Gene Conway MD; Connie Pollard
RN.
Licensure Skilled care; Intermediate care. *Beds*
SNF 100; ICF. *Certified* Medicaid;
Medicare.
Owner Proprietary Corp.
Admissions Requirements Medical
examination; Physician's request.
Staff Physicians 5 (pt); RNs 6 (ft), 3 (pt);
LPNs 10 (ft), 7 (pt); Nurses aides 34 (ft), 20
(pt); Physical therapists 1 (ft), 1 (pt);
Occupational therapists 1 (ft); Speech
therapists 1 (pt); Activities coordinators 1
(ft); Dietitians 1 (pt); Dentists 1 (pt);
Ophthalmologists 1 (pt); Podiatrists 1 (pt).
Facilities Dining room; Physical therapy
room; Activities room; Laundry room;
Barber/Beauty shop; Library.
Activities Arts & crafts; Cards; Games;
Reading groups; Prayer groups; Movies;
Shopping trips; Social/Cultural gatherings.

RITTMAN

**Americare Rittman Nursing & Rehabilitation
Center**
275 E Sunset Dr, Rittman, OH, 44270
(216) 927-2060
Admin Laura A Matthews. *Medical Dir/Dir of
Nursing* Dr Knapic; Dianna Carderas RN
DON.
Licensure Skilled care. *Beds* 100. *Certified*
Medicaid; Medicare.
Owner Proprietary Corp (Americare Corp).
Staff Physical therapists; Speech therapists;
Activities coordinators; Dietitians; Dentists;
Ophthalmologists.

Apostolic Christian Home Inc*
10680 Steiner Rd, Rittman, OH, 44270
(216) 927-1010
Licensure Intermediate care. *Beds* 51.
Certified Medicaid.
Owner Nonprofit Corp.
Affiliation Apostolic Christian

ROCK CREEK

Char-Lotte Nursing Home Inc*
Rte 45, Box 177, Rock Creek, OH, 44084
(216) 563-5547
Licensure Skilled care; Intermediate care. *Beds*
119. *Certified* Medicaid; Medicare.
Owner Proprietary Corp.

ROCKFORD

Colonial Nursing Home*
611 S Main St, Rockford, OH, 45882
(419) 363-2193
Licensure Intermediate care. *Beds* 34.
Certified Medicaid.
Owner Proprietary Corp.

Shane Hill Nursing Home
Rte 3, State Rte 118, Rockford, OH, 45882
(419) 363-2620
Admin John L Smith. *Medical Dir/Dir of
Nursing* Dr R D Bradrick, Dr Philip Masser;
Sue Barna DON.
Licensure Intermediate care. *Beds* ICF 100.
Certified Medicaid.
Owner Proprietary Corp.
Admissions Requirements Medical
examination; Physician's request.
Staff Physicians 6 (pt); RNs 5 (ft), 2 (pt);
LPNs 9 (ft), 5 (pt); Nurses aides 35 (ft), 5
(pt); Physical therapists 1 (pt); Recreational
therapists 2 (ft), 1 (pt); Speech therapists 1
(pt); Activities coordinators 1 (ft); Dietitians
1 (pt); Ophthalmologists 1 (pt).
Facilities Dining room; Physical therapy
room; Activities room; Chapel; Crafts room;
Laundry room; Barber/Beauty shop; Library.
Activities Arts & crafts; Cards; Games;
Reading groups; Prayer groups; Movies;
Social/Cultural gatherings.

ROCKY RIVER

Welsh Home for the Aged*
22199 Center Ridge Rd, Rocky River, OH,
44116
(216) 331-0420
Licensure Intermediate care. *Beds* 34.
Certified Medicaid.
Owner Nonprofit Corp.

SABINA

Autumn Years Nursing Center*
580 E Washington Ave, Sabina, OH, 45169
(513) 584-4440
Licensure Skilled care; Intermediate care. *Beds*
51. *Certified* Medicaid; Medicare.
Owner Proprietary Corp.

Deiber Nursing Home Inc
91 E Elm St, Sabina, OH, 45169-1330
(614) 773-2104
Licensure Intermediate care. *Beds* 33.
Certified Medicaid.
Owner Proprietary Corp.

Eden Manor Nursing Home*
273 S Howard St, Sabina, OH, 45169
(513) 584-4313
Licensure Intermediate care. *Beds* 30.
Certified Medicaid.
Owner Proprietary Corp.

SAINT CLAIRSVILLE

Belmont County Oakview Nursing Home*
Rte 1, Saint Clairsville, OH, 43950
(614) 695-4925
Licensure Intermediate care. *Beds* 71.
Certified Medicaid.
Owner Proprietary Corp (Health Care &
Retirement Corp).

Belmont Habilitation Center
320 Fox-Shannon Pl, Saint Clairsville, OH,
43950
Admin Jeff Egelston.
Licensure Intermediate care for mentally
retarded. *Beds* 85. *Certified* Medicaid.
Owner Nonprofit Corp.
Admissions Requirements Minimum age 18.
Staff Physicians 1 (pt); RNs 3 (ft); LPNs 3
(ft); Physical therapists 1 (pt); Occupational
therapists 3 (pt); Activities coordinators 1
(ft); Dietitians 1 (pt).
Facilities Dining room; Physical therapy
room; Activities room; Laundry room.
Activities Daily living skills & self-help
development.

Woodland Acres Nursing Home Inc*
Rte 4, Cresent Rd, Saint Clairsville, OH,
43950
(614) 695-0800
Licensure Nursing home. *Beds* 16.
Owner Proprietary Corp.

SAINT MARYS

Valley Nursing Home*
1140 Knoxville Ave, Saint Marys, OH, 45885
(419) 394-3308
Licensure Skilled care; Intermediate care. *Beds*
100. *Certified* Medicaid; Medicare.
Owner Proprietary Corp (Beverly Enterprises).

SALEM

Mary Fletcher Health Care Center 1*
767 Benton Rd, Salem, OH, 44460
(216) 332-0391
Licensure Intermediate care. *Beds* 24.
Certified Medicaid.
Owner Proprietary Corp.

Hutton Nursing Center I
2511 Bentley Dr, Salem, OH, 44460
(216) 337-9503
Admin Arnold C Yost, Jr. *Medical Dir/Dir of
Nursing* Sally Stamp RN DON.
Licensure Intermediate care. *Beds* ICF 100.
Certified Medicaid.
Owner Proprietary Corp (American Health
Care Centers).
Admissions Requirements Medical
examination.
Staff RNs; LPNs; Orderlies; Nurses aides;
Activities coordinators.
Facilities Dining room; Activities room;
Chapel; Laundry room; Barber/Beauty shop.
Activities Arts & crafts; Cards; Games; Prayer
groups; Shopping trips; Social/Cultural
gatherings.

Hutton Nursing Center II Inc*
250 Continental Drive, Salem, OH, 44460
Beds 100.

Salem Convalescent Center
1985 E Pershing St, Salem, OH, 44460
(216) 332-1588
Admin Duane Herron. *Medical Dir/Dir of
Nursing* W F Stevenson MD; Jacquelyn
McKeorsig RN.
Licensure Intermediate care; Rest home;
Assisted living. *Beds* ICF 90; Rest home 14;
Assisted living 8. *Certified* Medicaid.
Owner Privately owned.
Admissions Requirements Medical
examination; Physician's request.
Staff RNs 4 (ft), 2 (pt); LPNs 6 (ft), 5 (pt);
Nurses aides 26 (ft), 10 (pt); Activities
coordinators 2 (ft), 1 (pt).
Facilities Dining room; Activities room;
Chapel; Crafts room; Laundry room; Barber/
Beauty shop.
Activities Arts & crafts; Cards; Games;
Reading groups; Prayer groups; Movies;
Shopping trips; Social/Cultural gatherings;
Picnics; Outings to parks; Country rides.

Valley Road Nursing Home
451 Valley Rd, Salem, OH, 44460
(216) 537-4621
Admin Mariann Riley. *Medical Dir/Dir of
Nursing* Janet Holmes RN.
Licensure Intermediate care. *Beds* ICF 44.
Certified Medicaid.
Owner Proprietary Corp.
Admissions Requirements Minimum age 18.
Staff RNs 1 (ft); LPNs 4 (ft), 1 (pt); Nurses
aides 7 (ft), 4 (pt); Recreational therapists 1
(pt); Activities coordinators 1 (ft).
Facilities Dining room; Activities room;
Laundry room.
Activities Arts & crafts; Cards; Games; Prayer
groups; Movies; Shopping trips; Social/
Cultural gatherings.

SANDUSKY

Classic Care South
3423 S Columbus Ave, Sandusky, OH, 44839
(419) 625-6534
Admin Gloria Fidler. *Medical Dir/Dir of
Nursing* Jeannie VanCouwenbergh RN.
Licensure Intermediate care. *Beds* ICF 34.
Certified Medicaid.
Owner Proprietary Corp (Health Resources
Dev).
Staff Physicians 1 (pt); RNs 1 (ft); LPNs 4
(ft), 2 (pt); Nurses aides 11 (ft), 5 (pt);
Recreational therapists 1 (pt); Dietitians 1
(ft).
Facilities Dining room; Activities room;
Laundry room.
Activities Arts & crafts; Cards; Games;
Reading groups; Prayer groups; Movies;
Shopping trips; Social/Cultural gatherings.

Classic Center*
620 W Strub Rd, Sandusky, OH, 44870
(419) 626-5373
Medical Dir/Dir of Nursing D B Cuthbertson
MD.
Licensure Intermediate care. *Beds* 51.
Owner Proprietary Corp (Health Resources
Dev).
Admissions Requirements Medical
examination; Physician's request.
Staff Physicians 1 (ft), 4 (pt); RNs 2 (ft), 1
(pt); LPNs 3 (ft), 3 (pt); Nurses aides 10 (ft),
7 (pt); Physical therapists 1 (pt); Reality
therapists 1 (pt); Recreational therapists 1
(ft); Occupational therapists 1 (pt); Speech
therapists 1 (pt); Activities coordinators 1
(ft); Dietitians 1 (pt); Dentists 1 (pt);
Ophthalmologists 1 (pt); Podiatrists 2 (pt);
Audiologists 1 (pt).
Facilities Dining room; Activities room;
Chapel; Laundry room; Barber/Beauty shop;
Library.
Activities Arts & crafts; Cards; Games;
Reading groups; Prayer groups; Movies;
Shopping trips; Social/Cultural gatherings;
Outings.

Hospitality Care Center 1*
531 Wayne St, Sandusky, OH, 44870
(419) 625-4449
Licensure Nursing home. *Beds* 23.
Owner Proprietary Corp.

Hospitality Care Center 2
403 E Adams St, Sandusky, OH, 44870
(419) 626-5444
Admin E Maureen Leahy. *Medical Dir/Dir of
Nursing* Liz Wobser.
Licensure Intermediate care. *Beds* ICF 26.
Certified Medicaid.
Owner Privately owned.
Admissions Requirements Minimum age 18.
Staff Physicians 1 (pt); LPNs 2 (ft); Nurses
aides 9 (ft); Activities coordinators 1 (ft);
Dietitians 1 (pt); Ophthalmologists 1 (pt).
Facilities Dining room; Laundry room.
Activities Arts & crafts; Cards; Games;
Reading groups; Prayer groups; Movies;
Shopping trips; Social/Cultural gatherings.

Lutheran Memorial Home
795 Bardshar Rd, Sandusky, OH, 44870
(419) 625-4046
Admin Frances Landis. *Medical Dir/Dir of
Nursing* Dean J Reichenbach MD; Evelyn
Moore DON.
Licensure Intermediate care. *Beds* 50.
Owner Nonprofit organization/foundation.
Admissions Requirements Medical
examination.
Staff Physicians 1 (pt); RNs 1 (ft); LPNs 9
(pt); Nurses aides 13 (ft), 25 (pt); Physical
therapists 16 (ft), 14 (pt); Activities
coordinators 1 (ft); Dietitians 2 (ft).
Affiliation Lutheran
Facilities Dining room; Physical therapy
room; Activities room; Chapel; Crafts room;
Laundry room; Barber/Beauty shop.
Activities Arts & crafts; Cards; Games;
Reading groups; Prayer groups; Movies;
Shopping trips; Social/Cultural gatherings;
Group entertainment.

St Ann Skilled Nursing Center
1912 Hayes Ave, Sandusky, OH, 44870
(419) 625-8450 Ext 4257
Admin Sr Nancy Linen Kugel. *Medical Dir/
Dir of Nursing* Sidhaiyan Aiyappasamy MD;
Karen Campana.
Licensure Skilled care. *Beds* SNF 46. *Certified*
Medicaid; Medicare.
Owner Nonprofit Corp.
Admissions Requirements Medical
examination.
Staff Physicians; RNs 4 (ft), 4 (pt); LPNs 5
(ft), 8 (pt); Physical therapists; Occupational
therapists; Speech therapists; Activities
coordinators; Dietitians; Dentists;
Ophthalmologists; Podiatrists; Social Service
1 (pt).
Affiliation Roman Catholic
Facilities Dining room; Physical therapy
room; Activities room; Chapel; Crafts room;
Laundry room.
Activities Arts & crafts; Cards; Games;
Reading groups; Prayer groups; Movies;
Social/Cultural gatherings; Baking &
cooking; Reality orientation; Remotivation
groups; Individual activities; Physical
activities.

Sandusky Nursing Home Inc*
232 Jackson St, Sandusky, OH, 44870
(419) 626-6688
Medical Dir/Dir of Nursing W P Skirball MD.
Licensure Intermediate care; Intermediate care
for mentally retarded. *Beds* ICF 65; ICF/MR
64. *Certified* Medicaid.
Owner Proprietary Corp.
Staff Physicians 3 (pt); RNs 1 (ft), 2 (pt);
LPNs 9 (ft), 3 (pt); Nurses aides 30 (ft);
Physical therapists 1 (pt); Recreational
therapists 1 (ft); Occupational therapists 1
(pt); Speech therapists 1 (pt); Activities
coordinators 1 (pt); Dietitians 1 (pt);
Dentists 1 (pt); Ophthalmologists 1 (pt);
Podiatrists 1 (pt); Audiologists 1 (pt).
Facilities Dining room; Physical therapy
room; Activities room; Crafts room; Laundry
room; Barber/Beauty shop; Library.
Activities Arts & crafts; Cards; Games; Prayer
groups; Movies; Shopping trips; Social/
Cultural gatherings.

True Light Nursing Home*
507 Wayne St, Sandusky, OH, 44870
(419) 626-5444
Admin William J Hunt. *Medical Dir/Dir of
Nursing* Sidhaiyan Aiyappasamy MD.
Licensure Intermediate care. *Beds* 50.
Certified Medicaid.
Owner Proprietary Corp.
Admissions Requirements Medical
examination.
Staff Physicians 1 (pt); RNs 1 (pt); LPNs 6
(ft), 2 (pt); Orderlies 2 (ft); Nurses aides 12
(ft), 6 (pt); Physical therapists 1 (pt);
Occupational therapists 1 (pt); Speech
therapists 1 (pt); Activities coordinators 1

(ft); Dietitians 1 (pt); Dentists 1 (pt);
Ophthalmologists 1 (pt); Podiatrists 1 (pt);
Audiologists 1 (pt).
Facilities Dining room; Activities room;
Crafts room; Laundry room.
Activities Arts & crafts; Cards; Games;
Reading groups; Prayer groups; Movies;
Shopping trips; Social/Cultural gatherings.

SEBRING

Crandall Medical Center
800 S 15th St, Sebring, OH, 44672
(216) 938-9831
Medical Dir/Dir of Nursing George H Davies
MD.
Licensure Skilled care; Intermediate care; Rest
home. *Beds* 192. *Certified* Medicaid;
Medicare.
Owner Nonprofit Corp.
Admissions Requirements Medical
examination.
Staff Physicians 2 (pt); RNs 6 (ft), 7 (pt);
LPNs 13 (ft), 14 (pt); Orderlies 2 (ft), 3 (pt);
Nurses aides 32 (ft), 56 (pt); Physical
therapists 2 (pt); Occupational therapists 1
(pt); Speech therapists 1 (pt); Activities
coordinators 2 (pt); Dietitians 1 (pt); Dentists
1 (pt); Podiatrists 2 (pt).
Affiliation Methodist
Facilities Dining room; Physical therapy
room; Activities room; Chapel; Crafts room;
Laundry room; Barber/Beauty shop; Library.
Activities Arts & crafts; Cards; Games;
Reading groups; Prayer groups; Movies;
Shopping trips; Social/Cultural gatherings;
Discussion groups; Sing-alongs; Ceramics.

SEVILLE

Canterbury Villa of Seville*
76 High St, Seville, OH, 44256
Licensure Skilled care; Intermediate care. *Beds*
100. *Certified* Medicaid; Medicare.
Owner Proprietary Corp.

SHADYSIDE

Shadyside Care Center
60583 State Rte 7, Shadyside, OH, 43947
(614) 676-8381
Admin Anthony M Pucillo. *Medical Dir/Dir of
Nursing* Theron R Rolston MD; Joni Fox
RN DON.
Licensure Intermediate care. *Beds* ICF 100.
Certified Medicaid.
Owner Proprietary Corp.
Admissions Requirements Medical
examination; Physician's request.
Staff Physicians 8 (pt); Physical therapists 1
(pt); Recreational therapists 1 (ft);
Occupational therapists 1 (pt); Speech
therapists 1 (pt); Activities coordinators 1
(ft); Dietitians 1 (pt); Ophthalmologists 1
(pt); Podiatrists 1 (pt).
Facilities Dining room; Physical therapy
room; Activities room; Chapel; Crafts room;
Laundry room; Barber/Beauty shop.
Activities Arts & crafts; Cards; Games;
Reading groups; Prayer groups; Movies;
Shopping trips.

SHARONVILLE

Cottingham Retirement Community
3995 Cottingham Dr, Sharonville, OH, 45241
(513) 563-3600
Admin Michael J Scott. *Medical Dir/Dir of
Nursing* Steven Gerendel MD; Linda
McIntire DON.
Licensure Skilled care. *Beds* SNF 60. *Certified*
Medicare.
Owner Proprietary Corp.
Admissions Requirements Medical
examination.

Staff Physicians 3 (pt); RNs 4 (ft), 4 (pt); LPNs 3 (ft), 7 (pt); Nurses aides 19 (ft), 15 (pt); Physical therapists 1 (pt); Occupational therapists 1 (pt); Speech therapists 1 (pt); Activities coordinators 2 (ft), 1 (pt); Dietitians 1 (pt); Dentists 1 (pt); Ophthalmologists 1 (pt); Podiatrists 1 (pt).
Facilities Dining room; Physical therapy room; Activities room; Chapel; Crafts room; Laundry room; Barber/Beauty shop; Library; Tavern.
Activities Arts & crafts; Cards; Games; Prayer groups; Movies; Shopping trips; Social/Cultural gatherings.

SHELBY

Crestwood Care Center*
225 W Main St, Shelby, OH, 44875
(419) 526-3509
Licensure Skilled care; Intermediate care. *Beds* 127. *Certified* Medicaid; Medicare.
Owner Proprietary Corp.

Heritage Care Center
100 Rogers Ln, Shelby, OH, 44875
(419) 347-1313
Admin Stephen Nemeth. *Medical Dir/Dir of Nursing* F Renee Reber RN DON.
Licensure Skilled care. *Beds* 50. *Certified* Medicaid; Medicare.
Owner Proprietary Corp (Horizon Healthcare Corp).
Admissions Requirements Medical examination.
Staff RNs 2 (ft), 2 (pt); LPNs 3 (ft), 1 (pt); Nurses aides 12 (ft); Physical therapists 1 (pt); Activities coordinators 1 (ft); Dietitians 1 (ft).
Facilities Dining room; Activities room; Laundry room; Barber/Beauty shop.
Activities Arts & crafts; Cards; Games; Reading groups; Prayer groups; Movies; Shopping trips; Social/Cultural gatherings; Daily exercises.

SIDNEY

Fair Haven Shelby County Home
2901 Fair Rd, Sidney, OH, 45365
(513) 492-6900
Admin Bill S Stine NHA. *Medical Dir/Dir of Nursing* George J Schroer MD; F Barbara Ward RN DON.
Licensure Intermediate care; Custodial care. *Beds* ICF 125; Custodial care 20. *Certified* Medicaid.
Owner Publicly owned.
Admissions Requirements Minimum age 18; Medical examination.
Staff Physicians 1 (pt); RNs 6 (ft), 3 (pt); LPNs 10 (ft), 2 (pt); Nurses aides 41 (ft), 16 (pt); Activities coordinators 3 (ft); Licensed social workers 2 (ft); Administrative assistant 1 (ft); Chaplain 1 (pt); Dietitian-Cooks-Helpers 12 (ft), 8 (pt).
Facilities Dining room; Activities room; Chapel; Crafts room; Laundry room; Barber/Beauty shop; Library; Independent lounges for TV & visitation.
Activities Arts & crafts; Cards; Games; Reading groups; Prayer groups; Movies; Shopping trips; Social/Cultural gatherings; Church services; Music therapy; Pet therapy; Gardening.

Franklin Nursing Center of Sidney
510 Buckeye St, Sidney, OH, 45365
(513) 492-3171
Licensure Intermediate care. *Beds* 51. *Certified* Medicaid.
Owner Proprietary Corp.

Dorothy Love Retirement Community
3003 W Cisco Rd, Sidney, OH, 45365
(513) 498-2391

Admin Paul T Schultz. *Medical Dir/Dir of Nursing* Dr Robert Miller; Janice Maxson.
Licensure Skilled care; Intermediate care; Congregate; Housing. *Beds* SNF 96; ICF; Congregate 93; Housing 26. *Certified* Medicaid; Medicare.
Owner Nonprofit Corp (OH Presbyterian Homes).
Admissions Requirements Minimum age 55; Medical examination.
Staff RNs; LPNs; Nurses aides; Reality therapists; Recreational therapists; Activities coordinators; Dietitians.
Affiliation Presbyterian
Facilities Dining room; Physical therapy room; Activities room; Chapel; Crafts room; Laundry room; Barber/Beauty shop; Library; Greenhouse.
Activities Arts & crafts; Cards; Games; Reading groups; Prayer groups; Movies; Shopping trips; Social/Cultural gatherings; Volunteer program; Shuffleboard; Current events; Horseshoes; Fishing ponds; Gardening.

Sunny Acres Care Center*
705 Fulton St, Sidney, OH, 45365
(513) 492-9591
Licensure Skilled care; Intermediate care. *Beds* 60. *Certified* Medicaid; Medicare.
Owner Proprietary Corp.

SOUTH POINT

Pulley Care Center*
Rte 4, Box 349A, South Point, OH, 45680
(614) 894-3476
Licensure Skilled care; Intermediate care. *Beds* 100. *Certified* Medicaid; Medicare.
Owner Nonprofit Corp.

Pulley Nursing Home*
Rte 2, Box 44, South Point, OH, 45680
(614) 894-3442
Licensure Intermediate care. *Beds* 35. *Certified* Medicaid.
Owner Proprietary Corp.

SOUTH VIENNA

Sharonview Nursing Home
Box 447, South Vienna, OH, 45369
(513) 568-4342
Admin Susan K Rodabaugh. *Medical Dir/Dir of Nursing* Michael McKee; Janna Brown.
Licensure Intermediate care; Intermediate care for mentally retarded. *Beds* ICF 30; ICF/MR 20. *Certified* Medicaid.
Owner Proprietary Corp.
Admissions Requirements Minimum age 18; Medical examination.
Staff Physicians 2 (pt); RNs 2 (ft), 2 (pt); LPNs 4 (ft), 5 (pt); Nurses aides 12 (ft), 10 (pt); Physical therapists 1 (pt); Reality therapists 1 (pt); Recreational therapists 1 (pt); Occupational therapists 1 (pt); Speech therapists 2 (pt); Activities coordinators 2 (ft); Dietitians 1 (pt); Dentists 1 (pt); Ophthalmologists 1 (pt); Podiatrists 1 (pt).
Facilities Dining room; Activities room; Crafts room; Laundry room; Barber/Beauty shop; Habilitation; Programming room.
Activities Arts & crafts; Cards; Games; Reading groups; Prayer groups; Movies; Shopping trips; Social/Cultural gatherings; Ceramics.

SPENCERVILLE

Roselawn Manor
420 E 4th St, Spencerville, OH, 45887
(419) 647-6022
Admin Sean G Cleary NHA. *Medical Dir/Dir of Nursing* W T Wright MD; Elsie Wein DON.
Licensure Intermediate care. *Beds* ICF 100. *Certified* Medicaid.

Owner Proprietary Corp (Health Care Facilities Inc).
Staff Physicians 1 (pt); RNs 4 (ft); LPNs 10 (ft), 2 (pt); Nurses aides 40 (ft), 10 (pt); Physical therapists 1 (pt); Activities coordinators 1 (ft); Dietitians 1 (ft); Ophthalmologists 1 (pt); Podiatrists 1 (pt).
Facilities Dining room; Activities room; Crafts room; Laundry room; Barber/Beauty shop.
Activities Arts & crafts; Cards; Games; Reading groups; Prayer groups; Movies; Shopping trips; Social/Cultural gatherings.

SPRINGFIELD

Applin Nursing Home*
237 W Pleasant St, Springfield, OH, 45506
Licensure Intermediate care. *Beds* 22. *Certified* Medicaid.
Owner Nonprofit Corp.

Clark Memorial Home*
106 Kewbury Rd, Springfield, OH, 45504
(513) 399-4262
Licensure Rest home. *Beds* 20.
Owner Nonprofit Corp.

Fountain Care Center
1103 S Fountain Ave, Springfield, OH, 45506
(513) 322-6484
Admin J Pavkov. *Medical Dir/Dir of Nursing* P Preston DON.
Licensure Intermediate care. *Beds* ICF 20.
Owner Proprietary Corp.
Admissions Requirements Medical examination; Physician's request.
Staff Physicians 1 (pt); RNs 1 (ft); Nurses aides 1 (ft), 10 (pt); Recreational therapists 1 (pt); Dietitians 1 (pt).
Facilities Dining room; Activities room; Laundry room.
Activities Arts & crafts; Cards; Games; Social/Cultural gatherings.

The Good Shepherd Village*
422 N Burnett Rd, Springfield, OH, 45503
(513) 322-1911
Licensure Nursing home. *Beds* 61.
Owner Proprietary Corp.

Heartland of Springfield
2615 Derr Rd, Springfield, OH, 45503
(513) 390-0005
Admin Ann C Levy. *Medical Dir/Dir of Nursing* Barry Paxton MD; Sue Hartley RN DON.
Licensure Skilled care; Intermediate care. *Beds* 100. *Certified* Medicaid; Medicare.
Owner Proprietary Corp (Health Care & Retirement Corp).
Admissions Requirements Minimum age 55.
Staff Physicians; RNs; LPNs; Orderlies; Nurses aides; Physical therapists; Recreational therapists; Occupational therapists; Speech therapists; Activities coordinators; Dietitians; Dentists; Ophthalmologists; Podiatrists.
Facilities Dining room; Physical therapy room; Activities room; Laundry room; Barber/Beauty shop; Library.
Activities Arts & crafts; Cards; Games; Reading groups; Prayer groups; Movies; Shopping trips; Social/Cultural gatherings.

K W Hess Ohio Pythian Home*
901 W High St, Springfield, OH, 45506
(513) 322-3271
Licensure Intermediate care. *Beds* 98. *Certified* Medicaid.
Owner Nonprofit Corp.
Affiliation Knights of Pythias

Hope House Manor Inc
2317 E Home Rd, Springfield, OH, 45503
(513) 399-9217

Admin Chuck Komp. *Medical Dir/Dir of Nursing* Dr Vemana; Joyce Rutherford-Donner.
Licensure Skilled care; Intermediate care. *Beds* SNF 50; ICF 50. *Certified* Medicaid; Medicare; VA.
Owner Proprietary Corp.
Admissions Requirements Minimum age 10; Medical examination.
Staff Physicians 1 (ft); RNs 9 (ft), 4 (pt); LPNs 5 (ft), 3 (pt); Orderlies 3 (ft), 1 (pt); Nurses aides 28 (ft), 19 (pt); Physical therapists 1 (pt); Occupational therapists 1 (pt); Speech therapists 1 (pt); Activities coordinators 3 (ft), 1 (pt); Dietitians 2 (pt); Dentists 1 (pt); Ophthalmologists 1 (pt); Podiatrists 1 (pt); Social worker 1 (ft).
Facilities Dining room; Physical therapy room; Activities room; Crafts room; Laundry room; Barber/Beauty shop; Social services; Central lounge; 2 small lounges on each wing.
Activities Arts & crafts; Cards; Games; Reading groups; Prayer groups; Movies; Shopping trips; Social/Cultural gatherings.

IOOF Home of Ohio Inc
404 E McCreight Ave, Springfield, OH, 45503
(513) 399-8311
Admin Joseph Kramer. *Medical Dir/Dir of Nursing* Cheri Markle.
Licensure Intermediate care. *Beds* 100. *Certified* Medicaid.
Owner Nonprofit organization/foundation.
Admissions Requirements Medical examination.
Staff Physicians 1 (pt); RNs 5 (ft), 2 (pt); LPNs 7 (ft); Orderlies 5 (ft), 2 (pt); Nurses aides 33 (ft); Activities coordinators 1 (ft); Dietitians 1 (pt); Ophthalmologists 1 (pt).
Affiliation Independent Order of Odd Fellows & Rebekahs
Facilities Dining room; Physical therapy room; Activities room; Chapel; Crafts room; Laundry room; Barber/Beauty shop; Library.
Activities Arts & crafts; Cards; Games; Reading groups; Prayer groups; Movies; Shopping trips; Social/Cultural gatherings.

Max-Ull 1*
735 W North St, Springfield, OH, 45504
(513) 323-0321
Licensure Intermediate care. *Beds* 15. *Certified* Medicaid.
Owner Proprietary Corp.

F F Mueller Residential Center
2535 Kenton St, Springfield, OH, 45505
(513) 323-9125
Admin Dr Michael J O'Neill Dir Res Svcs. *Medical Dir/Dir of Nursing* Jenny Wallace DON.
Licensure Intermediate care for mentally retarded. *Beds* ICF/MR 88. *Certified* Medicaid.
Owner Publicly owned.
Admissions Requirements Medical examination.
Staff RNs 7 (ft), 5 (pt); LPNs 5 (pt); Recreational therapists 2 (ft), 8 (pt); Activities coordinators 1 (ft); Dietitians 1 (pt).
Languages Sign, Blissymbolics
Facilities Dining room; Activities room; Laundry room; Cottage style living.
Activities Arts & crafts; Cards; Games; Movies; Shopping trips; Social/Cultural gatherings; Sheltered workshop; Special Olympics; Softball; Basketball; Swimming.

New Horizon Nursing Home*
1157 Driscoll Ave, Springfield, OH, 45506
(513) 324-1831
Licensure Intermediate care. *Beds* 24. *Certified* Medicaid.
Owner Proprietary Corp.

The Ohio Masonic Home
2655 W National Rd, Springfield, OH, 45504
(513) 325-1531
Admin Thomas D Scott. *Medical Dir/Dir of Nursing* William C Fippin MD; Duane Szymanski DON.
Licensure Nursing home. *Beds* Nursing home 436.
Owner Nonprofit Corp.
Admissions Requirements Medical examination.
Staff Physicians 1 (ft); RNs 22 (ft), 11 (pt); LPNs 10 (ft), 2 (pt); Nurses aides 149 (ft), 28 (pt); Physical therapists 1 (ft); Activities coordinators 1 (ft); Dietitians 1 (ft); Ophthalmologists 1 (pt); Dentist 1 (pt).
Affiliation Masons
Facilities Dining room; Physical therapy room; Activities room; Chapel; Crafts room; Laundry room; Barber/Beauty shop; Library.
Activities Arts & crafts; Cards; Games; Reading groups; Movies; Shopping trips; Social/Cultural gatherings.

Pillars Nursing Home*
336 W Columbia St, PO Box 88, Springfield, OH, 45504
(513) 323-9104
Medical Dir/Dir of Nursing Nicholas B Pavlatos MD.
Licensure Intermediate care. *Beds* 46. *Certified* Medicaid.
Owner Proprietary Corp.
Staff Physicians 1 (pt); RNs 1 (ft), 2 (pt); LPNs 3 (ft), 4 (pt); Orderlies 3 (ft); Nurses aides 8 (ft), 2 (pt); Physical therapists; Speech therapists; Activities coordinators 1 (ft).
Facilities Dining room; Activities room; Laundry room; Barber/Beauty shop.
Activities Arts & crafts; Cards; Games; Reading groups; Prayer groups; Movies; Shopping trips; Social/Cultural gatherings.

Ridgewood Nursing Home*
1600 Saint Paris Pike, Springfield, OH, 45504
(513) 399-8131
Licensure Skilled care; Intermediate care. *Beds* 50. *Certified* Medicaid; Medicare.
Owner Proprietary Corp (Unicare).

St John's Center
100 W McCreight Ave, Springfield, OH, 45504
(513) 399-9910
Admin Gary L Wade. *Medical Dir/Dir of Nursing* Sally Abbott MD.
Licensure Skilled care; Intermediate care. *Beds* SNF 50; ICF 100. *Certified* Medicaid; Medicare.
Owner Nonprofit organization/foundation.
Admissions Requirements Medical examination.
Staff Physicians 1 (pt); RNs; LPNs; Orderlies; Nurses aides; Physical therapists 2 (ft); Recreational therapists 1 (ft); Occupational therapists 2 (ft); Activities coordinators 1 (ft); Dietitians 1 (pt); Pharmacists 2 (ft); Dentist 1 (pt); Chaplain 1 (pt).
Facilities Dining room; Physical therapy room; Activities room; Chapel; Crafts room; Laundry room; Barber/Beauty shop; Dental office; Pharmacy.
Activities Arts & crafts; Cards; Games; Reading groups; Prayer groups; Movies; Shopping trips; Social/Cultural gatherings.

Seminole Villa Care Center
1365 Seminole Ave, Springfield, OH, 45506
(513) 323-1471
Admin Janet R Pavkov. *Medical Dir/Dir of Nursing* S Delaveris; Eva Knipp DON.
Licensure Intermediate care for mentally retarded. *Beds* 34. *Certified* Medicaid; Medicare.
Owner Proprietary Corp (American Health Care Centers).
Admissions Requirements Minimum age 35.

Staff Physicians 3 (pt); RNs 2 (ft), 2 (pt); LPNs 3 (ft), 3 (pt); Orderlies 3 (ft), 2 (pt); Nurses aides 10 (ft), 9 (pt); Physical therapists 1 (pt); Occupational therapists 1 (ft), 1 (pt); Speech therapists 1 (pt); Activities coordinators 1 (ft), 1 (pt); Dietitians 2 (pt); Dentists 1 (pt); Ophthalmologists 1 (pt); Podiatrists 1 (pt); Dentist 1 (pt); Psychologist 1 (pt); Psychiatrist 1 (pt); Social worker 1 (ft), 1 (pt).
Facilities Dining room; Activities room; Crafts room; Laundry room; Resident kitchen.
Activities Arts & crafts; Cards; Games; Reading groups; Prayer groups; Movies; Shopping trips; Social/Cultural gatherings; Sewing; Cooking; Hospitality group; Gardening.

Springview Center*
3130 E Main St, Springfield, OH, 45505
(513) 325-9263
Licensure Intermediate care for mentally retarded. *Beds* 90.
Owner Publicly owned.

Sunnyland Villa*
1365 1/2 Seminole Ave, Springfield, OH, 45506
(513) 322-3436
Medical Dir/Dir of Nursing Dr Venema.
Licensure Skilled care; Intermediate care. *Beds* 100. *Certified* Medicaid; Medicare.
Owner Proprietary Corp.
Admissions Requirements Medical examination; Physician's request.
Staff Physicians 1 (ft); LPNs 16 (ft); Orderlies 7 (ft); Nurses aides 39 (ft); Physical therapists 1 (pt); Reality therapists 1 (pt); Recreational therapists 1 (pt); Occupational therapists 1 (pt); Speech therapists 1 (pt); Activities coordinators 1 (pt); Dietitians 1 (pt); Dentists 1 (pt); Ophthalmologists 1 (pt); Podiatrists 1 (pt); Audiologists 1 (pt).
Facilities Dining room; Physical therapy room; Activities room; Laundry room; Barber/Beauty shop.
Activities Arts & crafts; Cards; Games; Reading groups; Prayer groups; Movies; Shopping trips; Social/Cultural gatherings; Trips to zoos, fairs, museums.

STEUBENVILLE

Labelle View Nursing Center
1336 Maryland Ave, Steubenville, OH, 43952
(614) 282-4581
Admin Donald E Ickes. *Medical Dir/Dir of Nursing* Augusto P Fojas MD; Connie Miller RN DON.
Licensure Intermediate care. *Beds* ICF 101. *Certified* Medicaid.
Owner Proprietary Corp (American Health Care Centers).
Admissions Requirements Medical examination.
Staff RNs 2 (ft), 1 (pt); LPNs 10 (ft), 7 (pt); Nurses aides 30 (ft), 7 (pt); Reality therapists 1 (ft); Activities coordinators 2 (pt); Dietitians 1 (ft); Ophthalmologists 1 (pt); Podiatrists 1 (pt).
Facilities Dining room; Activities room; Laundry room; Barber/Beauty shop.
Activities Arts & crafts; Games; Prayer groups; Shopping trips; Social/Cultural gatherings.

Lancia Convalescent Center*
717 N 6th St, Steubenville, OH, 43952
(614) 282-3605
Medical Dir/Dir of Nursing John P Smarella MD.
Licensure Skilled care; Intermediate care. *Beds* 50. *Certified* Medicaid.
Owner Proprietary Corp.
Admissions Requirements Medical examination.

Staff Physicians 1 (pt); RNs 1 (ft); LPNs 5 (pt); Nurses aides 12 (ft), 6 (pt); Physical therapists 1 (pt); Speech therapists 1 (pt); Activities coordinators 1 (ft); Dietitians 1 (pt); Dentists 1 (pt); Podiatrists 1 (pt).
Facilities Dining room; Physical therapy room; Laundry room; Barber/Beauty shop.
Activities Arts & crafts; Cards; Games; Prayer groups; Shopping trips.

Lancia Villa Royale
1852 Sinclair Ave, Steubenville, OH, 43952
(614) 264-7101
Admin James J Bolger. *Medical Dir/Dir of Nursing* J P Smarrella MD; Mary Ann Lee RN DON.
Licensure Skilled care; Intermediate care. *Beds* 100. *Certified* Medicaid; Medicare.
Owner Proprietary Corp.
Admissions Requirements Medical examination; Physician's request.
Staff Physicians 6 (pt); RNs 5 (ft); LPNs 12 (ft); Nurses aides 34 (ft), 10 (pt); Physical therapists 2 (ft), 1 (pt); Speech therapists 1 (pt); Activities coordinators 2 (ft); Dietitians 2 (pt); Ophthalmologists 2 (pt).
Facilities Dining room; Physical therapy room; Activities room; Chapel; Crafts room; Laundry room; Barber/Beauty shop.
Activities Arts & crafts; Cards; Games; Reading groups; Prayer groups; Movies; Shopping trips; Social/Cultural gatherings; Sports events.

Martha Manor Home for Aged Women*
408 N 5th St, Steubenville, OH, 43952
(614) 282-5623
Admin Pat Dines.
Licensure Rest home. *Beds* 24.
Owner Nonprofit Corp.
Admissions Requirements Females only; Medical examination.
Staff RNs 1 (ft); LPNs 1 (ft), 1 (pt); Nurses aides 2 (ft), 4 (pt).
Facilities Dining room; Laundry room; Barber/Beauty shop.

Riverview Nursing Home*
925 N 4th St, Steubenville, OH, 43952
(614) 282-4158
Admin Joseph C Pino. *Medical Dir/Dir of Nursing* Laura K Mesaros MD.
Licensure Intermediate care. *Beds* 44. *Certified* Medicaid.
Owner Proprietary Corp.
Admissions Requirements Medical examination.
Staff Physicians 1 (pt); RNs 1 (ft), 7 (pt); LPNs 1 (pt); Orderlies 1 (ft); Nurses aides 13 (ft); Physical therapists 1 (pt); Recreational therapists 1 (pt).
Facilities Dining room; Activities room; Television lounge.
Activities Arts & crafts; Cards; Games; Movies; Shopping trips.

Royal Pavilion Extended Care Facility*
3102 Saint Charles Dr, Steubenville, OH, 43952
(614) 264-7161
Admin Robert J Sherrin. *Medical Dir/Dir of Nursing* Anthony V Scurti MD.
Licensure Skilled care; Intermediate care. *Beds* SNF 95; ICF 25. *Certified* Medicaid; Medicare.
Owner Proprietary Corp.
Admissions Requirements Physician's request.
Staff Physicians 1 (pt); RNs 5 (ft), 4 (pt); LPNs 1 (ft), 9 (pt); Nurses aides 12 (ft), 18 (pt); Physical therapists 1 (ft); Recreational therapists 1 (pt); Occupational therapists; Speech therapists; Activities coordinators 1 (pt); Dietitians; Dentists; Podiatrists; Audiologists.
Facilities Dining room; Physical therapy room; Activities room; Chapel; Crafts room; Laundry room; Barber/Beauty shop.

Activities Arts & crafts; Cards; Games; Prayer groups; Movies; Shopping trips; Social/Cultural gatherings.

Shaffer Plaza
256 John Scott Hwy, Steubenville, OH, 43952
(614) 264-7111
Admin Rick Pfannenschmidt. *Medical Dir/Dir of Nursing* Mary Jane Johnston.
Licensure Intermediate care for mentally retarded. *Beds* 33. *Certified* Medicaid.
Owner Publicly owned.
Admissions Requirements Minimum age 18; Medical examination.
Staff Physicians 1 (pt); RNs 1 (pt); LPNs 3 (ft), 3 (pt); Nurses aides 12 (ft), 11 (pt); Physical therapists 1 (pt); Recreational therapists 1 (ft); Occupational therapists 1 (pt); Speech therapists 1 (pt); Dietitians 1 (pt); Dentists 1 (pt); Ophthalmologists 1 (pt); Podiatrists 1 (pt).
Facilities Dining room; Physical therapy room; Activities room; Crafts room; Laundry room.
Activities Arts & crafts; Cards; Games; Movies; Shopping trips; Social/Cultural gatherings; Swimming; Bowling; Sheltered workshop.

STRONGSVILLE

Altenheim
15653 Pearl Rd, Strongsville, OH, 44136
(216) 238-3361
Admin Shawn Litten.
Licensure Skilled care. *Beds* SNF 100. *Certified* Medicaid; Medicare.
Owner Nonprofit Corp.
Admissions Requirements Medical examination.
Staff Physicians; RNs; LPNs; Orderlies; Nurses aides; Physical therapists; Recreational therapists; Occupational therapists; Speech therapists; Activities coordinators; Dietitians; Ophthalmologists; Podiatrists.
Languages German, Hungarian
Facilities Dining room; Physical therapy room; Activities room; Chapel; Crafts room; Laundry room; Barber/Beauty shop; Library.
Activities Arts & crafts; Cards; Games; Reading groups; Prayer groups; Movies; Shopping trips; Social/Cultural gatherings.

STRUTHERS

Maplecrest Nursing Home for the Aged*
400 Sexton St, Struthers, OH, 44471
(216) 755-1466
Medical Dir/Dir of Nursing Dr Jeffery Resch.
Licensure Nursing home. *Beds* 48.
Owner Proprietary Corp.
Admissions Requirements Medical examination.
Staff Physicians 1 (pt); RNs 2 (ft), 1 (pt); LPNs 2 (ft), 1 (pt); Nurses aides 13 (ft), 2 (pt); Physical therapists 1 (pt); Occupational therapists 1 (pt); Speech therapists 1 (pt); Dietitians 1 (pt); Podiatrists 1 (pt).
Facilities Dining room; Physical therapy room; Activities room; Laundry room; Barber/Beauty shop.
Activities Games; Prayer groups; Social/Cultural gatherings.

SUNBURY

Morning View Care Center III
14961 N Old CCC Hwy, Sunbury, OH, 43074
(614) 965-3984
Admin Jo Anne S Colfack. *Medical Dir/Dir of Nursing* Teresa Arndt DON.
Licensure Intermediate care. *Beds* ICF 50. *Certified* Medicaid.
Owner Proprietary Corp (Morning View Care Center).

Staff Physicians 1 (pt); RNs 2 (ft); LPNs 4 (pt); Nurses aides 20 (ft); Physical therapists 1 (pt); Recreational therapists 1 (ft), 1 (pt); Activities coordinators 1 (ft); Dietitians 1 (pt); Ophthalmologists 1 (pt).
Facilities Dining room; Activities room; Laundry room; Barber/Beauty shop.
Activities Arts & crafts; Cards; Games; Reading groups; Prayer groups; Movies; Shopping trips; Social/Cultural gatherings.

Sunbury Nursing Home
144 N Columbus St, Sunbury, OH, 43074
(614) 965-4915
Admin Dixie White. *Medical Dir/Dir of Nursing* Teresa Arndt.
Licensure Intermediate care. *Beds* ICF 30. *Certified* Medicaid.
Owner Proprietary Corp.
Staff LPNs 4 (ft), 2 (pt); Nurses aides 6 (ft), 2 (pt); Activities coordinators 1 (ft); Dietitians 1 (pt).
Facilities Dining room; Laundry room.
Activities Arts & crafts; Cards; Games; Reading groups; Prayer groups; Movies; Shopping trips; Social/Cultural gatherings.

SWANTON

Maple Tree Inn Inc
401 W Airpost Hwy, Swanton, OH, 43558
(419) 825-1111
Admin Susan Bender. *Medical Dir/Dir of Nursing* Dr Philip Lepkowski; Linda Rufenacht.
Licensure Intermediate care. *Beds* ICF 48. *Certified* Medicaid.
Owner Privately owned.
Admissions Requirements Medical examination.
Staff RNs 1 (ft), 4 (pt); LPNs 1 (ft), 4 (pt); Nurses aides 6 (ft), 10 (pt); Physical therapists; Occupational therapists; Speech therapists; Activities coordinators 1 (ft); Dietitians 1 (pt); Dentists; Ophthalmologists; Podiatrists.
Facilities Dining room; Activities room; Laundry room.
Activities Arts & crafts; Cards; Games; Reading groups; Prayer groups; Movies; Shopping trips; Social/Cultural gatherings; Individual programs for Alzheimer's Disease.

Mielke's Nursing Home
PO Box 38, Swanton, OH, 43558
(419) 826-4891
Admin Helen Brown. *Medical Dir/Dir of Nursing* Clara Mausser LPN.
Licensure Intermediate care. *Beds* 12. *Certified* Medicaid.
Owner Proprietary Corp.
Staff Physicians 2 (pt); RNs 1 (pt); LPNs 1 (ft), 2 (pt); Nurses aides 4 (ft), 6 (pt); Physical therapists 1 (pt); Recreational therapists 1 (pt); Activities coordinators 1 (pt); Dietitians 1 (pt); Podiatrists 1 (pt).
Facilities Dining room; Activities room; Laundry room.
Activities Arts & crafts; Cards; Games; Reading groups; Prayer groups; Shopping trips; Barber & beauty services available; Various religious services Sunday afternoon & Wednesday evening.

SYLVANIA

Briarfield Inc
5757 Whiteford Rd, Sylvania, OH, 43560
(419) 882-1875
Admin Joseph H Giauque; Daniel J Giauque. *Medical Dir/Dir of Nursing* Dr A M Quinto; Diana Waugh RN.
Licensure Skilled care; Intermediate care. *Beds* SNF 18; ICF 91. *Certified* Medicaid; Medicare.
Owner Proprietary Corp.

Admissions Requirements Medical examination.
Staff Physicians 1 (pt); RNs 7 (ft), 1 (pt); LPNs 10 (ft); Nurses aides 43 (ft); Reality therapists 1 (ft); Activities coordinators 2 (ft); Dietitians 1 (pt).
Facilities Dining room; Activities room; Crafts room; Laundry room; Barber/Beauty shop.
Activities Arts & crafts; Cards; Games; Reading groups; Prayer groups; Movies; Shopping trips; Social/Cultural gatherings; Outings; Camping; Volunteering at a facility for severely retarded children.

Lake Park Hospital & Nursing Care Center
5100 Harroun Rd, Sylvania, OH, 43560
(419) 885-1444
Admin Georgia A Poplar FACHCA. *Medical Dir/Dir of Nursing* R E Scherbarth MD.
Licensure Skilled care. *Beds* SNF 131; 65. *Certified* Medicaid Skilled only; Medicare.
Owner Nonprofit organization/foundation.
Admissions Requirements Minimum age 3 months; Physician's request.
Staff Physicians 1 (ft); RNs 15 (ft), 10 (pt); LPNs 16 (ft), 9 (pt); Orderlies 3 (ft), 2 (pt); Nurses aides 40 (ft), 40 (pt); Physical therapists 10 (ft); Recreational therapists 2 (ft), 1 (pt); Occupational therapists 4 (ft), 2 (pt); Speech therapists 3 (ft), 3 (pt); Dietitians 1 (ft), 1 (pt); Podiatrists 2 (pt); Dental Hygienist 1 (pt); MSW 2 (ft).
Languages Polish, Hungarian, Spanish
Affiliation Methodist
Facilities Dining room; Physical therapy room; Activities room; Chapel; Crafts room; Barber/Beauty shop; Library.
Activities Arts & crafts; Cards; Games; Reading groups; Prayer groups; Movies; Shopping trips; Social/Cultural gatherings.

TALLMADGE

Colonial Gardens Care Center
563 Colony Park Dr, Tallmadge, OH, 44278
(216) 630-9780
Admin Jana F Caplinger. *Medical Dir/Dir of Nursing* Carl J Mader MD; Gayle Sperry Rn.
Licensure Skilled care; Intermediate care. *Beds* SNF 15; ICF 190. *Certified* Medicaid; Medicare.
Owner Proprietary Corp (American Health Care Centers).
Admissions Requirements Minimum age 18.
Staff Physicians 30 (pt); RNs 3 (ft), 6 (pt); LPNs 17 (ft); Orderlies 3 (ft), 1 (pt); Nurses aides 33 (ft), 33 (pt); Physical therapists 1 (pt); Occupational therapists 1 (pt); Speech therapists 1 (pt); Activities coordinators 2 (ft), 4 (pt); Dietitians 1 (ft); Ophthalmologists 1 (pt); Podiatrists 1 (pt).
Facilities Dining room; Physical therapy room; Activities room; Crafts room; Laundry room; Barber/Beauty shop.
Activities Arts & crafts; Cards; Games; Reading groups; Prayer groups; Movies; Shopping trips; Social/Cultural gatherings.

Cooper Nursing Home Inc*
340 Southwest Ave, Tallmadge, OH, 44278
(216) 633-4723
Admin Robert L Zucker. *Medical Dir/Dir of Nursing* Dr Stuart Goldstein.
Licensure Intermediate care. *Beds* 31. *Certified* Medicaid.
Owner Proprietary Corp.
Admissions Requirements Minimum age 21; Females only; Medical examination; Physician's request.
Staff Physicians 1 (pt); RNs 1 (pt); LPNs 5 (ft), 1 (pt); Nurses aides 11 (ft), 4 (pt); Reality therapists 1 (pt); Activities coordinators 1 (pt); Dietitians 1 (pt); Dentists 1 (pt); Ophthalmologists 1 (pt); Podiatrists 1 (pt).

Facilities Dining room; Activities room; Laundry room; Kitchen; Lounge areas.
Activities Arts & crafts; Games; Prayer groups; Social/Cultural gatherings.

Summit County Nursing Home
1134 N Ave, Tallmadge, OH, 44278
(216) 688-8600
Admin Leah J Bryan. *Medical Dir/Dir of Nursing* Judith Gooding MD; Anne Richardson RN DON.
Licensure Intermediate care. *Beds* ICF 120. *Certified* Medicaid.
Owner Proprietary Corp.
Admissions Requirements Medical examination; Physician's request.
Staff RNs 5 (ft), 4 (pt); LPNs 10 (ft), 10 (pt); Orderlies 1 (ft); Nurses aides 50 (ft), 11 (pt); Physical therapists 1 (pt); Occupational therapists 1 (ft); Activities coordinators 1 (ft); Dietitians 1 (ft).
Facilities Dining room; Physical therapy room; Activities room; Laundry room; Barber/Beauty shop.
Activities Arts & crafts; Cards; Games; Reading groups; Prayer groups; Movies; Shopping trips; Social/Cultural gatherings.

THORNVILLE

Heatland-Fairfield*
7820 Pleasantville Rd, Thornville, OH, 43076
(614) 536-7381
Admin Carl M L Holbrook. *Medical Dir/Dir of Nursing* Dr Robert Sprouse.
Licensure Skilled care; Intermediate care. *Beds* SNF 150; ICF 150. *Certified* Medicaid; Medicare.
Owner Proprietary Corp (Health Care & Retirement Corp).
Admissions Requirements Medical examination; Physician's request.
Staff Physicians 2 (pt); RNs 10 (ft); LPNs 25 (ft), 2 (pt); Orderlies 10 (ft), 2 (pt); Nurses aides 90 (ft), 20 (pt); Physical therapists 2 (pt); Recreational therapists 2 (ft); Occupational therapists 1 (pt); Speech therapists 1 (pt); Activities coordinators 1 (ft); Dietitians 1 (pt); Dentists 2 (pt); Ophthalmologists 1 (pt); Podiatrists 1 (pt); Audiologists 1 (pt).
Facilities Dining room; Physical therapy room; Activities room; Crafts room; Laundry room; Barber/Beauty shop.
Activities Arts & crafts; Cards; Games; Reading groups; Prayer groups; Movies; Shopping trips; Social/Cultural gatherings.

TIFFIN

Alta Mira Nursing Home*
55 Seneca St, Tiffin, OH, 44883
(419) 447-7373
Licensure Intermediate care. *Beds* 40. *Certified* Medicaid.
Owner Proprietary Corp.

Autumnwood Care Center*
670 E State Rte 18, Tiffin, OH, 44883
(419) 447-7151
Licensure Skilled care; Intermediate care. *Beds* 100. *Certified* Medicaid; Medicare.
Owner Nonprofit Corp (Volunteers of America Care).

Riverfront Manor Inc*
Rte 2, New Haven Rd, Tiffin, OH, 44883
(419) 447-4662
Medical Dir/Dir of Nursing Dr Daniels.
Licensure Intermediate care. *Beds* 44. *Certified* Medicaid.
Owner Proprietary Corp.
Staff Physicians 1 (ft); RNs 1 (ft), 1 (pt); LPNs 3 (ft), 1 (pt); Orderlies 1 (ft); Nurses aides 12 (ft), 5 (pt); Activities coordinators 1 (ft); Dietitians 1 (pt).

Facilities Dining room; Activities room; Chapel; Crafts room; Laundry room; Barber/Beauty shop.
Activities Arts & crafts; Cards; Games; Reading groups; Prayer groups; Movies; Shopping trips; Social/Cultural gatherings.

St Francis Home for the Aged
182 Saint Francis Ave, Tiffin, OH, 44883
(419) 447-2723
Licensure Intermediate care; Rest home. *Beds* ICF 61; Rest home 56. *Certified* Medicaid.
Owner Nonprofit Corp.
Admissions Requirements Minimum age 70; Medical examination.
Staff RNs 3 (ft); LPNs 4 (ft), 3 (pt); Nurses aides 12 (ft), 15 (pt); Reality therapists 1 (pt); Recreational therapists 1 (ft); Activities coordinators 1 (pt); Dietitians 1 (pt).
Affiliation Roman Catholic
Facilities Dining room; Physical therapy room; Activities room; Chapel; Crafts room; Laundry room; Barber/Beauty shop; Library.
Activities Arts & crafts; Cards; Games; Prayer groups; Movies; Shopping trips; Social/Cultural gatherings.

South Washington Street Nursing Home*
248 S Washington St, Tiffin, OH, 44883
(419) 447-0773
Licensure Intermediate care. *Beds* 25. *Certified* Medicaid.
Owner Proprietary Corp.

Tiffin Developmental Center
600 N River Rd, Tiffin, OH, 44883
(419) 447-1450
Licensure Intermediate care for mentally retarded. *Beds* 220.
Owner Publicly owned.

Virginia Lee Care Center
PO Box 755, 235 N Sandusky St, Tiffin, OH, 44883-0755
(419) 447-8106
Licensure Intermediate care. *Beds* 20. *Certified* Medicaid.
Owner Proprietary Corp.
Admissions Requirements Medical examination.
Staff RNs 1 (pt); LPNs 2 (ft), 1 (pt); Nurses aides 6 (ft); Recreational therapists 1 (ft); Activities coordinators 1 (ft); Dietitians 1 (pt).
Facilities Dining room; Activities room; Crafts room; Laundry room.
Activities Arts & crafts; Cards; Games; Reading groups; Prayer groups; Shopping trips.

TIPP CITY

Feghtly Lutheran Home*
300 W Main St, Tipp City, OH, 45371
Licensure Rest home. *Beds* 15.
Owner Nonprofit Corp.

TOLEDO

Ashland Avenue Nursing Home*
2283 Ashland Ave, Toledo, OH, 43620
(419) 241-6457
Licensure Intermediate care. *Beds* 50. *Certified* Medicaid.
Owner Proprietary Corp.
Admissions Requirements Minimum age 18; Medical examination; Physician's request.
Staff RNs 1 (pt); LPNs 3 (ft), 5 (pt); Nurses aides 9 (ft), 11 (pt); Activities coordinators 1 (ft); Dietitians 1 (ft); Audiologists 1 (ft).
Facilities Dining room; Activities room; Chapel; Crafts room; Laundry room; Barber/Beauty shop; Library.
Activities Arts & crafts; Cards; Games; Reading groups; Prayer groups; Movies; Shopping trips; Social/Cultural gatherings.

Brookhaven Convalescent Center*
2051 Collingwood Blvd, Toledo, OH, 43620
(419) 243-5191
Medical Dir/Dir of Nursing Dr Antonio Paat.
Licensure Skilled care; Intermediate care. *Beds*
174. *Certified* Medicaid; Medicare.
Owner Proprietary Corp (Americare Corp).
Admissions Requirements Medical
examination.
Staff RNs 6 (ft), 6 (pt); LPNs 9 (ft), 16 (pt);
Nurses aides 38 (ft), 26 (pt); Activities
coordinators 1 (ft).
Facilities Dining room; Physical therapy
room; Activities room; Chapel; Laundry
room; Barber/Beauty shop; Patio.
Activities Arts & crafts; Cards; Games; Prayer
groups; Movies; Shopping trips; Social/
Cultural gatherings.

Byrnebrook Nursing Home
1011 N Byrne Rd, Toledo, OH, 43607
(419) 531-5321
Admin Cynthia M Allen. *Medical Dir/Dir of
Nursing* Dr Dan Williams; Barb Seiling RN
DON.
Licensure Skilled care; Intermediate care. *Beds*
SNF 18; ICF 55. *Certified* Medicaid;
Medicare.
Owner Proprietary Corp.
Admissions Requirements Medical
examination; Physician's request.
Staff Physicians 33 (ft); RNs 4 (ft), 2 (pt);
LPNs 9 (ft), 4 (pt); Nurses aides 23 (ft), 8
(pt); Reality therapists 1 (pt); Activities
coordinators 1 (ft), 1 (pt).
Languages Polish
Facilities Dining room; Physical therapy
room; Activities room; Crafts room; Laundry
room; Barber/Beauty shop.
Activities Arts & crafts; Cards; Games;
Reading groups; Prayer groups; Movies;
Social/Cultural gatherings.

Cherry Hill Nursing Home*
2900 Cherry St, Toledo, OH, 43608
(419) 242-7458
Licensure Skilled care; Intermediate care. *Beds*
100. *Certified* Medicaid; Medicare.
Owner Proprietary Corp (Arbor Health Care).

Colonial Nursing Home*
3121 Glanzman Rd, Toledo, OH, 43614
(419) 385-6616
Licensure Skilled care; Intermediate care. *Beds*
94. *Certified* Medicaid; Medicare.
Owner Proprietary Corp (Americare Corp).

Darlington House
2735 Darlington Rd, Toledo, OH, 43606
(419) 531-4465
Admin Aaron B Handler. *Medical Dir/Dir of
Nursing* Eli C Abramson MD; H JoAnne
Schwartzberg DON.
Licensure Skilled care. *Beds* 116. *Certified*
Medicaid; Medicare.
Owner Nonprofit organization/foundation.
Admissions Requirements Minimum age 65;
Medical examination.
Staff Physicians 2 (pt); RNs 12 (ft); LPNs 14
(ft), 4 (pt); Orderlies 4 (ft), 2 (pt); Nurses
aides 45 (ft); Physical therapists 2 (pt);
Recreational therapists 1 (pt); Occupational
therapists 1 (pt); Speech therapists 2 (pt);
Activities coordinators 1 (ft), 7 (pt);
Dietitians 1 (ft); Ophthalmologists 1 (pt).
Affiliation Jewish
Facilities Dining room; Physical therapy
room; Activities room; Chapel; Crafts room;
Laundry room; Barber/Beauty shop; Library;
Little theater; Garden.
Activities Arts & crafts; Cards; Games;
Reading groups; Movies; Shopping trips;
Social/Cultural gatherings; Baking; Singing;
Classical music.

Edgewood Nursing Home*
4848 Dorr St, Toledo, OH, 43615
(419) 531-2037

Licensure Nursing home. *Beds* 48.
Owner Proprietary Corp.
Staff LPNs 3 (ft); Nurses aides 10 (ft).
Facilities Dining room; Laundry room;
Barber/Beauty shop.
Activities Cards; Games; Social/Cultural
gatherings.

The Extended Care Center of Toledo
2005 Ashland Ave, Toledo, OH, 43620
(419) 255-5050
Admin Wm L Stewart CFACHCA. *Medical
Dir/Dir of Nursing* Charles E Rowan MD;
Mary Ellen Frye RN.
Licensure Skilled care; Intermediate care. *Beds*
SNF 98; ICF 114. *Certified* Medicaid;
Medicare.
Owner Proprietary Corp.
Admissions Requirements Physician's request.
Staff RNs 12 (ft), 8 (pt); LPNs 30 (ft), 20 (pt);
Nurses aides 60 (ft), 40 (pt); Physical
therapists; Occupational therapists; Speech
therapists; Activities coordinators 1 (ft), 1
(pt); Dietitians; Dentists; Ophthalmologists.
Facilities Dining room; Physical therapy
room; Activities room; Chapel; Crafts room;
Laundry room; Barber/Beauty shop.
Activities Arts & crafts; Cards; Games;
Reading groups; Prayer groups; Movies;
Shopping trips; Social/Cultural gatherings.

Fairview Manor Nursing Center
4420 South St, Toledo, OH, 43615
(419) 531-4201
Admin Bennett Balmer. *Medical Dir/Dir of
Nursing* Dr Margaret Miller; Barbara Kozek
RN.
Licensure Skilled care; Intermediate care. *Beds*
137. *Certified* Medicaid; Medicare.
Owner Proprietary Corp (Shive Nursing
Centers).
Staff Physicians 45 (ft); Physical therapists 1
(pt).
Facilities Dining room; Physical therapy
room; Activities room; Chapel; Crafts room;
Laundry room; Barber/Beauty shop; Library.
Activities Arts & crafts; Games; Reading
groups; Prayer groups; Movies; Shopping
trips; Social/Cultural gatherings; Parties.

Golden Haven Nursing Home
2901 Tremainsville Rd, Toledo, OH, 43613
(419) 472-2183
Admin Jeffery L Cohen; Dora Cohen. *Medical
Dir/Dir of Nursing* Dr Margaret Miller.
Licensure Skilled care; Intermediate care. *Beds*
SNF 94; ICF. *Certified* Medicaid; Medicare.
Owner Proprietary Corp.
Admissions Requirements Minimum age 18.
Staff RNs 2 (ft); LPNs 10 (ft); Orderlies 1 (ft),
1 (pt); Nurses aides 25 (ft); Activities
coordinators 1 (ft); Dietitians 1 (pt).
Languages Spanish, German, Polish
Facilities Dining room; Activities room;
Laundry room; Barber/Beauty shop; Library;
Screened porch; Patio.
Activities Arts & crafts; Cards; Games;
Reading groups; Prayer groups; Movies;
Social/Cultural gatherings.

Holly Glen Care Center Inc*
4293 Monroe St, Toledo, OH, 43606
(419) 474-6021
Licensure Nursing home. *Beds* 100.
Owner Proprietary Corp.

Hospitality Care Center Inc—Toledo*
3225 Glanzman Rd, Toledo, OH, 43614
(419) 382-5694
Licensure Intermediate care. *Beds* 26.
Certified Medicaid.
Owner Proprietary Corp.

Imperial Manor*
4816 Dorr St, Toledo, OH, 43615
(419) 536-7656
Licensure Intermediate care. *Beds* 29.
Certified Medicaid.
Owner Proprietary Corp.

Josina Lott Foundation Residential Center*
120 S Holland-Sylvania Rd, Toledo, OH,
43615
(419) 866-9013
Licensure Intermediate care for mentally
retarded. *Beds* 32.
Owner Nonprofit Corp.

Lutheran Old Folks Home
2411 Seaman St, Toledo, OH, 43605-1599
(419) 693-0751
Medical Dir/Dir of Nursing William Winslow
MD.
Licensure Skilled care; Intermediate care; Rest
home. *Beds* SNF 235; ICF; Rest home 8.
Certified Medicaid.
Owner Nonprofit Corp.
Admissions Requirements Minimum age 65;
Medical examination.
Languages German, Spanish
Affiliation Lutheran
Facilities Dining room; Physical therapy
room; Activities room; Chapel; Crafts room;
Laundry room; Barber/Beauty shop; Library;
Resident bakery; Auditorium; Picnic grove;
Shelter.
Activities Arts & crafts; Cards; Games;
Reading groups; Prayer groups; Movies;
Shopping trips; Social/Cultural gatherings;
Discussion groups; Couples club; Association
for residents' children.

Marigarde-Sylvania Nursing Home
4111 Holland-Sylvania Rd, Toledo, OH,
43623
(419) 882-2087, 882-2088
Admin Mr Tom Greiner. *Medical Dir/Dir of
Nursing* Mrs Mary Ellen Denko.
Licensure Intermediate care. *Beds* ICF 99.
Certified Medicaid.
Owner Proprietary Corp (Hillhaven Corp).
Admissions Requirements Medical
examination.
Staff Physicians 1 (ft); RNs 4 (ft); LPNs 5 (ft);
Orderlies 1 (ft); Physical therapists 1 (ft);
Reality therapists 1 (pt); Speech therapists 1
(pt); Activities coordinators 1 (ft); Dietitians
1 (ft); Ophthalmologists 1 (ft).
Languages Hungarian, Ukranian, Italian
Facilities Dining room; Activities room;
Laundry room; Barber/Beauty shop.
Activities Arts & crafts; Cards; Prayer groups;
Movies.

Northwest Ohio Development Center
1101 S Detroit Ave, Toledo, OH, 43614
(419) 385-0231
Admin Warren Karmol. *Medical Dir/Dir of
Nursing* Rae J Rehfeldt RN.
Licensure Intermediate care for mentally
retarded. *Beds* ICF/MR 170. *Certified*
Medicaid.
Owner Publicly owned.
Staff Physicians 10 (pt); RNs 6 (ft); LPNs 10
(ft); Nurses aides 100 (ft), 60 (pt);
Recreational therapists 3 (ft), 2 (pt);
Occupational therapists 1 (ft); Speech
therapists 3 (ft); Activities coordinators 1
(ft).
Activities Arts & crafts; Cards; Games;
Reading groups; Prayer groups; Movies;
Shopping trips; Social/Cultural gatherings.

Point North Nursing Home*
2803 117th St, Toledo, OH, 43611
(419) 726-9820
Licensure Intermediate care. *Beds* 19.
Certified Medicaid.
Owner Proprietary Corp.

Riverside Convalescent Home
1819 Summit St, Toledo, OH, 43611
(419) 729-0860
Admin Opal Evanoff RN. *Medical Dir/Dir of
Nursing* R O Naturdad MD; Opal Evanoff
RN.
Licensure Intermediate care. *Beds* ICF 10.
Certified Medicaid.

Owner Privately owned.
Admissions Requirements Medical examination.
Staff Physicians; RNs; LPNs; Nurses aides; Recreational therapists; Activities coordinators; Podiatrists.
Facilities Dining room; Activities room; Crafts room; Laundry room.
Activities Arts & crafts; Cards; Games; Reading groups; Movies; Shopping trips; Social/Cultural gatherings.

Robinwood Rest Home*
2024 Robinwood Ave, Toledo, OH, 43620
(419) 242-3702
Medical Dir/Dir of Nursing Isador Binzer MD.
Licensure Intermediate care. *Beds* 20. *Certified* Medicaid.
Owner Proprietary Corp.
Staff Physicians 1 (ft), 4 (pt); RNs 1 (pt); LPNs 2 (ft), 1 (pt); Nurses aides 7 (ft), 2 (pt); Dietitians 1 (ft); Podiatrists 1 (pt).
Facilities Dining room; Laundry room.
Activities Arts & crafts; Cards; Games.

Sunset House*
4020 Indian Rd, Toledo, OH, 43606
(419) 536-4645
Licensure Home for aged. *Beds* 80.
Owner Nonprofit Corp.

Toledo Mental Health Center
930 S Detroit Ave, Toledo, OH, 43699-0002
(419) 381-1881 ext 684
Admin Juanita H Price. *Medical Dir/Dir of Nursing* Bahdam Maryle MD; Jan Beauerson RN.
Licensure Intermediate care; Intermediate care for mentally retarded. *Beds* 24. *Certified* Medicaid; Medicare.
Owner Publicly owned.
Admissions Requirements Minimum age 18.
Staff Physicians; RNs; LPNs; Orderlies; Nurses aides; Physical therapists; Reality therapists; Recreational therapists; Occupational therapists; Speech therapists; Activities coordinators; Dietitians; Dentists; Ophthalmologists.
Facilities Dining room; Physical therapy room; Activities room; Chapel; Crafts room; Laundry room; Barber/Beauty shop; Library.
Activities Arts & crafts; Cards; Games; Reading groups; Prayer groups; Movies; Shopping trips; Social/Cultural gatherings.

Villa North Nursing Home*
4645 Lewis Ave, Toledo, OH, 43612
(419) 478-5131
Licensure Skilled care; Intermediate care. *Beds* 250. *Certified* Medicaid; Medicare.
Owner Proprietary Corp.

Waterford Commons
955 Garden Lake Parkway, Toledo, OH, 43614
(419) 382-2200
Admin Debra S Levitin. *Medical Dir/Dir of Nursing* Dr Mark Zilkowski; Becky Spitulski.
Licensure Skilled care; Intermediate care; Assisted living; Adult day care. *Beds* SNF 75; ICF; Assisted living 25. *Certified* Medicaid; Medicare.
Owner Proprietary Corp.
Admissions Requirements Medical examination; Physician's request.
Facilities Dining room; Physical therapy room; Activities room; Chapel; Crafts room; Laundry room; Barber/Beauty shop; Library; Gift shop with ice cream parlor; Patios.
Activities Arts & crafts; Cards; Games; Reading groups; Prayer groups; Movies; Shopping trips; Social/Cultural gatherings; Camping.

Wunderley Nursing Home*
2205 Parkwood Ave, Toledo, OH, 43620
(419) 244-8205

Licensure Intermediate care. *Beds* 29. *Certified* Medicaid.
Owner Proprietary Corp.

TROY

Highland View Nursing Home*
500 Crescent Dr, Troy, OH, 45373
(513) 335-7161
Licensure Nursing home. *Beds* 61. *Certified* Medicaid.
Owner Proprietary Corp.

Johnston Nursing Home*
845 N Harrison St, Troy, OH, 45373
(513) 335-2125
Licensure Intermediate care. *Beds* 18. *Certified* Medicaid.
Owner Proprietary Corp.

Miami Health Care Center
3232 N County Rd 25A, Troy, OH, 45373
(513) 339-5946
Medical Dir/Dir of Nursing Mark J Peters MD.
Licensure Intermediate care. *Beds* 150. *Certified* Medicaid.
Owner Nonprofit Corp.
Staff Physicians 30 (pt); RNs 5 (ft), 5 (pt); LPNs 9 (ft), 9 (pt); Orderlies 1 (ft); Nurses aides 25 (ft), 11 (pt); Physical therapists; Recreational therapists 3 (ft); Speech therapists; Activities coordinators 1 (ft); Dietitians 1 (pt); Dentists; Ophthalmologists; Podiatrists; Dentist.
Facilities Dining room; Physical therapy room; Activities room; Chapel; Crafts room; Laundry room; Barber/Beauty shop; Library.
Activities Arts & crafts; Cards; Games; Reading groups; Prayer groups; Movies; Shopping trips; Social/Cultural gatherings; Dinners; Theater; Special outings.

Villa Convalescent Center Inc*
512 Crescent Dr, Troy, OH, 45373
(513) 335-7161
Licensure Skilled care; Intermediate care. *Beds* 95. *Certified* Medicaid; Medicare.
Owner Proprietary Corp.

UHRICHSVILLE

Dove Nursing Facility*
Rte 1, Newport County Rd 28, Uhrichsville, OH, 44683
(614) 922-2629
Licensure Intermediate care. *Beds* 32. *Certified* Medicaid.
Owner Proprietary Corp.

Rohrigs Nursing Home Inc
449 E 4th St, Uhrichsville, OH, 44683
(614) 922-2610
Admin Margaret Rohrig LPN NHA.
Licensure Intermediate care. *Beds* ICF 17. *Certified* Medicaid.
Owner Privately owned.
Admissions Requirements Medical examination; Physician's request.
Staff RNs 1 (ft), 1 (pt); LPNs 2 (ft); Orderlies 1 (ft); Nurses aides 7 (ft), 1 (pt); Activities coordinators 2 (ft); Dietitians 1 (ft), 1 (pt); SSD 2 (ft).
Facilities Dining room; Activities room; Chapel; Crafts room; Laundry room.
Activities Arts & crafts; Cards; Games; Reading groups; Prayer groups; Shopping trips; Social/Cultural gatherings; Outings.

Twin City Health Care Center Inc
200 Spanson Dr, Uhrichsville, OH, 44683
(614) 922-2208
Admin Richard D McCloy. *Medical Dir/Dir of Nursing* Dr James Scott; Carole McCloy DON.
Licensure Intermediate care; Rest home. *Beds* ICF 67; Rest home 29. *Certified* Medicaid.
Owner Proprietary Corp.

Admissions Requirements Minimum age 18.
Staff RNs 4 (ft); LPNs 4 (ft); Orderlies 1 (ft); Nurses aides 19 (ft); Activities coordinators 1 (ft), 1 (pt); Dietitians 1 (pt).
Facilities Dining room; Physical therapy room; Activities room; Crafts room; Laundry room; Barber/Beauty shop.
Activities Arts & crafts; Cards; Games; Reading groups; Movies; Shopping trips; Social/Cultural gatherings.

UNION CITY

Crotinger Nursing Home
907 Central Ave, Union City, OH, 47390
(513) 968-5284, 968-3571
Admin Kim T Nye. *Medical Dir/Dir of Nursing* Dr C R Chambers; Sue Livingston.
Licensure Intermediate care. *Beds* ICF 50. *Certified* Medicaid.
Owner Proprietary Corp.
Staff RNs 1 (ft), 1 (pt); LPNs 3 (ft), 2 (pt); Orderlies 2 (ft), 1 (pt); Nurses aides 29 (ft), 3 (pt); Activities coordinators 1 (ft).
Facilities Activities room; Laundry room.
Activities Arts & crafts; Cards; Games; Reading groups; Prayer groups; Movies; Shopping trips; Social/Cultural gatherings.

Gade ICF/MR*
400 Gade Ave, Union City, OH, 47390
Licensure Intermediate care for mentally retarded. *Beds* 51. *Certified* Medicaid; Medicare.
Owner Proprietary Corp.

UPPER SANDUSKY

Fairhaven Retirement & Health Care Community
850 S Marseilles Ave, Upper Sandusky, OH, 43351
(419) 294-4973
Admin Gary E Ulrich. *Medical Dir/Dir of Nursing* Thomas Thornton MD; Lynn Altvater RN.
Licensure Skilled care; Intermediate care; Individual living units. *Beds* SNF 50; ICF 100; Apts 36. *Certified* Medicaid; Medicare.
Owner Nonprofit Corp (United Church Homes).
Admissions Requirements Minimum age 65.
Staff Physicians 1 (pt); RNs 16 (ft), 8 (pt); LPNs 7 (ft), 4 (pt); Nurses aides 44 (ft), 33 (pt); Physical therapists 1 (pt); Recreational therapists 1 (ft), 1 (pt); Activities coordinators 2 (ft), 2 (pt); Dietitians 1 (pt).
Affiliation Church of Christ
Facilities Dining room; Physical therapy room; Activities room; Chapel; Crafts room; Laundry room; Barber/Beauty shop; Library.
Activities Arts & crafts; Cards; Games; Reading groups; Prayer groups; Movies; Shopping trips; Social/Cultural gatherings.

Sunny Villa Care Center
342 S 8th St, Upper Sandusky, OH, 43351
(419) 294-3482
Medical Dir/Dir of Nursing N J Zohory MD; Diane Smith DON.
Licensure Intermediate care. *Beds* ICF 22. *Certified* Medicaid.
Owner Proprietary Corp.
Admissions Requirements Medical examination.
Staff RNs 1 (pt); LPNs 2 (ft), 2 (pt); Nurses aides 5 (ft), 3 (pt); Activities coordinators 1 (ft).
Facilities Dining room; Activities room; Laundry room.
Activities Arts & crafts; Cards; Games; Reading groups; Prayer groups; Movies; Shopping trips; Cooking; Gardening.

Wyandot County Nursing Home
Rte 2, 7830 N State Hwy 199, Upper
Sandusky, OH, 43351
(419) 294-1714
Admin Joseph D Jolliff. *Medical Dir/Dir of
Nursing* Jean Aller DON.
Licensure Intermediate care. *Beds* ICF 100.
Certified Medicaid.
Owner Publicly owned.
Staff RNs; LPNs; Orderlies; Nurses aides;
Recreational therapists; Activities
coordinators.
Facilities Dining room; Activities room;
Chapel; Crafts room; Laundry room; Barber/
Beauty shop.
Activities Arts & crafts; Cards; Games;
Reading groups; Movies; Shopping trips;
Social/Cultural gatherings.

Wyandot Manor HCF Inc
800 Mission Dr, Upper Sandusky, OH, 43351
(419) 294-3803
Admin Ann Stover-Wyatt. *Medical Dir/Dir of
Nursing* Dr William Kose; Nancy Crisler
DON.
Licensure Skilled care; Intermediate care. *Beds*
SNF 100; ICF. *Certified* Medicaid;
Medicare.
Owner Proprietary Corp (Health Care
Facilities Inc).
Admissions Requirements Medical
examination; Physician's request.
Staff Physicians 1 (ft), 5 (pt); RNs 5 (ft), 1
(pt); LPNs 4 (ft), 1 (pt); Nurses aides 30 (ft),
4 (pt); Physical therapists 1 (pt);
Recreational therapists 2 (ft), 1 (pt);
Occupational therapists 1 (pt); Speech
therapists 1 (pt); Activities coordinators 1
(ft); Dietitians 1 (ft); Dentists 1 (pt);
Ophthalmologists 1 (pt); Podiatrists 1 (pt).
Facilities Dining room (2); Physical therapy
room; Activities room; Laundry room;
Barber/Beauty shop; Library; 3 lounges.
Activities Arts & crafts; Cards; Games; Prayer
groups; Movies; Shopping trips; Social/
Cultural gatherings; Bingo; Church groups;
Welcome new residents; Birthdays; Cooking;
Bingo; Gardening.

URBANA

**Champaign County Residential Services Inc
Home No 1**
400 N Oakland, Urbana, OH, 43078
(513) 653-4076
Admin Than Johnson. *Medical Dir/Dir of
Nursing* Mark Schlater.
Licensure Intermediate care for mentally
retarded. *Beds* ICF/MR 18. *Certified*
Medicaid.
Owner Nonprofit Corp.
Admissions Requirements Minimum age 18;
Medical examination.
Staff LPNs 1 (ft); Orderlies 16 (ft), 17 (pt);
Occupational therapists 1 (pt); Activities
coordinators 1 (ft).
Facilities Dining room; Activities room;
Laundry room.
Activities Arts & crafts; Cards; Games;
Reading groups; Movies; Shopping trips;
Social/Cultural gatherings; Camping; Special
Olympics.

Champaign Nursing Home
PO Box 149, 2380 St, Rte 68, Urbana, OH,
43078
(513) 653-5291
Admin Dale R Long. *Medical Dir/Dir of
Nursing* Jae J Koh MD; Marty Castle DON.
Licensure Intermediate care; Intermediate care
for mentally retarded. *Beds* SNF 130; ICF/
MR 20. *Certified* Medicaid; Medicare.
Owner Nonprofit Corp.
Admissions Requirements Medical
examination; Physician's request.

Staff RNs 7 (ft), 1 (pt); LPNs 9 (ft), 6 (pt);
Nurses aides 44 (ft), 33 (pt); Occupational
therapists 1 (ft); Activities coordinators 1
(ft).
Facilities Dining room; Physical therapy
room; Activities room; Chapel; Crafts room;
Laundry room; Barber/Beauty shop.
Activities Arts & crafts; Cards; Games;
Reading groups; Prayer groups; Movies;
Shopping trips; Social/Cultural gatherings;
Cooking.

Heartland of Urbana
741 E Water St, Urbana, OH, 43078
(513) 652-1381
Admin Daniel Higgins. *Medical Dir/Dir of
Nursing* Dr Barry Paxton.
Licensure Skilled care; Intermediate care. *Beds*
SNF 100; ICF. *Certified* Medicaid;
Medicare.
Owner Proprietary Corp (Health Care &
Retirement Corp).
Admissions Requirements Minimum age 14;
Medical examination; Physician's request.
Staff RNs 5 (ft), 2 (pt); LPNs 6 (ft), 2 (pt);
Orderlies 1 (ft); Nurses aides 31 (ft), 18 (pt);
Physical therapists 1 (pt); Occupational
therapists 1 (pt); Speech therapists 1 (pt);
Activities coordinators 1 (ft), 1 (pt);
Dietitians 1 (ft).
Facilities Dining room; Physical therapy
room; Activities room; Crafts room; Laundry
room; Barber/Beauty shop; Library.
Activities Arts & crafts; Cards; Games;
Reading groups; Prayer groups; Movies;
Shopping trips; Social/Cultural gatherings.

UTICA

Utica Nursing Home
PO Box 618, 233 N Main St, Utica, OH,
43080
(614) 892-3414
Admin Karen A Rosser. *Medical Dir/Dir of
Nursing* Dr Hernando Posada; Mary C
Wilson.
Licensure Intermediate care. *Beds* ICF 35.
Certified Medicaid.
Owner Proprietary Corp.
Admissions Requirements Medical
examination.
Staff Physicians 1 (pt); RNs 2 (ft), 1 (pt);
LPNs 2 (ft), 1 (pt); Nurses aides 5 (ft), 8
(pt); Activities coordinators 1 (ft).
Facilities Dining room; Activities room;
Laundry room.
Activities Arts & crafts; Cards; Games; Prayer
groups; Shopping trips; Church.

VAN WERT

Van Wert Manor
160 Fox Rd, Van Wert, OH, 45891
(419) 238-6655
Admin Laurie Malsam NHA. *Medical Dir/Dir
of Nursing* Dr Osborn; Jacque Linder RN
DON.
Licensure Skilled care; Intermediate care. *Beds*
SNF 100; ICF. *Certified* Medicaid;
Medicare.
Owner Proprietary Corp (Health Care
Facilities Inc).
Admissions Requirements Medical
examination; Physician's request.
Staff Physicians 1 (pt); RNs 9 (ft), 1 (pt);
LPNs 9 (ft), 2 (pt); Nurses aides 52 (ft), 5
(pt); Physical therapists 1 (pt); Speech
therapists 1 (pt); Activities coordinators 1
(ft), 1 (pt); Dietitians 1 (pt); Dentists 1 (pt);
Ophthalmologists 1 (pt); Podiatrists 1 (pt);
Dentist 1 (pt) Social worker 1 (ft).
Facilities Dining room; Physical therapy
room; Activities room; Crafts room; Laundry
room; Barber/Beauty shop; Outside patio
areas; Indoor Florida room.

Activities Arts & crafts; Cards; Games; Prayer
groups; Movies; Shopping trips; Social/
Cultural gatherings; Discussion groups;
Bowling.

Vancrest Nursing Home
PO Box 558, R R 4, Van Wert, OH, 45891
(419) 238-4646
Admin Thelma L Thompson. *Medical Dir/Dir
of Nursing* A C Diller MD; Ann Warnecke
RN.
Licensure Skilled care; Intermediate care. *Beds*
104. *Certified* Medicaid; Medicare.
Owner Proprietary Corp.
Staff Physicians 2 (pt); RNs 1 (ft), 3 (pt);
LPNs 1 (ft), 5 (pt); Nurses aides 22 (ft), 14
(pt); Physical therapists 1 (pt); Activities
coordinators 1 (ft); Dietitians 1 (pt);
Ophthalmologists 1 (pt).
Facilities Dining room; Physical therapy
room; Activities room; Crafts room; Laundry
room; Barber/Beauty shop.
Activities Arts & crafts; Cards; Games;
Reading groups; Movies; Social/Cultural
gatherings.

VANDALIA

Franklin Nursing Center of Vandalia*
1208 Cassell Rd, Vandalia, OH, 45377
(513) 898-4202
Licensure Skilled care; Intermediate care. *Beds*
161. *Certified* Medicaid; Medicare.
Owner Proprietary Corp.

VERMILLION

Riverview Nursing Home*
5472 Liberty St, Vermillion, OH, 44089
(216) 967-6614
Admin C York.
Licensure Intermediate care. *Beds* 19.
Certified Medicaid.
Owner Proprietary Corp.
Admissions Requirements Medical
examination; Physician's request.
Staff RNs 1 (pt); LPNs 2 (ft), 4 (pt); Nurses
aides 9 (ft), 2 (pt); Reality therapists 1 (pt);
Activities coordinators 1 (ft); Dietitians 1
(ft); Podiatrists 1 (ft).
Facilities Dining room; Activities room;
Crafts room; Laundry room; Barber/Beauty
shop.
Activities Arts & crafts; Cards; Games;
Reading groups; Prayer groups; Movies;
Shopping trips.

VERSAILLES

Versailles Health Care Center
200 Marker Rd, Versailles, OH, 45380
(513) 526-5570
Admin Marilyn Barga. *Medical Dir/Dir of
Nursing* Dr C W Platt; Shirley Rockhold RN
DON.
Licensure Intermediate care. *Beds* ICF 50.
Certified Medicaid.
Owner Proprietary Corp (Community Care
Center).
Staff RNs 3 (ft); LPNs 2 (ft), 3 (pt); Nurses
aides 11 (ft), 15 (pt); Activities coordinators
1 (ft); Dietitians 1 (pt); Ophthalmologists 1
(pt).
Facilities Dining room; Activities room;
Chapel; Crafts room; Laundry room; Barber/
Beauty shop.
Activities Arts & crafts; Cards; Games;
Reading groups; Prayer groups; Movies;
Shopping trips; Social/Cultural gatherings.

WADSWORTH

Magnolia Care Center
365 Johnson Rd, Wadsworth, OH, 44281
(216) 335-1558

Admin Kevin J Sabo. *Medical Dir/Dir of Nursing* William Knapic MD; Peg Barber RN DON;.
Licensure Skilled care. *Beds* 109. *Certified* Medicaid; Medicare.
Owner Proprietary Corp (Beverly Enterprises).
Admissions Requirements Minimum age 18.
Staff Physicians; RNs; LPNs; Orderlies; Nurses aides; Physical therapists; Speech therapists; Activities coordinators; Dietitians; Dentists; Ophthalmologists; Podiatrists.
Facilities Dining room; Physical therapy room; Activities room; Chapel; Crafts room; Laundry room; Barber/Beauty shop.
Activities Arts & crafts; Games; Cards; Reading groups; Prayer groups; Movies; Shopping trips; Social/Cultural gatherings.

Wadsworth Health Care Center Inc*
147 Garfield St, Wadsworth, OH, 44281
(216) 335-2555
Licensure Skilled care; Intermediate care. *Beds* 112. *Certified* Medicaid; Medicare.
Owner Proprietary Corp.

WALNUT CREEK

Walnut Hills Nursing & Retirement Home
4748 Olde Pump St, Walnut Creek, OH,
(216) 852-2457
Admin David A Miller.
Licensure Intermediate care; Rest home; Residential apts. *Beds* ICF 102; Rest home 70; Residential apts 26. *Certified* Medicaid.
Owner Privately owned.
Staff Physicians; RNs; LPNs; Nurses aides; Activities coordinators.
Languages Pennsylvania Dutch
Facilities Dining room; Activities room; Crafts room; Laundry room; Barber/Beauty shop; Library.
Activities Arts & crafts; Cards; Games; Reading groups; Prayer groups; Movies; Shopping trips; Social/Cultural gatherings.

WAPAKONETA

Auglaize Acres
Rte 4, Infirmary Rd, Wapakoneta, OH, 45895
(419) 738-3816, 738-3819
Admin Alice Dewese. *Medical Dir/Dir of Nursing* Robert J Herman MD; Marie Perrin RN.
Licensure Intermediate care; Residential care. *Beds* ICF 142; Residential 18. *Certified* Medicaid.
Owner Publicly owned.
Admissions Requirements Minimum age 18; Medical examination.
Staff RNs 3 (ft), 8 (pt); LPNs 12 (ft), 3 (pt); Nurses aides 31 (ft), 12 (pt); Activities coordinators 3 (ft).
Facilities Dining room; Physical therapy room; Activities room; Chapel; Crafts room; Laundry room; Barber/Beauty shop; Solariums.
Activities Arts & crafts; Cards; Games; Reading groups; Prayer groups; Movies; Shopping trips; Social/Cultural gatherings.

Wapakoneta Manor
RR 4, St Rte 501, Wapakoneta, OH, 45885
(419) 738-3711
Admin Iva DeWitt Hoblet. *Medical Dir/Dir of Nursing* Charlotte E Newland.
Licensure Skilled care; Intermediate care. *Beds* 100. *Certified* Medicaid; Medicare.
Owner Proprietary Corp (Health Care Facilities Inc).
Staff Physicians 4 (pt); RNs 2 (ft), 3 (pt); LPNs 6 (ft), 6 (pt); Orderlies 2 (ft); Nurses aides 29 (ft), 17 (pt); Physical therapists 1 (pt); Occupational therapists 1 (pt); Speech therapists 1 (pt); Activities coordinators 1 (ft); Dietitians 1 (ft), 1 (pt); Dentists 1 (pt); Ophthalmologists 1 (pt); Podiatrists 1 (pt).

Facilities Dining room; Physical therapy room; Activities room; Laundry room; Barber/Beauty shop; Library.
Activities Arts & crafts; Games; Reading groups; Prayer groups; Movies; Social/Cultural gatherings.

WARREN

Albert's Nursing Home
2035 Van Wye SE, Warren, OH, 44484
(216) 369-2534
Admin Helen Albert. *Medical Dir/Dir of Nursing* Jagdish Patel MD; Arlene Jobe RN DON.
Licensure Skilled care; Intermediate care; Intermediate care for mentally retarded. *Beds* SNF 22; ICF; ICF/MR 28. *Certified* Medicaid; Medicare.
Owner Privately owned.
Admissions Requirements Medical examination; Physician's request.
Staff Physicians 3 (pt); RNs 1 (ft), 1 (pt); LPNs 4 (ft), 2 (pt); Orderlies 2 (ft); Nurses aides 24 (ft), 4 (pt); Physical therapists 1 (pt); Occupational therapists 1 (pt); Speech therapists 1 (pt); Activities coordinators 2 (ft); Dietitians 1 (pt); Ophthalmologists 1 (pt); Podiatrists 1 (pt); Psychologist 1 (pt).
Facilities Dining room; Physical therapy room; Activities room; Chapel; Crafts room; Laundry room.
Activities Arts & crafts; Cards; Games; Reading groups; Prayer groups; Movies; Shopping trips; Social/Cultural gatherings.

Albert's Nursing & Residential Facility*
2120 Van Wye St SE, Warren, OH, 44484
(216) 369-2137
Medical Dir/Dir of Nursing Dr Frank Guarnieri.
Licensure Intermediate care for mentally retarded. *Beds* 32. *Certified* Medicaid.
Owner Proprietary Corp.
Staff Physicians 1 (pt); RNs 1 (pt); LPNs 4 (ft), 1 (pt); Nurses aides 32 (ft), 8 (pt); Physical therapists 1 (pt); Occupational therapists 1 (pt); Speech therapists 1 (pt); Activities coordinators 1 (ft); Dietitians 1 (pt); Dentists 1 (pt); Ophthalmologists 1 (pt); Podiatrists 1 (pt); Audiologists 1 (pt).
Activities Arts & crafts; Cards; Games; Reading groups; Prayer groups; Movies; Shopping trips; Social/Cultural gatherings.

Community Skilled Nursing Centre
1320 Mahoning Ave NW, Warren, OH, 44483
(216) 373-1160
Admin Charles E Hogan. *Medical Dir/Dir of Nursing* Dr J N Cavalier.
Licensure Skilled care; Intermediate care. *Beds* 160. *Certified* Medicaid; Medicare.
Owner Nonprofit Corp.
Admissions Requirements Medical examination; Physician's request.
Staff Physicians 2 (ft); RNs 9 (ft), 7 (pt); LPNs 17 (ft), 6 (pt); Nurses aides 86 (ft), 3 (pt); Physical therapists 1 (pt); Reality therapists 1 (pt); Occupational therapists 1 (ft); Speech therapists 1 (pt); Activities coordinators 2 (ft); Dietitians 1 (ft); Ophthalmologists 1 (pt).
Facilities Dining room; Physical therapy room; Activities room; Chapel; Crafts room; Laundry room; Barber/Beauty shop.
Activities Arts & crafts; Cards; Games; Reading groups; Prayer groups; Movies; Shopping trips; Social/Cultural gatherings.

Gillette Nursing Home*
3214 Elm St, Warren, OH, 44483
(216) 372-4513
Medical Dir/Dir of Nursing Dr List.
Licensure Intermediate care. *Beds* 35. *Certified* Medicaid.
Owner Nonprofit Corp.

Admissions Requirements Medical examination; Physician's request.
Staff Physicians 1 (pt); RNs 1 (pt); LPNs 5 (ft); Nurses aides 9 (ft); Activities coordinators 1 (pt); Dietitians 1 (pt); Podiatrists 1 (pt).

Gillette's The Country Place
2473 North Rd NE, Warren, OH, 44483
(216) 372-2251
Admin Bruce E Maher. *Medical Dir/Dir of Nursing* Walter I Droba MD; Dolores Lehman RN DON.
Licensure Skilled care; Intermediate care. *Beds* 222. *Certified* Medicaid; Medicare.
Owner Proprietary Corp (Horizon Healthcare Corp).
Admissions Requirements Medical examination.
Staff Physicians 6 (pt); RNs 5 (ft), 2 (pt); LPNs 24 (ft), 1 (pt); Orderlies 1 (ft); Nurses aides 70 (ft), 5 (pt); Physical therapists 1 (pt); Occupational therapists 1 (pt); Speech therapists 1 (pt); Activities coordinators 1 (ft); Dietitians 1 (pt); Dentists 1 (pt); Ophthalmologists 1 (pt); Podiatrists 1 (pt); Social service coordinator 2 (pt).
Languages Greek
Facilities Dining room; Physical therapy room; Laundry room; Barber/Beauty shop.
Activities Arts & crafts; Cards; Games; Reading groups; Prayer groups; Movies; Shopping trips; Social/Cultural gatherings; Breakfast & lunch outings; Baking; Gardening; Personal grooming.

Imperial Skilled Care Center
4121 Tod Ave NW, Warren, OH, 44485
(216) 898-4033
Admin Betty Gowdy. *Medical Dir/Dir of Nursing* Walter Droba MD; Mary Dally RN DON.
Licensure Skilled care; Intermediate care. *Beds* SNF 121; ICF. *Certified* Medicaid; Medicare.
Owner Proprietary Corp.
Admissions Requirements Medical examination; Physician's request.
Staff Physicians 1 (pt); RNs 5 (ft), 2 (pt); LPNs 11 (ft), 6 (pt); Nurses aides 23 (ft), 13 (pt); Physical therapists 1 (ft); Speech therapists; Activities coordinators 1 (ft); Dietitians; Ophthalmologists 3 (pt).
Facilities Dining room; Physical therapy room; Activities room; Crafts room; Laundry room; Barber/Beauty shop.
Activities Arts & crafts; Cards; Games; Reading groups; Prayer groups; Movies; Shopping trips; Social/Cultural gatherings.

Washington Square Nursing Center
202 Washington St NW, Warren, OH, 44483
(216) 399-8997
Admin Kevin R Ruffing. *Medical Dir/Dir of Nursing* Dr Pollis, Dr McQuire.
Licensure Intermediate care. *Beds* ICF 100. *Certified* Medicaid.
Owner Proprietary Corp.
Admissions Requirements Medical examination.
Staff Physicians 2 (pt); RNs 4 (ft), 3 (pt); LPNs 6 (ft), 5 (pt); Orderlies 2 (pt); Nurses aides 18 (ft), 11 (pt); Activities coordinators 3 (pt); Dietitians 1 (ft); Dentists 1 (pt); Ophthalmologists 1 (pt); Podiatrists 1 (pt); Social service director 1 (ft).
Facilities Dining room; Activities room; Chapel; Crafts room; Laundry room; Barber/Beauty shop; Living rooms; Lounges; TV room.
Activities Arts & crafts; Games; Prayer groups; Movies; Shopping trips; Shopping trips; Reality orientation; Creative writing; Art expression; Current events.

WARRENSVILLE

Cuyahoga County Hospital—Sunny Acres Skilled Nursing Facility*
4310 Richmond Rd, Warrensville, OH, 44122
(216) 464-9500
Admin W J Wilson. *Medical Dir/Dir of Nursing* William G Ansley MD.
Licensure Skilled care; Intermediate care. *Beds* 320. *Certified* Medicaid; Medicare.
Owner Publicly owned.
Admissions Requirements Minimum age 15.
Staff Physicians 9 (ft); RNs 75 (ft), 20 (pt); LPNs 19 (ft), 3 (pt); Nurses aides 158 (ft); Physical therapists 4 (ft), 1 (pt); Recreational therapists 1 (ft); Occupational therapists 3 (ft); Activities coordinators 1 (ft); Dietitians 2 (ft); Dentists 1 (pt).
Facilities Dining room; Physical therapy room; Activities room; Chapel; Crafts room; Laundry room; Barber/Beauty shop; Library.
Activities Arts & crafts; Cards; Games; Reading groups; Prayer groups; Movies; Shopping trips; Special entertainments.

WARRENSVILLE HEIGHTS

Warrensville Center*
4325 Green Rd, Warrensville Heights, OH, 44128
Licensure Intermediate care for mentally retarded. *Beds* 261. *Certified* Medicaid.
Owner Publicly owned.

WARSAW

Echoing Hills Residential Center
Rte 2, Warsaw, OH, 43844
(614) 327-2311
Medical Dir/Dir of Nursing Jerold Meyer MD.
Licensure Intermediate care for Developmentally disabled. *Beds* 50.
Owner Proprietary Corp.
Admissions Requirements Minimum age 18; Medical examination.
Staff Physicians 1 (pt); RNs 5 (ft); LPNs 5 (ft), 2 (pt); Orderlies 10 (ft); Nurses aides 40 (ft), 1 (pt); Physical therapists 1 (pt); Occupational therapists 1 (pt); Speech therapists 1 (pt); Activities coordinators 1 (ft); Dietitians 1 (pt); Dentists 1 (pt); Ophthalmologists 1 (pt); Podiatrists 1 (pt).
Facilities Dining room; Physical therapy room; Activities room; Laundry room; Library.
Activities Arts & crafts; Prayer groups; Movies; Shopping trips; Social/Cultural gatherings; Camping; Travel.

WASHINGTON COURT HOUSE

Court House Manor
250 Glenn Ave, Washington Court House, OH, 43160
(614) 335-9290
Admin Linda S Luttrell. *Medical Dir/Dir of Nursing* Dr Ralph Gebhart; Elaine Hoover RN.
Licensure Skilled care; Intermediate care. *Beds* SNF 100. *Certified* Medicaid; Medicare.
Owner Proprietary Corp (Health Care Facilities Inc).
Admissions Requirements Medical examination; Physician's request.
Staff Physicians 1 (ft), 13 (pt); RNs 5 (ft); LPNs 8 (ft), 3 (pt); Nurses aides 26 (ft), 22 (pt); Physical therapists 1 (ft), 1 (pt); Recreational therapists 1 (pt); Occupational therapists 1 (pt); Speech therapists 1 (ft), 1 (pt); Activities coordinators 1 (ft), 1 (pt); Dietitians 1 (ft); Dentists 1 (pt); Ophthalmologists 1 (pt); Podiatrists 1 (pt).

Facilities Dining room; Physical therapy room; Activities room; Barber/Beauty shop.
Activities Arts & crafts; Cards; Games; Reading groups; Prayer groups; Movies; Shopping trips; Social/Cultural gatherings.

Deanview Nursing Home Inc*
719 Rawling St, Washington Court House, OH, 43160
(614) 335-1380
Medical Dir/Dir of Nursing Dr Hugh Payton.
Licensure Intermediate care. *Beds* 50. *Certified* Medicaid.
Owner Proprietary Corp.
Staff Physicians 5 (pt); RNs 1 (ft), 1 (pt); LPNs 4 (ft); Nurses aides 10 (ft), 6 (pt); Activities coordinators 1 (ft); Dietitians 1 (pt); Podiatrists 1 (pt).
Facilities Dining room; Activities room; Laundry room.
Activities Arts & crafts; Cards; Games; Reading groups; Prayer groups; Shopping trips.

Green Acres Nursing Home*
6674 Stafford Rd, Washington Court House, OH, 43160
(614) 335-2511
Licensure Intermediate care. *Beds* 25. *Certified* Medicaid.
Owner Proprietary Corp.
Admissions Requirements Medical examination; Physician's request.
Staff Physicians 1 (ft); RNs 1 (pt); LPNs 3 (ft); Nurses aides 7 (ft); Physical therapists 1 (ft); Activities coordinators 1 (ft); Dietitians 1 (ft); Dentists 1 (pt).
Facilities Dining room; Laundry room.
Activities Arts & crafts; Cards; Games; Prayer groups; Shopping trips.

Margaret Clark Oakfield Convalescent Center*
726 Rawling St, Washington Court House, OH, 43160
(614) 335-7143
Licensure Skilled care; Intermediate care. *Beds* 144. *Certified* Medicaid; Medicare.
Owner Proprietary Corp.

Quiet Acres Nursing Home Inc
1771 Palmer Rd NW, Washington Court House, OH, 43160
(614) 335-6391
Admin Pierre Sweeney. *Medical Dir/Dir of Nursing* Robert U Anderson MD; Cynthia Stoncrock DON.
Licensure Intermediate care. *Beds* ICF 50. *Certified* Medicaid.
Owner Privately owned.
Staff RNs 1 (ft); LPNs 3 (ft), 3 (pt); Nurses aides 10 (ft), 6 (pt); Activities coordinators 1 (ft); Dietitians 1 (pt).
Facilities Dining room; Activities room; Laundry room; Barber/Beauty shop.
Activities Arts & crafts; Cards; Games; Reading groups; Prayer groups; Movies; Shopping trips.

WATERVILLE

Hillcrest Care Center
555 Anthony Wayne Trail, Waterville, OH, 43566
(419) 878-3901
Admin William J Krech II. *Medical Dir/Dir of Nursing* Debbie Anello RN BSN.
Licensure Intermediate care. *Beds* ICF 100. *Certified* Medicaid.
Owner Proprietary Corp (Columbia Corp).
Admissions Requirements Medical examination.
Staff RNs 8 (ft), 2 (pt); LPNs 10 (ft), 2 (pt); Nurses aides 34 (ft), 16 (pt); Physical therapists 1 (pt); Reality therapists 1 (ft); Recreational therapists 1 (ft); Occupational therapists 1 (pt); Speech therapists 1 (pt); Dietitians 1 (pt).
Languages Sign

Facilities Dining room; Physical therapy room; Activities room; Barber/Beauty shop.
Activities Arts & crafts; Cards; Games; Reading groups; Prayer groups; Movies; Shopping trips; Social/Cultural gatherings.

WAUSEON

Detwiler Manor
604 S Shoop Ave, Wauseon, OH, 43567
(505) 337-9250
Admin Spence Tiffany. *Medical Dir/Dir of Nursing* Ben H Reed MD; Carol Hayes DON.
Licensure Intermediate care. *Beds* ICF 71. *Certified* Medicaid.
Owner Publicly owned.
Admissions Requirements Medical examination; Physician's request.
Staff RNs 3 (ft), 1 (pt); LPNs 6 (ft), 4 (pt); Orderlies 1 (pt); Nurses aides 16 (ft), 9 (pt); Activities coordinators 1 (ft), 1 (pt); Dietitians 1 (pt).
Facilities Dining room; Activities room; Chapel; Crafts room; Laundry room; Barber/Beauty shop.
Activities Arts & crafts; Cards; Games; Prayer groups; Movies; Shopping trips; Group singing; Piano & organ music entertainment.

Northwest Care Center*
303 W Leggett St, Wauseon, OH, 43567
(419) 337-3050
Licensure Skilled care; Intermediate care. *Beds* 51. *Certified* Medicaid; Medicare.
Owner Proprietary Corp.

WAVERLY

Buckeye Community Services—Grandview Avenue Homes*
207 Grandview Ave, Waverly, OH, 45690
Licensure Intermediate care for mentally retarded. *Beds* 8. *Certified* Medicaid.
Owner Nonprofit Corp.

WAYNESVILLE

Heffner's Ivy Cottage Nursing Home*
5596 Elbon Rd, Waynesville, OH, 45068
(513) 932-3950
Admin Phyllis D Arnold.
Licensure Intermediate care. *Beds* 25. *Certified* Medicaid.
Owner Proprietary Corp.
Admissions Requirements Minimum age 18; Medical examination.
Staff RNs 1 (pt); LPNs 2 (ft), 1 (pt); Orderlies 1 (pt); Nurses aides 5 (ft), 1 (pt); Activities coordinators 1 (pt).
Facilities Dining room; Activities room.
Activities Arts & crafts; Games; Movies; Shopping trips; Social/Cultural gatherings.

Quaker Heights Nursing Home*
514 W High St, Waynesville, OH, 45068
(513) 897-6050
Medical Dir/Dir of Nursing John Murphy III.
Licensure Skilled care; Intermediate care. *Beds* 98. *Certified* Medicaid; Medicare.
Owner Nonprofit Corp.
Admissions Requirements Medical examination.
Staff Physicians 6 (pt); RNs 7 (ft); LPNs 9 (ft); Orderlies 3 (ft); Nurses aides 37 (ft); Physical therapists 1 (pt); Activities coordinators 2 (ft); Dietitians 1 (ft); Dentists 1 (ft).
Affiliation Society of Friends
Facilities Dining room; Physical therapy room; Activities room; Crafts room; Laundry room; Barber/Beauty shop.
Activities Arts & crafts; Cards; Games; Reading groups; Prayer groups; Movies; Social/Cultural gatherings.

WELLINGTON

Elms Convalescent Home & Rehabilitation Center
136 S Main St, Wellington, OH, 44090
(216) 647-2414
Admin Janet A Ohman; Ralph S Keller.
Medical Dir/Dir of Nursing G T Derikito MD; Georgia A Anton.
Licensure Intermediate care. *Beds* ICF 74. *Certified* Medicaid.
Owner Proprietary Corp.
Admissions Requirements Minimum age 50.
Staff Physicians 8 (pt); RNs 2 (ft), 2 (pt); LPNs 4 (ft), 7 (pt); Nurses aides 14 (ft), 16 (pt); Physical therapists 1 (pt); Activities coordinators 1 (ft); Dietitians 1 (pt); Ophthalmologists 1 (pt).
Facilities Dining room; Physical therapy room; Laundry room; Barber/Beauty shop; Day room.
Activities Arts & crafts; Cards; Games; Reading groups; Prayer groups; Movies; Shopping trips; Social/Cultural gatherings; Monthly birthday parties; Sing-alongs.

Webers Nursing Home*
214 Herrick Ave E, Wellington, OH, 44090
(216) 647-2088
Licensure Intermediate care. *Beds* 69. *Certified* Medicaid.
Owner Proprietary Corp.

Wellington Manor Nursing Home Inc
PO Box 393, 116 Prospect St, Wellington, OH, 44090
(216) 647-3910
Medical Dir/Dir of Nursing G T Derikito MD; Kay Justice.
Licensure Intermediate care. *Beds* ICF 17. *Certified* Medicaid.
Owner Proprietary Corp.
Admissions Requirements Medical examination & TB test results.
Staff Physicians 1 (pt); RNs 1 (ft); LPNs 3 (ft); Nurses aides 13 (ft); Recreational therapists 1 (ft); Activities coordinators 1 (ft); Dietitians 1 (pt); Podiatrists 1 (pt).
Facilities Dining room; Activities room; Laundry room; Barber/Beauty shop.
Activities Arts & crafts; Cards; Games; Reading groups; Prayer groups; Movies; Shopping trips; Social/Cultural gatherings.

WELLSTON

Jenkins Memorial Nursing Home
142 Jenkins Memorial Rd, Wellston, OH, 45692
(614) 384-2119
Licensure Skilled care; Intermediate care. *Beds* 43. *Certified* Medicaid; Medicare.
Owner Nonprofit Corp.

Maple Heights Nursing Home Inc
406 E "A" St, Wellston, OH, 45692
(614) 384-2245
Admin Mary A Ingalls. *Medical Dir/Dir of Nursing* Douglas Jones MD; Jackie Shepherd RN.
Licensure Intermediate care. *Beds* ICF 16. *Certified* Medicaid; Medicare.
Owner Proprietary Corp.
Admissions Requirements Females only; Medical examination.
Staff Physicians 1 (pt); RNs 1 (pt); LPNs 2 (ft), 4 (pt); Nurses aides 4 (ft), 3 (pt); Physical therapists 1 (pt); Recreational therapists 1 (pt); Activities coordinators 1 (pt); Dietitians 1 (ft), 1 (pt); Ophthalmologists 1 (pt).
Facilities Dining room; Activities room.
Activities Arts & crafts; Cards; Games; Reading groups; Prayer groups; Movies; Shopping trips; Social/Cultural gatherings; Participation in parades.

Wellston Nursing Home*
405 N Park Ave, Wellston, OH, 45692
(614) 384-2880
Medical Dir/Dir of Nursing Dr A R Hambrick.
Licensure Intermediate care. *Beds* 50. *Certified* Medicaid.
Owner Proprietary Corp.
Admissions Requirements Medical examination.
Staff Physicians 1 (pt); RNs 1 (pt); LPNs 6 (ft); Nurses aides 12 (ft), 1 (pt); Recreational therapists 1 (ft); Activities coordinators 1 (ft); Dentists 1 (pt); Podiatrists 1 (pt); Audiologists 1 (pt).
Facilities Dining room; Activities room; Crafts room; Laundry room; Barber/Beauty shop.
Activities Arts & crafts; Cards; Games; Reading groups; Prayer groups; Movies; Shopping trips; Social/Cultural gatherings.

WELLSVILLE

Mary Fletcher Health Care Center 2*
1037 Main St, Wellsville, OH, 43968
(216) 532-2085
Licensure Intermediate care. *Beds* 21. *Certified* Medicaid.
Owner Proprietary Corp.

WEST CARROLLTON

Elm Creek Nursing Center
115 Elmwood Cir, West Carrollton, OH, 45449
(513) 866-3814
Admin David P Depp. *Medical Dir/Dir of Nursing* Dr C Y Rmee; Terry Quinn.
Licensure Skilled care; Intermediate care. *Beds* SNF 100; ICF. *Certified* Medicaid; Medicare.
Owner Proprietary Corp (Health Care Management).
Staff RNs; LPNs; Nurses aides; Physical therapists; Reality therapists; Recreational therapists; Occupational therapists; Speech therapists; Activities coordinators; Dietitians; Dentists; Ophthalmologists.
Facilities Dining room; Physical therapy room; Activities room; Crafts room; Laundry room; Barber/Beauty shop.
Activities Arts & crafts; Cards; Games; Reading groups; Prayer groups; Movies; Shopping trips; Social/Cultural gatherings.

WEST CHESTER

Willows Nursing Home*
9117 Cincinnati-Columbus Rd, West Chester, OH, 45069
(513) 777-6164
Licensure Skilled care; Intermediate care. *Beds* 105. *Certified* Medicaid; Medicare.
Owner Proprietary Corp.

WEST JEFFERSON

Hampton Court*
375 W Main St, West Jefferson, OH, 43162
Licensure Skilled care; Intermediate care. *Beds* 50. *Certified* Medicaid; Medicare.
Owner Proprietary Corp (Arbor Health Care).

WEST LAFAYETTE

Edgerton Manor—ICF/MR*
22059 Orchard St, Box 28, West Lafayette, OH, 43845
(614) 545-6366
Admin Renee1 Guilliams. *Medical Dir/Dir of Nursing* W R Agricola MD.
Licensure Intermediate care for mentally retarded. *Beds* 15.
Owner Proprietary Corp.

Admissions Requirements Minimum age 4; Medical examination.
Staff Physicians 1 (pt); RNs 1 (ft); LPNs 4 (ft), 1 (pt); Nurses aides 9 (ft), 3 (pt); Physical therapists 1 (pt); Recreational therapists 1 (ft); Occupational therapists 1 (pt); Speech therapists 1 (pt); Activities coordinators 1 (ft); Dietitians 2 (ft); Dentists 1 (pt); Ophthalmologists 1 (pt); Podiatrists 1 (pt); Audiologists 1 (pt).
Facilities Dining room; Activities room; Crafts room; Laundry room; Library.
Activities Arts & crafts; Cards; Games; Reading groups; Movies; Shopping trips; Social/Cultural gatherings.

Guilliams Family Home*
220 S Kirk, Box 28, West Lafayette, OH, 43845
(614) 545-6337
Admin Renee1 Guilliams. *Medical Dir/Dir of Nursing* W R Agricola MD.
Licensure Intermediate care for mentally retarded. *Beds* 5.
Owner Proprietary Corp.
Admissions Requirements Minimum age 16; Females only; Medical examination.
Staff Physicians 1 (pt); RNs 1 (pt); LPNs 1 (ft); Nurses aides 3 (ft), 1 (pt); Physical therapists 1 (pt); Recreational therapists 1 (pt); Occupational therapists 1 (pt); Speech therapists 1 (pt); Activities coordinators 1 (pt); Dentists 1 (pt); Ophthalmologists 1 (pt); Podiatrists 1 (pt); Audiologists 1 (pt).
Facilities Dining room; Activities room; Crafts room; Laundry room.
Activities Arts & crafts; Cards; Games; Reading groups; Movies; Shopping trips; Social/Cultural gatherings.

Rose Lawn ICF/MR*
21990 Orchard St, Box 28, West Lafayette, OH, 43845
(614) 545-6366
Admin Renee1 Guilliams. *Medical Dir/Dir of Nursing* W R Agricola MD.
Licensure Intermediate care for mentally retarded. *Beds* 30. *Certified* Medicaid.
Owner Proprietary Corp.
Admissions Requirements Minimum age 4; Medical examination.
Staff Physicians 1 (pt); RNs 1 (ft), 1 (pt); LPNs 5 (ft), 1 (pt); Nurses aides 13 (ft), 4 (pt); Physical therapists 1 (pt); Reality therapists 1 (pt); Occupational therapists 1 (pt); Speech therapists 1 (pt); Activities coordinators 1 (ft); Dietitians 4 (ft), 1 (pt); Dentists 1 (pt); Ophthalmologists 1 (pt); Podiatrists 1 (pt); Audiologists 1 (pt); Mental health technician; Behavior modification specialist; Social worker; Special education teacher; Qualified mental retardation professional.
Facilities Dining room; Activities room; Crafts room; Laundry room; Library; Program areas.
Activities Arts & crafts; Cards; Games; Reading groups; Movies; Shopping trips; Social/Cultural gatherings.

West Lafayette Care Center
620 E Main St, West Lafayette, OH, 43845
(614) 545-6355
Admin Atwood J Cool. *Medical Dir/Dir of Nursing* D Ruth Cheney RN.
Licensure Intermediate care. *Beds* ICF 96. *Certified* Medicaid.
Owner Proprietary Corp (Regency Health Care Centers).
Admissions Requirements Medical examination; Physician's request.
Staff RNs; LPNs; Nurses aides; Physical therapists; Occupational therapists; Activities coordinators; Dietitians.
Facilities Dining room; Physical therapy room; Activities room; Crafts room; Laundry room; Barber/Beauty shop.

Activities Arts & crafts; Cards; Games; Reading groups; Prayer groups; Shopping trips.

WEST LIBERTY

Green Hills Center
6557 US Rte 68 S, West Liberty, OH, 43357
(513) 465-5065
Admin Kathy Sommers. Medical Dir/Dir of Nursing James Steiner MD.
Licensure Skilled care; Intermediate care. Beds 105. Certified Medicaid; Medicare.
Owner Nonprofit Corp.
Admissions Requirements Medical examination; Physician's request.
Staff RNs 9 (ft), 11 (pt); Orderlies 1 (ft); Nurses aides 27 (ft), 21 (pt); Physical therapists 1 (pt); Occupational therapists 1 (pt); Speech therapists 1 (pt); Activities coordinators 2 (ft), 1 (pt); Dietitians 1 (pt); Dentists 1 (pt); Podiatrists 1 (pt).
Facilities Dining room; Physical therapy room; Activities room; Chapel; Crafts room; Laundry room; Barber/Beauty shop; Library; Speech therapy room; Soda Shoppe.
Activities Arts & crafts; Cards; Games; Reading groups; Prayer groups; Movies; Shopping trips; Social/Cultural gatherings.

WEST UNION

Adams County Manor Nursing Home*
10856 State Rte 41, West Union, OH, 45693
(513) 544-2205
Admin Glenda Walton & Rosalie Hughes. Medical Dir/Dir of Nursing Gary Greenlee MD.
Licensure Intermediate care. Beds 40. Certified Medicaid.
Owner Publicly owned.
Staff RNs 2 (pt); LPNs 4 (ft), 2 (pt); Nurses aides 11 (ft), 5 (pt); Recreational therapists 2 (pt); Activities coordinators 1 (ft); Dietitians 3 (pt).
Facilities Dining room; Activities room; Crafts room; Laundry room.
Activities Arts & crafts; Cards; Games; Reading groups; Prayer groups; Shopping trips; Social/Cultural gatherings.

Eagle Creek Nursing Center
141 Spruce Lane, West Union, OH, 45693
(513) 544-5531
Admin Mitchell J Durant. Medical Dir/Dir of Nursing Dale Mathias MD; Alice N Bailey BSN DON.
Licensure Skilled care; Intermediate care. Beds 100. Certified Medicaid; Medicare.
Owner Proprietary Corp (Health Care Management).
Staff Physicians 4 (pt); RNs 7 (ft); LPNs 10 (ft); Orderlies 4 (ft); Nurses aides 40 (ft), 20 (pt); Speech therapists; Activities coordinators 1 (ft); Dietitians 2 (pt); Dentists 1 (pt); Ophthalmologists 1 (pt).

Revmont Nursing Home*
7980 State Rte 125, West Union, OH, 45693
(513) 544-2923
Licensure Intermediate care. Beds 16. Certified Medicaid.
Owner Proprietary Corp.

WESTCHESTER

Bonnie's Nursing Home
PO Box 363, 9018 Cincinnati-Columbus Rd, Westchester, OH, 45069
(513) 777-6363
Admin Greg Carson. Medical Dir/Dir of Nursing Sandra Gilbert.
Licensure Intermediate care. Beds ICF 40.
Owner Proprietary Corp.
Admissions Requirements Medical examination.

Staff LPNs; Nurses aides; Activities coordinators; Dietitians.
Facilities Dining room; Activities room; Laundry room; Barber/Beauty shop.
Activities Arts & crafts; Cards; Games; Movies; Social/Cultural gatherings.

WESTERVILLE

Columbus Colony for the Elderly Care Inc*
1150 Colony Dr, Westerville, OH, 43081
(614) 891-5055
Admin Willliam L Stewart. Medical Dir/Dir of Nursing H T Villavacer MD.
Licensure Skilled care; Intermediate care. Beds 100. Certified Medicaid; Medicare.
Owner Nonprofit Corp.
Staff Physicians 1 (pt); RNs 5 (ft), 3 (pt); LPNs 5 (ft), 5 (pt); Nurses aides 23 (ft), 23 (pt); Recreational therapists 1 (ft), 1 (pt); Activities coordinators 1 (ft).
Facilities Dining room; Physical therapy room; Activities room; Crafts room; Laundry room; Barber/Beauty shop.
Activities Arts & crafts; Cards; Games; Reading groups; Prayer groups; Movies; Shopping trips; Social/Cultural gatherings; Outings; Special meals.

Edgewood Manor of Westerville
140 N State St, Westerville, OH, 43081
(614) 882-4055
Admin John H Law. Medical Dir/Dir of Nursing H T Villavacer MD; Kathy Dettore DON.
Licensure Intermediate care. Beds ICF 70. Certified Medicaid.
Owner Proprietary Corp.
Admissions Requirements Medical examination.
Staff Physicians 1 (ft); RNs 3 (ft), 3 (pt); LPNs 3 (ft), 5 (pt); Orderlies 3 (ft); Nurses aides 14 (ft), 4 (pt); Physical therapists 1 (pt); Recreational therapists 1 (pt); Occupational therapists 1 (pt); Speech therapists 1 (pt); Activities coordinators 1 (ft), 1 (pt); Dietitians 1 (pt); Dentists 1 (pt); Ophthalmologists 1 (pt).
Facilities Dining room; Activities room; Crafts room; Laundry room; Barber/Beauty shop.
Activities Arts & crafts; Cards; Games; Reading groups; Prayer groups; Movies; Shopping trips; Social/Cultural gatherings.

Mann Nursing Home
25 W Home St, Westerville, OH, 43081
(614) 882-2565
Admin Linda J Reash. Medical Dir/Dir of Nursing John Bohlen MD; Shirlee Tarfford RN.
Licensure Intermediate care. Beds 184. Certified Medicaid.
Owner Proprietary Corp (Altercare Inc).
Admissions Requirements Medical examination.
Staff Physicians 1 (ft), 11 (pt); RNs 5 (ft), 4 (pt); LPNs 20 (ft), 20 (pt); Orderlies 4 (ft); Physical therapists 1 (pt); Reality therapists 1 (pt); Recreational therapists 1 (pt); Occupational therapists 1 (pt); Activities coordinators 1 (ft); Dietitians 1 (pt).
Facilities Dining room; Activities room; Crafts room; Laundry room; Barber/Beauty shop.
Activities Arts & crafts; Cards; Games; Reading groups; Prayer groups; Movies; Shopping trips; Social/Cultural gatherings.

Manor Care—Westerville Nursing Center
140 County Line Rd, Westerville, OH, 43081
(614) 882-1511
Admin Robert Morris. Medical Dir/Dir of Nursing H T Villanecer MD; Patricia Custard MD.
Licensure Skilled care. Beds 180. Certified Medicaid; Medicare.
Owner Proprietary Corp (Manor Care).

Admissions Requirements Minimum age 18.
Staff RNs; LPNs; Orderlies; Nurses aides; Physical therapists 1 (ft); Occupational therapists 1 (pt); Speech therapists 1 (pt); Activities coordinators 2 (ft); Dietitians 1 (ft); Ophthalmologists 1 (pt).
Facilities Dining room; Physical therapy room; Activities room; Barber/Beauty shop.
Activities Arts & crafts; Cards; Games; Reading groups; Prayer groups; Movies; Shopping trips; Social/Cultural gatherings.

The Village at Westerville Nursing Center*
1060 Eastwind Rd, Westerville, OH, 43081
Beds 100.

WESTLAKE

Country Estate*
31156 Detroit Rd, Westlake, OH, 44145
(216) 871-2261
Licensure Intermediate care. Beds 44. Certified Medicaid.
Owner Proprietary Corp.

Dover Nursing Home*
28305 Detroit Rd, Westlake, OH, 44145
(216) 871-0500
Licensure Skilled care; Intermediate care. Beds 100. Certified Medicaid; Medicare.
Owner Proprietary Corp.

Lutheran Home
2116 Dover Center Rd, Westlake, OH, 44145-3194
(216) 871-0090
Licensure Skilled care; Intermediate care. Beds 222. Certified Medicaid; Medicare.
Owner Nonprofit Corp.
Admissions Requirements Minimum age 65; Females only.
Staff Physicians 6 (pt); RNs; LPNs; Nurses aides; Physical therapists 2 (pt); Occupational therapists 1 (pt); Activities coordinators 2 (ft); Dietitians 1 (pt); Podiatrists 1 (pt).
Affiliation Lutheran
Facilities Dining room; Physical therapy room; Activities room; Chapel; Crafts room; Laundry room; Barber/Beauty shop.
Activities Arts & crafts; Games; Movies; Social/Cultural gatherings.

Oakridge Home
26520 Center Ridge Rd, Westlake, OH, 44145
(216) 871-3030
Admin Bryan Newmyer. Medical Dir/Dir of Nursing James L Rush MD.
Licensure Skilled care; Intermediate care. Beds 117. Certified Medicaid; Medicare.
Owner Proprietary Corp.
Admissions Requirements Medical examination.
Staff RNs 4 (ft), 6 (pt); LPNs 6 (ft), 5 (pt); Nurses aides 33 (ft), 23 (pt); Physical therapists 1 (ft); Speech therapists 1 (pt); Activities coordinators 1 (ft); Dietitians 1 (pt).
Facilities Dining room; Physical therapy room; Activities room; Crafts room; Laundry room; Barber/Beauty shop.
Activities Arts & crafts; Cards; Games; Reading groups; Prayer groups; Movies; Shopping trips; Social/Cultural gatherings; Religious services; Resident suggested activities.

Rae-Ann Suburban*
29505 Detroit Rd, Westlake, OH, 44145
(216) 871-5181
Licensure Intermediate care. Beds 50. Certified Medicaid.
Owner Proprietary Corp.

Westbay Manor I
27601 Westchester Pkwy, Westlake, OH, 44145
(216) 871-5900

Admin Elizabeth T Benson. *Medical Dir/Dir of Nursing* Germaine R Hahnel MD; Susan Spillar RN DON.
Licensure Skilled care; Intermediate care. *Beds* SNF 12; ICF 141. *Certified* Medicaid; Medicare.
Owner Proprietary Corp.
Admissions Requirements Medical examination.
Staff Physicians; RNs; LPNs; Nurses aides; Physical therapists; Recreational therapists; Occupational therapists; Speech therapists; Activities coordinators; Dietitians; Podiatrists; Dentist; Optician.
Facilities Dining room; Physical therapy room; Activities room; Crafts room; Barber/Beauty shop; Library.
Activities Arts & crafts; Cards; Games; Reading groups; Prayer groups; Movies; Social/Cultural gatherings.

Westbay Manor II
27601 Westchester Parkway, Westlake, OH, 44145
(216) 871-5900
Admin Elizabeth T Benson. *Medical Dir/Dir of Nursing* Germaine R Hahnel MD; Carol Clancy RN DON.
Licensure Skilled care; Intermediate care. *Beds* SNF 10; ICF 96. *Certified* Medicare.
Owner Proprietary Corp.
Admissions Requirements Medical examination.
Staff Physicians; RNs; LPNs; Nurses aides; Physical therapists; Reality therapists; Recreational therapists; Occupational therapists; Speech therapists; Activities coordinators; Dietitians; Ophthalmologists; Podiatrists; Optician.
Facilities Dining room; Physical therapy room; Activities room; Crafts room; Laundry room; Barber/Beauty shop; Library.
Activities Arts & crafts; Cards; Games; Reading groups; Prayer groups; Movies; Social/Cultural gatherings.

WHEELERSBURG

Best Care Nursing Home*
2159 Dogwood Ridge, Wheelersburg, OH, 45694
(614) 574-2558
Medical Dir/Dir of Nursing W L Herrmann MD.
Licensure Skilled care; Intermediate care. *Beds* 151. *Certified* Medicaid; Medicare.
Owner Proprietary Corp.
Admissions Requirements Medical examination; Physician's request.
Staff Physicians; RNs; LPNs; Nurses aides; Physical therapists; Reality therapists; Recreational therapists; Occupational therapists; Speech therapists; Activities coordinators 2 (ft), 2 (pt); Dietitians; Dentists; Ophthalmologists; Podiatrists; Audiologists.
Facilities Dining room; Physical therapy room; Activities room; Chapel; Crafts room; Laundry room; Barber/Beauty shop; Library.
Activities Arts & crafts; Cards; Games; Reading groups; Prayer groups; Movies; Shopping trips; Social/Cultural gatherings.

Greenbriar Convalescent Center
PO Box 29, 1242 Crescent Dr, Wheelersburg, OH, 45694
(614) 574-8441
Licensure Skilled care; Intermediate care. *Beds* 151. *Certified* Medicaid; Medicare.
Owner Proprietary Corp.

WHITEHOUSE

Whitehouse Country Manor
11239 Waterville St, Whitehouse, OH, 43571
(419) 877-5338

Admin Carol Husing. *Medical Dir/Dir of Nursing* Dr Terry D Roode DO; Catherine Dotson RN DON.
Licensure Intermediate care. *Beds* ICF 100. *Certified* Medicaid.
Owner Proprietary Corp (Hillhaven Corp).
Admissions Requirements Medical examination.
Staff Physicians 1 (ft); RNs 2 (ft), 5 (pt); LPNs 5 (ft), 9 (pt); Orderlies 1 (pt); Nurses aides 24 (ft), 26 (pt); Physical therapists 1 (pt); Reality therapists 7 (ft); Occupational therapists 1 (pt); Speech therapists 1 (pt); Activities coordinators 1 (ft); Dietitians 1 (pt); Ophthalmologists 1 (pt); Podiatrists 1 (pt); Social worker 1 (ft).
Facilities Dining room; Activities room; Crafts room; Laundry room; Barber/Beauty shop.
Activities Arts & crafts; Cards; Games; Reading groups; Prayer groups; Movies; Social/Cultural gatherings; Discussion groups; Reality orientation; Birthday parties; Resident council; Eat-ins; Music; Grooming; Outings.

WICKLIFFE

Wickliffe Country Place
1919 Bishop Rd, Wickliffe, OH, 44092
(216) 944-9400
Admin Bartlett T Bell. *Medical Dir/Dir of Nursing* David M Berzon MD.
Licensure Skilled care; Intermediate care. *Beds* 189. *Certified* Medicare.
Owner Proprietary Corp.
Admissions Requirements Minimum age 15; Medical examination; Physician's request.
Staff Physicians 5 (pt); RNs 5 (ft), 6 (pt); Orderlies 3 (ft); Physical therapists 1 (ft); Reality therapists 1 (pt); Recreational therapists 2 (ft); Occupational therapists 1 (pt); Speech therapists 1 (pt); Activities coordinators 1 (ft); Dietitians 1 (ft); Dentists 1 (pt); Ophthalmologists 1 (pt); Podiatrists 1 (pt); Dentist 1 (pt).
Facilities Dining room; Physical therapy room; Activities room; Crafts room; Laundry room; Barber/Beauty shop; Library.
Activities Arts & crafts; Cards; Games; Reading groups; Prayer groups; Movies; Shopping trips; Social/Cultural gatherings.

WILLARD

Hillside Acres
370 E Howard St, Willard, OH, 44890
(419) 935-0148
Licensure Skilled care; Intermediate care. *Beds* 135. *Certified* Medicaid; Medicare.
Owner Proprietary Corp.
Staff Physicians; RNs; LPNs; Orderlies; Nurses aides; Physical therapists; Occupational therapists; Speech therapists; Activities coordinators; Dietitians; Ophthalmologists.
Facilities Dining room; Activities room; Chapel; Crafts room; Laundry room; Barber/Beauty shop.
Activities Arts & crafts; Cards; Games; Reading groups; Prayer groups; Movies; Shopping trips; Social/Cultural gatherings.

Willard Quality Care Nursing Center
725 Wessor Ave, Willard, OH, 44890
(419) 935-6511
Admin Tamara Thornton. *Medical Dir/Dir of Nursing* Dr John Russo; Sheryl L Long RN DON.
Licensure Intermediate care. *Beds* 51. *Certified* Medicaid.
Owner Proprietary Corp (Northwestern Service Corp).
Admissions Requirements Medical examination.

Staff Physicians 2 (ft), 4 (pt); RNs 1 (ft), 2 (pt); LPNs 3 (ft), 4 (pt); Nurses aides 10 (ft), 10 (pt); Physical therapists 1 (pt); Activities coordinators 1 (pt); Dietitians 1 (ft); Dentists 1 (pt); Ophthalmologists 1 (pt).
Languages Spanish
Facilities Dining room; Activities room; Crafts room; Laundry room; Barber/Beauty shop; Library.
Activities Arts & crafts; Cards; Games; Reading groups; Prayer groups; Movies; Shopping trips; Social/Cultural gatherings; Pet therapy.

WILLIAMSBURG

Locust Ridge Nursing Home Inc
12745 Elm Corner Rd, Williamsburg, OH, 45176
(513) 444-2920
Admin Howard L Meeker. *Medical Dir/Dir of Nursing* John H Wehby MD.
Licensure Skilled care; Intermediate care. *Beds* SNF 16; ICF 81. *Certified* Medicaid; Medicare.
Owner Proprietary Corp.
Staff Physicians 9 (pt); RNs 6 (ft), 1 (pt); LPNs 13 (ft), 1 (pt); Nurses aides 53 (ft), 1 (pt); Physical therapists 1 (ft); Activities coordinators 4 (ft); Dietitians 1 (ft).
Facilities Dining room; Physical therapy room; Activities room; Laundry room; Barber/Beauty shop.
Activities Arts & crafts; Games; Reading groups; Prayer groups; Movies; Shopping trips; Social/Cultural gatherings; Evening outings; Zoo trips; Mini-fair.

WILLISTON

Luther Home of Mercy
5810 N Main St, Williston, OH, 43468
(419) 836-7741
Admin Rev Donald L Wukotich. *Medical Dir/Dir of Nursing* Albert Perras MD; Dolores Schimming RN.
Licensure Intermediate care for mentally retarded. *Beds* ICF/MR 129. *Certified* Medicaid.
Owner Nonprofit Corp.
Staff Physicians 1 (pt); RNs 2 (ft), 8 (pt); LPNs 12 (ft), 10 (pt); Nurses aides 99 (ft), 29 (pt); Physical therapists 1 (pt); Recreational therapists 4 (pt); Occupational therapists 1 (pt); Speech therapists 1 (pt); Activities coordinators 1 (ft); Dietitians 1 (ft); Podiatrists 1 (ft).
Affiliation Lutheran
Facilities Dining room; Physical therapy room; Activities room; Chapel; Crafts room.
Activities Arts & crafts; Cards; Games; Reading groups; Prayer groups; Movies; Shopping trips; Social/Cultural gatherings.

WILLOUGHBY

Fairmount Health Center
36855 Ridge Rd, Willoughby, OH, 44094
(216) 942-4342
Admin Philip Braisted. *Medical Dir/Dir of Nursing* Ian Glass MD; Janet Bahr RN.
Licensure Skilled care; Intermediate care. *Beds* SNF 50; ICF 50. *Certified* Medicaid; Medicare.
Owner Nonprofit Corp (OH Presbyterian Homes).
Admissions Requirements Minimum age 60; Medical examination.
Staff Physicians 1 (pt); RNs 4 (ft), 2 (pt); LPNs 8 (ft), 3 (pt); Nurses aides 36 (ft), 5 (pt); Physical therapists 1 (pt); Activities coordinators 1 (ft), 2 (pt); Dietitians 1 (pt).
Affiliation Presbyterian
Facilities Dining room; Physical therapy room; Activities room; Chapel; Crafts room; Laundry room; Barber/Beauty shop.

Activities Arts & crafts; Games; Reading groups; Prayer groups; Movies; Shopping trips; Social/Cultural gatherings.

Manor Care—Willoughby
37603 Euclid Ave, Willoughby, OH, 44094
(216) 951-5551
Admin Anne Marie Johnson. *Medical Dir/Dir of Nursing* Edwin V Basquinez MD; Pat Butler RN DON.
Licensure Skilled care; Intermediate care. *Beds* SNF 157; ICF. *Certified* Medicaid; Medicare.
Owner Proprietary Corp (Manor Care).
Admissions Requirements Minimum age; Medical examination.
Staff Physicians; RNs; LPNs; Orderlies; Nurses aides; Physical therapists; Recreational therapists; Occupational therapists; Speech therapists; Activities coordinators; Dietitians 1 (ft).
Facilities Dining room; Physical therapy room; Activities room; Crafts room; Laundry room; Barber/Beauty shop; Library.
Activities Arts & crafts; Cards; Games; Reading groups; Prayer groups; Movies; Shopping trips; Social/Cultural gatherings.

WILMINGTON

Senior Health Care Center
201 E Locust St, Wilmington, OH, 45177
(513) 382-2695
Admin Ruth Reynolds NHA. *Medical Dir/Dir of Nursing* Zelma Johnson RN.
Licensure Intermediate care. *Beds* ICF 18. *Certified* Medicaid.
Owner Proprietary Corp.
Admissions Requirements Medical examination.
Staff Physicians 4 (pt); RNs 1 (ft), 1 (pt); LPNs 2 (pt); Nurses aides 6 (ft), 3 (pt); Activities coordinators 1 (pt); Dietitians 1 (pt); Ophthalmologists 1 (pt); 1 (pt) Social services.
Facilities Dining room.
Activities Reading groups; Prayer groups; Shopping trips.

Wilmington Extended Care Facility*
75 Hale St, Wilmington, OH, 45177
(513) 382-1621
Licensure Skilled care; Intermediate care. *Beds* 104. *Certified* Medicaid; Medicare.
Owner Proprietary Corp.

WINDSOR

Town Hall Estates Nursing Home
PO Box 48, Rts 322 & 534, Windsor, OH, 44099
(216) 272-5600
Admin Donald E Stair. *Medical Dir/Dir of Nursing* E DePasquale DO; Nancy Filiped RN DON.
Licensure Intermediate care. *Beds* ICF 99. *Certified* Medicaid.
Owner Nonprofit Corp.
Admissions Requirements Minimum age 55; Medical examination; Physician's request.
Staff Physicians 2 (pt); RNs 2 (ft); LPNs 6 (ft), 6 (pt); Nurses aides 26 (ft), 4 (pt); Activities coordinators 1 (ft), 1 (pt); Dietitians 1 (pt); Dentists 1 (pt); Ophthalmologists 1 (pt); Podiatrists 1 (pt).
Facilities Dining room; Laundry room; Barber/Beauty shop.
Activities Arts & crafts; Cards; Games; Reading groups; Prayer groups; Movies; Shopping trips; Kitchen groups; Exercise.

WINTERSVILLE

Forester Nursing Home Inc*
524 Canton Rd, Wintersville, OH, 43952
(614) 264-7788

Admin Ruth Eddy. *Medical Dir/Dir of Nursing* Carolyn Kennedy.
Licensure Nursing home. *Beds* 50.
Owner Proprietary Corp.
Admissions Requirements Minimum age 30; Medical examination; Physician's request.
Staff RNs 3 (ft), 1 (pt); LPNs 1 (ft), 3 (pt); Orderlies 1 (ft); Nurses aides 18 (ft), 5 (pt); Physical therapists 1 (pt); Speech therapists 1 (pt); Dentists 1 (pt); Ophthalmologists 1 (pt); Podiatrists 2 (pt).
Facilities Dining room; Activities room; Chapel; Crafts room; Laundry room; Barber/ Beauty shop.
Activities Arts & crafts; Cards; Games; Prayer groups; Movies; Shopping trips; Vegetable garden.

WOODSFIELD

Americare Woodsfield Nursing & Rehabilitation Center
Airport Rd, Woodsfield, OH, 43793
(614) 472-1678
Admin Mavis Wilson. *Medical Dir/Dir of Nursing* Dr Jack Matheny; Arlene Summers DON.
Licensure Skilled care; Intermediate care. *Beds* SNF 20; ICF 80. *Certified* Medicaid; Medicare.
Owner Proprietary Corp (Americare Corp).
Admissions Requirements Medical examination.
Staff Physicians; RNs; LPNs; Orderlies; Nurses aides; Physical therapists; Recreational therapists; Speech therapists; Activities coordinators; Dietitians; Dentists; Ophthalmologists; Podiatrists.
Facilities Dining room; Physical therapy room; Activities room; Laundry room; Barber/Beauty shop; Library.
Activities Arts & crafts; Cards; Games; Reading groups; Prayer groups; Movies; Shopping trips; Social/Cultural gatherings.

Monroe County Care Center
47045 Moore Ridge Road, Woodsfield, OH, 43793
(614) 472-0144
Admin Connie Hornbeck. *Medical Dir/Dir of Nursing* Donna Winland.
Licensure Intermediate care. *Beds* 49. *Certified* Medicaid.
Owner Nonprofit organization/foundation.
Admissions Requirements Females only.
Staff Physicians 2 (pt); RNs 1 (ft); LPNs 8 (ft); Nurses aides 30 (ft); Activities coordinators 1 (ft); Dietitians 1 (pt); Podiatrists 1 (pt).
Facilities Dining room; Activities room; Chapel; Laundry room; Barber/Beauty shop.
Activities Arts & crafts; Cards; Games; Prayer groups; Movies; Shopping trips.

WOODSTOCK

Fountain Park Nursing Home
1649 Park Rd, Woodstock, OH, 43084
(513) 826-3351
Admin Katherine B Engle. *Medical Dir/Dir of Nursing* Linda Strietenberger.
Licensure Skilled care; Intermediate care. *Beds* 51. *Certified* Medicaid; Medicare.
Owner Privately owned.
Staff Physicians 1 (ft); RNs 5 (ft); LPNs 6 (ft); Nurses aides 14 (ft); Recreational therapists 1 (ft); Activities coordinators 1 (ft).
Facilities Dining room; Physical therapy room; Activities room; Chapel; Crafts room; Laundry room; Barber/Beauty shop.
Activities Arts & crafts; Cards; Games; Reading groups; Prayer groups; Movies; Shopping trips; Social/Cultural gatherings.

WOOSTER

Glendora Nursing Home
1552 N Honeytown Rd, Wooster, OH, 44691
(216) 264-0912
Admin Robert Trivanovich.
Licensure Intermediate care. *Beds* ICF 36. *Certified* Medicaid.
Owner Proprietary Corp.
Admissions Requirements Medical examination.
Staff RNs 1 (pt); LPNs 2 (ft), 5 (pt); Nurses aides 11 (ft), 3 (pt); Activities coordinators 1 (pt); Dietitians 1 (pt); Social service 1 (pt).
Facilities Dining room; Activities room; Laundry room; Barber/Beauty shop.
Activities Arts & crafts; Cards; Games; Prayer groups; Movies; Shopping trips; Social/ Cultural gatherings.

Horn Nursing Home Inc
230 N Market St, Wooster, OH, 44691
(216) 262-2951
Admin Christopher Shook. *Medical Dir/Dir of Nursing* B J Stuart DON.
Licensure Intermediate care. *Beds* ICF 78. *Certified* Medicaid.
Owner Proprietary Corp.
Admissions Requirements Medical examination; Physician's request.
Staff RNs 3 (ft), 3 (pt); LPNs 4 (ft), 7 (pt); Orderlies 1 (ft); Nurses aides 21 (ft), 20 (pt); Physical therapists 1 (pt); Activities coordinators 1 (ft); Dietitians 1 (pt).
Facilities Dining room; Physical therapy room; Activities room; Chapel; Laundry room; Barber/Beauty shop; Library.
Activities Arts & crafts; Cards; Games; Reading groups; Prayer groups; Movies; Shopping trips; Social/Cultural gatherings; Spell down; Book reviews.

Smithville Western Care Center
4110 Smithville Western Rd, Wooster, OH, 44691
(216) 345-9050
Admin James M Horn. *Medical Dir/Dir of Nursing* John Robinson MD; Nancy Guldin RN DON.
Licensure Skilled care; Intermediate care. *Beds* 135. *Certified* Medicaid; Medicare.
Owner Proprietary Corp.
Admissions Requirements Medical examination; Physician's request.
Staff Physicians 1 (pt); RNs 3 (ft), 8 (pt); LPNs 8 (ft), 14 (pt); Nurses aides 23 (ft), 43 (pt); Physical therapists 1 (pt); Occupational therapists 1 (pt); Speech therapists 1 (pt); Activities coordinators 2 (pt); Dietitians 1 (pt); Dentists 1 (pt); Ophthalmologists 1 (pt); Podiatrists 1 (pt); Social service 1 (ft) Chaplain 1 (pt).
Facilities Dining room; Physical therapy room; Activities room; Chapel; Crafts room; Laundry room; Barber/Beauty shop; Private lounge.
Activities Arts & crafts; Cards; Games; Reading groups; Prayer groups; Movies; Group outings.

West View Manor Retirement Center
1715 Mechanicsburg Rd, Wooster, OH, 44691
(216) 264-8640
Admin Rev Gale D Crumrine. *Medical Dir/ Dir of Nursing* Marcella Lee RN.
Licensure Intermediate care; Rest home; Independent living. *Beds* ICF 93; Rest home 46; Independent living 18. *Certified* Medicaid.
Owner Nonprofit Corp.
Admissions Requirements Minimum age 62; Medical examination.
Staff RNs; LPNs; Orderlies; Nurses aides; Activities coordinators.
Affiliation Church of the Brethren
Facilities Dining room; Physical therapy room; Activities room; Chapel; Laundry room; Barber/Beauty shop.

Activities Arts & crafts; Cards; Games; Prayer groups; Movies; Bible study.

WORTHINGTON

Norworth Convalescent Center*
6830 High St, Worthington, OH, 43085
(614) 888-4553
Licensure Skilled care; Intermediate care. *Beds* 152. *Certified* Medicaid; Medicare.
Owner Proprietary Corp.

Willow Brook Christian Home
55 Lazelle Rd, Worthington, OH, 43085
(614) 885-3300
Admin Larry Harris. *Medical Dir/Dir of Nursing* Margaret Dronsfield DON.
Licensure Intermediate care. *Beds* ICF 50. *Certified* Medicaid.
Owner Nonprofit Corp.
Admissions Requirements Medical examination.
Staff RNs 2 (ft), 5 (pt); LPNs 3 (pt); Orderlies 1 (ft), 1 (pt); Nurses aides 6 (ft), 16 (pt); Physical therapists 1 (pt); Activities coordinators 1 (ft), 1 (pt); Dietitians 1 (pt).
Affiliation Church of Christ
Facilities Dining room; Physical therapy room; Activities room; Chapel; Crafts room; Laundry room; Barber/Beauty shop.
Activities Arts & crafts; Cards; Games; Reading groups; Prayer groups; Movies; Shopping trips; Social/Cultural gatherings.

Worthington Nursing & Convalescent Center*
1030 N High St, Worthington, OH, 43085
(614) 885-0408
Licensure Skilled care; Intermediate care. *Beds* 100. *Certified* Medicaid; Medicare.
Owner Proprietary Corp.

XENIA

Greenewood Manor
711 Dayton-Xenia Rd, Xenia, OH, 45385
(513) 376-7550
Admin N Caroline Frost. *Medical Dir/Dir of Nursing* R D Hendrickson MD; Wretha Haines RN DON.
Licensure Skilled care; Intermediate care. *Beds* SNF 100; ICF 100. *Certified* Medicaid; Medicare.
Owner Proprietary Corp (Blackeye Fam/ Nursing Hm).
Admissions Requirements Medical examination.
Staff RNs 5 (ft), 10 (pt); LPNs 5 (ft), 8 (pt); Nurses aides 26 (ft), 38 (pt); Physical therapists; Occupational therapists; Speech therapists; Activities coordinators 1 (ft); Dietitians; Ophthalmologists; Social workers 2 (ft).
Facilities Dining room; Physical therapy room; Activities room; Chapel; Crafts room; Laundry room; Barber/Beauty shop; Library.
Activities Arts & crafts; Cards; Games; Reading groups; Movies; Shopping trips; Social/Cultural gatherings; Pet therapy.

Heathergreene I*
126 Wilson Dr, Xenia, OH, 45385
(513) 376-2121
Licensure Skilled care; Intermediate care. *Beds* 100. *Certified* Medicaid; Medicare.
Owner Proprietary Corp.

Hospitality Home East*
1301 Monroe Dr, Xenia, OH, 45385
(513) 372-4495
Licensure Skilled care; Intermediate care. *Beds* 100. *Certified* Medicaid; Medicare.
Owner Proprietary Corp (Hannover Healthcare).

Hospitality Home West*
1384 Monroe Dr, Xenia, OH, 45385
(513) 372-8081

Licensure Skilled care; Intermediate care. *Beds* 90. *Certified* Medicaid; Medicare.
Owner Proprietary Corp (Hannover Healthcare).

Residential Services of Greene County Inc
115 Fairground Rd, Xenia, OH, 45385
(513) 376-3996
Admin Bethanne K Cliffe. *Medical Dir/Dir of Nursing* Fred Stockwell MD; Lesley Davis LPN DON.
Licensure Intermediate care for mentally retarded. *Beds* ICF/MR 3 8-bed group homes. *Certified* Medicaid.
Owner Nonprofit Corp.
Admissions Requirements Minimum age 18; Medical examination.
Staff Physicians 2 (pt); RNs 1 (pt); LPNs 1 (ft), 5 (pt); Physical therapists 1 (pt); Occupational therapists 1 (pt); Speech therapists 1 (pt); Dietitians 1 (pt); Dentists 1 (pt); Ophthalmologists 1 (pt); Podiatrists 1 (pt).
Languages Sign
Activities Movies; Shopping trips; Social/ Cultural gatherings.

YELLOW SPRINGS

Friends Care Center
150 E Herman St, Yellow Springs, OH, 45387
(513) 767-7363
Admin Don Brezine. *Medical Dir/Dir of Nursing* Carl Hyde MD; Dee Kennedy RN DON.
Licensure Skilled care; Intermediate care. *Beds* SNF 66; ICF 66. *Certified* Medicaid; Medicare.
Owner Nonprofit Corp.
Staff Physicians 1 (pt); RNs 6 (ft), 2 (pt); LPNs 6 (ft); Nurses aides 21 (ft), 20 (pt); Physical therapists 1 (ft); Occupational therapists 1 (pt); Speech therapists 1 (pt); Activities coordinators 2 (pt); Dietitians 1 (pt).
Facilities Dining room; Physical therapy room; Activities room; Chapel; Crafts room; Laundry room; Barber/Beauty shop; Library.
Activities Arts & crafts; Cards; Games; Reading groups; Prayer groups; Movies; Shopping trips; Social/Cultural gatherings.

YORKVILLE

Ford-Hull-Mar Nursing Home
212 4th St, Yorkville, OH, 43971
(614) 859-6496
Admin Hazel A Marinsnick. *Medical Dir/Dir of Nursing* Dr Mejia; Judy Fowler RN.
Licensure Intermediate care. *Beds* ICF 21. *Certified* Medicaid; Medicare.
Owner Nonprofit organization/foundation.
Admissions Requirements Minimum age 18; Medical examination; Physician's request.
Staff Physicians 1 (ft); RNs 1 (ft); LPNs 3 (ft), 1 (pt); Orderlies 1 (ft), 1 (pt); Nurses aides 3 (ft), 2 (pt); Physical therapists 1 (pt); Recreational therapists 1 (pt); Activities coordinators 2 (pt); Dietitians 1 (ft); Dentists 1 (pt); Ophthalmologists 1 (pt).
Facilities Dining room; Activities room; Chapel; Crafts room; Laundry room; Library.
Activities Arts & crafts; Cards; Games; Reading groups; Prayer groups; Movies; Shopping trips; Social/Cultural gatherings.

YOUNGSTOWN

Ashley Place Health Care Inc
PO Box 4240, 491 Ashley Cir, Youngstown, OH, 44515
(216) 793-3010
Admin Patricia Andrews. *Medical Dir/Dir of Nursing* Dr Joseph Ambrose; Julie Evancho RN DON.

Licensure Skilled care; Intermediate care. *Beds* SNF 47; ICF 53. *Certified* Medicaid; Medicare.
Owner Privately owned.
Staff RNs; LPNs; Orderlies; Nurses aides; Activities coordinators.
Facilities Dining room; Physical therapy room; Activities room; Crafts room; Laundry room; Barber/Beauty shop.
Activities Arts & crafts; Cards; Games; Reading groups; Prayer groups; Movies; Shopping trips.

Assumption Nursing Home
550 W Chalmers Ave, Youngstown, OH, 44511
(216) 743-1186
Admin Robert J Sherrin. *Medical Dir/Dir of Nursing* Dr Nicholas Garritano; Sr Mary Edwin DON.
Licensure Intermediate care. *Beds* ICF 126. *Certified* Medicaid.
Owner Nonprofit Corp.
Admissions Requirements Medical examination; Physician's request.
Facilities Dining room; Physical therapy room; Activities room; Chapel; Crafts room; Laundry room; Barber/Beauty shop; Library.
Activities Arts & crafts; Cards; Games; Reading groups; Movies; Shopping trips; Social/Cultural gatherings.

Camelot Arms Care Center
2958 Canfield Rd, Youngstown, OH, 44511
(216) 792-5511
Admin Frederick F Mattix Jr. *Medical Dir/Dir of Nursing* Sally Marx.
Licensure Intermediate care. *Beds* ICF 100. *Certified* Medicaid; Medicare.
Owner Proprietary Corp (American Health Care Centers).
Admissions Requirements Medical examination.
Staff Physicians 1 (ft), 4 (pt); RNs 4 (ft), 1 (pt); LPNs 6 (ft), 4 (pt); Orderlies 4 (ft), 2 (pt); Nurses aides 15 (ft), 20 (pt); Physical therapists 1 (ft), 1 (pt); Speech therapists 1 (ft); Activities coordinators 1 (ft), 1 (pt); Dietitians 2 (ft); Dentists 1 (pt); Ophthalmologists 1 (ft).
Languages Spanish, Italian, Swahili
Facilities Dining room; Physical therapy room; Activities room; Laundry room; Barber/Beauty shop.
Activities Arts & crafts; Cards; Games; Reading groups; Prayer groups; Movies; Shopping trips; Social/Cultural gatherings.

Colonial Manor Nursing Home
196 Colonial Dr, Youngstown, OH, 44505
(216) 759-3790
Admin Richard L Macaluso. *Medical Dir/Dir of Nursing* Brian Gordon MD; Mary Agnes Turkiewicz RN.
Licensure Skilled care; Intermediate care. *Beds* SNF 100. *Certified* Medicaid; Medicare.
Owner Proprietary Corp (Horizon Healthcare Corp).
Staff Physicians 2 (pt); RNs 3 (ft), 6 (pt); LPNs 6 (ft), 5 (pt); Nurses aides 24 (ft), 10 (pt); Physical therapists 1 (ft); Reality therapists 1 (ft); Recreational therapists 1 (pt); Occupational therapists 1 (pt); Speech therapists 1 (pt); Activities coordinators 1 (ft); Dietitians 1 (pt); Ophthalmologists 1 (pt); Podiatrists 1 (pt).
Facilities Dining room; Physical therapy room; Activities room; Chapel; Crafts room; Laundry room; Barber/Beauty shop.
Activities Arts & crafts; Cards; Games; Reading groups; Prayer groups; Movies; Shopping trips; Social/Cultural gatherings; Exercise program.

Danridge Nursing Home
1825 Oakhill Ave, Youngstown, OH, 44507
(216) 746-5157

Admin Ezell Armour. *Medical Dir/Dir of Nursing* Lorie Mickel.
Licensure Intermediate care. *Beds* 32. *Certified* Medicaid; Medicare.
Owner Privately owned.
Admissions Requirements Medical examination.
Staff Physicians 1 (ft); RNs 1 (ft); LPNs 3 (ft), 3 (pt); Orderlies 1 (ft); Nurses aides 6 (ft), 2 (pt); Activities coordinators 1 (ft); Dietitians 1 (ft); Ophthalmologists 1 (ft).
Facilities Dining room; Activities room; Laundry room.
Activities Arts & crafts; Games; Movies; Shopping trips; Social/Cultural gatherings.

Gateways to Better Living 1*
1406 5th Ave, Youngstown, OH, 44504
(216) 792-2854
Licensure Intermediate care for mentally retarded. *Beds* 10.
Owner Nonprofit Corp.
Admissions Requirements Minimum age 14.
Staff Physicians 1 (pt); RNs 1 (pt); LPNs 1 (pt); Recreational therapists 1 (pt); Speech therapists 1 (pt); Activities coordinators 1 (pt); Dietitians 1 (pt); Audiologists 1 (pt).
Facilities Dining room.
Activities Arts & crafts; Cards; Games; Reading groups; Movies; Shopping trips; Social/Cultural gatherings.

Gateways to Better Living 3*
1934 Volney Rd, Youngstown, OH, 44511
(216) 792-2854
Licensure Intermediate care for mentally retarded. *Beds* 12.
Owner Nonprofit Corp.
Admissions Requirements Minimum age 14.
Staff Physicians 1 (pt); RNs 1 (pt); LPNs 1 (pt); Recreational therapists 1 (pt); Speech therapists 1 (pt); Activities coordinators 1 (pt); Dietitians 1 (pt); Audiologists 1 (pt).
Facilities Dining room; Library.
Activities Arts & crafts; Cards; Games; Reading groups; Movies; Shopping trips; Social/Cultural gatherings.

Gateways to Better Living Inc—No 9*
660 Early Rd, Youngstown, OH, 44505
Licensure Intermediate care for mentally retarded. *Beds* 11. *Certified* Medicaid.
Owner Publicly owned.

Gateways to Better Living 16
359 Redondo Rd, Youngstown, OH, 44504
(216) 792-2854
Admin Dennis Allen. *Medical Dir/Dir of Nursing* Edgar Kornhauser DO; Karen Potts RN DON.
Licensure Intermediate care for mentally retarded. *Beds* ICF/MR 8. *Certified* Medicaid.
Owner Nonprofit Corp.
Admissions Requirements Minimum age 14; Females only; Medical examination.
Staff Physicians 1 (pt); RNs 1 (pt); LPNs 1 (pt); Nurses aides 4 (ft), 2 (pt); Recreational therapists 1 (pt); Speech therapists 1 (pt); Activities coordinators 1 (pt); Dietitians 1 (pt); Dentists 1 (pt); Ophthalmologists 1 (pt); Podiatrists 1 (pt); Medical specialist; Dentist; Social services; Counselors; Psychologist.
Facilities Dining room; Activities room; Crafts room; Laundry room.
Activities Arts & crafts; Games; Movies; Shopping trips; Social/Cultural gatherings; Habilitation services; Therapeutic services; Recreation/leisure time activities.

Heritage Manor
517 Gypsy Lane, Box 449, Youngstown, OH, 44501
(216) 746-1076
Admin Gary Weiss. *Medical Dir/Dir of Nursing* William D Loeser; Helen Schreiner DON.

Licensure Skilled care. *Beds* SNF 72. *Certified* Medicaid; Medicare.
Owner Nonprofit Corp.
Admissions Requirements Physician's request.
Staff Physicians 2 (pt); RNs 5 (ft), 3 (pt); LPNs 3 (ft), 1 (pt); Nurses aides 21 (ft), 1 (pt); Recreational therapists 1 (ft), 2 (pt); Occupational therapists 1 (pt); Speech therapists 1 (pt); Activities coordinators 1 (pt); Dietitians 1 (pt); Ophthalmologists 1 (pt).
Languages German, Yiddish, Hebrew, Russian, Hungarian
Affiliation Jewish
Facilities Dining room; Physical therapy room; Activities room; Chapel; Crafts room; Laundry room; Barber/Beauty shop.
Activities Arts & crafts; Cards; Games; Reading groups; Movies; Shopping trips; Social/Cultural gatherings.

Little Forest Medical Center*
5665 South Ave, Youngstown, OH, 44512
(216) 782-1173
Licensure Skilled care; Intermediate care. *Beds* 221. *Certified* Medicaid; Medicare.
Owner Proprietary Corp.

Manor House, Inc
259 Park Ave, Youngstown, OH, 44504
(216) 746-0043
Admin Mary Ann Robb. *Medical Dir/Dir of Nursing* Dr Ronald Fasline; Mrs Diane Wylie.
Licensure ICF Mild mental. *Beds* ICF Mild Mental 21. *Certified* Medicaid.
Owner Proprietary Corp.
Admissions Requirements Minimum age 30; Medical examination.
Staff Physicians 1 (pt); RNs 1 (pt); LPNs 3 (ft), 3 (pt); Nurses aides 5 (ft); Activities coordinators 1 (ft); Dietitians 1 (pt).
Facilities Dining room; Activities room; Laundry room.
Activities Arts & crafts; Cards; Games; Reading groups; Prayer groups; Movies; Shopping trips; Social/Cultural gatherings.

Millcreek Manor*
PO Box 3085, 721 Cohasset Dr, Youngstown, OH, 44511
(216) 747-6277
Licensure Intermediate care. *Beds* 20. *Certified* Medicaid.
Owner Proprietary Corp.

North Manor Center
115 Illinois Ave, Youngstown, OH, 44504
(216) 744-0188
Admin Edward J Fabian. *Medical Dir/Dir of Nursing* Karapenini Prasad MD; Carrie Bender DON.
Licensure Intermediate care. *Beds* ICF 100. *Certified* Medicaid.
Owner Proprietary Corp.
Admissions Requirements Minimum age 40; Medical examination.
Staff RNs 2 (ft); LPNs 10 (ft); Orderlies 6 (ft); Nurses aides 32 (ft); Recreational therapists 1 (ft); Speech therapists 1 (pt); Activities coordinators 2 (ft); Dietitians 1 (pt); Ophthalmologists 1 (pt).
Facilities Dining room; Activities room; Crafts room; Laundry room; Barber/Beauty shop; Library.
Activities Arts & crafts; Cards; Games; Reading groups; Prayer groups; Movies; Shopping trips; Social/Cultural gatherings.

North Side Nursing Home*
PO Box 2287, 480 Lora Ave, Youngstown, OH, 44504
(216) 743-5235
Licensure Intermediate care. *Beds* 31. *Certified* Medicaid.
Owner Proprietary Corp.

Omni Manor*
3245 Vestal Rd, Youngstown, OH, 44509
(216) 793-5648
Licensure Skilled care; Intermediate care. *Beds* 100. *Certified* Medicaid; Medicare.
Owner Proprietary Corp.

Paisley House for Aged Women*
1408 Mahoning Ave, Youngstown, OH, 44509
(216) 799-9431
Licensure Rest home. *Beds* 20.
Owner Proprietary Corp.
Admissions Requirements Females only.

Park Vista Retirement Community
1216 Fifth Ave, Youngstown, OH, 44504
(216) 746-2944
Admin David F Johnson Exec Dir. *Medical Dir/Dir of Nursing* James L Smeltzer MD; Shirley Armour RNC.
Licensure Skilled care; Intermediate care. *Beds* SNF 49; ICF 49. *Certified* Medicaid; Medicare.
Owner Nonprofit Corp (OH Presbyterian Homes).
Admissions Requirements Minimum age 65; Medical examination.
Staff Physicians 2 (pt); RNs 11 (ft), 7 (pt); LPNs 9 (ft), 11 (pt); Orderlies 3 (ft); Nurses aides 41 (ft), 7 (pt); Physical therapists 1 (pt); Speech therapists 1 (pt); Activities coordinators 1 (ft); Dietitians 1 (pt); Ophthalmologists 1 (pt); Dentist 1 (pt).
Affiliation Presbyterian
Facilities Dining room; Physical therapy room; Activities room; Chapel; Crafts room; Laundry room; Barber/Beauty shop; Library.
Activities Arts & crafts; Cards; Games; Reading groups; Prayer groups; Movies; Shopping trips; Social/Cultural gatherings; Trips to local entertainment; Sightseeing.

Ridgewood Nursing Center Inc*
1012 Glenwood Ave, Youngstown, OH, 44502
Licensure Intermediate care. *Beds* 38. *Certified* Medicaid.
Owner Proprietary Corp.

Seven Gables*
Box 2249, 264 Broadway Ave, Youngstown, OH, 44504
Licensure Intermediate care. *Beds* 28. *Certified* Medicaid.
Owner Proprietary Corp.

Sleigh Bell Residence
461 S Canfield-Niles Rd, Youngstown, OH, 44515
(216) 799-9791
Admin Carl L Casale.
Licensure Intermediate care. *Beds* ICF 98. *Certified* Medicaid.
Owner Proprietary Corp.
Staff RNs 8 (ft); LPNs 10 (ft); Nurses aides 60 (ft), 20 (pt); Physical therapists 1 (pt); Activities coordinators 1 (ft), 1 (pt); Dietitians & Aides 10 (ft).
Facilities Dining room; Physical therapy room; Activities room; Crafts room; Barber/Beauty shop.
Activities Arts & crafts; Cards; Games; Reading groups; Prayer groups; Movies; Shopping trips; Social/Cultural gatherings; Picnics; Shopping trips.

Windsor House
1735 Belmont Ave, Youngstown, OH, 44504
(216) 743-1393
Admin George Panno. *Medical Dir/Dir of Nursing* Dr Joseph Mersol MD; Gerri House DON.
Licensure Skilled care; Intermediate care. *Beds* 109. *Certified* Medicaid; Medicare.
Owner Proprietary Corp.
Admissions Requirements Medical examination.

Staff Physicians; RNs; LPNs; Orderlies;
Nurses aides; Physical therapists;
Occupational therapists; Speech therapists;
Activities coordinators; Dietitians;
Ophthalmologists.
Facilities Dining room; Physical therapy
room; Activities room; Crafts room; Laundry
room; Barber/Beauty shop.
Activities Arts & crafts; Cards; Games;
Reading groups; Prayer groups; Movies;
Shopping trips; Social/Cultural gatherings.

ZANESVILLE

Cedar Hill Care Center
PO Box 3326, Zanesville, OH, 43701
Beds 104.

Drake Nursing Home
750 Findley Ave, Zanesville, OH, 43701
(614) 452-3449
Admin Philip Drake. *Medical Dir/Dir of
Nursing* Carolee Frank.
Licensure Intermediate care. *Beds* 30.
Certified Medicaid.
Owner Privately owned.
Admissions Requirements Medical
examination.
Staff Physicians 1 (pt); RNs 1 (ft); LPNs 2
(ft), 4 (pt); Nurses aides 4 (ft), 5 (pt);
Activities coordinators 1 (pt); Dietitians 1
(pt).
Facilities Dining room; Activities room.
Activities Arts & crafts; Cards; Games;
Reading groups; Prayer groups.

Good Samaritan Medical Center
800 Forest Ave, Zanesville, OH, 43701
(614) 454-5000
Admin Daniel Rissing. *Medical Dir/Dir of
Nursing* Robert Thompson MD; Ed Fell
RN.
Licensure Skilled care; Intermediate care. *Beds*
SNF 18; ICF. *Certified* Medicare.
Owner Nonprofit organization/foundation.
Admissions Requirements Physician's request.
Staff RNs 2 (ft), 4 (pt); LPNs 5 (ft), 7 (pt);
Nurses aides 2 (ft), 3 (pt); Physical therapists
1 (pt); Occupational therapists 1 (pt); Speech
therapists 1 (pt); Activities coordinators 1
(pt); Dietitians 1 (pt).
Affiliation Roman Catholic

Facilities Dining room; Physical therapy
room; Activities room; Chapel; Laundry
room; Barber/Beauty shop; Library.
Activities Art: & crafts; Cards; Games;
Reading groups; Prayer groups; Movies;
Social/Cultural gatherings; Orientation
group.

Ohio District Council Nursing*
3125 E Pike, Zanesville, OH, 43701
(614) 452-4351
Medical Dir/Dir of Nursing Dr Eugene
Capocasale.
Licensure Skilled care; Intermediate care. *Beds*
100. *Certified* Medicaid; Medicare.
Owner Proprietary Corp.
Admissions Requirements Medical
examination; Physician's request.
Staff Physicians 1 (ft); RNs 3 (ft), 2 (pt);
LPNs 13 (ft); Physical therapists 1 (pt);
Reality therapists 2 (ft); Recreational
therapists 2 (ft); Occupational therapists;
Speech therapists; Activities coordinators 2
(ft); Dietitians; Dentists; Ophthalmologists;
Podiatrists; Audiologists.
Facilities Dining room; Physical therapy
room; Activities room; Chapel; Crafts room;
Laundry room; Barber/Beauty shop; Library.
Activities Arts & crafts; Cards; Games; Prayer
groups; Movies; Shopping trips; Social/
Cultural gatherings.

Helen Purcell Home
1854 Norwood Blvd, Zanesville, OH, 43701
(614) 453-1745
Licensure Home for aged. *Beds* 74.
Owner Nonprofit Corp.
Admissions Requirements Medical
examination.
Staff Physicians 1 (pt); RNs 1 (ft), 1 (pt);
LPNs 3 (ft), 4 (pt); Nurses aides 7 (ft), 5
(pt); Dietitians 1 (pt).
Facilities Dining room; Laundry room;
Barber/Beauty shop; Library.
Activities Arts & crafts; Cards; Prayer groups;
Shopping trips; Social/Cultural gatherings.

Sunny View Nursing Home
2991 Maple Ave, Zanesville, OH, 43701
(614) 454-4663
Admin Roger E Drake. *Medical Dir/Dir of
Nursing* Joe Booth MD; Lisa Feldner RN.
Licensure Skilled care. *Beds* 100.

Owner Nonprofit Corp.
Staff Physicians 1 (ft); RNs 1 (ft), 3 (pt);
LPNs 5 (ft), 3 (pt); Activities coordinators 2 (ft); Dietitians
1 (pt).
Facilities Dining room; Activities room;
Laundry room; Barber/Beauty shop; Garden;
Patios.
Activities Arts & crafts; Cards; Games; Prayer
groups; Movies; Shopping trips; Adult day
care program.

Willow Haven Nursing Home*
1122 Taylor St, Zanesville, OH, 43701
(614) 454-9747
Medical Dir/Dir of Nursing Dr David Klein.
Licensure Intermediate care. *Beds* 100.
Certified Medicaid.
Owner Proprietary Corp.
Admissions Requirements Minimum age 18;
Medical examination.
Staff RNs 3 (ft), 3 (pt); LPNs 6 (ft), 1 (pt);
Orderlies 1 (ft); Nurses aides 38 (ft), 15 (pt);
Physical therapists 1 (pt); Reality therapists
2 (ft); Recreational therapists 2 (ft);
Dietitians 1 (ft).
Facilities Dining room; Physical therapy
room; Activities room; Crafts room; Laundry
room; Barber/Beauty shop; Library.
Activities Arts & crafts; Cards; Games;
Reading groups; Prayer groups; Social/
Cultural gatherings.

Winter House*
1856 Adams Ln, Zanesville, OH, 43701
(614) 454-9769
Medical Dir/Dir of Nursing Thomas P
Forrestal MD.
Licensure Skilled care; Intermediate care. *Beds*
101. *Certified* Medicaid; Medicare.
Owner Proprietary Corp (Arbor Health Care).
Staff Physicians 1 (pt); RNs 4 (ft), 3 (pt);
LPNs 6 (ft), 1 (pt); Orderlies 4 (ft); Nurses
aides 41 (ft), 8 (pt); Activities coordinators 3
(ft); Dietitians 11 (ft).
Facilities Dining room; Activities room;
Crafts room; Laundry room; Barber/Beauty
shop.
Activities Arts & crafts; Cards; Games;
Reading groups; Prayer groups; Movies;
Shopping trips; Social/Cultural gatherings.

OKLAHOMA

ADA

Ada Retirement & Care Center*
PO Box 1185, 931 N Country Club Rd, Ada,
OK, 74820
(405) 332-3631
Admin Gussie J Corvin.
Licensure Intermediate care. *Beds* 85.
Certified Medicaid.

Ballard Nursing Center*
210 W 5th, Ada, OK, 74820
(405) 436-1414
Admin Gary Reed.
Licensure Intermediate care. *Beds* 73.
Certified Medicaid.

Jan Frances Care Center
815 N Country Club Rd, Ada, OK, 74820
(405) 332-5328
Admin Alandra Needham. *Medical Dir/Dir of
Nursing* Dr Martin Stokes.
Licensure Intermediate care. *Beds* ICF 120.
Certified Medicaid.
Owner Proprietary Corp (Beverly Enterprises).
Admissions Requirements Minimum age 18;
Physician's request.
Staff Physicians 6 (ft); RNs 1 (ft); LPNs 6 (ft),
4 (pt); Orderlies 5 (ft); Nurses aides 25 (ft),
25 (pt); Physical therapists 1 (ft), 1 (pt);
Reality therapists 1 (ft); Activities
coordinators 1 (ft); Dietitians 1 (ft).
Facilities Dining room; Physical therapy
room; Activities room; Chapel; Crafts room;
Laundry room; Barber/Beauty shop.
Activities Arts & crafts; Cards; Games;
Reading groups; Prayer groups; Movies;
Shopping trips; Social/Cultural gatherings.

McCalls Chapel School Inc
PO Box 232, Rte 7, Ada, OK, 74820
(405) 436-0373
Admin Ray G Lindsay. *Medical Dir/Dir of
Nursing* George K Stephens MD.
Licensure Intermediate care for mentally
retarded. *Beds* ICF/MR 98; Room & board
60. *Certified* Medicaid.
Owner Nonprofit Corp.
Admissions Requirements Minimum age 14;
Medical examination.
Staff LPNs; Nurses aides; Recreational
therapists.
Facilities Dining room; Activities room;
Crafts room; Laundry room; Barber/Beauty
shop; Library Gym; Classrooms.
Activities Arts & crafts; Games; Reading
groups; Prayer groups; Movies; Shopping
trips; Social/Cultural gatherings.

ALLEN

Woodland Hills Nursing Center*
200 N Easton, Allen, OK, 74825
(405) 857-2472
Admin Buford K Canaday.
Licensure Intermediate care. *Beds* 49.
Certified Medicaid.

ALTUS

Altus Home Nursing Home*
1059 E Pecan, Altus, OK, 73521
(405) 482-8342
Admin LaVerne Jackson.
Licensure Intermediate care. *Beds* 90.
Certified Medicaid.
Owner Proprietary Corp (Amity Care).
Admissions Requirements Medical
examination.
Staff RNs 1 (ft); LPNs 3 (ft); Nurses aides 23
(ft), 2 (pt); Activities coordinators 1 (ft);
Dietitians 1 (pt).
Facilities Dining room; Activities room;
Crafts room; Barber/Beauty shop.
Activities Arts & crafts; Games; Reading
groups; Prayer groups; Social/Cultural
gatherings.

English Village Manor Inc*
1515 Canterbury, Altus, OK, 73521
(405) 477-1133
Admin LaVerne Jackson.
Licensure Intermediate care. *Beds* 128.
Certified Medicaid.

Park Lane Manor*
702 N Park Lane, Altus, OK, 73521
(405) 482-8800
Admin Billy R Jones.
Licensure Intermediate care. *Beds* 55.
Certified Medicaid.

ALVA

Beadles Rest Home*
916 Noble, Alva, OK, 73717
(405) 327-1274
Admin Ruth Heitt.
Licensure Intermediate care. *Beds* 64.
Certified Medicaid.
Admissions Requirements Medical
examination; Physician's request.
Staff RNs 2 (ft); LPNs 2 (ft), 1 (pt); Orderlies
2 (ft); Nurses aides 16 (ft); Activities
coordinators 1 (ft); Dietitians 1 (pt).
Facilities Dining room; Activities room;
Library.
Activities Arts & crafts; Cards; Games;
Reading groups; Prayer groups; Movies;
Shopping trips; Special days each month.

Share Medical Center
730 Share Dr, Alva, OK, 73717
(405) 327-2800
Admin Jane Gaskill. *Medical Dir/Dir of
Nursing* Kirt Bierig MD.
Licensure Intermediate care. *Beds* ICF 80.
Certified Medicaid.
Owner Nonprofit organization/foundation.
Admissions Requirements Medical
examination.
Staff RNs 1 (pt); LPNs 3 (ft), 1 (pt); Orderlies
1 (pt); Physical therapists 1 (pt); Activities
coordinators 1 (ft); Dietitians 1 (ft).
Languages Spanish

Facilities Dining room; Physical therapy
room; Chapel; Barber/Beauty shop; Library;
Solarium; Van.
Activities Arts & crafts; Cards; Games; Prayer
groups; Movies; Shopping trips; Social/
Cultural gatherings; Intergenerational
programs with children.

ANADARKO

Friendship Manor*
201 W Kansas, Anadarko, OK, 73005
(405) 247-6611
Admin Charlotte Gibbs.
Licensure Intermediate care. *Beds* 224.
Certified Medicaid.

Silver Crest Manor Inc*
300 W Washington, Anadarko, OK, 73005
(405) 247-3347
Admin Wanda Silvers.
Licensure Intermediate care. *Beds* 92.
Certified Medicaid.

ANTLERS

Antlers Nursing Home*
507 E Main, Antlers, OK, 74523
(405) 298-3294
Admin Kathy Hannan Young.
Licensure Intermediate care. *Beds* 133.
Certified Medicaid.

ARDMORE

Ardmore Memorial Convalescent Home*
1037 15th NW, Ardmore, OK, 73401
(405) 223-8304
Admin Eugene Lutts.
Licensure Intermediate care. *Beds* 56.
Certified Medicaid.

Elmbrook Home*
1811 9th NW, Ardmore, OK, 73401
(405) 223-3303
Admin Bob Walker.
Licensure Intermediate care. *Beds* 100.
Certified Medicaid.

Lakeland Manor Inc*
604 Lake Murray Dr, Ardmore, OK, 73401
(405) 223-4501
Admin Michael Stringer.
Licensure Intermediate care. *Beds* 32.
Certified Medicaid.

Lu-Ken Manor*
832 Isabel SW, Ardmore, OK, 73401
(405) 223-5901
Admin James A Kenaga.
Licensure Intermediate care. *Beds* 104.
Certified Medicaid.

Silver Star Nursing Home
111 13th NW, Ardmore, OK, 73401
(405) 223-4803
Admin John D Mackey. *Medical Dir/Dir of
Nursing* Marian Ross LPN.

Licensure Intermediate care. *Beds* ICF 76.
Certified Medicaid.
Owner Privately owned.
Admissions Requirements Medical
examination; Physician's request.
Staff LPNs 4 (ft); Nurses aides 10 (ft);
Activities coordinators 1 (ft); Dietitians 1
(ft).
Facilities Dining room; Crafts room; Laundry
room; Barber/Beauty shop; Lobby.
Activities Arts & crafts; Cards; Games;
Reading groups; Prayer groups; Movies;
Shopping trips; Social/Cultural gatherings;
Bingo; Cooking class; Exercise; Beauty shop.

Woodview Home
1630 3rd NE, Ardmore, OK, 73401
(405) 226-5454
Admin Kenneth Walker. *Medical Dir/Dir of
Nursing* Melinda Blessing LPN.
Licensure Intermediate care. *Beds* ICF 43.
Certified Medicaid.
Owner Proprietary Corp.
Admissions Requirements Medical
examination; Physician's request.
Staff RNs 1 (pt); LPNs 3 (ft); Nurses aides 13
(ft); Physical therapists 1 (pt); Speech
therapists 1 (pt); Activities coordinators 1
(ft); Dietitians 1 (pt).
Facilities Dining room; Physical therapy
room; Activities room; Crafts room; Laundry
room; Barber/Beauty shop.
Activities Arts & crafts; Cards; Games;
Reading groups; Prayer groups; Movies;
Shopping trips; Social/Cultural gatherings;
Exercise class; Western day; Hawaiian luau.

ARKOMA

Medi-Home of Arkoma Inc
PO Box AJ, Arkoma, OK, 74901
(918) 875-3107
Admin Harold Babb. *Medical Dir/Dir of
Nursing* Cerise Travis RN DON.
Licensure Intermediate care. *Beds* ICF 56.
Certified Medicaid.
Owner Proprietary Corp.
Admissions Requirements Medical
examination; Physician's request.
Staff RNs 1 (ft); LPNs 4 (ft); Nurses aides 8
(ft); Activities coordinators 1 (ft); Dietitians
1 (ft).
Facilities Dining room; Chapel; Laundry
room; Barber/Beauty shop.
Activities Arts & crafts; Cards; Games;
Reading groups; Prayer groups; Movies.

ATOKA

Atoka Care Center*
323 W 6th, Atoka, OK, 74525
(405) 889-3373
Admin Beatrice Maxey. *Medical Dir/Dir of
Nursing* Edna Sheffield.
Licensure Intermediate care. *Beds* 96.
Certified Medicaid.
Admissions Requirements Medical
examination; Physician's request.

Atoka Colonial Manor Inc*
100 Virginia St, Atoka, OK, 74525
(405) 889-7341, 7342
Admin Louise Moore.
Licensure Intermediate care. *Beds* 80.
Certified Medicaid.

Plantation Manor Inc*
505 E "B" St, Atoka, OK, 74525
(405) 889-2517
Admin Mona A Simpson.
Licensure Intermediate care. *Beds* 85.
Certified Medicaid.
Admissions Requirements Minimum age 19;
Medical examination; Physician's request.
Staff RNs 1 (pt); LPNs 2 (ft); Nurses aides 23
(ft); Activities coordinators 1 (ft); Dietitians
1 (pt).

Facilities Dining room; Physical therapy
room; Activities room; Crafts room; Laundry
room.
Activities Arts & crafts; Cards; Games;
Reading groups; Shopping trips; Social/
Cultural gatherings.

BARNSDALL

Barnsdall Nursing Home
411 S 4th St, Barnsdall, OK, 74002
(918) 847-2826
Admin June Miller. *Medical Dir/Dir of
Nursing* Marjorie Schneider LPN.
Licensure Intermediate care. *Beds* ICF 40.
Certified Medicaid.
Owner Privately owned.
Admissions Requirements Medical
examination.
Staff Physicians 1 (ft), 1 (pt); RNs 1 (pt);
LPNs 3 (ft), 1 (pt); Nurses aides 12 (ft), 10
(pt); Activities coordinators 1 (ft); Dietitians
1 (ft).
Facilities Dining room; Activities room;
Laundry room; Barber/Beauty shop.
Activities Arts & crafts; Cards; Games;
Reading groups; Prayer groups; Movies;
Shopping trips; Social/Cultural gatherings.

BARTLESVILLE

Heritage House Nursing Home
1244 Woodland Loop, Bartlesville, OK,
74006-5223
(918) 336-1821
Admin M Colleen Jones.
Licensure Intermediate care. *Beds* 67.
Certified Medicaid.
Staff RNs 1 (pt); LPNs 6 (ft); Nurses aides 28
(ft); Physical therapists 1 (pt); Activities
coordinators 1 (ft); Dietitians 1 (pt).
Facilities Dining room; Physical therapy
room; Activities room; Crafts room; Laundry
room; Barber/Beauty shop; Library.
Activities Arts & crafts; Cards; Games;
Reading groups; Prayer groups; Movies;
Shopping trips; Social/Cultural gatherings.

**Heritage Manor Nursing & Convalescent
Center***
215 SE Howard, Bartlesville, OK, 74003
(918) 333-9545
Admin Paul A Roll.
Licensure Intermediate care. *Beds* 126.
Certified Medicaid.

BEAVER

Beaver County Nursing Home*
200 E 8th, Beaver, OK, 73932
(405) 625-4571
Admin LaVern Melton.
Licensure Intermediate care. *Beds* 62.
Certified Medicaid.

BEGGS

Beggs Nursing Home*
7th & Cherokee, Beggs, OK, 74421
(918) 267-3362
Admin Judy McKee.
Licensure Intermediate care. *Beds* 50.
Certified Medicaid.

BETHANY

Bethany Village Health Care Center
6900 NW 39th Expwy, Bethany, OK, 73008
(405) 495-6110
Admin Jan Prolst. *Medical Dir/Dir of Nursing*
John Pittman MD; Jana Gourley RN.
Licensure Intermediate care. *Beds* ICF 161.
Certified Medicaid.
Owner Proprietary Corp (Convalescent
Services).

Admissions Requirements Minimum age 45;
Medical examination.
Staff RNs 3 (ft); LPNs 12 (ft); Orderlies 6 (ft);
Nurses aides 37 (ft); Physical therapists 1
(pt); Recreational therapists 1 (ft); Speech
therapists 1 (pt); Activities coordinators 1
(ft); Dietitians 1 (pt).
Facilities Dining room; Physical therapy
room; Activities room; Chapel; Crafts room;
Laundry room; Barber/Beauty shop; Library.
Activities Arts & crafts; Cards; Games;
Reading groups; Prayer groups; Movies;
Shopping trips; Social/Cultural gatherings.

Evening Star Nursing Home*
6912 NW 23rd, Bethany, OK, 73008
(405) 789-8491
Admin Shirley Walker.
Licensure Intermediate care. *Beds* 55.
Certified Medicaid.
Owner Proprietary Corp (ARA Living
Centers).

Golden Acres Health Care Center*
7000 NW 32nd St, Bethany, OK, 73008
(405) 789-7242
Admin Barbara Breedlove.
Licensure Intermediate care. *Beds* 161.
Certified Medicaid.

Western Oaks Health Care Center
2200 N Flamingo Ave, Bethany, OK, 73008
(405) 787-2844
Admin R Paul Harvey. *Medical Dir/Dir of
Nursing* Dr Leon Gilbert; Joy Jones RN.
Licensure Intermediate care. *Beds* 235.
Certified Medicaid.
Owner Proprietary Corp.
Admissions Requirements Medical
examination.
Staff RNs 2 (ft); LPNs 8 (ft); Nurses aides 37
(ft), 26 (pt); Physical therapists 1 (ft);
Activities coordinators 3 (ft).
Languages Spanish
Facilities Dining room; Physical therapy
room; Activities room; Chapel; Crafts room;
Laundry room; Barber/Beauty shop; Library.
Activities Arts & crafts; Cards; Games;
Reading groups; Prayer groups; Movies;
Shopping trips; Social/Cultural gatherings.

BILLINGS

Billings Fairchild Center*
Hwy 15, Billings, OK, 74630
(405) 725-3533
Admin Albert Hardin.
Licensure Intermediate care. *Beds* 154.
Certified Medicaid.

BIXBY

Bixby Manor Nursing Home
15600 S Memorial Dr, Bixby, OK, 74008
(918) 366-4491
Admin Yvonne Roberts. *Medical Dir/Dir of
Nursing* Dana Quay.
Licensure Intermediate care. *Beds* 102.
Certified Medicaid.
Owner Proprietary Corp.
Admissions Requirements Minimum age 18;
Medical examination.
Staff Physicians 1 (pt); RNs 1 (pt); LPNs 5
(ft); Orderlies 4 (ft); Nurses aides 32 (ft);
Physical therapists 1 (pt); Speech therapists
1 (pt); Activities coordinators 1 (ft), 1 (pt);
Dietitians 1 (pt); Ophthalmologists 1 (pt).
Languages Spanish
Facilities Dining room; Physical therapy
room; Activities room; Crafts room; Laundry
room; Barber/Beauty shop.
Activities Arts & crafts; Cards; Games; Prayer
groups; Movies; Shopping trips; Social/
Cultural gatherings.

BLACKWELL

Blackwell Nursing Home Inc*
1200 W Coolidge, Blackwell, OK, 74631
(405) 363-1624
Admin John Johnson.
Licensure Intermediate care. *Beds* 71.
Certified Medicaid.

Hillcrest Manor*
1110 S 6th, Blackwell, OK, 74631
(405) 363-3244
Admin Adrian Taylor.
Licensure Intermediate care. *Beds* 110.
Certified Medicaid.

BLANCHARD

Senior Village Nursing Home
1100 N Madison, Blanchard, OK, 73010
(405) 485-3314
Admin Linda S Simmons.
Licensure Intermediate care. *Beds* 50.
Certified Medicaid.

BOISE CITY

Cimarron Nursing Home
100 S Ellis, Boise City, OK, 73933
(405) 544-2501
Admin Barbara Jo Wardlaw. *Medical Dir/Dir of Nursing* Mary Van Leer LPN.
Licensure Intermediate care. *Beds* 44.
Certified Medicaid.
Owner Publicly owned.
Admissions Requirements Medical examination.
Staff RNs 1 (pt); LPNs 3 (ft); Nurses aides 6 (ft), 11 (pt); Activities coordinators 1 (ft); Dietitians 1 (pt).
Languages Spanish
Facilities Dining room; Activities room; Barber/Beauty shop.
Activities Arts & crafts; Cards; Games; Reading groups; Prayer groups; Movies; Shopping trips.

BOLEY

Boley Intermediate Care Facility*
Hwy 62, Boley, OK, 74829
(918) 667-3311
Admin John B Bruner.
Licensure Intermediate care. *Beds* 25.
Certified Medicaid.

BRISTOW

Rainbow Nursing Home*
111 E Washington, Bristow, OK, 74010
(918) 367-2656
Admin Joe H Hamra.
Licensure Intermediate care. *Beds* 74.
Certified Medicaid.

BROKEN ARROW

Broken Arrow Nursing Home Inc*
425 N Date, Broken Arrow, OK, 74012
(918) 251-5343
Admin Tommy Cooper.
Licensure Intermediate care. *Beds* 81.
Certified Medicaid.

Franciscan Villa
17110 E 51st St S, Broken Arrow, OK, 74012
(918) 355-1596
Admin Sr Roseann Koskie. *Medical Dir/Dir of Nursing* Dr Keven Steichen, C Mark Teter.
Licensure Intermediate care. *Beds* ICF 60.
Certified Medicaid.
Owner Nonprofit Corp.
Admissions Requirements Minimum age 65; Medical examination.

Staff Physicians 2 (ft); RNs 3 (ft); LPNs 3 (ft); Nurses aides 27 (ft); Physical therapists 1 (ft); Activities coordinators 3 (ft); Dietitians 1 (ft); Ophthalmologists 1 (ft).
Affiliation Roman Catholic
Facilities Dining room; Physical therapy room; Activities room; Chapel; Crafts room; Laundry room; Barber/Beauty shop; Library; Solarium; Patio.
Activities Arts & crafts; Cards; Games; Reading groups; Prayer groups; Movies; Shopping trips; Social/Cultural gatherings.

Gatesway Foundation Inc
1217 E College, Broken Arrow, OK, 74012
(918) 251-2676
Admin Nina Honeyman. *Medical Dir/Dir of Nursing* Dorothy Terebesy RN.
Licensure Intermediate care for mentally retarded. *Beds* ICF/MR 84; Group homes 52. *Certified* Medicaid.
Owner Nonprofit Corp.
Admissions Requirements Minimum age 18; Medical examination.
Staff RNs 1 (ft); LPNs 3 (ft); Nurses aides 85 (ft); Physical therapists 1 (ft), 1 (pt); Recreational therapists 1 (ft); Occupational therapists 1 (ft); Speech therapists 1 (pt); Activities coordinators 3 (ft); Dietitians 1 (ft); Dentists 1 (pt); Ophthalmologists 1 (pt); Podiatrists 1 (pt).
Facilities Dining room; Physical therapy room; Activities room; Chapel; Crafts room; Laundry room; Barber/Beauty shop; Library; Indoor gym; Solar roof pool.
Activities Arts & crafts; Cards; Games; Reading groups; Prayer groups; Movies; Shopping trips; Social/Cultural gatherings; Educational facilities; Sheltered workshop.

Helen Raney Nursing Home Inc*
700 S Ash, Broken Arrow, OK, 74012
(918) 251-5384
Admin Reba Raney.
Licensure Intermediate care. *Beds* 52.
Certified Medicaid.

Senior Citizens Nursing Home*
1300 E College, Broken Arrow, OK, 74012
(918) 251-1571
Admin Leonard Brill.
Licensure Intermediate care. *Beds* 89.
Certified Medicaid.

Tidings of Peace Nursing Center Inc
1709 S Main, Broken Arrow, OK, 74012
(918) 251-2626
Admin Debbie Ary. *Medical Dir/Dir of Nursing* Leanne Kraft LPN.
Licensure Intermediate care. *Beds* ICF 80.
Certified Medicaid.
Owner Privately owned.
Admissions Requirements Medical examination; Physician's request.
Staff RNs 1 (pt); LPNs 6 (ft), 2 (pt); Orderlies 2 (ft); Nurses aides 30 (ft); Physical therapists 1 (pt); Speech therapists 1 (pt); Activities coordinators 1 (ft); Dietitians 1 (pt).
Facilities Dining room; Activities room; Crafts room; Laundry room; Barber/Beauty shop.
Activities Arts & crafts; Cards; Games; Reading groups; Prayer groups; Movies; Shopping trips; Social/Cultural gatherings; Field trips.

BROKEN BOW

Broken Bow Nursing Home*
805 N Bock St, Broken Bow, OK, 74728
(405) 584-6433
Admin Lois Hutchison.
Licensure Intermediate care. *Beds* 95.
Certified Medicaid.

McCurtain Manor Nursing Center*
Box 880, 1201 Dierks, Broken Bow, OK, 74728
(405) 584-9158
Admin John V Rich Jr.
Licensure Intermediate care. *Beds* 38.
Certified Medicaid.

BUFFALO

Western Nursing Home
Walnut Dr, Buffalo, OK, 73834
(405) 735-2415
Admin Debra Thompson. *Medical Dir/Dir of Nursing* Niodene McLaughlin DON.
Licensure Intermediate care. *Beds* 74.
Certified Medicaid.
Owner Proprietary Corp (Amity Care).
Facilities Dining room; Activities room; Crafts room; Laundry room; Barber/Beauty shop.
Activities Arts & crafts; Games; Reading groups; Prayer groups; Movies; Shopping trips; Social/Cultural gatherings.

CADDO

Caddo Nursing Home
Box 168, Caddo, OK, 74729
(405) 367-2264 or 367-2265
Admin Hatsene Milligan. *Medical Dir/Dir of Nursing* Judy Stallcup LPN.
Licensure Intermediate care. *Beds* ICF 34.
Certified Medicaid.
Owner Publicly owned.
Admissions Requirements Medical examination.
Staff LPNs; Nurses aides; Activities coordinators.
Facilities Dining room; Activities room; Crafts room; Laundry room; Barber/Beauty shop.
Activities Arts & crafts; Games; Reading groups; Prayer groups; Movies; Shopping trips; Social/Cultural gatherings.

CALERA

Calera Manor Nursing Home
Access & Blue Ave, Calera, OK, 74730
(405) 434-5727
Admin Gerald Buchanan. *Medical Dir/Dir of Nursing* Rao Sureddi MD.
Licensure Intermediate care. *Beds* 50.
Certified Medicaid; Medicare.
Owner Privately owned.
Admissions Requirements Medical examination; Physician's request.
Staff RNs 1 (pt); LPNs 2 (ft), 1 (pt); Nurses aides 10 (ft), 1 (pt); Activities coordinators 1 (ft); Dietitians 1 (pt); Medication aides 4 (ft); Office manager 1 (ft).
Facilities Dining room; Physical therapy room; Activities room; Laundry room.
Activities Arts & crafts; Cards; Games; Prayer groups; Shopping trips; Social/Cultural gatherings.

CARMEN

Carmen Home*
N Grand St, Box 158, Carmen, OK, 73726
(405) 987-2577
Admin J M Lemmon. *Medical Dir/Dir of Nursing* Betty Oakley.
Licensure Intermediate care. *Beds* 65.
Certified Medicaid.
Admissions Requirements Medical examination; Physician's request.
Staff RNs 1 (ft); LPNs 3 (ft), 1 (pt); Orderlies 1 (pt); Nurses aides 11 (ft), 10 (pt); Physical therapists 1 (pt); Recreational therapists 1 (pt); Activities coordinators 1 (ft); Dietitians 1 (pt); Dentists 1 (pt).
Affiliation Pentecostal Holiness

Facilities Dining room; Activities room; Chapel; Crafts room; Laundry room; Barber/ Beauty shop.
Activities Arts & crafts; Cards; Games; Prayer groups; Social/Cultural gatherings.

CARNEGIE

Carnegie Nursing Home*
225 N Broadway, Carnegie, OK, 73015
(405) 654-1439
Admin Lloyd Hilburn.
Licensure Intermediate care. *Beds* 100.
Certified Medicaid.

CHANDLER

Chandler Hillcrest Manor Inc*
401 W 1st, Chandler, OK, 74834
(405) 258-1131
Admin Judith Austin Cox.
Licensure Intermediate care. *Beds* 52.
Certified Medicaid.

Pioneer Estate
2nd & Steele, Chandler, OK, 74834
(405) 258-1375
Admin Peggy Inskeep. *Medical Dir/Dir of Nursing* Doris McCorkle.
Licensure Intermediate care. *Beds* 49.
Certified Medicaid.
Admissions Requirements Medical examination.
Staff RNs 1 (pt); LPNs 3 (ft); Nurses aides 12 (ft), 4 (pt); Physical therapists 1 (pt); Activities coordinators 1 (ft); Dietitians 1 (pt).
Facilities Dining room; Activities room; Chapel; Crafts room; Laundry room; Barber/ Beauty shop.
Activities Arts & crafts; Cards; Games; Reading groups; Prayer groups; Movies; Shopping trips.

CHECOTAH

Cedars Manor Inc
1001 W Gentry, Checotah, OK, 74426
(918) 473-2247
Admin Betty Kelsoe. *Medical Dir/Dir of Nursing* Dr John F Rice; Dorothy Stokes.
Licensure Intermediate care. *Beds* ICF 76.
Certified Medicaid.
Owner Proprietary Corp.
Admissions Requirements Physician's request.
Staff Physicians; RNs; LPNs; Orderlies; Nurses aides; Physical therapists; Speech therapists; Activities coordinators; Dietitians; Dentists.
Facilities Dining room; Physical therapy room; Activities room; Crafts room; Laundry room; Barber/Beauty shop.
Activities Arts & crafts; Cards; Games; Reading groups; Prayer groups; Movies; Shopping trips; Social/Cultural gatherings.

Checotah Manor Inc
112 SE 1st, Checotah, OK, 74426
(918) 473-2251
Admin Deborah Kelsoe. *Medical Dir/Dir of Nursing* Dian Leeper LPN.
Licensure Intermediate care. *Beds* ICF 82.
Certified Medicaid.
Owner Proprietary Corp.
Admissions Requirements Physician's request.
Staff Physicians; RNs; LPNs; Orderlies; Nurses aides; Physical therapists; Speech therapists; Activities coordinators; Dietitians; Dentists.
Facilities Dining room; Physical therapy room; Activities room; Crafts room; Laundry room; Barber/Beauty shop.
Activities Arts & crafts; Cards; Games; Prayer groups; Movies; Shopping trips; Social/ Cultural gatherings.

Odd Fellows Rest Home*
211 North Ave, Checotah, OK, 74426
(918) 473-5814
Admin Willie M Harris.
Licensure Intermediate care. *Beds* 28.
Certified Medicaid.
Affiliation Independent Order of Odd Fellows & Rebekahs

CHELSEA

Colonial Manor of Chelsea
401 Redbud Lane, Chelsea, OK, 74016
(918) 789-3215
Admin Henry R Malone. *Medical Dir/Dir of Nursing* Larry Lane DO; Wanda Robinson RN.
Licensure Intermediate care. *Beds* 60.
Certified Medicaid.
Owner Proprietary Corp (Beverly Enterprises).
Staff Physicians 1 (ft), 1 (pt); RNs 1 (ft); LPNs 1 (ft), 1 (pt); Orderlies 1 (ft); Nurses aides 20 (ft), 5 (pt); Physical therapists 1 (pt); Activities coordinators 1 (ft); Dietitians 1 (pt).
Facilities Dining room; Physical therapy room; Activities room; Crafts room; Laundry room; Barber/Beauty shop.
Activities Arts & crafts; Cards; Games; Prayer groups; Shopping trips; Social/Cultural gatherings.

CHEROKEE

Cherokee Manor
10th St & Memorial Dr, Cherokee, OK, 73728
(405) 596-2141
Admin Oliver Harris. *Medical Dir/Dir of Nursing* Dr Dean Vaughan; Jane Summers.
Licensure Intermediate care. *Beds* ICF 54.
Certified Medicaid.
Owner Proprietary Corp.
Admissions Requirements Minimum age Adult.
Staff Physicians 5 (ft); RNs 1 (ft); LPNs 3 (ft); Nurses aides 20 (ft); Physical therapists 1 (ft); Activities coordinators 1 (ft); Dietitians 1 (ft).
Facilities Dining room; Physical therapy room; Activities room; Chapel; Laundry room; Barber/Beauty shop.
Activities Arts & crafts; Cards; Games; Reading groups; Prayer groups; Movies; Shopping trips; Social/Cultural gatherings.

CHEYENNE

Cheyenne Convalescent Home
301 S 4th , Box 510, Cheyenne, OK, 73628
(405) 497-3328
Admin Lucille Dykes. *Medical Dir/Dir of Nursing* F K Buster MD; Betty Conway LPN.
Licensure Intermediate care. *Beds* 36.
Certified Medicaid.
Owner Proprietary Corp.
Admissions Requirements Medical examination.
Staff RNs 1 (pt); LPNs 1 (ft), 2 (pt); Orderlies 2 (ft); Nurses aides 9 (ft); Activities coordinators 2 (pt); Dietitians 1 (pt).
Facilities Dining room; Activities room; Crafts room; Laundry room; Whirlpool bath.
Activities Arts & crafts; Cards; Games; Prayer groups; Shopping trips; Sewing group; Church; Local bands; Remotivation.

CHICKASHA

Chickasha Nursing Center Inc*
2700 S 9th, Chickasha, OK, 73018
(405) 224-3593
Admin Linda Martin.
Licensure Intermediate care. *Beds* 60.
Certified Medicaid.

Eventide Care Center*
2300 Iowa Ave, Chickasha, OK, 73018
(405) 224-6456
Admin Patsy I Banks.
Licensure Intermediate care. *Beds* 100.
Certified Medicaid.

Shanoan Springs Residence Inc*
12th & Montana, Chickasha, OK, 73018
(405) 224-1397
Admin Paula McCathern.
Licensure Intermediate care. *Beds* 82.
Certified Medicaid.
Staff RNs 1 (ft); LPNs 2 (ft); Nurses aides 28 (ft); Recreational therapists 1 (ft); Occupational therapists 1 (ft); Dietitians 1 (ft).

Sunnytide Nursing Home*
2027 Idaho Ave, Chickasha, OK, 73018
(405) 224-1513
Admin Patsy I Banks.
Licensure Intermediate care. *Beds* 58.
Certified Medicaid.

CHOUTEAU

Meadowbrook Nursing Home*
113 E Jones Ave, Chouteau, OK, 74337
(918) 476-8918
Admin Tad Sampsel.
Licensure Intermediate care. *Beds* 55.
Certified Medicaid.

CLAREMORE

Claremore Nursing Home Inc
1500 N Sioux, Claremore, OK, 74017
(918) 341-4857
Admin Sam Lessley. *Medical Dir/Dir of Nursing* Gloria Hewling RN DON.
Licensure Intermediate care. *Beds* ICF 72.
Certified Medicaid.
Owner Proprietary Corp.
Admissions Requirements Physician's request.
Staff RNs 1 (ft), 1 (pt); LPNs 3 (ft), 1 (pt); Nurses aides 26 (ft); Activities coordinators 1 (ft), 1 (pt).
Facilities Dining room; Activities room; Crafts room; Laundry room; Barber/Beauty shop; Library.
Activities Arts & crafts; Cards; Games; Reading groups; Prayer groups; Movies; Shopping trips; Social/Cultural gatherings.

Wood Manor Inc*
630 N Dorothy, Claremore, OK, 74017
(918) 341-4365
Admin Wayne Wood.
Licensure Intermediate care. *Beds* 101.
Certified Medicaid.
Admissions Requirements Medical examination; Physician's request.
Staff RNs 1 (ft); LPNs 4 (ft); Orderlies 2 (ft); Nurses aides 37 (ft); Physical therapists 1 (pt); Speech therapists 1 (pt); Dietitians 1 (pt).
Facilities Dining room; Crafts room; Laundry room; Barber/Beauty shop.
Activities Arts & crafts; Cards; Games; Reading groups; Prayer groups; Shopping trips; Social/Cultural gatherings.

CLEVELAND

Cleveland Manor Nursing Home Inc
519 W Pawnee, Cleveland, OK, 74020
(918) 358-3135
Admin Mike Hawkins. *Medical Dir/Dir of Nursing* Edris P Cooper LPN DON.
Licensure Intermediate care. *Beds* ICF 50.
Certified Medicaid.
Owner Privately owned.
Admissions Requirements Medical examination; Physician's request.

Staff Physicians 5 (ft); RNs 1 (ft); LPNs 4 (ft); Nurses aides 16 (ft), 3 (pt); Activities coordinators 1 (ft); Dietitians 1 (ft); Dentists 1 (pt).
Facilities Dining room; Laundry room; Barber/Beauty shop.
Activities Arts & crafts; Cards; Games; Reading groups; Prayer groups; Shopping trips; Social/Cultural gatherings.

CLINTON

Highland Park Manor
2400 Modelle, Clinton, OK, 73601
(405) 323-1110
Admin Rebecca White.
Licensure Intermediate care. *Beds* 100.
Certified Medicaid.

The Methodist Home of Clinton Inc
PO Box 578, 2316 Modelle, Clinton, OK, 73601
(405) 323-0912
Admin Michael R Sewell. *Medical Dir/Dir of Nursing* Judy Unruh RN.
Licensure Intermediate care. *Beds* 101.
Certified Medicaid.
Owner Nonprofit Corp.
Admissions Requirements Medical examination; Physician's request.
Staff RNs 1 (ft); LPNs 7 (ft); Nurses aides 40 (ft), 10 (pt); Physical therapists 1 (ft); Recreational therapists 2 (ft); Activities coordinators 1 (ft); Dietitians 1 (ft).
Affiliation Methodist
Facilities Dining room; Physical therapy room; Activities room; Chapel; Crafts room; Laundry room; Barber/Beauty shop; Library.
Activities Arts & crafts; Cards; Games; Reading groups; Prayer groups.

COLLINSVILLE

Collinsville Manor*
2300 Broadway, Collinsville, OK, 74021
(918) 371-2545
Admin Jacquelyn Hudson.
Licensure Intermediate care. *Beds* 100.
Certified Medicaid.

COMANCHE

Carewell B & B Nursing Home
701 S 9th, Comanche, OK, 73529
(405) 439-5569
Admin Virginia Stringer.
Licensure Intermediate care. *Beds* 90.
Certified Medicaid.
Owner Privately owned.
Admissions Requirements Medical examination; Physician's request.
Staff Physicians; RNs; LPNs; Nurses aides; Physical therapists; Activities coordinators; Dietitians.
Facilities Dining room; Physical therapy room; Activities room; Crafts room; Laundry room; Barber/Beauty shop.
Activities Arts & crafts; Cards; Games; Reading groups; Prayer groups; Movies; Shopping trips; Social/Cultural gatherings.

Meridian Nursing Home*
Rte 2, Comanche, OK, 73529
(405) 439-2398
Admin Coweta Bishop.
Licensure Intermediate care. *Beds* 46.
Certified Medicaid.
Admissions Requirements Medical examination; Physician's request.
Staff Physicians 1 (pt); RNs 1 (ft); LPNs 6 (ft); Orderlies 1 (ft), 1 (pt); Nurses aides 11 (ft); Physical therapists 1 (ft); Recreational therapists 1 (ft); Activities coordinators 1 (ft); Dietitians 4 (ft); Social workers 1 (ft).
Facilities Dining room; Physical therapy room; Activities room; Crafts room; Laundry room; Barber/Beauty shop; Library.

Activities Cards; Games; Reading groups; Prayer groups; Shopping trips; Community plays; Seasonal parties.

COMMERCE

Eastwood Manor Nursing & Rehabilitation Center*
Hwy 66 & 6th St, Commerce, OK, 74339
(918) 675-4455
Admin Margaret Eastwood.
Licensure Intermediate care. *Beds* 53.
Certified Medicaid.

CORDELL

Cordell Christian Home
PO Box 250, 1400 N College St, Cordell, OK, 73632
(405) 832-3371
Admin Lowell Donley. *Medical Dir/Dir of Nursing* Denice Church RN.
Licensure Intermediate care. *Beds* 110.
Certified Medicaid.
Owner Nonprofit organization/foundation.
Admissions Requirements Medical examination; Physician's request.
Staff RNs 1 (ft); LPNs 5 (ft), 1 (pt); Nurses aides 40 (ft), 6 (pt); Recreational therapists 1 (ft); Activities coordinators 1 (ft); Dietitians 1 (pt).
Affiliation Church of Christ
Facilities Dining room; Physical therapy room; Activities room; Chapel; Crafts room; Laundry room; Barber/Beauty shop; Library; Gazebo.
Activities Arts & crafts; Cards; Games; Reading groups; Prayer groups; Movies; Shopping trips; Social/Cultural gatherings; Exercise classes.

CORN

Menonite Bretheren Home for the Aged*
207 S Dewey, Corn, OK, 73024
(405) 343-2295
Admin Loren Penner.
Licensure Intermediate care. *Beds* 61.
Certified Medicaid.
Affiliation Mennonite

COWETA

Coweta Manor*
Coweta, OK, 74429
(918) 251-6075
Admin Stella Maria Walker.
Licensure Intermediate care. *Beds* 100.
Certified Medicaid.

CRESCENT

Crescent Care Center*
E Sanderson, Crescent, OK, 73028
(405) 969-2680
Admin Elsie Hall.
Licensure Intermediate care. *Beds* 47.
Certified Medicaid.
Owner Proprietary Corp (ARA Living Centers).

CUSHING

Colonial Plaza Nursing Home Inc*
1405 E Moses, Cushing, OK, 74023
(918) 255-2220
Admin Genevieve Gary.
Licensure Intermediate care. *Beds* 67.
Certified Medicaid.

Rest Haven Nursing Home
310 N Central, Cushing, OK, 74023
(918) 225-1477
Admin Carrie L Meyers. *Medical Dir/Dir of Nursing* Agnes Rowland DON.

Licensure Intermediate care. *Beds* ICF 55.
Certified Medicaid.
Owner Privately owned.
Admissions Requirements Medical examination; Physician's request.
Staff RNs; LPNs; Nurses aides; Activities coordinators; Dietitians.
Facilities Dining room; Activities room; Laundry room; Barber/Beauty shop.
Activities Arts & crafts; Cards; Games; Shopping trips.

CYRIL

Cyril Nursing Home
410 S 4th, Cyril, OK, 73029
(405) 464-2242 or 464-2426
Admin Anna M McClung. *Medical Dir/Dir of Nursing* Gudrun Tendall.
Licensure Intermediate care. *Beds* ICF 80.
Certified Medicaid.
Owner Proprietary Corp (Texas Health Enterprises).
Admissions Requirements Medical examination; Physician's request.
Staff Physicians 1 (pt); RNs 1 (pt); LPNs 6 (ft); Nurses aides 25 (ft), 5 (pt); Physical therapists 1 (pt); Reality therapists 1 (pt); Recreational therapists 1 (ft); Activities coordinators 1 (ft); Dietitians 1 (pt).
Facilities Dining room; Activities room; Crafts room; Laundry room; Barber/Beauty shop; Patio.
Activities Arts & crafts; Cards; Games; Reading groups; Prayer groups; Movies; Social/Cultural gatherings.

DAVIS

Burford Manor*
505 S 7th, Davis, OK, 73030
(405) 369-2653
Admin Bill M Burford.
Licensure Intermediate care. *Beds* 51.
Certified Medicaid.

DEL CITY

Evergreen Nursing Home
400 S Scott, Del City, OK, 73155
(405) 677-3349
Admin Charles M Hocthaus. *Medical Dir/Dir of Nursing* Tracy Skolnick DO; Lorretta Gautt LPN.
Licensure Intermediate care. *Beds* ICF 61.
Certified Medicaid.
Owner Proprietary Corp (Amity Care).
Admissions Requirements Minimum age 18; Medical examination.
Staff Physicians 1 (pt); RNs 1 (pt); LPNs 3 (ft); Orderlies 1 (ft); Nurses aides 13 (ft); Physical therapists 1 (pt); Reality therapists 1 (pt); Recreational therapists 1 (pt); Activities coordinators 2 (ft); Dietitians 1 (pt); Dentists 1 (pt); Ophthalmologists 1 (pt).
Facilities Dining room; Activities room; Crafts room; Laundry room; Barber/Beauty shop; Library.
Activities Arts & crafts; Cards; Games; Reading groups; Prayer groups; Movies; Shopping trips; Social/Cultural gatherings.

DEWEY

Forrest Manor Nursing Home*
1410 N Choctaw, Dewey, OK, 74029
(918) 534-3355
Admin J D Fitzgerald.
Licensure Intermediate care. *Beds* 116.
Certified Medicaid.
Staff RNs; LPNs; Orderlies; Nurses aides; Physical therapists; Activities coordinators; Dietitians; Dentists.
Facilities Dining room; Physical therapy room; Activities room; Crafts room; Laundry room; Barber/Beauty shop.

Activities Arts & crafts; Cards; Games; Shopping trips; Social/Cultural gatherings.

Medicalodge of Dewey*
PO Box 520 Rte 1, Dewey, OK, 74029
(918) 534-2848
Admin Leila Arlene Dick.
Licensure Intermediate care. *Beds* 62.
Certified Medicaid.
Owner Proprietary Corp (Medicalodges).

DRUMRIGHT

Drumright Nursing Home*
Pine & Bristow, Drumright, OK, 74030
(918) 352-3249
Admin Marie Cooper.
Licensure Intermediate care. *Beds* 118.
Certified Medicaid.

DUNCAN

Duncan Care Center*
700 Palm, Duncan, OK, 73533
(405) 255-9000
Admin Phyllis Hill.
Licensure Intermediate care. *Beds* 180.
Certified Medicaid.
Owner Proprietary Corp (ARA Living Centers).

Kanukuk Nursing Home*
N Hwy 81, Duncan, OK, 73533
(405) 255-4600
Admin Jack Gregston.
Licensure Intermediate care. *Beds* 94.
Certified Medicaid.

Kenya Village Nursing Home
PO Box 1533, Duncan, OK, 73533
(405) 252-3955
Admin Worth McGee.
Licensure Intermediate care. *Beds* 31.
Certified Medicaid.
Admissions Requirements Minimum age 18; Medical examination.
Staff RNs 1 (pt); LPNs 2 (ft); Orderlies 1 (pt); Nurses aides 6 (ft), 3 (pt); Physical therapists 1 (pt); Recreational therapists 1 (pt); Activities coordinators 1 (ft); Dietitians 1 (pt).
Facilities Dining room; Physical therapy room; Laundry room; Barber/Beauty shop.
Activities Arts & crafts; Cards; Games; Reading groups; Prayer groups; Shopping trips.

Lahey's Nursing Home*
1004 N 5th St, Duncan, OK, 73533
(405) 255-6378
Admin Donald J Legner. *Medical Dir/Dir of Nursing* David Fisher MD.
Licensure Intermediate care. *Beds* 47.
Certified Medicaid.
Admissions Requirements Medical examination.
Staff RNs 1 (ft); LPNs 3 (ft); Nurses aides 15 (ft), 4 (pt); Physical therapists 1 (pt); Activities coordinators 1 (pt); Dietitians 1 (pt); Dentists 1 (pt).
Facilities Dining room; Physical therapy room; Activities room; Crafts room; Laundry room; Barber/Beauty shop.
Activities Arts & crafts; Cards; Games; Reading groups; Prayer groups; Movies; Shopping trips; Social/Cultural gatherings.

DURANT

Bryan County Manor*
1401 N Washington, Durant, OK, 74701
(405) 924-1263
Admin Kurt Stumpff.
Licensure Intermediate care. *Beds* 65.
Certified Medicaid.

Four Seasons Nursing Center*
1212 4-Seasons Dr, Durant, OK, 74701
(405) 924-5300
Admin Lloyd Allen Wheeler.
Licensure Intermediate care. *Beds* 110.
Certified Medicaid.

King's Daughters & Sons Nursing Home*
1223 Baltimore, Durant, OK, 74701
(405) 924-0496
Admin Bonnie A Bates.
Licensure Intermediate care. *Beds* 65.
Certified Medicaid.
Staff RNs; LPNs; Nurses aides.
Affiliation King's Daughters & Sons
Facilities Dining room; Physical therapy room; Activities room; Chapel; Crafts room; Laundry room; Barber/Beauty shop.
Activities Arts & crafts; Cards; Games; Prayer groups.

Oak Ridge Manor*
1100 Oak Ridge, Durant, OK, 74701
(405) 924-3244
Admin Erik Stumpff. *Medical Dir/Dir of Nursing* Patricia Henderson RN.
Licensure Intermediate care. *Beds* 84.
Certified Medicaid.
Admissions Requirements Minimum age 18; Medical examination; Physician's request.
Staff RNs 1 (ft); LPNs 2 (ft); Orderlies 1 (ft), 1 (pt); Nurses aides 24 (ft); Reality therapists 1 (pt); Recreational therapists 1 (pt); Activities coordinators 1 (ft); Dietitians 2 (pt).
Facilities Dining room; Physical therapy room; Activities room; Chapel; Crafts room; Laundry room; Barber/Beauty shop; Library.
Activities Arts & crafts; Cards; Games; Reading groups; Prayer groups; Movies; Shopping trips; Social/Cultural gatherings.

EDMOND

Edmond Nursing Center
39 SE 33rd, Edmond, OK, 73034
(405) 341-5555
Admin Pam Kovacs. *Medical Dir/Dir of Nursing* Loretta Slates.
Licensure Intermediate care. *Beds* ICF 109.
Certified Medicaid.
Owner Proprietary Corp (ARA Living Centers).
Staff LPNs 5 (ft), 3 (pt); Orderlies 1 (ft); Nurses aides 20 (ft), 9 (pt); Activities coordinators 2 (ft), 2 (pt); Dietitians 3 (ft), 5 (pt).

Oklahoma Christian Home Inc*
906 N Blvd, Edmond, OK, 73034
(405) 341-0810
Admin Charles D Hattendorf.
Licensure Intermediate care. *Beds* 122.
Certified Medicaid.
Owner Nonprofit Corp (Natl Bnvlnt Assn of Chrstn Homes).

Timberlane Manor Nursing Home
PO Box 2017, Edmond, OK, 73083
(405) 341-1433
Admin Shanna Shade. *Medical Dir/Dir of Nursing* Steffanie Rouselle.
Licensure Intermediate care. *Beds* ICF 100.
Certified Medicaid.
Owner Proprietary Corp (Amity Care).
Admissions Requirements Medical examination; Physician's request.
Staff RNs 1 (ft); LPNs 2 (ft), 1 (pt); Activities coordinators 1 (ft); Dietitians 1 (pt).
Facilities Dining room; Physical therapy room; Activities room; Crafts room; Laundry room; Barber/Beauty shop.
Activities Arts & crafts; Cards; Games; Prayer groups; Movies; Social/Cultural gatherings.

EL RENO

El Reno Nursing Center*
1901 Parkview Dr, PO Box 1399, El Reno, OK, 73036
(405) 262-2833
Admin Linda Jones.
Licensure Intermediate care. *Beds* 121.
Certified Medicaid.
Admissions Requirements Medical examination; Physician's request.
Staff RNs 3 (ft); LPNs 3 (ft); Nurses aides 23 (ft), 2 (pt); Activities coordinators 1 (ft); Dietitians 1 (ft).
Facilities Dining room; Activities room; Crafts room; Laundry room; Barber/Beauty shop; Library.
Activities Arts & crafts; Cards; Games; Reading groups; Prayer groups; Movies; Shopping trips; Social/Cultural gatherings.

Sunset Estates of El Reno Inc*
2100 Townsend Dr, El Reno, OK, 73036
(405) 262-3323
Admin Johnie L Harris.
Licensure Intermediate care. *Beds* 66.
Certified Medicaid.

ELK CITY

Hodges Nursing Home Inc
301 N Garrett, Elk City, OK, 73644
(405) 225-2811
Admin Mary E Porter. *Medical Dir/Dir of Nursing* R R Heine MD.
Licensure Intermediate care. *Beds* 112.
Certified Medicaid.
Admissions Requirements Medical examination; Physician's request.
Staff RNs 3 (ft); LPNs 4 (ft); Orderlies 4 (ft); Nurses aides 60 (ft); Physical therapists 1 (pt); Reality therapists 1 (ft); Activities coordinators 2 (ft); Dietitians 1 (pt); Dentists 1 (pt); Ophthalmologists 1 (pt).
Facilities Dining room; Physical therapy room; Activities room; Chapel; Crafts room; Laundry room; Barber/Beauty shop; Library.
Activities Arts & crafts; Cards; Games; Reading groups; Prayer groups; Movies; Shopping trips; Social/Cultural gatherings; Cooking class.

ENID

Enid Living Center*
1409 N 17th St, Enid, OK, 73701
(405) 234-1411
Admin Betty J Harris. *Medical Dir/Dir of Nursing* Dr Stafford.
Licensure Intermediate care. *Beds* 50.
Facilities Dining room; Physical therapy room; Activities room; Chapel; Crafts room; Laundry room; Barber/Beauty shop; Library.
Activities Arts & crafts; Cards; Games; Reading groups; Prayer groups; Movies; Shopping trips; Social/Cultural gatherings.

Greenbrier Nursing Home*
1121 E Owen Garriott, Enid, OK, 73701
(405) 233-0121
Admin Dortha Schmitz.
Licensure Intermediate care. *Beds* 52.
Certified Medicaid.

Highland Park Manor
1410 W Willow Rd, Enid, OK, 73701
(405) 234-2526
Licensure Intermediate care. *Beds* 110.
Certified Medicaid.

Kenwood Manor
502 W Pine, Enid, OK, 71263
(405) 233-2722
Admin Wanda Smith. *Medical Dir/Dir of Nursing* Dr Stafford; Sally Weingartner DON.

Licensure Intermediate care. *Beds* ICF 45.
Certified Medicaid.
Owner Nonprofit organization/foundation.
Admissions Requirements Medical
examination.
Staff Physicians 1 (ft); RNs 1 (pt); LPNs 3
(ft); Nurses aides 15 (ft), 4 (pt); Physical
therapists 4 (pt); Activities coordinators 1
(ft); Dietitians 1 (pt).
Facilities Dining room; Activities room;
Crafts room; Laundry room; Barber/Beauty
shop; Whirlpool baths.
Activities Arts & crafts; Cards; Games;
Reading groups; Prayer groups; Movies;
Shopping trips; Social/Cultural gatherings;
Outings; Picnics; Circus; Concerts.

Methodist Home of Enid Inc
PO Box 10489, 301 S Oakwood Rd, Enid,
OK, 73706
(405) 237-6164
Admin Janet Hardin. *Medical Dir/Dir of
Nursing* Barbara Lund RN DNS.
Licensure Skilled care; Intermediate care. *Beds*
SNF 30; ICF 99. *Certified* Medicaid.
Owner Nonprofit Corp.
Affiliation Methodist

Pekrul Manor*
313 E Oxford, Enid, OK, 73701
(405) 237-3871
Admin Virgil Pekrul.
Licensure Intermediate care. *Beds* 50.
Certified Medicaid.

Sunny Side Center*
1824 S Van Buren, Enid, OK, 73701
(405) 233-6422
Admin Anita Hartling. *Medical Dir/Dir of
Nursing* Jaspal Chawla MD.
Licensure Intermediate care. *Beds* 112.
Certified Medicaid.
Staff LPNs 4 (ft), 1 (pt); Orderlies 2 (ft);
Nurses aides 38 (ft); Physical therapists 1
(ft); Activities coordinators 1 (ft); Dietitians
1 (pt).
Facilities Dining room; Physical therapy
room; Activities room; Crafts room; Laundry
room; Barber/Beauty shop.
Activities Arts & crafts; Cards; Games;
Reading groups; Prayer groups; Movies;
Shopping trips; Social/Cultural gatherings;
Special Olympics.

Sunset Estates of Enid Inc*
410 N 30th St, Enid, OK, 73701
(405) 237-1973
Admin Joe Bussey.
Licensure Intermediate care. *Beds* 102.
Certified Medicaid.
Owner Proprietary Corp (Amity Care).

ERICK

Erick Nursing Home*
112 S Magnolia, Erick, OK, 73645
(405) 526-3088
Admin Joe Bauermeister.
Licensure Intermediate care. *Beds* 31.
Certified Medicaid.

EUFAULA

Eufaula Manor Inc*
107 McKinley, Eufaula, OK, 74432
(918) 689-3211
Admin Bonnie Brockman.
Licensure Intermediate care. *Beds* 80.
Certified Medicaid.
Facilities Dining room; Activities room;
Laundry room; Barber/Beauty shop.
Activities Arts & crafts; Cards; Games;
Reading groups; Prayer groups; Movies;
Shopping trips; Social/Cultural gatherings.

Friendly Manor Nursing Home
6th & Woodland, Eufaula, OK, 74432
(918) 689-2508

Admin James Nixon. *Medical Dir/Dir of
Nursing* Norma L Sneed MD; Barbara
Smith RN.
Licensure Intermediate care. *Beds* 70.
Certified Medicaid.
Owner Proprietary Corp.
Admissions Requirements Minimum age 16;
Medical examination; Physician's request.
Staff Physicians 5 (pt); RNs 1 (ft); LPNs 4
(ft); Nurses aides 22 (ft), 1 (pt); Physical
therapists 1 (pt); Recreational therapists 1
(ft); Occupational therapists 1 (pt); Speech
therapists 1 (pt); Activities coordinators 1
(ft); Dietitians 1 (pt).
Facilities Dining room; Physical therapy
room; Activities room; Chapel; Crafts room;
Laundry room; Barber/Beauty shop; Library.
Activities Arts & crafts; Cards; Games;
Reading groups; Prayer groups; Movies;
Shopping trips; Social/Cultural gatherings.

FAIRFAX

Fairfax Nursing Home*
401 S 8th, Fairfax, OK, 74637
(918) 642-3234
Admin Clayton Farmer.
Licensure Intermediate care. *Beds* 50.
Certified Medicaid.

FAIRLAND

Fairland Nursing Home*
12 E Conner, Fairland, OK, 74343
(918) 676-3685
Admin Jane A Wooley.
Licensure Intermediate care. *Beds* 29.
Certified Medicaid.
Admissions Requirements Medical
examination; Physician's request.
Staff RNs; LPNs; Nurses aides; Physical
therapists; Activities coordinators.
Facilities Dining room; Activities room;
Laundry room; Barber/Beauty shop.
Activities Arts & crafts; Games; Reading
groups; Prayer groups; Movies; Shopping
trips.

FAIRVIEW

Fairview Fellowship Home Inc
605 E State Rd, Fairview, OK, 73737
(405) 227-3784
Admin Don McCaskill. *Medical Dir/Dir of
Nursing* Johnie Skalicky RN.
Licensure Intermediate care. *Beds* ICF 100.
Certified Medicaid.
Owner Nonprofit Corp.
Admissions Requirements Medical
examination.
Staff RNs 2 (ft), 1 (pt); LPNs 4 (ft), 4 (pt);
Orderlies 1 (ft); Nurses aides 20 (ft), 18 (pt);
Physical therapists 1 (pt).
Facilities Dining room; Physical therapy
room; Activities room; Chapel; Crafts room;
Laundry room; Barber/Beauty shop.
Activities Arts & crafts; Games; Reading
groups; Movies; Shopping trips.

FORT GIBSON

Fort Gibson Nursing Home*
205 E Popular, Fort Gibson, OK, 74434
(918) 478-2456
Admin Michael Scott.
Licensure Intermediate care. *Beds* 48.
Certified Medicaid.

FREDERICK

Pioneer Manor
313 E Lucille, Frederick, OK, 73542
(405) 335-5591
Admin Kathryn Lee. *Medical Dir/Dir of
Nursing* Barbara Roden LPN.

Licensure Intermediate care. *Beds* ICF 110.
Owner Proprietary Corp.
Admissions Requirements Physician's request.
Staff RNs; LPNs; Orderlies; Nurses aides;
Activities coordinators.
Facilities Dining room; Physical therapy
room; Activities room; Crafts room; Laundry
room; Barber/Beauty shop.
Activities Arts & crafts; Cards; Games;
Reading groups; Prayer groups; Shopping
trips; Social/Cultural gatherings.

GARBER

Garber Nursing Home*
E Garber Rd, Garber, OK, 73738
(405) 863-2297
Admin Frank T Hagerman.
Licensure Intermediate care. *Beds* 57.
Certified Medicaid.

GEARY

Geary Community Nursing Home Inc*
PO Box 47, Geary, OK, 73040
(405) 884-5440
Admin William Perry. *Medical Dir/Dir of
Nursing* Dr R A Conley.
Licensure Intermediate care. *Beds* 47.
Certified Medicaid.
Owner Nonprofit Corp.
Admissions Requirements Medical
examination.
Staff Physicians 4 (pt); RNs 1 (pt); LPNs 3
(ft); Nurses aides 20 (ft); Activities
coordinators 1 (ft); Dietitians 1 (pt); Dentists
1 (pt).
Facilities Dining room; Laundry room;
Barber/Beauty shop.
Activities Arts & crafts; Cards; Games; Prayer
groups; Shopping trips; Social/Cultural
gatherings.

GLENPOOL

Glenpool Health Care Center
1700 E 141 St, Glenpool, OK, 74033
(918) 291-4230
Admin Dale Scott. *Medical Dir/Dir of Nursing*
Cindi Bangs.
Licensure Intermediate care. *Beds* ICF 100.
Owner Proprietary Corp.
Staff RNs 1 (ft); LPNs 5 (ft), 1 (pt); Nurses
aides 28 (ft), 3 (pt); Activities coordinators 1
(ft).

GRANDFIELD

Colonial Village*
900 Westfield St, Grandfield, OK, 73546
(405) 479-5244
Admin Frances Faye Sanders.
Licensure Intermediate care. *Beds* 40.
Certified Medicaid.

GROVE

Betty Ann Nursing Home*
1202 S Main, Grove, OK, 74344
(918) 786-2275
Admin Bob Maynard.
Licensure Intermediate care. *Beds* 60.
Certified Medicaid.
Staff RNs 1 (pt); LPNs 3 (ft); Nurses aides 20
(ft); Activities coordinators 1 (ft); Dietitians
1 (pt).
Facilities Dining room; Physical therapy
room; Activities room; Chapel; Crafts room;
Laundry room; Barber/Beauty shop; Library.
Activities Arts & crafts; Cards; Games;
Reading groups; Prayer groups; Movies;
Shopping trips; Social/Cultural gatherings.

Grand Lake Manor*
110 W 11th St, Grove, OK, 74344
(918) 786-2276

Admin Gary Dominguez. *Medical Dir/Dir of Nursing* Alice Wolf LPN.
Licensure Intermediate care. *Beds* 100.
Certified Medicaid.
Admissions Requirements Medical examination.
Staff RNs 1 (pt); LPNs 5 (ft), 1 (pt); Nurses aides 18 (ft), 3 (pt); Physical therapists 1 (pt); Activities coordinators 1 (ft); Dietitians 1 (pt).
Facilities Dining room; Physical therapy room; Laundry room; Barber/Beauty shop.
Activities Arts & crafts; Games; Movies; Shopping trips; Social/Cultural gatherings.

GUTHRIE

Coles Rest Haven Nursing Home
PO Box 956, 1310 E Oklahoma, Guthrie, OK, 73044
(405) 282-1686
Admin John Chambers. *Medical Dir/Dir of Nursing* Lenora Chambers.
Licensure Intermediate care. *Beds* ICF 72.
Certified Medicaid.
Owner Proprietary Corp.
Admissions Requirements Minimum age 16.
Staff RNs; LPNs; Orderlies; Nurses aides; Activities coordinators; Dietitians.
Facilities Dining room; Activities room; Laundry room; Barber/Beauty shop.
Activities Arts & crafts; Cards; Games; Reading groups; Prayer groups; Movies; Shopping trips; Social/Cultural gatherings; Activity bus.

Golden Age Nursing Home of Guthrie Inc*
419 E Okalhoma, Guthrie, OK, 73044
(405) 282-0144
Admin Gerald Duehning.
Licensure Intermediate care. *Beds* 72.
Certified Medicaid.
Staff RNs 1 (ft), 2 (pt); LPNs 3 (ft), 2 (pt); Nurses aides 35 (ft), 5 (pt); Dietitians 1 (pt).
Facilities Dining room; Physical therapy room; Barber/Beauty shop.
Activities Arts & crafts; Games; Shopping trips.

Guthrie Nursing Center*
405 N 20th, Guthrie, OK, 73044
(405) 282-1515
Admin Debra Ratliff.
Licensure Intermediate care. *Beds* 100.
Certified Medicaid.

Senior Citizens Nursing Home
PO Box 977, 1924 E Perkins, Guthrie, OK, 73044
(405) 282-3630
Admin Charles M Holthaus.
Licensure Intermediate care. *Beds* 81.
Certified Medicaid.

Westview Nursing Center*
1900 W Harrison, Guthrie, OK, 73044
(405) 282-0205
Admin Charles M Holthaus.
Licensure Intermediate care. *Beds* 51.
Certified Medicaid.

GUYMON

W F & Mada Dunaway Manor Inc
PO Box 831, 1401 N Lelia, Guymon, OK, 73942
(405) 338-3186
Admin Lee Pekrul. *Medical Dir/Dir of Nursing* Ruth Wadley MD; Elisa Padilla RN DON.
Licensure Intermediate care. *Beds* ICF 77.
Certified Medicaid.
Owner Nonprofit Corp.
Admissions Requirements Physician's request.
Staff RNs 1 (ft); LPNs 2 (ft); Orderlies; Nurses aides 30 (ft); Reality therapists; Recreational therapists; Activities coordinators 1 (ft), 1 (pt); Dietitians.

Languages Spanish
Affiliation Methodist
Facilities Dining room; Physical therapy room; Activities room; Chapel; Crafts room; Laundry room; Barber/Beauty shop; Library; Garden; Large patio.
Activities Arts & crafts; Cards; Games; Reading groups; Prayer groups; Movies; Shopping trips; Social/Cultural gatherings; Music groups.

HARTSHORNE

Twin City Nursing Home*
310 S 11th, Hartshorne, OK, 74547
(918) 297-2414
Admin Frances Mordecai.
Licensure Intermediate care. *Beds* 55.
Certified Medicaid.

HASKELL

Haskell Shamrock Care Center
PO Box 1319, Hwy 64 & Ash St, Haskell, OK, 74436
(918) 482-3310
Admin Ed R Turley. *Medical Dir/Dir of Nursing* Tina Yocham DON.
Licensure Intermediate care. *Beds* ICF 58.
Certified Medicaid.
Owner Privately owned.
Admissions Requirements Medical examination; Physician's request.
Staff RNs 1 (pt); LPNs 2 (ft); Nurses aides 18 (ft), 6 (pt); Activities coordinators 1 (ft).
Facilities Dining room; Activities room; Crafts room; Laundry room; Barber/Beauty shop.
Activities Arts & crafts; Cards; Games; Reading groups; Prayer groups; Movies; Social/Cultural gatherings.

HEALDTON

Healdton Nursing Home*
406 E Main, Healdton, OK, 73438
(405) 229-0737
Admin Patricia Garrison.
Licensure Intermediate care. *Beds* 51.
Certified Medicaid.
Owner Proprietary Corp (ARA Living Centers).

HEAVENER

Heavener Nursing Home
Box 1, Rte 1, Heavener, OK, 74937
(918) 653-2464
Admin Carolyn Yandell. *Medical Dir/Dir of Nursing* Ginger Lockhart RN.
Licensure Intermediate care. *Beds* ICF 41.
Certified Medicaid.
Owner Proprietary Corp.
Admissions Requirements Medical examination; Physician's request.
Staff RNs 1 (ft); LPNs 3 (ft); Nurses aides 15 (ft), 3 (pt); Activities coordinators 1 (ft); Dietitians 1 (pt).
Facilities Dining room; Activities room; Laundry room.
Activities Arts & crafts; Cards; Games; Movies; Shopping trips; Social/Cultural gatherings; Exercise group.

Vista Nursing Home
114 W 2nd, Heavener, OK, 74937
(918) 653-2472
Admin Mary E Foresee. *Medical Dir/Dir of Nursing* Donald Sutmiller DO; Linda Strong RN DON.
Licensure Intermediate care. *Beds* ICF 51.
Certified Medicaid.
Owner Proprietary Corp.
Admissions Requirements Physician's request.
Staff RNs; Activities coordinators; Dietitians.

Facilities Dining room; Laundry room; Barber/Beauty shop.
Activities Arts & crafts; Cards; Games; Reading groups; Prayer groups; Movies; Shopping trips.

HELENA

Ro-Mel Guest Manor Inc*
200 W 3rd, Helena, OK, 73741
(405) 852-3286
Admin Jerry Vilhauer. *Medical Dir/Dir of Nursing* Dr Gaylon Crawford.
Licensure Intermediate care. *Beds* 50.
Certified Medicaid.
Admissions Requirements Medical examination; Physician's request.
Staff Physicians 1 (pt); RNs 1 (pt); LPNs 1 (ft); Nurses aides 12 (ft), 3 (pt); Physical therapists 2 (pt); Reality therapists 1 (pt); Recreational therapists 1 (pt); Activities coordinators 1 (ft), 1 (pt); Dietitians 1 (ft); Dentists 1 (pt).
Facilities Dining room; Physical therapy room; Activities room; Crafts room; Laundry room; Barber/Beauty shop.
Activities Arts & crafts; Cards; Games; Reading groups; Prayer groups; Movies; Shopping trips; Church services.

HENNESSEY

Hennessey Care Center*
705 E 3rd, Hennessey, OK, 73742
(405) 853-6027
Admin Maxine Day.
Licensure Intermediate care. *Beds* 50.
Certified Medicaid.
Owner Proprietary Corp (ARA Living Centers).

HENRYETTA

Bono Nursing Home
212 N Antes, Henryetta, OK, 74437
(918) 652-8797
Admin Toni Johnson. *Medical Dir/Dir of Nursing* Kathy Cox RN.
Licensure Intermediate care. *Beds* ICF 53.
Certified Medicaid.
Owner Privately owned.
Admissions Requirements Medical examination.
Staff Physicians 1 (ft); RNs 1 (ft); LPNs 2 (ft), 1 (pt); Nurses aides 20 (ft); Recreational therapists 1 (ft); Activities coordinators 1 (ft); Dietitians 1 (pt).
Facilities Dining room; Activities room; Crafts room; Laundry room; Barber/Beauty shop.
Activities Arts & crafts; Cards; Games; Reading groups; Prayer groups; Movies; Shopping trips; Social/Cultural gatherings.

Fountain View Manor*
Box 520, Barclay & Lake Rds, Henryetta, OK, 74437
(918) 652-7021
Admin Opal Molet.
Licensure Intermediate care. *Beds* 140.
Certified Medicaid.

Lake Drive Nursing Home Inc*
600 Lake Rd, Henryetta, OK, 74437
(918) 652-8101
Admin Judith Cochran.
Licensure Intermediate care. *Beds* 60.
Certified Medicaid.

HINTON

Red Rock Manor Nursing Home Inc*
501 W Main, Hinton, OK, 73047
(405) 542-6677
Admin Anita Reimers.

Licensure Intermediate care. *Beds* 40.
Certified Medicaid.
Admissions Requirements Medical
examination; Physician's request.
Staff Physicians 1 (ft); RNs 1 (pt); LPNs 1
(ft), 2 (pt); Nurses aides 16 (ft); Physical
therapists 1 (pt); Reality therapists 1 (pt);
Recreational therapists 1 (ft); Activities
coordinators 1 (ft); Dietitians 1 (pt); Dentists
1 (pt); Podiatrists 1 (pt).
Facilities Dining room; Activities room;
Laundry room; Barber/Beauty shop.
Activities Arts & crafts; Cards; Games;
Reading groups; Prayer groups; Shopping
trips.

HOBART

B & K Nursing Center*
100 S Main St, Hobart, OK, 73651
(405) 726-3394
Admin Robert Lyde.
Licensure Intermediate care. *Beds* 50.
Certified Medicaid.

Good Samaritan Center*
PO Box 680, 709 N Lowe, Hobart, OK, 73651
(405) 726-3381
Admin Paul Hierstein.
Licensure Intermediate care. *Beds* 60.
Certified Medicaid.
Owner Nonprofit Corp (Evangelical Lutheran/
Good Samaritan).

Hobart Good Samaritan Home
PO Box 680, 330 N Randlett, Hobart, OK,
73651
(405) 726-5696
Admin Marla Hierstein. *Medical Dir/Dir of
Nursing* Margaret Medrano.
Licensure Intermediate care. *Beds* ICF 28.
Certified Medicaid.
Owner Nonprofit Corp (Evangelical Lutheran/
Good Samaritan).
Admissions Requirements Medical
examination; Physician's request.
Staff RNs 1 (pt); LPNs 2 (ft); Nurses aides 12
(ft); Activities coordinators 1 (ft).
Affiliation Lutheran
Facilities Dining room; Physical therapy
room; Activities room; Chapel; Laundry
room; Barber/Beauty shop.
Activities Arts & crafts; Cards; Games;
Reading groups; Prayer groups; Movies;
Shopping trips.

HOLDENVILLE

Boyce Manor Inc*
1600 E Hwy St, Holdenville, OK, 74848
(405) 379-3560
Admin Jerry L Boyce. *Medical Dir/Dir of
Nursing* T E Trow MD.
Licensure Intermediate care. *Beds* 125.
Certified Medicaid.
Admissions Requirements Minimum age 17;
Medical examination; Physician's request.
Staff Physicians 1 (pt); RNs 1 (ft); LPNs 11
(ft); Orderlies 3 (ft); Nurses aides 35 (ft);
Physical therapists 1 (ft); Reality therapists 1
(ft); Recreational therapists 1 (ft); Speech
therapists 1 (pt); Activities coordinators 1
(pt); Dietitians 1 (pt); Dentists 1 (pt).

Holdenville Nursing Home*
515 S Chestnut, Holdenville, OK, 74848
(405) 379-2126
Admin Gerrol Adkins. *Medical Dir/Dir of
Nursing* Ruth White.
Licensure Intermediate care. *Beds* 51.
Certified Medicaid.
Admissions Requirements Minimum age 18;
Medical examination.
Staff Physicians; RNs; LPNs; Nurses aides;
Physical therapists; Activities coordinators;
Dietitians.

Facilities Dining room; Crafts room; Laundry
room; Barber/Beauty shop.
Activities Arts & crafts; Games; Prayer groups;
Shopping trips; Social/Cultural gatherings.

HOLLIS

Colonial Manor I*
400 E Sycamore, Hollis, OK, 73550
(405) 688-2223
Admin Robert P Metcalf.
Licensure Intermediate care. *Beds* 69.
Certified Medicaid.

Colonial Manor II*
120 W Versa, Hollis, OK, 73550
(405) 688-2828
Admin Robert P Metcalf.
Licensure Intermediate care. *Beds* 92.
Certified Medicaid.

HOMINY

Hominy Nursing Home*
700 N Katy, Box 577, Hominy, OK, 74035
(918) 885-4746
Admin Zoe Kinney. *Medical Dir/Dir of
Nursing* Carol Passmore LPN.
Licensure Intermediate care. *Beds* 63.
Certified Medicaid.
Admissions Requirements Medical
examination; Physician's request.
Staff LPNs 2 (ft), 1 (pt); Orderlies 1 (ft);
Nurses aides 15 (ft); Activities coordinators
1 (pt); Dietitians 1 (pt).
Facilities Dining room; Activities room;
Chapel; Crafts room; Laundry room; Barber/
Beauty shop.
Activities Arts & crafts; Cards; Games; Prayer
groups; Shopping trips; Social/Cultural
gatherings.

HUGO

Hugo Golden Age Home*
1200 W Finley, Hugo, OK, 74743
(405) 326-9628
Admin Sam L Garner.
Licensure Intermediate care. *Beds* 100.
Certified Medicaid.

Hugo Manor Nursing Home*
601 N Broadway, Hugo, OK, 74743
(405) 326-6278
Admin W M McEwing.
Licensure Intermediate care. *Beds* 80.
Certified Medicaid.
Admissions Requirements Medical
examination.
Staff Physicians 1 (pt); RNs 1 (pt); LPNs 2
(ft); Activities coordinators 1 (ft); Dietitians
1 (pt); Dentists 1 (pt).
Facilities Dining room; Physical therapy
room; Activities room; Crafts room; Laundry
room; Barber/Beauty shop.
Activities Arts & crafts; Cards; Games;
Reading groups; Prayer groups; Movies;
Shopping trips; Social/Cultural gatherings.

Rose Haven Health Care Center
PO Box 387, 605 S "A", Hugo, OK, 74743
(405) 326-3677
Admin Florence E Harrison RN. *Medical Dir/
Dir of Nursing* Dr James Grimand DO; Joe
Scramage PA.
Licensure Intermediate care. *Beds* ICF 30.
Certified Medicaid.
Owner Privately owned.
Admissions Requirements Medical
examination; Physician's request.
Staff Physicians 1 (pt); RNs 1 (pt); LPNs 7
(ft); Nurses aides 5 (pt); Reality therapists 1
(pt); Activities coordinators 1 (ft); Dietitians
1 (pt).
Languages Choctaw, German

Facilities Dining room; Physical therapy
room; Activities room; Crafts room; Laundry
room; Barber/Beauty shop; Library.
Activities Arts & crafts; Cards; Games;
Reading groups; Prayer groups; Movies;
Shopping trips; Social/Cultural gatherings.

HYDRO

Hydro Manor Inc
800 Arapaho, Hydro, OK, 73048
(405) 663-2455
Admin Jerry Unruh. *Medical Dir/Dir of
Nursing* Dr Ralph Buller.
Licensure Intermediate care. *Beds* 42.
Certified Medicaid.
Staff RNs 1 (ft), 1 (pt); LPNs 1 (ft); Nurses
aides 12 (ft), 4 (pt); Activities coordinators 1
(ft).
Affiliation Mennonite

IDABEL

Hill Nursing Home*
808 NW 1st, Idabel, OK, 74745
(405) 286-5398
Admin Gladys Hill.
Licensure Intermediate care. *Beds* 51.
Certified Medicaid.

Memorial Heights Nursing Center
1305 SE Adams, Idabel, OK, 74745
(405) 286-3366
Admin Brenda Hunter.
Licensure Intermediate care. *Beds* ICF 122.
Certified Medicaid.
Owner Proprietary Corp.
Staff RNs 1 (ft); LPNs 6 (ft); Orderlies 3 (ft);
Nurses aides 66 (ft), 6 (pt); Physical
therapists 1 (pt); Activities coordinators 1
(ft); Dietitians 1 (pt); Dentists 1 (pt);
Ophthalmologists 1 (pt); Podiatrists 1 (pt).
Facilities Dining room; Physical therapy
room; Activities room; Crafts room; Laundry
room; Barber/Beauty shop.
Activities Arts & crafts; Cards; Games;
Reading groups; Prayer groups; Movies;
Shopping trips; Social/Cultural gatherings.

Oak Grove Manor Inc
PO Box 299, Idabel, OK, 74745
(405) 286-2537
Admin Julie K Bivin RN. *Medical Dir/Dir of
Nursing* Faye Pugh RN.
Licensure Intermediate care. *Beds* ICF 81.
Certified Medicaid.
Owner Proprietary Corp.
Admissions Requirements Physician's request.
Staff Physicians 1 (pt); RNs 2 (ft); LPNs 3
(ft), 2 (pt); Nurses aides 30 (ft), 3 (pt);
Physical therapists 1 (pt); Reality therapists
1 (pt); Recreational therapists 1 (pt);
Occupational therapists 1 (pt); Speech
therapists 1 (pt); Activities coordinators 1
(ft); Dietitians 1 (pt); Dentists 1 (pt);
Ophthalmologists 1 (pt); Podiatrists 1 (pt).
Facilities Dining room; Activities room;
Crafts room; Laundry room; Lounges;
Whirlpool baths; Patio sitting area; Covered
deck with swing.
Activities Arts & crafts; Cards; Games;
Reading groups; Prayer groups; Movies;
Shopping trips; Social/Cultural gatherings.

JAY

Guinn Nursing Home 1*
N Main, Jay, OK, 74346
(918) 253-4500
Admin Danny Guinn.
Licensure Intermediate care. *Beds* 48.
Certified Medicaid.

Guinn Nursing Home 2*
E Monroe, Jay, OK, 74346
(918) 253-4226
Admin Charles Guinn.

Licensure Intermediate care. *Beds* 50.
Certified Medicaid.

JENKS

Ambassador Manor South
711 N 5th, Jenks, OK, 74037
(918) 299-8502
Admin Brenda McLaughlin. *Medical Dir/Dir of Nursing* Nancy Turpin.
Licensure Intermediate care. *Beds* ICF 80.
Certified Medicaid.
Owner Privately owned.
Staff LPNs; Orderlies; Nurses aides; Physical therapists; Activities coordinators; Dietitians; Ophthalmologists.
Facilities Dining room; Activities room; Crafts room; Laundry room; Barber/Beauty shop.
Activities Arts & crafts; Cards; Games; Reading groups; Prayer groups; Movies; Shopping trips; Social/Cultural gatherings.

Riverside Nursing Home Inc
601 N 5th, Jenks, OK, 74037
(918) 299-9444
Admin JoAnne O Posey. *Medical Dir/Dir of Nursing* Barbara Sutterfield.
Licensure Intermediate care. *Beds* ICF 102.
Certified Medicaid.
Owner Proprietary Corp.
Admissions Requirements Medical examination; Physician's request.
Staff RNs 1 (ft); LPNs 6 (ft); Nurses aides 31 (ft); Recreational therapists 1 (pt); Occupational therapists 1 (pt); Activities coordinators 1 (ft); Dietitians 1 (ft).
Facilities Dining room; Physical therapy room; Activities room; Crafts room; Laundry room; Barber/Beauty shop.
Activities Arts & crafts; Cards; Games; Reading groups; Prayer groups; Movies; Shopping trips; Social/Cultural gatherings.

JONES

Oak Hills Nursing Home*
1100 W Georgia, Jones, OK, 73049
(405) 399-2294
Admin Phyllis Murry.
Licensure Intermediate care. *Beds* 106.
Certified Medicaid.

KINGFISHER

Care Villa Nursing Center
PO Box 1227, 1415 S Main, Kingfisher, OK, 73750
(405) 375-3157
Admin Wanda D Willms.
Licensure Intermediate care. *Beds* 55.
Certified Medicaid.

Second Shamrock Care Center
200 Will Rogers Dr, Kingfisher, OK, 73750
(405) 375-3106
Admin Delores Armstrong. *Medical Dir/Dir of Nursing* Donna H Treece LPN.
Licensure Intermediate care. *Beds* ICF 48.
Certified Medicaid.
Owner Proprietary Corp.
Admissions Requirements Medical examination.
Staff RNs; LPNs; Nurses aides; Activities coordinators; Dietitians.
Languages Spanish
Facilities Dining room; Activities room; Crafts room; Laundry room; Barber/Beauty shop.
Activities Arts & crafts; Cards; Games; Reading groups; Prayer groups; Movies; Shopping trips; Social/Cultural gatherings; Monthly birthday parties.

KINGSTON

Texoma Health Care Center Inc*
Hwy 32 W, Box 156, Kingston, OK, 73439
(405) 564-2351
Admin Juanima Davis.
Licensure Intermediate care. *Beds* 60.
Certified Medicaid.

KONAWA

New Horizons Nursing Home*
P O Box 217, 500 E Main, Konawa, OK, 74849
(405) 925-3645
Admin F C Williamson. *Medical Dir/Dir of Nursing* Martin Stokes MD.
Licensure Intermediate care. *Beds* 208.
Certified Medicaid.
Owner Proprietary Corp (Medicalodges).
Admissions Requirements Minimum age 18; Medical examination.
Staff Physicians 1 (pt); RNs 1 (ft); LPNs 7 (ft), 2 (pt); Orderlies 14 (ft); Nurses aides 59 (ft); Reality therapists 1 (ft); Recreational therapists 1 (ft); Activities coordinators 5 (ft); Dietitians 1 (pt); Dentists 1 (pt); Ophthalmologists 1 (pt); Podiatrists 1 (pt).
Facilities Dining room; Physical therapy room; Activities room; Chapel; Crafts room; Laundry room; Barber/Beauty shop; Library.
Activities Arts & crafts; Cards; Games; Reading groups; Prayer groups; Movies; Shopping trips; Social/Cultural gatherings.

LAWTON

Arlington Manor*
1202 Arlington, Lawton, OK, 73501
(405) 353-3373
Admin Don W Greb.
Licensure Intermediate care. *Beds* 54.
Certified Medicaid.

Cedar Crest Manor
1700 Fort Sill Blvd, Lawton, OK, 73507
(405) 355-1616
Admin Don W Greb. *Medical Dir/Dir of Nursing* Sandy Pappan RN.
Licensure Skilled care; Intermediate care. *Beds* 95. *Certified* Medicaid; Medicare.
Owner Proprietary Corp.
Admissions Requirements Medical examination; Physician's request.
Staff Physicians 12 (pt); RNs 1 (ft), 1 (pt); LPNs 7 (ft), 2 (pt); Nurses aides 36 (ft), 5 (pt); Physical therapists 1 (ft); Recreational therapists 1 (ft); Activities coordinators 1 (ft), 1 (pt); Dietitians 1 (ft); Dentists; Ophthalmologists 1 (pt); Podiatrists 1 (pt).
Facilities Dining room; Physical therapy room; Activities room; Chapel; Crafts room; Laundry room; Barber/Beauty shop; Library.
Activities Arts & crafts; Cards; Games; Reading groups; Prayer groups; Movies; Shopping trips; Social/Cultural gatherings.

Cotton's Nursing Home*
7403 W Gore, Lawton, OK, 73505
(405) 536-7401
Admin Larry Cotton.
Licensure Intermediate care. *Beds* 100.
Certified Medicaid.

Joseph's Nursing Home*
5396 NW Cache Rd, Lawton, OK, 73505
(405) 353-3653
Admin Joseph Amyx. *Medical Dir/Dir of Nursing* Thomas Leckman.
Licensure Intermediate care. *Beds* 130.
Certified Medicaid.
Admissions Requirements Minimum age 21; Medical examination; Physician's request.

Staff RNs 1 (pt); LPNs 6 (ft), 2 (pt); Nurses aides 48 (ft); Physical therapists 1 (ft), 1 (pt); Reality therapists 1 (pt); Speech therapists 1 (pt); Activities coordinators 1 (ft); Dietitians 1 (pt).
Activities Arts & crafts; Cards; Games; Reading groups; Prayer groups; Movies; Shopping trips; Social/Cultural gatherings; Grandfriends program; Visiting pets program; Residents advisory council.

Lawton Heights Nursing Center
1301 NW Andrews, Lawton, OK, 73507-3599
(405) 355-5720
Admin David H Dennis. *Medical Dir/Dir of Nursing* Grace Morrow LPN.
Licensure Intermediate care. *Beds* ICF 96.
Certified Medicaid.
Owner Proprietary Corp.
Admissions Requirements Minimum age 5; Medical examination; Physician's request.
Staff Physicians 1 (pt); RNs 1 (pt); LPNs 9 (ft), 2 (pt); Nurses aides 30 (ft), 4 (pt); Physical therapists 1 (pt); Speech therapists 1 (pt); Activities coordinators 1 (ft), 2 (pt); Dietitians 1 (pt).
Languages German
Facilities Dining room; Activities room; Crafts room; Laundry room; Barber/Beauty shop; Fenced patios.
Activities Arts & crafts; Cards; Games; Reading groups; Prayer groups; Movies; Shopping trips; Social/Cultural gatherings.

McMahon Tomlinson Nursing Center
3126 Arlington, Lawton, OK, 73505
(405) 357-3240
Admin Floyd Sanders.
Licensure Intermediate care. *Beds* ICF 118.
Certified Medicaid.
Owner Publicly owned.
Staff RNs 1 (ft); LPNs 13 (ft); Nurses aides 45 (ft); Recreational therapists 1 (ft); Activities coordinators 1 (ft).
Facilities Dining room; Physical therapy room; Activities room; Chapel; Laundry room; Barber/Beauty shop; Library.
Activities Arts & crafts; Cards; Games; Reading groups; Prayer groups; Movies; Shopping trips; Social/Cultural gatherings.

LEXINGTON

Lexington Nursing Home*
632 SE 3rd, Lexington, OK, 73051
(405) 527-6531
Admin Bonnie R Hackney.
Licensure Intermediate care. *Beds* 60.
Certified Medicaid.
Admissions Requirements Medical examination.
Staff RNs; LPNs; Nurses aides; Physical therapists; Reality therapists; Recreational therapists; Activities coordinators; Dietitians.
Facilities Dining room; Activities room; Crafts room; Laundry room; Barber/Beauty shop.
Activities Arts & crafts; Cards; Games; Reading groups; Prayer groups; Movies; Shopping trips; Social/Cultural gatherings.

Sunset Manor
PO Box 520, 2nd & Broadway, Lexington, OK, 73051
(405) 527-6519
Admin Tony Baird. *Medical Dir/Dir of Nursing* Michaele Cole.
Licensure Intermediate care. *Beds* ICF 101.
Certified Medicaid.
Owner Proprietary Corp.
Admissions Requirements Medical examination.
Staff RNs 1 (ft), 1 (pt); LPNs 4 (ft), 1 (pt); Orderlies 1 (ft); Nurses aides 26 (ft), 3 (pt); Physical therapists 1 (ft); Activities coordinators 1 (ft); Dietitians 1 (ft).

Facilities Dining room; Activities room; Crafts room; Laundry room; Barber/Beauty shop.
Activities Arts & crafts; Cards; Games; Reading groups; Prayer groups; Movies; Shopping trips; Social/Cultural gatherings.

LINDSAY

Lindsay Care Center*
Rte 1, Box 3, Lindsay, OK, 73052
(405) 756-4334
Admin H Joan Wood.
Licensure Intermediate care. *Beds* 106. *Certified* Medicaid.
Owner Proprietary Corp (ARA Living Centers).
Staff LPNs 4 (ft); Nurses aides 28 (ft); Activities coordinators 1 (ft).
Facilities Dining room; Physical therapy room; Activities room; Crafts room; Barber/Beauty shop; Library.
Activities Arts & crafts; Cards; Games; Shopping trips; Social/Cultural gatherings.

LOCUST GROVE

Parkhill East Nursing Home*
Park & Radcliffe, Locust Grove, OK, 74352
(918) 479-8411
Admin Burl H Trickett.
Licensure Intermediate care. *Beds* 50. *Certified* Medicaid.

Parkhill South Nursing Home*
Wyandotte & Ross, Locust Grove, OK, 74352
(918) 479-5784
Admin Burl H Trickett.
Licensure Intermediate care. *Beds* 54. *Certified* Medicaid.

MADILL

Brookside Manor Nursing Home
PO Box 848, Hwy 99 S, Madill, OK, 73446
(405) 795-2100
Admin Phillip W Stumpff. *Medical Dir/Dir of Nursing* Phyllis J Williams RN.
Licensure Intermediate care. *Beds* ICF 140. *Certified* Medicaid.
Owner Privately owned.
Admissions Requirements Physician's request.
Staff Physicians; RNs 1 (ft); LPNs 5 (ft); Orderlies 1 (ft); Physical therapists 1 (ft); Activities coordinators 2 (ft); Dietitians 1 (ft).
Facilities Dining room; Activities room; Chapel; Crafts room; Laundry room; Barber/Beauty shop.
Activities Arts & crafts; Cards; Games; Reading groups; Prayer groups; Dominoes; Bingo.

MANGUM

Mangum Nursing Center*
320 Carey, Mangum, OK, 73554
(405) 782-3346
Admin John H Fish. *Medical Dir/Dir of Nursing* R Kay Staton LPN.
Licensure Intermediate care. *Beds* 112. *Certified* Medicaid.
Owner Proprietary Corp (Amity Care).
Admissions Requirements Minimum age 18; Physician's request.
Staff RNs 1 (ft); LPNs 4 (pt); Orderlies 1 (pt); Nurses aides 49 (pt); Physical therapists 1 (ft); Speech therapists 1 (ft).
Facilities Dining room; Physical therapy room; Activities room; Laundry room.
Activities Arts & crafts; Cards; Games; Reading groups; Prayer groups; Movies; Shopping trips; Social/Cultural gatherings.

MARIETTA

Lake Country Manor
401 Medical Dr, Marietta, OK, 73448
(405) 276-3318
Admin Virginia Howard. *Medical Dir/Dir of Nursing* Joni Harrison.
Licensure Intermediate care. *Beds* ICF 62. *Certified* Medicaid.
Owner Privately owned.
Admissions Requirements Physician's request.
Staff RNs 1 (pt); LPNs 3 (ft), 1 (pt); Nurses aides 20 (ft), 2 (pt); Activities coordinators 1 (ft); Dietitians 6 (ft), 1 (pt).
Facilities Dining room; Activities room; Chapel; Crafts room; Laundry room; Barber/Beauty shop; Library.
Activities Arts & crafts; Cards; Games; Reading groups; Prayer groups; Movies; Shopping trips; Social/Cultural gatherings.

MARLOW

Gregston Nursing Home*
711 S Broadway, Marlow, OK, 73055
(405) 658-2319
Admin JoJean Gregston. *Medical Dir/Dir of Nursing* Charlotte Loughridge.
Licensure Intermediate care. *Beds* 86. *Certified* Medicaid.
Staff Physicians 1 (ft); RNs 1 (pt); LPNs 3 (ft), 1 (pt); Nurses aides 16 (ft); Physical therapists 1 (pt); Recreational therapists 1 (ft); Activities coordinators 1 (ft); Dietitians 1 (ft), 1 (pt); Dentists 2 (pt).
Facilities Dining room; Physical therapy room; Activities room; Chapel; Crafts room; Laundry room; Barber/Beauty shop; Library.
Activities Arts & crafts; Cards; Games; Reading groups; Prayer groups; Shopping trips; Singing groups; Band groups; Bingo; Quilting.

Marlow Manor Inc*
702 S 9th, PO Box 148, Marlow, OK, 73055
(405) 658-5468
Admin Barbara Besherse. *Medical Dir/Dir of Nursing* Dr W K Walker.
Licensure Intermediate care. *Beds* 69. *Certified* Medicaid.
Owner Proprietary Corp (ARA Living Centers).
Admissions Requirements Medical examination.
Staff RNs 1 (pt); LPNs 2 (ft), 5 (pt); Orderlies 1 (pt); Nurses aides 45 (ft); Physical therapists 1 (pt); Recreational therapists 1 (ft); Activities coordinators 1 (ft); Dietitians 1 (pt); Dentists 1 (pt).
Facilities Dining room; Activities room; Crafts room; Laundry room; Barber/Beauty shop.
Activities Arts & crafts; Cards; Games; Reading groups; Prayer groups.

MAUD

Sunset Estates of Maud
PO Box 769, 409 W King, Maud, OK, 74854
(405) 374-2207
Admin Jeff Van Arnam. *Medical Dir/Dir of Nursing* Farrelee Dean DON.
Licensure Intermediate care. *Beds* ICF 62. *Certified* Medicaid.
Owner Proprietary Corp (Beverly Enterprises).
Admissions Requirements Minimum age 18; Medical examination; Physician's request.
Staff Physicians; RNs; LPNs; Orderlies; Nurses aides; Physical therapists; Recreational therapists; Activities coordinators; Dietitians.
Facilities Dining room; Physical therapy room; Activities room; Crafts room; Laundry room; Barber/Beauty shop.
Activities Arts & crafts; Cards; Games; Reading groups; Prayer groups; Movies; Shopping trips; Social/Cultural gatherings.

MAYSVILLE

McCaskill Nursing Home Inc*
903 Parkview Dr, Maysville, OK, 73057
(405) 867-4412
Admin B H McCaskill.
Licensure Intermediate care. *Beds* 58. *Certified* Medicaid.

MCALESTER

Blevins Retirement & Care Center*
1220 E Electric, McAlester, OK, 74501
(918) 423-9095
Admin Charles H Blevins. *Medical Dir/Dir of Nursing* Donna Guthrie.
Licensure Intermediate care. *Beds* 55. *Certified* Medicaid.
Admissions Requirements Medical examination.
Staff RNs 1 (ft); LPNs 3 (ft); Orderlies 2 (ft); Nurses aides 15 (ft); Dietitians 1 (ft).
Facilities Dining room; Activities room; Chapel; Crafts room; Laundry room; Barber/Beauty shop.
Activities Arts & crafts; Cards; Games; Prayer groups; Movies; Shopping trips; Social/Cultural gatherings.

Colonial Lodge Nursing Home*
614 W Harrison, McAlester, OK, 74501
(918) 423-6011
Admin Lee Stephens.
Licensure Intermediate care. *Beds* 80. *Certified* Medicaid.
Owner Proprietary Corp (Manor Care).

Colonial Park Nursing Home*
1600 N "D" St, McAlester, OK, 74501
(918) 423-0330
Admin Carol Bullett. *Medical Dir/Dir of Nursing* William Gupton MD.
Licensure Intermediate care. *Beds* 55. *Certified* Medicaid.
Owner Proprietary Corp (Manor Care).
Admissions Requirements Medical examination; Physician's request.
Staff RNs 1 (pt); LPNs 2 (ft), 4 (pt); Orderlies 1 (ft); Nurses aides 14 (ft), 4 (pt); Activities coordinators 1 (ft); Dietitians 1 (pt); Dentists 1 (pt).
Facilities Dining room; Activities room; Crafts room; Laundry room; Barber/Beauty shop.
Activities Arts & crafts; Cards; Games; Reading groups; Prayer groups; Movies; Shopping trips; Social/Cultural gatherings.

Heritage Hills
411 N West St, McAlester, OK, 74502
(918) 423-2920
Admin Nema Davis. *Medical Dir/Dir of Nursing* Debbie Fassino.
Licensure Intermediate care. *Beds* ICF 56. *Certified* Medicaid.
Owner Privately owned.
Admissions Requirements Physician's request.
Staff Physicians; RNs 1 (ft); LPNs 3 (ft), 4 (pt); Orderlies; Nurses aides 7 (ft), 4 (pt); Dietitians 1 (pt).
Facilities Dining room; Activities room; Crafts room; Laundry room; Barber/Beauty shop.
Activities Arts & crafts; Cards; Games; Reading groups; Prayer groups; Movies; Shopping trips; Social/Cultural gatherings.

McAlester Regional Skilled Nursing Facility
1 Clark Bass Blvd, McAlester, OK, 74501
(918) 426-1800 ext 7008
Admin Vicki Warren. *Medical Dir/Dir of Nursing* Dr Larry Lewis; Cyndi Lang RN DON.
Licensure Skilled care. *Beds* SNF 21. *Certified* Medicare.
Owner Proprietary Corp.

Staff RNs 2 (ft); LPNs 4 (ft), 1 (pt); Nurses aides 3 (ft), 1 (pt); Physical therapists 2 (ft); Activities coordinators 1 (ft); Dietitians 2 (ft).
Facilities Activities room.
Activities Arts & crafts; Cards; Games; Prayer groups; Movies; Singing; Guest speakers.

Mitchell Manor Nursing Home*
Hickory & Electric, McAlester, OK, 74501
(918) 423-4661
Admin Oleta Mitchell.
Licensure Intermediate care. *Beds* 50.
Certified Medicaid.

Regency House Convalescent Center
615 E Morris, McAlester, OK, 74501
(918) 426-0850
Admin Margaret Cravins. *Medical Dir/Dir of Nursing* Shirley Sennett DON.
Licensure Intermediate care. *Beds* ICF 63.
Certified Medicaid.
Owner Proprietary Corp (ARA Living Centers).
Admissions Requirements Minimum age 25; Physician's request.
Staff RNs 1 (ft); LPNs 3 (ft); Orderlies 3 (ft); Nurses aides 14 (ft); Recreational therapists 1 (ft); Activities coordinators 1 (ft); Dietitians 1 (ft); Social service; Beautician; Barber.
Languages Choctaw
Facilities Dining room; Physical therapy room; Activities room; Crafts room; Laundry room; Barber/Beauty shop.
Activities Arts & crafts; Cards; Games; Reading groups; Prayer groups; Movies; Shopping trips; Social/Cultural gatherings.

MEDFORD

Medford Nursing Home
616 S Front St, Medford, OK, 73759
(405) 395-2105
Admin Opal M Stocker. *Medical Dir/Dir of Nursing* Lora Ramsey LPN.
Licensure Intermediate care. *Beds* 84.
Certified Medicaid; Medicare.
Owner Privately owned.
Facilities Dining room; Activities room; Laundry room; Barber/Beauty shop.
Activities Arts & crafts; Cards; Games; Reading groups; Prayer groups; Movies; Shopping trips.

MIAMI

Care Nursing Home
130 W Steve Owens, Miami, OK, 74354
(918) 542-9324
Admin Patti Henson. *Medical Dir/Dir of Nursing* Berta Carder.
Licensure Intermediate care. *Beds* ICF 58.
Certified Medicaid.
Owner Proprietary Corp (Health Enterprises of America).
Admissions Requirements Medical examination; Physician's request.
Staff RNs; LPNs; Orderlies; Nurses aides; Activities coordinators; Dietitians.
Facilities Dining room; Activities room; Crafts room; Laundry room; Barber/Beauty shop.
Activities Arts & crafts; Cards; Games; Prayer groups; Shopping trips; Social/Cultural gatherings; Church groups.

Heritage House*
1410 E Steve Owens, Miami, OK, 74354
(918) 542-8407
Admin Ronald Marquette.
Licensure Intermediate care. *Beds* 100.
Certified Medicaid.
Staff RNs 1 (pt); LPNs 5 (ft); Orderlies 2 (ft); Nurses aides 20 (ft); Physical therapists 1 (pt); Speech therapists 1 (pt); Activities coordinators 1 (ft); Dietitians 1 (pt).

Facilities Dining room; Activities room; Laundry room; Barber/Beauty shop.
Activities Arts & crafts; Games; Prayer groups; Shopping trips; Social/Cultural gatherings; Daily exercise class.

Miami Nursing Center*
1100 E St NE, Miami, OK, 74354
(918) 542-3335
Admin Louis D Eastwood.
Licensure Intermediate care. *Beds* 82.
Certified Medicaid.

MIDWEST CITY

Colonial Manor Nursing Home
8016 SE 15th, Midwest City, OK, 73110
(405) 737-5685
Admin J C Matlock. *Medical Dir/Dir of Nursing* Mary Ann Bell.
Licensure Intermediate care. *Beds* ICF 100.
Certified Medicaid.
Owner Proprietary Corp.
Admissions Requirements Medical examination; Physician's request.
Staff Physicians 1 (ft); LPNs 4 (ft), 1 (pt); Orderlies 2 (ft); Nurses aides 40 (ft), 10 (pt); Activities coordinators 1 (ft); Dietitians 1 (ft).
Facilities Dining room; Physical therapy room; Activities room; Crafts room; Laundry room; Barber/Beauty shop.
Activities Arts & crafts; Cards; Games; Reading groups; Prayer groups; Movies; Shopping trips; Social/Cultural gatherings.

Four Seasons Nursing Center of Midwest City*
2900 Parklawn Dr, Midwest City, OK, 73110
(405) 373-6601
Admin Linda Coventon.
Licensure Intermediate care. *Beds* 112.
Certified Medicaid.
Owner Proprietary Corp (Manor Care).

MOORE

Hillcrest Nursing Center*
2120 N Broadway, Moore, OK, 73160
(405) 794-4429
Admin Sheila Dattolie. *Medical Dir/Dir of Nursing* Perry Taaca MD.
Licensure Intermediate care. *Beds* 154.
Certified Medicaid.
Admissions Requirements Medical examination; Physician's request.
Staff RNs 1 (ft); LPNs 5 (ft); Orderlies 2 (ft); Nurses aides 48 (ft); Physical therapists 1 (pt); Activities coordinators 1 (ft); Dietitians 1 (ft).
Facilities Dining room; Activities room; Crafts room; Laundry room; Barber/Beauty shop; Library.
Activities Arts & crafts; Cards; Games; Reading groups; Prayer groups; Movies; Shopping trips; Social/Cultural gatherings.

MOORELAND

Mooreland Golden Age Nursing Home*
402 SE 6th, Mooreland, OK, 73852
(405) 994-5570
Admin Virginia Shaw. *Medical Dir/Dir of Nursing* Lois Roedell LPN.
Licensure Intermediate care. *Beds* 52.
Certified Medicaid.
Owner Publicly owned.
Staff RNs 1 (ft); LPNs 3 (ft).
Facilities Dining room; Laundry room; Barber/Beauty shop.
Activities Arts & crafts; Cards; Games; Prayer groups; Movies; Shopping trips; Social/Cultural gatherings.

MOUNTAIN VIEW

Mountain View Nursing Home*
320 N 7th, Mountain View, OK, 73062
(405) 347-2120
Admin Peggy Hines. *Medical Dir/Dir of Nursing* J B Tolbert MD.
Licensure Intermediate care. *Beds* 32.
Certified Medicaid.
Admissions Requirements Medical examination; Physician's request.
Staff RNs 1 (pt); LPNs 3 (ft), 2 (pt); Orderlies 1 (ft); Nurses aides 14 (ft), 3 (pt); Activities coordinators 1 (ft); Dietitians 1 (pt).
Facilities Dining room; Activities room; Crafts room; Laundry room.
Activities Arts & crafts; Cards; Games; Reading groups; Prayer groups; Movies; Shopping trips; Social/Cultural gatherings.

MULDROW

Muldrow Nursing Home*
308 S Main, Muldrow, OK, 74948
(918) 427-3441
Admin Judith Henry.
Licensure Intermediate care. *Beds* 33.
Certified Medicaid.

MUSKOGEE

Azalea Park Manor
4717 W Okmulgee, Muskogee, OK, 74401
(918) 683-2914
Admin Kathy Parris. *Medical Dir/Dir of Nursing* Connie Rinehart RN.
Licensure Intermediate care. *Beds* ICF 105.
Certified Medicaid.
Owner Proprietary Corp.
Staff RNs 1 (ft); LPNs 3 (ft); Nurses aides 8 (ft), 1 (pt); Activities coordinators 1 (ft); Dietitians 1 (pt).
Facilities Dining room; Physical therapy room; Activities room; Crafts room; Laundry room; Barber/Beauty shop.
Activities Arts & crafts; Cards; Games; Reading groups; Prayer groups; Movies; Shopping trips; Social/Cultural gatherings.

Broadway Manor*
1622 E Broadway, Muskogee, OK, 74401
(918) 683-2851
Admin Samuel D Scott.
Licensure Intermediate care. *Beds* 95.
Certified Medicaid.

Heritage Nursing Center Inc
3317 Denver, Muskogee, OK, 74401
(918) 683-3227
Admin Brenda S Workman. *Medical Dir/Dir of Nursing* Judy Tinker RN.
Licensure Intermediate care. *Beds* ICF 119.
Certified Medicaid.
Owner Privately owned.
Staff Physicians; RNs; LPNs; Orderlies; Nurses aides; Activities coordinators; Dietitians; Administrator; Office manager; Laundry; Maintenance; Housekeeping personnel.

Honor Heights Nursing Center*
4717 W Okmulgee, Muskogee, OK, 74401
(918) 683-2914
Admin Dennis Cheek.
Licensure Intermediate care. *Beds* 105.
Certified Medicaid.

McIntosh Nursing Homes Inc
2100 W Fondulac, Muskogee, OK, 74401
(918) 682-1970
Admin Johnnie C McIntosh. *Medical Dir/Dir of Nursing* Evelyn Jefferson RN.
Licensure Intermediate care. *Beds* 64.
Certified Medicaid; Medicare.
Owner Nonprofit Corp.
Admissions Requirements Medical examination.

Staff Physicians 2 (pt); RNs 2 (ft); LPNs 5 (ft), 2 (pt); Orderlies 2 (ft); Nurses aides 7 (ft), 7 (pt); Physical therapists 1 (pt); Reality therapists 1 (ft); Recreational therapists 1 (pt); Occupational therapists 1 (pt); Speech therapists 1 (pt); Activities coordinators 1 (ft); Dietitians 1 (pt); Dentists 1 (pt); Ophthalmologists 1 (pt); Podiatrists 1 (pt).
Facilities Dining room; Physical therapy room; Activities room; Chapel; Crafts room; Laundry room; Barber/Beauty shop.
Activities Arts & crafts; Cards; Games; Reading groups; Prayer groups; Movies; Shopping trips; Social/Cultural gatherings.

Muskogee Convalescent Center*
602 N "M", Muskogee, OK, 74401
(918) 682-9232
Admin Fern Knight.
Licensure Intermediate care. *Beds* 58. *Certified* Medicaid.
Staff Physicians 1 (pt); RNs 1 (pt); LPNs 2 (ft); Orderlies 2 (ft); Nurses aides 20 (ft); Activities coordinators 1 (pt); Dietitians 1 (pt); Dentists 1 (pt).
Facilities Dining room; Laundry room; Barber/Beauty shop.
Activities Arts & crafts; Cards; Games; Reading groups; Prayer groups; Shopping trips; Social/Cultural gatherings.

Pleasant Valley Health Care Center*
1120 Illinois, Muskogee, OK, 74401
(918) 682-5391
Admin Louis Nevitt. *Medical Dir/Dir of Nursing* Velma Trussell RN.
Licensure Intermediate care. *Beds* 68. *Certified* Medicaid.
Staff RNs 1 (ft), 1 (pt); LPNs 3 (ft), 2 (pt); Nurses aides 18 (ft); Reality therapists 1 (ft); Recreational therapists 1 (ft); Activities coordinators 1 (ft); Dietitians 1 (ft); Dentists 1 (ft); Podiatrists 1 (ft).
Facilities Dining room; Activities room; Chapel; Laundry room; Barber/Beauty shop.
Activities Arts & crafts; Cards; Games; Reading groups; Prayer groups; Movies; Shopping trips; Social/Cultural gatherings.

Tower Hill Nursing Home*
PO Box 1310, 424 Tower Hill Dr, Muskogee, OK, 74401
(918) 683-2983
Admin Samuel D Scott.
Licensure Intermediate care. *Beds* 48. *Certified* Medicaid.

Van Orden Adult Living Center
841 N 38th St, Muskogee, OK, 74401
(918) 683-8070
Admin Charles E Wetz. *Medical Dir/Dir of Nursing* Lu Harrison.
Licensure Intermediate care. *Beds* ICF 90. *Certified* Medicaid.
Owner Privately owned.
Admissions Requirements Medical examination; Physician's request.
Staff RNs; LPNs; Orderlies; Nurses aides; Activities coordinators.
Facilities Dining room; Physical therapy room; Activities room; Crafts room; Laundry room; Barber/Beauty shop; Library.
Activities Arts & crafts; Cards; Games; Prayer groups; Movies; Shopping trips; Social/Cultural gatherings; Exercise classes.

York Manor Nursing Home*
500 S York, Muskogee, OK, 74401
(918) 682-6724
Admin Elaine Peters.
Licensure Intermediate care. *Beds* 60. *Certified* Medicaid.
Admissions Requirements Medical examination.
Staff Physicians 1 (pt); RNs 1 (ft); LPNs 2 (ft); Nurses aides 15 (ft), 4 (pt); Dietitians 1 (pt).

NEWKIRK

Newkirk Nursing Center
Box 427, Newkirk, OK, 74647
(405) 362-3277
Admin W F Eichor. *Medical Dir/Dir of Nursing* Dr Palmer; Mary Wilson RN DON.
Licensure Intermediate care. *Beds* ICF 42. *Certified* Medicaid.
Owner Privately owned.
Admissions Requirements Medical examination; Physician's request.
Staff Physicians; RNs; LPNs; Nurses aides; Physical therapists; Recreational therapists; Speech therapists; Activities coordinators; Dietitians; Ophthalmologists.
Facilities Dining room; Physical therapy room; Activities room; Chapel; Crafts room; Laundry room; Barber/Beauty shop; Library.
Activities Arts & crafts; Cards; Games; Reading groups; Prayer groups; Movies; Shopping trips; Social/Cultural gatherings.

NORMAN

Four Seasons Nursing Center of Norman
1210 W Robinson, Norman, OK, 73069
(405) 321-8824
Admin Lori Hitchcock RN. *Medical Dir/Dir of Nursing* Edith Jones RN.
Licensure Skilled care. *Beds* SNF 118; ICF. *Certified* Medicare.
Owner Proprietary Corp (Manor Care).
Staff Physicians; RNs; LPNs; Orderlies; Nurses aides; Physical therapists; Reality therapists; Recreational therapists; Occupational therapists; Speech therapists; Activities coordinators; Dietitians.

Holiday Heights Nursing Home*
301 E Dale, Norman, OK, 73069
(405) 321-7932
Admin Bob Simmons.
Licensure Intermediate care. *Beds* 51. *Certified* Medicaid.

Morningside Nursing Home*
512 N Interstate Rd, Norman, OK, 73069
(405) 321-7483
Admin Kay Simmons.
Licensure Intermediate care. *Beds* 52. *Certified* Medicaid.

Rosewood Manor Ltd*
501 E Robinson, Norman, OK, 73071
(405) 321-6666
Admin Ben Primrose.
Licensure Intermediate care. *Beds* 200. *Certified* Medicaid.

NOWATA

Hays House Nursing Home*
300 S Mississippi, Nowata, OK, 74048
(918) 273-2002
Admin Ramona B Wilson.
Licensure Intermediate care. *Beds* 112. *Certified* Medicaid.
Admissions Requirements Medical examination.
Staff RNs 1 (ft); LPNs 2 (ft), 1 (pt); Orderlies 2 (ft); Nurses aides 28 (ft), 4 (pt); Recreational therapists 6 (ft); Activities coordinators 1 (ft); Dietitians 1 (ft), 1 (pt).
Facilities Dining room; Activities room; Crafts room; Laundry room; Barber/Beauty shop.
Activities Arts & crafts; Cards; Games; Reading groups; Prayer groups; Movies; Shopping trips; Social/Cultural gatherings.

Nowata Nursing Home*
516 S Joe, Nowata, OK, 74048
(918) 273-2236
Admin Patricia Lee Harris.
Licensure Intermediate care. *Beds* 43. *Certified* Medicaid.

Osage Nursing Home*
725 W Osage, Nowata, OK, 74048
(918) 273-2012
Admin James L Cooper.
Licensure Intermediate care. *Beds* 50. *Certified* Medicaid.

OKARCHE

Center of Family Love
PO Box 245, 6th & Texas, Okarche, OK, 73762
(405) 263-4658
Admin Bonnie B Page. *Medical Dir/Dir of Nursing* Vicki Cain LPM.
Licensure Intermediate care for mentally retarded. *Beds* 54. *Certified* Medicaid; Medicare.
Owner Nonprofit Corp.
Admissions Requirements Minimum age 18; Medical examination.
Staff RNs; LPNs; Orderlies; Nurses aides; Recreational therapists; Speech therapists; Activities coordinators; Dietitians.
Facilities Dining room; Physical therapy room; Activities room; Crafts room; Laundry room; Barber/Beauty shop; Occupational therapy room; Home economics room.
Activities Arts & crafts; Games; Prayer groups; Movies; Shopping trips; Social/Cultural gatherings; Music.

OKEENE

Buchanan Nursing Home of Okeene Inc*
119 N 6th, Okeene, OK, 73763
(405) 822-4441
Admin Mildred Buchanan.
Licensure Intermediate care. *Beds* 119. *Certified* Medicaid.

OKEMAH

Okemah Pioneer Nursing Home Inc
202 N Division, Okemah, OK, 74859
(918) 623-1126
Admin Francine Schmidt. *Medical Dir/Dir of Nursing* Florence Holdaway.
Licensure Intermediate care. *Beds* ICF 76. *Certified* Medicaid.
Owner Proprietary Corp.
Admissions Requirements Medical examination.
Staff RNs 1 (ft); LPNs 3 (ft); Nurses aides 16 (ft); Physical therapists 1 (ft); Occupational therapists 1 (ft); Activities coordinators 1 (ft); Dietitians 1 (ft).
Facilities Dining room; Activities room; Laundry room; Barber/Beauty shop.
Activities Arts & crafts; Cards; Games; Reading groups; Prayer groups; Movies; Shopping trips; Social/Cultural gatherings.

OKLAHOMA CITY

Bellevue Nursing Center*
6500 N Portland, Oklahoma City, OK, 73116
(405) 843-5796
Admin Norman L Thompson. *Medical Dir/Dir of Nursing* Hugh A Stout MD.
Licensure Skilled care. *Beds* 160.
Staff Physicians 1 (pt); RNs 4 (ft); LPNs 5 (ft), 1 (pt); Physical therapists 2 (ft); Occupational therapists 1 (ft), 1 (pt); Speech therapists 1 (pt); Activities coordinators 1 (ft); Dietitians 1 (pt); Dentists 1 (pt).
Facilities Dining room; Physical therapy room; Activities room; Chapel; Crafts room; Laundry room; Barber/Beauty shop.
Activities Arts & crafts; Cards; Games; Reading groups; Prayer groups; Movies; Social/Cultural gatherings.

Central Oklahoma Christian Home
6312 N Portland, Oklahoma City, OK, 73112
(405) 946-6932

Admin Royce W Dunn. *Medical Dir/Dir of Nursing* Gohla Lowery RN DON.
Licensure Intermediate care. *Beds* ICF 148. *Certified* Medicaid.
Owner Nonprofit Corp.
Admissions Requirements Medical examination.
Staff RNs 1 (ft); LPNs 9 (ft); Orderlies 3 (ft); Nurses aides 37 (ft); Physical therapists 1 (ft); Occupational therapists 1 (ft); Activities coordinators 1 (ft).
Affiliation Church of Christ
Facilities Dining room; Physical therapy room; Activities room; Chapel; Crafts room; Laundry room; Barber/Beauty shop.
Activities Arts & crafts; Cards; Games; Prayer groups; Movies; Shopping trips; Religious services; Music therapy.

The Convalescent Center of Oklahoma City
3233 NW 10th, Oklahoma City, OK, 73107
(405) 943-8366
Admin Claudia Hansbro. *Medical Dir/Dir of Nursing* Rae Roberts DON.
Licensure Intermediate care. *Beds* ICF 142. *Certified* Medicaid.
Owner Proprietary Corp.
Admissions Requirements Medical examination; Physician's request.
Staff Physicians 1 (ft); RNs 1 (ft); LPNs 5 (ft), 2 (pt); Orderlies 5 (ft); Nurses aides 33 (ft); Activities coordinators 1 (ft); Dietitians 1 (ft).
Languages Spanish, Vietnamese
Facilities Dining room; Activities room; Crafts room; Laundry room; Barber/Beauty shop; Library; Lobby area; 2 sitting rooms.
Activities Arts & crafts; Cards; Games; Reading groups; Prayer groups; Movies; Shopping trips; Social/Cultural gatherings; Dances; Concerts; Church groups; Family council; Resident council.

Fairview Manor Nursing Center*
3233 NW 10th, Oklahoma City, OK, 73107
(405) 943-8366
Admin Anna Warner.
Licensure Intermediate care. *Beds* 142. *Certified* Medicaid.
Owner Proprietary Corp (Amity Care).

Four Seasons Nursing Care of Northwest Oklahoma City
5301 N Brookline Rd, Oklahoma City, OK, 73112
(405) 946-3351
Admin Lola Whitlock. *Medical Dir/Dir of Nursing* Rita Lophem.
Licensure Skilled care. *Beds* SNF 14; ICF 122. *Certified* Medicare.
Owner Proprietary Corp (Manor Care).
Admissions Requirements Medical examination.
Facilities Dining room; Physical therapy room; Activities room; Laundry room; Barber/Beauty shop.
Activities Arts & crafts; Cards; Games; Reading groups; Prayer groups; Movies; Shopping trips; Social/Cultural gatherings.

Four Seasons Nursing Center of Southwest Oklahoma City*
5600 S Walker, Oklahoma City, OK, 73109
(405) 632-7771
Admin Jackie Bosler.
Licensure Intermediate care. *Beds* 120. *Certified* Medicaid.
Owner Proprietary Corp (Manor Care).

Four Seasons Nursing Center of Warr Acres*
6501 N MacArthur, Oklahoma City, OK, 73132
(405) 721-5444
Admin Linda Swain.
Licensure Intermediate care. *Beds* 103. *Certified* Medicaid.
Owner Proprietary Corp (Manor Care).

Four Seasons Nursing Center of Windsor Hills*
2416 N Ann Arbor, Oklahoma City, OK, 73127
(405) 942-8566
Admin Glenda Kauba.
Licensure Skilled care. *Beds* 112. *Certified* Medicaid.
Owner Proprietary Corp (Manor Care).

Ghana Village Home Inc
3000 NE 17th, Oklahoma City, OK, 73121
(405) 427-8364
Admin Rose Greer.
Licensure Intermediate care. *Beds* 44. *Certified* Medicaid.
Owner Proprietary Corp.
Admissions Requirements Physician's request.
Facilities Dining room; Activities room; Crafts room; Laundry room.
Activities Arts & crafts; Cards; Games; Reading groups; Prayer groups; Shopping trips; Field Trips; Attending sporting events.

Hefner Village Nursing Center*
5701 W Britton Rd, Oklahoma City, OK, 73132
(405) 722-1010
Admin Chiquita Henderson.
Licensure Intermediate care. *Beds* 173. *Certified* Medicaid.
Admissions Requirements Medical examination; Physician's request.
Staff RNs 2 (ft), 1 (pt); LPNs 7 (ft), 1 (pt); Nurses aides 40 (ft); Physical therapists 1 (ft); Activities coordinators 3 (ft); Dietitians 1 (ft).
Facilities Dining room; Physical therapy room; Activities room; Crafts room; Laundry room; Barber/Beauty shop.
Activities Arts & crafts; Cards; Games; Reading groups; Prayer groups; Movies; Shopping trips; Social/Cultural gatherings.

Hillcrest Health Center Skilled Nursing Facility
2129 SW 59th St, Oklahoma City, OK, 73119
(405) 680-2210
Admin James MacCallum. *Medical Dir/Dir of Nursing* Kim King DO; Vickie Casey RN DON.
Licensure Skilled care. *Beds* SNF 14. *Certified* Medicare.
Owner Nonprofit organization/foundation.
Admissions Requirements Medical examination.
Staff Physicians; RNs 2 (ft), 1 (pt); LPNs 2 (ft), 2 (pt); Nurses aides 4 (ft), 2 (pt); Physical therapists; Speech therapists; Activities coordinators; Dietitians.
Languages Spanish
Facilities Dining room; Activities room.
Activities Arts & crafts; Cards; Games.

Lackey Manor Nursing Home
9700 Mashburn Blvd, Oklahoma City, OK, 73132
(405) 721-2466
Admin Josephine Kelly. *Medical Dir/Dir of Nursing* Sylvia Hyde.
Licensure Intermediate care. *Beds* ICF 121. *Certified* Medicaid.
Owner Nonprofit Corp.
Admissions Requirements Medical examination.
Staff Physicians 1 (pt); RNs 1 (ft); LPNs 6 (ft); Orderlies 2 (ft); Nurses aides 35 (ft), 5 (pt); Physical therapists 1 (pt); Activities coordinators 2 (ft); Dietitians 1 (pt); Chaplain 1 (ft).
Affiliation Baptist
Facilities Dining room; Activities room; Chapel; Crafts room; Laundry room; Barber/Beauty shop; Library.
Activities Arts & crafts; Games; Reading groups; Prayer groups; Movies.

Mid-Del Manor Nursing Center
1511 Duffner Dr, Oklahoma City, OK, 73118
(405) 733-1794
Admin Edward Price.
Licensure Intermediate care. *Beds* 170. *Certified* Medicaid.

Morning Star Nursing Home*
3804 N Barr, Oklahoma City, OK, 73122
(405) 787-0522
Admin Judy Smith.
Licensure Intermediate care. *Beds* 55. *Certified* Medicaid.
Owner Proprietary Corp (ARA Living Centers).
Admissions Requirements Minimum age 18; Medical examination; Physician's request.
Staff Physicians 11 (pt); RNs 1 (pt); LPNs 6 (ft), 1 (pt); Orderlies 4 (ft); Nurses aides 11 (ft); Activities coordinators 1 (ft); Dietitians 1 (pt).
Facilities Dining room; Activities room; Laundry room; Barber/Beauty shop.
Activities Arts & crafts; Cards; Games; Reading groups; Prayer groups; Movies; Shopping trips; Social/Cultural gatherings.

Northeast Nursing Center*
1215 NE 34th, Oklahoma City, OK, 73111
(405) 424-4000
Admin Patricia Ann Hurt.
Licensure Intermediate care. *Beds* 72. *Certified* Medicaid.

Northwest Nursing Center*
2801 NW 61st, Oklahoma City, OK, 73112
(405) 842-6601
Admin T G Barker. *Medical Dir/Dir of Nursing* Hugh A Stout MD.
Licensure Intermediate care. *Beds* 100. *Certified* Medicaid.
Admissions Requirements Medical examination; Physician's request.
Staff RNs 3 (ft); LPNs 4 (ft), 1 (pt); Physical therapists 1 (ft); Activities coordinators 1 (ft).
Facilities Dining room; Physical therapy room; Activities room; Laundry room; Barber/Beauty shop.
Activities Arts & crafts; Cards; Games; Reading groups; Prayer groups; Movies; Shopping trips; Social/Cultural gatherings.

Oklahoma County Home*
7401 NE 23rd, Oklahoma City, OK, 73141
(405) 427-2426
Admin Mary Thomas.
Licensure Intermediate care. *Beds* 84. *Certified* Medicaid.

Park Manor Nursing Home*
1214 N Broadway Dr, Oklahoma City, OK, 73103
(405) 235-7488
Admin Kaylene Bass. *Medical Dir/Dir of Nursing* Perry Taaca MD.
Licensure Intermediate care. *Beds* 120. *Certified* Medicaid.
Admissions Requirements Minimum age 18; Medical examination; Physician's request.
Staff RNs 1 (pt); LPNs 4 (ft), 3 (pt); Orderlies 3 (ft), 1 (pt); Nurses aides 22 (ft); Physical therapists 1 (pt); Occupational therapists 1 (pt); Speech therapists 1 (pt); Activities coordinators 1 (ft); Dietitians 1 (pt); Dentists 1 (pt); Ophthalmologists 1 (pt); Podiatrists 1 (pt); Audiologists 1 (pt).
Facilities Dining room; Physical therapy room; Activities room; Chapel; Crafts room; Laundry room; Barber/Beauty shop; 2 indoor patios.
Activities Arts & crafts; Cards; Games; Reading groups; Prayer groups; Movies; Shopping trips; Social/Cultural gatherings.

Portland Health Care Facility*
3718 N Portland, Oklahoma City, OK, 73112
(405) 942-1014

Admin Stephen Terrell. *Medical Dir/Dir of Nursing* Mayuri Shah MD.
Licensure Intermediate care. *Beds* 24.
Certified Medicaid.
Staff RNs 1 (ft), 1 (pt); LPNs 1 (pt); Nurses aides 16 (ft); Reality therapists 1 (ft); Recreational therapists 1 (ft); Activities coordinators 1 (ft); Dietitians 1 (ft).
Facilities Dining room; Activities room; Crafts room; Laundry room; Barber/Beauty shop.
Activities Arts & crafts; Cards; Games; Reading groups; Prayer groups; Movies; Shopping trips; Social/Cultural gatherings.

St Ann's Nursing Home Inc
3825 NW 19th St, Oklahoma City, OK, 73107
(405) 942-8607
Admin Sr Marcellina ASC.
Licensure Intermediate care. *Beds* 82.
Certified Medicaid.
Owner Nonprofit organization/foundation.
Admissions Requirements Medical examination.
Staff Physicians; RNs; LPNs; Orderlies; Nurses aides; Physical therapists; Recreational therapists; Speech therapists; Activities coordinators; Dietitians; Ophthalmologists.
Affiliation Roman Catholic
Facilities Dining room; Physical therapy room; Activities room; Chapel; Crafts room; Laundry room; Barber/Beauty shop.
Activities Arts & crafts; Cards; Games; Reading groups; Prayer groups; Movies; Shopping trips; Social/Cultural gatherings; Singing; Parties; Outings.

Saints Nursing Home*
1913 NE 50th, Oklahoma City, OK, 73111
(405) 427-5414
Admin Wanda Boyd Rucker.
Licensure Intermediate care. *Beds* 107.
Certified Medicaid.

Shady View Nursing Home*
1163 E Madison, Oklahoma City, OK, 73111
(405) 424-1486
Admin Riley Brown.
Licensure Intermediate care. *Beds* 70.
Certified Medicaid.

South Park Health Care Center*
5725 S Ross, Oklahoma City, OK, 73119
(405) 685-4791
Admin Troy Matchen.
Beds 113.

Southern Oaks Manor Nursing Home*
301 SW 74th, Oklahoma City, OK, 73139
(405) 634-0573
Admin Chiquita Henderson.
Licensure Intermediate care. *Beds* 105.
Certified Medicaid.

Southwestern Convalescent Manor*
5512 S Western, Oklahoma City, OK, 73109
(405) 632-2318
Admin Thomas D Scott. *Medical Dir/Dir of Nursing* Roger Lienke MD.
Licensure Intermediate care. *Beds* 59.
Certified Medicaid.
Admissions Requirements Minimum age 21.
Staff RNs 1 (pt); LPNs 4 (ft); Nurses aides 16 (ft); Activities coordinators 1 (ft).
Facilities Dining room; Activities room; Laundry room; Barber/Beauty shop.
Activities Arts & crafts; Games; Prayer groups; Movies; Shopping trips.

Suburban Square Nursing Center*
225 SW 35th, Oklahoma City, OK, 73109
(405) 634-3323
Admin Arthur A Durkee.
Licensure Intermediate care. *Beds* 30.
Certified Medicaid.

Staff Physicians 3 (pt); RNs 2 (pt); LPNs 1 (ft), 3 (pt); Nurses aides 9 (ft), 3 (pt); Activities coordinators 2 (pt); Dietitians 1 (pt); Dentists 1 (pt); Podiatrists 1 (pt).
Facilities Dining room; Laundry room.
Activities Arts & crafts; Games; Prayer groups; Shopping trips; Social/Cultural gatherings.

Terrace Gardens Nursing Home
1921 NE 21st St, Oklahoma City, OK, 73111
(405) 424-1449
Admin Betty L Heiliger. *Medical Dir/Dir of Nursing* Kim Pack.
Licensure Intermediate care. *Beds* ICF 105.
Certified Medicaid.
Owner Proprietary Corp.
Admissions Requirements Medical examination; Physician's request.
Staff RNs; LPNs; Nurses aides; Activities coordinators; Dietitians.
Facilities Dining room; Activities room; Laundry room; Barber/Beauty shop.
Activities Arts & crafts; Cards; Games; Reading groups; Prayer groups; Movies; Social/Cultural gatherings.

United Cerebral Palsy Intermediate Care Facility
2901 SE 22nd, Oklahoma City, OK, 73129
(405) 677-0502
Admin Arthur A Durkee. *Medical Dir/Dir of Nursing* Claudia Bellows.
Licensure Intermediate care; Intermediate care for mentally retarded. *Beds* ICF 18; ICF/MR 75. *Certified* Medicaid.
Owner Nonprofit Corp.
Staff RNs; LPNs; Orderlies; Nurses aides; Physical therapists; Occupational therapists; Speech therapists; Activities coordinators; Dietitians; Ophthalmologists; Podiatrists.
Facilities Dining room; Activities room; Crafts room; Laundry room.
Activities Arts & crafts; Cards; Games; Reading groups; Prayer groups; Movies; Shopping trips; Social/Cultural gatherings.

Walnut Creek Nursing Home*
2400 SW 55th, Oklahoma City, OK, 73119
(405) 681-5381
Admin Delories Gilliland.
Licensure Intermediate care. *Beds* 100.
Certified Medicaid.
Owner Proprietary Corp (Amity Care).

Watkins Stephens Skyview Nursing Home*
2200 Coltrane Rd, Oklahoma City, OK, 73121
(405) 427-1322
Admin Betty R Lynch.
Licensure Intermediate care. *Beds* 60.
Certified Medicaid.

Wilshire Nursing Home*
505 E Wilshire, Oklahoma City, OK, 73105
(405) 478-0531
Admin Anna Warner.
Licensure Intermediate care. *Beds* 52.
Certified Medicaid.
Owner Proprietary Corp (Amity Care).
Staff LPNs 2 (ft), 1 (pt); Nurses aides 14 (ft), 4 (pt); Activities coordinators 1 (ft); Dietitians 1 (ft).

Woodside Nursing Center*
3601 N Eastern, Oklahoma City, OK, 73111
(405) 427-6533
Admin Rosalie Richardson.
Licensure Intermediate care. *Beds* 137.
Certified Medicaid.

OKMULGEE

Highland Park Manor*
1300 E Walnut, Okmulgee, OK, 74447
(918) 756-5611
Admin Donna Wells.
Licensure Intermediate care. *Beds* 100.
Certified Medicaid.

Leisure Manor Nursing Home*
1535 E 6th, Okmulgee, OK, 74447
(918) 756-3355
Admin Bob Barnard.
Licensure Intermediate care. *Beds* 63.
Certified Medicaid.

Okmulgee Terrace Nursing Home Inc*
1st & Miami, Okmulgee, OK, 74447
(918) 756-3556
Admin Judith Cochran.
Licensure Intermediate care. *Beds* 63.
Certified Medicaid.

Rebold Manor*
1701 E 6th, Okmulgee, OK, 74447
(918) 756-1967
Admin Bob Barnard.
Licensure Intermediate care. *Beds* 114.
Certified Medicaid.

PAULS VALLEY

Colonial Nursing Home
105 Washington, Pauls Valley, OK, 73075
(405) 238-5528
Admin Sue D Horton. *Medical Dir/Dir of Nursing* Connie Walls.
Licensure Intermediate care. *Beds* ICF 104.
Certified Medicaid.
Owner Proprietary Corp.

Pauls Valley Health Care Facility*
1413 S Chickasaw, Pauls Valley, OK, 73075
(405) 238-6411
Admin Gussie J Corvin.
Licensure Intermediate care. *Beds* 51.
Certified Medicaid.

PAWHUSKA

Pawhuska Nursing Home*
Box 959, Pawhuska, OK, 74056
(918) 287-3940
Admin Jerry L Cline.
Licensure Intermediate care. *Beds* 80.
Certified Medicaid.
Staff RNs 1 (pt); LPNs 2 (ft), 1 (pt); Dietitians 1 (pt).
Facilities Dining room; Crafts room; Laundry room; Barber/Beauty shop.
Activities Arts & crafts; Cards; Games; Prayer groups; Shopping trips.

PAWNEE

Pawnee Care Center
PO Box 190, 800 9th St, Pawnee, OK, 74058
(918) 762-2515
Admin Mary Hurt. *Medical Dir/Dir of Nursing* Susan Buckner.
Licensure Intermediate care. *Beds* 52.
Certified Medicaid.
Owner Proprietary Corp (ARA Living Centers).
Admissions Requirements Minimum age 18.
Staff RNs 1 (pt); LPNs 3 (ft); Nurses aides 20 (ft), 5 (pt); Activities coordinators 1 (ft), 1 (pt); Dietitians 1 (pt); Ophthalmologists 1 (pt).
Facilities Dining room; Physical therapy room; Activities room; Crafts room; Laundry room; Barber/Beauty shop.
Activities Arts & crafts; Cards; Games; Prayer groups; Movies; Shopping trips; Social/Cultural gatherings.

PERRY

Perry Green Valley Nursing Center*
1103 Birch St, Perry, OK, 73077
(405) 336-2285
Admin Anita Schwandt.
Licensure Intermediate care. *Beds* 82.
Certified Medicaid.

Perry Nursing Home*
410 15th St, Perry, OK, 73077
(405) 336-4461
Admin Anita Schwandt.
Licensure Intermediate care. *Beds* 51.
Certified Medicaid.

PICHER

Rest Haven Nursing Home*
2nd & Francis, Picher, OK, 74360
(918) 673-1660
Admin James A Patrick.
Licensure Intermediate care. *Beds* 26.
Certified Medicaid.

PONCA CITY

Highland Nursing Center*
1401 W Highland, Ponca City, OK, 74601
(405) 765-4454
Admin Joe M Nimmo.
Licensure Intermediate care. *Beds* 97.
Certified Medicaid.

Ponca City Nursing Home
PO Box 267, Ponca City, OK, 74602
(405) 762-6668
Admin Wesley E Nimmo. *Medical Dir/Dir of Nursing* Grace Paige.
Licensure Intermediate care. *Beds* ICF 143.
Certified Medicaid.
Owner Privately owned.
Staff Physicians; RNs; LPNs; Nurses aides; Physical therapists; Recreational therapists; Occupational therapists; Activities coordinators; Dietitians.
Facilities Dining room; Physical therapy room; Activities room; Chapel; Crafts room; Laundry room; Barber/Beauty shop; Library.
Activities Arts & crafts; Cards; Games; Reading groups; Prayer groups; Movies; Shopping trips; Social/Cultural gatherings.

Shawn Manor Nursing Home
2024 Turner Rd, Ponca City, OK, 74604
(405) 765-3364
Admin Pauline Bivin. *Medical Dir/Dir of Nursing* Carolyn Sissons RN.
Licensure Intermediate care. *Beds* ICF 86.
Certified Medicaid.
Owner Proprietary Corp.
Staff RNs 1 (ft); LPNs 4 (ft); Orderlies 3 (ft); Nurses aides 30 (ft); Activities coordinators 1 (ft), 1 (pt).
Facilities Dining room; Activities room; Chapel; Crafts room; Laundry room; Barber/Beauty shop.
Activities Arts & crafts; Cards; Games; Reading groups; Prayer groups; Movies.

Westminster Village
1601 Academy Rd, Ponca City, OK, 74604
(405) 762-9332
Admin James E Rosenbaum FACHE. *Medical Dir/Dir of Nursing* Helen S Beck RN.
Licensure Intermediate care; Retirement Center. *Beds* ICF 18; apts 70.
Owner Nonprofit Corp.
Admissions Requirements Minimum age 55; Membership fee.
Staff RNs 2 (ft); LPNs 4 (ft); Nurses aides 8 (ft); Activities coordinators 1 (ft); Dietitians 1 (pt).
Facilities Dining room; Activities room; Chapel; Crafts room; Laundry room; Barber/Beauty shop; Library.
Activities Arts & crafts; Cards; Games; Reading groups; Prayer groups; Movies; Shopping trips; Social/Cultural gatherings.

POTEAU

Eastern Oklahoma Medical Center Skilled Nursing Facility*
105 Wall, Poteau, OK,
(918) 647-8161

Admin Bobby D Cox. *Medical Dir/Dir of Nursing* M Kemp MD; Pam Henderson RN DON.
Licensure Skilled care. *Beds* SNF 8. *Certified* Medicare.
Owner Nonprofit organization/foundation.
Admissions Requirements Physician's request.
Staff Physicians 12 (ft), 4 (pt); RNs 2 (ft), 1 (pt); LPNs 2 (ft), 2 (pt); Nurses aides 1 (pt); Physical therapists 1 (ft); Speech therapists 1 (pt); Activities coordinators 1 (ft); Dietitians 1 (pt); Dentists 1 (pt); Podiatrists 1 (pt).
Facilities Dining room; Activities room; Library.
Activities Arts & crafts; Cards; Games; Reading groups; Prayer groups; Movies.

LeFlore Nursing Home
410 Carter St, Poteau, OK, 74953
(918) 647-4194
Admin Don Farmer. *Medical Dir/Dir of Nursing* Toni Fry RN DON.
Licensure Intermediate care. *Beds* ICF 63.
Certified Medicaid.
Owner Proprietary Corp.
Staff RNs; LPNs; Nurses aides; Activities coordinators; Dietitians.
Facilities Dining room; Physical therapy room; Activities room; Laundry room.
Activities Arts & crafts; Cards; Games; Reading groups; Prayer groups; Movies; Shopping trips; Social/Cultural gatherings.

Poteau Nursing Home*
1212 Reynolds, Poteau, OK, 74953
(918) 647-4247
Admin Arthur Wayne Hoffman.
Licensure Intermediate care. *Beds* 81.
Certified Medicaid.

PRAGUE

Parkland Manor*
1400 D Ave, Prague, OK, 74864
(405) 567-2201
Admin Dorothea Thomas.
Licensure Intermediate care. *Beds* 58.
Certified Medicaid.

PRYOR

Colonial Terrace Care Center Inc*
1320 NE 1st Pl, Pryor, OK, 74361
(918) 825-5311
Admin Dorothy Hagerman.
Licensure Intermediate care. *Beds* 51.
Certified Medicaid.

Grand Valley Care Center Inc*
201 N Kentucky, Pryor, OK, 74361
(918) 825-2558
Admin Frank Hagerman.
Licensure Intermediate care. *Beds* 65.
Certified Medicaid.

Shady Rest Care Center Inc
210 S Adair, Pryor, OK, 74361
(918) 825-4455
Admin Glenda Thomas. *Medical Dir/Dir of Nursing* Mary Lou Estes.
Licensure Intermediate care. *Beds* ICF 65.
Certified Medicaid.
Owner Proprietary Corp.
Admissions Requirements Medical examination.
Staff RNs 1 (pt); LPNs 2 (ft), 2 (pt); Nurses aides 18 (ft); Activities coordinators 1 (ft); Dietitians 1 (pt).
Facilities Dining room; Chapel; Laundry room; Barber/Beauty shop.
Activities Arts & crafts; Cards; Games; Reading groups; Prayer groups; Movies; Shopping trips; Social/Cultural gatherings.

PURCELL

Broadlawn Manor*
915-1017 N 7th, Purcell, OK, 73080
(405) 527-2122
Admin Louise Deane. *Medical Dir/Dir of Nursing* Dr John Rollins.
Licensure Intermediate care. *Beds* 69.
Certified Medicaid.
Admissions Requirements Minimum age 29; Medical examination.
Staff Physicians; RNs; LPNs; Nurses aides; Reality therapists; Recreational therapists; Activities coordinators; Dietitians; Dentists.
Facilities Dining room; Activities room; Crafts room; Laundry room; Barber/Beauty shop; Library.
Activities Arts & crafts; Cards; Games; Reading groups; Prayer groups; Movies; Shopping trips; Social/Cultural gatherings; Easter egg hunt.

Purchell Nursing Home*
639 Van Buren, Purcell, OK, 73080
(405) 527-3129
Admin Kenneth Greiner.
Licensure Intermediate care. *Beds* 105.
Certified Medicaid.
Owner Proprietary Corp (Amity Care).
Staff Physicians 1 (ft); RNs 1 (pt); LPNs 4 (ft); Orderlies 1 (ft); Nurses aides 30 (ft), 5 (pt); Recreational therapists 1 (ft); Occupational therapists 1 (pt); Activities coordinators 1 (ft); Dietitians 6 (ft).
Facilities Dining room; Physical therapy room; Activities room; Crafts room; Laundry room; Barber/Beauty shop.
Activities Arts & crafts; Cards; Games; Reading groups; Prayer groups; Movies; Shopping trips; Social/Cultural gatherings.

QUAPAW

Quapaw Nursing Home*
407 Whitebird, Quapaw, OK, 74363
(918) 674-2464
Admin Tom Housh.
Licensure Intermediate care. *Beds* 66.
Certified Medicaid.

QUINTON

Quinton Nursing Home Inc*
1209 W Main, Quinton, OK, 74561
(918) 469-2655
Admin Mike A Hawkins.
Licensure Intermediate care. *Beds* 63.
Certified Medicaid.
Staff Physicians 1 (ft), 1 (pt); RNs 1 (pt); LPNs 5 (ft); Nurses aides 16 (ft); Activities coordinators 1 (ft); Dietitians 1 (pt); Dentists 2 (pt); Podiatrists 1 (pt).
Facilities Dining room; Activities room; Crafts room; Laundry room; Barber/Beauty shop.
Activities Arts & crafts; Cards; Games; Reading groups; Shopping trips; Social/Cultural gatherings.

RINGLING

Ringling Nursing Home*
2nd & H Sts, Ringling, OK, 73456
(405) 662-2262
Admin Bobbie Woodall.
Licensure Intermediate care. *Beds* 50.
Certified Medicaid.
Owner Proprietary Corp (ARA Living Centers).

ROLAND

Sequoyah East Nursing Center*
East of Roland, Roland, OK, 74954
(918) 427-7401
Admin Bob G Mitchell.

Licensure Intermediate care. *Beds* 60.
Certified Medicaid.

RYAN

Ryan Nursing Home Inc
703 Lee Ave, Ryan, OK, 73565
(405) 757-2517
Admin Jimmy L Thorn. *Medical Dir/Dir of Nursing* Sharon Howe.
Licensure Intermediate care. *Beds* ICF 69.
Certified Medicaid.
Owner Proprietary Corp.
Admissions Requirements Medical examination.
Staff Physicians; RNs; LPNs; Nurses aides; Physical therapists; Recreational therapists; Activities coordinators; Dietitians.
Facilities Dining room; Physical therapy room; Activities room; Chapel; Crafts room; Laundry room; Barber/Beauty shop; Library.
Activities Arts & crafts; Cards; Games; Reading groups; Prayer groups; Movies; Shopping trips; Social/Cultural gatherings.

SALINA

Parkhill North Nursing Home*
Hwys 20 & 82, Salina, OK, 74365
(918) 434-5600
Admin Caroline Trickett.
Licensure Intermediate care. *Beds* 53.
Certified Medicaid.

SALLISAW

Sequoyah Manor
PO Box 427, 615 E Redwood, Sallisaw, OK, 74955
(918) 775-4881
Admin Laveta Kyle.
Licensure Intermediate care. *Beds* 154.
Certified Medicaid.

SAND SPRINGS

Oak Dale Manor*
1025 N Adams, Sand Springs, OK, 74063
(918) 245-5908
Admin T A Connery.
Licensure Intermediate care. *Beds* 207.
Certified Medicaid.

SAPULPA

North Side Nursing Home
PO Box 1110, 102 E Line, Sapulpa, OK, 74067
(918) 224-0833
Admin Nellie Blair. *Medical Dir/Dir of Nursing* Louis Martin MD; Ginger Mathews LPN DON.
Licensure Intermediate care. *Beds* 33.
Certified Medicaid.
Owner Privately owned.
Admissions Requirements Medical examination; Physician's request.
Staff Physicians; RNs; LPNs; Nurses aides; Physical therapists; Recreational therapists; Occupational therapists; Activities coordinators; Dietitians; Dentist 1 (ft).
Facilities Dining room; Activities room; Crafts room; Laundry room; Barber/Beauty shop.
Activities Arts & crafts; Cards; Games; Reading groups; Prayer groups; Movies; Shopping trips; Social/Cultural gatherings.

Pleasant Manor Nursing Home
310 W Taft, Sapulpa, OK, 74066
(918) 224-6012
Admin Patricia C Legrant. *Medical Dir/Dir of Nursing* Philip Joseph MD; Terry Nichols RN DON.
Licensure Intermediate care. *Beds* ICF 142.
Certified Medicaid.

Owner Proprietary Corp (Beverly Enterprises).
Admissions Requirements Minimum age 65.
Staff RNs; LPNs; Orderlies; Nurses aides; Activities coordinators; Ophthalmologists.
Facilities Dining room; Activities room; Chapel; Laundry room; Barber/Beauty shop.
Activities Arts & crafts; Cards; Games; Reading groups; Prayer groups; Movies; Shopping trips; Social/Cultural gatherings.

Ranch Terrace Nursing Home Inc
1310 E Cleveland, Sapulpa, OK, 74066
(918) 224-2578
Admin L D Lawson. *Medical Dir/Dir of Nursing* Teresa Morgan.
Licensure Intermediate care. *Beds* ICF 85.
Certified Medicaid.
Owner Privately owned.
Admissions Requirements Medical examination; Physician's request.
Staff Physicians 1 (pt); RNs 1 (ft); LPNs 3 (ft); Orderlies 11 (ft); Nurses aides 17 (ft); Physical therapists 1 (pt); Activities coordinators 1 (ft); Dietitians 1 (pt).
Activities Arts & crafts; Cards; Games; Reading groups; Prayer groups; Movies.

Sapulpa Nursing Center Inc*
1701 S Main, PO Box 1108, Sapulpa, OK, 74066
(918) 224-5790
Admin Coy V Cardin.
Licensure Intermediate care. *Beds* 57.
Certified Medicaid.
Staff Physicians 2 (pt); RNs 1 (pt); LPNs 2 (ft); Nurses aides 28 (ft); Physical therapists 1 (pt); Activities coordinators 1 (ft); Dietitians 1 (pt); Dentists 1 (pt).
Facilities Dining room; Physical therapy room; Activities room; Crafts room; Laundry room; Barber/Beauty shop.
Activities Arts & crafts; Cards; Games; Prayer groups; Shopping trips.

SAYRE

Hensley Nursing Home*
Rte 4, Box 136, Sayre, OK, 73662
(405) 928-2494
Admin Elmer Barr.
Licensure Intermediate care. *Beds* 67.
Certified Medicaid.

Town Hall Estates Nursing Center*
501 E Grand, Sayre, OK, 73662
(405) 928-3374
Admin Lawrence Thomas.
Licensure Intermediate care. *Beds* 101.
Certified Medicaid.

SEILING

Seiling Nursing Center*
Hwy 60 N, Seiling, OK, 73663
(405) 922-4433
Admin Jeneva Helterbrake.
Licensure Intermediate care. *Beds* 31.
Certified Medicaid.

SEMINOLE

Seminole Pioneer Nursing Home Inc*
1705 State St, Seminole, OK, 74868
(405) 382-1270
Admin Marchetta Black. *Medical Dir/Dir of Nursing* Auttis Johnson.
Licensure Intermediate care. *Beds* 146.
Certified Medicaid.

SENTINEL

Sentinel Nursing Home*
221 S 7th, Sentinel, OK, 73664
(405) 393-4385
Admin Albert Gray.

Licensure Intermediate care. *Beds* 25.
Certified Medicaid.

SHATTUCK

Convalescent Center of Shuttuck*
201 N Alfalfa, Box 189, Shattuck, OK, 73858
(405) 938-2501
Admin Karen Bittman.
Licensure Intermediate care. *Beds* 60.
Certified Medicaid.
Owner Proprietary Corp (Amity Care).
Admissions Requirements Minimum age 18; Medical examination.
Staff RNs 1 (pt); LPNs 2 (ft), 1 (pt); Nurses aides 13 (ft), 2 (pt); Physical therapists 1 (pt); Recreational therapists 1 (pt); Activities coordinators 1 (pt); Dietitians 1 (pt).
Facilities Dining room; Activities room; Crafts room; Laundry room; Barber/Beauty shop.
Activities Arts & crafts; Cards; Games; Prayer groups; Movies; Shopping trips; Social/Cultural gatherings.

SHAWNEE

Golden Rule Home Inc*
W Hardesty Rd, Shawnee, OK, 74801
(405) 273-7106
Admin Charles R Smith.
Licensure Intermediate care. *Beds* 34.
Certified Medicaid.

Independence Manor*
909 E Independence, Shawnee, OK, 74801
(405) 273-7156
Admin Jimmy E Rose.
Licensure Intermediate care. *Beds* 100.
Certified Medicaid.

Parkview Nursing Home Inc*
1100 E Edwards, Shawnee, OK, 74801
(405) 273-4835
Admin Jearl Smart.
Licensure Intermediate care. *Beds* 78.
Certified Medicaid.

Shawnee Care Center*
1202 W Gilmore, Shawnee, OK, 74801
(405) 273-8043
Admin Dennis P Wodowski.
Licensure Intermediate care. *Beds* 114.
Certified Medicaid.
Owner Proprietary Corp (Beverly Enterprises).

Shawnee Colonial Estates Nursing Home Inc
535 W Federal, Shawnee, OK, 74801
(405) 273-1826
Admin Sue Kanady. *Medical Dir/Dir of Nursing* Betty Wood RN.
Licensure Intermediate care. *Beds* 106.
Certified Medicaid.
Owner Proprietary Corp.
Admissions Requirements Minimum age 18; Medical examination.
Staff RNs 2 (ft); LPNs 7 (ft); Nurses aides 60 (ft), 20 (pt); Activities coordinators 1 (ft); Social Service 1 (ft).
Facilities Dining room; Physical therapy room; Activities room; Crafts room; Laundry room; Barber/Beauty shop.
Activities Arts & crafts; Cards; Games; Reading groups; Prayer groups; Movies; Social/Cultural gatherings; Current events.

Shawnee Sunset Estates
1402 E Independence, Shawnee, OK, 74801
(405) 275-1574
Admin William R Stewart II. *Medical Dir/Dir of Nursing* Lloyd Tucker.
Licensure Intermediate care. *Beds* ICF 72.
Certified Medicaid.
Owner Proprietary Corp.
Staff RNs 1 (ft); LPNs 4 (ft); Orderlies 4 (ft); Nurses aides 40 (ft); Activities coordinators 1 (ft); Dietitians 1 (pt).

Activities Arts & crafts; Cards; Games; Prayer groups; Movies; Shopping trips; Social/ Cultural gatherings.

SKIATOOK

Skiatook Nursing Home*
318 S Cherry, Skiatook, OK, 74070
(918) 396-2149
Admin Evelyn Reed.
Licensure Intermediate care. *Beds* 70.
Certified Medicaid.

SNYDER

Ayers Nursing Home*
801 B St, Snyder, OK, 73566
(405) 569-2258
Admin Jerry W Ayers.
Licensure Intermediate care. *Beds* 87.
Certified Medicaid.

SPIRO

Spiro Nursing Home*
401 S Main, Spiro, OK, 74959
(918) 962-2308
Admin Gary McClure.
Licensure Intermediate care. *Beds* 95.
Certified Medicaid.

STIGLER

Stigler Nursing Home
114 NE 3rd & B St, Stigler, OK, 74462
(918) 967-2389
Admin Georgett A Duvall. *Medical Dir/Dir of Nursing* Ealine Bigger RN.
Licensure Intermediate care. *Beds* ICF 100.
Certified Medicaid.
Owner Proprietary Corp.
Admissions Requirements Physician's request.
Staff Physicians; RNs; LPNs; Nurses aides; Dietitians.
Facilities Dining room; Activities room; Crafts room; Laundry room; Barber/Beauty shop.
Activities Arts & crafts; Cards; Games; Prayer groups; Movies; Shopping trips.

STILLWATER

Hearthstone Nursing Home Inc*
PO Box 2437, 3014 S Main, Stillwater, OK, 74076
(405) 372-9526
Admin Gary Smart.
Licensure Intermediate care. *Beds* 84.
Certified Medicaid.

Stillwater Nursing Home Inc*
1215 W 10th, Stillwater, OK, 74074
(405) 372-1000
Admin Jeannie Fitzgerald.
Licensure Intermediate care. *Beds* 104.
Certified Medicaid.
Owner Proprietary Corp (Amity Care).
Staff RNs 1 (ft), 1 (pt); LPNs 3 (ft); Orderlies 27 (ft), 6 (pt); Physical therapists 1 (pt); Activities coordinators 1 (ft); Dietitians 1 (pt); Dentists 1 (pt).

Stillwater Rosewood Nursing Home Inc*
1601 S Main, PO Box 2437, Stillwater, OK, 74076
(405) 377-4000
Admin Gary Smart. *Medical Dir/Dir of Nursing* Dr Sid Williams.
Licensure Intermediate care. *Beds* 104.
Certified Medicaid.
Staff Physicians 3 (pt); RNs 2 (pt); LPNs 3 (ft), 3 (pt); Activities coordinators 2 (ft); Dietitians 1 (pt).
Facilities Dining room; Physical therapy room; Activities room; Crafts room; Laundry room; Barber/Beauty shop.

Activities Arts & crafts; Cards; Games; Prayer groups; Movies; Shopping trips; Social/ Cultural gatherings; Remotivation.

Westhaven Nursing Home Inc
1215 S Western, Stillwater, OK, 74074
(405) 743-1140
Admin LaDonna Ross; Wendy Lott, Assist Admin. *Medical Dir/Dir of Nursing* Betty Foster.
Licensure Intermediate care. *Beds* ICF 112.
Certified Medicaid.
Facilities Dining room; Activities room; Laundry room; Barber/Beauty shop.
Activities Arts & crafts; Cards; Games; Reading groups; Prayer groups; Movies; Shopping trips; Social/Cultural gatherings.

STILWELL

Stilwell Nursing Home*
422 W Locust, Stilwell, OK, 74960
(918) 696-7715
Admin Fredna Latta.
Licensure Intermediate care. *Beds* 104.
Certified Medicaid.

STONEWALL

Stonegate Nursing Center
6th & Collins, Stonewall, OK, 74871
(405) 265-4247
Admin Betty Hilton. *Medical Dir/Dir of Nursing* Jeannie Ables.
Licensure Intermediate care. *Beds* 53.
Certified Medicaid.
Owner Privately owned.
Admissions Requirements Minimum age 18; Physician's request.
Staff Physicians 1 (pt); RNs 1 (pt); Nurses aides 20 (ft); Physical therapists 1 (pt); Activities coordinators 1 (ft); Dietitians 1 (pt).
Facilities Dining room; Activities room; Crafts room; Laundry room; Barber/Beauty shop.
Activities Arts & crafts; Cards; Games; Reading groups; Prayer groups; Movies; Shopping trips; Social/Cultural gatherings.

STRATFORD

Stratford Nursing Center
131 N Cottonwood, Stratford, OK, 74872
(405) 759-2268
Admin Dolores Tucker. *Medical Dir/Dir of Nursing* Melva Henderson.
Licensure Intermediate care. *Beds* ICF 106.
Certified Medicaid.
Owner Privately owned.
Admissions Requirements Medical examination; Physician's request.
Staff RNs 1 (ft); LPNs 5 (ft), 2 (pt); Orderlies 3 (ft); Nurses aides 25 (ft), 6 (pt); Physical therapists 1 (ft); Recreational therapists 1 (ft); Activities coordinators 1 (ft); Dietitians 1 (pt).
Facilities Dining room; Physical therapy room; Activities room; Crafts room; Laundry room; Barber/Beauty shop.
Activities Arts & crafts; Cards; Games; Reading groups; Prayer groups; Movies; Shopping trips; Social/Cultural gatherings.

STROUD

Care Manor Nursing Center*
721 W Olive, Stroud, OK, 74079
(918) 968-2075
Admin Susan Williams.
Licensure Intermediate care. *Beds* 58.
Certified Medicaid.

Stroud Health Care Center*
416 N 7th Ave, Stroud, OK, 74079
(918) 968-2507

Admin Roberta Snow.
Licensure Intermediate care. *Beds* 40.
Certified Medicaid.

SULPHUR

Artesian Home*
1415 W 15th, Sulphur, OK, 73086
(405) 622-2030
Admin Robert H Walker.
Licensure Intermediate care. *Beds* 62.
Certified Medicaid.

Callaway Nursing Home*
1300 W Lindsay, Sulphur, OK, 73086
(405) 622-2416
Admin Billy G Lance.
Licensure Intermediate care. *Beds* 86.
Certified Medicaid.

TAHLEQUAH

Davis Nursing Home*
1201 N Vinita Ave, Tahlequah, OK, 74464
(918) 456-6181
Admin Billie Davis.
Licensure Intermediate care. *Beds* 139.
Certified Medicaid.

Go Ye Village Medical Center
1201 W 4th St, Tahlequah, OK, 74464
(918) 456-4542
Admin James Richardson. *Medical Dir/Dir of Nursing* John F Porter DO; Frann Thompson LPN.
Licensure Intermediate care. *Beds* ICF 32.
Owner Nonprofit Corp.
Admissions Requirements Minimum age 55; Medical examination; Physician's request.
Staff Physicians 1 (ft); RNs 1 (ft), 1 (pt); LPNs 4 (ft), 2 (pt); Orderlies 1 (ft); Nurses aides 15 (ft), 5 (pt); Physical therapists 1 (pt); Reality therapists 1 (pt); Occupational therapists 1 (pt); Activities coordinators 1 (ft); Dietitians 1 (pt); Chaplains 2 (ft).
Facilities Dining room; Physical therapy room; Activities room; Chapel; Crafts room; Laundry room; Barber/Beauty shop; Library; Store.
Activities Arts & crafts; Cards; Games; Reading groups; Prayer groups; Movies; Shopping trips; Social/Cultural gatherings.

Tahlequah Nursing Home*
614 E Cherry, Tahlequah, OK, 74464
(918) 456-2573
Admin Billie Davis.
Licensure Intermediate care. *Beds* 125.
Certified Medicaid.

Ward Nursing Home*
124 E Chickasaw, Tahlequah, OK, 74464
(918) 456-3456
Admin Dennis Cheek.
Licensure Intermediate care. *Beds* 45.
Certified Medicaid.

TALIHINA

Talihina Manor Nursing Home*
1st & Thomas, Talihina, OK, 74571
(918) 567-2279
Admin Gilbert F Green.
Licensure Intermediate care. *Beds* 69.
Certified Medicaid.

TECUMSEH

Sunset Estates Inc*
201 W Walnut, Tecumseh, OK, 74873
(405) 598-2167
Admin Ken Prator. *Medical Dir/Dir of Nursing* Robert Zumwalt MD.
Licensure Intermediate care. *Beds* 100.
Certified Medicaid.
Admissions Requirements Minimum age 18; Physician's request.

Staff RNs 1 (ft); LPNs 6 (ft), 2 (pt); Orderlies 4 (ft); Nurses aides 39 (ft); Physical therapists 1 (pt); Activities coordinators 1 (ft); Dietitians 1 (pt).
Facilities Dining room; Physical therapy room; Activities room; Crafts room; Laundry room; Barber/Beauty shop.
Activities Arts & crafts; Cards; Games; Prayer groups; Movies; Shopping trips; Social/Cultural gatherings.

TEMPLE

Temple Manor Inc*
100 W Green, Temple, OK, 73568
(405) 342-6411
Admin Virginia Faye Stringer.
Licensure Intermediate care. *Beds* 48.
Certified Medicaid.

THOMAS

Thomas Nursing Center
PO Box 38, 601 E Frisco, Thomas, OK, 73669
(405) 661-2171
Admin Charleen Jantz. *Medical Dir/Dir of Nursing* Marilyn Marsh RN.
Licensure Intermediate care. *Beds* 60.
Certified Medicaid.
Owner Nonprofit Corp.
Admissions Requirements Medical examination.
Staff RNs 1 (ft); LPNs 2 (ft), 2 (pt); Orderlies 1 (pt); Nurses aides 13 (ft), 11 (pt); Physical therapists 1 (pt); Activities coordinators 1 (ft), 1 (pt); Dietitians 1 (pt).
Facilities Dining room; Physical therapy room; Activities room; Chapel; Crafts room; Laundry room; Barber/Beauty shop; Patio.
Activities Arts & crafts; Cards; Games; Prayer groups; Movies; Shopping trips; Social/Cultural gatherings.

TISHOMINGO

Hillcrest Nursing Home*
1200 E Main, Tishomingo, OK, 73460
(405) 371-2636
Admin Frank Harris.
Licensure Intermediate care. *Beds* 50.
Certified Medicaid.

Lawn View Nursing Home
607 S Byrd, Tishomingo, OK, 73460
(405) 371-2317
Admin Vearlene Burchett.
Licensure Intermediate care. *Beds* 60.
Certified Medicaid.

TONKAWA

Willow Haven
1301 N 5th St, Tonkawa, OK, 74653
(405) 628-2529
Admin Pat Scott. *Medical Dir/Dir of Nursing* Sharon Davis.
Licensure Intermediate care. *Beds* ICF 49.
Certified Medicaid.
Admissions Requirements Medical examination; Physician's request.
Staff RNs 1 (pt); LPNs 2 (ft); Nurses aides 14 (ft), 1 (pt); Activities coordinators 1 (ft); Dietitians 1 (pt).
Facilities Dining room; Activities room; Crafts room; Laundry room; Barber/Beauty shop.
Activities Arts & crafts; Cards; Games; Reading groups; Prayer groups; Movies; Shopping trips; Bingo.

TULSA

Ambassador Manor Nursing Center Inc
1340 E 61st St, Tulsa, OK, 74136
(918) 743-8978

Admin Sharon Covey. *Medical Dir/Dir of Nursing* Marla McMillian.
Licensure Intermediate care. *Beds* 142.
Certified Medicaid.
Owner Proprietary Corp.
Admissions Requirements Minimum age 55; Medical examination.
Staff Physicians 1 (ft); RNs 2 (ft); LPNs 8 (ft); Orderlies 3 (ft); Nurses aides 40 (ft); Physical therapists 1 (ft); Recreational therapists 1 (ft); Activities coordinators 1 (ft); Dietitians 1 (ft); Ophthalmologists 1 (ft); Dentist 1 (ft).
Facilities Dining room; Physical therapy room; Activities room; Chapel; Crafts room; Laundry room; Barber/Beauty shop; Library.
Activities Arts & crafts; Cards; Games; Reading groups; Prayer groups; Movies; Shopping trips; Social/Cultural gatherings; Opera; Ballet; Concerts.

Black's Nursing Home
3601 N Columbia, Tulsa, OK, 74110
(918) 425-1668
Admin Mary Henderson.
Licensure Intermediate care. *Beds* 54.
Certified Medicaid.
Admissions Requirements Minimum age 18; Medical examination; Physician's request.
Staff Physicians 1 (pt); LPNs 3 (ft); Nurses aides 14 (ft), 2 (pt); Dietitians 1 (pt).
Facilities Dining room; Laundry room; Barber/Beauty shop.
Activities Arts & crafts; Cards; Games; Reading groups; Prayer groups; Movies; Shopping trips; Social/Cultural gatherings.

Chamor Nursing Center*
2550 E 36th N, Tulsa, OK, 74110
(918) 425-7548
Admin T Oscar Chappelle.
Licensure Intermediate care. *Beds* 100.
Certified Medicaid.

Colonial Manor Nursing Home*
1815 E Skelly Dr, Tulsa, OK, 74105
(918) 743-7838
Admin Robert H Gary.
Licensure Intermediate care. *Beds* 120.
Certified Medicaid.

Convalescent Center Inc*
3333 E 28th, Tulsa, OK, 74114
(918) 747-8008
Admin Robert H Gray.
Licensure Intermediate care. *Beds* 56.
Certified Medicaid.

Four Seasons Nursing Center of Tulsa*
2425 S Memorial Dr, Tulsa, OK, 74129
(918) 628-0932
Admin Lewisa Gouker. *Medical Dir/Dir of Nursing* Dr Robert Gray.
Licensure Intermediate care. *Beds* 118.
Certified Medicaid.
Owner Proprietary Corp (Manor Care).
Admissions Requirements Medical examination; Physician's request.
Staff RNs 1 (ft); Nurses aides 42 (ft).
Facilities Dining room; Physical therapy room; Activities room; Laundry room; Barber/Beauty shop.
Activities Arts & crafts; Cards; Games; Movies; Shopping trips; Social/Cultural gatherings.

Georgian Court Nursing Home of Tulsa*
2552 E 21st, Tulsa, OK, 74114
(918) 742-7319
Admin Dan E Johnson. *Medical Dir/Dir of Nursing* Dr G Bryant Boyd.
Licensure Skilled care. *Beds* 48.
Admissions Requirements Physician's request.
Staff Physicians 1 (pt); RNs 1 (ft), 1 (pt); LPNs 5 (ft), 4 (pt); Orderlies 1 (pt); Nurses aides 12 (ft), 7 (pt); Physical therapists 1 (pt); Activities coordinators 1 (ft); Dietitians 1 (pt); Dentists 1 (pt); Podiatrists 1 (pt).

Facilities Dining room; Laundry room; Barber/Beauty shop.
Activities Arts & crafts; Cards; Games; Reading groups; Movies; Shopping trips; Social/Cultural gatherings.

Homestead Nursing Home
1021 Charles Page Blvd, Tulsa, OK, 74127
(918) 587-4189
Admin Larry L Cain. *Medical Dir/Dir of Nursing* Richard Gary MD; Terry Williams DON.
Licensure Intermediate care. *Beds* ICF 53.
Certified Medicaid.
Owner Proprietary Corp.
Admissions Requirements Minimum age 16; Medical examination; Physician's request.
Staff Physicians; RNs; LPNs 3 (ft); Physical therapists; Reality therapists 1 (ft); Dietitians 1 (pt); Ophthalmologists 1 (pt); Podiatrists 1 (pt).
Facilities Dining room; Activities room; Crafts room; Laundry room; Barber/Beauty shop.
Activities Arts & crafts; Cards; Games; Reading groups; Prayer groups; Movies; Shopping trips.

Leisure Village Nursing Center*
2154 S 85th E Ave, Tulsa, OK, 74129
(918) 622-4747
Admin Joe H Hamra.
Licensure Intermediate care. *Beds* 117.
Certified Medicaid.

The Mayfair Nursing Home
7707 S Memorial Dr, Tulsa, OK, 74133
(918) 250-8571
Admin Tandalynn L Sammer Exec Dir.
Licensure Skilled care. *Beds* SNF 100.
Owner Proprietary Corp (Hillhaven Corp).
Admissions Requirements Medical examination; Physician's request.
Staff RNs; LPNs; Orderlies; Nurses aides.
Facilities Dining room; Physical therapy room; Activities room; Crafts room; Barber/Beauty shop; Library.
Activities Arts & crafts; Cards; Games; Reading groups; Prayer groups; Movies; Shopping trips; Social/Cultural gatherings; Wine & cheese; Ceramics; Cooking.

Oklahoma Methodist Home for the Aged Inc
4134 E 31st St, Tulsa, OK, 74135
(918) 743-2565
Admin M Douglas Fleming. *Medical Dir/Dir of Nursing* Vivian Adair RN DON.
Licensure Intermediate care; Assisted retirement living; Independent retirement living. *Beds* 100. *Certified* Medicaid.
Owner Nonprofit Corp.
Admissions Requirements Minimum age 60; Medical examination.
Staff RNs 4 (ft); LPNs 12 (ft); Nurses aides 26 (ft); Physical therapists 1 (ft); Activities coordinators 2 (ft); Dietitians 1 (ft).
Affiliation Methodist
Facilities Dining room; Physical therapy room; Activities room; Chapel; Crafts room; Laundry room; Barber/Beauty shop; Library; Dental office.
Activities Arts & crafts; Cards; Games; Prayer groups; Movies; Shopping trips; Social/Cultural gatherings.

Park Terrace Convalescent Center*
5115 E 51st, Tulsa, OK, 74135
(918) 627-5961
Admin J Janice Meredith.
Licensure Intermediate care. *Beds* 126.
Admissions Requirements Medical examination.
Staff RNs; LPNs; Nurses aides; Recreational therapists; Activities coordinators.
Facilities Dining room; Activities room; Crafts room; Laundry room; Barber/Beauty shop.

Activities Arts & crafts; Cards; Games; Reading groups; Movies; Shopping trips.

Regency Park Manor Health Care Center*
3910 Park Rd, Tulsa, OK, 74115
(918) 425-1354
Admin Colette Capper.
Licensure Intermediate care. *Beds* 105.
Certified Medicaid.
Owner Proprietary Corp (ARA Living Centers).

Rest Haven Nursing Home*
1944 N Iroquois, Tulsa, OK, 74106
(918) 583-1509
Admin T Oscar Chappelle. *Medical Dir/Dir of Nursing* Dr Angelo Dagessandro.
Licensure Intermediate care. *Beds* 100.
Certified Medicaid.
Admissions Requirements Minimum age 21; Medical examination; Physician's request.
Staff Physicians 3 (pt); RNs 2 (ft); LPNs 3 (ft); Orderlies 4 (ft); Nurses aides 23 (ft); Physical therapists 1 (pt); Reality therapists 1 (ft); Recreational therapists 1 (pt); Activities coordinators 1 (ft); Dietitians 1 (pt).
Facilities Dining room; Physical therapy room; Activities room; Chapel; Laundry room; Barber/Beauty shop.
Activities Arts & crafts; Games; Reading groups; Prayer groups; Movies; Shopping trips; Social/Cultural gatherings.

St John Medical Center
1923 S Utica Ave, Tulsa, OK, 74104
(918) 744-2312
Admin Sr M Therese Gottschalk. *Medical Dir/ Dir of Nursing* Elaine Hadley.
Licensure Skilled care. *Beds* SNF 30. *Certified* Medicaid; Medicare.
Owner Nonprofit organization/foundation.
Admissions Requirements Physician's request.
Staff Physicians; RNs; LPNs; Orderlies; Nurses aides; Physical therapists; Recreational therapists; Occupational therapists; Speech therapists; Dietitians.
Affiliation Roman Catholic
Facilities Dining room; Physical therapy room; Activities room; Chapel; Crafts room; Barber/Beauty shop; Library.
Activities Arts & crafts; Cards; Games; Reading groups; Prayer groups; Movies; Social/Cultural gatherings.

St Simeon's Episcopal Home Inc*
3701 N Cincinnati, Tulsa, OK, 74106
(918) 425-3583
Admin Jerry D Pinson.
Licensure Intermediate care. *Beds* 25.
Certified Medicaid.
Affiliation Episcopal

Sherwood Manor Nursing Home*
2415 W Skelly Dr, Tulsa, OK, 74107
(918) 446-4284
Admin Opal Carter.
Licensure Intermediate care. *Beds* 102.
Certified Medicaid.

Skyline Terrace Nursing Center*
6202 E 61st, Tulsa, OK, 74136
(918) 494-8830
Admin Joyce Lyons, Carl Lyons, & Cindy Lyons. *Medical Dir/Dir of Nursing* Arthur Hale MD.
Licensure Skilled care. *Beds* 209. *Certified* Medicare.
Admissions Requirements Medical examination; Physician's request.
Facilities Dining room; Physical therapy room; Activities room; Chapel; Crafts room; Laundry room; Barber/Beauty shop; Library.
Activities Arts & crafts; Cards; Games; Reading groups; Prayer groups; Movies; Shopping trips; Social/Cultural gatherings.

Southern Hills Nursing Center*
5170 S Vandalia, Tulsa, OK, 74135
(918) 496-3963
Admin Julia Galvin.
Licensure Intermediate care. *Beds* 118.
Certified Medicaid.

Tulsa Christian Home Inc
6201 E 36th St, Tulsa, OK, 74135
(918) 622-3430
Admin Jewell Dessinger. *Medical Dir/Dir of Nursing* Dr Robert Mahaffey; Charline Dyer RN.
Licensure Intermediate care. *Beds* ICF 100.
Certified Medicaid.
Owner Nonprofit Corp.
Admissions Requirements Medical examination; Physician's request.
Staff Physicians 1 (pt); RNs 1 (ft); LPNs 6 (ft); Orderlies 1 (ft); Nurses aides 34 (ft), 1 (pt); Physical therapists 1 (pt); Activities coordinators 2 (ft); Dietitians 1 (pt).
Affiliation Church of Christ
Facilities Dining room; Physical therapy room; Activities room; Crafts room; Laundry room; Barber/Beauty shop; Library.
Activities Arts & crafts; Games; Reading groups; Movies; Shopping trips.

Tulsa Nursing Center*
10912 E 14th St, Tulsa, OK, 74128
(918) 438-2440
Admin Wilma Corley.
Licensure Intermediate care. *Beds* 150.
Certified Medicaid.

University Village Inc*
8555 S Lewis, Tulsa, OK, 74137
(918) 299-2661
Admin Don Steele. *Medical Dir/Dir of Nursing* Dr Edward Slothour.
Licensure Skilled care. *Beds* 70.
Admissions Requirements Medical examination.
Staff Physicians 1 (ft); RNs 5 (ft), 1 (pt); LPNs 3 (ft), 2 (pt); Orderlies 4 (ft); Nurses aides 24 (ft), 6 (pt); Physical therapists 1 (ft); Activities coordinators 1 (ft); Dietitians 1 (ft).
Affiliation Oral Roberts Ministries
Facilities Dining room; Physical therapy room; Activities room; Chapel; Crafts room; Laundry room; Barber/Beauty shop; Library.
Activities Arts & crafts; Cards; Games; Reading groups; Prayer groups; Movies; Shopping trips; Social/Cultural gatherings.

Woodland Park Home*
5707 S Memorial Dr, Tulsa, OK, 74145
(918) 252-2521
Admin Genevieve Gary.
Licensure Intermediate care. *Beds* 101.
Certified Medicaid.

TUTTLE

Care Manor Nursing Center of Tuttle*
108 S 12th, Tuttle, OK, 73089
(405) 381-3363
Admin Thelma Green.
Licensure Intermediate care. *Beds* 52.
Certified Medicaid.

VALLIANT

Valliant Care Center Inc
PO Box 957, 300 N Dalton, Valliant, OK, 74764
(405) 933-7803
Admin Phillip Gilbert. *Medical Dir/Dir of Nursing* Irene Farris RN.
Licensure Intermediate care. *Beds* ICF 65.
Certified Medicaid.
Owner Proprietary Corp.
Admissions Requirements Medical examination.

Staff RNs 1 (ft); LPNs 3 (ft), 1 (pt); Nurses aides 26 (ft); Activities coordinators 1 (ft).
Facilities Dining room; Laundry room; Barber/Beauty shop.
Activities Arts & crafts; Games; Prayer groups; Movies; Social/Cultural gatherings.

VIAN

Vian Nursing Home*
Thornton St, Vian, OK, 74962
(918) 773-5258
Admin Billy E Fullbright.
Licensure Intermediate care. *Beds* 112.
Certified Medicaid.

VICI

Town of Vici Nursing Home
619 Speck, Vici, OK, 73859
(405) 995-4216
Admin Ileta Allen.
Licensure Intermediate care. *Beds* 61.
Certified Medicaid.

VINITA

Autumn Nursing Centers Inc 1
240 N Scraper, Vinita, OK, 74301
(918) 256-7861
Admin Kunigunda M Lodes. *Medical Dir/Dir of Nursing* Nancy Stanley RN.
Licensure Intermediate care. *Beds* ICF 62.
Certified Medicaid.
Owner Privately owned.
Admissions Requirements Medical examination.
Staff RNs 1 (ft); LPNs 1 (ft), 2 (pt); Orderlies 1 (ft), 3 (pt); Nurses aides 9 (ft), 6 (pt); Activities coordinators 1 (ft); Dietitians 1 (ft), 1 (pt).
Facilities Dining room; Laundry room; Barber/Beauty shop.
Activities Arts & crafts; Cards; Games; Reading groups; Prayer groups; Movies; Shopping trips; Social/Cultural gatherings; Trips to park.

Autumn Nursing Centers Inc 2*
1200 W Canadian, Vinita, OK, 74301
(918) 256-6366
Admin Edwina Hoskin.
Licensure Intermediate care. *Beds* 121.
Certified Medicaid.

Home of Hope Inc
Hope Blvd & N Adair, Vinita, OK, 74301
(918) 256-7825
Admin Charlotte McComb.
Licensure Intermediate care for mentally retarded. *Beds* 94. *Certified* Medicaid.
Admissions Requirements Minimum age 18; Medical examination.
Facilities Dining room; Activities room; Crafts room; Laundry room; Barber/Beauty shop.
Activities Arts & crafts; Games; Reading groups; Movies; Shopping trips; Social/Cultural gatherings.

WAGONER

Ross Nursing Home 1 Inc*
205 N Lincoln, Wagoner, OK, 74467
(918) 485-2203
Admin Dwana Barnes.
Licensure Intermediate care. *Beds* 73.
Certified Medicaid.

Ross Nursing Home 2 Inc*
109 S Harrill, Wagoner, OK, 74467
(918) 485-3972
Admin Dwana Barnes.
Licensure Intermediate care. *Beds* 54.
Certified Medicaid.

WAKITA

Community Health Center
Cherokee St, Wakita, OK, 73771
(405) 594-2292
Admin Adena Rogers. *Medical Dir/Dir of Nursing* R J Helton DO.
Licensure Intermediate care. *Beds* 47.
Certified Medicaid.
Staff Physicians 1 (ft), 1 (pt); RNs 5 (ft), 4 (pt); LPNs 2 (ft); Nurses aides 27 (ft); Physical therapists 1 (pt); Activities coordinators 1 (ft); Dietitians 1 (ft); Dentists 1 (ft).
Facilities Dining room; Physical therapy room; Activities room; Chapel; Crafts room; Laundry room; Barber/Beauty shop; Library; Sunroom.
Activities Arts & crafts; Cards; Games; Reading groups; Prayer groups; Movies; Shopping trips; Social/Cultural gatherings.

WALTERS

Parkview Manor
600 E California, Walters, OK, 73752
(405) 875-3376
Admin Eva Miller.
Licensure Intermediate care. *Beds* 54.
Certified Medicaid.

WARNER

Countryside Estates Inc*
Box 629, Warner, OK, 74469
(918) 463-5143
Admin Margie Burris.
Licensure Intermediate care. *Beds* 90.
Certified Medicaid.
Staff Physicians 1 (pt); RNs 1 (pt); LPNs 5 (ft); Nurses aides 27 (ft); Physical therapists 1 (pt); Activities coordinators 1 (ft); Dietitians 1 (pt).
Facilities Dining room; Laundry room; Barber/Beauty shop; TV area.
Activities Arts & crafts; Cards; Games; Prayer groups; Shopping trips; Social/Cultural gatherings.

WATONGA

Hillcrest of Watonga Inc*
816 N Hook, Watonga, OK, 73772
(405) 623-7249
Admin Walter C Deane. *Medical Dir/Dir of Nursing* Regina Stinson RN.
Licensure Intermediate care. *Beds* 70.
Certified Medicaid.
Staff Physicians 4 (pt); RNs 1 (ft); LPNs 3 (pt); Nurses aides 19 (ft), 3 (pt); Activities coordinators 1 (ft); Dietitians 1 (pt).
Facilities Dining room; Activities room; Crafts room; Laundry room; Barber/Beauty shop.
Activities Arts & crafts; Cards; Games; Reading groups; Prayer groups; Movies; Shopping trips; Social/Cultural gatherings.

WAURIKA

Wood Nursing & Convalescent Center
PO Box 390, 1100 N Ash, Waurika, OK, 73573
(405) 228-2249
Admin Virgil L Wood Jr.
Licensure Intermediate care. *Beds* 83.
Certified Medicaid.

WAYNOKA

Waynoka Nursing Home
PO Box 50, Rte 2, Waynoka, OK, 73860
(405) 824-5661
Admin Michael L Wallace. *Medical Dir/Dir of Nursing* Becky Kath LPN.

Licensure Intermediate care. *Beds* ICF 40.
Certified Medicaid.
Owner Proprietary Corp.
Admissions Requirements Physician's request.
Staff Physicians; RNs; LPNs; Nurses aides; Dietitians.
Languages Spanish
Facilities Dining room; Activities room; Laundry room; Barber/Beauty shop; Whirlpool tub.
Activities Arts & crafts; Cards; Games; Reading groups; Prayer groups; Movies; Shopping trips; Social/Cultural gatherings.

WEATHERFORD

Little Bird Nursing Home Inc*
801 N Washington, Weatherford, OK, 73096
(405) 772-3993
Admin Lola Little Bird.
Licensure Intermediate care. *Beds* 81.
Certified Medicaid.

Weatherford Nursing Center
1015 N 7th, Weatherford, OK, 73096
(405) 772-3368
Admin Vonda R Carroll. *Medical Dir/Dir of Nursing* Iris Ainsworth DON.
Licensure Intermediate care. *Beds* ICF 52.
Certified Medicaid.
Owner Proprietary Corp.
Admissions Requirements Medical examination.
Staff RNs 1 (pt); LPNs 3 (ft); Orderlies 4 (ft), 1 (pt); Nurses aides 8 (ft); Activities coordinators 1 (ft), 1 (pt); Dietitians 1 (pt); CMAs 3 (ft), 2 (pt).
Facilities Dining room; Laundry room; Barber/Beauty shop.
Activities Arts & crafts; Cards; Games; Reading groups; Prayer groups; Movies; Shopping trips; Social/Cultural gatherings; Voluntary church organizations.

WELEETKA

Adkins Nursing Home*
300 W 9th, Weleetka, OK, 74880
(405) 786-2244
Admin Gerrol Adkins.
Licensure Intermediate care. *Beds* 60.
Certified Medicaid.

Adkins-Weleetka Nursing Home*
122 E 10th, Weleetka, OK, 74880
(405) 786-2401
Admin Gerrol Akins.
Licensure Intermediate care. *Beds* 45.
Certified Medicaid.

WEST SILOAM SPRINGS

Quail Ridge Living Center
PO Box 1005, Stateline Rd & Jefferson, West Siloam Springs, OK, 72761
(918) 422-5138
Admin John S Carlile. *Medical Dir/Dir of Nursing* Glenda Copeland.
Licensure Intermediate care. *Beds* ICF 100.
Certified Medicaid; Medicare.
Owner Proprietary Corp.
Admissions Requirements Medical examination; Physician's request.
Staff Physicians 1 (ft); RNs 1 (pt); LPNs 5 (ft); Orderlies 2 (ft); Nurses aides 25 (ft), 4 (pt); Physical therapists 1 (ft); Recreational therapists 1 (ft); Activities coordinators 1 (ft); Dietitians 1 (ft), 1 (pt).
Languages Cherokee
Facilities Dining room; Activities room; Crafts room; Laundry room; Barber/Beauty shop.
Activities Arts & crafts; Cards; Games; Reading groups; Prayer groups; Movies; Shopping trips; Social/Cultural gatherings.

WESTVILLE

Westville Nursing Home*
308 Williams St, Westville, OK, 74965
(918) 723-5476
Admin Sadie Blackwood.
Licensure Intermediate care. *Beds* 79.
Certified Medicaid.

WETUMKA

Pioneer Nursing Home of Hughes Inc*
620 S Alabama, Wetumka, OK, 74883
(405) 452-3296
Admin Helen Robinson-Knight. *Medical Dir/Dir of Nursing* Jane Gustin LPN.
Licensure Intermediate care. *Beds* 50.
Certified Medicaid.
Staff Physicians; RNs; LPNs; Orderlies; Nurses aides; Physical therapists; Activities coordinators; Dietitians; Dentists; Ophthalmologists.
Facilities Dining room; Activities room; Crafts room; Laundry room; Barber/Beauty shop.
Activities Arts & crafts; Games; Reading groups; Prayer groups; Shopping trips; Social/Cultural gatherings.

Wetumka Nursing Home Inc
700 N Main, Wetumka, OK, 74883
(405) 452-5126
Admin Loretta Goodin. *Medical Dir/Dir of Nursing* Dr Wade Warren; Pauline Jacobs DON.
Licensure Intermediate care. *Beds* ICF 50.
Certified Medicare.
Owner Proprietary Corp.
Admissions Requirements Physician's request.
Staff Physicians 2 (ft); RNs 1 (ft); LPNs 2 (ft); Nurses aides 17 (ft); Activities coordinators 1 (ft); Dietitians 1 (ft).
Facilities Dining room; Physical therapy room; Activities room; Chapel; Crafts room; Laundry room; Barber/Beauty shop; Library.
Activities Arts & crafts; Cards; Games; Reading groups; Prayer groups; Shopping trips; Social/Cultural gatherings.

WEWOKA

Elmwood Manor Inc*
300 S Seminole, Wewoka, OK, 74884
(405) 257-2576
Admin John Grimes.
Licensure Intermediate care. *Beds* 47.
Certified Medicaid.

Oakridge Home Inc*
7th & Compton, Wewoka, OK, 74884
(405) 257-5800
Admin Max Filson.
Licensure Intermediate care. *Beds* 160.
Certified Medicaid.
Staff Physicians 1 (pt); RNs 1 (ft); LPNs 6 (ft); Orderlies 4 (ft); Nurses aides 30 (ft); Recreational therapists 1 (ft); Activities coordinators 4 (ft); Dietitians 1 (ft).

Wewoka Nursing Home Inc*
200 E 4th, Wewoka, OK, 74884
(405) 257-3393
Admin James Robert Smart.
Licensure Intermediate care. *Beds* 57.
Certified Medicaid.

WILBURTON

Community Nursing Home*
200 NE 1st, Box 607, Wilburton, OK, 74578
(918) 465-2221
Admin Philip M Green. *Medical Dir/Dir of Nursing* Deborah Morgan LPN.
Licensure Intermediate care. *Beds* 29.
Certified Medicaid.
Admissions Requirements Medical examination.

Staff Physicians 1 (pt); RNs 1 (pt); LPNs 2 (ft); Nurses aides 11 (ft); Reality therapists 1 (ft); Recreational therapists 1 (ft); Activities coordinators 1 (ft); Dietitians 1 (pt); Dentists 1 (pt); Ophthalmologists 1 (pt); Podiatrists 1 (pt).
Facilities Dining room; Activities room; Chapel; Crafts room; Laundry room; Barber/Beauty shop; Library.
Activities Arts & crafts; Cards; Games; Prayer groups; Movies; Shopping trips; Social/Cultural gatherings.

Latimer Nursing Home*
Hwy 2 N, Wilburton, OK, 74578
(918) 465-2255
Admin Frances Mordecai.
Licensure Intermediate care. *Beds* 39.
Certified Medicaid.

Ranchwood Lodge Home*
900 W Ranchwood Dr, Wilburton, OK, 74578
(918) 465-2314
Admin Rosie Foster. *Medical Dir/Dir of Nursing* Liz Hawthorne.
Licensure Intermediate care. *Beds* 55.
Certified Medicaid.
Owner Proprietary Corp (ARA Living Centers).
Admissions Requirements Medical examination; Physician's request.
Staff Physicians; RNs; LPNs; Orderlies; Nurses aides; Physical therapists; Reality therapists; Recreational therapists; Occupational therapists; Activities coordinators; Dietitians; Dentists; Podiatrists; Audiologists.
Facilities Dining room; Activities room; Chapel; Crafts room; Laundry room; Barber/Beauty shop.
Activities Arts & crafts; Cards; Games; Prayer groups; Movies; Shopping trips; Social/Cultural gatherings.

WILSON

Wilson Nursing Center
406 E Main, Wilson, OK, 73463
(405) 668-2012

Admin Linda Curtis. *Medical Dir/Dir of Nursing* Nadine Goode.
Licensure Intermediate care. *Beds* ICF 60.
Certified Medicaid.
Owner Proprietary Corp (ARA Living Centers).
Admissions Requirements Medical examination; Physician's request.
Staff RNs; LPNs; Nurses aides; Reality therapists; Recreational therapists; Activities coordinators; Dietitians 1 (pt).
Facilities Dining room; Activities room; Crafts room; Laundry room; Barber/Beauty shop.
Activities Arts & crafts; Games; Reading groups; Prayer groups; Movies; Shopping trips; Social/Cultural gatherings; Family nights; Exercise group.

WOODWARD

Colonial Manor Nursing Home of Woodward Inc
2608 Reardon Rd, Woodward, OK, 73801
(405) 254-3456
Admin Kenneth Morrison.
Licensure Intermediate care. *Beds* 70.
Certified Medicaid.

Woodward Nursing Center*
429 Downs Ave, Woodward, OK, 73801
(405) 256-6448
Admin Nina Clabaugh.
Licensure Intermediate care. *Beds* 80.
Certified Medicaid.
Owner Proprietary Corp (Amity Care).

WYNNEWOOD

Wynnewood Nursing Center*
810 E California, Wynnewood, OK, 73098
(405) 665-2330
Admin Jo Ann Clayton.
Licensure Intermediate care. *Beds* 79.
Certified Medicaid.

YALE

Yale Nursing Home*
E Chicago & H St, Yale, OK, 74085
(918) 387-2412
Admin Susan G Williams.
Licensure Intermediate care. *Beds* 50.
Certified Medicaid.
Staff RNs 1 (pt); LPNs 2 (ft); Orderlies 1 (ft); Nurses aides 26 (ft); Physical therapists 1 (pt); Activities coordinators 1 (ft); Dietitians 1 (pt); Dentists 1 (pt).
Facilities Dining room; Physical therapy room; Activities room; Chapel; Crafts room; Laundry room; Barber/Beauty shop.
Activities Arts & crafts; Cards; Games; Prayer groups; Shopping trips; Social/Cultural gatherings.

YUKON

Cottonwood Manor Nursing Home*
300 Walnut, Yukon, OK, 73099
(405) 354-2563
Admin Liz Cummings.
Licensure Intermediate care. *Beds* 122.
Certified Medicaid.

Yukon Convalescent Center*
1110 Cornwell, Yukon, OK, 73099
(405) 354-5373
Admin Judy Greenameyer. *Medical Dir/Dir of Nursing* Dianne Lee.
Licensure Intermediate care. *Beds* 69.
Certified Medicaid.
Owner Proprietary Corp (ARA Living Centers).
Admissions Requirements Medical examination.
Staff Physicians 1 (ft); RNs 1 (pt); LPNs 6 (ft); Orderlies 1 (pt); Nurses aides 17 (ft), 1 (pt); Physical therapists 1 (pt); Occupational therapists 1 (pt); Activities coordinators 2 (ft); Dietitians 1 (pt); Podiatrists 1 (pt).
Facilities Dining room; Activities room; Crafts room; Laundry room; Barber/Beauty shop.
Activities Arts & crafts; Cards; Games; Reading groups; Prayer groups; Movies; Shopping trips; Social/Cultural gatherings.

OREGON

ALBANY

Albany Care Center
805 E 19th, Albany, OR, 97321
(503) 926-4741
Admin Kent Van Winckel. *Medical Dir/Dir of Nursing* Dr Lear; Donna Selig DON.
Licensure Intermediate care. *Beds* ICF 92. *Certified* Medicaid.
Owner Proprietary Corp.
Admissions Requirements Medical examination; Physician's request.
Staff RNs 8 (ft), 5 (pt); LPNs 6 (ft), 5 (pt); Orderlies 4 (ft), 1 (pt); Nurses aides 40 (ft), 15 (pt); Physical therapists 1 (pt); Recreational therapists 1 (pt); Occupational therapists; Activities coordinators 1 (ft); Dietitians 1 (ft); Dentists; Ophthalmologists; Podiatrists.
Facilities Dining room; Physical therapy room; Activities room; Barber/Beauty shop.
Activities Arts & crafts; Games; Prayer groups; Shopping trips.

Linn Care Center
1023 W 6th Ave, Albany, OR, 97321
(503) 926-8664
Admin Mary J Prentice. *Medical Dir/Dir of Nursing* Benjamin Bonnlander & Daniel Mulkey; Carol Mara DON.
Licensure Skilled care; Intermediate care. *Beds* SNF 16; ICF 82. *Certified* Medicaid; Medicare.
Owner Proprietary Corp (Beverly Enterprises).
Admissions Requirements Medical examination; Physician's request.
Staff RNs 7 (ft); Nurses aides 27 (ft); Physical therapists 1 (pt); Recreational therapists 3 (pt); Occupational therapists 1 (pt); Speech therapists 1 (pt); Activities coordinators 1 (ft); Dietitians 1 (pt).
Facilities Dining room; Physical therapy room; Activities room; Crafts room; Laundry room; Barber/Beauty shop; TV room.
Activities Arts & crafts; Games; Reading groups; Prayer groups; Movies; Shopping trips.

Mennonite Home
5353 SE Columbus, Albany, OR, 97321
(503) 928-7232
Admin Karl Birky. *Medical Dir/Dir of Nursing* Donald Kerr MD; Helen McGovern RN.
Licensure Intermediate care; Independent living apartments; Residential care. *Beds* ICF 95; Independent living units 133; Residential 58. *Certified* Medicaid.
Owner Nonprofit Corp.
Admissions Requirements Medical examination; Physician's request.
Staff RNs 5 (ft), 7 (pt); LPNs 2 (ft), 2 (pt); Nurses aides 36 (ft), 22 (pt); Physical therapists 1 (ft); Activities coordinators 1 (ft); Dietitians 1 (pt).
Affiliation Mennonite
Facilities Dining room; Activities room; Crafts room; Laundry room; Barber/Beauty shop; Library.

Activities Arts & crafts; Games; Reading groups; Prayer groups; Movies; Shopping trips; Social/Cultural gatherings.

ASHLAND

Linda Vista Care Center
135 Maple St, Ashland, OR, 97520
(503) 482-2341
Admin Mary H Boles. *Medical Dir/Dir of Nursing* Jerome Nitzberg MD.
Licensure Intermediate care. *Beds* ICF 83. *Certified* Medicaid.
Owner Proprietary Corp (Prestige Care Inc).
Facilities Dining room; Physical therapy room; Activities room; Crafts room; Laundry room; Barber/Beauty shop.
Activities Arts & crafts; Cards; Games; Reading groups; Prayer groups; Movies; Shopping trips; Social/Cultural gatherings.

ASTORIA

Clatsop Care & Rehabilitation Center
646 16th St, Astoria, OR, 97103
(503) 325-0313
Admin Kenneth M Taylor. *Medical Dir/Dir of Nursing* Paul Voeller MD; Jean Still DNS.
Licensure Skilled care; Intermediate care; Residential care; Apartments. *Beds* SNF; ICF 30; Residential 15; Apts 11. *Certified* Medicaid; Medicare.
Owner Nonprofit organization/foundation.
Admissions Requirements Minimum age 18; Medical examination; Physician's request.
Staff Physicians 1 (pt); RNs 4 (ft), 1 (pt); LPNs 3 (ft), 1 (pt); Nurses aides 16 (ft), 7 (pt); Physical therapists 1 (pt); Occupational therapists 1 (pt); Speech therapists 1 (pt); Activities coordinators 1 (ft); Dietitians 1 (pt); Ophthalmologists 1 (pt).
Facilities Dining room; Physical therapy room; Chapel; Laundry room; Barber/Beauty shop.
Activities Arts & crafts; Cards; Games; Reading groups; Shopping trips; Social/Cultural gatherings.

Crestview Care Center*
263 W Exchange, Astoria, OR, 97103
(503) 325-1753
Admin Don Johnston.
Licensure Intermediate care. *Beds* 82. *Certified* Medicaid.

BAKER

Cedar Manor*
4000 Cedar St, Baker, OR, 97814
(503) 523-6333
Admin Chuck Williams.
Licensure Intermediate care. *Beds* 55. *Certified* Medicaid.
Admissions Requirements Physician's request.

Staff RNs 1 (ft), 1 (pt); LPNs 4 (ft), 1 (pt); Orderlies 1 (ft); Nurses aides 25 (ft), 5 (pt); Activities coordinators 1 (ft); Dietitians 1 (pt).
Facilities Dining room; Activities room; Laundry room; Barber/Beauty shop; Library.
Activities Arts & crafts; Cards; Games; Reading groups; Movies; Shopping trips; Social/Cultural gatherings.

St Elizabeth Health Care Center
Box 1046, 3985 Midway Dr, Baker, OR, 97814
(503) 523-4452, 4453
Admin Sr Isabel Marie Haughey. *Medical Dir/Dir of Nursing* Sr Jacqueline Christian RN.
Licensure Intermediate care. *Beds* ICF 80. *Certified* Medicaid.
Owner Nonprofit Corp.
Admissions Requirements Physician's request.
Staff RNs 2 (ft), 2 (pt); LPNs 1 (ft), 4 (pt); Nurses aides 24 (ft), 6 (pt); Activities coordinators 2 (ft), 1 (pt).
Affiliation Roman Catholic
Facilities Dining room; Physical therapy room; Activities room; Chapel; Crafts room; Laundry room; Barber/Beauty shop; Library; TV room; Solarium; Courtyard; Smoking room.
Activities Arts & crafts; Cards; Games; Reading groups; Prayer groups; Movies; Shopping trips; Social/Cultural gatherings.

BANDON

Oceanview Care Center of Care Centers West
PO Box 552, 2790 Beach Loop Rd, Bandon, OR, 97411
(503) 347-4424
Admin Carolyn Schwindt. *Medical Dir/Dir of Nursing* Carolyn Schwindt RN DON.
Licensure Intermediate care. *Beds* ICF 37. *Certified* Medicaid; Medicare.
Owner Privately owned.
Admissions Requirements Medical examination; Physician's request.
Staff Physicians; RNs 2 (ft), 1 (pt); LPNs; Nurses aides 19 (ft); Activities coordinators 1 (ft); Dietitians.
Facilities Dining room; Activities room; Crafts room; Laundry room; Barber/Beauty shop; Library.
Activities Arts & crafts; Cards; Games; Reading groups; Prayer groups; Movies; Shopping trips; Social/Cultural gatherings; Pool; Bowling.

BEAVERTON

Bel Air Care Center*
11850 SW Allen Blvd, Beaverton, OR, 97005
(503) 646-7164
Admin Robert Berger.
Licensure Intermediate care. *Beds* 104. *Certified* Medicaid.
Owner Proprietary Corp (Hillhaven Corp).

Maryville Nursing Home*
14645 SW Farmington Rd, Beaverton, OR,
97005
(503) 643-8626
Admin Sr M Theresa Margaret. *Medical Dir/
Dir of Nursing* Donald R Alson MD.
Licensure Intermediate care. *Beds* 132.
Certified Medicaid.
Staff RNs 10 (ft); LPNs 3 (ft); Orderlies 3 (ft);
Nurses aides 36 (ft); Physical therapists 2
(pt); Recreational therapists 2 (ft); Activities
coordinators 1 (ft); Dietitians 1 (pt); Dentists
1 (pt); Ophthalmologists 1 (pt); Podiatrists 1
(pt).
Affiliation Roman Catholic
Facilities Dining room; Physical therapy
room; Activities room; Chapel; Crafts room;
Laundry room; Barber/Beauty shop; Library;
Lounge.
Activities Arts & crafts; Cards; Games; Prayer
groups; Movies; Social/Cultural gatherings;
Sing-alongs.

BEND

Bachelor Butte Nursing Center
119 SE Wilson Ave, Bend, OR, 97702
(503) 382-7161
Admin Joan Holbrook Bowen. *Medical Dir/
Dir of Nursing* Paul Johnson MD; Linda
Campbell RN DON.
Licensure Intermediate care. *Beds* ICF 87.
Certified Medicaid.
Owner Proprietary Corp.
Admissions Requirements Medical
examination.
Staff Physicians 1 (pt); RNs 6 (ft); LPNs 5
(ft); Nurses aides 30 (ft); Physical therapists
1 (pt); Recreational therapists 1 (ft);
Occupational therapists 1 (pt); Speech
therapists 1 (pt); Activities coordinators 1
(ft); Dietitians 1 (ft); Dentists 1 (pt);
Ophthalmologists 1 (pt); Podiatrists 1 (pt).
Facilities Dining room; Activities room;
Crafts room; Laundry room; Barber/Beauty
shop.
Activities Arts & crafts; Cards; Games;
Reading groups; Prayer groups; Movies;
Shopping trips; Exercise classes.

Central Oregon Health Care Center*
1876 NE Hwy 20, Bend, OR, 97701
(503) 382-5531
Admin Craig Riley.
Licensure Skilled care; Intermediate care. *Beds*
100. *Certified* Medicaid; Medicare.

Harmony House Nursing Home*
95 E Xerxes St, Bend, OR, 97701
(503) 382-0479
Admin Phyllis Field.
Licensure Intermediate care. *Beds* 18.
Certified Medicaid.

BROOKINGS

Curry Good Samaritan Center*
PO Box 1217, Park Ave, Brookings, OR,
97415
(503) 469-3111
Admin Rosemary Rosengren.
Licensure Intermediate care. *Beds* 71.
Certified Medicaid.
Owner Nonprofit Corp (Evangelical Lutheran/
Good Samaritan).

BURNS

Burns Nursing Home
348 W Adams, Burns, OR, 97720
(503) 573-6888
Admin Karen R Dinsmore. *Medical Dir/Dir of
Nursing* Christina Delepierre.
Licensure Intermediate care. *Beds* 40.
Certified Medicaid.
Owner Privately owned.
Admissions Requirements Physician's request.

Staff RNs 2 (ft); LPNs 2 (pt); Nurses aides 10
(ft), 5 (pt); Activities coordinators 1 (ft);
Dietitians 1 (pt).
Facilities Dining room; Activities room;
Crafts room; Laundry room.
Activities Arts & crafts; Cards; Games;
Reading groups; Prayer groups; Movies;
Shopping trips; Social/Cultural gatherings.

CANBY

Canby Care Center
390 NW 2nd Ave, Canby, OR, 97013
(503) 266-5541
Admin Miriam Larson. *Medical Dir/Dir of
Nursing* Erna Virene.
Licensure Intermediate care. *Beds* ICF 48.
Certified Medicaid.
Owner Proprietary Corp.
Admissions Requirements Physician's request.
Staff RNs 1 (ft), 2 (pt); LPNs 1 (ft), 3 (pt);
Orderlies 10 (ft), 10 (pt).
Facilities Dining room; Activities room;
Laundry room.
Activities Arts & crafts; Cards; Games;
Reading groups; Prayer groups; Movies;
Shopping trips; Church; Musical groups.

Elmhurst Nursing Home
1105 S Elm St, Canby, OR, 97013
(503) 266-1131
Admin Dale Stephens. *Medical Dir/Dir of
Nursing* Clara McDonald.
Licensure Intermediate care. *Beds* ICF 43.
Certified Medicaid.
Owner Proprietary Corp.
Admissions Requirements Minimum age 20;
Physician's request.
Staff RNs 4 (ft); LPNs 2 (ft); Orderlies 2 (ft);
Nurses aides 30 (ft); Physical therapists 1
(ft); Reality therapists 1 (ft); Recreational
therapists 1 (ft); Activities coordinators 1
(ft).
Facilities Dining room; Activities room;
Crafts room; Laundry room.
Activities Arts & crafts; Cards; Games;
Reading groups; Prayer groups; Movies;
Shopping trips.

CENTRAL POINT

Central Point Care Center
155 S 1st St, Central Point, OR, 97539
(503) 664-3355
Admin Verna A Pove. *Medical Dir/Dir of
Nursing* Mike Robinson DO; Don Vogel.
Licensure Intermediate care. *Beds* 33.
Certified Medicare.
Owner Privately owned.
Admissions Requirements Physician's request.
Staff Physicians; RNs 1 (ft), 1 (pt); LPNs 3
(ft); Nurses aides 15 (ft), 2 (pt); Physical
therapists 1 (pt); Activities coordinators 1
(ft); Dietitians 1 (pt).
Facilities Dining room.
Activities Arts & crafts; Cards; Games;
Reading groups; Shopping trips; Social/
Cultural gatherings.

CONDON

Condon Nursing Home*
311 W Gilliam, Condon, OR, 97823
(503) 384-2323
Admin Elvira McQuain.
Licensure Intermediate care. *Beds* 31.
Certified Medicaid.

COOS BAY

Coos Bay Care Center
2625 Coos Bay Blvd, Coos Bay, OR, 97420
(503) 267-2161
Admin Sharon Duerst. *Medical Dir/Dir of
Nursing* Dr Wayne Murray; Pearl E Derrick
DON.

Licensure Intermediate care; Residential care.
Beds ICF 91; Residential 1. *Certified*
Medicaid.
Owner Proprietary Corp (National Heritage).
Admissions Requirements Physician's request.
Staff RNs 4 (ft); LPNs 5 (ft); Nurses aides 35
(ft); Physical therapists 1 (ft); Activities
coordinators 1 (ft).
Facilities Dining room; Physical therapy
room; Activities room; Crafts room; Laundry
room; Barber/Beauty shop; Library.
Activities Arts & crafts; Cards; Games;
Reading groups; Prayer groups; Movies;
Shopping trips; Social/Cultural gatherings.

Life Care Center of Coos Bay
2890 Ocean Blvd, Coos Bay, OR, 97420
(503) 267-5433
Admin Patrick Burke. *Medical Dir/Dir of
Nursing* Ennis Keiser MD.
Licensure Skilled care; Intermediate care;
Residential care. *Beds* SNF 12; ICF 96;
Residential 6. *Certified* Medicaid; Medicare.
Admissions Requirements Physician's request.
Staff RNs 5 (ft), 2 (pt); LPNs 4 (ft), 1 (pt);
Nurses aides 50 (ft), 10 (pt); Physical
therapists 1 (ft); Reality therapists 1 (ft);
Activities coordinators 1 (ft); Dietitians 1
(ft).
Facilities Dining room; Physical therapy
room; Activities room; Chapel; Crafts room;
Laundry room; Barber/Beauty shop; Library.
Activities Arts & crafts; Cards; Games;
Reading groups; Prayer groups; Movies;
Social/Cultural gatherings.

COQUILLE

Coquille Care Center
HC 83 Box 5610, Coquille, OR, 97423
(503) 396-2302
Admin Debra Dalton. *Medical Dir/Dir of
Nursing* Debra Dalton RN DON.
Licensure Intermediate care. *Beds* ICF 37.
Certified Medicaid.
Owner Privately owned.
Admissions Requirements Medical
examination; Physician's request.
Staff RNs 3 (ft), 1 (pt); LPNs 1 (ft); Nurses
aides 13 (ft), 4 (pt); Activities coordinators 1
(ft).
Facilities Dining room; Activities room;
Crafts room; Laundry room.
Activities Arts & crafts; Cards; Games;
Reading groups; Prayer groups; Movies;
Shopping trips; Cooking club; Picnics; Van
outings.

CORNELIUS

**Good Shepherd Lutheran Home for Mentally
Retarded**
Box 96, Rte 4, Cornelius, OR, 97113
(503) 648-8976
Admin Ron Drews. *Medical Dir/Dir of
Nursing* Otto Loehden MD.
Licensure Intermediate care for mentally
retarded. *Beds* 87. *Certified* Medicaid.
Admissions Requirements Medical
examination.
Staff RNs 3 (ft), 1 (pt); LPNs 4 (ft), 2 (pt);
Orderlies 50 (ft), 4 (pt); Physical therapists 1
(pt); Recreational therapists 1 (ft), 1 (pt);
Occupational therapists 1 (ft), 1 (pt); Speech
therapists 1 (ft), 1 (pt); Dietitians 1 (pt).
Affiliation Lutheran
Facilities Dining room; Activities room;
Chapel; Crafts room; Laundry room;
Library.
Activities Arts & crafts; Cards; Games;
Reading groups; Movies; Shopping trips;
Social/Cultural gatherings.

CORVALLIS

Corvallis Care Center*
980 NW Spruce St, Corvallis, OR, 97330
(503) 757-0151
Admin Velda Fancher. *Medical Dir/Dir of Nursing* James W Gulick MD.
Licensure Intermediate care. *Beds* 84. *Certified* Medicaid; Medicare.
Owner Proprietary Corp (Beverly Enterprises).
Staff RNs 8 (ft); LPNs 3 (ft); Orderlies 1 (ft), 1 (pt); Nurses aides 30 (ft), 4 (pt); Physical therapists 1 (pt); Occupational therapists 1 (pt); Speech therapists 1 (pt); Activities coordinators 1 (ft); Dietitians 1 (pt); Podiatrists 1 (pt); Audiologists 1 (pt).
Facilities Dining room; Activities room; Laundry room; Barber/Beauty shop.
Activities Arts & crafts; Cards; Reading groups; Prayer groups; Movies; Shopping trips; Social/Cultural gatherings; Music & crafts.

Corvallis Manor
160 NE Conifer Ave, Corvallis, OR, 97330
(503) 757-1651
Admin Merlin Hart. *Medical Dir/Dir of Nursing* Dr Norman Castillo.
Licensure Skilled care; Intermediate care. *Beds* SNF 30; ICF 104. *Certified* Medicaid; Medicare.
Admissions Requirements Physician's request.
Staff Physicians 1 (pt); RNs 6 (ft), 5 (pt); LPNs 2 (ft), 1 (pt); Orderlies 4 (ft), 4 (pt); Nurses aides 30 (ft), 20 (pt); Physical therapists 1 (pt); Occupational therapists 1 (ft), 1 (pt); Speech therapists 1 (pt); Activities coordinators 1 (ft), 1 (pt); Dietitians 1 (pt).
Facilities Dining room; Physical therapy room; Activities room; Laundry room; Barber/Beauty shop; Library.
Activities Arts & crafts; Cards; Games; Reading groups; Prayer groups; Movies; Shopping trips; Social/Cultural gatherings.

Heart of the Valley Center
2700 NW Harrison Blvd, Corvallis, OR, 97330
(503) 757-1763
Admin Richard J Prout. *Medical Dir/Dir of Nursing* Dr James Gallant; Marla Wimer.
Licensure Intermediate care; Adult Residential Care. *Beds* ICF 72; Adult Residential 85. *Certified* Medicaid.
Owner Proprietary Corp.
Staff RNs 6 (ft); LPNs 6 (ft); Nurses aides 25 (ft); Recreational therapists 1 (ft); Activities coordinators 2 (ft).
Facilities Dining room; Physical therapy room; Activities room; Crafts room; Laundry room; Barber/Beauty shop; Library; Resident & guest lounges; Companion motel room.
Activities Arts & crafts; Cards; Games; Reading groups; Prayer groups; Movies; Shopping trips.

COTTAGE GROVE

Cottage Grove Hospital Skilled Nursing Facility
1340 Birch Ave, Cottage Grove, OR, 97424
Admin John L Hoopes. *Medical Dir/Dir of Nursing* Judy Spangler RN.
Licensure Skilled care. *Beds* 30. *Certified* Medicaid.
Owner Nonprofit Corp.
Admissions Requirements Medical examination; Physician's request.
Staff Physicians 19 (ft); RNs 2 (ft); LPNs 2 (ft), 2 (pt); Nurses aides 2 (ft), 12 (pt); Physical therapists 1 (ft), 1 (pt); Activities coordinators 1 (ft); Dietitians 1 (ft); Dentists 1 (ft); Ophthalmologists 1 (ft); Dentist 8 (pt).

Facilities Dining room; Physical therapy room; Activities room; Laundry room.
Activities Arts & crafts; Cards; Games; Reading groups; Prayer groups; Movies; Shopping trips; Social/Cultural gatherings.

Edgewood Nursing Center*
515 Grant St, Cottage Grove, OR, 97424
(503) 942-5528
Admin Charles D Fogg.
Licensure Skilled care; Intermediate care. *Beds* SNF 12; ICF 68. *Certified* Medicaid; Medicare.
Facilities Dining room; Physical therapy room; Activities room; Chapel; Crafts room; Laundry room; Barber/Beauty shop; Library.
Activities Arts & crafts; Cards; Games; Reading groups; Prayer groups; Movies; Shopping trips; Social/Cultural gatherings.

CRESWELL

Creswell Care Center
525 S 2nd, Creswell, OR, 97426
(503) 895-3333
Admin Connie Johnson.
Licensure Intermediate care. *Beds* 80. *Certified* Medicaid.
Owner Proprietary Corp.
Admissions Requirements Medical examination; Physician's request.
Facilities Dining room; Physical therapy room; Activities room; Crafts room; Laundry room; Barber/Beauty shop; Library.
Activities Arts & crafts; Cards; Games; Reading groups; Prayer groups; Movies; Shopping trips; Social/Cultural gatherings.

DALLAS

Birch Street Manor
862 SW Birch St, Dallas, OR, 97338
(503) 623-8131
Admin A Jeanine Knight. *Medical Dir/Dir of Nursing* Dr R A Regier; Verna Norris DON.
Licensure Intermediate care. *Beds* ICF 43. *Certified* Medicaid.
Owner Privately owned.
Admissions Requirements Medical examination; Physician's request.
Staff RNs 2 (ft), 1 (pt); LPNs 2 (ft), 2 (pt); Orderlies 1 (ft); Nurses aides 15 (ft), 5 (pt); Recreational therapists 1 (pt); Activities coordinators 1 (pt).
Facilities Dining room; Activities room; Crafts room; Laundry room; Barber/Beauty shop; Library.
Activities Arts & crafts; Cards; Games; Reading groups; Prayer groups; Movies; Social/Cultural gatherings; Social/Cultural gatherings.

Dallas Nursing Home
348 W Ellendale, Dallas, OR, 97338
(503) 623-5581
Admin Elizabeth Anderson. *Medical Dir/Dir of Nursing* Dr Tom Flaming; Rita Snyder DON.
Licensure Intermediate care. *Beds* ICF 117. *Certified* Medicaid.
Owner Nonprofit organization/foundation.
Admissions Requirements Minimum age birth; Physician's request.
Staff Physicians 1 (pt); RNs 6 (ft), 2 (pt); LPNs 4 (ft), 1 (pt); Nurses aides 64 (ft); Activities coordinators 1 (ft); Dietitians 1 (pt).
Languages Spanish, German
Affiliation Mennonite
Facilities Dining room; Activities room; Chapel; Crafts room; Laundry room; Barber/Beauty shop; TV room; Day room; Conference room.
Activities Arts & crafts; Games; Reading groups; Prayer groups; Movies; Shopping trips; Ceramics class; Church services.

DALLES

Columbia Basin Nursing Home
PO Box 93, 1015 Webber Rd, The Dalles, OR, 97058
(503) 296-2156
Admin Joyce Williams. *Medical Dir/Dir of Nursing* Thomas Hodge MD; Nancy Hammel RN DON.
Licensure Skilled care; Intermediate care. *Beds* SNF 14; ICF 106. *Certified* Medicaid; Medicare.
Owner Nonprofit organization/foundation.
Admissions Requirements Medical examination; Physician's request.
Staff RNs 8 (ft); LPNs 7 (ft); Orderlies 4 (ft); Nurses aides 35 (ft); Physical therapists 1 (ft); Speech therapists 1 (pt); Activities coordinators 1 (ft); Dietitians 1 (ft); Dentists 1 (pt); Ophthalmologists 1 (pt); Podiatrists 1 (pt).
Facilities Dining room; Physical therapy room; Activities room; Crafts room; Laundry room; Barber/Beauty shop; Store.
Activities Arts & crafts; Games; Reading groups; Prayer groups; Movies; Shopping trips; Social/Cultural gatherings; Bus trips; Gourmet cooking class.

Valle Vista Care Center*
1023 W 25th Ave, PO Box 6, The Dalles, OR, 97058
(503) 298-5158
Admin Vera McDowell.
Licensure Intermediate care. *Beds* 80. *Certified* Medicaid.
Admissions Requirements Medical examination; Physician's request.
Facilities Dining room; Physical therapy room; Activities room; Crafts room; Laundry room; Barber/Beauty shop.
Activities Arts & crafts; Cards; Games; Reading groups; Prayer groups; Movies; Shopping trips; Social/Cultural gatherings; Community activities.

ENTERPRISE

Wallowa County Nursing Home
207 E Park, Enterprise, OR, 97828
(503) 426-3111
Admin Ron Bender. *Medical Dir/Dir of Nursing* Barbara Biamont.
Licensure Intermediate care. *Beds* ICF 32. *Certified* Medicaid.
Owner Publicly owned.
Staff RNs 2 (ft); LPNs 2 (ft); Nurses aides 8 (ft); Recreational therapists.

EUGENE

Cascade Manor*
65 W 30th Ave, Eugene, OR, 97405
(503) 344-4851
Admin Doris Keown.
Licensure Intermediate care. *Beds* 21.

Emerald Nursing Center
2360 Chambers St, Eugene, OR, 97405
(503) 687-1310
Admin David A Jenness. *Medical Dir/Dir of Nursing* Gordon Anderson MD; Carolyn Walter RN DON.
Licensure Skilled care; Intermediate care; Day care/Respite care. *Beds* 138. *Certified* Medicaid; Medicare; VA.
Owner Nonprofit Corp (Adventist Health Sys-USA).
Admissions Requirements Medical examination; Physician's request.
Staff Physicians 1 (pt); RNs 6 (ft), 5 (pt); LPNs 7 (ft), 6 (pt); Orderlies 9 (ft); Nurses aides 36 (ft), 3 (pt); Physical therapists 1 (pt); Reality therapists 1 (pt); Recreational therapists 2 (ft); Occupational therapists 1

(pt); Speech therapists 1 (pt); Activities coordinators 1 (ft); Dietitians 1 (ft); Dentist 1 (pt).
Affiliation Seventh-Day Adventist
Facilities Dining room; Physical therapy room; Activities room; Crafts room; Laundry room; Barber/Beauty shop; Library.
Activities Arts & crafts; Cards; Games; Reading groups; Prayer groups; Movies; Shopping trips; Shopping trips; Social/Cultural gatherings; Bowling; Van trips; Picnics; Fishing; Ice cream socials; BBQs during summer; Sewing clubs; Cooking clubs.

Eugene Good Samaritan Center
3500 Hilyard St, Eugene, OR, 97405
(503) 687-9211
Admin Gunter Brunk. *Medical Dir/Dir of Nursing* Richard A Anderson MD; Barbara Rock RN DNS.
Licensure Skilled care; Intermediate care. *Beds* SNF 34; ICF 120. *Certified* Medicaid; Medicare.
Owner Nonprofit Corp (Evangelical Lutheran/ Good Samaritan).
Staff RNs; LPNs; Nurses aides; Physical therapists; Occupational therapists; Activities coordinators; Dietitians.
Facilities Dining room; Physical therapy room; Activities room; Chapel; Crafts room; Laundry room; Barber/Beauty shop.
Activities Arts & crafts; Cards; Games; Reading groups; Prayer groups; Movies; Shopping trips.

Garber's University Nursing Center*
1166 E 28th, PO Box 505, Eugene, OR, 97405
(503) 345-0534
Admin Aaron Garber. *Medical Dir/Dir of Nursing* Donald England MD.
Licensure Skilled care; Intermediate care. *Beds* SNF 14; ICF 124. *Certified* Medicaid; Medicare.
Admissions Requirements Medical examination; Physician's request.
Staff Physicians 1 (pt); RNs 6 (ft), 1 (pt); LPNs 1 (ft), 1 (pt); Nurses aides 31 (ft), 2 (pt); Physical therapists 1 (pt); Occupational therapists 1 (pt); Speech therapists 1 (pt); Activities coordinators 1 (ft); Dietitians 1 (pt); Podiatrists 1 (pt).
Facilities Dining room; Activities room; Laundry room; Barber/Beauty shop.
Activities Arts & crafts; Cards; Games; Reading groups; Prayer groups; Movies; Shopping trips; Social/Cultural gatherings.

Green Valley Care Center Inc
1735 Adkins St, Eugene, OR, 97401
(503) 683-5032
Admin Gary Snyder. *Medical Dir/Dir of Nursing* Jeffery Beckwith MD; Helen Schaefer.
Licensure Skilled care. *Beds* 104. *Certified* Medicaid; Medicare.
Admissions Requirements Physician's request.
Staff Physicians; RNs; LPNs; Nurses aides; Physical therapists; Recreational therapists; Occupational therapists; Speech therapists; Activities coordinators; Dietitians; Ophthalmologists.
Languages German
Facilities Dining room; Activities room; Laundry room; Barber/Beauty shop; Library.
Activities Arts & crafts; Cards; Games; Reading groups; Movies; Social/Cultural gatherings.

Hillside Heights Convalescent Center
1201 McLean Blvd, Eugene, OR, 97405
(503) 683-2155
Admin Martha J Jensen. *Medical Dir/Dir of Nursing* Dr Dwight Johnson; Diane Banos RN DNS.
Licensure Skilled care; Intermediate care. *Beds* SNF 22; ICF 58. *Certified* Medicaid; Medicare.

Owner Proprietary Corp (Beverly Enterprises).
Admissions Requirements Medical examination.
Staff RNs 7 (ft); LPNs 5 (ft); Nurses aides 25 (ft), 5 (pt); Physical therapists 1 (ft); Occupational therapists 1 (pt); Speech therapists 1 (pt); Activities coordinators 1 (ft); Dietitians 1 (ft).
Languages Spanish
Facilities Dining room; Physical therapy room; Activities room; Chapel; Crafts room; Laundry room; Barber/Beauty shop.
Activities Arts & crafts; Games; Reading groups; Prayer groups; Movies; Shopping trips; Social/Cultural gatherings.

Ivorena Care Center*
687 Cheshire Ave, Eugene, OR, 97402
(503) 484-2117
Admin J Brandt Spence.
Licensure Intermediate care. *Beds* 102. *Certified* Medicaid.

River Park Living Center
425 Alexander Loop, Eugene, OR, 97401
(503) 687-0019
Admin Millicent Redford. *Medical Dir/Dir of Nursing* Dwayne Rice MD; Mary Ann Fix RN DON.
Licensure Skilled care; Intermediate care. *Beds* SNF 6; ICF 60; Assisted living 40. *Certified* Medicaid; Medicare.
Owner Privately owned.
Admissions Requirements Minimum age 18; Physician's request.
Staff Physicians; RNs; LPNs; Orderlies; Nurses aides; Activities coordinators; Dietitians.
Languages German
Facilities Dining room; Physical therapy room; Activities room; Chapel; Crafts room; Laundry room; Barber/Beauty shop; Library.
Activities Arts & crafts; Cards; Games; Reading groups; Prayer groups; Shopping trips; Social/Cultural gatherings.

Twilight Acres Nursing Home
85434 Dilley Ln, Eugene, OR, 97405
(503) 746-7611
Admin Hazel Stebbeds.
Licensure Intermediate care. *Beds* 60. *Certified* Medicaid.
Admissions Requirements Medical examination; Physician's request.
Staff RNs 2 (ft), 2 (pt); LPNs 2 (ft), 2 (pt); Orderlies 2 (ft); Nurses aides 18 (ft), 6 (pt); Activities coordinators 1 (ft); Dietitians 1 (pt).
Facilities Dining room; Activities room; Barber/Beauty shop.
Activities Arts & crafts; Cards; Games; Reading groups; Movies; Shopping trips; Outings; BBQs.

Valley West Health Care Center
2300 Warren St, Eugene, OR, 97405
(503) 686-2828
Admin Jane F Boren. *Medical Dir/Dir of Nursing* Dwayne Rice MD.
Licensure Skilled care. *Beds* SNF 121. *Certified* Medicare.
Owner Proprietary Corp (Life Care Centers of America).
Admissions Requirements Medical examination; Physician's request.
Staff Physicians 3 (pt); RNs 18 (ft); Nurses aides 50 (ft); Physical therapists 1 (pt); Recreational therapists 2 (ft); Occupational therapists 1 (pt); Speech therapists 1 (pt); Activities coordinators 2 (ft); Dietitians 1 (pt); Ophthalmologists 1 (pt); Dentist 1 (pt).
Facilities Dining room; Physical therapy room; Activities room; Crafts room; Laundry room; Barber/Beauty shop; Library.
Activities Arts & crafts; Cards; Games; Reading groups; Prayer groups; Movies; Shopping trips; Social/Cultural gatherings; Alzheimer's activities.

FLORENCE

Siuslaw Care Center
1951 21st St, Florence, OR, 97439
(503) 997-8436
Admin Hal Elliot. *Medical Dir/Dir of Nursing* Becky Landcaster DNS.
Licensure Skilled care; Intermediate care. *Beds* SNF 8; ICF 57; RCF 15. *Certified* Medicaid; Medicare.
Owner Proprietary Corp (Beverly Enterprises).
Staff Physicians 1 (pt); RNs 3 (ft), 2 (pt); LPNs 6 (ft), 3 (pt); Nurses aides 28 (ft), 12 (pt); Physical therapists 2 (pt); Recreational therapists 1 (ft); Occupational therapists 1 (pt); Speech therapists 1 (pt); Activities coordinators 1 (ft); Dietitians 1 (pt); Dentists 1 (pt); Ophthalmologists 1 (pt); Podiatrists 1 (pt).
Activities Arts & crafts; Cards; Games; Reading groups; Prayer groups; Movies; Shopping trips; Social/Cultural gatherings.

FOREST GROVE

Camelot Care Center
3900 Pacific Ave, Forest Grove, OR, 97116
(503) 359-0449
Admin Gary Snyder. *Medical Dir/Dir of Nursing* Winona Reimers RN.
Licensure Skilled care; Intermediate care; Residential care. *Beds* SNF 41; ICF 73; Residential 14. *Certified* Medicaid; Medicare.
Owner Proprietary Corp (Beverly Enterprises).
Admissions Requirements Physician's request.
Staff RNs; LPNs; Orderlies; Nurses aides; Physical therapists; Recreational therapists; Occupational therapists; Speech therapists; Activities coordinators; Dietitians.
Facilities Dining room; Physical therapy room; Activities room; Crafts room; Laundry room; Barber/Beauty shop.
Activities Arts & crafts; Cards; Games; Reading groups; Prayer groups; Movies; Shopping trips; Social/Cultural gatherings.

Forest View Care Center
3300 19th Ave, Forest Grove, OR, 97116
(503) 357-7119
Admin Brad Mikesell. *Medical Dir/Dir of Nursing* Dorothy Jurgensen DON.
Licensure Intermediate care. *Beds* ICF 114. *Certified* Medicaid.
Owner Proprietary Corp (Beverly Enterprises).
Admissions Requirements Minimum age 18; Physician's request.
Staff RNs 4 (ft), 3 (pt); LPNs 3 (ft), 2 (pt); Nurses aides 33 (ft), 13 (pt); Activities coordinators 1 (ft); Dietitians 1 (pt).
Facilities Dining room; Physical therapy room; Activities room; Laundry room; Barber/Beauty shop.
Activities Arts & crafts; Cards; Games; Reading groups; Prayer groups; Movies.

Lou Del Health Care*
2122 Oak St, Forest Grove, OR, 97116
(503) 357-9780
Admin Arliss Roman. *Medical Dir/Dir of Nursing* Dr Robert Martens.
Licensure Intermediate care. *Beds* 40. *Certified* Medicaid.
Admissions Requirements Minimum age 18; Medical examination; Physician's request.
Staff RNs 1 (ft); LPNs 5 (pt); Nurses aides 14 (ft), 5 (pt); Activities coordinators 1 (ft); 1 (ft).
Facilities Dining room; Laundry room.
Activities Arts & crafts; Games; Reading groups; Prayer groups; Movies; Shopping trips; Social/Cultural gatherings.

Masonic & Eastern Star Home*
3505 Pacific Ave, Forest Grove, OR, 97116
(503) 359-4465
Admin Bob Surina.

Licensure Intermediate care. *Beds* 49.
Affiliation Masons

GASTON

Laurelwood Manor Nursing Home*
Rte 2, Box 145, Gaston, OR, 97119-9511
(503) 985-7484
Admin Ruth J Moreno.
Licensure Intermediate care. *Beds* 20.
Certified Medicaid.

GLADSTONE

Clackamas Terrace Convalescent Center*
340 1st St, Gladstone, OR, 97027
(503) 656-1646
Admin Maureen Kehoe.
Licensure Intermediate care. *Beds* 126.
Certified Medicaid.

Franklin Care Center
220 E Hereford, Gladstone, OR, 97027
(503) 656-0393
Admin Jessie L Curtis. *Medical Dir/Dir of Nursing* Dr Anna Bahr.
Licensure Intermediate care. *Beds* ICF 91.
Certified Medicaid.
Owner Proprietary Corp (Prestige Care Inc).
Staff RNs 2 (ft), 2 (pt); LPNs 3 (ft); Orderlies 3 (ft), 1 (pt); Nurses aides 30 (ft), 10 (pt); Activities coordinators 2 (ft); Dietitians 1 (pt).
Facilities Dining room; Physical therapy room; Activities room; Chapel; Crafts room; Laundry room; Barber/Beauty shop; Library.
Activities Arts & crafts; Cards; Games; Reading groups; Prayer groups; Movies; Shopping trips; Social/Cultural gatherings.

Gladstone Convalescent Care
18000 Webster Rd, Gladstone, OR, 97027
(503) 656-1644
Admin John H Stormset. *Medical Dir/Dir of Nursing* Roy Payne MD; Caroline Mills DON.
Licensure Intermediate care. *Beds* 130.
Certified Medicaid.
Owner Proprietary Corp (Beverly Enterprises).
Admissions Requirements Medical examination; Physician's request.
Staff Physicians 1 (pt); RNs 6 (ft), 1 (pt); LPNs 3 (ft), 2 (pt); Nurses aides 50 (ft), 13 (pt); Physical therapists 1 (pt); Occupational therapists 1 (pt); Speech therapists 1 (pt); Activities coordinators 2 (ft); Dietitians 1 (pt).
Facilities Dining room; Physical therapy room; Activities room; Crafts room; Laundry room; Barber/Beauty shop.
Activities Arts & crafts; Cards; Games; Reading groups; Prayer groups; Movies; Shopping trips; Social/Cultural gatherings.

GRANTS PASS

Highland House Nursing Home
2201 NW Highland, Grants Pass, OR, 97526
(503) 474-1901
Admin Phil Stephens. *Medical Dir/Dir of Nursing* Dr George Bailey.
Licensure Skilled care. *Beds* 134. *Certified* Medicaid.
Owner Proprietary Corp.
Admissions Requirements Medical examination; Physician's request.
Staff RNs 12 (ft), 9 (pt); LPNs 9 (ft), 9 (pt); Nurses aides 40 (ft), 28 (pt); Physical therapists 1 (ft); Reality therapists 1 (ft); Recreational therapists 2 (ft); Occupational therapists 1 (pt); Speech therapists 1 (pt); Activities coordinators 1 (ft); Dietitians 1 (pt); Dentists 1 (pt); Ophthalmologists 1 (pt); Podiatrists 1 (pt).
Facilities Dining room; Physical therapy room; Activities room; Chapel; Crafts room; Laundry room; Barber/Beauty shop.

Activities Arts & crafts; Cards; Games; Reading groups; Prayer groups; Movies; Shopping trips; Social/Cultural gatherings.

Laurel Hill Nursing Center
859 NE 6th, Grants Pass, OR, 97526
(503) 479-3700
Admin Jon Deasen. *Medical Dir/Dir of Nursing* Ardythe Hoffman DON.
Licensure Intermediate care. *Beds* 41.
Certified Medicaid.
Owner Proprietary Corp.
Admissions Requirements Physician's request.
Staff Physicians 1 (ft), 4 (pt); RNs 2 (ft), 4 (pt); LPNs 1 (ft), 4 (pt); Nurses aides 5 (ft), 4 (pt); Physical therapists 1 (ft), 4 (pt); Activities coordinators 1 (ft), 4 (pt); Dietitians 1 (ft), 4 (pt); Podiatrists 1 (ft), 4 (pt).
Languages Spanish
Facilities Dining room; Activities room; Laundry room.
Activities Arts & crafts; Cards; Games; Reading groups; Prayer groups; Movies.

Mariola Nursing Home*
1450 NE Fairview Ave, Grants Pass, OR, 97526
(503) 479-2606
Admin Kenneth Selvey.
Licensure Skilled care; Intermediate care. *Beds* 102. *Certified* Medicaid; Medicare.

Royale Gardens Health Care Facility
2075 NW Highland, Grants Pass, OR, 97526
(503) 476-8891
Admin Robert Puntney. *Medical Dir/Dir of Nursing* Thomas M Turek MD.
Licensure Skilled care; Intermediate care. *Beds* 194. *Certified* Medicaid; Medicare.
Admissions Requirements Minimum age 18.
Staff Physicians 1 (pt); RNs 8 (ft), 1 (pt); LPNs 7 (ft), 2 (pt); Orderlies 56 (ft), 23 (pt); Nurses aides 56 (ft), 23 (pt); Physical therapists 1 (pt); Reality therapists 1 (ft), 1 (pt); Recreational therapists 1 (pt); Speech therapists 1 (pt); Activities coordinators 1 (ft); Dietitians 1 (ft); Dentists 1 (pt); Podiatrists 1 (pt).
Activities Arts & crafts; Cards; Games; Reading groups; Movies; Shopping trips; Social/Cultural gatherings.

GRESHAM

Colbert Nursing Home Inc
405 NE 5th St, Gresham, OR, 97030-7345
(503) 666-5541
Admin Kathleen Schwerzler.
Licensure Intermediate care. *Beds* 71.
Certified Medicaid.

Fairlawn Care Center*
3457 NE Division, Gresham, OR, 97030
(503) 667-1965
Admin John E Palmer. *Medical Dir/Dir of Nursing* Dr MacKay.
Licensure Skilled care. *Beds* 123. *Certified* Medicaid; Medicare.
Admissions Requirements Minimum age 60; Medical examination; Physician's request.
Staff RNs 4 (ft), 17 (pt); LPNs 3 (ft), 6 (pt); Nurses aides 46 (ft), 25 (pt); Recreational therapists 2 (ft); Activities coordinators 1 (ft); Dietitians 1 (ft).
Affiliation Lutheran
Facilities Dining room; Physical therapy room; Activities room; Chapel; Laundry room; Barber/Beauty shop; Library.
Activities Arts & crafts; Cards; Games; Prayer groups; Movies; Shopping trips; Current events; Bus trips; Music appreciation; Gardening; Church services; Grandparent program.

Neighbors of Woodcraft Home*
1250 SE Roberts, Gresham, OR, 97030
(503) 667-5430

Admin Jessie Johnson, Jr.
Licensure Intermediate care. *Beds* 4.

Rest Harbor Nursing Home
PO Box 525, 5905 E Powell Blvd, Gresham, OR, 97030
(503) 665-1151
Admin Greg Dempsey. *Medical Dir/Dir of Nursing* Thomas Hickerson MD; Ruthann Eaton DNS.
Licensure Skilled care; Intermediate care. *Beds* SNF 56; ICF 72. *Certified* Medicaid; Medicare.
Owner Proprietary Corp.
Admissions Requirements Medical examination; Physician's request.
Staff Physicians 3 (pt); RNs 9 (ft), 3 (pt); LPNs 5 (ft), 6 (pt); Nurses aides 40 (ft), 17 (pt); Physical therapists 3 (pt); Reality therapists 1 (pt); Recreational therapists 1 (ft), 1 (pt); Occupational therapists 2 (pt); Speech therapists 3 (pt); Activities coordinators 1 (ft); Dietitians 1 (pt).
Affiliation Seventh-Day Adventist
Facilities Dining room; Physical therapy room; Activities room; Crafts room; Laundry room; Barber/Beauty shop; Library; Pharmacy.
Activities Arts & crafts; Cards; Games; Reading groups; Prayer groups; Movies; Shopping trips; Social/Cultural gatherings; Puppy therapy; Traveling zoo; Dining.

Village Convalescent Center
3955 SE 182nd Ave, Gresham, OR, 97030
(503) 665-0183
Admin John L Mack. *Medical Dir/Dir of Nursing* Dr Donald K Bohlman; Karen Robinson RN.
Licensure Skilled care; Intermediate care; Residential care. *Beds* SNF 34; ICF 62; Residential 10. *Certified* Medicaid; Medicare.
Owner Nonprofit Corp.
Admissions Requirements Medical examination; Physician's request.
Staff RNs 10 (ft), 2 (pt); LPNs 8 (ft), 2 (pt); Orderlies 10 (ft); Nurses aides 45 (ft); Physical therapists 1 (ft); Occupational therapists 1 (pt); Speech therapists 1 (pt); Activities coordinators 1 (ft); Dietitians 1 (pt); Ophthalmologists 1 (pt).
Languages Spanish
Facilities Dining room; Physical therapy room; Activities room; Crafts room; Laundry room; Barber/Beauty shop; Library.
Activities Arts & crafts; Cards; Games; Reading groups; Prayer groups; Movies.

Willow Tree Care Center*
311 NE Division, Gresham, OR, 97030
(503) 667-8050
Admin Gayle Palmer.
Licensure Intermediate care. *Beds* 40.
Certified Medicaid.

HEPPNER

Pioneer Memorial Hospital & Nursing Home
PO Box 9, 564 Pioneer Dr, Heppner, OR, 97836
(503) 676-9133
Admin Ernest R Wick. *Medical Dir/Dir of Nursing* Wallace Wolff MD.
Licensure Intermediate care. *Beds* ICF 32.
Certified Medicaid.
Owner Publicly owned.
Admissions Requirements Medical examination.
Staff Physicians 1 (ft); RNs 2 (ft), 8 (pt); LPNs 3 (ft), 2 (pt); Nurses aides 15 (ft), 5 (pt); Physical therapists 1 (pt); Activities coordinators 2 (pt); Dietitians 1 (ft).
Facilities Dining room; Activities room; Crafts room; Laundry room; Barber/Beauty shop; Solarium; Patio.

Activities Arts & crafts; Cards; Games;
Reading groups; Prayer groups; Movies;
Shopping trips.

HERMISTON

Hermiston Good Samaritan Center
970 W Juniper Ave, Hermiston, OR, 97838
(503) 567-8337
Admin Richard Alexander. *Medical Dir/Dir of
Nursing* Pat Duff.
Licensure Intermediate care. *Beds* ICF 95;
RCF 15. *Certified* Medicaid.
Owner Nonprofit Corp (Evangelical Lutheran/
Good Samaritan).
Admissions Requirements Medical
examination; Physician's request.
Staff RNs 3 (ft); LPNs 5 (ft), 5 (pt); Orderlies
1 (ft); Nurses aides 22 (ft), 18 (pt); Physical
therapists 1 (pt); Activities coordinators 2
(ft); Dietitians 1 (pt); Ophthalmologists 1
(pt); Dentist 1 (pt).
Facilities Dining room; Physical therapy
room; Activities room; Chapel; Crafts room;
Laundry room; Barber/Beauty shop; Library.
Activities Arts & crafts; Cards; Games;
Reading groups; Prayer groups; Movies;
Shopping trips; Social/Cultural gatherings.

HILLSBORO

Gardenview Care Center
33465 SW Tualatin Valley Hwy, Hillsboro,
OR, 97123
(503) 648-7181
Admin Donald V Terry. *Medical Dir/Dir of
Nursing* Marjorie Thaanum.
Licensure Intermediate care; Residential care.
Beds ICF 36; Residential 1. *Certified*
Medicaid.
Owner Privately owned.
Admissions Requirements Physician's request.
Staff RNs 2 (ft), 2 (pt); Nurses aides 10 (ft), 4
(pt); Activities coordinators 1 (ft); Dietitians
1 (pt); MRQ 1 (pt).
Facilities Dining room; Activities room;
Crafts room; Laundry room; Patio.
Activities Arts & crafts; Games; Reading
groups; Prayer groups; Dine-out; Bingo;
Music; Dancing; Exercises.

Oak Villa Health Care*
650 Oak St E, Hillsboro, OR, 97123
(503) 648-8588
Admin Joyce Gallovich.
Licensure Intermediate care. *Beds* 104.
Certified Medicaid.

HOOD RIVER

Hood River Care Center
729 Henderson Rd, Hood River, OR, 97031
(503) 386-2688
Admin Bruce Dillon. *Medical Dir/Dir of
Nursing* Paul Hamada MD; Linda Grunke
RN DON.
Licensure Skilled care; Intermediate care. *Beds*
SNF 12; ICF 116; Residential 3. *Certified*
Medicaid; Medicare.
Owner Proprietary Corp (Prestige Care Inc).
Admissions Requirements Physician's request.
Staff RNs 5 (ft); LPNs 6 (ft); Orderlies 2 (ft);
Nurses aides 23 (ft), 3 (pt); Physical
therapists 1 (pt); Recreational therapists 1
(ft); Occupational therapists 1 (pt); Speech
therapists 1 (pt); Activities coordinators 1
(ft); Dietitians 1 (pt); Dentists 1 (pt);
Ophthalmologists 1 (pt); Podiatrists 1 (pt).
Facilities Dining room; Physical therapy
room; Activities room; Crafts room; Laundry
room; Barber/Beauty shop; Library.
Activities Arts & crafts; Cards; Games;
Reading groups; Prayer groups; Movies;
Shopping trips; Social/Cultural gatherings.

INDEPENDENCE

Cedarwood Care Center*
1525 Monmouth Ave, Independence, OR,
97351
(503) 838-0001
Admin Betty Martin.
Licensure Intermediate care; Intermediate care
for mentally retarded. *Beds* ICF 48; ICF/MR
32. *Certified* Medicaid.

JUNCTION CITY

Grandview Manor Care Center*
530 Birch St, Junction City, OR, 97448
(503) 998-2395
Admin Judy Wittekind.
Licensure Intermediate care. *Beds* 72.
Certified Medicaid.

KLAMATH FALLS

Highland Care*
2555 Main St, Klamath Falls, OR, 97601
(503) 882-6341
Admin Hal Elliott. *Medical Dir/Dir of Nursing*
Dr Raymond Tice.
Licensure Intermediate care; Residential care.
Beds ICF 92; Residential 15. *Certified*
Medicaid.
Admissions Requirements Minimum age 18;
Medical examination; Physician's request.
Staff Physicians 1 (pt); RNs 4 (ft); LPNs 3
(ft), 2 (pt); Nurses aides 24 (ft), 12 (pt);
Physical therapists 1 (pt); Activities
coordinators 1 (ft); Dietitians 1 (pt); Dentists
1 (pt).
Facilities Dining room; Physical therapy
room; Activities room; Crafts room; Laundry
room; Barber/Beauty shop; Sunroom; TV
room; Smoking area.
Activities Arts & crafts; Cards; Games;
Movies; Shopping trips; Social/Cultural
gatherings; Religious services; Singing.

Klamath County Convalescent Center
1401 Campus Dr, Klamath Falls, OR, 97601
(503) 882-6691
Admin W F Barrett. *Medical Dir/Dir of
Nursing* Mary Caron RN DON.
Licensure Skilled care; Intermediate care. *Beds*
SNF 60; ICF 60. *Certified* Medicaid;
Medicare.
Owner Nonprofit organization/foundation.
Admissions Requirements Physician's request.
Staff RNs 9 (ft), 3 (pt); LPNs 9 (ft), 3 (pt);
Nurses aides 55 (ft), 17 (pt); Physical
therapists 1 (ft); Occupational therapists 1
(ft); Activities coordinators 2 (ft).
Languages Spanish
Facilities Dining room; Physical therapy
room; Activities room; Chapel; Crafts room;
Laundry room; Barber/Beauty shop; Library.
Activities Arts & crafts; Games; Reading
groups; Prayer groups; Movies; Social/
Cultural gatherings.

Mountain View
711 Washburn Way, Klamath Falls, OR,
97601
(503) 882-4471
Admin Ed Sorrels. *Medical Dir/Dir of Nursing*
Al Glidden; H Mauer RN DON.
Licensure Skilled care; Intermediate care. *Beds*
SNF; ICF 113. *Certified* Medicaid;
Medicare.
Owner Proprietary Corp (Unicare).
Admissions Requirements Physician's request.
Staff Physicians; RNs; LPNs; Orderlies;
Nurses aides; Physical therapists;
Occupational therapists; Speech therapists;
Activities coordinators; Dietitians;
Podiatrists.
Facilities Dining room; Physical therapy
room; Activities room; Crafts room; Laundry
room; Barber/Beauty shop.

Activities Arts & crafts; Cards; Games;
Reading groups; Prayer groups; Movies;
Shopping trips; Social/Cultural gatherings.

LAGRANDE

LaGrande Nursing Center*
95 Aries Way, LaGrande, OR, 97850
(503) 963-8678
Admin Dave Slaght.
Licensure Intermediate care. *Beds* 80.
Certified Medicaid.

Valley View Care Center
Rte 1, Box 1855, LaGrande, OR, 97850
(503) 963-4184
Admin Judith A Nitz. *Medical Dir/Dir of
Nursing* Arlette Patrow RN.
Licensure Intermediate care. *Beds* ICF 83.
Certified Medicaid.
Owner Proprietary Corp.
Admissions Requirements Physician's request.
Staff RNs 3 (ft), 1 (pt); LPNs 4 (ft); Nurses
aides 26 (ft), 7 (pt); Activities coordinators 1
(ft), 1 (pt); Dietitians 1 (pt).
Facilities Dining room; Physical therapy
room; Activities room; Laundry room;
Barber/Beauty shop.
Activities Arts & crafts; Cards; Games;
Reading groups; Prayer groups; Movies;
Social/Cultural gatherings; Drives.

LAKE OSWEGO

Mountain Park Convalescent Care Facility
PO Box 527, 4 Greenridge Ct, Lake Oswego,
OR, 97034
(503) 636-9614
Admin Tom Pollock. *Medical Dir/Dir of
Nursing* Gary Geddes MD; Mary Doak RN
DNS.
Licensure Intermediate care. *Beds* 182.
Certified Medicaid.
Owner Proprietary Corp (Beverly Enterprises).
Admissions Requirements Medical
examination; Physician's request.
Staff Physicians 1 (pt); RNs; LPNs; Orderlies;
Nurses aides; Physical therapists;
Occupational therapists; Speech therapists;
Activities coordinators; Dietitians;
Ophthalmologists.
Facilities Dining room; Physical therapy
room; Activities room; Crafts room; Laundry
room; Barber/Beauty shop; Library.
Activities Arts & crafts; Cards; Games;
Reading groups; Prayer groups; Movies;
Shopping trips; Social/Cultural gatherings.

LAKEVIEW

Lake District Hospital*
700 S J St, Lakeview, OR, 97630
(503) 947-2114, 2115
Admin Frank Occhuito.
Licensure Skilled care. *Beds* 47. *Certified*
Medicare.

LEBANON

Villa Cascade Nursing Home
PO Box 217, 350 S 8th, Lebanon, OR, 97355
(503) 259-1221
Admin Jerry Yost.
Licensure Intermediate care. *Beds* 107.
Certified Medicaid.

LINCOLN CITY

Evergreen Care Center
3011 NE Park Dr, Lincoln City, OR, 97367
(503) 994-8111
Admin Lavonne Davis. *Medical Dir/Dir of
Nursing* E Oksenholt DO; Earlene Morgan
RN DON.
Licensure Intermediate care. *Beds* 80.
Certified Medicaid.

Admissions Requirements Minimum age 16; Medical examination.
Staff Physicians 15 (ft); RNs 3 (ft), 1 (pt); LPNs 4 (ft); Orderlies 3 (ft); Nurses aides 20 (ft), 2 (pt); Physical therapists 1 (ft); Activities coordinators 1 (ft); Dietitians 1 (pt).
Facilities Dining room; Activities room; Crafts room; Laundry room; Barber/Beauty shop; Library.
Activities Arts & crafts; Cards; Games; Reading groups; Prayer groups; Movies; Shopping trips; Social/Cultural gatherings.

MADRAS

Mountain View Hospital*
1270 A St, Madras, OR, 97741
(503) 475-3882
Admin Ken Jones.
Licensure Intermediate care. *Beds* 68.
Certified Medicaid.

MALLALA

Lutheran Pioneer Home
32746 Shooge Rd, Mallala, OR, 97038
(503) 824-3311
Admin Beverly Rice.
Licensure Intermediate care. *Beds* 28.
Certified Medicaid.
Affiliation Lutheran

MCMINNVILLE

Carousel Care Center*
1309 E 27th St, McMinnville, OR, 97128
(503) 472-4678
Admin Stan Smith.
Licensure Skilled care; Intermediate care. *Beds* SNF 11; ICF 96. *Certified* Medicaid.

Hillside Manor Inc
900 N Hill Rd, McMinnville, OR, 97128
(503) 472-9534
Admin Robert Donohue. *Medical Dir/Dir of Nursing* Donalda Webster.
Licensure Skilled care; Intermediate care. *Beds* ICF 19.
Owner Nonprofit Corp.
Staff RNs 3 (ft), 3 (pt); LPNs 3 (ft); Nurses aides 14 (ft).
Facilities Dining room; Activities room; Chapel; Crafts room; Barber/Beauty shop; Library.
Activities Arts & crafts; Cards; Games; Reading groups; Prayer groups; Movies.

Oak Glen Care Center
421 S Evans St, McMinnville, OR, 97128
(503) 472-3141
Admin Bill Hoard. *Medical Dir/Dir of Nursing* Mark Olson MD.
Licensure Intermediate care. *Beds* 127.
Certified Medicaid.
Owner Privately owned.
Admissions Requirements Minimum age 18; Physician's request.
Staff RNs 3 (ft), 3 (pt); LPNs 5 (ft), 2 (pt); Orderlies 2 (ft); Nurses aides 30 (ft), 5 (pt); Activities coordinators 3 (ft), 1 (pt).
Facilities Dining room; Physical therapy room; Activities room; Laundry room; Barber/Beauty shop.
Activities Arts & crafts; Cards; Games; Reading groups; Prayer groups; Movies; Shopping trips; Social/Cultural gatherings.

MEDFORD

Hearthstone Manor
2901 E Barnett Rd, Medford, OR, 97504
(503) 779-4221
Admin Dan Gregory. *Medical Dir/Dir of Nursing* Warren G Bishop MD; Mary Ellen Mower RN DON.

Licensure Skilled care; Intermediate care; Residential care. *Beds* SNF 161; ICF.
Certified Medicaid; Medicare.
Owner Nonprofit Corp.
Admissions Requirements Medical examination; Physician's request.
Staff Physicians; RNs; LPNs; Orderlies; Nurses aides; Physical therapists; Reality therapists; Recreational therapists; Occupational therapists; Speech therapists; Activities coordinators.
Facilities Dining room; Physical therapy room; Activities room; Crafts room; Barber/Beauty shop.
Activities Arts & crafts; Cards; Games; Reading groups; Prayer groups; Movies; Shopping trips; Social/Cultural gatherings; College classes.

Rogue Valley Care Center
3693 S Pacific Hwy, Medford, OR, 97501
(503) 535-4636
Admin Jackie Connell. *Medical Dir/Dir of Nursing* Dr John Shonerd.
Licensure Intermediate care. *Beds* ICF 36.
Certified Medicaid.
Owner Proprietary Corp.
Admissions Requirements Medical examination; Physician's request.
Staff Physicians 1 (pt); RNs 1 (ft), 1 (pt); LPNs 4 (ft); Nurses aides 12 (ft), 2 (pt); Physical therapists 1 (pt); Activities coordinators 1 (ft); Dietitians 1 (pt); Ophthalmologists 1 (pt); Restorative aide 1 (ft).
Facilities Dining room; Physical therapy room; Activities room; Laundry room; Barber/Beauty shop; Library.
Activities Arts & crafts; Cards; Games; Reading groups; Prayer groups; Movies; Shopping trips; Social/Cultural gatherings; Old time fidlers.

Rogue Valley Manor
1200 Mira Mar Ave, Medford, OR, 97504
(503) 773-7411
Admin Thomas R Becker. *Medical Dir/Dir of Nursing* Patricia Kauffman.
Licensure Skilled care. *Beds* SNF 60.
Owner Nonprofit Corp.
Admissions Requirements Minimum age 62.
Staff Physicians; RNs; LPNs; Nurses aides; Physical therapists; Recreational therapists; Occupational therapists; Speech therapists; Activities coordinators; Dietitians; Dentists; Ophthalmologists; Podiatrists; Dentist.
Facilities Dining room; Physical therapy room; Activities room; Chapel; Crafts room; Laundry room; Barber/Beauty shop; Library; Pool; Fitness center.
Activities Arts & crafts; Cards; Games; Prayer groups; Movies; Shopping trips; Social/Cultural gatherings; Swimming; Exercise.

The Three Fountains
835 Crater Lake Ave, Medford, OR, 97504
(503) 773-7717
Admin Shirley A Inge CFACHCA. *Medical Dir/Dir of Nursing* Warren Bishop MD; Susan Lewis RN BS DON.
Licensure Skilled care. *Beds* SNF 156.
Certified Medicaid; Medicare.
Owner Proprietary Corp.
Admissions Requirements Minimum age 12; Physician's request.
Staff RNs 16 (ft); LPNs 4 (ft); Orderlies 5 (ft); Nurses aides 78 (ft), 4 (pt); Physical therapists 1 (ft); Occupational therapists 1 (ft); Speech therapists 1 (ft); Activities coordinators 3 (ft); Dietitians 1 (ft).
Facilities Dining room; Physical therapy room; Activities room; Crafts room; Laundry room; Barber/Beauty shop; Library.
Activities Arts & crafts; Cards; Games; Reading groups; Prayer groups; Movies; Shopping trips; Social/Cultural gatherings.

Villa Royal Health Care Center
625 Stevens St, Medford, OR, 97501
(503) 779-3551
Admin David Allen Scott. *Medical Dir/Dir of Nursing* Steven Brummer; Pam Cross DON.
Licensure Skilled care; Intermediate care. *Beds* 130. *Certified* Medicaid; Medicare.
Owner Proprietary Corp (Hillhaven Corp).
Staff Physicians; RNs; LPNs; Orderlies; Nurses aides; Physical therapists; Reality therapists; Recreational therapists; Occupational therapists; Speech therapists; Activities coordinators; Dietitians.
Languages Spanish
Facilities Dining room; Physical therapy room; Activities room; Crafts room; Laundry room; Barber/Beauty shop; Library.
Activities Arts & crafts; Cards; Games; Reading groups; Prayer groups; Movies; Shopping trips; Social/Cultural gatherings.

MERLIN

Merlin Health Retreat*
PO Box 340, 816 Sanitarium Rd, Merlin, OR, 97532
(503) 476-5300
Admin Charles Werner.
Licensure Intermediate care. *Beds* 40.
Certified Medicaid.
Facilities Dining room; Activities room; Chapel.
Activities Games; Prayer groups; Movies; Social/Cultural gatherings.

MILTON-FREEWATER

Elzora Manor
PO Box D, 120 Elzora St, Milton-Freewater, OR, 97862
(503) 938-3318
Admin Uva Berry. *Medical Dir/Dir of Nursing* Dr Ronald Zleck; Pat Gomes.
Licensure Skilled care; Intermediate care. *Beds* 127. *Certified* Medicaid; Medicare.
Owner Proprietary Corp.
Admissions Requirements Physician's request.
Staff Physicians 1 (pt); RNs 9 (ft); LPNs 5 (ft), 3 (pt); Orderlies 5 (ft); Nurses aides 35 (ft); Physical therapists 1 (pt); Reality therapists 1 (pt); Recreational therapists 1 (pt); Occupational therapists 1 (pt); Speech therapists 1 (pt); Activities coordinators 2 (ft); Dietitians 1 (pt); Dentists 1 (pt); Ophthalmologists 1 (pt); Podiatrists 1 (pt).
Languages Spanish
Facilities Dining room; Physical therapy room; Activities room; Crafts room; Laundry room; Barber/Beauty shop; Library.
Activities Arts & crafts; Cards; Games; Reading groups; Prayer groups; Movies; Shopping trips; Social/Cultural gatherings.

MILWAUKIE

Milwaukie Convalescent Center*
12045 SE Stanley Ave, Milwaukie, OR, 97222
(503) 659-2323
Admin Nash Barinaga.
Licensure Intermediate care. *Beds* 68.
Certified Medicaid.

Rose Villa Inc*
13505 SE River Rd, Milwaukie, OR, 97222
(503) 654-3171
Admin James Sturgis.
Licensure Skilled care. *Beds* 55.

Willamette Methodist Convalescent Center
13021 SE River Rd, Milwaukie, OR, 97222
(503) 652-6200
Admin Ruth Slick. *Medical Dir/Dir of Nursing* Dr Roy Payne.
Licensure Skilled care; Intermediate care. *Beds* SNF 54; ICF 66. *Certified* Medicaid; Medicare.

Admissions Requirements Minimum age 21;
Medical examination; Physician's request.
Staff RNs 9 (ft), 10 (pt); LPNs 2 (ft);
Orderlies 4 (ft); Nurses aides 47 (ft), 15 (pt);
Physical therapists 4 (pt); Occupational
therapists 1 (pt); Speech therapists 1 (pt);
Activities coordinators 1 (ft); Dietitians 1
(pt); Dentists 1 (pt); Podiatrists 1 (pt).
Affiliation Methodist
Facilities Dining room; Physical therapy
room; Activities room; Chapel; Crafts room;
Laundry room; Barber/Beauty shop; Library.
Activities Arts & crafts; Cards; Games;
Reading groups; Prayer groups; Movies;
Shopping trips; Social/Cultural gatherings.

MOLALLA

Molalla Manor Care Center
301 Ridings Ave, Molalla, OR, 97038
(503) 829-5591
Admin Kathleen C Weitz. *Medical Dir/Dir of
Nursing* Dr A B Willeford MD; Kathleen A
Williams DNS.
Licensure Skilled care; Intermediate care;
Respite care; Day care. *Beds* SNF 15; ICF
77. *Certified* Medicaid; Medicare.
Owner Proprietary Corp.
Admissions Requirements Medical
examination; Physician's request.
Staff RNs 3 (ft); LPNs 7 (ft); Orderlies 2 (ft);
Nurses aides 15 (ft), 13 (pt); Physical
therapists 1 (pt); Occupational therapists 1
(pt); Speech therapists 1 (pt); Activities
coordinators 1 (ft); Dietitians 1 (pt);
Ophthalmologists 1 (pt).
Languages Spanish
Facilities Dining room; Physical therapy
room; Activities room; Laundry room;
Barber/Beauty shop; Fireside; Multipurpose
Room.
Activities Arts & crafts; Games; Prayer groups;
Movies; Social/Cultural gatherings.

MOUNT ANGEL

Benedictine Nursing Center
540 S Main St, Mount Angel, OR, 97362
(503) 845-6841
Admin John H Hogan. *Medical Dir/Dir of
Nursing* Joy Smith DNS.
Licensure Skilled care; Intermediate care. *Beds*
SNF 127; ICF 108.
Owner Nonprofit Corp.
Admissions Requirements Minimum age 16;
Medical examination; Physician's request.
Staff RNs 12 (ft), 22 (pt); LPNs 1 (ft), 1 (pt);
Nurses aides 51 (ft), 11 (pt); Physical
therapists 6 (ft), 2 (pt); Occupational
therapists 2 (ft), 1 (pt); Speech therapists;
Activities coordinators 1 (ft); Dietitians 1
(ft).
Affiliation Roman Catholic
Facilities Dining room; Physical therapy
room; Activities room; Chapel; Barber/
Beauty shop; Quiet room.
Activities Games; Reading groups; Prayer
groups; Movies; Shopping trips; Social/
Cultural gatherings.

MYRTLE POINT

Myrtle Point Care Center
637 Ash St, Myrtle Point, OR, 97458
(503) 572-2066
Admin Don Veverka. *Medical Dir/Dir of
Nursing* Sharon Brockapp.
Licensure Intermediate care. *Beds* ICF 32;
RCF 8. *Certified* Medicaid.
Owner Proprietary Corp.
Admissions Requirements Medical
examination; Physician's request.
Staff Physicians 3 (pt); RNs 1 (ft), 1 (pt);
LPNs 2 (pt); Nurses aides 6 (ft), 10 (pt);
Activities coordinators 1 (ft); Dietitians 1
(ft).

Facilities Dining room; Physical therapy
room; Activities room; Chapel; Barber/
Beauty shop; Library.
Activities Arts & crafts; Cards; Games;
Reading groups; Prayer groups; Movies;
Shopping trips; Social/Cultural gatherings;
Van outing; Exercise groups; Lunch outings;
Fairs; Community programs.

NEWBERG

Chehalem Care Center
1900 E Fulton St, Newberg, OR, 97132
(503) 538-2108
Admin Paul Jensen. *Medical Dir/Dir of
Nursing* Dorothy Henderson.
Licensure Intermediate care; ARC. *Beds* ICF
90; ARC 10. *Certified* Medicaid.
Owner Proprietary Corp (Beverly Enterprises).
Admissions Requirements Medical
examination; Physician's request.
Staff RNs 5 (ft), 2 (pt); LPNs 2 (ft), 2 (pt);
Orderlies 5 (ft); Nurses aides 30 (ft);
Recreational therapists 1 (ft); Activities
coordinators 1 (ft); Dietitians 1 (ft).
Facilities Dining room; Physical therapy
room; Activities room; Laundry room;
Barber/Beauty shop.
Activities Arts & crafts; Cards; Games; Prayer
groups; Movies; Social/Cultural gatherings.

Newberg Care Home*
1500 E 1st St, Newberg, OR, 97132
(503) 538-9436
Admin John P Jones. *Medical Dir/Dir of
Nursing* John Cummings.
Licensure Skilled care. *Beds* SNF 9; ICF 58.
Certified Medicaid.
Owner Proprietary Corp.
Admissions Requirements Minimum age
Geriatrics only; Medical examination;
Physician's request.
Staff Physicians 1 (pt); RNs 4 (ft); LPNs 3
(ft); Orderlies 1 (ft); Nurses aides 35 (ft), 5
(pt); Physical therapists 1 (pt); Activities
coordinators 1 (ft), 1 (pt); Dietitians 1 (pt).
Facilities Dining room; Physical therapy
room; Activities room; Chapel; Crafts room;
Laundry room; Barber/Beauty shop.
Activities Arts & crafts; Cards; Games;
Reading groups; Prayer groups; Movies;
Shopping trips; Social/Cultural gatherings.

NEWBURG

Friendsview Manor Healthcenter
1301 E Fulton St, Newburg, OR, 97132
(503) 538-3144
Admin Stuart C Willcuts. *Medical Dir/Dir of
Nursing* LaVina Stram DON.
Licensure Intermediate care; RCF. *Beds* ICF
37; RCF 15.
Owner Nonprofit Corp.
Admissions Requirements Minimum age 65;
Medical examination; Physician's request.
Staff RNs 2 (ft), 7 (pt); LPNs 1 (ft); Nurses
aides 10 (ft), 6 (pt); Reality therapists 1 (ft);
Activities coordinators 1 (ft); Dietitians 1
(ft).
Languages Spanish, Portuguese
Affiliation Society of Friends
Facilities Dining room; Activities room;
Chapel; Crafts room; Laundry room; Barber/
Beauty shop; Library; Sunroom.
Activities Arts & crafts; Cards; Games;
Reading groups; Prayer groups; Movies;
Shopping trips; Social/Cultural gatherings;
Dinning out; Church meetings.

NEWPORT

Yaquina Care Center Inc*
835 SW 11th, Newport, OR, 97365
(503) 265-5356
Admin Julie Carlson.

Licensure Intermediate care. *Beds* 80.
Certified Medicaid.

NORTH BEND

St Catherine's Residence & Nursing Center
3959 Sheridan Ave, North Bend, OR, 97459
(503) 756-4151
Admin Sr Mary Laetice Williams RSM.
Medical Dir/Dir of Nursing Charles Lindsay
MD; Sr Mary Flavian DON.
Licensure Skilled care; Intermediate care;
Residential care. *Beds* SNF 10; ICF 151;
Residential 5. *Certified* Medicaid; Medicare.
Owner Nonprofit Corp.
Admissions Requirements Medical
examination; Physician's request.
Staff Physicians 1 (pt); RNs 10 (ft), 1 (pt);
LPNs 6 (ft), 4 (pt); Orderlies 3 (ft), 2 (pt);
Nurses aides 83 (ft), 7 (pt); Physical
therapists 1 (pt); Activities coordinators 1
(ft); Dietitians 1 (ft).
Affiliation Roman Catholic
Facilities Dining room; Physical therapy
room; Activities room; Chapel; Crafts room;
Barber/Beauty shop; Library.
Activities Arts & crafts; Cards; Games; Prayer
groups; Movies; Shopping trips; Social/
Cultural gatherings.

NYSSA

Malheur Memorial Hospital*
1109 Park Ave, Nyssa, OR, 97913
(503) 372-2211
Admin Richard W Jones. *Medical Dir/Dir of
Nursing* David W Sarazin MD.
Admissions Requirements Physician's request.
Staff Physicians 5 (ft); RNs 1 (ft), 3 (pt);
LPNs 6 (ft); Nurses aides 18 (ft); Physical
therapists 1 (pt); Recreational therapists 1
(pt); Activities coordinators 1 (ft); Dietitians
1 (ft); Dentists 1 (pt); Ophthalmologists 1
(pt); Podiatrists 1 (pt).
Facilities Dining room; Physical therapy
room; Activities room; Crafts room; Laundry
room; Barber/Beauty shop; Library Special
dining room for residents needing assistance.
Activities Arts & crafts; Cards; Games;
Reading groups; Prayer groups; Movies;
Shopping trips; Social/Cultural gatherings.

ONTARIO

Presbyterian Nursing Home Inc
1085 N Oregon, Ontario, OR, 97914
(503) 889-9133
Admin Barbara J Morgan. *Medical Dir/Dir of
Nursing* Joseph Burdic MD; Joan Bentz RN
DON.
Licensure Skilled care; Intermediate care. *Beds*
SNF 18; ICF 106. *Certified* Medicaid;
Medicare.
Admissions Requirements Minimum age 16;
Medical examination; Physician's request.
Staff Physicians 1 (pt); RNs 4 (ft), 2 (pt);
LPNs 10 (ft); Orderlies 5 (ft); Nurses aides
65 (ft), 10 (pt); Physical therapists 1 (ft);
Activities coordinators 3 (ft).
Affiliation Presbyterian
Facilities Dining room; Physical therapy
room; Activities room; Chapel; Crafts room;
Laundry room; Barber/Beauty shop; Library;
Classroom.
Activities Arts & crafts; Cards; Games;
Reading groups; Prayer groups; Movies;
Guest entertainments; BBQs; Picnics.

OREGON CITY

Golden Age Care Center*
1506 Division St, Oregon City, OR, 97045
(503) 656-1973
Admin Eleanor Johnson. *Medical Dir/Dir of
Nursing* Joseph Intile.
Licensure Intermediate care. *Beds* 48.
Certified Medicaid.

Admissions Requirements Minimum age 18.
Staff RNs 2 (ft), 2 (pt); LPNs 1 (ft); Orderlies 1 (ft), 1 (pt); Nurses aides 25 (ft), 5 (pt); Activities coordinators 1 (ft).
Facilities Dining room; Activities room.
Activities Arts & crafts; Cards; Games; Prayer groups; Movies.

Mountain View Convalescent Care Center
1400 Division St, Oregon City, OR, 97045
(503) 656-0367
Admin Victor D Kintz. *Medical Dir/Dir of Nursing* Dr Payne; Linda Campbell-Thurman RN DNS.
Licensure Skilled care; Intermediate care. *Beds* SNF; ICF; Medicare Certified; 120. *Certified* Medicaid; Medicare.
Owner Proprietary Corp (Beverly Enterprises).
Admissions Requirements Physician's request.
Staff Physicians 20 (pt); RNs 15 (ft), 5 (pt); LPNs 5 (ft), 2 (pt); Orderlies 6 (ft); Nurses aides 40 (ft); Physical therapists 1 (ft); Occupational therapists; Speech therapists; Activities coordinators 1 (ft), 1 (pt); Dietitians 1 (pt); Dentists 1 (pt); Ophthalmologists 1 (pt).
Facilities Dining room; Physical therapy room; Activities room; Crafts room; Barber/Beauty shop.
Activities Arts & crafts; Cards; Games; Reading groups; Prayer groups; Movies; Shopping trips; Social/Cultural gatherings; Rhythm band.

Oregon City Nursing Home*
148 Hood St, Oregon City, OR, 97045
(503) 656-4035
Admin Sharon Miller Hart. *Medical Dir/Dir of Nursing* Dr Julian Markin.
Licensure Intermediate care. *Beds* 45. *Certified* Medicaid.
Admissions Requirements Physician's request.
Staff RNs 1 (ft); LPNs 6 (ft); Orderlies 2 (ft); Nurses aides 22 (ft); Activities coordinators 1 (ft); Dietitians 1 (pt); Dentists 1 (pt); Podiatrists 1 (pt).
Facilities Dining room; Activities room; Crafts room; Laundry room; Barber/Beauty shop.
Activities Arts & crafts; Games; Prayer groups; Movies; Shopping trips.

Sierra Vista Care Center*
1680 Molalla Ave, PO Box 644, Oregon City, OR, 97045
(503) 655-2588
Admin Carol Prael.
Licensure Intermediate care. *Beds* 102. *Certified* Medicaid.
Admissions Requirements Medical examination; Physician's request.
Staff Physicians 5 (pt); RNs 3 (ft); LPNs 6 (ft); Orderlies 35 (ft), 10 (pt); Nurses aides 35 (ft), 10 (pt); Physical therapists 1 (pt); Recreational therapists 1 (pt); Speech therapists 1 (pt); Activities coordinators 1 (ft); Dietitians 1 (ft).
Facilities Dining room; Activities room; Crafts room; Laundry room; Barber/Beauty shop.
Activities Arts & crafts; Movies; Shopping trips.

PENDLETON

Amber Valley Care Center*
707 SW 37th St, Pendleton, OR, 97801
(503) 276-3374
Admin Nancy Nielsen.
Licensure Intermediate care. *Beds* 99. *Certified* Medicaid; Medicare.

Delamarter Care Center
PO Box 35, Rte 1, Mission Rd, Pendleton, OR, 97801
(503) 276-7157

Admin Shirley Weissenbuehler. *Medical Dir/ Dir of Nursing* Jules Bittner MD; Jeanne Reeve RN DNS.
Licensure Intermediate care. *Beds* ICF 84. *Certified* Medicaid; VA.
Owner Proprietary Corp.
Admissions Requirements Medical examination; Physician's request.
Staff Physicians 1 (ft); RNs 1 (ft), 2 (pt); LPNs 2 (ft), 4 (pt); Orderlies 2 (ft); Nurses aides 20 (ft), 5 (pt); Activities coordinators 1 (ft), 1 (pt); Beautician.
Languages Spanish
Facilities Dining room; Barber/Beauty shop; Multi-purpose room.
Activities Arts & crafts; Cards; Games; Reading groups; Prayer groups; Movies; Shopping trips; Social/Cultural gatherings; Van outings.

Eastern Oregon Hospital & Training Center*
PO Box A, Pendleton, OR, 97801
(503) 276-1711
Admin Al Baxter.
Licensure Intermediate care; Intermediate care for mentally retarded. *Beds* 370. *Certified* Medicaid.

PORTLAND

Baptist Manor
900 NE 81st Ave, Portland, OR, 97213
(503) 255-0860
Admin Lawrence Bienert. *Medical Dir/Dir of Nursing* Lois Williamson RN DON.
Licensure Intermediate care. *Beds* ICF 94. *Certified* Medicaid.
Owner Nonprofit Corp.
Admissions Requirements Medical examination; Physician's request.
Staff RNs 4 (ft), 3 (pt); LPNs 7 (ft), 3 (pt); Nurses aides 40 (ft); Activities coordinators 1 (ft), 1 (pt); Dietitians 1 (ft).
Affiliation Baptist
Facilities Dining room; Activities room; Chapel; Crafts room; Laundry room; Barber/ Beauty shop; Library.
Activities Arts & crafts; Cards; Games; Reading groups; Prayer groups; Movies; Social/Cultural gatherings.

Belmont Care Center
4914 SE Belmont St, Portland, OR, 97215
(503) 235-3179
Admin Robert Allen. *Medical Dir/Dir of Nursing* Carl Wilcox MD; Baya Young.
Licensure Intermediate care. *Beds* ICF 59. *Certified* Medicaid.
Owner Privately owned.
Staff RNs 2 (ft); LPNs 3 (ft), 2 (pt); Orderlies; Nurses aides 26 (ft); Recreational therapists 1 (ft), 1 (pt); Activities coordinators 1 (ft), 1 (pt); Dietitians 1 (ft).
Facilities Dining room; Activities room; Crafts room; Laundry room; Barber/Beauty shop; Library.
Activities Arts & crafts; Cards; Games; Reading groups; Prayer groups; Movies; Shopping trips; Social/Cultural gatherings.

Care Center East*
11325 NE Weidler, Portland, OR, 97220
(503) 253-1181
Admin David G Johnson.
Licensure Intermediate care. *Beds* 93. *Certified* Medicaid.

Care Vista
9911 SE Mt Scott Blvd, Portland, OR, 97266
(503) 777-5642
Admin Barbara J Foster. *Medical Dir/Dir of Nursing* Rebecca Stephens.
Licensure Intermediate care. *Beds* ICF 137. *Certified* Medicaid.
Owner Proprietary Corp.

Staff Physicians 4 (pt); RNs 10 (ft), 2 (pt); LPNs 2 (ft); Orderlies 2 (ft); Nurses aides 28 (ft); Physical therapists 1 (pt); Activities coordinators 2 (ft); Dietitians 1 (pt).
Facilities Dining room; Physical therapy room; Activities room; Crafts room; Laundry room; Barber/Beauty shop; Library.
Activities Arts & crafts; Cards; Games; Reading groups; Prayer groups; Movies; Shopping trips; Social/Cultural gatherings.

CareWest Plaza Inc*
2250 NW Kearney St, Portland, OR, 97210
(503) 224-3910
Admin Ellen Engelent.
Licensure Skilled care; Intermediate care. *Beds* SNF 24; ICF 88. *Certified* Medicaid; Medicare.

Cascade Terrace Nursing Center
5601 SE 122, Portland, OR, 97236
(503) 761-3181
Admin Charles D Fogg. *Medical Dir/Dir of Nursing* Dr Fennesseey; Juni Bailey DNS.
Licensure Intermediate care. *Beds* ICF 95; Residential care 10. *Certified* Medicaid.
Owner Proprietary Corp.
Staff RNs; LPNs; Orderlies; Nurses aides; Physical therapists; Occupational therapists; Speech therapists; Activities coordinators; Dietitians.
Facilities Dining room; Physical therapy room; Activities room; Chapel; Crafts room; Laundry room; Barber/Beauty shop.
Activities Arts & crafts; Cards; Games; Reading groups; Prayer groups; Movies; Shopping trips; Social/Cultural gatherings.

Centennial Health Care Center
725 SE 202nd Ave, Portland, OR, 97233
(503) 665-3118
Admin Ray Finch. *Medical Dir/Dir of Nursing* Faith Schiell DON.
Licensure Intermediate care. *Beds* ICF 106. *Certified* Medicaid.
Owner Proprietary Corp (Beverly Enterprises).
Admissions Requirements Medical examination.
Staff RNs; LPNs; Orderlies; Nurses aides; Activities coordinators; Dietitians.
Facilities Dining room; Physical therapy room; Activities room; Chapel; Laundry room; Barber/Beauty shop.
Activities Arts & crafts; Cards; Games; Reading groups; Prayer groups; Movies; Shopping trips; Social/Cultural gatherings.

Columbia Manor Convalescent Center
6010 SW Shattuck Rd, Portland, OR, 97221
(503) 246-8811
Admin Eleanor Johnson. *Medical Dir/Dir of Nursing* William Spisak MD.
Licensure Intermediate care. *Beds* ICF 102. *Certified* Medicaid.
Admissions Requirements Medical examination; Physician's request.
Staff RNs 2 (ft); LPNs 6 (ft); Orderlies 34 (ft), 4 (pt); Reality therapists 1 (ft); Recreational therapists 1 (ft); Activities coordinators 1 (ft).
Facilities Dining room; Activities room; Crafts room; Laundry room; Barber/Beauty shop; Library.
Activities Arts & crafts; Cards; Games; Reading groups; Prayer groups; Movies; Shopping trips; Social/Cultural gatherings.

Crestview Convalescent*
6530 SW 30th Ave, Portland, OR, 97201
(503) 244-7533
Admin Jean Glanz.
Licensure Skilled care. *Beds* 99. *Certified* Medicare.

Del's Care Center Inc*
319 NE Russett, Portland, OR, 97211
(503) 289-5571
Admin Caroline Schie. *Medical Dir/Dir of Nursing* Dr. Gordon Myers.

Licensure Intermediate care. *Beds* ICF 70; 20 RCF. *Certified* Medicaid.

Friendship Health Center*
3320 SE Holgate, Portland, OR, 97202
(503) 231-1411
Admin Tom DeJardin. *Medical Dir/Dir of Nursing* H Lenox H Dick MD.
Licensure Skilled care; Intermediate care. *Beds* SNF 40; ICF 60. *Certified* Medicaid; Medicare.
Admissions Requirements Minimum age 18; Medical examination.
Staff Physicians 5 (pt); RNs 12 (ft), 5 (pt); LPNs 5 (ft), 4 (pt); Orderlies 1 (ft), 2 (pt); Nurses aides 47 (ft), 13 (pt); Physical therapists 1 (ft); Recreational therapists 2 (ft); Occupational therapists 1 (pt); Speech therapists 1 (pt); Dietitians 1 (ft); Dentists 1 (pt); Podiatrists 1 (pt); Audiologists 1 (pt).
Facilities Dining room; Physical therapy room; Activities room; Chapel; Crafts room; Laundry room; Barber/Beauty shop; Library.
Activities Arts & crafts; Cards; Games; Reading groups; Prayer groups; Movies; Shopping trips; Social/Cultural gatherings.

Gateway Care Center
39 NE 102nd Ave, Portland, OR, 97220
(503) 252-2461
Admin Gayla L Brown. *Medical Dir/Dir of Nursing* Steve Jones MD; Gayla L Brown RN.
Licensure Intermediate care; Residential care. *Beds* ICF 42; Residential 20. *Certified* Medicaid.
Owner Proprietary Corp.
Admissions Requirements Medical examination; Physician's request.
Staff Physicians 1 (ft); RNs 2 (ft); LPNs 4 (ft), 2 (pt); Nurses aides 12 (ft); Physical therapists 1 (pt); Activities coordinators 1 (ft); Dietitians 1 (ft), 1 (pt); Ophthalmologists 1 (pt).
Facilities Dining room; Physical therapy room; Activities room; Laundry room; Barber/Beauty shop.
Activities Arts & crafts; Cards; Games; Reading groups; Social/Cultural gatherings; Exercise class; Discussion of current events.

Glenaire Care Center*
12441 SE Stark St, Portland, OR, 97233
(503) 255-7040
Admin Ray Finch. *Medical Dir/Dir of Nursing* Estill Deitz.
Licensure Intermediate care. *Beds* 95. *Certified* Medicaid.
Admissions Requirements Medical examination; Physician's request.
Staff RNs 4 (ft), 1 (pt); LPNs 4 (ft), 1 (pt); Nurses aides 34 (ft), 2 (pt); Activities coordinators 1 (ft).
Facilities Dining room; Activities room; Laundry room.
Activities Arts & crafts; Games; Prayer groups; Movies.

Glisan Care Center Inc
9750 NE Glisan St, Portland, OR, 97220
(503) 256-3920
Admin Beth Delamarter. *Medical Dir/Dir of Nursing* Bonnie Butler.
Licensure Skilled care; Intermediate care. *Beds* SNF 15; ICF 85. *Certified* Medicare.
Owner Proprietary Corp (Prestige Care Inc).
Admissions Requirements Physician's request.
Staff RNs 4 (ft), 2 (pt); LPNs 5 (ft), 1 (pt); Nurses aides 39 (ft), 3 (pt); Physical therapists 2 (ft); Reality therapists 1 (ft); Recreational therapists 1 (ft); Occupational therapists 1 (ft); Speech therapists 1 (ft); Activities coordinators 1 (ft); Dietitians 1 (pt).
Languages Japanese
Facilities Dining room; Physical therapy room; Activities room; Crafts room; Barber/ Beauty shop.

Activities Arts & crafts; Cards; Games; Reading groups; Prayer groups; Movies; Shopping trips; Social/Cultural gatherings.

Graystone Manor Convalescent Center*
12640 SE Bush, Portland, OR, 97236
(503) 761-6621
Admin David Heeb.
Licensure Intermediate care. *Beds* 36. *Certified* Medicaid.

Har-Lyn Care Center
10948 SE Boise St, Portland, OR, 97266
(503) 760-1727
Admin Linda M Glidden. *Medical Dir/Dir of Nursing* Dr Julia Markin.
Licensure Intermediate care. *Beds* ICF 80. *Certified* Medicaid.
Owner Proprietary Corp; Privately owned.
Staff Physicians 1 (ft); RNs 4 (ft); LPNs 3 (ft); Orderlies 3 (ft); Nurses aides 63 (ft), 12 (pt); Physical therapists 1 (ft); Reality therapists 1 (ft); Recreational therapists 1 (ft); Activities coordinators 1 (ft); Dietitians 1 (ft); Dentists 1 (ft); Ophthalmologists 1 (ft); Podiatrists 1 (ft).
Facilities Dining room; Activities room; Crafts room; Laundry room; Barber/Beauty shop; Library; Patio; Yard.
Activities Arts & crafts; Cards; Games; Reading groups; Prayer groups; Movies; Shopping trips; Social/Cultural gatherings; Community events.

Hillside Convalescent Inc
800 NW 25th Ave, Portland, OR, 97210
(503) 224-0535
Admin JoAnn Bavier RN. *Medical Dir/Dir of Nursing* David Perry MD; Lisa Claunch RN DON.
Licensure Intermediate care. *Beds* ICF 25.
Owner Proprietary Corp.
Admissions Requirements Medical examination; Physician's request.
Staff RNs; LPNs; Nurses aides; Activities coordinators.
Facilities Dining room; Activities room; Barber/Beauty shop.
Activities Arts & crafts; Cards; Games; Reading groups; Prayer groups; Movies; Shopping trips; Social/Cultural gatherings.

Holladay Park Plaza
1300 NE 16th Ave, Portland, OR, 97232
(503) 288-6671
Admin Ernest W Vetter. *Medical Dir/Dir of Nursing* Marian Danley RN.
Licensure Intermediate care. *Beds* ICF 33.
Owner Nonprofit Corp.
Admissions Requirements Minimum age 62; Physician's request.
Staff RNs 3 (ft), 5 (pt); LPNs 1 (pt); Nurses aides 8 (ft), 8 (pt); Activities coordinators 1 (ft); Dietitians 1 (ft).
Affiliation Presbyterian
Facilities Dining room; Physical therapy room; Chapel; Barber/Beauty shop; Library.
Activities Arts & crafts; Cards; Games; Reading groups; Prayer groups; Movies; Shopping trips; Social/Cultural gatherings; Pleasure trips; Cooking sessions; Good grooming sessions.

House of Care Inc
6003 SE 136th, Portland, OR, 97236
(503) 761-1155
Admin Janice Hill. *Medical Dir/Dir of Nursing* Edward R Tallman MD.
Licensure Intermediate care; Residential care. *Beds* 69; Residential 104.
Owner Privately owned.
Staff Physicians 2 (pt); RNs 3 (ft); LPNs 5 (ft); Nurses aides 35 (ft); Recreational therapists 3 (ft); Activities coordinators 1 (ft); Dietitians 1 (ft); Ophthalmologists 1 (pt).

Facilities Dining room; Activities room; Crafts room; Laundry room; Barber/Beauty shop; Library.
Activities Arts & crafts; Cards; Games; Reading groups; Movies; Shopping trips; Social/Cultural gatherings.

Jallo's Nursing Home*
5737 NE 37th Ave, Portland, OR, 97211
(503) 288-5967
Admin Caroline Schie.
Licensure Intermediate care. *Beds* 63. *Certified* Medicaid.
Facilities Dining room; Activities room; Laundry room; Barber/Beauty shop.
Activities Arts & crafts; Cards; Games; Reading groups; Prayer groups; Movies; Shopping trips; Social/Cultural gatherings.

Laurelhurst Care Center
2827 SE Salmon St, Portland, OR, 97214
(503) 232-8504
Admin Lin Neff. *Medical Dir/Dir of Nursing* Stephen Jones MD.
Licensure Intermediate care. *Beds* ICF 84. *Certified* Medicaid.
Owner Proprietary Corp (Beverly Enterprises).
Admissions Requirements Physician's request.
Staff RNs 4 (ft); LPNs 2 (ft); Nurses aides 20 (ft); Activities coordinators 1 (ft).
Facilities Dining room; Physical therapy room; Activities room; Laundry room; Barber/Beauty shop; Solarium.
Activities Arts & crafts; Cards; Games; Reading groups; Prayer groups; Movies.

Lawrence Convalescent Center*
812 SE 48th, Portland, OR, 97215
(503) 236-2624
Admin Alex Fehrer. *Medical Dir/Dir of Nursing* Martha Gail DO.
Licensure Intermediate care. *Beds* 40. *Certified* Medicaid.
Admissions Requirements Medical examination; Physician's request.
Staff RNs 1 (ft); LPNs 2 (ft), 1 (pt); Orderlies 2 (ft); Nurses aides 22 (ft); Reality therapists 1 (ft); Recreational therapists 1 (ft); Occupational therapists 1 (pt); Speech therapists 1 (pt); Activities coordinators 1 (ft); Dietitians 1 (pt); Dentists 1 (pt); Podiatrists 1 (pt).
Facilities Dining room; Laundry room; Barber/Beauty shop.
Activities Arts & crafts; Games; Prayer groups; Movies.

Menlo Park Health Care Center
745 NE 122nd Ave, Portland, OR, 97230
(503) 252-0241
Admin Judy Dove. *Medical Dir/Dir of Nursing* T Hickerson MD; Esther Murphy RN.
Licensure Skilled care. *Beds* SNF; ICF 83. *Certified* Medicaid; Medicare.
Owner Proprietary Corp.
Admissions Requirements Medical examination; Physician's request.
Staff RNs 4 (ft), 7 (pt); LPNs 2 (ft), 1 (pt); Orderlies 2 (ft); Nurses aides 25 (ft); Activities coordinators 1 (ft).
Facilities Dining room; Physical therapy room; Activities room; Crafts room; Laundry room; Barber/Beauty shop; Library.
Activities Arts & crafts; Cards; Games; Reading groups; Prayer groups; Movies; Social/Cultural gatherings.

Midway Care Center Inc*
5601 SE 122nd, Portland, OR, 97236
(503) 761-3181
Admin Antonette Petrecca.
Licensure Intermediate care. *Beds* 43. *Certified* Medicaid.

Bishop Morris Care Center
2430 NW Marshall, Portland, OR, 97210
(503) 227-3791

Admin Mary Jaeger. *Medical Dir/Dir of Nursing* Stephen R Jones MD; Kenda Carter RN.
Licensure Intermediate care. *Beds* ICF 108. *Certified* Medicaid.
Owner Nonprofit Corp.
Admissions Requirements Medical examination.
Staff Physicians; RNs; LPNs; Nurses aides; Physical therapists; Reality therapists; Recreational therapists; Occupational therapists; Speech therapists; Activities coordinators; Dietitians.
Affiliation Episcopal
Activities Arts & crafts; Cards; Games; Reading groups; Prayer groups; Movies; Shopping trips; Social/Cultural gatherings.

Mt St Joseph Extended Care Center
3060 SE Stark St, Portland, OR, 97214
(503) 232-6193
Admin Sr Madeleva Comiskey. *Medical Dir/Dir of Nursing* Charles Darby MD; Harriet Bennett RN MS DON.
Licensure Skilled care; Intermediate care; Residential care. *Beds* SNF 6; ICF 185; Residential 99. *Certified* Medicaid; Medicare.
Owner Nonprofit Corp.
Admissions Requirements Medical examination; Physician's request.
Staff RNs; LPNs; Nurses aides; Occupational therapists; Activities coordinators; Pastoral care; Social worker; Medical aides.
Languages Spanish
Affiliation Roman Catholic
Facilities Dining room; Physical therapy room; Activities room; Chapel; Crafts room; Laundry room; Barber/Beauty shop; Library; Dental office.
Activities Arts & crafts; Cards; Games; Reading groups; Prayer groups; Movies; Shopping trips; Social/Cultural gatherings; Picnics.

Mt Tabor Care Center
7100 SE Division, Portland, OR, 97206
(503) 775-8601
Admin Marcia Johnson. *Medical Dir/Dir of Nursing* Richard Orth DO.
Licensure Intermediate care. *Beds* ICF 120. *Certified* Medicaid.
Owner Proprietary Corp (American Health Care Inc).
Admissions Requirements Medical examination; Physician's request.
Staff RNs 4 (ft), 2 (pt); LPNs 5 (ft), 2 (pt); Orderlies 1 (ft); Nurses aides 27 (ft), 15 (pt); Restorative aides.
Facilities Dining room; Physical therapy room; Activities room; Laundry room.
Activities Arts & crafts; Cards; Games; Reading groups; Prayer groups; Movies; Shopping trips; Social/Cultural gatherings.

Park Forest Care Center*
8643 NE Beech St, Portland, OR, 97220
(503) 256-2151
Admin David Park.
Licensure Intermediate care. *Beds* 68. *Certified* Medicaid.

Park View Nursing Home*
2425 SW 6th, Portland, OR, 97201
(503) 228-6684
Admin Jeanne Dawson.
Licensure Intermediate care. *Beds* 102.

Parkrose Nursing Home*
10336 NE Wygant, Portland, OR, 97220
(503) 255-7677
Admin Roger Stewart. *Medical Dir/Dir of Nursing* Sharon Faulk.
Licensure Intermediate care. *Beds* 56. *Certified* Medicaid.
Admissions Requirements Minimum age 14; Medical examination; Physician's request.

Staff RNs 3 (ft); LPNs 2 (ft); Orderlies 3 (ft); Nurses aides 14 (ft), 5 (pt); Activities coordinators 1 (ft).
Facilities Dining room.
Activities Arts & crafts; Cards; Games; Reading groups; Prayer groups; Movies; Social/Cultural gatherings; Individualized activities.

Porthaven Care Center
5330 NE Prescott, Portland, OR, 97218
(503) 288-6585
Admin Jacquelyn H Janes.
Licensure Skilled care. *Beds* SNF 99. *Certified* Medicare.
Owner Proprietary Corp.
Admissions Requirements Medical examination.
Staff RNs 6 (ft), 5 (pt); LPNs 3 (ft), 1 (pt); Nurses aides 29 (ft), 1 (pt); Activities coordinators 1 (ft); Dietitians 1 (pt); CMAs 2 (ft), 1 (pt).
Facilities Dining room; Physical therapy room; Laundry room; Barber/Beauty shop; Library.
Activities Arts & crafts; Games; Movies; Social/Cultural gatherings; Picnics; Van trips.

Portland Adventist Convalescent Center
6045 SE Belmont, Portland, OR, 97215
(503) 231-7166
Admin Harley Clendenon. *Medical Dir/Dir of Nursing* John Griffin MD; Judy DePrada DON.
Licensure Skilled care; Intermediate care. *Beds* SNF 67; ICF 108. *Certified* Medicaid; Medicare.
Owner Nonprofit Corp (Adventist Health Sys-USA).
Admissions Requirements Minimum age 2; Medical examination; Physician's request.
Staff Physicians 1 (pt); RNs 11 (ft), 16 (pt); LPNs 13 (ft), 20 (pt); Orderlies; Nurses aides 63 (ft), 16 (pt); Physical therapists 2 (ft), 3 (pt); Occupational therapists 1 (ft), 1 (pt); Speech therapists 1 (ft), 1 (pt); Activities coordinators 1 (ft); Dietitians 1 (pt).
Languages Spanish
Affiliation Seventh-Day Adventist
Activities Arts & crafts; Cards; Games; Reading groups; Prayer groups; Movies; Shopping trips; Social/Cultural gatherings.

Powellhurst Nursing Home*
13033 SE Holgate Blvd, Portland, OR, 97236
(503) 761-1533
Admin Margaret K Covert. *Medical Dir/Dir of Nursing* Martha Gail DO.
Licensure Intermediate care. *Beds* 77. *Certified* Medicaid.
Facilities Dining room; Physical therapy room; Activities room; Crafts room; Laundry room; Barber/Beauty shop.
Activities Arts & crafts; Cards; Games; Reading groups; Prayer groups; Movies; Shopping trips; Social/Cultural gatherings.

Providence Children's Nursing Center*
830 NE 47th Ave, Portland, OR, 97213
(503) 234-9991
Admin Sr Katherine Smith. *Medical Dir/Dir of Nursing* Margaret M Wayson MD.
Licensure Skilled care. *Beds* 54. *Certified* Medicaid.
Admissions Requirements Medical examination; Physician's request.
Staff Physicians 1 (pt); RNs 6 (ft), 6 (pt); LPNs 3 (ft); Nurses aides 40 (ft), 28 (pt); Physical therapists 1 (pt); Speech therapists 1 (ft); Activities coordinators 1 (ft); Dietitians 1 (ft), 2 (pt).
Affiliation Roman Catholic
Facilities Physical therapy room; Activities room; Chapel; Laundry room.
Activities Games; Reading groups; Shopping trips; Social/Cultural gatherings; Outings; Swimming.

Raleigh Care Center*
6630 SW Beaverton-Hillsdale Hwy, Portland, OR, 97225
(503) 292-4488
Admin Allen Cortez. *Medical Dir/Dir of Nursing* Juliana Markin MD.
Licensure Intermediate care. *Beds* 90. *Certified* Medicaid.
Staff Physicians 1 (pt); RNs 4 (ft), 1 (pt); LPNs 3 (ft), 3 (pt); Orderlies 1 (ft), 1 (pt); Nurses aides 20 (ft), 25 (pt); Physical therapists 1 (pt); Speech therapists 1 (pt); Activities coordinators 1 (ft); Dietitians 1 (pt); Dentists 1 (pt); Podiatrists 1 (pt).
Facilities Dining room; Physical therapy room; Activities room; Laundry room; Barber/Beauty shop.
Activities Arts & crafts; Cards; Games; Reading groups; Prayer groups; Movies; Shopping trips; Social/Cultural gatherings.

Reedwood Extended Care Center
3540 SE Francis St, Portland, OR, 97202
(503) 232-5240
Admin Glenn Nelson.
Licensure Skilled care. *Beds* 60. *Certified* Medicare.
Admissions Requirements Minimum age 21.
Staff Physicians 1 (pt); RNs 5 (ft), 3 (pt); LPNs 1 (ft), 1 (pt); Orderlies 2 (ft); Nurses aides 25 (ft), 2 (pt); Physical therapists 1 (pt); Recreational therapists 1 (pt); Occupational therapists 1 (pt); Speech therapists 1 (pt); Dietitians 1 (pt).
Facilities Dining room; Activities room; Chapel; Laundry room.
Activities Arts & crafts; Cards; Games; Reading groups; Prayer groups; Movies.

Robison Jewish Home
6125 SW Boundary St, Portland, OR, 97221
(503) 246-7706
Admin Al A Mendlovitz. *Medical Dir/Dir of Nursing* Sam Miller MD; Linda Duggan DON.
Licensure Skilled care; Intermediate care. *Beds* 75. *Certified* Medicaid; Medicare.
Owner Nonprofit organization/foundation.
Admissions Requirements Medical examination; Physician's request.
Staff RNs 5 (ft), 6 (pt); LPNs 9 (ft), 1 (pt); Nurses aides 43 (ft), 10 (pt); Physical therapists 1 (pt); Occupational therapists 1 (ft); Speech therapists 1 (pt); Activities coordinators 3 (ft); Dietitians 1 (pt); Ophthalmologists 1 (pt); Dentist 1 (pt).
Languages Yiddish, Hebrew, Russian
Affiliation Jewish
Facilities Dining room; Physical therapy room; Activities room; Chapel; Crafts room; Laundry room; Barber/Beauty shop.
Activities Arts & crafts; Cards; Games; Reading groups; Movies; Shopping trips; Social/Cultural gatherings.

Rose City Nursing Home*
34 NE 20th Ave, Portland, OR, 97232
(503) 231-0276
Admin David Graber. *Medical Dir/Dir of Nursing* Dr Gerald Durris.
Licensure Intermediate care. *Beds* 30. *Certified* Medicaid.
Staff Physicians; RNs 1 (ft), 4 (pt); LPNs 2 (ft), 2 (pt); Orderlies 2 (ft); Nurses aides 15 (ft); Activities coordinators 1 (ft).
Facilities Dining room; Activities room; Laundry room; Barber/Beauty shop.
Activities Arts & crafts; Cards; Games; Reading groups; Prayer groups; Movies; Shopping trips; Social/Cultural gatherings.

Sunny Vista Care Center
10435 SE Cora St, Portland, OR, 97266
(503) 760-1737
Admin Maureen Chaklai. *Medical Dir/Dir of Nursing* Juliana Markiw MD; Gloria Beevor RN DON.
Licensure Intermediate care. *Beds* ICF 53.

Owner Proprietary Corp (National Heritage).
Admissions Requirements Medical
examination; Physician's request.
Staff RNs 4 (ft); LPNs 2 (ft); Nurses aides 12
(ft); Recreational therapists 1 (ft);
Occupational therapists; Activities
coordinators 1 (ft); Music therapist 1 (ft).
Languages Spanish
Facilities Dining room; Activities room;
Laundry room; Barber/Beauty shop;
Enclosed-secure garden/courtyard.
Activities Arts & crafts; Cards; Games;
Reading groups; Prayer groups; Movies;
Shopping trips; Social/Cultural gatherings;
Bell choir.

Terwilliger Plaza Inc
2545 SW Terwilliger Blvd, Portland, OR,
97201
(503) 299-4211
Admin Carmen Lawson. *Medical Dir/Dir of
Nursing* Carmen Lawson RN DON.
Licensure Intermediate care. *Beds* ICF 9.
Owner Nonprofit Corp.
Admissions Requirements Must be a member
of Terwilliger Plaza.
Staff RNs 1 (pt); LPNs 6 (pt); Nurses aides 1
(ft), 6 (pt); Activities coordinators;
Dietitians; Ophthalmologists.
Activities Arts & crafts; Cards; Games;
Reading groups; Prayer groups.

Victoria Nursing Home*
3339 SE Division St, Portland, OR, 97202
(503) 235-4135
Admin Esther Pearson.
Licensure Intermediate care. *Beds* 44.
Certified Medicaid.

West Hills Convalescent Center*
5701 SW Multnomah Blvd, Portland, OR,
97219
(503) 244-1107
Admin Margaret M Danner. *Medical Dir/Dir
of Nursing* Hester Fieldhouse MD.
Licensure Skilled care; Intermediate care. *Beds*
116. *Certified* Medicaid; Medicare.
Admissions Requirements Physician's request.
Staff RNs 10 (ft); LPNs 6 (ft); Orderlies 5 (ft);
Nurses aides 35 (ft); Physical therapists 2
(ft); Recreational therapists 1 (pt); Speech
therapists 1 (pt); Activities coordinators 1
(ft); Dietitians 1 (pt).
Facilities Dining room; Physical therapy
room; Activities room; Crafts room; Laundry
room; Barber/Beauty shop; Library.
Activities Arts & crafts; Cards; Games;
Reading groups; Prayer groups; Movies;
Shopping trips; Social/Cultural gatherings.

Willamette Nursing Home Inc*
3125 N Willamette Blvd, Portland, OR, 97217
(503) 285-8334
Admin Miriam M Drake.
Licensure Intermediate care. *Beds* 43.
Certified Medicaid.

PRAIRIE CITY

Blue Mountain Nursing Home
112 E 5th St, Prairie City, OR, 97869
(503) 820-3541
Admin Phyllis McCarthy.
Licensure Intermediate care. *Beds* 52.
Certified Medicaid.
Admissions Requirements Minimum age 16;
Medical examination; Physician's request.
Staff RNs 2 (ft), 1 (pt); LPNs 1 (ft), 1 (pt);
Nurses aides 18 (ft), 2 (pt); Occupational
therapists 1 (pt); Activities coordinators 1
(ft), 1 (pt).
Facilities Dining room; Physical therapy
room; Activities room; Laundry room;
Barber/Beauty shop.
Activities Cards; Games; Reading groups;
Prayer groups; Movies; Shopping trips;
Social/Cultural gatherings.

PRINEVILLE

Crook County Nursing Home
1201 N Elm, Prineville, OR, 97754
(503) 447-1287
Admin Jose A Gorbea. *Medical Dir/Dir of
Nursing* Craig Wilson RN.
Licensure Intermediate care; Residential care.
Beds 42.
Owner Publicly owned.
Admissions Requirements Medical
examination; Physician's request.
Staff RNs 1 (ft); LPNs 3 (ft), 5 (pt); Orderlies
1 (pt); Nurses aides 9 (ft), 5 (pt); Activities
coordinators 1 (ft), 1 (pt); Dietitians 1 (ft).
Facilities Dining room; Activities room;
Chapel; Crafts room; Laundry room; Barber/
Beauty shop; Library; Sunroom.
Activities Arts & crafts; Cards; Games;
Reading groups; Prayer groups; Movies;
Shopping trips; Social/Cultural gatherings;
Outdoor activity.

Ochoco Nursing Home
950 N Elm St, Prineville, OR, 97754
(503) 447-7667
Admin Tim Brown. *Medical Dir/Dir of
Nursing* Judy Walton.
Licensure Intermediate care. *Beds* ICF 63.
Certified Medicaid.
Owner Proprietary Corp.
Admissions Requirements Physician's request.
Staff RNs 1 (ft), 2 (pt); LPNs 4 (ft), 2 (pt);
Nurses aides 12 (ft), 7 (pt).
Facilities Dining room; Physical therapy
room; Activities room; Laundry room;
Barber/Beauty shop.
Activities Arts & crafts; Games; Prayer groups;
Movies; Shopping trips; Social/Cultural
gatherings.

REDMOND

Opportunity Foundation of Central Oregon
PO Box 430, Redmond, OR, 97756
(503) 548-8444
Admin Darrel Wilson. *Medical Dir/Dir of
Nursing* Laura Brown.
Licensure Intermediate care for mentally
retarded. *Beds* ICF/MR 16. *Certified*
Medicaid.
Owner Nonprofit organization/foundation.
Admissions Requirements Minimum age 18;
Medical examination.
Staff RNs 1 (ft); LPNs 7 (ft); Orderlies 14 (ft);
Recreational therapists 1 (ft).
Facilities Dining room; Activities room;
Laundry room.
Activities Arts & crafts; Cards; Games;
Movies; Shopping trips; Social/Cultural
gatherings.

Redmond Health Care Center
3025 SW Reservoir Dr, Redmond, OR, 97756
(503) 548-5066
Admin Tim Larkin. *Medical Dir/Dir of
Nursing* Mary Bowen Scallorn.
Licensure Intermediate care. *Beds* ICF 67.
Certified Medicaid.
Owner Proprietary Corp.
Staff RNs 1 (ft), 1 (pt); LPNs 3 (ft), 1 (pt);
Nurses aides 17 (ft); Activities coordinators
1 (ft); Rehabilitation aide 1 (ft).
Facilities Dining room; Barber/Beauty shop.
Activities Arts & crafts; Cards; Games; Prayer
groups; Movies; Shopping trips.

REEDSPORT

Lower Umpqua Hospital*
PO Box 6, Reedsport, OR, 97567
(503) 271-2171
Admin Richard Bell.
Licensure Intermediate care. *Beds* 20.
Certified Medicaid.

ROSEBURG

Grandview Care Center
1199 NW Grandview Dr, Roseburg, OR,
97490
(503) 672-1638
Admin Steven E Higgins. *Medical Dir/Dir of
Nursing* Matthew Sacks MD; Betty Farris
RN DON.
Licensure Intermediate care. *Beds* ICF 83.
Certified Medicaid.
Owner Proprietary Corp.
Admissions Requirements Physician's request.
Staff RNs 6 (ft), 2 (pt); LPNs 2 (ft), 2 (pt);
Orderlies 2 (ft), 1 (pt); Nurses aides 20 (ft),
9 (pt); Activities coordinators 1 (ft).
Facilities Dining room; Activities room;
Laundry room; Barber/Beauty shop.
Activities Arts & crafts; Cards; Games;
Reading groups; Prayer groups; Movies;
Shopping trips; Social/Cultural gatherings.

Rose Haven Nursing Center
740 NW Hill Pl, Roseburg, OR, 97470
(503) 672-1631
Admin Duane Miner. *Medical Dir/Dir of
Nursing* Dr Timothy Powell; Debbie Ebner
DON.
Licensure Skilled care; Intermediate care. *Beds*
SNF 17; ICF 182. *Certified* Medicaid;
Medicare.
Owner Privately owned.
Admissions Requirements Medical
examination.
Staff RNs 10 (ft); Orderlies 10 (ft); Nurses
aides 90 (ft); Physical therapists 2 (ft);
Reality therapists; Recreational therapists;
Occupational therapists; Speech therapists;
Activities coordinators 3 (ft).
Facilities Dining room; Physical therapy
room; Activities room; Crafts room; Laundry
room; Barber/Beauty shop.
Activities Arts & crafts; Cards; Games;
Reading groups; Prayer groups; Movies;
Shopping trips; Social/Cultural gatherings.

SAINT HELENS

Meadow Park Care Center
75 Shore Dr, Saint Helens, OR, 97051
(503) 397-2713
Admin Richard D Hellie. *Medical Dir/Dir of
Nursing* Dory Walrod MD; Melinda
Palmquist RN DON.
Licensure Intermediate care. *Beds* ICF 92.
Certified Medicaid.
Owner Proprietary Corp (Unicare).
Admissions Requirements Medical
examination; Physician's request.
Staff Physicians 1 (pt); RNs 3 (ft), 3 (pt);
LPNs 3 (ft), 2 (pt); Orderlies 1 (ft); Nurses
aides 28 (ft), 4 (pt); Physical therapists 1
(pt); Occupational therapists 1 (pt);
Activities coordinators 1 (ft); Dietitians 1
(pt); Ophthalmologists 1 (pt).
Facilities Dining room; Physical therapy
room; Activities room; Crafts room; Laundry
room; Barber/Beauty shop; TV room.
Activities Arts & crafts; Cards; Games; Prayer
groups; Movies; Social/Cultural gatherings;
Birthday parties; Anniversary parties; Open
house.

SALEM

Capitol Manor*
PO Box 5000, 1955 Salem-Dallas Hwy NE,
Salem, OR, 97304
(503) 362-4101
Admin Eric Kuhn.
Licensure Intermediate care. *Beds* 43.

Capitol View Health Care Center
875 Oak St SE, Salem, OR, 97301
(503) 581-1457

Admin Victor D Kintz. *Medical Dir/Dir of Nursing* Paul Young MD; Edie Cowan RN DON.
Licensure Skilled care; Intermediate care. *Beds* SNF 31; ICF 38. *Certified* Medicaid; Medicare.
Owner Proprietary Corp (Beverly Enterprises).
Admissions Requirements Physician's request.
Staff RNs 8 (ft); LPNs 8 (ft); Orderlies; Nurses aides 37 (ft); Physical therapists 1 (ft); Occupational therapists 1 (ft); Speech therapists 1 (ft); Activities coordinators 1 (ft); Dietitians 1 (ft).
Facilities Dining room; Physical therapy room; Activities room; Crafts room; Laundry room; Barber/Beauty shop; Day room.
Activities Arts & crafts; Cards; Games; Reading groups; Prayer groups; Movies; Shopping trips; Social/Cultural gatherings; Van outings to the coast; Zoo trips.

Colonial Arms Nursing Home*
1687 Summer St NE, Salem, OR, 97303
(503) 585-4602
Admin Mabel Baughman.
Licensure Intermediate care. *Beds* 46. *Certified* Medicaid.

Fairview Training Center*
2250 Strong Rd SE, Salem, OR, 97310
(503) 378-2268
Admin Martha Warkentin.
Licensure Intermediate care for mentally retarded. *Beds* 1475. *Certified* Medicaid.

Imperial Manor Convalescent Center
2630 Church St, Salem, OR, 97303
(503) 585-6712
Admin Kathleen C Weitz. *Medical Dir/Dir of Nursing* Betty C Ranch RN DON.
Licensure Intermediate care. *Beds* ICF 65. *Certified* Medicaid.
Owner Proprietary Corp.
Admissions Requirements Medical examination; Physician's request.
Staff RNs 2 (ft); LPNs 3 (ft), 1 (pt); Orderlies 2 (ft); Nurses aides 14 (ft), 2 (pt); Activities coordinators 1 (ft); Medical aides 2 (ft).
Languages Spanish
Facilities Dining room; Activities room; Laundry room; Barber/Beauty shop.
Activities Arts & crafts; Cards; Games; Reading groups; Prayer groups; Shopping trips.

Keizer Retirement & Health Care Center
2360 Grear St, Salem, OR, 97301
(503) 363-8554
Admin Greg Gortmaker. *Medical Dir/Dir of Nursing* Paul Young.
Licensure Intermediate care. *Beds* ICF 32. *Certified* Medicaid.
Owner Proprietary Corp.
Admissions Requirements Minimum age 65; Physician's request.
Staff RNs 2 (ft); LPNs 2 (pt); Orderlies 1 (ft), 1 (pt); Nurses aides 14 (ft), 1 (pt); Activities coordinators 1 (pt); Dietitians.
Facilities Dining room; Physical therapy room; Activities room; Chapel; Crafts room; Laundry room; Barber/Beauty shop; Day room.
Activities Arts & crafts; Cards; Games; Reading groups; Prayer groups; Movies; Shopping trips; Social/Cultural gatherings.

Oak Crest Care Center*
2933 Center St NE, Salem, OR, 97301
(503) 585-5850
Admin Ron Colburn. *Medical Dir/Dir of Nursing* Dr Casterline.
Licensure Intermediate care. *Beds* 110. *Certified* Medicaid.
Owner Proprietary Corp (Hillhaven Corp).
Staff Physicians; RNs; LPNs; Orderlies; Nurses aides; Physical therapists; Recreational therapists; Activities coordinators; Dietitians; Dentists.

Facilities Dining room; Activities room; Crafts room; Laundry room; Barber/Beauty shop.
Activities Arts & crafts; Cards; Games; Reading groups; Prayer groups; Movies; Shopping trips; Social/Cultural gatherings.

Plantation Care Center Inc
820 Cottage St NE, Salem, OR, 97301
(503) 399-1135
Admin Betty Fillmore. *Medical Dir/Dir of Nursing* Ruth Speaker.
Licensure Intermediate care. *Beds* ICF 100. *Certified* Medicaid.
Owner Proprietary Corp (National Heritage).
Admissions Requirements Medical examination; Physician's request.
Staff RNs; LPNs; Orderlies; Nurses aides; Physical therapists; Activities coordinators; Dietitians.
Facilities Dining room; Activities room; Laundry room; Barber/Beauty shop.
Activities Arts & crafts; Cards; Games; Reading groups; Prayer groups; Movies; Shopping trips; Social/Cultural gatherings.

Shangri-La*
2887 74th SE, Salem, OR, 97301
(503) 581-1732
Admin Nancy Glass.
Licensure Intermediate care for mentally retarded. *Beds* 70. *Certified* Medicaid.
Admissions Requirements Minimum age 6; Medical examination; Physician's request.
Staff Physicians 1 (pt); RNs 2 (ft), 1 (pt); Orderlies 31 (ft), 15 (ft); Physical therapists 1 (pt); Recreational therapists 5 (ft); Occupational therapists 1 (pt); Speech therapists 1 (pt); Activities coordinators 1 (ft); Dietitians 1 (pt).
Facilities Dining room; Activities room; Laundry room.
Activities Arts & crafts; Cards; Games; Movies; Shopping trips; Social/Cultural gatherings.

Sherwood Park Nursing Home*
4062 Arleta Ave NE, Salem, OR, 97303
(503) 390-2271
Admin Scott R Turner.
Licensure Intermediate care. *Beds* 44. *Certified* Medicaid.

South Salem Care Center*
4620 Kurth St S, Salem, OR, 97302
(503) 581-8666
Admin Loretta A Androes. *Medical Dir/Dir of Nursing* Chris Edwardson.
Licensure Intermediate care. *Beds* 72. *Certified* Medicaid.
Owner Proprietary Corp (National Heritage).
Admissions Requirements Medical examination.
Staff Physicians 1 (pt); RNs 2 (ft); LPNs 5 (ft); Orderlies 5 (ft); Nurses aides 30 (ft), 4 (pt); Physical therapists 1 (pt); Reality therapists 1 (pt); Recreational therapists 1 (ft); Occupational therapists 1 (pt); Speech therapists 1 (pt); Activities coordinators 1 (pt); Dietitians 1 (pt); Dentists 1 (pt); Ophthalmologists 1 (pt); Podiatrists 1 (pt); Audiologists 1 (pt).
Facilities Dining room; Activities room; Laundry room; Barber/Beauty shop.
Activities Arts & crafts; Cards; Games; Reading groups; Prayer groups; Movies; Shopping trips; Social/Cultural gatherings.

Spruce Villa Inc
1960 Center St NE, Salem, OR, 97301
(503) 399-7924
Admin Anson Bell. *Medical Dir/Dir of Nursing* Pat Seeber.
Licensure Intermediate care for mentally retarded; Semi-independent living. *Certified* Medicaid.
Owner Nonprofit Corp.
Admissions Requirements Minimum age 18.

Staff Physicians 1 (pt); RNs 1 (ft); Nurses aides 28 (ft); Recreational therapists 1 (ft); Activities coordinators 1 (ft); Skill trainers 7 (ft).
Languages Sign
Facilities Apartments & homes.
Activities Shopping trips; Social/Cultural gatherings; Counseling; Behavior management; Skill acquisition; Support.

Sunnyside Care Center
4515 Sunnyside Rd SE, Salem, OR, 97302
(503) 370-8284
Admin Loris Gielczyk. *Medical Dir/Dir of Nursing* Paul Young MD.
Licensure Intermediate care. *Beds* ICF 124. *Certified* Medicaid.
Owner Proprietary Corp (Hillhaven Corp).
Staff Physicians 1 (pt); RNs 7 (ft); LPNs 6 (ft); Orderlies 5 (ft); Nurses aides 35 (ft); Physical therapists 1 (ft); Activities coordinators 2 (ft); Dietitians 1 (pt).
Facilities Dining room; Physical therapy room; Activities room; Crafts room; Barber/Beauty shop.
Activities Arts & crafts; Cards; Games; Reading groups; Prayer groups; Movies; Shopping trips; Social/Cultural gatherings; Picnics.

Willamette Lutheran Homes Inc
PO Box 169, 7693 Wheatland Rd N, Salem, OR, 97303
(503) 393-1491
Admin David Barnet. *Medical Dir/Dir of Nursing* Flora Pinell.
Licensure Intermediate care; Retirement apartments. *Beds* ICF 20; Retirement apts 110.
Owner Nonprofit organization/foundation.
Admissions Requirements Minimum age 62.
Staff RNs 2 (ft); LPNs 3 (ft); Orderlies; Nurses aides 5 (ft), 8 (pt); Activities coordinators 1 (ft); Dietitians 1 (ft).
Affiliation Lutheran
Facilities Dining room; Physical therapy room; Activities room; Chapel; Crafts room; Laundry room; Barber/Beauty shop; Library.
Activities Arts & crafts; Cards; Games; Reading groups; Prayer groups; Movies; Shopping trips; Social/Cultural gatherings.

SANDY

Orchard Crest Care Center
19130 SE Bornstedt Rd, Sandy, OR, 97055
(503) 668-5551
Admin Beverly Wilmoth. *Medical Dir/Dir of Nursing* Dr Levenburg; Jean Lerch RN DON.
Licensure Intermediate care. *Beds* ICF 28. *Certified* Medicaid.
Owner Privately owned.
Admissions Requirements Physician's request.
Staff RNs 1 (ft), 1 (pt); LPNs 2 (ft), 4 (pt); Orderlies 1 (ft); Nurses aides 9 (ft), 2 (pt); Activities coordinators 1 (ft).
Facilities Dining room; Activities room; Crafts room; Laundry room; Barber/Beauty shop; Pet therapy program; Horticulture therapy program.
Activities Arts & crafts; Cards; Games; Reading groups; Prayer groups; Movies; Shopping trips; Social/Cultural gatherings.

SCAPPOOSE

Victorian Manor*
33910 Columbia Blvd, Box 1068, Scappoose, OR, 97056
(503) 543-7131
Admin Howard Lavin.
Licensure Intermediate care. *Beds* 41. *Certified* Medicaid.
Admissions Requirements Minimum age 18; Medical examination; Physician's request.

Staff RNs 1 (ft); LPNs 3 (pt); Orderlies 1 (ft),
  1 (pt); Nurses aides 5 (ft), 15 (pt); Activities
  coordinators 1 (ft), 1 (pt).
Facilities Dining room; Activities room;
  Barber/Beauty shop.
Activities Arts & crafts; Games; Reading
  groups; Prayer groups; Movies; Social/
  Cultural gatherings.

SEASIDE

Ocean Park Nursing Home*
1420 E 10th, PO Box 836, Seaside, OR, 97138
(503) 738-6142
Admin Kathy Park.
Licensure Intermediate care. *Beds* 22.
  Certified Medicaid.
Admissions Requirements Physician's request.
Staff RNs 1 (ft), 1 (pt); LPNs 1 (ft), 3 (pt);
  Nurses aides 9 (ft), 9 (pt); Activities
  coordinators 1 (ft).
Facilities Dining room; Activities room;
  Laundry room.
Activities Arts & crafts; Cards; Games;
  Reading groups; Prayer groups; Movies;
  Shopping trips; Social/Cultural gatherings.

Seaside Care Center
822 Necanicum Dr, Seaside, OR, 97138
(503) 738-8383
Admin Eleanor M Johnson. *Medical Dir/Dir
  of Nursing* Linda Briggs RN.
Licensure Intermediate care. *Beds* ICF 100.
  Certified Medicaid.
Owner Proprietary Corp (Summit Health Ltd).
Admissions Requirements Minimum age 18;
  Medical examination; Physician's request.
Staff Physicians; RNs; LPNs; Orderlies;
  Nurses aides; Physical therapists; Reality
  therapists; Activities coordinators; Dietitians.
Facilities Dining room; Physical therapy
  room; Activities room; Crafts room; Laundry
  room; Barber/Beauty shop.
Activities Arts & crafts; Cards; Games;
  Reading groups; Prayer groups; Movies;
  Social/Cultural gatherings.

SHERIDAN

Sheridan Care Center*
411 SE Sheridan Rd, Sheridan, OR, 97378
(503) 843-2204
Admin Linda Hill.
Licensure Intermediate care. *Beds* 54.
  Certified Medicaid.

SILVERTON

Silver Gardens Care Home Inc
115 S James Ave, Silverton, OR, 97381
(503) 873-5362
Licensure Intermediate care. *Beds* ICF 52.
  Certified Medicaid.
Owner Proprietary Corp.
Admissions Requirements Physician's request.
Staff RNs 2 (ft), 2 (pt); LPNs 4 (ft), 1 (pt);
  Nurses aides 17 (ft), 7 (pt); Activities
  coordinators 1 (ft).
Facilities Dining room; Activities room;
  Barber/Beauty shop.
Activities Arts & crafts; Cards; Games;
  Reading groups; Prayer groups; Movies;
  Social/Cultural gatherings.

Silverton Nursing Home*
1164 S Water St, Silverton, OR, 97381
(503) 873-5391
Admin Dorothy Yost. *Medical Dir/Dir of
  Nursing* Michael Grady MD.
Licensure Intermediate care. *Beds* 64.
  Certified Medicaid.
Staff RNs 2 (ft); LPNs 3 (ft), 2 (pt); Nurses
  aides 18 (ft), 4 (pt); Activities coordinators 1
  (ft); Dietitians 1 (ft), 1 (pt).
Facilities Dining room; Physical therapy
  room; Activities room; Crafts room; Laundry
  room; Barber/Beauty shop; 2 Solariums.

Activities Arts & crafts; Cards; Games;
  Reading groups; Prayer groups; Movies;
  Shopping trips; Social/Cultural gatherings.

SPRINGFIELD

McKenzie Manor Nursing Home
1333 N 1st St, Springfield, OR, 97477
(503) 746-6581
Admin Florence Miller. *Medical Dir/Dir of
  Nursing* Wallace Baldwin MD; Lynn Tromp
  DON.
Licensure Skilled care. *Beds* SNF 153.
  Certified Medicaid; Medicare.
Owner Privately owned.
Admissions Requirements Medical
  examination; Physician's request.
Staff Physicians 1 (pt); RNs 8 (ft), 8 (pt);
  LPNs 7 (ft), 6 (pt); Orderlies 4 (ft), 2 (pt);
  Nurses aides 65 (ft), 21 (pt); Physical
  therapists 1 (pt); Reality therapists 1 (pt);
  Occupational therapists 1 (pt); Speech
  therapists 1 (pt); Activities coordinators 2
  (ft); Dietitians 1 (pt); Dentists 1 (pt);
  Ophthalmologists 1 (pt); Podiatrists 1 (pt);
  Therapy aides 3 (ft).
Facilities Dining room; Physical therapy
  room; Activities room; Crafts room; Laundry
  room; Barber/Beauty shop; Library.
Activities Arts & crafts; Cards; Games;
  Reading groups; Movies; Shopping trips;
  Social/Cultural gatherings.

SUBLIMITY

Marian Nursing Home
360 Church St, Sublimity, OR, 97385
Stayton (503) 769-3499, Salem (503) 581-2006
Admin Maurice Reece.
Licensure Intermediate care; Home for aged;
  Apartments. *Beds* ICF 174; Home for the
  Aged 21; Apartments 37. *Certified* Medicaid.
Admissions Requirements Minimum age 43;
  Medical examination; Physician's request.
Staff Physicians 2 (pt); RNs 12 (ft); LPNs 14
  (ft); Physical therapists 2 (pt); Occupational
  therapists 1 (pt); Speech therapists 1 (pt);
  Activities coordinators 2 (ft); Dietitians 1
  (ft), 1 (pt); Dentists 1 (pt); Ophthalmologists
  1 (pt); Dentist 1 (pt).
Facilities Dining room; Activities room;
  Chapel; Crafts room; Laundry room; Barber/
  Beauty shop.
Activities Arts & crafts; Cards; Games;
  Reading groups; Prayer groups; Movies;
  Shopping trips; Social/Cultural gatherings;
  Short trips to mountains, coast park.

SWEET HOME

Twin Oaks Care Center Inc
950 Nandina St, Sweet Home, OR, 97386
(503) 367-2191
Admin Alice Hyland. *Medical Dir/Dir of
  Nursing* Patricia Ridinger.
Licensure Intermediate care. *Beds* ICF 44.
  Certified Medicaid.
Owner Proprietary Corp.
Admissions Requirements Physician's request.
Staff RNs 1 (ft), 1 (pt); LPNs 1 (ft); Physical
  therapists 1 (pt); Speech therapists 1 (pt);
  Activities coordinators 1 (ft); Dietitians 1
  (pt).
Facilities Dining room; Activities room;
  Laundry room; Multi-purpose room.
Activities Arts & crafts; Cards; Games;
  Reading groups; Prayer groups; Movies;
  Shopping trips; Social/Cultural gatherings.

TIGARD

King City Convalescent Center
16485 SW Pacific Hwy, Tigard, OR, 97224
(503) 620-5141
Admin R J Baker. *Medical Dir/Dir of Nursing*
  Dorothy Miles RN.

Licensure Skilled care; Intermediate care. *Beds*
  SNF 148; ICF. *Certified* Medicaid;
  Medicare.
Owner Proprietary Corp (Beverly Enterprises).
Admissions Requirements Physician's request.
Staff RNs 14 (ft); LPNs 5 (ft); Nurses aides 42
  (ft); Physical therapists 3 (ft); Occupational
  therapists 2 (ft); Speech therapists 1 (ft);
  Activities coordinators 1 (ft); Dietitians 1
  (ft).
Facilities Dining room; Physical therapy
  room; Activities room; Crafts room; Laundry
  room; Barber/Beauty shop.
Activities Arts & crafts; Reading groups;
  Prayer groups; Movies.

Tigard Care Center*
14145 SW 105th St, Tigard, OR, 97223
(503) 639-1144
Admin Dennis Wade.
Licensure Intermediate care. *Beds* 112.
  Certified Medicaid.

TILLAMOOK

Tillamook Care Center
2500 Nielson Rd, Tillamook, OR, 97141
(503) 842-6664
Admin Allan Tschiegg. *Medical Dir/Dir of
  Nursing* Delores McGee.
Licensure Skilled care; Intermediate care. *Beds*
  SNF 15; ICF 86. *Certified* Medicaid;
  Medicare.
Owner Proprietary Corp.
Staff RNs 5 (ft), 1 (pt); LPNs 4 (ft); Nurses
  aides 19 (ft), 23 (pt); Physical therapists 1
  (pt); Speech therapists 1 (pt); Activities
  coordinators 1 (ft); Dietitians 1 (pt);
  Ophthalmologists 1 (pt); Dentist 1 (pt).
Facilities Dining room; Physical therapy
  room; Activities room; Crafts room; Laundry
  room; Barber/Beauty shop.
Activities Arts & crafts; Cards; Games;
  Reading groups; Prayer groups; Movies;
  Shopping trips; Social/Cultural gatherings.

TOLEDO

New Lincoln Hospital*
PO Box 490, Toledo, OR, 97391
(503) 336-2237
Admin David Bloomer, Jr.
Licensure Skilled care. *Beds* 18. *Certified*
  Medicare.

TROUTDALE

Edgefield Manor Nursing Home*
2126 SW Halsey St, Troutdale, OR, 97060
(503) 665-0161
Admin Laverne E Jones.
Licensure Intermediate care. *Beds* 91.
  Certified Medicaid.

Wood Village Nursing Manor Inc
2060 NE 238th Dr, Troutdale, OR, 97060
(503) 666-3863
Admin Robbe Redford. *Medical Dir/Dir of
  Nursing* Laurel Demorest.
Licensure Intermediate care. *Beds* ICF 56.
  Certified Medicaid.
Owner Proprietary Corp.
Admissions Requirements Minimum age 18.
Staff RNs 3 (ft); LPNs 2 (ft), 1 (pt); Nurses
  aides 16 (ft); Activities coordinators 1 (ft);
  Audiologists CMA 3 (ft); Social worker 1
  (ft).
Facilities Dining room; Activities room;
  Laundry room; Barber/Beauty shop;
  Sunroom.
Activities Arts & crafts; Cards; Games; Prayer
  groups; Movies; Shopping trips; Social/
  Cultural gatherings.

VALE

Pioneer Nursing Home*
1060 D St W, Vale, OR, 97918
(503) 473-3131
Admin Gaynelle Edmondson. *Medical Dir/Dir of Nursing* D W Sarazin MD.
Licensure Intermediate care; Residential care. *Beds* ICF 51; Residential 9. *Certified* Medicaid.
Admissions Requirements Medical examination; Physician's request.
Staff RNs 1 (ft), 1 (pt); LPNs 4 (ft), 3 (pt); Orderlies 1 (ft), 1 (pt); Nurses aides 17 (ft), 1 (pt); Activities coordinators 1 (ft).
Facilities Dining room; Physical therapy room; Activities room; Crafts room; Laundry room; Barber/Beauty shop.
Activities Arts & crafts; Cards; Games; Reading groups; Prayer groups; Movies; Shopping trips; Social/Cultural gatherings.

WEST LINN

West Linn Care Center Inc
2330 DeBok Rd, West Linn, OR, 97068
(503) 655-6331
Admin Nancy Paulk. *Medical Dir/Dir of Nursing* Rosemary Hidalgo.
Licensure Intermediate care. *Beds* ICF 62. *Certified* Medicaid.
Owner Proprietary Corp (Prestige Care Inc).
Admissions Requirements Medical examination.
Staff RNs; LPNs; Orderlies; Nurses aides.
Languages Spanish

Facilities Dining room; Activities room; Laundry room.
Activities Arts & crafts; Games; Reading groups; Prayer groups; Movies; Shopping trips; Social/Cultural gatherings.

WHEELER

Nehalem Valley Care Center
PO Box 16, Wheeler, OR, 97147-0016
(503) 368-5119
Admin Ken Cafferty. *Medical Dir/Dir of Nursing* Dr Oscar Marin.
Licensure Intermediate care. *Beds* 50. *Certified* Medicaid.
Owner Publicly owned.
Admissions Requirements Medical examination; Physician's request.
Staff Physicians 4 (ft); RNs 2 (ft), 4 (pt); LPNs 1 (ft); Orderlies 2 (ft), 1 (pt); Nurses aides 21 (ft); Physical therapists 1 (ft); Recreational therapists 1 (ft); Occupational therapists 1 (pt); Speech therapists 1 (pt); Activities coordinators 1 (pt); Dietitians 1 (pt); Podiatrists 1 (pt); Dentist 1 (pt).
Facilities Dining room; Physical therapy room; Activities room; Chapel; Crafts room; Laundry room; Barber/Beauty shop; Library; Family room; Lounges.
Activities Arts & crafts; Games; Prayer groups; Social/Cultural gatherings; Exercise programs; Community education; Bus sightseeing weekly; Pets.

WOODBURN

French Prairie Care Center
601 Evergreen Rd, Woodburn, OR, 97071
(503) 982-9946
Admin Mr Rene F Dumas. *Medical Dir/Dir of Nursing* Gordon D Haynie MD; Joyce Park RN DON.
Licensure Skilled care; Intermediate care. *Beds* SNF 9; ICF 71.
Owner Privately owned.
Admissions Requirements Minimum age No pediatrics; Physician's request.
Staff RNs; LPNs; Orderlies; Nurses aides; Activities coordinators; Dietitians.
Languages Spanish, German
Facilities Dining room; Physical therapy room; Activities room; Crafts room; Laundry room; Barber/Beauty shop.
Activities Arts & crafts; Cards; Games; Reading groups; Prayer groups; Movies; Shopping trips; Social/Cultural gatherings.

Woodburn Convalescent Center*
540 Settlemier St, Woodburn, OR, 97071
(503) 981-9566
Admin Dixie Irwin.
Licensure Intermediate care. *Beds* 60. *Certified* Medicaid.
Admissions Requirements Minimum age 18; Physician's request.
Staff RNs 1 (ft), 1 (pt); LPNs 3 (ft), 2 (pt); Activities coordinators 1 (ft); Dietitians 1 (pt).
Facilities Dining room; Laundry room.
Activities Arts & crafts; Cards; Games; Reading groups; Prayer groups; Movies; Shopping trips; Social/Cultural gatherings.

PENNSYLVANIA

ABBOTTSTOWN

Childrens Developmental Center Inc*
PO Box 236, Abbottstown, PA, 17301
(717) 624-2455
Licensure Intermediate care for mentally
retarded. *Beds* 64. *Certified* Medicaid.
Owner Proprietary Corp.

AKRON

Maple Farm Nursing Center
PO Box F, Akron, PA, 17501
(717) 859-1191
Admin Mary Ann Russell. *Medical Dir/Dir of
Nursing* Ms McCloskey.
Licensure Skilled care. *Beds* SNF 123.
Certified Medicare.
Owner Proprietary Corp.
Admissions Requirements Medical
examination.
Facilities Dining room; Physical therapy
room; Activities room; Crafts room; Barber/
Beauty shop; Library.
Activities Arts & crafts; Games; Reading
groups; Movies; Shopping trips.

ALIQUIPPA

Golfview Manor Nursing Home*
616 Golf Course Rd, Aliquippa, PA, 15001
(412) 375-0345
Medical Dir of Nursing Dr Glenn Roberts.
Licensure Skilled care. *Beds* 59. *Certified*
Medicaid; Medicare.
Owner Proprietary Corp.
Admissions Requirements Medical
examination.
Staff Physicians 1 (pt); RNs 1 (ft), 10 (pt);
LPNs 2 (pt); Orderlies 1 (ft); Nurses aides
15 (ft), 12 (pt); Physical therapists 1 (pt);
Recreational therapists 2 (ft); Speech
therapists 1 (pt); Activities coordinators 1
(pt); Dietitians 1 (pt); Dentists 1 (pt);
Podiatrists 2 (pt).
Facilities Dining room; Activities room;
Crafts room; Laundry room; Barber/Beauty
shop.
Activities Arts & crafts; Cards; Games;
Reading groups; Prayer groups; Movies;
Social/Cultural gatherings.

ALLENTOWN

Cedarbrook
PO Box 508, 350 S Cedarbrook Rd,
Allentown, PA, 18105-0508
(215) 395-3727
Admin Warren L Grasse. *Medical Dir/Dir of
Nursing* Nancy Urankar MD; Francis J
Pecuch Jr RN MS.
Licensure Skilled care; Intermediate care. *Beds*
624. *Certified* Medicaid; Medicare.
Owner Nonprofit organization/foundation;
Publicly owned.
Admissions Requirements Minimum age 18;
Medical examination.

Staff RNs 35 (ft), 23 (pt); LPNs 45 (ft), 11
(pt); Nurses aides 212 (ft), 78 (pt); Physical
therapists 1 (ft); Recreational therapists 2
(ft); Occupational therapists 1 (pt); Speech
therapists 1 (pt); Activities coordinators 1
(ft); Dietitians 1 (ft); Dentists 1 (pt);
Ophthalmologists 2 (pt); Podiatrists 1 (pt).
Facilities Dining room; Physical therapy
room; Activities room; Chapel; Crafts room;
Barber/Beauty shop; Library.
Activities Arts & crafts; Cards; Games;
Reading groups; Prayer groups; Movies;
Shopping trips; Social/Cultural gatherings.

**The Good Shepherd Home Long-Term Care
Facility Inc***
Sixth & Saint John Sts, Allentown, PA, 18103
(215) 776-3111
Medical Dir/Dir of Nursing E Joel Carpenter
IV.
Licensure Skilled care; Intermediate care. *Beds*
135. *Certified* Medicaid; Medicare.
Owner Nonprofit Corp.
Admissions Requirements Minimum age 12;
Medical examination.
Staff Physicians 2 (pt); RNs 15 (ft), 9 (pt);
LPNs 9 (ft), 1 (pt); Nurses aides 52 (ft), 16
(pt); Physical therapists 1 (ft), 1 (pt);
Recreational therapists 1 (ft); Occupational
therapists 1 (ft); Speech therapists 1 (pt);
Activities coordinators 1 (ft); Dietitians 1
(ft); Dentists 1 (pt); Podiatrists 1 (pt).
Affiliation Lutheran
Facilities Dining room; Physical therapy
room; Activities room; Chapel; Crafts room;
Laundry room; Barber/Beauty shop;
Academic educational center; Vocational
evaluation center.
Activities Arts & crafts; Cards; Games;
Reading groups; Prayer groups; Movies;
Shopping trips; Social/Cultural gatherings.

Liberty Nursing Center
N 17th & Allen Sts, Allentown, PA, 18104
(215) 432-4351
Admin Jim Adamowicz. *Medical Dir/Dir of
Nursing* Donna Frank.
Licensure Skilled care. *Beds* SNF 150.
Certified Medicaid; Medicare.
Owner Proprietary Corp (Health Care &
Retirement Corp).
Admissions Requirements Minimum age 17;
Medical examination; Physician's request.
Staff Physicians 4 (pt); RNs 15 (ft), 8 (pt);
LPNs 4 (ft), 3 (pt); Nurses aides 42 (ft), 19
(pt); Physical therapists 1 (ft); Recreational
therapists 2 (ft), 1 (pt); Occupational
therapists 1 (pt); Speech therapists 1 (pt);
Activities coordinators 1 (ft); Dietitians 1
(pt); Ophthalmologists 2 (pt); Social service
3 (ft), 2 (pt).
Languages Dutch, German, Italian, Greek,
Ukranian
Facilities Dining room; Physical therapy
room; Activities room; Chapel; Crafts room;
Laundry room; Barber/Beauty shop; Library.

Activities Arts & crafts; Cards; Games;
Movies; Social/Cultural gatherings; Lunch in
restaurants; Pet shows.

Luther Crest
800 Hausman Rd, Allentown, PA, 18104
(215) 398-8011
Admin Carol M Hoeschele. *Medical Dir/Dir of
Nursing* Ward Becker MD; Deborah
Rhinehart.
Licensure Skilled care. *Beds* SNF 60. *Certified*
Medicaid; Medicare.
Owner Nonprofit organization/foundation.
Admissions Requirements Minimum age 60;
Medical examination.
Staff Physicians 1 (ft); RNs 5 (ft), 2 (pt);
LPNs 3 (ft), 4 (pt); Nurses aides 24 (ft), 8
(pt); Physical therapists 2 (ft); Reality
therapists 1 (pt); Recreational therapists 1
(pt); Occupational therapists 1 (ft), 1 (pt);
Speech therapists 1 (pt); Activities
coordinators 1 (ft), 1 (pt); Dietitians 1 (pt);
Dentists 1 (pt); Ophthalmologists 1 (pt);
Podiatrists 1 (pt).
Affiliation Lutheran
Facilities Dining room; Physical therapy
room; Activities room; Chapel; Laundry
room; Barber/Beauty shop; Library.
Activities Arts & crafts; Cards; Games;
Reading groups; Prayer groups; Movies;
Shopping trips; Social/Cultural gatherings;
Residential study group.

Parkway Rest Home Inc
3600 Hamilton St, Allentown, PA, 18104
(215) 395-3508, 395-4011
Admin Donald Lanquell. *Medical Dir/Dir of
Nursing* Dr E Baum.
Licensure Intermediate care. *Beds* 28.
Certified Medicaid.
Owner Proprietary Corp.
Admissions Requirements Minimum age 35;
Medical examination.
Staff Physicians 4 (pt); RNs 4 (ft); LPNs 4
(ft); Nurses aides 10 (ft); Physical therapists
1 (pt); Recreational therapists 1 (pt);
Occupational therapists 1 (pt); Activities
coordinators 1 (ft); Dietitians 1 (pt); Dentists
1 (pt); Podiatrists 1 (pt).
Facilities Dining room; Activities room;
Laundry room.
Activities Arts & crafts; Cards; Games;
Reading groups; Prayer groups; Movies;
Social/Cultural gatherings.

Phoebe Home Inc
1925 Turner St, Allentown, PA, 18104
(215) 435-9037
Admin William C Soldrich. *Medical Dir/Dir of
Nursing* Dr Warren H Endres MD; Jean
Homanick.
Licensure Skilled care; Intermediate care. *Beds*
SNF 184; ICF 144. *Certified* Medicaid;
Medicare.
Owner Nonprofit Corp.
Admissions Requirements Minimum age 62;
Medical examination.

Staff Physicians 1 (ft), 3 (pt); RNs 25 (ft), 31 (pt); LPNs 16 (ft), 3 (pt); Nurses aides 104 (ft), 68 (pt); Physical therapists 1 (ft), 2 (pt); Reality therapists 2 (ft); Recreational therapists 2 (ft); Occupational therapists 2 (ft); Activities coordinators 1 (ft); Dietitians 2 (ft); Ophthalmologists 1 (pt); Dentist 1 (pt).
Affiliation Church of Christ
Facilities Dining room; Physical therapy room; Activities room; Chapel; Crafts room; Laundry room; Barber/Beauty shop; Library.
Activities Arts & crafts; Cards; Games; Reading groups; Prayer groups; Movies; Shopping trips; Social/Cultural gatherings.

Westminster Village
803 N Wahneta St, Allentown, PA, 18103
(215) 434-6245
Admin James F Bernardo. *Medical Dir/Dir of Nursing* George Provost MD; Jeraldine Kohut RN MA.
Licensure Skilled care; Intermediate care. *Beds* SNF; ICF 111. *Certified* Medicaid; Medicare.
Owner Nonprofit Corp.
Admissions Requirements Minimum age 65.
Staff Physicians; RNs 12 (ft), 5 (pt); LPNs 1 (ft), 2 (pt); Orderlies; Nurses aides 30 (ft), 25 (pt); Physical therapists 1 (ft), 3 (pt); Recreational therapists 1 (ft); Occupational therapists 1 (ft); Speech therapists; Activities coordinators; Dietitians; Dentists; Ophthalmologists; Podiatrists.
Affiliation Presbyterian
Facilities Dining room; Physical therapy room; Activities room; Chapel; Crafts room; Laundry room; Barber/Beauty shop; Library; Gift shop; Occupational therapy room; Kitchen; Dental office; Exercise room.
Activities Arts & crafts; Cards; Games; Reading groups; Prayer groups; Movies; Shopping trips; Social/Cultural gatherings; Cooking group; Lunch trips.

White Haven Center Annex—Allentown*
1700 Hanover Ave, Allentown, PA, 18103
(215) 821-6201
Licensure Intermediate care for mentally retarded. *Beds* 43. *Certified* Medicaid.
Owner Nonprofit Corp.

ALLISON PARK

Regency Hall Nursing Home Inc
9399 Babcock Blvd, Allison Park, PA, 15101
(412) 366-8540
Admin Sr M Carmelita Avero. *Medical Dir/ Dir of Nursing* Robert Carroll MD.
Licensure Skilled care; Personal care; Adult day care. *Beds* 133. *Certified* Medicaid; Medicare.
Owner Proprietary Corp (Vari-Care Inc).
Admissions Requirements Medical examination.
Staff Physicians 10 (pt); RNs 3 (ft), 17 (pt); LPNs 4 (ft), 6 (pt); Orderlies 3 (ft); Nurses aides 41 (ft), 27 (pt); Physical therapists 1 (pt); Reality therapists 1 (ft); Recreational therapists 1 (ft); Speech therapists 1 (pt); Activities coordinators 1 (pt); Dietitians 1 (pt); Dentists 1 (pt); Ophthalmologists 1 (pt); Podiatrists 1 (pt); Audiologists 1 (pt).
Affiliation Roman Catholic
Facilities Dining room; Physical therapy room; Activities room; Chapel; Barber/ Beauty shop.
Activities Arts & crafts; Cards; Games; Reading groups; Prayer groups; Movies; Social/Cultural gatherings.

ALTOONA

Altoona Center
1515 Fourth St, Altoona, PA, 16601
(814) 946-6900

Admin Barry C Benford. *Medical Dir/Dir of Nursing* Jules Netreba MD.
Licensure Intermediate care for mentally retarded. *Beds* ICF/MR 138. *Certified* Medicaid; Medicare.
Owner Publicly owned.
Staff Physicians 1 (ft); RNs 16 (ft); LPNs 3 (ft); Nurses aides 93 (ft); Physical therapists 1 (ft); Recreational therapists 17 (ft); Occupational therapists 1 (ft); Speech therapists 2 (ft); Activities coordinators 1 (ft); Dietitians 1 (ft); Dentists 1 (pt); Ophthalmologists 1 (pt).
Facilities Dining room; Physical therapy room; Activities room; Crafts room; Laundry room; Barber/Beauty shop; Library.
Activities Arts & crafts; Games; Reading groups; Prayer groups; Movies; Shopping trips; Social/Cultural gatherings; Individualized activites.

Hillview Care Center
700 S Cayuga Ave, Altoona, PA, 16602
(814) 946-0471
Admin Virginia D Claar. *Medical Dir/Dir of Nursing* Dr Sheedy; Charlene Monahan DON.
Licensure Skilled care; Intermediate care. *Beds* SNF 30; ICF 98. *Certified* Medicaid; Medicare.
Owner Proprietary Corp (Beverly Enterprises).
Admissions Requirements Minimum age 65; Medical examination; Physician's request.
Staff Physicians 1 (pt); RNs 6 (ft); LPNs 9 (ft); Nurses aides 46 (ft); Physical therapists 1 (pt); Speech therapists 1 (pt); Activities coordinators 1 (ft); Dietitians 1 (ft); Dentists 1 (pt); Ophthalmologists 1 (pt); Podiatrists 1 (pt).
Facilities Dining room; Physical therapy room; Activities room; Chapel; Barber/ Beauty shop.
Activities Arts & crafts; Cards; Games; Reading groups; Prayer groups; Social/ Cultural gatherings.

Mid State ICFMR Broad*
2605 Broad Ave, Altoona, PA, 16601
(717) 946-4618
Licensure Residential MR care. *Beds* 8. *Certified* Medicaid.
Owner Proprietary Corp.

Mid State ICFMR Inc*
1908 8th Ave, Altoona, PA, 16602
(814) 946-4623
Licensure Residential MR care. *Beds* 8. *Certified* Medicaid.
Owner Proprietary Corp.

Mid State ICFMR Inc*
2210 16th St, Altoona, PA, 16601
(814) 946-4637
Licensure Residential MR care. *Beds* 8. *Certified* Medicaid.
Owner Proprietary Corp.

Valley View Home*
301 Pleasant Valley Blvd, Altoona, PA, 16602
(814) 944-0845
Licensure Skilled care; Intermediate care. *Beds* SNF 78; ICF 166. *Certified* Medicaid; Medicare.
Owner Nonprofit Corp.

AMBLER

Ambler Rest Center
Bethlehem & Butler Pikes, Ambler, PA, 19002
(215) 646-7050
Admin Selma Kron. *Medical Dir/Dir of Nursing* Samuel D Kron MD.
Licensure Skilled care. *Beds* SNF 100. *Certified* Medicaid; Medicare.
Owner Proprietary Corp.
Staff RNs 8 (ft), 5 (pt); LPNs 2 (ft), 6 (pt); Orderlies 3 (ft); Nurses aides 33 (ft), 12 (pt); Physical therapists 1 (pt); Occupational

therapists 1 (pt); Speech therapists 1 (pt); Activities coordinators 1 (ft); Dietitians 1 (pt); Ophthalmologists 1 (pt).
Facilities Dining room; Physical therapy room; Activities room; Laundry room; Barber/Beauty shop.
Activities Arts & crafts; Cards; Games; Reading groups; Movies; Shopping trips; Social/Cultural gatherings.

Artman Lutheran Home
250 Behtlehem Pike, Ambler, PA, 19002
(215) 643-6333
Admin Florence D Thaler NHA. *Medical Dir/ Dir of Nursing* Dr Henry Borska MD; Anne Gattuso RN DON.
Licensure Skilled care. *Beds* SNF 30. *Certified* Medicaid.
Owner Nonprofit Corp.
Admissions Requirements Minimum age 65.
Staff Physicians 1 (pt); RNs 3 (ft), 7 (pt); LPNs 3 (pt); Nurses aides 8 (ft), 5 (pt); Recreational therapists 1 (ft), 1 (pt); Activities coordinators 1 (ft); Dietitians 1 (pt); Dentists 1 (pt); Ophthalmologists 1 (pt).
Affiliation Lutheran
Facilities Dining room; Activities room; Chapel; Laundry room; Barber/Beauty shop; Library.
Activities Arts & crafts; Cards; Games; Reading groups; Prayer groups; Movies; Shopping trips; Social/Cultural gatherings.

ANNVILLE

Lebanon Valley Home*
550 E Main St, Annville, PA, 17003
(717) 867-4467
Licensure Skilled care. *Beds* 53. *Certified* Medicaid; Medicare.
Owner Nonprofit Corp.

United Christian Church Home
Drawer E, Annville, PA, 17003-0404
(717) 867-4636
Admin Roy J Kreider.
Licensure Skilled care; Personal care. *Beds* 57. *Certified* Medicaid; Medicare.
Owner Nonprofit Corp.
Admissions Requirements Minimum age 65.
Staff Physicians; RNs; LPNs; Nurses aides; Physical therapists; Speech therapists; Activities coordinators; Dietitians; Ophthalmologists; Dentist.
Facilities Dining room; Physical therapy room; Activities room; Chapel; Crafts room; Laundry room; Barber/Beauty shop.
Activities Arts & crafts; Games; Reading groups; Prayer groups; Movies; Shopping trips.

APOLLO

West Haven Nursing Home
PO Box 278, Apollo, PA, 15613
(412) 727-3451
Admin Sylvia J Smith. *Medical Dir/Dir of Nursing* Pat Anthony.
Licensure Skilled care; Intermediate care. *Beds* 179. *Certified* Medicaid; Medicare.
Owner Privately owned.
Admissions Requirements Medical examination.
Staff Physicians 10 (pt); RNs 5 (ft), 6 (pt); LPNs 9 (ft), 12 (pt); Orderlies 6 (ft), 2 (pt); Nurses aides 53 (ft), 9 (pt).
Facilities Dining room; Physical therapy room; Activities room; Chapel; Laundry room; Barber/Beauty shop.
Activities Arts & crafts; Cards; Games; Prayer groups; Movies; Social/Cultural gatherings; Individualized activities.

ASHLAND

Ashland State General Hospital Geriatric Center
Rte 61, RFD 1, Fountain Springs, Ashland, PA, 17921
(717) 875-2000
Admin Joan A Medlinsky. *Medical Dir/Dir of Nursing* Vincent Mirarchi MD; Marilyn Connell RN.
Licensure Skilled care. *Beds* SNF 18. *Certified* Medicaid; Medicare.
Owner Nonprofit organization/foundation.
Admissions Requirements Medical examination; Physician's request.
Staff Physicians 1 (pt); RNs 5 (ft), 2 (pt); LPNs 4 (ft); Nurses aides 4 (ft); Physical therapists 1 (pt); Occupational therapists 1 (pt); Speech therapists 1 (pt); Activities coordinators 1 (pt); Dietitians 1 (pt); Dentists 1 (pt); Ophthalmologists 1 (pt); Podiatrists 1 (pt).
Facilities Dining room; Physical therapy room; Activities room; Chapel; Crafts room; Barber & beautician services are available.
Activities Arts & crafts; Cards; Games; Reading groups; Prayer groups; Movies; Social/Cultural gatherings.

ATHENS

Heritage Nursing Home Inc*
200 S Main St, Athens, PA, 18810
(717) 885-5805
Licensure Skilled care; Intermediate care. *Beds* SNF 65; ICF 56. *Certified* Medicaid; Medicare.
Owner Proprietary Corp.

BADEN

Naugle Manor Inc
1061 Phillips St, Baden, PA, 15005
(412) 869-2730
Medical Dir/Dir of Nursing C Nadiga MD.
Licensure Intermediate care. *Beds* 19.
Owner Proprietary Corp.
Admissions Requirements Minimum age 18; Medical examination.
Staff Physicians 1 (pt); RNs 1 (ft); LPNs 1 (ft), 4 (pt); Orderlies 1 (ft); Nurses aides 2 (ft), 4 (pt); Activities coordinators 1 (pt); Dietitians 1 (ft), 1 (pt).
Facilities Dining room; Activities room.
Activities Arts & crafts; Cards; Games; Prayer groups.

BALA CYNWYD

Mary J Drexel Home*
238 Belmont Ave, Bala Cynwyd, PA, 19004
(215) 664-5967
Medical Dir/Dir of Nursing William Miller MD.
Licensure Skilled care. *Beds* 27. *Certified* Medicaid.
Owner Nonprofit Corp.
Admissions Requirements Minimum age 65; Medical examination.
Staff Physicians 1 (pt); RNs 2 (ft); LPNs 6 (ft); Nurses aides 18 (ft); Physical therapists 1 (pt); Recreational therapists 1 (pt); Occupational therapists 1 (pt); Speech therapists 1 (pt); Activities coordinators 1 (ft); Dietitians 1 (ft); Dentists 1 (pt); Podiatrists 3 (pt); Audiologists 1 (pt).
Affiliation Lutheran
Facilities Dining room; Physical therapy room; Activities room; Chapel; Crafts room; Laundry room; Barber/Beauty shop; Library.
Activities Arts & crafts; Cards; Games; Reading groups; Movies; Shopping trips.

BANGOR

Slate Belt Medical Center Inc
701 Slate Belt Blvd, RD 3, Bangor, PA, 18013
(215) 588-6161
Admin Joseph H Fortenbaugh III. *Medical Dir/Dir of Nursing* John G Oliver MD; Nancy E Bahl RN.
Licensure Skilled care; Intermediate care; Primary care. *Beds* SNF 96; ICF. *Certified* Medicaid; Medicare.
Owner Nonprofit Corp.
Admissions Requirements Medical examination; Physician's request.
Staff Physicians 2 (ft); RNs 13 (ft), 15 (pt); LPNs 7 (ft), 3 (pt); Nurses aides 32 (ft), 12 (pt); Physical therapists 2 (ft); Occupational therapists 1 (ft); Speech therapists 1 (ft); Activities coordinators 1 (ft); Dietitians 1 (pt); Ophthalmologists 3 (pt); Podiatrists 1 (pt); Dentist 1 (pt).
Facilities Dining room; Physical therapy room; Activities room; Chapel; Laundry room; Barber/Beauty shop.
Activities Arts & crafts; Cards; Games; Reading groups; Prayer groups; Movies; Picnics; Family parties.

BEAR CREEK

Bear Creek Health Care Center
7001 Bear Creek Blvd, PO Box 58, Bear Creek, PA, 18602-0058
(717) 472-3785
Medical Dir/Dir of Nursing Dr Gregory Fino; Don Alonzo RN DON.
Licensure Intermediate care. *Beds* 32. *Certified* Medicaid.
Owner Proprietary Corp.
Admissions Requirements Medical examination; Physician's request.
Staff Physicians 1 (pt); RNs 1 (ft); LPNs 2 (ft), 4 (pt); Orderlies 2 (ft); Nurses aides 6 (ft), 6 (pt); Physical therapists 1 (pt); Speech therapists 1 (pt); Activities coordinators 1 (ft).
Facilities Dining room; Activities room; Crafts room; Laundry room; Barber/Beauty shop.
Activities Arts & crafts; Cards; Games; Reading groups; Prayer groups; Movies; Shopping trips; Social/Cultural gatherings.

BEAVER

Beaver Valley Geriatrics Center
Dutch Ridge Rd, Beaver, PA, 15009
(412) 775-7100
Admin William R Jubeck NHA. *Medical Dir/Dir of Nursing* Nicholas Vasilopolous MD; Cynthia Phillips RN NHA.
Licensure Skilled care; Intermediate care. *Beds* SNF 130; ICF 546. *Certified* Medicaid; Medicare.
Owner Nonprofit organization/foundation.
Admissions Requirements Medical examination.
Staff Physicians 2 (pt); RNs 52 (ft), 29 (pt); LPNs 39 (ft), 19 (pt); Orderlies 3 (ft), 2 (pt); Nurses aides 192 (ft), 81 (pt); Physical therapists 1 (ft); Occupational therapists 1 (pt); Speech therapists 1 (ft); Activities coordinators 1 (ft), 1 (pt); Dietitians 1 (ft), 1 (pt); Ophthalmologists 1 (pt); Podiatrists 1 (pt).
Facilities Dining room; Physical therapy room; Activities room; Crafts room; Laundry room; Barber/Beauty shop; Library; Auditorium; Pharmacy; Clinic; X-ray room.
Activities Arts & crafts; Cards; Games; Reading groups; Prayer groups; Movies; Shopping trips; Social/Cultural gatherings.

BEAVER FALLS

Beaver Valley Nursing Center*
RD 1, Georgetown Rd, Beaver Falls, PA, 15070
(412) 846-8200
Medical Dir/Dir of Nursing Dr Nelson Kennedy.
Licensure Skilled care; Intermediate care. *Beds* SNF 60; ICF 60. *Certified* Medicaid; Medicare.
Owner Proprietary Corp (Unicare).
Admissions Requirements Medical examination.
Staff Physicians 4 (pt); RNs 2 (ft), 7 (pt); LPNs 7 (ft), 4 (pt); Orderlies 2 (ft); Nurses aides 37 (ft), 12 (pt); Physical therapists 1 (ft); Speech therapists 1 (ft); Activities coordinators 2 (ft); Dietitians 1 (ft); Dentists 2 (pt); Podiatrists 1 (pt).
Facilities Dining room; Physical therapy room; Activities room; Chapel; Crafts room; Laundry room; Barber/Beauty shop; Library.
Activities Arts & crafts; Cards; Games; Reading groups; Prayer groups; Movies; Shopping trips; Social/Cultural gatherings.

Blair Nursing Home Inc-Blair Personal Care Homes Inc
Rte 2, Box 196, Beaver Falls, PA, 15010
(412) 843-2209
Admin M W Blair. *Medical Dir/Dir of Nursing* Dr E Damazo.
Licensure Skilled care; Personal care. *Beds* SNF 28; Personal 50.
Owner Proprietary Corp.
Admissions Requirements Medical examination.
Staff Physicians 1 (pt); RNs 3 (ft); LPNs 2 (ft), 2 (pt); Nurses aides 4 (ft), 9 (pt); Physical therapists 1 (pt); Activities coordinators 1 (ft); Dietitians 1 (pt); Podiatrists 1 (pt).
Facilities Dining room; Activities room; Laundry room.
Activities Arts & crafts; Cards; Games; Reading groups; Prayer groups; Movies.

Providence Health Care Center
900 3rd Ave, Beaver Falls, PA, 15010
(412) 846-8504
Admin Bruce T Pickens. *Medical Dir/Dir of Nursing* Dr William Fiden; Sherry Crees DON.
Licensure Skilled care. *Beds* SNF 180. *Certified* Medicaid; Medicare.
Owner Proprietary Corp (Health Care Facilities Inc).
Admissions Requirements Medical examination.
Staff Physicians; RNs; LPNs; Orderlies; Nurses aides; Physical therapists; Recreational therapists; Occupational therapists; Speech therapists; Activities coordinators; Dietitians; Ophthalmologists; Optometrist.
Languages Italian, Spanish
Facilities Dining room; Physical therapy room; Activities room; Chapel; Crafts room; Laundry room; Barber/Beauty shop.
Activities Arts & crafts; Cards; Games; Reading groups; Prayer groups; Movies; Social/Cultural gatherings.

BEDFORD

Donahoe Manor*
Rte 5, Box 55, Bedford, PA, 15522
(814) 623-9075
Licensure Skilled care; Intermediate care. *Beds* SNF 48; ICF 24. *Certified* Medicaid; Medicare.
Owner Proprietary Corp (Health Care & Retirement Corp).

BELLEFONTE

Centre Crest
502 E Haward St, Bellefonte, PA, 16823
(814) 355-6777
Admin Geraldine S Kline RN NHA. *Medical Dir/Dir of Nursing* Dr Mark A Knox.
Licensure Skilled care; Intermediate care. *Beds* SNF 24; ICF 201. *Certified* Medicaid; Medicare.
Owner Nonprofit organization/foundation.
Admissions Requirements Medical examination; Physician's request.
Staff Physicians 1 (ft); RNs 3 (ft), 11 (pt); LPNs 40 (ft), 10 (pt); Orderlies 4 (pt); Nurses aides 40 (ft), 10 (pt); Physical therapists 1 (ft); Reality therapists 1 (ft); Recreational therapists 3 (ft); Occupational therapists 1 (pt); Speech therapists 1 (pt); Activities coordinators 1 (ft); Dietitians 1 (pt); Dentists 1 (pt); Ophthalmologists 1 (pt); Podiatrists 1 (pt).
Facilities Dining room; Physical therapy room; Activities room; Chapel; Crafts room; Laundry room; Barber/Beauty shop; Library.
Activities Arts & crafts; Cards; Games; Reading groups; Prayer groups; Movies; Shopping trips; Social/Cultural gatherings; Boating; Fishing; Theatre.

BELLEVILLE

Valley View Retirement Community
PO Box 827, Belleville, PA, 17004
(717) 935-2105
Admin R David Metzler Exec Dir; Isabelle Felmlee Acting Admin. *Medical Dir/Dir of Nursing* Dorothy Yoder DON.
Licensure Skilled care; Intermediate care; Personal care. *Beds* SNF 120; ICF; Personal care 12. *Certified* Medicaid.
Owner Nonprofit organization/foundation.
Admissions Requirements Minimum age 21; Medical examination.
Staff RNs 2 (ft), 5 (pt); LPNs 11 (ft), 12 (pt); Orderlies 2 (ft); Nurses aides 26 (ft), 39 (pt); Activities coordinators 1 (pt).
Facilities Dining room; Physical therapy room; Activities room; Chapel; Laundry room; Barber/Beauty shop.
Activities Arts & crafts; Games; Reading groups; Prayer groups; Movies; Shopping trips; Social/Cultural gatherings.

BERLIN

Maple Mountain Manor
1401 Hay St, Berlin, PA, 15530
(814) 267-3412
Admin James C Mitchell; Valerie S Lechliter. *Medical Dir/Dir of Nursing* Deborah Baceski; Sandra Grenke.
Licensure Intermediate care. *Beds* 162. *Certified* Medicaid.
Owner Publicly owned.
Admissions Requirements Medical examination.
Staff Physicians 7 (pt); RNs 6 (ft), 3 (pt); LPNs 10 (pt); Nurses aides 45 (ft), 22 (pt); Physical therapists 3 (pt); Occupational therapists 1 (pt); Speech therapists 1 (pt); Activities coordinators 1 (ft); Dietitians 1 (pt); Ophthalmologists 1 (pt); Podiatrists 1 (pt).
Facilities Dining room; Physical therapy room; Activities room; Chapel; Crafts room; Laundry room; Barber/Beauty shop; Library.
Activities Arts & crafts; Cards; Games; Reading groups; Prayer groups; Movies; Shopping trips; Social/Cultural gatherings; Bingo; Trivia teams; Reality orientation; Sensory stimulation groups; Luaus; Carnivals; Petting zoo; Special events.

BERWICK

Berwick Retirement Village Nursing Home
801 E 16th St, Berwick, PA, 18603
(717) 759-5400
Admin Ann Fletcher. *Medical Dir/Dir of Nursing* Frank Gegwich MD; D Krolikowski RN DON.
Licensure Skilled care; Intermediate care. *Beds* SNF 60; ICF 60. *Certified* Medicaid; Medicare.
Owner Nonprofit Corp.
Admissions Requirements Medical examination; Physician's request.
Staff Physicians; RNs 5 (ft), 7 (pt); LPNs 6 (ft), 11 (pt); Orderlies 1 (ft); Nurses aides 27 (ft), 31 (pt); Physical therapists 1 (pt); Recreational therapists 1 (ft); Occupational therapists 1 (pt); Speech therapists 1 (pt); Activities coordinators 1 (ft); Dietitians 1 (pt); Dentists 1 (pt); Ophthalmologists 1 (pt); Podiatrists 1 (pt).
Facilities Dining room; Physical therapy room; Activities room; Crafts room; Laundry room; Barber/Beauty shop; Library.
Activities Arts & crafts; Cards; Games; Reading groups; Prayer groups; Movies; Shopping trips; Social/Cultural gatherings; Intergenerational activities; Rock & roll; Resident council.

BETHEL PARK

Meadow Crest Inc
1200 Braun Rd, Bethel Park, PA, 15102
(412) 854-5500
Admin Diane L Ott. *Medical Dir/Dir of Nursing* Walter Hoover MD; Kathleen Gastan DON.
Licensure Skilled care; Intermediate care. *Beds* SNF 50; ICF 50 Interchangeable. *Certified* Medicare.
Owner Proprietary Corp.
Staff Physicians 2 (pt); RNs 4 (ft), 5 (pt); LPNs 2 (pt); Nurses aides 9 (ft), 7 (pt); Physical therapists; Occupational therapists; Speech therapists; Activities coordinators; Dietitians; Ophthalmologists.
Facilities Dining room; Physical therapy room; Activities room; Barber/Beauty shop; Library.
Activities Arts & crafts; Cards; Games; Reading groups; Prayer groups; Movies; Social/Cultural gatherings; Reality orientation; Resocialization; Music activities.

BETHLEHEM

Blough Nursing Home Inc
316 E Market St, Bethlehem, PA, 18018
(215) 868-4982
Admin Sandra A Massetti. *Medical Dir/Dir of Nursing* Jack Cole MD; Mae Anderson RN DON.
Licensure Skilled care. *Beds* SNF 41. *Certified* Medicare.
Owner Proprietary Corp.
Admissions Requirements Medical examination.
Staff RNs 1 (ft), 4 (pt); LPNs 2 (ft), 1 (pt); Nurses aides 8 (ft), 15 (pt); Activities coordinators 1 (ft).
Facilities Dining room; Physical therapy room; Activities room; Laundry room; Barber/Beauty shop.
Activities Arts & crafts; Cards; Games; Prayer groups; Movies.

Cedarbrook Fountain Hill Annex*
724 Delaware Ave, Bethlehem, PA, 18015
(215) 691-6700
Licensure Skilled care. *Beds* 197. *Certified* Medicaid; Medicare.
Owner Nonprofit Corp.

Holy Family Manor*
1200 Spring St, Bethlehem, PA, 18018
(215) 865-5595
Licensure Skilled care; Intermediate care. *Beds* SNF 158; ICF 40. *Certified* Medicaid; Medicare.
Owner Nonprofit Corp.
Affiliation Roman Catholic

Leader Nursing & Rehabilitation Center I
Westgate Dr & Catasauqua Rd, Bethlehem, PA, 18017
(215) 865-6077
Admin Christopher Donati. *Medical Dir/Dir of Nursing* Deborah Csaszar DON.
Licensure Skilled care; Intermediate care. *Beds* SNF 153; ICF 60. *Certified* Medicaid; Medicare.
Owner Proprietary Corp (Manor Care).
Staff RNs; LPNs; Nurses aides; Physical therapists; Recreational therapists; Occupational therapists; Activities coordinators.
Activities Arts & crafts; Cards; Games; Reading groups; Prayer groups; Movies; Shopping trips; Social/Cultural gatherings; Chaplain program.

BLOOMSBURG

Bloomsburg Health Care Center*
211 E 1st St, Bloomsburg, PA, 17815
(717) 784-5930
Licensure Skilled care. *Beds* 85. *Certified* Medicaid.
Owner Proprietary Corp.

BLUE BALL

Wetzler Convalescent Home Inc*
Box 115, Blue Ball, PA, 17506
(717) 354-7601
Licensure Skilled care. *Beds* 17. *Certified* Medicaid.
Owner Proprietary Corp.

BOOTHWYN

Longwood Villa Geriatric Nursing Center
1194 Naamans Creek Rd, Boothwyn, PA, 19061
(215) 459-9150
Admin Elizabeth A Thummel. *Medical Dir/Dir of Nursing* Dr John Giuliano; Elizabeth Hisler.
Licensure Skilled care; Intermediate care. *Beds* SNF 28; ICF 25. *Certified* Medicaid.
Owner Proprietary Corp.
Admissions Requirements Medical examination; Physician's request.
Staff Physicians; RNs; LPNs; Nurses aides; Physical therapists; Reality therapists; Recreational therapists; Occupational therapists; Speech therapists; Activities coordinators; Dietitians; Dentists; Ophthalmologists.
Facilities Dining room; Activities room; Chapel; Crafts room; Laundry room; Barber/Beauty shop.
Activities Arts & crafts; Cards; Games; Reading groups; Prayer groups; Movies; Shopping trips; Social/Cultural gatherings.

BRACKENRIDGE

Georgian Manor Nursing Home
1050 Broadview Blvd, Brackenridge, PA, 15014
(224-9200
Admin Helen E Kunca RN NHA. *Medical Dir/Dir of Nursing* Dr Frank Kush; Teresa DeCroo DON.
Licensure Skilled care. *Beds* SNF 97. *Certified* Medicaid; Medicare.
Owner Proprietary Corp (Genesis Health Ventures).

Staff RNs 5 (ft), 4 (pt); LPNs 11 (ft); Nurses aides 30 (ft), 2 (pt); Activities coordinators 2 (ft).
Facilities Dining room; Physical therapy room; Activities room; Crafts room; Laundry room; Barber/Beauty shop.
Activities Arts & crafts; Cards; Games; Reading groups; Prayer groups; Movies; Shopping trips.

Highland Nursing & Rehabilitation Center
1050 Broadview Blvd, Brackenridge, PA, 15014
(412) 224-9200
Admin Helen Kunca.
Beds 97.
Owner Proprietary Corp (Genesis Health Ventures).

BRADFORD

Bradford Nursing Pavilion
200 Pleasant St, Bradford, PA, 16701
(814) 362-4533
Admin Michael G Guley. *Medical Dir/Dir of Nursing* Dr Edward Roche; Karen Cordner RN.
Licensure Skilled care. *Beds* 95. *Certified* Medicaid; Medicare.
Owner Nonprofit Corp.
Admissions Requirements Minimum age 18.
Staff Physicians 1 (ft); RNs 6 (ft); LPNs 13 (ft); Nurses aides 33 (ft); Physical therapists 1 (ft); Recreational therapists 2 (ft); Speech therapists 1 (pt); Dietitians 1 (ft); Dentists 1 (pt); Ophthalmologists 1 (pt).
Facilities Dining room; Physical therapy room; Activities room; Laundry room.
Activities Arts & crafts; Cards; Games; Reading groups; Prayer groups; Movies; Shopping trips; Social/Cultural gatherings.

Dresser Memorial Presbyterian Home*
149 Jackson Ave, Bradford, PA, 16701
(814) 362-5585
Licensure Intermediate care. *Beds* 32. *Certified* Medicaid.
Owner Nonprofit Corp.
Affiliation Presbyterian

Hannum Memorial Rest Home Inc*
139 Minard Run Rd, Bradford, PA, 16701
(814) 368-5648
Admin Deborah M Sprague.
Licensure Intermediate care. *Beds* 34. *Certified* Medicaid.
Owner Nonprofit Corp.
Staff Physicians 1 (pt); RNs 2 (ft), 2 (pt); LPNs 1 (ft), 2 (pt); Nurses aides 8 (ft), 4 (pt); Physical therapists 1 (pt); Speech therapists 1 (pt); Activities coordinators 1 (ft); Dietitians 1 (pt); Podiatrists 1 (pt); Audiologists 1 (pt).
Affiliation Baptist
Facilities Dining room; Activities room; Laundry room; Barber/Beauty shop.
Activities Arts & crafts; Cards; Games; Reading groups; Movies; Shopping trips; Social/Cultural gatherings.

Ramsbottom Center Inc
800 E Main St, Bradford, PA, 16701
(814) 362-7401
Licensure Intermediate care for mentally retarded. *Beds* 24. *Certified* Medicaid.
Owner Nonprofit Corp.

BRIDGEVILLE

Mayview State Hospital*
Bridgeville, PA, 15017
(412) 221-7500
Licensure Intermediate care for mentally retarded. *Beds* 120. *Certified* Medicaid.
Owner Publicly owned.

Mayview State Hospital—Long-Term Care Unit*
Bridgeville, PA, 15017
(412) 343-2700
Admin Joan Malarbey. *Medical Dir/Dir of Nursing* Charles L Squires MD.
Licensure Intermediate care. *Beds* 184. *Certified* Medicaid.
Owner Publicly owned.
Staff Physicians 2 (ft); RNs 17 (ft), 1 (pt); LPNs 9 (ft); Nurses aides 70 (ft).
Facilities Dining room; Activities room; Chapel; Crafts room; Laundry room; Barber/Beauty shop; Conference room.
Activities Arts & crafts; Cards; Games; Reading groups; Prayer groups; Movies; Shopping trips; Social/Cultural gatherings; Bowling.

BRISTOL

Medicenter of America—Bristol*
King St & Fayette Dr, Bristol, PA, 19007
(215) 785-3201
Licensure Skilled care. *Beds* 174. *Certified* Medicaid; Medicare.
Owner Proprietary Corp (HBA Management Inc).

BROOKVILLE

Jefferson Manor*
RD 5 RT 28, Brookville, PA, 15825
(814) 849-2386
Licensure Skilled care; Intermediate care. *Beds* SNF 112; ICF 112. *Certified* Medicaid.
Owner Proprietary Corp (Unicare).

Pennsylvania Memorial Home*
51 Euclid Ave, Brookville, PA, 15825
(814) 849-2368
Licensure Skilled care; Intermediate care. *Beds* SNF 51; ICF 49. *Certified* Medicaid; Medicare.
Owner Nonprofit Corp.

BROOMALL

Broomall Presbyterian Home
146 Marple Road, Broomall, PA, 19008-2099
(215) 356-0100
Licensure Skilled care. *Beds* SNF 147. *Certified* Medicaid; Medicare.
Owner Nonprofit Corp (PA Presbyterian Homes).
Admissions Requirements Minimum age 65; Medical examination.
Staff Physicians 3 (pt); RNs 7 (ft), 15 (pt); LPNs 7 (ft), 2 (pt); Orderlies 1 (ft); Nurses aides 70 (ft), 20 (pt); Physical therapists 1 (pt); Recreational therapists 1 (ft); Speech therapists 1 (pt); Activities coordinators 1 (ft); Dietitians 1 (pt); Ophthalmologists 1 (pt); Podiatrists 1 (pt).
Affiliation Presbyterian
Facilities Dining room; Physical therapy room; Activities room; Crafts room; Laundry room; Barber/Beauty shop; Library.
Activities Arts & crafts; Cards; Games; Reading groups; Prayer groups; Movies; Shopping trips; Social/Cultural gatherings; Remotivation therapy; Touch therapy.

Central Park Lodge
50 N Malin Rd, Broomall, PA, 19008
(215) 356-0800
Admin David Z Ross. *Medical Dir/Dir of Nursing* Madeline Long MD; Dolores Jaquith RN.
Licensure Skilled care; Intermediate care. *Beds* SNF 286; ICF. *Certified* Medicaid; Medicare.
Owner Proprietary Corp.
Admissions Requirements Minimum age 60; Medical examination.

Staff RNs 10 (ft), 15 (pt); LPNs 6 (ft), 10 (pt); Orderlies 2 (ft), 1 (pt); Nurses aides 75 (ft), 40 (pt); Physical therapists 1 (pt); Recreational therapists 3 (ft); Occupational therapists 1 (pt); Speech therapists 1 (pt); Dietitians 1 (pt); Ophthalmologists 2 (pt); Podiatrists 1 (pt).
Facilities Dining room; Physical therapy room; Activities room; Crafts room; Laundry room; Barber/Beauty shop.
Activities Arts & crafts; Cards; Games; Reading groups; Prayer groups; Movies; Shopping trips; Social/Cultural gatherings; Sports events.

Church Lane Health Care Center
43 Church Ln, Broomall, PA, 19008
356-3003
Admin Robert Kopansky. *Medical Dir/Dir of Nursing* Dr William Kozin; N Kopitsig.
Licensure Skilled care; Intermediate care. *Beds* 132. *Certified* Medicaid; Medicare.
Owner Proprietary Corp.
Admissions Requirements Minimum age 65.
Staff RNs; LPNs; Nurses aides; Physical therapists; Recreational therapists; Occupational therapists; Speech therapists; Activities coordinators; Dietitians; Dentists; Ophthalmologists; Podiatrists.
Facilities Dining room; Physical therapy room; Activities room; Crafts room; Laundry room; Barber/Beauty shop.
Activities Arts & crafts; Cards; Games; Reading groups; Prayer groups; Movies; Shopping trips; Social/Cultural gatherings.

BROWNSVILLE

Brownsville Golden Age*
501 Church St, Brownsville, PA, 15417
(412) 785-3900
Licensure Skilled care. *Beds* 68. *Certified* Medicaid; Medicare.
Owner Proprietary Corp.

BRYN MAWR

Bryn Mawr Terrace Convalescent*
Haverford & Rugby Rds, Bryn Mawr, PA, 19010
(215) 525-8300
Licensure Skilled care. *Beds* 160. *Certified* Medicare.
Owner Proprietary Corp.

The Chateau Nursing & Rehabilitation Center
956 Railroad Ave, Bryn Mawr, PA, 19010
(215) 525-8412
Admin Anne A O'Rourke. *Medical Dir/Dir of Nursing* Dr Koryeni; Jeanne Schell DON.
Licensure Skilled care; Intermediate care. *Beds* 170. *Certified* Medicaid; Medicare.
Owner Proprietary Corp.
Admissions Requirements Minimum age; Medical examination.
Facilities Dining room; Physical therapy room; Activities room; Crafts room; Laundry room; Barber/Beauty shop.

BUCKINGHAM

Buckingham Valley Nursing Home*
PO Box 447, Buckingham, PA, 18912
(215) 598-7781
Licensure Skilled care. *Beds* 100. *Certified* Medicaid; Medicare.
Owner Proprietary Corp.

BUTLER

Sunnyview Home
711 Morton Ave Ext, Butler, PA, 16001
(412) 282-1800
Admin Thomas S Finucane. *Medical Dir/Dir of Nursing* William A Dicuccio MD; Sheila A Scanlon RN.

Licensure Skilled care; Intermediate care. *Beds* SNF 60; ICF 180. *Certified* Medicaid.
Owner Publicly owned.
Admissions Requirements Minimum age 18; Medical examination; Physician's request.
Staff Physicians 3 (pt); RNs 7 (ft), 11 (pt); LPNs 33 (ft), 5 (pt); Nurses aides 98 (ft), 6 (pt); Physical therapists 4 (pt); Recreational therapists 3 (ft); Speech therapists 1 (pt); Activities coordinators 1 (ft); Dietitians 1 (pt); Ophthalmologists 1 (pt); Podiatrists 1 (pt).
Facilities Dining room; Physical therapy room; Activities room; Chapel; Crafts room; Laundry room; Barber/Beauty shop; Library.
Activities Arts & crafts; Cards; Games; Reading groups; Prayer groups; Movies; Shopping trips; Social/Cultural gatherings.

CABOT

Lutheran Welfare Concordia Home
615 N Pike Rd, Cabot, PA, 16023
(412) 352-1571
Admin Kieth E Frndak. *Medical Dir/Dir of Nursing* Fred Fioravanti MD; Michelene Neubert DON.
Licensure Skilled care; Intermediate care; Personal Care. *Beds* SNF 60; ICF 60; Personal 20. *Certified* Medicaid; Medicare.
Owner Nonprofit Corp.
Admissions Requirements Minimum age 65; Medical examination.
Staff Physicians 1 (pt); RNs 5 (ft), 3 (pt); LPNs 6 (ft), 9 (pt); Nurses aides 31 (ft), 15 (pt); Physical therapists 1 (pt); Speech therapists 1 (pt); Dietitians 1 (pt).
Languages German
Affiliation Lutheran
Facilities Dining room; Physical therapy room; Activities room; Chapel; Crafts room; Laundry room; Barber/Beauty shop.
Activities Arts & crafts; Cards; Games; Reading groups; Movies; Shopping trips.

CAMBRIDGE SPRINGS

Presbyterian Home
229 N Main St, Cambridge Springs, PA, 16403
(814) 398-2813
Admin Margaret Skeens RN BSN. *Medical Dir/Dir of Nursing* E J Owens DO.
Licensure Intermediate care; Personal care. *Beds* ICF 10; Personnel care 15. *Certified* Medicaid.
Owner Nonprofit Corp.
Admissions Requirements Medical examination.
Staff RNs 4 (pt); LPNs 6 (pt); Nurses aides 10 (pt); Activities coordinators 1 (ft); Dietitians 1 (ft).
Affiliation Presbyterian
Facilities Dining room; Laundry room; Barber/Beauty shop; Kitchen.
Activities Arts & crafts; Cards; Games; Reading groups; Prayer groups; Movies; Social/Cultural gatherings; Current events; Poetry class; Self esteem workshops; Exercise.

Springs Manor
110 Canfield St, Cambridge Springs, PA, 16403
(814) 398-4626
Admin Don McDowell. *Medical Dir/Dir of Nursing* Dr Edward Owens; S Kathleen Varner RN.
Licensure Skilled care; Intermediate care; Personal care. *Beds* 105. *Certified* Medicaid; Medicare.
Owner Proprietary Corp (Beverly Enterprises).
Admissions Requirements Medical examination; Physician's request.

Staff RNs 1 (ft); LPNs 1 (ft); Nurses aides 1 (ft), 1 (pt); Physical therapists 1 (ft); Speech therapists 1 (pt); Activities coordinators 1 (ft); Dietitians 1 (ft).
Facilities Dining room; Physical therapy room; Activities room; Chapel; Laundry room; Barber/Beauty shop.
Activities Arts & crafts; Cards; Games; Reading groups; Prayer groups; Movies; Bowling league.

CAMP HILL

Blue Ridge Haven Convalescent Center West*
770 Poplar Church Rd, Camp Hill, PA, 17011
(717) 763-7070
Licensure Skilled care; Intermediate care. *Beds* SNF 120; ICF 214. *Certified* Medicaid; Medicare.
Owner Proprietary Corp (Beverly Enterprises).

Camp Hill Care Center
46 Erford Rd, Camp Hill, PA, 17011
(717) 763-7361
Admin Kenneth B Shaffer. *Medical Dir/Dir of Nursing* Jean Mortini DON.
Licensure Skilled care; Intermediate care. *Beds* SNF 36; ICF 82. *Certified* Medicaid; Medicare.
Owner Proprietary Corp (Beverly Enterprises).
Staff RNs 6 (ft); LPNs 6 (ft), 4 (pt); Orderlies 2 (ft); Nurses aides 44 (ft), 14 (pt); Physical therapists 1 (ft); Recreational therapists 2 (ft); Activities coordinators 1 (ft); Dietitians 1 (ft).
Facilities Dining room; Physical therapy room; Activities room; Laundry room; Barber/Beauty shop.
Activities Arts & crafts; Cards; Games; Reading groups; Prayer groups; Movies; Shopping trips; Social/Cultural gatherings.

Leader Nursing & Rehabilitation Center
1700 Market St, Camp Hill, PA, 17011
(717) 737-8551
Admin Stacey E Radcliff MGS NHA. *Medical Dir/Dir of Nursing* Earl Moyer MD; Sonna Schneider RN.
Licensure Skilled care; Personal care. *Beds* 94. *Certified* Medicaid; Medicare.
Owner Proprietary Corp (Manor Care).
Staff Physicians 1 (ft); RNs; LPNs; Orderlies; Nurses aides; Physical therapists; Speech therapists; Activities coordinators 1 (ft); Dietitians 2 (ft); Ophthalmologists.
Facilities Dining room; Physical therapy room; Activities room; Barber/Beauty shop.
Activities Arts & crafts; Cards; Games; Reading groups; Prayer groups; Movies; Shopping trips; Social/Cultural gatherings.

CAMPBELLTOWN

Twin Oaks Nursing Home
90 W Main St, Campbelltown, PA, 17010
(717) 838-2231
Admin Mary Snyder. *Medical Dir/Dir of Nursing* Harold Engle MD; Audry Scipioni DON.
Licensure Intermediate care. *Beds* ICF 42. *Certified* Medicaid.
Owner Privately owned.
Admissions Requirements Medical examination; Physician's request.
Staff LPNs 4 (ft), 1 (pt); Nurses aides 10 (ft), 5 (pt); Activities coordinators 1 (ft).
Facilities Dining room; Activities room; Barber/Beauty shop.
Activities Arts & crafts; Cards; Games; Reading groups.

CANONSBURG

Meadowlands Health Care Center
PO Box 146, RD 1, Rte 519 S, Canonsburg, PA, 15317
(412) 745-8000

Admin James O'Shea. *Medical Dir/Dir of Nursing* Patience Grummick.
Licensure Skilled care. *Beds* SNF 40 Speculiazing in head injury rehabilitation.
Owner Proprietary Corp (New Medico Assoc).
Admissions Requirements Minimum age 16.
Staff Physicians 1 (ft), 4 (pt); RNs 12 (ft), 4 (pt); LPNs 12 (ft), 8 (pt); Nurses aides 41 (ft), 16 (pt); Physical therapists 4 (ft); Recreational therapists 6 (ft); Occupational therapists 4 (ft); Speech therapists 4 (ft); Activities coordinators 1 (ft); Dietitians 1 (pt); Dentists 1 (pt); Ophthalmologists 1 (pt); Podiatrists 1 (pt); Adaptive equipment technician 1 (ft); Family counselors 3 (ft); Case managers 3 (ft); Behavior specialist 1 (ft).
Facilities Dining room; Physical therapy room; Activities room; Crafts room; Laundry room; Barber/Beauty shop; Library.
Activities Arts & crafts; Cards; Games; Reading groups; Prayer groups; Movies; Shopping trips; Social/Cultural gatherings; Adaptive aquatics; Equestrian therapy.

South Hills Convalescent Center
201 Village Dr, Canonsburg, PA, 15317
(412) 341-9191
Medical Dir/Dir of Nursing Robert G Lesnock MD.
Licensure Skilled care. *Beds* 104. *Certified* Medicaid; Medicare.
Owner Proprietary Corp (Beverly Enterprises).
Admissions Requirements Minimum age 18; Medical examination.
Staff Physicians 1 (ft); RNs 7 (ft), 5 (pt); LPNs 6 (ft), 13 (pt); Nurses aides 32 (ft), 21 (pt); Physical therapists 1 (pt); Speech therapists 1 (pt); Activities coordinators 1 (ft); Dietitians 1 (ft).
Facilities Dining room; Physical therapy room; Activities room; Chapel; Crafts room; Laundry room; Barber/Beauty shop; Library.
Activities Arts & crafts; Cards; Games; Reading groups; Prayer groups; Movies; Shopping trips; Social/Cultural gatherings.

Western Center*
333 Curry Hill Rd, Canonsburg, PA, 15317
(412) 745-0700
Licensure Intermediate care for mentally retarded. *Beds* 474. *Certified* Medicaid.
Owner Nonprofit Corp.

CARBONDALE

Carbondale Nursing Home Inc*
57 N Main St, Carbondale, PA, 18407
(717) 282-1020
Medical Dir/Dir of Nursing Dr John W Keyes.
Licensure Skilled care. *Beds* 105. *Certified* Medicaid; Medicare.
Owner Proprietary Corp.
Staff Physicians 1 (ft), 6 (pt); RNs 10 (ft); LPNs 15 (ft); Orderlies 6 (ft); Nurses aides 15 (ft); Physical therapists 2 (pt); Recreational therapists 1 (ft); Occupational therapists 2 (pt); Speech therapists 2 (pt); Activities coordinators 1 (ft); Dietitians 1 (pt); Dentists 1 (pt); Podiatrists 1 (pt).

CARLISLE

The Alliance Home of Carlisle Pennsylvania
770 S Hanover St, Carlisle, PA, 17013
(717) 249-1363
Admin Jack R Seward. *Medical Dir/Dir of Nursing* Beverly Osborn.
Licensure Skilled care; Intermediate care; Personal care. *Beds* 185. *Certified* Medicaid.
Owner Nonprofit Corp.
Admissions Requirements Minimum age 65; Medical examination; Physician's request.
Staff Physicians 1 (pt); RNs 3 (ft), 3 (pt); LPNs 5 (ft), 7 (pt); Nurses aides 22 (ft), 4 (pt); Physical therapists 1 (pt); Recreational

therapists 1 (ft), 1 (pt); Speech therapists 1 (pt); Activities coordinators 1 (ft); Dietitians 1 (pt).
Facilities Dining room; Physical therapy room; Activities room; Chapel; Crafts room; Laundry room; Barber/Beauty shop; Library.
Activities Arts & crafts; Cards; Games; Reading groups; Prayer groups; Movies; Shopping trips; Social/Cultural gatherings.

Church of God Home, Inc
801 N Hanover St, Carlisle, PA, 17013
(717) 249-5322
Admin Ronald F Madeira. *Medical Dir/Dir of Nursing* Dr Kenneth AGluistwite.
Licensure Skilled care; Personal care. *Beds* SNF 109; personal care 34. *Certified* Medicaid.
Owner Nonprofit Corp.
Admissions Requirements Medical examination.
Staff Physicians 1 (pt); RNs 7 (ft), 1 (pt); LPNs 6 (ft), 5 (pt); Nurses aides 1 (ft); Nurses aides 45 (ft), 14 (pt); Physical therapists 1 (pt); Recreational therapists 2 (ft); Occupational therapists 1 (pt); Speech therapists 1 (pt); Activities coordinators 1 (ft); Dietitians 1 (pt); Dentists 1 (pt); Ophthalmologists 1 (pt); Podiatrists 1 (pt).
Affiliation Church of God
Facilities Dining room; Physical therapy room; Activities room; Chapel; Crafts room; Laundry room; Barber/Beauty shop.
Activities Arts & crafts; Cards; Games; Prayer groups; Movies; Shopping trips.

Cumberland County Home*
Box 50, Rte 10, Carlisle, PA, 17013
(717) 243-2031
Licensure Skilled care; Intermediate care. *Beds* SNF 195; ICF 192. *Certified* Medicaid.
Owner Nonprofit Corp.

Forest Park Health Center
700 Walnut Bottom Rd, Carlisle, PA, 17013
(717) 243-1032
Admin Mary I Baker. *Medical Dir/Dir of Nursing* Dr Harold G Kretzing; Stephanie L Rupp DON.
Licensure Skilled care; Intermediate care. *Beds* SNF 34; ICF 66. *Certified* Medicaid; Medicare.
Owner Nonprofit Corp.
Admissions Requirements Medical examination; Physician's request.
Staff RNs 5 (ft), 3 (pt); LPNs 5 (ft), 3 (pt); Nurses aides 32 (ft), 7 (pt); Recreational therapists 2 (ft); Speech therapists 1 (pt); Dietitians 1 (pt).
Affiliation Presbyterian
Facilities Dining room; Physical therapy room; Activities room; Crafts room; Laundry room; Barber/Beauty shop.
Activities Arts & crafts; Games; Reading groups; Prayer groups; Movies; Shopping trips; Social/Cultural gatherings.

Thornwald Home*
422 Walnut Bottom Rd, Carlisle, PA, 17013
(717) 249-4118
Licensure Skilled care. *Beds* 79. *Certified* Medicaid.
Owner Nonprofit Corp.

Sarah A Todd Memorial Homes
50 Mooreland Ave & 1000 W South St, Carlisle, PA, 17013
(717) 249-1614, 245-2187
Admin Susan B Hench. *Medical Dir/Dir of Nursing* Dr Kenneth Guistwite; Jean Lane RN DON.
Licensure Skilled care; Intermediate care; Personal care. *Beds* SNF 11; ICF 49; Personal 44 Independent living apts 25. *Certified* Medicaid; Medicare.
Owner Nonprofit Corp.
Admissions Requirements Medical examination; Physician's request.

Staff RNs 3 (ft), 3 (pt); LPNs 4 (ft), 3 (pt); Nurses aides 14 (ft), 18 (pt); Recreational therapists 1 (ft), 1 (pt); Dietitians 1 (pt).
Facilities Dining room; Physical therapy room; Activities room; Crafts room; Laundry room; Barber/Beauty shop; Library; Multi-purpose activity room.
Activities Arts & crafts; Cards; Games; Reading groups; Prayer groups; Movies; Shopping trips; Social/Cultural gatherings; Sensory groups; Adopt-a-grandparent.

CARNEGIE

Step by Step Inc*
112 7th Ave, Carnegie, PA, 15106
(412) 279-8943
Licensure Intermediate care for mentally retarded. *Beds* 8. *Certified* Medicaid.
Owner Nonprofit Corp.

CHAMBERSBURG

Franklin County Nursing Home
201 Franklin Farm Ln, Chambersburg, PA, 17201
(717) 264-2715
Admin Joanne V Wible. *Medical Dir/Dir of Nursing* Joseph Thornton MD; Dorothy McMullen DON.
Licensure Skilled care; Intermediate care. *Beds* SNF 40; ICF 184. *Certified* Medicaid; Medicare.
Owner Publicly owned.
Admissions Requirements Minimum age 18; Medical examination.
Staff Physicians 3 (pt); RNs 7 (ft), 5 (pt); LPNs 18 (ft), 18 (pt); Orderlies 22 (ft), 20 (pt); Nurses aides 22 (ft), 20 (pt); Physical therapists 1 (pt); Activities coordinators 1 (ft); Dietitians 1 (pt); Ophthalmologists 2 (pt).
Facilities Dining room; Physical therapy room; Activities room; Chapel; Crafts room; Laundry room; Barber/Beauty shop.
Activities Arts & crafts; Cards; Games; Reading groups; Prayer groups; Movies.

Leader Nursing & Rehabilitation Center—Chambersburg*
1070 Stouffer Ave, Chambersburg, PA, 17201
(717) 263-9463
Licensure Skilled care; Intermediate care. *Beds* SNF 120; ICF 60. *Certified* Medicaid; Medicare.
Owner Proprietary Corp (Manor Care).

Menno-Haven/Menno-Village
2075 Scotland Ave, Chambersburg, PA, 17201
(717) 263-8545
Admin E Lewis Leaman. *Medical Dir/Dir of Nursing* James K Vankirk MD; Joan Winter RN DON.
Licensure Skilled care; Intermediate care; Personal care; Adult day care; Independent living; Assisted living. *Beds* SNF 132; ICF; Personal units 80; Independent living units 188; Assisted living units 29. *Certified* Medicaid; Medicare.
Owner Nonprofit Corp.
Admissions Requirements Minimum age 55; Medical examination.
Staff Physicians 4 (pt); RNs 12 (ft); LPNs 12 (ft); Orderlies 10 (ft); Nurses aides 40 (ft); Physical therapists 3 (pt); Reality therapists 1 (ft); Recreational therapists 1 (ft); Occupational therapists 1 (pt); Speech therapists 1 (pt); Activities coordinators 1 (ft); Dietitians 1 (ft); Ophthalmologists 2 (pt); Podiatrists 1 (pt).
Affiliation Mennonite
Facilities Dining room; Physical therapy room; Activities room; Chapel; Crafts room; Laundry room; Barber/Beauty shop; Library; Therapy pool; Coffee shop; Corner store; Wood shop.

Activities Arts & crafts; Cards; Games; Reading groups; Prayer groups; Movies; Shopping trips; Social/Cultural gatherings.

John H Shook Home for the Aged
PO Box 226, 55 S 2nd St, Chambersburg, PA, 17201
(717) 264-6815
Admin Frederick S Wood. *Medical Dir/Dir of Nursing* Lois C Bitner RN DON.
Licensure Intermediate care. *Beds* ICF 64. *Certified* Medicaid.
Owner Nonprofit Corp.
Admissions Requirements Minimum age 65; Medical examination.
Staff RNs 4 (ft); LPNs 6 (ft), 6 (pt); Nurses aides 18 (ft), 9 (pt); Activities coordinators 2 (ft), 2 (pt); Dietitians 1 (pt).
Facilities Dining room; Activities room; Crafts room; Laundry room; Barber/Beauty shop.
Activities Arts & crafts; Cards; Games; Reading groups; Movies; Shopping trips; Church & Sunday school classes; Birthday parties; Current events.

CHATHAM

Chatham Acres
London Grove Rd, Chatham, PA, 19318
(215) 869-2456
Admin Maureen Zagorskie. *Medical Dir/Dir of Nursing* David Callahan.
Licensure Intermediate care. *Beds* ICF 121. *Certified* Medicaid.
Owner Privately owned.
Admissions Requirements Medical examination; Physician's request.
Staff Physicians 1 (pt); RNs 2 (ft); LPNs 11 (ft), 1 (pt); Orderlies 2 (ft); Nurses aides 31 (ft), 4 (pt); Physical therapists 1 (pt); Recreational therapists 2 (ft); Activities coordinators 1 (pt); Dietitians 1 (pt); Ophthalmologists 1 (pt).
Languages Spanish
Facilities Dining room; Physical therapy room; Activities room; Crafts room; Laundry room; Barber/Beauty shop.
Activities Arts & crafts; Cards; Games; Reading groups; Prayer groups; Movies; Shopping trips.

CHESTER

The Belvedere
2507 Chestnut St, Chester, PA, 19013
(215) 872-5373
Admin Thomas P Connor. *Medical Dir/Dir of Nursing* Barry Holms DO; Mary Flacco RN.
Licensure Skilled care. *Beds* SNF 120. *Certified* Medicaid; Medicare.
Owner Proprietary Corp.
Staff Physicians; RNs; LPNs; Orderlies; Nurses aides; Physical therapists; Occupational therapists; Speech therapists; Activities coordinators; Dietitians; Dentists; Ophthalmologists; Podiatrists; Audiologists.
Facilities Dining room; Physical therapy room; Activities room; Laundry room; Barber/Beauty shop; Lounges.
Activities Arts & crafts; Cards; Games; Reading groups; Prayer groups; Movies; Shopping trips; Social/Cultural gatherings.

Chester Care Center
15th St & Shaw Terrace, Chester, PA, 19013
(215) 499-8800
Admin Anna E Helfrich. *Medical Dir/Dir of Nursing* Peter Binnion MD; Betsy Ramaika RN.
Licensure Skilled care; Intermediate care. *Beds* SNF 93; ICF 97. *Certified* Medicaid.
Owner Proprietary Corp.
Admissions Requirements Minimum age 16; Medical examination.

Staff RNs 9 (ft); LPNs 30 (ft), 6 (pt); Orderlies 10 (ft); Nurses aides 69 (ft), 2 (pt); Physical therapists 1 (pt); Reality therapists 1 (ft); Recreational therapists 5 (ft); Occupational therapists 1 (pt); Activities coordinators 1 (ft); Dietitians 1 (pt).
Facilities Dining room; Physical therapy room; Activities room; Crafts room; Laundry room; Barber/Beauty shop.
Activities Arts & crafts; Cards; Games; Reading groups; Prayer groups; Movies; Shopping trips; Remotivation.

Chester Care Center*
210 W 14th St, Chester, PA, 19013
Admin Aubrey C Smith. *Medical Dir/Dir of Nursing* Dr Leonard Haltrecht.
Licensure Intermediate care. *Beds* 97. *Certified* Medicaid.
Owner Proprietary Corp.
Admissions Requirements Medical examination.
Staff Physicians 8 (pt); RNs 1 (pt); LPNs 9 (ft), 12 (pt); Orderlies 3 (ft), 1 (pt); Nurses aides 27 (ft), 20 (pt); Physical therapists 1 (pt); Reality therapists 1 (pt); Recreational therapists 1 (pt); Occupational therapists 1 (pt); Speech therapists 1 (pt); Activities coordinators 1 (ft); Dietitians 1 (pt); Podiatrists 1 (pt).
Facilities Dining room; Physical therapy room; Activities room; Crafts room; Laundry room; Barber/Beauty shop; Library.
Activities Arts & crafts; Cards; Games; Reading groups; Prayer groups; Movies; Shopping trips; Social/Cultural gatherings.

CHESTNUT HILL

Harston Hall Nursing Home Inc*
350 Haws Ln, Chestnut Hill, PA, 19118
(215) 233-0700
Licensure Skilled care. *Beds* 72. *Certified* Medicaid.
Owner Proprietary Corp.

CHESWICK

Valley View Nursing Home
RD 2, Box 234, Cheswick, PA, 15024
(412) 767-4998
Admin Bonita L Readie. *Medical Dir/Dir of Nursing* Dr Nick Bourdakos; Mary Ann Montgomery RN DON.
Licensure Skilled care; Intermediate care 79. *Beds* SNF 49; ICF 79. *Certified* Medicaid; Medicare; VA.
Owner Proprietary Corp (Columbia Corp).
Staff Physicians 10 (pt); RNs 4 (ft), 7 (pt); LPNs 6 (ft), 5 (pt); Nurses aides 36 (ft), 10 (pt); Physical therapists 1 (pt); Recreational therapists 1 (ft); Occupational therapists 1 (pt); Speech therapists 1 (pt); Activities coordinators 1 (pt); Dietitians 1 (pt); Ophthalmologists 1 (pt).
Facilities Dining room; Physical therapy room; Crafts room; Laundry room; Barber/Beauty shop.
Activities Arts & crafts; Cards; Games; Reading groups; Prayer groups; Movies; Social/Cultural gatherings; Adopt-a-grandparent program; Music therapy; Pet therapy; Horticulture.

CHICORA

Chicora Medical Center Inc*
Rte 2, Chicora, PA, 16025
(412) 445-2000
Admin Yvonne De Bacco. *Medical Dir/Dir of Nursing* E P Molchany MD.
Licensure Skilled care. *Beds* 60. *Certified* Medicaid; Medicare.
Owner Proprietary Corp.
Admissions Requirements Minimum age 16.

Staff RNs 4 (ft), 1 (pt); LPNs 4 (ft); Nurses aides 22 (ft), 4 (pt); Physical therapists 1 (ft); Recreational therapists 1 (ft); Speech therapists 1 (ft); Activities coordinators 1 (ft); Dietitians 1 (ft); Dentists 1 (pt); Ophthalmologists 1 (pt); Podiatrists 1 (pt); Audiologists 1 (ft).
Facilities Dining room; Physical therapy room; Activities room; Laundry room; Barber/Beauty shop; Library.
Activities Arts & crafts; Cards; Games; Movies; Shopping trips.

CHRISTIANA

Harrison House*
41 Newport Pike, Christiana, PA, 17509
(219) 593-6901
Medical Dir/Dir of Nursing Paul W Herr DO.
Licensure Skilled care. *Beds* 139. *Certified* Medicaid; Medicare.
Owner Proprietary Corp.
Admissions Requirements Minimum age 16.
Staff RNs 3 (ft), 10 (pt); LPNs 5 (ft), 10 (pt); Nurses aides 24 (ft), 58 (pt); Activities coordinators 2 (ft); Dietitians 1 (ft); Physical therapists; Occupational therapists; Speech therapists.
Facilities Dining room; Physical therapy room; Activities room; Chapel; Crafts room; Laundry room; Barber/Beauty shop; Greenhouse.
Activities Arts & crafts; Cards; Games; Reading groups; Prayer groups; Movies; Shopping trips; Social/Cultural gatherings; Church; Sunday school.

CLAIRTON

Beatrice Lawson Nursing Home Inc*
540 Coal Valley Rd, Clairton, PA, 15025
(412) 466-8448
Licensure Skilled care. *Beds* 55.
Owner Proprietary Corp.

CLARION

Clarion Care Center
999 Heidrick St, Clarion, PA, 16214
(814) 226-6380
Admin Arlene Greenawalt. *Medical Dir/Dir of Nursing* Dr Charles Huston MD.
Licensure Skilled care; Intermediate care. *Beds* SNF 25; ICF 127. *Certified* Medicaid; Medicare.
Owner Proprietary Corp (Beverly Enterprises).
Admissions Requirements Minimum age 18; Medical examination; Physician's request.
Staff RNs 5 (ft), 1 (pt); LPNs 15 (ft), 1 (pt); Orderlies 1 (ft); Nurses aides 39 (ft), 10 (pt); Activities coordinators 2 (ft).
Facilities Dining room; Physical therapy room; Activities room; Crafts room; Laundry room; Barber/Beauty shop.
Activities Arts & crafts; Cards; Games; Reading groups; Prayer groups; Movies; Shopping trips; Social/Cultural gatherings.

CLARKS SUMMIT

Abington Manor Nursing & Rehabilitation Center
100 Edella Rd, Clarks Summit, PA, 18411
(717) 586-1002
Admin Michael Wylie.
Beds 120.
Owner Proprietary Corp (Genesis Health Ventures).

Clarks Summit State Hospital—Long-Term Care Facility*
Clarks Summit, PA, 18411
(717) 586-2011
Licensure Skilled care. *Beds* 179. *Certified* Medicaid.
Owner Nonprofit Corp.

White Haven Annex at Clark Summit*
Clark Summit State Hospital, Clarks Summit, PA, 18411
(717) 586-2011
Licensure Intermediate care. *Beds* 52. *Certified* Medicaid.
Owner Nonprofit Corp.

CLEARFIELD

Clear Haven Nursing Center*
700 Leonard St, Clearfield, PA, 16830
(814) 765-7546
Licensure Skilled care; Intermediate care. *Beds* SNF 82; ICF 160. *Certified* Medicaid; Medicare.
Owner Proprietary Corp.

COALDALE

Coaldale State General Hospital*
7th St, Coaldale, PA, 18218
(717) 645-2131
Licensure Skilled care. *Beds* 48. *Certified* Medicaid; Medicare.
Owner Nonprofit Corp.

COATESVILLE

Embreeville Center
Rte 162, Coatesville, PA, 19320
(215) 486-8000
Admin Marguerite M Conley. *Medical Dir/Dir of Nursing* Resa Epel MD.
Licensure Intermediate care for mentally retarded. *Beds* ICF/MR 280. *Certified* Medicaid.
Owner Publicly owned.

COLUMBIA

Heatherbank
745 Chiques Hill Rd, Columbia, PA, 17512
(717) 684-7555
Admin Ann Reynolds. *Medical Dir/Dir of Nursing* Ray Wilson MD; Judith Garman DON.
Licensure Skilled care; Intermediate care. *Beds* SNF 49; ICF 131. *Certified* Medicaid; Medicare.
Owner Proprietary Corp.
Admissions Requirements Physician's request.
Staff RNs 6 (ft), 5 (pt); LPNs 15 (ft), 5 (pt); Nurses aides 46 (ft), 28 (pt); Physical therapists 1 (ft); Recreational therapists 1 (ft); Occupational therapists 1 (ft); Speech therapists 1 (ft); Activities coordinators 1 (pt); Dietitians 1 (ft).
Facilities Dining room; Physical therapy room; Activities room; Crafts room; Laundry room; Barber/Beauty shop; Library; Solarium; TV lounges; Smoking areas; Speech & OT rooms.
Activities Arts & crafts; Cards; Games; Reading groups; Prayer groups; Movies; Shopping trips; Social/Cultural gatherings; Adopt-a-grandparent; Resident council.

St Anne's Home
RD2, Columbia, PA, 17512
(717) 285-5443
Admin Sr Carmela Ginto. *Medical Dir/Dir of Nursing* Dr Wm Landis; Sr M Daniele Brought.
Licensure Skilled care; Intermediate care. *Beds* SNF; ICF. *Certified* Medicaid.
Owner Nonprofit Corp.
Admissions Requirements Medical examination; Physician's request.
Staff RNs; LPNs; Orderlies; Nurses aides; Physical therapists; Recreational therapists; Occupational therapists; Activities coordinators; Dietitians.
Affiliation Roman Catholic

Facilities Dining room; Physical therapy room; Activities room; Chapel; Crafts room; Laundry room; Barber/Beauty shop; Library; Occupational Therapy.
Activities Arts & crafts; Cards; Games; Reading groups; Prayer groups; Movies; Shopping trips; Social/Cultural gatherings; Many.

CONCORDVILLE

Concord Villa Convalescent
US Rte 1, Scott Rd, Concordville, PA, 19331
(215) 459-2900
Medical Dir/Dir of Nursing Ronald Carlucci MD.
Licensure Skilled care. *Beds* 101. *Certified* Medicare.
Owner Proprietary Corp.
Admissions Requirements Minimum age 18.
Staff Physicians 4 (pt); RNs 9 (ft), 4 (pt); LPNs 3 (ft); Recreational therapists 1 (ft), 1 (pt); Occupational therapists 1 (pt); Speech therapists 1 (pt); Dietitians 1 (pt); Dentists 1 (pt); Podiatrists 1 (pt).
Facilities Dining room; Physical therapy room; Activities room; Crafts room; Laundry room; Barber/Beauty shop.
Activities Arts & crafts; Cards; Games; Movies.

CONNEAUTVILLE

Rolling Fields Healthcare Community
PO Box AD, Rte 198, Conneautville, PA, 16406
(814) 587-2012
Admin Kimberly Braham-Moody. *Medical Dir/Dir of Nursing* Kimberly K Paterson MD.
Licensure Skilled care; Intermediate care. *Beds* SNF 30; ICF 91. *Certified* Medicaid; Medicare.
Owner Proprietary Corp.
Admissions Requirements Medical examination.
Staff Physicians 1 (pt); RNs 8 (ft), 1 (pt); LPNs 7 (ft), 3 (pt); Orderlies 2 (ft); Nurses aides; Physical therapists; Occupational therapists 1 (pt); Speech therapists 1 (pt); Activities coordinators; Dietitians 1 (pt); Dentists 1 (pt); Ophthalmologists 1 (pt); Podiatrists 1 (pt).
Facilities Dining room; Physical therapy room; Activities room; Chapel; Crafts room; Laundry room; Barber/Beauty shop; Library.
Activities Arts & crafts; Cards; Games; Reading groups; Prayer groups; Movies; Shopping trips; Social/Cultural gatherings; Pet therapy; Fishing.

COOPERSBURG

Valley Manor Nursing Center
PO Box 163, Rte 309, Coopersburg, PA, 18036
(215) 282-1919
Admin Diane G Fonzone. *Medical Dir/Dir of Nursing* Dr Garry Sussman DO Medical Director; Roseanne Girard RN DON.
Licensure Skilled care; Intermediate care. *Beds* SNF 30; ICF 150. *Certified* Medicaid; Medicare.
Owner Proprietary Corp (Unicare).
Admissions Requirements Medical examination.
Staff RNs; LPNs; Nurses aides; Activities coordinators; Dietitians.
Facilities Dining room; Physical therapy room; Activities room; Crafts room; Laundry room; Barber/Beauty shop.
Activities Arts & crafts; Cards; Games; Reading groups; Prayer groups; Movies; Shopping trips; Social/Cultural gatherings.

CORAOPOLIS

Allegheny Valley School for Exceptional Children*
1992 Ewing Mill Rd, Coraopolis, PA, 15108
(412) 262-3500
Licensure Intermediate care for mentally retarded. *Beds* 160. *Certified* Medicaid.
Owner Nonprofit Corp.

Sycamore Creek Nursing Center
234 Coraopolis Rd, Coraopolis, PA, 15108
(412) 331-6060
Admin Mark D Bondi. *Medical Dir/Dir of Nursing* Drs Bader, Dickinson; M Lorah DON.
Licensure Skilled care; Intermediate care. *Beds* SNF 20; ICF 100. *Certified* Medicaid; Medicare.
Owner Proprietary Corp (Health Care Management).
Admissions Requirements Medical examination; Physician's request.
Staff Physicians 2 (pt); RNs 10 (ft); LPNs 19 (ft); Orderlies; Nurses aides 30 (ft), 20 (pt); Physical therapists 1 (pt); Reality therapists 1 (pt); Recreational therapists 1 (ft), 1 (pt); Occupational therapists 1 (pt); Speech therapists 1 (pt); Activities coordinators 1 (ft); Dietitians 1 (ft), 1 (pt); Dentists 1 (pt); Ophthalmologists 1 (pt); Podiatrists 1 (pt).
Facilities Dining room; Physical therapy room; Activities room; Crafts room; Laundry room; Barber/Beauty shop.
Activities Arts & crafts; Cards; Games; Reading groups; Prayer groups; Movies; Shopping trips; Social/Cultural gatherings.

CORNWALL

Cornwall Manor of the United Methodist Church
Boyd St, Cornwall, PA, 17016
(717) 273-2647
Admin Steven Hassinger. *Medical Dir/Dir of Nursing* Robert Nielsen MD; Susan E Fisher DON.
Licensure Skilled care; Intermediate care. *Beds* SNF 47; ICF 78. *Certified* Medicaid; Medicare.
Owner Nonprofit organization/foundation.
Admissions Requirements Medical examination; Physician's request.
Staff Physicians 4 (pt); RNs 5 (ft); LPNs 20 (ft), 15 (pt); Nurses aides 30 (ft), 20 (pt); Physical therapists 1 (pt); Activities coordinators 1 (ft); Dietitians 1 (ft).
Affiliation Methodist
Facilities Dining room; Physical therapy room; Activities room; Chapel; Laundry room; Barber/Beauty shop.
Activities Arts & crafts; Cards; Games; Reading groups; Prayer groups; Movies; Shopping trips; Social/Cultural gatherings; Remotivation; Reality orientation.

CORNWELL HEIGHTS

Muffett Nursing Home*
958 Flushing Rd, Cornwell Heights, PA, 19020
(215) 639-3568
Licensure Skilled care. *Beds* 23.
Owner Proprietary Corp.

CORRY

Corry Manor Nursing Home
640 Worth St, Corry, PA, 16407
(814) 664-9606
Admin Kathleen Cunningham. *Medical Dir/Dir of Nursing* Dr G R Lloyd MD; Marnie Hy RN DON.
Licensure Skilled care; Intermediate care. *Beds* SNF 121; ICF. *Certified* Medicaid; Medicare.

Owner Proprietary Corp (Health Care Facilities Inc).
Admissions Requirements Medical examination; Physician's request.
Staff RNs; LPNs; Orderlies; Nurses aides; Physical therapists 1 (pt); Speech therapists 1 (pt); Activities coordinators 1 (pt), 1 (pt).
Facilities Dining room; Physical therapy room; Activities room; Laundry room; Barber/Beauty shop; Library; Patios; Lounges; Soda shop.
Activities Arts & crafts; Cards; Games; Reading groups; Prayer groups; Movies; Shopping trips; Social/Cultural gatherings; Bowling; Bingo; Nail clinic.

COUDERSPORT

Charles Cole Memorial Hospital-ECF*
Rd 3, Coudersport, PA, 16915
(814) 274-9300
Licensure Skilled care; Intermediate care. *Beds* SNF 32; ICF 50. *Certified* Medicaid; Medicare.
Owner Nonprofit Corp.

DALLAS

Lakeside Nursing Center
PO Box 357, Rte 4, Dallas, PA, 18612
(717) 639-1885
Admin Frank J Berleth. *Medical Dir/Dir of Nursing* Dr Gary Smith; Patricia Shupp RN.
Licensure Skilled care; Personal care. *Beds* SNF 30; Personal 25. *Certified* Medicaid; Medicare.
Owner Proprietary Corp.
Admissions Requirements Medical examination; Physician's request.
Staff Physicians 6 (pt); RNs 1 (ft), 2 (pt); LPNs 4 (ft); Nurses aides 7 (ft), 6 (pt); Physical therapists 1 (pt); Recreational therapists 1 (pt); Occupational therapists 1 (pt); Speech therapists 1 (pt); Activities coordinators 1 (ft); Dietitians 3 (ft), 4 (pt); Ophthalmologists 2 (pt).
Facilities Dining room; Physical therapy room; Activities room; Laundry room.
Activities Arts & crafts; Cards; Games; Prayer groups; Movies; Shopping trips; Social/Cultural gatherings.

Maple Hill Nursing Home
PO Box 391, RD 2, Dallas, PA, 18612
(717) 675-1787
Admin Maureen Cerniglia NHA. *Medical Dir/Dir of Nursing* Ernest Gelb DO; Marlene Konopke RN.
Licensure Intermediate care. *Beds* 24. *Certified* Medicaid.
Owner Proprietary Corp.
Admissions Requirements Medical examination; Physician's request.
Staff RNs 1 (ft); LPNs 5 (pt); Nurses aides 5 (ft), 4 (pt); Activities coordinators 1 (ft).
Facilities Dining room.
Activities Arts & crafts; Cards; Games; Reading groups; Prayer groups; Shopping trips.

Meadows Nursing Center
55 W Center Hill Rd, Dallas, PA, 18612
(717) 675-8600
Admin Thomas J Sweeney. *Medical Dir/Dir of Nursing* Dorothy Flynn MD; Bette Segrave-Daly DON.
Licensure Skilled care. *Beds* SNF 120. *Certified* Medicaid; Medicare.
Owner Nonprofit Corp.
Admissions Requirements Minimum age 18; Medical examination; Physician's request.
Staff RNs 6 (ft), 7 (pt); LPNs 11 (ft), 12 (pt); Nurses aides 34 (ft), 34 (pt); Activities coordinators 1 (ft).
Facilities Dining room; Physical therapy room; Activities room; Chapel; Laundry room; Barber/Beauty shop.

Activities Arts & crafts; Games; Reading groups; Prayer groups; Movies; Shopping trips; Social/Cultural gatherings; Coffee klatch; Birthday parties; Exercises; Bingo; Music program.

DALLASTOWN

Leader Nursing & Rehabilitation Center*
100 W Queen St, Dallastown, PA, 17313
(717) 246-1671
Licensure Skilled care; Intermediate care. Beds SNF 120; ICF 60. Certified Medicaid; Medicare.
Owner Proprietary Corp (Manor Care).

Seitz Nursing Home
623 E Main St, Dallastown, PA, 17313
(717) 244-2295
Admin Sylvia E Snyder. Medical Dir/Dir of Nursing Edward F Holland MD; Maud Rupp DON.
Licensure Skilled care. Beds SNF 24.
Owner Privately owned.
Admissions Requirements Minimum age 16; Medical examination.
Staff RNs 1 (ft), 3 (pt); LPNs 1 (ft), 3 (pt); Nurses aides 6 (ft), 6 (pt); Recreational therapists 1 (pt); Activities coordinators 1 (pt).
Facilities Dining room; Activities room; Chapel; Crafts room; Laundry room.
Activities Arts & crafts; Cards; Games; Reading groups; Prayer groups; Movies; Shopping trips; Social/Cultural gatherings.

DANVILLE

Danville State Hospital Long-Term Care Facility
PO Box 700, Danville, PA, 17821-0700
(717) 275-7133
Admin Barbara A Long. Medical Dir/Dir of Nursing Benjamin Corteza MD; Jill Rhodes RN DON.
Licensure Skilled care; Intermediate care. Beds 143. Certified Medicare.
Owner Publicly owned.
Staff Physicians 1 (ft), 2 (pt); RNs 24 (ft), 3 (pt); LPNs 18 (ft); Nurses aides 48 (ft); Physical therapists 1 (pt); Occupational therapists 1 (pt); Activities coordinators 3 (ft); Dietitians 2 (pt); Ophthalmologists 1 (pt); Social worker 2 (ft).
Facilities Dining room; Activities room; Chapel; Crafts room; Laundry room; Barber/Beauty shop; Library.
Activities Arts & crafts; Cards; Games; Reading groups; Prayer groups; Movies; Shopping trips; Social/Cultural gatherings; Community trips.

Gold Star Nursing Home
School House Rd, Danville, PA, 17821
(717) 275-4946
Licensure Intermediate care. Beds 100. Certified Medicaid.
Owner Proprietary Corp.
Admissions Requirements Medical examination.
Staff Physicians 11 (pt); RNs 4 (ft), 2 (pt); LPNs 6 (ft), 1 (pt); Orderlies 3 (ft); Nurses aides 25 (ft), 1 (pt); Physical therapists 1 (pt); Speech therapists 1 (pt); Activities coordinators 1 (ft); Dietitians 1 (pt); Dentists 1 (pt); Podiatrists 1 (pt).
Facilities Dining room; Physical therapy room; Activities room; Crafts room; Laundry room; Barber/Beauty shop.
Activities Arts & crafts; Cards; Games; Reading groups; Prayer groups; Movies; Social/Cultural gatherings.

Grandview Health Homes Inc
Woodbine Lane, Danville, PA, 17821
(717) 275-5240

Admin Jerry E Boone. Medical Dir/Dir of Nursing Norman Ekberg MD; Jane Campbell DON.
Licensure Skilled care; Intermediate care. Beds SNF 20; ICF 130. Certified Medicaid; Medicare.
Owner Proprietary Corp.
Admissions Requirements Medical examination.
Staff RNs 3 (ft), 3 (pt); LPNs 13 (ft), 3 (pt); Orderlies; Nurses aides 43 (ft), 7 (pt); Physical therapists 1 (pt); Recreational therapists 3 (pt); Speech therapists 1 (pt); Activities coordinators 1 (ft); Dietitians 1 (ft), 1 (pt); Ophthalmologists 1.
Facilities Dining room; Physical therapy room; Activities room; Crafts room; Laundry room; Barber/Beauty shop; Library.
Activities Arts & crafts; Cards; Games; Movies; Social/Cultural gatherings; Church; Group patient murals.

Maria Joseph Manor
PO Box 3, RD 4, Danville, PA, 17821
(717) 275-4221
Admin Sr M Jeanetto. Medical Dir/Dir of Nursing John V McCormick MD.
Licensure Intermediate care; Residential care. Beds ICF 47; Residential 48. Certified Medicaid.
Owner Nonprofit Corp.
Admissions Requirements Minimum age 65; Medical examination.
Staff Physicians 2 (pt); RNs 3 (ft), 5 (pt); LPNs 5 (ft), 3 (pt); Nurses aides 22 (ft), 15 (pt); Physical therapists 1 (ft), 2 (pt); Recreational therapists 1 (ft); Dietitians 1 (ft).
Affiliation Roman Catholic
Facilities Dining room; Physical therapy room; Activities room; Chapel; Crafts room; Laundry room; Barber/Beauty shop; Lounges; Auditorium; Outdoor pavillion/patio.
Activities Arts & crafts; Cards; Games; Reading groups; Prayer groups; Movies; Shopping trips; Cocktail hour; Ice cream social; Various parties.

DARBY

Little Flower Manor
PO Box 190, 1201 Springfield Rd, Darby, PA, 19023
(215) 534-6000
Admin Sr M Nicolette. Medical Dir/Dir of Nursing Morris F Guirguis MD; Catherine Roche DON.
Licensure Skilled care. Beds SNF 122. Certified Medicaid.
Owner Nonprofit organization/foundation.
Admissions Requirements Minimum age 65; Medical examination; Physician's request.
Staff Physicians 6 (pt); RNs 7 (ft), 18 (pt); LPNs 3 (ft), 4 (pt); Nurses aides 23 (ft), 49 (pt); Physical therapists 3 (pt); Recreational therapists 2 (ft), 1 (pt); Occupational therapists 1 (pt); Speech therapists 1 (pt); Activities coordinators 1 (ft); Dietitians 1 (ft); Dentists 1 (pt); Ophthalmologists 1 (pt); Podiatrists 1 (pt).
Affiliation Roman Catholic
Facilities Dining room; Physical therapy room; Activities room; Chapel; Crafts room; Laundry room; Barber/Beauty shop; Library.
Activities Arts & crafts; Cards; Games; Reading groups; Prayer groups; Movies; Social/Cultural gatherings.

St Francis Country Home
14th & Lansdowne Ave, Darby, PA, 19023
(215) 461-6510
Admin Sr Anne Lutz CBS. Medical Dir/Dir of Nursing Ronald E Rossman MD; Marion Nimey DON.
Licensure Skilled care. Beds SNF 318. Certified Medicaid; Medicare.

Owner Nonprofit Corp (Bon Secours Health Sys).
Admissions Requirements Medical examination.
Staff RNs 10 (ft), 10 (pt); LPNs 15 (ft), 15 (pt); Orderlies 5 (ft), 5 (pt); Nurses aides 88 (ft), 88 (pt); Physical therapists 1 (pt); Occupational therapists 1 (pt); Speech therapists 1 (pt); Activities coordinators 1 (ft); Dietitians 1 (ft).
Affiliation Roman Catholic
Facilities Dining room; Physical therapy room; Activities room; Chapel; Crafts room; Barber/Beauty shop.
Activities Arts & crafts; Cards; Games; Reading groups; Prayer groups; Movies; Shopping trips.

DEVON

Cathcart Health Center
445 N Valley Forge Rd, Devon, PA, 19333
(215) 688-0833
Admin Jeffrey L Shireman NHA. Medical Dir/Dir of Nursing Alexander O'Neal MD; Rita Harkins RN.
Licensure Skilled care. Beds SNF 63. Certified Medicaid; Medicare.
Owner Nonprofit Corp.
Admissions Requirements Medical examination; Physician's request.
Staff RNs; LPNs; Orderlies; Nurses aides; Physical therapists; Speech therapists; Activities coordinators; Dietitians; Ophthalmologists.
Facilities Dining room; Physical therapy room; Activities room; Chapel; Laundry room; Barber/Beauty shop.
Activities Arts & crafts; Cards; Games; Prayer groups; Movies; Shopping trips.

Devon Manor Retirement Center
235 Lancaster Ave, Devon, PA, 19333
(215) 688-8080
Admin Peter W Grim. Medical Dir/Dir of Nursing Dr William Lander; Dorothy Riggs RN DON.
Licensure Skilled care; Personal care; Residential living; Adult day care. Beds SNF 92; Personal 94 Residential units 105. Certified Medicare.
Owner Proprietary Corp.
Admissions Requirements Medical examination.
Staff Physicians 4 (pt); RNs 14 (ft), 7 (pt); LPNs 3 (ft); Orderlies 1 (pt); Nurses aides 26 (ft), 9 (pt); Physical therapists 1 (ft); Reality therapists 1 (pt); Recreational therapists 3 (ft), 1 (pt); Occupational therapists 2 (pt); Speech therapists 1 (pt); Activities coordinators 1 (ft); Dietitians 2 (ft), 1 (pt); Dentists 1 (pt); Podiatrists 1 (pt); 1 (pt).
Languages French
Facilities Dining room; Physical therapy room; Activities room; Chapel; Crafts room; Laundry room; Barber/Beauty shop; Library; Health club; Cocktail lounge; Billiards room.
Activities Arts & crafts; Cards; Games; Reading groups; Prayer groups; Movies; Shopping trips; Social/Cultural gatherings; Lectures; Shows; Classical music groups; Big band groups.

DOYLESTOWN

Briarleaf Nursing & Convalescent Center
252 Belmont Ave, Doylestown, PA, 18901
(215) 348-2983
Admin Diane L McGerr. Medical Dir/Dir of Nursing Dr Laudenslager MD; Pat Buess RN DON.
Licensure Skilled care; Intermediate care. Beds 178. Certified Medicaid; Medicare.
Owner Privately owned.
Admissions Requirements Medical examination.

Staff RNs; LPNs; Orderlies; Nurses aides; Physical therapists; Recreational therapists; Occupational therapists; Speech therapists; Activities coordinators; Dietitians.
Facilities Dining room; Physical therapy room; Activities room; Crafts room; Laundry room; Barber/Beauty shop; Library.
Activities Arts & crafts; Cards; Games; Reading groups; Prayer groups; Movies; Shopping trips; Social/Cultural gatherings.

Bucks County Association of Retarded Citizens*
252 Belmont Dr, Doylestown, PA, 18901
(215) 348-3524
Licensure Intermediate care for mentally retarded. *Beds* 8. *Certified* Medicaid.
Owner Nonprofit Corp.

Doylestown Manor*
Maple Ave & East St, Doylestown, PA, 18901
(215) 345-1452
Admin Harry K Hobbs.
Licensure Skilled care; Intermediate care. *Beds* 120. *Certified* Medicaid; Medicare.
Owner Proprietary Corp (Beverly Enterprises).
Staff RNs 8 (ft), 3 (pt); LPNs 5 (ft), 2 (pt); Nurses aides 30 (ft), 10 (pt); Physical therapists 1 (ft), 1 (pt); Reality therapists 2 (ft); Activities coordinators 1 (ft).
Facilities Dining room; Physical therapy room; Activities room; Crafts room; Laundry room; Barber/Beauty shop.
Activities Arts & crafts; Cards; Games; Reading groups; Prayer groups; Movies; Shopping trips; Social/Cultural gatherings.

Greenleaf Nursing & Convalescent Center Inc
400 S Main St, Doylestown, PA, 18901
(215) 348-2980
Admin David R Devereaux. *Medical Dir/Dir of Nursing* Dr E C Laudenslager; Carol De Ricci DON.
Licensure Skilled care; Intermediate care. *Beds* SNF 16; ICF 114. *Certified* Medicaid; Medicare.
Owner Proprietary Corp.
Facilities Dining room; Physical therapy room; Activities room; Laundry room; Barber/Beauty shop.
Activities Arts & crafts; Cards; Games; Prayer groups; Movies; Shopping trips.

Heritage Towers
200 Veterans Lane, Doylestown, PA, 18901
(215) 345-4300
Admin Bruce L Lenich. *Medical Dir/Dir of Nursing* Charles W Burmeister MD; Myra Berest RN DON.
Licensure Skilled care; Intermediate care. *Beds* 60. *Certified* Medicaid; Medicare.
Owner Nonprofit Corp.
Admissions Requirements Medical examination; Physician's request.
Staff Physicians; RNs 4 (ft), 4 (pt); LPNs 1 (ft), 2 (pt); Orderlies 1 (ft); Nurses aides 9 (ft), 10 (pt); Physical therapists 1 (pt); Reality therapists 1 (pt); Recreational therapists 1 (pt); Occupational therapists 1 (pt); Speech therapists 1 (pt); Activities coordinators 1 (ft); Dietitians 1 (ft); Dentist 1 (pt).
Facilities Dining room; Physical therapy room; Activities room; Chapel; Crafts room; Laundry room; Barber/Beauty shop; Library; Auditorium.
Activities Arts & crafts; Cards; Games; Prayer groups; Social/Cultural gatherings.

Medical Center for Aging—Doylestown
777 Ferry St, Doylestown, PA, 18901
(215) 345-9000, 348-7770, (800) 992-8992
Admin Patricia C Knowles. *Medical Dir/Dir of Nursing* Dr Gary Sussman; Patricia Demusz.
Licensure Skilled care; Intermediate care; Personal care. *Beds* 236. *Certified* Medicaid; Medicare.
Owner Proprietary Corp.

Admissions Requirements Medical examination.
Staff Physicians; RNs; LPNs; Orderlies; Nurses aides; Physical therapists; Reality therapists; Recreational therapists; Occupational therapists; Speech therapists; Dietitians; Dentists; Ophthalmologists; Podiatrists.
Facilities Dining room; Physical therapy room; Activities room; Crafts room; Laundry room; Barber/Beauty shop; Library; Podiatrist office.
Activities Arts & crafts; Cards; Games; Reading groups; Prayer groups; Movies; Shopping trips; Social/Cultural gatherings; Drama club; Editorial club; Garden club.

Neshaminy Manor
Rte 611 & Almhouse Rd, Doylestown, PA, 18901
(215) 345-3205
Admin James C Bailey LNHA. *Medical Dir/Dir of Nursing* Dr Vern Harrison.
Licensure Skilled care; Intermediate care. *Beds* SNF 60; ICF 300. *Certified* Medicaid; Medicare.
Owner Publicly owned.
Admissions Requirements Medical examination; Physician's request.
Staff Physicians 1 (ft), 3 (pt); RNs 50 (ft), 15 (pt); LPNs 20 (ft), 13 (pt); Orderlies; Nurses aides 112 (ft), 43 (pt); Physical therapists 5 (ft); Recreational therapists 4 (ft); Occupational therapists 2 (pt); Speech therapists 1 (pt); Activities coordinators 1 (ft); Dietitians 3 (ft); Dentists 1 (pt); Ophthalmologists 1 (pt).
Facilities Dining room; Physical therapy room; Activities room; Chapel; Crafts room; Laundry room; Barber/Beauty shop; Library.
Activities Arts & crafts; Cards; Games; Reading groups; Prayer groups; Movies; Shopping trips; Social/Cultural gatherings.

DRESHER

American Medical Nursing Center Inc-Dresher Hill*
1390 Camp Hill Rd, Dresher, PA, 19025
(215) 641-1710
Licensure Skilled care. *Beds* 120. *Certified* Medicaid; Medicare.
Owner Proprietary Corp (Unicare).

DRUMS

Butler Valley Manor*
Rte 1, Box 206, Drums, PA, 18222
(717) 788-4175
Licensure Skilled care. *Beds* 37. *Certified* Medicaid; Medicare.
Owner Proprietary Corp.

DUBOIS

Christ the King Manor
PO Box 448, 1100 W Long Ave, Dubois, PA, 15801
(814) 371-3180
Medical Dir/Dir of Nursing Dr Stanley Lang.
Licensure Skilled care; Intermediate care. *Beds* 160. *Certified* Medicaid; Medicare.
Owner Nonprofit Corp.
Admissions Requirements Medical examination.
Staff Physicians 3 (pt); RNs 11 (ft), 2 (pt); LPNs 20 (ft), 2 (pt); Orderlies 1 (ft); Nurses aides 60 (ft), 16 (pt); Physical therapists 3 (pt); Recreational therapists 1 (ft); Occupational therapists 1 (pt); Speech therapists 1 (pt); Activities coordinators 1 (ft); Dietitians 1 (ft); Dentists 1 (pt); Ophthalmologists 1 (pt); Podiatrists 1 (pt).
Affiliation Roman Catholic

Facilities Dining room; Physical therapy room; Activities room; Chapel; Crafts room; Laundry room; Barber/Beauty shop.
Activities Arts & crafts; Cards; Games; Reading groups; Prayer groups; Movies; Shopping trips; Social/Cultural gatherings.

Dubois Nursing Home
200 S 8th St, Dubois, PA, 15801
(814) 375-9100
Admin Robert Buzzell. *Medical Dir/Dir of Nursing* Dr Jawahar Suvarnakar; Bette Iley DON.
Licensure Skilled care; Intermediate care. *Beds* SNF 36; ICF 144. *Certified* Medicaid; Medicare.
Owner Proprietary Corp (Unicare).
Admissions Requirements Medical examination; Physician's request.
Staff Physicians 7 (pt); RNs 5 (ft), 1 (pt); LPNs 14 (ft); Nurses aides 56 (ft); Recreational therapists 3 (ft); Occupational therapists 1 (pt); Speech therapists 1 (pt); Activities coordinators 3 (ft); Dietitians 1 (ft).
Facilities Dining room; Physical therapy room; Crafts room; Laundry room; Barber/Beauty shop.
Activities Arts & crafts; Cards; Games; Reading groups; Prayer groups; Movies; Shopping trips; Social/Cultural gatherings.

DUNCANNON

Kin Kora Pythian Home
PO Box 220, Rte 3, Duncannon, PA, 17020
(717) 834-4887
Admin Doris Miller. *Medical Dir/Dir of Nursing* Sandra Willis.
Licensure Intermediate care; Residential care. *Beds* ICF 27; Residential 8. *Certified* Medicaid.
Owner Nonprofit Corp.
Admissions Requirements Minimum age 18; Medical examination.
Staff Physicians 1 (ft); RNs 4 (ft); LPNs 4 (ft); Nurses aides 20 (ft); Activities coordinators 1 (ft); Dietitians 1 (ft); Ophthalmologists 1 (ft).
Affiliation Knights of Pythias
Facilities Dining room; Activities room; Crafts room; Laundry room; Library; Living room.
Activities Arts & crafts; Cards; Games; Reading groups; Prayer groups; Movies; Shopping trips.

DUNMORE

Laurel Hill Inc
Smith & Mill Sts, Dunmore, PA, 18512
(717) 342-7624
Admin Bruce N Harding. *Medical Dir/Dir of Nursing* Mary Ann Alabovitz RN DON.
Licensure Skilled care; Intermediate care. *Beds* SNF 20; ICF 107. *Certified* Medicaid; Medicare.
Owner Proprietary Corp.
Admissions Requirements Minimum age 21; Medical examination; Physician's request.
Staff RNs 5 (ft), 4 (pt); LPNs 6 (ft), 8 (pt); Nurses aides 24 (ft), 20 (pt); Activities coordinators 3 (ft).
Facilities Dining room; Activities room; Laundry room.
Activities Arts & crafts; Games; Reading groups; Prayer groups; Movies; Shopping trips.

EAST LANSDOWNE

Lansdowne Rest Home*
246 Melrose Ave, East Lansdowne, PA, 19050
(215) 623-2233
Licensure Intermediate care. *Beds* 26.
Owner Proprietary Corp.

Staff RNs 4 (pt); LPNs 2 (ft); Nurses aides 4 (ft), 6 (pt); Activities coordinators 1 (pt); Dietitians 1 (pt).
Facilities Dining room; Activities room; Laundry room.
Activities Arts & crafts; Cards; Games; Reading groups; Social/Cultural gatherings.

EAST NORRISTOWN

Leader Nursing & Rehabilitation Center*
Johnson Hwy & Old Arch Rd, East Norristown, PA, 19401
(215) 275-6401
Medical Dir/Dir of Nursing Joseph Maerz MD.
Licensure Skilled care. *Beds* 120. *Certified* Medicaid; Medicare.
Owner Proprietary Corp.
Facilities Dining room; Physical therapy room; Activities room; Chapel; Crafts room; Laundry room; Barber/Beauty shop; Library; Head trauma & spinal cord rehabilitation program.
Activities Arts & crafts; Cards; Games; Reading groups; Prayer groups; Movies; Shopping trips; Social/Cultural gatherings.

EAST STROUDSBURG

Stroud Manor Inc*
229 E Brown St, East Stroudsburg, PA, 18301
(717) 421-6200
Licensure Skilled care. *Beds* 129. *Certified* Medicaid; Medicare.
Owner Proprietary Corp (Beverly Enterprises).

EASTON

The Easton Home for Aged Women
1022 Northampton St, Easton, PA, 18042
(215) 258-7773
Admin Janice A Hoffman. *Medical Dir/Dir of Nursing* T R Liberta MD; Mary Linton RN DON.
Licensure Skilled care; Personal care. *Beds* SNF 26; Personal 31.
Owner Nonprofit organization/foundation.
Admissions Requirements Minimum age 65; Females only; Medical examination.
Staff RNs 1 (ft), 6 (pt); LPNs 2 (ft), 1 (pt); Nurses aides 2 (ft), 10 (pt); Activities coordinators 1 (ft); Social services 1 (ft).
Facilities Dining room; Activities room; Chapel; Crafts room; Laundry room; Barber/Beauty shop; Library.
Activities Arts & crafts; Cards; Games; Reading groups; Prayer groups; Movies; Shopping trips; Social/Cultural gatherings.

Eastwood Convalescent Home Inc
2125 Fairview Ave, Easton, PA, 18042
(215) 258-2801
Admin Robert E Irving & Mitchell Richman. *Medical Dir/Dir of Nursing* G B Miles DO; Ilene K Turner RN DON.
Licensure Long-term care. *Beds* Long-term care 107. *Certified* Medicare.
Owner Privately owned.
Staff RNs 6 (ft), 8 (pt); LPNs 5 (ft), 2 (pt); Nurses aides 30 (ft), 17 (pt); Activities coordinators 2 (ft); Dietitians 1 (pt).
Facilities Dining room; Physical therapy room; Activities room; Laundry room; Barber/Beauty shop; Lift-equipped bus.
Activities Arts & crafts; Games; Reading groups; Prayer groups; Movies; Shopping trips; Social/Cultural gatherings; Bus trips; Group discussions.

Leader Nursing & Rehabilitation Center*
2600 Northampton St, Easton, PA, 18042
(215) 250-0150
Licensure Skilled care. *Beds* 120. *Certified* Medicaid; Medicare.
Owner Proprietary Corp (Manor Care).

Praxis Nursing Home
500 Washington St, Easton, PA, 18042
(215) 253-3573
Admin Martha Marino NHA. *Medical Dir/Dir of Nursing* Dr Spool; Doris Zuck RN.
Licensure Skilled care; Intermediate care for Alzheimer's & related disorders. *Beds* 110. *Certified* Medicare.
Owner Proprietary Corp.
Admissions Requirements Medical examination.
Facilities Dining room; Physical therapy room; Activities room; Crafts room; Laundry room; Barber/Beauty shop.
Activities Arts & crafts; Cards; Games; Reading groups; Prayer groups; Movies; Shopping trips; Social/Cultural gatherings.

EBENSBURG

Ebensburg Center
Rte 22, Ebensburg, PA, 15931
(814) 472-7350
Admin Alan M Bellomo. *Medical Dir/Dir of Nursing* Edward Shertz MD.
Licensure Intermediate care for mentally retarded. *Beds* ICF/MR 624. *Certified* Medicaid.
Owner Nonprofit Corp.
Staff Physicians 5 (ft); RNs 38 (ft), 6 (pt); Nurses aides 378 (ft), 2 (pt); Physical therapists 4 (pt); Recreational therapists 8 (ft); Occupational therapists 1 (ft); Speech therapists 8 (ft); Activities coordinators 1 (ft); Dietitians 3 (ft); Dentists 1 (pt); Ophthalmologists 1 (ft); Podiatrists 1 (ft).
Facilities Dining room; Physical therapy room; Activities room; Chapel; Crafts room; Laundry room; Barber/Beauty shop; Vocational training room; Visually handicapped & communications training units; Behavior therapy unit.
Activities Arts & crafts; Games; Movies; Shopping trips; Social/Cultural gatherings.

EFFORT

Brookmont Health Care Center Inc
PO Box 50, Brookmont Dr, Effort, PA, 18330
(215) 681-4070
Admin Alan W Pedersen. *Medical Dir/Dir of Nursing* Thomas Harakal MD; Sherrill Rosetti DON.
Licensure Skilled care; Intermediate care. *Beds* SNF 43; ICF 60. *Certified* Medicaid; Medicare.
Owner Privately owned.
Admissions Requirements Medical examination.
Staff Physicians 1 (pt); RNs 4 (ft), 2 (pt); LPNs 6 (ft), 2 (pt); Nurses aides 30 (ft); Physical therapists 1 (ft); Recreational therapists 2 (ft).
Facilities Dining room; Physical therapy room; Activities room; Chapel; Crafts room; Laundry room; Barber/Beauty shop; Library.
Activities Arts & crafts; Cards; Games; Reading groups; Prayer groups; Movies; Shopping trips; Social/Cultural gatherings.

ELIZABETHTOWN

Leader Nursing & Rehabilitation Center
320 S Market St, Elizabethtown, PA, 17022
(717) 367-1377
Admin Donald Allen. *Medical Dir/Dir of Nursing* Henry Kreider MD; Minerva Ensminger RN DON.
Licensure Skilled care. *Beds* SNF 61. *Certified* Medicaid; Medicare.
Owner Proprietary Corp (Manor Care).
Admissions Requirements Medical examination.
Staff Physicians 1 (ft), 3 (pt); RNs 6 (ft), 1 (pt); LPNs 3 (ft), 1 (pt); Nurses aides 34 (ft), 16 (pt); Physical therapists 1 (ft);

Recreational therapists 1 (ft); Occupational therapists 1 (pt); Speech therapists 1 (pt); Activities coordinators 1 (ft); Dietitians 1 (ft); Dentists 1 (pt); Ophthalmologists 1 (pt); Podiatrists 1 (pt).
Facilities Dining room; Physical therapy room; Activities room; Chapel; Crafts room; Laundry room; Barber/Beauty shop; Library.
Activities Arts & crafts; Cards; Games; Reading groups; Prayer groups; Movies; Shopping trips; Social/Cultural gatherings.

Masonic Homes
Elizabethtown, PA, 17022
(717) 367-1121
Admin Joseph E Murphy. *Medical Dir/Dir of Nursing* Dr William W Longenecker; Martha M Wess RN DON.
Licensure Skilled care; Intermediate care; Residential. *Beds* 761. *Certified* Medicaid; Medicare.
Owner Nonprofit organization/foundation.
Admissions Requirements Medical examination.
Staff Physicians 4 (ft); RNs 24 (ft), 10 (pt); LPNs 54 (ft), 11 (pt); Nurses aides 156 (ft), 55 (pt); Physical therapists 1 (ft); Recreational therapists 1 (ft); Activities coordinators 1 (ft); Dietitians 1 (ft); Dentists 2 (pt); Ophthalmologists 1 (pt).
Affiliation Masons
Facilities Dining room; Physical therapy room; Activities room; Chapel; Crafts room; Laundry room; Barber/Beauty shop; Library; Museum; Post office; Snack shop; Ice cream palor; Gift shop; Theatre.
Activities Arts & crafts; Cards; Games; Reading groups; Prayer groups; Movies; Shopping trips; Social/Cultural gatherings.

ELIZABETHVILLE

The Kepler Home Inc
44 S Market St, Elizabethville, PA, 17023
(717) 362-8370
Admin Kathryn Hendershot.
Licensure Intermediate care. *Beds* ICF 36. *Certified* Medicaid.
Owner Proprietary Corp.
Admissions Requirements Medical examination.
Staff RNs 1 (ft), 2 (pt); LPNs 2 (ft), 2 (pt); Activities coordinators 1 (ft); Dietitians 1 (pt).
Languages Pennsylvania Dutch
Facilities Dining room; Activities room; Crafts room; Barber/Beauty shop.
Activities Arts & crafts; Cards; Games; Reading groups; Prayer groups; Movies; Shopping trips; Social/Cultural gatherings; Picnics; Sight-seeing trips.

ELKINS PARK

American Medical Nursing Centers—Township Manor*
265 Township Line Rd, Elkins Park, PA, 19117
(215) 379-2700
Licensure Skilled care; Intermediate care. *Beds* SNF 102; ICF 48. *Certified* Medicaid; Medicare.
Owner Proprietary Corp (Unicare).

ELLWOOD CITY

Mary Evans Extended Care Facility*
724 Pershing St, Ellwood City, PA, 16117
(412) 752-0081
Licensure Skilled care. *Beds* 19. *Certified* Medicaid; Medicare.
Owner Nonprofit Corp.

ELMHURST

St Mary's Villa Nursing Home
St Mary's Villa Rd, Elmhurst, PA, 18416
(717) 842-7621
Admin Sr Mary Anne Kaporch. *Medical Dir/
Dir of Nursing* Joseph Demko MD; Sr Ann
Long RN DON.
Licensure Skilled care. *Beds* SNF 121.
Certified Medicaid; Medicare.
Owner Nonprofit Corp.
Admissions Requirements Minimum age 65;
Medical examination; Physician's request.
Staff RNs 10 (ft), 11 (pt); LPNs 9 (ft), 5 (pt);
Nurses aides 40 (ft), 15 (pt); Physical
therapists 1 (pt); Activities coordinators 1
(ft); Dietitians 1 (ft); Ophthalmologists 2
(pt).
Languages Lithuanian
Affiliation Roman Catholic
Facilities Dining room; Physical therapy
room; Activities room; Chapel; Crafts room;
Laundry room; Barber/Beauty shop; Library;
Lounges; Patio; Pavillion; Porches; Coffee/
snack shop; Gift shop.
Activities Arts & crafts; Cards; Games;
Reading groups; Prayer groups; Movies;
Shopping trips; Social/Cultural gatherings;
Intergenerational program (pre-school
children).

EMPORIUM

Guy & Mary Felt Manor Inc
110 E 4th St, Emporium, PA, 15834
(814) 486-3736
Admin Nancy Umbenhauer. *Medical Dir/Dir
of Nursing* Dr J M Blackburn; Frances
English.
Licensure Skilled care; Intermediate care. *Beds*
SNF 20; ICF 20. *Certified* Medicaid;
Medicare.
Owner Nonprofit Corp.
Admissions Requirements Minimum age 18;
Medical examination; Physician's request.
Staff RNs 2 (ft), 2 (pt); LPNs 1 (ft), 2 (pt);
Nurses aides 10 (ft), 10 (pt); Activities
coordinators 1 (ft); Dietitians 1 (pt).
Facilities Dining room; Physical therapy
room; Activities room; Crafts room; Laundry
room; Barber/Beauty shop.
Activities Arts & crafts; Cards; Games;
Reading groups; Prayer groups; Movies.

EPHRATA

Ephrata Nursing Home Inc*
25 W Locust St, Ephrata, PA, 17522
(717) 733-2189
Admin C M Wagner. *Medical Dir/Dir of
Nursing* Dr William Noller.
Licensure Skilled care; Residential care. *Beds*
SNF 24; Residential 6. *Certified* Medicaid;
Medicare.
Owner Proprietary Corp.
Admissions Requirements Minimum age 45;
Medical examination.
Staff Physicians 4 (pt); RNs 1 (ft), 2 (pt);
LPNs 2 (ft), 2 (pt); Nurses aides 5 (ft), 6
(pt); Physical therapists 1 (pt); Reality
therapists 1 (pt); Recreational therapists 1
(ft); Occupational therapists 1 (pt); Speech
therapists 1 (pt); Activities coordinators 1
(ft); Dietitians 1 (pt); Dentists 1 (pt);
Ophthalmologists 1 (pt); Podiatrists 1 (pt).
Facilities Dining room; Physical therapy
room; Activities room; Laundry room.
Activities Arts & crafts; Cards; Games;
Reading groups; Prayer groups.

Fairmont Rest Home*
Rte 4, Ephrata, PA, 17522
(717) 354-4111
Licensure Skilled care. *Beds* 112. *Certified*
Medicaid.
Owner Nonprofit Corp.

ERIE

Alpine Manor Health Center
4114 Schaper Ave, Erie, PA, 16509
(814) 868-0831
Admin Renee Brown. *Medical Dir/Dir of
Nursing* Dr Merjia Wright.
Licensure Skilled care; Intermediate care. *Beds*
SNF 60; ICF 61. *Certified* Medicaid;
Medicare.
Owner Proprietary Corp (Integrated Health
Services Inc).
Admissions Requirements Medical
examination.
Staff Physicians 1 (ft), 1 (pt); RNs 12 (ft), 3
(pt); LPNs 2 (pt); Nurses aides 30 (ft);
Physical therapists 2 (ft); Recreational
therapists 1 (ft); Occupational therapists 1
(ft); Speech therapists 1 (ft); Activities
coordinators 1 (ft); Dietitians 1 (ft);
Ophthalmologists 1 (pt).
Facilities Dining room; Physical therapy
room; Activities room; Laundry room;
Barber/Beauty shop.
Activities Arts & crafts; Cards; Games;
Reading groups; Prayer groups; Movies;
Social/Cultural gatherings.

Ball Pavilion Inc*
5416 E Lake Rd, Erie, PA, 16511
(814) 899-3102
Licensure Skilled care; Intermediate care. *Beds*
SNF 31; ICF 53. *Certified* Medicaid;
Medicare.
Owner Nonprofit Corp.

Dr Gertrude A Barber Center Inc
136 East Ave, Erie, PA, 16506
(814) 453-7661
Admin Gertrude A Barber. *Medical Dir/Dir of
Nursing* Joseph DeFranco MD.
Licensure Intermediate care for mentally
retarded. *Beds* ICF/MR 43. *Certified*
Medicaid.
Owner Nonprofit Corp.
Admissions Requirements Minimum age 18;
Medical examination; Primary diagnosis of
mental retardation.
Staff Physicians 1 (pt); RNs 2 (ft), 1 (pt);
LPNs 2 (ft); Orderlies 24 (ft), 10 (pt);
Physical therapists 1 (pt); Recreational
therapists 2 (ft); Occupational therapists 1
(pt); Speech therapists 1 (ft); Dietitians 1
(pt); Dentists 1 (pt); Ophthalmologists 1 (pt);
Podiatrists 1 (pt); Psychologists 1 (pt); Social
worker 1 (pt).
Facilities Dining room; Physical therapy
room; Activities room; Chapel; Laundry
room; Library; Gymnasium; Vocational
workshops; Rehabilitation area; Pool.
Activities Arts & crafts; Cards; Games; Prayer
groups; Movies; Shopping trips; Social/
Cultural gatherings; Community activities.

Battersby Convalescent Home*
2686 Peach St, Erie, PA, 16508
(814) 453-6641
Licensure Skilled care. *Beds* 115. *Certified*
Medicaid; Medicare.
Owner Proprietary Corp (Beverly Enterprises).

Erie County Geriatric Annex*
4728 Lake Pleasant Rd, Erie, PA, 16522
(814) 864-3001
Licensure Skilled care. *Beds* 80. *Certified*
Medicaid; Medicare.
Owner Nonprofit Corp.

Lake Erie Institute of Rehabilitation
137 W 2nd St, Erie, PA, 16507
(814) 453-5602
Admin Urban LaRiccia. *Medical Dir/Dir of
Nursing* Thomas Klaus MD; Linda Sproat
RN CRRN.
Licensure Skilled care; Acute Rehabilitation.
Beds SNF 59; Acute Rehabilitation 59.
Certified Medicaid; Medicare.
Owner Proprietary Corp.

Staff Physicians 3 (ft), 2 (pt); RNs 25 (ft), 6
(pt); LPNs 7 (ft), 1 (pt); Nurses aides 48 (ft),
19 (pt); Physical therapists 6 (ft);
Recreational therapists 5 (ft); Occupational
therapists 8 (ft); Speech therapists 8 (ft);
Dietitians 1 (pt); Respiratory therapist;
Dentist 1 (pt).
Facilities Dining room; Physical therapy
room; Activities room; Crafts room; Laundry
room; EEG & evoked potential lab; Research
department; Occupational therapy rooms;
Recreation therapy rooms; Speech therapy
rooms.
Activities Arts & crafts; Cards; Games;
Movies; Shopping trips; Social/Cultural
gatherings; Stimulation groups.

Lutheran Home for the Aged
149 W 22nd St, Erie, PA, 16502
(814) 452-3271
Admin Joseph S Bieniek. *Medical Dir/Dir of
Nursing* Virginia Shaffer RN NHA.
Licensure Skilled care; Intermediate care;
Personal care. *Beds* SNF 57; ICF 57; 28
Personal care. *Certified* Medicaid; Medicare.
Owner Nonprofit Corp.
Admissions Requirements Minimum age 65;
Medical examination.
Staff Physicians 1 (pt); RNs 1 (ft), 1 (pt);
LPNs 3 (pt); Orderlies 1 (pt); Nurses aides
20 (ft), 8 (pt); Physical therapists 1 (pt);
Recreational therapists 1 (pt); Occupational
therapists 1 (pt); Speech therapists 1 (pt);
Activities coordinators 1 (ft); Dietitians 1
(ft); Dentists 1 (pt); Ophthalmologists 1 (pt);
Podiatrists 1 (pt).
Languages Language interpretation available
Affiliation Lutheran
Facilities Dining room; Physical therapy
room; Activities room; Chapel; Crafts room;
Laundry room; Barber/Beauty shop; Library.
Activities Arts & crafts; Cards; Games;
Reading groups; Prayer groups; Movies;
Shopping trips; Social/Cultural gatherings.

Manor Home for the Aged*
3401 Poplar St, Erie, PA, 16508
(814) 866-7449
Licensure Intermediate care. *Beds* 33.
Certified Medicaid.
Owner Proprietary Corp.

Pennsylvania Soldiers' & Sailors' Home
PO Box 6239, 560 E 3rd St, Erie, PA, 16512
(814) 871-4531
Admin Stanley E Snyder. *Medical Dir/Dir of
Nursing* Dr William O Rowane DO; R Jane
Smith RN DON.
Licensure Skilled care; Intermediate care;
Personal care; Domiciliary care. *Beds* SNF
38; ICF 37; Personal 52; Domiciliary care
48.
Owner Publicly owned.
Admissions Requirements Medical
examination.
Staff Physicians 1 (ft); RNs 26 (ft), 2 (pt);
LPNs 7 (ft); Orderlies 5 (ft); Nurses aides 26
(ft); Physical therapists 1 (ft); Occupational
therapists; Speech therapists 1 (pt); Activities
coordinators 1 (ft); Dietitians 1 (ft); Dentists
1 (pt); Ophthalmologists 1 (pt).
Facilities Dining room; Physical therapy
room; Activities room; Chapel; Crafts room;
Laundry room; Barber/Beauty shop; Library;
Exercise room; Snack bar.
Activities Arts & crafts; Cards; Games;
Movies; Shopping trips; Social/Cultural
gatherings; Fishing/Camping trips; Sports
events.

Presbyterian Lodge
2628 Elmwood Ave, Erie, PA, 16508
(814) 864-4802
Admin Doris E Johnson NHA. *Medical Dir/
Dir of Nursing* Ronald P Leemhuis MD;
Jean A Reichert RN.

Licensure Skilled care; Intermediate care; Personal care. *Beds* SNF 18; ICF 37; Personal 25. *Certified* Medicaid; Medicare.
Owner Nonprofit Corp.
Admissions Requirements Minimum age 65; Medical examination; Physician's request.
Staff Physicians; RNs; LPNs; Nurses aides; Physical therapists; Recreational therapists; Occupational therapists; Speech therapists; Activities coordinators; Dietitians; Ophthalmologists.
Affiliation Presbyterian
Facilities Dining room; Physical therapy room; Activities room; Crafts room; Laundry room; Barber/Beauty shop; Library.
Activities Arts & crafts; Cards; Games; Prayer groups; Movies; Shopping trips; Social/Cultural gatherings.

Sarah A Reed Retirement Center
2214 Sassafras St, Erie, PA, 16502
(814) 453-6797
Admin Florence R Adameck. *Medical Dir/Dir of Nursing* Robert R Stuart MD; Sandra Nelson DON.
Licensure Skilled care; Intermediate care; Residential/personal. *Beds* SNF 43; ICF 36; Residential/personal 54. *Certified* Medicaid; Medicare.
Owner Nonprofit Corp.
Admissions Requirements Medical examination.
Staff Physicians; RNs; LPNs; Orderlies; Nurses aides; Physical therapists; Reality therapists; Recreational therapists; Activities coordinators; Dietitians; Ophthalmologists.
Facilities Dining room; Physical therapy room; Activities room; Chapel; Crafts room; Laundry room; Barber/Beauty shop; Library.
Activities Arts & crafts; Cards; Games; Reading groups; Prayer groups; Movies; Shopping trips; Social/Cultural gatherings.

Rondale Nursing & Convalescent Home*
1267 S Hill Rd, Erie, PA, 16509
(814) 864-4081
Admin Mary Ann Balsign. *Medical Dir/Dir of Nursing* Dr Ronald W Pearson.
Licensure Skilled care; Intermediate care. *Beds* SNF 50; ICF 30. *Certified* Medicaid; Medicare.
Owner Proprietary Corp (Unicare).
Admissions Requirements Minimum age 16; Medical examination; Physician's request.
Staff RNs 4 (ft), 4 (pt); LPNs 4 (ft), 4 (pt); Orderlies 1 (ft), 1 (pt); Nurses aides 21 (ft), 10 (pt); Physical therapists 1 (pt); Recreational therapists 1 (ft); Activities coordinators 1 (ft).
Facilities Dining room; Physical therapy room; Activities room; Chapel; Crafts room; Barber/Beauty shop.
Activities Arts & crafts; Cards; Games; Movies; Social/Cultural gatherings.

St Marys Home of Erie
607 E 26th St, Erie, PA, 16504
(814) 459-0621
Admin Sr Anastasia Valimont. *Medical Dir/Dir of Nursing* Sr Phyllis McCracken DON.
Licensure Skilled care; Intermediate care. *Beds* SNF 100; ICF 96. *Certified* Medicaid; Medicare.
Owner Nonprofit Corp.
Admissions Requirements Medical examination; Physician's request.
Staff Physicians 1 (pt); RNs 13 (ft), 7 (pt); LPNs 8 (ft), 1 (pt); Nurses aides 66 (ft), 27 (pt); Physical therapists 1 (pt); Recreational therapists 2 (ft); Occupational therapists 1 (pt); Speech therapists 1 (pt); Activities coordinators 1 (pt); Dietitians 1 (ft), 1 (pt); Ophthalmologists 1 (pt); Podiatrists 1 (pt).
Affiliation Roman Catholic
Facilities Dining room; Physical therapy room; Activities room; Chapel; Crafts room; Laundry room; Barber/Beauty shop.

Activities Arts & crafts; Cards; Games; Reading groups; Prayer groups; Movies; Social/Cultural gatherings; Outdoor picnics.

Twinbrook Medical Center
3805 Field St, Erie, PA, 16511
(814) 899-0651
Admin Lloyd R Berkey. *Medical Dir/Dir of Nursing* Julie Breski RN DON.
Licensure Skilled care. *Beds* 124. *Certified* Medicaid; Medicare.
Owner Proprietary Corp (Health Care & Retirement Corp).
Facilities Dining room; Physical therapy room; Activities room; Chapel; Crafts room; Laundry room; Barber/Beauty shop; Library.
Activities Arts & crafts; Cards; Games; Reading groups; Prayer groups; Movies; Shopping trips; Social/Cultural gatherings.

Western Reserve Convalescent Home of Erie*
1521 W 54th St, Erie, PA, 16509
(814) 864-0671
Licensure Skilled care. *Beds* 133. *Certified* Medicaid; Medicare.
Owner Proprietary Corp (Beverly Enterprises).

EVERETT

Pennknoll Village Nursing Home
PO Box 420, RD 1, Everett, PA, 15537
(814) 623-9018
Admin Brenda Barefoot. *Medical Dir/Dir of Nursing* Dr Eyler MD; Kay Will DON.
Licensure Skilled care; Intermediate care. *Beds* SNF 29; ICF 104. *Certified* Medicaid; Medicare.
Owner Nonprofit Corp (Tressler-Lutheran Services Assoc).
Admissions Requirements Minimum age 65.
Staff RNs 6 (ft), 8 (pt); LPNs 8 (ft), 8 (pt); Nurses aides 37 (ft), 32 (pt); Activities coordinators 1 (ft).
Facilities Dining room; Physical therapy room; Activities room; Chapel; Crafts room; Laundry room; Barber/Beauty shop; Library.
Activities Arts & crafts; Cards; Games; Reading groups; Prayer groups; Movies; Shopping trips; Social/Cultural gatherings.

FAIRVIEW

Fairview Manor
900 Manchester Rd, Fairview, PA, 16415
(814) 838-4822
Admin Mary Ann Bryan NHA. *Medical Dir/Dir of Nursing* Thomas C Klaus MD; Gayle Weidner RN DON.
Licensure Skilled care. *Beds* SNF 121. *Certified* Medicaid; Medicare.
Owner Proprietary Corp (Health Care Facilities Inc).
Admissions Requirements Medical examination; Physician's request.
Staff RNs 6 (ft); LPNs 10 (ft), 1 (pt); Nurses aides 44 (ft), 12 (pt); Activities coordinators 1 (ft).
Facilities Dining room; Physical therapy room; Activities room; Crafts room; Laundry room; Barber/Beauty shop; Library.
Activities Arts & crafts; Cards; Games; Reading groups; Prayer groups; Movies; Shopping trips; Social/Cultural gatherings.

FAYETTE CITY

Waddington Convalescent Home*
Rte 1, Fayette City, PA, 15438
(412) 326-4077
Licensure Skilled care. *Beds* 40.
Owner Proprietary Corp.

FAYETTEVILLE

Guilford Convalesarium*
3301 Lincoln Way East, Fayetteville, PA, 17222
(717) 352-2101
Licensure Skilled care. *Beds* 64. *Certified* Medicaid; Medicare.
Owner Proprietary Corp.

Piney Mountain Home*
Rte 2, Fayetteville, PA, 17222
(717) 352-2721
Licensure Skilled care. *Beds* 92. *Certified* Medicaid.
Owner Nonprofit Corp.

FEASTERVILLE

Ridge Crest Convalescent Center
1730 Buck Rd N, Feasterville, PA, 19047
(215) 355-3131
Admin Francis J Lee Jr. *Medical Dir/Dir of Nursing* Robert B Davis MD; Edwina M Corry RN DON.
Licensure Skilled care. *Beds* SNF 128. *Certified* Medicaid; Medicare.
Owner Proprietary Corp.
Admissions Requirements Minimum age 16.
Staff RNs 10 (ft), 1 (pt); LPNs 3 (ft), 2 (pt); Orderlies 3 (ft), 1 (pt); Nurses aides 41 (ft), 8 (pt); Activities coordinators 2 (ft), 1 (pt).
Facilities Dining room; Physical therapy room; Activities room; Laundry room; Barber/Beauty shop.
Activities Arts & crafts; Cards; Games; Reading groups; Prayer groups; Movies; Social/Cultural gatherings.

FLOURTOWN

St Josephs Villa
Stenton & Wissahickon Aves, Flourtown, PA, 19031
(215) 836-4179
Admin Terry C Tressler. *Medical Dir/Dir of Nursing* Jude Damian MD.
Licensure Skilled care; Intermediate care; Residential. *Beds* SNF 54; ICF 54; Residential 215. *Certified* Medicare.
Owner Nonprofit Corp.
Admissions Requirements Medical examination; Physician's request.
Staff RNs; LPNs; Nurses aides; Physical therapists; Recreational therapists; Occupational therapists; Speech therapists; Activities coordinators; Dietitians.
Affiliation Roman Catholic
Facilities Dining room; Physical therapy room; Activities room; Chapel; Crafts room; Laundry room; Barber/Beauty shop; Library.
Activities Arts & crafts; Cards; Games; Reading groups; Prayer groups; Shopping trips; Social/Cultural gatherings; Ceramics; Flower club.

FORKSVILLE

Dar-Way Nursing Home Inc
RD 1, Forksville, PA, 18616
(717) 924-3411
Admin Dora A McCarty. *Medical Dir/Dir of Nursing* Marylou Adams RN DON.
Licensure Intermediate care. *Beds* ICF 70. *Certified* Medicaid.
Owner Privately owned.
Admissions Requirements Medical examination; Physician's request.
Staff Physicians 3 (pt); RNs 3 (ft), 2 (pt); LPNs 3 (ft), 3 (pt); Nurses aides 25 (ft), 7 (pt); Occupational therapists 1 (ft); Dietitians 1 (pt).
Facilities Dining room; Activities room; Chapel; Barber/Beauty shop.
Activities Arts & crafts; Cards; Games; Reading groups; Prayer groups; Movies.

FORT WASHINGTON

Dresher Hill Nursing Center
1390 Camp Hill Rd, Fort Washington, PA, 19034
(215) 641-1710
Admin Linda Sloane NHA. *Medical Dir/Dir of Nursing* Suzanne Cochran RN DON.
Licensure Skilled care; Intermediate care. *Beds* SNF 118; ICF. *Certified* Medicaid; Medicare.
Owner Proprietary Corp (Unicare).
Admissions Requirements Minimum age 16; Medical examination.
Facilities Dining room; Physical therapy room; Activities room; Crafts room; Laundry room; Barber/Beauty shop; Library.
Activities Arts & crafts; Cards; Games; Reading groups; Prayer groups; Movies; Shopping trips; Social/Cultural gatherings.

Fort Washington Estates*
Fort Washington Ave & Susquehanna Rd, Fort Washington, PA, 19034
(215) 542-8111
Licensure Skilled care. *Beds* 62.
Owner Nonprofit Corp.

FRACKVILLE

Broad Mountain Nursing Home
500 Laurel St, Frackville, PA, 17931
(717) 874-0696
Admin Rose Ann Dyszel RN. *Medical Dir/Dir of Nursing* Gursharan Singh MD; Barbara Merwine DON.
Licensure Skilled care; Intermediate care. *Beds* SNF 129; ICF. *Certified* Medicaid; Medicare.
Owner Proprietary Corp (Unicare).
Admissions Requirements Minimum age 18.
Staff RNs 4 (ft), 4 (pt); LPNs 6 (ft), 11 (pt); Orderlies 1 (ft), 1 (pt); Nurses aides 27 (ft), 24 (pt); Physical therapists 1 (ft); Activities coordinators 2 (ft); Dietitians 2 (ft).
Facilities Dining room; Physical therapy room; Activities room; Crafts room; Laundry room; Barber/Beauty shop; Library; Outside patio.
Activities Arts & crafts; Cards; Games; Reading groups; Prayer groups; Movies; Shopping trips; Social/Cultural gatherings; Pet therapy; Birthday parties; Welcoming parties.

FRANKLIN

Granview Health Care Inc—Franklin*
1 Dale Ave, Franklin, PA, 16323
(814) 437-6802
Licensure Skilled care; Intermediate care. *Beds* SNF 76; ICF 29. *Certified* Medicaid; Medicare.
Owner Proprietary Corp.

Venango Manor
PO Box 29, Rte 3, Franklin, PA, 16323
(814) 437-6522
Admin Judith Billingsley RN NHA. *Medical Dir of Nursing* Dr Kamal Aoun; Joyce Gibson RN BSN.
Licensure Skilled care; Intermediate care. *Beds* SNF 53; ICF 125. *Certified* Medicaid.
Owner Publicly owned.
Admissions Requirements Medical examination; Physician's request.
Staff Physicians; RNs; LPNs; Orderlies; Nurses aides; Physical therapists; Recreational therapists; Speech therapists; Activities coordinators; Dietitians; Dentists; Ophthalmologists; Podiatrists.
Facilities Dining room; Physical therapy room; Activities room; Crafts room; Laundry room; Barber/Beauty shop.
Activities Arts & crafts; Cards; Games; Reading groups; Prayer groups; Movies; Shopping trips; Social/Cultural gatherings.

FREDERICK

Frederick Mennonite Home*
Rte 73, Frederick, PA, 19435
(215) 754-7878
Licensure Skilled care. *Beds* 50. *Certified* Medicaid.
Owner Nonprofit Corp.
Affiliation Mennonite

GETTYSBURG

Gettysburg Lutheran Retirement Village
1075 Old Harrisburg Rd, Gettysburg, PA, 17325
(717) 334-6204
Admin Geary Millikan NHA. *Medical Dir/Dir of Nursing* Joyce McLaughlin RN.
Licensure Skilled care; Intermediate care. *Beds* SNF 69; ICF 23. *Certified* Medicaid; Medicare.
Owner Nonprofit Corp.
Admissions Requirements Medical examination; Physician's request.
Staff RNs 4 (ft), 6 (pt); LPNs 9 (ft), 6 (pt); Nurses aides 21 (ft), 15 (pt); Activities coordinators 1 (ft).
Affiliation Lutheran
Facilities Dining room; Physical therapy room; Activities room; Laundry room; Barber/Beauty shop; Library.
Activities Arts & crafts; Cards; Games; Reading groups; Movies; Shopping trips; Social/Cultural gatherings; Bible study.

Green Acres Adams County Home
595 Biglerville Rd, Gettysburg, PA, 17325
(717) 334-6249
Admin Carol A Knisely. *Medical Dir/Dir of Nursing* Robert S Lefever MD; Alice Routsong DON.
Licensure Skilled care; Intermediate care; Personal care. *Beds* SNF 12; ICF 144; Personal 12. *Certified* Medicaid.
Owner Publicly owned.
Admissions Requirements Minimum age 18.
Staff Physicians 2 (pt); RNs 5 (ft), 2 (pt); LPNs 20 (ft), 4 (pt); Orderlies 2 (ft); Nurses aides 35 (ft), 11 (pt); Activities coordinators 2 (ft), 1 (pt); Dietitians 1 (ft).
Facilities Dining room; Physical therapy room; Activities room; Chapel; Crafts room; Laundry room; Barber/Beauty shop.
Activities Arts & crafts; Cards; Games; Reading groups; Prayer groups; Movies; Shopping trips; Social/Cultural gatherings.

Michael Manor
741 Chambersburg Rd, Gettysburg, PA, 17325
(717) 334-6764
Admin George S Repchick MS NHA.
Licensure Skilled care; Intermediate care. *Beds* SNF 26; ICF 80. *Certified* Medicaid; Medicare.
Owner Proprietary Corp (Beverly Enterprises).
Admissions Requirements Minimum age 18.
Staff RNs; LPNs; Nurses aides; Physical therapists; Recreational therapists; Speech therapists.
Facilities Dining room; Physical therapy room; Activities room; Crafts room; Laundry room; Barber/Beauty shop.
Activities Arts & crafts; Cards; Games; Reading groups; Prayer groups; Movies; Shopping trips.

GIBSONIA

St Barnabas Nursing Home
5850 Meridian Rd, Gibsonia, PA, 15044
(412) 443-0700
Admin William V Day. *Medical Dir/Dir of Nursing* Dr Philip Schumacher; Judith Wagner RN DON.
Licensure Skilled care. *Beds* SNF 107. *Certified* Medicaid; Medicare.
Owner Nonprofit organization/foundation.

Admissions Requirements Minimum age 10; Medical examination; Physician's request.
Staff Physicians; RNs; LPNs; Orderlies; Nurses aides; Physical therapists 1 (ft); Recreational therapists 2 (ft); Speech therapists 1 (pt); Activities coordinators 1 (ft); Dietitians 1 (pt); Ophthalmologists 1 (pt); Podiatrists 1 (pt).
Facilities Dining room; Physical therapy room; Activities room; Chapel; Crafts room; Laundry room; Barber/Beauty shop; Library.
Activities Arts & crafts; Cards; Games; Reading groups; Prayer groups; Movies; Shopping trips; Social/Cultural gatherings.

GIRARD

Erie County Geriatric Center*
Rte 2, Girard, PA, 16417
(814) 474-5521
Licensure Skilled care; Intermediate care. *Beds* SNF 398; ICF 41. *Certified* Medicaid; Medicare.
Owner Nonprofit Corp.

GLENSIDE

Edgehill Nursing & Rehabilitation Center
146 Edgehill Rd, Glenside, PA, 19038
(215) 886-1043
Admin Douglas Foulke. *Medical Dir/Dir of Nursing* Dr Howard Fein; Betsy Sevitski DON.
Licensure Skilled care. *Beds* 60. *Certified* Medicaid.
Owner Proprietary Corp (GraceCare, Inc).
Admissions Requirements Medical examination.
Staff RNs 2 (ft), 5 (pt); LPNs 5 (ft); Nurses aides 18 (ft), 4 (pt); Activities coordinators 1 (ft).
Facilities Dining room; Physical therapy room; Laundry room; Library; Multipurpose room used for chapel, activities room, and crafts room.
Activities Arts & crafts; Cards; Games; Reading groups; Prayer groups; Movies; Shopping trips; Social/Cultural gatherings.

GRANVILLE

Malta Home for the Aging
PO Box E, Granville, PA, 17029
(717) 248-3988
Admin Gary A Bontrager. *Medical Dir/Dir of Nursing* Lakshman Rao MD.
Licensure Skilled care; Personal care. *Beds* SNF 24; Personal 38. *Certified* Medicaid; Medicare.
Owner Nonprofit organization/foundation.
Admissions Requirements Medical examination.
Staff Physicians 2 (pt); RNs 1 (ft), 2 (pt); LPNs 5 (ft), 1 (pt); Nurses aides 11 (ft), 6 (pt); Physical therapists 1 (pt); Speech therapists 1 (pt); Activities coordinators 1 (ft); Dietitians 1 (pt).
Affiliation Knights of Malta
Facilities Dining room; Physical therapy room; Activities room; Crafts room; Laundry room; Barber/Beauty shop; Library.
Activities Arts & crafts; Cards; Games; Prayer groups; Social/Cultural gatherings; Spring & fall bus trips.

GREENSBURG

Greensburg Home
6 Garden Center Dr, Greensburg, PA, 15601
(412) 832-8400
Admin John A Mobley.
Licensure Intermediate care; Residential care. *Beds* 64. *Certified* Medicaid.
Owner Nonprofit Corp.
Admissions Requirements Minimum age 62; Medical examination.

Staff Physicians 1 (pt); RNs 3 (ft), 3 (pt); LPNs 4 (ft), 3 (pt); Nurses aides 16 (ft), 9 (pt); Activities coordinators 2 (ft), 1 (pt); Dietitians 1 (pt); Ophthalmologists 1 (pt).
Affiliation Presbyterian
Facilities Dining room; Physical therapy room; Activities room; Chapel; Crafts room; Laundry room; Barber/Beauty shop; Library.
Activities Arts & crafts; Cards; Games; Reading groups; Prayer groups; Movies; Shopping trips; Social/Cultural gatherings.

Greensburg Nursing & Convalescent Center Inc
PO Box 956, Greensburg, PA, 15601-0956
(412) 836-2480
Admin Melba L Galonis. *Medical Dir/Dir of Nursing* Thomas DeGregory MD; Eleanor Pennington DON.
Licensure Skilled care; Intermediate care. *Beds* SNF 120; ICF. *Certified* Medicaid; Medicare.
Owner Privately owned.
Admissions Requirements Medical examination; Physician's request.
Staff RNs 3 (ft), 6 (pt); LPNs 8 (ft), 7 (pt); Nurses aides 25 (ft), 21 (pt); Activities coordinators 1 (ft); Dietitians 1 (ft).
Languages German, Slavic, Italian
Facilities Dining room; Physical therapy room; Activities room; Laundry room; Barber/Beauty shop.
Activities Arts & crafts; Cards; Games; Reading groups; Prayer groups; Movies; Social/Cultural gatherings.

Mt View Nursing Center
Rte 7, Box 249, Greensburg, PA, 15601
(412) 837-6499
Admin Janice C Reeping. *Medical Dir/Dir of Nursing* Michael Zorch MD; Joan Silvis RN.
Licensure Skilled care; Intermediate care. *Beds* SNF 43; ICF 94. *Certified* Medicaid; Medicare.
Owner Proprietary Corp (Integrated Health Services Inc).
Admissions Requirements Minimum age 16.
Staff Physicians 1 (ft); RNs 9 (ft), 9 (pt); LPNs 4 (ft), 3 (pt); Nurses aides 28 (ft), 25 (pt); Physical therapists 1 (pt); Occupational therapists 1 (pt); Speech therapists 1 (pt); Activities coordinators 1 (ft); Dietitians 1 (ft).
Facilities Dining room; Physical therapy room; Activities room; Crafts room; Laundry room; Barber/Beauty shop.
Activities Arts & crafts; Cards; Games; Reading groups; Prayer groups; Movies; Shopping trips; Social/Cultural gatherings.

Oak Hill Home of Rest & Care*
Rte 7, Box 77A, Luxor Rd, Greensburg, PA, 15601
(412) 837-7100
Licensure Skilled care. *Beds* 48.
Owner Proprietary Corp.

St Anne Home for the Elderly
685 Angela Dr, Greensburg, PA, 15601
(412) 837-6070
Admin Sr Jean F Simok. *Medical Dir/Dir of Nursing* Theodore A Schultz MD; Marie Cardella DON.
Licensure Skilled care; Intermediate care. *Beds* SNF 39; ICF 86. *Certified* Medicaid; Medicare.
Owner Proprietary Corp (Pinnacle Care Corp).
Admissions Requirements Minimum age 65; Medical examination.
Staff Physicians 2 (pt); RNs 3 (ft), 7 (pt); LPNs 8 (ft), 11 (pt); Nurses aides 39 (ft), 36 (pt); Physical therapists 2 (ft); Recreational therapists 1 (ft), 1 (pt); Speech therapists 1 (pt); Activities coordinators 1 (ft); Dietitians 1 (ft), 1 (pt); Dentists 1 (pt); Ophthalmologists 1 (pt).
Affiliation Roman Catholic

Facilities Dining room; Physical therapy room; Activities room; Chapel; Crafts room; Laundry room; Barber/Beauty shop; Library.
Activities Arts & crafts; Cards; Games; Prayer groups; Movies; Social/Cultural gatherings.

Westmoreland Manor*
Box 10, Greensburg, PA, 15601
(412) 834-0200
Licensure Skilled care. *Beds* 540. *Certified* Medicaid; Medicare.
Owner Nonprofit Corp.

GREENVILLE

Gilmores White Cliff Nursing Home
110 Fredonia Rd, Greenville, PA, 16125
(412) 588-8090
Licensure Skilled care. *Beds* 134. *Certified* Medicaid; Medicare.
Owner Proprietary Corp.

St Paul Homes
339 E Jamestown Rd, Greenville, PA, 16125
(412) 588-4070
Admin L Collins Defibaugh. *Medical Dir/Dir of Nursing* Kathy Burcin DO; Lois M Eastlick DON.
Licensure Skilled care; Intermediate care; Assisted retirement living; Individual living. *Beds* SNF 29; ICF 197; Assisted retirement living 28; Individual living 26. *Certified* Medicaid; Medicare.
Owner Nonprofit Corp.
Admissions Requirements Minimum age 62; Medical examination; Physician's request.
Staff Physicians 15 (pt); RNs 19 (ft); LPNs 37 (ft); Nurses aides 103 (ft); Physical therapists 1 (ft); Reality therapists 2 (ft); Recreational therapists 2 (ft), 1 (pt); Occupational therapists 2 (ft); Speech therapists 1 (pt); Activities coordinators 1 (ft); Dietitians 1 (pt).
Affiliation Church of Christ
Facilities Dining room; Physical therapy room; Activities room; Chapel; Crafts room; Laundry room; Barber/Beauty shop; Library.
Activities Arts & crafts; Cards; Games; Reading groups; Prayer groups; Movies; Shopping trips; Social/Cultural gatherings.

GROVE CITY

Grove Manor*
435 N Broad St, Grove City, PA, 16127
(412) 452-7800
Admin Mary C Gray.
Licensure Skilled care. *Beds* 52. *Certified* Medicaid; Medicare.
Owner Nonprofit Corp.
Admissions Requirements Medical examination.
Staff RNs 2 (ft), 4 (pt); LPNs 2 (ft), 1 (pt); Nurses aides 17 (ft), 8 (pt); Physical therapists 1 (ft); Speech therapists 1 (pt); Dietitians 1 (pt).
Affiliation Church of God
Facilities Dining room; Physical therapy room; Chapel; Crafts room; Laundry room; Barber/Beauty shop.
Activities Arts & crafts; Games; Reading groups; Prayer groups; Movies.

Orchard Manor Inc
Rte 3, Grove City, PA, 16127
(412) 458-7760
Medical Dir/Dir of Nursing William C Menzies MD.
Licensure Skilled care. *Beds* 120. *Certified* Medicaid.
Owner Nonprofit Corp.
Staff Physicians 2 (pt); RNs 8 (ft), 2 (pt); LPNs 5 (pt), 1 (pt); Orderlies 2 (pt); Nurses aides 40 (ft), 3 (pt); Physical therapists 1 (pt); Activities coordinators 1 (ft); Dietitians 1 (pt); Ophthalmologists 1 (pt); Physical therapy aides 1 (ft).

Affiliation Independent Order of Odd Fellows & Rebekahs
Facilities Dining room; Physical therapy room; Activities room; Chapel; Crafts room; Laundry room; Barber/Beauty shop; Library; Podiatrist room.
Activities Arts & crafts; Cards; Games; Reading groups; Prayer groups; Movies; Shopping trips; Social/Cultural gatherings; Trips in van.

GWYNEDD

Foulkeways at Gwynedd Inc
Meeting House Rd, Gwynedd, PA, 19436
(215) 643-2200
Medical Dir/Dir of Nursing Dr Laurence Beck; Jane Kummerer.
Licensure Skilled care; Personal care. *Beds* SNF 62; Personal 32. *Certified* Medicare.
Owner Nonprofit Corp.
Admissions Requirements Minimum age 65; Medical examination.
Affiliation Society of Friends
Facilities Dining room; Physical therapy room; Activities room; Crafts room; Laundry room; Barber/Beauty shop; Library; Indoor swimming pool; Therapy pool.
Activities Arts & crafts; Games; Reading groups; Movies; Shopping trips; Social/Cultural gatherings.

HAMBURG

Hamburg Center
Old Rte 22, Hamburg, PA, 19526
(215) 562-6000
Admin Carl E Elser.
Licensure Intermediate care for mentally retarded. *Beds* 448. *Certified* Medicaid.
Owner Publicly owned.
Staff Physicians 4 (ft); RNs 46 (ft), 5 (pt); LPNs 15 (ft); Physical therapists 1 (ft); Recreational therapists 5 (ft); Occupational therapists 1 (ft); Speech therapists 7 (ft); Activities coordinators 1 (ft); Dietitians 2 (ft); Podiatrists 1 (ft).
Facilities Dining room; Physical therapy room; Activities room; Chapel; Barber/Beauty shop; Library.
Activities Arts & crafts; Movies; Shopping trips; Social/Cultural gatherings; Therapeutic.

Laurel Living Center
PO Box 3885, Rte 3, Hamburg, PA, 19526
(215) 562-2284
Admin Dennis Hill. *Medical Dir/Dir of Nursing* Daniel Lyons MD.
Licensure Skilled care; Intermediate care; Residential-personal care. *Beds* SNF 60; ICF 60; Personal 42. *Certified* Medicaid; Medicare.
Owner Nonprofit Corp (Adventist Health Sys-USA).
Admissions Requirements Minimum age 18; Medical examination.
Staff RNs 6 (ft), 13 (pt); LPNs 8 (ft), 8 (pt); Orderlies 1 (pt); Nurses aides 31 (ft), 37 (pt); Physical therapists 2 (ft), 3 (pt); Occupational therapists 1 (pt); Speech therapists 1 (pt); Activities coordinators 2 (ft), 2 (pt); Dietitians 1 (pt); Ophthalmologists 1 (pt).
Affiliation Seventh-Day Adventist
Facilities Dining room; Physical therapy room; Activities room; Crafts room; Laundry room; Barber/Beauty shop.
Activities Arts & crafts; Cards; Games; Prayer groups; Movies; Shopping trips; Social/Cultural gatherings; Cooking; Choir.

HANOVER

Hanover Hall
267 Frederick St, Hanover, PA, 17331
(717) 637-8937

Admin Christine F Lorah. *Medical Dir/Dir of Nursing* Dr James Miller; Anita Buie.
Licensure Skilled care; Intermediate care. *Beds* SNF 106; ICF 50. *Certified* Medicaid; Medicare.
Owner Proprietary Corp.
Admissions Requirements Medical examination & chest x-ray.
Staff RNs 5 (ft), 5 (pt); LPNs 12 (ft), 5 (pt); Nurses aides 30 (ft), 28 (pt); Physical therapists 1 (ft); Recreational therapists 1 (ft), 2 (pt).
Facilities Dining room; Physical therapy room; Activities room; Chapel; Laundry room; Barber/Beauty shop; Lounges.
Activities Arts & crafts; Cards; Games; Reading groups; Prayer groups; Movies; Shopping trips; Social/Cultural gatherings; Adopt-a-grandparent; Pet therapy; Church services.

Hillview House—Hanover General Hospital*
Highland Ave & Charles St, Hanover, PA, 17331
(717) 637-3711
Licensure Skilled care. *Beds* 41. *Certified* Medicaid; Medicare.
Owner Nonprofit Corp.

Homewood Retirement Center*
11 York St, Hanover, PA, 17331
(717) 637-4160
Medical Dir/Dir of Nursing Ralph E Bittinger MD.
Licensure Skilled care. *Beds* 39. *Certified* Medicaid.
Owner Nonprofit Corp (Homewood Retire Centers/UCC).
Admissions Requirements Minimum age 60; Medical examination.
Staff Physicians 1 (pt); RNs 2 (ft), 2 (pt); LPNs 3 (ft), 1 (pt); Nurses aides 11 (ft), 12 (pt); Physical therapists 1 (pt); Reality therapists 1 (pt); Activities coordinators 2 (ft); Dietitians 1 (pt); Dentists 1 (pt); Ophthalmologists 1 (pt); Podiatrists 1 (pt); Audiologists 1 (pt).
Affiliation Church of Christ
Facilities Dining room; Physical therapy room; Activities room; Chapel; Crafts room; Laundry room; Barber/Beauty shop; Library.
Activities Arts & crafts; Cards; Games; Reading groups; Prayer groups; Movies; Shopping trips; Social/Cultural gatherings.

HARLEYSVILLE

Peter Becker Community
Maple Ave & Yoder Rd, Harleysville, PA, 19438
(215) 256-9501
Admin Ronald R M Moyer. *Medical Dir/Dir of Nursing* Dennis L Moyer MD; Judith Trumboire RN DON.
Licensure Skilled care; Intermediate care; Retirement apartments; Personal care. *Beds* SNF 81; Retirement apts 120; Personal 35. *Certified* Medicaid; Medicare.
Owner Nonprofit Corp.
Admissions Requirements Minimum age 62; Medical examination.
Staff RNs 5 (ft), 10 (pt); LPNs 4 (ft), 8 (pt); Nurses aides 25 (ft), 28 (pt); Physical therapists 1 (pt); Recreational therapists 1 (pt); Occupational therapists 1 (pt); Speech therapists 1 (pt); Activities coordinators 2 (ft), 1 (pt); Dietitians 1 (ft); Dentists 3 (pt); Ophthalmologists 3 (pt); Podiatrists 1 (pt).
Affiliation Church of the Brethren
Facilities Dining room; Physical therapy room; Activities room; Chapel; Crafts room; Laundry room; Barber/Beauty shop; Library; Pharmacy.
Activities Arts & crafts; Cards; Games; Reading groups; Prayer groups; Movies; Shopping trips.

HARMONY

Evergreen Convalescent Home*
Box 189, Harmony, PA, 16037
(412) 452-6970
Licensure Skilled care. *Beds* 51. *Certified* Medicaid; Medicare.
Owner Proprietary Corp.

HARRISBURG

Aspin Center
1205 S 28th St, Harrisburg, PA, 17111
(717) 558-1155
Admin Joanne MacCollum. *Medical Dir/Dir of Nursing* Dr Anjana Popat.
Licensure Intermediate care for mentally retarded. *Beds* ICF/MR 22. *Certified* Medicaid.
Owner Nonprofit organization/foundation.
Admissions Requirements Medical examination.
Staff Physicians 1 (ft); RNs 3 (ft), 3 (pt); LPNs 1 (ft), 3 (pt); Orderlies 1 (ft); Nurses aides 17 (ft), 11 (pt); Physical therapists 1 (pt); Occupational therapists 1 (pt); Speech therapists 1 (pt); Dietitians 1 (pt); Dentists 1 (pt); Podiatrists 1 (pt); Dentist 1 (pt).
Facilities Dining room; Physical therapy room; Activities room; Laundry room.
Activities Arts & crafts; Games; Movies; Shopping trips; Social/Cultural gatherings.

Blue Ridge Haven East Convalescent Center Inc
3625 N Progress Ave, Harrisburg, PA, 17110
(717) 652-2345
Admin Nancy Merisko. *Medical Dir/Dir of Nursing* Maurice Lewis MD; Terri L Baker RN DON.
Licensure Skilled care; Intermediate care. *Beds* SNF 38; ICF 29. *Certified* Medicaid; Medicare.
Owner Proprietary Corp (Beverly Enterprises).
Admissions Requirements Minimum age 18; Medical examination; Physician's request.
Staff RNs 3 (ft), 4 (pt); LPNs 2 (ft), 4 (pt); Nurses aides 13 (ft), 19 (pt); Physical therapists 1 (pt); Speech therapists 1 (pt); Activities coordinators 1 (pt); Dietitians 1 (pt); Dentists 1 (pt); Ophthalmologists 1 (pt); Podiatrists 1 (pt).
Facilities Dining room; Activities room; Barber/Beauty shop.
Activities Arts & crafts; Cards; Games; Reading groups; Prayer groups; Movies; Shopping trips; Social/Cultural gatherings.

Dauphin Manor
1205 S 28th St, Harrisburg, PA, 17111
(717) 558-1000
Admin James H Hetrick. *Medical Dir/Dir of Nursing* S Sava Macut MD; D L Mengel RN DON.
Licensure Skilled care; Intermediate care. *Beds* SNF 48; ICF 376. *Certified* Medicaid; Medicare.
Owner Publicly owned.
Admissions Requirements Minimum age 18; Females only.
Staff Physicians 9 (pt); RNs 29 (ft), 10 (pt); LPNs 28 (ft), 3 (pt); Orderlies 22 (ft); Nurses aides 133 (ft), 4 (pt); Physical therapists 2 (pt); Reality therapists 1 (ft); Recreational therapists 5 (ft); Speech therapists 1 (pt); Activities coordinators 1 (pt); Dietitians 3 (ft); Ophthalmologists 1 (pt); Podiatrists 1 (pt); Audiologists 1 (pt); Patient Advocate 1 (ft).
Facilities Dining room; Physical therapy room; Activities room; Chapel; Crafts room; Laundry room; Barber/Beauty shop; Library.
Activities Arts & crafts; Cards; Games; Reading groups; Prayer groups; Movies; Shopping trips; Social/Cultural gatherings; Gardening; Resident newspaper/mail grams.

Homeland
1901 N 5th St, Harrisburg, PA, 17102
(717) 232-0883
Admin Mrs Isabelle C Smith. *Medical Dir/Dir of Nursing* Donald B Freeman MD; Julie Giroux RN.
Licensure Skilled care; Intermediate care; Residential/personal care. *Beds* SNF 60; 60. *Certified* Medicaid; Medicare.
Owner Nonprofit Corp.
Admissions Requirements Minimum age 65; Medical examination.
Staff RNs 6 (ft), 5 (pt); LPNs 3 (ft), 1 (pt); Nurses aides 25 (ft), 15 (pt); Physical therapists 1 (pt); Recreational therapists 2 (ft); Occupational therapists 1 (pt); Speech therapists 1 (pt); Activities coordinators 1 (pt); Dietitians 1 (pt); Ophthalmologists 1 (pt); Podiatrists 1 (pt).
Facilities Dining room; Activities room; Chapel; Crafts room; Laundry room; Barber/Beauty shop; Library; Enclosed courtyard.
Activities Arts & crafts; Cards; Games; Reading groups; Prayer groups; Movies; Shopping trips; Social/Cultural gatherings; Cooking groups.

Jewish Home of Greater Harrisburg*
4000 Linglestown Rd, Harrisburg, PA, 17112
(717) 657-0700
Medical Dir/Dir of Nursing Dr Maurice Lewis.
Licensure Skilled care. *Beds* 120. *Certified* Medicaid; Medicare.
Owner Nonprofit Corp.
Admissions Requirements Minimum age 18.
Staff RNs 6 (ft), 4 (pt); LPNs 3 (pt); Nurses aides 19 (ft), 17 (pt); Recreational therapists 2 (pt); Activities coordinators 1 (pt).
Affiliation Jewish
Facilities Dining room; Physical therapy room; Activities room; Chapel; Crafts room; Laundry room; Barber/Beauty shop.
Activities Arts & crafts; Cards; Games; Reading groups; Prayer groups; Movies; Shopping trips; Social/Cultural gatherings.

Leader Nursing Rehabilitation Center
800 King Russ Rd, Harrisburg, PA, 17109
(717) 657-1520
Admin Joanne Denise NHA. *Medical Dir/Dir of Nursing* Dr Peter Brier; Betty Bollinger DON.
Licensure Skilled care; Intermediate care. *Beds* SNF 52; ICF 188. *Certified* Medicaid; Medicare.
Owner Proprietary Corp (Manor Care).
Admissions Requirements Medical examination; Physician's request.
Facilities Dining room; Physical therapy room; Activities room; Chapel; Crafts room; Laundry room; Barber/Beauty shop; Lounges.
Activities Arts & crafts; Cards; Games; Reading groups; Prayer groups; Movies; Shopping trips; Social/Cultural gatherings.

Polyclinic Medical Center Ltc Unit
2601 N 3rd St, Bldg 56, Harrisburg, PA, 17105
(717) 782-4124
Licensure Skilled care. *Beds* 80.
Owner Proprietary Corp.

Susquehanna Center for Nursing & Rehabilitation
1909 N Front St, Harrisburg, PA, 17102
(717) 234-4660
Admin Frank M Caswell Jr. *Medical Dir/Dir of Nursing* Dr Lawrence Zimmerman; Betsy Garman RN DON.
Licensure Skilled care; Intermediate care; Special rehabilitation. *Certified* Medicaid; Medicare.
Owner Proprietary Corp Partnership.
Admissions Requirements Minimum age 18; Physician's request.

Staff Physicians 1 (pt); Physical therapists 1 (ft), 1 (pt); Recreational therapists 2 (ft); Occupational therapists 1 (pt); Speech therapists 1 (pt); Activities coordinators 1 (ft); Dietitians 1 (pt); Ophthalmologists 1 (pt); Podiatrists 1 (pt).
Facilities Dining room; Physical therapy room; Activities room; Crafts room; Laundry room; Barber/Beauty shop; TV room; Patio.
Activities Arts & crafts; Cards; Games; Reading groups; Prayer groups; Movies; Shopping trips; Social/Cultural gatherings; Sing-alongs; Church groups; River cruises.

Villa Teresa Nursing Home*
1051 Avilla Rd, Harrisburg, PA, 17109
(717) 652-5900
Licensure Skilled care; Intermediate care. *Beds* SNF 135; ICF 45. *Certified* Medicaid; Medicare.
Owner Nonprofit Corp.

HARRISVILLE

Bonetti Health Care Center Inc
Main St, Harrisville, PA, 16038
(412) 735-2655
Admin Larry G Bonetti. *Medical Dir/Dir of Nursing* A W Donan MD; Helen Rankin RN DON.
Licensure Skilled care. *Beds* SNF 103; ICF. *Certified* Medicaid; Medicare.
Owner Proprietary Corp.
Staff RNs 3 (ft), 3 (pt); LPNs 2 (ft); Orderlies 1 (ft); Nurses aides 37 (ft), 3 (pt); Physical therapists 1 (ft); Activities coordinators 2 (ft).
Facilities Dining room; Physical therapy room; Activities room; Crafts room; Laundry room; Barber/Beauty shop.
Activities Arts & crafts; Cards; Games; Reading groups; Prayer groups; Movies; Shopping trips; Social/Cultural gatherings; Bingo; Baseball games; Farm shows.

HASTINGS

Haida Manor
3rd Ave Extension, Hastings, PA, 16646
(814) 247-6578
Admin John R Fantini. *Medical Dir/Dir of Nursing* Joseph Sabo MD; Joan Anna RN DON.
Licensure Skilled care; Intermediate care. *Beds* SNF 26; ICF 76. *Certified* Medicaid; Medicare.
Owner Proprietary Corp (Beverly Enterprises).
Admissions Requirements Medical examination; Physician's request.
Staff Physicians 5 (pt); RNs 4 (ft), 4 (pt); LPNs 8 (ft), 8 (pt); Orderlies 2 (pt); Nurses aides 33 (ft), 13 (pt); Physical therapists 1 (pt); Speech therapists 1 (pt); Activities coordinators 1 (ft); Dietitians 1 (ft); Ophthalmologists 1 (pt); Podiatrists 1 (pt).
Facilities Dining room; Physical therapy room; Activities room; Crafts room; Laundry room; Barber/Beauty shop.
Activities Arts & crafts; Cards; Games; Reading groups; Prayer groups; Movies; Shopping trips; Social/Cultural gatherings.

HATBORO

Luther Woods Convalescent Center
313 County Line Rd, Hatboro, PA, 19040
(215) 675-5005
Admin Ellen G Tetor. *Medical Dir/Dir of Nursing* E Noble Wagner DO; Patricia Kiel RN DON.
Licensure Skilled care. *Beds* SNF 140. *Certified* Medicaid; Medicare.
Owner Privately owned.
Staff RNs 13 (ft), 4 (pt); LPNs 16 (ft), 7 (pt); Orderlies 7 (ft), 2 (pt); Nurses aides 40 (ft), 23 (pt); Physical therapists 3 (ft);

Recreational therapists 4 (ft); Occupational therapists 2 (ft); Speech therapists 2 (ft); Activities coordinators 1 (ft); Dietitians 1 (ft).
Affiliation Lutheran
Facilities Dining room; Physical therapy room; Activities room; Chapel; Laundry room; Barber/Beauty shop.
Activities Arts & crafts; Cards; Games; Prayer groups; Movies.

Orange Home Inc
2815 Byberry, Hatboro, PA, 19040
(215) 675-0103
Admin Michael R Boyle. *Medical Dir/Dir of Nursing* Dr Judy-Girard Ciminera, Dr Gregory Ciminera.
Licensure Intermediate care; Retirement home. *Beds* ICF 14; Retirement home 39. *Certified* Medicaid.
Owner Nonprofit Corp.
Admissions Requirements Minimum age 55; Medical examination; Physician's request.
Staff Physicians 2 (ft); RNs 2 (ft), 1 (pt); LPNs 1 (ft), 4 (pt); Nurses aides 4 (ft), 10 (pt); Recreational therapists 1 (pt); Speech therapists 1 (pt); Activities coordinators 1 (ft); Dietitians 3 (ft), 1 (pt); Ophthalmologists 1 (pt); Podiatrists 1 (pt); Pharmacist 1 (ft).
Facilities Dining room; Activities room; Chapel; Crafts room; Laundry room; Barber/Beauty shop.
Activities Arts & crafts; Games; Reading groups; Prayer groups; Movies; Shopping trips; Social/Cultural gatherings.

The White Billet
412 S York Rd, Hatboro, PA, 19040
(215) 675-2828
Admin Ellen Shraeger. *Medical Dir/Dir of Nursing* Dr R Bruce Lutz, Jr MD; Elaine Streeper DON.
Licensure Skilled care. *Beds* 36.
Owner Proprietary Corp (GraceCare, Inc).
Admissions Requirements Medical examination.
Staff RNs 1 (ft), 5 (pt); LPNs 1 (ft), 3 (pt); Nurses aides 8 (ft), 9 (pt); Recreational therapists 1 (pt).
Facilities Dining room; Activities room; Chapel; Crafts room; Barber/Beauty shop.
Activities Arts & crafts; Cards; Games; Reading groups; Movies; Social/Cultural gatherings.

HAVERTOWN

Haverford Nursing & Rehabilitation Center*
2050 Old West Chester Pike, Havertown, PA, 19083
(215) 449-8600
Licensure Skilled care. *Beds* 100. *Certified* Medicare.
Owner Proprietary Corp.

HAZELTON

St Luke Manor
1711 E Broad St, Hazelton, PA, 18201
(717) 455-8571
Admin Jerome G Panisak. *Medical Dir/Dir of Nursing* Theresa Warnagiris RN.
Licensure Skilled care; Intermediate care. *Beds* 104. *Certified* Medicaid; Medicare.
Owner Nonprofit Corp.
Admissions Requirements Physician's request.
Staff Physicians 8 (pt); RNs 5 (ft), 5 (pt); LPNs 15 (ft), 5 (pt); Nurses aides 25 (ft), 20 (pt); Physical therapists 1 (ft); Recreational therapists 1 (pt); Occupational therapists 1 (pt); Speech therapists 1 (pt); Activities coordinators 1 (ft); Dietitians 1 (pt); Dentists 1 (pt); Ophthalmologists 1 (pt).
Languages Slavic
Affiliation Lutheran

Facilities Dining room; Physical therapy room; Laundry room; Barber/Beauty shop; Alzheimer care unit.
Activities Arts & crafts; Cards; Games; Reading groups; Prayer groups; Movies; Shopping trips; Social/Cultural gatherings.

St Luke Pavilion
1000 Stacie Dr, Hazelton, PA, 18201
(717) 455-7578
Admin Rose F Somers. *Medical Dir/Dir of Nursing* Arthur L Koch DO; Jane L Tormay RN DON.
Licensure Skilled care; Intermediate care. *Beds* SNF 44; ICF 76. *Certified* Medicaid; Medicare.
Owner Nonprofit Corp.
Admissions Requirements Minimum age 16.
Staff RNs 4 (ft), 5 (pt); LPNs 7 (ft), 6 (pt); Nurses aides 20 (ft), 25 (pt); Physical therapists 1 (ft); Speech therapists 1 (pt); Activities coordinators 1 (ft).
Affiliation Lutheran
Facilities Dining room; Physical therapy room; Activities room; Chapel; Laundry room; Barber/Beauty shop.
Activities Arts & crafts; Games; Movies; Shopping trips.

Sparr Convalescent Home
PO Box 2307, Hazelton, PA, 18201
(717) 788-4178
Licensure Skilled care. *Beds* 27. *Certified* Medicaid.
Owner Proprietary Corp.

HELLERTOWN

Mary Ellen Convalescent Home Inc*
204 Leithsville Rd, Hellertown, PA, 18055
(215) 838-7901
Licensure Intermediate care. *Beds* 52. *Certified* Medicare.
Owner Proprietary Corp.
Admissions Requirements Medical examination.
Staff RNs 3 (ft), 3 (pt); LPNs 3 (ft), 3 (pt); Nurses aides 30 (ft); Physical therapists 1 (pt); Reality therapists 1 (pt); Recreational therapists 1 (pt); Occupational therapists 1 (pt); Speech therapists 1 (pt); Activities coordinators 1 (pt); Dietitians 1 (pt); Dentists 1 (pt); Ophthalmologists 1 (pt); Podiatrists 1 (pt); Audiologists 1 (pt).
Facilities Dining room; Activities room; Library.
Activities Arts & crafts; Cards; Games; Reading groups; Prayer groups; Shopping trips; Social/Cultural gatherings.

HERMITAGE

Hospitality Care Center of Hermitage Inc
3726 E State St, Hermitage, PA, 16148
(412) 342-5279
Admin Steven E Bible. *Medical Dir/Dir of Nursing* John Scmibli MD; Jean Puhl DON.
Licensure Skilled care; Intermediate care. *Beds* 28. *Certified* Medicaid; Medicare.
Owner Privately owned.
Admissions Requirements Medical examination; Physician's request.
Staff RNs 3 (ft), 1 (pt); LPNs 1 (ft), 4 (pt); Nurses aides 6 (ft), 4 (pt); Activities coordinators 1 (ft); Dietitians 1 (ft).
Facilities Dining room; Activities room; Laundry room.
Activities Arts & crafts; Cards; Games; Reading groups; Prayer groups; Movies.

John XXIII Home For Senior Citizens
2250 Shenango Valley Fwy, Hermitage, PA, 16148
(412) 981-3200
Admin Sr Phyllis Schleicher. *Medical Dir/Dir of Nursing* Dr Amanto D'Amore; Irene Walsh RN DON.

Licensure Skilled care; Intermediate care; Personal care. *Beds* 142. *Certified* Medicaid.
Owner Nonprofit Corp.
Admissions Requirements Minimum age 65; Medical examination.
Staff RNs 5 (ft), 3 (pt); LPNs 7 (ft), 6 (pt); Nurses aides 19 (ft), 44 (pt); Recreational therapists; Activities coordinators 1 (ft), 2 (pt).
Affiliation Roman Catholic
Facilities Dining room; Physical therapy room; Activities room; Chapel; Crafts room; Laundry room; Barber/Beauty shop.
Activities Arts & crafts; Cards; Games; Reading groups; Prayer groups; Movies; Shopping trips; Social/Cultural gatherings.

Nugent Convalescent Home, Inc
500 Clarksville Rd, Hermitage, PA, 16148
(412) 981-6610
Admin Lillian E Nugent. *Medical Dir/Dir of Nursing* Dr T Armour DO, Dr W McDowell DO, & Dr J Bolotin MD; Patricia Antus Acting DON.
Licensure Skilled care. *Beds* SNF 101. *Certified* Medicaid; Medicare.
Owner Proprietary Corp.
Admissions Requirements Minimum age 18; Medical examination.
Staff RNs 4 (ft), 5 (pt); LPNs 7 (ft), 5 (pt); Orderlies 7 (ft), 2 (pt); Nurses aides 16 (ft), 8 (pt); Activities coordinators 1 (ft).
Facilities Dining room; Physical therapy room; Activities room; Crafts room; Laundry room.
Activities Arts & crafts; Cards; Games; Reading groups; Prayer groups; Movies; Social/Cultural gatherings.

HERSHEY

The Alpine Health Care Center
PO Box 377, Hershey, PA, 17033
(717) 533-3351
Admin William Landis. *Medical Dir/Dir of Nursing* Dr William Heffley; Kathryn Light RN DON.
Licensure Skilled care; Intermediate care; Residential care. *Beds* 245. *Certified* Medicaid; Medicare.
Owner Proprietary Corp (Cambridge Grp Inc).
Admissions Requirements Medical examination.
Staff Physicians; RNs; LPNs; Nurses aides; Physical therapists; Recreational therapists; Speech therapists; Activities coordinators; Dietitians.
Facilities Dining room; Physical therapy room; Activities room; Chapel; Crafts room; Laundry room; Barber/Beauty shop; Ice cream parlour.
Activities Arts & crafts; Cards; Games; Reading groups; Prayer groups; Movies; Shopping trips; Social/Cultural gatherings.

HILLSDALE

Mountain View Manor
PO Box 138, Hillsdale, PA, 15746
(814) 743-6614 or (412) 254-2244
Admin Jeff Lee Rentner. *Medical Dir/Dir of Nursing* Dr Chester Kauffman; Marlie Smith RN.
Licensure Skilled care; Intermediate care. *Beds* SNF 25; ICF 64. *Certified* Medicaid; Medicare.
Owner Proprietary Corp (Beverly Enterprises).
Admissions Requirements Minimum age 21; Medical examination; Physician's request.
Staff Physicians 5 (pt); RNs 2 (ft), 3 (pt); LPNs 10 (ft), 8 (pt); Orderlies 1 (pt); Nurses aides 25 (ft), 20 (pt); Physical therapists 3 (pt); Recreational therapists 1 (pt); Speech therapists 3 (pt); Activities coordinators 1 (ft); Dietitians 1 (ft).

Facilities Dining room; Physical therapy room; Activities room; Chapel; Crafts room; Laundry room; Barber/Beauty shop; Library; Enclosed garden/courtyard.
Activities Arts & crafts; Cards; Games; Reading groups; Prayer groups; Movies; Shopping trips; Social/Cultural gatherings; Special holiday events & outings.

HOLLAND

Gloria Dei Village Health Care Center*
280 Middle Holland Rd, Holland, PA, 18966
(215) 322-6100
Licensure Skilled care. *Beds* 80. *Certified* Medicaid; Medicare.
Owner Nonprofit Corp.

St Joseph's Home for the Aged
1182 Holland Rd, Holland, PA, 18966
(215) 357-5511
Admin Sr Mary Lawrence. *Medical Dir/Dir of Nursing* Dr Thomas Kardish; Dorothy Wendland.
Licensure Skilled care; Personal care. *Beds* SNF 38; Personal 58. *Certified* Medicaid.
Owner Nonprofit Corp.
Admissions Requirements Minimum age 65; Medical examination; Physician's request.
Staff Physicians; RNs; LPNs; Nurses aides; Physical therapists; Recreational therapists; Occupational therapists; Speech therapists; Activities coordinators; Dietitians; Ophthalmologists; Podiatrists.
Languages Lithuanian
Affiliation Roman Catholic
Facilities Dining room; Physical therapy room; Activities room; Chapel; Crafts room; Laundry room; Barber/Beauty shop.
Activities Arts & crafts; Cards; Games; Prayer groups; Movies; Shopping trips; Tours.

HOLLIDAYSBURG

Allegheny Lutheran Home
916 Hickory St, Hollidaysburg, PA, 16648
(814) 696-3501
Admin Lois J Gutshall. *Medical Dir/Dir of Nursing* Dr Johannes DeKoning; Virginia Townsend RN DON.
Licensure Skilled care; Intermediate care. *Beds* SNF 22; ICF 67; Personal care 21. *Certified* Medicaid; Medicare.
Owner Nonprofit Corp.
Admissions Requirements Minimum age 65; Medical examination.
Staff Physicians 2 (pt); RNs 3 (ft), 6 (pt); LPNs 8 (ft), 8 (pt); Nurses aides 22 (ft), 10 (pt); Physical therapists 3 (ft); Recreational therapists 3 (ft), 1 (pt); Speech therapists 1 (pt); Activities coordinators 1 (ft); Dietitians 1 (ft); Podiatrists 1 (pt).
Affiliation Lutheran
Facilities Dining room; Physical therapy room; Activities room; Crafts room; Barber/Beauty shop.
Activities Arts & crafts; Cards; Games; Prayer groups; Movies; Shopping trips; Social/Cultural gatherings.

Garvey Manor*
Logan Blvd, Hollidaysburg, PA, 16648
(814) 695-5571
Medical Dir/Dir of Nursing Dr John Sheedy.
Licensure Skilled care; Intermediate care. *Beds* SNF 29; ICF 127. *Certified* Medicaid; Medicare.
Owner Nonprofit Corp.
Admissions Requirements Minimum age 65; Medical examination; Physician's request.
Staff RNs 6 (ft), 3 (pt); LPNs 13 (ft), 9 (pt); Nurses aides 56 (ft); Physical therapists 1 (pt); Reality therapists 1 (pt); Recreational therapists 1 (pt); Occupational therapists 1 (pt); Activities coordinators; Dietitians; Podiatrists.
Affiliation Roman Catholic

Facilities Dining room; Physical therapy room; Activities room; Chapel; Crafts room; Laundry room; Barber/Beauty shop; Library.
Activities Arts & crafts; Cards; Games; Reading groups; Prayer groups; Movies; Shopping trips; Social/Cultural gatherings.

Hollidaysburg Veterans Home
PO Box 319, Hollidaysburg, PA, 16648
(814) 696-5201
Admin David J Langguth MPA NHA. *Medical Dir/Dir of Nursing* Dr Edward Sarp; Mary Ellen Healy.
Licensure Skilled care; Intermediate care; Personal care; Domiciliary care. *Beds* 379. *Certified* Medicare.
Owner Publicly owned.
Admissions Requirements Veterans of Pennsylvania.
Staff Physicians 2 (ft), 3 (pt); RNs 45 (ft); LPNs 6 (ft); Nurses aides 20 (ft); Physical therapists 1 (ft); Recreational therapists 1 (ft); Occupational therapists 1 (pt); Activities coordinators 1 (ft); Dietitians 2 (ft).
Facilities Dining room; Physical therapy room; Activities room; Crafts room; Barber/Beauty shop; Library.
Activities Arts & crafts; Cards; Games; Movies; Shopping trips; Social/Cultural gatherings.

United Presbyterian Home of Hollidaysburg*
220 Newry St, Hollidaysburg, PA, 16648
(814) 695-5095
Medical Dir/Dir of Nursing K L Beers MD.
Licensure Skilled care. *Beds* 67. *Certified* Medicaid.
Owner Nonprofit Corp.
Staff Physicians 1 (pt); RNs 5 (ft), 5 (pt); LPNs 5 (ft), 6 (pt); Nurses aides 29 (ft), 8 (pt); Physical therapists 1 (pt); Occupational therapists 1 (pt); Activities coordinators 1 (ft).
Affiliation Presbyterian
Facilities Dining room; Physical therapy room; Chapel; Laundry room; Barber/Beauty shop.
Activities Arts & crafts; Games; Reading groups; Prayer groups; Shopping trips; Local groups provide entertainment.

HOMESTEAD

Willis Nursing Center
1800 West St, Homestead, PA, 15120
(412) 464-6220
Admin Edith Smith. *Medical Dir/Dir of Nursing* Shin H Choi MD.
Licensure Skilled care. *Beds* SNF 74. *Certified* Medicaid; Medicare.
Owner Nonprofit Corp.
Admissions Requirements Medical examination; Physician's request.
Staff Physical therapists 2 (ft); Recreational therapists 1 (ft); Occupational therapists 1 (ft); Speech therapists 1 (ft); Dietitians 1 (ft); Dentists 2 (ft); Ophthalmologists 1 (ft); Podiatrists 1 (ft).
Facilities Dining room; Physical therapy room; Activities room; Chapel; Barber/Beauty shop; Library.
Activities Arts & crafts; Cards; Games; Reading groups; Prayer groups; Movies; Social/Cultural gatherings; Weekly church services.

HONESDALE

Ellen Memorial Health Care Center
PO Box 1147, Rte 1, Honesdale, PA, 18431
(717) 253-5690
Medical Dir/Dir of Nursing Young Woo Lee MD; Marilyn L Turner RN.
Licensure Skilled care; Intermediate care. *Beds* SNF 80; ICF 49. *Certified* Medicaid; Medicare.
Owner Proprietary Corp.

Admissions Requirements Physician's request.
Staff Physicians 1 (pt); RNs 5 (ft), 4 (pt);
Occupational therapists 3 (pt); Speech
therapists 1 (pt); Activities coordinators 2
(ft); Dietitians 1 (pt).
Facilities Dining room; Physical therapy
room; Activities room; Chapel; Crafts room;
Laundry room; Barber/Beauty shop.
Activities Arts & crafts; Cards; Games;
Reading groups; Prayer groups; Movies;
Social/Cultural gatherings; Community plays;
Concerts; Circus.

Peck's Convalescent Home
814 Court St, Honesdale, PA, 18431
(717) 253-0390
Admin Norma Nonnenmacher.
Licensure Personal care. *Beds* 27.
Owner Privately owned.
Admissions Requirements Physician's request.
Staff RNs 2 (pt); LPNs 1 (ft), 2 (pt); Nurses
aides 6 (ft), 3 (pt); Occupational therapists 1
(pt); Activities coordinators 1 (ft); Dietitians
1 (pt).
Facilities Dining room; Activities room;
Laundry room.
Activities Arts & crafts; Cards; Games;
Reading groups; Prayer groups; Movies;
Social/Cultural gatherings.

**Wayne County Memorial Hospital Skilled
Nursing Facility**
Park & West Sts, Honesdale, PA, 18431
(717) 253-1300
Admin John M Sherwood. *Medical Dir/Dir of
Nursing* William F Davis MD; Ellen Malloy
RN.
Licensure Skilled care. *Beds* SNF 28. *Certified*
Medicaid; Medicare.
Owner Nonprofit Corp.
Admissions Requirements Medical
examination; Physician's request.
Staff RNs; LPNs; Orderlies; Nurses aides.
Facilities Dining room; Activities room;
Chapel; Crafts room.
Activities Arts & crafts; Cards; Games;
Reading groups; Prayer groups; Movies;
Shopping trips; Social/Cultural gatherings.

HONEYBROOK

Hickory House Nursing Home Inc
Rte 3, Box 84, Honeybrook, PA, 19344
(215) 273-2915
Licensure Skilled care; Intermediate care. *Beds*
SNF 70; ICF 30. *Certified* Medicaid;
Medicare.
Owner Proprietary Corp.

Tel Hai Retirement Community
PO Box 190, Beaver Dam Road, Honeybrook,
PA, 19344
(215) 273-3149
Admin LeRoy Petersheim. *Medical Dir/Dir of
Nursing* Dr Richard Smith; Anna Skiles.
Licensure Skilled care; Continuous care
retirement community; Adult day care;
Personal care. *Beds* SNF 130; Adult Day
care 15 Individual living 118 Personal 126.
Certified Medicaid; Medicare.
Owner Nonprofit Corp.
Admissions Requirements Medical
examination.
Staff Physicians 15 (pt); RNs 8 (ft), 7 (pt);
LPNs 6 (ft), 3 (pt); Nurses aides 42 (ft), 21
(pt); Physical therapists 3 (pt); Recreational
therapists 1 (pt); Occupational therapists 1
(pt); Speech therapists 1 (pt); Activities
coordinators 3 (ft); Dietitians 1 (ft); Dentists
1 (pt); Ophthalmologists 1 (pt); Podiatrists 1
(pt); Chaplain.
Affiliation Mennonite
Facilities Dining room; Physical therapy
room; Activities room; Chapel; Crafts room;
Laundry room; Barber/Beauty shop; Library.
Activities Arts & crafts; Cards; Games;
Reading groups; Prayer groups; Movies;
Shopping trips; Social/Cultural gatherings.

HUNTINGDON

Huntingdon County Nursing Home
Warm Springs Ave, Huntingdon, PA, 16652
(814) 643-4210
Admin Sr M Constance Loeffler. *Medical Dir/
Dir of Nursing* Dr Thomas Meloy MD; Vera
M Patton DON.
Licensure Skilled care; Intermediate care. *Beds*
SNF 15; ICF 78. *Certified* Medicaid;
Medicare.
Owner Publicly owned.
Admissions Requirements Medical
examination; Physician's request.
Staff RNs 4 (ft), 4 (pt); LPNs 6 (ft), 6 (pt);
Orderlies 3 (ft), 3 (pt); Nurses aides 19 (ft),
19 (pt).
Facilities Dining room; Activities room;
Crafts room; Laundry room; Barber/Beauty
shop.
Activities Arts & crafts; Cards; Games; Prayer
groups; Movies; Social/Cultural gatherings.

IMMACULATA

Camilla Hall*
Immaculata, PA, 19345
(215) 644-1152
Licensure Skilled care. *Beds* 150.
Owner Nonprofit Corp.

INDIANA

Cameron Manor Inc
1515 Wayne Ave, Indiana, PA, 15701
(412) 349-5300
Admin Rita R Immel RN. *Medical Dir/Dir of
Nursing* Dr Daniel Loisel; Patricia Drak
DON.
Licensure Skilled care; Intermediate care;
Alzheimer's unit (ICF). *Beds* SNF 25; ICF
93. *Certified* Medicaid; Medicare.
Owner Privately owned.
Admissions Requirements Medical
examination; Physician's request.
Staff Physicians; RNs 4 (ft); LPNs 17 (ft);
Orderlies 1 (ft); Nurses aides 40 (ft);
Physical therapists 1 (ft); Reality therapists;
Recreational therapists 2 (ft); Occupational
therapists 1 (ft); Speech therapists 1 (ft);
Activities coordinators 1 (ft).
Languages Spanish, Italian, Polish, Slavic
Facilities Dining room; Physical therapy
room; Activities room; Crafts room; Laundry
room; Barber/Beauty shop; TV room/lounge;
2 indoor courtyards.
Activities Arts & crafts; Cards; Games;
Reading groups; Prayer groups; Movies;
Shopping trips; Social/Cultural gatherings.

Indian Haven Nursing Home
PO Box 1377, 1671 Saltsburg Ave, Indiana,
PA, 15701
(412) 465-3900
Admin Ruth McCurdy RN. *Medical Dir/Dir of
Nursing* Dr William C Vernocy; Jean A
Zbur RN.
Licensure Skilled care; Intermediate care. *Beds*
SNF 31; ICF 94. *Certified* Medicaid.
Owner Publicly owned.
Admissions Requirements Medical
examination; Physician's request.
Staff Physicians; RNs 8 (ft), 3 (pt); LPNs 13
(ft), 3 (pt); Orderlies 1 (ft); Nurses aides 58
(ft), 2 (pt); Recreational therapists 2 (ft);
Dietitians 1 (ft).
Facilities Dining room; Physical therapy
room; Activities room; Chapel; Barber/
Beauty shop.
Activities Arts & crafts; Games; Reading
groups; Prayer groups; Movies; Shopping
trips.

Indiana Presbyterian Homes*
1155 Indian Springs Rd, Indiana, PA, 15701
(412) 349-4870

Licensure Skilled care; Intermediate care. *Beds*
SNF 60; ICF 60. *Certified* Medicaid.
Owner Nonprofit Corp.
Affiliation Presbyterian

Scenery Hill Manor Inc*
Rte 5, Lions Health Camp Rd, Indiana, PA,
15701
(412) 463-7600
Licensure Skilled care. *Beds* 58. *Certified*
Medicaid; Medicare.
Owner Proprietary Corp.

JEANNETTE

Trinity Haven
206 N 1st St, Jeannette, PA, 15644
(412) 527-1509
Licensure Residential/Personal. *Beds*
Residential/Personal 27. *Certified* State
licensed.
Owner Proprietary Corp.
Admissions Requirements Minimum age 21.
Staff Orderlies 1 (ft), 1 (pt); Nurses aides 6
(ft), 6 (pt); Speech therapists 1 (ft); Activities
coordinators 1 (ft).
Languages Italian, Polish, Spanish
Facilities Dining room; Physical therapy
room; Activities room; Crafts room; Laundry
room; Sunroom.
Activities Arts & crafts; Cards; Games;
Reading groups; Prayer groups; Picnics.

JERSEY SHORE

Leader Nursing & Rehabilitation Center
Thompson Street & Kerr Ave, Jersey Shore,
PA, 17740
(717) 398-4747
Admin Charles J Miller. *Medical Dir/Dir of
Nursing* Lloyd R Forcey MD; Lois Hensler.
Licensure Skilled care; Intermediate care. *Beds*
SNF 27; ICF 93. *Certified* Medicaid;
Medicare.
Owner Proprietary Corp (Manor Care).
Admissions Requirements Medical
examination; Physician's request.
Staff Physicians 8 (pt); RNs 7 (ft), 3 (pt);
LPNs 7 (ft), 3 (pt); Nurses aides 60 (ft), 20
(pt); Speech therapists 1 (pt); Activities
coordinators 1 (ft), 1 (pt); Dietitians 1 (ft);
Ophthalmologists 1 (pt); Podiatrists 1 (pt).
Facilities Dining room; Activities room;
Chapel; Laundry room; Barber/Beauty shop;
Library.
Activities Arts & crafts; Cards; Games;
Reading groups; Prayer groups; Movies;
Shopping trips; Social/Cultural gatherings.

JOHNSTOWN

Allegheny Lutheran Home
807 Goucher St, Johnstown, PA, 15905-2999
(814) 255-6844
Admin Paula Schechter. *Medical Dir/Dir of
Nursing* Victor Bantly MD; Dorothy
Charney RN DON.
Licensure Skilled care; Intermediate care;
Personal care; Cottages. *Beds* SNF 40; ICF
29; Personal care 38; cottages 18. *Certified*
Medicaid; Medicare.
Owner Nonprofit Corp.
Admissions Requirements Minimum age 65;
Medical examination.
Staff RNs 3 (ft), 4 (pt); LPNs 5 (ft), 4 (pt);
Nurses aides 16 (ft), 12 (pt); Activities
coordinators 1 (ft); Audiologists 38 (ft), 19
(pt).
Affiliation Lutheran
Facilities Dining room; Physical therapy
room; Activities room; Chapel; Crafts room;
Laundry room; Barber/Beauty shop; Library.

Activities Arts & crafts; Cards; Games; Reading groups; Prayer groups; Movies; Shopping trips; Social/Cultural gatherings; Remotivation; Reality orientation; Special interest groups; Cooking.

Hiram G Andrews Center*
727 Goucher St, Johnstown, PA, 15905
(814) 225-5881
Licensure Intermediate care. *Beds* 61. *Certified* Medicare.
Owner Nonprofit Corp.

Arbutus Park Manor Inc*
207 Ottawa St, Johnstown, PA, 15904
(814) 266-3559
Licensure Intermediate care. *Beds* 102. *Certified* Medicaid.
Owner Nonprofit Corp.

Mercy Hospital Nursing Care Center
1017 Franklin St, Johnstown, PA, 15905
(814) 533-1934
Admin Wanda Tarsovich. *Medical Dir/Dir of Nursing* Richard Stadtmiller MD; Gertrude Fiscus RN DON.
Licensure Skilled care. *Beds* SNF 75. *Certified* Medicaid; Medicare.
Owner Nonprofit Corp.
Admissions Requirements Medical examination.
Staff Physicians 3 (pt); RNs 5 (ft), 2 (pt); LPNs 5 (ft), 6 (pt); Nurses aides 18 (ft), 1 (pt); Physical therapists 1 (pt); Reality therapists 1 (ft); Recreational therapists 1 (ft); Occupational therapists 2 (pt); Speech therapists 1 (pt); Activities coordinators 1 (ft); Dietitians 1 (pt).
Facilities Dining room; Physical therapy room; Activities room; Laundry room.
Activities Arts & crafts; Cards; Games; Reading groups; Prayer groups; Movies; Bowling; Bingo.

Presbyterian Home—Johnstown
787 Goucher St, Johnstown, PA, 15905
(814) 255-5539
Admin Leah H Williams. *Medical Dir/Dir of Nursing* Dr Richard Cartwright.
Licensure Intermediate care. *Beds* 23. *Certified* Medicaid.
Owner Nonprofit Corp.
Admissions Requirements Minimum age 62; Medical examination.
Staff RNs 1 (ft); LPNs 7 (ft); Nurses aides 13 (ft); Activities coordinators 1 (ft); Dietitians 1 (pt).
Affiliation Presbyterian
Facilities Dining room; Activities room; Chapel; Laundry room; Barber/Beauty shop; Library.
Activities Games; Reading groups; Prayer groups; Movies; Shopping trips.

KANE

Lutheran Home at Kane
Clay St Ext, Kane, PA, 16735
(814) 837-6706
Admin Linda D Carlson. *Medical Dir/Dir of Nursing* C R Bentz MD.
Licensure Skilled care; Intermediate care. *Beds* SNF 33; ICF 57. *Certified* Medicaid.
Owner Nonprofit Corp.
Admissions Requirements Medical examination.
Staff RNs; LPNs; Nurses aides; Physical therapists; Activities coordinators; Dietitians.
Affiliation Lutheran
Facilities Dining room; Physical therapy room; Chapel; Laundry room; Barber/Beauty shop.
Activities Arts & crafts; Games; Prayer groups; Movies.

KENNETT SQUARE

Linden Hall Nursing Home
147 W State St, Kennett Square, PA, 19348
(215) 444-0741
Admin Mary Lou Hovde. *Medical Dir/Dir of Nursing* Clifton M Durning MD.
Licensure Skilled care. *Beds* SNF 16.
Owner Nonprofit Corp.
Admissions Requirements Medical examination; Physician's request.
Staff RNs 1 (ft), 5 (pt); LPNs 1 (ft), 2 (pt); Nurses aides 8 (ft); Activities coordinators 1 (pt).
Affiliation Society of Friends
Facilities Dining room; Activities room; Crafts room; Barber/Beauty shop.
Activities Arts & crafts; Cards; Games; Reading groups; Movies; Social/Cultural gatherings.

KING OF PRUSSIA

Fair Villa Nursing Home
PO Box 1030, King of Prussia, PA, 19406-0477
(215) 275-6799
Medical Dir/Dir of Nursing Dr Yu Jen Tsai.
Licensure Skilled care. *Beds* 57. *Certified* Medicaid.
Owner Proprietary Corp.
Admissions Requirements Medical examination; Physician's request.
Staff Physicians 10 (pt); RNs 1 (ft), 1 (pt); LPNs 3 (ft), 1 (pt); Nurses aides 31 (ft), 14 (pt); Physical therapists 1 (pt); Speech therapists 1 (pt); Activities coordinators 1 (ft); Dietitians 1 (pt); Dentists 1 (pt); Podiatrists 1 (pt).
Facilities Dining room; Activities room; Crafts room; Laundry room; Library.
Activities Arts & crafts; Cards; Games; Reading groups; Prayer groups; Movies; Shopping trips; Social/Cultural gatherings.

KINGSTON

Leader Nursing & Rehabilitation Center—East*
200 2nd Ave, Kingston, PA, 18704
(717) 299-9315
Licensure Skilled care; Intermediate care. *Beds* SNF 160; ICF 20. *Certified* Medicaid; Medicare.
Owner Proprietary Corp (Manor Care).

Leader Nursing & Rehabilitation Center—West*
Wyoming Ave & Dorrance St, Kingston, PA, 18704
(717) 288-5496
Admin Cathy Nally. *Medical Dir/Dir of Nursing* Richard Crompton MD; Patricia Toole RN DON.
Licensure Skilled care. *Beds* 153. *Certified* Medicaid; Medicare.
Owner Proprietary Corp (Manor Care).
Staff RNs 8 (ft), 2 (pt); LPNs 5 (ft), 7 (pt); Nurses aides 44 (ft), 11 (pt); Physical therapists 1 (ft); Recreational therapists 3 (pt); Occupational therapists 1 (pt); Speech therapists 1 (pt); Activities coordinators 1 (ft).
Facilities Dining room; Physical therapy room; Activities room; Chapel; Laundry room; Barber/Beauty shop; Library.
Activities Arts & crafts; Cards; Games; Reading groups; Prayer groups; Movies; Shopping trips; Social/Cultural gatherings.

KITTANNING

Armstrong County Health Center*
Kittanning, PA, 16201
(412) 548-2222
Admin James R Bender. *Medical Dir/Dir of Nursing* Dr Cyrus Slease.

Licensure Skilled care. *Beds* 126. *Certified* Medicaid.
Owner Nonprofit Corp.
Admissions Requirements Medical examination; Physician's request.
Staff Physicians 1 (ft), 1 (pt); RNs 11 (ft), 3 (pt); LPNs 16 (ft), 4 (pt); Orderlies 5 (ft); Nurses aides 57 (ft), 8 (pt); Physical therapists 1 (pt); Speech therapists 1 (pt); Activities coordinators 1 (ft); Dietitians 1 (pt); Dentists 1 (pt); Ophthalmologists 1 (pt); Podiatrists 1 (pt).
Facilities Dining room; Physical therapy room; Activities room; Crafts room; Laundry room; Barber/Beauty shop.
Activities Arts & crafts; Cards; Games; Reading groups; Prayer groups; Movies; Shopping trips; Social/Cultural gatherings.

Wesley Manor Health Care Center Inc*
Rte 1, Box 27C, Rte 422, Kittanning, PA, 16201
(412) 545-2273
Admin Carol A Rohrabaugh. *Medical Dir/Dir of Nursing* Jeffrey Minteer MD.
Licensure Skilled care; Intermediate care. *Beds* SNF 60; ICF 60. *Certified* Medicaid; Medicare.
Owner Proprietary Corp.
Admissions Requirements Medical examination.
Staff Physicians 2 (pt); RNs 5 (ft), 7 (pt); LPNs 5 (ft), 11 (pt); Orderlies 2 (pt); Nurses aides 28 (ft), 20 (pt); Physical therapists; Speech therapists; Activities coordinators 1 (ft); Dietitians 1 (pt); Dentists; Podiatrists.
Facilities Dining room; Physical therapy room; Activities room; Crafts room; Laundry room; Barber/Beauty shop.
Activities Arts & crafts; Cards; Games; Prayer groups; Movies; Social/Cultural gatherings.

KUTZTOWN

Kutztown Manor Inc
120 Trexler Ave, Kutztown, PA, 19530
(215) 683-6220
Admin Jessica E Palazzi. *Medical Dir/Dir of Nursing* Cheryl A Magee RN DON.
Licensure Skilled care; Intermediate care. *Beds* SNF 65; ICF 65. *Certified* Medicaid; Medicare.
Owner Proprietary Corp.
Admissions Requirements Medical examination.
Staff RNs 9 (ft), 4 (pt); LPNs 10 (ft), 1 (pt); Orderlies 2 (ft), 1 (pt); Nurses aides 28 (ft), 29 (pt); Physical therapists 1 (ft); Occupational therapists 1 (ft); Speech therapists 1 (ft); Activities coordinators 1 (ft); Dietitians 1 (ft).
Languages Pennsylvania Dutch
Facilities Dining room; Physical therapy room; Activities room; Crafts room; Laundry room; Barber/Beauty shop.
Activities Arts & crafts; Cards; Games; Reading groups; Prayer groups; Movies; Shopping trips; Social/Cultural gatherings; Garden group; Cooking.

LAFAYETTE HILL

Masonic Home of Pennsylvania
801 Ridge Pike, Lafayette Hill, PA, 19444
(215) 825-6100
Admin Kenneth R Mills.
Licensure Skilled care; Intermediate care; Personal care. *Beds* SNF 23; ICF 52; Personal 94. *Certified* Medicaid.
Owner Nonprofit Corp.
Admissions Requirements Minimum age 75; Medical examination.
Staff Physicians 2 (pt); RNs 9 (ft); LPNs 4 (ft); Nurses aides 31 (ft), 10 (pt); Physical therapists 1 (pt); Recreational therapists 2 (ft); Occupational therapists 1 (pt); Ophthalmologists 1 (pt).

Affiliation Masons
Facilities Dining room; Physical therapy room; Activities room; Chapel; Crafts room; Laundry room; Barber/Beauty shop; Library.
Activities Arts & crafts; Cards; Games; Movies; Shopping trips; Social/Cultural gatherings.

LAKE ARIEL

Julia Ribaudo Home*
297-298 Center Dr, Lake Ariel, PA, 18436
(717) 937-4381
Licensure Skilled care. *Beds* 100. *Certified* Medicaid; Medicare.
Owner Proprietary Corp.

LANCASTER

Brethren Village
3001 Lititz Pike, Lancaster, PA, 17601
(717) 569-2657
Admin Gary N Clouser. *Medical Dir/Dir of Nursing* Dr Eugene Engle; Linda Sorrentino.
Licensure Skilled care; Intermediate care; Residential care. *Beds* SNF 67; ICF 81; Residential 450. *Certified* Medicaid; Medicare.
Owner Nonprofit Corp.
Admissions Requirements Minimum age 62; Medical examination.
Staff RNs 12 (ft), 4 (pt); LPNs 16 (ft), 9 (pt); Nurses aides 46 (ft), 27 (pt); Physical therapists 1 (ft); Activities coordinators 1 (ft); Dietitians 1 (ft).
Affiliation Church of the Brethren
Facilities Dining room; Physical therapy room; Activities room; Chapel; Crafts room; Laundry room; Barber/Beauty shop; Library.
Activities Arts & crafts; Cards; Games; Reading groups; Prayer groups; Movies; Shopping trips; Social/Cultural gatherings.

Calvary Fellowship Home Inc
502 Elizabeth Dr, Lancaster, PA, 17601
(717) 393-0711
Admin George L Baumgartner. *Medical Dir/Dir of Nursing* Richard Moncrief MD; Elizabeth Greider DON.
Licensure Skilled care. *Beds* SNF 45. *Certified* Medicaid; Medicare.
Owner Nonprofit Corp.
Admissions Requirements Medical examination.
Staff RNs 2 (ft), 3 (pt); LPNs 1 (ft), 1 (pt); Nurses aides 17 (ft), 7 (pt); Activities coordinators 1 (ft); Dietitians 1 (pt).
Facilities Dining room; Physical therapy room; Activities room; Chapel; Crafts room; Laundry room; Barber/Beauty shop; Library.
Activities Arts & crafts; Games; Prayer groups; Movies.

Conestoga View*
900 E King St, Lancaster, PA, 17602
(717) 299-7854
Licensure Skilled care; Intermediate care. *Beds* SNF 132; ICF 320. *Certified* Medicaid.
Owner Nonprofit Corp.

Duke Convalescent Residence
425 N Duke St, Lancaster, PA, 17602
(717) 397-4281
Admin Joan Schwartz. *Medical Dir/Dir of Nursing* James Wolf; Glenn Thomas RN DON.
Licensure Skilled care. *Beds* 139. *Certified* Medicaid; Medicare.
Owner Proprietary Corp (Beverly Enterprises).
Admissions Requirements Medical examination.
Staff RNs 5 (ft); LPNs 8 (ft), 4 (pt); Orderlies 3 (ft); Nurses aides 27 (ft), 6 (pt); Physical therapists 1 (ft); Occupational therapists 1 (pt); Speech therapists 1 (pt); Activities coordinators 1 (ft); Dietitians 1 (ft).

Facilities Dining room; Physical therapy room; Activities room; Crafts room; Laundry room; Barber/Beauty shop.
Activities Arts & crafts; Cards; Games; Prayer groups; Movies; Shopping trips; Social/Cultural gatherings.

Hamilton Arms of Pennsylvania*
336 S West End Ave, Lancaster, PA, 17603
(717) 393-0419
Licensure Skilled care. *Beds* 56. *Certified* Medicaid; Medicare.
Owner Proprietary Corp (Geriatric & Medical Centers).

Lancashire Hall Inc*
2829 Lititz Pike, Lancaster, PA, 17601
(717) 569-3211
Licensure Skilled care; Intermediate care. *Beds* SNF 96; ICF 96. *Certified* Medicaid; Medicare.
Owner Proprietary Corp.

Henry G Long Asylum*
200 N West End Ave, Lancaster, PA, 17603
(717) 397-3926
Medical Dir/Dir of Nursing Peter J Altiman MD.
Licensure Skilled care. *Beds* 16.
Owner Nonprofit Corp.
Admissions Requirements Minimum age 45; Medical examination.
Staff Physicians 4 (ft); RNs 3 (ft), 10 (pt); LPNs 1 (ft), 1 (pt); Nurses aides 5 (ft), 2 (pt); Physical therapists 1 (pt); Reality therapists 1 (pt); Recreational therapists 1 (pt); Occupational therapists 1 (pt); Activities coordinators 1 (pt); Dietitians 1 (pt); Dentists 1 (pt); Ophthalmologists 1 (pt); Podiatrists 1 (pt).
Facilities Dining room; Physical therapy room; Activities room; Chapel; Crafts room; Laundry room; Barber/Beauty shop; Library.
Activities Cards; Games; Shopping trips.

Mennonite Home
1520 Old Harrisburg Pike, Lancaster, PA, 17601
(717) 393-1301
Admin Paul G Leaman. *Medical Dir/Dir of Nursing* Dr Harry H Hoffman; Charlotte Yoder.
Licensure Skilled care; Intermediate care; Personal care. *Beds* SNF 92; ICF 52; Personal 189. *Certified* Medicaid; Medicare.
Owner Nonprofit Corp.
Admissions Requirements Minimum age 65; Medical examination.
Staff Physicians 3 (pt); RNs 3 (ft), 4 (pt); LPNs 28 (ft), 12 (pt); Orderlies 1 (pt); Nurses aides 20 (ft), 26 (pt); Physical therapists 1 (ft); Recreational therapists 4 (ft), 1 (pt); Activities coordinators 1 (pt); Dietitians 1 (ft); Administrative, dietary, housekeeping, laundry and maintenance staff 46 (ft), 36 (pt).
Affiliation Mennonite
Facilities Dining room; Physical therapy room; Activities room; Chapel; Crafts room; Laundry room; Barber/Beauty shop; Library; Therapy pool.
Activities Arts & crafts; Cards; Games; Reading groups; Prayer groups; Shopping trips; Social/Cultural gatherings.

Village Vista Skilled Nursing Facility*
1941 Benmar Dr, Lancaster, PA, 17603
(717) 397-5583
Medical Dir/Dir of Nursing J D Kemrer MD.
Licensure Skilled care. *Beds* 31. *Certified* Medicaid.
Owner Proprietary Corp.
Staff RNs 1 (ft), 3 (pt); LPNs 4 (ft), 1 (pt); Nurses aides 6 (ft), 9 (pt); Physical therapists; Activities coordinators 1 (pt); Dietitians.

Facilities Dining room; Activities room; Laundry room.
Activities Arts & crafts; Games; Reading groups; Prayer groups.

Whitehall Nursing & Convalescent Center*
100 Abbeyville Rd, Lancaster, PA, 17603
(717) 397-4261
Licensure Skilled care; Intermediate care. *Beds* SNF 145; ICF 30. *Certified* Medicaid; Medicare.
Owner Proprietary Corp (Manor Care).

LANDISVILLE

Community Services Inc-Main*
180 Main St, Landisville, PA, 17538
(717) 898-6323
Licensure Intermediate care for mentally retarded. *Beds* 6. *Certified* Medicaid.
Owner Proprietary Corp.

Community Services Inc-Stanley*
180 Stanley Rd, Landisville, PA, 17538
(717) 569-5970
Licensure Intermediate care for mentally retarded. *Beds* 4. *Certified* Medicaid.
Owner Nonprofit Corp.

LANGHORNE

Attleboro Nursing & Rehabilitation Center
300 E Winchester Ave, Langhorne, PA, 19047
(215) 757-3739
Admin Henry R Gureck. *Medical Dir/Dir of Nursing* Frank Madden MD; Judy Wagner RN.
Licensure Skilled care; Intermediate care; Rehabilitative. *Beds* SNF 60; ICF 120. *Certified* Medicaid; Medicare.
Owner Proprietary Corp.
Admissions Requirements Minimum age 18.
Staff RNs; LPNs; Nurses aides; Physical therapists 1 (ft); Recreational therapists 1 (ft); Activities coordinators 1 (ft); Dietitians 1 (ft).
Facilities Dining room; Physical therapy room; Activities room; Crafts room; Laundry room; Barber/Beauty shop; Library.
Activities Arts & crafts; Cards; Games; Reading groups; Movies; Shopping trips; Social/Cultural gatherings.

Crestview North Nursing & Rehabilitation Center*
262 Toll Gate Rd, Langhorne, PA, 19047
(215) 968-4650
Medical Dir/Dir of Nursing Robert Kane DO.
Licensure Skilled care. *Beds* 131. *Certified* Medicaid; Medicare.
Owner Proprietary Corp (Geriatric & Medical Centers).
Admissions Requirements Medical examination.
Staff Physicians 8 (ft); RNs 5 (ft), 6 (pt); LPNs 9 (ft), 7 (pt); Orderlies 2 (ft), 1 (pt); Nurses aides 37 (ft), 15 (pt); Physical therapists 1 (ft); Occupational therapists 1 (pt); Speech therapists 1 (ft); Activities coordinators 2 (ft), 1 (pt); Dietitians 1 (ft); Dentists 1 (ft); Ophthalmologists 1 (ft); Podiatrists 1 (ft).
Facilities Physical therapy room; Laundry room; Barber/Beauty shop; Library; Lounges.
Activities Arts & crafts; Cards; Games; Reading groups; Prayer groups; Movies; Shopping trips; Social/Cultural gatherings.

Langhorne Gardens Nursing Center
350 Manor Ave, Langhorne, PA, 19047
(215) 757-7667
Admin Ethel J Wiser. *Medical Dir/Dir of Nursing* Arnold Goldstein MD; Brenda Barats RN DON.
Licensure Skilled care; Intermediate care. *Beds* SNF 60; ICF 60. *Certified* Medicaid; Medicare.

Owner Proprietary Corp (Unicare).
Admissions Requirements Minimum age 16; Medical examination.
Staff Physicians 16 (pt); RNs 8 (pt); LPNs 4 (ft), 6 (pt); Orderlies 1 (ft); Nurses aides 23 (ft), 19 (pt); Physical therapists 1 (pt); Recreational therapists 1 (ft), 1 (pt); Speech therapists 1 (pt); Dietitians 1 (pt); Podiatrists 1 (pt).
Facilities Dining room; Physical therapy room; Activities room; Chapel; Crafts room; Laundry room; Barber/Beauty shop; Library.
Activities Arts & crafts; Games; Prayer groups; Movies; Shopping trips.

LANSDALE

Dock Terrace
275 Dock Dr, Lansdale, PA, 19446
(215) 362-5757
Admin Marcus A Clemens. *Medical Dir/Dir of Nursing* Judy Truscott RN.
Licensure Skilled care; Intermediate care. *Beds* SNF 72; ICF. *Certified* Medicaid; Medicare.
Owner Nonprofit organization/foundation.
Staff RNs 4 (ft), 7 (pt); LPNs 1 (ft); Nurses aides 26 (ft); Physical therapists 1 (pt); Occupational therapists 1 (pt); Speech therapists 1 (pt); Activities coordinators 1 (pt); Dietitians 1 (pt).
Affiliation Mennonite
Facilities Dining room; Physical therapy room; Activities room; Chapel; Crafts room; Laundry room; Barber/Beauty shop.
Activities Arts & crafts; Cards; Games; Reading groups; Prayer groups; Movies.

Elm Terrace Gardens
660 N Broad St, Lansdale, PA, 19446
(215) 362-6087
Admin Mike Metropole NHA. *Medical Dir/Dir of Nursing* Barbara Leo RN.
Licensure Skilled care. *Beds* SNF 45. *Certified* Medicaid; Medicare.
Owner Nonprofit Corp.
Admissions Requirements Minimum age 60; Medical examination; Physician's request.
Staff RNs; LPNs; Nurses aides; Activities coordinators.
Facilities Dining room; Physical therapy room; Activities room; Crafts room; Laundry room; Barber/Beauty shop; Library.
Activities Arts & crafts; Cards; Games; Reading groups; Prayer groups; Movies.

Gwynedd Square for Nursing Convalescent Care*
773 Sumneytown Pike, Lansdale, PA, 19446
(215) 699-7571
Licensure Skilled care; Intermediate care. *Beds* SNF 111; ICF 70. *Certified* Medicaid; Medicare.
Owner Proprietary Corp.
Facilities Dining room; Physical therapy room; Activities room; Chapel; Laundry room; Barber/Beauty shop.
Activities Arts & crafts; Cards; Games; Reading groups; Prayer groups; Movies; Shopping trips; Shopping trips; Social/Cultural gatherings.

North Pennsylvania Convalescent Residence Inc
25 W 5th St, Lansdale, PA, 19446
(215) 855-9765
Admin Thomas E Howells. *Medical Dir/Dir of Nursing* Dr T Detweiler; Linda Foehl.
Licensure Skilled care; Intermediate care. *Beds* SNF 33; ICF 100. *Certified* Medicaid; Medicare.
Owner Proprietary Corp (Beverly Enterprises).
Admissions Requirements Minimum age 16.
Staff RNs; LPNs; Orderlies; Nurses aides; Physical therapists; Activities coordinators; Dietitians.
Facilities Dining room; Physical therapy room; Activities room; Laundry room; Barber/Beauty shop.

Activities Arts & crafts; Cards; Games; Reading groups; Prayer groups; Movies; Shopping trips; Swimming.

St Marys Manor
Lansdale Ave, Lansdale, PA, 19446
(215) 368-0900
Admin George C Stauffer. *Medical Dir/Dir of Nursing* Leonardo V Arano MD.
Licensure Skilled care; Personal care. *Beds* SNF 70; Personal 80. *Certified* Medicaid; Medicare.
Owner Nonprofit Corp.
Admissions Requirements Minimum age 60; Medical examination.
Staff Physicians 1 (pt); RNs 3 (ft), 13 (pt); LPNs 1 (ft), 7 (pt); Nurses aides 13 (ft), 17 (pt); Physical therapists 1 (pt); Occupational therapists 1 (pt); Activities coordinators 1 (ft), 1 (pt); Dietitians 1 (ft); Podiatrists 1 (pt).
Affiliation Roman Catholic
Facilities Dining room; Physical therapy room; Activities room; Chapel; Crafts room; Laundry room; Barber/Beauty shop; Library; Auditorium; Canteen; Gift shop.
Activities Arts & crafts; Cards; Games; Reading groups; Prayer groups; Movies; Social/Cultural gatherings; Entertainment provided by clubs.

Villa of Divine Providence*
1001 Valley Forge Rd, Lansdale, PA, 19446
(215) 855-9700
Licensure Skilled care. *Beds* 82.
Owner Nonprofit Corp.

LAURELDALE

Leader Nursing & Rehabilitation Center
2125 Elizabeth Ave, Laureldale, PA, 19605
(215) 921-9292
Admin Linda Koch. *Medical Dir/Dir of Nursing* Carolyn Fick RN DON.
Licensure Skilled care; Intermediate care. *Beds* SNF 120; ICF 60. *Certified* Medicaid; Medicare.
Owner Proprietary Corp (Manor Care).
Admissions Requirements Medical examination.
Staff RNs 10 (ft), 5 (pt); LPNs 7 (ft), 14 (pt); Orderlies 3 (ft), 3 (pt); Nurses aides 44 (ft), 37 (pt); Physical therapists 5 (ft), 1 (pt); Recreational therapists 3 (ft), 1 (pt); Occupational therapists 1 (ft); Activities coordinators 1 (ft).
Facilities Dining room; Physical therapy room; Activities room; Chapel; Crafts room; Laundry room; Barber/Beauty shop.
Activities Arts & crafts; Cards; Games; Reading groups; Prayer groups; Shopping trips; Social/Cultural gatherings.

LAURELTON

Laurelton Center
Rte 45, Laurelton, PA, 17835-0300
(717) 922-3311
Admin S Reeves Power. *Medical Dir/Dir of Nursing* James R Kodlick; Lynn Libby RN DON.
Licensure Intermediate care for mentally retarded. *Beds* ICF/MR 400. *Certified* Medicaid.
Owner Nonprofit organization/foundation.
Admissions Requirements Medical examination.
Staff Physicians 1 (pt); RNs 13 (ft); LPNs 43 (ft), 2 (pt); Recreational therapists 5 (ft); Occupational therapists 1 (ft); Speech therapists 3 (ft); Dietitians 2 (ft); Podiatrists 2 (ft); Residential services aides 172 (ft), 1 (pt).
Facilities Dining room; Physical therapy room; Activities room; Crafts room; Barber/Beauty shop; Library.

Activities Arts & crafts; Cards; Games; Prayer groups; Movies; Shopping trips; Social/Cultural gatherings.

LEBANON

Cedar Haven
590 S 5th Ave, Lebanon, PA, 17042
(717) 274-0421
Admin Lee A Stickler. *Medical Dir/Dir of Nursing* Peter B Flowers MD; Ellen M Walker RN DON.
Licensure Skilled care; Intermediate care. *Beds* SNF 40; ICF 320. *Certified* Medicaid; Medicare.
Owner Nonprofit organization/foundation.
Staff Physicians 2 (pt); RNs 10 (ft), 3 (pt); LPNs 26 (ft), 10 (pt); Nurses aides 100 (ft), 50 (pt); Activities coordinators 3 (ft), 4 (pt).
Facilities Dining room; Physical therapy room; Activities room; Chapel; Crafts room; Laundry room; Barber/Beauty shop; Library.
Activities Arts & crafts; Cards; Games; Reading groups; Prayer groups; Movies; Shopping trips; Social/Cultural gatherings; Patio picnics; Exercise.

Leader Nursing and Rehabilitation Center
900 Tuck St, Lebanon, PA, 17042
(717) 273-8595
Admin William G Boyer Jr. *Medical Dir/Dir of Nursing* Dr Dale Brown-Bieber MD.
Licensure Skilled care; Intermediate care. *Beds* SNF 62; ICF 72. *Certified* Medicaid; Medicare.
Owner Proprietary Corp (Manor Care).
Admissions Requirements Medical examination.
Staff RNs 3 (ft), 10 (pt); LPNs 11 (ft), 7 (pt); Nurses aides 37 (ft), 42 (pt); Physical therapists 1 (ft); Recreational therapists 1 (ft); Occupational therapists 1 (ft), 1 (pt); Speech therapists 1 (pt); Activities coordinators 1 (ft).
Facilities Dining room; Physical therapy room; Activities room; Chapel; Crafts room; Laundry room; Barber/Beauty shop.
Activities Arts & crafts; Cards; Games; Reading groups; Prayer groups; Movies; Shopping trips; Social/Cultural gatherings; Field trips; Intergenerational groups.

Lebanon County Life Support
25 Metro Dr, Lebanon, PA, 17042
(717) 274-0493
Medical Dir/Dir of Nursing Bruce Yeamans MD & Drew Coutney MD.
Licensure Intermediate care for mentally retarded. *Beds* 25. *Certified* Medicaid.
Owner Nonprofit Corp.
Admissions Requirements Medical examination; Physician's request.
Staff Orderlies 1 (ft); Nurses aides 15 (ft), 5 (pt); Speech therapists 1 (pt); Activities coordinators 1 (pt); Dietitians 1 (pt); Program assistants 3 (ft).
Facilities Activities room.
Activities Arts & crafts; Games; Movies; Shopping trips.

Oakview
1407 Oak St, Lebanon, PA, 17042
(717) 273-5541
Admin C Franklin Helt. *Medical Dir/Dir of Nursing* Dr Glenn Hirsch; Sandra Geib RN DON.
Licensure Intermediate care; Residential living. *Beds* ICF 28; Residential living 24. *Certified* Medicaid.
Owner Nonprofit Corp.
Admissions Requirements Medical examination; Physician's request.
Staff RNs 1 (ft), 2 (pt); LPNs 1 (ft), 4 (pt); Nurses aides 8 (ft), 4 (pt); Recreational therapists 1 (ft); Occupational therapists 1 (pt).

Facilities Dining room; Activities room; Chapel; Crafts room; Laundry room; Barber/Beauty shop; Library.
Activities Arts & crafts; Cards; Games; Reading groups; Prayer groups; Movies; Shopping trips; Social/Cultural gatherings; Pet therapy; Kitchen band; Morning exercises.

Spang Crest Home*
1000 Quentin Rd, Lebanon, PA, 17042
(717) 272-4115
Licensure Skilled care; Intermediate care. *Beds* SNF 35; ICF 70. *Certified* Medicaid; Medicare.
Owner Nonprofit Corp.

LEHIGHTON

Gnaden Huetten Nursing & Convalescent Home
11th & Hamilton Sts, Lehighton, PA, 18235
(215) 377-1300
Admin Lee Lanning. *Medical Dir/Dir of Nursing* Delores Zaengle.
Licensure Skilled care. *Beds* 82. *Certified* Medicaid; Medicare.
Owner Nonprofit Corp.
Admissions Requirements Females only; Medical examination.
Staff Physicians 8 (ft), 5 (pt); RNs 6 (ft), 6 (pt); LPNs 7 (ft), 6 (pt); Orderlies 3 (ft), 1 (pt); Nurses aides 18 (ft), 17 (pt); Physical therapists 1 (ft); Recreational therapists 1 (ft); Occupational therapists 1 (ft); Speech therapists 1 (ft); Activities coordinators 1 (ft); Dietitians 1 (pt); Ophthalmologists 4 (pt); Podiatrists 2 (pt).
Languages German, Pennsylvania Dutch
Facilities Dining room; Physical therapy room; Activities room; Laundry room; Multi-purpose room.
Activities Arts & crafts; Games; Reading groups; Prayer groups; Movies; Social/Cultural gatherings; Facility olympics.

Mahoning Valley Nursing & Rehabilitation Center*
Rte 1, Box 46, Lehighton, PA, 18235-9640
(717) 386-5522
Medical Dir/Dir of Nursing Dr Robert Frantz.
Licensure Skilled care; Intermediate care. *Beds* SNF 59; ICF 61. *Certified* Medicaid; Medicare.
Owner Nonprofit Corp.
Staff Physicians 3 (pt); RNs 4 (ft), 2 (pt); LPNs 9 (ft); Orderlies 5 (ft); Nurses aides 28 (ft); Physical therapists 1 (pt); Occupational therapists 1 (pt); Speech therapists 1 (pt); Activities coordinators 1 (ft); Dietitians 1 (pt); Dentists 1 (pt); Ophthalmologists 1 (pt); Podiatrists 1 (pt); Audiologists 1 (pt).
Facilities Dining room; Physical therapy room; Activities room; Crafts room; Barber/Beauty shop.
Activities Arts & crafts; Cards; Games; Reading groups; Movies; Shopping trips.

LEOLA

Community Services Inc*
312 Pleasant Valley Dr, Leola, PA, 17540
(717) 656-8005
Licensure Intermediate care for mentally retarded. *Beds* 5. *Certified* Medicaid.
Owner Proprietary Corp.

LEVITTOWN

American Medical Nursing Centers—Statesman*
2629 Trenton Rd, Levittown, PA, 19056
(215) 943-7777
Licensure Skilled care; Intermediate care. *Beds* SNF 70; ICF 32. *Certified* Medicaid; Medicare.
Owner Proprietary Corp (Unicare).

LEWISBURG

Buffalo Valley Lutheran Village
Fairground Rd, Lewisburg, PA, 17837
(717) 524-2221
Admin Dennis E Horn. *Medical Dir/Dir of Nursing* Carol L Moyer RN DON.
Licensure Skilled care; Intermediate care. *Beds* SNF 21; ICF 89. *Certified* Medicaid; Medicare.
Owner Nonprofit Corp (Tressler-Lutheran Services Assoc).
Admissions Requirements Minimum age 65; Medical examination.
Staff RNs 4 (ft), 3 (pt); LPNs 4 (ft), 3 (pt); Nurses aides 24 (ft), 24 (pt); Activities coordinators 1 (ft).
Affiliation Lutheran
Facilities Dining room; Physical therapy room; Activities room; Chapel; Crafts room; Laundry room; Barber/Beauty shop.
Activities Arts & crafts; Cards; Games; Reading groups; Prayer groups; Movies; Shopping trips; Social/Cultural gatherings.

Lewisburg United Methodist Homes
Lewisburg, PA, 17837-9799
(717) 524-2271
Admin David L Reed. *Medical Dir/Dir of Nursing* John H Persing MD; Bonnie Haas RN DON.
Licensure Skilled care; Intermediate care. *Beds* SNF 90; ICF 140; Residential 165. *Certified* Medicaid; Medicare.
Owner Nonprofit organization/foundation.
Admissions Requirements Minimum age Retirement facilities 65; Medical examination.
Staff RNs 11 (ft), 5 (pt); LPNs 29 (ft), 12 (pt); Nurses aides 88 (ft), 58 (pt); Physical therapists; Activities coordinators 1 (ft), 3 (pt).
Affiliation Methodist
Facilities Dining room; Physical therapy room; Activities room; Chapel; Crafts room; Laundry room; Barber/Beauty shop; Library.
Activities Arts & crafts; Cards; Games; Reading groups; Prayer groups; Movies; Shopping trips; Social/Cultural gatherings; Regular church services.

LEWISTOWN

Ohesson Manor*
350 Green Ave Extension, Lewistown, PA, 17044
(717) 242-1417
Licensure Skilled care; Intermediate care. *Beds* SNF 35; ICF 99. *Certified* Medicaid; Medicare.
Owner Nonprofit Corp (Tressler-Lutheran Services Assoc).

William Penn Nursing Center
163 Summit Dr, Lewistown, PA, 17044
(717) 248-3941
Admin Stephen K Ott. *Medical Dir/Dir of Nursing* Dr John Zornosa; Ramona Byler RN DON.
Licensure Skilled care; Intermediate care. *Beds* SNF 25; ICF 96. *Certified* Medicaid; Medicare.
Owner Proprietary Corp (Beverly Enterprises).
Admissions Requirements Medical examination; Physician's request.
Staff RNs 5 (ft), 5 (pt); LPNs 9 (ft), 7 (pt); Nurses aides 25 (ft), 31 (pt); Physical therapists 1 (ft), 1 (pt); Recreational therapists 1 (ft), 1 (pt); Speech therapists 1 (pt).
Facilities Dining room; Physical therapy room; Activities room; Crafts room; Laundry room; Barber/Beauty shop; Lounges.
Activities Arts & crafts; Cards; Games; Reading groups; Prayer groups; Movies; Shopping trips; Social/Cultural gatherings; Individual programs.

LIGONIER

Bethlen Home of the Hungarian Reformed Federation of America
PO Box 657, Ligonier, PA, 15658
(412) 238-6711
Admin Rev Paul Kovacs. *Medical Dir/Dir of Nursing* G Jeanie Short.
Licensure Skilled care; Intermediate care. *Beds* SNF 45; ICF 58. *Certified* Medicaid; Medicare.
Owner Nonprofit Corp.
Admissions Requirements Medical examination; Physician's request.
Staff RNs 3 (ft), 10 (pt); LPNs 1 (ft), 2 (pt); Nurses aides; Activities coordinators; Dietitians 1 (ft).
Affiliation Christian Reformed Hungarian Church
Facilities Dining room; Physical therapy room; Activities room; Chapel; Crafts room; Laundry room; Barber/Beauty shop.
Activities Arts & crafts; Cards; Games; Reading groups; Prayer groups; Movies; Shopping trips; Social/Cultural gatherings.

Pine Hurst Nursing & Convalescent Home*
Rte 4, Ligonier, PA, 15658
(412) 593-7720
Licensure Skilled care. *Beds* 23.
Owner Proprietary Corp.

LIMA

Fair Acres Geriatric Center*
Rte 352, Middletown Rd, Lima, PA, 19037
(215) 891-7411
Licensure Skilled care; Intermediate care. *Beds* SNF 706; ICF 211. *Certified* Medicaid; Medicare.
Owner Nonprofit Corp.

Lima Estates*
411 N Middletown Rd, Lima, PA, 19037
(215) 565-7020
Licensure Skilled care. *Beds* 60.
Owner Nonprofit Corp.

LITITZ

Audubon Villa*
125 S Broad St, Lititz, PA, 17543
(717) 626-0211
Licensure Skilled care. *Beds* 32.
Owner Proprietary Corp.

Friendship Community
Rte 3, Box 254, Lititz, PA, 17543
(717) 656-2466
Admin Charles Bauman. *Medical Dir/Dir of Nursing* Flo Harnish.
Licensure Intermediate care for mentally retarded. *Beds* ICF/MR 21. *Certified* Medicaid.
Owner Nonprofit organization/foundation.
Admissions Requirements Minimum age 18; Medical examination; Physician's request.
Staff RNs 1 (pt); LPNs 3 (pt); Activities coordinators 1 (pt).
Facilities Dining room; Laundry room.
Activities Arts & crafts; Cards; Games; Reading groups; Prayer groups; Movies; Shopping trips; Social/Cultural gatherings.

Landis Home
Rd 3, Lititz, PA, 17543
(717) 569-3271
Admin Edward M Longenecker. *Medical Dir/Dir of Nursing* John Wolgemuth MD; Ruth Johnson RN DON.
Licensure Skilled care; Intermediate care; Personal care; Continuing care Retirement Community. *Beds* 365. *Certified* Medicaid; Medicare.
Owner Nonprofit Corp.
Admissions Requirements Minimum age 65.

Staff RNs 4 (ft), 6 (pt); LPNs 14 (ft), 9 (pt); Orderlies 1 (pt); Nurses aides 12 (ft), 47 (pt); Recreational therapists 3 (ft), 1 (pt); Activities coordinators.
Languages Pennsylvania Dutch
Affiliation Mennonite
Facilities Dining room; Physical therapy room; Activities room; Chapel; Crafts room; Laundry room; Barber/Beauty shop; Library.
Activities Arts & crafts; Games; Reading groups; Prayer groups; Movies; Shopping trips; Social/Cultural gatherings; Cooking.

Luther Acres
600 E Main St, Lititz, PA, 17543
(717) 626-1171
Licensure Skilled care; Intermediate care; Personal care. *Beds* SNF 19; ICF 87; Personal 27. *Certified* Medicaid; Medicare.
Owner Nonprofit Corp.
Affiliation Lutheran

Moravian Manor
300 W Lemon St, Lititz, PA, 17543
(717) 626-0214
Admin Nancy H O'Hara. *Medical Dir/Dir of Nursing* Reyer O Swan MD; Lillian Podlesny RN DON.
Licensure Skilled care; Intermediate care; Personal care. *Beds* SNF 63; ICF 47; Personal 88. *Certified* Medicaid; Medicare.
Owner Nonprofit Corp.
Admissions Requirements Minimum age 62.
Affiliation Moravian
Facilities Dining room; Physical therapy room; Activities room; Chapel; Crafts room; Laundry room; Barber/Beauty shop; Library.
Activities Arts & crafts; Cards; Games; Reading groups; Prayer groups; Movies; Shopping trips.

United Zion Home Inc*
Rte 2, Lititz, PA, 17543
(717) 626-2071
Licensure Skilled care. *Beds* 46. *Certified* Medicaid.
Owner Nonprofit Corp.

LIVERPOOL

Good Samaritan Home*
Front St, Liverpool, PA, 17045
(717) 444-3713
Admin Esther J Mohler. *Medical Dir/Dir of Nursing* Dr James Minahan.
Licensure Intermediate care. *Beds* 25. *Certified* Medicaid.
Owner Proprietary Corp.
Admissions Requirements Minimum age 16; Medical examination.
Staff RNs 1 (ft), 2 (pt); LPNs 4 (pt); Nurses aides 8 (pt); Recreational therapists 1 (pt); Activities coordinators 1 (pt).
Facilities Dining room.
Activities Arts & crafts; Cards; Games; Reading groups; Prayer groups; Movies; Shopping trips; Social/Cultural gatherings.

Nipple Convalescent Home
100 S Front St, Liverpool, PA, 17045
(717) 444-3413
Admin Rae A Adams. *Medical Dir/Dir of Nursing* Joseph R Kreiser MD.
Licensure Skilled care; Intermediate care. *Beds* 37. *Certified* Medicaid; Medicare.
Owner Privately owned.
Admissions Requirements Minimum age 18; Medical examination; Physician's request.
Staff Physicians 1 (pt); RNs 1 (ft), 1 (pt); LPNs 4 (ft), 2 (pt); Nurses aides 15 (ft), 5 (pt); Physical therapists 1 (pt); Recreational therapists 1 (pt); Speech therapists; Activities coordinators 1 (pt); Dietitians; Dentists; Ophthalmologists; Podiatrists.
Languages Pennsylvania Dutch
Facilities Dining room; Activities room; Crafts room; Laundry room; Barber/Beauty shop.

Activities Arts & crafts; Cards; Games; Reading groups; Prayer groups; Movies.

LOCK HAVEN

Lock Haven Hospital—Extended Care Facility*
Fourth & Nelson Sts, Lock Haven, PA, 17745
(717) 748-7721
Licensure Skilled care; Intermediate care. *Beds* SNF 60; ICF 60. *Certified* Medicaid; Medicare.
Owner Nonprofit Corp.

Susque View Home Inc
Cree Dr, Lock Haven, PA, 17745
(717) 748-9377
Admin Jack Spayd. *Medical Dir/Dir of Nursing* James Dolan MD; Barbara Jackson DON.
Licensure Skilled care; Intermediate care. *Beds* SNF 40; ICF 120. *Certified* Medicaid; Medicare.
Owner Nonprofit Corp.
Admissions Requirements Medical examination; Physician's request.
Staff Physicians 10 (pt); RNs 6 (ft), 4 (pt); LPNs 15 (ft), 8 (pt); Orderlies 1 (ft), 1 (pt); Nurses aides 44 (ft), 24 (pt); Physical therapists 2 (pt); Reality therapists 1 (pt); Recreational therapists 1 (ft); Occupational therapists 1 (pt); Speech therapists 1 (pt); Activities coordinators 1 (ft); Dietitians 1 (pt); Dentists 1 (pt); Ophthalmologists 1 (pt); Podiatrists 1 (pt).
Facilities Dining room; Physical therapy room; Activities room; Chapel; Crafts room; Laundry room; Barber/Beauty shop; Library.
Activities Arts & crafts; Cards; Games; Reading groups; Prayer groups; Movies; Shopping trips; Social/Cultural gatherings.

LOWER BURRELL

Belair Nursing Center
Chester Dr & Little Rd, Lower Burrell, PA, 15068
(412) 339-1071
Medical Dir/Dir of Nursing Valley Family Practice Center MD; Patricia Dolimade DON.
Licensure Skilled care; Intermediate care. *Beds* SNF 31; ICF 76. *Certified* Medicaid; Medicare.
Owner Proprietary Corp (Unicare).
Admissions Requirements Medical examination.
Staff Activities coordinators 2 (ft); Dietitians 1 (ft).
Facilities Dining room; Physical therapy room; Activities room; Chapel; Crafts room; Barber/Beauty shop.
Activities Arts & crafts; Cards; Games; Reading groups; Prayer groups; Movies; Shopping trips; Social/Cultural gatherings.

MANHEIM

Mt Hope Dunkard Brethren Church Home
Mount Hope Rd, Box 312 RD 3, Manheim, PA, 17545
(717) 665-6365
Admin Glen K Ziegler. *Medical Dir/Dir of Nursing* Dr William Stout; Anna S Kellen RN.
Licensure Skilled care. *Beds* SNF 39; ICF 26. *Certified* Medicaid.
Owner Nonprofit Corp.
Admissions Requirements Minimum age 65; Medical examination.
Staff RNs 3 (ft), 2 (pt); LPNs 4 (ft), 4 (pt); Orderlies 3 (pt); Nurses aides 12 (ft), 18 (pt); Activities coordinators 1 (ft); Dietitians 1 (pt).

Facilities Dining room; Activities room; Chapel; Crafts room; Laundry room.
Activities Arts & crafts; Games; Reading groups; Prayer groups; Shopping trips.

Pleasant View Rest Home Inc*
Box 487, Manheim, PA, 17545
(717) 665-2445
Medical Dir/Dir of Nursing Dr Terrence Jones.
Licensure Skilled care. *Beds* 130. *Certified* Medicaid.
Owner Nonprofit Corp.
Admissions Requirements Medical examination.
Staff Physicians; RNs; LPNs; Nurses aides; Physical therapists; Reality therapists; Recreational therapists; Activities coordinators; Dietitians; Dentists; Ophthalmologists; Podiatrists.
Facilities Dining room; Physical therapy room; Activities room; Chapel; Crafts room; Laundry room; Barber/Beauty shop.
Activities Arts & crafts; Games; Reading groups; Prayer groups; Movies; Shopping trips.

MARKLESBURG

Spear Convalescent Home*
PO Box 37, Marklesburg, PA, 15459
(412) 329-4830
Licensure Skilled care. *Beds* 79. *Certified* Medicaid.
Owner Nonprofit Corp.

MARS

St John Lutheran Care Center
PO Box 928, 500 Wittenberg Way, Mars, PA, 16046
(412) 625-1571
Admin Rev Dar W Vriesman. *Medical Dir/Dir of Nursing* William Schwerin MD; Ann Rice RN.
Licensure Skilled care; Intermediate care; Personal care; Independent living. *Beds* SNF 56; ICF 189; Personal 43; Apts 10. *Certified* Medicaid; Medicare.
Owner Nonprofit Corp.
Admissions Requirements Minimum age 60; Medical examination.
Staff Physicians 2 (pt); RNs 7 (ft), 15 (pt); LPNs 18 (ft), 17 (pt); Nurses aides 79 (ft), 39 (pt); Physical therapists 2 (pt); Reality therapists 2 (ft); Recreational therapists 2 (ft); Speech therapists 2 (pt); Activities coordinators 2 (ft); Dietitians 1 (pt); Ophthalmologists 1 (pt).
Affiliation Lutheran
Facilities Dining room; Physical therapy room; Activities room; Chapel; Crafts room; Laundry room; Barber/Beauty shop; Library.
Activities Arts & crafts; Cards; Games; Reading groups; Prayer groups; Movies; Shopping trips; Social/Cultural gatherings; Reality orientation; Music therapy; Remotivation therapy; Choir.

Sherwood Oaks & Cranberry Lake Health Center*
100 Norman Dr, Mars, PA, 16046
Admin Jace Gerie. *Medical Dir/Dir of Nursing* Dr J Robert Love.
Licensure Skilled care; Residential care. *Beds* SNF 59; Residential 37. *Certified* Medicaid; Medicare.
Owner Nonprofit Corp.
Admissions Requirements Medical examination.
Staff Physicians 2 (pt); RNs 5 (ft), 4 (pt); LPNs 3 (ft), 3 (pt); Nurses aides 14 (ft), 8 (pt); Recreational therapists 1 (ft); Occupational therapists 1 (pt); Speech therapists 1 (pt); Dietitians 1 (pt); Dentists 1

(pt); Ophthalmologists; Podiatrists 1 (pt); Occupational therapy aides 1 (pt); Physical therapy aides 1 (pt).
Facilities Dining room; Physical therapy room; Activities room; Chapel; Crafts room; Laundry room; Barber/Beauty shop; Library; Indoor heated pool & jacuzzi; Greenhouse; Bank; Convenience store; Woodworking shop; Lapidary shop.
Activities Arts & crafts; Cards; Games; Reading groups; Prayer groups; Movies; Shopping trips; Social/Cultural gatherings; Bible study.

MARTINSBURG

Homewood Retirement Center
430 S Market St, Martinsburg, PA, 16662
(814) 793-3728
Admin Linda N Frederick NHA. *Medical Dir/ Dir of Nursing* Diane K Golomb RN.
Licensure Intermediate care. *Beds* ICF 67. *Certified* Medicaid.
Owner Nonprofit Corp (Homewood Retire Center/UCC).
Admissions Requirements Minimum age 70; Medical examination.
Staff Physicians 4 (pt); RNs 4 (ft), 3 (pt); LPNs 6 (ft), 3 (pt); Nurses aides 12 (ft), 8 (pt); Physical therapists 2 (pt); Activities coordinators 1 (ft); Dietitians 1 (ft).
Affiliation Church of Christ
Facilities Dining room; Physical therapy room; Activities room; Chapel; Crafts room; Laundry room; Barber/Beauty shop.
Activities Arts & crafts; Cards; Games; Reading groups; Prayer groups; Movies; Shopping trips; Social/Cultural gatherings.

Morrisons Cove Home
429 S Market St, Martinsburg, PA, 16662
(814) 793-2104
Admin Lona B Norris. *Medical Dir/Dir of Nursing* Lunda Weaver MD; Ada Spaeth DON.
Licensure Skilled care; Intermediate care; Personal care; Independent/Residential. *Beds* SNF 47; ICF 57; Personal 65. *Certified* Medicaid; Medicare.
Owner Nonprofit Corp.
Admissions Requirements Minimum age 65; Medical examination.
Staff RNs 6 (ft), 6 (pt); LPNs 10 (ft), 8 (pt); Nurses aides 25 (ft), 20 (pt); Occupational therapists; Activities coordinators 1 (ft).
Affiliation Church of the Brethren
Facilities Dining room; Activities room; Chapel; Crafts room; Laundry room; Barber/ Beauty shop; Library.
Activities Arts & crafts; Cards; Games; Reading groups; Prayer groups; Shopping trips; Social/Cultural gatherings.

MCCONNELLSBURG

Fulton County Medical Center
216 S 1st St, McConnellsburg, PA, 17233-1399
(717) 485-3155
Admin Thomas A Fite. *Medical Dir/Dir of Nursing* James E Witt MD; Onda Borngesser RN DON.
Licensure Skilled care; Intermediate care. *Beds* SNF 15; ICF 42. *Certified* Medicaid; Medicare.
Owner Nonprofit Corp.
Admissions Requirements Medical examination; Physician's request.
Staff Physicians 1 (ft), 5 (pt); RNs 1 (ft), 1 (pt); LPNs 6 (ft), 6 (pt); Nurses aides 11 (ft), 21 (pt); Physical therapists 2 (pt); Speech therapists 1 (pt); Activities coordinators 1 (pt); Dietitians 1 (ft); Dentists 1 (pt); Ophthalmologists 1 (pt); Podiatrists 1 (pt).
Facilities Dining room; Physical therapy room; Activities room; Chapel; Laundry room; Barber/Beauty shop.

Activities Arts & crafts; Cards; Games; Reading groups; Prayer groups; Movies; Shopping trips; Social/Cultural gatherings.

MCKEES ROCKS

Robinson Developmental Center
Clever Rd, McKees Rocks, PA, 15136
(412) 787-2350
Admin Donald D DiMichele. *Medical Dir/Dir of Nursing* Louis D Pietragallo MD; Carol A Neuman RN.
Licensure Intermediate care for mentally retarded. *Beds* 132. *Certified* Medicaid.
Owner Nonprofit Corp.
Admissions Requirements Minimum age 21; Medical examination.
Staff Physicians 6 (pt); RNs 5 (ft); LPNs 6 (ft); Orderlies 96; Recreational therapists 1 (ft); Occupational therapists 1 (pt); Speech therapists 3 (ft); Activities coordinators 3 (ft); Dietitians 1 (ft); Dentists 1 (pt); Physical therapists aides 3 (ft), 1 (pt).
Languages Sign
Facilities Dining room; Physical therapy room; Activities room; Laundry room; Library.
Activities Active developmental programming.

MCMURRAY

McMurray Hills Manor Inc
249 W McMurray Rd, McMurray, PA, 15317
(412) 561-4406
Admin Paul D Kwiecinski. *Medical Dir/Dir of Nursing* Dr Jon Adler MD.
Licensure Skilled care; Intermediate care; Apartments. *Beds* SNF 97; ICF 22; 8 apartments. *Certified* Medicare.
Owner Proprietary Corp.
Admissions Requirements Minimum age 40; Medical examination.
Staff Physicians 3 (pt); RNs 16 (ft), 6 (pt); LPNs 3 (pt); Nurses aides 1 (pt); Physical therapists 1 (pt); Recreational therapists 1 (pt); Occupational therapists 1 (pt); Speech therapists 1 (pt); Activities coordinators 1 (ft); Dietitians 1 (pt); Dentists 1 (pt); Ophthalmologists 1 (pt); Podiatrists 1 (pt).
Facilities Dining room; Physical therapy room; Activities room; Crafts room; Laundry room; Barber/Beauty shop.
Activities Arts & crafts; Cards; Games; Reading groups; Prayer groups; Movies; Shopping trips; Social/Cultural gatherings.

MEADOWBROOK

St Josephs Manor
1616 Huntingdon Pike, Meadowbrook, PA, 19046
(215) 938-4000
Admin J Gregory Cauterucci. *Medical Dir/Dir of Nursing* Robert V Peruzzi Jr MD; Joseph F Mugford RN DON.
Licensure Skilled care. *Beds* 262. *Certified* Medicaid; Medicare.
Owner Nonprofit Corp.
Admissions Requirements Minimum age 65; Medical examination.
Staff Physicians; RNs; LPNs; Orderlies; Nurses aides; Activities coordinators; Dietitians.
Facilities Dining room; Physical therapy room; Activities room; Chapel; Crafts room; Laundry room; Barber/Beauty shop.
Activities Arts & crafts; Cards; Games; Reading groups; Prayer groups; Movies; Shopping trips; Social/Cultural gatherings.

MEADVILLE

Mead Nursing Home*
N Park Ave Extension, Meadville, PA, 16335
(814) 337-4229

Licensure Skilled care. *Beds* 150. *Certified* Medicaid.
Owner Proprietary Corp.

Meadville Hillside Home*
535 Williamson Rd, Meadville, PA, 16335
(814) 724-3117
Licensure Intermediate care. *Beds* 17. *Certified* Medicaid.
Owner Nonprofit Corp.

Westbury United Methodist Community
31 N Park Ave, Meadville, PA, 16335
(814) 724-8000
Admin William L Brown. *Medical Dir/Dir of Nursing* Dr Spiro E Moutsas; Diane Rudler.
Licensure Skilled care; Intermediate care; Independent, Residential, and Personal care. *Beds* 341. *Certified* Medicaid; Medicare.
Owner Nonprofit organization/foundation.
Admissions Requirements Medical examination; Physician's request.
Staff RNs 10 (ft), 7 (pt); LPNs 13 (ft), 9 (pt); Nurses aides 43 (ft), 65 (pt); Occupational therapists 1 (ft); Activities coordinators 1 (ft), 4 (pt); Dietitians 1 (ft).
Affiliation Methodist
Facilities Dining room; Physical therapy room; Activities room; Chapel; Crafts room; Laundry room; Barber/Beauty shop; Library; Nature trail.
Activities Arts & crafts; Cards; Games; Reading groups; Prayer groups; Movies; Shopping trips; Social/Cultural gatherings.

MECHANICSBURG

Bethany Village Retirement Center
325 Wesley Dr, Mechanicsburg, PA, 17055
(717) 766-0279
Admin James R Wilkins. *Medical Dir/Dir of Nursing* Kenneth Smeltier MD; Carol H Fleisher DON.
Licensure Skilled care; Intermediate care; Personal care. *Beds* 69. *Certified* Medicaid; Medicare.
Owner Nonprofit Corp.
Admissions Requirements Minimum age 62; Medical examination; Physician's request.
Staff Physicians 3 (pt); RNs 5 (ft), 12 (pt); LPNs 2 (ft), 8 (pt); Orderlies 4 (pt); Nurses aides 5 (ft), 28 (pt); Physical therapists 1 (pt); Recreational therapists 1 (ft), 1 (pt); Occupational therapists 1 (pt); Speech therapists 1 (pt); Activities coordinators 1 (ft); Dietitians 1 (pt); Dentists 1 (pt); Ophthalmologists 2 (pt); Podiatrists 1 (pt).
Affiliation Methodist
Facilities Dining room; Physical therapy room; Activities room; Chapel; Crafts room; Laundry room; Barber/Beauty shop; Library.
Activities Arts & crafts; Cards; Games; Reading groups; Prayer groups; Movies; Shopping trips; Social/Cultural gatherings.

Messiah Village
100 Mt Allen Dr, Mechanicsburg, PA, 17055
(717) 697-4666
Admin George Kibler. *Medical Dir/Dir of Nursing* Paul A Kase MD; Mary Lou Kuntzweiler DON.
Licensure Skilled care; Intermediate care. *Beds* 90. *Certified* Medicaid; Medicare.
Owner Nonprofit organization/foundation.
Admissions Requirements Minimum age 65; Medical examination.
Staff RNs 7 (ft), 1 (pt); LPNs 3 (pt); Nurses aides 23 (ft), 26 (pt); Activities coordinators 1 (ft).
Affiliation Brethren In Christ Church
Facilities Dining room; Physical therapy room; Activities room; Chapel; Crafts room; Laundry room; Barber/Beauty shop; Library.
Activities Arts & crafts; Games; Prayer groups; Movies; Shopping trips.

Seidle Memorial Hospital—Extended Care Unit
Simpson & Filbert Sts, Mechanicsburg, PA, 17055
(717) 766-7691
Licensure Skilled care. *Beds* 35. *Certified* Medicaid; Medicare.
Owner Nonprofit Corp.

MEDIA

Bishop Nursing Home Inc*
318 S Orange St, Media, PA, 19063
(215) 565-4836
Medical Dir/Dir of Nursing Peter Binnion MD.
Licensure Skilled care. *Beds* 164. *Certified* Medicaid.
Owner Proprietary Corp.
Staff Physicians 1 (pt); RNs 4 (ft), 8 (pt); LPNs 5 (ft), 8 (pt); Orderlies 4 (ft); Nurses aides 56 (ft), 8 (pt); Physical therapists 1 (pt); Occupational therapists 1 (pt); Activities coordinators 1 (ft); Dietitians 1 (pt).
Facilities Dining room; Physical therapy room; Activities room; Chapel; Crafts room; Laundry room; Barber/Beauty shop; Library.
Activities Arts & crafts; Cards; Games; Reading groups; Prayer groups; Movies; Shopping trips; Social/Cultural gatherings; Van trips; Bus trips; Special parties; Weekly BBQ; Community speakers.

Care Center at Martins Run*
11 Martins Run, Marple Township, Media, PA, 19063
(215) 353-7660
Licensure Skilled care. *Beds* 60. *Certified* Medicaid; Medicare.
Owner Nonprofit Corp.

Manchester House Nursing Home*
411 Manchester Ave, Media, PA, 19063
(215) 565-1800
Licensure Skilled care. *Beds* 297. *Certified* Medicaid.
Owner Proprietary Corp.

Workmens Circle Home
3rd & Jackson Sts, Media, PA, 19063
(215) 566-8703
Admin Raymond Rudich MBA. *Medical Dir/Dir of Nursing* Dr Di Wan; Mrs Spence RN.
Licensure Intermediate care; Residential care. *Beds* ICF 32; Residential 66. *Certified* Medicaid.
Owner Nonprofit Corp.
Admissions Requirements Medical examination.
Staff Physicians 1 (pt); RNs 2 (ft), 1 (pt); LPNs 2 (ft), 6 (pt); Orderlies 2 (ft), 1 (pt); Nurses aides 10 (ft), 4 (pt); Activities coordinators 1 (ft), 1 (pt); Dietitians 1 (pt).
Languages Yiddish, Hebrew
Facilities Dining room; Activities room; Chapel; Laundry room; Barber/Beauty shop.
Activities Arts & crafts; Cards; Games; Reading groups; Prayer groups; Movies; Shopping trips; Social/Cultural gatherings.

MERCER

Countryside Convalescent Home*
Rte 7, Mercer, PA, 16137
(412) 662-5860
Admin Gerald Furma. *Medical Dir/Dir of Nursing* V A Ciambotti DO.
Licensure Skilled care. *Beds* 48. *Certified* Medicaid.
Owner Proprietary Corp.
Admissions Requirements Medical examination; Physician's request.

Staff RNs 4 (ft); LPNs 5 (ft); Nurses aides 22 (ft); Physical therapists 1 (ft); Recreational therapists 2 (ft); Activities coordinators 1 (ft); Dietitians 1 (ft); Dentists 1 (pt); Podiatrists 1 (pt).
Facilities Dining room; Physical therapy room; Activities room; Chapel; Crafts room; Laundry room; Barber/Beauty shop.
Activities Arts & crafts; Cards; Games; Reading groups; Prayer groups; Movies; Social/Cultural gatherings.

Mercer County Living Center
Rd 2, Box 2060, Mercer, PA, 16137
(412) 662-5400
Admin D C Hogue. *Medical Dir/Dir of Nursing* Connie Eves.
Licensure Skilled care; Intermediate care. *Beds* SNF 21; ICF 104. *Certified* Medicaid.
Owner Publicly owned.
Staff Physicians 3 (pt); RNs 6 (ft), 3 (pt); LPNs 14 (ft), 1 (pt); Nurses aides 41 (ft), 12 (pt); Physical therapists 2 (ft); Recreational therapists 1 (ft); Activities coordinators 1 (ft); Dietitians 1 (pt); Dentists 1 (pt); Ophthalmologists 1 (pt).
Facilities Dining room; Physical therapy room; Activities room; Chapel; Crafts room; Barber/Beauty shop; Library.
Activities Arts & crafts; Cards; Games; Reading groups; Prayer groups; Movies; Social/Cultural gatherings.

MIDDLETOWN

Frey Village
1020 N Union St, Middletown, PA, 17057
(717) 944-0451
Admin H Dixon Hemma. *Medical Dir/Dir of Nursing* Joseph P Leaser MD; Joan Rivers RN; Agnes Fuoti RN Asst DON.
Licensure Skilled care; Intermediate care; Residential care. *Beds* SNF 25; ICF 111; Personal 35; Apts 58. *Certified* Medicaid; Medicare.
Owner Nonprofit Corp (Tressler-Lutheran Services Assoc).
Admissions Requirements Minimum age 62; Medical examination.
Staff Physicians 1 (pt); RNs 6 (ft), 10 (pt); LPNs 7 (ft), 6 (pt); Nurses aides 29 (ft), 29 (pt); Physical therapists 1 (ft); Speech therapists 1 (pt); Activities coordinators 1 (ft); Dietitians 2 (pt); Dentists 1 (pt); Podiatrists 2 (pt).
Affiliation Lutheran
Facilities Dining room; Physical therapy room; Activities room; Chapel; Crafts room; Laundry room; Barber/Beauty shop; Library; Guest house.
Activities Arts & crafts; Cards; Games; Reading groups; Prayer groups; Movies; Shopping trips; Social/Cultural gatherings.

Odd Fellows Home of Pennsylvania Inc*
999 W Harrisburg Pike, Middletown, PA, 17057
(717) 944-3351
Licensure Skilled care; Intermediate care; Residential care. *Beds* SNF 51; ICF 51; Residential 71. *Certified* Medicaid; Medicare.
Owner Nonprofit Corp.
Affiliation Independent Order of Odd Fellows & Rebekahs
Facilities Dining room; Physical therapy room; Activities room; Chapel; Crafts room; Laundry room; Barber/Beauty shop; Library.
Activities Arts & crafts; Cards; Games; Reading groups; Prayer groups; Movies; Shopping trips; Social/Cultural gatherings.

MIFFLIN

Locust Grove Retirement Village
Box 7, HCR 67, Mifflin, PA, 17058
(717) 436-8921

Admin Homer P Smith. *Medical Dir/Dir of Nursing* L G Guiser MD; Jane Yohn RN DON.
Licensure Skilled care; Intermediate care. *Beds* SNF 14; ICF 65. *Certified* Medicaid; Medicare.
Owner Nonprofit Corp (Tressler-Lutheran Services Assoc).
Admissions Requirements Minimum age 65.
Staff RNs; LPNs; Nurses aides; Recreational therapists; Activities coordinators; Dietitians; Ophthalmologists.
Facilities Dining room; Physical therapy room; Activities room; Chapel; Crafts room; Laundry room; Barber/Beauty shop.
Activities Arts & crafts; Cards; Games; Reading groups; Prayer groups; Movies.

MIFFLINTOWN

Brookline Manor Convalescent Home*
Rte 1, Box 63, Mifflintown, PA, 17059
(717) 436-2178
Licensure Skilled care; Intermediate care. *Beds* SNF 55; ICF 28. *Certified* Medicaid; Medicare.
Owner Proprietary Corp.

MILFORD

Hillcrest Home Inc*
404 E Harford St, Milford, PA, 18337
(717) 296-6812
Licensure Skilled care. *Beds* 50. *Certified* Medicaid; Medicare.
Owner Proprietary Corp.

Milford Valley Convalescent Home Inc
Rte 6 & 209, Milford, PA, 18337
(717) 296-6311
Admin Constance A Pizzol. *Medical Dir/Dir of Nursing* Dr Harrison Murray; Yvonne Krieger.
Licensure Skilled care. *Beds* SNF 80. *Certified* Medicaid; Medicare.
Owner Proprietary Corp.
Staff RNs 5 (ft), 4 (pt); LPNs 1 (ft), 4 (pt); Nurses aides 25 (ft), 6 (pt); Activities coordinators 1 (ft), 1 (pt).

MILLERSBURG

Susquehanna Lutheran Village
990 Medical Rd, Millersburg, PA, 17061
(717) 692-4751
Admin Becky Ulsh. *Medical Dir/Dir of Nursing* Robert Ettlinger MD; Diann Snyder RN DON.
Licensure Skilled care; Intermediate care. *Beds* SNF 45; ICF 152. *Certified* Medicaid; Medicare.
Owner Nonprofit Corp (Tressler-Lutheran Services Assoc).
Admissions Requirements Minimum age 65; Medical examination; Physician's request.
Staff RNs 5 (ft), 5 (pt); LPNs 11 (ft), 7 (pt); Nurses aides 28 (ft), 67 (pt).
Affiliation Lutheran
Facilities Dining room; Physical therapy room; Activities room; Chapel; Crafts room; Laundry room; Barber/Beauty shop; Recreation/sitting room.
Activities Arts & crafts; Cards; Games; Reading groups; Prayer groups; Movies; Shopping trips; Social/Cultural gatherings.

MILLMONT

Friendly Nursing Home*
Rte 1, Millmont, PA, 17845
(717) 922-3177
Medical Dir/Dir of Nursing Dr Charles Fasano.
Licensure Skilled care. *Beds* 60. *Certified* Medicaid; Medicare.
Owner Proprietary Corp.

Admissions Requirements Medical examination.
Staff RNs 1 (ft), 1 (pt); LPNs 4 (ft), 3 (pt); Nurses aides 9 (ft), 13 (pt); Physical therapists 1 (pt); Recreational therapists 1 (ft); Dietitians 1 (pt).
Facilities Dining room; Activities room; Chapel; Crafts room; Laundry room.
Activities Arts & crafts; Games; Reading groups; Prayer groups; Movies; Shopping trips.

MILLVILLE

Boone Nursing Home
Rte 1, Eyers Grove, Millville, PA, 17846
(717) 458-6751
Medical Dir/Dir of Nursing Dr Clark.
Licensure Intermediate care. *Beds* 60. *Certified* Medicaid.
Owner Proprietary Corp.
Admissions Requirements Minimum age 18; Medical examination; Physician's request.
Staff Physicians 1 (pt); RNs 3 (ft), 2 (pt); LPNs 2 (ft), 2 (pt); Nurses aides 18 (ft), 8 (pt); Physical therapists 1 (pt); Occupational therapists 1 (pt); Speech therapists 1 (pt); Activities coordinators 1 (ft); Dietitians 1 (pt); Dentists 1 (pt); Podiatrists 1 (pt);; Dentist 1 (pt).

MILTON

Gold Star Nursing Home*
560 E Broadway, Milton, PA, 17847
(717) 742-7651
Admin Maheon L Fritz. *Medical Dir/Dir of Nursing* Barclay M Wilson DO.
Licensure Intermediate care. *Beds* 39. *Certified* Medicaid.
Owner Proprietary Corp.
Admissions Requirements Medical examination.
Staff RNs 1 (ft); LPNs 6 (ft), 1 (pt); Nurses aides 11 (ft), 5 (pt); Physical therapists 1 (pt); Activities coordinators 1 (ft).
Facilities Dining room; Physical therapy room; Activities room; Crafts room; Laundry room; Barber/Beauty shop.
Activities Arts & crafts; Cards; Games; Reading groups; Movies.

Kramm Healthcare Center Inc*
743 Mahoning St, Milton, PA, 17847
(717) 742-2681
Admin Randall D Kramm. *Medical Dir/Dir of Nursing* Dr Robert Yannaccone.
Licensure Skilled care; Intermediate care. *Beds* SNF 61; ICF 59. *Certified* Medicaid; Medicare.
Owner Proprietary Corp.
Admissions Requirements Medical examination.
Staff Physicians 10 (pt); RNs 3 (ft), 4 (pt); LPNs 3 (ft), 4 (pt); Nurses aides 20 (ft), 20 (pt); Physical therapists 1 (pt); Recreational therapists 1 (ft); Activities coordinators 1 (ft); Dietitians 1 (pt); Dentists 1 (pt); Podiatrists 1 (pt).
Facilities Dining room; Physical therapy room; Activities room; Crafts room; Laundry room; Barber/Beauty shop.
Activities Arts & crafts; Cards; Games; Reading groups; Prayer groups; Movies; Shopping trips; Social/Cultural gatherings.

MONONGAHELA

Haven Crest Inc*
1277 Country Club Rd, Monongahela, PA, 15063
(412) 258-3000
Licensure Skilled care. *Beds* 48. *Certified* Medicaid.
Owner Proprietary Corp.

MONT CLARE

Janney House*
Rte 29, River Crest Center, Mont Clare, PA, 19453
(215) 935-1581
Licensure Intermediate care for mentally retarded. *Beds* 6. *Certified* Medicaid.
Owner Nonprofit Corp.

River Crest Center/Ken Crest Services
Rte 29, Mont Clare, PA, 19453
(215) 248-5120
Admin Beth I Barol. *Medical Dir/Dir of Nursing* Virginia Shontz RN.
Licensure Intermediate care for mentally retarded. *Beds* ICF/MR 77. *Certified* Medicaid.
Owner Nonprofit Corp.
Admissions Requirements Minimum age 6; Medical examination; Behavior problems or severe skill deficits plus a primary diagnosis of MR is required.
Staff Physicians 1 (pt); RNs 4 (ft), 1 (pt); LPNs 3 (pt); Physical therapists 1 (ft); Recreational therapists 3 (ft); Speech therapists 2 (ft); Dietitians 1 (pt).
Languages Sign
Affiliation Lutheran
Facilities Dining room; Each resident lives in an 8-person group home.
Activities Arts & crafts; Games; Shopping trips; Social/Cultural gatherings; Habilitative therapy.

Ye Olde House*
Rte 29, River Crest Center, Mont Clare, PA, 19453
(215) 935-1581
Licensure Intermediate care for mentally retarded. *Beds* 8. *Certified* Medicaid.
Owner Nonprofit Corp.

MONTOURSVILLE

Lysock View Nursing Home
RD 2, Montoursville, PA, 17754
(717) 433-3161
Admin Marcia F Bastress. *Medical Dir/Dir of Nursing* Dr Edith Murphy; Shirley Ferreri.
Licensure Skilled care; Intermediate care. *Beds* SNF; ICF 208. *Certified* Medicaid; Medicare.
Owner Publicly owned.
Admissions Requirements Medical examination.
Staff Physicians 1 (ft); RNs 8 (ft), 1 (pt); LPNs 26 (ft), 7 (pt); Orderlies 3 (ft); Nurses aides 57 (ft), 30 (pt); Physical therapists 2 (pt); Reality therapists 1 (pt); Recreational therapists 3 (ft); Speech therapists 2 (pt); Activities coordinators 1 (ft); Dietitians 2 (ft); Ophthalmologists 3 (pt).
Facilities Dining room; Physical therapy room; Activities room; Chapel; Crafts room; Laundry room; Barber/Beauty shop.
Activities Arts & crafts; Cards; Games; Reading groups; Prayer groups; Movies; Shopping trips; Social/Cultural gatherings; Dinner trips.

Sycamore Manor Nursing Home
Rte 3, Montoursville, PA, 17754
(717) 326-2037
Admin Edward Parks. *Medical Dir/Dir of Nursing* Dr Nancy Story; Carol Kopp RN.
Licensure Skilled care; Intermediate care. *Beds* SNF 40; ICF 83. *Certified* Medicaid; Medicare.
Owner Nonprofit Corp.
Staff RNs 4 (ft), 7 (pt); LPNs 10 (ft), 3 (pt); Orderlies 2 (ft); Nurses aides 36 (ft), 13 (pt); Physical therapists 1 (ft); Occupational therapists 1 (ft), 1 (pt); Dietitians 1 (pt).
Affiliation Presbyterian

Facilities Dining room; Physical therapy room; Activities room; Chapel; Laundry room; Barber/Beauty shop; Library.
Activities Arts & crafts; Games; Prayer groups; Movies; Shopping trips.

MONTROSE

Medical Arts Nursing Center Inc (Asa Park Manor)
Park St, Montrose, PA, 18801
(717) 278-3836
Admin Nancy Landes RN. *Medical Dir/Dir of Nursing* Paul B Kerr MD; Janet Daniels RN.
Licensure Skilled care. *Beds* SNF 63. *Certified* Medicaid; Medicare.
Owner Proprietary Corp.
Admissions Requirements Medical examination; Physician's request.
Staff Physicians 5 (ft); RNs 6 (ft), 7 (pt); LPNs 2 (ft), 2 (pt); Orderlies 1 (ft), 1 (pt); Nurses aides 16 (ft), 16 (pt); Physical therapists 1 (pt); Recreational therapists 1 (ft), 1 (pt); Speech therapists 1 (pt); Activities coordinators 1 (pt); Dietitians 1 (pt); Dentists 1 (pt); Ophthalmologists 1 (pt).
Facilities Dining room; Physical therapy room; Activities room; Chapel; Crafts room; Laundry room; Barber/Beauty shop.
Activities Arts & crafts; Cards; Games; Prayer groups; Movies; Social/Cultural gatherings.

MOUNTAINTOP

Davis Nursing Home Inc*
Rte 309, Mountaintop, PA, 18707
(717) 474-6378
Medical Dir/Dir of Nursing Dr Basil Rudusky.
Licensure Skilled care. *Beds* 79. *Certified* Medicaid; Medicare.
Owner Proprietary Corp.
Staff Physicians; RNs 11 (ft); LPNs 8 (ft); Nurses aides 40 (ft), 15 (pt); Physical therapists; Reality therapists 1 (ft), 1 (pt); Recreational therapists 1 (ft); Occupational therapists 1 (pt); Speech therapists 1 (pt); Activities coordinators 1 (ft), 1 (pt); Dietitians 1 (pt); Dentists 1 (pt); Ophthalmologists 1 (pt); Podiatrists 1 (ft); Audiologists 1 (pt).
Facilities Dining room; Physical therapy room; Activities room; Crafts room; Laundry room; Barber/Beauty shop.
Activities Arts & crafts; Cards; Games; Prayer groups; Shopping trips; Social/Cultural gatherings.

Smith Nursing & Convalescent Home of Mountaintop*
453 Main Rd, Mountaintop, PA, 18707
(717) 868-3664
Licensure Skilled care. *Beds* 16. *Certified* Medicaid.
Owner Proprietary Corp.

MUNCY

Muncy Valley Hospital—Skilled Nursing Facility*
215 E Water St, Muncy, PA, 17756
(717) 546-8282
Admin Sybil R Harriman. *Medical Dir/Dir of Nursing* Howard Weaner Jr MD.
Licensure Skilled care. *Beds* 59. *Certified* Medicaid; Medicare.
Owner Nonprofit Corp.
Admissions Requirements Medical examination; Physician's request.
Staff RNs 3 (ft); LPNs 4 (ft), 6 (pt); Nurses aides 15 (ft), 6 (pt); Speech therapists; Activities coordinators; Dietitians; Dentists; Ophthalmologists; Podiatrists.
Facilities Dining room; Physical therapy room; Activities room; Crafts room; Laundry room; Barber/Beauty shop.

Activities Arts & crafts; Cards; Games;
Reading groups; Prayer groups; Movies;
Shopping trips; Social/Cultural gatherings.

MUNHALL

Elder Crest Nursing Home*
2600 W Run Rd, Munhall, PA, 15120
(412) 462-8002
Admin Clara Radesausz. *Medical Dir/Dir of
Nursing* John C Wain MD.
Licensure Skilled care. *Beds* 48. *Certified*
Medicare.
Owner Proprietary Corp.
Admissions Requirements Minimum age 17.
Staff Physicians 1 (pt); RNs 2 (ft), 6 (pt);
Nurses aides 12 (ft), 13 (pt); Physical
therapists 1 (pt); Activities coordinators 1
(ft); Dietitians 1 (pt); Dentists 1 (pt);
Ophthalmologists 1 (pt); Podiatrists 1 (pt).
Facilities Dining room; Physical therapy
room; Activities room; Crafts room; Laundry
room; Barber/Beauty shop.
Activities Arts & crafts; Cards; Games;
Reading groups; Social/Cultural gatherings.

MURRAYSVILLE

Murray Manor Convalescent Center
3300 Logans Ferry Rd, Murraysville, PA,
15668
(412) 325-1500
Admin Daniel Landis. *Medical Dir/Dir of
Nursing* Walter Beam MD.
Licensure Skilled care; Intermediate care. *Beds*
SNF 35; ICF 88. *Certified* Medicaid;
Medicare.
Owner Proprietary Corp (Beverly Enterprises).
Admissions Requirements Medical
examination.
Staff RNs 8 (ft), 4 (pt) 13C 5 (ft), 3 (pt);
Nurses aides 25 (ft), 20 (pt); Physical
therapists 1 (pt); Occupational therapists 1
(pt); Speech therapists 1 (pt); Activities
coordinators 1 (ft), 1 (pt); Dietitians 1 (ft);
Dentists 1 (pt); Ophthalmologists 1 (pt).
Facilities Dining room; Physical therapy
room; Activities room; Laundry room;
Barber/Beauty shop; Library.
Activities Arts & crafts; Cards; Games;
Reading groups; Prayer groups; Movies;
Shopping trips; Social/Cultural gatherings;
Stroke group; Adopt-a-grandparent program.

MYERSTOWN

**Evangelical Congregational Church Retirement
Village**
S Railroad St, Myerstown, PA, 17067
(717) 866-6541
Admin Franklin H Schock. *Medical Dir/Dir of
Nursing* Dr Jose Sayson; Carol Johnston
DON.
Licensure Skilled care; Residential. *Beds* SNF
152; Residential 51. *Certified* Medicaid;
Medicare.
Owner Nonprofit Corp.
Admissions Requirements Minimum age 65
for residential; Medical examination.
Staff RNs 15 (ft); LPNs 13 (ft), 5 (pt); Nurses
aides 40 (ft), 40 (pt); Physical therapists 1
(ft); Recreational therapists 3 (ft), 1 (pt);
Occupational therapists 1 (pt); Speech
therapists 1 (pt); Activities coordinators 1
(ft); Dietitians 1 (pt); Dentists 1 (pt);
Ophthalmologists 1 (pt); Podiatrists 1 (pt).
Affiliation Congregational
Facilities Dining room; Physical therapy
room; Activities room; Chapel; Crafts room;
Laundry room; Barber/Beauty shop; Library.
Activities Arts & crafts; Cards; Games;
Reading groups; Prayer groups; Movies;
Shopping trips; Social/Cultural gatherings.

NANTICOKE

Birchwood Nursing Center
395 E Middle Rd, Nanticoke, PA, 18634
(717) 735-2973
Admin Michael P Kelly. *Medical Dir/Dir of
Nursing* Michael Kotch MD.
Licensure Skilled care; Intermediate care. *Beds*
SNF 60; ICF 61. *Certified* Medicaid;
Medicare.
Owner Proprietary Corp.
Staff Physicians 3 (pt); RNs 5 (ft), 3 (pt);
LPNs 7 (ft), 4 (pt); Nurses aides 25 (ft), 20
(pt); Physical therapists 1 (pt); Occupational
therapists 2 (pt); Activities coordinators 1
(ft), 2 (pt); Dietitians 1 (pt).
Languages Polish
Facilities Dining room; Physical therapy
room; Activities room; Crafts room; Laundry
room; Barber/Beauty shop; Smoking room;
Occupational therapy room.
Activities Arts & crafts; Cards; Games;
Reading groups; Prayer groups; Movies;
Shopping trips; Social/Cultural gatherings;
Baking; Photography; Music.

St Stanislaus Medical Care Center Inc
Newport St, Nanticoke, PA, 18634
(717) 735-7300
Admin Robert D Williams. *Medical Dir/Dir of
Nursing* Dr John Kennedy; Donald McHale.
Licensure Skilled care. *Beds* 100. *Certified*
Medicaid; Medicare.
Owner Nonprofit Corp.
Staff Physicians 5 (pt); RNs 7 (ft), 3 (pt);
LPNs 14 (ft), 1 (pt); Nurses aides 23 (ft), 19
(pt); Physical therapists 1 (pt); Recreational
therapists 1 (ft); Occupational therapists 1
(ft), 1 (pt); Speech therapists 1 (pt);
Activities coordinators 1 (ft); Dietitians 1
(pt); Dentists 1 (pt); Ophthalmologists 1 (pt);
Podiatrists 1 (pt).
Affiliation Roman Catholic
Facilities Dining room; Physical therapy
room; Activities room; Chapel; Laundry
room; Library.
Activities Arts & crafts; Cards; Games; Prayer
groups; Movies; Social/Cultural gatherings;
Musical events.

NARVON

Zerbe Sisters Nursing Center Inc
PO Box 209, Rte 1, Hammertown Rd,
Narvon, PA, 17555
(215) 445-4551
Admin Helen L Zerbe. *Medical Dir/Dir of
Nursing* Richard Bacon MD; Nancy Groff
RN DON.
Licensure Skilled care; Intermediate care;
Residential. *Beds* 79. *Certified* Medicaid;
Medicare.
Owner Proprietary Corp.
Admissions Requirements Medical
examination; Financial statement.
Staff Physicians 4 (pt); RNs 5 (ft), 5 (pt);
LPNs 3 (ft), 1 (pt); Nurses aides 24 (ft), 20
(pt); Occupational therapists 1 (pt); Speech
therapists 1 (pt); Activities coordinators 1
(ft); Dietitians 1 (pt); Ophthalmologists 1
(pt).
Languages Pennsylvania Dutch
Facilities Dining room; Physical therapy
room; Activities room; Crafts room; Laundry
room; Barber/Beauty shop; Recreation room.
Activities Arts & crafts; Cards; Games;
Reading groups; Prayer groups; Movies;
Social/Cultural gatherings; Recreational day
trips.

NAZARETH

Bible Fellowship Church Home
7 S New St, Nazareth, PA, 18064
(215) 759-5121
Admin Thomas Heimer. *Medical Dir/Dir of
Nursing* Dr Robert Vaughn; Barbara Greggo.

Licensure Intermediate care. *Beds* ICF 28.
Certified Medicaid.
Owner Nonprofit Corp.
Admissions Requirements Minimum age 65;
Medical examination.
Staff RNs 3 (pt); LPNs 1 (ft), 3 (pt); Nurses
aides 2 (ft), 9 (pt); Activities coordinators 1
(ft); Dietitians 1 (pt); Ophthalmologists 1
(pt).
Affiliation Bible Fellowship Church
Facilities Dining room; Chapel; Barber/Beauty
shop.
Activities Arts & crafts; Games; Reading
groups; Prayer groups; Shopping trips.

Northhampton County Home—Gracedale
Gracedale Avenue, Nazareth, PA, 18064-9213
(215) 759-3200
Admin Harold W Russell Jr. *Medical Dir/Dir
of Nursing* Wesley R Stancombe MD;
Marjorie M Milanak.
Licensure Skilled care; Intermediate care. *Beds*
SNF 200; ICF 591. *Certified* Medicaid;
Medicare.
Owner Nonprofit Corp.
Staff Physicians 1 (ft), 3 (pt); RNs 53 (ft), 50
(pt); LPNs 69 (ft), 41 (pt); Nurses aides 154
(ft), 189 (pt); Physical therapists 1 (ft);
Recreational therapists 7 (ft); Occupational
therapists 3 (ft); Speech therapists 1 (ft);
Activities coordinators 1 (ft); Dietitians 1
(ft); Dentists 1 (ft); Ophthalmologists 1 (ft);
Podiatrists 1 (ft); Audiologists 1 (ft).
Facilities Dining room; Physical therapy
room; Activities room; Chapel; Crafts room;
Laundry room; Barber/Beauty shop; Library.
Activities Arts & crafts; Cards; Games;
Reading groups; Prayer groups; Movies;
Shopping trips; Social/Cultural gatherings.

NEW BLOOMFIELD

Perry Village Nursing Home
PO Box 68, Rte 2, New Bloomfield, PA,
17068-9608
(717) 582-4346
Admin Willis A Smith Jr. *Medical Dir/Dir of
Nursing* Dr H Robert Gasull.
Licensure Skilled care; Intermediate care. *Beds*
SNF 13; ICF 110. *Certified* Medicaid;
Medicare.
Owner Nonprofit Corp (Tressler-Lutheran
Services Assoc).
Admissions Requirements Minimum age 65.
Staff Physicians 3 (pt); RNs 3 (ft), 10 (pt);
LPNs 4 (ft), 10 (pt); Nurses aides 22 (ft), 35
(pt); Physical therapists 1 (pt); Speech
therapists 1 (pt); Activities coordinators 1
(ft), 1 (pt); Dietitians 1 (pt); Dentists 1 (pt);
Ophthalmologists 1 (pt); Podiatrists 1 (pt).
Affiliation Lutheran
Facilities Dining room; Physical therapy
room; Activities room; Chapel; Crafts room;
Laundry room; Barber/Beauty shop; Library.
Activities Arts & crafts; Cards; Games;
Reading groups; Prayer groups; Movies;
Shopping trips; Social/Cultural gatherings;
Bus tours.

NEW BRIGHTON

**McGuire Memorial Home for Retired
Children***
2119 Mercer Rd, New Brighton, PA, 15066
(412) 843-3400
Licensure Intermediate care for mentally
retarded. *Beds* 99. *Certified* Medicaid.
Owner Nonprofit Corp.

NEW CASTLE

Almira Home*
1001 E Washington St, New Castle, PA,
16101
(412) 652-4131

Licensure Intermediate care. Beds 17.
Owner Nonprofit Corp.

Golden Hill Nursing Home Inc*
520 Friendship St, New Castle, PA, 16101
(412) 654-7791
Licensure Skilled care. Beds 204. Certified
Medicaid; Medicare.
Owner Proprietary Corp.

Haven Convalescent Home Inc
725 Paul St, New Castle, PA, 16101
(412) 654-8833
Admin Charles Tanner. Medical Dir/Dir of
Nursing M Abul Ela MD; Jean Dzemyan
RN.
Licensure Intermediate care. Beds 91.
Certified Medicaid.
Owner Proprietary Corp.
Admissions Requirements Minimum age 16;
Medical examination; Physician's request.
Staff Physicians; RNs; LPNs; Orderlies;
Nurses aides; Physical therapists; Reality
therapists; Speech therapists; Activities
coordinators; Dentists; Ophthalmologists.
Languages Italian
Facilities Dining room; Physical therapy
room; Activities room; Chapel; Crafts room;
Laundry room; Barber/Beauty shop.
Activities Arts & crafts; Cards; Games;
Reading groups; Prayer groups; Movies;
Shopping trips; Social/Cultural gatherings.

Highland Hall Care Center
239 W Pittsburgh Rd, New Castle, PA, 16101
(412) 658-4781
Admin Linda M Plowey NHA. Medical Dir/
Dir of Nursing Dr Raymond Seniow; Rita
June Hainer RN DON.
Licensure Intermediate care. Beds ICF 83.
Certified Medicaid.
Owner Proprietary Corp.
Admissions Requirements Medical
examination.
Staff RNs 3 (ft); LPNs 6 (ft), 1 (pt); Nurses
aides 24 (ft), 3 (pt); Recreational therapists 1
(ft); Activities coordinators 1 (ft); Dietitians
1 (ft).
Facilities Dining room; Activities room;
Crafts room; Laundry room; TV lounge.
Activities Arts & crafts; Cards; Games;
Reading groups; Movies; Shopping trips;
Social/Cultural gatherings; Special theme
days.

Hill View Manor
2801 Ellwood Rd, New Castle, PA, 16101
(412) 654-3672
Admin Mary Lou Corsi. Medical Dir/Dir of
Nursing Mohammad Ali MD; Ann Matteoni
DON.
Licensure Intermediate care. Beds ICF 136.
Certified Medicaid.
Owner Publicly owned.
Admissions Requirements Medical
examination.
Staff Physicians 1 (pt); RNs 6 (ft), 3 (pt);
LPNs 18 (ft); Orderlies 4 (ft), 1 (pt); Nurses
aides 40 (ft), 7 (pt); Recreational therapists 2
(ft); Activities coordinators 1 (ft);; Dietitians
1 (ft), 1 (pt); Activities aides 2 (ft).
Facilities Dining room; Activities room;
Chapel; Crafts room; Laundry room; Barber/
Beauty shop; Library.
Activities Arts & crafts; Cards; Games;
Reading groups; Prayer groups; Movies;
Shopping trips; Social/Cultural gatherings;
Adopt-a-grandparent program.

Indian Creek Nursing Center*
222 W Edison Ave, New Castle, PA, 16101
(412) 652-6340
Licensure Skilled care; Intermediate care. Beds
SNF 61; ICF 59. Certified Medicaid;
Medicare.
Owner Proprietary Corp (Health Care
Management).

Jack Rees Nursing & Rehabilitation Center*
715 Harbor St, New Castle, PA, 16101
(412) 652-3863
Medical Dir/Dir of Nursing Dr Ross Houston.
Licensure Skilled care; Intermediate care. Beds
SNF 51; ICF 33. Certified Medicaid;
Medicare.
Owner Proprietary Corp.
Admissions Requirements Minimum age 18.
Staff Physicians 2 (pt); RNs 3 (ft), 3 (pt);
LPNs 3 (ft), 4 (pt); Physical therapists 2 (pt);
Recreational therapists 1 (pt); Speech
therapists 1 (pt); Activities coordinators 1
(ft); Dietitians 1 (ft); Podiatrists 1 (pt).
Facilities Dining room; Physical therapy
room; Activities room; Crafts room; Laundry
room; Barber/Beauty shop; Library.
Activities Arts & crafts; Cards; Games;
Reading groups; Prayer groups; Movies;
Shopping trips; Social/Cultural gatherings.

NEW OXFORD

The Brethren Home
PO Box 128, 2990 Carlisle Pike, New Oxford,
PA, 17350
(717) 624-2161
Admin Harvey S Kline. Medical Dir/Dir of
Nursing David E Zickafoose MD; Ruth R
Carpenter RN DON.
Licensure Skilled care; Intermediate care;
Intermediate care for mentally retarded;
Independent living. Beds 284. Certified
Medicaid; Medicare.
Owner Nonprofit organization/foundation.
Admissions Requirements Minimum age 65;
Medical examination.
Staff RNs 11 (ft), 11 (pt); LPNs 18 (ft), 31
(pt); Orderlies 2 (pt); Nurses aides 39 (ft), 41
(pt); Activities coordinators 1 (ft); Dietitians
1 (ft).
Affiliation Church of the Brethren
Facilities Dining room; Physical therapy
room; Activities room; Chapel; Crafts room;
Laundry room; Barber/Beauty shop; Library;
Landscaped rural campus.
Activities Arts & crafts; Cards; Games;
Reading groups; Prayer groups; Movies;
Shopping trips; Social/Cultural gatherings.

NEW WILMINGTON

Overlook Medical Clinic Inc*
408 New Castle St, New Wilmington, PA,
16142
(412) 946-6113
Licensure Skilled care. Beds 105. Certified
Medicaid; Medicare.
Owner Proprietary Corp.

Shenango United Presbyterian Home
238 S Market St, New Wilmington, PA, 16142
(412) 946-3516
Admin Rev Ross Byers. Medical Dir/Dir of
Nursing Ella V DeSilvey RN.
Licensure Intermediate care; Residential care.
Beds ICF 25; Residential 41.
Owner Nonprofit Corp.
Admissions Requirements Minimum age 65;
Medical examination.
Staff RNs; LPNs; Nurses aides; Reality
therapists; Recreational therapists; Activities
coordinators; Dietitians.
Affiliation Presbyterian
Facilities Dining room; Activities room;
Chapel; Crafts room; Laundry room; Barber/
Beauty shop; Library; Lounges.
Activities Arts & crafts; Games; Reading
groups; Prayer groups; Movies; Social/
Cultural gatherings; Entertainment by college
& community groups.

NEWFOUNDLAND

Holiday Hill Nursing Home
PO Box 27A, Rte 7, Newfoundland, PA,
18445
(717) 676-3237
Admin Mary Seeley. Medical Dir/Dir of
Nursing Dr E Harasym; Mrs B Caldwell
DON.
Licensure Intermediate care; Intermediate care
for mentally retarded. Beds ICF 18; ICF/MR
7. Certified Medicaid.
Owner Nonprofit organization/foundation.
Admissions Requirements Medical
examination; Physician's request.
Staff RNs 3 (ft); LPNs 5 (ft); Nurses aides 8
(ft), 1 (pt); Activities coordinators 1 (ft);
Dietitians 1 (pt); Ophthalmologists 1 (pt).
Facilities Dining room; Activities room;
Laundry room.
Activities Arts & crafts; Cards; Games;
Reading groups; Prayer groups; Movies;
Shopping trips; Social/Cultural gatherings.

NEWTOWN

Chandler Hall Health Services
Barclay St & Buck Rd, Newtown, PA, 18940
(215) 860-4000
Licensure Skilled care. Beds 55. Certified
Medicaid; Medicare.
Owner Nonprofit Corp.

Pennswood Village
Rte 413, Newtown, PA, 18940
(215) 493-2177
Admin Michael Levengood. Medical Dir/Dir
of Nursing James C Alden MD; Patricia
Smith DON.
Licensure Skilled care; Independent living.
Beds SNF 45; Independent living 252.
Certified Medicare.
Owner Nonprofit Corp.
Admissions Requirements Minimum age 65.
Staff Physicians 1 (ft), 1 (pt); RNs 6 (ft), 7
(pt); LPNs 9 (ft), 4 (pt); Orderlies 1 (ft);
Nurses aides 17 (ft), 10 (pt); Physical
therapists 1 (ft); Occupational therapists 1
(pt); Speech therapists 1 (pt); Activities
coordinators 2 (ft); Dietitians 2 (ft).
Affiliation Society of Friends
Facilities Dining room; Physical therapy
room; Activities room; Crafts room; Laundry
room; Barber/Beauty shop; Library; Game
room; Auditorium; Greenhouse; Resident
meeting rooms.
Activities Arts & crafts; Cards; Games;
Reading groups; Movies; Shopping trips;
Social/Cultural gatherings.

Pickering Manor*
Lincoln Ave, Newtown, PA, 18940
(215) 968-3878
Medical Dir/Dir of Nursing Blaine R Garner
MD.
Licensure Skilled care. Beds 47. Certified
Medicaid; Medicare.
Owner Nonprofit Corp.
Admissions Requirements Minimum age 18.
Facilities Dining room; Physical therapy
room; Activities room; Laundry room;
Barber/Beauty shop; Library.
Activities Arts & crafts; Cards; Games;
Reading groups; Prayer groups; Movies;
Shopping trips; Social/Cultural gatherings.

NEWTOWN SQUARE

Dowden Nursing Home
3503 Rhoads Ave, Newtown Square, PA,
19073
(215) 356-7423
Admin Anna E Helfrich. Medical Dir/Dir of
Nursing Robert McAndrew DO.
Licensure Skilled care. Beds 51.
Owner Proprietary Corp.

Staff RNs 4 (ft); LPNs 4 (ft), 2 (pt); Nurses aides 19 (ft), 3 (pt); Physical therapists 1 (pt); Reality therapists 1 (ft); Recreational therapists 2 (pt); Activities coordinators 1 (ft); Dietitians 1 (pt); Art therapists 1 (pt).
Facilities Dining room; Activities room; Laundry room; Barber/Beauty shop.
Activities Arts & crafts; Cards; Games; Reading groups; Movies; Shopping trips; Social/Cultural gatherings.

Dunwoody Home Medical Center*
3500 West Chester Pike, Newtown Square, PA, 19073
(215) 359-4400
Licensure Skilled care. *Beds* 71. *Certified* Medicare.
Owner Nonprofit Corp.

NEWVILLE

Swaim Health Center
Green Ridge Village, Big Spring Rd, Newville, PA, 17241
(717) 776-3192
Admin Linda H Blunning. *Medical Dir/Dir of Nursing* J A Townsend MD; Martha Yerger RN DON.
Licensure Continuing care; Retirement community. *Beds* SNF 60; Residential 13; ILU 72. *Certified* Medicaid; Medicare.
Owner Nonprofit Corp.
Admissions Requirements Medical examination; Physician's request.
Staff Physicians; RNs 2 (ft), 2 (pt); LPNs 3 (ft), 4 (pt); Physical therapists 1 (pt); Occupational therapists; Speech therapists; Activities coordinators 1 (ft), 3 (pt); Dietitians; Ophthalmologists; Podiatrists.
Affiliation Presbyterian
Facilities Dining room; Physical therapy room; Activities room; Chapel; Crafts room; Laundry room; Barber/Beauty shop; Library; Conference; Community.
Activities Arts & crafts; Cards; Games; Reading groups; Prayer groups; Movies; Shopping trips; Social/Cultural gatherings; Trips.

NORRISTOWN

Leader Health Care Center*
2004 Old Arch Rd, Norristown, PA, 19401
(215) 277-0380
Medical Dir/Dir of Nursing John McLoone MD.
Licensure Skilled care. *Beds* 120. *Certified* Medicaid; Medicare.
Owner Proprietary Corp (Manor Care).
Admissions Requirements Medical examination.
Staff RNs 14 (ft); LPNs 11 (ft); Nurses aides 45 (ft); Physical therapists 1 (ft); Reality therapists 1 (ft); Recreational therapists 1 (ft); Occupational therapists 1 (pt); Speech therapists 1 (ft); Activities coordinators 1 (ft); Dietitians 1 (ft); Audiologists 1 (pt).

Plymouth House Health Care Center
900 E Germantown Pike, Norristown, PA, 19401
(215) 279-7300
Admin Sally Lucas. *Medical Dir/Dir of Nursing* James Bard MD; Barbara Koch RN DON.
Licensure Skilled care; Intermediate care. *Beds* SNF 30; ICF 120. *Certified* Medicaid; Medicare.
Owner Proprietary Corp.
Admissions Requirements Minimum age 18; Medical examination.
Staff Physicians 54 (pt); RNs 12 (ft), 8 (pt); LPNs 7 (ft), 3 (pt); Orderlies 1 (ft); Nurses aides 52 (ft), 21 (pt); Physical therapists 1 (pt); Recreational therapists 1 (ft), 1 (pt); Occupational therapists 1 (pt); Speech

therapists 1 (pt); Activities coordinators 1 (ft); Dietitians 1 (ft); Dentists 1 (pt); Ophthalmologists 1 (pt); Podiatrists 1 (pt).
Facilities Dining room; Physical therapy room; Activities room; Chapel; Crafts room; Laundry room; Barber/Beauty shop; Library.
Activities Arts & crafts; Cards; Games; Reading groups; Prayer groups; Movies; Shopping trips; Social/Cultural gatherings.

Regina Community Nursing Center
550 E Fornance St, Norristown, PA, 19401
(215) 272-5600
Admin Joseph Stimmler. *Medical Dir/Dir of Nursing* Charles Cutler MD; Alice M Hagel RN DON.
Licensure Skilled care. *Beds* SNF 121. *Certified* Medicaid; Medicare.
Owner Nonprofit Corp.
Facilities Dining room; Physical therapy room; Activities room; Crafts room; Laundry room; Barber/Beauty shop.
Activities Arts & crafts; Cards; Games; Prayer groups; Movies; Shopping trips; Social/Cultural gatherings.

NORTH HUNTINGDON

Briarcliff Pavilion Special Care
249 Maus Dr, North Huntingdon, PA, 15642
(412) 863-4374
Admin Janet Maxwell. *Medical Dir/Dir of Nursing* John M Aber MD; Mary Ann Nye RN.
Licensure Skilled care; Intermediate care. *Beds* SNF 55; ICF 65. *Certified* Medicaid; Medicare; VA.
Owner Proprietary Corp.
Admissions Requirements Minimum age 18; Medical examination; Physician's request.
Staff Physicians 1 (pt); RNs 7 (ft), 3 (pt); LPNs 6 (ft), 3 (pt); Nurses aides 33 (ft), 14 (pt); Physical therapists 1 (pt); Reality therapists 1 (pt); Occupational therapists 1 (pt); Speech therapists 1 (pt); Activities coordinators 2 (ft); Dietitians 1 (pt); Dentists 1 (pt); Podiatrists 1 (pt); Psychiatrist 1 (pt); Social worker 1 (ft).
Facilities Dining room; Physical therapy room; Activities room; Crafts room; Laundry room; Barber/Beauty shop.
Activities Arts & crafts; Cards; Games; Reading groups; Prayer groups; Movies; Shopping trips; Social/Cultural gatherings; Nationality day each month.

NORTH WALES

Angeline Nursing Home Inc*
Rte 309 & N Wales Rd, North Wales, PA, 19545
(215) 855-8670
Licensure Skilled care. *Beds* 32. *Certified* Medicaid.
Owner Proprietary Corp.

NORTHUMBERLAND

Nottingham Village*
Strawbridge Rd, Northumberland, PA, 17857
(717) 473-8366
Licensure Skilled care. *Beds* 121. *Certified* Medicaid; Medicare.
Owner Proprietary Corp.

Pleasant View Convalescent Home*
Rte 1, Northumberland, PA, 17857
(717) 473-9433
Licensure Skilled care. *Beds* 26. *Certified* Medicaid.
Owner Proprietary Corp.

OAKMONT

Oakmont Nursing Center
26 Ann St, Oakmont, PA, 15139
(412) 828-7300
Admin James E Neely. *Medical Dir/Dir of Nursing* T J Ferguson MD; Delores Bracco DON.
Licensure Skilled care; Intermediate care. *Beds* SNF 35; ICF 46. *Certified* Medicaid; Medicare.
Owner Proprietary Corp (Beverly Enterprises).
Staff Physicians 10 (pt); RNs 3 (ft), 1 (pt); LPNs 4 (ft), 2 (pt); Orderlies 1 (ft); Nurses aides 13 (ft), 4 (pt); Physical therapists 1 (pt); Occupational therapists 1 (pt); Speech therapists 1 (pt); Activities coordinators 1 (ft); Dietitians 1 (pt); Ophthalmologists 1 (pt).

Presbyterian Medical Center of Oakmont
1205 Hulton Rd, Oakmont, PA, 15139
(412) 828-5600
Admin Paul A Winkler. *Medical Dir/Dir of Nursing* Judith Ferguson RN.
Licensure Skilled care; Intermediate care; Post-acute rehabilitation care. *Beds* SNF 46; ICF 156. *Certified* Medicaid; Medicare.
Owner Nonprofit organization/foundation.
Admissions Requirements Medical examination; Physician's request.
Staff Physicians; RNs; LPNs; Orderlies; Nurses aides; Physical therapists; Recreational therapists; Occupational therapists; Speech therapists; Activities coordinators; Dietitians; Dentists; Ophthalmologists; Podiatrists.
Affiliation Presbyterian
Facilities Dining room; Physical therapy room; Activities room; Chapel; Crafts room; Laundry room; Barber/Beauty shop; Library; Occupational therapy room; Speech & hearing clinic; Soda fountain; Gift shop.
Activities Arts & crafts; Cards; Games; Reading groups; Prayer groups; Movies; Shopping trips; Social/Cultural gatherings.

OIL CITY

Grandview Health Care Inc—Oil City*
1293 Grandview Rd, Oil City, PA, 16301
(814) 676-8208
Medical Dir/Dir of Nursing Dr Gold.
Licensure Skilled care; Intermediate care. *Beds* SNF 25; ICF 124. *Certified* Medicaid; Medicare.
Owner Proprietary Corp (Beverly Enterprises).
Admissions Requirements Minimum age 16; Medical examination.
Staff Physicians 1 (pt); RNs 3 (ft), 1 (pt); LPNs 1 (ft), 3 (pt); Nurses aides 13 (ft), 5 (pt); Speech therapists 1 (pt); Activities coordinators 1 (ft), 1 (pt); Dietitians 1 (ft).
Facilities Dining room; Physical therapy room; Activities room; Crafts room; Laundry room; Barber/Beauty shop.
Activities Arts & crafts; Cards; Games; Reading groups; Movies; Shopping trips; Social/Cultural gatherings.

Oil City Presbyterian Home
10 Vo Tech Dr, Oil City, PA, 16301
(814) 676-8686
Admin Yvonne D Atkinson. *Medical Dir/Dir of Nursing* Edward Kepp MD; Sandra Leta DON.
Licensure Skilled care; Intermediate care. *Beds* SNF 31; ICF 90. *Certified* Medicaid; Medicare.
Owner Nonprofit Corp.
Admissions Requirements Minimum age 18; Medical examination.
Staff Physicians 1 (pt); RNs 6 (ft), 2 (pt); LPNs 8 (ft), 11 (pt); Nurses aides 35 (ft), 19 (pt); Activities coordinators 1 (ft), 2 (pt).
Affiliation Presbyterian

Facilities Dining room; Physical therapy room; Activities room; Crafts room; Laundry room; Barber/Beauty shop; Library.
Activities Arts & crafts; Cards; Games; Reading groups; Prayer groups; Movies; Shopping trips; Social/Cultural gatherings.

Presbyterian Home
701 N Perry St, Oil City, PA, 16354
(814) 827-1221
Admin Carol B Cauvel.
Licensure Personal care. *Beds* 25.
Owner Nonprofit Corp.
Staff LPNs; Nurses aides.

OLYPHANT

Lackawanna County Home*
Rte 1, Olyphant, PA, 18447
(717) 489-8611
Medical Dir/Dir of Nursing Dr Clause.
Licensure Skilled care; Intermediate care. *Beds* SNF 150; ICF 50. *Certified* Medicaid; Medicare.
Owner Publicly owned.
Staff Physicians 4 (pt); RNs 9 (ft); LPNs 12 (ft); Orderlies 6 (ft); Nurses aides 74 (ft); Physical therapists 1 (ft); Reality therapists; Recreational therapists 1 (ft); Occupational therapists; Speech therapists; Activities coordinators; Dietitians; Dentists; Ophthalmologists; Podiatrists; Audiologists.
Facilities Dining room; Physical therapy room; Activities room; Crafts room; Laundry room; Barber/Beauty shop; Library.
Activities Arts & crafts; Cards; Games; Reading groups; Prayer groups; Movies; Shopping trips; Social/Cultural gatherings.

ORANGEVILLE

Char Mund Nursing Home*
Rte 2, Orangeville, PA, 17859
(717) 683-5333
Licensure Skilled care. *Beds* 36. *Certified* Medicaid; Medicare.
Owner Proprietary Corp.

Klingerman Nursing Center
Rte 2, Orangeville, PA, 17859
(717) 683-5036
Admin Mahlon L Fritz, Sr. *Medical Dir/Dir of Nursing* Richard Delp; Gayl Klingerman.
Licensure Intermediate care. *Beds* ICF 118. *Certified* Medicaid.
Owner Proprietary Corp.
Admissions Requirements Physician's request.
Staff Physicians 2 (ft), 5 (pt); RNs 4 (ft), 6 (pt); LPNs 4 (ft), 1 (pt); Orderlies 1 (ft), 1 (pt); Nurses aides 28 (ft), 13 (pt); Physical therapists 1 (pt); Reality therapists 1 (ft), 1 (pt); Recreational therapists 1 (ft), 1 (pt); Activities coordinators 1 (ft), 1 (pt); Dietitians 1 (pt); Dentists 1 (pt); Podiatrists 2 (pt).
Facilities Dining room; Activities room; Chapel; Crafts room; Laundry room; Barber/Beauty shop.
Activities Arts & crafts; Cards; Games; Reading groups; Prayer groups; Movies; Shopping trips; Social/Cultural gatherings.

ORBISONIA

Woodland Retirement Center
PO Box 280, Rte 522, Orbisonia, PA, 17243
(814) 447-5563
Admin Phyullis S Bard NHA. *Medical Dir/Dir of Nursing* Dr Gary Wertman DO; Sandra Whitsel DON.
Licensure Skilled care; Intermediate care. *Beds* SNF 90; ICF. *Certified* Medicaid; Medicare; VA.
Owner Proprietary Corp.
Admissions Requirements Minimum age 18; Medical examination; Physician's request.

Staff Physicians 1 (ft); RNs 4 (ft), 3 (pt); LPNs 7 (ft), 6 (pt); Nurses aides 24 (ft), 26 (pt); Physical therapists 1 (pt); Recreational therapists 1 (ft), 1 (pt); Occupational therapists 1 (pt); Speech therapists 1 (pt); Activities coordinators 1 (ft); Dietitians 1 (pt); Dentists 1 (pt); Ophthalmologists 1 (pt).
Facilities Dining room; Physical therapy room; Activities room; Chapel; Crafts room; Laundry room; Barber/Beauty shop; Library Medical.
Activities Arts & crafts; Cards; Games; Reading groups; Prayer groups; Movies; Shopping trips; Social/Cultural gatherings.

OXFORD

Oxford Manor, The Steward Home & The Woods at Oxford Manor
7 E Locust St, Oxford, PA, 19363
(215) 932-2900
Admin Geoffrey L Henry. *Medical Dir/Dir of Nursing* Dr Faye R Doyle; Roberta Zaffarano RN DON.
Licensure Skilled care; Intermediate care; Continuing care retirement community. *Beds* SNF 100; PCB 40; ILU 34. *Certified* Medicaid; Medicare.
Owner Nonprofit Corp.
Admissions Requirements Medical examination.
Staff Physicians 10 (pt); RNs 4 (ft), 5 (pt); LPNs 2 (ft), 2 (pt); Nurses aides 40 (ft); Physical therapists 1 (pt); Occupational therapists 1 (pt); Activities coordinators 1 (ft); Dietitians 1 (ft).
Affiliation Presbyterian
Facilities Dining room; Physical therapy room; Activities room; Crafts room; Laundry room; Barber/Beauty shop; Library.
Activities Arts & crafts; Cards; Games; Reading groups; Prayer groups; Movies; Shopping trips; Social/Cultural gatherings.

PALMYRA

Lebanon Valley Brethren Home*
1200 Grubb St, Palmyra, PA, 17078
(717) 838-5406
Licensure Skilled care; Intermediate care. *Beds* SNF 60; ICF 40. *Certified* Medicaid; Medicare.
Owner Nonprofit Corp.

Palmyra Nursing Home
341-45 N Railroad St, Palmyra, PA, 17078
(717) 838-3011
Admin Juan B Brouch. *Medical Dir/Dir of Nursing* Harold H Engle MD.
Licensure Skilled care. *Beds* 39. *Certified* Medicaid; Medicare.
Owner Proprietary Corp.
Staff Physicians 1 (pt); RNs 2 (ft), 2 (pt); LPNs 1 (ft), 2 (pt); Nurses aides 7 (ft), 9 (pt); Physical therapists 1 (ft), 1 (pt); Recreational therapists 1 (ft); Speech therapists 1 (pt); Activities coordinators 1 (ft); Dietitians 1 (pt); Dentists 1 (pt); Ophthalmologists 1 (pt); Podiatrists 1 (pt); Dentist 1 (pt).
Facilities Dining room; Physical therapy room; Activities room; Laundry room; Barber/Beauty shop.
Activities Arts & crafts; Cards; Games; Reading groups; Prayer groups; Movies; Shopping trips; Social/Cultural gatherings.

PAOLI

Main Line Nursing & Rehabilitation Center
PO Box E, 283 E Lancaster Ave, Paoli, PA, 19301
(215) 296-4170
Admin Donna M Howard RN. *Medical Dir/Dir of Nursing* Ernest F Gillan MD; Sandra C Lutte RN.

Licensure Skilled care; Intermediate care. *Beds* SNF 120; ICF 60. *Certified* Medicaid; Medicare.
Owner Nonprofit Corp.
Staff Physicians 1 (ft); RNs 14 (ft); LPNs 19 (ft), 3 (pt); Orderlies 5 (ft); Nurses aides 55 (ft); Physical therapists 1 (ft); Recreational therapists 2 (ft); Occupational therapists 1 (pt); Speech therapists 1 (pt); Activities coordinators 1 (ft); Dietitians 1 (pt); Ophthalmologists 1 (pt); Dentist 1 (pt).
Languages Spanish, Italian, German, Polish
Facilities Dining room; Physical therapy room; Activities room; Crafts room; Laundry room; Barber/Beauty shop.
Activities Arts & crafts; Cards; Games; Reading groups; Prayer groups; Movies; Social/Cultural gatherings.

PENNSBURG

Pennsburg Manor
5th and Macoby Sts, Pennsburg, PA, 18073
(215) 679-8076
Admin Carole L Monahan RN NHA. *Medical Dir/Dir of Nursing* Norbert Leska MD; Mary Camargo RN DON.
Licensure Skilled care. *Beds* 120. *Certified* Medicaid; Medicare.
Owner Proprietary Corp (GraceCare, Inc).
Staff Physicians 8 (pt); RNs 5 (ft), 10 (pt); LPNs 3 (ft), 8 (pt); Nurses aides 27 (ft), 39 (pt); Physical therapists 1 (pt); Speech therapists 1 (pt); Activities coordinators 1 (ft); Dietitians 1 (ft); Dentists 1 (pt); Ophthalmologists 2 (pt); Podiatrists 1 (pt).
Languages Pennsylvania Dutch, Spanish
Facilities Dining room; Physical therapy room; Activities room; Laundry room; Barber/Beauty shop.
Activities Arts & crafts; Cards; Games; Reading groups; Prayer groups; Movies; Social/Cultural gatherings.

PHILADELPHIA

Ashton Hall Nursing & Convalescent Home*
2109 Red Lion Rd, Philadelphia, PA, 19114
(215) 673-7000
Licensure Skilled care. *Beds* 148. *Certified* Medicaid; Medicare.
Owner Proprietary Corp.

The Baptist Home of Philadelphia
8301 Roosevelt Blvd, Philadelphia, PA, 19152
(215) 624-7575
Admin David A Smiley NHA. *Medical Dir/Dir of Nursing* Dr Vernando Jaurique; Emily Cervonka.
Licensure Skilled care; Intermediate care; Residential care. *Beds* SNF 111; ICF 98; Residential 176. *Certified* Medicaid; Medicare.
Owner Nonprofit Corp.
Admissions Requirements Minimum age 65; Medical examination.
Staff Physicians 5 (pt); RNs 4 (ft), 1 (pt); LPNs 12 (ft), 11 (pt); Nurses aides 59 (ft), 18 (pt); Physical therapists 1 (ft); Recreational therapists 4 (ft), 1 (pt); Activities coordinators 2 (ft); Dietitians 1 (ft).
Affiliation Baptist
Facilities Dining room; Physical therapy room; Activities room; Chapel; Crafts room; Laundry room; Barber/Beauty shop; Library; Gift shop.
Activities Arts & crafts; Cards; Games; Prayer groups; Shopping trips; Social/Cultural gatherings; Bingo; Basketball (with Nurf ball); Gardening.

Boulevard Nursing Home
7950 Roosevelt Blvd, Philadelphia, PA, 19152
(215) 332-3700

Admin Catherine Dowd. *Medical Dir/Dir of Nursing* Bernard Cramer MD; Mary Antonio RN DON.
Licensure Skilled care; Intermediate care. *Beds* SNF 90; ICF 45. *Certified* Medicaid; Medicare.
Owner Proprietary Corp.
Admissions Requirements Minimum age 25; Medical examination; Physician's request.
Staff Physicians; RNs; LPNs; Nurses aides; Physical therapists; Recreational therapists; Occupational therapists; Speech therapists; Activities coordinators; Dietitians; Dentists; Ophthalmologists; Podiatrists.
Facilities Dining room; Physical therapy room; Activities room; Crafts room; Laundry room; Barber/Beauty shop.
Activities Arts & crafts; Cards; Games; Reading groups; Prayer groups; Movies; Shopping trips; Social/Cultural gatherings.

Care Pavilion of Walnut Park*
6212 Walnut St, Philadelphia, PA, 19139
(215) 476-6264
Medical Dir/Dir of Nursing Dr R Weisberg.
Licensure Skilled care; Intermediate care. *Beds* SNF 258; ICF 120. *Certified* Medicaid; Medicare.
Owner Proprietary Corp (Geriatric & Medical Centers).
Staff Physicians 6 (pt); RNs 20 (ft), 6 (pt); LPNs 30 (ft), 10 (pt); Nurses aides 180 (ft), 20 (pt); Physical therapists 1 (ft), 1 (pt); Recreational therapists 4 (ft), 1 (pt); Occupational therapists 1 (pt); Speech therapists 1 (ft); Activities coordinators 1 (ft); Dietitians 1 (ft).
Facilities Dining room; Physical therapy room; Activities room; Laundry room; Barber/Beauty shop.
Activities Arts & crafts; Cards; Games; Reading groups; Prayer groups; Movies; Shopping trips; Social/Cultural gatherings.

Cathedral Village
600 E Cathedral Rd, Philadelphia, PA, 19128
(215) 487-1300
Admin Judith A Hernan BSN NHA. *Medical Dir/Dir of Nursing* Dr Robert V Smith; Carol Joyce DON.
Licensure Skilled care. *Beds* SNF 148. *Certified* Medicaid; Medicare.
Owner Nonprofit Corp.
Admissions Requirements Minimum age 65 & must need nursing home care.
Staff Physicians 2 (pt); RNs 5 (ft), 20 (pt); LPNs 2 (ft), 4 (pt); Nurses aides 32 (ft), 47 (pt); Physical therapists 1 (ft); Recreational therapists 1 (ft), 1 (pt); Occupational therapists 1 (pt); Speech therapists 1 (pt); Activities coordinators 1 (ft), 1 (pt); Dietitians 1 (ft), 1 (pt); Dentists 1 (pt); Ophthalmologists 1 (pt); Podiatrists 1 (pt).
Affiliation Episcopal
Facilities Dining room; Physical therapy room; Activities room; Crafts room; Laundry room; Barber/Beauty shop; Library.
Activities Arts & crafts; Cards; Games; Reading groups; Prayer groups; Movies; Shopping trips; Social/Cultural gatherings; Exercise group; Current events group; SPCA visits; Childrens hour; Cocktail parties.

Central Park Lodge—Chestnut Hill
8833 Stenton Ave, Philadelphia, PA, 19118
(215) 247-8800
Admin Jeffrey T Brown. *Medical Dir/Dir of Nursing* Lawrence Kessel MD; Betty Boclair RN.
Licensure Skilled care. *Beds* 195. *Certified* Medicaid; Medicare.
Owner Proprietary Corp.
Staff Physicians 45 (pt); RNs 8 (ft), 9 (pt); LPNs 8 (ft), 5 (pt); Nurses aides 53 (ft), 18 (pt); Physical therapists 1 (pt); Activities coordinators 2 (ft), 1 (pt); Dietitians 1 (pt).

Facilities Dining room; Physical therapy room; Activities room; Laundry room; Barber/Beauty shop.
Activities Arts & crafts; Cards; Games; Reading groups; Movies; Shopping trips; Social/Cultural gatherings.

Central Park Lodge Nursing Home-Whitemarsh
9209 Ridge Pike, Philadelphia, PA, 19128
(215) 825-6560
Admin Jeanne V Bund. *Medical Dir/Dir of Nursing* Patricia Cubbin DON.
Licensure Skilled care. *Beds* 227. *Certified* Medicaid; Medicare.
Owner Proprietary Corp.
Staff Physicians 1 (ft); RNs 12 (ft), 4 (pt); LPNs 16 (ft), 4 (pt); Orderlies; Nurses aides 100 (ft), 30 (pt); Physical therapists 1 (ft); Reality therapists; Recreational therapists 3 (ft), 1 (pt); Occupational therapists 1 (pt); Speech therapists 1 (pt); Activities coordinators; Dietitians 1 (ft); Dentists 1 (pt); Ophthalmologists 1 (pt); Podiatrists 1 (pt).
Languages Spanish, Korean
Facilities Dining room; Physical therapy room; Activities room; Laundry room; Barber/Beauty shop.
Activities Arts & crafts; Cards; Games; Reading groups; Prayer groups; Movies; Shopping trips; Social/Cultural gatherings; Cocktail hour.

Chapel Manor Nursing & Convalescent Home*
1104 Welsh Rd, Philadelphia, PA, 19115
(215) 676-9191
Licensure Skilled care. *Beds* 144. *Certified* Medicaid; Medicare.
Owner Proprietary Corp.

Cheltenham Nursing & Rehabilitation Center
600 W Cheltenham Ave, Philadelphia, PA, 19126
(215) 927-7300
Licensure Skilled care. *Beds* 255. *Certified* Medicaid; Medicare.
Owner Proprietary Corp (Geriatric & Medical Centers).

Cheltenham-York Road Nursing Rehabilitation Center*
7107 Old York Rd, Philadelphia, PA, 19126
(215) 424-4090
Licensure Skilled care. *Beds* 125. *Certified* Medicaid.
Owner Proprietary Corp (Geriatric & Medical Centers).

Cobbs Creek Nursing Inc*
6900 Cobbs Creek Pkwy, Philadelphia, PA, 19142
(215) 729-1414
Licensure Skilled care. *Beds* 219. *Certified* Medicaid; Medicare.
Owner Proprietary Corp.

Combined Rehabilitation Services Inc
9990 Verree Rd, Philadelphia, PA, 19115
(215) 677-9500
Admin Joseph W Lista. *Medical Dir/Dir of Nursing* Richard Mirabelli MD; Delores Redner RN.
Licensure Intermediate care for mentally retarded. *Beds* ICF/MR 161. *Certified* Medicaid.
Owner Nonprofit Corp.
Admissions Requirements Medical examination.
Staff Physicians; RNs; LPNs; Orderlies; Nurses aides; Physical therapists; Recreational therapists; Occupational therapists; Speech therapists; Activities coordinators; Dietitians; Dentists; Ophthalmologists; Podiatrists.
Facilities Dining room; Physical therapy room; Activities room; Crafts room; Laundry room.

Activities Arts & crafts; Cards; Games; Prayer groups; Movies; Shopping trips; Social/Cultural gatherings; Developmental training.

Elmira Jeffries Memorial Home*
1500-1514 N Fifteenth St, Philadelphia, PA, 19121
(215) 785-3201
Licensure Skilled care. *Beds* 180. *Certified* Medicaid; Medicare.
Owner Proprietary Corp (HBA Management Inc).

Evangelical Manor
8401 Roosevelt Blvd, Philadelphia, PA, 19152
(215) 624-5800
Medical Dir/Dir of Nursing Dr John C Crawford; Irene Contino RN DON.
Licensure Skilled care; Intermediate care; Retirement Apartments. *Beds* SNF 60; ICF 60; Retirement Apts 194. *Certified* Medicaid; Medicare.
Owner Nonprofit Corp.
Admissions Requirements Minimum age 65; Medical examination.
Staff Physicians 1 (ft); RNs; LPNs; Orderlies; Nurses aides; Physical therapists 1 (ft); Recreational therapists 2 (ft); Occupational therapists 1 (pt); Speech therapists 1 (pt); Activities coordinators 1 (ft); Dietitians 1 (ft); Dentists 1 (pt); Ophthalmologists 1 (pt); Podiatrists 1 (pt).
Affiliation Methodist
Facilities Dining room; Physical therapy room; Activities room; Chapel; Crafts room; Laundry room; Barber/Beauty shop; Library.
Activities Arts & crafts; Cards; Games; Reading groups; Prayer groups; Movies; Shopping trips; Social/Cultural gatherings; Senior Olympics; Theme dinners; Drug holiday program.

Fairmount Geriatric Center
4001 Ford Rd, Philadelphia, PA, 19131
(215) 877-5400
Admin Arnold Leof. *Medical Dir/Dir of Nursing* Dr Eric Shore; Evelyn Ebora RN DON.
Licensure Skilled care; Intermediate care. *Beds* SNF 30; ICF 85. *Certified* Medicaid; Medicare.
Owner Nonprofit Corp.
Admissions Requirements Minimum age 65; Medical examination; Physician's request.
Staff Physicians; RNs 5 (ft); LPNs 7 (ft); Orderlies 2 (ft); Nurses aides 40 (ft); Physical therapists; Recreational therapists 1 (ft); Speech therapists; Activities coordinators 1 (ft); Dietitians; Dentists; Ophthalmologists; Podiatrists.
Languages Hebrew, Yiddish
Affiliation Jewish
Facilities Dining room; Physical therapy room; Activities room; Chapel; Crafts room; Laundry room; Barber/Beauty shop; Library.
Activities Arts & crafts; Cards; Games; Reading groups; Prayer groups; Movies; Shopping trips; Social/Cultural gatherings.

Fairview Care Center of Bethlehem Pike
184 Bethlehem Pike, Philadelphia, PA, 19118
(215) 247-5311
Admin Frank J Marchese III. *Medical Dir/Dir of Nursing* Dr Harry Borgersen DO; Laura Stauffer RN.
Licensure Intermediate care. *Beds* 153. *Certified* Medicaid.
Owner Proprietary Corp (Geriatric & Medical Centers).
Admissions Requirements Medical examination; Physician's request.
Staff Physicians 1 (pt); RNs 3 (ft), 2 (pt); LPNs 5 (ft), 2 (pt); Nurses aides 65 (ft), 25 (pt); Physical therapists 2 (ft); Recreational therapists 2 (ft), 1 (pt); Activities coordinators 1 (ft); Dietitians 1 (ft); Dentists 1 (pt); Ophthalmologists 1 (pt); Podiatrists 1 (pt).

Facilities Dining room; Physical therapy room; Activities room; Crafts room; Laundry room; Barber/Beauty shop.
Activities Arts & crafts; Cards; Games; Reading groups; Prayer groups.

Fairview Care Center of Papermill Rd
850 Papermill Rd, Philadelphia, PA, 19118
(215) 247-0595
Admin R June Hudak. *Medical Dir/Dir of Nursing* Louis A Pegel MD; Pat Fritz DON.
Licensure Skilled care; Intermediate care. *Beds* SNF 37; ICF 107. *Certified* Medicaid; Medicare.
Owner Proprietary Corp (Geriatric & Medical Centers).
Admissions Requirements Medical examination.
Staff Physicians 20 (pt); RNs 9 (ft), 5 (pt); LPNs 10 (ft), 4 (pt); Nurses aides 50 (ft), 25 (pt); Physical therapists 1 (ft); Recreational therapists 1 (ft); Occupational therapists 1 (pt); Speech therapists 1 (pt); Activities coordinators 2 (ft); Dietitians 1 (ft); Dentists 1 (pt); Ophthalmologists 1 (pt); Podiatrists 1 (pt).
Facilities Dining room; Physical therapy room; Activities room; Crafts room; Laundry room; Barber/Beauty shop; Library; Lounges.
Activities Arts & crafts; Cards; Games; Reading groups; Prayer groups; Movies; Shopping trips; Social/Cultural gatherings.

Friends Hall at Fox Chase
Hartel & Hasbrook Aves, Philadelphia, PA, 19111
(215) 728-4800
Admin Mark E Pressman NHA. *Medical Dir/Dir of Nursing* Marcia C Boroas MD; Sarah Ziska RN.
Licensure Skilled care. *Beds* SNF 27. *Certified* Medicare.
Owner Nonprofit organization/foundation.
Admissions Requirements Physician's request.
Staff Physicians 1 (pt); RNs 7 (ft), 11 (pt); LPNs 5 (ft), 7 (pt); Nurses aides 9 (ft), 20 (pt).
Affiliation Society of Friends
Facilities Dining room; Physical therapy room; Activities room.
Activities Arts & crafts; Cards.

Germantown Home
6950 Germantown Ave, Philadelphia, PA, 19119
(215) 848-3306
Admin Rev John G Huber. *Medical Dir/Dir of Nursing* Bruce Silver MD; Mary Bayer RN DON.
Licensure Skilled care; Intermediate care; Personal care; Apartment living. *Beds* SNF 20; ICF 149; Personal 14; Apartment living 118. *Certified* Medicaid; Medicare.
Owner Nonprofit Corp.
Admissions Requirements Minimum age 62; Medical examination; Physician's request.
Staff Physicians 3 (pt); Physical therapists 1 (ft); Reality therapists 1 (ft); Recreational therapists 3 (ft); Activities coordinators 1 (ft); Dietitians 1 (pt); Dentists 1 (pt); Ophthalmologists 2 (pt); Dentist 1 (pt); Optometrist 1 (pt).
Affiliation Lutheran
Facilities Dining room; Physical therapy room; Activities room; Chapel; Laundry room; Barber/Beauty shop; Library; Greenhouse.
Activities Arts & crafts; Games; Reading groups; Prayer groups; Movies; Shopping trips; Social/Cultural gatherings; Food fun; Ceramics; Manicure magic; Bedside sensory stimulation; Senior Olympics; Food fun; Gardening; Sewing groups; Music appreciation & therapy; Flower arranging.

Greystone on the Greene Inc
6400 Greene St, Philadelphia, PA, 19119
(215) 844-6401

Licensure Skilled care. *Beds* 180. *Certified* Medicaid; Medicare.
Owner Proprietary Corp.

George L Harrison Memorial*
Front St & Lehigh Ave, Philadelphia, PA, 19125
(215) 427-7000
Licensure Skilled care. *Beds* 35. *Certified* Medicaid; Medicare.
Owner Nonprofit Corp.

Holy Family Home
5300 Chester Ave, Philadelphia, PA, 19143
(215) 729-5153
Admin Sr Joseph Grenon. *Medical Dir/Dir of Nursing* Ronald Fronduti MD; Sr Gabrielle Garrett RN.
Licensure Skilled care; Intermediate care; Personal care. *Beds* SNF 19; ICF 83. *Certified* Medicaid; Medicare.
Owner Nonprofit Corp.
Admissions Requirements Minimum age 60; Medical examination.
Staff Physicians 3 (pt); RNs 4 (ft), 1 (pt); LPNs 9 (ft), 3 (pt); Nurses aides 24 (ft), 9 (pt); Physical therapists 1 (pt); Speech therapists 1 (pt); Activities coordinators 2 (ft); Dietitians 1 (pt); Dentists 1 (pt); Ophthalmologists 1 (pt); Podiatrists 1 (pt).
Languages French, Spanish
Affiliation Roman Catholic
Facilities Dining room; Physical therapy room; Activities room; Chapel; Crafts room; Laundry room; Barber/Beauty shop; Library.
Activities Arts & crafts; Cards; Games; Reading groups; Prayer groups; Movies; Shopping trips; Social/Cultural gatherings.

Home for the Jewish Aged*
5301 Old York Rd, Philadelphia, PA, 19141
(215) 455-6100
Licensure Skilled care; Intermediate care. *Beds* SNF 443; ICF 25. *Certified* Medicaid.
Owner Nonprofit Corp.
Affiliation Jewish

Immaculate Mary Home
Holmes Circle & Welsh Rd, Philadelphia, PA, 19136
(215) 335-2100
Admin Sr Corda Marie OSF. *Medical Dir/Dir of Nursing* Herbert M Bergman MD; Helen Turchi RN DON.
Licensure Skilled care; Intermediate care. *Beds* SNF 146; ICF 150. *Certified* Medicaid; Medicare.
Owner Nonprofit Corp.
Admissions Requirements Minimum age 60; Medical examination.
Languages Spanish, Polish, Italian
Affiliation Roman Catholic
Facilities Dining room; Physical therapy room; Activities room; Chapel; Crafts room; Laundry room; Barber/Beauty shop.
Activities Arts & crafts; Cards; Games; Reading groups; Prayer groups; Movies; Shopping trips; Social/Cultural gatherings.

Inglis House—The Philadelphia Home for Physically Disabled Persons
2600 Belmont Ave, Philadelphia, PA, 19131
(215) 878-5600
Admin Frank E Gable. *Medical Dir/Dir of Nursing* Dr Francis G Harrison Jr.
Licensure Skilled & intermediate care for physically disabled adults. *Beds* 296. *Certified* Medicaid; Medicare.
Owner Nonprofit organization/foundation.
Admissions Requirements Minimum age 17; Medical examination; Physically disabled, Mentally alert.
Staff Physicians 1 (ft), 5 (pt); RNs 28 (ft), 11 (pt); LPNs 40 (ft), 2 (pt); Nurses aides 169 (ft), 27 (pt); Physical therapists 2 (ft), 2 (pt); Recreational therapists 4 (ft); Occupational therapists 5 (pt); Speech therapists 1 (pt);

Dietitians 1 (ft); Dentists 1 (pt); Ophthalmologists 2 (pt); Social workers 5 (ft); Teachers 4 (ft).
Facilities Physical therapy room; Activities room; Chapel; Laundry room; Barber/Beauty shop; Library; Occupational therapy room; Recreational therapy room; Pet room; Work activities room; Computer lab.
Activities Arts & crafts; Cards; Games; Reading groups; Prayer groups; Movies; Shopping trips; Social/Cultural gatherings; Ham radio club; Photography; Gardening; Pet therapy; GED & college classes.

Ivy Ridge Nursing Home Inc*
5627 Ridge Ave, Philadelphia, PA, 19128
(215) 483-7522
Admin Annette Fabrican. *Medical Dir/Dir of Nursing* Mark Warren Cohen DO.
Licensure Intermediate care. *Beds* 47. *Certified* Medicaid.
Owner Proprietary Corp.
Staff RNs 1 (ft); LPNs 3 (ft); Nurses aides 8 (ft); Activities coordinators 1 (ft), 1 (pt).
Facilities Dining room; Activities room; Laundry room.
Activities Arts & crafts; Cards; Games; Reading groups; Prayer groups; Movies; Social/Cultural gatherings; Bazaars.

Kearsley/Christ Church Hospital
49th St & Monument Rd, Philadelphia, PA, 19131-2698
(215) 877-1565
Admin Pamela A DeLissio-Johnson NHA. *Medical Dir/Dir of Nursing* Gordon W Webster MD;Sandy J Beckius RN.
Licensure Skilled care; Independent living. *Beds* SNF 20; 87 Independent living units. *Certified* Medicaid.
Owner Nonprofit Corp.
Admissions Requirements Minimum age 62; Medical examination; Physician's request.
Staff Physicians 1 (pt); RNs 2 (ft), 1 (pt); LPNs 1 (ft); Nurses aides 4 (ft), 1 (pt); Recreational therapists 1 (ft); Activities coordinators 1 (ft); Dietitians 1 (pt); 1 (pt) Chaplain.
Affiliation Episcopal
Facilities Dining room; Chapel; Laundry room; Barber/Beauty shop.
Activities Games; Movies; Shopping trips; Social/Cultural gatherings.

The Lafayette-Philadelphia
8580 Verree Rd, Philadelphia, PA, 19111
(215) 728-8168
Admin Kate Jameson. *Medical Dir/Dir of Nursing* Dr Albert Paul; Rebecca Wilkes DON.
Licensure Skilled care; Intermediate care. *Beds* SNF 60; ICF 60. *Certified* Medicaid; Medicare.
Owner Proprietary Corp (Forum Grp).
Staff RNs 5 (ft), 3 (pt); LPNs 10 (ft), 10 (pt); Orderlies 4 (ft); Nurses aides 23 (ft), 15 (pt); Physical therapists 1 (pt); Recreational therapists 1 (ft); Occupational therapists 1 (pt); Speech therapists 1 (pt); Activities coordinators 1 (ft); Dietitians 1 (ft); Ophthalmologists 1 (pt); Podiatrists 1 (pt).
Languages Spanish
Facilities Dining room; Physical therapy room; Activities room; Laundry room; Barber/Beauty shop; Library; Day rooms; Screened porches; Country store.
Activities Arts & crafts; Cards; Games; Reading groups; Prayer groups; Movies; Shopping trips; Social/Cultural gatherings; Resident council.

Logan Square East Care Center
2 Franklin Town Blvd, Philadelphia, PA, 19103
(215) 557-0636
Admin John J Hurley. *Medical Dir/Dir of Nursing* Dr Sarle Cohen; Diane Rojewski DON.

Licensure Skilled care; Intermediate care. *Certified* Medicaid; Medicare.
Owner Nonprofit Corp.
Admissions Requirements Medical examination.
Staff Physicians; RNs; LPNs; Orderlies; Nurses aides; Physical therapists; Occupational therapists; Speech therapists; Activities coordinators; Dietitians; Dentists; Ophthalmologists.
Facilities Dining room; Physical therapy room; Laundry room; Barber/Beauty shop.
Activities Arts & crafts; Cards; Games; Reading groups; Movies; Social/Cultural gatherings.

Maple Wood Manor Convalescent Center
125 W School House Ln, Philadelphia, PA, 19144
(215) 844-8806
Admin Jonathan A Schultz. *Medical Dir/Dir of Nursing* Paul Moyer MD; Verna Womack RN.
Licensure Intermediate care. *Beds* ICF 180. *Certified* Medicaid.
Owner Proprietary Corp.
Admissions Requirements Minimum age 18; Medical examination.
Staff Physicians 4 (pt); RNs 5 (ft), 3 (pt); LPNs 15 (ft), 8 (pt); Nurses aides 65 (ft), 40 (pt); Physical therapists 1 (pt); Recreational therapists 2 (ft), 2 (pt); Speech therapists 1 (pt); Activities coordinators 1 (ft); Dietitians 2 (ft); Dentists 1 (pt); Ophthalmologists 1 (pt); Podiatrists 1 (pt).
Facilities Dining room; Physical therapy room; Activities room; Laundry room; Barber/Beauty shop.
Activities Arts & crafts; Cards; Games; Reading groups; Prayer groups; Movies; Shopping trips; Social/Cultural gatherings.

Marwood Rest Home Inc
1020 Oak Lane Ave, Philadelphia, PA, 19126
(215) 224-9898
Admin R Lyle Carpenter. *Medical Dir/Dir of Nursing* Leonard Cinberg MD; Icyline Morris DON.
Licensure Skilled care; Intermediate care. *Beds* SNF 87; ICF. *Certified* Medicaid; Medicare.
Owner Proprietary Corp.
Admissions Requirements Minimum age 65; Medical examination.
Staff Physicians 3 (pt); RNs 5 (ft), 5 (pt); LPNs 6 (ft), 5 (pt); Orderlies 2 (ft); Nurses aides 24 (ft), 10 (pt); Physical therapists 1 (pt); Recreational therapists 1 (ft); Occupational therapists 1 (pt); Speech therapists 1 (pt); Dietitians 1 (ft); Dentists 2 (pt); Ophthalmologists 1 (pt); Podiatrists 1 (pt).
Facilities Dining room; Physical therapy room; Activities room; Laundry room; Barber/Beauty shop; Outdoor areas.
Activities Arts & crafts; Cards; Games; Reading groups; Prayer groups; Movies; Shopping trips; Social/Cultural gatherings; Cooking; Horticulture; Music; Music therapy; Exercise groups; Bedside programs.

Mayo Nursing Center
650 Edison Ave, Philadelphia, PA, 19116
(213) 673-5700
Admin Liz Kopman. *Medical Dir/Dir of Nursing* R J Kane DO; Eileen McGlynn DON.
Licensure Skilled care; Intermediate care. *Beds* SNF 114; ICF 121. *Certified* Medicaid; Medicare.
Owner Proprietary Corp (Geriatric & Medical Centers).
Admissions Requirements Medical examination.
Staff Physicians 4 (ft); RNs 6 (ft), 3 (pt); LPNs 10 (ft), 4 (pt); Orderlies 1 (ft); Nurses aides 70 (ft), 15 (pt); Physical therapists 1 (pt); Recreational therapists 1 (pt); Occupational therapists 1 (pt); Speech

therapists 1 (pt); Activities coordinators 1 (ft); Dietitians 1 (pt); Dentists 1 (pt); Ophthalmologists 1 (pt); Podiatrists 1 (pt).
Facilities Dining room; Physical therapy room; Activities room; Barber/Beauty shop.
Activities Arts & crafts; Cards; Games; Movies; Social/Cultural gatherings.

Mercy Douglass Human Service Center*
4508-39 Chestnut St, Philadelphia, PA, 19139
(215) 382-9495
Admin Jessie D James. *Medical Dir/Dir of Nursing* Nathaniel H Copeland MD.
Licensure Skilled care. *Beds* 180. *Certified* Medicaid; Medicare.
Owner Nonprofit Corp.
Admissions Requirements Minimum age 60; Medical examination; Physician's request.
Staff Physicians 5 (pt); RNs 6 (ft), 3 (pt); LPNs 10 (ft), 3 (pt); Orderlies 5 (ft), 2 (pt); Nurses aides 50 (ft), 15 (pt); Physical therapists 1 (pt); Recreational therapists 3 (ft); Speech therapists 1 (pt); Activities coordinators 1 (pt); Dietitians 1 (ft), 1 (pt); Dentists 2 (pt); Ophthalmologists 1 (pt); Podiatrists 1 (pt); Audiologists 1 (pt).
Facilities Dining room; Physical therapy room; Activities room; Chapel; Crafts room; Laundry room; Barber/Beauty shop; Library.
Activities Arts & crafts; Cards; Games; Reading groups; Prayer groups; Movies.

Northwood Nursing Home
4621 Castor Ave, Philadelphia, PA, 19124
(215) 744-6464
Admin Robert Robalsky. *Medical Dir/Dir of Nursing* Dr Terry Waldman; Cindy Mezico.
Licensure Skilled care; Intermediate care. *Beds* SNF 72; ICF 76. *Certified* Medicaid; Medicare.
Owner Proprietary Corp.
Admissions Requirements Medical examination.
Staff Physicians 1 (ft), 8 (pt); RNs 3 (ft), 3 (pt); LPNs 6 (ft), 7 (pt); Orderlies 1 (ft), 1 (pt); Nurses aides 39 (ft), 15 (pt); Physical therapists 2 (pt); Recreational therapists 1 (pt); Occupational therapists 1 (pt); Speech therapists 1 (pt); Activities coordinators 1 (ft), 1 (pt); Dietitians 1 (ft), 1 (pt); Dentists 1 (pt); Ophthalmologists 1 (pt); Podiatrists 1 (pt).
Facilities Dining room; Physical therapy room; Activities room; Crafts room; Laundry room; Barber/Beauty shop.
Activities Arts & crafts; Cards; Games; Prayer groups; Movies; Social/Cultural gatherings; Pet therapy.

Park Pleasant Inc*
Drawer D University City, 4712-16 Chester Ave, Philadelphia, PA, 19143
(215) 727-4450
Licensure Skilled care. *Beds* 121. *Certified* Medicaid.
Owner Proprietary Corp.

Pauls Run
9896 Bustleton Ave, Philadelphia, PA, 19115
(215) 934-3000
Admin Norma E Coyle RN. *Medical Dir/Dir of Nursing* Donald Lieberman MD; Gloria Banks DON.
Licensure Skilled care; Intermediate care. *Beds* SNF 120; ICF. *Certified* Medicare.
Owner Nonprofit Corp.
Admissions Requirements Medical examination; Physician's request.
Staff Physicians 5 (pt); RNs 9 (ft), 6 (pt); LPNs 8 (ft), 8 (pt); Nurses aides 35 (ft), 35 (pt); Physical therapists 1 (ft); Recreational therapists 1 (ft); Occupational therapists 1 (pt); Speech therapists 1 (pt); Activities coordinators 1 (pt); Dietitians 1 (ft); Dentists 1 (pt); Ophthalmologists 1 (pt); Podiatrists 1 (pt).
Affiliation Lutheran

Facilities Dining room; Physical therapy room; Activities room; Chapel; Crafts room; Laundry room; Barber/Beauty shop.
Activities Arts & crafts; Cards; Games; Reading groups; Prayer groups; Movies; Social/Cultural gatherings; Pets; Bus trips.

Penny Pack Manor Nursing Home*
8015 Lawndale St, Philadelphia, PA, 19111
(215) 725-2525
Licensure Skilled care. *Beds* 56. *Certified* Medicare.
Owner Proprietary Corp.

Perkins Convalescent Home*
2107 W Tioga St, Philadelphia, PA, 19140
(215) 226-0407
Licensure Skilled care. *Beds* 27. *Certified* Medicaid.
Owner Proprietary Corp.

Philadelphia Nursing Home*
Girard & Corinthian Aves, Philadelphia, PA, 19130
(215) 978-2100
Licensure Skilled care; Intermediate care. *Beds* SNF 426; ICF 74. *Certified* Medicaid; Medicare.
Owner Nonprofit Corp.

Philadelphia Nursing Home*
7979 State Rd, Philadelphia, PA, 19136
(215) 335-8715
Medical Dir/Dir of Nursing Richard Gibbon MD.
Licensure Intermediate care. *Beds* 129. *Certified* Medicaid.
Owner Publicly owned.
Admissions Requirements Medical examination; Physician's request.
Staff Physicians 1 (ft), 1 (pt); RNs 8 (ft), 4 (pt); Recreational therapists 1 (ft); Dietitians 1 (pt); Dentists 1 (pt); Ophthalmologists 1 (pt); Podiatrists 1 (pt); Audiologists 1 (pt).
Facilities Dining room; Physical therapy room; Chapel; Crafts room; Laundry room; Barber/Beauty shop.
Activities Arts & crafts; Cards; Games; Reading groups; Prayer groups; Movies; Shopping trips; Social/Cultural gatherings.

The Philadelphia Protestant Home
6500 Tabor Rd, Philadelphia, PA, 19111
(215) 697-8000
Admin Rev Nevin Kershner. *Medical Dir/Dir of Nursing* Dr Anthony Palazzolo; Peter Ojeda RN DON.
Licensure Skilled care; Intermediate care; Personal care; Residential care. *Beds* SNF 53; ICF 53; Personal; Residential 126. *Certified* Medicaid.
Owner Nonprofit Corp.
Admissions Requirements Minimum age 62; Medical examination.
Staff Physicians 3 (pt); Physical therapists 5 (ft); Recreational therapists 2 (ft); Occupational therapists 1 (pt); Speech therapists 1 (pt); Activities coordinators 2 (ft); Dietitians 1 (ft); Dentists 1 (pt); Ophthalmologists 2 (pt); Podiatrists 1 (pt).
Languages German, Spanish
Facilities Dining room; Physical therapy room; Activities room; Chapel; Crafts room; Laundry room; Barber/Beauty shop; Library; Pool.
Activities Arts & crafts; Cards; Games; Reading groups; Prayer groups; Movies; Shopping trips; Social/Cultural gatherings; Swimming; Fitness classes.

The Presbyterian Home at 58th St
58th St & Greenway Ave, Philadelphia, PA, 19143
(215) 724-2218
Admin Carolyn Baxter. *Medical Dir/Dir of Nursing* Donald J Corey MD.
Licensure Skilled care. *Beds* SNF 50. *Certified* Medicaid; Medicare.
Owner Nonprofit Corp.

Admissions Requirements Medical examination.
Staff Physicians 1 (pt); RNs 2 (ft), 2 (pt), LPNs 4 (ft), 8 (pt); Nurses aides 15 (ft), 15 (pt); Physical therapists 1 (pt); Occupational therapists 1 (pt); Speech therapists 1 (pt); Activities coordinators 1 (ft); Dietitians 1 (ft); Dentists 1 (pt); Ophthalmologists 1 (pt); Podiatrists 1 (pt).
Affiliation Presbyterian
Facilities Dining room; Physical therapy room; Activities room; Chapel; Crafts room; Laundry room; Barber/Beauty shop; Library.
Activities Arts & crafts; Cards; Games; Reading groups; Prayer groups; Movies; Shopping trips; Social/Cultural gatherings.

Ralston House*
3615 Chestnut St, Philadelphia, PA, 19104
(215) 386-2984
Medical Dir/Dir of Nursing Dr Herb Cohen.
Licensure Skilled care; Intermediate care. *Beds* SNF 120; ICF 12. *Certified* Medicaid.
Owner Nonprofit Corp.
Staff Physicians 1 (pt); RNs 7 (ft); LPNs 5 (ft), 6 (pt); Orderlies 3 (ft), 1 (pt); Nurses aides 50 (ft), 9 (pt); Physical therapists 1 (ft); Recreational therapists 2 (ft); Occupational therapists 1 (ft); Activities coordinators 1 (ft); Dietitians 1 (ft).
Facilities Dining room; Physical therapy room; Activities room; Chapel; Crafts room; Laundry room; Barber/Beauty shop; Library.
Activities Arts & crafts; Games; Reading groups; Prayer groups; Movies; Shopping trips; Social/Cultural gatherings.

Regina Community Nursing Center
230 N 65th, Philadelphia, PA, 19139
(215) 472-0541
Admin Philomena Cummins RN NHA. *Medical Dir/Dir of Nursing* Martin J Kearney MD; Mary Coyne RN DON.
Licensure Skilled care; Intermediate care. *Beds* 44. *Certified* Medicaid.
Owner Nonprofit Corp.
Admissions Requirements Minimum age 40; Medical examination.
Staff Physicians 4 (pt); RNs 3 (ft), 2 (pt); LPNs 1 (ft), 2 (pt); Orderlies 1 (ft); Nurses aides 11 (ft), 8 (pt); Physical therapists 1 (pt); Recreational therapists 1 (pt); Dietitians 1 (pt).
Languages Italian
Facilities Dining room; Physical therapy room; Activities room.
Activities Cards; Games; Prayer groups; Movies.

Rittenhouse Care Center*
1526 Lombrd St, Philadelphia, PA, 19146
(215) 546-5960
Licensure Skilled care. *Beds* 198. *Certified* Medicaid; Medicare.
Owner Proprietary Corp (Geriatric & Medical Centers).

Sacred Heart Free Home*
1315 W Hunting Park Ave, Philadelphia, PA, 19140
(215) 329-8800
Licensure Skilled care (Terminal cancer patients only). *Beds* SNF 45.
Owner Nonprofit Corp.

Sacred Heart Manor
6445 Germantown Ave, Philadelphia, PA, 19119
(215) 438-5268
Admin Sr M Patricia Michael Sweeney. *Medical Dir/Dir of Nursing* Wilfreta Baugh MD; Sr Jeanne Francis.
Licensure Skilled care; Intermediate care; Personal care. *Beds* SNF 41; ICF 39; Personal 52. *Certified* Medicaid.
Owner Nonprofit Corp.
Admissions Requirements Minimum age 65; Medical examination.

Staff Physicians 12 (pt); RNs 5 (ft), 3 (pt); LPNs 7 (ft), 3 (pt); Nurses aides 35 (ft), 13 (pt); Physical therapists 1 (pt); Occupational therapists 1 (pt); Speech therapists 1 (pt); Activities coordinators 1 (ft); Dietitians 1 (pt); Ophthalmologists 2 (pt).
Affiliation Roman Catholic
Facilities Dining room; Physical therapy room; Activities room; Chapel; Crafts room; Laundry room; Barber/Beauty shop; Library.
Activities Arts & crafts; Cards; Games; Reading groups; Prayer groups; Movies; Shopping trips; Social/Cultural gatherings; Pet therapy.

St Ignatius Nursing Home
4401 Haverford Ave, Philadelphia, PA, 19104
(215) 349-8800
Admin Sr Mary Agatha Cebula. *Medical Dir/Dir of Nursing* L Walker MD; P Sturgis RN DON.
Licensure Skilled care; Intermediate care. *Beds* SNF 62; ICF 114. *Certified* Medicaid.
Owner Nonprofit Corp.
Staff RNs 3 (ft), 7 (pt); LPNs 12 (ft), 6 (pt); Nurses aides 63 (ft), 8 (pt); Physical therapists 1 (pt); Activities coordinators 1 (ft); Dietitians 1 (ft), 1 (pt); Dentists 1 (pt).

St John Neumann Nursing Home
10400 Roosevelt Blvd, Philadelphia, PA, 19116
(215) 698-5600
Admin Sr M Beata. *Medical Dir/Dir of Nursing* Robert E Chmielewski MD; Jane Oleksiak RN DON.
Licensure Skilled care. *Beds* SNF 218. *Certified* Medicaid; Medicare.
Owner Nonprofit Corp.
Admissions Requirements Minimum age 16; Medical examination.
Staff Physicians 1 (ft); RNs 6 (ft), 6 (pt); LPNs 5 (ft), 3 (pt); Orderlies 1 (pt); Nurses aides 100 (ft), 23 (pt); Physical therapists 1 (pt); Recreational therapists 1 (pt); Speech therapists 1 (pt); Activities coordinators 1 (ft); Dietitians 1 (ft); Dentists 1 (pt); Ophthalmologists 4 (pt); Podiatrists 1 (pt).
Languages French, Polish, Spanish, Italian, Hindi, Chinese
Affiliation Roman Catholic
Facilities Dining room; Physical therapy room; Activities room; Chapel; Crafts room; Laundry room; Barber/Beauty shop; Library; Multi-purpose room; 5 inner courts; Gift shop.
Activities Arts & crafts; Cards; Games; Reading groups; Prayer groups; Movies; Shopping trips; Social/Cultural gatherings; Exercise sessions; Reality orientation; Discussion groups; Wheel chair races.

Saunders House
100 Lancaster Ave, Philadelphia, PA, 19151
(215) 896-7955
Admin Milton Jacobs. *Medical Dir/Dir of Nursing* Bruce G Silver MD.
Licensure Skilled care; Intermediate care; Residential care. *Beds* SNF 135; ICF 45; Residential 30. *Certified* Medicaid; Medicare.
Owner Nonprofit Corp.
Admissions Requirements Minimum age 62; Medical examination.
Staff Physicians 3 (pt); RNs 29 (ft); LPNs 5 (ft); Orderlies 14 (ft); Nurses aides 85 (ft); Physical therapists 1 (pt); Reality therapists 3 (ft), 3 (pt); Recreational therapists 3 (ft), 3 (pt); Occupational therapists 1 (pt); Speech therapists 1 (pt); Activities coordinators 2 (ft); Dietitians 2 (ft); Dentists 1 (pt); Ophthalmologists 6 (pt); Podiatrists 1 (pt); Psychiatrists 2 (pt).
Facilities Dining room; Physical therapy room; Activities room; Chapel; Crafts room; Laundry room; Barber/Beauty shop; Library; Outdoor patio; Fitness field.

Activities Arts & crafts; Cards; Games; Reading groups; Prayer groups; Movies; Shopping trips; Social/Cultural gatherings; Special theme days.

Simpson House of the United Methodist Church
Belmont & Monument Aves, Philadelphia, PA, 19131
(215) 878-3600
Admin Rev David W Powell. *Medical Dir/Dir of Nursing* Edward W Closson MD; Betty Laucks RN DON.
Licensure Skilled care; Intermediate care; Residential care. *Beds* SNF 31; ICF 95; Residential 160. *Certified* Medicaid; Medicare.
Owner Nonprofit Corp.
Admissions Requirements Minimum age 65; Medical examination; Physician's request.
Staff Physicians 3 (pt); Orderlies 2 (ft), 2 (pt); Physical therapists 2 (pt); Recreational therapists 2 (pt); Occupational therapists 1 (pt); Speech therapists 1 (pt); Activities coordinators 1 (ft); Dietitians 1 (ft); Dentists 1 (pt); Ophthalmologists 1 (pt); Podiatrists 1 (pt).
Affiliation Methodist
Facilities Dining room; Physical therapy room; Activities room; Chapel; Crafts room; Laundry room; Barber/Beauty shop; Library.
Activities Arts & crafts; Cards; Games; Prayer groups; Movies; Shopping trips; Social/Cultural gatherings.

Stenton Hall Nursing & Convalescent Center
7310 Stenton Ave, Philadelphia, PA, 19150
(215) 242-2727
Admin Ronnie R Scicchitano NHA. *Medical Dir/Dir of Nursing* Richard Rosenfeld MD; Rick Keller RN DON.
Licensure Skilled care; Intermediate care. *Beds* 95. *Certified* Medicaid; Medicare.
Owner Proprietary Corp (Beverly Enterprises).
Staff Physicians 1 (pt); RNs 5 (ft), 1 (pt); LPNs 4 (ft), 2 (pt); Nurses aides 30 (ft); Physical therapists 1 (pt); Recreational therapists 1 (ft); Occupational therapists 1 (pt); Speech therapists 1 (pt); Activities coordinators 1 (ft); Dietitians 1 (pt); Dentists 1 (pt); Podiatrists 1 (pt).
Affiliation Jewish
Facilities Dining room; Physical therapy room; Activities room; Laundry room; Barber/Beauty shop.
Activities Arts & crafts; Cards; Games; Reading groups; Prayer groups; Movies; Shopping trips; Social/Cultural gatherings.

Stephen Smith Home for the Aged*
4400 W Girard Ave, Philadelphia, PA, 19104
(215) 581-4700
Licensure Skilled care. *Beds* 180. *Certified* Medicaid.
Owner Nonprofit Corp.

Tucker House
1001 Wallace St, Philadelphia, PA, 19123
(215) 235-1600
Admin Sidney Malamut. *Medical Dir/Dir of Nursing* Nathaniel Copeland MD; Vivian Nicholson DON.
Licensure Skilled care; Intermediate care. *Beds* SNF 60; ICF 120. *Certified* Medicaid; Medicare.
Owner Nonprofit Corp.
Admissions Requirements Minimum age 18; Medical examination; Physician's request.
Staff RNs 7 (ft), 4 (pt); LPNs 11 (ft), 6 (pt); Nurses aides 100 (ft), 40 (pt); Recreational therapists 2 (ft); Activities coordinators 1 (ft).
Facilities Dining room; Physical therapy room; Activities room; Chapel; Crafts room; Laundry room; Barber/Beauty shop.
Activities Arts & crafts; Cards; Games; Reading groups; Prayer groups; Movies; Social/Cultural gatherings.

Unitarian Universalist House
224 W Tulpehocken St, Philadelphia, PA,
19144
(215) 843-0809
Admin Beth Provkov. *Medical Dir/Dir of
Nursing* Norman Stahlheber MD; Delores
Salamone RN.
Licensure Skilled care; Intermediate care. *Beds*
39. *Certified* Medicaid.
Owner Nonprofit Corp.
Admissions Requirements Minimum age 60;
Medical examination.
Staff Physicians; RNs 5 (ft), 2 (pt); LPNs 3
(ft), 1 (pt); Nurses aides 12 (ft), 10 (pt);
Physical therapists; Recreational therapists;
Speech therapists; Activities coordinators 1
(pt); Dietitians 1 (ft); Social workers.
Affiliation Unitarian Universalist
Facilities Dining room; Activities room;
Laundry room; Barber/Beauty shop; Library;
Multi-purpose rooms.
Activities Arts & crafts; Cards; Games;
Reading groups; Movies; Shopping trips;
Social/Cultural gatherings; Music.

Uptown Home for the Aged*
7800 Bustleton Ave, Philadelphia, PA, 19152
(215) 722-2300
Admin Samuel T Lewis. *Medical Dir/Dir of
Nursing* Sidney Brenner MD.
Licensure Skilled care; Intermediate care. *Beds*
SNF 84; ICF 156. *Certified* Medicaid;
Medicare.
Owner Nonprofit Corp.
Admissions Requirements Minimum age 65;
Medical examination.
Staff Physicians 2 (pt); RNs 7 (ft), 6 (pt);
LPNs 11 (ft), 17 (pt); Orderlies 5 (ft), 3 (pt);
Nurses aides 51 (ft), 26 (pt); Physical
therapists 1 (pt); Recreational therapists 1
(ft); Occupational therapists 1 (pt); Speech
therapists 1 (pt); Activities coordinators 1
(ft); Dietitians 1 (pt); Dentists 1 (pt);
Ophthalmologists 1 (pt); Podiatrists 1 (pt);
Audiologists 1 (pt); Ward clerks 3 (ft).
Facilities Dining room; Physical therapy
room; Activities room; Chapel; Crafts room;
Laundry room; Barber/Beauty shop; Library.
Activities Arts & crafts; Cards; Games;
Reading groups; Prayer groups; Movies;
Shopping trips; Social/Cultural gatherings.

Willowcrest Bamberger
York & Tabor Rds, Philadelphia, PA, 19141
(215) 456-8613
Admin Robert V Stutz. *Medical Dir/Dir of
Nursing* Raymond Cogen MD; Helen
Downey RN.
Licensure Skilled care. *Beds* 102. *Certified*
Medicaid; Medicare.
Owner Nonprofit organization/foundation.
Admissions Requirements Minimum age 21;
Medical examination; Physician's request.
Staff Physicians 1 (pt); RNs 15 (ft), 6 (pt);
LPNs 1 (ft); Nurses aides 16 (ft), 2 (pt);
Recreational therapists 1 (ft); Occupational
therapists 1 (ft), 1 (pt); Dietitians 1 (pt).
Facilities Physical therapy room; Activities
room; Crafts room; Library.
Activities Arts & crafts; Games; Reading
groups; Movies; Social/Cultural gatherings;
Religious services.

PHILIPSBURG

United Presbyterian Home of Philipsburg*
Presqueisle & 2nd Sts, Philipsburg, PA, 16866
(814) 342-0340
Licensure Skilled care. *Beds* 38. *Certified*
Medicaid; Medicare.
Owner Nonprofit Corp.
Affiliation Presbyterian

PHOENIXVILLE

Phoenixville Convalescent Manor Inc
833 S Main St, Phoenixville, PA, 19460
(215) 933-5867
Licensure Skilled care. *Beds* 144. *Certified*
Medicaid; Medicare.
Owner Proprietary Corp (Beverly Enterprises).

PITMAN

Friendly Nursing Home
RD 1, Box 118, Pitman, PA, 17964
(717) 644-0489
Admin Dolly A Straight. *Medical Dir/Dir of
Nursing* Gregg Bannett DO; Jean Neye RN.
Licensure Skilled care. *Beds* SNF 48. *Certified*
Medicaid; Medicare.
Owner Proprietary Corp.
Staff RNs 1 (ft), 5 (pt); LPNs 2 (pt); Nurses
aides 5 (ft), 18 (pt); Activities coordinators 1
(ft).
Facilities Dining room; Activities room;
Crafts room.
Activities Arts & crafts; Cards; Games;
Reading groups; Prayer groups; Movies;
Shopping trips; Social/Cultural gatherings.

PITTSBURGH

Angelus Convalescent Center Inc*
200 Amber St, Pittsburgh, PA, 15206
(412) 362-6300
Licensure Skilled care. *Beds* 84. *Certified*
Medicaid; Medicare.
Owner Proprietary Corp.

Asbury Heights
700 Bower Hill Rd, Mount Lebanon,
Pittsburgh, PA, 15243
(412) 341-1030
Admin Howard F Peters. *Medical Dir/Dir of
Nursing* Lawrence Wilson MD.
Licensure Skilled care; Intermediate care;
Personal care; Independent care. *Beds* SNF
55; ICF 90; Personal 22. *Certified* Medicaid;
Medicare.
Owner Nonprofit Corp.
Admissions Requirements Minimum age 65;
Medical examination.
Staff Physicians 1 (ft); RNs 12 (ft), 15 (pt);
LPNs 10 (ft), 17 (pt); Orderlies 1 (pt);
Nurses aides 35 (ft), 34 (pt); Physical
therapists 1 (ft); Recreational therapists 2
(ft); Occupational therapists 1 (ft); Speech
therapists 1 (ft); Activities coordinators 4
(ft); Dietitians 1 (ft); Dentists 1 (ft);
Ophthalmologists 1 (ft); Dentist 1 (pt).
Affiliation Methodist
Facilities Dining room; Physical therapy
room; Activities room; Chapel; Crafts room;
Laundry room; Barber/Beauty shop; Library;
Ice cream shop; Country store; Medical
complex; Skylight mall.
Activities Arts & crafts; Cards; Games;
Reading groups; Prayer groups; Movies;
Shopping trips; Social/Cultural gatherings;
Trips to local points of interest.

Baptist Homes Nursing Center
489 Castle Shannon Blvd, Pittsburgh, PA,
15234
(412) 563-6550
Admin Kathleen S Anderson. *Medical Dir/Dir
of Nursing* Dr Joyce Sandberg; Jean
Wengryn RN DON.
Licensure Skilled care; Intermediate care. *Beds*
SNF 42; ICF 84. *Certified* Medicaid;
Medicare.
Owner Nonprofit Corp.
Admissions Requirements Medical
examination; Physician's request.
Staff RNs 7 (ft), 14 (pt); LPNs 8 (ft), 3 (pt);
Nurses aides 24 (ft), 38 (pt); Physical
therapists 1 (ft); Recreational therapists 1
(ft); Occupational therapists 1 (pt); Activities
coordinators 1 (ft); Dietitians 1 (ft).

Affiliation Baptist
Facilities Dining room; Physical therapy
room; Activities room; Chapel; Crafts room;
Laundry room; Barber/Beauty shop;
Lounges; Solarium; Family Rooms; Gift
shop.
Activities Arts & crafts; Cards; Games;
Reading groups; Prayer groups; Movies;
Shopping trips; Social/Cultural gatherings;
Sewing; Cooking; Exercise classes.

Canterbury Place
4001 Penn Ave, Pittsburgh, PA, 15224
(412) 682-0153
Admin Kathleen S Martindale NHA. *Medical
Dir/Dir of Nursing* Dr David Martin; June
Tyniec RN.
Licensure Skilled care; Intermediate care. *Beds*
SNF 28; ICF. *Certified* Medicaid; Medicare.
Owner Nonprofit Corp.
Admissions Requirements Minimum age 65;
Medical examination.
Staff Physicians 2 (pt); RNs 2 (ft), 2 (pt);
LPNs 3 (ft), 4 (pt); Nurses aides 13 (ft), 7
(pt); Physical therapists 1 (pt); Activities
coordinators 1 (ft); Ophthalmologists 1 (pt);
Physical therapy aide 1 (ft); Social worker 1
(pt); Nurse practitioner 1 (pt).
Languages Polish, Slavic
Affiliation Episcopal
Facilities Dining room; Physical therapy
room; Activities room; Chapel; Laundry
room; Barber/Beauty shop; Library.
Activities Arts & crafts; Cards; Games;
Reading groups; Prayer groups; Movies;
Shopping trips; Social/Cultural gatherings;
Pet therapy; Resident council; Music
therapy.

Collins Nursing Home Inc*
5511 Baum Blvd, Pittsburgh, PA, 15232
(412) 661-1740
Medical Dir/Dir of Nursing Dr Maranatti.
Licensure Skilled care; Intermediate care. *Beds*
SNF 31; ICF 41. *Certified* Medicaid;
Medicare.
Owner Proprietary Corp.
Admissions Requirements Minimum age 65;
Medical examination; Physician's request.
Staff Physicians 1 (pt); RNs 4 (ft), 3 (pt);
LPNs 6 (ft), 3 (pt); Physical therapists 1 (ft);
Recreational therapists 1 (ft); Speech
therapists 1 (pt); Activities coordinators 1
(ft); Dietitians 1 (ft); Dentists 1 (pt);
Ophthalmologists 1 (pt); Podiatrists 1 (pt).
Facilities Dining room; Physical therapy
room; Activities room; Laundry room;
Barber/Beauty shop.
Activities Arts & crafts; Cards; Games;
Reading groups.

Forbes Center for Gerontology*
Frankstown Ave at Washington Blvd,
Pittsburgh, PA, 15206
(412) 665-3165
Medical Dir/Dir of Nursing Dr J F O'Keefe &
Dr J R Friday.
Licensure Skilled care. *Beds* 132. *Certified*
Medicaid; Medicare.
Owner Proprietary Corp.
Admissions Requirements Minimum age 16;
Medical examination; Physician's request.
Staff Physicians 2 (ft); RNs 8 (ft), 4 (pt);
LPNs 12 (ft); Nurses aides 30 (ft); Physical
therapists 1 (ft); Reality therapists 1 (ft);
Recreational therapists 2 (ft); Occupational
therapists 1 (pt); Speech therapists 1 (pt);
Activities coordinators 1 (ft); Dietitians 1
(ft).
Facilities Dining room; Physical therapy
room; Activities room; Chapel; Laundry
room; Barber/Beauty shop; Library; Music
therapy room.
Activities Arts & crafts; Games; Prayer groups;
Movies; Shopping trips; Social/Cultural
gatherings.

The Health Center at Friendship Village of South Hills
1290 Boyce Rd, Pittsburgh, PA, 15241
(412) 941-3100
Admin Mary E Meindl NHA. *Medical Dir/Dir of Nursing* Walter Robison MD; Judith DiGorio RN DON.
Licensure Skilled care. *Beds* SNF 60. *Certified* Medicaid.
Owner Nonprofit Corp (Life Care Services Corp).
Admissions Requirements Minimum age 18; Physician's request.
Staff Physicians 3 (pt); RNs 4 (ft), 4 (pt); LPNs 5 (ft), 6 (pt); Nurses aides 13 (ft), 15 (pt); Physical therapists 1 (ft); Occupational therapists 1 (pt); Speech therapists 1 (pt); Activities coordinators 1 (ft); Dietitians 1 (pt); Ophthalmologists 1 (pt); Dentist 1 (pt).
Facilities Dining room; Physical therapy room; Activities room; Laundry room; Barber/Beauty shop.
Activities Arts & crafts; Cards; Games; Reading groups; Movies; Shopping trips; Social/Cultural gatherings.

Home for Aged Protestant Women*
900 Rebecca Ave, Pittsburgh, PA, 15221
(412) 731-2338
Medical Dir/Dir of Nursing Noel Gillette MD.
Licensure Intermediate care. *Beds* 37.
Owner Nonprofit Corp.
Admissions Requirements Minimum age 65; Females only; Medical examination; Physician's request.
Staff Physicians 1 (pt); RNs 1 (ft), 4 (pt); LPNs 3 (ft), 2 (pt); Nurses aides 8 (ft), 5 (pt); Physical therapists 1 (pt); Speech therapists 1 (pt); Activities coordinators 1 (ft).
Facilities Dining room; Physical therapy room; Activities room; Chapel; Crafts room; Laundry room; Barber/Beauty shop; Library.
Activities Arts & crafts; Cards; Games; Reading groups; Prayer groups; Movies; Social/Cultural gatherings.

Ivy Nursing Home Inc
5609 5th Ave, Pittsburgh, PA, 15232
(412) 362-3500
Admin M Murray. *Medical Dir/Dir of Nursing* Dr Margaret Kush; Patricia Bernd RN.
Licensure Skilled care; Intermediate care. *Beds* SNF 50; ICF 100. *Certified* Medicaid; Medicare.
Owner Proprietary Corp (Health Care & Retirement Corp).
Admissions Requirements Minimum age 18; Medical examination.
Staff Physicians 8 (pt); RNs 7 (ft), 1 (pt); LPNs 8 (ft), 6 (pt); Nurses aides 29 (ft), 24 (pt); Physical therapists 1 (ft); Recreational therapists 1 (ft); Occupational therapists 1 (pt); Speech therapists 1 (pt); Dietitians 1 (ft); Dentists; Ophthalmologists 1 (pt); Podiatrists.
Facilities Dining room; Physical therapy room; Activities room; Crafts room; Laundry room; Barber/Beauty shop.
Activities Arts & crafts; Cards; Games; Reading groups; Prayer groups; Movies; Shopping trips; Social/Cultural gatherings; Picnics; Concerts; Individual visits.

Jefferson Hills Manor Inc*
PO Box 10805, Pittsburgh, PA, 15236
(412) 653-1128
Licensure Skilled care. *Beds* 57.
Owner Proprietary Corp.

John J Kane Allegheny County Home
Vanadium Rd, Pittsburgh, PA, 15243
(412) 928-1400
Licensure Skilled care; Intermediate care. *Beds* SNF 1087; ICF 378. *Certified* Medicaid; Medicare.
Owner Nonprofit Corp.

Ladies GAR Home*
2622 Woodstock Ave, Pittsburgh, PA, 15218
(412) 271-1316
Medical Dir/Dir of Nursing Dr Mangan.
Licensure Intermediate care. *Beds* ICF 65. *Certified* Medicaid.
Owner Nonprofit Corp.
Admissions Requirements Females only; Medical examination.
Staff Physicians 2 (ft); RNs 1 (ft), 4 (pt); LPNs 2 (ft), 2 (pt); Nurses aides 15 (ft); Physical therapists 1 (pt); Reality therapists 1 (ft); Occupational therapists 1 (pt); Activities coordinators 1 (ft); Dietitians 1 (ft); Dentists 1 (ft).
Facilities Dining room; Activities room; Chapel; Crafts room; Laundry room; Barber/Beauty shop; Library.
Activities Arts & crafts; Cards; Games; Reading groups; Prayer groups; Movies; Shopping trips; Social/Cultural gatherings.

Lemington Home for the Aged
1625 Lincoln Ave, Pittsburgh, PA, 15206
(412) 441-3700
Admin Delores M Cureton. *Medical Dir/Dir of Nursing* Labib Rizk; Yvonne Bankston.
Licensure Intermediate care. *Beds* 34. *Certified* Medicaid.
Owner Nonprofit Corp.
Admissions Requirements Minimum age 60; Medical examination; Physician's request.
Staff Physicians 3 (pt); RNs 4 (ft), 4 (pt); LPNs 15 (ft), 1 (pt); Orderlies 13 (ft); Nurses aides 50 (ft), 2 (pt); Physical therapists 2 (pt); Recreational therapists 1 (ft); Activities coordinators 1 (pt); Dietitians 1 (pt); Dentists 1 (pt); Ophthalmologists 1 (pt); Podiatrists 1 (pt); Social worker 1 (ft).
Facilities Dining room; Physical therapy room; Activities room; Chapel; Crafts room; Laundry room; Barber/Beauty shop.
Activities Arts & crafts; Cards; Games; Reading groups; Prayer groups; Movies; Shopping trips; Social/Cultural gatherings.

Little Sisters of the Poor Home for the Aged
1028 Benton Ave, Pittsburgh, PA, 15212
(412) 761-5373
Admin Sr Regina. *Medical Dir/Dir of Nursing* Sr Anne Joseph Doyle.
Licensure Skilled care; Intermediate care; Residential care; Apartments; Congregate living. *Beds* SNF 26; ICF 51; Residential 26; Apts 18. *Certified* Medicaid.
Owner Nonprofit Corp.
Admissions Requirements Minimum age 60; Medical examination.
Staff RNs 3 (ft), 6 (pt); LPNs 6 (ft), 7 (pt); Nurses aides 24 (ft), 20 (pt); Physical therapists 1 (pt); Activities coordinators 2 (ft); Dietitians 1 (pt).
Languages Italian, Spanish, French
Affiliation Roman Catholic
Facilities Dining room; Physical therapy room; Activities room; Chapel; Crafts room; Laundry room; Barber/Beauty shop; Library.
Activities Arts & crafts; Cards; Games; Reading groups; Prayer groups; Movies; Shopping trips; Social/Cultural gatherings.

C Howard Marcy State Hospital*
Leech Farm Rd, Pittsburgh, PA, 15206
(412) 665-5373
Licensure Intermediate care for mentally retarded. *Beds* 128. *Certified* Medicaid.
Owner Nonprofit Corp.

Marian Manor*
2695 Winchester Dr, Pittsburgh, PA, 15220
(412) 563-6866
Licensure Skilled care; Intermediate care. *Beds* SNF 72; ICF 50. *Certified* Medicaid.
Owner Nonprofit Corp.

McDonough Home*
1540 Evergreen Ave, Pittsburgh, PA, 15209
(412) 821-3088

Licensure Intermediate care. *Beds* 25.
Owner Proprietary Corp.

Mt Lebanon Manor
350 Old Gilkeson Rd, Pittsburgh, PA, 15228
(412) 257-4444
Admin David W Thomas. *Medical Dir/Dir of Nursing* Michael Kavic MD; Shirley Jenkins RN DON.
Licensure Skilled care; Intermediate care. *Beds* SNF 60; ICF 61; Apartments 5. *Certified* Medicaid; Medicare.
Owner Proprietary Corp (Beverly Enterprises).
Admissions Requirements Medical examination; Physician's request.
Staff Physicians 11 (pt); RNs 6 (ft), 6 (pt); LPNs 6 (ft), 6 (pt); Nurses aides 20 (ft), 20 (pt); Activities coordinators; Dietitians 1 (ft).
Facilities Dining room; Physical therapy room; Activities room; Crafts room; Laundry room; Barber/Beauty shop; Library.
Activities Arts & crafts; Cards; Games; Reading groups; Prayer groups; Movies; Shopping trips; Social/Cultural gatherings.

Negley House Nursing Center
550 S Negley Ave, Pittsburgh, PA, 15232
(412) 665-2400
Admin Joan Franceschi. *Medical Dir/Dir of Nursing* Grant J Shevchik MD.
Licensure Skilled care; Intermediate care. *Beds* 224. *Certified* Medicaid; Medicare.
Owner Proprietary Corp (Health Care & Retirement Corp).
Admissions Requirements Minimum age 18; Medical examination.
Staff Physicians 4 (pt); RNs 11 (ft), 5 (pt); LPNs 15 (ft), 10 (pt); Orderlies 4 (ft); Nurses aides 30 (ft), 50 (pt); Physical therapists 1 (ft); Recreational therapists 3 (ft); Occupational therapists 1 (ft); Speech therapists 1 (ft); Dietitians 1 (ft); Dentists 1 (pt); Ophthalmologists 1 (pt); Podiatrists 1 (pt).
Facilities Dining room; Physical therapy room; Activities room; Barber/Beauty shop; Library.
Activities Arts & crafts; Cards; Games; Reading groups; Prayer groups; Movies; Shopping trips; Social/Cultural gatherings; Field trips to ball games; Picnics; Professional entertainment.

Rebecca Residence for Protestant Ladies
900 Rebecca Ave, Pittsburgh, PA, 15221
(412) 731-2338
Admin Mary E Wilson. *Medical Dir/Dir of Nursing* A J Zido MD; H Terry RN.
Licensure Intermediate care. *Beds* 24.
Owner Nonprofit Corp.
Admissions Requirements Minimum age 65; Females only; Medical examination.
Staff Physicians 1 (pt); RNs 3 (ft), 1 (pt); LPNs 3 (ft), 1 (pt); Nurses aides 5 (ft), 3 (pt); Recreational therapists; Activities coordinators 1 (ft); Dietitians 1 (pt); Podiatrists 1 (pt).
Facilities Dining room; Physical therapy room; Activities room; Chapel; Crafts room; Laundry room; Barber/Beauty shop; Library.
Activities Arts & crafts; Cards; Games; Prayer groups; Movies; Shopping trips; Social/Cultural gatherings.

Reformed Presbyterian Home
2344 Perrysville Ave, Pittsburgh, PA, 15214
(412) 321-4139
Admin William J Weir NHA. *Medical Dir/Dir of Nursing* Marjorie Russell RN.
Licensure Skilled care; Intermediate care; Residential care; Personal care. *Beds* SNF 58; Residential 46. *Certified* Medicaid; Medicare.
Owner Nonprofit Corp.
Staff RNs; LPNs; Nurses aides; Physical therapists; Recreational therapists; Activities coordinators; Dietitians.
Affiliation Presbyterian

Riverview Center for Jewish Seniors
4724 Browns Hill Rd, Pittsburgh, PA, 15217
(412) 521-5900
Admin Stanley M Schiffman. *Medical Dir/Dir of Nursing* Patricia Fallon DON.
Licensure Skilled care; Intermediate care; Respite care; Adult day care. *Beds* SNF 106; ICF 320. *Certified* Medicaid; Medicare; VA.
Owner Nonprofit Corp.
Admissions Requirements Minimum age 62; Medical examination; Physician's request.
Staff RNs; LPNs; Nurses aides 152 (ft), 59 (pt); Physical therapists 5 (ft), 2 (pt); Reality therapists 1 (ft); Recreational therapists 5 (ft), 7 (pt); Occupational therapists 2 (pt); Speech therapists 1 (pt); Activities coordinators 1 (ft); Dietitians 1 (ft).
Languages Yiddish, Hebrew, Russian
Affiliation Jewish
Facilities Dining room; Physical therapy room; Activities room; Chapel (large & small Shul); Crafts room; Laundry room; Barber/Beauty shop; Library; Gift shop; Dairy/kosher snack bar; Two adult day care centers (one specific to memory-impaired); Pharmacy.
Activities Arts & crafts; Cards; Games; Reading groups; Prayer groups; Movies; Shopping trips; Social/Cultural gatherings; Residents council; Men's club; Women's club; In-house TV channel with intergenerational programs; Garden club.

St Joseph Nursing & Health Care Center
5324 Penn Ave, Pittsburgh, PA, 15224
(412) 665-5100
Admin Sr Maria Goretti Zamberlan. *Medical Dir/Dir of Nursing* Frank Kush MD; Nadine Plummer RN.
Licensure Skilled care. *Beds* SNF 161. *Certified* Medicaid; Medicare.
Owner Nonprofit Corp.
Admissions Requirements Minimum age Primarily 60; Medical examination.
Staff Physicians 4 (pt); RNs 5 (ft), 4 (pt); LPNs 11 (ft), 7 (pt); Orderlies 5 (ft), 2 (pt); Nurses aides 43 (ft), 20 (pt); Physical therapists 1 (pt); Recreational therapists 1 (ft); Occupational therapists 1 (pt); Speech therapists 1 (pt); Dietitians 1 (pt); Dentists 1 (pt); Ophthalmologists 2 (pt); Podiatrists 1 (pt); Therapy aides 3 (ft).
Affiliation Roman Catholic
Facilities Dining room; Physical therapy room; Activities room; Chapel; Crafts room; Laundry room; Barber/Beauty shop; Library; Snack & gift shop.
Activities Arts & crafts; Cards; Games; Reading groups; Prayer groups; Movies; Shopping trips; Social/Cultural gatherings.

Sky Vue Terrace Nursing Center
2170 Rhine St, Pittsburgh, PA, 15212
(412) 323-0420
Admin Conne Civiterla. *Medical Dir/Dir of Nursing* Dr Harry L Heck; Callie Todhunter DON.
Licensure Skilled care; Intermediate care. *Beds* SNF 60; ICF 40. *Certified* Medicaid; Medicare; VA.
Owner Proprietary Corp (Health Care & Retirement Corp).
Admissions Requirements Medical examination.
Staff Physicians 1 (ft), 5 (pt); RNs 5 (ft), 7 (pt); LPNs 6 (ft), 5 (pt); Nurses aides 32 (ft), 4 (pt); Physical therapists 1 (ft); Occupational therapists 1 (ft); Speech therapists 1 (ft); Activities coordinators 1 (ft); Dietitians 1 (pt); Dentists 1 (pt); Ophthalmologists 1 (pt); Podiatrists 1 (pt); Dentist 1 (pt).
Facilities Dining room; Physical therapy room; Chapel; Laundry room; Barber/Beauty shop; Patient lounges.
Activities Arts & crafts; Cards; Games; Prayer groups; Movies; Shopping trips; Social/Cultural gatherings.

United Presbyterian Womens Association Home for Aged
306 Pennsylvania Ave, Pittsburgh, PA, 15221
(412) 242-3606
Admin Georgette Renze Miller. *Medical Dir/Dir of Nursing* J Gleason MD; C Gehringer.
Licensure Continuing care Retirement. *Beds* 120.
Owner Nonprofit Corp.
Admissions Requirements Minimum age 65; Medical examination.
Affiliation Presbyterian
Facilities Dining room; Activities room; Chapel; Crafts room; Laundry room; Barber/Beauty shop; Library.
Activities Arts & crafts; Cards; Games; Reading groups; Prayer groups; Movies; Shopping trips.

Villa Demarillac Nursing Home Inc*
5300 Stanton Ave, Pittsburgh, PA, 15206
(412) 361-2833
Licensure Skilled care. *Beds* 50. *Certified* Medicaid.
Owner Nonprofit Corp.

Vincention Home
Perrymont Rd, Pittsburgh, PA, 15237
(412) 366-5600
Admin Sr Anne Kull VSC.
Licensure Skilled care. *Beds* SNF 219. *Certified* Medicaid; Medicare.
Owner Proprietary Corp (Vari-Care Inc).
Admissions Requirements Medical examination.
Affiliation Roman Catholic
Facilities Dining room; Physical therapy room; Activities room; Chapel; Barber/Beauty shop.
Activities Cards; Games; Reading groups; Prayer groups; Movies; Movies; Shopping trips; Social/Cultural gatherings.

Western Pennsylvania Eastern Star Home*
226 Bellevue Rd, Pittsburgh, PA, 15229
(412) 931-2256
Licensure Skilled care. *Beds* 40.
Owner Nonprofit Corp.
Affiliation Order of Eastern Star

Western Restoration Center*
2851 Bedford Ave, Pittsburgh, PA, 15219
(412) 683-5000
Licensure Skilled care; Intermediate care. *Beds* SNF 66; ICF 35. *Certified* Medicaid.
Owner Nonprofit Corp.

Wightman Health Center*
2025 Wightman St, Pittsburgh, PA, 15217
(412) 421-8443
Medical Dir/Dir of Nursing Martin H Nalrath III MD.
Licensure Skilled care; Intermediate care. *Beds* SNF 134; ICF 47. *Certified* Medicaid; Medicare.
Owner Proprietary Corp.
Admissions Requirements Minimum age 16; Medical examination.
Staff Physicians 6 (pt); RNs 7 (ft), 8 (pt); LPNs 15 (ft), 2 (pt); Orderlies 3 (ft); Nurses aides 58 (ft), 2 (pt); Physical therapists 1 (ft); Recreational therapists 1 (ft); Occupational therapists 1 (ft), 1 (pt); Speech therapists 1 (pt); Activities coordinators 3 (ft); Dietitians 1 (pt).
Facilities Dining room; Physical therapy room; Activities room; Crafts room; Laundry room; Barber/Beauty shop; Library; Dental office; Occupational therapy room.
Activities Arts & crafts; Cards; Games; Prayer groups; Movies; Shopping trips; Social/Cultural gatherings.

PITTSTON

Wesley Village
Laflin Rd, Pittston, PA, 18640-3197
(717) 655-2891

Admin Mrs R Campenni NHA. *Medical Dir/Dir of Nursing* Joseph Lombardo MD; Margaret Loefflad RN DON.
Licensure Skilled care; Intermediate care. *Beds* 183. *Certified* Medicaid; Medicare.
Owner Nonprofit Corp.
Admissions Requirements Minimum age 65.
Staff RNs; LPNs; Orderlies; Nurses aides; Physical therapists 2 (ft); Dietitians 1 (ft), 1 (pt).
Affiliation Methodist
Facilities Dining room; Physical therapy room; Activities room; Chapel; Crafts room; Laundry room; Barber/Beauty shop; Library; Gift shop; Wheelchair van.
Activities Arts & crafts; Cards; Games; Reading groups; Prayer groups; Movies; Nature trips.

PLYMOUTH MEETING

Clara Burke Nursing Home
251 Stenton Ave, Plymouth Meeting, PA, 19462
(215) 828-2272
Admin Dawn Delore. *Medical Dir/Dir of Nursing* Dr Stewart McCracken; Judith Shearer.
Licensure Skilled care. *Beds* 69.
Owner Proprietary Corp (Integrated Health Services Inc).
Staff RNs; LPNs; Orderlies; Nurses aides; Physical therapists; Reality therapists; Recreational therapists; Occupational therapists; Speech therapists; Activities coordinators; Dietitians; Private duty nurses.
Facilities Dining room; Activities room; Library.
Activities Arts & crafts; Cards; Games; Reading groups; Prayer groups; Movies; Shopping trips; Social/Cultural gatherings; Shows; Concerts.

POTTSTOWN

Coventry Manor Nursing Home Inc
PO Star Rte, Pottstown, PA, 19464
(215) 469-6228, 323-3798
Admin David T Boyer. *Medical Dir/Dir of Nursing* Jack Wennersten MD; Vinga Brown RN DON.
Licensure Skilled care. *Beds* SNF 41. *Certified* Medicaid.
Owner Proprietary Corp.
Admissions Requirements Minimum age 18; Medical examination.
Staff Physicians 1 (pt); RNs 2 (ft), 3 (pt); LPNs 4 (pt); Nurses aides 11 (ft), 12 (pt); Physical therapists 1 (pt); Occupational therapists 1 (pt); Speech therapists 1 (pt); Activities coordinators 1 (ft); Dietitians 1 (pt); Dentists 1 (pt); Ophthalmologists 1 (pt); Podiatrists 1 (pt).
Facilities Dining room; Physical therapy room; Activities room; Chapel; Crafts room; Laundry room; Barber/Beauty shop; Library.
Activities Arts & crafts; Cards; Games; Reading groups; Prayer groups; Movies; Shopping trips; Social/Cultural gatherings.

Leader Nursing & Rehabilitation Center—Pottstown
724 N Charlotte St, Pottstown, PA, 19464
(215) 323-1837
Admin Janis L Brackbill. *Medical Dir/Dir of Nursing* Joseph Zukoski MD; Shirley Cheek RN.
Licensure Skilled care; Intermediate care. *Beds* SNF 165; ICF. *Certified* Medicaid; Medicare.
Owner Proprietary Corp (Manor Care).
Staff Physical therapists 1 (ft); Occupational therapists 1 (ft), 1 (pt); Speech therapists 1 (pt); Activities coordinators 1 (ft); Dietitians 2 (ft); Podiatrists 1 (pt).

Facilities Dining room; Physical therapy room; Activities room; Chapel; Laundry room; Barber/Beauty shop.
Activities Arts & crafts; Cards; Games; Reading groups; Prayer groups; Movies; Shopping trips; Social/Cultural gatherings.

Manatawny Manor
Box 799, Old Schuylkill Rd, Pottstown, PA, 19464
(215) 327-0840
Admin Deborah Dollar-Reid RN, NHA. *Medical Dir/Dir of Nursing* John A Lupas MD; Debra Phillips RN DON.
Licensure Skilled care; Residential; Adult day care. *Beds* SNF 99; Residential 113; Adult day care 21. *Certified* Medicaid; Medicare.
Owner Proprietary Corp.
Admissions Requirements Minimum age 18; Medical examination; Physician's request.
Staff RNs 7 (ft), 16 (pt); LPNs 6 (ft), 10 (pt); Nurses aides 39 (ft), 23 (pt); Nurses aides 2 (pt); Recreational therapists 1 (ft); Occupational therapists 2 (pt); Speech therapists 2 (pt); Activities coordinators 2 (ft); Dietitians 1 (pt); Ophthalmologists 1 (pt).
Facilities Dining room; Physical therapy room; Activities room; Chapel; Crafts room; Laundry room; Barber/Beauty shop; Library; Greenhouse; Gift shop.
Activities Arts & crafts; Cards; Games; Reading groups; Prayer groups; Movies; Shopping trips; Social/Cultural gatherings; Exercise class; Remotivation; Sensory stimulation.

POTTSVILLE

Leader Nursing Rehabilitation Center*
Leader & Pulaski Dr, Pottsville, PA, 17091
(717) 622-9582
Licensure Skilled care. *Beds* 152. *Certified* Medicaid; Medicare.
Owner Proprietary Corp (Manor Care).

York Terrace Nursing Center
24th & W Market Sts, Pottsville, PA, 17901
(717) 622-3982
Admin Arlene S Postupak.
Licensure Skilled care; Intermediate care. *Beds* SNF 32; ICF 48. *Certified* Medicaid; Medicare.
Owner Proprietary Corp (Beverly Enterprises).
Admissions Requirements Medical examination.
Staff RNs; LPNs; Nurses aides; Recreational therapists; Activities coordinators.
Facilities Dining room; Physical therapy room; Activities room; Crafts room; Laundry room; Barber/Beauty shop; Courtyard with patio.
Activities Arts & crafts; Cards; Games; Reading groups; Prayer groups; Movies; Shopping trips; Social/Cultural gatherings.

PROSPECT PARK

Prospect Park Care Center
815 Chester Pike, Prospect Park, PA, 19076
(215) 586-6262
Admin Rosemary Kuhlman. *Medical Dir/Dir of Nursing* Dr Barry Chase; Joyce Brown DON.
Licensure Skilled care; Intermediate care. *Beds* SNF 60; ICF 120. *Certified* Medicaid; Medicare.
Owner Proprietary Corp (Geriatric & Medical Centers).
Staff Physicians; RNs; LPNs; Nurses aides; Physical therapists; Recreational therapists; Occupational therapists; Speech therapists; Activities coordinators; Dietitians; Ophthalmologists; Podiatrists.
Facilities Dining room; Physical therapy room; Activities room; Laundry room; Barber/Beauty shop.

Activities Arts & crafts; Cards; Games; Reading groups; Prayer groups; Movies; Shopping trips; Social/Cultural gatherings.

PUNXSUTAWNEY

Blose McGregor Health Care Center Inc
407 1/2 W Mahoning St, Punxsutawney, PA, 15767
(814) 938-6020
Admin Barbara P Bose. *Medical Dir/Dir of Nursing* Dr Joseph Kernich, Dr Jay Elder; Mary Jo Hoeh RN DON.
Licensure Skilled care; Intermediate care. *Beds* 86. *Certified* Medicaid; Medicare.
Owner Proprietary Corp.
Admissions Requirements Minimum age 21; Medical examination.
Staff RNs 4 (ft), 2 (pt); LPNs 7 (ft), 5 (pt); Orderlies 1 (ft); Nurses aides 19 (ft), 18 (pt); Activities coordinators.
Facilities Dining room; Physical therapy room; Activities room; Laundry room; Barber/Beauty shop.
Activities Arts & crafts; Games; Prayer groups; Movies; Social/Cultural gatherings.

QUAKERTOWN

Belle Haven Nursing Home Inc*
1320 Mill Rd, Quakertown, PA, 18951
(215) 536-7666
Medical Dir/Dir of Nursing Walter Tice MD.
Licensure Skilled care; Intermediate care. *Beds* SNF 30; ICF 23. *Certified* Medicaid; Medicare.
Owner Proprietary Corp.
Admissions Requirements Minimum age 18; Medical examination.
Staff Physicians 11 (pt); RNs 2 (ft), 1 (pt); LPNs 6 (ft), 2 (pt); Nurses aides 30 (ft), 8 (pt); Physical therapists 1 (pt); Reality therapists 1 (ft); Recreational therapists 1 (ft); Occupational therapists 1 (pt); Speech therapists 1 (pt); Activities coordinators 1 (ft); Dentists 1 (pt); Ophthalmologists 2 (pt); Podiatrists 3 (pt); Audiologists 1 (pt).
Facilities Dining room; Physical therapy room; Activities room; Crafts room; Laundry room; Barber/Beauty shop; Library.
Activities Arts & crafts; Cards; Games; Reading groups; Prayer groups; Movies; Shopping trips; Social/Cultural gatherings; Cooking classes; Church every Sunday; Pet therapy.

Quakertwon Manor Convalescent & Rehabilitation Center*
1020 S Main St, Quakertown, PA, 18951
(215) 536-9300
Licensure Skilled care. *Beds* 126. *Certified* Medicaid; Medicare.
Owner Proprietary Corp.

Upper Bucks Nursing & Convalescent Center*
Rte 5, Box 56, Quakertown, PA, 18951
(215) 536-2400
Licensure Skilled care. *Beds* 55. *Certified* Medicaid; Medicare.
Owner Nonprofit Corp.

Yingst Nursing Home Inc
Rte 663, Quakertown, PA, 18951
(215) 536-4240
Licensure Skilled care. *Beds* 41. *Certified* Medicaid.
Owner Proprietary Corp.

QUARRYVILLE

The Quarryville Presbyterian Home
625 Robert Fulton Hwy, Quarryville, PA, 17566
(717) 786-7321
Admin G Keith Mitchell Jr. *Medical Dir/Dir of Nursing* William Hunt; Bertelle Rintz DON.

Licensure Skilled care; Continuing care retirement community. *Beds* SNF 160; Residential 215. *Certified* Medicaid; Medicare.
Owner Nonprofit Corp.
Admissions Requirements Minimum age 65; Medical examination.
Staff RNs 8 (ft), 8 (pt); LPNs 10 (ft), 18 (pt); Orderlies 3 (ft), 2 (pt); Nurses aides 32 (ft), 27 (pt); Activities coordinators 2 (ft).
Affiliation Presbyterian
Facilities Dining room; Physical therapy room; Activities room; Chapel; Crafts room; Laundry room; Barber/Beauty shop; Library.
Activities Arts & crafts; Games; Reading groups; Prayer groups; Movies; Shopping trips; Social/Cultural gatherings.

QUINCY

Donely House ICFMR*
PO Box 217, Quincy, PA, 17247
(717) 749-3151
Licensure Intermediate care for mentally retarded. *Beds* 8. *Certified* Medicaid.
Owner Nonprofit Corp.

Quincy United Methodist Home & Quincy Village
PO Box 217, Quincy, PA, 17247
(717) 749-3151
Admin Kathleen R Pell. *Medical Dir/Dir of Nursing* Dr Douglas Hess; Elizabeth Kaiser RN DON.
Licensure Skilled care; Intermediate care; Intermediate care for mentally retarded. *Beds* SNF 94; ICF 101; ICF/MR 8; Child Day care 35. *Certified* Medicaid; Medicare.
Owner Nonprofit Corp.
Admissions Requirements Medical examination.
Staff Physicians 1 (pt); RNs 12 (ft), 5 (pt); LPNs 18 (ft), 15 (pt); Nurses aides 46 (ft), 45 (pt); Physical therapists 1 (pt); Speech therapists 1 (pt); Activities coordinators 1 (ft); Dietitians 1 (pt); Dentists 1 (pt); Ophthalmologists 2 (pt).
Affiliation Methodist
Facilities Dining room; Physical therapy room; Activities room; Chapel; Crafts room; Laundry room; Barber/Beauty shop; Library.
Activities Arts & crafts; Cards; Games; Reading groups; Prayer groups; Movies; Shopping trips; Social/Cultural gatherings; Weekly worship services.

READING

Berks County Home*
PO Box 1495, Reading, PA, 19603
(215) 376-4847
Medical Dir/Dir of Nursing Lynwood V Keller MD.
Licensure Skilled care; Intermediate care. *Beds* SNF 125; ICF 670. *Certified* Medicaid; Medicare.
Owner Nonprofit Corp.
Admissions Requirements Minimum age 55; Medical examination.
Staff Physicians 14 (pt); RNs 32 (ft), 6 (pt); LPNs 73 (ft), 6 (pt); Nurses aides 309 (ft), 90 (pt); Physical therapists 1 (ft), 1 (pt); Recreational therapists 2 (ft); Occupational therapists 1 (pt); Speech therapists 1 (ft); Activities coordinators 1 (ft); Dietitians 2 (ft), 1 (pt); Dentists 1 (pt); Ophthalmologists 1 (pt); Podiatrists 1 (pt); Audiologists 1 (pt).
Facilities Dining room; Physical therapy room; Activities room; Chapel; Crafts room; Laundry room; Barber/Beauty shop; Library.
Activities Arts & crafts; Cards; Games; Reading groups; Prayer groups; Movies; Shopping trips; Social/Cultural gatherings.

The Hawthorne
1501 Mineral Spring Rd, Reading, PA, 19602
(215) 375-2221

Admin Margaret Layland. *Medical Dir/Dir of Nursing* Irving H Jones MD; Elizabeth Jozwiak DON.
Licensure Personal care boarding home. *Beds* 44.
Owner Privately owned.
Admissions Requirements Medical examination; Physician's request.
Staff RNs 1 (ft); LPNs 1 (ft), 1 (pt); Nurses aides 4 (ft); Student nurses 2 (pt).
Facilities Dining room; Activities room; Laundry room; Barber/Beauty shop; Library.
Activities Cards; Games; Prayer groups; Shopping trips.

Wyomissing Lodge
1000 E Wyomissing Blvd, Reading, PA, 19611
(215) 376-3991
Medical Dir/Dir of Nursing Robert Demby MD.
Licensure Skilled care. *Beds* 107. *Certified* Medicare.
Owner Proprietary Corp.
Staff Physicians 20 (pt); RNs 5 (ft), 12 (pt); LPNs 4 (ft), 3 (pt); Nurses aides 27 (ft), 10 (pt); Physical therapists 1 (pt); Recreational therapists 1 (pt); Occupational therapists 1 (pt); Speech therapists 1 (pt); Activities coordinators 1 (pt); Dietitians 1 (pt); Podiatrists 1 (pt).
Facilities Dining room; Physical therapy room; Activities room; Crafts room; Barber/Beauty shop; Library.
Activities Arts & crafts; Cards; Games; Prayer groups; Movies; Shopping trips; Wine & cheese gatherings.

RENOVO

Bucktail Medical Center*
Pine St, Renovo, PA, 17764
(717) 923-1000
Admin Donna C Paloskey. *Medical Dir/Dir of Nursing* Rizalito Advinceila MD.
Licensure Skilled care. *Beds* 33. *Certified* Medicaid; Medicare.
Owner Nonprofit Corp.
Staff Physicians 2 (ft); RNs 5 (ft), 4 (pt); LPNs 5 (ft), 3 (pt); Nurses aides 10 (ft), 12 (pt); Physical therapists 1 (ft); Recreational therapists 1 (ft); Occupational therapists 1 (pt); Speech therapists 1 (pt); Activities coordinators 1 (ft); Dietitians 1 (ft); Dentists 1 (pt); Podiatrists 1 (pt).
Facilities Dining room; Physical therapy room; Activities room; Chapel; Crafts room; Laundry room; Barber/Beauty shop; Library.
Activities Arts & crafts; Cards; Games; Reading groups; Prayer groups; Movies; Shopping trips; Social/Cultural gatherings.

RHEEMS

Lehmans Guest & Nursing Home
Broad St, Rheems, PA, 17570
(717) 367-1831
Admin Patricia G Baker.
Licensure Skilled care. *Beds* 18.
Owner Proprietary Corp.
Staff Physicians 1 (pt); RNs 2 (ft), 3 (pt); LPNs 2 (ft), 2 (pt); Nurses aides 4 (ft), 6 (pt); Recreational therapists 1 (pt); Activities coordinators 1 (pt); Dietitians 1 (pt).
Facilities Dining room; Activities room; Laundry room; Barber/Beauty shop.
Activities Arts & crafts; Cards; Games; Reading groups; Prayer groups; Shopping trips.

RICHBORO

Richboro Care Center
253 Twining Ford Rd, Richboro, PA, 18954
(215) 357-2032

Admin Charles A Kane NHA. *Medical Dir/Dir of Nursing* Wm Saponaro OD; Estella Ortego RN DON.
Licensure Skilled care; Intermediate care. *Beds* SNF 64; ICF. *Certified* Medicaid; Medicare.
Owner Proprietary Corp (Continental Medical Systems).
Admissions Requirements Medical examination; Physician's request.
Staff RNs 4 (ft), 5 (pt); LPNs 6 (ft), 7 (pt); Nurses aides 20 (ft), 12 (pt); Physical therapists 1 (pt); Reality therapists 1 (pt); Recreational therapists 1 (ft); Occupational therapists 1 (pt); Speech therapists 1 (pt); Activities coordinators 1 (pt); Dietitians 1 (ft); Podiatrists 1 (pt).
Facilities Dining room; Physical therapy room; Activities room; Laundry room.
Activities Arts & crafts; Cards; Games; Reading groups; Prayer groups; Movies; Social/Cultural gatherings.

RICHFIELD

The Zendt Home
PO Box 248, Main St, Richfield, PA, 17086
(717) 694-3434
Admin Nancy M Merisko. *Medical Dir/Dir of Nursing* Dr L Geiser; Lavonda Weaver DON.
Licensure Intermediate care. *Beds* ICF 46. *Certified* Medicaid.
Owner Proprietary Corp.
Admissions Requirements Medical examination.
Staff RNs 1 (pt); LPNs 6 (pt); Nurses aides 39 (pt); Activities coordinators 1 (ft); Dietitians 1 (pt).
Facilities Dining room; Activities room; Laundry room; Barber/Beauty shop.
Activities Arts & crafts; Cards; Games; Reading groups; Prayer groups; Movies; Shopping trips; Social/Cultural gatherings.

RICHLANDTOWN

Zohlman Nursing Home
108 S Main St, Richlandtown, PA, 18955
(215) 536-2252
Admin Debora Bartsch RN LNHA. *Medical Dir/Dir of Nursing* Dr Alfred Vasta.
Licensure Skilled care. *Beds* SNF 169. *Certified* Medicaid; Medicare.
Owner Proprietary Corp.
Admissions Requirements Minimum age 16; Medical examination.
Staff RNs 7 (ft), 15 (pt); LPNs 7 (ft), 4 (pt); Orderlies 4 (ft); Nurses aides 40 (ft), 11 (pt); Recreational therapists 2 (pt); Activities coordinators 1 (ft).
Languages Spanish
Facilities Dining room; Physical therapy room; Activities room; Crafts room; Laundry room; Barber/Beauty shop.
Activities Arts & crafts; Cards; Games; Reading groups; Prayer groups; Movies; Shopping trips; Social/Cultural gatherings.

RIDLEY PARK

Conner-Williams
105 Morton Ave, Ridley Park, PA, 19078
(215) 521-1331
Admin H Skiddell.
Licensure Skilled care; Intermediate care. *Beds* 52. *Certified* Medicaid.
Owner Privately owned.
Admissions Requirements Medical examination.
Facilities Dining room; Activities room; Laundry room; Barber/Beauty shop.
Activities Arts & crafts; Cards; Games; Movies.

Ross Manor Nursing Home*
316 E Hinckley Ave, Ridley Park, PA, 19078
(215) 521-0193
Licensure Skilled care. *Beds* 25. *Certified* Medicaid.
Owner Proprietary Corp.

ROSEMONT

Rosemont Manor*
35 Rosemont Ave, Rosemont, PA, 19010
(215) 525-1500
Admin Susan L Ulmer. *Medical Dir/Dir of Nursing* Dr Ian C Deener.
Licensure Skilled care. *Beds* 76. *Certified* Medicaid; Medicare.
Owner Proprietary Corp (Beverly Enterprises).
Admissions Requirements Minimum age 16.
Staff RNs; LPNs; Nurses aides; Physical therapists; Recreational therapists; Occupational therapists; Speech therapists; Activities coordinators; Dietitians; Dentists; Podiatrists; Audiologists; Social workers.
Facilities Dining room; Physical therapy room; Activities room; Crafts room; Laundry room; Barber/Beauty shop.
Activities Arts & crafts; Cards; Games; Reading groups; Prayer groups; Movies; Social/Cultural gatherings; Adopt-a-grandparent.

ROSLYN

Roslyn Nursing & Rehabilitation Center
2630 Woodland Rd, Roslyn, PA, 19001
(215) 884-6776
Admin Maureen K Humphreys. *Medical Dir/Dir of Nursing* Leonard A Winegrad DO; Joan Rarick DON.
Licensure Skilled care. *Beds* SNF 85. *Certified* Medicaid; Medicare.
Owner Proprietary Corp (GraceCare, Inc).
Admissions Requirements Minimum age 16.
Staff RNs 7 (ft), 10 (pt); LPNs 1 (ft), 1 (pt); Nurses aides 22 (ft), 20 (pt); Activities coordinators 1 (ft), 2 (pt); Dietitians 1 (pt).
Facilities Dining room; Physical therapy room; Activities room; Crafts room; Barber/Beauty shop.
Activities Arts & crafts; Cards; Games; Reading groups; Prayer groups; Movies; Shopping trips; Social/Cultural gatherings.

ROYERSFORD

Montgomery Country Geriatric & Rehabilitation Center
1600 Black Rock Rd, Royersford, PA, 19468
(215) 948-8800
Admin Jean L John NHA. *Medical Dir/Dir of Nursing* John J Maron MD; L A Ciarletta RN.
Licensure Skilled care; Intermediate care. *Beds* SNF 150; ICF 441. *Certified* Medicaid; Medicare.
Owner Nonprofit Corp.
Admissions Requirements Medical examination; Physician's request.
Staff Physicians; RNs; LPNs; Orderlies; Nurses aides; Physical therapists; Recreational therapists; Occupational therapists; Speech therapists; Activities coordinators; Dietitians; Dentists; Ophthalmologists; Podiatrists.
Facilities Dining room; Physical therapy room; Activities room; Chapel; Crafts room; Laundry room; Barber/Beauty shop; Library.
Activities Arts & crafts; Cards; Games; Reading groups; Prayer groups; Movies; Shopping trips; Social/Cultural gatherings.

RYDAL

Rydal Park of Philadelphia Presbyterian Homes on the Fairway
1515 The Fairway, Rydal, PA, 19046
(215) 885-6800
Admin Nancy W Weikert. *Medical Dir/Dir of Nursing* Charles Ewing MD; Carol Gerhart DON.
Licensure Skilled care. *Beds* SNF 120. *Certified* Medicaid; Medicare.
Owner Nonprofit Corp (PA Presbyterian Homes).
Admissions Requirements Minimum age 65.
Staff Physicians 1 (ft); RNs 10 (ft), 9 (pt); LPNs 4 (ft), 3 (pt); Nurses aides 34 (ft), 45 (pt); Recreational therapists 1 (ft); Occupational therapists 1 (ft); Activities coordinators 1 (ft); Dietitians 1 (ft); Ophthalmologists 1 (pt).
Affiliation Presbyterian
Facilities Dining room; Physical therapy room; Activities room; Chapel; Crafts room; Laundry room; Barber/Beauty shop; Library.
Activities Arts & crafts; Cards; Games; Reading groups; Prayer groups; Movies; Shopping trips; Social/Cultural gatherings.

SAEGERTOWN

Crawford County Home, Smith Institute
RD 1 Box 9, Saegertown, PA, 16433
(814) 763-2445
Admin Gordon C Foltz NHA. *Medical Dir/Dir of Nursing* Dr Gerald M Brooks; Sandra K Travis RN DON.
Licensure Intermediate care. *Beds* ICF 179. *Certified* Medicaid.
Owner Nonprofit organization/foundation.
Admissions Requirements Medical examination; Physician's request.
Staff Physicians 1 (ft); RNs 3 (ft), 3 (pt); LPNs 9 (ft), 2 (pt); Orderlies 4 (ft); Nurses aides 60 (ft), 4 (pt); Recreational therapists 2 (ft); Activities coordinators 1 (ft); Dietitians 1 (ft), 1 (pt).
Languages Polish
Facilities Dining room; Physical therapy room; Activities room; Crafts room; Laundry room; Barber/Beauty shop; Library.
Activities Arts & crafts; Cards; Games; Reading groups; Prayer groups; Movies; Shopping trips; Social/Cultural gatherings.

SAINT MARYS

Elk Haven Nursing Home*
RT 255 Box 271, Johnsonburg Rd, Saint Marys, PA, 15857
(814) 834-4256
Licensure Skilled care; Intermediate care. *Beds* SNF 60; ICF 60. *Certified* Medicaid; Medicare.
Owner Proprietary Corp (Unicare).

Andrew Kaul Memorial Hospital—Extended Care Facility
Johnsonburg Rd, Saint Marys, PA, 15857
(814) 781-7500
Admin Michael V Fragale. *Medical Dir/Dir of Nursing* Bernard L Coppolo MD; Mary Beth Ireland RN DON.
Licensure Skilled care; Intermediate care. *Beds* SNF 92; ICF 46. *Certified* Medicaid; Medicare.
Owner Nonprofit Corp.
Admissions Requirements Medical examination; Physician's request.
Staff Physicians 1 (pt); RNs 9 (ft), 4 (pt); LPNs 11 (ft), 11 (pt); Nurses aides 37 (ft), 36 (pt); Physical therapists 2 (ft); Recreational therapists 1 (ft), 1 (pt); Speech therapists 1 (pt); Activities coordinators 1 (ft); Dietitians 1 (ft).
Facilities Dining room; Physical therapy room; Activities room; Chapel; Crafts room; Laundry room; Barber/Beauty shop; Library.

Activities Arts & crafts; Cards; Games; Reading groups; Prayer groups; Movies; Shopping trips; Social/Cultural gatherings.

SALISBURY

Greenleaf House Nursing Home
335 Elm St, Salisbury, PA, 01952
(717) 462-3111
Admin Marcella A Costin.
Licensure Intermediate care. *Beds* ICF 60. *Certified* Medicaid.
Owner Proprietary Corp.
Admissions Requirements Minimum age 21; Medical examination.
Staff Physicians 1 (pt); RNs 2 (ft), 3 (pt); LPNs 2 (ft); Nurses aides 12 (ft), 14 (pt); Physical therapists 1 (pt); Occupational therapists 1 (pt); Activities coordinators 1 (ft), 1 (pt); Dietitians 1 (pt).
Facilities Dining room; Activities room; Crafts room; Laundry room.
Activities Arts & crafts; Cards; Games; Reading groups; Prayer groups; Movies; Shopping trips; Social/Cultural gatherings.

SARVER

Fair Winds Inc*
126 Iron Bridge Rd, Sarver, PA, 16055
(412) 353-1531
Licensure Skilled care. *Beds* 66. *Certified* Medicaid; Medicare.
Owner Proprietary Corp.

SAXONBURG

Saxony Health Center
PO Box 458, Saxonburg Blvd, Saxonburg, PA, 16056
(412) 352-9445
Admin Marjorie Hankey. *Medical Dir/Dir of Nursing* William Knab DO; Marlene Huss.
Licensure Skilled care. *Beds* 63. *Certified* Medicaid; Medicare.
Owner Proprietary Corp.
Staff Physicians 2 (pt); RNs 4 (ft), 4 (pt); LPNs 4 (ft), 1 (pt); Nurses aides 20 (ft), 9 (pt); Physical therapists 3 (pt); Speech therapists 1 (pt); Activities coordinators 1 (ft); Dietitians 1 (pt); Dentists 1 (pt); Ophthalmologists 1 (pt); Podiatrists 1 (pt).
Facilities Dining room; Physical therapy room; Crafts room; Laundry room; Barber/Beauty shop; Library.
Activities Arts & crafts; Cards; Games; Reading groups; Movies; Social/Cultural gatherings.

SAYRE

Sayre House Inc*
N Elmer Ave, Sayre, PA, 18840
(717) 883-1401
Licensure Skilled care. *Beds* 50. *Certified* Medicaid; Medicare.
Owner Proprietary Corp.

SCHUYLKILL HAVEN

Green View Nursing & Convalescent Center*
Rte 1, Schuylkill Haven, PA, 17972
(717) 866-2661
Licensure Skilled care. *Beds* 30. *Certified* Medicaid.
Owner Proprietary Corp.

Schuylkill County Home Rest Haven
PO Box 401, Rte 61, Schuylkill Haven, PA, 17972
(717) 385-0331
Admin James R Bender NHA. *Medical Dir/Dir of Nursing* Dr Joseph Weber; Elaine M Schaeffer RN.

Licensure Skilled care; Intermediate care. *Beds* SNF 37; ICF 225. *Certified* Medicaid; Medicare.
Owner Nonprofit organization/foundation.
Admissions Requirements Medical examination; Physician's request.
Staff Physicians 3 (pt); RNs 9 (ft), 3 (pt); LPNs 23 (ft), 10 (pt); Orderlies 2 (ft); Nurses aides 72 (ft), 20 (pt); Physical therapists 1 (ft); Occupational therapists 1 (pt); Speech therapists 1 (pt); Activities coordinators 1 (ft); Dietitians 2 (pt); Dentists 1 (pt); Ophthalmologists 1 (pt); Podiatrists 1 (pt); Dentist 1 (pt); Pharmacist 1 (pt); Psychiatrist 1 (pt).
Facilities Dining room; Physical therapy room; Activities room; Chapel; Crafts room; Laundry room; Barber/Beauty shop; Library; Gift shop.
Activities Arts & crafts; Cards; Games; Reading groups; Prayer groups; Movies; Shopping trips; Social/Cultural gatherings; Cooking class; Reality orientation groups.

SCOTTDALE

Wolfe Nursing Home Inc*
521 Overholt St, Scottdale, PA, 15683
(412) 887-7680
Licensure Skilled care. *Beds* 20.
Owner Proprietary Corp.

SCRANTON

Adams Manor
824 Adams Ave, Scranton, PA, 18510
(717) 346-5704
Admin Susan A York. *Medical Dir/Dir of Nursing* Dr Kondash; Peg Shaughnessy RN.
Licensure Skilled care; Intermediate care. *Beds* SNF 35; ICF 104. *Certified* Medicaid; Medicare.
Owner Proprietary Corp (Beverly Enterprises).
Facilities Dining room; Physical therapy room; Crafts room; Laundry room; Barber/Beauty shop.
Activities Arts & crafts; Cards; Games; Reading groups; Prayer groups; Movies; Shopping trips; Social/Cultural gatherings.

Allied Services—Long-Term Care Facility
PO Box 1103, 303 Smallcombe Dr, Scranton, PA, 18501
(717) 348-1424
Admin Ann P Rebar. *Medical Dir/Dir of Nursing* Richard Gratz MD; Diane Breslin RN DON.
Licensure Skilled care; Intermediate care. *Beds* SNF 240; ICF 120. *Certified* Medicaid; Medicare.
Owner Nonprofit Corp.
Admissions Requirements Minimum age 18; Medical examination; Physician's request.
Staff RNs 18 (ft); LPNs 27 (ft); Nurses aides 131 (ft); Physical therapists 1 (ft); Recreational therapists 5 (ft); Activities coordinators 1 (ft); Dietitians 1 (ft).
Facilities Dining room; Physical therapy room; Activities room; Chapel; Crafts room; Laundry room; Barber/Beauty shop.
Activities Arts & crafts; Cards; Games; Prayer groups; Movies; Shopping trips; Social/Cultural gatherings.

Allied Services—Lynett Village*
475 Morgan Hwy, Scranton, PA, 18508
(717) 347-1373
Medical Dir/Dir of Nursing Daniel Parsick MD.
Licensure Intermediate care for mentally retarded. *Beds* 89. *Certified* Medicaid.
Owner Nonprofit Corp.
Admissions Requirements Minimum age 18; Medical examination.
Staff Physicians 1 (pt); RNs 7 (ft), 12 (pt); Orderlies 64 (ft); Recreational therapists 3 (ft); Dietitians 1 (ft).

Facilities Dining room; Physical therapy room; Laundry room; Barber/Beauty shop.
Activities Arts & crafts; Games; Prayer groups; Movies; Shopping trips; Social/Cultural gatherings.

Ellen Memorial Convalescent Home
1554 Sanderson Ave, Scranton, PA, 18509
(717) 343-8688
Admin Marilyn L Turner. *Medical Dir/Dir of Nursing* Dr Eugene Stec; Margaret Hilderbrandt DON.
Licensure Skilled care. *Beds* SNF 34. *Certified* Medicaid; Medicare.
Owner Proprietary Corp.
Admissions Requirements Medical examination; Physician's request.
Staff RNs 2 (ft), 1 (pt); LPNs 2 (ft), 2 (pt); Orderlies 2 (ft); Nurses aides 10 (ft), 6 (pt); Activities coordinators 1 (ft).
Facilities Dining room; Activities room; Laundry room.
Activities Arts & crafts; Cards; Games; Reading groups; Prayer groups; Movies; Shopping trips; Social/Cultural gatherings.

Green Ridge Nursing Center
1530 Sanderson Ave, Scranton, PA, 18509
(717) 344-6121
Admin Carmen D Scrimalli. *Medical Dir/Dir of Nursing* Michael J Turock MD; Dolores Trycinski RN DON.
Licensure Skilled care; Intermediate care. *Beds* SNF 16; ICF 49. *Certified* Medicaid; Medicare.
Owner Privately owned.
Admissions Requirements Medical examination; Physician's request.
Staff Physicians; RNs; LPNs; Nurses aides; Physical therapists; Reality therapists; Recreational therapists; Occupational therapists; Speech therapists; Activities coordinators; Dietitians; Ophthalmologists.
Facilities Dining room; Physical therapy room; Activities room; Crafts room; Laundry room; Barber/Beauty shop.
Activities Arts & crafts; Cards; Games; Reading groups; Prayer groups; Movies; Shopping trips; Social/Cultural gatherings.

Holiday Manor*
Franklin Ave & Mulberry Sts, Scranton, PA, 18503
(717) 347-3303
Licensure Intermediate care. *Beds* 154. *Certified* Medicaid.
Owner Proprietary Corp.

Holy Family Residence*
2500 Adams Ave, Scranton, PA, 18509
(717) 343-4065
Medical Dir/Dir of Nursing Dr Thomas Clause.
Licensure Skilled care; Intermediate care. *Beds* SNF 41; ICF 41. *Certified* Medicaid.
Owner Nonprofit Corp.
Admissions Requirements Minimum age 60; Medical examination.
Affiliation Roman Catholic
Facilities Dining room; Physical therapy room; Activities room; Chapel; Crafts room; Laundry room; Barber/Beauty shop; Library.
Activities Arts & crafts; Games; Reading groups; Prayer groups; Movies; Shopping trips; Social/Cultural gatherings.

Hoyt Cresthome Inc*
712 Harrison Ave, Scranton, PA, 18510
(717) 346-2045
Admin Paul Magida. *Medical Dir/Dir of Nursing* Lee Besen MD.
Licensure Skilled care. *Beds* 40. *Certified* Medicaid.
Owner Proprietary Corp.
Admissions Requirements Minimum age 16; Medical examination; Physician's request.

Staff Physicians 1 (pt); RNs 3 (ft), 1 (pt); LPNs 3 (ft); Nurses aides 18 (ft); Activities coordinators 1 (ft); Dietitians 1 (pt); Dentists 1 (pt); Podiatrists 1 (pt).
Facilities Dining room; Activities room; Laundry room; Barber/Beauty shop.
Activities Arts & crafts; Cards; Games; Reading groups; Prayer groups; Movies; Shopping trips; Social/Cultural gatherings.

Jewish Home of Eastern Pennsylvania
1101 Vine St, Scranton, PA, 18510
(717) 344-6177
Licensure Skilled care. *Beds* 175. *Certified* Medicaid; Medicare.
Owner Nonprofit Corp.
Affiliation Jewish

Moses Taylor Hospital—Skilled Nursing Facility*
700 Quincy Ave, Scranton, PA, 18510
(717) 346-3801
Licensure Skilled care. *Beds* 32. *Certified* Medicaid; Medicare.
Owner Nonprofit Corp.

Mountain Rest Nursing Home Inc
Linwood Ave, Scranton, PA, 18505
(717) 346-7381
Admin Colleen Lando NHA. *Medical Dir/Dir of Nursing* Alfonso Gomar MD; Carol Lazzeri RN DON.
Licensure Skilled care. *Beds* SNF 29; ICF 79. *Certified* Medicaid; Medicare.
Owner Proprietary Corp.
Admissions Requirements Medical examination; Physician's request.
Staff RNs; LPNs; Nurses aides; Activities coordinators.
Facilities Dining room; Activities room; Chapel; Crafts room; Laundry room; Barber/Beauty shop.
Activities Arts & crafts; Cards; Games; Reading groups; Prayer groups; Movies; Shopping trips; Social/Cultural gatherings.

St Josephs Center*
2010 Adams Ave, Scranton, PA, 18509
(717) 342-8379
Licensure Intermediate care for mentally retarded. *Beds* 85. *Certified* Medicaid.
Owner Nonprofit Corp.

SECANE

Haskins Nursing Home
1009 Rhoads Ave, Secane, PA, 19018
(215) 623-3624
Admin Elizabeth M. Vernot, NHA. *Medical Dir/Dir of Nursing* Joseph J. Armao, MD; P. Dolan RN.
Licensure Skilled care. *Beds* 22. *Certified* Medicaid.
Owner Privately owned.
Admissions Requirements Physician's request.
Staff Physicians; RNs; Nurses aides; Activities coordinators; Dietitians.
Facilities Dining room; Laundry room.
Activities Arts & crafts; Cards; Reading groups; Prayer groups; Movies; Shopping trips.

SELINSGROVE

The Doctors' Convalescent Center Inc*
800 Broad St, Selinsgrove, PA, 17870-1299
(717) 374-8181
Admin Rae A Adams. *Medical Dir/Dir of Nursing* Robert A Grubb MD.
Licensure Skilled care; Intermediate care. *Beds* SNF 79; ICF 118. *Certified* Medicaid; Medicare.
Owner Proprietary Corp.
Staff Physicians 1 (ft), 1 (pt); RNs 4 (ft), 12 (pt); LPNs 10 (ft), 13 (pt); Nurses aides 48 (ft), 34 (pt); Physical therapists 3 (pt);

Recreational therapists 1 (ft), 1 (pt); Speech therapists 1 (pt); Dietitians 1 (ft); Podiatrists 1 (pt).
Facilities Dining room; Physical therapy room; Activities room; Chapel; Crafts room; Laundry room; Barber/Beauty shop; Library.
Activities Arts & crafts; Cards; Games; Reading groups; Prayer groups; Movies; Shopping trips; Social/Cultural gatherings.

Rathfons Convalescent Home*
308 S Market St, Selinsgrove, PA, 17870
(717) 374-5331
Admin Jean A Rathfon. *Medical Dir/Dir of Nursing* Dr Robert Heinback.
Licensure Intermediate care. *Beds* 44. *Certified* Medicaid.
Owner Proprietary Corp.
Admissions Requirements Medical examination.
Staff Physicians 1 (pt); RNs 2 (ft), 1 (pt); LPNs 1 (ft), 3 (pt); Nurses aides 14 (ft); Physical therapists 1 (pt); Activities coordinators 1 (pt); Dietitians 1 (pt).
Facilities Dining room; Activities room.
Activities Arts & crafts; Cards; Games; Reading groups; Prayer groups; Shopping trips.

Selinsgrove Center
Box 500, Selinsgrove, PA, 17870
(717) 374-2911
Admin Joseph J Scartelli. *Medical Dir/Dir of Nursing* William J Yingling MD.
Licensure Intermediate care for mentally retarded. *Beds* ICF/MR 978. *Certified* Medicaid.
Owner Publicly owned.
Staff Physicians 7 (ft), 2 (pt); RNs 48 (ft); LPNs 30 (ft); Orderlies 700 (ft); Physical therapists 2 (ft); Recreational therapists 10 (ft); Occupational therapists 2 (ft); Speech therapists 10 (ft); Activities coordinators 10 (ft); Dietitians 4 (ft); Podiatrists 5 (ft).
Languages Spanish
Facilities Dining room; Physical therapy room; Activities room; Chapel; Crafts room; Laundry room; Barber/Beauty shop; Library.
Activities Arts & crafts; Games; Prayer groups; Movies; Shopping trips; Social/Cultural gatherings.

SELLERSVILLE

Community Foundation for Human Development
22 Almont Rd, Sellersville, PA, 18960
(215) 257-1155
Admin David W S Austin PhD. *Medical Dir/Dir of Nursing* Dr Joseph Gerone; Kathryn Becker.
Licensure Intermediate care for mentally retarded. *Beds* ICF/MR 37. *Certified* Medicaid.
Owner Nonprofit Corp.
Admissions Requirements Minimum age Birth.
Staff Physicians 9 (pt); RNs 3 (ft), 1 (pt); LPNs 3 (ft), 4 (pt); Nurses aides 21 (ft), 20 (pt); Physical therapists 1 (pt); Recreational therapists 1 (pt); Occupational therapists 1 (pt); Speech therapists 1 (pt); Dietitians 1 (pt); Dentists 1 (pt); Ophthalmologists 1 (pt); Podiatrists 1 (pt).
Facilities Dining room; Activities room; Laundry room.
Activities Arts & crafts; Games; Movies; Shopping trips; Social/Cultural gatherings.

Grand View Hospital SNF/Senior Care Center
700 Lawn Ave, Sellersville, PA, 18960
(215) 257-3611
Admin Elyse Fox. *Medical Dir/Dir of Nursing* Beverly J Ewer DON.
Licensure Skilled care; Respite/residential care; senior day care. *Beds* 20. *Certified* Medicaid; Medicare.
Owner Nonprofit Corp.

Admissions Requirements Medical examination; Physician's request.
Staff RNs 10 (ft), 15 (pt); Orderlies 2 (ft), 2 (pt); Nurses aides 3 (ft), 3 (pt); Physical therapists 1 (ft); Recreational therapists 1 (ft); Occupational therapists 1 (ft); Speech therapists 1 (pt); Activities coordinators 1 (ft); Dietitians 1 (ft); Podiatrists 1 (pt).
Languages German, Pennsylvania Dutch, Spanish
Facilities Dining room; Physical therapy room; Activities room; Chapel; Crafts room; Barber/Beauty shop; Library.
Activities Arts & crafts; Cards; Games; Reading groups; Prayer groups; Movies; Social/Cultural gatherings.

Rockhill Mennonite Community
PO Box 21, Rte 152, Sellersville, PA, 18960
(215) 257-2751
Admin Randy L Shelly. *Medical Dir/Dir of Nursing* Dr Winfield Hedrick; Susan Stubbs RN DON.
Licensure Skilled care. *Beds* SNF 96. *Certified* Medicaid; Medicare.
Owner Nonprofit Corp.
Admissions Requirements Minimum age 62; Medical examination.
Staff RNs 4 (ft), 4 (pt); LPNs 2 (ft), 2 (pt); Orderlies 2 (ft), 2 (pt); Nurses aides 10 (ft), 20 (pt); Recreational therapists 1 (ft); Activities coordinators 1 (ft); Dietitians 1 (ft).
Languages Spanish
Affiliation Mennonite
Facilities Dining room; Physical therapy room; Activities room; Chapel; Crafts room; Laundry room; Barber/Beauty shop; Library.
Activities Arts & crafts; Cards; Games; Reading groups; Prayer groups; Movies; Shopping trips; Social gatherings.

SEWICKLY

Verland Foundation Inc
Iris Rd, RD 2, Sewickly, PA, 15143
(412) 741-2375
Admin Carol B Mitchell. *Medical Dir/Dir of Nursing* Maureen Sleben.
Licensure Intermediate care for mentally retarded. *Beds* ICF/MR 99. *Certified* Medicaid.
Owner Nonprofit Corp.
Staff RNs 15 (ft); Nurses aides 120 (ft); Physical therapists 3 (ft); Recreational therapists 3 (ft); Occupational therapists 3 (ft); Speech therapists 3 (ft); Activities coordinators 1 (ft); Dietitians 1 (ft).
Facilities Dining room; Physical therapy room; Activities room; Laundry room; Library.
Activities Arts & crafts; Games; Shopping trips; Social/Cultural gatherings.

SHAMOKIN

Northumberland County Mountain View Manor
Rte 1, Box 228, Shamokin, PA, 17872
(717) 644-4400
Admin Una M Kinchella. *Medical Dir/Dir of Nursing* Dr James C Gehris; Kay Doty.
Licensure Skilled care; Intermediate care. *Beds* SNF 60; ICF 257. *Certified* Medicaid; Medicare.
Owner Publicly owned.
Admissions Requirements Minimum age 40; Medical examination.
Staff Physicians 5 (pt); RNs 12 (ft), 11 (pt); LPNs 31 (ft), 2 (pt); Orderlies 24 (ft); Nurses aides 103 (ft), 2 (pt); Physical therapists 1 (pt); Occupational therapists 1 (pt); Speech therapists 1 (pt); Activities coordinators 1 (ft); Dietitians 1 (ft), 1 (pt); Dentists 1 (pt); Ophthalmologists 1 (pt); Podiatrists 1 (pt).
Facilities Dining room; Physical therapy room; Activities room; Chapel; Crafts room; Barber/Beauty shop.

Activities Arts & crafts; Cards; Games; Reading groups; Prayer groups; Movies; Shopping trips; Social/Cultural gatherings.

SHARON

Clepper Convalescent Home*
959 E State St, Sharon, PA, 16146
(412) 981-2750
Licensure Skilled care. *Beds* 61. *Certified* Medicaid; Medicare.
Owner Proprietary Corp.

SHARON HILL

Kearney Home*
753 Woodland Terrace, Sharon Hill, PA, 19079
(215) 586-1662
Licensure Intermediate care. *Beds* 17. *Certified* Medicaid; Medicare.
Owner Proprietary Corp.

SHENANDOAH

Shenandoah Manor Nursing Center
101 E Washington St, Shenandoah, PA, 17976
(717) 462-1908
Admin Edith Rothwell NHA. *Medical Dir/Dir of Nursing* Mary Lou Legg RN.
Licensure Skilled care; Intermediate care. *Beds* SNF 37; ICF 88. *Certified* Medicaid; Medicare.
Owner Proprietary Corp.
Admissions Requirements Minimum age 18; Medical examination; Physician's request.
Staff RNs 5 (ft), 3 (pt); LPNs 6 (ft), 11 (pt); Nurses aides 20 (ft), 36 (pt); Activities coordinators 2 (ft).
Facilities Dining room; Physical therapy room; Activities room; Chapel; Crafts room; Laundry room; Barber/Beauty shop; Library.
Activities Arts & crafts; Cards; Games; Reading groups; Prayer groups; Movies; Shopping trips; Social/Cultural gatherings.

SHILLINGTON

Mifflin Healthcare Centers
500 E Philadelphia Ave, Shillington, PA, 19607
(215) 777-7841
Admin Carl N Kline. *Medical Dir/Dir of Nursing* Brooke Cutler.
Licensure Skilled care; Intermediate care. *Beds* SNF 96; ICF 40. *Certified* Medicaid; Medicare.
Owner Proprietary Corp (Genesis Health Ventures).
Admissions Requirements Minimum age 16.
Staff RNs; LPNs; Orderlies; Nurses aides; Physical therapists; Occupational therapists; Speech therapists; Activities coordinators; Dietitians; Ophthalmologists; Podiatrists.
Facilities Dining room; Physical therapy room; Activities room; Crafts room; Laundry room; Barber/Beauty shop.
Activities Arts & crafts; Cards; Games; Reading groups; Prayer groups; Movies; Shopping trips; Social/Cultural gatherings; Adopt-a-grandparent.

SHINGLEHOUSE

Hewitt Manor Inc
59 Honeoye St, Shinglehouse, PA, 16748
(814) 697-6340
Admin Evelyn P Thomson. *Medical Dir/Dir of Nursing* Dilbagh Singh MD; Arlene Risser RN DON.
Licensure Skilled care; Intermediate care. *Beds* SNF 24; ICF 4. *Certified* Medicaid; Medicare.
Owner Proprietary Corp.

Admissions Requirements Minimum age 60; Medical examination; Physician's request.
Staff Physicians 2 (pt); RNs 3 (ft), 1 (pt); LPNs 2 (ft), 3 (pt); Nurses aides 11 (ft), 10 (pt).
Facilities Dining room; Activities room; Crafts room; Laundry room.
Activities Arts & crafts; Cards; Games; Reading groups; Prayer groups; Movies; Shopping trips; Social/Cultural gatherings.

SHREWSBURY

Shrewsbury Lutheran Retirement Village
200 Luther Rd, Shrewsbury, PA, 17361
(717) 235-6895
Admin Barbara J Egan.
Licensure Skilled care; Intermediate care. *Beds* SNF 6; ICF 94. *Certified* Medicaid; Medicare.
Owner Nonprofit organization/foundation.
Admissions Requirements Minimum age 65.
Staff RNs 7 (ft), 10 (pt); LPNs 4 (ft), 4 (pt); Nurses aides 42 (ft), 13 (pt); Physical therapists 1 (pt); Activities coordinators 1 (ft); Dietitians 1 (ft), 1 (pt).
Affiliation Lutheran
Facilities Dining room; Physical therapy room; Activities room; Chapel; Crafts room; Laundry room; Barber/Beauty shop; Library.
Activities Arts & crafts; Cards; Games; Reading groups; Prayer groups; Movies; Shopping trips; Social/Cultural gatherings.

SINKING SPRING

Leader Nursing & Rehabilitation Center
3000 Windmill Rd, Sinking Spring, PA, 19608
(215) 670-2100
Admin Richard C Raffensperger. *Medical Dir/Dir of Nursing* Brian Wummer.
Licensure Skilled care; Intermediate care. *Beds* SNF 122; ICF 62. *Certified* Medicaid; Medicare.
Owner Proprietary Corp (Manor Care).
Staff RNs 6 (ft), 9 (pt); LPNs 16 (ft), 11 (pt); Nurses aides 44 (ft), 39 (pt); Physical therapists 2 (ft); Occupational therapists 1 (ft); Speech therapists 1 (ft); Activities coordinators 1 (ft); Dietitians 1 (ft); Ophthalmologists 1 (pt); Podiatrists 1 (pt).
Facilities Dining room; Physical therapy room; Activities room; Chapel; Crafts room; Laundry room; Barber/Beauty shop; Library.
Activities Arts & crafts; Cards; Games; Reading groups; Prayer groups; Movies; Shopping trips; Social/Cultural gatherings; Cooking; Picnics; Field trips.

SLIGO

Clarview Rest Home*
Rte 1, Sligo, PA, 16255
(814) 745-2031
Licensure Skilled care; Intermediate care. *Beds* SNF 60; ICF 60. *Certified* Medicaid; Medicare.
Owner Proprietary Corp (Unicare).

SMETHPORT

Sena Kean Manor
Marvin St, RD 1, Smethport, PA, 16749
(814) 887-5601
Admin Linda Babola. *Medical Dir/Dir of Nursing* Dr Fayez Roumani; Linda Babuln DON.
Licensure Skilled care; Intermediate care. *Beds* SNF 27; ICF 131. *Certified* Medicaid.
Owner Publicly owned.
Admissions Requirements Minimum age 18; Medical examination; Physician's request.
Staff Physicians 4 (pt); RNs 5 (ft), 5 (pt); LPNs 11 (ft), 10 (pt); Orderlies 7 (ft), 2 (pt); Nurses aides 41 (ft), 16 (pt); Physical

therapists 1 (pt); Speech therapists 1 (pt); Activities coordinators 2 (ft); Dietitians 1 (pt); Ophthalmologists 1 (pt); Dentist 1 (pt).
Facilities Dining room; Physical therapy room; Activities room; Crafts room; Laundry room; Barber/Beauty shop; Library; TV lounges.
Activities Arts & crafts; Cards; Games; Reading groups; Prayer groups; Movies; Shopping trips; Social/Cultural gatherings; Gardening; Fishing.

C K Stones Manor Inc*
15 W Willow St, Smethport, PA, 16749
(814) 887-5716
Licensure Intermediate care. *Beds* 34. *Certified* Medicaid.
Owner Proprietary Corp.

SOMERSET

Seimon Lakeview Manor Estate*
Rte 7, Box 195A, Somerset, PA, 15501
(814) 443-2811
Medical Dir/Dir of Nursing Dr Wayne McKee.
Licensure Skilled care; Intermediate care. *Beds* SNF 30; ICF 90. *Certified* Medicaid; Medicare.
Owner Proprietary Corp.
Admissions Requirements Minimum age 18.
Facilities Dining room; Physical therapy room; Activities room; Crafts room; Laundry room; Barber/Beauty shop.
Activities Arts & crafts; Cards; Games; Reading groups; Prayer groups; Movies; Shopping trips; Social/Cultural gatherings; Fishing.

Somerset Community Hospital
225 S Center Ave, Somerset, PA, 15501
(814) 443-2626
Admin Nancy A Rayman.
Licensure Skilled care. *Beds* 18. *Certified* Medicaid; Medicare.
Owner Nonprofit Corp.
Staff Physicians; RNs; LPNs; Nurses aides; Physical therapists; Recreational therapists; Occupational therapists; Speech therapists; Dietitians.
Facilities Dining room; Physical therapy room; Activities room; Crafts room; Acute care facility adjacent to skilled nursing facility.
Activities Arts & crafts; Cards; Games; Reading groups; Prayer groups.

Somerset State Hospital—Mentally Retarded Unit*
PO Box 631, Somerset, PA, 15501
(814) 445-6501
Licensure Intermediate care for mentally retarded. *Beds* 127. *Certified* Medicaid.
Owner Nonprofit Corp.

SOUDERTON

Souderton Mennonite Homes
207 W Summit St, Souderton, PA, 18964
(215) 723-9881
Admin Paul D Moyer. *Medical Dir/Dir of Nursing* Dr John D Nuschke.
Licensure Skilled care; Personal care; Independent living. *Beds* SNF 59; Personal 104; Independent living 196. *Certified* Medicaid; Medicare.
Owner Nonprofit organization/foundation.
Admissions Requirements Medical examination.
Staff RNs 1 (ft), 10 (pt); LPNs 3 (ft), 5 (pt); Nurses aides 16 (ft), 21 (pt); Activities coordinators 1 (ft); Dietitians 1 (ft).
Affiliation Mennonite
Facilities Dining room; Physical therapy room; Activities room; Chapel; Laundry room; Barber/Beauty shop; Library; Multi-purpose activites room.

Activities Arts & crafts; Games; Reading groups; Movies; Shopping trips; Bible study; Choir & sing-along; Birthday parties; Physical fitness; Spelling bee.

SOUTH MOUNTAIN

South Mountain Restoration Center
South Mountain, PA, 17261
(717) 749-3121
Admin Bruce Darney. *Medical Dir/Dir of Nursing* Emmett P Davis MD; Nancy L Evans RN DON.
Licensure Skilled care; Intermediate care. *Beds* SNF 20; ICF 598. *Certified* Medicaid; Medicare.
Owner Publicly owned.
Admissions Requirements Minimum age 40; Medical examination; Physician's request.
Staff Physicians 3 (ft), 3 (pt); RNs 27 (ft); LPNs 94 (ft); Nurses aides 220 (ft); Physical therapists 1 (pt); Occupational therapists 1 (ft); Speech therapists 1 (ft); Activities coordinators 4 (ft); Dietitians 4 (ft); Ophthalmologists 1 (pt); Dentist 1 (ft).
Facilities Dining room; Physical therapy room; Activities room; Chapel; Crafts room; Laundry room; Barber/Beauty shop; Library.
Activities Arts & crafts; Cards; Games; Reading groups; Prayer groups; Movies; Shopping trips; Social/Cultural gatherings.

SOUTH WILLIAMSPORT

Freezers Home for the Aged*
6 E Central Ave, South Williamsport, PA, 17701
(717) 323-5954
Licensure Intermediate care. *Beds* 20. *Certified* Medicaid.
Owner Proprietary Corp.

SOUTHAMPTON

Southhampton Estates
238 Street Rd, Southampton, PA, 18966
(215) 364-2551
Medical Dir/Dir of Nursing Arthur Lintgen.
Licensure Skilled care. *Beds* 60. *Certified* Medicare.
Owner Nonprofit Corp.

SPRING CITY

Pennhurst Modular Home Community*
Spring City, PA, 19475
(215) 948-3500
Licensure Intermediate care for mentally retarded. *Beds* 150. *Certified* Medicaid.
Owner Nonprofit Corp.

SPRING HOUSE

Silverstream Nursing & Rehabilitation Home
905 Penmllyn Pike, Spring House, PA, 19477
(215) 646-1500
Admin Florence Werlinsky. *Medical Dir/Dir of Nursing* Dr Robert Leopold; Jean Mundy DON.
Licensure Skilled care; Intermediate care; Residential care. *Beds* SNF 51; ICF 57; Residential 20. *Certified* Medicaid; Medicare.
Owner Proprietary Corp (Geriatric & Medical Centers).
Admissions Requirements Medical examination.
Staff Physicians 20 (pt); RNs 7 (ft), 4 (pt); LPNs 4 (ft), 4 (pt); Orderlies 1 (ft), 2 (pt); Nurses aides 26 (ft), 10 (pt); Physical therapists 1 (pt); Recreational therapists 1 (ft), 3 (pt); Occupational therapists 1 (pt); Speech therapists 1 (pt); Dietitians 1 (pt); Dentists 1 (pt); Ophthalmologists 2 (pt); Podiatrists 1 (pt).

Facilities Dining room; Physical therapy room; Activities room; Crafts room; Laundry room; Barber/Beauty shop; Library.
Activities Arts & crafts; Cards; Games; Reading groups; Prayer groups; Movies; Shopping trips; Social/Cultural gatherings.

Spring House Estates Medical Care Facility
Norristown Rd & McKean St, Spring House, PA, 19477
(215) 628-3545 or 628-3546
Admin Elaine R Reimet. *Medical Dir/Dir of Nursing* Arthur B Lintgen MD; Beverly Whitman RN DON.
Licensure Skilled care. *Beds* SNF 60. *Certified* Medicare.
Owner Nonprofit Corp.
Admissions Requirements Physician's request.
Staff RNs 3 (ft), 6 (pt); LPNs 1 (ft), 3 (pt); Orderlies 1 (pt); Nurses aides 17 (ft), 22 (pt); Recreational therapists 1 (ft); Activities coordinators 1 (ft); Dietitians 1 (ft).
Facilities Dining room; Physical therapy room; Activities room; Crafts room; Laundry room; Barber/Beauty shop.
Activities Arts & crafts; Cards; Games; Reading groups; Prayer groups; Movies; Shopping trips; Social/Cultural gatherings.

SPRINGFIELD

C R Center
1799 S Sproul Rd, Springfield, PA, 19064
(215) 543-3380
Medical Dir/Dir of Nursing Dr Rocco Sciubba.
Licensure Intermediate care for mentally retarded. *Beds* 93. *Certified* Medicaid.
Owner Nonprofit Corp.
Admissions Requirements Minimum age 21; Males only; Medical examination.
Staff Physicians 1 (ft); RNs 1 (ft), 1 (pt); LPNs 1 (ft); Occupational therapists 1 (ft); Speech therapists 2 (ft); Activities coordinators 1 (ft); Dietitians 1 (ft).
Affiliation Roman Catholic
Facilities Dining room; Activities room; Chapel; Crafts room; Laundry room; Barber/Beauty shop; Library.
Activities Arts & crafts; Cards; Games; Reading groups; Prayer groups; Movies; Shopping trips; Social/Cultural gatherings.

Harlee Manor*
463 W Sproul Rd, Springfield, PA, 19064
(215) 544-2200
Licensure Skilled care. *Beds* 173. *Certified* Medicare.
Owner Proprietary Corp.

STATE COLLEGE

State College Manor Ltd
450 Waupelani Dr, State College, PA, 16801
(814) 238-5065
Admin Gerald J Boyle. *Medical Dir/Dir of Nursing* Thomas Bem MD; Eleanor Kraft RN.
Licensure Skilled care; Intermediate care. *Beds* SNF 41; ICF 132. *Certified* Medicaid; Medicare.
Owner Proprietary Corp.
Admissions Requirements Physician's request.
Staff Physicians 12 (pt); RNs 5 (ft), 8 (pt); LPNs 12 (ft), 11 (pt); Orderlies 7 (ft), 4 (pt); Nurses aides 33 (ft), 31 (pt); Physical therapists 1 (ft); Recreational therapists 1 (ft); Speech therapists 1 (ft); Activities coordinators 1 (ft), 2 (pt); Dietitians 1 (ft); Ophthalmologists 1 (pt).
Facilities Dining room; Physical therapy room; Activities room; Laundry room; Barber/Beauty shop.
Activities Arts & crafts; Games; Reading groups; Prayer groups; Movies; Shopping trips.

STEVENS

Denver Nursing Home
400 Lancaster Ave, Stevens, PA, 17578
(215) 267-3878, (717) 627-1123
Admin Walter L Wentzel Jr. *Medical Dir/Dir of Nursing* Dr Ronald B Laukaitis; Judi Bachman DON.
Licensure Skilled care; Intermediate care. *Beds* SNF 22; ICF 51. *Certified* Medicaid; Medicare.
Owner Proprietary Corp.
Admissions Requirements Medical examination.
Facilities Dining room; Physical therapy room; Activities room; Crafts room; Laundry room; Barber/Beauty shop.
Activities Arts & crafts; Cards; Games; Reading groups; Prayer groups; Movies; Shopping trips; Social/Cultural gatherings.

STILLWATER

Bonham Nursing Center
Register Rd 1, Stillwater, PA, 17878
(717) 864-3174
Medical Dir/Dir of Nursing Robert Campbell MD.
Licensure Skilled care; Intermediate care. *Beds* 58. *Certified* Medicaid; Medicare; VA.
Owner Privately owned.
Staff Physicians 4 (ft); RNs 2 (ft), 4 (pt); LPNs 4 (pt); Orderlies 1 (ft); Nurses aides 15 (ft), 16 (pt); Physical therapists 1 (pt); Activities coordinators 1 (ft), 1 (pt); Dietitians 1 (pt); Ophthalmologists 1 (pt); Dentist 1 (pt).
Facilities Dining room; Activities room; Laundry room; Barber/Beauty shop; Ambulance; Recreational park; Bus.
Activities Arts & crafts; Games; Prayer groups; Movies; Shopping trips; Social/Cultural gatherings; Fairs; Circus; Bible study.

STROUDSBURG

Laurel Manor*
1170 W Main St, Stroudsburg, PA, 18360
(717) 421-1240
Medical Dir/Dir of Nursing James G Kitchen II MD.
Licensure Intermediate care. *Beds* 54. *Certified* Medicaid.
Owner Nonprofit Corp.
Admissions Requirements Medical examination.
Staff Physicians 1 (pt); RNs 10 (ft); LPNs 5 (ft); Nurses aides 13 (ft); Reality therapists 1 (pt); Activities coordinators 1 (ft); Dietitians 1 (pt).
Facilities Dining room; Activities room; Crafts room.
Activities Arts & crafts; Cards; Games; Reading groups; Prayer groups; Movies; Social/Cultural gatherings.

Pleasant Valley Manor*
Rte 2, Stroudsburg, PA, 18360
(717) 992-4172
Medical Dir/Dir of Nursing John Lim MD.
Licensure Skilled care; Intermediate care. *Beds* SNF 28; ICF 146. *Certified* Medicaid; Medicare.
Owner Nonprofit Corp.
Admissions Requirements Medical examination.
Staff Physicians 1 (ft); RNs 5 (ft), 3 (pt); LPNs 6 (ft), 6 (pt); Orderlies 2 (ft), 1 (pt); Nurses aides 42 (ft); Reality therapists 1 (ft); Recreational therapists 3 (pt); Occupational therapists 1 (pt); Activities coordinators 1 (ft); Dietitians 1 (ft); Podiatrists 1 (pt).
Facilities Dining room; Physical therapy room; Activities room; Chapel; Crafts room; Laundry room; Barber/Beauty shop.

Activities Arts & crafts; Games; Prayer groups; Movies; Shopping trips; Social/Cultural gatherings.

SUNBURY

Leader Nursing & Rehabilitation Center
800 Court St Circle Dr, Sunbury, PA, 17801
(717) 286-7121
Admin Sandra Deppen. *Medical Dir/Dir of Nursing* Mohammed Munir MD; Alice Marks DON.
Licensure Skilled care; Intermediate care. *Beds* 122. *Certified* Medicaid; Medicare.
Owner Proprietary Corp (Manor Care).
Admissions Requirements Medical examination.
Staff RNs 4 (ft), 4 (pt); LPNs 8 (ft), 11 (pt); Orderlies 2 (pt); Nurses aides 15 (ft), 46 (pt); Physical therapists 1 (ft); Recreational therapists 1 (ft), 1 (pt); Occupational therapists 1 (ft).
Facilities Dining room; Physical therapy room; Activities room; Chapel; Crafts room; Laundry room; Barber/Beauty shop; Library; Occupational therapy facilities.
Activities Arts & crafts; Cards; Games; Reading groups; Prayer groups; Movies; Shopping trips; Social/Cultural gatherings; Family programs; Musicals; Religious activities.

Mansion Nursing & Convalescent Home Inc*
1040-1052 Market St, Sunbury, PA, 17801
(717) 286-6922
Licensure Skilled care. *Beds* 71. *Certified* Medicaid; Medicare.
Owner Proprietary Corp (Beverly Enterprises).

Sunbury Community Hospital—Skilled Nursing Unit
305 N 11th St, Sunbury, PA, 17801
(717) 286-3333
Admin Sherwin O Albert Jr NHA.
Licensure Skilled care; Intermediate care. *Beds* 29. *Certified* Medicaid; Medicare.
Owner Nonprofit Corp.
Admissions Requirements Medical examination; Physician's request.
Staff RNs 3 (ft); LPNs 17 (ft); Physical therapists 1 (ft), 1 (pt); Recreational therapists 1 (pt); Dietitians 1 (ft).
Activities Arts & crafts; Cards; Games; Reading groups; Prayer groups; Movies; Shopping trips; Social/Cultural gatherings.

SUSQUEHANNA

Barnes-Kasson County Hospital Skilled Nursing Facility
400 Turnpike St, Susquehanna, PA, 18847
(717) 853-3135
Admin Sara C Iveson. *Medical Dir/Dir of Nursing* Robert M Shelly MD; Joan Hurley RN.
Licensure Skilled care; Intermediate care. *Beds* 49. *Certified* Medicaid; Medicare.
Owner Nonprofit Corp.
Admissions Requirements Physician's request.
Staff Physicians 1 (pt); RNs 3 (ft), 2 (pt); LPNs 5 (ft), 1 (pt); Nurses aides 14 (ft), 8 (pt); Physical therapists 2 (ft), 1 (pt); Speech therapists 1 (pt); Activities coordinators 1 (ft), 2 (pt); Dietitians 1 (ft); Dentists 2 (pt); Ophthalmologists 1 (pt).
Facilities Dining room; Physical therapy room; Activities room; Crafts room; Barber/Beauty shop; Solarium.
Activities Arts & crafts; Cards; Games; Reading groups; Prayer groups; Movies; Shopping trips; Social/Cultural gatherings; Activities for bed-bound.

TELFORD

Lutheran Home—Telford
235 N Washington Ave, Telford, PA, 18969
(215) 723-9819
Licensure Skilled care. *Beds* 55. *Certified* Medicaid.
Owner Nonprofit Corp.
Affiliation Lutheran

THOMPSONTOWN

Meda Nipple Convalescent Home*
Rte 1, Box 109, Thompsontown, PA, 17094
(717) 463-2632
Licensure Skilled care. *Beds* 23. *Certified* Medicaid; Medicare.
Owner Proprietary Corp.
Staff RNs 2 (ft), 1 (pt); LPNs 1 (ft), 1 (pt); Nurses aides 2 (ft), 5 (pt); Physical therapists 1 (pt); Recreational therapists 1 (pt); Occupational therapists 1 (pt); Speech therapists 1 (pt); Activities coordinators 1 (ft); Dietitians 1 (pt); Dentists 1 (pt); Podiatrists 1 (pt); Audiologists 1 (pt).

TITUSVILLE

Sunset Manor
81 Dillon Dr, Titusville, PA, 16354
(814) 827-2727
Admin Arlene Greenawalt. *Medical Dir/Dir of Nursing* William Sonnenberg MD; Susan Hollo RN DON.
Licensure Intermediate care. *Beds* ICF 65. *Certified* Medicaid.
Owner Proprietary Corp (Beverly Enterprises).
Admissions Requirements Minimum age 18; Medical examination.
Staff RNs 2 (ft), 1 (pt); LPNs 4 (ft), 2 (pt); Nurses aides 15 (ft), 5 (pt); Activities coordinators 1 (ft); Dietitians 1 (ft).
Facilities Dining room; Physical therapy room; Activities room; Laundry room.
Activities Arts & crafts; Cards; Games; Reading groups; Prayer groups; Movies; Shopping trips; Social/Cultural gatherings; Bingo; Exercises; Family socials; Resident council.

TOPTON

Lutheran Home at Topton
Topton, PA, 19562
(215) 682-2145
Admin Paul L Buehrle. *Medical Dir/Dir of Nursing* Raymond Hauser MD; Jean Fox DON.
Licensure Skilled care; Intermediate care. *Beds* SNF 120; ICF 109. *Certified* Medicaid; Medicare.
Owner Nonprofit organization/foundation.
Admissions Requirements Minimum age 62.
Staff Physicians 3 (ft); RNs 16 (ft), 11 (pt); LPNs 16 (ft); Orderlies 1 (ft); Nurses aides 42 (ft), 92 (pt); Physical therapists 2 (ft); Reality therapists 1 (ft); Recreational therapists 1 (ft); Occupational therapists 4 (ft); Speech therapists 1 (pt); Activities coordinators 2 (ft); Dietitians 1 (pt); Dentists 1 (pt); Ophthalmologists 1 (pt); Podiatrists 1 (pt); Dentist 1 (pt).
Affiliation Lutheran
Facilities Dining room; Physical therapy room; Activities room; Chapel; Crafts room; Laundry room; Barber/Beauty shop; Library.
Activities Arts & crafts; Cards; Games; Reading groups; Prayer groups; Movies; Shopping trips; Social/Cultural gatherings.

TORRANCE

Torrance State Hospital—IMR Unit*
PO Box 103, Torrance, PA, 15779
(412) 459-8000

Licensure Intermediate care for mentally retarded. *Beds* 94. *Certified* Medicaid.
Owner Nonprofit Corp.

Torrance State Hospital—Long-Term Care Facility*
PO Box 103, Torrance, PA, 15779
(412) 459-8000
Licensure Skilled care; Intermediate care. *Beds* SNF 141; ICF 137. *Certified* Medicaid.
Owner Nonprofit Corp.

TOWANDA

Memorial Hospital Inc & Skilled Nursing Unit
1 Hospital Dr, Towanda, PA, 18848
(717) 265-2191
Medical Dir/Dir of Nursing Raymond A Perry MD.
Licensure Skilled care. *Beds* SNF 44. *Certified* Medicaid; Medicare.
Owner Nonprofit Corp.
Admissions Requirements Physician's request.
Staff Physicians 15 (pt); RNs 2 (ft), 2 (pt); LPNs 5 (ft), 5 (pt); Nurses aides 12 (ft), 12 (pt); Physical therapists 1 (ft); Speech therapists 1 (pt); Activities coordinators 1 (ft); Dietitians 1 (pt); Dentists 1 (pt); Ophthalmologists 1 (pt); Podiatrists 1 (pt).
Facilities Dining room; Physical therapy room; Activities room; Laundry room; Barber/Beauty shop.
Activities Arts & crafts; Cards; Games; Reading groups; Shopping trips; Social/Cultural gatherings.

TREMONT

Tremont Nursing Center
44 Donaldson Rd, Tremont, PA, 17981
(717) 695-3141
Admin Roseanne Makarczyk. *Medical Dir/Dir of Nursing* Sung H Park MD; Charlene Hentz DON.
Licensure Skilled care; Intermediate care. *Beds* SNF 60; ICF 60. *Certified* Medicaid; Medicare.
Owner Proprietary Corp (Unicare).
Admissions Requirements Medical examination.
Staff Physicians; RNs; LPNs; Orderlies; Nurses aides; Physical therapists; Reality therapists.
Facilities Dining room; Physical therapy room; Activities room; Crafts room; Laundry room; Barber/Beauty shop; Library.
Activities Arts & crafts; Cards; Games; Reading groups; Prayer groups; Movies; Shopping trips; Social/Cultural gatherings.

TREXLERTOWN

Mosser Nursing Home Inc*
Old Rte 222, Trexlertown, PA, 18087
(215) 395-5661
Licensure Skilled care. *Beds* 54. *Certified* Medicaid; Medicare.
Owner Proprietary Corp.

TROY

Bradford County Manor
PO Box 322, Rte 3, Troy, PA, 16947
(717) 297-4111
Admin Dale L Nolen. *Medical Dir/Dir of Nursing* Vance A Good MD; Sonya Powell RN.
Licensure Skilled care; Intermediate care. *Beds* SNF 40; ICF 186. *Certified* Medicaid; Medicare.
Owner Publicly owned.
Admissions Requirements Medical examination; Physician's request.
Staff Physicians 7 (pt); RNs 8 (ft), 4 (pt); LPNs 20 (ft), 10 (pt); Nurses aides 64 (ft), 35 (pt); Physical therapists 1 (pt); Speech

therapists 1 (pt); Activities coordinators 1 (ft), 4 (pt); Dietitians 1 (ft); Ophthalmologists 1 (pt); Podiatrists 1 (pt); Optometrist 1 (pt) Pharmacist 1 (pt).
Facilities Dining room; Physical therapy room; Activities room; Chapel; Crafts room; Laundry room; Barber/Beauty shop.
Activities Arts & crafts; Cards; Games; Reading groups; Prayer groups; Movies; Shopping trips; Social/Cultural gatherings.

Martha Lloyd School—Camelot ICF/MR
W Main St, Troy, PA, 16947
(717) 297-2185
Admin LuAnn Simcoe.
Licensure Intermediate care for mentally retarded. *Beds* 18.
Owner Nonprofit Corp.
Admissions Requirements Females only; Medical examination.
Staff RNs 1 (pt); LPNs 3 (ft), 1 (pt); Nurses aides 9 (ft), 3 (pt); Activities coordinators 1 (ft).
Facilities Dining room; Activities room; Crafts room; Laundry room; Barber/Beauty shop; Library; Gym; Work shop; School store; Home economics room.
Activities Arts & crafts; Cards; Games; Prayer groups; Movies; Shopping trips; Social/Cultural gatherings; Ceramics; Music.

TUNKHANNOCK

Carpenter Care Center Inc*
Rte 3, Virginia Ave, Tunkhannock, PA, 18657
Admin Virginia Carpenter. *Medical Dir/Dir of Nursing* Dr Arthur Sherwood.
Owner Proprietary Corp (Beverly Enterprises).
Admissions Requirements Minimum age 18; Medical examination.
Staff Physicians 7 (pt); Orderlies 4 (ft); Physical therapists 1 (ft); Reality therapists 1 (ft); Recreational therapists 3 (ft), 1 (pt); Occupational therapists 2 (ft), 1 (pt); Speech therapists 1 (pt); Activities coordinators 1 (pt); Dietitians 1 (ft); Dentists 1 (pt); Ophthalmologists 1 (pt); Podiatrists 1 (pt); Audiologists 1 (pt).
Facilities Dining room; Physical therapy room; Activities room; Chapel; Crafts room; Laundry room; Barber/Beauty shop; Library.
Activities Arts & crafts; Cards; Games; Reading groups; Prayer groups; Movies; Shopping trips; Social/Cultural gatherings.

TYRONE

Epworth Manor
951 Washington Ave, Tyrone, PA, 16686
(814) 684-0320
Admin Paul D Schroeder. *Medical Dir/Dir of Nursing* Carlos A Wiegering MD.
Licensure Skilled care; Intermediate care. *Beds* SNF 68; ICF 34. *Certified* Medicaid; Medicare.
Owner Nonprofit Corp.
Admissions Requirements Minimum age 62; Medical examination.
Staff Physicians 1 (pt); RNs 1 (ft); LPNs 3 (ft); Nurses aides 13 (ft); Physical therapists 1 (pt); Speech therapists 1 (pt); Activities coordinators 1 (ft); Dietitians 1 (pt); Dentists 1 (pt); Ophthalmologists 1 (pt); Podiatrists 1 (pt).
Affiliation Methodist
Facilities Dining room; Physical therapy room; Activities room; Chapel; Crafts room; Laundry room; Barber/Beauty shop.
Activities Arts & crafts; Cards; Games; Reading groups; Prayer groups; Movies; Shopping trips; Social/Cultural gatherings.

UNIONTOWN

Fayette Health Care Center
RD 4 Box 30, Uniontown, PA, 15401
(412) 439-5700
Admin James Filippone. *Medical Dir/Dir of Nursing* Honorio Pineda MD; Maryellen Gumro DON.
Licensure Skilled care; Intermediate care. *Beds* SNF 25; ICF 95. *Certified* Medicaid; Medicare.
Owner Proprietary Corp (Beverly Enterprises).
Admissions Requirements Medical examination; Physician's request.
Staff RNs; LPNs; Orderlies; Nurses aides; Activities coordinators.
Facilities Dining room; Physical therapy room; Activities room; Crafts room; Laundry room.
Activities Arts & crafts; Cards; Games; Reading groups; Prayer groups; Movies; Shopping trips; Social/Cultural gatherings.

Lafayette Manor*
Rte 4, Box 682, New Salem Rd, Uniontown, PA, 15401
(412) 437-9804
Licensure Skilled care. *Beds* 98. *Certified* Medicaid.
Owner Nonprofit Corp.

Laurel Health Center
75 Hickle St, Uniontown, PA, 15401
(412) 437-9871
Admin Charles Rossi.
Licensure Skilled care; Residential care. *Beds* SNF 55; Residential 8. *Certified* Medicare.
Owner Proprietary Corp.
Admissions Requirements Minimum age 18; Medical examination; Physician's request.
Staff RNs 3 (ft), 2 (pt); LPNs 5 (ft), 1 (pt); Orderlies 2 (ft); Nurses aides 20 (ft), 3 (pt); Physical therapists 2 (pt); Reality therapists 1 (ft); Recreational therapists 1 (ft); Occupational therapists 1 (pt); Speech therapists 1 (pt); Activities coordinators 1 (ft); Dietitians 1 (pt); Ophthalmologists 1 (pt).
Facilities Dining room; Physical therapy room; Activities room; Laundry room; Barber/Beauty shop.
Activities Arts & crafts; Cards; Games; Reading groups; Prayer groups.

Mt Macrina Manor Nursing Home
520 W Main St, Uniontown, PA, 15401
(412) 437-1400
Admin Sr Dorothy Balock.
Licensure Skilled care. *Beds* 54. *Certified* Medicaid; Medicare.
Owner Nonprofit Corp.
Admissions Requirements Medical examination; Physician's request.
Staff Physicians 5 (pt); RNs 3 (ft), 1 (pt); LPNs 10 (ft), 1 (pt); Orderlies 2 (ft); Nurses aides 26 (ft), 3 (pt); Physical therapists 1 (pt); Occupational therapists 1 (pt); Speech therapists 1 (pt); Activities coordinators 2 (ft); Dietitians 1 (ft); Ophthalmologists 1 (pt).
Languages Slavic
Affiliation Roman Catholic
Facilities Dining room; Physical therapy room; Activities room; Chapel; Laundry room; Barber/Beauty shop; Lounge; solarium; porches.
Activities Arts & crafts; Cards; Games; Reading groups; Prayer groups; Movies; Exercises; bowling.

VALENCIA

Grahams Nursing Home Inc*
Rte 1, Sandy Hill Rd, Valencia, PA, 16059
(412) 898-1894
Admin Herbert S White. *Medical Dir/Dir of Nursing* Donald L Kelley MD.

Licensure Intermediate care. Beds 24.
Certified Medicaid.
Owner Proprietary Corp.
Staff Physicians 1 (pt); RNs 4 (ft), 1 (pt);
LPNs 2 (ft), 2 (pt); Nurses aides 22 (ft);
Physical therapists 1 (pt); Reality therapists
1 (pt); Recreational therapists 1 (pt);
Activities coordinators 1 (ft); Dietitians 1
(pt).
Facilities Dining room; Physical therapy
room; Activities room; Crafts room; Laundry
room.
Activities Arts & crafts; Cards; Games;
Reading groups; Prayer groups; Movies;
Shopping trips; Social/Cultural gatherings.

Valencia Woods Nursing Center
Rte 4, Box 357, Valencia, PA, 16059
(412) 625-1561
Admin Linda K Lewis. Medical Dir/Dir of
Nursing Dr Jack Heck III; Esther
Tomaszewski RN DON.
Licensure Skilled care; Intermediate care. Beds
SNF 75; ICF. Certified Medicaid; Medicare.
Owner Nonprofit Corp.
Admissions Requirements Medical
examination.
Staff Physicians 1 (pt); RNs 6 (ft), 3 (pt);
LPNs 5 (pt); Nurses aides 17 (ft), 15 (pt);
Physical therapists 2 (pt); Recreational
therapists 1 (ft); Occupational therapists 1
(pt); Speech therapists 1 (pt); Activities
coordinators 1 (ft); Dietitians 1 (pt);
Ophthalmologists 1 (pt); Social worker 1
(pt).
Facilities Dining room; Physical therapy
room; Barber/Beauty shop; Patient lounge.
Activities Arts & crafts; Cards; Games;
Reading groups; Prayer groups; Movies;
Shopping trips; Social/Cultural gatherings.

WALLINGFORD

The Wallingford*
115 S Providence Rd, Wallingford, PA, 19086
(215) 565-3232
Licensure Skilled care. Beds 207. Certified
Medicaid; Medicare.
Owner Proprietary Corp.

WARMINSTER

Centennial Spring Health Care Center*
333 Newtown Rd, Warminster, PA, 18974
(215) 672-9082
Licensure Skilled care. Beds 180. Certified
Medicaid; Medicare.
Owner Proprietary Corp (HBA Management
Inc).

Christs Home Retirement Center
1220 W Street Rd, Warminster, PA, 18974
(215) 956-2270
Admin Richard B Barnes. Medical Dir/Dir of
Nursing Alan J Miller MD; Carol Baltera
DON.
Licensure Skilled care. Beds SNF 18. Certified
Medicaid; Medicare.
Owner Nonprofit Corp.
Admissions Requirements Minimum age 65;
Medical examination; Physician's request.
Staff Physicians 2 (pt); RNs 4 (ft), 5 (pt);
LPNs 2 (ft), 3 (pt); Nurses aides 9 (ft), 10
(pt); Physical therapists 1 (pt); Occupational
therapists 1 (pt); Speech therapists 1 (pt);
Activities coordinators 1 (ft); Dietitians 1
(pt); Dentists 1 (pt); Ophthalmologists 1 (pt);
Podiatrists 1 (pt).
Languages German
Facilities Dining room; Activities room;
Chapel; Crafts room; Laundry room; Barber/
Beauty shop.
Activities Arts & crafts; Games; Reading
groups; Prayer groups; Movies; Shopping
trips.

Eastern Pennsylvania Eastern Star Home
850 Norristown Rd, Warminster, PA, 18974
(215) 672-2500
Admin Lorraine Lardani. Medical Dir/Dir of
Nursing David Davis III DO; Patricia Strang
DON.
Licensure Skilled care; Personal care. Beds
SNF 26; Personal 35. Certified Medi-Cal.
Owner Nonprofit Corp.
Admissions Requirements Minimum age 65,
Must be member of the Eastern Star;
Medical examination.
Staff Physicians 2 (pt); RNs 2 (ft), 4 (pt);
LPNs 10 (pt); Nurses aides 10 (ft), 12 (pt);
Physical therapists; Recreational therapists 2
(ft); Occupational therapists; Speech
therapists; Dietitians; Dentists;
Ophthalmologists 2 (pt); Podiatrists.
Affiliation Eastern Star
Facilities Dining room; Physical therapy
room; Activities room; Chapel; Crafts room;
Laundry room; Barber/Beauty shop; Library.
Activities Arts & crafts; Cards; Games;
Reading groups; Prayer groups; Movies;
Shopping trips; Social/Cultural gatherings.

WARREN

Warren Manor
682 Pleasant Dr, Warren, PA, 16365
(814) 723-7060
Admin Royce E Freebourn. Medical Dir/Dir of
Nursing Dr Stephen Mory; Donna Fellows
DON.
Licensure Skilled care. Beds SNF 121.
Certified Medicaid; Medicare.
Owner Proprietary Corp (Health Care
Facilities Inc).
Admissions Requirements Medical
examination.
Staff Physicians 11 (pt); RNs 8 (ft), 4 (pt);
LPNs 5 (ft), 8 (pt); Nurses aides 32 (ft), 18
(pt); Physical therapists 5 (pt); Recreational
therapists 2 (ft), 2 (pt); Speech therapists 2
(pt); Activities coordinators 1 (ft); Dietitians
3 (pt); Dentists 1 (pt); Ophthalmologists 1
(pt); Ophthalmologists 1 (pt); Podiatrists 1
(pt); Respiratory therapists 2 (pt); EKG
technician 1 (pt); X-ray technician 1 (pt).
Facilities Dining room; Physical therapy
room; Activities room; Crafts room; Laundry
room; Barber/Beauty shop; Library; Two
large lounges; Seven large patios; 7 acres of
land; Therapy rooms.
Activities Arts & crafts; Cards; Games;
Reading groups; Prayer groups; Movies;
Shopping trips; Social/Cultural gatherings;
Soda shop.

Warren Medical Services*
205 Water St, Warren, PA, 16365
(814) 726-0820)
Admin Joseph P Darrington. Medical Dir/Dir
of Nursing Dr Robert Donaldson.
Licensure Skilled care. Beds 111. Certified
Medicaid; Medicare.
Owner Proprietary Corp.
Admissions Requirements Medical
examination; Physician's request.
Staff Physicians 1 (pt); RNs 3 (ft), 6 (pt);
LPNs 6 (ft), 5 (pt); Orderlies 3 (ft), 2 (pt);
Nurses aides 26 (ft), 18 (pt); Physical
therapists 1 (pt); Reality therapists 1 (ft);
Recreational therapists 1 (ft); Occupational
therapists 1 (pt); Speech therapists 1 (pt);
Dietitians 1 (pt); Dentists 1 (pt);
Ophthalmologists 1 (pt); Podiatrists 1 (pt);
Audiologists 1 (pt).
Facilities Dining room; Physical therapy
room; Activities room; Laundry room;
Barber/Beauty shop.
Activities Arts & crafts; Cards; Games;
Reading groups; Movies; Shopping trips;
Social/Cultural gatherings; Music therapy.

Warren Nursing Home Inc*
121 Central Ave, Warren, PA, 16365
(814) 726-1420
Admin D C Deal. Medical Dir/Dir of Nursing
Ronald Simonsen MD.
Licensure Skilled care. Beds 48. Certified
Medicaid.
Owner Proprietary Corp.
Staff Physicians 1 (pt); RNs 4 (ft), 2 (pt);
LPNs 1 (ft), 1 (pt); Nurses aides 14 (ft), 12
(pt); Physical therapists 1 (pt); Reality
therapists 1 (pt); Recreational therapists 1
(pt); Activities coordinators 1 (ft); Dietitians
1 (pt); Podiatrists 1 (pt).
Facilities Dining room; Physical therapy
room; Activities room; Crafts room; Laundry
room; Barber/Beauty shop.
Activities Arts & crafts; Cards; Games;
Reading groups; Prayer groups; Movies;
Shopping trips; Social/Cultural gatherings.

**Warren State Hospital—Long-Term Care
Facility**
PO Box 249, Warren, PA, 16365
(814) 723-5500
Admin Gizella Bunce. Medical Dir/Dir of
Nursing Dr William S Wolters; Victoria
Schmader.
Licensure Intermediate care. Beds 24.
Certified Medicaid.
Owner Publicly owned.
Admissions Requirements Minimum age 21;
Medical examination.
Staff Physicians 2 (pt); RNs 4 (ft); LPNs 7
(ft); Nurses aides 6 (ft); Recreational
therapists 1 (ft) 13I 2 (ft); Speech therapists
1 (ft); Activities coordinators 1 (ft);
Dietitians 3 (ft).
Facilities Dining room; Activities room;
Chapel; Crafts room; Laundry room; Barber/
Beauty shop; Library.
Activities Arts & crafts; Cards; Games;
Reading groups; Prayer groups; Movies;
Shopping trips; Social/Cultural gatherings.

WARRINGTON

Fox Nursing and Rehabilitation Center
PO Box 678, 2644 Bristol Rd, Warrington,
PA, 18976
(215) 343-2700
Admin Margaret W Crighton NHA RN.
Medical Dir/Dir of Nursing Dr Paul Moyer;
Sandi Meadow DON.
Licensure Skilled care; Critical Care. Certified
Medicare.
Owner Proprietary Corp (GraceCare, Inc).
Admissions Requirements Minimum age 25;
Medical examination.
Staff RNs 6 (ft), 6 (pt); LPNs 7 (ft), 3 (pt);
Nurses aides 8 (ft), 9 (pt); Recreational
therapists 1 (pt); Dietitians 1 (pt).
Facilities Dining room; Physical therapy
room; Activities room; Crafts room; Laundry
room.
Activities Arts & crafts; Cards; Games;
Reading groups; Movies; Shopping trips;
Social/Cultural gatherings.

WASHINGTON

Kade Nursing Home*
1198 W Wylie Ave Ext, Washington, PA,
15301
(412) 222-2148
Admin Janice Marianna. Medical Dir/Dir of
Nursing Dr John McCarrell.
Licensure Skilled care. Beds 57. Certified
Medicaid.
Owner Proprietary Corp.
Staff RNs; LPNs; Nurses aides; Physical
therapists; Speech therapists; Activities
coordinators; Dietitians.
Facilities Dining room; Physical therapy
room; Activities room; Laundry room;
Barber/Beauty shop.

Activities Arts & crafts; Cards; Games; Prayer groups; Shopping trips.

Washington County Health Center
Rte 1, Box 94, Washington, PA, 15301
(412) 228-5010
Admin Barry W Parks. *Medical Dir/Dir of Nursing* Dennis Davis; Margaret Boxton RN DON.
Licensure Skilled care; Intermediate care. *Beds* SNF 50; ICF 200. *Certified* Medicaid; Medicare.
Owner Publicly owned.
Admissions Requirements Minimum age 21; Medical examination.
Staff Physicians 3 (pt); RNs 12 (ft), 6 (pt); LPNs 14 (ft), 8 (pt); Nurses aides 87 (ft), 16 (pt); Physical therapists 1 (pt); Speech therapists 1 (pt); Activities coordinators 1 (ft); Dietitians 1 (pt); Dentists 1 (pt); Podiatrists 1 (pt).
Facilities Dining room; Physical therapy room; Activities room; Chapel; Crafts room; Laundry room; Barber/Beauty shop; Library.
Activities Arts & crafts; Cards; Games; Reading groups; Prayer groups; Movies; Shopping trips; Social/Cultural gatherings.

Washington Senior Care
PO Box 677, 825 S Main St, Washington, PA, 15301-0677
(412) 222-4300
Admin Evelyn M Vandever. *Medical Dir/Dir of Nursing* Jesus S Evangelista MD; Jeanne H Steele RN.
Licensure Skilled care; Intermediate care; Independent Housing; Personal care. *Beds* SNF 48; ICF 102; Congregate apts 150; Independent apts 30. *Certified* Medicaid; Medicare.
Owner Nonprofit Corp.
Admissions Requirements Minimum age 62; Medical examination; Physician's request.
Staff Physicians 1 (pt); RNs 11 (ft); LPNs 15 (ft); Nurses aides 59 (ft); Physical therapists 1 (pt); Recreational therapists 1 (ft); Occupational therapists 1 (pt); Speech therapists 1 (pt); Activities coordinators 2 (pt); Dietitians 1 (pt); Dentists 1 (pt); Ophthalmologists 1 (pt); Podiatrists 1 (pt); Dentist 1 (pt).
Affiliation Presbyterian
Facilities Dining room; Physical therapy room; Activities room; Crafts room; Laundry room; Barber/Beauty shop; Library; Soda fountain; Conference rooms; Patios; Atrium; Community rooms; Walkways.
Activities Arts & crafts; Cards; Games; Reading groups; Prayer groups; Movies; Shopping trips; Social/Cultural gatherings; Vesper services; Sewing.

WATSONTOWN

Kramm Nursing Home Inc*
245-47 E 8th St, Watsontown, PA, 17777
(717) 538-1160
Admin Randall D Kramm. *Medical Dir/Dir of Nursing* Dr Robert Yannaccone.
Licensure Skilled care. *Beds* 74. *Certified* Medicaid.
Owner Proprietary Corp.
Admissions Requirements Medical examination.
Staff Physicians 9 (pt); RNs 2 (ft), 2 (pt); LPNs 2 (ft), 3 (pt); Nurses aides 20 (ft), 14 (pt); Physical therapists 1 (pt); Activities coordinators 1 (ft); Dietitians 1 (pt); Dentists 1 (pt); Ophthalmologists 1 (pt); Podiatrists 1 (pt).
Facilities Dining room; Physical therapy room; Activities room; Crafts room; Laundry room; Barber/Beauty shop; Library.
Activities Arts & crafts; Cards; Games; Reading groups; Prayer groups; Movies; Shopping trips; Social/Cultural gatherings.

WAYNE

Wayne Nursing & Rehabilitation Center
30 West Ave, Wayne, PA, 19087
(215) 688-3635
Admin Marjorie Walker. *Medical Dir/Dir of Nursing* Ian Ballard MD.
Licensure Skilled care; Intermediate care. *Beds* 108. *Certified* Medicaid; Medicare.
Owner Proprietary Corp.
Staff Physicians 3 (pt); RNs 9 (ft), 8 (pt); LPNs 4 (ft), 2 (pt); Orderlies 3 (ft); Nurses aides 25 (ft), 20 (pt); Physical therapists 1 (ft); Recreational therapists 1 (ft); Occupational therapists 1 (pt); Speech therapists 1 (pt); Activities coordinators 1 (ft); Dietitians 1 (pt); Dentists 1 (pt); Ophthalmologists 1 (pt); Podiatrists 1 (pt); Audiologists 1 (pt).
Facilities Dining room; Physical therapy room; Activities room; Laundry room; Barber/Beauty shop; Library.
Activities Arts & crafts; Cards; Games; Reading groups; Prayer groups; Movies; Shopping trips; Wine & cheese parties; Theme lunches; Weekend & evening activities.

WAYNESBURG

Curry Memorial Home
RD 2 Box 60, Waynesburg, PA, 15370
(412) 627-3153
Admin Diane W McCauley NHA. *Medical Dir/Dir of Nursing* Dr Jeffrey Smith; Cathy Brezovsky DON.
Licensure Skilled care; Intermediate care. *Beds* SNF 37; ICF 74. *Certified* Medicaid; Medicare.
Owner Publicly owned.
Staff Physicians 1 (pt); RNs 7 (ft), 5 (pt); LPNs 22 (ft), 8 (pt); Nurses aides 37 (ft), 10 (pt); Physical therapists 1 (pt); Speech therapists 1 (pt); Activities coordinators 1 (ft); Dietitians 1 (pt); Dentists 1 (pt); Ophthalmologists 1 (pt); Podiatrists 1 (pt).
Facilities Dining room; Physical therapy room; Activities room; Chapel; Crafts room; Laundry room; Barber/Beauty shop; Library.
Activities Arts & crafts; Cards; Games; Reading groups; Prayer groups; Movies; Shopping trips; Social/Cultural gatherings.

WEATHERLY

Carbon County Home
Evergreen Ave, Rte 2, Weatherly, PA, 18255
(717) 427-8683
Admin Frank E Wehr. *Medical Dir/Dir of Nursing* Dr Larry Antolick; Margaret Lewis.
Licensure Skilled care; Intermediate care. *Beds* SNF 50; ICF 150. *Certified* Medicaid; Medicare.
Owner Nonprofit Corp.
Admissions Requirements Minimum age 17; Medical examination; Physician's request.
Staff Physicians 1 (ft), 1 (pt); RNs 8 (ft), 6 (pt); LPNs 15 (ft), 2 (pt); Nurses aides 62 (ft), 24 (pt); Physical therapists 1 (ft); Dentists 1 (ft); Ophthalmologists 1 (ft); Podiatrists 1 (ft); Dentist 1 (ft).
Facilities Dining room; Physical therapy room; Activities room; Chapel; Crafts room; Laundry room; Barber/Beauty shop; Game room.
Activities Arts & crafts; Cards; Games; Reading groups; Prayer groups; Movies; Shopping trips; Social/Cultural gatherings; Olympics; Fishing trips; Picnics.

WELLSBORO

Broad Acres Nursing Home
Rte 6 RD 3, Wellsboro, PA, 16901
(717) 724-3913

Admin Maureen Phelps NHA. *Medical Dir/Dir of Nursing* Preston Erway MD; Jeanine Coolidge RN.
Licensure Skilled care; Intermediate care. *Beds* SNF 60; ICF 60. *Certified* Medicaid; Medicare.
Owner Proprietary Corp (Unicare).
Admissions Requirements Medical examination.
Staff RNs 4 (ft), 3 (pt); LPNs 11 (ft), 2 (pt); Nurses aides 33 (ft), 13 (pt); Activities coordinators 2 (ft); Dietitians 1 (ft).
Facilities Dining room; Physical therapy room; Activities room; Crafts room; Laundry room; Barber/Beauty shop.
Activities Arts & crafts; Cards; Games; Prayer groups; Movies; Shopping trips; Social/Cultural gatherings; Resident committees; Music therapy.

Carleton Nursing Home*
10 West Ave, Wellsboro, PA, 16901
(717) 724-2631
Licensure Skilled care. *Beds* 26. *Certified* Medicaid.
Owner Proprietary Corp.

The Green Home Inc
PO Box 836, 37 Central Ave, Wellsboro, PA, 16901
(717) 724-3131
Admin Graydon E Fanning. *Medical Dir/Dir of Nursing* Anne K Butler MD.
Licensure Skilled care. *Beds* SNF 122. *Certified* Medicaid; Medicare; VA.
Owner Nonprofit Corp.
Admissions Requirements Medical examination; Physician's request.
Staff Physicians 1 (pt); RNs 6 (ft), 5 (pt); LPNs 10 (ft), 2 (pt); Orderlies 2 (ft); Nurses aides 40 (ft), 27 (pt); Physical therapists 1 (pt); Speech therapists 1 (pt); Activities coordinators 2 (ft); Dietitians 1 (ft); Ophthalmologists 1 (pt).
Facilities Dining room; Physical therapy room; Activities room; Laundry room; Barber/Beauty shop.
Activities Arts & crafts; Cards; Games; Reading groups; Prayer groups; Movies; Social/Cultural gatherings.

WERNERSVILLE

Hamburg Center Annex
Wernersville, PA, 19565
(215) 678-3411
Admin Todd M Carsen. *Medical Dir/Dir of Nursing* Dr Richard Bick.
Licensure Skilled care; Intermediate care. *Beds* SNF 214; ICF 86. *Certified* Medicaid; Medicare.
Owner Proprietary Corp (Beverly Enterprises).
Admissions Requirements Minimum age 16; Physician's request.
Staff Physicians; RNs; LPNs; Orderlies; Nurses aides; Physical therapists; Recreational therapists; Occupational therapists; Speech therapists; Activities coordinators; Dietitians; Dentists; Ophthalmologists; Podiatrists.
Facilities Dining room; Physical therapy room; Activities room; Chapel; Crafts room; Laundry room; Barber/Beauty shop.
Activities Arts & crafts; Games; Prayer groups; Movies; Shopping trips; Social/Cultural gatherings; Adopt-a-grandparent.

Wernersville State Hospital—Long-Term Care Unit
Wernersville, PA, 19565-0300
(215) 678-3311
Admin John D Sholly. *Medical Dir/Dir of Nursing* Phyllis A Murr MD; Fern R Wawrzyniak RN DON.
Licensure Skilled care; Intermediate care. *Beds* SNF 33; ICF 113. *Certified* Medicaid.
Owner Publicly owned.

Admissions Requirements Minimum age 18; Medical examination; Physician's request.
Staff Physicians 1 (ft), 1 (pt); RNs 23 (ft), 4 (pt); LPNs 34 (ft), 6 (pt); Nurses aides 16 (ft), 2 (pt); Physical therapists 1 (ft); Occupational therapists 1 (ft); Activities coordinators 1 (ft); Dietitians 1 (ft); Dentists 1 (pt).
Facilities Dining room; Physical therapy room; Activities room; Chapel; Crafts room; Laundry room; Barber/Beauty shop; Library.
Activities Arts & crafts; Cards; Games; Reading groups; Movies; Shopping trips; Social/Cultural gatherings.

WEST CHESTER

Brandywine Hall Care Center
PO Box 524, 800 W Miner St, West Chester, PA, 19382
(215) 696-3120
Admin Lois Eltonhead. *Medical Dir/Dir of Nursing* Philip Kistler MD; Julia Thomson DON.
Licensure Skilled care. *Beds* SNF 120. *Certified* Medicaid; Medicare.
Owner Proprietary Corp (Geriatric & Medical Centers).
Admissions Requirements Medical examination; Physician's request.
Staff Physicians; RNs; LPNs; Orderlies; Nurses aides; Physical therapists; Reality therapists; Recreational therapists; Occupational therapists; Speech therapists; Activities coordinators; Dietitians; Podiatrists.
Facilities Dining room; Physical therapy room; Activities room; Crafts room; Laundry room; Barber/Beauty shop; Library; Occupational therapy; Dietary exam room; Physician's room.
Activities Arts & crafts; Cards; Games; Reading groups; Prayer groups; Movies; Shopping trips; Social/Cultural gatherings; Rhythm band; Bell choir.

Friends Hall at West Chester*
424 N Matlack St, West Chester, PA, 19380
(215) 696-5211
Licensure Skilled care. *Beds* 80.
Owner Nonprofit Corp.

Pocopson Home
1695 Lenape Rd, West Chester, PA, 19382
(215) 793-1212
Admin Peter S Perry. *Medical Dir/Dir of Nursing* Dan S Butoi.
Licensure Skilled care; Intermediate care. *Beds* SNF 46; ICF 315. *Certified* Medicaid; Medicare.
Owner Publicly owned.
Admissions Requirements Medical examination.
Staff Physicians 3 (ft); RNs 13 (ft), 11 (pt); LPNs 29 (ft), 15 (pt); Nurses aides 150 (ft), 4 (pt); Physical therapists 1 (ft); Recreational therapists 7 (ft), 2 (pt); Speech therapists 1 (ft); Activities coordinators 1 (ft); Dietitians 2 (ft); Dentists 1 (ft); Ophthalmologists 1 (ft); Podiatrists 1 (ft).
Facilities Dining room; Physical therapy room; Activities room; Chapel; Crafts room; Laundry room; Barber/Beauty shop; Library.
Activities Arts & crafts; Cards; Games; Reading groups; Prayer groups; Movies; Shopping trips; Social/Cultural gatherings.

West Chester Arms of Pennsylvania Inc*
1130 West Chester Pike, West Chester, PA, 19380
(215) 692-3636
Medical Dir/Dir of Nursing Dr Ben Reniello.
Licensure Skilled care; Intermediate care. *Beds* SNF 90; ICF 150. *Certified* Medicaid; Medicare.
Owner Proprietary Corp (Geriatric & Medical Centers).

Staff Physical therapists 1 (ft); Recreational therapists 3 (ft); Occupational therapists; Speech therapists; Activities coordinators; Dietitians; Dentists; Podiatrists.
Facilities Physical therapy room; Activities room; Crafts room; Laundry room; Barber/Beauty shop.
Activities Arts & crafts; Cards; Games; Reading groups; Prayer groups; Movies; Shopping trips; Social/Cultural gatherings.

WEST READING

Leader Nursing & Rehabilitation Center*
425 Buttonwood St, West Reading, PA, 19611
(215) 373-5166
Licensure Skilled care; Intermediate care. *Beds* SNF 120; ICF 60. *Certified* Medicaid; Medicare.
Owner Proprietary Corp (Manor Care).
Admissions Requirements Medical examination; Physician's request.
Staff RNs 8 (ft), 8 (pt); LPNs 14 (ft), 6 (pt); Nurses aides 54 (ft), 36 (pt); Physical therapists 1 (ft); Reality therapists 1 (ft); Recreational therapists 1 (ft), 2 (pt); Activities coordinators 1 (ft); Dietitians 1 (ft).
Facilities Dining room; Physical therapy room; Activities room; Chapel; Laundry room; Barber/Beauty shop; Library.
Activities Arts & crafts; Cards; Reading groups; Prayer groups; Shopping trips; Social/Cultural gatherings.

Reading Nursing Center*
4th & Spruce Sts, West Reading, PA, 19602
(215) 374-5175
Admin Diane G Fonzone. *Medical Dir/Dir of Nursing* Dr Henry Bialas.
Licensure Skilled care; Intermediate care. *Beds* SNF 50; ICF 150. *Certified* Medicaid; Medicare.
Owner Proprietary Corp (Unicare).
Staff RNs 6 (ft), 4 (pt); LPNs 11 (ft), 12 (pt); Orderlies 2 (ft); Nurses aides 41 (ft), 43 (pt); Physical therapists 1 (ft); Occupational therapists 1 (pt); Speech therapists 1 (pt); Activities coordinators 4 (ft); Dietitians 1 (ft); Podiatrists 1 (pt); Audiologists 1 (pt).
Facilities Dining room; Physical therapy room; Activities room; Crafts room; Laundry room; Barber/Beauty shop.
Activities Arts & crafts; Cards; Games; Reading groups; Prayer groups; Movies; Shopping trips; Social/Cultural gatherings.

WEST SUNBURY

Allegheny Valley School—Butler Campus*
Rte 1, West Sunbury, PA, 16061
(412) 637-2981
Licensure Intermediate care for mentally retarded. *Beds* 15. *Certified* Medicaid.
Owner Nonprofit Corp.

WEXFORD

Pineview Manor*
PO Box 191, Swinderman Rd, Wexford, PA, 15090
(412) 935-3781
Licensure Skilled care. *Beds* 32. *Certified* Medicaid.
Owner Proprietary Corp.

Wexford House
9850 Old Perry Hwy, Wexford, PA, 15090
(412) 366-7900
Admin Joel F Camp. *Medical Dir/Dir of Nursing* Arlene Moran.
Licensure Skilled care. *Beds* 224. *Certified* Medicaid; Medicare.
Owner Proprietary Corp.
Admissions Requirements Medical examination; Physician's request.

Staff Physicians; RNs; LPNs; Orderlies; Nurses aides; Physical therapists; Recreational therapists; Occupational therapists; Speech therapists; Activities coordinators; Dietitians; Podiatrists.
Facilities Dining room; Physical therapy room; Activities room; Chapel; Crafts room; Laundry room; Barber/Beauty shop; Library.
Activities Arts & crafts; Cards; Games; Reading groups; Prayer groups; Movies; Shopping trips; Social/Cultural gatherings.

WHITE HAVEN

White Haven Center*
Oley Valley Rd, White Haven, PA, 18661
(717) 443-9564
Licensure Intermediate care for mentally retarded. *Beds* 567. *Certified* Medicaid.
Owner Nonprofit Corp.

WILKES-BARRE

Hampton House*
Sans Souci Pkwy, Wilkes-Barre, PA, 18702
(717) 825-8725
Licensure Skilled care. *Beds* 104. *Certified* Medicaid; Medicare.
Owner Proprietary Corp.

Heritage House
80 E Northampton St, Wilkes-Barre, PA, 18701-3098
(717) 826-1031
Admin Margaret R Spencer. *Medical Dir/Dir of Nursing* Dr Joseph M Lombardo; Barbara Aleo RN.
Licensure Skilled care; Residential care. *Beds* SNF 50; Residential 61. *Certified* Medicaid; Medicare.
Owner Nonprofit Corp.
Admissions Requirements Minimum age 62; Medical examination; Physician's request.
Staff Physicians 1 (pt); RNs 3 (ft), 3 (pt); LPNs 3 (ft), 2 (pt); Nurses aides 11 (ft), 14 (pt); Physical therapists 1 (pt); Occupational therapists 1 (pt); Speech therapists 1 (pt); Activities coordinators 1 (pt); Dietitians 1 (pt); Dentists 1 (pt); Ophthalmologists 1 (pt).
Facilities Dining room; Physical therapy room; Activities room; Crafts room; Laundry room; Barber/Beauty shop; Library; Outdoor patio.
Activities Arts & crafts; Cards; Games; Reading groups; Prayer groups; Movies; Shopping trips; Social/Cultural gatherings.

Little Flower Manor*
200 S Meade St, Wilkes-Barre, PA, 18702
(717) 823-6131
Medical Dir/Dir of Nursing John Valenti MD.
Licensure Skilled care. *Beds* 127. *Certified* Medicaid; Medicare.
Owner Nonprofit Corp.
Staff Physicians 3 (ft); RNs 6 (ft), 4 (pt); LPNs 13 (ft), 6 (pt); Nurses aides 36 (ft), 30 (pt); Recreational therapists 1 (ft); Dietitians 1 (ft); Dentists 1 (pt); Ophthalmologists 1 (pt); Podiatrists 1 (pt).
Affiliation Roman Catholic
Facilities Dining room; Physical therapy room; Activities room; Chapel; Crafts room; Laundry room; Barber/Beauty shop.
Activities Arts & crafts; Cards; Games; Prayer groups; Movies; Shopping trips; Social/Cultural gatherings.

Riverstreet Manor Nursing & Rehabilitation Center
440 N River St, Wilkes-Barre, PA, 18702
(717) 825-5611
Admin Paul Davies.
Beds 120.
Owner Proprietary Corp (Genesis Health Ventures).

Step by Step Inc
293 S Franklin St, Wilkes-Barre, PA, 18702
(717) 823-6891
Admin Ann Chester.
Licensure Intermediate care for mentally retarded. *Beds* ICF/MR 16. *Certified* Medicaid.
Owner Nonprofit Corp.
Admissions Requirements Medical examination; Physician's request.
Staff Physicians 2 (pt); RNs 1 (ft); LPNs 3 (pt); Physical therapists 1 (pt); Occupational therapists 1 (pt); Speech therapists 1 (pt); Activities coordinators 1 (pt); Dietitians 1 (pt); Dentists 1 (pt); Ophthalmologists 1 (pt); Podiatrists 1 (pt); Activities coordinator 1 (pt).
Facilities Dining room; Activities room; Laundry room.
Activities Arts & crafts; Games; Movies; Shopping trips; Social/Cultural gatherings.

Summit Health Care Center
50 N Pennsylvania Ave, Wilkes-Barre, PA, 18701
(714) 825-3488
Admin Lori Gerhard. *Medical Dir/Dir of Nursing* Isadore Robbins MD; Diane Hazur DON.
Licensure Skilled care; Intermediate care. *Beds* SNF 60; ICF 60. *Certified* Medicaid; Medicare.
Owner Proprietary Corp (Beverly Enterprises).
Admissions Requirements Medical examination.
Facilities Dining room; Physical therapy room; Activities room; Laundry room; Barber/Beauty shop.
Activities Arts & crafts; Games; Prayer groups; Movies; Shopping trips; Social/Cultural gatherings.

Valley Crest Nursing Home*
Rte 115, Plains Twp, Wilkes-Barre, PA, 18711
(717) 826-1011
Admin Robert A Reed. *Medical Dir/Dir of Nursing* David W Greenwald MD.
Licensure Skilled care. *Beds* 386. *Certified* Medicaid; Medicare.
Owner Nonprofit Corp.
Admissions Requirements Minimum age 18.
Staff Physicians 7 (ft); RNs 30 (ft), 2 (pt); LPNs 45 (ft); Nurses aides 177 (ft); Physical therapists 1 (pt); Occupational therapists 1 (pt); Speech therapists 1 (pt); Activities coordinators 1 (ft); Dietitians 2 (ft); Dentists 1 (pt); Ophthalmologists 1 (pt); Podiatrists 1 (pt); Audiologists 1 (pt).
Facilities Dining room; Physical therapy room; Activities room; Chapel; Crafts room; Laundry room; Barber/Beauty shop; Library.
Activities Arts & crafts; Cards; Games; Reading groups; Prayer groups; Movies; Shopping trips; Social/Cultural gatherings.

WILLIAMSPORT

Divine Providence—Extended Care Facility*
1100 Gramrion Blvd, Williamsport, PA, 17701
(717) 326-8181
Licensure Skilled care. *Beds* 34. *Certified* Medicaid; Medicare.
Owner Nonprofit Corp.

Hope Intermediate Residences Inc
PO Box 1837, Williamsport, PA, 17703
(717) 326-3745
Admin LeAnn Rock.
Licensure Intermediate care for mentally retarded. *Beds* ICF/MR 23. *Certified* Medicaid.
Owner Nonprofit Corp.
Admissions Requirements Medical examination.
Staff RNs 2 (ft); LPNs 4 (ft); Nurses aides 1 (pt).

Facilities Dining room; Activities room; Laundry room.
Activities Arts & crafts; Cards; Games; Movies; Shopping trips; Social/Cultural gatherings; Church; Camp; Adult Day Care Program.

Leader Nursing & Rehabilitation Center—North
300 Leader Dr, Williamsport, PA, 17701
(717) 323-8627
Admin Roberta McClintock. *Medical Dir/Dir of Nursing* James Montague MD; James Williams RN.
Licensure Skilled care; Intermediate care. *Beds* SNF 60; ICF 90. *Certified* Medicaid; Medicare.
Owner Proprietary Corp (Manor Care).
Admissions Requirements Physician's request.
Staff RNs 8 (ft), 2 (pt); LPNs 12 (ft), 7 (pt); Orderlies 3 (pt); Nurses aides 36 (ft), 27 (pt); Physical therapists; Recreational therapists 2 (ft), 1 (pt); Occupational therapists 1 (pt); Speech therapists 1 (pt); Dietitians 1 (ft).
Facilities Dining room; Physical therapy room; Activities room; Chapel; Laundry room; Barber/Beauty shop.
Activities Arts & crafts; Cards; Games; Prayer groups; Movies; Shopping trips.

Leader Nursing Rehabilitation Center—South
101 Leader Dr, Williamsport, PA, 17701
(717) 323-3758
Admin Roberta McClintock. *Medical Dir/Dir of Nursing* Dr Tobias; Judy Sullivan.
Licensure Skilled care; Intermediate care; Residential care. *Beds* SNF 33; ICF 77; Residential 10. *Certified* Medicaid; Medicare.
Owner Proprietary Corp (Manor Care).
Staff RNs 6 (ft), 4 (pt); LPNs 5 (ft), 6 (pt); Orderlies 2 (ft); Nurses aides 28 (ft), 26 (pt); Physical therapists 1 (pt); Recreational therapists 1 (ft), 2 (pt).
Facilities Dining room; Physical therapy room; Activities room; Chapel; Crafts room; Laundry room; Barber/Beauty shop; Library.
Activities Arts & crafts; Cards; Games; Reading groups; Prayer groups; Movies; Shopping trips; Social/Cultural gatherings.

Williamsport Home*
1900 Ravine Rd, Williamsport, PA, 17701
(717) 323-8781
Licensure Skilled care; Intermediate care. *Beds* SNF 8; ICF 141. *Certified* Medicaid.
Owner Nonprofit Corp.

WILLOW GROVE

The Homestead Nursing & Rehabilitation Center
1113 N Easton Rd, Willow Grove, PA, 19090
(215) 659-3060
Admin Dennis H Gregory. *Medical Dir/Dir of Nursing* Walter Krantz MD; Carol Lichtenwalner.
Licensure Skilled care; Intermediate care. *Beds* SNF 185. *Certified* Medicaid; Medicare.
Owner Proprietary Corp (Genesis Health Ventures).
Admissions Requirements Medical examination; Physician's request.
Staff RNs 6 (ft), 2 (pt); LPNs 9 (ft), 6 (pt); Nurses aides 40 (ft), 50 (pt); Physical therapists 1 (ft); Recreational therapists 4 (ft); Occupational therapists 1 (pt); Speech therapists 1 (ft); Activities coordinators; Dietitians 1 (pt).
Facilities Dining room; Physical therapy room; Activities room; Barber/Beauty shop.
Activities Arts & crafts; Games; Reading groups; Prayer groups; Movies; Shopping trips.

The Homestead Nursing & Rehabilitation Center
1113 N Easton Rd, Willow Grove, PA, 19090
(215) 659-3060
Admin Dennis Gregory.
Beds 185.
Owner Proprietary Corp (Genesis Health Ventures).

WINDBER

Church of the Brethren Home*
1005 Hoffman Ave, Windber, PA, 15963
(814) 467-5505
Licensure Skilled care; Intermediate care. *Beds* SNF 76; ICF 71. *Certified* Medicaid; Medicare.
Owner Nonprofit Corp.

WORTHINGTON

Sugar Creek Rest Inc
PO Box 80, RD 2, Worthington, PA, 16262
(412) 445-3146
Admin Kenneth Tack. *Medical Dir/Dir of Nursing* Dr D W Minteer; Kathy James.
Licensure Skilled care; Intermediate care. *Beds* SNF 30; ICF 73. *Certified* Medicaid; Medicare.
Owner Proprietary Corp.
Staff Physicians 4 (pt); RNs 5 (ft), 4 (pt); LPNs 3 (ft), 8 (pt); Orderlies; Nurses aides 23 (ft), 17 (pt); Physical therapists 2 (ft); Reality therapists 1 (pt); Recreational therapists 2 (ft); Occupational therapists 1 (pt); Speech therapists 1 (pt); Activities coordinators 1 (ft); Dietitians 1 (ft); Dentists 1 (pt); Ophthalmologists 1 (pt); Podiatrists 1 (pt).
Facilities Dining room; Physical therapy room; Activities room; Crafts room; Laundry room; Barber/Beauty shop; Library.
Activities Arts & crafts; Cards; Games; Reading groups; Prayer groups; Movies; Social/Cultural gatherings.

WYNCOTE

Hopkins House Nursing & Rehabilitation Center
8100 Washington Ln, Wyncote, PA, 19095
(215) 576-8000
Admin Arlene S Monroe. *Medical Dir/Dir of Nursing* Dr Leonard Winegrad; Nancy Randolph RN.
Licensure Skilled care; Intermediate care; Respite care. *Beds* SNF 99. *Certified* Medicaid; Medicare.
Owner Proprietary Corp (Columbia Corp).
Admissions Requirements Medical examination; Physician's request.
Staff RNs 4 (ft), 6 (pt); LPNs 10 (ft), 7 (pt); Orderlies 1 (ft); Nurses aides 27 (ft), 24 (pt); Physical therapists 1 (ft); Reality therapists 1 (ft); Occupational therapists 1 (pt); Speech therapists 1 (pt); Activities coordinators 1 (ft); Dietitians 1 (ft); Dentists 1 (pt); Ophthalmologists 1 (pt); Podiatrists 1 (pt); Social Services 1 (ft), 1 (pt).
Facilities Dining room; Physical therapy room; Activities room; Laundry room; Barber/Beauty shop; Library; Occupational therapy room; Speech therapy room; Respite care.
Activities Arts & crafts; Cards; Games; Prayer groups; Movies; Shopping trips; Social/Cultural gatherings; Religious services.

The Oaks Nursing & Rehabilitation Center
240 Barker Rd, Wyncote, PA, 19095
(215) 884-3639
Admin Susan Montague RN NHA. *Medical Dir/Dir of Nursing* Dr Giammanco; Daun Barrett RN DON.
Licensure Skilled care; Intermediate care. *Beds* SNF 51; ICF. *Certified* Medicaid; Medicare.

Owner Proprietary Corp (Genesis Health Ventures).
Staff RNs 1 (ft), 2 (pt); LPNs 4 (ft), 2 (pt); Nurses aides 20 (ft), 10 (pt); Physical therapists 1 (pt); Recreational therapists 1 (ft); Occupational therapists 1 (pt); Speech therapists; Dietitians 1 (pt).

The Oaks Nursing & Rehabilitation Center
Church Rd & Greenwood Ave, Wyncote, PA, 19095
(215) 884-3639
Admin Susan Montague.
Beds 53.
Owner Proprietary Corp (Genesis Health Ventures).

Wyncote Church Home
Fernbrook & Maple Aves, Wyncote, PA, 19095
(215) 885-2620
Admin Donald R Fulmer. *Medical Dir/Dir of Nursing* Earl S Krick MD; Elizabeth A Geiger RN DON.
Licensure Skilled care; Intermediate care; Residential care. *Beds* SNF 29; ICF 31; Residential 70. *Certified* Medicaid; Medicare.
Owner Nonprofit Corp.
Admissions Requirements Minimum age 65; Medical examination.
Staff Physicians 1 (pt); RNs 2 (ft), 9 (pt); LPNs 2 (pt); Nurses aides 21 (ft), 11 (pt); Physical therapists 1 (pt); Recreational therapists 2 (pt); Occupational therapists 1 (pt); Speech therapists 1 (pt); Activities coordinators 1 (pt); Dietitians 1 (ft); Dentists 1 (pt); Ophthalmologists 1 (pt); Podiatrists 1 (pt).
Affiliation Church of Christ
Facilities Dining room; Activities room; Chapel; Crafts room; Laundry room; Barber/Beauty shop; Library.
Activities Arts & crafts; Cards; Games; Reading groups; Prayer groups; Movies; Shopping trips; Social/Cultural gatherings; Remotivation; Choir groups.

WYNDMOOR

All Sts Rehabilitation Hospital/Springfield Retirement Residence
8601 Stenton Ave, Wyndmoor, PA, 19118
(215) 233-6200
Medical Dir/Dir of Nursing Richard A Sullivan MD.
Licensure Skilled care; Rehabilitation hospital. *Beds* SNF 31; Rehab 52. *Certified* Medicaid; Medicare.
Owner Nonprofit Corp.
Admissions Requirements Physician's request.
Staff Physicians 5 (ft), 1 (pt); RNs 24 (ft); LPNs 3 (ft); Nurses aides 20 (ft), 10 (pt); Physical therapists 6 (ft), 2 (pt); Recreational therapists 3 (ft); Occupational therapists 6 (ft); Speech therapists 1 (ft); Dietitians 1 (pt); Dentists 1 (pt); Podiatrists 1 (pt).
Affiliation Episcopal
Facilities Dining room; Physical therapy room; Activities room; Chapel; Crafts room; Laundry room; Barber/Beauty shop; Library; Various sitting areas.
Activities Arts & crafts; Cards; Games; Reading groups; Prayer groups; Movies; Shopping trips; Social/Cultural gatherings.

Green Acres Home for Convalescence Inc*
1401 Ivy Hill Rd, Wyndmoor, PA, 19150
(215) 233-5605
Licensure Skilled care. *Beds* 120. *Certified* Medicaid; Medicare.
Owner Proprietary Corp.

YEADON

Leader Nursing & Rehabilitation Center
Lansdowne & Lincoln Aves, Yeadon, PA, 19050
(215) 626-7700
Admin Regina MacArthur. *Medical Dir/Dir of Nursing* Dr James Kelly; Pat Johnson DON.
Licensure Skilled care; Intermediate care; Personal care. *Beds* SNF 120; ICF 48; Personal 30. *Certified* Medicaid; Medicare.
Owner Proprietary Corp (Manor Care).
Admissions Requirements Minimum age 16; Medical examination.
Staff RNs 5 (ft), 2 (pt); LPNs 14 (ft), 10 (pt); Nurses aides 45 (ft), 24 (pt); Physical therapists 1 (pt); Reality therapists 1 (pt); Recreational therapists 1 (ft); Occupational therapists 1 (pt); Speech therapists 1 (pt); Activities coordinators 2 (pt); Dietitians 1 (pt); Dentists 1 (pt); Ophthalmologists 1 (pt); Podiatrists 1 (pt); Chaplain 1 (pt).
Facilities Dining room; Physical therapy room; Activities room; Chapel; Crafts room; Laundry room; Barber/Beauty shop.
Activities Arts & crafts; Cards; Games; Reading groups; Prayer groups; Movies; Shopping trips; Social/Cultural gatherings.

YORK

Barley Convalescent Home—North
1775 Barley Rd, York, PA, 17404
(717) 767-6530
Licensure Skilled care. *Beds* 121. *Certified* Medicaid; Medicare.
Owner Proprietary Corp.

Barley Convalescent Home—South Nursing & Rehabilitation Center
200 Pauline Dr, York, PA, 17402
(717) 741-0824
Admin Lori A Mason. *Medical Dir/Dir of Nursing* Dr Merle Bacastow; Diana Lynn.
Licensure Skilled care; Intermediate care. *Beds* 102. *Certified* Medicaid; Medicare.
Owner Proprietary Corp (Manor Care).
Admissions Requirements Medical examination.
Staff Physicians 1 (pt); RNs 7 (ft), 2 (pt); LPNs 6 (ft), 3 (pt); Nurses aides 23 (ft), 11 (pt); Physical therapists 2 (pt); Recreational therapists 1 (ft), 2 (pt); Occupational therapists 1 (pt); Speech therapists 1 (pt).
Languages Pennsylvania Dutch, German
Facilities Dining room; Physical therapy room; Activities room; Chapel; Laundry room; Barber/Beauty shop; Telephone room; O T room; Conference room.
Activities Arts & crafts; Cards; Games; Reading groups; Prayer groups; Movies; Shopping trips; Social/Cultural gatherings.

Colonial Manor Nursing Home*
970 Colonial Ave, York, PA, 17403
(717) 845-2661
Licensure Skilled care; Intermediate care. *Beds* SNF 123; ICF 96. *Certified* Medicaid; Medicare.
Owner Proprietary Corp.

Manor Care of Barley Kingston Court
2400 Kingston Court, York, PA, 17402
(717) 755-5911
Medical Dir/Dir of Nursing Merle Bacastow.
Licensure Skilled care. *Beds* 121. *Certified* Medicaid; Medicare.
Owner Proprietary Corp (Manor Care).
Admissions Requirements Minimum age 16; Medical examination.
Staff RNs; LPNs; Nurses aides; Physical therapists; Recreational therapists 1 (ft); Occupational therapists; Speech therapists; Activities coordinators 1 (ft).

Facilities Dining room; Physical therapy room; Activities room; Crafts room; Laundry room; Barber/Beauty shop; 4 Large lounges/TV rooms.
Activities Arts & crafts; Cards; Games; Reading groups; Prayer groups; Movies; Shopping trips; Social/Cultural gatherings; Residents council; Current events; Discussion group; Spelling bees; Pokeno; Chaplaincy program.

Misericordia Convalescent Home
998 S Russell St, York, PA, 17402
(717) 755-1964
Admin Sr Rosella Marie DM. *Medical Dir/Dir of Nursing* Edward T Lis MD; Sr M Concepta DM.
Licensure Skilled care. *Beds* SNF 55. *Certified* Medicaid.
Owner Nonprofit organization/foundation.
Admissions Requirements Medical examination; Physician's request.
Staff Physicians 2 (pt); RNs 3 (ft), 2 (pt); LPNs 2 (ft), 3 (pt); Nurses aides 18 (ft), 15 (pt); Physical therapists 2 (pt); Recreational therapists 1 (ft), 1 (pt); Activities coordinators 1 (ft), 1 (pt); Dietitians 4 (ft), 1 (pt); Ophthalmologists 1 (pt).
Affiliation Roman Catholic
Facilities Dining room; Activities room; Chapel; Crafts room; Laundry room; Barber/Beauty shop.
Activities Games; Prayer groups; Movies; Social/Cultural gatherings; Sing-alongs.

Margaret E Moul Home
2050 Barley Rd, York, PA, 17404
Admin Dennis V Reese. *Medical Dir/Dir of Nursing* James Harberger MD.
Licensure Intermediate care. *Beds* 52. *Certified* Medicaid.
Owner Nonprofit Corp.
Admissions Requirements Minimum age 18; Medical examination; Physician's request.
Staff RNs 3 (ft), 3 (pt); LPNs 3 (ft), 4 (pt); Nurses aides 16 (ft), 13 (pt); Physical therapists 1 (ft), 1 (pt); Recreational therapists 1 (ft), 1 (pt); Speech therapists 1 (pt); Dietitians 1 (pt).
Facilities Dining room; Physical therapy room; Activities room; Chapel; Crafts room; Laundry room.
Activities Arts & crafts; Cards; Games; Reading groups; Prayer groups; Movies; Shopping trips; Social/Cultural gatherings.

Rest Haven-York
1050 S George St, York, PA, 17403
(717) 843-9866
Admin Margaret B Miller. *Medical Dir/Dir of Nursing* Dr Andrew Hickey; Geraldine Stoltzfus DON.
Licensure Skilled care. *Beds* SNF 167. *Certified* Medicaid; Medicare.
Owner Proprietary Corp.
Staff Physicians 1 (ft); RNs 10 (ft), 4 (pt); LPNs 22 (ft), 4 (pt) 13E 29 (ft), 27 (pt); Recreational therapists 1 (ft); Occupational therapists 2 (pt); Speech therapists 1 (pt); Activities coordinators 1 (ft), 4 (pt); Dietitians 1 (ft); Dentists 1 (pt); Ophthalmologists 1 (pt); Podiatrists 1 (pt); Psychologist 1 (pt).
Facilities Dining room; Physical therapy room; Activities room; Chapel; Crafts room; Laundry room; Barber/Beauty shop.
Activities Arts & crafts; Games; Reading groups; Prayer groups; Movies; Shopping trips; Social/Cultural gatherings.

York County Hospital & Home*
118 Pleasant Acres Rd, York, PA, 17402
(717) 755-9601
Admin Eileen Jenkins. *Medical Dir/Dir of Nursing* Dr Kenneth Yinger.
Licensure Skilled care; Intermediate care. *Beds* SNF 114; ICF 485. *Certified* Medicaid; Medicare.

Owner Nonprofit Corp.
Admissions Requirements Minimum age 18.
Staff Physicians 3 (ft), 1 (pt); RNs 20 (ft), 10 (pt); LPNs 45 (ft), 13 (pt); Nurses aides 120 (ft), 119 (pt); Physical therapists 5 (ft); Reality therapists 3 (ft); Recreational therapists 6 (ft); Speech therapists 1 (pt); Activities coordinators 1 (ft); Dietitians 1 (pt); Dentists 1 (pt); Ophthalmologists 1 (pt); Podiatrists 3 (pt); Audiologists 1 (pt).
Facilities Dining room; Physical therapy room; Activities room; Chapel; Crafts room; Laundry room; Barber/Beauty shop; Library.
Activities Arts & crafts; Cards; Games; Reading groups; Prayer groups; Movies; Shopping trips; Social/Cultural gatherings; Boating; Bowling; Voting.

York Lutheran Home
750 Kelly Dr, York, PA, 17404
(717) 848-2585
Admin Jeanne M Wildasin.
Licensure Skilled care; Intermediate care. *Beds* SNF 33; ICF 103. *Certified* Medicaid; Medicare.
Owner Nonprofit Corp.
Affiliation Lutheran

Yorkview Convalescent & Nursing Home
2091 Herman Ct, York, PA, 17402
(717) 755-6454
Licensure Skilled care. *Beds* 19.
Owner Proprietary Corp.

YOUNGSTOWN

Edgewood Nursing Center Inc
PO Box 277, E Main St, Youngstown, PA, 15696
(412) 537-4441

Admin Grace Mitchell. *Medical Dir/Dir of Nursing* Francis Meyers DO; Patricia Smith RN DON.
Licensure Intermediate care. *Beds* ICF 107. *Certified* Medicaid.
Owner Proprietary Corp.
Admissions Requirements Minimum age 16; Medical examination; Physician's request.
Staff Physicians 3 (pt); RNs 6 (ft), 2 (pt); LPNs 6 (ft), 4 (pt); Nurses aides 25 (ft), 9 (pt); Physical therapists 1 (pt); Recreational therapists 1 (pt); Speech therapists 1 (pt); Activities coordinators 2 (ft); Dietitians 1 (pt); Dentists 1 (pt); Ophthalmologists 1 (pt).
Facilities Dining room; Activities room; Crafts room; Laundry room; Barber/Beauty shop; Library; Lounges.
Activities Arts & crafts; Cards; Games; Reading groups; Prayer groups; Movies; Social/Cultural gatherings; Bingo.

YOUNGSVILLE

Rouse-Warren County Home
PO Box 207, Rte 1, Youngsville, PA, 16371
(814) 563-7561
Admin Max E Knickerbocker NHA. *Medical Dir/Dir of Nursing* Stanley J Sivak MD; Heather Probst RN DON.
Licensure Skilled care; Intermediate care. *Beds* SNF 46; ICF 133. *Certified* Medicaid; Medicare.
Owner Nonprofit organization/foundation.
Admissions Requirements Physician's request.
Staff Physicians 1 (pt); RNs 6 (ft), 4 (pt); LPNs 21 (ft), 6 (pt); Nurses aides 51 (ft), 19 (pt); Reality therapists 10 (ft); Recreational therapists 1 (ft); Occupational therapists 1 (ft); Speech therapists 1 (pt); Activities coordinators 1 (ft); Dietitians 1 (ft); Ophthalmologists 1 (pt); Podiatrists 1 (pt).
Facilities Dining room; Physical therapy room; Activities room; Chapel; Crafts room; Laundry room; Barber/Beauty shop.
Activities Arts & crafts; Cards; Games; Reading groups; Prayer groups; Movies; Shopping trips; Social/Cultural gatherings.

ZELLENOPLE

Passavant Retirement & Health Center
401 S Main St, Zellenople, PA, 16063
(412) 452-5400
Admin Elvin L Schlegel, Jr. *Medical Dir/Dir of Nursing* Linda Raymundo MD; Chervyl Wehr DON.
Licensure Skilled care; Intermediate care. *Beds* SNF 22; ICF 162. *Certified* Medicaid; Medicare.
Owner Nonprofit Corp.
Admissions Requirements Minimum age 65; Medical examination.
Staff Physicians 3 (ft); RNs 9 (ft), 2 (pt); LPNs 17 (ft), 6 (pt); Nurses aides 64 (ft), 16 (pt); Physical therapists 1 (ft); Reality therapists 1 (ft); Recreational therapists 2 (ft), 3 (pt); Activities coordinators 1 (ft); Dietitians 1 (pt); Ophthalmologists.
Affiliation Lutheran
Facilities Dining room; Physical therapy room; Activities room; Chapel; Crafts room; Laundry room; Barber/Beauty shop; Library.
Activities Arts & crafts; Cards; Games; Reading groups; Prayer groups; Movies; Shopping trips; Social/Cultural gatherings.

RHODE ISLAND

BRISTOL

Metacom Manor Health Center*
1 Dawn Hill, Bristol, RI, 02809
(401) 253-2300
Admin Ursula M Beauregard.
Licensure Skilled care; Intermediate care. *Beds* 121. *Certified* Medicaid; Medicare.

Silver Creek Manor
7 Creek Ln, Bristol, RI, 02809
(401) 253-3000
Admin Gerald P Romano. *Medical Dir/Dir of Nursing* Peter J Sansone MD.
Licensure Skilled care; Intermediate care. *Beds* 128. *Certified* Medicaid; Medicare.
Owner Privately owned.
Staff Physicians 20 (pt); RNs 6 (ft), 3 (pt); LPNs 3 (ft), 3 (pt); Orderlies 1 (ft); Nurses aides 27 (ft), 20 (pt); Physical therapists 1 (pt); Recreational therapists 1 (ft); Speech therapists 1 (pt); Activities coordinators 1 (ft), 1 (pt); Dietitians 1 (pt); Dentists 1 (pt); Ophthalmologists 2 (pt); Podiatrists 1 (pt).
Languages French, Portuguese, Polish
Facilities Dining room; Physical therapy room; Activities room; Crafts room; Laundry room; Barber/Beauty shop.
Activities Arts & crafts; Cards; Games; Reading groups; Prayer groups; Movies; Shopping trips; Social/Cultural gatherings.

BURRILLVILLE

Nicole Manor*
130 Sayles Ave, Burrillville, RI, 02859
(401) 568-6978
Admin Joan Sabella.
Licensure Intermediate care. *Beds* 14. *Certified* Medicaid.
Staff Physicians 3 (pt); RNs 1 (pt); LPNs 1 (ft), 1 (pt); Nurses aides 2 (ft), 3 (pt); Recreational therapists 1 (ft); Activities coordinators 1 (ft); Dentists 2 (pt); Ophthalmologists 2 (pt); Podiatrists 1 (pt).
Facilities Dining room; Activities room; Crafts room; Laundry room; Barber/Beauty shop; Library.
Activities Arts & crafts; Cards; Games; Reading groups; Prayer groups; Movies; Shopping trips; Social/Cultural gatherings.

Overlook Nursing Home*
14 Rock Ave, Burrillville, RI, 02859
(401) 568-2549
Admin Harold Kenoian.
Licensure Skilled care; Intermediate care. *Beds* 100. *Certified* Medicaid; Medicare.

Rest Well Rest Home Inc*
132 Sayles Ave, Burrillville, RI, 02859
(401) 568-3000
Admin Anthony Annarino.
Licensure Intermediate care. *Beds* 19. *Certified* Medicaid.

CENTRAL FALLS

Cartie's Health Center*
21 Lincoln Ave, Central Falls, RI, 02863
(401) 727-0900
Admin John Prew. *Medical Dir/Dir of Nursing* Eugene Gaudet MD.
Licensure Skilled care; Intermediate care. *Beds* 210. *Certified* Medicaid; Medicare.
Admissions Requirements Minimum age 14; Medical examination; Physician's request.
Staff Physicians 35 (pt); RNs 5 (ft), 8 (pt); LPNs 14 (ft), 11 (pt); Orderlies 5 (ft); Nurses aides 77 (ft), 23 (pt); Physical therapists 1 (ft), 1 (pt); Occupational therapists 1 (pt); Speech therapists 1 (pt); Activities coordinators 3 (ft); Dietitians 1 (pt); Dentists 1 (pt); Ophthalmologists 1 (pt); Podiatrists 1 (pt); Audiologists 1 (ft); Bed makers 2 (ft), 3 (pt).
Facilities Dining room; Physical therapy room; Activities room; Crafts room; Laundry room; Barber/Beauty shop.
Activities Arts & crafts; Cards; Games; Reading groups; Prayer groups; Movies; Social/Cultural gatherings.

Frigon Nursing Home Inc*
60 Eben Brown Ln, Central Falls, RI, 02863
(401) 726-0371
Admin James H Frigon.
Licensure Intermediate care. *Beds* 27. *Certified* Medicaid.

Mansion Nursing Home
104 Clay St, Central Falls, RI, 02863
(401) 722-0830, 726-5020
Admin Andrew Chopoorian. *Medical Dir/Dir of Nursing* Eugene Gaudette MD; Lois Hunt RN.
Licensure Intermediate care. *Beds* 62. *Certified* Medicaid.
Owner Proprietary Corp.
Staff RNs 4 (ft); LPNs 3 (ft); Nurses aides 11 (ft); Activities coordinators 1 (ft).
Languages French, Portuguese, Armenian
Facilities Dining room; Activities room; Laundry room; Porches; Yard with picnic table.
Activities Arts & crafts; Cards; Games; Reading groups; Prayer groups; Movies; Shopping trips; Social/Cultural gatherings; Picnics; Trips to park; Christmas lights; Penny socials; Auctions; Birthday parties; Family days.

Paquette Home Inc*
649 Broad St, Central Falls, RI, 02863
(401) 725-7045
Admin Ronald Paquette.
Licensure Intermediate care. *Beds* 30. *Certified* Medicaid.

Rose Cottage Health Care Center*
151 Hunt St, Central Falls, RI, 02863
(401) 722-4610
Admin Leonard Lamphear.
Licensure Skilled care; Intermediate care. *Beds* 104. *Certified* Medicaid; Medicare.

COVENTRY

Alpine Rest Home Inc
PO Box 457, Weaver Hill Rd, Coventry, RI, 02816
(401) 397-5001
Admin Elizabeth A Gauvin.
Licensure Intermediate care. *Beds* 28. *Certified* Medicaid.
Admissions Requirements Minimum age 50; Medical examination.
Staff RNs 1 (pt); LPNs 1 (ft), 1 (pt); Nurses aides 6 (ft); Recreational therapists 1 (ft); Dietitians 1 (pt); Podiatrists 1 (pt).
Facilities Dining room; Activities room; Crafts room; Laundry room; Barber/Beauty shop.
Activities Arts & crafts; Cards; Games; Reading groups; Prayer groups; Movies; Shopping trips; Social/Cultural gatherings.

Coventry Health Center
10 Woodland Dr, Coventry, RI, 02816
(401) 826-2000
Admin Richard Lewis. *Medical Dir/Dir of Nursing* Anthony Kazlauskas; Barbara Clarkin DON.
Licensure Skilled care; Intermediate care. *Beds* SNF 50; ICF 250. *Certified* Medicaid; Medicare.
Owner Proprietary Corp.
Admissions Requirements Medical examination.
Staff RNs; LPNs; Orderlies; Nurses aides; Physical therapists; Recreational therapists; Occupational therapists; Speech therapists; Activities coordinators; Dietitians.
Facilities Dining room; Physical therapy room; Activities room; Chapel; Crafts room; Barber/Beauty shop; Library.
Activities Arts & crafts; Cards; Games; Reading groups; Prayer groups; Movies; Shopping trips; Social/Cultural gatherings.

Laurel Foster Home Inc*
51 Laurel Ave, Coventry, RI, 02893
(401) 821-0136
Admin Thomas Whipple. *Medical Dir/Dir of Nursing* Dr Anthony Kazlauskas.
Licensure Intermediate care. *Beds* 57. *Certified* Medicaid.
Admissions Requirements Females only; Medical examination; Physician's request.
Staff RNs 1 (pt); LPNs 1 (ft), 1 (pt); Orderlies 1 (ft); Nurses aides 8 (ft), 10 (pt); Activities coordinators 1 (ft); Dietitians 1 (pt).
Facilities Dining room; Activities room; Chapel; Crafts room; Barber/Beauty shop; Library.
Activities Arts & crafts; Cards; Games; Reading groups; Prayer groups; Movies; Shopping trips; Social/Cultural gatherings; Resident council; Gardening club; Bowling trips weekly.

Riverview Nursing Home Inc
546 Main St, Coventry, RI, 02816
(401) 821-6837

Admin Lois Richard. *Medical Dir/Dir of Nursing* Dr J Winters.
Licensure Skilled care; Intermediate care. *Beds* 65. *Certified* Medicaid.
Staff Physicians 5 (pt); RNs 5 (ft); LPNs 7 (ft); Nurses aides 20 (ft); Activities coordinators 1 (ft); Dietitians 1 (pt); Dentists 1 (pt); Ophthalmologists 1 (pt); Podiatrists 1 (pt).
Facilities Dining room; Activities room; Crafts room; Barber/Beauty shop.
Activities Arts & crafts; Games; Prayer groups; Movies; Outings; Gardening; Sing-alongs; Parties.

Woodpecker Hill Foster Home*
Plainfield Pike, Coventry, RI, 02827
(401) 397-7504
Admin Thomas Haynes. *Medical Dir/Dir of Nursing* Dr Robert Spencer.
Licensure Intermediate care. *Beds* 31. *Certified* Medicaid.
Admissions Requirements Medical examination.
Staff RNs; LPNs; Orderlies; Nurses aides; Activities coordinators; Dietitians; Dentists; Ophthalmologists; Podiatrists; Audiologists.
Facilities Dining room; Activities room; Laundry room.
Activities Arts & crafts; Cards; Games; Movies; Shopping trips; Social/Cultural gatherings.

CRANSTON

Cedar Crest Nursing Centre Inc*
125 Scituate Ave, Cranston, RI, 02920
(401) 944-8500
Admin Mary DeConti.
Licensure Skilled care; Intermediate care. *Beds* 135. *Certified* Medicaid; Medicare.

Cra-Mar Nursing Home Inc*
575 7-Mile Rd, Cranston, RI, 02831
(401) 828-5010
Admin Thomas J Grzych.
Licensure Skilled care; Intermediate care. *Beds* 40. *Certified* Medicaid; Medicare.

Scandinavian Home for the Aged
1811 Broad St, Cranston, RI, 02905
(401) 461-1433
Admin John C Woulfe. *Medical Dir/Dir of Nursing* Lois Goff RN.
Licensure Skilled care; Intermediate care. *Beds* SNF 16; ICF 54. *Certified* Medicaid; Medicare.
Owner Nonprofit Corp.
Admissions Requirements Medical examination.
Staff RNs 4 (ft), 10 (pt); LPNs 1 (ft), 9 (pt); Nurses aides 14 (ft), 16 (pt); Physical therapists 1 (pt); Dietitians 1 (ft), 1 (pt); Dietitians 1 (pt).
Facilities Dining room; Activities room; Chapel; Crafts room; Laundry room; Barber/Beauty shop; Library.
Activities Arts & crafts; Cards; Games; Reading groups; Prayer groups; Movies; Shopping trips; Social/Cultural gatherings; Bus trip; Outings.

CUMBERLAND

Diamond Hill Nursing Center Inc
3579 Diamond Hill Rd, Cumberland, RI, 02864
(401) 333-5050
Admin Jeanne Abbruzzese. *Medical Dir/Dir of Nursing* Patricia Saccoccio DNS.
Licensure Intermediate care. *Beds* ICF ICF I 44; ICF II 4. *Certified* Medicaid.
Owner Proprietary Corp.
Admissions Requirements Physician's request.
Staff RNs 1 (ft), 4 (pt); LPNs 3 (ft), 3 (pt); Nurses aides 8 (ft), 12 (pt); Activities coordinators; Dietitians.

Facilities Dining room; Activities room; Barber/Beauty shop.
Activities Arts & crafts; Cards; Games; Prayer groups; Movies; Shopping trips.

Grandview Nursing Home Inc*
Chambers & John Sts, Cumberland, RI, 02864
(401) 724-7500
Admin Frances McDermott.
Licensure Skilled care; Intermediate care. *Beds* 72. *Certified* Medicaid; Medicare.

EAST GREENWICH

Greenwich Bay Manor*
945 Main St, East Greenwich, RI, 02818
(401) 885-3334
Admin R L Tetreault.
Licensure Intermediate care. *Beds* 45. *Certified* Medicaid.

EAST PROVIDENCE

Hattie Ide Chaffee Home
200 Wampanoag Trail, East Providence, RI, 02914
(401) 434-1520
Admin Adeline Frederick Schwartz. *Medical Dir/Dir of Nursing* Fred Vohr MD; Carol Northup.
Licensure Skilled care. *Beds* SNF 58. *Certified* Medicaid; Medicare.
Owner Nonprofit Corp.
Admissions Requirements Minimum age 16; Medical examination.
Staff Physicians 7 (pt); RNs 12 (ft), 4 (pt); Nurses aides 27 (ft), 16 (pt); Recreational therapists 2 (ft); Speech therapists 1 (pt); Dietitians 1 (pt); Dentists 1 (pt); Ophthalmologists 1 (pt).
Languages Italian, Portuguese, French
Facilities Dining room; Physical therapy room; Activities room; Chapel; Crafts room; Laundry room; Barber/Beauty shop.
Activities Arts & crafts; Cards; Games; Prayer groups; Movies.

East Side Manor*
2424 Pawtucket Ave, East Providence, RI, 02914
(401) 438-6925
Admin George Von Housen.
Licensure Intermediate care. *Beds* 12. *Certified* Medicaid.

Evergreen House Health Center*
1 Evergreen Dr, East Providence, RI, 02914
(401) 438-3250
Admin Richard A Lewis.
Licensure Skilled care; Intermediate care. *Beds* 156. *Certified* Medicaid; Medicare.
Owner Proprietary Corp (Life Care Centers of America).

Harris Nursing Home Inc
833 Broadway, East Providence, RI, 02914
(401) 434-7404
Admin Charles L Harris. *Medical Dir/Dir of Nursing* Peter J Sansone MD.
Licensure Intermediate care. *Beds* ICF 36. *Certified* Medicaid.
Owner Proprietary Corp.
Admissions Requirements Medical examination; Physician's request.
Staff Physicians 1 (pt); RNs 1 (ft), 2 (pt); LPNs 4 (ft), 2 (pt); Orderlies 2 (ft); Nurses aides 10 (ft), 6 (pt); Physical therapists 1 (pt); Reality therapists 1 (pt); Recreational therapists 1 (pt); Occupational therapists 1 (pt); Speech therapists 1 (pt); Activities coordinators 1 (ft), 1 (pt); Dietitians 1 (pt); Dentists 1 (pt); Ophthalmologists 1 (pt); Podiatrists 1 (pt).
Languages French, Portuguese

Facilities Dining room; Activities room; Crafts room.
Activities Arts & crafts; Cards; Games; Reading groups; Prayer groups; Movies; Shopping trips; Social/Cultural gatherings.

Health Havens Inc*
100 Wampanoag Trail, East Providence, RI, 02915
(401) 438-4275
Admin Barbara M Lagerquist. *Medical Dir/Dir of Nursing* A Lloyd Lagerquist MD.
Licensure Skilled care; Intermediate care. *Beds* 58. *Certified* Medicaid; Medicare.
Admissions Requirements Minimum age 25.
Staff RNs 3 (ft), 4 (pt); LPNs 1 (ft), 4 (pt); Nurses aides 18 (ft), 12 (pt); Physical therapists 1 (pt); Speech therapists 1 (pt); Dietitians 1 (pt).
Facilities Dining room; Activities room.
Activities Arts & crafts; Cards; Games; Movies.

Hillcrest Nursing Home Inc*
198 Waterman Ave, East Providence, RI, 02914
(401) 434-5960
Admin Paul Marra.
Licensure Intermediate care. *Beds* 76. *Certified* Medicaid.
Staff Physicians 4 (pt); RNs 3 (ft); LPNs 1 (ft); Orderlies 1 (ft) 13E 18 (ft); Activities coordinators 1 (ft); Dietitians 1 (pt); Podiatrists 1 (pt).
Facilities Dining room; Activities room; Laundry room; Library.
Activities Arts & crafts; Cards; Games; Reading groups; Movies; Shopping trips; Social/Cultural gatherings.

The Nicholas Marra Nursing Home*
135 Tripps Ln, East Providence, RI, 02915
(401) 438-2250
Admin Orlando J Bisbano Jr.
Licensure Skilled care; Intermediate care. *Beds* 180. *Certified* Medicaid; Medicare.

Riverside Nursing Home*
336 Willett Ave, East Providence, RI, 02915
(401) 433-0844
Admin Barbara Monteleone. *Medical Dir/Dir of Nursing* Dr Howard Perrone.
Licensure Intermediate care. *Beds* 27. *Certified* Medicaid.
Staff Physicians 7 (pt); RNs 1 (ft), 4 (pt); LPNs 1 (ft), 3 (pt); Nurses aides 3 (ft), 12 (pt); Activities coordinators 1 (ft); Dietitians 1 (pt); Dentists 1 (pt); Ophthalmologists 1 (pt); Podiatrists 1 (pt); Audiologists 1 (pt).
Facilities Dining room; Activities room; Laundry room.
Activities Arts & crafts; Cards; Games; Reading groups; Prayer groups; Movies; Shopping trips.

United Methodist Health Care Center
30 Alexander Ave, East Providence, RI, 02914
(401) 438-7210
Admin T J Peters III. *Medical Dir/Dir of Nursing* Dr John Demicco.
Licensure Intermediate care. *Beds* 83. *Certified* Medicare.
Admissions Requirements Medical examination; Physician's request.
Staff Physicians 1 (pt); RNs 4 (ft), 2 (pt); LPNs 2 (ft), 1 (pt); Orderlies 1 (ft); Nurses aides 24 (ft), 4 (pt); Reality therapists 1 (pt); Recreational therapists 1 (ft), 1 (pt); Activities coordinators 1 (ft); Dietitians 1 (pt).
Affiliation Methodist
Facilities Dining room; Activities room; Chapel; Crafts room; Laundry room; Barber/Beauty shop; Library.
Activities Arts & crafts; Cards; Games; Reading groups; Prayer groups; Movies; Shopping trips; Social/Cultural gatherings.

Waterview Villa
1275 S Broadway, East Providence, RI, 02914
438-7020
Admin Linda Monteleone. *Medical Dir/Dir of
Nursing* Dr Rocco Marzilli; Ena Ward.
Licensure Skilled care; Intermediate care. *Beds*
SNF 132; ICF. *Certified* Medicaid;
Medicare.
Owner Proprietary Corp.
Admissions Requirements Medical
examination.
Staff Physicians 42 (pt); RNs 8 (ft), 4 (pt);
LPNs 9 (ft), 2 (pt); Orderlies 1 (ft); Nurses
aides 37 (ft), 14 (pt); Physical therapists 1
(pt); Occupational therapists 1 (pt); Speech
therapists 1 (pt); Activities coordinators 1
(ft), 1 (pt); Dietitians 1 (pt); Dentists 1 (pt);
Ophthalmologists 3 (pt); Podiatrists 1 (pt).
Languages Portuguese
Facilities Dining room; Physical therapy
room; Activities room; Chapel; Crafts room;
Laundry room; Barber/Beauty shop; Library;
Dining facilities on 3 floors.
Activities Arts & crafts; Cards; Games;
Reading groups; Prayer groups; Movies;
Shopping trips; Social/Cultural gatherings;
Spelling groups; Restaurant nite at the
facility once monthly; Weekly cocktail hours
w/hors d'oeuvres.

EXETER

Shady Acres Inc*
Gardiner Rd, Exeter, RI, 02892
(401) 295-8520
Admin Charles W Miga.
Licensure Intermediate care. *Beds* 60.
Certified Medicaid.

FOSTER

Nancy Ann Convalescent Home*
E Killingly Rd, Box 180, Foster, RI, 02825
(401) 647-2170
Admin Esther O'Dette.
Licensure Intermediate care. *Beds* 18.
Certified Medicaid.
Admissions Requirements Minimum age 50;
Medical examination; Physician's request.
Staff RNs 1 (pt); LPNs 3 (ft); Orderlies 1 (pt);
Nurses aides 2 (ft), 4 (pt); Recreational
therapists 1 (pt); Activities coordinators 1
(pt); Podiatrists 1 (pt).
Facilities Dining room; Laundry room;
Barber/Beauty shop; All purpose room.
Activities Arts & crafts; Cards; Games; Prayer
groups; Movies; Social/Cultural gatherings.

HARRISVILLE

Lakeview Health Center
Steere Farm Rd, Harrisville, RI, 02859
(401) 568-6242
Admin Michael Monteleone. *Medical Dir/Dir
of Nursing* Clayton Lanphear DO.
Licensure Skilled care; Intermediate care. *Beds*
SNF 37; ICF 168. *Certified* Medicaid;
Medicare.
Owner Privately owned.
Staff RNs 8 (ft), 4 (pt); LPNs 6 (ft), 10 (pt);
Nurses aides 40 (ft), 60 (pt); Activities
coordinators 1 (ft), 1 (pt).
Facilities Dining room; Physical therapy
room; Activities room; Chapel; Crafts room;
Barber/Beauty shop.
Activities Arts & crafts; Cards; Games; Prayer
groups; Movies; Cooking classes.

JOHNSTON

Briarcliffe Healthcare Facility*
Old Pocasset Rd, PO Box 7236, Johnston, RI,
02919
(401) 944-2450
Admin Alphonse R Cardi.

Licensure Skilled care; Intermediate care. *Beds*
120. *Certified* Medicaid; Medicare.
Admissions Requirements Medical
examination; Physician's request.
Staff RNs 3 (ft), 5 (pt); LPNs 6 (ft), 4 (pt);
Nurses aides 28 (ft), 26 (pt); Activities
coordinators 1 (ft), 3 (pt).
Facilities Dining room; Physical therapy
room; Activities room; Chapel; Crafts room;
Laundry room; Barber/Beauty shop; Library.
Activities Arts & crafts; Cards; Games;
Reading groups; Prayer groups; Movies;
Social/Cultural gatherings.

Cherry Hill Manor
2 Cherry Hill Rd, Johnston, RI, 02919
(401) 231-3102
Admin Elena Pisaturo. *Medical Dir/Dir of
Nursing* Michael Baccari MD.
Licensure Skilled care; Intermediate care. *Beds*
168. *Certified* Medicaid; Medicare.
Owner Proprietary Corp.
Staff RNs; LPNs; Orderlies; Nurses aides;
Physical therapists; Recreational therapists;
Occupational therapists; Speech therapists;
Activities coordinators; Dietitians; Dentists;
Ophthalmologists; Podiatrists; Dentist.
Languages Italian, Polish
Facilities Dining room; Physical therapy
room; Activities room; Chapel; Crafts room;
Laundry room; Barber/Beauty shop.
Activities Arts & crafts; Cards; Games;
Reading groups; Prayer groups; Movies;
Shopping trips; Social/Cultural gatherings;
Painting; Baking; Picnics.

Marie Josephine Rest Home*
203 Greenville Ave, Johnston, RI, 02919
(401) 231-1950
Admin Kim A Dehn.
Licensure Intermediate care. *Beds* 16.
Certified Medicaid.

Morgan Health Center
80 Morgan Ave, Johnston, RI, 02919
(401) 944-7800
Admin Eugene Abbruzzese. *Medical Dir/Dir of
Nursing* Dr Kazlauskas; Joyce Morton RN.
Licensure Skilled care; Intermediate care. *Beds*
SNF 40; ICF 80. *Certified* Medicaid;
Medicare.
Owner Proprietary Corp (Health Concepts).
Staff RNs; LPNs; Orderlies; Activities
coordinators; Ophthalmologists.
Languages Italian
Facilities Dining room; Activities room;
Crafts room; Laundry room; Barber/Beauty
shop; Library; Dining Rooms; Gift Shop.
Activities Arts & crafts; Cards; Games;
Reading groups; Prayer groups; Movies;
Shopping trips; Social/Cultural gatherings;
An array of social groups & clubs.

LINCOLN

Holiday Retirement Home Inc
30 Sayles Hill Rd, Lincoln, RI, 02838
(401) 765-1440, 521-4590
Admin Marcia Stevens. *Medical Dir/Dir of
Nursing* Hao Huang MD; Doris Charrette
RN.
Licensure Skilled care; Intermediate care. *Beds*
129. *Certified* Medicaid; Medicare; VA.
Owner Proprietary Corp.
Staff RNs 6 (ft), 7 (pt); LPNs 3 (ft), 3 (pt);
Nurses aides 37 (ft), 14 (pt); Activities
coordinators 1 (ft).
Languages French, Polish, Italian
Facilities Dining room; Activities room;
Laundry room; Barber/Beauty shop.
Activities Arts & crafts; Cards; Games;
Reading groups; Prayer groups; Movies;
Shopping trips; Social/Cultural gatherings;
Trips other than shopping.

MIDDLETOWN

Bayview Nursing Home Inc
93 Miantonomi Ave, Middletown, RI, 02840
(401) 847-6300
Admin Diane W Keane. *Medical Dir/Dir of
Nursing* Suzanne E Grant.
Licensure Intermediate care. *Beds* ICF 51.
Certified Medicaid.
Owner Privately owned.
Staff Physicians 1 (pt); RNs 2 (ft), 3 (pt);
LPNs 2 (pt); Nurses aides 11 (ft), 13 (pt);
Activities coordinators 1 (ft); Dietitians 1
(pt).
Facilities Dining room; Activities room;
Laundry room.
Activities Arts & crafts; Cards; Games;
Reading groups; Prayer groups; Movies;
Shopping trips; Social/Cultural gatherings.

The John Clarke Retirement Center
600 Valley Rd, Middletown, RI, 02840
(401) 846-0743
Admin M Harry Randall. *Medical Dir/Dir of
Nursing* Charlotte Monk RN.
Licensure Skilled care; Intermediate care. *Beds*
SNF 4; ICF 48. *Certified* Medicaid;
Medicare.
Owner Nonprofit Corp.
Admissions Requirements Minimum age 62;
Medical examination.
Staff RNs; LPNs; Orderlies; Nurses aides;
Activities coordinators; Dietitians.
Languages Portuguese
Affiliation Baptist
Facilities Dining room; Physical therapy
room; Activities room; Chapel; Crafts room;
Laundry room; Barber/Beauty shop.
Activities Arts & crafts; Cards; Games;
Reading groups; Movies; Shopping trips;
Social/Cultural gatherings.

Forest Farm Health Care Centre Inc
201 Forest Ave, Middletown, RI, 02840
(401) 847-2786
Admin Karl Lyon.
Licensure Skilled care; Intermediate care. *Beds*
67. *Certified* Medicaid; Medicare.

Grand Islander Health Care Center Inc
333 Green End Ave, Middletown, RI, 02840
(401) 849-7100
Admin Jeffrey S Waddell. *Medical Dir/Dir of
Nursing* Dr Anthony Caputi; Mrs Janice
Letiecq RN.
Licensure Skilled care; Intermediate care. *Beds*
148. *Certified* Medicaid; Medicare.
Owner Proprietary Corp.
Staff RNs; LPNs; Orderlies; Nurses aides;
Recreational therapists; Activities
coordinators.
Facilities Dining room; Physical therapy
room; Activities room; Crafts room; Laundry
room; Barber/Beauty shop; Library; 5 day
rooms.
Activities Arts & crafts; Cards; Games;
Reading groups; Prayer groups; Movies;
Shopping trips; Social/Cultural gatherings.

NEWPORT

Bellevue-Newport Health Center*
Bellevue Ave, Newport, RI, 02840
(401) 849-6600
Admin Madeline Ernest.
Licensure Skilled care; Intermediate care. *Beds*
116. *Certified* Medicaid; Medicare.

Catherine Manor
44 Catherine St, Newport, RI, 02840
(401) 847-7455
Admin Edwina Sebest. *Medical Dir/Dir of
Nursing* Deborah Troncone LPN.
Licensure Intermediate care. *Beds* ICF 19.
Owner Proprietary Corp.
Admissions Requirements Medical
examination.

Staff RNs 1 (pt); LPNs 2 (ft), 1 (pt); Nurses aides 2 (ft), 5 (pt); Activities coordinators 1 (ft); Dietitians 1 (ft).
Facilities Dining room; Activities room; Library; Large porch & yard.
Activities Cards; Games; Prayer groups; Dance exercise classes; Weekly rap group; Bingo; Sing-alongs; Ceramics; Religious services.

St Clare Home
309 Spring St, Newport, RI, 02840
(401) 849-3204
Admin Mary Ann Altrui. *Medical Dir/Dir of Nursing* Sr Marjorie Furze RN.
Licensure Intermediate care. *Beds* 44.
Certified Medicaid.
Owner Nonprofit Corp.
Admissions Requirements Medical examination.
Staff RNs 1 (ft), 3 (pt); LPNs 1 (ft), 1 (pt); Nurses aides 10 (ft), 4 (pt); Activities coordinators 1 (ft); Dietitians 1 (pt).
Facilities Dining room; Activities room; Chapel; Crafts room; Laundry room; Barber/ Beauty shop; Library.
Activities Arts & crafts; Cards; Games; Reading groups; Prayer groups; Movies; Shopping trips; Social/Cultural gatherings.

Village House Convalescent Home Inc
70 Harrison Ave, Newport, RI, 02840
(401) 849-5222
Admin Sally J Ryan. *Medical Dir/Dir of Nursing* Elizabeth A Lord.
Licensure Skilled care; Intermediate care. *Beds* SNF 4; ICF 46. *Certified* Medicaid; Medicare.
Owner Proprietary Corp.
Staff RNs 3 (ft), 6 (pt); LPNs 2 (pt); Orderlies 1 (ft); Nurses aides 20 (ft), 10 (pt); Physical therapists 1 (pt); Reality therapists 1 (pt); Recreational therapists 1 (pt); Occupational therapists 1 (pt); Speech therapists 1 (pt); Activities coordinators 1 (pt); Dietitians 1 (pt).
Facilities Dining room; Activities room; Laundry room; Barber/Beauty shop.
Activities Arts & crafts; Games; Prayer groups; Movies; Shopping trips; Social/Cultural gatherings.

NORTH KINGSTOWN

Lafayette Nursing Home Inc*
691 10-Rod Rd, North Kingstown, RI, 02852
(401) 295-8816
Admin Domenic Mandolfi.
Licensure Skilled care; Intermediate care. *Beds* 52. *Certified* Medicaid; Medicare.

Roberts Health Centre Inc*
990 10-Rod Rd, North Kingstown, RI, 02852
(401) 884-6661
Admin Richard A. Catallozzi. *Medical Dir/Dir of Nursing* Dr Capalbo.
Licensure Intermediate care. *Beds* 61.
Certified Medicaid.
Staff Physicians 1 (pt); RNs 2 (ft), 6 (pt); LPNs 3 (ft), 2 (pt); Nurses aides 15 (ft), 8 (pt); Physical therapists 1 (pt); Reality therapists 1 (pt); Recreational therapists 1 (ft); Occupational therapists 1 (pt); Speech therapists 1 (pt); Activities coordinators 1 (ft); Dietitians 1 (pt); Dentists 1 (pt); Ophthalmologists 1 (pt); Podiatrists 1 (pt); Audiologists 1 (pt).
Facilities Dining room; Physical therapy room; Activities room; Chapel; Crafts room; Laundry room; Barber/Beauty shop; Library.
Activities Arts & crafts; Cards; Games; Reading groups; Prayer groups; Movies; Shopping trips.

Scalabrini Villa*
860 N Quidnesset Rd, North Kingstown, RI, 02852
(401) 884-1802
Admin Oscar Kenneth Swanson.

Licensure Skilled care; Intermediate care. *Beds* 70. *Certified* Medicaid; Medicare.

South County Nursing Centre*
Rte 4 & Oak Hill Rd, North Kingstown, RI, 02852
(401) 294-4545
Admin Domenic Mandolfi. *Medical Dir/Dir of Nursing* Charles Sawson MD.
Licensure Skilled care; Intermediate care. *Beds* 120. *Certified* Medicaid; Medicare.
Staff RNs 7 (ft), 12 (pt); LPNs 3 (ft), 3 (pt); Orderlies 1 (ft), 1 (pt); Nurses aides 80 (ft), 80 (pt); Activities coordinators 2 (ft); Dietitians 1 (ft).
Facilities Dining room; Physical therapy room; Activities room; Chapel; Crafts room; Laundry room; Barber/Beauty shop.
Activities Arts & crafts; Cards; Games; Reading groups; Prayer groups; Movies; Shopping trips; Social/Cultural gatherings.

NORTH PROVIDENCE

Golden Crest Nursing Center Inc*
100 Smithfield Rd, North Providence, RI, 02904
(410) 353-1710, 1711
Admin Susan Catalozzi.
Licensure Skilled care; Intermediate care. *Beds* 145. *Certified* Medicaid; Medicare.

Hopkins Health Center*
610 Smithfield Rd, North Providence, RI, 02904
(401) 353-6300
Admin Ronald Robidoux. *Medical Dir/Dir of Nursing* Dr Robert Brochu.
Licensure Skilled care; Intermediate care. *Beds* 200. *Certified* Medicaid; Medicare.
Admissions Requirements Medical examination.
Staff Physicians 1 (ft); RNs 8 (ft), 5 (pt); LPNs 6 (ft), 8 (pt); Nurses aides 55 (ft), 33 (pt); Physical therapists 1 (ft); Reality therapists 1 (ft); Recreational therapists 2 (ft), 1 (pt); Occupational therapists 1 (pt); Speech therapists 1 (pt); Dietitians 1 (ft); Social workers 2 (ft).
Facilities Dining room; Physical therapy room; Activities room; Chapel; Crafts room; Barber/Beauty shop; Library.
Activities Arts & crafts; Cards; Games; Reading groups; Prayer groups; Movies; Shopping trips; Social/Cultural gatherings.

NORTH SMITHFIELD

St Antoine Residence
400 Mendon Rd, North Smithfield, RI, 02895
(401) 767-3500
Admin Sr Yvonne Pouliot. *Medical Dir/Dir of Nursing* Agnes Bolduc RN.
Licensure Intermediate care. *Beds* ICF 243.
Certified Medicaid.
Owner Nonprofit Corp.
Admissions Requirements Minimum age 18; Medical examination; Physician's request.
Staff Physicians 8 (pt); RNs 8 (ft), 4 (pt); LPNs 14 (ft), 3 (pt); Orderlies 2 (ft), 1 (pt); Nurses aides 75 (ft), 6 (pt); Activities coordinators 2 (ft); Dietitians 1 (pt); Ophthalmologists 1 (pt); Social worker 1 (ft).
Languages French, Italian
Affiliation Roman Catholic
Facilities Dining room; Activities room; Chapel; Crafts room; Laundry room; Barber/ Beauty shop; Library.
Activities Arts & crafts; Cards; Games; Reading groups; Prayer groups; Movies; Shopping trips; Social/Cultural gatherings.

Woodland Convalescent Center Inc*
70 Woodland St, North Smithfield, RI, 02895
(401) 765-0499
Admin Mary Ann Abbruzzi.

Licensure Intermediate care. *Beds* 40.
Certified Medicaid.

PASCOAG

Jolly Rest Home Inc*
RFD 1, Box A33, S Main St, Pascoag, RI, 02859
(401) 568-3091
Admin T Lloyd Ryan. *Medical Dir/Dir of Nursing* Dr Louis Moran.
Licensure Intermediate care. *Beds* 36.
Certified Medicaid.
Staff Physicians 1 (ft), 5 (pt); RNs 1 (ft); LPNs 2 (pt); Nurses aides 1 (ft), 11 (pt); Physical therapists 1 (pt); Reality therapists 1 (pt); Recreational therapists 1 (pt); Occupational therapists 1 (pt); Speech therapists 1 (pt); Activities coordinators 1 (ft); Dietitians 1 (ft), 3 (pt); Dentists 1 (pt); Ophthalmologists 3 (pt); Podiatrists 1 (pt); Audiologists 1 (pt).
Facilities Dining room; Activities room; Crafts room; Laundry room; Library.
Activities Arts & crafts; Cards; Games; Prayer groups; Movies; Shopping trips; Social/ Cultural gatherings.

PAWTUCKET

Darlington Care Center
123 Armistice Blvd, Pawtucket, RI, 02860
(401) 725-2400
Admin Susan Gesualdi. *Medical Dir/Dir of Nursing* Dr Reenes MD.
Licensure Intermediate care. *Beds* 20.
Certified Medicaid.
Owner Privately owned.
Admissions Requirements Medical examination.
Staff Physicians 1 (ft); Nurses aides 5 (ft); Activities coordinators 1 (ft); Dentists 1 (ft); Ophthalmologists 1 (ft).
Affiliation Roman Catholic
Facilities Dining room; Laundry room; Barber/Beauty shop.
Activities Arts & crafts; Cards; Games; Prayer groups; Movies; Shopping trips.

Elsie May's Rest Home Inc*
105 Beechwood Ave, Pawtucket, RI, 02860
(401) 722-2630
Admin Stella Mandolfi.
Licensure Intermediate care. *Beds* 14.
Certified Medicaid.

Jeanne Jugan Residence*
964 Main St, Pawtucket, RI, 02860
(401) 723-4314
Admin Regina Jones.
Licensure Skilled care; Intermediate care. *Beds* 120. *Certified* Medicaid; Medicare.

Maynard Rest Home*
56 Maynard St, Pawtucket, RI, 02860
(401) 725-0517
Admin Linda Bertrand.
Licensure Intermediate care. *Beds* 18.
Certified Medicaid.
Staff Physicians 1 (ft); RNs 1 (pt); LPNs 2 (ft); Nurses aides 3 (ft), 4 (pt); Activities coordinators 1 (ft); Dentists 1 (pt); Podiatrists 1 (pt).
Facilities Dining room; Activities room; Crafts room; Laundry room.
Activities Arts & crafts; Cards; Games; Reading groups; Prayer groups; Movies; Shopping trips; Social/Cultural gatherings.

Neighborhood Convalescent Home Inc*
362 Daggett Ave, Pawtucket, RI, 02861
(401) 724-2111
Admin Raymond Dumas. *Medical Dir/Dir of Nursing* Dr R Boucher MD.
Licensure Intermediate care. *Beds* 17.
Certified Medicaid.

Admissions Requirements Medical
    examination.
Staff RNs 1 (ft), 1 (pt); LPNs 2 (ft), 4 (pt);
    Nurses aides 3 (ft), 4 (pt); Activities
    coordinators 1 (ft).
Facilities Dining room; Activities room;
    Laundry room.
Activities Arts & crafts; Cards; Games; Prayer
    groups; Movies; Shopping trips; Social/
    Cultural gatherings.

Oak Hill Nursing Home Inc*
544 Pleasant St, Pawtucket, RI, 02864
(401) 725-8888
Admin John Almeida.
Licensure Skilled care; Intermediate care. *Beds*
    104. *Certified* Medicaid; Medicare.

Pawtucket Institute for Health Services
70 Gill Ave, Pawtucket, RI, 02861
(401) 722-7900
Admin George Dassenko. *Medical Dir/Dir of
    Nursing* Biswa N Paul MD; Mildred
    Golembiesky RN.
Licensure Skilled care; Intermediate care. *Beds*
    SNF 42; ICF 118. *Certified* Medicaid;
    Medicare.
Owner Nonprofit Corp.
Admissions Requirements Minimum age 14;
    Medical examination; Physician's request.
Staff Physicians 6 (pt); RNs 8 (ft), 4 (pt);
    LPNs 6 (ft), 5 (pt); Orderlies 4 (ft), 3 (pt);
    Nurses aides 60 (ft), 12 (pt); Physical
    therapists 1 (pt); Speech therapists 1 (pt);
    Activities coordinators 1 (ft); Dietitians 1
    (pt); Dentists 1 (pt); Ophthalmologists 1 (pt);
    Podiatrists 1 (pt).
Languages Portuguese, French
Affiliation Seventh-Day Adventist
Facilities Dining room; Physical therapy
    room; Activities room; Chapel; Barber/
    Beauty shop.
Activities Arts & crafts; Cards; Games; Prayer
    groups; Movies; Shopping trips; Social/
    Cultural gatherings.

PROVIDENCE

Ann's Rest Home*
599 Broad St, Providence, RI, 02907
(401) 421-7576
Admin Diane Arzoumanian.
Licensure Intermediate care. *Beds* 14.
    Certified Medicaid.

Bannister Nursing Care Center
135 Dodge St, Providence, RI, 02907
(401) 274-3220
Admin Richard E Miller.
Licensure Skilled care; Intermediate care. *Beds*
    164. *Certified* Medicaid; Medicare.

Bay Tower Nursing Center*
101 Plain St, Providence, RI, 02903
Admin Genevieve A Francis. *Medical Dir/Dir
    of Nursing* John Demicco MD.
Licensure Skilled care; Intermediate care. *Beds*
    160. *Certified* Medicaid; Medicare.
Owner Proprietary Corp.
Admissions Requirements Physician's request.
Staff Physicians 6 (pt); RNs 8 (ft), 3 (pt);
    LPNs 8 (ft), 3 (pt); Nurses aides 1 (pt);
    Physical therapists 1 (pt); Occupational
    therapists 1 (pt); Speech therapists 1 (pt);
    Activities coordinators 2 (ft), 1 (pt);
    Dietitians 1 (pt); Dentists 1 (pt);
    Ophthalmologists 1 (pt); Podiatrists 1 (pt).
Facilities Dining room; Physical therapy
    room; Activities room; Chapel; Laundry
    room; Barber/Beauty shop.

Bethany Home of Rhode Island*
111 S Angell St, Providence, RI, 02906
(401) 831-2870
Admin Margaret Shippee.
Licensure Intermediate care. *Beds* 30.
    Certified Medicaid.

Charlesgate Nursing Center*
100 Randall St, Providence, RI, 02904
(401) 861-5858
Admin Robert S Gerskoff.
Licensure Skilled care; Intermediate care. *Beds*
    200. *Certified* Medicaid; Medicare.

Elmwood Health Center Inc
225 Elmwood Ave, Providence, RI, 02907
(401) 272-0600
Admin Norma J Ryan. *Medical Dir/Dir of
    Nursing* Hao Huang MD.
Licensure Skilled care; Intermediate care. *Beds*
    SNF; ICF 76. *Certified* Medicaid; Medicare.
Owner Privately owned.
Facilities Dining room; Physical therapy
    room; Activities room; Chapel; Crafts room;
    Laundry room; Barber/Beauty shop; Library.
Activities Arts & crafts; Cards; Games;
    Reading groups; Prayer groups; Movies;
    Shopping trips; Social/Cultural gatherings.

Hallworth House*
66 Benefit St, Providence, RI, 02904
(401) 274-4505
Admin Donald C Baker. *Medical Dir/Dir of
    Nursing* Paul J Conley MD.
Licensure Skilled care. *Beds* 51. *Certified*
    Medicaid; Medicare.
Admissions Requirements Medical
    examination; Physician's request.
Staff RNs 16 (ft); LPNs 1 (ft); Nurses aides 22
    (ft); Physical therapists 1 (pt); Recreational
    therapists 1 (pt); Dietitians 1 (pt).
Facilities Dining room; Physical therapy
    room; Activities room; Chapel; Crafts room;
    Barber/Beauty shop; Library.
Activities Arts & crafts; Cards; Games;
    Reading groups; Prayer groups; Movies.

Jewish Home for the Aged of Rhode Island
99 Hillside Ave, Providence, RI, 02906
(401) 351-4750
Admin William A Edelstein. *Medical Dir/Dir
    of Nursing* Henry Izeman MD; Judith
    Arredondo.
Licensure Skilled care; Intermediate care. *Beds*
    254. *Certified* Medicaid; Medicare.
Owner Nonprofit Corp.
Admissions Requirements Minimum age 62.
Staff RNs 32 (pt); LPNs 16 (ft), 8 (pt); Nurses
    aides 53 (ft), 56 (pt); Recreational therapists
    1 (ft), 3 (pt); Dietitians 1 (ft).
Affiliation Jewish
Facilities Dining room; Physical therapy
    room; Activities room; Chapel; Crafts room;
    Laundry room; Barber/Beauty shop; Library.
Activities Arts & crafts; Cards; Games;
    Movies; Shopping trips; Social/Cultural
    gatherings.

Park View Nursing Home
31 Parade St, Providence, RI, 02909
(401) 351-2600
Admin Lloyd H Turoff. *Medical Dir/Dir of
    Nursing* Dr Hao Huang; Rosanna Fontaine
    RN DNS.
Licensure Skilled care; Intermediate care. *Beds*
    SNF 20; ICF 55. *Certified* Medicaid;
    Medicare.
Owner Proprietary Corp.
Staff Physicians; RNs 2 (ft); LPNs 2 (ft);
    Orderlies 4 (ft); Nurses aides 28 (ft);
    Physical therapists 1 (pt); Recreational
    therapists 1 (ft); Occupational therapists 1
    (pt); Speech therapists 1 (pt); Activities
    coordinators 2 (ft); Dietitians 1 (pt).
Facilities Dining room; Physical therapy
    room; Activities room; Crafts room; Barber/
    Beauty shop; Library.
Activities Arts & crafts; Cards; Games; Prayer
    groups; Movies; Shopping trips; Social/
    Cultural gatherings.

St Elizabeth Home
109 Melrose St, Providence, RI, 02907
(401) 941-0200

Admin Steven J Horowitz. *Medical Dir/Dir of
    Nursing* Daniel Moore MD; Ann Schwarber
    DON.
Licensure Skilled care; Intermediate care. *Beds*
    SNF 24; ICF 84. *Certified* Medicaid;
    Medicare.
Admissions Requirements Medical
    examination.
Staff RNs 11 (ft); LPNs 5 (ft); Orderlies 3 (ft);
    Physical therapists 2 (ft); Nurses aides 52
    (ft); Physical therapists 2 (ft); Occupational
    therapists 1 (ft); Dietitians 1 (ft); Nurse
    practitioner 1 (pt).
Facilities Dining room; Physical therapy
    room; Activities room; Chapel; Crafts room;
    Barber/Beauty shop; Library; Solarium.
Activities Arts & crafts; Cards; Games;
    Reading groups; Movies; Social/Cultural
    gatherings.

Steere House
807 Broad St, Providence, RI, 02907
(401) 461-3340
Admin Harmon P B Jordan Jr.
Licensure Intermediate care. *Beds* 90.
    Certified Medicaid.

Summit Medical Center Inc*
1085 N Main St, Providence, RI, 02904
(401) 272-9600
Admin Thelma Kerzner.
Licensure Skilled care; Intermediate care. *Beds*
    138. *Certified* Medicaid; Medicare.

Tockwotton Home
180 George M Cohan Memorial Blvd,
    Providence, RI, 02906
(401) 272-5280 & 751-1550
Admin Joseph T Runner. *Medical Dir/Dir of
    Nursing* Richard Perry MD.
Licensure Intermediate care; Respite care.
    Beds 48. *Certified* Medicaid.
Owner Nonprofit Corp.
Admissions Requirements Minimum age 65;
    Females only; Medical examination.
Staff Physicians 2 (pt); RNs 5 (ft), 3 (pt);
    Nurses aides 8 (ft), 6 (pt); Physical therapists
    1 (pt); Occupational therapists 1 (pt);
    Activities coordinators 1 (pt); Dietitians 1
    (pt); Ophthalmologists 2 (pt); Dentist 1 (pt).
Facilities Dining room; Activities room;
    Crafts room; Laundry room; Barber/Beauty
    shop; Library.
Activities Arts & crafts; Cards; Movies;
    Shopping trips; Social/Cultural gatherings.

Wayland Health Center*
140 Pitman St, Providence, RI, 02906
(401) 274-4200
Admin Frank Pezzelli.
Licensure Skilled care; Intermediate care. *Beds*
    146. *Certified* Medicaid; Medicare.

SCITUATE

Oak Crest Manor Inc*
334 Chopmist Hill Rd, Scituate, RI, 02857
(401) 647-3890
Admin Muriel Beauregard.
Licensure Intermediate care. *Beds* 50.
    Certified Medicaid.

SMITHFIELD

Elm Brook Home Inc
40 Farnum Pike, Smithfield, RI, 02917
(401) 231-4646
Admin Paul Pezzelli. *Medical Dir/Dir of
    Nursing* Dr C K Lee; Lorraine Laprey DON.
Licensure Intermediate care. *Beds* ICF 65.
    Certified Medicaid.
Owner Proprietary Corp.
Admissions Requirements Medical
    examination; Physician's request.
Staff RNs 4 (ft); LPNs 3 (ft); Nurses aides 26
    (ft); Activities coordinators 1 (ft); Dietitians
    1 (pt); Dentist 1 (pt).

Facilities Dining room; Activities room;
  Crafts room.
Activities Arts & crafts; Cards; Games; Prayer
  groups; Shopping trips; Social/Cultural
  gatherings.

Hebert's Nursing Home Inc*
Log Rd, Smithfield, RI, 02917
(401) 231-7016
Admin Paul J Hebert.
Licensure Skilled care; Intermediate care. *Beds*
  86. *Certified* Medicaid; Medicare.

Heritage Hills Nursing Centre*
RFD 3, Douglas Pike, Smithfield, RI, 02917
(401) 231-2700
Admin John W Sormanti. *Medical Dir/Dir of
  Nursing* Dr Ovid Vezza.
Licensure Skilled care; Intermediate care. *Beds*
  110. *Certified* Medicaid; Medicare.
Staff RNs 5 (ft), 6 (pt); LPNs 4 (ft), 3 (pt);
  Nurses aides 20 (ft), 24 (pt); Physical
  therapists 1 (ft); Activities coordinators 2
  (pt); Dietitians 1 (ft); Podiatrists 1 (pt).
Facilities Dining room; Physical therapy
  room; Activities room; Chapel; Crafts room;
  Laundry room; Barber/Beauty shop; Library.
Activities Arts & crafts; Games; Prayer groups;
  Movies; Social/Cultural gatherings; Cooking.

Waterman Heights Nursing Home Ltd
Putnam Pike, Smithfield, RI, 02828
(401) 949-1200
Admin Claire Thibeault. *Medical Dir/Dir of
  Nursing* Robert F Spencer MD; Judith
  Robidoux RN.
Licensure Skilled care; Intermediate care;
  Custodial care. *Beds* SNF 34; ICF 63;
  Custodial care 8. *Certified* Medicaid;
  Medicare.
Owner Proprietary Corp.
Admissions Requirements Minimum age 14;
  Medical examination.
Staff RNs 5 (ft), 20 (pt); LPNs 5 (ft), 5 (pt);
  Nurses aides 30 (ft), 27 (pt); Physical
  therapists 1 (pt); Activities coordinators 1
  (ft); Ophthalmologists 1 (pt).
Facilities Dining room; Physical therapy
  room; Activities room; Chapel; Barber/
  Beauty shop; Lounge.
Activities Arts & crafts; Cards; Games; Prayer
  groups; Movies; Social/Cultural gatherings;
  Annual western day.

SOUTH KINGSTOWN

Allen's Health Centre Inc*
S County Trail, South Kingstown, RI, 02892
(401) 884-0425
Admin Mary Crossen.
Licensure Skilled care; Intermediate care. *Beds*
  101. *Certified* Medicaid; Medicare.

Scallop Shell Nursing Home Inc*
Kingstown Rd, South Kingstown, RI, 02883
(401) 789-3006
Admin Neil Mahoney.
Licensure Skilled care; Intermediate care. *Beds*
  67. *Certified* Medicaid; Medicare.

WARREN

Grace Barker Nursing Home Inc
54 Barker Ave, Warren, RI, 02885
(401) 245-9100
Admin Joseph E Sousa. *Medical Dir/Dir of
  Nursing* Dr Victor Medeiros; Marilyn Serbst
  RN DNS.
Licensure Skilled care; Intermediate care;
  Intermediate care for mentally retarded.
  Beds SNF 28; ICF 56. *Certified* Medicaid;
  Medicare.
Owner Privately owned.
Staff RNs; LPNs; Nurses aides; Activities
  coordinators.
Languages Portuguese

Facilities Dining room; Physical therapy
  room; Activities room; Chapel; Crafts room;
  Laundry room; Barber/Beauty shop.
Activities Arts & crafts; Cards; Games; Prayer
  groups; Movies; Shopping trips; Social/
  Cultural gatherings.

Crestwood Nursing & Convalescent Home Inc
568 Child St, Warren, RI, 02885
(401) 245-1574
Admin Donna A St Ours. *Medical Dir/Dir of
  Nursing* Dr Howard Perrone; Agnes M
  Medeiros RN DNS.
Licensure Skilled care; Intermediate care. *Beds*
  SNF 15; ICF 51. *Certified* Medicaid;
  Medicare.
Owner Privately owned.
Admissions Requirements Minimum age 18.
Staff RNs 12 (ft), 5 (pt); LPNs 6 (ft), 5 (pt);
  Orderlies 1 (pt); Nurses aides 38 (ft), 24 (pt);
  Activities coordinators 2 (ft).
Languages Italian, Portuguese, Polish
Facilities Dining room; Activities room;
  Crafts room; Barber/Beauty shop; Library.
Activities Arts & crafts; Cards; Games;
  Reading groups; Prayer groups; Movies;
  Shopping trips; Social/Cultural gatherings;
  Cruises; Senior Olympics; Exercise program.

Desilets Nursing Home Inc*
642 Metacom Ave, Warren, RI, 02885
(401) 245-2860
Admin Richard Desilets.
Licensure Skilled care; Intermediate care. *Beds*
  80. *Certified* Medicaid; Medicare.

WARWICK

Avalon Nursing Home Inc*
57 Stokes, Warwick, RI, 02889
(401) 738-1200
Admin Francis Kowalik. *Medical Dir/Dir of
  Nursing* Stanley Cate MD.
Licensure Skilled care; Intermediate care. *Beds*
  30. *Certified* Medicaid; Medicare.
Staff RNs; LPNs; Nurses aides; Activities
  coordinators.
Facilities Dining room; Activities room.
Activities Arts & crafts; Cards; Games; Prayer
  groups; Movies.

Brentwood Nursing Home Inc*
3986 Post Rd, Warwick, RI, 02886
(401) 884-8020
Admin Richard Miga.
Licensure Skilled care; Intermediate care. *Beds*
  96. *Certified* Medicaid; Medicare.

Burdick Convalescent Home Inc
57 Fair St, Warwick, RI, 02888
(401) 781-6628
Admin Elizabeth Moone. *Medical Dir/Dir of
  Nursing* Rapheal Perez MD.
Licensure Intermediate care. *Beds* 13.
  Certified Medicaid.
Owner Proprietary Corp.
Staff RNs 1 (pt); LPNs 2 (ft); Orderlies 1 (ft);
  Nurses aides 3 (ft), 3 (pt); Activities
  coordinators 1 (pt).
Facilities Dining room; Activities room;
  Chapel; Laundry room.
Activities Cards; Games; Reading groups;
  Prayer groups; Shopping trips; Social/
  Cultural gatherings.

Buttonwoods Crest Home
139 Hemlock Ave, Warwick, RI, 02886
(401) 739-6176
Admin Roger A Handy. *Medical Dir/Dir of
  Nursing* Stanley Cate MD.
Licensure Intermediate care. *Beds* ICF 31.
  Certified Medicaid.
Owner Privately owned.
Staff RNs 1 (ft), 7 (pt); LPNs 4 (pt); Nurses
  aides 2 (ft), 11 (pt); Physical therapists 1
  (pt); Recreational therapists 1 (pt); Activities
  coordinators 1 (pt); Dietitians 1 (pt);
  Ophthalmologists 1 (pt).

Facilities Dining room; Activities room;
  Crafts room; Laundry room.
Activities Arts & crafts; Cards; Games; Prayer
  groups; Shopping trips; Social/Cultural
  gatherings.

Greenwood House Nursing Home Inc*
1139 Main Ave, Warwick, RI, 02886
(401) 739-6600 & 737-9609
Admin Paul T Buonaiuto.
Licensure Skilled care; Intermediate care. *Beds*
  88. *Certified* Medicaid; Medicare.

Greenwood Oaks Rest Home*
14 Lake St, Warwick, RI, 02886
(401) 739-3297
Admin Dorothy Von Housen.
Licensure Intermediate care. *Beds* 16.
  Certified Medicaid.

Kent Nursing Home Inc
660 Commonwealth Ave, Warwick, RI, 02886
(401) 739-4241
Admin Joan Williams. *Medical Dir/Dir of
  Nursing* Dr Hossein Shushtari.
Licensure Skilled care; Intermediate care. *Beds*
  153. *Certified* Medicaid; Medicare.
Facilities Dining room; Physical therapy
  room; Activities room; Crafts room; Laundry
  room; Barber/Beauty shop.
Activities Arts & crafts; Cards; Games;
  Reading groups; Prayer groups; Movies;
  Shopping trips.

Pawtuxet Village Nursing Home
270 Post Rd, Warwick, RI, 02888
(401) 467-3555
Admin Steven McLeod. *Medical Dir/Dir of
  Nursing* Pat Bonn RN.
Licensure Skilled care; Intermediate care. *Beds*
  SNF 131; ICF. *Certified* Medicaid;
  Medicare.
Owner Proprietary Corp.
Facilities Dining room; Activities room;
  Chapel; Crafts room; Laundry room; Barber/
  Beauty shop.
Activities Arts & crafts; Cards; Games;
  Movies; Shopping trips; Social/Cultural
  gatherings.

Royal Manor Inc*
159 Division St, Warwick, RI, 02818
(401) 884-5590
Admin Jeannette E Del Padre.
Licensure Intermediate care. *Beds* 55.
Admissions Requirements Medical
  examination; Physician's request.
Staff RNs 5 (ft); Nurses aides 24 (ft);
  Activities coordinators 1 (ft); Dietitians 1
  (pt).
Facilities Dining room; Barber/Beauty shop.
Activities Arts & crafts; Cards; Prayer groups;
  Movies; Shopping trips; Social/Cultural
  gatherings.

Sunny View Nursing Home*
83 Corona St, Warwick, RI, 02886
(401) 737-9193
Admin Patricia Miga.
Licensure Skilled care; Intermediate care. *Beds*
  37. *Certified* Medicaid; Medicare.

Warwick Health Centre
109 W Shore Rd, Warwick, RI, 02889
(401) 739-9440
Admin Harry Nahigian.
Licensure Skilled care; Intermediate care. *Beds*
  149. *Certified* Medicaid; Medicare.
Admissions Requirements Medical
  examination.
Staff RNs 18 (ft), 7 (pt); LPNs 12 (ft), 5 (pt);
  Nurses aides 60 (ft), 20 (pt); Physical
  therapists 1 (pt); Speech therapists 1 (pt);
  Activities coordinators 1 (pt); Dentists 1
  (pt); Ophthalmologists 1
  (pt); Podiatrists 1 (pt); Dentist 1 (pt).
Facilities Dining room; Physical therapy
  room; Activities room; Chapel; Crafts room;
  Barber/Beauty shop.

Activities Arts & crafts; Cards; Games; Prayer groups; Movies; Social/Cultural gatherings.

Warwick Rest Home Inc*
348 Warwick Neck Ave, Warwick, RI, 02889
(401) 737-4909
Admin Pasquale P Squillante Jr.
Licensure Intermediate care. *Beds* 16.
Certified Medicaid.

West Bay Manor*
2783 W Shore Rd, Warwick, RI, 02886
(401) 739-7300
Admin David R Velander.
Licensure Intermediate care. *Beds* 45.
Certified Medicaid.

WEST WARWICK

West View Nursing Home Inc*
239 Legris Ave, West Warwick, RI, 02983
(401) 828-9000
Admin Robert Horton. *Medical Dir/Dir of Nursing* Frank Fallon DO.
Licensure Skilled care; Intermediate care. *Beds* 120. *Certified* Medicaid; Medicare.
Staff Physicians 23 (pt); RNs 6 (ft), 4 (pt); LPNs 6 (ft), 3 (pt); Orderlies 1 (ft); Nurses aides 40 (ft), 25 (pt); Physical therapists 1 (pt); Recreational therapists 2 (ft); Speech therapists 1 (pt); Activities coordinators 1 (ft); Dietitians 1 (pt); Dentists 1 (pt); Ophthalmologists 1 (pt); Podiatrists 2 (pt); Audiologists 1 (pt).
Facilities Dining room; Physical therapy room; Activities room; Chapel; Laundry room; Barber/Beauty shop.
Activities Arts & crafts; Cards; Games; Reading groups; Prayer groups; Movies; Shopping trips; Social/Cultural gatherings.

WESTERLY

Watch Hill Manor Ltd*
RR 1, Watch Hill Rd, Box 78, Westerly, RI, 02891
(401) 596-2664
Admin Philip Hovey. *Medical Dir/Dir of Nursing* Bruce M Gillie MD.
Licensure Skilled care; Intermediate care. *Beds* 59. *Certified* Medicaid; Medicare.
Admissions Requirements Medical examination; Physician's request.
Staff Recreational therapists.
Facilities Dining room; Activities room; Barber/Beauty shop.
Activities Arts & crafts; Games; Prayer groups; Shopping trips.

Westerly Health Center
PO Box 81A, RR 4, Westerly, RI, 02891
(401) 348-0020
Admin Mary Louise Kicinski. *Medical Dir/Dir of Nursing* Dr Walter J Lentz; Andrea Sellins RN DON.
Licensure Skilled care; Intermediate care. *Beds* SNF 60; ICF 60. *Certified* Medicaid; Medicare.
Owner Proprietary Corp (Health Concepts Corp).
Staff RNs 8 (ft), 4 (pt); LPNs 6 (ft), 3 (pt); Nurses aides 32 (ft), 17 (pt); Physical therapists 1 (pt); Activities coordinators 1 (ft), 2 (pt).
Facilities Dining room; Physical therapy room; Activities room; Crafts room; Laundry room; Barber/Beauty shop; Library.
Activities Arts & crafts; Cards; Games; Reading groups; Prayer groups; Movies; Social/Cultural gatherings.

Westerly Nursing Home Inc
81 Beach St, Westerly, RI, 02891
(401) 596-4925
Admin Paul V Martin. *Medical Dir/Dir of Nursing* Starlyne Davis RN DNS.
Licensure Skilled care; Intermediate care. *Beds* 60. *Certified* Medicaid; Medicare.
Owner Proprietary Corp.
Admissions Requirements Physician's request.
Staff Physicians; RNs; LPNs; Nurses aides; Physical therapists; Recreational therapists; Speech therapists; Activities coordinators; Dietitians; Dentists; Ophthalmologists.
Facilities Dining room; Physical therapy room; Activities room; Crafts room; Laundry room; Barber/Beauty shop.
Activities Arts & crafts; Cards; Games; Reading groups; Prayer groups; Movies; Shopping trips; Social/Cultural gatherings.

WOONSOCKET

Ballou Home for the Aged
60 Mendon Rd, Woonsocket, RI, 02895
(401) 769-0437
Admin Louise Boulet.
Licensure Intermediate care. *Beds* ICF 27.
Owner Nonprofit Corp.
Admissions Requirements Minimum age 65; Medical examination; Physician's request.
Staff RNs 1 (ft), 1 (pt); LPNs 1 (ft), 4 (pt); Nurses aides 4 (ft), 9 (pt); Activities coordinators 1 (pt).
Facilities Dining room; Activities room; Laundry room; Barber/Beauty shop; Library.
Activities Arts & crafts; Cards; Games; Movies; Shopping trips; Social/Cultural gatherings.

Evergreens Nursing Home Inc*
116 Greene St, Woonsocket, RI, 02895
(401) 769-8042
Admin Jeannette Kelly.
Licensure Intermediate care. *Beds* 35.
Certified Medicaid.

The Friendly Home Inc
303 Rhodes Ave, Woonsocket, RI, 02895
(401) 769-7220
Admin Angelo S Rotella. *Medical Dir/Dir of Nursing* Catello Scarano; Catherine Schenk.
Licensure Skilled care; Intermediate care. *Beds* SNF 24; ICF 86; ICF/MR 16. *Certified* Medicaid; Medicare.
Owner Proprietary Corp.
Staff RNs; LPNs; Orderlies; Nurses aides; Activities coordinators.
Languages French
Facilities Dining room; Physical therapy room; Activities room; Laundry room; Barber/Beauty shop; Library.
Activities Arts & crafts; Cards; Games; Prayer groups; Movies; Shopping trips; Social/Cultural gatherings.

Mt St Francis Health Center
4 St Joseph St, Woonsocket, RI, 02891
(401) 765-5844
Admin Carol F Sabella RN. *Medical Dir/Dir of Nursing* Nicolas Passarelli Jr RN DON.
Licensure Skilled care; Intermediate care. *Beds* SNF 198; ICF. *Certified* Medicaid; Medicare.
Owner Proprietary Corp.
Admissions Requirements Minimum age 18.
Staff Physicians; RNs; LPNs; Orderlies; Nurses aides; Physical therapists; Recreational therapists; Occupational therapists; Speech therapists; Activities coordinators; Dietitians; Dentists; Ophthalmologists; Podiatrists.
Languages French, Armenian
Affiliation Roman Catholic
Facilities Dining room; Physical therapy room; Activities room; Chapel; Crafts room; Laundry room; Barber/Beauty shop; Multi-purpose room.
Activities Arts & crafts; Cards; Games; Reading groups; Prayer groups; Movies; Shopping trips; Social/Cultural gatherings; Outings; Exercise groups; Ethnic cooking.

Woonsocket Health Centre*
262 Poplar St, Woonsocket, RI, 02895
(401) 765-2100
Admin Norma Pezzelli.
Licensure Skilled care; Intermediate care. *Beds* 275. *Certified* Medicaid; Medicare.

SOUTH CAROLINA

ABBEVILLE

Abbeville Nursing Home Inc*
PO Box 190, Abbeville, SC, 29620
(803) 459-5122
Admin Ethel L Hughes.
Licensure Skilled care; Intermediate care. *Beds*
50. *Certified* Medicaid; Medicare.

AIKEN

Aiken Nursing Home
123 DuPont Dr, Aiken, SC, 29801
(803) 648-0434
Admin George Butler. *Medical Dir/Dir of*
Nursing H A Langston; Marilyn Baugh.
Licensure Skilled care; Intermediate care. *Beds*
86. *Certified* Medicaid; Medicare.
Owner Proprietary Corp (Beverly Enterprises).
Admissions Requirements Minimum age 12;
Physician's request.
Staff Physicians 1 (pt); RNs 3 (ft), 5 (pt);
LPNs 5 (ft), 8 (pt); Orderlies 1 (ft); Nurses
aides 27 (ft), 6 (pt); Physical therapists 1
(pt); Speech therapists 1 (pt); Activities
coordinators 1 (ft), 1 (pt); Ophthalmologists
1 (pt); Dental 1 (pt).
Facilities Dining room; Physical therapy
room; Activities room; Laundry room;
Barber/Beauty shop.
Activities Arts & crafts; Cards; Games;
Reading groups; Prayer groups; Movies;
Shopping trips; Social/Cultural gatherings.

Mattie C Hall Health Care Center
830 Laurens St N, Aiken, SC, 29801
(803) 649-6264
Admin Vicki Lollis Major. *Medical Dir/Dir of*
Nursing T Mark Meger MD; Shirley S
Cooper RN DON.
Licensure Skilled care; Intermediate care. *Beds*
SNF 44; ICF 88. *Certified* Medicaid;
Medicare.
Owner Publicly owned.
Admissions Requirements Minimum age 18;
Medical examination; Physician's request.
Staff RNs 4 (ft), 1 (pt); LPNs 13 (ft), 3 (pt);
Nurses aides 65 (ft), 10 (pt); Physical
therapists 1 (pt); Occupational therapists 1
(pt); Speech therapists 1 (pt); Activities
coordinators 1 (ft), 2 (pt); Dietitians 1 (pt);
Ophthalmologists 1 (pt).
Facilities Dining room; Physical therapy
room; Activities room; Crafts room; Barber/
Beauty shop.
Activities Arts & crafts; Cards; Games;
Reading groups; Prayer groups; Movies;
Shopping trips; Social/Cultural gatherings.

Laurens Community Residence
625 Cushman Rd, Aiken, SC, 29801
(803) 649-7712
Admin Richard M Weldon. *Medical Dir/Dir of*
Nursing Randy Watson MD.
Licensure Intermediate care for mentally
retarded. *Beds* ICF/MR. *Certified* Medicaid.
Owner Nonprofit organization/foundation.

Admissions Requirements Minimum age 21;
Males only; Medical examination.
Staff Physicians 1 (pt); RNs 1 (pt); LPNs 1
(ft); Physical therapists 1 (pt); Recreational
therapists 1 (pt); Occupational therapists 1
(pt); Speech therapists 1 (pt); Dietitians 1
(pt); Mental retardation specialists 5 (ft).
Facilities Dining room; Activities room;
Laundry room; Basketball court.
Activities Arts & crafts; Games; Movies;
Shopping trips; Social/Cultural gatherings.

Richland Community Residence
1111 Richland Ave, Aiken, SC, 29801
(803) 649-7590
Admin Sally James.
Licensure Intermediate care for mentally
retarded. *Beds* ICF/MR 8. *Certified*
Medicare.
Owner Nonprofit organization/foundation.
Admissions Requirements Minimum age 16;
Females only.
Staff Physicians 8 (pt); RNs 1 (ft), 16 (pt);
LPNs 3 (ft), 8 (pt); MRSs 3 (ft), 8 (pt).
Facilities Activities room; Laundry room;
Family type home.
Activities Arts & crafts; Games; Movies;
Shopping trips; Social/Cultural gatherings.

Rudnick Community Residence
629 Chesterfield N, Aiken, SC, 29801
649-7174
Admin Sally James.
Licensure Intermediate care. *Beds* ICF/MR 8.
Certified Medicare.
Owner Nonprofit organization/foundation.
Admissions Requirements Minimum age 16;
Males only.
Staff Physicians 1 (ft), 16 (pt); RNs 1 (ft), 16
(pt); LPNs 3 (ft), 8 (pt); MRS's 3 (ft), 8 (pt).
Facilities Family style home.

Sanders Community Residence
625 Chesterfield St, Aiken, SC, 29801
(803) 649-7315
Admin Richard M Weldon. *Medical Dir/Dir of*
Nursing Randy Watson MD.
Licensure Intermediate care for mentally
retarded. *Beds* ICF/MR. *Certified* Medicaid.
Owner Nonprofit organization/foundation.
Admissions Requirements Minimum age 21;
Females only; Medical examination.
Staff Physicians 1 (pt); RNs 1 (pt); LPNs 2
(ft); Physical therapists 1 (pt); Recreational
therapists 1 (pt); Occupational therapists 1
(pt); Speech therapists 1 (pt); Dietitians 1
(pt); Mental retardation specialists 5 (ft).
Facilities Dining room; Activities room;
Laundry room.
Activities Arts & crafts; Games; Movies;
Shopping trips; Social/Cultural gatherings.

ANDERSON

Anderson Health Care Center*
PO Box 989, 1501 E Greenville St, Anderson,
SC, 29622
(803) 226-8356

Admin Betty J Finley.
Licensure Skilled care; Intermediate care. *Beds*
146. *Certified* Medicaid; Medicare.
Owner Proprietary Corp (National Health
Corp).

Ellenburg Nursing Center Inc
611 E Hampton, Anderson, SC, 29624
(803) 226-5054
Admin M L Ellenburg. *Medical Dir/Dir of*
Nursing Dr Warren White; Helen C Lusk
RN DON.
Licensure Skilled care; Intermediate care. *Beds*
176. *Certified* Medicaid; Medicare.
Owner Proprietary Corp.
Admissions Requirements Medical
examination; Physician's request.
Facilities Dining room; Physical therapy
room; Activities room; Laundry room;
Barber/Beauty shop.
Activities Arts & crafts; Games; Reading
groups; Prayer groups; Movies.

Latham Nursing Home
208 James St, Anderson, SC, 29621
(803) 226-3427
Admin Loneta L Dunn. *Medical Dir/Dir of*
Nursing Warren W White MD; Lana S
Willis RN.
Licensure Skilled care; Intermediate care. *Beds*
44. *Certified* Medicaid; Medicare.
Admissions Requirements Minimum age 14;
Medical examination; Physician's request.
Staff Physicians 21 (pt); RNs 3 (ft), 2 (pt);
LPNs 2 (ft), 1 (pt); Orderlies 1 (ft); Nurses
aides 10 (ft), 4 (pt); Occupational therapists
1 (pt); Speech therapists 1 (pt); Activities
coordinators 1 (pt); Dietitians 1 (pt); Dentists
1 (pt); Podiatrists 1 (pt); Social workers 1
(pt).
Facilities Dining room; Physical therapy
room; Activities room; Chapel; Crafts room;
Laundry room; Barber/Beauty shop.
Activities Arts & crafts; Cards; Games;
Reading groups; Prayer groups; Movies;
Social/Cultural gatherings.

AUGUSTA

Anna Maria ICF
PO Box 6277, 412 Main St, Augusta, SC,
29841-6277
(803) 652-2230
Admin D Annette Hobbs.
Licensure Intermediate care. *Beds* 26.
Certified Medicaid; Medicare.

Anne Maria Medical Care Nursing Home Inc*
Talisman Drive, Augusta, SC, 29841
(803) 278-2170
Admin Marianne Luckey. *Medical Dir/Dir of*
Nursing J W Thurmond III MD.
Licensure Skilled care; Intermediate care. *Beds*
120. *Certified* Medicaid; Medicare.
Admissions Requirements Medical
examination.

Staff Physicians 1 (ft); RNs 2 (ft), 3 (pt); LPNs 10 (ft), 6 (pt); Nurses aides 43 (ft), 6 (pt); Physical therapists 1 (pt); Activities coordinators 1 (ft), 2 (pt); Dietitians 1 (pt); Podiatrists 1 (pt).
Facilities Dining room; Physical therapy room; Activities room; Chapel; Crafts room; Laundry room; Barber/Beauty shop; Library.
Activities Arts & crafts; Cards; Games; Reading groups; Prayer groups; Social/Cultural gatherings; Garden club.

BAMBERG

Bamberg County Memorial Nursing Center*
North & McGee Sts, Bamberg, SC, 29003
(803) 245-4321
Admin Charles V Morgan. *Medical Dir/Dir of Nursing* Dr M C Watson.
Licensure Skilled care; Intermediate care. *Beds* 22. *Certified* Medicaid; Medicare.
Admissions Requirements Medical examination; Physician's request.
Facilities Dining room; Activities room; Laundry room.
Activities Arts & crafts; Games; Reading groups; Prayer groups.

BARNWELL

Barnwell County Nursing Home
PO Box 807, Wren St, Barnwell, SC, 29812
(803) 259-5547
Admin Paula E Birt. *Medical Dir/Dir of Nursing* Nedra C Mobley DON.
Licensure Skilled care; Intermediate care. *Beds* 40. *Certified* Medicaid; Medicare.
Owner Publicly owned.
Admissions Requirements Medical examination; Physician's request.
Staff Physicians 4 (pt); RNs 4 (ft); LPNs 4 (ft); Orderlies 2 (ft); Nurses aides 20 (ft); Physical therapists 1 (pt); Recreational therapists 1 (ft); Ophthalmologists 1 (pt).
Facilities Dining room; Physical therapy room; Activities room; Barber/Beauty shop.
Activities Arts & crafts; Cards; Games; Reading groups; Prayer groups; Movies; Shopping trips.

BEAUFORT

Bay View Nursing Center Inc*
PO Box 1103, S Todd Dr, Beaufort, SC, 29902
(803) 524-8911
Admin Danny Charpentier.
Licensure Skilled care; Intermediate care. *Beds* 132. *Certified* Medicaid; Medicare.

BENNETTSVILLE

Dundee Nursing Home
PO Box 858, 401 Bypass, Bennettsville, SC, 29512
(803) 479-6251
Admin Harold D Branton. *Medical Dir/Dir of Nursing* John May MD; Marie Hester DON.
Licensure Skilled care; Intermediate care. *Beds* SNF 87; ICF 24. *Certified* Medicaid; Medicare.
Owner Proprietary Corp.
Staff Physicians 5 (ft); RNs 4 (ft), 3 (pt); LPNs 8 (ft), 7 (pt); Nurses aides 28 (ft), 16 (pt); Dietitians; Dietitians 1 (pt).
Facilities Dining room; Physical therapy room; Activities room; Chapel; Laundry room; Barber/Beauty shop; Library.
Activities Arts & crafts; Cards; Games; Reading groups; Prayer groups; Movies; Shopping trips; Social/Cultural gatherings.

BLACKVILLE

Wildwood Health Care Center
PO Box 215, Jonesbridge Rd, Blackville, SC, 29817
(803) 284-2213, 284-2214
Admin Pace B Hungerford. *Medical Dir/Dir of Nursing* Emily Phail.
Licensure Intermediate care. *Beds* ICF 85. *Certified* Medicaid; Medicare.
Owner Privately owned.
Staff Physicians 1 (ft); RNs 2 (ft); LPNs 11 (ft); Orderlies 10 (ft); Nurses aides 10 (ft); Activities coordinators 1 (ft); Dietitians 1 (ft); Ophthalmologists 1 (ft).
Facilities Dining room; Activities room; Crafts room; Laundry room; Barber/Beauty shop.
Activities Arts & crafts; Cards; Games; Reading groups; Prayer groups; Movies; Shopping trips; Social/Cultural gatherings.

CAMDEN

A Sam Karesh LTC Center
1315 Roberts St, Camden, SC, 29020
(803) 432-4311
Admin L H Young. *Medical Dir/Dir of Nursing* John Dubose MD; Susan Outen RN.
Licensure Skilled care; Intermediate care. *Beds* 88. *Certified* Medicaid; Medicare.
Owner Publicly owned.
Admissions Requirements Physician's request.
Staff Physicians 1 (pt); RNs 4 (ft), 1 (pt); LPNs 13 (ft), 1 (pt); Orderlies 2 (ft), 1 (pt); Nurses aides 26 (ft), 4 (pt); Physical therapists 1 (pt); Speech therapists 1 (pt); Activities coordinators 1 (ft); Dietitians 1 (pt).
Facilities Dining room; Physical therapy room; Activities room; Laundry room; Barber/Beauty shop.
Activities Arts & crafts; Cards; Games; Reading groups; Prayer groups; Shopping trips.

CHARLESTON

Driftwood Health Care Center*
341 Calhoun St, Charleston, SC, 29407
(803) 723-9276
Admin Calvin D Lipscomb. *Medical Dir/Dir of Nursing* Dr Alexander Marshall.
Licensure Skilled care; Intermediate care. *Beds* 77. *Certified* Medicaid; Medicare.
Admissions Requirements Physician's request.
Staff Physicians 1 (pt); RNs 4 (ft), 1 (pt); LPNs 11 (ft), 4 (pt); Orderlies 1 (ft), 1 (pt); Nurses aides 27 (ft), 14 (pt); Physical therapists 1 (pt); Reality therapists 2 (ft); Recreational therapists 2 (ft); Speech therapists 1 (pt); Activities coordinators 2 (ft); Dietitians 1 (ft); Podiatrists 1 (pt).
Facilities Dining room; Activities room; Laundry room; Barber/Beauty shop.
Activities Arts & crafts; Cards; Games; Reading groups; Prayer groups; Movies; Shopping trips.

Driftwood Health Care Center—Long-Term Care Facility*
341 Calhoun St, Charleston, SC, 29407
(803) 723-9276
Admin Calvin D Lipscomb. *Medical Dir/Dir of Nursing* Dr Alexander Marshall.
Licensure Nursing care. *Beds* 102. *Certified* Medicaid; Medicare.
Staff Physicians; RNs; LPNs; Orderlies; Nurses aides; Physical therapists; Reality therapists; Recreational therapists; Speech therapists; Activities coordinators; Dietitians; Dentists.

Facilities Dining room; Activities room; Laundry room; Barber/Beauty shop.
Activities Arts & crafts; Cards; Games; Reading groups; Prayer groups; Movies; Shopping trips; Social/Cultural gatherings.

Firestone Community Residence
3641 Firestone Rd, Charleston, SC, 29418
(803) 552-7201, 767-1007
Admin Alice Q Libet. *Medical Dir/Dir of Nursing* Claudia Freeman RN.
Licensure Intermediate care for mentally retarded. *Beds* ICF/MR 14. *Certified* Medicaid.
Owner Publicly owned.
Admissions Requirements Males only.
Staff Physicians 1 (pt); RNs 1 (pt); LPNs 1 (ft); Physical therapists 1 (pt); Recreational therapists 1 (pt); Occupational therapists 1 (pt); Speech therapists 1 (pt); Dietitians 1 (pt); Podiatrists 1 (pt).
Facilities Dining room; Activities room; Laundry room.
Activities Arts & crafts; Cards; Games; Movies; Shopping trips; Social/Cultural gatherings; Work activity.

Lenevar Community Residence
1435 W Lenevar Dr, Charleston, SC, 29407
(803) 571-2916
Admin Alice Q Libet PhD. *Medical Dir/Dir of Nursing* Eugenia Felsinger RN PhD.
Licensure Intermediate care for mentally retarded. *Beds* ICF/MR 9. *Certified* Medicaid.
Owner Nonprofit organization/foundation.
Admissions Requirements Males only.
Staff Physicians 1 (pt); RNs 1 (pt); LPNs 1 (ft); Physical therapists 1 (pt); Recreational therapists 1 (pt); Occupational therapists 1 (pt); Speech therapists 1 (pt); Dietitians 1 (pt); Podiatrists 1 (pt).
Facilities Dining room; Activities room; Laundry room.
Activities Arts & crafts; Cards; Games; Movies; Shopping trips; Social/Cultural gatherings; Work Activity.

Manor Care of Charleston Inc
1137 Sam Rittenberg Blvd, Charleston, SC, 29407
(803) 763-0233
Admin Robert W Dougherty. *Medical Dir/Dir of Nursing* Donald Schweiger; Ann Tinley DON.
Licensure Skilled care. *Beds* SNF 132. *Certified* Medicare.
Owner Proprietary Corp (Manor Care).
Admissions Requirements Minimum age 16; Medical examination; Physician's request.
Staff RNs 7 (ft), 2 (pt); LPNs 14 (ft), 3 (pt); Orderlies 2 (ft); Nurses aides 42 (ft), 15 (pt); Physical therapists 2 (ft); Recreational therapists 1 (ft); Occupational therapists 1 (pt); Speech therapists 1 (ft); Activities coordinators 2 (ft); Dietitians 1 (ft); Ophthalmologists 1 (pt).
Languages Spanish
Facilities Dining room; Physical therapy room; Activities room; Chapel; Crafts room; Laundry room; Barber/Beauty shop.
Activities Arts & crafts; Cards; Games; Reading groups; Prayer groups; Movies; Shopping trips; Social/Cultural gatherings.

North Charleston Convalescent Center
9319 Medical Plaza Dr, Charleston, SC, 29418
(803) 797-8282
Admin Ted P Jones. *Medical Dir/Dir of Nursing* Dr Paul Deaton; Lynn Giles.
Licensure Skilled care; Intermediate care. *Beds* 132. *Certified* Medicaid; Medicare.
Owner Proprietary Corp (White Oak Manor Inc).
Staff Physicians 2 (ft), 1 (pt); RNs 6 (ft), 1 (pt); LPNs 13 (ft), 8 (pt); Nurses aides 48 (ft), 9 (pt); Physical therapists 3 (pt); Reality therapists 1 (pt); Recreational therapists 2

(pt); Occupational therapists 1 (pt); Speech therapists 1 (pt); Activities coordinators 1 (pt); Dietitians 1 (pt); Ophthalmologists 1 (pt).
Facilities Dining room; Physical therapy room; Activities room; Crafts room; Laundry room; Barber/Beauty shop.
Activities Arts & crafts; Cards; Games; Reading groups; Prayer groups; Movies; Shopping trips; Social/Cultural gatherings.

Rutledge Community Residence
887 Rutledge Ave, Charleston, SC, 29401
(803) 722-7547, 723-6078
Admin Alice Q Libet. *Medical Dir/Dir of Nursing* Claudia Freeman RN.
Licensure Intermediate care for mentally retarded. *Beds* ICF/MR 8. *Certified* Medicaid.
Owner Publicly owned.
Admissions Requirements Females only.
Staff Physicians 1 (pt); RNs 1 (pt); LPNs 1 (ft); Physical therapists 1 (pt); Recreational therapists 1 (pt); Occupational therapists 1 (pt); Speech therapists 1 (pt); Dietitians 1 (pt); Podiatrists 1 (pt).
Facilities Dining room; Activities room; Laundry room.
Activities Arts & crafts; Cards; Games; Movies; Shopping trips; Social/Cultural gatherings; Work activity.

CHERAW

Cheraw Nursing Home Inc*
Hwy 9 W, PO Box 1321, Cheraw, SC, 29520
(803) 537-3621
Admin Ruth S Laney. *Medical Dir/Dir of Nursing* Winston Y Godwin Sr MD.
Licensure Skilled care; Intermediate care. *Beds* 100. *Certified* Medicaid; Medicare.
Staff Physicians 1 (ft), 5 (pt); RNs 3 (ft); LPNs 7 (ft), 4 (pt); Orderlies 4 (ft); Nurses aides 33 (ft); Physical therapists 2 (pt); Reality therapists 1 (ft); Activities coordinators 1 (ft), 1 (pt); Dietitians 1 (ft); Dentists 1 (pt).
Facilities Dining room; Physical therapy room; Activities room; Laundry room; Barber/Beauty shop.
Activities Arts & crafts; Games; Prayer groups; Social/Cultural gatherings.

CHESTER

Chester County Hospital & Nursing Center Inc
Great Falls Rd, Chester, SC, 29706
(803) 377-3151
Admin Ron V Hunter. *Medical Dir/Dir of Nursing* J N Gaston Jr MD; Gwen Brown RN.
Licensure Dual swing. *Beds* 62.
Owner Nonprofit Corp.
Staff Physicians 22 (ft); RNs 2 (ft); LPNs 10 (ft); Nurses aides 33 (ft); Physical therapists 1 (ft); Activities coordinators 1 (ft); Dietitians 1 (ft).
Facilities Dining room; Physical therapy room; Activities room; Chapel; Barber/Beauty shop.
Activities Arts & crafts; Games; Reading groups; Prayer groups; Shopping trips; Social/Cultural gatherings.

CLEMSON

Clemson Health Care Center
500 Downs Loop, Clemson, SC, 29631
(803) 654-1155
Admin Rock A Reinhart. *Medical Dir/Dir of Nursing* H P Cooper Jr MD; Anita Davis RN DON.
Licensure Skilled care. *Beds* SNF 44.
Owner Proprietary Corp.
Admissions Requirements Medical examination; Physician's request.

Staff Physicians 11 (pt); RNs 5 (ft), 4 (pt); LPNs 3 (ft), 3 (pt); Orderlies 2 (ft); Nurses aides 13 (ft), 8 (pt); Activities coordinators 1 (pt); Dietitians 1 (ft); Dentists 1 (pt); Podiatrists 1 (pt).
Facilities Dining room; Physical therapy room; Activities room; Laundry room; Barber/Beauty shop; Library; Patio; Sunroom.
Activities Arts & crafts; Cards; Games; Reading groups; Prayer groups; Movies; Shopping trips; Social/Cultural gatherings; Pets.

CLINTON

Bailey Nursing Home*
Jacobs Hwy, Clinton, SC, 29325
(803) 833-2550
Admin Clem P Ham.
Licensure Skilled care; Intermediate care. *Beds* 43. *Certified* Medicaid; Medicare.
Admissions Requirements Medical examination; Physician's request.
Staff Physicians 10 (pt); RNs 2 (ft), 1 (pt); LPNs 7 (ft); Orderlies 3 (ft); Nurses aides 22 (ft), 5 (pt); Physical therapists 1 (pt); Reality therapists 1 (pt); Recreational therapists 1 (ft); Activities coordinators 1 (ft); Dietitians 1 (ft); Dentists 1 (pt).
Facilities Dining room; Activities room; Laundry room; Barber/Beauty shop.
Activities Games; Reading groups; Prayer groups; Shopping trips.

Whitten Center
Hwy 76, PO Drawer 239, Clinton, SC, 29325
(803) 833-2733 Ext 176
Admin Armicia M Lilley. *Medical Dir/Dir of Nursing* Dr George Dellaportas.
Licensure Intermediate care for mentally retarded. *Beds* ICF/MR 220.
Owner Publicly owned.
Admissions Requirements Minimum age 21.
Staff Physicians 3 (pt); RNs 2 (ft), 1 (pt); LPNs 20 (ft); Physical therapists 1 (pt); Recreational therapists 2 (ft); Occupational therapists 1 (pt); Speech therapists 4 (pt); Activities coordinators 1 (pt); Dietitians 1 (pt); Dentists 1 (pt); Podiatrists 1 (pt).
Facilities Dining room; Physical therapy room; Activities room; Chapel; Crafts room; Laundry room; Barber/Beauty shop; Library.
Activities Arts & crafts; Cards; Games; Reading groups; Prayer groups; Movies; Shopping trips; Social/Cultural gatherings.

COLUMBIA

Brian Center of Nursing Care—Columbia*
3514 Sidney Rd, Columbia, SC, 29210
(803) 798-9715
Admin Sarah Kirchman. *Medical Dir/Dir of Nursing* Dr Shawn Chillag.
Licensure Skilled care; Intermediate care. *Beds* 60. *Certified* Medicaid; Medicare.
Owner Proprietary Corp (Brian Center Management Corp).
Staff Physicians 1 (pt); RNs 4 (ft), 4 (pt); LPNs 7 (ft), 3 (pt); Orderlies 5 (ft), 2 (pt); Nurses aides 34 (ft), 5 (pt); Physical therapists 1 (pt); Speech therapists; Activities coordinators 1 (ft), 1 (pt); Dentists; Ophthalmologists; Podiatrists; Audiologists.
Facilities Dining room; Physical therapy room; Activities room; Chapel; Crafts room; Laundry room; Barber/Beauty shop.
Activities Arts & crafts; Cards; Games; Reading groups; Prayer groups; Social/Cultural gatherings.

Capitol Convalescent Center
PO Box 4276, 3001 Beechaven Rd, Columbia, SC, 29240
(803) 782-4363
Admin Anne O Winn. *Medical Dir/Dir of Nursing* Waitus O Tanner.

Licensure Skilled care; Intermediate care. *Beds* 120. *Certified* Medicaid; Medicare.
Admissions Requirements Medical examination; Physician's request.
Staff Physicians 5 (pt); RNs 5 (ft), 1 (pt); LPNs 9 (ft), 3 (pt); Orderlies 2 (ft), 2 (pt); Nurses aides 40 (ft), 9 (pt); Physical therapists 1 (pt); Recreational therapists 2 (ft); Speech therapists 1 (pt); Dentists 1 (pt); Podiatrists 1 (pt).
Facilities Dining room; Physical therapy room; Activities room; Crafts room; Laundry room; Barber/Beauty shop.
Activities Arts & crafts; Cards; Games; Reading groups; Prayer groups; Movies; Shopping trips; Social/Cultural gatherings.

First Midlands ICMRF*
8301 Farrow Rd, Columbia, SC, 29203
Admin Curtis Murph.
Licensure Skilled care; Intermediate care. *Beds* 112.

Forest Hills Nursing Center*
2451 Forest Dr, Columbia, SC, 29204
(803) 254-5960
Admin George H Butler.
Licensure Skilled care; Intermediate care. *Beds* 146. *Certified* Medicaid; Medicare.

Lexington West Inc*
PO Box 3817, Columbia, SC, 29230
Admin Ralph E Courtney.
Licensure Intermediate care for mentally retarded. *Beds* 8. *Certified* Medicaid.
Owner Nonprofit Corp.
Admissions Requirements Minimum age; Females only 18.
Staff RNs 1 (pt); LPNs 1 (ft); Nurses aides 3 (ft), 1 (pt); Occupational therapists 1 (pt); Speech therapists 1 (pt); Dietitians 1 (pt).
Facilities Dining room; Activities room; Laundry room.
Activities Arts & crafts; Cards; Games; Prayer groups; Movies; Shopping trips; Social/Cultural gatherings.

Manor Care—Columbia Nursing Center
2601 Forest Dr, Columbia, SC, 29223
(803) 256-4983
Admin Joyce M Pyle. *Medical Dir/Dir of Nursing* Dr James Vardell.
Licensure Skilled care; Intermediate care. *Beds* 118. *Certified* Medicaid; Medicare.
Owner Proprietary Corp (Manor Care).
Admissions Requirements Minimum age 16; Medical examination.
Staff RNs 12 (ft), 8 (pt); LPNs 7 (ft), 5 (pt); Nurses aides 2 (ft); Nurses aides 40 (ft), 12 (pt); Physical therapists 1 (ft); Recreational therapists 2 (ft); Occupational therapists 1 (pt); Speech therapists 1 (pt); Activities coordinators 2 (ft); Dietitians 1 (ft).
Facilities Dining room; Physical therapy room; Activities room; Chapel; Crafts room; Laundry room; Barber/Beauty shop.
Activities Arts & crafts; Cards; Games; Reading groups; Prayer groups; Movies; Shopping trips; Social/Cultural gatherings; Reality orientation; Happy hour; Family dinners.

Midlands Center Infant Care Unit*
8301 Farrow Rd, Columbia, SC, 29203
(803) 758-4668
Admin Olieda B Ress.
Licensure Skilled care; Intermediate care. *Beds* 22. *Certified* Medicaid; Medicare.
Owner Publicly owned.

Pine Lake ICF/MR—Babcock Center
140 Flora Dr, Columbia, SC, 29223
(803) 788-7872
Admin Katharine H Bradley. *Medical Dir/Dir of Nursing* J William Pitts; JoAnn Bahelka.
Licensure Intermediate care for mentally retarded. *Beds* ICF/MR 44. *Certified* Medicaid.
Owner Nonprofit Corp.

Admissions Requirements Medical examination; Physician's request; Psychological evaluation; Social evaluation.
Staff Physicians 1 (pt); RNs 2 (ft), 1 (pt); LPNs 4 (ft); Orderlies 50 (ft); Physical therapists 2 (pt); Recreational therapists 3 (ft); Occupational therapists 1 (pt); Speech therapists 1 (pt); Dietitians 1 (pt); Dentists 1 (pt); Ophthalmologists 1 (pt); Podiatrists 1 (pt); Dentist 1 (pt); Lifeguard Secretary QMRPs 10 (ft), 10 (pt).
Languages Sign
Facilities Dining room; Physical therapy room; Activities room; Crafts room; Laundry room; Lounges; Instruction areas; Work activities center.
Activities Arts & crafts; Cards; Games; Reading groups; Movies; Shopping trips; Social/Cultural gatherings; Habilitative training.

Richland Convalescent Center*
PO Drawer 4600, 4112 Hartford St, Columbia, SC, 29240
(803) 754-4203
Admin Judith R Clark.
Licensure Intermediate care. *Beds* 152. *Certified* Medicaid; Medicare.

Second Midlands ICMRF*
8301 Farrow Rd, Columbia, SC, 29203
Admin Dorothea Friday.
Licensure Skilled care; Intermediate care. *Beds* 226. *Certified* Medicaid; Medicare.

C M Tucker Jr Human Resources Center*
2200 Harden St, Columbia, SC, 29203
(803) 758-8155
Medical Dir/Dir of Nursing Charles N Still MD.
Licensure Skilled care; Intermediate care. *Beds* SNF 100; ICF 458; Dual Certified 50. *Certified* Medicaid; Medicare.
Admissions Requirements Minimum age 18; Medical examination; Physician's request.
Staff Physicians 6 (ft), 6 (pt); RNs 24 (ft), 4 (pt); LPNs 37 (ft), 2 (pt); Nurses aides 213 (ft); Physical therapists 1 (ft); Recreational therapists 8 (ft); Occupational therapists 1 (pt); Speech therapists 1 (ft); Activities coordinators 1 (ft); Dietitians 2 (ft); Dentists 1 (pt); Audiologists 1 (ft); Pharmacists 4 (ft).
Facilities Dining room; Physical therapy room; Activities room; Crafts room; Laundry room; Barber/Beauty shop; Library.
Activities Arts & crafts; Cards; Games; Reading groups; Movies; Shopping trips; Social/Cultural gatherings.

Mary E White Developmental Center
8301 S Farrow Rd, Columbia, SC, 29203
(803) 737-7500
Admin Alice R Tollison. *Medical Dir/Dir of Nursing* Louis Gold MD; Carolyn Dukes RN.
Licensure Skilled care; Intermediate care for mentally retarded. *Beds* 112. *Certified* Medicaid; Medicare.
Owner Publicly owned.
Admissions Requirements Minimum age 18; Must be classified as mentally retarded.
Staff Physicians 1 (ft); RNs 14 (ft); LPNs 19 (ft); Nurses aides 64 (ft); Physical therapists 2 (pt); Recreational therapists 4 (pt); Occupational therapists 2 (pt); Speech therapists 2 (pt); Activities coordinators 1 (pt); Dietitians 1 (pt); Ophthalmologists 1 (pt); Podiatrists 1 (pt); Record clerk 2 (ft); Chaplain 1 (pt).
Facilities Dining room; Physical therapy room; Activities room; Chapel; Crafts room; Laundry room; Medical clinic.
Activities Arts & crafts; Games; Reading groups; Prayer groups; Movies; Shopping trips; Social/Cultural gatherings.

Woodrow Intermediate Care Facility
1625 College St, Columbia, SC, 29208
(803) 777-5178
Admin Cameron McGinnis.
Licensure Intermediate care. *Beds* 8. *Certified* Medicaid; Medicare.
Owner Publicly owned.
Admissions Requirements Minimum age College age; Medical examination; Comprehensive evaluation & interview.
Facilities Dining room; Library; All USC facilities.
Activities All student-oriented activities associated with the University of South Carolina.

CONWAY

Conway Nursing Center Inc
3300 4th Ave, Conway, SC, 29526
(803) 248-5728
Admin Melanie H Connelly. *Medical Dir/Dir of Nursing* Dr R L Ramseur; Judith Russ DON.
Licensure Skilled care; Intermediate care. *Beds* 130. *Certified* Medicaid; Medicare.
Owner Proprietary Corp.
Admissions Requirements Minimum age 12; Medical examination.
Staff RNs 5 (ft), 1 (pt); LPNs 11 (ft), 3 (pt); Nurses aides 47 (ft), 3 (pt); Physical therapists 1 (pt); Occupational therapists 1 (pt); Activities coordinators 2 (ft); Dietitians 1 (pt).
Facilities Dining room; Physical therapy room; Activities room; Crafts room; Laundry room; Barber/Beauty shop; Library.
Activities Arts & crafts; Cards; Games; Reading groups; Prayer groups; Movies; Shopping trips; Social/Cultural gatherings; Trips to restaurants & gardens.

DARLINGTON

Bethea Baptist Home*
PO Drawer 4000, Florence-Darlington Hwy, Darlington, SC, 29532
(803) 393-2867
Admin J Thomas Garrett.
Licensure Skilled care. *Beds* 88.
Owner Nonprofit Corp.

Darlington Convalescent Center*
PO Box 185, 352 Pearl St, Darlington, SC, 29532
Admin Shirley L Morse.
Licensure Intermediate care. *Beds* 44. *Certified* Medicaid; Medicare.

Oakhaven Inc
PO Box 516, 131 Oak St, Darlington, SC, 29532
(803) 393-5892
Admin Mary Lou Blackmon. *Medical Dir/Dir of Nursing* George L Timmons MD; Phyllis Morris RN DON.
Licensure Skilled care; Intermediate care. *Beds* 88. *Certified* Medicaid; Medicare; VA.
Owner Proprietary Corp.
Admissions Requirements Medical examination; Physician's request.
Staff Physicians 1 (pt); RNs 4 (ft); LPNs 8 (ft), 4 (pt); Orderlies 2 (ft); Nurses aides 30 (ft); Physical therapists 1 (pt); Occupational therapists 1 (pt); Speech therapists 1 (pt); Activities coordinators 1 (ft), 2 (pt); Dietitians 1 (pt); Ophthalmologists 1 (pt); Social worker 1 (pt).
Facilities Dining room; Activities room; Crafts room; Laundry room; Barber/Beauty shop; Van.
Activities Arts & crafts; Cards; Games; Reading groups; Prayer groups; Movies; Shopping trips; Social/Cultural gatherings; Holiday events.

DILLON

The Pines Nursing & Convalescent Home
203 Lakeside Dr, Dillon, SC, 29536
(803) 774-2741
Admin Richard C Cooke. *Medical Dir/Dir of Nursing* SC Black MD; Margaret Arnette RN.
Licensure Skilled care; Intermediate care. *Beds* SNF 84; ICF. *Certified* Medicaid; Medicare.
Owner Proprietary Corp (Beverly Enterprises).
Admissions Requirements Medical examination; Physician's request.
Staff Physicians; RNs; LPNs; Orderlies 3 (ft); Nurses aides; Physical therapists; Activities coordinators 1 (ft); Dietitians 1 (ft).
Facilities Dining room; Physical therapy room; Laundry room; Barber/Beauty shop.
Activities Arts & crafts; Games; Prayer groups; Movies; Social/Cultural gatherings.

EASLEY

Alta Vista Inc*
Anne Dr, Easley, SC, 29640
(803) 859-9754
Admin Margaret B Lollis.
Licensure Skilled care; Intermediate care. *Beds* 103. *Certified* Medicaid; Medicare.

EDGEFIELD

Edgefield Health Care Center*
PO Box 668, 1 Medical Park Dr, Edgefield, SC, 29824
(803) 637-5312
Admin Cynthia R Vann. *Medical Dir/Dir of Nursing* Dr H R Kylstra.
Licensure Intermediate care. *Beds* 81. *Certified* Medicaid; Medicare.
Owner Proprietary Corp (Stuckey Health Care).
Admissions Requirements Medical examination.
Staff RNs 3 (ft), 2 (pt); LPNs 2 (ft), 6 (pt); Nurses aides 23 (ft), 10 (pt); Physical therapists 1 (pt); Activities coordinators 1 (ft); Dietitians 6 (ft), 1 (pt).
Facilities Dining room; Physical therapy room; Laundry room; Barber/Beauty shop; TV & recreation room.
Activities Arts & crafts; Games; Prayer groups; Movies; Social/Cultural gatherings; Cookouts; Pet therapy.

ESTILL

Stiles M Harper Convalescent Center
PO Box 386, S Liberty Ave, Estill, SC, 29918
(803) 625-3852
Admin Athalene B Mole. *Medical Dir/Dir of Nursing* Marie Benton LPN.
Licensure Intermediate care. *Beds* 44. *Certified* Medicaid.
Owner Nonprofit Corp.
Admissions Requirements Medical examination; Physician's request.
Staff RNs 1 (ft), 1 (pt).
Facilities Dining room; Activities room; Laundry room; Barber/Beauty shop.
Activities Arts & crafts; Cards; Games; Reading groups; Prayer groups; Movies; Social/Cultural gatherings.

FAIRFAX

John Edward Harter Nursing Center
Hwy 278 W, Fairfax, SC, 29827
(803) 632-3334
Admin M K Hiatt. *Medical Dir/Dir of Nursing* H L Laffitte MD.
Licensure Skilled care; Intermediate care. *Beds* 44. *Certified* Medicaid; Medicare.
Owner Publicly owned.
Admissions Requirements Medical examination; Physician's request.

Staff RNs 2 (ft), 2 (pt); LPNs 5 (ft); Orderlies 3 (ft), 1 (pt); Physical therapists 1 (pt); Recreational therapists 1 (pt); Speech therapists 1 (pt); Activities coordinators 1 (ft); Dietitians 1 (ft).
Facilities Dining room; Activities room.
Activities Arts & crafts; Games; Prayer groups; Movies.

FLORENCE

Clyde Street Home*
PO Box 3209, 509 Clyde St, Florence, SC, 29502
Admin Kenneth Ward.
Licensure Intermediate care for mentally retarded. *Beds* 20. *Certified* Medicare.

Coit Street Community Residence
654 S Coit St, Florence, SC, 29501
(803) 665-0013
Admin Belinda Calcutt NHA. *Medical Dir/Dir of Nursing* Bobbie Odum RN.
Licensure Intermediate care for mentally retarded. *Beds* 8. *Certified* Medicaid.
Owner Publicly owned.
Admissions Requirements Males only; Medical examination; MR.
Staff RNs 1 (pt); LPNs 1 (pt); Recreational therapists 1 (pt); Dietitians 1 (pt); QMRP 1 (pt) Nursing Home Aide 1 (pt) Social worker 1 (pt) Unit manager 1 (pt) Direct care 5 (ft).
Facilities Dining room; Laundry room.
Activities Arts & crafts; Games; Reading groups; Movies; Shopping trips; Social/Cultural gatherings; Habilitation - Active treatment.

Commander Nursing Home*
Rte 3, Pamplico Hwy, Florence, SC, 29501
(803) 669-3502
Admin Joe Commander III.
Licensure Skilled care; Intermediate care. *Beds* 133. *Certified* Medicaid; Medicare.

Faith Health Care Facility Inc*
PO Box 908, 617 W Marion St, Florence, SC, 29503
(803) 662-5148, 669-2534
Admin Rayshaw L Gaddy.
Licensure Skilled care; Intermediate care. *Beds* 44. *Certified* Medicaid; Medicare.

Florence Convalescent Center
Clarke Rd, Florence, SC, 29501
(803) 669-4374
Admin Genevieve M Lawrence. *Medical Dir/ Dir of Nursing* Dr H H Jeter.
Licensure Intermediate care. *Beds* 88. *Certified* Medicaid.
Staff Physicians 5 (pt); RNs 2 (ft); LPNs 6 (ft), 1 (pt); Orderlies 1 (ft); Nurses aides 20 (ft); Activities coordinators 1 (ft); Dietitians 7 (pt); Social workers 1 (ft).
Facilities Dining room; Activities room; Crafts room; Laundry room; Barber/Beauty shop.
Activities Arts & crafts; Cards; Games; Reading groups; Prayer groups; Movies; Shopping trips; Social/Cultural gatherings; Cookouts.

Folk Convalescent Home*
Rte 9, Box 64, Pamplico Hwy, Florence, SC, 29501
(803) 669-4403
Admin Charles S Commander.
Licensure Intermediate care. *Beds* 88. *Certified* Medicaid; Medicare.

Heritage Home of Florence Inc*
515 S Warley St, Florence, SC, 29501
(803) 662-4573
Admin Eileen Harris.
Licensure Intermediate care. *Beds* 44. *Certified* Medicaid; Medicare.

Honorage Nursing Center*
1207 N Cashua Rd, Florence, SC, 29501
(803) 665-6212
Admin Howard W Clarke. *Medical Dir/Dir of Nursing* Harold H Jeter Jr MD.
Licensure Skilled care; Intermediate care. *Beds* 88. *Certified* Medicaid; Medicare.
Admissions Requirements Medical examination.
Staff RNs 7 (ft); LPNs 7 (ft); Orderlies 2 (ft); Nurses aides 30 (ft); Activities coordinators 1 (ft).
Facilities Dining room; Activities room; Chapel; Crafts room; Laundry room; Barber/ Beauty shop.
Activities Arts & crafts; Games; Reading groups; Prayer groups; Movies; Social/ Cultural gatherings.

Mulberry Park*
PO Box 3029, Florence, SC, 29502
Admin Kenneth Ward.
Licensure Skilled care; Intermediate care. *Beds* 112.

Pamplico Road Residence*
PO Box 3209, 801 Pamplico Hwy, Florence, SC, 29502
Admin Fred Fuller.
Licensure Intermediate care for mentally retarded. *Beds* 8. *Certified* Medicare.

Pecan Lane*
PO Box 3209, Florence, SC, 29502
Admin Kenneth Ward.
Licensure Skilled care; Intermediate care. *Beds* 160.

FORK

Sunny Acres Nursing Home Inc*
Rte 1, Box 115, Fork, SC, 29543
(803) 464-6212
Admin Tony R Cooke. *Medical Dir/Dir of Nursing* Ira Barth MD.
Licensure Skilled care; Intermediate care. *Beds* SNF 57; ICF 54. *Certified* Medicaid; Medicare.
Staff Physicians 3 (ft); RNs 4 (ft), 3 (pt); LPNs 11 (ft), 3 (pt); Orderlies 3 (ft), 1 (pt); Nurses aides 28 (ft), 4 (pt); Recreational therapists 2 (ft), 2 (pt); Dietitians 9 (ft).
Facilities Dining room; Physical therapy room; Activities room; Chapel; Crafts room; Laundry room; Barber/Beauty shop.
Activities Arts & crafts; Games; Reading groups; Prayer groups; Movies; Shopping trips; Social/Cultural gatherings.

FOUNTAIN INN

Fountain Inn Convalescent Home
PO Box 67, 501 Gulliver St, Fountain Inn, SC, 29644
(803) 862-2554, 862-2555
Admin Alan Lee Hughes. *Medical Dir/Dir of Nursing* Walter R McLawhorn MD; Cecile McFarland RN DON.
Licensure Intermediate care. *Beds* ICF 44. *Certified* Medicaid.
Owner Proprietary Corp.
Admissions Requirements Medical examination.
Staff RNs 2 (ft); LPNs 2 (ft), 1 (pt); Nurses aides 11 (ft), 2 (pt); Activities coordinators 1 (ft); Dietitians 1 (ft); Social worker 1 (ft).
Facilities Dining room; Activities room; Laundry room; Barber/Beauty shop.
Activities Arts & crafts; Cards; Games; Reading groups; Prayer groups; Movies; Social/Cultural gatherings.

GAFFNEY

Brookview House Inc*
Thompson St, Gaffney, SC, 29340
(803) 489-3101

Admin Charles L Blanton Jr. *Medical Dir/Dir of Nursing* L L DuBose MD.
Licensure Skilled care; Intermediate care. *Beds* 44. *Certified* Medicaid; Medicare.
Staff RNs 3 (ft), 4 (pt); LPNs 10 (ft), 5 (pt); Orderlies 1 (ft), 3 (pt); Nurses aides 35 (ft), 10 (pt); Activities coordinators 3 (pt); Dietitians 1 (ft).
Facilities Dining room; Activities room; Crafts room; Laundry room; Barber/Beauty shop; Library.
Activities Arts & crafts; Games; Movies; Social/Cultural gatherings.

Cherokee County Hospital—Long-Term Care Unit*
1420 N Limestone St, Gaffney, SC, 29340
(803) 487-4271
Admin Nicholas Marzocco. *Medical Dir/Dir of Nursing* W K Brumbach MD.
Licensure Skilled care; Intermediate care. *Beds* 44. *Certified* Medicaid; Medicare.
Admissions Requirements Medical examination.
Staff Physicians 9 (pt); RNs 3 (pt); LPNs 8 (pt); Orderlies 2 (pt); Nurses aides 9 (pt); Physical therapists 1 (pt); Activities coordinators 1 (ft); Dietitians 1 (ft); Dentists 1 (pt).
Facilities Dining room; Activities room; Crafts room; Barber/Beauty shop.
Activities Arts & crafts; Games; Reading groups; Prayer groups; Movies; Shopping trips; Social/Cultural gatherings; Exercise; Music groups.

J Claude Fort Community Residence
816-818 W Montgomery St, Gaffney, SC, 29340
(803) 487-4786, 489-7025
Admin J Arthur Bridges Jr. *Medical Dir/Dir of Nursing* Kathryn Humphries RN.
Licensure Intermediate care for mentally retarded. *Beds* ICF/MR 2-8. *Certified* Medicaid.
Owner Nonprofit organization/foundation.
Admissions Requirements Minimum age 10; Males only; Medical examination.
Staff RNs 1 (ft), 2 (pt); LPNs 2 (ft); Nurses aides 12 (ft), 2 (pt); Activities coordinators 1 (ft).
Facilities Dining room; Activities room; Laundry room.
Activities Arts & crafts; Cards; Games; Movies; Shopping trips; Social/Cultural gatherings; Sports.

GEORGETOWN

Winyah Extended Care Center Inc*
PO Box 8158, S Island Rd, Georgetown, SC, 29440
(803) 546-4123
Admin W William Mitchell.
Licensure Skilled care; Intermediate care. *Beds* 84. *Certified* Medicaid; Medicare.

GREENVILLE

Grady H Hipp Nursing Center*
661 Rutherford Rd, Greenville, SC, 29609
(803) 232-2442
Admin Agnes D Roe.
Licensure Skilled care; Intermediate care. *Beds* 102. *Certified* Medicaid; Medicare.

NHE—Greenville Inc*
411 Ansel St, Greenville, SC, 29601
(803) 232-5368
Admin Jane B Owings.
Licensure Skilled care; Intermediate care. *Beds* 78. *Certified* Medicaid; Medicare.
Owner Proprietary Corp (Hillhaven Corp).

Oakmont East Nursing Center*
601 Sulphur Springs Rd, Greenville, SC,
29611
(803) 246-9941
Admin Wiley M Crittenden Jr.
Licensure Skilled care; Intermediate care. *Beds*
132. *Certified* Medicaid; Medicare.

Oakmont Nursing Home*
600 Sulphur Springs Rd, Greenville, SC,
29611
(803) 246-2721
Admin David S Harper. *Medical Dir/Dir of
Nursing* W W Goodlett MD.
Licensure Intermediate care. *Beds* 125.
Certified Medicaid; Medicare.
Staff Physicians 5 (ft); LPNs 8 (ft); Nurses
aides 40 (ft); Dietitians 1 (ft).
Facilities Dining room; Activities room;
Chapel; Barber/Beauty shop.
Activities Arts & crafts; Cards; Games; Prayer
groups; Movies; Shopping trips; Social/
Cultural gatherings.

Piedmont Nursing Center Inc*
809 Laurens Rd, Greenville, SC, 29607
(803) 232-8196
Admin Otis E Ridgeway Jr.
Licensure Skilled care; Intermediate care. *Beds*
44. *Certified* Medicaid; Medicare.

Resthaven Geriatric Center*
423 Vardry St, Greenville, SC, 29601
(803) 242-4730
Admin Joan T King. *Medical Dir/Dir of
Nursing* Norris Boone MD.
Licensure Skilled care. *Beds* 30.
Admissions Requirements Minimum age 16;
Medical examination; Physician's request.
Staff RNs 1 (ft), 1 (pt); LPNs 3 (ft), 2 (pt);
Orderlies 1 (ft); Nurses aides 10 (ft), 2 (pt).
Facilities Activities room; Laundry room.
Activities Prayer groups.

Ridge Road Residence
PO Box 17007, Greenville, SC, 29606
(803) 297-0712
Admin Marian W Blackwell.
Licensure Intermediate care for mentally
retarded. *Beds* 16.

Westside Health Care
8 N Texas Ave, Greenville, SC, 29611
Admin Thelma James. *Medical Dir/Dir of
Nursing* Dr Melvin Porter MD; Bettini
Barnwell RN DON.
Licensure Dual care. *Beds* 88. *Certified*
Medicaid; Medicare.
Owner Nonprofit Corp.
Admissions Requirements Minimum age 16;
Medical examination; Physician's request.
Staff RNs 4 (ft); LPNs 5 (ft); Nurses aides 29
(ft), 2 (pt); Physical therapists 2 (ft);
Activities coordinators 2 (ft); Dietitians 1
(ft).
Facilities Dining room; Physical therapy
room; Activities room; Crafts room; Laundry
room; Barber/Beauty shop.
Activities Arts & crafts; Cards; Games; Prayer
groups; Social/Cultural gatherings.

GREENWOOD

Greenwood Community Residence*
Rte 1, Box 146, S Main St, Greenwood, SC,
29646
(803) 223-1306
Admin Vicki A Neely.
Licensure Intermediate care for mentally
retarded. *Beds* 8. *Certified* Medicare.

Greenwood Nursing Home Inc*
PO Box 3109, 437 E Cambridge Ave,
Greenwood, SC, 29646
(803) 223-1950
Admin Effie N Dorn.

Licensure Skilled care; Intermediate care. *Beds*
89. *Certified* Medicaid; Medicare.
Owner Proprietary Corp (National Health
Corp).

Nursing Center Greenwood Methodist Home
1110 Marshall Rd, Greenwood, SC, 29646
(803) 227-6655
Admin Ingrid L Speer. *Medical Dir/Dir of
Nursing* O L Thomas MD; Lillian Thomas
RN DON.
Licensure Skilled care; Intermediate care. *Beds*
102. *Certified* Medicaid; Medicare.
Owner Nonprofit Corp.
Admissions Requirements Physician's request.
Staff Physicians 1 (pt); RNs 6 (ft), 3 (pt);
LPNs 3 (ft); Orderlies 5 (ft), 5 (pt); Nurses
aides 30 (ft), 9 (pt); Physical therapists 1
(pt); Activities coordinators 3 (ft); Dietitians
1 (ft).
Affiliation Methodist
Facilities Dining room; Physical therapy
room; Activities room; Chapel; Crafts room;
Laundry room; Barber/Beauty shop.
Activities Arts & crafts; Cards; Games;
Reading groups; Prayer groups; Movies;
Shopping trips; Social/Cultural gatherings.

GREER

Greer Health Care Inc
PO Box 1148, Chandler Rd at Memorial Dr
Ext, Greer, SC, 29651
(803) 879-7474
Admin Nekoda L McCauley. *Medical Dir/Dir
of Nursing* Lewis M Davis MD; Katherine
Schuker RN DON.
Licensure Skilled care; Intermediate care. *Beds*
132. *Certified* Medicaid; Medicare.
Owner Proprietary Corp.
Admissions Requirements Minimum age 13;
Medical examination; Physician's request.
Staff Physicians 18 (pt); RNs 8 (ft); LPNs 16
(ft); Orderlies 6 (ft); Nurses aides 56 (ft);
Physical therapists 2 (pt); Recreational
therapists 1 (pt); Occupational therapists 1
(pt); Speech therapists 1 (pt); Activities
coordinators 1 (ft); Dietitians 2 (ft);
Ophthalmologists 1 (pt); Podiatrists 1 (pt);
Dental 1 (pt); Psychiatrist 1 (pt); Social
workers 2 (ft).
Facilities Dining room; Physical therapy
room; Activities room; Crafts room; Laundry
room; Barber/Beauty shop; Library.
Activities Arts & crafts; Cards; Games;
Reading groups; Prayer groups; Movies;
Shopping trips; Social/Cultural gatherings;
Music therapy.

Roger Huntington Nursing Center
PO Box 1149, Greer, SC, 29652
(803) 879-0200
Admin Michael W Massey. *Medical Dir/Dir of
Nursing* Martha H Armstrong MD.
Licensure Skilled care; Intermediate care;
Dual. *Beds* 88. *Certified* Medicaid;
Medicare.
Owner Nonprofit Corp.
Admissions Requirements Medical
examination; Physician's request.
Staff RNs 6 (ft), 1 (pt); LPNs 5 (ft), 3 (pt);
Orderlies 3 (ft), 1 (pt); Nurses aides 18 (ft),
11 (pt); Activities coordinators 1 (ft);
Dietitians 1 (ft).
Facilities Dining room; Activities room;
Laundry room; Barber/Beauty shop.
Activities Arts & crafts; Games; Prayer groups;
Movies; Shopping trips.

HARTSVILLE

Morrell Memorial Convalescent Center Inc
PO Box 1318, Hartsville, SC, 29550
(803) 383-5164
Admin Thomas S Stewart. *Medical Dir/Dir of
Nursing* Dr Darrel Gant; Marcia B Stegner
DON.

Licensure Skilled care; Intermediate care. *Beds*
132. *Certified* Medicaid; Medicare.
Admissions Requirements Medical
examination; Physician's request.
Staff Physicians 1 (ft); RNs 3 (ft), 1 (pt);
LPNs 14 (ft), 3 (pt); Orderlies 9 (ft); Nurses
aides 48 (ft), 1 (pt); Activities coordinators 1
(ft).
Facilities Dining room; Physical therapy
room; Activities room; Chapel; Crafts room;
Laundry room; Barber/Beauty shop.
Activities Arts & crafts; Cards; Games;
Reading groups; Prayer groups.

Thad E Saleeby Developmental Center
714 Lewellen Ave, Hartsville, SC, 29550
(803) 332-4104
Admin Dr Brent J Koyle. *Medical Dir/Dir of
Nursing* James O Morphis, Jesse T Cox MD;
Celia Hinds RN DON.
Licensure Skilled care; Intermediate care for
mentally retarded. *Beds* 132. *Certified*
Medicare.
Owner Publicly owned.
Admissions Requirements Medical
examination.
Staff Physicians 2 (ft); Physical therapists 1
(pt); Recreational therapists 1 (ft);
Occupational therapists 1 (pt); Speech
therapists 1 (ft); Activities coordinators 1
(ft); Dietitians 1 (ft); Dentists 1 (pt);
Podiatrists 1 (pt).
Facilities Dining room; Physical therapy
room; Activities room; Crafts room; Laundry
room; Barber/Beauty shop; Library.
Activities Arts & crafts; Games; Reading
groups; Movies; Shopping trips; Social/
Cultural gatherings.

HILTON HEAD ISLAND

Hilton Head Center of South Carolina Inc*
PO Box 4926, Hilton Head Island, SC, 29938
Admin Stephani G Johnson. *Medical Dir/Dir
of Nursing* Dr Paul Long.
Licensure Skilled care; Intermediate care. *Beds*
44. *Certified* Medicaid; Medicare.
Owner Publicly owned.
Admissions Requirements Medical
examination.
Staff Physicians 7 (pt); RNs 3 (ft), 3 (pt);
LPNs 3 (ft), 5 (pt); Orderlies 2 (ft); Nurses
aides 20 (ft), 5 (pt); Physical therapists 1
(pt); Reality therapists 1 (pt); Recreational
therapists 1 (ft); Occupational therapists 1
(pt); Speech therapists 1 (pt); Activities
coordinators 1 (pt); Dietitians 1 (ft); Dentists
1 (pt); Podiatrists 1 (pt); Audiologists 1 (pt).
Facilities Dining room; Activities room;
Laundry room; Barber/Beauty shop.
Activities Arts & crafts; Cards; Games;
Reading groups; Prayer groups; Shopping
trips.

The Seabrook of Hilton Head Annex
300 Woodhaven Dr, Hilton Head Island, SC,
29928
(803) 842-3747
Admin Annette R Martin. *Medical Dir/Dir of
Nursing* J Cattell MD; Carol Abbott DON.
Licensure Skilled care; Intermediate care. *Beds*
44. *Certified* Medicare.
Owner Nonprofit organization/foundation.
Admissions Requirements Minimum age 65;
Medical examination.
Staff Physicians 1 (pt); RNs 2 (ft), 2 (pt);
LPNs 4 (ft), 4 (pt); Nurses aides 15 (ft), 10
(pt); Physical therapists 1 (pt); Recreational
therapists 1 (pt); Speech therapists 1 (pt);
Activities coordinators 1 (ft);
Ophthalmologists 1 (pt).
Facilities Dining room; Physical therapy
room; Activities room; Crafts room; Laundry
room; Barber/Beauty shop; Library;
Auditorium.

Activities Arts & crafts; Cards; Games;
Reading groups; Prayer groups; Movies;
Shopping trips; Social/Cultural gatherings;
Concerts; Classes.

HOPKINS

Stanton Pines Inc
PO Box 241, 124 Ridge Rd, Rte 2, Hopkins,
SC, 29061
(803) 776-3536
Admin James E Stanton. *Medical Dir/Dir of
Nursing* Daisy N Stanton RN.
Licensure Intermediate care. *Beds* ICF 26.
Owner Proprietary Corp.
Admissions Requirements Medical
examination; Physician's request.
Staff Physicians 1 (ft); RNs 1 (ft); LPNs 1 (ft);
Nurses aides 12 (ft); Dietitians 1 (ft).
Facilities Dining room; Activities room;
Laundry room; Barber/Beauty shop.
Activities Cards; Games; Prayer groups;
Movies.

INMAN

Camp Care Inc*
PO Box 847, Inman, SC, 29349
(803) 472-2028
Admin Carole N Camp. *Medical Dir/Dir of
Nursing* Dr Thomas Malone.
Licensure Intermediate care. *Beds* 88.
Certified Medicaid; Medicare.
Staff Physicians 1 (pt); RNs 1 (ft); LPNs 8
(ft), 2 (pt); Nurses aides 24 (ft), 3 (pt);
Recreational therapists 1 (ft); Activities
coordinators 1 (ft); Dietitians 1 (pt); Dentists
1 (pt).
Facilities Dining room; Activities room;
Crafts room; Laundry room; Barber/Beauty
shop.
Activities Arts & crafts; Games; Prayer groups;
Movies; Shopping trips; Social/Cultural
gatherings.

Camphaven Nursing Home*
Rte 4, Box 1, Blackstock Rd, Inman, SC,
29349
(803) 472-9055
Admin W R Camp.
Licensure Skilled care; Intermediate care. *Beds*
176. *Certified* Medicaid; Medicare.

Inman Nursing Home
PO Box 266, 51 N Main St, Inman, SC,
29349
(803) 472-9370
Admin H Wayne Johnson. *Medical Dir/Dir of
Nursing* Dr Barry Henderson; Lisa Laughter
RN DON.
Licensure Skilled care; Intermediate care. *Beds*
SNF 40; ICF. *Certified* Medicaid; Medicare.
Owner Privately owned.
Admissions Requirements Medical
examination; Physician's request.
Staff Physicians 1 (pt); RNs 1 (ft), 2 (pt);
LPNs 3 (ft), 2 (pt); Nurses aides 15 (ft), 7
(pt); Activities coordinators 1 (ft), 1 (pt);
Dietitians 1 (ft), 1 (pt).
Facilities Dining room; Activities room;
Laundry room; Barber/Beauty shop.
Activities Arts & crafts; Cards; Games;
Reading groups.

C W Johnson Intermediate Care Facility
82 N Main St, Inman, SC, 29349
(803) 472-6636
Admin Timothy A Johnson. *Medical Dir/Dir
of Nursing* Barry H Henderson.
Licensure Intermediate care. *Beds* ICF 44.
Certified Medicaid.
Owner Proprietary Corp.
Admissions Requirements Minimum age 21;
Medical examination; Physician's request.
Staff Physicians 1 (pt); RNs 1 (pt); LPNs 4
(ft), 1 (pt); Orderlies 1 (ft); Nurses aides 8
(ft), 6 (pt); Activities coordinators 1 (ft).

Facilities Dining room; Activities room;
Barber/Beauty shop.
Activities Arts & crafts; Cards; Games; Prayer
groups; Shopping trips.

IVA

Golden Acres Intermediate Care Facility
PO Box 505, Iva, SC, 29655
(803) 348-7433
Admin Loneta L Dunn. *Medical Dir/Dir of
Nursing* Gregory Baird MD.
Licensure Intermediate care. *Beds* ICF 26.
Certified Medicaid.
Owner Proprietary Corp.
Admissions Requirements Physician's request.
Staff Physicians 2 (pt); RNs 1 (ft), 1 (pt);
LPNs 2 (ft), 1 (pt); Nurses aides 8 (ft), 2
(pt); Physical therapists 1 (pt); Activities
coordinators 1 (ft); Dietitians 1 (pt);
Ophthalmologists 1 (pt).
Facilities Dining room; Activities room;
Chapel; Crafts room; Laundry room; Barber/
Beauty shop.
Activities Arts & crafts; Cards; Games;
Reading groups; Prayer groups; Movies;
Shopping trips; Social/Cultural gatherings.

JOHNS ISLAND

Hermina Traeye Memorial Nursing Home
PO Box 689, Johns Island, SC, 29455
(803) 559-5501
Admin Mary F Brown. *Medical Dir/Dir of
Nursing* Allen Rashford MD; Karen Klein
DON.
Licensure Skilled care; Intermediate care. *Beds*
SNF 44; ICF 44. *Certified* Medicaid;
Medicare.
Owner Nonprofit Corp.
Admissions Requirements Medical
examination.
Staff Physicians 2 (pt); RNs 3 (ft); LPNs 8
(ft), 3 (pt); Nurses aides 27 (ft); Physical
therapists 1 (pt); Activities coordinators 2
(ft); Dietitians 1 (pt).
Facilities Dining room; Physical therapy
room; Activities room; Crafts room; Laundry
room; Barber/Beauty shop.
Activities Arts & crafts; Games; Reading
groups; Prayer groups; Movies; Shopping
trips; Social/Cultural gatherings.

KINGSTREE

Kingstree Community Residence
Frierson Homes, 1037-"B" Lexington St,
Kingstree, SC, 29556
(803) 354-9670 or 354-9679
Admin John H Hines.
Licensure Intermediate care for mentally
retarded. *Beds* ICF/MR 14. *Certified*
Medicaid; Medicare.
Owner Publicly owned.
Admissions Requirements Minimum age 45.
Staff Physicians 1 (pt); RNs 1 (pt); LPNs 2
(ft), 3 (pt); Physical therapists 1 (pt);
Occupational therapists 1 (pt); Speech
therapists 1 (pt); Dietitians 1 (pt); Dentists 1
(pt).
Activities Work skills; Training in ADL,
mobility, community awareness.

Kingstree Nursing Facility Inc*
PO Box 359, 110 Mill St, Kingstree, SC,
29556
(803) 354-6116
Admin Carlyle Cooke.
Licensure Skilled care; Intermediate care. *Beds*
44. *Certified* Medicaid; Medicare.

LADSOM

Coastal Center—Live Oak Village*
12 Jamison Rd, Ladsom, SC, 29456
(803) 871-2335

Admin Chanson A Wieters.
Licensure Skilled care; Intermediate care. *Beds*
50.

LADSON

**South Carolina Department of Mental
Retardation-Coastal Regional Center**
Jamison Rd, Ladson, SC, 29456
(803) 873-5750
Admin Erbert F Cicenia Ed Dir. *Medical Dir/
Dir of Nursing* John D Fletcher MD; Mary
Christensen RN DON.
Licensure Skilled care; Intermediate care;
Intermediate care for mentally retarded.
Beds SNF 125; ICF; ICF/MR 342 Includes
16-bed facility in the community. *Certified*
Medicaid.
Owner Publicly owned.
Admissions Requirements Medical
examination.
Staff Physicians 2 (ft); RNs 18 (ft); LPNs 45
(ft); Nurses aides 351 (ft) Mental retardation
specialists; Physical therapists 1 (ft);
Recreational therapists 12 (ft); Occupational
therapists 2 (ft); Speech therapists 4 (ft);
Dietitians 2 (ft).
Facilities Dining room; Physical therapy
room; Activities room; Library; Gymnasium.
Activities Arts & crafts; Games; Movies;
Shopping trips; Social/Cultural gatherings;
Pony carts; Annual summer camp; Rhythm
band; Chorus.

LANCASTER

Lancaster County Care Center
Rte 10 Box 379, Hwy 9 E, Lancaster, SC,
29720
(803) 285-7907
Admin Kent Clary. *Medical Dir/Dir of
Nursing* Lee Thomas MD; Frances Jones
RN DON.
Licensure Skilled care; Intermediate care. *Beds*
SNF 44; ICF 66. *Certified* Medicaid;
Medicare.
Owner Publicly owned.
Admissions Requirements Medical
examination; Physician's request.
Staff Physicians 3 (pt); RNs 4 (ft); LPNs 12
(ft), 4 (pt); Nurses aides 38 (ft), 12 (pt);
Physical therapists 1 (pt); Activities
coordinators 2 (ft); Dietitians 2 (pt).
Facilities Dining room; Physical therapy
room; Activities room; Laundry room;
Barber/Beauty shop.
Activities Arts & crafts; Games; Reading
groups; Prayer groups; Movies; Shopping
trips; Social/Cultural gatherings.

Marion Sims Nursing Center*
800 W Meeting St, Lancaster, SC, 29720
(803) 285-4311
Admin Dace W Jones Jr.
Licensure Skilled care; Intermediate care. *Beds*
111. *Certified* Medicaid; Medicare.

LAURENS

Martha Franks Baptist Retirement Center
1 Martha Franks Dr, Laurens, SC, 29360-1799
(803) 984-4541
Admin Joe R Babb. *Medical Dir/Dir of
Nursing* Linda B Nelson.
Licensure Skilled care; Retirement center.
Beds 122.
Owner Nonprofit Corp.
Admissions Requirements Minimum age 65;
Medical examination; Must be ambulatory.
Staff Physicians; RNs; LPNs; Orderlies;
Nurses aides; Physical therapists.
Affiliation Baptist
Facilities Dining room; Physical therapy
room; Activities room; Chapel; Crafts room;
Laundry room; Barber/Beauty shop; Library.

Activities Arts & crafts; Cards; Games; Prayer groups; Movies; Shopping trips.

Laurens Nursing Center
Rt 5 Box 526, 301 Pinehaven St Ext, Laurens, SC, 29360
(803) 984-6584
Admin J B Kinney Jr. *Medical Dir/Dir of Nursing* Julian Atkinson MD; Kathy W Cheely RN DON.
Licensure Skilled care; Intermediate care. *Beds* SNF 88; ICF 44. *Certified* Medicaid; Medicare; VA.
Owner Proprietary Corp (National Health Corp).
Admissions Requirements Minimum age 18; Medical examination; Physician's request.
Staff Physicians 12 (pt); RNs 4 (ft), 4 (pt); LPNs 9 (ft), 2 (pt); Orderlies 6 (ft), 2 (pt); Nurses aides 26 (ft), 3 (pt); Physical therapists 1 (pt); Speech therapists 1 (pt); Activities coordinators 1 (ft); Dietitians 1 (ft); Podiatrists 1 (pt).
Facilities Dining room; Physical therapy room; Activities room; Chapel; Crafts room; Laundry room; Barber/Beauty shop; Library.
Activities Arts & crafts; Games; Reading groups; Prayer groups; Movies; Shopping trips; Social/Cultural gatherings.

LEXINGTON

Lexington Clusters
201 Duffie Dr, Lexington, SC, 29072
(803) 359-1509
Admin B Terrell Ball. *Medical Dir/Dir of Nursing* Joann Bahelka.
Licensure Intermediate care for mentally retarded. *Beds* ICF/MR 48. *Certified* Medicare.
Owner Nonprofit Corp.
Admissions Requirements Minimum age 18; Males only.
Staff Physicians 1 (pt); RNs 2 (pt); LPNs 5 (ft), 2 (pt); Physical therapists 1 (pt); Recreational therapists 2 (ft); Occupational therapists 1 (pt); Speech therapists 1 (ft); Dietitians 1 (pt); Dentists 1 (pt); Podiatrists 1 (pt); Mental retardation specialists.
Languages Sign
Facilities Dining room; Activities room; Laundry room.
Activities Arts & crafts; Cards; Games; Prayer groups; Movies; Shopping trips; Social/Cultural gatherings.

Rikard Nursing Home—Rikard Convalescent Bldg*
PO 517, Old Cherokee Rd, Lexington, SC, 29072
(803) 359-5181
Admin Melvin Ellis.
Licensure Skilled care; Intermediate care. *Beds* 63. *Certified* Medicaid; Medicare.

Rikard Nursing Homes—Keisler & Holstedt Bldgs*
PO Box 517, Lexington, SC, 29072
(803) 359-5181
Admin Joseph D Wright.
Licensure Skilled care; Intermediate care. *Beds* 212. *Certified* Medicaid; Medicare.

LORIS

Loris Hospital—Extended Care Facility
3212 Casey St, Loris, SC, 29569
(803) 756-4011
Admin Frank M Watts. *Medical Dir/Dir of Nursing* W H Johnson MD; Ovaline Barberousse.
Licensure Skilled care; Intermediate care. *Beds* 40. *Certified* Medicaid; Medicare.
Owner Publicly owned.
Admissions Requirements Medical examination.

Staff RNs 3 (ft); LPNs 6 (ft), 2 (pt); Orderlies 4 (ft), 1 (pt); Nurses aides 15 (ft); Activities coordinators 1 (ft).
Facilities Dining room; Activities room; Laundry room; Barber/Beauty shop.
Activities Arts & crafts; Cards; Games.

MANNING

Briggs Nursing Home*
Rte 3, Box 265, Manning, SC, 29102
Admin Jerry E Spann.
Licensure Skilled care; Intermediate care. *Beds* 38. *Certified* Medicare.

MARIETTA

Stroud Memorial Intermediate Care Facility
PO Box 216, Hwy 276, Marietta, SC, 29661
(803) 836-6381
Admin Earlene G Jones. *Medical Dir/Dir of Nursing* James E Barnett; Nelle B Taylor RN DON.
Licensure Intermediate care. *Beds* ICF 44. *Certified* Medicaid.
Admissions Requirements Medical examination.
Staff RNs 2 (ft); LPNs 4 (ft); Nurses aides 10 (ft), 2 (pt); Recreational therapists 1 (ft), 1 (pt); Activities coordinators 1 (ft), 1 (pt); Dietitians 1 (ft).
Facilities Dining room; Activities room; Chapel; Crafts room; Laundry room; Barber/Beauty shop.
Activities Arts & crafts; Cards; Games; Reading groups; Prayer groups; Movies.

MARION

Jenkins Nursing Home Inc
PO Box 917, 401 Murray St, Marion, SC, 29571
(803) 423-6947
Admin Simon M Jenkins.
Licensure Skilled care; Intermediate care. *Beds* 22. *Certified* Medicaid; Medicare.

Marion County Convalescent Center*
PO Drawer 1106, Hwy 501, Marion, SC, 29571
(803) 423-2601
Admin Crystal H Isom.
Licensure Skilled care; Intermediate care. *Beds* 62. *Certified* Medicaid; Medicare.
Owner Proprietary Corp (National Healthcare).

MONCKS CORNER

Berkeley Convalescent Center
PO Box 1467, Moncks Corner, SC, 29461
(803) 761-8368
Admin Richard L Ellickson. *Medical Dir/Dir of Nursing* John Fletcher MD; Jan Polkow RN DON.
Licensure Skilled care; Intermediate care. *Beds* SNF 44; ICF 88. *Certified* Medicaid; Medicare.
Owner Proprietary Corp.
Admissions Requirements Physician's request.
Facilities Dining room; Physical therapy room; Activities room; Crafts room; Laundry room; Barber/Beauty shop.
Activities Arts & crafts; Cards; Games; Reading groups; Prayer groups; Movies; Shopping trips; Social/Cultural gatherings.

MOUNT PLEASANT

Cooper Hall Nursing Center
921 Bowman Rd, Mount Pleasant, SC, 29464
(803) 884-8903
Admin James B Connelly. *Medical Dir/Dir of Nursing* George G Durst Sr MD.

Licensure Skilled care; Intermediate care. *Beds* SNF 132; ICF. *Certified* Medicaid; Medicare.
Owner Proprietary Corp.
Admissions Requirements Medical examination; Physician's request.
Staff Physicians 1 (pt); RNs 6 (ft), 3 (pt); LPNs 8 (ft), 4 (pt); Nurses aides 46 (ft); Physical therapists 1 (pt); Recreational therapists 1 (pt); Occupational therapists 1 (pt); Speech therapists 1 (pt); Activities coordinators 2 (ft); Dietitians 1 (ft).
Facilities Dining room; Physical therapy room; Activities room; Laundry room; Barber/Beauty shop.
Activities Arts & crafts; Cards; Games; Reading groups; Prayer groups; Movies; Shopping trips; Social/Cultural gatherings.

Sandpiper Convalescent Center*
1049 Anna Knapp Blvd, Mount Pleasant, SC, 29464
Admin Richard Poole.
Licensure Skilled care. *Beds* 88. *Certified* Medicaid.

MYRTLE BEACH

Myrtle Beach Manor*
PO Box 7337, Hwy 17 N, Myrtle Beach, SC, 29577
(803) 449-5283
Admin Juana C Newber.
Licensure Skilled care; Intermediate care. *Beds* 50. *Certified* Medicaid; Medicare.
Owner Proprietary Corp (Forum Grp).

Sandstrom Home Intermediate Care Facility*
6309-11 Hawthorne Ln, Myrtle Beach, SC, 29577
(803) 449-5615
Admin Grace Sandstrom.
Licensure Intermediate care. *Beds* 30. *Certified* Medicaid.
Admissions Requirements Minimum age 30; Medical examination.
Staff RNs 1 (ft), 1 (pt); LPNs 4 (ft); Orderlies 1 (ft); Nurses aides 14 (ft); Activities coordinators 1 (ft).
Facilities Dining room; Activities room; Laundry room; Barber/Beauty shop.
Activities Arts & crafts; Cards; Games; Prayer groups; Shopping trips.

NEWBERRY

J F Hawkins Nursing Home
1330 Kinard St, Newberry, SC, 29108
(803) 276-2601
Admin Fred K Taylor. *Medical Dir/Dir of Nursing* James A Underwood Jr MD.
Licensure Skilled care; Intermediate care. *Beds* 78. *Certified* Medicaid; Medicare.
Owner Nonprofit Corp.
Admissions Requirements Medical examination.
Staff RNs 5 (ft); LPNs 8 (ft), 3 (pt); Orderlies 1 (ft); Nurses aides 34 (ft); Activities coordinators 2 (ft); Dietitians 1 (ft).
Facilities Dining room; Activities room; Chapel; Crafts room; Barber/Beauty shop; Dayrooms.
Activities Arts & crafts; Games; Reading groups; Prayer groups; Social/Cultural gatherings; Outings.

Newberry Convalescent Center
Kinard St, Newberry, SC, 29108
(803) 276-6060
Admin Edith C Goforth. *Medical Dir/Dir of Nursing* Dr E E Epting.
Licensure Skilled care; Intermediate care. *Beds* 44. *Certified* Medicaid; Medicare.
Admissions Requirements Medical examination; Physician's request.

Staff RNs 4 (ft), 3 (pt); LPNs 4 (ft), 1 (pt); Nurses aides 26 (ft); Recreational therapists 1 (ft); Activities coordinators 1 (ft); Dietitians; Dentists.
Facilities Dining room; Activities room; Laundry room; Barber/Beauty shop.
Activities Arts & crafts; Games; Reading groups; Prayer groups; Social/Cultural gatherings.

ORANGEBURG

Amelia Community Residence
550 Amelia St, Orangeburg, SC, 29115
(803) 534-1615
Admin Dorothy Hartzog. *Medical Dir/Dir of Nursing* Sandee Gingrich RN.
Licensure Intermediate care for mentally retarded. *Beds* ICF/MR 8. *Certified* Medicaid.
Owner Nonprofit organization/foundation.
Admissions Requirements Minimum age 15; Males only; Medical examination.
Staff Physicians 1 (pt); RNs 1 (ft); LPNs 2 (ft); Nurses aides 3 (ft), 3 (pt); Physical therapists 1 (pt); Recreational therapists 1 (ft); Occupational therapists 1 (pt); Speech therapists 1 (pt); Activities coordinators 1 (ft); Dietitians 1 (pt); Dentists 1 (pt); Ophthalmologists 1 (pt); Podiatrists 1 (pt).
Facilities Dining room; Laundry room.
Activities Arts & crafts; Games; Movies; Shopping trips; Social/Cultural gatherings.

Boulevard Community Residence
612 Boulevard NE, Orangeburg, SC, 29115
(803) 536-1361
Admin Dorothy Hartzog. *Medical Dir/Dir of Nursing* Sandee Gingrich RN.
Licensure Intermediate care for mentally retarded. *Beds* ICF/MR 8. *Certified* Medicaid.
Owner Nonprofit organization/foundation.
Admissions Requirements Minimum age 15; Females only.
Staff Physicians 1 (pt); RNs 1 (ft); LPNs 2 (ft); Nurses aides 3 (ft), 3 (pt); Physical therapists 1 (pt); Recreational therapists 1 (ft); Occupational therapists 1 (pt); Speech therapists 1 (pt); Activities coordinators 1 (ft); Dietitians 1 (pt); Dentists 1 (pt); Ophthalmologists 1 (pt); Podiatrists 1 (pt).
Facilities Dining room; Laundry room.
Activities Arts & crafts; Games; Movies; Shopping trips; Social/Cultural gatherings.

Edisto Convalescent Center
500 Enterprise St SW, Orangeburg, SC, 29115
(803) 534-7771
Admin Ervin A Green. *Medical Dir/Dir of Nursing* Elizabeth O Green RN DON.
Licensure Skilled care; Intermediate care. *Beds* SNF 43; ICF 43. *Certified* Medicaid; Medicare.
Owner Proprietary Corp.
Admissions Requirements Medical examination.
Facilities Dining room; Activities room; Crafts room; Laundry room; Barber/Beauty shop.
Activities Arts & crafts; Cards; Games; Reading groups; Prayer groups; Movies; Social/Cultural gatherings.

Jolley Acres Nursing Home Inc
PO Drawer 1909, 1180 Wolfe Trail SW, Orangeburg, SC, 29115
(803) 534-1001
Admin Jimmie E Boland.
Licensure Skilled care; Intermediate care. *Beds* 43. *Certified* Medicaid; Medicare.

The Methodist Home
PO Box 327, Orangeburg, SC, 29116-0327
(803) 534-1212
Admin Rev C Burton Sheffield. *Medical Dir/Dir of Nursing* Vann Beth Shuler MD; James Brunson MD.

Licensure Skilled care; Intermediate care. *Beds* SNF 132; ICF. *Certified* Medicaid; Medicare.
Owner Nonprofit organization/foundation.
Admissions Requirements Minimum age 62; Medical examination.
Staff Physicians; RNs; LPNs; Orderlies; Nurses aides; Physical therapists; Reality therapists; Recreational therapists; Occupational therapists; Speech therapists; Activities coordinators; Dietitians; Dentists; Ophthalmologists; Podiatrists.
Affiliation Methodist
Facilities Dining room; Physical therapy room; Activities room; Chapel; Crafts room; Laundry room; Barber/Beauty shop; Library.
Activities Arts & crafts; Cards; Games; Reading groups; Prayer groups; Movies; Shopping trips; Social/Cultural gatherings.

Orangeburg Nursing Home
755 Whitman SE, Orangeburg, SC, 29115
(803) 534-7036
Admin Catherine D Young. *Medical Dir/Dir of Nursing* W O Whetsell MD.
Licensure Skilled care; Intermediate care. *Beds* 73. *Certified* Medicaid; Medicare.
Admissions Requirements Medical examination; Physician's request.
Staff Physicians 5 (pt); RNs 4 (ft), 5 (pt); LPNs 3 (ft), 4 (pt); Nurses aides 23 (ft), 7 (pt); Physical therapists 1 (pt); Speech therapists 1 (pt); Activities coordinators 1 (ft); Dietitians 1 (pt); Dentists 1 (pt).
Facilities Dining room; Laundry room; Barber/Beauty shop.
Activities Arts & crafts; Cards; Games; Reading groups; Prayer groups; Movies; Shopping trips; Social/Cultural gatherings.

PALMETTO

South Carolina Crippled Children's Convalescent Center*
2310 W Palmetto St, Palmetto, SC, 29502
(803) 669-0931
Admin Dorothy M Asman.
Licensure Skilled care; Intermediate care. *Beds* 44.

PICKENS

Laurel Hill Nursing Center Inc
PO Box 972, Pickens, SC, 29671
(803) 878-4739
Admin W Bird Lewis. *Medical Dir/Dir of Nursing* David W Mauldin; Christine Wood.
Licensure Skilled care; Intermediate care. *Beds* 80. *Certified* Medicaid; Medicare.
Owner Proprietary Corp.
Admissions Requirements Medical examination; Physician's request.
Staff RNs 2 (ft), 2 (pt); LPNs 7 (ft), 4 (pt); Nurses aides 24 (ft), 9 (pt); Activities coordinators 1 (ft).
Facilities Dining room; Physical therapy room; Activities room; Chapel; Crafts room; Laundry room; Barber/Beauty shop.
Activities Arts & crafts; Cards; Games; Reading groups; Prayer groups; Movies; Social/Cultural gatherings.

McKinney Intensive Care Facility
PO Box 895, 113 Rosemond St, Pickens, SC, 29671
(803) 878-2266
Admin Iris L Robinson.
Licensure Intermediate care. *Beds* 44. *Certified* Medicaid; Medicare.

PORT ROYAL

Port Royal Community Residence
1508 Old Shell Rd, Port Royal, SC, 29935
(803) 524-3001
Admin Wilson Inabinet Jr.

Licensure Intermediate care for mentally retarded. *Beds* ICF/MR 16. *Certified* Medicaid.
Owner Nonprofit organization/foundation.
Admissions Requirements Minimum age 17; Medical examination; Physician's request; Certification as MR.
Staff Physicians 1 (pt); RNs 1 (pt); LPNs 2 (ft); Speech therapists 1 (pt); Dietitians 1 (pt); Podiatrists 1 (pt); MRSPsychologist 1 (pt).
Facilities Dining room; Activities room; Laundry room.
Activities Arts & crafts; Games; Shopping trips; Social/Cultural gatherings; Skill training.

RIDGELAND

Ridgecrest Convalescent Center
PO Box 1570, Grays Rd, Hwy 278, Ridgeland, SC, 29936
(803) 726-5581
Admin Faye Cleland.
Licensure Skilled care; Intermediate care. *Beds* 88. *Certified* Medicaid; Medicare.

RIDGEWAY

Fairfield Homes*
PO Drawer 157, Longtown Rd, Ridgeway, SC, 29130
(803) 337-2257
Admin Annette B Cooper.
Licensure Intermediate care. *Beds* 112. *Certified* Medicaid; Medicare.

Tanglewood Health Care Center*
PO Drawer 68, Third St, Ridgeway, SC, 29130
(803) 337-3211
Admin James R Fulmer. *Medical Dir/Dir of Nursing* J E Campbell MD.
Licensure Intermediate care. *Beds* 150. *Certified* Medicaid; Medicare.
Owner Proprietary Corp (Wessex Corp).
Admissions Requirements Minimum age 35; Medical examination.
Staff Physicians 1 (pt); RNs 1 (ft), 1 (pt); LPNs 10 (ft), 7 (pt); Orderlies 8 (ft); Nurses aides 37 (ft), 4 (pt); Activities coordinators 2 (ft); Dietitians 1 (pt); Dentists 1 (pt); Ophthalmologists 1 (pt); Podiatrists 1 (pt); Audiologists 1 (pt).
Facilities Dining room; Activities room; Chapel; Crafts room; Laundry room; Barber/Beauty shop; Library.
Activities Arts & crafts; Cards; Games; Prayer groups; Movies; Shopping trips; Social/Cultural gatherings.

ROCK HILL

Magnolia Manor North
127 Murrah Dr, Rock Hill, SC, 29730
(803) 328-6518
Admin J David Niday. *Medical Dir/Dir of Nursing* Patricia Blanton.
Licensure Intermediate care. *Beds* 62. *Certified* Medicaid.
Owner Proprietary Corp.
Admissions Requirements Minimum age 18; Medical examination; Physician's request.
Staff RNs 1 (pt); LPNs 6 (ft), 6 (pt); Nurses aides 20 (ft), 12 (pt); Physical therapists 1 (pt); Recreational therapists 1 (pt); Occupational therapists 1 (pt); Speech therapists 1 (pt); Activities coordinators 1 (ft); Dietitians 1 (pt); Ophthalmologists 1 (pt).
Facilities Dining room; Physical therapy room; Activities room; Crafts room; Laundry room; Barber/Beauty shop.
Activities Arts & crafts; Cards; Games; Prayer groups; Movies; Shopping trips; Social/Cultural gatherings.

Magnolia Manor North
127 Murrah Dr, Rock Hill, SC, 29730
(803) 328-6518
Admin J David Niday. *Medical Dir/Dir of Nursing* Patricia Blanton DON.
Licensure Intermediate care. *Beds* ICF 62. *Certified* Medicaid.
Owner Proprietary Corp.
Admissions Requirements Medical examination; Physician's request.
Staff RNs 1 (pt); LPNs 4 (ft), 4 (pt); Nurses aides 16 (ft), 8 (pt); Activities coordinators 1 (ft); Dietitians 1 (pt).
Facilities Dining room; Physical therapy room; Activities room; Chapel; Crafts room; Laundry room; Barber/Beauty shop.
Activities Arts & crafts; Games; Reading groups; Prayer groups; Movies; Shopping trips; Social/Cultural gatherings; Happy hour.

Meadow Haven Nursing Center
205 S Herlong Ave, Rock Hill, SC, 29730
(803) 366-7133
Admin James J Burke. *Medical Dir/Dir of Nursing* J Luke Lentz; Lois Cox DON.
Licensure Skilled care; Intermediate care. *Beds* SNF 44; ICF 88. *Certified* Medicaid; Medicare.
Owner Proprietary Corp (Beverly Enterprises).
Admissions Requirements Medical examination.
Facilities Dining room; Physical therapy room; Activities room; Crafts room; Laundry room; Barber/Beauty shop.
Activities Arts & crafts; Cards; Games; Reading groups; Prayer groups; Movies; Shopping trips; Social/Cultural gatherings.

Rock Hill Convalescent Center
1915 Ebenezer Rd, Rock Hill, SC, 29730
(803) 366-8155
Admin Stephanie G Johnson. *Medical Dir/Dir of Nursing* Dr Robert Patton; Sharlene Plyler RN.
Licensure Skilled care; Intermediate care. *Beds* 141. *Certified* Medicaid; Medicare.
Owner Proprietary Corp (White Oak Manor Inc).
Staff RNs 4 (ft), 2 (pt); LPNs 15 (ft), 1 (pt); Orderlies 5 (ft); Nurses aides 51 (ft), 10 (pt); Physical therapists 2 (ft); Activities coordinators 1 (ft); Dietitians 1 (ft).
Facilities Dining room; Physical therapy room; Activities room; Laundry room; Barber/Beauty shop.
Activities Arts & crafts; Cards; Games; Reading groups; Prayer groups; Movies; Shopping trips; Social/Cultural gatherings.

SAINT GEORGE

St George Health Care Center Inc*
PO Box 187, Saint George, SC, 29477
Admin William M Rogers Sr.
Licensure Skilled care. *Beds* 88. *Certified* Medicaid.

SALUDA

Saluda Nursing Center*
Hwy 121, PO Box 398, Saluda, SC, 29138
(803) 445-2146
Admin Robert F Bowles. *Medical Dir/Dir of Nursing* Robert L Sawyer MD.
Licensure Skilled care; Intermediate care. *Beds* SNF 88; ICF 44. *Certified* Medicaid; Medicare.
Admissions Requirements Minimum age 14; Medical examination.
Staff Physicians 3 (ft); RNs 5 (ft), 4 (pt); LPNs 14 (ft); Nurses aides 52 (ft), 2 (pt); Activities coordinators 2 (ft), 1 (pt).
Facilities Dining room; Physical therapy room; Activities room; Chapel; Crafts room; Laundry room; Barber/Beauty shop.

Activities Arts & crafts; Cards; Games; Reading groups; Prayer groups; Movies; Shopping trips; Social/Cultural gatherings.

SENECA

Lila Doyle Nursing Care Facility*
Westminster Hwy 123, PO Box 858, Seneca, SC, 29678
(803) 882-3351
Admin W H Hudson. *Medical Dir/Dir of Nursing* D A Richardson MD.
Licensure Skilled care; Intermediate care. *Beds* 79. *Certified* Medicaid; Medicare.
Staff Physicians 20 (pt); RNs 3 (ft), 6 (pt); LPNs 9 (ft), 3 (pt); Orderlies 3 (ft), 1 (pt); Nurses aides 26 (ft), 9 (pt); Physical therapists 2 (pt); Activities coordinators 1 (ft); Dietitians 1 (ft).
Facilities Dining room; Physical therapy room; Activities room; Chapel; Crafts room; Barber/Beauty shop; Library.
Activities Arts & crafts; Cards; Games; Reading groups; Prayer groups; Movies; Shopping trips.

Oconee Geriatric Center Inc*
Rt 6 PO Box 189, Hwy 59, Seneca, SC, 29678
(803) 882-1642
Admin Leslie D Parks.
Licensure Skilled care; Intermediate care. *Beds* 88. *Certified* Medicaid; Medicare.
Owner Proprietary Corp (National Health Corp).

Seneca Community Residence*
Rte 1, Box 31-A, Hwy 188, Seneca, SC, 29678
(803) 882-2126
Admin Vicki Neely.
Licensure Intermediate care for mentally retarded. *Beds* 16. *Certified* Medicare.

SIMPSONVILLE

Palmetto Convalescent Center Inc*
721 W Curtis St, Simpsonville, SC, 29681
(803) 967-7191
Admin Joseph D Schofield.
Licensure Intermediate care. *Beds* 42. *Certified* Medicaid; Medicare.

SIX MILE

Harveys Love & Care Home Inc
Rte 1, Drawer C, Hwy 183 W, Six Mile, SC, 29682
(803) 868-2307
Admin Helen D Towe. *Medical Dir/Dir of Nursing* Dr David Mauldin.
Licensure Intermediate care. *Beds* ICF 40. *Certified* Medicaid.
Owner Proprietary Corp.
Admissions Requirements Medical examination.
Staff RNs 1 (pt); LPNs 1 (ft), 4 (pt); Nurses aides 11 (ft), 6 (pt); Activities coordinators 1 (ft); Dietitians 3 (ft), 3 (pt); Ophthalmologists 1 (pt).
Facilities Dining room; Activities room; Chapel; Crafts room; Laundry room; Barber/Beauty shop.
Activities Arts & crafts; Cards; Games; Reading groups; Movies; Social/Cultural gatherings.

SPARTANBURG

Lakeview Nursing Center
Hwy 585, 223 Smith Road, Spartanburg, SC, 29303
(803) 578-2523
Admin Bert Robinette. *Medical Dir/Dir of Nursing* Dr Barry Henderson.
Licensure Skilled care; Intermediate care. *Beds* 52. *Certified* Medicaid; Medicare; VA.
Owner Proprietary Corp.

Admissions Requirements Minimum age 18; Medical examination; Physician's request.
Staff Physicians 1 (ft); RNs 2 (ft), 1 (pt); Nurses aides 16 (ft), 7 (pt); Physical therapists 1 (pt); Speech therapists 1 (pt); Activities coordinators 1 (ft); Dietitians 1 (ft), 1 (pt); Dentists 1 (pt); Ophthalmologists 1 (pt).
Facilities Dining room; Activities room; Crafts room.
Activities Arts & crafts; Cards; Games; Reading groups; Prayer groups; Movies; Social/Cultural gatherings.

Mountainview Nursing Home*
340 Cedar Springs Rd, Spartanburg, SC, 29302
(803) 582-4175
Admin Wilson K Dillard.
Licensure Skilled care; Intermediate care. *Beds* 88. *Certified* Medicaid; Medicare.

Pinewood Convalescent Center
375 Serpentine Dr, Spartanburg, SC, 29303
(803) 585-0218
Admin Geraldine G Finch. *Medical Dir/Dir of Nursing* Warren C Lovett MD; Shirley Kinsland RN DON.
Licensure Skilled care; Intermediate care. *Beds* 95. *Certified* Medicaid; Medicare.
Owner Proprietary Corp.
Admissions Requirements Minimum age 12; Physician's request.
Staff Physicians 1 (ft), 18 (pt); RNs 5 (ft), 4 (pt); LPNs 8 (ft), 3 (pt); Nurses aides 34 (ft); Physical therapists 1 (pt); Reality therapists 1 (ft), 1 (pt); Recreational therapists 1 (pt); Occupational therapists 1 (pt); Speech therapists 1 (pt); Activities coordinators 1 (ft), 1 (pt); Dietitians 1 (ft); Ophthalmologists 1 (pt); Podiatrists 1 (pt).
Facilities Dining room; Physical therapy room; Activities room; Crafts room; Laundry room; Barber/Beauty shop; Bookmobile.
Activities Arts & crafts; Games; Reading groups; Prayer groups; Movies; Shopping trips.

Spartanburg Community Residence 1*
29 Long Dr, Spartanburg, SC, 29302
(803) 582-8842
Admin R B Williams. *Medical Dir/Dir of Nursing* Dr Ron Tollison.
Licensure Intermediate care for mentally retarded. *Beds* 15. *Certified* Medicare.
Admissions Requirements Medical examination.
Staff Physicians 1 (ft); RNs 1 (ft); LPNs 2 (ft); Recreational therapists 1 (ft); Activities coordinators 1 (ft); Dietitians 1 (ft).
Facilities Dining room; Activities room; Crafts room; Laundry room.
Activities Arts & crafts; Cards; Games; Reading groups; Movies; Shopping trips; Social/Cultural gatherings.

Spartanburg Commununity Residence 2*
29 Long Dr, Spartanburg, SC, 29302
(803) 582-8842
Admin R B Williams. *Medical Dir/Dir of Nursing* Dr Ron Tollison.
Licensure Intermediate care for mentally retarded. *Beds* 15. *Certified* Medicare.
Admissions Requirements Medical examination.
Staff Physicians 1 (ft); RNs 1 (ft); LPNs 2 (ft); Recreational therapists 1 (ft); Activities coordinators 1 (ft); Dietitians 1 (ft).
Facilities Dining room; Activities room; Crafts room; Laundry room.
Activities Arts & crafts; Cards; Games; Reading groups; Movies; Shopping trips; Social/Cultural gatherings.

Spartanburg Convalescent Center
PO Box 4246, 295 E Pearl St, Spartanburg, SC, 29303
(803) 585-0241

Admin Barbara H Adams. *Medical Dir/Dir of Nursing* Millie D Stein DON.
Licensure Skilled care; Intermediate care. *Beds* SNF 148; ICF 44. *Certified* Medicaid; Medicare.
Owner Privately owned.
Admissions Requirements Minimum age 18; Medical examination; Physician's request.
Staff Physicians; RNs; LPNs; Orderlies; Nurses aides; Physical therapists; Reality therapists; Recreational therapists; Speech therapists; Activities coordinators; Dietitians; Ophthalmologists; Dentist; Social workers.
Languages Greek, German
Facilities Dining room; Physical therapy room; Activities room; Chapel; Crafts room; Laundry room; Barber/Beauty shop; Library.
Activities Arts & crafts; Cards; Games; Reading groups; Prayer groups; Movies; Shopping trips; Social/Cultural gatherings.

SUMMERVILLE

Presbyterian Home of South Carolina—Summerville*
Box 140, 9th N, Summerville, SC, 29483
(803) 873-2550
Admin Charles R Tapp.
Licensure Skilled care; Intermediate care. *Beds* 90.
Owner Nonprofit Corp.
Affiliation Presbyterian

SUMTER

Community Intermediate Care Facility*
PO Box 6051, 703 Broad St, Sumter, SC, 29150-0051
(803) 773-6525
Admin Harold Hallums. *Medical Dir/Dir of Nursing* Dr Brenda Williams.
Licensure Intermediate care. *Beds* 20. *Certified* Medicaid; Medicare.
Staff LPNs 3 (ft), 1 (pt); Nurses aides 5 (ft), 2 (pt); Activities coordinators 1 (ft), 1 (pt).
Facilities Dining room; Laundry room.
Activities Arts & crafts; Games; Shopping trips.

Cypress Nurs Facility Inc
PO Box 1526, Carolina Ave, Sumter, SC, 29151
(803) 775-5394
Admin Lynda Charpentier. *Medical Dir/Dir of Nursing* R Lee Denny MD; Pat Boykin RN DON.
Licensure Skilled care. *Beds* SNF 88. *Certified* Medicaid; Medicare.
Owner Proprietary Corp (Pinnacle Care Corp).
Admissions Requirements Minimum age 18; Medical examination; Physician's request.
Staff RNs 3 (ft); LPNs 10 (ft); Orderlies 3 (ft); Nurses aides 26 (ft), 6 (pt); Physical therapists 2 (pt); Speech therapists 1 (pt); Activities coordinators 2 (ft); Dietitians 2 (pt).
Facilities Dining room; Physical therapy room; Activities room; Crafts room; Laundry room; Barber/Beauty shop.
Activities Arts & crafts; Cards; Games; Reading groups; Prayer groups; Movies; Social/Cultural gatherings.

Hampton Nursing Center Inc*
975 Miller Rd, Sumter, SC, 29150
(803) 795-8376
Admin Wade H Jones Jr. *Medical Dir/Dir of Nursing* Lee Denny MD.
Licensure Skilled care; Intermediate care. *Beds* 88. *Certified* Medicaid; Medicare.
Admissions Requirements Medical examination.
Staff RNs; LPNs; Orderlies; Nurses aides; Physical therapists; Occupational therapists.
Facilities Dining room; Physical therapy room; Activities room; Laundry room; Barber/Beauty shop.

Activities Arts & crafts; Cards; Games; Reading groups; Prayer groups.

Hopewell Healthcare Center
PO Box 818, 1761 Pinewood Rd, Sumter, SC, 29151
(803) 481-8591
Admin Mayes P Warr, Acting Admin. *Medical Dir/Dir of Nursing* Sandy Minoughan RN DON.
Licensure Intermediate care. *Beds* ICF 96. *Certified* Medicaid.
Owner Proprietary Corp (National Health Corp).
Admissions Requirements Minimum age 14; Medical examination; Physician's request.
Staff Physicians; RNs; LPNs; Orderlies; Nurses aides; Activities coordinators; Dietitians.
Activities Arts & crafts; Cards; Games; Reading groups; Prayer groups; Movies; Shopping trips.

Williamsburg Nursing Center*
PO Box 1524, 1018 N Guignard Dr, Sumter, SC, 29150
(803) 773-5567
Admin William P Betchman.
Licensure Skilled care; Intermediate care. *Beds* 100. *Certified* Medicaid; Medicare.

TRAVELERS REST

Oakmont North Nursing Center
6 Hart St, Travelers Rest, SC, 29690
Admin Christine M Wechsler. *Medical Dir/Dir of Nursing* John Holliday MD; Deborah Aiken RN DON.
Licensure Skilled care; Intermediate care. *Beds* 22. *Certified* Medicaid; Medicare.
Owner Proprietary Corp (Health Care & Retirement Corp).
Admissions Requirements Minimum age 18; Medical examination; Physician's request.
Staff RNs 1 (ft), 3 (pt); LPNs 2 (ft); Nurses aides 6 (ft), 5 (pt); Activities coordinators 1 (pt); Dietitians 1 (pt).
Facilities Dining room; Activities room; Barber/Beauty shop.
Activities Arts & crafts; Games; Prayer groups; Remotivation therapy.

UNION

Oakmont of Union
201 Rice St Extension, Union, SC, 29379
(803) 427-0306
Admin Frances A Harvey. *Medical Dir/Dir of Nursing* David Keith MD; Tomi O Vaughn DON.
Licensure Skilled care; Intermediate care. *Beds* SNF 44; ICF 44. *Certified* Medicaid; Medicare; VA Contract.
Owner Proprietary Corp (Health Care & Retirement Corp).
Admissions Requirements Medical examination; Physician's request.
Staff Physicians 8 (pt); RNs 3 (ft), 4 (pt); LPNs 8 (ft), 2 (pt); Orderlies 3 (ft), 2 (pt); Nurses aides 23 (ft), 6 (pt); Activities coordinators 1 (ft); Dietitians 1 (ft); Social worker 1 (ft).
Facilities Dining room; Physical therapy room; Activities room; Chapel; Laundry room; Barber/Beauty shop; Library.
Activities Arts & crafts; Cards; Games; Reading groups; Prayer groups; Movies; Shopping trips; Social/Cultural gatherings.

Ellen Sagar Nursing Home
Spartanburg Hwy 176, Union, SC, 29379
(803) 427-9533
Admin Leo Melle Newton. *Medical Dir/Dir of Nursing* Dr Boyd Hames; Rubye Cheek DON.
Licensure Skilled care; Intermediate care. *Beds* 64. *Certified* Medicaid; Medicare.

Owner Nonprofit organization/foundation.
Admissions Requirements Minimum age 15.
Staff RNs 4 (ft), 1 (pt); LPNs 6 (ft); Nurses aides 23 (ft), 2 (pt); Physical therapists 1 (pt); Speech therapists 1 (pt); Activities coordinators 1 (ft); Dietitians 1 (pt).
Facilities Dining room; Physical therapy room; Activities room; Chapel; Laundry room; Barber/Beauty shop.
Activities Arts & crafts; Cards; Games; Reading groups; Prayer groups; Movies; Social/Cultural gatherings.

WALTERBORO

Oakwood Health Care Center Inc
PO Box 1427, 401 Witsell St, Walterboro, SC, 29488
(803) 549-5546
Admin Mack B Whittle. *Medical Dir/Dir of Nursing* Patricia Ackerman RN DON.
Licensure Skilled care; Intermediate care. *Beds* SNF 74; ICF 58. *Certified* Medicaid; Medicare.
Owner Proprietary Corp (Wessex Corp).
Admissions Requirements Minimum age 16; Medical examination; Physician's request.
Staff RNs 2 (ft), 2 (pt); LPNs 18 (ft), 2 (pt); Nurses aides 39 (ft), 16 (pt); Activities coordinators 2 (ft); Dietitians 1 (ft).
Languages Spanish
Facilities Dining room; Activities room; Laundry room; Barber/Beauty shop.
Activities Arts & crafts; Prayer groups; Movies.

Walterboro Community Residence*
505 Forest Circle, Walterboro, SC, 29488
Admin Wilson V Inabiet, Jr.
Licensure Skilled care; Intermediate care. *Beds* 8.

WEST COLUMBIA

Manor Care Rehabilitation & Nursing Center
2416 Sunset Blvd, West Columbia, SC, 29169
(803) 796-8024
Admin Robin Miller. *Medical Dir/Dir of Nursing* Fred Clemenz MD; Terri Smith RN DON.
Licensure Skilled care; Intermediate care. *Beds* 106. *Certified* Medicaid; Medicare.
Owner Proprietary Corp (Manor Care).
Admissions Requirements Medical examination.
Staff Physicians 1 (pt); Physical therapists 1 (ft), 1 (pt); Recreational therapists 1 (ft); Occupational therapists 1 (ft); Speech therapists 2 (ft), 1 (pt); Activities coordinators 1 (ft); Dietitians 1 (ft).
Languages French
Facilities Dining room; Physical therapy room; Activities room; Chapel; Crafts room; Laundry room; Barber/Beauty shop; Library.
Activities Arts & crafts; Cards; Games; Reading groups; Prayer groups; Movies; Shopping trips; Social/Cultural gatherings.

South Carolina Episcopal Home at Still Hopes
100 7th St Extension, West Columbia, SC, 29169-7151
(803) 796-6490
Admin Diana B Jones. *Medical Dir/Dir of Nursing* James Ebersole MD; Carol Mercer RN DON.
Licensure Skilled care; Intermediate care; Residential care & cottages. *Beds* 145.
Owner Nonprofit Corp.
Admissions Requirements Minimum age 55; Medical examination; Physician's request.
Staff RNs 2 (ft), 1 (pt); LPNs 2 (ft), 1 (pt); Nurses aides 9 (ft), 7 (pt); Activities coordinators 1 (ft).
Affiliation Episcopal

Facilities Dining room; Physical therapy
room; Activities room; Chapel; Crafts room;
Laundry room; Barber/Beauty shop; Library;
Residents kitchen; Gift shop; Outdoor
walking paths.
Activities Arts & crafts; Cards; Games;
Reading groups; Prayer groups; Movies;
Shopping trips; Social/Cultural gatherings;
Entertainment; Outings; Youth visits; Pet
visits.

**South Carolina Vocational Rehabilitation
Comprehensive Center***
1400 Boston Ave, West Columbia, SC, 29169
(803) 758-8731
Admin Jack B Herndon. *Medical Dir/Dir of
Nursing* J Robert Dunn III MD.
Licensure Intermediate care. *Beds* 18.
Certified Medicare.
Staff Physicians 1 (pt); RNs 1 (ft), 2 (pt);
LPNs 4 (ft), 1 (pt); Nurses aides 1 (ft), 3
(pt); Physical therapists 1 (ft); Recreational
therapists 2 (ft); Occupational therapists 1
(ft); Speech therapists 1 (ft); Dietitians 1 (ft).
Facilities Dining room; Physical therapy
room; Activities room; Crafts room; Laundry
room; Library.
Activities Arts & crafts; Cards; Games;
Reading groups; Movies; Shopping trips;
Social/Cultural gatherings.

WHITE ROCK

The Lowman Home
PO Box 444, White Rock, SC, 29177
(803) 732-3000
Admin Louetta A Slice. *Medical Dir/Dir of
Nursing* Marie Connelly DON.
Licensure Skilled care; Intermediate care;
Residential care; Adult day care. *Beds* SNF
85; ICF 44; Residential 171; Adult day care
15. *Certified* Medicaid; Medicare.
Owner Nonprofit Corp.
Admissions Requirements Minimum age 18;
Medical examination; Physician's request.
Staff Physicians 3 (pt); RNs 8 (ft), 2 (pt);
LPNs 10 (ft), 2 (pt); Orderlies 5 (ft); Nurses
aides 110 (ft), 10 (pt); Physical therapists 1
(pt); Recreational therapists 3 (ft); Activities
coordinators 1 (ft); Dietitians 1 (ft).
Affiliation Lutheran
Facilities Dining room; Activities room;
Chapel; Crafts room; Laundry room; Barber/
Beauty shop; Library.
Activities Arts & crafts; Cards; Games;
Reading groups; Prayer groups; Movies;
Shopping trips; Social/Cultural gatherings;
Music; Choir; Handbell choir.

WILLISTON

Kirkland Convalescent Home Inc*
PO Box 250, Hwy 78, Williston, SC, 29853
(803) 266-3229
Admin Barbara T Kirkland.
Licensure Intermediate care. *Beds* 20.
Certified Medicaid; Medicare.

YORK

Divine Saviour Nursing Home
PO Box 629, 111 S Congress St, York, SC,
29745
(803) 684-4231
Admin John W Bailey. *Medical Dir/Dir of
Nursing* Nancy W Sherer RN.
Licensure Dual licensed. *Beds* Dual licensed
51. *Certified* Medicaid; Medicare.
Owner Nonprofit Corp.
Staff RNs; LPNs; Orderlies; Nurses aides;
Physical therapists; Speech therapists;
Activities coordinators; Dietitians.
Facilities Dining room; Activities room;
Chapel; Crafts room.
Activities Arts & crafts; Cards; Games;
Reading groups; Prayer groups; Movies;
Shopping trips; Social/Cultural gatherings.

SOUTH DAKOTA

ABERDEEN

Aberdeen Nursing Center*
1700 N Hwy 281, Aberdeen, SD, 57401
(605) 225-7315
Admin Craig Prokupek.
Licensure Skilled care; Intermediate care. *Beds* SNF 46; ICF 126. *Certified* Medicaid.

Americana Healthcare Center*
400 8th Ave NW, Aberdeen, SD, 57401
(605) 225-2550
Admin Dolores Inman.
Licensure Skilled care. *Beds* 69. *Certified* Medicaid; Medicare.
Owner Proprietary Corp (Manor Care).

Bethesda Home of Aberdeen
1224 S High St, Aberdeen, SD, 57401
(605) 225-7580
Admin Bob Vevle. *Medical Dir/Dir of Nursing* Dr William Bormes.
Licensure Skilled care. *Beds* SNF 86. *Certified* Medicaid.
Owner Nonprofit Corp.
Admissions Requirements Minimum age 60.
Staff RNs; LPNs; Orderlies; Nurses aides; Activities coordinators.
Affiliation Lutheran
Facilities Dining room; Physical therapy room; Activities room; Chapel; Crafts room; Laundry room; Barber/Beauty shop; Library; Children's day care.
Activities Arts & crafts; Cards; Games; Reading groups; Prayer groups; Movies; Shopping trips; Social/Cultural gatherings.

Mother Joseph Manor*
1002 N Jay, Aberdeen, SD, 57401
(605) 229-0550
Admin Gertrude Mangan. *Medical Dir/Dir of Nursing* J P Chang MD.
Licensure Skilled care; Intermediate care. *Beds* SNF 50; ICF 30. *Certified* Medicaid.
Admissions Requirements Medical examination; Physician's request.
Staff RNs 2 (ft), 3 (pt); LPNs 1 (ft), 4 (pt); Orderlies 2 (pt); Nurses aides 5 (ft), 15 (pt); Activities coordinators 1 (ft); Dietitians 1 (ft).
Affiliation Roman Catholic
Facilities Dining room; Physical therapy room; Activities room; Chapel; Crafts room; Laundry room; Barber/Beauty shop; Library.
Activities Arts & crafts; Cards; Games; Reading groups; Prayer groups; Movies; Shopping trips; Social/Cultural gatherings.

ALCESTER

Morningside Manor*
Box 188, Alcester, SD, 57001
(605) 934-2011
Admin Dorothy Millage. *Medical Dir/Dir of Nursing* James Daggett MD.
Licensure Skilled care; Intermediate care. *Beds* SNF 42; ICF 42. *Certified* Medicaid; Medicare.

Staff Physicians; RNs; LPNs; Orderlies; Nurses aides; Physical therapists; Recreational therapists; Occupational therapists; Speech therapists; Activities coordinators; Dietitians; Dentists.
Facilities Dining room; Physical therapy room; Activities room; Crafts room; Laundry room; Barber/Beauty shop; Library.
Activities Arts & crafts; Cards; Games; Reading groups; Prayer groups; Movies; Shopping trips; Social/Cultural gatherings.

ARLINGTON

Arlington Care Center*
403 N 4th St, Arlington, SD, 57212
(605) 983-5796
Admin Layne Gross.
Licensure Skilled care. *Beds* 52. *Certified* Medicaid.
Owner Proprietary Corp (Beverly Enterprises).
Staff RNs 3 (ft), 2 (pt); LPNs 1 (ft), 1 (pt); Orderlies 4 (ft); Nurses aides 8 (ft), 3 (pt); Activities coordinators 2 (ft); Dietitians 1 (pt).
Facilities Dining room; Activities room; Chapel; Crafts room; Laundry room; Barber/Beauty shop.
Activities Arts & crafts; Cards; Games; Reading groups; Prayer groups; Movies; Shopping trips; Social/Cultural gatherings.

ARMOUR

Colonial Manor
PO Box 489, Hwy 281 S, Armour, SD, 57313
(605) 724-2546
Admin Charlene R Nash. *Medical Dir/Dir of Nursing* Dr Ronald Price; Mary Mimmack DNS.
Licensure Skilled care. *Beds* SNF 45. *Certified* Medicaid.
Owner Proprietary Corp (Beverly Enterprises).
Admissions Requirements Medical examination; Physician's request.
Staff RNs 2 (ft), 2 (pt); LPNs 1 (ft), 3 (pt); Nurses aides 9 (ft), 6 (pt); Physical therapists 1 (pt); Recreational therapists 1 (pt); Occupational therapists 1 (pt); Speech therapists 1 (pt); Activities coordinators 1 (ft), 1 (pt); Dietitians 1 (pt).
Facilities Dining room; Physical therapy room; Activities room; Chapel; Laundry room; Barber/Beauty shop; Library.
Activities Arts & crafts; Cards; Games; Reading groups; Prayer groups; Movies; Shopping trips; Social/Cultural gatherings; Competitive bowling.

BELLE FOURCHE

Belle Fourche Health Care Center—Long-Term Care Unit*
2200 13th Ave, Belle Fourche, SD, 57717
(605) 892-3331
Admin Larry Potter.

Licensure Skilled care; Intermediate care. *Beds* SNF 50; ICF 50. *Certified* Medicaid.

Julia Olson Rest Home*
1112 6th St, Belle Fourche, SD, 57717
(605) 892-4187
Admin Julia Olson.
Licensure Supervised care. *Beds* 4.

BERESFORD

Bethesda Home for the Aged
606 W Cedar, Beresford, SD, 57004
(605) 763-2050
Admin Paul Collins. *Medical Dir/Dir of Nursing* Dr Chris Bucy; Diane Landon DON.
Licensure Skilled care. *Beds* SNF 83. *Certified* Medicaid.
Owner Nonprofit Corp.
Admissions Requirements Medical examination.
Staff RNs 5 (ft); LPNs 3 (ft); Nurses aides 15 (ft), 20 (pt); Recreational therapists 2 (ft), 1 (pt); Activities coordinators 1 (ft).
Affiliation Lutheran
Facilities Dining room; Physical therapy room; Activities room; Chapel; Crafts room; Laundry room; Barber/Beauty shop.
Activities Arts & crafts; Cards; Games; Reading groups; Prayer groups; Movies; Shopping trips; Social/Cultural gatherings.

BOWDLE

Bowdle Nursing Home
PO Box 308, Bowdle, SD, 57428
(605) 285-6391
Admin Dave Green. *Medical Dir/Dir of Nursing* Dr Stephen Grant; Gail Jeschke RN DON.
Licensure Skilled care. *Beds* SNF 38. *Certified* Medicaid.
Owner Nonprofit organization/foundation.
Staff RNs 3 (ft); LPNs 2 (ft); Nurses aides 9 (ft), 2 (pt); Physical therapists 1 (pt); Activities coordinators 1 (ft); Dietitians 1 (pt).
Languages German
Facilities Dining room; Physical therapy room; Activities room; Laundry room; Barber/Beauty shop.
Activities Arts & crafts; Cards; Games; Reading groups; Prayer groups; Movies; Shopping trips; Social/Cultural gatherings.

BRIDGEWATER

Diamond Care Center
PO Box 300, Bridgewater, SD, 57319
(605) 729-2525
Admin Ivo J Weber. *Medical Dir/Dir of Nursing* Dorothy Brendan.
Licensure Intermediate care. *Beds* ICF 56. *Certified* Medicaid.

Owner Proprietary Corp.
Staff Physicians; RNs; LPNs; Nurses aides;
Recreational therapists; Activities
coordinators; Dietitians.

BRISTOL

Sun Dial Manor Inc
PO Box 337, Bristol, SD, 57219
(605) 492-3615
Admin Sally Damm. *Medical Dir/Dir of
Nursing* Diane Warrington RN; Brenda
Sletten RN.
Licensure Skilled care. *Beds* 37. *Certified*
Medicaid; Medicare.
Owner Nonprofit Corp.
Admissions Requirements Medical
examination; Physician's request.
Staff RNs 2 (pt); LPNs 2 (pt); Orderlies 1 (ft);
Nurses aides 8 (ft), 20 (pt); Activities
coordinators 1 (ft); Dietitians 1 (ft).
Facilities Dining room; Activities room;
Chapel; Crafts room; Laundry room; Barber/
Beauty shop.
Activities Arts & crafts; Cards; Games;
Reading groups; Prayer groups; Movies;
Shopping trips; Social/Cultural gatherings.

BRITTON

Marshall Manor
W Hwy 10, Britton, SD, 57430
(605) 448-2252
Admin Robert B Marx. *Medical Dir/Dir of
Nursing* J Bull.
Licensure Intermediate care. *Beds* ICF 63.
Certified Medicaid.
Owner Proprietary Corp.
Staff RNs 1 (ft), 1 (pt); LPNs 2 (ft); Nurses
aides 18 (ft), 6 (pt); Activities coordinators 2
(ft); Dietitians 2 (ft), 3 (pt).
Facilities Dining room; Activities room;
Chapel; Laundry room; Barber/Beauty shop.
Activities Arts & crafts; Cards; Games;
Reading groups; Prayer groups; Movies;
Shopping trips; Social/Cultural gatherings.

BROOKINGS

Brookview Manor
300 22nd Ave, Brookings, SD, 57006
(605) 692-6351
Admin David Johnson. *Medical Dir/Dir of
Nursing* Bruce Lushbough MD; Gloria
Gerberding RN DON.
Licensure Skilled care. *Beds* SNF 79. *Certified*
Medicaid.
Owner Publicly owned.
Admissions Requirements Physician's request.
Staff RNs 2 (ft), 11 (pt); LPNs 3 (ft), 4 (pt);
Orderlies 2 (ft), 1 (pt); Nurses aides 8 (ft),
24 (pt); Reality therapists 1 (pt); Activities
coordinators 1 (ft), 1 (pt); Dietitians 1 (pt).
Facilities Dining room; Physical therapy
room; Activities room; Chapel; Crafts room;
Laundry room; Barber/Beauty shop; Dental
room.
Activities Arts & crafts; Cards; Games;
Reading groups; Prayer groups; Movies;
Shopping trips; Social/Cultural gatherings;
Fishing; Camping.

United Retirement Center
405 1st Ave, Brookings, SD, 57006
(605) 692-5351
Admin Arnold M Brown. *Medical Dir/Dir of
Nursing* Bette Johnson DON.
Licensure Intermediate care. *Beds* ICF 60.
Certified Medicaid.
Owner Nonprofit Corp.
Admissions Requirements Medical
examination.
Staff RNs 1 (ft), 5 (pt); LPNs 2 (pt); Nurses
aides 3 (ft), 20 (pt); Reality therapists 1 (pt);
Activities coordinators 1 (ft).

Facilities Dining room; Physical therapy
room; Activities room; Chapel; Crafts room;
Laundry room; Barber/Beauty shop.
Activities Arts & crafts; Cards; Games;
Reading groups; Prayer groups; Movies;
Shopping trips; Social/Cultural gatherings;
Campouts; Outings.

BRYANT

Parkview Care Center*
Bryant, SD, 57221
(605) 628-2771
Admin Robert Gergen. *Medical Dir/Dir of
Nursing* Dr G R Bell.
Licensure Intermediate care. *Beds* 52.
Certified Medicaid.
Admissions Requirements Medical
examination.
Staff RNs 1 (ft), 3 (pt); LPNs 2 (ft), 2 (pt);
Orderlies 1 (ft); Nurses aides 9 (ft), 12 (pt);
Physical therapists 1 (pt); Activities
coordinators 1 (ft); Dietitians 1 (pt).
Facilities Dining room; Activities room;
Chapel; Crafts room; Laundry room; Barber/
Beauty shop.
Activities Arts & crafts; Cards; Games;
Reading groups; Prayer groups; Movies;
Shopping trips; Social/Cultural gatherings.

CANISTOTA

Canistota Good Samaritan Center
PO Box 6, 700 W Main, Canistota, SD, 57012
(605) 296-3442
Admin Richard L Osborne. *Medical Dir/Dir of
Nursing* Phyllis Arends RN.
Licensure Intermediate care. *Beds* ICF 64.
Certified Medicaid.
Owner Nonprofit Corp (Evangelical Lutheran/
Good Samaritan).
Admissions Requirements Medical
examination.
Staff RNs 2 (ft); LPNs 5 (ft); Nurses aides 18
(ft); Physical therapists 1 (pt); Activities
coordinators 1 (ft), 1 (pt); Dietitians 1 (pt).
Facilities Dining room; Activities room;
Chapel; Crafts room; Laundry room; Barber/
Beauty shop.
Activities Arts & crafts; Cards; Games;
Reading groups; Prayer groups; Movies;
Shopping trips; Social/Cultural gatherings.

CANTON

Canton Good Samaritan Center
1022 N Oak Ave, Canton, SD, 57013
(605) 987-2696
Admin Don W Toft. *Medical Dir/Dir of
Nursing* Dr Gene Regier; Joyce Paulson.
Licensure Skilled care; Intermediate care. *Beds*
SNF 68; ICF 10. *Certified* Medicaid.
Owner Nonprofit Corp (Evangelical Lutheran/
Good Samaritan).
Admissions Requirements Medical
examination; Physician's request.
Staff RNs 5 (ft), 5 (pt); LPNs 2 (ft), 2 (pt);
Nurses aides 16 (ft), 14 (pt); Activities
coordinators 2 (ft), 3 (pt); Dietitians 7 (ft), 7
(pt); Physical Therapy Aides 1 (ft), 2 (pt).
Languages Norwegian, German
Affiliation Lutheran
Facilities Dining room; Physical therapy
room; Activities room; Chapel; Crafts room;
Laundry room; Barber/Beauty shop.
Activities Arts & crafts; Cards; Games;
Reading groups; Prayer groups; Movies;
Shopping trips; Social/Cultural gatherings;
Special events.

CENTERVILLE

Good Samaritan Center*
500 Vermillion, PO Box 190, Centerville, SD,
57014
(605) 563-2251

Licensure Intermediate care; Supervised care.
Beds ICF 56; Supervised care 4. *Certified*
Medicaid.
Owner Nonprofit Corp (Evangelical Lutheran/
Good Samaritan).
Admissions Requirements Medical
examination; Physician's request.
Staff RNs 1 (ft).
Facilities Dining room; Physical therapy
room; Activities room; Chapel; Crafts room;
Laundry room; Barber/Beauty shop; Library.
Activities Arts & crafts; Cards; Games;
Reading groups; Prayer groups; Movies;
Shopping trips; Social/Cultural gatherings.

CHAMBERLAIN

Sunset Valley Haven
111 W 16th St, Chamberlain, SD, 57325
(605) 734-6518
Admin Janet Evangelisto. *Medical Dir/Dir of
Nursing* Dr C F Binder; Vicki L Mills RN
DON.
Licensure Skilled care. *Beds* SNF 58. *Certified*
Medicaid.
Owner Nonprofit Corp.
Admissions Requirements Medical
examination; Physician's request.
Staff RNs; LPNs; Orderlies; Nurses aides;
Activities coordinators.
Facilities Dining room; Activities room;
Crafts room; Laundry room; Barber/Beauty
shop.
Activities Arts & crafts; Cards; Games;
Reading groups; Prayer groups; Movies;
Shopping trips; Social/Cultural gatherings.

CLARK

Clark Care Center
201 NW 8th Ave, Clark, SD, 57225
(605) 532-3431
Admin Joyce M Helkenn. *Medical Dir/Dir of
Nursing* G R Bartron MD; Betty Poppen
RN.
Licensure Skilled care. *Beds* SNF 45. *Certified*
Medicaid.
Owner Proprietary Corp (Beverly Enterprises).
Admissions Requirements Medical
examination; Physician's request.
Staff RNs 4 (ft), 3 (pt); Nurses aides 15 (ft),
20 (pt); Activities coordinators 1 (ft).
Facilities Dining room; Activities room;
Laundry room; Barber/Beauty shop; Library.
Activities Arts & crafts; Cards; Games;
Reading groups; Prayer groups; Movies;
Shopping trips; Social/Cultural gatherings.

CLEAR LAKE

Deuel County Good Samaritan Center
PO Box 666, 913 4th Ave S, Clear Lake, SD,
57226-0666
(605) 874-2159
Admin Daisy Bergjord. *Medical Dir/Dir of
Nursing* Dr H Dean Hughes; Julia V
Schumacher RN.
Licensure Skilled care; Intermediate care. *Beds*
SNF 44; ICF 41. *Certified* Medicaid.
Owner Nonprofit Corp (Evangelical Lutheran/
Good Samaritan).
Admissions Requirements Medical
examination.
Staff RNs; LPNs; Orderlies; Nurses aides;
Activities coordinators.
Affiliation Lutheran
Facilities Dining room; Physical therapy
room; Activities room; Chapel; Crafts room;
Laundry room; Barber/Beauty shop.
Activities Arts & crafts; Cards; Games;
Reading groups; Prayer groups; Movies;
Shopping trips; Social/Cultural gatherings.

CORSICA

Pleasant View Nursing Home
Rte 1, PO Box 300, Corsica, SD, 57328
(605) 946-5467
Licensure Intermediate care. *Beds* 62.
Certified Medicaid.
Admissions Requirements Medical
examination; Physician's request.
Staff RNs 1 (ft), 3 (pt); LPNs 1 (ft), 2 (pt);
Nurses aides 21 (pt); Physical therapists 1
(pt); Reality therapists 1 (pt); Speech
therapists 1 (pt); Activities coordinators 1
(ft), 1 (pt); Dietitians 1 (pt).
Affiliation Lutheran
Facilities Dining room; Activities room;
Chapel; Crafts room; Laundry room; Barber/
Beauty shop; Library; Conference room.
Activities Arts & crafts; Cards; Games;
Reading groups; Prayer groups; Movies;
Shopping trips; Social/Cultural gatherings;
Bible study.

CUSTER

Colonial Manor of Custer
1065 Montgomery St, Custer, SD, 57730
(605) 673-2237
Admin Gerald Woodford. *Medical Dir/Dir of
Nursing* Dennis Wicks MD; Barb Nordstrom
RN DON.
Licensure Skilled care; Intermediate care. *Beds*
80. *Certified* Medicaid; Medicare.
Owner Proprietary Corp (Beverly Enterprises).
Admissions Requirements Medical
examination; Physician's request.
Staff Physicians; RNs; LPNs; Nurses aides;
Physical therapists; Recreational therapists;
Activities coordinators.
Facilities Dining room; Physical therapy
room; Activities room; Chapel; Crafts room;
Laundry room; Barber/Beauty shop.
Activities Arts & crafts; Cards; Games;
Reading groups; Prayer groups; Movies;
Shopping trips; Social/Cultural gatherings.

DE SMET

Good Samaritan Center*
411 Calumet Ave, De Smet, SD, 57231
(605) 854-3327
Admin Jerry Keller.
Licensure Intermediate care; Supervised care.
Beds ICF 62; Supervised care 10. *Certified*
Medicaid.
Owner Nonprofit Corp (Evangelical Lutheran/
Good Samaritan).
Staff RNs 1 (ft), 2 (pt); LPNs 1 (ft), 4 (pt);
Nurses aides 10 (ft), 18 (pt); Activities
coordinators 1 (ft), 1 (pt).
Facilities Dining room; Activities room;
Chapel; Crafts room; Laundry room; Barber/
Beauty shop; Library.
Activities Arts & crafts; Cards; Games;
Reading groups; Prayer groups; Movies;
Shopping trips; Social/Cultural gatherings.

DEADWOOD

Friendship Home
HC 73, Box 500, 48 Highland, Deadwood,
SD, 57732
(605) 578-2482
Admin LaEtta Heltibridle.
Licensure Supervised care. *Beds* 8.

DELL RAPIDS

Odd Fellows Home*
100 W 10th St, Dell Rapids, SD, 57022
(605) 428-3398
Admin Ervin Ommen.
Licensure Intermediate care. *Beds* 54.
Certified Medicaid.
Admissions Requirements Medical
examination.

Staff Physicians 4 (pt); RNs 2 (ft), 2 (pt);
LPNs 4 (ft), 1 (pt); Orderlies 1 (pt); Nurses
aides 12 (ft); Activities coordinators 1 (ft);
Dietitians 1 (pt); Dentists 1 (pt).
Affiliation Independent Order of Odd Fellows
& Rebekahs
Facilities Dining room; Activities room;
Chapel; Crafts room; Laundry room; Barber/
Beauty shop.
Activities Arts & crafts; Cards; Games;
Reading groups; Prayer groups; Movies;
Shopping trips; Social/Cultural gatherings.

Terrace Manor*
1400 Thresher Dr, Dell Rapids, SD, 57022
(605) 428-5478
Admin Linda Ljunggren.
Licensure Skilled care. *Beds* 76. *Certified*
Medicaid.

ELK POINT

Prairie Estates
Box 486, Elk Point, SD, 57025
(605) 356-2622
Admin Alexander G Willford. *Medical Dir/Dir
of Nursing* Janet Limoug.
Licensure Intermediate care. *Beds* ICF 50.
Certified Medicaid.
Owner Proprietary Corp.
Admissions Requirements Medical
examination; Physician's request.
Staff Physicians 2 (ft); RNs 4 (ft); LPNs 2 (ft);
Nurses aides 20 (ft); Physical therapists 1
(ft); Speech therapists 1 (ft); Activities
coordinators 1 (ft); Dietitians 1 (ft).
Facilities Dining room; Activities room;
Chapel; Crafts room; Laundry room; Barber/
Beauty shop; Library.
Activities Arts & crafts; Games; Reading
groups; Prayer groups; Movies; Shopping
trips; Social/Cultural gatherings; Field trips.

ELKTON

Elkton Rest Home*
PO Box 327, Elkton, SD, 57026
(605) 542-7251
Admin Roween Cameron.
Licensure Supervised care. *Beds* 10.

ESTELLINE

Estelline Nursing & Care Center
PO Box 130, N Main, Estelline, SD, 57234
(605) 873-2278
Admin Evelyn Saathoff. *Medical Dir/Dir of
Nursing* S Feeney MD; G Casjens RN DON.
Licensure Skilled care. *Beds* SNF 60. *Certified*
Medicaid.
Owner Nonprofit Corp.
Admissions Requirements Medical
examination; Physician's request.
Staff RNs 2 (ft), 2 (pt); LPNs 2 (ft), 4 (pt);
Nurses aides 13 (ft), 12 (pt); Activities
coordinators 1 (ft).
Facilities Dining room; Activities room;
Crafts room; Laundry room; Barber/Beauty
shop.
Activities Arts & crafts; Cards; Games;
Reading groups; Movies; Shopping trips;
Social/Cultural gatherings; Sing-alongs;
Ladies groups; Mens groups.

EUREKA

Lutheran Home*
Eureka, SD, 57437
(605) 284-2534
Admin V R Just. *Medical Dir/Dir of Nursing*
Dr Susan Ostrowski.
Licensure Intermediate care. *Beds* 62.
Certified Medicaid.
Owner Nonprofit Corp (Luth Hosp & Homes
Socty).

Admissions Requirements Medical
examination; Physician's request.
Staff Physicians 2 (ft); RNs 2 (ft), 1 (pt);
LPNs 2 (ft); Nurses aides 16 (ft), 14 (pt);
Recreational therapists 1 (ft), 1 (pt);
Occupational therapists 1 (ft); Activities
coordinators 1 (ft), 1 (pt); Dietitians 1 (ft);
Dentists 1 (ft); Ophthalmologists 1 (ft).
Affiliation Lutheran
Facilities Dining room; Activities room;
Chapel; Crafts room; Laundry room; Barber/
Beauty shop.
Activities Arts & crafts; Cards; Games;
Reading groups; Prayer groups; Movies;
Shopping trips; Social/Cultural gatherings;
Fishing trips; Farm outings.

FAULKTON

John P Shirk Memorial Home
PO Box 249, Pearl & 13th Sts, Faulkton, SD,
57438
(605) 598-6214
Admin Karen Collins. *Medical Dir/Dir of
Nursing* Dr Kenneth Bartholomew; Eva
Hansen RN.
Licensure Skilled care; Intermediate care. *Beds*
SNF 27; ICF 27. *Certified* Medicaid.
Owner Proprietary Corp (North Central
Health Services).
Admissions Requirements Medical
examination.
Staff RNs 1 (ft), 7 (pt); LPNs 1 (ft), 1 (pt);
Nurses aides 6 (ft), 24 (pt); Activities
coordinators 1 (ft), 1 (pt).
Facilities Dining room; Physical therapy
room; Activities room; Crafts room; Laundry
room; Barber/Beauty shop.
Activities Arts & crafts; Cards; Games;
Reading groups; Prayer groups; Movies;
Shopping trips; Social/Cultural gatherings.

FLANDREAU

Riverview Manor*
611 E 2nd Ave, Flandreau, SD, 57028
(605) 997-2481
Admin JoAnn Lind.
Licensure Skilled care. *Beds* 80. *Certified*
Medicaid.

FREEMAN

Freeman Community Nursing Home*
PO Box 370, Freeman, SD, 57029
(605) 925-4231
Admin Larry Ravenburg.
Licensure Skilled care; Intermediate care. *Beds*
SNF 54; ICF 5. *Certified* Medicaid.

Salem Mennonite Home for the Aged
PO Box 140A, 106 W 7th St, Freeman, SD,
57029
(605) 925-4774
Admin Evelyn Hagemann. *Medical Dir/Dir of
Nursing* Evelyn Hagemann RN.
Licensure Supervised care. *Beds* 50. *Certified*
Medicaid; Medicare.
Owner Proprietary Corp.
Admissions Requirements Females only;
Medical examination.
Staff RNs 2 (pt); Nurses aides 10 (ft);
Activities coordinators 2 (pt); Dietitians 1
(ft); Administrator 1 (ft); Maintenance 1 (ft);
Diet aides & cooks 3 (ft), 3 (pt); Cleaning 3
(ft); Laundry 1 (ft), 1 (pt); Med aides 1 (ft),
3 (pt).
Languages German
Affiliation Mennonite
Facilities Dining room; Physical therapy
room; Activities room; Chapel; Crafts room;
Laundry room; Barber/Beauty shop; Library.
Activities Arts & crafts; Cards; Games;
Reading groups; Prayer groups; Movies;
Shopping trips; Social/Cultural gatherings.

GARRETSON

Palisade Manor*
920 4th St, Garretson, SD, 57030
(605) 594-3466
Admin Gloria Schultz.
Licensure Skilled care; Intermediate care. *Beds*
SNF 16; ICF 62. *Certified* Medicaid.

GETTYSBURG

Oahe Manor*
700 E Garfield, Gettysburg, SD, 57442
(605) 765-2461
Admin Timothy J Tracy.
Licensure Intermediate care. *Beds* 70.
Certified Medicaid.
Admissions Requirements Medical
examination; Physician's request.
Staff RNs 1 (ft); LPNs 4 (ft); Nurses aides 34
(ft); Activities coordinators 1 (ft); Dietitians
1 (ft).
Facilities Dining room; Activities room;
Chapel; Crafts room; Laundry room; Barber/
Beauty shop.
Activities Arts & crafts; Cards; Games;
Reading groups; Prayer groups; Movies.

GREGORY

Rosebud Nursing Home*
300 Park St, Gregory, SD, 57533
(605) 835-8296
Admin Terry E Davis.
Licensure Skilled care. *Beds* 58. *Certified*
Medicaid; Medicare.
Owner Nonprofit Corp (Luth Hosp & Homes
Socty).

GROTON

Colonial Manor of Groton
PO Box 418, Groton, SD, 57445
(605) 397-2365
Admin Bruce Glanzer.
Licensure Skilled care. *Beds* 60. *Certified*
Medicaid.
Owner Proprietary Corp (Beverly Enterprises).

HERREID

Good Samaritan Center*
Herreid, SD, 57632
(605) 437-2425
Admin Dolores Riedlinger.
Licensure Supervised care. *Beds* 27.
Admissions Requirements Medical
examination.
Staff RNs 1 (pt); LPNs 1 (pt); Nurses aides 7
(ft).
Affiliation Lutheran
Facilities Dining room; Laundry room.
Activities Games; Shopping trips.

HIGHMORE

Highmore Nursing Home*
Highmore, SD, 57345
(605) 852-2255
Admin Robert Bonato. *Medical Dir/Dir of
Nursing* Kathy Freier.
Licensure Intermediate care. *Beds* 48.
Certified Medicaid.
Admissions Requirements Medical
examination; Physician's request.
Staff Physicians 2 (pt); RNs 3 (pt); LPNs 4
(ft); Nurses aides 16 (ft), 3 (pt); Physical
therapists 1 (pt); Reality therapists 1 (pt);
Recreational therapists 1 (pt); Activities
coordinators 1 (pt); Dietitians 1 (pt);
Dentists 1 (pt); Podiatrists 1 (pt).

Facilities Dining room; Activities room;
Laundry room; Barber/Beauty shop.
Activities Arts & crafts; Cards; Games;
Reading groups; Prayer groups; Movies;
Shopping trips; Social hour.

HOSMER

Senior Citizens Home
PO Box 67, Hosmer, SD, 57448
(605) 283-2203
Admin John L Jacobs. *Medical Dir/Dir of
Nursing* Dr John McFee; Geralyn Malsom
RN DON.
Licensure Intermediate care. *Beds* ICF 40.
Certified Medicaid.
Owner Publicly owned.
Admissions Requirements Medical
examination; Physician's request.
Staff RNs 3 (ft); Nurses aides 15 (ft);
Activities coordinators 1 (ft).
Languages German
Facilities Dining room; Activities room;
Chapel; Crafts room; Laundry room; Barber/
Beauty shop.
Activities Arts & crafts; Cards; Games;
Reading groups; Prayer groups; Movies;
Shopping trips; Social/Cultural gatherings.

HOT SPRINGS

Lutheran Nursing Home
209 N 16th St, Hot Springs, SD, 57747
(605) 745-5071
Admin Ronald J Cork. *Medical Dir/Dir of
Nursing* Sarah R Flesner DON.
Licensure Intermediate care. *Beds* 48.
Certified Medicaid.
Owner Nonprofit Corp (Luth Hosp & Homes
Socty).
Staff Physicians 6 (ft); RNs 13 (ft), 2 (pt);
LPNs 5 (ft), 1 (pt); Nurses aides 15 (ft), 3
(pt); Physical therapists 1 (ft); Activities
coordinators 1 (ft); Dietitians 1 (pt); Social
service 1 (ft).
Affiliation Lutheran
Facilities Dining room; Physical therapy
room; Activities room; Chapel; Crafts room;
Laundry room; Barber/Beauty shop; Library.
Activities Arts & crafts; Cards; Games;
Reading groups; Prayer groups; Movies;
Shopping trips; Social/Cultural gatherings.

HOWARD

Howard Good Samaritan Center
PO Box 92, Rte 1, Howard, SD, 57349
(605) 772-4481
Admin Dennis Beeman. *Medical Dir/Dir of
Nursing* H J Sample MD; Lorna Koch RN
DON.
Licensure Skilled care; Supervised care. *Beds*
SNF 74; Supervised care 2. *Certified*
Medicaid.
Owner Nonprofit Corp (Evangelical Lutheran/
Good Samaritan).
Admissions Requirements Physician's request.
Staff Physicians 4 (pt); RNs 3 (ft), 7 (pt);
LPNs 1 (ft), 2 (pt); Nurses aides 12 (ft), 23
(pt); Physical therapists 1 (pt); Activities
coordinators 1 (ft), 2 (pt); Dietitians 1 (pt).
Affiliation Lutheran
Facilities Dining room; Physical therapy
room; Activities room; Crafts room; Laundry
room; Barber/Beauty shop.
Activities Arts & crafts; Cards; Games;
Reading groups; Prayer groups; Movies;
Shopping trips; Social/Cultural gatherings.

HUDSON

Colonial Manor of Hudson*
Hwy 46 W, Hudson, SD, 57032
(605) 984-2244
Admin Leonard Dahl. *Medical Dir/Dir of
Nursing* Monte Harvey DO.

Licensure Intermediate care. *Beds* 42.
Certified Medicaid.
Admissions Requirements Medical
examination; Physician's request.
Staff Physicians 1 (pt); RNs 1 (ft), 1 (pt);
LPNs 3 (pt); Nurses aides 24 (pt); Activities
coordinators 1 (ft); Dietitians 1 (pt).
Facilities Dining room; Activities room;
Chapel; Crafts room; Laundry room; Barber/
Beauty shop; Library.
Activities Arts & crafts; Cards; Games;
Reading groups; Prayer groups; Movies;
Shopping trips.

HURON

Huron Nursing Home*
PO Box 1277, Huron, SD, 57350
(605) 352-8471
Admin Sharon Grayson.
Licensure Skilled care; Intermediate care. *Beds*
SNF 125; ICF 38. *Certified* Medicaid;
Medicare.

Violet Tschetter Memorial Home
50 7th St SE, Huron, SD, 57350
(605) 352-8533
Admin Peggy Roy. *Medical Dir/Dir of Nursing*
Dr Paul Hohm; Joyce Kogel RN DON.
Licensure Skilled care. *Beds* SNF 58. *Certified*
Medicaid.
Owner Nonprofit Corp.
Admissions Requirements Medical
examination; Physician's request.
Staff RNs 1 (ft), 6 (pt); LPNs 1 (ft), 4 (pt);
Nurses aides 16 (ft), 13 (pt); Activities
coordinators 1 (ft); Dietitians 1 (pt).
Facilities Dining room; Activities room;
Chapel; Crafts room; Laundry room; Barber/
Beauty shop.
Activities Arts & crafts; Cards; Games;
Reading groups; Prayer groups; Movies;
Shopping trips; Social/Cultural gatherings.

IPSWICH

Colonial Manor of Ipswich
617 Bloemendaal Dr, Ipswich, SD, 57451
(605) 426-6622
Admin Diane M Horning. *Medical Dir/Dir of
Nursing* John L McFee MD; Lydia
Leafgreen RN DON.
Licensure Skilled care. *Beds* SNF 59. *Certified*
Medicaid.
Owner Proprietary Corp (Beverly Enterprises).
Admissions Requirements Minimum age 16;
Medical examination.
Staff Physicians 1 (pt); RNs 3 (ft), 1 (pt);
LPNs 3 (ft), 2 (pt); Nurses aides 20 (ft), 8
(pt); Physical therapists 1 (pt); Activities
coordinators 2 (ft), 2 (pt); Dietitians 1 (pt).
Languages German, French, Spanish
Facilities Dining room; Physical therapy
room; Activities room; Crafts room; Laundry
room; Barber/Beauty shop.
Activities Arts & crafts; Cards; Games;
Reading groups; Prayer groups; Movies;
Shopping trips; Social/Cultural gatherings;
Current events; Ethnic celebrations;
Exercises.

IRENE

Sunset Manor*
Irene, SD, 57037
(605) 263-3318
Admin Kathleen Stanage.
Licensure Intermediate care. *Beds* 66.
Certified Medicaid.

KADOKA

Kadoka Care Center
Box 310, Kadoka, SD, 57543
(605) 837-2270

Admin Nona Prang. *Medical Dir/Dir of Nursing* Nancy Pettyjohn.
Licensure Intermediate care. *Beds* ICF 34. *Certified* Medicaid.
Owner Nonprofit Corp.
Staff Physicians; RNs; LPNs; Orderlies; Nurses aides; Activities coordinators; Dietitians.
Languages Sioux
Facilities Dining room; Crafts room; Laundry room.
Activities Arts & crafts; Games; Prayer groups; Movies; Shopping trips; Social/Cultural gatherings.

LAKE ANDES

Lake Andes Health Care Center
PO Box 130, Lake Andes, SD, 57356
(605) 487-7674
Admin Robert A Bonato. *Medical Dir/Dir of Nursing* Jeanette Westerdorf RN.
Licensure Skilled care; Intermediate care. *Beds* SNF 10; ICF 42. *Certified* Medicaid.
Owner Proprietary Corp.
Admissions Requirements Medical examination.
Staff Physicians 5 (pt); RNs 4 (pt); LPNs 5 (pt); Nurses aides 20 (pt); Physical therapists 1 (pt); Recreational therapists 1 (pt); Activities coordinators 1 (pt); Dietitians 1 (pt).
Facilities Dining room; Activities room; Laundry room; Barber/Beauty shop.
Activities Arts & crafts; Cards; Games; Reading groups; Prayer groups; Movies; Shopping trips.

LAKE NORDEN

Lake Norden Care Center
PO Box 38, West Side St, Lake Norden, SD, 57248
(605) 785-3654
Admin Joe Ward. *Medical Dir/Dir of Nursing* G R Bartron MD; Margaret Boldt DON.
Licensure Skilled care. *Beds* SNF 63. *Certified* Medicaid.
Owner Proprietary Corp (Beverly Enterprises).
Admissions Requirements Medical examination; Physician's request.
Staff Physicians 1 (pt); RNs 3 (ft); LPNs 3 (ft), 1 (pt); Nurses aides 11 (ft), 10 (pt); Physical therapists 1 (pt); Activities coordinators 1 (ft), 1 (pt); Dietitians 1 (pt).
Facilities Dining room; Activities room; Chapel; Crafts room; Laundry room; Barber/ Beauty shop.
Activities Arts & crafts; Cards; Games; Reading groups; Prayer groups; Movies; Shopping trips; Social/Cultural gatherings; Outdoor outings.

LAKE PRESTON

Kingsbury Memorial Manor
700 4 SE, Lake Preston, SD, 57249
(605) 847-4405
Admin Bob Houser. *Medical Dir/Dir of Nursing* Dr David Halliday; Sherry Nielsen DON.
Licensure Skilled care; Intermediate care. *Beds* SNF 30; ICF 35. *Certified* Medicaid.
Owner Proprietary Corp (North Central Health Services).
Admissions Requirements Medical examination; Physician's request.
Staff Physicians 2 (ft); RNs 4 (ft), 1 (pt); LPNs 2 (ft), 1 (pt); Nurses aides 20 (ft), 15 (pt); Physical therapists 1 (pt); Recreational therapists 2 (ft); Speech therapists 1 (pt); Activities coordinators 1 (ft); Dietitians 1 (pt).

Facilities Dining room; Physical therapy room; Activities room; Chapel; Crafts room; Laundry room; Barber/Beauty shop; Library; TV room.
Activities Arts & crafts; Cards; Games; Reading groups; Prayer groups; Movies; Shopping trips; Social/Cultural gatherings.

LEMMON

Five Counties Nursing Home
PO Box 449, Lemmon, SD, 57638
(605) 374-3872
Admin Helen S Lindquist. *Medical Dir/Dir of Nursing* Elizabeth Holm RN.
Licensure Skilled care. *Beds* SNF 32. *Certified* Medicaid.
Owner Nonprofit Corp.
Admissions Requirements Physician's request.
Staff RNs; LPNs; Nurses aides; Physical therapists; Activities coordinators.
Facilities Dining room; Physical therapy room; Laundry room.
Activities Arts & crafts; Cards; Games; Reading groups; Prayer groups; Movies; Picnics.

LENNOX

Good Samaritan Center*
PO Box 78, Lennox, SD, 57039
(605) 647-2251
Admin J Lynn Thomas.
Licensure Skilled care; Intermediate care. *Beds* SNF 60; ICF 9. *Certified* Medicaid.
Owner Nonprofit Corp (Evangelical Lutheran/ Good Samaritan).

LETCHER

Storla Sunset Home*
PO Box 46, Letcher, SD, 57359
(605) 248-2244
Admin L Burdell Nelson.
Licensure Intermediate care. *Beds* 53. *Certified* Medicaid.

MADISON

Bethel Lutheran Home
1001 S Egan Ave, Madison, SD, 57042
(605) 256-4539
Admin James T Iverson. *Medical Dir/Dir of Nursing* Dr Richard Sample MD; Joan Johnson RN DON.
Licensure Skilled care. *Beds* SNF 59. *Certified* Medicaid.
Owner Nonprofit Corp.
Admissions Requirements Minimum age 18; Medical examination; Physician's request.
Staff RNs 3 (ft), 4 (pt); LPNs 3 (ft); Orderlies 2 (ft); Nurses aides 20 (ft), 15 (pt); Activities coordinators 1 (ft), 1 (pt); Dietitians 1 (ft).
Affiliation Lutheran
Facilities Dining room; Activities room; Crafts room; Laundry room; Barber/Beauty shop.
Activities Arts & crafts; Cards; Games; Reading groups; Prayer groups; Movies; Shopping trips; Social/Cultural gatherings.

North American Baptist Home*
718 NE 8th St, Madison, SD, 57042
(605) 256-6621
Admin Mary DeWaard.
Licensure Skilled care; Intermediate care. *Beds* SNF 42; ICF 20. *Certified* Medicaid.
Owner Proprietary Corp (Beverly Enterprises).
Affiliation Baptist

MARION

The Tieszen Memorial Home
437 State St, Marion, SD, 57043
(605) 648-3384, 648-3611

Admin Paul I Engbrecht. *Medical Dir/Dir of Nursing* Kay Weeldreyer.
Licensure Intermediate care; Intermediate care for mentally retarded. *Beds* 64. *Certified* Medicaid.
Owner Nonprofit organization/foundation.
Admissions Requirements Medical examination.
Languages German
Facilities Dining room; Physical therapy room; Activities room; Chapel; Crafts room; Laundry room; Barber/Beauty shop; Library.
Activities Arts & crafts; Cards; Games; Reading groups; Movies; Shopping trips; Social/Cultural gatherings.

MARTIN

Bennett County Nursing Home*
PO Box 70-D, Martin, SD, 57551
Admin Darvin Jemming. *Medical Dir/Dir of Nursing* John Krecht MD.
Licensure Skilled care. *Beds* 50. *Certified* Medicaid.
Owner Publicly owned.
Staff Physicians 2 (ft); RNs 1 (ft), 2 (pt); LPNs 2 (ft), 6 (pt); Nurses aides 7 (ft), 9 (pt); Occupational therapists 1 (pt); Activities coordinators 1 (ft); Dietitians 1 (pt).

MENNO

Menno-Olivet Care Center*
Menno, SD, 57045
(605) 387-5139
Admin Ted Boese. *Medical Dir/Dir of Nursing* Dr Kaufman.
Licensure Intermediate care. *Beds* 49. *Certified* Medicaid.
Admissions Requirements Minimum age 21; Medical examination; Physician's request.
Staff RNs 1 (pt); LPNs 1 (ft), 2 (pt); Nurses aides 8 (ft), 4 (pt); Reality therapists 1 (ft); Recreational therapists 2 (pt); Activities coordinators 1 (ft); Dietitians 1 (ft).
Facilities Dining room; Physical therapy room; Activities room; Crafts room; Laundry room; Barber/Beauty shop.
Activities Arts & crafts; Cards; Games; Reading groups; Prayer groups; Movies; Shopping trips.

MILBANK

St Williams Home for Aged*
901 E Virgil Ave, Milbank, SD, 57252
(605) 432-4538
Admin Sr Bernardine Kauffmann. *Medical Dir/Dir of Nursing* V Janavs MD.
Licensure Intermediate care; Supervised care. *Beds* ICF 60; Supervised care 15. *Certified* Medicaid.
Admissions Requirements Medical examination; Physician's request.
Staff Physicians 3 (pt); RNs 1 (ft); LPNs 4 (ft), 3 (pt); Nurses aides 13 (ft), 15 (pt); Activities coordinators 2 (ft).
Affiliation Roman Catholic
Facilities Dining room; Activities room; Chapel; Crafts room; Laundry room; Barber/ Beauty shop.
Activities Arts & crafts; Cards; Games; Reading groups; Prayer groups; Movies.

Whetstone Valley Nursing Home
1103 S 2nd St, Milbank, SD, 57252
(605) 432-4556
Admin Robert Hanson. *Medical Dir/Dir of Nursing* E A Johnson MD; Joyce Kasuske DON.
Licensure Skilled care. *Beds* SNF 83. *Certified* Medicaid; Medicare.
Owner Proprietary Corp (Beverly Enterprises).
Admissions Requirements Medical examination.

Staff RNs 1 (ft), 2 (pt); LPNs 3 (ft), 4 (pt);
Nurses aides 19 (ft), 25 (pt); Physical
therapists 1 (ft); Activities coordinators 1
(ft); Dietitians 1 (ft).
Facilities Dining room; Physical therapy
room; Activities room; Crafts room; Laundry
room; Barber/Beauty shop.
Activities Arts & crafts; Cards; Games;
Reading groups; Prayer groups; Movies;
Social/Cultural gatherings.

MILLER

Prairie Good Samaritan Center
421 E 4th St, Miller, SD, 57362
(605) 853-2701
Admin Douglas B Cruff. *Medical Dir/Dir of
Nursing* Stephan Schroeder MD.
Licensure Skilled care; Supervised care. *Beds*
SNF 73; Supervised care 5. *Certified*
Medicaid.
Owner Nonprofit Corp (Evangelical Lutheran/
Good Samaritan).
Admissions Requirements Medical
examination; Physician's request.
Staff RNs 3 (ft), 7 (pt); LPNs 1 (ft), 4 (pt);
Nurses aides 12 (ft), 27 (pt); Activities
coordinators 2 (ft), 1 (pt).
Affiliation Lutheran
Facilities Dining room; Physical therapy
room; Activities room; Chapel; Crafts room;
Laundry room; Barber/Beauty shop.
Activities Arts & crafts; Games; Reading
groups; Prayer groups; Movies; Shopping
trips; Social/Cultural gatherings; Bus trips;
Community programs.

MITCHELL

Brady Memorial Home
500 S Ohlman, Mitchell, SD, 57301
(605) 996-7701
Admin Roberta Clark. *Medical Dir/Dir of
Nursing* L N Margallo MD.
Licensure Skilled care. *Beds* SNF 61. *Certified*
Medicaid.
Owner Nonprofit Corp.
Admissions Requirements Medical
examination.
Staff RNs 3 (ft), 4 (pt); LPNs 2 (pt); Nurses
aides 6 (ft), 27 (pt); Activities coordinators 1
(ft), 1 (pt).
Affiliation Roman Catholic
Facilities Dining room; Activities room;
Chapel; Crafts room; Laundry room; Barber/
Beauty shop.
Activities Arts & crafts; Cards; Games;
Reading groups; Movies; Social/Cultural
gatherings.

Firesteel Heights Nursing Home*
1120 E 7th St, Mitchell, SD, 57301
(605) 996-6526
Admin Fred Janklow.
Licensure Skilled care; Intermediate care. *Beds*
SNF 66; ICF 20. *Certified* Medicaid.
Admissions Requirements Medical
examination; Physician's request.
Facilities Dining room; Physical therapy
room; Activities room; Crafts room; Laundry
room; Barber/Beauty shop.
Activities Arts & crafts; Cards; Games;
Reading groups; Prayer groups; Movies;
Shopping trips; Social/Cultural gatherings.

Mitchell Retirement Home
101 S Main St, Mitchell, SD, 57301
(605) 996-6251
Admin Ronald D Gates.
Licensure Intermediate care. *Beds* 51.
Certified Medicaid.
Admissions Requirements Medical
examination; Physician's request.
Staff RNs 2 (ft), 1 (pt); LPNs 3 (ft), 5 (pt);
Orderlies 1 (ft); Nurses aides 14 (ft), 8 (pt);
Recreational therapists 1 (ft); Activities
coordinators 1 (ft); Dietitians 1 (pt).

Facilities Dining room; Activities room;
Chapel; Crafts room.
Activities Arts & crafts; Cards; Games;
Reading groups; Prayer groups; Movies;
Shopping trips; Social/Cultural gatherings.

Mogck Home for Aged
1520 E 1st Ave, Mitchell, SD, 57301
(605) 996-2221
Admin Dolores Juhnke Sheffield. *Medical Dir/
Dir of Nursing* Elsie Juhnke.
Licensure Supervised care. *Beds* 11.
Owner Privately owned.
Admissions Requirements Females only.
Staff LPNs 1 (ft); Nurses aides 3 (ft).
Facilities Dining room; Laundry room.
Activities Games; Movies; Shopping trips;
Bingo.

Mogck Rest Home
1510 E 1st Ave, Mitchell, SD, 57301
(605) 996-2221
Admin Dolores Juhnke Sheffield. *Medical Dir/
Dir of Nursing* Elsie Juhnke.
Licensure Supervised care. *Beds* 11.
Owner Privately owned.
Admissions Requirements Females only;
Medical examination.
Staff LPNs; Nurses aides.
Facilities Dining room; Laundry room.
Activities Cards; Movies; Bingo.

Wilge Memorial Home
619 N Kittridge, Mitchell, SD, 57301
(605) 996-4280
Admin Patricia Miles. *Medical Dir/Dir of
Nursing* Marty Andrzejewski.
Licensure Intermediate care. *Beds* ICF 23.
Certified Medicaid.
Owner Privately owned.
Admissions Requirements Medical
examination.
Staff RNs 1 (ft); LPNs 1 (ft), 4 (pt); Orderlies
1 (pt); Nurses aides 7 (pt); Activities
coordinators 1 (pt); Dietitians 1 (pt).
Facilities Dining room; Activities room;
Crafts room; Laundry room; Barber/Beauty
shop.
Activities Arts & crafts; Cards; Games;
Reading groups; Prayer groups; Movies;
Shopping trips; Social/Cultural gatherings.

MOBRIDGE

Mobridge Care Center*
1100 4th Ave E, Mobridge, SD, 57601
(605) 845-7201
Admin John Miller. *Medical Dir/Dir of
Nursing* Dr Leonard Linde.
Licensure Skilled care. *Beds* 127. *Certified*
Medicaid.
Owner Proprietary Corp (Beverly Enterprises).
Staff Physicians.
Facilities Dining room; Physical therapy
room; Activities room; Chapel; Crafts room;
Laundry room; Barber/Beauty shop.
Activities Arts & crafts; Cards; Games;
Reading groups; Prayer groups; Movies;
Shopping trips; Social/Cultural gatherings.

NEW UNDERWOOD

New Underwood Good Samaritan Center
PO Box 327, 412 S Madison, New
Underwood, SD, 57761
(605) 754-6489
Admin Scott M Pick. *Medical Dir/Dir of
Nursing* Ann Simon.
Licensure Intermediate care. *Beds* ICF 49.
Certified Medicaid.
Owner Nonprofit Corp (Evangelical Lutheran/
Good Samaritan).
Admissions Requirements Medical
examination.
Staff RNs 1 (ft); LPNs 1 (ft), 2 (pt); Nurses
aides 11 (ft), 4 (pt); Activities coordinators 1
(ft); Dietitians 1 (ft).

Languages German
Facilities Dining room; Activities room;
Chapel; Crafts room; Laundry room; Barber/
Beauty shop; Library.
Activities Arts & crafts; Cards; Games;
Reading groups; Prayer groups; Movies;
Shopping trips; Social/Cultural gatherings.

NEWELL

Lee's Rest Home
218 S Girard, Newell, SD, 57760
(605) 456-2108
Admin Norman & Joan Lee.
Licensure Intermediate care. *Beds* ICF 5.
Owner Privately owned.
Admissions Requirements Males only.
Staff RNs; Orderlies; Dietitians.
Facilities Dining room; Activities room;
Laundry room.
Activities Arts & crafts; Shopping trips; Social/
Cultural gatherings.

PARKER

Hilltop Nursing Home
PO Box 218, Parker, SD, 57053
(605) 297-3488
Admin M L Turner. *Medical Dir/Dir of
Nursing* Charlene Turner RN DON.
Licensure Intermediate care. *Beds* ICF 40.
Certified Medicaid.
Owner Proprietary Corp.
Admissions Requirements Medical
examination; Physician's request.
Staff RNs 3 (ft), 1 (pt); LPNs 1 (ft), 3 (pt);
Nurses aides 28 (pt); Physical therapists 1
(pt); Reality therapists 2 (pt); Recreational
therapists 1 (pt); Activities coordinators 1
(ft); Dietitians 1 (pt); Dentists 1 (pt).
Facilities Dining room; Activities room;
Chapel; Crafts room; Laundry room; Barber/
Beauty shop; Library.
Activities Arts & crafts; Cards; Games;
Reading groups; Prayer groups; Movies;
Shopping trips; Social/Cultural gatherings.

PARKSTON

Good Samaritan Center*
205 E Ash, Parkston, SD, 57366
(605) 928-3561
Admin William B Bender.
Licensure Supervised care. *Beds* 26. *Certified*
Medicaid.
Owner Nonprofit Corp.
Admissions Requirements Medical
examination; Physician's request.
Staff LPNs 1 (pt); Nurses aides 7 (pt);
Activities coordinators 1 (pt); Dietitians 1
(pt).
Affiliation Lutheran
Facilities Dining room; Activities room;
Chapel; Crafts room.
Activities Arts & crafts; Games; Movies;
Social/Cultural gatherings.

Good Samaritan Nursing Center*
501 W Main, Parkston, SD, 57366
(605) 928-3384
Admin William B Bender.
Licensure Intermediate care. *Beds* 47.
Certified Medicaid.
Owner Nonprofit Corp.
Admissions Requirements Medical
examination; Physician's request.
Staff RNs 1 (ft); LPNs 4 (ft); Nurses aides 4
(ft), 19 (pt); Activities coordinators 1 (ft), 1
(pt); Dietitians 1 (ft).
Affiliation Lutheran
Facilities Dining room; Activities room;
Chapel; Crafts room; Laundry room.
Activities Arts & crafts; Cards; Games;
Reading groups; Movies; Social/Cultural
gatherings.

PHILIP

Philip Nursing Home
603 W Pine, Philip, SD, 57567
(605) 859-2511
Admin E Jeanne Hunt. *Medical Dir/Dir of Nursing* George Mangulis MD; Jessica Dale RN.
Licensure Skilled care. *Beds* SNF 30. *Certified* Medicaid.
Owner Nonprofit Corp.
Admissions Requirements Medical examination; Physician's request.
Staff Physicians 1 (ft), 6 (pt); RNs 1 (ft), 5 (pt); LPNs 2 (ft), 4 (pt); Nurses aides 4 (ft), 6 (pt); Physical therapists 1 (pt); Activities coordinators 1 (ft); Dietitians 1 (pt).
Facilities Dining room; Physical therapy room; Activities room; Laundry room; Barber/Beauty shop.
Activities Arts & crafts; Cards; Games; Reading groups; Prayer groups; Movies; Shopping trips; Social/Cultural gatherings.

PIERRE

Maryhouse Inc
717 E Dakota, Pierre, SD, 57501
(605) 224-4434
Admin Jane Vogt. *Medical Dir/Dir of Nursing* R C Jahraus MD; Judy Schwartz RN DON.
Licensure Skilled care. *Beds* 105. *Certified* Medicaid; Medicare.
Owner Nonprofit Corp.
Admissions Requirements Medical examination; Physician's request.
Staff RNs 7 (ft), 1 (pt); LPNs 10 (ft), 2 (pt); Orderlies 2 (ft); Nurses aides 30 (ft), 10 (pt); Activities coordinators 2 (ft), 2 (pt).
Languages German, Lakota Sioux
Affiliation Roman Catholic
Facilities Dining room; Activities room; Chapel; Crafts room; Laundry room; Barber/Beauty shop; Library.
Activities Arts & crafts; Cards; Games; Reading groups; Prayer groups; Movies; Shopping trips; Social/Cultural gatherings.

Rivercrest Manor*
951 E Dakota, Pierre, SD, 57501
(605) 224-8628
Admin Jan Paulson. *Medical Dir/Dir of Nursing* Thomas Huber MD.
Licensure Skilled care; Intermediate care. *Beds* SNF 64; ICF 8. *Certified* Medicaid.
Owner Proprietary Corp (Beverly Enterprises).
Admissions Requirements Medical examination; Physician's request.
Staff RNs 4 (ft); LPNs 6 (ft); Orderlies 1 (ft); Nurses aides 9 (ft), 13 (pt); Physical therapists 1 (ft); Activities coordinators 1 (ft); Dietitians 1 (ft).
Facilities Dining room; Activities room; Crafts room; Laundry room; Barber/Beauty shop.
Activities Arts & crafts; Cards; Games; Reading groups; Prayer groups; Movies; Shopping trips; Social/Cultural gatherings.

PLATTE

Platte Nursing Home
Platte, SD, 57369
(605) 337-3131
Admin Patricia Biddle. *Medical Dir/Dir of Nursing* Dr J W Bents.
Licensure Skilled care; Intermediate care. *Beds* 48. *Certified* Medicaid.
Admissions Requirements Physician's request.
Staff Physical therapists 1 (pt); Activities coordinators 1 (ft), 1 (pt); Dietitians 1 (pt).
Facilities Dining room; Activities room; Crafts room; Barber/Beauty shop.
Activities Arts & crafts; Cards; Games; Reading groups; Prayer groups; Shopping trips.

QUINN

Hilltop Retirement Home*
PO Box 8, Quinn, SD, 57775
(605) 386-2421
Admin Augusta Murphy.
Licensure Supervised care. *Beds* 8.

RAPID CITY

Black Hills Retirement Center
1620 N 7th St, Rapid City, SD, 57701
(605) 343-4958
Admin Karen Jensen. *Medical Dir/Dir of Nursing* Brenda Anton RN DON.
Licensure Intermediate care. *Beds* ICF 74. *Certified* Medicaid.
Owner Proprietary Corp (Beverly Enterprises).
Admissions Requirements Medical examination; Physician's request.
Staff RNs 1 (ft), 2 (pt); LPNs 2 (ft), 4 (pt); Orderlies 1 (pt); Nurses aides 12 (ft), 14 (pt); Activities coordinators 1 (ft), 1 (pt).
Facilities Dining room; Activities room; Crafts room; Laundry room; Barber/Beauty shop; Dayroom; Solarium.
Activities Arts & crafts; Games; Reading groups; Prayer groups; Movies; Social/Cultural gatherings.

Boardman Community Care Home
6604 Green Willow Dr, Rapid City, SD, 57701
(605) 342-0885
Admin Dottie Boardman.
Licensure Supervised care. *Beds* 7.

Clarkson Mountain View Guest Home*
1015 Mountain View Rd, Rapid City, SD, 57701
(605) 343-5882
Admin Corrinne Haedt.
Licensure Skilled care. *Beds* 52. *Certified* Medicaid.

Hillview Nursing Home*
302 Saint Cloud St, Rapid City, SD, 57701
(605) 343-4738
Admin Chet Beebe. *Medical Dir/Dir of Nursing* Dr Finely.
Licensure Skilled care. *Beds* 70. *Certified* Medicaid.
Owner Proprietary Corp (Beverly Enterprises).
Admissions Requirements Medical examination.
Staff RNs 2 (ft), 2 (pt); LPNs 2 (ft), 2 (pt); Nurses aides 21 (ft), 6 (pt); Physical therapists 1 (pt); Activities coordinators 2 (ft); Dietitians 1 (ft); Dentists 1 (pt).
Facilities Dining room; Physical therapy room; Activities room; Chapel; Crafts room; Laundry room; Barber/Beauty shop; Library.
Activities Arts & crafts; Games; Reading groups; Prayer groups; Movies; Shopping trips; Social/Cultural gatherings.

Meadowbrook Manor
2500 Arrowhead Dr, Rapid City, SD, 57702
(605) 348-0285
Admin Jeannette Hull. *Medical Dir/Dir of Nursing* Barney Nichols DON.
Licensure Skilled care. *Beds* SNF 76. *Certified* Medicaid.
Owner Proprietary Corp (Beverly Enterprises).
Admissions Requirements Medical examination; Physician's request.
Staff RNs 6 (ft); LPNs 4 (ft); Orderlies 6 (ft); Nurses aides 33 (ft); Activities coordinators 2 (ft); Dietitians 1 (ft).
Facilities Dining room; Physical therapy room; Activities room; Crafts room; Laundry room; Barber/Beauty shop.
Activities Arts & crafts; Cards; Games; Reading groups; Prayer groups; Movies; Shopping trips; Social/Cultural gatherings.

O'Brien's Rest Home*
1131 Wood Ave, Rapid City, SD, 57701
(605) 342-4570
Admin Elizabeth O'Brien.
Licensure Supervised care. *Beds* 6.

Rapid City Care Center*
916 Mountain View Rd, Rapid City, SD, 57701
(605) 343-8500
Admin Ron Ross.
Licensure Intermediate care. *Beds* 99. *Certified* Medicaid.
Owner Proprietary Corp (Beverly Enterprises).

Rapid City Nursing Center*
2908 5th St, Rapid City, SD, 57701
(605) 343-8500
Admin Roland Marinkovic.
Licensure Skilled care. *Beds* 51. *Certified* Medicaid.

REDFIELD

Eastern Star Home Inc
PO Box 150, 126 W 12th Ave, Redfield, SD, 574690150
(605) 472-2053
Admin Mary Fountain. *Medical Dir/Dir of Nursing* Judy Scnabel, RN.
Licensure Intermediate care. *Beds* ICF 30.
Owner Nonprofit Corp.
Admissions Requirements Medical examination.
Staff RNs 1 (ft), 2 (pt); LPNs 2 (pt); Nurses aides 3 (ft), 7 (pt); Activities coordinators 1 (ft).
Affiliation Eastern Star
Facilities Dining room; Activities room; Chapel; Crafts room; Laundry room; Barber/Beauty shop; Library.
Activities Arts & crafts; Cards; Games; Reading groups; Prayer groups; Movies; Shopping trips; Social/Cultural gatherings.

James Valley Nursing Home*
1015 3rd St E, Redfield, SD, 57469
(605) 472-2288
Admin Joan Williams.
Licensure Skilled care. *Beds* 87. *Certified* Medicaid.
Owner Proprietary Corp (Beverly Enterprises).

ROSHOLT

Rosholt Nursing Home
Box 108, Rosholt, SD, 57260
(605) 537-4272
Admin Shirleen Fossum. *Medical Dir/Dir of Nursing* Dr Joseph Kass.
Licensure Intermediate care. *Beds* ICF 49. *Certified* Medicaid.
Owner Proprietary Corp.
Admissions Requirements Medical examination; Physician's request.
Staff Physicians 2 (pt); RNs 1 (ft); LPNs 1 (ft), 5 (pt); Nurses aides 7 (ft), 15 (pt); Physical therapists 1 (pt); Activities coordinators 1 (ft), 2 (pt); Dietitians 1 (pt); Pharmacists 1 (pt).
Facilities Dining room; Activities room; Crafts room; Laundry room; Barber/Beauty shop.
Activities Arts & crafts; Cards; Games; Reading groups; Prayer groups; Movies; Shopping trips; Social/Cultural gatherings; Baking; Gardening; Dining out.

ROSLYN

Strand-Kjorsvig Community Rest Home
PO Box 195, Roslyn, SD, 57261
(605) 486-4523
Admin Bernie H P Hanson. *Medical Dir/Dir of Nursing* Barbara Stueland.
Licensure Intermediate care. *Beds* ICF 36. *Certified* Medicaid.

Owner Nonprofit Corp.
Admissions Requirements Medical examination; Physician's request.
Staff RNs 1 (ft), 1 (pt); Nurses aides 6 (ft), 11 (pt); Occupational therapists 1 (pt); Activities coordinators 1 (ft); Dietitians 1 (pt).
Facilities Dining room; Activities room; Chapel; Laundry room; Barber/Beauty shop.
Activities Arts & crafts; Cards; Games; Reading groups; Prayer groups; Social/ Cultural gatherings.

SALEM

Colonial Manor of Salem
500 Colonial Dr, Salem, SD, 57058
(605) 425-2203
Admin Dennis C Gourley.
Licensure Skilled care. *Beds* 63. *Certified* Medicaid.
Owner Proprietary Corp (Beverly Enterprises).
Admissions Requirements Physician's request.
Staff RNs; LPNs; Orderlies; Nurses aides; Activities coordinators; Dietitians.
Facilities Dining room; Physical therapy room; Activities room; Chapel; Laundry room; Barber/Beauty shop.
Activities Arts & crafts; Cards; Games; Reading groups; Prayer groups; Movies; Shopping trips; Social/Cultural gatherings.

SCOTLAND

Scotland Good Samaritan Center
Box 428, Scotland, SD, 57059
(605) 583-2216
Admin Tom Hoy. *Medical Dir/Dir of Nursing* Dr M Ramos & Dr E Mueller; Gladys Hasz DON.
Licensure Intermediate care. *Beds* ICF 62. *Certified* Medicaid.
Owner Nonprofit Corp (Evangelical Lutheran/ Good Samaritan).
Admissions Requirements Minimum age 18; Medical examination; Physician's request.
Staff RNs 2 (ft); LPNs 4 (pt); Orderlies; Nurses aides 15 (ft), 15 (pt); Recreational therapists 2 (ft); Activities coordinators 1 (ft).
Languages German, Bohemian, Czech
Affiliation Lutheran
Facilities Dining room; Physical therapy room; Activities room; Chapel; Crafts room; Laundry room; Barber/Beauty shop; Library; Adult day care room.
Activities Arts & crafts; Cards; Games; Reading groups; Prayer groups; Movies; Shopping trips; Social/Cultural gatherings; Worship services & devotions; Volunteer & auxiliary programs.

SELBY

Good Samaritan Center
4861 Lincoln Ave, Selby, SD, 57472
(605) 649-7744
Admin Dolores Riedlinger.
Licensure Intermediate care. *Beds* 64. *Certified* Medicaid.
Owner Nonprofit Corp (Evangelical Lutheran/ Good Samaritan).
Admissions Requirements Medical examination.
Staff RNs 1 (ft); LPNs 4 (ft); Nurses aides 9 (ft), 18 (pt); Activities coordinators 1 (ft); Dietitians 1 (pt).
Affiliation Lutheran
Facilities Dining room; Activities room; Chapel; Crafts room; Laundry room; Barber/ Beauty shop.
Activities Arts & crafts; Cards; Games; Reading groups; Prayer groups; Movies.

SIOUX FALLS

Bethany Lutheran Home*
1901 S Holly, Sioux Falls, SD, 57105
(605) 338-2351
Admin John Roth. *Medical Dir/Dir of Nursing* Tim Hurley.
Licensure Skilled care. *Beds* 112. *Certified* Medicaid.
Admissions Requirements Medical examination; Physician's request.
Staff RNs 9 (ft), 7 (pt); LPNs 5 (ft), 4 (pt); Nurses aides 31 (ft), 49 (pt); Reality therapists 2 (ft), 1 (pt); Recreational therapists 2 (ft), 2 (pt); Activities coordinators 1 (ft); Dietitians 1 (pt).
Affiliation Lutheran
Facilities Dining room; Physical therapy room; Activities room; Crafts room; Laundry room; Barber/Beauty shop; Hospitality room.
Activities Arts & crafts; Cards; Games; Reading groups; Prayer groups; Movies; Shopping trips; Exercises.

Covington Heights Health Care Center
3900 Cathy Ave, Sioux Falls, SD, 58106
(605) 361-8822
Admin Gary L Brink. *Medical Dir/Dir of Nursing* Dr S Devick; Shelly Clauson RN DON.
Licensure Skilled care. *Beds* SNF 109. *Certified* Medicaid; Medicare.
Owner Proprietary Corp (Beverly Enterprises).
Admissions Requirements Medical examination.
Staff RNs; LPNs; Orderlies; Nurses aides; Activities coordinators; Dietitians.
Facilities Dining room; Physical therapy room; Activities room; Crafts room; Laundry room; Barber/Beauty shop.
Activities Arts & crafts; Cards; Games; Reading groups; Prayer groups; Movies; Shopping trips; Social/Cultural gatherings.

Dow-Rummel Village
1000 N Lake Ave, Sioux Falls, SD, 57104
(605) 336-1490
Admin Ralph Jensen. *Medical Dir/Dir of Nursing* Helen Carlson RN.
Licensure Intermediate care; Self care; Cottage apts. *Beds* ICF 28; Self care 73; Cottage apts 11. *Certified* Medicaid.
Owner Nonprofit Corp.
Admissions Requirements Medical examination.
Staff RNs 3 (ft), 4 (pt); LPNs 1 (ft), 1 (pt); Nurses aides 7 (ft), 4 (pt); Activities coordinators 1 (ft).
Facilities Dining room; Activities room; Chapel; Crafts room; Laundry room; Barber/ Beauty shop; Library; Private dining room.
Activities Arts & crafts; Cards; Prayer groups; Movies; Shopping trips.

Good Samaritan Center*
401 W 2nd, Sioux Falls, SD, 57104
(605) 336-6252
Admin Norman Stordahl. *Medical Dir/Dir of Nursing* Dr P E Lakstigala.
Licensure Skilled care. *Beds* 141. *Certified* Medicaid.
Owner Nonprofit Corp (Evangelical Lutheran/ Good Samaritan).
Admissions Requirements Minimum age 14; Medical examination.
Staff Physicians 1 (pt); RNs 7 (ft), 4 (pt); LPNs 7 (ft), 2 (pt); Orderlies 3 (ft); Nurses aides 39 (ft), 28 (pt); Physical therapists 2 (pt); Recreational therapists 2 (ft); Occupational therapists 1 (pt); Speech therapists 1 (pt); Activities coordinators 1 (ft), 1 (pt); Dietitians 1 (pt); Dentists 1 (pt); Podiatrists 1 (pt); Audiologists 1 (pt).
Facilities Dining room; Physical therapy room; Activities room; Chapel; Crafts room; Laundry room; Barber/Beauty shop.

Activities Arts & crafts; Cards; Games; Reading groups; Prayer groups; Movies; Shopping trips; Social/Cultural gatherings; Bible study.

Good Samaritan Luther Manor
2900 S Lake Ave, Sioux Falls, SD, 57105
(605) 336-1997
Admin Kayln H Johnson. *Medical Dir/Dir of Nursing* Dr Devick; Peggy Roberts.
Licensure Skilled care. *Beds* SNF 118. *Certified* Medicaid.
Owner Nonprofit Corp (Evangelical Lutheran/ Good Samaritan).
Admissions Requirements Medical examination.
Staff Physicians 1 (pt); RNs 2 (ft), 12 (pt); LPNs 1 (ft), 7 (pt); Orderlies 5 (ft); Nurses aides 35 (ft), 30 (pt); Physical therapists 5 (ft); Activities coordinators 2 (ft), 2 (pt); Dietitians 1 (pt); Ophthalmologists 1 (pt).
Affiliation Lutheran
Facilities Dining room; Physical therapy room; Activities room; Chapel; Laundry room; Barber/Beauty shop; Privacy room; Chapel/Dining combination.
Activities Games; Reading groups; Movies; Social/Cultural gatherings.

Mom & Dad's Home & Health Care Center
3600 S Norton Ave, Sioux Falls, SD, 57105
(605) 338-9891
Admin Barbara Severson. *Medical Dir/Dir of Nursing* Dr A P Reding; Nita Birk RN.
Licensure Skilled care; Intermediate care. *Beds* SNF 109; ICF 59. *Certified* Medicaid.
Owner Proprietary Corp.
Admissions Requirements Medical examination.
Staff RNs 9 (ft); LPNs 11 (ft), 4 (pt); Orderlies 7 (ft), 2 (pt); Nurses aides 47 (ft), 34 (pt); Activities coordinators 2 (ft), 2 (pt); Dietitians 1 (ft).
Facilities Dining room; Physical therapy room; Activities room; Chapel; Crafts room; Laundry room; Barber/Beauty shop; Library.
Activities Arts & crafts; Cards; Games; Reading groups; Prayer groups; Movies; Shopping trips; Social/Cultural gatherings.

Sioux Falls Good Samaritan Village
3901 S Marion Rd, Sioux Falls, SD, 57106
(605) 361-3311
Admin John B Larson. *Medical Dir/Dir of Nursing* Larry Sittner MD; Lael Smith RN DON.
Licensure Skilled care; Intermediate care; Supervised living. *Beds* SNF 55; ICF 90; Supervised living 77. *Certified* Medicaid.
Owner Nonprofit Corp (Evangelical Lutheran/ Good Samaritan).
Admissions Requirements Medical examination; Physician's request.
Staff RNs; LPNs; Orderlies; Nurses aides 110 (ft); Activities coordinators 1 (ft); Dietitians 1 (pt).
Facilities Dining room; Activities room; Chapel; Crafts room; Laundry room; Barber/ Beauty shop; Library; Restorative nursing; Meeting room.
Activities Arts & crafts; Cards; Games; Reading groups; Prayer groups; Movies; Shopping trips; Social/Cultural gatherings.

Wee Rest Home*
5405 Romar Dr, Sioux Falls, SD, 57107
(605) 332-0280
Admin Dewey Hartsuiker.
Licensure Supervised care. *Beds* 5.
Admissions Requirements Females only.
Facilities Dining room; Laundry room.

SISSETON

Tekakwitha Nursing Home
6 E Chestnut, Sisseton, SD, 57262
(605) 698-7693

Admin Sr Siena Wald. *Medical Dir/Dir of Nursing* David Oey MD; Carolyn Hanson.
Licensure Skilled care; Intermediate care. *Beds* SNF 46; ICF 55. *Certified* Medicaid.
Owner Nonprofit Corp (Missionary Oblates of Mary Imm).
Admissions Requirements Medical examination; Physician's request.
Staff RNs 2 (ft), 1 (pt); LPNs 5 (ft), 3 (pt); Recreational therapists 1 (pt); Activities coordinators 1 (ft), 1 (pt); Dietitians 1 (ft).
Facilities Dining room; Physical therapy room; Activities room; Chapel; Crafts room; Laundry room; Barber/Beauty shop.
Activities Arts & crafts; Cards; Games; Reading groups; Prayer groups; Movies; Shopping trips; Social/Cultural gatherings.

SPEARFISH

David M Dorsett Health Care Facility
1020 10th St, Spearfish, SD, 57783-2297
(605) 642-2716
Admin James L Haeder. *Medical Dir/Dir of Nursing* Dr Warren Golliher; Barbara Jordan RN.
Licensure Skilled care. *Beds* SNF 62; ICF 58. *Certified* Medicaid.
Owner Proprietary Corp (North Central Health Services).
Admissions Requirements Minimum age 18; Medical examination; Physician's request.
Staff RNs 4 (ft), 3 (pt); LPNs 2 (ft), 3 (pt); Orderlies 3 (ft), 1 (pt); Nurses aides 35 (ft), 16 (pt); Activities coordinators 1 (ft).
Facilities Dining room; Physical therapy room; Activities room; Crafts room; Laundry room; Barber/Beauty shop; Library.
Activities Arts & crafts; Cards; Games; Reading groups; Prayer groups; Movies; Social/Cultural gatherings.

Upper Valley Rest Home
262 Upper Valley Rd, Spearfish, SD, 57783
(605) 642-5021
Admin Lowell & Joyce Carlson.
Licensure Supervised care. *Beds* 9. *Certified* Medicaid.
Owner Privately owned.
Admissions Requirements Medical examination; Physician's request.
Staff Nurses aides.
Facilities Dining room; Laundry room.
Activities Arts & crafts; Prayer groups; Shopping trips; Social/Cultural gatherings.

Walker's Veterans Home*
1004 5th St, Spearfish, SD, 57783
(605) 642-3911
Admin Ronald Walker.
Licensure Supervised care. *Beds* 8.
Admissions Requirements Minimum age 18; Medical examination.
Staff Nurses aides; Recreational therapists; Activities coordinators.
Facilities Dining room; Activities room; Crafts room; Laundry room.
Activities Arts & crafts; Cards; Shopping trips.

STURGIS

B & C Rest Home
341 9th St, Sturgis, SD, 57785
(605) 347-3659 or 347-4384
Admin Charles E Jones.
Licensure Rest home. *Beds* 25.
Owner Privately owned.
Admissions Requirements Medical examination; Physician's request.
Staff Orderlies 2 (ft); Nurses aides 2 (ft).
Facilities Dining room; Activities room; Laundry room; Barber/Beauty shop.
Activities Arts & crafts; Cards; Games; Movies; Shopping trips; Social/Cultural gatherings.

Nelson's Rest Home*
1124 2nd St, Sturgis, SD, 57785
(605) 347-2405
Admin Wayne Nelson & Betty Nelson.
Licensure Supervised care. *Beds* 9.

Pina Home for the Aged
1542 Davenport St, Sturgis, SD, 57785
(605) 347-2770
Admin Eugene Flaglore.
Licensure Supervised personal home care. *Beds* Home care 13.
Owner Privately owned.
Admissions Requirements Medical examination.
Facilities Dining room.
Activities Cards; Games; Reading groups.

Sturgis Community Health Care Center
PO Box 279, 949 Harmon St, Sturgis, SD, 57785
(605) 347-2536
Admin Michael Penticoff. *Medical Dir/Dir of Nursing* LL Massa DO.
Licensure Skilled care; Intermediate care. *Beds* SNF 39; ICF 45. *Certified* Medicaid.
Admissions Requirements Physician's request.
Staff RNs 2 (ft), 3 (pt); LPNs 2 (ft), 7 (pt); Nurses aides 21 (ft), 24 (pt); Physical therapists 1 (pt); Activities coordinators 2 (ft); Dietitians 1 (pt).
Facilities Dining room; Physical therapy room; Activities room; Chapel; Crafts room; Laundry room; Barber/Beauty shop.
Activities Arts & crafts; Cards; Games; Reading groups; Prayer groups; Movies; Shopping trips; Social/Cultural gatherings.

We Care Home for the Aged*
1733 Davenport St, Sturgis, SD, 57785
(605) 347-2251
Admin Allen Moeller & Sandra Moeller.
Licensure Supervised care. *Beds* 8.

TRIPP

Good Samaritan Center*
PO Box 370, Tripp, SD, 57376
(605) 935-6101
Admin Daniel J Fosness.
Licensure Intermediate care; Supervised care. *Beds* ICF 62; Supervised care 5. *Certified* Medicaid.
Owner Nonprofit Corp (Evangelical Lutheran/ Good Samaritan).

TYNDALL

St Michael's Nursing Home
PO Box 27, Tyndall, SD, 57066
(605) 589-3341
Admin Gale Walker.
Licensure Skilled care. *Beds* 9. *Certified* Medicaid.

Tyndall Good Samaritan Center
PO Box 460, 800 N State St, Tyndall, SD, 57066
(605) 589-3350
Admin Lynden R Heiman. *Medical Dir/Dir of Nursing* Teri VaVruska.
Licensure Intermediate care. *Beds* ICF 71. *Certified* Medicaid.
Owner Nonprofit Corp (Evangelical Lutheran/ Good Samaritan).
Admissions Requirements Medical examination; Physician's request.
Staff RNs 1 (ft), 1 (pt); LPNs 5 (ft); Nurses aides 20 (ft); Activities coordinators 1 (ft); Restorative aides 1 (ft), 2 (pt).
Languages Czech, German, Dutch
Affiliation Lutheran
Facilities Dining room; Physical therapy room; Activities room; Chapel; Crafts room; Laundry room; Barber/Beauty shop; Library; Family room; Solarium.

Activities Arts & crafts; Cards; Games; Reading groups; Prayer groups; Movies; Shopping trips; Social/Cultural gatherings; Cooking; Baking.

VERMILLION

Southeastern Dakota Nursing Home
102 S Plum St, Vermillion, SD, 57069
(605) 624-4481
Admin Dale Garris.
Licensure Intermediate care. *Beds* ICF 66. *Certified* Medicaid.
Owner Nonprofit Corp.
Admissions Requirements Medical examination.
Staff RNs 4 (ft), 4 (pt); LPNs 3 (ft), 1 (pt); Orderlies 6 (pt); Nurses aides 12 (ft), 20 (pt); Activities coordinators 3 (ft).
Facilities Dining room; Physical therapy room; Activities room; Chapel; Crafts room; Barber/Beauty shop; Library on wheels.
Activities Arts & crafts; Cards; Games; Reading groups; Prayer groups; Movies; Shopping trips; Social/Cultural gatherings.

VIBORG

Pioneer Memorial Nursing Home
PO Box 368, Viborg, SD, 57070
(605) 326-5161
Admin Douglas R Ekeren. *Medical Dir/Dir of Nursing* E G Nelson MD.
Licensure Intermediate care. *Beds* ICF 52. *Certified* Medicaid.
Owner Nonprofit Corp.
Staff RNs 2 (ft); LPNs 1 (ft), 2 (pt); Nurses aides 6 (ft), 17 (pt); Physical therapists 1 (pt); Activities coordinators 1 (ft); Dietitians 1 (pt).
Facilities Dining room; Physical therapy room; Activities room; Chapel; Crafts room; Laundry room; Barber/Beauty shop; Library.
Activities Arts & crafts; Cards; Games; Reading groups; Prayer groups; Movies; Shopping trips; Social/Cultural gatherings; Current events; Bowling.

VOLGA

Parkview Home*
PO Box 328, Volga, SD, 57071
(605) 627-9141
Admin Mabel Eggebraaten.
Licensure Supervised care. *Beds* 25.

WAGNER

Wagner Good Samaritan Center
W Hwy 46, Wagner, SD, 57380
(605) 384-3661
Admin Sarah Jane Goldhammer. *Medical Dir/ Dir of Nursing* Gloria Buhler RN DON.
Licensure Intermediate care; Supervised care. *Beds* 77. *Certified* Medicaid.
Owner Nonprofit Corp (Evangelical Lutheran/ Good Samaritan).
Admissions Requirements Physician's request.
Staff RNs 1 (ft), 3 (pt); LPNs 1 (ft); Nurses aides 8 (ft), 9 (pt); Activities coordinators 1 (ft), 2 (pt); Dietitians 1 (pt).
Affiliation Lutheran
Facilities Dining room; Physical therapy room; Activities room; Chapel; Crafts room; Laundry room; Barber/Beauty shop.
Activities Arts & crafts; Cards; Games; Reading groups; Prayer groups; Movies; Shopping trips.

WAKONDA

Wakonda Heritage Manor
Box 327, Wakonda, SD, 57073
(605) 267-2081

Admin Warren G Kuhler. *Medical Dir/Dir of Nursing* Marilyn Rhymer DON.
Licensure Intermediate care; Supervised care. *Beds* ICF 44; Supervised care 1. *Certified* Medicare.
Owner Nonprofit Corp.
Admissions Requirements Physician's request.
Staff RNs 4 (pt); LPNs 2 (ft); Nurses aides 3 (ft), 10 (pt); Activities coordinators 2 (ft); Dietitians 1 (pt).
Facilities Dining room; Activities room; Crafts room; Laundry room; Barber/Beauty shop; Library.
Activities Arts & crafts; Cards; Games; Reading groups; Prayer groups; Movies; Shopping trips; Social/Cultural gatherings.

WATERTOWN

Brugman Home
1365 2nd St NW, Watertown, SD, 57201
(605) 886-8395
Admin Joyce Brugman.
Licensure Supervised care. *Beds* 4.
Owner Privately owned.
Admissions Requirements Medical examination.
Facilities Dining room.
Activities Arts & crafts; Cards; Games; Movies.

Hazels Rest Home
520 2nd Ave SE, Watertown, SD, 57201
(605) 882-1768
Admin Hazel Pekelder.
Licensure Supervised care. *Beds* 6.
Owner Privately owned.
Admissions Requirements Medical examination.
Facilities Dining room; Activities room.

Jenkins Methodist Home Inc
12 2nd Ave SE, Watertown, SD, 57201
(605) 886-5777
Admin Allen D Swan. *Medical Dir/Dir of Nursing* G R Bartron MD.
Licensure Skilled care; Intermediate care. *Beds* SNF 166; ICF 16. *Certified* Medicaid; Medicare.
Owner Nonprofit Corp.
Admissions Requirements Medical examination.
Staff RNs 2 (ft), 10 (pt); LPNs 3 (ft), 15 (pt); Nurses aides 40 (ft), 54 (pt); Recreational therapists 3 (pt), 1 (pt); Activities coordinators 1 (ft); Dietitians 1 (ft), 1 (pt).
Affiliation Methodist
Facilities Dining room; Physical therapy room; Activities room; Chapel; Crafts room; Laundry room; Barber/Beauty shop; Library.
Activities Arts & crafts; Cards; Games; Reading groups; Prayer groups; Movies; Shopping trips; Social/Cultural gatherings.

Prairie Lakes Nursing Home
420 4th St NE, Watertown, SD, 57201
(605) 886-8431
Admin Edmond L Weiland. *Medical Dir/Dir of Nursing* G R Bartron MD; Sr Augusta Johnson, Director of Aging.
Licensure Skilled care. *Beds* SNF 51. *Certified* Medicaid.
Owner Nonprofit Corp.
Admissions Requirements Medical examination; Physician's request.
Staff RNs 2 (ft), 1 (pt); LPNs 4 (ft), 6 (pt); Nurses aides 13 (ft), 8 (pt); Physical therapists 1 (ft); Activities coordinators 1 (ft), 1 (pt); Dietitians 1 (ft).
Facilities Dining room; Physical therapy room; Activities room; Chapel; Crafts room; Laundry room; Barber/Beauty shop.
Activities Arts & crafts; Cards; Games; Reading groups; Prayer groups; Movies; Shopping trips; Social/Cultural gatherings.

WAUBAY

Waubay Rest Home*
1st Ave W, Waubay, SD, 57273
(605) 947-4361
Admin Mildred Gregerson & Mary Warns.
Licensure Supervised care. *Beds* 9.
Admissions Requirements Medical examination.
Staff Orderlies 2 (ft); Nurses aides 2 (ft).
Facilities Dining room; Laundry room.
Activities Cards; Prayer groups; Shopping trips; Social/Cultural gatherings.

WEBSTER

Bethesda Home
W Hwy 12, Webster, SD, 57274
(605) 345-3331
Admin Robert E Faehn. *Medical Dir/Dir of Nursing* Dr Kevin Bjordahl; Miriam Skilbred RN DON.
Licensure Skilled care. *Beds* SNF 58. *Certified* Medicaid.
Owner Nonprofit organization/foundation.
Admissions Requirements Physician's request.
Staff Physicians 1 (pt); RNs 2 (ft), 5 (pt); LPNs 2 (pt); Orderlies 1 (pt); Nurses aides 30 (pt); Physical therapists 1 (pt); Reality therapists 2 (pt); Recreational therapists 1 (pt); Activities coordinators 1 (ft), 2 (pt); Dietitians 1 (pt).
Affiliation Lutheran
Facilities Dining room; Physical therapy room; Activities room; Crafts room; Laundry room; Barber/Beauty shop.
Activities Arts & crafts; Cards; Games; Reading groups; Prayer groups; Movies; Shopping trips.

WESSINGTON SPRINGS

Springs Senior Citizens Home Inc Weskota Manor
PO Box S, 611 1st St NE, Wessington Springs, SD, 57382
(605) 539-1621
Admin Thomas V Richter. *Medical Dir/Dir of Nursing* Dr R E Dean; Dorothy Willman RN DON.
Licensure Intermediate care. *Beds* ICF 40. *Certified* Medicaid.
Owner Nonprofit Corp.
Admissions Requirements Medical examination.
Staff RNs 2 (ft); LPNs 1 (pt); Nurses aides 4 (ft), 17 (pt); Activities coordinators 1 (ft); Dietitians 1 (ft).
Facilities Dining room; Activities room; Chapel; Crafts room; Laundry room; Barber/Beauty shop; Library; TV lounge.
Activities Cards; Games; Reading groups; Prayer groups; Movies; Shopping trips; School programs.

WHITE

White Care Center Inc
PO Box 68, White, SD, 57276
(605) 629-2881
Admin Allen P Svennes. *Medical Dir/Dir of Nursing* Delores Jorenby RN.
Licensure Intermediate care. *Beds* ICF 61. *Certified* Medicaid.
Owner Nonprofit Corp.
Staff RNs 2 (ft), 2 (pt); LPNs 3 (ft), 20 (pt); Orderlies 2 (ft); Nurses aides 7 (ft), 12 (pt); Reality therapists 1 (ft); Recreational therapists 1 (ft); Activities coordinators 1 (ft).
Facilities Dining room; Physical therapy room; Activities room; Chapel; Laundry room; Barber/Beauty shop.
Activities Arts & crafts; Cards; Games; Reading groups; Prayer groups; Movies; Shopping trips; Social/Cultural gatherings.

WHITE LAKE

Aurora-Brule Nursing Home*
PO Box 217, White Lake, SD, 57383
(605) 249-2216
Admin Larry Fredericksen.
Licensure Intermediate care. *Beds* 77. *Certified* Medicaid.

WHITE RIVER

Heritage of White River*
Box 310, White River, SD, 57579
(605) 259-3161
Admin Jon Covault.
Licensure Intermediate care. *Beds* 52. *Certified* Medicaid.
Admissions Requirements Medical examination.
Staff RNs 1 (ft), 1 (pt); LPNs 1 (ft); Orderlies 1 (ft); Nurses aides 15 (ft), 2 (pt); Activities coordinators 1 (ft), 1 (pt).
Facilities Dining room; Physical therapy room; Activities room; Chapel; Crafts room; Laundry room; Barber/Beauty shop.
Activities Arts & crafts; Cards; Games; Reading groups; Movies; Shopping trips.

WILMOT

Wilmot Community Home
RR 2 Box 3, Wilmot, SD, 57279
(605) 938-4418
Admin Audrey Utley. *Medical Dir/Dir of Nursing* Colette Weyh RN DON.
Licensure Intermediate care. *Beds* ICF 46. *Certified* Medicaid.
Owner Proprietary Corp.
Admissions Requirements Medical examination; Physician's request.
Staff RNs 1 (ft); LPNs 2 (pt); Nurses aides 23 (pt); Activities coordinators 1 (ft).
Facilities Dining room; Activities room; Crafts room; Laundry room; Barber/Beauty shop; Patio.
Activities Arts & crafts; Cards; Games; Reading groups; Prayer groups; Movies; Shopping trips; Social/Cultural gatherings; Residents council.

WINNER

Winner Nursing Home
956 E 7th St, Winner, SD, 57580
(605) 842-3483
Admin Elsie S Jensen. *Medical Dir/Dir of Nursing* Rhonda L Olson DON.
Licensure Skilled care. *Beds* SNF 81. *Certified* Medicaid.
Owner Proprietary Corp (Beverly Enterprises).
Admissions Requirements Medical examination; Physician's request.
Staff RNs 3 (ft); LPNs 6 (ft); Nurses aides 35 (ft); Activities coordinators 2 (ft); Dietitians 1 (ft).
Facilities Dining room; Activities room; Laundry room; Barber/Beauty shop.
Activities Arts & crafts; Cards; Games; Reading groups; Prayer groups; Movies; Social/Cultural gatherings.

WOONSOCKET

Prairie View Care Center*
Woonsocket, SD, 57385
(605) 796-4467
Admin Charlene Nash.
Licensure Intermediate care. *Beds* 52. *Certified* Medicaid.
Admissions Requirements Medical examination; Physician's request.
Staff RNs 1 (ft), 2 (pt); LPNs 3 (ft); Orderlies 2 (pt); Nurses aides 7 (ft), 6 (pt); Activities coordinators 1 (ft), 1 (pt).

Facilities Dining room; Activities room; Chapel; Laundry room; Barber/Beauty shop.
Activities Arts & crafts; Cards; Games; Reading groups; Prayer groups; Movies; Shopping trips; Social/Cultural gatherings.

YANKTON

Sister James' Nursing Home
1000 W 4th St, Yankton, SD, 57078
(605) 665-9371
Admin Pamela Rezac. *Medical Dir/Dir of Nursing* Dr T H Sattler; Lou Moore RN DON.
Licensure Skilled care; Intermediate care; Intermediate care for mentally retarded. *Beds* SNF 53; ICF 60. *Certified* Medicaid.
Owner Nonprofit Corp.
Admissions Requirements Medical examination; Physician's request.

Staff RNs 5 (ft), 4 (pt); LPNs 3 (ft), 2 (pt); Orderlies 1 (pt); Nurses aides 18 (ft), 25 (pt).
Affiliation Roman Catholic
Facilities Dining room; Activities room; Chapel; Crafts room; Laundry room; Barber/Beauty shop.
Activities Arts & crafts; Cards; Games; Prayer groups; Movies; Shopping trips; Social/Cultural gatherings.

Sunshine Nursing Home*
1014 W 8th St, Yankton, SD, 57078
(605) 665-5348
Admin Margaret Jansen.
Licensure Intermediate care. *Beds* 15. *Certified* Medicaid.

Yankton Care Center
PO Box 714, 1212 W 8th, Yankton, SD, 57078
(605) 665-9429

Admin Anthony D Cates. *Medical Dir/Dir of Nursing* Mary Hladky.
Licensure Intermediate care. *Beds* ICF 74. *Certified* Medicaid.
Owner Privately owned.
Admissions Requirements Medical examination.
Staff RNs 3 (ft), 2 (pt); LPNs 2 (ft), 2 (pt); Nurses aides 12 (ft), 13 (pt); Physical therapists 1 (pt); Activities coordinators 1 (ft); Dietitians 1 (pt).
Facilities Dining room; Physical therapy room; Activities room; Chapel; Crafts room; Laundry room; Barber/Beauty shop; Library; Solarium; Lounge.
Activities Arts & crafts; Cards; Games; Reading groups; Prayer groups; Movies; Shopping trips; Social/Cultural gatherings; Fishing; Zoo; Picnics.

TENNESSEE

ADAMSVILLE

Tri-County Convalescent Home Inc*
Park Ave, PO Box 325, Adamsville, TN,
38310
(901) 632-3301
Medical Dir/Dir of Nursing Harry L Peeler
   MD.
Licensure Skilled care. *Beds* 124. *Certified*
   Medicaid; Medicare.
Admissions Requirements Minimum age 16;
   Medical examination; Physician's request.
Staff Physicians 7 (pt); RNs 1 (ft), 2 (pt);
   LPNs 9 (ft), 4 (pt); Nurses aides 34 (ft), 2
   (pt); Physical therapists 1 (pt); Speech
   therapists 1 (pt); Activities coordinators 1
   (ft); Dietitians 1 (pt); Dentists 1 (pt).
Facilities Dining room; Physical therapy
   room; Activities room; Crafts room; Laundry
   room; Barber/Beauty shop.
Activities Arts & crafts; Cards; Games;
   Movies; Shopping trips; Social/Cultural
   gatherings; Daily devotions.

ALAMO

Crockett County Nursing Home
PO Box 40, 372 W Main St, Alamo, TN,
38001
(901) 696-4541
Admin G F Harber.
Licensure Intermediate care. *Beds* ICF 121.
   Certified Medicaid.
Owner Proprietary Corp.
Admissions Requirements Minimum age 16;
   Medical examination.
Staff Physicians 2 (pt); RNs 1 (ft); LPNs 11
   (ft); Nurses aides 42 (ft); Physical therapists
   1 (pt); Reality therapists 1 (pt); Recreation
   therapists 1 (ft); Activities coordinators 1
   (ft); Dietitians 1 (pt).
Facilities Dining room; Physical therapy
   room; Activities room; Crafts room; Chapel;
   Laundry room; Barber/Beauty shop.
Activities Arts & crafts; Cards; Games;
   Reading groups; Prayer groups; Movies;
   Shopping trips.

ALGOOD

Masters Health Care Center
278 Dry Valley Rd, Algood, TN, 38501
(615) 537-6524
Admin Laura Mansfield. *Medical Dir/Dir of
   Nursing* Dr J T Moore MD; Phyllis Davis
   DON.
Licensure Skilled care; Intermediate care. *Beds*
   SNF 22; ICF 148. *Certified* Medicaid;
   Medicare.
Owner Proprietary Corp (Hillhaven Corp).
Admissions Requirements Minimum age 14;
   Medical examination; Physician's request.
Staff Physicians 1 (pt); RNs 3 (ft), 3 (pt);
   LPNs 12 (ft), 10 (pt); Orderlies 3 (ft); Nurses
   aides 50 (ft), 8 (pt); Physical therapists 1 (ft);

Occupational therapists 1 (pt); Speech
   therapists 1 (pt); Activities coordinators 1
   (ft); Dietitians 1 (pt); Podiatrists.
Facilities Dining room; Physical therapy
   room; Activities room; Crafts room; Laundry
   room; Barber/Beauty shop.
Activities Arts & crafts; Cards; Games;
   Reading groups; Prayer groups; Movies;
   Social/Cultural gatherings.

ANDERSONVILLE

Wayside Health Care Center*
Rte 2, Box 34-A, Andersonville, TN, 37705
(615) 494-0986
Beds 90.

ARDMORE

Ardmore Nursing Home Inc*
Hwy 31, Box 257, Ardmore, TN, 38449
(615) 427-2143
Admin Ted Barnett. *Medical Dir/Dir of
   Nursing* A C Foronda.
Licensure Intermediate care. *Beds* 70.
   Certified Medicaid.
Admissions Requirements Medical
   examination.
Staff Physicians 3 (pt); RNs 1 (pt); LPNs 2
   (ft), 4 (pt); Nurses aides 16 (ft), 2 (pt);
   Physical therapists; Recreational therapists;
   Occupational therapists; Speech therapists;
   Activities coordinators 1 (ft); Dietitians 1
   (ft).
Facilities Dining room; Activities room;
   Laundry room; Lobby; 2 Sunrooms.
Activities Arts & crafts; Cards; Games;
   Reading groups; Prayer groups; Social/
   Cultural gatherings.

ASHLAND CITY

Cheatham County Rest Home*
Rte 6, River Rd, Ashland City, TN, 37015
(615) 792-4948
Medical Dir/Dir of Nursing James Baldwin
   MD.
Licensure Intermediate care. *Beds* 100.
   Certified Medicaid.
Admissions Requirements Minimum age 14.
Facilities Dining room; Activities room;
   Chapel; Crafts room; Laundry room; Barber/
   Beauty shop.
Activities Arts & crafts; Cards; Games; Prayer
   groups; Shopping trips; Social/Cultural
   gatherings.

Montgomery County Nursing Home*
Rte 5, Box 292, Ashland City, TN, 37015
(615) 362-3203
Licensure Intermediate care. *Beds* 81.
   Certified Medicaid.

ATHENS

Athens Convalescent & Nursing Center*
214 Grove St NW, Athens, TN, 37303
(615) 745-0434
Licensure Skilled care; Intermediate care. *Beds*
   87. *Certified* Medicaid; Medicare.

Athens Health Care Center
214 Grove Ave, Athens, TN, 37303
(615) 745-0795
Admin Walter H Heath. *Medical Dir/Dir of
   Nursing* Nancy Long.
Licensure Skilled care; Intermediate care. *Beds*
   SNF 38; ICF 49. *Certified* Medicaid;
   Medicare.
Owner Proprietary Corp (National Health
   Corp).
Admissions Requirements Physician's request.
Facilities Dining room; Physical therapy
   room; Activities room; Crafts room; Laundry
   room; Barber/Beauty shop; Library.
Activities Arts & crafts; Cards; Games;
   Reading groups.

Life Care Center—Athens
1234 Frye St, Athens, TN, 37303
(615) 745-8181
Admin William W Wright. *Medical Dir/Dir of
   Nursing* James Cleveland MD; Dot Green
   RN DON.
Licensure Intermediate care. *Beds* ICF 128.
   Certified Medicaid.
Owner Proprietary Corp (Life Care Centers of
   America).
Admissions Requirements Physician's request.
Staff RNs 1 (ft); LPNs 12 (ft); Orderlies 5 (ft);
   Nurses aides 37 (ft); Physical therapists 1
   (pt); Activities coordinators 1 (ft); Dietitians
   1 (ft).
Facilities Dining room; Physical therapy
   room; Activities room; Chapel; Crafts room;
   Laundry room; Barber/Beauty shop.
Activities Arts & crafts; Cards; Games;
   Reading groups; Prayer groups; Movies;
   Shopping trips; Social/Cultural gatherings.

BLOUNTVILLE

Care Inn Blountville*
Dunlap Rd, Blountville, TN, 37617
(615) 323-7112
Medical Dir/Dir of Nursing Dr T H Raberson.
Licensure Intermediate care. *Beds* 170.
   Certified Medicaid.
Admissions Requirements Minimum age 14;
   Medical examination; Physician's request.
Staff Physicians 13 (ft); RNs 1 (ft), 1 (pt);
   LPNs 12 (ft), 3 (pt); Orderlies 5 (ft); Nurses
   aides 44 (ft), 6 (pt); Physical therapists 1
   (pt); Reality therapists 2 (pt); Speech
   therapists 1 (pt); Activities coordinators 1
   (ft); Dietitians 1 (ft).
Facilities Dining room; Physical therapy
   room; Activities room; Laundry room;
   Barber/Beauty shop.

Activities Arts & crafts; Games; Reading
groups; Prayer groups; Movies; Holiday
parties; Western day; Mexican day.

BOLIVAR

Brint Nursing Home*
214 N Water St, Bolivar, TN, 38008
(901) 658-5287
Licensure Intermediate care. *Beds* 42.
Certified Medicaid.

Care Inn—Bolivar*
700 Nuckols Rd, Bolivar, TN, 38008
(901) 658-4707
Licensure Intermediate care. *Beds* 132.
Certified Medicaid.

BRISTOL

Bristol Nursing Home Inc*
261 North St, Bristol, TN, 37620
(615) 764-6151
Licensure Intermediate care. *Beds* 240.
Certified Medicaid.

BROWNSVILLE

Crestview Nursing Home
704 Dupree St, Brownsville, TN, 38012
(901) 772-3356
Admin Joyce Phillpott. *Medical Dir/Dir of
Nursing* Jack G Pettigrew MD.
Licensure Intermediate care. *Beds* ICF 140.
Certified Medicaid.
Owner Proprietary Corp (American Health
Centers Inc).
Admissions Requirements Medical
examination.
Staff LPNs 8 (ft), 7 (pt); Nurses aides 41 (ft),
8 (pt); Activities coordinators 1 (ft);
Dietitians 7 (ft), 1 (pt).
Facilities Dining room; Activities room;
Laundry room; Barber/Beauty shop.
Activities Arts & crafts; Cards; Games;
Reading groups; Prayer groups; Movies;
Social/Cultural gatherings.

BRUCETON

Life Care Center of Bruceton Hollow Rock
105 Rowland Ave, Bruceton, TN, 38317
(901) 586-2061
Admin Peggy J Elkins. *Medical Dir/Dir of
Nursing* Dr Jerry Atkins; Brenda Woodruff
DON.
Licensure Intermediate care. *Beds* ICF 88.
Certified Medicaid.
Owner Proprietary Corp (Life Care Centers of
America).
Admissions Requirements Medical
examination; Physician's request.
Staff RNs 1 (ft); LPNs 8 (ft), 4 (pt); Orderlies
1 (ft); Nurses aides 27 (ft), 9 (pt); Activities
coordinators 1 (ft); Dietitians 1 (ft).
Facilities Dining room; Activities room;
Crafts room; Laundry room; Barber/Beauty
shop.
Activities Arts & crafts; Cards; Games;
Reading groups; Prayer groups; Movies;
Shopping trips; Social/Cultural gatherings.

BYRDSTOWN

Pickett County Nursing Home
PO Box 388, Byrdstown, TN, 38549
(615) 864-3162
Admin Erline S Myrick. *Medical Dir/Dir of
Nursing* Larry Mason MD; Charlet G
Holman DON.
Licensure Intermediate care. *Beds* ICF 48.
Certified Medicaid.
Owner Publicly owned.
Facilities Dining room; Activities room;
Crafts room; Laundry room; Barber/Beauty
shop.

Activities Arts & crafts; Games; Prayer groups;
Movies; Social/Cultural gatherings.

CAMDEN

Hillhaven Convalescent Center
197 Hospital Drive, Camden, TN, 38320
(901) 584-3500
Admin Kathy Farmer.
Licensure Intermediate care. *Beds* ICF 186.
Certified Medicaid.
Owner Proprietary Corp (Hillhaven Corp).
Admissions Requirements Medical
examination.
Staff RNs 2 (ft); LPNs 15 (ft); Orderlies 2 (ft);
Nurses aides 60 (ft); Physical therapists 1
(pt); Activities coordinators 2 (ft); Dietitians
1 (pt).
Facilities Dining room; Activities room;
Chapel; Crafts room; Laundry room; Barber/
Beauty shop.
Activities Arts & crafts; Cards; Games;
Reading groups; Prayer groups; Movies;
Shopping trips; Social/Cultural gatherings.

CARTHAGE

Smith County Manor*
Hospital Dr, Carthage, TN, 37030
(615) 735-0570
Licensure Intermediate care. *Beds* 48.
Certified Medicaid.
Owner Proprietary Corp (Hillhaven Corp).

CELINA

Clay County Manor Inc
Box 201A, Celina, TN, 38551
(615) 243-3130
Admin Henry L Van Essen. *Medical Dir/Dir
of Nursing* Dr R Mauricio; Linda J Kendall
DON.
Licensure Intermediate care. *Beds* ICF 66.
Certified Medicaid.
Owner Proprietary Corp (American Health
Centers Inc).
Admissions Requirements Medical
examination; Physician's request.
Staff Physicians 3 (pt); RNs 1 (pt); Physical
therapists 1 (pt); Reality therapists 1 (ft);
Recreational therapists 1 (ft); Speech
therapists 1 (pt); Activities coordinators 1
(ft); Dietitians 1 (pt); Podiatrists 1 (pt).
Facilities Dining room; Physical therapy
room; Activities room; Crafts room; Laundry
room; Barber/Beauty shop; Library.
Activities Arts & crafts; Cards; Games;
Reading groups; Prayer groups; Movies;
Shopping trips; Social/Cultural gatherings;
Picnics; Campouts; Parties.

CENTERVILLE

Centerville Health Care Center
112 Old Dickson Rd, Centerville, TN, 37033
(615) 729-4236
Admin Charles P Harris Jr. *Medical Dir/Dir of
Nursing* Jeff Fosnes MD; Joyce Pace RN
DON.
Licensure Intermediate care. *Beds* ICF 122.
Certified Medicaid.
Owner Proprietary Corp.
Admissions Requirements Minimum age 14.
Staff Physicians 5 (pt); RNs 1 (ft); LPNs 9
(ft), 1 (pt); Orderlies; Nurses aides 45 (ft);
Activities coordinators 1 (ft); Dietitians 1
(pt).
Facilities Dining room; Physical therapy
room; Activities room; Chapel; Crafts room;
Laundry room; Barber/Beauty shop; Library.
Activities Arts & crafts; Games; Reading
groups; Prayer groups; Movies; Shopping
trips; Social/Cultural gatherings.

Hickman County Nursing Home
135 E Swan St, Centerville, TN, 37033
(615) 729-3513
Medical Dir/Dir of Nursing B L Holladay MD.
Licensure Intermediate care. *Beds* 40.
Certified Medicaid.
Admissions Requirements Medical
examination; Physician's request.
Staff Physicians 2 (pt); RNs 2 (ft); LPNs 2
(ft), 4 (pt); Nurses aides 12 (ft), 3 (pt);
Physical therapists; Occupational therapists;
Speech therapists; Activities coordinators 1
(pt); Dietitians 1 (pt).
Facilities Dining room; Activities room;
Barber/Beauty shop.
Activities Arts & crafts; Cards; Games; Prayer
groups; Movies.

CHATTANOOGA

Asbury Center at Oak Manor*
716 Dodds Ave, Chattanooga, TN, 37404
(615) 622-6424
Licensure Home for aged. *Beds* 49.

Caldsted Foundation Inc*
3701 Cherryton Dr, Chattanooga, TN, 37411
(615) 624-9906
Licensure Home for aged. *Beds* 52.

Dempsey Nursing Home Inc*
8249 Standifer Gap Rd, Chattanooga, TN,
37421
Licensure Intermediate care. *Beds* 34.

Friendship Haven*
950 Dodson Ave, Chattanooga, TN, 37406
(615) 629-2847
Admin Mabel Abernathy.
Licensure Home for aged. *Beds* 25.
Admissions Requirements Minimum age 47;
Females only; Medical examination.
Facilities Dining room; Laundry room.
Activities Prayer groups; Shopping trips;
Exercise groups.

Hamilton County Nursing Home
2626 Walker Rd, Chattanooga, TN, 37421
(615) 892-9442
Admin H Doke Cage. *Medical Dir/Dir of
Nursing* Irene J Labrador MD; Billie
Watkins RN DON.
Licensure Skilled care; Intermediate care;
Adult day care; Apartments for the elderly;
Home for aged. *Beds* 831. *Certified*
Medicaid; Medicare.
Owner Nonprofit organization/foundation.
Admissions Requirements Minimum age 14;
Medical examination.
Staff Physicians; RNs; LPNs; Orderlies;
Nurses aides; Physical therapists;
Recreational therapists; Speech therapists;
Activities coordinators; Dietitians.
Facilities Dining room; Physical therapy
room; Activities room; Chapel; Crafts room;
Laundry room; Barber/Beauty shop; Library.

Heritage Manor Nursing Home Inc*
708 Dwight St, Chattanooga, TN, 37406
(615) 622-4301
Licensure Intermediate care. *Beds* 78.
Certified Medicaid.
Owner Proprietary Corp (Life Care Centers of
America).

Mountain View Nursing Home*
PO Box 2318, 5410 Lee Ave, Chattanooga,
TN, 37410
(615) 821-4836
Licensure Intermediate care. *Beds* 28.
Certified Medicaid.

Mountain View Rest Home*
PO Box 2318, 5412 Lee Ave, Chattanooga,
TN, 37410
(615) 821-4836
Licensure Intermediate care. *Beds* 19.
Certified Medicaid.

Parkwood Health Care Center*
2700 Parkwood Ave, Chattanooga, TN, 37404
(615) 624-1533
Medical Dir/Dir of Nursing Dr Paul Hawkins.
Licensure Skilled care. *Beds* 212. *Certified*
Medicaid; Medicare.
Owner Proprietary Corp (National Health
Corp).
Admissions Requirements Minimum age 14;
Medical examination.
Staff Physicians 2 (ft); RNs 7 (ft), 5 (pt);
LPNs 14 (ft), 14 (pt); Orderlies 7 (ft), 3 (pt);
Nurses aides 54 (ft), 12 (pt); Physical
therapists 1 (ft); Recreational therapists 2
(ft); Speech therapists 1 (pt); Activities
coordinators 1 (ft); Dietitians 1 (ft); Dentists
1 (pt); Podiatrists 1 (pt); Assistant physical
therapists 3 (ft).
Facilities Dining room; Physical therapy
room; Activities room; Chapel; Crafts room;
Laundry room; Barber/Beauty shop; Library.
Activities Arts & crafts; Games; Movies;
Shopping trips; Social/Cultural gatherings.

St Barnabas Nursing Home
Pine & W 6th, Chattanooga, TN, 37402
(615) 267-3764
Licensure Skilled care; Intermediate care. *Beds*
87. *Certified* Medicaid; Medicare.
Staff RNs 4 (ft), 3 (pt); LPNs 6 (ft), 3 (pt);
Orderlies 3 (ft), 1 (pt); Nurses aides 27 (ft),
16 (pt); Physical therapists 1 (pt); Activities
coordinators 1 (ft); Dietitians 1 (ft); Dentists
1 (pt).
Facilities Dining room; Physical therapy
room; Activities room; Chapel; Barber/
Beauty shop; Library.
Activities Arts & crafts; Games; Reading
groups; Prayer groups; Movies; Pet program.

CHUCKEY

Durham-Hensley Nursing Homes Inc*
Rte 3, Chuckey, TN, 36741
(615) 257-6761
Medical Dir/Dir of Nursing Dr Ronald Cole.
Licensure Intermediate care. *Beds* 100.
Certified Medicaid.
Staff Physicians 7 (pt); RNs 2 (ft); LPNs 9
(ft); Nurses aides 21 (ft), 6 (pt); Physical
therapists 1 (pt); Speech therapists 1 (pt);
Activities coordinators 1 (ft); Dietitians 1
(pt).
Facilities Dining room; Physical therapy
room; Activities room; Laundry room;
Barber/Beauty shop.
Activities Arts & crafts; Cards; Games;
Reading groups; Prayer groups; Movies;
Shopping trips; Social/Cultural gatherings.

CHURCH HILL

Life Care Center of Church Hill
W Main St, Church Hill, TN, 37642
(615) 357-7178
Admin James H Griffitt. *Medical Dir/Dir of
Nursing* T H Roberson MD; Patty Schad
RN DON.
Licensure Intermediate care. *Beds* ICF 124.
Certified Medicaid.
Owner Proprietary Corp (Life Care Centers of
America).
Admissions Requirements Minimum age 14;
Medical examination; Physician's request.
Staff Physicians 6 (pt); RNs 2 (ft); LPNs 9
(ft), 3 (pt); Orderlies 4 (ft), 1 (pt); Nurses
aides 30 (ft), 6 (pt); Physical therapists 1
(pt); Speech therapists 1 (pt); Activities
coordinators 1 (ft); Dietitians 1 (pt);
Ophthalmologists 1 (pt); Podiatrists 1 (pt).
Languages Spanish, German
Facilities Dining room; Physical therapy
room; Activities room; Crafts room; Laundry
room; Barber/Beauty shop.
Activities Arts & crafts; Cards; Games;
Reading groups; Prayer groups; Movies;
Shopping trips; Social/Cultural gatherings.

CLARKSVILLE

Clarksville Manor Nursing Center*
2134 Ashland City Rd, Clarksville, TN, 37040
(615) 552-3002
Licensure Intermediate care. *Beds* 66.
Certified Medicaid.
Owner Proprietary Corp (American Health
Centers Inc).

General Care Convalescent Center*
111 Usery Rd, Clarksville, TN, 37040
(615) 647-0269
Licensure Skilled care; Intermediate care. *Beds*
120. *Certified* Medicaid; Medicare.
Owner Proprietary Corp (American Health
Centers Inc).

CLEVELAND

Bradley County Nursing Home
2910 Peerless Rd NW, Cleveland, TN, 37312
(615) 472-7116
Admin Ernest M Vincett. *Medical Dir/Dir of
Nursing* Stanley Pettit MD; Jane Tollett RN
DON.
Licensure Skilled care; Intermediate care. *Beds*
SNF 33; ICF 192. *Certified* Medicaid;
Medicare.
Owner Publicly owned.
Admissions Requirements Medical
examination; Physician's request.
Staff RNs 6 (ft), 1 (pt); LPNs 15 (ft), 4 (pt);
Orderlies 9 (ft); Nurses aides 69 (ft), 6 (pt);
Physical therapists 1 (ft); Speech therapists 1
(pt); Activities coordinators 1 (ft); Dietitians
1 (ft); Ophthalmologists 1 (pt).
Facilities Dining room; Physical therapy
room; Activities room; Chapel; Crafts room;
Laundry room; Barber/Beauty shop; Library.
Activities Arts & crafts; Cards; Games;
Reading groups; Prayer groups; Movies;
Shopping trips; Social/Cultural gatherings.

Life Care Center of Cleveland
3530 Keith St NW, Cleveland, TN, 37311
(615) 476-7243, 476-3254
Admin Barbara C Kiser. *Medical Dir/Dir of
Nursing* Dr Vance; Cindy Johnson DON.
Licensure Intermediate care. *Beds* ICF 163.
Certified Medicaid.
Owner Proprietary Corp (Life Care Centers of
America).
Admissions Requirements Minimum age 14;
Medical examination; Physician's request.
Staff RNs 2 (ft); LPNs 11 (ft), 2 (pt);
Orderlies 5 (ft); Nurses aides 41 (ft), 9 (pt);
Activities coordinators 1 (pt); Recreational
therapist aide 1 (ft).
Facilities Dining room; Physical therapy
room; Activities room; Crafts room; Laundry
room; Barber/Beauty shop; Library;
Conference room.
Activities Arts & crafts; Cards; Games;
Reading groups; Prayer groups; Movies;
Shopping trips; Social/Cultural gatherings.

CLINTON

Anderson County Health Care Center
220 Longmire Rd, Clinton, TN, 37716
(615) 457-6925
Admin Sandra L Reynolds LNHA. *Medical
Dir/Dir of Nursing* Dr R W Robinson; Mary
R Silcox RN.
Licensure Skilled care; Intermediate care. *Beds*
SNF 30; ICF 90. *Certified* Medicaid;
Medicare.
Owner Proprietary Corp (Beverly Enterprises).
Admissions Requirements Medical
examination.
Staff Physicians 3 (pt); RNs 2 (ft), 1 (pt);
LPNs 10 (ft), 7 (pt); Orderlies 5 (ft); Nurses
aides 24 (ft), 16 (pt); Activities coordinators
1 (ft).

Facilities Dining room; Physical therapy
room; Activities room; Laundry room;
Barber/Beauty shop; (2) TV/sitting rooms.
Activities Arts & crafts; Cards; Games;
Reading groups; Prayer groups; Movies;
Shopping trips; Social/Cultural gatherings;
Exercise class.

COLLEGEDALE

Life Care Center of Collegedale*
Apison Pike, PO Box 658, Collegedale, TN,
37315
(615) 396-2182
Licensure Intermediate care. *Beds* 124.
Certified Medicaid.
Owner Proprietary Corp (Life Care Centers of
America).
Staff RNs 2 (ft), 1 (pt); LPNs 13 (ft), 3 (pt);
Orderlies 1 (ft); Nurses aides 33 (ft);
Physical therapists 1 (ft); Reality therapists 1
(pt); Recreational therapists 1 (pt);
Occupational therapists 1 (pt); Speech
therapists 1 (pt); Activities coordinators 1
(ft); Dietitians 1 (ft).
Facilities Dining room; Physical therapy
room; Activities room; Chapel; Laundry
room; Barber/Beauty shop.
Activities Arts & crafts; Games; Movies;
Shopping trips; Social/Cultural gatherings.

COLLIERVILLE

Care Inn Collierville
490 Hwy 57 W, Collierville, TN, 38017
(615) 853-8561
Admin Brenda Stewart. *Medical Dir/Dir of
Nursing* Rachel Kelsey.
Licensure Skilled care. *Beds* SNF 114.
Certified Medicaid; Medicare.
Owner Proprietary Corp (Southmark Heritage
Corp).
Admissions Requirements Physician's request.
Facilities Dining room; Activities room;
Crafts room; Laundry room; Barber/Beauty
shop; Library.
Activities Arts & crafts; Cards; Games;
Reading groups; Prayer groups; Movies;
Shopping trips; Social/Cultural gatherings.

COLUMBIA

Bel-Air Health Care Inc*
105 N Campbell Blvd, Columbia, TN, 38401
(615) 389-5035
Medical Dir/Dir of Nursing Dr William A
Robinson.
Licensure Intermediate care. *Beds* 95.
Certified Medicaid.
Owner Proprietary Corp (Regency Health
Care Centers).
Admissions Requirements Medical
examination; Physician's request.
Staff RNs 1 (ft); LPNs 5 (ft), 3 (pt); Orderlies
1 (pt); Nurses aides 23 (ft), 8 (pt); Physical
therapists 1 (pt); Speech therapists 1 (pt);
Activities coordinators 1 (pt); Dietitians 1
(pt); Dentists 1 (pt); Podiatrists 1 (pt).
Facilities Dining room; Activities room;
Laundry room; Barber/Beauty shop.
Activities Arts & crafts; Cards; Games;
Reading groups; Prayer groups; Movies;
Shopping trips; Social/Cultural gatherings.

Columbia Health Care Center
101 Walnut Ln, Columbia, TN, 38401
(615) 381-3112
Admin Mary K Sellars. *Medical Dir/Dir of
Nursing* Dr C A Ball; Lynda Ponder.
Licensure Skilled care; Intermediate care. *Beds*
SNF 48; ICF 72. *Certified* Medicaid;
Medicare.
Owner Proprietary Corp (National Health
Corp).
Admissions Requirements Medical
examination.

Staff RNs 3 (ft); LPNs 10 (ft); Nurses aides 45 (ft); Physical therapists 1 (ft); Speech therapists 1 (ft); Activities coordinators 1 (ft), 5 (pt).
Facilities Dining room; Physical therapy room; Activities room; Laundry room; Barber/Beauty shop.

Graymere Nursing Center Inc*
1410 Trotwood Ave, Columbia, TN, 38401
(615) 388-6443
Licensure Intermediate care. *Beds* 171.
Certified Medicaid.

Hillview Health Care Center Inc*
2710 Trotwood Ave, Columbia, TN, 38401
(615) 388-7182
Medical Dir/Dir of Nursing Dr Carl C Gardner.
Licensure Skilled care; Intermediate care. *Beds* 98. *Certified* Medicaid; Medicare.
Owner Proprietary Corp (National Health Corp).
Admissions Requirements Minimum age 18; Physician's request.
Staff Physicians 1 (pt); RNs 6 (ft), 4 (pt); LPNs 5 (ft), 2 (pt); Orderlies 3 (ft); Nurses aides 22 (ft), 5 (pt); Physical therapists 1 (ft); Speech therapists 1 (ft); Activities coordinators 1 (ft); Dietitians 1 (ft); Dentists 1 (pt); Podiatrists 1 (pt); Audiologists 1 (pt).
Facilities Dining room; Physical therapy room; Activities room; Chapel; Crafts room; Laundry room; Barber/Beauty shop; Library.
Activities Arts & crafts; Cards; Games; Reading groups; Prayer groups; Movies; Shopping trips; Social/Cultural gatherings.

COOKEVILLE

Cookeville Health Care Center Inc
PO Box 2829, 815 Bunker Hill Rd, Cookeville, TN, 38501
(615) 528-5516
Admin John R Strawn. *Medical Dir/Dir of Nursing* Clarence Jones MD; Susan Adermann RN.
Licensure Skilled care; Intermediate care. *Beds* 96. *Certified* Medicaid; Medicare.
Owner Proprietary Corp (National Health Corp).
Admissions Requirements Minimum age 18; Medical examination.
Staff Physicians 1 (pt); RNs 3 (pt); LPNs 9 (ft), 8 (pt); Orderlies 3 (ft); Nurses aides 27 (ft), 15 (pt); Physical therapists 1 (ft), 1 (pt); Speech therapists 1 (pt); Activities coordinators 1 (ft); Dietitians 1 (ft).
Facilities Dining room; Physical therapy room; Activities room; Laundry room.
Activities Arts & crafts; Cards; Games; Reading groups; Prayer groups; Movies; Shopping trips; Social/Cultural gatherings.

Cookeville Manor Nursing Home*
215 W 6th St, Cookeville, TN, 38501
(615) 528-7466
Licensure Intermediate care. *Beds* 49.
Certified Medicaid.
Owner Proprietary Corp (American Health Centers Inc).

CORDOVA

Hillhaven Convalescent Center Germantown
955 Germantown Rd, Cordova, TN, 38018-9601
(901) 754-1393
Admin Samuel R Scarbro. *Medical Dir/Dir of Nursing* Patrick J Murphy MD.
Licensure Intermediate care. *Beds* ICF 274.
Certified Medicaid.
Owner Proprietary Corp (Hillhaven Corp).

COVINGTON

Covington Manor Inc
PO Box 827, 1992 Hwy 51 S, Covington, TN, 38019
(901) 476-1820
Admin Donald Lee Jones. *Medical Dir/Dir of Nursing* Dr N L Hyatt; Bettye Morgan.
Licensure Intermediate care. *Beds* 196.
Certified Medicaid.
Owner Proprietary Corp (American Health Centers Inc).
Admissions Requirements Medical examination; Physician's request.
Staff RNs 1 (ft); LPNs; Orderlies; Nurses aides; Physical therapists; Reality therapists; Recreational therapists; Occupational therapists; Speech therapists; Activities coordinators; Dietitians.
Facilities Dining room; Activities room; Crafts room; Laundry room; Barber/Beauty shop.
Activities Arts & crafts; Cards; Games; Reading groups; Prayer groups; Movies; Shopping trips; Social/Cultural gatherings; Beauty groups; Men's fellowship; Outings.

CROSSVILLE

Life Care Center of Crossville*
407 Wayne Ave, Crossville, TN, 38555
(615) 484-6129
Licensure Intermediate care. *Beds* 109.
Certified Medicaid.
Owner Proprietary Corp (Life Care Centers of America).
Staff Physicians 8 (pt); RNs 1 (ft), 1 (pt); LPNs 8 (ft), 2 (pt); Orderlies 4 (ft), 2 (pt); Nurses aides 32 (ft), 6 (pt); Physical therapists 1 (pt); Activities coordinators 1 (ft); Dietitians 1 (pt); Dentists 1 (pt).
Facilities Dining room; Physical therapy room; Activities room; Crafts room; Laundry room; Barber/Beauty shop; Library.
Activities Arts & crafts; Cards; Games; Reading groups; Prayer groups; Movies; Shopping trips; Social/Cultural gatherings.

DANDRIDGE

Jefferson County Nursing Home*
Rte 5, Box 369, Dandridge, TN, 37725
(615) 397-3163
Licensure Intermediate care. *Beds* 83.
Certified Medicaid.

DAYTON

Laurelbrook Sanitarium
PO Box 352, Ogden Rd, Rte 3, Dayton, TN, 37321
(615) 775-3338, 775-0771, 267-1620
Admin Steve Marlow. *Medical Dir/Dir of Nursing* Lester Littell MD.
Licensure Intermediate care. *Beds* ICF 50; Provide care for those w/tube feeders & tracheostomics feedings. *Certified* Medicaid.
Owner Nonprofit Corp.
Staff Physicians 1 (pt); RNs 2 (ft), 1 (pt); LPNs 2 (ft), 2 (pt); Orderlies 1 (ft), 5 (pt); Nurses aides 7 (ft), 11 (pt); Activities coordinators 1 (ft), 1 (pt); Dietitians 1 (ft), 7 (pt); Dietitian aides 2 (ft).
Affiliation Seventh-Day Adventist
Facilities Dining room; Activities room; Chapel.
Activities Arts & crafts; Games; Prayer groups; Movies; Shopping trips; Social/Cultural gatherings.

Rhea County Nursing Home
PO Box 629, Hwy 27 N, Dayton, TN, 37321
(615) 775-1121
Admin Barbara J Heath. *Medical Dir/Dir of Nursing* Lester F Littell MD; Betty Holland RN.

Licensure Intermediate care. *Beds* ICF 107.
Certified Medicaid.
Owner Publicly owned.
Admissions Requirements Medical examination.
Staff Physicians 5 (ft); RNs 2 (ft); LPNs 11 (ft); Orderlies 2 (ft); Nurses aides 26 (ft), 5 (pt); Physical therapists 1 (pt); Activities coordinators 1 (ft); Dietitians 1 (ft).
Facilities Dining room; Physical therapy room; Activities room; Chapel; Crafts room; Barber/Beauty shop; Library; Courtyard with BBQ pit; Large sunporch.
Activities Arts & crafts; Cards; Games; Reading groups; Prayer groups; Movies; Shopping trips; Social/Cultural gatherings; Fishing trips; Character visits.

DICKSON

Dickson County Nursing Home
901 N Charlotte St, Dickson, TN, 37055
(615) 446-5171
Admin JoAnn Brown. *Medical Dir/Dir of Nursing* Dr W A Bell; Betty Carpenter.
Licensure Intermediate care. *Beds* 69.
Certified Medicaid.
Owner Nonprofit Corp.
Admissions Requirements Minimum age 18; Medical examination; Physician's request.
Staff LPNs 4 (ft), 6 (pt); Nurses aides 19 (ft), 15 (pt); Physical therapists 2 (ft); Activities coordinators 1 (ft); Dietitians 1 (ft).
Facilities Dining room; Physical therapy room; Activities room; Laundry room; Barber/Beauty shop; Library.
Activities Arts & crafts; Cards; Games; Reading groups; Prayer groups; Movies; Shopping trips; Social/Cultural gatherings.

Green Valley Health Care Center Inc
812 Charlotte St, Dickson, TN, 37055
(615) 446-8046
Admin Wesley Felts. *Medical Dir/Dir of Nursing* W A Bell MD; Norma Wall RN DON.
Licensure Skilled care; Intermediate care. *Beds* SNF 70; ICF 87. *Certified* Medicaid; Medicare.
Owner Proprietary Corp (National Health Corp).
Admissions Requirements Medical examination; Physician's request.
Staff RNs 6 (ft), 2 (pt); LPNs 18 (ft), 6 (pt); Orderlies 2 (ft); Nurses aides 37 (ft), 19 (pt); Physical therapists 2 (ft); Recreational therapists 1 (ft); Occupational therapists 1 (ft), 1 (pt); Speech therapists 1 (ft); Activities coordinators 1 (ft); Dietitians 1 (ft).
Languages Spanish
Facilities Dining room; Physical therapy room; Activities room; Crafts room; Laundry room; Barber/Beauty shop; Library.
Activities Arts & crafts; Cards; Games; Reading groups; Prayer groups; Movies; Shopping trips; Social/Cultural gatherings.

DOVER

Manor House of Dover
PO Box 399, Hwy 49E, Dover, TN, 37058
(615) 232-6902
Admin Patricia Lee. *Medical Dir/Dir of Nursing* Dr Robert Lee; Marian Watson RN DON.
Licensure Skilled care; Intermediate care. *Beds* SNF 30; ICF 58. *Certified* Medicaid; Medicare; VA.
Owner Proprietary Corp (Wessex Corp).
Admissions Requirements Minimum age 14; Medical examination; Physician's request.
Staff Physicians 1 (pt); RNs 2 (ft), 2 (pt); LPNs 7 (ft), 3 (pt); Orderlies 1 (ft); Nurses aides 28 (ft), 11 (pt); Physical therapists 1 (pt); Occupational therapists 1 (pt); Speech

therapists 1 (pt); Activities coordinators 1 (ft); Dietitians 1 (pt); Dentists 1 (pt); Ophthalmologists 1 (pt); Podiatrists 1 (pt).
Facilities Dining room; Activities room; Crafts room; Laundry room; Barber/Beauty shop.
Activities Arts & crafts; Cards; Games; Reading groups; Prayer groups; Movies; Shopping trips; Social/Cultural gatherings.

DRESDEN

Hillview Nursing Home Corp
PO Box 377, Rte 1, Dresden, TN, 38225
(901) 364-3886
Admin Mary Ellis. *Medical Dir/Dir of Nursing* Fran Allen.
Licensure Intermediate care. *Beds* ICF 70. *Certified* Medicaid.
Owner Proprietary Corp.
Admissions Requirements Medical examination.
Staff LPNs 7 (ft), 4 (pt); Nurses aides 17 (ft), 6 (pt); Activities coordinators 1 (ft); Dietitians 1 (ft); Social service 1 (ft).
Facilities Dining room; Activities room; Chapel; Laundry room; Barber/Beauty shop; Patio.
Activities Arts & crafts; Cards; Games; Reading groups; Shopping trips.

Weakley County Nursing Home
PO Box 787, Dresden, TN, 38225
(901) 364-3158
Admin Kenneth Wainscott. *Medical Dir/Dir of Nursing* Dr R E Owens; Pat Mitchell DON.
Licensure Intermediate care. *Beds* ICF 139. *Certified* Medicaid.
Owner Nonprofit organization/foundation.
Admissions Requirements Minimum age 14; Medical examination; Physician's request.
Staff RNs 1 (ft); LPNs 14 (ft), 4 (pt); Orderlies 3 (ft), 2 (pt); Nurses aides 46 (ft), 12 (pt); Activities coordinators 1 (ft), 1 (pt); Dietitians 1 (pt).
Facilities Dining room; Activities room; Laundry room; Barber/Beauty shop.
Activities Arts & crafts; Cards; Games; Movies; Shopping trips; Social/Cultural gatherings; Local parades; Fishing trips.

DUNLAP

Sequatchie Health Care Center
PO Box 685, Taylor St, Dunlap, TN, 37327
(615) 949-4651
Admin Cheri Cropper. *Medical Dir/Dir of Nursing* Susan Merriman.
Licensure Skilled care; Intermediate care. *Beds* SNF 22; ICF 38. *Certified* Medicaid; Medicare.
Owner Proprietary Corp (National Health Corp).
Admissions Requirements Minimum age 18; Medical examination; Physician's request.
Staff Physicians 1 (pt); RNs 2 (ft), 1 (pt); LPNs 5 (ft), 5 (pt); Nurses aides 11 (ft), 12 (pt); Physical therapists 1 (ft), 1 (pt); Speech therapists 1 (pt); Activities coordinators 1 (pt); Dietitians 1 (ft); Dentists 1 (pt).
Facilities Dining room; Physical therapy room; Activities room; Barber/Beauty shop.
Activities Arts & crafts; Reading groups; Shopping trips; Social/Cultural gatherings.

DYERSBURG

Nucare Convalescent Center
1636 Woodlawn, Dyersburg, TN, 38024
(901) 285-6400
Admin Bettie Motley. *Medical Dir/Dir of Nursing* W I Thornton MD; Wayne Leonard DON.
Licensure Intermediate care. *Beds* ICF 50. *Certified* Medicaid.
Owner Proprietary Corp.

Admissions Requirements Physician's request.
Staff LPNs 5 (ft), 3 (pt); Nurses aides 14 (ft), 2 (pt); Activities coordinators 1 (ft); Dietitians 1 (ft).
Facilities Dining room; Activities room; Laundry room; Barber/Beauty shop; Library.
Activities Arts & crafts; Cards; Games; Prayer groups; Movies; Shopping trips.

Parkview Convalescent Unit
350 Tickle St, Dyersburg, TN, 38024
(901) 285-9710
Admin Randall Hoover. *Medical Dir/Dir of Nursing* Roy Chu MD; Sue Meeks RN.
Licensure Intermediate care. *Beds* ICF 113. *Certified* Medicaid.
Owner Nonprofit Corp.
Admissions Requirements Medical examination.
Staff Physicians; RNs; LPNs; Nurses aides; Physical therapists; Recreational therapists; Activities coordinators; Dietitians.
Affiliation Methodist
Facilities Dining room; Laundry room; Barber/Beauty shop; Library.
Activities Arts & crafts; Cards; Games; Prayer groups; Social/Cultural gatherings.

EAST RIDGE

Life Care Center of East Ridge
1500 Fincher Ave, East Ridge, TN, 37412
(615) 894-1254
Admin Joy Hambleton. *Medical Dir/Dir of Nursing* Dr Winters; Jeanine Gentry DON.
Licensure Intermediate care. *Beds* ICF 120. *Certified* Medicaid.
Owner Proprietary Corp (Life Care Centers of America).
Admissions Requirements Medical examination.
Staff Physicians 1 (pt); RNs 2 (ft); LPNs 6 (ft), 4 (pt); Orderlies 2 (ft); Nurses aides 25 (ft), 15 (pt); Physical therapists 1 (pt); Recreational therapists 1 (ft); Activities coordinators 1 (ft); Dietitians 1 (ft), 1 (pt); Ophthalmologists 1 (pt).
Facilities Dining room; Physical therapy room; Activities room; Crafts room; Laundry room; Barber/Beauty shop.
Activities Arts & crafts; Cards; Games; Reading groups; Prayer groups; Movies; Shopping trips; Social/Cultural gatherings.

ELIZABETHTON

Heritage Manor of Elizabethton
1641 Hwy 19E, Elizabethton, TN, 37643
(615) 542-4133
Admin Leroy A Policky. *Medical Dir/Dir of Nursing* R Eugene Galloway MD & Jerry Gastineau MD.
Licensure Intermediate care. *Beds* ICF 158. *Certified* Medicaid.
Owner Proprietary Corp (National Heritage).
Admissions Requirements Minimum age 18; Medical examination; Physician's request.
Staff Physicians 2 (pt); RNs 2 (ft); LPNs 12 (ft), 1 (pt); Nurses aides 48 (ft), 7 (pt); Physical therapists 1 (pt); Speech therapists 1 (pt); Activities coordinators 1 (ft), 1 (pt); Dietitians 1 (ft), 1 (pt).
Facilities Dining room; Physical therapy room; Activities room; Laundry room; Barber/Beauty shop.
Activities Arts & crafts; Cards; Games; Reading groups; Prayer groups; Movies; Shopping trips; Social/Cultural gatherings.

Hermitage Nursing Home Inc
1633 Hillview Dr, Elizabethton, TN, 37643
(615) 543-2571
Admin Jeannette F Bradshaw. *Medical Dir/Dir of Nursing* Royce L Holsey Jr.
Licensure Intermediate care. *Beds* 58. *Certified* Medicaid.

Admissions Requirements Minimum age 14; Medical examination; Physician's request.
Staff Physicians 1 (pt); RNs 1 (ft), 1 (pt); LPNs 3 (ft), 3 (pt); Orderlies 1 (ft); Nurses aides 12 (ft), 7 (pt); Physical therapists 1 (pt); Activities coordinators 1 (ft); Dietitians 1 (pt).
Facilities Dining room; Physical therapy room; Activities room; Laundry room; Barber/Beauty shop; Library.
Activities Arts & crafts; Cards; Games; Reading groups; Prayer groups; Movies; Shopping trips; Social/Cultural gatherings.

Hillview Nursing Home
1666 Hillview Dr, Elizabethton, TN, 37643
(615) 542-5061
Admin Carol Hutchins.
Licensure Intermediate care. *Beds* 42. *Certified* Medicaid.
Admissions Requirements Minimum age 14; Physician's request.
Staff Physicians 6 (pt); RNs 2 (ft); LPNs 4 (ft), 1 (pt); Nurses aides 10 (ft), 4 (pt); Activities coordinators 1 (ft); Dietitians 1 (pt).
Facilities Dining room; Laundry room; Outdoor activities shed.
Activities Arts & crafts; Games; Reading groups; Prayer groups; Shopping trips.

Ivy Hall Nursing Home*
301 Watauga Ave, Elizabethton, TN, 37643
(615) 542-6512
Admin Judy C Taylor. *Medical Dir/Dir of Nursing* Dr E E Perry.
Licensure Intermediate care. *Beds* 76. *Certified* Medicaid.
Admissions Requirements Medical examination; Physician's request.
Staff Physicians 1 (ft), 5 (pt); RNs 1 (ft); LPNs 6 (ft), 2 (pt); Orderlies 2 (ft), 1 (pt); Nurses aides 28 (ft), 5 (pt); Physical therapists 1 (pt); Speech therapists 1 (pt); Activities coordinators 1 (ft); Dietitians 1 (ft), 1 (pt); Dentists 1 (pt); Ophthalmologists 1 (pt); Podiatrists 1 (pt); Audiologists 1 (pt).
Facilities Dining room; Physical therapy room; Activities room; Crafts room; Laundry room; Barber/Beauty shop; Library.
Activities Arts & crafts; Cards; Games; Reading groups; Prayer groups; Movies; Shopping trips; Social/Cultural gatherings.

Southwood Nursing Home
1200 Spruce Lane/ Pineridge Circle, Elizabethton, TN, 37643
(615) 543-3202
Admin Gerry Woods. *Medical Dir/Dir of Nursing* Dr Steve May; Patsy McKinney.
Licensure Intermediate care. *Beds* 86. *Certified* Medicaid.
Owner Proprietary Corp (Southwood Health Care).
Admissions Requirements Medical examination.
Staff Physicians 1 (pt); RNs 1 (ft); LPNs 9 (ft); Orderlies 3 (ft); Nurses aides 15 (ft), 15 (pt); Physical therapists 1 (pt); Activities coordinators 1 (ft); Dietitians 1 (ft).
Facilities Dining room; Physical therapy room; Activities room; Crafts room; Laundry room; Barber/Beauty shop.
Activities Arts & crafts; Cards; Games; Prayer groups; Movies; Shopping trips.

ERIN

Royal Care of Erin Inc*
Knight Rd, Rte 3, Box 137-B, Erin, TN, 37061
(615) 289-4141
Admin Helen L Stout. *Medical Dir/Dir of Nursing* Daniel Martin MD.
Licensure Intermediate care. *Beds* 100. *Certified* Medicaid.
Admissions Requirements Minimum age 18; Medical examination.

Staff Physicians 3 (ft), 1 (pt); RNs 3 (ft);
LPNs 4 (ft), 4 (pt); Nurses aides 20 (ft), 12
(pt); Physical therapists 1 (pt); Activities
coordinators 1 (ft), 1 (pt); Dietitians 1 (pt).
Facilities Dining room; Physical therapy
room; Activities room; Chapel; Crafts room;
Laundry room; Barber/Beauty shop; Library.
Activities Arts & crafts; Games; Reading
groups; Prayer groups; Movies; Social/
Cultural gatherings.

ERWIN

Unicoi County Nursing Home*
Greenway Circle, Erwin, TN, 37650
(615) 743-3141
Licensure Skilled care; Intermediate care. *Beds*
46. *Certified* Medicaid; Medicare.

ETOWAH

Etowah Health Care Center*
Old Grady Rd, Etowah, TN, 37331
(615) 263-1138
Medical Dir/Dir of Nursing Dr Thomas W
Williams.
Licensure Intermediate care. *Beds* 120.
Certified Medicaid.
Admissions Requirements Minimum age 18;
Medical examination; Physician's request.
Staff Physicians 1 (pt); RNs 1 (ft); LPNs 7
(ft), 3 (pt); Orderlies 4 (ft), 2 (pt); Nurses
aides 30 (ft), 8 (pt); Physical therapists 1
(pt); Speech therapists 1 (pt); Activities
coordinators 1 (ft), 1 (pt); Dietitians 1 (pt).
Facilities Dining room; Physical therapy
room; Activities room; Laundry room;
Barber/Beauty shop.
Activities Arts & crafts; Games; Prayer groups;
Movies; Social/Cultural gatherings.

McMinn Memorial Nursing Home
PO Box 410, Old Grady Rd, Hwy 411 N,
Etowah, TN, 37331
(615) 263-3646
Admin Wanda Watson. *Medical Dir/Dir of
Nursing* T W Williams MD.
Licensure Intermediate care. *Beds* ICF 44.
Certified Medicaid.
Owner Nonprofit organization/foundation.
Admissions Requirements Medical
examination; Physician's request.
Staff RNs 1 (ft); LPNs 5 (ft); Orderlies 1 (ft);
Nurses aides 10 (ft), 3 (pt); Physical
therapists 1 (pt); Speech therapists 1 (pt);
Activities coordinators 1 (pt); Dietitians 1
(ft); Social worker 1 (pt).
Facilities Dining room; Activities room;
Barber/Beauty shop.
Activities Arts & crafts; Cards; Games;
Reading groups; Prayer groups; Movies;
Shopping trips; Social/Cultural gatherings.

FAYETTEVILLE

Donalson Care Center
510 W Market St, Fayetteville, TN, 37334
(615) 433-7156
Admin Kathleen M Closson. *Medical Dir/Dir
of Nursing* Dr A U Bolner; Gayle Sullivan
DON.
Licensure Intermediate care. *Beds* ICF 43.
Certified Medicaid; Medicare.
Owner Nonprofit organization/foundation.
Admissions Requirements Minimum age 14;
Medical examination; Physician's request.
Staff RNs 1 (ft); LPNs 6 (ft), 2 (pt); Nurses
aides 12 (ft), 2 (pt); Dietitians 1 (pt).
Languages Spanish
Facilities Dining room; Activities room;
Crafts room.
Activities Arts & crafts; Cards; Games;
Reading groups; Prayer groups; Movies;
Shopping trips; Social/Cultural gatherings.

Health Inn Inc
Rte 7, Thornton Pkwy, Fayetteville, TN,
37334
(615) 433-9973
Admin Jewell Barnett. *Medical Dir/Dir of
Nursing* Douie Meeks LPN.
Licensure Intermediate care. *Beds* ICF 54.
Certified Medicaid.
Owner Proprietary Corp.
Staff RNs 1 (pt); LPNs 5 (ft), 3 (pt); Orderlies
1 (ft); Nurses aides 14 (ft), 1 (pt); Activities
coordinators 1 (ft); Dietitians 3 (ft), 3 (pt).
Facilities Dining room; Laundry room;
Barber/Beauty shop.

Lincoln Care Center
501 Morgan Ave, Fayetteville, TN, 37334
(615) 433-6146
Admin Kathy M Closson. *Medical Dir/Dir of
Nursing* Anne U Bolner MD; G Sullivan, V
Groce DON.
Licensure Skilled care; Intermediate care. *Beds*
SNF 37; ICF 182. *Certified* Medicaid;
Medicare.
Owner Nonprofit organization/foundation.
Admissions Requirements Medical
examination.
Staff Physicians 1 (pt); RNs 7 (ft); LPNs 22
(ft); Nurses aides 72 (ft); Physical therapists
1 (ft); Occupational therapists 1 (ft); Speech
therapists 1 (ft); Activities coordinators 1
(ft); Dietitians 1 (ft); Dentists 1 (pt);
Ophthalmologists 1 (pt).
Languages Spanish
Facilities Dining room; Physical therapy
room; Activities room; Barber/Beauty shop;
In-house pharmacy.
Activities Arts & crafts; Cards; Games;
Reading groups; Prayer groups; Movies;
Shopping trips; Social/Cultural gatherings;
Monthly luncheon buffets; Swimming;
Coffee breaks; Cookouts; Exercise classes;
Fishing; Quilting; Bingo; Sensory
stimulation.

FRANKLIN

Claiborne & Hughes Convalescent Center Inc
200 Strahl St, Franklin, TN, 37064
(615) 791-1103
Admin John W Jones. *Medical Dir/Dir of
Nursing* Robert Hollister MD; Pauline
Pewitz RN DON.
Licensure Skilled care; Intermediate care. *Beds*
SNF 43; ICF 114. *Certified* Medicaid;
Medicare.
Owner Proprietary Corp.
Admissions Requirements Medical
examination.
Staff RNs 2 (ft), 1 (pt); LPNs 13 (ft), 2 (pt);
Nurses aides 40 (ft), 15 (pt); Activities
coordinators 2 (ft), 2 (pt).
Facilities Dining room; Physical therapy
room; Activities room; Crafts room; Laundry
room; Barber/Beauty shop.
Activities Arts & crafts; Cards; Games;
Reading groups; Prayer groups; Movies;
Shopping trips; Social/Cultural gatherings;
Resident council.

Franklin Health Care Center*
216 Fairground St, Franklin, TN, 37064
(615) 794-9287
Licensure Skilled care; Intermediate care. *Beds*
76. *Certified* Medicaid; Medicare.
Owner Proprietary Corp (National Health
Corp).

Graystone Home Inc
157 4th Ave S, Franklin, TN, 37064
(615) 794-4877
Admin Dorothy S Stone. *Medical Dir/Dir of
Nursing* Margurietta P Church RN DON.
Licensure Intermediate care. *Beds* ICF 37.
Owner Privately owned.
Admissions Requirements Minimum age 14;
Medical examination.

Staff Physicians 1 (pt); RNs 1 (ft); LPNs 3
(ft), 2 (pt); Nurses aides 11 (ft), 4 (pt);
Activities coordinators 1 (ft); Dietitians 1
(pt).
Facilities Activities room; Barber/Beauty shop.
Activities Arts & crafts; Cards; Games; Prayer
groups; Group singing.

Harpeth Terrace Convalescent Center Inc
1287 W Main St, Franklin, TN, 37064
(615) 794-8417
Admin Boris Georgeff. *Medical Dir/Dir of
Nursing* Dr H Bryant Savage; Judy Michael.
Licensure Skilled care; Intermediate care. *Beds*
SNF 30; ICF 89. *Certified* Medicaid;
Medicare.
Owner Proprietary Corp.
Admissions Requirements Medical
examination.
Staff Physicians 3 (ft); RNs 3 (ft); LPNs 5 (ft);
Nurses aides 26 (ft); Activities coordinators
1 (ft); Dietitians 1 (pt); Social worker 1 (ft).
Facilities Dining room; Physical therapy
room; Activities room; Laundry room;
Barber/Beauty shop.
Activities Arts & crafts; Cards; Games;
Reading groups; Prayer groups; Movies;
Shopping trips; Social/Cultural gatherings.

Lofton Nursing Home Inc*
1501 Columbia Ave, Franklin, TN, 37064
(615) 794-2624
Beds 49.

GAINESBORO

Theo Spivey Nursing Home*
Rte 2, Box 271-A, Gainesboro, TN, 38562
(615) 268-0291
Licensure Intermediate care. *Beds* 64.
Certified Medicaid.

GALLATIN

Brandywood Nursing Home*
555 E Bledsoe St, Gallatin, TN, 37066
(615) 452-7132
Licensure Skilled care; Intermediate care. *Beds*
100. *Certified* Medicaid; Medicare.
Owner Proprietary Corp (Beverly Enterprises).

Gallatin Health Care Associates
438 N Water Ave, Gallatin, TN, 37066
(615) 452-2322
Admin Marie Lane. *Medical Dir/Dir of
Nursing* Family Practice Associates MD.
Licensure Skilled care; Intermediate care. *Beds*
SNF 52; ICF 151. *Certified* Medicaid;
Medicare.
Owner Privately owned.
Admissions Requirements Physician's request.
Staff RNs 3 (ft); LPNs 25 (ft); Nurses aides
100 (ft); Physical therapists 1 (ft);
Occupational therapists 1 (ft); Speech
therapists 1 (ft); Activities coordinators 1
(ft); Dietitians 1 (ft).
Facilities Dining room; Physical therapy
room; Activities room; Crafts room; Laundry
room; Barber/Beauty shop; Sunrooms.
Activities Arts & crafts; Prayer groups;
Movies; Shopping trips; Social/Cultural
gatherings.

L M Swanson Nursing Home*
647 Pace St, Gallatin, TN, 37066
(615) 452-0611
Licensure Intermediate care. *Beds* 25.
Certified Medicaid.

GALLAWAY

Layton W Watson Nursing Home
PO Box 128, 435 Old Brownsville Rd,
Gallaway, TN, 38036
(901) 867-2010

Admin Doris L Morris. *Medical Dir/Dir of Nursing* Dr Patrick Murphy; Donna Beasley DON.
Licensure Intermediate care. *Beds* ICF 130. *Certified* Medicaid.
Owner Nonprofit Corp.
Admissions Requirements Minimum age 14; Medical examination; Physician's request.
Staff LPNs 10 (ft), 5 (pt); Nurses aides 33 (ft), 10 (pt); Activities coordinators 1 (ft).
Facilities Dining room; Physical therapy room; Activities room; Chapel; Crafts room; Laundry room; Barber/Beauty shop; Library.
Activities Arts & crafts; Cards; Games; Reading groups; Prayer groups; Movies; Shopping trips; Social/Cultural gatherings.

GOODLETTSVILLE

Vanco Manor Nursing Home
813 S Dickerson Rd, Goodlettsville, TN, 37072
(615) 859-6600
Admin Billy R Talbert. *Medical Dir/Dir of Nursing* Erma Hoover.
Licensure Intermediate care. *Beds* ICF 66. *Certified* Medicaid.
Owner Proprietary Corp (American Health Centers Inc).
Staff RNs 1 (ft); LPNs 4 (ft); Nurses aides 18 (ft); Activities coordinators 1 (ft); Dietitians 1 (ft).

GRAY

Anderson Health Care Center
PO Box 8275, Rte 15, Gray, TN, 37615
(615) 477-7146
Admin Mrs Billie S Anderson. *Medical Dir/Dir of Nursing* Jacqueline Lloyd MD; Mrs Terri Nave RN DON.
Licensure Skilled care; Intermediate care. *Beds* SNF 20; ICF 85. *Certified* Medicaid; Medicare.
Owner Proprietary Corp.
Staff Physicians 14 (pt); RNs 2 (ft), 1 (pt); LPNs 10 (ft), 2 (pt); Nurses aides 35 (ft), 10 (pt); Physical therapists 2 (pt); Speech therapists 1 (pt); Activities coordinators 1 (ft); Dietitians 1 (ft); Dentists 1 (pt); Ophthalmologists 1 (pt); Podiatrists 1 (pt); Dentist 1 (pt).
Facilities Dining room; Physical therapy room; Activities room; Laundry room; Barber/Beauty shop.
Activities Arts & crafts; Cards; Games; Reading groups; Prayer groups; Social/Cultural gatherings.

GRAYSVILLE

Graysville Nursing Home*
Star Rte, Graysville, TN, 37338
(615) 775-1262
Licensure Nursing home. *Beds* 19.
Admissions Requirements Medical examination.
Staff RNs 1 (pt); LPNs 1 (ft), 1 (pt); Nurses aides 6 (ft), 3 (pt).
Facilities Dining room; Laundry room.

GREENEVILLE

Life Care Center of Greeneville*
725 Crum St, Greeneville, TN, 37743
(615) 639-8131
Licensure Intermediate care. *Beds* 161. *Certified* Medicaid.
Owner Proprietary Corp (Life Care Centers of America).
Facilities Dining room; Physical therapy room; Activities room; Chapel; Crafts room; Laundry room; Barber/Beauty shop; EKG; X-ray; IPPB.

Activities Arts & crafts; Games; Reading groups; Movies; Shopping trips; Social/Cultural gatherings.

Life Care—West Nursing Center
210 Holt Court, Greeneville, TN, 37743
(615) 639-0213
Admin Charles R Sherer. *Medical Dir/Dir of Nursing* Dr Richard Aasheim; Betty Laster DON.
Licensure Intermediate care. *Beds* ICF 124. *Certified* Medicaid.
Owner Proprietary Corp (Life Care Centers of America).
Admissions Requirements Medical examination; Physician's request.
Staff Physicians 1 (pt); RNs 2 (ft); LPNs 11 (ft); Orderlies 4 (ft); Nurses aides 32 (ft), 10 (pt); Physical therapists 1 (pt); Speech therapists 1 (pt); Activities coordinators 1 (ft); Dietitians 1 (pt).
Facilities Dining room; Physical therapy room; Activities room; Chapel; Crafts room; Laundry room; Barber/Beauty shop.
Activities Arts & crafts; Cards; Games; Reading groups; Prayer groups; Movies; Shopping trips; Social/Cultural gatherings; Fishing trips; Hayride; Bingo; Christmas parade; County fair.

HARRIMAN

Johnson's Health Care Center Inc*
Box 290, Hannah Rd, Harriman, TN, 37748
(615) 882-9159
Licensure Intermediate care. *Beds* 160. *Certified* Medicaid.

HARTSVILLE

Hartsville Convalescent Center
Rte 2 Box 18B, Hartsville, TN, 37074
(615) 374-2167
Admin Dorothy D Evinss. *Medical Dir/Dir of Nursing* E K Bratton MD; Lucille Seelow DON.
Licensure Intermediate care. *Beds* ICF 80. *Certified* Medicaid.
Owner Proprietary Corp.
Admissions Requirements Medical examination.
Staff Physicians 1 (pt); LPNs 9 (ft); Nurses aides 23 (ft); Physical therapists 1 (pt); Activities coordinators 1 (ft); Dietitians 5 (ft), 3 (pt).
Facilities Dining room; Activities room; Laundry room; Barber/Beauty shop.
Activities Arts & crafts; Cards; Games; Reading groups; Prayer groups; Movies.

HENDERSON

Chester County Nursing Home
831 E Main St, Henderson, TN, 38340
(901) 989-7598
Admin Tommie Archer. *Medical Dir/Dir of Nursing* R L Wilson MD; Bonnie Hudson DON.
Licensure Intermediate care. *Beds* ICF 89. *Certified* Medicaid.
Owner Privately owned.
Admissions Requirements Minimum age 18; Medical examination; Physician's request.
Staff RNs 1 (ft); LPNs 7 (ft), 2 (pt); Orderlies 1 (ft); Nurses aides 20 (ft), 8 (pt); Activities coordinators 1 (ft); Dietitians 1 (pt).
Facilities Dining room; Activities room; Laundry room; Barber/Beauty shop.
Activities Arts & crafts; Cards; Games; Reading groups; Prayer groups; Movies; Shopping trips; Social/Cultural gatherings.

HENDERSONVILLE

Hendersonville Nursing Home*
672 W Main St, Hendersonville, TN, 37075
(615) 824-8301
Beds 32.

HERMITAGE

McKendree Village Inc
4347 Lebanon Rd, Hermitage, TN, 37076
(615) 889-6990
Admin Winfrey C Link. *Medical Dir/Dir of Nursing* Dr Edward King.
Licensure Skilled care; Intermediate care. *Beds* 300. *Certified* Medicaid; Medicare.
Owner Nonprofit Corp.
Admissions Requirements Minimum age 55; Medical examination.
Staff Physicians 1 (pt); RNs 7 (ft), 5 (pt); LPNs 8 (ft), 6 (pt); Nurses aides 55 (ft), 22 (pt); Physical therapists 2 (ft); Recreational therapists 2 (ft), 1 (pt); Occupational therapists 1 (pt); Speech therapists 1 (pt); Activities coordinators 1 (ft); Dietitians 1 (ft), 1 (pt); Ophthalmologists 1 (pt); Podiatrists 1 (pt).
Affiliation Methodist
Facilities Dining room; Physical therapy room; Activities room; Chapel; Crafts room; Laundry room; Barber/Beauty shop; Library.
Activities Arts & crafts; Cards; Games; Reading groups; Prayer groups; Movies; Shopping trips; Social/Cultural gatherings.

HOHENWALD

Lewis County Manor
PO Box 147, Linden Hwy, Hohenwald, TN, 38462
(615) 796-3233
Admin Thelma Blocker. *Medical Dir/Dir of Nursing* Jean Allsop.
Licensure Intermediate care. *Beds* ICF 61. *Certified* Medicaid.
Owner Proprietary Corp (American Health Centers Inc).
Staff RNs 2 (pt); LPNs 4 (ft); Orderlies 3 (ft); Nurses aides 13 (ft), 3 (pt); Activities coordinators 1 (ft); Dietitians 1 (ft).
Facilities Dining room; Activities room; Laundry room; Barber/Beauty shop.
Activities Arts & crafts; Cards; Games; Reading groups; Movies; Shopping trips; Social/Cultural gatherings.

HUMBOLDT

Nucare Convalescent Center
2400 Mitchell St, Humboldt, TN, 38343
(901) 784-5183
Admin Nichols L Nevius. *Medical Dir/Dir of Nursing* Dr Robert Routon; M E Duncan RN.
Licensure Intermediate care. *Beds* ICF 142. *Certified* Medicaid.
Owner Proprietary Corp.
Admissions Requirements Medical examination; Physician's request.
Staff Physicians 14 (pt); RNs 1 (ft); LPNs 13 (ft); Nurses aides 52 (ft); Physical therapists 1 (pt); Speech therapists 1 (pt); Activities coordinators 1 (ft); Dietitians 1 (ft); Dentists 1 (pt).
Facilities Dining room; Physical therapy room; Activities room; Laundry room; Barber/Beauty shop; Library.
Activities Games; Social/Cultural gatherings; Bingo; Ball games; Fishing trips.

HUNTINGDON

Care Inn—Huntingdon*
635 High St, Huntingdon, TN, 38344
(901) 986-8943
Admin William W Wright.

Licensure Intermediate care. *Beds* 132.
Certified Medicaid.
Staff RNs 1 (ft); LPNs 13 (ft); Nurses aides 26
(ft); Physical therapists 1 (pt); Activities
coordinators 1 (ft); Dietitians 1 (ft).
Facilities Dining room; Activities room;
Crafts room; Laundry room; Barber/Beauty
shop.
Activities Arts & crafts; Cards; Games;
Reading groups; Prayer groups; Movies;
Shopping trips; Social/Cultural gatherings.

HUNTSVILLE

Stonehenge Health Care Center Inc*
Hunt St, Huntsville, TN, 37756
(615) 663-3600
Admin William J Stout Jr. *Medical Dir/Dir of
Nursing* Dr George Kline.
Licensure Intermediate care. *Beds* 79.
Certified Medicaid.
Owner Proprietary Corp (Tullock
Management).
Admissions Requirements Minimum age 14;
Medical examination; Physician's request.
Staff RNs 1 (pt); LPNs 5 (ft); Orderlies 3 (ft);
Nurses aides 11 (ft), 5 (pt); Physical
therapists 1 (pt); Activities coordinators 1
(ft); Dietitians 1 (pt); Dentists 1 (pt);
Ophthalmologists 1 (pt).
Facilities Dining room; Physical therapy
room; Activities room; Laundry room;
Barber/Beauty shop; Library.
Activities Arts & crafts; Cards; Games;
Reading groups; Prayer groups; Movies;
Shopping trips; Social/Cultural gatherings.

JACKSON

Forest Cove Nursing Center*
45 Forest Cove, Jackson, TN, 38301
(901) 424-4200
Licensure Intermediate care. *Beds* 150.
Certified Medicaid.
Owner Proprietary Corp (American Health
Centers Inc).
Admissions Requirements Minimum age 18.
Staff RNs 2 (ft); LPNs 12 (ft), 3 (pt); Nurses
aides 36 (ft), 13 (pt); Recreational therapists
1 (pt); Activities coordinators 1 (ft).
Facilities Dining room; Activities room;
Crafts room; Barber/Beauty shop.
Activities Arts & crafts; Cards; Games; Prayer
groups; Movies.

Jackson Manor
131 Cloverdale St, Jackson, TN, 38301
(901) 423-8750
Admin Jane C Pendergrass. *Medical Dir/Dir of
Nursing* Curtis Clark MD; M Kirby
Buchanan RN DON.
Licensure Intermediate care. *Beds* ICF 107.
Certified Medicaid.
Owner Proprietary Corp (Tullock
Management).
Admissions Requirements Minimum age 14;
Medical examination; Physician's request.
Staff Physicians 1 (pt); RNs 1 (ft); LPNs 8
(ft), 2 (pt); Orderlies 1 (ft); Nurses aides 31
(ft), 6 (pt); Physical therapists 1 (pt);
Activities coordinators 1 (ft), 1 (pt);
Dietitians 1 (pt).
Facilities Dining room; Activities room;
Crafts room; Laundry room; Barber/Beauty
shop.
Activities Arts & crafts; Cards; Games; Prayer
groups; Movies; Social/Cultural gatherings.

Laurel Wood Health Care Inc*
200 Birch St, Jackson, TN, 38301
(901) 422-5641
Admin Leonard L Usery. *Medical Dir/Dir of
Nursing* Robert Tucker.
Licensure Intermediate care. *Beds* 66.
Certified Medicaid.
Admissions Requirements Minimum age 14;
Medical examination; Physician's request.

Staff Physicians 2 (ft), 8 (pt); RNs 1 (pt);
LPNs 4 (ft), 3 (pt); Nurses aides 28 (ft), 10
(pt); Physical therapists 2 (pt); Reality
therapists ' (ft); Recreational therapists 1
(ft); Occupational therapists 1 (pt); Activities
coordinators 1 (ft); Dietitians 1 (ft); Dentists
1 (pt); Podiatrists 1 (pt).
Facilities Dining room; Physical therapy
room; Activities room; Chapel; Laundry
room; Barber/Beauty shop.
Activities Arts & crafts; Cards; Games;
Reading groups; Prayer groups; Movies;
Shopping trips.

Maplewood Health Care Center*
100 Cherrywood Pl, Jackson, TN, 38301
(901) 668-1900
Licensure Intermediate care. *Beds* 133.
Certified Medicaid.

Mission Convalescent Home
118 Glass St, Jackson, TN, 38301
(901) 424-2951, 424-2954
Admin F L Cherry. *Medical Dir/Dir of
Nursing* Dr Ronald Weaver; Brenda Bray
LPN.
Licensure Intermediate care. *Beds* 30.
Certified Medicaid; Medicare.
Owner Nonprofit organization/foundation.
Admissions Requirements Minimum age 16;
Medical examination; Physician's request.
Facilities Dining room; Activities room;
Chapel; Laundry room.
Activities Arts & crafts; Cards; Games; Prayer
groups; Movies; Social/Cultural gatherings.

JAMESTOWN

Fentress County Nursing Home
PO Box 968, Hwy 52 W, Jamestown, TN,
38556
(615) 879-5859
Admin Gale C Potter. *Medical Dir/Dir of
Nursing* D N Joshi MD; Glenna Hall RN
DON.
Licensure Intermediate care. *Beds* ICF 100.
Certified Medicaid.
Owner Nonprofit organization/foundation.
Admissions Requirements Medical
examination; Physician's request.
Staff Physicians 5 (pt); RNs 2 (ft); LPNs;
Orderlies 9 (ft); Nurses aides 27 (ft);
Physical therapists 1 (pt); Speech therapists
1 (pt); Activities coordinators 1 (ft);
Dietitians 1 (ft).
Facilities Dining room; Physical therapy
room; Activities room; Laundry room;
Barber/Beauty shop.
Activities Arts & crafts; Cards; Games;
Reading groups; Prayer groups; Movies;
Shopping trips; In room visits.

JEFFERSON CITY

Hillhaven Health Care—Jefferson City
101 Universal Road, Hwy 11 East, Jefferson
City, TN, 37760
(615) 475-4034
Admin Rodney Worley. *Medical Dir/Dir of
Nursing* Henry J Presutti MD; Katherine
Mahan RN DON.
Licensure Intermediate care. *Beds* ICF 186.
Certified Medicaid.
Owner Proprietary Corp (Hillhaven Corp).
Admissions Requirements Minimum age 18;
Medical examination; Physician's request.
Staff RNs 3 (ft); LPNs 10 (ft), 8 (pt);
Orderlies 4 (ft), 2 (pt); Nurses aides 40 (ft),
26 (pt); Activities coordinators 2 (ft);
Dietitians 1 (ft).
Facilities Dining room; Activities room;
Crafts room; Laundry room; Barber/Beauty
shop; Library; TV lounge.
Activities Arts & crafts; Cards; Games;
Reading groups; Prayer groups; Movies;
Shopping trips; Social/Cultural gatherings;
Resident council.

JOHNSON CITY

Appalachian Christian Village
2012 Sherwood Dr, Johnson City, TN, 37601
(615) 928-3168
Admin Garry L Phillips. *Medical Dir/Dir of
Nursing* Gwen Hendrix.
Licensure Intermediate care; Continuing care
retirement community. *Beds* ICF 101.
Certified Medicaid.
Owner Nonprofit organization/foundation.
Admissions Requirements Minimum age 62;
Medical examination.
Staff RNs 2 (ft), 2 (pt); LPNs 10 (ft), 4 (pt);
Orderlies 5 (ft), 1 (pt); Nurses aides 40 (ft),
6 (pt); Physical therapists 1 (pt); Activities
coordinators 1 (ft), 1 (pt); Dietitians 1 (ft);
Dentists 1 (pt); Ophthalmologists 1 (pt);
Podiatrists 1 (pt); Ward clerks 2 (ft); Social
worker 1.
Affiliation Church of Christ
Facilities Dining room; Physical therapy
room; Activities room; Chapel; Crafts room;
Laundry room; Barber/Beauty shop; Library.
Activities Games; Movies; Social/Cultural
gatherings.

**Asbury Center Health Care & Retirement
Facility**
400 N Boone St, Johnson City, TN, 37604
(615) 929-1161
Admin Sam W Ware, James R Deck. *Medical
Dir/Dir of Nursing* Robert C Allen MD;
Nancy Hidalgo RN DON.
Licensure Skilled care; Intermediate care;
Retirement facility. *Beds* SNF 22; ICF 152;
Apartment units 90. *Certified* Medicaid;
Medicare.
Owner Nonprofit Corp.
Admissions Requirements Medical
examination; Physician's request.
Staff RNs; LPNs; Orderlies; Nurses aides;
Physical therapists; Speech therapists;
Activities coordinators; Dietitians.
Facilities Dining room; Physical therapy
room; Activities room; Chapel; Crafts room;
Laundry room; Barber/Beauty shop; Library;
Garden with fountain; Gazebo; Shuffleboard;
Putting green.
Activities Arts & crafts; Cards; Games;
Reading groups; Prayer groups; Shopping
trips; Social/Cultural gatherings.

Colonial Hill Health Care Center
PO Box 3218, 3209 Bristol Hwy, Johnson
City, TN, 37602
(615) 282-3311
Admin Ronald Dean. *Medical Dir/Dir of
Nursing* Dr Richard Morrison; Joyce
Walwick RN DON.
Licensure Skilled care; Intermediate care. *Beds*
SNF 74; ICF 103. *Certified* Medicaid;
Medicare.
Owner Proprietary Corp (National Health
Corp).
Admissions Requirements Medical
examination; Physician's request.
Staff Physicians 2 (pt); RNs 8 (ft), 3 (pt);
LPNs 12 (ft), 12 (pt); Orderlies 1 (ft), 3 (pt);
Nurses aides 43 (ft), 18 (pt); Physical
therapists 2 (pt); Occupational therapists 2
(ft), 2 (pt); Speech therapists 2 (ft); Activities
coordinators 2 (pt); Dietitians 1 (ft).
Facilities Dining room; Physical therapy
room; Activities room; Crafts room; Laundry
room; Barber/Beauty shop; Library.
Activities Arts & crafts; Cards; Games;
Reading groups; Prayer groups; Movies;
Shopping trips; Social/Cultural gatherings.

JONESBOROUGH

Four Oaks Health Care Center
Drawer 39, Persimmon Ridge Rd,
Jonesborough, TN, 37659
(615) 753-8711

Admin Suzanne Ervin. *Medical Dir/Dir of Nursing* David Doane MD, Forrest Lang MD; Alice Ford RN DON.
Licensure Skilled care; Intermediate care. *Beds* SNF 21; ICF 52. *Certified* Medicaid; Medicare.
Owner Proprietary Corp.
Admissions Requirements Medical examination.
Staff Physicians 2 (pt); RNs 1 (ft), 2 (pt); LPNs 4 (ft), 3 (pt); Orderlies 1 (ft); Nurses aides 25 (ft), 5 (pt); Physical therapists 1 (pt); Recreational therapists 1 (ft); Occupational therapists 1 (pt); Speech therapists 1 (pt); Activities coordinators 1 (ft); Dietitians 1 (pt); Dentists 1 (pt); Ophthalmologists 1 (pt); Podiatrists 1 (pt).
Facilities Dining room; Physical therapy room; Activities room; Crafts room; Laundry room; Barber/Beauty shop; Library.
Activities Arts & crafts; Cards; Games; Reading groups; Prayer groups; Movies; Social/Cultural gatherings.

Jonesboro Nursing Home Inc
300 W Jackson Blvd, Jonesborough, TN, 37659
(615) 753-4281
Admin Linda Jennings. *Medical Dir/Dir of Nursing* Marvine Boggs RN DON.
Licensure Intermediate care. *Beds* 365. *Certified* Medicaid.
Owner Proprietary Corp.
Admissions Requirements Medical examination; Physician's request.
Staff Physicians 2 (pt); RNs 1 (ft); LPNs 5 (ft), 1 (pt); Orderlies 3 (ft); Nurses aides 18 (ft), 2 (pt); Activities coordinators 1 (ft); Dietitians 1 (pt).
Facilities Dining room; Activities room; Crafts room; Laundry room; Barber/Beauty shop.
Activities Arts & crafts; Cards; Games; Reading groups; Prayer groups; Social/Cultural gatherings.

KINGSPORT

Netherland Health Center
100 Netherland Ln, Kingsport, TN, 37660
(615) 245-6193
Admin Terryll H Brown. *Medical Dir/Dir of Nursing* Barbara Campbell.
Licensure Intermediate care. *Beds* ICF 40.
Owner Nonprofit Corp.
Admissions Requirements Medical examination; Physician's request.
Staff Physicians 1 (pt); RNs 1 (ft); LPNs 5 (ft), 2 (pt); Orderlies 1 (pt); Nurses aides 14 (ft), 3 (pt); Physical therapists 1 (pt); Speech therapists 1 (pt); Activities coordinators 1 (pt); Dietitians 1 (pt).
Facilities Dining room; Physical therapy room; Activities room; Crafts room; Laundry room; Barber/Beauty shop; Library.
Activities Arts & crafts; Games; Reading groups; Prayer groups; Movies.

KNOXVILLE

Brakebill Nursing Homes Inc
5837 Lyons View Pike, Knoxville, TN, 37919
(615) 584-3902
Admin W Lynn Brakebill. *Medical Dir/Dir of Nursing* Susan Titlow.
Licensure Skilled care; Intermediate care. *Beds* SNF 54; ICF 168. *Certified* Medicaid; Medicare.
Owner Proprietary Corp.
Admissions Requirements Medical examination; Physician's request.
Staff Physicians 20 (pt); RNs 6 (ft), 2 (pt); LPNs 12 (ft), 2 (pt); Nurses aides 50 (ft), 5 (pt); Physical therapists 1 (ft), 2 (pt); Speech therapists 1 (pt); Activities coordinators 3 (ft); Dietitians 1 (pt).

Facilities Dining room; Physical therapy room; Activities room; Crafts room; Laundry room; Barber/Beauty shop; Library.
Activities Arts & crafts; Cards; Games; Reading groups; Prayer groups; Movies; Shopping trips; Social/Cultural gatherings.

Hillcrest Central
5321 Tazewell Pike, Knoxville, TN, 37918
(615) 687-1321
Admin Thomas E Hicks. *Medical Dir/Dir of Nursing* Thomas B Drinnen MD; Alda Maranville RN.
Licensure Skilled care; Intermediate care. *Beds* SNF 53; ICF 120. *Certified* Medicaid; Medicare.
Owner Publicly owned.
Admissions Requirements Medical examination; Physician's request.
Facilities Dining room; Physical therapy room; Activities room; Laundry room; Barber/Beauty shop.
Activities Arts & crafts; Cards; Reading groups; Prayer groups; Movies; Shopping trips.

Hillcrest—North*
Rte 12, Maloneyville Rd, Knoxville, TN, 37918
Licensure Nursing home. *Beds* 386.

Hillcrest—South*
1758 Hillwood Ave, Knoxville, TN, 37920
(615) 573-9621
Licensure Intermediate care. *Beds* 106. *Certified* Medicaid.

Hillcrest—West*
6801 Middlebrook Pike, Knoxville, TN, 37919
(615) 588-7661
Licensure Skilled care; Intermediate care. *Beds* 212. *Certified* Medicaid; Medicare.

Knoxville Convalescent & Nursing Home Inc*
809 Emerald Ave, Knoxville, TN, 37917
(615) 524-7366
Licensure Skilled care; Intermediate care. *Beds* 152. *Certified* Medicaid; Medicare.
Owner Proprietary Corp (National Health Corp).

Knoxville Health Care Center Inc*
2120 Highland Ave, Knoxville, TN, 37916
(615) 525-4131
Licensure Skilled care; Intermediate care. *Beds* 180. *Certified* Medicaid; Medicare.
Owner Proprietary Corp (National Health Corp).

Little Creek Sanitarium
1810 Little Creek Ln, Knoxville, TN, 37922
(615) 690-6727
Admin Roger F Goodge. *Medical Dir/Dir of Nursing* Ann Goodge RN.
Licensure Skilled care. *Beds* SNF 38.
Owner Nonprofit organization/foundation.
Admissions Requirements Minimum age 14; Medical examination.
Staff RNs 4 (ft), 4 (pt); LPNs 2 (ft), 2 (pt); Orderlies 2 (pt); Nurses aides 6 (ft), 22 (pt); Activities coordinators 1 (pt).
Affiliation Seventh-Day Adventist
Facilities Dining room; Chapel; Barber/Beauty shop.
Activities Games; Reading groups; Prayer groups; Movies; Holiday & seasonal parties; Hayrides.

Northhaven Health Care Center*
3300 Broadway NE, Knoxville, TN, 37917
(615) 698-2052
Medical Dir/Dir of Nursing Dr Mosley.
Licensure Intermediate care. *Beds* 96. *Certified* Medicaid.
Owner Proprietary Corp (Hillhaven Corp).
Admissions Requirements Minimum age 14; Medical examination; Physician's request.

Staff RNs 2 (ft), 3 (pt); LPNs 2 (ft), 4 (pt); Nurses aides 24 (ft), 8 (pt); Physical therapists 2 (pt); Activities coordinators 1 (ft); Dietitians 1 (pt); Dentists 1 (pt); Ophthalmologists 1 (pt); Podiatrists 1 (pt); Audiologists 1 (pt).
Facilities Dining room; Physical therapy room; Activities room; Crafts room; Laundry room; Barber/Beauty shop.
Activities Arts & crafts; Cards; Games; Reading groups; Prayer groups; Movies; Pet therapy.

Serene Manor Medical Center
970 Wray St, Knoxville, TN, 37917
(615) 523-9171
Admin Rita Kidd. *Medical Dir/Dir of Nursing* Dr Steve Master; Nancy Bowman RNC.
Licensure Intermediate care. *Beds* ICF 73. *Certified* Medicaid.
Owner Nonprofit Corp.
Admissions Requirements Minimum age 14; Medical examination; Physician's request.
Staff Physicians 1 (pt); RNs 2 (ft); LPNs 10 (ft); Orderlies 5 (ft), 5 (pt); Nurses aides 15 (ft), 10 (pt); Physical therapists 1 (pt); Recreational therapists 1 (pt); Activities coordinators 1 (ft); Dietitians 1 (ft); Ophthalmologists 1 (pt).
Facilities Dining room; Physical therapy room; Activities room; Crafts room; Barber/Beauty shop.
Activities Arts & crafts; Cards; Games; Reading groups; Prayer groups; Movies; Shopping trips; Social/Cultural gatherings; Birthday parties; Cook-outs.

Shannondale Retirement Home*
801 Vanosdale Rd, Knoxville, TN, 37919
(615) 690-3411
Medical Dir/Dir of Nursing Dr Harry K Ogden.
Licensure Skilled care; Intermediate care; Home for aged. *Beds* 349. *Certified* Medicaid; Medicare.
Admissions Requirements Minimum age 62.
Staff Physicians 1 (pt); RNs 1 (ft), 2 (pt); LPNs 2 (ft), 1 (pt); Activities coordinators 1 (ft); Dietitians 1 (ft); Podiatrists 1 (pt).
Affiliation Presbyterian
Facilities Dining room; Activities room; Chapel; Crafts room; Laundry room; Barber/Beauty shop; Library.
Activities Arts & crafts; Cards; Games; Prayer groups; Movies; Shopping trips; Social/Cultural gatherings; Theatre; Zoo; Dogwood Arts Festival; Art shows.

LAFAYETTE

Janwynella Nursing Home Inc*
405 Times Ave, Lafayette, TN, 37083
(615) 666-3170
Medical Dir/Dir of Nursing C C Chitwood Jr MD.
Beds 39.
Admissions Requirements Minimum age 14; Medical examination.
Staff RNs 1 (ft); LPNs 1 (ft); Orderlies 2 (ft); Nurses aides 15 (ft); Activities coordinators 1 (ft); Dietitians 1 (pt).

LAFOLLETTE

LaFollette Community Nursing Home
PO Box 1301, 106 E Ave, LaFollette, TN, 37766
(615) 562-2211
Admin J B Wright. *Medical Dir/Dir of Nursing* Dr L J Seargeant; Carol Leach RN DON.
Licensure Skilled care; Intermediate care. *Beds* SNF 50; ICF 48. *Certified* Medicaid; Medicare.
Owner Nonprofit organization/foundation.
Admissions Requirements Minimum age 14; Medical examination; Physician's request.

Staff Physicians 10 (ft); RNs 1 (ft), 1 (pt);
LPNs 12 (ft), 7 (pt); Orderlies 1 (ft), 1 (pt);
Nurses aides 27 (ft), 40 (pt); Physical
therapists 1 (ft), 1 (pt); Speech therapists 1
(ft); Activities coordinators 2 (ft); Dietitians
1 (ft); Dentists 1 (ft); Ophthalmologists 1
(ft).
Facilities Dining room; Physical therapy
room; Activities room; Chapel; Crafts room;
Barber/Beauty shop; Library.
Activities Arts & crafts; Cards; Games;
Reading groups; Prayer groups; Movies;
Social/Cultural gatherings.

LAKE CITY

Lake City Health Care Center
PO Box 659, Industrial Park Dr, Lake City,
TN, 37769
(615) 426-2147
Admin Anita L Wilmoth. *Medical Dir/Dir of
Nursing* James Giles MD; Elizabeth Templin
RN DON.
Licensure Intermediate care. *Beds* ICF 115.
Certified Medicaid.
Owner Privately owned.
Admissions Requirements Minimum age 18;
Medical examination.
Staff RNs 1 (ft), 1 (pt); LPNs 8 (ft), 4 (pt);
Nurses aides 18 (ft), 15 (pt); Activities
coordinators 1 (ft); Dietitians 1 (ft); Social
service 1 (ft).
Facilities Dining room; Physical therapy
room; Activities room; Crafts room; Laundry
room; Barber/Beauty shop; Library.
Activities Arts & crafts; Cards; Games;
Reading groups; Prayer groups; Movies;
Shopping trips; Social/Cultural gatherings;
Field trips.

LAWRENCEBURG

Laurenceburg Health Care Center
PO Box 767, 324 Kennedy St, Lawrenceburg,
TN, 38464
(615) 762-9418
Admin Betty T Pape. *Medical Dir/Dir of
Nursing* Leon Everett MD; Jeanette McGee
RN DON.
Licensure Skilled care; Intermediate care. *Beds*
37. *Certified* Medicaid; Medicare.
Owner Proprietary Corp (National Health
Corp).
Staff RNs 2 (ft), 3 (pt); LPNs 3 (ft), 2 (pt);
Nurses aides 10 (ft), 8 (pt); Physical
therapists 1 (pt); Speech therapists 1 (pt);
Activities coordinators 1 (ft).
Facilities Dining room; Activities room.
Activities Arts & crafts; Cards; Games;
Reading groups; Prayer groups; Exercise
groups.

Lawrence County Lions Nursing Home Inc
PO Box 906, 374 Brink St, Lawrenceburg, TN,
38464
Licensure Intermediate care. *Beds* 88.
Certified Medicaid.

Royal Care of Lawrenceburg
3501 Buffalo Rd, Rte 1, Lawrenceburg, TN,
38464
(615) 762-7518
Admin Kaun Porter. *Medical Dir/Dir of
Nursing* J Carmack Hudgins MD.
Licensure Skilled care; Intermediate care. *Beds*
SNF 64; ICF 88. *Certified* Medicaid;
Medicare.
Admissions Requirements Minimum age 14;
Medical examination; Physician's request.
Staff RNs 4 (ft), 1 (pt); LPNs 11 (ft), 5 (pt);
Orderlies 1 (pt); Nurses aides 6 (ft), 35 (pt);
Physical therapists; Speech therapists;
Activities coordinators 1 (ft); Dietitians 1
(ft); Dentists; Social workers 1 (ft); Physical
therapy aides 2 (ft).

Facilities Dining room; Physical therapy
room; Activities room; Crafts room; Laundry
room; Barber/Beauty shop; Library.
Activities Arts & crafts; Cards; Games;
Reading groups; Prayer groups; Movies;
Shopping trips; Social/Cultural gatherings;
Painting classes; Quilting bees; Special
singing; Church services.

LEBANON

Cedars Nursing Home*
933 Baddour Parkway, Lebanon, TN, 37087
(615) 444-1836
Medical Dir/Dir of Nursing Morris Ferguson
MD.
Licensure Skilled care. *Beds* 60. *Certified*
Medicaid; Medicare.
Staff RNs 4 (ft), 1 (pt); LPNs 5 (ft); Nurses
aides 28 (ft); Physical therapists 1 (ft);
Activities coordinators 1 (ft).
Facilities Dining room; Physical therapy
room; Laundry room; Barber/Beauty shop.
Activities Arts & crafts; Cards; Games;
Reading groups; Movies; Shopping trips;
Social/Cultural gatherings.

Margie Anna Nursing Home
152 S College St, Lebanon, TN, 37087
(615) 444-2882
Admin Terry L Stafford. *Medical Dir/Dir of
Nursing* R C Kash MD; Louise Patterson
DON.
Licensure Intermediate care. *Beds* ICF 46.
Certified Medicaid.
Owner Proprietary Corp.
Admissions Requirements Minimum age 16;
Physician's request.
Staff RNs 1 (pt); LPNs 4 (ft), 3 (pt); Nurses
aides 15 (ft), 8 (pt); Activities coordinators 1
(ft); Dietitians 1 (pt).
Facilities Dining room; Laundry room.
Activities Arts & crafts; Games; Movies.

Quality Care Health Center
932 Baddour Pkwy, Lebanon, TN, 37087
(615) 444-1836
Admin Dixie Taylor. *Medical Dir/Dir of
Nursing* Morris Ferguson MD; Wilma
Moore LPN DON.
Licensure Intermediate care. *Beds* ICF 170.
Certified Medicaid.
Owner Privately owned.
Staff Physicians 1 (ft); RNs 1 (ft); LPNs 11
(ft); Nurses aides 53 (ft); Reality therapists 1
(pt); Activities coordinators 11 (ft);
Dietitians 1 (pt).
Facilities Dining room; Physical therapy
room; Barber/Beauty shop; Library.
Activities Arts & crafts; Cards; Games; Prayer
groups; Social/Cultural gatherings.

LENOIR CITY

Baptist Health Care Center
Route 1, Williams Ferry Rd, Lenoir City, TN,
37771
(615) 986-3583
Admin Carl S Burkhalter. *Medical Dir/Dir of
Nursing* Walter Shea MD; Deborah
Symington RN DON.
Licensure Intermediate care; Private. *Beds*
ICF 40; 62. *Certified* Medicaid.
Owner Nonprofit Corp.
Admissions Requirements Minimum age 16;
Medical examination.
Staff RNs 2 (ft); LPNs 10 (ft); Nurses aides 45
(ft); Physical therapists 1 (pt); Recreational
therapists 1 (pt); Occupational therapists 1
(pt); Speech therapists 1 (pt); Activities
coordinators 1 (ft); Dietitians 1 (pt);
Ophthalmologists 1 (pt).
Affiliation Baptist
Facilities Dining room; Physical therapy
room; Activities room; Chapel; Crafts room;
Laundry room; Barber/Beauty shop; Library.

Activities Arts & crafts; Cards; Games;
Reading groups; Prayer groups; Movies;
Shopping trips; Social/Cultural gatherings.

LEWISBURG

Merihil Health Care Center Inc
PO Box 251, 1653 Mooresville Hwy,
Lewisburg, TN, 37091
(615) 359-4506
Admin Alecia E Pollock. *Medical Dir/Dir of
Nursing* Jack Phelps MD; Paulette Thacker
DON.
Licensure Skilled care; Intermediate care. *Beds*
SNF 41; ICF 54. *Certified* Medicaid;
Medicare; VA.
Owner Proprietary Corp (National Health
Corp).
Admissions Requirements Medical
examination; Physician's request.
Facilities Dining room; Physical therapy
room; Activities room; Chapel; Crafts room;
Laundry room; Barber/Beauty shop; Library.
Activities Arts & crafts; Cards; Games;
Reading groups; Prayer groups; Movies;
Social/Cultural gatherings.

Oakwood Health Care Center Inc
PO Box 685, 244 Oakwood Dr, Lewisburg,
TN, 37091
(615) 359-3563
Admin Alecia E Pollock. *Medical Dir/Dir of
Nursing* Dr Joseph Von Almen; Sudie
Milam DON.
Licensure Skilled care; Intermediate care. *Beds*
62. *Certified* Medicaid; Medicare.
Owner Proprietary Corp (National Health
Corp).
Admissions Requirements Minimum age 14;
Physician's request.
Staff Physicians 14 (pt); RNs 3 (ft); LPNs 6
(ft), 3 (pt); Nurses aides 20 (ft), 4 (pt);
Physical therapists 1 (ft); Recreational
therapists 2 (pt); Speech therapists 1 (ft);
Dietitians 1 (ft).
Facilities Dining room; Physical therapy
room; Activities room; Crafts room; Laundry
room; Barber/Beauty shop; Library.
Activities Arts & crafts; Cards; Games; Prayer
groups; Movies; Social/Cultural gatherings;
Exercise class; Glamour hour.

LEXINGTON

Lexington Manor Nursing Center
727 E Church St, Lexington, TN, 38351
(901) 968-6095
Admin Gail Crawford. *Medical Dir/Dir of
Nursing* Waren Ramer Jr MD; Lavonda
Roberts DON.
Licensure Intermediate care. *Beds* ICF 119.
Certified Medicaid.
Owner Proprietary Corp.
Staff RNs; LPNs; Orderlies; Nurses aides.
Facilities Dining room; Activities room;
Laundry room; Barber/Beauty shop.
Activities Arts & crafts; Cards; Games;
Reading groups; Prayer groups; Movies;
Shopping trips; Social/Cultural gatherings.

Nucare Convalescent Center
41 Hospital Dr, Lexington, TN, 38351
(901) 968-6629
Admin Della Raines. *Medical Dir/Dir of
Nursing* Dr Tim Linder; Joyce Thompson
DON.
Licensure Intermediate care. *Beds* ICF 55.
Certified Medicaid.
Owner Proprietary Corp (Southeastern Health
Care Inc).
Admissions Requirements Physician's request.
Staff RNs; LPNs; Nurses aides; Physical
therapists; Activities coordinators; Dietitians.
Facilities Dining room; Activities room;
Crafts room; Laundry room; Barber/Beauty
shop.

Activities Arts & crafts; Cards; Games; Reading groups; Prayer groups; Shopping trips; Social/Cultural gatherings.

LIMESTONE

John M Reed Nursing Home
PO Box 301, Rte 2, Limestone, TN, 37681
(615) 257-6122
Admin Leon Dutka. *Medical Dir/Dir of Nursing* N F Garland MD; Constance Fine DON.
Licensure Intermediate care. *Beds* ICF 56. *Certified* Medicaid.
Owner Nonprofit Corp.
Admissions Requirements Minimum age 60; Medical examination; Physician's request.
Staff Physicians 2 (pt); RNs 1 (ft); LPNs 4 (ft), 2 (pt); Nurses aides 24 (ft); Physical therapists 1 (ft); Recreational therapists 1 (ft); Activities coordinators 1 (ft); Dietitians 1 (ft).
Affiliation Church of the Brethren
Facilities Dining room; Physical therapy room; Activities room; Crafts room; Laundry room; Barber/Beauty shop.
Activities Arts & crafts; Cards; Games; Reading groups; Prayer groups; Movies; Social/Cultural gatherings.

LINDEN

Perry County Nursing Home
PO Box 71, Rte 4, Linden, TN, 37096
(615) 589-2134
Admin David Ramey. *Medical Dir/Dir of Nursing* Dr Stephen Averett; Peggie Ramey DON.
Licensure Intermediate care. *Beds* ICF 72. *Certified* Medicaid.
Owner Proprietary Corp.
Admissions Requirements Physician's request.
Staff Physicians 1 (pt); RNs 2 (ft); LPNs 7 (ft), 1 (pt); Orderlies 1 (ft); Nurses aides 22 (ft), 3 (pt); Activities coordinators 1 (ft); Dietitians 1 (pt).
Facilities Dining room; Activities room; Laundry room; Barber/Beauty shop.
Activities Arts & crafts; Cards; Games; Prayer groups; Movies.

LIVINGSTON

Overton County Nursing Home
Bilbrey St, Livingston, TN, 38570
(615) 823-6403
Admin R Gay Lane. *Medical Dir/Dir of Nursing* Dr J Roe.
Licensure Intermediate care. *Beds* 162. *Certified* Medicaid.
Admissions Requirements Medical examination; Physician's request.
Staff Physicians 1 (pt); RNs 1 (ft), 1 (pt); LPNs 16 (ft), 5 (pt); Orderlies 8 (ft), 2 (pt); Nurses aides 36 (ft), 20 (pt); Recreational therapists 2 (ft); Activities coordinators 1 (ft); Dietitians 1 (pt).
Facilities Dining room; Physical therapy room; Activities room; Crafts room; Barber/Beauty shop; Laundry services; Solarium; Whirpool bathing facilities.
Activities Arts & crafts; Games; Prayer groups; Movies; Ceramics; Prayer study.

LOUDON

Care Inn—Loudon*
1320 Grove St, Loudon, TN, 37774
(615) 458-5436
Licensure Intermediate care. *Beds* 186. *Certified* Medicaid.
Admissions Requirements Medical examination.
Staff RNs 3 (ft); LPNs 9 (ft); Orderlies 1 (ft); Nurses aides 23 (ft), 5 (pt); Activities coordinators 2 (ft); Dietitians 1 (ft).

Facilities Dining room; Physical therapy room; Activities room; Crafts room; Laundry room; Barber/Beauty shop.
Activities Arts & crafts; Cards; Games; Reading groups; Prayer groups; Movies; Shopping trips; Social/Cultural gatherings.

MADISON

Hillhaven Convalescent Center*
431 Larkin Springs Rd, Madison, TN, 37115
(615) 865-8520
Licensure Skilled care; Intermediate care. *Beds* 96. *Certified* Medicaid; Medicare.
Owner Proprietary Corp (Hillhaven Corp).

Imperial Manor Convalescent Center
300 W Due West Ave, Madison, TN, 37115
(615) 865-5001
Licensure Skilled care; Intermediate care. *Beds* 201. *Certified* Medicaid; Medicare.
Owner Proprietary Corp (Sunbelt Healthcare Centers).

MADISONVILLE

East Tennessee Health Care Center
728 Isbill Rd, Madisonville, TN, 37354
(615) 442-3990
Admin Steven H Martin. *Medical Dir/Dir of Nursing* Houston Lowry MD; Ronda Hodge DON.
Licensure Intermediate care. *Beds* ICF 87. *Certified* Medicaid.
Owner Proprietary Corp (American Health Centers Inc).
Admissions Requirements Physician's request.
Staff RNs; LPNs; Orderlies; Nurses aides; Activities coordinators.
Facilities Dining room; Activities room; Crafts room; Laundry room; Barber/Beauty shop.
Activities Arts & crafts; Cards; Games; Movies; Social/Cultural gatherings.

MANCHESTER

Coffee Medical Center Nursing Home
1001 McArthur Dr, Manchester, TN, 37355
(615) 728-3586
Admin Ervin C Crosslin. *Medical Dir/Dir of Nursing* Coulter S Young MD.
Licensure Intermediate care. *Beds* ICF 66. *Certified* Medicaid.
Owner Publicly owned.
Admissions Requirements Minimum age 18; Medical examination; Physician's request.
Staff Physicians 7 (ft); RNs 1 (ft), 1 (pt); LPNs 9 (ft), 2 (pt); Orderlies 2 (ft); Nurses aides 24 (ft), 3 (pt); Physical therapists 1 (ft); Occupational therapists 1 (ft); Activities coordinators 1 (ft); Dietitians 1 (ft); Social Service 1 (ft).
Facilities Dining room; Physical therapy room; Activities room; Barber/Beauty shop; Library.
Activities Arts & crafts; Cards; Games; Reading groups; Prayer groups; Movies.

Crestwood Nursing Home
Rte 1, Taylor St, Manchester, TN, 37355
(615) 728-7549
Admin Rachel Carlene White. *Medical Dir of Nursing* Mary Arwood.
Licensure Intermediate care. *Beds* ICF 59. *Certified* Medicaid.
Owner Privately owned.
Admissions Requirements Minimum age 18; Medical examination.
Staff RNs 1 (pt); LPNs 7 (ft), 3 (pt); Orderlies 1 (ft); Nurses aides 16 (ft), 6 (pt); Activities coordinators 1 (ft); Dietitians 1 (ft); Dietary 6 (ft), 1 (pt); Laundry 1 (ft); Housekeeping 2 (ft); Maintenance 1 (ft).
Facilities Dining room; Activities room; Crafts room; Laundry room; Barber/Beauty shop; Kitchen.

Activities Arts & crafts; Cards; Games; Reading groups; Prayer groups; Shopping trips; Social/Cultural gatherings.

MARTIN

Van Ayer Manor Nursing Center
640 Hannings Ln, Martin, TN, 38237
(901) 587-3193
Admin Nina W Snyder. *Medical Dir/Dir of Nursing* H H Beale MD; Betty F Goff DON.
Licensure Intermediate care. *Beds* ICF 80. *Certified* Medicaid.
Owner Proprietary Corp (American Health Centers Inc).
Admissions Requirements Minimum age 14; Medical examination.
Staff RNs 1 (pt); LPNs 4 (ft), 6 (pt); Nurses aides 7 (ft), 20 (pt); Physical therapists 1 (pt); Activities coordinators 1 (ft); Dietitians 4 (ft), 4 (pt).
Facilities Dining room; Activities room; Crafts room; Laundry room; Barber/Beauty shop.
Activities Arts & crafts; Cards; Games; Reading groups; Prayer groups; Movies.

MARYVILLE

Asbury Acres Retirement Home
Sevierville Rd, Maryville, TN, 37801
(615) 984-1660
Admin Betty Turner. *Medical Dir/Dir of Nursing* Dr O L Simpson.
Licensure Home for aged. *Beds* 99.
Admissions Requirements Minimum age 65; Medical examination.
Staff Physicians; RNs; Nurses aides; Physical therapists; Activities coordinators; Dietitians.
Affiliation Methodist
Facilities Dining room; Activities room; Chapel; Crafts room; Laundry room; Barber/Beauty shop; Library.
Activities Arts & crafts; Cards; Games; Reading groups; Prayer groups; Movies; Shopping trips; Social/Cultural gatherings.

Asbury Centers Inc
2648 Sevierville Rd, Maryville, TN, 37801-3699
(615) 984-1660
Admin Melba B Bruce. *Medical Dir/Dir of Nursing* O L Simpson MD; Jean Coleman DON.
Licensure Skilled care; Intermediate care. *Beds* SNF 35; ICF 160. *Certified* Medicaid; Medicare.
Owner Nonprofit organization/foundation.
Admissions Requirements Minimum age 14; Medical examination; Physician's request.
Staff RNs 7 (ft), 4 (pt); LPNs 15 (ft), 5 (pt); Physical therapists 2 (pt); Recreational therapists 3 (ft); Activities coordinators 1 (ft); Dietitians 18 (ft), 7 (pt).
Affiliation Methodist
Facilities Dining room; Physical therapy room; Activities room; Crafts room; Laundry room; Barber/Beauty shop.
Activities Arts & crafts; Cards; Games; Reading groups; Prayer groups; Movies; Shopping trips; Social/Cultural gatherings; Church services; Current events.

Care Inn—Maryville*
1602 Montvale Station Rd, Maryville, TN, 37801
(615) 984-7400
Licensure Intermediate care. *Beds* 186. *Certified* Medicaid.
Owner Proprietary Corp.

Colonial Hills Nursing Center
2034 Cochran Rd, Maryville, TN, 37801
(615) 982-6161
Admin Peggy G Savage. *Medical Dir/Dir of Nursing* J Thomas Mandrell MD; Annette Everett RN DON.

Licensure Skilled care; Intermediate care. *Beds*
SNF 6; ICF 197. *Certified* Medicaid;
Medicare.
Owner Proprietary Corp.
Admissions Requirements Minimum age 14;
Medical examination.
Staff RNs 7 (ft); LPNs 20 (ft), 4 (pt);
Orderlies 4 (ft); Nurses aides 60 (ft), 6 (pt);
Physical therapists 1 (pt); Speech therapists
1 (pt); Activities coordinators 2 (ft);
Dietitians 1 (ft).
Languages Italian
Facilities Dining room; Physical therapy
room; Activities room; Crafts room; Laundry
room; Barber/Beauty shop; Library;
Solarium; Music room; Whirlpool baths.
Activities Arts & crafts; Cards; Games;
Reading groups; Prayer groups; Movies;
Shopping trips; Social/Cultural gatherings.

Montvale Health Center*
Montvale Rd, Rte 6, Maryville, TN, 37801
(615) 982-6161
Licensure Intermediate care. *Beds* 107.
Certified Medicaid.

MCKENZIE

Oak Manor Nursing Home*
Rte 4, McKenzie, TN, 38201
(901) 352-5317
Admin Larry Hardy.
Licensure Intermediate care. *Beds* 49.
Certified Medicaid.

MCMINNVILLE

McMinnville Health Care Center
PO Box 528, Old Smithville Hwy,
McMinnville, TN, 37110
(615) 473-8431
Admin Clay F Crosson. *Medical Dir/Dir of
Nursing* Dr J F Fisher; Alma Stone RN.
Licensure Skilled care; Intermediate care. *Beds*
SNF 52; ICF 30. *Certified* Medicaid;
Medicare.
Owner Proprietary Corp (National Health
Corp).
Admissions Requirements Minimum age 18.
Staff Physicians 10 (pt); RNs 2 (ft), 2 (pt);
LPNs 11 (ft), 4 (pt); Orderlies 1 (ft); Nurses
aides 30 (ft), 10 (pt); Physical therapists 1
(pt); Recreational therapists 1 (ft);
Occupational therapists 1 (pt); Speech
therapists 1 (pt); Activities coordinators 1
(ft); Dietitians 1 (ft); Dentists 1 (pt);
Ophthalmologists 1 (pt); Podiatrists 1 (pt).
Facilities Dining room; Physical therapy
room; Activities room; Crafts room; Laundry
room; Barber/Beauty shop.
Activities Arts & crafts; Cards; Games;
Reading groups; Prayer groups; Movies;
Social/Cultural gatherings.

South Oaks Health Care Inc
South Oaks Ln, McMinnville, TN, 37110
(615) 668-2011
Admin Gilbert E Salter. *Medical Dir/Dir of
Nursing* Dr T L Pedigo.
Licensure Skilled care; Intermediate care. *Beds*
154. *Certified* Medicaid; Medicare.
Owner Proprietary Corp.
Admissions Requirements Medical
examination; Physician's request.
Staff Physicians 1 (pt); RNs 1 (ft); LPNs 7
(ft), 2 (pt); Orderlies 1 (ft); Nurses aides 29
(ft), 15 (pt); Physical therapists 1 (pt);
Speech therapists 1 (pt); Activities
coordinators 1 (ft); Dietitians 1 (ft); Dentists
1 (pt).
Facilities Dining room; Physical therapy
room; Activities room; Crafts room; Laundry
room; Barber/Beauty shop; Library.
Activities Arts & crafts; Cards; Games;
Reading groups; Prayer groups; Shopping
trips; Social/Cultural gatherings.

MEMPHIS

Allenbrooke Health Care Center
3933 Allenbrooke Cove, Memphis, TN, 38118
(901) 795-2444
Admin Michael J. Carney. *Medical Dir/Dir of
Nursing* Mark Hammond; Paula Bain.
Licensure Skilled care; Intermediate care. *Beds*
SNF 60; ICF 120. *Certified* Medicaid;
Medicare.
Owner Proprietary Corp (Beverly Enterprises).
Admissions Requirements Medical
examination.
Staff Physicians; RNs; LPNs; Orderlies;
Nurses aides; Physical therapists; Reality
therapists; Recreational therapists;
Occupational therapists; Speech therapists;
Activities coordinators; Dietitians;
Ophthalmologists; Podiatrists.
Facilities Dining room; Physical therapy
room; Activities room; Crafts room; Laundry
room; Barber/Beauty shop; Library;
Courtyard.
Activities Arts & crafts; Cards; Games;
Reading groups; Prayer groups; Movies;
Shopping trips.

Ave Maria Home
2805 Charles Bryan Rd, Memphis, TN, 38134
(901) 386-3211
Admin Patricia Curtis. *Medical Dir/Dir of
Nursing* Basil A Bland Jr MD; Charlotte
Blair RN.
Licensure Intermediate care. *Beds* ICF 73.
Certified Medicaid.
Owner Nonprofit Corp.
Admissions Requirements Minimum age 60;
Medical examination.
Staff Physicians 1 (pt); RNs 2 (ft), 1 (pt);
LPNs 5 (ft), 1 (pt); Nurses aides 22 (ft), 5
(pt); Activities coordinators 1 (ft); Dietitians
1 (pt); Ophthalmologists 1 (pt); Dentist 1
(pt).
Facilities Dining room; Activities room;
Chapel; Crafts room; Barber/Beauty shop;
Dental Clinic; Spacious landscaped grounds.
Activities Arts & crafts; Cards; Games; Prayer
groups; Movies; Shopping trips; Social/
Cultural gatherings.

Bright Glade Convalescent Center*
5070 Sanderlin Ave, Memphis, TN, 38117
(615) 682-5677
Medical Dir/Dir of Nursing Saul Seigel MD.
Beds 77.
Owner Proprietary Corp (American Health
Centers Inc).
Admissions Requirements Minimum age 16;
Physician's request.
Staff Physicians 1 (ft), 1 (pt); RNs 2 (ft);
LPNs 5 (ft), 1 (pt); Nurses aides 11 (ft), 5
(pt); Physical therapists 1 (pt); Recreational
therapists 1 (pt); Podiatrists 1 (pt).
Facilities Dining room; Activities room;
Crafts room; Barber/Beauty shop.
Activities Cards; Games; Prayer groups.

Care Inn—Memphis*
2491 Joy Ln, Memphis, TN, 38114
(615) 743-7700
Licensure Intermediate care. *Beds* 110.
Certified Medicaid.
Owner Proprietary Corp (Southmark Heritage
Corp).

Collins Chapel Health Care Center*
409 N Ayers, Memphis, TN, 38105
(615) 522-9243
Medical Dir/Dir of Nursing Cary Anderson
MD.
Licensure Intermediate care. *Beds* 88.
Certified Medicaid.
Admissions Requirements Medical
examination; Physician's request.

Staff Physicians 1 (ft), 1 (pt); RNs 1 (pt);
LPNs 7 (ft); Orderlies 4 (ft); Nurses aides 18
(ft); Physical therapists 1 (pt); Activities
coordinators 1 (ft); Dietitians 6 (ft); Dentists
1 (ft).
Affiliation Christian Methodist Episcopal
Facilities Dining room; Physical therapy
room; Activities room; Crafts room; Laundry
room; Barber/Beauty shop.
Activities Arts & crafts; Cards; Games;
Reading groups; Prayer groups; Movies;
Social/Cultural gatherings.

Durham Retirement Center
6005 Stage Rd, Memphis, TN, 38134
(901) 386-4531
Admin Thomas H Durham Jr. *Medical Dir/
Dir of Nursing* Margaret Moffitt.
Licensure Independent living. *Beds*
Retirement Community 80.
Owner Nonprofit organization/foundation.
Admissions Requirements Minimum age 55;
Medical examination.
Staff Activities coordinators 1 (pt); Dietitians
1 (ft), 1 (pt).
Facilities Dining room; Activities room;
Chapel; Barber/Beauty shop; Library; Patio;
3 sun porches; 4 open air porches;
Walkpath.
Activities Cards; Games; Reading groups;
Prayer groups; Movies; Shopping trips;
Social/Cultural gatherings; Community &
church interaction.

Evergreen Care Center
6444 Keswick, Memphis, TN, 38119
(615) 278-3840
Admin Bea Boyd. *Medical Dir/Dir of Nursing*
Leslie Shumaker MD.
Licensure Intermediate care. *Beds* 49.
Certified Medicaid.
Admissions Requirements Minimum age 21;
Medical examination; Physician's request.
Staff RNs 1 (pt); LPNs 6 (ft); Orderlies 2 (ft);
Nurses aides 20 (ft), 2 (pt); Physical
therapists 1 (ft); Activities coordinators 1
(ft); Dietitians 1 (ft).
Facilities Dining room; Activities room;
Laundry room.
Activities Arts & crafts; Cards; Games;
Reading groups; Shopping trips.

Mary Galloway Home for the Aged Women
5389 Poplar Ave, Memphis, TN, 38119
(901) 682-6646
Admin Helen N Miller.
Licensure Home for aged. *Beds* 46.
Owner Nonprofit organization/foundation.
Admissions Requirements Minimum age 60;
Females only; Medical examination.
Staff Dietitians 1 (ft).
Facilities Dining room; Activities room;
Crafts room; Laundry room; Barber/Beauty
shop.
Activities Prayer groups; Shopping trips;
Various programs.

Hillhaven Convalescent Center
6025 Primacy Pkwy, Memphis, TN, 38119
(901) 767-1040
Admin Martha A Johnson. *Medical Dir/Dir of
Nursing* Robert Kilpatrick MD; Carroll
Johnson DNS.
Licensure Skilled care; Intermediate care. *Beds*
SNF 10; ICF 110. *Certified* Medicare.
Owner Proprietary Corp (Hillhaven Corp).
Admissions Requirements Minimum age 12;
Medical examination; Physician's request.
Staff RNs; LPNs; Orderlies; Nurses aides;
Physical therapists; Reality therapists;
Recreational therapists; Occupational
therapists; Speech therapists; Activities
coordinators; Dietitians.
Facilities Dining room; Physical therapy
room; Activities room; Crafts room; Laundry
room; Barber/Beauty shop.

Activities Arts & crafts; Cards; Games;
Reading groups; Prayer groups; Movies;
Shopping trips; Social/Cultural gatherings.

Hillhaven Health Care Center of Raleigh
3909 Covington Pike, Memphis, TN, 38134
(901) 377-1011
Admin Susan P Morganelli. *Medical Dir/Dir
of Nursing* Dr E E Hines; Christine Russell
DON.
Licensure Skilled care; Intermediate care. *Beds*
SNF 16; ICF 230. *Certified* Medicaid.
Owner Proprietary Corp (Hillhaven Corp).
Admissions Requirements Medical
examination; Physician's request.
Staff RNs; LPNs; Orderlies; Nurses aides;
Physical therapists; Reality therapists;
Recreational therapists; Occupational
therapists; Speech therapists; Activities
coordinators; Dietitians; Dentists;
Ophthalmologists.
Languages Spanish
Facilities Dining room; Physical therapy
room; Activities room; Chapel; Crafts room;
Laundry room; Barber/Beauty shop.
Activities Arts & crafts; Cards; Games;
Reading groups; Prayer groups; Movies;
Shopping trips; Social/Cultural gatherings.

Johnson Nursing Home
1279 Peabody, Memphis, TN, 38104-3551
(615) 274-6201
Beds 22.
Admissions Requirements Minimum age 75;
Medical examination; Physician's request.
Staff RNs 1 (ft); LPNs 4 (ft), 4 (pt); Nurses
aides 6 (ft), 6 (pt); Occupational therapists 1
(pt); Speech therapists 1 (pt); Activities
coordinators 1 (ft); Dietitians 1 (ft); Dentists
1 (pt); Ophthalmologists 1 (pt); Podiatrists 1
(pt).
Facilities Dining room; Activities room;
Chapel; Laundry room; Barber/Beauty shop.
Activities Arts & crafts; Cards; Games;
Reading groups; Prayer groups; Movies.

**James E Kerwin Housing for the Elderly &
Elderly Disabled***
1150 Dovercrest Rd, Memphis, TN, 38134
(615) 382-1700
Licensure Intermediate care. *Beds* 100.
Certified Medicaid.

Kings Daughters & Sons Home
1467 E McLemore Ave, Memphis, TN, 38016
(901) 272-7405
Admin Ronald B Arrison. *Medical Dir/Dir of
Nursing* Jean McFarland.
Licensure Intermediate care. *Beds* ICF 107.
Certified Medicaid.
Owner Nonprofit Corp.
Admissions Requirements Minimum age 18.
Staff Physicians 1 (pt); RNs 1 (ft), 1 (pt);
LPNs 12 (ft), 5 (pt); Nurses aides 45 (ft), 3
(pt); Physical therapists 1 (pt); Activities
coordinators 1 (ft); Dietitians 1 (pt).
Affiliation King's Daughters & Sons
Facilities Dining room; Physical therapy
room; Activities room; Chapel; Crafts room;
Laundry room; Barber/Beauty shop.
Activities Arts & crafts; Cards; Games;
Reading groups; Prayer groups; Movies;
Shopping trips; Social/Cultural gatherings;
Ceramics.

Memphis Health Care Center
6733 Quince Rd, Memphis, TN, 38119
(901) 755-3860
Admin Jeanette McKinion. *Medical Dir/Dir of
Nursing* Mark Hammond MD; Darla Grant.
Licensure Skilled care; Intermediate care. *Beds*
SNF 28; ICF 152. *Certified* Medicaid;
Medicare.
Owner Proprietary Corp (Beverly Enterprises).
Admissions Requirements Minimum age 18;
Medical examination; Physician's request.

Staff Physicians 1 (pt); RNs 2 (ft), 2 (pt);
LPNs 13 (ft); Orderlies 1 (ft); Nurses aides
67 (ft), 12 (pt); Activities coordinators 2 (ft);
Social director 2 (ft); Dietary service
manager 1 (ft).
Facilities Dining room; Physical therapy
room; Activities room; Crafts room; Laundry
room; Barber/Beauty shop.
Activities Arts & crafts; Cards; Games;
Reading groups; Prayer groups; Movies;
Shopping trips; Social/Cultural gatherings.

Memphis Sunshine Home for Aged Men*
3411 Poplar Ave, Memphis, TN, 38111
(901) 452-6532
Licensure Home for aged. *Beds* 36.
Admissions Requirements Males only.

Mid-City Care Center*
1428 Monroe, Memphis, TN, 38104
(615) 726-5171
Medical Dir/Dir of Nursing George Bassett.
Licensure Intermediate care. *Beds* 79.
Certified Medicaid.
Admissions Requirements Medical
examination.
Staff Physicians 1 (ft); RNs 1 (ft); LPNs 12
(ft); Orderlies 3 (ft); Nurses aides 25 (ft);
Physical therapists 2 (ft); Reality therapists 2
(ft); Recreational therapists 2 (ft);
Occupational therapists 1 (pt); Speech
therapists 1 (pt); Activities coordinators 2
(ft); Dietitians 1 (ft); Dentists 1 (pt);
Ophthalmologists 1 (pt); Podiatrists 1 (pt);
Audiologists 1 (pt).
Facilities Dining room; Physical therapy
room; Activities room; Chapel; Crafts room;
Laundry room; Barber/Beauty shop; Library.
Activities Arts & crafts; Cards; Games;
Reading groups; Prayer groups; Movies;
Shopping trips; Social/Cultural gatherings.

Mid-South Christian Nursing Home
2380 James Rd, Memphis, TN, 38127
(901) 358-1707
Admin John Faught. *Medical Dir/Dir of
Nursing* Dr J H Ijams.
Licensure Intermediate care. *Beds* ICF 162.
Certified Medicaid.
Owner Nonprofit Corp.
Admissions Requirements Minimum age 25;
Medical examination; Physician's request.
Staff Physicians 1 (pt); RNs 1 (ft); LPNs 13
(ft), 8 (pt); Orderlies 2 (ft); Nurses aides 36
(ft), 27 (pt); Recreational therapists 1 (ft);
Activities coordinators 2 (ft); Dietitians 1
(ft); Ophthalmologists 1 (pt).
Affiliation Church of Christ
Facilities Dining room; Activities room;
Chapel; Crafts room; Laundry room; Barber/
Beauty shop.
Activities Arts & crafts; Cards; Games;
Reading groups; Prayer groups; Movies;
Shopping trips.

The Allen Morgan Nursing Center
177 N Highland, Memphis, TN, 38111
(901) 325-4003
Admin Rebecca D DeRousse. *Medical Dir/Dir
of Nursing* Charles L Clarke MD; Suzanne
Sydow RN DON.
Licensure Skilled care. *Beds* SNF 66. *Certified*
Medicare.
Owner Nonprofit organization/foundation.
Admissions Requirements Minimum age 15;
Medical examination; Physician's request.
Staff Physicians 1 (pt); RNs 2 (ft), 5 (pt);
LPNs 2 (ft), 1 (pt); Nurses aides 17 (ft), 5
(pt); Recreational therapists 1 (ft); Activities
coordinators 1 (ft); Dietitians 1 (pt);
Ophthalmologists 1 (pt).
Facilities Dining room; Physical therapy
room; Activities room; Chapel; Crafts room;
Laundry room; Barber/Beauty shop; Library.
Activities Arts & crafts; Games; Reading
groups; Prayer groups; Movies; Shopping
trips; Social/Cultural gatherings.

NHE—Memphis*
1414 Court St, Memphis, TN, 38104
(615) 272-2494
Licensure Intermediate care. *Beds* 96.
Certified Medicaid.

The Oaks Care Center Inc*
642 Semmes St, Memphis, TN, 38111
(615) 454-0048
Admin Buford Street. *Medical Dir/Dir of
Nursing* Karen Hensley DO.
Licensure Intermediate care. *Beds* 56.
Certified Medicaid.
Admissions Requirements Medical
examination; Physician's request.
Staff Physicians 1 (pt); RNs 1 (pt); LPNs 4
(ft), 3 (pt); Orderlies 1 (ft); Nurses aides 15
(ft), 1 (pt); Physical therapists 1 (ft); Reality
therapists 1 (ft); Recreational therapists 1
(ft); Activities coordinators 1 (ft); Dietitians
1 (ft); Dentists 1 (pt); Ophthalmologists 1
(pt); Podiatrists 1 (pt); Audiologists 1 (pt).
Facilities Dining room; Physical therapy
room; Activities room; Laundry room;
Barber/Beauty shop.
Activities Arts & crafts; Games; Reading
groups; Prayer groups; Shopping trips.

Oakville Health Care Center
3391 Old Getwell Rd, Memphis, TN, 38118
(901) 369-9100
Admin Paul C Chapman. *Medical Dir/Dir of
Nursing* George P Jones Jr MD; Wanda
Jane Alexander DON.
Licensure Skilled care; Intermediate care. *Beds*
SNF; ICF 314. *Certified* Medicaid;
Medicare.
Owner Publicly owned.
Admissions Requirements Physician's request.
Staff Physicians 2 (ft); RNs 13 (ft), 1 (pt);
LPNs 56 (ft); Nurses aides 126 (ft); Physical
therapists 1 (pt); Recreational therapists 2
(ft); Occupational therapists 1 (pt); Activities
coordinators 2 (ft); Dietitians 1 (ft).
Facilities Dining room; Physical therapy
room; Activities room; Chapel; Crafts room;
Barber/Beauty shop; Library.
Activities Arts & crafts; Cards; Games;
Reading groups; Prayer groups; Movies;
Shopping trips; Social/Cultural gatherings.

Resthaven Nursing Home*
300 N Bellevue, Memphis, TN, 38105
(615) 726-9786
Medical Dir/Dir of Nursing Billie Jeanne
Johnson.
Beds 64.
Owner Proprietary Corp (American Health
Centers Inc).
Admissions Requirements Minimum age 20;
Medical examination; Physician's request.
Staff Physicians; RNs 2 (ft), 2 (pt); LPNs 2
(ft), 2 (pt); Nurses aides 15 (ft), 2 (pt);
Physical therapists 1 (pt); Recreational
therapists 1 (ft); Occupational therapists 1
(pt); Speech therapists 1 (pt); Activities
coordinators 1 (ft); Dietitians 1 (pt).
Facilities Dining room; Activities room;
Laundry room; Barber/Beauty shop.
Activities Cards; Games; Reading groups;
Prayer groups; Social/Cultural gatherings.

Rosewood Manor
3030 Walnut Grove Rd, Memphis, TN, 38111
(901) 458-1146
Licensure Skilled care; Intermediate care. *Beds*
211. *Certified* Medicaid; Medicare.

St Francis Hospital Nursing Home
5959 Park Ave, Memphis, TN, 38119-5150
( ) 765-3110
Admin Tom Hanlen. *Medical Dir/Dir of
Nursing* Dr Mickey Busby; Susan Hudson
RN DON.
Licensure Skilled care; Intermediate care. *Beds*
196. *Certified* Medicaid; Medicare.
Owner Nonprofit Corp.
Admissions Requirements Physician's request.

Staff RNs 2 (ft); LPNs 21 (ft), 16 (pt); Nurses aides 39 (ft), 41 (pt); Activities coordinators 1 (ft).
Facilities Dining room; Physical therapy room; Activities room; Chapel; Crafts room; Laundry room; Barber/Beauty shop.
Activities Arts & crafts; Cards; Games; Reading groups; Prayer groups; Movies; Social/Cultural gatherings.

St Peter Villa Nursing Home
141 N McLean, Memphis, TN, 38104
(901) 276-2021
Medical Dir/Dir of Nursing Dr Mohamad Akbik; Vicki L Sherrard RN DON.
Licensure Skilled care; Intermediate care. *Beds* SNF 60; ICF 120. *Certified* Medicaid; Medicare.
Admissions Requirements Medical examination; Physician's request.
Staff RNs 2 (ft), 1 (pt); LPNs 20 (ft), 4 (pt); Orderlies 3 (ft), 3 (pt); Nurses aides 36 (ft), 20 (pt); Physical therapists 1 (ft); Occupational therapists 1 (pt); Speech therapists 1 (pt); Activities coordinators 1 (ft); Dietitians 1 (pt); Ophthalmologists 1 (pt); Podiatrists 1 (pt).
Affiliation Roman Catholic
Facilities Dining room; Physical therapy room; Activities room; Chapel; Barber/Beauty shop.
Activities Arts & crafts; Cards; Games; Reading groups; Prayer groups; Movies; Shopping trips; Social/Cultural gatherings.

Shelby County Health Care Center
1075 Mullins Station Rd, Memphis, TN, 38134
(901) 386-4361
Admin James D Brown. *Medical Dir/Dir of Nursing* George Jones MD; Nelda McCarter RN DON.
Licensure Intermediate care. *Beds* ICF 575. *Certified* Medicaid.
Owner Publicly owned.
Admissions Requirements Medical examination; Physician's request.
Staff Physicians 2 (ft), 1 (pt); RNs 16 (ft); LPNs 56 (ft); Nurses aides 255 (ft); Physical therapists 1 (pt); Recreational therapists 4 (ft); Activities coordinators 1 (ft); Dietitians 2 (ft), 1 (pt); Dentists 1 (pt); Ophthalmologists 1 (pt).
Facilities Dining room; Physical therapy room; Activities room; Chapel; Crafts room; Laundry room; Barber/Beauty shop; Library.
Activities Arts & crafts; Cards; Games; Reading groups; Prayer groups; Movies; Shopping trips; Social/Cultural gatherings; Fashion shows.

Wesley Highland Manor
3549 Norriswood, Memphis, TN, 38111
(615) 458-7186
Admin Joyce Farnsworth. *Medical Dir/Dir of Nursing* William Bounds MD; Rodney Holladay MD; Jennell Monroe DON.
Licensure Skilled care; Intermediate care. *Beds* 150. *Certified* Medicaid; Medicare.
Owner Nonprofit organization/foundation.
Admissions Requirements Minimum age 18; Physician's request.
Staff Physicians 2 (pt); RNs 2 (ft), 5 (pt); LPNs 11 (ft), 7 (pt); Nurses aides 40 (ft), 11 (pt); Activities coordinators 1 (ft).
Affiliation Methodist
Facilities Dining room; Physical therapy room; Activities room; Laundry room; Barber/Beauty shop; Library.
Activities Cards; Games; Reading groups; Prayer groups; Movies; Trips to ballgames; Plays.

Whitehaven Care Center
1076 Chambliss, Memphis, TN, 38116
(901) 396-8470

Admin Carole B Stengel. *Medical Dir/Dir of Nursing* Charles Parrott MD; Doris Walker RN DON.
Licensure Intermediate care. *Beds* 90. *Certified* Medicaid.
Owner Proprietary Corp (Southeastern Health Care Inc).
Admissions Requirements Minimum age 21; Medical examination; Physician's request.
Staff RNs 1 (ft); LPNs 8 (ft), 2 (pt); Orderlies 2 (ft); Nurses aides 36 (ft), 6 (pt); Activities coordinators 1 (ft).
Facilities Dining room; Barber/Beauty shop.
Activities Arts & crafts; Cards; Games; Reading groups; Prayer groups; Movies; Shopping trips.

MILAN

Douglas Nursing Home Inc*
235 W Main St, Milan, TN, 38358
(901) 686-8321
Licensure Intermediate care. *Beds* 72. *Certified* Medicaid.

Milan Health Care Inc
PO Box 650, Milan, TN, 38358
(901) 686-8364
Admin Jack W Tipton. *Medical Dir/Dir of Nursing* Mildred Braddy.
Licensure Intermediate care. *Beds* ICF 66. *Certified* Medicaid.
Owner Proprietary Corp.
Admissions Requirements Physician's request.
Staff Physicians; RNs; LPNs; Nurses aides; Physical therapists; Speech therapists; Dietitians.
Facilities Dining room; Activities room; Laundry room; Barber/Beauty shop.
Activities Games; Reading groups; Prayer groups; Movies; Social/Cultural gatherings.

Ridgewood Health Care Center*
Dogwood Ln, Milan, TN, 38358
(901) 686-8311
Admin Timothy Sullivan. *Medical Dir/Dir of Nursing* Fred Friedman MD.
Licensure Skilled care; Intermediate care. *Beds* 119. *Certified* Medicaid; Medicare.
Owner Proprietary Corp (National Health Corp).
Admissions Requirements Minimum age 21; Medical examination; Physician's request.
Staff RNs 5 (ft), 1 (pt); LPNs 10 (ft), 1 (pt); Orderlies 1 (ft); Nurses aides 39 (ft), 4 (pt); Physical therapists 1 (ft); Speech therapists 1 (ft); Activities coordinators 1 (ft); Dietitians 1 (ft).
Facilities Dining room; Physical therapy room; Activities room; Laundry room; Barber/Beauty shop; Library.
Activities Arts & crafts; Cards; Games; Reading groups; Prayer groups; Movies; Social/Cultural gatherings.

MONTEAGLE

Regency Health Care Center*
218 2nd St NE, Box 429, Monteagle, TN, 37356
(615) 924-2041
Licensure Intermediate care. *Beds* 140. *Certified* Medicaid.
Owner Proprietary Corp (Regency Health Care Centers).
Admissions Requirements Minimum age 14.
Staff Physicians 5 (pt); RNs 4 (ft); LPNs 7 (ft); Nurses aides 45 (ft); Physical therapists 1 (pt); Occupational therapists 1 (pt); Speech therapists 1 (pt); Activities coordinators 1 (ft); Dietitians 1 (pt).
Facilities Dining room; Physical therapy room; Activities room; Crafts room; Laundry room; Barber/Beauty shop; Library.
Activities Arts & crafts; Cards; Games; Reading groups; Prayer groups; Movies; Shopping trips; Social/Cultural gatherings.

MONTEREY

Standing Stone Health Care Center
410 W Crawford Ave, Monterey, TN, 38574
(615) 839-2244
Admin Joyce Hicks. *Medical Dir/Dir of Nursing* Danny Hall MD.
Licensure Intermediate care. *Beds* 104. *Certified* Medicaid.
Owner Proprietary Corp.
Admissions Requirements Minimum age 14; Medical examination; Physician's request.
Staff Physicians 5 (pt); RNs 2 (ft); LPNs 5 (ft), 6 (pt); Orderlies 1 (pt); Nurses aides 24 (ft), 11 (pt); Physical therapists 1 (pt); Speech therapists 1 (pt); Activities coordinators 1 (ft); Dietitians 1 (pt).
Facilities Dining room; Physical therapy room; Activities room; Chapel; Crafts room; Laundry room; Barber/Beauty shop.
Activities Arts & crafts; Games; Reading groups; Prayer groups; Shopping trips; Social/Cultural gatherings.

MORRISTOWN

Life Care Center of Morristown
501 W Economy Rd, Morristown, TN, 37814
(615) 581-5435
Admin Marvin Frey. *Medical Dir/Dir of Nursing* Faye Proffitt DON.
Licensure Intermediate care. *Beds* ICF 161. *Certified* Medicaid.
Owner Proprietary Corp (Life Care Centers of America).
Admissions Requirements Medical examination.
Staff RNs 2 (ft); LPNs 10 (ft), 4 (pt); Nurses aides 41 (ft), 11 (pt); Activities coordinators 1 (ft); Dietitians 1 (ft).
Facilities Dining room; Physical therapy room; Activities room; Crafts room; Laundry room; Barber/Beauty shop; Library.
Activities Arts & crafts; Cards; Games; Reading groups; Prayer groups; Movies; Shopping trips; Social/Cultural gatherings.

MOUNT PLEASANT

Hidden Acres Manor*
Hidden Acres Dr, Mount Pleasant, TN, 38474
(615) 379-5502
Licensure Intermediate care. *Beds* 60. *Certified* Medicaid.

MOUNTAIN CITY

Johnson County Health Care
919 Medical Park Dr, Mountain City, TN, 37683
(615) 727-7800
Admin Gerry Woods. *Medical Dir/Dir of Nursing* Jack Whitlock MD; Tami King DON.
Licensure Intermediate care. *Beds* ICF 110. *Certified* Medicaid.
Owner Privately owned.
Admissions Requirements Minimum age 14; Medical examination; Physician's request.
Staff Physicians 8 (pt); RNs 1 (pt); LPNs 7 (ft), 4 (pt); Orderlies 8 (ft), 1 (pt); Nurses aides 20 (ft), 9 (pt); Physical therapists 1 (pt); Reality therapists 1 (pt); Recreational therapists 1 (ft); Occupational therapists 1 (pt); Speech therapists 1 (pt); Activities coordinators 1 (ft); Dietitians 1 (ft); Dentists 1 (pt); Ophthalmologists 1 (pt); Podiatrists 1 (pt).
Facilities Dining room; Physical therapy room; Activities room; Crafts room; Laundry room; Barber/Beauty shop.
Activities Arts & crafts; Cards; Games; Reading groups; Prayer groups; Movies; Shopping trips; Social/Cultural gatherings.

MURFREESBORO

Boulevard Terrace Nursing Home
915 S Tennessee Blvd, Murfreesboro, TN, 37130
(615) 896-4504
Licensure Intermediate care. *Beds* 100. *Certified* Medicaid.
Admissions Requirements Medical examination; Physician's request.
Facilities Dining room; Activities room; Crafts room; Laundry room; Barber/Beauty shop.
Activities Arts & crafts; Cards; Games; Reading groups; Prayer groups; Movies; Shopping trips; Social/Cultural gatherings.

Murfreesboro Health Care Center*
420 N University St, Murfreesboro, TN, 37130
(615) 893-2602
Medical Dir/Dir of Nursing Dr Susan Andrews.
Licensure Skilled care. *Beds* 184. *Certified* Medicaid; Medicare.
Owner Proprietary Corp (National Health Corp).
Admissions Requirements Physician's request.
Staff RNs 10 (ft); LPNs 20 (ft); Nurses aides 40 (ft); Physical therapists 2 (ft); Recreational therapists 2 (ft); Occupational therapists 1 (ft); Speech therapists 2 (ft); Activities coordinators 1 (ft); Dietitians 1 (ft).
Facilities Dining room; Physical therapy room; Activities room; Crafts room; Laundry room; Barber/Beauty shop; Library.
Activities Arts & crafts; Games; Reading groups; Prayer groups; Movies; Shopping trips; Social/Cultural gatherings.

Rutherford County Nursing Home
Rte 1, County Farm Rd, Murfreesboro, TN, 37130
(615) 893-2624
Licensure Intermediate care. *Beds* 130. *Certified* Medicaid.
Admissions Requirements Physician's request.
Facilities Dining room; Crafts room; Laundry room; Barber/Beauty shop.
Activities Arts & crafts; Cards; Games; Reading groups; Prayer groups; Movies.

Stones River Manor
205 Haynes Dr, Murfreesboro, TN, 37130
(615) 893-5617
Admin Janet Swift. *Medical Dir/Dir of Nursing* Pam Lamb.
Licensure Home for aged. *Beds* 59.
Owner Nonprofit organization/foundation.
Admissions Requirements Minimum age 65; Medical examination.
Staff LPNs; Nurses aides; Activities coordinators; Dietitians.
Affiliation Church of Christ
Facilities Dining room; Activities room; Crafts room; Laundry room; Barber/Beauty shop; Library.
Activities Arts & crafts; Cards; Games; Prayer groups; Movies; Shopping trips; Social/Cultural gatherings.

NASHVILLE

Belcourt Terrace Nursing Home*
1710 Belcourt Ave, Nashville, TN, 37312
(615) 383-3570
Licensure Intermediate care. *Beds* 49. *Certified* Medicaid.

Carriage Health Care Center
1400 18th Ave S, Nashville, TN, 37203
(615) 383-4715
Admin Brenda Dunn. *Medical Dir/Dir of Nursing* Dr Dee Baker; Judy Ferguson.
Licensure Intermediate care. *Beds* ICF 212. *Certified* Medicaid; Medicare.
Owner Privately owned.

Admissions Requirements Medical examination.
Staff Physicians 4 (ft); RNs 5 (ft); LPNs 20 (ft); Orderlies 8 (ft); Nurses aides 60 (ft), 20 (pt); Physical therapists 1 (ft); Reality therapists; Recreational therapists 2 (ft); Speech therapists 1 (ft); Activities coordinators 1 (ft); Dietitians 2 (ft); Dentists 1 (pt); Ophthalmologists 1 (pt); Podiatrists 1 (pt).
Facilities Dining room; Activities room; Chapel; Crafts room; Laundry room; Barber/Beauty shop.
Activities Arts & crafts; Cards; Games; Prayer groups; Movies; Social/Cultural gatherings; Exercise classes daily.

Church of Christ Home for Aged*
1900 Eastland Ave, Nashville, TN, 37206
(615) 227-9566
Licensure Home for aged. *Beds* 44.
Affiliation Church of Christ

Crestview Nursing Home Inc*
2030 25th Ave N, Nashville, TN, 37208
(615) 256-4697
Licensure Intermediate care. *Beds* 111. *Certified* Medicaid.

Jackson Park Christian Home*
4107 Gallatin Rd, Nashville, TN, 37216
(615) 228-0356
Licensure Home for aged. *Beds* 49.

Joseph B Knowles Home for the Aged
625 Benton Ave, Nashville, TN, 37204
(615) 259-6429
Admin Caroline M Skelton.
Licensure Home for aged. *Beds* 68.
Owner Publicly owned.
Admissions Requirements Minimum age 55.
Staff RNs 1 (ft); Activities coordinators 1 (ft); Group care workers 16 (ft); Custodians 3 (ft); Social workers 2 (ft).
Facilities Dining room; Activities room; Chapel; Crafts room; Laundry room; Barber/Beauty shop; Library.
Activities Arts & crafts; Cards; Games; Reading groups; Prayer groups; Movies; Shopping trips; Social/Cultural gatherings; Exercise.

Lakeshore Estates Inc
3025 Fernbrook Ln, Nashville, TN, 37214
(615) 885-2320
Admin George Chatfield Dir; David Grady, Craig Underwood Adms. *Medical Dir/Dir of Nursing* Eva Rich.
Licensure Skilled care; Intermediate care; Assisted living; Independent living. *Beds* SNF 28; ICF 164; Assisted living 48; Independent living 173.
Owner Nonprofit Corp.
Staff Physicians 1 (pt); RNs 10 (ft); LPNs 30 (ft); Nurses aides 50 (ft); Activities coordinators 3 (ft); Dietitians 3 (ft).

Lakeshore Home for the Aged
832 Wedgewood Ave, Nashville, TN, 37203
(615) 383-4006
Admin David Grady. *Medical Dir/Dir of Nursing* Dr Richard Garman; Eva Rich DON.
Licensure Intermediate care; Independent retirement rooms. *Beds* ICF 44; Independent retirement rooms 138.
Owner Nonprofit Corp.
Admissions Requirements Medical examination; Physician's request.
Staff Physicians; RNs; LPNs; Nurses aides; Physical therapists; Activities coordinators; Dietitians; Ophthalmologists; Podiatrists.
Affiliation Church of Christ
Facilities Dining room; Activities room; Crafts room; Laundry room; Barber/Beauty shop; Library.
Activities Arts & crafts; Cards; Games; Reading groups; Prayer groups; Movies; Shopping trips; Social/Cultural gatherings.

Life Care Center of Donelson
2733 McCampbell Rd, Nashville, TN, 37214
(615) 885-0483
Admin David L Tripp. *Medical Dir/Dir of Nursing* Phyllis Poe RN DON.
Licensure Skilled care; Intermediate care. *Beds* SNF 17; ICF 107. *Certified* Medicaid; Medicare.
Owner Proprietary Corp.
Admissions Requirements Minimum age 18; Medical examination; Physician's request.
Staff Physicians 2 (pt); RNs 5 (ft); LPNs 10 (ft); Orderlies 4 (ft); Nurses aides 25 (ft), 10 (pt); Physical therapists 1 (ft), 1 (pt); Recreational therapists 1 (ft); Occupational therapists 1 (pt); Speech therapists 1 (pt); Activities coordinators 1 (ft); Dietitians 1 (ft); Social worker 1 (ft).
Facilities Dining room; Physical therapy room; Activities room; Crafts room; Laundry room; Barber/Beauty shop; Library.
Activities Arts & crafts; Cards; Games; Reading groups; Prayer groups; Movies; Shopping trips; Social/Cultural gatherings.

Meharry-Hubbard Hospital-Skilled Nursing Facility
PO Box 61-A, 1005 D B Todd Blvd, Nashville, TN, 37208
(615) 327-5550
Admin Duane Farnham Interim NHA. *Medical Dir/Dir of Nursing* Charles A Wiggins MD; Juanita J Polite RN DON.
Licensure Skilled care. *Beds* SNF 20. *Certified* Medicaid; Medicare.
Owner Nonprofit organization/foundation.
Admissions Requirements Physician's request.
Staff Physicians; RNs; LPNs; Physical therapists; Recreational therapists; Occupational therapists; Speech therapists; Activities coordinators; Dietitians.
Facilities Dining room; Physical therapy room; Activities room; Chapel.
Activities Arts & crafts; Cards; Games; Reading groups; Prayer groups; Movies; Social/Cultural gatherings; Quiet hour.

Nashville Health Care Center
2215 Patterson St, Nashville, TN, 37203
(615) 327-3011
Admin Martha Ulm. *Medical Dir/Dir of Nursing* Richard Garman MD.
Licensure Skilled care; Intermediate care. *Beds* SNF 52; ICF 50. *Certified* Medicaid; Medicare.
Owner Proprietary Corp (National Health Corp).
Admissions Requirements Medical examination.
Staff Physicians 1 (ft); RNs 5 (ft); LPNs 10 (ft); Nurses aides 77 (ft); Physical therapists 2 (ft); Occupational therapists 2 (ft); Speech therapists 1 (ft); Activities coordinators 2 (ft); Dietitians 1 (ft); Ophthalmologists 1 (pt).
Facilities Dining room; Physical therapy room; Activities room; Crafts room; Barber/Beauty shop.
Activities Arts & crafts; Games; Movies; Social/Cultural gatherings.

Nashville Manor Nursing Home
1306 Katie Ave, Nashville, TN, 37207
(615) 228-3494
Admin Mildred Ray. *Medical Dir/Dir of Nursing* Charles Wiggins MD; Delores Burton.
Licensure Intermediate care. *Beds* ICF 79. *Certified* Medicaid.
Owner Privately owned.
Admissions Requirements Minimum age 14; Medical examination; Physician's request.
Staff Physicians 1 (pt); RNs 1 (ft); LPNs 4 (ft); Orderlies 3 (ft); Nurses aides 22 (ft), 4 (pt); Physical therapists 1 (pt); Activities coordinators 1 (pt); Dietitians 1 (pt).

Facilities Dining room; Activities room;
Crafts room; Laundry room; Barber/Beauty
shop; 2 TV Rooms.
Activities Arts & crafts; Cards; Games;
Reading groups; Prayer groups; Movies;
Social/Cultural gatherings.

Porter House Health Care
701 Porter Rd, Nashville, TN, 37206
(615) 226-3264
Admin Doris J Dismuke. *Medical Dir/Dir of
Nursing* Dr William Pettit.
Licensure Intermediate care. *Certified*
Medicaid.
Owner Proprietary Corp.
Admissions Requirements Minimum age 14;
Medical examination; Physician's request.
Staff RNs 2 (ft); LPNs 10 (ft); Orderlies 65
(ft), 10 (pt); Activities coordinators 1 (ft), 1
(pt); Dietitians 1 (ft); Social Svcs 1 (ft).
Facilities Dining room; Physical therapy
room; Laundry room; Barber/Beauty shop;
Day rooms.
Activities Arts & crafts; Cards; Games; Prayer
groups; Movies.

Trevecca Health Care Center*
329 Murfreesboro Rd, Nashville, TN, 37210
(615) 244-6900
Admin M L McCaskell. *Medical Dir/Dir of
Nursing* Earl E Vastbinder MD.
Licensure Skilled care; Intermediate care. *Beds*
240. *Certified* Medicaid; Medicare.
Owner Proprietary Corp (Crowne
Management).
Admissions Requirements Minimum age 45;
Medical examination.
Staff Physicians 6 (pt); RNs 6 (ft), 4 (pt);
LPNs 18 (ft), 6 (pt); Orderlies 4 (ft), 3 (pt);
Nurses aides 82 (ft), 14 (pt); Physical
therapists 1 (ft), 1 (pt); Occupational
therapists 1 (pt); Speech therapists 1 (pt);
Activities coordinators 2 (ft); Dietitians 1
(pt); Dentists 1 (pt); Ophthalmologists 1 (pt);
Podiatrists 1 (pt); Audiologists 1 (pt).
Facilities Dining room; Activities room;
Chapel; Crafts room; Laundry room; Barber/
Beauty shop; Library.
Activities Arts & crafts; Cards; Games;
Movies; Shopping trips; Social/Cultural
gatherings.

University Health Care Center Inc*
2015 Terrace Pl, Nashville, TN, 37203
(615) 327-2144
Medical Dir/Dir of Nursing B H Webster MD.
Licensure Intermediate care. *Beds* 49.
Certified Medicaid.
Owner Proprietary Corp (National Health
Corp).
Staff Physicians 1 (pt); RNs 3 (ft); LPNs 4
(ft); Orderlies 1 (pt); Nurses aides 14 (ft), 5
(pt); Physical therapists 1 (pt); Speech
therapists 1 (pt); Activities coordinators 1
(pt); Dietitians 1 (ft).
Facilities Dining room; Physical therapy
room; Activities room; Laundry room;
Barber/Beauty shop.
Activities Games; Movies; Shopping trips.

NEW TAZEWELL

Laurel Manor Health Care Facility
PO Box 505, 902 Buchanan Rd, New
Tazewell, TN, 37825
(615) 626-8215
Admin Richard E Fields. *Medical Dir/Dir of
Nursing* Dr William N Smith.
Licensure Skilled care; Intermediate care. *Beds*
SNF 67; ICF 67. *Certified* Medicaid;
Medicare.
Owner Proprietary Corp (Wessex Corp).
Admissions Requirements Minimum age 14;
Medical examination; Physician's request.
Staff Physicians 12 (pt); RNs 4 (ft), 1 (pt);
LPNs 12 (ft), 2 (pt); Orderlies 12 (ft), 3 (pt);
Nurses aides 28 (ft), 7 (pt); Physical
therapists 1 (pt); Occupational therapists 1

(pt); Speech therapists 1 (ft); Activities
coordinators 1 (ft); Dietitians 1 (pt); Dentists
1 (pt).
Facilities Dining room; Physical therapy
room; Activities room; Crafts room; Laundry
room; Barber/Beauty shop.
Activities Arts & crafts; Cards; Games;
Movies; Shopping trips; Social/Cultural
gatherings; Bingo.

NEWPORT

Cocke County Baptist Convalescent Center
603 College St, Newport, TN, 37821
(615) 625-2196
Admin Mary E Seay. *Medical Dir/Dir of
Nursing* Dr David McConnell; Debra Holt
RN DON.
Licensure Intermediate care. *Beds* ICF 56.
Certified Medicaid.
Owner Nonprofit organization/foundation.
Admissions Requirements Minimum age 18;
Medical examination.
Staff RNs 1 (ft); LPNs 6 (ft); Orderlies 4 (ft);
Nurses aides 13 (ft), 2 (pt); Physical
therapists 1 (pt); Activities coordinators 1
(ft); Dietitians 1 (ft).
Affiliation Baptist
Facilities Dining room; Physical therapy
room; Activities room; Laundry room;
Barber/Beauty shop.
Activities Arts & crafts; Cards; Games;
Reading groups; Prayer groups; Movies;
Social/Cultural gatherings.

Regency Health Care Center
PO Box 489, Hwy 25 at 70 & 411, Newport,
TN, 37821
(615) 623-0929
Admin Craig N Ethridge. *Medical Dir/Dir of
Nursing* Kenneth Hill MD; Arnolene
Seahorn RN DON.
Licensure Skilled care; Intermediate care. *Beds*
SNF 18; ICF 120. *Certified* Medicaid;
Medicare.
Owner Proprietary Corp (Regency Health
Care Centers).
Admissions Requirements Minimum age 15;
Medical examination; Physician's request.
Staff RNs 4 (ft); LPNs 12 (ft); Orderlies 6 (ft),
1 (pt); Nurses aides 30 (ft), 8 (pt); Physical
therapists 1 (pt); Speech therapists 1 (ft);
Activities coordinators 1 (ft); Dietitians 1
(ft).
Facilities Dining room; Physical therapy
room; Activities room; Chapel; Crafts room;
Laundry room; Barber/Beauty shop; Library.
Activities Arts & crafts; Cards; Games;
Reading groups; Prayer groups; Movies;
Shopping trips; Social/Cultural gatherings;
Gardening.

OAK RIDGE

Oak Ridge Health Care Center*
300 Laboratory Rd, Oak Ridge, TN, 37830
(615) 482-7698
Medical Dir/Dir of Nursing Anthony Garton.
Licensure Skilled care; Intermediate care. *Beds*
120. *Certified* Medicaid; Medicare.
Owner Proprietary Corp (National Health
Corp).
Staff Physicians 2 (pt); RNs 4 (ft), 5 (pt);
LPNs 13 (ft), 8 (pt); Nurses aides 23 (ft), 15
(pt); Physical therapists 1 (ft); Recreational
therapists 1 (ft); Speech therapists 1 (pt);
Activities coordinators 1 (ft); Dietitians 1
(ft).
Facilities Dining room; Physical therapy
room; Activities room; Crafts room; Laundry
room; Barber/Beauty shop.
Activities Arts & crafts; Cards; Games;
Reading groups; Prayer groups; Movies;
Shopping trips; Social/Cultural gatherings.

ONEIDA

Scott County Nursing Home
PO Box 308, Alberta Ave, Oneida, TN, 37841
(615) 569-8521
Admin Nancy Meidinger. *Medical Dir/Dir of
Nursing* Dr Maxwell Huff; Peggy Smithers
LPN.
Licensure Intermediate care. *Beds* ICF 52.
Certified Medicaid.
Owner Publicly owned.
Admissions Requirements Physician's request.
Staff LPNs 7 (ft), 1 (pt).
Facilities Dining room; Activities room;
Barber/Beauty shop; Family visitation room.
Activities Arts & crafts; Games; Reading
groups; Prayer groups; Shopping trips;
Social/Cultural gatherings.

PALMYRA

**Palmyra Intermediate Care Center & New
Dawn**
PO Box 8, Palmyra, TN, 37142
(615) 326-5252
Admin Frances H Warren. *Medical Dir/Dir of
Nursing* Linda Newberry.
Licensure Skilled care; Intermediate care;
Intermediate care for mentally retarded.
Beds SNF 22; ICF 33; ICF/MR 20. *Certified*
Medicaid; Medicare.
Owner Privately owned.
Admissions Requirements Minimum age 21;
Medical examination; Physician's request.
Staff RNs 2 (ft), 2 (pt); LPNs 5 (ft), 4 (pt);
Orderlies 2 (ft), 2 (pt); Nurses aides 8 (ft), 9
(pt); Recreational therapists 1 (ft), 1 (pt);
Activities coordinators 1 (ft); Physical
therapy aide 1 (ft); Developmental
technicians 10 (ft), 13 (pt); Social workers 2
(ft); Medical records 1 (ft).
Languages Sign
Facilities Dining room; Activities room;
Crafts room; Laundry room; Barber/Beauty
shop; Dental office; Training center for
ADLS & vocational skills training.
Activities Arts & crafts; Cards; Games;
Reading groups; Prayer groups; Movies;
Shopping trips; Social/Cultural gatherings;
Community service projects; Ceramics;
Outings; Senior Olympics; Cook-outs.

PARIS

Henry County Nursing Home*
Hospital Circle, Paris, TN, 38242
(901) 642-5700
Licensure Intermediate care. *Beds* 114.
Certified Medicaid.

Paris Manor Nursing Center
PO Box 1408, Rte 3, Old Murray Rd, Paris,
TN, 38242
(901) 642-2535
Admin Ramon C Snyder.
Licensure Intermediate care. *Beds* 132.
Certified Medicaid.
Owner Proprietary Corp (American Health
Centers Inc).

PARSONS

Decatur County Manor Nursing Center
1501 Kentucky Ave S, Parsons, TN, 38363
(910) 847-6371
Admin Thomas E Feeback. *Medical Dir/Dir of
Nursing* Nancy Palmer DON.
Licensure Intermediate care. *Beds* ICF 95.
Certified Medicaid.
Owner Proprietary Corp (American Health
Centers Inc).
Admissions Requirements Medical
examination.

Staff RNs 1 (ft); LPNs 11 (ft); Nurses aides 27 (ft); Physical therapists 1 (pt); Recreational therapists 1 (ft); Activities coordinators 1 (ft).
Facilities Dining room; Activities room; Chapel; Crafts room; Laundry room; Barber/Beauty shop.
Activities Arts & crafts; Cards; Games; Reading groups; Prayer groups; Movies; Shopping trips; Social/Cultural gatherings.

PIKEVILLE

Bledsoe County Nursing Home*
Hwy 30 W, Pikeville, TN, 37367
(615) 447-6811
Licensure Intermediate care. *Beds* 49.
Certified Medicaid.

PLEASANT HILL

May Cravath Wharton Nursing Home
PO Box 168, Lake Dr, Pleasant Hill, TN, 38578
(615) 277-3511
Admin Lela W Swank. *Medical Dir/Dir of Nursing* Dr Fred Lake; Verlee Fischer RN DON.
Licensure Intermediate care. *Beds* ICF 80.
Owner Nonprofit Corp.
Admissions Requirements Minimum age 65; Medical examination.
Staff Physicians 2 (pt); RNs 1 (ft); LPNs 3 (ft), 3 (pt); Nurses aides 17 (ft), 13 (pt); Activities coordinators 1 (ft).
Affiliation Church of Christ
Facilities Dining room; Activities room; Crafts room; Laundry room; Barber/Beauty shop; Library; Lounges; Patios.
Activities Arts & crafts; Cards; Games; Reading groups; Prayer groups; Movies; Shopping trips; Social/Cultural gatherings; Coffee & conversation.

PORTLAND

Highland Manor Nursing Home
PO Box 104, Rte 4, Portland, TN, 37148
(615) 325-9263
Admin Richard L Mountz. *Medical Dir/Dir of Nursing* James Ladd MD; Jean Crittenden RN DON.
Licensure Intermediate care. *Beds* ICF 110.
Certified Medicaid.
Owner Proprietary Corp (Sunbelt Healthcare Centers).
Admissions Requirements Medical examination; Physician's request.
Staff RNs 1 (ft), 1 (pt); LPNs 11 (ft), 7 (pt); Nurses aides 40 (ft), 2 (pt); Activities coordinators 1 (ft); Dietitians 1 (pt).
Facilities Dining room; Activities room; Chapel; Crafts room; Barber/Beauty shop.
Activities Arts & crafts; Cards; Games; Prayer groups; Movies; Social/Cultural gatherings.

PULASKI

Hewitt House Retirement Center
322 E Washington St, Pulaski, TN, 38478
(615) 363-2222
Admin Janice M. Clark. *Medical Dir/Dir of Nursing* Helen Malone, LPN.
Licensure Retirement living facility. *Beds* 35.
Owner Privately owned.
Admissions Requirements Medical examination.
Staff LPNs; Nurses aides; Activities coordinators; Dietitians; Attendants.
Facilities Dining room; Activities room; Laundry room; Library.
Activities Cards; Games; Reading groups; Prayer groups; Movies; Shopping trips; Social/Cultural gatherings; Country drives; Sing-alongs; Birthday parties; Exercise.

Meadowbrook Nursing Home*
Hwy 64 E, Pulaski, TN, 38478
(615) 363-7548
Admin Christine Edwards.
Licensure Intermediate care. *Beds* 71.
Certified Medicaid.
Owner Proprietary Corp (American Health Centers Inc).
Admissions Requirements Minimum age 18; Medical examination.
Staff RNs 1 (ft); LPNs 5 (ft); Nurses aides 17 (ft); Activities coordinators 1 (ft).
Facilities Dining room; Activities room; Laundry room; Barber/Beauty shop.
Activities Arts & crafts; Cards; Games; Reading groups; Prayer groups; Movies; Shopping trips; Social/Cultural gatherings.

Pulaski Health Care Center*
Rte 4, Hwy 64 E, Pulaski, TN, 38478
(615) 363-3572
Admin Betty T Pope. *Medical Dir/Dir of Nursing* W K Owen MD.
Licensure Skilled care; Intermediate care. *Beds* 75. *Certified* Medicaid; Medicare.
Owner Proprietary Corp (National Health Corp).
Staff RNs 3 (ft), 1 (pt); LPNs 11 (ft); Orderlies 1 (ft); Nurses aides 13 (ft), 13 (pt); Physical therapists 1 (ft); Speech therapists 1 (pt); Activities coordinators 1 (ft); Dietitians 1 (ft); Dentists 1 (pt).
Facilities Dining room; Activities room; Barber/Beauty shop.
Activities Arts & crafts; Cards; Games; Reading groups; Prayer groups; Movies.

PURYEAR

Puryear Nursing Home
PO Box 38, 223 W Chestnut St, Puryear, TN, 38251
(901) 247-3205
Admin Peggy J Nichols. *Medical Dir/Dir of Nursing* Virginia A Sawyers.
Licensure Private. *Beds* 25. *Certified* Medicaid.
Owner Privately owned.
Admissions Requirements Minimum age 14; Medical examination.
Staff RNs 1 (ft); LPNs 4 (ft); Nurses aides 12 (ft); Activities coordinators 1 (ft); Dietitians 1 (ft).
Facilities Dining room; Activities room; Barber/Beauty shop; Library.
Activities Arts & crafts; Cards; Games; Reading groups; Movies; Church; Sunday school.

RED BOILING SPRINGS

Regency Health Care Center*
Hwy 52, Red Boiling Springs, TN, 37150
(615) 699-2238
Licensure Intermediate care. *Beds* 109.
Certified Medicaid.
Owner Proprietary Corp (Regency Health Care Centers).

RIDGETOP

Ridgetop Haven Inc*
Box 138, Woodruff, Ridgetop, TN, 37152
(615) 643-4548
Beds 32.

RIPLEY

Care Inn—Ripley*
118 Halliburton St, Ripley, TN, 38063
(901) 635-5180
Licensure Intermediate care. *Beds* 130.
Certified Medicaid.

Hillhaven Convalescent Center Ripley
118 Halliburton Rd, Ripley, TN, 38063
(901) 635-5180
Admin Gregory H Mitchell. *Medical Dir/Dir of Nursing* William Tucker MD; Carolyn Drumwright RN DON.
Licensure Skilled care; Intermediate care. *Beds* SNF 10; ICF 168. *Certified* Medicaid; Medicare.
Owner Proprietary Corp (Hillhaven Corp).
Admissions Requirements Medical examination; Physician's request.
Staff RNs 5 (ft); LPNs 16 (ft); Nurses aides 65 (ft); Recreational therapists 1 (ft), 1 (pt); Activities coordinators 1 (ft); Dietitians 1 (ft).
Facilities Dining room; Physical therapy room; Activities room; Barber/Beauty shop.
Activities Arts & crafts; Games; Reading groups; Prayer groups; Movies; Shopping trips; Social/Cultural gatherings.

Lauderdale County Nursing Home*
Lackey Ln, Ripley, TN, 38063
(901) 635-1331
Licensure Intermediate care. *Beds* 71.
Certified Medicaid.

ROCKWOOD

Rockwood Health Care Center*
PO Box 476, Hwy 70 E, Rockwood, TN, 37854
(615) 354-3366
Licensure Intermediate care. *Beds* 120.
Certified Medicaid.

ROGERSVILLE

Heritage Manor of Rogersville
Rte 4, Box 30, Rogersville, TN, 37857
(615) 272-3099
Admin A E Luttrell. *Medical Dir/Dir of Nursing* R B Baird Jr MD; Anna Ethridge RN DON.
Licensure Intermediate care. *Beds* ICF 150.
Certified Medicaid.
Owner Proprietary Corp.
Admissions Requirements Medical examination.
Staff Physicians 4 (pt); RNs 2 (ft), 1 (pt); LPNs 12 (ft), 2 (pt); Orderlies 3 (ft); Nurses aides 36 (ft), 10 (pt); Physical therapists 1 (pt); Speech therapists 1 (pt); Activities coordinators 1 (ft), 1 (pt); Dietitians 1 (ft), 1 (pt).
Facilities Dining room; Physical therapy room; Activities room; Crafts room; Laundry room; Barber/Beauty shop.
Activities Arts & crafts; Games; Reading groups; Prayer groups; Social/Cultural gatherings; Bus rides.

RUTLEDGE

Ridgeview Terrace Convalescent & Nursing Center*
Rte 2, Coffey Ln, Rutledge, TN, 37861
(615) 828-5295
Medical Dir/Dir of Nursing Dr John Kinser.
Licensure Intermediate care. *Beds* 132.
Certified Medicaid.
Owner Proprietary Corp (Life Care Centers of America).
Staff Physicians 8 (pt); RNs 1 (ft); LPNs 9 (ft); Nurses aides 8 (ft); Physical therapists 1 (pt); Reality therapists 1 (pt); Speech therapists 1 (pt); Activities coordinators 1 (ft); Dietitians 1 (pt).
Facilities Dining room; Physical therapy room; Activities room; Crafts room; Laundry room; Barber/Beauty shop; Library.
Activities Arts & crafts; Games; Prayer groups; Movies; Shopping trips.

SAVANNAH

Harbert Hills Academy Nursing Home
PO Box 212, Lonesome Pine Rd, Rte 2,
Savannah, TN, 38372
(901) 925-5495
Admin Lester L Dickman. *Medical Dir/Dir of
Nursing* John Lay MD; Geraldine Dickman
RN DON.
Licensure Intermediate care. *Beds* ICF 49.
Certified Medicaid.
Owner Proprietary Corp.
Staff Physicians 5 (pt); RNs 1 (ft); LPNs 5
(ft); Orderlies 10 (pt); Nurses aides 60 (ft),
20 (pt); Activities coordinators 1 (ft);
Dietitians 1 (pt).
Facilities Dining room; Activities room;
Chapel; Laundry room; Barber/Beauty shop.
Activities Arts & crafts; Movies; Shopping
trips.

Hardin County Nursing Home
2006 Wayne Rd, Savannah, TN, 38372
(901) 925-4954
Admin Rowena Davis. *Medical Dir/Dir of
Nursing* Janet K Lard MD; Margie Tall
LPN.
Licensure Intermediate care. *Beds* ICF 48.
Certified Medicaid.
Owner Publicly owned.
Admissions Requirements Medical
examination; Physician's request.
Staff RNs 1 (pt); LPNs 6 (ft), 2 (pt); Orderlies
4 (ft), 3 (pt); Nurses aides 7 (ft), 6 (pt);
Activities coordinators 1 (pt).
Facilities Dining room; Activities room;
Laundry room; Barber/Beauty shop; Library.
Activities Arts & crafts; Games; Reading
groups; Movies; Social/Cultural gatherings.

Hardin Home Nursing Home*
Hwy 64 E, Savannah, TN, 38372
(901) 925-4004
Licensure Intermediate care. *Beds* 52.
Certified Medicaid.

SELMER

Maple Hill Nursing Home*
6th St S, Selmer, TN, 38375
(901) 645-7908
Licensure Intermediate care. *Beds* 31.
Certified Medicaid.

SEVIERVILLE

**Fort Sanders—Sevier Medical Center Nursing
Home***
Middle Creek Rd, Sevierville, TN, 37862
(615) 453-7111
Admin Samuel McGahn. *Medical Dir/Dir of
Nursing* Charles H Bozeman MD.
Licensure Skilled care; Intermediate care. *Beds*
54. *Certified* Medicaid; Medicare.
Admissions Requirements Medical
examination; Physician's request.
Staff Physicians 1 (pt); RNs 3 (ft), 3 (pt);
LPNs 3 (ft), 4 (pt); Nurses aides 19 (ft), 5
(pt); Physical therapists 3 (pt); Occupational
therapists 1 (pt); Speech therapists 1 (pt);
Activities coordinators 1 (ft); Dietitians 1
(pt); Dentists 1 (pt); Social workers 1 (pt).
Facilities Dining room; Physical therapy
room; Activities room; Chapel; Crafts room;
Barber/Beauty shop; Library.
Activities Arts & crafts; Cards; Games;
Reading groups; Prayer groups; Movies;
Shopping trips; Social/Cultural gatherings.

Sevier County Health Care Center Inc*
415 Catlett Rd, Sevierville, TN, 37862
(615) 453-4747
Licensure Skilled care; Intermediate care. *Beds*
120. *Certified* Medicaid; Medicare.

SHELBYVILLE

Bedford County Nursing Home
845 Union St, Shelbyville, TN, 37160
(615) 684-3426
Medical Dir/Dir of Nursing Sara Womack
MD.
Licensure Intermediate care. *Beds* 88.
Certified Medicaid.
Owner Publicly owned.
Admissions Requirements Medical
examination; Physician's request.
Staff RNs 2 (ft); LPNs 8 (ft), 4 (pt); Orderlies
2 (pt); Nurses aides 17 (ft), 19 (pt); Physical
therapists 1 (pt); Activities coordinators 1
(pt); Dietitians 1 (pt).
Facilities Dining room; Physical therapy
room; Activities room; Chapel; Crafts room;
Laundry room; Barber/Beauty shop; Library.
Activities Arts & crafts; Cards; Games;
Reading groups; Prayer groups; Shopping
trips; Social/Cultural gatherings.

Glen Oaks Convalescent Center
1101 Glen Oaks Rd, Shelbyville, TN, 37160
(615) 684-8340
Admin Palyce W Jones. *Medical Dir/Dir of
Nursing* Dr A T Richards; Rebecca
Patterson RN.
Licensure Intermediate care. *Beds* ICF 130.
Certified Medicaid.
Owner Privately owned.
Admissions Requirements Medical
examination.
Staff Physicians 1 (pt); RNs 2 (ft); LPNs 14
(ft), 2 (pt); Nurses aides 42 (ft), 6 (pt);
Physical therapists 1 (pt); Occupational
therapists 1 (pt); Speech therapists 1 (pt);
Activities coordinators 1 (ft), 1 (pt);
Dietitians 1 (pt).
Facilities Dining room; Physical therapy
room; Activities room; Crafts room; Laundry
room; Barber/Beauty shop.
Activities Arts & crafts; Cards; Games;
Reading groups; Prayer groups; Movies;
Shopping trips; Social/Cultural gatherings.

SIGNAL MOUNTAIN

Alexian Village of Tennesse Inc
100 James Blvd, Signal Mountain, TN, 37377
(615) 870-0101, 870-0100
Admin Dan Gray. *Medical Dir/Dir of Nursing*
Arch Y Smith MD; Chris Tarziers RN
DON.
Licensure Skilled care; Intermediate care. *Beds*
124. *Certified* Medicaid; Medicare.
Owner Nonprofit Corp (Alexian Bros Health
Sys).
Admissions Requirements Medical
examination; Physician's request.
Staff RNs 2 (ft), 2 (pt); LPNs 12 (ft), 2 (pt);
Orderlies 1 (ft); Nurses aides 37 (ft), 2 (pt);
Physical therapists 2 (pt); Speech therapists
1 (pt); Activities coordinators 1 (ft);
Dietitians 1 (pt).
Affiliation Roman Catholic
Facilities Dining room; Physical therapy
room; Activities room; Chapel; Crafts room;
Laundry room; Barber/Beauty shop; Library;
Pharmacy.
Activities Arts & crafts; Cards; Games;
Reading groups; Prayer groups; Movies;
Shopping trips; Social/Cultural gatherings.

SMITHVILLE

Sunny Point Health Care Center Inc*
Rte 1, Spring St, Smithville, TN, 37166
(615) 597-4284 or (615) 597-6271
Licensure Skilled care; Intermediate care. *Beds*
76. *Certified* Medicaid; Medicare.
Owner Proprietary Corp (National Health
Corp).

SMYRNA

Smyrna Nursing Center*
202 Enon Springs Rd, Smyrna, TN, 37167
(615) 459-5621
Licensure Intermediate care. *Beds* 89.
Certified Medicaid.
Owner Proprietary Corp (Wessex Corp).

SOMERVILLE

Somerville Health Care Center*
PO Drawer D, Lakeview Dr, Somerville, TN,
38068
(901) 465-9861
Licensure Skilled care; Intermediate care. *Beds*
80. *Certified* Medicaid; Medicare.
Owner Proprietary Corp (National Health
Corp).

SOUTH PITTSBURG

Rivermont Convalescent & Nursing Center
201 E 10th St, South Pittsburg, TN, 37380
(615) 837-7981
Admin Douglas L Malin. *Medical Dir/Dir of
Nursing* Dr Russ Adcock; Rebecca
Chambers DON.
Licensure Intermediate care. *Beds* ICF 165.
Certified Medicaid.
Owner Proprietary Corp (National Heritage).
Admissions Requirements Medical
examination.
Staff RNs 2 (ft); LPNs 14 (ft), 4 (pt); Nurses
aides 53 (ft), 14 (pt); Activities coordinators
1 (ft); Dietitians 1 (pt).
Facilities Dining room; Physical therapy
room; Activities room; Crafts room; Laundry
room; Barber/Beauty shop; Library.
Activities Arts & crafts; Cards; Games;
Reading groups; Prayer groups; Movies;
Shopping trips; Social/Cultural gatherings.

SPARTA

Sparta Health Care Center Inc*
Box 298, 108 E Gracey St, Sparta, TN, 38583
(615) 836-2211
Licensure Skilled care; Intermediate care. *Beds*
120. *Certified* Medicaid; Medicare.
Owner Proprietary Corp (National Health
Corp).

SPRINGFIELD

Elm Hurst Nursing Home Inc
705 5th Ave E, Springfield, TN, 37172
(615) 384-7977
Admin Anita Willis. *Medical Dir/Dir of
Nursing* J R Quarles MD; Donna Henry
DON.
Licensure Intermediate care. *Beds* ICF 70.
Certified Medicaid.
Owner Publicly owned.
Admissions Requirements Minimum age 14.
Staff Physicians 1 (ft); RNs 2 (ft); LPNs 5 (ft),
4 (pt); Nurses aides 23 (ft), 7 (pt); Activities
coordinators 1 (ft); Rehab aide 1 (pt).
Facilities Activities room; Chapel; Crafts
room; Laundry room; Barber/Beauty shop;
Library.
Activities Arts & crafts; Cards; Games; Social/
Cultural gatherings; Birthday parties; Group
exercise; Special occasion parties.

Robertson County Health Care Center
PO Box 236, Rte 6, Springfield, TN, 37172
(615) 384-9565
Admin Eleta Grimmett. *Medical Dir/Dir of
Nursing* John Bassel; Wendy Lowe.
Licensure Skilled care; Intermediate care. *Beds*
SNF 34; ICF 86. *Certified* Medicaid;
Medicare.
Owner Proprietary Corp (Beverly Enterprises).
Admissions Requirements Medical
examination; Physician's request.

Staff RNs 3 (ft), 1 (pt); LPNs 7 (ft); Orderlies 4 (ft), 2 (pt); Physical therapists 1 (pt); Speech therapists 1 (pt); Activities coordinators 1 (ft), 1 (pt); Dietitians 1 (ft).
Facilities Dining room; Physical therapy room; Activities room; Laundry room; Barber/Beauty shop.
Activities Arts & crafts; Cards; Games; Reading groups; Prayer groups; Movies; Shopping trips; Social/Cultural gatherings.

Springfield Health Care Center
608 8th Ave E, Springfield, TN, 37172
(615) 384-8453
Admin Edna McClurlcan. *Medical Dir/Dir of Nursing* John B Turner MD; JoAnne Nicholson RN.
Licensure Skilled care; Intermediate care. *Beds* SNF 32; ICF 80. *Certified* Medicaid; Medicare.
Owner Proprietary Corp (National Health Corp).
Admissions Requirements Medical examination; Physician's request.
Staff RNs 3 (ft), 2 (pt); LPNs 6 (ft), 3 (pt); Nurses aides 31 (ft), 13 (pt); Physical therapists 1 (ft); Speech therapists 1 (pt); Activities coordinators 1 (ft); Dietitians 1 (pt); Ophthalmologists 1 (pt).
Facilities Dining room; Physical therapy room; Activities room; Crafts room; Laundry room; Barber/Beauty shop; Library.
Activities Arts & crafts; Cards; Games; Reading groups; Prayer groups; Movies; Shopping trips; Social/Cultural gatherings.

SWEETWATER

Sweetwater Valley Convalescent & Nursing Home Inc*
S Lee Hwy, Sweetwater, TN, 37874
(615) 337-6631
Licensure Intermediate care. *Beds* 93. *Certified* Medicaid.

Wood Presbyterian Home Inc*
310 S High St, Sweetwater, TN, 37874
(615) 337-5326
Admin Corinne Erickson. *Medical Dir/Dir of Nursing* Jean Edmonds RN.
Licensure Intermediate care. *Beds* 30. *Certified* Medicaid.
Admissions Requirements Medical examination.
Staff RNs 1 (ft); LPNs 3 (ft), 3 (pt); Nurses aides 10 (ft), 3 (pt); Activities coordinators 1 (pt); Dietitians 1 (pt).
Affiliation Presbyterian
Facilities Dining room; Activities room; Laundry room.
Activities Cards; Games; Reading groups; Movies.

TAZEWELL

Claiborne County Nursing Home
1000 Old Knoxville Rd, Tazewell, TN, 37879
(615) 626-4211
Admin Patricia Gray. *Medical Dir/Dir of Nursing* Dr Stanley Thompson; Bonnie Jamison DON.
Licensure Skilled care; Intermediate care. *Beds* 50. *Certified* Medicaid; Medicare.
Owner Publicly owned.
Admissions Requirements Medical examination; Physician's request.
Facilities Dining room; Physical therapy room; Activities room; Crafts room; Laundry room; Barber/Beauty shop.
Activities Arts & crafts; Cards; Games; Reading groups; Prayer groups; Movies; Shopping trips; Social/Cultural gatherings.

TIPTONVILLE

Reelfoot Manor Nursing Home
1034 Reelfoot Dr, Tiptonville, TN, 38079
(901) 253-6681
Admin Johnny H Rea. *Medical Dir/Dir of Nursing* Terry Byrd RN.
Licensure Intermediate care. *Beds* 120. *Certified* Medicaid.
Owner Proprietary Corp (Beverly Enterprises).
Admissions Requirements Minimum age 18; Medical examination.
Staff Physicians; RNs; LPNs; Orderlies; Nurses aides; Physical therapists; Reality therapists; Activities coordinators; Dietitians; Podiatrists.
Languages Spanish
Facilities Dining room; Physical therapy room; Activities room; Chapel; Laundry room; Barber/Beauty shop.
Activities Arts & crafts; Games; Reading groups; Prayer groups; Movies; Social/Cultural gatherings; Fishing trips; Outings; Tours.

TRENTON

Forum Convalescent Center
Box 168, Trenton, TN, 38382
(901) 855-4500
Admin Karen Utley. *Medical Dir/Dir of Nursing* Debra Harris RN.
Licensure Intermediate care. *Beds* ICF 44. *Certified* Medicaid; Medicare.
Owner Privately owned.
Admissions Requirements Medical examination.
Staff Physicians 5 (ft); RNs 1 (ft); LPNs 6 (ft); Nurses aides 10 (ft).
Facilities Dining room; Activities room; Crafts room; Barber/Beauty shop.
Activities Arts & crafts; Cards; Games; Reading groups; Prayer groups; Movies; Shopping trips; Social/Cultural gatherings; Womanless beauty review.

Harlan Morris Home
400 Harlan Morris Dr, Trenton, TN, 38382
(901) 855-0702
Licensure Home for aged. *Beds* 49.
Admissions Requirements Minimum age 50; Medical examination.
Facilities Dining room; Activities room; Barber/Beauty shop; Library.
Activities Arts & crafts; Games; Reading groups; Prayer groups; Shopping trips; Birthday parties once a month.

TULLAHOMA

Life Care Center of Tullahoma*
1715 N Jackson St, Tullahoma, TN, 37388
(615) 455-8557
Licensure Intermediate care. *Beds* 169. *Certified* Medicaid.
Owner Proprietary Corp (Life Care Centers of America).

UNION CITY

Obion County Rest Home*
Rte 1, Box 207, Union City, TN, 38261
(901) 885-9065
Admin Bill Jordan. *Medical Dir/Dir of Nursing* Dr Grover Schleifer.
Licensure Intermediate care. *Beds* 52. *Certified* Medicaid.
Admissions Requirements Medical examination; Physician's request.
Staff Physicians 1 (pt); RNs 1 (ft); LPNs 5 (ft); Orderlies 4 (ft); Nurses aides 9 (ft); Activities coordinators 1 (ft); Dietitians 1 (ft).

Facilities Dining room; Activities room; Laundry room; Barber/Beauty shop.
Activities Arts & crafts; Games; Reading groups; Prayer groups; Movies; Social/Cultural gatherings.

Union City Health Care Center*
1105 Sunswept Dr, Union City, TN, 38261
(901) 885-6400
Licensure Skilled care; Intermediate care. *Beds* 120. *Certified* Medicaid; Medicare.
Owner Proprietary Corp (Beverly Enterprises).

Union City Manor Nursing Center
PO Box 509, 1630 Reelfoot Ave, Union City, TN, 38261
(901) 885-8095, 885-8096
Admin Gary K Snyder. *Medical Dir/Dir of Nursing* Dr Paul Hill; Beth Huff DON.
Licensure Intermediate care. *Beds* ICF 81. *Certified* Medicaid.
Owner Proprietary Corp (American Health Centers Inc).
Admissions Requirements Minimum age 14; Physician's request.
Staff Physicians 1 (pt); RNs 1 (ft); LPNs 5 (ft), 2 (pt); Orderlies 1 (ft); Nurses aides 20 (ft), 5 (pt); Activities coordinators 1 (ft); Dietitians 1 (ft).
Facilities Dining room; Activities room; Crafts room; Laundry room; Barber/Beauty shop.
Activities Arts & crafts; Cards; Games; Reading groups; Prayer groups; Movies; Shopping trips; Social/Cultural gatherings.

WARTBURG

Life Care Center of Morgan County
Potters Falls Rd, Wartburg, TN, 37887
(615) 346-6691
Admin Walt Cross. *Medical Dir/Dir of Nursing* Dwight Willett MD; Peggy Vespie DON.
Licensure Intermediate care. *Beds* ICF 124. *Certified* Medicaid.
Owner Proprietary Corp (Life Care Centers of America).
Admissions Requirements Minimum age 14; Medical examination; Physician's request.
Staff Physicians 4 (pt); RNs 2 (ft); LPNs 11 (ft); Orderlies 1 (ft); Nurses aides 30 (ft), 15 (pt); Physical therapists 1 (pt); Reality therapists 1 (pt); Recreational therapists 1 (pt); Occupational therapists 1 (pt); Speech therapists 1 (pt); Activities coordinators 1 (ft); Dietitians 1 (pt).
Facilities Dining room; Physical therapy room; Activities room; Crafts room; Laundry room; Barber/Beauty shop; Courtyard; Minibus.
Activities Arts & crafts; Cards; Games; Reading groups; Prayer groups; Movies; Shopping trips; Social/Cultural gatherings.

WAVERLY

Humphreys County Nursing Home Inc
PO Box 476, S Church St, Waverly, TN, 37185-0476
(615) 296-2532
Admin Steve Lee. *Medical Dir/Dir of Nursing* Shelly Jackson DON.
Licensure Intermediate care. *Beds* ICF 73. *Certified* Medicaid.
Owner Nonprofit Corp.
Admissions Requirements Minimum age 18; Physician's request; Humphreys County residents only.
Staff RNs; LPNs; Orderlies; Nurses aides; Physical therapists; Recreational therapists; Activities coordinators; Dietitians.
Facilities Dining room; Activities room; Crafts room; Laundry room; Barber/Beauty shop.

Activities Arts & crafts; Cards; Games;
  Reading groups; Prayer groups; Movies;
  Shopping trips; Social/Cultural gatherings.

WAYNESBORO

Nelson's Health Care Center Inc
Box 580, 500 S High St, Waynesboro, TN,
  38485-0580
(615) 722-5832
Licensure Intermediate care. *Beds* 46.
  Certified Medicaid.

Wayne County Nursing Home
PO Box 510, Waynesboro, TN, 38485
(615) 722-3641
Licensure Intermediate care. *Beds* 72.
  Certified Medicaid.

WHITES CREEK

**Brookside Manor Nursing Home & Home for
the Aged**
3425 Knight Rd, Whites Creek, TN, 37189-
  9189
(615) 876-2754
Admin Gerald D Williams.
Licensure Intermediate care. *Beds* ICF; Home
  54. *Certified* Medicaid.
Owner Privately owned.
Admissions Requirements Minimum age 14.

Facilities Dining room.
Activities Arts & crafts; Cards; Games;
  Reading groups; Prayer groups; Movies;
  Social/Cultural gatherings.

WINCHESTER

Franklin County Health Care Center
Rte 3, 41-A Bypass, Winchester, TN, 37398
(615) 967-7082
Admin Joseph R Hagan. *Medical Dir/Dir of
  Nursing* Dudley Fort MD; Vallerie Rose RN
  DON.
Licensure Skilled care; Intermediate care.
  Certified Medicaid; Medicare.
Owner Proprietary Corp (Beverly Enterprises).
Admissions Requirements Medical
  examination.
Staff Physicians; RNs; LPNs; Nurses aides;
  Physical therapists; Activities coordinators;
  Dietitians.
Facilities Dining room; Physical therapy
  room; Activities room; Barber/Beauty shop;
  Day rooms on each wing.
Activities Arts & crafts; Cards; Games; Prayer
  groups; Movies; Shopping trips; Social/
  Cultural gatherings; Bingo; Bunko; Daily
  coffee break; Birthday parties; Wine &
  cheese parties.

Lakeside Manor Home for the Aged*
Rte 4, Lynchburg Rd, Winchester, TN, 37398
(615) 967-0865

Licensure Home for aged. *Beds* 12.

Methodist Nursing Home of Middle Tennessee
Cowan Rd, Winchester, TN, 37398
(615) 967-8249, 967-8389
Admin Robert Rose. *Medical Dir/Dir of
  Nursing* Louvena Glass DON.
Licensure Intermediate care. *Beds* 36.
  Certified Medicaid; Medicare.
Owner Nonprofit Corp.
Admissions Requirements Medical
  examination; Physician's request.
Staff RNs 3 (ft); LPNs 3 (ft), 1 (pt); Nurses
  aides 9 (ft), 3 (pt); Physical therapists;
  Activities coordinators 1 (ft); Activities
  coordinators.
Affiliation Methodist
Facilities Dining room; Physical therapy
  room; Activities room; Laundry room;
  Barber/Beauty shop.
Activities Arts & crafts; Cards; Games;
  Reading groups; Prayer groups; Movies;
  Shopping trips; Social/Cultural gatherings;
  Rhythm band.

WOODBURY

Woodbury Nursing Center Inc*
119 W High St, Woodbury, TN, 37190
(615) 563-5930
Licensure Intermediate care. *Beds* 82.
  Certified Medicaid.

TEXAS

ABILENE

Bur-Mont Nursing Center*
725 Medical Dr, Abilene, TX, 79601
(915) 672-3236
Admin Carolyn Martin.
Licensure Intermediate care. *Beds* 118.
  Certified Medicaid.
Owner Proprietary Corp.

Care Inn of Abilene*
4934 S 7th St, Abilene, TX, 79605
(915) 692-2172
Admin Joyce Pylant.
Licensure Intermediate care. *Beds* 106.
  Certified Medicaid.
Owner Proprietary Corp (ARA Living
  Centers).

Happy Haven Nursing Center*
1751 N 15th St, Abilene, TX, 79603
(915) 673-8892
Admin Ernest C Valle. *Medical Dir/Dir of
  Nursing* S Daggubati MD.
Licensure Intermediate care. *Beds* 235.
  Certified Medicaid.
Staff RNs 3 (ft); LPNs 18 (ft); Orderlies 10
  (ft); Nurses aides 70 (ft); Activities
  coordinators 1 (ft); Dietitians 1 (ft).
Facilities Dining room; Activities room;
  Crafts room; Laundry room; Barber/Beauty
  shop.
Activities Arts & crafts; Cards; Games;
  Reading groups; Prayer groups; Movies;
  Shopping trips; Social/Cultural gatherings.

Sears Memorial Methodist Nursing Center
3202 S Willis St, Abilene, TX, 79605
(915) 692-6145
Admin Chris Spence. *Medical Dir/Dir of
  Nursing* Dr W Kenneth Day MD; Pearl
  Merritt DON.
Licensure Intermediate care; Custodial care.
  Beds ICF 159; Custodial 51. *Certified*
  Medicaid.
Owner Nonprofit Corp.
Admissions Requirements Minimum age 62;
  Medical examination; Physician's request.
Staff Physicians 1 (pt); RNs 1 (ft); LPNs 20
  (ft), 4 (pt); Nurses aides 48 (ft), 25 (pt);
  Activities coordinators 2 (ft); Dietitians 1
  (ft), 1 (pt).
Languages Spanish
Affiliation Methodist
Facilities Dining room; Physical therapy
  room; Activities room; Crafts room; Laundry
  room; Barber/Beauty shop; Library; Enclosed
  courtyard; Family parlor.
Activities Arts & crafts; Cards; Games; Prayer
  groups; Movies; Shopping trips; Social/
  Cultural gatherings; Birthday parties;
  Religious; Educational; Family activities.

Shady Oaks Lodge 1*
2722 Old Anson Rd, Abilene, TX, 79603
(915) 673-7358
Admin Melba Fisher.

Licensure Intermediate care. *Beds* 114.
  Certified Medicaid.
Owner Proprietary Corp.

Shady Oaks Lodge 2*
2722 Old Anson Rd, Abilene, TX, 79603
(915) 673-7358
Admin Velda Howard. *Medical Dir/Dir of
  Nursing* Jack S Haynes MD.
Licensure Skilled care. *Beds* 100. *Certified*
  Medicaid.
Admissions Requirements Medical
  examination; Physician's request.
Staff Physicians 1 (pt); RNs 1 (ft), 3 (pt);
  LPNs 12 (ft), 2 (pt); Nurses aides 26 (ft);
  Activities coordinators 1 (ft); Dietitians 1
  (pt); Dentists 1 (pt).
Facilities Dining room; Physical therapy
  room; Activities room; Crafts room; Laundry
  room; Barber/Beauty shop; Library.
Activities Arts & crafts; Cards; Games;
  Reading groups; Prayer groups; Movies;
  Shopping trips.

West Texas Nursing Center*
2630 Old Anson Rd, Abilene, TX, 79603
(915) 673-5101
Admin Lexie L Hutchison.
Licensure Intermediate care. *Beds* 114.
  Certified Medicaid.
Owner Proprietary Corp.

Western Hills Nursing Center*
2102 Amy Lyn Ave, Abilene, TX, 79603
(915) 677-2296
Admin Leslie Kay Lane.
Licensure Intermediate care. *Beds* 118.
  Certified Medicaid.
Owner Proprietary Corp.

ALBANY

Bluebonnet Nursing Home
PO Box 608, Baird Hwy, Albany, TX, 76430
(915) 762-3329
Admin William D Wakefield.
Licensure Intermediate care. *Beds* ICF 80.
  Certified Medicaid.
Owner Proprietary Corp (Beverly Enterprises).
Admissions Requirements Minimum age 18;
  Medical examination; Physician's request.
Staff Physicians; RNs; LPNs; Orderlies;
  Nurses aides; Physical therapists; Reality
  therapists; Recreational therapists;
  Occupational therapists; Speech therapists;
  Activities coordinators; Dietitians.
Languages Spanish
Facilities Dining room; Physical therapy
  room; Activities room; Crafts room; Laundry
  room; Barber/Beauty shop.
Activities Arts & crafts; Cards; Games;
  Reading groups; Prayer groups; Movies;
  Social/Cultural gatherings.

ALICE

Hospitality House Inc
PO Box 1458, 218-219 N King St, Alice, TX,
78332
(512) 664-4366
Admin Phyl E Drake. *Medical Dir/Dir of
  Nursing* Dr R O Albert.
Licensure Skilled care; Intermediate care;
  Supervised living. *Beds* SNF 81; ICF 50;
  Supervised living 15. *Certified* Medicaid;
  Medicare.
Owner Proprietary Corp.
Staff Physicians 1 (pt); RNs 1 (ft), 4 (pt);
  LPNs 12 (ft); Nurses aides 65 (ft), 15 (pt);
  Physical therapists 1 (pt); Activities
  coordinators 2 (ft); Dietitians 2 (ft), 1 (pt).
Languages Spanish
Activities Arts & crafts; Cards; Games;
  Reading groups; Movies; Shopping trips;
  Social/Cultural gatherings; Churches.

Retama Manor Nursing Center*
606 Coyote Trail, Alice, TX, 78332
(512) 664-5479
Admin Mary Lou Van Alstyne.
Licensure Intermediate care. *Beds* 140.
  Certified Medicaid.
Owner Proprietary Corp (ARA Living
  Centers).

ALPINE

Valley Star Nursing Home
1003 Loop Rd, Alpine, TX, 79830
(915) 837-3344
Admin Tom Wright. *Medical Dir/Dir of
  Nursing* Ruth Apolinar.
Licensure Intermediate care. *Beds* 56.
  Certified Medicaid.
Admissions Requirements Physician's request.
Staff Physicians; RNs; Orderlies; Nurses aides;
  Activities coordinators; Dietitians.
Facilities Dining room; Activities room;
  Crafts room; Laundry room; Barber/Beauty
  shop.
Activities Arts & crafts; Cards; Games;
  Reading groups; Prayer groups; Movies;
  Shopping trips; Social/Cultural gatherings;
  Field trips.

ALVARADO

Alvarado Nursing Home*
R6t 3, Box 320, 500 Glenwood Dr, Alvarado,
TX, 76009
(817) 783-3304
Admin Genevieve H Tucker.
Licensure Skilled care. *Beds* 60. *Certified*
  Medicaid.
Owner Proprietary Corp.

ALVIN

Alvin Convalescent Center*
416 N Shirley, Alvin, TX, 77511
(713) 585-8484

Admin Roberta Miller.
Licensure Intermediate care. *Beds* 98.
Certified Medicaid.
Owner Proprietary Corp (Cantex Healthcare Centers).
Admissions Requirements Medical examination; Physician's request.
Staff RNs 1 (ft); LPNs 7 (ft), 1 (pt); Orderlies 1 (ft); Nurses aides 20 (ft), 2 (pt); Physical therapists 1 (pt); Occupational therapists 1 (pt); Speech therapists 1 (pt); Activities coordinators 1 (ft), 1 (pt); Dietitians 1 (pt).
Facilities Dining room; Crafts room; Laundry room; Barber/Beauty shop.
Activities Arts & crafts; Cards; Games; Prayer groups; Movies; Shopping trips; Social/ Cultural gatherings.

Winchester Lodge Nursing Home
1112 Smith Dr, Alvin, TX, 77511
(713) 331-6125
Admin Sylvia Donelly. *Medical Dir/Dir of Nursing* Lolly Dickson RN.
Licensure Intermediate care. *Beds* ICF 96; Personal care 25 Supervised living 21. *Certified* Medicaid.
Owner Proprietary Corp (ARA Living Centers).
Admissions Requirements Medical examination.
Staff RNs 1 (ft); LPNs 6 (ft); Orderlies 1 (ft); Nurses aides 12 (ft); Activities coordinators 1 (ft); Dietitians 1 (ft).
Languages Spanish
Facilities Dining room; Activities room; Crafts room; Laundry room; Barber/Beauty shop; Library.
Activities Arts & crafts; Cards; Games; Reading groups; Prayer groups; Movies; Shopping trips; Social/Cultural gatherings.

AMARILLO

Amarillo Good Samaritan Retirement Center
2200 7th St, Amarillo, TX, 79106
(806) 374-6896
Admin Virginia Langston. *Medical Dir/Dir of Nursing* Mickey Suit.
Licensure Intermediate care. *Beds* ICF 59. *Certified* Medicaid.
Owner Nonprofit Corp (Evangelical Lutheran/ Good Samaritan).
Admissions Requirements Physician's request.
Staff RNs 1 (ft), 1 (pt); LPNs 6 (ft), 4 (pt); Nurses aides 22 (ft), 2 (pt); Activities coordinators 1 (ft); Dietitians 1 (ft).
Facilities Dining room; Physical therapy room; Activities room; Chapel; Crafts room; Laundry room; Barber/Beauty shop; Library.
Activities Arts & crafts; Cards; Games; Reading groups; Prayer groups; Movies; Shopping trips; Social/Cultural gatherings.

Amarillo Nursing Center*
4033 W 51st St, Amarillo, TX, 79109
(806) 355-4488
Admin Peggy Richburg. *Medical Dir/Dir of Nursing* Suzane Porter.
Licensure Intermediate care; Personal care. *Beds* ICF 130; Personal 30. *Certified* Medicaid.
Owner Proprietary Corp (Beverly Enterprises).
Staff RNs 1 (ft); LPNs 5 (ft); Nurses aides 10 (ft); Activities coordinators 1 (ft); Dietitians 1 (ft).
Facilities Dining room; Activities room; Crafts room; Laundry room; Barber/Beauty shop.
Activities Arts & crafts; Cards; Games; Reading groups; Prayer groups; Movies; Shopping trips; Social/Cultural gatherings.

Elizabeth Jane Bivins Home for the Aged
PO Box 31450, 3115 Tee Anchor Blvd, Amarillo, TX, 79120
(806) 373-7671

Admin Maggie Cleo Cox. *Medical Dir/Dir of Nursing* Patricia Bloom MD; Marquitta Elliott DON.
Licensure Intermediate care. *Beds* ICF 36. *Certified* Medicaid.
Owner Nonprofit organization/foundation.
Admissions Requirements Minimum age 60; Medical examination.
Staff LPNs; Nurses aides; Physical therapists; Activities coordinators.
Facilities Dining room; Physical therapy room; Activities room; Chapel; Crafts room; Laundry room; Barber/Beauty shop; Library.
Activities Arts & crafts; Cards; Games; Prayer groups; Movies; Shopping trips; Social/ Cultural gatherings; Activities in the city; Ice capades; Fair; Circus.

Bivins Memorial Nursing Home
1001 Wallace Blvd, Amarillo, TX, 79106
(806) 355-7453
Admin Landis Oran Clark. *Medical Dir/Dir of Nursing* Patricia Bloom MD.
Licensure Skilled care; Intermediate care. *Beds* SNF 72; ICF 68. *Certified* Medicaid; Medicare.
Owner Nonprofit organization/foundation.
Admissions Requirements Medical examination; Physician's request.
Staff Physicians 1 (pt); RNs 7 (ft), 1 (pt); LPNs 36 (ft); Nurses aides 65 (ft), 10 (pt); Physical therapists 2 (ft); Activities coordinators 3 (ft); Dietitians 1 (ft); Music therapist 1 (ft).
Languages Spanish
Facilities Dining room; Physical therapy room; Activities room; Chapel; Crafts room; Laundry room; Barber/Beauty shop; Training/Social.
Activities Arts & crafts; Cards; Games; Reading groups; Prayer groups; Movies; Shopping trips; Social/Cultural gatherings.

Bryanwood Care Center*
2423 Line Ave, Amarillo, TX, 79106
(806) 376-7241
Admin Margurite Van Zandt.
Licensure Intermediate care. *Beds* 74. *Certified* Medicaid.
Owner Proprietary Corp (ARA Living Centers).

Country Club Manor
9 Medical Dr, Amarillo, TX, 79106
(806) 352-2731
Admin Wayne Campbell. *Medical Dir/Dir of Nursing* Rita Arthur.
Licensure Intermediate care. *Beds* ICF 102. *Certified* Medicaid.
Owner Proprietary Corp (ARA Living Centers).
Staff LPNs; Orderlies; Nurses aides; Physical therapists; Speech therapists; Activities coordinators; Dietitians.

Georgia Manor Nursing Home
2611 SW 46th St, Amarillo, TX, 79110
(806) 355-6517
Admin Laverne Munoz. *Medical Dir/Dir of Nursing* Mary Amerson RN DON.
Licensure Intermediate care. *Beds* ICF 56. *Certified* Medicaid; VA Contracts.
Owner Privately owned.
Admissions Requirements Medical examination; Physician's request.
Staff LPNs 5 (ft), 1 (pt); Nurses aides 8 (ft); Activities coordinators; Dietitians.
Facilities Dining room; Activities room; Laundry room; Barber/Beauty shop.
Activities Arts & crafts; Cards; Games; Reading groups; Prayer groups; Movies; Social/Cultural gatherings; Parties; Resident Council; Family dinner night.

Golden Age Care Center
1601 Kirkland Dr, Amarillo, TX, 79106
(806) 355-8281

Admin Sarah Rice. *Medical Dir/Dir of Nursing* Terri Pace RN DON.
Licensure Intermediate care. *Beds* ICF 98. *Certified* Medicaid.
Owner Nonprofit organization/foundation.
Admissions Requirements Medical examination; Physician's request.
Staff RNs 1 (pt); LPNs 8 (ft), 1 (pt); Nurses aides 22 (ft), 5 (pt); Activities coordinators 2 (ft); Dietitians 1 (pt).
Facilities Dining room; Activities room; Laundry room; Barber/Beauty shop.
Activities Arts & crafts; Cards; Games; Reading groups; Prayer groups; Shopping trips; Social/Cultural gatherings.

Heritage Convalescent Center
1009 Clyde, Amarillo, TX, 79106
(806) 352-5295
Admin Myrtis Mosley. *Medical Dir/Dir of Nursing* Dr Donald Frank.
Licensure Skilled care; Intermediate care. *Beds* 116. *Certified* Medicaid; Medicare.
Staff Physicians 2 (pt); RNs 3 (ft); LPNs 6 (ft); Orderlies 3 (ft); Nurses aides 18 (ft); Physical therapists 1 (ft); Recreational therapists 1 (ft); Occupational therapists 1 (pt); Speech therapists 1 (pt); Activities coordinators 1 (ft); Dietitians 1 (pt).
Facilities Dining room; Activities room; Crafts room; Laundry room; Barber/Beauty shop.
Activities Arts & crafts; Cards; Games; Social/ Cultural gatherings.

Medi Park Care Center Inc*
1931 Medi Park Dr, Amarillo, TX, 79106
(806) 353-7433
Admin Wayne Gray. *Medical Dir/Dir of Nursing* Harlan Wilson.
Licensure Intermediate care. *Beds* 124. *Certified* Medicaid.
Staff RNs 1 (ft); LPNs 9 (ft); Orderlies 6 (ft); Nurses aides 25 (ft); Physical therapists 1 (pt); Occupational therapists 1 (pt); Speech therapists 1 (pt); Activities coordinators 1 (ft); Dietitians 1 (ft).
Facilities Dining room; Activities room; Crafts room; Laundry room; Barber/Beauty shop.
Activities Arts & crafts; Cards; Games; Reading groups; Prayer groups; Movies; Shopping trips; Social/Cultural gatherings.

Olsen Manor Nursing Home*
3350 Olsen Blvd, Amarillo, TX, 79109
(806) 355-9726
Admin Phillip E Kielpinski.
Licensure Intermediate care; Custodial care. *Beds* ICF 60; Custodial care 60. *Certified* Medicaid.
Owner Proprietary Corp (Comprehensive Health Care Assn).

Vivian's Nursing Home*
508 N Taylor St, Amarillo, TX, 79107
(806) 372-6822
Admin Jack D Rude.
Licensure Intermediate care. *Beds* 53. *Certified* Medicaid.
Owner Proprietary Corp.

AMHERST

Amherst Manor
700 Main St, Box 489, Amherst, TX, 79312
(806) 246-3583
Admin Mamie Dangerfield. *Medical Dir/Dir of Nursing* Carol Warren.
Licensure Intermediate care. *Beds* ICF 30. *Certified* Medicaid.
Owner Proprietary Corp.
Admissions Requirements Medical examination; Physician's request.
Staff Nurses aides 8 (ft); Activities coordinators 1 (ft); Dietitians; LVNs 4 (ft).

Facilities Dining room; Activities room; Crafts room; Laundry room; Lobby.
Activities Arts & crafts; Cards; Games; Reading groups; Prayer groups; Movies; Shopping trips; Social/Cultural gatherings.

ANAHUAC

Leisure Lodge—Anahuac*
Drawer W, Front St, Anahuac, TX, 77514
(713) 267-3164
Admin Joy Lee Green.
Licensure Intermediate care. *Beds* 100.
Certified Medicaid.
Owner Proprietary Corp (Beverly Enterprises).

ANDREWS

Andrews Nursing Center*
620 Hospital Dr, Andrews, TX, 79714
(915) 523-4986
Admin Virginia S Clegg.
Licensure Intermediate care. *Beds* 98.
Certified Medicaid.
Owner Proprietary Corp (Beverly Enterprises).

ANGLETON

Angleton-Danbury Convalescent Center
135 1/2 Hospital Dr, Angleton, TX, 77515
(409) 849-8221
Admin Juanita Benton. *Medical Dir/Dir of Nursing* Janet Klinkenberg.
Licensure Intermediate care. *Beds* ICF 104.
Certified Medicaid.
Owner Proprietary Corp.
Admissions Requirements Medical examination; Physician's request.
Staff RNs; Nurses aides; Activities coordinators; Dietitians.
Facilities Dining room; Activities room; Crafts room; Laundry room; Barber/Beauty shop.
Activities Arts & crafts; Games; Movies.

Golden Villa Nursing Home*
721 W Mulberry St, Angleton, TX, 77515
(713) 849-8281
Admin Joy Teague.
Licensure Intermediate care. *Beds* 103.
Certified Medicaid.
Owner Proprietary Corp.

ANSON

Briarstone Manor
125 Ave J, Anson, TX, 79501
(915) 823-3471, 823-3131
Admin Lorene Beason. *Medical Dir/Dir of Nursing* Diana Moore.
Licensure Intermediate care. *Beds* ICF 70.
Certified Medicaid.
Owner Proprietary Corp (Beverly Enterprises).
Staff RNs 1 (pt); LPNs 5 (ft), 3 (pt); Nurses aides 15 (ft), 3 (pt); Activities coordinators 1 (ft).
Facilities Dining room; Activities room; Chapel; Laundry room; Barber/Beauty shop.
Activities Arts & crafts; Games; Prayer groups; Social/Cultural gatherings.

Valley View Care Center*
101 Liberty Ln, Anson, TX, 79501
(915) 823-2141
Admin Frances A Ward.
Licensure Intermediate care. *Beds* 36.
Certified Medicaid.
Admissions Requirements Medical examination; Physician's request.
Staff RNs 1 (pt); LPNs 3 (ft), 2 (pt); Orderlies 2 (pt); Nurses aides 9 (ft), 2 (pt); Activities coordinators 1 (ft); Dietitians 1 (pt).
Facilities Dining room; Activities room; Chapel; Crafts room; Laundry room; Barber/Beauty shop.

Activities Arts & crafts; Cards; Games; Reading groups; Prayer groups; Shopping trips; Social/Cultural gatherings.

ARANSAS PASS

Aransas Pass Nursing & Convalescent Center
1661 W Yoakum St, Aransas Pass, TX, 78336
(512) 758-7686
Admin Joyce Corry. *Medical Dir/Dir of Nursing* Louise Wheeler RN.
Licensure Intermediate care. *Beds* 170.
Certified Medicaid.
Owner Proprietary Corp (Diversicare Corp).
Admissions Requirements Medical examination; Physician's request.
Staff RNs 1 (ft); LPNs 12 (ft), 2 (pt); Nurses aides 20 (ft), 12 (pt); Activities coordinators 1 (ft); Dietitians 1 (ft).
Languages Spanish
Facilities Dining room; Activities room; Crafts room; Laundry room; Barber/Beauty shop.
Activities Arts & crafts; Cards; Games; Reading groups; Prayer groups; Movies; Shopping trips; Social/Cultural gatherings.

ARCHER CITY

Archer Nursing Home
201 E Chestnut, Archer City, TX, 76351
(817) 574-4551
Admin Edith V Lawrence.
Licensure Intermediate care. *Beds* 46.
Certified Medicaid.
Admissions Requirements Medical examination.
Staff RNs 1 (pt); LPNs 2 (ft), 1 (pt); Nurses aides 13 (ft), 2 (pt); Activities coordinators 1 (ft); Dietitians 1 (ft).
Facilities Dining room; Activities room; Laundry room.
Activities Arts & crafts; Cards; Games; Reading groups; Prayer groups; Movies; Social/Cultural gatherings; Church; Singing; Square dancing.

ARLINGTON

Arlington Nursing Center*
301 W Randol Mill Rd, Arlington, TX, 76010
(817) 460-2002
Admin Victoria Ray.
Licensure Intermediate care. *Beds* 120.
Certified Medicaid.
Owner Proprietary Corp.

Arlington Villa for Senior Citizens*
2601 W Randol Mill Rd, Arlington, TX, 76012
(817) 274-5571
Admin Genevieve Sims.
Licensure Intermediate care. *Beds* 148.
Certified Medicaid.
Admissions Requirements Minimum age 62; Medical examination; Physician's request.
Staff RNs 1 (ft), 1 (pt); LPNs 7 (ft), 1 (pt); Nurses aides 14 (ft); Activities coordinators 1 (ft); Dietitians 1 (ft).
Facilities Dining room; Activities room; Chapel; Laundry room; Barber/Beauty shop; Library.
Activities Arts & crafts; Games; Prayer groups; Movies; Shopping trips; Social/Cultural gatherings.

Dalworth Care Center*
405 Duncan Perry Rd, Arlington, TX, 76010
(817) 649-3366
Admin Ann Collins.
Licensure Intermediate care. *Beds* 120.
Certified Medicaid.
Owner Proprietary Corp (ARA Living Centers).

Eastern Star Home
1201 E Division St, Arlington, TX, 76011
(817) 265-1513
Admin Evelyn J Lutz. *Medical Dir/Dir of Nursing* Dr Reichelt; Louise McDonald.
Licensure Intermediate care. *Beds* ICF 40.
Owner Nonprofit organization/foundation.
Admissions Requirements Females only.
Staff Physicians; RNs; LPNs; Nurses aides; Activities coordinators; Dietitians; Ophthalmologists.
Affiliation Order of Eastern Star
Facilities Dining room; Chapel; Crafts room; Laundry room; Barber/Beauty shop; Library.
Activities Arts & crafts; Cards; Games; Movies; Shopping trips.

Knights Templar Clinic*
1501 W Division, Arlington, TX, 76012
(817) 275-2893
Admin Dorothy B Health.
Licensure Intermediate care. *Beds* 60.
Owner Nonprofit Corp.
Affiliation Masons

Oakhaven Nursing Center*
1112 Gibbins Rd, Arlington, TX, 76012
(817) 261-6881
Admin Kathy Blasingame. *Medical Dir/Dir of Nursing* Dr Dorab Patel.
Licensure Skilled care. *Beds* 175. *Certified* Medicaid.
Staff RNs 6 (ft); Nurses aides 40 (ft), 15 (pt); Physical therapists 2 (ft); Activities coordinators 1 (ft); Dietitians 1 (ft); Dentists; Podiatrists; LVNs 8 (ft), 4 (pt).
Facilities Dining room; Activities room; Crafts room; Laundry room; Barber/Beauty shop; Library.
Activities Arts & crafts; Cards; Games; Reading groups; Prayer groups; Movies; Shopping trips; Social/Cultural gatherings.

Villa Nursing Center Inc*
2645 W Randol Mill Rd, Arlington, TX, 76012
(817) 277-6789
Admin Barbara J Perkins.
Licensure Intermediate care. *Beds* 120.
Certified Medicaid.
Owner Proprietary Corp (Convalescent Services).
Admissions Requirements Medical examination.
Staff RNs 2 (ft); LPNs 8 (ft); Orderlies 2 (ft); Nurses aides 30 (ft); Activities coordinators 1 (ft); Dietitians 1 (ft).
Facilities Dining room; Physical therapy room; Activities room; Laundry room; Barber/Beauty shop.
Activities Arts & crafts; Cards; Games; Prayer groups; Movies; Social/Cultural gatherings.

ASPERMONT

Gibson Nursing Center
1000 N Broadway, Aspermont, TX, 79502
(817) 989-3526
Admin Beth Thomas. *Medical Dir/Dir of Nursing* Mary Daniel DON.
Licensure Intermediate care. *Beds* ICF 80.
Certified Medicaid.
Owner Proprietary Corp (Beverly Enterprises).
Staff LPNs 4 (ft); Nurses aides 6 (ft), 5 (pt); Activities coordinators 1 (ft); Dietitians 1 (pt).
Activities Arts & crafts; Cards; Games; Reading groups; Prayer groups; Movies; Social/Cultural gatherings.

ATHENS

Athens Nursing Home
305 S Palestine St, Athens, TX, 75751
(214) 675-5604
Admin Mike Kirby. *Medical Dir/Dir of Nursing* Wanda Henson.

Licensure Intermediate care. *Beds* ICF 65.
Certified Medicaid; Medicare.
Owner Proprietary Corp (Health Enter of America).
Admissions Requirements Medical examination.
Staff LPNs; Nurses aides; Physical therapists; Activities coordinators; Dietitians; Ophthalmologists.
Facilities Dining room; Activities room; Laundry room; Barber/Beauty shop; Feeder room.
Activities Cards; Games; Reading groups; Movies; Social/Cultural gatherings.

Park Highlands*
711 Lucas, Athens, TX, 75751
(214) 675-7156, 8538
Admin Melba L Edwards.
Licensure Intermediate care. *Beds* 140.
Certified Medicaid.
Owner Proprietary Corp (ARA Living Centers).

Valvista Pavillion*
500 Valle Vista Dr, Athens, TX, 75751
(214) 675-8591
Admin Marie J Wood. *Medical Dir/Dir of Nursing* Dr A Dyphrone.
Licensure Intermediate care. *Beds* 118.
Certified Medicaid.
Staff Physicians 1 (pt); RNs 1 (ft), 1 (pt); LPNs 8 (ft); Nurses aides 33 (ft), 2 (pt); Activities coordinators 2 (ft); Dietitians 1 (ft), 1 (pt).
Facilities Dining room; Laundry room; Barber/Beauty shop.
Activities Arts & crafts; Games; Prayer groups; Movies; Shopping trips; Social/Cultural gatherings; Exercise class.

ATLANTA

Pine Lodge Nursing Home*
201 E 3rd St, Atlanta, TX, 75551
(214) 796-4461
Admin Theodore T Asimos.
Licensure Intermediate care. *Beds* 109.
Certified Medicaid.
Owner Proprietary Corp.

Rose Haven Retreat Inc*
Live Oak & Williams, Atlanta, TX, 75551
(214) 796-4127
Admin Leonard M Jester Jr. *Medical Dir/Dir of Nursing* James Morris MD.
Licensure Skilled care; Intermediate care. *Beds* SNF 45; ICF 63. *Certified* Medicaid.
Admissions Requirements Medical examination; Physician's request.
Staff Physicians 8 (pt); RNs 2 (ft), 1 (pt); LPNs 6 (ft), 2 (pt); Nurses aides 22 (ft), 6 (pt); Activities coordinators 1 (ft); Dietitians 1 (pt); Dentists 1 (pt); Ophthalmologists 1 (pt).
Facilities Dining room; Physical therapy room; Activities room; Chapel; Crafts room; Laundry room; Barber/Beauty shop.
Activities Arts & crafts; Cards; Games; Reading groups; Prayer groups; Movies; Shopping trips; Social/Cultural gatherings.

AUSTIN

Anderson Lane Nursing Home
7901 Lazy Ln, Austin, TX, 78758
(512) 454-5621
Admin Rebecca Boyd-Hubik. *Medical Dir/Dir of Nursing* Dr Peggy Russell; Barbara Johnson.
Licensure Intermediate care. *Beds* 48.
Certified Medicaid.
Owner Proprietary Corp.
Staff LPNs 2 (ft); Nurses aides 10 (ft); Activities coordinators 1 (ft).

Facilities Dining room; Activities room; Crafts room; Laundry room.
Activities Arts & crafts; Cards; Games; Reading groups; Prayer groups; Movies; Shopping trips; Social/Cultural gatherings; Cooking.

Arnold's Care Center*
3101 Govalle Ave, Austin, TX, 78702
(512) 926-8117
Admin Marjorie D Austin.
Licensure Intermediate care. *Beds* 83.
Certified Medicaid.
Owner Proprietary Corp.

Austin Manor Nursing Home*
5413 Guadalupe St, Austin, TX, 78751
(512) 452-7316
Admin Lillian B Laughlin.
Licensure Intermediate care. *Beds* 60.
Certified Medicaid.
Owner Proprietary Corp.

Austin Nursing Center
110 E Live Oak, Austin, TX, 78704
(512) 444-3511
Admin Charles N Taylor. *Medical Dir/Dir of Nursing* Odilia San Miguel DON.
Licensure Intermediate care. *Beds* ICF 170.
Certified Medicaid.
Owner Proprietary Corp.
Admissions Requirements Medical examination.
Staff RNs; Nurses aides; Physical therapists; Occupational therapists; Speech therapists; Activities coordinators; Dietitians; Ophthalmologists.
Languages Spanish
Facilities Dining room; Activities room; Crafts room; Laundry room; Barber/Beauty shop; Library.
Activities Arts & crafts; Cards; Games; Reading groups; Prayer groups; Movies; Shopping trips; Social/Cultural gatherings.

Barton Heights Nursing Home Inc*
1606 Nash St, Austin, TX, 78704
(512) 444-6708
Admin Mary E Zumwalt.
Licensure Intermediate care. *Beds* 60.
Certified Medicaid.
Owner Proprietary Corp.

Buckner Monte Siesta Home
4700 Dudmar Dr, Austin, TX, 78735
(512) 892-1131
Admin Sammie M Black. *Medical Dir/Dir of Nursing* Barbara Nelson RN.
Licensure Intermediate care. *Beds* ICF 128.
Certified Medicaid.
Owner Nonprofit Corp (Buckner Bapt Retire Vlg).
Admissions Requirements Medical examination.
Staff RNs 1 (ft); LPNs 13 (ft); Orderlies 1 (ft); Nurses aides 30 (ft); Activities coordinators 2 (ft); Dietitians 1 (ft).
Affiliation Baptist
Facilities Dining room; Activities room; Crafts room; Barber/Beauty shop.
Activities Arts & crafts; Games; Reading groups; Movies; Shopping trips.

Buckner Villa Siesta Home*
1001 E Braker Ln, Austin, TX, 78753
(512) 836-1515
Admin James H Cantrell.
Licensure Intermediate care. *Beds* 128.
Certified Medicaid.
Owner Nonprofit Corp.
Affiliation Baptist

Cameron Villa Rest Home*
1109 E 52nd St, Austin, TX, 78723
(512) 451-1673
Admin Charles Collins.
Licensure Intermediate care. *Beds* 41.
Certified Medicaid.
Owner Proprietary Corp.

Capitol City Nursing Home*
9052 Galewood Dr, Austin, TX, 78758
(512) 836-9172
Admin Rita Balmforth. *Medical Dir/Dir of Nursing* Dr George Robison.
Licensure Skilled care. *Beds* 120. *Certified* Medicaid.
Owner Proprietary Corp (Beverly Enterprises).
Admissions Requirements Medical examination.
Staff RNs 1 (ft), 1 (pt); LPNs 10 (ft), 5 (pt); Orderlies 2 (ft); Nurses aides 27 (ft), 2 (pt); Activities coordinators 2 (ft); Dietitians 1 (ft).
Facilities Dining room; Activities room; Laundry room; Barber/Beauty shop; Library.
Activities Arts & crafts; Cards; Games; Reading groups; Prayer groups; Movies; Shopping trips; Social/Cultural gatherings.

Central Texas Care Center
8007 Burnet Rd, Austin, TX, 78758
(512) 453-7389
Admin Mildred O Scheumack. *Medical Dir/Dir of Nursing* Elsie Dixon LVN DON.
Licensure Intermediate care. *Beds* ICF 96.
Certified Medicaid.
Owner Privately owned.
Admissions Requirements Medical examination.
Staff Nurses aides; Activities coordinators; Dietitians; LVNs.
Languages Spanish
Facilities Dining room; Activities room; Laundry room; Barber/Beauty shop.
Activities Arts & crafts; Cards; Games; Reading groups; Prayer groups; Movies; Shopping trips; Social/Cultural gatherings.

Cresthaven Childrens Center
4800 S 1st St, Austin, TX, 78745
(512) 444-8551
Admin Robert Wolszon. *Medical Dir/Dir of Nursing* Larry Lewellyn DO; Debbie Robinson RN.
Licensure Intermediate care for mentally retarded. *Beds* 72. *Certified* Medicaid.
Owner Proprietary Corp (Beverly Enterprises).
Admissions Requirements Minimum age 2 to 12.
Staff Physicians 1 (pt); RNs 1 (ft); LPNs 9 (ft); Nurses aides 39 (ft), 8 (pt); Reality therapists 1 (pt); Activities coordinators 2 (ft); Dietitians 1 (ft); Social worker 1 (ft).
Facilities Dining room; Physical therapy room; Activities room; Laundry room.
Activities Games; Shopping trips; Social/Cultural gatherings.

Cresthaven Nursing Center
6400 E Martin Luther King Blvd, Austin, TX, 78724
(512) 926-5976
Admin Jerry Nelson. *Medical Dir/Dir of Nursing* Linda Trout RN.
Licensure Intermediate care for mentally retarded. *Beds* ICF/MR 96. *Certified* Medicaid.
Owner Nonprofit Corp.
Admissions Requirements Minimum age 21.
Staff Physicians 3 (pt); RNs 3 (ft), 5 (pt); LPNs 6 (ft), 4 (pt); Nurses aides 80 (ft); Physical therapists 1 (pt); Occupational therapists 1 (pt); Speech therapists 1 (pt); Activities coordinators 1 (ft); Dietitians 1 (ft); Dentists 1 (pt); Ophthalmologists 1 (pt); Podiatrists 1 (pt).
Languages Spanish
Facilities Dining room; Activities room; Crafts room; Laundry room.
Activities Arts & crafts; Cards; Games; Reading groups; Prayer groups; Movies; Shopping trips; Social/Cultural gatherings; As required & meet needs & abilities of clients.

Cullen Avenue Rest Home*
2105 Cullen, Austin, TX, 78757
(512) 454-2731
Admin Bobby Dockal. *Medical Dir/Dir of Nursing* Louise Eeds MD.
Licensure Intermediate care. *Beds* 60.
Certified Medicaid.
Staff Physicians 1 (ft), 2 (pt); RNs 1 (pt); LPNs 2 (ft), 4 (pt); Orderlies 5 (ft), 1 (pt); Nurses aides 14 (ft), 3 (pt); Physical therapists 1 (pt); Speech therapists 1 (pt); Activities coordinators 1 (ft); Dietitians 1 (pt); Dentists 1 (pt); Podiatrists 1 (pt).
Facilities Dining room; Activities room; Crafts room; Laundry room; Barber/Beauty shop.
Activities Arts & crafts; Cards; Games; Reading groups; Prayer groups; Movies; Shopping trips; Social/Cultural gatherings.

Delwood Nursing Center Inc*
4407 Red River St, Austin, TX, 78751
(512) 452-2533
Admin Billie G McGee.
Licensure Intermediate care. *Beds* 40.
Certified Medicaid.
Staff RNs 1 (ft); LPNs 2 (ft), 3 (pt); Nurses aides 11 (ft), 3 (pt); Activities coordinators 1 (pt).
Facilities Dining room; Activities room.
Activities Arts & crafts; Games; Prayer groups; Social/Cultural gatherings.

Four Seasons Nursing Center
500 E Saint Johns, Austin, TX, 78752
(512) 454-9581
Admin Kenny Owings. *Medical Dir/Dir of Nursing* Alan Sonstien MD.
Licensure Skilled care; Intermediate care. *Beds* 233. *Certified* Medicaid; Medicare.
Owner Proprietary Corp (Manor Care).
Admissions Requirements Medical examination; Physician's request.
Staff RNs 9 (ft), 10 (pt); LPNs 4 (ft), 12 (pt); Nurses aides 18 (ft), 32 (pt); Physical therapists 1 (pt); Reality therapists 2 (ft), 1 (pt); Occupational therapists 1 (pt); Speech therapists 1 (pt); Dentists 1 (pt); Ophthalmologists 1 (pt); Activities coordinators 1 (ft); Dietitians 1 (pt).
Facilities Dining room; Physical therapy room; Activities room; Crafts room; Laundry room; Barber/Beauty shop.
Activities Arts & crafts; Cards; Games; Reading groups; Prayer groups; Movies; Shopping trips; Social/Cultural gatherings.

Maggie Johnson's Nursing Center*
3406 E 17th St, Austin, TX, 78721
(512) 926-4760
Admin Johnny E Slaughter.
Licensure Intermediate care. *Beds* 48.
Certified Medicaid.
Owner Proprietary Corp.

Miller's Rest Home Inc
PO Box 49262, 4606 Connelly, Austin, TX, 78765
(512) 452-0155
Admin Rosalie M Miller.
Licensure Intermediate care. *Beds* 38.
Certified Medicaid.
Owner Proprietary Corp.

Northwest Mediplex*
11612 Angus Rd, Austin, TX, 78759
(512) 345-1805
Admin Irene G Richter. *Medical Dir/Dir of Nursing* Ernest Schmatolla.
Licensure Intermediate care. *Beds* 388.
Certified Medicaid.
Owner Proprietary Corp (Beverly Enterprises).
Facilities Dining room; Physical therapy room; Activities room; Laundry room; Barber/Beauty shop; Library.

Oakcrest Manor*
9507 Hwy 290 E, Austin, TX, 78724
(512) 272-5511

Admin Mary A Neal.
Licensure Intermediate care. *Beds* 60.
Certified Medicaid.
Owner Proprietary Corp.

Resthaven Nursing Home
6222 N Lamar, Austin, TX, 78752
(512) 453-6658
Admin Beatrice V Burrell. *Medical Dir/Dir of Nursing* Dr Eeds; Darlene Martin DON.
Licensure Intermediate care. *Beds* ICF 80.
Owner Privately owned.
Admissions Requirements Physician's request.
Staff Physicians; RNs; Orderlies 1 (ft); Nurses aides 12 (ft), 3 (pt); Activities coordinators 1 (ft); Dietitians 1 (ft).
Languages Spanish
Facilities Dining room; Activities room; Crafts room; Laundry room; Barber/Beauty shop.
Activities Arts & crafts; Cards; Games; Reading groups; Prayer groups; Movies; Shopping trips; Social/Cultural gatherings.

Retirement & Nursing Center
6909 Burnet Ln, Austin, TX, 78757
(512) 454-5719
Admin Carolyn Perdue. *Medical Dir/Dir of Nursing* Debbie Rexroad.
Licensure Private. *Beds* Private 104. *Certified* .
Owner Privately owned.
Admissions Requirements Physician's request.
Staff RNs; LPNs; Orderlies; Nurses aides; Activities coordinators; Dietitians.
Facilities Dining room; Activities room; Crafts room; Laundry room; Barber/Beauty shop.
Activities Arts & crafts; Cards; Games; Reading groups; Prayer groups; Movies; Social/Cultural gatherings.

Southwest Mediplex*
1015 William Cannon Dr, Austin, TX, 78745
(512) 443-1640
Admin Lisa Wilson. *Medical Dir/Dir of Nursing* Dr Allen Sonstein.
Licensure Intermediate care. *Beds* 120.
Certified Medicaid.
Owner Proprietary Corp (Beverly Enterprises).
Admissions Requirements Medical examination; Physician's request.
Staff RNs 2 (ft), 3 (pt); LPNs 6 (ft), 1 (pt); Nurses aides 21 (ft), 6 (pt); Activities coordinators 1 (ft); Dietitians 1 (ft).
Facilities Dining room; Laundry room; Barber/Beauty shop.
Activities Arts & crafts; Cards; Games; Reading groups; Prayer groups; Movies; Shopping trips; Social/Cultural gatherings.

Francis Southwood Nursing Home Inc*
3759 Valley View Rd, Austin, TX, 78704
(512) 443-3436
Admin Irene G Richter.
Licensure Intermediate care. *Beds* 120.
Certified Medicaid.
Owner Proprietary Corp.

Stonebrook Nursing Home*
2806 Real St, Austin, TX, 78722
(512) 474-1411
Admin Linda Matlock.
Licensure Skilled care; Intermediate care. *Beds* 204. *Certified* Medicaid; Medicare.
Owner Proprietary Corp.

Walnut Hills Convalescent Center
3509 Rogge Ln, Austin, TX, 78723
(512) 926-2070
Admin Bobby Dockal. *Medical Dir/Dir of Nursing* Joyce Adams.
Licensure Intermediate care. *Beds* ICF 120.
Certified Medicaid.
Owner Proprietary Corp.
Facilities Dining room; Physical therapy room; Activities room; Chapel; Crafts room; Laundry room; Barber/Beauty shop.

Activities Arts & crafts; Cards; Games; Reading groups; Prayer groups; Movies; Movies; Shopping trips; Social/Cultural gatherings.

AZLE

Azle Manor Inc
225 Church St, Azle, TX, 76020
(817) 444-2536
Admin McKinley Wayne Pack. *Medical Dir/Dir of Nursing* Jim Savage MD.
Licensure Skilled care. *Beds* 127. *Certified* Medicaid.
Staff RNs 1 (ft), 2 (pt); Nurses aides 35 (ft), 7 (pt); Activities coordinators 1 (ft); Dietitians 1 (pt); Dentists 1 (pt); Ophthalmologists 1 (pt); LVNs 12 (ft), 5 (pt); Dentist 2 (pt).
Facilities Dining room; Activities room; Crafts room; Laundry room; Barber/Beauty shop.
Activities Arts & crafts; Cards; Games; Reading groups; Prayer groups; Movies; Shopping trips.

BAIRD

Canterbury Villa of Baird
240 E 6th St, Baird, TX, 79504
(915) 854-1307
Admin Monica A Hawes. *Medical Dir/Dir of Nursing* Thelma Spann.
Licensure Intermediate care. *Beds* ICF 78.
Certified Medicaid.
Owner Proprietary Corp (Texas Health Enterprises).
Admissions Requirements Minimum age 18; Medical examination; Physician's request.
Staff LPNs 7 (ft); Orderlies; Nurses aides; Activities coordinators; Dietitians 1 (ft).
Languages Spanish
Facilities Dining room; Activities room; Crafts room; Laundry room; Barber/Beauty shop.
Activities Arts & crafts; Cards; Games; Prayer groups; Shopping trips; Social/Cultural gatherings.

BALCH SPRINGS

Balch Springs Nursing Home
4200 Shepherd Ln, Balch Springs, TX, 75180
(214) 286-0335
Admin Merril M Grey. *Medical Dir/Dir of Nursing* Paul Schorr.
Licensure Intermediate care. *Beds* 120.
Certified Medicaid.
Owner Proprietary Corp (Beverly Enterprises).
Admissions Requirements Medical examination; Physician's request.
Staff RNs 1 (ft); LPNs 10 (ft), 3 (pt); Orderlies 1 (ft), 1 (pt); Nurses aides 22 (ft), 4 (pt); Activities coordinators 1 (ft); Dietitians 1 (ft).
Facilities Dining room; Activities room; Chapel; Crafts room; Laundry room; Barber/Beauty shop; Library.
Activities Arts & crafts; Cards; Games; Reading groups; Prayer groups; Movies; Shopping trips; Social/Cultural gatherings.

BALLINGER

Ballinger Manor
PO Box 309, Ballinger, TX, 76821
(915) 365-2538
Admin D W Sims. *Medical Dir/Dir of Nursing* Dr Antoine Albert.
Licensure Intermediate care. *Beds* 154.
Certified Medicaid.
Staff Physicians 4 (pt); LPNs 4 (ft), 2 (pt); Orderlies 1 (ft); Nurses aides 9 (ft), 7 (pt); Physical therapists 1 (pt); Activities coordinators 1 (ft); Dietitians 2 (ft).

Facilities Dining room; Physical therapy room; Activities room; Chapel; Crafts room; Laundry room; Barber/Beauty shop; Library.
Activities Arts & crafts; Cards; Games; Reading groups; Prayer groups; Movies; Shopping trips; Social/Cultural gatherings.

Ballinger Nursing Center*
PO Box 622, 1400 Country Club Ave, Ballinger, TX, 76821
(915) 365-2632
Admin Darlene McDaniel.
Licensure Intermediate care. *Beds* 48. *Certified* Medicaid.
Owner Proprietary Corp.

BANDERA

Purple Hills Manor Inc
PO Box 836, Montague Dr, Bandera, TX, 78003
(512) 796-3767
Admin Preston Gray. *Medical Dir/Dir of Nursing* Alice Warnecke LVN.
Licensure Intermediate care. *Beds* ICF 62. *Certified* Medicaid.
Owner Privately owned.
Staff LPNs 3 (ft); Nurses aides 18 (ft); Physical therapists 1 (ft); Recreational therapists 1 (ft); Activities coordinators 1 (ft); Dietitians 1 (ft).
Languages Spanish
Facilities Dining room; Activities room; Laundry room; Barber/Beauty shop.
Activities Cards; Games; Reading groups; Prayer groups; Social/Cultural gatherings; Music; BBQs; Exercise.

BANGS

Bangs Nursing Home
1400 Fitzgerald St, Bangs, TX, 76823
(915) 752-6321
Admin Glorris A Wolford. *Medical Dir/Dir of Nursing* Delores Daub.
Licensure Intermediate care. *Beds* ICF 48. *Certified* Medicaid.
Owner Proprietary Corp (ARA Living Centers).
Admissions Requirements Physician's request.
Staff LPNs 4 (ft); Orderlies 1 (ft), 1 (pt); Nurses aides 7 (ft), 4 (pt); Activities coordinators 1 (ft); Dietitians 3 (ft), 2 (pt).
Activities Arts & crafts; Cards; Games; Reading groups; Prayer groups; Shopping trips; Social/Cultural gatherings.

Twilight Nursing Home Inc*
205 S West St, Bangs, TX, 76823
(915) 752-6322
Admin Wendell H Byler.
Licensure Intermediate care. *Beds* 41. *Certified* Medicaid.
Owner Proprietary Corp.

BARTLETT

Will-O-Bell Inc*
412 N Dalton, Bartlett, TX, 76511
(817) 527-3371
Admin June D Fugate. *Medical Dir/Dir of Nursing* Ralph Clearman MD.
Licensure Intermediate care. *Beds* 60. *Certified* Medicaid.
Staff Physicians 2 (pt); RNs 1 (pt); LPNs 3 (ft), 2 (pt); Nurses aides 45 (ft); Activities coordinators 1 (ft); Dietitians 1 (pt).
Facilities Dining room; Activities room; Laundry room; Barber/Beauty shop.
Activities Arts & crafts; Cards; Games; Reading groups; Prayer groups; Movies; Shopping trips.

BASTROP

Bastrop Nursing Center
PO Box 649, 400 Old Austin Hwy, Bastrop, TX, 78602
(512) 321-2529
Admin Christopher C Bland. *Medical Dir/Dir of Nursing* Dr Talley; Anne Saegert.
Licensure Intermediate care. *Beds* ICF 96. *Certified* Medicaid.
Owner Proprietary Corp (ARA Living Centers).
Admissions Requirements Minimum age 18; Medical examination.
Staff RNs; LPNs; Orderlies; Nurses aides; Recreational therapists; Activities coordinators; Dietitians.
Facilities Dining room; Activities room; Chapel; Laundry room; Barber/Beauty shop.
Activities Arts & crafts; Cards; Games; Reading groups; Prayer groups; Movies; Shopping trips; Social/Cultural gatherings; Fishing trips.

BAY CITY

Bay Villa Nursing Center
1800 13th St, Bay City, TX, 77414
(409) 245-6327
Admin Polly Hedrick. *Medical Dir/Dir of Nursing* Dr H C Matthes; Geraldine Sprys RN.
Licensure Skilled care; Intermediate care. *Beds* SNF 47; ICF 58. *Certified* Medicaid; Medicare.
Owner Proprietary Corp (ARA Living Centers).
Admissions Requirements Medical examination; Physician's request.
Staff RNs 4 (ft); LPNs 11 (ft), 2 (pt); Orderlies 2 (ft), 1 (pt); Nurses aides 32 (ft), 3 (pt); Activities coordinators 1 (ft); Dietitians 1 (ft).
Languages Spanish
Facilities Dining room; Activities room; Laundry room; Barber/Beauty shop.
Activities Arts & crafts; Cards; Games; Reading groups; Prayer groups; Movies; Shopping trips; Social/Cultural gatherings.

Matagorda House
1115 Ave G, Bay City, TX, 77414
(409) 245-6383
Admin Pat Matthes. *Medical Dir/Dir of Nursing* H C Matthes MD; Louise Matthews RN DON.
Licensure Skilled care. *Beds* SNF 28. *Certified* Medicaid; Medicare.
Owner Nonprofit Corp.
Admissions Requirements Medical examination; Physician's request.
Staff RNs 2 (ft); LPNs 4 (ft), 2 (pt); Nurses aides 14 (ft); Activities coordinators 1 (ft); Dietitians 1 (pt); Dentists 1 (pt); Ophthalmologists 1 (pt); Podiatrists 1 (pt).
Languages Spanish
Facilities Dining room; Chapel; Barber/Beauty shop.
Activities Cards; Games; Reading groups; Prayer groups; All kinds of parties.

BAYTOWN

Allenbrook Healthcare Center
4109 Allenbrook Dr, Baytown, TX, 77521
(713) 422-3546
Admin Jack E Hogston. *Medical Dir/Dir of Nursing* Susan Beth Shaffer.
Licensure Intermediate care. *Beds* ICF 120. *Certified* Medicaid.
Owner Proprietary Corp (ARA Living Centers).
Admissions Requirements Medical examination.
Staff RNs 1 (ft); Nurses aides 23 (ft), 1 (pt); Activities coordinators 1 (ft); Dietitians 1 (ft).

Facilities Dining room; Activities room; Crafts room; Laundry room; Barber/Beauty shop; Whirlpool room (2).
Activities Arts & crafts; Cards; Games; Movies; Shopping trips.

Baytown Nursing Home*
1106 Park St, Baytown, TX, 77520
(713) 427-1644, 1421
Admin Edward R Garrett.
Licensure Intermediate care. *Beds* 90. *Certified* Medicaid.
Owner Proprietary Corp.

Green Acres Convalescent Center*
2000 Beaumont, Baytown, TX, 77520
(713) 427-4774
Admin Beverly Miller.
Licensure Intermediate care. *Beds* 100. *Certified* Medicaid.
Owner Proprietary Corp (ARA Living Centers).

St James House of Baytown
5800 Baker Rd, Baytown, TX, 77520
(713) 424-4541
Admin Elizabeth R Alexander. *Medical Dir/Dir of Nursing* Joy M Crow RN DON.
Licensure Intermediate care; Custodial care. *Beds* ICF 68; Custodial care 37. *Certified* Medicaid.
Owner Nonprofit Corp.
Admissions Requirements Minimum age 65; Medical examination.
Staff RNs 1 (ft); LPNs 9 (ft), 2 (pt); Nurses aides 15 (ft), 5 (pt); Activities coordinators 2 (ft); Dietitians 1 (ft); Physical activity aides 2 (ft).
Languages Spanish
Affiliation Episcopal
Facilities Dining room; Physical therapy room; Activities room; Chapel; Crafts room; Laundry room; Barber/Beauty shop; 3 Kitchens for residents; Gift shop; Chaplains office; Small sitting rooms.
Activities Arts & crafts; Cards; Games; Reading groups; Prayer groups; Movies; Shopping trips; Social/Cultural gatherings; Happy hour; Overnight & day trips.

BEAUMONT

Adaptive Living Center—Southeast Texas*
3755 Corley St, Beaumont, TX, 77701
(713) 842-5900
Admin Martha Kirkpatrick.
Licensure Intermediate care for mentally retarded. *Beds* 130. *Certified* Medicaid.

Centerbury Villa—Beaumont*
1175 Denton Dr, Beaumont, TX, 77704
(713) 842-3120
Admin Margie Anders. *Medical Dir/Dir of Nursing* Dr J S Douglas.
Licensure Intermediate care. *Beds* 122. *Certified* Medicaid.
Owner Proprietary Corp (Health Enter of America).
Staff Physicians 1 (pt); RNs 1 (ft); LPNs 8 (ft), 1 (pt); Nurses aides 16 (ft), 2 (pt); Activities coordinators 1 (ft); Dietitians 1 (ft), 1 (pt); Podiatrists 1 (pt).
Facilities Dining room; Activities room; Crafts room; Laundry room; Barber/Beauty shop.
Activities Arts & crafts; Cards; Games; Reading groups; Prayer groups; Movies; Shopping trips; Social/Cultural gatherings.

College Street Nursing Center*
4150 College Ave, Beaumont, TX, 77707
(713) 842-0333
Admin Kaye Vaden.
Licensure Intermediate care. *Beds* 80. *Certified* Medicaid.
Owner Proprietary Corp.

Glad Day Nursing Center*
795 Lindberg Dr, Beaumont, TX, 77707
(713) 842-0311
Admin Maggie E Davis.
Licensure Skilled care; Intermediate care. *Beds*
84. *Certified* Medicaid.
Facilities Dining room; Physical therapy
room; Chapel; Crafts room.
Activities Arts & crafts; Cards; Games;
Reading groups; Prayer groups; Movies;
Shopping trips; Social/Cultural gatherings.

Green Acres Convalescent Center—Parkdale*
11025 Old Voth Rd, Beaumont, TX, 77708
(713) 892-9722
Admin Ruby L Marrero.
Licensure Intermediate care. *Beds* 150.
Certified Medicaid.
Owner Proprietary Corp (ARA Living
Centers).

Hamilton Nursing Home Inc
2660 Brickyard Rd, Beaumont, TX, 77703
(409) 892-1533
Admin Martha Kirkpatrick. *Medical Dir/Dir
of Nursing* June Shell DON.
Licensure Intermediate care. *Beds* ICF 121.
Certified Medicaid.
Owner Proprietary Corp.
Admissions Requirements Minimum age 18;
Medical examination; Physician's request.
Staff Nurses aides 47 (ft), 9 (pt); Activities
coordinators 2 (ft); Dietitians 1 (ft); LVNs
11 (ft), 2 (pt).
Facilities Dining room; Activities room;
Laundry room; Barber/Beauty shop.
Activities Arts & crafts; Cards; Games;
Reading groups; Music; Church services;
Western band; Gospel quartet.

Sabine Oaks Home
1945 Pennsylvania Ave, Beaumont, TX,
77701
(713) 833-1989
Admin Rose M Stinnett. *Medical Dir/Dir of
Nursing* Dorothy Bryan.
Licensure Custodial care. *Beds* 40. *Certified*
Medicaid.
Owner Nonprofit Corp.
Admissions Requirements Minimum age 60;
Medical examination.
Staff RNs 1 (pt); LPNs 1 (ft), 3 (pt); Nurses
aides 8 (ft), 2 (pt); Activities coordinators 1
(ft); Dietitians 1 (ft).
Languages French
Facilities Dining room; Activities room;
Chapel; Laundry room; Barber/Beauty shop.
Activities Arts & crafts; Cards; Games;
Reading groups; Prayer groups; Movies;
Social/Cultural gatherings; Exercise; Service
projects; Quizzes.

A W Schlesinger Geriatric Center
PO Box 1990, 4195 Milan, Beaumont, TX,
77707
(409) 842-4550
Admin Emma Jo Smith. *Medical Dir/Dir of
Nursing* Nicolas Rodriguez MD; Shirley
Dingle RN.
Licensure Skilled care; Intermediate care. *Beds*
412. *Certified* Medicaid; Medicare.
Owner Nonprofit organization/foundation.
Admissions Requirements Minimum age 18;
Medical examination; Physician's request.
Staff RNs 5 (ft), 3 (pt); LPNs 34 (ft); Nurses
aides; Physical therapists 2 (pt);
Occupational therapists 1 (pt); Speech
therapists 1 (pt); Activities coordinators 1
(ft); Dietitians 1 (ft).
Facilities Dining room; Physical therapy
room; Activities room; Chapel; Crafts room;
Laundry room; Barber/Beauty shop; Library.
Activities Arts & crafts; Cards; Games;
Reading groups; Prayer groups; Movies;
Shopping trips; Social/Cultural gatherings;
Bingo.

BEDFORD

La Dora Lodge Nursing Home
1960 Bedford Rd, Bedford, TX, 76021
(817) 283-4771
Admin Mary T Uebelhart. *Medical Dir/Dir of
Nursing* Berradine Lupa.
Licensure Intermediate care. *Beds* ICF 66.
Owner Proprietary Corp.
Admissions Requirements Medical
examination.
Staff RNs 1 (ft); LPNs 5 (ft); Nurses aides 15
(ft); Activities coordinators 1 (ft); Dietitians
1 (ft).
Facilities Dining room; Activities room;
Crafts room; Laundry room; Barber/Beauty
shop.
Activities Arts & crafts; Cards; Games;
Reading groups; Prayer groups; Movies;
Shopping trips; Social/Cultural gatherings.

Stanford Convalescent Center—Bedford*
2716 Tibbets Dr, Bedford, TX, 76021
(817) 283-5511
Admin Sandra Hale.
Licensure Skilled care; Intermediate care. *Beds*
160. *Certified* Medicaid.
Owner Proprietary Corp (Beverly Enterprises).

BEEVILLE

Hillside Lodge Nursing Home
600 Hillside Dr, Beeville, TX, 78102
(512) 358-8880
Admin Judith Martin. *Medical Dir/Dir of
Nursing* J L Reagan MD; Shirley R Jefferson
RN DON.
Licensure Intermediate care. *Beds* 120.
Certified Medicaid.
Owner Proprietary Corp (Diversicare Corp).
Admissions Requirements Physician's request.
Staff Physicians; RNs; LPNs; Orderlies;
Nurses aides; Physical therapists; Activities
coordinators; Dietitians; Dentists;
Ophthalmologists.
Languages Spanish
Facilities Dining room; Physical therapy
room; Activities room; Laundry room;
Barber/Beauty shop.
Activities Arts & crafts; Games; Prayer groups;
Movies; Shopping trips; Social/Cultural
gatherings.

Meridian Nursing Center—Beeville
4901 N St Marys, Beeville, TX, 78102
(512) 358-5612
Admin William L Phelps Jr. *Medical Dir/Dir
of Nursing* Tom Reagan MD.
Licensure Skilled care; Intermediate care. *Beds*
SNF 50; ICF 50. *Certified* Medicaid.
Staff Physicians 1 (pt); RNs 3 (ft), 1 (pt);
LPNs 3 (ft), 6 (pt); Nurses aides 26 (ft), 10
(pt); Physical therapists 1 (pt); Reality
therapists 1 (pt); Speech therapists 1 (pt);
Activities coordinators 1 (ft); Dietitians 1
(pt); Dentists 1 (pt); Podiatrists 1 (pt).

BELLVILLE

Colonial Belle Nursing Home*
104 N Baron St, Bellville, TX, 77418
(713) 865-3689
Medical Dir/Dir of Nursing J B Harle MD.
Licensure Skilled care. *Beds* 73. *Certified*
Medicaid.
Admissions Requirements Medical
examination; Physician's request.
Staff Physicians 4 (ft); RNs 2 (ft), 1 (pt);
LPNs 9 (ft); Orderlies 4 (ft); Physical
therapists 1 (pt); Recreational therapists 1
(pt); Activities coordinators 1 (pt); Dietitians
1 (pt); Dentists 1 (pt); Ophthalmologists 1
(pt); Podiatrists 1 (pt).
Facilities Dining room; Physical therapy
room; Activities room; Chapel; Laundry
room; Barber/Beauty shop; Library.

Activities Arts & crafts; Cards; Games;
Reading groups; Prayer groups; Movies;
Shopping trips; Social/Cultural gatherings.

Sweetbriar Nursing Home
PO Box 638, Hwy 36 N, Bellville, TX, 77418
(409) 865-5144
Admin Lucile Kiemsteadt. *Medical Dir/Dir of
Nursing* Katie Woods.
Licensure Intermediate care. *Beds* ICF 170.
Certified Medicaid.
Owner Privately owned.
Admissions Requirements Physician's request.
Staff LPNs; Nurses aides; Activities
coordinators.
Languages German, Czech
Facilities Dining room; Activities room;
Laundry room; Barber/Beauty shop.
Activities Arts & crafts; Games; Reading
groups; Prayer groups; Movies; Social/
Cultural gatherings; Square dancing.

BELTON

Crestview Manor Nursing Center*
1103 Mary Jane St, Belton, TX, 76513
(817) 939-9327
Admin Bettye H Evans. *Medical Dir/Dir of
Nursing* William B Long MD.
Licensure Skilled care; Intermediate care. *Beds*
91. *Certified* Medicaid.
Owner Proprietary Corp (Beverly Enterprises).
Admissions Requirements Minimum age 18;
Medical examination; Physician's request.
Staff RNs 1 (ft), 1 (pt); LPNs 10 (ft); Nurses
aides 40 (ft); Activities coordinators 1 (ft).
Facilities Dining room; Activities room;
Laundry room; Barber/Beauty shop; Living
room.
Activities Arts & crafts; Cards; Games;
Reading groups; Prayer groups; Movies;
Shopping trips; Social/Cultural gatherings.

BENBROOK

Benbrook Sweetbriar Nursing Home*
1000 McKinley St, Benbrook, TX, 76126
(817) 249-0020
Admin Alma B Schumacher. *Medical Dir/Dir
of Nursing* Dr James T Hawa.
Licensure Intermediate care. *Beds* 133.
Certified Medicaid.
Staff Physicians 1 (ft); RNs 1 (ft), 1 (pt);
LPNs 8 (ft); Orderlies 5 (ft); Nurses aides 21
(ft); Physical therapists 1 (pt); Speech
therapists 1 (pt); Activities coordinators 1
(ft); Dietitians 2 (pt); Dentists 1 (pt);
Podiatrists 1 (pt).
Facilities Dining room; Physical therapy
room; Activities room; Chapel; Crafts room;
Laundry room; Barber/Beauty shop; Library.
Activities Arts & crafts; Cards; Games;
Reading groups; Prayer groups; Movies;
Shopping trips; Social/Cultural gatherings.

BERTRAM

Bertram Nursing Home*
Hwy 29, Box 209, Bertram, TX, 78605
(512) 355-2116
Admin Dixie Ann Westen. *Medical Dir/Dir of
Nursing* H James Wall MD.
Licensure Intermediate care. *Beds* 32.
Certified Medicaid.
Owner Nonprofit Corp.
Admissions Requirements Medical
examination; Physician's request.
Staff Physicians 1 (pt); RNs 1 (pt); LPNs 6
(pt); Nurses aides 11 (ft), 6 (pt); Reality
therapists 1 (pt); Recreational therapists 1
(pt); Occupational therapists 1 (pt); Speech
therapists 1 (pt); Activities coordinators 1
(ft); Dietitians 1 (pt).

Facilities Dining room; Activities room; Laundry room; Barber/Beauty shop.
Activities Arts & crafts; Cards; Games; Reading groups; Movies; Shopping trips; Parties; Church; Sing-alongs; Recreational outings.

BIG SPRING

Mountain View Lodge Inc*
2009 Virginia, Big Spring, TX, 79720
(915) 263-1271
Admin Billy M Hendrix.
Licensure Intermediate care. *Beds* 92.
  Certified Medicaid.
Owner Proprietary Corp.

United Health Care Center*
901 Goliad St, Big Spring, TX, 79720
(915) 263-7633
Admin Raymond Junker.
Licensure Intermediate care. *Beds* 200.
  Certified Medicaid.
Owner Proprietary Corp.

BLANCO

Blanco Health Care Center
PO Box 327, 3rd & Elm St, Blanco, TX, 78606
(512) 833-4710
Admin Sophie A Johnson. *Medical Dir/Dir of Nursing* Dorothy Wright.
Licensure Intermediate care. *Beds* ICF 42; Personal care 20. *Certified* Medicaid.
Owner Proprietary Corp.
Admissions Requirements Medical examination; Physician's request.
Staff RNs 1 (pt); Orderlies 2 (ft); Nurses aides 12 (ft); Activities coordinators 1 (ft); LVNs 2 (ft), 2 (pt).
Activities Arts & crafts; Cards; Games; Reading groups; Prayer groups; Movies; Shopping trips; Social/Cultural gatherings.

Live Oak Medical Center
PO Box 356, 300 E 7th, Blanco, TX, 78606
(512) 833-4567
Admin Mary F Toms. *Medical Dir/Dir of Nursing* Mary Evans.
Licensure Intermediate care. *Beds* ICF 64.
  Certified Medicaid.
Owner Proprietary Corp.
Admissions Requirements Medical examination; Physician's request.
Staff RNs 1 (ft); LPNs 4 (ft); Orderlies 1 (ft); Nurses aides 15 (ft); Physical therapists 1 (ft); Recreational therapists 1 (ft); Activities coordinators 2 (ft); Dietitians 1 (ft).
Facilities Dining room; Activities room; Crafts room; Laundry room.
Activities Arts & crafts; Cards; Games; Reading groups; Prayer groups; Movies; Shopping trips.

BOERNE

Hill Top Nursing Home*
200 Ryan St, Boerne, TX, 78006
(512) 249-2594
Admin Betty Buel Price.
Licensure Intermediate care. *Beds* 72.
  Certified Medicaid.

Town & Country Manor Inc*
625 N Main, Boerne, TX, 78006
(512) 249-3085
Admin Lois F Wertheim.
Licensure Intermediate care. *Beds* 131.
  Certified Medicaid.
Owner Proprietary Corp (Summit Health Ltd).

BOGATA

Red River Haven Nursing Home Inc*
319 Paris Rd, Bogata, TX, 75417
(214) 632-5756
Admin Bobbie Lee Cawley.
Licensure Intermediate care. *Beds* 154.
  Certified Medicaid.
Owner Proprietary Corp (Beverly Enterprises).

BONHAM

Bonham Nursing Center*
709 W 5th St, Bonham, TX, 75418
(214) 583-8551
Admin Juanita Awbrey.
Licensure Intermediate care. *Beds* 65.
  Certified Medicaid.
Owner Proprietary Corp (ARA Living Centers).
Admissions Requirements Physician's request.
Staff LPNs 8 (ft); Nurses aides 10 (ft); Activities coordinators 1 (ft); Dietitians 3 (ft), 2 (pt).
Facilities Dining room; Activities room; Crafts room; Laundry room; Barber/Beauty shop.
Activities Arts & crafts; Cards; Games; Reading groups; Prayer groups; Movies; Shopping trips; Social/Cultural gatherings; Exercise; Field trips.

Fairview Nursing Home
1500 Kennedy St, Bonham, TX, 75418
(214) 583-2148
Admin Helen E Moser. *Medical Dir/Dir of Nursing* Dr W Sisk Medical Director; Claire Skotnik RN DON.
Licensure Intermediate care; VA Contract. *Beds* ICF 103. *Certified* Medicaid.
Owner Proprietary Corp (ARA Living Centers).
Admissions Requirements Minimum age 45; Medical examination; Physician's request.
Staff RNs 1 (ft); LPNs 3 (ft), 2 (pt); Nurses aides 9 (ft), 2 (pt); Activities coordinators 1 (ft); Dietitians 1 (pt).
Facilities Dining room; Activities room; Crafts room; Laundry room; Barber/Beauty shop.
Activities Arts & crafts; Cards; Games; Reading groups; Prayer groups; Movies; Shopping trips; Social/Cultural gatherings.

Seven Oaks Convalescent Care Center
901 Seven Oaks Rd, Bonham, TX, 75020
(214) 583-2191
Admin K Ann Duckworth. *Medical Dir/Dir of Nursing* Hope Grantland.
Licensure Intermediate care. *Beds* 108.
  Certified Medicaid.
Owner Proprietary Corp (Health Enter of America).
Admissions Requirements Physician's request.
Staff RNs 1 (ft); LPNs 9 (ft); Nurses aides 36 (ft), 3 (pt); Activities coordinators 1 (ft); Dietitians 1 (pt); Ophthalmologists 1 (pt); Podiatrists 1 (pt).
Languages Spanish
Facilities Dining room; Laundry room; Barber/Beauty shop; Library.
Activities Arts & crafts; Cards; Games; Reading groups; Prayer groups; Movies; Shopping trips; Social/Cultural gatherings.

BORGER

Borger Nursing Center
1316 S Florida, Borger, TX, 79007
(806) 273-3785
Admin Dorothy Blumer. *Medical Dir/Dir of Nursing* A L Sherer MD; Elaine Cleek DON.
Licensure Intermediate care. *Beds* 120.
Owner Proprietary Corp (Beverly Enterprises).
Staff LPNs 8 (ft); Orderlies 2 (ft); Nurses aides 24 (ft), 2 (pt); Activities coordinators 1 (ft); Dietitians 1 (ft).

Languages Sign
Facilities Dining room; Laundry room; Barber/Beauty shop.
Activities Arts & crafts; Games; Reading groups; Prayer groups; Movies; Social/Cultural gatherings.

Magic Star Nursing Home
PO Box 409, 200 Tyler St, Borger, TX, 79007
(806) 273-3725
Admin Don F York. *Medical Dir/Dir of Nursing* Georgia Siebert.
Licensure Intermediate care. *Beds* ICF 49.
  Certified Medicaid.
Owner Proprietary Corp.
Admissions Requirements Minimum age 18; Medical examination; Physician's request.
Staff RNs 1 (pt); LPNs 2 (ft), 3 (pt); Nurses aides 10 (ft), 5 (pt); Activities coordinators 1 (ft); Dietitians 1 (pt).
Languages Spanish, German
Facilities Dining room; Activities room; Crafts room; Laundry room.
Activities Arts & crafts; Cards; Games; Reading groups; Prayer groups; Movies; Shopping trips; Social/Cultural gatherings.

BOWIE

Bellmire Home Inc*
PO Box 1227, 1101 Rock St, Bowie, TX, 76230
(817) 872-2283
Admin Mary H Duvall.
Licensure Intermediate care. *Beds* 201.
  Certified Medicaid.
Owner Proprietary Corp.

Bowie Convalescing Home*
601 Central Ave, Bowie, TX, 76230
(817) 872-1231
Admin Carol S Brewer.
Licensure Intermediate care. *Beds* 95.
  Certified Medicaid.
Owner Proprietary Corp.

BRADY

Leisure Lodge of Brady
PO Box 551, Menard Hwy, Brady, TX, 76825
(915) 597-2906
Admin Stephen M Goode. *Medical Dir/Dir of Nursing* Dr McCullough; Carol Brawner.
Licensure Intermediate care. *Beds* ICF 110.
  Certified Medicaid.
Owner Proprietary Corp (Beverly Enterprises).
Admissions Requirements Physician's request.
Staff Physicians 4 (ft), 1 (pt); LPNs 7 (ft); Nurses aides 16 (ft); Activities coordinators 1 (ft); Dietitians 1 (pt).
Languages Spanish
Facilities Dining room; Barber/Beauty shop.
Activities Arts & crafts; Cards; Games; Prayer groups; Movies; Shopping trips; Picnics; Outings.

Shuffield Nursing Home Inc 1
PO Box 349, 1605 S Bradley, Brady, TX, 76825
(915) 597-2916
Admin Eugene E Frost. *Medical Dir/Dir of Nursing* Pam Wilkinson RN.
Licensure Intermediate care. *Beds* ICF 67.
  Certified Medicaid.
Owner Proprietary Corp.
Admissions Requirements Minimum age 18; Medical examination; Physician's request.
Staff RNs 1 (ft); LPNs 5 (ft), 2 (pt); Orderlies 1 (pt); Nurses aides 25 (ft), 5 (pt); Activities coordinators 1 (ft); Dietitians 1 (pt).
Languages Spanish
Facilities Dining room; Physical therapy room; Activities room; Crafts room; Laundry room; Barber/Beauty shop.
Activities Arts & crafts; Cards; Games; Reading groups; Prayer groups; Movies; Shopping trips; Social/Cultural gatherings.

Shuffield Rest Home Inc No 2
PO Box 990, US Hwy 87 S, Brady, TX, 76825
(915) 597-2947
Admin Patsy E Lohn. *Medical Dir/Dir of Nursing* Ellen Johnson RN.
Licensure Intermediate care. *Beds* ICF 60. *Certified* Medicaid.
Owner Proprietary Corp.
Admissions Requirements Medical examination; Physician's request.
Staff RNs; LPNs; Nurses aides; Activities coordinators.
Facilities Dining room; Activities room; Chapel; Crafts room; Laundry room; Barber/Beauty shop.
Activities Arts & crafts; Cards; Games; Reading groups; Prayer groups; Movies; Shopping trips; Social/Cultural gatherings.

BRECKENRIDGE

Town Hall Estates*
1900 W Elliott, Breckenridge, TX, 76024
(817) 559-3303
Admin Kenneth V Campbell.
Licensure Intermediate care. *Beds* 72. *Certified* Medicaid.
Owner Nonprofit Corp.

Villa Haven*
300 S Jackson, Breckenridge, TX, 76024
(817) 559-3386
Admin Marjorie A Duncan.
Licensure Intermediate care. *Beds* 92. *Certified* Medicaid.
Owner Proprietary Corp (Unicare).
Staff RNs 2 (pt); LPNs 6 (ft), 3 (pt); Activities coordinators 1 (ft); Dietitians 1 (pt).
Facilities Dining room; Activities room; Crafts room; Laundry room; Barber/Beauty shop.
Activities Arts & crafts; Cards; Games; Reading groups; Prayer groups; Movies; Shopping trips; Social/Cultural gatherings.

BREMOND

Bremond Nursing Center
PO Box 520, 200 N Main St, Bremond, TX, 76629
(817) 746-7666
Admin Holis U McGee. *Medical Dir/Dir of Nursing* Dr Dan Saylak.
Licensure Intermediate care. *Beds* ICF 82. *Certified* Medicaid.
Owner Proprietary Corp (Unicare).
Staff Physicians 2 (pt); RNs 1 (pt); LPNs 4 (ft), 3 (pt); Nurses aides 28 (ft), 5 (pt); Activities coordinators 1 (ft); Dietitians 1 (pt); Dentist 1 (pt).
Facilities Dining room; Physical therapy room; Activities room; Chapel; Crafts room; Laundry room; Barber/Beauty shop; Library.
Activities Arts & crafts; Games; Reading groups; Prayer groups; Movies; Shopping trips; Social/Cultural gatherings.

BRENHAM

Brenham Rest Home Inc*
406 Cottonwood St, Brenham, TX, 77833
(409) 836-3434
Admin H S Hughes.
Licensure Intermediate care. *Beds* 108. *Certified* Medicaid.
Admissions Requirements Medical examination; Physician's request.
Staff RNs 1 (ft), 1 (pt); LPNs 7 (ft); Nurses aides 28 (ft), 12 (pt); Activities coordinators 1 (ft), 1 (pt).
Facilities Dining room; Activities room; Crafts room; Laundry room.
Activities Arts & crafts; Cards; Games; Reading groups; Prayer groups; Movies; Social/Cultural gatherings.

Sweetbriar Nursing Home
401 E Horton St, Brenham, TX, 77833
(409) 836-6611
Admin Betty C Fife. *Medical Dir/Dir of Nursing* W F Hasskarl Jr MD ; Dolores Kocurek.
Licensure Skilled care; Intermediate care. *Beds* 265. *Certified* Medicaid; Medicare.
Owner Privately owned.
Admissions Requirements Minimum age 21.
Staff Physicians 1 (ft), 233 (pt); RNs 5 (ft); LPNs 27 (ft); Orderlies 1 (ft); Nurses aides 113 (ft), 233 (pt); Activities coordinators 3 (ft).
Languages German, Spanish
Facilities Dining room; Activities room; Laundry room; Barber/Beauty shop.
Activities Arts & crafts; Cards; Games; Prayer groups; Movies; Shopping trips; Social/Cultural gatherings.

BRIDGE CITY

Green Acres Convalescent & Development Center
PO Box 606, 625 Meadowlawn, Bridge City, TX, 77611
(409) 735-3528
Admin James E Trussell Jr. *Medical Dir/Dir of Nursing* Dr Joseph Vadas; Joan Adams LVN DON.
Licensure Intermediate care; Intermediate care for mentally retarded. *Beds* ICF 106; ICF/MR 40. *Certified* Medicaid.
Owner Proprietary Corp (ARA Living Centers).
Admissions Requirements Minimum age 22; Medical examination.
Staff Physicians 11 (pt); LPNs 11 (ft); Orderlies 3 (ft); Nurses aides 38 (ft); Physical therapists 1 (ft); Recreational therapists 1 (ft); Occupational therapists 1 (pt); Speech therapists 1 (pt); Activities coordinators 1 (ft); Dietitians 1 (pt); Dentists 1 (pt); Ophthalmologists 1 (pt); Podiatrists 1 (pt); Psychologist 1 (pt).
Facilities Dining room; Activities room; Chapel; Crafts room; Laundry room; Barber/Beauty shop.
Activities Arts & crafts; Cards; Games; Movies; Shopping trips; Social/Cultural gatherings.

BRIDGEPORT

Golden Years Retreat*
1st at Cates, Bridgeport, TX, 76026
(817) 683-4615
Admin Maxine Smith.
Licensure Intermediate care. *Beds* 98. *Certified* Medicaid.
Owner Proprietary Corp.

BRONTE

Bronte Nursing Home*
900 State St, Bronte, TX, 76933
(915) 473-3621
Admin Joy F Bagwell. *Medical Dir/Dir of Nursing* Lloyd L Downing MD.
Licensure Intermediate care. *Beds* 40. *Certified* Medicaid.
Admissions Requirements Minimum age 18; Medical examination; Physician's request.
Staff LPNs 3 (ft), 3 (pt); Nurses aides 14 (ft), 2 (pt); Activities coordinators 1 (ft).
Facilities Dining room; Activities room; Crafts room; Laundry room; Barber/Beauty shop; Library.
Activities Arts & crafts; Cards; Games; Reading groups; Prayer groups; Shopping trips; Social/Cultural gatherings.

BROOKSHIRE

Brookshire Arms Inc*
Hwy 359, Brookshire, TX, 77423
(713) 934-2224
Admin Marvin E Cole. *Medical Dir/Dir of Nursing* Gail Bernhausen MD.
Licensure Intermediate care. *Beds* 134. *Certified* Medicaid.
Admissions Requirements Medical examination; Physician's request.
Staff RNs 2 (ft); LPNs 9 (ft); Orderlies 6 (ft); Nurses aides 28 (ft), 7 (pt); Activities coordinators 2 (ft); Dietitians 1 (ft); 27 (ft).
Facilities Dining room; Activities room; Chapel; Laundry room.
Activities Arts & crafts; Cards; Games; Shopping trips.

BROWNFIELD

Brownfield Nursing Home*
510 S 1st St, Brownfield, TX, 79316
(806) 637-4307, 4626
Admin Denton O'Dell Bates.
Licensure Intermediate care. *Beds* 54. *Certified* Medicaid.
Owner Proprietary Corp.

South Plains Memorial Home*
1101 E Lake St, Brownfield, TX, 79316
(806) 637-7561
Admin Julia Merrill.
Licensure Intermediate care. *Beds* 116. *Certified* Medicaid.
Owner Proprietary Corp (Beverly Enterprises).

BROWNSVILLE

Brownsville Good Samaritan Center*
510 Parades Line Rd, Brownsville, TX, 78520
(512) 546-5358
Admin Cletus M Solar. *Medical Dir/Dir of Nursing* Marcos Reis.
Licensure Skilled care; Intermediate care. *Beds* 112. *Certified* Medicaid.
Owner Nonprofit Corp (Evangelical Lutheran/Good Samaritan).
Admissions Requirements Physician's request.
Staff RNs; LPNs; Orderlies; Nurses aides; Physical therapists; Reality therapists; Recreational therapists; Activities coordinators; Dietitians.
Facilities Dining room; Physical therapy room; Activities room; Crafts room; Laundry room; Barber/Beauty shop; Library.
Activities Arts & crafts; Cards; Games; Prayer groups; Movies; Shopping trips; Social/Cultural gatherings.

Mother of Perpetual Help Home*
519 E Madison at 6th, Brownsville, TX, 78520
(512) 546-6745
Admin Mary P Collins.
Licensure Intermediate care. *Beds* 37. *Certified* Medicaid.

Retama Manor Nursing Center*
1415 W Washington, Brownsville, TX, 78520
(512) 546-3711
Admin Dalona Riggs Murphy.
Licensure Intermediate care; Intermediate care for mentally retarded. *Beds* ICF 91; ICF/MR 74. *Certified* Medicaid.
Owner Proprietary Corp (ARA Living Centers).

Valley Grande Manor Inc
901 Wild Rose Ln, Brownsville, TX, 78520
(512) 546-4568
Admin Ruben Mohan Raj Moses. *Medical Dir/Dir of Nursing* Gustavo F Stern.
Licensure Skilled care; Intermediate care. *Beds* SNF 121; ICF 59. *Certified* Medicaid; Medicare.

Admissions Requirements Medical
examination; Physician's request.
Staff RNs 3 (ft), 2 (pt); LPNs 20 (ft), 4 (pt);
Orderlies 11 (ft), 2 (pt); Nurses aides 52 (ft),
3 (pt); Physical therapists 1 (pt); Activities
coordinators 2 (ft).
Languages Spanish
Affiliation Seventh-Day Adventist
Facilities Dining room; Physical therapy
room; Activities room; Chapel; Crafts room;
Laundry room; Barber/Beauty shop; Library.
Activities Arts & crafts; Cards; Games;
Reading groups; Prayer groups; Movies;
Shopping trips; Social/Cultural gatherings;
Zoo trips; Beach trips.

BROWNWOOD

Brownwood Care Center*
101 Miller Dr, Brownwood, TX, 76801
(915) 643-1596
Admin Betty F Turner.
Licensure Intermediate care. *Beds* 130.
Certified Medicaid.
Owner Proprietary Corp (Manor Care).
Admissions Requirements Minimum age 18;
Medical examination; Physician's request.
Staff RNs 1 (ft); LPNs 15 (ft); Nurses aides 40
(ft), 5 (pt); Physical therapists 5 (pt);
Activities coordinators 1 (ft); Dietitians 1
(ft).
Facilities Dining room; Activities room;
Chapel; Crafts room; Laundry room; Barber/
Beauty shop; TV room.
Activities Arts & crafts; Cards; Games; Prayer
groups; Movies; Shopping trips; Social/
Cultural gatherings; Bingo; Dominoes;
Happy hour.

C.A.R.E., Inc Nursing Center
PO Box 6-A, Star Rte 3, Brownwood, TX,
76801
(915) 646-5521
Admin Jerry D McGuffey. *Medical Dir/Dir of
Nursing* Dr Fred Spencer; Margaret
Copeland RN DON.
Licensure Skilled care; Intermediate care. *Beds*
SNF 21; ICF 76. *Certified* Medicaid.
Owner Proprietary Corp.
Admissions Requirements Minimum age 16;
Medical examination; Physician's request.
Staff Physicians 1 (ft), 1 (pt); RNs 1 (ft), 1 (pt);
LPNs 9 (ft), 5 (pt); Orderlies 1 (ft), 1 (pt);
Nurses aides 25 (ft), 5 (pt); Activities
coordinators 1 (ft); Dietitians 1 (ft).
Languages Spanish
Facilities Dining room; Physical therapy
room; Activities room; Chapel; Crafts room;
Barber/Beauty shop; Library; Hydro therapy.
Activities Arts & crafts; Cards; Games;
Reading groups; Prayer groups; Movies;
Shopping trips; Social/Cultural gatherings.

Cross Country Care Center
1514 Indian Creek Rd, Brownwood, TX,
76801
(915) 646-6529
Admin Pamela Minich. *Medical Dir/Dir of
Nursing* Gary Butka MD; Gladys Camp
DON.
Licensure Intermediate care. *Beds* 146.
Certified Medicaid.
Owner Proprietary Corp (Beverly Enterprises).
Admissions Requirements Medical
examination; Physician's request.
Staff RNs 1 (ft); LPNs 10 (ft); Orderlies 5 (ft);
Nurses aides 30 (ft); Activities coordinators
1 (ft).
Facilities Dining room; Activities room;
Chapel; Crafts room; Laundry room; Barber/
Beauty shop.
Activities Arts & crafts; Cards; Games;
Reading groups; Prayer groups; Movies;
Shopping trips; Social/Cultural gatherings.

Plantation Nursing Home*
405 W Anderson, Brownwood, TX, 76801
(915) 643-3606

Admin Patrick H McLaughlin III.
Licensure Intermediate care. *Beds* 46.
Certified Medicaid.
Staff LPNs 3 (ft); Nurses aides 12 (ft), 3 (pt);
Activities coordinators 1 (ft).
Facilities Dining room; Laundry room.
Activities Arts & crafts; Cards; Games;
Movies; Social/Cultural gatherings.

South Park Development Center*
Morris-Sheppard Dr, Brownwood, TX, 76801
(915) 646-9531
Admin Ann Daniel.
Licensure Intermediate care for mentally
retarded. *Beds* 108. *Certified* Medicaid.
Admissions Requirements Minimum age 18.
Staff RNs 1 (ft); LPNs 5 (ft); Orderlies 25 (ft);
Physical therapists 1 (pt); Reality therapists
1 (ft); Recreational therapists 1 (ft);
Occupational therapists 1 (pt); Speech
therapists 1 (pt); Activities coordinators 1
(ft); Dietitians 1 (pt); Dentists 1 (pt);
Ophthalmologists 1 (pt); Podiatrists 1 (pt);
Audiologists 1 (pt).
Facilities Dining room; Physical therapy
room; Activities room; Crafts room; Laundry
room.
Activities Arts & crafts; Cards; Games;
Reading groups; Movies; Shopping trips;
Social/Cultural gatherings.

BRYAN

Crestview Methodist Retirement Community
2501 Villa Maria Rd, Bryan, TX, 77805
(409) 776-4778
Admin Rhonda M Morales. *Medical Dir/Dir
of Nursing* Madeline Klintworth RN.
Licensure Intermediate care; Independent
living. *Beds* ICF 57; Independent living
units 182. *Certified* Medicaid.
Owner Nonprofit Corp.
Admissions Requirements Minimum age 62;
Medical examination; Physician's request.
Staff RNs 1 (ft), 1 (pt); LPNs 6 (ft), 8 (pt);
Nurses aides 8 (ft), 6 (pt); Activities
coordinators 2 (ft); Dietitians 1 (ft).
Affiliation Methodist
Facilities Dining room; Physical therapy
room; Activities room; Chapel; Crafts room;
Laundry room; Barber/Beauty shop; Library.
Activities Arts & crafts; Cards; Games;
Reading groups; Prayer groups; Movies;
Shopping trips; Social/Cultural gatherings.

Leisure Lodge Bryan*
2001 E 29th St, Bryan, TX, 77801
(713) 822-7361
Admin Loretta Henk.
Licensure Intermediate care. *Beds* 150.
Certified Medicaid.
Owner Proprietary Corp (Beverly Enterprises).
Facilities Dining room; Physical therapy
room; Laundry room; Barber/Beauty shop.
Activities Arts & crafts; Cards; Games;
Reading groups; Prayer groups; Shopping
trips; Social/Cultural gatherings.

Sherwood Health Care Inc
1401 Memorial Dr, Bryan, TX, 77801
(409) 776-7521
Admin Edwin P Sulik. *Medical Dir/Dir of
Nursing* Council Mills MD.
Licensure Skilled care; Intermediate care. *Beds*
246. *Certified* Medicaid; Medicare.
Staff RNs 5 (pt); LPNs 24 (pt); Nurses aides
78 (pt); Physical therapists 2 (pt); Activities
coordinators 2 (pt); Dietitians 1 (pt); Dentist
1 (ft).
Facilities Dining room; Physical therapy
room; Chapel; Barber/Beauty shop.
Activities Arts & crafts; Games; Prayer groups;
Movies; Shopping trips; Bowling; Plays;
Ballet; Fishing.

BUFFALO

Buffalo Nursing Center*
Pearlstone St at Hospital Dr, Buffalo, TX,
75831
(214) 322-4208
Admin Pauline Bulen.
Licensure Intermediate care. *Beds* 60.
Certified Medicaid.
Owner Proprietary Corp (Beverly Enterprises).

BUNA

Buna Nursing Home
PO Box 1088, Buna, TX, 77612
(409) 994-3576
Admin Wayne Daniel Butchee. *Medical Dir/
Dir of Nursing* J L Sessions MD; Pat
Wiggins LVN DON.
Licensure Intermediate care. *Beds* ICF 60.
Certified Medicaid.
Owner Proprietary Corp.

BURKBURNETT

Care Manor Nursing Center
800 Red River Expwy, Burkburnett, TX,
76354
(817) 569-1466
Admin Janice Sanders. *Medical Dir/Dir of
Nursing* Ruby Lange.
Licensure Intermediate care. *Beds* ICF 74.
Certified Medicaid.
Owner Proprietary Corp.
Admissions Requirements Physician's request.
Staff RNs 1 (pt); LPNs 6 (ft); Nurses aides 20
(ft); Activities coordinators 1 (ft); Dietitians
1 (pt); Ophthalmologists 1 (pt).
Facilities Dining room; Activities room;
Laundry room; Barber/Beauty shop.
Activities Arts & crafts; Cards; Games;
Reading groups; Prayer groups; Shopping
trips; Social/Cultural gatherings.

Evergreen Care Center*
406 E 7th, Burkburnett, TX, 76354
(817) 569-2236
Admin Susie M Brown.
Licensure Intermediate care. *Beds* 60.
Certified Medicaid.
Owner Proprietary Corp (Beverly Enterprises).

BURLESON

Burleson Nursing Center
144 SW Thomas St, Burleson, TX, 76028
(817) 295-2216
Admin Ann Walker. *Medical Dir/Dir of
Nursing* Geraldine Grieve.
Licensure Skilled care; Intermediate care. *Beds*
SNF 60; ICF 66. *Certified* Medicaid;
Medicare.
Owner Proprietary Corp (Summit Health Ltd).
Admissions Requirements Minimum age 21;
Medical examination; Physician's request.
Staff RNs 1 (ft), 1 (pt); LPNs 8 (ft); Orderlies
2 (ft); Nurses aides 25 (ft); Activities
coordinators 1 (ft); Dietitians 1 (ft).
Facilities Dining room; Activities room;
Laundry room; Barber/Beauty shop.
Activities Arts & crafts; Cards; Games;
Reading groups; Prayer groups; Movies;
Shopping trips.

Silver Haven Care Center*
600 Maple, Burleson, TX, 76028
(817) 295-8118
Admin Richard L Nelson.
Licensure Intermediate care. *Beds* 120.
Certified Medicaid.
Owner Nonprofit Corp.

BURNET

Oaks Nursing Home*
507 W Jackson, Burnet, TX, 78611
(512) 756-6044
Admin Judy Edgar Allen. *Medical Dir/Dir of Nursing* Billy B Ozier MD.
Licensure Intermediate care. *Beds* 92.
Certified Medicaid.
Owner Nonprofit Corp.
Staff RNs 1 (ft); LPNs 5 (ft); Nurses aides 32 (ft), 3 (pt); Activities coordinators 1 (ft); Dietitians 1 (pt).
Facilities Dining room; Activities room; Laundry room; Barber/Beauty shop.
Activities Cards; Games; Prayer groups; Movies; Shopping trips.

CALDWELL

Leisure Lodge—Caldwell
701 N Broadway, Caldwell, TX, 77836
(409) 567-3237
Admin Lavern E Balcar. *Medical Dir/Dir of Nursing* Barker Stigler; Nancy Keller.
Licensure Intermediate care. *Beds* ICF 156.
Certified Medicaid; Medicare.
Owner Proprietary Corp (Beverly Enterprises).
Admissions Requirements Minimum age 16; Medical examination; Physician's request.
Staff RNs 2 (ft), 1 (pt); LPNs 8 (ft), 1 (pt); Nurses aides 38 (ft), 10 (pt); Activities coordinators 1 (ft), 2 (pt).
Languages Spanish, Czech
Facilities Dining room; Physical therapy room; Activities room; Chapel; Crafts room; Laundry room; Barber/Beauty shop; Library.
Activities Arts & crafts; Games; Reading groups; Prayer groups; Movies; Shopping trips; Social/Cultural gatherings; Family council; Resident council; Ministerial alliance.

CALVERT

Calvert Nursing Center
PO Box 418, 701 Browning, Calvert, TX, 77837
(713) 364-2391, 364-2023
Admin Audrey G Williamson. *Medical Dir/Dir of Nursing* Hazel L Brown DON.
Licensure Intermediate care. *Beds* 32.
Certified Medicaid.
Owner Privately owned.
Admissions Requirements Minimum age 21; Medical examination; Physician's request.
Staff LPNs; Nurses aides; Physical therapists; Speech therapists; Activities coordinators.
Facilities Dining room; Laundry room; Barber/Beauty shop.
Activities Arts & crafts; Cards; Games; Reading groups; Prayer groups; Movies; Social/Cultural gatherings.

CAMERON

Cameron Nursing Home*
PO Box 831, 700 E 11th St, Cameron, TX, 76520
(817) 697-6564
Admin Donna Sue Stephenson.
Licensure Intermediate care. *Beds* 43.
Certified Medicaid.
Owner Proprietary Corp.

Colonial Nursing Home
PO Box 831, 1002 E 10th St, Cameron, TX, 76520
(817) 697-6578
Admin Connie Biffle. *Medical Dir/Dir of Nursing* Pat Kettett.
Licensure Intermediate care. *Beds* ICF 84.
Certified Medicaid.
Owner Proprietary Corp.
Admissions Requirements Minimum age 21; Medical examination; Physician's request.

Staff RNs 1 (ft); LPNs 8 (ft); Nurses aides 18 (ft), 6 (pt); Recreational therapists 1 (ft); Activities coordinators 1 (ft); Dietitians 1 (pt).
Languages German
Facilities Dining room; Activities room; Barber/Beauty shop; "Gathering" room; Living room.
Activities Arts & crafts; Cards; Games; Reading groups; Prayer groups; Movies; Shopping trips; Social/Cultural gatherings.

CANADIAN

Edward Abraham Memorial Home
803 Birch, Canadian, TX, 79014
(806) 323-6453
Admin Sue Flanagan Collier.
Licensure Intermediate care. *Beds* 59.
Certified Medicaid.
Facilities Dining room; Activities room; Chapel; Laundry room; Barber/Beauty shop.
Activities Arts & crafts; Cards; Games; Reading groups; Prayer groups; Movies; Shopping trips; Social/Cultural gatherings.

CANTON

Canton Nursing Center*
1661 S Buffalo St, Canton, TX, 75103
(214) 567-4135
Admin Barbara Jeanine Rutherford.
Licensure Intermediate care. *Beds* 66.
Certified Medicaid.
Owner Proprietary Corp (Beverly Enterprises).

Canton Residential Center*
1755 Elliott St, Canton, TX, 75103
(214) 567-2901
Admin Debbie Davenport.
Licensure Intermediate care. *Beds* 42.
Certified Medicaid.

Heritage Manor*
901 W College St, Canton, TX, 75103
(214) 567-4169
Admin Curtis D Bjornlie.
Licensure Intermediate care. *Beds* 110.
Certified Medicaid.
Owner Proprietary Corp.

CANYON

Golden Plains Care Center
15 Hospital Dr, Canyon, TX, 79015
(805) 655-2161
Admin Fern B Yell. *Medical Dir/Dir of Nursing* Andy Conrad.
Licensure Intermediate care. *Beds* ICF 90.
Certified Medicaid.
Owner Privately owned.
Admissions Requirements Medical examination; Physician's request.
Staff RNs; LPNs; Orderlies; Nurses aides; Activities coordinators.
Facilities Dining room; Activities room; Laundry room; Barber/Beauty shop.
Activities Arts & crafts; Cards; Games; Prayer groups; Movies; Shopping trips; Social/Cultural gatherings.

CARRIZO SPRINGS

Carrizo Springs Nursing Home Inc*
8th & Clark Sts, Carrizo Springs, TX, 78834
(512) 876-5090, 2320
Admin Margaret Terrell.
Licensure Skilled care; Intermediate care; Personal care. *Beds* ICF 100; Personal 24.
Certified Medicaid.
Owner Proprietary Corp.

CARROLLTON

Carrollton Manor*
1618 Kirby, Carrollton, TX, 75006
(214) 245-1573
Admin Sybil Perrin.
Licensure Intermediate care. *Beds* 120.
Certified Medicaid.
Owner Proprietary Corp (ARA Living Centers).

Northwood Manor Nursing Home*
2135 Denton Dr, Carrollton, TX, 75006
(214) 242-0666
Admin Charles William Hames.
Licensure Intermediate care. *Beds* 150.
Certified Medicaid.
Owner Proprietary Corp (Beverly Enterprises).

CARTHAGE

Leisure Lodge—Carthage*
701 S Market, Carthage, TX, 75633
(214) 693-6671
Admin Tommie Hight.
Licensure Intermediate care. *Beds* 96.
Certified Medicaid.
Owner Proprietary Corp (Beverly Enterprises).
Staff RNs 1 (ft); LPNs 5 (ft), 4 (pt); Nurses aides 20 (ft), 4 (pt); Activities coordinators 1 (ft).
Facilities Dining room; Activities room; Chapel; Crafts room; Laundry room; Barber/Beauty shop.
Activities Arts & crafts; Cards; Games; Reading groups; Prayer groups; Movies; Shopping trips; Social/Cultural gatherings.

Panola Nursing Home
PO Box 170, 501 Cottage Rd, Carthage, TX, 75633
(214) 693-7141
Admin Janet S Chamness. *Medical Dir/Dir of Nursing* June Alexander RN DON.
Licensure Skilled care; Intermediate care. *Beds* 108. *Certified* Medicaid; Medicare.
Owner Nonprofit Corp.
Admissions Requirements Physician's request.
Staff RNs 1 (ft), 1 (pt); LPNs 10 (ft), 5 (pt); Nurses aides 32 (ft), 10 (pt); Activities coordinators 1 (ft); Dietitians 1 (ft).
Facilities Dining room; Activities room; Crafts room; Barber/Beauty shop.
Activities Arts & crafts; Cards; Games; Reading groups; Prayer groups; Movies; Shopping trips; Social/Cultural gatherings.

CEDAR HILL

Cedar Hill Nursing Center
303 S Clark Rd, Cedar Hill, TX, 75104
(214) 291-7877
Admin Kerri G Etminan. *Medical Dir/Dir of Nursing* Deanna Green DON.
Licensure Intermediate care. *Beds* ICF 120.
Certified Medicaid.
Owner Proprietary Corp (Beverly Enterprises).
Staff Physicians; RNs; LPNs; Orderlies; Nurses aides; Physical therapists; Reality therapists; Recreational therapists; Occupational therapists; Speech therapists; Activities coordinators; Dietitians.

CELINA

Belinda Care Center
PO Box 158, Celina, TX, 75009
(214) 382-2356
Admin Peggy Jones. *Medical Dir/Dir of Nursing* Glen Mitchell MD; Jane Sullivan RN.
Licensure Intermediate care. *Beds* ICF 88.
Certified Medicaid.
Owner Privately owned.
Admissions Requirements Medical examination; Physician's request.

Staff RNs 1 (ft); LPNs 4 (ft); Orderlies 2 (ft); Nurses aides 19 (ft); Activities coordinators 1 (ft); Dietitians 1 (ft).
Facilities Dining room; Activities room; Crafts room; Laundry room; Barber/Beauty shop.
Activities Arts & crafts; Cards; Games; Reading groups; Prayer groups; Movies; Shopping trips; Social/Cultural gatherings.

CENTER

Green Acres Convalescent Center*
501 Timpson, Center, TX, 75935
(409) 598-2483
Admin Evelyn R Russell.
Licensure Intermediate care. *Beds* 102. *Certified* Medicaid.
Owner Proprietary Corp (ARA Living Centers).
Admissions Requirements Medical examination; Physician's request.
Staff RNs 1 (ft); LPNs 8 (ft); Orderlies 1 (ft); Nurses aides 27 (ft); Physical therapists 1 (ft); Activities coordinators 1 (ft); Podiatrists 1 (pt).
Facilities Dining room; Activities room; Chapel; Crafts room; Laundry room; Barber/Beauty shop.
Activities Arts & crafts; Cards; Games; Reading groups; Prayer groups; Movies.

Holiday Nursing Home*
100 Holiday Circle, Center, TX, 75935
(713) 598-3371
Admin Gayla Adams.
Licensure Skilled care; Intermediate care. *Beds* 137. *Certified* Medicaid.
Owner Proprietary Corp.

CENTERVILLE

Leisure Lodge—Ctrville*
103 Teakwood Center, Centerville, TX, 75833
(214) 536-2596
Admin Beth J Rodell.
Licensure Intermediate care. *Beds* 102. *Certified* Medicaid.
Owner Proprietary Corp (Beverly Enterprises).

CHILDRESS

Childress Nursing Center
1200 7th St NW, Childress, TX, 79201
(817) 937-8668
Admin Shirley Southard. *Medical Dir/Dir of Nursing* Sharon Bowen.
Licensure Intermediate care; Personal care. *Beds* ICF 110; Personal 10. *Certified* Medicaid.
Owner Proprietary Corp (Beverly Enterprises).
Admissions Requirements Physician's request.
Staff RNs 1 (ft); LPNs 8 (ft); Nurses aides 18 (ft); Activities coordinators 1 (ft); Dietitians 1 (ft).
Facilities Dining room; Activities room; Crafts room; Laundry room; Barber/Beauty shop.
Activities Arts & crafts; Cards; Games; Prayer groups; Movies.

Turner Nursing Home*
1610 Ave G NW, Childress, TX, 79201
(817) 937-3675
Admin Linda Bohannon.
Licensure Intermediate care. *Beds* 60. *Certified* Medicaid.
Admissions Requirements Medical examination; Physician's request.
Staff RNs 2 (pt); LPNs 5 (ft); Nurses aides 18 (ft), 2 (pt); Physical therapists 2 (pt); Speech therapists 1 (pt); Activities coordinators 1 (ft); Dietitians 1 (pt); Dentists 1 (pt); Ophthalmologists 1 (pt).

Facilities Dining room; Activities room; Laundry room; Barber/Beauty shop; Library.
Activities Arts & crafts; Cards; Games; Prayer groups; Movies; Shopping trips; Social/Cultural gatherings.

CHILLICOTHE

Iris Haven Nursing Home
PO Box 667, 209 Ave I, Chillicothe, TX, 79225
(817) 852-5151
Admin Helen W Holt. *Medical Dir/Dir of Nursing* Vivian Ford DON.
Licensure Intermediate care. *Beds* ICF 46. *Certified* Medicaid.
Owner Proprietary Corp.
Admissions Requirements Medical examination; Physician's request.
Staff LPNs; Nurses aides; Activities coordinators 1 (ft).
Facilities Dining room; Activities room; Barber/Beauty shop.
Activities Games; Prayer groups.

CHRISTOVAL

Christoval Golden Years Nursing Home Inc
116 McKee St, PO Box 45, Christoval, TX, 76935
(915) 896-2391
Admin June Pettitt. *Medical Dir/Dir of Nursing* Betty Henry.
Licensure Intermediate care. *Beds* 45. *Certified* Medicaid.
Owner Proprietary Corp.
Staff Physicians 1 (ft); RNs 1 (ft); LPNs 5 (ft); Orderlies 1 (ft); Nurses aides 13 (ft); Activities coordinators 1 (ft); Dietitians 1 (ft).
Languages Spanish
Facilities Dining room; Activities room; Laundry room.
Activities Arts & crafts; Cards; Games; Reading groups; Prayer groups; Movies.

CISCO

Canterburry Villa of Cisco
1404 Front St, Cisco, TX, 76437
(817) 442-4202
Admin Patricia R Monroe. *Medical Dir/Dir of Nursing* Nova George DON.
Licensure Intermediate care. *Beds* 106. *Certified* Medicaid.
Owner Proprietary Corp (Texas Health Enterprises).
Admissions Requirements Physician's request.
Staff Physicians 1 (pt); RNs 1 (pt); LPNs 8 (ft); Orderlies 2 (ft); Nurses aides 25 (ft); Activities coordinators 1 (ft); Dietitians 1 (ft), 1 (pt).
Facilities Dining room; Physical therapy room; Activities room; Chapel; Crafts room; Laundry room; Barber/Beauty shop; Library.
Activities Arts & crafts; Cards; Games; Reading groups; Prayer groups; Shopping trips; Social/Cultural gatherings.

CLARENDON

Medical Center Nursing Home
Box 1007, Hwy 70 N, Clarendon, TX, 79226
(806) 874-3760
Admin Larry White. *Medical Dir/Dir of Nursing* Sue Leeper RN.
Licensure Intermediate care. *Beds* 43. *Certified* Medicaid.
Owner Nonprofit Corp.
Admissions Requirements Medical examination.
Staff Physicians 1 (pt); RNs 1 (ft), 1 (pt); LPNs 9 (ft); Nurses aides 27 (ft); Reality therapists 1 (pt); Recreational therapists 1 (pt); Activities coordinators 2 (pt); Dietitians 1 (ft), 1 (pt).

Facilities Dining room; Physical therapy room; Activities room; Crafts room; Barber/Beauty shop.
Activities Arts & crafts; Cards; Games; Reading groups; Prayer groups; Movies; Social/Cultural gatherings.

CLARKSVILLE

Clarksville Nursing Center*
300 E Baker St, Clarksville, TX, 75426
(214) 427-2236
Admin Edna Nelson. *Medical Dir/Dir of Nursing* Dr B C Muthappa.
Licensure Intermediate care. *Beds* 132. *Certified* Medicaid.
Owner Proprietary Corp (Beverly Enterprises).
Staff RNs 1 (ft); LPNs 10 (ft), 2 (pt); Nurses aides 35 (ft); Physical therapists 1 (pt); Activities coordinators 1 (ft); Dietitians 1 (pt).
Facilities Dining room; Chapel; Laundry room; Barber/Beauty shop.
Activities Arts & crafts; Games; Reading groups; Prayer groups; Movies; Shopping trips; Social/Cultural gatherings.

CLAUDE

Palo Duro Convalescent Home Inc
PO Box 42D, 405 S Collins St, Claude, TX, 79019
(806) 226-5121
Admin Sharon K Kelley. *Medical Dir/Dir of Nursing* Peter Knight MD; Dianne Hill RN DON.
Licensure Skilled care. *Beds* SNF 56. *Certified* Medicaid; Medicare.
Owner Proprietary Corp.
Admissions Requirements Minimum age 18; Medical examination; Physician's request.
Staff RNs 3 (ft), 2 (pt); LPNs 4 (ft), 2 (pt); Nurses aides 18 (ft), 5 (pt); Activities coordinators 1 (ft); Dietitians 1 (pt).
Languages Spanish
Facilities Dining room; Activities room; Crafts room; Laundry room; Barber/Beauty shop.
Activities Arts & crafts; Cards; Games; Reading groups; Prayer groups; Movies; Social/Cultural gatherings.

CLEBURNE

Colonial Manor Nursing & Convalescent Center*
2035 N Granbury St, Cleburne, TX, 76031
(817) 645-9134, 477-3009
Admin Harold D Werning.
Licensure Skilled care; Intermediate care. *Beds* 150. *Certified* Medicaid.
Owner Proprietary Corp (Beverly Enterprises).

Fireside Lodge
301 Lincoln Park Dr, Cleburne, TX, 76031
(817) 641-3433, 641-3434
Admin Wanda Dean. *Medical Dir/Dir of Nursing* Betty Huddleston.
Owner Proprietary Corp.
Staff RNs 2 (ft), 1 (pt); Nurses aides 32 (ft); Activities coordinators 2 (ft); LVNs 11 (ft), 1 (pt).

Golden Age Nursing Home Inc*
1102 Williams Ave, Cleburne, TX, 76031
(817) 645-8049
Admin Wanda Dean.
Licensure Intermediate care. *Beds* 102. *Certified* Medicaid.
Owner Proprietary Corp.

Leisure Lodge—Cleburne*
PO Box 138, 1108 W Kilpatrick St, Cleburne, TX, 76031
(817) 645-3931
Admin Donna Poteet.

Licensure Intermediate care. *Beds* 120.
 Certified Medicaid.
Owner Proprietary Corp.

CLEVELAND

Galaxy Manor Nursing Home*
903 E Houston, Cleveland, TX, 77327
(713) 592-8775
Admin Ann Yeager.
Licensure Intermediate care. *Beds* 160.
 Certified Medicaid.
Owner Proprietary Corp (Beverly Enterprises).

CLIFTON

Clifton Lutheran Sunset Home
PO Box 71, College Hill, Clifton, TX, 76634
(817) 675-8637
Admin Elmer F Luckenbach. *Medical Dir/Dir of Nursing* Dr D A Gloff; Sarah Turner.
Licensure Skilled care; Intermediate care. *Beds* SNF 60; ICF 120; Residential 40; Apartments 41. *Certified* Medicaid; Medicare.
Owner Nonprofit Corp.
Staff RNs 3 (ft); LPNs 11 (ft); Nurses aides 66 (ft); Physical therapists 1 (pt); Activities coordinators 2 (ft), 1 (pt); Dietitians 1 (pt).
Affiliation Lutheran
Facilities Dining room; Physical therapy room; Activities room; Chapel; Crafts room; Laundry room; Barber/Beauty shop; Library.
Activities Arts & crafts; Cards; Games; Reading groups; Prayer groups; Movies; Shopping trips; Social/Cultural gatherings.

CLUTE

Sunset Nursing Home*
914 N Hwy 288, Clute, TX, 77531
(713) 265-4794
Admin Glenna L Morlan.
Licensure Intermediate care. *Beds* 120.
 Certified Medicaid.
Owner Proprietary Corp.

Wood Lake Nursing Home*
603 E Plantation Rd, Clute, TX, 77531
(713) 265-4221
Admin Polly Hedrick.
Licensure Intermediate care. *Beds* 98.
 Certified Medicaid.
Owner Proprietary Corp (ARA Living Centers).

CLYDE

Leisure Lodge—Clyde*
Rte 3, Box 148, Old Hwy 80, Clyde, TX, 79510
(915) 893-4288
Admin Glenn R Gray.
Licensure Intermediate care. *Beds* 48.
 Certified Medicaid.
Owner Proprietary Corp.

COLEMAN

Coleman Care Center
FM 53, Box 392, Coleman, TX, 76834
(915) 625-4157
Admin Jimmy D Simpson. *Medical Dir/Dir of Nursing* Toni Burrage.
Licensure Intermediate care; Retirement apartments. *Beds* ICF 74; Retirement apts 8. *Certified* Medicaid.
Owner Nonprofit Corp.
Admissions Requirements Physician's request.
Staff LPNs 8 (ft), 2 (pt); Nurses aides 26 (ft), 11 (pt); Activities coordinators 1 (ft); Dietitians 1 (pt).
Languages Spanish
Facilities Dining room; Activities room; Chapel; Crafts room; Laundry room; Barber/Beauty shop.

Activities Arts & crafts; Games; Prayer groups.

Leisure Lodge—Coleman*
PO Box 853, 2713 Commercial Ave, Coleman, TX, 76834
(915) 625-4105
Admin Jimmie Don Simpson.
Licensure Intermediate care. *Beds* 64.
 Certified Medicaid.
Owner Proprietary Corp (Beverly Enterprises).

COLLEGE STATION

Brazos Valley Geriatric Center*
1115 Anderson, College Station, TX, 77840
(713) 693-1515
Admin Freddie M White. *Medical Dir/Dir of Nursing* Sally Perez LVN.
Licensure Intermediate care. *Beds* 150.
 Certified Medicaid.
Owner Proprietary Corp (ARA Living Centers).
Admissions Requirements Medical examination; Physician's request.
Staff LPNs 7 (ft), 3 (pt); Orderlies 1 (ft); Nurses aides 16 (ft), 2 (pt); Activities coordinators 1 (ft); Dietitians 1 (ft).
Facilities Dining room; Physical therapy room; Activities room; Crafts room; Laundry room; Barber/Beauty shop.
Activities Arts & crafts; Cards; Games; Shopping trips; Social/Cultural gatherings; Birthday parties; Church; Singing.

COLLINSVILLE

Collinsville Care Home Inc*
400 Main St, Collinsville, TX, 76233
(214) 429-6426
Admin Anita Murphree. *Medical Dir/Dir of Nursing* John Galewaler DO.
Licensure Intermediate care. *Beds* 88.
 Certified Medicaid.
Owner Proprietary Corp (Health Enter of America).
Admissions Requirements Medical examination; Physician's request.
Staff RNs 1 (ft); LPNs 5 (ft); Nurses aides 20 (ft), 6 (pt); Activities coordinators 1 (ft); Dietitians 1 (ft).
Facilities Dining room; Activities room; Chapel; Crafts room; Laundry room; Barber/Beauty shop.
Activities Arts & crafts; Games; Prayer groups; Movies; Shopping trips; Social/Cultural gatherings; Picnics; Olympics.

COLORADO CITY

Kristi Lee Manor Inc*
1941 Chestnut St, Colorado City, TX, 79512
(915) 728-5247
Admin Chester C Moody.
Licensure Intermediate care. *Beds* 118.
 Certified Medicaid.
Owner Proprietary Corp.

Valley Fair Lodge
1541 Chestnut St, Colorado City, TX, 79512
(915) 728-2634
Admin Marsha Rickard. *Medical Dir/Dir of Nursing* Thomas Aquillion MD; Elia Gonzalez DON.
Licensure Intermediate care. *Beds* ICF 50.
 Certified Medicaid.
Owner Publicly owned.
Admissions Requirements Medical examination; Physician's request.
Staff Physicians 1 (pt); RNs 1 (pt); LPNs 12 (ft); Nurses aides 18 (ft); Physical therapists 1 (ft); Recreational therapists 1 (pt); Activities coordinators 1 (ft); Dietitians 1 (ft), 1 (pt).
Facilities Dining room; Physical therapy room; Activities room; Chapel; Laundry room; Barber/Beauty shop.

Activities Arts & crafts; Games; Reading groups; Prayer groups; Shopping trips; Social/Cultural gatherings.

COLUMBUS

Columbus Convalescent Center*
300 N St, Columbus, TX, 78934
(713) 732-2347
Admin Robert E Gay III. *Medical Dir/Dir of Nursing* R Cecil Marburger MD.
Licensure Intermediate care. *Beds* 90.
 Certified Medicaid.
Admissions Requirements Medical examination.
Staff Activities coordinators 1 (ft).
Facilities Dining room; Activities room; Laundry room; Barber/Beauty shop; Library.
Activities Cards; Games; Reading groups; Prayer groups; Movies; Shopping trips; Social/Cultural gatherings.

Sweetbriar Nursing Home
103 Sweetbriar Ln, Columbus, TX, 78934
(409) 732-5716
Admin Marian J Werland. *Medical Dir/Dir of Nursing* R Cecil Marburger MD.
Licensure Intermediate care; Personal care; Alzheimer's unit. *Beds* ICF 116; Personal 24. *Certified* Medicaid.
Owner Proprietary Corp (ARA Living Centers).
Admissions Requirements Minimum age 18; Medical examination; Physician's request.
Staff RNs; LPNs 6 (ft); Nurses aides 18 (ft); Physical therapists; Speech therapists; Activities coordinators; Dietitians.
Languages Spanish, German
Facilities Dining room; Activities room; Crafts room; Laundry room; Barber/Beauty shop.
Activities Arts & crafts; Cards; Games; Reading groups; Prayer groups; Movies; Shopping trips; Social/Cultural gatherings; Cook outs; Field trips; Costume days.

COMANCHE

Western Hills Nursing Home*
Rte 5, Box 26, Comanche, TX, 76442
(915) 356-2571
Admin Bobbie Nichols.
Licensure Skilled care; Intermediate care. *Beds* 166. *Certified* Medicaid.
Staff RNs 1 (ft); Physical therapists 1 (pt).
Facilities Dining room; Physical therapy room; Activities room; Crafts room; Laundry room; Barber/Beauty shop.
Activities Arts & crafts; Cards; Games; Reading groups; Prayer groups; Shopping trips.

COMMERCE

Care Inn of Commerce*
2901 Sterling Hart Dr, Commerce, TX, 75428
(214) 886-2510
Admin Shelby Weatherbee.
Licensure Intermediate care. *Beds* 116.
 Certified Medicaid.
Owner Proprietary Corp.

CONROE

Autumn Hills—Conroe
2019 N Frazier, Conroe, TX, 77356
(409) 756-5536
Admin Faye D Thompson. *Medical Dir/Dir of Nursing* Donald Stillwagon MD; Joyce Coulter RN.
Licensure Intermediate care. *Beds* ICF 108.
 Certified Medicaid.
Owner Proprietary Corp.
Admissions Requirements Minimum age 50; Medical examination; Physician's request.

Staff Physicians 1 (pt); RNs 1 (ft); LPNs 10 (ft); Nurses aides 25 (ft).
Facilities Dining room; Activities room; Chapel; Crafts room; Laundry room; Barber/ Beauty shop; Library.
Activities Arts & crafts; Cards; Games; Reading groups; Prayer groups; Movies; Shopping trips; Social/Cultural gatherings.

Care Inn of Conroe Inc*
99 Rigby Owen Rd, Conroe, TX, 77301
(713) 539-1701
Admin Charles T Smith.
Licensure Intermediate care. *Beds* 150. *Certified* Medicaid.
Admissions Requirements Medical examination.
Staff RNs; LPNs; Orderlies; Nurses aides; Physical therapists; Speech therapists; Activities coordinators; Dietitians; Podiatrists.
Facilities Dining room; Activities room; Crafts room; Laundry room; Barber/Beauty shop; Library.
Activities Arts & crafts; Cards; Games; Prayer groups; Movies; Shopping trips; Social/ Cultural gatherings.

COOPER

Birchwood Manor Nursing Home*
Hwy 64 W, Cooper, TX, 75432
(214) 395-2125
Admin Delma Wintermute.
Licensure Intermediate care. *Beds* 100. *Certified* Medicaid.

Delta Nursing Home
101 SE 8th St, Cooper, TX, 75432
(214) 395-2184
Admin Shelby J Weatherbee.
Licensure Intermediate care; Personal care. *Beds* ICF 38; Personal 24. *Certified* Medicaid.
Admissions Requirements Medical examination; Physician's request.
Staff LPNs 2 (ft), 2 (pt); Nurses aides 9 (ft); Activities coordinators 1 (ft), 1 (pt).
Facilities Dining room; Laundry room; Barber/Beauty shop.
Activities Arts & crafts; Games; Reading groups; Prayer groups; Social/Cultural gatherings.

COPPERAS COVE

Wind Crest Nursing Center Inc
607 W Ave B, Copperas Cove, TX, 76522
(817) 547-1033
Admin Darrell Cross. *Medical Dir/Dir of Nursing* Dr Franklin House MD.
Licensure Skilled care; Intermediate care. *Beds* SNF 96; ICF 32. *Certified* Medicaid; Medicare.
Owner Proprietary Corp.
Staff RNs 1 (ft), 3 (pt); LPNs 16 (ft), 4 (pt); Orderlies 1 (ft); Nurses aides 44 (ft), 4 (pt); Physical therapists 1 (ft); Activities coordinators 1 (ft), 1 (pt); Dietitians 1 (pt).
Languages Spanish
Facilities Dining room; Physical therapy room; Activities room; Laundry room; Barber/Beauty shop.
Activities Arts & crafts; Cards; Games; Reading groups; Prayer groups; Movies; Shopping trips; Social/Cultural gatherings.

CORPUS CHRISTI

Corpus Christi Nursing Center
5607 Everhart Rd, Corpus Christi, TX, 78411
(512) 854-4601
Admin Elma Gomez. *Medical Dir/Dir of Nursing* Zulema Garcia RN DON.
Licensure Skilled care. *Certified* Medicaid; Medicare.
Owner Proprietary Corp (Beverly Enterprises).

Admissions Requirements Physician's request.
Languages Spanish
Facilities Dining room; Physical therapy room; Activities room; Chapel; Crafts room; Laundry room; Barber/Beauty shop; Library.
Activities Arts & crafts; Cards; Games; Reading groups; Prayer groups; Movies; Shopping trips; Social/Cultural gatherings; Boat rides; Picnics.

Del Mar Health Care Center
4130 Santa Elena, Corpus Christi, TX, 78405
(512) 882-3655
Admin Chet Clark. *Medical Dir/Dir of Nursing* Tony Nerios DON.
Licensure Intermediate care. *Beds* ICF 108. *Certified* Medicaid.
Owner Proprietary Corp.
Admissions Requirements Medical examination.
Staff RNs 1 (ft); LPNs 6 (ft); Orderlies 3 (ft); Nurses aides 11 (ft); Activities coordinators 1 (ft); Dietitians 1 (pt).
Languages Spanish
Facilities Dining room; Physical therapy room; Activities room; Crafts room; Laundry room; Barber/Beauty shop.
Activities Arts & crafts; Cards; Games; Prayer groups; Movies; Shopping trips; Social/ Cultural gatherings.

The Hearth*
1125 S 19th St, Corpus Christi, TX, 78405
(512) 884-5522
Admin Betty Fleet Carcamo.
Licensure Skilled care; Intermediate care. *Beds* 107. *Certified* Medicaid.
Owner Publicly owned.

Hillhaven Convalescent Center
1314 3rd St, Corpus Christi, TX, 78404
(512) 888-5511
Admin Jerry E Bell. *Medical Dir/Dir of Nursing* Dr B B Grossman.
Licensure Skilled care; Intermediate care. *Beds* 174. *Certified* Medicaid; Medicare.
Owner Proprietary Corp (Hillhaven Corp).
Admissions Requirements Physician's request.
Staff Physicians 1 (ft); RNs 4 (ft); LPNs 25 (ft); Orderlies 2 (ft); Nurses aides 60 (ft); Physical therapists 1 (ft); Recreational therapists 1 (ft); Occupational therapists 1 (pt); Speech therapists 1 (pt); Activities coordinators 1 (ft); Dietitians 1 (ft).
Facilities Dining room; Physical therapy room; Activities room; Laundry room; Barber/Beauty shop; Library; Country store.
Activities Arts & crafts; Cards; Games; Prayer groups; Movies; Shopping trips; Social/ Cultural gatherings; Happy hours; Religious services; Bowling.

Human Development Center
3031 McArdle Rd, Corpus Christi, TX, 78415
(512) 854-1458
Admin Lillie O Bryant. *Medical Dir/Dir of Nursing* Dr Antonio Hernandez; Dr Girish Patel; M Spencer F N.
Licensure Intermediate care for mentally retarded. *Beds* ICF/MR 100. *Certified* Medicaid.
Owner Proprietary Corp (ARA Living Centers).
Admissions Requirements Minimum age 1 yr.
Staff RNs 2 (ft); Nurses aides 42 (ft), 11 (pt); Activities coordinators 1 (ft); LVNs 11 (ft), 6 (pt).
Facilities Dining room; Physical therapy room; Activities room; Recreation room.

Lynnhaven Nursing Center Inc
3030 Fig St, Corpus Christi, TX, 78404
(512) 882-1948
Admin Robert W Harman. *Medical Dir/Dir of Nursing* Yolanda Taylor RN.
Licensure Intermediate care. *Beds* ICF 180. *Certified* Medicaid.
Owner Proprietary Corp.

Admissions Requirements Minimum age 20; Medical examination; Physician's request.
Staff RNs 1 (ft); LPNs 15 (ft); Nurses aides 58 (ft); Dietitians 1 (pt).
Facilities Dining room; Activities room; Crafts room; Laundry room; Barber/Beauty shop.

Retama Manor Nursing Center—North*
2322 Morgan Ave, Corpus Christi, TX, 78405
(512) 882-4242
Admin Lillie O Bryant.
Licensure Skilled care; Intermediate care. *Beds* 180. *Certified* Medicaid.
Owner Proprietary Corp.

Retirement & Nursing Center*
3050 Sunnybrook, Corpus Christi, TX, 78415
(512) 853-9981
Admin Richard Stebbins.
Licensure Skilled care; Intermediate care. *Beds* 178. *Certified* Medicaid.
Owner Proprietary Corp.

South Park Manor*
3115 McArdle, Corpus Christi, TX, 78415
(512) 853-2577
Admin F E Deere.
Licensure Intermediate care. *Beds* 194. *Certified* Medicaid.
Owner Proprietary Corp.

Westwood Manor
801 Cantwell, Corpus Christi, TX, 78408
(512) 882-4284
Admin Dorothy Westbrook. *Medical Dir/Dir of Nursing* Marie Fischer RN.
Licensure Intermediate care. *Beds* ICF 60. *Certified* Medicaid.
Owner Privately owned.
Admissions Requirements Minimum age 18; Medical examination; Physician's request.
Staff Physicians 1 (ft); RNs 1 (ft); LPNs 6 (ft); Nurses aides 23 (ft); Activities coordinators 1 (ft); Dietitians 1 (ft).
Facilities Dining room; Activities room; Crafts room; Laundry room; Barber/Beauty shop.
Activities Arts & crafts; Games; Prayer groups; Shopping trips; Social/Cultural gatherings.

CORRIGAN

Pineywood Acres Nursing Home
300 Hospital St, Corrigan, TX, 75939
(409) 398-2584, 398-2585
Admin Steve Devries. *Medical Dir/Dir of Nursing* Brenda Harris DON.
Licensure Intermediate care ICF III. *Beds* ICF ICF III 90. *Certified* Medicaid.
Owner Proprietary Corp.
Admissions Requirements Medical examination; Physician's request.
Staff Nurses aides; Activities coordinators; Dietitians; LVNs.
Facilities Dining room; Activities room; Laundry room; Barber/Beauty shop; Library; Covered patio.
Activities Arts & crafts; Cards; Games; Reading groups; Prayer groups; Movies; Social/Cultural gatherings.

CORSICANA

Corsicana Nursing Home
1500 N 45th, Corsicana, TX, 75110
(214) 872-4606
Admin Todd E Mayfield. *Medical Dir/Dir of Nursing* J H Barnebee MD; Pat Coppode DON.
Licensure Intermediate care. *Beds* ICF 120. *Certified* Medicaid.
Owner Proprietary Corp (Beverly Enterprises).
Admissions Requirements Minimum age 18; Medical examination; Physician's request.

Staff Physicians 1 (ft); RNs 1 (pt); LPNs 8 (ft); Nurses aides 21 (ft), 8 (pt); Physical therapists 2 (pt); Activities coordinators 1 (ft); Dietitians 1 (ft); Dentists 1 (pt); Ophthalmologists 1 (pt); Podiatrists 1 (pt); Medical aids 5 (ft), 2 (pt).
Facilities Dining room; Physical therapy room; Activities room; Crafts room; Laundry room; Barber/Beauty shop.
Activities Arts & crafts; Cards; Games; Reading groups; Prayer groups; Movies; Shopping trips; Social/Cultural gatherings.

Leisure Lodge—Corsicana*
3301 Park Row, Corsicana, TX, 75110
(214) 872-2455
Admin Alla Mae Capps.
Licensure Intermediate care. *Beds* 102.
Certified Medicaid.
Owner Proprietary Corp.

Mel-Haven Convalescent Home*
901 E 16th Ave, Corsicana, TX, 75110
(214) 874-7454
Admin Mildred J Jennings. *Medical Dir/Dir of Nursing* Dr J H Barnebee.
Licensure Skilled care; Intermediate care. *Beds* 106. *Certified* Medicaid.
Admissions Requirements Minimum age 18; Medical examination; Physician's request.
Staff Physicians 1 (pt); RNs 2 (ft), 1 (pt); LPNs 7 (ft); Nurses aides 23 (ft), 4 (pt); Activities coordinators 1 (ft); Dietitians 1 (pt).
Facilities Dining room; Physical therapy room; Activities room; Crafts room; Laundry room; Barber/Beauty shop.
Activities Arts & crafts; Cards; Games; Prayer groups; Shopping trips; Social/Cultural gatherings.

Northside Nursing Center*
106 W Gorman, Corsicana, TX, 75110
(214) 874-7520
Admin Pauline Bulen.
Licensure Intermediate care. *Beds* 51.
Certified Medicaid.
Staff Nurses aides 9 (ft); Physical therapists 2 (pt); Activities coordinators 1 (ft).

Twilight Home
3001 W 4th Ave, Corsicana, TX, 75110
(214) 872-2521
Admin Mary B Beamon. *Medical Dir/Dir of Nursing* Ann E Corley DON.
Licensure Intermediate care. *Beds* ICF 106.
Certified Medicaid.
Owner Nonprofit Corp.
Admissions Requirements Medical examination; Physician's request.
Staff RNs 3 (ft), 1 (pt); LPNs 9 (ft), 5 (pt); Nurses aides 33 (ft), 9 (pt); Activities coordinators 2 (ft); Dentist 1 (pt).
Facilities Dining room; Laundry room; Barber/Beauty shop.
Activities Arts & crafts; Cards; Games; Reading groups; Prayer groups; Movies; Shopping trips; Social/Cultural gatherings.

Westside Development Center*
421 N 40th St, Corsicana, TX, 75110
(214) 874-6543
Admin Billy Bruce Apperson.
Licensure Intermediate care for mentally retarded. *Beds* 71. *Certified* Medicaid.

CRANE

Golden Manor Nursing Home*
PO Box 1026, 1205 S Sue St, Crane, TX, 79731
(915) 558-3888
Admin Carolyn Belshe.
Licensure Intermediate care. *Beds* 30.
Certified Medicaid.
Owner Proprietary Corp.

CROCKETT

Houston County Nursing Home Inc
210 E Pease St, Crockett, TX, 75835
(409) 544-7884
Admin Loraine E Baker. *Medical Dir/Dir of Nursing* Donna J Hendrix.
Licensure Intermediate care. *Beds* ICF 60.
Certified Medicaid.
Owner Proprietary Corp.
Admissions Requirements Medical examination; Physician's request.
Staff RNs 1 (pt); LPNs 4 (ft), 1 (pt); Nurses aides 10 (ft); Physical therapists 1 (pt); Occupational therapists 1 (pt); Speech therapists 1 (pt); Activities coordinators 1 (ft); Dietitians 1 (pt).
Facilities Dining room; Activities room; Chapel; Barber/Beauty shop.
Activities Arts & crafts; Games; Prayer groups; Social/Cultural gatherings.

Leisure Lodge—Crockett*
Loop 304 E, Crockett, TX, 75835
(713) 544-2051
Admin Andrea K Hill.
Licensure Intermediate care. *Beds* 120.
Certified Medicaid.
Owner Proprietary Corp (Beverly Enterprises).
Staff RNs 1 (ft); LPNs 5 (ft); Nurses aides 14 (ft); Activities coordinators 2 (ft).
Facilities Dining room; Activities room; Laundry room; Barber/Beauty shop.
Activities Arts & crafts; Games; Prayer groups; Movies; Shopping trips; Social/Cultural gatherings.

Whitehall Nursing Center Inc*
PO Box 998, 1116 E Loop 304, Crockett, TX, 75835
(713) 544-2163
Admin Terri Smith Hutcherson.
Licensure Skilled care. *Beds* 71. *Certified* Medicaid.
Owner Proprietary Corp.

CROSBYTON

Crosbyton Care Center*
222 N Farmer St, Crosbyton, TX, 79322
(806) 675-2415
Admin Vickie Dian Griffin.
Licensure Intermediate care. *Beds* 62.
Certified Medicaid.
Owner Proprietary Corp.

CROSS PLAINS

Colonial Oaks Nursing Home
PO Box 398, 1431 E 14th & Ave A, Cross Plains, TX, 76443
(817) 725-6175
Admin Frances M Wolf. *Medical Dir/Dir of Nursing* Peggy Hilburn LVN DON.
Licensure Intermediate care. *Beds* ICF 41.
Certified Medicaid.
Owner Privately owned.
Admissions Requirements Medical examination; Physician's request.
Staff LPNs; Nurses aides; Activities coordinators.
Languages German
Facilities Dining room; Barber/Beauty shop.
Activities Games; Reading groups; Prayer groups; Social/Cultural gatherings.

CROWELL

Crowell Nursing Center*
200 S "B" Ave, Crowell, TX, 79227
(817) 684-1422
Admin Pat Keen.
Licensure Intermediate care. *Beds* 80.
Certified Medicaid.
Owner Proprietary Corp (Beverly Enterprises).

Staff Physicians; RNs; LPNs; Orderlies; Nurses aides; Physical therapists; Reality therapists; Recreational therapists; Occupational therapists; Speech therapists; Activities coordinators; Dietitians.
Facilities Dining room; Physical therapy room; Activities room; Crafts room; Laundry room; Barber/Beauty shop; Library.
Activities Arts & crafts; Cards; Games; Reading groups; Prayer groups; Shopping trips; Shopping trips; Social/Cultural gatherings.

CUERO

Retama Manor East—Cuero
1010 McArthur, Cuero, TX, 77954
(512) 275-6133
Admin Kathrin Moore. *Medical Dir/Dir of Nursing* Barbara Nuckels.
Licensure Intermediate care; Personal care. *Beds* 86. *Certified* Medicaid.
Owner Proprietary Corp (ARA Living Centers).
Staff LPNs 3 (ft), 1 (pt); Nurses aides 13 (ft); Activities coordinators 1 (ft).
Languages Spanish
Facilities Dining room; Chapel; Crafts room; Laundry room; Barber/Beauty shop; Library.
Activities Arts & crafts; Cards; Games; Reading groups; Prayer groups; Movies; Shopping trips; Social/Cultural gatherings.

Retama Manor Nursing Center—Cuero*
PO Box 630, Hwy 77-A, Cuero, TX, 77954
(512) 275-3421
Admin Orlo W Lang.
Licensure Intermediate care. *Beds* 98.
Certified Medicaid.
Owner Proprietary Corp.

CUSHING

Cushing Care Center Inc
PO Box 338, Hwy 225 N, Cushing, TX, 75760
(409) 326-4529
Admin Yvonne Williamson. *Medical Dir/Dir of Nursing* Florence Barrett DON.
Licensure Intermediate care. *Beds* ICF 90.
Certified Medicaid.
Owner Proprietary Corp.
Admissions Requirements Minimum age 18; Medical examination; Physician's request.
Staff RNs 1 (ft); Nurses aides 20 (ft), 5 (pt); Activities coordinators 1 (ft); LVN 7 (ft), 1 (pt).
Facilities Dining room; Activities room; Crafts room; Laundry room; Barber/Beauty shop.
Activities Arts & crafts; Games; Prayer groups; Movies; Shopping trips; Social/Cultural gatherings.

DAINGERFIELD

Pinecrest Convalescent Home
PO Box 519, 507 E Watson Blvd, Daingerfield, TX, 75638
(214) 645-3791, 645-3915
Admin Judy L Dodd. *Medical Dir/Dir of Nursing* Dr Buddy Smith; Linda Pilgrim.
Licensure Intermediate care. *Beds* ICF 117.
Certified Medicaid.
Owner Proprietary Corp (Hillhaven Corp).
Admissions Requirements Medical examination.
Staff Physicians Medical director; LPNs 6 (ft); Nurses aides 13 (ft); Activities coordinators 1 (ft); Dietitians 1 (pt); Ophthalmologists 1 (pt).
Facilities Dining room; Activities room; Crafts room; Laundry room; Barber/Beauty shop; Library.
Activities Arts & crafts; Cards; Games; Prayer groups; Movies; Shopping trips; Social/Cultural gatherings.

DALHART

Coon Memorial Home
210 Texas Blvd, Dalhart, TX, 79022
(806) 249-4571
Admin Jimmie Sue Chisum. *Medical Dir/Dir of Nursing* Elsie Sullivan RN.
Licensure Intermediate care. *Beds* ICF 88. *Certified* Medicaid.
Owner Nonprofit Corp.
Admissions Requirements Medical examination; Physician's request.
Staff RNs 2 (ft); Orderlies 1 (ft); Nurses aides 37 (ft), 2 (pt); Activities coordinators 2 (ft); LVNs 4 (ft), 3 (pt).
Languages Spanish
Affiliation Roman Catholic
Facilities Dining room; Activities room; Crafts room; Laundry room; Barber/Beauty shop; Library.
Activities Arts & crafts; Cards; Games; Reading groups; Prayer groups; Movies; Social/Cultural gatherings.

DALLAS

Autumn Leaves
1010 Emerald Isle Dr, Dallas, TX, 75214
(214) 328-4161
Admin Marvin Kayse. *Medical Dir/Dir of Nursing* Shirley Hornack DON.
Licensure Skilled care; Intermediate care; Personal care. *Beds* 88. *Certified* Medicaid.
Owner Privately owned.
Staff RNs 1 (ft); LPNs 5 (ft); Nurses aides 10 (ft); Activities coordinators 1 (ft); Dietitians 1 (ft).
Facilities Dining room; Activities room; Chapel; Crafts room; Laundry room; Barber/Beauty shop; Library; Van.
Activities Arts & crafts; Cards; Games; Reading groups; Movies; Shopping trips; Social/Cultural gatherings.

Brentwood Place One
8069 Scyene Circle, Dallas, TX, 75227
(214) 388-0609
Admin Larry J Ayres Jr. *Medical Dir/Dir of Nursing* Veronica Johnson.
Licensure Skilled care. *Beds* SNF 120. *Certified* Medicaid; Medicare.
Owner Proprietary Corp (National Heritage).
Admissions Requirements Medical examination; Physician's request.
Staff Physicians 1 (ft); RNs 5 (ft); LPNs 12 (ft); Nurses aides 38 (ft), 3 (pt); Activities coordinators 1 (ft), 1 (pt); Dietitians 1 (pt).
Languages Spanish, Sign
Facilities Dining room; Activities room; Laundry room; Barber/Beauty shop.
Activities Arts & crafts; Cards; Games; Reading groups; Prayer groups; Movies; Shopping trips; Social/Cultural gatherings.

Bryan Manor Nursing Home*
3401 Bryan St, Dallas, TX, 75204
(214) 823-9071
Admin Bonnie B Gayton.
Licensure Intermediate care. *Beds* 80. *Certified* Medicaid.
Owner Proprietary Corp.

Buckner Baptist Trew Retirement Center*
4800 Samuell Blvd, Dallas, TX, 75228
(214) 388-2171
Admin Robert L Herring Jr.
Licensure Skilled care; Custodial care. *Beds* SNF 104; Custodial care 75. *Certified* Medicaid.
Owner Nonprofit Corp (Buckner Bapt Retire Vlg).
Affiliation Baptist

Central Park Manor Inc
3922 Capitol Ave, Dallas, TX, 75204
(214) 823-5641
Admin Sarah Kirkpatrick. *Medical Dir/Dir of Nursing* Dr L S Thompson Jr; Robin Recer.

Licensure Skilled care. *Beds* 64.
Admissions Requirements Minimum age 16; Medical examination; Physician's request.
Staff Physicians 1 (pt); RNs 1 (ft); LPNs 10 (ft), 2 (pt); Nurses aides 18 (ft), 2 (pt); Physical therapists 1 (pt); Occupational therapists 1 (pt); Speech therapists 1 (pt); Dietitians 1 (pt); Dentists 1 (pt); Podiatrists 1 (pt).
Facilities Dining room.

Christian Care Center North
9009 Forest Ln, Dallas, TX, 75243
(214) 783-1771
Admin E Eugene Standifer. *Medical Dir/Dir of Nursing* Karen Cash.
Licensure Intermediate care. *Beds* ICF 120. *Certified* Medicaid.
Owner Nonprofit Corp.
Admissions Requirements Minimum age 21; Medical examination; Physician's request.
Staff LPNs 12 (ft), 1 (ft); Orderlies 3 (ft); Nurses aides 20 (ft); Physical therapists; Reality therapists; Recreational therapists; Occupational therapists; Speech therapists; Activities coordinators 1 (ft); Dietitians 1 (ft).
Affiliation Church of Christ
Facilities Dining room; Activities room; Crafts room; Laundry room; Barber/Beauty shop.
Activities Arts & crafts; Games; Reading groups; Prayer groups; Movies; Shopping trips; Social/Cultural gatherings; Adopt-A-Friend.

Cliff Gardens Nursing Home
801 W 10th St, Dallas, TX, 75208
(214) 946-8709
Admin Gayle Copeland. *Medical Dir/Dir of Nursing* Wanella Walker.
Licensure Intermediate care. *Beds* ICF 34. *Certified* Medicaid.
Owner Proprietary Corp.
Admissions Requirements Medical examination; Physician's request.
Staff LPNs 4 (ft), 1 (pt); Nurses aides 8 (ft), 2 (pt); Activities coordinators 1 (pt).
Facilities Dining room; Chapel; Crafts room.
Activities Arts & crafts; Cards; Games; Reading groups; Prayer groups; Movies; Shopping trips.

Cliff Towers Nursing Home*
329 E Colorado Blvd, Dallas, TX, 75203
(214) 942-8425
Admin Jack L Anders. *Medical Dir/Dir of Nursing* B Northam DO & T V Nguyen MD.
Licensure Skilled care; Intermediate care; Custodial care. *Beds* SNF 214; Custodial care 37. *Certified* Medicaid.
Admissions Requirements Medical examination; Physician's request.
Staff LPNs 23 (ft), 4 (pt); Orderlies 4 (ft), 1 (pt); Nurses aides 55 (ft), 16 (pt); Physical therapists 1 (ft); Reality therapists 1 (pt); Recreational therapists 1 (pt); Occupational therapists 1 (pt); Speech therapists 1 (pt); Activities coordinators 2 (ft); Dietitians 1 (ft).
Facilities Dining room; Physical therapy room; Activities room; Chapel; Crafts room; Laundry room; Barber/Beauty shop.
Activities Arts & crafts; Cards; Games; Reading groups; Prayer groups; Movies; Shopping trips; Social/Cultural gatherings.

The Convalescent Center
4005 Gaston Ave, Dallas, TX, 75246
(214) 826-3891
Admin W Edward McLendon. *Medical Dir/Dir of Nursing* Dr Ben Northam; Linda Bishop RN.
Licensure Intermediate care; Intermediate care for mentally retarded. *Beds* ICF 140; ICF/MR 104. *Certified* Medicaid.
Owner Proprietary Corp (Unicare).

Admissions Requirements Medical examination; Physician's request.
Staff Physicians 1 (pt); RNs 2 (ft); LPNs 20 (ft); Physical therapists 1 (pt); Recreational therapists 1 (pt); Occupational therapists 1 (pt); Speech therapists 1 (pt); Activities coordinators 1 (ft); Dietitians 1 (ft); Dentists 1 (ft); Ophthalmologists 1 (pt); Podiatrists 1 (pt).
Facilities Dining room; Physical therapy room; Activities room; Crafts room; Laundry room; Barber/Beauty shop; Library.
Activities Arts & crafts; Cards; Games; Reading groups; Prayer groups; Movies; Shopping trips; Social/Cultural gatherings.

Crystal Hill Nursing Home Inc
630 Elsbeth Ave, Dallas, TX, 75208
(214) 948-3996
Admin Regina Rideaux. *Medical Dir/Dir of Nursing* William Preston MD; Helen Evans LVN DON.
Licensure Intermediate care. *Beds* ICF 60. *Certified* Medicaid.
Owner Proprietary Corp.
Admissions Requirements Medical examination.
Staff Physicians 5 (pt); RNs 1 (ft); LPNs 5 (ft); Orderlies 3 (ft); Nurses aides 19 (pt); Physical therapists 1 (pt); Occupational therapists 1 (pt); Speech therapists 1 (pt); Activities coordinators 1 (ft); Dietitians 1 (pt); Dentists 1 (pt); Ophthalmologists 1 (pt); Podiatrists 1 (pt).
Languages Spanish
Facilities Dining room; Activities room; Laundry room; Barber/Beauty shop.
Activities Arts & crafts; Cards; Games; Reading groups; Prayer groups; Movies; Shopping trips; Social/Cultural gatherings.

Dallas Home for Jewish Aged
2525 Centerville Rd, Dallas, TX, 75228
(214) 327-4503
Admin Mary Jo Pompeo. *Medical Dir/Dir of Nursing* David Bornstein MD; Justine Thompson RN.
Licensure Intermediate care. *Beds* ICF 265. *Certified* Medicaid.
Owner Nonprofit Corp.
Staff Physicians 4 (pt); RNs 14 (ft); LPNs 40 (ft); Nurses aides 95 (ft); Physical therapists 2 (ft); Recreational therapists 3 (ft); Occupational therapists 4 (ft); Activities coordinators 1 (ft); Dietitians 2 (ft); Ophthalmologists 1 (pt); Social workers 4 (ft), 1 (pt).
Languages Yiddish, Hebrew, Russian
Affiliation Jewish
Activities Arts & crafts; Cards; Games; Reading groups; Prayer groups; Movies; Shopping trips; Social/Cultural gatherings.

Doctor's Nursing Center Foundation Inc
9009 White Rock Trail, Dallas, TX, 75238
(214) 348-8100
Admin Frank Jimenez. *Medical Dir/Dir of Nursing* Dr Jose Pilatovsky; Janet Boyden DON.
Licensure Intermediate care; Custodial care. *Beds* ICF 283; Custodial care 45.
Admissions Requirements Minimum age 16; Medical examination; Physician's request.
Staff Physicians 8 (ft), 1 (pt); RNs 8 (ft), 6 (pt); LPNs 16 (ft), 8 (pt); Orderlies 2 (ft), 2 (pt); Nurses aides 58 (ft), 24 (pt); Physical therapists 1 (ft); Recreational therapists 1 (ft); Occupational therapists 1 (pt); Speech therapists 1 (pt); Activities coordinators 2 (ft); Dietitians 1 (ft); Dentists 1 (pt); Podiatrists 1 (pt); Pharmacist 1 (ft).
Facilities Dining room; Activities room; Chapel; Crafts room; Laundry room; Barber/Beauty shop; Library; Pharmacy.
Activities Arts & crafts; Cards; Games; Reading groups; Prayer groups; Movies; Shopping trips; Social/Cultural gatherings; Cocktail hours; Resident's council.

Fair Park Health Care Center
2815 Martin Luther King Jr Blvd, Dallas, TX, 75215
(214) 421-2159
Admin Peggy Higgins. *Medical Dir/Dir of Nursing* Jewel Holick RN DON.
Licensure Intermediate care. *Beds* ICF 120. *Certified* Medicaid.
Owner Proprietary Corp.
Admissions Requirements Medical examination; Physician's request.
Staff Physicians; RNs 1 (ft), 1 (pt); LPNs 10 (ft); Orderlies 1 (ft); Nurses aides 35 (ft); Physical therapists; Reality therapists; Recreational therapists; Occupational therapists; Speech therapists; Activities coordinators 2 (ft); Dietitians 1 (pt); Ophthalmologists 1 (pt).
Facilities Dining room; Activities room; Laundry room.
Activities Arts & crafts; Cards; Games; Reading groups; Prayer groups; Movies; Shopping trips; Social/Cultural gatherings.

Ferguson Nursing Center*
7626 Ferguson Rd, Dallas, TX, 75228
(214) 327-9321
Admin Jerry Amsler. *Medical Dir/Dir of Nursing* Vickie Lowry.
Licensure Intermediate care. *Beds* 92. *Certified* Medicaid.
Admissions Requirements Medical examination; Physician's request.
Staff Physicians 1 (pt); RNs 1 (ft); LPNs 8 (ft), 5 (pt); Orderlies 3 (ft); Nurses aides 14 (ft), 6 (pt); Physical therapists 1 (pt); Activities coordinators 1 (ft); Dietitians 1 (pt).
Facilities Dining room; Activities room; Laundry room; Barber/Beauty shop.
Activities Arts & crafts; Games; Prayer groups; Movies.

Four Seasons Nursing Center — Dallas
3326 Burgoyne St, Dallas, TX, 75233
(214) 330-9291
Admin Margaret V Wheeler. *Medical Dir/Dir of Nursing* J D Johnson MD; Pat Getman RN DON.
Licensure Skilled care; Personal care. *Beds* 208. *Certified* Medicare.
Owner Proprietary Corp (Manor Care).
Admissions Requirements Medical examination; Physician's request.
Staff RNs 5 (ft), 2 (pt); LPNs 15 (ft), 4 (pt); Orderlies 4 (ft); Nurses aides 44 (ft), 1 (pt); Physical therapists 1 (ft); Activities coordinators 2 (ft); Physical therapist aides 2 (pt).
Languages Spanish
Facilities Dining room; Physical therapy room; Activities room; Crafts room; Laundry room; Barber/Beauty shop; Library; TV rooms.
Activities Arts & crafts; Cards; Games; Reading groups; Prayer groups; Movies; Shopping trips; Social/Cultural gatherings.

Juliette Fowler Homes
PO Box 140129, 100 S Fulton St, Dallas, TX, 75214
(214) 827-0813
Admin Marcela L Wentzel Ph D.
Licensure Intermediate care. *Beds* ICF 131. *Certified* Medicaid.
Owner Nonprofit Corp (Natl Bnvlnt Assn of Chrstn Homes).
Admissions Requirements Medical examination.
Staff Physicians; RNs; LPNs; Nurses aides; Physical therapists; Recreational therapists; Occupational therapists; Speech therapists; Activities coordinators; Dietitians; Ophthalmologists.
Affiliation Disciples of Christ
Facilities Dining room; Activities room; Chapel; Crafts room; Laundry room; Barber/Beauty shop; Library.

Activities Arts & crafts; Cards; Games; Reading groups; Prayer groups; Movies; Shopping trips; Social/Cultural gatherings; Resident council; Resident food consultants committee; Extensive recreational/therapeutic activities.

Garrett Park Manor
1407 N Garrett, Dallas, TX, 75206
(214) 824-8030
Admin Nora Hauck.
Licensure Skilled care; Intermediate care. *Beds* 77. *Certified* Medicaid.
Admissions Requirements Minimum age 18; Medical examination; Physician's request.
Staff Physicians 3 (pt); RNs 1 (pt); LPNs 8 (pt); Orderlies 1 (pt); Nurses aides 30 (pt); Activities coordinators 1 (ft); Dietitians 1 (pt).
Facilities Dining room; Activities room.
Activities Arts & crafts; Cards; Games; Reading groups; Prayer groups; Movies; Shopping trips; Social/Cultural gatherings.

Greenery Rehabilitation Center
7850 Brookhollow Rd, Dallas, TX, 75235
(214) 637-0000
Admin William J McGinley.
Licensure Skilled care. *Beds* SNF 66.
Owner Proprietary Corp (Greenery Rehab Grp).
Admissions Requirements Medical examination.
Staff Physicians; RNs; LPNs; Orderlies; Nurses aides; Physical therapists; Recreational therapists; Occupational therapists; Speech therapists; Activities coordinators; Dietitians; Dentists; Ophthalmologists; Podiatrists; Psychiatrist; Neuropsychologist.
Languages Spanish
Facilities Dining room; Physical therapy room; Activities room; Crafts room; Laundry room; Barber/Beauty shop; Library; Hydrotherapy department.
Activities Arts & crafts; Cards; Games; Reading groups; Prayer groups; Movies; Shopping trips; Social/Cultural gatherings.

Holiday Hills Retirement & Nursing Center Inc*
2428 Bahama, Dallas, TX, 75211
(214) 948-3811
Admin Mae E Maddox.
Licensure Skilled care; Intermediate care. *Beds* 135. *Certified* Medicaid.
Owner Proprietary Corp (Beverly Enterprises).

Kensington Manor*
8039 Scyene Circle, Dallas, TX, 75227
(214) 388-0424
Admin Billie C Hardin.
Licensure Intermediate care. *Beds* 120. *Certified* Medicaid.
Owner Proprietary Corp (ARA Living Centers).

Kenwood Nursing Home*
2922 Duncanville Rd, Dallas, TX, 75211
(214) 339-8341
Admin Mary G Squiers. *Medical Dir/Dir of Nursing* Carl Willeford.
Licensure Intermediate care. *Beds* 60. *Certified* Medicaid.
Owner Proprietary Corp (Cantex Healthcare Centers).
Admissions Requirements Medical examination.
Staff RNs 1 (pt); LPNs 5 (ft), 3 (pt); Orderlies 2 (ft); Nurses aides 10 (ft), 3 (pt); Activities coordinators 1 (ft).
Facilities Dining room; Activities room; Barber/Beauty shop.
Activities Arts & crafts; Prayer groups; Movies.

La Boure Care Center*
1950 Record Crossing, Dallas, TX, 75235
(214) 638-8050

Admin Douglas Daugherty.
Licensure Skilled care. *Beds* 168. *Certified* Medicaid; Medicare.
Owner Proprietary Corp.

The Meadowgreen
8383 Meadow Rd, Dallas, TX, 75231
(214) 369-7811
Admin Herman D Sabrsula. *Medical Dir/Dir of Nursing* Paul Cary MD; Earnestine Melton RN.
Licensure Skilled care; Custodial care. *Beds* SNF 128; Custodial care 26. *Certified* Medicare.
Owner Proprietary Corp (Convalescent Services).
Admissions Requirements Minimum age 18; Medical examination; Physician's request.
Staff Physicians 1 (ft); RNs 5 (ft); LPNs 18 (ft); Orderlies 3 (ft); Nurses aides 33 (ft); Physical therapists 1 (ft); Activities coordinators 2 (ft); Dietitians 1 (ft).
Facilities Dining room; Physical therapy room; Laundry room; Barber/Beauty shop; Library; Covered patio.
Activities Arts & crafts; Cards; Games; Reading groups; Prayer groups; Movies; Shopping trips.

Northaven Nursing Center*
11301 Dennis Rd, Dallas, TX, 75229
(214) 241-2551
Admin Evelyn R Artall. *Medical Dir/Dir of Nursing* Stan Pull MD & S A Redfern MD.
Licensure Intermediate care. *Beds* 208. *Certified* Medicaid.
Owner Proprietary Corp (Summit Health Ltd).
Admissions Requirements Minimum age 21; Medical examination; Physician's request.
Staff Physicians 1 (ft); RNs 3 (ft), 2 (pt); LPNs 14 (ft), 6 (pt); Nurses aides 37 (ft), 10 (pt); Activities coordinators 1 (ft); Dietitians 1 (ft); Dentists 1 (ft); Podiatrists 1 (ft).
Facilities Dining room; Activities room; Crafts room; Barber/Beauty shop; Library.
Activities Arts & crafts; Cards; Games; Reading groups; Prayer groups; Movies; Shopping trips; Social/Cultural gatherings.

Nottingham Manor*
8059 Scyene Circle, Dallas, TX, 75227
(214) 388-0519
Admin Jeanine Rutherford. *Medical Dir/Dir of Nursing* Dr Bill Morgan.
Licensure Intermediate care. *Beds* 120. *Certified* Medicaid.
Owner Proprietary Corp (Beverly Enterprises).
Admissions Requirements Physician's request.
Staff Physicians 1 (ft); LPNs 6 (ft), 1 (pt); Nurses aides 28 (ft), 4 (pt); Physical therapists 1 (pt); Recreational therapists 1 (ft); Occupational therapists 1 (pt); Activities coordinators 1 (ft); Podiatrists 1 (pt); Rehab LVNs 1 (ft).
Facilities Dining room; Activities room; Crafts room; Laundry room; Barber/Beauty shop; Rehab room.
Activities Arts & crafts; Cards; Games; Reading groups; Prayer groups; Movies; Shopping trips; Social/Cultural gatherings.

Presbyterian Village Inc
550 E Ann Arbor, Dallas, TX, 75216
(214) 376-1701
Admin Galen K Ewer. *Medical Dir/Dir of Nursing* Allen M Fain MD; Nancy Torrealba RN.
Licensure Skilled care; Intermediate care; Private pay. *Beds* SNF 160; ICF. *Certified* Medicaid; Medicare.
Owner Nonprofit Corp.
Admissions Requirements Medical examination; Physician's request.
Staff Physicians 4 (ft); RNs 8 (ft), 1 (pt); LPNs 15 (ft), 4 (pt); Nurses aides 52 (ft), 5 (pt); Physical therapists 1 (ft); Occupational therapists 1 (ft); Ophthalmologists 1 (ft).
Languages Spanish

Affiliation Presbyterian
Facilities Dining room; Physical therapy room; Activities room; Chapel; Crafts room; Laundry room; Barber/Beauty shop; Library.
Activities Arts & crafts; Cards; Games; Reading groups; Prayer groups; Movies; Shopping trips; Social/Cultural gatherings.

Presbyterian Village North
8600 Skyline Dr, Dallas, TX, 75243
(214) 349-3960
Admin C Lynn McGowan. *Medical Dir/Dir of Nursing* Lisa Clark MD; Ruth Matthews RN DON.
Licensure Skilled care; Intermediate care; Independent living; Personal care. *Beds* SNF 122; ICF 57.
Owner Nonprofit Corp.
Admissions Requirements Minimum age 62; Medical examination; Private Pay (financial statement approval).
Staff Physicians 1 (pt); RNs 7 (ft), 1 (pt); Nurses aides 62 (ft), 1 (pt); Occupational therapists 1 (ft); Activities coordinators 1 (ft); Dietitians 1 (pt); Chaplain 1 (ft); Ambulation aide 1 (ft); Assistant Administrator 1 (ft); LVNs 23 (ft), 2 (pt).
Facilities Dining room; Activities room; Chapel; Crafts room; Laundry room; Barber/Beauty shop; Library; Whirlpool; Pharmacy; Gift shop.
Activities Arts & crafts; Cards; Games; Reading groups; Prayer groups; Movies; Shopping trips; Social/Cultural gatherings; Cooking project; Current events; Reality orientation; Exercise; In-room activities for bed-fast.

Ryburn Nursing Center
4810 Samuell Blvd, Dallas, TX, 75228
(214) 388-0426
Admin John Wilson. *Medical Dir/Dir of Nursing* Marilyn Krantz.
Licensure Intermediate care. *Beds* ICF 120.
Certified Medicaid.
Owner Nonprofit organization/foundation.
Admissions Requirements Minimum age 62; Medical examination; Physician's request.
Affiliation Baptist
Facilities Dining room; Physical therapy room; Activities room; Crafts room; Laundry room; Barber/Beauty shop; Library.
Activities Arts & crafts; Cards; Games; Prayer groups; Movies; Shopping trips; Social/Cultural gatherings.

St Joseph's Residence
330 W Pembroke St, Dallas, TX, 75208
(214) 948-3597
Admin Sr Adelaide R Bocanegra. *Medical Dir/Dir of Nursing* Dr Ross M Carmichael.
Licensure Custodial care. *Beds* Custodial care 49. *Certified* Private.
Owner Nonprofit organization/foundation.
Admissions Requirements Minimum age 70; Medical examination.
Staff Physicians; RNs; LPNs; Nurses aides; Activities coordinators; Dietitians; Pharmacist.
Languages Spanish
Affiliation Roman Catholic
Facilities Dining room; Chapel; Laundry room; Barber/Beauty shop; Library.
Activities Arts & crafts; Cards; Games; Reading groups; Prayer groups; Movies; Social/Cultural gatherings; Musicals; Bus trips; Sightseeing.

South Dallas Nursing Home*
3808 S Central Expwy, Dallas, TX, 75215
(214) 428-2851
Admin Leona Hawkins.
Licensure Intermediate care. *Beds* 76.
Certified Medicaid.
Admissions Requirements Physician's request.
Staff RNs; LPNs; Orderlies; Nurses aides; Occupational therapists; Speech therapists; Activities coordinators; Dietitians.

Facilities Dining room; Activities room; Chapel; Crafts room; Laundry room.
Activities Arts & crafts; Cards; Games; Reading groups; Prayer groups; Movies; Social/Cultural gatherings.

Sunnyvale Manor
5300 Houston School Rd, Dallas, TX, 75241
(214) 372-1496
Admin Don L Brewer.
Licensure Intermediate care. *Beds* ICF 200.
Certified Medicaid.
Owner Proprietary Corp.

The Traymore
7602 Culcourt, Dallas, TX, 75209
(214) 358-3131
Admin Jessie E Wolkowicz. *Medical Dir/Dir of Nursing* James Walter Galbraith MD.
Licensure Skilled care; Intermediate care. *Beds* 150. *Certified* Private pay.
Owner Proprietary Corp.
Admissions Requirements Medical examination; Physician's request.
Languages Spanish
Facilities Dining room; Activities room; Crafts room; Laundry room; Barber/Beauty shop; Library.
Activities Arts & crafts; Cards; Games; Reading groups; Prayer groups; Movies; Shopping trips; Social/Cultural gatherings.

Treemot Health Care Center
5550 Harvest Hill Rd, Dallas, TX, 75230
(214) 661-1862
Admin Stephen Jones. *Medical Dir/Dir of Nursing* Beth Shapiro RN DON.
Licensure Skilled care; Intermediate care; Custodial care. *Beds* 114.
Owner Proprietary Corp (Cambridge Grp Inc).
Admissions Requirements Medical examination; Physician's request.
Staff Physicians 2 (pt); RNs 5 (ft), 2 (pt); LPNs 4 (ft), 1 (pt); Orderlies 5 (ft); Nurses aides 18 (ft), 3 (pt); Physical therapists 1 (ft); Activities coordinators 1 (ft), 1 (pt); Dietitians 1 (ft), 1 (pt); Podiatrists 1 (pt).
Facilities Dining room; Physical therapy room; Activities room; Crafts room; Laundry room; Barber/Beauty shop; Library.
Activities Arts & crafts; Cards; Games; Reading groups; Prayer groups; Movies; Shopping trips; Social/Cultural gatherings.

Walnut Place
5515 Glen Lakes Dr, Dallas, TX, 75231
(214) 361-8923
Admin Richard M Pratt. *Medical Dir/Dir of Nursing* Irwin Korngut MD; Gene Ragsdale RN.
Licensure Skilled care; Personal care. *Beds* SNF 285; Personal 100.
Owner Privately owned.
Admissions Requirements Medical examination; Physician's request.
Staff RNs; LPNs; Orderlies; Nurses aides; Physical therapists; Recreational therapists; Occupational therapists; Activities coordinators; Dietitians.
Facilities Dining room; Physical therapy room; Activities room; Chapel; Crafts room; Laundry room; Barber/Beauty shop; Library.
Activities Arts & crafts; Cards; Games; Reading groups; Prayer groups; Movies; Shopping trips; Social/Cultural gatherings.

Westminster Manor*
7979 Scyene Circle, Dallas, TX, 75227
(214) 388-0549
Admin L Clay Stephenson.
Licensure Custodial care. *Beds* 96.
Owner Proprietary Corp (Southmark Heritage Corp).

C C Young Memorial Home—Young Health Center*
4829 W Lawther Dr, Dallas, TX, 75214
(214) 827-8080
Admin Julian D Thomas.

Licensure Intermediate care; Personal care. *Beds* ICF 244; Personal 60. *Certified* Medicaid.
Owner Nonprofit Corp.
Affiliation Methodist

DAYTON

Heritage Manor Care Center*
310 E Lawrence, Dayton, TX, 77535
(713) 258-5562
Admin Jack Mallard.
Licensure Skilled care. *Beds* 60. *Certified* Medicaid.
Owner Proprietary Corp.

DE LEON

De Leon Nursing Home*
205 E Ayers, De Leon, TX, 76444
(817) 893-6676
Admin Billie R Butler.
Licensure Intermediate care. *Beds* 53.
Certified Medicaid.
Admissions Requirements Medical examination; Physician's request.
Staff RNs 1 (ft); LPNs 2 (ft); Nurses aides 8 (ft); Activities coordinators 1 (ft); Dietitians 1 (pt).
Facilities Dining room; Activities room; Laundry room; Barber/Beauty shop.
Activities Arts & crafts; Games; Reading groups; Prayer groups; Shopping trips; Social/Cultural gatherings.

Natatana Care Center*
PO Box 287, Hwy 6 E, De Leon, TX, 76444
(817) 893-2075
Admin Charles L Pollock.
Licensure Intermediate care. *Beds* 102.
Certified Medicaid.
Owner Proprietary Corp.

DECATUR

Decatur Convalescent Center*
PO Box 68, 605 W Mulberry St, Decatur, TX, 76234
(817) 627-5444
Admin Geneva Galloway.
Licensure Intermediate care. *Beds* 42.
Certified Medicaid.
Owner Proprietary Corp.

Golden Years Haven*
Hwy 81 S, Rte 2, Box 226, Decatur, TX, 76234
(817) 627-2234
Admin Lezlie McWhorter. *Medical Dir/Dir of Nursing* Verda Slimp.
Licensure Intermediate care. *Beds* 42.
Certified Medicaid.
Admissions Requirements Medical examination.
Staff Physicians 5 (ft); RNs 1 (ft); LPNs 3 (ft), 1 (pt); Orderlies 4 (ft); Nurses aides 16 (ft); Activities coordinators 1 (ft); Dietitians 1 (ft); Dentists 1 (ft).
Facilities Dining room; Activities room; Crafts room; Laundry room; Barber/Beauty shop.
Activities Arts & crafts; Cards; Games; Prayer groups; Movies.

Sunny Hills Nursing Center*
200 E Thompson, Decatur, TX, 76234
(817) 627-2165
Admin Gary M Hendrix.
Licensure Intermediate care. *Beds* 102.
Certified Medicaid.
Owner Proprietary Corp.

DEER PARK

San Jacinto Heritage Manor*
206 W Ave P, Deer Park, TX, 77536
(713) 479-8471
Admin Pat Monroe.
Licensure Intermediate care. *Beds* 96.
Certified Medicaid.
Owner Proprietary Corp (Southmark Heritage Corp).

DEKALB

Sunny Acres of Dekalb Inc
540 S E Front St, Dekalb, TX, 75559
(214) 667-2011
Admin Dora S Perry. *Medical Dir/Dir of Nursing* Donna Hawkins RN.
Licensure Skilled care; Intermediate care. *Beds* SNF 86; ICF. *Certified* Medicaid.
Owner Privately owned.
Admissions Requirements Physician's request.
Staff RNs 1 (ft), 86 (pt); LPNs 8 (ft), 86 (pt); Nurses aides 35 (ft), 86 (pt); Activities coordinators 1 (ft), 86 (pt).
Facilities Dining room; Activities room; Chapel; Laundry room; Barber/Beauty shop.
Activities Arts & crafts; Cards; Games; Reading groups; Prayer groups.

DEL RIO

Del Rio Nursing Home Inc
301 Moore St, Del Rio, TX, 78840
(512) 775-2459
Admin Nell T Gardner. *Medical Dir/Dir of Nursing* Carleen White LVN DON.
Licensure Intermediate care. *Beds* ICF 52.
Certified Medicaid.
Owner Proprietary Corp.
Admissions Requirements Minimum age 16; Medical examination; Physician's request.
Staff RNs 1 (pt); LPNs 6 (ft), 5 (pt); Orderlies 1 (ft); Nurses aides 16 (ft), 2 (pt); Activities coordinators 1 (ft); Dietitians 1 (ft).
Languages Spanish
Facilities Dining room; Activities room; Laundry room; Barber/Beauty shop.
Activities Arts & crafts; Cards; Games; Reading groups; Prayer groups; Movies; Shopping trips; Social/Cultural gatherings.

Retama Manor Nursing Center—Del Rio*
100 Herrmann Dr, Del Rio, TX, 78840
(512) 775-7477
Admin Janet Tennis.
Licensure Intermediate care. *Beds* 88.
Certified Medicaid.
Owner Proprietary Corp (ARA Living Centers).

DENISON

Cantex Healthcare Center—Denison*
801 W Washington St, Denison, TX, 75020
(214) 465-9670
Admin Nancy Raulston.
Licensure Intermediate care. *Beds* 50.
Certified Medicaid.
Owner Proprietary Corp (Cantex Healthcare Centers).

Care Inn of Denison*
1300 Memorial Dr, Denison, TX, 75020
(214) 465-7442
Admin Adelia Shepherd.
Licensure Intermediate care. *Beds* 150.
Certified Medicaid.
Owner Proprietary Corp (ARA Living Centers).

Denison Manor Inc*
601 E Hwy 69, Denison, TX, 75020
(214) 465-2438
Admin Ruth E Brinson. *Medical Dir/Dir of Nursing* M Y Stokes MD.

Licensure Skilled care; Intermediate care. *Beds* 71. *Certified* Medicaid.
Owner Proprietary Corp (ARA Living Centers).
Admissions Requirements Medical examination; Physician's request.
Staff RNs 2 (ft), 2 (pt); LPNs 5 (ft), 2 (pt); Orderlies 1 (ft); Nurses aides 14 (ft), 4 (pt); Activities coordinators 1 (ft).
Facilities Dining room; Activities room; Crafts room; Barber/Beauty shop.
Activities Arts & crafts; Games.

DENTON

The Beaumont Nursing Home*
2224 N Carroll Blvd, Denton, TX, 76201
(817) 387-6656, 382-5713
Admin Pat B Kayser.
Licensure Intermediate care. *Beds* 55.
Certified Medicaid.
Owner Proprietary Corp.

Denton Development Center
909 N Loop 288, Denton, TX, 76201
(817) 387-8525
Admin Mark D Abell. *Medical Dir/Dir of Nursing* Stephen Schulman MD.
Licensure Intermediate care for mentally retarded. *Beds* ICF/MR 68. *Certified* Medicaid.
Owner Proprietary Corp (Texas Health Enterprises).
Admissions Requirements Minimum age 3; Medical examination.
Facilities Dining room; Physical therapy room; Activities room; Laundry room; Barber/Beauty shop.
Activities Games; Movies; Shopping trips; Social/Cultural gatherings.

Denton Good Samaritan Village*
2500 Hinkle Dr, Denton, TX, 76201
(817) 383-2651
Admin Douglas F Wuenschel.
Licensure Skilled care. *Beds* 92. *Certified* Medicaid.
Owner Nonprofit Corp (Evangelical Lutheran/Good Samaritan).
Affiliation Lutheran

Denton Nursing Center*
2229 Carroll Blvd, Denton, TX, 76201
(817) 387-8508
Admin Arveta M Shields.
Licensure Intermediate care. *Beds* 148.
Certified Medicaid.
Owner Proprietary Corp (Truco Inc).

DENVER CITY

Stonebrook Nurse Center*
315 Mustang, Denver City, TX, 79323
(806) 592-2127
Admin Virginia Clegg. *Medical Dir/Dir of Nursing* Carol Jones RN.
Licensure Intermediate care. *Beds* 100.
Certified Medicaid.

DEPORT

Deport Nursing Home
US Hwy 271, Deport, TX, 75435
(214) 652-4410
Admin Martha Castlebury. *Medical Dir/Dir of Nursing* T H Glover MD.
Licensure Intermediate care. *Beds* 102.
Certified Medicaid.
Admissions Requirements Physician's request.
Staff Physicians 1 (pt); RNs 1 (ft); LPNs 5 (ft), 4 (pt); Nurses aides 24 (ft), 6 (pt); Activities coordinators 1 (ft); Dietitians 1 (pt).

Facilities Dining room; Laundry room; Barber/Beauty shop.
Activities Arts & crafts; Cards; Games; Reading groups; Prayer groups; Shopping trips; Social/Cultural gatherings.

DESOTO

DeSoto Nursing Home
1101 N Hampton, DeSoto, TX, 75115
(214) 223-3944
Admin Sylvia Bush. *Medical Dir/Dir of Nursing* Dr McLean; Rebecca Adams DON.
Licensure Intermediate care. *Beds* ICF 120.
Certified Medicaid; Private pay.
Owner Proprietary Corp (Beverly Enterprises).
Admissions Requirements Medical examination; Physician's request.
Staff Physicians; RNs; LPNs; Nurses aides; Physical therapists; Reality therapists; Recreational therapists; Occupational therapists; Speech therapists; Activities coordinators; Dietitians; Dentists; Ophthalmologists; Podiatrists.
Facilities Dining room; Activities room; Crafts room; Laundry room; Barber/Beauty shop.
Activities Arts & crafts; Cards; Games; Reading groups; Prayer groups; Movies; Shopping trips; Social/Cultural gatherings.

Skyline Nursing Home*
PO Box 489, Parkerville Rd at 135 E, DeSoto, TX, 75115
(214) 223-6311
Admin Mike Henrie.
Licensure Intermediate care. *Beds* 110.
Certified Medicaid.
Owner Proprietary Corp (Cantex Healthcare Centers).

DEVINE

Heritage Manor Inc*
104 Enterprize, Devine, TX, 78016
(512) 663-4451 & 663-4452
Admin Eileen Lyall.
Licensure Intermediate care. *Beds* 100.
Certified Medicaid.
Staff RNs 1 (ft); LPNs 4 (ft), 4 (pt); Activities coordinators 1 (ft); Dietitians 1 (pt).
Facilities Dining room; Physical therapy room; Activities room; Chapel; Crafts room; Laundry room; Barber/Beauty shop; Library.
Activities Arts & crafts; Cards; Games; Reading groups; Prayer groups; Movies; Shopping trips; Social/Cultural gatherings.

Heritage Residential Care Center
307 Briscoe Ave, Devine, TX, 78016
(512) 663-2832
Admin Brenda Burford. *Medical Dir/Dir of Nursing* Angel Chapa.
Licensure Custodial care. *Beds* 45.
Owner Proprietary Corp.
Staff LPNs; Orderlies; Nurses aides; Activities coordinators; Dietitians.
Facilities Dining room; Activities room; Laundry room.
Activities Arts & crafts; Cards; Games; Reading groups; Prayer groups; Movies; Shopping trips; Social/Cultural gatherings.

DIBOLL

South Meadows Nursing Home*
900 S Temple Dr, Diboll, TX, 75941
(713) 829-5581
Admin Jo Nell Placker.
Licensure Intermediate care. *Beds* 54.
Certified Medicaid.
Owner Proprietary Corp.

DIMMITT

South Hills Manor*
1619 Butler Blvd, Dimmitt, TX, 79027
(806) 647-3117
Admin Jean B Holt.
Licensure Intermediate care. *Beds* 118.
Certified Medicaid.
Owner Proprietary Corp.

DUBLIN

Dublin Nursing Center
715 Sheehan St, Dublin, TX, 76446
(817) 445-2257
Admin C W Swanner. *Medical Dir/Dir of Nursing* Frances Rinehart.
Licensure Intermediate care. *Beds* 102.
Certified Medicaid.
Owner Privately owned.
Admissions Requirements Medical examination.
Staff RNs; LPNs; Orderlies; Nurses aides; Activities coordinators; Dietitians; Ophthalmologists.
Languages Spanish
Facilities Dining room; Activities room; Laundry room; Barber/Beauty shop.
Activities Arts & crafts; Cards; Games; Reading groups; Prayer groups; Movies; Shopping trips; Social/Cultural gatherings; Meals on Wheels.

Golden Age Manor Nursing Center
Rte 5, Box 4A, 704 Dobkins St, Dublin, TX, 76446
(817) 445-3370
Admin Bobbie M Nichols. *Medical Dir/Dir of Nursing* Jimmie D Walker RN.
Licensure Skilled care; Intermediate care. *Beds* SNF 90. *Certified* Medicaid; Medicare.
Owner Privately owned.
Admissions Requirements Medical examination.
Staff RNs; LPNs; Orderlies; Nurses aides; Activities coordinators.
Facilities Dining room; Activities room; Laundry room; Barber/Beauty shop.
Activities Arts & crafts; Cards; Games; Reading groups; Prayer groups; Movies; Shopping trips; Social/Cultural gatherings.

DUMAS

Dumas Memorial Home*
1009 S Maddox Ave, Dumas, TX, 79029
(806) 935-4143
Admin Faye Lockhart.
Licensure Intermediate care. *Beds* 47.
Certified Medicaid.
Staff LPNs 4 (ft), 2 (pt); Nurses aides 15 (ft), 3 (pt); Activities coordinators 1 (ft); Dietitians 2 (ft).

DUNCANVILLE

Shadyside Nursing Home Inc
330 W Camp Wisdom Rd, Duncanville, TX, 75116
(214) 298-3398
Admin Beverly V Johnson. *Medical Dir/Dir of Nursing* Dr Don E Christiansen.
Licensure Intermediate care. *Beds* 61.
Certified Medicaid.
Admissions Requirements Minimum age 50; Physician's request.
Staff Physicians 5 (pt); RNs 1 (ft); LPNs 4 (ft), 1 (pt); Nurses aides 11 (ft), 5 (pt); Physical therapists 2 (pt) Occupational therapists 1 (pt); Speech therapists 1 (pt); Activities coordinators 1 (ft), 1 (pt); Ophthalmologists 1 (pt); Dentist 1 (pt).

Facilities Dining room; Activities room; Chapel; Laundry room; Barber/Beauty shop.
Activities Arts & crafts; Cards; Games; Prayer groups.

EAGLE LAKE

Heritage House
200 Heritage Ln, Eagle Lake, TX, 77434
(409) 234-3591
Admin Richard A Luebke. *Medical Dir/Dir of Nursing* Raymond R Thomas MD.
Licensure Intermediate care. *Beds* ICF 98.
Certified Medicaid.
Owner Proprietary Corp (ARA Living Centers).
Admissions Requirements Medical examination; Physician's request.
Staff Physicians; LPNs; Orderlies; Nurses aides; Physical therapists; Occupational therapists; Speech therapists; Activities coordinators; Dietitians.
Languages Spanish, Czech, German
Facilities Dining room; Activities room; Crafts room; Laundry room; Barber/Beauty shop.
Activities Arts & crafts; Cards; Games; Reading groups; Prayer groups; Movies; Shopping trips; Social/Cultural gatherings; Senior Olympics.

EAGLE PASS

Canterbury Villa of Eagle Pass
PO Box 1530, 2550 Zacatecas, Eagle Pass, TX, 78852
(512) 773-4488
Admin Faye J Martin. *Medical Dir/Dir of Nursing* Doris Linder LVN.
Licensure Intermediate care. *Beds* ICF 120.
Certified Medicaid.
Owner Privately owned.
Admissions Requirements Medical examination; Physician's request.
Staff RNs 1 (pt); LPNs 7 (ft); Orderlies 7 (ft); Nurses aides 25 (ft); Reality therapists 1 (ft); Recreational therapists 1 (ft); Activities coordinators 1 (ft); Dietitians 5 (ft).
Languages Spanish
Facilities Dining room; Activities room; Chapel; Laundry room; Barber/Beauty shop; Library.
Activities Arts & crafts; Cards; Games; Reading groups; Prayer groups; Movies; Shopping trips; Social/Cultural gatherings.

EASTLAND

Eastland Manor*
1405 W Commerce St, Eastland, TX, 76448
(817) 629-2686
Admin Phillip Dalgleish.
Licensure Intermediate care. *Beds* 102.
Certified Medicaid.
Owner Proprietary Corp (Beverly Enterprises).

Northview Development Center*
411 W Moss St, Eastland, TX, 76448
(817) 629-2624
Admin Lauretta Davis Lawler.
Licensure Intermediate care for mentally retarded. *Beds* 54. *Certified* Medicaid.
Admissions Requirements Minimum age 18; Medical examination; Physician's request.
Staff Physicians 1 (pt); RNs 1 (ft); LPNs 3 (ft), 3 (pt); Nurses aides 14 (ft), 6 (pt); Physical therapists 1 (pt); Recreational therapists 1 (ft); Occupational therapists 1 (pt); Speech therapists 1 (pt); Dietitians 1 (pt); Dentists 1 (pt); Ophthalmologists 1 (pt); Audiologists 1 (pt).
Facilities Dining room; Activities room; Crafts room; Laundry room; Barber/Beauty shop.

Activities Arts & crafts; Cards; Games; Reading groups; Movies; Shopping trips; Social/Cultural gatherings; Camping; Swimming; Hiking; Exercise classes; Make-up classes.

Valley View Lodge*
PO Box 552, 700 S Ostrom St, Eastland, TX, 76448
(817) 629-1779
Admin Judith M Chaney.
Licensure Intermediate care. *Beds* 102.
Certified Medicaid.
Owner Proprietary Corp (Beverly Enterprises).

EDEN

Concho Nursing Center*
PO Box 838, Eaker & Burleson Sts, Eden, TX, 76837
(915) 869-5531
Admin Pearl Murrah.
Licensure Intermediate care. *Beds* 82.
Certified Medicaid.
Owner Proprietary Corp (Unicare).

EDINBURG

Colonial Manor of Edinburg
PO Drawer 308, 1401 S 2nd St, Edinburg, TX, 78540
(512) 383-4978
Admin Harlin L Sadler. *Medical Dir/Dir of Nursing* Phyllis Karr.
Licensure Intermediate care. *Beds* ICF 44.
Certified Medicaid.
Owner Privately owned.
Admissions Requirements Medical examination.
Staff RNs 1 (ft); LPNs 3 (ft); Nurses aides 14 (ft); Activities coordinators 1 (ft); Dietitians 1 (pt).
Languages Spanish
Facilities Dining room; Activities room; Crafts room; Laundry room.
Activities Arts & crafts; Cards; Games; Reading groups; Prayer groups; Movies; Shopping trips; Social/Cultural gatherings.

Retama Manor Nursing Center
1505 S Closner, Edinburg, TX, 78539
(512) 383-5656
Admin Leonides E Molina.
Licensure Intermediate care. *Beds* 104.
Certified Medicaid.
Owner Proprietary Corp (ARA Living Centers).
Staff LPNs 9 (ft); Orderlies 1 (ft); Nurses aides 26 (ft); Activities coordinators 1 (ft); Dietitians 7 (pt); Social workers 1 (ft).
Facilities Dining room; Activities room; Crafts room; Laundry room; Barber/Beauty shop.
Activities Arts & crafts; Cards; Games; Reading groups; Prayer groups; Movies; Shopping trips; Social/Cultural gatherings.

EDNA

Care Inn of Edna
1204 N Wells, Edna, TX, 77957
(512) 782-3581
Admin John E Kraemer. *Medical Dir/Dir of Nursing* Marty Gibson.
Licensure Intermediate care. *Beds* ICF 60.
Certified Medicaid.
Owner Proprietary Corp (ARA Living Centers).
Admissions Requirements Physician's request.
Staff RNs 1 (ft); LPNs 6 (ft), 2 (pt); Nurses aides 20 (pt); Activities coordinators 1 (ft); Dietitians 1 (ft).
Languages Spanish
Facilities Dining room; Activities room; Crafts room; Laundry room; Barber/Beauty shop.

Activities Arts & crafts; Cards; Games; Reading groups; Prayer groups; Movies; Shopping trips.

EL CAMPO

Czech Catholic Home for the Aged
Rte 3, Box 40, El Campo, TX, 77437
(713) 648-2628
Admin Edith Sohrt Molberg. *Medical Dir/Dir of Nursing* Kathy Moore.
Licensure Intermediate care. *Beds* ICF 59. *Certified* Medicaid.
Owner Nonprofit Corp.
Staff RNs 1 (pt); LPNs 7 (ft); Nurses aides 20 (ft), 4 (pt); Activities coordinators 1 (ft); Dietitians 1 (pt).
Affiliation Roman Catholic

Garden Villa Nursing Home*
106 Del Norte Dr, El Campo, TX, 77437
(713) 543-6762
Admin Robert B Reeves.
Licensure Intermediate care. *Beds* 150. *Certified* Medicaid.
Owner Proprietary Corp.

EL PASO

Coronado Nursing Center Inc*
223 S Resler, El Paso, TX, 79912
(915) 584-9417
Admin William Jabalie.
Licensure Intermediate care. *Beds* 120. *Certified* Medicaid.
Facilities Dining room; Activities room; Laundry room; Barber/Beauty shop; Library.
Activities Arts & crafts; Games; Prayer groups; Movies; Social/Cultural gatherings.

El Paso Convalescent Center
11525 Vista Del Sol Dr, El Paso, TX, 79936
(915) 855-3636
Admin Joyce Williams. *Medical Dir/Dir of Nursing* Celia Duron DON.
Licensure Intermediate care. *Beds* ICF 150. *Certified* Medicaid.
Owner Proprietary Corp (Beverly Enterprises).
Admissions Requirements Minimum age 21; Medical examination; Physician's request.
Staff LPNs; Orderlies; Nurses aides; Physical therapists; Occupational therapists; Speech therapists; Activities coordinators; Dietitians.
Languages Spanish
Facilities Dining room; Physical therapy room; Activities room; Crafts room; Laundry room; Barber/Beauty shop; Library.
Activities Arts & crafts; Cards; Games; Reading groups; Prayer groups; Movies; Shopping trips; Social/Cultural gatherings.

Four Seasons Nursing Center of El Paso*
1600 Murchison Rd, El Paso, TX, 79902
(915) 544-2002
Admin Betty Turner.
Licensure Skilled care; Intermediate care. *Beds* 208. *Certified* Medicaid.
Owner Proprietary Corp (Manor Care).

Hillhaven Convalescent Center
2301 N Oregon St, El Paso, TX, 79902
(915) 532-8941
Admin Ann E Albert. *Medical Dir/Dir of Nursing* Robert Zurek MD; Karen Fico RN DON.
Licensure Skilled care; Intermediate care. *Beds* 247. *Certified* Medicaid; Medicare.
Owner Proprietary Corp (Hillhaven Corp).
Admissions Requirements Minimum age 18; Medical examination; Physician's request.
Staff RNs; LPNs; Orderlies; Nurses aides; Physical therapists; Speech therapists; Activities coordinators; Dietitians; Ophthalmologists; Podiatrists.
Languages Spanish

Facilities Dining room; Physical therapy room; Activities room; Crafts room; Laundry room; Barber/Beauty shop.
Activities Arts & crafts; Cards; Games; Reading groups; Prayer groups; Movies; Shopping trips; Social/Cultural gatherings.

Nazareth Hall
4614 Trowbridge Dr, El Paso, TX, 79903
(915) 565-4677
Admin Sr Bernice B Juen. *Medical Dir/Dir of Nursing* Colleen M Gillmouthe RN.
Licensure Intermediate care. *Beds* ICF 50. *Certified* Medicaid.
Owner Nonprofit Corp.
Admissions Requirements Minimum age 18; Medical examination; Physician's request.
Staff Physicians 50 (pt); RNs; LPNs; Nurses aides; Physical therapists; Activities coordinators; Ophthalmologists.
Languages Spanish
Affiliation Roman Catholic
Facilities Dining room; Activities room; Chapel; Crafts room; Laundry room; Barber/Beauty shop; Library.
Activities Arts & crafts; Games; Prayer groups; Movies.

Rest Haven Nursing Home*
2729 Porter Ave, El Paso, TX, 79930
(915) 566-2111
Admin Joseph B Johns.
Licensure Intermediate care. *Beds* 51.
Owner Proprietary Corp.

RN Nursing & Convalescent Home Inc
180 Croom Rd, El Paso, TX, 79915
(915) 772-5480
Admin Joseph Johns. *Medical Dir/Dir of Nursing* Dr W C Autroy; T Saavedra.
Licensure Intermediate care. *Beds* ICF 48.
Owner Privately owned.
Admissions Requirements Medical examination; Physician's request.
Staff Physicians 1 (pt); RNs 1 (pt); LPNs 4 (ft); Orderlies 1 (ft); Nurses aides 15 (ft); Physical therapists 1 (pt); Recreational therapists 1 (pt); Occupational therapists 1 (ft); Activities coordinators 1 (ft); Dietitians 1 (pt); Ophthalmologists 1 (pt).
Languages Spanish
Facilities Dining room; Activities room; Crafts room; Laundry room; Barber/Beauty shop.
Activities Arts & crafts; Cards; Games; Reading groups; Prayer groups; Shopping trips; Social/Cultural gatherings; Picnics; BBQs; Gardening.

Sunset Haven Nursing Center Ltd*
9001 N Loop Dr, El Paso, TX, 79907
(915) 859-1650
Admin Pamela Z Elrod.
Licensure Intermediate care. *Beds* 120. *Certified* Medicaid.
Owner Proprietary Corp.

Vista Hills Health Care Center*
1599 Lomaland Dr, El Paso, TX, 79935
(915) 593-1131
Admin Miguel M Martinez.
Licensure Skilled care; Intermediate care. *Beds* 120. *Certified* Medicaid.
Owner Proprietary Corp (Beverly Enterprises).

White Acres-Good Samaritan Retirement Village & Nursing Center
7304 Good Samaritan Ct, El Paso, TX, 79912
(915) 581-4683
Admin Ronald Fechner. *Medical Dir/Dir of Nursing* Rosa Ninojos DON.
Licensure Intermediate care. *Beds* ICF 60. *Certified* Medicaid.
Owner Nonprofit Corp (Evangelical Lutheran/ Good Samaritan).
Admissions Requirements Medical examination; Physician's request.

Staff RNs 1 (ft); LPNs 7 (ft); Orderlies 5 (ft); Nurses aides 15 (ft); Recreational therapists 1 (ft); Dietitians 1 (ft); Chaplain 1 (ft); Social services 1 (ft).
Languages Spanish
Affiliation Lutheran
Facilities Dining room; Activities room; Chapel; Laundry room; Barber/Beauty shop; Library.
Activities Arts & crafts; Games; Reading groups; Movies; Social/Cultural gatherings.

ELDORADO

Schleicher County Medical Center*
305 Murchison St, Eldorado, TX, 76936
(915) 853-2507
Admin Lilliam M Kroeger. *Medical Dir/Dir of Nursing* Dr H Shih.
Licensure Intermediate care. *Beds* 38. *Certified* Medicaid.
Admissions Requirements Medical examination.
Staff Physicians; RNs; LPNs 7 (ft); Orderlies 2 (ft); Nurses aides 8 (ft); Activities coordinators 1 (ft); Dietitians 4 (ft).
Facilities Dining room; Activities room; Laundry room; Barber/Beauty shop.
Activities Arts & crafts; Cards; Games; Prayer groups; Shopping trips; Annual barbeque for residents' families; Monthly birthday parties.

ELGIN

Elgin Golden Years Retirement Nursing Home*
605 N US Hwy 290, Elgin, TX, 78621
(512) 285-3444
Admin Patricia Ann McCullough.
Licensure Intermediate care. *Beds* 56. *Certified* Medicaid.
Staff RNs 1 (pt); LPNs 4 (ft); Nurses aides 24 (ft), 2 (pt); Activities coordinators 1 (ft), 2 (pt); Dietitians 1 (pt).
Facilities Dining room; Activities room; Laundry room; Barber/Beauty shop.
Activities Arts & crafts; Cards; Games; Prayer groups.

ELKHART

Elkhart Nursing Home Inc*
PO Drawer 7, Jones Rd, Elkhart, TX, 75839
(214) 764-2291
Admin Frank M Bryan.
Licensure Intermediate care. *Beds* 99. *Certified* Medicaid.
Owner Proprietary Corp.

ENNIS

Claystone Manor
PO Box 795, 1107 S Clay, Ennis, TX, 75119
(214) 875-8411
Admin Dorothy Mahoney.
Licensure Intermediate care. *Beds* 120. *Certified* Medicaid.
Owner Proprietary Corp (Beverly Enterprises).

Four Seasons Nursing Center*
1200 S Hall St, Ennis, TX, 75119
(214) 875-2673
Admin Mark R Cummings. *Medical Dir/Dir of Nursing* W D Kinzie MD.
Licensure Skilled care; Intermediate care. *Beds* 154. *Certified* Medicaid.
Admissions Requirements Minimum age 18.
Staff Physicians 9 (pt); RNs 6 (ft); LPNs 13 (ft), 6 (pt); Orderlies 2 (ft); Nurses aides 39 (ft), 11 (pt); Physical therapists 2 (pt); Recreational therapists 1 (ft); Occupational therapists 1 (pt); Speech therapists 1 (pt); Activities coordinators 2 (ft); Dietitians 1 (pt); Dentists 1 (pt); Ophthalmologists 1 (pt); Podiatrists 1 (pt); Audiologists 1 (pt).

Facilities Dining room; Activities room;
Chapel; Crafts room; Barber/Beauty shop;
Library; Living & lounge rooms.
Activities Arts & crafts; Cards; Games;
Reading groups; Prayer groups; Movies;
Shopping trips; Social/Cultural gatherings;
Outside trips; Garden club; College classes.

Odd Fellow & Rebekah Nursing Home*
Rte 1, Oak Grove Rd, Ennis, TX, 75119
(214) 875-8641
Admin David A Dunnahoo.
Licensure Intermediate care. *Beds* 58.
Certified Medicaid.
Owner Nonprofit Corp.
Affiliation Independent Order of Odd Fellows
& Rebekahs

EULESS

Euless Nursing Center
901 Clinic Dr, Euless, TX, 76039
(817) 283-5326
Admin Tina L Johnson. *Medical Dir/Dir of
Nursing* Charles Maxville; Pam Homsher.
Licensure Intermediate care. *Beds* ICF 120.
Certified Medicaid.
Owner Proprietary Corp (Beverly Enterprises).
Admissions Requirements Physician's request.
Staff RNs 1 (pt); LPNs 12 (ft); Nurses aides
26 (ft); Activities coordinators 1 (ft).
Facilities Dining room; Crafts room; Laundry
room; Barber/Beauty shop; Library.
Activities Arts & crafts; Cards; Games;
Reading groups; Prayer groups; Movies;
Social/Cultural gatherings; Monthly outings.

EVANT

January Care Home
506 Circle Dr, Evant, TX, 76525
(817) 471-5526
Admin Sammie Lemons. *Medical Dir/Dir of
Nursing* C B Wright MD; Anita Lofland
DON.
Licensure Intermediate care. *Beds* ICF 53.
Certified Medicaid.
Owner Privately owned.
Admissions Requirements Medical
examination; Physician's request.
Staff Physicians 2 (ft); RNs 1 (ft); Nurses
aides 20 (ft); Activities coordinators 2 (ft);
Dietitians 1 (ft).
Facilities Dining room; Activities room;
Crafts room; Laundry room.
Activities Arts & crafts; Cards; Games;
Reading groups; Movies; Social/Cultural
gatherings.

FAIRFIELD

Fairview Manor*
PO Box 166, Ray at Reunion St, Fairfield,
TX, 75840
(214) 389-4121
Admin Nellie H Halbert.
Licensure Intermediate care. *Beds* 90.
Certified Medicaid.
Owner Proprietary Corp.

FALFURRIAS

Retama Manor Nursing Center*
1301 S Terrell St, Falfurrias, TX, 78355
(512) 325-3691
Admin Ann P Rotge.
Licensure Intermediate care. *Beds* 100.
Certified Medicaid.
Owner Proprietary Corp (ARA Living
Centers).

FARMERS BRANCH

Brookhaven Nursing Center*
5 Medical Pkwy, Farmers Branch, TX, 75234
(214) 247-1000

Admin William A Rohloff. *Medical Dir/Dir of
Nursing* Roger Beaudoing MD.
Licensure Skilled care. *Beds* 102. *Certified*
Medicaid; Medicare.
Admissions Requirements Medical
examination; Physician's request.
Staff RNs 7 (ft), 5 (pt); LPNs 8 (ft); Orderlies
1 (ft); Nurses aides 30 (ft), 6 (pt); Physical
therapists 2 (ft); Occupational therapists 1
(ft), 1 (pt); Speech therapists 1 (ft); Activities
coordinators 2 (ft); Dietitians 1 (ft); Dentists
1 (ft); Ophthalmologists 2 (ft).
Affiliation Lutheran
Facilities Dining room; Physical therapy
room; Activities room; Chapel; Crafts room;
Barber/Beauty shop.
Activities Arts & crafts; Cards; Games; Prayer
groups; Movies; Shopping trips; Social/
Cultural gatherings.

FARMERSVILLE

Hinton Home Inc*
205 Beach St, Farmersville, TX, 75031
(214) 782-6191
Admin Opal Hinton.
Licensure Intermediate care. *Beds* 74.
Certified Medicaid.
Staff RNs 1 (pt); Orderlies 4 (pt); Nurses
aides 28 (ft), 2 (pt); Activities coordinators 1
(ft); Dietitians 1 (pt).
Facilities Dining room; Activities room;
Chapel; Laundry room; Barber/Beauty shop.
Activities Cards; Games; Prayer groups;
Movies; Shopping trips.

FARWELL

Farwell Convalescent Center
PO Box 890, Farwell, TX, 79325
(806) 481-9027
Admin Cara Mirabella. *Medical Dir/Dir of
Nursing* William T Green MD; Mary Kay
Hays DON.
Licensure Intermediate care. *Beds* 94.
Certified Medicaid.
Owner Publicly owned.
Staff LPNs 7 (ft); Nurses aides 35 (ft), 2 (pt);
Activities coordinators 1 (ft).
Languages Spanish
Facilities Dining room; Activities room;
Chapel; Laundry room; Barber/Beauty shop.
Activities Arts & crafts; Cards; Games; Prayer
groups; Movies; Shopping trips; Social/
Cultural gatherings.

FERRIS

Ferris Nursing Care Center
201 E 5th St, Ferris, TX, 75125
(214) 225-7130
Admin Gabriel G Bach PhD. *Medical Dir/Dir
of Nursing* Dr B Nordham; Terri Palos RN.
Licensure Intermediate care. *Beds* ICF 88.
Certified Medicaid.
Owner Proprietary Corp.
Admissions Requirements Medical
examination; Physician's request.
Staff Physicians 1 (pt); RNs 2 (ft); LPNs 6
(ft); Nurses aides 20 (ft); Activities
coordinators 1 (ft); Dietitians 1 (ft).
Languages Spanish, German
Facilities Dining room; Activities room;
Laundry room; Barber/Beauty shop.
Activities Arts & crafts; Cards; Games;
Reading groups; Prayer groups; Movies;
Social/Cultural gatherings.

FLATONIA

Oak Manor Nursing Center*
624 N Converse St, Flatonia, TX, 78941
(512) 865-3571
Admin Debbie Grosenbacher.
Licensure Intermediate care. *Beds* 90.
Certified Medicaid.

Staff Physicians 1 (pt); RNs 1 (pt); LPNs 8
(ft), 2 (pt); Nurses aides 20 (ft), 5 (pt);
Physical therapists 1 (pt); Activities
coordinators 1 (ft); Dietitians 1 (pt); Dentists
1 (pt); Podiatrists 1 (pt).
Facilities Dining room; Activities room;
Crafts room; Laundry room; Barber/Beauty
shop; Library.
Activities Arts & crafts; Cards; Games;
Reading groups; Prayer groups; Movies;
Shopping trips; Social/Cultural gatherings.

FLORESVILLE

Floresville Nursing Home*
1811 6th St, Floresville, TX, 78114
(512) 393-2561
Admin James R Moses.
Licensure Intermediate care. *Beds* 84.
Certified Medicaid.
Owner Proprietary Corp.

FLOYDADA

Floydada Nursing Home*
Box 609, 925 W Crockett, Floydada, TX,
79235
(806) 983-3704
Admin Steve Westbrook.
Licensure Intermediate care. *Beds* 52.
Certified Medicaid.
Owner Proprietary Corp.

FORT STOCKTON

Comanche View Nursing Home*
PO Box 128, 101 N Rooney, Fort Stockton,
TX, 79735
(915) 336-5261
Admin David B Herrell.
Licensure Intermediate care. *Beds* 68.
Certified Medicaid.
Owner Proprietary Corp.

FORT WORTH

Alta Mesa Nursing Center
5300 Alta Mesa Blvd, Fort Worth, TX, 76133
(817) 346-1800
Admin Ruth Cahall. *Medical Dir/Dir of
Nursing* Irving Rapfogel MD.
Licensure Intermediate care. *Beds* ICF 154.
Owner Proprietary Corp.
Admissions Requirements Physician's request.
Staff Physicians 1 (ft); RNs 2 (ft); LPNs 16
(ft); Orderlies 1 (ft); Nurses aides 52 (ft);
Physical therapists 1 (pt); Recreational
therapists 2 (pt); Occupational therapists 3
(pt); Speech therapists 1 (pt); Activities
coordinators 2 (ft); Dietitians 1 (ft);
Ophthalmologists 1 (pt); Podiatrists 1 (pt).
Facilities Dining room; Physical therapy
room; Activities room; Crafts room; Laundry
room; Barber/Beauty shop; Library; Enclosed
patios.
Activities Arts & crafts; Cards; Games;
Reading groups; Prayer groups; Movies;
Shopping trips; Social/Cultural gatherings.

Arlington Heights Nursing Center Inc*
4825 Wellesley St, Fort Worth, TX, 76107
(817) 732-6608
Admin Lisbeth Miller. *Medical Dir/Dir of
Nursing* Randall E Hayes DO.
Licensure Skilled care; Intermediate care. *Beds*
180. *Certified* Medicaid.
Owner Proprietary Corp (Convalescent
Services).
Admissions Requirements Medical
examination; Physician's request.
Staff RNs 3 (ft), 2 (pt); LPNs 22 (ft); Nurses
aides 46 (ft); Activities coordinators 1 (ft);
Dietitians 1 (ft); Psychotherapist 1 (ft).
Facilities Dining room; Physical therapy
room; Activities room; Laundry room;
Barber/Beauty shop.

Activities Arts & crafts; Cards; Games; Reading groups; Prayer groups; Movies; Shopping trips; Social/Cultural gatherings.

Autumn Place*
1617 W Cannon, Fort Worth, TX, 76014
(817) 336-7283
Admin Betty J Ezell.
Licensure Skilled care; Intermediate care. *Beds* 104. *Certified* Medicaid.
Owner Proprietary Corp.

Autumn Years Lodge Inc
424 S Adams, Fort Worth, TX, 76104
(817) 335-5781
Admin Betty L Giaimo. *Medical Dir/Dir of Nursing* George McIlheran Jr MD; Doris Croyle DON.
Licensure Skilled care; Intermediate care. *Beds* SNF 111; ICF 84. *Certified* Medicaid; Medicare.
Owner Proprietary Corp.
Admissions Requirements Medical examination; Physician's request.
Staff Physicians 3 (pt); RNs 3 (ft); LPNs 14 (ft), 3 (pt); Nurses aides 54 (ft), 2 (pt); Physical therapists 1 (pt); Recreational therapists 1 (pt); Occupational therapists 1 (pt); Speech therapists 1 (pt); Activities coordinators 1 (ft); Dietitians 1 (pt); Dentist 1 (pt).
Facilities Dining room; Physical therapy room; Activities room; Chapel; Barber/Beauty shop; Library; Sun lobby.
Activities Arts & crafts; Cards; Games; Reading groups; Prayer groups; Movies; Social/Cultural gatherings.

Brookhaven Nursing & Convalescent Center
4208 E Lancaster, Fort Worth, TX, 76104
(817) 535-0816
Admin Jeannette Medlenka. *Medical Dir/Dir of Nursing* Harold Gaaitzer DO; Therressa Houston LVN.
Licensure Intermediate care. *Beds* ICF 61. *Certified* Medicaid.
Owner Proprietary Corp (Summit Health Ltd).
Admissions Requirements Medical examination; Physician's request.
Staff RNs 1 (ft); LPNs 6 (ft); Nurses aides 16 (ft), 4 (pt); Activities coordinators 1 (ft); Dietitians 1 (ft).
Facilities Dining room; Activities room; Barber/Beauty shop; Sunroom.
Activities Arts & crafts; Cards; Games; Reading groups; Prayer groups; Movies; Shopping trips; Social/Cultural gatherings.

Canteburg Villa of Fort Worth
8401 Jacksboro Hwy, Fort Worth, TX, 76135
(817) 237-3335
Admin Mary E Wolff. *Medical Dir/Dir of Nursing* Dr Howard Graitzer DON; Cameron Farris RN.
Licensure Intermediate care. *Beds* ICF 104. *Certified* Medicaid.
Owner Proprietary Corp (Texas Health Enterprises).
Staff Physicians 1 (ft), 4 (pt); RNs 1 (ft); LPNs 8 (ft), 2 (pt); Nurses aides 24 (ft), 2 (pt); Physical therapists 1 (pt); Speech therapists 1 (pt); Activities coordinators 1 (ft); Dietitians 1 (pt); Dentists 1 (pt); Ophthalmologists 1 (pt); Podiatrists 1 (pt).
Languages Spanish
Activities Arts & crafts; Cards; Games; Reading groups; Prayer groups; Movies; Social/Cultural gatherings.

Colonial Manor Nursing Center
400 S Beach St, Fort Worth, TX, 76105
(817) 535-2135
Admin Ann E Williams. *Medical Dir/Dir of Nursing* Raj VenKatappan; Connie Fincher.
Licensure Skilled care; Intermediate care. *Beds* SNF 62; ICF 119. *Certified* Medicaid; Medicare.
Owner Proprietary Corp.

Admissions Requirements Medical examination; Physician's request.
Staff RNs 2 (ft); LPNs 15 (ft); Orderlies 2 (ft); Nurses aides 54 (ft); Activities coordinators 2 (ft); Dietitians 1 (ft); Dietary Manager 1 (ft).
Facilities Dining room; Activities room; Chapel; Crafts room; Laundry room; Barber/Beauty shop.
Activities Arts & crafts; Games; Movies; Shopping trips; Social/Cultural gatherings.

Crossroads Development Center
5700 Midway, Fort Worth, TX, 76111
(817) 831-6471
Admin Lee A Brown. *Medical Dir/Dir of Nursing* Judy LeMay.
Licensure Intermediate care for mentally retarded. *Beds* ICF/MR 80. *Certified* Medicaid.
Owner Nonprofit organization/foundation.
Admissions Requirements Minimum age 6; Medical examination.
Staff RNs 2 (ft); LPNs 7 (ft); Physical therapists 1 (pt); Recreational therapists 5 (ft); Occupational therapists 1 (pt); Speech therapists 1 (ft); Dietitians 1 (pt).
Facilities Dining room; Physical therapy room; Activities room; Crafts room.
Activities Arts & crafts; Cards; Games; Movies; Shopping trips; Social/Cultural gatherings.

East Park Manor
1000 Park Manor Dr, Fort Worth, TX, 76104
(817) 332-4042
Admin Don King. *Medical Dir/Dir of Nursing* Raj Venkentappen; Sandy McCann-Montez.
Licensure Intermediate care. *Beds* 130. *Certified* Medicaid.
Owner Proprietary Corp.
Staff RNs 1 (pt); LPNs 4 (ft), 4 (pt); Orderlies 4 (ft); Nurses aides 20 (ft); Physical therapists 1 (pt); Recreational therapists 1 (pt); Occupational therapists 1 (pt); Speech therapists 1 (pt); Activities coordinators 1 (ft); Dietitians 1 (pt).
Languages Spanish
Facilities Dining room; Activities room; Crafts room; Laundry room; Barber/Beauty shop.
Activities Arts & crafts; Cards; Games; Reading groups; Prayer groups; Movies; Shopping trips; Social/Cultural gatherings.

Eastwood Village Nursing & Retirement Center*
3825 Village Creek Rd, Fort Worth, TX, 76119
(817) 531-3696
Admin Dovie J Webber.
Licensure Intermediate care. *Beds* 100. *Certified* Medicaid.
Owner Proprietary Corp.

Fireside Lodge Retirement Center Inc
4800 White Settlement Rd, Fort Worth, TX, 76114
(817) 738-6556
Admin Terry McGrath. *Medical Dir/Dir of Nursing* Rita Prestage RN.
Licensure Skilled care; Intermediate care. *Beds* 92. *Certified* All private pay.
Owner Proprietary Corp.
Admissions Requirements Minimum age 21; Medical examination; Physician's request.
Staff RNs 2 (ft); LPNs 4 (ft), 2 (pt); Nurses aides 25 (ft), 8 (pt); Physical therapists 1 (pt); Recreational therapists 1 (ft); Activities coordinators 1 (ft).
Facilities Dining room; Physical therapy room; Activities room; Chapel; Crafts room; Laundry room; Barber/Beauty shop; Library.
Activities Arts & crafts; Cards; Games; Reading groups; Movies; Shopping trips; Social/Cultural gatherings.

Forest Hill Nursing Center Inc*
4607 California Pkwy E, Fort Worth, TX, 76119
(817) 535-0851
Admin Lois M Jenkins. *Medical Dir/Dir of Nursing* William A Griffith DO.
Licensure Skilled care. *Beds* 120. *Certified* Medicaid.
Owner Proprietary Corp (Summmit Health Ltd).
Admissions Requirements Medical examination; Physician's request.
Staff RNs 1 (ft), 2 (pt); LPNs 12 (ft), 3 (pt); Nurses aides 32 (ft), 2 (pt); Reality therapists 1 (ft); Dietitians 1 (pt).
Facilities Dining room; Activities room; Laundry room; Barber/Beauty shop.
Activities Arts & crafts; Cards; Games; Prayer groups; Shopping trips; Social/Cultural gatherings.

Fort Worth Western Hills Nursing Home Inc*
8001 Western Hills Blvd, Fort Worth, TX, 76108
(817) 246-4953
Admin Dorothy Sullivan. *Medical Dir/Dir of Nursing* Dr C E Everett.
Licensure Intermediate care. *Beds* 270. *Certified* Medicaid; Medicare.
Admissions Requirements Minimum age 18; Medical examination; Physician's request.
Staff Physicians 1 (ft); RNs 4 (ft), 1 (pt); LPNs 20 (ft), 1 (pt); Orderlies 1 (pt); Nurses aides 67 (ft), 2 (pt); Physical therapists 1 (ft); Activities coordinators 1 (ft), 1 (pt); Dietitians 1 (ft).
Facilities Dining room; Physical therapy room; Activities room; Chapel; Crafts room; Laundry room; Barber/Beauty shop; TV lounges.
Activities Arts & crafts; Cards; Games; Reading groups; Prayer groups; Movies; Shopping trips; Social/Cultural gatherings; Exercise class.

Four Seasons Nursing Center—North Richland Hills
7625 Glenview Dr, Fort Worth, TX, 76180
(817) 284-1427
Admin Lisbeth Miller. *Medical Dir/Dir of Nursing* Alexander Graham MD; Sue Whitlow RN DON.
Licensure Skilled care; Intermediate care. *Beds* 109. *Certified* Medicaid; Medicare.
Owner Proprietary Corp (Manor Care).
Admissions Requirements Minimum age 21; Medical examination; Physician's request.
Staff RNs 6 (ft), 1 (pt); LPNs 7 (ft), 2 (pt); Nurses aides 29 (ft), 3 (pt); Physical therapists 1 (pt); Speech therapists 1 (pt); Activities coordinators 1 (ft), 1 (pt); Dietitians 1 (pt).
Facilities Dining room; Physical therapy room; Activities room; Laundry room; Barber/Beauty shop; Library.
Activities Arts & crafts; Cards; Games; Reading groups; Prayer groups; Movies; Shopping trips; Social/Cultural gatherings; Adult education; Cooking; Gardening; Pet-a-pet.

Four Seasons Nursing Center—Northwest*
2129 Skyline Dr, Fort Worth, TX, 76114
(817) 626-1956
Admin Kay Severson. *Medical Dir/Dir of Nursing* Barry Ungerleider DO.
Licensure Skilled care; Intermediate care. *Beds* 108. *Certified* Medicaid; Medicare.
Owner Proprietary Corp (Manor Care).
Admissions Requirements Medical examination; Physician's request.
Staff Physicians 1 (ft); RNs 2 (ft), 3 (pt); LPNs 7 (ft), 3 (pt); Orderlies 1 (pt); Nurses aides 27 (ft), 3 (pt); Activities coordinators 1 (ft).
Facilities Dining room; Physical therapy room; Activities room; Laundry room; Barber/Beauty shop.

Activities Games; Prayer groups; Shopping trips; Social/Cultural gatherings.

Francis Convalescent Center*
1000 6th Ave, Fort Worth, TX, 76104
(817) 336-2586
Admin Joan Bingman.
Licensure Skilled care; Intermediate care. *Beds* 130. *Certified* Medicaid.
Staff Physicians 2 (ft); RNs 2 (ft), 3 (pt); LPNs 9 (ft), 3 (pt); Nurses aides 25 (ft), 4 (pt); Physical therapists 1 (ft); Occupational therapists 1 (pt); Speech therapists 1 (pt); Activities coordinators 2 (ft), 1 (pt); Dietitians 1 (ft), 1 (pt); Dentists 1 (pt); Ophthalmologists 1 (pt); Podiatrists 1 (pt); Medical aides 1 (ft), 1 (pt).
Facilities Dining room; Activities room; Crafts room; Laundry room; Barber/Beauty shop; Sunroom.
Activities Arts & crafts; Cards; Games; Reading groups; Prayer groups; Movies; Shopping trips; Social/Cultural gatherings.

Haltom Convalescent Center*
2936 Markum Dr, Fort Worth, TX, 76117
(817) 831-0545
Admin Joan Bellah. *Medical Dir/Dir of Nursing* Charles Riddle MD.
Licensure Intermediate care. *Beds* 146. *Certified* Medicaid.
Owner Proprietary Corp (Convalescent Services).
Admissions Requirements Minimum age 18; Medical examination; Physician's request.
Staff RNs 1 (ft); LPNs 9 (ft); Orderlies 2 (ft); Nurses aides 44 (ft); Activities coordinators 2 (ft).
Facilities Dining room; Activities room; Crafts room; Barber/Beauty shop.
Activities Arts & crafts; Cards; Games; Reading groups; Prayer groups; Movies; Shopping trips; Social/Cultural gatherings.

Hearthstone Nursing Home*
701 Saint Louis, Fort Worth, TX, 76104
(817) 335-4151
Admin Elizabeth A Strange.
Licensure Intermediate care. *Beds* 103. *Certified* Medicaid.
Owner Proprietary Corp.

Jackson Square East Nursing Center
814 Weiler Blvd, Fort Worth, TX, 76112
(817) 451-8111
Admin Mamie Jo Gentry. *Medical Dir/Dir of Nursing* Sherrie A Thomas.
Licensure Skilled care. *Beds* 60. *Certified* Medicaid; Medicare.
Owner Proprietary Corp.
Admissions Requirements Females only.
Staff RNs; Nurses aides; Activities coordinators; Dietitians; LVN.
Facilities Dining room; Activities room; Laundry room; Barber/Beauty shop.
Activities Games; Reading groups; Prayer groups; Movies; Social/Cultural gatherings.

Jackson Square Nursing Center of Texas Inc*
921 W Cannon, Fort Worth, TX, 76104
(817) 332-9261
Admin Linda M Hazel.
Licensure Intermediate care. *Beds* 53. *Certified* Medicaid.
Owner Proprietary Corp.

Jarvis Heights Nursing Center*
3601 Hardy St, Fort Worth, TX, 76106
(817) 625-2739
Admin Carol M Egbert. *Medical Dir/Dir of Nursing* Harold C Shilling MD PA.
Licensure Skilled care. *Beds* 124. *Certified* Medicaid.
Owner Proprietary Corp (Summit Health Ltd).
Admissions Requirements Medical examination; Physician's request.

Staff Physicians 1 (ft); RNs 3 (ft), 2 (pt); LPNs 10 (ft), 7 (pt); Orderlies 1 (pt); Nurses aides 36 (ft), 5 (pt); Activities coordinators 1 (ft), 1 (pt).
Facilities Dining room; Activities room; Laundry room; Library.
Activities Arts & crafts; Cards; Games; Reading groups; Movies; Social/Cultural gatherings.

Kent's Nursing Center
900 W Leuda St, Fort Worth, TX, 76104
(817) 332-7003
Admin Cheryl L Killian.
Licensure Intermediate care. *Beds* ICF 107. *Certified* Medicaid.
Owner Proprietary Corp (Life Care Centers of America).
Admissions Requirements Medical examination; Physician's request.
Staff RNs 1 (ft); LPNs 10 (ft); Nurses aides 30 (ft); Activities coordinators 1 (ft), 1 (pt).
Languages Spanish
Facilities Dining room; Activities room; Crafts room; Barber/Beauty shop; Library.
Activities Arts & crafts; Cards; Games; Reading groups; Prayer groups; Movies.

Lake Worth Nursing Home
4220 Wells Dr, Fort Worth, TX, 76135
(817) 237-6101
Admin Eleanor Hewes. *Medical Dir/Dir of Nursing* H B Stilwell DO.
Licensure Skilled care. *Beds* 104. *Certified* Medicaid; Medicare; VA.
Admissions Requirements Minimum age 16; Medical examination; Physician's request.
Staff RNs 3 (ft); Orderlies 2 (ft); Nurses aides 60 (ft); Activities coordinators 2 (ft); LVNs 15 (ft).
Languages Spanish
Facilities Dining room; Laundry room.
Activities Arts & crafts; Cards; Games; Prayer groups; Movies; Shopping trips; Social/Cultural gatherings.

Lakewood Village Med Center
5100 Randol Mill Rd, Fort Worth, TX, 76112
(817) 451-8001
Admin Weldon Newton. *Medical Dir/Dir of Nursing* Sally Quasada.
Licensure Skilled care. *Beds* SNF 30. *Certified* Medicare.
Owner Nonprofit Corp.
Admissions Requirements Minimum age 62 or disabled; Medical examination.
Staff Physicians 1 (pt); RNs 2 (ft), 2 (pt); LPNs 5 (ft); Nurses aides 13 (ft); Physical therapists 1 (pt); Reality therapists 1 (pt); Recreational therapists 1 (pt); Occupational therapists 1 (pt); Speech therapists 1 (pt); Activities coordinators 1 (ft); Dietitians 1 (pt); Dentists 1 (pt); Ophthalmologists 1 (pt); Podiatrists 1 (pt).
Affiliation Church of Christ
Facilities Dining room; Physical therapy room; Activities room; Chapel; Crafts room; Laundry room; Barber/Beauty shop; Library.
Activities Arts & crafts; Cards; Games; Reading groups; Prayer groups; Movies; Shopping trips; Social/Cultural gatherings; Special programs & entertainment.

Meadowbrook Nursing Home*
3301 View St, Fort Worth, TX, 76103
(817) 531-3616
Admin Phyllis M Massey.
Licensure Skilled care; Intermediate care. *Beds* 187. *Certified* Medicaid.
Owner Proprietary Corp (Beverly Enterprises).

Richland Hills Nursing Home*
3109 Kings Ct, Fort Worth, TX, 76118
(817) 589-2431
Admin Yvonne Jabri. *Medical Dir/Dir of Nursing* John Byarley MD.
Licensure Skilled care; Intermediate care. *Beds* 92. *Certified* Medicaid.

Owner Proprietary Corp (Unicare).
Admissions Requirements Minimum age 16; Medical examination; Physician's request.
Staff RNs 1 (ft), 3 (pt); LPNs 6 (ft), 2 (pt); Orderlies 2 (ft); Nurses aides 34 (ft); Activities coordinators 1 (ft); Dietitians 1 (pt).
Facilities Dining room; Activities room; Laundry room; Barber/Beauty shop.
Activities Arts & crafts; Cards; Games; Prayer groups; Movies; Shopping trips; Social/Cultural gatherings.

Ridgewood Manor*
201 Sycamore School Rd, Fort Worth, TX, 76134
(817) 293-7610
Admin Ruth Cahall. *Medical Dir/Dir of Nursing* David Engleking MD.
Licensure Intermediate care. *Beds* 150. *Certified* Medicaid.
Owner Proprietary Corp (Beverly Enterprises).
Admissions Requirements Medical examination; Physician's request.
Staff Physicians 1 (pt); RNs 1 (ft), 2 (pt); LPNs 9 (ft), 3 (pt); Nurses aides 31 (ft), 5 (pt); Physical therapists 1 (pt); Recreational therapists 1 (pt); Occupational therapists 1 (pt); Speech therapists 1 (pt); Activities coordinators 1 (ft); Dietitians 1 (pt); Dentists 1 (pt); Ophthalmologists 1 (pt); Podiatrists 1 (pt).
Facilities Dining room; Activities room; Chapel; Crafts room; Laundry room; Barber/Beauty shop; Library; Living room; Covered patio; Smoking areas.
Activities Arts & crafts; Cards; Games; Reading groups; Prayer groups; Movies; Shopping trips; Social/Cultural gatherings; Swimming; Baking group; Residents council; Meet the new residents.

River Oaks Care Center
2416 NW 18th St, Fort Worth, TX, 76106
(817) 626-5454
Admin Wesley J Bellah. *Medical Dir/Dir of Nursing* Charles Maxvilldo; Mary Lou Tuey.
Licensure Intermediate care. *Beds* ICF 120. *Certified* Medicaid.
Owner Proprietary Corp.
Admissions Requirements Minimum age 18; Medical examination; Physician's request.
Staff RNs 1 (ft); LPNs 11 (ft); Nurses aides 24 (ft); Activities coordinators 1 (ft); Dietitians 1 (ft).
Languages Spanish
Facilities Dining room; Physical therapy room; Activities room; Barber/Beauty shop; Formal living room; TV room.
Activities Arts & crafts; Cards; Games; Reading groups; Prayer groups; Movies; Social/Cultural gatherings.

Stanford Convalescent Center—Eighth Ave*
1535 Pennsylvania, Fort Worth, TX, 76104
(817) 336-2786
Admin Ollie C Wilson.
Licensure Intermediate care. *Beds* 89. *Certified* Medicaid.

Stanford Convalescent Center Hemphill
1617 Hemphill, Fort Worth, TX, 76104
(817) 926-9201
Admin Patricia Sanders. *Medical Dir/Dir of Nursing* Kenneth Jorns MD; Vera Smith RN DON.
Licensure Skilled care; Intermediate care. *Beds* SNF 59; ICF 73. *Certified* Medicaid; Medicare; VA.
Owner Proprietary Corp (Beverly Enterprises).
Admissions Requirements Physician's request.
Staff RNs 1 (ft); LPNs 11 (ft); Orderlies 6 (ft); Nurses aides 34 (ft), 54 (pt); Occupational therapists; Speech therapists; Activities coordinators; Dietitians; Ophthalmologists; Podiatrists.

Facilities Dining room; Physical therapy room; Activities room; Laundry room; Barber/Beauty shop.
Activities Arts & crafts; Cards; Games; Reading groups; Prayer groups; Movies; Shopping trips; Social/Cultural gatherings.

Stanford Convalescent Center—Jennings
929 Hemphill St, Fort Worth, TX, 76104
(817) 336-9191
Admin Linda Batchelor. *Medical Dir/Dir of Nursing* Dr David Stone; Peggy Watts, RN DON.
Licensure Intermediate care. *Beds* ICF 120. *Certified* Medicaid.
Owner Proprietary Corp (Beverly Enterprises).
Admissions Requirements Minimum age 18; Medical examination; Physician's request.
Staff RNs 1 (ft); LPNs 4 (ft), 1 (pt); Orderlies 2 (ft); Nurses aides 10 (ft); Activities coordinators 1 (ft).
Languages Spanish
Facilities Dining room; Activities room; Crafts room; Laundry room; Barber/Beauty shop; Library.
Activities Arts & crafts; Cards; Games; Reading groups; Prayer groups; Movies; Social/Cultural gatherings.

Stanford Convalescent Center—Pennsylvania*
901 Pennsyvlania, Fort Worth, TX, 76104
(817) 335-3030
Admin Kathleen A Gerrity.
Licensure Intermediate care. *Beds* 125. *Certified* Medicaid.
Owner Proprietary Corp (Beverly Enterprises).

Trinity Terrace
1600 Texas St, Fort Worth, TX, 76101
(817) 338-2400
Admin Wendell D Wilson. *Medical Dir/Dir of Nursing* Candace Burks RN.
Licensure Skilled care. *Beds* SNF 60.
Owner Nonprofit Corp.
Admissions Requirements Minimum age 62; Medical examination; Physician's request.
Staff RNs 3 (ft); LPNs 6 (ft), 3 (pt); Nurses aides 20 (ft); Activities coordinators 1 (ft).
Affiliation Presbyterian
Facilities Dining room; Activities room; Chapel; Barber/Beauty shop; Library.
Activities Arts & crafts; Cards; Games; Reading groups; Prayer groups; Movies; Shopping trips; Social/Cultural gatherings.

Watson Nursing Home
5000 E Lancaster, Fort Worth, TX, 76103
(817) 535-3447
Admin Fred M Reed. *Medical Dir/Dir of Nursing* Tishey G Hughes LVN.
Licensure Intermediate care. *Beds* 69. *Certified* Medicaid.
Owner Proprietary Corp.
Admissions Requirements Medical examination; Physician's request.
Facilities Activities room; Barber/Beauty shop.
Activities Arts & crafts; Cards; Games; Reading groups; Prayer groups; Movies.

Webber Nursing Center
4900 E Berry St, Fort Worth, TX, 76105
(817) 531-3707
Admin Christene Moss. *Medical Dir/Dir of Nursing* Dr Marion J Brooks MD; Patsy Dockery DON.
Licensure Intermediate care. *Beds* ICF 145. *Certified* Medicaid.
Owner Proprietary Corp.
Admissions Requirements Medical examination; Physician's request.
Staff Physicians 1 (ft); RNs 1 (pt); LPNs 10 (ft); Orderlies 1 (ft); Nurses aides 27 (ft), 1 (pt); Physical therapists 1 (pt); Recreational therapists 1 (pt); Occupational therapists 1 (pt); Recreational therapists 1 (pt); Activities coordinators 2 (ft); Dietitians 1 (pt); Ophthalmologists 1 (pt).
Languages Spanish

Facilities Dining room; Activities room; Laundry room; Barber/Beauty shop.
Activities Arts & crafts; Cards; Games; Reading groups; Prayer groups; Movies; Shopping trips; Social/Cultural gatherings; Glee club; Newsletter.

Wedgewood Nursing Home*
6621 Old Granbury Rd, Fort Worth, TX, 76133
(817) 292-6330
Admin Henry C Hames.
Licensure Skilled care. *Beds* 129. *Certified* Medicaid.
Owner Proprietary Corp (Beverly Enterprises).

White Settlement Nursing Center
7820 Skyline Park Dr, Fort Worth, TX, 76108
(817) 246-4671
Admin Betty S Martin. *Medical Dir/Dir of Nursing* Robert Irwin DO; Marcia Spacher.
Licensure Skilled care. *Beds* 108. *Certified* Medicaid; Medicare.
Owner Proprietary Corp (Beverly Enterprises).
Admissions Requirements Minimum age 21; Females only; Medical examination.
Staff Physicians 3 (ft); RNs 4 (ft); LPNs 100 (ft); Orderlies 1 (ft); Nurses aides 29 (ft); Physical therapists 1 (ft); Reality therapists 1 (ft); Recreational therapists 1 (ft); Occupational therapists 1 (ft); Speech therapists 1 (ft); Activities coordinators 1 (ft); Dietitians 1 (ft); Ophthalmologists 1 (ft); Podiatrists 1 (ft).
Facilities Dining room; Activities room; Crafts room; Laundry room; Barber/Beauty shop.
Activities Arts & crafts; Cards; Games; Prayer groups; Movies; Shopping trips; Social/Cultural gatherings.

FRANKSTON

Frankston Nursing Center
PO Box 66, Hwy 155, Frankston, TX, 75763
(214) 876-3208, 876-3209
Admin Ann Davis. *Medical Dir/Dir of Nursing* JoAnn Baxter DON.
Licensure Intermediate care. *Certified* Medicaid.
Owner Proprietary Corp (Beverly Enterprises).
Admissions Requirements Medical examination; Physician's request.
Staff Nurses aides 9 (ft); Activities coordinators 1 (ft); LVNs 3 (ft).
Facilities Dining room; Laundry room; Barber/Beauty shop.
Activities Games; Prayer groups; Movies; Social/Cultural gatherings.

FREDERICKSBURG

Brown's Nursing Home Inc*
Kerr Rte Box 12, W Live Oak Rd, Fredericksburg, TX, 78624
(512) 997-4391
Admin Bernice Dryden. *Medical Dir/Dir of Nursing* Leona Black LVN.
Licensure Intermediate care. *Beds* 92. *Certified* Medicaid.
Staff RNs 1 (pt); Orderlies 2 (pt); Nurses aides 24 (pt); Physical therapists 1 (pt); Occupational therapists 1 (pt); Speech therapists 1 (pt); Dietitians 1 (pt).
Facilities Dining room; Activities room; Chapel; Crafts room; Laundry room; Barber/Beauty shop.

Fredericksburg Nursing Home*
1117 S Adams, Fredericksburg, TX, 78624
(512) 997-4364
Admin Lynn J Hecht.
Licensure Intermediate care. *Beds* 90. *Certified* Medicaid.
Owner Nonprofit Corp.
Affiliation Seventh-Day Adventist

Knopp Nursing Home 2 Inc
Rte 1, Box 311, 202 Hollmig Ln, Fredericksburg, TX, 78624
(512) 997-7924
Admin Jerry M Luckenbach. *Medical Dir/Dir of Nursing* Dr Lorence Fellen; Magdalena Wendel RN DON.
Licensure Intermediate care. *Beds* ICF 60. *Certified* Medicaid.
Owner Proprietary Corp.
Admissions Requirements Minimum age State req; Physician's request.
Staff LPNs 5 (ft), 3 (pt); Nurses aides 12 (ft), 4 (pt); Activities coordinators 1 (ft); Dietitians 1 (ft).
Languages German, Spanish
Facilities Dining room; Activities room; Crafts room; Laundry room; Barber/Beauty shop.
Activities Arts & crafts; Games; Reading groups; Prayer groups; Social/Cultural gatherings.

Knopp Nursing Home Inc 1
1208 N Llano, Fredericksburg, TX, 78624
(512) 997-3704
Admin Irene Luckenbach. *Medical Dir/Dir of Nursing* Joan Lindley.
Licensure Skilled care; Intermediate care; VA contract. *Beds* SNF 44; ICF 89. *Certified* Medicaid; Medicare.
Owner Proprietary Corp.
Admissions Requirements Minimum age State.
Staff RNs; LPNs; Orderlies; Nurses aides; Activities coordinators; Dietitians.
Languages German, Spanish
Facilities Dining room; Physical therapy room; Activities room; Crafts room; Laundry room; Barber/Beauty shop.
Activities Arts & crafts; Games; Reading groups; Prayer groups; Social/Cultural gatherings.

FRIENDSWOOD

Friendswood Arms Convalescent Center*
213 Heritage Dr, Friendswood, TX, 77546
(713) 482-1281
Admin Patricia A Beem.
Licensure Skilled care; Intermediate care. *Beds* 121. *Certified* Medicaid.
Owner Proprietary Corp.

FRIONA

Prairie Acres
201 E 15th St, Friona, TX, 79035
(806) 247-3922
Admin Jo Gene Blackwell. *Medical Dir/Dir of Nursing* Mary Johnston RN DON.
Licensure Intermediate care. *Beds* ICF 65. *Certified* Medicaid; VA.
Owner Publicly owned.
Admissions Requirements Medical examination; Physician's request.
Staff Physicians 2 (pt); RNs 1 (ft); LPNs 5 (ft), 2 (pt); Nurses aides 21 (ft); Physical therapists 1 (pt); Activities coordinators 1 (ft), 1 (pt); Dietitians 1 (ft).
Languages Spanish
Facilities Dining room; Activities room; Chapel; Crafts room; Laundry room; Barber/Beauty shop; Library.
Activities Arts & crafts; Cards; Games; Reading groups; Prayer groups; Movies; Shopping trips; Social/Cultural gatherings; Church services; Exercise classes; Dominos.

GAINESVILLE

Frontier Manor*
1907 Refinery Rd, Gainesville, TX, 76240
(817) 665-0386
Admin Leo A Ladouceur.

Licensure Intermediate care. *Beds* 118.
Certified Medicaid.
Owner Proprietary Corp (ARA Living
Centers).

Gainesville Convalescent Center*
1900 O'Neal St, Gainesville, TX, 76240
(817) 665-2826
Admin Milie P Belcher.
Licensure Intermediate care. *Beds* 120.
Certified Medicaid.
Owner Proprietary Corp (ARA Living
Centers).

Oak Tree Lodge*
Hwy 51, Black Hill Dr, Gainesville, TX,
76240
(817) 665-5221
Admin Linda Edgett. *Medical Dir/Dir of
Nursing* Dr William Powell.
Licensure Intermediate care. *Beds* 48.
Certified Medicaid.
Owner Proprietary Corp (Cantex Healthcare
Centers).
Admissions Requirements Medical
examination; Physician's request.
Staff Physicians 1 (ft); RNs 1 (ft); Nurses
aides 7 (ft), 2 (pt); Physical therapists 2 (ft);
Activities coordinators 1 (ft); Dietitians 1
(ft); Dentists 1 (ft).

GALVESTON

Edgewater Methodist Retirement Community
2228 Seawall Blvd, Galveston, TX, 77550
(409) 765-4403
Admin Andrea F Keith. *Medical Dir/Dir of
Nursing* Edward Lefeber MD; Carol Waters
DON.
Licensure Intermediate care. *Beds* 164.
Certified Medicaid.
Admissions Requirements Minimum age 62;
Medical examination; Physician's request.
Staff Physicians 1 (pt); RNs 7 (pt); LPNs 3
(ft), 13 (pt); Nurses aides 5 (ft), 45 (pt);
Physical therapists 1 (pt); Recreational
therapists 1 (ft); Occupational therapists 1
(ft); Speech therapists 1 (pt); Activities
coordinators 1 (ft); Dietitians 2 (ft); Music
therapist 1 (ft); Social worker 1 (ft); Director
1 (ft).
Affiliation Methodist
Facilities Dining room; Physical therapy
room; Activities room; Chapel; Crafts room;
Laundry room; Barber/Beauty shop; Private
showers in each room.
Activities Arts & crafts; Cards; Games;
Reading groups; Prayer groups; Movies;
Shopping trips; Social/Cultural gatherings;
Cooking club.

GANADO

Care Inn of Ganado*
205 W Rogers St, Ganado, TX, 77962
(512) 771-3315
Admin Judy A Liberda.
Licensure Intermediate care. *Beds* 57.
Certified Medicaid.
Owner Proprietary Corp (ARA Living
Centers).

GARLAND

Castle Manor Nursing Home
1922 Castle Dr, Garland, TX, 75040
(214) 494-1471
Admin Martin Tomerlin.
Licensure Intermediate care. *Beds* 100.
Certified Medicaid.
Owner Proprietary Corp (ARA Living
Centers).
Admissions Requirements Medical
examination.

Staff Physicians 3 (pt); RNs 1 (ft); LPNs 7
(ft), 3 (pt); Orderlies 1 (ft); Nurses aides 20
(ft); Occupational therapists 1 (pt); Speech
therapists 1 (pt); Speech therapists 1 (pt);
Ophthalmologists 1 (pt).
Facilities Dining room; Activities room;
Crafts room; Laundry room; Barber/Beauty
shop.
Activities Arts & crafts; Cards; Prayer groups;
Movies; Social/Cultural gatherings.

Garland Convalescent Center*
321 N Shiloh Rd, Garland, TX, 75042
(214) 276-9571
Admin Henry C Hames. *Medical Dir/Dir of
Nursing* James R McLean DO.
Licensure Intermediate care. *Beds* 120.
Certified Medicaid.
Owner Proprietary Corp (Summit Health Ltd).
Admissions Requirements Minimum age 18;
Physician's request.
Staff Physicians 1 (pt); RNs 1 (ft); LPNs 8
(ft), 1 (pt); Nurses aides 22 (ft); Physical
therapists 1 (pt); Reality therapists 1 (pt);
Recreational therapists 1 (pt); Occupational
therapists 1 (ft); Speech therapists 1 (ft);
Activities coordinators 1 (ft); Dietitians 1
(pt).
Facilities Dining room; Activities room;
Crafts room; Laundry room; Barber/Beauty
shop.
Activities Arts & crafts; Cards; Games;
Reading groups; Prayer groups; Movies;
Shopping trips; Social/Cultural gatherings.

Garland Manors Nursing Home Inc*
2101 W Walnut, Garland, TX, 75042
(214) 276-8547
Admin Billy Ray Jacobs.
Licensure Intermediate care; Custodial care.
Beds ICF 52; Custodial care 8. *Certified*
Medicaid.

Serenity Haven Nursing Home*
106 N Beltline Rd, Garland, TX, 75040
(214) 495-7700
Admin Lois Y Jabri.
Licensure Skilled care; Intermediate care. *Beds*
120. *Certified* Medicaid.
Owner Proprietary Corp (Beverly Enterprises).

Silver Leaves Inc*
505 W Centerville Rd, Garland, TX, 75041
(214) 278-3566
Admin George E Powell.
Licensure Intermediate care. *Beds* 250.
Certified Medicaid.
Owner Proprietary Corp (Beverly Enterprises).
Admissions Requirements Minimum age 18;
Medical examination; Physician's request.
Staff LPNs 13 (pt); Nurses aides 39 (pt);
Reality therapists 1 (ft); Recreational
therapists 1 (ft); Activities coordinators 2
(ft); Dietitians 1 (ft), 1 (pt).
Facilities Dining room; Activities room;
Chapel; Crafts room; Laundry room; Barber/
Beauty shop; Library.
Activities Arts & crafts; Cards; Games; Prayer
groups; Movies; Shopping trips; Social/
Cultural gatherings; Modified sports.

GARRISON

Garrison Nursing Home Inc
PO Box 600, Elm St, Garrison, TX, 75946
(713) 347-2234
Admin Darrell G Yarbrough.
Licensure Intermediate care. *Beds* 43.
Certified Medicaid.
Owner Proprietary Corp.

GATESVILLE

Canterbury Villa of Gatesville
2525 Osage Rd, Gatesville, TX, 76528
(817) 865-2231

Admin Truett Johnson. *Medical Dir/Dir of
Nursing* Rose Mary Colbet DON.
Licensure Skilled care; Intermediate care. *Beds*
SNF 58; ICF 152. *Certified* Medicaid;
Medicare.
Owner Proprietary Corp (Truco Inc).
Admissions Requirements Physician's request.
Staff RNs; LPNs; Orderlies; Nurses aides;
Activities coordinators.
Facilities Dining room; Activities room;
Laundry room; Barber/Beauty shop.
Activities Games; Prayer groups; Shopping
trips.

Hillside Manor Nursing Center*
101 S 34th St, Gatesville, TX, 76528
Admin Vicki Pressley. *Medical Dir/Dir of
Nursing* William F Floyd MD.
Licensure Intermediate care. *Beds* 110.
Certified Medicaid.
Owner Proprietary Corp.
Admissions Requirements Physician's request.
Staff RNs 1 (pt); LPNs 5 (ft), 2 (pt); Nurses
aides 16 (ft); Activities coordinators 1 (ft);
Dietitians 1 (ft).
Facilities Dining room; Activities room;
Laundry room; Barber/Beauty shop.
Activities Arts & crafts; Games; Prayer groups.

GEORGETOWN

Georgetown Sweetbriar Nursing Home Inc
N San Gabriel Park Dr, Georgetown, TX,
78626
(512) 255-2746
Admin Linda L Duncan. *Medical Dir/Dir of
Nursing* Dorothy Hill LN.
Licensure Intermediate care. *Beds* 120.
Certified Medicaid.
Owner Proprietary Corp.
Admissions Requirements Physician's request.
Staff LPNs 10 (ft), 1 (pt); Nurses aides.
Facilities Dining room; Laundry room;
Barber/Beauty shop.
Activities Arts & crafts; Games; Reading
groups; Prayer groups; Movies; Social/
Cultural gatherings.

Wesleyan Nursing Home
2001 Scenic Dr, Georgetown, TX, 78626
(512) 863-9511
Admin Charles Bostock. *Medical Dir/Dir of
Nursing* Dr Douglas Benold; Elaine McAfee
DON.
Licensure Intermediate care. *Beds* ICF 180.
Certified Medicaid.
Owner Nonprofit organization/foundation.
Admissions Requirements Medical
examination; Physician's request.
Staff RNs 2 (ft); LPNs 12 (ft), 4 (pt); Nurses
aides 25 (ft), 12 (pt); Physical therapists 1
(pt); Activities coordinators 1 (ft); Dietitians
1 (ft).
Affiliation Methodist
Facilities Dining room; Activities room;
Chapel; Laundry room; Barber/Beauty shop;
Library.
Activities Arts & crafts; Cards; Games;
Reading groups; Prayer groups; Movies;
Shopping trips.

GIDDINGS

Giddings Convalescent Center
1747 E Hempstead, Giddings, TX, 78942
(409) 542-2150
Admin Mary Halliburton.
Licensure Intermediate care. *Beds* 50.
Certified Medicaid.
Owner Proprietary Corp.

Hennesey Nursing Home Inc
PO Box 540, Giddings, TX, 78942
(409) 542-3611
Admin Tommy G Jackson. *Medical Dir/Dir of
Nursing* Freda Vincent RN DON.

Licensure Intermediate care. *Beds* ICF 92.
Certified Medicaid.
Owner Proprietary Corp.
Admissions Requirements Physician's request.
Staff RNs; LPNs; Orderlies; Nurses aides;
Activities coordinators; Dietitians.
Languages German
Facilities Dining room; Activities room;
Chapel; Crafts room; Laundry room; Barber/
Beauty shop.
Activities Arts & crafts; Games; Prayer groups;
Movies; Shopping trips; Social/Cultural
gathcrings.

GILMER

Gilmer Convalescent & Nursing Center
703 N Titus St, Gilmer, TX, 75644
(214) 843-5529
Admin JoAnn Hinson. *Medical Dir/Dir of
Nursing* Anita Steelman RN.
Licensure Skilled care; Intermediate care. *Beds*
SNF 50; ICF 59. *Certified* Medicaid;
Medicare.
Owner Nonprofit organization/foundation.
Admissions Requirements Medical
examination; Physician's request.
Staff RNs 2 (ft), 2 (pt); LPNs 15 (ft); Nurses
aides 33 (ft), 3 (pt); Activities coordinators 1
(ft); Dietitians 1 (pt).
Affiliation Baptist
Facilities Dining room; Activities room;
Crafts room; Laundry room; Barber/Beauty
shop; Lounges.
Activities Arts & crafts; Cards; Games;
Reading groups; Prayer groups; Social/
Cultural gatherings.

Leisure Lodge—Gilmer*
1704 Bradford St, Gilmer, TX, 75644
(214) 843-5696
Admin J Louise Knight.
Licensure Intermediate care. *Beds* 102.
Certified Medicaid.
Owner Proprietary Corp (Beverly Enterprises).

GLADEWATER

Oak Manor Nursing Home
PO Box 1467, Hwy 80 E, Gladewater, TX,
75647
(214) 845-6933
Admin Alan Loyd. *Medical Dir/Dir of Nursing*
Pat Steelman.
Licensure Intermediate care. *Beds* 120.
Certified Medicaid.
Owner Proprietary Corp (Truco Inc).
Admissions Requirements Minimum age 21;
Medical examination; Physician's request.
Staff LPNs 10 (ft); Orderlies 6 (ft); Nurses
aides 65 (ft); Activities coordinators 2 (ft).
Facilities Dining room; Activities room;
Crafts room; Laundry room; Barber/Beauty
shop.
Activities Arts & crafts; Cards; Games;
Reading groups; Prayer groups; Movies;
Shopping trips; Social/Cultural gatherings.

GLEN ROSE

Harris Manor
PO Box 997, 1309 Holden St, Glen Rose, TX,
76043
(817) 897-2215
Admin Gary A Marks. *Medical Dir/Dir of
Nursing* Jane Wise RN.
Licensure Intermediate care. *Beds* ICF 42.
Certified Medicaid.
Owner Nonprofit Corp.
Admissions Requirements Physician's request.
Staff RNs 1 (ft); LPNs 6 (ft), 2 (pt); Nurses
aides 16 (ft); Activities coordinators 1 (ft);
Dietitians 1 (ft).
Affiliation Methodist

Facilities Dining room; Activities room;
Crafts room; Laundry room; Barber/Beauty
shop; Library.
Activities Arts & crafts; Games; Reading
groups; Prayer groups; Movies; Social/
Cultural gatherings; Church services twice
weekly.

GOLDTHWAITE

Gold Star Nursing Home
1207 Reynolds, Goldthwaite, TX, 76844
(915) 648-2258
Admin Lovell Jewell. *Medical Dir/Dir of
Nursing* Dr Richard Penly; Kyla Berry RN
DON.
Licensure Skilled care; Intermediate care. *Beds*
SNF 50; ICF 84. *Certified* Medicaid;
Medicare VA.
Owner Proprietary Corp.
Admissions Requirements Medical
examination.
Staff RNs 1 (ft), 1 (pt); LPNs 11 (ft), 1 (pt);
Orderlies 3 (ft); Nurses aides 25 (ft), 10 (pt);
Activities coordinators 1 (ft); Dietitians 1
(ft).
Facilities Dining room; Activities room;
Barber/Beauty shop; Library.
Activities Arts & crafts; Games; Reading
groups; Prayer groups; Movies; Social/
Cultural gatherings; Shopping trips.

Heritage Nursing Home Inc*
1207 Reynolds, Goldthwaite, TX, 76844
(915) 648-2258
Admin Beverly K Freeman. *Medical Dir/Dir
of Nursing* Dr M A Childress.
Licensure Skilled care; Intermediate care. *Beds*
134. *Certified* Medicaid.
Staff RNs 1 (ft), 1 (pt); LPNs 6 (ft), 5 (pt);
Orderlies 2 (ft); Nurses aides 22 (ft), 10 (pt);
Activities coordinators 1 (ft); Dietitians 1
(pt).
Facilities Dining room; Activities room;
Crafts room; Laundry room; Barber/Beauty
shop; Library.
Activities Games; Reading groups; Prayer
groups; Shopping trips; Social/Cultural
gatherings.

Hillview Manor
PO Box 588, 1110 Rice St, Goldthwaite, TX,
76844
(915) 648-2247
Admin Beverly Yarborough. *Medical Dir/Dir
of Nursing* Polly Womack.
Licensure Intermediate care. *Beds* ICF 60.
Certified Medicaid.
Owner Proprietary Corp (ARA Living
Centers).
Admissions Requirements Medical
examination.
Staff RNs 1 (ft); LPNs 5 (ft), 1 (pt); Nurses
aides 11 (ft), 3 (pt); Activities coordinators 1
(ft); Dietitians 1 (ft).
Facilities Dining room; Activities room;
Crafts room; Laundry room; Barber/Beauty
shop.
Activities Arts & crafts; Cards; Games;
Reading groups; Prayer groups; Movies;
Social/Cultural gatherings.

GOLIAD

Goliad Manor Inc
106 N Welch St, Goliad, TX, 77963
(512) 645-3352 or 645-2481
Admin Doris Hiilsmeier.
Licensure Intermediate care. *Beds* ICF 60.
Certified Medicaid.
Owner Proprietary Corp (Diversicare Corp).
Admissions Requirements Medical
examination; Physician's request.
Staff LPNs 6 (ft); Nurses aides 20 (ft), 5 (pt);
Activities coordinators 1 (ft); Dietitians 1
(ft).

Facilities Dining room; Activities room;
Laundry room; Barber/Beauty shop.
Activities Arts & crafts; Games; Prayer groups;
Movies; Shopping trips; Social/Cultural
gatherings.

GONZALES

Care Inn of Gonzales
Box 145, Rte 4, Gonzales, TX, 78629
(512) 672-2867
Admin Judith A Pleshek. *Medical Dir/Dir of
Nursing* Lunetta Low.
Licensure Intermediate care. *Beds* ICF 90.
Certified Medicaid.
Owner Proprietary Corp (ARA Living
Centers).
Admissions Requirements Minimum age 18;
Physician's request.
Staff RNs 1 (ft); LPNs 4 (ft), 1 (pt); Nurses
aides 22 (ft), 3 (pt); Activities coordinators 1
(ft).
Languages Spanish
Facilities Dining room; Laundry room.
Activities Arts & crafts; Cards; Games;
Reading groups; Prayer groups; Movies;
Shopping trips; Social/Cultural gatherings;
Exercise class; Reality orientation.

Cartwheel Lodge—Gonzales*
PO Box 659, 1800 Cartwheel Dr, Gonzales,
TX, 78629
(512) 672-2887
Admin Kathy E Powell.
Licensure Intermediate care. *Beds* 98.
Certified Medicaid.
Owner Proprietary Corp.

GORMAN

Canterbury Villa of Gorman
PO Box 668, 600 W Roosevelt St, Gorman,
TX, 76454
(817) 734-2202
Admin Deane Christian. *Medical Dir/Dir of
Nursing* Rena F Rhyne.
Licensure Intermediate care. *Beds* ICF 97.
Certified Medicaid.
Owner Proprietary Corp (Texas Health
Enterprises).
Admissions Requirements Physician's request.
Staff RNs 1 (ft); LPNs 8 (ft); Activities
coordinators 1 (ft); Dietitians 1 (ft).
Languages Spanish
Facilities Dining room; Activities room;
Chapel; Laundry room; Barber/Beauty shop.
Activities Arts & crafts; Cards; Games;
Reading groups; Prayer groups; Movies;
Shopping trips; Social/Cultural gatherings.

GRAHAM

Burgess Manor Nursing Center
1309 Brazos St, Graham, TX, 76046
(817) 549-3760
Admin James D Roberts. *Medical Dir/Dir of
Nursing* Deana J Walker DON.
Licensure Intermediate care. *Beds* ICF 64.
Certified Medicaid.
Owner Proprietary Corp (Beverly Enterprises).
Admissions Requirements Medical
examination; Physician's request.
Staff Physicians 1 (pt); LPNs 3 (ft), 3 (pt).
Facilities Dining room; Activities room;
Crafts room; Laundry room; Barber/Beauty
shop.
Activities Arts & crafts; Cards; Games;
Reading groups; Prayer groups; Movies;
Shopping trips.

Cherry Oaks Nursing Center*
1201 Cherry St, Graham, TX, 76046
(817) 549-3677
Admin Brenda Freeman. *Medical Dir/Dir of
Nursing* Dr R G McDaniels.
Licensure Intermediate care. *Beds* 66.
Certified Medicaid.

Staff LPNs 5 (ft); Orderlies 1 (ft); Nurses aides 11 (ft); Activities coordinators 1 (ft); Dietitians 1 (ft).
Facilities Dining room; Activities room; Chapel; Laundry room; Barber/Beauty shop.
Activities Arts & crafts; Games; Reading groups; Prayer groups; Movies; Shopping trips.

Garden Terrace Nursing Center*
1224 Corvadura St, Graham, TX, 76046
(817) 549-4646
Admin Mary L Shabay.
Licensure Intermediate care. Beds 120. Certified Medicaid.
Owner Proprietary Corp (Beverly Enterprises).

GRANBURY

Granbury Care Center
PO Box 40, 301 Park Dr at Doyle St, Granbury, TX, 76048
(817) 573-3726
Admin Dean E Lindner. Medical Dir/Dir of Nursing Larry G Padget DO.
Licensure Intermediate care. Beds 101. Certified Medicaid.
Admissions Requirements Medical examination; Physician's request.
Staff LPNs 6 (ft), 6 (pt); Nurses aides 29 (ft), 7 (pt); Activities coordinators 1 (ft).
Facilities Dining room; Physical therapy room; Activities room; Chapel; Laundry room; Barber/Beauty shop; Library.
Activities Arts & crafts; Cards; Games; Prayer groups; Movies; Social/Cultural gatherings.

Valley View Home
PO Box 998, Drawer M, 600 Reunion St, Granbury, TX, 76048
(817) 573-3773
Admin Carolyn Sue Wilson.
Licensure Intermediate care. Beds 108. Certified Medicaid.
Owner Proprietary Corp.

GRAND PRAIRIE

Great Southwest Convalescent Center*
2337 Doreen St, Grand Prairie, TX, 75050
(214) 641-2921
Admin Scott W Donaldson. Medical Dir/Dir of Nursing Ben Capote MD.
Licensure Skilled care. Beds 120. Certified Medicaid.
Owner Proprietary Corp (Hillhaven Corp).
Staff RNs 1 (ft), 1 (pt); LPNs 8 (ft), 3 (pt); Orderlies 3 (ft); Nurses aides 55 (ft); Activities coordinators 1 (ft); Dietitians 1 (pt).
Facilities Dining room; Activities room; Crafts room; Laundry room; Barber/Beauty shop.
Activities Arts & crafts; Cards; Games; Reading groups; Prayer groups; Movies.

Kern Place
820 Small St, Grand Prairie, TX, 75050
(214) 262-1351
Admin Millie Westbrook. Medical Dir/Dir of Nursing Philip Pearson DO; Nell Dees RN DON.
Licensure Skilled care; Intermediate care. Beds SNF 150; ICF. Certified Medicaid; Medicare.
Owner Proprietary Corp (Texas Health Enterprises).
Admissions Requirements Medical examination; Physician's request.
Staff Physicians; RNs 2 (ft); LPNs 7 (ft); Nurses aides 13 (ft); Activities coordinators 1 (ft); Dietitians 1 (ft); Social services 1 (ft).
Facilities Dining room; Physical therapy room; Activities room; Chapel; Crafts room; Laundry room; Barber/Beauty shop; Library; 3 courtyards.

Activities Arts & crafts; Cards; Games; Reading groups; Prayer groups; Movies; Shopping trips; Social/Cultural gatherings.

Metroplex Care Center*
658 SW 3rd St, Grand Prairie, TX, 75051
(214) 264-2464
Admin Elma Gloria Gomez.
Licensure Intermediate care. Beds 150. Certified Medicaid.
Owner Proprietary Corp (ARA Living Centers).

GRAND SALINE

Anderson Memorial Care Homes Inc*
PO Drawer K, Bradburn Rd at High St, Grand Saline, TX, 75140
(214) 962-4234
Admin Carolyn E La Prade.
Licensure Intermediate care. Beds 76. Certified Medicaid.
Owner Proprietary Corp.

Grand Saline Manor*
441 Spring Creek Rd, Grand Saline, TX, 75140
(214) 962-4226
Admin James Fleet.
Licensure Intermediate care. Beds 76.
Owner Proprietary Corp (Health Enter of America).

GRANDVIEW

Grandview Nursing Home*
501 W Criner, Grandview, TX, 76050
(817) 866-3367
Admin Linda Rae Smith.
Licensure Intermediate care. Beds 68. Certified Medicaid.
Owner Nonprofit Corp.

GRANGER

Bluebonnet Nursing Center of Granger
Hwy 95 N, Granger, TX, 76530
(512) 859-2800
Admin Lydia Kurtin. Medical Dir/Dir of Nursing Barbara Starling.
Licensure Intermediate care. Beds 68. Certified Medicaid.
Owner Proprietary Corp.
Admissions Requirements Minimum age 18; Medical examination.
Staff RNs 1 (pt); LPNs 4 (ft), 2 (pt); Nurses aides 13 (ft), 6 (pt); Activities coordinators 1 (ft).
Languages Spanish, Czech
Facilities Dining room; Chapel; Laundry room; Barber/Beauty shop.
Activities Arts & crafts; Games; Reading groups; Prayer groups; Social/Cultural gatherings.

GRAPELAND

Grapeland Nursing Home
US 287 at Church St, Grapeland, TX, 75844
(409) 687-4655
Admin Patricia A Jeffcoat. Medical Dir/Dir of Nursing Doris Brown RN.
Licensure Intermediate care. Beds ICF 68. Certified Medicaid.
Owner Proprietary Corp.
Admissions Requirements Physician's request.
Staff RNs 1 (ft); LPNs 6 (ft), 3 (pt); Activities coordinators 1 (ft).
Facilities Dining room; Activities room; Laundry room; Barber/Beauty shop.
Activities Arts & crafts; Games; Reading groups; Movies; Shopping trips; Social/Cultural gatherings.

GRAPEVINE

Brookhollow Manor Nursing Home Inc*
925 Minters Chapel Rd, Grapevine, TX, 76051
(817) 481-1551
Admin Dorothy Johnson. Medical Dir/Dir of Nursing E L Lancaster MD.
Licensure Skilled care; Intermediate care. Beds 78. Certified Medicaid.
Admissions Requirements Medical examination; Physician's request.
Staff Physicians 1 (pt); RNs 2 (ft), 1 (pt); Orderlies 2 (ft); Nurses aides 20 (ft), 1 (pt); Dentists 1 (pt); Podiatrists 1 (pt); LVNs 7 (ft), 1 (pt).
Facilities Dining room; Activities room; Barber/Beauty shop.
Activities Arts & crafts; Cards; Games; Shopping trips; Social/Cultural gatherings.

Grapevine Nursing Home*
1500 Autumn Dr, Grapevine, TX, 76051
(817) 488-8585, 481-3622
Admin Terry J Barcelo.
Licensure Intermediate care. Beds 142. Certified Medicaid.
Owner Proprietary Corp.

GREENVILLE

Greencrest Manor Inc
Box 278A, Rte 6, Greenville, TX, 75401
(214) 455-7942
Admin Martha L Ford. Medical Dir/Dir of Nursing John C Vallancey MD; June Casey Rn DON.
Licensure Intermediate care. Beds ICF 112. Certified Medicaid.
Owner Proprietary Corp (Hillhaven Corp).
Admissions Requirements Medical examination; Physician's request.
Staff RNs 2 (ft); LPNs 9 (ft); Nurses aides 17 (ft); Physical therapists 1 (pt); Speech therapists 1 (pt); Activities coordinators 1 (ft); Dietitians 1 (pt); Dentists 1 (pt); Ophthalmologists 1 (pt); Podiatrists 1 (pt).
Facilities Dining room; Activities room; Laundry room; Barber/Beauty shop.
Activities Arts & crafts; Cards; Games; Reading groups; Prayer groups; Movies; Shopping trips; Social/Cultural gatherings.

Greenville Nursing Home Inc*
4910 Wellington, Greenville, TX, 75401
(214) 454-3772
Admin Myra L Porter.
Licensure Skilled care; Intermediate care. Beds 120. Certified Medicaid.
Owner Proprietary Corp (Beverly Enterprises).

Home for Aged Pythians Inc
6017 Interstate 30, Greenville, TX, 75401
(214) 455-0180
Admin Barbara Thomas. Medical Dir/Dir of Nursing John C Vallancey MD; Diana Straach LVN DON.
Licensure Intermediate care. Beds ICF 48. Certified Medicaid.
Owner Nonprofit organization/foundation.
Admissions Requirements Minimum age 62; Physician's request.
Staff Physicians; Nurses aides 6 (ft); Activities coordinators 1 (ft); LVNs 7 (ft).
Affiliation Knights of Pythias
Facilities Dining room; Activities room; Crafts room; Laundry room; Barber/Beauty shop; Library.
Activities Arts & crafts; Games; Reading groups; Prayer groups; Movies; Shopping trips; Social/Cultural gatherings.

Park Haven Nursing Center Inc
3500 Park St, Greenville, TX, 75401
(214) 455-2220
Admin Carolyn Vinson. Medical Dir/Dir of Nursing John C Vallancey MD; Lee Frazier RN.

Licensure Skilled care. *Beds* SNF 100.
Certified Medicaid; Medicare.
Owner Proprietary Corp (Hillhaven Corp).
Admissions Requirements Physician's request.
Staff Physicians 1 (pt); RNs 3 (ft), 1 (pt);
LPNs 10 (ft), 2 (pt); Nurses aides 30 (ft);
Activities coordinators 1 (ft).
Facilities Dining room; Activities room;
Chapel; Crafts room; Laundry room; Barber/
Beauty shop; Library.
Activities Arts & crafts; Games; Reading
groups; Prayer groups; Movies; Social/
Cultural gatherings.

GROESBECK

Park Plaza Nursing Center
607 Parkside Dr, Groesbeck, TX, 76642
(817) 729-3245
Admin Martha Saling. *Medical Dir/Dir of
Nursing* Dorothy Outlaw.
Licensure Intermediate care. *Beds* ICF 90.
Certified Medicaid.
Owner Proprietary Corp.
Admissions Requirements Minimum age 18;
Medical examination.
Staff Physicians 4 (ft); RNs 1 (ft); LPNs 6 (ft);
Orderlies 2 (ft); Nurses aides 18 (ft);
Physical therapists 1 (ft); Speech therapists 1
(ft); Activities coordinators 1 (ft); Dietitians
1 (ft); Ophthalmologists 1 (ft); Podiatrists 1
(ft).
Facilities Dining room; Physical therapy
room; Activities room; Crafts room; Laundry
room; Barber/Beauty shop.
Activities Arts & crafts; Cards; Games;
Reading groups; Prayer groups; Movies;
Shopping trips; Social/Cultural gatherings;
Picnics.

GROVES

Cresthaven Nursing Residence*
4400 Gulf Ave, Groves, TX, 77619
(713) 962-5785
Admin Joyce N Lewis. *Medical Dir/Dir of
Nursing* Dr H H Randolph Jr.
Licensure Skilled care; Intermediate care. *Beds*
138. *Certified* Medicaid.
Owner Proprietary Corp (Cantex Healthcare
Centers).
Staff Physicians 1 (pt); RNs 1 (ft), 2 (pt);
LPNs 13 (ft); Orderlies 2 (ft); Nurses aides
29 (pt); Activities coordinators 1 (ft), 1 (pt);
Dietitians 1 (ft), 1 (pt); Dentists 1 (pt).
Facilities Dining room; Activities room;
Chapel; Crafts room; Laundry room; Barber/
Beauty shop.
Activities Arts & crafts; Cards; Games;
Reading groups; Prayer groups; Movies;
Social/Cultural gatherings.

Oak Grove Nursing Home Inc*
6230 Warren St, Groves, TX, 77619
(713) 963-1266
Admin Lois Rushing.
Licensure Intermediate care. *Beds* 100.
Certified Medicaid.
Owner Proprietary Corp.

GROVETON

Groveton Hospital & Nursing Home
PO Box 890, Hwy 287, Groveton, TX, 75845
(409) 642-1221
Admin Beth Thornton. *Medical Dir/Dir of
Nursing* Reatha Duke LVN.
Licensure Intermediate care. *Beds* ICF 35.
Certified Medicaid.
Owner Nonprofit organization/foundation.
Admissions Requirements Minimum age 18.
Staff RNs; LPNs; Nurses aides; Activities
coordinators.
Facilities Dining room; Activities room;
Barber/Beauty shop.
Activities Arts & crafts; Games; Prayer groups.

GUNTER

Hilltop Haven Home for the Aged
308 E College St, Gunter, TX, 75058
(214) 433-2415
Admin Linda Morrison.
Licensure Intermediate care; Custodial care.
Beds ICF 215. *Certified* Medicaid.
Admissions Requirements Minimum age 16;
Medical examination; Physician's request.
Staff RNs 1 (ft); LPNs 13 (ft), 6 (pt);
Orderlies 1 (ft), 1 (pt); Nurses aides 53 (ft),
7 (pt); Activities coordinators 2 (ft);
Dietitians 18 (ft), 5 (pt).
Affiliation Church of Christ
Facilities Dining room; Activities room;
Chapel; Crafts room; Laundry room; Barber/
Beauty shop; Library.
Activities Arts & crafts; Cards; Games; Prayer
groups; Movies; Shopping trips.

HALE CENTER

Hi-Plains Nursing Home*
202 W 3rd, Hale Center, TX, 79041
(806) 839-2471
Admin Gordon Russell.
Licensure Intermediate care. *Beds* 44.
Certified Medicaid.
Owner Nonprofit Corp.

HALLETTSVILLE

Stevens Convalescent Center Inc
PO Box 526, 106 Kahn St, Hallettsville, TX,
77964
(512) 798-3606
Admin Joseph C Bonck JR. *Medical Dir/Dir
of Nursing* Mary Lynn Hamel RN DON.
Licensure Intermediate care. *Beds* ICF 190.
Certified Medicaid; VA.
Owner Proprietary Corp (National Heritage).
Staff Physicians 4 (ft); RNs 1 (ft); LPNs 25
(ft); Orderlies 2 (ft); Nurses aides 84 (ft);
Physical therapists 1 (ft); Activities
coordinators 3 (ft); Dietitians 1 (ft).
Languages Spanish, German
Facilities Dining room; Physical therapy
room; Activities room; Chapel; Crafts room;
Laundry room; Barber/Beauty shop.
Activities Arts & crafts; Cards; Games;
Reading groups; Prayer groups; Movies;
Shopping trips; Social/Cultural gatherings.

HAMILTON

Forest Oaks Nursing Home*
726 E Coke St, Hamilton, TX, 76531
(817) 386-5319
Admin Forrest S Tatum.
Licensure Intermediate care. *Beds* 28.
Certified Medicaid.
Staff RNs 1 (pt); LPNs 3 (ft); Nurses aides 5
(ft), 1 (pt); Activities coordinators 1 (ft);
Dietitians 1 (ft).
Facilities Dining room; Activities room.
Activities Arts & crafts; Cards; Games;
Movies; Social/Cultural gatherings.

Hamilton Nursing Home
205 W Gentry St, Hamilton, TX, 76531
(817) 386-3106
Admin Georgia M Robinson. *Medical Dir/Dir
of Nursing* Foster Lee Wilcox.
Licensure Intermediate care. *Beds* ICF 41.
Certified Medicare.
Owner Privately owned.
Admissions Requirements Minimum age 21.
Staff RNs 2 (ft); LPNs 4 (ft); Nurses aides 10
(ft); Activities coordinators 1 (ft); Dietitians
1 (ft).
Facilities Dining room; Barber/Beauty shop.
Activities Arts & crafts; Games; Movies;
Shopping trips; Social/Cultural gatherings.

Hillcrest Nursing Home
400 W Grogan, Hamilton, TX, 76531
(817) 386-3171
Admin Martin R Hubbartt. *Medical Dir/Dir of
Nursing* C B Wright; Martha Willis RN
DON.
Licensure Intermediate care. *Beds* ICF 78.
Certified Medicaid.
Owner Privately owned.
Admissions Requirements Medical
examination; Physician's request.
Staff Physicians 2 (pt); RNs 1 (ft), 1 (pt);
LPNs 5 (ft), 2 (pt); Orderlies 2 (ft), 1 (pt);
Nurses aides 16 (ft), 4 (pt); Activities
coordinators 1 (ft); Dietitians 1 (ft), 1 (pt);
Chaplain 1 (ft).
Languages Spanish, Portuguese
Facilities Dining room; Activities room;
Chapel; Laundry room; Barber/Beauty shop;
Billard room.
Activities Cards; Games; Prayer groups;
Movies; Social/Cultural gatherings.

Leisure Lodge—Hamilton*
910 E Pierson, Hamilton, TX, 76531
(817) 386-8113
Admin Dennis P Dorton.
Licensure Intermediate care. *Beds* 96.
Certified Medicaid.
Owner Proprietary Corp (Beverly Enterprises).

HAMLIN

Holiday Lodge*
PO Box 381, 425 SW Ave F, Hamlin, TX,
79520
(915) 576-3643
Admin James B Crowley.
Licensure Intermediate care. *Beds* 60.
Certified Medicaid.
Owner Proprietary Corp.

HAMPSTEAD

Hampstead Nursing Home*
1111 San Antonio, Hampstead, TX, 77445
(713) 816-3382, 6220
Admin Joyce Brokmeyer.
Licensure Skilled care; Intermediate care. *Beds*
110. *Certified* Medicaid; Medicare.
Owner Proprietary Corp.

HARLINGEN

Harlingen Good Samaritan Center
4301 S "F" St, Harlingen, TX, 78550
(512) 423-4959
Admin Darrold Nies. *Medical Dir/Dir of
Nursing* Betty Randgaard RN.
Licensure Intermediate care. *Beds* ICF 112.
Certified Medicaid.
Owner Nonprofit Corp (Evangelical Lutheran/
Good Samaritan).
Admissions Requirements Physician's request.
Staff RNs 1 (ft); LPNs 10 (ft), 4 (pt);
Orderlies; Nurses aides; Activities
coordinators 1 (ft).
Languages Spanish, German
Affiliation Lutheran
Facilities Dining room; Physical therapy
room; Laundry room; Barber/Beauty shop.
Activities Arts & crafts; Cards; Games; Prayer
groups; Movies; Shopping trips.

Retama Manor Nursing Center—Harlingen*
2201 Pease St, Harlingen, TX, 78550
(512) 423-2663
Admin Edelmira Resendez.
Licensure Intermediate care. *Beds* 197.
Certified Medicaid.
Owner Proprietary Corp (ARA Living
Centers).

TLC Nursing Center*
2204 Pease, Harlingen, TX, 78550
(512) 425-2812

Admin Martha Ann Hamby. *Medical Dir/Dir of Nursing* Sam Carter MD.
Licensure Skilled care; Intermediate care. *Beds* 120. *Certified* Medicaid.
Owner Proprietary Corp (Hillhaven Corp).
Admissions Requirements Medical examination.
Staff RNs 3 (ft), 4 (pt); LPNs 12 (ft), 3 (pt); Orderlies 4 (ft), 2 (pt); Nurses aides 24 (ft), 4 (pt); Activities coordinators 1 (ft), 1 (pt); Dietitians 1 (ft).
Facilities Dining room; Activities room; Crafts room; Laundry room; Barber/Beauty shop.

HASKELL

Haskell Nursing Center
PO Box 1086, 1504 N 1st St, Haskell, TX, 79521-1086
(817) 864-3556
Admin Lorene A Beason.
Licensure Intermediate care. *Beds* 68. *Certified* Medicaid.
Owner Proprietary Corp (Beverly Enterprises).

Rice Springs Care Home Inc
Box 640, Rte 1, 1302 N 1st St, Haskell, TX, 79521
(817) 864-2652, 864-2653
Admin Ruth Ann Klose. *Medical Dir/Dir of Nursing* Donna Tidrow.
Licensure Intermediate care. *Beds* ICF 82. *Certified* Medicaid.
Owner Proprietary Corp.
Admissions Requirements Medical examination; Physician's request.
Staff RNs; LPNs; Orderlies; Nurses aides; Activities coordinators; Dietitians.
Facilities Dining room; Activities room; Crafts room; Laundry room; Barber/Beauty shop.
Activities Arts & crafts; Cards; Games; Reading groups; Prayer groups; Movies; Shopping trips; Social/Cultural gatherings.

HAWKINS

Hawkins Care Center
PO Box 430, Hawkins, TX, 75765
(214) 769-2941
Admin Lavonia J Stone. *Medical Dir/Dir of Nursing* Dr R A Lester III; Imarene Anders DON.
Licensure Intermediate care. *Beds* ICF 46. *Certified* Medicaid.
Owner Proprietary Corp (Health Enter of America).
Admissions Requirements Physician's request.
Staff Physicians 1 (ft); RNs 1 (pt); LPNs 4 (ft), 1 (pt); Nurses aides 10 (ft), 3 (pt); Physical therapists 1 (pt); Reality therapists 1 (pt); Recreational therapists 1 (pt); Occupational therapists 1 (pt); Speech therapists 1 (pt); Activities coordinators 1 (ft); Dietitians 1 (ft); Ophthalmologists 1 (pt).
Facilities Dining room; Laundry room; Barber/Beauty shop.
Activities Arts & crafts; Cards; Games; Reading groups; Prayer groups; Movies; Shopping trips; Social/Cultural gatherings.

HEARNE

Leisure Lodge—Hearne*
1100 Brown St, Hearne, TX, 77859
(713) 279-5361
Admin Velma Windham.
Licensure Intermediate care. *Beds* 148. *Certified* Medicaid.
Owner Proprietary Corp (Beverly Enterprises).

HENDERSON

Leisure Lodge—Henderson*
1010 W Main, Henderson, TX, 75652
(214) 657-6513
Admin Marilyn A Johnson.
Licensure Intermediate care. *Beds* 179. *Certified* Medicaid.
Owner Proprietary Corp (Beverly Enterprises).
Staff LPNs 9 (ft), 2 (pt); Nurses aides 44 (ft), 7 (pt).
Facilities Dining room; Laundry room; Barber/Beauty shop.
Activities Arts & crafts; Games; Reading groups; Prayer groups; Movies; Social/Cultural gatherings.

Southwood Convalescent Center Inc
PO Box 1066, Henderson, TX, 75653
(214) 657-6506
Admin Gloria L George. *Medical Dir/Dir of Nursing* Barbara Tate.
Licensure Intermediate care. *Beds* ICF 160. *Certified* Medicaid.
Owner Privately owned.
Staff RNs; LPNs; Nurses aides; Activities coordinators; Dietitians.
Activities Arts & crafts; Cards; Games; Reading groups; Movies; Social/Cultural gatherings.

HENRIETTA

Bur-Mont Nursing Center*
Hwy 287 E, Henrietta, TX, 76365
(817) 538-5665
Admin Rebecca Rae Spikes.
Licensure Intermediate care. *Beds* 90. *Certified* Medicaid.
Owner Nonprofit Corp.

Henrietta Care Center
PO Box 7635, 807 W Bois D'Arc, Henrietta, TX, 76365
(817) 538-4303
Admin Robert G Holmes.
Licensure Intermediate care. *Beds* 60. *Certified* Medicaid.
Owner Proprietary Corp (Comprehensive Health Care Assn).

HEREFORD

King's Manor Methodist Home*
430 Ranger Dr, Hereford, TX, 79045
(806) 364-0661
Admin Joyce L Lyons.
Licensure Intermediate care. *Beds* 79. *Certified* Medicaid.
Admissions Requirements Medical examination; Physician's request.
Staff Physicians 5 (ft); RNs 1 (ft), 1 (pt); LPNs 12 (ft); Nurses aides 35 (ft); Activities coordinators 2 (ft); Dietitians 1 (pt).
Affiliation Methodist
Facilities Dining room; Chapel; Laundry room; Barber/Beauty shop; Library.
Activities Arts & crafts; Cards; Games; Shopping trips.

HICO

Village Nursing Home*
Hemphill & Railroad Sts, Hico, TX, 76457
(817) 796-2111
Admin Velaine Swedelius.
Licensure Intermediate care. *Beds* 114. *Certified* Medicaid.
Admissions Requirements Physician's request.
Staff LPNs 8 (ft); Nurses aides 32 (ft); Activities coordinators 1 (ft); Dietitians 1 (ft).

Facilities Dining room; Activities room; Laundry room.
Activities Arts & crafts; Cards; Games; Reading groups; Prayer groups; Movies; Shopping trips; Social/Cultural gatherings.

HILLSBORO

Canterbury Villa of Hillsboro
Rte 3, Box 304, Hillsboro, TX, 76645
(817) 582-8416
Admin Verna Gibson. *Medical Dir/Dir of Nursing* Nancy Coffey.
Licensure Intermediate care. *Beds* ICF 166. *Certified* Medicaid.
Owner Proprietary Corp (Health Enter of America).
Admissions Requirements Medical examination; Physician's request.
Staff RNs 1 (ft); LPNs 11 (ft); Orderlies 2 (ft); Nurses aides 50 (ft); Activities coordinators 1 (ft); Dietitians 1 (ft).
Facilities Dining room; Activities room; Chapel; Crafts room; Laundry room; Barber/Beauty shop.
Activities Arts & crafts; Cards; Games; Reading groups; Prayer groups; Movies; Social/Cultural gatherings.

Town Hall Estates
300 Happy Ln, Hillsboro, TX, 76645
(817) 582-8482
Admin R Edward Lowe. *Medical Dir/Dir of Nursing* Sharon Maass.
Licensure Intermediate care. *Beds* 118. *Certified* Medicaid.
Owner Nonprofit Corp.
Staff RNs 1 (pt); LPNs 11 (ft), 1 (pt); Nurses aides 40 (ft), 10 (pt); Activities coordinators 1 (ft).
Facilities Dining room; Chapel; Barber/Beauty shop.
Activities Games; Social/Cultural gatherings.

HITCHCOCK

Hitchcock Nursing Home*
6701 FM 2004, Hitchcock, TX, 77563
(713) 986-6516
Admin Ann Wallace.
Licensure Intermediate care. *Beds* 60. *Certified* Medicaid.
Admissions Requirements Physician's request.
Staff Physicians 1 (pt); RNs 1 (pt); LPNs 4 (ft); Nurses aides 15 (ft), 5 (pt); Physical therapists 1 (pt); Recreational therapists 1 (pt); Activities coordinators 1 (ft); Dietitians 1 (pt).
Facilities Dining room; Activities room; Crafts room; Laundry room; Barber/Beauty shop.
Activities Arts & crafts; Cards; Games; Prayer groups; Shopping trips; Social/Cultural gatherings.

HOLLAND

K'Way Kare Nursing Home
PO Box 209, 610 Josephine St, Holland, TX, 76534
(817) 657-2494
Admin Gilbert W Goodnight. *Medical Dir/Dir of Nursing* Cynthia Pacha LVN.
Licensure Intermediate care. *Beds* ICF 31. *Certified* Medicaid.
Owner Privately owned.
Admissions Requirements Medical examination.
Facilities Dining room; Activities room; Crafts room; Laundry room.
Activities Arts & crafts; Cards; Games; Reading groups; Prayer groups; Movies; Social/Cultural gatherings.

HONDO

Community Care Center
2001 Ave E, Hondo, TX, 78861
(512) 426-3087
Admin Virginia Lamza. *Medical Dir/Dir of Nursing* Betty Frieda.
Licensure Skilled care. *Beds* SNF 75. *Certified* Medicaid; Medicare.
Owner Proprietary Corp (Columbia Corp).
Admissions Requirements Minimum age 14; Medical examination.
Staff Physicians 4 (pt); RNs 1 (ft), 1 (pt); LPNs 7 (ft), 1 (pt); Nurses aides 30 (ft); Physical therapists 1 (pt); Reality therapists 1 (pt); Activities coordinators 1 (ft); Dietitians 1 (pt); Dentists 1 (pt); Dentist 1 (pt).
Languages Spanish, German
Facilities Dining room; Activities room; Crafts room; Laundry room; Barber/Beauty shop.
Activities Arts & crafts; Cards; Games; Reading groups; Prayer groups; Movies; Shopping trips; Social/Cultural gatherings.

Heritage Manor Care Center of Hondo Inc
3002 Ave Q, Hondo, TX, 78861
(512) 426-3057
Admin Myrtle Andrews. *Medical Dir/Dir of Nursing* Dr John Meyer; Gia Sabiat RN DON.
Licensure Skilled care; Intermediate care. *Beds* SNF 118; ICF. *Certified* Medicaid; Medicare.
Owner Proprietary Corp.
Admissions Requirements Medical examination; Physician's request.
Staff RNs; LPNs 4 (ft); Orderlies 1 (ft); Nurses aides 13 (ft); Activities coordinators 1 (ft).
Languages Spanish, Italian, German
Facilities Dining room; Physical therapy room; Activities room; Laundry room; Barber/Beauty shop.
Activities Arts & crafts; Cards; Games; Reading groups; Prayer groups; Movies; Shopping trips; Social/Cultural gatherings; Picnics.

HONEY GROVE

Grove Manor Nursing Home Inc
Rte 2, Honey Grove, TX, 75446
(214) 378-2293
Admin Alice J Edelhauser. *Medical Dir/Dir of Nursing* Jeff Duncan MD; Sheryl Brinlee RN DON.
Licensure Intermediate care. *Beds* ICF 90. *Certified* Medicaid.
Owner Proprietary Corp.
Admissions Requirements Medical examination; Physician's request.
Staff RNs 1 (ft); LPNs 5 (ft), 3 (pt); Nurses aides 17 (ft), 2 (pt); Physical therapists 1 (pt); Activities coordinators 1 (ft); Dietitians 1 (pt); Ophthalmologists 1 (pt).
Facilities Dining room; Activities room; Chapel; Laundry room; Barber/Beauty shop.
Activities Games; Prayer groups; Movies; Social/Cultural gatherings.

HOUSTON

Afton Oaks Nursing Center
7514 Kingsley, Houston, TX, 77087
(713) 644-8393
Admin Leonard C Goodin. *Medical Dir/Dir of Nursing* A O'Dwyer MD; Sherlyn Gidney RN DON.
Licensure Skilled care; Intermediate care. *Beds* 170. *Certified* Medicaid; Medicare.
Owner Proprietary Corp.
Admissions Requirements Minimum age 21; Medical examination; Physician's request.

Staff Physicians 1 (pt); RNs 9 (ft); LPNs 28 (ft); Nurses aides 42 (ft); Physical therapists 3 (pt); Recreational therapists 1 (pt); Occupational therapists 2 (pt); Speech therapists 1 (pt); Activities coordinators 1 (ft); Dietitians 1 (pt); Ophthalmologists 1 (pt); Podiatrists 1 (pt).
Facilities Dining room; Activities room; Chapel; Crafts room; Laundry room; Barber/Beauty shop; Library.
Activities Arts & crafts; Cards; Games; Reading groups; Prayer groups; Movies; Shopping trips; Social/Cultural gatherings.

Autumn Hills Convalescent Center
617 W Janisch, Houston, TX, 77018
(713) 697-2891
Admin Mr Del Waggoner. *Medical Dir/Dir of Nursing* Mrs Martha Sellers RN DON.
Licensure Intermediate care. *Beds* ICF 119. *Certified* Medicaid.
Owner Proprietary Corp.
Admissions Requirements Medical examination; Physician's request.
Staff RNs; LPNs; Orderlies; Nurses aides; Activities coordinators; Dietitians.
Facilities Dining room; Activities room; Crafts room; Laundry room; Barber/Beauty shop; Library.
Activities Arts & crafts; Cards; Games; Reading groups; Prayer groups; Movies; Shopping trips; Social/Cultural gatherings.

Bayou Glen Jones Road
10851 Crescent Moon Rd, Houston, TX, 77064
(713) 890-0171
Admin Sherry A Reid. *Medical Dir/Dir of Nursing* B Vu MD; Velma Gleason RN DON.
Licensure Intermediate care. *Beds* ICF 120; Private 60. *Certified* Medicaid.
Owner Proprietary Corp (Convalescent Services).
Admissions Requirements Medical examination.
Staff RNs 5 (ft), 4 (pt); LPNs 8 (ft), 3 (pt); Orderlies 1 (ft); Nurses aides 50 (ft); Activities coordinators 2 (ft); Dietitians 1 (ft).
Facilities Dining room; Physical therapy room; Activities room; Crafts room; Laundry room; Barber/Beauty shop; Library; TV room.
Activities Arts & crafts; Cards; Games; Reading groups; Prayer groups; Movies; Shopping trips; Social/Cultural gatherings.

Bayou Glen Nursing Center*
8820 Town Park Dr, Houston, TX, 77036
(713) 777-7241
Admin Barbara L Martin.
Licensure Skilled care; Intermediate care. *Beds* 180. *Certified* Medicaid.
Owner Proprietary Corp (Convalescent Services).

Bayou Glen-Northwest Nursing Center*
9303 W Gulfbank Rd, Houston, TX, 77040
(713) 466-8933
Admin Nancy L Wood.
Licensure Skilled care; Intermediate care. *Beds* 180. *Certified* Medicaid.
Owner Proprietary Corp (Convalescent Services).

Bayou Manor
4141 S Braeswood, Houston, TX, 77025
(713) 666-2651
Admin Vivian H Davis. *Medical Dir/Dir of Nursing* Dr John Borland.
Licensure Skilled care. *Beds* 26.
Owner Nonprofit organization/foundation.
Admissions Requirements Minimum age 65; Must be a resident of Bayou Manor (a CCRC). Does not take patients from the community.

Staff RNs 3 (ft), 2 (pt); LPNs 2 (ft); Nurses aides 10 (ft), 4 (pt); Activities coordinators 1 (ft); Dietitians 1 (pt).
Facilities Dining room; Activities room; Chapel; Crafts room; Laundry room; Barber/Beauty shop; Library.
Activities Arts & crafts; Cards; Games; Movies; Social/Cultural gatherings; Exercise.

Benner Convalescent Center
3510 Sherman St, Houston, TX, 77003
(713) 224-5344
Admin Elsie L Hawkins. *Medical Dir/Dir of Nursing* Clydell Rhodes LVN DON.
Licensure Intermediate care. *Beds* ICF 117. *Certified* Medicaid.
Owner Proprietary Corp.
Admissions Requirements Minimum age 18; Medical examination; Physician's request.
Staff LPNs 8 (ft), 3 (pt); Nurses aides 22 (ft), 4 (pt); Activities coordinators 1 (ft).
Languages Spanish, Italian
Facilities Dining room; Activities room; Crafts room; Laundry room; Barber/Beauty shop.
Activities Arts & crafts; Cards; Games; Reading groups; Prayer groups; Social/Cultural gatherings.

Blalock Nursing Home—East*
1405 Holland Ave, Houston, TX, 77029
(713) 455-1744
Admin Golden Wiltz.
Licensure Intermediate care. *Beds* 160. *Certified* Medicaid.
Owner Proprietary Corp.

Blalock Nursing Home—North*
5329 N Freeway, Houston, TX, 77022
(713) 695-5821
Admin Claude Anderson.
Licensure Skilled care; Intermediate care. *Beds* 169. *Certified* Medicaid.
Owner Proprietary Corp.

Buckner Baptist Haven
12601 Memorial Dr, Houston, TX, 77024-4892
(713) 465-3406
Admin Elaine W Brewer. *Medical Dir/Dir of Nursing* Mary Ellen Gay DON.
Licensure Intermediate care; Custodial care. *Beds* ICF 60; Custodial care 93. *Certified* Medicaid.
Owner Nonprofit Corp (Buckner Bapt Retire Vlg).
Admissions Requirements Minimum age 65; Medical examination.
Affiliation Baptist
Facilities Dining room; Activities room; Chapel; Crafts room; Laundry room; Barber/Beauty shop; Library.
Activities Cards; Games; Movies; Social/Cultural gatherings; Church services in chapel.

Center for the Retarded—Cullen*
810 Marston, Houston, TX, 77019
(713) 523-6741
Admin Dalona L Riggs.
Licensure Intermediate care for mentally retarded. *Beds* 86. *Certified* Medicaid.

Clarewood House Infirmary*
7400 Clarewood, Houston, TX, 77036
(713) 774-5821
Admin Lynn E Eads.
Licensure Intermediate care. *Beds* 24.
Owner Nonprofit Corp.
Admissions Requirements Minimum age 65; Medical examination.
Staff RNs 3 (ft), 6 (pt); Nurses aides 3 (ft), 5 (pt).
Facilities Dining room; Activities room; Chapel; Crafts room; Laundry room; Barber/Beauty shop; Library.

Courtyard Convalescent Center*
7499 Stanwick Dr, Houston, TX, 77087
(713) 644-8048
Admin Delight L Finnell. *Medical Dir/Dir of Nursing* J Winston Morrison MD.
Licensure Intermediate care. *Beds* 120.
Certified Medicaid.
Owner Proprietary Corp (Beverly Enterprises).
Admissions Requirements Minimum age 21; Medical examination; Physician's request.
Staff Physicians 1 (pt); RNs 1 (ft); LPNs 8 (ft), 4 (pt); Orderlies 1 (ft), 1 (pt); Nurses aides 30 (ft), 2 (pt); Physical therapists 1 (pt); Occupational therapists 1 (pt); Speech therapists 1 (pt); Activities coordinators 1 (ft); Dietitians 1 (pt); Dentists 1 (pt); Ophthalmologists 1 (pt); Podiatrists 1 (pt); Audiologists 1 (pt).
Facilities Dining room; Activities room; Barber/Beauty shop.
Activities Arts & crafts; Cards; Games; Reading groups; Prayer groups; Movies; Shopping trips; Social/Cultural gatherings.

Dever Nursing Home*
3310 W Main St, Houston, TX, 77098
(713) 529-1218
Admin Grace French.
Licensure Intermediate care. *Beds* 37.
Owner Proprietary Corp.

Golden Age Manor
6500 Rookin St, Houston, TX, 77074
(713) 774-9736
Admin Linda Roman. *Medical Dir/Dir of Nursing* Jean M Samaan MD; Carolyn Monn DON.
Licensure Skilled care; Intermediate care; Private. *Beds* SNF 57; ICF 189; Private 58.
Certified Medicaid; Medicare.
Owner Proprietary Corp.
Admissions Requirements Medical examination; Physician's request.
Staff RNs 10 (ft), 5 (pt); LPNs 29 (ft), 6 (pt); Orderlies 4 (ft); Nurses aides 149 (ft), 7 (pt); Physical therapists 1 (ft); Activities coordinators 3 (ft), 1 (pt); Dietitians 1 (ft).
Languages Spanish, Hindi, Nigerian, Chinese, Tagalog, French
Facilities Dining room; Physical therapy room; Activities room; Crafts room; Laundry room; Barber/Beauty shop; Library.
Activities Arts & crafts; Cards; Games; Reading groups; Movies; Shopping trips; Social/Cultural gatherings.

Golden Age Manor—Bellfort*
7633 Bellfort Blvd, Houston, TX, 77061
(713) 644-2101
Admin Mary Lee Seeley. *Medical Dir/Dir of Nursing* L W Johnson MD.
Licensure Skilled care; Intermediate care. *Beds* 200. *Certified* Medicaid.
Owner Proprietary Corp (Hillhaven Corp).
Admissions Requirements Medical examination; Physician's request.
Staff RNs 5 (ft), 2 (pt); LPNs 14 (ft), 3 (pt); Nurses aides 60 (ft); Physical therapists 2 (ft); Activities coordinators 2 (ft).
Facilities Dining room; Physical therapy room; Activities room; Barber/Beauty shop; Library.
Activities Arts & crafts; Cards; Games; Reading groups; Prayer groups; Movies; Social/Cultural gatherings.

Golden Age Manor—Holmes*
6150 S Loop E, Houston, TX, 77087
(713) 643-2628
Admin Mildred M Stanley.
Licensure Intermediate care. *Beds* 120.
Certified Medicaid.
Owner Proprietary Corp (Hillhaven Corp).

Golden Age Manor—Long Point*
8810 Long Point Rd, Houston, TX, 77055
(713) 468-7833
Admin Marion L Martin.

Licensure Intermediate care. *Beds* 174.
Certified Medicaid.
Owner Proprietary Corp (Hillhaven Corp).

Golden Age Manor—North Loop
1737 North Loop W, Houston, TX, 77008
(713) 869-5551
Admin Robert A Kalin. *Medical Dir/Dir of Nursing* Dr William Cruce.
Licensure Skilled care; Intermediate care. *Beds* 200. *Certified* Medicaid; Medicare.
Owner Proprietary Corp (Hillhaven Corp).
Admissions Requirements Medical examination; Physician's request.
Staff Physicians 1 (pt); RNs 4 (ft), 1 (pt); LPNs 15 (ft), 5 (pt); Nurses aides 62 (ft), 5 (pt); Physical therapists 2 (pt); Occupational therapists 1 (pt); Speech therapists 1 (pt); Activities coordinators 2 (ft); Dietitians 1 (ft); Dentists 1 (pt); Ophthalmologists 1 (pt); Podiatrists 1 (pt).
Facilities Dining room; Physical therapy room; Activities room; Crafts room; Laundry room; Barber/Beauty shop; Library.
Activities Arts & crafts; Cards; Games; Reading groups; Prayer groups; Movies; Shopping trips; Social/Cultural gatherings; Exercise classes.

Graystone Manor Nursing Home 2*
1911 Aldine Mail Rte, Houston, TX, 77039
(713) 442-8436
Admin Mary Lou McMillan.
Licensure Intermediate care. *Beds* 49.
Certified Medicaid.
Owner Proprietary Corp.

Hallmark-Anderson Health Care Center
4718 Hallmark Ln, Houston, TX, 77056
(713) 622-6633
Admin Helen S Hampton. *Medical Dir/Dir of Nursing* Lucy C Shields DON.
Licensure Private nursing. *Beds* Private nursing 42.
Owner Nonprofit Corp.
Admissions Requirements Minimum age 65; Medical examination.
Staff Physicians 4 (ft); RNs 2 (ft); LPNs 5 (ft); Nurses aides 20 (ft); Activities coordinators 1 (ft); Dietitians 2 (ft); Ophthalmologists 1 (pt).
Facilities Dining room; Activities room; Crafts room; Laundry room; Barber/Beauty shop; Library; Swimming pool.
Activities Arts & crafts; Games; Reading groups; Prayer groups; Movies; Shopping trips; Social/Cultural gatherings.

Hermann Park Manor
5600 Chenevert, Houston, TX, 77024
(713) 523-6831
Admin Forest B Smith. *Medical Dir/Dir of Nursing* Margaret Saw MD.
Licensure Skilled care; Intermediate care. *Beds* 185. *Certified* Medicaid; Medicare.
Owner Proprietary Corp (American Health Centers Inc).
Admissions Requirements Minimum age 45; Medical examination.
Staff Physicians 1 (pt); RNs 2 (ft); LPNs 26 (ft); Nurses aides 65 (ft); Physical therapists 1 (ft); Reality therapists 1 (ft); Recreational therapists 1 (ft); Activities coordinators 2 (ft); Dietitians 1 (ft); Ophthalmologists 1 (pt).
Facilities Dining room; Physical therapy room; Activities room; Crafts room; Laundry room; Barber/Beauty shop.
Activities Arts & crafts; Cards; Games; Reading groups; Prayer groups; Movies; Shopping trips; Social/Cultural gatherings.

Highland Park Care Center*
2714 Morrison, Houston, TX, 77009
(713) 869-1491
Admin Charlene Hinton.
Licensure Intermediate care. *Beds* 67.
Certified Medicaid.

Admissions Requirements Medical examination; Physician's request.
Staff RNs 1 (pt); LPNs 4 (ft); Nurses aides 16 (ft); Activities coordinators 1 (ft); Podiatrists 1 (pt).
Facilities Dining room; Activities room; Laundry room; Barber/Beauty shop.
Activities Arts & crafts; Cards; Games; Prayer groups; Movies.

Holly Hall
8304 Knight Rd, Houston, TX, 77054
(713) 799-9031
Admin Wesley F Stevens. *Medical Dir/Dir of Nursing* Juliette Buchanan DON.
Licensure Skilled care; Intermediate care; Independent living. *Beds* SNF 46; ICF 24; Independent living 85; Cottages 12; Duplexes 4.
Owner Nonprofit Corp.
Admissions Requirements Minimum age 65; Medical examination.
Staff RNs 2 (ft), 1 (pt); LPNs 8 (ft), 2 (pt); Nurses aides 15 (ft), 3 (pt); Dietitians 2 (ft).
Facilities Dining room; Activities room; Chapel; Barber/Beauty shop; Library.
Activities Arts & crafts; Games; Prayer groups; Shopping trips.

Jewish Home for the Aged*
6200 N Braeswood, Houston, TX, 77074
(713) 771-4111
Admin Anita Cabelli.
Licensure Skilled care; Intermediate care. *Beds* 218. *Certified* Medicaid.
Owner Nonprofit Corp.
Affiliation Jewish

Leisure Arms Nursing Home*
4225 Denmark, Houston, TX, 77016
(713) 631-0200
Admin Geraldine L McElroy.
Licensure Intermediate care. *Beds* 83.
Certified Medicaid.
Owner Proprietary Corp (ARA Living Centers).
Admissions Requirements Minimum age 20; Medical examination; Physician's request.
Staff Physicians 1 (ft); LPNs 4 (ft), 3 (pt); Nurses aides 12 (ft), 6 (pt).
Facilities Dining room; Activities room; Crafts room; Laundry room.
Activities Arts & crafts; Cards; Games; Prayer groups; Movies; Shopping trips; Social/Cultural gatherings.

Manda Ann Convalescent Home Inc
7441 Coffee St, Houston, TX, 77033
(713) 733-9471
Admin Grace Thomas. *Medical Dir/Dir of Nursing* Jo Ann Hampton.
Licensure Intermediate care. *Beds* ICF 216.
Certified Medicaid.
Owner Proprietary Corp.
Admissions Requirements Physician's request.
Staff Physicians; RNs; Orderlies; Nurses aides; Physical therapists; Occupational therapists; Activities coordinators; Dietitians; Ophthalmologists.
Facilities Dining room; Activities room; Crafts room; Laundry room; Barber/Beauty shop; Courtyard.
Activities Arts & crafts; Cards; Games; Reading groups; Prayer groups; Movies; Shopping trips; Social/Cultural gatherings.

Manor Care—Sharpview Rehabilitation & Nursing Center
7505 Bellerive, Houston, TX, 77036
(713) 774-9611
Admin Margaret L Dunn. *Medical Dir/Dir of Nursing* Dr Arvind Bhandari MD; Lynette Lawson.
Licensure Skilled care; Intermediate care. *Beds* SNF 51; ICF 109. *Certified* Medicare.
Owner Proprietary Corp (Manor Care).
Admissions Requirements Physician's request.

Staff RNs 6 (ft); LPNs 7 (pt); Orderlies 4 (ft);
Nurses aides 43 (ft); Physical therapists 1
(ft); Occupational therapists 1 (ft); Speech
therapists 1 (pt); Activities coordinators 1
(ft), 1 (pt); Ophthalmologists 1 (pt).
Languages Spanish
Facilities Dining room; Physical therapy
room; Activities room; Chapel; Crafts room;
Laundry room; Barber/Beauty shop; Library.
Activities Arts & crafts; Games;
Reading groups; Prayer groups; Movies;
Shopping trips; Social/Cultural gatherings;
Special pals.

Mercy Nursing Home Inc*
3901 Los Angeles St, Houston, TX, 77026
(713) 672-7654
Admin Brenda Joyce H Edwards.
Licensure Intermediate care. *Beds* 65.
Certified Medicaid.
Owner Proprietary Corp.

Montrose Care Center*
3508 Milam St, Houston, TX, 77002
(713) 529-3071
Admin Ronald Betterton.
Licensure Intermediate care. *Beds* 159.
Certified Medicaid.
Owner Proprietary Corp (ARA Living
Centers).

Northline Manor*
7210 Northline Dr, Houston, TX, 77076
(713) 697-4771
Admin W William Jahn.
Licensure Intermediate care; Personal care.
Beds ICF 180; Personal 24. *Certified*
Medicaid.
Owner Proprietary Corp (Cantex Healthcare
Centers).
Admissions Requirements Minimum age 18;
Medical examination.
Staff RNs 1 (ft); LPNs 10 (ft); Orderlies 4 (ft);
Nurses aides 65 (ft); Physical therapists 1
(ft); Occupational therapists 1 (pt); Speech
therapists 1 (pt); Activities coordinators 1
(ft), 1 (pt); Dietitians 1 (pt).
Facilities Dining room; Physical therapy
room; Activities room; Chapel; Laundry
room; Barber/Beauty shop; Library.
Activities Arts & crafts; Cards; Games;
Reading groups; Prayer groups; Movies;
Shopping trips; Social/Cultural gatherings.

Northshore Healthcare Center
12350 Wood Bayou Dr, Houston, TX, 77013
(713) 453-0446
Admin Catherine A Golden. *Medical Dir/Dir
of Nursing* Cynthia Douglas RN DON.
Licensure Intermediate care. *Beds* ICF 150.
Certified Medicaid; Medicare.
Owner Proprietary Corp (ARA Living
Centers).
Admissions Requirements Minimum age 18;
Medical examination.
Staff RNs 1 (ft); LPNs 12 (ft), 2 (pt);
Orderlies 2 (ft); Nurses aides 30 (ft), 8 (pt);
Activities coordinators 1 (ft), 1 (pt).
Facilities Dining room; Activities room;
Crafts room; Laundry room; Barber/Beauty
shop; Library.
Activities Arts & crafts; Cards; Games;
Movies; Social/Cultural gatherings; Stroke
group.

Pharmcare—Aldine*
PO Box 38392, 10110 Airline Dr, Houston,
TX, 77037
(713) 447-0376
Admin Richard Lewis Simpson.
Licensure Intermediate care. *Beds* 197.
Certified Medicaid.
Owner Proprietary Corp.

St Anthony Center*
6301 Almeda Rd, Houston, TX, 77021
(713) 748-5021
Admin Sr Mary Alma Murphy. *Medical Dir/
Dir of Nursing* Bernard Flanz MD.

Licensure Skilled care; Intermediate care. *Beds*
325. *Certified* Medicaid; Medicare.
Admissions Requirements Physician's request.
Staff Physicians 2 (ft); RNs 24 (ft); LPNs 48
(ft); Nurses aides 128 (ft); Physical therapists
7 (ft); Recreational therapists 2 (ft);
Occupational therapists 9 (ft), 2 (pt); Speech
therapists 2 (ft); Activities coordinators 1
(ft); Dietitians 1 (ft); Dentists 2 (ft);
Podiatrists 1 (pt); Audiologists 2 (ft).
Affiliation Roman Catholic
Facilities Dining room; Physical therapy
room; Activities room; Chapel; Crafts room;
Laundry room; Barber/Beauty shop; Library.
Activities Arts & crafts; Games; Prayer groups;
Movies; Shopping trips.

St Dominic Nursing Home
6502 Grand Blvd, Houston, TX, 77021
741-8701
Admin Ruth Whigham. *Medical Dir/Dir of
Nursing* Susan Jadlowski RN DON.
Licensure Intermediate care. *Beds* ICF 120.
Certified Medicaid.
Owner Nonprofit Corp.
Admissions Requirements Medical
examination.
Staff RNs 1 (ft); LPNs 19 (ft); Nurses aides 60
(ft); Activities coordinators 2 (ft).
Languages Spanish
Facilities Dining room; Activities room;
Chapel; Laundry room; Barber/Beauty shop.
Activities Arts & crafts; Cards; Games; Prayer
groups; Movies; Shopping trips; Social/
Cultural gatherings.

St Thomas Convalescent Center*
5925 Almeda Rd, Houston, TX, 77004
(713) 522-5107
Admin Majorie Turner.
Licensure Intermediate care. *Beds* 125.
Certified Medicaid.
Owner Proprietary Corp.

Silver Threads Nursing Center*
3402 Vintage St, Houston, TX, 77026
(713) 675-8105
Admin Helen M Spencer.
Licensure Intermediate care. *Beds* 82.
Certified Medicaid.
Owner Proprietary Corp (Beverly Enterprises).

Spring Branch Healthcare Center
8955 Long Point Rd, Houston, TX, 77055
(713) 464-7625
Admin Carolyn Barten. *Medical Dir/Dir of
Nursing* Donna DiIorio RN.
Licensure Intermediate care. *Beds* ICF/MR
106. *Certified* Medicaid.
Owner Proprietary Corp (ARA Living
Centers).
Admissions Requirements Medical
examination.
Staff Physicians; RNs; LPNs; Nurses aides;
Physical therapists; Occupational therapists;
Speech therapists; Activities coordinators;
Dietitians; Dentists; Ophthalmologists;
Podiatrists.
Facilities Dining room; Activities room;
Laundry room; Barber/Beauty shop; Van
with wheelchair lift; individual a/c units.
Activities Arts & crafts; Cards; Games;
Reading groups; Prayer groups; Movies;
Shopping trips; Social/Cultural gatherings;
Fieldtrips; Stroke support group.

Stoneybrook Healthcare Center
2808 Stoney Brook, Houston, TX, 77063
(713) 782-4355
Admin Olive Moffit RN. *Medical Dir/Dir of
Nursing* P R Pingitore MD; Oneta Poole RN
DON.
Licensure Intermediate care. *Beds* ICF 112.
Certified Medicaid.
Owner Proprietary Corp (ARA Living
Centers).
Admissions Requirements Minimum age 18;
Medical examination; Physician's request.

Staff RNs 1 (ft); LPNs 6 (ft); Nurses aides 25
(ft); Activities coordinators 1 (ft); Dietitians
1 (ft).
Languages Spanish
Facilities Dining room; Activities room;
Barber/Beauty shop; Library.
Activities Arts & crafts; Cards; Games;
Reading groups; Prayer groups; Movies;
Shopping trips; Social/Cultural gatherings.

Thomas Care Centers Inc*
3827 W Fuqua St, Houston, TX, 77045
(713) 433-7206
Admin James R Hale. *Medical Dir/Dir of
Nursing* Dr William L Mize.
Licensure Intermediate care; Intermediate care
for mentally retarded. *Beds* 250. *Certified*
Medicaid.
Owner Proprietary Corp (ARA Living
Centers).
Staff Physicians 2 (ft), 4 (pt); RNs 8 (ft), 12
(pt); LPNs 10 (ft), 10 (pt); Nurses aides 25
(ft), 35 (pt); Physical therapists 3 (ft);
Recreational therapists 4 (ft); Occupational
therapists 4 (ft); Speech therapists 2 (ft);
Activities coordinators 2 (ft); Dietitians 2
(ft); Dentists 1 (ft); Ophthalmologists 1 (pt);
Podiatrists 1 (pt); Audiologists 1 (ft).
Facilities Dining room; Physical therapy
room; Activities room; Crafts room; Laundry
room; Barber/Beauty shop.
Activities Arts & crafts; Cards; Games;
Reading groups; Prayer groups; Movies;
Shopping trips; Social/Cultural gatherings.

Treemont Health Care Center*
2501 Westerland Dr, Houston, TX, 77042
(713) 783-4100
Admin Jean C Rogers. *Medical Dir/Dir of
Nursing* William J Wylie.
Licensure Intermediate care; Custodial care.
Beds ICF 70; Custodial care 54.
Admissions Requirements Minimum age 60;
Medical examination; Physician's request.
Staff RNs 2 (ft); LPNs 10 (ft), 1 (pt);
Orderlies 1 (ft); Nurses aides 40 (ft), 3 (pt);
Recreational therapists 1 (ft); Dietitians 1
(ft).
Facilities Dining room; Activities room;
Crafts room; Laundry room; Barber/Beauty
shop; Library.
Activities Arts & crafts; Cards; Games; Prayer
groups; Movies; Shopping trips; Social/
Cultural gatherings.

Isla Carroll Turner Health Care Center
4141 S Braeswood, Houston, TX, 77025
(713) 666-2651
Admin Vivian H Davis. *Medical Dir/Dir of
Nursing* Kelly Langford RN DON.
Licensure Skilled care. *Beds* 25.
Owner Nonprofit organization/foundation.
Admissions Requirements Minimum age 65;
Medical examination.
Staff RNs 1 (ft), 2 (pt); LPNs 3 (ft), 1 (pt);
Nurses aides 12 (ft); Activities coordinators
1 (ft).
Facilities Dining room; Activities room;
Chapel; Crafts room; Laundry room; Barber/
Beauty shop; Library.
Activities Arts & crafts; Cards; Games; Prayer
groups; Movies; Shopping trips.

Villa Northwest Convalescent Center
17600 Cali Dr, Houston, TX, 77090
(713) 440-9000
Admin Arthur C Johnson III. *Medical Dir/Dir
of Nursing* M Javed Aslam MD; Patsy
Tschudy DON.
Licensure Skilled care; Intermediate care. *Beds*
165. *Certified* Medicaid.
Owner Proprietary Corp (Convalescent
Services).
Admissions Requirements Minimum age 21.
Staff Physicians 1 (pt); RNs 7 (ft), 1 (pt);
LPNs 10 (ft), 2 (pt); Nurses aides 43 (ft), 6
(pt); Activities coordinators 1 (ft), 2 (pt);
Dietitians 11 (ft), 1 (pt).

Facilities Dining room; Physical therapy room; Activities room; Laundry room; Barber/Beauty shop.
Activities Arts & crafts; Cards; Games; Reading groups; Prayer groups; Movies; Exercise; Church services; Special entertainment; Music therapy; Resident's council.

The Village Healthcare Center
1341 Blalock Dr, Houston, TX, 77055
(713) 468-7821
Admin Sue Morgan. *Medical Dir/Dir of Nursing* Colleen Caswell RN DON.
Licensure Intermediate care. *Beds* ICF 240.
Certified Medicaid.
Owner Proprietary Corp (ARA Living Centers).
Admissions Requirements Medical examination.
Staff RNs 1 (ft); LPNs 12 (ft); Nurses aides 40 (ft); Physical therapists 1 (pt); Reality therapists 1 (ft); Occupational therapists 1 (pt); Speech therapists 1 (pt); Activities coordinators 2 (ft); Dietitians 1 (pt); Dentists 1 (pt); Ophthalmologists 1 (pt); Podiatrists 1 (pt).
Languages French, Spanish
Facilities Dining room; Activities room; Crafts room; Laundry room; Barber/Beauty shop; Library.
Activities Arts & crafts; Cards; Games; Reading groups; Prayer groups; Movies; Shopping trips; Social/Cultural gatherings.

Manda Ann Watkins
730 W 23rd Rd, Houston, TX, 77008
862-9584
Admin Betty Philips. *Medical Dir/Dir of Nursing* B Echols MD; Irene Adams DON.
Licensure Intermediate care. *Beds* ICF 116.
Certified Medicaid.
Owner Privately owned.
Admissions Requirements Medical examination.
Staff Physicians 1 (ft); LPNs 6 (ft); Nurses aides 50 (ft); Physical therapists 2 (ft); Reality therapists 1 (ft); Recreational therapists 1 (ft); Occupational therapists 1 (ft); Speech therapists 1 (ft); Activities coordinators 1 (ft); Dietitians 1 (ft); Dentists 1 (ft); Ophthalmologists 1 (ft).
Languages Spanish
Facilities Dining room; Physical therapy room; Activities room; Laundry room; Barber/Beauty shop.
Activities Arts & crafts; Cards; Games; Reading groups; Prayer groups; Shopping trips; Social/Cultural gatherings.

The Westbury Place Nursing & Retirement Center
5201 S Willow Dr, Houston, TX, 77035
(713) 721-0297
Admin Hazel Reaves. *Medical Dir/Dir of Nursing* Margueritte Sluder RN.
Licensure Private Pay. *Beds* 148. *Certified* Private Pay.
Owner Proprietary Corp (Convalescent Services).
Admissions Requirements Medical examination; Physician's request.
Staff Physicians; RNs; LPNs; Nurses aides; Physical therapists; Activities coordinators; Dietitians; Ophthalmologists.
Languages Spanish, Italian, German
Facilities Dining room; Physical therapy room; Activities room; Chapel; Crafts room; Laundry room; Barber/Beauty shop; Library.
Activities Arts & crafts; Cards; Games; Reading groups; Prayer groups; Movies; Shopping trips; Social/Cultural gatherings.

Wileyvale Community Nursing Home*
7915 Wileyvale Rd, Houston, TX, 77016
(713) 633-2890
Admin Claude Anderson.

Licensure Intermediate care. *Beds* 130.
Certified Medicaid.
Staff Physicians 3 (pt); RNs 1 (pt); LPNs 15 (pt); Nurses aides 35 (pt); Activities coordinators 1 (ft), 1 (pt); Dietitians 1 (ft); Dentists 3 (pt); Ophthalmologists 1 (pt); Podiatrists 1 (pt).
Facilities Dining room; Activities room; Laundry room.
Activities Cards; Games; Prayer groups.

Winter Haven Nursing Home
6534 Stuebner Airline Dr, Houston, TX, 77091
(713) 692-5137
Admin Glenda C Donahue.
Licensure Intermediate care. *Beds* 151.
Certified Medicaid.
Staff RNs 1 (ft); LPNs 10 (ft), 4 (pt); Nurses aides 42 (ft); Physical therapists 3 (pt); Activities coordinators 2 (ft); Dietitians 1 (ft); Medical aides 4 (pt).
Facilities Dining room; Physical therapy room; Activities room; Crafts room; Laundry room; Barber/Beauty shop; Library; Gift shop.
Activities Arts & crafts; Cards; Games; Prayer groups; Movies; Shopping trips; Social/Cultural gatherings.

HUBBARD

Oakview Manor Nursing Home
PO Box 561, 6th & Hickory, Hubbard, TX, 76648
(817) 576-2518
Admin Janet C Marek. *Medical Dir/Dir of Nursing* Patsy Reeves.
Licensure Intermediate care. *Beds* 60.
Certified Medicaid.
Owner Proprietary Corp.
Staff LPNs; Nurses aides; Activities coordinators; Dietitians.
Facilities Dining room; Activities room; Crafts room; Laundry room; Barber/Beauty shop; Library.
Activities Arts & crafts; Cards; Games; Reading groups; Prayer groups; Movies.

HUGHES SPRINGS

Theron Grainger Nursing Home
PO Box 1390, Hwy 161 South, Hughes Springs, TX, 75656
(214) 639-2561
Admin Betty Traylor. *Medical Dir/Dir of Nursing* Kathryn Brimhall.
Licensure Intermediate care. *Beds* ICF 69.
Certified Medicaid.
Owner Proprietary Corp.
Admissions Requirements Physician's request.
Staff LPNs 9 (ft); Nurses aides 25 (ft); Activities coordinators 1 (ft).
Facilities Dining room; Activities room; Laundry room; Barber/Beauty shop.
Activities Arts & crafts; Cards; Games; Reading groups; Prayer groups; Movies; Shopping trips; Social/Cultural gatherings.

Hughes Springs Convalescent Center*
N Taylor St, Hughes Springs, TX, 75656
(214) 639-2531
Admin Betty M McCarley.
Licensure Intermediate care. *Beds* 60.
Certified Medicaid.
Owner Proprietary Corp (Hillhaven Corp).
Staff RNs 1 (pt); LPNs 4 (ft); Nurses aides 25 (ft); Physical therapists 1 (pt); Occupational therapists 1 (pt); Speech therapists 1 (pt); Activities coordinators 1 (ft).
Facilities Dining room; Activities room; Crafts room; Laundry room; Barber/Beauty shop.
Activities Arts & crafts; Games; Prayer groups; Movies; Shopping trips; Social/Cultural gatherings.

HUMBLE

Green Acres Convalescent Center—Humble
93 Isaacks Rd, Humble, TX, 77338
(713) 446-7159, 446-7150, 446-8483
Admin Bob E Standard. *Medical Dir/Dir of Nursing* Dr Guerinni; Linda Barr.
Licensure Intermediate care. *Beds* ICF 134.
Certified Medicaid.
Owner Proprietary Corp (ARA Living Centers).
Staff Physicians 1 (pt); RNs 1 (ft); LPNs 8 (ft), 2 (pt); Orderlies 4 (ft); Nurses aides 38 (ft), 10 (pt); Physical therapists 1 (pt); Recreational therapists 1 (ft); Speech therapists 1 (pt); Activities coordinators 1 (ft); Dietitians 1 (pt); Dentists 1 (pt); Ophthalmologists 1 (pt); Podiatrists 1 (pt).

Humble Skilled Care Facility*
18903 Memorial S, Humble, TX, 77338
Medical Dir/Dir of Nursing Dr N N Izzat.
Admissions Requirements Minimum age 6 months; Medical examination; Physician's request.
Staff Physicians 22 (ft), 8 (pt); RNs 11 (ft), 5 (pt); LPNs 26 (ft), 7 (pt); Nurses aides 43 (ft), 15 (pt); Physical therapists 14 (ft), 7 (pt); Recreational therapists 1 (ft); Occupational therapists 9 (ft); Speech therapists 3 (ft); Activities coordinators 1 (ft); Dietitians 1 (ft); Dentists 4 (ft); Ophthalmologists 2 (ft); Podiatrists 2 (ft); Audiologists 1 (ft).
Facilities Dining room; Physical therapy room; Activities room; Chapel; Crafts room; Laundry room; Barber/Beauty shop; Library.
Activities Cards; Games; Reading groups; Prayer groups; Social/Cultural gatherings.

HUNTSVILLE

Fair Park Nursing Center
2628 Milam St, Huntsville, TX, 77340
(713) 295-6464
Admin Jerry N Schaff. *Medical Dir/Dir of Nursing* Pam Jeffcoat.
Licensure Skilled care; Intermediate care. *Beds* 109. *Certified* Medicaid; Medicare.
Owner Proprietary Corp (Beverly Enterprises).
Admissions Requirements Minimum age 18; Medical examination; Physician's request.
Staff Physicians 1 (pt); RNs 2 (ft), 4 (pt); LPNs 12 (ft), 3 (pt); Orderlies 1 (ft), 1 (pt); Nurses aides 51 (ft), 4 (pt); Physical therapists 1 (pt); Recreational therapists 1 (pt); Occupational therapists 1 (pt); Speech therapists 1 (pt); Activities coordinators 1 (ft); Dietitians 1 (pt); Dentists 1 (pt); Ophthalmologists 1 (pt); Podiatrists 1 (pt).
Languages Spanish
Facilities Dining room; Physical therapy room; Activities room; Chapel; Laundry room; Barber/Beauty shop; Library; Den; Sitting rooms.
Activities Arts & crafts; Cards; Games; Reading groups; Prayer groups; Movies; Shopping trips; Social/Cultural gatherings; Reality orientation; Individualized activities.

Green Acres Convalescent Center*
1302 Inverness, Huntsville, TX, 77340
(713) 295-6313
Admin Anna E Carpenter. *Medical Dir/Dir of Nursing* Hugh Poindexter MD.
Licensure Intermediate care. *Beds* 102.
Certified Medicaid.
Owner Proprietary Corp (ARA Living Centers).
Staff Physicians 1 (pt); RNs 1 (ft); Nurses aides 15 (ft); Reality therapists 1 (ft); Recreational therapists 1 (pt); Activities coordinators 1 (ft); Dietitians 1 (ft); LVNs 8 (ft).
Facilities Dining room; Activities room; Chapel; Crafts room; Laundry room; Barber/Beauty shop.

Activities Arts & crafts; Cards; Games;
Reading groups; Prayer groups; Movies;
Shopping trips; Social/Cultural gatherings.

Ella Smither Geriatric Center
PO Box 6169, Huntsville, TX, 77340
(409) 295-0216
Admin Geri Farris. *Medical Dir/Dir of
Nursing* Dalia Harrelson.
Licensure Skilled care; Intermediate care;
Residential. *Beds* SNF 46; ICF 50;
Residential 13. *Certified* Medicaid;
Medicare.
Owner Nonprofit Corp.
Admissions Requirements Physician's request.
Staff RNs 5 (ft), 2 (pt); LPNs 11 (ft), 7 (pt);
Nurses aides 25 (ft), 14 (pt); Activities
coordinators 1 (ft); Dietitians 1 (ft).
Facilities Dining room; Activities room;
Chapel; Barber/Beauty shop.
Activities Arts & crafts; Cards; Games;
Reading groups; Prayer groups; Movies;
Social/Cultural gatherings.

HURST

Autumn Leaf Lodge*
215 E Plaza Blvd, Hurst, TX, 76053
(817) 282-6777
Admin Mary Tharp.
Licensure Skilled care; Intermediate care. *Beds*
116. *Certified* Medicaid.
Owner Proprietary Corp (ARA Living
Centers).

Bishop Davies Center Inc
2712 N Hurstview, Hurst, TX, 76054
(817) 281-6708
Admin Robert C Murphy Jr. *Medical Dir/Dir
of Nursing* Sara C Vaughan RN DON.
Licensure Skilled care. *Beds* SNF 100.
Certified Medicaid; Medicare.
Owner Nonprofit Corp.
Admissions Requirements Minimum age 55;
Physician's request.
Staff Physicians 1 (pt); RNs 3 (ft), 3 (pt);
LPNs 12 (ft), 2 (pt); Orderlies 2 (ft); Nurses
aides 27 (ft); Physical therapists 1 (pt);
Recreational therapists 1 (ft); Occupational
therapists 1 (pt); Speech therapists 1 (pt);
Activities coordinators 1 (ft); Dietitians 1
(ft).
Affiliation Episcopal
Facilities Dining room; Physical therapy
room; Activities room; Chapel; Crafts room;
Laundry room; Barber/Beauty shop; Library;
Parlour.
Activities Arts & crafts; Cards; Games;
Reading groups; Prayer groups; Movies;
Shopping trips; Social/Cultural gatherings;
Family nights; Family sharing sessions; Van;
Registered music therapist.

IOWA PARK

Electra Nursing Center
511 S Bailey, Iowa Park, TX, 76360
(817) 495-2184
Admin Betty D Guyette. *Medical Dir/Dir of
Nursing* Dr E Banez; Cleta Beggs.
Licensure Intermediate care. *Beds* ICF/MR
69. *Certified* Medicaid.
Owner Proprietary Corp (Beverly Enterprises).
Admissions Requirements Physician's request.
Staff RNs 1 (pt); LPNs 7 (ft); Orderlies 1 (pt);
Nurses aides 1 (ft), 1 (pt); Activities
coordinators 1 (ft); Dietitians 1 (pt).
Facilities Dining room; Activities room;
Laundry room; Barber/Beauty shop.
Activities Arts & crafts; Games; Reading
groups; Prayer groups; Movies; Social/
Cultural gatherings; Speakers;
Demonstrations; Rodeos; Pet days; Garage
sales.

Heritage Manor of Iowa Park
1109 N 3rd St, Iowa Park, TX, 76367
(817) 592-4139
Admin Novella Gilbreath.
Licensure Intermediate care. *Beds* 77.
Certified Medicaid.
Owner Proprietary Corp (Southmark Heritage
Corp).
Staff Physicians 3 (pt); RNs 1 (pt); LPNs 9
(ft); Nurses aides 34 (ft), 6 (pt); Activities
coordinators 1 (ft); Dietitians 1 (ft).
Facilities Dining room; Laundry room;
Barber/Beauty shop.
Activities Arts & crafts; Games; Prayer groups;
Movies; Shopping trips; Social/Cultural
gatherings.

IRVING

Irving Campus of Care*
2021 Shoaf Dr, Irving, TX, 75061
(214) 579-1919
Medical Dir/Dir of Nursing James Galbraith
MD.
Licensure Skilled care; Intermediate care. *Beds*
360. *Certified* Medicaid; Medicare.
Owner Proprietary Corp (Summit Health Ltd).
Staff Physicians 6 (ft); RNs 5 (ft); LPNs 17
(ft); Orderlies 4 (ft); Nurses aides 42 (ft);
Physical therapists 1 (ft); Reality therapists 1
(ft); Recreational therapists 1 (ft);
Occupational therapists 1 (ft); Speech
therapists 1 (ft); Activities coordinators 2
(ft); Dietitians 1 (pt); Dentists 1 (pt);
Ophthalmologists 1 (pt); Podiatrists 1 (pt).
Facilities Dining room; Physical therapy
room; Activities room; Chapel; Crafts room;
Laundry room; Barber/Beauty shop; Library.
Activities Arts & crafts; Cards; Games; Prayer
groups; Movies; Shopping trips; Social/
Cultural gatherings.

Irving Care Center*
619 N Britain Rd, Irving, TX, 75060
(214) 438-4161
Admin Lisa J Dillard.
Licensure Intermediate care. *Beds* 86.
Certified Medicaid.
Owner Proprietary Corp (Manor Care).

Pioneer Place Nursing Home
225 Sowers Rd, Irving, TX, 75061
(214) 253-4173
Admin Robbi Stewart. *Medical Dir/Dir of
Nursing* James Galbraith MD.
Licensure Intermediate care. *Beds* ICF 120.
Certified Medicaid.
Owner Proprietary Corp (Beverly Enterprises).
Admissions Requirements Medical
examination; Physician's request.
Staff Physicians 1 (ft); LPNs 10 (ft); Orderlies
3 (ft); Nurses aides 28 (ft); Activities
coordinators 1 (ft); Dietitians 1 (ft);
Ophthalmologists 1 (ft).
Facilities Dining room; Activities room;
Laundry room; Barber/Beauty shop; Library;
Large living room; Front & back patios.
Activities Arts & crafts; Cards; Games;
Reading groups; Prayer groups; Shopping
trips; Social/Cultural gatherings; Sing-alongs;
Manicures; Adopt-a-grandparent program;
Residents council; Reminiscence therapy;
Exercise.

ITALY

Italy Convalescent Center*
Hwy 77, Italy, TX, 76651
(214) 483-6369
Admin Billie Farrington. *Medical Dir/Dir of
Nursing* Zenaida Robles.
Licensure Intermediate care. *Beds* 61.
Certified Medicaid.
Owner Proprietary Corp (Southmark Heritage
Corp).
Admissions Requirements Medical
examination; Physician's request.

Staff Physicians 1 (pt); RNs 1 (pt); LPNs 8
(ft), 3 (pt); Nurses aides 18 (ft), 6 (pt);
Physical therapists 1 (pt); Activities
coordinators 1 (ft); Dietitians 1 (pt); Dentists
1 (pt); Podiatrists 1 (pt).
Facilities Dining room; Laundry room;
Barber/Beauty shop; Library.
Activities Arts & crafts; Cards; Games;
Reading groups; Prayer groups; Movies;
Shopping trips; Social/Cultural gatherings.

ITASCA

Itasca Nursing Home
409 S Files St, Itasca, TX, 76055
(817) 687-2383
Admin Elizabeth Dianne Taylor. *Medical Dir/
Dir of Nursing* Charles Allen MD; Martha
McWhorter RN DON.
Licensure Intermediate care. *Beds* ICF 82.
Certified Medicaid.
Owner Proprietary Corp (Health Enter of
America).
Staff RNs; LPNs; Orderlies; Nurses aides;
Activities coordinators; Dietitians.
Facilities Dining room; Activities room;
Chapel; Crafts room; Laundry room; Barber/
Beauty shop; Library.
Activities Arts & crafts; Cards; Games;
Reading groups; Prayer groups; Movies;
Shopping trips; Social/Cultural gatherings;
Fishing trips; Picnics; Safari trips; Adopt-a-
grandparent; Resident council; Family
council.

Sanford Nursing Home*
107 Marion St, Itasca, TX, 76055
(817) 687-2358
Admin Alan L Lee.
Licensure Intermediate care. *Beds* 52.
Certified Medicaid.

JACKSBORO

Cox Convalescent Center
527 W Belknap, Jacksboro, TX, 76056
(817) 567-2371
Admin Joye Anastas. *Medical Dir/Dir of
Nursing* Joyce Guthrie.
Licensure Intermediate care. *Beds* 40.
Certified Medicaid.
Owner Proprietary Corp (ARA Living
Centers).
Admissions Requirements Medical
examination; Physician's request.
Staff Nurses aides; Dietitians; LVN.
Facilities Dining room; Activities room;
Crafts room; Laundry room; Barber/Beauty
shop.
Activities Arts & crafts; Cards; Games;
Reading groups; Prayer groups; Movies;
Shopping trips; Social/Cultural gatherings.

Jacksboro Nursing Center*
211 E Jasper, Jacksboro, TX, 76056
(817) 567-2686
Admin Patsy Snow.
Licensure Intermediate care. *Beds* 108.
Certified Medicaid.
Owner Proprietary Corp (Beverly Enterprises).

JACKSONVILLE

Gardendale Nursing Home*
Hwy 79 E, Jacksonville, TX, 75766
(214) 586-3626
Admin Pattie Gray. *Medical Dir/Dir of
Nursing* D B Turner MD.
Licensure Skilled care; Intermediate care. *Beds*
120. *Certified* Medicaid.
Owner Proprietary Corp (Beverly Enterprises).
Admissions Requirements Physician's request.

Sunset Care Center*
407 Bonita St, Jacksonville, TX, 75766
(214) 586-3616
Admin Jean C Allen.

Licensure Intermediate care. *Beds* 53.
Certified Medicaid.
Owner Proprietary Corp (Beverly Enterprises).

Twin Oaks Convalescent Center*
PO Box 1271, 1123 N Bolton, Jacksonville,
TX, 75766
(214) 586-9031
Admin Jeffie Caldwell.
Licensure Intermediate care. *Beds* 96.
Certified Medicaid.
Owner Proprietary Corp.

JASPER

Jasper Convalescent Center Inc*
350 Springhill Rd, Jasper, TX, 75951
(713) 384-5411
Admin Lillie Carrell.
Licensure Intermediate care. *Beds* 88.
Certified Medicaid.
Admissions Requirements Medical
examination.
Staff RNs 2 (ft); LPNs 6 (ft), 3 (pt); Nurses
aides 25 (ft), 3 (pt); Physical therapists 1
(pt); Occupational therapists 1 (pt); Speech
therapists 1 (pt); Activities coordinators 1
(ft); Dietitians 1 (ft); Podiatrists 1 (pt).
Facilities Dining room; Activities room;
Laundry room; Barber/Beauty shop.
Activities Arts & crafts; Cards; Games;
Movies; Shopping trips; Social/Cultural
gatherings.

Pinewood Manor Nursing Home*
315 W Gibson, Jasper, TX, 75951
(713) 384-5768
Admin Doris Evelyn Chapman.
Licensure Intermediate care. *Beds* 120.
Certified Medicaid.
Owner Proprietary Corp.

JAYTON

Kent County Nursing Home*
Hwy 70 W, Jayton, TX, 79528
(806) 237-3036
Admin O Joyce Reynolds.
Licensure Intermediate care. *Beds* 33.
Certified Medicaid.
Owner Proprietary Corp.

JEFFERSON

Douglas Memorial Nursing Home*
PO Box 527, 100-06 Walnut St, Jefferson, TX,
75657
(214) 665-8541
Admin Willie Mae Douglas.
Licensure Intermediate care. *Beds* 42.
Certified Medicaid.
Owner Proprietary Corp.

Magnolia Manor
510 E Bonham St, Jefferson, TX, 75657
(214) 665-3903
Admin Brenda J Cox. *Medical Dir/Dir of
Nursing* W S Terry MD; Mary Green DON.
Licensure Intermediate care. *Beds* ICF 60.
Certified Medicaid.
Owner Proprietary Corp.
Admissions Requirements Medical
examination; Physician's request.
Staff RNs 1 (ft); Nurses aides 17 (ft), 2 (pt);
Activities coordinators 1 (ft).
Facilities Dining room; Laundry room;
Barber/Beauty shop.
Activities Arts & crafts; Cards; Games; Prayer
groups; Movies; Shopping trips; Social/
Cultural gatherings.

JOHNSON CITY

Lyndon B Johnson Memorial Nursing Home*
Ave C & 10th St, Johnson City, TX, 78636
(512) 868-7115

Admin Lucille M Newman.
Licensure Intermediate care. *Beds* 24.
Certified Medicaid.
Owner Nonprofit Corp.

JOURDANTON

Retama Manor Nursing Center Inc*
1504 Oak, Jourdanton, TX, 78026
(512) 769-3531
Admin Zettie B McLerran.
Licensure Skilled care. *Beds* 48. *Certified*
Medicaid.
Owner Proprietary Corp (ARA Living
Centers).
Admissions Requirements Minimum age 21.
Staff Physicians 1 (pt); RNs 2 (ft); LPNs 4
(ft); Nurses aides 12 (ft), 4 (pt); Physical
therapists 1 (pt); Reality therapists 1 (pt);
Recreational therapists 1 (pt); Occupational
therapists 1 (pt); Speech therapists 1 (pt);
Activities coordinators 1 (ft); Dietitians 1
(pt).
Facilities Dining room; Crafts room; Laundry
room; Barber/Beauty shop.
Activities Arts & crafts; Cards; Games;
Reading groups; Prayer groups; Movies;
Social/Cultural gatherings.

JUNCTION

Leisure Lodge—Junction*
111 Hospital Dr, Junction, TX, 76849
(915) 446-3351
Admin Marion L Seba. *Medical Dir/Dir of
Nursing* Ronald A Graham MD.
Licensure Intermediate care. *Beds* 70.
Certified Medicaid.
Owner Proprietary Corp (Beverly Enterprises).
Admissions Requirements Medical
examination; Physician's request.
Staff Physicians 1 (pt); RNs 1 (pt); LPNs 3
(ft); Orderlies 3 (ft); Nurses aides 13 (ft), 2
(pt); Activities coordinators 1 (ft); Dietitians
1 (pt).
Facilities Dining room; Activities room;
Chapel; Crafts room; Laundry room; Barber/
Beauty shop; Library.
Activities Arts & crafts; Cards; Games; Prayer
groups; Movies; Shopping trips; Social/
Cultural gatherings.

KARNES CITY

Karnes City Care Center
PO Box 430, 209 Country Club Dr, Karnes
City, TX, 78118
(512) 780-2426
Admin Freddie M White. *Medical Dir/Dir of
Nursing* Patricia A Bednorz RN DON.
Licensure Skilled care. *Beds* SNF 60. *Certified*
Medicaid; Medicare.
Owner Proprietary Corp (Columbia Corp).
Admissions Requirements Medical
examination; Physician's request.
Staff RNs 2 (ft); LPNs 4 (ft), 1 (pt); Nurses
aides 15 (ft), 4 (pt); Activities coordinators 1
(ft).
Languages Spanish, Polish, Czech, German
Facilities Dining room; Laundry room;
Barber/Beauty shop.
Activities Arts & crafts; Games; Prayer groups;
Movies.

KATY

Katyville Healthcare Center
5129 E 5th St, Katy, TX, 77449
(713) 391-7087
Admin Lera E Phillips. *Medical Dir/Dir of
Nursing* Cheryl Crozier RN.
Licensure Intermediate care. *Beds* ICF 98.
Certified Medicaid.
Owner Proprietary Corp.
Admissions Requirements Minimum age 18.

Staff RNs; LPNs; Nurses aides; Activities
coordinators; Dietitians.
Facilities Dining room; Activities room;
Crafts room; Laundry room; Barber/Beauty
shop; Library.
Activities Arts & crafts; Cards; Games;
Reading groups; Prayer groups; Movies;
Shopping trips; Social/Cultural gatherings.

KAUFMAN

Leisure Lodge—Kaufman
PO Box 191, 3001 S Houston St, Kaufman,
TX, 75142
(214) 932-2118
Admin Mary E Grant. *Medical Dir/Dir of
Nursing* David Ellis MD; Rusty Simmons
LVN DON.
Licensure Intermediate care. *Beds* ICF 115.
Certified Medicaid.
Owner Proprietary Corp (Beverly Enterprises).
Admissions Requirements Minimum age 18;
Medical examination; Physician's request.
Staff LPNs 8 (ft), 3 (pt); Nurses aides 25 (ft),
3 (pt); Activities coordinators 1 (ft).
Facilities Dining room; Activities room;
Crafts room; Laundry room; Barber/Beauty
shop; Library; Whirlpool.
Activities Arts & crafts; Cards; Games;
Reading groups; Prayer groups; Movies;
Shopping trips; Social/Cultural gatherings;
Dominoes; Exercise; Friendly visitor
program; International programs.

Rose Haven of Kaufman Inc*
102 E 9th St, Kaufman, TX, 75142
(214) 932-2326
Admin Richard Mullin.
Licensure Intermediate care. *Beds* 37.
Certified Medicaid.
Owner Proprietary Corp.

KEENE

Town Hall Estates
PO Box 673, 207 Old Betsy Rd, Keene, TX,
76059
(817) 641-9843
Admin Alberta Ann Bunnell.
Licensure Intermediate care. *Beds* 75.
Certified Medicaid.
Staff RNs 2 (ft); LPNs 5 (ft); Nurses aides 23
(ft); Activities coordinators 1 (ft); Dietitians
1 (pt).
Facilities Dining room; Laundry room;
Barber/Beauty shop.
Activities Arts & crafts; Games; Reading
groups; Prayer groups; Movies.

KELLER

Mimosa Manor Care Center
PO Box 485, 459 E Price St, Keller, TX,
76248
(817) 431-2518
Admin Andre F Villarreal. *Medical Dir/Dir of
Nursing* Dr B Domagus; Linda Chambers
LVN.
Licensure Intermediate care. *Beds* ICF 150.
Certified Medicaid.
Owner Proprietary Corp.
Admissions Requirements Minimum age 21.
Staff LPNs 6 (ft); Orderlies 4 (ft); Nurses
aides 30 (ft).
Languages Spanish
Facilities Dining room; Physical therapy
room; Activities room; Crafts room; Laundry
room; Barber/Beauty shop.
Activities Arts & crafts; Cards; Games;
Reading groups; Prayer groups; Movies;
Shopping trips; Social/Cultural gatherings.

KEMP

Kemp Care Center Inc*
600 N Adams St, Kemp, TX, 75143
(214) 498-5701
Admin A W Baldwin.
Licensure Intermediate care. *Beds* 60.
Certified Medicaid.
Admissions Requirements Medical
examination; Physician's request.
Staff Physicians; RNs; LPNs; Nurses aides;
Physical therapists; Reality therapists;
Recreational therapists; Occupational
therapists; Speech therapists; Activities
coordinators; Dietitians; Podiatrists.
Facilities Dining room; Physical therapy
room; Activities room; Chapel; Crafts room;
Laundry room; Barber/Beauty shop; Library.
Activities Cards; Games; Prayer groups;
Movies; Shopping trips.

KENEDY

Green's Nursing Center
505 W Main St, Kenedy, TX, 78119
(512) 583-3406
Admin Patsy L Marchant. *Medical Dir/Dir of
Nursing* Stephanie Martignoni.
Licensure Intermediate care. *Beds* ICF 61.
Certified Medicaid; Medicare.
Owner Proprietary Corp.
Admissions Requirements Minimum age 16;
Physician's request.
Staff LPNs; Nurses aides.
Languages Spanish
Facilities Dining room; Activities room;
Crafts room; Laundry room; Barber/Beauty
shop.
Activities Arts & crafts; Games; Reading
groups; Prayer groups; Movies; Shopping
trips; Social/Cultural gatherings.

John Paul II Nursing Center*
215 Tilden, Kenedy, TX, 78119
(512) 583-2784
Admin Pauline Wernli.
Licensure Intermediate care; Personal care.
Beds ICF 73; Personal 21. *Certified*
Medicaid.
Owner Nonprofit Corp.
Affiliation Roman Catholic

Restful Acres Nursing Home Inc*
Box E, Hwy 181 S, Kenedy, TX, 78119
(512) 583-3421
Admin Lana K Green.
Licensure Intermediate care. *Beds* 60.
Certified Medicaid.
Owner Proprietary Corp.

KENNEDALE

Kennedale Nursing Home*
PO Box 447, Old Mansfield Rd, Kennedale,
TX, 76060
(817) 478-5454
Admin Mildred K Garrett.
Licensure Skilled care. *Beds* 60. *Certified*
Medicaid.
Owner Proprietary Corp (Summit Health Ltd).

KERENS

Maywood Manor Inc
PO Box 30, Rte 1, Kerens, TX, 75144
(214) 396-2905
Admin Joan K Kilcrease. *Medical Dir/Dir of
Nursing* Margaret Burden.
Licensure Intermediate care. *Beds* 60.
Certified Medicaid.
Owner Proprietary Corp.
Admissions Requirements Medical
examination; Physician's request.
Staff RNs 1 (pt); LPNs 4 (ft), 1 (pt); Nurses
aides 13 (ft), 8 (pt); Activities coordinators 1
(ft), 1 (pt); Dietitians 1 (pt).

Facilities Dining room; Laundry room;
Barber/Beauty shop.
Activities Arts & crafts; Games.

KERMIT

Kermit Nursing Center*
PO Box 1035, School St, Kermit, TX, 79745
(915) 586-6665
Admin Jemmie Nell Cooke.
Licensure Skilled care. *Beds* 100. *Certified*
Medicaid.
Owner Proprietary Corp (Beverly Enterprises).

KERRVILLE

**Alpine Terrace Retirement & Convalescent
Center**
746 Alpine Dr, Kerrville, TX, 78028
(512) 896-2323
Admin Andrew B Seibert. *Medical Dir/Dir of
Nursing* Gregory G McKenzie MD; Mary
Ann Parker RN.
Licensure Intermediate care; Custodial care.
Beds ICF 60; Custodial care 60.
Owner Proprietary Corp (Vari-Care Inc).
Admissions Requirements Medical
examination.
Staff Physicians 1 (pt); RNs 1 (ft); LPNs 5
(ft), 2 (pt); Nurses aides 15 (ft), 3 (pt);
Activities coordinators 2 (ft); Dietitians 1
(pt).
Facilities Dining room; Physical therapy
room; Activities room; Crafts room; Laundry
room; Barber/Beauty shop; Library;
Courtyard.
Activities Arts & crafts; Cards; Games;
Reading groups; Prayer groups; Movies;
Shopping trips; Social/Cultural gatherings.

Edgewater Care Center
1213 Water St, Kerrville, TX, 78028
(512) 896-2411
Admin James Vaughn. *Medical Dir/Dir of
Nursing* Ann K Hardee RN; Dan W Bacon
MD.
Licensure Skilled care; Intermediate care. *Beds*
SNF 79; ICF 104. *Certified* Medicaid;
Medicare.
Owner Proprietary Corp.
Admissions Requirements Minimum age 55;
Medical examination; Physician's request.
Staff Physicians 1 (pt); RNs 3 (ft), 1 (pt);
LPNs 10 (ft), 8 (pt); Orderlies 4 (ft), 4 (pt);
Nurses aides 38 (ft), 8 (pt); Physical
therapists 1 (pt); Activities coordinators 1
(ft), 2 (pt); Dietitians 1 (ft), 1 (pt);
Ophthalmologists 1 (pt).
Languages Spanish, German
Facilities Dining room; Physical therapy
room; Activities room; Crafts room; Laundry
room; Barber/Beauty shop; Library.
Activities Arts & crafts; Cards; Games;
Reading groups; Prayer groups; Movies;
Shopping trips; Social/Cultural gatherings.

Hilltop Village*
Hilltop Circle, Kerrville, TX, 78028
(512) 895-3200
Admin Jack Reynolds.
Licensure Intermediate care; Custodial care.
Beds ICF 90; Custodial care 60. *Certified*
Medicaid.
Owner Proprietary Corp (Vari-Care Inc).
Admissions Requirements Medical
examination; Physician's request.
Staff RNs 3 (ft), 1 (pt); LPNs 14 (ft), 2 (pt);
Orderlies 2 (ft); Nurses aides 39 (ft), 5 (pt);
Activities coordinators 2 (ft); Dietitians 1
(ft).
Facilities Dining room; Activities room;
Chapel; Crafts room; Laundry room; Barber/
Beauty shop; Library.
Activities Arts & crafts; Cards; Games; Prayer
groups; Movies; Shopping trips; Social/
Cultural gatherings.

Meadowview Care Center*
600 Leslie Dr, Kerrville, TX, 78028
(512) 896-3711
Admin Paul Toops.
Licensure Intermediate care; Personal care.
Beds ICF 96; Personal care 22. *Certified*
Medicaid.
Admissions Requirements Medical
examination; Physician's request.
Staff RNs 1 (ft); Activities coordinators 1 (ft).
Facilities Dining room; Activities room;
Crafts room; Laundry room; Barber/Beauty
shop.
Activities Arts & crafts; Cards; Games;
Reading groups; Prayer groups; Movies;
Shopping trips; Exercise groups.

KILGORE

Gregg Home for the Aged Inc
Rte 5 Box 135 Hwy 42N, Kilgore, TX, 75662
(214) 984-5688, 4391
Admin Barbara A Garner. *Medical Dir/Dir of
Nursing* Sharon L McCabe LVN.
Licensure Intermediate care. *Beds* ICF 62.
Certified Medicaid.
Owner Nonprofit Corp.
Admissions Requirements Minimum age 21;
Medical examination; Physician's request.
Staff RNs 1 (pt); LPNs 6 (ft); Nurses aides 12
(ft); Physical therapists; Reality therapists;
Occupational therapists; Speech therapists;
Activities coordinators 1 (ft); Dietitians 1
(ft); Dentists; Ophthalmologists; Podiatrists.
Facilities Dining room; Activities room;
Chapel; Crafts room; Laundry room; Barber/
Beauty shop; Library; Sunrooms.
Activities Arts & crafts; Cards; Games;
Reading groups; Prayer groups; Movies;
Shopping trips; Social/Cultural gatherings;
Field trips; Mini-golf course; Volleyball.

Kilgore Nursing Center
2700 S Henderson Blvd, Kilgore, TX, 75662
(214) 984-3511
Admin Mike Chaney. *Medical Dir/Dir of
Nursing* Linda Hutchison.
Licensure Skilled care. *Beds* SNF 115.
Certified Medicaid; Medicare.
Owner Proprietary Corp (Hillhaven Corp).
Admissions Requirements Physician's request.
Staff RNs; LPNs; Orderlies; Nurses aides;
Activities coordinators.
Facilities Dining room; Activities room;
Laundry room; Barber/Beauty shop.
Activities Arts & crafts; Cards; Games; Prayer
groups; Movies; Shopping trips; Social/
Cultural gatherings.

Stone Road Nursing Center Inc
PO Box 1317, 3607 Stone Rd, Kilgore, TX,
75662
(214) 984-5036
Admin Glenda R Jones. *Medical Dir/Dir of
Nursing* Sue Braswell LVN.
Licensure Intermediate care. *Beds* ICF 60.
Certified Medicaid.
Owner Proprietary Corp.
Staff LPNs; Nurses aides; Activities
coordinators.
Activities Arts & crafts; Cards; Games;
Reading groups; Prayer groups; Movies;
Shopping trips; Social/Cultural gatherings;
Picnics; Outings.

KILLEEN

Killeen Nursing Home*
710 W Rancier Ave, Killeen, TX, 76544
(817) 526-3130, 6398
Admin Sandra Springwater.
Licensure Skilled care. *Beds* 50. *Certified*
Medicaid.
Owner Proprietary Corp (Beverly Enterprises).

KINGSLAND

Kingsland Hills Care Center
Drawer 1079, Hwy 1431, Kingsland, TX, 78639
(915) 388-4538
Admin Wanda M Laxson. *Medical Dir/Dir of Nursing* Wilma Dehnel.
Licensure Intermediate care. *Beds* ICF 108. *Certified* Medicaid.
Owner Proprietary Corp.
Admissions Requirements Medical examination; Physician's request.
Staff RNs 1 (ft); LPNs 12 (ft); Nurses aides 43 (ft); Activities coordinators 1 (ft); Dietitians 1 (ft).
Languages German, Spanish
Facilities Dining room; Laundry room; Barber/Beauty shop.
Activities Cards; Games; Prayer groups; Movies; Social/Cultural gatherings; Exercise.

KINGSVILLE

Retama Manor*
316 Military Hwy, Kingsville, TX, 78363
(512) 592-9366
Admin Emma Aguilar.
Licensure Intermediate care; Custodial care. *Beds* ICF 156; Custodial care 42. *Certified* Medicaid.
Owner Proprietary Corp (ARA Living Centers).
Admissions Requirements Medical examination; Physician's request.
Staff RNs 1 (ft); LPNs 8 (ft), 2 (pt); Activities coordinators 1 (ft).
Facilities Dining room; Activities room; Chapel; Crafts room; Laundry room; Barber/Beauty shop.
Activities Arts & crafts; Cards; Games; Prayer groups; Movies.

KNOX CITY

Brazos Valley Care Home Inc*
605 Ave "F" S, Knox City, TX, 79529
(817) 658-3543
Admin Doyle Graham. *Medical Dir/Dir of Nursing* Dr Hooker.
Licensure Intermediate care. *Beds* 70. *Certified* Medicaid.
Owner Proprietary Corp (Truco Inc).
Admissions Requirements Minimum age 18; Medical examination.
Staff Physicians 3 (pt); RNs 1 (pt); LPNs 5 (ft), 5 (pt); Nurses aides 16 (ft); Physical therapists 1 (pt); Recreational therapists 1 (pt); Activities coordinators 1 (ft); Dietitians 1 (pt); Dentists 1 (pt).
Facilities Dining room; Activities room; Crafts room; Laundry room; Barber/Beauty shop.
Activities Arts & crafts; Games; Prayer groups; Movies; Shopping trips; Social/Cultural gatherings.

KOUNTZE

Kountze Nursing Center
PO Box 940, FM Rd 1293, Kountze, TX, 77625
(409) 246-3418
Admin Saundra Rhame. *Medical Dir/Dir of Nursing* H A Hooks MD; Diane Haddon RN.
Licensure Skilled care. *Beds* SNF 60. *Certified* Medicaid; Medicare.
Owner Proprietary Corp (ARA Living Centers).
Admissions Requirements Medical examination; Physician's request.
Staff RNs 1 (ft), 3 (pt); LPNs 6 (ft), 1 (pt); Nurses aides 15 (ft); Physical therapists 1 (pt); Activities coordinators 1 (ft); Dietitians 1 (ft), 1 (pt).

Facilities Dining room; Physical therapy room; Activities room; Crafts room; Laundry room; Barber/Beauty shop.
Activities Arts & crafts; Games; Reading groups; Prayer groups; Movies; Shopping trips; Social/Cultural gatherings.

LA GRANGE

Care Inn of La Grange*
PO Box 398, 457 N Main, La Grange, TX, 78945
(713) 968-5865
Admin Marjorie Heinrich.
Licensure Intermediate care. *Beds* 98. *Certified* Medicaid.
Owner Proprietary Corp (ARA Living Centers).

LA PORTE

Happy Harbor Methodist Home*
PO Box 1337, 1106 Bayshore Dr, La Porte, TX, 77571
(713) 471-1210
Admin H Frank Carter.
Licensure Intermediate care. *Beds* 140. *Certified* Medicaid.
Owner Nonprofit Corp.
Affiliation Methodist

La Porte Care Center*
208 S Utah, La Porte, TX, 77571
(713) 471-1810
Admin Norma J Shamblin.
Licensure Intermediate care. *Beds* 58. *Certified* Medicaid.
Owner Proprietary Corp (Beverly Enterprises).
Staff RNs 1 (pt); LPNs 4 (ft); Nurses aides 13 (ft); Activities coordinators 1 (ft); Dietitians 1 (ft); 8 (ft).
Facilities Dining room; Chapel; Laundry room; Barber/Beauty shop.
Activities Arts & crafts; Cards; Games; Reading groups; Prayer groups; Movies; Shopping trips; Social/Cultural gatherings.

LAKE JACKSON

Lake Jackson Nursing Home*
413 Garland Dr, Lake Jackson, TX, 77566
(713) 297-3266
Admin Rebecca Grether. *Medical Dir/Dir of Nursing* A O McCary MD.
Licensure Skilled care; Intermediate care. *Beds* 120. *Certified* Medicaid; Medicare.
Owner Proprietary Corp (Beverly Enterprises).
Admissions Requirements Medical examination; Physician's request.
Staff Physicians 1 (ft), 2 (pt); RNs 4 (ft); LPNs 11 (ft); Orderlies 1 (ft); Nurses aides 45 (ft); Physical therapists 1 (pt); Occupational therapists 1 (pt); Speech therapists 1 (pt); Activities coordinators 1 (ft); Dietitians 1 (pt); Dentists 1 (pt); Podiatrists 1 (pt).
Facilities Dining room; Activities room; Crafts room; Laundry room; Barber/Beauty shop.
Activities Arts & crafts; Cards; Games; Reading groups; Prayer groups; Movies; Shopping trips; Social/Cultural gatherings.

LAKE WORTH

Lake Lodge Retirement & Nursing Center
3800 Marina Dr, Lake Worth, TX, 76135
(817) 237-7231
Admin Donna J Snyder. *Medical Dir/Dir of Nursing* Charles Maxville; Myrna Jurica.
Licensure Intermediate care; Quadriplegic wing. *Beds* 150. *Certified* Medicaid.
Owner Proprietary Corp (Texas Health Enterprises).
Admissions Requirements Medical examination.

Staff Physicians 1 (pt); RNs 2 (ft); LPNs 10 (ft); Orderlies 17 (ft); Physical therapists 1 (pt); Occupational therapists 1 (pt); Speech therapists 1 (pt); Activities coordinators 1 (ft); Dietitians 1 (ft); Dentists 1 (pt); Ophthalmologists 1 (pt); Podiatrists 1 (pt).
Facilities Dining room; Activities room; Crafts room; Laundry room; Barber/Beauty shop; Library; 2 sunrooms; Sun deck; Large patio.
Activities Arts & crafts; Cards; Games; Reading groups; Prayer groups; Movies; Shopping trips; Social/Cultural gatherings.

LAMESA

Heritage Nursing Manor*
PO Box 1285, 1201 N 15th St, Lamesa, TX, 79331
(806) 872-2141
Admin David O Crowson.
Licensure Intermediate care. *Beds* 80. *Certified* Medicaid.
Owner Proprietary Corp (Beverly Enterprises).

Lamesa Nursing Center*
1818 N 7th St, Lamesa, TX, 79331
(806) 872-8351
Admin Eugenia F Herrin.
Licensure Intermediate care. *Beds* 48. *Certified* Medicaid.
Owner Proprietary Corp (Beverly Enterprises).

LAMPASAS

Lampasas Manor*
PO Box 970, 611 N Broad St, Lampasas, TX, 76550
(512) 556-3688
Admin Don Carlos Lacey.
Licensure Skilled care. *Beds* 68. *Certified* Medicaid.
Owner Proprietary Corp.

Leisure Lodge—Lampasas*
FM Rd 580 E, Lampasas, TX, 76550
(512) 556-6267
Admin Ima B Kelley.
Licensure Intermediate care. *Beds* 96. *Certified* Medicaid.
Owner Proprietary Corp (Beverly Enterprises).

LANCASTER

Lancaster Nursing Home Inc*
1515 N Elm, Lancaster, TX, 75134
(214) 227-6066
Admin Mina L Ellison. *Medical Dir/Dir of Nursing* Charles Waldrop MD.
Licensure Skilled care; Intermediate care. *Beds* 120. *Certified* Medicaid.
Owner Proprietary Corp (Beverly Enterprises).
Admissions Requirements Medical examination; Physician's request.
Facilities Dining room; Activities room; Laundry room; Barber/Beauty shop.
Activities Arts & crafts; Games; Prayer groups; Shopping trips; Social/Cultural gatherings.

Lancaster Residential Center*
3901 N Dallas Ave, Lancaster, TX, 75134
(214) 224-3554
Admin James L Roberts Jr.
Licensure Intermediate care for mentally retarded. *Beds* 68. *Certified* Medicaid.

Silent Night Nursing Home*
346 W Redbud, Lancaster, TX, 75146
(214) 227-1205, 1255
Admin Helen G Robinson.
Licensure Intermediate care. *Beds* 62. *Certified* Medicaid.
Owner Proprietary Corp.

Texas Healthcare Center*
1241 Westridge, Lancaster, TX, 75146
(214) 227-5110

Admin Joyce Steuer.
Licensure Intermediate care. *Beds* 120.
Certified Medicaid.
Owner Proprietary Corp.

LAREDO

Retama Manor Nursing Center—East*
2520 Arkansas, Laredo, TX, 78040
(512) 722-0584
Admin Virginia Rodriguez.
Licensure Skilled care. *Beds* 100. *Certified*
Medicaid.

Retama Manor Nursing Center—South*
1100 Galveston, Laredo, TX, 78040
(512) 723-2068
Admin Virginia Rodriguez.
Licensure Intermediate care. *Beds* 120.
Certified Medicaid.
Owner Proprietary Corp (ARA Living
Centers).

Retama Manor Nursing Center—West*
1200 Lane, Laredo, TX, 78040
(512) 722-0031
Admin Betty Funkhouser.
Licensure Intermediate care; Custodial care.
Beds ICF 168; Custodial care 40. *Certified*
Medicaid.
Owner Proprietary Corp (ARA Living
Centers).

LEONARD

Gilbert Nursing Home*
PO Box 358, E Hackberry St, Leonard, TX,
75452
(214) 587-2282
Admin Billy Wayne Gilbert.
Licensure Intermediate care. *Beds* 80.
Certified Medicaid.
Owner Proprietary Corp.

LEVELLAND

Levelland Development Center
1515 5th St, Levelland, TX, 79336
(806) 894-4902
Admin Don Whiteside.
Licensure Intermediate care for mentally
retarded. *Beds* 42. *Certified* Medicaid.

Levelland Nursing Home
210 W Ave, Levelland, TX, 79336
(806) 894-5053
Admin Charlene T Turner. *Medical Dir/Dir of
Nursing* Judy Choate.
Licensure Intermediate care. *Beds* 89.
Certified Medicaid.
Owner Proprietary Corp (ARA Living
Centers).
Staff LPNs 7 (ft), 3 (pt); Nurses aides 20 (ft),
4 (pt); Recreational therapists 2 (ft), 2 (pt);
Activities coordinators 1 (ft).
Facilities Dining room; Activities room;
Barber/Beauty shop.

LEWISVILLE

Edmond Oaks Center
1680 Edmonds Lane, Lewisville, TX, 75067
(214) 436-4538
Admin Douglas L Adams. *Medical Dir/Dir of
Nursing* Claire Ruffin RN.
Licensure Intermediate care for mentally
retarded. *Beds* ICF/MR 116. *Certified*
Medicaid.
Owner Proprietary Corp.
Admissions Requirements Minimum age 16.
Staff Physicians 1 (pt); RNs 1 (pt); LPNs 6
(ft); Nurses aides 120 (ft); Physical therapists
1 (pt); Recreational therapists 1 (ft);
Occupational therapists 1 (pt); Speech

therapists 1 (pt); Dietitians 1 (pt); Dentists 1
(pt); Ophthalmologists 1 (pt); Podiatrists 1
(pt).
Facilities Dining room; Physical therapy
room; Activities room; Off-campus training
center.
Activities Arts & crafts; Cards; Games; Social/
Cultural gatherings; Habilitative training.

Lewisville Nursing Home*
740 Edmonds Ln, Lewisville, TX, 75067
(214) 436-3314
Admin Casandra Ann Kalina.
Licensure Intermediate care. *Beds* 60.
Certified Medicaid.
Owner Proprietary Corp.

Twin Pines Nursing Center
169 Lake Park Rd, Lewisville, TX, 76054
(214) 436-7571
Admin Michelle Arthur. *Medical Dir/Dir of
Nursing* Marie Nole RN.
Licensure Intermediate care. *Beds* ICF 120.
Certified Medicaid.
Owner Privately owned.
Admissions Requirements Medical
examination.
Staff RNs; Orderlies; Nurses aides; Physical
therapists; Recreational therapists;
Occupational therapists; Speech therapists;
Activities coordinators; Dietitians;
Ophthalmologists.
Languages Spanish
Facilities Dining room; Activities room;
Crafts room; Laundry room; Barber/Beauty
shop; Library.
Activities Arts & crafts; Cards; Games;
Reading groups; Prayer groups; Movies;
Shopping trips; Social/Cultural gatherings.

LIBERTY

Golden Charm Nursing Home*
1206 N Travis, Liberty, TX, 77575
(713) 336-7247
Admin Rita Aalund. *Medical Dir/Dir of
Nursing* Dr Sergio Rodriquez.
Licensure Skilled care; Intermediate care. *Beds*
120. *Certified* Medicaid.
Owner Proprietary Corp (Beverly Enterprises).
Admissions Requirements Minimum age 21;
Medical examination; Physician's request.
Staff Physicians 6 (pt); RNs 1 (ft), 1 (pt);
LPNs 9 (ft); Nurses aides 19 (ft); Physical
therapists 1 (pt); Speech therapists 1 (pt);
Activities coordinators 1 (pt); Dietitians 1
(pt); Dentists 1 (pt); Podiatrists 1 (pt).
Facilities Dining room; Activities room;
Laundry room; Barber/Beauty shop.
Activities Arts & crafts; Games; Movies;
Shopping trips; Social/Cultural gatherings.

Liberty Nursing Home*
521 Travis, Liberty, TX, 77575
(713) 336-3691
Admin Joy L Green.
Licensure Intermediate care. *Beds* 82.
Certified Medicaid.
Admissions Requirements Medical
examination; Physician's request.
Staff Activities coordinators 1 (ft); Dietitians
1 (ft).
Facilities Dining room; Activities room;
Chapel; Crafts room; Laundry room; Barber/
Beauty shop.
Activities Arts & crafts; Games; Reading
groups; Prayer groups; Movies; Shopping
trips; Social/Cultural gatherings.

LINDALE

Lindale Nursing Center*
PO Box 188, 800 N College St, Lindale, TX,
75771
(214) 882-3118, 6037
Admin Juanita Awbrey.

Licensure Intermediate care. *Beds* 89.
Certified Medicaid.
Owner Proprietary Corp (Beverly Enterprises).

LINDEN

Oak Manor Nursing Home*
Hwy 11 W, Linden, TX, 75563
(214) 756-5575
Admin Wallace D Roberts Jr.
Licensure Intermediate care. *Beds* 107.
Certified Medicaid.
Owner Proprietary Corp (Truco Inc).
Facilities Dining room; Activities room;
Barber/Beauty shop.
Activities Arts & crafts; Cards; Games; Prayer
groups; Movies; Social/Cultural gatherings.

LITTLEFIELD

Knight's Nursing Home
Box 328, 520 Ash, Littlefield, TX, 79339
(806) 385-3921
Admin Nelda Jean Cheshier. *Medical Dir/Dir
of Nursing* Faye Jackson LVN DON.
Licensure Intermediate care. *Beds* ICF 59.
Certified Medicaid.
Owner Privately owned.
Staff Physicians 7 (pt); RNs 1 (pt); LPNs 6
(ft), 1 (pt); Nurses aides 30 (ft), 1 (pt);
Physical therapists 1 (pt); Activities
coordinators 1 (ft); Dietitians 1 (pt); Dentists
1 (pt); Ophthalmologists 1 (pt).
Languages Spanish, German
Facilities Dining room; Activities room;
Chapel; Crafts room; Laundry room.
Activities Arts & crafts; Cards; Games;
Reading groups; Prayer groups; Social/
Cultural gatherings.

Littlefield Hospitality House*
PO Box 589, 1609 W 10th St, Littlefield, TX,
79339
(806) 385-5952
Admin Vera L Reynolds.
Licensure Intermediate care. *Beds* 63.
Certified Medicaid.
Owner Proprietary Corp.

LIVINGSTON

Bur-Mont Nursing Center*
154 Banks Dr, Livingston, TX, 77351
(713) 327-5415
Admin Velma Walker.
Licensure Intermediate care. *Beds* 120.
Certified Medicaid.
Staff LPNs 10 (ft); Nurses aides 30 (ft);
Activities coordinators 1 (ft); Dietitians 2
(ft).
Facilities Dining room; Activities room;
Chapel; Crafts room; Laundry room; Barber/
Beauty shop.
Activities Arts & crafts; Prayer groups;
Movies; Social/Cultural gatherings.

Livngston Convalescent Center*
PO Box 929, 1810 N Washington, Livingston,
TX, 77351
(713) 327-4341
Admin Virginia L Williams.
Licensure Intermediate care. *Beds* 52.
Certified Medicaid.
Owner Proprietary Corp (Cantex Healthcare
Centers).

LLANO

Care Inn of Llano*
800 W Haynie, Llano, TX, 78643
(915) 247-4194
Admin Audrey Sue Rice.
Licensure Intermediate care. *Beds* 122.
Certified Medicaid.
Owner Proprietary Corp (ARA Living
Centers).

Hill Country Manor
507 E Green St, Llano, TX, 78643
(915) 247-4115
Admin Mildred Overstreet. *Medical Dir/Dir of
Nursing* Karen Powell.
Licensure Intermediate care. *Beds* ICF 86.
Certified Medicaid.
Owner Proprietary Corp (Beverly Enterprises).
Admissions Requirements Physician's request.
Staff Physicians 4 (ft); RNs 1 (ft); LPNs 6 (ft);
Orderlies 2 (ft); Nurses aides 13 (ft);
Physical therapists 1 (pt); Activities
coordinators; Dietitians 1 (ft).
Facilities Dining room; Activities room;
Chapel; Crafts room; Laundry room; Barber/
Beauty shop.
Activities Arts & crafts; Cards; Games;
Reading groups; Prayer groups; Movies;
Shopping trips; Social/Cultural gatherings;
Senior Olympics; Adopt-a-grandparent
program.

LOCKHART

Cartwheel Lodge—Lockhart
107 N Medina, Lockhart, TX, 78644
(512) 398-5213
Admin Mr Jack Keys. *Medical Dir/Dir of
Nursing* Mary Soliz LUN DON.
Licensure Intermediate care. *Beds* ICF 100.
Certified Medicaid.
Owner Proprietary Corp (Diversicare Corp).
Admissions Requirements Physician's request.
Staff LPNs 4 (ft), 1 (pt); Orderlies 5 (ft), 1
(pt); Nurses aides 22 (ft), 1 (pt); Activities
coordinators 1 (ft); Dietitians 1 (ft).
Languages Spanish
Facilities Dining room; Activities room;
Laundry room; Barber/Beauty shop.
Activities Arts & crafts; Cards; Games;
Reading groups; Prayer groups; Movies;
Shopping trips; Social/Cultural gatherings.

Golden Age Home
PO Box 870, S Main St, Lockhart, TX, 78644
(512) 398-2362
Admin Robert J Reeb. *Medical Dir/Dir of
Nursing* P A Wales MD; Judy Dalrymple
DON.
Licensure Intermediate care. *Beds* ICF 100.
Certified Medicaid.
Owner Nonprofit organization/foundation.
Admissions Requirements Minimum age 62;
Physician's request; Ambulatory.
Staff Physicians 1 (pt); RNs 1 (ft), 5 (pt);
LPNs 3 (ft); Nurses aides 17 (ft), 13 (pt);
Activities coordinators 1 (ft); Dietitians 1
(ft).
Languages Spanish
Affiliation Methodist
Facilities Dining room; Activities room;
Chapel; Crafts room; Laundry room; Barber/
Beauty shop; Library.
Activities Arts & crafts; Cards; Games; Prayer
groups; Movies; Shopping trips; Exercise
classes.

LOCKNEY

Lockney Care Center
401 N Main, Lockney, TX, 79241
(806) 652-2502 or 652-2513
Admin Lavona Pitchford. *Medical Dir/Dir of
Nursing* Marilyn Ellis.
Licensure Intermediate care. *Beds* ICF 52.
Certified Medicaid.
Owner Proprietary Corp (Unicare).
Admissions Requirements Medical
examination; Physician's request.
Staff LPNs 4 (ft); Nurses aides 13 (ft), 2 (pt);
Activities coordinators 1 (ft).
Facilities Dining room; Laundry room;
Barber/Beauty shop.
Activities Arts & crafts; Cards; Games;
Reading groups; Prayer groups; Movies;
Shopping trips.

LONGVIEW

Cleaver Memorial Convalescent Center
1000 Sapphire St, Longview, TX, 75601
(214) 753-8608
Admin Edwin C Cuington. *Medical Dir/Dir of
Nursing* Edna M McNeil.
Licensure Intermediate care. *Beds* ICF 100.
Certified Medicaid.
Owner Proprietary Corp.
Admissions Requirements Physician's request.
Staff RNs 2 (ft); LPNs 8 (ft), 2 (pt); Nurses
aides 10 (ft), 5 (pt); Activities coordinators 1
(ft); Dietitians 2 (ft).
Facilities Dining room; Activities room;
Chapel; Crafts room; Laundry room; Barber/
Beauty shop.
Activities Arts & crafts; Cards; Games; Prayer
groups; Social/Cultural gatherings.

Highland Pines*
1100 N 4th St, Longview, TX, 75601
(214) 753-7661
Admin Gladys M Riggs. *Medical Dir/Dir of
Nursing* Charles E Gaye MD.
Licensure Intermediate care. *Beds* 114.
Certified Medicaid.
Admissions Requirements Medical
examination; Physician's request.
Staff Physicians 1 (pt); RNs 1 (ft); LPNs 9
(ft); Nurses aides 19 (ft); Physical therapists;
Reality therapists 2 (ft); Recreational
therapists 2 (ft); Occupational therapists;
Speech therapists; Activities coordinators 1
(pt); Dietitians 1 (pt); Dentists 1 (pt);
Podiatrists 1 (pt); Audiologists 1 (pt).
Facilities Dining room; Activities room;
Chapel; Crafts room; Laundry room; Barber/
Beauty shop; Library; Two sunrooms.
Activities Arts & crafts; Cards; Games;
Reading groups; Prayer groups; Shopping
trips; Social/Cultural gatherings.

Holiday Lodge Nursing Home
1301 Eden Dr, Longview, TX, 75601
(214) 753-7651
Admin Billie Sue Cooper. *Medical Dir/Dir of
Nursing* Mimi Gonzalez RN.
Licensure Skilled care; Intermediate care. *Beds*
SNF 56; ICF 102. *Certified* Medicaid;
Medicare.
Owner Proprietary Corp (ARA Living
Centers).
Admissions Requirements Minimum age 16.
Staff RNs; LPNs; Nurses aides; Physical
therapists; Activities coordinators; Dietitians.
Facilities Dining room; Activities room;
Crafts room; Laundry room; Barber/Beauty
shop.
Activities Arts & crafts; Cards; Games;
Reading groups; Prayer groups; Movies;
Shopping trips; Social/Cultural gatherings.

Lynn Lodge Nursing Home
111 Ruthlynn Dr, Longview, TX, 75601
(214) 757-2557
Admin Benjamin C Delmonico Jr. *Medical
Dir/Dir of Nursing* Kenneth Marshall MD;
Hilda Wallin RN DON.
Licensure Intermediate care. *Beds* ICF 118.
Certified Medicaid.
Owner Proprietary Corp (ARA Living
Centers).
Admissions Requirements Medical
examination.
Staff RNs 1 (ft); LPNs 10 (ft); Nurses aides 25
(ft); Activities coordinators 1 (ft).
Facilities Dining room; Activities room;
Laundry room; Barber/Beauty shop.
Activities Arts & crafts; Cards; Games; Prayer
groups; Movies; Social/Cultural gatherings.

Pine Tree Lodge Nursing Center*
PO Box 5968, 2711 Pine Tree Rd, Longview,
TX, 75601
(214) 759-3994
Admin Sharon L Gray.

Licensure Intermediate care. *Beds* 60.
Certified Medicaid.
Owner Proprietary Corp.

Willowbrook Manor Nursing Home
112 Ruthlynn Dr, Longview, TX, 75604
(214) 753-8611
Admin Bob E Standard. *Medical Dir/Dir of
Nursing* Dr Roger Kiser; Bonnie Castle.
Licensure Skilled care; Intermediate care. *Beds*
SNF 70; ICF 80. *Certified* Medicaid;
Medicare.
Owner Proprietary Corp (Beverly Enterprises).
Admissions Requirements Minimum age 18;
Medical examination.
Staff Physicians 2 (ft); RNs 2 (ft); LPNs 15
(ft); Orderlies 2 (ft); Nurses aides 35 (ft);
Physical therapists 1 (ft); Reality therapists 1
(ft); Recreational therapists 1 (ft); Activities
coordinators 1 (ft); Dietitians 1 (ft).
Languages Spanish
Facilities Dining room; Physical therapy
room; Activities room; Crafts room; Laundry
room; Barber/Beauty shop.
Activities Arts & crafts; Cards; Games;
Reading groups; Prayer groups; Movies;
Shopping trips; Social/Cultural gatherings;
Outdoor activities; Current events; Quilting.

LORAINE

Loraine Nursing Home
219 Campbell Ave, Loraine, TX, 79532
(915) 737-2209
Admin Linda Barrick. *Medical Dir/Dir of
Nursing* Marie Graham DNS.
Licensure Intermediate care. *Beds* ICF 60.
Certified Medicaid.
Owner Proprietary Corp (Beverly Enterprises).
Admissions Requirements Medical
examination; Physician's request.
Staff RNs 1 (pt); LPNs 4 (ft), 2 (pt); Orderlies
1 (ft); Nurses aides 8 (ft), 1 (pt); Activities
coordinators 1 (ft); Dietitians 1 (pt).
Languages Spanish
Facilities Dining room; Activities room;
Laundry room; Barber/Beauty shop.
Activities Arts & crafts; Cards; Games;
Reading groups; Prayer groups; Movies;
Shopping trips; Social/Cultural gatherings;
Exercise.

LUBBOCK

Bender Terrace Nursing Home*
4510 27th St, Lubbock, TX, 79410
(806) 795-4368
Admin Deborah R Moore.
Licensure Intermediate care. *Beds* 60.
Certified Medicaid.
Owner Proprietary Corp (Summit Health Ltd).
Staff RNs 1 (pt); LPNs 4 (ft); Nurses aides 15
(ft); Activities coordinators 1 (ft); Dietitians
1 (pt).
Facilities Dining room; Activities room;
Laundry room; Barber/Beauty shop.
Activities Arts & crafts; Cards; Games;
Reading groups; Prayer groups; Movies;
Shopping trips; Social/Cultural gatherings.

Brentwood Manor Care Center*
4320 W 19th St, Lubbock, TX, 79407
(806) 795-7147
Admin Maxine H Smith. *Medical Dir/Dir of
Nursing* Dr Pappas.
Licensure Skilled care; Intermediate care. *Beds*
110. *Certified* Medicaid.
Admissions Requirements Minimum age 20;
Medical examination; Physician's request.
Staff RNs 1 (ft), 3 (pt); LPNs 7 (ft), 1 (pt);
Orderlies 2 (ft); Nurses aides 20 (ft), 2 (pt);
Recreational therapists 1 (ft); Activities
coordinators 1 (ft).
Facilities Dining room; Physical therapy
room; Activities room; Chapel; Crafts room;
Laundry room; Barber/Beauty shop.

Activities Arts & crafts; Cards; Games; Reading groups; Prayer groups; Movies; Shopping trips; Social/Cultural gatherings.

Golden Age Nursing Home*
2613 34th St, Lubbock, TX, 79410
(806) 792-2196
Admin Sidney Z Pospisil.
Licensure Intermediate care. Beds 42.
Certified Medicaid.
Owner Proprietary Corp.

John Knox Village
1717 Norfolk Ave, Lubbock, TX, 79416
(806) 791-6000
Admin Rita E Mullins. Medical Dir/Dir of Nursing Linda Villalobos DON.
Licensure Private pay. Beds 62. Certified Medicaid; Medicare.
Owner Nonprofit organization/foundation.
Admissions Requirements Medical examination; Physician's request.
Staff Physicians 1 (ft); RNs 1 (ft); LPNs 8 (ft); Nurses aides 20 (ft); Activities coordinators 1 (ft); Dietitians 1 (ft).
Facilities Dining room; Activities room; Chapel; Barber/Beauty shop.
Activities Arts & crafts; Cards; Games; Reading groups; Prayer groups; Movies; Shopping trips; Social/Cultural gatherings.

Lakeside Memorial Home*
4306 24th St, Lubbock, TX, 79410
(806) 793-2555
Admin Norma E Visage.
Licensure Intermediate care. Beds 93.
Certified Medicaid.
Owner Proprietary Corp.

Lubbock Hospitality House Inc
4710 Slide Rd, Lubbock, TX, 79414
(806) 797-3481
Admin Lois E Hays.
Licensure Intermediate care. Beds 110.
Certified Medicaid.
Staff Physicians 1 (pt); RNs 2 (ft), 1 (pt); LPNs 9 (ft); Nurses aides 28 (ft), 2 (pt); Activities coordinators 1 (ft); Dietitians 1 (ft).
Facilities Dining room; Activities room; Crafts room; Laundry room; Barber/Beauty shop; Library.
Activities Arts & crafts; Cards; Games; Reading groups; Prayer groups; Movies; Shopping trips; Social/Cultural gatherings.

Lubbock Nursing Home Inc*
4120 22nd Pl, Lubbock, TX, 79407
(806) 793-3252
Admin Judy D Bobbitt.
Licensure Skilled care. Beds 120. Certified Medicaid.
Owner Proprietary Corp.

Lutheran Home of West Texas
2418 6th St, Lubbock, TX, 79401
(806) 744-5775
Admin Mary Nell Griffin. Medical Dir/Dir of Nursing Nita Terry RN.
Licensure Intermediate care. Beds 67.
Certified Medicaid.
Owner Nonprofit organization/foundation.
Admissions Requirements Medical examination.
Languages German, Spanish
Facilities Dining room; Activities room; Crafts room; Laundry room; Barber/Beauty shop; Library.
Activities Arts & crafts; Cards; Games; Reading groups; Prayer groups; Movies; Shopping trips; Social/Cultural gatherings.

Parkway Manor Care Center
114 Cherry Ave, Lubbock, TX, 79403
(806) 763-4186
Admin Lisa Owens. Medical Dir/Dir of Nursing Patrick H Pappas MD; Shelley Arick RN DON.

Licensure Skilled care. Beds SNF 61. Certified Medicaid; Medicare.
Owner Proprietary Corp (Southeastern Health Care Inc).
Admissions Requirements Medical examination; Physician's request.
Languages Spanish
Facilities Dining room; Physical therapy room; Laundry room; Barber/Beauty shop.
Activities Arts & crafts; Cards; Games; Reading groups; Prayer groups; Movies; Shopping trips; Social/Cultural gatherings.

Parkway Manor Nursing Home*
114 Cherry Ave, Lubbock, TX, 79403
(806) 763-4186
Admin Lisa L Owens. Medical Dir/Dir of Nursing Patrick H Pappas MD.
Licensure Skilled care. Beds 61. Certified Medicaid; Medicare.
Admissions Requirements Medical examination; Physician's request.
Staff RNs 2 (ft); LPNs 6 (ft), 1 (pt); Nurses aides 18 (ft); Physical therapists 1 (pt); Recreational therapists 1 (pt); Dietitians 1 (pt).
Facilities Dining room; Barber/Beauty shop.

Quaker Villa*
4403 74th St, Lubbock, TX, 79424
(806) 795-0668
Admin James T Swanner.
Licensure Intermediate care. Beds 96.
Certified Medicaid.
Owner Proprietary Corp (Hillhaven Corp).

Sherwood Healthcare Center of Lubbock*
5502 W 4th St, Lubbock, TX, 79416
(806) 739-1111
Admin Nell Casey. Medical Dir/Dir of Nursing Richard Mayer DO.
Licensure Intermediate care. Beds 150.
Certified Medicaid.
Admissions Requirements Medical examination; Physician's request.
Staff LPNs 6 (ft); Orderlies 1 (ft); Nurses aides 26 (ft); Activities coordinators 1 (ft).
Facilities Dining room; Chapel; Laundry room; Barber/Beauty shop.
Activities Arts & crafts; Cards; Games; Prayer groups; Movies; Shopping trips; Social/Cultural gatherings.

University Manor
2400 Quaker, Lubbock, TX, 79410
(806) 792-2831
Admin Janet Morris. Medical Dir/Dir of Nursing Carl F Page MD; Clowe Niell RN.
Licensure Skilled care; Intermediate care. Beds SNF 45; ICF 50. Certified Medicaid; Medicare.
Owner Proprietary Corp (Hillhaven Corp).
Staff RNs 3 (ft), 2 (pt); LPNs 6 (ft), 1 (pt); Orderlies 2 (ft); Nurses aides 19 (ft), 3 (pt); Activities coordinators 1 (ft); Dietitians 1 (ft).
Languages Spanish
Facilities Dining room; Activities room; Laundry room; Barber/Beauty shop.
Activities Arts & crafts; Cards; Games; Reading groups; Prayer groups; Movies; Shopping trips; Social/Cultural gatherings.

LUFKIN

Angelina Nursing Home Inc*
504 N John Redditt Dr, Lufkin, TX, 75901
(713) 632-3331
Admin Patricia R Culbertson.
Licensure Intermediate care. Beds 132.
Certified Medicaid.
Owner Proprietary Corp.

Cantex Convalescent Center (Westwood)
1514 Ellis Ave, Lufkin, TX, 75901
(713) 632-5571
Admin Dr John H Barnes. Medical Dir/Dir of Nursing La Dell Dominey DON.

Licensure Intermediate care. Beds ICF 68.
Certified Medicaid; Medicare.
Owner Proprietary Corp (Cantex Healthcare Centers).
Staff RNs 1 (pt); LPNs 8 (ft); Orderlies 1 (ft); Nurses aides 15 (ft); Physical therapists 1 (pt); Activities coordinators 1 (ft); Dietitians 1 (pt); Dentists 1 (pt); Ophthalmologists 1 (pt); Podiatrists 1 (pt).
Facilities Dining room; Activities room; Laundry room; Barber/Beauty shop; Library.
Activities Arts & crafts; Games; Reading groups; Prayer groups; Movies; Shopping trips; Social/Cultural gatherings.

Lufkin Nursing Center*
2313 N Raguet St, Lufkin, TX, 75901
(713) 634-2264
Admin Jesse B Pugh.
Licensure Intermediate care. Beds 150.
Certified Medicaid.
Owner Proprietary Corp (Beverly Enterprises).
Admissions Requirements Medical examination; Physician's request.
Staff Physicians 1 (ft); RNs 1 (ft); LPNs 5 (ft); Nurses aides 15 (ft); Occupational therapists 1 (ft); Speech therapists 1 (ft); Activities coordinators 1 (ft); Dietitians 1 (ft).
Facilities Dining room; Physical therapy room; Activities room; Laundry room; Barber/Beauty shop.
Activities Cards; Games; Reading groups; Prayer groups; Movies; Shopping trips; Social/Cultural gatherings.

Pine Haven Nursing Home*
1712 N Timberland, Lufkin, TX, 75901
(713) 632-3346
Admin Beth A Thornton.
Licensure Intermediate care. Beds 100.
Certified Medicaid.
Owner Proprietary Corp.

Progressive Living Center
PO BOX 2427, 2404 Medford Dr, Lufkin, TX, 75901
(713) 639-1206
Admin David Milem. Medical Dir/Dir of Nursing Philis Costner.
Licensure Intermediate care for mentally retarded. Beds ICF/MR 60. Certified Medicaid; Medicare.
Owner Privately owned.
Staff Physicians 1 (ft); RNs 1 (pt); LPNs 5 (ft); Nurses aides 27 (ft); Physical therapists 1 (pt); Recreational therapists 1 (ft); Occupational therapists 1 (pt); Speech therapists 1 (pt); Activities coordinators 1 (ft); Dietitians 1 (pt); Dentists 1 (pt); Ophthalmologists 1 (pt); Podiatrists 1 (pt).
Facilities Dining room; Physical therapy room; Activities room; Crafts room; Laundry room; Barber/Beauty shop; Recreation room; Training room.
Activities Arts & crafts; Cards; Games; Reading groups; Movies; Shopping trips; Social/Cultural gatherings; Community events.

LULING

Cartwheel Lodge of Luling*
PO Drawer 912, Hwy 183 N, Luling, TX, 78648
(512) 875-5606
Admin Jon L Miller.
Licensure Intermediate care. Beds 96.
Certified Medicaid; Medicare.

Hillcrest Manor
PO Box 230, Hwy 90 E, Luling, TX, 78648
(512) 875-5219
Admin Joyce Corry. Medical Dir/Dir of Nursing Opal Valenta.
Licensure Intermediate care. Beds ICF 60.
Certified Medicaid.
Owner Proprietary Corp (Diversicare Corp).

Admissions Requirements Medical
examination; Physician's request.
Staff RNs; LPNs; Nurses aides; Physical
therapists; Activities coordinators; Dietitians.
Languages Spanish
Facilities Dining room; Activities room;
Laundry room; Barber/Beauty shop.
Activities Arts & crafts; Prayer groups;
Movies; Shopping trips.

Luling Care Center
PO Box 312, 501 W Austin St, Luling, TX,
78648
(512) 875-5628
Admin Genevieve McCleary. *Medical Dir/Dir
of Nursing* Sue Clay DON.
Licensure Intermediate care. *Beds* ICF 56.
Certified Medicaid.
Owner Privately owned.
Admissions Requirements Medical
examination.
Staff RNs 1 (pt); LPNs 5 (ft); Orderlies 1 (ft);
Nurses aides 14 (ft); Activities coordinators
1 (ft); Dietitians 1 (ft).
Facilities Dining room; Activities room;
Crafts room; Laundry room; Barber/Beauty
shop.
Activities Arts & crafts; Games; Prayer groups;
Movies; Shopping trips; Social/Cultural
gatherings.

LYTLE

Lytle Nursing Home Inc
614 Oak St, Lytle, TX, 78052
(512) 772-3557
Admin Nancy L Pawelek. *Medical Dir/Dir of
Nursing* Dr Emanuel DeNoia.
Licensure Intermediate care. *Beds* 70.
Certified Medicaid.
Staff RNs 1 (pt); LPNs 5 (ft); Orderlies 1 (ft);
Nurses aides 18 (ft); Activities coordinators
1 (ft); Dietitians 1 (pt).
Facilities Dining room; Activities room;
Chapel; Crafts room; Laundry room; Barber/
Beauty shop.
Activities Arts & crafts; Games; Movies;
Shopping trips; Social/Cultural gatherings.

MABANK

Mabank Nursing Home*
Rte 1, Box 9, 110 W Trouple, Mabank, TX,
75147
(214) 887-2436
Admin Johnny M Adams.
Licensure Intermediate care. *Beds* 60.
Certified Medicaid.
Owner Proprietary Corp.

MADISONVILLE

Madisonville Nursing Home No 1
PO Box 40, 411 E Collard St, Madisonville,
TX, 77864
(409) 348-2735
Admin Norman G Morris.
Licensure Intermediate care; Nursing home.
Beds ICF 136. *Certified* Medicaid; Private
Pay.
Owner Privately owned.
Admissions Requirements Medical
examination; Physician's request.
Staff RNs; LPNs; Nurses aides; Activities
coordinators; Dietitians.
Facilities Dining room; Activities room;
Laundry room; Barber/Beauty shop.
Activities Arts & crafts; Games;
Reading groups; Movies; Parties; Special
gatherings, etc.

Madisonville Nursing Home No 2
PO Box 40, 410 E Collard St, Madisonville,
TX, 77864
(409) 348-6166
Admin Susanne Morris.

Licensure Intermediate care. *Beds* ICF 136.
Certified Medicaid; Private Pay.
Owner Privately owned.
Admissions Requirements Medical
examination; Physician's request.
Staff RNs; LPNs; Nurses aides; Activities
coordinators; Dietitians.
Facilities Dining room; Activities room;
Laundry room; Barber/Beauty shop.
Activities Arts & crafts; Cards; Games;
Reading groups; Movies; Parties; Special
gatherings.

Madisonville Nursing Home No 3
PO Box 40, 413 E Collard St, Madisonville,
TX, 77864
(409) 348-3860
Admin Larry Goodrum.
Licensure Intermediate care. *Beds* ICF 136.
Certified Medicaid; Private Pay.
Owner Privately owned.
Admissions Requirements Medical
examination; Physician's request.
Staff RNs; LPNs; Nurses aides; Activities
coordinators; Dietitians.
Facilities Dining room; Activities room;
Laundry room; Barber/Beauty shop.
Activities Arts & crafts; Cards; Games;
Reading groups; Movies; Parties; Special
gatherings, etc.

MALAKOFF

Cedar Lake Nursing Home
Rte 3, Hwy 31 W, Malakoff, TX, 75148
(214) 489-1702, 489-1706
Admin Douglas B Humble III. *Medical Dir/
Dir of Nursing* Jo Sparks.
Licensure Intermediate care. *Beds* ICF 90.
Certified Medicaid.
Owner Proprietary Corp.
Admissions Requirements Medical
examination; Physician's request.
Staff Physicians 1 (pt); RNs 2 (ft); Nurses
aides 15 (ft), 5 (pt); Physical therapists 1
(pt); Activities coordinators 1 (ft); Dietitians
1 (pt); Dentists 1 (pt); Ophthalmologists 1
(pt); 25 (ft); LVNs 6 (ft).
Languages Spanish
Facilities Dining room; Physical therapy
room; Activities room; Crafts room; Laundry
room; Barber/Beauty shop; Library.
Activities Arts & crafts; Cards; Games;
Reading groups; Prayer groups; Movies;
Shopping trips; Social/Cultural gatherings;
Newspaper.

MANSFIELD

Mansfield Nursing Home*
1402 E Broad St, Mansfield, TX, 76063
(817) 477-2176
Admin Peggy M Snow. *Medical Dir/Dir of
Nursing* Larry Myer MD.
Licensure Skilled care. *Beds* 127. *Certified*
Medicaid.
Owner Proprietary Corp (Summit Health Ltd).
Admissions Requirements Minimum age 21;
Medical examination; Physician's request.
Staff RNs 1 (ft), 3 (pt); Activities coordinators
1 (ft); Dietitians 1 (pt).
Facilities Dining room; Physical therapy
room; Activities room; Chapel; Crafts room;
Laundry room; Barber/Beauty shop.
Activities Arts & crafts; Cards; Games;
Reading groups; Prayer groups; Movies;
Shopping trips; Social/Cultural gatherings.

MARBLE FALLS

Northwood Healthcare Center
1109 Northwood Dr, Marble Falls, TX, 78654
(512) 693-3551
Admin Darlene Cayce. *Medical Dir/Dir of
Nursing* Richard Repert MD; Carol Klotz
DON.

Licensure Intermediate care. *Beds* ICF 110.
Certified Medicaid.
Owner Proprietary Corp (ARA Living
Centers).
Admissions Requirements Minimum age 16;
Medical examination; Physician's request.
Staff RNs 1 (ft); LPNs 8 (ft), 2 (pt); Orderlies
1 (ft); Nurses aides 26 (ft); Activities
coordinators 1 (ft); Dietitians 1 (ft).
Languages Spanish, German
Facilities Dining room; Physical therapy
room; Activities room; Laundry room;
Barber/Beauty shop.
Activities Arts & crafts; Cards; Games;
Reading groups; Prayer groups; Movies;
Shopping trips; Social/Cultural gatherings.

MARLIN

Elmwood Nursing Center*
221 Virginia St, Marlin, TX, 76661
(817) 883-5548
Admin William E Hazel. *Medical Dir/Dir of
Nursing* Frank McKinley MD.
Licensure Skilled care; Intermediate care;
Custodial care. *Beds* 141. *Certified*
Medicaid.
Admissions Requirements Physician's request.
Staff Physicians 1 (ft); RNs 1 (ft), 1 (pt);
LPNs 14 (ft); Orderlies 3 (ft); Nurses aides
20 (ft); Dietitians 1 (pt).
Facilities Dining room; Activities room;
Crafts room; Laundry room; Barber/Beauty
shop.
Activities Arts & crafts; Cards; Games;
Reading groups; Prayer groups; Movies;
Social/Cultural gatherings.

Golden Years Rest Home*
351 Coleman St, Marlin, TX, 76661
(817) 883-5508
Admin Carolyn Liberty. *Medical Dir/Dir of
Nursing* William F McKinley.
Licensure Intermediate care. *Beds* 96.
Certified Medicaid.
Owner Proprietary Corp (ARA Living
Centers).
Staff RNs 1 (ft); Orderlies 4 (ft), 1 (pt);
Nurses aides 15 (ft), 4 (pt); Activities
coordinators 1 (ft); Dietitians 1 (pt).
Facilities Dining room; Activities room;
Crafts room; Laundry room; Barber/Beauty
shop.
Activities Arts & crafts; Cards; Games;
Reading groups; Prayer groups; Movies;
Shopping trips; Social/Cultural gatherings.

MARSHALL

Colonial Park Nursing Home
509 S Grove, Marshall, TX, 75670
(214) 935-7886
Admin Douglas R Mehling. *Medical Dir/Dir of
Nursing* Nancy Pringle RN.
Licensure Skilled care; Intermediate care. *Beds*
SNF 40; ICF 120. *Certified* Medicaid;
Medicare.
Owner Proprietary Corp (Beverly Enterprises).
Staff RNs 3 (ft), 2 (pt); LPNs 22 (ft), 4 (pt);
Orderlies 3 (ft), 2 (pt); Nurses aides 42 (ft),
4 (pt); Activities coordinators 2 (ft).
Facilities Dining room; Physical therapy
room; Activities room; Chapel; Crafts room;
Laundry room; Barber/Beauty shop; Library.
Activities Arts & crafts; Cards; Games;
Movies; Shopping trips; Social/Cultural
gatherings.

Marshall Manor Nursing Home Inc
1007 S Washington St, Marshall, TX, 75670
(214) 935-7971
Admin Julius E Cox Jr. *Medical Dir/Dir of
Nursing* George E Bennett MD; Patricia
Salituro RN.
Licensure Skilled care; Intermediate care. *Beds*
SNF 50; ICF 129. *Certified* Medicaid;
Medicare.

Owner Proprietary Corp.
Admissions Requirements Physician's request.
Staff RNs 3 (ft), 1 (pt); LPNs 22 (ft), 1 (pt); Nurses aides 45 (ft), 6 (pt); Activities coordinators 4 (ft), 1 (pt).
Facilities Dining room; Activities room; Crafts room; Laundry room; Barber/Beauty shop; Library.
Activities Arts & crafts; Cards; Games; Reading groups; Prayer groups; Movies; Shopping trips; Social/Cultural gatherings.

Merritt Plaza Nursing Home*
207 W Merritt, Marshall, TX, 75670
(214) 938-3793
Admin Tom Bowen. *Medical Dir/Dir of Nursing* Dr George E Bennett.
Licensure Intermediate care. *Beds* 170. *Certified* Medicaid.
Owner Proprietary Corp (Beverly Enterprises).
Admissions Requirements Medical examination; Physician's request.
Staff RNs 1 (ft); LPNs 15 (ft); Orderlies 2 (ft); Nurses aides 34 (ft); Physical therapists 1 (ft); Speech therapists 1 (ft); Activities coordinators 2 (ft); Dietitians 1 (ft).
Facilities Dining room; Activities room; Laundry room; Barber/Beauty shop.
Activities Arts & crafts; Games; Reading groups; Prayer groups; Movies; Shopping trips; Social/Cultural gatherings.

Suburban Acres Nursing Center*
PO Box 366, Elysian Fields Rd, Marshall, TX, 75670
(214) 938-6679
Admin Gloria J Johnson.
Licensure Intermediate care. *Beds* 74. *Certified* Medicaid.
Owner Proprietary Corp.

MART

Park Plaza Nursing Home*
1201 McLennan Ave, Mart, TX, 76664
(817) 876-2531
Admin John W O'Connor.
Licensure Intermediate care. *Beds* 117. *Certified* Medicaid.
Owner Proprietary Corp.

MASON

Anna L Lee Nursing Home*
401 W Moreland, Mason, TX, 76856
(915) 347-6480
Admin Anna L Lee. *Medical Dir/Dir of Nursing* Betty Aulrey DON.
Licensure Intermediate care. *Beds* 33. *Certified* Medicaid.
Staff Physicians 2 (ft); LPNs 2 (ft), 2 (pt); Nurses aides 19 (pt).
Facilities Dining room; Laundry room; Lobby for entertainment.
Activities Arts & crafts; Games; Reading groups; Prayer groups; Movies; Grooming parties; Sing-alongs; Poetry classes; History classes.

Mason Care Center*
101 College, Mason, TX, 76856
(915) 347-5181
Admin Harvey W Zombro Sr. *Medical Dir/Dir of Nursing* Michael Richey MD.
Licensure Intermediate care. *Beds* 41. *Certified* Medicaid.
Admissions Requirements Minimum age 18; Medical examination; Physician's request.
Staff Physicians 2 (ft); LPNs 6 (ft); Nurses aides 12 (ft); Physical therapists 1 (ft); Speech therapists 1 (ft); Activities coordinators 1 (ft); Dietitians 1 (pt); Dentists 1 (pt).
Facilities Dining room; Physical therapy room; Activities room; Crafts room; Laundry room; Barber/Beauty shop.

Activities Arts & crafts; Cards; Games; Reading groups; Prayer groups; Movies; Shopping trips; Social/Cultural gatherings.

MCALLEN

Colonial Manor of McAllen
209 Hackberry, McAllen, TX, 78501
(512) 686-2243
Admin Elma N Martinez. *Medical Dir/Dir of Nursing* Rosemary Knowles RN DON.
Licensure Intermediate care. *Beds* ICF 59. *Certified* Medicaid.
Owner Proprietary Corp (Beverly Enterprises).
Admissions Requirements Physician's request.
Staff Physicians 1 (pt); RNs 1 (ft); LPNs 5 (ft), 3 (pt); Orderlies 2 (ft), 1 (pt); Nurses aides 14 (ft), 5 (pt); Activities coordinators 1 (ft); Dietitians 1 (pt).
Languages Spanish
Facilities Dining room; Activities room; Crafts room; Laundry room.
Activities Cards; Games; Prayer groups; Movies; Shopping trips; Social/Cultural gatherings.

McAllen Good Samaritan Center
812 Houston Ave, McAllen, TX, 78501
(512) 682-6331
Admin William B Yancy Jr.
Licensure Intermediate care. *Beds* 100. *Certified* Medicaid.
Owner Nonprofit Corp (Evangelical Lutheran/Good Samaritan).
Affiliation Lutheran

McAllen Nursing Center
600 N Cynthia, McAllen, TX, 78501
(512) 631-2265
Admin Betty Lofton. *Medical Dir/Dir of Nursing* Dr Popek; Ronnie Barrera RN DON.
Licensure Skilled care; Intermediate care. *Beds* SNF; ICF 120. *Certified* Medicaid; Medicare.
Owner Proprietary Corp (Beverly Enterprises).
Admissions Requirements Physician's request.
Staff Physicians 2 (ft), 20 (pt); RNs 3 (ft), 1 (pt); LPNs 15 (ft), 4 (pt); Orderlies 8 (ft), 2 (pt); Nurses aides 20 (ft), 6 (pt); Speech therapists 1 (pt); Activities coordinators 1 (ft); Dietitians 1 (ft); Dentists 1 (pt); Ophthalmologists 1 (pt).
Languages Spanish
Facilities Dining room; Physical therapy room; Activities room; Crafts room; Laundry room; Barber/Beauty shop.
Activities Arts & crafts; Cards; Games; Prayer groups; Movies; Outings.

Retama Manor Nursing Center
900 S 12th St, McAllen, TX, 78501
(512) 682-4171
Admin Maria Dalia Welch. *Medical Dir/Dir of Nursing* Richard Barrera MD; Alta Quiroz RN DON.
Licensure Skilled care; Intermediate care; Supervised living; Personal care. *Beds* SNF 40; ICF 60; Personal 27. *Certified* Medicaid; Medicare.
Owner Proprietary Corp (ARA Living Centers).
Admissions Requirements Minimum age 18; Medical examination; Physician's request.
Staff RNs 1 (ft); LPNs 12 (ft); Orderlies 2 (ft), 1 (pt); Nurses aides 30 (ft), 4 (pt); Activities coordinators 1 (ft).
Facilities Dining room; Physical therapy room; Activities room; Chapel; Crafts room; Laundry room; Barber/Beauty shop; Library.
Activities Arts & crafts; Cards; Games; Reading groups; Prayer groups; Movies; Shopping trips; Social/Cultural gatherings; Entertainment.

Twinbrooke South—McAllen*
1000 N McColl Rd, McAllen, TX, 78501
(512) 682-6101

Admin Carl F Lueg Jr.
Licensure Intermediate care. *Beds* 63. *Certified* Medicaid.
Owner Proprietary Corp.

Village Convalescent Center*
615 N Ware Rd, McAllen, TX, 78501
(512) 682-4161
Admin Coral Ann Rung. *Medical Dir/Dir of Nursing* Monique Popek MD.
Licensure Skilled care; Intermediate care. *Beds* 114. *Certified* Medicaid; Medicare.
Admissions Requirements Physician's request.
Staff Physicians 1 (pt); RNs 2 (ft), 1 (pt); LPNs 10 (ft); Orderlies 2 (ft); Nurses aides 26 (ft), 3 (pt); Physical therapists 1 (pt); Reality therapists 1 (pt); Occupational therapists 1 (pt); Speech therapists 1 (pt); Activities coordinators 1 (ft); Dietitians 1 (pt); Dentists 1 (pt).
Facilities Dining room; Physical therapy room; Activities room; Crafts room; Laundry room; Barber/Beauty shop.
Activities Arts & crafts; Cards; Games; Prayer groups; Movies; Shopping trips; Social/Cultural gatherings.

MCCAMEY

Upton County Convalescent Center
PO Box 1200, 305 S Burleson, McCamey, TX, 79752
(915) 652-8626
Admin James R Queen Jr. *Medical Dir/Dir of Nursing* Beverly J Nichols LVN DON.
Licensure Intermediate care. *Beds* ICF 30. *Certified* Medicaid.
Owner Publicly owned.
Admissions Requirements Medical examination.
Staff Physicians 5 (pt); RNs 1 (pt); LPNs 3 (ft), 3 (pt); Orderlies 1 (ft); Nurses aides 10 (ft); Activities coordinators 1 (ft); Dietitians 2 (pt).
Languages Spanish
Facilities Dining room; Activities room; Chapel; Laundry room; Barber/Beauty shop.
Activities Arts & crafts; Cards; Games; Prayer groups; Social/Cultural gatherings.

MCGREGOR

Westview Manor*
414 Johnson Dr, McGregor, TX, 76657
(817) 840-3281
Admin Ray Dean Elliott.
Licensure Skilled care; Intermediate care. *Beds* 122. *Certified* Medicaid.
Owner Proprietary Corp.

MCKINNEY

Pavilion Nursing Homne*
PO Box 556, N Hwy 5, McKinney, TX, 75069
(214) 542-3565, 4418
Admin Peggy Jones.
Licensure Intermediate care. *Beds* 140. *Certified* Medicaid.
Owner Proprietary Corp (ARA Living Centers).

University Nursing Center*
2030 W University Dr, McKinney, TX, 75069
(214) 542-2695
Admin Billy Hill.
Licensure Skilled care. *Beds* 112. *Certified* Medicaid.
Owner Proprietary Corp.

MCLEAN

Thomas Nursing Center Inc*
7th & Cedar, Box 280, McLean, TX, 79057
(806) 779-2469
Admin Billy W Thomas. *Medical Dir/Dir of Nursing* H F Fabian.

Licensure Intermediate care. *Beds* 59. *Certified* Medicaid.
Admissions Requirements Minimum age 18; Medical examination; Physician's request.
Staff RNs 2 (pt); LPNs 5 (ft); Orderlies 2 (ft); Nurses aides 9 (ft); Activities coordinators 1 (ft).
Facilities Dining room; Activities room; Chapel; Crafts room; Laundry room; Barber/ Beauty shop.
Activities Arts & crafts; Cards; Games; Prayer groups; Movies; Shopping trips; Social/ Cultural gatherings.

MEMPHIS

Memphis Convalescent Center*
1415 N 18th St, Memphis, TX, 79245
(806) 259-3566
Admin Henry W Hall.
Licensure Intermediate care. *Beds* 80. *Certified* Medicaid.
Admissions Requirements Physician's request.
Staff RNs 1 (pt); LPNs 7 (ft); Orderlies 1 (ft), 1 (pt); Activities coordinators 1 (ft).
Facilities Dining room; Activities room; Laundry room; Barber/Beauty shop.
Activities Arts & crafts; Games; Reading groups; Prayer groups; Shopping trips; Social/Cultural gatherings.

MENARD

Menard Manor*
100 Gay St, Menard, TX, 76859
(915) 396-4541
Admin Edward Zachary.
Licensure Intermediate care. *Beds* 40. *Certified* Medicaid.
Staff LPNs 3 (ft), 1 (pt); Nurses aides 11 (ft), 6 (pt); Activities coordinators 1 (ft).
Facilities Dining room; Physical therapy room; Activities room; Chapel; Laundry room; Barber/Beauty shop.
Activities Arts & crafts; Cards; Games; Reading groups; Prayer groups; Movies; Shopping trips; Social/Cultural gatherings.

MERIDIAN

Meridian Geriatric Center
1110 N Main, Meridian, TX, 76665
(817) 435-2357
Admin Linda M Hazel. *Medical Dir/Dir of Nursing* Sandra Schranck DON.
Licensure Intermediate care. *Beds* 92. *Certified* Medicaid.
Owner Nonprofit Corp.
Admissions Requirements Medical examination.
Staff RNs 1 (ft), 1 (pt); Nurses aides 26 (ft); Activities coordinators 1 (ft); Dietitians 1 (ft); LVN 8 (ft), 2 (pt).
Facilities Dining room; Chapel; Laundry room; Barber/Beauty shop.
Activities Arts & crafts; Cards; Games; Prayer groups; Movies; Social/Cultural gatherings.

MERKEL

Starr Nursing Home*
Old Hwy 80 W, Merkel, TX, 79536
(915) 928-5673
Admin Brenda J Quinn.
Licensure Intermediate care. *Beds* 45. *Certified* Medicaid.
Owner Proprietary Corp.

MESQUITE

Big Town Nursing Home*
2231 Hwy 80 E, Mesquite, TX, 75149
(214) 279-3601
Admin Barbara E Thomas.

Licensure Skilled care; Intermediate care. *Beds* 252. *Certified* Proprietary Corp.
Owner Proprietary Corp.

Christian Care Center
1000 Wiggins Pkwy, Mesquite, TX, 75150
(214) 270-4466
Admin Lucy Withrow. *Medical Dir/Dir of Nursing* Roy Wagoner; Jackie Frantz RN DON.
Licensure Skilled care; Intermediate care. *Beds* SNF 60; ICF 60. *Certified* Medicaid; Medicare.
Owner Nonprofit Corp.
Admissions Requirements Medical examination; Physician's request.
Staff Physicians 1 (pt); RNs 3 (ft); LPNs 12 (ft); Orderlies 3 (ft); Nurses aides 35 (ft); Activities coordinators 2 (ft); Dietitians 1 (ft), 1 (pt).
Languages Spanish
Affiliation Church of Christ
Facilities Dining room; Physical therapy room; Activities room; Chapel; Laundry room; Barber/Beauty shop.
Activities Arts & crafts; Cards; Games; Prayer groups; Shopping trips; Holiday & birthday parties.

Heritage Place
825 W Kearney, Mesquite, TX, 75149
(214) 288-7668
Admin Harvey Junker. *Medical Dir/Dir of Nursing* John Pataki MD; Lynn Craft RN DON.
Licensure Intermediate care. *Beds* ICF 152. *Certified* Medicare.
Owner Proprietary Corp.
Admissions Requirements Minimum age 60; Medical examination; Physician's request.
Staff RNs 3 (ft), 1 (pt); LPNs 8 (ft), 5 (pt); Orderlies; Nurses aides 27 (ft), 6 (pt); Physical therapists; Recreational therapists; Speech therapists; Activities coordinators 1 (ft); Dietitians 1 (ft).
Facilities Dining room; Activities room; Chapel; Laundry room; Barber/Beauty shop; Library.
Activities Arts & crafts; Cards; Games; Reading groups; Prayer groups; Movies; Shopping trips; Social/Cultural gatherings.

Mesquite Tree Nursing Center
434 Paza Dr, Mesquite, TX, 75049
(214) 288-6489
Admin Barbara Roblin. *Medical Dir/Dir of Nursing* Linus Miller MD; Tony Jackson DON.
Licensure Intermediate care. *Beds* ICF 148. *Certified* Medicaid.
Owner Proprietary Corp (Beverly Enterprises).
Admissions Requirements Medical examination.
Staff LPNs; Orderlies; Nurses aides.
Facilities Dining room; Activities room; Laundry room; Barber/Beauty shop.
Activities Arts & crafts; Cards; Games; Reading groups; Prayer groups; Movies; Shopping trips; Social/Cultural gatherings.

MEXIA

Haven Nursing Home
601 Terrace Ln, Mexia, TX, 76667
(817) 562-5400
Admin Lola M Compton. *Medical Dir/Dir of Nursing* Margaret Bumpas RN.
Licensure Intermediate care. *Beds* ICF 74. *Certified* Medicaid.
Owner Privately owned.
Admissions Requirements Medical examination; Physician's request.
Staff Physicians; RNs; LPNs; Nurses aides; Physical therapists; Reality therapists; Recreational therapists; Occupational therapists; Speech therapists; Activities coordinators; Dietitians; Ophthalmologists.

Facilities Dining room; Activities room; Crafts room; Laundry room; Barber/Beauty shop.
Activities Arts & crafts; Cards; Games; Reading groups; Prayer groups; Movies; Shopping trips; Social/Cultural gatherings.

The Manor Retirement & Convalescent Center*
PO Box 710, 831 Tehuacana Hwy, Mexia, TX, 76667
(817) 562-3867
Admin Ronald R Huggins.
Licensure Intermediate care. *Beds* 80. *Certified* Medicaid.
Owner Proprietary Corp.

Mexia Nursing Home*
501 E Sumpter St, Mexia, TX, 76667
(817) 562-5542
Admin John Thomas Wright.
Licensure Intermediate care. *Beds* 40. *Certified* Medicaid.
Admissions Requirements Medical examination; Physician's request.
Staff Physicians 1 (ft); LPNs 3 (ft), 4 (pt); Nurses aides 5 (ft), 8 (pt); Activities coordinators 1 (ft).
Facilities Dining room; Activities room; Laundry room.
Activities Arts & crafts; Cards; Games; Prayer groups; Shopping trips; Social/Cultural gatherings; Community events.

MIDLAND

The Lutheran Home—Permian Basin
3203 Sage, Midland, TX, 79705-5798
(915) 683-5403
Admin Marion Seba. *Medical Dir/Dir of Nursing* Debbie Shultz LVN.
Licensure Intermediate care. *Beds* ICF 114. *Certified* Medicaid.
Owner Nonprofit organization/foundation.
Admissions Requirements Minimum age 18; Medical examination; Physician's request.
Affiliation Lutheran
Facilities Dining room; Activities room; Chapel; Laundry room; Barber/Beauty shop.
Activities Arts & crafts; Cards; Games; Reading groups; Prayer groups; Movies; Shopping trips; Social/Cultural gatherings.

Midland Care Center Inc*
2000 N Main, Midland, TX, 79701
(915) 684-6613
Admin Betty R Gardner.
Licensure Intermediate care. *Beds* 118. *Certified* Medicaid.
Owner Proprietary Corp.

Sage Healthcare Center*
3203 Sage, Midland, TX, 79701
(915) 683-5403
Admin Edna Goodin.
Licensure Intermediate care. *Beds* 114. *Certified* Medicaid.
Owner Proprietary Corp.

Terrace Gardens Nursing Home*
2901 W Ohio, Midland, TX, 79701
(915) 694-8831
Admin Delores T Cregg.
Licensure Skilled care. *Beds* 60. *Certified* Medicaid.
Owner Proprietary Corp (Hillhaven Corp).

Terrace West*
2800 N Midland Dr, Midland, TX, 79701
(915) 697-3108
Admin J H Black. *Medical Dir/Dir of Nursing* Dr H F Page.
Licensure Intermediate care. *Beds* 150. *Certified* Medicaid.
Owner Proprietary Corp (Hillhaven Corp).
Admissions Requirements Medical examination.

Staff Physicians 1 (pt); RNs 4 (ft); LPNs 12 (ft); Orderlies 4 (ft); Nurses aides 31 (ft); Physical therapists 1 (pt); Occupational therapists 1 (pt); Speech therapists 1 (pt); Activities coordinators 1 (ft); Dietitians 1 (pt); Dentists 1 (pt).
Facilities Dining room; Physical therapy room; Activities room; Chapel; Crafts room; Laundry room; Barber/Beauty shop.
Activities Arts & crafts; Cards; Games; Reading groups; Prayer groups; Movies; Shopping trips; Social/Cultural gatherings.

Trinity Towers*
2800 W Illinois, Midland, TX, 79701
(915) 694-1691
Admin William G Saxton.
Licensure Intermediate care; Custodial care. *Beds* ICF 31; Custodial care 19.
Owner Nonprofit Corp.
Affiliation Presbyterian

MINEOLA

Wood Memorial Nursing Center
320 Greenville Ave, Mineola, TX, 75773
(214) 569-3852
Admin Dana L Gentry. *Medical Dir/Dir of Nursing* R O Moore MD; Mary Cloud RN DON.
Licensure Intermediate care. *Beds* ICF 75. *Certified* Medicaid.
Owner Proprietary Corp.
Staff RNs 2 (ft); LPNs 4 (ft); Nurses aides 20 (ft); Physical therapists 1 (pt); Recreational therapists 1 (pt); Occupational therapists 1 (pt); Speech therapists 1 (pt); Activities coordinators 1 (ft); Dietitians 1 (pt); Ophthalmologists 1 (pt); Podiatrists 1 (pt).
Facilities Dining room; Barber/Beauty shop.
Activities Arts & crafts; Cards; Games; Prayer groups; Movies; Shopping trips; Social/Cultural gatherings.

MINERAL WELLS

Mineral Wells Care Center
316 SW 25th Ave, Mineral Wells, TX, 76067
(817) 325-1358
Admin Linda Ratzlaff. *Medical Dir/Dir of Nursing* Audred Stewart.
Licensure Skilled care; Intermediate care. *Beds* SNF 61; ICF 61. *Certified* Medicaid; Medicare.
Owner Proprietary Corp (ARA Living Centers).
Admissions Requirements Physician's request.
Staff RNs; LPNs; Orderlies; Nurses aides; Activities coordinators.
Languages Spanish
Facilities Dining room; Activities room; Laundry room; Barber/Beauty shop.
Activities Arts & crafts; Cards; Games; Reading groups; Prayer groups; Movies; Social/Cultural gatherings.

Palo Pinto Nursing Center*
Star Rt, Box 23, Mineral Wells, TX, 76067
(817) 325-7813
Admin Terry W Matthews.
Licensure Intermediate care. *Beds* 106. *Certified* Medicaid.
Owner Proprietary Corp (Beverly Enterprises).

Resort Lodge Inc*
401 NW 4th St, Mineral Wells, TX, 76067
(817) 325-3744
Admin Florence W Kearby.
Licensure Skilled care. *Beds* 52. *Certified* Medicaid.
Owner Proprietary Corp.

MONAHANS

Ward County Nursing Home*
1200 W 15th St, Monahans, TX, 79756
(915) 943-4329

Admin Julia Martinez.
Licensure Intermediate care. *Beds* 98. *Certified* Medicaid.
Admissions Requirements Medical examination; Physician's request.
Staff RNs 1 (pt); LPNs 5 (pt); Nurses aides 10 (ft); Activities coordinators 1 (ft); Dietitians 1 (pt).
Facilities Dining room; Activities room; Crafts room; Laundry room; Barber/Beauty shop.
Activities Arts & crafts; Cards; Games; Reading groups; Prayer groups; Movies; Shopping trips; Social/Cultural gatherings.

MOODY

Moody Care Center
Box 218, Fm Rd 107, 7th & Church Sts, Moody, TX, 76557
(817) 853-2591, 853-2631
Admin Claudia Evans. *Medical Dir/Dir of Nursing* Jane Smith DON.
Licensure Intermediate care. *Beds* ICF 57. *Certified* Medicaid.
Owner Proprietary Corp (Manor Care).
Admissions Requirements Minimum age 18; Medical examination; Physician's request.
Staff RNs 1 (pt); LPNs 3 (ft); Nurses aides 17 (ft), 6 (pt); Activities coordinators 1 (ft); Dietitians 1 (ft).
Facilities Dining room; Activities room; Chapel; Crafts room; Laundry room; Barber/Beauty shop.
Activities Arts & crafts; Cards; Games; Reading groups; Prayer groups; Movies; Shopping trips; Social/Cultural gatherings.

MORTON

Roberts Memorial Nursing Home*
PO Box 952, 211 W Garfield, Morton, TX, 79346
(806) 266-8866
Admin Clota M Templeton.
Licensure Intermediate care. *Beds* 30. *Certified* Medicaid.
Owner Proprietary Corp.

MOULTON

Shady Oak Nursing Home Inc*
101 S Lancaster, Moulton, TX, 77975
(512) 596-7777
Admin Edward A Darilek.
Licensure Intermediate care. *Beds* 61. *Certified* Medicaid.
Admissions Requirements Minimum age 21; Medical examination; Physician's request.
Staff RNs 1 (pt); LPNs 7 (ft); Nurses aides 13 (ft), 8 (pt); Activities coordinators 1 (ft); Dietitians 1 (pt).
Facilities Dining room; Activities room; Laundry room.
Activities Arts & crafts; Cards; Games.

MOUNT PLEASANT

Currey Nursing Home Inc
901 N Jefferson, Mount Pleasant, TX, 75455
(214) 572-4361
Admin Thelma Lee Landers. *Medical Dir/Dir of Nursing* G B Taylor DO; Reba Jefferson DON.
Licensure Intermediate care. *Beds* ICF 56. *Certified* Medicaid.
Owner Proprietary Corp.
Admissions Requirements Physician's request.
Staff LPNs; Nurses aides; Dietitians.
Facilities Dining room; Activities room; Laundry room; Barber/Beauty shop; Library.
Activities Arts & crafts; Cards; Games; Reading groups; Prayer groups; Shopping trips; Social/Cultural gatherings.

Geras Nursing Home*
316 W 7th St, Mount Pleasant, TX, 75455
(214) 572-3693
Admin Janice K Graham.
Licensure Intermediate care. *Beds* 101. *Certified* Medicaid.
Owner Proprietary Corp (Summit Health Ltd).
Staff RNs 1 (ft); LPNs 7 (ft), 1 (pt); Nurses aides 23 (ft), 2 (pt); Activities coordinators 1 (ft); Dietitians 1 (ft).
Facilities Dining room; Activities room; Crafts room.
Activities Arts & crafts; Cards; Games; Prayer groups; Social/Cultural gatherings.

Golden Years Lodge
1606 Memorial St, Mount Pleasant, TX, 75455
(214) 572-3618
Admin Margaret R Strain. *Medical Dir/Dir of Nursing* Georgia Lide RN.
Licensure Skilled care. *Beds* SNF 128. *Certified* Medicaid; Medicare.
Owner Proprietary Corp (Truco Inc).
Admissions Requirements Physician's request.
Staff Physicians 1 (pt); RNs 2 (ft), 10 (pt); LPNs 11 (ft); Orderlies 1 (ft); Nurses aides 30 (ft), 5 (pt); Reality therapists 1 (ft); Activities coordinators 1 (ft); Dietitians 2 (pt).
Languages Spanish
Facilities Dining room; Physical therapy room; Activities room; Chapel; Laundry room; Barber/Beauty shop.
Activities Arts & crafts; Cards; Games; Prayer groups; Movies; Shopping trips; Social/ Cultural gatherings.

Physicians Nursing & Convalescent Center
2101 N Mulberry, Mount Pleasant, TX, 75455
(214) 572-6621
Admin Mary Sue Quarles.
Licensure Skilled care; Intermediate care. *Beds* 80. *Certified* Medicaid; Medicare.
Owner Proprietary Corp (Beverly Enterprises).
Admissions Requirements Physician's request.
Staff RNs 2 (ft); LPNs 7 (ft); Nurses aides 20 (ft), 4 (pt); Physical therapists; Speech therapists; Activities coordinators 1 (ft); Dietitians.
Facilities Dining room; Activities room; Laundry room; Barber/Beauty shop.
Activities Arts & crafts; Games; Prayer groups; Movies; Social/Cultural gatherings.

Villa Nursing Center
FM 1734 & I30, Mount Pleasant, TX, 75455
(214) 572-5511, 572-4328
Admin Milton R Kelley. *Medical Dir/Dir of Nursing* Dr Gary Taylor MD; Phyllis Aurty RN DON.
Licensure Skilled care. *Beds* SNF 90. *Certified* Medicaid; Medicare.
Owner Proprietary Corp.
Admissions Requirements Physician's request.
Staff Physicians; RNs; LPNs; Orderlies; Nurses aides; Physical therapists; Reality therapists; Occupational therapists; Speech therapists; Activities coordinators; Dietitians; Dentists; Ophthalmologists; Podiatrists.
Facilities Dining room; Physical therapy room; Activities room; Chapel; Crafts room; Laundry room; Barber/Beauty shop; Library.
Activities Arts & crafts; Cards; Games; Reading groups; Prayer groups; Movies; Shopping trips; Social/Cultural gatherings.

MOUNT VERNON

Mission Manor Nursing Home Inc
PO Box 600, 600 Yates St, Mount Vernon, TX, 75457
(214) 537-4424
Admin Diane Newsom. *Medical Dir/Dir of Nursing* Debbie Stout.
Licensure Intermediate care. *Beds* ICF 101. *Certified* Medicaid.
Owner Privately owned.

Admissions Requirements Medical examination; Physician's request.
Staff RNs 1 (ft), 101 (pt); LPNs 5 (ft); Nurses aides 22 (ft), 4 (pt); Physical therapists; Activities coordinators 1 (ft); Dietitians.
Facilities Dining room; Activities room; Crafts room; Laundry room; Barber/Beauty shop.
Activities Arts & crafts; Cards; Games; Reading groups; Prayer groups; Movies; Social/Cultural gatherings.

Terry Haven Nursing Home Inc
PO Box 519, Hwy 67 W, Mount Vernon, TX, 75457
(214) 537-4332 or 537-2571
Admin Edna Nelson. *Medical Dir/Dir of Nursing* Vicki Atkison.
Licensure Intermediate care. *Beds* ICF 65. *Certified* Medicaid.
Owner Proprietary Corp (Health Enter of America).
Admissions Requirements Medical examination; Physician's request.
Staff Physicians 4 (pt); LPNs 6 (ft), 2 (pt); Orderlies 1 (pt); Nurses aides 14 (ft), 3 (pt); Activities coordinators 1 (ft); Dietitians 1 (pt); Ophthalmologists 1 (pt).
Facilities Dining room; Activities room; Crafts room; Laundry room; Barber/Beauty shop; Library.
Activities Arts & crafts; Cards; Games; Reading groups; Prayer groups; Movies; Shopping trips; Social/Cultural gatherings.

MUENSTER

St Richard's Villa Inc*
US Hwy 82 W, Muenster, TX, 76252
(817) 759-2219
Admin Wesley D Fuson.
Licensure Intermediate care. *Beds* 30. *Certified* Medicaid.
Owner Proprietary Corp.

MULESHOE

Muleshoe Nursing Home
106 W Ave H, Muleshoe, TX, 79347
(806) 272-3861
Admin Jim Swanner. *Medical Dir/Dir of Nursing* Helen Bayless.
Licensure Intermediate care. *Beds* ICF 57. *Certified* Medicare.
Owner Nonprofit Corp.
Admissions Requirements Minimum age 16; Medical examination; Physician's request.
Staff LPNs 4 (ft); Activities coordinators 1 (ft); Dietitians 1 (ft).
Languages Spanish
Facilities Dining room; Activities room; Crafts room; Laundry room; Barber/Beauty shop.
Activities Arts & crafts; Cards; Games; Reading groups; Movies; Social/Cultural gatherings.

MUNDAY

Munday Nursing Center*
PO Box 199, 421 W "F" St, Munday, TX, 76371
(817) 422-4541
Admin Joyce Hardin.
Licensure Intermediate care. *Beds* 61. *Certified* Medicaid.
Owner Proprietary Corp (Beverly Enterprises).

NACOGDOCHES

Nacogdoches Convalescent Center
3305 N St, Nacogdoches, TX, 75961
(409) 564-0256
Admin Cynthia Motley. *Medical Dir/Dir of Nursing* Gwen McClendon.

Licensure Intermediate care. *Beds* ICF 68. *Certified* Medicaid.
Owner Proprietary Corp (Cantex Healthcare Centers).
Facilities Dining room; Laundry room; Barber/Beauty shop.
Activities Arts & crafts; Games; Prayer groups; Movies.

Oak Manor Nursing Home
1200 Ferguson, Nacogdoches, TX, 75961
(409) 564-7359
Admin Debbie Y Williams. *Medical Dir/Dir of Nursing* Curtisa Christian DON.
Licensure Intermediate care. *Beds* ICF 64. *Certified* Medicaid.
Owner Proprietary Corp (ARA Living Centers).
Facilities Dining room; Activities room; Laundry room; Barber/Beauty shop.
Activities Arts & crafts; Cards; Games; Reading groups; Prayer groups; Movies; Shopping trips; Social/Cultural gatherings.

Pine Crest Nursing Home
2612 Williams St, Nacogdoches, TX, 75961
(713) 564-7603
Admin Charles F Williams.
Licensure Intermediate care. *Beds* 56. *Certified* Medicaid.
Admissions Requirements Medical examination; Physician's request.
Staff Physicians 1 (pt); RNs 2 (pt); LPNs (LVN) 2 (ft), 2 (pt); Nurses aides 10 (ft); Activities coordinators 1 (ft); Dietitians 3 (ft), 2 (pt); Dentists 1 (pt).
Facilities Dining room; Activities room; Laundry room; Library.
Activities Arts & crafts; Games; Prayer groups; Movies; Shopping trips.

The Rock Haven Nursing Home*
401 SE Stallings Dr, Nacogdoches, TX, 75961
(713) 569-9411
Admin C Wayne Hopson.
Licensure Skilled care. *Beds* 60. *Certified* Medicaid.
Owner Proprietary Corp.

Westridge Manor Inc
PO Box 1951, 611 SW Stallings Dr, Nacogdoches, TX, 75961
(409) 564-1138
Admin Edward Williamson. *Medical Dir/Dir of Nursing* Jean Nichols.
Licensure Intermediate care; Personal care. *Beds* ICF 86; Personal 10. *Certified* Medicaid.
Owner Proprietary Corp.
Staff RNs 1 (pt); LPNs 8 (ft), 2 (pt); Nurses aides 21 (ft), 4 (pt); Activities coordinators 1 (ft); Dietitians 1 (pt).
Facilities Dining room; Barber/Beauty shop.
Activities Arts & crafts; Games; Prayer groups; Movies; Shopping trips; Social/Cultural gatherings.

NAPLES

Redbud Retreat
R2 Box 2, Floyd St, Naples, TX, 75568
(214) 897-5694
Admin Faye Sullivan. *Medical Dir/Dir of Nursing* Lana Foster.
Licensure Intermediate care. *Beds* ICF 86. *Certified* Medicaid.
Owner Proprietary Corp (Truco Inc).
Admissions Requirements Physician's request.
Staff RNs 2 (ft); LPNs 8 (ft); Orderlies 2 (ft); Nurses aides 38 (ft); Activities coordinators 1 (ft); Dietitians 6 (ft).
Facilities Dining room; Activities room; Chapel; Crafts room; Laundry room; Barber/Beauty shop.
Activities Arts & crafts; Cards; Games; Reading groups; Prayer groups; Shopping trips; Social/Cultural gatherings.

NAVASOTA

Canterbury Villa of Navasota*
1405 E Washington, Navasota, TX, 77868
(713) 825-6463
Admin Irene E Higdon.
Licensure Intermediate care. *Beds* 172. *Certified* Medicaid.
Owner Proprietary Corp (Health Enter of America).
Admissions Requirements Minimum age 18; Medical examination.
Staff RNs 1 (ft); LPNs 6 (ft), 2 (pt); Orderlies 2 (ft); Nurses aides 48 (ft), 6 (pt); Activities coordinators 2 (ft).
Facilities Dining room; Physical therapy room; Activities room; Crafts room; Laundry room; Barber/Beauty shop.
Activities Arts & crafts; Cards; Games; Prayer groups; Shopping trips; Social/Cultural gatherings.

Heart Manor Nursing Home*
1310 Grimes, Navasota, TX, 77868
(713) 825-7557 or 825-7553
Admin Wilma Kile.
Beds 120.
Admissions Requirements Minimum age 34; Medical examination; Physician's request.
Staff RNs 2 (ft); Nurses aides 1 (ft); Activities coordinators 1 (ft); Dietitians 1 (ft).
Facilities Dining room; Activities room; Laundry room; Barber/Beauty shop.

NEDERLAND

Nederland Nursing Home Inc*
3600 N Twin City Hwy, Nederland, TX, 77627
(713) 727-3143
Admin Thyria M McConley.
Licensure Intermediate care. *Beds* 110. *Certified* Medicaid.
Owner Proprietary Corp (Beverly Enterprises).

NEEDVILLE

SPJST Rest Home 2
PO Box 347, 8611 Main St, Needville, TX, 77461
(409) 793-4256
Admin Harvey L Marx.
Licensure Intermediate care. *Beds* 58. *Certified* Medicaid.
Owner Nonprofit Corp.

NEW BOSTON

New Boston Nursing Center
210 Rice St, New Boston, TX, 75570
(214) 628-5551
Admin James R Goodwin. *Medical Dir/Dir of Nursing* E B McGee MD; Pauline Jump DON.
Licensure Skilled care. *Beds* SNF 120. *Certified* Medicaid; Medicare.
Owner Proprietary Corp (Truco Inc).
Admissions Requirements Medical examination.
Staff Physicians 1 (pt); RNs 1 (ft), 1 (pt); LPNs 12 (ft), 3 (pt); Nurses aides 35 (ft), 7 (pt); Physical therapists 1 (pt); Speech therapists 1 (pt); Activities coordinators 2 (ft); Dietitians 1 (pt); Ophthalmologists 1 (pt); Dentist 1 (pt).
Facilities Dining room; Activities room; Crafts room; Laundry room; Barber/Beauty shop.
Activities Arts & crafts; Games; Prayer groups; Movies; Shopping trips.

NEW BRAUNFELS

Colonial Manor Nursing Home*
821 US Hwy 81 W, New Braunfels, TX,
78130
(512) 625-7526
Admin John W Greer.
Licensure Skilled care. *Beds* 160. *Certified*
Medicaid; Medicare.
Owner Proprietary Corp (Summit Health Ltd).

Eden Home Inc
631 Lakeview Blvd, New Braunfels, TX,
78130
(512) 625-6291
Admin Kenneth A Triesch. *Medical Dir/Dir of*
Nursing Charles Berger MD; Lorraine
Kennemer RN DON.
Licensure Skilled care; Intermediate care. *Beds*
178. *Certified* Medicaid; Medicare.
Owner Nonprofit Corp.
Admissions Requirements Minimum age 62;
Medical examination; Physician's request.
Staff RNs 3 (ft); LPNs 16 (ft); Nurses aides 62
(ft), 2 (pt); Physical therapists 1 (ft);
Recreational therapists 2 (ft); Dietitians 2
(pt).
Languages Spanish, German
Affiliation Church of Christ
Facilities Dining room; Physical therapy
room; Activities room; Chapel; Crafts room;
Laundry room; Barber/Beauty shop; Library.
Activities Arts & crafts; Cards; Games;
Reading groups; Prayer groups; Movies;
Shopping trips; Social/Cultural gatherings;
Bible study; Choral group; Reality
orientation.

Oak Crest Inn
1310 Hwy 35 W, New Braunfels, TX, 78130
(512) 625-6941
Admin Winona Oberkampf.
Licensure Intermediate care. *Beds* ICF 139.
Certified Medicaid.
Owner Proprietary Corp (ARA Living
Centers).
Admissions Requirements Medical
examination.
Staff RNs 12 (ft); LPNs 2 (ft); Nurses aides 30
(ft); Reality therapists 1 (ft); Activities
coordinators 1 (ft); Dietitians 1 (ft).
Languages German, Spanish
Facilities Dining room; Activities room;
Crafts room; Barber/Beauty shop.
Activities Arts & crafts; Cards; Games;
Reading groups; Prayer groups; Movies;
Shopping trips; Social/Cultural gatherings;
Cooking clubs; Resident council; In-room
activities.

NEW LONDON

Sunshine Nursing Home Inc
PO Box 378, 100 E Humble Dr, New London,
TX, 75682
(214) 895-4804
Admin Gladys Riggs. *Medical Dir/Dir of*
Nursing Ann Tinsley.
Licensure Intermediate care. *Beds* ICF 69.
Certified Medicaid.
Owner Nonprofit Corp.
Admissions Requirements Physician's request.
Staff RNs; LPNs; Nurses aides; Reality
therapists; Recreational therapists; Activities
coordinators; Dietitians.
Facilities Dining room; Activities room;
Chapel; Crafts room; Laundry room; Barber/
Beauty shop; Library.
Activities Arts & crafts; Cards; Games;
Reading groups; Prayer groups; Movies;
Shopping trips; Social/Cultural gatherings.

NEWTON

Shady Acres Health Care Center
Drawer E, Newton, TX, 75966
(409) 379-8121

Admin Betty L Hines. *Medical Dir/Dir of*
Nursing Carolyn Reed RN.
Licensure Skilled care. *Beds* SNF 82. *Certified*
Medicaid; Medicare.
Owner Proprietary Corp.
Admissions Requirements Medical
examination.
Staff RNs 1 (ft), 1 (pt); LPNs 4 (ft), 2 (pt);
Orderlies 1 (ft), 1 (pt); Nurses aides 19 (ft),
4 (pt); Activities coordinators 1 (ft);
Dietitians 1 (pt).
Facilities Dining room; Physical therapy
room; Activities room; Chapel; Crafts room;
Laundry room; Barber/Beauty shop; Library.
Activities Arts & crafts; Cards; Games;
Reading groups; Prayer groups; Movies;
Shopping trips.

NIXON

Colonial Convalescent & Nursing Home
406 S Parker, Nixon, TX, 78140
(512) 582-1811, 582-1081
Admin Mike Millington. *Medical Dir/Dir of*
Nursing Dr W G Millington; Rose Anne
Medina RN DON.
Licensure Intermediate care. *Beds* ICF 89.
Certified Medicaid.
Owner Proprietary Corp.
Admissions Requirements Minimum age 21.
Staff Physicians 1 (pt); RNs 1 (pt); LPNs 6
(ft); Nurses aides 29 (ft), 7 (pt); Activities
coordinators 1 (ft); Dietitians 1 (pt);
Ophthalmologists 1 (pt).
Languages Spanish
Facilities Dining room; Activities room;
Laundry room; Barber/Beauty shop.
Activities Arts & crafts; Games; Reading
groups; Prayer groups; Movies; Shopping
trips; Social/Cultural gatherings.

NOCONA

Horizon Manor
PO Box 449, Nocona, TX, 76255
(817) 825-3258
Admin Mary Adams.
Licensure Intermediate care. *Beds* 64.
Certified Medicaid.
Owner Proprietary Corp (Comprehensive
Health Care Assn).

Nocona Nursing Home
306 Carolyn Rd, Nocona, TX, 76255
(817) 825-3288
Admin Becky Spikes. *Medical Dir/Dir of*
Nursing Mary Rose Underwood DON.
Licensure Intermediate care. *Beds* ICF 91.
Certified Medicaid.
Owner Privately owned.
Admissions Requirements Medical
examination; Physician's request.
Staff LPNs 6 (ft), 2 (pt); Orderlies 1 (ft);
Nurses aides 12 (ft), 4 (pt); Activities
coordinators 1 (ft); Dietitians 1 (pt).
Facilities Dining room; Activities room;
Chapel; Crafts room; Laundry room; Barber/
Beauty shop.
Activities Arts & crafts; Games; Reading
groups; Prayer groups.

ODESSA

Deerings Nursing Home
1020 W County Rd, Odessa, TX, 79763
(915) 332-0371
Admin Fred Cullens. *Medical Dir/Dir of*
Nursing Phyllis Young DON.
Licensure Intermediate care. *Beds* ICF 89;
Private 22. *Certified* Medicaid.
Owner Proprietary Corp (Hillhaven Corp).
Staff LPNs; Orderlies; Nurses aides; Activities
coordinators; Dietitians.

Deerings West Nursing Home
2510 W 8th St, Odessa, TX, 79763
(915) 333-4511

Admin Daniel Lopez. *Medical Dir/Dir of*
Nursing Kim Thompson.
Licensure Skilled care; Intermediate care. *Beds*
150. *Certified* Medicaid; Medicare.
Owner Proprietary Corp (Hillhaven Corp).
Admissions Requirements Medical
examination; Physician's request.
Staff RNs; LPNs; Orderlies; Nurses aides;
Activities coordinators; Dietitians.
Languages Spanish, Sign
Facilities Dining room; Physical therapy
room; Activities room; Laundry room;
Barber/Beauty shop.
Activities Arts & crafts; Cards; Games;
Reading groups; Prayer groups; Movies;
Shopping trips; Social/Cultural gatherings.

Four Seasons Nursing Center
3800 Englewood Ln, Odessa, TX, 79762
(915) 362-2583
Admin Betty Turner. *Medical Dir/Dir of*
Nursing Kirby Tatum MD; Beverly Martin
RN DON.
Licensure Intermediate care. *Beds* ICF 113.
Certified Medicaid.
Owner Proprietary Corp (Manor Care).
Admissions Requirements Medical
examination; Physician's request.
Staff RNs 2 (ft), 1 (pt); LPNs 6 (ft), 1 (pt);
Nurses aides 19 (ft), 2 (pt); Reality therapists
1 (pt); Activities coordinators 1 (ft);
Dietitians 1 (pt).
Facilities Dining room; Activities room;
Laundry room; Barber/Beauty shop.
Activities Arts & crafts; Cards; Games;
Reading groups; Prayer groups; Movies;
Social/Cultural gatherings.

Westview Manor*
2443 W 16th St, Odessa, TX, 79763
(915) 333-2904
Admin William L Ketcham.
Licensure Intermediate care. *Beds* 97.
Certified Medicaid; Medicare.

OLNEY

Olney Nursing Center*
1302 W Payne, Box 68, Olney, TX, 76374
(817) 564-5626
Admin Elisabeth E Neal. *Medical Dir/Dir of*
Nursing Dr C V Wright.
Licensure Intermediate care. *Beds* 72.
Certified Medicaid.
Owner Proprietary Corp (Beverly Enterprises).
Staff RNs 1 (pt); LPNs 4 (ft), 2 (pt); Orderlies
1 (ft); Nurses aides 12 (ft); Activities
coordinators 1 (ft); Dietitians 1 (pt).

Seven Oaks Nursing Home*
PO Box 157, 1402 W Elm St, Olney, TX,
76374
(817) 564-5631
Admin Katherine B Bennett.
Licensure Skilled care. *Beds* 90. *Certified*
Medicaid.
Owner Proprietary Corp (Comprehensive
Health Care Assn).

OMAHA

Elmwood Nursing Home*
PO Box 1087, Giles St, Omaha, TX, 75571
(214) 884-2341
Admin Clayton D Elliott.
Licensure Intermediate care. *Beds* 54.
Certified Medicaid.
Owner Proprietary Corp (Truco Inc).

ORANGE

Jones Health Center Inc*
3000 Cardinal Dr, Orange, TX, 77630
(713) 883-5727
Admin Mary F Dupuy.

Licensure Skilled care; Intermediate care. *Beds*
109. *Certified* Medicaid.
Owner Proprietary Corp.

Polley's Rest Home Inc
501 N 3rd St, Orange, TX, 77630
(713) 886-8677
Admin Rose Marie Gordon.
Licensure Intermediate care. *Beds* 112.
Certified Medicaid.
Owner Proprietary Corp.

OVERTON

Leisure Lodge—Overton
PO Drawer K, Hwy 135 S, Overton, TX,
75684
(214) 834-6166
Admin Linda B Jones. *Medical Dir/Dir of
Nursing* James Hamilton MD; Carolyn
Smith RN.
Licensure Skilled care; Intermediate care. *Beds*
100. *Certified* Medicaid; Medicare.
Owner Proprietary Corp (Beverly Enterprises).
Admissions Requirements Minimum age 18
months; Medical examination; Physician's
request.
Staff RNs 2 (ft), 3 (pt); LPNs 10 (ft); Nurses
aides 44 (ft), 4 (pt); Activities coordinators 1
(ft); Dietitians 1 (ft).
Facilities Dining room; Activities room;
Crafts room; Laundry room; Barber/Beauty
shop.
Activities Arts & crafts; Cards; Games;
Reading groups; Prayer groups; Movies;
Shopping trips; Social/Cultural gatherings.

OZONA

Crockett County Care Center*
Ave H & 1st St, Ozona, TX, 76943
(915) 392-3096
Admin Elvira Caldwell.
Licensure Intermediate care. *Beds* 36.
Certified Medicaid.
Admissions Requirements Minimum age 16;
Medical examination; Physician's request.
Staff Physicians 2 (ft); RNs 1 (pt); LPNs 3
(ft); Orderlies 1 (ft); Nurses aides 23 (ft);
Reality therapists 1 (pt); Speech therapists 1
(pt); Activities coordinators 1 (pt); Dietitians
1 (pt).
Facilities Dining room; Activities room;
Chapel; Crafts room; Laundry room; Barber/
Beauty shop.
Activities Arts & crafts; Cards; Games;
Reading groups; Prayer groups; Movies;
Shopping trips; Social/Cultural gatherings.

PADUCAH

Cottle County Nursing Home*
800 7th St, Paducah, TX, 79248
(806) 492-3517
Admin Gwynna Marie Stoffel.
Licensure Intermediate care. *Beds* 46.
Certified Medicaid.
Owner Proprietary Corp.

PALACIOS

Leisure Lodge—Palacios*
1414 4th St, Palacios, TX, 77465
(512) 972-2542
Admin Minnie Smith.
Licensure Intermediate care. *Beds* 102.
Certified Medicaid.
Owner Proprietary Corp (Beverly Enterprises).
Staff LPNs 4 (ft); Nurses aides 12 (ft);
Physical therapists 1 (pt); Occupational
therapists 1 (pt); Speech therapists 1 (pt);
Activities coordinators 1 (ft); Dietitians 1
(pt).

Facilities Dining room; Activities room;
Chapel; Laundry room; Barber/Beauty shop.
Activities Arts & crafts; Games; Prayer groups;
Movies; Shopping trips; Social/Cultural
gatherings.

PALESTINE

Cartmell Home for Aged*
2212 W Reagan, Palestine, TX, 75801
(214) 729-2268
Admin Peggy Howland.
Licensure Intermediate care; Custodial care.
Beds ICF 44; Custodial care 16.
Admissions Requirements Minimum age 65;
Medical examination.
Staff Physicians 1 (pt); LPNs 4 (ft), 4 (pt);
Nurses aides 13 (ft), 3 (pt); Activities
coordinators 1 (ft); Dietitians 1 (pt).
Facilities Dining room; Physical therapy
room; Activities room; Crafts room; Laundry
room; Barber/Beauty shop; Garden.
Activities Arts & crafts; Cards; Games; Prayer
groups; Movies; Shopping trips; Local trips;
Picnics.

Oak Haven Nursing Home*
606 E Kolstad, Palestine, TX, 75801
(214) 729-6901
Admin Patricia A Jeffcoat.
Licensure Intermediate care. *Beds* 54.
Certified Medicaid.
Owner Proprietary Corp.

Palestine Nursing Center
2404 Hwy 155 N, Palestine, TX, 75801
(214) 729-6024
Admin Ruben L Goatcher. *Medical Dir/Dir of
Nursing* Margaret Sherman.
Licensure Intermediate care. *Beds* ICF 120.
Certified Medicaid.
Owner Proprietary Corp.
Admissions Requirements Medical
examination.
Staff LPNs 12 (ft); Nurses aides 30 (ft);
Physical therapists 1 (pt); Recreational
therapists 1 (ft); Occupational therapists 1
(pt); Speech therapists 1 (pt); Activities
coordinators 1 (ft); Dietitians 2 (pt);
Ophthalmologists 1 (pt); Podiatrists 1 (pt).
Facilities Dining room; Physical therapy
room; Laundry room; Barber/Beauty shop.
Activities Arts & crafts; Cards; Games;
Reading groups; Prayer groups; Movies;
Shopping trips; Social/Cultural gatherings.

Park Place Nursing Home*
505 Sylvan Ave, Palestine, TX, 75801
(214) 729-3246
Admin Danny Swabado.
Licensure Skilled care. *Beds* 108. *Certified*
Medicaid.
Owner Proprietary Corp.

Villa Inn Nursing Center
1816 Tile Factory Rd, Palestine, TX, 75801
(214) 729-2261
Admin Brenda Bryant. *Medical Dir/Dir of
Nursing* Kay Caufield.
Licensure Skilled care; Intermediate care;
Intermediate care for mentally retarded.
Beds 112. *Certified* Medicaid; Medicare.
Owner Proprietary Corp (Beverly Enterprises).
Admissions Requirements Physician's request.
Staff RNs; LPNs; Nurses aides; Physical
therapists; Activities coordinators; Dietitians.
Facilities Dining room; Laundry room;
Barber/Beauty shop.
Activities Cards; Games; Prayer groups;
Movies; Shopping trips.

PAMPA

Coronado Nursing Center*
PO Box 539, 1504 W Kentucky St, Pampa,
TX, 79065
(806) 665-5746

Admin Jimmie Lee Moore.
Licensure Intermediate care. *Beds* 120.
Certified Medicaid.
Owner Proprietary Corp (Beverly Enterprises).

Pampa Nursing Center
PO Box 582, 1321 W Kentucky St, Pampa,
TX, 79065-0582
(806) 669-2551
Admin Dorris Houck. *Medical Dir/Dir of
Nursing* Jesse Hardy.
Licensure Intermediate care. *Beds* 100.
Certified Medicaid.
Owner Proprietary Corp (ARA Living
Centers).
Admissions Requirements Medical
examination; Physician's request.
Staff LPNs 4 (ft); Nurses aides 14 (ft);
Activities coordinators 1 (ft); Dietitians 1
(ft).

PANHANDLE

St Ann's Nursing Home
PO Box 1179, Spur 293, Panhandle, TX,
79068
(806) 537-3194
Admin Sr M Consilia Feuchtenhofer.
Licensure Skilled care. *Beds* 52. *Certified*
Medicaid.
Owner Nonprofit Corp.
Affiliation Roman Catholic

PARIS

Cherry Street Annex
2185 E Cherry St, Paris, TX, 75460
(214) 784-7108
Admin Julie P Hopper. *Medical Dir/Dir of
Nursing* Dr E Sidney White; Donnie Dee
VanVoast RN DON.
Licensure Intermediate care. *Beds* ICF 122.
Certified Medicaid.
Owner Proprietary Corp.
Admissions Requirements Physician's request.
Staff Physicians 1 (ft); RNs 1 (ft); LPNs 8 (ft),
5 (pt); Nurses aides 35 (ft), 9 (pt); Physical
therapists 1 (pt); Speech therapists 1 (pt);
Activities coordinators 1 (ft); Dietitians 2
(pt); Medical aides 6 (ft), 1 (pt).
Facilities Dining room; Activities room;
Crafts room; Laundry room; Barber/Beauty
shop; TV lobbies; Conversation area.
Activities Arts & crafts; Cards; Games;
Reading groups; Prayer groups; Movies;
Shopping trips; Social/Cultural gatherings.

Cherry Street Manor*
2193 E Cherry St, Paris, TX, 75460
(214) 784-2244
Admin Jack L Marshall.
Licensure Intermediate care. *Beds* 122.
Certified Medicaid.
Owner Proprietary Corp.

Medical Plaza Nursing Center
610 Deshong Dr, Paris, TX, 75460
(214) 784-6638
Admin Teressa J Whitley. *Medical Dir/Dir of
Nursing* Richard Bercher MD; Barbara Rose
RN DON.
Licensure Intermediate care. *Beds* ICF 98.
Certified Medicaid.
Owner Proprietary Corp (Beverly Enterprises).
Admissions Requirements Medical
examination.
Staff RNs 1 (ft); LPNs 10 (ft); Nurses aides 40
(ft), 5 (pt); Activities coordinators 1 (ft).
Facilities Dining room; Activities room;
Crafts room; Laundry room; Barber/Beauty
shop; Library.
Activities Arts & crafts; Cards; Games;
Reading groups; Prayer groups; Shopping
trips; Social/Cultural gatherings.

Park View Convalescent Center*
2895 Lewis Ln, Paris, TX, 75460
(214) 784-4111
Admin Bert Armstrong. *Medical Dir/Dir of Nursing* Sidney White MD.
Licensure Intermediate care. *Beds* 102. *Certified* Medicaid.
Admissions Requirements Physician's request.
Staff Physicians 1 (ft); RNs 1 (ft); LPNs 7 (ft); Nurses aides 30 (ft), 6 (pt); Physical therapists 1 (ft); Activities coordinators 1 (ft); Dietitians 1 (ft).
Facilities Dining room; Activities room; Laundry room; Barber/Beauty shop.
Activities Arts & crafts; Games; Prayer groups; Movies; Shopping trips; Social/Cultural gatherings.

Pleasant Grove Nursing Home*
3055 Clarksville St, Paris, TX, 75460
(214) 785-1601
Admin Robbi Ann Stewart.
Licensure Intermediate care; Personal care. *Beds* ICF 144; Personal 22. *Certified* Medicaid.
Owner Proprietary Corp.

PASADENA

Blalock Nursing Home—Southeast*
802 Fresa St, Pasadena, TX, 77501
(713) 946-3360
Admin Karen Young.
Licensure Skilled care; Intermediate care. *Beds* 210. *Certified* Medicaid.
Owner Proprietary Corp.

Faith Memorial Nursing Home*
811 Garner Rd, Pasadena, TX, 77502
(713) 473-8573
Admin Phyllis C Ayres.
Licensure Intermediate care. *Beds* 120. *Certified* Medicaid.
Owner Proprietary Corp (ARA Living Centers).
Facilities Dining room; Activities room; Crafts room.
Activities Arts & crafts; Cards; Games; Reading groups; Prayer groups; Movies; Shopping trips; Social/Cultural gatherings.

Pasadena Care Center
4006 Vista Rd, Pasadena, TX, 77504
(713) 943-1592
Admin Jerald W Myers Sr.
Licensure Intermediate care. *Beds* 120. *Certified* Medicaid.
Owner Proprietary Corp (ARA Living Centers).

Vista Continuing Care Center
4300 Vista Rd, Pasadena, TX, 77504
(713) 946-6787
Admin Coral Ann Rung. *Medical Dir/Dir of Nursing* W B Herlong MD; Elaine Burnham RN.
Licensure Intermediate care. *Beds* ICF 131. *Certified* Medicaid; VA.
Owner Proprietary Corp.
Staff Physicians 1 (pt); RNs 1 (ft); LPNs 9 (ft), 1 (pt); Orderlies 2 (ft); Nurses aides 37 (ft), 2 (pt); Physical therapists 1 (pt); Occupational therapists 1 (pt); Speech therapists 1 (pt); Activities coordinators 1 (ft), 1 (pt); Dietitians 1 (pt); Ophthalmologists 1 (pt); Podiatrists 1 (pt).

PEARLAND

Windsong Village Convalescent Center*
3400 E Walnut St, Pearland, TX, 77581
(713) 485-2776
Admin Cecil W Barcelo.
Licensure Intermediate care. *Beds* 96. *Certified* Medicaid.
Owner Proprietary Corp.

PEARSALL

Frio County Nursing Center*
311 Hackberry, Pearsall, TX, 78061
(512) 334-3371
Admin Beverly Roberts.
Licensure Intermediate care. *Beds* 104. *Certified* Medicaid.
Owner Proprietary Corp.

Pearsall Manor*
320 S Ash, Pearsall, TX, 78061
(512) 334-4197
Admin William D Mutzig.
Licensure Intermediate care. *Beds* 52. *Certified* Medicaid.
Owner Proprietary Corp.

PECOS

Pecos Nursing Home
PO Box 1461, 1819 Memorial Dr, Pecos, TX, 79772
(915) 447-2183
Admin Elizabeth Z Peters. *Medical Dir/Dir of Nursing* Bruce Hay MD; Gloria Gonzales LVN DON.
Licensure Intermediate care. *Beds* ICF 60. *Certified* Medicaid.
Owner Privately owned.
Admissions Requirements Minimum age 53; Medical examination; Physician's request.
Staff RNs 1 (pt); LPNs 4 (ft); Nurses aides 15 (ft); Activities coordinators 1 (ft); Dietitians 1 (pt).
Facilities Dining room; Activities room; Laundry room; Barber/Beauty shop.
Activities Arts & crafts; Cards; Games; Reading groups; Prayer groups; Movies; Shopping trips; Social/Cultural gatherings.

PERRYTON

Senior Village Nursing Home
Hwy 83 South, Perryton, TX, 79070
(806) 435-5403
Admin Rita A Hargrove. *Medical Dir/Dir of Nursing* Pat Atkinson.
Licensure Intermediate care. *Beds* 60. *Certified* Medicaid.
Owner Proprietary Corp (Beverly Enterprises).
Admissions Requirements Physician's request.
Staff LPNs 4 (ft), 2 (pt); Nurses aides 15 (ft), 1 (pt); Activities coordinators 1 (ft); Dietitians 1 (pt).
Facilities Dining room; Activities room; Laundry room; Barber/Beauty shop.
Activities Arts & crafts; Games; Reading groups; Prayer groups; Movies; Shopping trips; Social/Cultural gatherings.

PHARR

Pharr Nursing Home
PO Drawer D, 204 S Casa Rd, Pharr, TX, 78577
(512) 787-2735
Admin Dorothy Sadler. *Medical Dir/Dir of Nursing* Socorro Rodriguez.
Licensure Intermediate care. *Beds* ICF 45. *Certified* Medicaid.
Owner Privately owned.
Admissions Requirements Medical examination.
Staff RNs 1 (ft); LPNs 3 (ft); Nurses aides 14 (ft); Activities coordinators 1 (ft); Dietitians 1 (ft).
Languages Spanish
Facilities Dining room; Activities room; Crafts room; Laundry room.
Activities Arts & crafts; Cards; Games; Reading groups; Prayer groups; Movies; Shopping trips; Social/Cultural gatherings.

PILOT POINT

Sundial Manors Nursing Home
202 N Prairie St, Pilot Point, TX, 75258
(817) 686-2272
Admin Ray Dane. *Medical Dir/Dir of Nursing* Marion A Groff DO.
Licensure Skilled care. *Beds* 70. *Certified* Medicaid; Medicare.
Admissions Requirements Minimum age 18; Medical examination; Physician's request.
Staff RNs 2 (ft), 1 (pt); LPNs 11 (ft); Orderlies 1 (ft); Nurses aides 13 (ft), 5 (pt); Physical therapists 1 (pt); Speech therapists 1 (pt); Activities coordinators 1 (ft); Dietitians 1 (ft), 1 (pt).
Facilities Dining room; Barber/Beauty shop; Library.
Activities Arts & crafts; Cards; Games; Reading groups; Prayer groups; Movies; Shopping trips; Social/Cultural gatherings.

PINELAND

Hines Nursing Home
PO Box 806, Hwy 83, Pineland, TX, 75968
(713) 584-2174
Admin Patricia Bradberry.
Licensure Intermediate care. *Beds* 90. *Certified* Medicaid.
Owner Proprietary Corp.

PITTSBURG

Moore's Nursing Home
618 Quitman St, Pittsburg, TX, 75686
(214) 856-6634
Admin Elizabeth Massie. *Medical Dir/Dir of Nursing* Betty L London.
Licensure Intermediate care. *Beds* 24. *Certified* Medicaid.
Owner Privately owned.
Admissions Requirements Minimum age 16; Medical examination; Physician's request.
Staff LPNs; Nurses aides 4 (ft), 1 (pt); Activities coordinators 1 (ft); Podiatrists 1 (pt).
Activities Arts & crafts; Cards; Games; Reading groups; Prayer groups; Movies; Shopping trips; Social/Cultural gatherings.

Pittsburg Nursing Center*
123 Pecan Grove, Pittsburg, TX, 75686
(214) 856-3633
Admin Billie Pittman.
Licensure Intermediate care. *Beds* 106. *Certified* Medicaid.
Owner Proprietary Corp (Beverly Enterprises).

PLAINVIEW

Care Inn of Plainview
224 Saint Louis, Plainview, TX, 79072
(806) 293-5201
Admin Janice W Rogers. *Medical Dir/Dir of Nursing* Shirley Rawlinson.
Licensure Intermediate care. *Beds* ICF 52. *Certified* Medicaid.
Owner Proprietary Corp (ARA Living Centers).
Admissions Requirements Medical examination; Physician's request.
Staff LPNs; Nurses aides; Activities coordinators.
Languages Spanish
Facilities Dining room; Activities room; Chapel; Crafts room; Laundry room; Barber/Beauty shop; Library.
Activities Arts & crafts; Cards; Games; Reading groups; Movies; Shopping trips; Social/Cultural gatherings.

Heritage Home
2510 W 24th St, Plainview, TX, 79072
(806) 296-5584

Admin Lila R Hawkins. *Medical Dir/Dir of Nursing* Joquita Linquist RN.
Licensure Skilled care; Intermediate care. *Beds* SNF 62; ICF 50. *Certified* Medicaid; Medicare.
Owner Proprietary Corp (Southmark Heritage Corp).
Admissions Requirements Medical examination.
Staff RNs 1 (ft); LPNs 10 (ft); Nurses aides 20 (ft), 10 (pt); Activities coordinators 1 (ft).
Languages Spanish
Facilities Dining room; Activities room; Crafts room; Laundry room; Barber/Beauty shop; Library.
Activities Arts & crafts; Cards; Games; Reading groups; Prayer groups; Movies; Shopping trips; Social/Cultural gatherings.

Plains Convalescent Center
2813 W 8th St, Plainview, TX, 79072
(806) 293-2581
Admin Victoria Hutton. *Medical Dir/Dir of Nursing* C L Busby MD; Melba Dolois Palmer DON.
Licensure Intermediate care. *Beds* ICF 52. *Certified* Medicaid.
Owner Proprietary Corp (Southmark Heritage Corp).
Admissions Requirements Medical examination; Physician's request.
Staff LPNs; Nurses aides; Activities coordinators.
Facilities Dining room; Laundry room; Barber/Beauty shop.
Activities Arts & crafts; Games; Reading groups; Prayer groups; Movies; Social/Cultural gatherings.

PLANO

Heritage Manor
1621 Coit Rd, Plano, TX, 75075
(214) 596-7930
Admin Bobbie Sechovec RN. *Medical Dir/Dir of Nursing* A A Acosta MD; Lyn Goerot RN DON.
Licensure Intermediate care. *Beds* ICF 152. *Certified* Medicaid.
Owner Privately owned.
Admissions Requirements Medical examination; Physician's request.
Staff Physicians 25 (pt); RNs 3 (ft), 3 (pt); LPNs 8 (ft), 2 (pt); Nurses aides 26 (ft), 7 (pt); Physical therapists 1 (pt); Recreational therapists 1 (pt); Occupational therapists 1 (pt); Speech therapists 1 (pt); Activities coordinators 1 (ft); Dietitians 1 (ft); Dentists 2 (pt); Ophthalmologists 2 (pt); Podiatrists 1 (pt).
Facilities Dining room; Physical therapy room; Activities room; Chapel; Laundry room; Barber/Beauty shop; Library; Sunrooms.
Activities Arts & crafts; Games; Reading groups; Prayer groups; Movies; Shopping trips; Social/Cultural gatherings; Music therapy; Pet therapy.

Heritage Park
3208 Thunderbird Ln, Plano, TX, 75075
(214) 422-2214
Admin Evelyn R Artall. *Medical Dir/Dir of Nursing* Dr Varsha Solanki; Mary McDermott RN.
Licensure Intermediate care. *Beds* ICF 120. *Certified* Medicaid; VA.
Owner Proprietary Corp.
Admissions Requirements Medical examination; Physician's request.
Staff Physicians 1 (ft); RNs 3 (ft); LPNs 9 (ft); Orderlies 1 (ft); Nurses aides 31 (ft); Physical therapists 1 (ft); Reality therapists 1 (ft); Recreational therapists 1 (ft); Occupational therapists 1 (ft); Speech

therapists 1 (ft); Activities coordinators 1 (ft); Dietitians 1 (ft); Dentists 1 (ft); Ophthalmologists 1 (ft); Podiatrists 1 (ft).
Languages Spanish
Facilities Dining room; Activities room; Laundry room; Barber/Beauty shop; Library.
Activities Arts & crafts; Cards; Games; Reading groups; Prayer groups; Movies; Shopping trips; Social/Cultural gatherings.

Plano Nursing Home*
3100 S Rigsbee Dr, Plano, TX, 75074
(214) 423-6217
Admin Ann Bridges.
Licensure Intermediate care. *Beds* 120. *Certified* Medicaid.
Owner Proprietary Corp (Beverly Enterprises).

PLEASANTON

Retama Manor North
404 Goodwin St, Pleasanton, TX, 78064
(512) 657-4205
Admin Ruth Brewster. *Medical Dir/Dir of Nursing* Lucille Williams RN DON.
Licensure Intermediate care. *Beds* ICF 50. *Certified* Medicaid.
Owner Proprietary Corp (ARA Living Centers).
Admissions Requirements Physician's request.
Staff RNs 1 (ft); LPNs 5 (ft), 1 (pt); Activities coordinators 1 (ft).
Languages Spanish
Facilities Dining room; Activities room; Laundry room; Barber/Beauty shop.
Activities Arts & crafts; Cards; Games; Reading groups; Prayer groups; Movies; Shopping trips; Social/Cultural gatherings.

Retama Manor Nursing Center—South*
905 Oaklawn, Pleasanton, TX, 78064
(512) 569-3861
Admin Sue Hines.
Licensure Intermediate care. *Beds* 96. *Certified* Medicaid.
Owner Proprietary Corp (ARA Living Centers).

PORT ARTHUR

Gaspard's Nursing Care Center Inc*
2689 65th St, Port Arthur, TX, 77640
(713) 736-1541
Admin Velma M Gaspard.
Licensure Skilled care. *Beds* 102. *Certified* Medicaid.
Owner Proprietary Corp.

Golden Triangle Convalescent Center*
8825 Lamplighter, Port Arthur, TX, 77640
(713) 727-1651
Admin Hulon A Walker.
Licensure Intermediate care. *Beds* 200. *Certified* Medicaid.
Owner Proprietary Corp.

PORT LAVACA

Coastal Healthcare Center
524 Village Rd, Port Lavaca, TX, 77979
(512) 552-3741
Admin Hannah M Kinsey. *Medical Dir/Dir of Nursing* Barbara Turk RN.
Licensure Intermediate care. *Beds* ICF 120. *Certified* Medicaid.
Owner Proprietary Corp (ARA Living Centers).
Admissions Requirements Medical examination.
Staff RNs 1 (ft), 1 (pt); LPNs 9 (ft); Nurses aides 35 (ft); Activities coordinators 1 (ft); Dietitians 1 (ft).
Languages Spanish
Facilities Dining room; Physical therapy room; Activities room; Laundry room; Barber/Beauty shop.

Activities Arts & crafts; Cards; Games; Prayer groups; Movies; Social/Cultural gatherings.

PORTER

Pine Shadow Retreat*
PO Box 889, 123 Pine Shadow Ln, Porter, TX, 77365
(713) 354-2155
Admin Betty Swabado.
Licensure Intermediate care. *Beds* 74. *Certified* Medicaid.
Owner Proprietary Corp.

POST

Twin Cedar Nursing Home
107 W 7th, Post, TX, 79356
(806) 495-2022
Admin Bobbie Self. *Medical Dir/Dir of Nursing* Bonnie Medlin DON.
Licensure Intermediate care. *Beds* ICF 24. *Certified* Medicaid.
Owner Privately owned.
Admissions Requirements Physician's request.
Staff LPNs 3 (ft); Nurses aides 6 (ft); Activities coordinators 1 (ft).
Languages Spanish
Facilities Dining room; Activities room; Crafts room; Laundry room; Barber/Beauty shop.
Activities Arts & crafts; Games; Prayer groups; Movies; Shopping trips.

United Convalescent of Post*
605 W 7th St, Post, TX, 79356
(806) 495-2848
Admin Bobbie Edler.
Licensure Intermediate care. *Beds* 75. *Certified* Medicaid.
Owner Proprietary Corp.

POTEET

Poteet Nursing Home
PO Box 995, 101 School Dr, Poteet, TX, 78065
(512) 742-3525
Admin Rebecca M Parker. *Medical Dir/Dir of Nursing* Gerald Phillips MD; Debra J Buck RN DON.
Licensure Skilled care. *Beds* SNF 60. *Certified* Medicaid.
Owner Proprietary Corp.
Admissions Requirements Physician's request.
Staff RNs 1 (ft); LPNs 6 (ft), 2 (pt); Nurses aides 15 (ft), 1 (pt); Activities coordinators 1 (ft); Rehabilitation Aide 1 (ft).
Languages Spanish
Facilities Dining room; Activities room; Laundry room.
Activities Arts & crafts; Cards; Games; Prayer groups; Movies; Shopping trips; Social/Cultural gatherings; Bingo.

PREMONT

Premont Rest Home Inc*
PO Drawer Q, 431 NW 3rd St, Premont, TX, 78375
(512) 348-3812
Admin Janie S Dunn.
Licensure Intermediate care. *Beds* 48. *Certified* Medicaid.
Owner Proprietary Corp.

QUANAH

Wood Convalescent Center 1*
1106 W 14th St, Quanah, TX, 79252
(817) 663-5369
Admin Mary Catherine Morgan. *Medical Dir/Dir of Nursing* Dr W A Brooks.
Licensure Intermediate care. *Beds* 62. *Certified* Medicaid.

Admissions Requirements Minimum age 21; Medical examination; Physician's request.
Staff RNs 1 (pt); LPNs 3 (ft), 2 (pt); Nurses aides 12 (ft); Physical therapists 1 (ft), 2 (pt); Speech therapists 1 (pt); Activities coordinators 1 (ft); Dietitians 1 (pt); 17 (ft), 4 (pt).
Facilities Dining room; Laundry room; Barber/Beauty shop.
Activities Arts & crafts; Cards; Games; Reading groups; Prayer groups; Movies; Shopping trips; Social/Cultural gatherings.

QUITMAN

Heritage Nursing Home
1026 E Goode St, Quitman, TX, 75783
(214) 763-2284
Admin Annette Simpkins. *Medical Dir/Dir of Nursing* Ben F Merritt MD.
Licensure Intermediate care. *Beds* 165.
Certified Medicaid.
Owner Proprietary Corp.
Admissions Requirements Minimum age 18; Medical examination; Physician's request.
Staff RNs 2 (ft); LPNs 8 (ft), 2 (pt); Orderlies 2 (ft); Nurses aides 35 (ft), 2 (pt); Physical therapists 1 (pt); Speech therapists 1 (pt); Activities coordinators 1 (ft), 1 (pt); Dietitians 1 (ft); Podiatrists 1 (pt).
Facilities Dining room; Physical therapy room; Activities room; Crafts room; Laundry room; Barber/Beauty shop; Library; Multi-purpose room; Gift shop; Training center.
Activities Arts & crafts; Cards; Games; Reading groups; Prayer groups; Movies; Shopping trips; Social/Cultural gatherings.

Quitman Nursing Home Inc*
503 N College St, Quitman, TX, 75783
(214) 763-2753
Admin Jo Ann Petrea.
Licensure Intermediate care. *Beds* 62.
Certified Medicaid.
Staff RNs 1 (ft); LPNs 3 (ft), 3 (pt); Nurses aides 13 (ft), 6 (pt); Activities coordinators 1 (ft); Dietitians 1 (ft); 8 (ft), 5 (pt).
Facilities Dining room; Activities room; Laundry room; Barber/Beauty shop; Library.
Activities Arts & crafts; Cards; Games; Prayer groups; Movies.

RALLS

Ralls Nursing Home
1111 Ave P Box 486, Ralls, TX, 79357
(806) 253-2314, 243-2415
Admin Betty J Abell. *Medical Dir/Dir of Nursing* Betty Kelsey DON.
Licensure Intermediate care. *Beds* ICF 46.
Certified Medicaid.
Owner Proprietary Corp (ARA Living Centers).
Admissions Requirements Medical examination.
Staff Physicians; LPNs; Nurses aides; Activities coordinators.
Languages Spanish
Facilities Dining room; Laundry room.
Activities Arts & crafts; Cards; Games; Reading groups; Prayer groups; Shopping trips.

RANGER

Western Manor
460 W Main St, Ranger, TX, 76470
(817) 647-3111
Admin Lauretta Lawler. *Medical Dir/Dir of Nursing* Lavelle Hallmark.
Licensure Intermediate care. *Beds* ICF 50.
Certified Medicaid.
Owner Privately owned.
Admissions Requirements Minimum age 18; Medical examination; Physician's request.

Staff RNs 1 (pt); LPNs 4 (ft), 3 (pt); Nurses aides 15 (ft), 8 (pt); Activities coordinators 1 (ft); Dietitians 1 (pt).
Languages Spanish
Facilities Dining room; Activities room; Laundry room.
Activities Arts & crafts; Cards; Games; Reading groups; Prayer groups; Movies; Shopping trips.

RAYMONDVILLE

Retama Manor Nursing Center*
PO Box 445, State Hwy 186 E, Raymondville, TX, 78580
(512) 689-2126
Admin Jimmy W Lowe.
Licensure Intermediate care. *Beds* 48.
Certified Medicaid.
Owner Proprietary Corp (ARA Living Centers).

REFUGIO

Refugio Manor
109 Swift St, Refugio, TX, 78377
(512) 526-4641
Admin Joyce L Cox. *Medical Dir/Dir of Nursing* Debra A Shirley LUN DON.
Licensure Intermediate care. *Beds* ICF 64.
Certified Medicaid.
Owner Proprietary Corp (Diversicare Corp).
Admissions Requirements Medical examination; Physician's request.
Staff LPNs 7 (ft), 3 (pt); Nurses aides 17 (ft), 3 (pt); Activities coordinators 1 (ft); Dietitians 1 (pt).
Facilities Dining room; Activities room; Laundry room; Barber/Beauty shop.
Activities Arts & crafts; Cards; Games; Prayer groups; Shopping trips.

RICHARDSON

Heritage Village
1111 Rockingham St, Richardson, TX, 75080
(214) 231-8833
Admin Beverly J Holt. *Medical Dir/Dir of Nursing* Jean Atwood.
Licensure Intermediate care. *Beds* ICF 280.
Certified Medicaid.
Owner Privately owned.
Admissions Requirements Medical examination; Physician's request.
Staff RNs 6 (ft), 1 (pt); LPNs 19 (ft), 3 (pt); Orderlies 6 (ft); Nurses aides 49 (ft), 2 (pt); Physical therapists 1 (ft); Occupational therapists 1 (ft); Speech therapists 1 (ft); Activities coordinators 1 (ft), 1 (pt); Dietitians 1 (ft); Dentists 1 (ft); Ophthalmologists 1 (ft); Podiatrists 1 (ft); Social worker 1 (ft).
Languages Spanish
Facilities Dining room; Physical therapy room; Activities room; Chapel; Crafts room; Laundry room; Barber/Beauty shop; Library; Ice cream parlor; Outdoor enclosed patio.
Activities Arts & crafts; Cards; Games; Reading groups; Prayer groups; Movies; Shopping trips; Social/Cultural gatherings.

Richardson Manor Care Center
1510 N Plano Rd, Richardson, TX, 75081
(214) 234-4786
Admin Gabriel G Bach. *Medical Dir/Dir of Nursing* Dee Kaulbach RN.
Licensure Intermediate care. *Beds* ICF 142.
Certified Medicaid.
Owner Proprietary Corp.
Admissions Requirements Medical examination; Physician's request.
Staff Physicians 1 (ft); RNs 2 (ft); LPNs 12 (ft); Nurses aides 38 (ft); Physical therapists 1 (pt); Reality therapists 1 (pt); Recreational therapists 1 (pt); Occupational therapists 1 (pt); Speech therapists 1 (pt); Activities

coordinators 1 (pt); Dietitians 1 (pt); Dentists 1 (pt); Ophthalmologists 1 (pt); Podiatrists 1 (pt).
Languages Spanish, German, French
Facilities Dining room; Activities room; Crafts room; Laundry room; Barber/Beauty shop.
Activities Arts & crafts; Cards; Games; Reading groups; Prayer groups.

RICHLAND HILLS

Boulevard Manor Care Center*
7146 Baker Blvd, Richland Hills, TX, 76118
(817) 284-1484
Admin Catherine M Costa.
Licensure Intermediate care. *Beds* 122.
Certified Medicaid; Medicare.

RICHMOND

Autumn Hills Convalescent Center—Richmond
705 Jackson St, Richmond, TX, 77469
(713) 342-5493
Admin Mildred M Stanley. *Medical Dir/Dir of Nursing* Cathy Stearns RN DON.
Licensure Intermediate care. *Beds* ICF 98.
Certified Medicaid.
Owner Proprietary Corp.
Admissions Requirements Medical examination; Physician's request.
Staff RNs 1 (ft); LPNs 8 (ft), 3 (pt); Nurses aides 23 (ft); Occupational therapists 1 (pt); Speech therapists 1 (pt); Activities coordinators 1 (ft); Dietitians 1 (pt); Dentists 1 (pt); Ophthalmologists 1 (pt); Podiatrists 1 (pt).
Facilities Dining room; Activities room; Crafts room; Laundry room; Barber/Beauty shop.
Activities Arts & crafts; Cards; Games; Reading groups; Prayer groups; Movies; Shopping trips; Social/Cultural gatherings.

Brazosview Healthcare Center*
2127 Preston Rd, Richmond, TX, 77469
(713) 342-2801
Admin Robin Baschnagel.
Licensure Intermediate care. *Beds* 56.
Certified Medicaid.
Owner Proprietary Corp (ARA Living Centers).

RIO GRANDE CITY

Retama Manor Nursing Center*
400 S Pete Diaz, Jr, Rio Grande City, TX, 78582
(512) 487-2513
Admin Rosemary Decker.
Licensure Intermediate care. *Beds* 100.
Certified Medicaid; Medicare.
Owner Proprietary Corp (ARA Living Centers).

RISING STAR

Rising Star Nursing Center*
411 S Miller, Rising Star, TX, 76471
(817) 643-2691
Admin Glenn R Gray. *Medical Dir/Dir of Nursing* Terry Horton.
Licensure Intermediate care. *Beds* 61.
Certified Medicaid.
Admissions Requirements Medical examination; Physician's request.
Staff LPNs 6 (ft), 1 (pt); Nurses aides 15 (ft); Activities coordinators 1 (ft), 1 (pt).
Facilities Dining room; Activities room; Laundry room; Barber/Beauty shop.
Activities Arts & crafts; Cards; Games; Prayer groups; Shopping trips; Social/Cultural gatherings.

ROBERT LEE

West Coke County Hospital District Nursing Home
PO Box 1209, 307 W 8th St, Robert Lee, TX, 76945
(915) 453-2511
Admin Jeanene Andrews Baucum. *Medical Dir/Dir of Nursing* Guno Kletter MD; Golda Brown LUN DON.
Licensure Intermediate care. *Beds* ICF 86. *Certified* Medicaid.
Owner Publicly owned.
Admissions Requirements Physician's request.
Staff Physicians 1 (pt); LPNs 8 (ft), 2 (pt); Orderlies 3 (ft); Nurses aides 30 (ft), 2 (pt); Activities coordinators 1 (ft); Dietitians 1 (pt).
Languages Spanish
Facilities Dining room; Physical therapy room; Activities room; Chapel; Crafts room; Laundry room; Barber/Beauty shop; Library; Physician exam room; X-Ray.
Activities Arts & crafts; Cards; Games; Prayer groups; Movies; Social/Cultural gatherings.

ROBINSON

Robinson Nursing Home & Development Center*
305 S Andrews, Robinson, TX, 76706
(817) 662-4010
Admin Ann Duckworth.
Licensure Intermediate care. *Beds* 136. *Certified* Medicaid.
Owner Proprietary Corp (ARA Living Centers).
Staff Physicians; RNs; Orderlies; Nurses aides; Physical therapists; Occupational therapists; Speech therapists; Dietitians.
Facilities Dining room; Activities room; Crafts room; Laundry room; Barber/Beauty shop.
Activities Arts & crafts; Reading groups; Shopping trips.

ROBSTOWN

Retama Manor Nursing Center—Robstown
603 E Ave J, Robstown, TX, 78380
(512) 387-1568
Admin Kerri G White. *Medical Dir/Dir of Nursing* Eutie Burnett.
Licensure Intermediate care. *Beds* ICF 98. *Certified* Medicaid.
Owner Proprietary Corp (ARA Living Centers).
Admissions Requirements Medical examination; Physician's request.
Staff LPNs 6 (ft); Orderlies 1 (ft); Nurses aides 30 (ft); Activities coordinators 1 (ft); Dietitians 1 (ft).
Languages Spanish
Facilities Dining room; Activities room; Chapel; Crafts room; Laundry room; Barber/Beauty shop.
Activities Arts & crafts; Cards; Games; Reading groups; Prayer groups; Movies; Shopping trips; Social/Cultural gatherings.

ROBY

Golden Haven Home*
PO Box 307, 107 N 2nd, Roby, TX, 79543
(915) 776-2391
Admin Greta N Finch.
Licensure Intermediate care. *Beds* 34. *Certified* Medicaid.
Owner Proprietary Corp.

ROCKDALE

Manor Oaks Nursing Home*
Rte 1, Box 7, Rockdale, TX, 76567
(512) 446-5893
Admin Charlotte Rogers. *Medical Dir/Dir of Nursing* Dr Phillip Young.
Licensure Intermediate care. *Beds* 60. *Certified* Medicaid.
Admissions Requirements Medical examination.
Staff Physicians; RNs; LPNs; Nurses aides; Physical therapists; Occupational therapists; Speech therapists; Activities coordinators; Dietitians; Dentists.

Rockdale Nursing Home
700 Dyer St, Rockdale, TX, 76567
(512) 446-2548
Admin Esta Faye Lay. *Medical Dir/Dir of Nursing* Dr Philip M Young; Alice Duncum RN DON.
Licensure Intermediate care. *Beds* ICF 59. *Certified* Medicaid.
Admissions Requirements Physician's request.
Staff RNs 1 (ft); LPNs 4 (ft); Nurses aides 16 (ft), 3 (pt); Physical therapists 1 (pt); Activities coordinators 1 (ft); Dietitians 1 (pt); Dentists 1 (pt); Ophthalmologists 1 (pt); Dentist 1 (pt).
Facilities Dining room; Activities room; Crafts room; Barber/Beauty shop; TV room; Piano room.
Activities Arts & crafts; Cards; Games; Reading groups; Prayer groups; Shopping trips; Social/Cultural gatherings; Daily exercise program.

ROCKWALL

Rockwall Nursing Home*
206 Storr's St, Rockwall, TX, 75087
(214) 226-7591
Admin Don E Miller.
Licensure Intermediate care. *Beds* 134. *Certified* Medicaid.
Admissions Requirements Medical examination; Physician's request.
Staff Physicians 1 (pt); RNs 4 (ft); LPNs ; 6 (ft); Nurses aides 35 (ft); Physical therapists 1 (pt); Reality therapists 1 (pt); Recreational therapists 1 (pt); Occupational therapists 1 (pt); Speech therapists 1 (pt); Activities coordinators 1 (pt); Dietitians 1 (pt).
Facilities Dining room; Laundry room; Barber/Beauty shop.
Activities Arts & crafts; Cards; Games; Reading groups; Prayer groups; Movies; Social/Cultural gatherings.

ROSCOE

Roscoe Nursing Home
201 Cypress, Roscoe, TX, 79545
(915) 766-3374
Admin Mary Wooddell. *Medical Dir/Dir of Nursing* Dr Larry McEachern; Patricia Featherstone DON.
Licensure Intermediate care. *Beds* 60. *Certified* Medicaid.
Owner Proprietary Corp (Beverly Enterprises).
Admissions Requirements Physician's request.
Staff Physicians; RNs; LPNs 6 (ft); Orderlies 1 (ft); Nurses aides 11 (ft); Activities coordinators 1 (ft); Dietitians 1 (ft).
Facilities Dining room; Activities room; Crafts room; Laundry room; Barber/Beauty shop; Designated areas serve as library, chapel, physical therapy and treatment rooms.
Activities Arts & crafts; Cards; Games; Reading groups; Prayer groups; Movies; Shopping trips; Social/Cultural gatherings; Adopt-a-grandparent.

ROSEBUD

Heritage House
College & Ave F, Rosebud, TX, 76570
(817) 583-7904
Admin Judy S Robison. *Medical Dir/Dir of Nursing* Clarence D Snyder MD; Jane Sammon RN DON.
Licensure Skilled care; Intermediate care. *Beds* SNF 60; ICF 64. *Certified* Medicaid; Medicare.
Staff Physicians 2 (pt); RNs 1 (ft), 2 (pt); LPNs 10 (ft), 4 (pt); Orderlies 1 (ft), 1 (pt); Nurses aides 44 (ft), 2 (pt); Physical therapists 1 (pt); Activities coordinators 1 (ft), 1 (pt); Dietitians 1 (pt); Dentists 1 (pt).
Languages Spanish, Czech, German
Facilities Dining room; Activities room; Laundry room; Barber/Beauty shop.
Activities Arts & crafts; Cards; Games; Reading groups; Prayer groups; Movies; Shopping trips; Social/Cultural gatherings.

ROSENBERG

Fort Bend Nursing Home*
3010 Bamore Rd, Rosenberg, TX, 77471
(713) 342-2142
Admin Tamara D Hall.
Licensure Intermediate care. *Beds* 56. *Certified* Medicaid.
Owner Proprietary Corp.

Leisure Lodge—Rosenberg*
1419 Manlman St, Rosenberg, TX, 77471
(713) 232-6471
Admin Olivia Manning. *Medical Dir/Dir of Nursing* R L Yelderman MD.
Licensure Intermediate care. *Beds* 142. *Certified* Medicaid.
Owner Proprietary Corp (Beverly Enterprises).
Staff RNs 1 (ft); LPNs 8 (ft); Nurses aides 30 (ft); Activities coordinators 1 (ft); Dietitians 1 (pt).
Facilities Dining room; Laundry room; Barber/Beauty shop.
Activities Arts & crafts; Games; Reading groups; Prayer groups; Movies; Shopping trips.

ROTAN

Fisher County Nursing Home*
110 W Johnson, Rotan, TX, 79546
(915) 735-3291
Admin Mary Sue Hitt.
Licensure Intermediate care. *Beds* 35. *Certified* Medicaid.
Owner Proprietary Corp.

Rotan Nursing Center*
711 E 5th, Rotan, TX, 79546
(915) 735-2233
Admin Peggy Richburg.
Licensure Intermediate care. *Beds* 48. *Certified* Medicaid.
Owner Proprietary Corp (Beverly Enterprises).

ROUND ROCK

Trinity Lutheran Home—Round Rock
PO Box 8, 1000 E Main Ave, Round Rock, TX, 78664
(512) 255-2521
Admin Kenneth M Keller. *Medical Dir/Dir of Nursing* Dr Hal Gaddy.
Licensure Intermediate care. *Beds* ICF 119; Personal care 24. *Certified* Medicaid.
Owner Nonprofit Corp.
Admissions Requirements Medical examination; Physician's request.
Staff Physicians 1 (pt); RNs 1 (ft); LPNs 10 (ft), 2 (pt); Nurses aides 24 (ft), 6 (pt); Physical therapists 1 (pt); Reality therapists 1 (pt); Activities coordinators 1 (ft); Dietitians 1 (pt).
Languages Spanish
Affiliation Lutheran

Facilities Dining room; Physical therapy room; Activities room; Chapel; Crafts room; Laundry room; Barber/Beauty shop; Library; Many extra dayrooms; 3 enclosed courtyards.
Activities Arts & crafts; Cards; Games; Reading groups; Prayer groups; Movies; Shopping trips; Social/Cultural gatherings; Picnic; Open house; Bazaar; Fishing.

RUSK

Leisure Lodge—Rusk*
2205 E Johnson, Rusk, TX, 75785
(214) 683-5444
Admin Elizabeth Doss. Medical Dir/Dir of Nursing Dr Roger McLarry.
Licensure Intermediate care. Beds 96. Certified Medicaid.
Owner Proprietary Corp (Beverly Enterprises).
Staff LPNs 5 (ft), 2 (pt); Orderlies 2 (ft); Nurses aides 18 (ft), 4 (pt); Activities coordinators 1 (ft); Dietitians 1 (ft).
Facilities Dining room; Physical therapy room; Activities room; Laundry room; Barber/Beauty shop.
Activities Arts & crafts; Games; Prayer groups; Movies.

Rusk Nursing Home Inc*
PO Box 347, 1216 W 6th St, Rusk, TX, 75785
(214) 683-5421
Admin Eleanor E Gabbert.
Licensure Intermediate care. Beds 42. Certified Medicaid.
Owner Proprietary Corp.

Town Hall Estates
1900 E Bagley Rd, Rusk, TX, 75785
(214) 683-5438
Admin Steven M Tandy. Medical Dir/Dir of Nursing Roger A Meharry MD; Nancy DeFoor DON.
Licensure Skilled care; Intermediate care; Private. Beds SNF 56; ICF 60; Private 24. Certified Medicaid; Medicare.
Owner Nonprofit Corp.
Admissions Requirements Medical examination; Physician's request.
Staff RNs 3 (ft); LPNs 22 (ft); Orderlies 4 (ft); Nurses aides 56 (ft); Physical therapists 1 (ft); Activities coordinators 1 (ft), 1 (pt).
Affiliation American Religious Town Hall Meeting
Facilities Dining room; Physical therapy room; Activities room; Crafts room; Laundry room; Barber/Beauty shop; Library; Books on wheels; Lobby.
Activities Arts & crafts; Games; Reading groups; Prayer groups; Movies; Shopping trips; Social/Cultural gatherings.

SAN ANGELO

Baptist Memorial Geriatric Center*
PO Box 5661, 902 N Main St, San Angelo, TX, 76901
(915) 655-7391
Admin Walter D McDonald.
Licensure Skilled care; Intermediate care. Beds 208. Certified Medicaid; Medicare.
Owner Nonprofit Corp.
Affiliation Baptist

Colonial Nursing Home
4215 Armstrong, San Angelo, TX, 76903
(915) 655-8986
Admin Stephen Hicks. Medical Dir/Dir of Nursing Marlene Keith.
Licensure Intermediate care. Beds 60. Certified Medicaid.
Owner Proprietary Corp.
Admissions Requirements Physician's request.
Staff RNs 1 (ft); LPNs 4 (ft), 2 (pt); Orderlies 1 (pt); Nurses aides 12 (ft), 3 (pt); Activities coordinators 1 (ft); Dietitians 1 (ft).
Languages Spanish

Facilities Dining room; Physical therapy room; Activities room; Crafts room; Laundry room; Barber/Beauty shop.
Activities Arts & crafts; Cards; Games; Reading groups; Prayer groups; Movies; Shopping trips; Social/Cultural gatherings.

Park Plaza Nursing Center*
2210 Howard St, San Angelo, TX, 76901
(915) 944-0561
Admin James D Loudermilk.
Licensure Intermediate care. Beds 269. Certified Medicaid.
Owner Proprietary Corp.

Riverside Manor*
609 Rio Concho Dr, San Angelo, TX, 76901
(915) 653-1266
Admin J W Kendall. Medical Dir/Dir of Nursing Dr Lloyd Downing.
Licensure Intermediate care. Beds 148. Certified Medicaid.
Owner Proprietary Corp (Beverly Enterprises).
Admissions Requirements Physician's request.
Staff Physicians 1 (pt); RNs 2 (ft); LPNs 6 (ft); Orderlies 1 (ft); Nurses aides 40 (ft); Reality therapists 1 (ft); Activities coordinators 1 (ft); Dietitians 1 (pt).
Facilities Dining room; Physical therapy room; Activities room; Chapel; Laundry room; Barber/Beauty shop.
Activities Arts & crafts; Cards; Games; Prayer groups; Movies; Shopping trips; Social/Cultural gatherings; Parties.

San Angelo Development Center
701 E 19th St, San Angelo, TX, 76903
(915) 655-3106
Admin Connie Jeffers. Medical Dir/Dir of Nursing Dr James Womack.
Licensure Intermediate care for mentally retarded. Beds ICF/MR 58. Certified Medicaid.
Owner Proprietary Corp (ARA Living Centers).
Admissions Requirements Minimum age 17; Medical examination.
Staff Physicians 1 (pt); RNs 1 (ft); LPNs 3 (ft), 1 (pt); Nurses aides 18 (ft); Recreational therapists 1 (ft); Speech therapists 1 (pt); Dietitians 1 (pt).
Languages Spanish
Facilities Dining room; Activities room; Crafts room; Laundry room; Barber/Beauty shop.
Activities Arts & crafts; Cards; Games; Reading groups; Movies; Shopping trips; Social/Cultural gatherings; Academic & vocational training.

SAN ANTONIO

Air Force Village I Health Care Center
4917 Ravenswood Dr, San Antonio, TX, 78227
(512) 673-7110
Admin Jean Nagle. Medical Dir/Dir of Nursing Patricia Hague.
Licensure Intermediate care. Beds ICF 68.
Owner Nonprofit organization/foundation.
Admissions Requirements Minimum age 62; Physician's request.
Staff Physicians 2 (pt); RNs 3 (ft), 2 (pt); LPNs 3 (ft), 2 (pt); Orderlies 6 (ft); Nurses aides 9 (ft), 12 (pt); Occupational therapists 1 (ft); Activities coordinators 1 (ft); Dietitians 1 (pt); Ophthalmologists 1 (pt).
Languages Spanish
Facilities Dining room; Activities room; Chapel; Laundry room; Barber/Beauty shop.
Activities Arts & crafts; Cards; Reading groups; Movies; Birthday parties; Dining out; Exercise class; Social hour.

Arms of Mercy Care Center Inc*
225 W Laurel, San Antonio, TX, 78212
(512) 227-0267
Admin Mary Eleanor Foreman.

Licensure Intermediate care. Beds 75. Certified Medicaid.
Owner Proprietary Corp.

Bethesda Care Center*
1939 Bandera Rd, San Antonio, TX, 78228
(512) 434-0671
Admin Paul Richard Love.
Licensure Intermediate care. Beds 144. Certified Medicaid.
Owner Nonprofit Corp.

Broadway Lodge*
1841 Flamingo, San Antonio, TX, 78209
(512) 824-5324, 5326
Admin Jeaneane Enke.
Licensure Intermediate care; Personal care. Beds ICF 66; Personal 26. Certified Medicaid.
Owner Proprietary Corp (ARA Living Centers).

Camlu Care Center of Oak Hills*
7302 Oak Manor Dr, San Antonio, TX, 78229
(512) 344-8537
Admin Susan Distelhorst. Medical Dir/Dir of Nursing Dr Norman Jacobson.
Licensure Skilled care; Intermediate care; Alzheimer's unit. Beds SNF 192; Alzheimer's unit 48. Certified Medicaid.
Admissions Requirements Minimum age 18; Medical examination.
Staff Physical therapists; Occupational therapists; Speech therapists; Dietitians; Podiatrists.
Facilities Dining room; Physical therapy room; Activities room; Chapel; Crafts room; Laundry room; Barber/Beauty shop; Library.
Activities Arts & crafts; Cards; Games; Reading groups; Prayer groups; Movies; Shopping trips; Social/Cultural gatherings.

Camlu Care Center of Woodlawn Hills*
3031 W Woodlawn Ave, San Antonio, TX, 78228
(512) 432-2381
Admin Paul W Nettle. Medical Dir/Dir of Nursing Luis E Perez-Montes MD.
Licensure Skilled care; Intermediate care. Beds 204. Certified Medicaid.
Admissions Requirements Minimum age 18; Physician's request.
Staff RNs 3 (ft), 1 (pt); LPNs 22 (ft), 7 (pt); Orderlies 8 (ft), 3 (pt); Nurses aides 34 (ft), 12 (pt); Physical therapists 1 (ft); Reality therapists 1 (ft); Recreational therapists 2 (ft); Occupational therapists 1 (pt); Activities coordinators 1 (ft), 1 (pt); Dietitians 1 (pt).
Facilities Dining room; Physical therapy room; Activities room; Chapel; Crafts room; Laundry room; Barber/Beauty shop; Library.
Activities Arts & crafts; Cards; Games; Reading groups; Prayer groups; Movies; Shopping trips; Social/Cultural gatherings; Van rides; Outings.

Camlu Care Center-Louis Pasteur*
7602 Louis Pasteur Dr, San Antonio, TX, 78229
(512) 690-9974
Admin Paul W Nettle. Medical Dir/Dir of Nursing Emanuel P DeNoia MD.
Licensure Skilled care. Beds 87. Certified Medicaid.
Admissions Requirements Physician's request.
Staff RNs 2 (ft), 1 (pt); LPNs 12 (ft), 1 (pt); Orderlies 8 (ft), 2 (pt); Nurses aides 18 (ft), 4 (pt); Physical therapists 1 (pt); Recreational therapists 1 (ft); Occupational therapists 1 (pt); Activities coordinators 1 (ft), 1 (pt); Dietitians 1 (ft).
Facilities Dining room; Physical therapy room; Activities room; Chapel; Crafts room; Laundry room; Barber/Beauty shop; Library.

Activities Arts & crafts; Cards; Games; Reading groups; Prayer groups; Movies; Shopping trips; Social/Cultural gatherings; Outside events—rides, ball games, park outings.

Carriage Square Nursing Home*
8020 Blanco Rd, San Antonio, TX, 78216
(512) 344-4553
Admin Carolyn A Barten.
Licensure Skilled care. *Beds* 143. *Certified* Medicaid.
Owner Proprietary Corp.

Casa de San Antonio
603 Corinne, San Antonio, TX, 78218
(512) 824-7331
Admin Myrna J Eavenson. *Medical Dir/Dir of Nursing* Carol Ann Chamberlain.
Licensure Intermediate care. *Beds* ICF 80; Private pay 40. *Certified* Medicaid.
Owner Privately owned.
Admissions Requirements Medical examination.
Staff RNs; LPNs; Orderlies; Nurses aides; Activities coordinators; Dietitians; Podiatrists.
Facilities Dining room; Activities room; Laundry room; Barber/Beauty shop; Library.
Activities Arts & crafts; Cards; Games; Reading groups; Prayer groups; Movies; Shopping trips; Social/Cultural gatherings; Van rides.

Cresthaven Childrens Center
3018 E Commerce St, San Antonio, TX, 78220
(512) 224-4271
Admin Joe Ward. *Medical Dir/Dir of Nursing* Janet Phillips; Yolanda Threat.
Licensure Intermediate care for mentally retarded. *Beds* ICF/MR 208. *Certified* Medicaid.
Owner Proprietary Corp (Beverly Enterprises).
Admissions Requirements Minimum age 5.
Staff Physicians 3 (pt); RNs 3 (ft); Physical therapists 1 (pt); Occupational therapists 1 (pt); Speech therapists 1 (pt); Activities coordinators 2 (ft); Dietitians 1 (ft); LVNs 15 (ft); Qualified Mental Retardation Professionals 8 (ft).
Languages Spanish
Facilities Dining room; Physical therapy room; Activities room; Crafts room; Laundry room.
Activities Arts & crafts; Games; Reading groups; Movies; Shopping trips; Social/Cultural gatherings.

Desha's Rest Home*
1405 S Hackberry, San Antonio, TX, 78210
(512) 532-5841
Admin Beatrice W Desha.
Licensure Intermediate care. *Beds* 22. *Certified* Medicaid.
Admissions Requirements Medical examination; Physician's request.
Staff RNs 1 (pt); LPNs 1 (ft), 6 (pt); Nurses aides 5 (ft), 4 (pt); Activities coordinators 1 (ft); Dietitians 1 (pt).
Facilities Dining room; Laundry room.
Activities Arts & crafts; Games; Reading groups; Prayer groups; Shopping trips; Social/Cultural gatherings.

Four Seasons Nursing Center—Babcock
1975 Babcock Rd, San Antonio, TX, 78229
(512) 341-8681
Admin Catherine Ferguson. *Medical Dir/Dir of Nursing* E DeNoia MD; E Parker RN.
Licensure Skilled care; Intermediate care. *Beds* SNF 224; ICF; Non Certified. *Certified* Medicaid; Medicare.
Owner Proprietary Corp (Manor Care).
Admissions Requirements Minimum age 21; Medical examination; Physician's request.

Staff RNs 8 (ft), 3 (pt); LPNs 14 (ft), 1 (pt); Orderlies 3 (ft), 3 (pt); Nurses aides 59 (ft), 7 (pt); Physical therapists 1 (ft); Occupational therapists 1 (ft); Speech therapists 1 (ft); Activities coordinators 2 (ft).
Languages Spanish
Facilities Dining room; Physical therapy room; Activities room; Laundry room; Barber/Beauty shop.
Activities Arts & crafts; Cards; Games; Reading groups; Prayer groups; Movies; Shopping trips; Social/Cultural gatherings.

Four Seasons Nursing Center—North*
7703 Briaridge Dr, San Antonio, TX, 78230
(512) 341-6121
Admin Wayne W Young. *Medical Dir/Dir of Nursing* Dr Norman Jacobson.
Licensure Intermediate care. *Beds* 109. *Certified* Medicaid.
Owner Proprietary Corp (Manor Care).
Staff RNs 5 (ft); LPNs 6 (ft); Nurses aides 30 (ft); Activities coordinators 1 (ft), 2 (pt).
Facilities Dining room; Activities room; Laundry room; Barber/Beauty shop.
Activities Arts & crafts; Games; Prayer groups; Movies; Shopping trips; Social/Cultural gatherings.

Four Seasons Nursing Center—Northwest*
8300 Wurzbach Rd, San Antonio, TX, 78229
(512) 690-1040
Admin Ruth Anne VanBlaricum. *Medical Dir/Dir of Nursing* Dr Norman Jacobson.
Licensure Intermediate care. *Beds* 164. *Certified* Medicaid.
Owner Proprietary Corp (Manor Care).
Admissions Requirements Medical examination; Physician's request.
Staff RNs; LPNs; Orderlies; Nurses aides; Physical therapists; Reality therapists; Recreational therapists; Activities coordinators; Dietitians; Dentists; Podiatrists.
Facilities Dining room; Activities room; Crafts room; Barber/Beauty shop; Library.
Activities Arts & crafts; Cards; Games; Reading groups; Prayer groups; Movies; Shopping trips; Social/Cultural gatherings.

Four Seasons Nursing Center—Pecan Valley*
5027 Pecan Grove, San Antonio, TX, 78222
(512) 333-6815
Admin Linda K Young.
Licensure Skilled care; Intermediate care. *Beds* 206. *Certified* Medicaid.
Owner Proprietary Corp (Manor Care).

Four Seasons Nursing Center—South
1339 W Chavaneaux Rd, San Antonio, TX, 78214
(512) 924-6211
Admin Jeannie M Warren.
Licensure Intermediate care. *Beds* 90. *Certified* Medicaid.
Owner Proprietary Corp (Manor Care).

Four Seasons Nursing Center—Windcrest*
8800 Fourwinds Dr, San Antonio, TX, 78239
(512) 656-7800
Admin Della M Torres.
Licensure Skilled care; Intermediate care. *Beds* 208. *Certified* Medicaid.
Owner Proprietary Corp (Manor Care).

Sarah Roberts French Home
1315 Texas Ave, San Antonio, TX, 78201
(512) 736-4238
Admin David Williams. *Medical Dir/Dir of Nursing* Francis Brown.
Licensure Intermediate care. *Beds* 60. *Certified* Medicaid.
Owner Nonprofit organization/foundation.
Admissions Requirements Minimum age 60; Females only.
Staff LPNs; Nurses aides 17 (ft); Activities coordinators 1 (ft); Dietitians 1 (ft).
Languages Spanish

Facilities Dining room; Activities room; Crafts room; Laundry room; Barber/Beauty shop; Library.
Activities Arts & crafts; Cards; Games; Reading groups; Prayer groups; Movies; Shopping trips; Social/Cultural gatherings.

Golden Manor Jewish Home for the Aged*
130 Spencer Ln, San Antonio, TX, 78201
(512) 736-4544
Admin Sue S Bornstein.
Licensure Skilled care. *Beds* 59. *Certified* Medicaid.
Owner Nonprofit Corp.
Affiliation Jewish

Grayson Square Health Care Center Inc*
818 E Grayson, San Antonio, TX, 78208
(512) 226-8181
Admin Terrence R Hayes. *Medical Dir/Dir of Nursing* Allen Ritch MD.
Licensure Intermediate care. *Beds* 81. *Certified* Medicaid.
Admissions Requirements Physician's request.
Staff RNs 1 (ft); LPNs 8 (ft); Nurses aides 19 (ft); Activities coordinators 2 (ft); Dietitians 1 (ft).

Highland Nursing Home*
5819 Pecan Valley Dr, San Antonio, TX, 78223
(512) 532-1911
Admin Michael A Triana.
Licensure Skilled care; Custodial care. *Beds* SNF 59; Custodial 22. *Certified* Medicaid.
Owner Proprietary Corp.

Hillside Manor Nursing Home Inc
8310 Gault Ln, San Antonio, TX, 78209
(512) 828-0606
Admin Diana Geis Vandel. *Medical Dir/Dir of Nursing* Curtis Ryder.
Licensure Skilled care; Intermediate care. *Beds* 237. *Certified* Medicaid; Medicare; Private pay.
Admissions Requirements Minimum age 18; Medical examination; Physician's request.
Staff Physicians 1 (pt); RNs 8 (ft); LPNs 19 (ft); Orderlies 5 (ft); Nurses aides 41 (ft), 1 (pt); Physical therapists 1 (pt); Dietitians 1 (ft).
Facilities Dining room; Physical therapy room; Activities room; Chapel; Crafts room; Laundry room; Barber/Beauty shop; Library; Vegetable garden.
Activities Arts & crafts; Cards; Games; Reading groups; Prayer groups; Movies; Shopping trips; Social/Cultural gatherings; Bible study; Church services; Communion services; Current events; Ceramics; Exercise classes; Bookcart; Bingo; Volunteer group; Residents council.

Leon Valley Lodge*
6518 Samaritan Dr, San Antonio, TX, 78238
(512) 684-3194
Admin Faye Lobert.
Licensure Intermediate care. *Beds* 66. *Certified* Medicaid.
Owner Proprietary Corp.

Manor Square Convalescent Home*
414 N Hackberry, San Antonio, TX, 78202
(512) 226-6397
Admin Jeannette Cade.
Licensure Intermediate care. *Beds* 41. *Certified* Medicaid.

Memorial Medical Nursing Center*
315 Lewis St, San Antonio, TX, 78212
(512) 223-5521
Admin Robert W Knoebel. *Medical Dir/Dir of Nursing* J Rolando Rojas.
Licensure Skilled care; Intermediate care; Personal care. *Beds* SNF 60; ICF 119; Personal 26. *Certified* Medicaid.
Owner Proprietary Corp (ARA Living Centers).

Admissions Requirements Minimum age 18;
Medical examination; Physician's request.
Staff Physicians 1 (pt); RNs 2 (ft), 4 (pt);
Orderlies 1 (ft); Nurses aides 44 (ft);
Physical therapists; Occupational therapists;
Speech therapists; Activities coordinators 1
(ft), 1 (pt); Dietitians 1 (ft); Dentists 1 (pt);
Ophthalmologists 1 (pt); Podiatrists 1 (pt).
Facilities Dining room; Physical therapy
room; Activities room; Barber/Beauty shop.
Activities Arts & crafts; Cards; Games; Prayer
groups; Movies; Social/Cultural gatherings.

Morningside Manor
602 Babcock Rd, San Antonio, TX, 78284
(517) 731-1000
Admin Glenn Brown. *Medical Dir/Dir of
Nursing* Rowan Fisher MD; Caroline
Sorensen.
Licensure Skilled care; Intermediate care;
Personal care; Alzheimer's care. *Beds* SNF
95; ICF 202; Personal 78. *Certified*
Medicaid; Medicare.
Owner Nonprofit Corp.
Admissions Requirements Minimum age 62;
Medical examination; Physician's request.
Staff Physicians 1 (pt); RNs 5 (ft), 3 (pt);
LPNs 28 (ft), 5 (pt); Orderlies 8 (ft), 2 (pt);
Nurses aides 90 (ft), 12 (pt); Physical
therapists 1 (pt); Occupational therapists 4
(ft); Activities coordinators 5 (ft); Dietitians
1 (pt).
Languages Spanish
Facilities Dining room; Physical therapy
room; Activities room; Chapel; Crafts room;
Laundry room; Barber/Beauty shop; Library.
Activities Arts & crafts; Cards; Games;
Reading groups; Prayer groups; Movies;
Shopping trips; Social/Cultural gatherings.

Normandy Terrace Inc*
841 Rice Rd, San Antonio, TX, 78220
(512) 648-0101
Admin Betty Lou Roberts. *Medical Dir/Dir of
Nursing* Dr Ruskin Norman.
Licensure Skilled care; Intermediate care. *Beds*
320. *Certified* Medicaid; Medicare.
Admissions Requirements Medical
examination; Physician's request.
Staff RNs 6 (ft), 4 (pt); LPNs 21 (ft);
Orderlies 1 (ft); Nurses aides 109 (ft);
Physical therapists 3 (ft); Recreational
therapists 2 (ft); Occupational therapists 2
(ft); Activities coordinators 1 (ft); Dietitians
1 (ft).
Facilities Dining room; Physical therapy
room; Activities room; Chapel; Crafts room;
Laundry room; Barber/Beauty shop.
Activities Arts & crafts; Cards; Games;
Reading groups; Prayer groups; Movies;
Shopping trips; Social/Cultural gatherings.

Normandy Terrace Inc—Northeast*
8607 Village Dr, San Antonio, TX, 78217
(512) 656-6733
Admin Charles H Koll.
Licensure Skilled care. *Beds* 240. *Certified*
Medicaid.
Owner Proprietary Corp.

Retama Manor—North*
501 Ogden, San Antonio, TX, 78212
(512) 225-4588
Admin Mary S Jakob.
Licensure Intermediate care. *Beds* 136.
Certified Medicaid.
Owner Proprietary Corp (ARA Living
Centers).

Retama Manor Nursing Center—South*
3030 S Roosevelt, San Antonio, TX, 78214
(512) 924-8151
Admin Billy Bruce Apperson.
Licensure Intermediate care. *Beds* 150.
Certified Medicaid.
Owner Proprietary Corp (ARA Living
Centers).

Retama Manor Nursing Center—West
636 Cupples Rd, San Antonio, TX, 78237
(512) 434-0611
Admin Deborah L Lally.
Licensure Intermediate care. *Beds* 150.
Certified Medicaid.
Owner Proprietary Corp (ARA Living
Centers).

St Benedict Nursing Home*
323 E Johnson St, San Antonio, TX, 78204
(512) 222-0171
Admin Sr Mary John Sapp.
Licensure Skilled care; Intermediate care. *Beds*
197. *Certified* Medicaid; Medicare.
Owner Nonprofit Corp.
Affiliation Roman Catholic

St Francis Nursing Home*
2717 N Flores, San Antonio, TX, 78212
(512) 736-3177
Admin Patsy Sue Block.
Licensure Intermediate care. *Beds* 143.
Certified Medicaid.
Owner Nonprofit Corp.
Affiliation Roman Catholic

San Antonio Convalescent Center*
921 Nolan, San Antonio, TX, 78202
(512) 227-5341
Admin Patricia Mullen.
Licensure Intermediate care. *Beds* 100.
Certified Medicaid.
Owner Proprietary Corp (ARA Living
Centers).

San Jose Nursing Center
406 Sharmain, San Antonio, TX, 78221
(512) 924-8136
Admin Marilyn Kowalik.
Licensure Intermediate care. *Beds* ICF 70.
Certified Medicaid.
Owner Privately owned.
Staff LPNs; Orderlies; Nurses aides; Activities
coordinators.

San Pedro Manor
515 W Ashby Pl, San Antonio, TX, 78212
(512) 732-5181
Admin Bessie B Parkin. *Medical Dir/Dir of
Nursing* Patricia Perritano RN DON.
Licensure Skilled care; Intermediate care. *Beds*
152. *Certified* Medicaid; Medicare; Private
pay.
Owner Proprietary Corp.
Admissions Requirements Physician's request.
Staff RNs 5 (ft), 3 (pt); LPNs 13 (ft), 6 (pt);
Orderlies 2 (ft); Nurses aides 30 (ft), 15 (pt);
Activities coordinators 1 (ft), 1 (pt);
Dietitians 1 (ft).
Languages Spanish
Facilities Dining room; Barber/Beauty shop.
Activities Arts & crafts; Cards; Games; Prayer
groups; Movies; Exercise groups; Resident
council.

Skyview Living Center—San Antonio*
4703 Goldfield, San Antonio, TX, 78218
(512) 661-6751
Admin Joyce M Latham.
Licensure Intermediate care for mentally
retarded. *Beds* 150. *Certified* Medicaid.

Southeast Nursing Center*
4302 Southcross Blvd, San Antonio, TX,
78220
(512) 333-1223
Admin Marcella M Costanzi.
Licensure Intermediate care. *Beds* 120.
Certified Medicaid.
Owner Proprietary Corp (Beverly Enterprises).

Southwest Care Centers Inc*
PO Box 21156, 903 Leahy St, San Antonio,
TX, 78221
(512) 922-2761
Admin Samuel W Hardy.

Licensure Intermediate care. *Beds* 92.
Certified Medicaid.
Owner Proprietary Corp.

The Village at Vance Jackson
2730 NW Loop 410, San Antonio, TX, 78213
(512) 344-3047
Admin Donna M Weimer. *Medical Dir/Dir of
Nursing* Dr Edward Sargent; Nancy Spilka.
Licensure Custodial assisted living center.
Beds Custodial 120.
Owner Proprietary Corp (Manor Care).
Admissions Requirements Medical
examination.
Staff RNs; LPNs; Nurses aides; Activities
coordinators.
Languages Spanish
Facilities Dining room; Activities room;
Crafts room; Laundry room; Barber/Beauty
shop; Library; Garden.
Activities Arts & crafts; Cards; Games; Prayer
groups; Movies; Shopping trips; Social/
Cultural gatherings; Cocktail hour.

Welcome Home for the Blind & Aged Inc
618 Hudson St, San Antonio, TX, 78202
(512) 227-3812
Admin Rev Thomas B Lee. *Medical Dir/Dir of
Nursing* Sara Higgs.
Licensure Intermediate care. *Beds* ICF 36.
Owner Nonprofit Corp.
Admissions Requirements Minimum age 21;
Medical examination.
Staff LPNs; Nurses aides; Physical therapists;
Reality therapists; Recreational therapists;
Activities coordinators; Dietitians.
Languages Spanish
Facilities Dining room; Activities room;
Barber/Beauty shop.

Wood Nursing Home
2700 Pleasanton Rd, San Antonio, TX, 78221
(512) 924-8183
Admin Yvonne B Wood. *Medical Dir/Dir of
Nursing* Anita Esparza DON.
Licensure Intermediate care. *Beds* ICF 49.
Owner Privately owned.
Admissions Requirements Physician's request.
Staff Physicians; RNs 1 (pt); LPNs 4 (ft);
Nurses aides 13 (ft), 4 (pt); Activities
coordinators 1 (ft); Dietitians 1 (pt).
Languages Spanish
Facilities Dining room; Physical therapy
room; Activities room; Laundry room.
Activities Arts & crafts; Cards; Games; Prayer
groups; Shopping trips; Social/Cultural
gatherings.

Wright Nursing Home Inc
328 W Mayfield Blvd, San Antonio, TX,
78221
(512) 924-8533
Admin Georgia W Holmes. *Medical Dir/Dir of
Nursing* Dr David Madonsky; Susan
Quezada DON.
Licensure Intermediate care; Personal. *Beds*
ICF 60; Personal 20. *Certified* Medicaid.
Owner Proprietary Corp.
Admissions Requirements Minimum age 21.
Staff LPNs 5 (ft), 3 (pt); Orderlies 5 (ft), 2
(pt); Nurses aides 15 (ft), 5 (pt); Activities
coordinators 1 (ft); Dietitians 1 (pt).
Languages Spanish
Facilities Dining room; Activities room;
Library.
Activities Arts & crafts; Cards; Games;
Reading groups; Prayer groups; Movies;
Shopping trips; Social/Cultural gatherings;
Picnics.

SAN AUGUSTINE

East Texas Convalescent Home*
806 N Clark St, San Augustine, TX, 75972
(713) 275-2522, 5609
Admin Jeanette B Davidson.

Licensure Intermediate care. *Beds* 70.
Certified Medicaid.
Owner Proprietary Corp.

San Augustine Nursing & Development Center
Hwy 96 at FM 1277, San Augustine, TX, 75972
(713) 275-3466
Admin Patsy R Thomas. *Medical Dir/Dir of Nursing* Carol Moore DON.
Licensure Intermediate care; Intermediate care for mentally retarded. *Beds* ICF 58; ICF/MR 56. *Certified* Medicaid; Medicare.
Owner Proprietary Corp (ARA Living Centers).
Admissions Requirements Minimum age 21; Medical examination; Physician's request.
Staff RNs 3 (ft); Nurses aides 32 (ft); Recreational therapists 1 (ft); Activities coordinators 1 (ft); Dietitians 1 (pt); LVN 8 (ft).
Activities Arts & crafts; Cards; Games; Reading groups; Prayer groups; Movies; Shopping trips; Social/Cultural gatherings.

Twin Lakes Care Center
Rte 1, Box 725, Hwy 96, San Augustine, TX, 75972
(409) 275-2900
Admin Jeanette Davidson. *Medical Dir/Dir of Nursing* Diana Whitehead.
Licensure Intermediate care. *Beds* ICF 90. *Certified* Medicaid.
Owner Privately owned.
Admissions Requirements Medical examination.
Staff RNs 1 (ft); LPNs 6 (ft); Nurses aides 40 (ft); Activities coordinators 1 (ft).
Facilities Dining room; Activities room; Chapel; Crafts room; Laundry room; Barber/Beauty shop; Library.
Activities Arts & crafts; Prayer groups; Shopping trips; Social/Cultural gatherings.

SAN BENITO

Twinbrooke South—San Benito*
502 E Expressway, San Benito, TX, 78586
(512) 399-3732
Admin Rebecca M Berry.
Licensure Intermediate care. *Beds* 52. *Certified* Medicaid.
Owner Proprietary Corp.

SAN DIEGO

La Hacienda Nursing Home Inc*
4408 Hwy 44 E, San Diego, TX, 78384
(512) 279-3860
Admin James M Baker.
Licensure Skilled care; Intermediate care. *Beds* 114. *Certified* Medicaid.
Owner Proprietary Corp.

SAN JUAN

San Juan Nursing Home Inc*
300 N Nebraska Ave, San Juan, TX, 78589
(512) 787-1771
Admin Sr Lucille M Belisle.
Licensure Skilled care. *Beds* 60. *Certified* Medicaid.
Owner Nonprofit Corp.
Affiliation Roman Catholic

SAN MARCOS

Hillside Manor—San Marcos*
Thorpe Ln, San Marcos, TX, 78666
(512) 392-3383
Admin George E Dimmick. *Medical Dir/Dir of Nursing* Holland St John MD.
Licensure Skilled care; Intermediate care. *Beds* 135. *Certified* Medicaid; Medicare.
Admissions Requirements Minimum age 18; Medical examination; Physician's request.

Staff RNs 6 (ft), 2 (pt); LPNs 10 (ft), 2 (pt); Orderlies 4 (ft), 2 (pt); Nurses aides 50 (ft); Physical therapists 1 (ft); Recreational therapists 2 (ft); Dietitians.
Facilities Dining room; Physical therapy room; Activities room; Crafts room; Laundry room; Barber/Beauty shop; Library.
Activities Arts & crafts; Cards; Games; Reading groups; Prayer groups; Movies; Shopping trips; Social/Cultural gatherings.

SAN SABA

Eventide Nursing Home Inc
1405 W Storey, San Saba, TX, 76877
(915) 372-3675
Admin Alice M Brown. *Medical Dir/Dir of Nursing* Marietta Adams.
Licensure Intermediate care. *Beds* ICF 80. *Certified* Medicaid.
Owner Privately owned.
Admissions Requirements Medical examination; Physician's request.
Staff RNs 1 (ft); LPNs 7 (ft); Nurses aides 20 (ft); Activities coordinators 1 (ft).
Languages Spanish
Facilities Dining room; Activities room; Laundry room; Barber/Beauty shop.
Activities Arts & crafts; Games; Prayer groups; Movies; Shopping trips; Social/Cultural gatherings.

San Saba Nursing Home Inc*
608 S Edgewood St, San Saba, TX, 76877
(915) 372-5179
Admin Joyce Lusty.
Licensure Intermediate care. *Beds* 63. *Certified* Medicaid.
Owner Proprietary Corp.

SANGER

Care Inn of Sanger*
600 N Stemmons Fwy, Sanger, TX, 76226
(817) 458-3202
Admin Opal Faye Morrison. *Medical Dir/Dir of Nursing* J Clyde Chapman DO.
Licensure Intermediate care. *Beds* 67. *Certified* Medicaid.
Owner Proprietary Corp (ARA Living Centers).
Admissions Requirements Minimum age 18.
Staff RNs 1 (ft); LPNs 7 (ft), 2 (pt); Orderlies 1 (ft); Nurses aides 12 (ft), 1 (pt).
Facilities Dining room; Activities room; Crafts room; Laundry room; Barber/Beauty shop; Library.
Activities Arts & crafts; Games; Reading groups; Social/Cultural gatherings.

SANTA ANNA

Ranger Park Inn Nursing Home
PO Box 159, Brownwood Hwy, Santa Anna, TX, 76878
(915) 348-3158
Admin Herbert C Houser. *Medical Dir/Dir of Nursing* Lila Tucker RN.
Licensure Skilled care. *Beds* SNF 70. *Certified* Medicaid; Medicare.
Owner Proprietary Corp.
Admissions Requirements Medical examination; Physician's request.
Staff RNs 1 (ft); LPNs 6 (ft); Nurses aides 11 (ft); Physical therapists 1 (pt); Activities coordinators 1 (ft); Dietitians 1 (pt).
Facilities Dining room; Activities room; Crafts room; Laundry room; Barber/Beauty shop.
Activities Arts & crafts; Games; Prayer groups; Social/Cultural gatherings.

SAVOY

Canterbury Villa of Savoy*
Hwy 82 E, Savoy, TX, 75479
(214) 965-4285
Admin Joan F Pierce.
Licensure Intermediate care. *Beds* 96. *Certified* Medicaid.
Owner Proprietary Corp (Health Enter of America).
Admissions Requirements Medical examination.
Staff RNs 1 (ft); LPNs 2 (ft); Nurses aides 20 (ft); Activities coordinators 1 (ft); Dietitians 1 (ft).
Facilities Dining room; Physical therapy room; Activities room; Chapel; Crafts room; Laundry room; Barber/Beauty shop.
Activities Arts & crafts; Cards; Games; Shopping trips; Social/Cultural gatherings.

Mullican Nursing Home*
PO Box 426, Main St, Savoy, TX, 75479
(214) 965-4964
Admin Mary A Little.
Licensure Intermediate care. *Beds* 93. *Certified* Medicaid.
Owner Proprietary Corp.

SCHERTZ

Autumn Winds Retirement Lodge
FM 3009, Schertz, TX, 78154
(512) 658-6338
Admin Darlene T Pruitt.
Licensure Custodial care. *Beds* 96. *Certified* Medicaid.
Staff RNs 2 (ft); LPNs 7 (ft); Nurses aides 19 (ft); Activities coordinators 2 (ft); Dietitians 1 (ft).
Facilities Dining room; Activities room; Crafts room; Laundry room; Barber/Beauty shop; Library.
Activities Arts & crafts; Cards; Prayer groups; Movies; Shopping trips; Social/Cultural gatherings.

SCHULENBURG

Colonial Nursing Home Inc
507 West Ave, Schulenburg, TX, 78956
(409) 743-4150
Admin Rita Brossmann. *Medical Dir/Dir of Nursing* Evelyn Meyer DON.
Licensure Intermediate care. *Beds* ICF 90. *Certified* Medicaid.
Owner Proprietary Corp.
Admissions Requirements Medical examination; Physician's request.
Staff Nurses aides; Physical therapists; Recreational therapists; Occupational therapists; Speech therapists; Activities coordinators; Dietitians.
Languages Spanish, Czech, German
Facilities Dining room; Activities room; Chapel; Crafts room; Laundry room; Barber/Beauty shop.
Activities Arts & crafts; Cards; Games; Reading groups; Prayer groups; Movies; Shopping trips; Social/Cultural gatherings.

SEAGOVILLE

Carter Nursing Home
111 Fisk Rd, Seagoville, TX, 75159
(214) 287-2322
Admin Doyle J Graham.
Licensure Intermediate care. *Beds* ICF 121. *Certified* Medicaid.
Owner Proprietary Corp.
Admissions Requirements Minimum age 21; Medical examination; Physician's request.
Staff Physicians 3 (ft); RNs 2 (ft); LPNs 6 (ft); Orderlies 12 (ft); Nurses aides 28 (ft); Physical therapists 1 (ft); Reality therapists 1 (ft); Recreational therapists 1 (ft); Speech

therapists 1 (ft); Activities coordinators 1 (ft); Dietitians 1 (ft); Ophthalmologists 1 (ft); Podiatrists 1 (ft).
Languages Spanish
Facilities Dining room; Activities room; Crafts room; Laundry room; Barber/Beauty shop.
Activities Arts & crafts; Cards; Games; Reading groups; Prayer groups; Movies; Shopping trips; Social/Cultural gatherings.

Seago Manor
2416 Elizabeth Ln, Seagoville, TX, 75159
(214) 287-1201
Admin Barbara Perryman. *Medical Dir/Dir of Nursing* Larry Stubblefield MD.
Licensure Intermediate care. *Beds* ICF 142.
Certified Medicaid.
Owner Proprietary Corp (Cantex Healthcare Centers).
Admissions Requirements Minimum age 18; Medical examination; Physician's request.
Staff RNs 1 (pt); LPNs 8 (ft), 1 (pt); Orderlies 1 (ft); Nurses aides 31 (ft); Activities coordinators 1 (ft); Dietitians 1 (ft), 1 (pt).
Facilities Dining room; Physical therapy room; Activities room; Chapel; Crafts room; Laundry room; Barber/Beauty shop; Library.
Activities Arts & crafts; Cards; Games; Reading groups; Prayer groups; Movies; Shopping trips; Social/Cultural gatherings.

SEALY

Azalea Manor*
207 N Meyer, Sealy, TX, 77474
(409) 885-2191
Admin Phylis Avant.
Licensure Intermediate care. *Beds* 90.
Certified Medicaid.
Admissions Requirements Medical examination; Physician's request.
Staff RNs 1 (ft); LPNs 5 (ft), 2 (pt); Nurses aides 20 (ft), 4 (pt); Activities coordinators 1 (ft); Dietitians 1 (pt).
Facilities Dining room; Physical therapy room; Laundry room; Barber/Beauty shop.
Activities Arts & crafts; Cards; Games; Reading groups; Prayer groups; Shopping trips; Social/Cultural gatherings.

SEGUIN

Care Inn of Seguin*
1219 Eastwood Dr, Seguin, TX, 78155
(512) 379-7777
Admin Jeaneane Y Enke. *Medical Dir/Dir of Nursing* Dr Robert Fretz.
Licensure Intermediate care. *Beds* 141.
Certified Medicaid.
Owner Proprietary Corp (ARA Living Centers).
Admissions Requirements Medical examination; Physician's request.
Staff Physicians; RNs; LPNs; Nurses aides; Activities coordinators; Dietitians.
Facilities Dining room; Activities room; Laundry room; Barber/Beauty shop; Restorative care room.
Activities Arts & crafts; Cards; Games; Reading groups; Prayer groups; Shopping trips; Ceramics; One-to-one activities; Country western band; Family night dinners.

Nesbit Nursing Home
1215 E Ashby, Seguin, TX, 78155
(512) 379-1606
Admin David W Nesbit.
Licensure Intermediate care. *Beds* 120.
Certified Medicaid.
Admissions Requirements Medical examination; Physician's request.
Staff RNs 1 (ft); LPNs 10 (ft), 2 (pt); Nurses aides 37 (ft), 4 (pt); Activities coordinators 2 (ft); Dietitians 1 (ft).

Facilities Dining room; Activities room; Crafts room; Laundry room; Barber/Beauty shop.
Activities Arts & crafts; Cards; Games; Reading groups; Prayer groups; Movies; Shopping trips; Social/Cultural gatherings.

Seguin Convalescent Home
1637 N King St, Seguin, TX, 78155
(512) 379-3784, 379-3787
Admin John W Greer. *Medical Dir/Dir of Nursing* Jennette Muenich.
Licensure Skilled care; Intermediate care. *Beds* SNF 44; ICF 69. *Certified* Medicaid; Medicare.
Owner Proprietary Corp.
Admissions Requirements Minimum age 18; Medical examination; Physician's request.
Staff RNs 3 (ft); LPNs 7 (ft); Nurses aides 25 (ft); Physical therapists 1 (ft); Reality therapists 1 (ft); Occupational therapists 1 (ft); Speech therapists 1 (ft); Activities coordinators 1 (ft); Dietitians 1 (ft).
Languages German, Spanish
Facilities Dining room; Physical therapy room; Activities room; Chapel; Crafts room; Laundry room; Barber/Beauty shop.
Activities Arts & crafts; Cards; Games; Reading groups; Prayer groups; Movies; Shopping trips.

SEMINOLE

Seminole Nursing Center Inc*
306 NW 3rd, Seminole, TX, 79360
(915) 758-9401
Admin David O Crowson.
Licensure Intermediate care. *Beds* 32.
Certified Medicaid.
Admissions Requirements Minimum age 18; Medical examination; Physician's request.
Staff LPNs 4 (ft); Nurses aides 12 (ft); Activities coordinators 1 (ft).
Facilities Dining room; Laundry room; Barber/Beauty shop.
Activities Arts & crafts; Cards; Games; Reading groups; Prayer groups; Movies; Shopping trips; Social/Cultural gatherings.

SEYMOUR

Westview Care Center
PO Box 1291, 1100 Westview Dr, Seymour, TX, 76380
(817) 888-3176
Admin W Faye Hollar.
Licensure Intermediate care. *Beds* 100.
Certified Medicaid.
Owner Proprietary Corp (Beverly Enterprises).
Admissions Requirements Minimum age 18.
Staff RNs 1 (pt); LPNs 8 (ft); Orderlies 4 (ft); Nurses aides 25 (ft), 3 (pt); Activities coordinators 1 (ft).
Languages Spanish
Facilities Dining room; Activities room; Crafts room; Laundry room; Barber/Beauty shop.
Activities Arts & crafts; Cards; Games; Reading groups; Prayer groups; Movies; Shopping trips; Social/Cultural gatherings.

SHAMROCK

Care Inn of Shamrock*
Hwy 83 S, Shamrock, TX, 79079
(806) 256-2153
Admin Daniel G Wylie.
Licensure Intermediate care. *Beds* 64.
Certified Medicaid.
Owner Proprietary Corp (ARA Living Centers).

SHERMAN

Chapel of Care Nursing Center
1518 S Sam Rayburn Fwy, Sherman, TX, 75090
(214) 893-5553
Admin Adelia F Shepherd. *Medical Dir/Dir of Nursing* Dr Stanley Monroe; Valeria Shelby RN DON.
Licensure Skilled care; Intermediate care. *Beds* SNF 200; ICF. *Certified* Medicaid; Medicare.
Owner Proprietary Corp (Meridan Healthcare).
Staff Physicians 3 (pt); RNs 6 (ft); LPNs 20 (ft); Orderlies 4 (ft); Nurses aides 85 (ft); Physical therapists 3 (pt); Activities coordinators 2 (ft); Dietitians 1 (ft); Ophthalmologists 1 (ft).
Languages Spanish
Facilities Dining room; Physical therapy room; Activities room; Chapel; Laundry room; Barber/Beauty shop; Sun porch; Sitting rooms; TV room; Lobby.
Activities Arts & crafts; Cards; Games; Reading groups; Prayer groups; Movies; Shopping trips; Social/Cultural gatherings; Exercises; Manicures.

Heritage Manor Nursing Home*
315 W McLain, Sherman, TX, 75090
(214) 893-0149
Admin Annabelle Grissom.
Licensure Intermediate care; Intermediate care for mentally retarded. *Beds* ICF 64; ICF/MR 66. *Certified* Medicaid.
Owner Proprietary Corp (ARA Living Centers).

Meridian Nursing Center—Shady Oaks*
Loy Lake Rd & Hwy 82, Sherman, TX, 75090
(214) 893-9636
Admin Wanda J Howard. *Medical Dir/Dir of Nursing* Stanley Monroe MD.
Licensure Skilled care. *Beds* 135. *Certified* Medicaid.
Owner Proprietary Corp (Meridan Healthcare).
Admissions Requirements Minimum age 18.
Staff Physicians 1 (pt); RNs 1 (ft), 3 (pt); LPNs 11 (ft); Nurses aides 39 (ft); Activities coordinators 1 (ft); Dietitians 1 (ft).
Facilities Dining room; Physical therapy room; Activities room; Chapel; Crafts room; Laundry room; Barber/Beauty shop; Library; Greenhouse.
Activities Arts & crafts; Cards; Games; Prayer groups; Movies; Social/Cultural gatherings.

Sherman Nursing Center*
817 W Center St, Sherman, TX, 75090
(214) 893-6348
Admin Jerry L Jones.
Licensure Intermediate care. *Beds* 122.
Certified Medicaid.
Owner Proprietary Corp (Truco Inc).

SHINER

Trinity Lutheran Home
1213 N Ave B, Rte 3, Box 19, Shiner, TX, 77984
(512) 594-3353
Admin Mary Lynn Campbell. *Medical Dir/Dir of Nursing* Dr Maurice G Wilkinson.
Licensure Intermediate care. *Beds* ICF 89.
Certified Medicaid.
Admissions Requirements Medical examination; Physician's request.
Staff LPNs 8 (ft), 1 (pt); Nurses aides 19 (ft), 11 (pt); Activities coordinators 1 (ft), 1 (pt).
Languages Czech, German, Spanish
Affiliation Lutheran
Facilities Dining room; Activities room; Chapel; Crafts room; Laundry room; Barber/Beauty shop.

Activities Arts & crafts; Cards; Games; Reading groups; Prayer groups; Movies; Shopping trips; Social/Cultural gatherings; Parties involving guests from other nursing homes in the area.

SILSBEE

Bur-Mont Nursing Center
1680 Hwy 327 W, Silsbee, TX, 77656
(713) 385-5571
Admin Anna L Tanton.
Licensure Skilled care. *Beds* 120. *Certified* Medicaid; VA.
Owner Proprietary Corp.
Staff Physicians; RNs; LPNs; Nurses aides; Physical therapists; Occupational therapists; Speech therapists; Activities coordinators.

Silsbee Convalescent Center*
1105 W Hwy 418, Silsbee, TX, 77656
(713) 385-3784
Admin Martha J Reeves.
Licensure Intermediate care. *Beds* 68.
Certified Medicaid.
Owner Proprietary Corp (Cantex Healthcare Centers).

SINTON

Sinton Manor Nursing Home
936 W 4th St, Sinton, TX, 78387
(512) 364-3478
Admin Norma Apple. *Medical Dir/Dir of Nursing* Venilde Marez-Mejias.
Licensure Intermediate care. *Certified* Medicaid.
Owner Proprietary Corp.
Staff Physicians 1 (pt); RNs 1 (pt); LPNs 3 (ft), 2 (pt); Nurses aides 10 (ft), 2 (pt); Activities coordinators 1 (ft); Dietitians 1 (ft), 1 (pt).
Facilities Dining room; Activities room; Crafts room; Laundry room.
Activities Arts & crafts; Games; Reading groups; Prayer groups; Movies; Shopping trips; Social/Cultural gatherings.

SLATON

Slaton Rest Home
630 S 19th St, Slaton, TX, 79364
(806) 828-6268
Admin Wanda Barclay.
Licensure Intermediate care. *Beds* 120.
Certified Medicaid.
Owner Proprietary Corp.

SMITHVILLE

Towers Nursing Home*
PO Box 89, 907 Garwood St, Smithville, TX, 78957
(512) 237-2442
Admin James R Sikes.
Licensure Intermediate care. *Beds* 60.
Certified Medicaid.
Owner Nonprofit Corp.

SNYDER

Snyder Nursing Center*
5311 Big Spring Hwy, Snyder, TX, 79549
(915) 573-6332
Admin Jerry Miller.
Licensure Intermediate care; Personal care.
Beds ICF 80; Personal 20. *Certified* Medicaid.
Owner Proprietary Corp (Beverly Enterprises).
Staff LPNs 4 (ft); Nurses aides 25 (ft); Reality therapists 1 (ft); Activities coordinators 1 (ft); Dietitians 4 (ft).
Facilities Dining room; Physical therapy room; Activities room; Laundry room; Barber/Beauty shop.

Activities Arts & crafts; Cards; Games; Reading groups; Prayer groups; Movies; Shopping trips; Social/Cultural gatherings.

Snyder Oaks Care Center*
210 E 37th St, Snyder, TX, 79549
(915) 573-9377
Admin Nelda Pearl Kruger.
Licensure Intermediate care. *Beds* 97.
Certified Medicaid.
Owner Proprietary Corp.

SONORA

Lillian M Hudspeth Nursing Home
PO Box 455, 310 Hudspeth, Sonora, TX, 76950
(915) 387-3030
Admin M Scott Gilmore. *Medical Dir/Dir of Nursing* Gregory Lind MD; Rebecca Becknell DON.
Licensure Intermediate care. *Beds* ICF 39.
Certified Medicaid.
Owner Nonprofit Corp.
Admissions Requirements Minimum age 18; Physician's request.
Staff Physicians 2 (ft); LPNs 6 (ft); Nurses aides 14 (ft); Activities coordinators 1 (ft); Dietitians 1 (ft); Ophthalmologists 1 (pt).
Languages Spanish
Facilities Dining room; Activities room; Chapel; Laundry room; Barber/Beauty shop.
Activities Arts & crafts; Cards; Games; Reading groups; Movies; Social/Cultural gatherings.

SPEARMAN

Hansford Manor*
707 S Roland, Spearman, TX, 79081
Admin Raymond Wasil.
Licensure Intermediate care. *Beds* 39.
Certified Medicaid.
Owner Publicly owned.
Admissions Requirements Medical examination.
Staff LPNs 6 (ft); Nurses aides 16 (ft), 1 (pt); Physical therapists 1 (pt); Activities coordinators 1 (ft).
Facilities Dining room; Physical therapy room; Activities room; Crafts room; Barber/Beauty shop.
Activities Arts & crafts; Cards; Games; Reading groups; Prayer groups; Movies; Shopping trips.

SPUR

Spur Care Center*
E State Hwy 70, Spur, TX, 79370
(806) 271-3343
Admin Margurite Van Zandt.
Licensure Intermediate care. *Beds* 40.
Certified Medicaid.
Admissions Requirements Medical examination; Physician's request.
Staff LPNs; Nurses aides; Activities coordinators; Dietitians.
Facilities Dining room; Activities room; Laundry room; Barber/Beauty shop.
Activities Arts & crafts; Games; Prayer groups; Movies; Shopping trips; Social/Cultural gatherings.

STAMFORD

Skyview Living Center of Stamford*
1101 Columbia, Stamford, TX, 79553
(915) 773-2791
Admin Patsy R Newland.
Licensure Intermediate care for mentally retarded. *Beds* 102. *Certified* Medicaid.

Teakwood Manor
1003 Columbia, Stamford, TX, 79553
(915) 773-3671

Admin Judy Doster. *Medical Dir/Dir of Nursing* Vickie Wilhelm.
Licensure Intermediate care. *Beds* 150.
Certified Medicaid.
Owner Proprietary Corp (Truco Inc).
Admissions Requirements Minimum age 18.
Staff RNs 1 (pt); LPNs 4 (ft); Orderlies 2 (ft); Nurses aides 30 (ft); Physical therapists; Reality therapists; Recreational therapists; Occupational therapists; Speech therapists; Activities coordinators 1 (ft); Dietitians 1 (pt).
Facilities Dining room; Activities room; Chapel; Crafts room; Laundry room; Barber/Beauty shop.
Activities Arts & crafts; Cards; Games; Reading groups; Prayer groups; Movies; Shopping trips.

STANTON

Stanton Care Center
1100 W Broadway, Stanton, TX, 79782
(915) 756-3387
Admin Charlene Allmon. *Medical Dir/Dir of Nursing* Charlotte Locke DON.
Licensure Intermediate care. *Beds* ICF 65.
Certified Medicaid.
Owner Proprietary Corp (Manor Care).
Admissions Requirements Medical examination; Physician's request.
Staff RNs; LPNs; Orderlies; Nurses aides; Physical therapists; Activities coordinators; Dietitians.
Languages Spanish
Facilities Dining room; Activities room; Laundry room; Barber/Beauty shop.
Activities Arts & crafts; Games; Reading groups; Prayer groups; Movies; Shopping trips; Exercises.

STEPHENVILLE

Canterbury Villa of Stephenville
2309 W Washington St, Stephenville, TX, 76401
(817) 968-4191
Admin Deltha McDonald.
Licensure Intermediate care. *Beds* ICF 88.
Certified Medicaid; VA; Private pay.
Owner Proprietary Corp.
Admissions Requirements Medical examination.
Staff RNs 1 (ft); LPNs 6 (ft); Orderlies 1 (ft); Nurses aides 12 (ft); Physical therapists 1 (ft); Speech therapists 1 (ft); Activities coordinators 1 (ft); Dietitians 1 (ft); Dentists 1 (ft); Ophthalmologists 1 (ft); Podiatrists 1 (ft).
Facilities Dining room; Activities room; Laundry room; Barber/Beauty shop.
Activities Arts & crafts; Games; Reading groups; Prayer groups; Shopping trips; Social/Cultural gatherings.

Community Nursing Home
2025 NW Loop, Stephenville, TX, 76401
(817) 968-4649
Admin Johnny Mel Serratt. *Medical Dir/Dir of Nursing* Martha Anderson.
Licensure Intermediate care. *Beds* ICF 103.
Certified Medicaid; Medicare.
Owner Privately owned.
Admissions Requirements Medical examination; Physician's request.
Staff RNs 1 (ft); LPNs 10 (ft), 2 (pt); Orderlies 4 (ft); Nurses aides 30 (ft); Activities coordinators; Dietitians.
Facilities Dining room; Physical therapy room; Activities room; Chapel; Crafts room; Laundry room; Barber/Beauty shop.
Activities Arts & crafts; Cards; Games; Reading groups; Prayer groups; Shopping trips; Social/Cultural gatherings.

Mulberry Manor
1670 Lingleville Rd, Stephenville, TX, 76401
(817) 968-2158
Admin Bill Wakefield.
Licensure Skilled care. *Beds* 118. *Certified* Medicaid.
Owner Proprietary Corp (ARA Living Centers).

Stephenville Nursing Inc*
2311 W Washington St, Stephenville, TX, 76401
(817) 968-3313
Admin Helen Allen.
Licensure Intermediate care. *Beds* 46. *Certified* Medicaid.
Staff RNs 1 (ft); LPNs 1 (ft), 2 (pt); Orderlies 12 (ft); Activities coordinators 1 (ft).
Facilities Dining room; Laundry room; Barber/Beauty shop.
Activities Arts & crafts; Cards; Games; Reading groups; Prayer groups; Movies; Shopping trips; Social/Cultural gatherings.

STERLING CITY

Sterling County Nursing Home
Box 3, 5th Ave, Sterling City, TX, 76951
(915) 378-3201
Admin Cindy Stokes.
Licensure Intermediate care. *Beds* 29. *Certified* Medicaid.
Owner Publicly owned.

STOCKDALE

Stockdale Nursing Home*
PO Box 36, 300 Solomon St, Stockdale, TX, 78160
(512) 996-3721
Admin Jonnie L Staggs.
Licensure Skilled care. *Beds* 68. *Certified* Medicaid.
Owner Proprietary Corp.

STRATFORD

Coldwater Manor Nursing Home
1111 Beaver, Stratford, TX, 79084
(806) 396-5568
Admin J Gennell York. *Medical Dir/Dir of Nursing* Dr Claude Harlow; Shirley Plunk RN DON.
Licensure Intermediate care. *Beds* ICF 38. *Certified* Medicaid.
Owner Nonprofit organization/foundation.
Admissions Requirements Medical examination; Physician's request.
Staff Physicians 1 (ft); RNs 1 (ft); Nurses aides 16 (ft); Recreational therapists 1 (ft); Activities coordinators 1 (ft); Dietitians 1 (ft); Dentists 1 (ft); Ophthalmologists 1 (ft); Podiatrists 1 (ft); LVNs 5 (ft).
Facilities Dining room; Physical therapy room; Activities room; Chapel; Crafts room; Laundry room; Barber/Beauty shop.
Activities Arts & crafts; Cards; Games; Reading groups; Prayer groups; Movies; Shopping trips; Social/Cultural gatherings; Art classes; Ceramic classes.

SUGAR LAND

Autumn Hills Convalescent Center
333 Matlage Way, Sugar Land, TX, 77478
(713) 491-3011
Admin Paul A Smith Jr. *Medical Dir/Dir of Nursing* Kas Saranathan MD; Delores Alaniz, DON.
Licensure Intermediate care. *Beds* ICF 150. *Certified* Medicaid.
Owner Proprietary Corp.
Admissions Requirements Minimum age 65; Medical examination; Physician's request.

Staff Physicians 6 (pt); RNs 1 (ft), 1 (pt); LPNs 11 (ft); Orderlies 3 (ft), 1 (pt); Nurses aides 37 (ft); Physical therapists 2 (pt); Speech therapists 1 (pt); Activities coordinators 1 (ft), 1 (pt); Dietitians 1 (pt).
Facilities Dining room; Activities room; Crafts room; Barber/Beauty shop; Living room; 2 Lounges.
Activities Arts & crafts; Cards; Games; Reading groups; Prayer groups; Movies; Social/Cultural gatherings.

SULPHUR SPRINGS

Hopkins County Nursing Home
1333 Jefferson, Sulphur Springs, TX, 76482
(214) 885-7642
Admin Alvie L Morgan. *Medical Dir/Dir of Nursing* Loretta McKay.
Licensure Intermediate care. *Beds* ICF 119. *Certified* Medicaid.
Owner Proprietary Corp.
Admissions Requirements Medical examination; Physician's request.
Staff RNs 1 (ft); LPNs 7 (ft), 1 (pt); Nurses aides 24 (ft); Activities coordinators 1 (ft).
Facilities Dining room; Activities room; Chapel; Crafts room; Laundry room; Barber/Beauty shop; Library.
Activities Arts & crafts; Cards; Games; Reading groups; Prayer groups; Movies; Shopping trips; Social/Cultural gatherings; Outings to other senior gatherings & dances.

Leisure Lodge—Sulphur Springs
411 Airport Rd, Sulphur Springs, TX, 75482
(214) 885-7668
Admin Brian Bailey. *Medical Dir/Dir of Nursing* Dr Claude Reynolds; Miriam Carpenter DON.
Licensure Skilled care; Intermediate care. *Beds* SNF 38; ICF 88. *Certified* Medicaid.
Owner Proprietary Corp (Beverly Enterprises).
Admissions Requirements Medical examination; Physician's request.
Staff RNs 3 (ft); LPNs 8 (ft); Nurses aides 30 (ft); Activities coordinators 1 (ft); Dietitians 1 (pt).
Facilities Dining room; Activities room; Chapel; Crafts room; Laundry room; Barber/ Beauty shop.
Activities Arts & crafts; Cards; Games; Reading groups; Prayer groups; Movies; Shopping trips; Social/Cultural gatherings; Exercise; Resident council; Family council; Birthday parties.

Sulphur Springs Nursing Home
301 Oak Ave, Sulphur Springs, TX, 75482
(214) 885-3596
Admin Mary Pamela Folowell. *Medical Dir/ Dir of Nursing* Pam Burnett.
Licensure Intermediate care. *Beds* ICF 60. *Certified* Medicaid.
Owner Privately owned.
Admissions Requirements Medical examination; Physician's request.
Staff RNs 1 (ft); LPNs 3 (ft), 1 (pt); Nurses aides 24 (ft), 3 (pt); Activities coordinators 1 (ft).
Facilities Dining room; Activities room; Laundry room; Barber/Beauty shop.
Activities Arts & crafts; Cards; Games; Reading groups; Movies; Shopping trips; Social/Cultural gatherings.

Woodhaven Nursing Home*
1200 N Jackson, Sulphur Springs, TX, 75482
(214) 885-6571
Admin William F Rettmann.
Licensure Intermediate care. *Beds* 95. *Certified* Medicaid.
Owner Proprietary Corp.

SWEENY

Sweeny House
109 N McKinney, Sweeny, TX, 77480
(409) 548-3383
Admin Sylvia M Donelly. *Medical Dir/Dir of Nursing* Donna Winebrenner DON.
Licensure Intermediate care; Personal care. *Beds* ICF 82; Personal 20. *Certified* Medicaid.
Owner Proprietary Corp (ARA Living Centers).
Admissions Requirements Medical examination; Physician's request.
Staff RNs 1 (ft); LPNs 8 (ft); Nurses aides 35 (ft), 4 (pt); Activities coordinators 1 (ft).
Languages Spanish
Facilities Dining room; Activities room; Laundry room; Barber/Beauty shop; In-house doctors office.
Activities Arts & crafts; Cards; Games; Reading groups; Prayer groups; Movies; Shopping trips; Social/Cultural gatherings; In-room activities; Awareness; Dominoes; Holiday activities; Field trips; Residents council.

SWEETWATER

Holiday Retirement Center*
PO Box 1369, 1901 Lamar, Sweetwater, TX, 79556
(915) 235-5417
Admin Katherine Owen.
Licensure Skilled care. *Beds* 78. *Certified* Medicaid.
Owner Proprietary Corp (Hillhaven Corp).

Sweetwater Nursing Center*
1600 Josephine, Sweetwater, TX, 79556
(915) 236-6653
Admin Donna Hallman. *Medical Dir/Dir of Nursing* Bruce Carpenter MD.
Licensure Intermediate care. *Beds* 100. *Certified* Medicaid.
Owner Proprietary Corp (Beverly Enterprises).
Admissions Requirements Physician's request.
Staff LPNs 5 (ft), 4 (pt); Nurses aides 14 (ft), 4 (pt); Activities coordinators 1 (ft); Dietitians 1 (ft).
Facilities Dining room; Crafts room; Laundry room; Barber/Beauty shop.
Activities Arts & crafts; Cards; Games; Reading groups; Prayer groups; Movies; Shopping trips; Social/Cultural gatherings.

TAFT

Shoreliner Healthcare Center*
1201 Gregory St, Taft, TX, 78390
(512) 528-2523
Admin Norma Brandt.
Licensure Intermediate care. *Beds* 200. *Certified* Medicaid.
Owner Proprietary Corp (ARA Living Centers).

Taft Hospital District
1220 Gregory St, Taft, TX, 78390
(512) 528-2545
Admin Douglas Langley. *Medical Dir/Dir of Nursing* Y S Jenkins MD; Cynthia Keese DON.
Licensure Private. *Beds* Private 30.
Owner Publicly owned.
Admissions Requirements Minimum age 18; Medical examination; Physician's request.
Staff RNs 1 (ft); LPNs 4 (ft); Nurses aides 4 (ft); Physical therapists 1 (pt); Activities coordinators 1 (pt); Dietitians 1 (pt).
Facilities Dining room; Physical therapy room; Activities room; Chapel; Crafts room; Laundry room; Library.
Activities Arts & crafts; Cards; Games; Reading groups; Prayer groups.

TAHOKA

Tahoka Care Center
PO Box 449, 1829 S 7th St, Tahoka, TX, 79373
(806) 998-5018
Admin Diana Riojas. *Medical Dir/Dir of Nursing* Ruby Groves.
Licensure Intermediate care. *Beds* ICF 42. *Certified* Medicaid.
Owner Nonprofit organization/foundation.
Admissions Requirements Medical examination; Physician's request.
Staff Nurses aides; Activities coordinators.
Languages German, Spanish
Facilities Dining room; Laundry room; Barber/Beauty shop.
Activities Arts & crafts; Cards; Games; Reading groups; Prayer groups; Movies; Shopping trips; Social/Cultural gatherings.

TAYLOR

SPJST Rest Home 1
500 E Lake Dr, Taylor, TX, 76574
(512) 352-6337
Admin Frances Schwenker. *Medical Dir/Dir of Nursing* Ilyn Kaspar.
Licensure Intermediate care. *Beds* ICF 72. *Certified* Medicaid.
Owner Nonprofit Corp.
Admissions Requirements Physician's request.
Staff LPNs 10 (ft); Nurses aides 60 (ft); Activities coordinators 1 (ft); Dietitians 1 (ft).
Facilities Dining room; Activities room; Laundry room.
Activities Arts & crafts; Games; Reading groups; Prayer groups; Shopping trips.

Sunnyside Retirement Center 2
PO Box 1129, 212 E Lake Dr, Taylor, TX, 76574
(512) 352-6825
Admin Bholanath B Nadkarni. *Medical Dir/Dir of Nursing* Melissa Kelley.
Licensure Intermediate care. *Beds* ICF 89. *Certified* Medicaid.
Owner Proprietary Corp.
Admissions Requirements Minimum age 18; Medical examination.
Staff Physicians 1 (pt); RNs 1 (pt); LPNs 5 (ft); Orderlies 2 (ft); Nurses aides 16 (pt); Physical therapists 1 (pt); Occupational therapists 1 (pt); Speech therapists 1 (pt); Activities coordinators 1 (ft), 1 (pt); Dietitians 1 (ft), 1 (pt); Dentists 1 (pt); Ophthalmologists 1 (pt); Podiatrists 1 (pt).
Languages Spanish, German, French, Czech
Facilities Dining room; Laundry room; Barber/Beauty shop; Library.
Activities Arts & crafts; Cards; Games; Reading groups; Prayer groups; Shopping trips; Social/Cultural gatherings; Wheelchair basketball; Sports.

Sweetbriar Nursing Home
PO Box 831, Granger Hwy, Taylor, TX, 76574
(512) 352-3684
Admin Dorothy Phillips. *Medical Dir/Dir of Nursing* Pat Maxwell.
Licensure Intermediate care; Personal care. *Beds* ICF 150; Personal care 40; Licensed 66. *Certified* Medicaid.
Owner Proprietary Corp (ARA Living Centers).
Admissions Requirements Medical examination.
Staff Physicians; RNs; LPNs; Orderlies; Nurses aides; Physical therapists; Reality therapists; Recreational therapists; Occupational therapists; Speech therapists; Activities coordinators; Dietitians; Dentists; Ophthalmologists; Podiatrists.
Languages Czech, German, Spanish

Facilities Dining room; Activities room; Crafts room; Laundry room; Barber/Beauty shop; Library.
Activities Arts & crafts; Cards; Games; Reading groups; Prayer groups; Shopping trips; Social/Cultural gatherings; Alzheimer's support group.

TEAGUE

McGee Nursing Home*
615 S 8th Ave, Teague, TX, 75860
(817) 739-2566
Beds 82. *Certified* Medicaid.
Admissions Requirements Minimum age 21.
Staff Physicians 1 (ft); RNs 1 (ft); LPNs 4 (ft); Nurses aides 30 (ft); Activities coordinators 1 (ft); Dietitians 1 (ft); Dentists 1 (ft).
Facilities Dining room; Activities room; Crafts room; Laundry room; Barber/Beauty shop; Library.
Activities Arts & crafts; Cards; Games; Reading groups; Prayer groups; Movies; Shopping trips.

Teague Nursing Home
PO Box 89, Teague, TX, 75860
(817) 739-2541
Admin Eugenia Lummus. *Medical Dir/Dir of Nursing* Marion Williams.
Licensure Intermediate care. *Beds* ICF 102. *Certified* Medicaid.
Owner Proprietary Corp.
Admissions Requirements Physician's request.
Staff Orderlies 1 (ft); Nurses aides 20 (ft), 3 (pt); Activities coordinators 1 (ft); LVN 7 (ft), 1 (pt).
Facilities Dining room; Chapel; Laundry room; Barber/Beauty shop.
Activities Arts & crafts; Games; Prayer groups; Movies; Shopping trips; Social/Cultural gatherings.

TEMPLE

Bur-Mont Nursing Center*
612 Industrial Blvd, Temple, TX, 76501
(817) 773-5640
Admin Rose M Mondrik.
Licensure Intermediate care. *Beds* 120. *Certified* Medicaid.
Owner Proprietary Corp.

Four Seasons Nursing Center
1700 Marland Wood Rd, Temple, TX, 76502
(817) 773-1591
Admin C D Elliott. *Medical Dir/Dir of Nursing* Jack Weinblatt MD; Jackie Young DON.
Licensure Skilled care; Private-intermediate care. *Beds* SNF 24; Private 81. *Certified* Medicaid; Medicare.
Owner Proprietary Corp (Manor Care).
Staff RNs 2 (ft), 2 (pt); LPNs 9 (ft); Orderlies 3 (ft); Nurses aides 27 (ft), 3 (pt); Activities coordinators 1 (ft).
Languages Spanish, Tagalog
Facilities Dining room; Physical therapy room; Activities room; Crafts room; Laundry room; Barber/Beauty shop; Heritage lounge.
Activities Arts & crafts; Games; Reading groups; Movies; Shopping trips; Social/Cultural gatherings.

Golden Heritage Care Center*
1511 Marland Wood Rd, Temple, TX, 76501
(817) 778-6616
Admin Ruth Haptonstall.
Licensure Intermediate care. *Beds* 91. *Certified* Medicaid.
Owner Proprietary Corp.

Regency Manor Nursing Center*
3011 W Adams, Temple, TX, 76501
(817) 773-1626
Admin G Jo Beach. *Medical Dir/Dir of Nursing* Jack Weinblott MD.

Licensure Intermediate care. *Beds* 140. *Certified* Medicaid.
Owner Proprietary Corp (Beverly Enterprises).
Admissions Requirements Medical examination.
Staff RNs; LPNs; Orderlies; Nurses aides; Physical therapists; Recreational therapists; Occupational therapists; Speech therapists; Activities coordinators; Dietitians.
Facilities Dining room; Activities room; Crafts room; Laundry room; Barber/Beauty shop.
Activities Arts & crafts; Cards; Games; Reading groups; Prayer groups; Movies; Shopping trips; Social/Cultural gatherings.

Southern Manor Inc*
1802 S 31st St, Temple, TX, 76501
(817) 778-4231
Admin Barbara A Doyle. *Medical Dir/Dir of Nursing* Jack Weinblatt MD.
Licensure Skilled care; Intermediate care. *Beds* 145. *Certified* Medicaid.
Admissions Requirements Medical examination; Physician's request.
Staff RNs 1 (ft), 2 (pt); LPNs 9 (ft), 4 (pt); Orderlies 1 (ft); Nurses aides 43 (ft), 3 (pt); Activities coordinators 1 (ft); Dietitians 1 (ft).
Facilities Dining room; Physical therapy room; Activities room; Crafts room; Laundry room; Barber/Beauty shop.
Activities Arts & crafts; Cards; Games; Prayer groups; Movies; Shopping trips; Social/Cultural gatherings.

Southland Villa Nursing Center*
2222 S 5th, Temple, TX, 76501
(817) 773-1641
Admin Margaret F Jackson. *Medical Dir/Dir of Nursing* James D Wilson Sr MD.
Licensure Skilled care. *Beds* 134. *Certified* Medicaid.
Owner Proprietary Corp (Summith Health Ltd).
Admissions Requirements Medical examination.
Staff Physicians 6 (ft); RNs 3 (ft); LPNs 29 (ft); Nurses aides 42 (ft); Physical therapists 1 (ft); Reality therapists 1 (ft); Recreational therapists 1 (ft); Activities coordinators 1 (ft); Dietitians 1 (ft); Dentists 1 (ft).
Facilities Dining room; Activities room; Crafts room; Laundry room; Barber/Beauty shop.
Activities Arts & crafts; Cards; Games; Reading groups; Prayer groups; Movies; Shopping trips; Social/Cultural gatherings; Picnics; Trips to park; Rides out to the lake & countryside; Dining out.

Tutor Nursing Home Inc
119 S 33rd St, Temple, TX, 76504
(817) 778-7740, 778-3301
Admin Ray Van Tutor. *Medical Dir/Dir of Nursing* Mary Tutor RN.
Licensure Intermediate care. *Beds* 45. *Certified* Medicaid.
Owner Proprietary Corp.
Admissions Requirements Medical examination; Physician's request.
Staff RNs 1 (ft); LPNs 4 (pt); Orderlies 1 (ft); Nurses aides 9 (ft); Activities coordinators 1 (ft); Dietitians 1 (ft).
Languages Spanish
Facilities Dining room; Activities room; Chapel; Crafts room; Library.
Activities Arts & crafts; Cards; Games; Prayer groups; Shopping trips; Social/Cultural gatherings; BBQ; Fishing; Sight-seeing trips.

TERRELL

Rose Hill Personal Care Center*
1010 Rose Hill Rd, Terrell, TX, 75160
(214) 563-5796
Admin Bilile R Simmons.

Licensure Intermediate care. *Beds* 68.
Certified Medicaid.
Owner Proprietary Corp (Southmark Heritage Corp).

Terrell Care Center
204 W Nash, Terrell, TX, 75160
(214) 563-7668
Admin Berneice Hill. *Medical Dir/Dir of Nursing* Becky Slagle.
Licensure Intermediate care. *Beds* ICF 94.
Certified Medicaid.
Owner Proprietary Corp (National Heritage).
Admissions Requirements Medical examination; Physician's request.
Staff LPNs 20 (ft); Nurses aides 35 (ft); Activities coordinators 1 (ft); Dietitians 7 (ft).
Facilities Dining room; Activities room; Chapel; Crafts room; Barber/Beauty shop.
Activities Cards; Games; Reading groups; Prayer groups; Movies; Social/Cultural gatherings.

Terrell Convalescent Center 1*
1800 N Frances, Terrell, TX, 75160
(214) 563-2652
Admin Edward C Black.
Licensure Intermediate care; Personal care. *Beds* ICF 101; Personal 28. *Certified* Medicaid.
Owner Proprietary Corp (Southmark Heritage Corp).

Terrell Convalescent Center 2
1900 N Frances, Terrell, TX, 75160
(214) 563-6428
Admin Marjorie D Looker.
Licensure Intermediate care. *Beds* 122.
Certified Medicaid.
Owner Proprietary Corp (Southmark Heritage Corp).

TEXARKANA

Edgewood Manor Nursing Home
4925 Elizabeth St, Texarkana, TX, 75503
(214) 793-4645
Admin Peggy Fomby. *Medical Dir/Dir of Nursing* Dr Charles Marrow; Jo Ann Griffin.
Licensure Intermediate care. *Beds* ICF 120.
Certified Medicaid.
Admissions Requirements Physician's request.
Staff LPNs 10 (ft); Nurses aides 32 (ft); Activities coordinators 1 (ft); Dietary Staff 10 (ft); Housekeeping, laundry and maintenance staff 9 (ft).
Facilities Dining room; Activities room; Crafts room; Laundry room; Barber/Beauty shop; Library.
Activities Arts & crafts; Games; Reading groups; Prayer groups; Movies; Shopping trips; Social/Cultural gatherings.

Four States Nursing Home
PO Box 5368, 8 E Midway Dr, Texarkana, TX, 75501
(214) 838-9526
Admin Norma Z Dozier. *Medical Dir/Dir of Nursing* Dr Donald Middleton; Donna Murphy.
Licensure Intermediate care. *Beds* ICF 180.
Certified Medicaid.
Owner Proprietary Corp (Hillhaven Corp).
Admissions Requirements Medical examination; Physician's request.
Staff RNs; LPNs; Orderlies; Nurses aides; Activities coordinators.
Facilities Dining room; Laundry room; Barber/Beauty shop.
Activities Arts & crafts; Games; Reading groups; Prayer groups; Movies; Social/Cultural gatherings.

Leisure Lodge Texarkana
4808 Elizabeth, Texarkana, TX, 75503
(214) 794-3826

Admin Erma Cooper. *Medical Dir/Dir of Nursing* Kathy Wilson LUN DON.
Licensure Intermediate care. *Beds* 120.
Certified Medicaid.
Owner Proprietary Corp (Beverly Enterprises).
Admissions Requirements Medical examination.
Staff RNs 1 (ft); LPNs 10 (ft); Nurses aides; Activities coordinators.
Facilities Dining room; Activities room; Crafts room; Laundry room; Barber/Beauty shop; Library.
Activities Arts & crafts; Cards; Games; Reading groups; Prayer groups; Movies; Shopping trips; Social/Cultural gatherings.

Oak Manor Nursing Home of Texarkana*
PO Box 5398, 3120 Smith St, Texarkana, TX, 75501
(214) 838-7566
Admin Ronald E Duke.
Licensure Intermediate care. *Beds* 56.
Certified Medicaid.
Owner Proprietary Corp.

Texarkana Nursing Center
4920 Elizabeth, Texarkana, TX, 75503
(214) 792-3812
Admin Alandra Needham. *Medical Dir/Dir of Nursing* Dr Thomas Alston; Judy Beasley RN DON.
Licensure Intermediate care. *Beds* ICF 120.
Certified Medicaid.
Owner Proprietary Corp (Beverly Enterprises).
Admissions Requirements Medical examination; Physician's request.
Staff RNs 2 (ft); LPNs 10 (ft); Orderlies 3 (ft), 1 (pt); Nurses aides 30 (ft), 5 (pt); Activities coordinators 1 (ft); Dietitians 1 (ft).
Facilities Dining room; Physical therapy room; Activities room; Crafts room; Laundry room; Barber/Beauty shop; Library.
Activities Arts & crafts; Cards; Games; Reading groups; Prayer groups; Movies; Shopping trips; Social/Cultural gatherings.

TEXAS CITY

Coastal Care Center*
501 8th Ave N, Texas City, TX, 77590
(713) 948-3502
Admin Ione M Filer.
Licensure Intermediate care. *Beds* 117.
Certified Medicaid.
Owner Proprietary Corp (Hillhaven Corp).
Admissions Requirements Medical examination.
Staff Physicians; RNs; LPNs; Nurses aides; Physical therapists; Reality therapists; Recreational therapists; Occupational therapists; Speech therapists; Activities coordinators; Dietitians; Dentists; Ophthalmologists; Podiatrists; Audiologists.
Facilities Dining room; Physical therapy room; Activities room; Crafts room; Laundry room; Barber/Beauty shop.
Activities Arts & crafts; Cards; Games; Reading groups; Prayer groups; Movies; Shopping trips; Social/Cultural gatherings.

College Park Care Center*
424 N Tarpey Rd, Texas City, TX, 77590
(713) 938-8431
Admin Peggy E Thomas. *Medical Dir/Dir of Nursing* Weldon Kolb MD.
Licensure Skilled care; Intermediate care. *Beds* 114. *Certified* Medicaid.
Owner Proprietary Corp (Beverly Enterprises).
Staff Physicians 1 (pt); RNs 2 (ft); LPNs 10 (ft); Nurses aides 30 (ft), 5 (pt); Physical therapists 1 (pt); Occupational therapists 1 (pt); Speech therapists 1 (pt); Activities coordinators 1 (ft); Dietitians 1 (pt); Dentists 1 (pt).
Facilities Dining room; Activities room; Crafts room; Laundry room; Barber/Beauty shop.

Activities Arts & crafts; Cards; Games; Reading groups; Movies; Shopping trips; Social/Cultural gatherings.

Fifth Avenue Home
815 5th Ave N, Texas City, TX, 77590
(409) 945-7429
Admin M Nancee Manning.
Licensure Intermediate care. *Beds* 65.
Certified Medicaid.
Admissions Requirements Medical examination.
Staff LPNs 7 (ft); Orderlies 1 (ft); Nurses aides 18 (ft); Physical therapists 1 (ft); Activities coordinators 1 (ft).
Facilities Dining room; Activities room; Crafts room; Laundry room; Barber/Beauty shop; Library.
Activities Arts & crafts; Cards; Games; Reading groups; Prayer groups; Movies; Shopping trips; Social/Cultural gatherings.

Manor Care Texas City
210 Gulf Fwy, Texas City, TX, 77591
(409) 938-4271 or (713) 488-0624
Admin Pauline Kaper. *Medical Dir/Dir of Nursing* R E Sullivan MD; Ann Wright DON.
Licensure Skilled care; Intermediate care. *Beds* SNF 52; ICF 58. *Certified* Medicaid; Medicare.
Owner Proprietary Corp (Manor Care).
Admissions Requirements Medical examination.
Staff RNs 3 (ft), 3 (pt); LPNs 9 (ft), 6 (pt); Orderlies 2 (ft); Nurses aides 32 (ft), 9 (pt); Physical therapists 1 (pt); Occupational therapists 1 (pt); Speech therapists 1 (pt); Activities coordinators 1 (ft); Dietitians 1 (ft); Ophthalmologists 1 (pt); Podiatrists 1 (pt).
Languages Spanish
Facilities Dining room; Physical therapy room; Activities room; Crafts room; Laundry room; Barber/Beauty shop.
Activities Arts & crafts; Cards; Games; Reading groups; Prayer groups; Movies; Shopping trips; Social/Cultural gatherings.

Seabreeze Care Center*
6602 Memorial Dr, Texas City, TX, 77590
(713) 935-2451
Admin Nancy Gail van Cleave.
Licensure Intermediate care. *Beds* 103.
Certified Medicaid.
Owner Proprietary Corp (ARA Living Centers).

THREE RIVERS

Roma Memorial Nursing Home*
Smith Blvd, Three Rivers, TX, 78071
(512) 786-2256
Admin Evelyn Huebotter.
Licensure Intermediate care. *Beds* 51.
Certified Medicaid.
Staff RNs 1 (pt); LPNs 4 (ft); Nurses aides 15 (ft); Activities coordinators 1 (ft); Dietitians 1 (pt).
Facilities Dining room; Laundry room; Barber/Beauty shop.
Activities Arts & crafts; Cards; Games; Prayer groups; Social/Cultural gatherings.

THROCKMORTON

Throckmorton Nursing Center*
1000 Minter Ave, Throckmorton, TX, 76083
(817) 849-2861
Admin Betty Mahan.
Licensure Intermediate care. *Beds* 58.
Certified Medicaid.
Owner Proprietary Corp (Beverly Enterprises).

TOMBALL

Autumn Hills Convalescent Center—Tomball*
615 Lawrence St, Tomball, TX, 77375
(713) 351-7231
Admin Martha G Conn. *Medical Dir/Dir of Nursing* George Murillo MD.
Licensure Skilled care; Intermediate care. *Beds* 150. *Certified* Medicaid.
Admissions Requirements Medical examination.
Staff Physicians 12 (ft); RNs 4 (ft), 1 (pt); LPNs 15 (ft), 2 (pt); Orderlies 1 (ft); Nurses aides 33 (ft); Activities coordinators 2 (ft); Dietitians 1 (ft); Dentists 1 (ft); Podiatrists 1 (ft).
Facilities Dining room; Activities room; Laundry room; Barber/Beauty shop.
Activities Arts & crafts; Cards; Games; Reading groups; Prayer groups; Shopping trips; Social/Cultural gatherings.

L & J Winslow Memorial Nursing Home
815 N Peach St, Tomball, TX, 77375
(713) 351-5443
Admin Evelyn Bolds. *Medical Dir/Dir of Nursing* Arvind Pai MD.
Licensure Skilled care; Intermediate care. *Beds* SNF 60; ICF 62. *Certified* Medicaid.
Owner Proprietary Corp (Cantex Healthcare Centers).
Admissions Requirements Minimum age 16; Medical examination; Physician's request.
Staff Physicians 1 (pt); RNs 1 (ft); LPNs 6 (ft); Nurses aides 12 (ft); Activities coordinators 1 (ft), 1 (pt); Dietitians 1 (ft).
Facilities Dining room; Activities room; Chapel; Laundry room; Barber/Beauty shop.
Activities Arts & crafts; Cards; Games; Reading groups; Prayer groups; Movies; Shopping trips; Social/Cultural gatherings.

TRINITY

Trinity Memorial Hospital*
PO Box 471, 900 Prospect Dr, Trinity, TX, 75862
(713) 594-3588
Admin Glea Ramey Jr.
Licensure Intermediate care. *Beds* 28. *Certified* Medicaid.
Owner Publicly owned.

TROUP

Westwood Convalescent Home Inc*
PO Box 399, 1204 W Noble St, Troup, TX, 75789
(214) 842-3118
Admin Arthur P Mowery.
Licensure Intermediate care. *Beds* 60. *Certified* Medicaid.
Owner Proprietary Corp.

TULIA

Tulia Care Center*
714 S Austin, Tulia, TX, 79088
(806) 995-4810
Admin Mary Ann Resch.
Licensure Intermediate care. *Beds* 52. *Certified* Medicaid.
Admissions Requirements Medical examination.
Staff RNs 1 (ft), 1 (pt); LPNs 4 (ft); Orderlies 3 (ft); Nurses aides 10 (ft), 2 (pt) 13J 1 (pt); Activities coordinators 1 (ft), 1 (pt); Dietitians 1 (pt).
Facilities Dining room; Physical therapy room; Activities room; Laundry room; Barber/Beauty shop.
Activities Arts & crafts; Games; Prayer groups; Movies; Shopping trips; Social/Cultural gatherings.

TYLER

All Seasons Nursing Home
2901 E Front St, Tyler, TX, 75702
(214) 592-6584
Admin Betty Hill. *Medical Dir/Dir of Nursing* Juanita White; Carole Monday.
Licensure Intermediate care. *Beds* ICF 168. *Certified* Medicaid.
Owner Proprietary Corp (Texas Health Enterprises).
Staff Physicians; RNs; LPNs; Nurses aides; Activities coordinators.
Facilities Dining room; Activities room; Crafts room; Laundry room; Barber/Beauty shop; Library; TV Lounge.
Activities Arts & crafts; Cards; Games; Reading groups; Prayer groups; Movies; Shopping trips; Social/Cultural gatherings.

Colonial Manor of Tyler*
930 S Baxter St, Tyler, TX, 75701
(214) 597-2068
Admin Sue Burford. *Medical Dir/Dir of Nursing* Dr Irving Brown.
Licensure Skilled care; Intermediate care. *Beds* 124. *Certified* Medicaid; Medicare.
Activities Arts & crafts; Cards; Games; Reading groups; Prayer groups; Shopping trips; Social/Cultural gatherings.

Eastview Nursing Home
2902 Hwy 31 E, Tyler, TX, 75702
(214) 597-1323
Admin Ralph J King LNHA. *Medical Dir/Dir of Nursing* Kay Ritch LVN DON.
Licensure Intermediate care. *Beds* ICF 120. *Certified* Medicaid.
Owner Proprietary Corp.
Staff Physicians 1 (pt); LPNs 8 (ft); Orderlies 2 (ft); Nurses aides 20 (ft); Activities coordinators 1 (ft).

Glenview of Tyler Nursing Home Inc*
3526 W Erwin, Tyler, TX, 75702
(214) 593-6441
Admin Barbara Gill.
Licensure Intermediate care. *Beds* 120. *Certified* Medicaid.
Admissions Requirements Medical examination; Physician's request.
Facilities Dining room; Activities room; Crafts room; Laundry room; Barber/Beauty shop; Library.
Activities Arts & crafts; Cards; Games; Movies; Social/Cultural gatherings.

Hearthstone Nursing Home*
800 Clinic Dr, Tyler, TX, 75701
(214) 593-2471
Admin Kenneth W Hagan. *Medical Dir/Dir of Nursing* C D Albright MD.
Licensure Skilled care; Intermediate care. *Beds* 108.
Admissions Requirements Medical examination; Physician's request.
Staff Physicians 1 (pt); RNs 1 (ft), 3 (pt); LPNs 8 (ft), 3 (pt); Nurses aides 38 (ft), 10 (pt); Physical therapists 1 (pt); Recreational therapists 1 (ft); Occupational therapists 1 (ft); Speech therapists 1 (pt); Activities coordinators 1 (ft); Dietitians 1 (ft); Dentists 1 (pt).
Facilities Dining room; Physical therapy room; Activities room; Laundry room; Barber/Beauty shop; Library.
Activities Arts & crafts; Cards; Games; Reading groups; Prayer groups; Movies; Shopping trips; Social/Cultural gatherings; Pet therapy.

Leisure Lodge—Tyler*
810 S Porter, Tyler, TX, 75701
(214) 593-2463
Admin Joyce Handorf.
Licensure Intermediate care. *Beds* 196. *Certified* Medicaid.
Owner Proprietary Corp (Beverly Enterprises).

Mel-Rose Convalescent Home*
1501 W 29th St, Tyler, TX, 75702
(214) 592-8148
Admin Clark Broadhurst.
Licensure Intermediate care. *Beds* 100. *Certified* Medicaid.
Owner Proprietary Corp.

UVALDE

Amistad Nursing Home Inc*
615 Garden St, Uvalde, TX, 78801
(512) 278-5641
Admin John M Wade. *Medical Dir/Dir of Nursing* J M Barton MD.
Licensure Skilled care; Intermediate care. *Beds* 120. *Certified* Medicaid.
Admissions Requirements Physician's request.

Amistad II Care Center
535 N Park St, Uvalde, TX, 78801
(512) 278-2505
Admin Marilyn R Sweeten. *Medical Dir/Dir of Nursing* J M Barton MD; Lupe Hinojosa DON.
Licensure Intermediate care. *Beds* ICF 122. *Certified* Medicaid.
Owner Proprietary Corp.
Admissions Requirements Physician's request.
Staff LPNs; Orderlies; Nurses aides; Activities coordinators.
Languages Spanish
Facilities Dining room; Activities room; Barber/Beauty shop.
Activities Arts & crafts; Cards; Games; Prayer groups; Movies.

VALLEY MILLS

Golden Heritage Nursing Home 2*
PO Box 138, 1st St & Ave E, Valley Mills, TX, 76689
(817) 932-6288
Admin Cleo D Jones.
Licensure Intermediate care. *Beds* 61. *Certified* Medicaid.
Owner Proprietary Corp.

VAN

Country Inn Care Center*
615 E Main, Van, TX, 75790
(214) 963-8646
Admin Dana L Fleming.
Licensure Intermediate care. *Beds* 61. *Certified* Medicaid.
Owner Proprietary Corp (Beverly Enterprises).

Villa Siesta Nursing Home*
PO Box 1030, 201 S Oak, Van, TX, 75790
(214) 963-8642
Admin Valta L Carcamo.
Licensure Intermediate care. *Beds* 60. *Certified* Medicaid.
Owner Proprietary Corp (Beverly Enterprises).

VAN ALSTYNE

Meadowbrook Care Center*
PO Box 307, 100 Windsor Dr, Van Alstyne, TX, 75095
(214) 482-5941, 532-6543
Admin Cheryl Ann Littrell.
Licensure Intermediate care. *Beds* 60. *Certified* Medicaid.
Owner Proprietary Corp.

VERNON

Vernon Care Center*
2301 Texas St, Vernon, TX, 76384
(817) 552-9316
Admin Norma J Gatewood.
Licensure Intermediate care. *Beds* 90. *Certified* Medicaid.
Owner Proprietary Corp (Beverly Enterprises).

Wood Nursing Convalescent Center*
4301 Hospital Dr, Vernon, TX, 76384
(817) 552-2568
Admin James L Wood.
Licensure Intermediate care. *Beds* 206.
  Certified Medicaid.
Owner Proprietary Corp.

VICTORIA

Linwood Place
3401 E Airline Dr, Victoria, TX, 77901
(512) 573-2467
Admin Linda L Hoffman. *Medical Dir/Dir of
  Nursing* Nancy Kolafa RN DON.
Licensure Private pay. *Beds* Private pay 80.
  Certified Medicaid.
Owner Proprietary Corp (ARA Living
  Centers).
Admissions Requirements Physician's request;
  All private pay.
Staff Physicians 1 (pt); RNs 1 (ft); LPNs 6
  (ft); Orderlies 3 (ft); Nurses aides 30 (ft);
  Physical therapists 1 (pt); Reality therapists
  1 (pt); Recreational therapists 1 (pt);
  Occupational therapists 1 (pt); Speech
  therapists 1 (pt); Activities coordinators 1
  (ft), 1 (pt); Dietitians 1 (ft), 1 (pt); Dentists 1
  (pt); Ophthalmologists 1 (pt); Podiatrists 1
  (pt).
Activities Arts & crafts; Cards; Games;
  Reading groups; Prayer groups; Movies;
  Shopping trips; Social/Cultural gatherings.

Retama Manor Nursing Center—West*
3007 N Navarro, Victoria, TX, 77901
(512) 575-2356
Admin Judith Martin.
Licensure Intermediate care. *Beds* 184.
  Certified Medicaid.
Owner Proprietary Corp (ARA Living
  Centers).

Retama Manor—South 098
3103 Airline Dr, Victoria, TX, 77901
(512) 575-6457
Admin Kathy Moore. *Medical Dir/Dir of
  Nursing* Pat Jacob RN.
Licensure Intermediate care. *Beds* ICF 148.
  Certified Medicaid.
Owner Proprietary Corp (ARA Living
  Centers).
Admissions Requirements Minimum age 18;
  Medical examination; Physician's request.
Staff RNs 2 (ft); LPNs 10 (ft), 10 (pt);
  Orderlies 3 (ft); Nurses aides 45 (ft), 5 (pt);
  Activities coordinators 1 (ft); Dietitians 1
  (ft).
Languages Spanish, Czech, Russian
Facilities Dining room; Activities room;
  Crafts room; Laundry room; Barber/Beauty
  shop.
Activities Arts & crafts; Cards; Games;
  Reading groups; Prayer groups; Movies;
  Shopping trips; Social/Cultural gatherings.

Twin Pines Nursing Home*
3301 Mockingbird Ln, Victoria, TX, 77901
(512) 573-3201
Admin Betty J Hedgclough.
Licensure Intermediate care. *Beds* 148.
  Certified Medicaid.
Owner Nonprofit Corp.

VIDOR

Changing Seasons Commuity Care Complex*
545 Denver St, Vidor, TX, 77662
(713) 769-4542, 4510
Admin Neda E Wilson.
Licensure Intermediate care. *Beds* 55.
  Certified Medicaid.
Owner Proprietary Corp.

Green Acres Convalescent Center*
470 Moore St, Vidor, TX, 77662
(713) 769-2454

Admin Maybelle Chandler.
Licensure Intermediate care. *Beds* 150.
  Certified Medicaid.
Owner Proprietary Corp (ARA Living
  Centers).

Oakwood Manor Nursing Home*
225 S Main St, Vidor, TX, 77662
(713) 769-3692, 5697
Admin Charlene Evans.
Licensure Intermediate care. *Beds* 61.
  Certified Medicaid.
Owner Proprietary Corp (Cantex Healthcare
  Centers).

WACO

Adaptive Livng Center—Central Texas*
1916 Seley St, Waco, TX, 76705
(817) 799-6291
Admin Ruby Faye Sumerior.
Licensure Intermediate care for mentally
  retarded. *Beds* 100. *Certified* Medicaid.

Bellmead Nursing Home Inc*
4601 Wisconsin, Waco, TX, 76705
(817) 799-5581
Admin Helen Atkinson.
Licensure Intermediate care. *Beds* 49.
  Certified Medicaid.
Admissions Requirements Medical
  examination.
Staff RNs 1 (ft); LPNs 4 (ft), 1 (pt); Orderlies
  4 (ft); Nurses aides 11 (ft); Activities
  coordinators 1 (ft); Dietitians 1 (ft).
Facilities Dining room; Activities room;
  Laundry room; Barber/Beauty shop.
Activities Arts & crafts; Cards; Games;
  Reading groups; Prayer groups; Movies;
  Shopping trips; Social/Cultural gatherings.

Care Inn of Waco
5900 Clover Ln, Waco, TX, 76710
(817) 772-0610
Admin Helen Atkinson. *Medical Dir/Dir of
  Nursing* Dr E W Schwartze MD; Kay Vines
  RN DON.
Licensure Intermediate care. *Beds* ICF 74.
  Certified Medicaid.
Owner Proprietary Corp (ARA Living
  Centers).
Admissions Requirements Medical
  examination.
Staff RNs 1 (ft); LPNs 8 (ft), 2 (pt); Orderlies
  2 (ft); Nurses aides 18 (ft), 4 (pt); Activities
  coordinators 1 (ft); Dietitians 1 (ft).
Facilities Dining room; Physical therapy
  room; Activities room; Laundry room;
  Barber/Beauty shop; Library; Patio.
Activities Arts & crafts; Cards; Games;
  Reading groups; Prayer groups; Movies;
  Shopping trips; Social/Cultural gatherings.

**Crestview Manor Retirement & Convalescent
Center***
PO Drawer 5301, 1400 Lake Shore Dr, Waco,
  TX, 76708
(817) 753-0291
Admin Ruby Faye Sumerour.
Licensure Intermediate care. *Beds* 150.
  Certified Medicaid.
Owner Proprietary Corp.

Greenview Manor*
401 Owen Ln, Waco, TX, 76710
(817) 772-8900
Admin Helen Goss.
Licensure Intermediate care. *Beds* 130.
  Certified Medicaid.
Owner Proprietary Corp (ARA Living
  Centers).

Haven Manor Nursing Home
1701 W Waco Dr, Waco, TX, 76707
(817) 754-2347
Admin Rodney E Harris. *Medical Dir/Dir of
  Nursing* Richard Kleiman; Melba
  Niswanger.

Licensure Intermediate care. *Beds* ICF 102.
  Certified Medicaid.
Owner Proprietary Corp (ARA Living
  Centers).
Facilities Dining room; Activities room;
  Chapel; Laundry room; Barber/Beauty shop.
Activities Arts & crafts; Games; Prayer groups;
  Movies; Social/Cultural gatherings.

Hillcrest Manor Nursing Home
3008 Lyle Ave, Waco, TX, 76708
(817) 752-2596
Admin Sylvia Brown. *Medical Dir/Dir of
  Nursing* Monnie Williams.
Licensure Intermediate care. *Beds* ICF 60.
  Certified Medicaid.
Owner Proprietary Corp.
Admissions Requirements Physician's request.
Staff Physicians 1 (pt); RNs 1 (ft); LPNs 6
  (ft); Nurses aides 14 (ft); Activities
  coordinators 1 (ft); Dietitians 1 (ft).
Facilities Dining room; Laundry room;
  Barber/Beauty shop.
Activities Arts & crafts; Games; Reading
  groups; Movies; Individual activities.

Jeffrey Place Nursing Center*
820 Jeffrey Dr, Waco, TX, 76710
(817) 772-9480
Admin Sandra Balcar.
Licensure Intermediate care. *Beds* 106.
  Certified Medicaid.
Owner Proprietary Corp (Beverly Enterprises).

Parkview Nursing Home*
2120 N 4th St, Waco, TX, 76708
(817) 756-5446
Admin Marian A Garcia.
Licensure Intermediate care. *Beds* 70.
  Certified Medicaid.
Owner Proprietary Corp (ARA Living
  Centers).

Quality Care of Waco*
2501 Maple Ave, Waco, TX, 76707
(817) 752-0311
Admin Geraldine Hatchett. *Medical Dir/Dir of
  Nursing* Robert Gassler MD.
Licensure Intermediate care. *Beds* 121.
  Certified Medicare.
Admissions Requirements Medical
  examination; Physician's request.
Staff RNs 5 (ft), 7 (pt); LPNs 6 (ft), 6 (pt);
  Nurses aides 21 (ft), 18 (pt); Occupational
  therapists 1 (pt); Speech therapists 1 (pt);
  Activities coordinators 1 (ft); Dietitians 1
  (pt); Dentists 1 (pt).
Facilities Dining room; Activities room;
  Crafts room; Laundry room; Barber/Beauty
  shop.
Activities Arts & crafts; Cards; Games;
  Reading groups; Prayer groups; Movies;
  Shopping trips; Social/Cultural gatherings.

St Elizabeth Nursing Home
400 Austin Ave, Waco, TX, 76703
(817) 756-5441
Admin Keith Perry. *Medical Dir/Dir of
  Nursing* Jan Irons, RN FNP.
Licensure Intermediate care. *Beds* 179.
  Certified Medicaid.
Owner Nonprofit Corp.
Staff Physicians 1 (pt); RNs 4 (ft), 1 (pt);
  LPNs 17 (ft); Orderlies 3 (ft); Nurses aides
  42 (ft); Physical therapists 1 (pt); Speech
  therapists 1 (pt); Activities coordinators 3
  (ft); Dietitians 1 (pt); Pastoral counselor 1
  (ft); Social worker 2 (ft).
Affiliation Roman Catholic
Facilities Dining room; Physical therapy
  room; Activities room; Chapel; Crafts room;
  Laundry room; Barber/Beauty shop; Library.
Activities Arts & crafts; Cards; Games;
  Reading groups; Prayer groups; Movies;
  Shopping trips; Social/Cultural gatherings.

Twin Oaks Retirement Center
2329 N 39th St, Waco, TX, 76708
(817) 756-3701

Admin Stephen Adams.
Licensure Intermediate care. *Beds* ICF 94.
Certified Medicaid.
Owner Proprietary Corp (ARA Living
Centers).
Facilities Dining room; Activities room;
Crafts room; Laundry room; Barber/Beauty
shop.
Activities Arts & crafts; Cards; Games;
Reading groups; Prayer groups; Movies;
Shopping trips; Social/Cultural gatherings;
Pool; Crochet; Chartered trips.

Woodland Springs Nursing Home
1010 Dallas St, Waco, TX, 76704
(817) 752-9774
Admin Virginia Atkinson. *Medical Dir/Dir of
Nursing* Carolyn C B Harmon RN.
Licensure Intermediate care. *Beds* ICF 152.
Certified Medicaid.
Owner Nonprofit Corp.
Admissions Requirements Minimum age 55;
Medical examination.
Staff RNs; LPNs; Orderlies; Nurses aides;
Activities coordinators; Dietitians;
Ophthalmologists.
Languages Spanish
Facilities Dining room; Activities room;
Crafts room; Laundry room; Barber/Beauty
shop.
Activities Arts & crafts; Cards; Games; Prayer
groups; Movies.

WAXAHACHIE

Pleasant Manor Nursing Home—Waxahachie
Access Rd, S Hwy 35, Waxahachie, TX,
75165
(214) 937-7320
Admin Steven V Cook.
Licensure Intermediate care. *Beds* ICF 102.
Certified Medicaid.
Owner Privately owned.
Admissions Requirements Minimum age 18;
Medical examination; Physician's request.
Staff RNs 1 (ft); LPNs 8 (ft), 2 (pt); Nurses
aides 24 (ft), 6 (pt); Activities coordinators 1
(ft); Dietitians 1 (ft).
Facilities Dining room; Activities room;
Chapel; Laundry room; Barber/Beauty shop.
Activities Arts & crafts; Cards; Games;
Reading groups; Prayer groups; Movies;
Shopping trips; Social/Cultural gatherings.

Renfro Nursing Home
1413 W Main St, Waxahachie, TX, 75165
(214) 937-2298
Admin Larry L Walker. *Medical Dir/Dir of
Nursing* John G Compton MD.
Licensure Skilled care; Intermediate care. *Beds*
SNF 58; ICF 98. *Certified* Medicaid;
Medicare.
Owner Proprietary Corp (Beverly Enterprises).
Admissions Requirements Physician's request.
Staff Physicians 7 (ft); RNs 2 (ft), 1 (pt);
LPNs 5 (ft), 4 (pt); Orderlies 4 (ft); Nurses
aides 17 (ft), 3 (pt); Physical therapists 1 (ft);
Reality therapists 1 (ft); Recreational
therapists 1 (ft); Occupational therapists 1
(ft); Speech therapists 1 (ft); Activities
coordinators 1 (ft), 1 (pt); Dietitians 1 (pt);
Dentists 1 (pt); Ophthalmologists 1 (pt);
Podiatrists 1 (pt).
Facilities Dining room; Activities room;
Laundry room; Barber/Beauty shop.
Activities Arts & crafts; Cards; Games;
Reading groups; Prayer groups; Movies;
Shopping trips.

WEATHERFORD

Keeneland Nursing Home*
700 S Bowie, Weatherford, TX, 76086
(817) 594-2715
Admin Luther Shuffield.

Licensure Skilled care. *Beds* 72. *Certified*
Medicaid.
Owner Proprietary Corp (Southmark Heritage
Corp).

Leisure Lodge—Weatherford*
1205 Santa Fe Dr, Weatherford, TX, 76086
(817) 594-2786
Admin Janelle Lynch. *Medical Dir/Dir of
Nursing* Dr John L Roan.
Licensure Intermediate care. *Beds* 120.
Certified Medicaid.
Owner Proprietary Corp (Beverly Enterprises).
Admissions Requirements Medical
examination; Physician's request.
Staff Physicians 19 (pt); RNs 1 (ft); LPNs 9
(ft); Nurses aides 28 (ft); Activities
coordinators 1 (ft); Dietitians 1 (ft).
Facilities Dining room; Physical therapy
room; Laundry room; Barber/Beauty shop.
Activities Arts & crafts; Cards; Games;
Reading groups; Prayer groups; Movies;
Shopping trips; Social/Cultural gatherings.

Weatherford Care Center 1*
Peaster Hwy, Weatherford, TX, 76086
(817) 594-8713
Admin John DeGrand. *Medical Dir/Dir of
Nursing* Dr John Roon.
Licensure Skilled care; Intermediate care. *Beds*
122. *Certified* Medicaid.
Owner Proprietary Corp (ARA Living
Centers).
Staff RNs 2 (ft); LPNs 10 (ft); Activities
coordinators 1 (ft); Dietitians 1 (ft).
Facilities Dining room; Physical therapy
room; Activities room; Laundry room;
Barber/Beauty shop.
Activities Arts & crafts; Cards; Games; Prayer
groups; Movies.

Weatherford Care Center 2*
315 Anderson St, Weatherford, TX, 76086
(817) 594-6461
Admin Deborah L Whitaker.
Licensure Intermediate care. *Beds* 59.
Certified Medicaid.
Owner Proprietary Corp.

WEBSTER

Manor Care—Webster
750 Texas Ave, Webster, TX, 77598
(713) 332-3496
Admin Sharan Nunn. *Medical Dir/Dir of
Nursing* Michael J Austin MD; Mollie
Jamison RN DON.
Licensure Skilled care; Intermediate care;
Non-certified. *Beds* SNF 28; ICF 65; Non-
certified 26. *Certified* Medicaid; Medicare.
Owner Proprietary Corp (Manor Care).
Admissions Requirements Minimum age 18;
Medical examination; Physician's request.
Staff Physicians; RNs; LPNs; Nurses aides;
Physical therapists; Recreational therapists;
Occupational therapists; Speech therapists;
Activities coordinators; Dietitians;
Ophthalmologists.
Facilities Dining room; Physical therapy
room; Activities room; Laundry room;
Barber/Beauty shop.
Activities Arts & crafts; Cards; Games;
Reading groups; Prayer groups; Movies;
Shopping trips; Social/Cultural gatherings;
Happy hour; Pet therapy.

WEIMAR

Parkview Manor
206 N Smith St, Weimar, TX, 78962
(409) 725-8564
Admin Carolyn Poenitzsch. *Medical Dir/Dir of
Nursing* Ottilia Klare.
Licensure Intermediate care. *Beds* ICF 68.
Certified Medicaid.
Owner Nonprofit organization/foundation.

Admissions Requirements Females only;
Medical examination.
Staff Physicians; RNs; LPNs; Nurses aides;
Activities coordinators; Dietitians.
Affiliation Methodist
Facilities Dining room; Activities room;
Crafts room; Laundry room; Barber/Beauty
shop.
Activities Arts & crafts; Cards; Games;
Reading groups; Prayer groups; Movies;
Social/Cultural gatherings.

WELLINGTON

Wellington Care Center
1506 Childress St, Wellington, TX, 79095
(806) 447-2777
Admin Angelin Anderson. *Medical Dir/Dir of
Nursing* Dr K N Kumar.
Licensure Intermediate care. *Beds* ICF 84.
Certified Medicaid.
Owner Proprietary Corp.
Admissions Requirements Physician's request.
Staff RNs 1 (pt); LPNs 6 (ft), 2 (pt);
Orderlies; Nurses aides 23 (ft), 2 (pt);
Activities coordinators 1 (ft); Dietitians 1
(pt).
Facilities Dining room; Activities room;
Crafts room; Laundry room; Barber/Beauty
shop.
Activities Arts & crafts; Cards; Games;
Reading groups; Prayer groups; Shopping
trips; Social/Cultural gatherings.

WELLS

Wells Nursing Home*
PO Box 359, May St at 2nd St, Wells, TX,
75976
(713) 867-4707
Admin Robert D Winfield.
Licensure Intermediate care. *Beds* 60.
Certified Medicaid.
Owner Proprietary Corp.

WESLACO

John Knox Village
1300 S Border Ave, Weslaco, TX, 78596
(512) 968-4575
Admin Audrey L Earl. *Medical Dir/Dir of
Nursing* Barbara Jackson RN.
Licensure Life care Retirement Community.
Beds SNF 60; Personal 16. *Certified*
Medicare.
Owner Nonprofit Corp.
Staff RNs; LPNs; Nurses aides; Activities
coordinators; Dietitians.
Facilities Dining room; Activities room;
Chapel; Crafts room; Laundry room; Barber/
Beauty shop; Library; Billards; Ice cream
parlor; Exercise room; Swimming pool;
Jacuzzi.
Activities Arts & crafts; Cards; Games;
Reading groups; Prayer groups; Movies;
Shopping trips; Social/Cultural gatherings.

Retama Manor Nursing Center—Weslaco*
721 Airport Dr, Weslaco, TX, 78596
(512) 968-8502
Admin William N Lowe.
Licensure Intermediate care. *Beds* 120.
Certified Medicaid.
Owner Proprietary Corp (ARA Living
Centers).

Valley Grande Manor
1212 S Bridge Ave, Weslaco, TX, 78596
(512) 968-2121
Admin Diane Butler. *Medical Dir/Dir of
Nursing* Janet Louitt RN.
Licensure Skilled care; Intermediate care. *Beds*
SNF 143. *Certified* Medicaid; Medicare.
Owner Nonprofit Corp.
Admissions Requirements Medical
examination; Physician's request.

Staff RNs; LPNs; Orderlies; Nurses aides; Activities coordinators; Dietitians.
Languages Spanish
Affiliation Seventh-Day Adventist
Facilities Dining room; Physical therapy room; Activities room; Chapel; Crafts room; Laundry room; Barber/Beauty shop; Library.
Activities Arts & crafts; Cards; Games; Reading groups; Prayer groups; Movies; Social/Cultural gatherings.

WEST

West Rest Haven Inc
300 Haven St, West, TX, 76691
(817) 826-5354
Admin Zona M Donohue. *Medical Dir/Dir of Nursing* Dr George Smith; Helen Kubacak.
Licensure Skilled care; Intermediate care. *Beds* SNF 91. *Certified* Medicaid; Medicare.
Owner Proprietary Corp.
Admissions Requirements Medical examination; Physician's request.
Staff Physicians 1 (ft); RNs 2 (ft); Orderlies 12 (ft); Nurses aides 22 (ft); Physical therapists 1 (ft); Occupational therapists 1 (ft); Speech therapists 1 (ft); Activities coordinators 1 (ft); Dietitians 1 (ft).
Facilities Dining room; Activities room; Chapel; Crafts room; Laundry room; Barber/Beauty shop.
Activities Arts & crafts; Social/Cultural gatherings; Pet therapy.

WEST COLUMBIA

Sweetbriar Development Center*
212 N 14th, West Columbia, TX, 77486
(713) 345-3191
Admin Leanne M K Martinsen.
Licensure Intermediate care for mentally retarded. *Beds* 120. *Certified* Medicaid.

WHARTON

Wharton Manor*
418 N Rusk St, Wharton, TX, 77488
(713) 532-5020
Admin Willa Dean Roades.
Licensure Intermediate care. *Beds* 116. *Certified* Medicaid.
Owner Proprietary Corp (ARA Living Centers).

WHEELER

Wheeler Care Center
PO Box 525, 1000 S Kiowa, Wheeler, TX, 79096
(806) 826-3505
Admin B A Hyatt. *Medical Dir/Dir of Nursing* Jessie Bailey LVN.
Licensure Intermediate care. *Beds* ICF 90. *Certified* Medicaid.
Owner Proprietary Corp.
Admissions Requirements Physician's request.
Staff RNs 1 (pt); LPNs 8 (ft), 2 (pt); Orderlies 3 (ft), 2 (pt); Nurses aides 27 (ft), 4 (pt); Activities coordinators 1 (ft); Dietitians 1 (pt).
Facilities Dining room; Activities room; Laundry room; Barber/Beauty shop; Smoking lounge.
Activities Arts & crafts; Games; Prayer groups; Movies; Shopping trips; Field trips.

WHITESBORO

Whitesboro Nursing Home Inc
1204 Sherman Dr, Whitesboro, TX, 76273
(214) 564-3508
Admin Darrell Reed. *Medical Dir/Dir of Nursing* Macel Hood DON.
Licensure Skilled care. *Beds* ICF 82. *Certified* Medicaid.

Owner Proprietary Corp.
Admissions Requirements Minimum age 21; Medical examination.
Staff RNs 1 (pt); LPNs 10 (ft), 2 (pt); Nurses aides 21 (ft), 2 (pt); Activities coordinators 1 (ft), 1 (pt).
Facilities Dining room; Physical therapy room; Activities room; Chapel; Crafts room; Laundry room; Barber/Beauty shop; Library.
Activities Arts & crafts; Games; Reading groups; Prayer groups; Movies; Social/Cultural gatherings.

WHITEWRIGHT

Whitewright Nursing Home Inc*
PO Box 808, S Bond St, Whitewright, TX, 75491
(214) 364-2772, 2774
Admin Rosalie S Geers.
Licensure Skilled care; Custodial care. *Beds* SNF 137; Custodial care 12. *Certified* Medicaid.
Owner Proprietary Corp.

WHITNEY

Park Plaza Nursing Home
1244 State Park Rd, Whitney, TX, 76692
(817) 694-2239
Admin Millie L Westbrook. *Medical Dir/Dir of Nursing* Morris R Hill MD; Sherry Jumper DON.
Licensure Intermediate care. *Beds* ICF 110. *Certified* Medicaid.
Owner Proprietary Corp (Health Enter of America).
Admissions Requirements Physician's request.
Staff RNs; LPNs; Nurses aides; Physical therapists; Recreational therapists; Speech therapists; Activities coordinators; Dietitians; Ophthalmologists; Podiatrists.
Facilities Dining room; Activities room; Laundry room; Barber/Beauty shop.
Activities Arts & crafts; Cards; Games; Reading groups; Prayer groups; Movies; Shopping trips; Social/Cultural gatherings.

Town Hall Estates Nursing Home
PO Box 878, Brazos at Washington, Whitney, TX, 76692
(817) 694-2233 or 694-5204
Admin Sue Murphy. *Medical Dir/Dir of Nursing* Maggie Williams DON.
Licensure Intermediate care. *Beds* ICF 39. *Certified* Medicaid.
Owner Nonprofit Corp.
Admissions Requirements Medical examination.
Staff LPNs 5 (ft); Nurses aides 11 (ft); Activities coordinators 1 (ft).
Affiliation Seventh-Day Adventist
Facilities Dining room; Laundry room.
Activities Arts & crafts; Games; Prayer groups; Movies; Shopping trips.

WICHITA FALLS

Care Manor—Parkway*
5105 Professional Dr, Wichita Falls, TX, 76302
(817) 766-3594
Admin Eileen M Addison.
Licensure Intermediate care. *Beds* 54. *Certified* Medicaid.
Admissions Requirements Medical examination; Physician's request.
Staff RNs 1 (pt); LPNs 3 (ft); Orderlies 2 (ft); Nurses aides 18 (pt); Activities coordinators 1 (ft); Dietitians 1 (pt).
Facilities Dining room; Activities room; Crafts room; Laundry room; Barber/Beauty shop.
Activities Arts & crafts; Games; Reading groups; Prayer groups; Shopping trips; Social/Cultural gatherings.

Cottonwood Care Center*
100 Bailey St, Wichita Falls, TX, 76307
(817) 766-0279
Admin Stephen Taras Jr.
Licensure Intermediate care. *Beds* 58. *Certified* Medicaid.
Owner Proprietary Corp (Beverly Enterprises).

Highland Nursing Center
4822 Lake Rd, Wichita Falls, TX, 76308
(817) 692-2820
Admin Eileen M Addison. *Medical Dir/Dir of Nursing* Georgia Cargal.
Licensure Intermediate care; Personal care. *Beds* ICF 90; Personal 24. *Certified* Medicaid.
Owner Proprietary Corp (Health Enter of America).
Staff LPNs 8 (ft); Orderlies 4 (ft); Nurses aides 34 (ft); Activities coordinators 1 (ft); Dietitians 1 (pt).
Activities Arts & crafts; Games; Reading groups; Prayer groups; Movies; Shopping trips.

Lane's Convalescent Home Inc*
1908 6th St, Wichita Falls, TX, 76301
(817) 322-2193
Admin Carlton Jack Lane.
Licensure Intermediate care. *Beds* 62. *Certified* Medicaid.
Owner Proprietary Corp.

Lane's Nursing Home Inc*
608 Denver, Wichita Falls, TX, 76301
(817) 322-7852
Admin Frederick D Lane.
Licensure Intermediate care. *Beds* 81. *Certified* Medicaid.
Owner Proprietary Corp.

Midwestern Parkway Heritage Manor
601 Midwestern Pkwy, Wichita Falls, TX, 76302
(817) 723-0885
Admin David Reaves.
Licensure Intermediate care. *Beds* ICF 120. *Certified* Medicaid.
Owner Proprietary Corp (National Heritage).

Monterey Care Center*
3101 10th St, Wichita Falls, TX, 76301
(817) 766-0281
Admin Marjorie Sue Moncrief.
Licensure Skilled care. *Beds* 91. *Certified* Medicaid.
Owner Proprietary Corp (Beverly Enterprises).

Pioneer Care Center—Wichita Falls*
2501 Taylor St, Wichita Falls, TX, 76309
(817) 723-7511
Admin Betty D Guyette. *Medical Dir/Dir of Nursing* Dr C F Fuller.
Licensure Intermediate care. *Beds* 52. *Certified* Medicaid.
Admissions Requirements Physician's request.
Staff RNs 1 (pt); LPNs 3 (ft); Orderlies 2 (ft); Nurses aides 8 (ft); Activities coordinators 1 (ft); Dietitians 1 (pt); Podiatrists 1 (pt).
Facilities Dining room; Activities room; Crafts room; Laundry room; Barber/Beauty shop.
Activities Arts & crafts; Cards; Games; Reading groups; Prayer groups; Movies; Shopping trips; Social/Cultural gatherings; Fishing; Sightseeing; Shows.

Pleasant Hill Nursing Home
4445 Sisk Rd, Wichita Falls, TX, 76310
(817) 692-3977
Admin Freeda Patterson. *Medical Dir/Dir of Nursing* A Chitale; Karen Liss.
Licensure Intermediate care. *Beds* ICF 35. *Certified* Medicaid.
Staff Physicians 1 (ft); RNs 1 (pt); LPNs 3 (ft), 1 (pt); Orderlies 1 (pt); Nurses aides 5 (ft), 2 (pt); Physical therapists 1 (pt); Reality

therapists 1 (pt); Activities coordinators 1
(ft); Dietitians 1 (ft); Ophthalmologists 1
(pt).
Languages Spanish
Facilities Dining room; Activities room;
Crafts room; Laundry room.
Activities Arts & crafts; Cards; Games;
Reading groups; Prayer groups; Movies;
Shopping trips; Social/Cultural gatherings.

Presbyterian Manor Inc
4600 Taft Blvd, Wichita Falls, TX, 76308
(817) 691-1710
Admin Jimmy Oakley. *Medical Dir/Dir of
Nursing* Helen Talley DON.
Licensure Intermediate care; Custodial care.
Beds ICF 43; Custodial care 14.
Owner Nonprofit Corp.
Staff RNs 2 (ft), 3 (pt); LPNs 5 (ft), 4 (pt);
Nurses aides 15 (ft), 6 (pt); Activities
coordinators 2 (ft); Dietitians 1 (ft).
Affiliation Presbyterian

Ridgeview Nursing & Convalescent Center*
4411 Henry S Grace Fwy S, Wichita Falls,
TX, 76302
(817) 767-8322
Admin Dennis Ferguson.
Licensure Intermediate care. *Beds* 148.
Certified Medicaid.
Owner Proprietary Corp (Hillhaven Corp).

Texhoma Christian Care Center
300 Loop 11, Wichita Falls, TX, 76305
(817) 723-8420
Admin Kale Martin. *Medical Dir/Dir of
Nursing* Francis Skinner LVN.
Licensure Intermediate care. *Beds* ICF 151.
Certified Medicaid.
Owner Nonprofit organization/foundation.
Admissions Requirements Minimum age 18;
Medical examination.
Staff Physicians 1 (pt); RNs 1 (ft); LPNs 15
(ft); Orderlies 2 (ft); Nurses aides 68 (ft), 2
(pt); Activities coordinators 1 (ft), 1 (pt);
Dietitians 1 (pt).
Affiliation Church of Christ
Facilities Dining room; Activities room;
Chapel; Crafts room; Laundry room; Barber/
Beauty shop.
Activities Arts & crafts; Cards; Games; Prayer
groups; Movies; Social/Cultural gatherings.

University Park Heritage Manor*
4511 Coronado, Wichita Falls, TX, 76301
(817) 692-8001
Admin Frank Conyea.
Licensure Intermediate care. *Beds* 100.
Certified Medicaid.
Owner Proprietary Corp (Southmark Heritage
Corp).

Wichita Falls Convalescent Center*
1501 7th St, Wichita Falls, TX, 76301
(817) 322-0741
Admin Elisha Y Ashcraft.
Licensure Intermediate care. *Beds* 197.
Certified Medicaid.
Owner Proprietary Corp.

Wood Convalescent Center
2400 Southwest Pkwy, Wichita Falls, TX,
76308
(817) 691-5301
Admin Mary F Wood. *Medical Dir/Dir of
Nursing* Mark Mleak MD; Gloria Jordan.
Licensure Intermediate care. *Beds* ICF 98.
Certified Medicaid.
Owner Proprietary Corp.
Admissions Requirements Medical
examination; Physician's request.
Staff RNs 1 (pt); LPNs 9 (ft), 2 (pt); Orderlies
8 (ft); Nurses aides 14 (ft), 4 (pt); Physical
therapists 1 (pt); Reality therapists 1 (pt);
Recreational therapists 1 (pt); Occupational
therapists 1 (pt); Speech therapists 1 (pt);
Activities coordinators 1 (ft); Dietitians 1
(pt).

Facilities Dining room; Activities room;
Laundry room; Barber/Beauty shop.
Activities Arts & crafts; Cards; Games;
Reading groups; Prayer groups; Shopping
trips; Social/Cultural gatherings.

WILLIS

Willis Convalescent Center*
3000 N Danville, Willis, TX, 77378
(713) 856-4312, 7013
Admin Jeanne Young.
Licensure Intermediate care. *Beds* 120.
Certified Medicaid.
Owner Proprietary Corp (ARA Living
Centers).

WILLS POINT

Free State Crestwood Inc
PO Box 368, 1448 Houston St, Wills Point,
TX, 75169
(214) 873-2542
Admin Mike Henrie. *Medical Dir/Dir of
Nursing* Sherry Martin.
Licensure Intermediate care. *Beds* ICF 120.
Certified Medicaid.
Owner Proprietary Corp.
Admissions Requirements Physician's request.
Staff RNs 1 (pt); LPNs 12 (ft); Nurses aides
38 (ft), 3 (pt); Activities coordinators 1 (ft);
Dietitians 1 (pt).
Languages Spanish
Facilities Dining room; Activities room;
Chapel; Crafts room; Laundry room; Barber/
Beauty shop; Library.
Activities Arts & crafts; Cards; Games;
Reading groups; Prayer groups; Movies;
Shopping trips; Social/Cultural gatherings.

Locust Grove Nursing Home
PO Box 393, Rte 1, Wills Point, TX, 75169
(214) 563-9445
Admin William A Reed.
Licensure Intermediate care. *Beds* 60.
Certified Medicaid.
Owner Proprietary Corp.

WINNSBORO

Whispering Pines Nursing Home Inc
910 Beech St, Winnsboro, TX, 75494
(214) 342-6616
Admin Jo Ann Milner. *Medical Dir/Dir of
Nursing* Lynda Combs.
Licensure Intermediate care. *Beds* ICF 120.
Certified Medicaid.
Owner Proprietary Corp.
Admissions Requirements Physician's request.
Staff LPNs 8 (ft), 6 (pt); Nurses aides 25 (ft),
10 (pt); Activities coordinators 1 (ft);
Dietitians 1 (ft).
Facilities Dining room; Activities room;
Crafts room; Laundry room; Barber/Beauty
shop.
Activities Arts & crafts; Cards; Games;
Reading groups; Prayer groups; Shopping
trips.

Winnsboro Nursing Home
PO Box 554, 402 S Chestnut St, Winnsboro,
TX, 75494
(214) 342-6156
Admin Mary Helen Lawrence.
Licensure Intermediate care. *Beds* 60.
Certified Medicaid.
Owner Proprietary Corp.

Winnwood Nursing Home Inc
PO Box 24, 502 E Coke Rd, Winnsboro, TX,
75494
(214) 342-6951
Admin Glennis Christenberry. *Medical Dir/Dir
of Nursing* Dr Tom Jones.
Licensure Intermediate care. *Beds* 60.
Certified Medicaid.

Owner Proprietary Corp (Southmark Heritage
Corp).
Staff Orderlies 1 (ft); Nurses aides 7 (ft);
Activities coordinators 1 (ft); 20 (ft).
Facilities Dining room; Activities room;
Crafts room; Laundry room; Barber/Beauty
shop; Library.
Activities Arts & crafts; Cards; Games; Prayer
groups; Shopping trips; Social/Cultural
gatherings.

WINTERS

Senior Citizens Nursing Home
PO Box 66, 506 Van Ness St, Winters, TX,
79567
(915) 754-4566
Admin Wanda M Laxson. *Medical Dir/Dir of
Nursing* Dr Y K Lee; Tommye J O'Dell.
Licensure Intermediate care. *Beds* ICF 48.
Certified Medicaid.
Owner Proprietary Corp.
Admissions Requirements Medical
examination; Physician's request.
Staff RNs 1 (pt); LPNs 6 (ft), 1 (pt);
Orderlies; Nurses aides 14 (ft), 3 (pt);
Physical therapists 1 (pt); Activities
coordinators 1 (ft), 1 (pt); Dietitians 1 (pt).
Facilities Dining room; Physical therapy
room; Activities room; Chapel; Laundry
room; Barber/Beauty shop; Whirlpool/spa.
Activities Arts & crafts; Cards; Games;
Reading groups; Prayer groups; Movies;
Shopping trips; Social/Cultural gatherings.

WOLFE CITY

Smith's Nursing Home*
PO Box 107, 300 Crockett, Wolfe City, TX,
75496
(214) 496-2261
Admin S E Smith.
Licensure Intermediate care. *Beds* 46.
Certified Medicaid.
Owner Proprietary Corp.

WOODVILLE

Holiday Pines Manor*
Cardinal Dr, Woodville, TX, 75979
(409) 283-3397
Admin Sondra Lankford.
Licensure Intermediate care. *Beds* 112.
Certified Medicaid.
Admissions Requirements Medical
examination.
Staff Physicians 1 (pt); RNs 1 (ft); LPNs 6
(ft); Nurses aides 60 (ft); Physical therapists
1 (pt); Occupational therapists 1 (pt); Speech
therapists 1 (pt); Activities coordinators 1
(ft); Dietitians 1 (pt); Dentists 1 (pt);
Podiatrists 1 (pt).
Facilities Dining room; Physical therapy
room; Activities room; Chapel; Crafts room;
Laundry room; Barber/Beauty shop.
Activities Arts & crafts; Cards; Games;
Reading groups; Prayer groups; Movies;
Shopping trips; Social/Cultural gatherings;
Gardening.

Woodville Convalescent Center*
102 N Beach St, Woodville, TX, 75979
(713) 283-2555
Admin Judy G McKee.
Licensure Intermediate care. *Beds* 98.
Certified Medicaid.
Owner Proprietary Corp (Cantex Healthcare
Centers).

WORTHAM

Leisure Lodge—Wortham
Twin Circle Addition, Wortham, TX, 76693
(817) 765-3377

Admin Margaret W Brown. *Medical Dir/Dir of Nursing* N D Buchmeyer MD; Janet McDade DON.
Licensure Intermediate care. *Beds* ICF 102. *Certified* Medicaid.
Owner Proprietary Corp (Beverly Enterprises).
Admissions Requirements Physician's request.
Staff RNs 1 (ft); LPNs 5 (ft), 1 (pt); Nurses aides 14 (ft), 3 (pt); Activities coordinators 1 (ft); Dietitians 1 (ft).
Facilities Dining room; Physical therapy room; Chapel; Laundry room; Barber/Beauty shop.
Activities Arts & crafts; Cards; Games; Prayer groups; Shopping trips.

WYLIE

Hillcrest Manor
PO Box 550, 300 E Brown St, Wylie, TX, 75098
(214) 442-3553
Admin Theresa Ward. *Medical Dir/Dir of Nursing* Mildred Cole RN DON, Edward Brown MD.
Licensure Intermediate care. *Beds* ICF 102. *Certified* Medicaid.
Owner Proprietary Corp (Summit Health Ltd).
Admissions Requirements Medical examination; Physician's request.
Staff Physicians 1 (pt); RNs 1 (ft); LPNs 10 (ft); Orderlies 1 (ft); Nurses aides 30 (ft); Physical therapists 1 (pt); Reality therapists 1 (pt); Recreational therapists 1 (pt); Occupational therapists 1 (pt); Speech therapists 1 (pt); Activities coordinators 1 (ft); Dietitians 1 (ft); Podiatrists 1 (pt).
Facilities Dining room; Activities room; Laundry room; Barber/Beauty shop; 2 sunrooms.
Activities Arts & crafts; Games; Reading groups.

YOAKUM

Stevens Nursing Home Inc*
205 Walters St, Yoakum, TX, 77995
(512) 293-3544
Admin Chesley Stevens. *Medical Dir/Dir of Nursing* F L Merian MD.
Licensure Skilled care; Intermediate care. *Beds* 106. *Certified* Medicaid.
Admissions Requirements Minimum age 16; Medical examination; Physician's request.
Staff RNs 2 (ft), 1 (pt); LPNs 8 (ft), 6 (pt); Activities coordinators 1 (ft); Dietitians 1 (ft), 1 (pt).
Facilities Dining room; Activities room; Chapel; Crafts room; Laundry room; Barber/Beauty shop.
Activities Arts & crafts; Games; Movies; Social/Cultural gatherings.

Yoakum Memorial Nursing Home*
Hwy 77-A Business Rte, Yoakum, TX, 77995
(512) 293-2533
Admin C R Jamison.

Licensure Intermediate care. *Beds* 60. *Certified* Medicaid.
Staff RNs 1 (pt); LPNs 2 (ft), 3 (pt); Nurses aides 10 (ft), 4 (pt); Activities coordinators 1 (ft); 12 (ft), 5 (pt).
Facilities Dining room; Activities room; Laundry room; Barber/Beauty shop.
Activities Arts & crafts; Games; Prayer groups; Shopping trips.

YORKTOWN

Yorktown Manor Home
670 W 4th St, Yorktown, TX, 78164
(512) 564-2275
Admin Lyndal S Pattillo. *Medical Dir/Dir of Nursing* Gloria Suggs LVN.
Licensure Intermediate care. *Beds* ICF 92. *Certified* Medicaid; Medicare.
Owner Proprietary Corp (Diversicare Corp).
Admissions Requirements Minimum age 16; Physician's request.
Staff Physicians 2 (ft); RNs 1 (pt); LPNs 3 (ft); Orderlies 4 (ft); Nurses aides 17 (ft); Physical therapists 1 (pt); Activities coordinators 2 (ft); Dietitians 1 (ft); Dentists 1 (ft); Podiatrists 1 (pt).
Languages Spanish, Polish
Facilities Dining room; Activities room; Chapel; Laundry room; Barber/Beauty shop.
Activities Arts & crafts; Cards; Games; Reading groups; Prayer groups; Movies; Shopping trips; Social/Cultural gatherings; Parties.

UTAH

AMERICAN FORK

Utah State Training School
765 N 900 E, American Fork, UT, 84003
(801) 756-6022
Admin Jerry Pandoy. *Medical Dir/Dir of Nursing* David Green MD.
Licensure Intermediate care for mentally retarded. *Beds* ICF/MR 550. *Certified* Medicaid; Medicare.
Owner Publicly owned.
Staff Physicians 2 (ft), 20 (pt); RNs 16 (ft); LPNs 45 (ft); Physical therapists 4 (ft); Recreational therapists 10 (ft); Occupational therapists 4 (ft); Speech therapists 10 (ft); Dietitians 2 (ft).

BLANDING

Four Corners Regional Care Center
930 N 400 W (39-3), Blanding, UT, 84511
(801) 678-2251
Admin Rayburn E Jack. *Medical Dir/Dir of Nursing* James D Redd; Kathleen G Lyman.
Licensure Skilled care. *Beds* SNF 78. *Certified* Medicaid; Medicare.
Owner Proprietary Corp.
Admissions Requirements Medical examination; Physician's request.
Staff RNs; LPNs; Orderlies; Nurses aides; Speech therapists.
Languages Ute, Navajo
Facilities Dining room; Physical therapy room; Activities room; Laundry room; Barber/Beauty shop; Library.
Activities Arts & crafts; Cards; Games; Reading groups; Movies; Shopping trips; Social/Cultural gatherings; Church services (3 denominations).

BOUNTIFUL

Bountiful Convalescent Center*
350 S 400 E, Bountiful, UT, 84010
(801) 298-2291
Admin Kelly Gill. *Medical Dir/Dir of Nursing* Dr Joseph Jensen.
Licensure Skilled care; Intermediate care. *Beds* 112. *Certified* Medicaid; Medicare.
Owner Proprietary Corp (Care Enterprises).
Admissions Requirements Physician's request.
Staff Physicians 1 (pt); RNs 5 (ft), 3 (pt); LPNs 5 (ft), 5 (pt); Nurses aides 36 (ft), 10 (pt); Recreational therapists 1 (ft); Occupational therapists 1 (pt); Speech therapists 1 (pt); Activities coordinators 1 (ft); Dietitians 1 (pt); Podiatrists 1 (pt).
Facilities Dining room; Physical therapy room; Activities room; Laundry room; Barber/Beauty shop; Library; Lobby.
Activities Cards; Games; Reading groups; Prayer groups; Shopping trips; Parties; Bingo; Excercises.

Bountiful Nursing Home*
130 E 100 N, Bountiful, UT, 84010
(801) 295-3003
Admin Sybel Simmonds.
Licensure Intermediate care. *Beds* 23.
Certified Medicaid; Medicare.

Brookside Manor Nursing Home*
340 N 100 W, Bountiful, UT, 84010
(801) 295-8112
Admin Jennifer Ready.
Licensure Intermediate care. *Beds* 24.
Certified Medicaid.

Park View Nursing Home
PO Box 520, 523 N Main St, Bountiful, UT, 84010
(801) 298-2234
Admin Dean Allen Bithell. *Medical Dir/Dir of Nursing* Annette Bithell.
Licensure Intermediate care. *Beds* ICF 38.
Certified Medicaid.
Owner Privately owned.
Admissions Requirements Medical examination; Physician's request.
Staff Physicians 1 (pt); RNs 1 (pt); LPNs 5 (ft); Orderlies 3 (ft); Nurses aides 12 (ft); Recreational therapists 1 (ft); Dietitians 1 (pt).
Languages Spanish, German
Facilities Dining room; Activities room; Crafts room; Laundry room; Barber/Beauty shop.
Activities Arts & crafts; Cards; Games; Reading groups; Prayer groups; Movies; Shopping trips; Social/Cultural gatherings; Touring rides; Picnic outings.

South Davis Community Hospital Inc
401 S 400 E, Bountiful, UT, 84010
(801) 295-2361
Admin Gordon W Bennett. *Medical Dir/Dir of Nursing* Philip L Bryson MD; Ione Ca.
Licensure Skilled care; Sub-Acute Hospital. *Beds* SNF 60; Sub-Acute Hospital 17.
Certified Medicaid; Medicare.
Owner Nonprofit Corp.
Admissions Requirements Minimum age Birth (pediatric unit).
Staff Physicians 3 (pt); RNs 4 (ft), 7 (pt); LPNs 9 (ft), 6 (pt); Orderlies 1 (ft); Nurses aides 12 (ft), 9 (pt); Physical therapists 1 (ft), 1 (pt); Recreational therapists 2 (ft); Occupational therapists 1 (pt); Speech therapists 1 (ft); Activities coordinators 1 (ft); Dietitians 1 (ft); Dentists 1 (pt); Ophthalmologists 1 (pt); Podiatrists 1 (pt); Social workers 1 (ft).
Facilities Dining room; Physical therapy room; Activities room; Crafts room; Barber/Beauty shop; Small store.
Activities Arts & crafts; Cards; Games; Reading groups; Prayer groups; Movies; Social/Cultural gatherings; Van rides.

BRIGHAM CITY

Godfrey's Foothill Retreat*
775 N 2nd E, Brigham City, UT, 84302
(801) 723-6038 or 723-8772

Admin Michael J Godfrey Sr. *Medical Dir/Dir of Nursing* John R Markeson.
Licensure Intermediate care. *Beds* 50.
Certified Medicaid.
Facilities Dining room; Physical therapy room; Activities room; Chapel; Crafts room; Laundry room; Barber/Beauty shop.
Activities Arts & crafts; Cards; Games; Reading groups; Prayer groups; Movies; Shopping trips.

Pioneer Memorial Nursing Home
815 S 200 W, Brigham City, UT, 84302
(801) 723-5289
Admin Margo Eberhard. *Medical Dir/Dir of Nursing* Dr Lynn Q Beard; Marie Olsen RN DON.
Licensure Skilled care; Intermediate care. *Beds* SNF 34; ICF 42. *Certified* Medicaid; Medicare.
Owner Publicly owned.
Admissions Requirements Medical examination; Physician's request.
Staff RNs 2 (ft), 5 (pt); LPNs 2 (ft), 3 (pt); Orderlies 1 (ft); Nurses aides 21 (ft), 6 (pt); Physical therapists 1 (pt); Recreational therapists 2 (ft); Occupational therapists 1 (pt); Speech therapists 1 (pt); Activities coordinators; Dietitians 1 (pt); Dentist.
Facilities Dining room; Physical therapy room; Activities room; Crafts room; Laundry room; Barber/Beauty shop.
Activities Arts & crafts; Cards; Games; Reading groups; Movies; Shopping trips; Social/Cultural gatherings; Bus rides; Exercises; Church service.

CEDAR CITY

Cedar Manor*
679 S Sunset Dr, Cedar City, UT, 84720
(801) 586-6481
Admin F Lee Bistline. *Medical Dir/Dir of Nursing* Robert D Corry MD.
Licensure Intermediate care. *Beds* 27.
Certified Medicaid.
Admissions Requirements Medical examination; Physician's request.
Staff Physicians 1 (pt); RNs 2 (ft); LPNs 1 (ft); Orderlies 1 (pt); Nurses aides 6 (ft), 4 (pt); Physical therapists 1 (pt); Recreational therapists 1 (ft); Occupational therapists 1 (pt); Speech therapists 1 (pt); Activities coordinators 1 (ft); Dietitians 1 (pt); Dentists 1 (pt); Ophthalmologists 1 (pt); Podiatrists 1 (pt); Audiologists 1 (pt).
Affiliation Church of Latter-Day Saints (Mormon)
Facilities Dining room; Activities room; Crafts room; Laundry room.
Activities Arts & crafts; Cards; Games; Reading groups; Prayer groups; Movies; Shopping trips; Social/Cultural gatherings.

Valley View Medical Center
595 S 75 E, Cedar City, UT, 84720
(801) 586-6587

Admin Mark Dalley. *Medical Dir/Dir of Nursing* Nancy Willets RN.
Licensure Skilled care. *Beds* 48. *Certified* Medicaid; Medicare.
Owner Nonprofit organization/foundation.
Admissions Requirements Physician's request.
Staff Physicians 21 (ft); RNs 32 (ft); LPNs 2 (ft); Nurses aides 3 (ft); Physical therapists 1 (ft); Recreational therapists 1 (ft); Speech therapists 1 (ft); Activities coordinators 1 (ft); Dietitians 1 (ft); Dentists 1 (ft); Ophthalmologists 1 (ft); Podiatrists 1 (ft).
Languages Spanish
Facilities Dining room; Physical therapy room; Activities room; Crafts room; Laundry room.
Activities Arts & crafts; Cards; Games; Reading groups; Movies; Social/Cultural gatherings.

CLEARFIELD

CareWest Clearfield Nursing & Rehabilitation Center
1450 S 1500 E, Clearfield, UT, 84015
(801) 773-6553
Admin Karen Stoddard. *Medical Dir/Dir of Nursing* Dr De J Cutler; Rose Bauman RN DON.
Licensure Skilled care; Intermediate care. *Beds* SNF 100; Residential Retirement care 10. *Certified* Medicaid; Medicare.
Owner Proprietary Corp (Care Enterprises).
Admissions Requirements Medical examination; Physician's request.
Staff Physicians 1 (pt); RNs 6 (ft); LPNs 7 (ft); Orderlies 2 (ft); Nurses aides 50 (ft); Physical therapists 2 (ft); Recreational therapists 1 (ft); Occupational therapists 1 (pt); Speech therapists 1 (pt); Dietitians 1 (ft); Ophthalmologists 1 (pt).
Languages Spanish, Sign
Facilities Dining room; Physical therapy room; Activities room; Chapel; Crafts room; Laundry room; Barber/Beauty shop; Library.
Activities Arts & crafts; Cards; Games; Reading groups; Prayer groups; Movies; Shopping trips; Social/Cultural gatherings; BBQs.

DELTA

West Millard Care Center
275 W 100 S, Delta, UT, 84624
(801) 864-2944
Admin Roy E Barraclough. *Medical Dir/Dir of Nursing* Brent Black MD; Margaret Baker RN DON.
Licensure Intermediate care. *Beds* ICF 36. *Certified* Medicaid; Medicare.
Admissions Requirements Medical examination; Physician's request.
Staff Physicians 1 (ft); RNs 1 (ft); LPNs 4 (ft); Orderlies 1 (ft); Nurses aides 10 (ft); Physical therapists; Recreational therapists; Dietitians.
Languages Spanish, German, French
Facilities Dining room; Physical therapy room; Activities room; Crafts room; Laundry room; Library.
Activities Arts & crafts; Games; Reading groups; Movies; Shopping trips; Visits to parks.

DRAPER

Lanore's Nursing Home*
12701 S 950 E, Draper, UT, 84020
(801) 571-2704
Admin Don B Searle.
Licensure Skilled care; Intermediate care. *Beds* SNF 9; ICF 63. *Certified* Medicaid.

FERRON

Emery County Nursing Home
PO Box 936, Ferron, UT, 84523
(801) 384-2303, 384-2301
Admin John W Bramall. *Medical Dir/Dir of Nursing* Dr Konrad Kotrady; Marianna Pugmire.
Licensure Skilled care; Intermediate care. *Beds* SNF 50. *Certified* Medicaid; Medicare; VA.
Owner Publicly owned.
Admissions Requirements Medical examination; Physician's request.
Staff Physicians 1 (pt); RNs 2 (ft), 1 (pt); LPNs 5 (ft), 2 (pt); Nurses aides 10 (ft), 5 (pt); Physical therapists 1 (pt); Reality therapists 1 (pt); Recreational therapists 1 (ft); Speech therapists 1 (pt); Activities coordinators 1 (ft); Dietitians 1 (ft).
Facilities Dining room; Physical therapy room; Activities room; Chapel; Crafts room; Laundry room; Barber/Beauty shop.
Activities Arts & crafts; Cards; Games; Reading groups; Movies; Shopping trips; Social/Cultural gatherings.

GUNNISON

Gunnison Valley Hospital*
60 E 1st N, Gunnison, UT, 84634
(801) 528-7246
Admin Dale A Rosenlund.
Licensure Skilled care; Intermediate care. *Beds* SNF 12; ICF 9.

HEBER CITY

CareWest Heber Nursing Center
160 W 500 N, Heber City, UT, 84032
(801) 654-0521, 654-4417
Admin Todd V Winder. *Medical Dir/Dir of Nursing* Dr William Ferguson; Janet Matthews DON.
Licensure Intermediate care. *Beds* ICF 49. *Certified* Medicaid.
Owner Proprietary Corp (Care Enterprises).
Admissions Requirements Medical examination; Physician's request.
Staff Physicians 1 (pt); RNs 1 (pt); LPNs 4 (ft); Nurses aides 9 (ft), 4 (pt); Physical therapists 1 (pt); Recreational therapists 1 (pt); Occupational therapists 1 (pt); Speech therapists 1 (pt); Activities coordinators 1 (pt); Dietitians 1 (pt); Ophthalmologists 1 (pt); Volunteers.
Facilities Dining room; Activities room; Crafts room; Laundry room; Barber/Beauty shop; Resident park; Conversation patio.
Activities Arts & crafts; Cards; Games; Reading groups; Movies; Shopping trips; Social/Cultural gatherings; Field trips; Exercise groups; Church service.

Wasatch County Hospital—Skilled Nursing Facility*
55 S 500 E, Heber City, UT, 84032
(801) 654-2500
Admin Wayne Terry. *Medical Dir/Dir of Nursing* Dr G D Pitts.
Licensure Skilled care; Intermediate care. *Beds* 15. *Certified* Medicaid; Medicare.
Admissions Requirements Medical examination; Physician's request.
Staff RNs 1 (ft); LPNs 1 (ft), 1 (pt); Nurses aides 5 (ft); Physical therapists 1 (ft); Recreational therapists 1 (ft); Speech therapists 1 (pt); Activities coordinators 1 (ft); Dietitians 1 (pt).
Facilities Dining room; Physical therapy room; Activities room.
Activities Arts & crafts; Cards; Games; Reading groups; Prayer groups; Movies.

HURRICANE

Birk's Mountain Home*
PO Box 904, Hurricane, UT, 84737
(801) 635-2558
Admin Norene Birk.
Licensure Intermediate care. *Beds* 24. *Certified* Medicaid.
Staff Physicians 1 (pt); RNs 1 (ft); LPNs 2 (ft); Nurses aides 7 (ft), 2 (pt); Recreational therapists 1 (pt); Dietitians 1 (pt); Dentists 1 (pt); Ophthalmologists 1 (pt); Podiatrists 1 (pt).
Facilities Dining room; Physical therapy room; Activities room; Laundry room; Barber/Beauty shop.
Activities Arts & crafts; Games; Reading groups; Movies; Shopping trips.

KANAB

Kane County Hospital—Skilled Nursing Facility
200 W 300 N, Kanab, UT, 84741
(801) 644-5811
Admin Mark P Toohey. *Medical Dir/Dir of Nursing* Rosalie Esplin RN.
Licensure Skilled care; Intermediate care; Acute care. *Beds* SNF 13; ICF; Acute care 20. *Certified* Medicaid; Medicare.
Owner Publicly owned.
Staff Physicians 3 (ft); RNs 5 (ft); LPNs 2 (ft); Nurses aides 12 (ft); Physical therapists 1 (ft); Recreational therapists 1 (ft); Activities coordinators 1 (ft); Dietitians 1 (ft); Ophthalmologists 1 (ft).
Facilities Dining room; Physical therapy room; Activities room; Laundry room.
Activities Arts & crafts; Games; Reading groups.

LEHI

Larsen Nursing Home*
651 E 2nd S, Lehi, UT, 84043
(801) 768-3631
Admin Maxine H Larsen.
Licensure Intermediate care. *Beds* 26. *Certified* Medicaid.

LINDON

Lindon Care & Training Center
680 N State Rd, PO Box 457, Lindon, UT, 84062
(801) 785-2179
Admin Joyce Halling. *Medical Dir/Dir of Nursing* William Parker MD.
Licensure Intermediate care for mentally retarded. *Beds* 66.
Admissions Requirements Minimum age 12; Females only; Medical examination; Physician's request.
Staff Physicians 1 (pt); RNs 1 (pt); LPNs 6 (ft); Nurses aides 25 (ft), 25 (pt); Physical therapists 1 (pt); Reality therapists 1 (ft); Recreational therapists 1 (pt); Occupational therapists 1 (pt); Speech therapists 1 (pt); Activities coordinators 1 (ft); Dietitians 1 (pt); Dentists 1 (pt); Ophthalmologists 1 (pt); Podiatrists 1 (pt).
Facilities Dining room; Activities room; Crafts room; Laundry room; Barber/Beauty shop.
Activities Arts & crafts; Cards; Games; Reading groups; Prayer groups; Movies; Shopping trips; Social/Cultural gatherings.

LOGAN

Sunshine Terrace Foundation Inc
PO Box 3207, 225 N 200 W, Logan, UT, 84321
(801) 752-0411

Admin Sara V Sinclair. *Medical Dir/Dir of Nursing* Merrill C Daines MD; Alyn Bosch RN DON.
Licensure Skilled care; Intermediate care; Adult day center; Alzheimer's wing. *Beds* SNF 96; ICF 76. *Certified* Medicaid; Medicare; VA.
Owner Nonprofit organization/foundation.
Admissions Requirements Medical examination; Physician's request; Must have need for 24-hour care.
Staff RNs 12 (ft), 24 (pt); LPNs 16 (ft), 8 (pt); Orderlies; Nurses aides 12 (ft), 53 (pt); Recreational therapists 6 (ft); Activities coordinators 1 (ft); Rehabilitation aides 10 (ft), 1 (pt); Social workers 2 (ft).
Languages Spanish, French
Facilities Dining room; Physical therapy room; Activities room; Crafts room; Laundry room; Barber/Beauty shop; Library; Pharmacy; Dental room; Patios; Outdoor walking paths; Handicapped van & bus; Adult day center.
Activities Arts & crafts; Cards; Games; Reading groups; Prayer groups; Movies; Shopping trips; Social/Cultural gatherings; Residents council; Family council; Lecture series; Reality orientation; Current events; Cooking; Woodworking; Reminiscence group.

MAYFIELD

Mayfield Manor*
Center St, Mayfield, UT, 84643
(801) 528-3550
Admin Eugene S Bartholonew.
Licensure Intermediate care. *Beds* 37.
Certified Medicaid.

MENDON

Mendon Care Center
125 E 1st E, Mendon, UT, 84325
(801) 753-6490
Admin Richard L Wheeler. *Medical Dir/Dir of Nursing* Galen S McQuarrie MD.
Licensure Intermediate care. *Beds* ICF 43. *Certified* Medicaid.
Owner Proprietary Corp (National Heritage).
Staff RNs 2 (ft), 1 (pt); LPNs 3 (ft); Orderlies 4 (ft); Nurses aides 7 (ft), 3 (pt); Recreational therapists 1 (ft); Activities coordinators 1 (ft); Dietitians 1 (pt).
Facilities Dining room; Physical therapy room; Activities room; Chapel; Crafts room; Laundry room; Barber/Beauty shop.
Activities Arts & crafts; Cards; Games; Reading groups; Prayer groups; Movies; Shopping trips; Social/Cultural gatherings.

MILFORD

Milford Valley Memorial—Skilled Nursing Facility
451 N Main St, Milford, UT, 84751
(801) 387-2411
Admin Mary Wiseman.
Licensure Skilled care; Intermediate care. *Beds* SNF 6; ICF 18. *Certified* Medicaid; Medicare.
Owner Nonprofit Corp.
Admissions Requirements Physician's request.
Staff Physicians 2 (ft); RNs 6 (ft); LPNs 1 (ft); Nurses aides 6 (ft), 6 (pt); Recreational therapists 2 (pt); Dietitians 1 (pt).
Facilities Dining room; Activities room; Laundry room; Barber/Beauty shop; Library.
Activities Arts & crafts; Games; Reading groups; Prayer groups; Social/Cultural gatherings; Bus rides.

NEPHI

Colonial Manor Nursing & Convalescent Center*
71 N Main, Nephi, UT, 84648
(801) 623-0511
Admin Juanita Crawford. *Medical Dir/Dir of Nursing* Dr Catrett.
Licensure Intermediate care. *Beds* 64. *Certified* Medicaid.
Admissions Requirements Medical examination; Physician's request.
Staff RNs 2 (ft), 2 (pt); LPNs 2 (pt); Orderlies 2 (pt); Nurses aides 26 (ft); Recreational therapists 1 (ft); Activities coordinators 1 (ft); Dietitians 1 (pt).
Facilities Dining room; Activities room; Chapel; Laundry room; Barber/Beauty shop.
Activities Arts & crafts; Cards; Games; Reading groups; Prayer groups; Movies; Shopping trips; Social/Cultural gatherings.

OGDEN

Aspen Care Center*
2325 Madison Ave, Ogden, UT, 84401
(801) 399-5846
Admin Merle Bellon. *Medical Dir/Dir of Nursing* John Newton MD.
Licensure Skilled care; Intermediate care. *Beds* SNF 54; ICF 18. *Certified* Medicaid; Medicare.
Admissions Requirements Medical examination; Physician's request.
Staff Physicians 1 (ft); RNs 3 (ft); LPNs 13 (ft); Orderlies 4 (ft); Nurses aides 24 (ft); Physical therapists 1 (pt); Reality therapists 1 (pt); Recreational therapists 1 (pt); Occupational therapists 1 (pt); Speech therapists 1 (pt); Activities coordinators 1 (ft); Dietitians 1 (ft); Dentists 1 (pt); Ophthalmologists 1 (pt); Podiatrists 1 (pt); Audiologists 1 (pt).
Facilities Dining room; Physical therapy room; Activities room; Laundry room; Barber/Beauty shop; Library; Lounge/ smoking area.
Activities Arts & crafts; Cards; Games; Reading groups; Prayer groups; Movies; Shopping trips; Social/Cultural gatherings; Fishing trips; Song fest weekly.

CareWest Mt Ogden
375 E 5350 South, Ogden, UT, 84403
(801) 479-5700
Admin Gary Kelso. *Medical Dir/Dir of Nursing* Dr J Newton; Pam Russell.
Licensure Skilled care. *Beds* SNF 120. *Certified* Medicaid; Medicare.
Owner Proprietary Corp (Care Enterprises).
Admissions Requirements Medical examination; Physician's request.
Staff RNs 16 (ft), 2 (pt); LPNs 2 (ft), 1 (pt); Orderlies 3 (ft); Nurses aides 45 (ft), 5 (pt); Physical therapists 5 (ft), 1 (pt); Reality therapists 1 (ft), 1 (pt); Recreational therapists 1 (ft), 1 (pt); Occupational therapists 1 (pt); Speech therapists 1 (pt); Activities coordinators 1 (pt); Dietitians 1 (pt).
Facilities Dining room; Physical therapy room; Activities room; Crafts room; Laundry room; Barber/Beauty shop; Library.
Activities Arts & crafts; Cards; Games; Reading groups; Prayer groups; Movies; Shopping trips; Social/Cultural gatherings.

Country Meadows*
5865 Wasatch Dr, Ogden, UT, 84403
(801) 479-8480
Admin Eva Barney. *Medical Dir/Dir of Nursing* LaMar Rogers MD.
Licensure Skilled care; Intermediate care. *Beds* SNF 32; ICF 60. *Certified* Medicaid.
Staff Physicians 1 (ft), 6 (pt); RNs 3 (ft), 2 (pt); LPNs 5 (pt), 4 (pt); Orderlies 3 (ft), 1 (pt); Nurses aides 20 (ft), 14 (pt); Physical

therapists 1 (ft); Recreational therapists 1 (ft); Occupational therapists 1 (ft); Speech therapists 1 (ft); Activities coordinators 1 (ft); Dietitians 1 (ft); Podiatrists 1 (ft).

Crestwood Care Center*
3665 Brinker Ave, Ogden, UT, 84403
(801) 399-0964
Admin Inge Glover.
Licensure Skilled care; Intermediate care. *Beds* SNF 32; ICF 25. *Certified* Medicaid.

McKay-Dee Transitional Care Center
3939 Harrison Blvd, Ogden, UT, 84409
(801) 625-2380
Admin Kent F Meacham. *Medical Dir/Dir of Nursing* Paul Southwick MD; Marie Willis DON.
Licensure Skilled care. *Beds* SNF 31. *Certified* Medicaid; Medicare.
Owner Nonprofit Corp.
Staff RNs 3 (ft), 4 (pt); Nurses aides 5 (ft), 6 (pt); Recreational therapists 1 (pt).
Languages Spanish
Facilities Dining room; Activities room.
Activities Arts & crafts; Cards; Games.

Ogden Care Center North
524 E 800 N, Ogden, UT, 84404
(801) 782-3740
Admin Patricia M Rothey. *Medical Dir/Dir of Nursing* Jack D Wahlen MD; Keely Bunderson DNS.
Licensure Skilled care; Intermediate care. *Beds* SNF 33; ICF 71. *Certified* Medicaid; Medicare.
Owner Proprietary Corp.
Admissions Requirements Medical examination; Physician's request.
Staff Physicians 1 (ft); RNs 8 (ft); LPNs 7 (ft); Orderlies 2 (ft); Nurses aides 32 (ft); Physical therapists 1 (ft); Recreational therapists 1 (ft); Occupational therapists 1 (ft); Speech therapists 1 (ft); Activities coordinators 1 (ft); Dietitians 1 (ft); Ophthalmologists 1 (ft); Podiatrists 1 (ft).
Languages Spanish
Facilities Dining room; Physical therapy room; Activities room; Crafts room; Laundry room; Barber/Beauty shop; Library.
Activities Arts & crafts; Cards; Games; Reading groups; Prayer groups; Movies; Shopping trips; Social/Cultural gatherings.

Wasatch Care Center
3430 Harrison Blvd, Ogden, UT, 84403
(801) 399-5609
Admin Steven L Call. *Medical Dir/Dir of Nursing* Barbara Stratford RN.
Licensure Skilled care. *Beds* SNF 69. *Certified* Medicaid; Medicare.
Owner Proprietary Corp (Hillhaven Corp).
Admissions Requirements Minimum age 21; Medical examination; Physician's request.
Staff Physicians 1 (pt); RNs 2 (ft), 4 (pt); LPNs 4 (pt), 4 (pt); Orderlies 4 (ft), 1 (pt); Nurses aides 18 (ft), 10 (pt); Physical therapists 1 (pt); Reality therapists 1 (pt); Recreational therapists 1 (pt); Occupational therapists 1 (pt); Speech therapists 1 (pt); Activities coordinators 1 (ft); Dietitians 1 (pt).
Languages Spanish
Facilities Dining room; Physical therapy room; Activities room; Barber/Beauty shop.
Activities Arts & crafts; Games; Reading groups; Prayer groups; Movies; Shopping trips; Social/Cultural gatherings.

Wide Horizons Care Center
910 Monroe Blvd, Ogden, UT, 84404
(801) 399-5876
Admin Dale Sweat. *Medical Dir/Dir of Nursing* Laureen Jacobson.
Licensure Intermediate care for mentally retarded. *Beds* ICF/MR 83. *Certified* Medicaid.
Owner Proprietary Corp (National Heritage).

Staff RNs 1 (ft); LPNs 3 (ft), 1 (pt); Nurses aides 31 (ft); Physical therapists 1 (ft), 1 (pt); Recreational therapists 1 (ft); Occupational therapists 1 (pt); Speech therapists 1 (pt); Activities coordinators 1 (ft); Dietitians 1 (pt); Ophthalmologists 1 (pt); Podiatrists 1 (pt); QMRPs 8 (ft).
Languages Spanish
Facilities Dining room; Physical therapy room; Activities room; Crafts room; Laundry room; Barber shop.
Activities Arts & crafts; Cards; Games; Reading groups; Movies; Shopping trips; Social/Cultural gatherings.

OREM

Central Utah Rehabilitation & Convalescent Center*
575 E 1400 S, Orem, UT, 84057
(801) 225-4741
Admin Robert G Conley.
Licensure Skilled care; Intermediate care. *Beds* SNF 100; ICF 20. *Certified* Medicaid; Medicare.
Owner Proprietary Corp (Care Enterprises).

Hidden Hollow Rest Home*
261 W 20th S, Orem, UT, 84057
(801) 225-2145
Admin H Dale Goodwin. *Medical Dir/Dir of Nursing* Dr Kraig Jenson.
Licensure Intermediate care for mentally retarded. *Beds* 43.
Staff Physicians; RNs 1 (pt); LPNs 1 (ft), 3 (pt); Orderlies 7 (ft); Nurses aides 8 (ft); Recreational therapists 1 (ft); Activities coordinators 1 (ft), 4 (pt).
Facilities Dining room; Physical therapy room; Activities room; Chapel; Crafts room; Laundry room.
Activities Arts & crafts; Cards; Games; Reading groups; Prayer groups; Movies; Shopping trips; Social/Cultural gatherings.

Lakecrest Development Center*
394 W 4th N, Orem, UT, 84057
(801) 225-9292
Admin Rich Dunkley. *Medical Dir/Dir of Nursing* Dr Robert Clark.
Licensure Intermediate care for mentally retarded. *Beds* 75.
Staff Physicians; RNs; LPNs; Orderlies; Nurses aides; Physical therapists; Reality therapists; Recreational therapists; Occupational therapists; Speech therapists; Activities coordinators; Dietitians; Dentists; Ophthalmologists; Podiatrists; Audiologists.
Facilities Dining room; Physical therapy room; Activities room; Crafts room; Laundry room; Barber/Beauty shop.
Activities Arts & crafts; Cards; Games; Reading groups; Prayer groups; Movies; Shopping trips; Social/Cultural gatherings; Programing for the mentally retarded.

Timpanogos Valley Care Center*
740 N 300 E, Orem, UT, 84057
(801) 224-0921
Admin Dave Scott.
Licensure Skilled care; Intermediate care. *Beds* SNF 48; ICF 40. *Certified* Medicaid; Medicare.
Staff Physicians 2 (ft); RNs 4 (ft), 2 (pt); LPNs 12 (ft), 8 (pt); Orderlies 4 (ft), 2 (pt); Nurses aides 14 (ft), 6 (pt); Physical therapists 1 (ft); Reality therapists 2 (ft); Recreational therapists 2 (ft); Occupational therapists 1 (ft); Speech therapists 2 (ft); Activities coordinators 1 (ft); Dietitians 1 (ft); Dentists 1 (ft); Podiatrists 1 (ft); Audiologists 2 (ft).
Facilities Dining room; Physical therapy room; Activities room; Chapel; Crafts room; Laundry room; Barber/Beauty shop.
Activities Arts & crafts; Cards; Games; Reading groups; Prayer groups; Movies; Shopping trips; Social/Cultural gatherings.

Topham's Tiny Tots Care Center
247 N 100 E, Orem, UT, 84057
(801) 225-0323
Admin Lorraine Topham. *Medical Dir/Dir of Nursing* Richard Farnsworth MD; Linda Hallet LPN DON.
Licensure Intermediate care for mentally retarded. *Beds* ICF/MR 50. *Certified* Medicaid.
Owner Proprietary Corp.
Admissions Requirements Minimum age 0-11; Medical examination; Physician's request.
Staff Physicians 1 (pt); RNs 1 (pt); LPNs 5 (pt); Nurses aides 40 (ft); Physical therapists 2 (pt); Recreational therapists 1 (pt); Occupational therapists 3 (pt); Speech therapists 1 (pt); Activities coordinators 1 (ft); Dietitians 1 (pt).
Facilities Dining room; Physical therapy room; Activities room; Chapel; Crafts room; Laundry room; Barber/Beauty shop; Library.
Activities Arts & crafts; Games; Reading groups; Movies; Sunday school.

PANGUITCH

Garfield Memorial Hospital
200 N 400 E, Panguitch, UT, 84759
(801) 676-8811
Admin Wayne R Ross. *Medical Dir/Dir of Nursing* Linda Holdaway.
Licensure Skilled care; Intermediate care. *Beds* 20. *Certified* Medicaid; Medicare.
Owner Nonprofit Corp.
Staff Physicians 3 (ft); RNs 4 (ft), 6 (pt); LPNs 1 (ft), 3 (pt); Nurses aides 2 (ft), 10 (pt); Physical therapists 1 (ft); Recreational therapists 1 (pt); Dietitians 1 (pt).
Languages Spanish, French, German
Facilities Dining room; Physical therapy room.
Activities Cards; Games; Reading groups; Movies.

PAROWAN

Iron County Nursing Home*
69 E 100 S, Parowan, UT, 84761
(801) 477-3615
Admin Clarence J Benson. *Medical Dir/Dir of Nursing* David L Wilkerson MD.
Licensure Intermediate care. *Beds* 30. *Certified* Medicaid.
Admissions Requirements Medical examination.
Staff Physicians 4 (pt); RNs 1 (pt); LPNs 4 (ft); Nurses aides 6 (ft), 3 (pt); Physical therapists 1 (pt); Recreational therapists 1 (ft); Occupational therapists 1 (pt); Speech therapists 1 (pt); Activities coordinators 1 (ft); Dietitians 1 (pt); Dentists 1 (pt); Ophthalmologists 1 (pt); Podiatrists 1 (pt); Audiologists 1 (pt).

PAYSON

El Rancho Rest Home*
Box 726, E Hwy 91, Payson, UT, 84651
(801) 465-9211
Admin Steve A Lassen.
Licensure Intermediate care. *Beds* 51. *Certified* Medicaid.

Mountain View Hospital*
1000 E Hwy 91, Payson, UT, 84057
(801) 465-9201
Admin Val Christensen.
Licensure Skilled care; Intermediate care. *Beds* SNF 5; ICF 89.

PLEASANT GROVE

Alpine Valley Care Center*
25 E Alpine Dr, Pleasant Grove, UT, 84062
(801) 785-3568
Admin Gary M Kelso.

Licensure Skilled care; Intermediate care. *Beds* SNF 36; ICF 14. *Certified* Medicaid.
Owner Proprietary Corp (National Heritage).

PRICE

Carbon County Nursing Home*
250 E 6th N, Price, UT, 84501
(801) 637-2621
Admin John Bugel.
Licensure Skilled care. *Beds* 58. *Certified* Medicaid.

Price Care Center
1340 E 3rd N, Price, UT, 84501
(801) 637-6111
Admin Linda Hofling.
Licensure Intermediate care. *Beds* 100. *Certified* Medicaid.

PROVO

Bunce Care Center
1530 S 500 W, Provo, UT, 84601
(801) 374-1468
Admin Hilda Bunce. *Medical Dir/Dir of Nursing* Kim Bunce.
Licensure Intermediate care; Intermediate care for mentally retarded. *Beds* 72. *Certified* Medicaid; Medicare.
Owner Privately owned.
Admissions Requirements Medical examination; Physician's request.
Staff Physicians; RNs; LPNs; Orderlies; Nurses aides; Physical therapists; Reality therapists; Recreational therapists; Occupational therapists; Speech therapists; Occupational therapists; Dietitians; Ophthalmologists; Podiatrists.
Facilities Dining room; Physical therapy room; Activities room; Chapel; Crafts room; Laundry room; Barber/Beauty shop.
Activities Arts & crafts; Cards; Games; Reading groups; Prayer groups; Movies; Shopping trips; Social/Cultural gatherings.

Crestview Convalescent Care Center
1020 S 1053 W, Provo, UT, 84601
(801) 373-2630
Admin Richard Dunkley. *Medical Dir/Dir of Nursing* Dr Jeffrey Johnson; Gail James RN.
Licensure Skilled care; Intermediate care. *Beds* SNF 74; ICF 25. *Certified* Medicaid.
Owner Proprietary Corp (National Heritage).
Staff Physicians; RNs; LPNs; Orderlies; Nurses aides; Physical therapists; Recreational therapists; Occupational therapists; Speech therapists; Activities coordinators; Dietitians; Ophthalmologists; Podiatrists.

Evergreen Nursing Home*
1560 S 552 W, Provo, UT, 84601
(801) 375-5505
Admin Joseph Bunce.
Licensure Intermediate care. *Beds* 36. *Certified* Medicaid.

Medallion Manor Inc*
1701 W 600 S, Provo, UT, 84601
(801) 375-2710
Admin Dennis R Wright.
Licensure Intermediate care. *Beds* 35. *Certified* Medicaid.

Phillips Nursing Home*
2901 W Center St, Provo, UT, 84601
(801) 373-5079
Admin Alice B Goodwin.
Licensure Intermediate care. *Beds* 47. *Certified* Medicaid.

Provo Care Center
256 E Center St, Provo, UT, 84601
(801) 373-8771
Admin David Halling. *Medical Dir/Dir of Nursing* Paul Smith MD; Deanna Young DON.

Licensure Intermediate care. *Beds* ICF 35. *Certified* Medicaid.
Owner Proprietary Corp.
Admissions Requirements Medical examination; Physician's request.
Staff Physicians 1 (pt); RNs 1 (pt); LPNs 3 (ft); Nurses aides 10 (ft); Recreational therapists 1 (pt); Activities coordinators 1 (ft); Dietitians 2 (pt).
Facilities Dining room; Activities room; Crafts room; Laundry room; Barber/Beauty shop.
Activities Arts & crafts; Cards; Games; Reading groups; Movies; Shopping trips; Social/Cultural gatherings; Swimming; Bowling.

Timpanogos Psychiatric Unit*
1701 S Dakota Ln, Provo, UT, 84601
(801) 373-7393
Admin Glen R Brown.
Licensure Skilled care. *Beds* 24.

RICHFIELD

Richfield Care Center
83 E 1100 N, Richfield, UT, 84701
(801) 896-8211
Admin Ronald L Nielsen. *Medical Dir/Dir of Nursing* Elaine Blackburn.
Licensure Skilled care; Intermediate care. *Beds* SNF 76; ICF 22. *Certified* Medicaid; Medicare.
Owner Proprietary Corp (Care Enterprises).
Admissions Requirements Minimum age 15; Medical examination; Physician's request.
Staff RNs 5 (ft), 3 (pt); LPNs 4 (ft), 2 (pt); Orderlies 4 (ft); Nurses aides 20 (ft), 2 (pt); Recreational therapists 1 (ft), 1 (pt); Dietitians 1 (ft).
Facilities Dining room; Physical therapy room; Activities room; Crafts room; Laundry room; Barber/Beauty shop; Library.
Activities Arts & crafts; Games; Reading groups; Prayer groups; Movies; Shopping trips; Social/Cultural gatherings; Exercise class.

ROOSEVELT

Cedar Crest Convalescent Center Inc*
187 Lagoon St, Roosevelt, UT, 84066
(801) 722-2456
Admin Jon Robertson. *Medical Dir/Dir of Nursing* Gary White MD.
Licensure Skilled care; Intermediate care. *Beds* SNF 22; ICF 29. *Certified* Medicaid.
Admissions Requirements Medical examination; Physician's request.
Staff Physicians; RNs; LPNs; Orderlies; Nurses aides; Recreational therapists; Activities coordinators; Dietitians; Dentists; Ophthalmologists; Podiatrists.
Facilities Dining room; Activities room; Crafts room; Laundry room; Barber/Beauty shop.
Activities Arts & crafts; Cards; Games; Reading groups; Prayer groups; Movies; Shopping trips; Social/Cultural gatherings.

ROY

Weber Memorial Care Center
2700 W 5600 S, Roy, UT, 84078
(801) 825-9731
Admin Mark F Dunn.
Licensure Skilled care. *Beds* 176. *Certified* Medicaid; Medicare.
Owner Proprietary Corp (National Heritage).

SAINT GEORGE

Porters Nursing Home
126 W 200 N, Saint George, UT, 84770
(801) 628-1601

Admin James Porter. *Medical Dir/Dir of Nursing* Carol Wood.
Licensure Intermediate care. *Beds* ICF 53. *Certified* Medicaid.
Owner Privately owned.
Admissions Requirements Minimum age 21; Medical examination.
Staff Physicians 1 (pt); RNs 1 (pt); LPNs 4 (ft), 2 (pt); Orderlies; Nurses aides 12 (ft), 5 (pt); Physical therapists 1 (pt); Recreational therapists 1 (ft); Activities coordinators 1 (ft); Dietitians 1 (pt); Ophthalmologists 1 (pt); Podiatrists 1 (pt).
Languages Spanish
Facilities Dining room; Activities room; Chapel; Crafts room; Laundry room; Barber/Beauty shop.
Activities Arts & crafts; Cards; Games; Reading groups; Prayer groups; Shopping trips; Social/Cultural gatherings.

St George Care Center*
1032 E 100 S, Saint George, UT, 84770
(801) 628-0488
Admin H Paul Harker.
Licensure Skilled care; Intermediate care. *Beds* SNF 40; ICF 60. *Certified* Medicaid; Medicare.
Owner Proprietary Corp (Hillhaven Corp).

Southern Hospitality Living Center
35 S 100 E, Saint George, UT, 84770
(801) 673-3682, 673-9530
Admin Laurel Stinson. *Medical Dir/Dir of Nursing* Mona Small DON.
Licensure Intermediate care. *Beds* ICF 34. *Certified* Medicaid.
Owner Proprietary Corp.
Admissions Requirements Medical examination; Physician's request.
Staff Physicians 1 (pt); RNs 1 (pt); LPNs 2 (ft), 1 (pt); Orderlies 4 (ft), 2 (pt); Nurses aides 5 (ft), 2 (pt); Physical therapists 1 (pt); Recreational therapists 1 (pt); Activities coordinators 1 (ft); Dietitians 1 (pt).
Languages Spanish
Facilities Dining room; Activities room; Laundry room.
Activities Arts & crafts; Cards; Games; Prayer groups; Movies; Shopping trips; Social/Cultural gatherings Swimming; Bowling; Picnics.

SALT LAKE CITY

A & E Nursing Home
3094 S State St, Salt Lake City, UT, 84115
(801) 487-7837
Admin Edna Price. *Medical Dir/Dir of Nursing* Margaret Nightingale.
Licensure Intermediate care. *Beds* SNF 37. *Certified* Medicaid.
Owner Proprietary Corp.
Admissions Requirements Minimum age 21; Medical examination.
Staff Physicians; RNs; LPNs; Orderlies; Nurses aides; Physical therapists; Reality therapists; Recreational therapists; Occupational therapists; Speech therapists; Activities coordinators; Dietitians; Dentists; Ophthalmologists; Podiatrists.
Languages Spanish
Facilities Dining room; Activities room; Crafts room; Laundry room; Smoking room.
Activities Arts & crafts; Cards; Games; Reading groups; Prayer groups; Movies; Shopping trips; Social/Cultural gatherings; Van rides.

Alpine-Chavis Care Center*
3855 S 7th E, Salt Lake City, UT, 84106
(801) 268-4766
Medical Dir/Dir of Nursing Victor Kassel MD.
Licensure Intermediate care. *Beds* 72. *Certified* Medicaid.
Admissions Requirements Physician's request.

Staff Physicians 1 (pt); RNs 3 (ft), 1 (pt); LPNs 8 (ft), 3 (pt); Orderlies 4 (ft), 1 (pt); Nurses aides 30 (ft), 10 (pt); Physical therapists 1 (ft); Recreational therapists 1 (ft); Occupational therapists 1 (pt); Speech therapists 1 (pt); Activities coordinators 1 (ft); Dietitians 1 (pt); Dentists 1 (pt); Ophthalmologists 1 (pt); Podiatrists 1 (pt); Audiologists 1 (pt).
Facilities Dining room; Physical therapy room; Activities room; Laundry room; Barber/Beauty shop; Library.
Activities Arts & crafts; Cards; Games; Reading groups; Prayer groups; Movies; Shopping trips; Social/Cultural gatherings.

Alta Care Center
4035 S 500 E, Salt Lake City, UT, 84107
(801) 262-9181
Admin H Stephen Poulson. *Medical Dir/Dir of Nursing* Randall Daynes MD.
Licensure Skilled care. *Beds* 99. *Certified* Medicaid; Medicare.
Owner Proprietary Corp.
Admissions Requirements Minimum age 25; Medical examination; Physician's request.
Staff Physicians 2 (pt); RNs 2 (ft), 3 (pt); LPNs 4 (ft), 4 (pt); Nurses aides 23 (ft), 8 (pt); Physical therapists 1 (pt); Recreational therapists 1 (ft), 1 (pt); Occupational therapists 1 (pt); Speech therapists 1 (pt); Activities coordinators 1 (ft); Dietitians 1 (pt); Ophthalmologists 1 (pt); Podiatrists 1 (pt).
Languages Spanish, German
Facilities Dining room; Physical therapy room; Activities room; Crafts room; Laundry room; Library; TV room.
Activities Arts & crafts; Cards; Games; Reading groups; Prayer groups; Movies; Shopping trips; Social/Cultural gatherings.

Ann's Rest Home*
3944 S 400 E, Salt Lake City, UT, 84107
(801) 266-4339
Admin Trudy Rojas.
Licensure Intermediate care. *Beds* 60. *Certified* Medicaid.
Admissions Requirements Males only.

Bennion Care Center*
6246 S Redwood Rd, Salt Lake City, UT, 84107
(801) 969-1451
Admin Pat Johnson.
Licensure Skilled care; Intermediate care. *Beds* SNF 42; ICF 58. *Certified* Medicaid; Medicare.

The Bungalow
645 S 13th E, Salt Lake City, UT, 84102
(801) 582-1457
Admin Lois Hendricksen. *Medical Dir/Dir of Nursing* Dr John Tudor.
Licensure Intermediate care. *Beds* 25. *Certified* Medicaid.
Admissions Requirements Females only; Medical examination.
Staff Physicians; RNs; LPNs; Nurses aides; Physical therapists; Reality therapists; Recreational therapists; Occupational therapists; Speech therapists; Activities coordinators; Dietitians; Dentists; Ophthalmologists; Podiatrists.
Facilities Dining room; Activities room; Crafts room; Laundry room; Barber/Beauty shop; Library.
Activities Arts & crafts; Cards; Games; Reading groups; Prayer groups; Movies; Shopping trips; Social/Cultural gatherings.

CareWest-Salt Lake Nursing & Rehabilitation Center
165 S 10th E, Salt Lake City, UT, 84102
(801) 322-5521
Admin Nora Vorheis. *Medical Dir/Dir of Nursing* Victor Kassel MD.

Licensure Skilled care. *Beds* SNF 106.
Certified Medicaid; Medicare.
Owner Proprietary Corp.
Admissions Requirements Medical
examination; Physician's request.
Staff Physicians 1 (pt); RNs 5 (ft), 5 (pt);
LPNs 7 (ft), 3 (pt); Nurses aides 39 (ft), 2
(pt); Recreational therapists 1 (ft), 2 (pt);
Occupational therapists 1 (pt); Dentists 1
(pt); Ophthalmologists 1 (pt); Podiatrists 1
(pt).
Facilities Dining room; Physical therapy
room; Activities room; Crafts room; Laundry
room; Barber/Beauty shop.
Activities Arts & crafts; Cards; Games;
Reading groups; Prayer groups; Movies;
Shopping trips; Social/Cultural gatherings;
Community service projects; Painting; Music
appreciation; Cooking.

Doxie-Hatch Medical Center*
1255 E 3900 S, Salt Lake City, UT, 84117
(801) 262-3401
Admin Jan Mikesell.
Licensure Skilled care. *Beds* 150. *Certified*
Medicaid; Medicare.

Eva Dawn Care Center
1001 N Featherstone Dr, Salt Lake City, UT,
84116
(801) 531-0257
Admin Donna Featherstone. *Medical Dir/Dir
of Nursing* Dr John Marshall.
Licensure Intermediate care. *Beds* ICF 60.
Certified Medicaid.
Owner Privately owned.
Admissions Requirements Medical
examination; Physician's request.
Staff Physicians 1 (pt); RNs 1 (ft), 1 (pt);
LPNs 5 (ft); Orderlies 4 (ft); Nurses aides 6
(ft), 4 (pt); Physical therapists 1 (pt); Reality
therapists 1 (ft); Recreational therapists 1
(ft); Occupational therapists 1 (pt); Speech
therapists 1 (pt); Activities coordinators 1
(ft); Dietitians 1 (pt); Dentists 1 (pt);
Ophthalmologists 1 (pt).
Languages Spanish
Facilities Dining room; Physical therapy
room; Activities room; Crafts room; Laundry
room; Barber/Beauty shop; Library;
Whirlpool.
Activities Arts & crafts; Cards; Games;
Reading groups; Prayer groups; Movies;
Shopping trips; Social/Cultural gatherings;
Trips.

Fairview Convalescent Center*
876 W 7th S, Salt Lake City, UT, 84104
(801) 355-9649
Admin Dale E Peterson.
Licensure Intermediate care. *Beds* 36.
Certified Medicaid.

Fairview Nursing Home*
455 S 9th E, Salt Lake City, UT, 84102
(801) 355-6891
Admin Joseph D Petersen.
Licensure Intermediate care. *Beds* 36.
Certified Medicaid.

Fay Case Nursing Home
294 E Robert Ave, Salt Lake City, UT, 84115
(801) 486-1154
Admin Jan L Mikesell. *Medical Dir/Dir of
Nursing* David W Fiegal MD; Rose T
Gillespie DON.
Licensure Intermediate care. *Beds* 68.
Certified Medicaid.
Admissions Requirements Medical
examination.
Staff LPNs 10 (ft); Orderlies 1 (ft); Nurses
aides 20 (ft); Recreational therapists 1 (ft).
Facilities Dining room; Activities room;
Laundry room; Barber/Beauty shop.
Activities Arts & crafts; Cards; Games;
Reading groups; Prayer groups; Movies;
Shopping trips; Social/Cultural gatherings.

Glenwood Care*
404 E 5600 S, Salt Lake City, UT, 84107
(801) 266-3588
Admin Sue Bowker. *Medical Dir/Dir of
Nursing* Dr Burtis Evans.
Licensure Skilled care; Intermediate care. *Beds*
119. *Certified* Medicaid; Medicare.
Admissions Requirements Medical
examination; Physician's request.
Staff Physicians 20 (pt); RNs 6 (ft), 2 (pt);
LPNs 8 (ft); Orderlies 5 (ft); Physical
therapists 1 (ft); Reality therapists 1 (ft);
Recreational therapists 1 (ft); Occupational
therapists 1 (ft); Speech therapists 1 (ft);
Activities coordinators 1 (ft); Dietitians 1
(pt); Dentists 1 (pt); Ophthalmologists 1 (pt);
Podiatrists 1 (pt); Audiologists 1 (pt).
Facilities Dining room; Physical therapy
room; Activities room; Crafts room; Laundry
room; Barber/Beauty shop.
Activities Arts & crafts; Cards; Games;
Reading groups; Prayer groups; Movies;
Shopping trips; Social/Cultural gatherings.

Golden Manor of Salt Lake*
4150 W 3375 S, Salt Lake City, UT, 84120
(801) 968-9028
Admin Kenneth Max Depew.
Licensure Skilled care; Intermediate care. *Beds*
SNF 48; ICF 28. *Certified* Medicaid;
Medicare.

Highland Care Center
4285 Highland Dr, Salt Lake City, UT, 84124
(801) 278-2839
Admin Terry Lemmon. *Medical Dir/Dir of
Nursing* John Hylen MD; Pam Wolf RN
DON.
Licensure Skilled care. *Beds* SNF 60. *Certified*
Medicaid; Medicare.
Owner Proprietary Corp.
Admissions Requirements Minimum age 65;
Medical examination; Physician's request.
Staff Physicians; RNs 2 (ft), 2 (pt); LPNs 3
(ft), 2 (pt); Nurses aides 15 (ft), 5 (pt);
Physical therapists 2 (pt); Recreational
therapists 1 (ft); Speech therapists 1 (pt);
Activities coordinators; Dietitians 1 (pt);
Ophthalmologists 1 (pt).
Languages Spanish
Affiliation Church of Latter-Day Saints
(Mormon)
Facilities Dining room; Physical therapy
room; Activities room; Laundry room;
Barber/Beauty shop.
Activities Arts & crafts; Cards; Games;
Reading groups; Prayer groups; Movies;
Shopping trips; Social/Cultural gatherings.

Hillhaven Convalescent Center*
41 S 9th E, Salt Lake City, UT, 84102
(801) 532-3539
Admin E Lynn Reed.
Licensure Skilled care. *Beds* 154. *Certified*
Medicaid; Medicare.
Owner Proprietary Corp (Hillhaven Corp).

Hillside Villa Inc
1216 E 1300 S, Salt Lake City, UT, 84105
(801) 487-5865
Admin Erich S Linner. *Medical Dir/Dir of
Nursing* James Pearl MD;.
Licensure Intermediate care. *Beds* ICF 115.
Certified Medicaid.
Owner Proprietary Corp.
Admissions Requirements Medical
examination; Physician's request.
Staff RNs 3 (ft); LPNs 7 (ft); Nurses aides 26
(ft); Activities coordinators 2 (ft);
Ophthalmologists 1 (ft); Podiatrists 1 (ft).
Facilities Dining room; Physical therapy
room; Activities room; Crafts room; Laundry
room; Barber/Beauty shop; Library.
Activities Arts & crafts; Cards; Games;
Reading groups; Movies; Shopping trips;
Social/Cultural gatherings; Outings; Picnics.

Johanna Nursing Home*
433 E 2700 S, Salt Lake City, UT, 84115
(801) 487-2248
Admin Johanna Syms. *Medical Dir/Dir of
Nursing* John Tudor MD.
Licensure Intermediate care. *Beds* 41.
Certified Medicaid.
Staff Physicians; RNs; LPNs; Orderlies;
Nurses aides; Recreational therapists;
Activities coordinators; Dietitians.
Facilities Dining room; Activities room;
Laundry room; Barber/Beauty shop; Library.
Activities Arts & crafts; Cards; Games;
Reading groups; Prayer groups; Movies;
Shopping trips.

Latham Nursing Home*
642 University St, Salt Lake City, UT, 84102
(801) 582-2195
Admin Belinda Latham.
Licensure Intermediate care. *Beds* 16.

New Horizons*
125 S 9th W, Salt Lake City, UT, 84104
(801) 363-6340
Admin John Pappadakis. *Medical Dir/Dir of
Nursing* Leo Sotiriou.
Licensure Skilled care; Intermediate care. *Beds*
SNF 30; ICF 42. *Certified* Medicaid.
Admissions Requirements Minimum age 18.
Staff Physicians; RNs; LPNs; Orderlies;
Nurses aides; Physical therapists;
Recreational therapists; Occupational
therapists; Speech therapists; Activities
coordinators; Dietitians; Dentists;
Ophthalmologists; Podiatrists; Audiologists;
Medical records; Social worker; Food service
supervisor.
Facilities Dining room; Physical therapy
room; Activities room; Crafts room; Laundry
room; Barber/Beauty shop; Day room.
Activities Arts & crafts; Cards; Games; Prayer
groups; Movies; Shopping trips; Social/
Cultural gatherings.

Olympus Care Center
950 E 3300 S, Salt Lake City, UT, 84106
(801) 486-5121
Admin T Ann Fagot. *Medical Dir/Dir of
Nursing* Margaret Hect MD; Carol Davis
DON.
Licensure Intermediate care. *Beds* ICF 72.
Certified Medicaid.
Owner Proprietary Corp.
Admissions Requirements Medical
examination; Physician's request.
Staff LPNs 8 (ft); Orderlies 4 (ft); Nurses
aides 12 (ft), 3 (pt); Recreational therapists 1
(ft); Activities coordinators 1 (ft).
Languages Spanish
Facilities Dining room; Activities room;
Crafts room; Laundry room; Barber/Beauty
shop.
Activities Arts & crafts; Cards; Games;
Reading groups; Prayer groups; Movies;
Shopping trips; Social/Cultural gatherings;
Trips; Camping; Bowling; Fishing; Cook-
outs.

Plantation Convalescent Center*
635 Vine St, Salt Lake City, UT, 84107
(801) 266-3852
Admin Steven L Eddy.
Licensure Intermediate care. *Beds* 80.
Certified Medicaid.

Rosewood Terrace
158 N 600 W, Salt Lake City, UT, 84116
(801) 363-4222
Admin Debbie Holling. *Medical Dir/Dir of
Nursing* King Udall; Jan Brotherton.
Licensure Skilled care. *Beds* 79. *Certified*
Medicaid; Medicare.
Owner Proprietary Corp.
Admissions Requirements Physician's request.
Staff RNs 4 (ft); LPNs 6 (ft); Orderlies;
Nurses aides; Activities coordinators 1 (ft);
Dietitians 1 (pt).

Facilities Dining room; Physical therapy room; Laundry room; Barber/Beauty shop; TV/smoking room.
Activities Arts & crafts; Cards; Games; Prayer groups; Movies; Shopping trips; Social/Cultural gatherings.

St Joseph Villa
475 Ramona Ave, Salt Lake City, UT, 84115-2299
(801) 487-7557
Admin G Richard Erick. *Medical Dir/Dir of Nursing* Victor Kassel MD; DeAnn Heide RN DON.
Licensure Skilled care; Intermediate care. *Beds* SNF 145; ICF 30. *Certified* Medicaid; Medicare.
Owner Proprietary Corp.
Admissions Requirements Minimum age 55; Medical examination; Physician's request.
Staff RNs 7 (ft), 5 (pt); LPNs 18 (ft), 3 (pt); Orderlies 5 (ft), 1 (pt); Nurses aides 58 (ft), 8 (pt); Recreational therapists 2 (ft), 1 (pt); Activities coordinators 1 (ft); Dietitians 1 (ft); MSW 1 (ft).
Affiliation Roman Catholic
Facilities Dining room; Physical therapy room; Activities room; Chapel; Crafts room; Laundry room; Barber/Beauty shop; Library; Movie & TV rooms.
Activities Arts & crafts; Cards; Games; Reading groups; Prayer groups; Movies; Social/Cultural gatherings; Resident council.

Salt Lake DD Center
252 S 500 E, Salt Lake City, UT, 84102
(801) 366-0220
Admin Dennis F Gehring.
Licensure Intermediate care for mentally retarded. *Beds* 112. *Certified* Medicaid.

Terrace Villa
4600 Highland Dr, Salt Lake City, UT, 84117
(801) 272-4411
Admin Mark D Bybee. *Medical Dir/Dir of Nursing* Dr John M Tudor; Clarine Moffit RN.
Licensure Skilled care; Intermediate care. *Beds* 100. *Certified* Medicaid; Medicare.
Owner Proprietary Corp (National Heritage).
Staff RNs 3 (ft), 2 (pt); Orderlies 5 (ft); Nurses aides 50 (ft); Physical therapists 2 (ft); Reality therapists 1 (ft); Recreational therapists 1 (ft); Dietitians 1 (ft).
Facilities Dining room; Physical therapy room; Activities room; Chapel; Crafts room; Laundry room; Barber/Beauty shop; Library.
Activities Arts & crafts; Cards; Games; Reading groups; Prayer groups; Movies; Social/Cultural gatherings.

Twin Pines Care Center*
3520 S Highland Dr, Salt Lake City, UT, 84106
(801) 484-7638
Admin Janene Daskalas.
Licensure Intermediate care. *Beds* 57. *Certified* Medicaid.

Wasatch Villa
2200 E 3300 S, Salt Lake City, UT, 84109
(801) 486-2096
Admin Wayne Dunbar. *Medical Dir/Dir of Nursing* John Marshall MD; Lois Laine.
Licensure Skilled care. *Beds* 118. *Certified* Medicaid; Medicare.
Owner Proprietary Corp (Hillhaven Corp).
Admissions Requirements Minimum age 21; Medical examination; Physician's request.
Staff Physicians 6 (pt); RNs 8 (ft), 1 (pt); LPNs 12 (ft), 1 (pt); Orderlies 8 (ft), 2 (pt); Nurses aides 32 (ft), 6 (pt); Physical therapists 21 (ft), 1 (pt); Reality therapists 2 (pt); Recreational therapists 1 (ft), 1 (pt); Occupational therapists 1 (pt); Speech therapists 1 (pt); Activities coordinators 1 (ft), 1 (pt); Dietitians 1 (pt); Dentists 1 (pt); Ophthalmologists 1 (pt); Podiatrists 1 (pt).

Affiliation Church of Latter-Day Saints (Mormon)
Facilities Dining room; Physical therapy room; Activities room; Chapel; Crafts room; Laundry room; Barber/Beauty shop; Library.
Activities Arts & crafts; Cards; Games; Reading groups; Prayer groups; Movies; Shopping trips; Social/Cultural gatherings.

Zion's Mountain View*
2730 E 33rd S, Salt Lake City, UT, 84109
(801) 487-0896
Admin Dirk Anjewierden.
Licensure Intermediate care. *Beds* 100. *Certified* Medicaid.
Staff Physicians 1 (ft); RNs 1 (ft); LPNs 6 (ft), 1 (pt); Nurses aides 45 (ft); Recreational therapists 1 (ft); Dietitians 1 (pt); Podiatrists 1 (pt).
Facilities Dining room; Laundry room; Barber/Beauty shop.
Activities Arts & crafts; Games; Reading groups; Movies; Shopping trips; Social/Cultural gatherings.

SANDY

Hillcrest Care Center
348 E 8000 S, Sandy, UT, 84091
(801) 566-4191
Admin Dottie Gonthier. *Medical Dir/Dir of Nursing* Sharon Jeffs RN.
Licensure Intermediate care for mentally retarded. *Beds* ICF/MR 60. *Certified* Medicaid; Medicare.
Owner Proprietary Corp (National Heritage).
Admissions Requirements Minimum age 21.
Staff Physicians 1 (pt); RNs 1 (pt); LPNs 4 (ft), 2 (pt); Nurses aides 25 (ft); Physical therapists 1 (pt); Recreational therapists 1 (ft), 2 (pt); Occupational therapists 1 (ft); Speech therapists 1 (ft); Dietitians 1 (ft), 1 (pt); Podiatrists 1 (pt).
Facilities Dining room; Activities room; Crafts room; Laundry room.
Activities Arts & crafts; Cards; Games; Movies; Shopping trips; Social/Cultural gatherings; Special Olympics.

SPANISH FORK

Hales Rest Home*
46 N 1st E, Spanish Fork, UT, 84660
(801) 798-6220
Admin Steven Bona.
Licensure Intermediate care. *Beds* 25. *Certified* Medicaid.
Admissions Requirements Females only; Medical examination; Physician's request.
Staff Physicians 3 (pt); RNs 1 (pt); LPNs 4 (ft); Nurses aides 9 (ft); Physical therapists 1 (pt); Recreational therapists 1 (ft); Occupational therapists 1 (pt); Speech therapists 1 (pt); Activities coordinators 1 (pt); Dietitians 1 (pt); Dentists 1 (pt); Ophthalmologists 1 (pt); Podiatrists 1 (pt); Audiologists 1 (pt).
Facilities Dining room; Activities room; Crafts room; Laundry room; Barber/Beauty shop.
Activities Arts & crafts; Cards; Games; Reading groups; Movies; Shopping trips.

SPRINGVILLE

Anns Siesta Villa
469 N Main, Springville, UT, 84663
(801) 489-9409
Admin Sharon Maestas. *Medical Dir/Dir of Nursing* Kathy Corona.
Licensure Intermediate care. *Beds* ICF 44. *Certified* Medicaid.
Owner Nonprofit Corp.
Admissions Requirements Physician's request.

Staff Physicians 1 (pt); RNs 1 (ft); LPNs 5 (ft), 1 (pt); Orderlies 6 (ft); Nurses aides 4 (ft); Physical therapists 1 (pt); Reality therapists 1 (pt); Recreational therapists 1 (ft); Occupational therapists 1 (pt); Speech therapists 1 (pt); Activities coordinators 1 (ft); Dietitians 1 (pt); Ophthalmologists 1 (pt); Podiatrists 1 (pt).
Facilities Dining room; Physical therapy room; Activities room; Crafts room; Laundry room; Barber/Beauty shop; Library; Smoking room.
Activities Arts & crafts; Cards; Games; Reading groups; Prayer groups; Movies; Shopping trips; Social/Cultural gatherings; Bowling; Swimming.

Todholm Care Center
321 E 800 S, Springville, UT, 84663
(801) 489-9461
Admin Margaret M Boyack. *Medical Dir/Dir of Nursing* L Colledge.
Licensure Intermediate care. *Beds* ICF 67. *Certified* Medicaid.
Owner Proprietary Corp.
Admissions Requirements Medical examination; Physician's request.
Staff LPNs 4 (ft), 3 (pt); Nurses aides 12 (ft), 8 (pt); Activities coordinators 1 (ft).
Facilities Dining room; Activities room; Laundry room; Barber/Beauty shop; Library; Outdoor recreational facilities.
Activities Arts & crafts; Cards; Games; Reading groups; Movies; Shopping trips; Social/Cultural gatherings; Various church groups.

TOOELE

Tooele Valley Nursing Home
140 E 2nd S, Tooele, UT, 84074
(801) 882-6130
Admin Beth Vowles. *Medical Dir/Dir of Nursing* Robert Rudas; Muriel Dufendach DON.
Licensure Skilled care; Intermediate care. *Beds* 48. *Certified* Medicaid.
Owner Publicly owned.
Staff Physicians 7 (pt); RNs 5 (ft), 1 (pt); LPNs 3 (ft), 1 (pt); Orderlies 2 (ft); Nurses aides 25 (ft), 5 (pt); Physical therapists 1 (ft); Reality therapists 1 (ft); Recreational therapists 2 (ft); Occupational therapists 1 (pt); Activities coordinators 1 (pt); Dietitians 1 (ft); Ophthalmologists 1 (pt); Podiatrists 1 (pt).
Facilities Dining room; Activities room; Crafts room; Laundry room; Barber/Beauty shop; Patio.
Activities Arts & crafts; Games; Reading groups; Prayer groups; Movies; Social/Cultural gatherings; Bus trips; Picnics.

TREMONTON

Box Elder County Nursing Home
460 W 600 N, Tremonton, UT, 84337
(801) 257-5356
Admin Lois Thompson. *Medical Dir/Dir of Nursing* Jack S Johnson MD; Carma Bradshaw RN DON.
Licensure Intermediate care. *Beds* ICF 38. *Certified* Medicaid.
Owner Publicly owned.
Admissions Requirements Medical examination; Physician's request.
Staff RNs; LPNs; Nurses aides; Activities coordinators; Dietitians; Dentist.
Facilities Dining room; Physical therapy room; Activities room; Crafts room; Laundry room; Barber/Beauty shop.
Activities Arts & crafts; Cards; Games; Reading groups; Movies; Shopping trips; Social/Cultural gatherings.

VERNAL

Uintah Care Center
510 S 500 W, Vernal, UT, 84078
(801) 789-8851
Admin Rossa Simmons. *Medical Dir/Dir of Nursing* Dr Paul Stringham.
Licensure Skilled care; Intermediate care. *Beds* SNF 50; ICF.
Owner Proprietary Corp (National Heritage).
Admissions Requirements Medical examination; Physician's request.
Staff RNs; LPNs; Orderlies; Nurses aides; Physical therapists; Reality therapists; Recreational therapists; Occupational therapists; Speech therapists; Activities coordinators; Dietitians; Dentists; Ophthalmologists; Podiatrists.
Facilities Dining room; Physical therapy room; Activities room; Crafts room; Laundry room; Barber/Beauty shop; Library; Smoking room; Large covered patio & backyard.
Activities Arts & crafts; Cards; Games; Reading groups; Prayer groups; Movies; Shopping trips; Social/Cultural gatherings; Reality orientation; Cooking classes; Wood shop.

WASHINGTON TERRACE

Mt Ogden Convalescent Center
375 E 5350 S, Washington Terrace, UT, 84403
(801) 479-5700
Admin Wiliam A Wortley. *Medical Dir/Dir of Nursing* Janet Akins RN DON.

Licensure Skilled care; Intermediate care. *Certified* Medicaid; Medicare.
Staff RNs 10 (ft), 1 (pt); LPNs 2 (ft), 1 (pt); Orderlies 3 (ft); Nurses aides 45 (ft); Physical therapists 5 (ft), 1 (pt); Reality therapists 1 (ft), 1 (pt); Recreational therapists 1 (ft), 1 (pt); Occupational therapists 1 (ft), 1 (pt); Speech therapists 1 (ft); Activities coordinators 1 (ft); Dietitians 1 (ft); Ophthalmologists 1 (pt); Podiatrists 1 (pt); Dentist 1 (pt).
Facilities Dining room; Physical therapy room; Activities room; Crafts room; Laundry room; Barber/Beauty shop; Library.
Activities Arts & crafts; Cards; Games; Reading groups; Prayer groups; Movies; Shopping trips; Social/Cultural gatherings.

WEST JORDAN

West Jordan Care Center*
3350 W 78th S, West Jordan, UT, 84084
(801) 566-0686
Admin Renee Maxwell. *Medical Dir/Dir of Nursing* Dr J Mumford.
Licensure Intermediate care for mentally retarded. *Beds* 80.
Admissions Requirements Minimum age 5; Medical examination; Physician's request.
Staff Physicians 1 (ft); RNs 2 (ft); LPNs 5 (ft), 1 (pt); Orderlies 6 (ft); Nurses aides 25 (ft), 4 (pt); Physical therapists 1 (ft); Reality therapists 1 (ft); Recreational therapists 1 (ft).

Facilities Dining room; Physical therapy room; Activities room; Crafts room; Laundry room; Barber/Beauty shop.
Activities Arts & crafts; Cards; Games; Reading groups; Prayer groups; Movies; Shopping trips; Social/Cultural gatherings.

WEST VALLEY CITY

Hazen Nursing Home
2520 S Redwood Rd, West Valley City, UT, 84119
(801) 972-1050
Admin Romaine P Tuft. *Medical Dir/Dir of Nursing* Dr David Feigal.
Licensure Intermediate care. *Beds* ICF 26. *Certified* Medicaid.
Owner Proprietary Corp.
Admissions Requirements Females only; Medical examination.
Staff Physicians 1 (pt); RNs 1 (pt); LPNs 2 (ft), 2 (pt); Nurses aides 12 (ft), 7 (pt); Recreational therapists 1 (ft); Activities coordinators 1 (ft); Dietitians 1 (pt).
Facilities Dining room; Activities room; Laundry room.
Activities Arts & crafts; Cards; Games; Reading groups; Prayer groups; Movies; Shopping trips; Social/Cultural gatherings; Van rides; Daily exercise class.

Pfeiffer's Community Home*
4028 S 4800 W, West Valley City, UT, 84120
(801) 968-8122
Admin Rosemarie T Rohde.
Licensure Intermediate care. *Beds* 28.

VERMONT

BARRE

Berlin Convalescent Center*
Rte 3, Airport Rd, Barre, VT, 05641
(802) 229-0308
Admin Carol C Carey. *Medical Dir/Dir of Nursing* Harry L Columbo MD.
Licensure Skilled care; Intermediate care. *Beds* SNF 48; ICF 104. *Certified* Medicaid; Medicare.
Admissions Requirements Minimum age 16; Medical examination; Physician's request.
Staff RNs 19 (ft), 11 (pt); LPNs 2 (ft), 7 (pt); Orderlies 2 (ft), 2 (pt); Nurses aides 18 (ft), 53 (pt); Physical therapists 1 (ft); Recreational therapists 1 (ft), 1 (pt); Speech therapists 1 (pt); Activities coordinators 1 (ft); Dietitians 1 (pt); Dentists 1 (pt).
Facilities Dining room; Physical therapy room; Activities room; Chapel; Crafts room; Laundry room; Barber/Beauty shop.
Activities Arts & crafts; Cards; Games; Reading groups; Prayer groups; Movies; Shopping trips; Social/Cultural gatherings.

McFarland House*
71 Washington St, Barre, VT, 05641
(802) 476-4164
Admin David C Tuholski.
Licensure Intermediate care. *Beds* 88. *Certified* Medicaid.

Rowan Court*
Prosect St, Barre, VT, 05641
(802) 476-4166
Admin Barbara J Kilmurry. *Medical Dir/Dir of Nursing* Dr George Lucchina.
Licensure Skilled care; Intermediate care. *Beds* SNF 10; ICF 104. *Certified* Medicaid.
Admissions Requirements Minimum age 16; Medical examination; Physician's request.
Staff RNs 8 (ft); LPNs 7 (ft); Nurses aides 69 (ft); Activities coordinators 1 (ft); Dietitians 1 (pt); Dentists 2 (pt); Ophthalmologists 2 (pt); Podiatrists 2 (pt); Audiologists 1 (pt).
Facilities Dining room; Physical therapy room; Activities room; Chapel; Crafts room; Laundry room; Barber/Beauty shop; Library; Greenhouse.
Activities Arts & crafts; Cards; Games; Reading groups; Prayer groups; Movies; Shopping trips; Social/Cultural gatherings; Bus with wheelchair lift for outings.

BARTON

Maple Lane Nursing Home*
Rte 1, Barton Hill Rd, Barton, VT, 05822
(802) 754-8575
Admin Gary Marcotte.
Licensure Intermediate care. *Beds* 37. *Certified* Medicaid.

BELLOWS FALLS

McGirr Nursing Home*
33 Atkinson St, Bellows Falls, VT, 05101
(802) 463-4387
Admin Margaret M Perry.
Licensure Intermediate care. *Beds* 30. *Certified* Medicaid.

BENNINGTON

Bennington Convalescent Center
360 Dewey St, Bennington, VT, 05201
(802) 442-8526
Admin Neil H Gruber. *Medical Dir/Dir of Nursing* Peter Peff MD.
Licensure Skilled care; Intermediate care. *Beds* SNF 26; ICF 74. *Certified* Medicaid; Medicare.
Owner Proprietary Corp.
Admissions Requirements Medical examination.
Staff RNs 5 (ft), 5 (pt); LPNs 10 (ft), 10 (pt); Nurses aides 15 (ft), 25 (pt); Physical therapists 1 (pt); Recreational therapists 2 (ft); Dietitians 1 (pt); Dentist 1 (pt).
Facilities Dining room; Physical therapy room; Activities room; Crafts room; Barber/Beauty shop.
Activities Arts & crafts; Cards; Games; Reading groups; Prayer groups; Movies; Shopping trips; Social/Cultural gatherings.

Crescent Manor Nursing Home
312 Crescent Blvd, Bennington, VT, 05201
(802) 447-1501
Admin Brendan Coogan. *Medical Dir/Dir of Nursing* Thelma Dubreud RN DON.
Licensure Intermediate care. *Beds* ICF 70. *Certified* Medicaid.
Owner Proprietary Corp.
Facilities Dining room; Activities room; Barber/Beauty shop.
Activities Arts & crafts; Cards; Games; Reading groups; Prayer groups; Movies; Shopping trips; Social/Cultural gatherings.

Vermont Veterans Home
325 North St, Bennington, VT, 05201
(802) 442-6353
Admin Phillip M Peterson. *Medical Dir/Dir of Nursing* Elizabeth Jenkins DON.
Licensure Intermediate care; Domiciliary. *Beds* ICF 135; Domiciliary 24. *Certified* Medicaid.
Owner Publicly owned.
Admissions Requirements Veterans & spouses.
Staff Physicians 2 (pt); RNs 8 (ft); LPNs 9 (ft), 10 (pt); Nurses aides 33 (ft), 20 (pt); Physical therapists 3 (ft), 1 (pt); Occupational therapists 2 (ft); Activities coordinators 1 (ft); Dietitians 1 (pt); DNS 1 (ft).
Facilities Dining room; Physical therapy room; Activities room; Chapel; Laundry room; Barber/Beauty shop; Library.

Activities Arts & crafts; Cards; Games; Prayer groups; Movies; Social/Cultural gatherings; Field trips.

BRATTLEBORO

Eden Park Nursing Home of Brattleboro*
Pine Heights, Brattleboro, VT, 05301
(802) 257-0307
Admin David G Selover.
Licensure Skilled care; Intermediate care. *Beds* SNF 40; ICF 84. *Certified* Medicaid; Medicare.
Owner Proprietary Corp (Eden Park Mngment).

Linden Lodge
75 Linden St, Brattleboro, VT, 05301
(802) 257-7785
Admin Roberta Bremmer RN. *Medical Dir/Dir of Nursing* Dr R Walker.
Licensure Intermediate care. *Beds* ICF 117. *Certified* Medicaid.

Thompson House Nursing Home
PO Box 1117, 30 Maple St, Brattleboro, VT, 05301-1117
(802) 254-4977
Admin Janet J Henningsen, CFACHCA. *Medical Dir/Dir of Nursing* Christopher J Schmidt MD; Annette Vigneau RN DNS.
Licensure Intermediate care. *Beds* ICF 35. *Certified* Medicaid.
Owner Nonprofit Corp.
Admissions Requirements Medical examination.
Staff RNs 2 (ft); LPNs 4 (ft), 4 (pt); Nurses aides 14 (ft), 4 (pt); Activities coordinators 2 (ft); Social services 1 (ft).
Facilities Dining room; Activities room; Crafts room; Barber/Beauty shop.
Activities Arts & crafts; Cards; Games; Reading groups; Prayer groups; Movies; Shopping trips; Social/Cultural gatherings; Sensory stimulation; Cooking group; Musical programs; Poetry; Current events.

BURLINGTON

Birchwood Terrace Healthcare
43 Starr Farm Rd, Burlington, VT, 05401
(802) 863-6384
Admin Patricia A Zeigler. *Medical Dir/Dir of Nursing* Maurice Walsh MD; Joan K Bombard RN DON.
Licensure Skilled care; Intermediate care. *Beds* SNF 60; ICF 100. *Certified* Medicaid; Medicare.
Owner Proprietary Corp (Hillhaven Corp).

Burlington Convalescent Center*
300 Pearl St, Burlington, VT, 05401
(802) 658-4200
Admin Ronald F Deal.
Licensure Skilled care; Intermediate care. *Beds* SNF 42; ICF 126. *Certified* Medicaid; Medicare.

Medical Center Nursing Home—DeGoesbriand Unit*
Medical Center Hospital of Vermont, Burlington, VT, 05401
(802) 656-3909
Admin Carol Trombley.
Licensure Skilled care. *Beds* 42. *Certified* Medicaid; Medicare.

DERBY

Patenaude Rest Home*
Main St, Derby, VT, 05829
(802) 766-2201
Admin Raymond J Gobeil. *Medical Dir/Dir of Nursing* Dr F P Fiermonte.
Licensure Intermediate care. *Beds* 19.
Staff Physicians 1 (pt); RNs 1 (ft), 1 (pt); LPNs 4 (ft); Nurses aides 4 (ft); Physical therapists 1 (pt); Speech therapists 1 (pt); Dietitians 1 (pt).
Facilities Dining room; Activities room.

FAIR HAVEN

Sager Nursing Home*
28 Prospect St, Fair Haven, VT, 05743
(802) 265-3263
Admin Mary Koldys. *Medical Dir/Dir of Nursing* Edward C Stannard.
Licensure Intermediate care. *Beds* 36. *Certified* Medicaid.
Admissions Requirements Medical examination; Physician's request.
Staff RNs 2 (ft), 6 (pt); LPNs 1 (pt); Nurses aides 6 (ft), 6 (pt); Reality therapists 1 (ft); Recreational therapists 1 (ft); Occupational therapists 1 (pt); Activities coordinators 1 (pt); Dietitians 1 (pt).
Facilities Dining room; Activities room; Crafts room; Laundry room; Barber/Beauty shop.
Activities Arts & crafts; Cards; Games; Reading groups; Prayer groups; Social/ Cultural gatherings.

GLOVER

Union House Nursing Home Inc*
Main St, Rte 16, RR 2, Box 1, Glover, VT, 05839
(802) 525-6600
Admin Patricia E Russell. *Medical Dir/Dir of Nursing* Dr George Linton.
Licensure Intermediate care. *Beds* 31. *Certified* Medicaid.
Admissions Requirements Minimum age 18; Medical examination.
Staff Physicians 1 (ft), 1 (pt); RNs 3 (ft); LPNs 4 (ft), 3 (pt); Nurses aides 14 (ft), 7 (pt); Physical therapists 1 (pt); Reality therapists 1 (ft); Recreational therapists 1 (ft); Occupational therapists 1 (pt); Speech therapists 1 (pt); Activities coordinators 1 (ft); Dietitians 1 (pt); Dentists 1 (pt).
Facilities Dining room; Activities room; Crafts room; Laundry room.
Activities Arts & crafts; Cards; Games; Reading groups; Prayer groups; Movies; Shopping trips; Social/Cultural gatherings; Fishing trips; Picnics; Gardening; Senior citizen groups.

GREENSBORO

Greensboro Nursing Home*
Rural Rt, Cemetary Rd, Greensboro, VT, 05481
(802) 533-7051
Admin Lorraine Comi.
Licensure Intermediate care. *Beds* ICF 26. *Certified* Medicaid; Medicare.

LUDLOW

Gill Odd Fellows Home of Vermont Inc
PO Box Drawer K, 8 Gill Terrace, Ludlow, VT, 05149
(802) 228-4571
Admin Joseph J Girouard. *Medical Dir/Dir of Nursing* Eugene M Bont MD; Betty A Demers RN DON.
Licensure Intermediate care; Community care home. *Beds* ICF 48; Community care home 14. *Certified* Medicaid.
Owner Nonprofit Corp.
Admissions Requirements Medical examination.
Staff RNs 1 (ft), 3 (pt); LPNs 4 (pt); Nurses aides 10 (ft), 12 (pt); Activities coordinators 2 (pt); Dietitians 1 (ft).
Affiliation Independent Order of Odd Fellows & Rebekahs
Facilities Dining room; Physical therapy room; Activities room; Crafts room; Laundry room; Barber/Beauty shop; Library.
Activities Arts & crafts; Cards; Games; Reading groups; Prayer groups; Movies; Shopping trips; Social/Cultural gatherings.

LYNDONVILLE

Pine Knoll Nursing Home*
Kirby Rd, Lyndonville, VT, 05851
(802) 626-3361
Admin Francis E Cheney Jr.
Licensure Intermediate care. *Beds* 44. *Certified* Medicaid.

MIDDLEBURY

Helen Porter Nursing Home
S St, Middlebury, VT, 05753
(802) 388-7901
Admin Susan J Bormolini. *Medical Dir/Dir of Nursing* Dr Clark W Bryant; Susan J Bormolini.
Licensure Skilled care. *Beds* SNF 50. *Certified* Medicaid; Medicare.
Owner Nonprofit Corp.
Admissions Requirements Minimum age 21; Medical examination; Physician's request.
Staff RNs 2 (ft), 12 (pt); LPNs 1 (ft), 5 (pt); Nurses aides 13 (ft), 18 (pt); Activities coordinators 1 (ft); Dietitians 1 (ft).
Facilities Dining room; Activities room; Barber/Beauty shop.
Activities Arts & crafts; Games; Reading groups; Prayer groups; Movies; Social/ Cultural gatherings; Resident council.

MONTPELIER

Heaton House*
Heaton St, Montpelier, VT, 05602
(802) 223-3424
Admin David C Tuholski.
Licensure Skilled care. *Beds* 57. *Certified* Medicaid; Medicare.

MORRISVILLE

Dumont Nursing & Convalescent Center*
Harrel St, Morrisville, VT, 05661
(802) 888-3131
Admin David Yacavone.
Licensure Intermediate care. *Beds* ICF 90. *Certified* Medicare.
Owner Proprietary Corp (Beverly Enterprises).

The Manor Nursing Home
204 Washington Hwy, Morrisville, VT, 05661
(802) 888-5201
Admin David W Yacovone. *Medical Dir/Dir of Nursing* Lincoln Jacobs MD; Kathy Cote DON.
Licensure Intermediate care. *Beds* ICF 51. *Certified* Medicaid.
Owner Proprietary Corp.

Admissions Requirements Medical examination.
Staff RNs 3 (ft), 1 (pt); LPNs 2 (ft), 4 (pt); Nurses aides 20 (ft); Physical therapists 1 (pt); Activities coordinators 2 (pt); Dietitians 1 (pt).
Facilities Dining room; Activities room; Chapel; Crafts room; Laundry room; Barber/ Beauty shop.
Activities Arts & crafts; Cards; Games; Reading groups; Prayer groups; Movies; Shopping trips; Social/Cultural gatherings.

MURRAY

CareWest-Murray
404 E 5600 S, Murray, VT, 84107
(801) 266-3588
Admin Ann Votava. *Medical Dir/Dir of Nursing* Dr John Hylen; Thelma Ennis DON.
Licensure Skilled care. *Beds* SNF 119. *Certified* Medicaid; Medicare.
Owner Proprietary Corp (Care Enterprises).
Staff Physicians; RNs 6 (ft), 1 (pt); Nurses aides 25 (ft), 10 (pt); Physical therapists 2 (ft); Reality therapists 1 (ft); Recreational therapists 1 (ft); Occupational therapists 20 (pt); Speech therapists 20 (pt); Activities coordinators 1 (ft); Dietitians 1 (ft); Ophthalmologists 10 (pt).
Facilities Dining room; Physical therapy room; Activities room; Laundry room; Barber/Beauty shop.
Activities Arts & crafts; Cards; Games; Reading groups; Prayer groups; Movies; Shopping trips; Social/Cultural gatherings.

NEWPORT

Bel-Aire Quality Care Nursing Home
PO Box 819, Bel-Aire Dr, Newport, VT, 05855
(802) 334-2878
Admin Marie Joseph. *Medical Dir/Dir of Nursing* Dr F Barber; Elaine Schurman.
Licensure Intermediate care. *Beds* ICF/MR 44. *Certified* Medicaid.
Owner Proprietary Corp (Northwestern Service Corp).
Facilities Dining room; Activities room; Crafts room; Laundry room; Barber/Beauty shop.
Activities Arts & crafts; Cards; Games; Reading groups; Prayer groups; Movies; Social/Cultural gatherings.

Newport Health Care Center
RR 2, Box 123, Newport, VT, 05855
(802) 334-7321
Admin David Silver. *Medical Dir/Dir of Nursing* Edna Silver.
Licensure Skilled care; Intermediate care. *Beds* SNF 25; ICF 35. *Certified* Medicaid; Medicare.
Owner Proprietary Corp.
Admissions Requirements Minimum age 16.
Staff RNs 3 (ft), 2 (pt); LPNs 5 (ft), 5 (pt); Nurses aides 12 (ft), 12 (pt); Reality therapists 1 (pt); Activities coordinators 1 (ft).
Facilities Dining room; Physical therapy room; Activities room; Crafts room; Laundry room; Barber/Beauty shop; Library.
Activities Arts & crafts; Games; Prayer groups; Movies.

NORTH BENNINGTON

Prospect Nursing Home*
34 Prospect St, North Bennington, VT, 05257
(802) 447-7144
Admin Edmond Morache Jr. *Medical Dir/Dir of Nursing* Oliver Durand MD.
Licensure Intermediate care. *Beds* 20. *Certified* Medicaid.

Admissions Requirements Medical examination.
Staff Physicians 1 (pt); RNs 1 (ft); LPNs 3 (ft); Nurses aides 5 (ft); Physical therapists 1 (pt); Recreational therapists 1 (ft); Activities coordinators 1 (ft); Dietitians 1 (pt).
Facilities Dining room; Activities room; Chapel; Crafts room; Laundry room; Barber/Beauty shop; Library.
Activities Arts & crafts; Games; Prayer groups; Movies; Shopping trips.

NORTHFIELD

Mayo Nursing Home
1 Richardson Ave, Northfield, VT, 05663
(802) 485-3161
Admin Lorraine R Day. *Medical Dir/Dir of Nursing* Dr Roger Kellogg; Audrey Engroff RN DON.
Licensure Skilled care; Intermediate care; Residential care. *Beds* SNF 20; ICF 30; Residential care 36. *Certified* Medicaid.
Owner Nonprofit Corp.
Admissions Requirements Medical examination; Physician's request.
Staff Physicians 3 (pt); RNs 8 (ft); LPNs 2 (ft); Orderlies 2 (ft); Nurses aides 20 (ft), 12 (pt); Physical therapists 2 (pt); Recreational therapists 1 (ft); Speech therapists 1 (pt); Activities coordinators 1 (ft); Dietitians 1 (pt); Ophthalmologists 2 (pt).
Facilities Dining room; Physical therapy room; Activities room; Crafts room; Laundry room; Barber/Beauty shop; Library.
Activities Arts & crafts; Cards; Games; Reading groups; Prayer groups; Movies; Shopping trips; Social/Cultural gatherings; Newspaper.

RANDOLPH

Tranquility Nursing Home
50 Randolph Ave, Randolph, VT, 05060
(802) 728-5607
Admin David Yacovone. *Medical Dir/Dir of Nursing* Sandra Patterson.
Licensure Intermediate care. *Beds* ICF 53. *Certified* Medicaid.
Owner Proprietary Corp.
Staff RNs 4 (ft); LPNs 3 (ft); Orderlies 1 (ft); Nurses aides 20 (ft); Activities coordinators 1 (ft), 1 (pt); Dietitians 1 (pt).
Facilities Dining room; Activities room; Chapel; Crafts room; Laundry room; Barber/Beauty shop.
Activities Arts & crafts; Cards; Games; Reading groups; Prayer groups; Movies; Shopping trips; Social/Cultural gatherings.

RUTLAND

Beverly Manor Convalescent Center*
9 Haywood Ave, Rutland, VT, 05701
(802) 775-0007
Admin Donald M Silliter.
Licensure Skilled care; Intermediate care. *Beds* SNF 49; ICF 117. *Certified* Medicaid; Medicare.
Owner Proprietary Corp (Beverly Enterprises).

Eden Park Nursing Home of Rutland*
99 Allen St, Rutland, VT, 05701
(802) 775-2331
Admin Joan B Fletcher.
Licensure Skilled care; Intermediate care. *Beds* SNF 40; ICF 84. *Certified* Medicaid; Medicare.
Owner Proprietary Corp (Eden Park Management).

Pleasant Manor Nursing Home*
46 Nichols St, Rutland, VT, 05701
(802) 775-2941
Admin Leon A Dion.
Licensure Intermediate care. *Beds* 119. *Certified* Medicaid.

Vermont Achievement Center—Pediatric Convalescent Unit
88 Park St, Rutland, VT, 05701
(802) 775-2395
Admin Rita Baccei. *Medical Dir/Dir of Nursing* P M Costello MD; Rita Baccei RN.
Licensure Skilled care; Pediatric. *Beds* SNF 20. *Certified* Medicaid.
Owner Nonprofit Corp.
Admissions Requirements Minimum age 0-21.
Staff Physicians 1 (pt); RNs 5 (ft), 3 (pt); LPNs 1 (pt); Nurses aides 12 (ft), 5 (pt); Physical therapists 1 (ft); Occupational therapists 1 (ft); Speech therapists 1 (pt); Activities coordinators 1 (ft); Dietitians 1 (pt).
Facilities Dining room; Physical therapy room; Activities room; Crafts room; Laundry room; Library.
Activities Arts & crafts; Cards; Games; Reading groups; Movies; Shopping trips; Social/Cultural gatherings.

SAINT ALBANS

Holiday House*
Sheldon Rd, Saint Albans, VT, 05478
(802) 524-2996
Admin Phillip H Condon.
Licensure Intermediate care. *Beds* 63. *Certified* Medicaid.

Redstone Villa*
7 Forest Hill Dr, Saint Albans, VT, 05478
(802) 524-3498
Admin Ronald F Deal. *Medical Dir/Dir of Nursing* Albert Brosseau MD.
Licensure Intermediate care. *Beds* 30. *Certified* Medicaid.
Admissions Requirements Medical examination; Physician's request.
Staff Physicians 7 (ft); RNs 2 (pt); LPNs 4 (ft), 2 (pt); Nurses aides 15 (ft), 6 (pt); Reality therapists 1 (ft); Recreational therapists 1 (ft); Activities coordinators 1 (ft); Dietitians 1 (ft).
Facilities Dining room; Laundry room; Barber/Beauty shop.
Activities Arts & crafts; Games; Reading groups; Prayer groups; Social/Cultural gatherings.

VerDelle Village
Box 80, Sheldon Rd, Saint Albans, VT, 05478
(802) 524-6534
Admin Raymond K Johnson. *Medical Dir/Dir of Nursing* Frank J Zsoldos MD; Phyllis Lucas RN DON.
Licensure Skilled care; Intermediate care. *Beds* SNF 24; ICF 96. *Certified* Medicaid; Medicare.
Owner Proprietary Corp.
Staff Physicians 3 (pt); RNs 6 (ft), 3 (pt); LPNs 15 (ft), 6 (pt); Orderlies 4 (ft), 2 (pt); Nurses aides 60 (ft), 20 (pt); Physical therapists 1 (ft); Recreational therapists 2 (ft); Occupational therapists 1 (pt); Speech therapists 1 (pt); Activities coordinators 1 (pt); Dietitians 1 (ft); Ophthalmologists 1 (pt).
Languages French
Activities Arts & crafts; Cards; Games; Reading groups; Prayer groups; Movies; Shopping trips; Social/Cultural gatherings.

SAINT JOHNSBURY

St Johnsbury Convalescent Center*
Hospital Dr, Saint Johnsbury, VT, 05819
(802) 748-8757
Admin Margaret M Cole.
Licensure Skilled care; Intermediate care. *Beds* SNF 27; ICF 83. *Certified* Medicaid; Medicare.
Staff Physicians 6 (pt); RNs 9 (ft), 2 (pt); LPNs 14 (ft), 1 (pt); Nurses aides 34 (ft), 3 (pt); Physical therapists 1 (ft); Recreational

therapists 1 (ft); Speech therapists; Activities coordinators 1 (ft); Dietitians 1 (ft); Dentists 1 (ft); Ophthalmologists 1 (pt); Podiatrists 1 (ft); Audiologists 1 (ft).
Facilities Dining room; Physical therapy room; Activities room; Chapel; Crafts room; Laundry room; Barber/Beauty shop.
Activities Arts & crafts; Cards; Games; Reading groups; Prayer groups; Movies; Shopping trips; Social/Cultural gatherings; Exercise class; Hymn sings; Band group; Special dinners.

SOUTH BARRE

Girouard St Jude Nursing Home Inc*
Box 300, South Barre, VT, 05670
(802) 476-7442
Admin Normand E Girouard Jr.
Licensure Intermediate care. *Beds* 36. *Certified* Medicaid.
Admissions Requirements Medical examination.
Staff RNs 2 (ft), 2 (pt); LPNs 2 (ft), 4 (pt); Nurses aides 10 (ft), 6 (pt); Activities coordinators.
Facilities Dining room; Activities room; Crafts room; Laundry room; 2 TV rooms.
Activities Arts & crafts; Cards; Games; Prayer groups; Movies; Shopping trips; Social/ Cultural gatherings.

SPRINGFIELD

Hanson Court Convalescent Center*
Summer St Extension, Springfield, VT, 05156
(802) 885-3408
Admin William F Morlock III.
Licensure Intermediate care. *Beds* 42. *Certified* Medicaid.

Springfield Convalescent Center
105 Chester Rd, Springfield, VT, 05156
(802) 885-5741
Admin Marcia DeRosia; Jean Julius. *Medical Dir/Dir of Nursing* Mark Hamilton; Judith Trout.
Licensure Skilled care; Intermediate care. *Beds* SNF 26; ICF 76. *Certified* Medicaid; Medicare.
Owner Proprietary Corp.
Admissions Requirements Physician's request.
Staff RNs 5 (ft), 3 (pt); LPNs 7 (ft), 8 (pt); Orderlies 3 (ft); Nurses aides 34 (ft), 27 (pt); Physical therapists 1 (pt); Recreational therapists 1 (ft); Occupational therapists 1 (pt); Speech therapists 1 (pt); Activities coordinators 1 (ft); Dietitians 1 (pt).
Facilities Dining room; Physical therapy room; Activities room; Crafts room; Laundry room; Barber/Beauty shop; Library; Adult day care.
Activities Arts & crafts; Cards; Games; Reading groups; Prayer groups; Movies; Shopping trips; Social/Cultural gatherings; Cooking; Activities; Day care.

TOWNSHEND

Stratton House Nursing Home
PO Box 216, Rte 35, Townshend, VT, 05353
(802) 365-7344
Admin Effie B Chamberlin. *Medical Dir/Dir of Nursing* R W Backus MD; Bess Richardson RN DON.
Licensure Intermediate care. *Beds* ICF 18. *Certified* Medicaid.
Owner Nonprofit Corp.
Staff Physicians 3 (pt); RNs 1 (ft), 1 (pt); LPNs 3 (ft); Nurses aides 5 (ft); Physical therapists 1 (ft); Occupational therapists 1 (pt); Speech therapists 1 (pt); Activities coordinators 1 (ft), 1 (pt); Dietitians 1 (ft).
Facilities Dining room; Physical therapy room; Activities room; Crafts room; Laundry room.

Activities Arts & crafts; Cards; Games; Reading groups; Prayer groups; Movies; Shopping trips; Social/Cultural gatherings; Tours; Dining out.

VERGENNES

Clark Nursing Home*
34 North St, Vergennes, VT, 05491
(802) 877-3562
Admin Donald B Clark.
Licensure Intermediate care. *Beds* 17.
Certified Medicaid.

VERNON

Vernon Green Nursing Home*
Rte 142, Vernon, VT, 05354
(802) 254-6041
Admin Lawrence B Knowles Jr. *Medical Dir/ Dir of Nursing* R Keith Clarke MD.
Licensure Skilled care; Intermediate care. *Beds* SNF 35; ICF 20. *Certified* Medicaid; Medicare.
Admissions Requirements Physician's request.
Staff RNs 3 (ft), 2 (pt); LPNs 3 (ft), 5 (pt); Orderlies 1 (ft); Nurses aides 18 (ft), 8 (pt); Physical therapists 1 (pt); Occupational therapists 1 (pt); Speech therapists 1 (pt); Activities coordinators 1 (ft).
Facilities Dining room; Physical therapy room; Activities room; Chapel; Crafts room; Laundry room; Barber/Beauty shop; Library.
Activities Arts & crafts; Cards; Games; Reading groups; Prayer groups; Movies; Shopping trips; Social/Cultural gatherings.

WHITE RIVER JUNCTION

Brookside Nursing Home*
120 Christian St, White River Junction, VT, 05001
(802) 295-7511

Admin Cathleen B Rice.
Licensure Skilled care; Intermediate care. *Beds* SNF 14; ICF 49. *Certified* Medicaid; Medicare.

WINDSOR

Cedar Manor Nursing Home Inc*
Star Rte 1, Windsor, VT, 05089
(802) 674-2050
Admin E Ingrid Anderson. *Medical Dir/Dir of Nursing* Dale Gephart MD.
Licensure Intermediate care. *Beds* 31. *Certified* Medicaid.
Admissions Requirements Minimum age 16; Medical examination.
Staff RNs 2 (ft), 1 (pt); LPNs 2 (ft), 3 (pt); Orderlies 1 (ft); Nurses aides 9 (ft), 4 (pt).
Facilities Dining room; Laundry room; Gardens; Swimming pool; Large yard; Picnic area.
Activities Arts & crafts; Cards; Games; Reading groups; Prayer groups; Movies; Shopping trips; Social/Cultural gatherings; Swimming pool; Outdoor programs (picnics, games, walks); Educational programs; Exercise class; Gardening; Bird-watching.

Mt Ascutney Hospital & Health Center
PO Box 6, County Rd, RR 1, Windsor, VT, 05089
(802) 674-6711
Admin Jeannette Lynch. *Medical Dir/Dir of Nursing* Jeannette Lynch.
Licensure Skilled care. *Beds* SNF 32. *Certified* Medicaid; Medicare.
Owner Nonprofit organization/foundation.
Admissions Requirements Minimum age 16; Medical examination; Physician's request.
Staff Physicians; RNs; LPNs; Nurses aides; Physical therapists; Occupational therapists; Speech therapists; Activities coordinators; Dietitians; Dentists; Ophthalmologists; Podiatrists.

Facilities Dining room; Physical therapy room; Activities room; Crafts room; Laundry room; Barber/Beauty shop; Library; Contact with VT State Library.
Activities Arts & crafts; Cards; Games; Reading groups; Prayer groups; Movies; Shopping trips; Social/Cultural gatherings; Exercise; Current events; Horticulture; Painting; Bowling; Sing-alongs; Cooking programs.

WINOOSKI

Green Mountain Nursing Home*
1102 Ethan Allen Ave, Winooski, VT, 05404
(802) 655-1025
Admin Gordon R Haslam. *Medical Dir/Dir of Nursing* John Lantman MD.
Licensure Skilled care; Intermediate care. *Beds* 73. *Certified* Medicaid.
Admissions Requirements Minimum age 18; Physician's request.
Staff Physicians 1 (pt); RNs 7 (ft), 6 (pt); LPNs 3 (ft), 3 (pt); Nurses aides 28 (ft), 15 (pt); Physical therapists 1 (pt); Recreational therapists 3 (ft); Activities coordinators 1 (ft); Dietitians 1 (pt); Dentists 1 (pt).
Facilities Dining room; Physical therapy room; Activities room; Chapel; Crafts room; Laundry room; Barber/Beauty shop; Library; TV lounges.
Activities Arts & crafts; Games; Reading groups; Prayer groups; Movies; Shopping trips; Social/Cultural gatherings; Cooking group.

VIRGINIA

ABINGDON

Cedar Lawn Convalescent Center
600 Walden Rd, Abingdon, VA, 24210
(703) 628-2111
Admin Herman A Hogston. *Medical Dir/Dir
of Nursing* Dr J S Shaffer.
Licensure Intermediate care. *Beds* 120.
Certified Medicaid.
Owner Privately owned.
Admissions Requirements Minimum age 14.
Staff Physicians 4 (ft); RNs 3 (ft), 1 (pt);
LPNs 11 (ft); Orderlies 3 (ft); Nurses aides
38 (ft); Physical therapists 1 (pt); Activities
coordinators 1 (ft); Dietitians 1 (pt).
Facilities Dining room; Activities room;
Laundry room; Barber/Beauty shop; Library.
Activities Arts & crafts; Cards; Games;
Reading groups; Prayer groups; Social/
Cultural gatherings.

ALEXANDRIA

Goodwin House—Nurs Care Unit
4800 Fillmore Ave, Alexandria, VA, 22311
(703) 578-1000
Admin James K Meharg Jr. *Medical Dir/Dir
of Nursing* James R Brayshaw MD; Kathy
Owens RN.
Licensure Skilled care; Intermediate care; Life
care. *Beds* SNF 60; ICF 34; Life care 278.
Certified Medicaid; Medicare.
Owner Nonprofit Corp.
Admissions Requirements Minimum age 65;
Medical examination; Physician's request.
Staff Physicians; RNs 6 (ft), 9 (pt); LPNs 8
(ft), 7 (pt); Nurses aides 46 (ft), 16 (pt);
Physical therapists 2 (pt); Recreational
therapists 1 (ft); Occupational therapists 1
(pt); Speech therapists; Activities
coordinators 1 (ft); Dietitians 1 (ft);
Ophthalmologists.
Affiliation Episcopal
Facilities Dining room; Physical therapy
room; Activities room; Chapel; Crafts room;
Laundry room; Barber/Beauty shop; Library;
Exercise.
Activities Arts & crafts; Cards; Games;
Reading groups; Prayer groups; Movies;
Shopping trips; Social/Cultural gatherings;
Language; Sculpture; Weaving classes.

Hermitage in Northern Virginia
5000 Fairbanks Ave, Alexandria, VA, 22311
(703) 820-2434
Admin Edwin G Burch. *Medical Dir/Dir of
Nursing* Lana Wingate DON.
Licensure Skilled care; Intermediate care. *Beds*
121.
Owner Nonprofit Corp.
Admissions Requirements Minimum age 65;
Medical examination.
Staff Physicians 1 (pt); RNs 16 (ft), 15 (pt);
LPNs 13 (ft), 5 (pt); Nurses aides 43 (ft), 3
(pt); Recreational therapists 1 (ft); Activities
coordinators 1 (ft), 1 (pt); Dietitians 1 (ft).
Affiliation Methodist

Facilities Dining room; Physical therapy
room; Activities room; Chapel; Crafts room;
Laundry room; Barber/Beauty shop; Library;
Auditorium; Solariums on each floor.
Activities Arts & crafts; Cards; Games;
Reading groups; Prayer groups; Movies;
Shopping trips; Social/Cultural gatherings;
Music programs.

Mt Vernon Nursing Center*
8111 Tiswell Dr, Alexandria, VA, 22306
(703) 360-4000
Admin Hazel N Engels.
Licensure Skilled care; Intermediate care. *Beds*
SNF 20; ICF 110. *Certified* Medicaid;
Medicare.
Owner Proprietary Corp.

Oak Meadow Nursing Center Inc
1510 Collingwood Rd, Alexandria, VA, 22308
(703) 765-6107
Admin Jean Moulds. *Medical Dir/Dir of
Nursing* Scott Robson MD; Patsy McLaurin
RN DON.
Licensure Skilled care; Intermediate care. *Beds*
SNF 13; ICF 83. *Certified* Medicaid;
Medicare.
Owner Proprietary Corp (Health Care &
Retirement Corp).
Admissions Requirements Medical
examination.
Staff RNs 5 (ft), 3 (pt); LPNs 4 (ft), 5 (pt);
Nurses aides 19 (ft), 31 (pt); Activities
coordinators 1 (ft), 1 (pt).
Languages Spanish
Facilities Dining room; Physical therapy
room; Activities room; Chapel; Crafts room;
Laundry room; Barber/Beauty shop; Day
rooms with TVs.
Activities Arts & crafts; Cards; Games;
Reading groups; Prayer groups; Movies;
Shopping trips; Social/Cultural gatherings;
Monthly lunch out.

The Washington House—Health Care Unit*
5100 Fillmore Ave, Alexandria, VA, 22311
(703) 379-9000
Admin Robert N Bianco. *Medical Dir/Dir of
Nursing* Dr Ronald Apter.
Beds 68.
Owner Nonprofit Corp.
Admissions Requirements Medical
examination.
Staff Physicians 2 (pt); Physical therapists 2
(pt); Recreational therapists 1 (ft); Activities
coordinators 1 (ft); Dietitians 1 (pt); Dentists
1 (pt); Podiatrists 1 (pt).

Woodbine Nursing & Convalescent Center*
2729 King St, Alexandria, VA, 22302
(703) 836-8838
Admin Vivian V Hewett.
Licensure Skilled care; Intermediate care. *Beds*
257. *Certified* Medicaid; Medicare.
Owner Proprietary Corp.

AMHERST

Ryan Nursing Home
PO Box 590, Rte 2, Amherst, VA, 24521
(804) 946-7781
Admin Claudette Canter. *Medical Dir/Dir of
Nursing* Fay Cox.
Licensure Intermediate care. *Beds* 51.
Certified Medicaid.
Owner Proprietary Corp.
Admissions Requirements Medical
examination; Physician's request.
Staff RNs; LPNs; Nurses aides; Recreational
therapists; Activities coordinators.
Facilities Dining room; Physical therapy
room; Activities room; Crafts room; Laundry
room; Library.
Activities Arts & crafts; Cards; Games;
Reading groups; Prayer groups; Movies;
Social/Cultural gatherings.

ANNANDALE

Leewood Nursing Home Inc*
7120 Braddock Rd, Annandale, VA, 22003
(703) 256-9770
Admin Cynthia L Butler. *Medical Dir/Dir of
Nursing* M Roy Nicholson.
Licensure Intermediate care. *Beds* 132.
Certified Medicaid.
Owner Proprietary Corp.
Admissions Requirements Minimum age 18;
Medical examination; Physician's request.
Staff Physicians 2 (pt); RNs 28 (ft); LPNs 16
(ft); Nurses aides 128 (ft); Physical therapists
1 (ft); Recreational therapists 1 (ft);
Activities coordinators 1 (ft); Dietitians 1
(pt); Dentists 1 (pt); Podiatrists 1 (pt).
Facilities Dining room; Physical therapy
room; Activities room; Chapel; Crafts room;
Laundry room; Barber/Beauty shop; Library.
Activities Arts & crafts; Cards; Games;
Reading groups; Prayer groups; Movies;
Shopping trips; Social/Cultural gatherings.

Sleepy Hollow Manor Nursing Home*
6700 Columbia Pike, Annandale, VA, 22003
(703) 256-7000
Admin Mary B Harrison.
Licensure Intermediate care. *Beds* 230.
Certified Medicaid.
Owner Proprietary Corp (Beverly Enterprises).

ARLINGTON

Camelot Hall Nursing Home
3710 Lee Hwy, Arlington, VA, 22207
(703) 243-7640
Admin Stephen L Forstenzer. *Medical Dir/Dir
of Nursing* Robert G Bullock MD; Robert
Spencer RN DON.
Licensure Skilled care; Intermediate care. *Beds*
SNF 10; ICF 230. *Certified* Medicaid;
Medicare.
Owner Proprietary Corp (Medical Facilities of
America).

Admissions Requirements Medical examination.
Staff RNs 8 (ft), 8 (pt); LPNs 18 (ft), 2 (pt); Nurses aides 71 (ft), 7 (pt); Physical therapists 1 (ft); Occupational therapists 1 (ft); Speech therapists 1 (ft); Activities coordinators 1 (ft); Dietitians 1 (pt).
Facilities Dining room; Physical therapy room; Activities room; Chapel; Crafts room; Laundry room; Barber/Beauty shop.
Activities Arts & crafts; Cards; Games; Reading groups; Prayer groups; Movies; Shopping trips; Stroke support club; Reminiscing workshop.

Carriage Hill—Arlington*
1785 S Hayes St, Arlington, VA, 22202
(703) 920-5700
Admin Denny G Dennis. *Medical Dir/Dir of Nursing* Ott Kurz MD.
Licensure Skilled care; Intermediate care. *Beds* 240. *Certified* Medicaid; Medicare.
Owner Proprietary Corp.
Admissions Requirements Minimum age 14; Medical examination; Physician's request.
Staff Physicians; RNs; LPNs; Orderlies; Nurses aides; Physical therapists; Recreational therapists; Occupational therapists O 1 (pt); Speech therapists 1 (ft); Activities coordinators 1 (ft); Dietitians 2 (ft).
Facilities Dining room; Physical therapy room; Activities room; Chapel; Crafts room; Laundry room; Barber/Beauty shop.
Activities Arts & crafts; Games; Reading groups; Prayer groups; Movies; Shopping trips; Social/Cultural gatherings; Special events; Cherry Blossom Trip; Dining out in local restaurants.

Crystal City Nursing Center
1785 S Hayes St, Arlington, VA, 22202
(703) 920-5700
Admin Barbara McKenna.
Beds 240.
Owner Proprietary Corp (Genesis Health Ventures).

Manor Care Arlington Nursing & Rehabilitation Center
550 S Carlin Springs Rd, Arlington, VA, 22204
(703) 379-7200
Admin Kathryn A Heflin. *Medical Dir/Dir of Nursing* Dr James Ambury MD; Kathleen Beeman RN DON.
Licensure Skilled care; Intermediate care. *Beds* 196. *Certified* Medicaid; Medicare.
Owner Proprietary Corp (Manor Care).
Admissions Requirements Minimum age 16; Medical examination; Physician's request.
Staff RNs 8 (ft), 11 (pt); LPNs 15 (ft), 22 (pt); Orderlies 3 (ft); Nurses aides 58 (ft), 9 (pt); Physical therapists 2 (ft); Recreational therapists 2 (ft), 1 (pt); Occupational therapists 1 (ft); Speech therapists 1 (ft); Dietitians 1 (ft).
Facilities Dining room; Physical therapy room; Activities room; Crafts room; Laundry room; Barber/Beauty shop.
Activities Arts & crafts; Cards; Games; Reading groups; Prayer groups; Movies; Shopping trips; Social/Cultural gatherings.

ARODA

Mountain View Nursing Home Inc
PO Box 186, Rte 5, Aroda, VA, 22709
(703) 948-6831
Admin Eldon Hochstetler. *Medical Dir/Dir of Nursing* William B Cave MD; Hilda Zook RN DON.
Licensure Intermediate care. *Beds* ICF 40. *Certified* Medicaid.
Owner Nonprofit Corp.
Admissions Requirements Medical examination.

Staff Physicians 3 (pt); RNs 2 (ft), 2 (pt); LPNs 2 (ft); Orderlies 4 (ft); Nurses aides 11 (ft); Activities coordinators 1 (ft); Dietitians 1 (ft).
Affiliation Mennonite
Facilities Dining room; Activities room; Crafts room; Laundry room; Barber/Beauty shop.
Activities Arts & crafts; Games; Reading groups; Prayer groups; Movies; Shopping trips.

ASHLAND

Ashland Convalescent Center Inc*
PO Box 2050, Rte 54 W, Ashland, VA, 23005
(804) 798-3291
Admin Joseph M Teefey.
Licensure Skilled care; Intermediate care. *Beds* SNF 15; ICF 115. *Certified* Medicaid; Medicare.
Owner Proprietary Corp.

BEDFORD

Bedford County Nursing Home
PO Box 413, Rte 4, Bedford, VA, 24523
(703) 586-3347
Admin Edith Whicker. *Medical Dir/Dir of Nursing* Lou P Brown RN DON.
Licensure Intermediate care. *Beds* 56. *Certified* Medicaid.
Owner Publicly owned.
Staff RNs 1 (ft); LPNs 4 (ft), 4 (pt); Orderlies 1 (ft); Nurses aides 16 (ft), 9 (pt); Activities coordinators 1 (ft).
Facilities Dining room; Activities room; Chapel; Laundry room; Barber/Beauty shop.
Activities Arts & crafts; Cards; Games; Reading groups; Prayer groups; Movies.

Oakwood Manor
PO Box 688, 1613 Oakwood St, Bedford, VA, 24523
(703) 586-2441
Admin John H Fretz. *Medical Dir/Dir of Nursing* Brian Buchanan MD.
Licensure Skilled care; Intermediate care. *Beds* 100. *Certified* Medicaid; Medicare.
Owner Nonprofit Corp.
Admissions Requirements Medical examination; Physician's request.
Staff Physicians; RNs; LPNs; Orderlies; Nurses aides; Recreational therapists; Speech therapists; Dietitians; Dentists; Ophthalmologists.
Facilities Dining room; Physical therapy room; Activities room; Chapel; Crafts room; Barber/Beauty shop.
Activities Arts & crafts; Cards; Games; Reading groups; Prayer groups; Music; Occasional meals out.

BERRYVILLE

Rose Hill Nursing Home
110 Chalmers Ct, Berryville, VA, 22611
(703) 955-9995
Admin Susan A York. *Medical Dir/Dir of Nursing* Sylvia Heishman RN DON.
Licensure Skilled care; Intermediate care. *Beds* 120. *Certified* Medicaid; Medicare; VA.
Owner Proprietary Corp (Beverly Enterprises).
Staff RNs; LPNs; Orderlies; Nurses aides; Physical therapists; Occupational therapists; Speech therapists; Activities coordinators; Dietitians; Dentists; Ophthalmologists; Podiatrists.
Facilities Dining room; Physical therapy room; Activities room; Crafts room; Barber/Beauty shop.
Activities Arts & crafts; Cards; Games; Prayer groups; Movies; Shopping trips; Social/Cultural gatherings.

BIG STONE GAP

Heritage Hall Health Care II
2045 Valley View Dr, Big Stone Gap, VA, 24219
(703) 523-3000
Admin Pat H Stallard. *Medical Dir/Dir of Nursing* Dr Lawrence Fleenor; Linda Ramsey RN.
Licensure Skilled care; Intermediate care; Intermediate care for mentally retarded. *Beds* SNF 22; ICF 158. *Certified* Medicaid; Medicare.
Owner Proprietary Corp.
Admissions Requirements Minimum age 14; Medical examination; Physician's request.
Staff Physicians 11 (ft); RNs 3 (ft), 2 (pt); LPNs 21 (ft), 6 (pt); Orderlies 3 (ft), 1 (pt); Nurses aides 34 (ft), 32 (pt); Activities coordinators 1 (ft); Dietitians 1 (ft).
Facilities Dining room; Physical therapy room; Activities room; Crafts room; Laundry room; Barber/Beauty shop; Library.
Activities Arts & crafts; Games; Prayer groups; Social/Cultural gatherings.

BLACKSBURG

Heritage Hall Health Care I
3610 S Main St, Blacksburg, VA, 24060
(703) 951-7000
Admin Robert Nelson. *Medical Dir/Dir of Nursing* Dr C L Boatwright; Carla Schwertz DON.
Licensure Intermediate care. *Beds* 194. *Certified* Medicaid.
Owner Proprietary Corp.
Admissions Requirements Medical examination; Physician's request.
Staff Physicians 15 (pt); RNs 4 (ft), 1 (pt); LPNs 16 (ft), 6 (pt); Nurses aides 57 (ft), 31 (pt); Physical therapists 2 (pt); Speech therapists 1 (pt); Activities coordinators 2 (ft); Dietitians 1 (pt); Ophthalmologists 2 (pt).
Facilities Dining room; Physical therapy room; Activities room; Laundry room; Barber/Beauty shop.
Activities Arts & crafts; Games; Reading groups; Prayer groups; Movies; Shopping trips; Social/Cultural gatherings.

BLACKSTONE

Heritage Hall Health Care IV
800 S Main St, Blackstone, VA, 23824
(804) 292-5301
Admin Chuck Rehnborg. *Medical Dir/Dir of Nursing* Dr Stuart B White.
Licensure Intermediate care. *Beds* 180. *Certified* Medicaid.
Owner Proprietary Corp.
Admissions Requirements Medical examination; Physician's request.
Staff Physicians 3 (ft), 18 (pt); RNs 5 (ft), 2 (pt); LPNs 16 (ft), 3 (pt); Orderlies 4 (ft); Nurses aides 62 (ft), 9 (pt); Physical therapists 1 (pt); Recreational therapists 1 (ft); Activities coordinators 1 (ft); Dietitians 1 (ft); Dentists 1 (pt); Ophthalmologists 1 (pt); Podiatrists 1 (pt).
Facilities Dining room; Physical therapy room; Activities room; Crafts room; Laundry room; Barber/Beauty shop.
Activities Arts & crafts; Cards; Games; Reading groups; Prayer groups; Movies; Shopping trips; Social/Cultural gatherings.

BLOXOM

Bi-County Clinic & Nursing Home Inc*
Rte 13, PO Box 85, Bloxom, VA, 23308
(804) 665-5005
Admin Isaac S White. *Medical Dir/Dir of Nursing* Edward S White.
Beds 24.

Owner Proprietary Corp.
Staff Physicians 2 (ft); RNs 1 (ft); LPNs 2 (ft),
2 (pt); Orderlies 1 (ft); Nurses aides 6 (ft);
Activities coordinators 1 (pt); Dietitians 1
(pt); Dentists 1 (pt); Podiatrists 1 (pt).
Facilities Dining room; Activities room.
Activities Games; Movies.

BRIDGEWATER

Bridgewater Home Inc*
Virginia Ave & 2nd St, Bridgewater, VA,
22812
(703) 828-2531
Admin John R Garber.
Licensure Intermediate care. *Beds* 200.
Certified Medicaid.
Owner Nonprofit Corp.
Admissions Requirements Minimum age 14;
Medical examination; Physician's request.
Staff RNs 11 (ft), 16 (pt); LPNs 7 (ft), 5 (pt);
Orderlies 39 (ft), 65 (pt); Physical therapists
1 (pt); Speech therapists 1 (pt); Activities
coordinators 1 (ft); Dietitians 1 (pt);
Audiologists 1 (pt).
Affiliation Church of the Brethren
Facilities Dining room; Physical therapy
room; Activities room; Chapel; Crafts room;
Laundry room; Barber/Beauty shop; Library.
Activities Arts & crafts; Cards; Games;
Reading groups; Prayer groups; Movies;
Shopping trips.

BRISTOL

Bristol Health Care Center
245 North St, Bristol, VA, 24201
(703) 669-4711
Admin William D Bishop.
Licensure Skilled care; Intermediate care. *Beds*
SNF 28; ICF 92. *Certified* Medicaid;
Medicare.
Owner Proprietary Corp (National Health
Corp).
Admissions Requirements Physician's request.
Staff RNs; LPNs; Orderlies; Nurses aides;
Physical therapists; Recreational therapists;
Speech therapists; Activities coordinators;
Dietitians.
Facilities Dining room; Physical therapy
room; Activities room; Crafts room; Laundry
room; Barber/Beauty shop.

Memorial Hall—Bristol Memorial Hospital*
North St, Bristol, VA, 24201
(615) 968-1121
Admin W W Fanning.
Licensure Skilled care. *Beds* 40. *Certified*
Medicaid; Medicare.
Owner Nonprofit Corp.

CHARLOTTESVILLE

The Cedars
1242 Cedars Ct, Charlottesville, VA, 22901
(804) 296-5611
Admin Jeffrey K Jellerson. *Medical Dir/Dir of
Nursing* Dr David Chester; Barbara Gruber
RN.
Licensure Skilled care; Intermediate care. *Beds*
143. *Certified* Medicaid; Medicare.
Owner Proprietary Corp (Beverly Enterprises).
Admissions Requirements Minimum age 14.
Staff RNs 10 (ft), 4 (pt); LPNs 12 (ft), 4 (pt);
Orderlies 2 (ft); Nurses aides 59 (ft), 1 (pt);
Physical therapists 1 (ft); Occupational
therapists 1 (ft); Speech therapists 1 (ft);
Activities coordinators 2 (ft); Dietitians 1
(ft).
Activities Arts & crafts; Cards; Games;
Reading groups; Prayer groups; Movies;
Shopping trips; Social/Cultural gatherings.

Eldercare Gardens
1150 Northwest Dr, Charlottesville, VA,
22901
(804) 973-7933

Admin Larry M Lucas. *Medical Dir/Dir of
Nursing* Dr William Tompkins; Allene
Brighton RN.
Licensure Skilled care; Intermediate care. *Beds*
SNF 30; ICF 150. *Certified* Medicaid;
Medicare; VA.
Owner Proprietary Corp.
Admissions Requirements Medical
examination; Physician's request.
Facilities Dining room; Physical therapy
room; Activities room; Crafts room; Laundry
room; Barber/Beauty shop; Library.
Activities Arts & crafts; Cards; Games;
Reading groups; Prayer groups; Movies;
Shopping trips; Social/Cultural gatherings.

Piedmont Health Care Center
1214 Jefferson Park Ave, Charlottesville, VA,
22901
(804) 295-1161
Admin Pamela D Doshier. *Medical Dir/Dir of
Nursing* Dr Joseph May.
Licensure Intermediate care; Home for adults.
Beds ICF 128; Home for adults 40. *Certified*
Medicaid.
Owner Proprietary Corp.
Admissions Requirements Medical
examination; Physician's request.
Facilities Dining room; Physical therapy
room; Activities room; Chapel; Crafts room;
Laundry room; Barber/Beauty shop; Library.
Activities Arts & crafts; Cards; Games;
Reading groups; Prayer groups; Movies;
Social/Cultural gatherings.

CHESAPEAKE

Autumn Care of Chesapeake*
PO Box 13680, 2701 Border Rd, Chesapeake,
VA, 23325-0680
(804) 545-2487
Admin Dona J Allison. *Medical Dir/Dir of
Nursing* Dr Rudolf Schuster.
Licensure Intermediate care. *Beds* 54.
Certified Medicaid.
Owner Proprietary Corp (Autumn Corp).
Admissions Requirements Minimum age 18;
Medical examination; Physician's request.
Staff RNs 1 (ft), 1 (pt); LPNs 4 (ft), 4 (pt);
Nurses aides 21 (ft), 4 (pt); Recreational
therapists 1 (pt); Dietitians 1 (pt).
Facilities Dining room; Activities room;
Crafts room; Laundry room; Barber/Beauty
shop.
Activities Arts & crafts; Cards; Games;
Reading groups; Prayer groups; Movies;
Shopping trips; Social/Cultural gatherings.

Autumn Care of Great Bridge*
PO Box 15224, 821 Cedar Rd, Chesapeake,
VA, 23320
(804) 547-4528
Admin Delores G Womack.
Licensure Intermediate care. *Beds* 55.
Certified Medicaid.
Owner Proprietary Corp (Autumn Corp).

Brent Lox Hall Nursing Center
1017 George Washington Hwy, Chesapeake,
VA, 23323
(804) 485-5500
Admin Norma R Spencer. *Medical Dir/Dir of
Nursing* Jonathan Manneu MD.
Licensure Intermediate care. *Beds* 120.
Certified Medicaid.
Owner Proprietary Corp.
Admissions Requirements Medical
examination.
Staff Physicians; RNs 4 (ft); LPNs 16 (ft);
Nurses aides 78 (ft); Physical therapists;
Occupational therapists 1 (ft); Speech
therapists; Activities coordinators 1 (ft);
Dietitians 1 (ft); Ophthalmologists.
Facilities Dining room; Physical therapy
room; Activities room; Crafts room; Laundry
room; Barber/Beauty shop; Library.

Activities Arts & crafts; Cards; Games;
Reading groups; Prayer groups; Movies;
Social/Cultural gatherings.

Camelot Hall Nursing Home
688 Kingsborough Square, Chesapeake, VA,
23320
(804) 547-9111
Admin John A Gryglewicz.
Licensure Skilled care; Intermediate care. *Beds*
240. *Certified* Medicaid; Medicare.
Owner Proprietary Corp.
Admissions Requirements Minimum age 16;
Medical examination; Physician's request.
Staff Physicians; RNs; LPNs; Orderlies;
Nurses aides; Physical therapists;
Recreational therapists; Speech therapists;
Activities coordinators; Dietitians;
Ophthalmologists.
Facilities Dining room; Physical therapy
room; Activities room; Chapel; Crafts room;
Laundry room; Barber/Beauty shop; Library.
Activities Arts & crafts; Cards; Games;
Reading groups; Prayer groups; Movies;
Shopping trips; Social/Cultural gatherings.

Oak Hill Convalescent Center*
776 Oak Grove Rd, PO Box 1277,
Chesapeake, VA, 23320
(804) 547-5156
Admin Joyce T Butler. *Medical Dir/Dir of
Nursing* L Jonathan Marven MD.
Licensure Intermediate care. *Beds* 102.
Certified Medicaid.
Owner Nonprofit Corp.
Admissions Requirements Minimum age 18;
Medical examination; Physician's request.
Staff Physicians 6 (pt); RNs 2 (ft); LPNs 16
(ft), 4 (pt); Orderlies 1 (ft); Nurses aides 46
(ft); Activities coordinators 1 (ft); Dietitians
1 (pt); Dentists 1 (pt); Podiatrists 1 (pt).

CHESTERFIELD

Lucy Corr Nursing Home
PO Drawer 170, Chesterfield, VA, 23832
(804) 748-1511
Admin Jacob W Mast Jr. *Medical Dir/Dir of
Nursing* Scott Woogen MD; Susan Phalen
DON.
Licensure Skilled care; Intermediate care. *Beds*
194. *Certified* Medicaid; Medicare.
Owner Publicly owned.
Admissions Requirements Medical
examination.
Staff Physicians 4 (pt); RNs 8 (ft), 2 (pt);
LPNs 14 (ft), 15 (pt); Nurses aides 49 (ft),
67 (pt); Physical therapists 1 (pt);
Occupational therapists 1 (ft); Activities
coordinators 1 (ft); Dietitians 1 (ft);
Ophthalmologists 1 (pt).
Facilities Dining room; Physical therapy
room; Activities room; Crafts room; Laundry
room; Barber/Beauty shop; Library.
Activities Arts & crafts; Cards; Games;
Reading groups; Prayer groups; Movies;
Shopping trips; Camping; Kings Dominion;
Fishing.

CHILHOWIE

Valley Health Care Center
PO Box 746, Chilhowie, VA, 24319
(703) 646-8911
Admin D R Wright. *Medical Dir/Dir of
Nursing* William N Greever MD.
Licensure Skilled care; Intermediate care;
Residential home for adults. *Beds* SNF 20;
ICF 160; Home for adults 27. *Certified*
Medicaid; Medicare.
Owner Proprietary Corp (Convalescent Care
Inc).
Admissions Requirements Medical
examination.
Staff RNs 6 (ft), 5 (pt); LPNs 20 (ft), 2 (pt);
Nurses aides 48 (ft), 4 (pt); Activities
coordinators 2 (ft).

Facilities Dining room; Physical therapy room; Activities room; Laundry room; Barber/Beauty shop.
Activities Arts & crafts; Games; Reading groups; Prayer groups; Movies; Social/Cultural gatherings; Ceramics.

Valley Health Care Center*
PO Box 746, Hwy 11 & Pine St, Chilhowie, VA, 24319
(703) 646-8911
Admin T R Wright Jr.
Licensure Skilled care; Intermediate care. *Beds* SNF 20; ICF 100. *Certified* Medicaid; Medicare.
Owner Proprietary Corp.

CLIFTON FORGE

Liberty House Nursing Home*
Rte 60 E, PO Box 167, Clifton Forge, VA, 24422
(703) 862-5791
Admin William R Snead. *Medical Dir/Dir of Nursing* Dr R S Goings.
Licensure Skilled care; Intermediate care. *Beds* 150. *Certified* Medicaid.
Owner Proprietary Corp (Beverly Enterprises).
Admissions Requirements Medical examination; Physician's request.
Staff Physicians 1 (pt); RNs 9 (ft); LPNs 7 (ft); Orderlies 33 (ft), 25 (pt); Physical therapists 1 (pt); Activities coordinators 1 (ft); Dietitians 1 (pt); Dentists 1 (pt); Podiatrists 1 (pt).
Facilities Dining room; Physical therapy room; Activities room; Chapel; Crafts room; Laundry room; Barber/Beauty shop; Library.
Activities Arts & crafts; Games; Movies; Shopping trips; Social/Cultural gatherings.

Shenandoah Manor
Fairview Heights, Clifton Forge, VA, 24422
(703) 862-7056
Admin Nile D Cutlid. *Medical Dir/Dir of Nursing* Dr Wallace Nunley MD; Shelbia Bayne RN DON.
Licensure Intermediate care. *Beds* ICF 47. *Certified* Medicaid.
Owner Proprietary Corp (Glenmark Assocs).
Staff Physicians 1 (pt); RNs 2 (ft); LPNs 4 (ft); Nurses aides 2 (ft); Activities coordinators 1 (ft); Dietitians 1 (pt).
Facilities Dining room; Physical therapy room; Activities room; Crafts room; Laundry room; Barber/Beauty shop; Library.
Activities Arts & crafts; Cards; Games; Reading groups; Prayer groups; Movies; Shopping trips; Social/Cultural gatherings.

CLINTWOOD

Heritage Hall Health Care VIII*
PO Box 909, Clintwood, VA, 24228
(703) 926-4693
Admin Dick Baker. *Medical Dir/Dir of Nursing* Dr Russel Schram.
Licensure Intermediate care. *Beds* 100. *Certified* Medicaid.
Owner Proprietary Corp.
Admissions Requirements Minimum age 14; Medical examination; Physician's request.
Staff Physicians 1 (pt); RNs 2 (ft), 1 (pt); LPNs 7 (ft), 4 (pt); Orderlies 3 (ft); Nurses aides 24 (ft), 5 (pt); Physical therapists 1 (pt); Reality therapists 1 (pt); Recreational therapists 1 (ft); Activities coordinators 1 (pt); Dietitians 1 (pt); Dentists 1 (pt); Ophthalmologists 2 (pt).
Facilities Dining room; Crafts room; Laundry room; Barber/Beauty shop.
Activities Arts & crafts; Cards; Games; Reading groups; Prayer groups; Shopping trips; Social/Cultural gatherings.

COLONIAL HEIGHTS

Colonial Heights Convalescent Center
831 E Ellerslie Ave, Colonial Heights, VA, 23834
(804) 541-3973
Admin Anne B McDaniel. *Medical Dir/Dir of Nursing* Dr Scott Knowles; Wanda Cassort DON.
Licensure Skilled care; Intermediate care. *Beds* SNF 18; ICF 118. *Certified* Medicaid; Medicare.
Owner Proprietary Corp (Convalescent Care Inc).
Admissions Requirements Minimum age 14; Medical examination; Physician's request.
Staff Physicians 10 (pt); RNs 8 (ft), 3 (pt); LPNs 16 (ft), 4 (pt); Orderlies 7 (ft); Nurses aides 72 (ft), 8 (pt); Physical therapists 1 (pt); Occupational therapists 1 (pt); Speech therapists 1 (pt); Activities coordinators 2 (ft); Dietitians 1 (pt); Podiatrists 1 (pt).
Facilities Dining room; Physical therapy room; Activities room; Chapel; Crafts room; Laundry room; Barber/Beauty shop; 2 outside courtyards; 4 dayrooms.
Activities Arts & crafts; Cards; Games; Reading groups; Shopping trips; Social/Cultural gatherings; Family night dinners; Resident council.

CULPEPER

Virginia Baptist Home Inc*
Box 191, Culpeper, VA, 22701
(703) 825-2411
Admin Raleigh O Baker. *Medical Dir/Dir of Nursing* Evelyn B Cunningham.
Beds 47.
Owner Nonprofit Corp.
Admissions Requirements Minimum age 65; Medical examination.
Staff Physicians 1 (pt); RNs 2 (ft), 3 (pt); LPNs 8 (ft), 1 (pt); Nurses aides 22 (ft), 16 (pt); Activities coordinators 1 (ft); Dietitians 1 (pt); Ophthalmologists 1 (pt).
Affiliation Baptist
Facilities Dining room; Activities room; Chapel; Crafts room; Laundry room; Barber/Beauty shop; Library.
Activities Arts & crafts; Cards; Games; Reading groups; Prayer groups; Shopping trips; Social/Cultural gatherings.

DANVILLE

Camelot Hall Nursing Home
450 Piney Forest Rd, Danville, VA, 245410
(804) 799-1565
Admin Sheena Mackenzie. *Medical Dir/Dir of Nursing* Dr Vincent Falgui.
Licensure Skilled care; Intermediate care. *Beds* SNF 14; ICF 106. *Certified* Medicaid; Medicare.
Owner Proprietary Corp (Medical Facilities of America).
Admissions Requirements Minimum age 14; Medical examination; Physician's request.
Staff Physicians 23 (pt); RNs 4 (ft), 4 (pt); LPNs 11 (ft), 4 (pt); Orderlies 1 (ft); Physical therapists 1 (pt); Speech therapists 1 (pt); Activities coordinators 1 (ft); Dietitians 1 (pt); Dentists; Ophthalmologists.
Facilities Dining room; Physical therapy room; Crafts room; Laundry room; Barber/Beauty shop.
Activities Arts & crafts; Cards; Games; Prayer groups; Movies; Shopping trips; Social/Cultural gatherings.

Riverside Health Care Center*
2344 Riverside Drive, Danville, VA, 24540
(804) 791-3800
Admin Tommy D Mathena.
Licensure Intermediate care. *Beds* 180. *Certified* Medicare.
Owner Proprietary Corp.

Roman Eagle Memorial Home Inc
2526 N Main St, Danville, VA, 24540
(804) 793-0111
Admin Bernice H Jennings. *Medical Dir/Dir of Nursing* G V Thompson Jr.
Licensure Skilled care; Intermediate care. *Beds* SNF 48; ICF 264. *Certified* Medicaid; Medicare.
Owner Nonprofit Corp.
Admissions Requirements Medical examination; Physician's request.
Staff RNs 12 (ft), 4 (pt); LPNs 24 (ft), 12 (pt); Orderlies 12 (ft); Nurses aides 112 (ft), 27 (pt); Physical therapists 1 (pt); Speech therapists 1 (pt); Activities coordinators 3 (ft); Dietitians 1 (ft).
Facilities Dining room; Physical therapy room; Activities room; Chapel; Crafts room; Laundry room; Barber/Beauty shop; Library; Pharmacy; Speech therapy room.
Activities Arts & crafts; Cards; Games; Reading groups; Prayer groups; Movies; Shopping trips.

DILLWYN

Heritage Hall Dillwyn
9 Brickyard Dr, Dillwyn, VA, 23936
(804) 983-2058
Admin Charles E Rehnborg. *Medical Dir/Dir of Nursing* Dr Irving Epperson.
Licensure Intermediate care. *Beds* ICF 60. *Certified* Medicaid.
Owner Proprietary Corp.
Admissions Requirements Medical examination; Physician's request.
Staff RNs 2 (ft), 1 (pt); LPNs 4 (ft), 4 (pt); Nurses aides 13 (ft), 12 (pt); Physical therapists 1 (pt); Recreational therapists 1 (pt); Occupational therapists 1 (pt); Speech therapists 1 (pt); Activities coordinators 1 (ft); Dietitians 1 (pt); Ophthalmologists 1 (pt).
Facilities Dining room; Physical therapy room; Activities room; Crafts room; Laundry room; Barber/Beauty shop; Library.
Activities Arts & crafts; Cards; Games; Prayer groups; Movies; Shopping trips; Social/Cultural gatherings.

DRYDEN

Carter Hall Nursing Home*
Alt Rte 58, Box 53, Dryden, VA, 24243
(703) 546-4114
Admin Dennis E Bowen.
Licensure Intermediate care. *Beds* 50. *Certified* Medicaid.
Owner Proprietary Corp (Beverly Enterprises).

DUBLIN

Highland Manor Nursing Home
PO Box 1087, Dublin, VA, 24084
(703) 674-4193
Admin Irene L Seeley. *Medical Dir/Dir of Nursing* James L Patterons Jr MD.
Licensure Intermediate care. *Beds* 132. *Certified* Medicaid.
Owner Proprietary Corp.
Admissions Requirements Minimum age 18; Medical examination.
Staff Physicians 6 (ft); RNs 2 (ft); LPNs 14 (ft); Orderlies 3 (ft); Nurses aides 30 (ft), 1 (pt); Physical therapists 1 (ft), 1 (pt); Recreational therapists 1 (ft); Activities coordinators 1 (ft); Dietitians 1 (ft), 1 (pt); Ophthalmologists 1 (pt); Dentist 1 (pt).
Facilities Dining room; Physical therapy room; Activities room; Crafts room; Barber/Beauty shop; Library; Day rooms; Enclosed outside courts; Laboratory; Whirlpool bathing areas.
Activities Arts & crafts; Cards; Games; Reading groups; Prayer groups; Movies; Shopping trips; Picnics; Planned outings;

Birthday parties; Current events discussion groups; Exercise classes; Coffee groups; Chapel services (all religions, various services).

DUFFIELD

Ridgecrest Manor Nursing Home*
PO Box 280, Thomas Village, Duffield, VA, 24244
(703) 431-2841
Admin Jim Daugherty.
Licensure Skilled care; Intermediate care. *Beds* SNF 30; ICF 90. *Certified* Medicare.
Owner Proprietary Corp (Beverly Enterprises).

DUNN LORING

Iliff Nursing Home
8000 Iliff Dr, Dunn Loring, VA, 22027
(703) 560-1000
Admin Dory Parker. *Medical Dir/Dir of Nursing* Otto Kurz MD; Barbara Arnold DON.
Licensure Intermediate care. *Beds* ICF 130. *Certified* Medicaid.
Owner Proprietary Corp (Continental Medical Systems).
Admissions Requirements Medical examination.
Staff RNs 7 (ft), 2 (pt); LPNs 8 (ft); Orderlies 3 (ft); Nurses aides 29 (ft), 11 (pt); Physical therapists 1 (ft); Occupational therapists 1 (pt); Speech therapists 1 (pt); Activities coordinators 2 (ft); Dietitians 1 (pt); Dentists 1 (pt); Ophthalmologists 1 (pt).
Facilities Dining room; Physical therapy room; Activities room; Chapel; Crafts room; Laundry room; Barber/Beauty shop; Library.
Activities Arts & crafts; Cards; Games; Reading groups; Prayer groups; Movies; Shopping trips.

EMPORIA

Avis B Adams Christian Convalescent Center
200 Weaver Ave, Emporia, VA, 23847
(804) 634-6581
Admin Robert S Tinder. *Medical Dir/Dir of Nursing* Dr James A Kirkland.
Licensure Intermediate care. *Beds* 120. *Certified* Medicaid.
Owner Proprietary Corp.
Admissions Requirements Minimum age 18; Medical examination; Physician's request.
Staff RNs 3 (ft); LPNs 10 (ft), 3 (pt); Orderlies 5 (ft), 5 (pt); Nurses aides 25 (ft), 14 (pt); Physical therapists 1 (pt); Recreational therapists 2 (ft); Speech therapists 1 (pt); Activities coordinators 1 (ft), 1 (pt); Dietitians 1 (pt); Ophthalmologists 1 (pt); Podiatrists 1 (pt).
Facilities Dining room; Physical therapy room; Activities room; Chapel; Laundry room; Barber/Beauty shop.
Activities Arts & crafts; Cards; Games; Reading groups; Prayer groups; Movies; Shopping trips; Social/Cultural gatherings.

FAIRFAX

Fairfax Nursing Center*
10701 Main St, Fairfax, VA, 22030
(703) 273-7705
Admin Robert Bainum.
Licensure Skilled care; Intermediate care. *Beds* 200. *Certified* Medicaid; Medicare.
Owner Proprietary Corp.

The Virginian
9229 Arlington Blvd, Fairfax, VA, 22031
(703) 385-0555
Admin Sonia Y Weaver. *Medical Dir/Dir of Nursing* Mary Fisher DON.
Licensure Private Pay. *Beds* 100.
Owner Nonprofit organization/foundation.

Admissions Requirements Medical examination.
Staff Physicians 5 (pt); RNs; LPNs; Nurses aides; Physical therapists 1 (pt); Recreational therapists 1 (ft); Activities coordinators 2 (ft), 1 (pt); Dietitians 1 (ft); Dentists 1 (ft); Ophthalmologists 1 (ft).
Facilities Dining room; Physical therapy room; Activities room; Chapel; Crafts room; Laundry room; Barber/Beauty shop; Library.
Activities Arts & crafts; Cards; Games; Reading groups; Prayer groups; Movies; Shopping trips; Social/Cultural gatherings.

FALLS CHURCH

Barcroft Institute
2960 Sleepy Hollow Rd, Falls Church, VA, 22044
(703) 536-2000
Admin Karen A Sartiano. *Medical Dir/Dir of Nursing* William Hart MD; Sue Zich RN DON.
Licensure Intermediate care. *Beds* ICF 58. *Certified* Medicaid.
Owner Proprietary Corp.
Admissions Requirements Minimum age 16; Medical examination; Physician's request.
Staff Physicians 30 (pt); RNs 5 (ft), 2 (pt); LPNs 5 (ft), 2 (pt); Nurses aides 17 (ft), 7 (pt); Physical therapists 1 (pt); Occupational therapists 1 (pt); Speech therapists 1 (pt); Activities coordinators 1 (ft); Dietitians 1 (ft), 1 (pt); Ophthalmologists 1 (pt); Podiatrists 1 (pt); Dentist 1 (pt).
Facilities Dining room; Activities room; Crafts room; Laundry room; Barber/Beauty shop.
Activities Arts & crafts; Cards; Games; Reading groups; Prayer groups; Movies; Shopping trips; Social/Cultural gatherings; Van rides; Planned activities off grounds.

Powhatan Nursing Home Inc*
2100 Powhatan St, Falls Church, VA, 22043
(703) 538-2400
Admin J T Butler. *Medical Dir/Dir of Nursing* Robert Communale MD.
Licensure Skilled care; Intermediate care. *Beds* 160. *Certified* Medicaid; Medicare.
Owner Proprietary Corp.
Admissions Requirements Minimum age 18.
Staff Physicians 48 (pt); RNs 21 (ft), 9 (pt); LPNs 7 (ft), 2 (pt); Nurses aides 71 (ft), 11 (pt); Physical therapists 1 (ft), 1 (pt); Reality therapists 1 (ft); Recreational therapists 3 (ft); Speech therapists 1 (pt); Activities coordinators 2 (pt); Dietitians 1 (ft); Dentists 1 (pt); Ophthalmologists 1 (pt); Podiatrists 1 (pt); Audiologists 1 (pt).
Facilities Dining room; Physical therapy room; Activities room; Chapel; Crafts room; Laundry room; Barber/Beauty shop; Library.
Activities Arts & crafts; Cards; Games; Reading groups; Prayer groups; Movies; Shopping trips; Social/Cultural gatherings.

FARMVILLE

Eldercare of Farmville
PO Box 487, Scott Drive, Farmville, VA, 23901
(804) 392-8806
Admin Rebecca McCaulley. *Medical Dir/Dir of Nursing* Carrill Benhoff.
Licensure Intermediate care. *Beds* ICF 120. *Certified* Medicare.
Owner Proprietary Corp.
Facilities Dining room; Physical therapy room; Activities room; Crafts room; Laundry room; Barber/Beauty shop.
Activities Arts & crafts; Cards; Games; Reading groups; Prayer groups; Movies; Shopping trips; Social/Cultural gatherings.

Holly Manor Nursing Home
2003 Cobb St, Farmville, VA, 23901
(804) 392-6106
Admin Earl B Lee. *Medical Dir/Dir of Nursing* Dr R A Moore Jr; Marsha Whitehurst DON.
Licensure Intermediate care. *Beds* ICF 115.
Owner Proprietary Corp.
Admissions Requirements Medical examination.
Staff RNs 3 (ft); LPNs 18 (ft), 2 (pt); Nurses aides 45 (ft), 3 (pt); Recreational therapists 2 (ft); Activities coordinators 1 (pt).
Languages Spanish
Facilities Dining room; Physical therapy room; Activities room; Crafts room; Laundry room; Barber/Beauty shop.
Activities Arts & crafts; Cards; Games; Reading groups; Prayer groups; Movies; Shopping trips; Social/Cultural gatherings.

FLOYD

Skyline Manor Nursing Home
PO Box 508, Rte 4, Floyd, VA, 24091
(901) 745-2016
Admin Karen T Thompson. *Medical Dir/Dir of Nursing* Clarence W Taylor Jr MD; Judy Thomas DON.
Licensure Intermediate care. *Beds* 60. *Certified* Medicaid.
Owner Proprietary Corp.
Staff Physicians 5 (ft); RNs 1 (ft); LPNs 5 (ft), 4 (pt); Orderlies 2 (ft), 3 (pt); Nurses aides 14 (ft), 1 (pt); Physical therapists 1 (ft), 20 (pt); Recreational therapists 2 (pt); Speech therapists 1 (pt); Activities coordinators 2 (pt); Dietitians 1 (ft).
Facilities Dining room; Physical therapy room; Laundry room; Barber/Beauty shop.
Activities Arts & crafts; Cards; Games; Reading groups; Prayer groups; Movies; Shopping trips; Social/Cultural gatherings; Spelling bees; Music/exercise; Pet therapy.

FRANKLIN

Southampton Memorial Hospital—East Pavilion
100 Fairview Dr, Franklin, VA, 23851
(804) 562-5161
Admin Edward J Patneshy. *Medical Dir/Dir of Nursing* Michael Ponder MD.
Licensure Intermediate care. *Beds* 116. *Certified* Medicaid.
Owner Nonprofit Corp.
Admissions Requirements Minimum age 14; Medical examination.
Staff RNs 2 (ft), 3 (pt); LPNs 12 (ft), 7 (pt); Nurses aides 32 (ft), 14 (pt); Physical therapists 1 (ft); Activities coordinators 2 (pt); Dietitians 1 (ft).
Facilities Dining room; Physical therapy room; Activities room; Crafts room; Laundry room; Barber/Beauty shop; Library.
Activities Arts & crafts; Cards; Games; Prayer groups; Movies; Social/Cultural gatherings; Bingo; Resident council.

FREDERICKSBURG

Fredericksburg Nursing Home*
3900 Plank Rd, Fredericksburg, VA, 22401
(703) 786-8351
Admin Herbert R Woodall.
Licensure Intermediate care. *Beds* 177. *Certified* Medicaid.
Owner Proprietary Corp (Beverly Enterprises).

Woodmont Nursing Home Inc*
PO Box 366, 120 Kings Hwy, Fredericksburg, VA, 22404
(703) 371-9414
Admin Lucille B Merritt.

Licensure Intermediate care. *Beds* 122.
Certified Medicaid.
Owner Proprietary Corp (National Healthcare
Affiliates).

FRONT ROYAL

Warren Memorial Hospital—Lynn Care Center
1000 Shenandoah Ave, Front Royal, VA,
22630
(703) 636-0300
Admin C Douglas Rosen. *Medical Dir/Dir of
Nursing* Roger K Westfall MD.
Licensure Intermediate care. *Beds* 40.
Certified Medicaid.
Owner Nonprofit Corp.
Admissions Requirements Minimum age 18;
Medical examination; Physician's request.
Staff RNs 1 (ft); LPNs 4 (ft); Orderlies 5 (ft);
Nurses aides 12 (ft); Physical therapists 1
(ft); Recreational therapists 1 (ft); Activities
coordinators; Dietitians; Dentist.
Facilities Dining room; Activities room;
Crafts room; Barber/Beauty shop.
Activities Arts & crafts; Games; Reading
groups; Prayer groups; Movies; Shopping
trips; Social/Cultural gatherings.

GALAX

Blue Ridge Highlands Nursing Home
PO Box 229, 836 Glendale Rd, Galax, VA,
24333
(703) 236-9991
Admin Fredia A McClung. *Medical Dir/Dir of
Nursing* Faye E Cole DON.
Licensure Intermediate care. *Beds* ICF 120.
Certified Medicaid.
Owner Proprietary Corp (Beverly Enterprises).
Admissions Requirements Minimum age 18;
Medical examination; Physician's request.
Staff RNs 4 (ft); LPNs 8 (ft), 6 (pt); Nurses
aides 51 (ft), 18 (pt); Activities coordinators
1 (ft).
Facilities Dining room; Physical therapy
room; Activities room; Crafts room; Laundry
room; Barber/Beauty shop.
Activities Arts & crafts; Cards; Games;
Reading groups; Prayer groups; Movies;
Shopping trips; Social/Cultural gatherings.

Waddell Nursing Home
202 Painter St, Galax, VA, 24333
(703) 236-5164
Admin David N Zopfi. *Medical Dir/Dir of
Nursing* Dr William Waddell; Doris W
Morris.
Licensure Skilled care; Intermediate care. *Beds*
SNF 32; ICF 103. *Certified* Medicaid;
Medicare.
Owner Privately owned.
Admissions Requirements Medical
examination; Physician's request.
Staff RNs 2 (ft), 2 (pt); LPNs 18 (ft), 4 (pt);
Orderlies 3 (ft), 3 (pt); Nurses aides 55 (ft),
15 (pt); Physical therapists 1 (pt); Speech
therapists 1 (pt); Activities coordinators 1
(ft); Dietitians 1 (ft).
Languages German, Spanish
Facilities Dining room; Physical therapy
room; Activities room; Crafts room; Laundry
room; Barber/Beauty shop; 3 Courtyards.
Activities Arts & crafts; Cards; Games;
Reading groups; Prayer groups; Movies;
Shopping trips; Social/Cultural gatherings.

GLEN ALLEN

Elizabeth Adam Crump Manor*
Mountain Rd, PO Box 1458, Glen Allen, VA,
23060
(804) 262-8625
Admin Jacob W Mast. *Medical Dir/Dir of
Nursing* Dr F Pitts.
Licensure Intermediate care. *Beds* 180.
Certified Medicaid.

Owner Publicly owned.
Admissions Requirements Medical
examination; Physician's request.
Staff RNs; LPNs; Orderlies; Nurses aides;
Physical therapists; Reality therapists;
Speech therapists; Activities coordinators;
Dietitians; Dentists; Podiatrists.
Facilities Dining room; Physical therapy
room; Activities room; Chapel; Crafts room;
Laundry room; Barber/Beauty shop.
Activities Arts & crafts; Cards; Games;
Reading groups; Prayer groups; Movies;
Shopping trips; Social/Cultural gatherings.

GLOUCESTER

Francis N Sanders Nursing Home Inc
PO Box 130, Gloucester, VA, 23061
(804) 693-2000
Admin Merlin R Steider. *Medical Dir/Dir of
Nursing* Dr Raymond S Brown; Frances F
Jackson RN.
Licensure Intermediate care. *Beds* ICF 55.
Owner Nonprofit Corp.
Admissions Requirements Minimum age 16;
Medical examination; Physician's request.
Staff RNs 2 (ft), 4 (pt); LPNs 1 (ft), 3 (pt);
Nurses aides 16 (ft), 17 (pt); Activities
coordinators 1 (pt); Dietitians 1 (pt).
Facilities Dining room; Activities room;
Chapel; Crafts room; Laundry room; Barber/
Beauty shop.
Activities Arts & crafts; Games; Reading
groups; Prayer groups; Movies; Social/
Cultural gatherings.

Walter Reed Convalescent Center
PO Box 87, Rte 17 & Meridith Drive,
Gloucester, VA, 23061
(804) 693-6503
Admin Hal D Bourque. *Medical Dir/Dir of
Nursing* Dr Sam R Stanford Jr MD: Sonya
Krista RN DON.
Licensure Intermediate care. *Beds* 164.
Certified Medicaid.
Owner Proprietary Corp.
Admissions Requirements Physician's request.
Staff RNs 6 (ft), 7 (pt); LPNs 8 (ft), 10 (pt);
Orderlies 1 (ft); Nurses aides 42 (ft), 35 (pt);
Physical therapists 1 (ft); Activities
coordinators 2 (ft); Dietitians 1 (ft).
Facilities Dining room; Physical therapy
room; Activities room; Crafts room; Laundry
room; Barber/Beauty shop; Library.
Activities Arts & crafts; Cards; Games; Prayer
groups; Movies; Social/Cultural gatherings.

GWYNN

Rosewood Convalescent Center*
Henry's Rd, Gwynn, VA, 23066
(804) 725-5200
Admin Guy K Shelton Jr.
Licensure Intermediate care. *Beds* 24.
Certified Medicaid.
Owner Proprietary Corp.

HAMPTON

Coliseum Park Nursing Home
305 Marcella Rd, Hampton, VA, 23666
(804) 827-8953
Admin Charles E Rehnborg. *Medical Dir/Dir
of Nursing* Dr Frank Robert; Gloria
Kenerley RN DON.
Licensure Intermediate care. *Certified*
Medicaid.
Owner Privately owned.
Admissions Requirements Minimum age 16;
Medical examination; Physician's request.
Staff Physicians 38 (ft); RNs 7 (ft); LPNs 10
(ft), 8 (pt); Orderlies 3 (ft); Nurses aides 25
(ft), 40 (pt); Activities coordinators 2 (ft);
Dietitians 1 (ft).

Facilities Dining room; Activities room;
Laundry room; Barber/Beauty shop.
Activities Arts & crafts; Cards; Games;
Reading groups; Prayer groups; Movies;
Shopping trips; Social/Cultural gatherings.

Hampton Convalescent Center
414 Algonquin Rd, Hampton, VA, 23661
(804) 722-9881
Admin Raymond J Franz. *Medical Dir/Dir of
Nursing* Louis Parham MD; Maureen Cash
RN DON.
Licensure Intermediate care. *Beds* ICF 140.
Certified Medicaid.
Owner Nonprofit Corp.
Admissions Requirements Medical
examination; Physician's request.
Staff RNs 3 (ft), 3 (pt); LPNs 15 (ft), 14 (pt);
Nurses aides 33 (ft), 26 (pt); Activities
coordinators 1 (ft).
Facilities Dining room; Physical therapy
room; Activities room; Crafts room; Laundry
room; Barber/Beauty shop.
Activities Arts & crafts; Cards; Games;
Reading groups; Prayer groups; Movies;
Shopping trips; Social/Cultural gatherings.

HARRISONBURG

Camelot Hall Nursing Home*
1225 Reservoir St, Harrisonburg, VA, 22801
(703) 433-2623
Admin J S Parker Jones IV.
Licensure Skilled care; Intermediate care. *Beds*
SNF 13; ICF 167. *Certified* Medicaid;
Medicare.
Owner Proprietary Corp.
Staff RNs 15 (ft); LPNs 9 (ft); Orderlies 59
(ft); Physical therapists 1 (pt); Speech
therapists 1 (pt); Activities coordinators 1
(ft); Dietitians 1 (ft); Dentists 1 (pt);
Audiologists 1 (pt).
Facilities Dining room; Physical therapy
room; Activities room; Chapel; Crafts room;
Laundry room; Barber/Beauty shop.
Activities Arts & crafts; Cards; Games;
Reading groups; Prayer groups; Movies;
Shopping trips; Social/Cultural gatherings.

Liberty House Nursing Home
94 South Ave, Harrisonburg, VA, 22801
(703) 433-2791
Admin Leonard E Wallace. *Medical Dir/Dir of
Nursing* Mark Kniss MD.
Licensure Skilled care; Intermediate care. *Beds*
SNF 8; ICF 109. *Certified* Medicaid;
Medicare.
Owner Proprietary Corp (Beverly Enterprises).
Admissions Requirements Medical
examination.
Staff Physicians 2 (pt); RNs 3 (ft); LPNs 7
(ft), 2 (pt); Orderlies 2 (ft); Nurses aides 31
(ft), 12 (pt); Physical therapists 1 (pt);
Speech therapists 1 (ft); Activities
coordinators 1 (ft); Dietitians 1 (ft);
Ophthalmologists 1 (pt); Podiatrists 1 (pt).
Facilities Dining room; Physical therapy
room; Activities room; Chapel; Laundry
room; Barber/Beauty shop; Library.
Activities Arts & crafts; Cards; Games;
Reading groups; Prayer groups; Movies;
Shopping trips; Social/Cultural gatherings.

Oak Lea Nursing Home
1475 Virginia Ave, Harrisonburg, VA, 22801
(703) 434-0084
Admin Earl L Schrock. *Medical Dir/Dir of
Nursing* Kathy Suter, Director of Nursing.
Licensure Intermediate care. *Beds* ICF 120.
Certified Medicaid.
Owner Nonprofit Corp.
Admissions Requirements Medical
examination.
Staff RNs 5 (ft), 7 (pt); LPNs 4 (pt); Nurses
aides; Recreational therapists 1 (ft), 1 (pt);
Dietitians; Social worker.
Affiliation Mennonite

Facilities Dining room; Physical therapy room; Activities room; Chapel; Laundry room; Barber/Beauty shop; Library.
Activities Arts & crafts; Cards; Games; Reading groups; Prayer groups; Movies; Shopping trips; Social/Cultural gatherings; Baking.

Sunnyside Presbyterian Retirement Community
PO Box 928, Harrisonburg, VA, 22801
(703) 568-8200
Admin Dick Lyons. *Medical Dir/Dir of Nursing* Karen Shiflet.
Licensure Intermediate care. *Beds* ICF 120. *Certified* Medicaid.
Owner Nonprofit Corp.
Admissions Requirements Minimum age 65.
Staff RNs 18 (ft); LPNs 20 (ft).
Affiliation Presbyterian
Facilities Dining room; Physical therapy room; Activities room; Chapel; Crafts room; Laundry room; Barber/Beauty shop; Library; Dental operatory.
Activities Arts & crafts; Cards; Games; Reading groups; Prayer groups; Movies; Shopping trips; Social/Cultural gatherings.

HOPEWELL

Hopewell Convalescent Center*
905 Cousin Ave, Hopewell, VA, 23860
(804) 458-6325
Admin Paula S Poole.
Licensure Skilled care; Intermediate care. *Beds* SNF 11; ICF 119. *Certified* Medicaid; Medicare.
Owner Proprietary Corp.

John Randolph Nursing Home Inc
PO Box 1626, 700 N 4th Ave, Hopewell, VA, 23860
(804) 541-7536
Admin Paula S Poole RN. *Medical Dir/Dir of Nursing* Dr Lee Weathington; Gwendolyn Cosslett RN DON.
Licensure Skilled care; Intermediate care. *Beds* SNF 18; ICF 106. *Certified* Medicaid; Medicare.
Owner Nonprofit Corp.
Admissions Requirements Physician's request.
Staff RNs 6 (ft), 8 (pt); LPNs 12 (ft), 12 (pt); Orderlies 2 (ft); Nurses aides 35 (ft), 22 (pt); Activities coordinators 1 (ft); Dietitians 1 (pt).
Facilities Dining room; Activities room; Crafts room; Laundry room; Barber/Beauty shop.
Activities Arts & crafts; Games; Reading groups; Prayer groups; Movies; Shopping trips; Social/Cultural gatherings.

IRVINGTON

Rappahannock Westminster-Canterbury
10 Lancaster Dr, Irvington, VA, 22480
(804) 438-4000
Admin Rexford Beckwith. *Medical Dir/Dir of Nursing* Ralph Robertson MD; Evelyn Johnston RN DON.
Licensure Skilled care; Intermediate care; Home for Adults; Retirement living. *Beds* SNF 10; ICF 24; Home for adults 66; Retirement living 78. *Certified* Medicaid; Medicare.
Owner Nonprofit Corp.
Admissions Requirements Minimum age 65 Retirement living; 14 Nursing home; Medical examination; Physician's request Nursing home.
Staff Physicians 5 (pt); RNs 5 (ft); LPNs 4 (ft); Nurses aides 22 (ft); Physical therapists 1 (pt); Activities coordinators 2 (pt); Dietitians 1 (ft); Ophthalmologists 1 (pt); Podiatrists 1 (pt).
Affiliation Episcopal

Facilities Dining room; Physical therapy room; Activities room; Crafts room; Laundry room; Barber/Beauty shop; Library; Store; Bank; Clinic; Auditorium; Private meeting rooms; Snack bar/cafe.
Activities Arts & crafts; Cards; Games; Reading groups; Prayer groups; Movies; Shopping trips; Social/Cultural gatherings; Trips; Lectures.

KILMARNOCK

The Lancashire
287 School St, Kilmarnock, VA, 22482
(804) 435-1684
Admin George W Crenshaw Jr. *Medical Dir/Dir of Nursing* Melvin B Lamberth Jr MD.
Licensure Intermediate care. *Beds* 120. *Certified* Medicaid.
Owner Proprietary Corp.
Admissions Requirements Minimum age 30; Medical examination; Physician's request.
Staff Physicians 3 (pt); RNs 6 (ft), 5 (pt); LPNs 8 (ft), 2 (pt); Nurses aides 42 (ft), 15 (pt); Activities coordinators 1 (ft), 2 (pt); Dietitians 12 (ft), 6 (pt); Podiatrists 1 (pt).
Facilities Dining room; Physical therapy room; Activities room; Crafts room; Laundry room; Barber/Beauty shop.
Activities Arts & crafts; Games; Reading groups; Prayer groups; Movies; Shopping trips; Social/Cultural gatherings.

LEESBURG

Heritage Hall Health Care V*
122 Morven Park Rd NW, Leesburg, VA, 22075
(703) 777-8700
Admin Stephanie Keelan.
Licensure Intermediate care. *Beds* 120. *Certified* Medicaid.
Owner Proprietary Corp.
Admissions Requirements Minimum age 14; Medical examination.
Staff RNs 5 (ft), 3 (pt); LPNs 4 (ft), 4 (pt); Orderlies 2 (ft); Nurses aides 35 (ft), 4 (pt); Activities coordinators 1 (ft); Dietitians 1 (ft); Social workers 1 (ft).
Facilities Dining room; Physical therapy room; Activities room; Crafts room; Laundry room; Barber/Beauty shop.
Activities Arts & crafts; Games; Prayer groups; Movies; Shopping trips; Social/Cultural gatherings.

Loudoun Long-Term Care Center
224 Cornwall St, NW, Leesburg, VA, 22075
(703) 771-2841
Admin Kent Stevens. *Medical Dir/Dir of Nursing* Cynthia H Mazurkiewicz RN DON.
Licensure Intermediate care. *Beds* ICF 100. *Certified* Medicaid.
Owner Nonprofit Corp.
Admissions Requirements Minimum age 16; Medical examination.
Staff RNs 3 (ft), 3 (pt); LPNs 10 (ft), 10 (pt); Nurses aides 24 (ft), 22 (pt); Activities coordinators 1 (ft).
Facilities Dining room; Physical therapy room; Activities room; Crafts room; Laundry room; Barber/Beauty shop; TV rooms; Dental room; Examination room.
Activities Arts & crafts; Cards; Games; Reading groups; Prayer groups; Movies; Shopping trips; Social/Cultural gatherings.

Wynkoop Nursing Home*
94 W Market St, Leesburg, VA, 22075
(703) 777-2377
Admin Belle C Wynkoop.
Beds 12.
Owner Proprietary Corp.

LEXINGTON

Stonewall Jackson Hospital Extended Care Facility
Spotswood Rd, Lexington, VA, 24450
(703) 463-9141
Admin L E Richardson. *Medical Dir/Dir of Nursing* Barbara N; Cathey BSN RN.
Licensure Skilled care; Intermediate care. *Beds* SNF 25; ICF 25. *Certified* Medicaid; Medicare.
Owner Nonprofit organization/foundation.
Staff Physicians 23 (ft); RNs 1 (ft); LPNs 5 (ft), 4 (pt); Orderlies 1 (ft), 2 (pt); Nurses aides 12 (ft), 11 (pt); Physical therapists 1 (ft); Recreational therapists 1 (pt); Speech therapists 1 (pt); Dietitians 1 (pt); Dentists 1 (pt).
Facilities Dining room; Physical therapy room; Activities room; Laundry room; Barber/Beauty shop.
Activities Arts & crafts; Games; Reading groups; Prayer groups; Movies; Social/Cultural gatherings.

LOCUST HILL

Mizpah Nursing Home Inc*
Box 7, Locust Hill, VA, 23092
(804) 758-5260
Admin Myrtle D Faulkner.
Licensure Intermediate care. *Beds* 60. *Certified* Medicaid.
Owner Proprietary Corp.

LURAY

MontVue Nursing Home
Montvue Dr, Luray, VA, 22835
(703) 743-4571
Admin Berit A Kuntz. *Medical Dir/Dir of Nursing* James R Holsinger MD.
Licensure Intermediate care. *Beds* ICF 120. *Certified* Medicaid.
Owner Proprietary Corp (Hillhaven Corp).
Admissions Requirements Minimum age 16; Medical examination.
Staff Physicians 5 (ft); RNs 2 (ft), 2 (pt); LPNs 8 (ft), 5 (pt); Nurses aides 37 (ft), 12 (pt); Physical therapists 1 (pt); Activities coordinators 1 (ft); Dietitians 1 (pt); Dentists 1 (pt); Ophthalmologists 1 (pt).
Facilities Dining room; Physical therapy room; Activities room; Crafts room; Laundry room; Barber/Beauty shop.
Activities Arts & crafts; Cards; Games; Reading groups; Prayer groups; Movies; Social/Cultural gatherings.

LYNCHBURG

Camelot Hall Nursing Home*
5615 Seminole Ave, Lynchburg, VA, 24502
(804) 239-2657
Admin C Benjamin Puckett. *Medical Dir/Dir of Nursing* Dr Alan Podosek.
Licensure Skilled care; Intermediate care. *Beds* 180. *Certified* Medicaid; Medicare.
Owner Proprietary Corp.
Admissions Requirements Minimum age Birth-14; Medical examination; Physician's request.
Staff RNs 9 (ft), 12 (pt); LPNs 7 (ft), 12 (pt); Orderlies 11 (ft), 2 (pt); Nurses aides 48 (ft), 8 (pt); Physical therapists 1 (pt); Activities coordinators 1 (ft); Dietitians 1 (pt).
Facilities Dining room; Physical therapy room; Activities room; Crafts room; Laundry room; Barber/Beauty shop; Library.
Activities Arts & crafts; Games; Prayer groups; Movies; Shopping trips; Social/Cultural gatherings.

Guggenheimer Nursing Home, Division of Centra Health Inc
Tate Springs Rd, Lynchburg, VA, 24506
(804) 528-5100
Admin L Darrell Powers. *Medical Dir/Dir of Nursing* Anjan M Ramachandriah MD; Wylie M DeJarnette RN DON.
Licensure Intermediate care. *Beds* ICF 110. *Certified* Medicaid.
Owner Nonprofit Corp.
Admissions Requirements Physician's request.
Staff RNs 5 (ft), 5 (pt); LPNs 17 (ft), 6 (pt); Nurses aides 34 (ft), 5 (pt).
Facilities Dining room; Physical therapy room; Activities room; Chapel; Crafts room; Laundry room; Barber/Beauty shop.
Activities Arts & crafts; Cards; Games; Reading groups; Prayer groups; Movies; Shopping trips; Social/Cultural gatherings.

Lynchburg Nursing Home
701 Hollins St, Lynchburg, VA, 24504
(804) 847-1341
Admin Kenneth E (Ed) Vest. *Medical Dir/Dir of Nursing* Lewis F Somers MD.
Licensure Intermediate care. *Beds* ICF 89. *Certified* Medicaid.
Owner Publicly owned.
Admissions Requirements Medical examination.
Staff Physicians 1 (pt); RNs 6 (ft); LPNs 7 (ft), 2 (pt); Orderlies 5 (ft), 1 (pt); Nurses aides 23 (ft), 2 (pt); Recreational therapists 1 (ft); Dietitians 1 (pt); Social worker 1 (ft).
Facilities Dining room; Activities room; Chapel; Crafts room; Laundry room; Barber/Beauty shop.
Activities Arts & crafts; Cards; Games; Reading groups; Prayer groups; Movies; Shopping trips; Social/Cultural gatherings.

Medical Care Center
2200 Landover Pl, Lynchburg, VA, 24501
(804) 846-4626
Admin Bonnie Ramey. *Medical Dir/Dir of Nursing* Charles Ashworth MD; Diane Marshall.
Licensure Skilled care; Intermediate care. *Beds* SNF 11; ICF 107. *Certified* Medicaid; Medicare.
Owner Proprietary Corp (Health Care & Retirement Corp).
Admissions Requirements Medical examination.
Staff Physicians 90 (pt); RNs 6 (ft), 8 (pt); LPNs 13 (ft), 5 (pt); Orderlies 1 (pt); Nurses aides 31 (ft), 10 (pt); Physical therapists 1 (ft), 1 (pt); Recreational therapists 1 (pt); Occupational therapists 1 (pt); Speech therapists 1 (ft), 1 (pt); Activities coordinators 1 (ft), 1 (pt); Dietitians 1 (pt); Dentists 1 (pt); Ophthalmologists 1 (pt); Podiatrists 1 (pt).
Facilities Dining room; Physical therapy room; Activities room; Crafts room; Laundry room; Barber/Beauty shop; Library.
Activities Arts & crafts; Cards; Games; Prayer groups; Movies; Shopping trips; Social/Cultural gatherings.

St John's Nursing Home Inc*
3500 Powhatan St, Lynchburg, VA, 24501
(804) 845-6045
Admin Norma S Staples.
Beds 45.
Owner Proprietary Corp.

Seven Hills Health Care Center
2081 Langhorne Rd, Lynchburg, VA, 24501
(804) 846-8437
Admin Justine C Stadtherr. *Medical Dir/Dir of Nursing* Doris Justice.
Licensure Skilled care; Intermediate care. *Beds* SNF 8; ICF 101. *Certified* Medicaid; Medicare.
Owner Proprietary Corp (Beverly Enterprises).
Admissions Requirements Physician's request.

Staff RNs; LPNs; Orderlies; Nurses aides; Activities coordinators; Social Services Coordinator.
Facilities Dining room; Physical therapy room; Activities room; Crafts room; Laundry room; Barber/Beauty shop.
Activities Arts & crafts; Cards; Games; Prayer groups; Movies; Shopping trips; Social/Cultural gatherings.

Virginia Baptist Hospital Skilled Nursing Unit
3300 Rivermont Ave, Lynchburg, VA, 24503
(804) 522-4000
Admin Thomas C Jividen. *Medical Dir/Dir of Nursing* Sandra Lewis.
Licensure Skilled care. *Beds* SNF 36. *Certified* Medicaid; Medicare.
Owner Nonprofit organization/foundation.
Admissions Requirements Minimum age 18; Physician's request.
Staff RNs 7 (ft), 4 (pt); LPNs 4 (ft), 6 (pt); Orderlies 1 (ft), 4 (pt); Nurses aides 12 (ft), 3 (pt); Physical therapists 7 (ft), 1 (pt); Recreational therapists 6 (ft); Occupational therapists 6 (ft); Speech therapists 3 (ft), 1 (pt); Dietitians 3 (ft); Podiatrists 2 (ft), 1 (pt).
Languages Spanish
Facilities Activities room; Laundry room; Barber/Beauty shop.
Activities Arts & crafts; Games; Prayer groups; Social/Cultural gatherings.

Westminster-Canterbury of Lynchburg Inc
501 VES Rd, Lynchburg, VA, 24503
(804) 386-3500
Admin Hundsdon Cary III.
Licensure Skilled care; Intermediate care. *Beds* SNF 19; ICF 61. *Certified* Medicaid; Medicare.
Owner Nonprofit Corp.

MANASSAS

Annaburg Manor
9201 Maple St, Manassas, VA, 22110
(703) 335-8300
Admin Harley L Tabak. *Medical Dir/Dir of Nursing* Dr J L Mathews Jr.
Licensure Skilled care; Intermediate care. *Beds* 245. *Certified* Medicaid; Medicare.
Owner Nonprofit Corp.
Admissions Requirements Minimum age 18; Medical examination.
Staff Physicians 4 (ft); RNs 11 (ft); LPNs 29 (ft); Orderlies 3 (ft); Nurses aides 104 (ft); Physical therapists 1 (ft); Occupational therapists 2 (ft); Speech therapists 1 (ft); Activities coordinators 1 (ft); Dietitians 1 (pt); Dentists; Ophthalmologists; Podiatrists; Audiologists; Physical therapy aides 1 (ft); Activities aides 2 (ft).
Facilities Dining room; Physical therapy room; Activities room; Crafts room; Laundry room; Barber/Beauty shop.
Activities Arts & crafts; Cards; Games; Reading groups; Prayer groups; Movies; Social/Cultural gatherings.

MARION

Francis Marion Manor*
PO Box 880, Marion, VA, 24354
(703) 783-7211
Admin D R Carlton.
Licensure Intermediate care. *Beds* 38. *Certified* Medicaid.
Owner Nonprofit Corp.

MARTINSVILLE

Commonwealth Health Care*
15 Starling Ave, Martinsville, VA, 24112
(703) 638-8701
Admin Nancy L Ritter. *Medical Dir/Dir of Nursing* John Kasterintious.

Licensure Intermediate care; Home for aged. *Beds* ICF 182; Home for aged 102. *Certified* Medicaid.
Owner Proprietary Corp.
Admissions Requirements Minimum age 18; Medical examination; Physician's request.
Staff Physicians 2 (pt); RNs 6 (ft); LPNs 22 (pt); Orderlies 15 (pt); Nurses aides 110 (pt); Speech therapists 1 (pt); Activities coordinators 1 (ft); Dietitians 1 (pt); Dentists 1 (pt); Ophthalmologists 1 (pt); Podiatrists 1 (pt); Audiologists 1 (pt).
Facilities Dining room; Activities room; Chapel; Crafts room; Laundry room; Barber/Beauty shop; Library.
Activities Arts & crafts; Cards; Games; Reading groups; Prayer groups; Movies; Shopping trips; Social/Cultural gatherings.

Martinsville Convalescent Home Inc*
Rte 8, Box 474, Spruce St, Martinsville, VA, 24112
(703) 632-7146
Admin Genevieve C Jones.
Licensure Intermediate care. *Beds* 141. *Certified* Medicaid.
Owner Proprietary Corp.

NASSAWADOX

Heritage Hall Health Care VI
PO Box 176, Medical Rd, Nassawadox, VA, 23413
(804) 442-5600
Admin Tom Malik. *Medical Dir/Dir of Nursing* Dr John Snyder; Lorraine Williams.
Licensure Intermediate care. *Beds* ICF 125. *Certified* Medicaid.
Owner Proprietary Corp.
Admissions Requirements Minimum age 18; Medical examination; Physician's request.
Staff RNs 2 (ft), 1 (pt); LPNs 8 (ft), 5 (pt); Nurses aides 28 (ft), 33 (pt); Activities coordinators 1 (ft).
Facilities Dining room; Activities room; Crafts room; Laundry room; Barber/Beauty shop.
Activities Arts & crafts; Cards; Games; Prayer groups; Movies; Shopping trips; Social/Cultural gatherings.

NEW POINT

Horn Harbor Nursing Home Inc*
PO Box 32, New Point, VA, 23125
(804) 725-7830
Admin Hal D Bourque.
Licensure Intermediate care. *Beds* 77. *Certified* Medicaid.
Owner Proprietary Corp.

NEWPORT NEWS

Huntington Convalescent Center*
5015 Huntington Ave, Newport News, VA, 23607
(804) 244-1734
Admin Robert M Burns Jr.
Licensure Intermediate care. *Beds* 246. *Certified* Medicaid.
Owner Proprietary Corp (Vantage Healthcare).

James River Convalescent Center*
540 Aberthaw Ave, Newport News, VA, 23601
(804) 595-2273
Admin Jeffrey L Mendelsohn.
Licensure Intermediate care. *Beds* 173. *Certified* Medicaid; Medicare.
Owner Proprietary Corp.

Newport Convalescent Center Inc*
11141 Warwick Blvd, Newport News, VA, 23601
(804) 595-3733
Admin John R Tew.
Beds 50.
Owner Proprietary Corp.

Newport News Baptist Retirement Community
PO Box 6010, 955 Harpersville Rd, Newport
News, VA, Mailing address 23606; Location
23601
(804) 599-4376
Admin R Furman Kenney. *Medical Dir/Dir of
Nursing* Judy Dozier RN.
Licensure Intermediate care. *Beds* ICF 52.
Certified Medicaid.
Owner Nonprofit Corp.
Admissions Requirements Minimum age 65;
Medical examination.
Staff Physicians; RNs; LPNs; Nurses aides;
Physical therapists; Recreational therapists;
Activities coordinators; Dietitians.
Affiliation Baptist
Facilities Dining room; Physical therapy
room; Activities room; Chapel; Crafts room;
Laundry room; Barber/Beauty shop; Library;
Large carpeted patio.
Activities Arts & crafts; Games; Reading
groups; Prayer groups; Movies; Shopping
trips; Bowling; Sing-alongs.

Patrick Henry Healthcare Center
1000 Old Denbigh Blvd, Newport News, VA,
23602
(804) 877-8001
Admin Patricia A Iannetta. *Medical Dir/Dir of
Nursing* Dr G S Mitchell; Lynda Burton
DON.
Licensure Skilled care; Intermediate care. *Beds*
385. *Certified* Medicaid; Medicare.
Owner Nonprofit Corp.
Admissions Requirements Medical
examination.
Staff Physicians 12 (pt); RNs 19 (ft), 5 (pt);
LPNs 25 (ft), 25 (pt); Nurses aides 123 (ft),
6 (pt); Physical therapists 1 (ft), 1 (pt);
Recreational therapists 1 (ft); Occupational
therapists 1 (ft); Speech therapists 1 (pt);
Dietitians 1 (ft), 1 (pt); Dentists 1 (pt);
Ophthalmologists 1 (pt); Podiatrists 1 (pt);
Dentist 1 (pt).
Facilities Physical therapy room; Activities
room; Chapel; Crafts room; Barber/Beauty
shop.
Activities Arts & crafts; Cards; Games;
Reading groups; Prayer groups; Movies;
Social/Cultural gatherings.

NORFOLK

Campen's Nursing Home Inc*
3401 Granby St, Norfolk, VA, 23504
(804) 625-7140
Admin C A Thoma.
Licensure Intermediate care. *Beds* 21.
Certified Medicaid.
Owner Proprietary Corp.

Ghent Arms Nursing Home
249 Newtown Rd S, Norfolk, VA, 23507
(804) 627-4345
Admin Anthony Fludd.
Licensure Intermediate care. *Beds* 65.
Certified Medicaid.
Owner Proprietary Corp.
Admissions Requirements Minimum age 50.
Staff Physicians 2 (ft); RNs 1 (ft), 2 (pt);
LPNs 4 (ft), 4 (pt); Orderlies 2 (ft), 1 (pt);
Nurses aides 13 (ft), 7 (pt); Physical
therapists 1 (pt); Activities coordinators 1
(ft); Dietitians 1 (ft); Podiatrists 1 (ft).
Facilities Dining room; Activities room;
Laundry room; Barber/Beauty shop; Library.
Activities Arts & crafts; Cards; Games;
Reading groups; Prayer groups; Movies;
Social/Cultural gatherings.

**Hillhaven Rehabilitation & Convalescent
Center**
1005 Hampton Blvd, Norfolk, VA, 23507
(804) 623-5602
Admin Vickie A Archer. *Medical Dir/Dir of
Nursing* Dr Robert Mann.

Licensure Skilled care; Intermediate care. *Beds*
SNF 58; ICF 131; Certified 20. *Certified*
Medicaid; Medicare.
Owner Proprietary Corp (Hillhaven Corp).
Admissions Requirements Medical
examination; Physician's request.
Staff RNs 7 (ft), 8 (pt); LPNs 13 (ft), 17 (pt);
Nurses aides 46 (ft), 40 (pt); Physical
therapists 2 (ft); Recreational therapists 2
(ft); Occupational therapists 1 (ft); Speech
therapists 1 (ft); Activities coordinators 1
(ft); Dietitians 1 (ft).
Facilities Dining room; Physical therapy
room; Activities room; Laundry room;
Barber/Beauty shop; Library.
Activities Arts & crafts; Cards; Games;
Reading groups; Prayer groups; Movies;
Shopping trips; Social/Cultural gatherings.

Lafayette Villa Health Care
3900 Llewellyn Ave, Norfolk, VA, 23504
(804) 625-5363
Admin Gary W Seay. *Medical Dir/Dir of
Nursing* Mary Ann Lucas RN.
Licensure Intermediate care. *Beds* 242.
Certified Medicaid.
Owner Proprietary Corp.
Admissions Requirements Minimum age 18.
Staff RNs 3 (ft), 2 (pt); LPNs 32 (ft); Nurses
aides 95 (ft), 5 (pt); Physical therapists 1
(pt); Activities coordinators 1 (ft); Dietitians
1 (pt); Ophthalmologists 1 (pt).
Facilities Dining room; Physical therapy
room; Activities room; Chapel; Crafts room;
Laundry room; Barber/Beauty shop.
Activities Arts & crafts; Cards; Games;
Reading groups; Prayer groups; Movies;
Social/Cultural gatherings; Outside
entertainment.

Lake Taylor City Hospital
1309 Kempsville Rd, Norfolk, VA, 23502
(804) 461-5001
Admin Dean F Martin. *Medical Dir/Dir of
Nursing* Andrew M Fekete MD; Marguerite
W White RN.
Licensure Skilled care; Intermediate care;
Chronic disease hospital beds. *Beds* SNF
106; ICF 120; Chronic disease hospital beds
104. *Certified* Medicaid; Medicare.
Owner Publicly owned.
Admissions Requirements Physician's request.
Staff Physicians 5 (ft), 32 (pt); RNs 35 (ft), 11
(pt); LPNs 42 (ft), 33 (pt); Nurses aides 91
(ft), 20 (pt); Physical therapists 2 (ft);
Recreational therapists 2 (ft); Occupational
therapists 1 (ft); Speech therapists 1 (ft);
Dietitians 2 (ft), 1 (pt); Dentists 1 (pt);
Ophthalmologists 1 (pt).
Facilities Dining room; Physical therapy
room; Activities room; Chapel; Crafts room;
Laundry room; Barber/Beauty shop.
Activities Arts & crafts; Cards; Games;
Reading groups; Prayer groups; Movies;
Shopping trips.

Louise C Godwin Nursing Home Inc*
918 Colonial Ave, Norfolk, VA, 23507
(804) 625-5514
Admin G F Rowe.
Licensure Intermediate care. *Beds* 26.
Certified Medicaid.
Owner Proprietary Corp.

Richardson Nursing Home*
419 W 28th St, Norfolk, VA, 23508
(804) 622-1094
Admin Lillian T Moseley. *Medical Dir/Dir of
Nursing* Sandra Thorogood.
Licensure Intermediate care. *Beds* 43.
Certified Medicaid.
Owner Proprietary Corp.
Admissions Requirements Medical
examination; Physician's request.
Staff RNs 1 (ft); LPNs 3 (ft), 1 (pt); Nurses
aides 14 (ft), 2 (pt); Activities coordinators 1
(ft).

Facilities Dining room; Activities room;
Laundry room.

St Mary's Infant Home Inc*
317 Chapel St, Norfolk, VA, 23504
(804) 622-2208
Admin William M Jolly.
Licensure Intermediate care for mentally
retarded. *Beds* 60. *Certified* Medicaid.
Owner Nonprofit Corp.

NORTON

St Mary's Hospital Long-Term Care
3rd St NE, Norton, VA, 24273
(703) 679-1151 ext 400
Admin Robert Spera. *Medical Dir/Dir of
Nursing* G S Kanawal MD.
Licensure Intermediate care. *Beds* ICF 44.
Certified Medicaid.
Owner Nonprofit organization/foundation.
Admissions Requirements Minimum age 16;
Medical examination; Physician's request.
Staff Physicians 12 (pt); RNs 1 (ft); LPNs 6
(ft), 4 (pt); Orderlies 2 (ft), 1 (pt); Nurses
aides 12 (ft), 7 (pt); Physical therapists 1
(pt); Recreational therapists 1 (ft); Activities
coordinators 1 (ft); Dietitians 1 (ft).
Affiliation Roman Catholic
Facilities Dining room; Physical therapy
room; Activities room; Laundry room;
Barber/Beauty shop.
Activities Arts & crafts; Cards; Games;
Reading groups; Prayer groups; Movies;
Shopping trips; Social/Cultural gatherings.

OAKTON

Oakton Nursing Home Inc*
10322 Blake Ln, Oakton, VA, 22124
(703) 281-4418
Admin Gwendolyn B Wright.
Licensure Intermediate care. *Beds* 27.
Certified Medicaid.
Owner Proprietary Corp.

ONANCOCK

**Hermitage on the Eastern Shore—Nurs Home
Unit**
PO Box 300, North St Ext, Onancock, VA,
23417
(804) 787-4343
Admin Charles M Johnson. *Medical Dir/Dir of
Nursing* E W Bosworth MD; Elizabeth Perry
RN DON.
Licensure Intermediate care. *Beds* ICF 35.
Owner Nonprofit Corp.
Admissions Requirements Minimum age 65;
Medical examination.
Staff Physicians 1 (pt); RNs 1 (ft); LPNs 4
(ft), 4 (pt); Nurses aides 18 (ft), 7 (pt);
Activities coordinators 1 (ft), 1 (pt);
Dietitians 1 (pt).
Affiliation Methodist
Facilities Dining room; Activities room;
Chapel; Crafts room; Laundry room; Barber/
Beauty shop; Library; Social hall; Lounges.
Activities Arts & crafts; Cards; Games;
Reading groups; Prayer groups; Movies;
Shopping trips; Social/Cultural gatherings;
Bible study; Vespers; Special outings.

ORANGE

**Orange County Nursing Home and Home for
Adults**
120 Dogwood Lane, Orange, VA, 22960
(703) 672-2611
Admin Delores C Darnell RNC. *Medical Dir/
Dir of Nursing* Dr R S LeGarde; Shirley A
Stone RN.
Licensure Intermediate care; Home for aged.
Beds ICF 134; Home for aged 34. *Certified*
Medicaid.
Owner Publicly owned.

Admissions Requirements Medical examination.
Staff RNs 5 (ft); LPNs 20 (ft), 4 (pt); Nurses aides 68 (ft), 18 (pt); Physical therapists 1 (pt); Recreational therapists 2 (ft), 1 (pt); Occupational therapists 1 (pt); Speech therapists 1 (pt); Activities coordinators 1 (ft); Dietitians 1 (pt); Ophthalmologists 1 (pt).
Facilities Dining room; Physical therapy room; Activities room; Chapel; Crafts room; Laundry room; Barber/Beauty shop; Library.
Activities Arts & crafts; Cards; Games; Reading groups; Prayer groups; Movies; Shopping trips; Social/Cultural gatherings.

PARKSLEY

Accomack County Nursing Home
Rte 1, PO Box 185, Parksley, VA, 23421
(804) 665-5133
Admin W J Bundick Jr. *Medical Dir/Dir of Nursing* Edward S White MD.
Licensure Intermediate care. *Beds* ICF 136. *Certified* Medicaid.
Owner Publicly owned.
Admissions Requirements Minimum age 14; Medical examination; Physician's request.
Staff Physicians 1 (pt); RNs 2 (ft), 2 (pt); LPNs 11 (ft), 4 (pt); Orderlies 5 (ft), 5 (pt); Nurses aides 32 (ft), 17 (pt); Occupational therapists 1 (pt); Activities coordinators 1 (ft); Dietitians 1 (pt); Ophthalmologists 1 (pt).
Facilities Dining room; Physical therapy room; Activities room; Chapel; Crafts room; Laundry room; Barber/Beauty shop; Library.
Activities Arts & crafts; Cards; Games; Reading groups; Prayer groups; Movies; Social/Cultural gatherings.

PETERSBURG

Battlefield Park Convalescent Center
250 Flank Rd, Petersburg, VA, 23805
(804) 861-2223
Admin Phyllis J Watson. *Medical Dir/Dir of Nursing* William S Sloan MD; Martha Spain RN DON.
Licensure Intermediate care. *Beds* 120. *Certified* Medicaid.
Owner Proprietary Corp (Beverly Enterprises).
Admissions Requirements Medical examination; Physician's request.
Staff Physicians; RNs; LPNs; Nurses aides; Physical therapists; Speech therapists; Activities coordinators; Dietitians; Ophthalmologists.
Facilities Dining room; Physical therapy room; Activities room; Chapel; Crafts room; Laundry room; Barber/Beauty shop; Enclosed garden.
Activities Arts & crafts; Cards; Games; Reading groups; Prayer groups; Movies; Shopping trips; Social/Cultural gatherings; Picnics; Zoo outings.

Walnut Hill Convalescent Center
287 South Blvd, Petersburg, VA, 23805
(804) 733-1190
Admin Hal Garland. *Medical Dir/Dir of Nursing* Peter Ault MD; Fred Long DON.
Licensure Skilled care; Intermediate care. *Beds* 120. *Certified* Medicaid; Medicare.
Owner Proprietary Corp (Beverly Enterprises).
Admissions Requirements Medical examination.
Staff RNs 4 (ft); LPNs 20 (ft); Orderlies 5 (ft); Nurses aides 50 (ft); Physical therapists 1 (pt); Recreational therapists 1 (ft), 1 (pt); Activities coordinators 1 (ft), 1 (pt); Dietitians 1 (pt); Ophthalmologists 1 (pt).
Facilities Dining room; Physical therapy room; Activities room; Crafts room; Laundry room; Barber/Beauty shop.
Activities Arts & crafts; Cards; Games; Prayer groups; Movies; Shopping trips; Social/Cultural gatherings.

PORTSMOUTH

Autumn Care of Portsmouth
3610 Winchester Dr, Portsmouth, VA, 23707
(804) 397-0725
Admin Thelma J Wilson. *Medical Dir/Dir of Nursing* Boniface Costa MD; Janice Turner RN DON.
Licensure Intermediate care. *Beds* ICF 73. *Certified* Medicaid.
Owner Proprietary Corp (Autumn Corp).
Admissions Requirements Medical examination; Physician's request.
Staff RNs 1 (ft); LPNs 5 (ft), 5 (pt); Nurses aides 26 (ft); Activities coordinators 1 (ft); Dietitians 1 (ft); Restorative nursing aides 3 (ft) Social worker 1 (ft).
Facilities Dining room; Activities room; Crafts room; Laundry room; Barber/Beauty shop; Social services; Staff development.
Activities Arts & crafts; Cards; Games; Reading groups; Prayer groups; Movies; Shopping trips; Social/Cultural gatherings; Picnics; Ferry trips; Dinning out.

Beverly Manor of Portsmouth*
900 London Blvd, Portsmouth, VA, 23704
Medical Dir/Dir of Nursing Faith Dajao MD.
Owner Proprietary Corp.
Admissions Requirements Minimum age 14; Medical examination; Physician's request.
Staff RNs 5 (ft), 5 (pt); LPNs 9 (ft), 8 (pt); Nurses aides 26 (ft), 30 (pt); Physical therapists; Occupational therapists; Speech therapists; Activities coordinators 1 (ft).
Facilities Dining room; Physical therapy room; Activities room; Chapel; Laundry room; Barber/Beauty shop.
Activities Arts & crafts; Cards; Games; Reading groups; Prayer groups; Movies; Shopping trips; Social/Cultural gatherings; Picnics & other outings.

William T Hall Memorial Convalescent Home
3301 N Armistead Dr, Portsmouth, VA, 23704
(804) 399-0691
Admin Anthony L Fludd. *Medical Dir/Dir of Nursing* Dr J Marven; Aleurta Hughes DON.
Licensure Intermediate care. *Beds* 32. *Certified* Medicaid.
Owner Nonprofit organization/foundation.
Staff RNs 1 (ft); LPNs 3 (ft), 6 (pt); Nurses aides 4 (ft), 9 (pt); Activities coordinators 1 (ft); Dietitians 1 (ft).
Facilities Dining room; Activities room; Laundry room.

Manning Convalescent Home
PO Box 430, 175 Hatton St, Portsmouth, VA, 23705-0430
(804) 399-1321
Admin Thurman W Manning. *Medical Dir/Dir of Nursing* Dr E A Barham Jr.
Licensure Skilled care; Intermediate care. *Beds* SNF 258; ICF. *Certified* Medicaid; Medicare.
Owner Privately owned.
Admissions Requirements Minimum age 14; Medical examination; Physician's request.
Staff Physicians 64 (ft); RNs 14 (ft), 9 (pt); LPNs 20 (ft), 7 (pt); Nurses aides 97 (ft), 16 (pt); Physical therapists 1 (ft); Occupational therapists 1 (ft); Speech therapists 1 (ft); Activities coordinators 1 (ft); Dietitians 1 (ft), 1 (pt); Ophthalmologists 2 (pt); Dentist 2 (pt).
Facilities Dining room; Physical therapy room; Activities room; Chapel; Crafts room; Laundry room; Barber/Beauty shop; Library; Dental Office.

PULASKI

Pulaski Health Care Center
PO Box 1268, 2401 Lee Hiway, Pulaski, VA, 24301
(703) 980-3111
Admin Francis Clarke.
Licensure Skilled care; Intermediate care. *Beds* SNF 4; ICF 56. *Certified* Medicaid; Medicare.
Owner Proprietary Corp.
Admissions Requirements Minimum age 14; Medical examination.
Facilities Dining room; Physical therapy room; Activities room; Crafts room; Laundry room; Barber/Beauty shop.
Activities Arts & crafts; Cards; Games; Reading groups; Prayer groups; Movies; Shopping trips; Social/Cultural gatherings; Success therapy; Flower cart; Visitation program.

RICH CREEK

Riverview Nursing Home Inc
PO Box 327, 120 Virginia Ave, Rich Creek, VA, 24147
(703) 726-2328
Admin W F Lambert. *Medical Dir/Dir of Nursing* L E Delap MD; Laurie Dobbs RN DON.
Licensure Intermediate care. *Beds* ICF 60. *Certified* Medicaid.
Owner Proprietary Corp.
Admissions Requirements Medical examination.
Staff Physicians 5 (pt); RNs 2 (ft), 2 (pt); LPNs 3 (ft), 4 (pt); Nurses aides 18 (ft), 9 (pt); Physical therapists 1 (pt); Activities coordinators 1 (ft); Dietitians 1 (pt); Dentists 1 (pt); Podiatrists 1 (pt); Dentist 1 (pt) Social worker 1 (ft).
Facilities Dining room; Activities room; Chapel; Crafts room; Laundry room; Barber/Beauty shop.
Activities Arts & crafts; Cards; Games; Reading groups; Prayer groups; Movies; Shopping trips; Social/Cultural gatherings.

RICHMOND

Beth Sholom Home of Central Virginia
5700 Fitzhugh Ave, Richmond, VA, 23226
(804) 282-5471
Admin Barbara K Gottlieb. *Medical Dir/Dir of Nursing* Marian Baxter DON.
Licensure Intermediate care. *Beds* ICF 116. *Certified* Medicaid.
Owner Nonprofit Corp.
Admissions Requirements Minimum age 65; Medical examination.
Staff Physicians 2 (pt); RNs 6 (ft); LPNs 17 (ft); Orderlies 5 (ft); Nurses aides 80 (ft); Physical therapists 1 (pt); Recreational therapists 2 (ft), 1 (pt); Activities coordinators 1 (ft); Dietitians 1 (pt); Dentists 1 (pt); Ophthalmologists 1 (pt).
Affiliation Jewish
Facilities Dining room; Physical therapy room; Activities room; Chapel; Crafts room; Laundry room; Barber/Beauty shop; Library.
Activities Arts & crafts; Cards; Games; Reading groups; Prayer groups; Movies; Shopping trips; Social/Cultural gatherings.

Cambridge Manor*
1776 Cambridge Drive, Richmond, VA, 23233
(804) 740-6174
Admin Mary E Beddoes.
Licensure Skilled care; Intermediate care. *Beds* SNF 11; ICF 120. *Certified* Medicaid; Medicare.

Owner Proprietary Corp.

Camelot Hall Nursing Home*
2400 E Parham Rd, Richmond, VA, 23228
(804) 264-9185
Admin John A Booth.
Licensure Skilled care; Intermediate care. *Beds*
SNF 13; ICF 167. *Certified* Medicaid;
Medicare.
Owner Proprietary Corp.

Chippenham Manor Inc*
7246 Forest Hill Ave, Richmond, VA, 23225
(804) 320-7901
Admin Linwood F Logan Jr. *Medical Dir/Dir
of Nursing* Justo T Perez MD.
Licensure Intermediate care. *Beds* 196.
Certified Medicaid.
Owner Proprietary Corp.
Admissions Requirements Minimum age 21;
Medical examination; Physician's request.
Staff RNs 10 (ft), 9 (pt); LPNs 10 (ft), 6 (pt);
Orderlies 8 (ft), 1 (pt); Nurses aides 69 (ft),
5 (pt); Physical therapists 1 (pt);
Recreational therapists 2 (ft), 1 (pt);
Dietitians 1 (pt).
Facilities Dining room; Physical therapy
room; Activities room; Crafts room; Laundry
room; Barber/Beauty shop.
Activities Arts & crafts; Cards; Games;
Reading groups; Prayer groups; Movies;
Shopping trips; Social/Cultural gatherings.

Convalescent Care, Inc
7204 Glen Forest Br, Ste 101, Richmond, VA,
23226
(804) 285-7600
Admin W W Willis Pres.
Licensure Skilled care; Intermediate care;
Home for Adults. *Beds* SNF 60; ICF 785;
Home for adults 55. *Certified* Medicaid;
Medicare.
Owner Proprietary Corp.
Admissions Requirements Minimum age 14;
Medical examination; Physician's request.
Facilities Dining room; Physical therapy
room; Activities room; Chapel; Crafts room;
Laundry room; Barber/Beauty shop; Library.
Activities Arts & crafts; Cards; Games;
Reading groups; Prayer groups; Movies;
Shopping trips; Social/Cultural gatherings.

Forest Hill Convalescent Center*
4403 Forest Hill Ave, Richmond, VA, 23225
(804) 231-0231
Admin T Fred Allen.
Licensure Intermediate care. *Beds* 174.
Certified Medicaid.
Owner Proprietary Corp.

Imperial Health Center*
1717 Bellevue Ave, Richmond, VA, 23227
(804) 262-7364
Admin Agnes M Martin.
Licensure Intermediate care. *Beds* 68.
Certified Medicaid.
Owner Proprietary Corp.

**Little Sisters of the Poor—St Joseph Home for
Aged**
1503 Michael Rd, Richmond, VA, 23229-4899
(804) 288-6245
Admin Sr Marie Candide McCabe.
Licensure Intermediate care. *Beds* 63.
Certified Medicaid.
Owner Nonprofit Corp.
Affiliation Roman Catholic

Masonic Home of Virginia—Health Care Unit*
4101 Nine Mile Rd, Richmond, VA, 23223
(804) 222-1694
Admin Charles O Franck Jr. *Medical Dir/Dir
of Nursing* J Earle Smith.
Beds 42.
Owner Nonprofit Corp.
Admissions Requirements Minimum age 65;
Medical examination.
Affiliation Masons

Facilities Dining room; Physical therapy
room; Activities room; Chapel; Crafts room;
Laundry room; Barber/Beauty shop; Library.
Activities Arts & crafts; Games; Prayer groups;
Movies; Shopping trips; Social/Cultural
gatherings.

Richmond Nursing Home*
1900 Cool Ln, Richmond, VA, 23223
(804) 780-4914
Admin Geneva D Austin.
Licensure Skilled care; Intermediate care. *Beds*
SNF 56; ICF 113. *Certified* Medicaid;
Medicare.
Owner Publicly owned.

Stratford Hall Nursing Home
2125 Hilliard Rd, Richmond, VA, 23228
(804) 266-9666
Admin Vivian D Thomas. *Medical Dir/Dir of
Nursing* Thomas W Murrell Jr MD.
Licensure Skilled care; Intermediate care. *Beds*
194. *Certified* Medicaid; Medicare.
Owner Proprietary Corp (Manor Care).
Staff RNs 7 (ft), 7 (pt); LPNs 10 (ft), 4 (pt);
Nurses aides 60 (ft), 5 (pt); Physical
therapists 1 (ft), 1 (pt); Recreational
therapists 2 (ft); Occupational therapists 1
(pt); Speech therapists 1 (ft); Activities
coordinators 1 (ft); Dietitians 1 (ft).
Facilities Dining room; Physical therapy
room; Activities room; Crafts room; Laundry
room; Barber/Beauty shop; Library.
Activities Arts & crafts; Cards; Games;
Reading groups; Prayer groups; Movies;
Shopping trips; Social/Cultural gatherings.

University Park
2420 Pemberton Rd, Richmond, VA, 23229
(804) 747-9200
Admin Walter W Regirer. *Medical Dir/Dir of
Nursing* H Chesley Decker MD.
Licensure Skilled care; Intermediate care;
Home of adults; Club homes; Home health
care. *Beds* SNF 18; ICF 162; Home of
adults 18; Club homes 6. *Certified* Medicaid;
Medicare; VA.
Owner Privately owned.
Admissions Requirements Medical
examination; Physician's request.
Staff Physicians 83 (pt); RNs 18 (ft); LPNs 20
(ft); Orderlies 5 (ft); Nurses aides 69 (ft);
Physical therapists 2 (ft); Reality therapists 1
(ft); Recreational therapists 4 (ft);
Occupational therapists 2 (ft); Speech
therapists 1 (pt); Activities coordinators 1
(ft); Dietitians 1 (ft); Dentists 1 (pt);
Ophthalmologists 1 (pt); Podiatrists 1 (pt).
Facilities Dining room; Physical therapy
room; Activities room; Chapel; Crafts room;
Laundry room; Barber/Beauty shop; Library;
Tavern; Dental; Gift shop.
Activities Arts & crafts; Cards; Games;
Reading groups; Prayer groups; Movies;
Shopping trips; Social/Cultural gatherings.

**Via Health Care Center for the Hermitage
Methodist Home**
1600 Westwood Ave at Hermitage Rd,
Richmond, VA, 23227
(804) 355-5721
Admin C Bruce Pfeiffer. *Medical Dir/Dir of
Nursing* Dr Ronald Artz; Lethea Hague RN.
Licensure Unskilled. *Beds* Unskilled 115.
Owner Nonprofit Corp.
Admissions Requirements Minimum age 65;
Medical examination.
Staff Physicians 1 (pt); RNs 5 (ft); LPNs 9
(ft), 3 (pt); Nurses aides 56 (ft), 13 (pt);
Physical therapists 1 (ft), 1 (pt); Activities
coordinators 1 (ft); Dietitians 1 (ft).
Affiliation Methodist
Facilities Dining room; Physical therapy
room; Activities room; Chapel; Crafts room;
Laundry room; Barber/Beauty shop; Library.
Activities Arts & crafts; Cards; Games;
Reading groups; Prayer groups; Movies;
Shopping trips; Social/Cultural gatherings.

The Virginia Home
1101 Hampton St, Richmond, VA, 23220
(804) 359-4093
Admin Jeffrey D Custer. *Medical Dir/Dir of
Nursing* Dr Gile Robertson; Cornelia Fields
DON.
Licensure Intermediate care. *Beds* ICF 113.
Certified Medicaid.
Owner Nonprofit Corp.
Admissions Requirements Minimum age 18;
Medical examination; Physician's request.
Staff Physicians 4 (pt); RNs 5 (ft), 3 (pt);
LPNs 9 (ft), 7 (pt); Orderlies 40 (ft), 13 (pt);
Physical therapists 1 (pt); Recreational
therapists 3 (ft); Occupational therapists 1
(ft); Speech therapists 1 (pt); Activities
coordinators 1 (ft); Dietitians 1 (ft); Dentists
1 (pt); Ophthalmologists 1 (pt); Podiatrists 1
(pt).
Facilities Dining room; Physical therapy
room; Activities room; Chapel; Crafts room;
Laundry room; Barber/Beauty shop; Library;
Recreation room; Sun parlors; Solarium;
Medical room; Dental room.
Activities Arts & crafts; Cards; Games;
Reading groups; Prayer groups; Movies;
Shopping trips; Social/Cultural gatherings;
Outings with vehicles.

Westminster-Canterbury House
1600 Westbrook Ave, Richmond, VA, 23227
(804) 264-6000
Admin W Thomas Cunningham Jr. *Medical
Dir/Dir of Nursing* Fleming W Gill MD;
Phyllis Moore RN.
Licensure Skilled care; Intermediate care. *Beds*
133. *Certified* Medicaid; Medicare.
Owner Nonprofit Corp.
Admissions Requirements Minimum age 14;
Medical examination; Physician's request.
Staff RNs 13 (ft), 9 (pt); LPNs 11 (ft), 10 (pt);
Orderlies 1 (ft), 1 (pt); Nurses aides 51 (ft),
9 (pt); Physical therapists 1 (ft); Recreational
therapists 2 (ft); Activities coordinators;
Dietitians 1 (ft).
Affiliation Episcopal
Facilities Dining room; Physical therapy
room; Activities room; Chapel; Crafts room;
Laundry room; Barber/Beauty shop; Library.
Activities Arts & crafts; Cards; Games;
Reading groups; Prayer groups; Movies;
Shopping trips; Social/Cultural gatherings;
Pets.

Westport Convalescent Center*
7300 Forest Ave, Richmond, VA, 23226
(804) 288-3152
Admin Miriam C Green RN. *Medical Dir/Dir
of Nursing* Melvin Fratkin MD.
Licensure Intermediate care. *Beds* 225.
Certified Medicaid.
Owner Proprietary Corp.
Admissions Requirements Minimum age 14;
Medical examination; Physician's request.
Staff RNs 13 (ft); LPNs 14 (ft); Orderlies 8
(ft); Nurses aides 61 (ft); Physical therapists
1 (ft); Reality therapists 2 (ft); Activities
coordinators 1 (ft).
Facilities Dining room; Physical therapy
room; Activities room; Chapel; Crafts room;
Laundry room; Barber/Beauty shop.
Activities Arts & crafts; Cards; Games;
Reading groups; Prayer groups; Movies;
Shopping trips.

The Windsor*
3600 Grove Ave, Richmond, VA, 23221
(804) 353-3881
Admin Ms Walter W Regirer.
Licensure Skilled care; Intermediate care. *Beds*
SNF 8; ICF 67. *Certified* Medicaid;
Medicare.
Owner Proprietary Corp.

ROANOKE

Friendship Manor Convalescent Center
215 Hershberger Rd NW, Roanoke, VA,
24012
(703) 366-7641
Admin H Lawrence Rice. *Medical Dir/Dir of Nursing* Dr Anthony R Stavola.
Licensure Skilled care; Intermediate care. *Beds* SNF 373; ICF. *Certified* Medicaid; Medicare.
Owner Nonprofit Corp.
Admissions Requirements Minimum age 50.
Staff Physicians; RNs 13 (ft), 8 (pt); LPNs 22 (ft), 11 (pt); Nurses aides 101 (ft), 40 (pt); Physical therapists 1 (ft), 2 (pt); Reality therapists 1 (ft); Recreational therapists 1 (ft); Occupational therapists 1 (ft); Speech therapists 1 (pt); Activities coordinators 2 (ft); Dietitians 1 (ft), 1 (pt).
Facilities Dining room; Physical therapy room; Activities room; Chapel; Crafts room; Laundry room; Barber/Beauty shop; Library.
Activities Arts & crafts; Cards; Games; Reading groups; Prayer groups; Movies; Shopping trips; Social/Cultural gatherings.

Liberty House Nursing Home
324 King George Ave SW, Roanoke, VA,
24016
(703) 345-8139
Admin Ron Covington. *Medical Dir/Dir of Nursing* A M Jacobson MD; Faye Angell DON.
Licensure Skilled care; Intermediate care. *Beds* 141. *Certified* Medicaid.
Owner Proprietary Corp.
Admissions Requirements Medical examination.
Staff Nurses aides; Physical therapists; Speech therapists; Social services.
Facilities Dining room; Physical therapy room; Activities room; Laundry room; Barber/Beauty shop.
Activities Arts & crafts; Cards; Games; Reading groups; Prayer groups; Movies; Shopping trips; Social/Cultural gatherings.

Roanoke City Nursing Home
Box 478, Rte 1, Roanoke, VA, 24012
(703) 977-1018
Admin Bernice F Jones. *Medical Dir/Dir of Nursing* Ronald Overstreet; Martha Hartley.
Licensure Intermediate care. *Beds* ICF 58. *Certified* Medicaid.
Owner Publicly owned.
Staff Physicians 2 (pt); RNs 3 (ft); LPNs 4 (ft), 1 (pt); Orderlies; Nurses aides 20 (ft), 3 (pt); Activities coordinators 1 (ft); Dietitians 1 (ft).
Facilities Dining room.
Activities Arts & crafts; Cards; Games; Movies; Shopping trips.

Roanoke United Methodist Home
PO Box 6339, 1009 Old Country Club Rd NW, Roanoke, VA, 24017
(703) 344-6248
Admin Thomas H Au. *Medical Dir/Dir of Nursing* Dr William Ward.
Licensure Intermediate care. *Beds* ICF 40.
Owner Nonprofit Corp.
Admissions Requirements Minimum age 65; Medical examination.
Staff Physicians 4 (pt); RNs 4 (ft), 4 (pt); LPNs 4 (ft), 7 (pt); Orderlies 1 (ft); Nurses aides 21 (ft), 5 (pt); Physical therapists 1 (pt); Activities coordinators 1 (ft); Dietitians 1 (ft); Ophthalmologists 2 (pt); Dentist 1 (pt).
Affiliation Methodist
Facilities Dining room; Activities room; Chapel; Crafts room; Laundry room; Barber/ Beauty shop; Library.
Activities Arts & crafts; Cards; Games; Reading groups; Prayer groups; Movies; Shopping trips; Social/Cultural gatherings; Shuffleboard; Greenhouse.

South Roanoke Nursing Home Inc*
3823 Franklin Rd SW, Roanoke, VA, 24014
(703) 344-4325
Admin Charles E Carter Jr.
Licensure Skilled care. *Beds* 104. *Certified* Medicaid; Medicare.
Owner Proprietary Corp.

Virginia Synod Lutheran Home at Roanoke
3804 Brandon Ave SW, Roanoke, VA, 24018-1499
(703) 774-1661
Admin Francis X Hayes Jr. *Medical Dir/Dir of Nursing* Kcith Edmunds MD; Doloris Dutton RN.
Licensure Intermediate care. *Beds* ICF 62. *Certified* Medicaid.
Owner Nonprofit Corp.
Staff RNs 2 (ft), 2 (pt); LPNs 6 (ft), 5 (pt); Orderlies 3 (ft), 2 (pt); Nurses aides 24 (ft), 6 (pt); Activities coordinators 1 (ft).
Affiliation Lutheran
Facilities Dining room; Physical therapy room; Activities room; Crafts room; Barber/ Beauty shop.
Activities Arts & crafts; Cards; Games; Reading groups; Prayer groups; Movies; Shopping trips; Social/Cultural gatherings.

Woodhaven Village Inc*
3164 Roundhill Ave NW, Roanoke, VA, 24012
(703) 947-2207
Admin Malcolm A Pace.
Beds 48.
Owner Proprietary Corp.

ROCKY MOUNT

Eldercare of Franklin County
Hatcher St, PO Box 739, Rocky Mount, VA, 24151
(703) 483-9261
Admin Paul C Miller. *Medical Dir/Dir of Nursing* Robert S Strong.
Licensure Skilled care; Intermediate care. *Beds* SNF 12; ICF 168. *Certified* Medicaid; Medicare.
Owner Privately owned.
Admissions Requirements Medical examination.
Staff Physicians; RNs; LPNs; Orderlies; Nurses aides; Physical therapists; Speech therapists; Activities coordinators; Dietitians; Dentists; Ophthalmologists; Podiatrists.
Facilities Dining room; Physical therapy room; Activities room; Crafts room; Laundry room; Barber/Beauty shop.
Activities Arts & crafts; Cards; Games; Reading groups; Prayer groups; Movies; Shopping trips; Social/Cultural gatherings.

SALEM

Camelot Hall Nursing Home
1945 Roanoke Blvd, Salem, VA, 24153
(703) 345-3894
Admin Charles M LeMaster. *Medical Dir/Dir of Nursing* H J Minarik & Esther Brown.
Licensure Skilled care; Intermediate care. *Beds* SNF 30; ICF 210. *Certified* Medicaid; Medicare.
Owner Proprietary Corp.
Admissions Requirements Medical examination; Physician's request.
Staff Physicians 2 (pt); RNs 16 (ft), 3 (pt); LPNs 20 (ft), 8 (pt); Orderlies 6 (ft); Nurses aides 70 (ft), 4 (pt); Physical therapists 1 (pt); Reality therapists 1 (ft); Recreational therapists 1 (ft); Speech therapists; Activities coordinators; Dentists; Ophthalmologists; Podiatrists.
Facilities Dining room; Physical therapy room; Activities room; Chapel; Crafts room; Laundry room; Barber/Beauty shop; Library.

Activities Arts & crafts; Cards; Games; Reading groups; Movies; Shopping trips; Social/Cultural gatherings.

McVitty House Inc*
US Rte 460 W, PO Box 1240, Salem, VA, 24153
(703) 389-0271
Admin William K Anglim. *Medical Dir/Dir of Nursing* Howard Lebow MD.
Licensure Skilled care; Intermediate care. *Beds* 327. *Certified* Medicaid; Medicare.
Owner Nonprofit Corp.
Admissions Requirements Medical examination; Physician's request.
Staff Physicians 12 (pt); LPNs 20 (ft); LPNs 25 (ft); Orderlies 16 (ft); Nurses aides 120 (ft); Physical therapists 1 (ft); Activities coordinators 2 (ft); Dietitians 1 (ft); Dentists 1 (pt); Podiatrists 1 (pt).
Facilities Dining room; Physical therapy room; Activities room; Chapel; Crafts room; Laundry room; Barber/Beauty shop.
Activities Arts & crafts; Games; Reading groups; Prayer groups; Movies.

Snyder Nursing Home Inc
11 N Broad St, Salem, VA, 24153
(703) 389-0160
Admin C H Givens.
Licensure Intermediate care. *Beds* 45. *Certified* Medicaid.
Owner Nonprofit Corp.

SALUDA

Saluda Home*
PO Box 303, US Rte 17, Saluda, VA, 23149
(804) 758-2363
Admin R W Phill Sr.
Licensure Intermediate care. *Beds* 60. *Certified* Medicaid.
Owner Nonprofit Corp.

SHAWSVILLE

Meadowbrook Inc*
PO Box 305, Shawsville, VA, 24162
(703) 268-2276
Admin George R Smith III. *Medical Dir/Dir of Nursing* Dr G R Smith Jr.
Licensure Intermediate care. *Beds* 120. *Certified* Medicaid.
Owner Proprietary Corp.
Admissions Requirements Medical examination; Physician's request.
Staff Physicians 3 (ft); RNs 4 (ft); LPNs 6 (ft); Orderlies 6 (ft); Nurses aides 30 (ft); Physical therapists 1 (pt); Speech therapists 1 (pt); Activities coordinators 1 (ft); Dietitians 1 (pt); Dentists 1 (pt).
Facilities Dining room; Physical therapy room; Activities room; Chapel; Crafts room; Laundry room; Barber/Beauty shop; Library; Enclosed courtyard.
Activities Arts & crafts; Cards; Games; Reading groups; Prayer groups; Social/ Cultural gatherings.

SMITHFIELD

Smithfield Home*
200 Lumar Rd, Smithfield, VA, 23430
(804) 357-3282
Admin J Natalie Kent.
Licensure Intermediate care. *Beds* 35. *Certified* Medicare.
Owner Nonprofit Corp.

SOUTH BOSTON

Berry Hill Nursing Home Inc*
PO Box 797, 621 Berry Hill Rd, South Boston, VA, 24592
(804) 572-8901

Admin G Carlton Stevens.
Licensure Intermediate care. *Beds* 120.
  Certified Medicaid.
Owner Proprietary Corp.

Twin Oaks Convalescent Home Inc
406 Oak Ln, South Boston, VA, 24592
(804) 572-2925
Admin Connie S Zamora. *Medical Dir/Dir of Nursing* Dr Warren C Hagood; Sandra D Ligon.
Licensure Intermediate care. *Beds* 54.
  Certified Medicaid.
Owner Proprietary Corp.
Admissions Requirements Medical examination.
Staff RNs 1 (ft), 1 (pt); LPNs 6 (ft), 5 (pt); Orderlies 3 (ft), 2 (pt); Nurses aides 13 (ft), 12 (pt); Activities coordinators 1 (ft); Dietitians 1 (pt).
Facilities Dining room; Activities room; Laundry room; Barber/Beauty shop.
Activities Arts & crafts; Cards; Games; Reading groups; Prayer groups; Movies; Social/Cultural gatherings.

The Woodview
103 Rosehill Dr, South Boston, VA, 24592
(804) 572-4906
Admin Harvey B Newbill. *Medical Dir/Dir of Nursing* W J Hagood Jr MD; Emma F Meeler RN.
Licensure Skilled care; Intermediate care. *Beds* SNF 19; ICF 161. *Certified* Medicaid; Medicare.
Owner Nonprofit Corp.
Admissions Requirements Medical examination; Physician's request.
Staff Physicians 9 (pt); RNs 4 (ft), 1 (pt); LPNs 26 (ft), 3 (pt); Orderlies 7 (ft), 4 (pt); Nurses aides 56 (ft), 8 (pt); Physical therapists 2 (ft), 1 (pt); Reality therapists 1 (pt); Recreational therapists 2 (pt); Activities coordinators 1 (ft), 1 (pt); Dietitians 1 (pt).
Facilities Dining room; Physical therapy room; Activities room; Chapel; Crafts room; Laundry room; Barber/Beauty shop; Library.
Activities Arts & crafts; Cards; Games; Reading groups; Prayer groups; Movies; Shopping trips; Social/Cultural gatherings.

SOUTH HILL

Community Memorial Hospital—W S Hundley Annex
125 Buena Vista Circle, South Hill, VA, 23970
(804) 447-3151
Admin Allene Reese. *Medical Dir/Dir of Nursing* F C Sturmer MD; Mary Ann Hager RN.
Licensure Skilled care; Intermediate care. *Beds* SNF 15; ICF 125. *Certified* Medicaid; Medicare.
Owner Nonprofit organization/foundation.
Admissions Requirements Minimum age 14; Medical examination.
Staff Physicians; RNs; LPNs; Orderlies; Nurses aides; Physical therapists; Speech therapists; Activities coordinators; Dietitians.
Facilities Dining room; Physical therapy room; Activities room; Chapel; Laundry room; Barber/Beauty shop; Library; Lounges; Patios.
Activities Arts & crafts; Cards; Games; Reading groups; Prayer groups; Movies; Shopping trips; Social/Cultural gatherings; Cookouts; Music.

STAFFORD

Brookwood Nursing Home
PO Box 85, Andrew Chapel Rd, Stafford, VA, 22554
(703) 659-4670
Admin Patricia D Bagley. *Medical Dir/Dir of Nursing* Vonzie Pitts.

Licensure Intermediate care. *Beds* 34.
  Certified Medicaid.
Owner Proprietary Corp.
Admissions Requirements Medical examination.
Staff RNs 1 (ft), 2 (pt); LPNs 8 (pt); Nurses aides 3 (ft), 11 (pt); Recreational therapists 1 (ft); Activities coordinators 1 (ft); Dietitians 1 (pt).
Facilities Dining room; Activities room; Laundry room; Barber/Beauty shop.
Activities Arts & crafts; Cards; Games; Reading groups; Prayer groups; Movies; Shopping trips; Social/Cultural gatherings.

STAUNTON

Oak Hill Nursing Home Inc*
PO Box 2565, 512 Houston St, Staunton, VA, 24401
(703) 886-2335
Admin Mary Lou DiGrassie. *Medical Dir/Dir of Nursing* Dr Leon Lenker.
Licensure Intermediate care; Home for aged. *Beds* ICF 130; Home for aged 27. *Certified* Medicaid.
Owner Proprietary Corp (National Healthcare Affiliates).
Admissions Requirements Medical examination.
Facilities Dining room; Activities room; Crafts room; Laundry room; Barber/Beauty shop.
Activities Arts & crafts; Cards; Games; Reading groups; Prayer groups; Movies; Shopping trips; Social/Cultural gatherings.

Staunton Manor Nursing Home Inc
1734 Churchville Ave, Staunton, VA, 24401
(703) 885-3611
Admin Daniel Sheets. *Medical Dir/Dir of Nursing* Myrtle Summers.
Licensure Intermediate care. *Beds* ICF 89.
  Certified Medicaid.
Owner Proprietary Corp.
Staff RNs; LPNs; Orderlies; Nurses aides; Activities coordinators; Dietitians.
Facilities Dining room; Activities room; Chapel; Crafts room; Laundry room.
Activities Arts & crafts; Cards; Games; Reading groups; Prayer groups; Movies; Social/Cultural gatherings.

STUART

Blue Ridge Nursing Home Inc
Commerce St, Stuart, VA, 24171
(703) 694-7161
Admin D Victor Williams LNHA. *Medical Dir/Dir of Nursing* Sam P Massie & Dr Robert Bowman; Sandra Harris RN.
Licensure Intermediate care. *Beds* ICF 120.
  Certified Medicaid.
Owner Proprietary Corp.
Staff Physicians 3 (pt); RNs 8 (ft), 2 (pt); LPNs 3 (ft); Orderlies 2 (ft), 2 (pt); Nurses aides 28 (ft), 23 (pt); Physical therapists 2 (pt); Speech therapists 1 (pt); Activities coordinators 1 (ft), 1 (pt); Dietitians 1 (pt).
Facilities Dining room; Physical therapy room; Activities room; Chapel; Crafts room; Laundry room; Barber/Beauty shop; Library.
Activities Arts & crafts; Games; Reading groups; Prayer groups; Movies; Social/Cultural gatherings.

SUFFOLK

Autumn Care of Suffolk*
2580 Pruden Blvd, Suffolk, VA, 23434
(804) 934-2363
Admin Mary G Taychert. *Medical Dir/Dir of Nursing* Beverly Holladay MD.
Licensure Intermediate care. *Beds* 120.
  Certified Medicaid.
Owner Proprietary Corp (Autumn Corp).

Admissions Requirements Minimum age 18; Medical examination; Physician's request.
Staff RNs 1 (ft); LPNs 11 (ft); Nurses aides 47 (ft); Recreational therapists; Activities coordinators 1 (ft); Dietitians 1 (pt); Podiatrists 1 (pt).
Facilities Dining room; Physical therapy room; Activities room; Crafts room; Laundry room; Barber/Beauty shop.
Activities Arts & crafts; Cards; Games; Reading groups; Prayer groups; Movies; Shopping trips; Social/Cultural gatherings.

Nansemond Convalescent Center Inc*
200 W Constance Rd, Suffolk, VA, 23434
(804) 539-8744
Admin Audrey B Butler.
Licensure Intermediate care. *Beds* 100.
  Certified Medicaid.
Owner Proprietary Corp (Hillhaven Corp).

TAPPAHANNOCK

Tappahannock Manor Convalescent Center & Home for Adults*
Marsh St, PO Box 1167, Tappahannock, VA, 22560
(804) 443-4308
Admin Katherine Gardner.
Licensure Intermediate care. *Beds* 60.
  Certified Medicaid.
Owner Proprietary Corp.
Admissions Requirements Minimum age 18.
Staff Physicians 7 (pt); RNs 1 (ft), 2 (pt); LPNs 4 (ft), 5 (pt); Nurses aides 13 (ft), 10 (pt); Physical therapists 1 (pt); Activities coordinators 1 (ft), 1 (pt); Dietitians 1 (pt).
Facilities Dining room; Physical therapy room; Activities room; Crafts room; Barber/Beauty shop.
Activities Arts & crafts; Cards; Games; Prayer groups; Movies; Shopping trips.

TAZEWELL

Heritage Hall III
121 Ben Bolt Ave, Tazewell, VA, 24651
(703) 988-2515
Admin Joy C Myers. *Medical Dir/Dir of Nursing* Dr James Thompson; Delores Troupe.
Licensure Intermediate care. *Beds* ICF 180.
  Certified Medicaid.
Owner Proprietary Corp.
Staff Physicians 14 (pt); RNs 3 (ft), 2 (pt); LPNs 12 (ft), 7 (pt); Nurses aides 48 (ft), 23 (pt); Activities coordinators 2 (ft); Dentist 2 (pt).
Facilities Dining room; Physical therapy room; Activities room; Chapel; Crafts room; Laundry room; Barber/Beauty shop.
Activities Arts & crafts; Cards; Games; Prayer groups; Movies; Shopping trips; Social/Cultural gatherings.

VINTON

The Berkshire Health Care Center
705 Clearview Dr, Vinton, VA, 24179
(703) 982-6691
Admin Jacqueline H Wood. *Medical Dir/Dir of Nursing* Robert Bondurant MD; Toni Pierce RN DON.
Licensure Intermediate care. *Beds* ICF 180.
  Certified Medicaid.
Owner Proprietary Corp (Medical Facilities of America).
Admissions Requirements Minimum age 14; Medical examination; Physician's request.
Staff RNs; LPNs; Nurses aides; Activities coordinators.
Facilities Dining room; Physical therapy room; Activities room; Laundry room; Barber/Beauty shop; Meditation room; Treatment room.

Activities Arts & crafts; Cards; Games; Reading groups; Prayer groups; Movies; Social/Cultural gatherings.

VIRGINIA BEACH

Beth Sholom Home of Eastern Virginia
6401 Auburn Dr, Virginia Beach, VA, 23464
(804) 420-2512
Admin Lee H Olitzky.
Licensure Intermediate care. *Beds* 120. *Certified* Medicaid.
Owner Nonprofit Corp (Beth Shalom Homes of VA).
Affiliation Jewish

Camelot Hall Nursing Home
1801 Camelot Dr, Virginia Beach, VA, 23454
(804) 481-3500
Admin Charles Weiden. *Medical Dir/Dir of Nursing* Dr Gregory Edinger; Mrs Jean Mann.
Licensure Intermediate care. *Beds* ICF 240. *Certified* Medicaid; Medicare.
Owner Proprietary Corp (Medical Facilities of America).
Admissions Requirements Minimum age 18; Medical examination.
Facilities Dining room; Physical therapy room; Activities room; Barber/Beauty shop.
Activities Arts & crafts; Cards; Games; Reading groups; Prayer groups; Movies; Shopping trips; Social/Cultural gatherings; Special programs.

Holmes Convalescent Center Inc*
4142 Bonney Rd, Virginia Beach, VA, 23452
(804) 340-0620
Admin Juanita L Snell.
Licensure Intermediate care. *Beds* 160. *Certified* Medicaid.
Owner Proprietary Corp (Hillhaven Corp).

Lynn Shores Manor
340 Lynn Shores Dr, Virginia Beach, VA, 23452
(804) 340-6611
Admin Tom Orsihi. *Medical Dir/Dir of Nursing* Louis Farano MD.
Licensure Intermediate care. *Beds* SNF 24; ICF 218. *Certified* Medicaid; Medicare.
Owner Proprietary Corp.
Admissions Requirements Minimum age 14; Medical examination; Physician's request.
Staff RNs 8 (ft), 6 (pt); LPNs 20 (ft), 10 (pt); Nurses aides 62 (ft), 92 (pt); Activities coordinators 1 (ft), 2 (pt); Dietitians 1 (ft).
Facilities Dining room; Physical therapy room; Activities room; Crafts room; Laundry room; Barber/Beauty shop; Library.
Activities Arts & crafts; Cards; Games; Reading groups; Prayer groups; Movies; Shopping trips; Social/Cultural gatherings.

Medicenter—Virginia Beach*
1148 1st Colonial Blvd, Virginia Beach, VA, 23454
(804) 481-3321
Admin Matthew C Farmer. *Medical Dir/Dir of Nursing* Marc Gaines.
Licensure Skilled care. *Beds* 118. *Certified* Medicaid; Medicare.
Owner Proprietary Corp (Hillhaven Corp).
Admissions Requirements Medical examination; Physician's request.
Staff RNs 7 (ft); LPNs 8 (ft), 9 (pt); Orderlies 8 (ft), 11 (pt); Nurses aides 33 (ft), 16 (pt); Physical therapists 2 (ft); Recreational therapists 1 (ft); Occupational therapists 1 (ft); Speech therapists 1 (ft); Activities coordinators 1 (ft); Dietitians 1 (ft); Dentists 1 (pt); Ophthalmologists 1 (pt); Podiatrists 1 (pt); Audiologists 1 (pt).
Facilities Dining room; Physical therapy room; Activities room; Laundry room; Barber/Beauty shop.

Activities Arts & crafts; Cards; Games; Reading groups; Prayer groups; Movies; Shopping trips; Social/Cultural gatherings.

Shore Drive Convalescent Home Inc*
3601 Shore Dr, Virginia Beach, VA, 23455
(804) 460-1169
Admin Martha S Sims. *Medical Dir/Dir of Nursing* Joseph O M Thatcher MD.
Licensure Intermediate care. *Beds* 22. *Certified* Medicaid.
Owner Proprietary Corp.
Admissions Requirements Medical examination.
Staff Physicians 1 (pt); RNs 1 (pt); LPNs 4 (ft); Nurses aides 6 (ft), 4 (pt); Recreational therapists 1 (pt); Activities coordinators 1 (ft); Dietitians 1 (pt); Podiatrists 1 (pt).
Facilities Dining room; Activities room; Laundry room.
Activities Arts & crafts; Games; Reading groups; Prayer groups; Social/Cultural gatherings.

Westminster-Canterbury in Virginia Beach
3100 Shore Dr, Virginia Beach, VA, 23451
(804) 496-1100
Admin Thomas E Clements. *Medical Dir/Dir of Nursing* Thomas Manser MD.
Licensure Skilled care; Intermediate care; Lifecare retirement. *Beds* SNF 15; ICF 60. *Certified* Medicaid; Medicare.
Owner Nonprofit Corp.
Admissions Requirements Medical examination; Physician's request.
Staff Physicians 2 (pt); RNs 10 (ft), 8 (pt); LPNs 8 (ft), 6 (pt); Nurses aides 25 (ft), 20 (pt); Physical therapists 1 (ft); Recreational therapists 1 (ft); Occupational therapists 1 (pt); Speech therapists 1 (pt); Activities coordinators 2 (ft); Dietitians 1 (ft); Ophthalmologists 1 (pt).
Affiliation Episcopal
Facilities Dining room; Physical therapy room; Activities room; Chapel; Crafts room; Laundry room; Barber/Beauty shop; Library; Woodworking shop; Convenience store; Clinic.
Activities Arts & crafts; Cards; Games; Reading groups; Prayer groups; Movies; Shopping trips; Social/Cultural gatherings; Weekly chapel services; Travelogues; Display of collections & hobbies.

WARRENTON

District Nursing Home
32 Waterloo St, Warrenton, VA, 22186
(703) 347-1881
Admin Bryan A Graham. *Medical Dir/Dir of Nursing* Dr Iden; Ms Savenner.
Licensure Intermediate care. *Beds* ICF 51. *Certified* Medicaid.
Owner Publicly owned.
Admissions Requirements Medical examination; Physician's request.
Facilities Dining room; Activities room; Barber/Beauty shop.
Activities Arts & crafts; Games; Prayer groups; Social/Cultural gatherings.

Oak Springs of Warrenton
1066 Hastings Ln, Warrenton, VA, 22186
(703) 347-4770
Admin Felicia K Kinney. *Medical Dir/Dir of Nursing* Dr Douglas Morris; Louann Toomey RN.
Licensure Intermediate care. *Beds* 130. *Certified* Medicaid.
Owner Privately owned.
Admissions Requirements Minimum age 17; Medical examination.
Staff RNs 5 (ft); LPNs 16 (ft), 3 (pt); Nurses aides 56 (ft), 7 (pt); Physical therapists 1 (pt); Recreational therapists 1 (ft); Occupational therapists 1 (pt); Speech therapists 1 (pt); Activities coordinators 1 (ft); Dietitians 1 (pt).

Facilities Dining room; Physical therapy room; Activities room; Crafts room; Laundry room; Barber/Beauty shop.
Activities Arts & crafts; Games; Reading groups; Prayer groups; Movies; Shopping trips; Social/Cultural gatherings.

WARSAW

Warsaw Health Care Center*
Box 39, Rte 1, 302 W Richmond Rd, Warsaw, VA, 22572
(804) 333-3616
Admin Richard Wager.
Licensure Skilled care; Intermediate care. *Beds* SNF 10; ICF 110. *Certified* Medicaid; Medicare.
Owner Proprietary Corp.

WAYNESBORO

District Home
1400 District Home Dr, Waynesboro, VA, 22980-9305
(703) 942-5237
Admin Jerry B Layman. *Medical Dir/Dir of Nursing* G C Ayers MD; Brenda Q Novene BS RN DON.
Licensure Intermediate care; Home for adults. *Beds* ICF 91; Home for adults 60. *Certified* Medicaid.
Owner Publicly owned.
Admissions Requirements Minimum age 18; Medical examination.
Staff Physicians 1 (pt); RNs 3 (ft); LPNs 14 (ft), 2 (pt); Orderlies 4 (ft); Nurses aides 41 (ft), 4 (pt); Physical therapists 1 (pt); Recreational therapists 1 (pt); Speech therapists 1 (pt); Activities coordinators 1 (ft); Dietitians 1 (pt); Dentists 1 (pt); Ophthalmologists 1 (pt).
Facilities Dining room; Activities room; Chapel; Crafts room; Barber/Beauty shop; Library.
Activities Arts & crafts; Cards; Games; Reading groups; Prayer groups; Movies; Shopping trips; Social/Cultural gatherings.

Liberty House Nursing Home
1221 Rosser Ave, Waynesboro, VA, 22980
(703) 942-7191
Admin John G Lambert.
Licensure Intermediate care. *Beds* SNF 9; ICF 100. *Certified* Medicaid.
Owner Proprietary Corp.

WILLIAMSBURG

Pines Convalescent Center*
1235 Mount Vernon Ave, Williamsburg, VA, 23185
(804) 229-4121
Admin Anne N Hurley.
Licensure Intermediate care. *Beds* 156. *Certified* Medicaid.
Owner Proprietary Corp (National Healthcare Affiliates).

Williamsburg Landing
5700 Williasmsburg Landing Dr, Williamsburg, VA, 23185
(804) 253-0303
Admin D Martin Trueblood, Exec Dir; Donald L Husi, Nursing Home Admin. *Medical Dir/Dir of Nursing* Florence Galing DON.
Licensure Intermediate care. *Beds* ICF 19.
Owner Nonprofit Corp.
Admissions Requirements Physician's request.
Staff RNs 4 (ft), 8 (pt); Nurses aides 5 (ft), 8 (pt); Activities coordinators 1 (ft); Dietitians.
Facilities Dining room; Physical therapy room; Activities room; Chapel; Library.
Activities Arts & crafts; Cards; Games; Reading groups; Prayer groups; Movies; Shopping trips; Social/Cultural gatherings.

WINCHESTER

Hillcrest Manor Nursing Home*
Rte 522 N, Sunnyside Station, Winchester, VA, 22601
(703) 662-3334
Admin Stelleda H Whitman.
Beds 60.
Owner Proprietary Corp.

Shawnee Springs Nursing Home*
380 Millwood Ave, Winchester, VA, 22601
(703) 667-7010
Admin Bonita S Brown.
Licensure Intermediate care. *Beds* 176.
Certified Medicaid.
Owner Proprietary Corp.

WISE

Heritage Hall—Wise
PO Box 1009, 1009 College Rd, Wise, VA, 24293
(703) 328-2721
Admin James H McVey Sr. *Medical Dir/Dir of Nursing* Charles Burkhart.
Licensure Intermediate care. *Beds* ICF 62.
Certified Medicaid.
Owner Proprietary Corp.
Staff RNs; LPNs; Nurses aides; Activities coordinators.
Facilities Dining room; Activities room; Laundry room; Barber/Beauty shop.
Activities Arts & crafts; Cards; Games; Prayer groups; Movies; Shopping trips; Social/Cultural gatherings.

WOODBRIDGE

Woodbridge Nursing Center Inc
14906 Jefferson Davis Hwy, Woodbridge, VA, 22191
(703) 491-6167
Admin W Russell Rodgers Jr. *Medical Dir/Dir of Nursing* William McCarthy MD.
Licensure Intermediate care. *Beds* 120.
Certified Medicaid; Medicare.
Owner Proprietary Corp.
Admissions Requirements Medical examination; Physician's request.
Staff Physicians 14 (pt); RNs 4 (ft), 6 (pt); LPNs 9 (ft), 4 (pt); Nurses aides 38 (ft), 26 (pt); Physical therapists 2 (ft), 1 (pt); Reality therapists 1 (ft); Recreational therapists 1 (pt); Speech therapists 2 (pt); Dietitians 1 (ft); Dentists 2 (pt); Ophthalmologists 2 (pt); Podiatrists 1 (pt); Dentist 1 (pt); Social workers 1 (ft).
Facilities Dining room; Physical therapy room; Activities room; Crafts room; Laundry room; Barber/Beauty shop.
Activities Arts & crafts; Cards; Games; Reading groups; Prayer groups; Movies; Shopping trips; Social/Cultural gatherings.

WOODSTOCK

Susan B Miller Nursing Homes Inc
118 N Muhlenberg St, Woodstock, VA, 22664
(703) 459-2118
Admin Marian E Foltz.
Licensure Intermediate care. *Beds* 54.
Certified Medicaid.
Owner Proprietary Corp.

Shenandoah County Memorial Hospital—Long-Term Care Unit*
Rte 11, Woodstock, VA, 22664
(703) 459-4021
Admin Stanley B Kamm.
Licensure Intermediate care. *Beds* 34.
Certified Medicaid.
Owner Nonprofit Corp.

Skyline Terrace Convalescent Home*
PO Box 191, 11 South & Lakeview Rd, Woodstock, VA, 22664
(703) 459-3738
Admin Jesse D Funkhouser.
Licensure Intermediate care. *Beds* 70.
Certified Medicaid.
Owner Proprietary Corp.

WYTHEVILLE

Asbury Center at Birdmont Retirement Community
990 Holston Rd, Wytheville, VA, 24382
(703) 228-5595
Admin William S Rodgers. *Medical Dir/Dir of Nursing* Julana Whitlow.
Licensure Intermediate care; Retirement community. *Beds* ICF 152; Retirement community 88. *Certified* Medicaid; Medicare.
Owner Nonprofit Corp.
Admissions Requirements Minimum age 65; Medical examination; Physician's request.
Staff RNs 8 (ft), 3 (pt); LPNs 6 (ft), 6 (pt); Orderlies 5 (ft), 1 (pt); Nurses aides 80 (ft), 10 (pt); Physical therapists 4 (pt); Speech therapists 1 (pt); Activities coordinators 3 (ft); Dietitians 1 (ft), 1 (pt).
Affiliation Methodist
Facilities Dining room; Physical therapy room; Activities room; Chapel; Crafts room; Laundry room; Barber/Beauty shop; Library.
Activities Arts & crafts; Cards; Games; Reading groups; Prayer groups; Movies; Shopping trips; Social/Cultural gatherings.

WASHINGTON

ABERDEEN

Grays Harbor Convalescent Center*
920 Anderson Dr, Aberdeen, WA, 98520
(206) 532-5122
Admin Terry J Almasi. *Medical Dir/Dir of Nursing* Dr James Baker.
Licensure Skilled care; Intermediate care. *Beds* 155. *Certified* Medicaid; Medicare.
Owner Proprietary Corp.
Admissions Requirements Medical examination; Physician's request.
Staff RNs 7 (ft), 1 (pt); LPNs 12 (ft), 3 (pt); Nurses aides 55 (ft), 10 (pt); Activities coordinators 3 (ft).
Facilities Dining room; Physical therapy room; Activities room; Chapel; Crafts room; Barber/Beauty shop; Library.
Activities Arts & crafts; Cards; Games; Reading groups; Prayer groups; Movies; Shopping trips; Social/Cultural gatherings.

Harbor Health Care
308 W King, Aberdeen, WA, 98520
(206) 533-3000
Admin Patty McMillan. *Medical Dir/Dir of Nursing* Rena Westerback.
Licensure Skilled care; Intermediate care. *Beds* SNF 91; ICF. *Certified* Medicaid.
Owner Proprietary Corp (Beverly Enterprises).
Admissions Requirements Medical examination; Physician's request.
Staff RNs 4 (ft); LPNs 5 (ft), 2 (pt); Orderlies 3 (ft); Nurses aides 25 (ft), 8 (pt); Physical therapists 1 (ft); Reality therapists 1 (ft), 1 (pt); Activities coordinators 1 (ft); Dietitians 1 (ft); Social service; Medical records.
Languages Finnish
Facilities Dining room; Activities room; Crafts room; Laundry room; Barber/Beauty shop.
Activities Arts & crafts; Cards; Games; Reading groups; Prayer groups; Movies; Shopping trips; Social/Cultural gatherings; Geriatric olympics; Beauty pagents.

ANACORTES

Anacortes Convalescent Center*
1105 26th St, Anacortes, WA, 98221
(206) 293-3174
Admin Terrell L Leno.
Licensure Skilled care; Intermediate care. *Beds* 119. *Certified* Medicaid; Medicare.
Owner Proprietary Corp.

Barth Nursing Home
1407 5th St, Anacortes, WA, 98221
(206) 293-6622
Admin Virginia Wiggins. *Medical Dir/Dir of Nursing* Joan Farmer.
Licensure Intermediate care. *Beds* ICF 26. *Certified* Medicaid.
Owner Privately owned.
Admissions Requirements Medical examination; Physician's request.
Staff LPNs 4 (ft); Orderlies 4 (ft); Nurses aides; Dietitians 1 (pt).

Facilities Dining room; Activities room; Barber/Beauty shop.
Activities Arts & crafts; Cards; Games; Reading groups; Prayer groups; Movies; Shopping trips; Social/Cultural gatherings.

San Juan Nursing Home
911 21st St, Anacortes, WA, 98221
(206) 293-7222
Admin Stephen R Johnson. *Medical Dir/Dir of Nursing* Marlene Kirkland DNS.
Licensure Skilled care; Intermediate care. *Beds* SNF 52; ICF. *Certified* Medicaid.
Owner Proprietary Corp.
Admissions Requirements Medical examination; Physician's request.
Staff RNs; LPNs; Nurses aides; Activities coordinators; Dietitians.
Facilities Dining room; Laundry room.
Activities Arts & crafts; Games; Reading groups; Prayer groups; Movies; Shopping trips.

ARLINGTON

Arlington Convalescent Center
Florence & Hazel St, Arlington, WA, 98223
(206) 435-5521
Admin Beaulah M Gibble. *Medical Dir/Dir of Nursing* Dr Mark Lucianna; Ann Tennyson DON.
Licensure Skilled care; Intermediate care. *Beds* SNF 96; ICF. *Certified* Medicaid.
Owner Proprietary Corp.
Admissions Requirements Medical examination; Physician's request.
Staff Physicians; RNs; LPNs; Orderlies; Nurses aides; Recreational therapists; Activities coordinators.
Facilities Dining room; Physical therapy room; Activities room; Chapel; Crafts room; Laundry room; Barber/Beauty shop.
Activities Arts & crafts; Cards; Games; Reading groups; Prayer groups; Movies; Social/Cultural gatherings; Reality orientation classes; Remotivation classes.

AUBURN

Applegate Care Center
414 17th SE, Auburn, WA, 98002
(206) 833-1740
Admin James K Osborn. *Medical Dir/Dir of Nursing* Dr Zerr; Shirley Larson.
Licensure Skilled care. *Beds* 96. *Certified* Medicaid.
Owner Proprietary Corp.
Staff RNs 8 (ft); LPNs 10 (ft); Nurses aides 45 (ft); Physical therapists 1 (pt); Reality therapists 1 (pt); Recreational therapists 1 (ft); Occupational therapists 1 (ft); Speech therapists 1 (ft); Activities coordinators 1 (ft); Dietitians 1 (ft); Dentists 1 (pt); Ophthalmologists 1 (pt); Podiatrists 1 (pt).
Facilities Dining room; Physical therapy room; Activities room; Crafts room; Laundry room; Barber/Beauty shop; Library.

Activities Arts & crafts; Cards; Games; Reading groups; Prayer groups; Movies; Shopping trips; Social/Cultural gatherings.

Green River Terrace Nursing Home*
2830 I St NE, Auburn, WA, 98002
(206) 854-4142
Admin John B Merz.
Licensure Skilled care; Intermediate care. *Beds* 139. *Certified* Medicaid; Medicare.
Owner Proprietary Corp (Beverly Enterprises).

Marine View Convalescent Center
PO Box 1678, 29601 8th Ave SW, Auburn, WA, 98071-1678
(206) 839-3782
Admin Barbara Altier.
Licensure Skilled care; Intermediate care. *Beds* 51. *Certified* Medicaid.
Owner Proprietary Corp.

BAINBRIDGE ISLAND

Messenger House Care Center
10861 Manitou Park Blvd NE, Bainbridge Island, WA, 98110
(206) 842-2654
Admin Ray Ramsdell. *Medical Dir/Dir of Nursing* Elinor Ringland.
Licensure Skilled care; Intermediate care. *Beds* SNF 96. *Certified* Medicaid.
Owner Proprietary Corp (Soundcare Inc).
Admissions Requirements Medical examination; Physician's request.
Staff Physicians 1 (pt); RNs 9 (ft); LPNs 8 (ft); Nurses aides 28 (ft); Physical therapists 1 (pt); Recreational therapists 1 (ft), 1 (pt); Occupational therapists 1 (pt); Speech therapists 1 (pt); Activities coordinators 1 (ft); Dietitians 1 (pt); Ophthalmologists 1 (pt); Social Services 1 (ft).
Facilities Dining room; Physical therapy room; Activities room; Laundry room; Barber/Beauty shop; Sunroom.
Activities Arts & crafts; Cards; Games; Reading groups; Prayer groups; Movies; Shopping trips; Social/Cultural gatherings.

Winslow Convalescent Center*
835 Madison Ave N, Bainbridge Island, WA, 98110
(206) 842-4765
Admin Steven R Lane. *Medical Dir/Dir of Nursing* Dr Keyes.
Licensure Skilled care; Intermediate care. *Beds* 92. *Certified* Medicaid.
Owner Proprietary Corp.
Admissions Requirements Medical examination.
Staff RNs 8 (ft), 5 (pt); LPNs 1 (pt); Orderlies 2 (ft), 3 (pt); Nurses aides 24 (ft), 14 (pt); Physical therapists 2 (pt); Reality therapists 1 (pt); Recreational therapists 2 (pt); Occupational therapists 2 (pt); Speech therapists 1 (pt); Activities coordinators 1 (ft), 1 (pt); Dietitians 1 (pt); Dentists 1 (pt); Ophthalmologists 1 (pt); Podiatrists 1 (pt); Audiologists 1 (pt).

Facilities Dining room; Physical therapy room; Activities room; Laundry room; Barber/Beauty shop.
Activities Arts & crafts; Cards; Games; Movies; Shopping trips; Social/Cultural gatherings; Church services; Current events discussion group; Visiting musical entertainment groups; Sensory stimulation groups.

BATTLE GROUND

Clark Institute of Restorative Tech*
PO Box 218, 103 N Parkway, Battle Ground, WA, 98604
(206) 687-3781
Admin James Morgan.
Licensure Intermediate care for mentally retarded. *Beds* 57. *Certified* Medicaid.
Owner Proprietary Corp.

Meadow Glade Manor
11117 NE 189th St, Battle Ground, WA, 98604
(206) 687-3151
Admin Kathleen Dhanens. *Medical Dir/Dir of Nursing* Dean Barth MD.
Licensure Intermediate care. *Beds* 65. *Certified* Medicare.
Owner Proprietary Corp (Beverly Enterprises).
Admissions Requirements Minimum age 21; Medical examination; Physician's request.
Staff Physicians 1 (ft); RNs 5 (ft); LPNs 4 (ft); Nurses aides 33 (ft); Physical therapists 1 (pt); Reality therapists 1 (ft); Recreational therapists 1 (ft); Occupational therapists 1 (pt); Speech therapists 1 (pt); Activities coordinators 1 (ft); Dietitians 1 (pt); Dentists 1 (pt); Podiatrists 1 (pt); Dentist 1 (pt).
Facilities Dining room; Physical therapy room; Activities room; Crafts room; Barber/Beauty shop; Day room.
Activities Arts & crafts; Cards; Games; Reading groups; Prayer groups; Movies; Shopping trips; Social/Cultural gatherings; Resident council; Church services; Special entertainment; Dining out; Beach trips; County fair; Relaxation; Exercises; Pet therapy.

Parkway North Care Center
PO Box 770, 404 N Parkway, Battle Ground, WA, 98604
(206) 687-5141
Admin Nancy T Gebhard. *Medical Dir/Dir of Nursing* Dr Dean Barth; Susan Gates DON.
Licensure Skilled care; Intermediate care. *Beds* 84. *Certified* Medicaid.
Owner Proprietary Corp (National Heritage).
Staff Physicians 1 (pt); RNs 4 (ft), 2 (pt); LPNs 4 (ft), 2 (pt); Orderlies 1 (ft); Nurses aides 31 (ft), 3 (pt); Physical therapists 1 (pt); Reality therapists 1 (pt); Recreational therapists 1 (pt); Occupational therapists 1 (pt); Speech therapists 1 (pt); Activities coordinators 2 (ft); Dietitians 1 (pt); Dentists 1 (pt); Podiatrists 1 (pt).
Facilities Dining room; Physical therapy room; Activities room; Crafts room; Laundry room; Barber/Beauty shop.
Activities Arts & crafts; Cards; Games; Reading groups; Prayer groups; Movies; Shopping trips; Social/Cultural gatherings.

BELLEVUE

Bellevue Center
1640 148th Ave SE, Bellevue, WA, 98007
(206) 746-8640
Admin Barbara Hancock. *Medical Dir/Dir of Nursing* H Angle MD.
Licensure Skilled care; Intermediate care for mentally retarded. *Beds* 109. *Certified* Medicaid.
Owner Proprietary Corp.

Staff Physicians 5 (pt); RNs 8 (ft), 4 (pt); LPNs 3 (ft), 1 (pt); Nurses aides 48 (ft), 6 (pt); Physical therapists 1 (pt); Recreational therapists 1 (ft); Occupational therapists 1 (ft); Speech therapists 1 (ft); Activities coordinators 1 (ft); Dietitians 1 (pt); Dentists 1 (pt).
Facilities Dining room; Physical therapy room; Activities room; Laundry room; Sensory stimulation therapy room.
Activities Arts & crafts; Cards; Games; Movies; Shopping trips; Social/Cultural gatherings; Art therapy with artists; Music therapy; Special Olympics; Wheelchair games; Bowling; Swimming.

Bellevue Terrace
150 102nd Ave SE, Bellevue, WA, 98004
(206) 454-6166
Admin Lee H Felton.
Licensure Skilled care; Intermediate care; Respite; Medicare. *Beds* SNF 182; ICF 42; Medicare 12. *Certified* Medicaid; Medicare.
Owner Proprietary Corp (Beverly Enterprises).
Admissions Requirements Minimum age; Medical examination; Physician's request.
Staff Physicians 3 (pt); RNs 10 (ft), 5 (pt); LPNs 11 (ft), 8 (pt); Nurses aides 51 (ft), 9 (pt); Physical therapists 1 (ft); Reality therapists 1 (ft); Recreational therapists 2 (ft); Occupational therapists 1 (pt); Speech therapists 1 (pt); Activities coordinators 1 (ft); Dietitians 1 (pt); Dentists 1 (pt); Ophthalmologists 1 (pt); Podiatrists 1 (pt).
Languages Spanish, French, Chinese, Tagalog
Facilities Dining room; Physical therapy room; Activities room; Crafts room; Laundry room; Barber/Beauty shop; Library.
Activities Arts & crafts; Cards; Games; Reading groups; Prayer groups; Movies; Shopping trips; Social/Cultural gatherings.

BELLINGHAM

Alderwood Park Convalescent Center
2726 Alderwood Ave, Bellingham, WA, 98226
(206) 733-2322
Admin Donna Nylund RN. *Medical Dir/Dir of Nursing* Patti Overdorf RN DNS.
Licensure Skilled care; Intermediate care. *Beds* 102. *Certified* Medicaid; Medicare.
Owner Proprietary Corp (Regency Health Care Centers).
Staff RNs 3 (ft), 1 (pt); LPNs 8 (ft), 2 (pt); Nurses aides 30 (ft); Recreational therapists 1 (pt); Activities coordinators 1 (ft).
Languages Spanish
Facilities Dining room; Physical therapy room; Activities room; Crafts room; Laundry room; Barber/Beauty shop.
Activities Arts & crafts; Cards; Games; Reading groups; Prayer groups; Movies; Shopping trips; Social/Cultural gatherings; Pet therapy.

Bellingham Care Center
1200 Birchwood Ave, Bellingham, WA, 98225
(206) 734-9295
Admin Wayne Gerner. *Medical Dir/Dir of Nursing* Dr Wynne; Christine Profic DON.
Licensure Skilled care; Intermediate care. *Beds* SNF 120; ICF. *Certified* Medicaid; Medicare.
Owner Proprietary Corp (Hillhaven Corp).
Admissions Requirements Medical examination; Physician's request.
Staff RNs 7 (ft); LPNs 8 (ft); Nurses aides 30 (ft), 6 (pt); Recreational therapists 3 (pt); Activities coordinators 1 (ft).
Facilities Dining room; Physical therapy room; Activities room; Laundry room; Barber/Beauty shop; Library.
Activities Arts & crafts; Cards; Games; Reading groups; Movies; Shopping trips.

Highland Convalescent Center
2400 Samish Way, Bellingham, WA, 98226
(206) 734-4800

Admin Richard Chasteen. *Medical Dir/Dir of Nursing* Mary Kruze DNS.
Licensure Skilled care; Intermediate care. *Beds* 44. *Certified* Medicaid; Medicare.
Owner Proprietary Corp.
Admissions Requirements Minimum age; Males only; Medical examination; Physician's request.
Staff RNs 3 (ft); LPNs 2 (ft); Nurses aides 9 (ft); Physical therapists 5 (ft); Recreational therapists 1 (ft); Dietitians 1 (ft).
Facilities Dining room; Activities room; Laundry room.
Activities Arts & crafts; Cards; Games; Reading groups; Prayer groups; Movies; Shopping trips.

Needhams Nursing Home
1509 E Victor St, Bellingham, WA, 98225
(206) 733-3141
Admin J F Wiley. *Medical Dir/Dir of Nursing* E Fairbanks MD.
Licensure Skilled care; Intermediate care. *Beds* 122. *Certified* Medicaid.
Owner Proprietary Corp.
Facilities Dining room; Activities room; Crafts room; Laundry room; Barber/Beauty shop; Library.
Activities Arts & crafts; Cards; Games; Prayer groups; Movies; Shopping trips; Field trips.

Nor-Bell Care Center
5280 Northwest Rd, Bellingham, WA, 98226
(206) 734-4181
Admin Dorothy A Durand. *Medical Dir/Dir of Nursing* Dr Stuart Andrews.
Licensure Skilled care; Intermediate care. *Beds* 70. *Certified* Medicaid.
Owner Publicly owned.
Admissions Requirements Medical examination.
Staff RNs 5 (ft), 2 (pt); LPNs 3 (ft), 2 (pt); Nurses aides 21 (ft), 8 (pt); Activities coordinators 3 (ft), 2 (pt); Dietitians 1 (ft), 1 (pt); Rehab aides 3 (ft), 2 (pt).
Facilities Dining room; Physical therapy room; Activities room; Chapel; Laundry room; Barber/Beauty shop; Sunroom; TV room.
Activities Arts & crafts; Cards; Games; Reading groups; Prayer groups; Movies; Shopping trips; Social/Cultural gatherings; Sing-along; Rhythm band; Exercise.

Sehome Park Care Center
700 32nd St, Bellingham, WA, 98225
(206) 734-9330
Admin Ralph M Kollarsky. *Medical Dir/Dir of Nursing* Joan L Humen.
Licensure Skilled care; Intermediate care. *Beds* SNF 137; ICF. *Certified* Medicaid; Medicare.
Owner Proprietary Corp.
Admissions Requirements Medical examination; Physician's request.
Facilities Dining room; Physical therapy room; Activities room; Crafts room; Laundry room; Barber/Beauty shop; Library.
Activities Arts & crafts; Cards; Games; Reading groups; Prayer groups; Movies; Shopping trips; Social/Cultural gatherings.

Shuksan Convalescent Center
1530 James St, Bellingham, WA, 98225
(206) 733-9161
Admin Everett Gimmaka. *Medical Dir/Dir of Nursing* Sharon Landcastle DON.
Licensure Skilled care; Intermediate care. *Beds* 61. *Certified* Medicaid; Medicare.
Owner Proprietary Corp.
Staff RNs; LPNs; Orderlies; Nurses aides; Activities coordinators.
Facilities Dining room; Physical therapy room; Activities room; Barber/Beauty shop; Library.
Activities Arts & crafts; Cards; Games; Reading groups; Prayer groups; Movies; Shopping trips.

BLAINE

Stafholt Good Samaritan Center
PO Box Z, 360 D St, Blaine, WA, 98230
(206) 332-8733
Admin Ann L Walter. *Medical Dir/Dir of Nursing* Stuart Andrews MD; Marilyn Matheson RN.
Licensure Skilled care; Intermediate care. *Beds* SNF 65; ICF. *Certified* Medicaid.
Owner Nonprofit Corp (Evangelical Lutheran/Good Samaritan).
Admissions Requirements Medical examination.
Staff RNs 4 (ft), 1 (pt); LPNs 6 (ft), 1 (pt); Nurses aides 18 (ft), 12 (pt); Recreational therapists 1 (ft); Activities coordinators 1 (ft); Dietitians 1 (pt).
Facilities Dining room; Physical therapy room; Activities room; Crafts room; Laundry room; Barber/Beauty shop; Library.
Activities Arts & crafts; Cards; Games; Reading groups; Prayer groups; Movies; Shopping trips; Social/Cultural gatherings.

BOTHELL

Eastern Star Nursing Home*
707 228th SW, Bothell, WA, 98011
(206) 481-8500
Admin Vivian B Spore.
Licensure Skilled care; Intermediate care. *Beds* 52. *Certified* Medicaid.
Owner Nonprofit Corp.

Northshore Manor
10909 NE 185th St, Bothell, WA, 98011
(206) 486-7174
Admin David R Crawford. *Medical Dir/Dir of Nursing* Dr James Monahan.
Licensure Skilled care; Intermediate care. *Beds* 135. *Certified* Medicaid.
Owner Nonprofit Corp.
Admissions Requirements Medical examination.
Staff RNs 11 (ft), 6 (pt); LPNs 5 (ft), 1 (pt); Orderlies 3 (ft), 2 (pt); Nurses aides 35 (ft), 27 (pt); Activities coordinators 2 (ft); Dietitians 1 (ft).
Facilities Dining room; Physical therapy room; Activities room; Chapel; Crafts room; Laundry room; Barber/Beauty shop.
Activities Arts & crafts; Cards; Games; Reading groups; Prayer groups; Movies; Social/Cultural gatherings.

BREMERTON

Belmont Terrace Inc
560 Lebo Blvd, Bremerton, WA, 98310
(206) 479-1515
Admin Sam Sutherland. *Medical Dir/Dir of Nursing* Ann Steele MD; Mary Beth Fennick DON.
Licensure Skilled care; Intermediate care. *Beds* 102. *Certified* Medicaid; Medicare.
Owner Proprietary Corp.
Staff RNs 10 (ft), 4 (pt); LPNs 4 (ft), 4 (pt); Orderlies 2 (ft), 1 (pt); Nurses aides 40 (ft), 4 (pt); Physical therapists 1 (pt); Reality therapists 1 (ft); Recreational therapists 3 (ft); Occupational therapists 2 (ft); Activities coordinators 1 (ft).
Facilities Dining room; Physical therapy room; Activities room; Crafts room; Laundry room; Barber/Beauty shop.
Activities Arts & crafts; Cards; Games; Reading groups; Prayer groups; Movies; Shopping trips; Rides; Make-up days; Cooking days.

Bremerton Convalescent Center
2701 Clare Ave, Bremerton, WA, 98310
(206) 377-3951
Admin Roger P Bright. *Medical Dir/Dir of Nursing* Dr Robert Bright.
Licensure Skilled care; Intermediate care. *Beds* 103. *Certified* Medicaid; Medicare.
Owner Proprietary Corp.
Admissions Requirements Medical examination; Physician's request.
Staff RNs 10 (ft); LPNs 5 (ft); Orderlies 2 (ft); Nurses aides 60 (ft); Physical therapists 1 (pt); Recreational therapists 1 (ft); Occupational therapists 1 (pt); Speech therapists 1 (pt); Activities coordinators 1 (ft); Dietitians 1 (pt).
Facilities Dining room; Physical therapy room; Activities room; Chapel; Crafts room; Laundry room; Barber/Beauty shop; Library; TV.
Activities Arts & crafts; Cards; Games; Reading groups; Prayer groups; Movies; Social/Cultural gatherings.

Forest Ridge Convalescent Center*
140 S Marion Ave, Bremerton, WA, 98312
(206) 479-4747
Admin Kathleen J Reed. *Medical Dir/Dir of Nursing* Dr William Seal.
Licensure Skilled care; Intermediate care. *Beds* 98. *Certified* Medicaid; Medicare.
Owner Proprietary Corp.
Staff RNs 7 (ft), 4 (pt); LPNs 3 (ft); Orderlies 1 (ft), 1 (pt); Nurses aides 31 (ft), 6 (pt); Physical therapists 1 (pt); Reality therapists 1 (pt); Occupational therapists 1 (pt); Speech therapists 1 (pt); Activities coordinators 1 (ft); Dietitians 1 (pt); Dentists 1 (pt); Podiatrists 1 (pt).
Facilities Dining room; Physical therapy room; Activities room; Laundry room; Barber/Beauty shop.
Activities Arts & crafts; Cards; Games; Reading groups; Prayer groups; Movies; Shopping trips; Social/Cultural gatherings.

Hope Street Group Home*
1322 E Hope St, Bremerton, WA, 98310
(206) 377-7231
Admin Roberta Soran.
Licensure Intermediate care for mentally retarded. *Beds* 5.
Owner Nonprofit Corp.

Resthaven Nursing Home—Bremerton*
3517 11th St, Bremerton, WA, 98310
(206) 377-5537
Admin Judith Ann Leaf. *Medical Dir/Dir of Nursing* Hugh Harkins MD.
Licensure Skilled care; Intermediate care. *Beds* 91. *Certified* Medicaid; Medicare.
Owner Proprietary Corp.
Admissions Requirements Medical examination; Physician's request.
Staff RNs 5 (ft), 3 (pt); LPNs 3 (ft), 3 (pt); Nurses aides 32 (ft), 3 (pt); Physical therapists 1 (pt); Recreational therapists 2 (pt); Occupational therapists 1 (pt); Speech therapists 1 (pt); Activities coordinators 1 (ft), 1 (pt); Dietitians 1 (pt).
Affiliation Lutheran
Facilities Dining room; Physical therapy room; Activities room; Crafts room; Laundry room; Barber/Beauty shop.
Activities Arts & crafts; Games; Reading groups; Prayer groups; Movies; Shopping trips; Social/Cultural gatherings; Crafty cookers; Gardening; Resident council events; Special speakers & presentations.

301 Sylvan Way*
5112 NW Taylor Rd, Bremerton, WA, 98312
(206) 377-6153
Admin Molly Harris.
Licensure Intermediate care for mentally retarded. *Beds* 6.
Owner Nonprofit Corp.

BREWSTER

Harmony House
PO Box 829, 100 River Plaza, Brewster, WA, 98812
(509) 689-2546
Admin Jerry R Tretwold. *Medical Dir/Dir of Nursing* Jim Edwards MD; Luanne Sevrin DON.
Licensure Skilled care. *Beds* SNF 73. *Certified* Medicaid.
Owner Privately owned.
Staff Physicians; RNs; LPNs; Orderlies; Nurses aides; Physical therapists; Recreational therapists; Occupational therapists; Speech therapists; Activities coordinators; Dietitians.
Activities Arts & crafts; Cards; Games; Reading groups; Prayer groups; Movies; Shopping trips; Social/Cultural gatherings.

BURLINGTON

Burton Nursing Home
1036 Victoria Ave, Burlington, WA, 98233
(206) 755-0711
Admin Stephen R Johnson. *Medical Dir/Dir of Nursing* Dr S M Aldrich; Patrice Hendricks RNC.
Licensure Intermediate care. *Beds* ICF 51. *Certified* Medicaid.
Owner Proprietary Corp.
Admissions Requirements Medical examination; Physician's request.
Staff RNs 2 (ft), 1 (pt); LPNs 2 (ft), 3 (pt); Nurses aides 16 (ft), 7 (pt); Physical therapists 1 (pt); Activities coordinators 1 (ft), 1 (pt); Dietitians 1 (ft); Restorative aide 1 (ft).
Facilities Dining room; Activities room; Living room; Solarium; Secure courtyard.
Activities Arts & crafts; Cards; Games; Movies; Social/Cultural gatherings.

CAMANO ISLAND

Camano Shores Nursing Home
1054 SW Camano Dr, Camano Island, WA, 98292
(206) 387-4711
Admin Loren Fassett. *Medical Dir/Dir of Nursing* Delores Isakson.
Licensure Intermediate care. *Beds* ICF 24. *Certified* Medicaid.
Owner Privately owned.
Staff Physicians 1 (ft); RNs 3 (ft); LPNs 3 (ft), 2 (pt); Nurses aides 3 (ft), 2 (pt); Activities coordinators 1 (pt).
Facilities Dining room; Activities room; Laundry room.
Activities Arts & crafts; Cards; Games; Reading groups; Prayer groups; Movies; Shopping trips; Weekly visits to senior center.

CAMAS

Highland Terrace Nursing Center*
640 NE Everett St, Camas, WA, 98607
(206) 834-5055
Admin Richard Halfhill.
Licensure Skilled care; Intermediate care. *Beds* 131. *Certified* Medicaid.
Owner Proprietary Corp (Beverly Enterprises).

CASHMERE

Cashmere Convalescent Center*
PO Box 626, 817 Pioneer Ave, Cashmere, WA, 98815
(509) 782-1251
Admin William A Dronen.
Licensure Skilled care; Intermediate care. *Beds* 90. *Certified* Medicaid; Medicare.
Owner Proprietary Corp.

CATHLAMET

Columbia View Nursing Home*
PO Box 338, 155 Alder, Cathlamet, WA,
98612
(206) 795-3234
Admin Crystal Stanley.
Licensure Skilled care; Intermediate care. *Beds*
53. *Certified* Medicaid.
Owner Proprietary Corp.
Admissions Requirements Medical
examination; Physician's request.
Staff RNs 5 (ft); LPNs 3 (ft); Nurses aides 20
(ft); Physical therapists 1 (pt); Speech
therapists 1 (pt); Activities coordinators 1
(ft); Dietitians 1 (pt); Dentists 1 (pt);
Ophthalmologists 1 (pt); Podiatrists 1 (pt);
Audiologists 1 (pt).
Facilities Dining room; Activities room;
Laundry room.
Activities Arts & crafts; Cards; Games;
Reading groups; Prayer groups; Movies;
Shopping trips; Social/Cultural gatherings.

CENTRALIA

Centralia Convalescent Center
1015 Long Rd, Centralia, WA, 98531
(206) 736-3381
Admin Debi L Thompson. *Medical Dir/Dir of
Nursing* Dr Kenneth Burden; Sharon Gadd
RN.
Licensure Skilled care. *Beds* SNF 96. *Certified*
Medicaid; Medicare.
Owner Proprietary Corp (Pleasant Valley
Services Corp).
Admissions Requirements Medical
examination; Physician's request.
Staff RNs; LPNs; Orderlies; Nurses aides;
Activities coordinators.
Facilities Dining room; Physical therapy
room; Activities room; Crafts room; Laundry
room; Barber/Beauty shop.
Activities Arts & crafts; Cards; Games; Prayer
groups; Movies; Shopping trips; Social/
Cultural gatherings; Exercises; Manicures;
Grooming; Banquets.

Edison Manor
PO Box 239, 708 G St, Centralia, WA, 98531
(206) 736-6848
Admin Paul S Miller.
Licensure Intermediate care. *Beds* 40.
Certified Medicaid.
Owner Proprietary Corp.

Liberty Manor Care Facility Inc
PO Box 1110, 1126 S Gold St, Centralia, WA,
98531
(206) 736-9384
Admin Herbert E Higaki. *Medical Dir/Dir of
Nursing* Kenneth H Burden MD; Darlene
Sellards RN DON.
Licensure Skilled care; Intermediate care. *Beds*
58. *Certified* Medicaid.
Owner Proprietary Corp.
Staff Physicians 1 (pt); RNs 2 (ft), 2 (pt);
LPNs 4 (ft), 3 (pt); Nurses aides 26 (ft), 3
(pt); Physical therapists 1 (pt); Reality
therapists 1 (pt); Occupational therapists 1
(pt); Activities coordinators 1 (ft), 1 (pt);
Dietitians 1 (pt).
Facilities Dining room; Activities room;
Laundry room; Barber/Beauty shop.
Activities Arts & crafts; Cards; Games;
Reading groups; Prayer groups; Movies;
Shopping trips; Social/Cultural gatherings.

Royal Care Convalescent Center*
1305 Alexander, Centralia, WA, 98531
(206) 736-2823
Admin Helen E Anderson.
Licensure Skilled care; Intermediate care. *Beds*
131. *Certified* Medicaid.
Owner Proprietary Corp.

Sharon Care Center
1509 Harrison Ave, Centralia, WA, 98531
(206) 736-0112
Admin William Hammond & Owner. *Medical
Dir/Dir of Nursing* Sandy Stevens.
Licensure Intermediate care. *Beds* ICF 42.
Certified Medicaid.
Owner Privately owned.
Admissions Requirements Medical
examination; Physician's request.
Staff RNs 1 (ft), 1 (pt); LPNs 3 (ft); Orderlies
1 (ft); Nurses aides 14 (ft), 3 (pt); Physical
therapists 1 (pt); Recreational therapists 1
(pt); Activities coordinators 1 (pt); Dietitians
1 (pt); Ophthalmologists 1 (pt); Podiatrists 1
(pt).
Facilities Dining room; Activities room;
Crafts room; Laundry room; Barber/Beauty
shop.
Activities Arts & crafts; Cards; Games;
Reading groups; Prayer groups; Movies;
Shopping trips; Social/Cultural gatherings.

South Tower Rest Home
PO Box 328, Centralia, WA, 98531
(206) 736-4729
Admin Paul S Miller.
Licensure Intermediate care. *Beds* 27.
Certified Medicaid.
Owner Proprietary Corp.

Walker Care Center
408 S King, Centralia, WA, 98531
(206) 736-1197
Admin Duane McCormies. *Medical Dir/Dir of
Nursing* Elaine Lawler DON.
Licensure Skilled care; Intermediate care. *Beds*
48. *Certified* Medicaid.
Owner Proprietary Corp (Soundcare Inc).
Admissions Requirements Physician's request.
Staff RNs 2 (ft), 1 (pt); LPNs 3 (ft), 2 (pt);
Orderlies 2 (ft); Nurses aides 15 (ft), 9 (pt);
Physical therapists 1 (pt); Occupational
therapists 1 (pt); Activities coordinators 1
(ft); Dietitians 1 (pt).
Facilities Dining room; Activities room;
Laundry room.
Activities Arts & crafts; Games; Reading
groups; Prayer groups; Movies; Shopping
trips; Social/Cultural gatherings.

CHELAN

Regency Manor
PO Box 609, 726 N Markeson, Chelan, WA,
98816
(509) 682-2551
Admin David L Rogge. *Medical Dir/Dir of
Nursing* Charles F Jame MD; Larita Bigelow
DNS.
Licensure Skilled care; Intermediate care. *Beds*
80. *Certified* Medicaid.
Owner Proprietary Corp (Regency Health
Care Centers).
Facilities Dining room; Physical therapy
room; Laundry room; Barber/Beauty shop.
Activities Arts & crafts; Cards; Games;
Reading groups; Prayer groups; Movies;
Shopping trips.

CHENEY

Cheney Care Center
2219 N 6th, Cheney, WA, 99004
(509) 235-6196
Admin Keith A Fauerso. *Medical Dir/Dir of
Nursing* Charles H B Hough MD; Elizabeth
M Fil RN.
Licensure Skilled care; Intermediate care. *Beds*
62. *Certified* Medicaid.
Owner Nonprofit Corp.
Admissions Requirements Medical
examination; Physician's request.
Staff RNs 4 (ft), 2 (pt); LPNs 5 (ft), 6 (pt);
Nurses aides 17 (ft), 25 (pt); Physical
therapists 1 (ft), 1 (pt); Recreational

therapists 1 (ft); Speech therapists 1 (pt);
Activities coordinators 1 (ft); Dietitians 1
(pt).
Facilities Dining room; Physical therapy
room; Activities room; Crafts room; Laundry
room; Barber/Beauty shop; Fenced back
yard; Security for wanderers.
Activities Arts & crafts; Cards; Games;
Reading groups; Prayer groups; Movies;
Shopping trips; Social/Cultural gatherings.

CLARKSTON

Clarkston Care Center*
1242 11th St, Clarkston, WA, 99403
(509) 758-2523
Admin Dennis M McDonald. *Medical Dir/Dir
of Nursing* Dr Walter Seibly.
Licensure Skilled care; Intermediate care. *Beds*
85. *Certified* Medicaid; Medicare.
Owner Proprietary Corp.

Tri-State Convalescent Center
PO Box 429, 1255 Belmont Way, Clarkston,
WA, 99403
(509) 758-5573
Admin Judith P Seubert. *Medical Dir/Dir of
Nursing* Walter Seibly MD; Diana Berndt
RN.
Licensure Skilled care; Intermediate care. *Beds*
SNF; ICF 115; Medicare certified beds 9.
Certified Medicaid; Medicare.
Owner Proprietary Corp (Life Care Centers of
America).
Admissions Requirements Medical
examination; Physician's request.
Staff RNs 8 (ft); LPNs 9 (ft), 3 (pt) 13D;
Nurses aides 33 (ft), 12 (pt); Activities
coordinators 2 (ft), 1 (pt).
Facilities Dining room; Activities room;
Laundry room; Barber/Beauty shop.
Activities Arts & crafts; Cards; Games;
Reading groups; Prayer groups; Movies;
Social/Cultural gatherings.

CLE ELUM

Pinecrest Manor Convalescent Home
601 Power St, Cle Elum, WA, 98922
(509) 674-4401
Admin Carol Detwiler. *Medical Dir/Dir of
Nursing* Dr Elizabeth Wise; Mary Eggen
RN.
Licensure Skilled care; Intermediate care. *Beds*
61. *Certified* Medicaid.
Owner Proprietary Corp (Community Care
Centers).
Admissions Requirements Minimum age 18;
Medical examination; Physician's request.
Staff RNs 6 (ft); LPNs 7 (ft); Nurses aides 32
(ft); Activities coordinators 1 (ft), 1 (pt).
Facilities Dining room; Physical therapy
room; Activities room; Laundry room;
Barber/Beauty shop.
Activities Arts & crafts; Cards; Games;
Reading groups; Prayer groups; Movies;
Shopping trips; Social/Cultural gatherings;
Cooking; Mental health sensory stimulation;
Music.

COLFAX

Palouse Nursing Center*
PO Box 551, S 907 Mill St, Colfax, WA,
99111
(509) 397-3433
Admin Roy J McDonald.
Licensure Skilled care; Intermediate care. *Beds*
74. *Certified* Medicaid; Medicare.
Owner Proprietary Corp.

COLLEGE PLACE

Blue Mountain Convalescent Center
1200 SE 12th St, College Place, WA, 99324
(509) 529-4080

Admin Kathleen Bowman. *Medical Dir/Dir of Nursing* Michael Kilfoyle MD; Mary Fowler RN DON.
Licensure Skilled care. *Beds* SNF 123. *Certified* Medicaid; Medicare.
Owner Proprietary Corp (Horizon Healthcare Corp).
Admissions Requirements Medical examination.
Staff RNs; LPNs; Nurses aides; Physical therapists; Activities coordinators; Dietitians.
Languages Spanish
Facilities Dining room; Physical therapy room; Activities room; Crafts room; Laundry room; Barber/Beauty shop.
Activities Arts & crafts; Cards; Games; Reading groups; Prayer groups; Movies; Shopping trips; Social/Cultural gatherings.

COLVILLE

Buena Vista Inc
Rte 2, Box 17, Colville, WA, 99114
(509) 684-4856
Admin Velda McCammon. *Medical Dir/Dir of Nursing* Dr J Herman.
Licensure Skilled care; Intermediate care. *Beds* SNF 40; ICF. *Certified* Medicaid.
Owner Proprietary Corp.
Staff Physicians 6 (pt); RNs 6 (ft), 2 (pt); LPNs 2 (ft); Nurses aides 30 (ft); Physical therapists 1 (pt); Recreational therapists 1 (pt); Occupational therapists 1 (pt); Activities coordinators 1 (ft); Dietitians 1 (pt); Ophthalmologists 1 (pt).
Facilities Dining room; Activities room; Crafts room; Barber/Beauty shop.
Activities Arts & crafts; Cards; Games; Reading groups; Prayer groups; Movies; Shopping trips; Social/Cultural gatherings.

Pinewood Terrace Nursing & Retirement Center
1000 E Elep St, Colville, WA, 99114
(509) 684-2573
Admin Steven H Wilson. *Medical Dir/Dir of Nursing* Dr William Doyle MD; Linda Winslow RN DON.
Licensure Skilled care; Intermediate care. *Beds* 93. *Certified* Medicaid; Medicare.
Owner Proprietary Corp (Beverly Enterprises).
Admissions Requirements Minimum age 21; Physician's request.
Staff RNs 3 (ft); LPNs 4 (ft), 1 (pt); Nurses aides 21 (ft), 1 (pt); Activities coordinators 1 (ft); Dietitians 1 (ft).
Facilities Dining room; Physical therapy room; Activities room; Laundry room; Barber/Beauty shop.
Activities Arts & crafts; Cards; Games; Reading groups; Prayer groups; Movies; Shopping trips; Social/Cultural gatherings; Ceramics.

DAVENPORT

Lincoln Hospital Nursing Home
Box 68, 10 Nichols St, Davenport, WA, 99122
(509) 725-7101
Admin Thomas J Martin. *Medical Dir/Dir of Nursing* Dr Donald Sebesta; Judith Van Pevenage RN DON.
Licensure Skilled care. *Beds* 93. *Certified* Medicaid; Medicare.
Owner Publicly owned.
Admissions Requirements Medical examination.
Staff Physicians 4 (pt); RNs 15 (ft), 7 (pt); LPNs 3 (ft); Nurses aides 40 (ft), 5 (pt); Physical therapists 2 (ft); Recreational therapists 2 (ft); Activities coordinators 1 (ft); Dietitians 3 (pt).
Facilities Dining room; Physical therapy room; Activities room; Crafts room; Laundry room; Barber/Beauty shop.

Activities Arts & crafts; Cards; Games; Movies; Shopping trips; Social/Cultural gatherings.

DAYTON

Booker Convalescent Annex
1012 S 3rd, Dayton, WA, 99328
(509) 382-2531
Admin Garvin G Olson. *Medical Dir/Dir of Nursing* S R Hevel MD.
Licensure Intermediate care. *Beds* 20.
Owner Publicly owned.
Admissions Requirements Medical examination; Physician's request.
Staff RNs 2 (ft); LPNs 1 (ft), 1 (pt); Nurses aides 4 (ft), 2 (pt); Activities coordinators 1 (ft); Dietitians 1 (pt).
Facilities Dining room; Physical therapy room; Activities room.
Activities Arts & crafts; Games; Prayer groups; Movies; Social/Cultural gatherings.

Robison Nursing Home Inc
221 E Washington, Dayton, WA, 99328
(509) 382-2531
Admin Garvin G Olson. *Medical Dir/Dir of Nursing* S R Hevel MD.
Licensure Skilled care; Intermediate care. *Beds* 46. *Certified* Medicaid.
Owner Publicly owned.
Admissions Requirements Medical examination; Physician's request.
Staff RNs 4 (ft); LPNs 4 (ft), 1 (pt); Nurses aides 17 (ft), 3 (pt); Physical therapists 1 (pt); Activities coordinators 1 (ft); Dietitians 1 (pt).
Facilities Dining room; Physical therapy room; Activities room.
Activities Arts & crafts; Games; Prayer groups; Movies; Social/Cultural gatherings.

DES MOINES

Caldwell Health Center at Judson Park
23620 Marine View Dr S, Des Moines, WA, 98198
(206) 824-4000
Admin Raymond P Westeren. *Medical Dir/Dir of Nursing* Eleanor Sutherland MD; Louise Ellis RN DON.
Licensure Skilled care; Intermediate care. *Beds* SNF 120; ICF. *Certified* Medicaid; Medicare.
Owner Nonprofit Corp.
Admissions Requirements Minimum age 62; Medical examination; Physician's request.
Staff Physicians 1 (pt); RNs 4 (ft), 144 (pt); LPNs 3 (ft), 4 (pt); Nurses aides 39 (ft), 24 (pt); Physical therapists 1 (pt); Recreational therapists 1 (ft); Speech therapists 1 (pt); Dietitians 1 (pt); Dentists 1 (pt); Ophthalmologists 1 (pt); Dentist 1 (pt).
Affiliation Baptist
Facilities Dining room; Physical therapy room; Activities room; Chapel; Crafts room; Laundry room; Barber/Beauty shop.
Activities Arts & crafts; Games; Reading groups; Prayer groups; Movies; Drives; Restaurants; Bowling.

Masonic Home of Washington
23660 Marine View Dr S, Des Moines, WA, 98188
(206) 878-8434
Admin Donna Mae Ketten. *Medical Dir/Dir of Nursing* Jackelene Baker.
Licensure Skilled care. *Beds* SNF 72.
Owner Nonprofit Corp.
Admissions Requirements Minimum age 65; Medical examination.
Staff Physicians 1 (pt); RNs 5 (ft), 4 (pt); LPNs 1 (ft); Orderlies 1 (ft); Nurses aides 12 (ft), 4 (pt); Physical therapists 1 (pt); Recreational therapists 1 (pt); Activities

coordinators 1 (pt); Dietitians 1 (pt); Dentists 1 (pt); Ophthalmologists 1 (pt); Podiatrists 1 (pt).
Affiliation Masons
Facilities Dining room; Physical therapy room; Activities room; Chapel; Crafts room; Laundry room; Barber/Beauty shop; Library.
Activities Arts & crafts; Cards; Games; Reading groups; Prayer groups; Movies; Shopping trips; Social/Cultural gatherings.

Wesley Care Center*
1122 S 216th St, Des Moines, WA, 98188
(206) 824-3663
Admin Calvin A Groenenberg.
Licensure Skilled care; Intermediate care. *Beds* 98. *Certified* Medicaid; Medicare.
Owner Nonprofit Corp.
Affiliation Methodist

Wesley Gardens—The Gardens*
815 S 216th St, Des Moines, WA, 98188
(206) 824-5000
Admin Leon F Bowers. *Medical Dir/Dir of Nursing* Stanley Harris MD.
Licensure Skilled care; Intermediate care. *Beds* 58. *Certified* Medicaid.
Owner Nonprofit Corp.
Staff RNs; LPNs; Nurses aides; Physical therapists; Recreational therapists; Occupational therapists; Speech therapists; Dietitians; Dentists; Ophthalmologists; Podiatrists; Audiologists.
Affiliation Methodist
Facilities Dining room; Physical therapy room; Activities room; Chapel; Crafts room; Laundry room; Barber/Beauty shop; Library.

Wesley Gardens—The Terrace*
816 S 216th St, Des Moines, WA, 98188
(206) 824-5000
Admin Leon F Bowers. *Medical Dir/Dir of Nursing* Stanley Harris MD.
Licensure Skilled care; Intermediate care. *Beds* 35. *Certified* Medicaid.
Owner Nonprofit Corp.
Staff RNs; LPNs; Nurses aides; Physical therapists; Recreational therapists; Occupational therapists; Activities coordinators; Dietitians; Dentists; Podiatrists; Audiologists.
Facilities Dining room; Physical therapy room; Activities room; Chapel; Crafts room; Laundry room; Barber/Beauty shop; Library.

DUVALL

Carlton Group Home
119 NE Virginia, Duvall, WA, 98019
(206) 788-4489
Admin Steve Skeen.
Licensure Intermediate care for mentally retarded. *Beds* 6.
Owner Nonprofit Corp.

Chelsea Group Home*
317 1st Ave NE, Duvall, WA, 98019
(206) 788-4585
Admin Steve Skeen.
Licensure Intermediate care for mentally retarded. *Beds* 6.
Owner Nonprofit Corp.

EAST WENATCHEE

Highline Convalescent Center
609 Highline Dr, East Wenatchee, WA, 98801
(509) 884-6602
Admin Terry Lee Mace. *Medical Dir/Dir of Nursing* Dr Robert Hoxsey; Delores Peterson RN.
Licensure Skilled care; Intermediate care. *Beds* SNF 101. *Certified* Medicaid; Medicare.
Owner Privately owned.
Admissions Requirements Medical examination; Physician's request.

Staff Physicians; RNs; LPNs; Orderlies;
Nurses aides; Physical therapists; Reality
therapists; Recreational therapists;
Occupational therapists; Speech therapists;
Activities coordinators; Dietitians;
Ophthalmologists.
Activities Arts & crafts; Cards; Games;
Reading groups; Prayer groups; Movies;
Shopping trips; Social/Cultural gatherings.

EDMONDS

Aurora-Edmonds Nursing Home*
8104 220th SW, Edmonds, WA, 98020
(206) 778-5703
Admin George R Nickell.
Licensure Intermediate care. *Beds* 33.
Certified Medicaid.
Owner Proprietary Corp.

Edmonds Care Center
21008 76th Ave W, Edmonds, WA, 98020
(206) 778-0107
Admin Linda Hofeling. *Medical Dir/Dir of
Nursing* Ardelle Marchand DON.
Licensure Skilled care; Intermediate care. *Beds*
SNF 93. *Certified* Medicaid; Medicare.
Owner Proprietary Corp (Hillhaven Corp).
Admissions Requirements Medical
examination; Physician's request History &
Physical.
Staff RNs 11 (ft); LPNs 4 (ft), 1 (pt); Nurses
aides 30 (ft), 4 (pt); Activities coordinators 1
(ft), 1 (pt); Dietitians 1 (ft).
Facilities Dining room; Physical therapy
room; Activities room; Laundry room;
Barber/Beauty shop.
Activities Arts & crafts; Cards; Games;
Reading groups; Prayer groups; Movies;
Social/Cultural gatherings.

Washington Health Care Center—Aldercrest
21400 72nd Ave W, Edmonds, WA, 98020
(206) 775-1961
Admin Joanne L Wheaton. *Medical Dir/Dir of
Nursing* Pamela Cooper MD.
Licensure Skilled care; Intermediate care. *Beds*
160. *Certified* Medicaid; Medicare.
Owner Proprietary Corp.
Staff RNs; LPNs; Orderlies; Nurses aides;
Physical therapists; Reality therapists;
Recreational therapists; Occupational
therapists; Speech therapists; Activities
coordinators; Dietitians; Dentists;
Ophthalmologists; Podiatrists.
Facilities Dining room; Physical therapy
room; Activities room; Crafts room; Laundry
room; Barber/Beauty shop.
Activities Arts & crafts; Cards; Games;
Reading groups; Prayer groups; Movies;
Shopping trips; Social/Cultural gatherings.

ELLENSBURG

Gold Leaf Care Center
1050 E Mountain View, Ellensburg, WA,
98926-3999
(509) 925-4171
Admin J D Ingram. *Medical Dir/Dir of
Nursing* Dr Alfred Grose; Claudia Eattock
RN.
Licensure Skilled care; Intermediate care. *Beds*
80. *Certified* Medicaid; Medicare.
Owner Proprietary Corp.
Admissions Requirements Physician's request.
Staff RNs 4 (ft), 4 (pt); LPNs 6 (ft); Orderlies
31 (ft); Physical therapists 1 (pt); Reality
therapists 1 (pt); Recreational therapists 1
(pt); Occupational therapists 1 (pt); Speech
therapists 1 (pt); Activities coordinators 1
(ft); Dietitians 1 (ft); Dentists 1 (pt);
Ophthalmologists 1 (pt); Podiatrists 1 (pt).
Facilities Dining room; Physical therapy
room; Activities room; Chapel; Laundry
room; Barber/Beauty shop; Library; TV
room; Lounge.

Activities Arts & crafts; Cards; Games;
Reading groups; Prayer groups; Movies;
Social/Cultural gatherings.

Royal Vista Care Center*
1506 Radio Rd, Ellensburg, WA, 98926
(509) 925-1404
Admin Larry Delamarter. *Medical Dir/Dir of
Nursing* Dr Messner.
Licensure Skilled care; Intermediate care. *Beds*
86. *Certified* Medicaid; Medicare.
Owner Proprietary Corp.
Staff RNs 5 (ft); LPNs 6 (ft); Nurses aides 60
(ft); Physical therapists 2 (ft); Reality
therapists 1 (ft); Recreational therapists 1
(ft), 1 (pt); Activities coordinators 1 (ft);
Dietitians 1 (ft).
Facilities Dining room; Physical therapy
room; Activities room; Crafts room; Laundry
room; Library.
Activities Arts & crafts; Cards; Games;
Reading groups; Prayer groups; Movies;
Shopping trips; Social/Cultural gatherings.

ELMA

Beechwood Nursing Home*
308 E Young St, Elma, WA, 98541
(206) 482-3234
Admin Cable J Wolverton.
Licensure Intermediate care. *Beds* 35.
Certified Medicaid.
Owner Proprietary Corp.
Admissions Requirements Physician's request.
Staff RNs 1 (ft), 1 (pt); LPNs 5 (pt); Nurses
aides 6 (ft), 6 (pt); Physical therapists;
Activities coordinators 1 (ft); Dietitians;
Dentists; Ophthalmologists; Podiatrists.
Facilities Dining room; Crafts room; Laundry
room.
Activities Arts & crafts; Cards; Games;
Reading groups; Movies; Shopping trips;
Social/Cultural gatherings.

Oakhurst Convalescent Center
PO Box 717, 506 E Young St, Elma, WA,
98541
(206) 482-2941
Admin Sharon Genson. *Medical Dir/Dir of
Nursing* Stanton Mccool MD; Irene Smith
DON.
Licensure Skilled care. *Beds* SNF 150; ICF
43. *Certified* Medicaid.
Owner Publicly owned.
Admissions Requirements Medical
examination 18.
Staff RNs 5 (ft), 1 (pt); LPNs 20 (ft), 2 (pt);
Orderlies 3 (ft); Nurses aides 50 (ft), 35 (pt);
Physical therapists 3 (ft); Reality therapists 3
(ft); Recreational therapists 3 (ft);
Occupational therapists 3 (ft); Speech
therapists 1 (pt); Activities coordinators 1
(ft); Dietitians 1 (ft); Ophthalmologists 1
(pt); Podiatrists 1 (pt).
Facilities Dining room; Physical therapy
room; Activities room; Crafts room; Laundry
room; Barber/Beauty shop.
Activities Arts & crafts; Cards; Games;
Reading groups; Prayer groups; Movies;
Shopping trips; Social/Cultural gatherings.

EVERETT

Bethany Home for the Aged Inc
3322 Broadway, Everett, WA, 98201
(206) 259-5508
Admin Jo Ann Beaumont. *Medical Dir/Dir of
Nursing* Barbara Tuck DNS.
Licensure Skilled care; Intermediate care. *Beds*
SNF 242; ICF. *Certified* Medicaid.
Owner Nonprofit Corp.
Admissions Requirements Medical
examination.
Staff RNs; LPNs; Nurses aides; Physical
therapists; Activities coordinators; Dietitians.
Affiliation Lutheran

Facilities Dining room; Physical therapy
room; Activities room; Chapel; Crafts room;
Laundry room; Barber/Beauty shop; Library.
Activities Arts & crafts; Cards; Games;
Reading groups; Prayer groups; Movies.

Colby Manor Nursing Home*
4230 Colby Ave, Everett, WA, 98203
(206) 259-5569
Admin Doris M Dewees.
Licensure Skilled care; Intermediate care. *Beds*
69. *Certified* Medicaid.
Owner Proprietary Corp.

Pleasant Acres*
5129 Hilltop Rd, Everett, WA, 98203
(206) 258-4474
Admin Dale H McKnight.
Licensure Skilled care; Intermediate care. *Beds*
60. *Certified* Medicaid.
Owner Proprietary Corp.

Sunrise View Convalescent Center
2520 Madison, Everett, WA, 98203
(206) 353-4040
Admin Charmaine Slattery.
Licensure Skilled care; Intermediate care. *Beds*
73. *Certified* Medicaid.
Owner Proprietary Corp.

Virginia Manor Convalescent Home Inc*
3515 Hoyt Ave, Everett, WA, 98201
(206) 259-0242
Admin Ulysses Rowell Jr. *Medical Dir/Dir of
Nursing* F J Reichmann MD.
Licensure Skilled care; Intermediate care. *Beds*
239. *Certified* Medicaid; Medicare.
Owner Proprietary Corp.
Facilities Dining room; Activities room;
Laundry room; Barber/Beauty shop.
Activities Arts & crafts; Cards; Games;
Reading groups; Movies; Social/Cultural
gatherings.

FAIRFIELD

Fairfield Good Samaritan Center
PO Box 131-A, Rte 1, Fairfield, WA, 99012
(509) 283-2118
Admin Donald Heeringa. *Medical Dir/Dir of
Nursing* Francis Thiel MD; Mary Surdez RN
DON.
Licensure Skilled care; Intermediate care;
Retirement Apts. *Beds* SNF 80; Retirement
apartments 19. *Certified* Medicaid;
Medicare.
Owner Nonprofit Corp (Evangelical Lutheran/
Good Samaritan).
Admissions Requirements Medical
examination; Physician's request.
Staff RNs 3 (ft), 3 (pt); LPNs 3 (ft), 6 (pt);
Orderlies 2 (pt); Nurses aides 14 (ft), 26 (pt);
Activities coordinators 1 (ft), 1 (pt);
Dietitians 1 (ft).
Languages German
Affiliation Lutheran
Facilities Dining room; Physical therapy
room; Activities room; Chapel; Crafts room;
Laundry room; Barber/Beauty shop; Library.
Activities Arts & crafts; Cards; Games;
Reading groups; Prayer groups; Movies;
Shopping trips; Social/Cultural gatherings.

FEDERAL WAY

Federal Way Convalescent Center
1045 S 308th, Federal Way, WA, 98003
(206) 946-2273
Admin Richard Dickson. *Medical Dir/Dir of
Nursing* Bertold Bruell MD; Beverly Myers
RN DON.
Licensure Skilled care; Intermediate care. *Beds*
157 (22 Medicare Certified). *Certified*
Medicaid; Medicare.
Owner Proprietary Corp (Life Care Centers of
America).

Admissions Requirements Minimum age 16; Medical examination; Physician's request.
Staff Physicians 30 (pt); RNs 12 (ft), 6 (pt); LPNs 8 (ft), 8 (pt); Orderlies 7 (ft), 3 (pt); Nurses aides 32 (ft), 11 (pt); Physical therapists 1 (pt); Reality therapists 1 (ft); Recreational therapists 2 (ft); Occupational therapists 1 (pt); Speech therapists 1 (pt); Activities coordinators 1 (ft); Dietitians 1 (pt); Dentists 1 (pt); Ophthalmologists 1 (pt).
Languages Spanish, Vietnamese
Facilities Dining room; Physical therapy room; Activities room; Crafts room; Laundry room; Barber/Beauty shop.
Activities Arts & crafts; Cards; Games; Reading groups; Prayer groups; Movies; Shopping trips; Social/Cultural gatherings.

FERNDALE

Pioneer Ridge Healthcare*
PO Box 608, 2185 Seamount St, Ferndale, WA, 98248
(206) 384-1277
Admin Everett Gimmaka.
Licensure Skilled care; Intermediate care. *Beds* 79. *Certified* Medicaid.
Owner Proprietary Corp.
Staff RNs 3 (ft); LPNs 2 (ft); Nurses aides 11 (ft); Activities coordinators 2 (ft); Dietitians 1 (pt).
Facilities Dining room; Activities room; Barber/Beauty shop.
Activities Arts & crafts; Cards; Games; Reading groups; Prayer groups; Movies; Shopping trips; Social/Cultural gatherings.

FORKS

Forks Community Hospital
PO Box 3575, Rte 3, Forks, WA, 98331
(206) 374-6271
Admin Dave McIvor. *Medical Dir/Dir of Nursing* R Keith Dobyns DO.
Licensure Skilled care; Intermediate care. *Beds* SNF 20; ICF. *Certified* Medicaid.
Owner Publicly owned.
Admissions Requirements Physician's request.
Staff RNs 1 (ft), 3 (pt); LPNs 3 (ft), 2 (pt); Nurses aides 5 (ft), 9 (pt); Activities coordinators 1 (ft), 1 (pt); Dietitians 1 (pt).
Facilities Dining room; Activities room; Crafts room; Laundry room; Barber/Beauty shop.
Activities Arts & crafts; Games; Movies.

FREELAND

Island Care Center
PO Box 1030, 1635 E Main, Freeland, WA, 98249
(206) 321-6232
Admin Shirley J Burch. *Medical Dir/Dir of Nursing* Dr Patrice Oneill; Ann Rudd RN.
Licensure Skilled care; Intermediate care. *Beds* SNF 61; ICF. *Certified* Medicaid.
Owner Privately owned.
Admissions Requirements Medical examination.
Facilities Dining room; Laundry room; Barber/Beauty shop.
Activities Arts & crafts; Cards; Games; Reading groups; Prayer groups; Movies; Shopping trips; Social/Cultural gatherings; Special luncheons; Dinners.

FRIDAY HARBOR

The Islands Convalescent Center Inc
PO Box 489, 660 Spring St, Friday Harbor, WA, 98250
(206) 378-2117
Admin Thelma M Howarth. *Medical Dir/Dir of Nursing* Burk Gossom MD; Lynne Barnes ARNP DON.

Licensure Skilled care; Intermediate care. *Beds* SNF 53; ICF. *Certified* Medicaid.
Owner Proprietary Corp.
Admissions Requirements Physician's request.
Staff RNs; LPNs; Orderlies; Nurses aides; Recreational therapists; Activities coordinators.
Facilities Dining room; Activities room; Barber/Beauty shop.
Activities Arts & crafts; Cards; Games; Reading groups; Prayer groups; Movies; Social/Cultural gatherings.

GIG HARBOR

Cottesmore Nursing Home Inc*
2909 14th Ave NW, Gig Harbor, WA, 98335
(206) 383-1268
Admin Inez L Glass. *Medical Dir/Dir of Nursing* Buel L Sever MD.
Licensure Nursing home. *Beds* 108.
Owner Proprietary Corp.
Admissions Requirements Medical examination; Physician's request.
Staff RNs 5 (ft), 7 (pt); LPNs 4 (ft), 4 (pt); Orderlies 1 (ft); Nurses aides 44 (ft), 2 (pt); Physical therapists 1 (pt); Speech therapists 1 (pt); Activities coordinators 1 (ft), 1 (pt); Dietitians 1 (pt).
Facilities Dining room; Physical therapy room; Activities room; Crafts room; Barber/Beauty shop.
Activities Arts & crafts; Games; Reading groups; Prayer groups; Movies.

Gig Harbor Group Home*
6823 Soundview Dr, Gig Harbor, WA, 98335
(206) 851-3716
Admin James W Mitchell.
Licensure Intermediate care for mentally retarded. *Beds* 15.
Owner Nonprofit Corp.

Rocky Bay Health Care Center*
Rte 4, Box 4679, Gig Harbor, WA, 98335
(206) 884-2277
Admin Edith M Moors. *Medical Dir/Dir of Nursing* G S Tatterson.
Licensure Intermediate care for mentally retarded. *Beds* 30. *Certified* Medicaid.
Owner Proprietary Corp.
Staff Physicians; RNs; LPNs; Nurses aides; Physical therapists; Recreational therapists; Occupational therapists; Speech therapists; Activities coordinators; Dietitians; Dentists.
Facilities Dining room; Activities room; Crafts room; Laundry room.
Activities Arts & crafts; Prayer groups; Movies; Shopping trips; Social/Cultural gatherings.

GOLDENDALE

Mt Adams Care Center
216 E Simcoe Dr, Goldendale, WA, 98620
(509) 773-5714
Admin Louis A Robert. *Medical Dir/Dir of Nursing* Miriam Nielsen RN DON.
Licensure Skilled care; Intermediate care. *Beds* 80. *Certified* Medicaid.
Owner Proprietary Corp.
Admissions Requirements Medical examination; Physician's request.
Staff RNs; LPNs; Orderlies; Nurses aides; Recreational therapists.
Facilities Dining room; Physical therapy room; Laundry room; Barber/Beauty shop.
Activities Arts & crafts; Cards; Games; Reading groups; Movies; Shopping trips; Singing; Special event dinners; Church.

GRAND COULEE

Coulee Community Hospital Nursing Home
Box H, Grand Coulee, WA, 99133
(509) 633-1753

Admin David Page. *Medical Dir/Dir of Nursing* Vicki Black MD; Betty Jean Hauber RN.
Licensure Skilled care. *Beds* SNF 20; Hospital acute care 28. *Certified* Medicaid.
Owner Nonprofit Corp.
Staff RNs 1 (ft), 3 (pt); LPNs 1 (ft), 3 (pt); Nurses aides 13 (ft), 2 (pt); Activities coordinators 1 (ft); Dietitians 1 (pt).
Facilities Dining room; Activities room; Crafts room.
Activities Arts & crafts; Cards; Games; Reading groups; Prayer groups; Movies; Social/Cultural gatherings; Exercise; Church; Cooking.

GRANDVIEW

Hillcrest Nursing Home
912 Hillcrest Ave, Grandview, WA, 98930
(509) 882-1200
Admin Ruth E Hall. *Medical Dir/Dir of Nursing* A C Tait MD; Opal Long DON.
Licensure Skilled care. *Beds* SNF 80. *Certified* Medicaid.
Owner Proprietary Corp (Beverly Enterprises).
Admissions Requirements Physician's request.
Staff RNs; LPNs; Nurses aides; Activities coordinators.
Facilities Dining room.
Activities Arts & crafts; Cards; Games; Reading groups; Prayer groups; Movies; Shopping trips.

Walnut Grove Nursing Home
PO Box 2438, Rte 2, Grandview, WA, 98930
(509) 882-2400, 786-3711
Admin Dean E Leffler Jr. *Medical Dir/Dir of Nursing* Robert Bush MD; Cathleen Hackett RN DON.
Licensure Skilled care; Intermediate care. *Beds* SNF 71; ICF. *Certified* Medicaid.
Owner Proprietary Corp (Pleasant Valley Services Corp).
Admissions Requirements Medical examination; Physician's request.
Staff RNs 6 (ft); LPNs 6 (ft), 2 (pt); Nurses aides 28 (ft); Physical therapists 1 (pt); Speech therapists 1 (pt); Activities coordinators 2 (ft); Dietitians 1 (pt); Ophthalmologists 1 (pt).
Languages Spanish
Facilities Dining room; Activities room; Crafts room; Laundry room; Barber/Beauty shop; Library.
Activities Arts & crafts; Cards; Games; Reading groups; Prayer groups; Movies; Shopping trips; Social/Cultural gatherings.

GREENACRES

Spokane Valley Good Samaritan Center
E 17121 8th Ave, Greenacres, WA, 99016
(509) 924-6161
Admin Harvey J Johnson. *Medical Dir/Dir of Nursing* Dr Arnold Lehmann; Beverly Smith DON.
Licensure Skilled care; Intermediate care. *Beds* SNF 201; ICF. *Certified* Medicaid; Medicare.
Owner Nonprofit Corp (Evangelical Lutheran/Good Samaritan).
Admissions Requirements Physician's request.
Staff RNs 13 (ft), 3 (pt); LPNs 16 (ft), 4 (pt); Orderlies 5 (ft); Nurses aides 80 (ft), 20 (pt); Activities coordinators 1 (ft); Chaplain 1 (ft); Social worker 1 (ft).
Affiliation Lutheran
Facilities Dining room; Physical therapy room; Activities room; Chapel; Laundry room; Barber/Beauty shop.
Activities Arts & crafts; Cards; Games; Reading groups; Prayer groups; Movies; Shopping trips; Social/Cultural gatherings; Individual in-room activities.

HOQUIAM

Grays Harbor Resthaven*
3035 Cherry St, Hoquiam, WA, 98550
(206) 532-7882
Admin Mark W Thompson.
Licensure Skilled care; Intermediate care. *Beds*
118. *Certified* Medicaid; Medicare.
Owner Proprietary Corp.

ISSAQUAH

Issaquah Villa Care Center*
805 Front St S, Issaquah, WA, 98027
(206) 392-1271
Admin Michael K Fitz.
Licensure Skilled care; Intermediate care. *Beds*
182. *Certified* Medicaid; Medicare.
Owner Proprietary Corp (Hillhaven Corp).

Marianwood Extended Health Care Facility
3725 Providence Dr SE, Issaquah, WA, 98027
(206) 391-2800
Admin Eva Sullivan. *Medical Dir/Dir of
Nursing* Maurice Doerfler MD; Madeline
Miller RN DON.
Licensure Skilled care. *Beds* SNF 120.
Certified Medicaid; Medicare.
Owner Nonprofit Corp.
Staff RNs; LPNs; Nurses aides; Physical
therapists; Recreational therapists 1 (ft), 1
(pt); Dietitians 1 (pt); Geriatric nurse
practioner 1 (ft).
Affiliation Roman Catholic
Facilities Dining room; Physical therapy
room; Activities room; Chapel; Laundry
room; Barber/Beauty shop; Library.

KELSO

Monticello Hall*
405 N 19th, Kelso, WA, 98626
(206) 423-4140
Admin Gregory Middlestetter.
Licensure Intermediate care. *Beds* 48.
Certified Medicaid.
Owner Proprietary Corp.
Admissions Requirements Minimum age 20;
Medical examination; Physician's request.

KENNEWICK

Life Care Center of Kennewick
1508 W 7th Ave, Kennewick, WA, 99336
(509) 586-9185
Admin Ann E Albert. *Medical Dir/Dir of
Nursing* Thomas Cooper MD; Judi Mcrkel
DON.
Licensure Skilled care; Intermediate care. *Beds*
136. *Certified* Medicaid; Medicare.
Owner Proprietary Corp (Life Care Centers of
America).
Admissions Requirements Medical
examination; Physician's request.
Staff RNs 6 (ft), 4 (pt); LPNs 4 (ft), 6 (pt);
Orderlies 2 (ft), 2 (pt); Nurses aides 36 (ft),
15 (pt); Activities coordinators 1 (ft).
Languages Spanish
Facilities Dining room; Physical therapy
room; Activities room; Laundry room;
Barber/Beauty shop.
Activities Arts & crafts; Games; Reading
groups; Prayer groups; Movies; Social/
Cultural gatherings.

Vistavue Care Center
1213 Morain Loop, Kennewick, WA, 99336
(509) 783-3213
Admin Hazel Batchelor. *Medical Dir/Dir of
Nursing* Dr Charles Krause; Agnes Barnett
RN.
Licensure Skilled care; Intermediate care. *Beds*
SNF 6; ICF 47. *Certified* Medicaid;
Medicare.
Owner Proprietary Corp.

Admissions Requirements Minimum age 21;
Medical examination; Physician's request.
Staff Physicians 6 (ft), 53 (pt); RNs 5 (ft);
LPNs 6 (ft); Orderlies 4 (ft); Nurses aides 18
(ft); Physical therapists 1 (ft); Recreational
therapists 1 (ft); Occupational therapists 1
(ft); Speech therapists 1 (ft); Activities
coordinators 1 (ft); Dietitians 1 (ft);
Ophthalmologists 1 (ft).
Languages Spanish, German
Facilities Dining room; Physical therapy
room; Activities room; TV lounge.
Activities Arts & crafts; Cards; Games;
Reading groups; Prayer groups; Movies;
Shopping trips; Social/Cultural gatherings.

KENT

Benson Heights Rehabilitation Center
22410 Benson Rd SE, Kent, WA, 98031
(206) 852-7755
Admin Gary L Miller. *Medical Dir/Dir of
Nursing* N Zemcuznikov; Nancy McCulley.
Licensure Intermediate care. *Beds* ICF 91.
Certified Medicaid.
Owner Proprietary Corp (Beverly Enterprises).
Admissions Requirements Minimum age 18;
Medical examination.
Staff RNs 7 (ft), 1 (pt); LPNs 9 (ft), 2 (pt);
Nurses aides 20 (ft), 3 (pt); Recreational
therapists 3 (ft); Dietitians 1 (pt).
Facilities Dining room; Activities room;
Chapel; Crafts room; Laundry room; Barber/
Beauty shop; Library.
Activities Arts & crafts; Cards; Games;
Reading groups; Prayer groups; Movies;
Shopping trips; Social/Cultural gatherings;
Reality orientation; Pet therapy.

Midway Manor Convalescent Center
24215 Pacific Hwy S, Kent, WA, 98032
(206) 824-1490
Admin Clenet Merrifield. *Medical Dir/Dir of
Nursing* Dr Thomas Deal; Charlotte Liddell
DON.
Licensure Intermediate care. *Beds* ICF 51.
Certified Medicaid.
Owner Proprietary Corp (Beverly Enterprises).
Admissions Requirements Minimum age 30;
Medical examination; Physician's request.
Staff RNs 1 (ft); LPNs 4 (ft), 2 (pt); Nurses
aides 6 (ft), 1 (pt); Activities coordinators 1
(ft).
Facilities Dining room; Activities room;
Crafts room; Laundry room; Pool room;
Smoking room.
Activities Arts & crafts; Cards; Games; Prayer
groups; Movies; Shopping trips; Social/
Cultural gatherings; Day bus outings.

Seatoma Convalescent Center*
PO Box 3806, 2800 S 224th St, Kent, WA,
98032
(206) 824-0600
Admin Kris F Bolt. *Medical Dir/Dir of
Nursing* Dr Janet Hodge.
Licensure Skilled care; Intermediate care. *Beds*
123. *Certified* Medicaid; Medicare.
Owner Proprietary Corp.
Admissions Requirements Medical
examination.
Staff Physicians 4 (ft), 8 (pt); RNs 15 (ft);
LPNs 12 (ft); Physical therapists 2 (ft);
Recreational therapists 2 (ft); Occupational
therapists 1 (ft); Speech therapists 1 (pt);
Activities coordinators 2 (ft); Dietitians 1
(pt); Dentists 1 (pt); Podiatrists 1 (pt).
Facilities Dining room; Physical therapy
room; Activities room; Chapel; Crafts room;
Laundry room; Barber/Beauty shop; TV
room; Solarium.
Activities Arts & crafts; Games; Reading
groups; Prayer groups; Movies; Shopping
trips; Social/Cultural gatherings.

KIRKLAND

Evergreen Vista Convalescent Center*
11800 NE 128th, Kirkland, WA, 98033
(206) 821-0404
Admin Pearl Barnes.
Licensure Skilled care; Intermediate care. *Beds*
132. *Certified* Medicaid; Medicare.
Owner Proprietary Corp.

Kirkland Convalescent Center
6505 Lakeview Dr, Kirkland, WA, 98033
(206) 822-6096
Admin Michael P Dorsey. *Medical Dir/Dir of
Nursing* Dr Peter Crane MD; Jane Waine
DON.
Licensure Skilled care; Intermediate care. *Beds*
85. *Certified* Medicaid.
Owner Proprietary Corp (Beverly Enterprises).
Admissions Requirements Minimum age 18.
Staff Physicians 1 (pt); RNs 6 (ft); LPNs 3
(ft); Nurses aides 40 (ft); Physical therapists
1 (pt); Occupational therapists 1 (pt); Speech
therapists 1 (pt); Activities coordinators 1
(ft); Dietitians 1 (pt); Dentists 1 (pt);
Ophthalmologists 1 (pt); Podiatrists 1 (pt);
Mental health staff 1 (pt).
Facilities Dining room; Physical therapy
room; Activities room; Laundry room;
Barber/Beauty shop; Mobile library.
Activities Arts & crafts; Cards; Games;
Reading groups; Prayer groups; Movies;
Shopping trips.

Lake Vue Gardens Convalescent Center
10101 NE 120th, Kirkland, WA, 98033
(206) 823-2323
Admin David Langdon. *Medical Dir/Dir of
Nursing* Paul Buchrens MD.
Licensure Skilled care; Intermediate care. *Beds*
190. *Certified* Medicaid; Medicare.
Owner Proprietary Corp.
Admissions Requirements Medical
examination; Physician's request.
Staff RNs 22 (ft), 4 (pt); LPNs 3 (ft), 1 (pt);
Orderlies 8 (ft); Nurses aides 74 (ft), 18 (pt);
Recreational therapists 1 (ft); Occupational
therapists 1 (ft), 1 (pt); Activities
coordinators 2 (ft); Dietitians 1 (ft).
Facilities Dining room; Physical therapy
room; Activities room; Crafts room; Laundry
room; Barber/Beauty shop; Library.
Activities Arts & crafts; Cards; Games;
Reading groups; Prayer groups; Movies;
Shopping trips; Social/Cultural gatherings.

LA CENTER

Moorehaven Care Center
PO Box 102, Rte 1, Box 440, La Center, WA,
98629
(206) 263-2147
Admin Don Bottemiller. *Medical Dir/Dir of
Nursing* Jan Boyd.
Licensure Skilled care; Intermediate care. *Beds*
55. *Certified* Medicaid.
Owner Proprietary Corp.
Admissions Requirements Physician's request.
Staff Physicians 1 (pt); RNs 2 (ft), 4 (pt);
LPNs 2 (ft), 1 (pt); Nurses aides 15 (ft), 8
(pt); Physical therapists 1 (ft); Occupational
therapists 1 (pt); Speech therapists 1 (pt);
Activities coordinators 1 (ft); Dietitians 1
(pt); Dentists 1 (pt); Ophthalmologists 1 (pt);
Podiatrists 1 (pt).
Facilities Dining room; Activities room;
Crafts room; Laundry room.
Activities Arts & crafts; Cards; Games; Prayer
groups; Movies; Shopping trips; Social/
Cultural gatherings.

LACY

**Panorama Convalescent & Rehabilitation
Center**
150 Circle Dr, Lacy, WA, 98503
(206) 456-0111 ext 4200

Admin Helen June Nelson. *Medical Dir/Dir of Nursing* Endre Mihalyi MD; Pat Albright DON.
Licensure Skilled care; Intermediate care. *Beds* SNF; ICF. *Certified* Medicaid; Medicare.
Owner Nonprofit Corp.
Admissions Requirements Medical examination; Physician's request.
Staff Physicians 1 (pt); RNs 6 (ft), 2 (pt); LPNs 18 (ft), 2 (pt); Orderlies 1 (ft), 1 (pt); Nurses aides 69 (ft), 2 (pt); Physical therapists 1 (pt); Occupational therapists 1 (pt); Speech therapists 1 (pt); Activities coordinators 3 (ft), 1 (pt); Dietitians 1 (pt); Dentists 1 (pt); Ophthalmologists 1 (pt); Podiatrists 1 (pt); Mental health 2 (pt).
Facilities Dining room; Physical therapy room; Activities room; Chapel; Crafts room; Laundry room; Barber/Beauty shop; Library.
Activities Arts & crafts; Cards; Games; Reading groups; Prayer groups; Movies; Shopping trips; Social/Cultural gatherings.

Roo-Lan Healthcare Center*
1505 SE Carpenter Rd, Lacy, WA, 98503
(206) 491-1765
Admin James W Tappero.
Licensure Skilled care; Intermediate care. *Beds* 102. *Certified* Medicaid; Medicare.
Owner Proprietary Corp.

LONG BEACH

New Seaera Convalescent Home
PO Box 619, 8th St & Washington, Long Beach, WA, 98631
(206) 642-3173
Admin Randy Wirick. *Medical Dir/Dir of Nursing* L C Neace MD; Donna Meed RN DON.
Licensure Skilled care; Intermediate care. *Beds* 53. *Certified* Medicaid; Medicare.
Owner Proprietary Corp.
Admissions Requirements Medical examination; Physician's request.
Staff Physicians 1 (pt); RNs 4 (ft), 1 (pt); LPNs 3 (ft), 1 (pt); Nurses aides 19 (ft), 2 (pt); Physical therapists 1 (pt); Recreational therapists 1 (ft); Occupational therapists 1 (pt); Speech therapists 1 (pt); Activities coordinators 1 (ft); Dietitians 1 (pt); Dentists 1 (pt); Ophthalmologists 1 (pt); Podiatrists 1 (pt).
Facilities Dining room; Physical therapy room; Activities room; Crafts room; Laundry room; Barber/Beauty shop.
Activities Arts & crafts; Cards; Games; Reading groups; Prayer groups; Movies; Shopping trips; Social/Cultural gatherings.

Ocean View Convalescent Center
Rte 1, Box 580, 211 Pioneer Rd, Long Beach, WA, 98631
(206) 642-3123
Admin Mary Jo Strope. *Medical Dir/Dir of Nursing* Dr L C Neace; Dorothy Owens DON.
Licensure Skilled care; Intermediate care; Congregate care facility. *Beds* SNF 62; ICF; Congregate care 19. *Certified* Medicaid.
Owner Proprietary Corp.
Admissions Requirements Medical examination; Physician's request.
Staff RNs 4 (ft); LPNs 6 (ft); Orderlies 5 (ft); Nurses aides 18 (ft); Activities coordinators 1 (ft).
Facilities Dining room; Physical therapy room; Activities room; Laundry room; Barber/Beauty shop; Day room for visits.
Activities Arts & crafts; Cards; Games; Reading groups; Prayer groups; Movies; Shopping trips; Social/Cultural gatherings; Individual activity plans.

LONGVIEW

Americana Convalescent Home
917 7th Ave, Longview, WA, 98632
(206) 425-5910
Admin Mary Barnes. *Medical Dir/Dir of Nursing* Dr James Davis.
Licensure Skilled care; Intermediate care. *Beds* 82. *Certified* Medicaid.
Owner Nonprofit Corp.
Admissions Requirements Medical examination; Physician's request.
Staff Physicians 1 (pt); RNs 5 (ft), 3 (pt); LPNs 3 (ft), 2 (pt); Nurses aides 45 (ft), 12 (pt); Physical therapists 1 (pt); Occupational therapists 1 (pt); Speech therapists 1 (pt); Activities coordinators 2 (ft); Dietitians 1 (ft); Dentists 1 (pt); Ophthalmologists 1 (pt); Podiatrists 1 (pt).
Facilities Dining room; Physical therapy room; Activities room; Chapel; Crafts room; Laundry room; Barber/Beauty shop; Patios.
Activities Arts & crafts; Cards; Games; Reading groups; Prayer groups; Movies; Shopping trips; Social/Cultural gatherings.

Cowlitz Convalescent Center
1541 11th Ave, Longview, WA, 98632
(206) 425-5840
Admin Karin Rutt. *Medical Dir/Dir of Nursing* L Hamilton MD; Carolyn Mott RN.
Licensure Skilled care; Intermediate care. *Beds* SNF 52; ICF. *Certified* Medicaid.
Owner Proprietary Corp.
Staff RNs 4 (ft), 1 (pt); LPNs 2 (ft), 1 (pt); Nurses aides 25 (ft), 6 (pt); Activities coordinators 1 (ft); Rehabilitation aides 2 (ft).
Facilities Dining room; Activities room.
Activities Arts & crafts; Cards; Games; Reading groups; Prayer groups; Movies; Shopping trips; Social/Cultural gatherings.

Frontier Extended Care Facility
1500 3rd Ave, Longview, WA, 98632
(206) 423-8800
Admin Patricia E Walker. *Medical Dir/Dir of Nursing* Dr James Davis.
Licensure Skilled care. *Beds* SNF 146. *Certified* Medicaid; Medicare.
Owner Proprietary Corp (Pleasant Valley Services Corp).
Admissions Requirements Medical examination; Physician's request.
Staff Physicians 1 (pt); RNs 12 (ft), 5 (pt); LPNs 8 (ft), 3 (pt); Nurses aides 44 (ft), 40 (pt); Physical therapists 1 (pt); Reality therapists 2 (pt); Recreational therapists 1 (ft), 1 (pt); Occupational therapists 1 (pt); Speech therapists 1 (pt); Activities coordinators 2 (ft); Dietitians 1 (ft); Dentists 1 (pt); Ophthalmologists 1 (pt); Podiatrists 1 (pt); Dentist 1 (pt).
Languages Spanish, Vietnamese, Sign
Facilities Dining room; Physical therapy room; Activities room; Crafts room; Laundry room; Barber/Beauty shop; Library.
Activities Arts & crafts; Cards; Games; Reading groups; Prayer groups; Movies; Shopping trips; Social/Cultural gatherings.

The Manor Nursing Home
1330 11th Ave, Longview, WA, 98632
(206) 425-6706
Admin Gregory Middlestetter. *Medical Dir/Dir of Nursing* Dr Frank Marre; Karlene Peterson DON.
Licensure Skilled care; Intermediate care. *Beds* SNF 55; ICF. *Certified* Medicaid; Medicare.
Owner Proprietary Corp (Pleasant Valley Services Corp).
Admissions Requirements Physician's request.
Staff RNs; LPNs; Orderlies; Nurses aides; Activities coordinators.

Facilities Dining room; Physical therapy room; Activities room; Barber/Beauty shop.
Activities Arts & crafts; Cards; Games; Reading groups; Prayer groups; Movies; Shopping trips; Social/Cultural gatherings.

Northwest Continuum Care Center
128 Beacon Hill Dr, Longview, WA, 98632
(206) 423-4060
Admin Thomas B Deutsch. *Medical Dir/Dir of Nursing* Jake Bergstrom MD; Nancy Arnett RN.
Licensure Intermediate care. *Beds* ICF 74. *Certified* Medicaid; Medicare.
Owner Proprietary Corp (Hillhaven Corp).
Admissions Requirements Physician's request.
Staff RNs 4 (ft); LPNs 7 (ft); Nurses aides 40 (ft); Activities coordinators 2 (ft).
Facilities Dining room; Physical therapy room; Activities room; Crafts room; Laundry room; Barber/Beauty shop; Library.
Activities Arts & crafts; Cards; Games; Reading groups; Prayer groups; Movies; Shopping trips; Social/Cultural gatherings.

Park Royal Medical Center
910 16th Ave, Longview, WA, 98632
(206) 423-2890
Admin Gail Davis. *Medical Dir/Dir of Nursing* Debbie Nida RN.
Licensure Skilled care; Intermediate care. *Beds* SNF 62; ICF. *Certified* Medicaid; Medicare.
Owner Privately owned.
Admissions Requirements Medical examination; Physician's request.
Staff Physicians; RNs; LPNs; Orderlies; Nurses aides; Physical therapists; Reality therapists; Recreational therapists; Occupational therapists; Speech therapists; Activities coordinators; Dietitians; Dentists; Ophthalmologists; Podiatrists.
Facilities Dining room; Activities room; Laundry room; Barber/Beauty shop; Library.
Activities Arts & crafts; Cards; Games; Reading groups; Prayer groups; Movies; Shopping trips; Social/Cultural gatherings.

LYNDEN

Christian Rest Home*
205 S British Columbia Ave, Lynden, WA, 98264
(206) 354-4434
Admin Angeline J Brouwer. *Medical Dir/Dir of Nursing* Dr Steven Alexandar.
Licensure Skilled care; Intermediate care. *Beds* 150. *Certified* Medicaid.
Owner Nonprofit Corp.
Admissions Requirements Minimum age 60; Medical examination; Physician's request.
Staff Physicians 1 (ft); RNs 6 (ft), 9 (pt); LPNs 3 (ft), 12 (pt); Orderlies 2 (ft), 1 (pt); Nurses aides 39 (ft), 66 (pt); Physical therapists 1 (ft), 1 (pt); Reality therapists 1 (ft), 1 (pt); Recreational therapists 1 (ft), 1 (pt); Activities coordinators 1 (ft); Dietitians 1 (ft).
Facilities Dining room; Activities room; Chapel; Crafts room; Barber/Beauty shop; Library.
Activities Arts & crafts; Cards; Games; Reading groups; Prayer groups; Movies; Shopping trips; Social/Cultural gatherings.

LYNNWOOD

Lynnwood Manor Health Care Center
5821 188th SW, Lynnwood, WA, 98037
(206) 776-5512
Admin Vonni Halvorson. *Medical Dir/Dir of Nursing* Dr Petrin; Denise Myers.
Licensure Skilled care; Intermediate care. *Beds* SNF 109; ICF. *Certified* Medicaid.
Owner Proprietary Corp.
Admissions Requirements Medical examination.

Staff RNs 5 (ft), 5 (pt); LPNs 5 (ft), 5 (pt); Nurses aides 44 (ft); Activities coordinators 1 (ft).
Languages French, Spanish, Japanese
Facilities Dining room; Physical therapy room; Activities room; Laundry room; Barber/Beauty shop; Library.
Activities Arts & crafts; Cards; Games; Prayer groups; Movies; Shopping trips; Social/Cultural gatherings.

MARYSVILLE

Havenwood Care Center Inc
1821 Grove St, Marysville, WA, 98270
(206) 659-3926
Admin Viola M Melnyk. *Medical Dir/Dir of Nursing* Carolyn Cochran.
Licensure Skilled care. *Beds* SNF 46. *Certified* Medicaid.
Owner Proprietary Corp.
Admissions Requirements Medical examination; Physician's request.
Staff RNs 8 (ft); LPNs 3 (ft), 1 (pt); Nurses aides 25 (ft), 2 (pt); Activities coordinators 1 (ft); Dietitians 5 (ft); Rehabilitation therapists 2 (ft).
Facilities Dining room; Activities room; Chapel; Crafts room; Laundry room; Barber/Beauty shop; Music.
Activities Arts & crafts; Cards; Games; Reading groups; Prayer groups; Movies.

Madeleine Villa Convalescent Center*
2nd & Liberty, Marysville, WA, 98270
(206) 659-1259
Admin E J & Michael E Downey.
Licensure Skilled care; Intermediate care. *Beds* 106. *Certified* Medicaid.
Owner Proprietary Corp.

MCKENNA

Nisqually Valley Care Center
PO Box B, McKenna, WA, 98558
(206) 458-3801
Admin John C Striker. *Medical Dir/Dir of Nursing* Cathrine Abbey.
Licensure Skilled care; Intermediate care. *Beds* 133. *Certified* Medicaid.
Owner Proprietary Corp (Soundcare Inc).
Admissions Requirements Medical examination; Physician's request.
Staff RNs 5 (ft); LPNs 10 (ft); Nurses aides 35 (ft); Physical therapists 1 (pt); Reality therapists 1 (pt); Recreational therapists 1 (pt); Occupational therapists 1 (pt); Speech therapists 1 (pt); Activities coordinators 1 (ft); Dietitians 1 (pt).
Facilities Dining room; Activities room; Crafts room; Laundry room.
Activities Arts & crafts; Cards; Games; Reading groups; Prayer groups; Movies; Social/Cultural gatherings; Many trips & scheduled outings.

MEDICAL LAKE

Interlake School
PO Box B, Medical Lake, WA, $6 99022
(509) 299-3111
Admin Mr Laurie Zapt. *Medical Dir/Dir of Nursing* Mary Harrison MD: Dorothy Stangler.
Licensure Intermediate care for mentally retarded. *Certified* Medicaid; Medicare.
Owner Publicly owned.
Staff Physicians 4 (ft); RNs 15; LPNs 36 (ft); Physical therapists 1 (ft); Recreational therapists 12 (ft), 1 (pt); Occupational therapists 10 (ft); Speech therapists 1 (ft); Dietitians 1 (ft); Dentists 1 (ft); Podiatrists 1 (ft); Attendant counselors 171 (ft).

Facilities Physical therapy room; Activities room; Library.
Activities Arts & crafts; Cards; Games; Reading groups; Prayer groups; Movies; Shopping trips; Social/Cultural gatherings.

MERCER ISLAND

Mercer Island Villa Care*
7445 SE 24th, Mercer Island, WA, 98040
(206) 232-6600
Admin Linda M Larson.
Licensure Skilled care. *Beds* 108. *Certified* Medicare.
Owner Proprietary Corp (Hillhaven Corp).
Facilities Dining room; Physical therapy room; Activities room; Barber/Beauty shop.
Activities Arts & crafts; Cards; Games; Reading groups; Prayer groups; Movies; Shopping trips; Social/Cultural gatherings.

MONROE

Monroe Convalescent Center
1355 W Main St, Monroe, WA, 98272
(206) 794-4011
Admin Margaret J Campbell. *Medical Dir/Dir of Nursing* Dr Trotter; Viola DeJonge.
Licensure Skilled care; Intermediate care. *Certified* Medicaid.
Owner Proprietary Corp.
Admissions Requirements Minimum age 14.
Staff RNs 6 (ft), 4 (pt); LPNs 4 (ft), 4 (pt); Nurses aides 21 (ft), 21 (pt); Physical therapists 1 (ft); Activities coordinators 1 (ft), 1 (pt).
Facilities Dining room; Physical therapy room; Activities room; Barber/Beauty shop.
Activities Arts & crafts; Cards; Games; Reading groups; Prayer groups; Movies; Shopping trips; Social/Cultural gatherings.

MONTESANO

Cedar Apartments*
PO Box 325, 1301 E Cedar St, Montesano, WA, 98563
(206) 249-3900
Admin William S Pine.
Licensure Intermediate care for mentally retarded. *Beds* 10.
Owner Proprietary Corp.

Edgewood Manor
514 E Broadway, Montesano, WA, 98563
(206) 249-4521
Admin Gerald A Cutler. *Medical Dir/Dir of Nursing* Dr Lindel; Bernice Porter RN DON.
Licensure Intermediate care. *Beds* ICF 37. *Certified* Medicaid.
Owner Proprietary Corp.
Admissions Requirements Medical examination; Physician's request.
Staff RNs 1 (ft); LPNs 1 (ft), 6 (pt); Nurses aides 9 (ft), 6 (pt); Physical therapists 1 (pt); Activities coordinators 1 (ft); Dietitians 2 (ft), 3 (pt); Ophthalmologists 1 (pt); Podiatrists 1 (pt).
Facilities Dining room; Activities room; Crafts room; Laundry room.
Activities Arts & crafts; Cards; Games; Reading groups; Prayer groups; Movies; Shopping trips.

Woodland Terrace Residential Training Center
PO Box 129, 414 E Ferndale, Montesano, WA, 98563
(206) 249-3822
Admin Carol Cutler. *Medical Dir/Dir of Nursing* Sandi Sikos.
Licensure Intermediate care for mentally retarded. *Beds* 30. *Certified* Medicaid; Medicare.
Owner Proprietary Corp.
Admissions Requirements Minimum age 18; Medical examination; Physician's request.

Staff Physicians 1 (pt); RNs 1 (pt); LPNs 2 (ft), 3 (pt); Nurses aides 15 (ft), 5 (pt); Recreational therapists 1 (pt); Occupational therapists 1 (pt); Speech therapists 1 (pt); Activities coordinators 1 (ft), 1 (pt); Dietitians 1 (pt).
Languages Sign
Facilities Dining room; Activities room; Laundry room; Day room.
Activities Arts & crafts; Games; Prayer groups; Movies; Shopping trips; Social/Cultural gatherings.

MORTON

Morton Nursing Home
PO Box 249, 180 Adams St, Morton, WA, 98356
(206) 496-5328
Admin Wilma M Milward. *Medical Dir/Dir of Nursing* Wanda Murphy.
Licensure Intermediate care. *Beds* ICF 23. *Certified* Medicaid.
Owner Proprietary Corp.
Admissions Requirements Medical examination; Physician's request.
Staff RNs 2 (ft); LPNs 3 (ft); Nurses aides 18 (ft); Physical therapists; Reality therapists; Recreational therapists; Occupational therapists; Speech therapists; Activities coordinators; Dietitians; Dentists; Ophthalmologists; Podiatrists.
Facilities Dining room; Physical therapy room; Activities room; Crafts room; Laundry room; Library.
Activities Arts & crafts; Cards; Games; Reading groups; Prayer groups; Movies; Shopping trips; Social/Cultural gatherings.

MOSES LAKE

Crestview Convalescent Center
817 E Plum St, Moses Lake, WA, 98837
(509) 763-7835
Admin James E McConnell. *Medical Dir/Dir of Nursing* David Miller MD; Jackie Boyle RN DON.
Licensure Skilled care; Intermediate care. *Beds* SNF 96. *Certified* Medicaid; Medicare.
Owner Proprietary Corp.
Admissions Requirements Physician's request.
Staff Physicians 10 (pt); RNs 4 (ft); LPNs 8 (ft); Nurses aides 30 (ft); Physical therapists 1 (pt); Reality therapists 1 (pt); Recreational therapists 1 (pt); Occupational therapists 1 (pt); Speech therapists 1 (pt); Activities coordinators 1 (ft); Dietitians 1 (pt); Dentists 1 (pt); Ophthalmologists 1 (pt); Podiatrists 1 (pt).
Languages Spanish
Facilities Dining room; Physical therapy room; Activities room; Chapel; Crafts room; Laundry room; Barber/Beauty shop; Library.
Activities Arts & crafts; Cards; Games; Reading groups; Prayer groups; Movies; Shopping trips; Social/Cultural gatherings.

MOUNT VERNON

Evergreen Terrace Nursing Center
2120 E Division St, Mount Vernon, WA, 98273
(206) 424-4254
Admin Donald Wilson. *Medical Dir/Dir of Nursing* Dr John W Erbstoeszer; Anna Nystoen RN.
Licensure Skilled care; Intermediate care. *Beds* SNF 141; ICF. *Certified* Medicaid; Medicare; VA.
Owner Proprietary Corp (Beverly Enterprises).
Staff RNs 4 (ft); LPNs 6 (ft); Nurses aides 20 (ft); Activities coordinators; Dietitians; Dentist.
Facilities Dining room; Physical therapy room; Activities room; Laundry room; Barber/Beauty shop.

Activities Arts & crafts; Cards; Games; Reading groups; Prayer groups; Movies; Shopping trips; Social/Cultural gatherings.

Mira-Vista Nursing Home*
PO Box 1305, 1020 N 8th, Mount Vernon, WA, 98273
(206) 424-1320
Admin David W Miller.
Licensure Skilled care; Intermediate care. *Beds* 58. *Certified* Medicaid.
Owner Proprietary Corp.

Valley Homes
1005 S 3rd Ave, Mount Vernon, WA, 98273
(206) 336-5717
Admin George Q Wheeler Jr. *Medical Dir/Dir of Nursing* John W Erbstoeszer MD; Sally Herman RN DON.
Licensure Intermediate care for mentally retarded. *Beds* ICF/MR 8. *Certified* Medicaid.
Owner Nonprofit organization/foundation.
Admissions Requirements Minimum age 18; Medical examination.
Facilities Dining room; Laundry room.
Activities Arts & crafts; Games; Movies; Shopping trips; Social/Cultural gatherings.

NACHES

Strawn Nursing Home Inc
30 Link Road, Naches, WA, 98937
(509) 966-5880
Admin Berdina M Faith. *Medical Dir/Dir of Nursing* William Cox DO; Doris Worby RN DON.
Licensure Intermediate care. *Beds* ICF 39. *Certified* Medicaid.
Owner Proprietary Corp.
Admissions Requirements Medical examination; Physician's request.
Staff Physicians Physician on call; RNs 3 (ft); LPNs 1 (ft), 3 (pt); Nurses aides 7 (ft), 3 (pt); Recreational therapists 1 (ft); Activities coordinators 1 (ft), 1 (pt).
Facilities Dining room; Activities room; Laundry room; Barber/Beauty shop.
Activities Arts & crafts; Cards; Games; Reading groups; Prayer groups; Movies; Shopping trips; Social/Cultural gatherings; Field trips.

NESPELEM

Collville Tribal Convalescent Center
PO Box 150, Nespelem, WA, 99155
(509) 634-4788
Admin Carol Frood-Aubertin. *Medical Dir/Dir of Nursing* G D Patterson DO; Helen Purdy RN.
Licensure Skilled care; Intermediate care. *Beds* SNF 52; ICF. *Certified* Medicaid.
Owner Proprietary Corp.
Admissions Requirements Medical examination; Physician's request.
Staff Physicians 2 (ft); RNs 2 (ft); LPNs 4 (ft); Orderlies 1 (ft); Nurses aides 16 (ft), 2 (pt); Physical therapists aide 1 (ft); Recreational therapists 1 (pt); Activities coordinators 1 (ft); Dietitians 1 (pt).
Languages Indian
Facilities Dining room; Physical therapy room; Activities room; Chapel; Crafts room; Laundry room; Barber/Beauty shop; Library.
Activities Arts & crafts; Cards; Games; Reading groups; Prayer groups; Movies; Shopping trips; Lunch outings.

NEWPORT

Pend Oreille Pines Nursing Home
PO Box 669, Scott & Pine Sts, Newport, WA, 99156
(509) 447-2441

Admin Ralph K Allen Jr Ph D. *Medical Dir/Dir of Nursing* A Peter Weir MD; Vonnie Carney RN.
Licensure Skilled care; Intermediate care. *Beds* SNF 50; ICF. *Certified* Medicaid.
Owner Publicly owned.
Staff Physicians 2 (ft), 2 (pt); RNs 3 (ft), 4 (pt); LPNs 2 (ft), 2 (pt); Orderlies 2 (ft), 2 (pt); Nurses aides 4 (ft), 7 (pt); Physical therapists 2 (pt); Activities coordinators 1 (ft), 1 (pt); Dietitians 1 (ft); Dentists 1 (pt); Ophthalmologists 1 (pt); MSW 1 (pt).
Facilities Dining room; Physical therapy room; Activities room; Crafts room; Laundry room; Barber/Beauty shop.
Activities Arts & crafts; Cards; Games; Reading groups; Prayer groups; Movies; Social/Cultural gatherings.

NORTH BEND

North Bend Nursing Center
PO Box 1405, 219 Cedar Ave S, North Bend, WA, 98045
(206) 888-2129
Admin Gary D Morical. *Medical Dir/Dir of Nursing* Dr Maurice Doerfler; Pat Mittness RN.
Licensure Skilled care; Intermediate care. *Beds* 94. *Certified* Medicaid; VA.
Owner Proprietary Corp (Regency Health Care Centers).
Admissions Requirements Minimum age 16; Medical examination; Physician's request.
Staff Physicians 8 (pt); RNs 7 (ft); LPNs 6 (ft); Orderlies 2 (ft); Nurses aides 25 (ft); Physical therapists 1 (pt); Reality therapists 2 (pt); Occupational therapists 1 (pt); Speech therapists 1 (pt); Activities coordinators 1 (ft); Dietitians 1 (pt); Dentists 1 (pt); Podiatrists 1 (pt).
Facilities Dining room; Physical therapy room; Activities room; Crafts room; Laundry room; Barber/Beauty shop; Day room.
Activities Arts & crafts; Cards; Games; Reading groups; Prayer groups; Movies; Social/Cultural gatherings; Van rides.

OAK HARBOR

Whibbey Island Manor Inc
PO Box 1900, 5425 500 Ave W, Oak Harbor, WA, 98277
(206) 675-5913
Admin Mark S Wiggins. *Medical Dir/Dir of Nursing* Pat Koontz RN.
Licensure Skilled care; Intermediate care. *Beds* 62. *Certified* Medicaid.
Owner Proprietary Corp.
Admissions Requirements Physician's request.
Staff RNs 4 (ft), 2 (pt); LPNs 3 (ft), 2 (pt); Nurses aides 30 (ft), 7 (pt); Physical therapists 1 (pt); Reality therapists 1 (pt); Recreational therapists 1 (pt); Occupational therapists 1 (pt); Speech therapists 1 (pt); Activities coordinators 1 (ft), 1 (pt); Dietitians 1 (pt).
Facilities Dining room; Laundry room.
Activities Arts & crafts; Games; Reading groups; Prayer groups; Movies; Social/Cultural gatherings.

ODESSA

Memorial Hospital/Conv Center
PO Box 368, 502 E Amende, Odessa, WA, 99159
(509) 982-2611
Admin Carol Schott. *Medical Dir/Dir of Nursing* Dr James Cornell; Marlene Brendell DON.
Licensure Skilled care; Intermediate care. *Beds* 26. *Certified* Medicaid.
Owner Publicly owned.
Admissions Requirements Physician's request.

Staff Physicians 1 (pt); RNs 1 (ft), 10 (pt); LPNs 2 (pt); Nurses aides 6 (ft), 12 (pt); Physical therapists 1 (ft), 1 (pt); Activities coordinators 1 (ft); Dietitians 1 (pt).
Facilities Dining room; Physical therapy room; Activities room; Crafts room.
Activities Arts & crafts; Cards; Reading groups; Movies; Social/Cultural gatherings.

OKANOGAN

Valley Care Center A Prestige Facility
PO Box 977, 520 2nd S, Okanogan, WA, 98840
(509) 422-3180
Admin Ann Kier. *Medical Dir/Dir of Nursing* Dr Dengel; Sandra Martellini RN.
Licensure Skilled care; Intermediate care. *Beds* SNF 89; ICF. *Certified* Medicaid; Medicare.
Owner Proprietary Corp.
Admissions Requirements Physician's request.
Staff RNs 8 (ft); LPNs 13 (ft); Nurses aides 45 (ft); Physical therapists 1 (pt); Occupational therapists 1 (pt); Speech therapists 1 (pt); Activities coordinators 1 (ft); Dietitians 1 (pt).
Facilities Dining room; Physical therapy room; Activities room; Laundry room; Barber/Beauty shop; Library.
Activities Arts & crafts; Cards; Games; Reading groups; Prayer groups; Movies; Shopping trips; Social/Cultural gatherings; Reality orientation; Sensory stimulation; Resident council; Music events; Social hour; Exercise group.

OLYMPIA

Bayview Inn
2221 E Bay Dr, Olympia, WA, 98506
(206) 357-3567
Admin Dorothy Hocking. *Medical Dir/Dir of Nursing* Noel Gates RN.
Licensure Intermediate care for mentally retarded. *Beds* ICF/MR 40.
Owner Proprietary Corp (Community Care Centers).
Staff RNs 1 (ft); LPNs 1 (ft), 3 (pt); Activities coordinators 2 (ft); Counselors 18 (ft), 1 (pt).

Olympia Manor*
1811 E 22nd Ave, Olympia, WA, 98501
(206) 943-0910
Admin Marilyn Lundberg. *Medical Dir/Dir of Nursing* Dr J M Brady.
Licensure Skilled care; Intermediate care. *Beds* 28. *Certified* Medicaid.
Owner Proprietary Corp.
Staff RNs 2 (ft), 3 (pt); LPNs 2 (ft), 3 (pt); Nurses aides 8 (ft); Activities coordinators 1 (ft).
Facilities Dining room.
Activities Arts & crafts; Cards; Games; Prayer groups; Movies.

Rest Haven Nursing Home
232 N Perry, Olympia, WA, 98502
(206) 357-8123
Admin Jerry B Hlousek. *Medical Dir/Dir of Nursing* Edmund Olson MD; V J Vander Maas DON.
Licensure Skilled care; Intermediate care. *Beds* 35.
Owner Proprietary Corp.
Admissions Requirements Medical examination; Physician's request.
Staff Physicians 1 (pt); RNs 2 (ft); LPNs 4 (ft), 1 (pt); Nurses aides 5 (ft), 2 (pt); Physical therapists 1 (pt); Recreational therapists 1 (ft); Dietitians 1 (pt).
Facilities Dining room; Activities room; Laundry room; Barber/Beauty shop.
Activities Arts & crafts; Cards; Games; Reading groups; Prayer groups; Movies; Shopping trips; Social/Cultural gatherings; Van rides.

OTHELLO

Othello Convalescent Center
495 N 13th St, Othello, WA, 99344
(509) 488-9609
Admin Gail McDowell. *Medical Dir/Dir of Nursing* Diane Bolin.
Licensure Skilled care. *Beds* 62. *Certified* Medicaid; Medicare.
Owner Proprietary Corp (Beverly Enterprises).
Staff RNs 7 (ft), 2 (pt); LPNs 2 (ft); Nurses aides 20 (ft); Physical therapists 1 (pt); Activities coordinators 1 (ft); Dietitians 1 (ft).
Languages Spanish
Facilities Dining room; Activities room; Laundry room; Barber/Beauty shop.
Activities Arts & crafts; Cards; Games; Reading groups; Prayer groups; Movies; Shopping trips; Social/Cultural gatherings.

PASCO

Hillcrest Convalescent Center*
2004 N 22nd St, Pasco, WA, 99301
(509) 747-8811
Admin Betty Deymonaz. *Medical Dir/Dir of Nursing* Mark Campbell.
Licensure Skilled care; Intermediate care. *Beds* 125. *Certified* Medicaid; Medicare.
Owner Proprietary Corp (Beverly Enterprises).
Facilities Dining room; Physical therapy room; Activities room; Laundry room; Barber/Beauty shop.
Activities Arts & crafts; Cards; Games; Reading groups; Prayer groups; Movies; Shopping trips.

POMEROY

Memory Manor*
PO Box 880, N 66 6th St, Pomeroy, WA, 99347
(509) 843-1794
Admin Garvin Olson. *Medical Dir/Dir of Nursing* Dr D Shirley Richardson.
Licensure Skilled care; Intermediate care. *Beds* 40. *Certified* Medicaid.
Owner Publicly owned.
Staff Physicians 2 (ft); RNs 2 (ft); LPNs 6 (ft); Nurses aides 19 (pt); Physical therapists 1 (pt); Occupational therapists 1 (pt); Activities coordinators 1 (ft); Dietitians 1 (pt); Dentists 1 (pt).
Facilities Dining room; Physical therapy room; Activities room; Chapel; Crafts room; Laundry room; Barber/Beauty shop.
Activities Arts & crafts; Cards; Games; Reading groups; Prayer groups; Movies; Shopping trips; Social/Cultural gatherings.

PORT ANGELES

Crestwood Convalescent Center
1116 E Lauridsen Blvd, Port Angeles, WA, 98362
(206) 452-9206
Admin H B Folden. *Medical Dir/Dir of Nursing* Sondyn Rose DON.
Licensure Skilled care. *Beds* SNF 103. *Certified* Medicaid; Medicare.
Owner Privately owned.
Staff RNs 11 (ft); LPNs 14 (ft); Nurses aides 25 (ft); Physical therapists 1 (ft); Reality therapists 1 (pt); Occupational therapists 1 (pt); Speech therapists 1 (pt); Activities coordinators 1 (ft); Dietitians 1 (pt).
Facilities Dining room; Physical therapy room; Activities room; Crafts room; Laundry room; Barber/Beauty shop; Library.
Activities Arts & crafts; Cards; Games; Reading groups; Prayer groups; Movies; Social/Cultural gatherings.

Port Angeles Care Center
825 E 5th, Port Angeles, WA, 98362
(206) 452-6213
Admin Neal Peisley. *Medical Dir/Dir of Nursing* Tricia Hall.
Licensure Skilled care; Intermediate care. *Beds* SNF 107; ICF. *Certified* Medicaid; Medicare; VA.
Owner Proprietary Corp (National Heritage).
Admissions Requirements Medical examination; Physician's request.
Staff RNs; LPNs; Orderlies; Nurses aides; Activities coordinators.
Languages Spanish
Facilities Dining room; Physical therapy room; Activities room; Crafts room; Laundry room; Barber/Beauty shop.
Activities Arts & crafts; Games; Reading groups; Prayer groups; Movies; Social/Cultural gatherings.

PORT ORCHARD

Long Lake Manor Inc
7242 Long Lake Rd SE, Port Orchard, WA, 98366
(206) 871-1210
Admin Ernest L Beals. *Medical Dir/Dir of Nursing* Michael Butler MD; Jeanne A Beals RN DON.
Licensure Skilled care; Intermediate care. *Beds* SNF 46; ICF. *Certified* Medicaid.
Owner Proprietary Corp.
Admissions Requirements Medical examination.
Staff RNs 3 (ft), 2 (pt); LPNs 3 (ft), 2 (pt); Nurses aides 18 (ft), 2 (pt); Reality therapists 1 (ft); Recreational therapists 1 (ft); Activities coordinators 1 (ft).
Facilities Dining room; Activities room.
Activities Arts & crafts; Cards; Games; Reading groups; Prayer groups; Movies; Shopping trips; Social/Cultural gatherings.

Port Orchard Care Center
2031 Pottery Ave, Port Orchard, WA, 98366
(206) 876-8035
Admin Keith Briggs. *Medical Dir/Dir of Nursing* Kitty Phillips.
Licensure Skilled care; Intermediate care; Medicare Approved. *Beds* SNF 125; ICF; Medicare 12. *Certified* Medicaid; Medicare.
Owner Proprietary Corp.
Admissions Requirements Medical examination; Physician's request.
Staff Physicians 1 (pt); RNs 7 (ft); LPNs 10 (ft), 3 (pt); Orderlies 4 (ft); Nurses aides 35 (ft); Physical therapists 1 (pt); Reality therapists 1 (pt); Recreational therapists 1 (ft); Occupational therapists 1 (pt); Speech therapists 1 (pt); Activities coordinators 1 (ft); Dietitians 1 (pt); Dentists 1 (pt); Ophthalmologists 1 (pt); Podiatrists 1 (pt); Dentist 1 (pt).
Languages Spanish
Facilities Dining room; Physical therapy room; Activities room; Crafts room; Laundry room; Barber/Beauty shop; Special dining area.
Activities Arts & crafts; Cards; Games; Reading groups; Prayer groups; Movies; Shopping trips; Social/Cultural gatherings; Social dinners; Alzheimer's support group.

Ridgemont Terrace Inc
2051 Pottery Ave, Port Orchard, WA, 98366
(206) 876-4461
Admin Eugene F Asa. *Medical Dir/Dir of Nursing* Dr Merley; Cheri Svensson.
Licensure Skilled care. *Beds* SNF 119. *Certified* Medicaid; Medicare.
Owner Proprietary Corp.
Admissions Requirements Medical examination.
Staff Physicians 1 (pt); RNs 11 (ft); LPNs 5 (ft); Nurses aides 29 (ft); Physical therapists 1 (pt); Recreational therapists 1 (ft);

Occupational therapists 1 (pt); Speech therapists 1 (pt); Activities coordinators 2 (pt); Dietitians 1 (pt); Podiatrists 1 (pt); Dentist 1 (pt).
Facilities Dining room; Physical therapy room; Activities room; Crafts room; Laundry room; Barber/Beauty shop.
Activities Arts & crafts; Cards; Games; Prayer groups; Movies; Shopping trips; Social/Cultural gatherings.

PORT TOWNSEND

Kah Tai Care Center
751 Kearney St, Port Townsend, WA, 98368
(206) 385-3555
Admin George Avis. *Medical Dir/Dir of Nursing* Tiffany Benton.
Licensure Skilled care. *Beds* 94. *Certified* Medicaid; Medicare.
Owner Proprietary Corp.
Admissions Requirements Medical examination; Physician's request.
Staff RNs 16 (ft); LPNs 3 (ft); Nurses aides 35 (ft), 6 (pt); Occupational therapists 1 (pt); Activities coordinators 1 (ft); Dietitians 1 (pt); Ophthalmologists 1 (pt).
Facilities Dining room; Physical therapy room; Activities room; Barber/Beauty shop.
Activities Arts & crafts; Reading groups; Prayer groups; Movies; Resident council; Sing-alongs; Monthly birthday parties.

POULSBO

Loop Street NE
112 12th St S, Poulsbo, WA, 98370
(206) 377-7231
Admin Roberta Soran.
Licensure Intermediate care for mentally retarded. *Beds* 6.
Owner Nonprofit Corp.

Martha & Mary Nursing Home
19160 Front St NE, Box 127, Poulsbo, WA, 98370
(206) 779-4517
Admin Jack Juhkentaal. *Medical Dir/Dir of Nursing* Dr Patrick Tracy; Marcia Weedman DON.
Licensure Skilled care; Intermediate care. *Beds* SNF 190; ICF. *Certified* Medicaid.
Owner Nonprofit Corp.
Admissions Requirements Minimum age 18; Medical examination; Physician's request.
Staff RNs 10 (ft), 20 (pt); LPNs 4 (ft), 5 (pt); Orderlies 3 (ft); Nurses aides 55 (ft), 30 (pt); Physical therapists 1 (pt); Recreational therapists 4 (ft); Occupational therapists 1 (pt); Speech therapists 1 (pt); Activities coordinators 1 (ft); Dietitians 1 (ft).
Affiliation Lutheran
Facilities Dining room; Physical therapy room; Activities room; Chapel; Crafts room; Laundry room; Barber/Beauty shop; Library; Day rooms.
Activities Arts & crafts; Cards; Games; Reading groups; Prayer groups; Movies; Shopping trips; Social/Cultural gatherings; Bus rides.

PULLMAN

Pullman Convalescent Center*
NW 1310 Deane, Pullman, WA, 99163
(509) 332-1566
Admin Edwin W Morgan. *Medical Dir/Dir of Nursing* David Magaret MD.
Licensure Skilled care; Intermediate care. *Beds* 82. *Certified* Medicaid; Medicare.
Owner Proprietary Corp.
Admissions Requirements Medical examination; Physician's request.
Staff Physicians 1 (pt); RNs 3 (ft), 2 (pt); LPNs 3 (ft), 2 (pt); Orderlies 6 (ft); Nurses aides 26 (ft); Physical therapists 1 (pt);

Recreational therapists 2 (ft); Occupational therapists 1 (pt); Activities coordinators 1 (ft); Dietitians 1 (ft).
Facilities Dining room; Physical therapy room; Activities room; Laundry room; Barber/Beauty shop.
Activities Arts & crafts; Cards; Games; Reading groups; Prayer groups; Movies; Shopping trips; Social/Cultural gatherings.

PUYALLUP

Pam Group Home IMR
619 7th Ave SE, Puyallup, WA, 98374
(206) 845-8871
Admin Peggy Wright.
Licensure Intermediate care for mentally retarded. *Beds* 8. *Certified* Medicaid.
Owner Nonprofit Corp.
Admissions Requirements Minimum age 21; DDD referral.
Facilities Dining room; Laundry room.
Activities Arts & crafts; Games; Movies; Shopping trips; Social/Cultural gatherings.

Riverwood Care Center
114 4th Ave NW, Puyallup, WA, 98371
(206) 848-4551
Admin Sandra Caban. *Medical Dir/Dir of Nursing* Scott Kronlund MD; Diane Tooke RN DON.
Licensure Skilled care; Intermediate care. *Beds* SNF 80; ICF. *Certified* Medicaid.
Owner Proprietary Corp (Pleasant Valley Services Corp).
Admissions Requirements Minimum age 14.
Staff RNs 7 (ft); LPNs 4 (ft); Nurses aides 22 (ft); Physical therapists 1 (pt); Occupational therapists 1 (pt); Speech therapists 1 (pt); Activities coordinators 2 (ft); Dietitians 1 (pt); Ophthalmologists 1 (pt); Podiatrists 1 (pt).
Languages German
Facilities Dining room; Physical therapy room; Activities room; Crafts room; Laundry room; Barber/Beauty shop.
Activities Arts & crafts; Cards; Games; Reading groups; Prayer groups; Movies; Shopping trips; Social/Cultural gatherings.

Sunrise Haven
PO Box 459, 1701 13th St SE, Puyallup, WA, 98371
(206) 845-1718
Admin Kenneth C Lane. *Medical Dir/Dir of Nursing* Linda Tresaugue DON.
Licensure Skilled care. *Beds* SNF 50; ICF; Sheltered care. *Certified* Medicare.
Owner Nonprofit Corp.
Admissions Requirements Must rely totally on Christian Science for healing.
Staff Nurses aides; Activities coordinators.
Affiliation Christian Science
Facilities Dining room; Laundry room; Barber/Beauty shop; Library; Reading room.
Activities Arts & crafts; Games; Reading groups; Prayer groups; Movies; Shopping trips; Musical groups.

Valley Terrace Nursing Center
511 10th Ave SE, Puyallup, WA, 98371
(206) 845-7566
Admin Richard C Halfhill. *Medical Dir/Dir of Nursing* Dr Thomas Clark.
Licensure Skilled care. *Beds* SNF 202. *Certified* Medicaid.
Owner Privately owned.
Staff Physicians 1 (pt); RNs 7 (ft); LPNs 18 (ft); Nurses aides 124 (ft); Physical therapists 1 (pt); Reality therapists 1 (pt); Occupational therapists 1 (pt); Speech therapists 1 (pt); Activities coordinators 1 (ft); Dietitians 1 (pt); Dentists 1 (pt); Ophthalmologists 1 (pt); Podiatrists 1 (pt).
Activities Arts & crafts; Cards; Games; Reading groups; Prayer groups; Movies; Shopping trips; Social/Cultural gatherings.

Wildwood Healthcare Center
909 S Meridian, Puyallup, WA, 98371
(206) 845-6631
Admin Moe Chaudry. *Medical Dir/Dir of Nursing* D Thomas Clark MD.
Licensure Skilled care; Intermediate care. *Beds* 138. *Certified* Medicaid; Medicare.
Owner Proprietary Corp (Beverly Enterprises).
Admissions Requirements Medical examination; Physician's request.
Staff Physicians 1 (pt); RNs 6 (ft); LPNs 13 (ft), 2 (pt); Nurses aides 40 (ft), 5 (pt); Physical therapists 1 (ft); Occupational therapists 1 (ft); Speech therapists 1 (ft); Speech therapists 1 (ft); Activities coordinators 2 (ft); Dietitians 1 (ft); Ophthalmologists 1 (pt); Podiatrists 1 (pt); Social workers 1 (ft), 1 (pt).
Facilities Dining room; Physical therapy room; Activities room; Chapel; Crafts room; Crafts room; Laundry room; Barber/Beauty shop; Library.
Activities Arts & crafts; Cards; Games; Reading groups; Prayer groups; Movies; Shopping trips; Social/Cultural gatherings; Reality orientation; Special programs for low-functioning patients.

RAYMOND

Willapa Harbor Care Center
PO Box 432, 1100 Jackson St, Raymond, WA, 98577
(206) 942-2424
Admin Paul Jeffers. *Medical Dir/Dir of Nursing* Frank Hing; Patsy Cook.
Licensure Skilled care; Intermediate care. *Beds* SNF 80; ICF. *Certified* Medicaid.
Owner Proprietary Corp (Beverly Enterprises).
Staff RNs 4 (ft); LPNs 7 (ft); Physical therapists 1 (pt); Activities coordinators 1 (ft); Dietitians 1 (ft); Ophthalmologists 1 (pt).

REDMOND

Cascade Vista Convalescent Center*
7900 Redmond Kirkland Hwy, Redmond, WA, 98052
(206) 885-0808
Admin Pearl K Barnes.
Licensure Skilled care; Intermediate care. *Beds* 139. *Certified* Medicaid; Medicare.
Owner Proprietary Corp.

Pinevilla Guest Home
PO Box 447, 8705 166th Ave NE, Redmond, WA, 98073
(206) 885-1432
Admin Alma O Kern. *Medical Dir/Dir of Nursing* Carol A Bean RN.
Licensure Intermediate care. *Beds* ICF 28. *Certified* Medicaid.
Owner Proprietary Corp.
Admissions Requirements Minimum age 45-50.
Staff RNs 3 (pt); LPNs 2 (ft), 2 (pt); Nurses aides 3 (ft), 3 (pt).
Facilities Dining room; Activities room; Laundry room; Day room.
Activities Cards; Games; Reading groups; Social/Cultural gatherings; Parties; Music; Exercise; Outings; Remotivation groups.

RENTON

Highlands Convalescent Center Inc
1110 Edmonds Ave NE, Renton, WA, 98056
(206) 226-6120
Admin Phyllis Wallace. *Medical Dir/Dir of Nursing* Frans Koning; Carol Rigney.
Licensure Skilled care; Intermediate care. *Beds* SNF 100. *Certified* Medicaid.
Owner Privately owned.
Admissions Requirements Minimum age 60; Medical examination; Physician's request.
Staff RNs; LPNs; Orderlies; Nurses aides; Physical therapists; Activities coordinators.
Facilities Dining room; Activities room; Chapel; Crafts room; Laundry room; Barber/Beauty shop.
Activities Arts & crafts; Cards; Games; Reading groups; Prayer groups; Movies.

Renton Terrace Nursing Center
80 SW 2nd St, Renton, WA, 98055
(206) 226-4610
Admin Joyce Kouell. *Medical Dir/Dir of Nursing* Dr Richard Niemann.
Licensure Skilled care; Intermediate care. *Beds* 160. *Certified* Medicaid; Medicare.
Owner Proprietary Corp (Beverly Enterprises).
Staff Physicians 12 (pt); RNs 7 (ft); LPNs 12 (ft); Orderlies 7 (ft); Nurses aides 31 (ft); Physical therapists 1 (ft); Recreational therapists 2 (ft); Occupational therapists 1 (ft); Speech therapists 1 (pt); Activities coordinators 2 (ft); Dietitians 1 (pt); Dentists 1 (pt); Ophthalmologists 1 (pt); Podiatrists 1 (pt).
Facilities Dining room; Physical therapy room; Activities room; Laundry room; Barber/Beauty shop.
Activities Arts & crafts; Cards; Games; Reading groups; Prayer groups; Movies; Shopping trips; Social/Cultural gatherings.

Valley Villa Care Center*
4430 Talbot Rd S, Renton, WA, 98055
(206) 226-7500
Admin Linda Larson.
Licensure Skilled care; Intermediate care. *Beds* 166. *Certified* Medicaid; Medicare.
Owner Proprietary Corp (Hillhaven Corp).

RICHLAND

Life Care Center of Richland
44 Goethals Dr, Richland, WA, 99352
(509) 943-1117
Admin Reita E Musser. *Medical Dir/Dir of Nursing* Justin DelosSantos MD; Debra Lang RN.
Licensure Skilled care; Intermediate care. *Beds* 104. *Certified* Medicaid; Medicare.
Owner Proprietary Corp (Life Care Centers of America).
Admissions Requirements Medical examination; Physician's request.
Staff RNs 10 (ft); LPNs 8 (ft); Nurses aides 38 (ft); Activities coordinators 1 (ft).
Facilities Dining room; Physical therapy room; Activities room; Crafts room; Laundry room; Barber/Beauty shop.
Activities Arts & crafts; Cards; Games; Reading groups; Prayer groups; Movies; Shopping trips.

Williams House IMR-E
761 Williams Blvd, Richland, WA, 99352
(509) 943-6794 or 943-1766
Admin Dorlan Hergesheimer.
Licensure IMR-E. *Beds* IMR-E 8. *Certified* Medicaid; Medicare.
Owner Nonprofit Corp.
Admissions Requirements Minimum age 18; Medical examination.
Staff Physicians 1 (pt); RNs 1 (pt); Physical therapists 1 (pt); Recreational therapists 1 (pt); Occupational therapists 1 (pt); Speech therapists 1 (pt); Dietitians 1 (pt).
Facilities Dining room; Laundry room.
Activities Arts & crafts; Games; Movies; Shopping trips; Social/Cultural gatherings.

RIDGEFIELD

Ridgefield Health Care*
PO Box 399, 104 Pioneer Ave, Ridgefield, WA, 98642
(206) 887-3121
Admin James Rutt.

Licensure Intermediate care. *Beds* 42.
  Certified Medicaid.
Owner Proprietary Corp.

RITZVILLE

Life Care Center of Ritzville
506 S Jackson, Ritzville, WA, 99169
(509) 659-1600
Admin Julie Schultz. *Medical Dir/Dir of
  Nursing* James J Jardee MD; Merrily Fagg
  RN DON.
Licensure Skilled care. *Beds* SNF 50. *Certified*
  Medicaid; Medicare.
Owner Proprietary Corp (Life Care Centers of
  America).
Staff Physicians 3 (ft); RNs 4 (ft); LPNs 3 (ft);
  Orderlies 4 (ft); Nurses aides 13 (ft), 5 (pt);
  Physical therapists 1 (pt); Speech therapists
  1 (pt); Activities coordinators 1 (ft);
  Dietitians 1 (ft); Dentists 2 (pt);
  Ophthalmologists 1 (pt); Dentist 2 (pt).
Facilities Dining room; Activities room;
  Crafts room; Laundry room; Barber/Beauty
  shop.
Activities Arts & crafts; Cards; Games;
  Reading groups; Prayer groups; Movies;
  Shopping trips; Social/Cultural gatherings;
  One to one visits.

SEATTLE

Anderson House Inc
17127 15th Ave NE, Seattle, WA, 98155
(206) 364-7131
Admin Larry Anderson.
Licensure Skilled care; Intermediate care. *Beds*
  SNF 112.
Owner Proprietary Corp.
Admissions Requirements Physician's request.
Staff Physicians; RNs; LPNs; Orderlies;
  Nurses aides; Physical therapists; Reality
  therapists; Recreational therapists;
  Occupational therapists; Speech therapists;
  Activities coordinators; Dietitians; Dentists;
  Ophthalmologists; Podiatrists.
Facilities Dining room; Physical therapy
  room; Activities room; Crafts room; Laundry
  room; Barber/Beauty shop; Library.
Activities Arts & crafts; Cards; Games;
  Reading groups; Prayer groups; Movies;
  Shopping trips; Social/Cultural gatherings.

Arden Nursing Home
16357 Aurora Ave N, Seattle, WA, 98133
(206) 542-3103
Admin Felecia Bly RN. *Medical Dir/Dir of
  Nursing* Anne Walker RN DNS.
Licensure Skilled care. *Beds* 100. *Certified*
  Medicare.
Owner Proprietary Corp (Hillhaven Corp).
Staff RNs 6 (ft), 2 (pt); LPNs 3 (ft), 2 (pt);
  Nurses aides 26 (ft), 8 (pt); Physical
  therapists 1 (ft); Recreational therapists 1
  (ft); Occupational therapists 1 (ft); Dietitians
  1 (ft).
Facilities Dining room; Physical therapy
  room; Activities room; Barber/Beauty shop.
Activities Arts & crafts; Cards; Games;
  Reading groups; Prayer groups; Movies;
  Shopping trips; Social/Cultural gatherings.

Austin Nursing Home*
9005 Roosevelt Way NE, Seattle, WA, 98115
(206) 523-4296
Admin Catherine Stockwell.
Licensure Nursing home. *Beds* 44.
Owner Proprietary Corp.

Ballard Convalescent Center
820 NW 95th St, Seattle, WA, 98117
(206) 782-0100
Admin David L Rogge. *Medical Dir/Dir of
  Nursing* Dr Martin Burkland, Dr Roger
  Higgs, Dr Laminack, Dr Leitzell; Bonnie
  Blachley DON.

Licensure Skilled care. *Beds* SNF 210.
  Certified Medicare.
Owner Proprietary Corp.
Admissions Requirements Physician's request.
Staff Physicians 4 (pt); RNs 16 (ft), 2 (pt);
  LPNs 4 (ft), 2 (pt); Orderlies 6 (ft); Nurses
  aides 65 (ft), 6 (pt); Physical therapists 2 (ft),
  1 (pt); Reality therapists 1 (ft); Recreational
  therapists 2 (ft), 2 (pt); Occupational
  therapists 1 (ft), 1 (pt); Speech therapists 1
  (pt); Activities coordinators 1 (ft); Dietitians
  1 (ft); Ophthalmologists 1 (pt).
Languages German, Spanish, Japanese
Facilities Dining room; Physical therapy
  room; Activities room; Crafts room; Laundry
  room; Barber/Beauty shop.
Activities Arts & crafts; Cards; Games;
  Reading groups; Prayer groups; Movies;
  Shopping trips; Social/Cultural gatherings.

Barcley Boarding Home*
1510 NE Perkins Way, Seattle, WA, 98155
(206) 365-9767
Admin Steve Skeen.
Licensure Intermediate care for mentally
  retarded. *Beds* 6.
Owner Nonprofit Corp.

Bayview Manor
11 W Aloha St, Seattle, WA, 98119
(206) 284-7330
Admin Marshall C Hjelte. *Medical Dir/Dir of
  Nursing* Marcelle Dunning MD; Elizabeth
  Zohn DNS.
Licensure Skilled care; Intermediate care. *Beds*
  SNF; ICF 50. *Certified* Medicaid.
Owner Nonprofit Corp.
Admissions Requirements Minimum age 62.
Staff RNs 10 (ft), 1 (pt); LPNs 6 (ft); Nurses
  aides 26 (ft), 7 (pt); Recreational therapists 1
  (ft); Occupational therapists 1 (pt).
Affiliation Methodist
Facilities Dining room; Physical therapy
  room; Activities room; Chapel; Crafts room;
  Laundry room; Barber/Beauty shop; Library.
Activities Arts & crafts; Cards; Games;
  Reading groups; Prayer groups; Movies;
  Shopping trips; Social/Cultural gatherings.

Branch Villa Health Care Center
2611 S Dearborn, Seattle, WA, 98144
(206) 325-6700
Admin Helen Sikov. *Medical Dir/Dir of
  Nursing* Dr K Hong MD; J Hammond RN
  DON.
Licensure Skilled care; Intermediate care. *Beds*
  SNF 177; ICF. *Certified* Medicaid.
Owner Proprietary Corp.
Admissions Requirements Medical
  examination.
Staff Physicians 18 (pt); RNs 13 (ft); LPNs 13
  (ft); Orderlies 5 (ft); Nurses aides 55 (ft), 5
  (pt); Physical therapists 1 (ft); Reality
  therapists 1 (ft); Recreational therapists 3
  (ft); Occupational therapists 1 (ft), 1 (pt);
  Speech therapists 1 (pt); Activities
  coordinators 1 (ft); Dietitians 1 (ft); Dentists
  1 (pt); Ophthalmologists 1 (pt); Podiatrists 1
  (pt); Social worker 2 (ft); Mental health team
  4 (ft).
Languages Tagalog, Chinese, Korean, East
  Indian
Facilities Dining room; Physical therapy
  room; Activities room; Crafts room; Laundry
  room; Barber/Beauty shop; 2 day rooms;
  Secured patio-lawn.
Activities Arts & crafts; Cards; Games;
  Reading groups; Prayer groups; Movies;
  Shopping trips; Social/Cultural gatherings;
  Community outings; Sensory Stimulation;
  Music therapy; Pet therapy.

Burien Terrace Nursing Center
1031 SW 130th St, Seattle, WA, 98146
(206) 242-3213
Admin Patricia L Swaner. *Medical Dir/Dir of
  Nursing* Dr Zerr; Carol Juhnke DNS.

Licensure Skilled care; Intermediate care. *Beds*
  SNF 140; ICF. *Certified* Medicaid;
  Medicare.
Owner Proprietary Corp.
Admissions Requirements Medical
  examination; Physician's request.
Staff Physicians 1 (pt); RNs 5 (ft); LPNs 11
  (ft); Nurses aides 50 (ft); Physical therapists
  1 (pt); Recreational therapists 1 (ft);
  Occupational therapists 1 (pt); Speech
  therapists 1 (pt); Activities coordinators 1
  (ft); Dietitians 1 (pt); Dentists 1 (pt);
  Ophthalmologists 1 (pt); Podiatrists 1 (pt).
Facilities Dining room; Physical therapy
  room; Activities room; Laundry room;
  Barber/Beauty shop; Library.
Activities Arts & crafts; Cards; Games;
  Reading groups; Prayer groups; Movies;
  Shopping trips; Social/Cultural gatherings.

Camelot Group Home*
9201 2nd NW, Seattle, WA, 98117
(206) 783-2373
Admin Steve Skeen.
Licensure Intermediate care for mentally
  retarded. *Beds* 8.
Owner Nonprofit Corp.

Columbia Lutheran Home
4700 Phinney Ave N, Seattle, WA, 98103
(206) 632-7400
Admin Rev Walter Morris.
Licensure Skilled care; Intermediate care. *Beds*
  122. *Certified* Medicaid.
Owner Nonprofit Corp.
Affiliation Lutheran

Crista Senior Community
19303 Fremont Ave N, Seattle, WA, 98177
(206) 546-7400
Admin Jeffery L Crandall. *Medical Dir/Dir of
  Nursing* Pamela Cooper MD; Vivian
  Johnson DON.
Licensure Skilled care; Intermediate care. *Beds*
  SNF; ICF 236. *Certified* Medicaid;
  Medicare.
Owner Nonprofit Corp.
Admissions Requirements Minimum age 62;
  Medical examination.
Staff RNs 26 (ft), 17 (pt); LPNs 5 (ft), 2 (pt);
  Nurses aides 69 (ft), 17 (pt); Physical
  therapists 1 (ft); Reality therapists 4 (ft);
  Recreational therapists 4 (ft); Occupational
  therapists; Activities coordinators 1 (ft);
  Dietitians 1 (pt).
Facilities Dining room; Physical therapy
  room; Activities room; Chapel; Crafts room;
  Laundry room; Barber/Beauty shop; Library;
  Van service.
Activities Arts & crafts; Cards; Games;
  Reading groups; Prayer groups; Movies;
  Shopping trips; Social/Cultural gatherings;
  Ceramics; Discussion groups; Bible study;
  Chapel services; Art classes; Exercise classes;
  Missionary fellowship; Cooking classes.

Exeter House
720 Seneca St, Seattle, WA, 98101
(206) 622-1300
Admin Arlene Temple. *Medical Dir/Dir of
  Nursing* Dr Robert Erickson; Helen Reed
  RN.
Licensure Nursing home. *Beds* SNF 20;
  Retirement units 130.
Owner Nonprofit Corp (Presbyterian
  Ministeries).
Admissions Requirements Minimum age 62;
  Medical examination; Physician's request.
Staff RNs 4 (ft), 2 (pt); LPNs 1 (ft), 1 (pt);
  Nurses aides 6 (ft), 4 (pt); Activities
  coordinators 1 (ft); Dietitians 1 (ft).
Affiliation Presbyterian
Facilities Dining room; Activities room;
  Chapel; Crafts room; Laundry room; Barber/
  Beauty shop; Library.
Activities Arts & crafts; Cards; Games;
  Reading groups; Prayer groups; Movies;
  Shopping trips; Social/Cultural gatherings.

Fircrest School
15230 15th NE, Seattle, WA, 98155
(206) 364-0300
Admin Norm Davis. *Medical Dir/Dir of Nursing* Rosh Doan.
Licensure Intermediate care for mentally retarded. *Beds* ICF/MR 496.
Owner Publicly owned.
Staff Physicians; RNs; LPNs; Physical therapists; Recreational therapists; Occupational therapists; Speech therapists; Dietitians.
Languages Sign
Facilities Dining room; Physical therapy room; Activities room; Chapel; Laundry room; Barber/Beauty shop; Library.
Activities Arts & crafts; Games; Prayer groups; Movies; Shopping trips; Social/Cultural gatherings.

First Hill Care Center
1334 Terry Ave, Seattle, WA, 98104
(206) 624-1484
Admin Ray Billings. *Medical Dir/Dir of Nursing* John Addison MD; Ellen Gerson.
Licensure Skilled care; Intermediate care. *Beds* SNF 181. *Certified* Medicaid; Medicare.
Owner Proprietary Corp (Hillhaven Corp).
Admissions Requirements Minimum age 18; Medical examination; Physician's request.
Staff Physicians 1 (ft); RNs 14 (ft); LPNs 18 (ft); Nurses aides 48 (ft), 27 (pt); Physical therapists 2 (ft); Occupational therapists 1 (ft); Speech therapists 1 (pt); Activities coordinators 1 (ft), 3 (pt); Dietitians 1 (ft); Dentists 1 (pt); Ophthalmologists 1 (pt); Podiatrists 1 (pt).
Facilities Dining room; Physical therapy room; Activities room; Crafts room; Laundry room; Barber/Beauty shop; Library.
Activities Arts & crafts; Cards; Games; Reading groups; Prayer groups; Movies; Shopping trips; Social/Cultural gatherings.

Foss Home
13023 Greenwood Ave N, Seattle, WA, 98133
(206) 364-1300
Admin Joseph J Breznau.
Licensure Skilled care; Intermediate care. *Beds* 211. *Certified* Medicaid.
Owner Nonprofit Corp.

Caroline K Galland Home*
7500 Seward Park Ave S, Seattle, WA, 98118
(206) 725-8800
Admin Joshua Gortler.
Licensure Skilled care; Intermediate care. *Beds* 145. *Certified* Medicaid.
Owner Nonprofit Corp.

Glen Terrace Nursing Center*
10344 14th Ave S, Seattle, WA, 98168
(206) 762-8481
Admin Paul S Groven.
Licensure Skilled care; Intermediate care. *Beds* 204. *Certified* Medicaid; Medicare.
Owner Proprietary Corp (Beverly Enterprises).

Greenery Rehabilitation Center
555 16th Ave, Seattle, WA, 98122
(206) 324-8200
Admin Marlyn M Hathaway. *Medical Dir/Dir of Nursing* Richard Arnold MD; Lani Spencer DON.
Licensure Skilled care; Intermediate care. *Beds* SNF 150; ICF. *Certified* Medicaid; Medicare.
Owner Proprietary Corp.
Admissions Requirements Minimum age 12; Physician's request.
Staff Physicians; RNs; LPNs; Orderlies; Nurses aides; Physical therapists; Recreational therapists; Occupational therapists; Speech therapists; Activities coordinators; Dietitians.
Languages Chinese, Vietnamese

Facilities Dining room; Physical therapy room; Activities room; Crafts room; Laundry room; Barber/Beauty shop; Library.
Activities Arts & crafts; Cards; Games; Reading groups; Prayer groups; Movies; Shopping trips; Social/Cultural gatherings.

Greenwood Park Care Center*
13333 Greenwood Ave N, Seattle, WA, 98133
(206) 362-0303
Admin Thomas E Imel.
Licensure Skilled care; Intermediate care. *Beds* 91. *Certified* Medicaid.
Owner Proprietary Corp.

The Hearthstone
6720 E Green Lake Way N, Seattle, WA, 98103
(206) 525-9666
Admin Richard J Milsow. *Medical Dir/Dir of Nursing* Dr Robert Erickson.
Licensure Skilled care; Intermediate care. *Beds* 51. *Certified* Medicaid; Medicare.
Owner Nonprofit Corp.
Admissions Requirements Minimum age 62; Medical examination; Physician's request.
Staff RNs 5 (ft), 5 (pt); LPNs 2 (ft), 2 (pt); Nurses aides 17 (ft), 8 (pt); Physical therapists 1 (pt); Occupational therapists 1 (pt); Speech therapists 1 (pt); Activities coordinators 1 (ft), 1 (pt); Dietitians 1 (pt); Podiatrists 1 (pt).
Affiliation Lutheran
Facilities Dining room; Activities room; Chapel; Crafts room; Laundry room; Barber/Beauty shop; Library.
Activities Arts & crafts; Cards; Games; Reading groups; Prayer groups; Movies; Shopping trips; Social/Cultural gatherings.

Highline Care Center
220 SW 160th, Seattle, WA, 98166
(206) 243-3056
Admin Elaine Salisbury. *Medical Dir/Dir of Nursing* Dr J M Claunch; Judy McTaggart.
Licensure Intermediate care for mentally retarded. *Beds* 86. *Certified* Medicaid.
Owner Proprietary Corp.
Admissions Requirements Developmental Disability.
Staff Physicians 20 (pt); RNs 3 (ft), 2 (pt); LPNs 6 (ft); Physical therapists 1 (pt); Recreational therapists 2 (ft), 3 (pt); Occupational therapists 1 (pt); Speech therapists 1 (pt); Dietitians 1 (pt); Dentists 1 (pt); Ophthalmologists 1 (pt); Podiatrists 1 (pt); QMRP 3 (ft); Attendant counselors 29 (ft), 4 (pt); Van drivers 3 (ft), 2 (pt).
Facilities Dining room; Physical therapy room; Activities room; Barber/Beauty shop.
Activities Arts & crafts; Games; Movies; Shopping trips; Social/Cultural gatherings; Camping trips; Special Olympics; Field trips.

Hilltop Inn
1625 W Dravus, Seattle, WA, 98119
(206) 722-3289
Admin Ron W Steele. *Medical Dir/Dir of Nursing* Dr Bowden.
Licensure Skilled care; Intermediate care. *Beds* 54. *Certified* Medicaid.
Owner Proprietary Corp.
Admissions Requirements Medical examination; Physician's request.
Staff Physicians 5 (pt); RNs 3 (ft); LPNs 4 (ft), 2 (pt); Orderlies 2 (ft); Nurses aides 17 (ft); Physical therapists 1 (pt); Reality therapists 1 (pt); Recreational therapists 1 (pt); Occupational therapists 1 (pt); Speech therapists 1 (pt); Activities coordinators 1 (ft); Dietitians 1 (pt); Dentists 1 (pt); Ophthalmologists 1 (pt); Podiatrists 1 (pt).
Facilities Dining room; Activities room; Laundry room.
Activities Arts & crafts; Cards; Games; Reading groups; Prayer groups; Movies; Shopping trips; Social/Cultural gatherings.

Horizon House Inc
900 University St, Seattle, WA, 98101
(206) 624-3700
Admin Ann Ewart Hughes. *Medical Dir/Dir of Nursing* Robert Y Erickson MD.
Licensure Skilled care; Intermediate care. *Beds* 56. *Certified* Medicare.
Owner Nonprofit Corp.
Admissions Requirements Medical examination; Physician's request.
Staff Physicians 2 (pt); RNs 9 (ft); LPNs 2 (ft); Nurses aides 27 (ft); Physical therapists 1 (ft); Recreational therapists 1 (ft); Occupational therapists 1 (pt); Speech therapists 1 (pt); Activities coordinators 1 (ft); Dietitians 1 (ft); Ophthalmologists 1 (pt).
Affiliation Church of Christ
Facilities Dining room; Physical therapy room; Activities room; Chapel; Crafts room; Laundry room; Barber/Beauty shop; Library; Dental clinic; Doctors clinic; Physical fitness center; Overnight guest rooms for family members.
Activities Arts & crafts; Cards; Games; Reading groups; Prayer groups; Movies; Shopping trips; Social/Cultural gatherings; Pet therapy.

Jacobsen Nursing Home*
1810 11th Ave, Seattle, WA, 98122
(206) 323-5321
Admin Howard Richardson.
Licensure Skilled care. *Beds* 45.
Owner Proprietary Corp.

Kenney Presbyterian Home
7125 Fauntleroy Way SW, Seattle, WA, 98136
(206) 937-2800
Admin Kenneth D Curry. *Medical Dir/Dir of Nursing* Samuel Peizer MD.
Licensure Skilled care; Intermediate care. *Beds* 53. *Certified* Medicaid.
Owner Nonprofit Corp.
Admissions Requirements Minimum age 60; Medical examination; Physician's request.
Staff Physicians 1 (pt); RNs 3 (ft), 3 (pt); LPNs 1 (ft), 4 (pt); Nurses aides 19 (ft), 3 (pt); Activities coordinators 1 (ft), 2 (pt).
Affiliation Presbyterian
Facilities Dining room; Physical therapy room; Activities room; Chapel; Crafts room; Laundry room; Barber/Beauty shop; Library; Recreation room; Lounges; Sewing room; Wood shop.
Activities Arts & crafts; Cards; Games; Reading groups; Prayer groups; Movies; Shopping trips; Social/Cultural gatherings; Literary guild; Little theatre group; Service projects.

Lockview Nursing Home
4646 36th Ave W, Seattle, WA, 98199
(206) 283-9322
Admin Jan R Reinking. *Medical Dir/Dir of Nursing* Karen Hardin DON.
Licensure Intermediate care. *Beds* ICF 34. *Certified* Medicaid.
Owner Privately owned.
Admissions Requirements Medical examination; Physician's request.
Staff RNs 2 (ft), 1 (pt); LPNs 1 (ft); Orderlies 3 (ft), 1 (pt); Nurses aides 4 (ft), 2 (pt); Activities coordinators 1 (ft).
Facilities Dining room; Activities room; Crafts room; Laundry room; Barber/Beauty shop; Patio areas.
Activities Arts & crafts; Cards; Games; Reading groups; Prayer groups; Movies; Shopping trips; Social/Cultural gatherings; Outdoor recreation.

Malden Nursing Home
PO Box 12011, 526 Malden Ave E, Seattle, WA, 98102
(206) 324-8133
Admin Donald D Dunnagan. *Medical Dir/Dir of Nursing* Danita Shelton.

Licensure Intermediate care. *Beds* 23. *Certified* Medicaid.
Owner Privately owned.
Admissions Requirements Minimum age 35.
Staff RNs 1 (ft); LPNs 3 (ft); Orderlies 2 (ft); Nurses aides 3 (ft); Activities coordinators 1 (ft); Dietitians 1 (ft).
Facilities Dining room; Activities room; Crafts room; Laundry room.
Activities Arts & crafts; Cards; Games; Reading groups; Prayer groups; Movies; Shopping trips; Social/Cultural gatherings; Van outing.

Meadowbrook Nursing & Convalescent Center
3540 NE 110th, Seattle, WA, 98125
(206) 363-7733
Admin Louis E Sternberg. *Medical Dir/Dir of Nursing* Dr Robert Haining; Janine Humphrey.
Licensure Skilled care. *Beds* 47.
Owner Proprietary Corp.
Admissions Requirements Minimum age 18; Medical examination; Physician's request.
Staff RNs 6 (ft), 4 (pt); LPNs 2 (pt); Nurses aides 12 (ft), 13 (pt); Activities coordinators 1 (ft).
Facilities Dining room; Physical therapy room; Activities room; Laundry room; Barber/Beauty shop; Library.
Activities Arts & crafts; Cards; Games; Reading groups; Prayer groups; Movies; Shopping trips.

Moderncare—West Seattle
4700 SW Admiral Way, Seattle, WA, 98116
(206) 935-2480
Admin John W Kirk. *Medical Dir/Dir of Nursing* Samuel Pizer.
Licensure Skilled care; Intermediate care. *Beds* 106. *Certified* Medicaid.
Owner Proprietary Corp.
Admissions Requirements Minimum age 21; Medical examination; Physician's request.
Staff Physicians 6 (ft), 1 (pt); LPNs 4 (ft); Nurses aides 25 (ft); Physical therapists 1 (pt); Reality therapists 1 (pt); Occupational therapists; Speech therapists; Activities coordinators 2 (ft); Dietitians; Dentists; Ophthalmologists; Podiatrists; Dentist.
Facilities Dining room; Physical therapy room; Activities room; Laundry room; Barber/Beauty shop.
Activities Arts & crafts; Cards; Games; Reading groups; Prayer groups; Movies; Shopping trips.

Mt St Vincent Nursing Center
4831 35th Ave SW, Seattle, WA, 98126
(206) 937-3700
Admin Robert Wildenhaus. *Medical Dir/Dir of Nursing* Dr Joseph C M Downs; Margarita Prentice DON.
Licensure Skilled care; Intermediate care. *Beds* 252. *Certified* Medicaid; Medicare.
Owner Nonprofit Corp.
Admissions Requirements Minimum age 18; Females only; Medical examination.
Staff RNs 17 (ft); LPNs 17 (ft); Nurses aides 83 (ft); Physical therapists 1 (ft); Reality therapists 5 (ft); Recreational therapists 5 (ft); Occupational therapists 1 (ft); Speech therapists 1 (ft); Dietitians 2 (ft); Podiatrists 1 (ft); Social workers 3 (ft).
Affiliation Roman Catholic
Facilities Dining room; Physical therapy room; Activities room; Chapel; Crafts room; Laundry room; Barber/Beauty shop; Library; Adult Day Center.
Activities Arts & crafts; Cards; Games; Reading groups; Prayer groups; Movies; Shopping trips; Social/Cultural gatherings; Special events; Bingo; Music therapy; Volunteer programs; Thrift shop.

Norse Home
5311 Phinney Ave N, Seattle, WA, 98103
(783-9600

Admin Dr Robert Solem. *Medical Dir/Dir of Nursing* Dr John Addison; Donna Hawkins MN DON.
Licensure Skilled care. *Beds* SNF 51. *Certified* Medicaid.
Owner Nonprofit Corp.
Admissions Requirements Minimum age 65; Physician's request.
Staff RNs 3 (ft), 2 (pt); LPNs 3 (ft), 3 (pt); Nurses aides 20 (ft), 7 (pt); Recreational therapists 1 (pt); Activities coordinators 1 (ft).
Facilities Dining room; Physical therapy room; Activities room; Barber/Beauty shop.
Activities Arts & crafts; Games; Reading groups; Movies; Social/Cultural gatherings; Music therapy; Pet therapy; Bible study.

Northgate Rehabilitation Center*
10509 Stone Ave N, Seattle, WA, 98133
(206) 524-8300
Admin Mary J Arthur.
Licensure Skilled care; Intermediate care. *Beds* 142. *Certified* Medicaid.
Owner Proprietary Corp (Beverly Enterprises).

Northwest Danish Home
10010 Des Moines Way S, Seattle, WA, 98168
(206) 762-0166
Admin Constance McCracken. *Medical Dir/Dir of Nursing* Thomas E Hulse MD.
Licensure Intermediate care. *Beds* 45. *Certified* Medicaid.
Owner Nonprofit Corp.
Admissions Requirements Minimum age 62; Medical examination.
Staff Physicians 1 (pt); RNs 1 (ft); LPNs 3 (pt); Nurses aides 5 (ft), 4 (pt); Physical therapists 1 (pt); Activities coordinators 1 (ft); Dietitians 1 (pt).
Facilities Dining room; Activities room; Crafts room; Laundry room; Barber/Beauty shop; Library.
Activities Arts & crafts; Cards; Games; Reading groups; Prayer groups; Movies; Social/Cultural gatherings.

Northwest Progressive Care Center
1545 N 120th, Seattle, WA, 98133
(206) 365-8100
Admin C W Schneider. *Medical Dir/Dir of Nursing* Sarah Goodlin MD; Sue Cooke RN DON.
Licensure Skilled care. *Beds* 182. *Certified* Medicaid; Medicare.
Owner Nonprofit Corp.
Admissions Requirements Medical examination.
Staff RNs 5 (ft), 29 (pt); LPNs 7 (ft), 22 (pt); Nurses aides 72 (ft), 15 (pt); Physical therapists 1 (ft); Recreational therapists 2 (ft), 1 (pt); Occupational therapists 1 (ft); Podiatrists Social worker 1 (ft).
Languages Taglog, Cambodian, Korean, Vietnamese, Hindi
Facilities Dining room; Physical therapy room; Activities room; Crafts room; Laundry room; Barber/Beauty shop; Library; Swimming pool; kiln.
Activities Arts & crafts; Cards; Games; Reading groups; Prayer groups; Movies; Shopping trips; Social/Cultural gatherings; Cooking/baking; Pet therapy; Child care program; Gardening; Bookmobile; Exercise; Sing-along; Bowling.

Olympic Crest Convalescent Center
21428 Pacific Hwy S, Seattle, WA, 98198
(206) 878-2042
Admin Myra King.
Licensure Skilled care; Intermediate care. *Beds* 110. *Certified* Medicaid.
Owner Proprietary Corp (Beverly Enterprises).
Facilities Dining room; Physical therapy room; Activities room; Crafts room; Laundry room; Barber/Beauty shop.

Activities Arts & crafts; Games; Reading groups; Prayer groups; Movies; Social/Cultural gatherings.

Park Ridge Care Center Inc
1250 NE 145th St, Seattle, WA, 98155-7134
(206) 363-5856
Admin Doug Swaim. *Medical Dir/Dir of Nursing* Dr George Langmyhr; Donna Chandler RN.
Licensure Skilled care; Intermediate care. *Beds* 128. *Certified* Medicare.
Owner Proprietary Corp.
Admissions Requirements Medical examination; Physician's request.
Staff Physicians 1 (ft); RNs 9 (ft); LPNs 6 (ft); Nurses aides 37 (ft); Activities coordinators 1 (ft).
Facilities Dining room; Physical therapy room; Activities room; Crafts room; Laundry room; Barber/Beauty shop; Library.
Activities Arts & crafts; Cards; Games; Reading groups; Prayer groups; Movies; Shopping trips; Bingo; Pet therapy; Entertainment.

Park Shore
1630 43rd Ave E, Seattle, WA, 98112
(206) 329-0770
Admin Donald R Mickey. *Medical Dir/Dir of Nursing* Dr James Dalton; Mary Schumacher.
Licensure Skilled care; Intermediate care; Nursing home. *Beds* 34.
Owner Nonprofit Corp (Presbyterian Ministeries).
Admissions Requirements Minimum age 62; Medical examination.
Staff Physicians 1 (pt); RNs 4 (ft), 4 (pt); Nurses aides 12 (ft), 6 (pt); Dietitians 1 (ft).
Affiliation Presbyterian
Facilities Dining room; Activities room; Chapel; Laundry room; Barber/Beauty shop; Library.
Activities Arts & crafts; Cards; Games; Reading groups; Prayer groups; Movies.

Park West Care Center
1703 California Ave SW, Seattle, WA, 98116
(206) 937-9750
Admin John W Nugent. *Medical Dir/Dir of Nursing* Dr Hugh Clark.
Licensure Skilled care; Intermediate care. *Beds* 152. *Certified* Medicaid; Medicare.
Owner Proprietary Corp.
Admissions Requirements Medical examination.
Staff Physicians; RNs; LPNs; Orderlies; Nurses aides; Physical therapists; Reality therapists; Recreational therapists; Occupational therapists; Speech therapists; Activities coordinators; Dietitians; Dentists; Ophthalmologists; Podiatrists; Social worker.
Facilities Dining room; Physical therapy room; Activities room; Crafts room; Laundry room; Secured courtyard.
Activities Arts & crafts; Cards; Games; Reading groups; Prayer groups; Movies; Shopping trips; Social/Cultural gatherings.

Parkside Health Care Inc*
620 19th Ave E, Seattle, WA, 98112
(206) 322-2293
Admin Robert E Johnson. *Medical Dir/Dir of Nursing* William Stewart MD.
Licensure Skilled care; Intermediate care. *Beds* 82. *Certified* Medicaid.
Owner Proprietary Corp.
Staff RNs 4 (ft); LPNs 4 (ft); Orderlies 8 (ft), 1 (pt); Nurses aides 28 (ft), 8 (pt); Recreational therapists 1 (ft); Occupational therapists 1 (ft); Activities coordinators 1 (ft); Dietitians 1 (pt).
Facilities Dining room; Physical therapy room; Activities room; Laundry room.
Activities Arts & crafts; Cards; Games; Reading groups; Prayer groups; Movies; Shopping trips.

Pedersen Nursing Home Inc
414 10th Ave, Seattle, WA, 98122
(206) 623-3635, 623-3637
Admin Ida E Israel. *Medical Dir/Dir of Nursing* Thomas Deal MD; Leriza DeCastro DON.
Licensure Intermediate care. *Beds* ICF 37. *Certified* Medicaid.
Owner Proprietary Corp.
Admissions Requirements Minimum age 18.
Staff RNs 1 (ft), 1 (pt); LPNs 1 (ft), 1 (pt); Orderlies 1 (ft), 1 (pt); Nurses aides 3 (ft), 3 (pt); Activities coordinators 1 (ft); Dietitians 1 (pt).
Languages Spanish
Facilities Dining room; Activities room; Crafts room; Laundry room; Barber/Beauty shop.
Activities Arts & crafts; Cards; Games; Reading groups; Prayer groups; Movies; Shopping trips; Social/Cultural gatherings.

Pinehurst Convalescent Center Inc*
11039 17th NE, Seattle, WA, 98125
(206) 363-5490
Admin David Masterjohn. *Medical Dir/Dir of Nursing* Dr Roys.
Licensure Intermediate care. *Beds* 61. *Certified* Medicaid.
Owner Proprietary Corp (Beverly Enterprises).
Admissions Requirements Physician's request.
Staff RNs 1 (ft); LPNs 5 (ft); Orderlies 2 (ft); Nurses aides 14 (pt); Physical therapists 1 (pt); Recreational therapists 1 (pt); Occupational therapists 1 (pt); Activities coordinators 1 (pt); Dietitians 1 (ft); Dentists 1 (pt); Ophthalmologists 1 (pt); Podiatrists 1 (pt).
Facilities Dining room; Activities room; Laundry room.
Activities Arts & crafts; Cards; Games; Reading groups; Prayer groups; Movies; Shopping trips; Social/Cultural gatherings; Horse races.

Pinehurst Park Terrace*
2818 NE 145th St, Seattle, WA, 98155
(206) 364-8810
Admin David A Ostlie. *Medical Dir/Dir of Nursing* George Zerr MD.
Licensure Skilled care; Intermediate care. *Beds* 200. *Certified* Medicaid.
Owner Proprietary Corp (Beverly Enterprises).
Facilities Dining room; Physical therapy room; Activities room; Crafts room; Laundry room; Barber/Beauty shop.
Activities Arts & crafts; Cards; Games; Reading groups; Prayer groups; Movies; Shopping trips.

Queen Anne Villa Care Center*
2717 Dexter Ave N, Seattle, WA, 98109
(206) 284-7012
Admin Joseph A Buck.
Licensure Skilled care; Intermediate care. *Beds* 174. *Certified* Medicaid; Medicare.
Owner Proprietary Corp (Hillhaven Corp).

Restorative Care Center
2821 S Walden St, Seattle, WA, 98144
(206) 725-2800
Admin David Langdon. *Medical Dir/Dir of Nursing* Shirley Gilday DON.
Licensure Skilled care; Intermediate care; Rehab/Restorative/Specialty. *Beds* 189. *Certified* Medicaid; Medicare.
Owner Proprietary Corp.
Admissions Requirements Medical examination; Physician's request.
Staff Physicians 1 (pt); RNs 6 (ft), 7 (pt); LPNs 11 (ft), 6 (pt); Nurses aides 70 (ft), 9 (pt); Physical therapists 1 (pt); Occupational therapists 1 (pt); Speech therapists 1 (pt); Activities coordinators 1 (ft); Dietitians 1 (pt); Dentists 1 (pt); Ophthalmologists 1 (pt); Podiatrists 1 (pt).

Facilities Dining room; Physical therapy room; Activities room; Chapel; Crafts room; Laundry room; Barber/Beauty shop.
Activities Arts & crafts; Cards; Games; Reading groups; Prayer groups; Movies; Shopping trips; Social/Cultural gatherings.

Riverton Heights Convalescent Home*
2849 S 127th, Seattle, WA, 98168
(206) 243-0200
Admin Henri G Trueba.
Licensure Skilled care; Intermediate care. *Beds* 70. *Certified* Medicaid.
Owner Proprietary Corp.

Seattle Keiro
1601 Yesler Way, Seattle, WA, 98122-5640
(206) 329-9575
Admin Russell Akiyama. *Medical Dir/Dir of Nursing* Ruby Inouye MD.
Licensure Skilled care; Intermediate care. *Beds* 63. *Certified* Medicaid.
Owner Nonprofit Corp.
Admissions Requirements Physician's request.
Staff RNs 6 (ft); LPNs 1 (ft), 2 (pt); Nurses aides 22 (ft), 6 (pt); Physical therapists 1 (pt); Occupational therapists 1 (pt); Speech therapists 1 (pt); Activities coordinators 1 (ft), 2 (pt); Dietitians 1 (pt); Dentists 1 (pt).
Facilities Dining room; Physical therapy room; Activities room; Chapel; Laundry room; Library.
Activities Arts & crafts; Games; Reading groups; Prayer groups; Movies; Shopping trips; Social/Cultural gatherings; Crafts; Flower arranging; Singing.

Seattle Specialized Group Home
7347 Dibble Ave NW, Seattle, WA, 98117
(206) 782-0149
Admin Jane Stangle.
Licensure Intermediate care for mentally retarded. *Beds* 6.
Owner Nonprofit Corp.

Sunshine Vista*
1732 16th Ave, Seattle, WA, 98122
(206) 329-5775
Admin Beverly R McKnight.
Licensure Skilled care; Intermediate care. *Beds* 37. *Certified* Medicaid; Medicare.
Owner Proprietary Corp.

Terrace View Convalescent Center Inc*
1701 18th Ave S, Seattle, WA, 98144
(206) 329-9586
Admin Philip Gayton. *Medical Dir/Dir of Nursing* James B Bushyhead MD.
Licensure Skilled care; Intermediate care. *Beds* 115. *Certified* Medicaid; Medicare.
Owner Proprietary Corp.
Admissions Requirements Minimum age 18; Medical examination; Physician's request.
Staff RNs 10 (ft), 2 (pt); LPNs 6 (ft), 2 (pt); Nurses aides 30 (ft), 15 (pt); Physical therapists 1 (ft), 1 (pt); Activities coordinators 1 (ft); Dietitians 1 (ft), 1 (pt).
Facilities Dining room; Physical therapy room; Activities room; Chapel; Crafts room; Laundry room; Barber/Beauty shop; Library.
Activities Arts & crafts; Cards; Games; Reading groups; Prayer groups; Movies; Shopping trips; Social/Cultural gatherings.

United Cerebral Palsy Residential Center
PO Box 77048, 14910 1st Ave NE, Seattle, WA, 98177
(206) 363-7303
Admin Paul McNain. *Medical Dir/Dir of Nursing* Kathryn Zufall-Larson MD.
Licensure Intermediate care for mentally retarded. *Beds* ICF/MR 110.
Owner Nonprofit Corp.
Admissions Requirements Minimum age 18.
Staff RNs; LPNs; Physical therapists; Recreational therapists; Occupational therapists; Speech therapists; Dietitians.

Facilities Dining room; Physical therapy room; Activities room; Chapel.
Activities Arts & crafts; Cards; Games; Reading groups; Movies; Shopping trips; Social/Cultural gatherings; Art Programs.

SEDRO WOOLLEY

Skagit Valley Convalescent Center Inc
2019 Hwy 20, Sedro Woolley, WA, 98284
(206) 856-6867
Admin Patricia Swaner. *Medical Dir/Dir of Nursing* Karen Axelson RN.
Licensure Skilled care; Intermediate care. *Beds* 104. *Certified* Medicaid; VA.
Owner Proprietary Corp.
Admissions Requirements Physician's request.
Staff RNs 6 (ft), 2 (pt); LPNs 10 (ft), 4 (pt); Nurses aides 30 (ft), 8 (pt); Activities coordinators 1 (ft); Dietitians 1 (ft).
Facilities Dining room; Physical therapy room; Activities room; Crafts room; Barber/Beauty shop.
Activities Arts & crafts; Cards; Games; Reading groups; Prayer groups; Movies; Shopping trips; Social/Cultural gatherings; Sign language class.

SELAH

Selah Convalescent Home Inc
PO Box 157, 203 W Naches Ave, Selah, WA, 98942
(509) 697-8503
Admin Carol J Hyatt. *Medical Dir/Dir of Nursing* Adelyn Mohagen.
Licensure Intermediate care. *Beds* 38. *Certified* Medicaid.
Owner Proprietary Corp.
Staff RNs 2 (ft), 1 (pt); LPNs 3 (ft), 1 (pt); Nurses aides 9 (ft); Activities coordinators 1 (pt); Dietitians 1 (pt); Ophthalmologists 1 (pt).
Languages Spanish
Activities Arts & crafts; Cards; Games; Reading groups; Prayer groups; Movies; Shopping trips; Social/Cultural gatherings; Bowling; Walking program.

SEQUIM

Olympic Health Care Inc
1000 5th Ave S, Sequim, WA, 98382
(206) 683-1112
Admin Kerry Hansen.
Licensure Skilled care; Intermediate care. *Beds* 60. *Certified* Medicaid; Medicare.
Owner Proprietary Corp.

Sequim Nursing Center
PO Box 726, 408 W Washington, Sequim, WA, 98382
(206) 683-4184
Admin Elmer A Erban. *Medical Dir/Dir of Nursing* Allen Berry MD; Iveigh B Erban RN DON.
Licensure Skilled care; Intermediate care; VA; Private. *Beds* 102. *Certified* Medicaid; Medicare; VA; Private.
Owner Proprietary Corp (International Health Care Management).
Admissions Requirements Medical examination.
Staff Physicians 1 (ft); RNs 5 (ft); LPNs 7 (ft); Orderlies 4 (ft); Nurses aides 40 (ft); Physical therapists 1 (ft); Reality therapists 1 (ft); Occupational therapists 1 (pt); Speech therapists 1 (pt); Activities coordinators 1 (ft); Dietitians 1 (pt); Dentists 1 (pt); Ophthalmologists 1 (pt); Podiatrists 1 (pt).
Facilities Dining room; Physical therapy room; Activities room; Crafts room; Laundry room; Barber/Beauty shop; Library.

Activities Arts & crafts; Cards; Games; Reading groups; Prayer groups; Movies; Shopping trips; Social/Cultural gatherings; Bingo; Teas; BBQs.

Sherwood Manor Inc*
PO Box 1630, 550 Hendrickson Rd, Sequim, WA, 98382
(206) 683-3348
Admin William Littlejohn.
Licensure Skilled care; Intermediate care. *Beds* 60. *Certified* Medicaid.
Owner Proprietary Corp.

SHELTON

Fir Lane Terrace Convalescent Center
2430 N 13th St, Shelton, WA, 98584
(206) 426-1651
Admin Roberta L Goodwin. *Medical Dir/Dir of Nursing* Dr Tim Weber; Linda Elvin DNS.
Licensure Skilled care; Intermediate care. *Beds* 120. *Certified* Medicaid; Medicare; VA.
Owner Proprietary Corp.
Admissions Requirements Physician's request.
Facilities Dining room; Physical therapy room; Activities room; Crafts room; Laundry room; Barber/Beauty shop.
Activities Arts & crafts; Cards; Games; Reading groups; Prayer groups; Movies; Social/Cultural gatherings.

SILVERDALE

Martin Street Group Home*
8814 Martin St, Silverdale, WA, 98370
(206) 692-3062
Admin Molly Harris.
Licensure Intermediate care for mentally retarded. *Beds* 6.
Owner Nonprofit Corp.

SNOHOMISH

Delta Rehabilitation Center*
1705 Terrace, Snohomish, WA, 98290
(206) 568-2168
Admin Wallace J Walsh.
Licensure Skilled care; Intermediate care. *Beds* 139. *Certified* Medicaid.
Owner Proprietary Corp.

Hollycrest Home Inc
124 Ave B, Snohomish, WA, 98290
(206) 568-1535
Admin Linda Moe.
Licensure Intermediate care for mentally retarded. *Beds* 32. *Certified* Medicaid.
Owner Nonprofit Corp.

Merry Haven Health Care Center
800 10th St, Snohomish, WA, 98290
(206) 568-3161
Admin Kathleen Taylor. *Medical Dir/Dir of Nursing* Karen Crawford.
Licensure Skilled care; Intermediate care. *Beds* 91. *Certified* Medicaid.
Owner Proprietary Corp.
Admissions Requirements Minimum age 18; Medical examination.
Staff RNs 10 (ft); LPNs 10 (ft); Orderlies 35; Nurses aides; Recreational therapists 2 (ft); Dietitians 1 (ft).
Facilities Dining room; Physical therapy room; Activities room; Chapel; Crafts room; Laundry room; Barber/Beauty shop.
Activities Arts & crafts; Cards; Games; Reading groups; Prayer groups; Movies; Shopping trips; Social/Cultural gatherings.

Parkway Nursing Center*
525 13th St, Snohomish, WA, 98290
(206) 568-8566
Admin Carroll E Heffron Jr. *Medical Dir/Dir of Nursing* Melvin Nelson MD.

Licensure Skilled care; Intermediate care. *Beds* 119. *Certified* Medicaid.
Owner Proprietary Corp.
Admissions Requirements Medical examination; Physician's request.
Staff RNs 6 (ft), 3 (pt); LPNs 3 (ft), 3 (pt); Nurses aides 37 (ft), 4 (pt); Physical therapists 1 (pt); Reality therapists 1 (ft); Recreational therapists 1 (ft); Occupational therapists 1 (pt); Speech therapists 1 (pt); Activities coordinators 1 (ft), 1 (pt); Dietitians 1 (pt); Dentists 1 (pt).
Facilities Dining room; Physical therapy room; Activities room; Chapel; Crafts room; Laundry room; Barber/Beauty shop; Library.
Activities Arts & crafts; Cards; Games; Reading groups; Prayer groups; Movies; Shopping trips; Social/Cultural gatherings.

SOAP LAKE

McKay Memorial
PO Box 818, Soap Lake, WA, 98851
(509) 246-1111
Admin Kenneth V Buell. *Medical Dir/Dir of Nursing* Sara Minor.
Licensure Skilled care; Intermediate care. *Beds* SNF 42; ICF. *Certified* Medicaid.
Owner Nonprofit Corp.
Admissions Requirements Medical examination; Physician's request.
Staff Physicians 5 (ft); RNs 3 (ft), 1 (pt); LPNs 3 (ft); Nurses aides 12 (ft), 9 (pt); Activities coordinators 1 (ft); Dietitians 1 (ft).
Facilities Dining room; Activities room; Crafts room; Laundry room; Barber/Beauty shop.
Activities Arts & crafts; Cards; Games; Reading groups; Prayer groups; Movies; Shopping trips; Social/Cultural gatherings.

SPOKANE

Alderwood Manor Nursing & Convalescent Center
3600 E Hartson Ave, Spokane, WA, 99216
(509) 535-2071
Admin Kay A Corder. *Medical Dir/Dir of Nursing* Eric Paulson MD.
Licensure Skilled care; Intermediate care. *Beds* SNF 85; ICF. *Certified* Medicaid; Medicare.
Owner Proprietary Corp.
Admissions Requirements Medical examination; Physician's request.
Staff Physicians 40 (pt); RNs 7 (ft); LPNs 6 (ft); Orderlies 3 (ft); Nurses aides 22 (ft), 4 (pt); Occupational therapists 1 (pt); Speech therapists 1 (pt); Activities coordinators 1 (ft); Dietitians 1 (pt); Ophthalmologists 1 (pt).
Facilities Dining room; Physical therapy room; Activities room; Crafts room; Laundry room; Barber/Beauty shop.
Activities Arts & crafts; Cards; Games; Reading groups; Prayer groups; Movies; Social/Cultural gatherings.

Cliff Manor*
W 427 7th Ave, Spokane, WA, 99204
(509) 624-2324
Admin Judith Emerson.
Licensure Skilled care; Intermediate care. *Beds* 88. *Certified* Medicaid.
Owner Proprietary Corp.

Echo Specialized Group Home*
W 631 Waverly Pl, Spokane, WA, 99205
(509) 328-8181
Admin Kathy Thorson.
Licensure Intermediate care for mentally retarded. *Beds* 8.
Owner Proprietary Corp.

Garden Terrace Manor*
W 424 7th, Spokane, WA, 99204
(509) 838-8233

Admin Grace Ellis.
Licensure Skilled care; Intermediate care. *Beds* 120. *Certified* Medicaid; Medicare.
Owner Proprietary Corp.

Hawthorne Manor Retirement Residence
E 101 Hawthorne Rd, Spokane, WA, 99218
(509) 466-0411
Admin Don Ratliff. *Medical Dir/Dir of Nursing* Pat Tolbert.
Licensure CCRC with Health care center. *Beds* Nursing home 20.
Owner Nonprofit Corp.
Admissions Requirements Minimum age 62; Medical examination.
Staff RNs 1 (ft), 6 (pt); LPNs 1 (ft), 2 (pt); Nurses aides 6 (ft), 7 (pt); Activities coordinators 1 (ft), 1 (pt).
Affiliation Presbyterian
Facilities Dining room; Activities room; Crafts room; Laundry room; Barber/Beauty shop; Library.
Activities Arts & crafts; Cards; Games; Reading groups; Prayer groups; Movies; Shopping trips; Social/Cultural gatherings; Community sings; Aerobic exercises; Music appreciation.

Keller Nursing Home
W 1117 10th Ave, Spokane, WA, 99204
(509) 624-7632
Admin Patsy Keller.
Licensure Nursing home. *Beds* 22.
Owner Proprietary Corp.

Kirbyhaven*
E 10506 10th Ave, Spokane, WA, 99206
(509) 924-6111
Admin LeAnn Springer.
Licensure Intermediate care for mentally retarded. *Beds* 57. *Certified* Medicaid.
Owner Proprietary Corp.

Latah Center Inc
S 5913 Inland Empire Way, Spokane, WA, 99204
(509) 448-2262
Admin Julie J Landwehr. *Medical Dir/Dir of Nursing* Hershel Zellman MD; Patti Hundeby RN DON.
Licensure Intermediate care for mentally retarded. *Beds* ICF/MR 40. *Certified* Medicaid.
Owner Proprietary Corp.
Admissions Requirements Minimum age 18.
Staff Physicians 1 (pt); RNs 2 (ft); LPNs 3 (ft); Nurses aides 14 (ft), 4 (pt); Physical therapists 1 (pt); Recreational therapists 2 (ft); Occupational therapists 1 (pt); Speech therapists 1 (pt); Dietitians 1 (pt); Dentists 1 (pt); Ophthalmologists 1 (pt); Podiatrists 1 (pt).
Facilities Dining room; Activities room; Laundry room.
Activities Arts & crafts; Cards; Games; Movies; Shopping trips; Social/Cultural gatherings.

Lilac City Convalescent Center
E 1707 Rowan Ave, Spokane, WA, 99207
(509) 489-1427
Admin Kerry Arbuckle. *Medical Dir/Dir of Nursing* Leonard Vanderbosch MD; Jay Waddell RN.
Licensure Skilled care. *Beds* SNF 52. *Certified* Medicaid.
Owner Proprietary Corp (Beverly Enterprises).
Admissions Requirements Minimum age 18; Physician's request.
Staff RNs 4 (ft), 1 (pt); LPNs 2 (ft); Orderlies; Nurses aides 24 (ft); Activities coordinators 1 (ft); Office manager.
Facilities Dining room; Physical therapy room; Activities room; Laundry room; Barber/Beauty shop.
Activities Arts & crafts; Cards; Games; Reading groups; Prayer groups; Movies; Shopping trips; Social/Cultural gatherings.

Mansion House Nursing Home*
E 3011 Wellesley, Spokane, WA, 99207
(509) 489-8825
Admin Donald Halverson. *Medical Dir/Dir of Nursing* Dr Van Veen.
Licensure Skilled care; Intermediate care. *Beds* 67. *Certified* Medicaid.
Owner Proprietary Corp.
Staff RNs 3 (ft); LPNs 6 (ft); Nurses aides 20 (ft); Physical therapists 1 (ft); Activities coordinators 1 (ft); Dietitians 1 (pt).
Facilities Dining room; Physical therapy room; Activities room; Crafts room; Laundry room; Barber/Beauty shop.
Activities Arts & crafts; Cards; Games; Reading groups; Prayer groups; Movies.

Northwest Convalescent Center*
W 618 Nora, Spokane, WA, 99205
(509) 328-6030
Admin Robert Avey Jr.
Licensure Skilled care; Intermediate care. *Beds* 101. *Certified* Medicaid.
Owner Proprietary Corp.

Regency Care Center of Spokane
E 44 Cozza Dr, Spokane, WA, 99208
(509) 489-5652
Admin Sharon Ahonen. *Medical Dir/Dir of Nursing* Arthur Craig MD; Alice J Brown RN.
Licensure Skilled care; Intermediate care. *Beds* 137. *Certified* Medicaid; VA.
Owner Proprietary Corp (Regency Health Care Centers).
Admissions Requirements Medical examination; Physician's request.
Staff RNs 7 (ft), 5 (pt); LPNs 7 (ft), 7 (pt); Nurses aides 49 (ft), 10 (pt); Occupational therapists 1 (pt); Speech therapists 1 (pt); Activities coordinators 2 (ft); Dietitians 1 (ft), 1 (pt); Ophthalmologists 1 (pt).
Facilities Dining room; Physical therapy room; Activities room; Laundry room; Barber/Beauty shop.
Activities Arts & crafts; Cards; Games; Reading groups; Prayer groups; Movies; Shopping trips; Social/Cultural gatherings.

Regency South Care Center*
S 518 Browne St, Spokane, WA, 99204
(509) 455-9710
Admin Kittie Lindsay. *Medical Dir/Dir of Nursing* Michael Higgins MD.
Licensure Skilled care; Intermediate care. *Beds* 84. *Certified* Medicaid.
Owner Proprietary Corp (Regency Health Care Centers).
Admissions Requirements Physician's request.
Staff Physicians 2 (pt); RNs 5 (ft), 2 (pt); LPNs 8 (ft), 1 (pt); Orderlies 2 (ft); Nurses aides 26 (ft), 2 (pt); Physical therapists 1 (pt); Recreational therapists 1 (pt); Activities coordinators 1 (pt); Dietitians 1 (pt); Dentists 1 (pt); Ophthalmologists 1 (pt); Podiatrists 1 (pt).
Facilities Dining room; Activities room; Crafts room; Laundry room.
Activities Arts & crafts; Cards; Games; Reading groups; Prayer groups; Movies; Shopping trips; Social/Cultural gatherings.

Riverpart Convalescent Center
W 4444 Downriver Dr, Spokane, WA, 99205
(509) 326-6711
Admin Robert Avey Jr. *Medical Dir/Dir of Nursing* Dr Frank Vanveen; Leslie Proctor.
Licensure Skilled care; Intermediate care. *Beds* SNF 136; ICF. *Certified* Medicaid.
Owner Proprietary Corp.
Staff RNs 5 (ft), 1 (pt); LPNs 7 (ft), 2 (pt); Orderlies 15 (ft); Nurses aides 31 (ft); Physical therapists 1 (ft); Occupational therapists 1 (ft); Activities coordinators 1 (ft); Dietitians 1 (ft).

Facilities Dining room; Activities room; Laundry room; Library.
Activities Arts & crafts; Cards; Games; Reading groups; Prayer groups; Movies; Shopping trips; Social/Cultural gatherings.

Riverview Lutheran Memorial Care Center
E 1841 Upriver Dr, Spokane, WA, 99207
(509) 489-4466
Admin Gene Larson. *Medical Dir/Dir of Nursing* Alex Van Derwilde MD.
Licensure Skilled care; Intermediate care. *Beds* 75. *Certified* Medicaid; Medicare.
Owner Nonprofit Corp.
Admissions Requirements Minimum age 55.
Affiliation Lutheran
Facilities Dining room; Physical therapy room; Activities room; Chapel; Crafts room; Laundry room; Barber/Beauty shop; Library.
Activities Arts & crafts; Cards; Games; Prayer groups; Movies; Shopping trips; Social/Cultural gatherings.

Rockwood Manor Infirmary
E 2903 25th Ave, Spokane, WA, 99223
(509) 536-6650
Admin Daniel M Chapman. *Medical Dir/Dir of Nursing* Eric Mahnke RN.
Licensure Skilled care; Intermediate care. *Beds* SNF 44. *Certified* Medicare.
Owner Nonprofit Corp.
Admissions Requirements Minimum age 65; Medical examination.
Staff RNs 9 (ft); LPNs 8 (ft); Orderlies 2 (ft); Nurses aides 15 (ft); Physical therapists 1 (pt); Recreational therapists 1 (ft); Occupational therapists 1 (pt); Speech therapists 1 (pt); Activities coordinators 1 (ft); Dietitians 1 (pt); Dentists 1 (pt); Ophthalmologists 1 (pt); Podiatrists 1 (pt).
Affiliation Methodist
Facilities Dining room; Physical therapy room; Activities room; Chapel; Crafts room; Laundry room; Barber/Beauty shop; Library.
Activities Arts & crafts; Cards; Games; Reading groups; Prayer groups; Movies; Shopping trips; Social/Cultural gatherings.

St Brendan Care Center
E 17 8th Ave, Spokane, WA, 99202
(509) 624-1161
Admin Kenneth J Corman. *Medical Dir/Dir of Nursing* Dr Arthur Craig.
Licensure Skilled care; Intermediate care; Respite care. *Beds* 177. *Certified* Medicaid; Medicare.
Owner Proprietary Corp.
Admissions Requirements Physician's request.
Staff Physicians 1 (pt); RNs 10 (ft); LPNs 15 (ft); Nurses aides 75 (ft); Physical therapists 1 (ft); Occupational therapists 1 (pt); Speech therapists 1 (pt); Activities coordinators 2 (ft); Dietitians 1 (ft); Dentists 1 (pt).
Facilities Dining room; Physical therapy room; Activities room; Crafts room; Laundry room; Barber/Beauty shop; Library.
Activities Arts & crafts; Cards; Games; Reading groups; Prayer groups; Movies; Shopping trips; Social/Cultural gatherings.

St Joseph Care Center
20 W 9th Ave, Spokane, WA, 99204
(509) 838-6437, 838-6438, 838-6439
Admin Sr Vincenza Dufresne. *Medical Dir/Dir of Nursing* Dr Richard Bale.
Licensure Skilled care; Intermediate care. *Beds* SNF 88; ICF 15. *Certified* Medicaid.
Owner Nonprofit Corp.
Admissions Requirements Medical examination; Physician's request.
Staff Physicians 1 (pt); RNs 12 (pt); LPNs 1 (pt); Nurses aides 36 (ft), 10 (pt); Physical therapists 3 (ft), 1 (pt); Recreational therapists 1 (pt); Occupational therapists 1 (pt); Speech therapists 1 (pt); Dietitians 1 (pt); Dentists 1 (pt); Ophthalmologists 1 (pt).
Languages French
Affiliation Roman Catholic

Facilities Dining room; Physical therapy room; Activities room; Chapel; Crafts room; Laundry room; Barber/Beauty shop; Library.
Activities Arts & crafts; Cards; Games; Reading groups; Prayer groups; Movies; Shopping trips.

St Jude's Health Care Center
1521 E Illinois, Spokane, WA, 99207
(509) 484-3132
Admin Florence Davis Reynolds. *Medical Dir/Dir of Nursing* F L Van Veen MD; Ronda Truppe RN DON.
Licensure Intermediate care. *Beds* ICF 45. *Certified* Medicaid.
Owner Privately owned.
Admissions Requirements Medical examination; Physician's request.
Staff Physicians 1 (ft); RNs 5 (ft), 1 (pt); LPNs 4 (ft); Orderlies 1 (ft), 1 (pt); Nurses aides 9 (ft), 2 (pt); Reality therapists 1 (ft); Activities coordinators 1 (ft); Dietitians 1 (pt).
Languages German, Japanese
Facilities Dining room; Laundry room.
Activities Arts & crafts; Cards; Games; Reading groups; Prayer groups; Movies; Shopping trips; Social/Cultural gatherings.

Senior Citizens Nursing Home
N 2659 Ash, Spokane, WA, 99205
(509) 327-7728
Admin L Jones. *Medical Dir/Dir of Nursing* Patricia A Friedland.
Licensure Intermediate care. *Beds* 24.
Owner Proprietary Corp (Regency Health Care Centers).
Staff Physicians; RNs; LPNs; Orderlies; Nurses aides; Physical therapists; Reality therapists; Recreational therapists; Occupational therapists; Speech therapists; Activities coordinators; Dietitians; Dentists; Ophthalmologists; Podiatrists.
Activities Arts & crafts; Cards; Games; Reading groups; Prayer groups; Movies.

Southcrest Convalescent Center*
W 110 Cliff ı Grand Blvd, Spokane, WA, 99204
(509) 456-8300
Admin Monica Roy. *Medical Dir/Dir of Nursing* Dr F Claude Manning.
Licensure Skilled care; Intermediate care. *Beds* 212. *Certified* Medicaid; Medicare.
Owner Proprietary Corp (Unicare).
Admissions Requirements Medical examination; Physician's request.
Staff RNs 15 (ft); LPNs 11 (ft); Nurses aides 57 (ft); Physical therapists 2 (ft); Recreational therapists 2 (ft); Speech therapists; Dietitians 1 (ft); Dentists; Podiatrists.
Facilities Dining room; Physical therapy room; Activities room; Chapel; Crafts room; Laundry room; Barber/Beauty shop; Library.
Activities Arts & crafts; Cards; Games; Reading groups; Prayer groups; Movies; Shopping trips; Social/Cultural gatherings.

Sunshine Gardens
10410 E 9th Ave, Spokane, WA, 99206
(509) 926-3547
Admin Margaret C Dikes. *Medical Dir/Dir of Nursing* Dr Robert Eastwood.
Licensure Intermediate care. *Beds* 57. *Certified* Medicaid.
Owner Proprietary Corp.
Staff RNs 1 (ft), 2 (pt); LPNs 1 (ft), 2 (pt); Orderlies 1 (ft), 2 (pt); Nurses aides 5 (ft), 5 (pt); Activities coordinators 1 (ft), 2 (pt).
Facilities Dining room; Activities room; Crafts room; Laundry room.
Activities Arts & crafts; Cards; Games; Reading groups; Prayer groups; Movies; Shopping trips; Social/Cultural gatherings.

Unicrest
S 414 University Rd, Spokane, WA, 99206
(509) 924-4650
Admin Cheryl Niccolls. *Medical Dir/Dir of Nursing* Robert Matthias; Mary Olmsted.
Licensure Skilled care; Intermediate care. *Beds* 115. *Certified* Medicaid; Medicare.
Owner Proprietary Corp (Unicare).
Admissions Requirements Medical examination; Physician's request.
Staff Physicians; RNs 5 (ft), 2 (pt); LPNs 11 (ft), 1 (pt); Orderlies; Nurses aides 66 (ft), 3 (pt); Activities coordinators 2 (ft); Dietitians 1 (ft); Ophthalmologists.
Facilities Dining room; Physical therapy room; Activities room; Laundry room; Barber/Beauty shop; Library.
Activities Arts & crafts; Cards; Games; Prayer groups; Movies; Shopping trips; Social/Cultural gatherings.

Washington Health Care Center—Northcrest
N 6021 Lidgerwood, Spokane, WA, 99207
(509) 489-3323
Admin Vicki McKenna. *Medical Dir/Dir of Nursing* Lana Boteler.
Licensure Skilled care. *Beds* SNF 163. *Certified* Medicaid; Medicare.
Owner Proprietary Corp (Unicare).
Staff RNs 5 (ft), 5 (pt).
Facilities Dining room; Physical therapy room; Activities room; Laundry room; Barber/Beauty shop.
Activities Arts & crafts; Cards; Games; Reading groups; Prayer groups; Movies; Shopping trips; Social/Cultural gatherings.

Washington Health Care Center—Valley Crest
E 12715 Mission Ave, Spokane, WA, 99216
(509) 924-3040
Admin David Murphy. *Medical Dir/Dir of Nursing* Laurina Worth MD; Kathi Wenzel.
Licensure Skilled care; Intermediate care. *Beds* SNF 190; ICF. *Certified* Medicaid; Medicare.
Owner Proprietary Corp (Unicare).
Staff RNs 7 (ft); LPNs 12 (ft); Nurses aides 40 (ft); Recreational therapists 1 (ft); Activities coordinators 1 (ft); Dietitians 1 (ft); Dentist 1 (pt).
Facilities Dining room; Physical therapy room; Activities room; Barber/Beauty shop.
Activities Arts & crafts; Cards; Games; Prayer groups; Movies; Shopping trips; Social/Cultural gatherings.

STANWOOD

Josephine Sunset Home*
PO Box 374, 9901 272nd Pl NW, Stanwood, WA, 98292
(206) 629-2126
Admin Kenneth M Taylor.
Licensure Skilled care; Intermediate care. *Beds* 160. *Certified* Medicaid.
Owner Nonprofit Corp.
Admissions Requirements Minimum age 19.
Staff Physicians 1 (pt); RNs 9 (ft), 8 (pt); LPNs 6 (ft), 9 (pt); Nurses aides 54 (ft), 10 (pt); Activities coordinators 1 (ft).
Affiliation Lutheran
Facilities Dining room; Physical therapy room; Activities room; Chapel; Crafts room; Laundry room; Barber/Beauty shop; Library.
Activities Arts & crafts; Cards; Games; Reading groups; Prayer groups; Movies; Shopping trips; Social/Cultural gatherings.

Warm Beach Health Care Center
20420 Marine Dr NW, Stanwood, WA, 98292
(206) 652-7585
Admin David M Belcher. *Medical Dir/Dir of Nursing* Dr Mark Spencer.
Licensure Skilled care; Intermediate care. *Beds* SNF 81; ICF. *Certified* Medicaid.
Owner Nonprofit Corp.

Staff RNs 5 (ft), 4 (pt); LPNs 3 (ft), 2 (pt); Nurses aides 30 (ft), 8 (pt); Physical therapists 1 (pt); Reality therapists 1 (pt); Activities coordinators 1 (ft); Dietitians 1 (pt).
Affiliation Methodist
Facilities Dining room; Physical therapy room; Activities room; Crafts room; Laundry room; Barber/Beauty shop; Library; Swimming pool; Atrium; Gazebo.
Activities Arts & crafts; Games; Prayer groups; Movies; Shopping trips; Bowling; Swimming; Ceramics; Sing-alongs.

SUMNER

Sumner Lodge
PO Box P, 1723 Bonney Ave, Sumner, WA, 98390
(206) 863-4425
Admin Kathleen A Kinkade.
Licensure Intermediate care for mentally retarded. *Beds* 43. *Certified* Medicaid.
Owner Proprietary Corp.

SUNNYSIDE

Hillcrest Manor—Sunnyside
PO Box 876, 721 Otis, Sunnyside, WA, 98944
(509) 837-2122
Admin Mary Arthur. *Medical Dir/Dir of Nursing* Dr Arnold Tait.
Licensure Skilled care; Intermediate care. *Beds* 84. *Certified* Medicaid; Medicare.
Owner Proprietary Corp (Beverly Enterprises).
Admissions Requirements Medical examination; Physician's request.
Staff RNs 6 (ft), 3 (pt); LPNs 4 (ft), 2 (pt); Nurses aides 18 (ft), 12 (pt); Physical therapists 1 (pt); Recreational therapists 1 (ft); Activities coordinators 1 (ft), 1 (pt); Dietitians 1 (ft).
Facilities Dining room; Physical therapy room; Activities room; Chapel; Crafts room; Laundry room; Barber/Beauty shop; Day room.
Activities Arts & crafts; Cards; Games; Reading groups; Prayer groups; Movies; Shopping trips; Social/Cultural gatherings.

Sunny Haven Convalescent Center
1313 S 6th, Sunnyside, WA, 98944
(509) 837-4200
Admin Chuck Gilman. *Medical Dir/Dir of Nursing* Arnold Tait MD; Theresa Scofield RN DON.
Licensure Intermediate care for mentally retarded. *Beds* ICF/MR 45. *Certified* Medicaid.
Owner Proprietary Corp (Beverly Enterprises).
Admissions Requirements Minimum age 18.
Staff Physicians 1 (pt); RNs 6 (ft); LPNs 3 (ft); Nurses aides 31 (ft); Physical therapists 1 (pt); Occupational therapists 1 (pt); Speech therapists 1 (pt); Activities coordinators 1 (ft); Dietitians 1 (pt); Podiatrists 1 (pt).
Languages Spanish, Sign
Facilities Dining room; Physical therapy room; Activities room; Laundry room; Barber/Beauty shop.
Activities Arts & crafts; Cards; Games; Reading groups; Prayer groups; Movies; Shopping trips; Social/Cultural gatherings; Special Olympics; 4-H Club; Shelter workshop developmental training classes.

TACOMA

Abilene House Inc
2901 Bridgeport Way W, Tacoma, WA, 98466
(206) 564-1643
Admin James C Edwards. *Medical Dir/Dir of Nursing* William Wright MD; Marion Ray RN DON.
Licensure Skilled care. *Beds* SNF 70.
Owner Proprietary Corp.

Staff RNs 3 (ft), 4 (pt); LPNs 4 (ft), 4 (pt); Nurses aides 30 (ft), 1 (pt); Physical therapists 1 (pt); Reality therapists 1 (pt); Recreational therapists 1 (pt); Occupational therapists 1 (pt); Speech therapists 1 (pt); Activities coordinators 2 (ft); Dietitians 1 (pt); Ophthalmologists 1 (pt).
Languages Lithuanian
Facilities Dining room; Physical therapy room; Activities room; Crafts room; Laundry room; Barber/Beauty shop.
Activities Arts & crafts; Cards; Games; Reading groups; Prayer groups; Movies; Shopping trips; Social/Cultural gatherings.

Bel Air Health Care Center
630 S Pearl St, Tacoma, WA, 98465
(206) 564-7111
Admin Kenneth S Rehusch. *Medical Dir/Dir of Nursing* James M Wilson Jr MD; Kimmi Munson-Walsh RN DON.
Licensure Skilled care; Intermediate care. *Beds* SNF 103; ICF. *Certified* Medicaid; Medicare.
Owner Proprietary Corp.
Admissions Requirements Minimum age 18; Medical examination.
Staff RNs 4 (ft), 2 (pt); LPNs 4 (ft), 2 (pt); Nurses aides 21 (ft), 2 (pt); Activities coordinators 2 (ft); Dietitians 1 (ft).
Facilities Dining room; Physical therapy room; Activities room; Barber/Beauty shop.
Activities Arts & crafts; Cards; Games; Movies; Shopping trips; Social/Cultural gatherings; Baking; Exercise classes; Breakfast club.

Bellevue Care Center Inc
515 S 64th St, Tacoma, WA, 98408
(206) 472-4481
Admin Sandra A Reynoldson. *Medical Dir/Dir of Nursing* Dr John Comfort; Joene M Timmons RN.
Licensure Skilled care; Intermediate care. *Beds* SNF 51; ICF. *Certified* Medicaid.
Owner Proprietary Corp.
Admissions Requirements Medical examination; Physician's request.
Staff RNs 5 (ft), 3 (pt); LPNs 4 (ft), 2 (pt); Nurses aides 11 (ft), 4 (pt); Physical therapists 1 (ft); Occupational therapists 1 (ft); Activities coordinators 1 (ft).
Languages German, Korean
Facilities Dining room; Activities room; Barber/Beauty shop; Library.
Activities Arts & crafts; Cards; Games; Reading groups; Prayer groups; Movies; Shopping trips; Social/Cultural gatherings.

Brentwood Care Center*
1401 N 5th St, Tacoma, WA, 98403
(206) 572-8141
Admin Jada Lynn. *Medical Dir/Dir of Nursing* David Brown MD.
Licensure Skilled care; Intermediate care. *Beds* 50. *Certified* Medicaid.
Owner Proprietary Corp.
Admissions Requirements Medical examination.
Staff Physicians 1 (pt); RNs 3 (ft), 2 (pt); LPNs 5 (ft), 3 (pt); Nurses aides 10 (ft), 5 (pt); Physical therapists 1 (pt); Activities coordinators 1 (ft), 1 (pt); Dietitians 1 (ft); Dentists 1 (pt).
Facilities Dining room; Physical therapy room; Activities room; Laundry room; Barber/Beauty shop.
Activities Arts & crafts; Cards; Games; Reading groups; Prayer groups; Movies; Shopping trips; Social/Cultural gatherings.

Clearview Manor Convalescent Center*
6844 Portland Ave, Tacoma, WA, 98404
(206) 474-9496
Admin Helen G Bales. *Medical Dir/Dir of Nursing* Bryan M Archer MD.
Licensure Skilled care; Intermediate care. *Beds* 136. *Certified* Medicaid.

Owner Proprietary Corp.
Admissions Requirements Medical examination; Physician's request.
Staff RNs; LPNs; Orderlies; Nurses aides; Physical therapists; Reality therapists; Recreational therapists; Occupational therapists; Activities coordinators; Restorative technician.
Facilities Dining room; Physical therapy room; Activities room; Crafts room; Barber/Beauty shop.
Activities Arts & crafts; Games; Reading groups; Prayer groups; Movies; Shopping trips; Social/Cultural gatherings.

Georgian House Health Care Center
8407 Steilacoom Blvd SW, Tacoma, WA, 98498-4799
(206) 588-2146
Admin Edward C Mawe. *Medical Dir/Dir of Nursing* Herman Judd MD.
Licensure Skilled care; Intermediate care. *Beds* SNF 73; ICF. *Certified* Medicaid; Medicare.
Owner Privately owned.
Admissions Requirements Minimum age 18.
Staff RNs 3 (ft), 6 (pt); LPNs 4 (ft), 3 (pt); Nurses aides 30 (ft), 5 (pt); Physical therapists 1 (pt); Recreational therapists 1 (ft); Occupational therapists 1 (pt); Activities coordinators 1 (ft); Dietitians 1 (pt); Dentists 1 (pt); Ophthalmologists 1 (pt).
Facilities Dining room; Physical therapy room; Activities room; Crafts room; Barber/Beauty shop.
Activities Arts & crafts; Cards; Games; Reading groups; Prayer groups; Movies; Shopping trips; Social/Cultural gatherings.

Heritage
7411 Pacific Ave, Tacoma, WA, 98408
(206) 474-8456
Admin Ronald Spinelli. *Medical Dir/Dir of Nursing* Raymond Dillworth MD; Kathie Makita RN GNP.
Licensure Skilled care; Intermediate care. *Beds* 89. *Certified* Medicaid; Medicare.
Owner Proprietary Corp.
Staff Physicians 1 (pt); RNs 5 (ft); LPNs 8 (ft); Nurses aides 30 (ft); Physical therapists 1 (pt); Reality therapists 1 (pt); Recreational therapists 1 (pt); Occupational therapists 1 (pt); Speech therapists 1 (pt); Activities coordinators 2 (ft); Dietitians 1 (pt); Dentists 1 (pt); Ophthalmologists 1 (pt).
Facilities Dining room; Physical therapy room; Activities room; Crafts room; Barber/Beauty shop.
Activities Arts & crafts; Cards; Games; Movies; Shopping trips; Social/Cultural gatherings; Bible study; Church services.

Jefferson House Care Center
1748 Jefferson Ave, Tacoma, WA, 98402
(206) 383-5495
Admin Tim Moore. *Medical Dir/Dir of Nursing* Bryan Archer; Kathryn Jensen.
Licensure Skilled care; Intermediate care. *Beds* 130. *Certified* Medicaid.
Owner Proprietary Corp (Soundcare Inc).
Admissions Requirements Minimum age 18; Medical examination; Physician's request.
Staff RNs 4 (ft), 5 (pt); LPNs 5 (ft), 2 (pt); Orderlies 4 (ft); Nurses aides 20 (ft), 1 (pt); Activities coordinators 2 (ft); Dietitians 1 (pt).
Facilities Dining room; Activities room; Laundry room.
Activities Arts & crafts; Cards; Games; Reading groups; Prayer groups; Movies; Shopping trips; Social/Cultural gatherings.

Franke Tobey Jones Home
5340 N Bristol, Tacoma, WA, 98407
(206) 752-6621
Admin Sarita Rebman. *Medical Dir/Dir of Nursing* Joseph Regimbal MD; Jo Ann Head RN DON.

Licensure Skilled care; Boarding home. *Beds* SNF 43; Boarding home 135.
Owner Nonprofit Corp.
Admissions Requirements Minimum age 18 Nursing home, 65 Boarding home; Medical examination; Physician's request.
Staff Physicians 1 (pt); LPNs 3 (ft); Recreational therapists 1 (ft); Activities coordinators 1 (ft); Dietitians 1 (ft).
Languages German, Scandinavian
Facilities Dining room; Activities room; Laundry room; Barber/Beauty shop; Library; Parlors; Spa with jacuzzi; Greenhouse.
Activities Arts & crafts; Cards; Games; Reading groups; Prayer groups; Movies; Shopping trips; Social/Cultural gatherings; Greenhouse.

Midland Manor
10816 18th Ave E, Tacoma, WA, 98445
(206) 537-5395
Admin Judy Prunty. *Medical Dir/Dir of Nursing* Dr Thomas Bowden; Judy Morford.
Licensure Intermediate care. *Beds* ICF 45. *Certified* Medicaid.
Owner Proprietary Corp.
Admissions Requirements Medical examination.
Staff LPNs; Nurses aides; Activities coordinators.
Facilities Dining room; Laundry room; Barber/Beauty shop.
Activities Arts & crafts; Cards; Games; Reading groups; Prayer groups; Movies; Shopping trips; Social/Cultural gatherings; Pet therapy.

Nesika I*
5210 S 'K' St, Tacoma, WA, 98408
(206) 752-2856
Admin Louise Shafer. *Medical Dir/Dir of Nursing* Charles Weatherby.
Licensure Intermediate care for mentally retarded. *Beds* 8. *Certified* Medicaid.
Owner Nonprofit Corp.
Admissions Requirements Minimum age 18; Medical examination; Physician's request.
Staff Physicians 1 (pt); RNs 1 (pt); LPNs 1 (pt); Nurses aides 5 (ft), 3 (pt); Physical therapists 1 (pt); Recreational therapists 1 (pt); Occupational therapists 1 (pt); Speech therapists 1 (pt); Dietitians 1 (pt); Dentists 2 (pt); Ophthalmologists 2 (pt); Audiologists 2 (pt).
Facilities Dining room; Crafts room; Laundry room.
Activities Arts & crafts; Cards; Games; Movies; Shopping trips; Social/Cultural gatherings.

Nesika II*
1724 Narrows Dr, Tacoma, WA, 98406
(206) 752-2856
Admin Louise Shafer. *Medical Dir/Dir of Nursing* Doug Jeffrey.
Licensure Intermediate care for mentally retarded. *Beds* 8. *Certified* Medicaid.
Owner Nonprofit Corp.
Admissions Requirements Minimum age 18; Medical examination; Physician's request.
Staff Physicians 1 (pt); RNs 1 (pt); LPNs 1 (pt); Nurses aides 5 (ft), 3 (pt); Physical therapists 1 (pt); Recreational therapists 1 (pt); Occupational therapists 1 (pt); Speech therapists 1 (pt); Dietitians 1 (pt); Dentists 2 (pt); Ophthalmologists 2 (pt); Audiologists 2 (pt).
Facilities Dining room; Physical therapy room; Activities room; Crafts room; Laundry room.
Activities Arts & crafts; Cards; Games; Reading groups; Movies; Shopping trips; Social/Cultural gatherings.

Nesika III*
9034 S Yakima, Tacoma, WA, 98444
(206) 752-2856

Admin Louise Shafer. *Medical Dir/Dir of Nursing* Cynthia Wilson.
Licensure Intermediate care for mentally retarded. *Beds* 8. *Certified* Medicaid.
Owner Nonprofit Corp.
Admissions Requirements Minimum age 18; Medical examination; Physician's request.
Staff Physicians 1 (pt); RNs 1 (pt); LPNs 1 (pt); Nurses aides 5 (ft), 3 (pt); Physical therapists 1 (pt); Recreational therapists 1 (pt); Occupational therapists 1 (pt); Speech therapists 1 (pt); Dietitians 1 (pt); Dentists 2 (pt); Ophthalmologists 2 (pt); Audiologists 2 (pt).
Facilities Dining room; Physical therapy room; Activities room; Laundry room.
Activities Arts & crafts; Games; Movies; Shopping trips; Social/Cultural gatherings.

Northwood Care Centre*
1415 N 5th St, Tacoma, WA, 98403
(206) 272-1206
Admin Jada Lynn.
Licensure Intermediate care. *Beds* 35. *Certified* Medicaid.
Owner Proprietary Corp.

Orchard Park
4755 S 48th, Tacoma, WA, 98409
(206) 475-4611
Admin William J J Baldwin. *Medical Dir/Dir of Nursing* Jim Wilson MD; Kathy Burr RN DON.
Licensure Skilled care; Intermediate care. *Beds* 144. *Certified* Medicaid; Medicare.
Owner Privately owned.
Admissions Requirements Minimum age 18; Medical examination; Physician's request.
Staff RNs 8 (ft), 8 (pt); LPNs 7 (ft), 7 (pt); Nurses aides 57 (ft), 3 (pt); Physical therapists 1 (ft); Occupational therapists 1 (ft); Speech therapists 1 (ft); Activities coordinators 1 (ft); Dietitians 1 (ft); Podiatrists 1 (pt).
Facilities Dining room; Physical therapy room; Activities room; Crafts room; Barber/Beauty shop.
Activities Arts & crafts; Cards; Games; Reading groups; Prayer groups; Movies; Shopping trips; Social/Cultural gatherings.

Park Rose Care Center*
3919 S 19th, Tacoma, WA, 98405
(206) 752-5677
Admin Leta Faust.
Licensure Skilled care; Intermediate care. *Beds* 148. *Certified* Medicaid; Medicare.
Owner Proprietary Corp.

Parkland Care Center*
321 S 116th St, Tacoma, WA, 98444
(206) 537-3022
Admin William T Rowe Jr. *Medical Dir/Dir of Nursing* Dr Thomas Bowden.
Licensure Nursing home. *Beds* 30.
Owner Proprietary Corp.
Admissions Requirements Medical examination; Physician's request.
Staff RNs 1 (ft); LPNs 5 (pt); Nurses aides 9 (ft), 1 (pt); Activities coordinators 1 (ft).
Facilities Dining room; Activities room; Laundry room.
Activities Arts & crafts; Cards; Games; Reading groups; Movies; Shopping trips; Social/Cultural gatherings; Church services; Special music.

Sherwood Terrace Nursing Center*
2102 S 96th, Tacoma, WA, 98444
(206) 582-4141
Admin John C Striker. *Medical Dir/Dir of Nursing* George Zerr.
Licensure Skilled care; Intermediate care. *Beds* 235. *Certified* Medicaid; Medicare.
Owner Proprietary Corp.
Staff RNs; LPNs; Orderlies; Nurses aides; Physical therapists; Reality therapists; Recreational therapists; Occupational

therapists; Speech therapists; Activities coordinators; Dietitians; Dentists; Ophthalmologists; Podiatrists; Audiologists.
Facilities Dining room; Physical therapy room; Activities room; Chapel; Crafts room; Laundry room; Barber/Beauty shop.
Activities Arts & crafts; Cards; Games; Reading groups; Prayer groups; Movies; Shopping trips; Social/Cultural gatherings.

Springhaven Care Center
PO Box 42279, 1645 E 72nd St, Tacoma, WA, 98042-0279
(206) 472-9027
Admin Nancy Kay Rowe. *Medical Dir/Dir of Nursing* Dr Kenneth Ritter.
Licensure Intermediate care. *Beds* 20. *Certified* Medicaid.
Owner Proprietary Corp.
Admissions Requirements Medical examination; Physician's request.
Staff RNs 1 (pt); LPNs 5 (ft); Nurses aides 7 (ft); Occupational therapists 1 (ft); Activities coordinators 1 (ft); Dietitians 1 (pt).

Tacoma Lutheran Home & Retirement Community
1301 Highlands Pkwy N, Tacoma, WA, 98406
(206) 752-7112
Admin Paul M Opgrande. *Medical Dir/Dir of Nursing* Dr Ray Miller; Zina Herbert DON.
Licensure Skilled care; Intermediate care. *Beds* SNF 220; ICF. *Certified* Medicaid.
Owner Nonprofit Corp.
Staff RNs 13 (ft), 8 (pt); LPNs 18 (ft), 9 (pt); Nurses aides 134 (ft), 36 (pt); Physical therapists 1 (ft); Activities coordinators 1 (ft); Dietitians 1 (pt).
Affiliation Lutheran
Facilities Dining room; Physical therapy room; Activities room; Chapel; Crafts room; Laundry room; Barber/Beauty shop; Library.
Activities Arts & crafts; Cards; Games; Reading groups; Prayer groups; Movies; Shopping trips; Social/Cultural gatherings; Pet-people partnership program.

Tacoma Narrows Care Center
5954 N 26th, Tacoma, WA, 98407
(206) 752-7713
Admin Chris Nickerson. *Medical Dir/Dir of Nursing* David Munoz MD.
Licensure Skilled care; Intermediate care. *Beds* 86. *Certified* Medicaid.
Owner Proprietary Corp.
Admissions Requirements Medical examination; Physician's request.
Staff Physical therapists 1 (pt); Activities coordinators 1 (ft)
Languages Italian
Facilities Dining room; Activities room; Crafts room; Laundry room; Barber/Beauty shop.
Activities Arts & crafts; Cards; Games; Movies; Shopping trips; Social/Cultural gatherings; Small groups for severely impaired.

Tacoma Terrace Convalescent Center
3625 E "B" St, Tacoma, WA, 98404
(206) 475-2507
Admin Arnie Schoenmoser. *Medical Dir/Dir of Nursing* Sharon Harrison.
Licensure Skilled care; Intermediate care. *Beds* 139. *Certified* Medicaid.
Owner Proprietary Corp.
Admissions Requirements Medical examination; Physician's request.
Staff RNs 7 (ft); LPNs 2 (ft), 10 (pt); Dietitians 1 (pt); Dentists 1 (pt); Ophthalmologists 1 (pt); Podiatrists 1 (pt); Dentist 1 (pt).
Facilities Dining room; Physical therapy room; Activities room; Laundry room; Barber/Beauty shop; Lounges.
Activities Arts & crafts; Cards; Games; Movies; Social/Cultural gatherings.

Tule Lake Manor*
901 Tule Lake Rd, Tacoma, WA, 98444
(206) 537-7887
Admin Linda Rouse.
Licensure Nursing home. *Beds* 15.
Owner Proprietary Corp.
Staff LPNs 1 (ft); Nurses aides 8 (ft).
Activities Arts & crafts; Cards; Games; Shopping trips.

Viewcrest Convalescent Center
4810 S Wilkeson St, Tacoma, WA, 98408
(206) 474-0733
Admin Jacqueline Folsom. *Medical Dir/Dir of Nursing* Lorraine LaRoche.
Licensure Skilled care; Intermediate care. *Beds* SNF 106; ICF. *Certified* Medicaid.
Owner Proprietary Corp (Community Care Centers).
Admissions Requirements Minimum age 18; Medical examination; Physician's request.
Staff RNs 4 (ft), 2 (pt); LPNs 8 (ft), 2 (pt); Orderlies 3 (ft); Nurses aides 39 (ft); Activities coordinators 2 (ft); Dietitians 1 (pt).
Facilities Dining room; Activities room; Laundry room; Barber/Beauty shop.
Activities Arts & crafts; Cards; Games; Reading groups; Prayer groups; Movies; Shopping trips; Social/Cultural gatherings; Adopt-a-grandparent program.

TEKOA

Tekoa Care Center
PO Box 350, Rte 1, Tekoa, WA, 99033
(509) 284-4501
Admin Dorothy I Fletcher. *Medical Dir/Dir of Nursing* Francis Thiel MD; Arlene Morgan RN DON.
Licensure Skilled care; Intermediate care. *Beds* SNF 62; ICF. *Certified* Medicaid.
Owner Privately owned.
Admissions Requirements Medical examination.
Staff Physicians 5 (pt); RNs 5 (ft), 2 (pt); LPNs 1 (ft), 1 (pt); Orderlies 4 (ft); Nurses aides 19 (ft), 17 (pt); Physical therapists 1 (pt); Reality therapists 1 (pt); Recreational therapists 1 (pt); Occupational therapists 1 (pt); Speech therapists 1 (pt); Activities coordinators 1 (ft); Dietitians 1 (pt); Dentists 1 (pt); Ophthalmologists 1 (pt); Podiatrists 1 (pt); Social worker 1 (pt).
Facilities Dining room; Physical therapy room; Activities room; Chapel; Crafts room; Laundry room; Barber/Beauty shop; Family visiting rooms.
Activities Arts & crafts; Games; Reading groups; Prayer groups; Movies; Shopping trips; Social/Cultural gatherings; Ceramics.

TOPPENISH

Mountain Vista Nursing Home
PO Box 352, 802 W 3rd St, Toppenish, WA, 98948
(509) 865-3955
Admin Richard Ensey. *Medical Dir/Dir of Nursing* Ruth Moore DON.
Licensure Skilled care; Intermediate care. *Beds* 125. *Certified* Medicaid; Medicare.
Owner Proprietary Corp (Beverly Enterprises).
Admissions Requirements Physician's request.
Staff RNs 6 (ft), 3 (pt); LPNs 4 (ft), 4 (pt); Orderlies 3 (ft); Nurses aides 37 (ft), 8 (pt); Occupational therapists 1 (ft); Activities coordinators 1 (ft), 1 (pt); Dietitians 1 (pt).
Languages Spanish
Facilities Dining room; Physical therapy room; Activities room; Crafts room; Laundry room; Barber/Beauty shop; Library.
Activities Arts & crafts; Cards; Games; Reading groups; Prayer groups; Movies; Social/Cultural gatherings.

TUMWATER

Capitol Park Care Center*
230 E Dennis, Tumwater, WA, 98501
(206) 943-4040
Admin Jerry Hlousek.
Licensure Skilled care; Intermediate care. *Beds* 117. *Certified* Medicaid.
Owner Proprietary Corp.

UNION GAP

Parkside Nursing Care Center
308 W Emma, Union Gap, WA, 98903
(509) 248-1985
Admin Clinton Neal Smith. *Medical Dir/Dir of Nursing* Joan Funk DON.
Licensure Skilled care; Intermediate care. *Beds* 88. *Certified* Medicaid.
Owner Proprietary Corp.
Staff RNs; LPNs; Orderlies; Nurses aides; Recreational therapists; Activities coordinators; Dietitians; Ophthalmologists.
Facilities Dining room; Activities room; Crafts room; Laundry room; Barber/Beauty shop.
Activities Arts & crafts; Cards; Games; Reading groups; Prayer groups; Movies; Shopping trips; Social/Cultural gatherings.

VANCOUVER

Emerald Terrace Nursing Center*
1015 N Garrison Rd, Vancouver, WA, 98664
(206) 694-7501
Admin Janice Lehner.
Licensure Skilled care; Intermediate care. *Beds* 152. *Certified* Medicaid; Medicare.
Owner Proprietary Corp (Beverly Enterprises).

Fort Vancouver Convalescent Center
8507 NE 8th Way, Vancouver, WA, 98664
(206) 254-5335
Admin Steve C Jackson. *Medical Dir/Dir of Nursing* Dorothy Barnaby.
Licensure Skilled care; Intermediate care. *Beds* 92. *Certified* Medicaid; Medicare.
Owner Privately owned.
Admissions Requirements Physician's request.
Staff RNs; LPNs; Nurses aides; Activities coordinators.
Facilities Dining room; Physical therapy room; Activities room; Chapel; Crafts room; Laundry room; Barber/Beauty shop.
Activities Arts & crafts; Games; Reading groups; Prayer groups; Movies; Exercises.

Hazel Dell Care Center*
5220 NE Hazel Dell Ave, Vancouver, WA, 98663
(206) 693-1474
Admin Jan Wilson.
Licensure Skilled care; Intermediate care. *Beds* 89. *Certified* Medicaid.
Owner Proprietary Corp (Beverly Enterprises).

Hewitt House*
4316 NE Saint James Rd, Vancouver, WA, 98663
(206) 693-0649
Admin Mary L Johnson.
Licensure Intermediate care for mentally retarded. *Beds* 6.
Owner Proprietary Corp.

Hillhaven Convalescent Center
400 E 33rd St, Vancouver, WA, 98663
(206) 696-2561
Admin Lennette Watson. *Medical Dir/Dir of Nursing* Dr Barth; Barbara Pederson DON.
Licensure Skilled care. *Beds* SNF 98. *Certified* Medicaid; Medicare.
Owner Proprietary Corp (Hillhaven Corp).
Admissions Requirements Physician's request.
Staff RNs 10 (ft), 4 (pt); LPNs 4 (ft), 2 (pt); Nurses aides 37 (ft), 6 (pt); Activities coordinators 1 (ft).

Facilities Dining room; Physical therapy room; Activities room; Barber/Beauty shop.

Hillhaven Nursing Home
3605 Y St, Vancouver, WA, 98663
(206) 693-5839
Admin Thomas J Adams. *Medical Dir/Dir of Nursing* Dr G Dean Barth.
Licensure Skilled care; Intermediate care. *Beds* SNF 53; ICF. *Certified* Medicaid.
Owner Proprietary Corp (Hillhaven Corp).
Admissions Requirements Physician's request.
Staff Physicians 1 (ft); RNs 6 (ft); LPNs 2 (ft); Nurses aides 11 (ft); Activities coordinators 1 (ft); Dietitians 1 (ft).
Facilities Dining room; Activities room; Crafts room.
Activities Arts & crafts; Cards; Games; Reading groups; Prayer groups; Movies; Shopping trips; Social/Cultural gatherings.

Oregon-Washington Pythian Home*
3409 Main St, Vancouver, WA, 98663
(206) 694-6401
Admin C Allen Small.
Licensure Skilled care; Intermediate care. *Beds* 34. *Certified* Medicaid.
Owner Nonprofit Corp.
Affiliation Knights of Pythias

Rose Vista Nursing Center*
5001 Columbia View Dr, Vancouver, WA, 98661
(206) 696-0161
Admin John Lanouette. *Medical Dir/Dir of Nursing* G Dean Barth MD.
Licensure Skilled care; Intermediate care. *Beds* 237. *Certified* Medicaid.
Owner Proprietary Corp (Beverly Enterprises).
Admissions Requirements Physician's request.
Staff RNs 8 (ft), 2 (pt); LPNs 11 (ft), 3 (pt); Nurses aides 65 (ft), 4 (pt); Activities coordinators 1 (ft).
Facilities Dining room; Physical therapy room; Activities room; Crafts room; Laundry room; Barber/Beauty shop; Library.
Activities Arts & crafts; Cards; Games; Reading groups; Prayer groups; Movies; Shopping trips; Social/Cultural gatherings.

VASHON ISLAND

Island Manor Nursing Center
PO Box 20, Rte 1, 15401 99th Ave SW, Vashon Island, WA, 98070
(206) 567-4421
Admin James Alexander. *Medical Dir/Dir of Nursing* Janet Hodge MD; Mary Ruth Hughes RN.
Licensure Skilled care; Intermediate care. *Beds* 50. *Certified* Medicaid.
Owner Privately owned.
Admissions Requirements Minimum age 50; Medical examination; Physician's request.
Staff RNs 4 (ft), 4 (pt); LPNs 2 (ft), 2 (pt); Nurses aides 15 (ft), 10 (pt); Physical therapists 1 (pt); Activities coordinators 1 (ft), 2 (pt); Dietitians 1 (pt).
Facilities Dining room; Activities room; Laundry room; Barber/Beauty shop; Library; TV room.
Activities Arts & crafts; Cards; Games; Reading groups; Movies; Shopping trips; Social/Cultural gatherings.

VERADALE

Rosewood Manor
4317 Ball Dr, Veradale, WA, 99037-9105
(509) 326-5252
Admin Kay Corder.
Licensure Skilled care; Intermediate care. *Beds* 44. *Certified* Medicaid.
Owner Proprietary Corp.

WALLA WALLA

Park Manor Convalescent Center
1710 Plaza Way, Walla Walla, WA, 99362
(509) 529-4218
Admin Pat Locati. *Medical Dir/Dir of Nursing* Robert Candill MD; Aileen Oye RN DON.
Licensure Skilled care. *Beds* SNF 81. *Certified* Medicaid; Medicare.
Owner Proprietary Corp (Hillhaven Corp).
Admissions Requirements Physician's request.
Staff RNs 5 (ft), 4 (pt); LPNs 2 (ft), 2 (pt); Nurses aides 28 (ft), 7 (pt); Physical therapists 1 (ft); Occupational therapists 1 (pt); Speech therapists 1 (pt); Activities coordinators 2 (ft), 2 (pt); Dietitians 1 (pt).
Activities Arts & crafts; Cards; Games; Reading groups; Prayer groups; Movies.

Pleasant View Nursing Home
PO Box 31, Rte 5, Walla Walla, WA, 99362
(509) 529-1882
Admin Jerry Doctor. *Medical Dir/Dir of Nursing* Aster Debeb DON.
Licensure Intermediate care. *Beds* ICF 17. *Certified* Medicaid.
Owner Privately owned.
Staff Physicians; RNs; LPNs; Nurses aides; Dietitians.
Facilities Dining room; Activities room; Chapel; Crafts room; Laundry room; Barber/Beauty shop.
Activities Arts & crafts; Cards; Games; Reading groups; Prayer groups; Movies; Social/Cultural gatherings.

Regency Care Center
225 Woodland Ave, Walla Walla, WA, 99362
(509) 529-4480
Admin Roger A Joice. *Medical Dir/Dir of Nursing* Michael J Kilfoyle; Jan Schmidt.
Licensure Skilled care; Intermediate care. *Beds* 102. *Certified* Medicaid; Medicare; VA.
Owner Proprietary Corp (Regency Health Care Centers).
Admissions Requirements Medical examination; Physician's request.
Staff Physicians 1 (pt); RNs 6 (ft), 4 (pt); LPNs 50 (ft), 5 (pt); Nurses aides 23 (ft), 10 (pt); Physical therapists 1 (pt); Recreational therapists 1 (ft), 1 (pt); Dietitians 1 (pt).
Facilities Dining room; Physical therapy room; Activities room; Crafts room; Laundry room; Barber/Beauty shop.
Activities Arts & crafts; Cards; Games; Prayer groups; Movies; Shopping trips; Social/Cultural gatherings; BBQs; Picnics.

Smith Nursing Home*
1865 E Alder, Walla Walla, WA, 99362
(509) 525-8762
Admin Dale I Smith.
Licensure Skilled care; Intermediate care. *Beds* 74. *Certified* Medicaid.
Owner Proprietary Corp.

Washington Odd Fellows Home
534 Boyer Ave, Walla Walla, WA, 99362
(509) 525-6463
Admin Jean Lienhard. *Medical Dir/Dir of Nursing* Dr James Johnson; Betty Martonick RN DON.
Licensure Skilled care; Intermediate care; Boarding care; Apartments. *Beds* SNF 100; ICF; Boarding 165; Apts 33. *Certified* Medicaid.
Owner Nonprofit Corp.
Admissions Requirements Minimum age 65; Medical examination; Physician's request.
Staff RNs 16 (ft), 9 (pt); LPNs 1 (ft), 1 (pt); Nurses aides 49 (ft), 7 (pt); Activities coordinators 3 (ft).
Affiliation Independent Order of Odd Fellows & Rebekahs
Facilities Dining room; Physical therapy room; Activities room; Crafts room; Laundry room; Barber/Beauty shop; Library; 2 auditoriums.

Activities Arts & crafts; Cards; Games; Reading groups; Prayer groups; Movies; Shopping trips; Social/Cultural gatherings.

WAPATO

Emerald Circle Convalescent Center
209 N Ahtanum Ave, Wapato, WA, 98951
(509) 877-3175
Admin Louis A Robert. *Medical Dir/Dir of Nursing* Wallace A Donaldson; Pauline Groth RN.
Licensure Skilled care; Intermediate care. *Beds* 82. *Certified* Medicaid; Medicare; VA.
Owner Proprietary Corp.
Admissions Requirements Medical examination; Physician's request.
Staff Physicians 1 (pt); RNs 10 (ft); LPNs 3 (ft); Physical therapists 1 (pt); Speech therapists 1 (pt); Activities coordinators 2 (ft); Dietitians 1 (pt); Nursing Assistants 26 (ft).
Languages Spanish
Facilities Dining room; Physical therapy room; Activities room; Laundry room; Barber/Beauty shop; Library; Outdoor patios.
Activities Arts & crafts; Cards; Games; Reading groups; Prayer groups; Movies; Shopping trips; Social/Cultural gatherings; Social outings.

WAUNA

Rocky Bay Health Care Facility
PO Box 99, Wauna, WA, 98395
(206) 884-2277
Admin Edith M Moore.
Licensure Intermediate care; Intermediate care for mentally retarded. *Beds* ICF/MR 30. *Certified* Medicaid; Medicare.
Owner Privately owned.
Admissions Requirements Medical examination; Physician's request.
Staff Physicians 1 (pt); RNs 2 (ft); LPNs 1 (ft), 2 (pt); Nurses aides 8 (ft), 7 (pt); Physical therapists 1 (pt); Recreational therapists 2 (pt); Occupational therapists 1 (pt); Speech therapists 1 (pt); Activities coordinators 2 (ft); Dietitians 1 (pt).
Facilities Dining room; Activities room; Laundry room.
Activities Arts & crafts; Cards; Games; Prayer groups; Movies; Shopping trips; Social/Cultural gatherings.

WENATCHEE

Colonial Vista Convalescent Center
PO Box 2569, 625 Okanogan Ave, Wenatchee, WA, 98801
(509) 663-1171
Admin Ron Stevens. *Medical Dir/Dir of Nursing* Dr Robert Hoxsey; Lee Ann Matson DON.
Licensure Skilled care; Intermediate care. *Beds* SNF 100; ICF. *Certified* Medicaid.
Owner Privately owned.
Admissions Requirements Medical examination; Physician's request.
Staff RNs 5 (ft); LPNs 5 (ft); Orderlies; Nurses aides 21 (ft); Activities coordinators 1 (ft).
Facilities Dining room; Physical therapy room; Activities room; Chapel; Crafts room; Laundry room; Barber/Beauty shop.
Activities Arts & crafts; Cards; Games; Reading groups; Prayer groups; Movies; Shopping trips; Social/Cultural gatherings.

Parkside Manor Convalescent Center
PO Box 2986, 1230 Monitor, Wenatchee, WA, 98801
(509) 663-1628

Admin Benjamin E Colson. *Medical Dir/Dir of Nursing* Robert Hoxsey MD; Dixie Wilkinson RN DON.
Licensure Skilled care. *Beds* SNF 156. *Certified* Medicaid.
Owner Proprietary Corp.
Admissions Requirements Medical examination; Physician's request.
Staff Physicians 15 (pt); RNs 18 (ft); LPNs 10 (ft); Nurses aides 45 (ft); Physical therapists 1 (pt); Occupational therapists 1 (pt); Speech therapists 1 (pt); Activities coordinators 3 (ft); Dietitians 1 (pt); Dentists 1 (pt); Ophthalmologists 2 (pt); Podiatrists 1 (pt).
Languages Spanish
Facilities Dining room; Activities room; Crafts room; Laundry room; Barber/Beauty shop; Secure & protected courtyards.
Activities Arts & crafts; Cards; Games; Reading groups; Prayer groups; Movies; Shopping trips; Social/Cultural gatherings.

WOODINVILLE

Bedford Group Home
12461 NE 173rd Pl, Woodinville, WA, 98072
(206) 488-7764
Admin Steve Skeen.
Licensure Intermediate care for mentally retarded. *Beds* ICF/MR 6. *Certified* Medicaid.
Owner Nonprofit organization/foundation.
Admissions Requirements Minimum age 18; Medical examination.
Staff Physicians 1 (pt); RNs 1 (pt); Physical therapists 1 (pt); Recreational therapists 1 (pt); Occupational therapists 1 (pt); Speech therapists 1 (pt); Dietitians 1 (pt).
Facilities Dining room; Activities room; Laundry room.
Activities Arts & crafts; Cards; Games; Movies; Shopping trips; Social/Cultural gatherings.

Brookhaven Group Home
17235 126th Pl NE, Woodinville, WA, 98072
(206) 488-8877
Admin Steve Skeen.
Licensure Intermediate care for mentally retarded. *Beds* ICF/MR 6. *Certified* Medicaid.
Owner Nonprofit organization/foundation.
Admissions Requirements Minimum age 18; Medical examination.
Staff Physicians 1 (pt); RNs 1 (pt); Physical therapists 1 (pt); Recreational therapists 1 (pt); Occupational therapists 1 (pt); Speech therapists 1 (pt); Dietitians 1 (pt).
Facilities Dining room; Activities room; Laundry room.
Activities Arts & crafts; Cards; Games; Movies; Shopping trips; Social/Cultural gatherings.

WOODLAND

Woodland Convalescent Center
PO Box 69, 310-4th St, Woodland, WA, 98674
(206) 225-9443, 695-2080
Admin Patricia Madsen. *Medical Dir/Dir of Nursing* Dr Dean Barth.
Licensure Skilled care; Intermediate care. *Beds* 62. *Certified* Medicaid; Medicare.
Owner Proprietary Corp.
Admissions Requirements Medical examination; Physician's request.
Staff RNs 7 (ft), 2 (pt); LPNs 2 (ft), 1 (pt); Nurses aides 23 (ft), 2 (pt); Activities coordinators 1 (ft).

Facilities Dining room; Physical therapy room; Activities room; Crafts room; Laundry room; Barber/Beauty shop.
Activities Arts & crafts; Cards; Games; Reading groups; Prayer groups; Movies; Shopping trips; Social/Cultural gatherings.

YAKIMA

Central Convalescent
206 S 10th Ave, Yakima, WA, 98902
(509) 453-4854
Admin David W Forsman.
Licensure Skilled care; Intermediate care. *Beds* 104. *Certified* Medicaid; Medicare.
Owner Nonprofit Corp.

Chalet Healthcare*
115 N 10th St, Yakima, WA, 98901
(509) 248-4173
Admin Johnny Gross.
Licensure Skilled care; Intermediate care. *Beds* 109. *Certified* Medicaid.
Owner Proprietary Corp.

Crescent Convalescent Center
505 N 40th Ave, Yakima, WA, 98908
(509) 248-4446
Admin Ron E Foster. *Medical Dir/Dir of Nursing* Stanley L Wilkinson MD; Julie Barr RN.
Licensure Skilled care; Intermediate care. *Beds* 122. *Certified* Medicaid; Medicare; VA.
Owner Proprietary Corp.
Admissions Requirements Medical examination; Physician's request.
Staff Physicians 1 (pt); RNs 10 (ft); LPNs 4 (ft); Nurses aides 52 (ft); Physical therapists 1 (pt); Speech therapists 1 (pt); Activities coordinators 2 (ft); Dietitians 1 (pt); Rehabilitation Nurse 1 (ft).
Facilities Dining room; Physical therapy room; Activities room; Laundry room; Barber/Beauty shop; Library; Outside patios.
Activities Arts & crafts; Cards; Games; Reading groups; Movies; Shopping trips; Social/Cultural gatherings; Church services; Social outings.

Eden House Convalescent Center
4007 Tieton Dr, Yakima, WA, 98908
(509) 966-4500
Admin Ron E Foster. *Medical Dir/Dir of Nursing* William Von Stubbe MD; Helen Doggett RN.
Licensure Skilled care; Intermediate care. *Beds* 83. *Certified* Medicaid; VA.
Owner Proprietary Corp.
Admissions Requirements Medical examination; Physician's request.
Staff Physicians 1 (pt); RNs 6 (ft); LPNs 4 (ft); Physical therapists 1 (pt); Speech therapists 1 (pt); Activities coordinators 1 (ft); Dietitians 1 (pt); Rehabilitation nurse 1 (ft) Nursing assistants 20 (ft).
Facilities Dining room; Physical therapy room; Activities room; Laundry room; Barber/Beauty shop; Library; Outdoor patios.
Activities Arts & crafts; Cards; Games; Reading groups; Prayer groups; Movies; Shopping trips; Social/Cultural gatherings; Social outings.

Fountains Convalescent Center
515 N 34th Ave, Yakima, WA, 98902
(509) 248-6220
Admin Richard E Exendine. *Medical Dir/Dir of Nursing* Molly Harrington.
Licensure Skilled care. *Beds* 82. *Certified* Medicaid; Medicare.

Owner Proprietary Corp.
Facilities Dining room; Physical therapy room; Activities room; Crafts room; Laundry room; Barber/Beauty shop; Library.
Activities Arts & crafts; Cards; Games; Reading groups; Prayer groups; Movies; Shopping trips; Social/Cultural gatherings.

Good Samaritan Health Care Center
702 N 16th Ave, Yakima, WA, 98902
(509) 248-5320
Admin Richard Chasteen. *Medical Dir/Dir of Nursing* William W Robinson MD; Mary Jane Funk DON.
Licensure Skilled care; Intermediate care. *Beds* 120. *Certified* Medicaid.
Owner Proprietary Corp (Regency Health Care Centers).
Admissions Requirements Medical examination; Physician's request.
Staff RNs 6 (ft); LPNs 6 (ft); Nurses aides 40 (ft); Activities coordinators 2 (ft), 1 (pt); Dietitians 1 (pt).
Facilities Dining room; Physical therapy room; Activities room; Crafts room; Laundry room; Barber/Beauty shop; Smoking & non-smoking lounges.
Activities Arts & crafts; Cards; Games; Reading groups; Prayer groups; Movies; Shopping trips; Social/Cultural gatherings; Religious services.

Summitview Manor
3905 Knobel Ave, Yakima, WA, 98902
(509) 966-6240
Admin Dave Forsman. *Medical Dir/Dir of Nursing* Dr Wilkinson; Sharon Alexander DON.
Licensure Skilled care; Intermediate care. *Beds* SNF 180; ICF. *Certified* Medicaid.
Owner Nonprofit Corp.
Admissions Requirements Medical examination.
Staff RNs 14 (ft); LPNs; Nurses aides 50 (ft); Activities coordinators 1 (ft); Dietitians 1 (ft).
Facilities Dining room; Physical therapy room; Activities room; Chapel; Crafts room; Laundry room; Barber/Beauty shop; Library.
Activities Arts & crafts; Cards; Games; Reading groups; Prayer groups; Movies; Shopping trips; Social/Cultural gatherings; Ceramics.

Yakima Convalescent
818 W Yakima Ave, Yakima, WA, 98902
(509) 248-4104
Admin Doug Bault. *Medical Dir/Dir of Nursing* Stanley Wilkinson MD; Karen Moore RN DON.
Licensure Skilled care; Intermediate care. *Beds* 93. *Certified* Medicaid; Medicare.
Owner Nonprofit Corp.
Admissions Requirements Medical examination; Physician's request.
Staff RNs 9 (ft), 5 (pt); LPNs 2 (ft); Physical therapists 1 (ft); Recreational therapists 1 (pt); Occupational therapists; Speech therapists; Activities coordinators 3 (ft); Dietitians 1 (pt); Ophthalmologists; Podiatrists.
Facilities Dining room; Physical therapy room; Activities room; Chapel; Barber/Beauty shop.
Activities Arts & crafts; Cards; Games; Reading groups; Prayer groups; Movies; Social/Cultural gatherings.

WEST VIRGINIA

ANSTED

Green Acres Convalescent Center*
PO Box 633, Ansted, WV, 25812
(304) 658-5271
Admin Joan K Todd.
Licensure Intermediate care. *Beds* 60.

BECKLEY

Heartland of Beckley
300 Dry Hill Rd, Beckley, WV, 25801
(304) 255-1591
Admin Pamela L White. *Medical Dir/Dir of Nursing* Dr T Rojas; Mary Berry RN DON.
Licensure Intermediate care. *Beds* 122.
Certified Medicaid.
Owner Proprietary Corp (Health Care & Retirement Corp).
Admissions Requirements Minimum age 18; Medical examination; Physician's request.
Staff Physicians 2 (pt); RNs 2 (ft), 1 (pt); LPNs 14 (ft), 9 (pt); Orderlies 4 (ft); Nurses aides 39 (ft), 15 (pt); Physical therapists 1 (pt); Activities coordinators 2 (ft); Dietitians 1 (ft), 1 (pt); Ophthalmologists 1 (pt); Podiatrists 1 (pt).
Facilities Dining room; Physical therapy room; Activities room; Chapel; Crafts room; Laundry room; Barber/Beauty shop; Library; Patio; Landscaped grounds.
Activities Arts & crafts; Cards; Games; Reading groups; Prayer groups; Movies; Shopping trips; Social/Cultural gatherings.

Pine Lodge Health Care*
405 Stanaford Rd, Beckley, WV, 25801
(304) 252-6317
Admin Tim Thompson. *Medical Dir/Dir of Nursing* John M Daniel.
Licensure Skilled care; Intermediate care. *Beds* 120. *Certified* Medicaid; Medicare.
Owner Proprietary Corp (Americare Corp).
Staff Physicians 2 (ft); RNs 3 (ft); LPNs 13 (ft); Orderlies 7 (ft); Nurses aides 40 (ft); Recreational therapists 1 (ft); Activities coordinators 1 (ft); Dietitians 1 (ft); Dentists 1 (ft); Ophthalmologists 1 (ft).
Facilities Dining room; Activities room; Laundry room; Barber/Beauty shop.
Activities Arts & crafts; Games; Prayer groups; Movies; Shopping trips.

BEECH BOTTOM

Jones Nursing Home*
444 Hill St, PO Box 35, Beech Bottom, WV, 26030
(304) 394-5321
Admin Nellie Baker. *Medical Dir/Dir of Nursing* Dr George Bontos.
Licensure Intermediate care. *Beds* 30.
Certified Medicaid.
Admissions Requirements Medical examination.
Staff Physicians; RNs; LPNs; Nurses aides; Activities coordinators.

BELINGTON

Barbour County Good Samaritan Center*
Rte 2, Belington, WV, 26250
(304) 823-2555
Admin Jonathan S Conrad.
Licensure Intermediate care. *Beds* 60.
Certified Medicaid.
Owner Nonprofit Corp (Evangelical Lutheran/ Good Samaritan).
Admissions Requirements Medical examination; Physician's request.
Staff RNs 1 (ft), 1 (pt); LPNs 1 (ft), 8 (pt); Orderlies 2 (pt); Nurses aides 9 (ft), 14 (pt); Activities coordinators 1 (ft).
Affiliation Lutheran
Facilities Dining room; Activities room; Chapel; Crafts room; Laundry room; Barber/ Beauty shop; Solarium.
Activities Arts & crafts; Cards; Games; Prayer groups; Movies; Shopping trips; Social/ Cultural gatherings.

BERKELEY SPRINGS

Valley View Nursing Home*
Rte 3, Box 277A, Berkeley Springs, WV, 25411
(304) 258-3673
Admin John E Richards Jr. *Medical Dir/Dir of Nursing* Romulo J Estigoy.
Licensure Intermediate care. *Beds* 120.
Staff Physicians 3 (ft); RNs 4 (ft); LPNs 9 (ft); Orderlies 3 (ft); Nurses aides 42 (ft), 16 (pt); Activities coordinators 2 (ft); Dentists 1 (pt); Ophthalmologists 1 (pt); Podiatrists 1 (pt); Audiologists 1 (pt).
Facilities Dining room; Activities room; Chapel; Crafts room; Laundry room; Barber/ Beauty shop; Library; Exercise room.
Activities Arts & crafts; Cards; Games; Reading groups; Prayer groups; Movies; Shopping trips; Social/Cultural gatherings.

BLUEFIELD

Bluefield Multi-Care*
Rogers & Pearis Sts, PO Box 410, Bluefield, WV, 24701
(304) 325-5448
Admin Nile D Cutlip. *Medical Dir/Dir of Nursing* David Bell.
Licensure Skilled care; Intermediate care. *Beds* 105. *Certified* Medicaid; Medicare.
Admissions Requirements Medical examination.
Staff Physicians 1 (ft), 1 (pt); RNs 6 (ft), 4 (pt); LPNs 8 (ft), 1 (pt); Nurses aides 43 (ft); Physical therapists 1 (pt); Reality therapists 1 (pt); Recreational therapists 3 (ft); Speech therapists 1 (pt); Activities coordinators 1 (ft); Dietitians 1 (pt); Dentists 1 (pt); Ophthalmologists 1 (pt); Podiatrists 1 (pt).
Facilities Dining room; Physical therapy room; Activities room; Laundry room; Barber/Beauty shop; Library.

Activities Arts & crafts; Cards; Games; Reading groups; Prayer groups; Shopping trips; Social/Cultural gatherings.

Contemporary Care Inc
PO Box 1958, 1201 Bland Street, Bluefield, WV, 24701
(304) 327-2485
Admin Linda B Tolley. *Medical Dir/Dir of Nursing* John Bryan MD; Vera Tomlinson RN DON.
Licensure Intermediate care. *Beds* 31.
Certified Medicaid.
Owner Proprietary Corp (US Care Corp).
Admissions Requirements Medical examination; Physician's request.
Staff Physicians 1 (ft); RNs 1 (ft); LPNs 3 (ft), 1 (pt); Nurses aides 6 (ft), 8 (pt); Recreational therapists 1 (pt); Activities coordinators 1 (ft); Dietitians 1 (ft); Dentists 1 (pt); Ophthalmologists 1 (pt).
Facilities Dining room; Activities room; Crafts room; Laundry room; Barber/Beauty shop.
Activities Arts & crafts; Cards; Games; Reading groups; Prayer groups; Movies; Shopping trips; Social/Cultural gatherings.

BRIDGEPORT

The Heritage*
Rte 3, Box 17, Bridgeport, WV, 26330
(304) 842-4135
Admin William E Morton.
Licensure Intermediate care. *Beds* 51.
Certified Medicaid.

Meadowview Manor Health Care Center
41 Crestview Terr, Bridgeport, WV, 26330
(304) 842-7101
Admin Roxanne McDaniel. *Medical Dir/Dir of Nursing* Dr Louis F Ortenzio; Nancy Strelow RN DON.
Licensure Intermediate care. *Beds* ICF 60.
Certified Medicaid.
Owner Privately owned.
Staff RNs 2 (ft), 2 (pt); LPNs 2 (ft), 5 (pt); Orderlies 1 (ft), 1 (pt); Nurses aides 12 (ft), 6 (pt); Activities coordinators 1 (ft).
Facilities Dining room; Physical therapy room; Activities room; Laundry room; Barber/Beauty shop.
Activities Arts & crafts; Cards; Games; Prayer groups; Movies; Shopping trips; Social/ Cultural gatherings.

BUCKHANNON

Holbrook on the Hill
346 S Florida St, Buckhannon, WV, 26201
(304) 472-3280
Admin Bonnie L Hitt. *Medical Dir/Dir of Nursing* R L Chamberlain MD.
Licensure Skilled care; Intermediate care. *Beds* 120. *Certified* Medicaid; Medicare.
Owner Proprietary Corp (Glenmark Assocs).

Staff Physicians 11 (pt); RNs 5 (ft); LPNs 12 (ft); Nurses aides 35 (ft); Physical therapists 1 (ft); Speech therapists 1 (pt); Activities coordinators 1 (ft), 1 (pt); Dietitians 1 (pt); Dentists 1 (pt); Ophthalmologists 1 (pt); Podiatrists 1 (pt).
Facilities Dining room; Physical therapy room; Activities room; Chapel; Crafts room; Laundry room; Barber/Beauty shop; Library.
Activities Arts & crafts; Cards; Games; Reading groups; Prayer groups; Movies; Shopping trips; Social/Cultural gatherings.

CAMERON

McConaughey Guest Home*
PO Box 56, Cameron, WV, 26033
(304) 686-3644
Admin John C McConaughey. *Medical Dir/ Dir of Nursing* Dr Meyer Sonneborn.
Licensure Intermediate care. *Beds* 19.
Certified Medicaid.
Staff Physicians 1 (pt); RNs 1 (pt); LPNs 4 (ft); Orderlies 1 (ft); Nurses aides 12 (ft); Activities coordinators 1 (ft); Dietitians 1 (pt); Dentists 1 (pt).
Facilities Dining room; Activities room; Laundry room.
Activities Prayer groups; Movies.

CEREDO

Aivert Nursing Home*
953 Airport Rd, Ceredo, WV, 25507
(304) 453-1851
Admin C M Bates. *Medical Dir/Dir of Nursing* W F Daniels Jr MD.
Licensure Intermediate care. *Beds* 20.
Admissions Requirements Medical examination; Physician's request.
Staff Physicians 1 (pt); RNs 1 (ft); LPNs 4 (ft); Orderlies 1 (ft); Nurses aides 4 (ft); Recreational therapists 1 (pt); Activities coordinators 1 (pt); Dietitians 1 (pt).
Facilities Dining room; Activities room; Laundry room.
Activities Arts & crafts; Cards; Games; Reading groups; Prayer groups; Movies; Social/Cultural gatherings.

CHARLES TOWN

Jeffersonian Manor
Rte 9, Box 220, Charles Town, WV, 25414
(304) 725-6575
Admin James S Hecker. *Medical Dir/Dir of Nursing* Konrad Nau MD; Janette Henderson RN.
Licensure Intermediate care. *Beds* ICF 118.
Certified Medicaid.
Owner Proprietary Corp.
Staff Physicians 12 (pt); RNs 3 (ft); LPNs 12 (ft); Orderlies 2 (ft); Nurses aides 51 (ft), 5 (pt); Activities coordinators 1 (ft), 1 (pt); Dietitians 1 (pt); Dentists 1 (pt); Podiatrists 1 (pt).
Facilities Dining room; Physical therapy room; Activities room; Crafts room; Laundry room; Barber/Beauty shop; Library.
Activities Arts & crafts; Cards; Games; Reading groups; Prayer groups; Shopping trips; Social/Cultural gatherings; Parties.

Knott Nursing Home*
115 W Congress St, Charles Town, WV, 25414
(304) 725-5124
Admin Kenna K Travell.
Licensure Intermediate care. *Beds* 30.

CHARLESTON

Heartland of Charleston
3819 Chesterfield Ave, Charleston, WV, 25304
(304) 925-4772

Admin Lynda G Kramer, Acting. *Medical Dir/ Dir of Nursing* Joseph Farris MD; Lauren Atkinson RN BSN.
Licensure Intermediate care. *Beds* ICF 192.
Certified Medicaid.
Owner Proprietary Corp (Health Care & Retirement Corp).
Admissions Requirements Medical examination; Physician's request.
Staff Physicians 2 (pt); RNs 2 (ft), 1 (pt); LPNs 13 (ft), 3 (pt); Orderlies 6 (ft); Nurses aides 46 (ft), 6 (pt); Physical therapists 1 (pt); Recreational therapists 1 (pt); Dietitians 1 (pt); Ophthalmologists 1 (pt).
Facilities Dining room; Activities room; Crafts room; Laundry room; Barber/Beauty shop.
Activities Arts & crafts; Cards; Games; Reading groups; Prayer groups; Movies; Shopping trips; Social/Cultural gatherings; Exercises.

Arthur B Hodges Center Inc
500 Morris St, Charleston, WV, 25301
(304) 345-6560
Admin Robert E Baer. *Medical Dir/Dir of Nursing* Kenneth Clark MD; Lee Myers RN.
Licensure Skilled care; Intermediate care. *Beds* 120. *Certified* Medicaid; Medicare.
Owner Nonprofit organization/foundation.
Admissions Requirements Medical examination; Physician's request.
Staff Physicians 1 (pt); RNs 6 (ft), 4 (pt); LPNs 12 (ft), 2 (pt); Nurses aides 40 (ft), 5 (pt); Physical therapists 1 (pt); Occupational therapists 1 (pt); Speech therapists 1 (pt); Activities coordinators 1 (pt); Dietitians 1 (pt); Podiatrists 1 (pt).
Facilities Dining room; Physical therapy room; Activities room; Crafts room; Laundry room; Barber/Beauty shop.
Activities Arts & crafts; Games; Prayer groups; Movies; Shopping trips; Social/Cultural gatherings; Cooking group; Sing-alongs.

Mountain State Nursing Home*
1301 Virginia St E, Charleston, WV, 25301
(304) 346-5725
Admin Frances A Harris.
Licensure Intermediate care. *Beds* 87.
Certified Medicaid.

CHESTER

Fox Nursing Home Inc
RD 1, Box 2, 1038 Pan Ave, Chester, WV, 26034
(304) 387-0101
Admin James E Fox. *Medical Dir/Dir of Nursing* Margaret Simmons.
Licensure Intermediate care. *Beds* ICF 60.
Certified Medicaid.
Owner Proprietary Corp.
Admissions Requirements Physician's request.
Staff RNs 2 (ft), 4 (pt); LPNs 3 (ft), 3 (pt); Orderlies 2 (ft); Nurses aides 12 (ft), 12 (pt); Activities coordinators 1 (ft).
Facilities Dining room; Physical therapy room; Activities room; Chapel; Barber/ Beauty shop.
Activities Arts & crafts; Games; Reading groups; Prayer groups; Movies.

CLARKSBURG

Lida Clark Nursing Home*
960 W Pike St, Clarksburg, WV, 26301
(304) 622-2621
Admin Roxanne McDaniel.
Licensure Nursing home. *Beds* 36.

Heartland of Clarksburg
100 Parkway Dr, Clarksburg, WV, 26301
(304) 624-6401
Admin Pamela White. *Medical Dir/Dir of Nursing* Robert Hess MD.

Licensure Intermediate care. *Beds* ICF 120.
Certified Medicaid.
Owner Proprietary Corp (Health Care & Retirement Corp).
Admissions Requirements Medical examination.
Staff Physicians 10 (ft); RNs 4 (ft); LPNs 6 (ft); Nurses aides 100 (ft); Activities coordinators 1 (ft); Dietitians 1 (ft).
Facilities Dining room; Physical therapy room; Activities room; Crafts room; Laundry room; Barber/Beauty shop; Library; Conference room; TV Lounges.
Activities Arts & crafts; Cards; Games; Reading groups; Prayer groups; Movies; Shopping trips; Social/Cultural gatherings.

DANVILLE

Americare Boone Nursing & Rehabilitation Center
PO Box 123, Danville, WV, 25053
(304) 369-5300
Admin Doug Altherr. *Medical Dir/Dir of Nursing* Dr A Fernandez, Dr Stolings, Dr Atkins; Paula White RN DON.
Licensure Skilled care; Intermediate care. *Beds* SNF 24; ICF 96. *Certified* Medicaid; Medicare.
Owner Proprietary Corp (Americare Corp).
Admissions Requirements Medical examination.
Staff RNs 4 (ft); LPNs 8 (ft), 3 (pt); Orderlies 2 (ft), 2 (pt); Nurses aides 50 (ft); Speech therapists 1 (pt); Activities coordinators 1 (ft); Dietitians 1 (pt); Dentists 1 (pt).
Facilities Dining room; Physical therapy room; Activities room; Crafts room; Laundry room; Barber/Beauty shop; Enclosed courtyard with barbecue.
Activities Arts & crafts; Cards; Games; Prayer groups; Movies; Shopping trips; Social/ Cultural gatherings.

DUNBAR

Americare Dunbar Nursing & Rehabilitation Center
501 Caldwell Ln, Dunbar, WV, 25064
(304) 744-4761
Admin Drema K Thompson. *Medical Dir/ Dir of Nursing* Dr John Merrifield & Dr Joseph Smith; Emma Coleman RN.
Licensure Skilled care; Intermediate care. *Beds* 120. *Certified* Medicaid; Medicare.
Owner Proprietary Corp (Americare Corp).
Staff Physicians 3 (pt); RNs 4 (ft); LPNs 7 (ft), 3 (pt); Nurses aides 40 (ft), 9 (pt); Physical therapists; Speech therapists 1 (ft); Activities coordinators 1 (ft); Dietitians 1 (pt); Ophthalmologists 1 (pt); Dentist 1 (pt).
Facilities Dining room; Physical therapy room; Activities room; Crafts room; Laundry room; Barber/Beauty shop; TV lounges.
Activities Arts & crafts; Games; Reading groups; Prayer groups; Movies; Shopping trips; Social/Cultural gatherings.

ELKINS

Nella's Inc*
PO Box 1639, Elkins, WV, 26241
(304) 636-1008
Admin Thomas R Eidell.
Licensure Skilled care; Intermediate care. *Beds* 100. *Certified* Medicaid; Medicare.

Nella's Nursing Home Inc
301 Central St, Elkins, WV, 26241
(304) 636-2033
Admin Carolyn Eidell. *Medical Dir/Dir of Nursing* Dr Samuel J Bucher.
Licensure Intermediate care. *Beds* 84.
Certified Medicaid.
Owner Proprietary Corp.

Admissions Requirements Females only; Medical examination.
Staff RNs 2 (ft); LPNs 11 (ft); Nurses aides 38 (ft); Activities coordinators 1 (ft); Dietitians 1 (pt).
Facilities Dining room; Activities room; Chapel; Crafts room; Barber/Beauty shop.
Activities Arts & crafts; Cards; Games; Reading groups; Prayer groups; Movies; Shopping trips; Social/Cultural gatherings.

ELLENBORO

Sheppard Health Care Inc
Rte 83, Box 10, Ellenboro, WV, 26346
(304) 869-3344
Admin P G Sheppard. *Medical Dir/Dir of Nursing* Asel P Hatfield MD; Judy M Terrell RN.
Licensure Intermediate care. *Beds* ICF 24.
Certified Medicaid.
Owner Proprietary Corp.
Admissions Requirements Medical examination; Physician's request.
Staff Physicians 1 (pt); RNs 2 (ft); LPNs 3 (ft); Orderlies 1 (ft); Nurses aides 12 (ft); Activities coordinators 1 (pt); Dietitians 1 (pt).
Facilities Dining room; Activities room; Crafts room; Laundry room.
Activities Arts & crafts; Games; Shopping trips.

FAIRMONT

Wishing Well Health Center*
1539 Country Club Rd, Fairmont, WV, 26554
(304) 366-9100
Admin Herman Haupstein.
Licensure Skilled care; Intermediate care. *Beds* 106. *Certified* Medicaid; Medicare.

FAYETTEVILLE

Fayette Continuous Care Center
100 Hresan Blvd, Fayetteville, WV, 25840
(304) 574-0770
Admin Darlene L Newell.
Licensure Intermediate care. *Beds* ICF 60.
Certified Medicaid.
Owner Proprietary Corp.
Admissions Requirements Medical examination.
Staff Physicians; RNs; LPNs; Nurses aides; Physical therapists; Speech therapists; Activities coordinators; Dietitians; Dentists.
Facilities Dining room; Physical therapy room; Activities room; Crafts room; Laundry room; Barber/Beauty shop; Library.
Activities Arts & crafts; Cards; Games; Reading groups; Prayer groups; Movies.

FOLLANSBEE

Brightwood Nursing Home
840 Lee Rd, Follansbee, WV, 26037
(304) 527-1100
Admin Winifred McCoy. *Medical Dir/Dir of Nursing* Dr Michael Giannamore; Chris Campbell DON.
Licensure Intermediate care. *Beds* ICF 60.
Certified Medicaid.
Owner Proprietary Corp (Glenmark Assocs).
Admissions Requirements Medical examination; Physician's request.
Staff Physicians 3 (pt); RNs 4 (ft); LPNs 2 (ft), 6 (pt); Orderlies 1 (ft); Nurses aides 14 (ft), 15 (pt); Recreational therapists 1 (ft); Speech therapists 1 (pt); Activities coordinators 1 (ft); Dentists 1 (pt); Ophthalmologists 1 (pt); Restorative aide 1 (ft); Dietary director.
Facilities Dining room; Physical therapy room; Activities room; Crafts room; Laundry room; Barber/Beauty shop; Library; Residents living room; Formal living room.

Activities Arts & crafts; Cards; Games; Reading groups; Prayer groups; Movies; Shopping trips; Social/Cultural gatherings.

FORT ASHBY

Dawn View Manor
General Delivery, Fort Ashby, WV, 26719
(304) 298-3602
Admin Mary E Billmyre. *Medical Dir/Dir of Nursing* Dr Robert R Brown.
Licensure Intermediate care. *Beds* 60.
Certified Medicaid.
Admissions Requirements Medical examination.
Staff RNs 2 (ft), 1 (pt); LPNs 6 (ft); Nurses aides 12 (ft), 11 (pt); Activities coordinators 1 (ft), 1 (pt).
Facilities Dining room; Physical therapy room; Activities room; Crafts room; Laundry room; Barber/Beauty shop.
Activities Arts & crafts; Cards; Games; Reading groups; Prayer groups; Shopping trips; Social/Cultural gatherings.

FRANKLIN

Pendleton Nursing Home
PO Box 700, Franklin, WV, 26807
(304) 358-2322
Admin Paul A Schulz. *Medical Dir/Dir of Nursing* Dr H Luke Eye.
Licensure Intermediate care. *Beds* 91.
Certified Medicaid.
Owner Nonprofit Corp (Evangelical Lutheran/ Good Samaritan).
Staff Recreational therapists 1 (pt); Occupational therapists 1 (pt); Activities coordinators 1 (ft), 1 (pt).
Facilities Dining room; Physical therapy room; Activities room; Crafts room; Laundry room; Barber/Beauty shop.
Activities Arts & crafts; Cards; Games; Reading groups; Movies; Shopping trips; Social/Cultural gatherings.

GLASGOW

Beverly Health Care Center*
PO Box 350, Melrose Dr, Glasgow, WV, 25086
(304) 595-1155
Admin Ladawna Payne.
Licensure Intermediate care. *Beds* 120.
Owner Proprietary Corp (Beverly Enterprises).

GLENVILLE

Americare Glenville Nursing & Rehabilitation Center
46 Fairground Rd, Glenville, WV, 26351
(304) 462-5718
Admin David Wilbur.
Licensure Intermediate care. *Beds* ICF 65.
Certified Medicaid.
Owner Proprietary Corp (Care Enterprises).
Admissions Requirements Medical examination; Physician's request.
Staff RNs 3 (ft), 2 (pt); LPNs 4 (ft), 2 (pt); Nurses aides 21 (ft), 6 (pt); Activities coordinators 1 (ft).
Facilities Dining room; Physical therapy room; Laundry room; Barber/Beauty shop.
Activities Arts & crafts; Cards; Games; Prayer groups; Movies; Shopping trips; Social/ Cultural gatherings.

GRAFTON

Rest Haven Nursing Home Inc*
PO Box 26, Grafton, WV, 26354
(304) 265-2423
Admin Homer W Winans. *Medical Dir/Dir of Nursing* Dr Christopher Villaraza.

Licensure Intermediate care. *Beds* 23.
Certified Medicaid.
Owner Proprietary Corp (Glenmark Assoc).
Admissions Requirements Medical examination.
Staff Physicians; RNs; LPNs; Nurses aides; Reality therapists; Recreational therapists; Activities coordinators; Dietitians; Dentists.
Facilities Dining room; Activities room; Barber/Beauty shop.
Activities Arts & crafts; Cards; Games; Reading groups; Prayer groups.

HARRISVILLE

Pine View Continuous Care Center
PO Box 200, 400 McKinley St, Harrisville, WV, 26362
(304) 643-2712
Admin Wilma Conaway NHA. *Medical Dir/ Dir of Nursing* Lynda Conaway Kiek NHA RN.
Licensure Skilled care; Intermediate care. *Beds* SNF 5; ICF 55; ICF/MR 29. *Certified* Medicaid.
Owner Proprietary Corp.
Admissions Requirements Minimum age 40.
Staff Physicians 2 (ft); RNs 4 (ft); LPNs 12 (ft); Orderlies 3 (ft); Nurses aides 37 (ft); Physical therapists 1 (ft); Reality therapists 1 (ft); Recreational therapists 1 (ft); Speech therapists 1 (ft); Activities coordinators 2 (ft); Dietitians 1 (ft).
Facilities Dining room; Physical therapy room; Activities room; Chapel; Crafts room; Laundry room; Barber/Beauty shop.
Activities Arts & crafts; Cards; Games; Reading groups; Prayer groups; Movies; Shopping trips; Social/Cultural gatherings.

HILLTOP

Hilltop Health Care Center
PO Box 125, Hilltop, WV, 25855
(304) 469-2966
Admin Sharon K Johnson. *Medical Dir/Dir of Nursing* D C Newell Jr DO; Gloria A Vest RN DON.
Licensure Skilled care; Intermediate care. *Beds* SNF 120; ICF. *Certified* Medicaid; Medicare.
Owner Proprietary Corp.
Admissions Requirements Medical examination; Physician's request.
Staff Physicians 5 (pt); RNs 4 (ft), 1 (pt); LPNs 12 (ft), 6 (pt); Nurses aides 32 (ft), 11 (pt); Physical therapists 1 (pt); Speech therapists 1 (pt); Activities coordinators 1 (ft); Dietitians 1 (pt); Dentists 1 (pt); Ophthalmologists 1 (pt); Podiatrists 1 (pt).
Facilities Dining room; Physical therapy room; Activities room; Laundry room; Barber/Beauty shop.
Activities Arts & crafts; Cards; Games; Reading groups; Prayer groups; Movies; Shopping trips; Social/Cultural gatherings.

Hilltop Nursing Home*
PO Box 207, Hilltop, WV, 25855
(304) 469-2988
Admin Richard H Clelland.
Licensure Intermediate care. *Beds* 30.
Certified Medicaid.

HINTON

Summers County Continuous Care Center*
PO Box 1240, Hinton, WV, 25951
Admin M J Goff. *Medical Dir/Dir of Nursing* Dr J D Woodrum.
Licensure Intermediate care. *Beds* 120.
Certified Medicaid.
Owner Proprietary Corp.
Admissions Requirements Minimum age 21; Medical examination; Physician's request.

Staff Physicians 2 (pt); RNs 4 (ft), 1 (pt); LPNs 18 (ft), 2 (pt); Orderlies 6 (ft); Nurses aides 40 (ft), 4 (pt); Physical therapists 2 (pt); Speech therapists 1 (pt); Activities coordinators 1 (ft); Dietitians 1 (pt); Dentists 1 (pt); Podiatrists 1 (pt); Social workers 1 (ft).
Facilities Dining room; Physical therapy room; Activities room; Chapel; Crafts room; Laundry room; Barber/Beauty shop; Library.
Activities Arts & crafts; Cards; Games; Reading groups; Prayer groups; Movies; Shopping trips; Social/Cultural gatherings.

HUNTINGTON

Fairhaven Rest Home*
302 Adams Ave, Huntington, WV, 25701
(304) 522-0032
Admin Everett Pulley Jr.
Licensure Skilled care; Intermediate care. *Beds* 41. *Certified* Medicaid; Medicare.

Hillview Nursing & Convalescent Center*
1720 17th St, Huntington, WV, 25701
(304) 529-6031
Admin Peter Hutchins.
Licensure Skilled care; Intermediate care. *Beds* 107. *Certified* Medicaid; Medicare.

Pleasant View Manor*
3100 Staunton Rd, Huntington, WV, 25702
(304) 523-8429
Admin Mark Dillon.
Licensure Nursing home. *Beds* 34.

Presbyterian Manor Inc
101 13th St, Huntington, WV, 25701
(304) 525-7622
Admin Frank William Armstrong. *Medical Dir/Dir of Nursing* Willard F Daniels MD; Joyce Seamonds RN DON.
Licensure Skilled care; Intermediate care. *Beds* SNF 120; ICF. *Certified* Medicaid; Medicare.
Owner Nonprofit Corp.
Admissions Requirements Minimum age 18; Medical examination; Physician's request.
Staff Physicians 1 (pt); RNs 6 (ft), 1 (pt); LPNs 10 (ft), 1 (pt); Orderlies 1 (ft); Nurses aides 52 (ft), 3 (pt); Physical therapists 1 (pt); Speech therapists 1 (pt); Activities coordinators 1 (ft); Dietitians 1 (pt); Social worker 1 (ft).
Affiliation Presbyterian
Facilities Dining room; Physical therapy room; Activities room; Chapel; Crafts room; Laundry room; Barber/Beauty shop; Library; Enclosed patio.
Activities Arts & crafts; Cards; Games; Reading groups; Prayer groups; Movies; Shopping trips; Social/Cultural gatherings; Exercise class; Professional entertainers.

HURRICANE

Americare Putnam Nursing & Rehabilitation Center
300 Seville Rd, Hurricane, WV, 25526
(304) 757-6805
Admin Bill Snook. *Medical Dir/Dir of Nursing* Dr Robert Hively; Mary Walker DON.
Licensure Skilled care; Intermediate care. *Beds* SNF 24; ICF 120. *Certified* Medicaid; Medicare.
Owner Proprietary Corp (Americare Corp).
Admissions Requirements Minimum age 17; Medical examination; Physician's request.
Staff Physicians 1 (ft); RNs 3 (ft), 3 (pt); LPNs 7 (ft), 6 (pt); Orderlies 81 (ft), 2 (pt); Nurses aides 27 (ft), 26 (pt); Activities coordinators 1 (ft).
Facilities Dining room; Physical therapy room; Activities room; Laundry room; Barber/Beauty shop; TV room/Lounge.

Activities Arts & crafts; Cards; Games; Reading groups; Prayer groups; Movies; Shopping trips; Social/Cultural gatherings.

JANE LEW

Potomac House of Jane Lew*
PO Box 40, Jane Lew, WV, 26378
(304) 884-7811
Admin Jerry Gallien. *Medical Dir/Dir of Nursing* Bennett D Orvik MD.
Licensure Intermediate care. *Beds* 60. *Certified* Medicaid.
Admissions Requirements Medical examination.
Staff Physicians 1 (ft), 1 (pt); RNs 1 (ft), 4 (pt); LPNs 3 (ft), 3 (pt); Orderlies 1 (ft), 1 (pt); Nurses aides 16 (ft), 9 (pt); Physical therapists 1 (ft); Reality therapists 1 (ft); Activities coordinators 1 (pt); Dietitians 1 (ft); Dentists 1 (ft); Ophthalmologists 1 (ft); Podiatrists 1 (ft); Audiologists 1 (ft).
Facilities Dining room; Physical therapy room; Activities room; Crafts room; Laundry room; Barber/Beauty shop.
Activities Arts & crafts; Cards; Games; Reading groups; Prayer groups; Movies; Shopping trips; Social/Cultural gatherings.

KEYSER

Heartland of Keyser
PO Box 848, 135 Southern Dr, Keyser, WV, 26726
(304) 788-3415
Admin Sharon A Nicol. *Medical Dir/Dir of Nursing* Dr Phillip Staggers; M Susan Harber.
Licensure Intermediate care. *Beds* ICF 120. *Certified* Medicaid.
Owner Proprietary Corp (Health Care & Retirement Corp).
Admissions Requirements Medical examination; Physician's request.
Staff Physicians 8 (pt); RNs 7 (ft), 2 (pt); LPNs 5 (ft); Nurses aides 39 (ft), 16 (pt); Physical therapists 1 (pt); Speech therapists 1 (pt); Activities coordinators 1 (ft); Dietitians 1 (ft); Podiatrists 1 (pt); Licensed Social worker 1 (pt).
Facilities Dining room; Physical therapy room; Activities room; Barber/Beauty shop; Nature trail.
Activities Arts & crafts; Cards; Games; Prayer groups; Movies; Social/Cultural gatherings.

KINGWOOD

Heartland of Preston County
300 Miller Rd, Kingwood, WV, 26537
(304) 329-3195
Admin Anna R Ruckman. *Medical Dir/Dir of Nursing* Dr Frederick Conley & Dr Claude Shannon.
Licensure Skilled care; Intermediate care. *Beds* 120. *Certified* Medicaid; Medicare.
Owner Proprietary Corp (Health Care & Retirement Corp).
Admissions Requirements Medical examination; Physician's request.
Staff Physicians 2 (pt); RNs 2 (ft), 3 (pt); LPNs 11 (ft), 1 (pt); Nurses aides 39 (ft), 15 (pt); Physical therapists 1 (pt); Occupational therapists 1 (pt); Speech therapists 1 (pt); Activities coordinators 1 (ft); Dietitians 1 (pt).
Facilities Dining room; Physical therapy room; Activities room; Crafts room; Laundry room; Barber/Beauty shop.
Activities Arts & crafts; Cards; Games; Reading groups; Prayer groups; Movies; Shopping trips; Social/Cultural gatherings.

LEWISBURG

Greenbrier Manor
PO Box 15A, Rte 2, Lewisburg, WV, 24901
(304) 645-3076
Admin Brownie Dunn. *Medical Dir/Dir of Nursing* Martin Smith DO; Ann Canterbury DON.
Licensure Intermediate care. *Beds* ICF 100. *Certified* Medicaid; VA.
Owner Nonprofit Corp.
Admissions Requirements Medical examination.
Staff Physicians 1 (pt); RNs 5 (ft); LPNs 14 (ft); Orderlies 5 (ft); Nurses aides 34 (ft), 3 (pt); Physical therapists 1 (pt); Activities coordinators 2 (ft); Dietitians 1 (ft), 1 (pt).
Facilities Dining room; Physical therapy room; Activities room; Laundry room; Barber/Beauty shop.
Activities Arts & crafts; Cards; Games; Reading groups; Prayer groups; Movies; Shopping trips; Social/Cultural gatherings.

LOGAN

Logan Park Care Center*
PO Box 990, Logan, WV, 25601
(304) 752-8724
Admin Willis M Elkins. *Medical Dir/Dir of Nursing* Dr Erwin R Chillag.
Licensure Intermediate care. *Beds* 120. *Certified* Medicaid.
Admissions Requirements Medical examination.
Staff Physicians 2 (pt); RNs 4 (ft); LPNs 12 (ft); Orderlies 4 (ft); Physical therapists 1 (pt); Activities coordinators 2 (ft), 1 (pt); Dietitians 1 (pt); Dentists 1 (pt); Podiatrists 1 (pt).
Facilities Dining room; Physical therapy room; Activities room; Crafts room; Laundry room; Barber/Beauty shop; Library; Resident lounges; Large visitors lounge.
Activities Arts & crafts; Cards; Games; Reading groups; Prayer groups; Movies; Shopping trips; Social/Cultural gatherings.

MARLINTON

Pocahontas Continuous Care Center Inc
PO Box 500, Rte 1, Marlinton, WV, 24954
(304) 799-7375
Admin Dana Moyers. *Medical Dir/Dir of Nursing* John Sharp MD; Susie Dolan RN DON.
Licensure Intermediate care; Personal care. *Beds* ICF 66; Personal care 2. *Certified* Medicaid.
Owner Proprietary Corp (Glenmark Assoc).
Admissions Requirements Medical examination; Physician's request.
Staff Physicians 6 (pt); RNs 4 (ft); LPNs 6 (ft); Orderlies 1 (ft); Nurses aides 12 (ft), 10 (pt); Physical therapists 1 (pt); Reality therapists 1 (ft); Recreational therapists 1 (ft); Occupational therapists 1 (pt); Speech therapists 1 (pt); Activities coordinators 2 (pt); Dietitians 1 (ft); Podiatrists 1 (pt).
Facilities Dining room; Physical therapy room; Activities room; Chapel; Crafts room; Laundry room; Barber/Beauty shop; Library.
Activities Arts & crafts; Reading groups; Prayer groups; Movies; Shopping trips; Sing-along; Frankle exercises.

MARTINSBURG

Heartland of Martinsburg*
PO Box 530, Martinsburg, WV, 25401
(304) 263-8921
Admin John F Speer. *Medical Dir/Dir of Nursing* R Estgoy & R Crisp.
Licensure Skilled care; Intermediate care. *Beds* 116. *Certified* Medicaid; Medicare.

Owner Proprietary Corp (Health Care & Retirement Corp).
Staff Physicians 2 (ft); RNs 8 (ft); LPNs 8 (ft); Orderlies 2 (ft); Nurses aides 40 (ft); Physical therapists 1 (pt); Activities coordinators 1 (ft); Dietitians 1 (pt); Dentists 1 (pt); Podiatrists 1 (pt).
Facilities Dining room; Physical therapy room; Activities room; Chapel; Crafts room; Laundry room; Barber/Beauty shop.
Activities Arts & crafts; Cards; Games; Reading groups; Prayer groups; Movies; Shopping trips.

MILTON

Morris Memorial Nursing & Convalescent Home*
PO Box 6, Milton, WV, 25541
(304) 743-6861
Admin John E Greene.
Beds 185.

MONONGAH

St Barbara's Memorial Nursing Home Inc
Off Rte 19, Maple Terrace, Lady Lane, Monongah, WV, 26554
(304) 534-5220
Admin Sr Mary Stephen Reynolds Ph D. *Medical Dir/Dir of Nursing* Joyce Pellillo RN.
Licensure Skilled care. *Beds* SNF Swing beds 57. *Certified* Medicaid; Medicare.
Owner Nonprofit Corp.
Admissions Requirements Physician's request; Patients request.
Staff Physicians 1 (pt); RNs 4 (ft); Nurses aides 18 (ft); Physical therapists 1 (ft), 1 (pt); Activities coordinators 1 (ft), 1 (pt); Dietitians 1 (ft), 1 (pt); Maintenance Technicians 1 (ft), 1 (pt).
Facilities Dining room; Physical therapy room; Activities room; Chapel; Barber/Beauty shop; Library.
Activities Arts & crafts; Games; Prayer groups; Movies; Social/Cultural gatherings.

MORGANTOWN

Morgan Manor Convalescent Center*
1379 Van Voorhis Rd, Morgantown, WV, 26505
(304) 599-9480
Admin Linda Bair.
Licensure Skilled care; Intermediate care. *Beds* 100. *Certified* Medicaid; Medicare.
Owner Proprietary Corp (Beverly Enterprises).

Morgantown Health Care Corporation*
995 Maple Dr, Morgantown, WV, 26505
(304) 599-9378
Admin Diana K Barnett. *Medical Dir/Dir of Nursing* Austin Thompson MD & Richard Emanuelson MD.
Licensure Skilled care; Intermediate care. *Beds* 101. *Certified* Medicare.
Owner Proprietary Corp (Americare Corp).
Admissions Requirements Medical examination; Physician's request.
Staff Physicians 2 (ft); RNs 3 (ft), 3 (pt); LPNs 6 (ft), 7 (pt); Orderlies 2 (ft); Nurses aides 28 (ft), 18 (pt); Physical therapists 1 (pt); Recreational therapists 1 (ft); Occupational therapists 1 (pt); Speech therapists 1 (pt); Activities coordinators 1 (ft); Dietitians 1 (pt); Dentists 1 (pt); Ophthalmologists 1 (pt); Podiatrists 1 (pt); Audiologists 1 (pt).
Facilities Dining room; Physical therapy room; Activities room; Laundry room; Barber/Beauty shop; Library.
Activities Arts & crafts; Cards; Games; Reading groups; Prayer groups; Movies; Social/Cultural gatherings.

Sundale Nursing Home
800 J D Anderson Dr, Morgantown, WV, 26505
(304) 599-0497
Admin Sherry Rice. *Medical Dir/Dir of Nursing* Edwin Boso; Margaret Rog.
Licensure Intermediate care. *Beds* 120. *Certified* Medicaid.
Owner Nonprofit Corp.
Admissions Requirements Medical examination; Physician's request.
Staff Physicians 2 (ft); RNs 2 (ft); LPNs 11 (ft), 6 (pt); Orderlies 1 (pt); Nurses aides 23 (ft), 26 (pt); Physical therapists 1 (ft), 2 (pt); Speech therapists 3 (ft); Activities coordinators 1 (ft); Dietitians 1 (ft); Ophthalmologists 1 (pt).
Facilities Dining room; Physical therapy room; Activities room; Chapel; Crafts room; Laundry room; Barber/Beauty shop.
Activities Arts & crafts; Cards; Games; Prayer groups; Movies; Shopping trips; Social/Cultural gatherings.

MOUNDSVILLE

Mound View Health Care Center
PO Box F, Moundsville, WV, 26101
(304) 843-1035
Admin Herman Conaway. *Medical Dir/Dir of Nursing* Dr Dolgovskij; Alma Cunningham.
Licensure Skilled care; Intermediate care. *Beds* 174. *Certified* Medicaid; Medicare.
Owner Proprietary Corp.
Admissions Requirements Minimum age 16.
Staff Physicians 1 (pt); RNs 12 (ft); LPNs 4 (ft); Orderlies 4 (ft); Nurses aides 39 (ft); Physical therapists 1 (ft); Recreational therapists 1 (pt); Occupational therapists 1 (pt); Speech therapists 1 (pt); Activities coordinators 2 (ft); Dietitians 1 (ft); Dentists 1 (pt); Podiatrists 1 (pt).
Facilities Dining room; Physical therapy room; Activities room; Chapel; Crafts room; Laundry room; Barber/Beauty shop; Library.
Activities Arts & crafts; Cards; Games; Reading groups; Prayer groups; Movies; Shopping trips; Social/Cultural gatherings.

Mound View Health Care Inc*
PO Box F, Moundsville, WV, 26041
(304) 843-1035
Admin Wilma Conaway.
Licensure Skilled care; Intermediate care. *Beds* 114. *Certified* Medicaid; Medicare.

NEW MARTINSVILLE

New Martinsville Health Care Center
225 Russell Ave, New Martinsville, WV, 26155
(304) 455-2600
Admin George G Couch. *Medical Dir/Dir of Nursing* Dr Robert D Morris; Lameta Funari RN.
Licensure Skilled care; Intermediate care. *Beds* SNF 120; ICF. *Certified* Medicaid; Medicare.
Owner Proprietary Corp.
Admissions Requirements Minimum age 55; Medical examination; Physician's request.
Staff Physicians 1 (pt); RNs 8 (ft), 4 (pt); LPNs 8 (ft), 4 (pt); Nurses aides 42 (ft), 12 (pt); Physical therapists 2 (pt); Recreational therapists 1 (ft); Speech therapists 1 (pt); Activities coordinators 1 (ft); Dietitians 1 (pt); Dentists 1 (pt); Ophthalmologists 1 (pt).
Facilities Dining room; Physical therapy room; Activities room; Crafts room; Laundry room; Barber/Beauty shop; Library; Courtyard; Lounges.
Activities Arts & crafts; Cards; Games; Reading groups; Prayer groups; Movies; Shopping trips; Social/Cultural gatherings.

PARKERSBURG

Arlington Health Care Inc*
1716 Gihon Rd, Parkersburg, WV, 26101
(304) 485-5511
Admin Jeffrey Arnold.
Licensure Intermediate care. *Beds* 66. *Certified* Medicaid.

Ohio Valley Health Care Inc*
Rte 5, Box 146, Parkersburg, WV, 26101
(304) 485-5137
Admin Michael A Miller.
Licensure Intermediate care. *Beds* 60. *Certified* Medicaid.

Park View Healthcare Inc
1600 27th St, Parkersburg, WV, 26101
(304) 485-6476
Admin Larry N Conaway. *Medical Dir/Dir of Nursing* R Biddle MD.
Licensure Skilled care; Intermediate care. *Beds* 104. *Certified* Medicare.
Owner Proprietary Corp (ARA Living Centers).
Staff Physicians 3 (pt); RNs 4 (ft), 7 (pt); LPNs 7 (ft); Orderlies 2 (ft); Nurses aides 29 (ft); Physical therapists 2 (ft); Occupational therapists 1 (pt); Speech therapists 1 (pt); Activities coordinators 2 (ft); Dietitians 1 (pt); Dentists 1 (pt); Ophthalmologists 1 (pt); Podiatrists 2 (pt).
Facilities Dining room; Physical therapy room; Activities room; Chapel; Crafts room; Laundry room; Barber/Beauty shop; Library.
Activities Arts & crafts; Cards; Games; Reading groups; Prayer groups; Movies; Shopping trips; Social/Cultural gatherings.

The Willows
PO Box 3059, 723 Summers St, Parkersburg, WV, 26103
(304) 428-5573
Admin Katheryn Gessler. *Medical Dir/Dir of Nursing* Beverly Hellein RN.
Licensure Skilled care; Intermediate care. *Beds* SNF 19; ICF 70. *Certified* Medicaid.
Owner Proprietary Corp (Glenmark Assoc).
Admissions Requirements Minimum age 18; Medical examination.
Staff Physicians 1 (pt); RNs 4 (ft), 5 (pt); LPNs 3 (ft), 3 (pt); Nurses aides 18 (ft), 12 (pt); Physical therapists 1 (pt); Activities coordinators 1 (ft); Dietitians 1 (ft).
Facilities Dining room; Physical therapy room; Activities room; Crafts room; Laundry room; Barber/Beauty shop; Private dining area.
Activities Arts & crafts; Cards; Games; Prayer groups; Movies; Shopping trips; Social/Cultural gatherings.

Worthington Manor Inc
PO Box 4010, 36th St & Core Rd, Parkersburg, WV, 26104
(304) 485-7447
Admin Norma Dunn. *Medical Dir/Dir of Nursing* George McCarty MD; Patricia Richardson RN DON.
Licensure Skilled care. *Beds* SNF 105. *Certified* Medicaid; Medicare.
Owner Privately owned.
Admissions Requirements Medical examination; Physician's request.
Staff Physicians 2 (pt); RNs 4 (ft), 2 (pt); LPNs 13 (ft); Orderlies 2 (ft); Nurses aides 39 (ft), 3 (pt); Physical therapists 1 (pt); Speech therapists 2 (pt); Activities coordinators 1 (ft); Dietitians 1 (pt); Dentists 1 (pt); Ophthalmologists 1 (pt).
Facilities Dining room; Physical therapy room; Activities room; Crafts room; Laundry room; Barber/Beauty shop; Library.
Activities Arts & crafts; Cards; Games; Reading groups; Prayer groups; Movies; Shopping trips; Social/Cultural gatherings.

PETERSBURG

Grant County Nursing Home
27 Early Ave, Petersburg, WV, 26847
(304) 257-4233
Admin Terry Shobe. *Medical Dir/Dir of Nursing* Dewey Bensenhaver MD; Connie Cover RN DON.
Licensure Intermediate care. *Beds* ICF 60. *Certified* Medicaid.
Owner Publicly owned.
Staff Physicians 3 (pt); RNs 4 (ft), 2 (pt); LPNs 3 (ft), 3 (pt); Orderlies 1 (ft); Nurses aides 12 (ft), 18 (pt); Physical therapists 1 (pt); Recreational therapists 1 (pt); Speech therapists 1 (pt); Activities coordinators 1 (ft), 1 (pt); Dietitians 1 (pt); Ophthalmologists 1 (pt); Social workers 1 (pt); Restorative aides 1 (ft).
Facilities Dining room; Physical therapy room; Activities room; Chapel; Crafts room; Laundry room; Barber/Beauty shop; Patio; 2 TV rooms.
Activities Arts & crafts; Cards; Games; Movies; Shopping trips; Bible study; Picnics; Recreational trips.

PRINCETON

Glenwood Park United Methodist Home*
Rte 1, Box 464, Princeton, WV, 24740
(304) 325-8164
Admin Daniel W Farley.
Licensure Skilled care; Intermediate care. *Beds* 56.
Affiliation Methodist

Princeton Health Care Center*
315 Court House Rd, Princeton, WV, 24740
(304) 487-3458
Admin Larry Hodge. *Medical Dir/Dir of Nursing* Dr Charles J Mirabile.
Licensure Intermediate care. *Beds* 120.
Admissions Requirements Medical examination.
Staff Physicians 1 (ft); RNs 2 (ft); LPNs 8 (ft), 2 (pt); Orderlies 3 (ft); Physical therapists 1 (pt); Reality therapists 1 (ft); Recreational therapists 1 (ft); Speech therapists 1 (pt); Activities coordinators 1 (ft); Dentists 1 (pt); Ophthalmologists 1 (pt); Podiatrists 1 (ft); Audiologists 1 (pt).
Facilities Dining room; Physical therapy room; Activities room; Laundry room; Barber/Beauty shop; Library.
Activities Arts & crafts; Cards; Games; Reading groups; Prayer groups; Movies; Shopping trips; Social/Cultural gatherings.

RAINELLE

Pomeroy-Davis-Heartland Memorial Nursing Home*
Pennsylvania & 16th St, Rainelle, WV, 25982
(304) 438-6127
Admin Brian S Allen.
Licensure Intermediate care. *Beds* 59. *Certified* Medicaid.
Owner Proprietary Corp (Health Care & Retirement Corp).

RANSON

Shenandoah Home Inc*
131 E 3rd St, Ranson, WV, 25438
(304) 725-3404
Admin James Bryan.
Licensure Intermediate care. *Beds* 48. *Certified* Medicaid.

RICHWOOD

Nicholas County Health Care Center Inc
18 4th St, Richwood, WV, 26261
(304) 846-2668
Admin Richard A Lemons. *Medical Dir/Dir of Nursing* Clemente Diaz MD; Sue Cogar RN DON.
Licensure Intermediate care. *Beds* ICF 120. *Certified* Medicaid.
Owner Proprietary Corp (Unicare).
Staff Physicians 5 (pt); RNs 4 (ft), 1 (pt); LPNs 5 (ft), 4 (pt); Orderlies 1 (ft); Nurses aides 30 (ft), 8 (pt); Physical therapists 3 (pt); Recreational therapists 1 (pt); Speech therapists 1 (pt); Activities coordinators 1 (ft); Dietitians 1 (pt); Podiatrists 1 (pt).
Facilities Dining room; Physical therapy room; Activities room; Crafts room; Laundry room; Barber/Beauty shop.
Activities Arts & crafts; Cards; Games; Prayer groups; Movies; Shopping trips; Social/Cultural gatherings.

RIPLEY

Care Inn*
107 Miller Dr, Ripley, WV, 25271
(304) 372-5115
Admin Ernest Eades. *Medical Dir/Dir of Nursing* Samuel Johnson MD.
Licensure Skilled care; Intermediate care. *Beds* 120. *Certified* Medicaid; Medicare.
Owner Proprietary Corp (Beverly Enterprises).
Admissions Requirements Medical examination.
Staff Physicians 2 (pt); RNs 6 (ft); LPNs 12 (ft); Orderlies 2 (ft); Nurses aides 49 (ft); Physical therapists 1 (pt); Recreational therapists 1 (pt); Activities coordinators 1 (ft); Dietitians 1 (pt); Dentists 2 (pt); Ophthalmologists 1 (pt); Podiatrists 1 (pt); Psychologists 1 (pt).
Facilities Dining room; Physical therapy room; Activities room; Chapel; Laundry room; Barber/Beauty shop.
Activities Arts & crafts; Games; Reading groups; Prayer groups; Movies; Shopping trips; Social/Cultural gatherings.

ROMNEY

Kidwell Rest Home*
550 Sioux Ln, Romney, WV, 26757
(304) 822-5330
Admin Nellie Kidwell.
Licensure Intermediate care. *Beds* 18. *Certified* Medicaid.

RONCEVERTE

Shenandoah Manor
608 Greenbrier Ave, Ronceverte, WV, 24970
(304) 645-7270
Admin Nile D Cutlip. *Medical Dir/Dir of Nursing* Dorris Ragsdale MD.
Licensure Intermediate care. *Beds* 96. *Certified* Medicaid.
Owner Proprietary Corp (Glenmark Assoc).
Admissions Requirements Medical examination; Physician's request.
Staff Physicians 3 (pt); RNs 3 (ft), 1 (pt); LPNs 12 (ft), 4 (pt); Orderlies 4 (ft); Nurses aides 27 (ft), 10 (pt); Physical therapists 1 (pt); Speech therapists 1 (pt); Activities coordinators 1 (ft), 1 (pt); Dietitians 1 (pt); Dentists 1 (pt); Ophthalmologists 1 (pt); Podiatrists 1 (pt).
Facilities Dining room; Physical therapy room; Activities room; Crafts room; Laundry room; Barber/Beauty shop.
Activities Arts & crafts; Cards; Games; Reading groups; Prayer groups; Movies; Shopping trips; Social/Cultural gatherings.

SAINT ALBANS

Riverside Nursing & Convalescent Center Inc*
6500 MacCorkle Ave SW, Saint Albans, WV, 25177
(304) 768-0002
Admin Ruth Duppee. *Medical Dir/Dir of Nursing* S L Henson MD.
Licensure Skilled care; Intermediate care. *Beds* 98. *Certified* Medicare.
Owner Proprietary Corp (Beverly Enterprises).
Staff Physicians 2 (pt); RNs 4 (ft), 2 (pt); LPNs 4 (ft), 2 (pt); Orderlies 4 (ft); Nurses aides 32 (ft); Recreational therapists 1 (ft); Activities coordinators 1 (ft); Dietitians 1 (ft); Dentists 1 (pt); Ophthalmologists 1 (pt); Podiatrists 1 (pt); Audiologists 1 (pt).
Facilities Dining room; Physical therapy room; Activities room; Chapel; Crafts room; Laundry room; Barber/Beauty shop.
Activities Arts & crafts; Cards; Games; Reading groups; Prayer groups; Movies; Shopping trips; Social/Cultural gatherings.

SALEM

Americare Salem Nursing & Rehabilitation Center
Rte 2, Box 427, 146 Water St, Salem, WV, 26426
(304) 782-3000
Admin Marie Brown Okronley. *Medical Dir/Dir of Nursing* Dr Arthur Calhoun; Dr Mark Godenick; Dr Connie Godenick.
Licensure Skilled care; Intermediate care. *Beds* SNF 28; ICF 100. *Certified* Medicaid; Medicare.
Owner Proprietary Corp (Americare Corp).
Admissions Requirements Medical examination.
Staff Physicians 3 (pt); RNs 4 (ft), 2 (pt); LPNs 8 (ft), 3 (pt); Orderlies 10 (ft); Nurses aides 35 (ft), 15 (pt); Physical therapists 1 (ft); Speech therapists 1 (pt); Activities coordinators 1 (ft); Dietitians 1 (ft).
Facilities Dining room; Physical therapy room; Activities room; Crafts room; Laundry room; Barber/Beauty shop.
Activities Arts & crafts; Cards; Games; Reading groups; Prayer groups; Movies; Shopping trips; Social/Cultural gatherings.

SISTERSVILLE

Magnolia Manor Nursing Home*
410 Wells St, Sistersville, WV, 26175
(304) 652-1551
Admin Herman Conaway.
Licensure Intermediate care. *Beds* 24. *Certified* Medicaid.

SPENCER

Gordon Memorial Health Care Facility*
400 Church St, Spencer, WV, 25276
(304) 927-5331
Admin Marybelle Hersman. *Medical Dir/Dir of Nursing* H L Gamposia MD.
Licensure Intermediate care. *Beds* 66. *Certified* Medicaid.
Admissions Requirements Medical examination; Physician's request.
Staff Physicians 1 (ft), 3 (pt); RNs 2 (ft); LPNs 6 (ft); Orderlies 2 (ft); Nurses aides 17 (ft), 2 (pt); Physical therapists 1 (pt); Recreational therapists 1 (ft); Occupational therapists 1 (ft), 2 (pt); Dietitians 1 (pt); Dentists 1 (pt); Ophthalmologists 1 (pt); Podiatrists 1 (pt).
Facilities Dining room; Activities room; Laundry room; Barber/Beauty shop.
Activities Arts & crafts; Cards; Games; Reading groups; Prayer groups; Movies; Shopping trips; Social/Cultural gatherings.

SUTTON

Braxton Health Care Center*
Rte 19/23, Old Dyer Rd, Sutton, WV, 26601
(304) 765-2861
Admin Larry Lawrence.
Licensure Intermediate care. *Beds* 60.

THOMAS

Portland Acres Nursing Home
Rte 1, Box 98, Thomas, WV, 26292
(304) 463-4181
Admin Dan Bucher. *Medical Dir/Dir of Nursing* Dr Samuel J Bucher; Anita Flanagan RN DON.
Licensure Skilled care; Intermediate care. *Beds* SNF 94; ICF. *Certified* Medicaid; Medicare.
Owner Nonprofit Corp.
Admissions Requirements Minimum age Elderly; Medical examination.
Staff Physicians 7 (pt); RNs 5 (ft), 4 (pt); LPNs 4 (ft), 6 (pt); Orderlies 2 (ft); Nurses aides 30 (ft), 15 (pt); Physical therapists 1 (ft), 1 (pt); Activities coordinators 1 (ft), 1 (pt); Dietitians 1 (pt); Ophthalmologists 1 (pt).
Facilities Dining room; Physical therapy room; Activities room; Chapel; Laundry room; Barber/Beauty shop.
Activities Arts & crafts; Cards; Games; Reading groups; Prayer groups; Movies; Shopping trips; Social/Cultural gatherings.

WEIRTON

Weirton Geriatric Center
2525 Pennsylvania Ave, Weirton, WV, 26062
(304) 723-4300
Admin Louis Serra. *Medical Dir/Dir of Nursing* Antonio Licata MD; Nancy Riggle RN.
Licensure Skilled care; Intermediate care. *Beds* 119. *Certified* Medicaid; Medicare.
Owner Proprietary Corp.
Staff Physicians 10 (pt); RNs 10 (ft), 4 (pt); LPNs 2 (pt); Nurses aides 55 (ft), 15 (pt); Physical therapists 1 (pt) 13J 1 (pt); Activities coordinators 1 (ft); Dietitians 1 (pt); Ophthalmologists 1 (pt); Podiatrists 1 (pt).
Facilities Dining room; Physical therapy room; Activities room; Chapel; Crafts room; Laundry room; Barber/Beauty shop.
Activities Arts & crafts; Cards; Games; Reading groups; Prayer groups; Movies; Shopping trips; Social/Cultural gatherings Exercise Program.

WELLSBURG

Valley Haven Geriatric Center & Personal Care Home Inc
Rte 2, Box 44, Wellsburg, WV, 26070
(304) 394-5322
Admin Alice M Couch. *Medical Dir/Dir of Nursing* Michael Voorhees MD.
Licensure Intermediate care; Personal care. *Beds* ICF 60; Personal 25. *Certified* Medicaid.
Owner Proprietary Corp.
Admissions Requirements Minimum age 18; Physician's request.
Staff Physicians 2 (pt); RNs 8 (ft), 2 (pt); LPNs 6 (ft), 3 (pt); Nurses aides 29 (ft), 2 (pt); Physical therapists 1 (pt); Recreational therapists 1 (pt); Speech therapists 1 (pt); Activities coordinators 1 (ft), 1 (pt); Dietitians 1 (pt); Dentists 1 (pt); Ophthalmologists 1 (pt); Podiatrists 1 (pt); Social Service 1 (ft).
Facilities Dining room; Physical therapy room; Activities room; Crafts room; Laundry room; Barber/Beauty shop; Library.
Activities Arts & crafts; Cards; Games; Reading groups; Prayer groups; Movies; Shopping trips; Social/Cultural gatherings; Lounge; Physical therapy; Speech therapy; Hearing therapy.

WHEELING

Good Shepherd Nursing Home*
159 Edgington Blvd, Wheeling, WV, 26003
(304) 242-1093
Admin Donald R Kirsch. *Medical Dir/Dir of Nursing* Dr John Battaglino.
Licensure Skilled care; Intermediate care. *Beds* 192. *Certified* Medicaid; Medicare.
Admissions Requirements Minimum age 55.
Staff RNs 4 (ft), 8 (pt); LPNs 19 (ft), 13 (pt); Nurses aides 63 (ft), 18 (pt); Physical therapists 2 (pt); Speech therapists 1 (pt); Activities coordinators 1 (ft); Dietitians 1 (pt).
Facilities Dining room; Physical therapy room; Activities room; Chapel; Laundry room.
Activities Arts & crafts; Cards; Games; Reading groups; Prayer groups; Movies; Shopping trips; Social/Cultural gatherings.

Bishop Joseph H Hodges Continuous Care Center
Medical Park, Wheeling, WV, 26003
(304) 243-3812
Admin Gary R Gould. *Medical Dir/Dir of Nursing* John J Battaglino Fr MD.
Licensure Skilled care; Intermediate care. *Beds* ICF 120. *Certified* Medicaid; Medicare.
Owner Nonprofit Corp.
Admissions Requirements Medical examination; Physician's request.
Staff Physicians 1 (pt); RNs 10 (ft), 15 (pt); LPNs 9 (ft), 5 (pt); Nurses aides 26 (ft), 41 (pt); Physical therapists 1 (ft); Speech therapists 1 (pt); Activities coordinators 2 (ft); Dietitians 1 (pt).
Facilities Dining room; Physical therapy room; Activities room; Chapel; Crafts room; Laundry room; Barber/Beauty shop; Library.
Activities Arts & crafts; Cards; Games; Reading groups; Prayer groups; Movies; Social/Cultural gatherings.

Wheeling Continuous Care Center*
109 Main St, Wheeling, WV, 26003
(304) 233-4330
Admin Patrick J Ward.
Licensure Skilled care; Intermediate care. *Beds* 76. *Certified* Medicaid; Medicare.

WILLIAMSON

Mingo Manor
Williamson, WV, 25661
(304) 235-7005
Admin Willis M Elkins. *Medical Dir/Dir of Nursing* Dr E R Chillag; Pat Harrah RN.
Licensure Skilled care. *Beds* 120. *Certified* Medicaid; Medicare.
Owner Privately owned.
Admissions Requirements Medical examination; Physician's request.
Staff Physicians; RNs; LPNs; Orderlies; Nurses aides; Physical therapists; Recreational therapists; Activities coordinators; Dietitians; Dentists; Ophthalmologists.
Facilities Dining room; Physical therapy room; Activities room; Crafts room; Laundry room; Barber/Beauty shop; Library; 3 lounges.
Activities Arts & crafts; Cards; Games; Reading groups; Prayer groups; Movies; Shopping trips; Social/Cultural gatherings.

WISCONSIN

ABBOTSFORD

Continental Manor
600 E Elm St, Abbotsford, WI, 54405
(715) 223-2359
Admin Jill Cleven. *Medical Dir/Dir of Nursing*
Renee Hinrichsen RN.
Licensure Skilled care; Intermediate care. *Beds*
60. *Certified* Medicaid.
Owner Proprietary Corp (Beverly Enterprises).
Staff RNs; LPNs; Nurses aides; Activities
coordinators.
Facilities Dining room; Physical therapy
room; Laundry room; Barber/Beauty shop.
Activities Arts & crafts; Games; Reading
groups; Movies; Social/Cultural gatherings.

ALGOMA

Algoma Memorial Long-Term Care Unit
1510 Fremont St, Algoma, WI, 54201
(414) 487-5511
Admin Ron Junco. *Medical Dir/Dir of Nursing*
J F March MD; Ardis R Junco DON.
Licensure Skilled care. *Beds* SNF 50. *Certified*
Medicaid.
Owner Publicly owned.
Admissions Requirements Physician's request.
Staff Physicians 4 (ft); RNs 1 (ft), 3 (pt);
LPNs 5 (ft), 3 (pt); Nurses aides 10 (ft), 6
(pt); Physical therapists 1 (ft); Reality
therapists 1 (pt); Recreational therapists 1
(pt); Occupational therapists 1 (pt); Speech
therapists 1 (pt); Activities coordinators 1
(ft); Dietitians 1 (ft).
Languages Italian, German
Facilities Dining room; Physical therapy
room; Activities room; Crafts room.
Activities Arts & crafts; Cards; Games;
Reading groups; Prayer groups; Movies;
Shopping trips; Social/Cultural gatherings.

ALTOONA

Henry Thodes Oakwood Villa
2512 New Pine Dr, Altoona, WI, 54720
(715) 833-0401
Admin Henry Thode. *Medical Dir/Dir of
Nursing* Judy Atkinson.
Licensure Skilled care; Intermediate care. *Beds*
88. *Certified* Medicaid.
Owner Proprietary Corp.
Admissions Requirements Minimum age 18.
Staff RNs; LPNs; Orderlies; Nurses aides;
Physical therapists; Recreational therapists;
Occupational therapists; Speech therapists;
Activities coordinators; Dietitians.
Facilities Dining room; Physical therapy
room; Activities room; Chapel; Crafts room;
Laundry room; Barber/Beauty shop; Library.
Activities Arts & crafts; Cards; Games;
Reading groups; Prayer groups; Movies;
Shopping trips; Social/Cultural gatherings.

AMERY

Amery Constant Care Inc
400 Deronda St, Amery, WI, 54001
(715) 268-8171
Admin Dean H Dixon. *Medical Dir/Dir of
Nursing* Bill Byrnes; Shannon Purinton.
Licensure Skilled care; Intermediate care. *Beds*
94. *Certified* Medicaid; Medicare.
Owner Proprietary Corp.
Admissions Requirements Medical
examination.
Staff RNs 1 (ft), 3 (pt); LPNs 2 (ft), 4 (pt);
Nurses aides 30 (ft), 14 (pt); Recreational
therapists 1 (ft); Activities coordinators 1
(ft); Dietitians 1 (pt).
Facilities Dining room; Activities room;
Laundry room; Barber/Beauty shop.
Activities Arts & crafts; Cards; Games;
Reading groups; Prayer groups; Movies;
Shopping trips; Social/Cultural gatherings.

Golden Age Manor*
220 Scholl St, Amery, WI, 54001
(715) 268-7107
Admin Gary E Taxdahl.
Licensure Skilled care; Intermediate care. *Beds*
114. *Certified* Medicaid.
Owner Publicly owned.

ANTIGO

Eastview Manor
729 Park St, Antigo, WI, 54409
(715) 623-2356
Admin Mary Ellen Draeger. *Medical Dir/Dir
of Nursing* John McKenna MD.
Licensure Skilled care; Intermediate care. *Beds*
173. *Certified* Medicaid.
Owner Proprietary Corp (Hillhaven Corp).
Admissions Requirements Minimum age 18;
Medical examination; Physician's request.
Staff RNs 1 (ft), 12 (pt); LPNs 1 (ft), 8 (pt);
Nurses aides 20 (ft), 47 (pt); Physical
therapists 1 (ft); Occupational therapists 1
(pt); Activities coordinators 1 (ft); Dietitians
1 (ft).
Facilities Dining room; Physical therapy
room; Activities room; Chapel; Crafts room;
Laundry room; Barber/Beauty shop.
Activities Arts & crafts; Cards; Games;
Reading groups; Prayer groups; Movies;
Shopping trips; Social/Cultural gatherings.

APPLETON

Americana Health Care Center
1330 S Oneida St, Appleton, WI, 54915
(414) 731-6646
Admin Mary Calhoun. *Medical Dir/Dir of
Nursing* Dr William Hale MD; Jeff Vander
Venter.
Licensure Skilled care. *Beds* 104. *Certified*
Medicaid; Medicare.
Owner Proprietary Corp (Manor Care).
Admissions Requirements Medical
examination; Physician's request.

Staff Physicians 1 (pt); RNs 3 (ft), 3 (pt);
LPNs 2 (ft), 10 (pt); Orderlies 1 (ft); Nurses
aides 15 (ft), 32 (pt); Physical therapists 1
(pt); Recreational therapists 1 (ft);
Occupational therapists 1 (pt); Speech
therapists 1 (pt); Dietitians 1 (pt);
Ophthalmologists 1 (pt).
Facilities Dining room; Physical therapy
room; Activities room; Crafts room; Laundry
room; Barber/Beauty shop; Library.
Activities Arts & crafts; Cards; Games;
Reading groups; Prayer groups; Movies;
Shopping trips; Social/Cultural gatherings;
Community involvement.

Appleton Extended Care Center*
2915 N Meade St, Appleton, WI, 54911
(414) 731-3184
Admin Charles R Barnum.
Licensure Skilled care; Intermediate care. *Beds*
235. *Certified* Medicaid.
Owner Proprietary Corp.

Colony Oaks Care Center
601 Briarcliff Dr, Appleton, WI, 54915
(414) 739-4466
Admin Holly Lindgren.
Licensure Skilled care; Intermediate care. *Beds*
102. *Certified* Medicaid; Medicare.
Owner Proprietary Corp (Hillhaven Corp).

Outagamie County Health Center
3400 W Brewster St, Appleton, WI, 54914-
1699
(414) 735-5400
Admin David Rothmann. *Medical Dir/Dir of
Nursing* Dr Terrance Meece.
Licensure Skilled care; Intermediate care;
Intermediate care for mentally retarded.
Beds 256. *Certified* Medicaid.
Owner Publicly owned.
Admissions Requirements Minimum age 18;
Medical examination; Physician's request.
Staff Physicians 24 (pt); RNs 12 (ft), 3 (pt);
LPNs 13 (ft), 12 (pt); Nurses aides 37 (ft),
70 (pt); Physical therapists 1 (pt);
Occupational therapists 4 (ft); Activities
coordinators 1 (ft); Dietitians 1 (pt); Dentist
2 (pt).
Facilities Dining room; Physical therapy
room; Activities room; Chapel; Crafts room;
Barber/Beauty shop.
Activities Arts & crafts; Cards; Games;
Reading groups; Prayer groups; Movies;
Shopping trips; Social/Cultural gatherings.

Peabody Manor Inc
720 W 5th ST, Appleton, WI, 54914
(414) 733-3724
Admin Robert J Bastian.
Licensure Skilled care. *Beds* 80.
Owner Nonprofit Corp.

ARCADIA

St Joseph Nursing Home*
464 S Saint Joseph Ave, Arcadia, WI, 54612
(608) 323-3341

Admin Bruce E Roesler.
Licensure Skilled care; Intermediate care. *Beds* 75. *Certified* Medicaid.
Owner Nonprofit Corp.

ARPIN

Bethel Living Center
8014 Bethel Rd, Arpin, WI, 54410
(715) 652-2103
Admin Walter A Schroeder. *Medical Dir/Dir of Nursing* Robert Phillips MD; Linda Skilton DON.
Licensure Skilled care. *Beds* 111. *Certified* Medicaid; Medicare.
Owner Nonprofit Corp (Adventist Health Sys-USA).
Admissions Requirements Minimum age 18; Medical examination; Physician's request.
Staff RNs 4 (ft), 4 (pt); LPNs 4 (ft), 4 (pt); Nurses aides 30 (ft), 30 (pt); Physical therapists 1 (pt); Activities coordinators 1 (ft); Dietitians 1 (pt).
Affiliation Seventh-Day Adventist
Facilities Dining room; Physical therapy room; Activities room; Chapel; Crafts room; Laundry room; Barber/Beauty shop; Library; Gym.
Activities Arts & crafts; Cards; Games; Reading groups; Prayer groups; Movies; Shopping trips; Social/Cultural gatherings; Bus rides.

ASHLAND

Ashland Health Care Center Inc
1319 Beaser Ave, Ashland, WI, 54806
(715) 682-3468
Admin Jeffrey L Ott. *Medical Dir/Dir of Nursing* Dr Joseph M Jauquet MD; Janet Bresette RN.
Licensure Skilled care. *Beds* 144. *Certified* Medicaid; Medicare.
Owner Privately owned.
Admissions Requirements Medical examination; Physician's request.
Staff RNs 6 (ft), 9 (pt); LPNs 7 (ft), 11 (pt); Orderlies 3 (ft), 5 (pt); Nurses aides 20 (ft), 32 (pt); Physical therapists 1 (pt); Activities coordinators 2 (ft), 1 (pt); Dietitians 1 (pt).
Languages German, Finish, Swedish
Facilities Dining room; Physical therapy room; Activities room; Chapel; Crafts room; Laundry room; Barber/Beauty shop; Physicians exam room; 15-passenger van with hydraulic wheelchar lift.
Activities Arts & crafts; Cards; Games; Reading groups; Prayer groups; Movies; Shopping trips; Social/Cultural gatherings; Religious services.

Court Manor
911 W 3rd St, Ashland, WI, 54806
(715) 682-8172
Admin Roy T Schoemaker. *Medical Dir/Dir of Nursing* Dr Joseph Jauquet.
Licensure Skilled care; Intermediate care. *Beds* 150. *Certified* Medicaid; Medicare; VA.
Owner Proprietary Corp (Beverly Enterprises).
Admissions Requirements Minimum age 18; Medical examination; Physician's request.
Staff Physicians 1 (ft), 1 (pt); RNs 6 (ft), 3 (pt); LPNs 8 (ft), 5 (pt); Orderlies 4 (ft), 3 (pt); Nurses aides 43 (ft), 21 (pt); Physical therapists 1 (ft); Recreational therapists 1 (ft), 1 (pt); Speech therapists 1 (pt); Activities coordinators 1 (ft); Dietitians 1 (pt).
Facilities Dining room; Physical therapy room; Activities room; Chapel; Crafts room; Laundry room; Barber/Beauty shop; Library.
Activities Arts & crafts; Cards; Games; Reading groups; Prayer groups; Movies; Shopping trips; Social/Cultural gatherings.

AUGUSTA

Augusta Area Nursing Home
215 Brown St, Augusta, WI, 54722
(715) 286-2266
Admin Joyce Richards. *Medical Dir/Dir of Nursing* Roberta Vandehey.
Licensure Intermediate care. *Beds* ICF 62.
Owner Nonprofit Corp.
Admissions Requirements Minimum age 18; Medical examination.
Staff RNs 1 (ft), 3 (pt); LPNs 4 (pt); Nurses aides 6 (ft), 20 (pt); Activities coordinators 1 (ft), 2 (pt); Dietitians 1 (pt).
Facilities Dining room; Chapel; Laundry room; Barber/Beauty shop; Library.
Activities Arts & crafts; Cards; Games; Reading groups; Prayer groups; Movies; Shopping trips; Social/Cultural gatherings.

BALDWIN

Baldwin Care Center*
640 Elm St, Baldwin, WI, 54002
(715) 684-3231
Admin Gary R Olson. *Medical Dir/Dir of Nursing* Dr Lennard B Torkelson.
Licensure Skilled care; Intermediate care. *Beds* 76. *Certified* Medicaid.
Admissions Requirements Minimum age 21; Medical examination.
Staff Physicians 1 (ft); RNs 1 (ft), 3 (pt); LPNs 9 (ft); Orderlies 1 (ft); Nurses aides 13 (ft), 17 (pt); Physical therapists 1 (pt); Activities coordinators 1 (ft); Dietitians 1 (pt); Dentists 2 (pt).
Facilities Dining room; Activities room; Laundry room.
Activities Cards; Games; Prayer groups; Movies; Shopping trips; Social/Cultural gatherings.

BARABOO

Jefferson Meadows Care Center
1414 Jefferson St, Baraboo, WI, 53913
(608) 356-4838
Admin Arthur E Uselding NHA. *Medical Dir/Dir of Nursing* John J Siebert MD; Rita Miller RN DON.
Licensure Skilled care; Community based residential facility. *Beds* SNF 102; Community based residential facility 32. *Certified* Medicaid; Medicare.
Owner Nonprofit Corp.
Admissions Requirements Minimum age 18; Medical examination; Physician's request.
Staff Physicians 1 (pt); RNs 2 (ft), 10 (pt); LPNs 1 (ft), 7 (pt); Nurses aides 7 (ft), 45 (pt); Physical therapists 1 (pt); Reality therapists 1 (pt); Recreational therapists 4 (pt); Occupational therapists 1 (pt); Speech therapists 1 (pt); Activities coordinators 1 (pt); Dietitians 1 (pt); Podiatrists 1 (pt).
Facilities Dining room; Physical therapy room; Activities room; Laundry room; Barber/Beauty shop; Ice cream parlor.
Activities Arts & crafts; Cards; Games; Movies; Shopping trips; Social/Cultural gatherings.

BARRON

Barron Memorial Medical Center SNF
1222 E Woodland Ave, Barron, WI, 54812
(715) 537-3186
Admin Gerald C Olson. *Medical Dir/Dir of Nursing* Dr Michael Damroth.
Licensure Skilled care. *Beds* SNF 50. *Certified* Medicaid.
Owner Nonprofit Corp.
Admissions Requirements Medical examination; Physician's request.
Staff Physicians 10 (pt); RNs 4 (ft); LPNs 4 (ft); Orderlies 1 (ft); Nurses aides 18 (ft), 6 (pt); Physical therapists 1 (pt); Occupational

therapists 1 (pt); Speech therapists 1 (pt); Activities coordinators 1 (ft); Dietitians 1 (pt); Ophthalmologists 1 (pt).
Languages Spanish
Facilities Dining room; Physical therapy room; Activities room; Chapel; Crafts room; Barber/Beauty shop; Library.
Activities Arts & crafts; Cards; Games; Reading groups; Prayer groups; Movies; Shopping trips; Social/Cultural gatherings; Fishing; Family picnics; Pets day.

Barron Riverside Manor
660 E Birch Ave, Barron, WI, 54812
(715) 537-5643
Admin Cora Ayers. *Medical Dir/Dir of Nursing* J R Hoefert MD; Phoebe Vik DON.
Licensure Skilled care; Intermediate care. *Beds* SNF 50; ICF. *Certified* Medicaid.
Owner Nonprofit Corp.
Admissions Requirements Minimum age 18; Medical examination; Physician's request.
Staff RNs 2 (ft), 2 (pt); LPNs 2 (ft), 2 (pt); Orderlies 1 (ft); Nurses aides 6 (ft), 16 (pt); Physical therapists 1 (pt); Recreational therapists 1 (pt); Occupational therapists 1 (pt); Speech therapists 1 (pt); Activities coordinators 1 (ft); Dietitians 1 (pt).
Facilities Dining room; Physical therapy room; Activities room; Crafts room; Laundry room; Barber/Beauty shop.
Activities Arts & crafts; Cards; Games; Reading groups; Prayer groups; Movies; Shopping trips; Social/Cultural gatherings; Gardening.

BEAVER DAM

Beaver Dam Care Center
410 Roedl Ct, Beaver Dam, WI, 53916
(414) 887-7191
Admin Richard F Rexrode Jr. *Medical Dir/Dir of Nursing* Dr Fred Karsten MD; Dawn E Lake RN DON.
Licensure Skilled care; Intermediate care. *Beds* 130. *Certified* Medicaid; Medicare.
Owner Proprietary Corp (Beverly Enterprises).
Admissions Requirements Minimum age 18; Medical examination; Physician's request.
Staff RNs 6 (ft), 4 (pt); LPNs 9 (ft), 5 (pt); Orderlies 1 (ft); Nurses aides 39 (ft), 14 (pt); Activities coordinators 1 (ft); Dietitians 1 (ft).
Facilities Dining room; Physical therapy room; Activities room; Chapel; Crafts room; Laundry room; Barber/Beauty shop; Library; Whirlpool with hydrolic lift.
Activities Arts & crafts; Cards; Games; Reading groups; Prayer groups; Movies; Shopping trips; Social/Cultural gatherings; Pet therapy.

Beaver Dam Lakeview Unit*
208 Lacrosse St, Beaver Dam, WI, 53916
(414) 887-7181
Admin Linda M Boyd.
Licensure Skilled care; Intermediate care. *Beds* 123. *Certified* Medicaid.
Owner Nonprofit Corp.

BELOIT

Beloit Convalescent Center*
1905 W Hart Rd, Beloit, WI, 53511
(608) 365-2554
Admin Betsy Larson. *Medical Dir/Dir of Nursing* Dr James Long.
Licensure Skilled care; Intermediate care. *Beds* 156. *Certified* Medicaid; Medicare.
Owner Proprietary Corp (Unicare).
Admissions Requirements Medical examination.
Facilities Dining room; Physical therapy room; Activities room; Chapel; Crafts room; Laundry room; Barber/Beauty shop.

Activities Arts & crafts; Cards; Games; Reading groups; Prayer groups; Movies; Shopping trips; Social/Cultural gatherings.

Caravilla
PO Box 75, Beloit, WI, 53511
(608) 365-8877
Admin Catherine H Smith. *Medical Dir/Dir of Nursing* James Miller MD.
Licensure Skilled care; Intermediate care; Community based residential facility. *Beds* 326. *Certified* Medicaid; Medicare.
Owner Proprietary Corp.
Admissions Requirements Minimum age 18; Medical examination; Physician's request.
Staff Physicians; RNs; LPNs; Orderlies; Nurses aides; Physical therapists; Recreational therapists; Occupational therapists; Speech therapists; Activities coordinators; Dietitians; Ophthalmologists; Podiatrists.
Facilities Dining room; Physical therapy room; Activities room; Chapel; Crafts room; Laundry room; Barber/Beauty shop; Library.
Activities Arts & crafts; Cards; Games; Reading groups; Prayer groups; Movies; Shopping trips; Social/Cultural gatherings; Church.

The Carlyle
2121 Pioneer Dr, Beloit, WI, 53511
(608) 365-9526
Admin Patricia Murphy. *Medical Dir/Dir of Nursing* Dr Ram Das; Sherry Georgeff DON.
Licensure Skilled care. *Beds* 262. *Certified* Medicaid; Medicare.
Owner Proprietary Corp.
Admissions Requirements Minimum age 18; Medical examination; Physician's request.
Staff Physicians 24 (pt); RNs 9 (ft), 16 (pt); LPNs 6 (ft), 7 (pt); Nurses aides 27 (ft), 57 (pt); Physical therapists 2 (ft); Reality therapists 2 (pt); Occupational therapists 1 (ft); Speech therapists 1 (pt); Dietitians 1 (pt); Ophthalmologists 2 (pt); Podiatrists 1 (pt).
Languages Italian
Facilities Dining room; Physical therapy room; Activities room; Chapel; Crafts room; Laundry room; Barber/Beauty shop; Library.
Activities Arts & crafts; Cards; Games; Reading groups; Prayer groups; Movies; Shopping trips; Social/Cultural gatherings; Singing groups; Bowling; Boating; Baseball games.

NCF Eastridge House*
2009 E Ridge Rd, Beloit, WI, 53511
(608) 365-4511
Admin Nancy Fennema.
Licensure Intermediate care. *Beds* 4. *Certified* Medicaid.
Owner Nonprofit Corp.

BERLIN

Fox View Acres*
284 Mound St, Berlin, WI, 54923
(414) 499-4892
Admin Glenn T Beaudry.
Licensure Intermediate care. *Beds* 10. *Certified* Medicaid.
Owner Nonprofit Corp.

Juliette Manor*
169 E Huron St, Berlin, WI, 54923
(414) 361-3092
Admin Charles P Clarey. *Medical Dir/Dir of Nursing* William Piotrowski MD.
Licensure Skilled care; Intermediate care. *Beds* 102. *Certified* Medicaid; Medicare.
Owner Proprietary Corp.
Admissions Requirements Medical examination; Physician's request.

Facilities Dining room; Physical therapy room; Activities room; Chapel; Crafts room; Laundry room; Barber/Beauty shop; Cocktail lounge.
Activities Arts & crafts; Cards; Games; Prayer groups; Movies; Shopping trips; Social/Cultural gatherings; Current events group.

BLACK EARTH

Black Earth Manor*
634 Center St, Black Earth, WI, 53515
(608) 767-2572
Admin Mary E Reines. *Medical Dir/Dir of Nursing* Dr Gerald Kempthorne.
Licensure Intermediate care. *Beds* 32. *Certified* Medicaid.
Owner Nonprofit Corp (Good Shepherd Health Fac).
Admissions Requirements Minimum age 18; Medical examination; Physician's request.
Staff RNs 1 (ft), 2 (pt); LPNs 3 (pt); Orderlies 1 (pt); Nurses aides 13 (pt); Activities coordinators 1 (pt); Dietitians 1 (pt).
Facilities Dining room; Several multipurpose lounge areas.
Activities Arts & crafts; Cards; Games; Reading groups; Prayer groups; Movies; Shopping trips; Social/Cultural gatherings; Outings & trips.

BLACK RIVER FALLS

Family Heritage Nursing Home*
1311 Tyler St, Black River Falls, WI, 54615
(715) 284-4396
Admin Jacqueline C Pavelski. *Medical Dir/Dir of Nursing* Dr Eugene Krohn.
Licensure Skilled care; Intermediate care. *Beds* 156. *Certified* Medicaid.
Owner Proprietary Corp.
Admissions Requirements Minimum age 18; Medical examination; Physician's request.
Staff RNs 4 (ft); LPNs 1 (ft), 12 (pt); Nurses aides 16 (ft), 32 (pt); Activities coordinators 2 (ft), 2 (pt).
Facilities Dining room; Physical therapy room; Activities room; Chapel; Crafts room; Laundry room; Barber/Beauty shop; Library; Meeting rooms.
Activities Arts & crafts; Cards; Games; Reading groups; Prayer groups; Movies; Shopping trips; Social/Cultural gatherings.

Pine View
400 Pine View Rd, Black River Falls, WI, 54615
(715) 284-5396
Admin Flora G Nay. *Medical Dir/Dir of Nursing* Diane Vlach DON.
Licensure Skilled care. *Beds* SNF 141. *Certified* Medicaid; Medicare.
Owner Publicly owned.
Admissions Requirements Minimum age 18; Medical examination.
Staff RNs 6 (ft), 6 (pt); LPNs 2 (ft), 7 (pt); Orderlies 22 (ft), 43 (pt); Activities coordinators 2 (ft), 2 (pt); Dietitians 1 (ft), 2 (pt).
Facilities Dining room; Physical therapy room; Activities room; Chapel; Crafts room; Laundry room; Barber/Beauty shop; Exam rooms; TV room; Lounges.
Activities Arts & crafts; Cards; Games; Movies; Shopping trips; Social/Cultural gatherings.

BLAIR

Grand View Care Center Inc
PO Box 27, 620 Grand View Ave, Blair, WI, 54616
(608) 989-2511
Admin Michael O Kittleson. *Medical Dir/Dir of Nursing* Sandra Erickson RN.

Licensure Skilled care; Intermediate care. *Beds* SNF 101; ICF. *Certified* Medicaid.
Owner Nonprofit Corp.
Admissions Requirements Medical examination.
Staff Physicians 2 (pt); RNs 3 (ft), 6 (pt); LPNs 1 (ft), 4 (pt); Nurses aides 7 (ft), 46 (pt); Physical therapists 1 (pt); Recreational therapists 1 (ft), 1 (pt); Dietitians 1 (pt).
Facilities Dining room; Physical therapy room; Activities room; Crafts room; Laundry room; Barber/Beauty shop; Library.
Activities Arts & crafts; Cards; Games; Reading groups; Prayer groups; Movies; Shopping trips; Social/Cultural gatherings; Music.

BLOOMER

Eagleton Nursing Home
Rte 3, Bloomer, WI, 54724
(715) 288-6311
Admin Thomas G Spagnoletti. *Medical Dir/Dir of Nursing* Brenda Ohly RN.
Licensure Skilled care. *Beds* 28. *Certified* Medicaid.
Owner Privately owned.
Admissions Requirements Physician's request.
Staff Physicians 3 (pt); RNs 1 (ft), 2 (pt); LPNs 2 (ft), 1 (pt); Nurses aides 6 (ft), 2 (pt); Activities coordinators 1 (ft); Dietitians 1 (pt).
Facilities Dining room; Activities room; Laundry room.
Activities Arts & crafts; Cards; Games; Reading groups; Prayer groups; Movies; Shopping trips; Social/Cultural gatherings.

Hetzel Care Center Inc
1840 Priddy St, Bloomer, WI, 54724
(715) 568-2503
Admin Gordon P Hetzel. *Medical Dir/Dir of Nursing* M W Asplund MD; Carol J Hable RN.
Licensure Skilled care; Community Residential care. *Beds* SNF 31; Community Residential 15. *Certified* Medicaid.
Owner Proprietary Corp.
Staff RNs 1 (ft), 4 (pt); LPNs 1 (ft), 1 (pt); Nurses aides 4 (ft), 5 (pt); Activities coordinators 2 (pt); Social worker 1 (pt).
Facilities Dining room; Physical therapy room; Activities room; Chapel; Crafts room; Barber/Beauty shop.
Activities Arts & crafts; Cards; Games; Reading groups; Prayer groups; Movies; Social/Cultural gatherings.

The Maple Wood
1501 Thompson St, Bloomer, WI, 54724
(715) 568-2000
Admin Don Babbitt. *Medical Dir/Dir of Nursing* R E Gladitsch MD; M D Crisp DON.
Licensure Skilled care. *Beds* 75. *Certified* Medicaid.
Owner Nonprofit Corp.
Staff RNs 4 (ft), 1 (pt); LPNs 3 (ft), 3 (pt); Nurses aides 16 (ft), 16 (pt); Physical therapists 1 (ft); Activities coordinators 1 (ft); Dietitians 1 (ft); Social worker 1 (ft).
Facilities Dining room; Physical therapy room; Activities room; Crafts room; Laundry room; Barber/Beauty shop.
Activities Arts & crafts; Cards; Games; Reading groups; Prayer groups; Movies; Shopping trips; Social/Cultural gatherings.

BOSCOBEL

Memorial Nursing Home*
205 Parker St, Boscobel, WI, 53805
(608) 375-4104
Admin Gerhard O Qualey.
Licensure Skilled care; Intermediate care. *Beds* 104. *Certified* Medicaid.
Owner Nonprofit Corp.

BROOKFIELD

Congregational Home Inc
13900 W Burleigh Rd, Brookfield, WI, 53005
(414) 781-0550
Admin Robert G Hankins. *Medical Dir/Dir of Nursing* Dr Nicholas Owen; Nancy M Tabor DON.
Licensure Skilled care; Intermediate care. *Beds* SNF 88; ICF.
Owner Nonprofit Corp.
Admissions Requirements Minimum age 18; Medical examination.
Staff Physicians 1 (pt); RNs 5 (ft), 11 (pt); LPNs 2 (ft), 11 (pt); Nurses aides 11 (ft), 14 (pt); Physical therapists 1 (pt); Occupational therapists 1 (ft); Activities coordinators 1 (pt); Dietitians 1 (pt).
Affiliation Congregational
Facilities Dining room; Physical therapy room; Activities room; Chapel; Crafts room; Laundry room; Barber/Beauty shop; Library.
Activities Arts & crafts; Cards; Games; Reading groups; Prayer groups; Movies; Shopping trips; Social/Cultural gatherings.

St Elizabeth Nursing Home
745 N Brookfield Rd, Brookfield, WI, 53005
(414) 782-8118
Admin Sr Mary Rita Amrhein. *Medical Dir/Dir of Nursing* Dr Joseph Bartos; Sr Angela Myers DON.
Licensure Intermediate care. *Beds* ICF 16.
Owner Nonprofit organization/foundation.
Admissions Requirements Minimum age 18; Females only; Medical examination; Physician's request.
Staff RNs 1 (ft), 1 (pt); LPNs 1 (ft), 1 (pt); Nurses aides 4 (ft), 1 (pt); Activities coordinators 1 (pt).
Languages German
Affiliation Roman Catholic
Facilities Activities room; Chapel; Crafts room; Solarium; Parlor.
Activities Arts & crafts; Cards; Games; Reading groups; Prayer groups; Movies.

Woodland Health Center
18740 W Bluemound Rd, Brookfield, WI, 53005
(414) 782-0230
Admin Charles T Nelson. *Medical Dir/Dir of Nursing* Jan Frodermann RN DON.
Licensure Skilled care; Intermediate care. *Beds* 226. *Certified* Medicaid.
Owner Proprietary Corp (American Medical Services Inc).
Admissions Requirements Medical examination; Physician's request.
Staff RNs; LPNs; Nurses aides; Activities coordinators.
Facilities Dining room; Physical therapy room; Activities room; Chapel; Crafts room; Barber/Beauty shop; Library.
Activities Arts & crafts; Cards; Games; Reading groups; Prayer groups; Movies; Social/Cultural gatherings.

BROWN DEER

Hearthside Rehabilitation Center
9325 N Green Bay Rd, Brown Deer, WI, 53209
(414) 354-4800
Admin Rick P Mehrer. *Medical Dir/Dir of Nursing* Dr Burton Zimmerman.
Licensure Skilled care; Intermediate care; Intermediate care for mentally retarded. *Beds* 246. *Certified* Medicaid.
Owner Proprietary Corp.
Admissions Requirements Minimum age 18; Medical examination.
Staff Physicians 5 (pt); RNs 9 (ft), 4 (pt); LPNs 18 (ft), 7 (pt); Nurses aides 77 (ft), 52 (pt); Physical therapists 1 (pt); Reality therapists 1 (pt); Recreational therapists 5 (ft), 3 (pt); Occupational therapists 3 (ft);

Speech therapists 2 (pt); Activities coordinators 2 (pt); Dietitians 1 (ft); Dentist 2 (pt).
Facilities Dining room; Physical therapy room; Laundry room; Barber/Beauty shop.
Activities Arts & crafts; Cards; Games; Reading groups; Prayer groups; Movies; Shopping trips; Social/Cultural gatherings.

BURLINGTON

Mt Carmel Care Center
677 E State St, Burlington, WI, 53105
(414) 763-9531
Admin Thomas W Polakowski. *Medical Dir/Dir of Nursing* R C Wheaton MD; Judy Bornfleth RN DNS.
Licensure Skilled care; Intermediate care. *Beds* 105. *Certified* Medicaid.
Owner Proprietary Corp (Hillhaven Corp).
Staff Physicians 1 (pt); RNs 2 (ft); LPNs 4 (ft); Orderlies 6 (ft); Nurses aides 8 (ft); Recreational therapists 1 (ft); Occupational therapists 1 (pt); Speech therapists 1 (pt); Activities coordinators 1 (ft); Dietitians 1 (ft).
Facilities Dining room; Physical therapy room; Activities room; Chapel; Crafts room; Laundry room; Barber/Beauty shop.
Activities Arts & crafts; Cards; Games; Reading groups; Prayer groups; Movies; Shopping trips; Social/Cultural gatherings; Annual resident senior prom.

CEDARBURG

Lasata
W76 N677 Wauwatosa Rd, Cedarburg, WI, 53012
(414) 377-5060
Admin Randall G Krentz. *Medical Dir/Dir of Nursing* Dr Celestino Perez; Marjorie Leach DON.
Licensure Skilled care. *Beds* SNF 204. *Certified* Medicaid; Medicare.
Owner Publicly owned.
Admissions Requirements Minimum age 18; Medical examination.
Staff Physicians 1 (pt); RNs 17 (ft), 16 (pt); LPNs 6 (ft), 5 (pt); Orderlies 2 (ft), 1 (pt); Nurses aides 42 (ft), 35 (pt); Physical therapists 2 (ft); Occupational therapists 2 (ft); Speech therapists 1 (ft); Activities coordinators 1 (ft); Dietitians 1 (pt).
Facilities Dining room; Physical therapy room; Activities room; Chapel; Crafts room; Laundry room; Barber/Beauty shop; Library.
Activities Arts & crafts; Cards; Games; Reading groups; Prayer groups; Movies; Shopping trips; Social/Cultural gatherings.

CENTURIA

Centuria Care Center
300 Michigan St, Centuria, WI, 54824
(715) 646-2010
Admin Darlene Romportl. *Medical Dir/Dir of Nursing* Dr M Schmidt; Wanda Nelson DON.
Licensure Intermediate care. *Beds* ICF 41. *Certified* Medicaid.
Owner Publicly owned.
Admissions Requirements Medical examination; Physician's request.
Staff Physicians 1 (pt); RNs 1 (ft), 1 (pt); LPNs 1 (ft), 4 (pt); Nurses aides 8 (ft), 5 (pt); Physical therapists 1 (pt); Recreational therapists 1 (pt); Occupational therapists 1 (pt); Activities coordinators 1 (ft); Dietitians 1 (ft).
Facilities Dining room; Physical therapy room; Activities room; Chapel; Crafts room; Laundry room; Barber/Beauty shop.
Activities Arts & crafts; Cards; Games; Reading groups; Movies; Shopping trips.

CHETEK

Knapp Haven Nursing Home
725 Knapp St, Chetek, WI, 54728
(715) 924-4891
Admin William L Burnham. *Medical Dir/Dir of Nursing* Howard Thalacker MD; Mary Huset DON.
Licensure Skilled care; Intermediate care. *Beds* 99. *Certified* Medicaid.
Owner Publicly owned.
Admissions Requirements Minimum age 18; Medical examination; Physician's request.
Staff RNs 3 (ft), 7 (pt); LPNs 1 (ft), 5 (pt); Nurses aides 15 (ft), 38 (pt); Physical therapists 1 (pt); Reality therapists 1 (pt); Recreational therapists 1 (ft); Occupational therapists 1 (pt); Speech therapists 1 (pt); Activities coordinators 1 (pt); Dietitians 1 (pt).
Facilities Dining room; Physical therapy room; Activities room; Chapel; Crafts room; Laundry room; Barber/Beauty shop; Library.
Activities Arts & crafts; Cards; Games; Reading groups; Prayer groups; Movies; Shopping trips; Social/Cultural gatherings.

CHILTON

Chilton Village Skilled Care Center
810 Memorial Dr, Chilton, WI, 53014
(414) 849-2308
Admin James Guschl. *Medical Dir/Dir of Nursing* Dawn Holsen DON.
Licensure Skilled care. *Beds* SNF 106. *Certified* Medicaid; Medicare.
Owner Proprietary Corp (Beverly Enterprises).
Admissions Requirements Minimum age 18; Physician's request.
Staff RNs 5 (ft); LPNs 9 (ft), 3 (pt); Nurses aides 39 (ft), 31 (pt); Physical therapists 1 (pt); Recreational therapists 1 (ft), 3 (pt); Occupational therapists 1 (pt); Speech therapists 1 (pt); Activities coordinators 1 (ft); Dietitians 1 (pt); Dentists 1 (pt); Ophthalmologists 1 (pt); Podiatrists 1 (pt).
Languages German
Facilities Dining room; Physical therapy room; Activities room; Chapel; Crafts room; Laundry room; Barber/Beauty shop; Library.
Activities Arts & crafts; Cards; Games; Reading groups; Prayer groups; Movies; Shopping trips; Social/Cultural gatherings.

CHIPPEWA FALLS

Chippewa Manor Nursing Home
222 Chapman Rd, Chippewa Falls, WI, 54729
(715) 723-4437
Admin Karen Davis. *Medical Dir/Dir of Nursing* Robert L Hendrickson MD; Nancy L Hanson DON.
Licensure Skilled care. *Beds* SNF 90. *Certified* Medicaid.
Owner Privately owned.
Admissions Requirements Minimum age 18; Medical examination; Physician's request.
Staff RNs 4 (ft), 5 (pt); Physical therapists 1 (pt); Activities coordinators 1 (ft), 1 (pt); Dietitians 1 (pt); Chaplain 1 (ft).
Facilities Dining room; Physical therapy room; Activities room; Chapel; Crafts room; Laundry room; Barber/Beauty shop; Library.
Activities Arts & crafts; Cards; Games; Reading groups; Prayer groups; Movies; Shopping trips; Social/Cultural gatherings.

Heyde Health System Inc
2821 County Trunk I, Chippewa Falls, WI, 54729
(715) 723-9341
Admin Martin C Metten. *Medical Dir/Dir of Nursing* John H Layer MD; Marianne Missfeldt.
Licensure Skilled care; Intermediate care for mentally retarded. *Beds* SNF 328; ICF/MR 25. *Certified* Medicaid; Medicare.

Owner Proprietary Corp.
Admissions Requirements Minimum age 18;
Medical examination; Physician's request.
Staff RNs 10 (ft), 14 (pt); LPNs 11 (ft), 19
(pt); Nurses aides 61 (ft), 111 (pt); Activities
coordinators 1 (ft); Dietitians 1 (ft).
Facilities Dining room; Physical therapy
room; Activities room; Chapel; Crafts room;
Laundry room; Barber/Beauty shop; Library.
Activities Arts & crafts; Cards; Games;
Reading groups; Prayer groups; Movies;
Shopping trips; Social/Cultural gatherings.

**Northern Wisconsin Center for the
Developmentally Disabled**
PO Box 340, Chippewa Falls, WI, 54729
(715) 723-5542
Admin Terry A Willkom. *Medical Dir/Dir of
Nursing* Helen Gonzaga MD.
Licensure Intermediate care for mentally
retarded. *Beds* 634. *Certified* Medicaid.
Owner Publicly owned.
Admissions Requirements Minimum age 6.
Staff Physicians 4 (ft); RNs 33 (ft), 15 (pt);
LPNs 41 (ft), 13 (pt); Nurses aides 357 (ft),
32 (pt); Recreational therapists 7 (ft); Speech
therapists 6 (ft); Activities coordinators 2
(ft); Dietitians 2 (ft).
Facilities Dining room; Physical therapy
room; Activities room; Chapel; Crafts room;
Laundry room; Barber/Beauty shop; Library;
Educational center.
Activities Arts & crafts; Cards; Games;
Reading groups; Prayer groups; Movies;
Shopping trips; Social/Cultural gatherings.

Hannah M Rutledge Home for the Aged
Eagle & Bridgewater Ave, Chippewa Falls, WI,
54729
(715) 723-5566
Admin Richard Foiles. *Medical Dir/Dir of
Nursing* Robert L Hendrickson MD; Sharon
Couey DON.
Licensure Skilled care. *Beds* 100. *Certified*
Medicaid.
Owner Nonprofit Corp.
Admissions Requirements Medical
examination.
Staff Physicians 2 (pt); RNs 1 (ft), 4 (pt);
LPNs 4 (ft), 3 (pt); Nurses aides 17 (ft), 7
(pt); Physical therapists 1 (pt); Activities
coordinators 1 (ft); Dietitians 1 (pt).
Facilities Dining room; Activities room;
Crafts room; Laundry room; Barber/Beauty
shop; Library.
Activities Arts & crafts; Cards; Games; Prayer
groups; Movies; Shopping trips; Social/
Cultural gatherings.

CLINTON

Meadow Park Nursing Home
709 Meadow Park Dr, Clinton, WI, 53525
(608) 676-2202
Admin David D Mickelson. *Medical Dir/Dir
of Nursing* Dr James P Long; JoAnn Shibley
RN.
Licensure Skilled care; Intermediate care. *Beds*
SNF 95; ICF. *Certified* Medicaid.
Owner Proprietary Corp.
Admissions Requirements Minimum age 18;
Medical examination; Physician's request.
Staff RNs 5 (ft), 3 (pt); LPNs 2 (ft), 5 (pt);
Nurses aides 15 (ft), 30 (pt); Physical
therapists 1 (pt); Activities coordinators 1
(ft), 2 (pt); Dietitians 1 (ft).
Facilities Dining room; Physical therapy
room; Activities room; Chapel; Crafts room;
Laundry room; Barber/Beauty shop; Library.
Activities Arts & crafts; Cards; Games;
Reading groups; Prayer groups; Movies;
Shopping trips; Social/Cultural gatherings.

CLINTONVILLE

Viola Behling Memorial Home Inc
38 N Main St, Clintonville, WI, 54929
(715) 823-2619
Admin Andrew V Lagatta. *Medical Dir/Dir of
Nursing* Dr Paulino Belgado.
Licensure Skilled care. *Beds* SNF 26.
Owner Proprietary Corp.
Admissions Requirements Medical
examination; Physician's request.
Staff RNs 2 (ft), 1 (pt); LPNs 2 (ft), 2 (pt);
Nurses aides 8 (ft), 5 (pt); Activities
coordinators 1 (pt); Social workers 1 (pt).
Facilities Dining room; Activities room;
Chapel; Barber/Beauty shop.
Activities Arts & crafts; Cards; Games; Prayer
groups; Movies; Social/Cultural gatherings.

Greentree Health Care Center
70 Greentree Rd, Clintonville, WI, 54929
(715) 823-2194
Admin John Simonson. *Medical Dir/Dir of
Nursing* Dr C Egan.
Licensure Skilled care; Intermediate care. *Beds*
78. *Certified* Medicaid; Medicare.
Owner Proprietary Corp (American Medical
Services Inc).
Admissions Requirements Minimum age 18;
Medical examination; Physician's request.
Staff Physicians 6 (pt); RNs 1 (ft), 4 (pt);
LPNs 1 (ft), 6 (pt); Activities coordinators 1
(ft), 1 (pt); Dietitians 1 (pt).
Facilities Dining room; Activities room;
Chapel; Barber/Beauty shop.
Activities Arts & crafts; Cards; Games;
Reading groups; Prayer groups; Movies;
Shopping trips; Social/Cultural gatherings.

Pine Manor
PO Box 30, Rte 3, Clintonville, WI, 54929
(715) 823-3135
Admin Mathew J Oreskovich. *Medical Dir/Dir
of Nursing* Dr L Heise.
Licensure Skilled care; Intermediate care. *Beds*
121. *Certified* Medicaid.
Owner Proprietary Corp (American Medical
Services Inc).
Staff RNs 3 (ft), 7 (pt); LPNs 3 (ft), 2 (pt);
Orderlies 1 (ft); Nurses aides 29 (ft), 13 (pt);
Physical therapists 1 (pt); Recreational
therapists 2 (pt); Occupational therapists 1
(pt); Speech therapists 1 (pt); Activities
coordinators 1 (ft); Dietitians 1 (ft).
Facilities Dining room; Physical therapy
room; Activities room; Chapel; Crafts room;
Laundry room; Barber/Beauty shop.
Activities Arts & crafts; Cards; Games; Prayer
groups; Movies; Shopping trips; Social/
Cultural gatherings.

COLBY

Colonial House Living Center
702 W Dolf St, Colby, WI, 54421
(715) 223-2352
Admin Paul Kenyon. *Medical Dir/Dir of
Nursing* D Pfefferkorn; Sharon Groschwitz
DON.
Licensure Skilled care; Intermediate care. *Beds*
SNF 95; ICF. *Certified* Medicaid; Medicare.
Owner Nonprofit Corp (Adventist Health Sys-
USA).
Admissions Requirements Minimum age 18;
Medical examination; Physician's request.
Staff RNs 5 (ft), 3 (pt); LPNs 2 (ft), 2 (pt);
Nurses aides 25 (ft), 14 (pt); Activities
coordinators 1 (ft); Dietitians 1 (ft).
Languages German
Affiliation Seventh-Day Adventist
Facilities Dining room; Physical therapy
room; Activities room; Chapel; Crafts room;
Laundry room; Barber/Beauty shop; Library.
Activities Arts & crafts; Cards; Games;
Reading groups; Prayer groups; Movies;
Shopping trips; Social/Cultural gatherings;
Fishing; Bingo.

COLFAX

Area Nursing Home Inc
PO Box 515, Colfax, WI, 54730
(715) 962-3186
Admin Jon A Suckow. *Medical Dir/Dir of
Nursing* P Schleifer; Jean Fox DON.
Licensure Skilled care; Intermediate care. *Beds*
SNF 97; ICF. *Certified* Medicaid.
Owner Proprietary Corp.
Admissions Requirements Minimum age 18;
Medical examination; Physician's request.
Staff Physicians 1 (pt); RNs 6 (ft); LPNs 7
(ft); Orderlies 2 (ft); Nurses aides 30 (ft), 22
(pt); Physical therapists 1 (pt); Recreational
therapists 2 (ft); Occupational therapists 1
(pt); Activities coordinators 1 (ft); Dietitians
1 (pt); Podiatrists.
Facilities Dining room; Physical therapy
room; Activities room; Chapel; Crafts room;
Laundry room; Barber/Beauty shop.
Activities Arts & crafts; Cards; Games;
Reading groups; Prayer groups; Movies;
Shopping trips; Social/Cultural gatherings.

COLUMBUS

Columbus Care Center
825 Western Ave, Columbus, WI, 53925
(414) 623-2520
Admin William J Sidesky.
Licensure Skilled care. *Beds* 99. *Certified*
Medicaid.
Owner Proprietary Corp (Hillhaven Corp).
Admissions Requirements Minimum age 18;
Medical examination; Physician's request.
Facilities Dining room; Physical therapy
room; Activities room; Chapel; Crafts room;
Laundry room; Barber/Beauty shop.
Activities Arts & crafts; Cards; Games;
Reading groups; Prayer groups; Movies;
Shopping trips; Social/Cultural gatherings.

CORNELL

Cornell Area Care Center Inc*
PO Box 125, Cornell, WI, 54732
(715) 239-6288
Admin Kenneth L Tayler. *Medical Dir/Dir of
Nursing* Robert L Henrickson MD.
Licensure Skilled care. *Beds* 50. *Certified*
Medicaid.
Owner Proprietary Corp.
Admissions Requirements Medical
examination; Physician's request.
Facilities Dining room; Physical therapy
room; Activities room; Chapel; Crafts room;
Laundry room; Barber/Beauty shop.
Activities Arts & crafts; Cards; Games;
Reading groups; Prayer groups; Movies;
Shopping trips; Social/Cultural gatherings.

CRANDON

Crandon Health Care Center Inc*
PO Box 366, Crandon, WI, 54520
(715) 478-3325
Admin Phillip J Orlenko. *Medical Dir/Dir of
Nursing* Daniel Johnson MD.
Licensure Skilled care; Intermediate care. *Beds*
111. *Certified* Medicaid.
Owner Proprietary Corp.
Staff RNs 4 (ft); LPNs 8 (ft); Orderlies 2 (ft);
Nurses aides 20 (ft), 5 (pt); Physical
therapists 1 (pt); Occupational therapists 1
(pt); Activities coordinators 1 (ft); Dietitians
1 (pt).
Facilities Dining room; Physical therapy
room; Activities room; Chapel; Crafts room;
Laundry room; Barber/Beauty shop.
Activities Arts & crafts; Cards; Games;
Movies; Shopping trips; Social/Cultural
gatherings.

CRIVITZ

McVane Memorial Nursing Home
PO Box 220, Crivitz, WI, 54114
(715) 854-2717
Admin Betty L Larsen. *Medical Dir/Dir of Nursing* Lois Hudson DON.
Licensure Intermediate care. *Beds* ICF 64. *Certified* Medicaid.
Owner Proprietary Corp.
Admissions Requirements Minimum age 18; Medical examination; Physician's request.
Staff RNs 1 (ft), 2 (pt); LPNs 2 (ft), 4 (pt); Nurses aides 3 (ft), 20 (pt); Physical therapists 1 (pt); Occupational therapists 1 (pt); Activities coordinators 1 (ft); Dietitians 1 (pt).
Facilities Dining room; Physical therapy room; Activities room; Chapel; Crafts room; Laundry room; Barber/Beauty shop.
Activities Arts & crafts; Cards; Games; Reading groups; Prayer groups; Movies; Shopping trips; Social/Cultural gatherings; Dinner nights out.

CUBA CITY

Southwest Health Center Nursing Home
808 S Washington St, Cuba City, WI, 53807
(608) 744-2161
Admin Kenneth W Creswick. *Medical Dir/Dir of Nursing* M F Stuessy MD; Pat Moxness RN DON.
Licensure Skilled care; Intermediate care. *Beds* SNF 94; ICF. *Certified* Medicaid; Medicare.
Owner Nonprofit Corp.
Staff Physicians 1 (pt); RNs 2 (ft), 6 (pt); LPNs 2 (ft), 8 (pt); Nurses aides 9 (ft), 38 (pt); Physical therapists 1 (pt); Occupational therapists 1 (pt); Speech therapists 1 (pt); Activities coordinators 1 (ft); Dietitians 1 (pt); Dentists 1 (pt); Ophthalmologists 1 (pt); Podiatrists 1 (pt).
Facilities Dining room; Physical therapy room; Activities room; Chapel; Crafts room; Laundry room; Barber/Beauty shop; Library.
Activities Arts & crafts; Cards; Games; Reading groups; Prayer groups; Movies; Social/Cultural gatherings.

CUMBERLAND

Cumberland Memorial Hospital—Extended Care Unit
1110 7th Ave, Cumberland, WI, 54829
(715) 822-4521
Admin Earl F Strub. *Medical Dir/Dir of Nursing* Tony Bormann.
Licensure Skilled care; Intermediate care. *Beds* 49. *Certified* Medicaid.
Owner Nonprofit Corp.
Admissions Requirements Minimum age 18.
Staff RNs 4 (ft), 3 (pt); LPNs 3 (ft), 3 (pt); Nurses aides 20 (ft), 18 (pt); Physical therapists 1 (pt); Occupational therapists 1 (pt); Speech therapists 1 (pt); Activities coordinators 1 (ft), 1 (pt); Dietitians 1 (pt).
Facilities Dining room; Activities room; Crafts room; Barber/Beauty shop.
Activities Arts & crafts; Cards; Games; Movies; Shopping trips.

DALLAS

Dallas Health & Rehabilitation Center
PO Box 165, Dallas, WI, 54733
(715) 837-1222
Admin Alvin B Knutson. *Medical Dir/Dir of Nursing* Mark Rholl MD; Barbara A Strangeway RN DON.
Licensure Skilled care. *Beds* 60. *Certified* Medicaid.
Owner Nonprofit Corp.
Admissions Requirements Medical examination; Physician's request.

Staff Physicians 1 (pt); RNs 1 (ft), 4 (pt); LPNs 7 (ft), 2 (pt); Nurses aides 12 (ft), 5 (pt); Activities coordinators 1 (ft); Dietitians 1 (pt).
Facilities Dining room; Physical therapy room; Activities room; Crafts room; Laundry room; Barber/Beauty shop.
Activities Arts & crafts; Games; Reading groups; Prayer groups; Movies; Shopping trips; Social/Cultural gatherings.

DARLINGTON

Lafayette Manor
PO Box 167, 719 E Catherine St, Darlington, WI, 53530
(608) 776-4472
Admin William Schoen. *Medical Dir/Dir of Nursing* Dr F Ruf; Juanita Burke DON.
Licensure Skilled care; Intermediate care. *Beds* SNF 123; ICF. *Certified* Medicaid; Medicare.
Owner Nonprofit Corp.
Admissions Requirements Minimum age 18; Physician's request.
Staff RNs 3 (ft), 6 (pt); LPNs 2 (ft), 3 (pt); Nurses aides 25 (ft), 22 (pt); Activities coordinators 3 (ft).
Facilities Dining room; Physical therapy room; Activities room; Chapel; Crafts room; Laundry room; Barber/Beauty shop.
Activities Arts & crafts; Cards; Games; Reading groups; Prayer groups; Movies; Shopping trips; Social/Cultural gatherings; Bus rides; Church services.

DE PERE

Anna John Home
828 EE Rd, De Pere, WI, 54115
(414) 869-2797
Admin Whitney J Mills. *Medical Dir/Dir of Nursing* Chris Parins DON.
Licensure Skilled care; Intermediate care. *Beds* 50. *Certified* Medicaid; Medicare.
Owner Publicly owned.
Admissions Requirements Minimum age 18.
Staff Physicians 1 (pt); RNs 1 (ft), 3 (pt); LPNs 7 (pt); Nurses aides 10 (ft), 10 (pt); Physical therapists 1 (pt); Recreational therapists 1 (ft), 1 (pt); Activities coordinators 1 (ft); Dietitians 1 (pt).
Facilities Dining room; Physical therapy room; Activities room; Chapel; Crafts room; Laundry room; Barber/Beauty shop; Library.
Activities Arts & crafts; Cards; Games; Reading groups; Prayer groups; Movies; Shopping trips; Social/Cultural gatherings.

Roseville of De Pere
3737 Dickinson Rd, De Pere, WI, 54115
(414) 336-7733
Admin Grace F Desotell.
Licensure Intermediate care. *Beds* 38. *Certified* Medicaid.
Owner Proprietary Corp.

DELAVAN

Willowfield Nursing Home
905 E Geneva St, Delavan, WI, 53115
(414) 728-6319
Admin Patricia Jankowski. *Medical Dir/Dir of Nursing* Dr John Martin; Ruth Rosenquist DON.
Licensure Skilled care. *Beds* SNF 51; ICF. *Certified* Medicaid; Medicare.
Owner Proprietary Corp (Unicare).
Admissions Requirements Medical examination; Physician's request.
Staff RNs 1 (ft), 5 (pt); LPNs 3 (pt); Orderlies 1 (pt); Nurses aides 5 (ft), 16 (pt); Activities coordinators 1 (ft).
Facilities Dining room; Physical therapy room; Activities room; Chapel; Crafts room; Laundry room; Barber/Beauty shop.

Activities Arts & crafts; Cards; Games; Prayer groups; Movies; Shopping trips; Social/Cultural gatherings.

DODGEVILLE

Bloomfield Manor Nursing Home
PO Box 55, Rte 3, Dodgeville, WI, 53533
(608) 935-3321
Admin Joseph D Alexander. *Medical Dir/Dir of Nursing* Harold P Breier; Mary Moll DON.
Licensure Skilled care; Intermediate care. *Beds* SNF 100; ICF. *Certified* Medicaid.
Owner Publicly owned.
Admissions Requirements Minimum age 18; Medical examination; Physician's request.
Staff Physicians 1 (pt); RNs 1 (ft), 7 (pt); LPNs 1 (ft), 6 (pt); Orderlies 2 (ft), 1 (pt); Nurses aides 6 (ft), 29 (pt); Physical therapists 1 (pt); Occupational therapists 1 (pt); Speech therapists 1 (pt); Activities coordinators 1 (ft); Dietitians 1 (pt).
Facilities Dining room; Physical therapy room; Activities room; Chapel; Crafts room; Laundry room; Barber/Beauty shop; Picnic areas.
Activities Arts & crafts; Cards; Games; Reading groups; Prayer groups; Shopping trips; Social/Cultural gatherings; Picnics; Camping.

Medical Care Facility of Memorial Hospital of Iowa Co
125 E North St, Dodgeville, WI, 53533
(608) 935-2711
Admin Cheryl Ortiz RN. *Medical Dir/Dir of Nursing* Dr Imlehman.
Licensure Skilled care; Intermediate care. *Beds* SNF 44; ICF. *Certified* Medicaid; Medicare.
Owner Nonprofit Corp.
Admissions Requirements Medical examination.
Staff Physicians 12 (ft); RNs 2 (ft), 4 (pt); LPNs 2 (ft), 3 (pt); Nurses aides 7 (ft), 10 (pt); Physical therapists 2 (ft); Occupational therapists 1 (pt); Activities coordinators; Activities coordinators 1 (pt); Dietitians 1 (ft).
Facilities Dining room; Physical therapy room; Activities room; Crafts room; Laundry room; Barber/Beauty shop.
Activities Arts & crafts; Cards; Games; Reading groups; Prayer groups; Movies; Shopping trips; Social/Cultural gatherings; Lunch bunch; Religious services; Reality orientation; Exercise classes.

DURAND

Oakview Care Center
1620 3rd Ave W, Durand, WI, 54736
(715) 672-4211
Admin Malcolm P Cole. *Medical Dir/Dir of Nursing* David L Castleberg MD; Laurel K Wicktor RN DNS.
Licensure Skilled care; Intermediate care. *Beds* 60. *Certified* Medicaid.
Owner Nonprofit Corp.
Admissions Requirements Minimum age 18; Medical examination; Physician's request.
Staff Physicians 5 (pt); RNs 2 (ft), 4 (pt); LPNs 3 (ft), 2 (pt); Nurses aides 6 (ft), 20 (pt); Physical therapists 1 (pt); Occupational therapists 1 (pt); Speech therapists 1 (pt); Activities coordinators 1 (pt); Dietitians 1 (pt); Dentists 1 (pt).
Affiliation Seventh-Day Adventist
Facilities Dining room; Physical therapy room; Activities room; Chapel; Crafts room; Barber/Beauty shop.
Activities Arts & crafts; Cards; Games; Reading groups; Prayer groups; Movies; Shopping trips; Social/Cultural gatherings.

EAGLE RIVER

Eagle River Healthcare Center Inc*
357 River St, Box 1149, Eagle River, WI, 54521
(715) 479-7465
Admin Mildred M Kiefer.
Licensure Skilled care; Intermediate care. *Beds* 97. *Certified* Medicaid.
Owner Proprietary Corp.

EAST TROY

Kiwanis Manor Inc
PO Box 292, 3271 North St, East Troy, WI, 53120
(414) 642-3995
Admin David B Henschel. *Medical Dir/Dir of Nursing* Dr Thomas Williams; Gayle Gramza.
Licensure Skilled care; Intermediate care. *Beds* SNF 60. *Certified* Medicaid.
Owner Nonprofit Corp.
Admissions Requirements Medical examination; Physician's request.
Staff Physicians 4 (pt); RNs 3 (ft), 4 (pt); LPNs 5 (ft), 1 (pt); Nurses aides 22 (ft), 9 (pt); Physical therapists 1 (ft); Occupational therapists 1 (pt); Speech therapists 1 (pt); Activities coordinators 1 (ft); Dietitians 1 (ft).
Facilities Dining room; Physical therapy room; Activities room; Crafts room; Laundry room; Barber/Beauty shop; Multi-purpose rooms.
Activities Arts & crafts; Cards; Games; Reading groups; Prayer groups; Movies; Shopping trips; Social/Cultural gatherings.

EAU CLAIRE

Center of Care
1405 Truax Blvd, Eau Claire, WI, 54703
(715) 839-4844
Admin Avon Karpenske. *Medical Dir/Dir of Nursing* Dr L J Wilson; Donna Scott RN DON.
Licensure Skilled care; Intermediate care. *Beds* 190. *Certified* Medicaid; Medicare.
Owner Publicly owned.
Admissions Requirements Minimum age 18.
Staff RNs 8 (ft), 8 (pt); LPNs 3 (ft), 3 (pt); Nurses aides 49 (ft), 35 (pt); Physical therapists contract 1 (pt); Occupational therapists contract 1 (pt); Speech therapists contract 1 (pt); Activities coordinators contract 2 (ft); Dietitians contract 1 (pt).
Facilities Dining room; Physical therapy room; Activities room; Chapel; Crafts room; Laundry room; Barber/Beauty shop; Library; Woodwork shop; Canteen.
Activities Arts & crafts; Cards; Games; Reading groups; Prayer groups; Movies; Shopping trips; Social/Cultural gatherings; Picnics; Special Olympics.

The Clairemont
2120 Heights Dr, Eau Claire, WI, 54701
(715) 832-1681
Admin Anita L Olds. *Medical Dir/Dir of Nursing* Dr Robert N Leasum; Jan Giedd DON.
Licensure Skilled care; Intermediate care. *Beds* SNF 223. *Certified* Medicaid; Medicare; VA contract.
Owner Privately owned.
Admissions Requirements Medical examination; Physician's request.
Staff Physicians 1 (pt); RNs 13 (ft), 8 (pt); LPNs 2 (ft), 17 (pt); Nurses aides 28 (ft), 83 (pt); Physical therapists 1 (ft), 3 (pt); Occupational therapists 1 (ft), 1 (pt); Speech therapists 1 (pt); Activities coordinators 1 (ft); Dietitians 1 (pt).

Facilities Dining room; Physical therapy room; Activities room; Chapel; Crafts room; Barber/Beauty shop; Library; Occupational therapy room; Speech therapy room.
Activities Arts & crafts; Cards; Games; Reading groups; Prayer groups; Movies; Shopping trips; Social/Cultural gatherings.

M B Syverson Lutheran Home*
816 Porter St, Eau Claire, WI, 54701
(715) 832-1644
Admin Sandra J Kilde.
Licensure Skilled care; Intermediate care. *Beds* 95. *Certified* Medicaid.
Owner Nonprofit Corp.
Affiliation Lutheran

EDGERTON

Memorial Community Hospital—Long-Term Care Facility
313 Stoughton Rd, Edgerton, WI, 53534
(608) 884-3441
Admin Harlan J Murphy. *Medical Dir/Dir of Nursing* Victor E Falk; Barbara Kerchoff.
Licensure Skilled care; Intermediate care. *Beds* 61. *Certified* Medicaid; Medicare.
Owner Nonprofit Corp.
Admissions Requirements Minimum age 18.
Staff Physicians 1 (ft); RNs 2 (ft), 1 (pt); LPNs 8 (ft), 2 (pt); Nurses aides 16 (ft), 4 (pt); Physical therapists 1 (ft), 1 (pt); Recreational therapists 2 (ft), 1 (pt); Occupational therapists 1 (pt); Speech therapists 1 (pt); Activities coordinators 1 (ft); Dietitians 1 (pt).
Facilities Dining room; Activities room; Crafts room; Laundry room.
Activities Arts & crafts; Cards; Games; Reading groups; Prayer groups; Movies; Shopping trips.

ELKHORN

Holton Manor*
638 N Broad St, Elkhorn, WI, 53121
(414) 723-4963
Admin James Stannard. *Medical Dir/Dir of Nursing* Dr I Bruhn.
Licensure Skilled care; Intermediate care. *Beds* 60. *Certified* Medicaid.
Owner Proprietary Corp.
Facilities Dining room; Activities room; Barber/Beauty shop.
Activities Arts & crafts; Cards; Games; Reading groups; Prayer groups; Movies; Shopping trips; Social/Cultural gatherings.

Lakeland Nursing Home of Walworth County
Box 1003, Hwy NN, Elkhorn, WI, 53121
(414) 741-3600
Admin Marilyn J Rantz. *Medical Dir/Dir of Nursing* Dr Menandro Tavera; Tari V Miller DON.
Licensure Skilled care. *Beds* 328. *Certified* Medicaid.
Owner Publicly owned.
Admissions Requirements Medical examination; Physician's request.
Staff Physicians 1 (pt); RNs 17 (ft), 18 (pt); LPNs 10 (ft), 17 (pt); Nurses aides 101 (ft), 119 (pt); Recreational therapists 7 (ft); Activities coordinators 2 (ft); Dietitians 2 (ft).
Facilities Dining room; Physical therapy room; Activities room; Chapel; Crafts room; Laundry room; Barber/Beauty shop.
Activities Arts & crafts; Cards; Games; Reading groups; Prayer groups; Movies; Shopping trips; Social/Cultural gatherings.

ELLSWORTH

Ellsworth Care Centers Inc*
403 N Maple St, Ellsworth, WI, 54011
(715) 273-5821

Admin Dale J Birkel. *Medical Dir/Dir of Nursing* F B Klaas MD.
Licensure Skilled care; Intermediate care. *Beds* 89. *Certified* Medicaid.
Owner Proprietary Corp.
Admissions Requirements Minimum age 18; Medical examination.
Staff Physicians 2 (pt); RNs 3 (ft), 4 (pt); LPNs 3 (ft), 3 (pt); Nurses aides 20 (ft), 21 (pt); Physical therapists 1 (pt); Reality therapists 1 (pt); Occupational therapists 1 (pt); Speech therapists 1 (pt); Activities coordinators 2 (ft); Dietitians 1 (ft).
Facilities Dining room; Physical therapy room; Activities room; Crafts room; Laundry room; Barber/Beauty shop.
Activities Arts & crafts; Cards; Games; Reading groups; Prayer groups; Movies.

Group Home I*
256 W Warner, Ellsworth, WI, 54011
(715) 273-5131
Admin Lucille M Strom.
Licensure Skilled care; Intermediate care for mentally retarded. *Beds* 15. *Certified* Medicaid.
Owner Proprietary Corp.

Piety Place*
120 S Piety St, Ellsworth, WI, 54011
(715) 273-3515
Admin James E Peterson.
Licensure Intermediate care. *Beds* 20. *Certified* Medicaid.
Owner Proprietary Corp.

ELMWOOD

Heritage of Elmwood Nursing Home
232 E Eau Galle Ave, Elmwood, WI, 54740-0086
(715) 639-2911
Admin Rodney J Gilles. *Medical Dir/Dir of Nursing* Carrie Jo Nelson MD; Jo Anne Meyer RN.
Licensure Skilled care. *Beds* 78. *Certified* Medicaid.
Owner Nonprofit Corp.
Admissions Requirements Minimum age 18; Medical examination; Physician's request.
Staff RNs 1 (ft), 3 (pt); LPNs 9 (pt); Nurses aides 11 (ft), 30 (pt); Activities coordinators 1 (pt).
Facilities Dining room; Physical therapy room; Activities room; Chapel; Laundry room; Barber/Beauty shop; Occupational therapy room.
Activities Arts & crafts; Cards; Games; Reading groups; Prayer groups; Social/Cultural gatherings; Music therapy.

ELROY

Heritage Manor Nursing Home
167 Royal Ave, Elroy, WI, 53929
(608) 462-8491
Admin Patricia A Schulz. *Medical Dir/Dir of Nursing* Dr Roy Balder MD; John Chute RN DON.
Licensure Skilled care. *Beds* 80. *Certified* Medicaid.
Owner Proprietary Corp (1st Am Care Fac).
Admissions Requirements Minimum age 16; Medical examination.
Staff RNs 6 (ft), 6 (pt); LPNs 1 (ft); Orderlies 1 (ft); Nurses aides 20 (ft), 20 (pt); Physical therapists 1 (pt); Recreational therapists 1 (pt); Occupational therapists 1 (pt); Speech therapists 1 (pt); Activities coordinators 1 (ft); Dietitians 1 (pt).
Facilities Dining room; Physical therapy room; Activities room; Chapel; Crafts room; Laundry room; Barber/Beauty shop; Library; TV room.
Activities Arts & crafts; Cards; Games; Reading groups; Prayer groups; Movies; Shopping trips; Social/Cultural gatherings.

EVANSVILLE

Evansville Manor
540 Garfield Ave, Evansville, WI, 53536
(608) 882-5700
Admin Clifford D Woolever. *Medical Dir/Dir of Nursing* R S Gray MD; Barbara Buttchen RN DON.
Licensure Skilled care; Intermediate care. *Beds* SNF 83; ICF. *Certified* Medicaid.
Owner Proprietary Corp.
Admissions Requirements Minimum age 18; Medical examination; Physician's request.
Staff Physicians 1 (pt); RNs 3 (ft), 8 (pt); LPNs 1 (ft), 4 (pt); Nurses aides 17 (ft), 45 (pt); Physical therapists 1 (pt); Occupational therapists 1 (pt); Speech therapists 1 (pt); Activities coordinators 1 (ft), 1 (pt); Dietitians 1 (pt); Ophthalmologists 1 (pt).
Languages German, Norwegian
Facilities Dining room; Physical therapy room; Activities room; Chapel; Crafts room; Laundry room; Barber/Beauty shop; Library.
Activities Arts & crafts; Cards; Games; Reading groups; Prayer groups; Movies; Shopping trips; Social/Cultural gatherings.

FAIRCHILD

Fairchild Nursing Home*
N Front St, Fairchild, WI, 54741
(715) 334-4311
Admin Twyland Wieland.
Licensure Intermediate care. *Beds* 71. *Certified* Medicaid.
Owner Proprietary Corp.

FALL CREEK

Fall Creek Valley Nursing Home*
PO Box 398, Fall Creek, WI, 54742
(715) 877-2411
Admin John B Gerberich Jr.
Licensure Skilled care; Intermediate care. *Beds* 76. *Certified* Medicaid.
Owner Publicly owned.

FENNIMORE

Fennimore Good Samaritan Center
1850 11th St, Fennimore, WI, 53809
(608) 822-6100
Admin Doug T Daechsel. *Medical Dir/Dir of Nursing* Dr R Stader; Donna Brugger DON.
Licensure Skilled care; Intermediate care. *Beds* SNF 88; ICF. *Certified* Medicaid.
Owner Nonprofit Corp (Evangelical Lutheran/ Good Samaritan).
Admissions Requirements Minimum age 18; Medical examination.
Staff RNs 3 (ft), 5 (pt); LPNs 3 (ft), 3 (pt); Nurses aides 20 (ft), 16 (pt); Physical therapists 1 (ft); Recreational therapists 2 (ft); Occupational therapists 1 (pt); Activities coordinators 1 (ft); Dietitians 1 (pt).
Affiliation Lutheran
Facilities Dining room; Physical therapy room; Activities room; Chapel; Laundry room; Barber/Beauty shop.
Activities Arts & crafts; Cards; Games; Reading groups; Prayer groups; Movies; Shopping trips; Social/Cultural gatherings.

FLORENCE

Florence Villa
1000 Chapin St, Florence, WI, 54121
(715) 528-4833
Admin Todd M Ramlet. *Medical Dir/Dir of Nursing* Jana M Clement.
Licensure Skilled care; Intermediate care. *Beds* SNF 74; ICF. *Certified* Medicaid; Medicare.
Owner Proprietary Corp (Beverly Enterprises).
Staff Physicians 1 (pt); RNs 3 (ft); LPNs 5 (ft); Orderlies 2 (ft); Nurses aides 30 (ft), 12 (pt); Activities coordinators 1 (pt).

Facilities Dining room; Physical therapy room; Laundry room; Barber/Beauty shop.
Activities Arts & crafts; Cards; Games; Prayer groups; Movies; Social/Cultural gatherings.

FOND DU LAC

Americana Healthcare Center*
265 S National Ave, Fond Du Lac, WI, 54935
(414) 922-7342
Admin Aaron Koelsch. *Medical Dir/Dir of Nursing* Dr R L Waffle.
Licensure Skilled care. *Beds* 108. *Certified* Medicaid; Medicare.
Owner Proprietary Corp (Manor Care).
Admissions Requirements Medical examination.
Facilities Dining room; Physical therapy room; Activities room; Laundry room; Barber/Beauty shop; Occupational therapy room.
Activities Arts & crafts; Games; Reading groups; Prayer groups; Movies; Shopping trips; Social/Cultural gatherings.

Care Center East
115 E Arndt St, Fond Du Lac, WI, 54935
(414) 923-7040
Admin Barbara Deitte. *Medical Dir/Dir of Nursing* Alfred Pennings MD; Genevieve Lewellyn DON.
Licensure Skilled care; Intermediate care. *Beds* 131. *Certified* Medicaid; Medicare.
Owner Proprietary Corp (Unicare).
Admissions Requirements Minimum age 18; Medical examination; Physician's request.
Staff RNs 3 (ft), 4 (pt); LPNs 3 (ft), 12 (pt); Nurses aides 6 (ft), 39 (pt); Activities coordinators 1 (ft); Dietitians 1 (ft).
Facilities Dining room; Physical therapy room; Activities room; Chapel; Laundry room; Barber/Beauty shop.
Activities Arts & crafts; Cards; Games; Reading groups; Prayer groups; Movies; Shopping trips; Social/Cultural gatherings.

Fond Du Lac County Health Care Center
459 E 1st St, Fond Du Lac, WI, 54935
(414) 929-3502
Admin Donald J Triggs. *Medical Dir/Dir of Nursing* Dr J R Musunuru; Lorna Friess RN BSN DON.
Licensure Skilled care; Intermediate care for mentally retarded. *Beds* SNF 123. *Certified* Medicaid; Medicare (acute only).
Owner Publicly owned.
Admissions Requirements Minimum age 18; Medical examination; Physician's request.
Staff Physicians 2 (ft), 3 (pt); RNs 5 (ft), 4 (pt); LPNs 9 (ft), 4 (pt); Recreational therapists 1 (ft); Occupational therapists 1 (ft); Dietitians 1 (ft).
Facilities Dining room; Activities room; Chapel; Crafts room; Laundry room; Barber/ Beauty shop; Library.
Activities Arts & crafts; Cards; Games; Reading groups; Prayer groups; Movies; Shopping trips; Social/Cultural gatherings.

Fond Du Lac Lutheran Home*
244 N Macy St, Fond Du Lac, WI, 54935
(414) 921-9520
Admin Leon C Tomchek.
Licensure Skilled care; Intermediate care. *Beds* 150. *Certified* Medicaid.
Owner Nonprofit Corp.
Affiliation Lutheran

Grancare Nursing Center
517 E Division St, Fond Du Lac, WI, 54935
(414) 921-6800
Admin Cindy J Idzik. *Medical Dir/Dir of Nursing* Robert E Cullen MD.
Licensure Skilled care. *Beds* 75.
Owner Proprietary Corp.

Staff Physicians 1 (pt); RNs 4 (ft), 3 (pt); LPNs 4 (ft), 4 (pt); Nurses aides 10 (ft), 14 (pt); Recreational therapists 1 (ft), 1 (pt); Activities coordinators 1 (pt).
Facilities Dining room; Physical therapy room; Activities room; Chapel; Crafts room; Laundry room; Barber/Beauty shop; Library; Personal day room.
Activities Arts & crafts; Cards; Games; Reading groups; Prayer groups; Movies; Shopping trips; Social/Cultural gatherings; Picnics; Luncheons.

Rolling Meadows
1155 S Military Rd, Fond Du Lac, WI, 54935
(414) 929-3585
Admin Genevieve Huck. *Medical Dir/Dir of Nursing* Gay D Trepanier MD; Constance Atkinson RN DON.
Licensure Skilled care; Intermediate care. *Beds* 177. *Certified* Medicaid.
Owner Publicly owned.
Admissions Requirements Medical examination; Physician's request.
Staff Physicians 1 (pt); RNs 7 (ft), 9 (pt); LPNs 2 (ft), 13 (pt); Nurses aides 27 (ft), 62 (pt); Physical therapists 1 (pt); Occupational therapists 1 (pt); Speech therapists 1 (pt); Activities coordinators 2 (ft), 1 (pt); Dietitians 1 (ft); Dentists 1 (pt).
Facilities Dining room; Physical therapy room; Activities room; Chapel; Crafts room; Laundry room; Barber/Beauty shop; Library.
Activities Arts & crafts; Cards; Games; Reading groups; Prayer groups; Movies; Shopping trips; Social/Cultural gatherings.

St Frances Home
365 Gillett St, Fond Du Lac, WI, 54935
(414) 921-2280
Admin Sr Irene Kohne. *Medical Dir/Dir of Nursing* Robert E Cullen MD; Eileen Dineen DON.
Licensure Skilled care; Intermediate care. *Beds* SNF 70. *Certified* Medicaid.
Owner Nonprofit Corp.
Admissions Requirements Minimum age 65; Medical examination.
Staff RNs 1 (ft), 3 (pt); LPNs 1 (ft), 6 (pt); Orderlies 1 (ft); Nurses aides 8 (ft), 14 (pt); Activities coordinators 1 (ft), 1 (pt); Dietitians 1 (ft).
Affiliation Roman Catholic
Facilities Dining room; Physical therapy room; Activities room; Chapel; Crafts room; Laundry room; Barber/Beauty shop; Library.
Activities Arts & crafts; Cards; Games; Reading groups; Prayer groups; Movies; Shopping trips; Social/Cultural gatherings.

FORT ATKINSON

Fort Atkinson Health Care Center
430 Wilcox St, Fort Atkinson, WI, 53538
(414) 563-5533
Admin Marilyn Perry. *Medical Dir/Dir of Nursing* H Lerring MD; Linda Meyer DON.
Licensure Skilled care. *Beds* SNF 126. *Certified* Medicaid; Medicare.
Owner Proprietary Corp (Beverly Enterprises).
Admissions Requirements Medical examination; Physician's request.
Staff Physicians 1 (pt); RNs 3 (ft), 3 (pt); LPNs 7 (ft), 9 (pt); Orderlies 2 (ft); Nurses aides 28 (ft), 15 (pt); Physical therapists 1 (ft); Activities coordinators 2 (ft); Dietitians 1 (pt).
Facilities Dining room; Physical therapy room; Activities room; Barber/Beauty shop.
Activities Arts & crafts; Cards; Games; Reading groups; Movies; Shopping trips; Social/Cultural gatherings.

FOUNTAIN CITY

St Michael's Evangelical Lutheran Home for the Aged
270 North St, RR 2, Fountain City, WI, 54629
(608) 687-7721
Admin Shirley Steckel. *Medical Dir/Dir of Nursing* Dr Andrew Edin; Jo Hassinger DON.
Licensure Skilled care. *Beds* 55. *Certified* Medicaid.
Owner Nonprofit organization/foundation.
Admissions Requirements Minimum age 60; Medical examination.
Staff Physicians 1 (pt); RNs 2 (ft), 2 (pt); LPNs 4 (ft), 3 (pt); Nurses aides 10 (ft), 13 (pt); Physical therapists 1 (pt); Occupational therapists 1 (pt); Speech therapists 1 (pt); Activities coordinators 1 (ft); Dietitians 1 (pt).
Affiliation Lutheran
Facilities Dining room; Physical therapy room; Activities room; Chapel; Crafts room; Laundry room; Barber/Beauty shop; Library.
Activities Arts & crafts; Cards; Games; Reading groups; Prayer groups; Movies; Shopping trips; Social/Cultural gatherings.

FRANKSVILLE

Oak Ridge Care Center*
18100 65th Ct, Franksville, WI, 53126
(414) 878-2788
Admin A P Kuranz.
Licensure Intermediate care. *Beds* 36. *Certified* Medicaid.
Owner Proprietary Corp.

FREDERIC

Frederic Municipal Nursing Home Inc
107 E Oak St, Frederic, WI, 54837
(715) 327-4297
Admin Nancy J Jappe. *Medical Dir/Dir of Nursing* Dr Richard Hartzell; Phyllis Kopecky RN.
Licensure Intermediate care. *Beds* ICF 30. *Certified* Medicaid.
Owner Publicly owned.
Admissions Requirements Medical examination; Physician's request.
Staff RNs 1 (ft), 1 (pt); LPNs 2 (ft), 2 (pt); Nurses aides 6 (ft), 13 (pt); Activities coordinators 2 (pt).
Facilities Dining room; Physical therapy room; Crafts room; Laundry room.
Activities Arts & crafts; Cards; Games; Reading groups; Prayer groups; Movies; Social/Cultural gatherings; Reminiscence; Current events; One to ones; Poetry; Music.

FRIENDSHIP

Adams County Memorial Hospital Nursing Care Unit
PO Box 40, 402 W Lake, Friendship, WI, 53934
(608) 339-3331
Admin Anita Van Beek. *Medical Dir/Dir of Nursing* Martin J Janssen MD.
Licensure Skilled care; Intermediate care. *Beds* 18. *Certified* Medicaid.
Owner Publicly owned.
Admissions Requirements Minimum age 18; Medical examination; Physician's request.
Staff RNs 1 (ft), 2 (pt); LPNs 1 (ft), 8 (pt); Nurses aides 3 (ft), 8 (pt); Physical therapists 1 (pt); Occupational therapists 1 (pt); Speech therapists 1 (pt); Activities coordinators 1 (pt); Dietitians 1 (pt); Podiatrists 1 (pt); Social service director 1 (pt).
Facilities Dining room; Physical therapy room; Activities room; Laundry room; Barber/Beauty shop; Century tub bather room.

Activities Arts & crafts; Cards; Games; Reading groups; Prayer groups; Movies; Shopping trips; Social/Cultural gatherings.

Villa Pines Living Center
201 S Park St, Friendship, WI, 53934
(608) 339-3361
Admin Robert L Frost. *Medical Dir/Dir of Nursing* Dr Martin Janssen.
Licensure Skilled care; Intermediate care. *Beds* 124. *Certified* Medicaid; Medicare.
Owner Nonprofit Corp (Adventist Health Sys-USA).
Staff Physicians 6 (ft); RNs 11 (ft), 2 (pt); LPNs 3 (ft), 1 (pt); Orderlies 1 (ft); Nurses aides 20 (ft), 18 (pt); Physical therapists 1 (ft), 1 (pt); Occupational therapists 1 (ft); Speech therapists 1 (ft); Activities coordinators 2 (pt); Dietitians 1 (ft); Dentists 1 (ft); Ophthalmologists 1 (ft).
Affiliation Seventh-Day Adventist
Facilities Dining room; Physical therapy room; Activities room; Chapel; Crafts room; Laundry room; Barber/Beauty shop.
Activities Arts & crafts; Cards; Games; Reading groups; Prayer groups; Movies; Shopping trips; Social/Cultural gatherings.

GALESVILLE

Marinuka Manor
PO Box 339, 100 Silver Creek Rd, Galesville, WI, 54630
(608) 582-2211
Admin Eileen M Nowak. *Medical Dir/Dir of Nursing* James Richardson; Nancy Smick RN DON.
Licensure Skilled care; Intermediate care. *Beds* SNF 59; ICF. *Certified* Medicaid.
Owner Publicly owned.
Admissions Requirements Medical examination.
Staff Physicians 3 (pt); RNs 7 (pt); LPNs 7 (pt); Nurses aides 10 (ft), 23 (pt); Physical therapists 1 (pt); Activities coordinators 1 (ft).
Facilities Dining room; Physical therapy room; Activities room; Crafts room; Laundry room; Barber/Beauty shop.
Activities Arts & crafts; Cards; Games; Prayer groups; Movies; Social/Cultural gatherings; one to one activities; Small group activities.

GENOA CITY

Highland Rest Home Inc
Rte 1, Box 2, Hwy H, Genoa City, WI, 53128
(414) 279-3345
Admin Myrna A Webster. *Medical Dir/Dir of Nursing* C Dekker MD; Karen M Klein DON.
Licensure Intermediate care. *Beds* 28. *Certified* Medicaid.
Owner Proprietary Corp.
Admissions Requirements Minimum age 18; Medical examination; Physician's request.
Staff RNs 1 (ft), 2 (pt); Nurses aides 6 (ft), 5 (pt); Activities coordinators 1 (pt); Dietitians 1 (pt).
Languages German, Spanish
Facilities Dining room; Activities room; Crafts room; Laundry room; Barber/Beauty shop.
Activities Arts & crafts; Cards; Games; Reading groups; Prayer groups; Movies; Shopping trips; Social/Cultural gatherings.

GILLETT

Gillett Nursing Home Inc
330 Robinhood Lane, Gillett, WI, 54124
(414) 855-2136
Admin Betty I Jones. *Medical Dir/Dir of Nursing* Dr Clyde Siefert; Barbara Smith.
Licensure Skilled care. *Beds* SNF 44. *Certified* Medicaid.

Owner Privately owned.
Admissions Requirements Minimum age 18.
Staff RNs 2 (ft), 1 (pt); LPNs 4 (ft), 1 (pt); Nurses aides 8 (ft), 4 (pt); Physical therapists 1 (pt); Occupational therapists 1 (pt); Speech therapists 1 (pt); Activities coordinators 1 (ft); Dietitians 1 (pt).
Languages German
Facilities Dining room; Physical therapy room; Laundry room.
Activities Arts & crafts; Cards; Games; Reading groups; Movies; Social/Cultural gatherings.

GILMAN

Gilman Nursing Home*
3531 Elder Dr N, Gilman, WI, 54433
(715) 447-8217
Admin Wayne C Zastrow. *Medical Dir/Dir of Nursing* R L Hendrickson.
Licensure Intermediate care. *Beds* 19. *Certified* Medicaid.
Owner Proprietary Corp.
Admissions Requirements Medical examination; Physician's request.
Staff RNs 1 (ft); LPNs 1 (pt); Nurses aides 3 (ft), 4 (pt); Physical therapists 1 (pt); Occupational therapists 1 (pt); Speech therapists 1 (pt); Activities coordinators 1 (ft); Dietitians 1 (pt); Dentists 1 (pt).
Facilities Dining room; Activities room; Crafts room; Laundry room.
Activities Arts & crafts; Cards; Games; Movies; Shopping trips; Social/Cultural gatherings.

Zastrow Care Center Inc*
N3531 Elder Dr, Gilman, WI, 54433
(715) 447-8217
Admin Wayne C Zastrow. *Medical Dir/Dir of Nursing* Robert L Hendrickson MD.
Licensure Intermediate care. *Beds* 24. *Certified* Medicaid.
Owner Proprietary Corp.
Admissions Requirements Medical examination; Physician's request.
Staff Physicians 1 (pt); RNs 1 (ft); LPNs 2 (pt); Nurses aides 3 (ft), 7 (pt); Physical therapists 1 (pt); Speech therapists 1 (pt); Activities coordinators 1 (ft); Dietitians 1 (pt); Dentists 1 (pt).
Facilities Dining room; Activities room; Crafts room; Laundry room.
Activities Arts & crafts; Cards; Games; Reading groups; Movies; Shopping trips; Social/Cultural gatherings.

GLENDALE

Colonial Manor Retirement & Convalescent Home
1616 W Bender Rd, Glendale, WI, 53209
(414) 228-8700
Admin Mary B Lesjak. *Medical Dir/Dir of Nursing* S GO; Suzanne Reading DON.
Licensure Skilled care; Intermediate care. *Beds* SNF 225; ICF. *Certified* Medicaid; Medicare.
Owner Proprietary Corp (Beverly Enterprises).
Admissions Requirements Minimum age 65; Medical examination; Physician's request.
Staff Physicians; RNs; LPNs; Orderlies; Nurses aides; Physical therapists; Reality therapists; Recreational therapists; Occupational therapists; Speech therapists; Activities coordinators; Dietitians; Dentists; Ophthalmologists; Podiatrists.
Facilities Dining room; Physical therapy room; Activities room; Chapel; Crafts room; Laundry room; Barber/Beauty shop; Library; Courtyard; Garden area; Tea room.
Activities Arts & crafts; Cards; Games; Reading groups; Prayer groups; Movies; Shopping trips; Social/Cultural gatherings; Diners club.

GLENWOOD CITY

Glenhaven
Rte 2, Box 153, Glenwood City, WI, 54013
(715) 265-4555
Admin Cheryl L Nelson. *Medical Dir/Dir of Nursing* Sandra Johnson DON.
Licensure Skilled care; Intermediate care. *Beds* 44. *Certified* Medicaid.
Owner Nonprofit Corp.
Admissions Requirements Minimum age 18; Medical examination.
Staff RNs 1 (ft), 2 (pt); LPNs 2 (ft), 3 (pt); Orderlies 1 (ft); Nurses aides 5 (ft), 14 (pt); Activities coordinators 1 (ft); Dietitians 1 (ft).
Facilities Dining room; Physical therapy room; Activities room; Barber/Beauty shop.
Activities Arts & crafts; Cards; Games; Prayer groups; Shopping trips.

GRANTSBURG

Burnett General Hospital—LTC*
Box 99, Grantsburg, WI, 54840
(715) 463-5353
Admin Stanley J Gaynor.
Licensure Skilled care; Intermediate care. *Beds* 53. *Certified* Medicaid.
Owner Nonprofit Corp.

GREEN BAY

Americana Health Care Center—East*
600 S Webster Ave, Green Bay, WI, 54301
(414) 432-3213
Admin Robert W Possanza Jr. *Medical Dir/Dir of Nursing* Dr Fred Walburn.
Licensure Skilled care. *Beds* 79. *Certified* Medicaid; Medicare.
Owner Proprietary Corp (Manor Care).
Admissions Requirements Medical examination.
Staff Physicians 1 (pt); RNs 1 (ft), 6 (pt); LPNs 2 (ft), 5 (pt); Nurses aides 14 (ft), 27 (pt); Physical therapists 1 (ft); Occupational therapists 1 (pt); Speech therapists 1 (pt); Activities coordinators 1 (ft); Dietitians 1 (pt); Dentists 1 (pt).
Facilities Dining room; Physical therapy room; Activities room; Laundry room; Barber/Beauty shop.
Activities Arts & crafts; Cards; Games; Prayer groups; Movies; Social/Cultural gatherings.

Americana Healthcare Center—West
1760 Shawano Ave, Green Bay, WI, 54303
(414) 499-5191
Admin Mary L Dettman. *Medical Dir/Dir of Nursing* Fred Walbrun MD; Sandy Fenendael RN DON.
Licensure Skilled care; Intermediate care. *Beds* SNF 105; ICF. *Certified* Medicaid; Medicare.
Owner Proprietary Corp (Manor Care).
Admissions Requirements Minimum age 18; Medical examination; Physician's request.
Staff RNs; LPNs; Orderlies; Nurses aides; Physical therapists 1 (pt); Occupational therapists 1 (pt); Speech therapists 1 (pt); Activities coordinators 1 (pt); Dietitians 1 (pt); Ophthalmologists 1 (pt); Dentist 1 (pt).
Facilities Dining room; Physical therapy room; Activities room; Crafts room; Laundry room; Barber/Beauty shop; Lounges.
Activities Arts & crafts; Cards; Games; Reading groups; Prayer groups; Movies; Shopping trips; Social/Cultural gatherings.

Bornemann Nursing Home
226 Bornemann, Green Bay, WI, 54302
(414) 468-8675
Admin Vera Bornemann.
Licensure Skilled care; Intermediate care. *Beds* 146. *Certified* Medicaid.
Owner Privately owned.
Admissions Requirements Minimum age 18.

Staff RNs; LPNs; Nurses aides; Activities coordinators.
Facilities Dining room; Physical therapy room; Activities room; Chapel; Crafts room; Laundry room; Barber/Beauty shop.
Activities Arts & crafts; Cards; Games; Reading groups; Prayer groups; Movies; Shopping trips; Social/Cultural gatherings.

Brown County Health Care Center
2900 Saint Anthony Dr, Green Bay, WI, 54301
(414) 468-1136
Admin James W Deprez. *Medical Dir/Dir of Nursing* Ernique Manabat MD; Dorothy E Riley DON.
Licensure Skilled care. *Beds* SNF 190. *Certified* Medicaid.
Owner Publicly owned.
Admissions Requirements Minimum age 18; Medical examination.
Staff Physicians; RNs; LPNs; Nurses aides; Recreational therapists; Occupational therapists; Dietitians.
Facilities Dining room; Activities room; Chapel; Crafts room; Laundry room; Barber/Beauty shop; Library.
Activities Arts & crafts; Cards; Games; Reading groups; Prayer groups; Movies; Shopping trips; Social/Cultural gatherings.

Demes Rehabilitation Center*
PO Box 8065, Green Bay, WI, 54308
(414) 468-4801
Admin David Miller. *Medical Dir/Dir of Nursing* Dr F Mansel.
Licensure Intermediate care for mentally retarded. *Beds* 53. *Certified* Medicaid.
Owner Proprietary Corp.
Admissions Requirements Minimum age 18; Medical examination.
Staff Physicians 1 (pt); RNs 1 (ft), 1 (pt); LPNs 1 (ft), 1 (pt); Nurses aides 10 (ft), 10 (pt); Physical therapists 1 (pt); Recreational therapists 1 (ft); Occupational therapists 1 (pt); Speech therapists 1 (pt); Activities coordinators 1 (ft); Dietitians 1 (pt).
Facilities Dining room; Activities room; Crafts room; Laundry room; Barber/Beauty shop.
Activities Arts & crafts; Cards; Games; Reading groups; Prayer groups; Movies; Shopping trips; Social/Cultural gatherings.

Grancare Nursing Center
1555 Dousman St, Green Bay, WI, 54303
(414) 494-4525
Admin Cindy J Idzik. *Medical Dir/Dir of Nursing* Barb Long.
Licensure Skilled care; Intermediate care. *Beds* 76.
Owner Proprietary Corp.
Admissions Requirements Minimum age 18; Medical examination; Physician's request.
Staff Physicians 1 (pt); RNs 4 (ft), 4 (pt); LPNs 6 (ft), 2 (pt); Nurses aides 20 (ft), 30 (pt); Physical therapists 1 (pt); Reality therapists 1 (pt); Recreational therapists 1 (ft); Occupational therapists 1 (pt); Speech therapists 1 (pt); Activities coordinators 2 (ft), 1 (pt); Dietitians 1 (pt); Ophthalmologists 1 (pt); Food service director 1 (ft).
Facilities Dining room; Physical therapy room; Activities room; Chapel; Crafts room; Laundry room; Barber/Beauty shop; Library.
Activities Arts & crafts; Cards; Games; Reading groups; Prayer groups; Movies; Shopping trips; Social/Cultural gatherings.

Guardian Angel Health Care Center*
2997 Saint Anthony Dr, Green Bay, WI, 54301
(414) 468-0734
Admin John Lippert.
Licensure Intermediate care. *Beds* 66. *Certified* Medicaid.
Owner Proprietary Corp (Beverly Enterprises).

Jefferson Manor
436 S Jefferson St, Green Bay, WI, 54301
(414) 437-9812
Admin Lori M Blaha. *Medical Dir/Dir of Nursing* Lee Ann Sachs.
Licensure Intermediate care for mentally retarded. *Beds* ICF/MR 42. *Certified* Medicaid.
Owner Proprietary Corp.
Admissions Requirements Minimum age 18; Medical examination; Physician's request.
Staff RNs 1 (ft); LPNs 1 (ft), 6 (pt); Nurses aides 4 (ft), 5 (pt); Activities coordinators 1 (ft); Dietitians 2 (ft), 2 (pt).
Facilities Dining room; Activities room; Crafts room; Laundry room.
Activities Arts & crafts; Cards; Games; Reading groups; Movies; Shopping trips; Social/Cultural gatherings.

Parkview Manor Nursing Center*
2961 Saint Anthony Dr, Green Bay, WI, 54301
(414) 468-0861
Admin William Bender. *Medical Dir/Dir of Nursing* Dr Rahr.
Licensure Skilled care; Intermediate care. *Beds* 142. *Certified* Medicaid; Medicare.
Owner Proprietary Corp (Beverly Enterprises).
Staff RNs 4 (ft), 4 (pt); LPNs 8 (ft), 6 (pt); Nurses aides 40 (ft), 38 (pt); Physical therapists 1 (pt); Occupational therapists 1 (pt); Speech therapists 1 (pt); Activities coordinators 1 (ft); Dietitians 1 (ft); Dentists 1 (pt).
Facilities Dining room; Physical therapy room; Activities room; Chapel; Laundry room; Barber/Beauty shop.
Activities Arts & crafts; Cards; Games; Reading groups; Prayer groups; Movies; Shopping trips; Social/Cultural gatherings.

San Luis Manor
2305 San Luis Pl, Green Bay, WI, 54304
(414) 494-5231
Admin Laverne L Larson. *Medical Dir/Dir of Nursing* Fred Walburn.
Licensure Skilled care; Intermediate care. *Beds* 180. *Certified* Medicaid.
Owner Proprietary Corp (Hillhaven Corp).
Admissions Requirements Medical examination; Physician's request.
Staff Physicians 1 (pt); RNs 4 (ft), 7 (pt); LPNs 9 (ft), 9 (pt); Nurses aides 40 (ft), 50 (pt); Physical therapists 1 (ft); Occupational therapists 1 (ft); Speech therapists 1 (pt); Activities coordinators 1 (ft); Dietitians 1 (pt); Dentists 1 (pt); Podiatrists 1 (pt).
Facilities Dining room; Physical therapy room; Activities room; Chapel; Crafts room; Laundry room; Barber/Beauty shop; Library.
Activities Arts & crafts; Cards; Games; Reading groups; Prayer groups; Movies; Shopping trips; Social/Cultural gatherings.

Santa Marie Nursing Home*
430 S Clay St, Green Bay, WI, 54301
(414) 432-5231
Admin Helen M Desotell.
Licensure Skilled care; Intermediate care. *Beds* 59. *Certified* Medicaid.
Owner Proprietary Corp.

Van Buren Hall
115 S Van Buren St, Green Bay, WI, 54301
(414) 437-5476
Admin Lori M Blaha. *Medical Dir/Dir of Nursing* Rae Blakesley.
Licensure Intermediate care for mentally retarded. *Beds* ICF/MR 50. *Certified* Medicaid.
Owner Proprietary Corp.
Admissions Requirements Minimum age 18; Medical examination; Physician's request.
Staff RNs 1 (ft); LPNs 2 (ft), 3 (pt); Nurses aides 5 (ft), 5 (pt); Activities coordinators 2 (ft); Dietitians 2 (ft), 2 (pt).

Facilities Dining room; Activities room; Crafts room; Laundry room; TV room; Pool room.
Activities Arts & crafts; Cards; Games; Reading groups; Movies; Shopping trips; Social/Cultural gatherings.

Western Village
1640 Shawano Ave, Green Bay, WI, 54303
(414) 499-5177
Admin Dale P Johnson.
Licensure Skilled care; Intermediate care. *Beds* 125. *Certified* Medicaid; Medicare.
Owner Proprietary Corp (Beverly Enterprises).

Wisconsin Odd Fellow-Rebekah Nursing Home*
1229 S Jackson St, Green Bay, WI, 54301
(414) 437-6523
Admin Leonard D Ferris.
Licensure Skilled care; Intermediate care. *Beds* 82. *Certified* Medicaid.
Owner Nonprofit Corp.
Affiliation Independent Order of Odd Fellows & Rebekahs

Woodside Lutheran Home*
1040 Pilgrim Way, Green Bay, WI, 54304
(414) 499-1481
Admin June K Mecklenburg.
Licensure Skilled care; Intermediate care. *Beds* 168. *Certified* Medicaid.
Owner Nonprofit Corp.
Affiliation Lutheran

GREENFIELD

Clement Manor
3939 S 92nd St, Greenfield, WI, 53228
(414) 321-1800
Admin Elizabeth M Halme. *Medical Dir/Dir of Nursing* John Wisniewski MD; Gloria Jenrich DON.
Licensure Skilled care. *Beds* SNF 164. *Certified* Medicaid; Medicare.
Owner Nonprofit Corp.
Admissions Requirements Minimum age 18; Medical examination; Physician's request.
Staff Physicians 1 (pt); RNs 9 (ft), 10 (pt); LPNs 6 (ft), 11 (pt); Nurses aides 47 (ft), 39 (pt); Physical therapists 2 (ft); Reality therapists 1 (ft); Recreational therapists 2 (ft); Occupational therapists 2 (ft); Speech therapists 1 (pt); Activities coordinators 1 (ft); Dietitians 1 (ft); Ophthalmologists 1 (pt); Podiatrists 1 (pt).
Languages German, Polish
Affiliation Roman Catholic
Facilities Dining room; Physical therapy room; Activities room; Chapel; Crafts room; Laundry room; Barber/Beauty shop; Library.
Activities Arts & crafts; Cards; Games; Reading groups; Prayer groups; Movies; Shopping trips; Social/Cultural gatherings; Reality orientation; Remotivation; Woodworking; Cooking classes.

HAMMOND

American Heritage Care Center
425 Davis St, Hammond, WI, 54015
(715) 796-2218
Admin Donald A Richardson. *Medical Dir/Dir of Nursing* Sharon Nyberg.
Licensure Skilled care. *Beds* 67. *Certified* Medicaid.
Owner Nonprofit Corp.
Admissions Requirements Physician's request.
Staff Physicians 1 (pt); RNs 5 (ft), 2 (pt); LPNs 7 (pt); Nurses aides 7 (ft), 28 (pt); Physical therapists 1 (pt); Occupational therapists 1 (pt); Speech therapists 1 (pt); Activities coordinators 1 (ft); Dietitians 1 (pt).
Facilities Dining room; Activities room; Chapel; Crafts room; Laundry room; Barber/Beauty shop.

Activities Arts & crafts; Cards; Games; Reading groups; Prayer groups; Movies; Shopping trips; Social/Cultural gatherings; Fishing; Dining out.

HARTFORD

Hartford Care Center*
1202 E Sumner St, Hartford, WI, 53027
(414) 673-2220
Admin Richard Sternke.
Licensure Skilled care; Intermediate care. *Beds* 115. *Certified* Medicaid.
Owner Proprietary Corp (Hillhaven Corp).

HAWTHORNE

Middle River Health Facility
Hwy 53, Hawthorne, WI, 54842
(715) 398-3523
Admin Marvin L Benedict. *Medical Dir/Dir of Nursing* Dr Alfred Lounsbury.
Licensure Skilled care; Intermediate care. *Beds* 124. *Certified* Medicaid; Medicare.
Owner Nonprofit Corp.
Admissions Requirements Medical examination; Physician's request.
Staff RNs 2 (ft), 4 (pt); LPNs 6 (ft), 10 (pt); Orderlies 2 (pt); Nurses aides 24 (ft), 21 (pt).
Facilities Dining room; Physical therapy room; Activities room; Chapel; Crafts room; Laundry room; Barber/Beauty shop; Library.
Activities Arts & crafts; Cards; Games; Reading groups; Movies; Shopping trips; Social/Cultural gatherings; Reality orientation.

HAYWARD

Hayward Nursing Home
Rte 3, Box 3999, Hayward, WI, 54843
(715) 634-8911
Admin Karen Churitch.
Licensure Skilled care; Intermediate care. *Beds* 76. *Certified* Medicaid.
Owner Nonprofit Corp.

Valley Health Care Center
PO Box 779, Nyman Ave, Hayward, WI, 54843
(715) 634-2202
Admin David J Attwood. *Medical Dir/Dir of Nursing* Richard L Eder MD; Karen Robert RN DON.
Licensure Skilled care; Intermediate care. *Beds* SNF 62; ICF. *Certified* Medicaid.
Owner Proprietary Corp (Beverly Enterprises).
Admissions Requirements Minimum age 18; Medical examination; Physician's request.
Staff RNs 2 (ft), 1 (pt); LPNs 1 (ft), 3 (pt); Nurses aides 8 (ft), 15 (pt); Physical therapists 1 (pt); Occupational therapists 11 (pt); Speech therapists 1 (pt); Activities coordinators 1 (ft), 1 (pt); Dietitians 1 (ft), 1 (pt).
Facilities Dining room; Physical therapy room; Activities room; Crafts room; Laundry room; Barber/Beauty shop; Library.
Activities Arts & crafts; Cards; Games; Reading groups; Prayer groups; Movies; Shopping trips; Social/Cultural gatherings.

HILLSBORO

St Joseph's Nursing Home*
400 Water Ave, Hillsboro, WI, 54634
(608) 489-2211
Admin Rolin H Johnson.
Licensure Skilled care; Intermediate care. *Beds* 65. *Certified* Medicaid.
Owner Nonprofit Corp.

HUDSON

Christian Community Home of Hudson*
1415 Laurel Ave, Hudson, WI, 54016
(715) 386-9303
Admin Paul J Connolly. *Medical Dir/Dir of Nursing* Dr Jeanne Diefenbach.
Licensure Skilled care; Intermediate care. *Beds* 75. *Certified* Medicaid.
Owner Nonprofit Corp.
Admissions Requirements Medical examination; Physician's request.
Staff RNs 3 (ft), 2 (pt); LPNs 3 (ft), 5 (pt); Nurses aides 28 (ft), 8 (pt); Activities coordinators 1 (ft); Dietitians 1 (ft).
Affiliation Methodist
Facilities Dining room; Physical therapy room; Activities room; Chapel; Crafts room; Barber/Beauty shop; Library; Smokers lounge; Atrium.
Activities Arts & crafts; Cards; Games; Prayer groups; Movies; Social/Cultural gatherings; Dining out.

L O Simenstad Nursing Care Unit
Box 218, 301 River St, Hudson, WI, 54020
(715) 294-2120
Admin Mark H Tibbetts. *Medical Dir/Dir of Nursing* A S Potek MD; Cheryl Zempel RN.
Licensure Skilled care; Intermediate care. *Beds* SNF 40; ICF. *Certified* Medicaid.
Owner Nonprofit organization/foundation.
Admissions Requirements Medical examination; Physician's request.
Facilities Dining room; Physical therapy room; Activities room; Chapel; Crafts room; Laundry room; Barber/Beauty shop.
Activities Arts & crafts; Cards; Games; Reading groups; Prayer groups; Movies; Shopping trips; Outings; Fishing trips; Picnics; Sightseeing.

Willow Park Care Facility*
Rte 2, Box 385, Hudson, WI, 54016
(715) 386-2222
Admin Colette Ruemmele. *Medical Dir/Dir of Nursing* Dr Frank H Hollar.
Licensure Intermediate care. *Beds* 39. *Certified* Medicaid.
Owner Proprietary Corp.
Admissions Requirements Medical examination; Physician's request.
Staff Physicians 1 (pt); RNs 2 (ft); LPNs 2 (ft); Orderlies 4 (ft); Nurses aides 2 (ft), 4 (pt); Reality therapists 1 (pt); Recreational therapists 1 (pt); Activities coordinators 1 (pt); Dietitians 1 (pt); Dentists 1 (pt).
Facilities Dining room; Activities room; Crafts room; Group meeting room.
Activities Arts & crafts; Cards; Games; Prayer groups; Movies; Shopping trips; Social/Cultural gatherings Library visits & mail-a-book service; AA in-house meetings.

HURLEY

Sky View Nursing Center*
309 Iron St, Hurley, WI, 54534
(715) 561-5646
Admin Dean A Jivery.
Licensure Intermediate care. *Beds* 36. *Certified* Medicaid.
Owner Proprietary Corp.

Villa Maria Healthcare Center*
Villa Dr, Hurley, WI, 54534
(715) 561-3200
Admin Lawrence J Kutz.
Licensure Skilled care; Intermediate care. *Beds* 70. *Certified* Medicaid.
Owner Proprietary Corp.

IOLA

Iola Nursing Home
PO Box 237, 185 S Washington, Iola, WI, 54945
(715) 445-2412
Admin Gary L Baehman. *Medical Dir/Dir of Nursing* Dr James Hanusa; Mary Bublizt.
Licensure Skilled care; Intermediate care. *Beds* SNF 38; ICF. *Certified* Medicaid.
Owner Nonprofit Corp.
Admissions Requirements Medical examination.
Staff Physicians 2 (ft); RNs 1 (ft), 3 (pt); LPNs 2 (ft), 5 (pt); Nurses aides 5 (ft), 10 (pt); Physical therapists 1 (pt); Recreational therapists 1 (ft); Activities coordinators 1 (ft); Dietitians 1 (pt).
Facilities Dining room; Physical therapy room; Activities room; Chapel; Crafts room; Laundry room; Barber/Beauty shop; Library.
Activities Arts & crafts; Cards; Games; Reading groups; Prayer groups; Movies; Social/Cultural gatherings.

JANESVILLE

Cedar Crest Health Center
1700 S River Rd, Janesville, WI, 53545
(608) 756-0344
Admin Jay E Smoke. *Medical Dir/Dir of Nursing* David Smith MD; Dorothy Osborne RN.
Licensure Skilled care; Intermediate care. *Beds* 95.
Owner Nonprofit Corp.
Staff RNs 4 (ft), 12 (pt); LPNs 2 (pt); Nurses aides 22 (ft), 31 (pt); Activities coordinators 1 (ft).

Dupoint House*
1947 Dupoint Dr, Janesville, WI, 53545
(608) 831-2055
Admin Nancy Fennema.
Licensure Skilled care; Intermediate care for mentally retarded. *Beds* 6. *Certified* Medicaid.
Owner Nonprofit Corp.

Janesville Health Care Center
119 S Parker Dr, Janesville, WI, 53545
(608) 756-0374
Admin Aaron L Chatterson. *Medical Dir/Dir of Nursing* Dr S Frazer MD; D Archer DON.
Licensure Skilled care. *Beds* 104. *Certified* Medicaid; Medicare.
Owner Proprietary Corp.
Admissions Requirements Minimum age; Medical examination; Physician's request.
Facilities Dining room; Physical therapy room; Activities room; Laundry room; Barber/Beauty shop.
Activities Arts & crafts; Cards; Games; Reading groups; Prayer groups; Movies; Shopping trips; Social/Cultural gatherings.

Rock County Health Care Center
PO Box 351, N Parker Dr, Janesville, WI, 53547
(608) 755-2522
Admin Terry A Scieszinski. *Medical Dir/Dir of Nursing* Paul F Frechette MD.
Licensure Skilled care; Intermediate care. *Beds* 388. *Certified* Medicaid; Medicare.
Owner Publicly owned.
Admissions Requirements Minimum age 18; Medical examination; Physician's request.
Staff Physicians 2 (ft), 2 (pt); RNs 11 (ft), 17 (pt); LPNs 8 (ft), 12 (pt); Nurses aides 102 (ft), 70 (pt); Physical therapists 1 (ft); Occupational therapists 3 (ft); Speech therapists 1 (ft); Activities coordinators 1 (ft); Dietitians 1 (ft); Ophthalmologists 1 (pt).

Facilities Dining room; Physical therapy room; Activities room; Chapel; Crafts room; Laundry room; Barber/Beauty shop; Library.
Activities Arts & crafts; Cards; Games; Reading groups; Prayer groups; Movies; Shopping trips; Social/Cultural gatherings.

St Elizabeth's Home
502 Saint Lawrence, Janesville, WI, 53545
(608) 752-6709
Admin Mary Denise Slocum. *Medical Dir/Dir of Nursing* Sr Mary Jacinta RN.
Licensure Intermediate care. *Beds* 43.
Owner Nonprofit Corp.
Admissions Requirements Medical examination; Physician's request.
Staff RNs 2 (ft); Nurses aides 10 (ft), 3 (pt); Activities coordinators 1 (ft), 1 (pt); Dietitians 1 (pt); Social worker 1 (pt).
Affiliation Roman Catholic
Activities Arts & crafts; Cards; Games; Reading groups; Prayer groups; Movies; Shopping trips; Bingo; Picnics.

JEFFERSON

Countryside Home
1425 Wisconsin Dr, Jefferson, WI, 53549
(414) 674-3170
Admin Phyllis T Williams RN NHA. *Medical Dir/Dir of Nursing* Dr H Leering; Sharon Erickson RN.
Licensure Skilled care; Intermediate care for mentally retarded. *Beds* 353. *Certified* Medicaid; Medicare.
Owner Publicly owned.
Admissions Requirements Minimum age 18; Medical examination; Physician's request.
Staff Physicians 1 (ft); RNs 12 (ft), 5 (pt); LPNs 24 (ft), 19 (pt); Nurses aides 84 (ft), 60 (pt); Recreational therapists 1 (ft); Activities coordinators 1 (ft); Dietitians 1 (pt).
Facilities Dining room; Physical therapy room; Activities room; Chapel; Crafts room; Laundry room; Barber/Beauty shop; Library.
Activities Arts & crafts; Cards; Games; Reading groups; Prayer groups; Movies; Shopping trips; Social/Cultural gatherings.

St Coletta School Alverno Cottage
W 4955 Hwy 18, Jefferson, WI, 53549
(414) 674-2045
Admin Ellen Haines. *Medical Dir/Dir of Nursing* Judith Kylmanen RN.
Licensure Intermediate care. *Beds* ICF/MR 76. *Certified* Medicaid.
Owner Nonprofit Corp.
Admissions Requirements Minimum age 18; Medical examination; Physician's request.
Staff RNs 1 (ft); LPNs 3 (pt); Nurses aides 19 (ft), 15 (pt); Occupational therapists 1 (ft); Speech therapists 1 (pt); Dietitians 1 (pt).
Facilities Dining room; Physical therapy room; Activities room; Chapel; Crafts room; Laundry room; Barber/Beauty shop; Library.
Activities Arts & crafts; Cards; Games; Reading groups; Prayer groups; Movies; Shopping trips; Social/Cultural gatherings.

JUNEAU

Clearview Nursing Home*
198 Home Rd, Juneau, WI, 53039
(414) 386-2631
Admin Michael W Berry. *Medical Dir/Dir of Nursing* Frederick Haessley.
Licensure Skilled care. *Beds* 243. *Certified* Medicaid.
Owner Publicly owned.
Admissions Requirements Minimum age 18; Medical examination; Physician's request.
Staff Physicians 1 (ft); RNs 4 (ft), 6 (pt); LPNs 13 (ft), 13 (pt); Nurses aides 62 (ft), 13 (pt); Recreational therapists 3 (ft); Activities coordinators 1 (ft); Dietitians 1 (ft).

Facilities Dining room; Physical therapy room; Activities room; Chapel; Crafts room; Laundry room; Barber/Beauty shop; Library.
Activities Arts & crafts; Cards; Games; Reading groups; Prayer groups; Movies; Shopping trips; Social/Cultural gatherings.

Dodge County Community Health Center*
199 Home Rd, Juneau, WI, 53039
(414) 386-2655
Admin Michael W Berry. *Medical Dir/Dir of Nursing* John Smith.
Licensure Skilled care; Intermediate care. *Beds* 233. *Certified* Medicaid.
Owner Publicly owned.
Admissions Requirements Minimum age 18; Medical examination; Physician's request.
Staff Physicians 1 (ft); RNs 5 (ft), 6 (pt); LPNs 11 (ft), 11 (pt); Nurses aides 71 (ft), 6 (pt); Occupational therapists 1 (ft), 1 (pt).
Facilities Dining room; Physical therapy room; Activities room; Chapel; Crafts room; Laundry room; Barber/Beauty shop; Library.
Activities Arts & crafts; Cards; Games; Reading groups; Prayer groups; Movies; Shopping trips; Social/Cultural gatherings.

KAUKAUNA

Riverview Health Center
200 Sanatorium Rd, Kaukauna, WI, 54130
(414) 766-4241
Admin Rick L Johnson. *Medical Dir/Dir of Nursing* James Jeffrey MD; Sharon Magmin.
Licensure Skilled care. *Beds* 77. *Certified* Medicaid.
Owner Nonprofit Corp.
Admissions Requirements Minimum age 18; Medical examination; Physician's request.
Staff RNs 2 (ft), 3 (pt); LPNs 7 (pt); Orderlies 1 (pt); Nurses aides 36 (pt); Occupational therapists 3 (pt).
Facilities Dining room; Physical therapy room; Activities room; Chapel; Crafts room; Barber/Beauty shop.
Activities Arts & crafts; Cards; Games; Reading groups; Prayer groups; Movies; Shopping trips; Social/Cultural gatherings.

St Paul Home
509 W Wisconsin, Kaukauna, WI, 54130
(414) 766-6020
Admin Sr Alanna Ring.
Licensure Skilled care; Intermediate care. *Beds* 52. *Certified* Medicaid.
Owner Nonprofit Corp.

KENOSHA

Brookside Care Center
3506 Washington Rd, Kenosha, WI, 53142
(414) 656-6700
Admin Darlene H Sanchez. *Medical Dir/Dir of Nursing* Dr D Boyd Horsley MD; Rebecca Brehm RN DON.
Licensure Skilled care. *Beds* SNF 262; ICF. *Certified* Medicaid.
Owner Publicly owned.
Admissions Requirements Minimum age 18; Medical examination; Physician's request.
Staff Physicians 1 (pt); RNs 11 (ft), 8 (pt); LPNs 15 (ft), 11 (pt); Nurses aides 80 (ft), 48 (pt); Physical therapists 1 (ft), 1 (pt); Recreational therapists 1 (ft); Occupational therapists 1 (ft), 1 (pt); Speech therapists 2 (pt); Dietitians 1 (ft).
Facilities Dining room; Physical therapy room; Activities room; Crafts room; Barber/ Beauty shop.
Activities Arts & crafts; Cards; Games; Reading groups; Prayer groups; Movies; Shopping trips; Social/Cultural gatherings.

Dayton Residential Care Facility
521 59th St, Kenosha, WI, 53140
(414) 652-0751
Admin Cie Idrizi.

Licensure Intermediate care. *Beds* 102.
Certified Medicaid.
Owner Proprietary Corp.
Admissions Requirements Minimum age 18.
Staff LPNs; Nurses aides; Activities
coordinators; Dietitians.
Facilities Dining room; Activities room;
Crafts room; Laundry room; Barber/Beauty
shop.
Activities Cards; Games; Social/Cultural
gatherings; Bingo; Exercise.

Hospitality Manor
8633 32nd Ave, Kenosha, WI, 53142
(414) 694-8300
Admin Clark D Nardberg. *Medical Dir/Dir of
Nursing* Kevin Benson MD.
Licensure Skilled care. *Beds* SNF 102.
Certified Medicaid; Medicare.
Owner Proprietary Corp (Unicare).
Admissions Requirements Medical
examination.
Staff Physicians 1 (pt); RNs 2 (ft), 3 (pt);
LPNs 1 (ft), 12 (pt); Orderlies 2 (pt); Nurses
aides 6 (ft), 60 (pt); Physical therapists 1
(pt); Recreational therapists 1 (ft), 1 (pt);
Occupational therapists 1 (pt); Speech
therapists 1 (pt); Activities coordinators 1
(ft); Dietitians 1 (pt); Dentists 1 (pt);
Ophthalmologists 1 (pt); Podiatrists 1 (pt).
Facilities Dining room; Physical therapy
room; Activities room; Crafts room; Laundry
room; Barber/Beauty shop.
Activities Arts & crafts; Cards; Games;
Reading groups; Prayer groups; Movies;
Social/Cultural gatherings.

Midway Manor Health Care Facility
1519 60th St, Kenosha, WI, 53140
(414) 658-8156
Admin Earl Hawley. *Medical Dir/Dir of
Nursing* L Newman.
Licensure Skilled care. *Beds* 96.
Owner Proprietary Corp.
Admissions Requirements Minimum age 18;
Medical examination; Physician's request.
Staff RNs 3 (ft), 2 (pt); LPNs 4 (ft); Orderlies
12 (ft), 12 (pt); Recreational therapists 1 (ft),
1 (pt); Occupational therapists 1 (ft);
Activities coordinators 1 (ft), 1 (pt);
Dietitians 1 (pt).
Facilities Dining room; Physical therapy
room; Activities room; Chapel; Crafts room;
Laundry room.
Activities Arts & crafts; Cards; Games;
Reading groups; Prayer groups; Movies;
Shopping trips; Social/Cultural gatherings.

St Joseph's Home
9244-29th Ave, Kenosha, WI, 53140
(414) 694-0080
Admin Sr Mary Therese Esselman. *Medical
Dir/Dir of Nursing* Rita Cox DON.
Licensure Skilled care. *Beds* SNF 93; ICF.
Certified Medicaid.
Owner Nonprofit organization/foundation.
Staff RNs 2 (ft), 4 (pt); LPNs 4 (ft), 7 (pt);
Nurses aides 17 (ft), 16 (pt); Activities
coordinators 1 (ft); Dietitians 1 (pt).

Shady Lawn Nursing Home—East
920 61st St, Kenosha, WI, 53140
(414) 658-4346
Admin Candace Lagerfeldt. *Medical Dir/Dir of
Nursing* Robin K Smith DON.
Licensure Intermediate care. *Beds* 80.
Certified Medicaid.
Owner Proprietary Corp.
Admissions Requirements Medical
examination; Physician's request.
Facilities Dining room; Activities room;
Chapel; Crafts room; Laundry room; Barber/
Beauty shop.
Activities Arts & crafts; Cards; Games; Prayer
groups; Movies; Shopping trips; Social/
Cultural gatherings; Bowling.

Shady Lawn West Nursing Home
1703 60th St, Kenosha, WI, 53140
(414) 658-4125
Admin Tim Herber. *Medical Dir/Dir of
Nursing* Michael Zeihen; Dorla Cecconie
DON.
Licensure Skilled care. *Beds* SNF 120.
Certified Medicaid; Medicare.
Owner Proprietary Corp (Vantage Healthcare).
Admissions Requirements Medical
examination; Physician's request.
Staff RNs 4 (ft), 6 (pt); LPNs 6 (ft), 7 (pt);
Orderlies 4 (pt); Nurses aides 30 (ft), 26 (pt);
Physical therapists 1 (pt); Occupational
therapists 1 (pt); Speech therapists 1 (pt);
Activities coordinators 1 (ft); Dietitians 1
(ft); Ophthalmologists 1 (pt).
Facilities Dining room; Physical therapy
room; Activities room; Crafts room; Barber/
Beauty shop.
Activities Arts & crafts; Cards; Games; Prayer
groups; Movies; Shopping trips; Social/
Cultural gatherings.

Sheridan Nursing Home
8400 Sheridan Rd, Kenosha, WI, 53140
(414) 658-4141
Admin Mary W Petersen. *Medical Dir/Dir of
Nursing* Dr Mitchell Ziarko; Ann Gainey
RN.
Licensure Skilled care; Intermediate care. *Beds*
106. *Certified* Medicaid; Medicare.
Owner Proprietary Corp (Hillhaven Corp).
Admissions Requirements Minimum age 18;
Medical examination; Physician's request.
Staff RNs; LPNs; Orderlies; Nurses aides;
Physical therapists; Reality therapists;
Recreational therapists; Occupational
therapists; Speech therapists; Activities
coordinators; Dietitians; Ophthalmologists.
Languages Italian
Facilities Dining room; Activities room;
Chapel; Crafts room; Barber/Beauty shop;
Library.
Activities Arts & crafts; Cards; Games;
Reading groups; Prayer groups; Movies;
Shopping trips; Social/Cultural gatherings;
Creative writing; Poetry.

Washington Manor
3100 Washington Rd, Kenosha, WI, 53142
(414) 658-4622
Admin Thomas F O'Neal. *Medical Dir/Dir of
Nursing* Dr David Goldstein; Judy Suter
DON.
Licensure Skilled care; Intermediate care. *Beds*
103. *Certified* Medicaid; Medicare.
Owner Proprietary Corp (Health Care &
Retirement Corp).
Admissions Requirements Minimum age 18;
Medical examination; Physician's request.
Staff RNs; LPNs; Orderlies; Nurses aides;
Physical therapists; Recreational therapists;
Occupational therapists; Speech therapists;
Activities coordinators; Dietitians;
Ophthalmologists.
Facilities Dining room; Physical therapy
room; Activities room; Barber/Beauty shop.
Activities Arts & crafts; Cards; Games;
Reading groups; Movies; Shopping trips.

Woodstock-Kenosha Health Center
3415 N Sheridan Rd, Kenosha, WI, 53140
(414) 657-6175
Admin John F Flynn RN. *Medical Dir/Dir of
Nursing* R Rustia MD: Janice Kafer RN
DON.
Licensure Skilled care. *Beds* SNF 183.
Certified Medicaid; Medicare.
Owner Proprietary Corp (Hillhaven Corp).
Admissions Requirements Minimum age 18;
Medical examination; Physician's request.
Staff Physicians 3 (pt); RNs 3 (ft), 12 (pt);
LPNs 6 (ft), 15 (pt); Orderlies; Nurses aides
13 (ft), 66 (pt); Physical therapists 2 (ft);
Occupational therapists 2 (ft); Speech
therapists 1 (ft); Activities coordinators 1

(ft), 7 (pt); Dietitians 1 (pt); Dentists 1 (pt);
Ophthalmologists 1 (pt); Podiatrists 1 (pt);
Volunteer Coordinator 1 (pt).
Facilities Dining room; Physical therapy
room; Activities room; Crafts room; Laundry
room; Barber/Beauty shop.
Activities Arts & crafts; Cards; Games;
Reading groups; Prayer groups; Movies;
Shopping trips; Social/Cultural gatherings;
Van equipped for the handicapped.

KEWASKUM

Beechwood Rest Home
Rte 1, 16-98 Hwy A, Kewaskum, WI, 53040
(414) 626-4258
Admin Lee L Rammer.
Licensure Intermediate care. *Beds* 26.
Certified Medicaid.
Owner Proprietary Corp.

KEWAUNEE

Kewaunee Health Care Center
1308 Lincoln St, Kewaunee, WI, 54216
(414) 388-4111
Admin Steven Bavers. *Medical Dir/Dir of
Nursing* Dr E Regehr; Dr R M Nesemann;
Gerald Tegen.
Licensure Skilled care; Intermediate care. *Beds*
106. *Certified* Medicaid; Medicare; VA.
Owner Proprietary Corp (Beverly Enterprises).
Admissions Requirements Minimum age 18;
Medical examination; Physician's request.
Staff Physicians 5 (pt); RNs 3 (ft), 1 (pt);
LPNs 4 (ft), 4 (pt); Orderlies 2 (ft); Nurses
aides 21 (ft), 24 (pt); Physical therapists 2
(pt); Occupational therapists 2 (pt);
Activities coordinators 1 (ft), 1 (pt);
Dietitians 1 (ft); Ophthalmologists 1 (pt).
Facilities Dining room; Physical therapy
room; Activities room; Laundry room;
Barber/Beauty shop.
Activities Arts & crafts; Cards; Games;
Reading groups; Prayer groups; Movies;
Shopping trips; Social/Cultural gatherings.

KING

Wisconsin Veterans Home
Burns-Clemens Bldg, King, WI, 54946
(715) 258-5586
Admin Lavern L Hanke. *Medical Dir/Dir of
Nursing* Paul Drinka MD; Karen Brown
DON.
Licensure Skilled care; Intermediate care. *Beds*
193. *Certified* Medicaid.
Owner Publicly owned.
Staff Physicians 1 (ft); RNs 6 (ft), 4 (pt);
LPNs 7 (ft), 4 (pt); Nurses aides 27 (ft), 7
(pt); Physical therapists 1 (ft); Recreational
therapists 1 (ft); Occupational therapists 1
(ft); Activities coordinators 1 (ft).
Languages German, Spanish, Polish
Activities Arts & crafts; Cards; Games;
Reading groups; Prayer groups; Movies;
Shopping trips; Social/Cultural gatherings;
Boat rides; Bowling.

Wisconsin Veterans Home No 422
McArthur Hall, King, WI, 54946
(715) 258-5586
Admin Lavern L Hanke. *Medical Dir/Dir of
Nursing* Paul Drinka MD; Dorothy Knopp.
Licensure Skilled care; Intermediate care;
Domiciliary. *Beds* 116. *Certified* Medicaid.
Owner Publicly owned.
Admissions Requirements Minimum age 50;
Medical examination; Physician's request.
Staff Physicians 1 (ft); RNs 7 (ft), 4 (pt);
LPNs 11 (ft), 5 (pt); Nurses aides 38 (ft), 2
(pt); Physical therapists 1 (ft); Recreational
therapists 1 (ft); Occupational therapists 1
(ft); Activities coordinators 1 (ft); Dietitians
1 (ft).
Languages German, Spanish, Polish

Facilities Dining room; Physical therapy room; Activities room; Chapel; Crafts room; Laundry room; Barber/Beauty shop; Library; Bowling alley.
Activities Arts & crafts; Cards; Games; Reading groups; Prayer groups; Movies; Shopping trips; Social/Cultural gatherings; Bowling; Boat trips.

Wisconsin Veterans Home No 600
Olson Hall, King, WI, 54946
(715) 258-5586
Admin Lavern L Hanke. *Medical Dir/Dir of Nursing* Paul Drinka MD; David Barncy RN DON.
Licensure Skilled care; Intermediate care; Domiciliary. *Beds* 200. *Certified* Medicaid.
Owner Publicly owned.
Admissions Requirements Minimum age 50; Medical examination; Physician's request.
Staff Physicians 1 (ft); RNs 6 (ft), 2 (pt); LPNs 11 (ft), 5 (pt); Nurses aides 54 (ft), 6 (pt); Physical therapists 1 (ft); Recreational therapists 1 (ft); Occupational therapists 1 (ft); Activities coordinators 1 (ft); Dietitians 1 (ft).
Languages German, Polish, Spanish
Facilities Dining room; Physical therapy room; Activities room; Chapel; Crafts room; Laundry room; Barber/Beauty shop; Library; Bowling alley.
Activities Arts & crafts; Cards; Games; Reading groups; Prayer groups; Movies; Shopping trips; Social/Cultural gatherings; Work therapy program; Bowling; Boat rides.

Wisconsin Veterans Home No 700
Stordock Hall, King, WI, 54946
(715) 258-5586
Admin Lavern L Hanke. *Medical Dir/Dir of Nursing* Paul A Drinka MD; Alice Rodriguez RN.
Licensure Skilled care; Intermediate care; Domiciliary. *Beds* 200. *Certified* Medicaid.
Owner Publicly owned.
Admissions Requirements Minimum age 50; Medical examination; Physician's request.
Staff Physicians 1 (ft); RNs 7 (ft), 1 (pt); LPNs 11 (ft), 5 (pt); Nurses aides 44 (ft), 8 (pt); Physical therapists 1 (ft); Recreational therapists 1 (ft); Occupational therapists 1 (ft); Activities coordinators 1 (ft); Dietitians 1 (ft).
Languages German, Spanish, Polish
Facilities Dining room; Physical therapy room; Activities room; Chapel; Crafts room; Laundry room; Barber/Beauty shop; Library; Bowling alley.
Activities Arts & crafts; Cards; Games; Reading groups; Prayer groups; Movies; Shopping trips; Social/Cultural gatherings; Bowling; Boat rides.

LA CROSSE

Bethany Riverside
2575 S 7th St, La Crosse, WI, 54601
(608) 784-3380
Admin Rev Howard Larsen. *Medical Dir/Dir of Nursing* Bruce Polender MD.
Licensure Skilled care; Intermediate care. *Beds* 123. *Certified* Medicaid.
Owner Nonprofit Corp.
Admissions Requirements Minimum age 21; Medical examination.
Affiliation Lutheran
Facilities Dining room; Physical therapy room; Activities room; Chapel; Crafts room; Laundry room; Barber/Beauty shop; Library.
Activities Arts & crafts; Cards; Games; Reading groups; Prayer groups; Movies; Shopping trips; Social/Cultural gatherings; Outings.

Bethany St Joseph Care Center
2501 Shelby Rd, La Crosse, WI, 54601
(608) 788-5700

Admin Thomas Rand. *Medical Dir/Dir of Nursing* Phil Utz MD; Beth Olson RN DON.
Licensure Skilled care; Intermediate care. *Beds* 226. *Certified* Medicaid; Medicare.
Owner Nonprofit Corp.
Admissions Requirements Minimum age 18; Medical examination; Physician's request.
Staff RNs 12 (ft), 20 (pt); LPNs 3 (ft), 21 (pt); Nurses aides 41 (ft), 63 (pt); Physical therapists 1 (ft), 2 (pt); Recreational therapists 1 (ft); Occupational therapists 2 (pt); Speech therapists 1 (ft); Activities coordinators 1 (ft); Dietitians 1 (ft), 2 (pt).
Facilities Dining room; Physical therapy room; Activities room; Chapel; Crafts room; Laundry room; Barber/Beauty shop; Library.
Activities Arts & crafts; Cards; Games; Reading groups; Prayer groups; Movies; Shopping trips; Social/Cultural gatherings; Music; Cooking.

Hillview Health Care Center
3501 Park Lane Dr, La Crosse, WI, 54601
(608) 788-6650
Admin Mary G Nichols. *Medical Dir/Dir of Nursing* Teddy Wais.
Licensure Skilled care. *Beds* SNF 228. *Certified* Medicaid.
Owner Publicly owned.
Admissions Requirements Medical examination; Physician's request.
Staff Physicians 1 (pt); RNs 8 (ft), 11 (pt); LPNs 5 (ft), 10 (pt); Nurses aides 45 (ft), 63 (pt); Physical therapists 1 (ft); Recreational therapists 1 (ft); Occupational therapists 1 (ft); Speech therapists 1 (pt); Activities coordinators 1 (ft); Dietitians 1 (ft).
Facilities Dining room; Physical therapy room; Activities room; Chapel; Crafts room; Laundry room; Barber/Beauty shop; Library.
Activities Arts & crafts; Cards; Games; Reading groups; Prayer groups; Movies; Social/Cultural gatherings.

St Francis Home/La Crosse Inc
620 S 11th St, La Crosse, WI, 54601
(608) 785-0966
Admin Carol A Strittmater. *Medical Dir/Dir of Nursing* Dr Phillip Utz; Richard Berendes RN DON.
Licensure Skilled care. *Beds* SNF 95. *Certified* Medicaid; Medicare.
Owner Nonprofit Corp.
Admissions Requirements Minimum age 18; Medical examination; Physician's request.
Staff RNs 4 (ft), 4 (pt); LPNs 1 (ft), 7 (pt); Nurses aides 24 (ft), 19 (pt); Physical therapists 1 (pt); Occupational therapists 1 (pt); Speech therapists 1 (pt); Activities coordinators 1 (ft), 2 (pt); Dietitians 1 (pt).
Facilities Dining room; Activities room; Chapel; Laundry room; Barber/Beauty shop.
Activities Arts & crafts; Cards; Games; Reading groups; Prayer groups; Movies; Shopping trips; Social/Cultural gatherings.

St Joseph's Nursing Home*
2902 East Ave S, La Crosse, WI, 54601
(608) 788-9870
Admin John J Newman.
Licensure Skilled care; Intermediate care. *Beds* 80. *Certified* Medicaid.
Owner Publicly owned.
Affiliation Roman Catholic

LADYSMITH

Ladysmith Nursing Home*
120 E 4th St, Ladysmith, WI, 54848
(715) 532-5546
Admin Michael W Kelley.
Licensure Intermediate care. *Beds* 43. *Certified* Medicaid.
Owner Proprietary Corp.

Rusk County Memorial Hospital Nursing Home
900 College Ave W, Ladysmith, WI, 54848
(715) 532-5561
Admin James M Shaw. *Medical Dir/Dir of Nursing* Robert Hackney; Juanita Patten.
Licensure Skilled care; Intermediate care. *Beds* 117. *Certified* Medicaid.
Owner Publicly owned.
Admissions Requirements Minimum age 18; Medical examination; Physician's request.
Staff Physicians 1 (pt); RNs 7 (ft), 4 (pt); LPNs 4 (ft), 3 (pt); Orderlies 2 (ft), 1 (pt); Nurses aides 14 (ft), 36 (pt); Activities coordinators 1 (ft); Dietitians 1 (pt).
Facilities Dining room; Physical therapy room; Activities room; Chapel; Laundry room; Barber/Beauty shop; Library.
Activities Arts & crafts; Cards; Games; Reading groups; Prayer groups; Movies; Shopping trips; Social/Cultural gatherings.

LAKE GENEVA

Geneva Lake Manor
211 S Curtis St, Lake Geneva, WI, 53147
(414) 248-3145
Admin Karen L Clapp. *Medical Dir/Dir of Nursing* Gregory Gerber MD; Kathy A Smith RN DON.
Licensure Skilled care; Intermediate care. *Beds* 60. *Certified* Medicaid.
Owner Proprietary Corp.
Admissions Requirements Minimum age 18; Medical examination; Physician's request.
Staff Physicians 14 (pt); RNs 4 (ft), 2 (pt); LPNs 4 (ft), 2 (pt); Orderlies 1 (ft), 1 (pt); Nurses aides 16 (ft), 8 (pt); Physical therapists 1 (pt); Occupational therapists 1 (pt); Speech therapists 1 (pt); Activities coordinators 1 (ft); Dietitians 1 (pt); Ophthalmologists 1 (pt); Podiatrists 1 (pt); Pharmacist 3 (pt).
Facilities Dining room; Physical therapy room; Activities room; Chapel; Crafts room; Laundry room; Barber/Beauty shop.
Activities Arts & crafts; Cards; Games; Reading groups; Prayer groups; Movies; Shopping trips; Social/Cultural gatherings.

LAKE MILLS

Willowbrook Nursing Home*
901 Mulberry St, Lake Mills, WI, 53551
(414) 648-8344
Admin Kathryn Rudel.
Licensure Skilled care; Intermediate care. *Beds* 60. *Certified* Medicaid; Medicare.
Owner Proprietary Corp.

LANCASTER

Lancaster Living Center*
1350 S Madison St, Lancaster, WI, 53813
(608) 723-4143
Admin Michael Flugstad. *Medical Dir/Dir of Nursing* Leo Becher MD.
Licensure Skilled care; Intermediate care. *Beds* 154. *Certified* Medicaid; Medicare.
Owner Nonprofit Corp (Adventist Health Sys-USA).
Staff Physicians 1 (pt); RNs 4 (ft), 3 (pt); LPNs 3 (ft), 4 (pt); Orderlies 1 (ft); Nurses aides 30 (ft), 19 (pt); Physical therapists 1 (pt); Recreational therapists 1 (pt); Speech therapists 1 (pt); Activities coordinators 1 (ft), 2 (pt); Dietitians 1 (pt); Dentists 1 (pt); Ophthalmologists 1 (pt).
Affiliation Seventh-Day Adventist
Facilities Dining room; Physical therapy room; Activities room; Chapel; Crafts room; Laundry room; Barber/Beauty shop; Library.
Activities Arts & crafts; Cards; Games; Reading groups; Prayer groups; Movies; Shopping trips; Social/Cultural gatherings.

Orchard Manor—North*
PO Box 431, Lancaster, WI, 53813
(608) 723-2113
Admin Gerald L Johnson.
Licensure Skilled care; Intermediate care. *Beds*
143. *Certified* Medicaid; Medicare.
Owner Publicly owned.

Orchard Manor—South
PO Box 431, Lancaster, WI, 53813
(608) 723-2113
Admin Matteo T Furno Jr. *Medical Dir/Dir of
Nursing* Donna Peterson.
Licensure Skilled care; Intermediate care for
mentally retarded. *Beds* 143. *Certified*
Medicaid; Medicare.
Owner Publicly owned.
Admissions Requirements Minimum age 18;
Medical examination.
Facilities Dining room; Physical therapy
room; Activities room; Chapel; Crafts room;
Laundry room; Barber/Beauty shop; Library.
Activities Arts & crafts; Cards; Games;
Reading groups; Prayer groups; Movies;
Social/Cultural gatherings.

LAONA

Nu-Roc Nursing Home
Rte 1, Laona, WI, 54541
(715) 674-4477
Admin Craig R Newton. *Medical Dir/Dir of
Nursing* Dr R D Niehause.
Licensure Skilled care; Intermediate care. *Beds*
61. *Certified* Medicaid.
Owner Proprietary Corp.
Admissions Requirements Medical
examination.
Staff RNs 3 (ft); LPNs 3 (ft), 1 (pt); Nurses
aides 6 (ft), 20 (pt); Physical therapists 1
(pt); Activities coordinators 1 (ft); Dietitians
1 (pt).
Facilities Dining room; Physical therapy
room; Activities room; Laundry room;
Barber/Beauty shop.
Activities Arts & crafts; Cards; Games; Prayer
groups; Social/Cultural gatherings; Dinner
club.

LITTLE CHUTE

Parkside Care Center*
1201 Garfield Ave, Little Chute, WI, 54140
(414) 788-5806
Admin Thomas Lesselyong. *Medical Dir/Dir of
Nursing* F X Van Lieshout MD.
Beds 103. *Certified* Medicaid.
Owner Proprietary Corp.
Admissions Requirements Minimum age 18;
Medical examination; Physician's request.
Staff RNs 3 (ft), 1 (pt); LPNs 4 (ft), 4 (pt);
Nurses aides 12 (ft), 30 (pt); Activities
coordinators 1 (ft), 2 (pt).
Facilities Dining room; Physical therapy
room; Activities room; Chapel; Crafts room;
Laundry room; Barber/Beauty shop.
Activities Arts & crafts; Cards; Games;
Reading groups; Prayer groups; Movies;
Social/Cultural gatherings.

LODI

Lodi Good Samaritan Center
700 Clark St, Lodi, WI, 53555
(608) 592-3241
Admin Gilbert M Singer. *Medical Dir/Dir of
Nursing* Dr Dale Fanney; Cristi L Maier
RN.
Licensure Skilled care. *Beds* SNF 100.
Certified Medicaid.
Owner Nonprofit Corp (Evangelical Lutheran/
Good Samaritan).
Admissions Requirements Minimum age 18;
Medical examination.

Staff Physicians 5 (ft); RNs 2 (ft), 8 (pt);
LPNs 1 (ft), 10 (pt); Nurses aides 16 (ft), 31
(pt); Physical therapists 1 (pt); Speech
therapists 1 (pt); Occupational therapists 1
(pt); Activities coordinators 1 (ft), 2 (pt);
Dietitians 1 (pt); Dentists 1 (pt); Podiatrists
1 (pt).
Affiliation Lutheran
Facilities Dining room; Physical therapy
room; Activities room; Chapel; Crafts room;
Laundry room; Barber/Beauty shop.
Activities Arts & crafts; Cards; Games;
Reading groups; Prayer groups; Movies;
Shopping trips; Social/Cultural gatherings;
Outings in van.

LOMIRA

Hope Nursing Home
438 Ashford Avenue, Lomira, WI, 53048
(414) 269-4386
Admin Sr Ann Josepha Lencioni Acting
Admin. *Medical/Dir of Nursing* Dr G P
Langenfeld; Elaine Muchlius RN DON.
Licensure Skilled care. *Beds* SNF 42. *Certified*
Medicaid.
Owner Nonprofit Corp.
Admissions Requirements Minimum age 21;
Medical examination.
Staff Physicians 3 (pt); RNs 1 (ft), 3 (pt);
LPNs 1 (ft), 4 (pt); Nurses aides 6 (ft), 16
(pt); Recreational therapists 1 (pt); Activities
coordinators 1 (pt); Dietitians 1 (pt).
Affiliation Roman Catholic
Facilities Dining room; Activities room;
Chapel; Laundry room; Barber/Beauty shop;
Library; Living room.
Activities Cards; Games; Reading groups;
Prayer groups; Movies; Social/Cultural
gatherings.

LUCK

United Pioneer Home*
Park Ave, Luck, WI, 54853
(715) 472-2164
Admin Stephan Rice. *Medical Dir/Dir of
Nursing* Dr Arnold Lagus.
Licensure Skilled care; Intermediate care. *Beds*
98. *Certified* Medicaid.
Owner Nonprofit Corp.
Staff RNs 5 (ft), 1 (pt); LPNs 2 (ft), 4 (pt);
Orderlies 1 (pt); Nurses aides 5 (ft), 20 (pt);
Physical therapists 1 (pt); Reality therapists
1 (pt); Recreational therapists 1 (ft), 1 (pt);
Occupational therapists 1 (pt); Activities
coordinators 1 (pt); Dietitians 1 (pt).
Facilities Dining room; Physical therapy
room; Activities room; Chapel; Crafts room;
Laundry room; Barber/Beauty shop.
Activities Arts & crafts; Cards; Games;
Reading groups; Movies; Shopping trips;
Social/Cultural gatherings.

MADISON

Arbor View Healthcare Center Inc*
1347 Fish Hatchery Rd, Madison, WI, 53715
(608) 257-0781
Admin Jeanne Hegerich.
Licensure Skilled care; Intermediate care. *Beds*
184. *Certified* Medicaid; Medicare.
Owner Proprietary Corp.

Attic Angel Nursing Home*
602 N Segoe Rd, Madison, WI, 53705
(608) 238-8282
Admin Helen M Kurth.
Licensure Skilled care. *Beds* 64.
Owner Nonprofit Corp.
Admissions Requirements Minimum age 18;
Medical examination.
Staff Physicians 1 (pt); RNs 3 (ft), 8 (pt);
LPNs 13 (ft), 26 (pt); Recreational therapists
1 (pt); Activities coordinators 1 (ft);
Dietitians 1 (pt).

Facilities Dining room; Physical therapy
room; Activities room; Crafts room; Laundry
room; Barber/Beauty shop; Library.
Activities Arts & crafts; Cards; Games;
Reading groups; Prayer groups; Movies;
Shopping trips; Social/Cultural gatherings.

**Central Wisconsin Center for the
Developmentally Disabled**
317 Knutson Dr, Madison, WI, 53704-1197
(608) 249-2151
Admin R Scheerenberger. *Medical Dir/Dir of
Nursing* John B Toussaint MD; Patricia C
McNelly RN DON.
Licensure Intermediate care for mentally
retarded. *Beds* ICF/MR 658. *Certified*
Medicaid.
Owner Publicly owned.
Admissions Requirements Minimum age birth;
Physician's request.
Staff Physicians 6 (ft), 1 (pt); RNs 31 (ft), 22
(pt); LPNs 57 (ft), 20 (pt); Nurses aides 394
(ft), 50 (pt); Physical therapists 9 (ft), 4 (pt);
Recreational therapists 10 (ft); Occupational
therapists 5 (ft), 6 (pt); Speech therapists 5
(ft), 1 (pt); Activities coordinators 1 (ft);
Dietitians 5 (ft), 1 (pt); Dentists 1 (ft).
Facilities Dining room; Physical therapy
room; Activities room; Chapel; Crafts room;
Laundry room; Barber/Beauty shop; Library.
Activities Arts & crafts; Games; Movies;
Shopping trips; Social/Cultural gatherings.

City View Nursing Home*
Rte 10, 3737 Burke Rd, Madison, WI, 53704
(608) 244-1313
Admin Thomas R Schroud.
Licensure Skilled care; Intermediate care. *Beds*
60. *Certified* Medicaid.
Owner Proprietary Corp.

Colonial Manor
110 Belmont Rd, Madison, WI, 53714
(608) 249-7391
Admin Bill Bender. *Medical Dir/Dir of
Nursing* Louise Keating.
Licensure Skilled care; Intermediate care. *Beds*
152. *Certified* Medicaid; Medicare.
Owner Proprietary Corp (Hillhaven Corp).
Admissions Requirements Minimum age 18;
Medical examination; Physician's request.
Staff RNs; LPNs; Orderlies; Nurses aides;
Physical therapists; Occupational therapists;
Activities coordinators; Dietitians.
Facilities Dining room; Physical therapy
room; Activities room; Crafts room; Laundry
room; Barber/Beauty shop; Library;
Pharmacy.
Activities Arts & crafts; Cards; Games;
Reading groups; Prayer groups; Movies;
Shopping trips; Social/Cultural gatherings.

Karmenta Health Care Center*
4502 Milwaukee St, Madison, WI, 53714
(608) 249-2137
Admin Arlene Peterson.
Licensure Skilled care; Intermediate care. *Beds*
105. *Certified* Medicaid; Medicare.
Owner Proprietary Corp.

Leader Nursing & Rehabilitation Center*
801 Braxton Pl, Madison, WI, 53715
(608) 251-1010
Admin Jack D Nelson. *Medical Dir/Dir of
Nursing* Dr Linda Farley.
Licensure Skilled care; Intermediate care. *Beds*
173. *Certified* Medicaid; Medicare.
Owner Proprietary Corp (Manor Care).
Staff RNs 10 (ft), 5 (pt); LPNs 6 (ft), 9 (pt);
Physical therapists 2 (ft), 2 (pt); Recreational
therapists 2 (ft), 1 (pt); Occupational
therapists 2 (ft); Speech therapists 1 (pt);
Dietitians 1 (pt); Dentists 1 (pt); Podiatrists
1 (pt); Audiologists 1 (pt).
Facilities Dining room; Physical therapy
room; Activities room; Chapel; Crafts room;
Laundry room; Barber/Beauty shop; Library.

Activities Arts & crafts; Cards; Games; Reading groups; Prayer groups; Movies; Shopping trips; Social/Cultural gatherings.

Madison Convalescent Center
2308 University Ave, Madison, WI, 53705
(608) 238-8401
Admin Barbara Clavette. *Medical Dir/Dir of Nursing* Dr Steven Babcock; Bonnie Fredrick DON.
Licensure Skilled care; Intermediate care. *Beds* SNF 150; ICF. *Certified* Medicaid; Medicare.
Owner Proprietary Corp (Unicare).
Admissions Requirements Minimum age 18; Medical examination; Physician's request.
Staff RNs 4 (ft), 8 (pt); LPNs 5 (ft), 6 (pt); Orderlies; Nurses aides 20 (ft), 39 (pt); Activities coordinators 1 (ft).
Facilities Dining room; Physical therapy room; Activities room; Chapel; Crafts room; Laundry room; Barber/Beauty shop.
Activities Arts & crafts; Cards; Games; Reading groups; Prayer groups; Movies; Shopping trips; Social/Cultural gatherings; Community outings.

Methodist Health Center
334 W Doty St, Madison, WI, 53703
(608) 258-2700
Medical Dir/Dir of Nursing Weldon Shelp MD; Janice K Proctor RN MS DON.
Licensure Skilled care; Intermediate care. *Beds* SNF 120; ICF. *Certified* Medicaid; Medicare.
Owner Nonprofit Corp.
Admissions Requirements Medical examination; Physician's request.
Staff RNs; LPNs; Orderlies; Nurses aides; Physical therapists 2 (ft); Occupational therapists; Speech therapists; Activities coordinators; Dietitians 1 (ft); Ophthalmologists.
Affiliation Methodist
Facilities Dining room; Physical therapy room; Activities room; Chapel; Crafts room; Laundry room; Barber/Beauty shop; Library.
Activities Arts & crafts; Cards; Games; Reading groups; Prayer groups; Movies; Shopping trips; Social/Cultural gatherings.

Monona Drive Rest Home
4202 Monona Dr, Madison, WI, 53716
(608) 222-5925
Admin Grace Johnson.
Licensure Intermediate care. *Beds* 17. *Certified* Medicaid.
Owner Proprietary Corp.

Oakwood Lutheran Homes Association Inc
6201 Mineral Point Rd, Madison, WI, 53705
(608) 231-3453
Admin Charles K Lamson. *Medical Dir/Dir of Nursing* John E Ewalt MD; Tracy Cisneros.
Licensure Skilled care; Intermediate care. *Beds* SNF 137; ICF. *Certified* Medicaid; Medicare.
Owner Nonprofit Corp.
Admissions Requirements Medical examination; Physician's request.
Staff RNs 6 (ft), 17 (pt); LPNs 2 (ft), 4 (pt); Nurses aides 16 (ft), 52 (pt); Activities coordinators 1 (ft).
Affiliation Lutheran
Facilities Dining room; Physical therapy room; Activities room; Chapel; Crafts room; Laundry room; Barber/Beauty shop; Pharmacy; 30 wooded acres.
Activities Arts & crafts; Cards; Games; Reading groups; Prayer groups; Movies; Shopping trips; Bible study.

RFDF Orchard Hill
2875 Fish Hatchery Rd, Madison, WI, 53713
(608) 274-4350
Admin Stephen Jones PhD. *Medical Dir/Dir of Nursing* Ron Shaw MD; Greta Janus RN DON.

Licensure Intermediate care for mentally retarded. *Beds* ICF/MR 96. *Certified* Medicaid; Medicare.
Owner Nonprofit organization/foundation.
Admissions Requirements Minimum age 18; Medical examination.
Staff Physicians 1 (pt); RNs 3 (ft); Nurses aides 2 (ft); Physical therapists 1 (pt); Recreational therapists 3 (ft), 1 (pt); Occupational therapists 2 (pt); Speech therapists 1 (pt); Activities coordinators 1 (ft); Dietitians 1 (pt); Social workers 2 (ft); Psychologist 1 (ft), 1 (pt).
Facilities Dining room; Activities room; Crafts room; Laundry room; Barber/Beauty shop; Gym.
Activities Arts & crafts; Cards; Games; Reading groups; Movies; Shopping trips; Social/Cultural gatherings; Horseback riding; Swimming; Bike hike; Bowling; Choir.

Sunny Hill Health Care Center
4325 Nakoma Rd, Madison, WI, 53711
(608) 271-7321
Admin Ellen E Fritsch. *Medical Dir/Dir of Nursing* Patricia Stauss DON.
Licensure Skilled care; Intermediate care. *Beds* 73. *Certified* Medicaid; Medicare.
Owner Proprietary Corp (American Medical Services Inc).
Admissions Requirements Minimum age 18; Medical examination; Physician's request.
Staff RNs 2 (ft), 5 (pt); LPNs 2 (pt); Nurses aides 11 (ft), 4 (pt); Occupational therapists 1 (pt); Activities coordinators 1 (ft), 2 (pt); Dietitians 1 (ft).
Facilities Dining room; Physical therapy room; Activities room; Crafts room; Laundry room; Barber/Beauty shop.
Activities Arts & crafts; Cards; Games; Reading groups; Prayer groups; Movies; Shopping trips; Social/Cultural gatherings.

MANAWA

Manawa Community Nursing Center Inc
4th & Grove St, Manawa, WI, 54949
(414) 596-2566
Admin Ann F Bonikowske. *Medical Dir/Dir of Nursing* Dr Lloyd Maasch MD; Paula Weisbrod RN DON.
Licensure Skilled care; Intermediate care. *Beds* SNF 68; ICF. *Certified* Medicaid; Medicare.
Owner Proprietary Corp.
Admissions Requirements Minimum age 18; Medical examination; Physician's request.
Staff Physicians 5 (pt); RNs 1 (ft), 2 (pt); LPNs 3 (ft), 4 (pt); Orderlies 1 (ft); Nurses aides 15 (ft), 12 (pt); Physical therapists 1 (pt); Occupational therapists 1 (pt); Speech therapists 1 (pt); Activities coordinators 1 (ft); Dietitians 1 (pt); Dentists 1 (pt); Ophthalmologists 1 (pt); Podiatrists 1 (pt).
Facilities Dining room; Physical therapy room; Activities room; Crafts room; Laundry room; Barber/Beauty shop.
Activities Arts & crafts; Cards; Games; Reading groups; Prayer groups; Movies; Shopping trips; Social/Cultural gatherings.

MANITOWOC

Manitowoc Health Care Center
4200 Calumet Ave, Manitowoc, WI, 54220
(414) 683-4100
Admin Thomas C Harter.
Licensure Skilled care; Intermediate care; Intermediate care for mentally retarded. *Beds* 294. *Certified* Medicaid.
Owner Publicly owned.

Michigan Shores
1028 S 9th St, Manitowoc, WI, 54220
(414) 682-0268
Admin Margaret Schmeling. *Medical Dir/Dir of Nursing* Julie Hardrath DON.

Licensure Intermediate care. *Beds* ICF 41. *Certified* Medicaid.
Owner Proprietary Corp (Beverly Enterprises).
Admissions Requirements Minimum age 18; Medical examination; Physician's request.
Staff Physicians 10 (pt); RNs 1 (ft), 2 (pt); LPNs 2 (ft), 3 (pt); Orderlies 1 (ft); Nurses aides 12 (ft); Physical therapists; Occupational therapists; Speech therapists; Activities coordinators 1 (ft), 2 (pt); Dietitians 1 (pt); Dentists; Podiatrists.
Facilities Dining room; Activities room; Laundry room.
Activities Arts & crafts; Cards; Games; Reading groups; Prayer groups; Movies; Shopping trips; Social/Cultural gatherings.

North Ridge Care Center
1445 N 7th St, Manitowoc, WI, 54220
(414) 682-0314
Admin Kenneth Zade. *Medical Dir/Dir of Nursing* Dr J L Stoune; Judy Holder.
Licensure Skilled care; Intermediate care. *Beds* 164. *Certified* Medicaid; Medicare.
Owner Proprietary Corp (Hillhaven Corp).
Staff Physicians 1 (pt); RNs 5 (ft), 3 (pt); LPNs 5 (ft), 8 (pt); Nurses aides 13 (ft), 44 (pt); Physical therapists 1 (pt); Occupational therapists 1 (pt); Activities coordinators 1 (ft).
Facilities Dining room; Activities room; Barber/Beauty shop.
Activities Cards; Games; Reading groups; Prayer groups; Movies; Social/Cultural gatherings; Lunch outings; Rides.

Park Lawn Home*
1308 S 22nd St, Manitowoc, WI, 54220
(414) 683-4330
Admin Marlys S Griffiths.
Licensure Skilled care; Intermediate care. *Beds* 99. *Certified* Medicaid.
Owner Publicly owned.

Rainbow House
610 S 29th St, Manitowoc, WI, 54220
(414) 684-4851
Admin Marcia M Christiansen. *Medical Dir/Dir of Nursing* Steven Driggers MD; Sharon Van Ells DON.
Licensure Intermediate care for mentally retarded. *Beds* ICF/MR 15. *Certified* Medicaid.
Owner Privately owned.
Admissions Requirements Minimum age 18; Developmentally disabled & ambulatory.
Staff RNs 2 (pt); LPNs 1 (pt), 1 (pt); Nurses aides 2 (ft), 4 (pt); Activities coordinators 1 (ft); Skill development aides 1 (ft), 2 (pt).
Facilities Dining room; Activities room; Laundry room.
Activities Arts & crafts; Cards; Games; Reading groups; Prayer groups; Movies; Shopping trips; Social/Cultural gatherings.

St Mary's Home for the Aged Inc
2005 Division St, Manitowoc, WI, 54220
(414) 684-7171
Admin Sr M Claude Szyperski. *Medical Dir/Dir of Nursing* Dr Gary Schmidt; Sr Noel Marie.
Licensure Skilled care; Intermediate care. *Beds* SNF 256; ICF. *Certified* Medicaid.
Owner Nonprofit Corp.
Admissions Requirements Minimum age 18; Medical examination.
Staff RNs 15 (ft), 3 (pt); LPNs 8 (ft), 7 (pt); Nurses aides 78 (ft), 311 (pt); Occupational therapists 1 (ft); Activities coordinators 4 (ft), 1 (pt); Dietitians 1 (ft).
Languages Polish
Affiliation Roman Catholic
Facilities Dining room; Physical therapy room; Activities room; Chapel; Crafts room; Laundry room; Barber/Beauty shop; Library; Swimming pool; Bowling alley; Wine cove; Coffee shop.

Activities Arts & crafts; Cards; Games; Reading groups; Prayer groups; Movies; Shopping trips; Social/Cultural gatherings.

Shady Lane Home Inc
1235 S 24th St, Manitowoc, WI, 54220
(414) 682-8254
Admin James E Mueller. *Medical Dir/Dir of Nursing* Dr Mary Govier; Karen Komoroski RN DON.
Licensure Skilled care. *Beds* 168. *Certified* Medicaid.
Owner Nonprofit Corp.
Admissions Requirements Minimum age 62 unless Board approval given; Medical examination; Physician's request.
Staff RNs 3 (ft), 3 (pt); LPNs 3 (ft), 11 (pt); Nurses aides 20 (ft), 27 (pt); Activities coordinators 1 (ft), 3 (pt).
Facilities Dining room; Physical therapy room; Activities room; Chapel; Crafts room; Laundry room; Barber/Beauty shop; Library; Snack shop.
Activities Arts & crafts; Cards; Games; Reading groups; Prayer groups; Movies; Shopping trips; Social/Cultural gatherings.

MARINETTE

Luther Home
831 Pine Beach Rd, Marinette, WI, 54143
(715) 732-0155
Admin Rev Kenneth Michaelis. *Medical Dir/Dir of Nursing* Lydia Taylor DON.
Licensure Skilled care; Intermediate care. *Beds* 161. *Certified* Medicaid.
Owner Nonprofit Corp.
Admissions Requirements Minimum age 18; Medical examination; Physician's request.
Affiliation Lutheran
Facilities Dining room; Physical therapy room; Activities room; Chapel; Crafts room; Laundry room; Barber/Beauty shop.
Activities Arts & crafts; Cards; Games; Reading groups; Prayer groups; Movies; Shopping trips; Social/Cultural gatherings.

MARKESAN

Riverdale Manor*
150 S Bridge St, Markesan, WI, 53946
(414) 398-2751
Admin James A Effenheim.
Licensure Skilled care; Intermediate care. *Beds* 72. *Certified* Medicaid.
Owner Nonprofit Corp.

MARSHFIELD

Marshfield Living Center
814 W 14th St, Marshfield, WI, 54449
(715) 387-1188
Admin David L Green. *Medical Dir/Dir of Nursing* Scott Erickson MD; Beverly Kermitz RN.
Licensure Skilled care; Intermediate care. *Beds* 206. *Certified* Medicaid; Medicare.
Owner Nonprofit Corp (Adventist Health Sys-USAW).
Admissions Requirements Medical examination; Physician's request.
Staff Physicians 2 (pt); RNs 17 (ft), 5 (pt); LPNs 8 (ft), 8 (pt); Orderlies 5 (ft), 1 (pt); Nurses aides 61 (ft), 54 (pt); Physical therapists 1 (ft); Occupational therapists 1 (pt); Speech therapists 1 (pt); Activities coordinators 1 (ft); Dietitians 1 (ft); Ophthalmologists 1 (pt).
Affiliation Seventh-Day Adventist
Facilities Dining room; Physical therapy room; Activities room; Chapel; Crafts room; Laundry room; Barber/Beauty shop; Library.
Activities Arts & crafts; Cards; Games; Reading groups; Prayer groups; Movies; Shopping trips; Social/Cultural gatherings; Outside meetings; Softball tournaments.

Norwood Health Center*
1600 N Chestnut, Marshfield, WI, 54449
(715) 384-2188
Admin Kurt Baker. *Medical Dir/Dir of Nursing* George Pagels MD.
Licensure Skilled care; Intermediate care. *Beds* 66. *Certified* Medicaid.
Owner Publicly owned.
Admissions Requirements Minimum age 18; Medical examination; Physician's request.
Staff Physicians 9 (pt); RNs 10 (ft), 5 (pt); LPNs 2 (ft), 1 (pt); Orderlies 55 (ft), 20 (pt); Nurses aides 60 (ft), 25 (pt); Recreational therapists 1 (pt); Occupational therapists 2 (ft); Speech therapists 1 (ft); Activities coordinators 3 (ft); Dietitians 1 (ft); Dentists 1 (ft); Ophthalmologists 1 (ft); Podiatrists 1 (ft); Audiologists 1 (ft).
Facilities Dining room; Activities room; Crafts room; Laundry room; Barber/Beauty shop; Library.
Activities Arts & crafts; Cards; Games; Reading groups; Prayer groups; Movies; Shopping trips; Social/Cultural gatherings.

MAUSTON

Fair View Home*
1050 Division St, Mauston, WI, 53948
(608) 847-6161
Admin Daniel L Manders. *Medical Dir/Dir of Nursing* Dr E Heaney.
Licensure Skilled care; Intermediate care. *Beds* 60. *Certified* Medicaid.
Owner Nonprofit Corp.
Admissions Requirements Medical examination; Physician's request.
Staff Physicians 9 (ft); RNs 9 (ft); LPNs 3 (pt); Nurses aides 10 (ft), 31 (pt); Physical therapists 2 (ft); Recreational therapists 2 (pt); Occupational therapists 1 (pt); Dietitians 1 (ft).
Facilities Dining room; Physical therapy room; Activities room; Barber/Beauty shop.
Activities Arts & crafts; Cards; Games; Reading groups; Prayer groups; Movies; Shopping trips; Social/Cultural gatherings.

MEDFORD

Memorial Nursing Home Long-Term Care Unit*
135 S Gibson St, Medford, WI, 54451
(715) 748-2600
Admin Eugene W Arnett.
Licensure Skilled care; Intermediate care. *Beds* 104. *Certified* Medicaid.
Owner Nonprofit Corp.
Staff RNs 4 (ft), 5 (pt); LPNs 3 (ft), 5 (pt); Nurses aides 32 (ft), 4 (pt); Physical therapists 2 (pt); Occupational therapists 1 (pt); Activities coordinators 3 (ft); Dietitians 1 (pt).
Facilities Dining room; Physical therapy room; Activities room; Chapel; Crafts room; Laundry room; Barber/Beauty shop.
Activities Arts & crafts; Cards; Games; Reading groups; Prayer groups; Movies; Shopping trips; Social/Cultural gatherings.

MENASHA

Oakridge Gardens Nursing Center Inc
1700 Midway Rd, Menasha, WI, 54952
(414) 739-0111
Admin Michael T Schanke. *Medical Dir/Dir of Nursing* G R Mich MD; Vivian A Schutte RN DON.
Licensure Skilled care; Intermediate care. *Beds* 111. *Certified* Medicaid.
Owner Privately owned.
Staff RNs 3 (ft), 4 (pt); LPNs 2 (ft), 10 (pt); Nurses aides 9 (ft), 35 (pt); Activities coordinators 1 (ft), 2 (pt).

Facilities Dining room; Physical therapy room; Activities room; Crafts room; Laundry room; Barber/Beauty shop.
Activities Arts & crafts; Games; Prayer groups; Movies; Shopping trips; Bingo; Exercises.

MENOMONEE FALLS

Menomonee Falls Nursing Home*
N84 W17049 Menomonee Ave, Menomonee Falls, WI, 53051
(414) 255-1180
Admin Ernest Winkelman.
Licensure Skilled care; Intermediate care. *Beds* 106. *Certified* Medicaid.
Owner Proprietary Corp.

MENOMONIE

American Lutheran Home—Menomonie Unit
915 Elm Ave, Menomonie, WI, 54751
(715) 235-9041
Admin LaNette Flunker. *Medical Dir/Dir of Nursing* Dr William Wright; Margaret Kinderman.
Licensure Skilled care. *Beds* 60. *Certified* Medicaid.
Owner Nonprofit Corp.
Staff RNs 3 (ft), 2 (pt); LPNs 4 (ft), 1 (pt); Nurses aides 10 (ft), 22 (pt); Activities coordinators 1 (ft); Dietitians 1 (ft).
Affiliation Lutheran
Facilities Dining room; Activities room; Chapel; Laundry room; Barber/Beauty shop.
Activities Cards; Games; Reading groups; Prayer groups; Movies; Shopping trips.

Dunn County Health Care Center
Rte 2, PO Box 150, Menomonie, WI, 54751
(715) 232-2661
Admin Gregory M Roberts.
Licensure Skilled care. *Beds* SNF 251. *Certified* Medicaid.
Owner Publicly owned.
Admissions Requirements Physician's request.
Staff Physicians; RNs; LPNs; Orderlies; Nurses aides; Physical therapists; Reality therapists; Recreational therapists; Occupational therapists; Speech therapists; Activities coordinators; Dietitians.
Facilities Dining room; Physical therapy room; Activities room; Chapel; Crafts room; Laundry room; Barber/Beauty shop; Greenhouse.
Activities Arts & crafts; Cards; Games; Reading groups; Prayer groups; Movies; Shopping trips; Social/Cultural gatherings.

MEQUON

Mequon Care Center Inc
10911 N Port Washington Rd, Mequon, WI, 53092
(414) 241-3950
Admin Richard J Rau; Mary T Zak. *Medical Dir/Dir of Nursing* Russell Robertson MD; Doris Kingman RN DON.
Licensure Skilled care. *Beds* SNF 213. *Certified* Medicaid; Medicare.
Owner Proprietary Corp.
Admissions Requirements Minimum age 18; Medical examination; Physician's request.
Staff RNs 12 (ft), 18 (pt); LPNs 15 (ft), 16 (pt); Nurses aides 70 (ft), 63 (pt); Physical therapists 1 (ft), 1 (pt); Activities coordinators 1 (ft); Dietitians 1 (pt).
Languages German
Facilities Dining room; Physical therapy room; Activities room; Crafts room; Laundry room; Barber/Beauty shop; Library; Private room for family visits.
Activities Arts & crafts; Cards; Games; Reading groups; Prayer groups; Movies; Social/Cultural gatherings; Music & art therapy; La Restaurante.

MERRILL

Pine Crest Nursing Home
2100 E 6th St, Merrill, WI, 54452
(715) 536-0355
Admin Elaine A Roskos. *Medical Dir/Dir of Nursing* Dr Roxana Saeger; Evelyn Sommi RN DON.
Licensure Skilled care; Intermediate care. *Beds* 180. *Certified* Medicaid; Medicare.
Owner Publicly owned.
Admissions Requirements Minimum age 18; Medical examination; Physician's request.
Staff RNs 7 (ft), 12 (pt); LPNs 4 (ft), 6 (pt); Orderlies 1 (pt); Nurses aides 43 (ft), 50 (pt); Physical therapists 1 (pt); Recreational therapists 3 (ft); Occupational therapists 1 (pt); Speech therapists 1 (pt); Activities coordinators 1 (ft); Dietitians 1 (ft); Dentists 1 (pt); Podiatrists 1 (pt).
Facilities Dining room; Physical therapy room; Activities room; Chapel; Crafts room; Laundry room; Barber/Beauty shop; Library.
Activities Arts & crafts; Cards; Games; Reading groups; Prayer groups; Movies; Shopping trips; Social/Cultural gatherings.

MIDDLETON

Middleton Village
PO Box 321, 6201 Elmwood Ave, Middleton, WI, 53562
(608) 831-8300
Admin Robert A Gorder. *Medical Dir/Dir of Nursing* Joyce Crates.
Licensure Skilled care. *Beds* SNF 80. *Certified* Medicaid; Medicare.
Owner Proprietary Corp.
Admissions Requirements Minimum age 55; Medical examination.
Staff Physicians 1 (pt); RNs 3 (ft), 6 (pt); LPNs 3 (ft), 3 (pt); Nurses aides 15 (ft), 44 (pt); Activities coordinators 1 (ft); Dietitians 1 (ft).
Facilities Dining room; Physical therapy room; Activities room; Chapel; Crafts room; Laundry room; Barber/Beauty shop; Library; Lounges.
Activities Arts & crafts; Cards; Games; Reading groups; Prayer groups; Movies; Shopping trips; Social/Cultural gatherings.

MILWAUKEE

Alexian Village of Milwaukee Inc
7979 W Glenbrook Rd, Milwaukee, WI, 53223
(414) 355-9300
Admin Daniel C Krejci. *Medical Dir/Dir of Nursing* Norbert Bauch MD; Janet I Fine RN DON.
Licensure Skilled care. *Beds* SNF 61. *Certified* Medicaid.
Owner Nonprofit Corp (Alexian Bros Health Sys).
Admissions Requirements Minimum age 18.
Staff RNs 5 (ft), 4 (pt); LPNs 2 (ft), 9 (pt); Nurses aides 9 (ft), 21 (pt); Recreational therapists 1 (ft); Activities coordinators 1 (ft).
Affiliation Roman Catholic
Facilities Dining room; Physical therapy room; Activities room; Chapel; Crafts room; Laundry room; Barber/Beauty shop; Library; Country store; Bank; Pharmacy.
Activities Arts & crafts; Cards; Games; Reading groups; Prayer groups; Movies; Shopping trips; Social/Cultural gatherings.

AMS Green Tree Health Care Center*
6925 N Port Washington Rd, Milwaukee, WI, 53217
(414) 352-3300
Admin Nancy A O'Donnell. *Medical Dir/Dir of Nursing* Marshall Mirviss MD.
Licensure Skilled care; Intermediate care. *Beds* 403. *Certified* Medicaid; Medicare.

Owner Proprietary Corp.
Admissions Requirements Medical examination; Physician's request.
Staff Physicians 1 (pt); RNs 15 (ft), 15 (pt); LPNs 19 (ft), 18 (pt); Nurses aides 81 (ft), 43 (pt); Physical therapists 2 (ft); Recreational therapists 6 (ft), 3 (pt); Occupational therapists 4 (ft); Speech therapists 1 (pt); Dietitians 1 (ft).
Facilities Dining room; Physical therapy room; Activities room; Chapel; Crafts room; Laundry room; Barber/Beauty shop; Library; Snack shop; Occupational therapy room.
Activities Arts & crafts; Cards; Games; Reading groups; Prayer groups; Movies; Shopping trips; Social/Cultural gatherings.

Bel Air Health Care Center Inc*
9350 W Fond Du Lac, Milwaukee, WI, 53225
(414) 464-2240
Admin Gene R Schwarze.
Licensure Skilled care; Intermediate care. *Beds* 310. *Certified* Medicaid.
Owner Proprietary Corp.

Bluemound Manor Nursing Home
6526 W Bluemound Rd, Milwaukee, WI, 53213
(414) 774-4290
Admin Lynn Vogt. *Medical Dir/Dir of Nursing* Dr A Moonilal Singh; Karen Forseth DON.
Licensure Skilled care; Intermediate care. *Beds* SNF 35; ICF. *Certified* Medicaid.
Owner Proprietary Corp.
Admissions Requirements Medical examination; Physician's request.
Staff Physicians 1 (pt); RNs 1 (ft), 3 (pt); LPNs 6 (pt); Nurses aides 8 (ft), 9 (pt); Recreational therapists 1 (ft); Occupational therapists 2 (pt); Activities coordinators 1 (pt); Dietitians 1 (pt); Dentists 1 (pt); Ophthalmologists 1 (pt).
Facilities Dining room; Activities room; Crafts room; Laundry room.
Activities Arts & crafts; Cards; Games; Reading groups; Prayer groups; Movies; Shopping trips; Social/Cultural gatherings.

Bradley Convalescent Center*
6735 W Bradley Rd, Milwaukee, WI, 53223
(414) 354-3300
Admin Michael R Zimmerman.
Licensure Skilled care; Intermediate care. *Beds* 270. *Certified* Medicaid; Medicare.
Owner Proprietary Corp (Beverly Enterprises).

Cameo Convalescent Center*
5790 S 27th St, Milwaukee, WI, 53221
(414) 282-1300
Admin Borislav Kresovic.
Licensure Skilled care; Intermediate care. *Beds* 112. *Certified* Medicaid.
Owner Proprietary Corp.

Comstock Nursing Home*
3025 W Mitchell, Milwaukee, WI, 53215
(414) 384-8550
Admin Raymond J Herrmann. *Medical Dir/Dir of Nursing* John Palese MD.
Licensure Skilled care; Intermediate care. *Beds* 70. *Certified* Medicaid.
Owner Proprietary Corp.
Admissions Requirements Minimum age 21; Medical examination.
Staff Physicians 4 (pt); RNs 3 (ft); LPNs 3 (ft), 6 (pt); Orderlies 2 (pt); Nurses aides 8 (ft), 19 (pt); Physical therapists 1 (pt); Occupational therapists 1 (pt); Speech therapists 1 (pt); Activities coordinators 3 (pt); Dietitians 1 (pt); Dentists 1 (pt); Podiatrists 1 (pt).
Facilities Dining room; Physical therapy room; Activities room; Crafts room; Laundry room; Barber/Beauty shop.
Activities Arts & crafts; Cards; Games; Prayer groups; Movies; Shopping trips; Social/Cultural gatherings.

De Paul Belleview Extended Care
1904 E Belleview Pl, Milwaukee, WI, 53211
(414) 964-8200
Admin John E Stager. *Medical Dir/Dir of Nursing* William McDaniel MD; Lucy Motley RN DON.
Licensure Skilled care; Intermediate care. *Beds* 95. *Certified* Medicaid.
Owner Nonprofit Corp.
Admissions Requirements Minimum age 18; Medical examination.
Staff Physicians 3 (pt); RNs 7 (ft), 6 (pt); LPNs 6 (ft), 8 (pt); Orderlies 8 (ft), 1 (pt); Nurses aides 7 (ft), 18 (pt); Physical therapists 2 (pt); Recreational therapists 2 (ft), 1 (pt); Occupational therapists 5 (ft); Speech therapists 1 (pt); Activities coordinators 1 (ft); Dietitians 1 (ft); Dentists 1 (pt); Ophthalmologists 1 (pt); Podiatrists 1 (pt); Counselors & social workers 11 (ft).
Facilities Dining room; Physical therapy room; Activities room; Chapel; Crafts room; Laundry room; Barber/Beauty shop; Library; Meeting rooms.
Activities Arts & crafts; Cards; Games; Reading groups; Prayer groups; Movies; Shopping trips; Social/Cultural gatherings; Community outings; Trips; AA; NA; OA; Support groups.

Family Nursing Home & Rehabilitation Center
2801 W Wisconsin Ave, Milwaukee, WI, 53208
(414) 937-8700
Admin Wayne Brow. *Medical Dir/Dir of Nursing* David Fischer.
Licensure Skilled care. *Beds* 174. *Certified* Medicaid; Medicare.
Owner Proprietary Corp.
Admissions Requirements Minimum age 18; Medical examination; Physician's request.
Staff Physicians 25 (pt); RNs 6 (ft), 3 (pt); LPNs 15 (ft), 6 (pt); Orderlies 7 (ft), 3 (pt); Nurses aides 20 (ft), 30 (pt); Physical therapists 1 (ft); Recreational therapists 1 (ft); Occupational therapists 1 (ft); Speech therapists 1 (ft); Activities coordinators 1 (ft); Dietitians 1 (pt); Dentists 1 (pt); Ophthalmologists 1 (pt).
Facilities Dining room; Physical therapy room; Activities room; Crafts room; Laundry room; Barber/Beauty shop; Library.
Activities Arts & crafts; Cards; Games; Reading groups; Prayer groups; Movies; Shopping trips; Social/Cultural gatherings.

Friendship Village of Greater Milwaukee Inc
7300 W Dean Rd, Milwaukee, WI, 53223
(414) 354-3700
Admin Paul W Leighton. *Medical Dir/Dir of Nursing* June Shilts.
Licensure Skilled care; Intermediate care. *Beds* SNF 67; ICF 22; 325.
Owner Nonprofit Corp.
Admissions Requirements Minimum age 62; Medical examination; Physician's request.
Staff Physicians 1 (pt); RNs 3 (ft), 6 (pt); LPNs 9 (ft), 1 (pt); Orderlies 1 (pt); Nurses aides 25 (ft), 9 (pt); Recreational therapists 1 (ft), 1 (pt); Activities coordinators 1 (ft); Dietitians 1 (pt); Ophthalmologists 1 (pt).
Facilities Dining room; Physical therapy room; Activities room; Chapel; Crafts room; Laundry room; Barber/Beauty shop; Library.
Activities Arts & crafts; Cards; Games; Reading groups; Prayer groups; Movies; Shopping trips; Social/Cultural gatherings; Field trips.

Glen Field Health Care Center*
1633 W Bender Rd, Milwaukee, WI, 53209
(414) 228-9440
Admin Thomas D Pollock.
Licensure Skilled care; Intermediate care. *Beds* 260. *Certified* Medicaid; Medicare.
Owner Proprietary Corp (Beverly Enterprises).

Heartland of Milwaukee
3216 W Highland Blvd, Milwaukee, WI, 53208
(414) 344-6515
Admin Betsy J Larsen. *Medical Dir/Dir of Nursing* Jean Neitzke.
Licensure Skilled care; Intermediate care. *Beds* 150. *Certified* Medicaid; Medicare.
Owner Proprietary Corp (Health Care & Retirement Corp).
Admissions Requirements Minimum age 18; Medical examination; Physician's request.
Staff Physicians 1 (pt); RNs 12 (ft), 4 (pt); LPNs 6 (ft), 15 (pt); Orderlies 1 (ft); Nurses aides 36 (ft), 84 (pt); Physical therapists 1 (pt); Recreational therapists 1 (ft), 2 (pt); Occupational therapists 1 (pt); Speech therapists 1 (pt); Activities coordinators 1 (ft); Dietitians 1 (pt).
Facilities Dining room; Physical therapy room; Activities room; Chapel; Crafts room; Laundry room; Barber/Beauty shop.
Activities Arts & crafts; Cards; Games; Reading groups; Prayer groups; Movies; Shopping trips; Social/Cultural gatherings.

Hillcrest Convalescent Home*
3281 N 15th St, Milwaukee, WI, 53206
(414) 264-2720
Admin Thelma Henderson.
Licensure Skilled care; Intermediate care. *Beds* 50. *Certified* Medicaid.
Owner Proprietary Corp.

Hillside Health Care Center, Inc
8726 W Mill Rd, Milwaukee, WI, 53225
(414) 353-4100
Admin Mary Lueck. *Medical Dir/Dir of Nursing* Nicholas C De Leo MD; Mrs. Pat Fuller RN DON.
Licensure Skilled care. *Beds* 39. *Certified* Medicaid.
Owner Proprietary Corp.
Admissions Requirements Minimum age 50; Medical examination; Physician's request.
Staff RNs 1 (ft), 1 (pt); LPNs 3 (ft), 3 (pt); Nurses aides 10 (ft), 10 (pt); Physical therapists; Recreational therapists 1 (ft); Occupational therapists; Speech therapists; Activities coordinators 1 (ft); Dietitians 1 (pt); Dentists.
Facilities Dining room; Physical therapy room; Activities room; Chapel; Laundry room; Barber/Beauty shop.
Activities Arts & crafts; Cards; Games; Reading groups; Prayer groups; Movies; Shopping trips; Social/Cultural gatherings.

Hillview Care Center
1615 S 22nd St, Milwaukee, WI, 53204
(414) 671-6830
Admin Gail Wolf. *Medical Dir/Dir of Nursing* Dr Randle Pollard; Ms Walker DON.
Licensure Skilled care. *Beds* SNF 114. *Certified* Medicaid.
Owner Proprietary Corp.
Admissions Requirements Minimum age 45.
Facilities Dining room; Physical therapy room; Activities room; Barber/Beauty shop.
Activities Arts & crafts; Cards; Games; Reading groups; Prayer groups; Movies; Shopping trips; Social/Cultural gatherings.

Jackson Center
1840 N 6th St, Milwaukee, WI, 53212
(414) 263-1933
Admin Joann Harris-Adams. *Medical Dir/Dir of Nursing* Dr Simplico Go; Jeff Tushaus.
Licensure Intermediate care for mentally retarded. *Beds* 125. *Certified* Medicaid.
Owner Proprietary Corp (Unicare).
Admissions Requirements Minimum age 18.
Staff Physicians 2 (pt); RNs 4 (ft), 2 (pt); LPNs 3 (ft), 8 (pt); Nurses aides 18 (ft), 21 (pt); Physical therapists 2 (pt); Recreational therapists 2 (ft), 4 (pt); Occupational

therapists 3 (pt); Speech therapists 4 (pt); Dietitians 1 (ft); Dentists 1 (pt); Ophthalmologists 1 (pt); Podiatrists 1 (pt).
Facilities Dining room; Physical therapy room; Laundry room.
Activities Arts & crafts; Cards; Games; Movies; Shopping trips; Social/Cultural gatherings.

Kilbourn Care Center Inc*
2125 W Kilbourn Ave, Milwaukee, WI, 53233
(414) 342-1312
Admin Sharron Berman. *Medical Dir/Dir of Nursing* Dr Mankiewicz.
Licensure Skilled care; Intermediate care. *Beds* 98. *Certified* Medicaid.
Owner Nonprofit Corp.
Admissions Requirements Medical examination.
Staff Physicians 8 (pt); RNs 3 (ft), 5 (pt); LPNs 6 (ft), 10 (pt); Orderlies 4 (ft), 1 (pt); Nurses aides 12 (ft), 16 (pt); Physical therapists 2 (pt); Recreational therapists 1 (ft), 2 (pt); Occupational therapists 1 (pt); Speech therapists 1 (pt); Dietitians 1 (ft); Dentists 1 (pt); Ophthalmologists 1 (pt).
Facilities Dining room; Physical therapy room; Activities room; Crafts room; Barber/Beauty shop.
Activities Arts & crafts; Cards; Games; Reading groups; Prayer groups; Movies; Shopping trips; Social/Cultural gatherings.

Lakewood Care Center
2115 E Woodstock Pl, Milwaukee, WI, 53202
(414) 271-1020
Admin Robert Gordon. *Medical Dir/Dir of Nursing* Dr Lillich.
Licensure Skilled care; Intermediate care. *Beds* 246. *Certified* Medicaid.
Owner Proprietary Corp (Beverly Enterprises).
Admissions Requirements Medical examination; Physician's request.
Staff RNs 15 (ft), 5 (pt); LPNs 36 (ft), 4 (pt); Nurses aides 87 (ft), 8 (pt); Recreational therapists 3 (ft); Activities coordinators 1 (ft); Dietitians 1 (ft).
Facilities Dining room; Physical therapy room; Activities room; Chapel; Barber/Beauty shop; Occupational Therapy; Speech Therapy.
Activities Arts & crafts; Cards; Games; Reading groups; Prayer groups; Movies; Shopping trips; Social/Cultural gatherings; Resident council; Family council.

Luther Manor*
4545 N 92nd St, Milwaukee, WI, 53225
(414) 464-3880
Admin Peter E Chang.
Licensure Skilled care; Intermediate care. *Beds* 201. *Certified* Medicaid; Medicare.
Owner Nonprofit Corp.
Affiliation Lutheran

Marian Catholic Home*
3333 W Highland Blvd, Milwaukee, WI, 53208
(414) 344-8100
Admin Merle H McDonald Jr.
Licensure Skilled care; Intermediate care. *Beds* 360. *Certified* Medicaid.
Owner Nonprofit Corp.
Affiliation Roman Catholic

Marian Franciscan Home
9632 W Appleton Ave, Milwaukee, WI, 53225
(414) 461-8850
Admin J Thomas Duncan. *Medical Dir/Dir of Nursing* Ruth N Springob RN.
Licensure Skilled care. *Beds* 465. *Certified* Medicaid.
Owner Nonprofit Corp.
Admissions Requirements Minimum age 18.
Affiliation Roman Catholic
Facilities Dining room; Physical therapy room; Activities room; Crafts room; Laundry room; Barber/Beauty shop.

Marina View Manor
1522 N Prospect Ave, Milwaukee, WI, 53202
(414) 273-4890
Admin Gail L Wolf. *Medical Dir/Dir of Nursing* Dr M Lauwasser; Barbara Schmitz RN DON.
Licensure Skilled care; Intermediate care. *Beds* SNF 357; ICF. *Certified* Medicaid; Medicare.
Owner Proprietary Corp (Health Care & Retire Corp).
Admissions Requirements Minimum age Adults.
Languages Polish, German, Spanish
Facilities Dining room; Physical therapy room; Activities room; Chapel; Crafts room; Laundry room; Barber/Beauty shop; Library.
Activities Arts & crafts; Cards; Games; Reading groups; Prayer groups; Movies; Shopping trips; Social/Cultural gatherings.

Mercy Residential & Rehabilitation Center
2727 W Mitchell St, Milwaukee, WI, 53215
(414) 383-3699
Admin Sandra K Maiers MSW, NHA. *Medical Dir/Dir of Nursing* Marilyn Venturi BSN.
Licensure Skilled care. *Beds* SNF 60.
Owner Proprietary Corp (Unicare).
Staff Physicians; RNs; LPNs; Orderlies; Nurses aides; Physical therapists; Occupational therapists; Speech therapists; Activities coordinators; Dietitians.
Facilities Dining room; Physical therapy room; Activities room; Crafts room; Laundry room; Barber/Beauty shop.
Activities Arts & crafts; Cards; Games; Reading groups; Prayer groups; Movies; Shopping trips; Social/Cultural gatherings.

Millway Nursing Home*
8534 W Mill Rd, Milwaukee, WI, 53225
(414) 353-2300
Admin Peter S Zlotocha.
Licensure Skilled care; Intermediate care. *Beds* 105. *Certified* Medicaid.
Owner Proprietary Corp.

Milwaukee Catholic Home*
2462 N Prospect Ave, Milwaukee, WI, 53211
(414) 224-9700
Admin Thomas A Schmit.
Licensure Skilled care; Intermediate care. *Beds* 44. *Certified* Medicaid.
Owner Nonprofit Corp.
Affiliation Roman Catholic

Milwaukee Jewish Convalescent Center
5151 W Silver Spring Dr, Milwaukee, WI, 53218
(414) 464-2300
Admin Benjamin E Lane. *Medical Dir/Dir of Nursing* Sanford Mallin; Madonna Booher.
Licensure Skilled care; Intermediate care. *Beds* 48. *Certified* Medicaid; Medicare.
Owner Nonprofit Corp.
Admissions Requirements Medical examination.
Staff Physicians 3 (pt); RNs 3 (ft); LPNs 3 (ft), 3 (pt); Nurses aides 12 (ft), 4 (pt); Physical therapists 2 (pt); Reality therapists 1 (pt); Recreational therapists 2 (ft), 5 (pt); Occupational therapists 1 (pt); Dietitians 1 (pt).
Languages Yiddish, Hebrew
Affiliation Jewish
Facilities Dining room; Physical therapy room; Activities room; Chapel; Crafts room; Barber/Beauty shop; Library.
Activities Arts & crafts; Cards; Games; Reading groups; Prayer groups; Movies; Shopping trips; Social/Cultural gatherings.

Milwaukee Jewish Home
1414 N Prospect Ave, Milwaukee, WI, 53202-3089
(414) 276-2627

Admin Nita L Corre. *Medical Dir/Dir of Nursing* Richard Kane MD; Walter Vine DON.
Licensure Skilled care. *Beds* SNF 208. *Certified* Medicaid; Medicare.
Owner Nonprofit Corp.
Admissions Requirements Medical examination.
Staff Physicians 1 (pt); RNs 17 (ft), 3 (pt); LPNs 12 (ft), 4 (pt); Orderlies 16 (ft), 6 (pt); Nurses aides 54 (ft), 35 (pt); Physical therapists 1 (ft); Occupational therapists 1 (pt); Activities coordinators 1 (ft); Dietitians 1 (ft); Physical therapist asst 1 (ft).
Languages Yiddish, Hebrew
Affiliation Jewish
Facilities Dining room; Physical therapy room; Activities room; Chapel; Crafts room; Barber/Beauty shop; Library; Soda shop; Gift shop.
Activities Arts & crafts; Cards; Games; Reading groups; Prayer groups; Movies; Shopping trips; Social/Cultural gatherings; Sheltered workshop.

Milwaukee Protestant Bradford Terrace*
2429 E Bradford Ave, Milwaukee, WI, 53211
(414) 332-8610
Admin James G Lehmkuhl.
Licensure Skilled care. *Beds* 50. *Certified* Medicare.
Owner Nonprofit Corp.

Milwaukee Protestant Home Infirmary*
2449 N Downer Ave, Milwaukee, WI, 53211
(414) 332-8610
Admin James G Luhmkuhl.
Licensure Skilled care. *Beds* 47.
Owner Nonprofit Corp.

Mt Carmel Health Care Center*
5700 W Layton Ave, Milwaukee, WI, 53220
(414) 281-7200
Admin Richard J Lesjak.
Licensure Skilled care; Intermediate care. *Beds* 666. *Certified* Medicaid.
Owner Proprietary Corp (Hillhaven Corp).

North Shore Health Care Center
601 W Glencoe Pl, Milwaukee, WI, 53217
(414) 351-3830
Admin Nicholas J Braumonte. *Medical Dir/Dir of Nursing* Dr A Cornfield.
Licensure Skilled care; Intermediate care. *Beds* SNF; ICF 282. *Certified* Medicaid.
Owner Proprietary Corp (Beverly Enterprises).
Admissions Requirements Medical examination; Physician's request.
Staff RNs 6 (ft), 2 (pt); LPNs 21 (ft), 8 (pt); Orderlies 4 (ft), 2 (pt); Nurses aides 62 (ft), 17 (pt); Physical therapists 1 (pt); Occupational therapists 2 (ft); Speech therapists 1 (pt); Activities coordinators 1 (ft); Dietitians 1 (ft).
Facilities Dining room; Physical therapy room; Activities room; Crafts room; Laundry room; Barber/Beauty shop.
Activities Arts & crafts; Cards; Games; Reading groups; Prayer groups; Movies; Shopping trips; Social/Cultural gatherings.

Northwest Health Center
7800 W Fond Du Lac Ave, Milwaukee, WI, 53218
(414) 464-3950
Admin Judy Riley. *Medical Dir/Dir of Nursing* Dr Michael Fehrer.
Licensure Skilled care; Intermediate care. *Beds* SNF 118; ICF. *Certified* Medicaid; Medicare.
Owner Proprietary Corp (American Medical Services Inc).
Admissions Requirements Minimum age 18; Medical examination.
Staff Physicians 1 (ft), 10 (pt); RNs 3 (ft), 8 (pt); LPNs 4 (ft), 9 (pt); Orderlies; Nurses aides 10 (ft), 49 (pt); Physical therapists 1 (pt); Recreational therapists 2 (ft), 1 (pt);

Occupational therapists 1 (pt); Speech therapists 1 (pt); Dietitians 1 (ft); Dentists 1 (pt); Ophthalmologists 1 (pt); Podiatrists 1 (pt); Dentist 1 (pt).
Facilities Dining room; Physical therapy room; Activities room; Chapel; Crafts room; Laundry room; Barber/Beauty shop; Library; Lounges.
Activities Arts & crafts; Cards; Games; Reading groups; Prayer groups; Movies; Shopping trips; Social/Cultural gatherings.

Oakland Manor*
3710 N Oakland Dr, Milwaukee, WI, 53211
(414) 964-6200
Admin Candace Lagerfeldt.
Licensure Skilled care; Intermediate care. *Beds* 288. *Certified* Medicaid; Medicare.
Owner Proprietary Corp.

Park Manor Health Care Center*
1824 E Park Pl, Milwaukee, WI, 53211
(414) 961-1115
Admin Dana E Bilder. *Medical Dir/Dir of Nursing* John Becker MD.
Licensure Skilled care; Intermediate care. *Beds* 118. *Certified* Medicaid; Medicare.
Owner Proprietary Corp (American Medical Services Inc).
Admissions Requirements Minimum age 18; Medical examination; Physician's request.
Staff Physicians 22 (pt); RNs 3 (ft), 7 (pt); LPNs 4 (ft), 7 (pt); Orderlies 5 (ft), 7 (pt); Nurses aides 9 (ft), 33 (pt); Physical therapists 3 (pt); Recreational therapists 1 (ft), 1 (pt); Occupational therapists 2 (pt); Speech therapists 1 (pt); Dietitians 1 (pt); Dentists 1 (pt); Podiatrists 1 (pt).
Facilities Dining room; Physical therapy room; Activities room; Chapel; Crafts room; Laundry room; Barber/Beauty shop; Library; Outdoor patio.
Activities Arts & crafts; Cards; Games; Reading groups; Prayer groups; Movies; Shopping trips; Social/Cultural gatherings; Music.

Parkview Care Center Inc
4615 W Hampton Ave, Milwaukee, WI, 53218
(414) 462-9590
Admin Thomas G Schanke. *Medical Dir/Dir of Nursing* Dr DeLeo; Marge Gozdowiak RN DON.
Licensure Skilled care; Intermediate care. *Beds* 74. *Certified* Medicaid.
Owner Proprietary Corp.
Staff RNs; LPNs; Nurses aides; Activities coordinators; Dietitians.
Facilities Dining room; Physical therapy room; Activities room; Laundry room; Barber/Beauty shop.
Activities Arts & crafts; Cards; Games; Prayer groups; Movies; Shopping trips; Social/Cultural gatherings.

Plymouth Manor Nursing
619 W Walnut St, Milwaukee, WI, 53212
(414) 263-1770
Admin I D Schug. *Medical Dir/Dir of Nursing* M R Sethi MD.
Licensure Skilled care; Intermediate care. *Beds* 166. *Certified* Medicaid.
Owner Proprietary Corp (Unicare).
Facilities Dining room; Physical therapy room; Activities room; Crafts room; Barber/Beauty shop; Occupational Therapy Room.
Activities Arts & crafts; Cards; Games; Reading groups; Prayer groups; Movies; Shopping trips; Social/Cultural gatherings; Afro-American Studies.

Regency Terrace South*
2919 W Parnell Ave, Milwaukee, WI, 53221
(414) 231-2810
Admin Norman F Stougaard.
Licensure Intermediate care. *Beds* 122. *Certified* Medicaid.
Owner Proprietary Corp.

River Hills East Health Care Center
1301 N Franklin Pl, Milwaukee, WI, 53202
(414) 273-3560
Admin Walter Bilski. *Medical Dir/Dir of Nursing* Richard Fritz MD.
Licensure Skilled care. *Beds* SNF 308. *Certified* Medicaid; Medicare.
Owner Proprietary Corp (American Medical Services Inc).
Admissions Requirements Minimum age 18; Medical examination; Physician's request.
Staff RNs 18 (ft), 7 (pt); LPNs 8 (ft); Orderlies 7 (ft), 3 (pt); Nurses aides 73 (ft), 28 (pt); Physical therapists 1 (ft); Recreational therapists 5 (ft), 1 (pt); Occupational therapists 2 (ft); Speech therapists 1 (ft); Dietitians 1 (ft).
Facilities Dining room; Physical therapy room; Activities room.
Activities Arts & crafts; Cards; Games; Reading groups; Prayer groups; Movies; Shopping trips; Social/Cultural gatherings.

River Hills Health Care Center—South
2730 W Ramsey, Milwaukee, WI, 53221
(414) 282-2600
Admin Judith N Stuver. *Medical Dir/Dir of Nursing* Dr Richard Kane; Betty Storm.
Licensure Skilled care; Intermediate care. *Beds* 196. *Certified* Medicaid; Medicare.
Owner Proprietary Corp (Southmark Heritage Corp).
Admissions Requirements Minimum age 18; Medical examination; Physician's request.
Staff Physicians 25 (pt); RNs 7 (ft), 7 (pt); LPNs 7 (ft), 17 (pt); Orderlies 5 (ft); Nurses aides 34 (ft), 37 (pt); Physical therapists 1 (ft), 1 (pt); Reality therapists 1 (pt); Recreational therapists 3 (ft), 1 (pt); Occupational therapists 1 (pt); Speech therapists 1 (pt); Activities coordinators 1 (ft); Dietitians 1 (pt); Dentists 1 (pt); Podiatrists 1 (pt); Audiologists 1 (pt).
Facilities Dining room; Physical therapy room; Activities room; Crafts room; Laundry room; Barber/Beauty shop.
Activities Arts & crafts; Cards; Games; Reading groups; Prayer groups; Movies; Shopping trips; Social/Cultural gatherings.

Roseville East
1825 N Prospect Ave, Milwaukee, WI, 53202
(414) 271-9160
Admin Julie A McKnight.
Licensure Skilled care; Intermediate care. *Beds* 122. *Certified* Medicaid; Medicare.
Owner Proprietary Corp.

Roseville Manor*
8526 W Mill Rd, Milwaukee, WI, 53225
(414) 358-1403
Admin David Beinlich.
Licensure Skilled care; Intermediate care. *Beds* 65. *Certified* Medicaid.
Owner Proprietary Corp.

Roseville Nursing Home*
6477 N 91st St, Milwaukee, WI, 53224
(414) 353-5780
Admin Nancy M Borkin.
Licensure Intermediate care for mentally retarded. *Beds* 16. *Certified* Medicaid.
Owner Proprietary Corp.

St Anne's Home for the Elderly*
3800 N 92nd St, Milwaukee, WI, 53222
(414) 463-7570
Admin Sr Cecilia Honigfort.
Licensure Skilled care; Intermediate care. *Beds* 156. *Certified* Medicaid.
Owner Nonprofit Corp (Little Sisters of the Poor).
Affiliation Roman Catholic

St Ann's Rest Home*
2020 S Muskego, Milwaukee, WI, 53204
(414) 383-2630
Admin Sr Lis M Columba.

Licensure Intermediate care. *Beds* 98.
Certified Medicaid.
Owner Nonprofit Corp.
Affiliation Roman Catholic

St John's Home of Milwaukee
1840 N Prospect Ave, Milwaukee, WI, 53202
(414) 272-2022
Admin Dennis M Gralinski. *Medical Dir/Dir
of Nursing* Parks LeTellier MD; Carol
Schrank RN DON.
Licensure Skilled care; Intermediate care;
Home health. *Beds* SNF; ICF 95. *Certified*
Medicaid; Medicare.
Owner Nonprofit Corp.
Admissions Requirements Minimum age 60;
Medical examination; Physician's request.
Staff Physicians 1 (ft), RNs 6 (ft), 2 (pt);
LPNs 5 (ft), 6 (pt); Orderlies 1 (ft); Nurses
aides 17 (ft), 30 (pt); Physical therapists 1
(ft); Occupational therapists 1 (ft), 2 (pt);
Activities coordinators 2 (ft); Dietitians 1
(pt); Podiatrists 1 (pt).
Affiliation Episcopal
Facilities Dining room; Physical therapy
room; Activities room; Chapel; Crafts room;
Laundry room; Barber/Beauty shop; Library;
Dental services.
Activities Arts & crafts; Cards; Games;
Reading groups; Prayer groups; Movies;
Shopping trips; Social/Cultural gatherings;
Service club; Special events.

St Marys Nursing Home
3516 W Center St, Milwaukee, WI, 53210
(414) 873-9250
Admin Michael R Zimmerman. *Medical Dir/
Dir of Nursing* Dr Eric Conradson;
Bernadetta Kolbeck MSN.
Licensure Skilled care. *Beds* 130. *Certified*
Medicaid.
Owner Nonprofit Corp.
Admissions Requirements Minimum age 18.
Staff RNs 4 (ft), 7 (pt); LPNs 8 (ft), 2 (pt);
Orderlies 1 (ft); Nurses aides 46 (ft), 24 (pt);
Physical therapists 1 (ft), 2 (pt); Recreational
therapists 2 (ft); Occupational therapists 1
(ft); Activities coordinators 1 (ft); Dietitians
1 (pt).
Affiliation Roman Catholic
Facilities Dining room; Physical therapy
room; Activities room; Chapel; Crafts room;
Laundry room; Barber/Beauty shop.
Activities Arts & crafts; Games; Reading
groups; Prayer groups; Movies; Social/
Cultural gatherings.

Silver Spring Convalescent Center*
1300 W Silver Spring Dr, Milwaukee, WI,
53209
(414) 228-8120
Admin Elaine Lukas.
Licensure Skilled care; Intermediate care. *Beds*
138. *Certified* Medicaid.
Owner Proprietary Corp (Beverly Enterprises).

Sunrise Nursing Home for the Blind Inc
827 N 34th St, Milwaukee, WI, 53208
(414) 933-6977
Admin Michael J Kern. *Medical Dir/Dir of
Nursing* Dr Raymond Moy; Fran Meyer RN
DON.
Licensure Skilled care; Intermediate care. *Beds*
SNF 99. *Certified* Medicaid.
Owner Nonprofit Corp.
Admissions Requirements Medical
examination; Physician's request.
Staff Physicians 4 (pt); RNs 5 (ft), 5 (pt);
LPNs 8 (ft), 2 (pt); Nurses aides 20 (ft), 10
(pt); Physical therapists 1 (pt); Occupational
therapists 1 (pt); Speech therapists 1 (pt);
Activities coordinators 1 (ft); Dietitians 3
(ft), 2 (pt).
Facilities Dining room; Physical therapy
room; Activities room; Chapel; Crafts room;
Laundry room; Barber/Beauty shop.

Activities Arts & crafts; Cards; Games;
Reading groups; Prayer groups; Movies;
Shopping trips; Social/Cultural gatherings.

Town & Country Manor*
9222 W Appleton, Milwaukee, WI, 53225
(414) 464-3050
Admin John R Werner.
Licensure Skilled care; Intermediate care. *Beds*
30. *Certified* Medicaid; Medicare.
Owner Proprietary Corp.

Westview Nursing Home*
3014 W McKinley, Milwaukee, WI, 53208
(414) 933-5217
Admin Joan M Langen. *Medical Dir/Dir of
Nursing* Dr Wiliam Kah.
Licensure Intermediate care. *Beds* 21.
Certified Medicaid.
Owner Proprietary Corp.
Admissions Requirements Minimum age 18;
Females only; Medical examination;
Physician's request.
Staff Physicians 2 (pt); RNs 1 (ft); LPNs 2
(pt); Nurses aides 4 (ft), 6 (pt); Recreational
therapists 1 (pt); Dietitians 1 (pt).
Facilities Dining room; Activities room;
Chapel; Crafts room; Laundry room.
Activities Arts & crafts; Cards; Games;
Reading groups; Prayer groups; Movies;
Shopping trips.

Wisconsin Lutheran Child & Family Service
PO Box 23980, 6800 N 76th St, Milwaukee,
WI, 53223
(414) 353-5000
Medical Dir/Dir of Nursing Marc Olsen MD.
Licensure Skilled care. *Beds* 161. *Certified*
Medicaid.
Owner Nonprofit Corp.
Admissions Requirements Medical
examination; Physician's request.
Staff Physicians 1 (pt); RNs 7 (ft), 11 (pt);
LPNs 2 (ft), 9 (pt); Orderlies 1 (ft), 4 (pt);
Nurses aides 35 (ft), 53 (pt); Physical
therapists 1 (pt); Occupational therapists 1
(pt); Speech therapists 1 (pt); Activities
coordinators 1 (ft); Dietitians 1 (pt).
Affiliation Lutheran
Facilities Dining room; Physical therapy
room; Activities room; Chapel; Crafts room;
Laundry room; Barber/Beauty shop.
Activities Arts & crafts; Cards; Games;
Reading groups; Prayer groups; Movies;
Shopping trips; Social/Cultural gatherings.

MINERAL POINT

Mineral Point Care Center*
109 N Iowa St, Mineral Point, WI, 53565
(608) 987-2381
Admin Virgil Strang.
Licensure Skilled care; Intermediate care. *Beds*
89. *Certified* Medicaid.
Owner Nonprofit Corp (Adventist Health Sys-
USA).

MONDOVI

American Lutheran Home—Mondovi Unit
158 E Main, Mondovi, WI, 54755
(715) 926-4962
Admin Shelia J Gibbs. *Medical Dir/Dir of
Nursing* Dr William Wright; Mary Jacobson
DON.
Licensure Skilled care. *Beds* SNF 55. *Certified*
Medicaid.
Owner Nonprofit organization/foundation.
Admissions Requirements Minimum age 18;
Medical examination; Physician's request.
Staff RNs 2 (ft), 2 (pt); LPNs 2 (ft), 1 (pt);
Nurses aides 12 (ft), 6 (pt); Recreational
therapists 1 (pt); Occupational therapists 1
(pt); Activities coordinators 1 (pt).
Affiliation Lutheran

Facilities Dining room; Physical therapy
room; Activities room; Chapel; Crafts room;
Laundry room; Barber/Beauty shop.
Activities Arts & crafts; Games; Reading
groups; Movies; Shopping trips.

Memorial Manor*
200 Memorial Dr, Mondovi, WI, 54755
(715) 926-4201
Admin Larry D Welsh.
Licensure Skilled care; Intermediate care. *Beds*
119. *Certified* Medicaid.
Owner Nonprofit Corp.

MONROE

Monroe Manor Nursing Home
516 26th Ave, Monroe, WI, 53566
(608) 325-9141
Admin Amanda Pas. *Medical Dir/Dir of
Nursing* Dr John Irvin; Kathy Ramsey.
Licensure Skilled care; Intermediate care. *Beds*
SNF 100; ICF. *Certified* Medicaid;
Medicare.
Owner Proprietary Corp (Unicare).
Admissions Requirements Minimum age 18;
Medical examination.
Staff RNs 6 (ft), 2 (pt); LPNs 2 (ft), 2 (pt);
Nurses aides 4 (ft), 36 (pt); Physical
therapists 1 (pt); Occupational therapists 1
(pt); Speech therapists 1 (pt); Activities
coordinators 1 (ft), 2 (pt); Dietitians 1 (ft);
Dentist 1 (pt).
Facilities Dining room; Physical therapy
room; Activities room; Chapel; Crafts room;
Laundry room; Barber/Beauty shop.
Activities Arts & crafts; Cards; Games;
Reading groups; Prayer groups; Movies;
Shopping trips; Social/Cultural gatherings.

Pleasant View Nursing Home
PO Box 768, Monroe, WI, 53566
(608) 325-2171
Admin Don Stoor. *Medical Dir/Dir of Nursing*
John Frantz MD.
Licensure Skilled care; Intermediate care. *Beds*
246. *Certified* Medicaid; Medicare.
Owner Publicly owned.
Admissions Requirements Medical
examination.
Staff RNs 8 (ft), 8 (pt); LPNs 6 (ft), 3 (pt);
Nurses aides 40 (ft), 70 (pt); Activities
coordinators 3 (ft), 1 (pt); Dietitians 1 (pt).
Facilities Dining room; Physical therapy
room; Activities room; Chapel; Crafts room;
Laundry room; Barber/Beauty shop; Library.
Activities Arts & crafts; Cards; Games;
Reading groups; Prayer groups; Movies;
Social/Cultural gatherings.

MONTELLO

Montello Care Center
PO Box 385, 251 Forest Ln, Montello, WI,
53949-9202
(608) 297-2153
Admin Ruth F Bornick. *Medical Dir/Dir of
Nursing* Dr Renato Baylon MD; Barbara
Holtz RN.
Licensure Skilled care; Intermediate care. *Beds*
62. *Certified* Medicaid.
Owner Proprietary Corp.
Admissions Requirements Medical
examination; Physician's request.
Staff RNs 2 (ft), 3 (pt); LPNs 2 (ft), 5 (pt);
Nurses aides 8 (ft), 22 (pt); Physical
therapists 1 (pt); Occupational therapists 1
(pt); Speech therapists 1 (pt); Activities
coordinators 1 (ft); Dietitians 1 (pt);
Podiatrists 1 (pt).
Facilities Dining room; Physical therapy
room; Activities room; Chapel; Crafts room;
Laundry room; Barber/Beauty shop; Library.
Activities Arts & crafts; Cards; Games;
Reading groups; Prayer groups; Movies;
Shopping trips; Social/Cultural gatherings.

MOUNT CALVARY

Villa Loretto Nursing Home
N8138 Calvary St, Mount Calvary, WI,
53057-9703
(414) 753-3211
Admin Sr Mary Rose Schulte. *Medical Dir/Dir
of Nursing* J A Strong MD; Sr Stephen
Bloesl RN DON.
Licensure Skilled care; Intermediate care. *Beds*
52. *Certified* Medicaid.
Owner Nonprofit Corp.
Admissions Requirements Minimum age 55;
Medical examination.
Staff RNs 1 (ft), 3 (pt); LPNs 1 (ft), 4 (pt);
Nurses aides 5 (ft), 18 (pt); Activities
coordinators 1 (ft), 2 (pt); Dietitians 1 (pt).
Facilities Dining room; Activities room;
Chapel; Crafts room; Laundry room; Barber/
Beauty shop; Outside patio; Garden; Petting
zoo.
Activities Arts & crafts; Cards; Games; Prayer
groups; Movies; Social/Cultural gatherings;
Bingo.

MOUNT HOREB

Ingleside
407 N 8th St, Mount Horeb, WI, 53572
(608) 437-5511
Admin Michael J Rock. *Medical Dir/Dir of
Nursing* Dr James Damos; Pat Stauss.
Licensure Skilled care; Assisted retirement
living center. *Beds* SNF 119; Assisted
retirement living center 20. *Certified* VA.
Admissions Requirements Medical
examination; Physician's request.
Staff RNs 5 (ft), 7 (pt); LPNs 3 (ft), 5 (pt);
Nurses aides 20 (ft), 44 (pt).
Facilities Dining room; Physical therapy
room; Activities room; Chapel; Crafts room;
Barber/Beauty shop.
Activities Arts & crafts; Cards; Games;
Reading groups; Prayer groups; Movies;
Shopping trips; Social/Cultural gatherings.

MUSCODA

Riverdale Manor
1000 N Wisconsin Ave, Muscoda, WI, 53573
(608) 739-3186
Admin Ronald L Bingham. *Medical Dir/Dir of
Nursing* Dale Sinnett MD; Rosaleen
Gibbons RN DON.
Licensure Skilled care; Intermediate care. *Beds*
SNF 80; ICF. *Certified* Medicaid; Medicare.
Owner Proprietary Corp (Beverly Enterprises).
Admissions Requirements Medical
examination; Physician's request.
Staff Physicians 3 (pt); RNs 3 (ft), 1 (pt);
LPNs 3 (ft), 2 (pt); Nurses aides 20 (ft), 20
(pt); Physical therapists 1 (pt); Reality
therapists 1 (pt); Recreational therapists 1
(ft), 1 (pt); Occupational therapists 1 (pt);
Speech therapists 1 (pt); Activities
coordinators 1 (ft); Dietitians 1 (pt);
Ophthalmologists 1 (pt).
Facilities Dining room; Physical therapy
room; Activities room; Chapel; Crafts room;
Laundry room; Barber/Beauty shop; Library.
Activities Arts & crafts; Cards; Games;
Reading groups; Prayer groups; Movies;
Shopping trips; Social/Cultural gatherings.

MUSKEGO

Muskego Nursing Home*
S77-W18690 Janesville Rd, Muskego, WI,
53150
(414) 679-0246
Admin Harold M Swanto Jr. *Medical Dir/Dir
of Nursing* Dr John Buhl.
Licensure Skilled care; Intermediate care. *Beds*
49. *Certified* Medicaid.

Owner Proprietary Corp.
Admissions Requirements Minimum age 18;
Medical examination; Physician's request.

Tudor Oaks Health Center
12929 McShane Drive, Muskego, WI, 53150
(414) 529-0100
Admin Earl J Hoagberg. *Medical Dir/Dir of
Nursing* Dr Scott Tilleson; Karen Boese.
Licensure Skilled care. *Beds* 61. *Certified*
Medicaid; Medicare.
Owner Nonprofit Corp.
Admissions Requirements Minimum age 18;
Medical examination; Physician's request.
Staff RNs 5 (ft), 6 (pt); LPNs 3 (ft), 6 (pt);
Nurses aides 15 (ft), 16 (pt); Physical
therapists 1 (pt); Recreational therapists 1
(ft); Occupational therapists 1 (pt); Dietitians
1 (ft).
Affiliation Baptist
Facilities Dining room; Physical therapy
room; Activities room; Chapel; Barber/
Beauty shop.
Activities Arts & crafts; Games; Reading
groups; Prayer groups; Movies; Shopping
trips; Animal visits; Pet therapy; Coffee
groups.

NEENAH

Vallhaven Care Center
125 Byrd Ave, Neenah, WI, 54956
(414) 725-2714
Admin Mary Sue Taylor. *Medical Dir/Dir of
Nursing* E Loftus MD; Rose Wendt RN
DON.
Licensure Skilled care. *Beds* 164. *Certified*
Medicaid.
Owner Proprietary Corp (Hillhaven Corp).
Admissions Requirements Minimum age 18.
Staff Physicians 1 (pt); RNs 8 (ft), 3 (pt);
LPNs 5 (ft), 9 (pt); Orderlies 3 (ft); Nurses
aides 24 (ft), 33 (pt); Physical therapists 1
(pt); Occupational therapists 1 (pt); Speech
therapists 1 (pt); Activities coordinators 2
(ft); Dietitians 1 (pt).
Facilities Dining room; Activities room;
Chapel; Crafts room; Laundry room; Barber/
Beauty shop; Library.
Activities Arts & crafts; Cards; Games;
Reading groups; Prayer groups; Movies;
Shopping trips; Social/Cultural gatherings;
Exercise.

NEILLSVILLE

Neillsville Memorial Home*
216 Sunset Pl, Neillsville, WI, 54456
(715) 743-3101
Admin Glen E Grady.
Licensure Skilled care; Intermediate care. *Beds*
176. *Certified* Medicaid.
Owner Nonprofit Corp.

NEW GLARUS

New Glarus Home Inc
700 2nd Ave, New Glarus, WI, 53574
(608) 527-2126
Admin Roger L Goepfert. *Medical Dir/Dir of
Nursing* Dr Aquino.
Licensure Skilled care; Intermediate care. *Beds*
96. *Certified* Medicaid.
Owner Nonprofit Corp.
Admissions Requirements Minimum age 65;
Medical examination; Physician's request.
Staff Physicians 5 (pt); RNs 1 (ft), 5 (pt);
LPNs 3 (ft), 4 (pt); Nurses aides 11 (ft), 21
(pt); Reality therapists 1 (pt); Recreational
therapists 3 (ft); Occupational therapists 1
(pt); Dietitians 1 (pt); Dentists 1 (pt).
Affiliation Church of Christ
Facilities Dining room; Physical therapy
room; Activities room; Chapel; Crafts room;
Laundry room; Barber/Beauty shop; Library.

Activities Arts & crafts; Cards; Games;
Reading groups; Prayer groups; Movies;
Shopping trips; Social/Cultural gatherings;
Entertainments.

NEW HOLSTEIN

Calumet Homestead
1712 Monroe St, New Holstein, WI, 53061
(414) 898-4296
Admin Nancy Steinke. *Medical Dir/Dir of
Nursing* Rosalie A Brocked RN.
Licensure Skilled care. *Beds* SNF 104.
Certified Medicaid.
Owner Publicly owned.
Admissions Requirements Medical
examination.
Staff Physicians.
Languages German
Facilities Dining room; Physical therapy
room; Activities room; Chapel; Crafts room;
Laundry room; Barber/Beauty shop.
Activities Arts & crafts; Cards; Prayer groups;
Movies; Social/Cultural gatherings; Exercise
class.

Willowdale Nursing Home*
1610 Hoover St, New Holstein, WI, 53061
(414) 898-5706
Admin Nola Feldkamp.
Licensure Intermediate care. *Beds* 51.
Certified Medicaid.
Owner Proprietary Corp (Unicare).

NEW LISBON

Pleasant Acres
W8741, County B, New Lisbon, WI, 53950
(608) 562-3667
Admin Herbert C Finger. *Medical Dir/Dir of
Nursing* Dr Tim Hinton.
Licensure Intermediate care. *Beds* ICF 70.
Certified Medicaid.
Owner Publicly owned.
Admissions Requirements Medical
examination; Physician's request.
Staff Physicians 1 (pt); RNs 2 (ft), 6 (pt);
LPNs 2 (ft), 2 (pt); Nurses aides 11 (ft), 17
(pt); Physical therapists 1 (pt); Occupational
therapists 1 (pt); Activities coordinators 2
(ft), 1 (pt); Dietitians 1 (ft);
Ophthalmologists 1 (pt); Dentist 1 (pt).
Facilities Dining room; Activities room;
Laundry room.
Activities Arts & crafts; Cards; Games;
Reading groups; Prayer groups; Movies;
Shopping trips; Social/Cultural gatherings.

NEW LONDON

St Joseph Residence Inc
1925 Division, New London, WI, 54961
(414) 982-5310
Admin Daniel W Orr. *Medical Dir/Dir of
Nursing* Alan Strobusch MD; Terrie Pralat
RN.
Licensure Skilled care; Intermediate care. *Beds*
107. *Certified* Medicaid.
Owner Nonprofit Corp.
Admissions Requirements Medical
examination; Physician's request.
Affiliation Roman Catholic
Facilities Dining room; Physical therapy
room; Activities room; Chapel; Crafts room;
Laundry room; Barber/Beauty shop; Library.
Activities Arts & crafts; Cards; Games;
Reading groups; Prayer groups; Movies;
Shopping trips; Social/Cultural gatherings.

NEW RICHMOND

Maple Manor Health Care Center
505 W 8th St, New Richmond, WI, 54017
(715) 246-6851
Admin Errol F Gooding. *Medical Dir/Dir of
Nursing* Dr Joseph Powell; Judy Knox RN.

Licensure Skilled care; Intermediate care. *Beds* 80. *Certified* Medicaid; Medicare.
Owner Proprietary Corp (Beverly Enterprises).
Admissions Requirements Minimum age 18; Medical examination; Physician's request.
Staff RNs 4 (ft), 3 (pt); LPNs 2 (ft), 3 (pt); Orderlies 1 (ft), 1 (pt); Nurses aides 16 (ft), 15 (pt); Physical therapists 1 (pt); Occupational therapists 1 (pt); Speech therapists 1 (pt); Activities coordinators 1 (ft); Dietitians 1 (pt).
Facilities Dining room; Physical therapy room; Activities room; Crafts room; Laundry room; Barber/Beauty shop.
Activities Arts & crafts; Cards; Games; Reading groups; Prayer groups; Movies; Shopping trips; Social/Cultural gatherings.

St Croix Health Center*
Rte 5, Box 33A, New Richmond, WI, 54017
(715) 246-6991
Admin Gary D Johnson.
Licensure Skilled care; Intermediate care. *Beds* 189. *Certified* Medicaid.
Owner Publicly owned.

NIAGARA

Maryhill Manor Inc
973 Main St, Niagara, WI, 54151
(715) 251-3172
Admin Sr Mary Francis Schwankle.
Licensure Intermediate care. *Beds* 49. *Certified* Medicaid.
Owner Nonprofit Corp (School Sisters of St Francis).
Affiliation Roman Catholic

OCONOMOWOC

Shorehaven Health Center
PO Box 208, 1306 West Wisconsin Ave, Oconomowoc, WI, 53066
(414) 567-8341
Admin Tim E Thiele. *Medical Dir/Dir of Nursing* Dr Robert Ballman; Lorna Gartzke RN.
Licensure Skilled care; Intermediate care. *Beds* 242. *Certified* Medicaid.
Owner Nonprofit Corp.
Admissions Requirements Medical examination; Physician's request.
Staff RNs; LPNs; Nurses aides; Activities coordinators; Dietitians.
Affiliation Lutheran
Facilities Dining room; Physical therapy room; Activities room; Chapel; Crafts room; Barber/Beauty shop.
Activities Arts & crafts; Cards; Games; Reading groups; Prayer groups; Movies; Shopping trips; Social/Cultural gatherings.

OCONTO

Riverside Nursing Center
100 Scherer Ave, Oconto, WI, 54153
(414) 834-4575
Admin Edward L Brady. *Medical Dir/Dir of Nursing* John S Honish MD; Jane Belongia DON.
Licensure Skilled care; Intermediate care. *Beds* 103. *Certified* Medicaid; Medicare; VA.
Owner Proprietary Corp (Beverly Enterprises).
Staff RNs; LPNs; Orderlies; Nurses aides; Physical therapists; Occupational therapists; Speech therapists; Activities coordinators; Dietitians.
Facilities Dining room; Physical therapy room; Activities room; Chapel; Crafts room; Laundry room; Barber/Beauty shop.
Activities Arts & crafts; Cards; Games; Reading groups; Prayer groups; Movies; Shopping trips; Social/Cultural gatherings.

OCONTO FALLS

Falls Nursing Home—East
PO Box 985, 855 S Main St, Oconto Falls, WI, 54154
(414) 846-3421
Admin Thomas A Lehmkuhl. *Medical Dir/Dir of Nursing* James R Wong MD; Karen Gagnon RN DON.
Licensure Skilled care; Intermediate care. *Beds* SNF 42; ICF. *Certified* Medicaid.
Owner Proprietary Corp.
Admissions Requirements Minimum age 18.
Staff RNs 2 (ft), 1 (pt); LPNs 3 (ft), 3 (pt); Orderlies 1 (ft); Nurses aides 7 (ft), 13 (pt); Activities coordinators 1 (ft).
Facilities Dining room; Physical therapy room; Activities room; Chapel; Crafts room; Laundry room; Barber/Beauty shop; Library.
Activities Arts & crafts; Cards; Games; Reading groups; Prayer groups; Movies; Shopping trips; Social/Cultural gatherings.

Falls Nursing Home—West
PO Box 985, Oconto Falls, WI, 54154
(414) 846-3272
Admin James M Sharpe. *Medical Dir/Dir of Nursing* James R Wong MD; Lou Ann Brown RN DON.
Licensure Skilled care; Intermediate care. *Beds* SNF 73; ICF. *Certified* Medicaid.
Owner Proprietary Corp.
Admissions Requirements Minimum age 18; Medical examination; Physician's request.
Staff RNs 4 (ft), 2 (pt); LPNs 4 (ft), 6 (pt); Nurses aides 20 (ft), 25 (pt); Activities coordinators 1 (ft), 2 (pt); Dietitians 1 (ft).
Facilities Dining room; Physical therapy room; Activities room; Laundry room; Barber/Beauty shop.
Activities Arts & crafts; Cards; Games; Reading groups; Prayer groups; Movies; Shopping trips; Social/Cultural gatherings; Picnics; Sightseeing; Dinner outings.

OMRO

Omro Care Center
500 S Grant St, Omro, WI, 54963
(414) 685-2755
Admin Kathleen M Regez. *Medical Dir/Dir of Nursing* Donald McDonald MD; Jeff Vander Venter.
Licensure Skilled care; Intermediate care. *Beds* 124. *Certified* Medicaid; Medicare.
Owner Proprietary Corp (Hillhaven Corp).
Admissions Requirements Minimum age 18; Medical examination; Physician's request.
Staff RNs; LPNs; Nurses aides; Occupational therapists; Speech therapists.
Facilities Dining room; Physical therapy room; Activities room; Chapel; Crafts room; Laundry room; Barber/Beauty shop; Library.
Activities Arts & crafts; Cards; Games; Reading groups; Prayer groups; Movies; Shopping trips; Social/Cultural gatherings.

ONALASKA

Onalaska Care Center
1600 Main St, Onalaska, WI, 54650
(608) 783-4681
Admin Ralph L Briggs. *Medical Dir/Dir of Nursing* Philip H Utz MD; Karen L McBeth RN DON.
Licensure Skilled care; Intermediate care. *Beds* 112. *Certified* Medicaid.
Owner Proprietary Corp.
Admissions Requirements Minimum age 18; Medical examination; Physician's request.
Staff Physicians 2 (pt); RNs 5 (ft), 6 (pt); LPNs 4 (ft), 7 (pt); Orderlies 2 (ft); Nurses aides 41 (ft), 27 (pt); Physical therapists 2 (pt); Reality therapists 1 (ft); Recreational therapists 1 (ft); Occupational therapists 1 (pt); Speech therapists 1 (pt); Activities coordinators 1 (ft); Dietitians 1 (ft).

Facilities Dining room; Physical therapy room; Activities room; Chapel; Crafts room; Laundry room; Barber/Beauty shop; Library.
Activities Arts & crafts; Cards; Games; Reading groups; Prayer groups; Movies; Shopping trips; Social/Cultural gatherings.

ONEIDA

Oneida Nursing Home*
PO Box 365, Oneida, WI, 54155
Admin Rick L Johnson. *Medical Dir/Dir of Nursing* Dr Fred H Walbrun.
Licensure Skilled care; Intermediate care. *Beds* 50. *Certified* Medicaid.
Owner Nonprofit Corp.
Admissions Requirements Minimum age 18; Medical examination; Physician's request.
Facilities Dining room; Physical therapy room; Activities room; Chapel; Crafts room; Laundry room; Barber/Beauty shop; Library.
Activities Arts & crafts; Cards; Games; Reading groups; Prayer groups; Movies; Shopping trips; Social/Cultural gatherings.

OREGON

Oregon Manor Ltd*
354 N Main St, Oregon, WI, 53575
(608) 835-3535
Admin Irmhild Micek.
Licensure Intermediate care. *Beds* 45. *Certified* Medicaid.
Owner Proprietary Corp.

OSHKOSH

Bethel Home
225 N Eagle St, Oshkosh, WI, 54901
(414) 235-4653
Admin Roberta K Messer. *Medical Dir/Dir of Nursing* R V Kuhn MD; Delores Wassmann RN.
Licensure Skilled care; Intermediate care; Medicaid Certified. *Beds* 200. *Certified* Medicaid.
Owner Nonprofit Corp.
Admissions Requirements Medical examination; Physician's request.
Affiliation Lutheran
Facilities Dining room; Physical therapy room; Activities room; Chapel; Crafts room; Laundry room; Barber/Beauty shop.
Activities Arts & crafts; Cards; Games; Reading groups; Prayer groups; Movies; Shopping trips; Social/Cultural gatherings.

Evergreen Manor Retirement Community
PO Box 1720, 1130 N Westfield St, Oshkosh, WI, 54901-1720
(414) 233-2340
Admin David A Green. *Medical Dir/Dir of Nursing* Paul Plueddeman MD; Carol Mueller DON.
Licensure Skilled care; Intermediate care. *Beds* 106. *Certified* Medicaid.
Owner Nonprofit Corp.
Admissions Requirements Minimum age 60.
Staff RNs 4 (ft), 14 (pt); LPNs 1 (ft), 14 (pt); Nurses aides 19 (ft), 47 (pt); Activities coordinators 1 (ft).
Affiliation Methodist
Facilities Dining room; Physical therapy room; Activities room; Chapel; Crafts room; Laundry room; Barber/Beauty shop; Library; Kitchen available for residents use.
Activities Arts & crafts; Cards; Games; Reading groups; Prayer groups; Movies; Shopping trips; Social/Cultural gatherings; Music appreciation; Dinner clubs; Supper clubs; Kaffee Klatsch.

Oshkosh Care Center
1850 Bowen St, Oshkosh, WI, 54901
(414) 233-4011
Admin David S Miller. *Medical Dir/Dir of Nursing* Lynn K Harron RN DON.

Licensure Skilled care; Intermediate care; Special care. *Beds* SNF 157; ICF; Special care 29. *Certified* Medicaid; Medicare.
Owner Proprietary Corp (Hillhaven Corp).
Admissions Requirements Medical examination; Physician's request.
Staff RNs 9 (ft), 6 (pt), 19 (pt); Nurses aides 125 (ft); Physical therapists 1 (ft), 2 (pt); Occupational therapists 2 (ft); Activities coordinators 1 (ft); Dietitians 1 (ft).
Facilities Dining room; Physical therapy room; Activities room; Chapel; Laundry room; Barber/Beauty shop; Occupational therapy room; Speech therapy; Privacy room.
Activities Arts & crafts; Cards; Games; Reading groups; Prayer groups; Movies; Shopping trips; Social/Cultural gatherings.

OSSEO

Osseo Area Municipal Hospital & Nursing Home
674 8th St, Osseo, WI, 54758
(715) 597-3121
Admin James Sokup. *Medical Dir/Dir of Nursing* Bradley G Garber; Arvis Crump RN DON.
Licensure Skilled care; Intermediate care. *Beds* 90. *Certified* Medicaid; Medicare.
Owner Nonprofit Corp.
Admissions Requirements Physician's request.
Staff Physicians 3 (ft); RNs 2 (ft), 2 (pt); LPNs 5 (ft); Orderlies 1 (ft); Nurses aides 10 (ft), 18 (pt); Physical therapists 1 (ft); Recreational therapists 2 (ft); Activities coordinators 1 (ft); Dietitians 1 (ft).
Languages Norwegian
Facilities Dining room; Physical therapy room; Activities room; Chapel; Crafts room; Laundry room; Barber/Beauty shop; Van for travel.
Activities Arts & crafts; Cards; Games; Reading groups; Prayer groups; Movies; Shopping trips; Social/Cultural gatherings.

OWEN

Clark County Health Care Center
Hwy 29 E, Owen, WI, 54460
(715) 229-2172
Admin Arlyn A Mills. *Medical Dir/Dir of Nursing* J W Johnson.
Licensure Skilled care; Intermediate care. *Beds* 275. *Certified* Medicaid; Medicare.
Owner Publicly owned.
Admissions Requirements Minimum age 18; Medical examination; Physician's request.
Facilities Dining room; Physical therapy room; Activities room; Chapel; Crafts room; Laundry room; Barber/Beauty shop; Library; Multipurpose gymnasium.
Activities Arts & crafts; Cards; Games; Reading groups; Prayer groups; Movies; Shopping trips; Social/Cultural gatherings.

OXFORD

Oxford Convalescent Home*
PO Box 47, Oxford, WI, 53952
(608) 586-4211
Admin Thomas Kuehn.
Licensure Skilled care; Intermediate care. *Beds* 58. *Certified* Medicaid.
Owner Proprietary Corp.

PARK FALLS

Park Manor
250 Lawrence Ave, Park Falls, WI, 54552
(715) 762-2449
Admin Wanda Preisler. *Medical Dir/Dir of Nursing* James L Murphy MD; Jane Sellers DON.

Licensure Skilled care; Intermediate care; Intermediate care for mentally retarded. *Beds* 171. *Certified* Medicaid.
Owner Proprietary Corp.
Admissions Requirements Medical examination; Physician's request.
Staff RNs 4 (ft), 6 (pt); LPNs 5 (ft), 7 (pt); Nurses aides 11 (ft), 66 (pt); Physical therapists 1 (pt); Activities coordinators 2 (ft).
Facilities Dining room; Physical therapy room; Activities room; Crafts room; Laundry room; Barber/Beauty shop; Library.
Activities Arts & crafts; Cards; Games; Reading groups; Prayer groups; Movies; Shopping trips; Social/Cultural gatherings.

PEPIN

Pepin Manor Care Center*
2nd & Locust St, Pepin, WI, 54759
(715) 442-4811
Admin Jeanette L Sass.
Licensure Skilled care; Intermediate care. *Beds* 100. *Certified* Medicaid.
Owner Proprietary Corp.

PESHTIGO

Larsen Memorial Home
Badger Park, Peshtigo, WI, 54157
(715) 582-4148
Admin Sandra O'Neil.
Licensure Intermediate care. *Beds* 77. *Certified* Medicaid.
Owner Proprietary Corp.
Staff RNs 1 (ft), 2 (pt); LPNs 2 (ft), 2 (pt); Nurses aides 51 (ft), 24 (pt); Speech therapists 1 (pt); Activities coordinators 1 (ft); Dietitians 1 (pt).

Pine View Health Care Center
PO Box 127, Peshtigo, WI, 54157
(715) 582-3962
Admin Karla K Brabender. *Medical Dir/Dir of Nursing* Dr Tom Mack; Georgetta Preg.
Licensure Skilled care. *Beds* SNF 155. *Certified* Medicaid.
Owner Publicly owned.
Admissions Requirements Minimum age 18; Medical examination; Physician's request.
Staff Physicians 2 (pt); RNs 10 (ft), 6 (pt); LPNs 3 (ft), 4 (pt); Nurses aides 20 (ft), 47 (pt); Physical therapists 1 (pt); Recreational therapists 1 (ft); Occupational therapists 1 (pt); Speech therapists 1 (pt); Activities coordinators 1 (ft); Dietitians 1 (pt).
Facilities Dining room; Physical therapy room; Activities room; Crafts room; Laundry room; Barber/Beauty shop; Library.
Activities Arts & crafts; Cards; Games; Reading groups; Prayer groups; Movies; Shopping trips; Social/Cultural gatherings.

Rennes Health Center
PO Box 147, 501 N Lake St, Peshtigo, WI, 54157
(715) 582-3906
Admin Karen M Brechlin. *Medical Dir/Dir of Nursing* Dr T Mack; Ruthie Carriveall DON.
Licensure Skilled care. *Beds* SNF 144. *Certified* Medicaid.
Owner Proprietary Corp.
Admissions Requirements Minimum age 18; Medical examination; Physician's request.
Staff Physicians 4 (pt); RNs 4 (ft), 9 (pt); LPNs 2 (ft), 13 (pt); Nurses aides 9 (ft), 65 (pt); Physical therapists 1 (pt); Recreational therapists 1 (ft); Occupational therapists 1 (pt); Speech therapists 1 (pt); Activities coordinators 1 (pt); Dietitians 1 (ft); Dentists 1 (pt); Ophthalmologists 1 (pt).
Facilities Dining room; Physical therapy room; Activities room; Chapel; Crafts room; Laundry room; Barber/Beauty shop; Library; Greenhouse; Whirlpool baths; Courtyards.

Activities Arts & crafts; Cards; Games; Reading groups; Prayer groups; Movies; Shopping trips; Social/Cultural gatherings; Community trips.

PEWAUKEE

River Hills Health Care Center—West*
321 Riverside Dr, Pewaukee, WI, 53072
(414) 691-2300
Admin Barry T Metevia.
Licensure Skilled care; Intermediate care. *Beds* 248. *Certified* Medicaid; Medicare.
Owner Proprietary Corp (American Medical Services Inc).

PHELPS

Lillian E Kerr Nursing Home
PO Box 26, Phelps, WI, 54554
(715) 545-2313
Admin Curtis A Johnson. *Medical Dir/Dir of Nursing* Thomas Richards DO.
Licensure Skilled care; Intermediate care. *Beds* SNF 81; ICF. *Certified* Medicaid.
Owner Nonprofit Corp.
Admissions Requirements Minimum age 16; Physician's request.
Staff Physicians 3 (ft); RNs 3 (ft), 3 (pt); LPNs 3 (ft), 5 (pt); Orderlies 2 (ft), 2 (pt); Nurses aides 18 (ft), 15 (pt); Physical therapists 1 (pt); Recreational therapists 2 (ft); Occupational therapists 1 (pt); Speech therapists 1 (pt); Dietitians 1 (pt).
Facilities Dining room; Physical therapy room; Activities room; Chapel; Crafts room; Laundry room; Barber/Beauty shop.
Activities Arts & crafts; Cards; Games; Reading groups; Prayer groups; Movies; Shopping trips; Social/Cultural gatherings.

PHILLIPS

Pleasant View Nursing Home*
Peterson Dr, Phillips, WI, 54555
(715) 339-3113
Admin Wayne R Sawallish. *Medical Dir/Dir of Nursing* Walter E Niebauer MD.
Licensure Skilled care; Intermediate care. *Beds* 86. *Certified* Medicaid.
Owner Nonprofit Corp.
Admissions Requirements Medical examination; Physician's request.
Staff Physicians 3 (pt); RNs 2 (ft), 4 (pt); LPNs 6 (pt); Nurses aides 14 (ft), 28 (pt); Physical therapists 1 (pt); Speech therapists 1 (pt); Activities coordinators 1 (ft), 2 (pt); Dietitians 1 (ft), 1 (pt); Dentists 1 (pt).
Facilities Dining room; Physical therapy room; Activities room; Crafts room; Laundry room; Barber/Beauty shop; Library.
Activities Arts & crafts; Cards; Games; Reading groups; Prayer groups; Movies; Shopping trips; Social/Cultural gatherings.

PIGEON FALLS

Pigeon Falls Nursing Home
PO Box 195, Pigeon Falls, WI, 54760
(715) 983-2293
Admin Laurie J Haines. *Medical Dir/Dir of Nursing* Reuben Adams MD; Doris A Johnson RN.
Licensure Skilled care; Intermediate care; Residential care. *Beds* SNF; ICF 41; CBRF 8. *Certified* Medicaid.
Owner Proprietary Corp.

PLATTEVILLE

Grays Nursing Home Inc
555 N Chestnut St, Platteville, WI, 53818
(608) 349-6741

Admin Bernice M Gray. *Medical Dir/Dir of Nursing* J Huekner; Karen Beckman RN DON.
Licensure Skilled care; Intermediate care. *Beds* 20. *Certified* Medicaid.
Owner Proprietary Corp.
Admissions Requirements Medical examination; Physician's request.
Staff RNs 2 (ft), 3 (pt); LPNs 3 (pt); Nurses aides 11 (pt); Activities coordinators 1 (ft); Dietitians 1 (pt); Social worker 1 (pt).
Facilities Dining room; Activities room; Chapel; Crafts room; Laundry room; Multi-purpose rooms.
Activities Arts & crafts; Cards; Games; Reading groups; Prayer groups; Movies; Shopping trips.

Parkview Terrace/HCR
1300 N Water St, Platteville, WI, 53818
(608) 348-2453
Admin Mary Ann Floerke. *Medical Dir/Dir of Nursing* Dr M F Stuessy; Sherry Franseen RN.
Licensure Skilled care; Adult day care services. *Beds* 100. *Certified* Medicaid; Medicare; VA.
Owner Proprietary Corp (Health Care & Retirement Corp).
Admissions Requirements Minimum age 18; Medical examination; Physician's request.
Facilities Dining room; Physical therapy room; Activities room; Chapel; Crafts room; Laundry room; Barber/Beauty shop; Library.
Activities Arts & crafts; Cards; Games; Reading groups; Prayer groups; Movies; Social/Cultural gatherings; Art therapy; Poetry group; Cooking; Residents council; Adult day care services.

Southwest Health Center Nursing Home
1100 5th Ave, Platteville, WI, 53818
(608) 348-2331
Admin Kenneth W Creswick. *Medical Dir/Dir of Nursing* Milton F Stuessy MD.
Licensure Skilled care; Intermediate care. *Beds* 34. *Certified* Medicaid.
Owner Nonprofit Corp.
Staff RNs 4 (pt); LPNs 3 (ft), 4 (pt); Nurses aides 8 (ft), 15 (pt); Physical therapists 1 (pt); Occupational therapists 1 (pt); Activities coordinators 1 (pt); Dietitians 1 (pt).
Facilities Dining room; Physical therapy room; Activities room; Crafts room.
Activities Arts & crafts; Cards; Games; Prayer groups; Movies; Shopping trips; Social/Cultural gatherings.

PLUM CITY

Plum Center Nursing Center
301 Cherry St, Plum City, WI, 54761
(715) 647-2401
Admin Lisa Gust. *Medical Dir/Dir of Nursing* Dr C W Docter; Patricia Sabello.
Licensure Skilled care. *Beds* 42. *Certified* Medicaid.
Owner Proprietary Corp.
Admissions Requirements Minimum age 18; Medical examination; Physician's request.
Staff RNs 1 (ft), 3 (pt); LPNs 1 (ft), 4 (pt); Nurses aides 7 (ft), 11 (pt); Activities coordinators 1 (pt).
Facilities Dining room; Physical therapy room; Activities room; Laundry room; Barber/Beauty shop.
Activities Arts & crafts; Games; Reading groups; Prayer groups; Social/Cultural gatherings; Bible tape; Baking.

PLYMOUTH

Rocky Knoll Health Care Facility
Plymouth, WI, 53073
(414) 467-6464

Admin Juanita K Wethington. *Medical Dir/Dir of Nursing* Curtiss Hancock MD; Nancy Slupski RN.
Licensure Skilled care; Intermediate care. *Beds* 263. *Certified* Medicaid; Medicare; VA.
Owner Publicly owned.
Admissions Requirements Medical examination; Physician's request.
Staff RNs 11 (ft), 6 (pt); LPNs 9 (ft), 8 (pt); Nurses aides 44 (ft), 43 (pt); Physical therapists 1 (pt); Recreational therapists 3 (ft); Occupational therapists 1 (pt); Speech therapists 1 (pt); Activities coordinators 1 (ft); Dietitians 1 (pt).
Facilities Dining room; Physical therapy room; Activities room; Chapel; Crafts room; Laundry room; Barber/Beauty shop; Library.
Activities Arts & crafts; Cards; Games; Reading groups; Prayer groups; Movies; Shopping trips; Social/Cultural gatherings; Music therapy.

Valley Manor Nursing Home
916 E Clifford St, Plymouth, WI, 53073
(414) 893-1771
Admin Patrick Trotter. *Medical Dir/Dir of Nursing* Dr George Schroeder; K Newell DON.
Licensure Skilled care; Intermediate care; Retirement apts. *Beds* 60; Retirement apts 32. *Certified* Medicaid; Medicare.
Owner Nonprofit Corp.
Admissions Requirements Medical examination; Physician's request.
Staff Physicians 1 (pt); RNs 3 (ft), 1 (pt); LPNs 3 (ft), 3 (pt); Nurses aides 4 (ft), 10 (pt); Physical therapists 1 (pt); Recreational therapists 1 (pt); Occupational therapists 1 (pt); Speech therapists 1 (pt); Activities coordinators 1 (ft), 1 (pt); Dietitians 1 (pt); Dentists 1 (pt); Podiatrists 1 (pt); Social workers 2 (ft).
Facilities Dining room; Physical therapy room; Activities room; Chapel; Laundry room; Barber/Beauty shop; Solarium.
Activities Arts & crafts; Cards; Games; Reading groups; Movies; Shopping trips.

PORT EDWARDS

Edgewater Haven Nursing Home
1351 Wisconsin River Dr, Port Edwards, WI, 54469
(715) 887-3200
Admin Steven R Sterzinger. *Medical Dir/Dir of Nursing* John E Thompson MD; Carol J Dean.
Licensure Skilled care; Intermediate care. *Beds* 164. *Certified* Medicaid; Medicare.
Owner Publicly owned.
Admissions Requirements Medical examination.
Staff RNs 4 (ft), 13 (pt); LPNs 3 (ft), 12 (pt); Nurses aides 44 (ft), 15 (pt); Physical therapists 2 (pt); Recreational therapists 1 (ft); Dietitians 1 (pt).
Facilities Dining room; Physical therapy room; Activities room; Chapel; Laundry room; Barber/Beauty shop.
Activities Arts & crafts; Cards; Games; Prayer groups; Movies; Shopping trips; Social/Cultural gatherings.

PORT WASHINGTON

Heritage Nursing Home
1119 N Wisconsin St, Port Washington, WI, 53092
(414) 284-5892
Admin Patricia E Treffert RN. *Medical Dir/Dir of Nursing* Dr Mark Bostwick; Ms Bernice Lubner RN.
Licensure Skilled care; Intermediate care. *Beds* 54. *Certified* Medicaid.
Owner Proprietary Corp.
Admissions Requirements Medical examination; Physician's request.

Staff RNs 1 (ft), 6 (pt); LPNs 4 (pt); Nurses aides 5 (ft), 38 (pt); Physical therapists 1 (pt); Recreational therapists 1 (pt); Speech therapists 1 (pt); Activities coordinators 1 (pt); Dietitians 1 (pt).
Facilities Dining room; Activities room; Crafts room; TV/Music lounge.
Activities Arts & crafts; Cards; Games; Reading groups; Prayer groups; Movies; Social/Cultural gatherings; Church services.

PORTAGE

Divine Savior Hospital & Nursing Home
715 W Pleasant St, Portage, WI, 53901
(608) 742-4131
Admin Michael D Hammer. *Medical Dir/Dir of Nursing* Dr Stuart Taylor Sr; Penny Finnegan DON.
Licensure Skilled care; Intermediate care; Self care. *Beds* SNF 111; Self care 14. *Certified* Medicaid.
Owner Nonprofit Corp.
Staff RNs 14 (ft); LPNs 5 (ft); Nurses aides 38 (ft); Physical therapists 1 (ft); Occupational therapists 1 (ft); Speech therapists 1 (ft); Activities coordinators 1 (ft); Dietitians 1 (ft); Podiatrists 1 (ft).
Affiliation Roman Catholic

PRAIRIE DU CHIEN

Prairie Living Center
1150 S 15th St, Prairie du Chien, WI, 53821
(608) 326-8471
Admin Morris Arnold. *Medical Dir/Dir of Nursing* Kirk D Berger.
Licensure Skilled care; Intermediate care. *Beds* 173. *Certified* Medicaid; Medicare.
Owner Nonprofit Corp (Adventist Health Sys-USA).
Admissions Requirements Medical examination.
Staff Physicians 1 (pt); RNs 5 (ft), 7 (pt); LPNs 2 (ft), 9 (pt); Nurses aides 20 (ft), 45 (pt); Speech therapists 1 (pt); Activities coordinators 1 (ft); Dietitians 1 (pt); Dentists 1 (pt); Podiatrists 1 (pt); Audiologists 1 (pt); Social workers 1 (pt).
Affiliation Seventh-Day Adventist
Facilities Dining room; Physical therapy room; Activities room; Chapel; Crafts room; Laundry room; Barber/Beauty shop.
Activities Arts & crafts; Cards; Games; Reading groups; Prayer groups; Movies; Shopping trips; Social/Cultural gatherings.

PRAIRIE FARM

Pioneer Nursing Home
PO Box 95, Prairie Farm, WI, 54762
(715) 455-1178
Admin Fred J Schlosser Jr. *Medical Dir/Dir of Nursing* J R Hoefert MD; Joanne Griffiths RN.
Licensure Skilled care. *Beds* SNF 42. *Certified* Medicaid.
Owner Nonprofit Corp.
Admissions Requirements Minimum age 18; Medical examination.
Staff RNs 1 (ft), 3 (pt); LPNs 1 (ft), 3 (pt); Nurses aides 5 (ft), 6 (pt); Physical therapists 1 (pt); Occupational therapists 1 (pt); Activities coordinators 1 (ft); Dietitians 1 (pt).
Facilities Dining room; Physical therapy room; Activities room; Laundry room; Barber/Beauty shop.
Activities Arts & crafts; Cards; Games; Prayer groups; Movies; Shopping trips; Social/Cultural gatherings.

PRINCETON

Sunnyview Village
900 Sunnyview Ln, Princeton, WI, 54968
(414) 295-6463
Admin Cheryl Milbrandt. *Medical Dir/Dir of Nursing* Robert House MD; Sharon Flood DON.
Licensure Skilled care. *Beds* SNF 66. *Certified* Medicaid.
Owner Proprietary Corp.
Admissions Requirements Minimum age 18; Medical examination; Physician's request.
Staff RNs 3 (ft), 1 (pt); LPNs 2 (ft), 3 (pt); Orderlies 2 (ft), 2 (pt); Nurses aides 7 (ft), 19 (pt); Physical therapists 1 (pt); Activities coordinators 1 (ft); Dietitians 1 (ft).
Facilities Dining room; Physical therapy room; Activities room; Chapel; Laundry room; Barber/Beauty shop; TV; Reading room; Family rooms.
Activities Arts & crafts; Cards; Games; Reading groups; Prayer groups; Movies; Shopping trips; Social/Cultural gatherings; Coffee hour; Exercises; Kitchen club.

RACINE

The Becker/Shoop Center
6101 16th St, Racine, WI, 53406
(414) 637-7486
Admin Daniel W Langenwalter. *Medical Dir/Dir of Nursing* Dr John Jamieson; Elaine M Oser RN DON.
Licensure Skilled care; Intermediate care; Adult day care for Alzheimer's diagnosed clients. *Beds* 110. *Certified* Medicaid.
Owner Nonprofit Corp (Lincoln Luth of Racine WI).
Admissions Requirements Medical examination; Physician's request.
Staff Physicians 1 (pt); RNs 8 (ft), 15 (pt); LPNs 1 (ft), 3 (pt); Nurses aides 16 (ft), 62 (pt); Physical therapists 1 (pt); Recreational therapists 1 (ft); Occupational therapists 1 (pt); Speech therapists 1 (pt); Activities coordinators 1 (ft); Dietitians 1 (pt); Dentists 1 (pt); Ophthalmologists 1 (pt); Podiatrists 1 (pt).
Languages German, Polish, Danish
Affiliation Lutheran
Facilities Dining room; Physical therapy room; Activities room; Chapel; Crafts room; Laundry room; Barber/Beauty shop; Solarium; Outdoor courtyard.
Activities Arts & crafts; Cards; Games; Reading groups; Prayer groups; Movies; Shopping trips; Social/Cultural gatherings.

Lincoln Lutheran Home
2015 Prospect St, Racine, WI, 53404
(414) 637-6531
Admin Lee D Morey. *Medical Dir/Dir of Nursing* Dr Wolkomir; Anita Getty DON.
Licensure Skilled care; Intermediate care. *Beds* 167. *Certified* Medicaid.
Owner Nonprofit Corp (Lincoln Luth of Racine WI).
Admissions Requirements Medical examination; Physician's request.
Staff Physicians 1 (pt); RNs 3 (ft), 17 (pt); LPNs 2 (ft), 13 (pt); Nurses aides 27 (ft), 52 (pt); Physical therapists 1 (pt); Recreational therapists 4 (ft); Activities coordinators 1 (ft); Dietitians 1 (ft); Dentists 1 (pt); Chaplain 1 (ft).
Affiliation Lutheran
Facilities Dining room; Activities room; Crafts room; Laundry room; Barber/Beauty shop.
Activities Arts & crafts; Cards; Prayer groups; Movies; Social/Cultural gatherings.

Lincoln Village Convalescent Center
1700 C A Becker Dr, Racine, WI, 53406
(414) 637-9751

Admin Joseph D Alexander. *Medical Dir/Dir of Nursing* Santiago Yllas MD.
Licensure Skilled care. *Beds* SNF 122. *Certified* Medicaid; Medicare.
Owner Nonprofit Corp (Lincoln Luth of Racine WI).
Admissions Requirements Minimum age 18; Medical examination; Physician's request.
Staff Physicians 1 (pt); RNs 4 (ft), 13 (pt); LPNs 15 (pt); Nurses aides 30 (ft), 52 (pt); Physical therapists 1 (pt); Recreational therapists 3 (pt); Occupational therapists 1 (pt); Speech therapists 1 (pt); Activities coordinators 1 (ft); Dietitians 1 (pt); Ophthalmologists 1 (pt); Dentist 1 (pt) Chaplain 1 (ft).
Affiliation Lutheran
Facilities Dining room; Physical therapy room; Activities room; Crafts room; Barber/Beauty shop; Library; Living room.
Activities Arts & crafts; Cards; Games; Reading groups; Prayer groups; Movies; Shopping trips; Social/Cultural gatherings.

Racine Residential Care*
1719 Washington Ave, Racine, WI, 53403
(414) 633-5348
Admin Norman L Steffen.
Licensure Intermediate care for mentally retarded. *Certified* Medicaid.
Owner Proprietary Corp.
Admissions Requirements Minimum age 18; Medical examination.
Staff RNs 1 (ft), 1 (pt); LPNs 2 (ft), 2 (pt); Nurses aides 9 (ft), 3 (pt); Recreational therapists 1 (ft); Occupational therapists 1 (ft); Dietitians 1 (pt); Social workers 2 (ft).
Facilities Dining room; Activities room.
Activities Arts & crafts; Games; Reading groups; Prayer groups; Movies; Shopping trips; Social/Cultural gatherings.

Ridgewood Care Center
5455 Durand Ave, Racine, WI, 53406
(414) 554-6440
Admin Brenda E Danculovich. *Medical Dir/Dir of Nursing* Dr William Haedike; Frances Petrick.
Licensure Skilled care; Intermediate care. *Beds* 210. *Certified* Medicaid.
Owner Publicly owned.
Admissions Requirements Minimum age 18; Medical examination; Physician's request.
Staff Physicians 3 (pt); RNs 10 (ft), 10 (pt); LPNs 13 (ft), 13 (pt); Nurses aides 38 (ft), 42 (pt); Physical therapists 1 (ft); Recreational therapists 1 (ft); Occupational therapists 2 (ft); Speech therapists 1 (pt); Activities coordinators 1 (ft); Dietitians 1 (ft); Ophthalmologists 1 (pt); Optometrist 1 (pt).
Facilities Dining room; Physical therapy room; Activities room; Chapel; Crafts room; Laundry room; Barber/Beauty shop; Library; Locked unit for court-ordered protectively placed; Secure care system for wanderers.
Activities Arts & crafts; Cards; Games; Reading groups; Prayer groups; Movies; Shopping trips; Social/Cultural gatherings.

St Catherine's Infirmary Inc
5635 Erie St, Racine, WI, 53402
(414) 639-4100
Admin Sr Mae M Schellinger. *Medical Dir/Dir of Nursing* Gloria Stedman-Brown.
Licensure Skilled care; Intermediate care. *Beds* 40. *Certified* Medicaid.
Owner Nonprofit organization/foundation.
Admissions Requirements Physician's request.
Staff RNs; LPNs; Nurses aides; Occupational therapists; Activities coordinators; Dietitians; Ophthalmologists.
Languages Spanish, Bohemian, German
Affiliation Roman Catholic
Facilities Dining room; Activities room; Chapel; Crafts room; Laundry room; Barber/Beauty shop; Library.
Activities Arts & crafts; Games; Prayer groups.

Westview Health Care Center Inc
1600 Ohio St, Racine, WI, 53406
(414) 637-7491
Admin Ronald A Chrsitner.
Licensure Skilled care; Intermediate care. *Beds* 320. *Certified* Medicaid; Medicare.
Owner Proprietary Corp.

RADISSON

Marian Nursing Home*
Rte 1, Radisson, WI, 54867
(715) 945-2203
Admin Frances A Mleczko. *Medical Dir/Dir of Nursing* Dr Larry Carlson.
Licensure Intermediate care. *Beds* 28. *Certified* Medicaid.
Owner Proprietary Corp.
Admissions Requirements Medical examination.
Staff Physicians 1 (pt); RNs 2 (ft), 2 (pt); LPNs 2 (pt); Nurses aides 5 (ft), 6 (pt); Physical therapists 1 (pt); Occupational therapists 1 (pt); Speech therapists 1 (pt); Activities coordinators 1 (pt); Dietitians 1 (pt); Dentists 1 (pt).
Facilities Dining room; Activities room; Chapel; Crafts room; Laundry room; Barber/Beauty shop; Library.
Activities Arts & crafts; Cards; Games; Reading groups; Prayer groups; Movies; Shopping trips.

RANDOLPH

Continental Manor Nursing Center
502 S High St, Randolph, WI, 53956
(414) 326-3171
Admin William H Disch. *Medical Dir/Dir of Nursing* Dr John Poser; Victoria Grant.
Licensure Skilled care; Intermediate care. *Beds* 84. *Certified* Medicaid; Medicare; VA.
Owner Proprietary Corp (Beverly Enterprises).
Admissions Requirements Medical examination; Physician's request.
Staff RNs 2 (ft), 4 (pt); LPNs 4 (ft), 7 (pt); Orderlies 2 (ft), 1 (pt); Nurses aides 18 (ft), 18 (pt); Activities coordinators 1 (pt).
Facilities Dining room; Physical therapy room; Activities room; Crafts room; Laundry room; Barber/Beauty shop; Library; 2 dayrooms; Living room; Multi-purpose room.
Activities Arts & crafts; Cards; Games; Reading groups; Prayer groups; Movies; Shopping trips; Social/Cultural gatherings; Monthly luncheons to local restaurants.

REEDSBURG

Sauk County Health Care Center
Rte 2, Reedsburg, WI, 53959
(608) 524-4371
Admin Donald W Erickson. *Medical Dir/Dir of Nursing* Frederick W Blancke MD; Joan Petron RN DON.
Licensure Skilled care. *Beds* SNF 275. *Certified* Medicaid; Medicare.
Owner Publicly owned.
Admissions Requirements Minimum age 21; Medical examination; Physician's request.
Staff Physicians 13 (pt); RNs 8 (ft), 12 (pt); LPNs 4 (ft), 8 (pt); Nurses aides 45 (ft), 80 (pt); Physical therapists 1 (pt); Recreational therapists 4 (ft), 6 (pt); Occupational therapists 1 (ft); Speech therapists 1 (pt); Activities coordinators 1 (ft); Dietitians 1 (pt); Podiatrists 1 (pt).
Facilities Dining room; Physical therapy room; Activities room; Chapel; Crafts room; Laundry room; Barber/Beauty shop; Library; In-house bakery.
Activities Arts & crafts; Cards; Games; Reading groups; Prayer groups; Movies; Shopping trips; Social/Cultural gatherings; Resident Council.

Edward Snyder Memorial Home
1104 21st St, Reedsburg, WI, 53959
(608) 524-6487
Admin George L Johnson. *Medical Dir/Dir of Nursing* Dr D Burnett.
Licensure Skilled care; Intermediate care. *Beds* SNF 50; ICF. *Certified* Medicaid.
Owner Nonprofit Corp.
Admissions Requirements Medical examination; Physician's request.
Staff RNs 2 (ft), 4 (pt); LPNs 2 (ft), 1 (pt); Nurses aides 8 (ft), 15 (pt); Physical therapists 1 (ft); Occupational therapists 1 (ft); Activities coordinators 1 (ft); Dietitians 1 (pt).
Facilities Dining room; Physical therapy room; Activities room; Chapel; Crafts room; Laundry room; Barber/Beauty shop.
Activities Arts & crafts; Cards; Games; Reading groups; Prayer groups; Movies; Shopping trips; Social/Cultural gatherings.

Zimmerman Nursing Home
617 4th St, Reedsburg, WI, 53959
(608) 524-3664
Admin Marion K Zimmerman. *Medical Dir/Dir of Nursing* Linda Splett RN.
Licensure Intermediate care. *Beds* ICF 12. *Certified* Medicaid.
Owner Privately owned.
Admissions Requirements Medical examination.
Staff RNs; LPNs; Nurses aides; Dietitians.
Facilities Dining room; Activities room; Chapel; Laundry room; Barber/Beauty shop.
Activities Games; Prayer groups; Movies.

RHINELANDER

The Friendly Village
PO Box 857, Rhinelander, WI, 54501
(715) 362-7676
Admin Carol Paradies. *Medical Dir/Dir of Nursing* Dr M J Henry; Rhae Ellen Schnoor.
Licensure Skilled care; Intermediate care. *Beds* SNF 152; ICF. *Certified* Medicaid.
Owner Proprietary Corp (Petersen Health Care of Wisconsin).
Admissions Requirements Medical examination.
Staff RNs; LPNs; Orderlies; Nurses aides; Physical therapists; Occupational therapists; Speech therapists; Activities coordinators; Dietitians.
Facilities Dining room; Physical therapy room; Activities room; Chapel; Crafts room; Laundry room; Barber/Beauty shop.
Activities Arts & crafts; Cards; Games; Reading groups; Prayer groups; Movies; Social/Cultural gatherings.

Horizons Unlimited
PO Box 857, Rhinelander, WI, 54501
(715) 362-7676
Admin Jean Jacobson. *Medical Dir/Dir of Nursing* Dr L D Eggman; Maureen Krouze.
Licensure Skilled care; Intermediate care for mentally retarded. *Beds* SNF 248; ICF/MR. *Certified* Medicaid.
Owner Proprietary Corp (Petersen Health Care of Wisconsin).
Admissions Requirements Minimum age 18; Medical examination.
Staff RNs; LPNs; Orderlies; Nurses aides; Physical therapists; Occupational therapists; Speech therapists; Dietitians.
Facilities Dining room; Physical therapy room; Activities room; Chapel; Crafts room; Laundry room; Barber/Beauty shop.
Activities Arts & crafts; Cards; Games; Movies; Shopping trips; Social/Cultural gatherings.

Passport
PO Box 857, Rhinelander, WI, 54501
(715) 362-7676
Admin Patricia Lietz. *Medical Dir/Dir of Nursing* Dr L D Eggman; Cathy Weingarten.

Licensure Intermediate care. *Beds* ICF 20. *Certified* Medicaid.
Owner Proprietary Corp (Petersen Health Care of Wisconsin).
Admissions Requirements Minimum age 18; Medical examination.
Staff RNs 1 (pt); LPNs 1 (ft), 1 (pt); Nurses aides 3 (ft), 3 (pt); Recreational therapists 1 (ft).
Facilities Dining room; Activities room; Crafts room; Laundry room.
Activities Arts & crafts; Cards; Games; Reading groups; Prayer groups; Movies; Shopping trips; Social/Cultural gatherings.

Taylor Park Health Care & Rehabilitation Center
PO Box 857, Rhinelander, WI, 54501
(715) 362-7676
Admin Phyllis Dable. *Medical Dir/Dir of Nursing* Dr M J Henry; Cheryle Bohnert.
Licensure Skilled care; Intermediate care. *Beds* SNF 100; ICF. *Certified* Medicaid; Medicare.
Owner Proprietary Corp (Petersen Health Care of Wisconsin).
Admissions Requirements Medical examination; Physician's request.
Staff RNs; LPNs; Orderlies; Nurses aides; Physical therapists; Occupational therapists; Speech therapists; Activities coordinators; Dietitians.
Facilities Dining room; Physical therapy room; Activities room; Chapel; Crafts room; Laundry room; Barber/Beauty shop.
Activities Arts & crafts; Cards; Games; Reading groups; Prayer groups; Movies; Shopping trips; Social/Cultural gatherings.

RIB LAKE

Rib Lake Health Care Center
PO Box 308, 650 Pearl St, Rib Lake, WI, 54470
(715) 427-5291
Admin Paul Kuenning.
Licensure Skilled care; Intermediate care. *Beds* 100. *Certified* Medicaid; Medicare.
Owner Proprietary Corp (Beverly Enterprises).

RICE LAKE

Heritage Manor
19 W Newton St, Rice Lake, WI, 54868
(715) 234-2161
Admin Daniel C Dixon. *Medical Dir/Dir of Nursing* Dr William Smith MD; Brenda Nelson RN DON.
Licensure Skilled care; Intermediate care. *Beds* SNF 101; ICF. *Certified* Medicaid; Medicare.
Owner Proprietary Corp.
Admissions Requirements Medical examination; Physician's request.
Staff RNs 5 (ft); LPNs 3 (ft); Orderlies 3 (pt); Nurses aides 23 (ft), 22 (pt); Physical therapists 2 (pt); Activities coordinators 1 (ft), 1 (pt); Dietitians 1 (ft); Social worker 1 (ft); Medical Records 1 (ft).
Facilities Dining room; Physical therapy room; Activities room; Chapel; Crafts room; Laundry room; Barber/Beauty shop; Library; Family dining room.
Activities Arts & crafts; Cards; Games; Reading groups; Prayer groups; Movies; Shopping trips; Social/Cultural gatherings; Pet therapy; Church services; Community outings; Family oriented activities.

Rice Lake Convalescent Center*
1016 Lakeshore Dr, Rice Lake, WI, 54868
(715) 234-9101
Admin Don L Fritz. *Medical Dir/Dir of Nursing* Dr Mark Nymo.
Licensure Skilled care. *Beds* 100. *Certified* Medicaid.
Owner Proprietary Corp (1st Am Care Fac).

Staff Physicians 1 (ft), 12 (pt); RNs 2 (ft), 9 (pt); LPNs 1 (ft), 3 (pt); Orderlies 3 (pt); Nurses aides 20 (ft), 27 (pt); Physical therapists 1 (pt); Occupational therapists 1 (pt); Speech therapists 1 (pt); Activities coordinators 1 (ft); Dietitians 1 (ft); Dentists 1 (pt); Ophthalmologists 1 (pt); Podiatrists 1 (pt); Audiologists 1 (pt).
Facilities Dining room; Physical therapy room; Activities room; Chapel; Crafts room; Laundry room; Barber/Beauty shop; Library.
Activities Arts & crafts; Cards; Games; Reading groups; Prayer groups; Movies; Shopping trips; Social/Cultural gatherings; Pet therapy; Choir; Rhythm band.

RICHLAND CENTER

Pine Valley Manor
PO Box 154, Rte 4, Richland Center, WI, 53581
(608) 647-2138
Admin Dale L Pauls. *Medical Dir/Dir of Nursing* John Jordon MD.
Licensure Skilled care; Intermediate care. *Beds* 176. *Certified* Medicaid; Medicare.
Owner Publicly owned.
Admissions Requirements Minimum age 18; Medical examination.
Staff Physicians 6 (pt); RNs 1 (ft), 8 (pt); LPNs 12 (ft), 3 (pt); Nurses aides 46 (ft), 32 (pt); Physical therapists 1 (ft); Recreational therapists 1 (ft); Occupational therapists 2 (ft); Speech therapists 1 (pt); Activities coordinators 1 (ft); Dietitians 1 (pt); Dentist 1 (pt).
Facilities Dining room; Physical therapy room; Activities room; Chapel; Laundry room; Barber/Beauty shop.
Activities Arts & crafts; Cards; Games; Reading groups; Prayer groups; Movies; Shopping trips; Social/Cultural gatherings.

Schmitt Woodland Hills Inc
1400 W Seminary St, Richland Center, WI, 53581
(608) 647-8931
Admin Ruth L McVay. *Medical Dir/Dir of Nursing* Dr Thomas Richardson; Shannon Trebus.
Licensure Skilled care; Intermediate care. *Beds* 25. *Certified* Medicaid.
Owner Nonprofit Corp.
Admissions Requirements Minimum age 65; Medical examination.
Staff RNs 2 (ft), 2 (pt); LPNs 2 (ft), 2 (pt); Nurses aides 5 (ft), 9 (pt); Activities coordinators 1 (ft); Dietitians 1 (ft).
Affiliation Methodist
Facilities Dining room; Physical therapy room; Activities room; Chapel; Crafts room; Laundry room; Barber/Beauty shop; Library.
Activities Arts & crafts; Cards; Games; Movies; Shopping trips; Social/Cultural gatherings.

RIPON

Parkview Nursing Home Inc
PO Box 509, 50 Wolverton Ave, Ripon, WI, 54971-0509
(414) 748-5638
Admin Emil Kesich.
Licensure Skilled care; Intermediate care. *Beds* 177. *Certified* Medicaid.
Owner Nonprofit Corp.

Ripon Area Residential Center
1002 Eureka St, Ripon, WI, 54971
(414) 748-6252
Admin Lisa Selthofner. *Medical Dir/Dir of Nursing* Paul Nelsen MD; Barb Prellwitz DON.
Licensure Intermediate care for mentally retarded. *Beds* ICF/MR 60. *Certified* Medicaid.
Owner Nonprofit Corp.

Admissions Requirements Minimum age 18;
Medical examination; Physician's request;
County Unified Services approval.
Staff RNs 2 (ft), 1 (pt); LPNs 2 (ft), 4 (pt);
Nurses aides 14 (ft), 10 (pt); Physical
therapists 1 (pt); Recreational therapists 2
(ft); Occupational therapists 1 (pt); Speech
therapists 1 (pt); Activities coordinators 1
(ft); Dietitians 1 (pt); Psychologist 1 (pt);
Social worker 1 (pt); Work activity trainer 1
(ft), 1 (pt).
Facilities Dining room; Physical therapy
room; Activities room; Crafts room; Laundry
room; Barber/Beauty shop; Work activity;
Visiting lounge; TV lounges.
Activities Cards; Games; Prayer groups;
Movies; Shopping trips; Social/Cultural
gatherings; Church; Bible study; Swimming;
Bowling.

RIVER FALLS

River Falls Area Hospital Kinnic Home Division
550 N Main St, River Falls, WI, 54022
(715) 425-7957
Admin Mary L Hanson. *Medical Dir/Dir of
Nursing* Dr R Hammer; Dorothy Symes.
Licensure Skilled care; Intermediate care;
Respite. *Beds* 68. *Certified* Medicaid.
Owner Nonprofit Corp.
Admissions Requirements Minimum age 18;
Medical examination; Physician's request.
Staff RNs 2 (ft), 3 (pt); LPNs 4 (ft), 6 (pt);
Orderlies 2 (ft), 5 (pt); Nurses aides 10 (ft),
23 (pt); Activities coordinators 1 (ft), 2 (pt);
Dietitians 1 (pt); Social worker 1 (ft), 1 (pt)
Pharmacist 1 (ft), 2 (pt).
Facilities Dining room; Physical therapy
room; Activities room; Chapel; Laundry
room; Barber/Beauty shop; Library; Hospital
with occupational therapy room; Speech/
physical therapy; Lab; X-ray; Emergency
room.
Activities Arts & crafts; Cards; Games;
Reading groups; Prayer groups; Movies;
Shopping trips; Social/Cultural gatherings;
Outings.

River Falls Care Center
640 N Main St, River Falls, WI, 54022
(715) 425-5353
Admin Glenda Zielski. *Medical Dir/Dir of
Nursing* Robert Johnson MD; Jean Clausen
RN DON.
Licensure Skilled care; Intermediate care;
Residential. *Beds* SNF 140; Residential 11.
Certified Medicaid; Medicare.
Owner Proprietary Corp.
Admissions Requirements Minimum age 18;
Medical examination; Physician's request.
Staff Physicians; RNs; LPNs; Orderlies;
Nurses aides; Physical therapists;
Occupational therapists; Speech therapists;
Activities coordinators; Dietitians.
Facilities Dining room; Physical therapy
room; Activities room; Chapel; Barber/
Beauty shop.
Activities Arts & crafts; Cards; Games;
Reading groups; Prayer groups; Movies;
Shopping trips; Social/Cultural gatherings.

SAINT CROIX FALLS

St Croix Valley Good Samaritan Center
750 Louisiana E, Saint Croix Falls, WI, 54024
(715) 483-9815
Admin Rev Max Dietze. *Medical Dir/Dir of
Nursing* Dr William Riegel; Sharon Loaney
RN DON.
Licensure Skilled care; Intermediate care. *Beds*
SNF 68; ICF. *Certified* Medicaid.
Owner Nonprofit Corp (Evangelical Lutheran/
Good Samaritan).
Admissions Requirements Minimum age 18;
Medical examination; Physician's request.

Staff Physicians 2 (pt); RNs 3 (ft), 4 (pt);
LPNs 2 (ft), 4 (pt); Orderlies 1 (pt); Nurses
aides 10 (ft), 17 (pt); Physical therapists 1
(pt); Occupational therapists 1 (pt); Speech
therapists 1 (pt); Activities coordinators 1
(ft).
Affiliation Lutheran
Facilities Dining room; Physical therapy
room; Activities room; Chapel; Crafts room;
Laundry room; Barber/Beauty shop; Library.
Activities Arts & crafts; Cards; Games;
Reading groups; Prayer groups; Movies;
Shopping trips; Social/Cultural gatherings.

SAINT FRANCIS

South Shore Manor
1915 E Tripoli Ave, Saint Francis, WI, 53207
(414) 483-3611
Admin Patricia Maurer. *Medical Dir/Dir of
Nursing* Greg Nierengarten DO.
Licensure Skilled care. *Beds* SNF 34; ICF.
Certified Medicaid.
Owner Proprietary Corp (Beverly Enterprises).
Admissions Requirements Minimum age 18;
Medical examination; Physician's request.
Staff Physicians 1 (pt); RNs 1 (ft), 1 (pt);
LPNs 3 (ft), 3 (pt); Activities coordinators 1
(pt); Dietitians 1 (ft), 3 (pt); Dentists 1 (pt);
Ophthalmologists 1 (pt).
Facilities Dining room; Physical therapy
room; Activities room; Laundry room;
Barber/Beauty shop; Library.
Activities Arts & crafts; Cards; Games;
Reading groups; Prayer groups; Movies;
Shopping trips; Social/Cultural gatherings;
Groups for confused & disoriented; Visits
from elementary and preschool age children.

SAUK CITY

Maplewood of Sauk Prairie*
245 Sycamore St, Sauk City, WI, 53583
(608) 643-3383
Admin Scott A Nelson.
Licensure Skilled care; Intermediate care. *Beds*
125. *Certified* Medicaid.
Owner Proprietary Corp.

SCHOFIELD

Heritage Haven Care Center
6001 Alderson St, Schofield, WI, 54476
(715) 359-4257
Admin Suzanne T Whitty. *Medical Dir/Dir of
Nursing* C Grauer MD.
Licensure Skilled care; Intermediate care. *Beds*
164. *Certified* Medicaid.
Owner Proprietary Corp (Hillhaven Corp).
Admissions Requirements Minimum age 18;
Medical examination; Physician's request.
Facilities Dining room; Physical therapy
room; Activities room; Chapel; Laundry
room; Barber/Beauty shop; Books available;
Social services.
Activities Arts & crafts; Cards; Games;
Reading groups; Prayer groups; Movies;
Shopping trips; Social/Cultural gatherings.

SEYMOUR

Good Shepherd Nursing Home Ltd
607 Bronson Rd, Seymour, WI, 54165
(414) 833-6856
Admin Shirley K Mielke. *Medical Dir/Dir of
Nursing* Dr Lindy Eatwell; Lori Schultz.
Licensure Skilled care; Intermediate care. *Beds*
97. *Certified* Medicaid.
Owner Nonprofit Corp.
Admissions Requirements Minimum age 18;
Medical examination; Physician's request.
Staff Physicians 8 (pt); RNs 1 (ft), 8 (pt);
LPNs 3 (ft), 6 (pt); Orderlies 1 (pt); Nurses
aides 16 (ft), 32 (pt); Physical therapists 1
(pt); Occupational therapists 1 (pt); Speech

therapists 1 (pt); Activities coordinators 1
(ft), 2 (pt); Dietitians 1 (pt);
Ophthalmologists 1 (pt).
Facilities Dining room; Physical therapy
room; Activities room; Chapel; Laundry
room; Barber/Beauty shop; Senior citizen
center; Conference room.
Activities Arts & crafts; Cards; Games;
Reading groups; Prayer groups; Movies;
Shopping trips; Social/Cultural gatherings;
Exercise program; Music therapy.

SHAWANO

Birch Hill Health Care Center
1475 Birch Hill Ln, Shawano, WI, 54166
(715) 526-3161
Admin Leonard J Kary. *Medical Dir/Dir of
Nursing* Ronald Lageman; Gail Mader.
Licensure Skilled care. *Beds* SNF 102.
Certified Medicaid; Medicare.
Owner Proprietary Corp.
Admissions Requirements Medical
examination; Physician's request.
Staff RNs 5 (ft), 3 (pt); LPNs 2 (ft), 2 (pt);
Nurses aides 21 (ft), 13 (pt); Activities
coordinators 1 (ft); Dietitians 1 (pt).
Facilities Dining room; Physical therapy
room; Activities room; Chapel; Crafts room;
Laundry room; Barber/Beauty shop.
Activities Arts & crafts; Cards; Games;
Reading groups; Prayer groups; Movies;
Shopping trips; Social/Cultural gatherings.

Evergreen Health Care Center Inc
1250 Evergreen St, Shawano, WI, 54166
(715) 526-3107
Admin Jane Wuench. *Medical Dir/Dir of
Nursing* R L Logemann MD; Kathleen Dey
RN DON.
Licensure Skilled care; Intermediate care. *Beds*
103. *Certified* Medicaid; Medicare.
Owner Proprietary Corp.
Admissions Requirements Medical
examination; Physician's request.
Facilities Dining room; Physical therapy
room; Activities room; Chapel; Crafts room;
Laundry room; Barber/Beauty shop.
Activities Arts & crafts; Cards; Games;
Reading groups; Prayer groups; Movies;
Shopping trips; Social/Cultural gatherings.

Heartland of Shawano*
PO Box 454, Shawano, WI, 54166
(715) 526-6111
Admin Lisa Schulte. *Medical Dir/Dir of
Nursing* Patricia Stuff MD.
Licensure Skilled care; Intermediate care. *Beds*
118. *Certified* Medicaid; Medicare.
Owner Proprietary Corp (Health Care &
Retirement Corp).
Admissions Requirements Minimum age 18;
Medical examination; Physician's request.
Staff RNs 2 (ft), 2 (pt); LPNs 4 (ft), 4 (pt);
Nurses aides 25 (ft), 15 (pt); Physical
therapists 1 (ft); Occupational therapists 1
(pt); Speech therapists 1 (pt); Activities
coordinators 1 (ft), 1 (pt); Dietitians 1 (pt).
Facilities Dining room; Physical therapy
room; Activities room; Chapel; Laundry
room; Barber/Beauty shop.
Activities Cards; Games; Reading groups;
Prayer groups; Movies; Shopping trips;
Social/Cultural gatherings.

Maple Lane Health Care Facility
PO Box 534, Shawano, WI, 54166
(715) 526-3158
Admin Thomas W Arvey. *Medical Dir/Dir of
Nursing* Alois J Sebesta; Mary Martin.
Licensure Skilled care; Intermediate care;
Intermediate care for mentally retarded.
Beds ICF 72; ICF/MR 30. *Certified*
Medicaid.
Owner Publicly owned.
Admissions Requirements Minimum age;
Medical examination.

Staff Physicians 1 (pt); RNs 3 (ft), 2 (pt);
LPNs 6 (pt); Nurses aides 22 (ft), 14 (pt);
Activities coordinators 1 (ft); Dietitians 1
(pt).
Facilities Dining room; Activities room;
Chapel; Crafts room; Laundry room; Barber/
Beauty shop; Library; Woodshop; Kitchen;
Dental exam room; Canteen.
Activities Arts & crafts; Cards; Games; Prayer
groups; Movies; Shopping trips; Social/
Cultural gatherings; Woodworking; Exercises;
Current events; Socialization.

SHEBOYGAN

Greendale Health Center*
3129 Michigan Ave, Sheboygan, WI, 53082
(414) 458-1155
Admin Suzanne M Groth. *Medical Dir/Dir of
Nursing* Dr Stephen Wescott.
Licensure Skilled care; Intermediate care. *Beds*
64. *Certified* Medicaid.
Owner Proprietary Corp.
Admissions Requirements Minimum age 18;
Medical examination; Physician's request.
Staff Physicians 1 (pt); Physical therapists 1
(pt); Reality therapists 1 (ft), 1 (pt);
Recreational therapists 1 (ft), 1 (pt);
Occupational therapists 1 (pt); Speech
therapists 1 (pt); Activities coordinators 1
(ft); Dietitians 1 (ft); Dentists 1 (pt);
Audiologists 1 (pt).
Facilities Dining room; Physical therapy
room; Activities room; Chapel; Crafts room;
Laundry room; Barber/Beauty shop; Library;
Luxurious lounges; Outside areas; Private
personal storage; Safety deposit box;
Specially equipped vans for patient
transportation or family use.
Activities Arts & crafts; Cards; Games;
Reading groups; Prayer groups; Movies;
Shopping trips; Social/Cultural gatherings;
Resident council; Geriatric/adult day care;
Outpatient physical therapy, occupational
therapy, speech therapy; Outpatient activities
program.

Heritage Nursing Center*
1902 Mead St, Sheboygan, WI, 53081
(414) 458-8333
Admin Virgil W Kalchthaler. *Medical Dir/Dir
of Nursing* Dr Robert A Helminiak.
Licensure Skilled care; Intermediate care. *Beds*
156. *Certified* Medicaid.
Owner Proprietary Corp.
Admissions Requirements Minimum age 18;
Medical examination; Physician's request.
Staff Physicians; RNs; LPNs; Orderlies;
Nurses aides; Physical therapists; Reality
therapists; Recreational therapists;
Occupational therapists; Speech therapists;
Activities coordinators; Dietitians; Dentists;
Ophthalmologists; Podiatrists; Audiologists.
Facilities Dining room; Activities room;
Crafts room; Laundry room; Barber/Beauty
shop.
Activities Arts & crafts; Cards; Games;
Reading groups; Prayer groups; Shopping
trips.

Meadow View Manor Nursing Home Inc
3613 S 13th St, Sheboygan, WI, 53081
(414) 458-4040
Admin Marilyn L Schmidtke. *Medical Dir/Dir
of Nursing* Jacolyn Stone DON.
Licensure Intermediate care. *Beds* ICF 74.
Certified Medicaid.
Owner Privately owned.
Admissions Requirements Physician's request.
Facilities Dining room; Activities room;
Laundry room; Barber/Beauty shop.
Activities Arts & crafts; Cards; Games;
Reading groups; Prayer groups; Movies;
Shopping trips; Social/Cultural gatherings.

Morningside Health Center
3431 N 13th St, Sheboygan, WI, 53081
(414) 457-5046

Admin Edith M Schmidt.
Licensure Skilled care; Intermediate care. *Beds*
72. *Certified* Medicaid.
Owner Proprietary Corp.

Olive Schaeffer Home*
1406 N 11th St, Sheboygan, WI, 53081
(414) 499-4892
Admin Glenn T Beaudry.
Licensure Intermediate care; Intermediate care
for mentally retarded. *Beds* 12. *Certified*
Medicaid.
Owner Nonprofit Corp.

**Sheboygan Retirement Home & Beach Health
Care Center Inc**
930 N 6th St, Sheboygan, WI, 53081
(414) 458-2137
Admin Michael J Basch. *Medical Dir/Dir of
Nursing* Vytas Kerpe MD; Pat Kolb RN
DON.
Licensure Skilled care; Intermediate care;
CBRF-Residential Apartments. *Beds* SNF
82; Residential 94. *Certified* Medicaid.
Owner Nonprofit organization/foundation.
Admissions Requirements Medical
examination.
Staff RNs 1 (ft), 3 (pt); LPNs 6 (ft), 11 (pt);
Orderlies 19 (ft), 38 (pt); Physical therapists
1 (ft); Activities coordinators 2 (ft), 1 (pt).
Affiliation Methodist
Facilities Dining room; Physical therapy
room; Activities room; Chapel; Crafts room;
Laundry room; Barber/Beauty shop; Library;
Patio; Sun deck; Wood working shop.
Activities Arts & crafts; Cards; Games;
Reading groups; Prayer groups; Movies;
Shopping trips; Social/Cultural gatherings.

Sunny Ridge
3014 Erie Ave, Sheboygan, WI, 53081
(414) 459-3028
Admin Mary Ann Drescher. *Medical Dir/Dir
of Nursing* Dr Curtis Hancock; Dorthea
Miller DON.
Licensure Skilled care; Intermediate care. *Beds*
398. *Certified* Medicaid.
Owner Publicly owned.
Admissions Requirements Minimum age 18.
Staff RNs 13 (ft), 17 (pt); LPNs 9 (ft), 16 (pt);
Nurses aides 65 (ft), 57 (pt); Occupational
therapists 1 (ft).
Facilities Dining room; Physical therapy
room; Activities room; Chapel; Crafts room;
Laundry room; Barber/Beauty shop; Library.
Activities Arts & crafts; Cards; Games;
Reading groups; Prayer groups; Movies;
Shopping trips; Social/Cultural gatherings.

SHEBOYGAN FALLS

Pine Haven Christian Home
531 Giddings Ave, Sheboygan Falls, WI,
53085
(414) 467-2401, 458-7999
Admin Daniel H Pastoor. *Medical Dir/Dir of
Nursing* Mary Veenendaal RN.
Licensure Intermediate care. *Beds* ICF 71.
Certified Medicaid.
Owner Nonprofit Corp.
Admissions Requirements Minimum age 65;
Medical examination.
Staff RNs 1 (ft), 3 (pt); LPNs 1 (ft), 5 (pt);
Nurses aides 32 (pt); Activities coordinators
2 (pt); Dietitians 1 (pt).
Facilities Dining room; Activities room;
Laundry room; Barber/Beauty shop; Library.
Activities Arts & crafts; Cards; Games;
Reading groups; Prayer groups; Movies;
Shopping trips.

Sheboygan Comprehensive Health Center
PO Box 265, Rte 2, Sheboygan Falls, WI,
53085
(414) 467-4648
Admin John Van Der Male. *Medical Dir/Dir
of Nursing* Dr William Forkner.

Licensure Skilled care; Intermediate care. *Beds*
174. *Certified* Medicaid.
Owner Publicly owned.
Admissions Requirements Minimum age 18;
Medical examination.
Staff Physicians 4 (pt); RNs 7 (ft), 8 (pt);
LPNs 10 (ft), 9 (pt); Nurses aides 38 (ft), 40
(pt); Physical therapists 1 (pt); Occupational
therapists 1 (ft); Speech therapists 1 (pt);
Dietitians 1 (ft); Dentists 1 (pt);
Ophthalmologists 1 (pt); Podiatrists 1 (pt);
Dentist 1 (pt).
Facilities Dining room; Activities room;
Chapel; Crafts room; Barber/Beauty shop;
Library.
Activities Arts & crafts; Cards; Games;
Reading groups; Prayer groups; Movies;
Shopping trips; Social/Cultural gatherings;
Swimming; Bowling; Fishing; Sheltered
workshop.

SHELL LAKE

Terraceview Living Center
PO Box 379, County Trunk B, Shell Lake, WI,
54871
(715) 468-7292
Admin Lindell W Weathers. *Medical Dir/Dir
of Nursing* Greg Thatcher MD.
Licensure Skilled care. *Beds* SNF 70. *Certified*
Medicaid; Medicare.
Owner Nonprofit organization/foundation.
Admissions Requirements Minimum age 18;
Medical examination; Physician's request.
Staff Physicians 11 (pt); RNs 1 (ft), 2 (pt);
LPNs 4 (ft), 2 (pt); Nurses aides 6 (ft), 13
(pt); Speech therapists 1 (pt); Activities
coordinators 1 (pt); Dietitians 1 (pt); Dentist
1 (pt).
Facilities Dining room; Physical therapy
room; Activities room; Chapel; Crafts room;
Laundry room; Barber/Beauty shop.
Activities Arts & crafts; Cards; Games;
Reading groups; Prayer groups; Movies;
Shopping trips; Social/Cultural gatherings.

SIREN

Capeside Cove Good Samaritan Center
PO Box 49, Siren, WI, 54872
(715) 349-2292
Admin Charlene L Borchers. *Medical Dir/Dir
of Nursing* Richard L Hartzell MD; Sharon
McNeil RN DON.
Licensure Skilled care. *Beds* SNF 100.
Certified Medicaid.
Owner Nonprofit Corp (Evangelical Lutheran/
Good Samaritan).
Admissions Requirements Medical
examination; Physician's request.
Staff RNs 5 (ft), 5 (pt); LPNs 3 (ft), 6 (pt);
Nurses aides 20 (ft), 30 (pt); Activities
coordinators 1 (ft), 2 (pt).
Affiliation Lutheran
Facilities Dining room; Activities room;
Chapel; Crafts room; Laundry room; Barber/
Beauty shop; Library; Visiting room;
Lounges.
Activities Arts & crafts; Cards; Games;
Reading groups; Movies; Shopping trips;
Social/Cultural gatherings; Exercise groups;
Walking groups.

SISTER BAY

Scandia Village Retirement Center
290 Smith Dr, Sister Bay, WI, 54234
(414) 854-2317
Admin Rev Steven P Gutzman. *Medical Dir/
Dir of Nursing* Dr William Meyer.
Licensure Skilled care. *Beds* 60. *Certified*
Medicaid.
Owner Nonprofit Corp (Evangelical Lutheran/
Good Samaritan).
Admissions Requirements Minimum age 16;
Medical examination; Physician's request.

Staff Physicians; RNs 2 (ft), 3 (pt); LPNs 1 (ft), 3 (pt); Orderlies 1 (ft); Nurses aides 8 (ft), 10 (pt); Physical therapists; Occupational therapists; Activities coordinators 1 (ft); Dietitians; Dentists.
Affiliation Lutheran
Facilities Dining room; Physical therapy room; Activities room; Chapel; Crafts room; Laundry room; Barber/Beauty shop; Library; Living room/lounge.
Activities Arts & crafts; Cards; Games; Reading groups; Prayer groups; Movies; Shopping trips; Social/Cultural gatherings.

SOLDIERS GROVE

Sannes
Hwy 61, Soldiers Grove, WI, 54655
(608) 624-5244
Admin Donald A Sannes. *Medical Dir/Dir of Nursing* Timothy Devitt MD; Marlene Norman DON.
Licensure Skilled care; Intermediate care. *Beds* 66. *Certified* Medicaid.
Owner Proprietary Corp.
Admissions Requirements Medical examination.
Staff RNs; LPNs; Nurses aides; Activities coordinators; Dietitians.
Facilities Dining room; Physical therapy room; Activities room; Chapel; Crafts room; Laundry room; Barber/Beauty shop; Library.
Activities Arts & crafts; Cards; Games; Reading groups; Prayer groups; Movies; Shopping trips; Social/Cultural gatherings.

SOUTH MILWAUKEE

Franciscan Villa of South Milwaukee
3601 S Chicago Ave, South Milwaukee, WI, 53172
(414) 764-4100
Admin Sr Rita Kraemer. *Medical Dir/Dir of Nursing* Antonio A Malapira MD; Donna Phillips RN BSN.
Licensure Skilled care; Intermediate care. *Beds* SNF; ICF 150. *Certified* Medicaid.
Owner Nonprofit Corp.
Staff RNs 9 (ft), 9 (pt); LPNs 7 (ft), 12 (pt); Nurses aides 22 (ft), 53 (pt); Physical therapists; Recreational therapists 1 (ft); Occupational therapists 1 (ft); Speech therapists 1 (pt); Activities coordinators 1 (ft); Dietitians 1 (pt); Ophthalmologists 2 (pt); Podiatrists 1 (pt); Art Therapist 1 (pt).
Affiliation Roman Catholic
Facilities Dining room; Physical therapy room; Activities room; Chapel; Crafts room; Laundry room; Barber/Beauty shop; Occupational therapy.
Activities Arts & crafts; Cards; Games; Reading groups; Movies; Shopping trips; Social/Cultural gatherings.

Willowcrest Nursing Home
3821 S Chicago Ave, South Milwaukee, WI, 53172
(414) 762-7336
Admin Gloria Glowinski. *Medical Dir/Dir of Nursing* Dr Wadie Abdallah MD; Julie Heuser DON.
Licensure Skilled care. *Beds* 51. *Certified* Medicaid; Medicare.
Owner Proprietary Corp (Unicare).
Admissions Requirements Medical examination; Physician's request.
Staff RNs 9 (ft), 6 (pt); LPNs 8 (ft), 7 (pt); Nurses aides 12 (ft), 10 (pt); Activities coordinators 1 (ft), 1 (pt); Dietitians 1 (ft).
Facilities Dining room; Physical therapy room; Activities room; Crafts room; Laundry room; Barber/Beauty shop.
Activities Arts & crafts; Cards; Games; Reading groups; Prayer groups; Movies; Shopping trips; Social/Cultural gatherings.

SPARTA

Morrow Memorial Home for the Aged*
331 S Water St, Sparta, WI, 54656
(608) 269-3168
Admin Larry W Alens. *Medical Dir/Dir of Nursing* Dr Paul G Albrecht.
Licensure Skilled care; Intermediate care. *Beds* 115. *Certified* Medicaid.
Owner Nonprofit Corp.
Admissions Requirements Medical examination; Physician's request.
Staff RNs 3 (ft), 5 (pt); LPNs 2 (ft), 5 (pt); Nurses aides 9 (ft), 27 (pt); Activities coordinators 1 (pt).
Affiliation Methodist
Facilities Dining room; Physical therapy room; Activities room; Chapel; Crafts room; Laundry room; Barber/Beauty shop; Library.
Activities Arts & crafts; Cards; Games; Reading groups; Prayer groups; Movies; Shopping trips; Social/Cultural gatherings.

Rolling Hills*
Rte 2, Sparta, WI, 54656
(608) 269-8800
Admin John D Brennan. *Medical Dir/Dir of Nursing* Dr Patricia Raftery.
Licensure Skilled care; Intermediate care. *Beds* 248. *Certified* Medicaid.
Owner Publicly owned.
Staff Physicians 3 (pt); RNs 11 (ft), 9 (pt); LPNs 6 (ft), 11 (pt); Nurses aides 78 (ft), 32 (pt); Physical therapists 1 (pt); Occupational therapists 1 (pt); Speech therapists 1 (pt); Activities coordinators 2 (ft); Dietitians 1 (pt); Dentists 1 (pt); Podiatrists 1 (pt).
Facilities Dining room; Physical therapy room; Activities room; Chapel; Crafts room; Laundry room; Barber/Beauty shop; Library.
Activities Arts & crafts; Cards; Games; Reading groups; Prayer groups; Movies; Shopping trips; Social/Cultural gatherings.

St Mary's Nursing Home
K & W Main Streets, Sparta, WI, 54656
(608) 269-2132
Admin Sr Julie Tydrich. *Medical Dir/Dir of Nursing* Susan Davis.
Licensure Skilled care. *Beds* 30. *Certified* Medicaid.
Owner Nonprofit Corp.
Admissions Requirements Medical examination.
Staff RNs 1 (ft), 6 (pt); LPNs 1 (ft), 2 (pt); Nurses aides 3 (ft), 9 (pt); Physical therapists 1 (ft), 1 (pt); Recreational therapists 1 (pt); Occupational therapists 1 (pt); Speech therapists 1 (pt); Activities coordinators 1 (pt); Dietitians 1 (pt).
Affiliation Roman Catholic
Facilities Dining room; Physical therapy room; Activities room; Chapel; Crafts room; Laundry room; Barber/Beauty shop.
Activities Arts & crafts; Cards; Games; Reading groups; Prayer groups; Movies; Shopping trips; Social/Cultural gatherings.

SPOONER

Spooner Hospital & Nursing Home
819 Ash St, Spooner, WI, 54801
(715) 635-2111
Admin Craig J Barness. *Medical Dir/Dir of Nursing* Dr Fredrick Goetsch MD; Nancy Detlefsen, RN DON.
Licensure Skilled care. *Beds* SNF 90. *Certified* Medicaid.
Owner Nonprofit Corp.
Admissions Requirements Medical examination; Physician's request.
Staff Physicians 10 (ft); RNs 8 (ft); LPNs 10 (ft), 5 (pt); Nurses aides 30 (ft), 15 (pt); Physical therapists 2 (ft), 1 (pt); Recreational therapists 2 (ft); Speech therapists 1 (ft); Activities coordinators 1 (ft); Dietitians 1 (ft); Dentists 2 (ft); Ophthalmologists 2 (ft).

Facilities Dining room; Physical therapy room; Activities room; Chapel; Crafts room; Laundry room; Barber/Beauty shop; Library.
Activities Arts & crafts; Cards; Games; Reading groups; Prayer groups; Movies; Shopping trips; Social/Cultural gatherings.

SPRING GREEN

Greenway Manor
501 S Winsted, Spring Green, WI, 53588
(608) 588-2586
Admin Mark W Scoles. *Medical Dir/Dir of Nursing* Dr Gerald Kempthorne; Theresa Young.
Licensure Skilled care; Intermediate care. *Beds* 60. *Certified* Medicaid; Medicare.
Owner Proprietary Corp.
Admissions Requirements Physician's request.
Staff RNs 2 (ft), 7 (pt); LPNs 1 (ft), 2 (pt); Nurses aides 10 (ft), 25 (pt); Physical therapists 1 (pt); Recreational therapists 1 (ft), 1 (pt).
Facilities Dining room; Physical therapy room; Activities room; Chapel; Crafts room; Laundry room; Barber/Beauty shop; Library.
Activities Arts & crafts; Cards; Games; Reading groups; Movies; Social/Cultural gatherings.

SPRING VALLEY

Spring Valley Municipal Nursing Home
Hwy 29, Spring Valley, WI, 54767
(715) 778-5545
Admin Craig D Ubbelohde. *Medical Dir/Dir of Nursing* Gale Murty; Gayle Schliep DON.
Licensure Skilled care; Intermediate care. *Beds* SNF 86; ICF. *Certified* Medicaid.
Owner Nonprofit Corp.
Admissions Requirements Minimum age 18; Medical examination; Physician's request.
Staff Physicians 1 (pt); RNs 3 (ft), 1 (pt); LPNs 5 (ft), 2 (pt); Nurses aides 10 (ft), 20 (pt); Physical therapists 1 (pt); Recreational therapists 1 (ft); Occupational therapists 1 (pt); Speech therapists 1 (pt); Activities coordinators 1 (ft); Dietitians 1 (ft); Dentists 1 (pt); Ophthalmologists 1 (pt); Podiatrists 1 (pt).
Languages Norwegian
Facilities Dining room; Physical therapy room; Activities room; Chapel; Crafts room; Laundry room; Barber/Beauty shop; Library.
Activities Arts & crafts; Cards; Games; Reading groups; Prayer groups; Movies; Shopping trips; Social/Cultural gatherings; Fishing trips; Van w/wheelchair lift; Lunch outings; Museums; Antique shops.

STANLEY

Victory Memorial Hospital & Nursing Home
230 E 4th Ave, Stanley, WI, 54768
(715) 644-5571
Admin John J Blahnik. *Medical Dir/Dir of Nursing* William Hopkins MD; Sharon Polanski RN.
Licensure Skilled care; Intermediate care. *Beds* SNF 86. *Certified* Medicaid.
Owner Nonprofit Corp.
Admissions Requirements Medical examination; Physician's request.
Staff Physicians 10 (ft); RNs 4 (ft), 8 (pt); LPNs 2 (ft), 9 (pt); Nurses aides 14 (ft), 28 (pt); Physical therapists 2 (ft); Occupational therapists 1 (ft); Speech therapists 1 (pt); Activities coordinators 1 (ft); Dietitians 1 (ft), 1 (pt); Podiatrists 1 (pt).
Languages Polish
Facilities Dining room; Physical therapy room; Activities room; Chapel; Crafts room; Laundry room; Barber/Beauty shop.
Activities Arts & crafts; Cards; Games; Reading groups; Prayer groups; Movies; Shopping trips; Social/Cultural gatherings.

STEVENS POINT

Portage County Home
825 Whiting Ave, Stevens Point, WI, 54481
(715) 346-1374
Admin George R Samardich. *Medical Dir/Dir of Nursing* Dr Daniel Brick; Elizabeth Rollo DON.
Licensure Skilled care; Intermediate care. *Beds* SNF 139; ICF. *Certified* Medicaid.
Owner Publicly owned.
Admissions Requirements Minimum age 18; Medical examination; Physician's request.
Staff Physicians 1 (pt); RNs 3 (ft), 8 (pt); LPNs 2 (ft), 6 (pt); Nurses aides 28 (ft), 37 (pt); Physical therapists 1 (pt); Recreational therapists 1 (pt); Occupational therapists 1 (pt); Activities coordinators 1 (pt); Dietitians 1 (pt); Ophthalmologists 1 (pt); Dentist 1 (pt).
Facilities Dining room; Physical therapy room; Activities room; Chapel; Crafts room; Laundry room; Barber/Beauty shop; Library.
Activities Arts & crafts; Cards; Games; Reading groups; Prayer groups; Movies; Shopping trips; Social/Cultural gatherings.

River Pines Living Center
1800 Sherman Ave, Stevens Point, WI, 54481
(715) 344-1800
Admin Lou Gasparo. *Medical Dir/Dir of Nursing* Daniel L Brick MD; Gail Viergutz.
Licensure Skilled care; Intermediate care. *Beds* 238. *Certified* Medicaid; Medicare.
Owner Nonprofit Corp (Adventist Health Sys-USA).
Admissions Requirements Minimum age 18; Medical examination.
Staff Physicians 8 (pt); RNs 4 (ft), 9 (pt); LPNs 1 (ft), 21 (pt); Nurses aides 107 (ft), 1 (pt); Physical therapists 1 (ft); Occupational therapists 1 (ft); Speech therapists 1 (ft); Activities coordinators 1 (ft); Dietitians 1 (ft).
Affiliation Seventh-Day Adventist
Facilities Dining room; Physical therapy room; Activities room; Chapel; Crafts room; Laundry room; Barber/Beauty shop; Library.
Activities Arts & crafts; Cards; Games; Reading groups; Prayer groups; Movies; Shopping trips; Social/Cultural gatherings.

STOUGHTON

McCarthy Nursing Home*
124 S Monroe St, Stoughton, WI, 53589
(608) 873-7462
Admin Michael J McCarthy. *Medical Dir/Dir of Nursing* Jean E Pecotte.
Licensure Intermediate care for mentally retarded. *Beds* 18. *Certified* Medicaid.
Owner Proprietary Corp.
Staff RNs 1 (ft); LPNs 1 (ft); Nurses aides 7 (ft); Activities coordinators 1 (pt); Dietitians 1 (pt).
Facilities Dining room; Activities room; Laundry room.
Activities Arts & crafts; Cards; Games; Reading groups; Prayer groups; Movies; Shopping trips; Social/Cultural gatherings.

Morningside Care Center*
PO Box 313, Stoughton, WI, 53589
(608) 873-6441
Admin Ruth C Jensen.
Licensure Intermediate care for mentally retarded. *Beds* 15. *Certified* Medicaid.
Owner Proprietary Corp.

Nazareth House
814 Jackson St, Stoughton, WI, 53589
(608) 873-6448
Admin Sr Rose Hoye. *Medical Dir/Dir of Nursing* Dr V W Nordholm.
Licensure Skilled care; Intermediate care. *Beds* 99. *Certified* Medicaid.
Owner Nonprofit Corp.

Admissions Requirements Minimum age 65; Medical examination.
Staff Physicians 2 (pt); RNs 4 (ft), 4 (pt); LPNs 2 (ft), 2 (pt); Nurses aides 30 (ft), 12 (pt); Physical therapists 1 (ft), 2 (pt); Reality therapists 1 (ft); Recreational therapists 1 (pt); Activities coordinators 1 (ft), 3 (pt); Dietitians 1 (ft); Dentist 1 (pt).
Affiliation Roman Catholic
Facilities Dining room; Physical therapy room; Activities room; Chapel; Crafts room; Laundry room; Barber/Beauty shop; Sunrooms.
Activities Arts & crafts; Cards; Games; Prayer groups; Movies; Social/Cultural gatherings.

Nygaard Manor
321 N Johnson St, Stoughton, WI, 53589
(608) 873-9072
Admin Kristine Gabert. *Medical Dir/Dir of Nursing* Clarice Lyke DON.
Licensure Intermediate care. *Beds* ICF 16.
Owner Nonprofit Corp.
Admissions Requirements Minimum age 65; Females only; Medical examination; Physician's request.
Staff Physicians 1 (pt); RNs 1 (ft), 1 (pt); LPNs 1 (ft), 3 (pt); Nurses aides 2 (ft), 4 (pt); Physical therapists 1 (pt); Occupational therapists 1 (pt); Activities coordinators 1 (pt); Dietitians 1 (pt).
Languages Norwegian
Affiliation Lutheran
Facilities Dining room; Activities room; Laundry room.
Activities Arts & crafts; Cards; Games; Reading groups; Prayer groups; Movies; Shopping trips; Social/Cultural gatherings.

Skaalen Sunset Home
400 N Morris St, Stoughton, WI, 53589
(608) 873-9454
Admin Mark Benson. *Medical Dir/Dir of Nursing* Dr David Nelson.
Licensure Skilled care; Intermediate care. *Beds* 270. *Certified* Medicaid.
Owner Nonprofit Corp.
Admissions Requirements Minimum age 65; Medical examination; Physician's request.
Staff RNs 7 (ft), 12 (pt); LPNs 5 (ft), 21 (pt); Orderlies 2 (ft); Nurses aides 33 (ft), 122 (pt); Recreational therapists 2 (ft), 1 (pt); Occupational therapists 1 (ft), 1 (pt); Activities coordinators 1 (ft); Dietitians 1 (pt).
Affiliation Lutheran
Facilities Dining room; Physical therapy room; Activities room; Chapel; Crafts room; Barber/Beauty shop; Library; Inservice education.
Activities Arts & crafts; Cards; Games; Reading groups; Prayer groups; Movies; Shopping trips; Social/Cultural gatherings.

STRUM

Strum Nursing Home
PO Box 217, 208 Elm St, Strum, WI, 54770
(715) 695-2611
Admin Mary Gullicksrud. *Medical Dir/Dir of Nursing* Dr William E Wright; Roberta Ross RN.
Licensure Skilled care; Intermediate care. *Beds* SNF 44; ICF 6. *Certified* Medicaid.
Owner Proprietary Corp.
Admissions Requirements Minimum age 18; Medical examination.
Staff Physicians 8 (pt); RNs 2 (ft), 3 (pt); LPNs 4 (ft), 1 (pt); Nurses aides 12 (ft), 9 (pt); Physical therapists 1 (pt); Occupational therapists 1 (pt); Speech therapists 1 (pt); Activities coordinators 1 (ft); Dietitians 1 (pt).
Languages Norwegian
Facilities Dining room; Physical therapy room; Activities room; Chapel; Laundry room; Barber/Beauty shop.

Activities Arts & crafts; Cards; Reading groups; Prayer groups; Social/Cultural gatherings.

STURGEON BAY

Door County Memorial Hospital—Skilled Nursing Facility
330 S 16th Pl, Sturgeon Bay, WI, 54235
(414) 743-5566
Admin Willard L Sperry. *Medical Dir/Dir of Nursing* Jeffery J Brook; Karen Bellin.
Licensure Skilled care; Intermediate care. *Beds* SNF 30. *Certified* Medicaid; Medicare.
Owner Nonprofit Corp.
Admissions Requirements Minimum age 18; Medical examination; Physician's request.
Staff Physicians 1 (pt); RNs 5 (pt); LPNs 2 (ft), 3 (pt); Nurses aides 4 (ft), 10 (pt); Activities coordinators 1 (pt); Dietitians 1 (pt).
Facilities Dining room; Activities room; Barber/Beauty shop.
Activities Arts & crafts; Cards; Reading groups; Movies.

Dorchester Nursing Center
200 N 7th Ave, Sturgeon Bay, WI, 54235
(414) 743-6274
Admin Jean Marsh. *Medical Dir/Dir of Nursing* George Roenning MD; Kathleen Russell RN.
Licensure Skilled care. *Beds* SNF 149. *Certified* Medicaid; Medicare.
Owner Proprietary Corp (Beverly Enterprises).
Admissions Requirements Medical examination; Physician's request.
Staff RNs 6 (ft), 6 (pt); LPNs 5 (ft), 5 (pt); Orderlies 5 (ft), 2 (pt); Nurses aides 44 (ft), 23 (pt); Activities coordinators 1 (ft).
Facilities Dining room; Physical therapy room; Activities room; Chapel; Crafts room; Laundry room; Barber/Beauty shop; Beautiful courtyard; Family visiting room.
Activities Arts & crafts; Cards; Games; Reading groups; Prayer groups; Movies; Shopping trips; Social/Cultural gatherings; Family socials.

SUN PRAIRIE

Sun Prairie Health Care Center*
228 W Main St, Sun Prairie, WI, 53590
(608) 837-5959
Admin Lars Rogeberg. *Medical Dir/Dir of Nursing* Dr M Schmidt MD.
Licensure Skilled care. *Beds* 32. *Certified* Medicaid; Medicare.
Owner Proprietary Corp.
Admissions Requirements Medical examination; Physician's request.
Staff Physicians 1 (pt); RNs 1 (ft), 3 (pt); LPNs 1 (ft), 4 (pt); Orderlies 2 (ft), 12 (pt); Physical therapists 1 (pt); Occupational therapists 1 (ft); Speech therapists 1 (pt); Activities coordinators 1 (pt); Dietitians 1 (pt); Dentists 1 (pt); Ophthalmologists 1 (pt); Podiatrists 1 (pt); Audiologists 1 (pt).
Facilities Dining room; Physical therapy room; Activities room; Crafts room; Laundry room; Barber/Beauty shop; Library.
Activities Arts & crafts; Cards; Games; Reading groups; Prayer groups; Movies; Shopping trips; Social/Cultural gatherings.

The Willows Nursing Home*
41 Rickel Rd, Sun Prairie, WI, 53590
(608) 837-8520
Admin Ellen E Fritsch. *Medical Dir/Dir of Nursing* Dr William Russell.
Licensure Skilled care. *Beds* 60. *Certified* Medicaid; Medicare.
Owner Proprietary Corp (Unicare).
Admissions Requirements Minimum age 18; Medical examination; Physician's request.

Staff RNs 1 (ft), 6 (pt); LPNs 7 (pt); Orderlies 2 (pt); Nurses aides 15 (ft), 10 (pt); Recreational therapists 1 (ft), 1 (pt).
Facilities Dining room; Physical therapy room; Activities room; Crafts room; Laundry room; Barber/Beauty shop; Library.
Activities Arts & crafts; Cards; Games; Reading groups; Prayer groups; Movies; Shopping trips; Social/Cultural gatherings; Many discussion groups; Self-help groups; Stroke groups.

SUPERIOR

Chaffey Nursing Home Inc
1419 Hill Ave, Superior, WI, 54880
(715) 392-6121
Admin Joy Jurgensen NHA. *Medical Dir/Dir of Nursing* R P Fruehauf MD; Janice LeMay RN DNS.
Licensure Skilled care; Intermediate care. *Beds* 50. *Certified* Medicaid.
Owner Proprietary Corp.
Admissions Requirements Minimum age 18 unless waivered; Medical examination; Physician's request.
Staff RNs 3 (ft), 1 (pt); LPNs 1 (ft), 9 (pt); Nurses aides 6 (ft), 26 (pt); Physical therapists; Occupational therapists; Speech therapists; Activities coordinators 1 (ft), 1 (pt).
Facilities Dining room; Activities room; Crafts room; Laundry room; Barber/Beauty shop; Library; Patio area for outdoor enjoyment.
Activities Arts & crafts; Cards; Games; Reading groups; Prayer groups; Movies; Shopping trips; Social/Cultural gatherings; Music therapy; Resident council; Baking/cooking; Intergenerational programs.

Colonial Health Care Services Inc
3120 N 21st St, Superior, WI, 54880
(715) 392-2922
Admin Patricia Ziburski. *Medical Dir/Dir of Nursing* Claudia Porter.
Licensure Intermediate care. *Beds* 42. *Certified* Medicaid.
Owner Proprietary Corp.
Admissions Requirements Medical examination; Physician's request.
Staff RNs 1 (ft); LPNs 2 (ft), 4 (pt); Nurses aides 8 (ft), 4 (pt); Activities coordinators 1 (ft); Dietitians 1 (ft).
Facilities Dining room; Activities room; Crafts room; Laundry room; Barber/Beauty shop.
Activities Arts & crafts; Cards; Games; Reading groups; Prayer groups; Movies; Shopping trips; Social/Cultural gatherings.

Fieldview Manor Healthcare*
1612 N 37th St, Superior, WI, 54880
(715) 392-5144
Admin Benjamin Prince.
Licensure Skilled care; Intermediate care. *Beds* 119. *Certified* Medicaid.
Owner Proprietary Corp (Beverly Enterprises).

St Francis Home Inc
1800 New York Ave, Superior, WI, 54880
(715) 394-5591
Admin Kurt M Graves. *Medical Dir/Dir of Nursing* Dr Selleas.
Licensure Skilled care. *Beds* 192. *Certified* Medicaid; Medicare.
Owner Nonprofit Corp.
Affiliation Roman Catholic

Southdale Health Care Services Inc
3712 Tower Ave, Superior, WI, 54880
(715) 392-6272
Admin Patricia Ziburski. *Medical Dir/Dir of Nursing* L Beth Carlson.
Licensure Intermediate care. *Beds* ICF 50. *Certified* Medicaid.
Owner Proprietary Corp.

Admissions Requirements Medical examination; Physician's request.
Staff RNs 1 (ft); LPNs 5 (ft), 2 (pt); Nurses aides 8 (ft), 9 (pt); Activities coordinators 1 (ft); Dietitians 1 (pt).
Facilities Dining room; Activities room; Crafts room; Laundry room; Barber/Beauty shop; Library.
Activities Arts & crafts; Cards; Games; Reading groups; Prayer groups; Movies; Shopping trips; Social/Cultural gatherings.

SURING

Woodland Village Nursing Home Inc
430 Manor Dr, Suring, WI, 54174
(414) 842-2191
Admin Helen J Newbury. *Medical Dir/Dir of Nursing* Randall Lewis DO; Carol Weber RN DON.
Licensure Skilled care. *Beds* SNF 60. *Certified* Medicaid; Medicare.
Owner Proprietary Corp.
Admissions Requirements Minimum age 18; Medical examination; Physician's request.
Staff Physicians 4 (pt); RNs 4 (pt); LPNs 6 (ft); Orderlies 1 (pt); Nurses aides 29 (ft); Physical therapists 1 (pt); Occupational therapists 1 (pt); Speech therapists 1 (pt); Activities coordinators 1 (pt); Dietitians 1 (pt); Podiatrists 1 (pt).
Languages Polish, Spanish, Menominee
Facilities Dining room; Physical therapy room; Activities room; Chapel; Crafts room; Laundry room; Barber/Beauty shop; Library.
Activities Arts & crafts; Cards; Games; Reading groups; Prayer groups; Movies; Shopping trips; Social/Cultural gatherings.

THORP

Thorp Care Center
PO Box 594, 206 W Prospect St, Thorp, WI, 54771
(715) 669-5321
Admin Ruth Ann Schmidt. *Medical Dir/Dir of Nursing* Dr William Hopkins; Lucy Hoffman RN DON.
Licensure Skilled care; Intermediate care. *Beds* SNF 58; ICF. *Certified* Medicaid.
Owner Proprietary Corp.
Admissions Requirements Minimum age 18; Medical examination; Physician's request.
Staff RNs 1 (ft), 4 (pt); LPNs 8 (pt); Nurses aides 25 (pt); Activities coordinators 1 (ft); Dietitians 1 (pt); Social workers 2 (pt).
Languages Polish, Ukranian, German, Finnish
Facilities Dining room; Physical therapy room; Activities room; Chapel; Crafts room; Laundry room; Barber/Beauty shop; Supervised smoking area; Day room.
Activities Arts & crafts; Cards; Games; Reading groups; Prayer groups; Movies; Shopping trips; Social/Cultural gatherings; Van trips.

TOMAH

Tomah Care Center
1505 Butts Ave, Tomah, WI, 54660
(608) 372-3241
Admin Judy Goldberg. *Medical Dir/Dir of Nursing* Michael Saunders MD; Janice Henry RN.
Licensure Skilled care. *Beds* 110. *Certified* Medicaid.
Owner Proprietary Corp (Beverly Enterprises).
Admissions Requirements Minimum age 18; Medical examination; Physician's request.
Staff RNs 5 (ft), 2 (pt); LPNs 3 (ft), 3 (pt); Nurses aides 32 (ft), 18 (pt); Physical therapists 1 (ft); Recreational therapists 1 (ft); Occupational therapists 1 (ft).

Facilities Dining room; Physical therapy room; Activities room; Crafts room; Laundry room; Barber/Beauty shop; Dayroom; Conference or visiting/privacy room; TV rooms.
Activities Arts & crafts; Cards; Games; Reading groups; Prayer groups; Movies; Shopping trips; Social/Cultural gatherings; Exercises; Small groups for sensory stimulation; Socialization skill level; Reminiscing; Church.

TOMAHAWK

Golden Age Nursing Home
720 E Kings Rd, Tomahawk, WI, 54487
(715) 453-2164
Admin David M Rademacher. *Medical Dir/Dir of Nursing* James L Carroll MD; Jean Richert DON.
Licensure Skilled care; Intermediate care. *Beds* 105. *Certified* Medicaid; Medicare.
Owner Proprietary Corp (Beverly Enterprises).
Admissions Requirements Medical examination; Physician's request.
Facilities Dining room; Physical therapy room; Activities room; Crafts room; Laundry room; Barber/Beauty shop; Library.
Activities Arts & crafts; Cards; Games; Reading groups; Prayer groups; Movies; Shopping trips; Social/Cultural gatherings.

Riverview Terrace*
428 N 6th St, Tomahawk, WI, 54487
(715) 453-2511
Admin John P Ley. *Medical Dir/Dir of Nursing* N L Bugarin.
Licensure Skilled care; Intermediate care. *Beds* 64. *Certified* Medicaid; Medicare.
Owner Proprietary Corp (Beverly Enterprises).
Admissions Requirements Minimum age 18; Medical examination; Physician's request.
Staff RNs 2 (ft), 1 (pt); LPNs 3 (ft), 2 (pt); Nurses aides 30 (ft), 14 (pt); Physical therapists 1 (pt); Occupational therapists 1 (pt); Speech therapists 1 (pt); Activities coordinators 1 (ft); Dietitians 1 (pt).
Facilities Dining room; Physical therapy room; Activities room; Laundry room; Barber/Beauty shop.
Activities Arts & crafts; Cards; Games; Prayer groups; Movies; Shopping trips; Social/Cultural gatherings.

TWIN LAKES

Hillcrest Nursing Home
Box 1025, Twin Lakes, WI, 53181
(414) 877-2118
Admin Jeffrey R Minor. *Medical Dir/Dir of Nursing* Dr Richard Rodarte; Kathleen Walker.
Licensure Intermediate care. *Beds* 84. *Certified* Medicaid.
Owner Proprietary Corp.
Admissions Requirements Minimum age 18; Medical examination.
Staff Physicians 6 (pt); RNs 3 (ft), 3 (pt); LPNs 4 (ft), 3 (pt); Orderlies 20 (ft), 20 (pt); Physical therapists 1 (pt); Occupational therapists 1 (pt); Speech therapists 1 (pt); Activities coordinators 1 (ft); Dietitians 1 (ft); Dentists 1 (pt); Ophthalmologists 1 (pt); Podiatrists 1 (pt).
Facilities Dining room; Laundry room; Barber/Beauty shop.
Activities Arts & crafts; Cards; Games; Reading groups; Prayer groups; Movies; Shopping trips; Social/Cultural gatherings.

TWO RIVERS

Hamilton Memorial Home
1 Hamilton Dr, Two Rivers, WI, 54241
(414) 793-2261

Admin Jack Gospodarek. *Medical Dir/Dir of Nursing* John E Nilles MD; Margaret Shikowski RN DON.
Licensure Skilled care; Intermediate care. *Beds* SNF 85; ICF. *Certified* Medicaid.
Owner Nonprofit Corp.
Admissions Requirements Minimum age 18; Medical examination; Physician's request.
Staff Physicians 8 (pt); RNs 3 (ft), 4 (pt); LPNs 3 (ft), 6 (pt); Nurses aides 10 (ft), 30 (pt); Physical therapists 1 (pt); Occupational therapists 1 (pt); Activities coordinators 1 (ft); Dietitians 1 (pt).
Facilities Dining room; Activities room; Chapel; Crafts room; Laundry room; Barber/Beauty shop.
Activities Arts & crafts; Cards; Games; Reading groups; Prayer groups; Movies; Shopping trips; Social/Cultural gatherings; Pet therapy.

UNION GROVE

Southern Wisconsin Center for the Developmentally Disabled
21425 Spring St, Union Grove, WI, 53182
(414) 878-2411
Admin Michael J Moore.
Licensure Intermediate care for mentally retarded. *Beds* ICF/MR 705. *Certified* Medicaid.
Owner Publicly owned.
Admissions Requirements Minimum age 3.
Staff Physicians 5 (ft), 10 (pt); RNs 33 (ft), 7 (pt); LPNs 17 (ft), 9 (pt); Nurses aides 452 (ft); Recreational therapists 14 (ft); Speech therapists 3 (ft); Dietitians 4 (ft); Podiatrists 1 (ft).
Facilities Dining room; Physical therapy room; Activities room; Chapel; Crafts room; Barber/Beauty shop.
Activities Arts & crafts; Games; Movies; Shopping trips; Social/Cultural gatherings.

VERONA

Badger Prairie Health Care Center
6748 Hwy 18-151, Verona, WI, 53593
(608) 845-6601
Admin Sharon Burns. *Medical Dir/Dir of Nursing* Sharon Burns.
Licensure Skilled care; Intermediate care; Intermediate care for mentally retarded. *Beds* SNF; ICF 178194. *Certified* Medicaid.
Owner Publicly owned.
Admissions Requirements Medical examination; Physician's request.
Staff Physicians 5 (pt); RNs 16 (ft); LPNs 9 (ft); Nurses aides 75 (ft); Recreational therapists 1 (ft); Occupational therapists 1 (ft); Dietitians 3 (ft).
Facilities Dining room; Activities room; Crafts room; Laundry room; Barber/Beauty shop; Library; Auditorium.
Activities Arts & crafts; Cards; Games; Movies; Shopping trips; Social/Cultural gatherings.

Dane County Home—West Building*
6748 Hwy 18-151, Verona, WI, 53593
(608) 845-6601
Admin David Dybdahl. *Medical Dir/Dir of Nursing* Steven Babcock MD.
Licensure Skilled care; Intermediate care. *Beds* 169. *Certified* Medicaid; Medicare.
Owner Publicly owned.
Staff RNs 12 (ft), 2 (pt); LPNs 10 (ft), 3 (pt); Nurses aides 62 (ft), 1 (pt); Physical therapists 1 (pt); Recreational therapists 2 (ft), 1 (pt); Occupational therapists 1 (pt); Dietitians 1 (pt); Dentists 1 (pt).
Facilities Dining room; Physical therapy room; Activities room; Crafts room; Laundry room; Barber/Beauty shop; Library.
Activities Arts & crafts; Games; Movies; Shopping trips; Social/Cultural gatherings.

Four Winds Manor*
303 S Jefferson, Verona, WI, 53593
(608) 845-6465
Admin Max Arthur.
Licensure Skilled care; Intermediate care. *Beds* 71. *Certified* Medicaid.
Owner Proprietary Corp.

Rest Haven Health Care Center
7672 Mineral Point Rd, Verona, WI, 53593
(608) 833-1691
Admin Marilyn J Rogeberg. *Medical Dir/Dir of Nursing* Don Janicek MD; Eleanor Abrams DON.
Licensure Skilled care. *Beds* 31.
Owner Proprietary Corp.
Admissions Requirements Medical examination; Physician's request.
Staff Physicians 1 (pt); RNs 1 (ft), 2 (pt); LPNs 1 (ft), 4 (pt); Nurses aides 2 (ft), 8 (pt); Recreational therapists 1 (ft); Dietitians 1 (pt); Dentist 1 (pt).
Facilities Dining room; Physical therapy room; Activities room; Crafts room; Laundry room.
Activities Arts & crafts; Cards; Games; Reading groups; Prayer groups; Movies; Social/Cultural gatherings.

VIROQUA

Bethel Home & Services Inc
614 S Rock St, Viroqua, WI, 54665
(608) 637-2171
Admin James B Olson. *Medical Dir/Dir of Nursing* Dr Edward Vig; Mary Herrlinger DON.
Licensure Skilled care; Intermediate care. *Beds* SNF 121. *Certified* Medicaid.
Owner Nonprofit Corp.
Admissions Requirements Medical examination; Physician's request.
Staff Physicians 6 (pt); RNs 7 (ft), 5 (pt); LPNs 2 (ft), 8 (pt); Nurses aides 20 (ft), 36 (pt); Physical therapists 1 (ft); Recreational therapists 1 (ft); Occupational therapists 1 (pt); Speech therapists 1 (pt); Activities coordinators 1 (ft); Dietitians 1 (pt); Dentist 3 (pt).
Languages Norwegian
Affiliation Lutheran
Facilities Dining room; Physical therapy room; Activities room; Chapel; Crafts room; Laundry room; Barber/Beauty shop; Library.
Activities Arts & crafts; Cards; Games; Reading groups; Prayer groups; Movies; Shopping trips; Social/Cultural gatherings.

Vernon Manor*
Rte 3, Box 300, Viroqua, WI, 54665
(608) 637-8311
Admin Myrtle M Jacobson. *Medical Dir/Dir of Nursing* De Verne W Vig MD.
Licensure Skilled care; Intermediate care. *Beds* 120. *Certified* Medicaid.
Owner Publicly owned.
Admissions Requirements Minimum age 18; Medical examination; Physician's request.
Staff Physicians 2 (pt); RNs 3 (ft), 4 (pt); LPNs 3 (ft), 5 (pt); Nurses aides 38 (ft), 28 (pt); Physical therapists 1 (pt); Activities coordinators; Dietitians.
Facilities Dining room; Physical therapy room; Activities room; Chapel; Crafts room; Barber/Beauty shop.
Activities Arts & crafts; Cards; Games; Reading groups; Prayer groups; Movies; Shopping trips; Social/Cultural gatherings.

WALWORTH

The Christian League for the Handicapped*
PO Box 948, Walworth, WI, 53184
Admin Clark Dempsey. *Medical Dir/Dir of Nursing* Sandra Anderson RN.
Licensure Residential care. *Beds* 68. *Certified* Medicaid.

Owner Nonprofit Corp.
Admissions Requirements Minimum age 18.
Staff RNs 1 (ft), 3 (pt); Orderlies 1 (pt); Nurses aides 3 (ft), 2 (pt); Activities coordinators 1 (ft).
Facilities Dining room; Physical therapy room; Activities room; Crafts room; Laundry room; Barber/Beauty shop; Library; Sheltered workshop; Conference & retreat center.
Activities Arts & crafts; Games; Reading groups; Prayer groups; Movies; Shopping trips; Social/Cultural gatherings; Camping sessions; Outings.

The Golden Years Home*
Rte 1, Box 91, Walworth, WI, 53184
(414) 275-6103
Admin Richard T Austin.
Beds 26.
Owner Proprietary Corp.

WASHBURN

Northern Lights Manor Nursing Home
322 Superior Ave, Washburn, WI, 54891
(715) 373-5621
Admin John J Blahnik. *Medical Dir/Dir of Nursing* Ed Vandenberg MD.
Licensure Skilled care; Intermediate care. *Beds* 86. *Certified* Medicaid.
Owner Nonprofit Corp.
Staff Physicians 4 (pt); RNs 3 (ft), 2 (pt); LPNs 5 (ft), 5 (pt); Orderlies 2 (ft), 2 (pt); Nurses aides 16 (ft), 16 (pt); Physical therapists 1 (ft); Recreational therapists 1 (ft); Occupational therapists 1 (pt); Speech therapists 1 (pt); Activities coordinators 1 (pt); Dietitians 1 (ft), 1 (pt); Dentists 3 (pt); Ophthalmologists 2 (pt); Podiatrists 1 (pt).
Facilities Dining room; Physical therapy room; Activities room; Crafts room; Barber/Beauty shop; Library.
Activities Arts & crafts; Cards; Games; Reading groups; Prayer groups; Movies; Shopping trips; Social/Cultural gatherings.

WATERTOWN

Bethesda-Ritter Dierker
700 Hoffmann Dr, Watertown, WI, 53094
(414) 261-3050
Admin Wayne A Kottmeyer. *Medical Dir/Dir of Nursing* John Heffelfinger MD; Joan Sofinowski DON.
Licensure Intermediate care for mentally retarded. *Beds* 454. *Certified* Medicaid.
Owner Nonprofit Corp.
Admissions Requirements Minimum age 8; Medical examination; Physician's request.
Staff Physicians 1 (ft), 6 (pt); RNs 24 (ft), 1 (pt); LPNs 17 (ft), 1 (pt); Nurses aides 138 (ft), 1 (pt); Physical therapists 2 (ft); Recreational therapists 10 (ft); Occupational therapists 3 (ft); Speech therapists 3 (ft); Activities coordinators 3 (ft); Dietitians 1 (ft).
Affiliation Lutheran
Facilities Dining room; Physical therapy room; Activities room; Chapel; Crafts room; Laundry room; Barber/Beauty shop; Library.
Activities Arts & crafts; Cards; Games; Movies; Shopping trips; Social/Cultural gatherings; Special dinners; Concerts.

Beverly Terrace Nursing Home
121 Hospital Dr, Watertown, WI, 53094
(414) 261-9220
Admin Duane Floyd.
Licensure Skilled care; Intermediate care. *Beds* 130. *Certified* Medicaid; Medicare.
Owner Proprietary Corp (Beverly Enterprises).
Staff Physicians 6 (pt); RNs 4 (pt); LPNs 8 (ft); Nurses aides 55 (ft); Physical therapists 1 (ft); Reality therapists 1 (pt); Recreational therapists 1 (pt); Occupational therapists 2 (pt); Speech therapists 1 (pt); Activities

coordinators 1 (ft); Dietitians 1 (pt); Dentists 1 (ft); Ophthalmologists 1 (ft); Podiatrists 1 (ft); Dentist 1 (ft).
Facilities Dining room; Physical therapy room; Activities room; Chapel; Crafts room; Laundry room; Barber/Beauty shop.
Activities Arts & crafts; Cards; Games; Reading groups; Movies; Social/Cultural gatherings.

Marquardt Memorial Manor Inc*
1020 Hill St, Watertown, WI, 53094
(414) 261-0400
Admin Boyd A Flater.
Licensure Skilled care; Intermediate care. *Beds* 140. *Certified* Medicaid.
Owner Nonprofit Corp.

Welbourne Hall*
1301 E Main St, Watertown, WI, 53094
(414) 261-1211
Admin Kenneth M Mueller Jr.
Licensure Intermediate care. *Beds* 80. *Certified* Medicaid.

Clara Werner Dormitory
700 Hoffmann Dr, Watertown, WI, 53094
(414) 261-3050
Admin Wayne A Kottmeyer. *Medical Dir/Dir of Nursing* John Heffelfinger MD; Joan Sofinowski DON.
Licensure Intermediate care; Intermediate care for mentally retarded. *Beds* 46. *Certified* Medicaid.
Owner Nonprofit Corp.
Admissions Requirements Medical examination; Physician's request.
Staff Physicians; RNs; LPNs; Nurses aides; Physical therapists; Recreational therapists; Occupational therapists; Speech therapists; Activities coordinators; Dietitians.
Affiliation Lutheran
Facilities Dining room; Physical therapy room; Activities room; Chapel; Crafts room; Laundry room; Barber/Beauty shop; Library.
Activities Arts & crafts; Cards; Games; Movies; Shopping trips; Social/Cultural gatherings; Special dinners; Concerts.

WAUKESHA

Avalon Manor Infirmary
222 Park Pl, Waukesha, WI, 53186
(414) 547-6741
Admin Mary Joan Evans.
Licensure Skilled care. *Beds* 22.
Owner Nonprofit Corp.
Admissions Requirements Minimum age 62; Medical examination; Physician's request.
Staff RNs 1 (ft), 4 (pt); LPNs 5 (pt); Nurses aides 12 (pt); Activities coordinators 1 (pt); Dietitians 1 (pt).
Facilities Dining room; Activities room; Crafts room; Laundry room; Barber/Beauty shop; Library.
Activities Arts & crafts; Cards; Games; Reading groups; Prayer groups; Movies; Social/Cultural gatherings.

LindenGrove—Northview
25042 W Northview Rd, Waukesha, WI, 53188
(414) 548-7866
Admin William T Pratt. *Medical Dir/Dir of Nursing* Peter Geiss; Mary Kelly-Powell.
Licensure Skilled care; Intermediate care. *Beds* SNF; ICF 405. *Certified* Medicaid; Medicare.
Owner Nonprofit Corp.
Admissions Requirements Minimum age 18; Medical examination; Physician's request.
Staff Physicians 2 (pt); RNs 16 (ft), 6 (pt); LPNs 28 (ft), 8 (pt); Nurses aides 101 (ft), 38 (pt); Physical therapists 7 (ft); Recreational therapists 9 (ft), 1 (pt); Occupational therapists 4 (ft); Speech therapists 1 (ft); Activities coordinators 1 (ft); Dietitians 2 (ft).

Facilities Dining room; Physical therapy room; Activities room; Chapel; Crafts room; Laundry room; Barber/Beauty shop; Library; Dental office; Speech & occupational therapy.
Activities Arts & crafts; Cards; Games; Reading groups; Prayer groups; Movies; Shopping trips; Social/Cultural gatherings; Pet therapy; Music therapy.

The Virginia Health Care Center
1471 Waukesha Ave, Waukesha, WI, 53186
(414) 547-2123
Admin Mary A Obermeier. *Medical Dir/Dir of Nursing* John Buhl MD; Susan E Bischmann RN DON.
Licensure Skilled care; Intermediate care. *Beds* SNF 102; ICF. *Certified* Medicaid.
Owner Proprietary Corp (American Medical Services Inc).
Admissions Requirements Minimum age Adult; Medical examination; Physician's request.
Staff RNs 1 (ft), 9 (pt); LPNs 3 (ft), 5 (pt); Nurses aides 21 (ft), 26 (pt); Physical therapists 1 (pt); Recreational therapists 1 (ft); Occupational therapists 1 (pt); Activities coordinators 1 (ft); Dietitians 1 (pt); Ophthalmologists 1 (pt).
Languages Laotian, Spanish
Facilities Dining room; Physical therapy room; Activities room; Chapel; Crafts room; Barber/Beauty shop.
Activities Arts & crafts; Cards; Games; Reading groups; Prayer groups; Movies; Shopping trips; Social/Cultural gatherings.

Westmoreland Health Center
1810 Kensington Dr, Waukesha, WI, 53188
(414) 548-1400
Admin Robert J Best. *Medical Dir/Dir of Nursing* Wilbur Rosenkranz MD; Susan Jackson RN DON.
Licensure Skilled care. *Beds* SNF 245. *Certified* Medicaid; Medicare.
Owner Proprietary Corp.
Admissions Requirements Minimum age 18; Medical examination; Physician's request.
Staff Physicians 48 (pt); RNs 7 (ft), 13 (pt); LPNs 10 (ft), 21 (pt); Orderlies 3 (ft); Nurses aides 44 (ft), 58 (pt); Physical therapists 3 (ft); Reality therapists 1 (ft); Recreational therapists 2 (ft); Occupational therapists 2 (pt); Speech therapists 2 (pt); Activities coordinators 2 (ft), 10 (pt); Dietitians 1 (pt); Dentists 1 (pt); Ophthalmologists 1 (pt); Podiatrists 1 (pt).
Languages German, Spanish, Sign
Facilities Dining room; Physical therapy room; Activities room; Chapel; Crafts room; Laundry room; Barber/Beauty shop; Library; Visitor dining area.
Activities Arts & crafts; Cards; Games; Reading groups; Prayer groups; Movies; Shopping trips; Social/Cultural gatherings; Oral history groups; Intergenerational programs.

WAUNAKEE

Waunakee Manor Health Care Center*
801 Klein Dr, Waunakee, WI, 53597
(608) 849-5016
Admin Edwin M Kruchten.
Licensure Skilled care; Intermediate care. *Beds* 104. *Certified* Medicaid; Medicare.
Owner Proprietary Corp.

WAUPACA

Bethany Home*
1226 Berlin St, Waupaca, WI, 54981
(715) 258-5521
Admin William N Parker.
Licensure Skilled care; Intermediate care. *Beds* 119. *Certified* Medicaid.
Owner Nonprofit Corp.

Pine Ridge Manor
1401 Churchill St, Waupaca, WI, 54981
(715) 258-8131
Admin Donna Barbian. *Medical Dir/Dir of Nursing* Dr G Burgstede MD; Jean Israels RN DON.
Licensure Skilled care; Intermediate care. *Beds* 80. *Certified* Medicaid; Medicare.
Owner Proprietary Corp (Unicare).
Admissions Requirements Minimum age 18; Medical examination; Physician's request.
Staff RNs; LPNs; Orderlies; Nurses aides; Physical therapists; Reality therapists; Occupational therapists; Speech therapists; Activities coordinators; Dietitians.
Facilities Dining room; Physical therapy room; Activities room; Chapel; Barber/Beauty shop.
Activities Arts & crafts; Cards; Games; Reading groups; Prayer groups; Movies; Shopping trips; Social/Cultural gatherings.

WAUPUN

Christian Home Inc
220 Grandview Ave, Waupun, WI, 53963
(414) 324-9051
Admin Joyce Buytendorp. *Medical Dir/Dir of Nursing* Mariano Rosales MD; Ruth Schrank RN DON.
Licensure Skilled care; Intermediate care. *Beds* SNF 84; ICF. *Certified* Medicaid.
Owner Nonprofit Corp.
Admissions Requirements Medical examination; Physician's request.
Staff Physicians 6 (pt); RNs 2 (ft), 6 (pt); LPNs 11 (pt); Orderlies; Nurses aides 10 (ft), 27 (pt); Physical therapists; Recreational therapists; Occupational therapists; Speech therapists; Activities coordinators 1 (ft); Dietitians 1 (pt); Ophthalmologists; Podiatrists.
Facilities Dining room; Chapel; Laundry room; Barber/Beauty shop.
Activities Arts & crafts; Cards; Games; Reading groups; Prayer groups; Movies; Social/Cultural gatherings.

WAUSAU

Colonial Manor of Wausau
1010 E Wausau Ave, Wausau, WI, 54401
(715) 842-2028
Admin Norma Jean Burgener. *Medical Dir/Dir of Nursing* J V Flannery Sr MD; Mary Ellen Schreiber DON.
Licensure Skilled care; Intermediate care. *Beds* 152. *Certified* Medicaid; Medicare.
Owner Proprietary Corp (Hillhaven Corp).
Admissions Requirements Minimum age 18; Physician's request.
Staff Physicians 1 (pt); RNs 1 (ft), 12 (pt); LPNs 7 (pt); Nurses aides 30 (ft), 27 (pt); Physical therapists 1 (pt); Recreational therapists 1 (ft), 3 (pt); Occupational therapists 1 (pt); Speech therapists 1 (pt); Activities coordinators 1 (ft); Dietitians 1 (ft); Podiatrists 1 (ft); Dentist 1 (ft).
Languages Polish, German
Facilities Dining room; Physical therapy room; Activities room; Chapel; Crafts room; Laundry room; Barber/Beauty shop.
Activities Arts & crafts; Cards; Games; Reading groups; Prayer groups; Movies; Shopping trips.

Marywood Convalescent Center*
1821 N 4th Ave, Wausau, WI, 54401
(715) 675-9451
Admin Christian E Spangberg.
Licensure Skilled care; Intermediate care. *Beds* 90. *Certified* Medicaid; Medicare.
Owner Nonprofit Corp.

Mt View Nursing Home*
1205 72nd Ave, Wausau, WI, 54401
(715) 845-2186

Admin William Chad McGrath.
Licensure Intermediate care. *Beds* 135.
Certified Medicaid.
Owner Publicly owned.

North Central Health Care Facility
1100 Lake View Dr, Wausau, WI, 54401-6799
(715) 848-4600
Admin William Chad McGrath. *Medical Dir/
Dir of Nursing* DR S N Basu; Molly Maguire
RN DON.
Licensure Skilled care; Intermediate care;
Intermediate care for mentally retarded.
Beds SNF 356; ICF/MR 26. *Certified*
Medicaid; Medicare.
Owner Publicly owned.
Admissions Requirements Medical
examination.
Staff Physicians 1 (ft), 2 (pt); RNs 19 (ft), 23
(pt); LPNs 9 (ft), 8 (pt); Nurses aides 108
(ft), 86 (pt); Recreational therapists 1 (pt);
Occupational therapists 4 (pt); Activities
coordinators 1 (pt); Dietitians 2 (pt).
Facilities Dining room; Physical therapy
room; Activities room; Chapel; Crafts room;
Laundry room; Barber/Beauty shop; Library.
Activities Arts & crafts; Cards; Games;
Reading groups; Prayer groups; Movies;
Shopping trips; Social/Cultural gatherings.

Sunny Vale Nursing Home*
1200 Lakeview Dr, Wausau, WI, 54401
(715) 845-6725
Admin William Chad McGrath. *Medical Dir/
Dir of Nursing* S N Basu.
Licensure Skilled care; Intermediate care. *Beds*
151. *Certified* Medicaid; Medicare.
Owner Publicly owned.
Staff Physicians 1 (pt); RNs 6 (ft), 10 (pt);
LPNs 2 (ft), 5 (pt); Nurses aides 51 (ft), 23
(pt); Physical therapists 2 (pt); Occupational
therapists 1 (pt); Speech therapists 2 (pt);
Dietitians 1 (pt); Dentists 1 (pt).
Facilities Dining room; Activities room;
Crafts room.
Activities Arts & crafts; Cards; Games;
Reading groups; Movies; Shopping trips;
Social/Cultural gatherings.

Wausau Manor*
3107 Westhill Dr, Wausau, WI, 54401
(715) 842-0575
Admin Stan C Jones. *Medical Dir/Dir of
Nursing* Frank Rubino MD; Peggy Larson
RN DON.
Licensure Skilled care. *Beds* SNF 60. *Certified*
Medicare.
Owner Privately owned.
Admissions Requirements Medical
examination; Physician's request.
Staff Physicians 1 (pt); RNs 5 (ft), 4 (pt);
LPNs 1 (ft), 1 (pt); Orderlies 1 (pt); Nurses
aides 20 (ft), 10 (pt); Physical therapists 2
(pt); Recreational therapists 1 (ft), 1 (pt);
Occupational therapists 1 (pt); Speech
therapists 1 (pt); Dietitians 1 (pt).
Facilities Dining room; Physical therapy
room; Activities room; Crafts room; Laundry
room; Barber/Beauty shop; Library.
Activities Arts & crafts; Cards; Games;
Reading groups; Prayer groups; Movies;
Shopping trips; Social/Cultural gatherings.

WAUTOMA

Wautoma Care Center Inc*
327 Waupaca St, Box 720, Wautoma, WI,
54982
(414) 787-3359
Admin James P Stannard. *Medical Dir/Dir of
Nursing* Dr Rodney Wichman MD.
Licensure Skilled care; Intermediate care. *Beds*
84. *Certified* Medicaid.
Owner Proprietary Corp.
Admissions Requirements Minimum age 18;
Medical examination; Physician's request.

Staff Physicians 9 (pt); RNs 3 (ft), 2 (pt);
LPNs 4 (ft); Orderlies 1 (ft), 1 (pt); Nurses
aides 21 (ft), 17 (pt); Physical therapists 1
(pt); Occupational therapists 1 (pt); Speech
therapists 1 (pt); Activities coordinators 1
(ft); Dietitians 1 (pt); Dentists 1 (pt);
Ophthalmologists 1 (pt); Podiatrists 1 (pt).
Facilities Dining room; Physical therapy
room; Activities room; Chapel; Laundry
room; Barber/Beauty shop.
Activities Arts & crafts; Cards; Games;
Reading groups; Prayer groups; Movies;
Shopping trips; Social/Cultural gatherings.

WAUWATOSA

Luther Manor*
4545 N 92nd St, Wauwatosa, WI, 53226
(414) 464-3880
Admin Peter E Chang. *Medical Dir/Dir of
Nursing* Dr Paul Nordin.
Licensure Skilled care; Intermediate care. *Beds*
201. *Certified* Medicaid.
Owner Nonprofit Corp.
Admissions Requirements Minimum age 68;
Medical examination; Physician's request.
Staff RNs 5 (ft), 22 (pt); LPNs 17 (pt);
Orderlies 18 (ft), 60 (pt); Recreational
therapists 4 (ft); Occupational therapists 1
(pt); Dietitians 1 (ft); Dentists 1 (pt);
Podiatrists 1 (pt).
Affiliation Lutheran
Facilities Dining room; Physical therapy
room; Activities room; Chapel; Crafts room;
Laundry room; Barber/Beauty shop; Library.
Activities Arts & crafts; Cards; Games;
Reading groups; Prayer groups; Movies;
Shopping trips; Social/Cultural gatherings.

Lutheran Home for the Aging Inc*
7500 W North Ave, Wauwatosa, WI, 53213
(414) 258-6170
Admin Roger A Sievers.
Licensure Skilled care; Intermediate care. *Beds*
290. *Certified* Medicaid.
Owner Nonprofit Corp.
Affiliation Lutheran

**Milwaukee County Mental Health Complex
Rehabilitation Center—Central**
9455 Watertown Plank Rd, Wauwatosa, WI,
53226
(414) 257-7339
Admin James Gresham. *Medical Dir/Dir of
Nursing* Jon E Gudeman MD.
Licensure Skilled care; Intermediate care. *Beds*
SNF 332; ICF. *Certified* Medicaid.
Owner Publicly owned.
Admissions Requirements Minimum age 18.
Staff Physicians 3 (ft), 5 (pt); RNs 39 (ft), 11
(pt); LPNs 57 (pt); Nurses aides 146 (ft);
Occupational therapists 7 (ft), 1 (pt);
Activities coordinators 1 (ft); Dietitians 2
(ft); Ophthalmologists 1 (pt).
Facilities Dining room; Physical therapy
room; Activities room; Chapel; Crafts room;
Laundry room; Barber/Beauty shop; Library.
Activities Arts & crafts; Cards; Games;
Reading groups; Prayer groups; Movies;
Shopping trips; Social/Cultural gatherings.

**Milwaukee County Mental Health Complex
Rehabilitation Center—West**
10437 Watertown Plank Rd, Wauwatosa, WI,
53226
(414) 257-7339
Admin James Gresham. *Medical Dir/Dir of
Nursing* Richard P Jahn MD.
Licensure Intermediate care. *Beds* ICF 220.
Certified Medicaid.
Owner Publicly owned.
Admissions Requirements Minimum age 18.
Staff Physicians 1 (ft); RNs 11 (ft); LPNs 13
(ft); Nurses aides 64 (ft); Recreational
therapists 1 (ft); Occupational therapists 3
(ft); Activities coordinators 1 (ft); Dietitians
1 (pt); Ophthalmologists 1 (pt); Psychiatrist
1 (pt); Dentist 1 (pt).

Facilities Dining room; Activities room;
Chapel; Crafts room; Laundry room; Barber/
Beauty shop; Library.
Activities Arts & crafts; Cards; Games;
Reading groups; Movies; Shopping trips;
Social/Cultural gatherings.

St Camillus Health Center Inc
10100 W Bluemound Rd, Wauwatosa, WI,
53226
(414) 258-1814
Admin Rick L Johnson. *Medical Dir/Dir of
Nursing* Illuminado Millar MD; Betty
Brunner.
Licensure Skilled care; Intermediate care. *Beds*
188. *Certified* Medicaid; Medicare.
Owner Nonprofit Corp.
Admissions Requirements Minimum age 18;
Medical examination.
Staff Physicians 1 (pt); RNs 10 (ft), 13 (pt);
LPNs 12 (ft), 13 (pt); Nurses aides 39 (ft),
45 (pt); Physical therapists 1 (ft); Reality
therapists 1 (ft); Recreational therapists 1
(ft); Occupational therapists 1 (ft); Speech
therapists 1 (pt); Dietitians 1 (pt).
Affiliation Roman Catholic
Facilities Dining room; Physical therapy
room; Activities room; Chapel; Crafts room;
Laundry room; Barber/Beauty shop; Library;
Auditorium.
Activities Arts & crafts; Cards; Games;
Reading groups; Prayer groups; Movies;
Shopping trips; Social/Cultural gatherings;
Pet therapy.

WENTWORTH

Parkland Health Facility
PO Box 58, Wentworth, WI, 54874
(715) 398-6616
Admin Jennifer Jarocki-Bieno NHA. *Medical
Dir/Dir of Nursing* Dr Robert Mataezynski;
Terri L Benedict RN MSN.
Licensure Skilled care; Intermediate care. *Beds*
119. *Certified* Medicaid.
Owner Publicly owned.
Admissions Requirements Minimum age 18;
Medical examination; Physician's request.
Staff Physicians 4 (ft); RNs 6 (ft); LPNs 22
(ft); Orderlies 5 (ft); Nurses aides 53 (ft);
Physical therapists 1 (pt); Reality therapists
2 (pt); Occupational therapists 1 (pt); Speech
therapists 1 (pt); Activities coordinators 1
(ft); Dietitians 1 (pt); Dentists 1 (pt);
Podiatrists 1 (pt).
Facilities Dining room; Physical therapy
room; Activities room; Chapel; Crafts room;
Laundry room; Barber/Beauty shop.
Activities Arts & crafts; Cards; Games;
Reading groups; Prayer groups; Movies;
Shopping trips; Social/Cultural gatherings;
Leep; Small business group; Healthy group.

WEST ALLIS

Adobe Nursing Home*
1950 S 96th St, West Allis, WI, 53227
(414) 321-4480
Admin Arthur P Kuranz.
Licensure Intermediate care for mentally
retarded. *Beds* 18. *Certified* Medicaid.
Owner Proprietary Corp.

Hillcrest Nursing Home*
1467 S 75th St, West Allis, WI, 53214
(414) 476-2928
Admin Dorothy M Sciano. *Medical Dir/Dir of
Nursing* Dr Roger Ruehl.
Licensure Intermediate care. *Beds* 25.
Certified Medicaid.
Owner Proprietary Corp.
Admissions Requirements Minimum age 18.
Staff Physicians 1 (pt); RNs 1 (ft); LPNs 2
(pt); Nurses aides 1 (ft), 10 (pt); Activities
coordinators 1 (pt); Dietitians 1 (pt).

Kappes Nursing Home
8300 W Beloit Rd, West Allis, WI, 53219
(414) 321-2420
Admin Ralph P Hibbard. *Medical Dir/Dir of Nursing* Donna Mathis.
Licensure Intermediate care. *Beds* ICF 28. *Certified* Medicaid.
Owner Proprietary Corp.
Admissions Requirements Minimum age 55.
Staff RNs 1 (ft), 2 (pt); LPNs 1 (ft), 2 (pt); Orderlies 3 (ft), 4 (pt); Nurses aides; Activities coordinators 2 (pt); Dietitians 1 (pt).
Facilities Dining room; Activities room; Barber/Beauty shop.
Activities Arts & crafts; Cards; Games; Prayer groups; Movies; Social/Cultural gatherings.

Mary-Jude Nursing Home
9806 W Lincoln Ave, West Allis, WI, 53227
(414) 543-5330
Admin Edward P Bartz. *Medical Dir/Dir of Nursing* Eugene Collins MD; Shirley Kubacki RN DON.
Licensure Skilled care; Intermediate care. *Beds* SNF 51; ICF. *Certified* Medicaid.
Owner Proprietary Corp.
Admissions Requirements Minimum age 18; Medical examination.
Staff RNs 1 (ft), 5 (pt); LPNs 1 (ft), 4 (pt); Nurses aides 12 (ft), 8 (pt); Activities coordinators 1 (ft); Dietitians 1 (pt).
Languages Polish, German
Facilities Dining room; Activities room; Chapel; Crafts room; Laundry room; Barber/Beauty shop.
Activities Arts & crafts; Cards; Games; Reading groups; Prayer groups; Movies; Shopping trips; Social/Cultural gatherings; Theatre; Zoo; Trips.

Rosewood Nursing Home
3161 S 112, West Allis, WI, 53227
(414) 543-1809
Admin Dorothy M Stadler NHA. *Medical Dir/Dir of Nursing* Dorothy M Stadler RN DON.
Licensure Intermediate care. *Beds* ICF 23. *Certified* Medicaid.
Owner Proprietary Corp.
Admissions Requirements Medical examination.
Staff RNs; LPNs; Nurses aides; Recreational therapists; Activities coordinators; Dietitians.
Facilities Dining room; Activities room.
Activities Arts & crafts; Cards; Games; Reading groups; Prayer groups; Movies; Shopping trips; Social/Cultural gatherings.

St Joan Antida Home
6700 W Beloit Rd, West Allis, WI, 53219
(414) 541-6575
Admin Sr Ann C Veierstahler. *Medical Dir/Dir of Nursing* Dr E Kuglitsch; Louise Besaw DON.
Licensure Skilled care; Intermediate care. *Beds* SNF 76; ICF. *Certified* Medicaid.
Owner Nonprofit organization/foundation.
Admissions Requirements Minimum age 65; Medical examination; Physician's request.
Staff Physicians 1 (pt); RNs 4 (ft); LPNs 3 (ft), 4 (pt); Nurses aides 20 (ft); Physical therapists 1 (pt); Reality therapists 1 (pt); Recreational therapists 1 (ft); Occupational therapists 1 (pt); Activities coordinators 1 (ft); Dietitians 1 (pt); Dentists 1 (pt); Ophthalmologists 1 (pt).
Languages Italian
Affiliation Roman Catholic
Facilities Dining room; Physical therapy room; Activities room; Chapel; Crafts room; Laundry room; Barber/Beauty shop; Library.
Activities Arts & crafts; Cards; Games; Prayer groups; Social/Cultural gatherings.

St Joseph's Home for the Aged
5301 W Lincoln Ave, West Allis, WI, 53219
(414) 541-8444

Admin Roger L DeMark. *Medical Dir/Dir of Nursing* Dr John Plase; Mary Ann Kovacic DON.
Licensure Intermediate care; CBRF. *Beds* ICF 74; CBRF 49. *Certified* Medicaid.
Owner Nonprofit Corp.
Affiliation Roman Catholic

Villa Clement
9047 W Greenfield, West Allis, WI, 53214
(414) 453-9290
Admin Gina Dennik Champion RN MSN. *Medical Dir/Dir of Nursing* John Wisniewski MD; Priscilla Rice RNMS.
Licensure Skilled care. *Beds* SNF 198. *Certified* Medicaid; Medicare.
Owner Nonprofit Corp (School Sisters of St Francis).
Staff Physicians 1 (pt); RNs 13 (ft), 22 (pt); LPNs 8 (ft), 11 (pt); Orderlies 59 (ft), 68 (pt); Physical therapists 1 (ft), 2 (pt); Recreational therapists 8 (pt); Occupational therapists 1 (pt); Speech therapists 3 (pt); Activities coordinators 1 (pt); Dietitians 1 (ft); Ophthalmologists 1 (pt).
Affiliation Roman Catholic
Facilities Dining room; Physical therapy room; Activities room; Chapel; Laundry room; Barber/Beauty shop.
Activities Arts & crafts; Cards; Games; Reading groups; Prayer groups; Movies; Social/Cultural gatherings; Planting.

WEST BEND

Cedar Lake Home Campus
5595 Hwy Z, West Bend, WI, 53095
(414) 334-9487
Admin Steven J Jaberg. *Medical Dir/Dir of Nursing* Dr Charles Holmburg; Amy Bauer RN DON.
Licensure Skilled care. *Beds* SNF 415. *Certified* Medicaid.
Owner Nonprofit Corp.
Admissions Requirements Minimum age 18; Medical examination.
Staff RNs 15 (ft), 27 (pt); LPNs 9 (ft), 17 (pt); Nurses aides 81 (ft), 110 (pt); Physical therapists 3 (ft); Recreational therapists 1 (ft); Occupational therapists 2 (ft), 1 (pt); Speech therapists 1 (pt); Activities coordinators 5 (ft), 1 (pt); Dietitians 1 (ft).
Languages Sign
Affiliation Church of Christ
Facilities Dining room; Physical therapy room; Activities room; Chapel; Crafts room; Laundry room; Barber/Beauty shop; Library; Educational buildings; Museum; Woodworking shop; Sewing room; Swimming pool; Greenhouse.
Activities Arts & crafts; Cards; Games; Reading groups; Prayer groups; Movies; Shopping trips; Social/Cultural gatherings; Intergenerational programs; Trail rides; Fishing clubs; Woodworking; Swimming; Sewing.

Samaritan Home*
531 E Washington St, West Bend, WI, 53095
(414) 338-4500
Admin Anne Tilt. *Medical Dir/Dir of Nursing* Dr F I Bush.
Licensure Skilled care; Intermediate care. *Beds* 251. *Certified* Medicaid; Medicare.
Owner Publicly owned.
Admissions Requirements Minimum age 21; Medical examination; Physician's request.
Staff Physicians 1 (ft), 2 (pt); RNs 12 (ft); LPNs 18 (ft), 6 (pt); Nurses aides 66 (ft), 47 (pt); Physical therapists 1 (ft); Occupational therapists 2 (pt); Speech therapists 1 (pt); Activities coordinators 1 (ft); Dietitians 1 (pt); Dentists 1 (pt).
Facilities Dining room; Physical therapy room; Activities room; Chapel; Crafts room; Laundry room; Barber/Beauty shop; Library; Occupational therapy department.

Activities Arts & crafts; Cards; Games; Reading groups; Prayer groups; Movies; Shopping trips; Social/Cultural gatherings; Bus trips; Picnics.

WEST SALEM

Lakeview Health Center
902 E Garland St, West Salem, WI, 54669-1399
(608) 786-1400
Admin Robert G Machotka. *Medical Dir/Dir of Nursing* William D Bateman MD; Karen Miller RN.
Licensure Skilled care. *Beds* 255. *Certified* Medicaid.
Owner Publicly owned.
Admissions Requirements Minimum age 18.
Staff Physicians 4 (pt); RNs 16 (ft), 7 (pt); LPNs 6 (ft), 4 (pt); Nurses aides 48 (ft), 44 (pt); Physical therapists 1 (pt); Occupational therapists 1 (pt); Speech therapists 1 (pt); Dietitians 1 (pt); Dentists 1 (pt); Ophthalmologists 1 (pt).
Facilities Dining room; Physical therapy room; Activities room; Chapel; Crafts room; Laundry room; Barber/Beauty shop; Library.
Activities Arts & crafts; Cards; Games; Reading groups; Prayer groups; Movies; Shopping trips; Social/Cultural gatherings.

Mulder Health Care Facility*
713 N Leonard St, West Salem, WI, 54669
(608) 786-1600
Admin Ronald G Gilbertson.
Licensure Skilled care; Intermediate care. *Beds* 106. *Certified* Medicaid; Medicare.
Owner Proprietary Corp.

WESTBY

Norseland Nursing Home*
323 Black River Rd, Westby, WI, 54667
(608) 634-3747
Admin Ned P Barstad.
Licensure Skilled care; Intermediate care. *Beds* 59. *Certified* Medicaid.
Owner Publicly owned.

WEYAUWEGA

Lakeview Manor*
Rte 1, Box X, Weyauwega, WI, 54983
(414) 867-2183
Admin Jeanne M Zempel. *Medical Dir/Dir of Nursing* Lloyd P Maasch MD.
Licensure Skilled care; Intermediate care. *Beds* 103. *Certified* Medicaid.
Owner Publicly owned.
Staff Physicians 2 (pt); RNs 6 (ft), 2 (pt); LPNs 8 (ft); Nurses aides 31 (ft); Physical therapists 1 (pt); Recreational therapists 2 (ft), 5 (pt); Occupational therapists 2 (pt); Activities coordinators 1 (ft); Dietitians 1 (pt); Podiatrists 1 (pt); Social workers 1 (ft), 1 (pt).
Facilities Dining room; Physical therapy room; Activities room; Chapel; Crafts room; Laundry room; Barber/Beauty shop; Workshop; Greenhouse.
Activities Arts & crafts; Cards; Games; Reading groups; Prayer groups; Movies; Shopping trips; Social/Cultural gatherings.

Weyauwega Health Care Center
PO Box 440, 717 E Alfred St, Weyauwega, WI, 54983
(414) 867-3121
Admin James Ignarski. *Medical Dir/Dir of Nursing* Dr Pete Hamel; Steve Otto RN.
Licensure Skilled care; Intermediate care. *Beds* SNF 103; ICF. *Certified* Medicaid; Medicare.
Owner Proprietary Corp (Unicare).
Admissions Requirements Medical examination; Physician's request.

Staff Physicians 1 (pt); RNs 5 (ft); LPNs 10 (ft); Orderlies 15 (ft), 20 (pt); Physical therapists 1 (pt); Occupational therapists 1 (pt); Speech therapists 1 (pt); Activities coordinators 1 (ft); Dietitians 1 (pt).
Facilities Dining room; Physical therapy room; Activities room; Chapel; Laundry room; Barber/Beauty shop.
Activities Arts & crafts; Cards; Games; Reading groups; Prayer groups; Movies; Shopping trips; Social/Cultural gatherings.

WHITEHALL

Trempealeau County Health Care Center
PO Box 150, RFD 2, Whitehall, WI, 54773
(715) 538-4312
Admin Phillip J Borreson. *Medical Dir/Dir of Nursing* Dr Rueben Adams.
Licensure Skilled care. *Beds* 167. *Certified* Medicaid.
Owner Publicly owned.
Admissions Requirements Minimum age 18.
Staff Physicians 1 (pt); RNs 12 (ft), 3 (pt); LPNs 7 (ft); Nurses aides 37 (ft), 23 (pt); Recreational therapists 3 (ft); Occupational therapists 1 (ft); Activities coordinators 1 (ft); Dietitians 1 (pt).
Facilities Dining room; Physical therapy room; Activities room; Chapel; Crafts room; Laundry room; Barber/Beauty shop; Library; Work activities.
Activities Arts & crafts; Cards; Games; Reading groups; Prayer groups; Movies; Shopping trips; Social/Cultural gatherings.

Tri-County Memorial Hospital—Nurs Home*
1801 Lincoln St, Whitehall, WI, 54773
(715) 538-4361
Admin Ronald B Fields.
Licensure Skilled care; Intermediate care. *Beds* 68. *Certified* Medicaid.
Owner Nonprofit Corp.

WHITEWATER

Fairhaven Corporation
435 Starin Rd, Whitewater, WI, 53190
(414) 473-2140
Admin Rev Dr Carroll J Olm. *Medical Dir/Dir of Nursing* L F Nelson MD; Olive Crawley RN DON.
Licensure Skilled care; Intermediate care. *Beds* SNF 84; ICF. *Certified* Medicaid.
Owner Nonprofit Corp.
Admissions Requirements Minimum age 65; Medical examination.
Staff RNs; LPNs; Nurses aides; Recreational therapists; Occupational therapists; Activities coordinators; Dietitians.
Affiliation Church of Christ
Facilities Dining room; Physical therapy room; Activities room; Crafts room; Laundry room; Barber/Beauty shop; Library.
Activities Arts & crafts; Cards; Games; Reading groups; Prayer groups; Movies; Shopping trips; Social/Cultural gatherings.

WILD ROSE

Wild Rose Manor
PO Box 295, 625 Summit St, Wild Rose, WI, 54984
(414) 622-4342
Admin Donna M Barbian. *Medical Dir/Dir of Nursing* T Romana MD; Valerie Grunwaldt RN DON.
Licensure Skilled care; Intermediate care. *Beds* 84. *Certified* Medicaid.
Owner Proprietary Corp.
Admissions Requirements Minimum age 18; Medical examination; Physician's request.

Staff RNs 2 (ft), 7 (pt); LPNs 2 (ft), 3 (pt); Nurses aides 10 (ft), 25 (pt); Physical therapists 1 (pt); Occupational therapists 1 (pt); Speech therapists 1 (pt); Activities coordinators 1 (ft), 1 (pt); Dietitians 1 (pt).
Facilities Dining room; Physical therapy room; Activities room; Chapel; Laundry room; Barber/Beauty shop; Library.
Activities Arts & crafts; Cards; Games; Reading groups; Prayer groups; Movies; Shopping trips; Social/Cultural gatherings.

WILLIAMS BAY

Sherwood Care Center
140 Clover, Box 310, Williams Bay, WI, 53191
(414) 245-6400
Admin John C Kalkirtz. *Medical Dir/Dir of Nursing* Dr Britt Kolar.
Licensure Skilled care. *Beds* 84. *Certified* Medicaid; Medicare.
Owner Proprietary Corp.
Facilities Dining room; Physical therapy room; Activities room; Chapel; Laundry room; Barber/Beauty shop.
Activities Arts & crafts; Cards; Games; Reading groups; Prayer groups; Movies; Shopping trips; Social/Cultural gatherings.

WINNEBAGO

Park View Health Center—Pleasant Acres*
725 Butler Ave, Winnebago, WI, 54985
(414) 235-5100
Admin Sylvia R Banville.
Licensure Skilled care; Intermediate care. *Beds* 212. *Certified* Medicaid.
Owner Publicly owned.

Park View Health Center—Rehab Pavilion*
725 Butler Ave, Winnebago, WI, 54985
(414) 235-5100
Admin Sylvia R Banville.
Licensure Skilled care; Intermediate care. *Beds* 173. *Certified* Medicaid.
Owner Publicly owned.

WISCONSIN DELLS

Continental Manor Nursing Home
300 Race St, Wisconsin Dells, WI, 53965
(608) 254-2574
Admin Scott Martens. *Medical Dir/Dir of Nursing* Dr Richard K Westphal.
Licensure Skilled care. *Beds* SNF 101. *Certified* Medicaid; Medicare.
Owner Proprietary Corp (Beverly Enterprises).
Admissions Requirements Minimum age 18; Medical examination; Physician's request.
Staff RNs 4 (ft), 2 (pt); LPNs 5 (ft), 3 (pt); Nurses aides 34 (ft), 12 (pt); Activities coordinators 1 (ft).
Facilities Dining room; Physical therapy room; Activities room; Crafts room; Laundry room; Barber/Beauty shop.
Activities Arts & crafts; Cards; Games; Reading groups; Prayer groups; Movies; Shopping trips; Social/Cultural gatherings.

WISCONSIN RAPIDS

Family Heritage Nursing Home*
130 Strawberry Ln, Wisconsin Rapids, WI, 54494
(715) 424-1600
Admin William L McKenzie.
Licensure Skilled care; Intermediate care. *Beds* 165. *Certified* Medicaid.
Owner Proprietary Corp (Hillhaven Corp).

Riverview Manor
921 3rd St S, Wisconsin Rapids, WI, 54494
(715) 421-7468

Admin William C Schloer. *Medical Dir/Dir of Nursing* Clifford Stair MD; Patricia Raymond RN DON.
Licensure Skilled care. *Beds* SNF 118. *Certified* Medicaid; Medicare.
Owner Nonprofit Corp.
Admissions Requirements Minimum age 18; Medical examination; Physician's request.
Staff RNs 3 (ft), 5 (pt); LPNs 5 (ft), 6 (pt); Nurses aides 21 (ft), 27 (pt); Physical therapists 1 (ft); Recreational therapists 1 (ft), 1 (pt); Occupational therapists 1 (pt); Speech therapists 1 (pt); Dietitians 1 (pt).
Languages Polish, German
Facilities Dining room; Physical therapy room; Activities room; Crafts room; Barber/Beauty shop.
Activities Arts & crafts; Cards; Games; Reading groups; Prayer groups; Movies; Shopping trips; Social/Cultural gatherings.

WITTENBERG

Homme Home for the Aging Inc
607 Webb St, Wittenberg, WI, 54499
(715) 253-2125
Admin Dufur M Peters. *Medical Dir/Dir of Nursing* Ralph Tauke MD; Ramona Morehouse DON.
Licensure Skilled care; Intermediate care; CBRF. *Beds* SNF 77; ICF; CBRF 59. *Certified* Medicaid.
Owner Nonprofit Corp.
Admissions Requirements Minimum age 18; Medical examination.
Staff Physicians 4 (pt); RNs 10 (ft), 1 (pt); LPNs 8 (ft), 7 (pt); Nurses aides 53 (ft), 25 (pt); Physical therapists 1 (pt); Activities coordinators 1 (ft); Dietitians 1 (ft).
Languages German, Polish, Norwegian
Facilities Dining room; Physical therapy room; Activities room; Chapel; Crafts room; Laundry room; Barber/Beauty shop; Library.
Activities Arts & crafts; Cards; Games; Reading groups; Prayer groups; Movies; Social/Cultural gatherings.

WOODRUFF

Lakeland Manor*
PO Box 859, Woodruff, WI, 54568
(715) 356-5355
Admin Patricia L Richardson. *Medical Dir/Dir of Nursing* George Nemec.
Licensure Skilled care; Intermediate care. *Beds* 61. *Certified* Medicaid.
Owner Proprietary Corp.
Staff Physicians 1 (pt); RNs 4 (ft), 1 (pt); LPNs 3 (ft), 2 (pt); Orderlies 1 (ft), 2 (pt); Nurses aides 15 (ft), 8 (pt); Physical therapists 1 (pt); Reality therapists 1 (pt); Reality therapists 1 (pt); Occupational therapists 1 (pt); Speech therapists 1 (pt); Activities coordinators 1 (ft); Dietitians 1 (ft); Ophthalmologists 1 (pt); Podiatrists 1 (pt); Audiologists 1 (pt).
Facilities Dining room; Physical therapy room; Activities room; Crafts room; Laundry room; Barber/Beauty shop.
Activities Arts & crafts; Games; Reading groups; Prayer groups; Movies; Shopping trips; Social/Cultural gatherings.

Doctor Kate Newcomb Convalescent Center
PO Box 829, 301 Elm St, Woodruff, WI, 54568
(715) 356-3223
Admin Michael D Girard. *Medical Dir/Dir of Nursing* Dr George Nemec; Joan Foeckler.
Licensure Skilled care; Intermediate care. *Beds* 65. *Certified* Medicaid.
Owner Nonprofit organization/foundation.
Admissions Requirements Medical examination; Physician's request.

Staff RNs 3 (ft), 1 (pt); LPNs 4 (ft), 2 (pt); Orderlies 2 (ft), 1 (pt); Nurses aides 18 (ft), 11 (pt); Activities coordinators 1 (ft), 1 (pt); Dietitians 1 (pt); Social worker 1 (pt).
Facilities Dining room; Physical therapy room; Activities room; Crafts room; Barber/Beauty shop; Library.
Activities Arts & crafts; Cards; Games; Reading groups; Prayer groups; Movies; Shopping trips; Social/Cultural gatherings.

WOODVILLE

Park View Home Inc
220 Lockwood St, Woodville, WI, 54028
(715) 698-2451
Admin Jeannette V Howard. *Medical Dir/Dir of Nursing* Dr Arthur Heiser.
Licensure Skilled care. *Beds* SNF 61. *Certified* Medicaid.
Owner Nonprofit Corp.

Admissions Requirements Minimum age 18; Medical examination.
Staff Physicians 5 (pt); RNs 2 (ft), 1 (pt); LPNs 5 (pt); Nurses aides 6 (ft), 14 (pt); Physical therapists 1 (pt); Recreational therapists 1 (ft), 1 (pt); Occupational therapists 1 (pt); Speech therapists 1 (pt); Dietitians 1 (pt).
Facilities Dining room; Physical therapy room; Activities room; Crafts room; Laundry room; Barber/Beauty shop; Library; Living room/lounge area.
Activities Arts & crafts; Cards; Games; Reading groups; Prayer groups; Movies; Social/Cultural gatherings.

WYOCENA

Columbia County Home
PO Box 895, Wyocena, WI, 53969
(608) 429-2181

Admin Gerald E Baldowin. *Medical Dir/Dir of Nursing* Bruce Kraus MD; Jean Wadsworth RN.
Licensure Skilled care; Intermediate care. *Beds* SNF 150. *Certified* Medicaid; Medicare.
Owner Publicly owned.
Admissions Requirements Minimum age 18.
Staff Physicians 1 (pt); RNs 3 (ft), 12 (pt); LPNs 3 (ft), 9 (pt); Nurses aides 25 (ft), 62 (pt); Recreational therapists 2 (ft); Activities coordinators 1 (ft); Dietitians 1 (ft).
Facilities Dining room; Physical therapy room; Activities room; Chapel; Crafts room; Laundry room; Barber/Beauty shop; Library; Pharmacy.
Activities Arts & crafts; Cards; Games; Reading groups; Prayer groups; Movies; Shopping trips; Social/Cultural gatherings.

WYOMING

BASIN

Wyoming Retirement Center
890 Highway 20 S, Basin, WY, 82410
(307) 568-2431
Admin Leon Clyde Pruett. *Medical Dir/Dir of Nursing* Patricia Fritz RN.
Licensure Skilled care; Intermediate care. *Beds* SNF 90; ICF. *Certified* Medicaid; Medicare.
Owner Publicly owned.
Admissions Requirements Medical examination.
Staff RNs 9 (ft), 2 (pt); LPNs 3 (ft), 2 (pt); Nurses aides 24 (ft), 6 (pt).
Facilities Dining room; Physical therapy room; Activities room; Chapel; Crafts room; Laundry room; Barber/Beauty shop; Library.
Activities Arts & crafts; Cards; Games; Reading groups; Prayer groups; Movies; Shopping trips; Social/Cultural gatherings.

BUFFALO

Amie Holt Care Center
497 W Lott St, Buffalo, WY, 82834
(307) 684-5521
Admin Jerry E Jurena. *Medical Dir/Dir of Nursing* Dr Pat Nolan; Phyllis Hepp DON.
Licensure Skilled care; Intermediate care. *Beds* SNF 54; ICF. *Certified* Medicaid.
Owner Publicly owned.
Staff RNs 2 (ft), 1 (pt); LPNs 4 (ft); Nurses aides 22 (ft), 3 (pt); Physical therapists 1 (pt); Speech therapists 1 (pt); Activities coordinators 1 (ft), 1 (pt); Dietitians 1 (pt); Podiatrists 1 (pt).
Facilities Dining room; Activities room; Chapel; Crafts room; Barber/Beauty shop.
Activities Arts & crafts; Cards; Games; Reading groups; Prayer groups; Movies; Shopping trips; Social/Cultural gatherings.

CASPER

Poplar Living Center
4305 S Poplar, Casper, WY, 82601
(307) 237-2561
Admin Lillian L Holder. *Medical Dir/Dir of Nursing* Dr Fred Deiss; LaRae Balzer RN DON.
Licensure Skilled care; Intermediate care. *Beds* 120. *Certified* Medicaid; Medicare.
Owner Proprietary Corp (ARA Living Centers).
Admissions Requirements Minimum age 21; Physician's request.
Staff RNs 6 (ft); LPNs 10 (ft); Nurses aides 42 (ft); Activities coordinators 1 (ft), 1 (pt); Dietitians 2 (pt).
Languages Spanish
Facilities Dining room; Physical therapy room; Activities room; Crafts room; Laundry room; Barber/Beauty shop; Library.

Activities Arts & crafts; Cards; Games; Reading groups; Prayer groups; Movies; Shopping trips; Social/Cultural gatherings; Ice cream social; Reality orientation classes; Pie social.

CHEYENNE

Mountain Towers Healthcare*
3129 Acacia Dr, Cheyenne, WY, 82001
(307) 634-7901
Admin Frank J Shaw.
Licensure Skilled care; Intermediate care. *Beds* 170. *Certified* Medicaid.
Owner Proprietary Corp (Hillhaven Corp).

CODY

West Park Long-Term Care Center
707 Sheridan Ave, Cody, WY, 82414
(307) 578-2434
Admin Patricia M Brown. *Medical Dir/Dir of Nursing* Peter Rutherford; Karen Liden DON.
Licensure Skilled care; Intermediate care. *Beds* SNF 47; ICF 58. *Certified* Medicaid; Medicare.
Owner Publicly owned.
Admissions Requirements Medical examination; Physician's request.
Staff Physicians 8 (ft); RNs 4 (ft), 3 (pt); LPNs 6 (ft), 2 (pt); Nurses aides 32 (ft); Physical therapists 1 (ft), 1 (pt); Activities coordinators 1 (ft), 2 (pt); Dentists 1 (ft); Podiatrists 1 (ft).
Facilities Dining room; Physical therapy room; Activities room; Chapel; Crafts room; Laundry room; Barber/Beauty shop; Library.
Activities Arts & crafts; Cards; Games; Reading groups; Prayer groups; Movies; Social/Cultural gatherings; BBQs; Outings.

EVANSTON

Rennie Memorial Nursing Home
1225 Uinta St, Evanston, WY, 82930
(307) 789-3636
Admin Terry E Davis. *Medical Dir/Dir of Nursing* Dr Eskens.
Licensure Intermediate care. *Beds* 26. *Certified* Medicaid.
Owner Nonprofit Corp.
Admissions Requirements Minimum age 50; Medical examination.
Staff RNs 1 (ft), 2 (pt); LPNs 1 (pt); Nurses aides 6 (ft), 2 (pt); Physical therapists 2 (pt); Reality therapists 1 (pt); Recreational therapists 1 (pt); Occupational therapists 1 (pt); Activities coordinators 1 (pt); Dietitians 1 (pt); Podiatrists 1 (pt).
Facilities Dining room; Physical therapy room; Activities room; Crafts room; Laundry room; Barber/Beauty shop; Patio.
Activities Arts & crafts; Cards; Games; Reading groups; Prayer groups; Movies; Shopping trips; Social/Cultural gatherings; Senior citizens organization.

FORT WASHAKIE

Morning Star Manor
PO Box 628, Fort Washakie, WY, 82514
(307) 332-6902
Admin Bruce Odenthal. *Medical Dir/Dir of Nursing* Marion Ute DON.
Licensure Intermediate care. *Beds* ICF 50. *Certified* Medicaid.
Owner Nonprofit organization/foundation.
Admissions Requirements Minimum age 18; Physician's request.
Staff RNs 2 (ft); LPNs 4 (ft), 2 (pt); LPNs 1 (ft); Orderlies 1 (ft); Nurses aides 8 (ft), 6 (pt); Physical therapists 1 (ft); Speech therapists 1 (pt); Activities coordinators 1 (ft), 1 (pt); Dietitians 1 (ft).
Languages Shoshoni, Arapahoe
Facilities Dining room; Activities room; Chapel; Crafts room; Laundry room; Barber/Beauty shop.
Activities Arts & crafts; Cards; Games; Reading groups; Prayer groups; Social/Cultural gatherings.

GILLETTE

Pioneer Manor*
900 W 8th St, Gillette, WY, 82716
(307) 682-4709
Admin Charles R Willey. *Medical Dir/Dir of Nursing* J E Taylor MD.
Licensure Skilled care; Intermediate care. *Beds* 120. *Certified* Medicaid; Medicare.
Owner Nonprofit Corp.
Staff RNs 7 (ft), 3 (pt); LPNs 6 (ft), 2 (pt); Orderlies 1 (ft); Nurses aides 41 (ft), 4 (pt); Activities coordinators 1 (ft); Dietitians 1 (ft).
Facilities Dining room; Physical therapy room; Activities room; Chapel; Crafts room; Laundry room; Barber/Beauty shop; Library.
Activities Arts & crafts; Cards; Games; Reading groups; Prayer groups; Movies; Shopping trips; Social/Cultural gatherings.

GREYBULL

Bonnie Bluejacket Memorial Nursing Home
PO Box 152, Greybull, WY, 82426
(307) 568-3311
Admin Donn Swartz. *Medical Dir/Dir of Nursing* Ron McLean; Donna Becker.
Licensure Skilled care; Intermediate care. *Beds* SNF 32; ICF. *Certified* Medicaid; Medicare.
Owner Nonprofit Corp (Adventist Health Sys-USA).
Admissions Requirements Medical examination.
Staff Physicians 1 (pt); RNs 1 (ft), 4 (pt); LPNs 3 (ft), 2 (pt); Orderlies 1 (ft); Nurses aides 6 (ft), 6 (pt); Physical therapists 1 (pt); Activities coordinators 1 (ft); Dietitians 1 (pt).
Facilities Dining room; Physical therapy room; Activities room; Chapel; Crafts room; Laundry room; Barber/Beauty shop.

Activities Arts & crafts; Games; Prayer groups; Movies; Shopping trips; Social/Cultural gatherings; Bingo; Birds; Fish.

JACKSON

St Johns Hospital Long-Term Care
PO Box 428, Jackson, WY, 83001
(307) 733-3636, ext 218
Admin Dale Morgan. *Medical Dir/Dir of Nursing* Bruce Hayse MD; Becky Rice DON.
Licensure Intermediate care. *Beds* ICF 12. *Certified* Medicaid.
Owner Publicly owned.
Admissions Requirements Physician's request.
Staff Physicians 20 (ft); RNs 1 (ft); LPNs 2 (ft); Orderlies 1 (ft); Nurses aides 6 (ft); Physical therapists 1 (ft); Occupational therapists 1 (pt); Speech therapists 1 (pt); Activities coordinators 1 (pt); Dietitians 1 (pt).
Languages German, French
Facilities Dining room; Physical therapy room; Activities room; Crafts room; Laundry room; Barber/Beauty shop; Library.
Activities Arts & crafts; Cards; Games; Reading groups; Prayer groups; Movies; Social/Cultural gatherings; Picnics; Bus trips.

LANDER

Westward Heights Nursing Home
150 Buena Vista, Lander, WY, 82520
(307) 332-5560
Admin Cindy Morrison MA NHA. *Medical Dir/Dir of Nursing* Dr Charles McMahon; Peggy Cox DON.
Licensure Skilled care; Intermediate care. *Beds* SNF 6; ICF 54. *Certified* Medicaid.
Owner Proprietary Corp (Beverly Enterprises).
Admissions Requirements Medical examination; Physician's request.
Staff RNs; LPNs; Nurses aides; Activities coordinators; Social service coordinator.
Facilities Dining room; Activities room; Chapel; Laundry room; Barber/Beauty shop; Library.
Activities Arts & crafts; Cards; Games; Reading groups; Prayer groups; Movies; Social/Cultural gatherings.

LARAMIE

Bethesda Care Center of Laramie
503 S 18th, Laramie, WY, 82070
(303) 742-3728
Admin William G Shipman. *Medical Dir/Dir of Nursing* Dr Chris Bolz; Jeannie Niemoller RN DON.
Licensure Skilled care. *Beds* SNF 143. *Certified* Medicaid.
Owner Nonprofit Corp (Bethesda Care Centers).
Admissions Requirements Medical examination; Physician's request.
Staff RNs 4 (ft), 3 (pt); LPNs 5 (ft), 4 (pt); Orderlies 2 (pt); Nurses aides 35 (ft), 15 (pt); Physical therapists 1 (pt); Occupational therapists 1 (pt); Activities coordinators 1 (ft); Dietitians 1 (pt).
Facilities Dining room; Physical therapy room; Activities room; Chapel; Laundry room; Barber/Beauty shop; Library; 3 dining rooms.
Activities Arts & crafts; Cards; Reading groups; Prayer groups; Movies; Shopping trips.

LOVELL

New Horizons Care Center
PO Box 518, 100 E 10th St, Lovell, WY, 82431
(307) 548-7354

Admin Imogene Hanson. *Medical Dir/Dir of Nursing* John M Welch MD; Jan Hansen DON.
Licensure Skilled care; Intermediate care. *Beds* 60. *Certified* Medicaid; Medicare.
Owner Publicly owned.
Admissions Requirements Physician's request.
Staff RNs; LPNs; Nurses aides; Recreational therapists; Activities coordinators; Dietitians.
Facilities Dining room; Physical therapy room; Activities room; Chapel; Crafts room; Laundry room; Barber/Beauty shop; Library.
Activities Arts & crafts; Cards; Games; Reading groups; Prayer groups; Movies; Shopping trips; Social/Cultural gatherings.

LUSK

Niobrara County Memorial Hospital Nursing Home*
939 Ballencee Ave, Lusk, WY, 82225
(307) 334-2900
Admin Duaine Kanwischer. *Medical Dir/Dir of Nursing* Kenneth Turner DO.
Licensure Skilled care; Intermediate care. *Beds* 36.
Owner Publicly owned.
Admissions Requirements Medical examination; Physician's request.
Staff Physicians 2 (ft); RNs 3 (ft), 1 (pt); LPNs 3 (ft), 1 (pt); Nurses aides 15 (ft); Activities coordinators 1 (ft), 1 (pt); Dentists 1 (ft).
Facilities Dining room; Physical therapy room; Activities room; Chapel; Crafts room; Laundry room; Barber/Beauty shop.
Activities Arts & crafts; Cards; Games; Reading groups; Movies; Shopping trips; Social/Cultural gatherings.

NEWCASTLE

Weston County Manor
1124 Washington Blvd, Newcastle, WY, 82701
(307) 746-2793
Admin Evonne Ulmer. *Medical Dir/Dir of Nursing* Kirby Duvall MD.
Licensure Skilled care; Intermediate care. *Beds* SNF; ICF 37. *Certified* Medicaid; Medicare.
Owner Publicly owned.
Admissions Requirements Medical examination.
Staff Physicians 3 (pt); RNs 2 (ft), 1 (pt); LPNs 1 (ft), 3 (pt); Nurses aides 12 (ft), 4 (pt); Physical therapists 1 (pt); Activities coordinators 2 (ft); Dietitians 1 (pt).
Facilities Dining room; Activities room; Crafts room; Barber/Beauty shop.
Activities Arts & crafts; Cards; Games; Reading groups; Prayer groups; Movies; Shopping trips; Social/Cultural gatherings.

PINEDALE

Sublette County Retirement Center
PO Box 788, 333 N Bridger Av, Pinedale, WY, 82941
(307) 367-4161
Admin Ellen Toth. *Medical Dir/Dir of Nursing* Dr J T Johnston; Gaye Fletcher.
Licensure Skilled care; Intermediate care. *Beds* SNF 34; ICF. *Certified* Medicaid; Medicare.
Owner Nonprofit Corp.
Admissions Requirements Minimum age 62; Medical examination; Physician's request.
Staff Physicians 3 (pt); RNs 3 (ft), 2 (pt); LPNs 2 (ft), 1 (pt); Nurses aides 7 (ft), 3 (pt); Physical therapists 1 (pt); Reality therapists 1 (ft); Activities coordinators 1 (ft); Dietitians 1 (ft).
Facilities Dining room; Physical therapy room; Activities room; Chapel; Crafts room; Laundry room; Barber/Beauty shop; Library.
Activities Arts & crafts; Cards; Games; Reading groups; Prayer groups; Movies; Shopping trips; Social/Cultural gatherings.

POWELL

Powell Nursing Home
639 Ave H, Powell, WY, 82435
(307) 754-5704
Admin Elaine R Knudson. *Medical Dir/Dir of Nursing* Lyle F Haberland; Mary Lois Jacobson RN.
Licensure Skilled care; Intermediate care. *Beds* 98. *Certified* Medicaid.
Owner Nonprofit Corp (Luth Hosp & Homes Socty).
Admissions Requirements Physician's request.
Staff Physicians 4 (pt); RNs 6 (ft); LPNs 5 (ft), 2 (pt); Nurses aides 35 (ft), 6 (pt); Physical therapists 1 (pt); Activities coordinators 1 (ft); Dietitians 1 (pt); Podiatrists 1 (pt); Activities aide 1 (ft); Restorative aide 1 (ft); Social service 1 (ft).
Languages Spanish, German
Facilities Dining room; Physical therapy room; Activities room; Chapel; Crafts room; Laundry room; Barber/Beauty shop; Library.
Activities Arts & crafts; Games; Reading groups; Prayer groups; Movies; Shopping trips; Picnics; Bus rides; County fair; Birthday parties.

RAWLINS

Park Manor Nursing & Convalescent Home
542 16th St, Rawlins, WY, 82301
(307) 324-2759
Medical Dir/Dir of Nursing Florence Jolley DON.
Licensure Skilled care; Intermediate care. *Beds* SNF; ICF 90.
Owner Proprietary Corp (Hillhaven Corp).
Staff Physicians; RNs; LPNs; Orderlies; Nurses aides; Physical therapists; Activities coordinators; Dietitians.

ROCK SPRINGS

Kimberly Manor Nursing & Convalescent Home*
1325 Sage, Rock Springs, WY, 82901
(307) 362-3780
Admin Jeanne Ruffini. *Medical Dir/Dir of Nursing* Howard Greaves MD.
Licensure Skilled care; Intermediate care. *Beds* 101. *Certified* Medicaid; Medicare.
Owner Proprietary Corp (Hillhaven Corp).
Admissions Requirements Medical examination; Physician's request.
Staff RNs 6 (ft); LPNs 5 (ft); Orderlies 30 (ft); Activities coordinators 1 (ft), 1 (pt); Dietitians 1 (pt); Dentists; Ophthalmologists; Podiatrists.
Facilities Dining room; Physical therapy room; Activities room; Chapel; Crafts room; Laundry room; Barber/Beauty shop.
Activities Arts & crafts; Cards; Games; Reading groups; Prayer groups; Movies; Shopping trips; Social/Cultural gatherings.

SARATOGA

Valley View Manor*
Box 630, Saratoga, WY, 82331
(307) 326-8212
Admin Lynn Christensen. *Medical Dir/Dir of Nursing* Dr John Lunt.
Licensure Intermediate care. *Beds* 48. *Certified* Medicaid.
Owner Proprietary Corp.
Admissions Requirements Physician's request.
Staff Physicians 1 (pt); RNs 1 (ft), 3 (pt); LPNs 1 (ft), 3 (pt); Orderlies 1 (ft); Nurses aides 12 (ft), 2 (pt); Physical therapists 1 (pt); Activities coordinators 1 (ft), 1 (pt); Dietitians 1 (ft), 1 (pt).
Facilities Dining room; Physical therapy room; Laundry room; Barber/Beauty shop; Library.

Activities Arts & crafts; Cards; Games; Reading groups; Movies; Shopping trips; Social/Cultural gatherings.

SHERIDAN

Eventide of Sheridan
PO Box 788, 1851 Big Horn Ave, Sheridan, WY, 82801
(307) 674-4416
Admin Darold S Melchior. *Medical Dir/Dir of Nursing* Kay Causer RN.
Licensure Skilled care; Intermediate care. *Beds* SNF 120. *Certified* Medicaid; Medicare.
Owner Proprietary Corp (ARA Living Centers).
Staff RNs; LPNs; Orderlies; Nurses aides.
Languages Spanish, German, Polish
Facilities Dining room; Activities room; Chapel; Laundry room; Barber/Beauty shop; Library.
Activities Arts & crafts; Cards; Games; Reading groups; Prayer groups; Movies; Shopping trips; Social/Cultural gatherings.

THERMAPOLIS

Canyon Hills Manor
1210 Canyon Hills Rd, Thermapolis, WY, 82443
(307) 864-5591, 864-5592
Admin Pat Van Syer. *Medical Dir/Dir of Nursing* Dr Howard Willson; Linda Conner DON.
Licensure Intermediate care. *Beds* ICF 80. *Certified* Medicaid.
Owner Proprietary Corp (North Central Health Services).
Admissions Requirements Physician's request.
Staff RNs 1 (ft), 1 (pt); LPNs 6 (ft); Orderlies 3 (ft); Nurses aides 20 (ft), 4 (pt); Activities coordinators 2 (ft), 1 (pt).

Facilities Dining room; Activities room; Crafts room; Laundry room; Barber/Beauty shop.
Activities Arts & crafts; Cards; Games; Reading groups; Prayer groups; Movies; Shopping trips; Social/Cultural gatherings; Swimming; Bathing in mineral springs.

TORRINGTON

Goshen County Memorial Nursing Wing
536 E 20th Ave, Torrington, WY, 82240
(307) 532-4038
Admin Jean M Zerwas. *Medical Dir/Dir of Nursing* Shirley Love RN DON.
Licensure Intermediate care. *Beds* ICF 75. *Certified* Medicaid.
Owner Nonprofit Corp (Luth Hosp & Homes Socty).
Staff RNs 3 (ft); LPNs 9 (ft); Nurses aides 18 (ft), 7 (pt); Activities coordinators 2 (ft), 1 (pt); Dietitians 1 (ft).
Facilities Dining room; Activities room; Chapel; Crafts room; Barber/Beauty shop; Library; Ceramics room.
Activities Arts & crafts; Cards; Games; Reading groups; Prayer groups; Movies; Social/Cultural gatherings; One on one; Bus rides; Sing-alongs.

WHEATLAND

Platte County Memorial Nursing Home*
201 14th St, Wheatland, WY, 82201
(307) 322-3636
Admin Duaine Kanwischer. *Medical Dir/Dir of Nursing* Jane Nickel.
Licensure Intermediate care. *Beds* 43. *Certified* Medicaid.
Owner Nonprofit Corp (Luth Hosp & Homes Socty).

Admissions Requirements Medical examination; Physician's request.
Staff RNs 1 (ft); LPNs 3 (ft), 4 (pt); Nurses aides 7 (ft), 14 (pt); Physical therapists 1 (pt); Speech therapists 1 (pt); Activities coordinators 2 (ft); Dietitians 1 (pt); Dentists 1 (pt).
Facilities Dining room; Physical therapy room; Activities room; Chapel; Crafts room; Laundry room; Barber/Beauty shop.
Activities Arts & crafts; Cards; Games; Reading groups; Prayer groups; Movies; Shopping trips; Social/Cultural gatherings.

WORLAND

Bethesda Care Center of Worland
1901 Howell Ave, Worland, WY, 82401
(307) 347-4285
Admin Eric B Jensen NHA. *Medical Dir/Dir of Nursing* Virginia Basse RN.
Licensure Intermediate care. *Beds* ICF 76. *Certified* Medicaid.
Owner Nonprofit Corp (Bethesda Care Centers).
Admissions Requirements Medical examination; Physician's request.
Staff RNs 2 (ft), 4 (pt); LPNs 2 (ft), 4 (pt); Nurses aides 20 (ft), 7 (pt); Physical therapists 1 (pt); Activities coordinators 2 (ft), 1 (pt); Dietitians 1 (pt); Social worker 1 (pt).
Languages Spanish
Facilities Dining room; Physical therapy room; Activities room; Chapel; Barber/Beauty shop; Library.
Activities Arts & crafts; Cards; Games; Reading groups; Prayer groups; Movies; Shopping trips; Social/Cultural gatherings; Van outings.

PUERTO RICO

CAGUAS

Caguas Regional Skilled Nursing Facility*
Box 1238, Caguas, PR, 00625
Licensure Skilled care. *Beds* 24. *Certified*
  Medicaid; Medicare.

GUAYAMAS

Santa Rosa Extended Care Facility
PO Box 988, Guayamas, PR, 00654
Licensure Acute. *Beds* 47. *Certified* Medicaid;
  Medicare.

HATO REY

Auxilio Mutuo Hospital*
Ponce de Leon Ave, Stop 37, Hato Rey, PR,
  00919
Licensure Skilled care. *Beds* 66. *Certified*
  Medicaid; Medicare.

HUMACAO

Ryder Memorial Skilled Nursing Facility
Call Box 859, Humacao, PR, 00661
(809) 852-0768
Admin Saturnino Pena Flores. *Medical Dir/
  Dir of Nursing* Dr Jose Rafael Alvarez.
Licensure Skilled care. *Beds* SNF 40. *Certified*
  Medicare.
Owner Nonprofit organization/foundation.

Admissions Requirements Medical
  examination; Physician's request.
Staff Physicians 1 (ft); RNs 8 (ft), 2 (pt);
  LPNs 15 (ft); Physical therapists 1 (ft), 1
  (pt); Occupational therapists 1 (ft); Speech
  therapists 1 (pt); Activities coordinators 1
  (ft); Dietitians 1 (ft); Dentists 1 (pt);
  Podiatrists 1 (pt).
Languages Spanish
Affiliation Church of Christ
Facilities Dining room; Physical therapy
  room; Activities room; Chapel; Crafts room;
  Laundry room; Library.
Activities Arts & crafts; Cards; Games;
  Reading groups; Prayer groups; Movies;
  Social/Cultural gatherings; Educative
  conferences.

VIRGIN ISLANDS

CHRISTIANSTED

Charles Harwood Memorial Hospital—Skilled Nursing Unit*
Estate Orange Grove, Christiansted, VI, 00820
Licensure Skilled care. *Beds* 115. *Certified* Medicaid; Medicare.
Owner Publicly owned.

SAINT THOMAS

Knud Hansen Memorial Hospital*
Hospital Ln, Saint Thomas, VI, 00801
Licensure Skilled care. *Beds* 201. *Certified* Medicaid; Medicare.
Owner Publicly owned.

AFFILIATION INDEX

ALABAMA

Baptist
Baptist Home for Senior Citizens Inc, Cook Springs, AL
Eufaula Geriatric Center, Eufaula, AL

Episcopal
St Martins-in-the-Pines, Birmingham, AL

Methodist
Methodist Home for the Aging, Birmingham, AL
Wesley Manor Methodist Home for the Aging, Dothan, AL

Presbyterian
John Knox Manor Inc II, Montgomery, AL

Roman Catholic
Father Purcell Memorial Exceptional Children's Center, Montgomery, AL
Father Walter Memorial Child Care Center, Montgomery, AL
Little Sisters of the Poor—Sacred Heart Home, Mobile, AL
Mercy Medical, Daphne, AL
Resurrection Catholic Nursing Home, Marbury, AL

ALASKA

Lutheran
Heritage Place, Soldotna, AK
Kodiak Island Hospital, Kodiak, AK

Methodist
Wesleyan Nursing Home Inc, Seward, AK

Roman Catholic
Our Lady of Compassion Care Center, Anchorage, AK

ARIZONA

Baptist
Orangewood Health Center, Phoenix, AZ

Jewish
Handmaker Jewish Geriatric Center, Tucson, AZ
Kivel Geriatric Center-Nursing Home-Kivel Care Center, Phoenix, AZ

Lutheran
Good Shepherd Retirement Center, Peoria, AZ
Prescott Samaritan Village, Prescott, AZ
Wooddale Health Centre, Sun City, AZ

Order of Eastern Star
Arizona Eastern Star Home, Phoenix, AZ

Roman Catholic
Crestview Convalescent Lodge, Phoenix, AZ
Villa Maria Geriatric Center, Tucson, AZ

Seventh-Day Adventist
Pueblo Norte Nursing Center, Scottsdale, AZ
Pueblo Norte Nursing Center, Show Low, AZ
Pueblo Norte-West Nursing Center, Peoria, AZ

Volunteers of America
Westchester Care Center, Tempe, AZ

ARKANSAS

Baptist
Longmeadow Nursing Home of Malvern, Malvern, AR

Lutheran
Good Samaritan Cedar Lodge, Hot Springs Village, AR

Mennonite
Hillcrest Home—Harrison, Harrison, AR

Methodist
Methodist Nursing Home Inc, Fort Smith, AR
Smackover Nursing Home, Smackover, AR

Presbyterian
Presbyterian Village Health Care Center, Little Rock, AR

Roman Catholic
Pinewood Nursing Home, Waldron, AR

CALIFORNIA

Altenheim Society
Altenheim Inc, Oakland, CA

Baptist
Piedmont Gardens Health Facility, Oakland, CA
Pilgrim Haven Home, Los Altos, CA
Plymouth Village Redlands Convalescent Hospital, Redlands, CA
Valle Verde Health Facility, Santa Barbara, CA

Christian Reformed
Inland Christian Home Inc, Ontario, CA
Pilgrims Convalescent Hospital, Artesia, CA

Church of Christ
Mount San Antonio Gardens/Congregational Homes, Pomona, CA
Plymouth Tower, Riverside, CA

Church of God
Grace Nursing Home, Livingston, CA

Congregational
Carmel Valley Manor, Carmel, CA
Plymouth Square, Stockton, CA

Disciples of Christ
Bethany Convalescent Hospital, San Jose, CA
Bethesda Manor & Convalescent Center, Los Gatos, CA
California Christian Home, Rosemead, CA

Episcopal
The Canterbury, Rancho Palos Verdes, CA
Canterbury Woods, Pacific Grove, CA
The Home for the Aged of the Protestant Episcopal Church of the Diocese of Los Angeles, Alhambra, CA
Los Gatos Meadows, Los Gatos, CA
St Paul's Health Care Center, San Diego, CA

Evangelical Covenant Church
Brandel Manor, Turlock, CA
Mt Miguel Covenant Village, Spring Valley, CA
Samarkand Health Center, Santa Barbara, CA

Jewish
Beverly Palms Rehabilitation Hospital, Los Angeles, CA
Hebrew Home for Aged Disabled, San Francisco, CA
Home for Jewish Parents, Oakland, CA
San Diego Hebrew Home for the Aged, San Diego, CA

Lutheran
Lutheran Health Facility, Alhambra, CA
Lutheran Health Facility of Anaheim, Anaheim, CA
Lutheran Health Facility of Carlsbad, Carlsbad, CA
Redwood Terrace Lutheran Home, Escondido, CA
St Luke Manor, Fortuna, CA
Salem Lutheran Home Skilled Nursing Facility, Oakland, CA
Solheim Lutheran Home for the Aged, Los Angeles, CA
Southland Geriatric Center, Norwalk, CA
Sunny View Manor, Cupertino, CA

Mennonite
Pleasant View Manor, Reedley, CA
Sierra View Homes Inc, Reedley, CA

Methodist
Lake Park Retirement Residence, Oakland, CA
Pacific Grove Convalescent Hospital, Pacific Grove, CA

Order of Eastern Star
Eastern Star Home, Los Angeles, CA

Presbyterian
Buena Vista Manor, Duarte, CA
Casa Verdugo Convalescent Lodge, Glendale, CA
Monte Vista Grove Homes, Pasadena, CA
Westminster Gardens Health Center, Duarte, CA
White Sands of La Jolla, La Jolla, CA

Reorganized Church of Jesus Christ of Latter-Day Saints
Pacific Haven Convalescent Home, Garden Grove, CA

Roman Catholic
Ave Maria Convalescent Hospital, Monterey, CA

Franciscan Convalescent Hospital, Merced, CA
Little Sisters of the Poor, San Pedro, CA
Marycrest Manor, Culver City, CA
Nazareth House, San Diego, CA
Nazareth House, Fresno, CA
Nazareth House, Los Angeles, CA
Our Lady of Fatima Villa, Saratoga, CA
St Annes Home, San Francisco, CA
St John of God Nursing Hospital & Residence Inc, Los Angeles, CA
St Joseph Medical Center Pavilion, Burbank, CA
St Josephs Convalescent Hospital, Ojai, CA

Russian Orthodox
St John Kronstadt Convalescent Center, Castro Valley, CA

Seventh-Day Adventist
Adventist Convalescent Hospital, Glendora, CA
Ventura Estates Health Manor, Newbury Park, CA
Ventura Estates Health Manor, Newbury Park, CA

Society of Friends
Quaker Gardens, Stanton, CA

Volunteers of America
Imperial Manor Inc, Imperial, CA

COLORADO

Baptist
Mountain Vista Nursing Home, Wheat Ridge, CO
Park Avenue Baptist Home, Denver, CO
Stovall Care Center, Denver, CO

Independent Order of Odd Fellows & Rebekahs
Hildebrand Care Center, Canon City, CO

Jewish
Beth Israel Hospital & Geriatric Center, Denver, CO

Lutheran
Boulder Good Samaritan Health Care Center, Boulder, CO
Eben Ezer Lutheran Care Center, Brush, CO
Fort Collins Good Samaritan Retirement Village, Fort Collins, CO
Good Shepard Lutheran Home of the West, Littleton, CO
Hampton Drive Home, Colorado Springs, CO
Hilltop Nursing Home, Cripple Creek, CO
Loveland Good Samaritan Village, Loveland, CO
Simla Good Samaritan Center, Simla, CO

Mennonite
Arkansas Valley Regional Medical Center Nursing Care Center, La Junta, CO
Pioneers Memorial Hospital & Nursing Home, Rocky Ford, CO

Methodist
Frasier Meadows Manor Health Care Center, Boulder, CO

Roman Catholic
Ivy Nursing Home, Denver, CO
St Joseph Manor, Florence, CO
St Joseph's Hospital & Nursing Home of Del Norte Inc, Del Norte, CO
St Thomas More Progressive Care Center, Canon City, CO

Seventh-Day Adventist
Asbury Circle Living Center, Denver, CO
Eden Valley Nursing Home, Loveland, CO

Volunteers of America
Laurel Manor Care Center, Colorado Springs, CO

CONNECTICUT

Baptist
The Elim Park Baptist Home Inc, Cheshire, CT
Evangelical Baptist Home, Ashford, CT
Pierce Memorial Baptist Home Inc, Brooklyn, CT

Congregational
Noble Building, Hartford, CT

Evangelical Covenant Church
Pilgrim Manor, Cromwell, CT

Independent Order of Odd Fellows & Rebekahs
Fairview, Groton, CT

Jewish
Hebrew Home & Hospital, Hartford, CT
Jewish Home for the Aged, New Haven, CT
Jewish Home for the Elderly, Fairfield, CT

Lutheran
Lutheran Home of Middletown Inc, Middletown, CT
Lutheran Home of Southbury, Southbury, CT

Masons
Ashlar of Newtown, Newtown, CT
Masonic Home & Hospital, Wallingford, CT

Methodist
United Methodist Conv Home of Connecticut Inc, Shelton, CT

Roman Catholic
Matulaitis Nursing Home, Putnam, CT
Mercyknoll Inc, West Hartford, CT
Monsignor Bojnowski Manor Inc, New Britain, CT
Notre Dame Convalescent Home Inc, Norwalk, CT
Rose Manor, Waterbury, CT
St Elizabeth Health Center, East Hartford, CT
St Joseph's Manor, Trumbull, CT
St Joseph's Residence, Enfield, CT
St Mary Home, West Hartford, CT
Waterbury Extended Care Facility Inc, Watertown, CT

Seventh-Day Adventist
Geer Memorial Health Center, Canaan, CT

DELAWARE

Episcopal
Episcopal Church Home, Hockessin, DE

Jewish
Milton & Hattie Kutz Home Inc, Wilmington, DE

Masons
Masonic Home, Wilmington, DE

Mennonite
Country Rest Home, Greenwood, DE

Methodist
Cokesbury Village, Hockessin, DE
Methodist Country House, Wilmington, DE
Methodist Manor House, Seaford, DE

Roman Catholic
Jeanne Jugan Residence, Newark, DE

DISTRICT OF COLUMBIA

Baptist
Thomas House, Washington, DC

Masons
Medlantic Manor at Lamond—Riggs, Washington, DC

Methodist
Methodist Home of DC, Washington, DC

Presbyterian
Presbyterian Home of DC, Washington, DC

FLORIDA

Baptist
Florida Baptist Retirement Center, Vero Beach, FL
Palm Shores Retirement Center, Saint Petersburg, FL

Christian & Missionary Alliance Foundation
Alliance Nursing Center, Deland, FL
Shell Point Village Nursing Pavilion, Fort Myers, FL

Christian Science
Daystar Inc, Fort Lauderdale, FL
Morningside Inc, Pinellas Park, FL

Church of Christ
Plymouth Harbor Inc, Sarasota, FL

Church of the Brethren
Palms Health Care Center, Sebring, FL

Disciples of Christ
Florida Christian Health Center, Jacksonville, FL

Episcopal
William L Hargrave Health Center, Davenport, FL
Suncoast Manor, Saint Petersburg, FL

Jewish
Aviva Manor, Lauderdale Lakes, FL
Hebrew Home for the Aged—North Dade, North Miami Beach, FL
King David Center at Palm Beach, West Palm Beach, FL
Miami Beach Hebrew Home for the Aged, Miami Beach, FL
Miami Jewish Home for the Aged at Douglas Gardens, Miami, FL
River Garden Hebrew Home for the Aged, Jacksonville, FL

Lutheran
Daytona Beach Olds Hall Good Samaritan Nursing Center, Daytona Beach, FL
Fair Havens Center, Miami, FL
Kissimmee Good Samaritan Nursing Center, Kissimmee, FL
Lutheran Haven, Oviedo, FL
Orlando Lutheran Towers, Orlando, FL
St Mark Village, Palm Harbor, FL
Swanholm Nursing & Rehabilitation Center, Saint Petersburg, FL

Masons
Masonic Home of Florida, Saint Petersburg, FL

Mennonite
Sunnyside Nursing Home, Sarasota, FL

Methodist
Asbury Towers, Bradenton, FL
Sunny Shores Villas Health Center, Saint Petersburg, FL
Wesley Manor Retirement Village, Jacksonville, FL

Presbyterian
Bay Village of Sarasota, Sarasota, FL
Bradenton Manor, Bradenton, FL
Leisure Manor, Saint Petersburg, FL
Osceola Inn, Clearwater, FL
Presbyterian Nursing Center—Florida Presbyterian Homes Inc, Lakeland, FL
Westminster Oaks Nursing Home, Tallahassee, FL
Westminster Towers, Orlando, FL
Winter Park Towers, Winter Park, FL

Roman Catholic
All Saints Catholic Nursing Home,
  Jacksonville, FL
Bon Secours Hospital/Villa Maria Nursing
  Center, North Miami, FL
Florida Manor Nursing Home, Orlando, FL
Haven of Our Lady of Peace, Pensacola, FL
Lourdes-Noreen McKeen Residence for
  Geriatric Care Inc, West Palm Beach, FL
Maria Manor Health Care, Saint Petersburg,
  FL
St Catherine Laboure Manor, Jacksonville, FL
St Johns Nursing & Rehabilitation Hospital/St
  John's Health Care Center, Lauderdale
  Lakes, FL
St Jude Manor Nursing Home, Jacksonville,
  FL

Royal Order of Moose
Moosehaven Health Center, Orange Park, FL

Seventh-Day Adventist
Florida Living Nursing Center, Forest City,
  FL
Lake Alfred Restorium & ACLF, Lake Alfred,
  FL
Lake Wales Convalescent Center, Lake Wales,
  FL

GEORGIA

Baptist
Banks-Jackson-Commerce Nursing Home,
  Commerce, GA
Baptist Village Inc, Waycross, GA
Bethany Home for Men, Millen, GA
Harvest Heights Baptist Home Center,
  Decatur, GA

Jewish
The Jewish Home for the Aged, Atlanta, GA

King's Daughters & Sons
Cohen's Retreat, Savannah, GA

Methodist
Budd Terrace Intermediate Care Home,
  Atlanta, GA
Magnolia Manor Methodist Nursing Home,
  Americus, GA
Wesley Woods Health Center, Atlanta, GA

Presbyterian
The Presbyterian Home Inc, Quitman, GA

Roman Catholic
Our Lady of Perpetual Help Home, Atlanta,
  GA

Seventh-Day Adventist
Lakeland Villa Convalescent Center, Lakeland,
  GA

HAWAII

Church of Christ
Arcadia Retirement Residence, Honolulu, HI

Lutheran
Pohai Nani Care Center, Kaneohe, HI

Roman Catholic
St Francis Hospital (DP), Honolulu, HI

IDAHO

Lutheran
Boise Samaritan Village, Boise, ID
Good Samaritan Center, Idaho Falls, ID
Good Samaritan Village, Moscow, ID
Silver Wood Good Samaritan Center,
  Silverton, ID

Roman Catholic
St Benedict's Long-Term Care Unit, Jerome,
  ID

ILLINOIS

Apostolic Christian
Apostolic Christian Home, Roanoke, IL
Apostolic Christian Home for the
  Handicapped, Morton, IL
Apostolic Christian Restmor I, Morton, IL
Eureka Apostolic Christian Home, Eureka, IL
Fairview Haven Inc, Fairbury, IL

Apostolic Christian Church
Apostolic Christian Home, Peoria, IL
Apostolic Christian Resthaven, Elgin, IL

Assembly of God
Parkway Terrace Nursing Home, Wheaton, IL

Baha'i Faith
Baha'i Home, Wilmette, IL

Baptist
Baptist Retirement Home, Maywood, IL
Barry Care Center of Litchfield, Litchfield, IL
Central Baptist Home for the Aged, Norridge,
  IL
Fairview Baptist Home, Downers Grove, IL

Christian Reformed
Rest Haven South, South Holland, IL
Rest Haven West Christian Nursing Center,
  Downers Grove, IL

Christian Science
Hill Top, Lake Bluff, IL

Church of Christ
The Anchorage Bensenville Home,
  Bensenville, IL
Beulah Land Christian Home, Flanagan, IL
Eden Retirement Center Inc, Edwardsville, IL
Fair Havens Christian Home, Decatur, IL
Faith Countryside Homes Nursing Center,
  Highland, IL
Good Samaritan Home of Quincy, Quincy, IL
Hitz Memorial Home, Alhambra, IL
Lewis Memorial Christian Village, Springfield,
  IL
Peace Memorial Home, Evergreen Park, IL
Peotone Bensenville Home, Peotone, IL
Pine View Care Center, Saint Charles, IL
Plymouth Place Inc, La Grange Park, IL
St Pauls House/Grace Convalescent Home,
  Chicago, IL
Washington Christian Village, Washington, IL

Church of the Brethren
Pleasant Hill Village, Girard, IL

Evangelical Covenant Church
Brandel Care Center, Northbrook, IL
Covenant Health Care Center Inc, Batavia, IL
Covenant Home, Chicago, IL

Evangelical Free Church
Fairhaven Christian Home, Rockford, IL

Independent Order of Odd Fellows & Rebekahs
Odd Fellow-Rebekah Home, Mattoon, IL

Jewish
Buckingham Pavilion, Chicago, IL
Home Association Jewish Blind, Chicago, IL
Jewish Peoples Convalescent Home, Chicago,
  IL
Lieberman Geriatric Health Centre, Skokie, IL
Selfhelp Home for the Aged, Chicago, IL

King's Daughters & Sons
Friendship Manor, Rock Island, IL

Lutheran
Augustana Center for Developmentally
  Disabled Children, Chicago, IL
Bethesda Home & Retirement Center,
  Chicago, IL
Carroll County Good Samaritan Center,
  Mount Carroll, IL
Country Health Inc, Gifford, IL
Good Samaritan Home of Flanagan, Flanagan,
  IL

Hoopeston Regional Nursing Home,
  Hoopeston, IL
Lutheran Care Center, Altamont, IL
The Lutheran Home, Peoria, IL
Lutheran Home & Services for Aged,
  Arlington Heights, IL
Mendota Lutheran Home, Mendota, IL
Metropolis Good Samaritan Home,
  Metropolis, IL
P A Peterson Home for the Aging, Rockford,
  IL
Pleasant View Luther Home, Ottawa, IL
Prairieview Lutheran Home, Danforth, IL
Prophets Riverview Good Samaritan Center,
  Prophetstown, IL
St Matthew Lutheran Home, Park Ridge, IL
Salem Village, Joliet, IL

Masons
Warren N Barr Pavilion, Chicago, IL
Illinois Knights Templar Home, Paxton, IL
Illinois Masonic Home, Sullivan, IL

Mennonite
Maple Lawn Health Center, Eureka, IL
Meadows Mennonite Home, Chenoa, IL

Methodist
Bethany Methodist Home, Chicago, IL
Bethany Terrace Retirement & Nursing Home,
  Morton Grove, IL
Evenglow Lodge, Pontiac, IL
The Methodist Home, Chicago, IL
North Rockford Convalescent Home,
  Rockford, IL
Oak Crest, DeKalb, IL
Sunset Home of the United Methodist
  Church, Quincy, IL
Sunset Manor, Woodstock, IL
The United Methodist Village Inc,
  Lawrenceville, IL
Wesley Village U M C Health Care Center,
  Macomb, IL
Wesley Wilcourt Willows Health Center,
  Rockford, IL

Order of Eastern Star
Eastern Star Home, Macon, IL

Presbyterian
Illinois Presbyterian Home, Springfield, IL
The Presbyterian Home, Evanston, IL
Titus Memorial Presbyterian Home, Sullivan,
  IL

Roman Catholic
Alvernia Manor Retirement Home, Lemont,
  IL
Brother James Court, Springfield, IL
Dammert Geriatric Center, Belleville, IL
Franciscan Nursing Home, Joliet, IL
Good Shepherd Manor, Momence, IL
Holy Family Health Center, Des Plaines, IL
Holy Family Villa, Lemont, IL
Little Sisters of the Poor, Chicago, IL
Maria Linden, Rockford, IL
A Merkle-C Knipprath Nursing Home,
  Clifton, IL
Misericordia Home, Chicago, IL
Mother Theresa Home Inc, Lemont, IL
Mt St Joseph, Lake Zurich, IL
Nazarethville, Des Plaines, IL
Our Lady of Angels Retirement, Joliet, IL
Our Lady of Victory Nursing Home,
  Bourbonnais, IL
Rosary Hill Home, Justice, IL
St Anthonys Continuing Care Center, Rock
  Island, IL
St Benedict Home for Aged, Niles, IL
St Joseph Home of Chicago Inc, Chicago, IL
St Joseph's Home for the Elderly, Palatine, IL
St Josephs Home of Peoria, Peoria, IL
St Joseph's Home of Springfield, Springfield,
  IL
St Patrick's Residence, Joliet, IL
Villa St Cyril, Highland Park, IL

Seventh-Day Adventist
Applewood Living Center, Matteson, IL
Colonial Hall Nursing Home, Princeton, IL
Crown Manor Living Center, Zion, IL
Douglas Living Center, Mattoon, IL
Elmwood Living Center, Aurora, IL
Lakewood Living Center, Plainfield, IL
Notre Dame Hills Living Center, Belleville, IL
Rivershores Living Center, Marseilles, IL

Slovak American Charitable Association
Rolling Hills Manor, Zion, IL

INDIANA

Apostolic Christian
Parkview Haven Retirement Home, Francesville, IN

Baptist
St Paul Baptist Church Home for the Aged, Indianapolis, IN

Church of Christ
Evansville Protestant Home Inc, Evansville, IN
Golden Years Homestead Inc, Fort Wayne, IN
The Good Samaritan Home Inc, Evansville, IN
Maple Manor Christian Home Inc—Adult Division, Sellersburg, IN

Church of the Brethren
Brethren's Home of Indiana Inc, Flora, IN
Grace Village Health Care Facility, Winona Lake, IN
Timbercrest—Church of the Brethren Home Inc, North Manchester, IN

Church of the Nazarene
Westside Christian Retirement Village Inc, Indianapolis, IN

Disciples of Christ
Flinn Memorial Home Inc, Marion, IN
Kennedy Memorial Christian Home Inc, Martinsville, IN

First Wesleyan Church
Wesleyan Health Care Center, Marion, IN

Independent Order of Odd Fellows & Rebekahs
Odd Fellows Home, Greensburg, IN

Jewish
Hooverwood, Indianapolis, IN

Knights of Pythias
Indiana Pythian Home, Lafayette, IN

Lutheran
Lutheran Community Home Inc, Seymour, IN
Lutheran Home of Northwest Indiana Inc, Crown Point, IN
Lutheran Homes Inc, Fort Wayne, IN
Lutheran Homes Inc, Kendallville, IN
Mulberry Lutheran Home, Mulberry, IN
Northwood Good Samaritan Center, Jasper, IN
Shakamak Good Samaritan Center, Jasonville, IN

Masons
Indiana Masonic Home, Franklin, IN

Mennonite
Greencroft Nursing Center, Goshen, IN
Swiss Village Inc, Berne, IN

Methodist
The Franklin United Methodist Home, Franklin, IN
Hamilton Grove, New Carlisle, IN
Indiana Asbury Towers United Methodist Home Inc, Greencastle, IN
United Methodist Memorial Home, Warren, IN
Wesley Manor Inc, Frankfort, IN

Missionary Church
Hubbard Hill Estates Inc, Elkhart, IN

Presbyterian
Englishton Park, Lexington, IN
Peabody Retirement Community, North Manchester, IN

Roman Catholic
Little Company of Mary Health Facility Inc, San Pierre, IN
Little Sisters of the Poor, Evansville, IN
Providence Retirement Home, New Albany, IN
The Regina Continuing Care Center, Evansville, IN
Sacred Heart Home, Avilla, IN
St Anne Home, Fort Wayne, IN
St Ann's Home, Hammond, IN
St Anthony Health Care Inc, Lafayette, IN
St Anthony Home Inc, Crown Point, IN
St Augustine Home for the Aged, Indianapolis, IN
St Elizabeth Healthcare Center, Delphi, IN
St Josephs Care Center—Lombardy, South Bend, IN
St Joseph's Care Center—Morningside, South Bend, IN
St Paul Hermitage, Beech Grove, IN

Seventh-Day Adventist
Bethel Sanitarium Inc, Evansville, IN
Prairie Village Living Center, Washington, IN
River Valley Living Center, Madison, IN
Scott Villa Living Center, Scottsburg, IN
Swiss Villa Living Center, Vevay, IN

IOWA

Baptist
Baptist Memorial Home Elm Crest Apartments, Harlan, IA
Crest Group Home, Des Moines, IA
Crest Group Home, Ottumwa, IA
Salsbury Baptist Home, Charles City, IA

Church of Christ
Mayflower Home, Grinnell, IA

Disciples of Christ
Ramsey Home, Des Moines, IA

Evangelical Free Church
Evangelical Free Church Home, Boone, IA

Independent Order of Odd Fellows & Rebekahs
Iowa Odd Fellows Home, Mason City, IA

Jewish
Iowa Jewish Home, Des Moines, IA

Lutheran
Algona Good Samaritan Center, Algona, IA
Bartels Lutheran Home Inc, Waverly, IA
Bethany Lutheran Home Inc, Council Bluffs, IA
Bethany Manor Inc, Story City, IA
Cedar Falls Lutheran Home, Cedar Falls, IA
Davenport Lutheran Home, Davenport, IA
Eventide Lutheran Home for the Aged, Denison, IA
Good Neighbor Home, Manchester, IA
Good Samaritan Center, Postville, IA
Good Samaritan Center, Ottumwa, IA
Good Samaritan Center, Forest City, IA
Lakeside Lutheran Home, Emmetsburg, IA
Luther Manor, Dubuque, IA
Luther Park Health Center, Des Moines, IA
Lutheran Home for the Aged, Vinton, IA
Lutheran Homes Society, Muscatine, IA
Lutheran Retirement Home Inc, Northwood, IA
Perry Lutheran Home, Perry, IA
St Luke Lutheran Home, Spencer, IA
Salem Lutheran Homes, Elk Horn, IA
Strawberry Point Lutheran Home, Strawberry Point, IA
Valborg Lutheran Home, Des Moines, IA
West Union Good Samaritan Center, West Union, IA

Masons
Iowa Masonic Nursing Home, Bettendorf, IA
Herman L Rowley Memorial Masonic Home, Perry, IA
Scottish Rite Park Health Care Center, Des Moines, IA

Mennonite
Parkview Home, Wayland, IA
Pleasant View Home, Kalona, IA

Methodist
Friendship Haven Inc, Fort Dodge, IA
Halcyon House, Washington, IA
Heritage House Continuing Care Community, Atlantic, IA
Methodist Manor, Storm Lake, IA
Meth-Wick Manor, Cedar Rapids, IA
St Luke's Methodist Hospital, Cedar Rapids, IA
Wesley Acres, Des Moines, IA
Western Home, Cedar Falls, IA

Order of Eastern Star
M A Barthell Order of Eastern Star Home, Decorah, IA
Eastern Star Masonic Home, Boone, IA

Presbyterian
Bethany Home, Dubuque, IA
Presbyterian Home of Ackley, Ackley, IA
United Presbyterian Home, Washington, IA

Roman Catholic
Alverno Health Care Facility, Clinton, IA
Bishop Drumm Care Center, Johnston City, IA
Hallmar Mercy Hospital, Cedar Rapids, IA
Happy Siesta Nursing, Remsen, IA
Kahl Home for the Aged, Davenport, IA
Marian Home, Fort Dodge, IA
Mercy Health Center, Dubuque, IA
Padre Pio Health Care Center, Dubuque, IA
St Anthony Nursing Home, Carroll, IA
St Francis Continuing Care & Nursing Home Center, Burlington, IA

KANSAS

Apostolic Christian
Apostolic Christian Home, Sabetha, KS

Baptist
Homestead Health Center Inc, Wichita, KS
Sunset Nursing Center, Concordia, KS

Church of Christ
Christ Villa Nursing Center, Wichita, KS
Winfield Rest Haven Inc, Winfield, KS

Church of the Brethren
The Cedars Inc, McPherson, KS

Congregational
Brewster Place—The Congregational Home, Topeka, KS

International Order of Odd Fellows & Rebekahs
Rebekah-Odd Fellow Care Home, Hutchinson, KS

Lutheran
Bethany Home Association of Lindsborg, Lindsborg, KS
Cedar View Nursing Center, Wellington, KS
Decatur County Good Samaritan Center, Oberlin, KS
Ellis Good Samaritan Center, Ellis, KS
Ellsworth Good Samaritan Center—Villa Grace, Ellsworth, KS
Ellsworth Good Samaritan Center—Villa Hope, Ellsworth, KS
Good Samaritan Center, Winfield, KS
Good Samaritan Center, Dodge City, KS
Good Samaritan Village, Saint Francis, KS
Hays Good Samaritan Center, Hays, KS

Hutchinson Good Samaritan Center,
  Hutchinson, KS
Junction City Good Samaritan Center,
  Junction City, KS
Liberal Good Samaritan Center, Liberal, KS
Linn Community Nursing Home Inc, Linn,
  KS
Lutheran Home Inc, Herington, KS
Lyons Good Samaritan Center, Lyons, KS
Manor Nursing Home, Independence, KS
Minneapolis Good Samaritan Center,
  Minneapolis, KS
Olathe Good Samaritan Center, Olathe, KS
Parsons Good Samaritan Center, Parsons, KS
Rush County Nursing Home, LaCrosse, KS
Shiloh Manor Nursing Home, Canton, KS
Trinity Lutheran Manor, Merriam, KS
Valley Vista Good Samaritan Center,
  Wamego, KS

Masons
Kansas Masonic Home, Wichita, KS

Mennonite
Bethel Home Inc, Montezuma, KS
Garden Valley Retirement Village, Garden
  City, KS
Kidron Bethel Retirement Services, Newton,
  KS
Memorial Home for the Aged, Moundridge,
  KS
Mennonite Friendship Manor Inc, South
  Hutchison, KS
Moundridge Manor, Moundridge, KS
Parkside Homes Inc, Hillsboro, KS
Schowalter Villa, Hesston, KS

Methodist
Aldersgate Village Health Unit, Topeka, KS
Friendly Acres Inc, Newton, KS
Trinity Manor Adult Care Home, Dodge City,
  KS
United Methodist Home, Topeka, KS
Wesley Towers Inc, Hutchinson, KS

Presbyterian
Arkansas City Presbyterian Manor, Arkansas
  City, KS
Clay Center Presbyterian Manor, Clay Center,
  KS
Emporia Presbyterian Manor, Emporia, KS
Hutchinson Heights, Hutchinson, KS
Kansas City Presbyterian Manor, Kansas City,
  KS
Lawrence Presbyterian Manor, Lawrence, KS
Newton Presbyterian Manor, Newton, KS
Parsons Presbyterian Manor, Parsons, KS
Salina Presbyterian Manor, Salina, KS
Sterling Presbyterian Manor, Sterling, KS
Topeka Presbyterian Manor Inc, Topeka, KS
Wichita Presbyterian Manor, Wichita, KS

Roman Catholic
Catholic Care Center, Wichita, KS
Mt Joseph, Concordia, KS
St John's of Hays, Hays, KS
St Johns Rest Home, Victoria, KS
St Joseph Home, Kansas City, KS
Villa Maria Inc, Mulvane, KS

Seventh-Day Adventist
Paradise Valley Living Center, Belle Plaine,
  KS

KENTUCKY

Baptist
Baptist Convalescent Center, Newport, KY
Baptist Home East, Louisville, KY
Mary Harding Home Inc, Owensboro, KY

Church of Christ
Sayre Christian Village Nursing Home,
  Lexington, KY

Episcopal
Episcopal Church Home, Louisville, KY
Home of the Innocents, Louisville, KY

King's Daughters & Sons
Kings Daughters & Sons Home, Louisville,
  KY
King's Daughters & Sons Home for Aged Men
  & Women, Ashland, KY

Lutheran
Cedar Lake Lodge, LaGrange, KY
Louisville Lutheran Home Inc, Jeffersontown,
  KY

Masons
Masonic Widows & Orphans Home &
  Infirmary Inc, Masonic Home, KY
Old Masons' Home of Kentucky, Shelbyville,
  KY

Methodist
Lewis Memorial Methodist Home, Franklin,
  KY
Wesley Manor Retirement Community,
  Louisville, KY

Order of Eastern Star
Eastern Star Home in Kentucky, Louisville,
  KY

Presbyterian
Rose Anna Hughes Presbyterian Home,
  Louisville, KY
Westminster Terrace, Louisville, KY

Roman Catholic
Carmel Manor, Fort Thomas, KY
Loretto Motherhouse Infirmary, Nerinx, KY
Marian Home, Louisville, KY
Nazareth Home, Louisville, KY
Sacred Heart Home, Louisville, KY
St Margaret of Cortona Home, Lexington, KY
Sansbury Memorial Infirmary, Saint
  Catherine, KY
Taylor Manor Nursing Home, Versailles, KY

Salvation Army
Salvation Army Adult Day Care Center,
  Newport, KY

Seventh-Day Adventist
Friendship Manor Nursing Home, Pewee
  Valley, KY
Memorial Hospital—SNF, Manchester, KY
Mills Manor, Mayfield, KY
Pinecrest Manor, Hopkinsville, KY

LOUISIANA

Baptist
Arcadia Baptist Home, Arcadia, LA
Madison Parish Baptist Nursing Home,
  Tallulah, LA

Challenge Ministries
Oak Park Care Center, Lake Charles, LA

Church of God
Prayer Tower Rest Home, New Orleans, LA

Jewish
Willow Wood, Algiers, LA

Lutheran
Lutheran Home of New Orleans, New
  Orleans, LA

Methodist
Lafon United Methodist Nursing Home, New
  Orleans, LA

Presbyterian
Evergreen Manor, Minden, LA
Presbyterian Village of Homer, Homer, LA

Roman Catholic
Bethany MHS Care Center, Lafayette, LA
Consolata Home, New Iberia, LA
Lafon Nursing Home of the Holy Family,
  New Orleans, LA
Martin de Porres Multi-Care Center, Lake
  Charles, LA

Mary-Joseph Residence for the Elderly, New
  Orleans, LA
Prompt Succor Nursing Home, Opelousas, LA
St Joseph's Home, Monroe, LA
St Margaret's Daughters Nursing Home, New
  Orleans, LA
St Mary's Residential Training School,
  Alexandria, LA

MAINE

Jewish
Jewish Home for the Aged, Portland, ME

Roman Catholic
d'Youville Pavilion Nursing Home, Lewiston,
  ME
St Andre Health Care Facility, Biddeford, ME
St Casimir Health Care Facility, Lewiston, ME
St Joseph Nursing Home, Upper Frenchville,
  ME
St Joseph's Manor, Portland, ME

Seventh-Day Adventist
Ledgeview Memorial Home, West Paris, ME

MARYLAND

Baptist
The Baptist Home of Maryland Del Inc,
  Owings Mills, MD
Maryland Baptist Aged Home, Baltimore, MD

Church of Christ
Homewood Retirement Center—Frederick,
  Frederick, MD

Church of the Brethren
Faheney-Keedy Memorial Home Inc,
  Boonsboro, MD

Episcopal
Uplands Home for Church Women,
  Baltimore, MD

Jewish
Hebrew Home of Greater Washington,
  Rockville, MD
Hurwitz House, Baltimore, MD
Jewish Convalescent & Nursing Home Inc,
  Baltimore, MD
Levindale Hebrew Geriatric Center &
  Hospital, Baltimore, MD
Milford Manor Nursing Home, Baltimore,
  MD
Pikesville Nursing & Convalescent Center,
  Pikesville, MD

Lutheran
Augsburg Lutheran Home of Maryland Inc,
  Pikesville, MD
John L Deaton Medical Center Inc, Baltimore,
  MD
Frostburg Village Nursing Home of Allegany
  County, Frostburg, MD
National Lutheran Home for the Aged,
  Rockville, MD
Ravenwood Lutheran Village Nursing Home,
  Hagerstown, MD
Roland Park Place, Baltimore, MD
St Luke Lutheran Home, Baltimore, MD

Masons
Maryland Masonic Homes, Cockeysville, MD

Mennonite
Goodwill Mennonite Home Inc, Grantsville,
  MD
Mennonite Old People's Home, Maugansville,
  MD

Methodist
Wesley Home Inc, Baltimore, MD

Presbyterian
Presbyterian Home of Maryland Inc, Towson,
  MD

Roman Catholic
Bon Secours Extended Care Facility, Ellicott
City, MD
Cardinal Shehan Center for the Aging,
Towson, MD
Carroll Manor Inc, Hyattsville, MD
Jenkins Memorial Nursing Home, Baltimore,
MD
Little Sisters of the Poor—St Martin's,
Baltimore, MD
St Joseph's Nursing Home, Catonsville, MD
Stella Maris, Baltimore, MD
Villa Rosa Nursing Home, Mitchellville, MD

Society of Friends
Broadmead, Cockeysville, MD
Friends Nursing Home Inc, Sandy Spring, MD

MASSACHUSETTS

Afro-American
Hurstdale Rest Home, Springfield, MA

Baptist
Baptist Home of Massachusetts, Newton, MA

Episcopal
St Monica's Home, Roxbury, MA
Taber Street Nursing Home, New Bedford,
MA

German Ladies Aid Society
Deutsches Altenheim Inc, West Roxbury, MA

Hellenic Women's Benevolent Society
Hellenic Nursing Home for The Aged, Canton,
MA

Independent Order of Odd Fellows & Rebekahs
Odd Fellows Home of Massachusetts,
Worcester, MA

Jewish
Chelsea Jewish Nursing Home, Chelsea, MA
Fall River Jewish Home for the Aged, Fall
River, MA
Jewish Home for the Aged, Worcester, MA
Jewish Nursing Home of Western
Massachusetts, Longmeadow, MA
Jewish Rehabilitation Center for Aged of the
North Shore Inc, Swampscott, MA
New Bedford Jewish Convalescent Home,
New Bedford, MA

Lutheran
Fair Havens Rest Home Inc, Middleboro, MA
Lutheran Home of Brockton Inc, Brockton,
MA
Lutheran Home of Worcester Inc, Worcester,
MA

Masons
Masonic Home, Charlton, MA

Methodist
Rivercrest Long-Term Care Facility, Concord,
MA

Order of Eastern Star
Eastern Star Home, Orange, MA

Roman Catholic
Beaven-Kelly Rest Home, Holyoke, MA
Campion Residence & Renewal Center,
Weston, MA
Catholic Memorial Home Inc, Fall River, MA
D'Youville Manor, Lowell, MA
Harborview Manor Nursing Home, South
Dartmouth, MA
Madonna Manor, North Attleboro, MA
Marian Manor Nursing Home, South Boston,
MA
MI Nursing & Restorative Center, Lawrence,
MA
Mt St Vincent Nursing Home Inc, Holyoke,
MA
Our Lady's Haven, Fairhaven, MA
Sacred Heart Nursing Home, New Bedford,
MA

St Francis Home, Worcester, MA
St Joseph's Manor, Boston, MA
St Lukes Home, Springfield, MA
St Patricks Manor Inc, Framingham, MA
Tower Hill Rest Home, Fitchburg, MA

Society of Friends
New England Friends Home, Hingham, MA

Unitarian Universalist
Doolittle Home Inc, Foxboro, MA

MICHIGAN

Baptist
Inter-City Christian Manor, Allen Park, MI
Michigan Christian Home, Grand Rapids, MI

Christian Reformed
Holland Home—Raybrook Manor, Grand
Rapids, MI

Church of Christ
Church of Christ Care Center, Mount
Clemens, MI
Evangelical Home—Detroit, Detroit, MI
Evangelical Home Port Huron, Port Huron,
MI
Pilgrim Manor Inc, Grand Rapids, MI

Episcopal
St Lukes Episcopal Home, Highland Park, MI

Independent Order of Odd Fellows & Rebekahs
Odd Fellow & Rebekah Home, Jackson, MI

Jewish
Jewish Home for the Aged 2, Detroit, MI
Prentis Manor Jewish Home for Aged 1,
Southfield, MI

Lutheran
Luther Haven, Detroit, MI
Luther Home, Grand Rapids, MI
Luther Manor, Saginaw, MI
Martin Luther Holt Home, Holt, MI
Martin Luther Memorial Home, South Haven,
MI
Martin Luther Memorial Home, South Lyon,
MI
Martin Luther Saginaw Home, Saginaw, MI
The Lutheran Home, Frankenmuth, MI
Lutheran Home—Monroe, Monroe, MI

Masons
Michigan Masonic Home, Alma, MI

Mennonite
Ausable Valley Home, Fairview, MI
Thurston Woods Village-Nursing Center,
Sturgis, MI

Methodist
Boulevard Temple United Methodist
Retirement Home, Detroit, MI
Chelsea United Methodist Retirement Home,
Chelsea, MI

Presbyterian
Porter Hills Presbyterian Village Inc, Grand
Rapids, MI

Roman Catholic
Dowagiac Nursing Home, Dowagiac, MI
Grand Blanc Convalescent Center Inc, Grand
Blanc, MI
Little Sisters of the Poor, Detroit, MI
Lourdes Inc, Pontiac, MI
Bishop Noa Home for Senior Citizens,
Escanaba, MI
Our Lady of Mercy Convalescent Home Inc,
Hubbell, MI
River Forest Nursing Care Center, Three
Rivers, MI
St Anthony Nursing Center, Warren, MI
St Francis Home, Saginaw, MI
St Jude Convalescent Center, Livonia, MI
St Lawrence Diamondale Center, Dimondale,
MI

St Martin Deporres Nursing Home, Detroit,
MI
Villa Elizabeth Inc, Grand Rapids, MI

Royal Order of Moose
Whitehall Convalescent Home 2, Novi, MI

Seventh-Day Adventist
Riveridge Manor, Inc, Niles, MI

MINNESOTA

Baptist
Castle Ridge Care Center & Manor House,
Eden Prairie, MN
Maranatha Baptist Care Center, Brooklyn
Center, MN
Thorne Crest Retirement Center, Albert Lea,
MN
Winnebago Baptist Home, Winnebago, MN

Christian Science
Clifton House, Minneapolis, MN

Church of Christ
Christian Manor Nursing Home, Tracy, MN
St Lucas Convalescent & Geriatric Center,
Faribault, MN
St Pauls Church Home, Saint Paul, MN
Samaritan Bethany Home, Rochester, MN

Episcopal
Episcopal Church Home of Minnesota, Saint
Paul, MN

Evangelical Covenant Church
Colonial Acres Health Care Center, Golden
Valley, MN
Ebenezer Covenant Home, Buffalo, MN

Evangelical Free Church
Elim Home, Milaca, MN
Elim Home, Princeton, MN
Elim Home, Watertown, MN

Independent Order of Odd Fellows & Rebekahs
Minnesota Odd Fellows Home, Northfield,
MN

Jewish
Minnesota Jewish Group Home 1—Chai
House, Saint Louis Park, MN
Minnesota Jewish Group Home II—Tivah,
Saint Paul, MN
Sholom Home, Saint Paul, MN

Lutheran
Adams Group Home, Adams, MN
Albert Lea Good Samaritan Center, Albert
Lea, MN
Arlington Good Samaritan Center, Arlington,
MN
Augustana Home of Minneapolis,
Minneapolis, MN
Baxter Group Home ICF/MR, Baxter, MN
Bethany Good Samaritan Center, Brainerd,
MN
Bethany Home, Litchfield, MN
Bethany Home/Bethel Manors, Alexandria,
MN
Bethany Samaritan Heights, Rochester, MN
Bethesda Lutheran Care Center, Saint Paul,
MN
Board of Social Ministry, Saint Paul, MN
Brainerd Good Samaritan Center, Brainerd,
MN
Broen Memorial Home, Fergus Falls, MN
Mary J Brown Good Samaritan Center,
Luverne, MN
Christus Group Home, Grand Rapids, MN
Clinton Good Samaritan Center, Clinton, MN
Crest View Lutheran Home, Columbia
Heights, MN
Ebenezer Hall, Minneapolis, MN
Ebenezer Ridges Geriatric Care Center,
Lakeville, MN
Ebenezer Society Luther & Field, Minneapolis,
MN
Elders Home Inc, New York Mills, MN

Emmanuel Home, Litchfield, MN
Emmanuel Nursing Home, Detroit Lakes, MN
Eventide Lutheran Home, Moorhead, MN
Gethsemane Group Home, Virginia, MN
Glenwood Retirement Home Inc, Glenwood, MN
Good Samaritan Center, Jackson, MN
Good Samaritan Center, Clearbrook, MN
Good Samaritan Nursing Center, East Grand Forks, MN
Good Samaritan Village, Pipestone, MN
Good Samaritan Village, Mountain Lake, MN
Good Shepherd Lutheran Home, Rushford, MN
Good Shepherd Lutheran Home, Sauk Rapids, MN
Halstad Lutheran Memorial Home, Halstad, MN
Kenyon Sunset Home, Kenyon, MN
Lafayette Good Samaritan Center, Lafayette, MN
Lakeshore Lutheran Home, Duluth, MN
Luther Haven Nursing Home, Montevideo, MN
Martin Luther Manor, Bloomington, MN
Luther Memorial Home, Madelia, MN
The Lutheran Home & Hope Residence, Belle Plaine, MN
Lutheran Memorial Nursing Home, Twin Valley, MN
Lutheran Retirement Home of Southern Minnesota, Truman, MN
Lyngblomsten Care Center, Saint Paul, MN
Mankato Lutheran Home, Mankato, MN
Minnewaska Lutheran Home, Starbuck, MN
Northern Pines Good Samaritan Center, Blackduck, MN
Northfield Retirement Center, Northfield, MN
Paynesville Good Samaritan Center, Paynesville, MN
Pelican Rapids Good Samaritan Center, Pelican Rapids, MN
Pelican Valley Health Center, Pelican Rapids, MN
Pioneer Home Inc, Fergus Falls, MN
Pleasant View Good Samaritan Center, Saint James, MN
Red Wing Group Home, Red Wing, MN
St John Lutheran Home, Springfield, MN
St Johns Lutheran Home, Albert Lea, MN
St Marks Lutheran Home, Austin, MN
St Olaf Residence, Minneapolis, MN
St Stephen Group Homes A & B, Bloomington, MN
Seminary Memorial Home, Red Wing, MN
Sogge Memorial Good Samaritan Center, Windom, MN
Tuff Memorial Home, Hills, MN
Tweeten Memorial Hospital—Nurs Home, Spring Grove, MN
Vasa Lutheran Home, Red Wing, MN
Whispering Pines Good Samaritan Center, Pine River, MN

Masons
Minnesota Masonic Care Center, Bloomington, MN

Methodist
Chapel View Inc, Hopkins, MN
Lakeview Methodist Health Care Center, Fairmont, MN
Methodist Hospital Extended Care Facility, Saint Louis Park, MN
Walker Methodist Health Center Inc, Minneapolis, MN

Moravian
Lake Auburn Home for Aged, Excelsior, MN

Presbyterian
Minneapolis Outreach Home, Minneapolis, MN
Presbyterian Homes Johanna Shores, Saint Paul, MN
Presbyterian Homes Langton Place, Saint Paul, MN
Presbyterian Homes-Johanna Shores, Arden Hills, MN

Roman Catholic
Assumption Home, Cold Spring, MN
Divine Providence Community Home, Sleepy Eye, MN
Divine Providence Hospital & Home, Ivanhoe, MN
Little Sisters of the Poor, Saint Paul, MN
Madonna Towers Inc, Rochester, MN
Mille Lacs Nursing Home, Onamia, MN
Mother of Mercy Nursing Home & Retirement Center, Albany, MN
Mother Teresa Home, Cold Spring, MN
Our Lady of Good Counsel Home, Saint Paul, MN
Sacred Heart Hospice, Austin, MN
St Annes Hospice, Winona, MN
St Anthony Eldercenter on Main, Minneapolis, MN
St Benedicts Center, Saint Cloud, MN
St Elizabeth Nursing Home, Wabasha, MN
St Francis Home, Waite Park, MN
St Francis Home, Breckenridge, MN
St Marys Villa Nursing Home, Pierz, MN
St Otto's Home, Little Falls, MN
St Therese Home, New Hope, MN
Villa of St Francis Nursing Home, Morris, MN
Villa St Vincent, Crookston, MN

Volunteers of America
Crystal Care Center, Crystal, MN
Sleepy Eye Care Center, Sleepy Eye, MN

MISSISSIPPI

Baptist
Crawford Nursing Home Inc, Jackson, MS

King's Daughters & Sons
King's Daughters & Sons Rest Home Inc, Meridian, MS

Seventh-Day Adventist
Adventist Health Center, Lumberton, MS

MISSOURI

Assembly of God
Maranatha Manor, Springfield, MO

Baptist
The Baptist Home, Ironton, MO
General Baptist Nursing Home, Independence, MO
General Baptist Nursing Home Inc, Campbell, MO
West Vue Home Inc, West Plains, MO

Christian Science
Great Oaks Inc, Kansas City, MO

Church of Christ
Good Samaritan Home, Saint Louis, MO
Parkside Meadows Inc, Saint Charles, MO

Disciples of Christ
Foxwood Springs Living Center, Raymore, MO
Lenoir Health Care Center, Columbia, MO

Independent Order of Odd Fellows & Rebekahs
Odd Fellows Home, Liberty, MO

Jewish
Jewish Center for Aged, Chesterfield, MO
Shalom Geriatric Center, Kansas City, MO

King's Daughters & Sons
King's Daughters Home, Mexico, MO

Lutheran
Beautiful Savior Home, Belton, MO
Luther Manor Retirement & Nursing Center, Hannibal, MO
Lutheran Altenheim Society of Missouri, Saint Louis, MO

Lutheran Good Shepherd Home, Concordia, MO
Lutheran Health Care Association Extended Care Facility, Webster Grove, MO
The Lutheran Home, Cape Girardeau, MO
Pine View Manor Inc, Stanberry, MO

Methodist
The Ozarks Methodist Manor, Marionville, MO

Presbyterian
Fulton Presbyterian Manor, Fulton, MO
Presbyterian Manor at Farmington, Farmington, MO
Presbyterian Manor at Rolla, Rolla, MO

Reorganized Church of Jesus Christ of Latter-Day Saints
Independence Regional Health Center—Extended Care, Independence, MO

Roman Catholic
DePaul Health Center St Anne's Division, Bridgeton, MO
Grand Manor, Saint Louis, MO
LaVerna Heights, Savannah, MO
LaVerna Village Nursing Home, Savannah, MO
Little Sisters of the Poor, Saint Louis, MO
Little Sisters of the Poor—St Alexis Home, Kansas City, MO
Mary, Queen & Mother Center, Saint Louis, MO
Mother of Good Counsel Nursing Home, Saint Louis, MO
Our Lady of Mercy Home, Kansas City, MO
St Agnes Home, Kirkwood, MO
St Francis Hopital—SNF/ICF Care Facility, Marceline, MO
St Johns Mercy Villa, Springfield, MO
St Joseph's Hill Infirmary Inc, Eureka, MO

MONTANA

Lutheran
Carbon County Memorial Nursing Home, Red Lodge, MT
Faith Lutheran Home, Wolf Point, MT
Immanuel Lutheran Home, Kalispell, MT
Lutheran Home of the Good Shepherd, Havre, MT
Mountain View Manor Nursing Center, Eureka, MT
Mountainview Memorial Hospital & Nursing Home, White Sulphur Springs, MT
St John's Lutheran Home, Billings, MT
Valley View Home, Glasgow, MT

NEBRASKA

Baptist
Maple-Crest, Omaha, NE

Evangelical Free Church
Christian Homes Inc, Holdrege, NE

Jewish
Rose Blumkin Jewish Home, Omaha, NE
Doctor Philip Sher Jewish Home, Omaha, NE

Lutheran
Atkinson Good Samaritan Center, Atkinson, NE
Bethpage at Axtell, Axtell, NE
Bethpage at Lincoln, Lincoln, NE
Bloomfield Good Samaritan Center, Bloomfield, NE
Blue Valley Lutheran Home Society Inc, Hebron, NE
Callaway Good Samaritan Home, Callaway, NE
Colonial Villa Good Samaritan Center, Alma, NE
Good Samaritan Center, Nelson, NE
Good Samaritan Center, Superior, NE
Good Samaritan Center, Syracuse, NE

Good Samaritan Home & Center, Beatrice, NE
Good Samaritan Village, Alliance, NE
Good Samaritan Village—Perkins Pavilion, Hastings, NE
Good Shepherd Lutheran Home, Blair, NE
Gordon Good Samaritan Center, Gordon, NE
Martin Luther Home, Beatrice, NE
The Lutheran Home, Omaha, NE
Mid-Nebraska Lutheran Home Inc, Newman Grove, NE
Millard Good Samaritan Center, Omaha, NE
C A Mues Memorial Good Samaritan Center, Arapahoe, NE
Nemaha County Good Samaritan Center, Auburn, NE
Pine View Good Samaritan Center, Valentine, NE
Ravenna Good Samaritan Home, Ravenna, NE
St John's Center, Kearney, NE
St Luke's Good Samaritan Village, Kearney, NE
Scribner Good Samaritan Center, Scribner, NE
Tabitha Home, Lincoln, NE
Villa Grace Good Samaritan Village, Hastings, NE
Wolf Memorial Good Samaritan Center, Albion, NE
Wymore Good Samaritan Center, Wymore, NE

Methodist
Methodist Memorial Homes Inc, Holdrege, NE

Reformed Church
Lakeview Rest Home, Firth, NE

Roman Catholic
Madonna Centers, Lincoln, NE
Mt Carmel Home—Keens Memorial, Kearney, NE
St Joseph Gerontology Center, Alliance, NE
St Josephs Villa Inc, David City, NE

Women's Christian Temperance Union
Mother Hull Home, Kearney, NE

NEW HAMPSHIRE

Church of Christ
Havenwood-Heritage Heights Retirement Community, Concord, NH

Independent Order of Odd Fellows & Rebekahs
New Hampshire Odd Fellows Home, Concord, NH

Masons
Masonic Home, Manchester, NH

Roman Catholic
Mt Carmel Nursing Home, Manchester, NH
St Frances Home for the Aged, Hampshire, NH
St Francis Home, Laconia, NH

NEW JERSEY

Christian Reformed
Christian Health Care Center, Wyckoff, NJ

Jewish
Central New Jersey Jewish Home for the Aged, Somerset, NJ
Daughters of Israel Pleasant Valley Home, West Orange, NJ
Jewish Geriatric Center, Cherry Hill, NJ
Westwood Hall Hebrew Home, Long Branch, NJ

Lutheran
Lutheran Home at Ocean View, Ocean View, NJ

Masons
Masonic Home of New Jersey, Burlington, NJ

Presbyterian
The Grove Health Care Center, Neptune, NJ
Haddonfield Presbyterian Home of Southern New Jersey, Haddonfield, NJ
The Lodge Intermediate Care Facility, Neptune, NJ
Presbyterian Home of Atlantic City—Madison House, Atlantic City, NJ

Roman Catholic
Mater Dei Nursing Home, Newfield, NJ
Bishop McCarthy Residence, Vineland, NJ
Our Lady's Residence, Pleasantville, NJ
St Vincent's Nursing Home, Montclair, NJ

Society of Friends
Cadbury Health Care Center, Cherry Hill, NJ
Friends Home at Woodstown, Woodstown, NJ
Medford Leas, Medford, NJ

NEW MEXICO

Church of Christ
Lakeview Christian Home—Northgate Unit, Carlsbad, NM

Lutheran
Betty Dare Good Samaritan Center, Alamogordo, NM
Four Corners Good Samaritan, Aztec, NM
Grants Good Samaritan Center, Grants, NM
Lovington Good Samaritan Center, Lovington, NM
Manzano del Sol Good Samaritan Village, Albuquerque, NM
Socorro Good Samaritan Village, Socorro, NM
University Terrace Good Samaritan Village, Las Cruces, NM

Methodist
Laundsun Homes Inc, Carlsbad, NM

Presbyterian
La Residencia, Santa Fe, NM
Retirement Ranch of Clovis, Clovis, NM

Roman Catholic
Casa Maria Health Care Centre, Roswell, NM
St Francis Gardens Inc, Albuquerque, NM

NEW YORK

Baptist
Baptist Home of Brooklyn New York, Rhinebeck, NY
Baptist Medical Center Nursing Home, Brooklyn, NY
Baptist Retirement Center, Scotia, NY
Fairport Baptist Home, Fairport, NY

Congregational
New York Congregational Home for the Aged, Brooklyn, NY

Episcopal
Good Shepherd-Fairview Home Inc, Binghamton, NY
St Johns Episcopal Homes for the Aged & the Blind, Brooklyn, NY
St Marys Hospital for Children Inc, Bayside, NY

Independent Order of Odd Fellows & Rebekahs
Odd Fellow & Rebekah Nursing Home Inc, Lockport, NY
United Odd Fellow & Rebekah Home, Bronx, NY

Jewish
Aishel Avraham Residential Health Facility Inc, Brooklyn, NY
Beth Abraham Hospital, Bronx, NY
Bezalel Nursing Home Company, Far Rockaway, NY
Bialystoker Home for the Aged, New York, NY

Rosa Coplon Jewish Home & Infirmary, Buffalo, NY
Daughters of Jacob Geriatric Center, Bronx, NY
Daughters of Sarah Nursing Home Company Inc, Albany, NY
Fort Tryon Nursing Home, New York, NY
Franklin Nursing Home, Flushing, NY
The Rosaline & Joseph Gurwin Jewish Geriatric Center of Long Island, Commack, NY
Haym Salomon Home for the Aged, Brooklyn, NY
The Hebrew Home for the Aged at Riverdale, New York, NY
Hebrew Home for the Aged/Fairfield Division, Bronx, NY
Hebrew Hospital for the Chronic Sick, Bronx, NY
Home for the Aged Blind, Yonkers, NY
The Jewish Home & Hospital for Aged-Kingsbridge Center, Bronx, NY
Jewish Home & Hospital for the Aged, New York, NY
Jewish Home of Central New York, Syracuse, NY
Jewish Home of Rochester, Rochester, NY
Jewish Institute for Geriatric Care Nursing Home Co Inc, New Hyde Park, NY
JHMCB Center for Nursing & Rehabilitation, Brooklyn, NY
Menorah Home & Hospital for the Aged & Infirm, Brooklyn, NY
Menorah Nursing Home Inc, Brooklyn, NY
Metropolitan Jewish Genatric Center, Brooklyn, NY
Port Chester Nursing Home, Port Chester, NY
Prospect Park Nursing Home Inc, Brooklyn, NY
Rutland Nursing Home Co Inc, Brooklyn, NY
Sephardic Home for the Aged Inc, Brooklyn, NY
Charles T Sitrin Nursing Home Company Inc, New Hartford, NY
United Home for Aged Hebrews, New Rochelle, NY
United Nursing Home for the Aged Inc, New Rochelle, NY
Workmens Circle Home & Infirmary, Bronx, NY

Lutheran
Augustana Lutheran Home for the Aged, Brooklyn, NY
Eger Nursing Home Inc, Staten Island, NY
Good Samaritan Nursing Home, Delmar, NY
Lutheran Center for the Aging, Smithtown, NY
Lutheran Retirement Home, Jamestown, NY
The Martin Luther Nursing Home Inc, Clinton, NY
Niagara Lutheran Home Inc, Buffalo, NY
The Wartburg Home of the Evangelical Lutheran Church, Mount Vernon, NY
Wartburg Lutheran Home for the Aging, Brooklyn, NY

Masons
German Masonic Home Corp, New Rochelle, NY
Masonic Home & Health Facility, Utica, NY

Methodist
Bethany Nursing Home & Health Related Facility Inc, Horseheads, NY
Bethel Nursing Home Company Inc, Ossining, NY
Brooklyn United Methodist Church Home, Brooklyn, NY
Elizabeth Church Manor, Binghamton, NY
Folts Home, Herkimer, NY
Gerry Nursing Home Co Inc, Gerry, NY
Methodist Church Home for the Aged, Bronx, NY
Niagra Frontier Methodist Home Inc Health Related Facility, Getzville, NY
Wesley Health Care Center Inc, Saratoga Springs, NY

Wesley-on-East Ltd, Rochester, NY

Order of Eastern Star
Eastern Star Home & Infirmary, Oriskany, NY

Presbyterian
Amherst Presbyterian Nursing Center, Williamsville, NY
Presbyterian Home for Central New York Inc, New Hartford, NY
Presbyterian Homes of Western New York Inc, Jamestown, NY
St Lukes Presbyterian Nursing Center, Buffalo, NY

Roman Catholic
A Barton Hepburn Hospital Skilled Nursing Facility, Ogdensburg, NY
Brothers of Mercy Nursing & Rehabilitation Center, Clarence, NY
Consolation Nursing Home Inc, West Islip, NY
Ferncliff Nursing Home Co Inc, Rhinebeck, NY
Good Samaritan Nursing Home, Sayville, NY
Holy Family Home for the Aged, Brooklyn, NY
Jeanne Jugan Residence, Bronx, NY
Kateri Residence, New York, NY
Kenmore Mercy Skilled Nursing Facility, Kenmore, NY
Lyden Nursing Home, Astoria, NY
Madonna Home of Mercy Hospital of Watertown, Watertown, NY
Madonna Residence Inc, Brooklyn, NY
Mercy Health & Rehabilitation Center Nursing Home Inc, Auburn, NY
Mercy Healthcare Center, Tupper Lake, NY
Mt Loretto Nursing Home, Amsterdam, NY
Nazareth Health Related Facility, Buffalo, NY
Our Lady of Hope Residence-Little Sisters of the Poor, Latham, NY
Ozanam Hall of Queens Nursing Home Inc, Bayside, NY
Sacred Heart Home, Bronx, NY
Sacred Heart Home Inc, Plattsburgh, NY
St Ann's Home for the Aged Inc—The Heritage, Rochester, NY
St Cabrini Nursing Home Inc, Dobbs Ferry, NY
St Camillus Residential Health Care Facility, Syracuse, NY
St Clare Manor, Lockport, NY
St Josephs Home, Ogdensburg, NY
St Josephs Hospital Nursing Home of Yonkers New York Inc, Yonkers, NY
St Josephs Manor, Olean, NY
St Luke Nursing Home Company Inc, Oswego, NY
St Patricks Home for the Aged & Infirm, Bronx, NY
St Teresas Nursing Home Inc, Middletown, NY
Frances Schervier Home & Hospital, Bronx, NY
Sisters of Charity Hospital—Skilled Nursing Facility, Buffalo, NY
Teresian House Nursing Home Co Inc, Albany, NY
Tibbits Health Care Facility, White Plains, NY
Uihlein Mercy Center, Lake Placid, NY
Villa Mary Immaculate, Albany, NY

Seventh-Day Adventist
Adventist Nursing Home Inc, Livingston, NY

Volunteer Firefighting Service
Firemans Home of the State of New York Volunteer Firemens Assoc, Hudson, NY

NORTH CAROLINA

Baptist
Baptist Retirement Homes of North Carolina Inc, Winston-Salem, NC

Church of Christ
J W Abernethy Center—United Church Retirement Homes Inc, Newton, NC
Piedmont Center-United Church Retirement Homes Inc, Thomasville, NC

Episcopal
Deerfield Episcopal Retirement Community Inc, Asheville, NC

First Wesleyan Church
Wesleyan Arms Inc, High Point, NC

Jewish
The Bluementhal Jewish Home for the Aged Inc, Clemmons, NC

Lutheran
Lutheran Nursing Homes Inc—Albemarle Unit, Albemarle, NC
Lutheran Nursing Homes Inc—Hickory Unit, Hickory, NC
Lutheran Nursing Homes Inc—Salisbury Unit, Salisbury, NC
Twin Lakes Care Center, Burlington, NC

Masons
Masonic & Eastern Star Home of North Carolina Inc, Greensboro, NC

Methodist
Brooks-Howell Home, Asheville, NC
Methodist Retirement Home—Wesley Pines, Lumberton, NC
Methodist Retirement Homes Inc, Durham, NC

Moravian
Moravian Home Inc, Winston-Salem, NC

Presbyterian
Covenant Village, Gastonia, NC
The Presbyterian Home at Charlotte Inc, Charlotte, NC
The Presbyterian Home of High Point, High Point, NC
The Presbyterian Home of Hawfields, Inc, Mebane, NC

Roman Catholic
Maryfield Nursing Home, High Point, NC

Seventh-Day Adventist
Pisgah Manor Inc, Candler, NC

Society of Friends
Friends Home Inc, Greensboro, NC

NORTH DAKOTA

Baptist
Baptist Home Inc, Bismarck, ND

Church of Christ
Elm Crest Manor, New Salem, ND
Wishek Home for the Aged, Wishek, ND

Evangelical Free Church
Elim Home, Fargo, ND

Lutheran
Arthur Good Samaritan Center, Arthur, ND
Enderlin Hillcrest Manor Ltd, Enderlin, ND
Good Samaritan—LTC, Rugby, ND
The Good Shepherd Home, Watford City, ND
Gronna Good Samaritan Center, Lakota, ND
Lake Region Lutheran Home, Devils Lake, ND
Larimore Good Samaritan Center, Larimore, ND
Luther Memorial Home, Mayville, ND
Lutheran Home of the Good Shepherd Inc, New Rockford, ND
Lutheran Sunset Home, Grafton, ND
Missouri Slope Lutheran Home Inc, Bismarck, ND
Mott Good Samaritan Nursing Center, Mott, ND
Oakes Manor Good Samaritan Center, Oakes, ND

Parkside Lutheran Home, Lisbon, ND
Pembina County Memorial Nursing Home, Cavalier, ND
St Luke's Home, Dickinson, ND
Souris Valley Care Center, Velva, ND
Sunset Home Inc, Bowman, ND
Tri-County Retirement & Nursing Home, Hatton, ND
Valley Memorial Home—Almonte, Grand Forks, ND
Valley Memorial Home—Medical Park, Grand Forks, ND
Westhope Home, Westhope, ND

Roman Catholic
Carrington Health Care LTC, Carrington, ND
Garrison Memorial Hospital—ICF, Garrison, ND
St Aloisius Skilled Nursing Home, Harvey, ND
St Andrew's Hospital & Nursing Home, Bottineau, ND
St Vincent's Nursing Home, Bismarck, ND

OHIO

Apostolic Christian
Apostolic Christian Home Inc, Rittman, OH

Baptist
Judson Village, Cincinnati, OH

Christian Reformed Hungarian Church
Lorantffy Care Center Inc, Akron, OH

Christian Science
Overlook House, Cleveland, OH

Church of Christ
Canton Christian Home, Canton, OH
Chapel Hill Home, Canal Fulton, OH
Fairhaven Retirement & Health Care Community, Upper Sandusky, OH
Mt Healthy Christian Home, Cincinnati, OH
Trinity Retirement Community, Dayton, OH
Willow Brook Christian Home, Worthington, OH

Church of God
Hester Memorial Nursing Home, Dayton, OH
Winebrenner Extended Care Facility, Findlay, OH
Winebrenner Haven, Findlay, OH

Church of the Brethren
Brethren Care Inc, Ashland, OH
The Brethren's Home, Greenville, OH
Good Shepherd Home, Fostoria, OH
West View Manor Retirement Center, Wooster, OH

Episcopal
Marjorie P Lee Retirement Community, Cincinnati, OH
Whetstone Convalescent Center, Columbus, OH

First Community Church
First Community Village Healthcare Center, Columbus, OH

Independent Order of Odd Fellows & Rebekahs
IOOF Home of Ohio Inc, Springfield, OH

Jewish
Covenant House—Jewish Home for Aged, Dayton, OH
Darlington House, Toledo, OH
Glen Manor Home for Jewish Aged, Cincinnati, OH
Heritage House-Columbus Jewish Home for the Aged, Columbus, OH
Heritage Manor, Youngstown, OH
Menorah Park Center for the Aging, Beachwood, OH
Orthodox Jewish Home for the Aged, Cincinnati, OH

King's Daughters & Sons
Belle Hoffman Michael Home, Bucyrus, OH

Knights of Pythias
K W Hess Ohio Pythian Home, Springfield, OH
Sophia Huntington Parker Home, Medina, OH

Lutheran
Bethany Lutheran Village, Dayton, OH
Filling Memorial Home of Mercy Inc, Napoleon, OH
Luther Home of Mercy, Williston, OH
Lutheran Home, Westlake, OH
Lutheran Memorial Home, Sandusky, OH
Lutheran Old Folks Home, Toledo, OH
Lutheran Senior City, Columbus, OH
St Luke Lutheran Home for the Aging, North Canton, OH
Shepherd of the Valley Nursing Home, Niles, OH

Masons
The Ohio Masonic Home, Springfield, OH

Mennonite
Fairlawn Haven, Archbold, OH
Mennonite Memorial Home, Bluffton, OH

Methodist
Crandall Medical Center, Sebring, OH
The Elyria United Methodist Home, Elyria, OH
Flat Rock Care Center, Flat Rock, OH
Healthaven Nursing Home, Akron, OH
Hill View Health Center, Portsmouth, OH
Lake Park Hospital & Nursing Care Center, Sylvania, OH
Otterbein Home, Lebanon, OH
Otterbein Portage Valley, Pemberville, OH
Riverside Methodist Hospital's Extended Care Unit, Columbus, OH
Twin Towers, Cincinnati, OH
Wesley Glen Inc, Columbus, OH
Wesley Hall Inc, Cincinnati, OH

Order of Eastern Star
Eastern Star Home of Cuyahoga County, East Cleveland, OH
Hamilton County Eastern Star Home Inc, Cincinnati, OH
Ohio Eastern Star Home, Mount Vernon, OH

Presbyterian
Fairmount Health Center, Willoughby, OH
Dorothy Love Retirement Community, Sidney, OH
Marietta Manor, Cleveland, OH
Mt Pleasant Nursing Home, Cleveland, OH
Mt Pleasant Village, Monroe, OH
Park Vista Retirement Community, Youngstown, OH
Westminster Thurber Community, Columbus, OH

Roman Catholic
Archbishop Leibold Home, Cincinnati, OH
Franciscan Terrace at St Clare Center, Cincinnati, OH
Good Samaritan Medical Center, Zanesville, OH
Holy Family Home, Parma, OH
Jennings Hall Inc, Garfield Heights, OH
Little Sisters of the Poor, Cleveland, OH
Madonna Hall, Cleveland, OH
Maria Care Center, Bowling Green, OH
The Maria-Joseph Center, Dayton, OH
Mother Margaret Hall, Mount Saint Joseph, OH
Mt Alverna Home, Parma, OH
Sacred Heart Home for Aged—Little Sisters of the Poor, Oregon, OH
St Ann Skilled Nursing Center, Sandusky, OH
St Edward Home, Akron, OH
St Francis Home for the Aged, Tiffin, OH
St Francis Rehabilitation Hospital & Nursing Home, Green Springs, OH
St Joseph Hospice Home for the Aged, Louisville, OH

St Raphaels Home for the Aged, Columbus, OH
St Rita's Home for the Aged Inc, Columbus, OH
St Theresa Home, Cincinnati, OH
Schroder Manor, Hamilton, OH

Seventh-Day Adventist
Meadowbrook Living Center, Montgomery, OH
Northside Manor Living Center, Mount Vernon, OH

Society of Friends
Quaker Heights Nursing Home, Waynesville, OH
Walton Retirement Home, Barnesville, OH

Swedenborgian
New Dawn Convalescent Center, Furnace, OH

Volunteers of America
Kettering Convalescent Center, Kettering, OH
Leisure Oaks Convalescent Center, Defiance, OH

OKLAHOMA

Baptist
Lackey Manor Nursing Home, Oklahoma City, OK

Church of Christ
Central Oklahoma Christian Home, Oklahoma City, OK
Cordell Christian Home, Cordell, OK
Tulsa Christian Home Inc, Tulsa, OK

Episcopal
St Simeon's Episcopal Home Inc, Tulsa, OK

Independent Order of Odd Fellows & Rebekahs
Odd Fellows Rest Home, Checotah, OK

King's Daughters & Sons
King's Daughters & Sons Nursing Home, Durant, OK

Lutheran
Hobart Good Samaritan Home, Hobart, OK

Mennonite
Hydro Manor Inc, Hydro, OK
Menonite Bretheren Home for the Aged, Corn, OK

Methodist
W F & Mada Dunaway Manor Inc, Guymon, OK
The Methodist Home of Clinton Inc, Clinton, OK
Methodist Home of Enid Inc, Enid, OK
Oklahoma Methodist Home for the Aged Inc, Tulsa, OK

Oral Roberts Ministries
University Village Inc, Tulsa, OK

Pentecostal Holiness
Carmen Home, Carmen, OK

Roman Catholic
Franciscan Villa, Broken Arrow, OK
St Ann's Nursing Home Inc, Oklahoma City, OK
St John Medical Center, Tulsa, OK

OREGON

Baptist
Baptist Manor, Portland, OR

Episcopal
Bishop Morris Care Center, Portland, OR

Jewish
Robison Jewish Home, Portland, OR

Lutheran

Fairlawn Care Center, Gresham, OR
Good Shepherd Lutheran Home for Mentally Retarded, Cornelius, OR
Lutheran Pioneer Home, Mallala, OR
Willamette Lutheran Homes Inc, Salem, OR

Masons
Masonic & Eastern Star Home, Forest Grove, OR

Mennonite
Dallas Nursing Home, Dallas, OR
Mennonite Home, Albany, OR

Methodist
Willamette Methodist Convalescent Center, Milwaukie, OR

Presbyterian
Holladay Park Plaza, Portland, OR
Presbyterian Nursing Home Inc, Ontario, OR

Roman Catholic
Benedictine Nursing Center, Mount Angel, OR
Maryville Nursing Home, Beaverton, OR
Mt St Joseph Extended Care Center, Portland, OR
Providence Children's Nursing Center, Portland, OR
St Catherine's Residence & Nursing Center, North Bend, OR
St Elizabeth Health Care Center, Baker, OR

Seventh-Day Adventist
Emerald Nursing Center, Eugene, OR
Portland Adventist Convalescent Center, Portland, OR
Rest Harbor Nursing Home, Gresham, OR

Society of Friends
Friendsview Manor Healthcenter, Newburg, OR

PENNSYLVANIA

Baptist
The Baptist Home of Philadelphia, Philadelphia, PA
Baptist Homes Nursing Center, Pittsburgh, PA
Hannum Memorial Rest Home Inc, Bradford, PA

Bible Fellowship Church
Bible Fellowship Church Home, Nazareth, PA

Brethren In Christ Church
Messiah Village, Mechanicsburg, PA

Christian Reformed Hungarian Church
Bethlen Home of the Hungarian Reformed Federation of America, Ligonier, PA

Church of Christ
Homewood Retirement Center, Martinsburg, PA
Homewood Retirement Center, Hanover, PA
Phoebe Home Inc, Allentown, PA
St Paul Homes, Greenville, PA
Wyncote Church Home, Wyncote, PA

Church of God
Church of God Home, Inc, Carlisle, PA
Grove Manor, Grove City, PA

Church of the Brethren
Peter Becker Community, Harleysville, PA
The Brethren Home, New Oxford, PA
Brethren Village, Lancaster, PA
Morrisons Cove Home, Martinsburg, PA

Congregational
Evangelical Congregational Church Retirement Village, Myerstown, PA

Eastern Star
Eastern Pennsylvania Eastern Star Home, Warminster, PA

Episcopal

All Sts Rehabilitation Hospital/Springfield Retirement Residence, Wyndmoor, PA
Canterbury Place, Pittsburgh, PA
Cathedral Village, Philadelphia, PA
Kearsley/Christ Church Hospital, Philadelphia, PA

Independent Order of Odd Fellows & Rebekahs
Odd Fellows Home of Pennsylvania Inc, Middletown, PA
Orchard Manor Inc, Grove City, PA

Jewish
Fairmount Geriatric Center, Philadelphia, PA
Home for the Jewish Aged, Philadelphia, PA
Jewish Home of Eastern Pennsylvania, Scranton, PA
Jewish Home of Greater Harrisburg, Harrisburg, PA
Riverview Center for Jewish Seniors, Pittsburgh, PA
Stenton Hall Nursing & Convalescent Center, Philadelphia, PA

Knights of Malta
Malta Home for the Aging, Granville, PA

Knights of Pythias
Kin Kora Pythian Home, Duncannon, PA

Lutheran
Allegheny Lutheran Home, Hollidaysburg, PA
Allegheny Lutheran Home, Johnstown, PA
Artman Lutheran Home, Ambler, PA
Buffalo Valley Lutheran Village, Lewisburg, PA
Mary J Drexel Home, Bala Cynwyd, PA
Frey Village, Middletown, PA
Germantown Home, Philadelphia, PA
Gettysburg Lutheran Retirement Village, Gettysburg, PA
The Good Shepherd Home Long-Term Care Facility Inc, Allentown, PA
Luther Acres, Lititz, PA
Luther Crest, Allentown, PA
Luther Woods Convalescent Center, Hatboro, PA
Lutheran Home at Kane, Kane, PA
Lutheran Home at Topton, Topton, PA
Lutheran Home for the Aged, Erie, PA
Lutheran Home—Telford, Telford, PA
Lutheran Welfare Concordia Home, Cabot, PA
Passavant Retirement & Health Center, Zellenople, PA
Pauls Run, Philadelphia, PA
Perry Village Nursing Home, New Bloomfield, PA
River Crest Center/Ken Crest Services, Mont Clare, PA
St John Lutheran Care Center, Mars, PA
St Luke Manor, Hazelton, PA
St Luke Pavilion, Hazelton, PA
Shrewsbury Lutheran Retirement Village, Shrewsbury, PA
Susquehanna Lutheran Village, Millersburg, PA
York Lutheran Home, York, PA

Masons
Masonic Home of Pennsylvania, Lafayette Hill, PA
Masonic Homes, Elizabethtown, PA

Mennonite
Dock Terrace, Lansdale, PA
Frederick Mennonite Home, Frederick, PA
Landis Home, Lititz, PA
Menno-Haven/Menno-Village, Chambersburg, PA
Mennonite Home, Lancaster, PA
Rockhill Mennonite Community, Sellersville, PA
Souderton Mennonite Homes, Souderton, PA
Tel Hai Retirement Community, Honeybrook, PA

Methodist
Asbury Heights, Pittsburgh, PA

Bethany Village Retirement Center, Mechanicsburg, PA
Cornwall Manor of the United Methodist Church, Cornwall, PA
Epworth Manor, Tyrone, PA
Evangelical Manor, Philadelphia, PA
Lewisburg United Methodist Homes, Lewisburg, PA
Quincy United Methodist Home & Quincy Village, Quincy, PA
Simpson House of the United Methodist Church, Philadelphia, PA
Wesley Village, Pittston, PA
Westbury United Methodist Community, Meadville, PA

Moravian
Moravian Manor, Lititz, PA

Order of Eastern Star
Western Pennsylvania Eastern Star Home, Pittsburgh, PA

Presbyterian
Broomall Presbyterian Home, Broomall, PA
Dresser Memorial Presbyterian Home, Bradford, PA
Forest Park Health Center, Carlisle, PA
Greensburg Home, Greensburg, PA
Indiana Presbyterian Homes, Indiana, PA
Oil City Presbyterian Home, Oil City, PA
Oxford Manor, The Steward Home & The Woods at Oxford Manor, Oxford, PA
Presbyterian Home, Cambridge Springs, PA
The Presbyterian Home at 58th St, Philadelphia, PA
Presbyterian Home—Johnstown, Johnstown, PA
Presbyterian Lodge, Erie, PA
Presbyterian Medical Center of Oakmont, Oakmont, PA
The Quarryville Presbyterian Home, Quarryville, PA
Reformed Presbyterian Home, Pittsburgh, PA
Rydal Park of Philadelphia Presbyterian Homes on the Fairway, Rydal, PA
Shenango United Presbyterian Home, New Wilmington, PA
Swaim Health Center, Newville, PA
Sycamore Manor Nursing Home, Montoursville, PA
United Presbyterian Home of Hollidaysburg, Hollidaysburg, PA
United Presbyterian Home of Philipsburg, Philipsburg, PA
United Presbyterian Womens Association Home for Aged, Pittsburgh, PA
Washington Senior Care, Washington, PA
Westminster Village, Allentown, PA

Roman Catholic
C R Center, Springfield, PA
Christ the King Manor, Dubois, PA
Garvey Manor, Hollidaysburg, PA
Holy Family Home, Philadelphia, PA
Holy Family Manor, Bethlehem, PA
Holy Family Residence, Scranton, PA
Immaculate Mary Home, Philadelphia, PA
John XXIII Home For Senior Citizens, Hermitage, PA
Maria Joseph Manor, Danville, PA
Little Flower Manor, Darby, PA
Little Flower Manor, Wilkes-Barre, PA
Little Sisters of the Poor Home for the Aged, Pittsburgh, PA
Misericordia Convalescent Home, York, PA
Mt Macrina Manor Nursing Home, Uniontown, PA
Regency Hall Nursing Home Inc, Allison Park, PA
Sacred Heart Manor, Philadelphia, PA
St Anne Home for the Elderly, Greensburg, PA
St Anne's Home, Columbia, PA
St Francis Country Home, Darby, PA
St John Neumann Nursing Home, Philadelphia, PA
St Joseph Nursing & Health Care Center, Pittsburgh, PA

St Joseph's Home for the Aged, Holland, PA
St Josephs Villa, Flourtown, PA
St Marys Home of Erie, Erie, PA
St Marys Manor, Lansdale, PA
St Mary's Villa Nursing Home, Elmhurst, PA
St Stanislaus Medical Care Center Inc, Nanticoke, PA
Vincention Home, Pittsburgh, PA

Seventh-Day Adventist
Laurel Living Center, Hamburg, PA

Society of Friends
Foulkeways at Gwynedd Inc, Gwynedd, PA
Friends Hall at Fox Chase, Philadelphia, PA
Linden Hall Nursing Home, Kennett Square, PA
Pennswood Village, Newtown, PA

Unitarian Universalist
Unitarian Universalist House, Philadelphia, PA

RHODE ISLAND

Baptist
The John Clarke Retirement Center, Middletown, RI

Jewish
Jewish Home for the Aged of Rhode Island, Providence, RI

Methodist
United Methodist Health Care Center, East Providence, RI

Roman Catholic
Darlington Care Center, Pawtucket, RI
Mt St Francis Health Center, Woonsocket, RI
St Antoine Residence, North Smithfield, RI

Seventh-Day Adventist
Pawtucket Institute for Health Services, Pawtucket, RI

SOUTH CAROLINA

Baptist
Martha Franks Baptist Retirement Center, Laurens, SC

Episcopal
South Carolina Episcopal Home at Still Hopes, West Columbia, SC

Lutheran
The Lowman Home, White Rock, SC

Methodist
The Methodist Home, Orangeburg, SC
Nursing Center Greenwood Methodist Home, Greenwood, SC

Presbyterian
Presbyterian Home of South Carolina—Summerville, Summerville, SC

SOUTH DAKOTA

Baptist
North American Baptist Home, Madison, SD

Eastern Star
Eastern Star Home Inc, Redfield, SD

Independent Order of Odd Fellows & Rebekahs
Odd Fellows Home, Dell Rapids, SD

Lutheran
Bethany Lutheran Home, Sioux Falls, SD
Bethel Lutheran Home, Madison, SD
Bethesda Home, Webster, SD
Bethesda Home for the Aged, Beresford, SD
Bethesda Home of Aberdeen, Aberdeen, SD
Canton Good Samaritan Center, Canton, SD
Deuel County Good Samaritan Center, Clear Lake, SD

Good Samaritan Center, Herreid, SD
Good Samaritan Center, Parkston, SD
Good Samaritan Center, Selby, SD
Good Samaritan Luther Manor, Sioux Falls, SD
Good Samaritan Nursing Center, Parkston, SD
Howard Good Samaritan Center, Howard, SD
Lutheran Home, Eureka, SD
Lutheran Nursing Home, Hot Springs, SD
Pleasant View Nursing Home, Corsica, SD
Prairie Good Samaritan Center, Miller, SD
Scotland Good Samaritan Center, Scotland, SD
Tyndall Good Samaritan Center, Tyndall, SD
Wagner Good Samaritan Center, Wagner, SD

Mennonite
Salem Mennonite Home for the Aged, Freeman, SD

Methodist
Jenkins Methodist Home Inc, Watertown, SD

Roman Catholic
Brady Memorial Home, Mitchell, SD
Maryhouse Inc, Pierre, SD
Mother Joseph Manor, Aberdeen, SD
St Williams Home for Aged, Milbank, SD
Sister James' Nursing Home, Yankton, SD

TENNESSEE

Baptist
Baptist Health Care Center, Lenoir City, TN
Cocke County Baptist Convalescent Center, Newport, TN

Christian Methodist Episcopal
Collins Chapel Health Care Center, Memphis, TN

Church of Christ
Appalachian Christian Village, Johnson City, TN
Church of Christ Home for Aged, Nashville, TN
Lakeshore Home for the Aged, Nashville, TN
Mid-South Christian Nursing Home, Memphis, TN
Stones River Manor, Murfreesboro, TN
May Cravath Wharton Nursing Home, Pleasant Hill, TN

Church of the Brethren
John M Reed Nursing Home, Limestone, TN

King's Daughters & Sons
Kings Daughters & Sons Home, Memphis, TN

Methodist
Asbury Acres Retirement Home, Maryville, TN
Asbury Centers Inc, Maryville, TN
McKendree Village Inc, Hermitage, TN
Methodist Nursing Home of Middle Tennessee, Winchester, TN
Parkview Convalescent Unit, Dyersburg, TN
Wesley Highland Manor, Memphis, TN

Presbyterian
Shannondale Retirement Home, Knoxville, TN
Wood Presbyterian Home Inc, Sweetwater, TN

Roman Catholic
Alexian Village of Tennesse Inc, Signal Mountain, TN
St Peter Villa Nursing Home, Memphis, TN

Seventh-Day Adventist
Laurelbrook Sanitarium, Dayton, TN
Little Creek Sanitarium, Knoxville, TN

TEXAS

American Religious Town Hall Meeting
Town Hall Estates, Rusk, TX

Baptist
Baptist Memorial Geriatric Center, San Angelo, TX
Buckner Baptist Haven, Houston, TX
Buckner Baptist Trew Retirement Center, Dallas, TX
Buckner Monte Siesta Home, Austin, TX
Buckner Villa Siesta Home, Austin, TX
Gilmer Convalescent & Nursing Center, Gilmer, TX
Ryburn Nursing Center, Dallas, TX

Church of Christ
Christian Care Center, Mesquite, TX
Christian Care Center North, Dallas, TX
Eden Home Inc, New Braunfels, TX
Hilltop Haven Home for the Aged, Gunter, TX
Lakewood Village Med Center, Fort Worth, TX
Texhoma Christian Care Center, Wichita Falls, TX

Disciples of Christ
Juliette Fowler Homes, Dallas, TX

Episcopal
Bishop Davies Center Inc, Hurst, TX
St James House of Baytown, Baytown, TX

Independent Order of Odd Fellows & Rebekahs
Odd Fellow & Rebekah Nursing Home, Ennis, TX

Jewish
Dallas Home for Jewish Aged, Dallas, TX
Golden Manor Jewish Home for the Aged, San Antonio, TX
Jewish Home for the Aged, Houston, TX

Knights of Pythias
Home for Aged Pythians Inc, Greenville, TX

Lutheran
Brookhaven Nursing Center, Farmers Branch, TX
Clifton Lutheran Sunset Home, Clifton, TX
Denton Good Samaritan Village, Denton, TX
Harlingen Good Samaritan Center, Harlingen, TX
The Lutheran Home—Permian Basin, Midland, TX
McAllen Good Samaritan Center, McAllen, TX
Trinity Lutheran Home, Shiner, TX
Trinity Lutheran Home—Round Rock, Round Rock, TX
White Acres-Good Samaritan Retirement Village & Nursing Center, El Paso, TX

Masons
Knights Templar Clinic, Arlington, TX

Methodist
Crestview Methodist Retirement Community, Bryan, TX
Edgewater Methodist Retirement Community, Galveston, TX
Golden Age Home, Lockhart, TX
Happy Harbor Methodist Home, La Porte, TX
Harris Manor, Glen Rose, TX
King's Manor Methodist Home, Hereford, TX
Parkview Manor, Weimar, TX
Sears Memorial Methodist Nursing Center, Abilene, TX
Wesleyan Nursing Home, Georgetown, TX
C C Young Memorial Home—Young Health Center, Dallas, TX

Order of Eastern Star
Eastern Star Home, Arlington, TX

Presbyterian
Presbyterian Manor Inc, Wichita Falls, TX

Presbyterian Village Inc, Dallas, TX
Trinity Terrace, Fort Worth, TX
Trinity Towers, Midland, TX

Roman Catholic
Coon Memorial Home, Dalhart, TX
Czech Catholic Home for the Aged, El Campo, TX
John Paul II Nursing Center, Kenedy, TX
Nazareth Hall, El Paso, TX
St Ann's Nursing Home, Panhandle, TX
St Anthony Center, Houston, TX
St Benedict Nursing Home, San Antonio, TX
St Elizabeth Nursing Home, Waco, TX
St Francis Nursing Home, San Antonio, TX
St Joseph's Residence, Dallas, TX
San Juan Nursing Home Inc, San Juan, TX

Seventh-Day Adventist
Fredericksburg Nursing Home, Fredericksburg, TX
Town Hall Estates Nursing Home, Whitney, TX
Valley Grande Manor, Weslaco, TX
Valley Grande Manor Inc, Brownsville, TX

UTAH

Church of Latter-Day Saints (Mormon)
Cedar Manor, Cedar City, UT
Highland Care Center, Salt Lake City, UT
Wasatch Villa, Salt Lake City, UT

Roman Catholic
St Joseph Villa, Salt Lake City, UT

VERMONT

Independent Order of Odd Fellows & Rebekahs
Gill Odd Fellows Home of Vermont Inc, Ludlow, VT

VIRGINIA

Baptist
Newport News Baptist Retirement Community, Newport News, VA
Virginia Baptist Home Inc, Culpeper, VA

Church of the Brethren
Bridgewater Home Inc, Bridgewater, VA

Episcopal
Goodwin House—Nurs Care Unit, Alexandria, VA
Rappahannock Westminster-Canterbury, Irvington, VA
Westminster-Canterbury in Virginia Beach, Virginia Beach, VA
Westminster-Canterbury House, Richmond, VA

Jewish
Beth Sholom Home of Central Virginia, Richmond, VA
Beth Sholom Home of Eastern Virginia, Virginia Beach, VA

Lutheran
Virginia Synod Lutheran Home at Roanoke, Roanoke, VA

Masons
Masonic Home of Virginia—Health Care Unit, Richmond, VA

Mennonite
Mountain View Nursing Home Inc, Aroda, VA
Oak Lea Nursing Home, Harrisonburg, VA

Methodist
Asbury Center at Birdmont Retirement Community, Wytheville, VA
Hermitage in Northern Virginia, Alexandria, VA
Hermitage on the Eastern Shore—Nurs Home Unit, Onancock, VA

Roanoke United Methodist Home, Roanoke, VA

Via Health Care Center for the Hermitage Methodist Home, Richmond, VA

Presbyterian
Sunnyside Presbyterian Retirement Community, Harrisonburg, VA

Roman Catholic
Little Sisters of the Poor—St Joseph Home for Aged, Richmond, VA

St Mary's Hospital Long-Term Care, Norton, VA

WASHINGTON

Baptist
Caldwell Health Center at Judson Park, Des Moines, WA

Christian Science
Sunrise Haven, Puyallup, WA

Church of Christ
Horizon House Inc, Seattle, WA

Independent Order of Odd Fellows & Rebekahs
Washington Odd Fellows Home, Walla Walla, WA

Knights of Pythias
Oregon-Washington Pythian Home, Vancouver, WA

Lutheran
Bethany Home for the Aged Inc, Everett, WA
Columbia Lutheran Home, Seattle, WA
Fairfield Good Samaritan Center, Fairfield, WA
The Hearthstone, Seattle, WA
Josephine Sunset Home, Stanwood, WA
Martha & Mary Nursing Home, Poulsbo, WA
Resthaven Nursing Home—Bremerton, Bremerton, WA
Riverview Lutheran Memorial Care Center, Spokane, WA
Spokane Valley Good Samaritan Center, Greenacres, WA
Tacoma Lutheran Home & Retirement Community, Tacoma, WA

Masons
Masonic Home of Washington, Des Moines, WA

Methodist
Bayview Manor, Seattle, WA
Rockwood Manor Infirmary, Spokane, WA
Warm Beach Health Care Center, Stanwood, WA
Wesley Care Center, Des Moines, WA
Wesley Gardens—The Gardens, Des Moines, WA

Presbyterian
Exeter House, Seattle, WA
Hawthorne Manor Retirement Residence, Spokane, WA
Kenney Presbyterian Home, Seattle, WA
Park Shore, Seattle, WA

Roman Catholic
Marianwood Extended Health Care Facility, Issaquah, WA
Mt St Vincent Nursing Center, Seattle, WA
St Joseph Care Center, Spokane, WA

WEST VIRGINIA

Lutheran
Barbour County Good Samaritan Center, Belington, WV

Methodist
Glenwood Park United Methodist Home, Princeton, WV

Presbyterian
Presbyterian Manor Inc, Huntington, WV

WISCONSIN

Baptist
Tudor Oaks Health Center, Muskego, WI

Church of Christ
Cedar Lake Home Campus, West Bend, WI
Fairhaven Corporation, Whitewater, WI
New Glarus Home Inc, New Glarus, WI

Congregational
Congregational Home Inc, Brookfield, WI

Episcopal
St John's Home of Milwaukee, Milwaukee, WI

Independent Order of Odd Fellows & Rebekahs
Wisconsin Odd Fellow-Rebekah Nursing Home, Green Bay, WI

Jewish
Milwaukee Jewish Convalescent Center, Milwaukee, WI
Milwaukee Jewish Home, Milwaukee, WI

Lutheran
American Lutheran Home—Menomonie Unit, Menomonie, WI
American Lutheran Home—Mondovi Unit, Mondovi, WI
The Becker/Shoop Center, Racine, WI
Bethany Riverside, La Crosse, WI
Bethel Home, Oshkosh, WI
Bethel Home & Services Inc, Viroqua, WI
Bethesda-Ritter Dierker, Watertown, WI
Capeside Cove Good Samaritan Center, Siren, WI
Fennimore Good Samaritan Center, Fennimore, WI
Fond Du Lac Lutheran Home, Fond Du Lac, WI
Lincoln Lutheran Home, Racine, WI
Lincoln Village Convalescent Center, Racine, WI
Lodi Good Samaritan Center, Lodi, WI
Luther Home, Marinette, WI
Luther Manor, Wauwatosa, WI
Luther Manor, Milwaukee, WI
Lutheran Home for the Aging Inc, Wauwatosa, WI
Nygaard Manor, Stoughton, WI
Oakwood Lutheran Homes Association Inc, Madison, WI
St Croix Valley Good Samaritan Center, Saint Croix Falls, WI
St Michael's Evangelical Lutheran Home for the Aged, Fountain City, WI
Scandia Village Retirement Center, Sister Bay, WI
Shorehaven Health Center, Oconomowoc, WI
Skaalen Sunset Home, Stoughton, WI
M B Syverson Lutheran Home, Eau Claire, WI
Clara Werner Dormitory, Watertown, WI
Wisconsin Lutheran Child & Family Service, Milwaukee, WI
Woodside Lutheran Home, Green Bay, WI

Methodist
Christian Community Home of Hudson, Hudson, WI
Evergreen Manor Retirement Community, Oshkosh, WI
Methodist Health Center, Madison, WI
Morrow Memorial Home for the Aged, Sparta, WI
Schmitt Woodland Hills Inc, Richland Center, WI
Sheboygan Retirement Home & Beach Health Care Center Inc, Sheboygan, WI

Roman Catholic
Alexian Village of Milwaukee Inc, Milwaukee, WI
Clement Manor, Greenfield, WI
Divine Savior Hospital & Nursing Home, Portage, WI
Franciscan Villa of South Milwaukee, South Milwaukee, WI
Hope Nursing Home, Lomira, WI
Marian Catholic Home, Milwaukee, WI
Marian Franciscan Home, Milwaukee, WI
Maryhill Manor Inc, Niagara, WI
Milwaukee Catholic Home, Milwaukee, WI
Nazareth House, Stoughton, WI
St Anne's Home for the Elderly, Milwaukee, WI
St Ann's Rest Home, Milwaukee, WI
St Camillus Health Center Inc, Wauwatosa, WI
St Catherine's Infirmary Inc, Racine, WI
St Elizabeth Nursing Home, Brookfield, WI
St Elizabeth's Home, Janesville, WI
St Frances Home, Fond Du Lac, WI
St Francis Home Inc, Superior, WI
St Joan Antida Home, West Allis, WI
St Joseph Residence Inc, New London, WI
St Joseph's Home for the Aged, West Allis, WI
St Joseph's Nursing Home, La Crosse, WI
St Mary's Home for the Aged Inc, Manitowoc, WI
St Marys Nursing Home, Milwaukee, WI
St Mary's Nursing Home, Sparta, WI
Villa Clement, West Allis, WI

Seventh-Day Adventist
Bethel Living Center, Arpin, WI
Colonial House Living Center, Colby, WI
Lancaster Living Center, Lancaster, WI
Marshfield Living Center, Marshfield, WI
Oakview Care Center, Durand, WI
Prairie Living Center, Prairie du Chien, WI
River Pines Living Center, Stevens Point, WI
Villa Pines Living Center, Friendship, WI

PUERTO RICO

Church of Christ
Ryder Memorial Skilled Nursing Facility, Humacao, PR

ALPHABETICAL LISTING OF FACILITIES

A & E Nursing Home, Salt Lake City, UT
AARC Group Home 2, Albuquerque, NM
AARC Group Home 3, Albuquerque, NM
Aaron Convalescent Home, Reading, OH
Aaron Manor Health Care Facility, Chester, CT
Aase Haugen Homes Inc, Decorah, IA
Abbe Center for Community Care, Marion, IA
Abbeville Heritage Manor, Abbeville, LA
Abbeville Nursing Home Inc, Abbeville, SC
Abbeville Nursing Home Intermediate Care Facility, Abbeville, GA
Abbey Convalescent & Nursing Home, Warren, MI
Abbey Forest Nursing Home, Waltham, MA
Abbey Hill Nursing Home, Saugus, MA
Abbey Manor Inc, Windham, CT
Abbey Nursing Home, Saint Petersburg, FL
Abbey Nursing Home, Kenmore, NY
Abbington House Inc, Roselle, IL
Abbot Group Home, Abbot, ME
Abbott House, Highland Park, IL
Abbott House Nursing Home, Lynn, MA
Abbott Manor Convalescent Center, Plainfield, NJ
ABC Health Center, Harrisonville, MO
ABCM Corporation—Bloomfield Care Center, Bloomfield, IA
Aberdeen Nursing Center, Aberdeen, SD
Aberdeen Nursing Home, Rochester, NY
Aberjona Nursing Home Inc, Winchester, MA
J W Abernethy Center—United Church Retirement Homes Inc, Newton, NC
Abilene House Inc, Tacoma, WA
Abilene Nursing Center, Abilene, KS
Abington Manor Nursing & Rehabilitation Center, Clarks Summit, PA
Able Manor Nursing Home, Cincinnati, OH
Acacias NRTA & AARP Nursing Home, Ojai, CA
Academy Manor of Andover, Andover, MA
Acadia—St Landry Guest Home, Church Point, LA
Acadiana Nursing Home, Lafayette, LA
Accomack County Nursing Home, Parksley, VA
Achenbach Learning Center, Hardtner, KS
Acocks Medical Facility, Marquette, MI
Acushnet Nursing Home, Acushnet, MA
Ada Municipal Hospital, Ada, MN
Ada I, Ada, MN
Ada Retirement & Care Center, Ada, OK
Adair Community Health Center Inc, Adair, IA
Avis B Adams Christian Convalescent Center, Emporia, VA
Adams County Manor Nursing Home, West Union, OH
Adams County Memorial Hospital Nursing Care Unit, Friendship, WI
Adams Group Home, Westminster, CO
Adams Group Home, Adams, MN
Adams Health Care Center, Adams, MN
Adams House Health Care, Torrington, CT
John Adams Nursing Home, Quincy, MA
Adams & Kinton Nursing Home Inc, Lillington, NC
Adams Manor, Scranton, PA

Adams Nursing Home, Alexander City, AL
The Adams Plaza, Jacksonville, FL
Quincy Adams Nursing Home, Brockton, MA
Adams Rest Home Inc, Adams, MA
Adaptive Living Center—Southeast Texas, Beaumont, TX
Adaptive Livng Center—Central Texas, Waco, TX
Adare Medical Center, Rockledge, FL
Addolorata Villa, Wheeling, IL
Adel Acres Care Center, Adel, IA
Adin Manor Nursing Home, Hopedale, MA
Adirondack Tri-County Nursing Home Inc, North Creek, NY
Adkins Nursing Home, Weleetka, OK
Adkins-Weleetka Nursing Home, Weleetka, OK
Adobe Nursing Home, West Allis, WI
Adrian Manor Nursing Home Inc, Adrian, MO
Advance Nursing Center, Inkster, MI
Adventist Convalescent Hospital, Glendora, CA
Adventist Health Center, Lumberton, MS
Adventist Nursing Home Inc, Livingston, NY
Affton Care Center, Saint Louis, MO
Aftenro Home, Duluth, MN
Afton Care Center Inc, Afton, IA
Afton Oaks Nursing Center, Houston, TX
Agape Halfway House Inc, Austin, MN
Agape House ICF/MR, Ellsworth, ME
Ah-Gwah-Ching, Ah-Gwah-Ching, MN
Aicota Nursing Home, Aitkin, MN
Aiken Nursing Home, Aiken, SC
Air Force Village I Health Care Center, San Antonio, TX
Aishel Avraham Residential Health Facility Inc, Brooklyn, NY
Aivert Nursing Home, Ceredo, WV
Akin's Convalescent Hospital, Long Beach, CA
Akron City Convalescent Care Center, Akron, IA
Al Mar Residence, Julesburg, CO
Ala Fern Intermediate Care Facility for Mental Health, Russell, KS
Aladdin's of Shelbina, Shelbina, MO
Alaimo Nursing Home, Rochester, NY
Alamance Memorial Hospital Skilled Nursing Division, Burlington, NC
Alamitos Belmont Rehabilitation Hospital, Long Beach, CA
Alamitos West Convalescent Hospital, Los Alamitos, CA
Alamo Nursing Home, Inc, Kalamazoo, MI
Barry Alan Nursing Home, Saint Louis, MO
Alaska Nursing Home, Cincinnati, OH
Alba Nursing Home, Lynn, MA
Albany Avenue Nursing Home Inc, Kingston, NY
Albany Care Center, Albany, OR
Albany County Nursing Home, Albany, NY
Albany Health Care, Albany, GA
Albany Nursing Care Inc, Albany, IN
Albemarle Health Care Center, Jackson, MS
Albemarle Villa, Williamston, NC
Albert Lea Good Samaritan Center, Albert Lea, MN

Albert Lea Health Care Center, Albert Lea, MN
Albert's Nursing Home, Warren, OH
Albert's Nursing & Residential Facility, Warren, OH
Albertville Nursing Home Inc, Albertville, AL
Albia Care Center, Albia, IA
Albia Manor, Albia, IA
Albion Manor, Albion, MI
Alby Residence, Godfrey, IL
Alcazar Home for the Aged Inc, Saint Louis, MO
Alcorn County Care Inn, Corinth, MS
Alcott Rehabilitation Hospital, Los Angeles, CA
Alden House, Fort Lauderdale, FL
Alden Nursing Center of Naperville, Naperville, IL
Alden Terrace Convalescent Hospital, Los Angeles, CA
Aldersgate Village Health Unit, Topeka, KS
Aldersly Inc—Danish Home Senior Citizens, San Rafael, CA
Alderson Convalescent Hospital, Woodland, CA
Alderwood Manor Convalescent Hospital, San Gabriel, CA
Alderwood Manor Nursing & Convalescent Center, Spokane, WA
Alderwood Park Convalescent Center, Bellingham, WA
Aldrich Board & Care, Minneapolis, MN
Aletha Lodge Nursing Home Inc, Booneville, MS
Alexander Continuing Care Center, Royal Oak, MI
Alexander Home, Willmar, MN
Alexander Human Development Center, Alexander, AR
Alexandria Convalescent Center, Alexandria, IN
Alexandria Convalescent Hospital, Los Angeles, CA
Alexian Village of Milwaukee Inc, Milwaukee, WI
Alexian Village of Tennesse Inc, Signal Mountain, TN
Mildred Alford Nursing Home, Abington, MA
Algart Health Care Inc, Cleveland, OH
Algoma Memorial Long-Term Care Unit, Algoma, WI
Algona Good Samaritan Center, Algona, IA
Alhambra Convalescent Home, Alhambra, CA
Alhambra Convalescent Hospital, Martinez, CA
The Alhambra Nursing Home Inc, Saint Petersburg, FL
Alice Byrd Tawes Nursing Home, Crisfield, MD
Aliceville Manor Nursing Home, Aliceville, AL
All American Nursing Home, Chicago, IL
All Saints Catholic Nursing Home, Jacksonville, FL
All Saints Convalescent Center, North Hollywood, CA
All Sts Rehabilitation Hospital/Springfield Retirement Residence, Wyndmoor, PA

All Seasons Nursing Home, Tyler, TX
Allamakee County Care Center, Waukon, IA
Allegan County Medical Care Facility, Allegan, MI
Allegany County Nursing Home, Cumberland, MD
Allegany Nursing Home, Allegany, NY
Allegheny Lutheran Home, Hollidaysburg, PA
Allegheny Lutheran Home, Johnstown, PA
Allegheny Valley School—Butler Campus, West Sunbury, PA
Allegheny Valley School for Exceptional Children, Coraopolis, PA
Allen County Inn for the Aged, Lima, OH
Allen Hall, Milledgeville, GA
Allen Home, Mexico, MO
Allen Memorial Home, Mobile, AL
Allen Park Convalescent Home, Allen Park, MI
Allenbrook Healthcare Center, Baytown, TX
Allenbrooke Health Care Center, Memphis, TN
Allendale Nursing Home, Allendale, NJ
Allen's Health Centre Inc, South Kingstown, RI
Allen's Rest Home, West Liberty, KY
The Alliance Home of Carlisle Pennsylvania, Carlisle, PA
Alliance Nursing Center, Deland, FL
Alliance Nursing Home Inc, Alliance, OH
Allied Services—Long-Term Care Facility, Scranton, PA
Allied Services—Lynett Village, Scranton, PA
Allison Care Center, Allison, IA
Allison Health Care Center, Lakewood, CO
Allison Manor Healthcare Center Inc, Litchfield, IL
Allison Nursing Home Inc, Poseyville, IN
Allston Manor Nursing Home, Allston, MA
Alma Manor Nursing Home, Alma, KS
Alma Nelson Manor, Rockford, IL
Almana Rest Home, Quincy, MA
Almeida Rest Home, Boston, MA
Almira Home, New Castle, PA
The Alois Alzheimer Center, Cincinnati, OH
Alondra Nursing Home, Gardena, CA
Alpha Annex Nursing Center, Detroit, MI
Alpha Convalescent Hospital, Oakland, CA
The Alpha Home, Indianapolis, IN
Alpha Home, Spicer, MN
Alpha Manor Nursing Home, Detroit, MI
Alpha & Omega Personal Care Home, Jackson, MS
Alpha Village Long-Term Care Facility, Middleboro, MA
Alpha-Wilshire Convalescent Hospital, Los Angeles, CA
Alpine Convalescent Center, Alpine, CA
Alpine Fireside Health Center, Rockford, IL
Alpine Guest Care Center, Ruston, LA
The Alpine Health Care Center, Hershey, PA
Alpine Manor, Thornton, CO
Alpine Manor Health Center, Erie, PA
Alpine Nursing Center, Saint Petersburg, FL
Alpine Nursing Home, Chelmsford, MA
Alpine Rest Home Inc, Coventry, RI
Alpine Terrace Retirement & Convalescent Center, Kerrville, TX
Alpine Valley Care Center, Pleasant Grove, UT
Alpine Village, Verdigre, NE
Alpine-Chavis Care Center, Salt Lake City, UT
Alps Manor Nursing Home, Wayne, NJ
Alshore House, Chicago, IL
Alta Care Center, Salt Lake City, UT
Alta Loma Convalescent Hospital, Alta Loma, CA
Alta Mesa Nursing Center, Fort Worth, TX
Alta Mira Nursing Home, Tiffin, OH
Alta Nursing Home Inc, Dayton, OH
Alta Vista Group Home, Trinidad, CO
Alta Vista Healthcare, Arlington, CA
Alta Vista Inc, Easley, SC
Altamaha Convalescent Center Inc, Jesup, GA
Altenheim, Strongsville, OH
Altenheim German Home, Forest Park, IL
Altenheim Inc, Oakland, CA

Altercare of North Ridgeville, North Ridgeville, OH
Alternative Residence 44-Cadiz Group Home, Cadiz, OH
Alternative Residence Two Inc—Middleton Estates, Gallipolis, OH
Althea Woodland Nursing Home, Silver Spring, MD
Altoona Center, Altoona, PA
Altoona Health Care Center, Altoona, AL
Altoona Manor Care Center, Altoona, IA
Altus Home Nursing Home, Altus, OK
Alum Crest, Columbus, OH
Alvarado Convalescent & Rehabilitation Hospital, San Diego, CA
Alvarado Nursing Home, Alvarado, TX
Alvernia Manor Retirement Home, Lemont, IL
Alverno Health Care Facility, Clinton, IA
Alvin Convalescent Center, Alvin, TX
Alvis House-Wittwer Hall, Columbus, OH
Alvista Care Home Inc, Greenville, GA
Amarillo Good Samaritan Retirement Center, Amarillo, TX
Amarillo Nursing Center, Amarillo, TX
Amasa Stone House Inc, Cleveland, OH
Ambassador Convalescent Hospital, West Covina, CA
Ambassador Healthcare Center, New Hope, MN
Ambassador Manor Nursing Center Inc, Tulsa, OK
Ambassador Manor South, Jenks, OK
Ambassador North, Cincinnati, OH
Ambassador Nursing Center, Detroit, MI
Ambassador Nursing Center, East Cleveland, OH
Ambassador Nursing Center Inc, Chicago, IL
Ambassador South, Cincinnati, OH
Amber Health Care Center, Columbus, OH
Amber House, Lexington Park, MD
Amber Valley Care Center, Pendleton, OR
Amberwood Convalescent Hospital, Los Angeles, CA
Ambler Rest Center, Ambler, PA
Amboy Care Center, Perth Amboy, NJ
Ambrosia Home Inc, Tampa, FL
Amelia Community Residence, Orangeburg, SC
Amelia Island Care Center, Fernandina Beach, FL
Amelia Manor Nursing Home, Lafayette, LA
Amenity Manor, Topsham, ME
American Beauty Nursing Home, West Frankfort, IL
American Care Center, Perryville, MO
American Finnish Nursing Home, Finnish-American Rest Home, Inc, Lake Worth, FL
American Heritage Care Center, Hammond, WI
American Indian Nursing Home, Laveen, AZ
American Lutheran Home—Menomonie Unit, Menomonie, WI
American Lutheran Home—Mondovi Unit, Mondovi, WI
American Marion Nursing & Rehabilitation Center, Marion, OH
American Medical Nursing Center Inc-Dresher Hill, Dresher, PA
American Medical Nursing Centers—Statesman, Levittown, PA
American Medical Nursing Centers—Township Manor, Elkins Park, PA
American Nursing Home, New York, NY
American Plaza Nursing Center, Evanston, IL
American Village Retirement Community, Indianapolis, IN
Americana Convalescent Home, Longview, WA
Americana-Family Tree, Anderson, IN
Americana Fremont Healthcare Center, Springfield, MO
Americana Health Care Center, Naples, FL
Americana Health Care Center, Decatur, GA
Americana Health Care Center, Appleton, WI
Americana Health Care Center—East, Green Bay, WI

Americana Health Care Center of Orlando, Orlando, FL
Americana Healthcare Center, Jacksonville, FL
Americana Healthcare Center, Winter Park, FL
Americana Healthcare Center, Marietta, GA
Americana Healthcare Center, Danville, IL
Americana Healthcare Center, Kankakee, IL
Americana Healthcare Center, Oak Lawn, IL
Americana Healthcare Center, Anderson, IN
Americana Healthcare Center, Cedar Rapids, IA
Americana Healthcare Center, Davenport, IA
Americana Healthcare Center, Dubuque, IA
Americana Healthcare Center, Mason City, IA
Americana Healthcare Center, Waterloo, IA
Americana Healthcare Center, Kingsford, MI
Americana Healthcare Center, Florissant, MO
Americana Healthcare Center, Aberdeen, SD
Americana Healthcare Center, Fond Du Lac, WI
Americana Healthcare Center—Elkhart, Elkhart, IN
Americana Healthcare Center—Fargo, Fargo, ND
Americana Healthcare Center—Indianapolis, Indianapolis, IN
Americana Healthcare Center—Indianapolis Midtown, Indianapolis, IN
Americana Healthcare Center—Indianapolis North, Indianapolis, IN
Americana Healthcare Center—Kokomo, Kokomo, IN
Americana Healthcare Center—Lafayette, Lafayette, IN
Americana Healthcare Center—Minot, Minot, ND
Americana Healthcare Center of Arlington Heights, Arlington Heights, IL
Americana Healthcare Center of Champaign, Champaign, IL
Americana Healthcare Center of Decatur, Decatur, IL
Americana Healthcare Center of Elgin, Elgin, IL
Americana Healthcare Center of Normal, Normal, IL
Americana Healthcare Center of Peoria, Peoria, IL
Americana Healthcare Center of Rolling Meadows, Rolling Meadows, IL
Americana Healthcare Center of Urbana, Urbana, IL
Americana Healthcare Center of Westmont, Westmont, IL
Americana Healthcare Center—West, Green Bay, WI
Americana Nursing Center, Naperville, IL
Americana-Monticello Convalescent Center, Oak Lawn, IL
Americare Boone Nursing & Rehabilitation Center, Danville, WV
Americare Circleville Nursing & Rehabilitation Center, Circleville, OH
Americare Columbus Nursing & Rehabilitation Center, Columbus, OH
Americare Convalescent Center, Detroit, MI
Americare Dunbar Nursing & Rehabilitation Center, Dunbar, WV
Americare Glenville Nursing & Rehabilitation Center, Glenville, WV
Americare-Homestead Nursing & Rehabilitation Center, Lancaster, OH
Americare-Ladera Health Care Center, Albuquerque, NM
Americare Nursing & Rehabilitation Center of Alliance, Alliance, OH
Americare of New Lexington, New Lexington, OH
Americare Pomeroy Nursing & Rehabilitation Center, Pomeroy, OH
Americare Putnam Nursing & Rehabilitation Center, Hurricane, WV
Americare Rittman Nursing & Rehabilitation Center, Rittman, OH
Americare Salem Nursing & Rehabilitation Center, Salem, WV

Americare Woodsfield Nursing &
Rehabilitation Center, Woodsfield, OH
Americare-Oregon Nursing & Rehabilitation
Center, Oregon, OH
Amery Constant Care Inc, Amery, WI
Ames Way House, Arvada, CO
Amesbury Nursing & Retirement Home,
Amesbury, MA
Amherst Home for Aged Women, Amherst,
MA
Amherst Manor, Amherst, OH
Amherst Manor, Amherst, TX
Amherst Nursing & Convalescent Home,
Amherst, NY
Amherst Nursing Home Inc, Amherst, MA
Amherst Presbyterian Nursing Center,
Williamsville, NY
Amie Holt Care Center, Buffalo, WY
Amistad Nursing Home Inc, Uvalde, TX
Amistad II Care Center, Uvalde, TX
Amite Nursing Home Inc, Amite, LA
Amory Manor Nursing Home, Amory, MS
AMS Green Tree Health Care Center,
Milwaukee, WI
Amsterdam House Nursing Home, New York,
NY
Amsterdam Memorial Hospital—Skilled
Nursing Facility, Amsterdam, NY
Anacortes Convalescent Center, Anacortes,
WA
Anaheim Terrace Care Center, Anaheim, CA
Anamosa Care Center, Anamosa, IA
Anchor Lodge Nursing Home, Lorain, OH
The Anchorage Bensenville Home,
Bensenville, IL
Anchorage Convalescent Home Inc, Detroit,
MI
Anchorage Nursing Home, Shelburne, MA
Andbe Home Inc, Norton, KS
Anderson County Health Care Center,
Clinton, TN
Anderson Health Care Center, Anderson, SC
Anderson Health Care Center, Gray, TN
Anderson Healthcare Center, Anderson, IN
Anderson House Inc, Seattle, WA
Anderson Lane Nursing Home, Austin, TX
Anderson Memorial Care Homes Inc, Grand
Saline, TX
Andover Intermediate Care Center, Andover,
NJ
Andrew House Healthcare, New Britain, CT
Andrew Michaud Nursing Home, Fulton, NY
Andrew Residence, Minneapolis, MN
Hiram G Andrews Center, Johnstown, PA
Andrews Nursing Center, Andrews, TX
Andrus Retirement Community, Hastings, NY
Andrys Retirement Community, Hastings on
Hudson, NY
Aneskarm III—Inisteige, Morris, MN
Aneskarn IV, Brookston, MN
Aneta Good Samaritan Center, Aneta, ND
Angel View Childrens Habilitation Center,
Desert Hot Springs, CA
Angelina Nursing Home Inc, Lufkin, TX
Angeline Nursing Home Inc, North Wales, PA
Angels Nursing Center, Los Angeles, CA
Angelus Convalescent Center East, Inglewood,
CA
Angelus Convalescent Center Inc, Pittsburgh,
PA
Angelus Convalescent Center—West,
Inglewood, CA
Angelus Convalescent Home, Minneapolis,
MN
Angleton-Danbury Convalescent Center,
Angleton, TX
Angola Nursing Home, Angola, IN
Anlaw Nursing Home, Lawrence, MA
Ann Pearl Intermediate Care Facility,
Kaneohe, HI
Ann Stock Center, Fort Lauderdale, FL
Anna John Home, De Pere, WI
Anna L Lee Nursing Home, Mason, TX
Anna Maria ICF, Augusta, SC
Anna Maria of Aurora Inc, Aurora, OH
Anna Maria Rest Home, Worcester, MA
Annaburg Manor, Manassas, VA
Anna-Henry Nursing Home, Edwardsville, IL

Annandale Care Center, Annandale, MN
Annapolis Convalescent Center, Annapolis,
MD
Anne Maria Medical Care Nursing Home Inc,
Augusta, SC
Annemark Nursing Home Inc, Revere, MA
Annie Mae Matthews Memorial Nursing
Home, Alexandria, LA
Annie Walker Nursing Home Inc, Mount
Sterling, KY
Anniston Nursing Home, Anniston, AL
Ann's Personal Care Home, Jackson, MS
Ann's Rest Home, Dorchester, MA
Ann's Rest Home, Providence, RI
Ann's Rest Home, Salt Lake City, UT
Anns Siesta Villa, Springville, UT
Anoka Maple Manor Care Center, Anoka, MN
Ansley Pavilion, Atlanta, GA
Anson County Hospital-SNF, Wadesboro, NC
Antelope Valley Convalescent Hospital &
Nursing Home, Lancaster, CA
Frances J Anthony, Winston-Salem, NC
Antioch Convalescent Hospital, Antioch, CA
Antlers Nursing Home, Antlers, OK
Anza Convalescent Hospital, El Cajon, CA
Apalachicola Health Care Center Inc,
Apalachicola, FL
Apalachicola Valley Nursing Center,
Blounstown, FL
Apostolic Christian Home, Peoria, IL
Apostolic Christian Home, Roanoke, IL
Apostolic Christian Home, Sabetha, KS
Apostolic Christian Home for the
Handicapped, Morton, IL
Apostolic Christian Home Inc, Rittman, OH
Apostolic Christian Resthaven, Elgin, IL
Apostolic Christian Restmor I, Morton, IL
Appalachian Christian Village, Johnson City,
TN
Apple Creek Developmental Center, Apple
Creek, OH
Apple Tree Inn, Fayetteville, AR
Apple Tree Lane Convalescent Home,
Romulus, MI
Apple Valley Health Center, Apple Valley,
MN
Applegarth Care Center, Hightstown, NJ
Applegate Care Center, Auburn, WA
Applegate East Nursing Home, Galesburg, IL
Applegate Manor Inc, Monmouth, IL
Appleton Extended Care Center, Appleton, WI
Appleton Municipal Hospital & Nursing
Home, Appleton, MN
Robert Appleton Nursing Home, Everett, MA
Applewood Care Center Inc, Chanute, KS
Applewood Hills Care Center Inc, Lakewood,
CO
Applewood Living Center, Longmont, CO
Applewood Living Center, Matteson, IL
Applewood Manor, Freehold, NJ
Applewood Manor Convalescent Center,
Bloomingdale, IL
Applewood Manor Inc, McMillan, MI
Applewood Nursing Center, Woodhaven, MI
Applin Nursing Home, Springfield, OH
Appling County Nursing Home, Baxley, GA
Approved Home Inc, Chicago, IL
Arah's Acres, Hallsville, MO
Aransas Pass Nursing & Convalescent Center,
Aransas Pass, TX
Ararat Convalescent Hospital, Los Angeles,
CA
Arbor of Itasca Inc, Itasca, IL
Arbor Manor Care Center, Spring Arbor, MI
Arbor Manor Inc, Fremont, NE
Arbor View Healthcare Center Inc, Madison,
WI
The Arbors at Hilliard, Hilliard, OH
The Arbors Nursing Center, Camp Verde, AZ
Arborway Manor Convalescent Home, Boston,
MA
Arbourway Rest Home, New Bedford, MA
Arbutus Park Manor Inc, Johnstown, PA
ARC Homes on Cummings, Arden Hills, MN
Arcadia Acres, Logan, OH
Arcadia Baptist Home, Arcadia, LA
Arcadia Children's Home, Arcadia, IN

Arcadia Convalescent Hospital Inc, Arcadia,
CA
Arcadia Manor, Cincinnati, OH
Arcadia Nursing Center, Coolville, OH
Arcadia Nursing Home, Lowell, MA
Arcadia Retirement Residence, Honolulu, HI
Arch Creek Nursing Home, Miami, FL
Archbishop Leibold Home, Cincinnati, OH
Archer Nursing Home, Archer City, TX
Archibald Memorial Home for Aged Deaf,
Brookston, IN
Archusa Convalescent Center Inc, Quitman,
MS
Arden House Inc, Hamden, CT
Arden Memorial Convalescent Hospital,
Sacramento, CA
Arden Nursing Home, Seattle, WA
Ardis Nursing Home Inc, Farwell, MI
Ardleigh Nursing Home Inc, Baltimore, MD
Ardmore Memorial Convalescent Home,
Ardmore, OK
Ardmore Nursing Home Inc, Ardmore, TN
Area Nursing Home Inc, Colfax, WI
Arena Manor Inc, Saint Louis, MO
Argyle House, Spring Valley, IL
Argyle Park Square, Denver, CO
Aristocrat Lakewood, Lakewood, OH
Aristocrat South, Parma Heights, OH
Aristocrat West Skilled Nursing Facility,
Cleveland, OH
Arizona Eastern Star Home, Phoenix, AZ
Arizona Elks Long-Term Care Unit, Tucson,
AZ
Arizona William-Wesley, Tucson, AZ
Arkadelphia Human Developmental Center,
Arkadelphia, AR
Arkansas City Presbyterian Manor, Arkansas
City, KS
Arkansas Easter Seals Residential Center,
Little Rock, AR
Arkansas Healthcare Nursing Center, Hot
Springs, AR
Arkansas Manor Nursing Home Inc, Denver,
CO
Arkansas Valley Regional Medical Center
Nursing Care Center, La Junta, CO
Arkhaven at Erie, Erie, KS
Arkhaven at Fort Scott, Fort Scott, KS
Arkhaven at Garnett, Garnett, KS
Arkhaven at Iola, Iola, KS
Arlington Care Center, Arlington, SD
Arlington Convalescent Center, Arlington, WA
Arlington Court Nursing Home, Columbus,
OH
Arlington Gardens Convalescent Hospital,
Riverside, CA
Arlington Good Samaritan Center, Arlington,
MN
Arlington Good Samaritan Center, Arlington,
OH
Arlington Health Care Inc, Parkersburg, WV
Arlington Heights Nursing Center Inc, Fort
Worth, TX
Arlington Manor, Lawton, OK
Arlington Manor Care Center, Jacksonville,
FL
Arlington Nursing Center, Arlington, TX
Arlington Nursing Home Inc, Newark, OH
Arlington Rest Home Inc, Arlington, MA
Arlington Villa for Senior Citizens, Arlington,
TX
Armacost Nursing Home Inc, Baltimore, MD
The Armenian Nursing Home, Jamaica Plain,
MA
Armour Heights Nursing Home Inc, Fort
Smith, AR
Armour Home, Kansas City, MO
Arms of Mercy Care Center Inc, San Antonio,
TX
Armstrong County Health Center, Kittanning,
PA
Armstrong Nursing Home, Worcester, MA
Armstrong's Personal Care Home I, Jackson,
MS
Armstrong's Personal Care Home II, Jackson,
MS
Army Distaff Hall—Health Services Center,
Washington, DC

Arnold Avenue Nursing Home, Greenville, MS
Arnold Home Inc, Detroit, MI
Arnold House Inc, Stoneham, MA
Arnold Memorial Nursing Home, Adrian, MN
Arnold Walter Nursing Home, Hazlet, NJ
Arnold's Care Center, Austin, TX
Arnot-Ogden Memorial Hospital—Skilled Nursing Unit, Elmira, NY
Arolyn Heights Nursing Home, Chanute, KS
The Aroostook Medical Center, Mars Hill, ME
The Aroostook Medical Center-Community General Hospital Division, Fort Fairfield, ME
Aroostook Residential Center, Presque Isle, ME
Arrington Nursing Home, Jackson, AL
Arrowhead Health Care Center—Eveleth, Eveleth, MN
Arrowhead Health Care Center—Virginia, Virginia, MN
Arrowhead Home, San Bernardino, CA
Arrowood Nursing Center, Battle Creek, MI
Arroyo Vista Convalescent Center, San Diego, CA
Arroyo-Creekside Convalescent Hospital, Walnut Creek, CA
Arterburn Home Inc, West Haven, CT
Artesia Good Samaritan Center, Artesia, NM
Artesian Home, Sulphur, OK
Arthur Good Samaritan Center, Arthur, ND
The Arthur Home, Arthur, IL
Artman Lutheran Home, Ambler, PA
Artrips Personal Care Home, Ashland, KY
Arundel Geriatric & Nursing Center, Glen Burnie, MD
Arundel Nursing Center Inc, Crownsville, MD
Arvada Health Center, Arvada, CO
Asbury Acres Retirement Home, Maryville, TN
Asbury Center at Birdmont Retirement Community, Wytheville, VA
Asbury Center at Oak Manor, Chattanooga, TN
Asbury Center Health Care & Retirement Facility, Johnson City, TN
Asbury Centers Inc, Maryville, TN
Asbury Circle Living Center, Denver, CO
Asbury Heights, Pittsburgh, PA
Asbury Towers, Bradenton, FL
Ash Flat Convalescent Center, Ash Flat, AR
Ash Grove Nursing Home Inc, Ash Grove, MO
Ashbrook Nursing Home, Scotch Plains, NJ
Ashburn Conver-Care Inc, Ashburn, GA
Ashburton Nursing Home, Baltimore, MD
Ashby Geriatric Hospital Inc, Berkeley, CA
Ashland Avenue Nursing Home, Toledo, OH
Ashland Convalescent Center Inc, Ashland, VA
Ashland Health Care Center Inc, Ashland, WI
Ashland Manor, Sacramento, CA
Ashland Manor Nursing Home, Ashland, MA
Ashland State General Hospital Geriatric Center, Ashland, PA
Ashland Terrace, Lexington, KY
Ashlar of Newtown, Newtown, CT
Ashley Manor, Wilmot, AR
Ashley Manor Care Center, Miami, FL
Ashley Manor Care Center, Boonville, MO
Ashley Medical Center SNF, Ashley, ND
Ashley Nursing Center, Denver, CO
Ashley Place Health Care Inc, Youngstown, OH
Ashmere Manor Nursing Home, Hinsdale, MA
Ashmore Estates, Ashmore, IL
Ashtabula County Nursing Home, Kingsville, OH
Ashtabula County Residential Services Corp Maples 2, Conneaut, OH
Ashtabula Medicare Nursing Center, Ashtabula, OH
Ashton Hall Nursing & Convalescent Home, Philadelphia, PA
Ashton Nursing Home, Ashton, ID
Ashton Woods Convalescent Center, Atlanta, GA

Ashville-Whitney Nursing Home Inc, Ashville, AL
Aspen Care Center, Ogden, UT
Aspen Care Center—West, Westminster, CO
Aspen Care East, Westminster, CO
Aspen Living Center, Colorado Springs, CO
The Aspen Siesta, Denver, CO
Aspin Center, Harrisburg, PA
Assembly Nursing Home of Poplar Bluff Inc, Poplar Bluff, MO
Assisi Residences of Fairbault County Inc, Blue Earth, MN
Assumption Health Care Center Inc, Napoleonville, LA
Assumption Home, Cold Spring, MN
Assumption Nursing Home, Youngstown, OH
Asthmatic Childrens Foundation of New York Inc, Ossining, NY
Aston Park Health Care Center Inc, Asheville, NC
Astor Gardens Nursing Home, Bronx, NY
Astoria Conv/Waldorf Astoria ICF, Sylmar, CA
Astoria Health Care Center, Astoria, IL
Atchison Senior Village, Atchison, KS
Athena Manor, Inc, Newark, OH
Athens Convalescent Center Inc, Athens, AL
Athens Convalescent & Nursing Center, Athens, TN
Athens Group Home, Athens, ME
Athens Health Care Center, Athens, TN
Athens Health Care Center Inc, Athens, GA
Athens Heritage Home Inc, Athens, GA
Athens Nursing Home, Athens, TX
Atkinson Good Samaritan Center, Atkinson, NE
Atlanta Health Care Center, Austell, GA
Atlantacare Convalescent Center, Decatur, GA
Atlantic Care Center, Atlantic, IA
Atlantic County Nursing Home—Meadowview, Northfield, NJ
Atlantic Highlands Nursing Home, Atlantic Highlands, NJ
Atlantic Rest Home, Lynn, MA
Atlantis Convalescent Center, Lantana, FL
Atmore Nursing Care Center, Atmore, AL
Atoka Care Center, Atoka, OK
Atoka Colonial Manor Inc, Atoka, OK
Atrium Village, Hills, IA
Attala County Nursing Center, Kosciusko, MS
Attalla Nursing Home Inc, Attalla, AL
Attic Angel Nursing Home, Madison, WI
Attleboro Nursing & Rehabilitation Center, Langhorne, PA
Attleboro Retirement Center Inc, Attleboro, MA
Atwater House, Atwater, MN
Atwood Manor, Galion, OH
Auburn Convalescent Hospital, Auburn, CA
Auburn House Nursing Home, Boston, MA
Auburn Nursing Center Inc, Auburn, KY
Auburn Nursing Home, Auburn, ME
Auburn Nursing Home, Auburn, NY
Auburn Park Club, Chicago, IL
Auburn Ravine Terrace, Auburn, CA
Audubon Health Care Center, New Orleans, LA
Audubon Villa, Lititz, PA
Auglaize Acres, Wapakoneta, OH
Augsburg Lutheran Home of Maryland Inc, Pikesville, MD
Augusta Area Nursing Home, Augusta, WI
Augusta Convalescent Center, Augusta, ME
Augusta Health Care Facility, Augusta, GA
Augusta Mental Health Institute, Augusta, ME
Augustana Center for Developmentally Disabled Children, Chicago, IL
Augustana Home of Minneapolis, Minneapolis, MN
Augustana Lutheran Home for the Aged, Brooklyn, NY
Aurora Australis Lodge, Columbus, MS
Aurora Care Center, Aurora, CO
Aurora Community Living Facility, Aurora, IL
Aurora House, Saint Paul, MN
Aurora Manor, Aurora, IL
Aurora Nursing Center, Aurora, MO

Aurora Park Health Care Center Inc, East Aurora, NY
Aurora-Brule Nursing Home, White Lake, SD
Aurora-Edmonds Nursing Home, Edmonds, WA
Ausable Valley Home, Fairview, MI
The Austin Home Inc, Warner, NH
Austin Manor Nursing Home, Austin, TX
Austin Nursing Center, Austin, TX
Austin Nursing Home, Seattle, WA
Austin Woods Nursing Center Inc, Austintown, OH
Autauga Health Care Center, Prattville, AL
Autumn Aegis Nursing Home, Lorain, OH
Autumn Breeze Nursing Home, Marietta, GA
Autumn Care of Brownsburg, Brownsburg, IN
Autumn Care of Chesapeake, Chesapeake, VA
Autumn Care of Clark's Creek, Plainfield, IN
Autumn Care of Drexel, Drexel, NC
Autumn Care of Great Bridge, Chesapeake, VA
Autumn Care of Marion, Marion, NC
Autumn Care of Mocksville, Mocksville, NC
Autumn Care of Portsmouth, Portsmouth, VA
Autumn Care of Suffolk, Suffolk, VA
Autumn Care of Waynesville, Waynesville, NC
Autumn Court Nursing Center, Columbia, MO
Autumn Heights Health Care Center, Denver, CO
Autumn Hills, Glendale, CA
Autumn Hills—Conroe, Conroe, TX
Autumn Hills Convalescent Center, Houston, TX
Autumn Hills Convalescent Center, Sugar Land, TX
Autumn Hills Convalescent Center—Richmond, Richmond, TX
Autumn Hills Convalescent Center—Tomball, Tomball, TX
Autumn Leaf Lodge, Hurst, TX
Autumn Leaves, Dallas, TX
Autumn Leaves Nursing Home, Winnfield, LA
Autumn Leaves Nursing Home Inc, Greenville, MS
Autumn Manor Inc 2, Yates Center, KS
Autumn Nursing Centers Inc 1, Vinita, OK
Autumn Nursing Centers Inc 2, Vinita, OK
Autumn Place, Fort Worth, TX
Autumn View Manor, Hamburg, NY
Autumn Winds Retirement Lodge, Schertz, TX
Autumn Years Lodge Inc, Fort Worth, TX
Autumn Years Nursing Center, Sabina, OH
Autumnfield Inc of Lowell, Gastonia, NC
Autumnfield of Asheville, Asheville, CA
Autumnfield of Danville, Danville, KY
Autumnwood Care Center, Tiffin, OH
Autumnwood Villa, McPherson, KS
Auxilio Mutuo Hospital, Hato Rey, PR
Avalon Manor, Hagerstown, MD
Avalon Manor Infirmary, Waukesha, WI
Avalon Nursing Home, Lynn, MA
Avalon Nursing Home, Saint Louis, MO
Avalon Nursing Home Inc, Warwick, RI
Ave Maria Convalescent Hospital, Monterey, CA
Ave Maria Home, Memphis, TN
Avery Nursing Home, Hartford, CT
Aveyron Homes Inc, Hutchinson, MN
Aviva Manor, Lauderdale Lakes, FL
Avon Convalescent Home Inc, Avon, CT
Avon Nursing Home, Dewitt, MI
Avon Nursing Home, Avon, NY
Avon Nursing Home Inc, Avon, IL
Avon Oaks Nursing Home, Avon, OH
Avondale Convalescent Home, Rochester, MI
Avonside Nursing Home, Detroit, MI
Avonwood Rest Home Inc, Birmingham, AL
Avoyelles Manor Nursing Home, Plaucheville, LA
Ayer-Lar Sanitarium, Gardena, CA
Ayers Nursing Home, Snyder, OK
Azalea Gardens Nursing Center, Wiggins, MS
Azalea Manor, Sealy, TX
Azalea Park Manor, Muskogee, OK
Azalea Trace, Pensacola, FL

Azalea Villa Nursing Home, New Iberia, LA
Azalealand Nursing Home Inc, Savannah, GA
Azle Manor Inc, Azle, TX
B & C Rest Home, Sturgis, SD
B & K Nursing Center, Hobart, OK
Bachelor Butte Nursing Center, Bend, OR
Bacon Nursing Home Inc, Harrisburg, IL
Badger Prairie Health Care Center, Verona, WI
Badillo Convalescent Hospital, Covina, CA
Bagwell Nursing Home Inc, Carrollton, GA
Baha'i Home, Wilmette, IL
Bailey Nursing Home, Clinton, SC
Bailie's Rest Home, Fairhaven, MA
Bainbridge Health Care Inc, Bainbridge, GA
Bainbridge Nursing Home, Bronx, NY
Baird Nursing Home, Rochester, NY
Baker Health Care Inc, Baker, LA
Baker Katz Nursing Home, Haverhill, MA
Baker Manor Rest Home, Lynn, MA
Baker's Rest Haven, Boonville, IN
Bakersfield Convalescent Hospital, Bakersfield, CA
Baker-Sumser Retirement Village, Canton, OH
Balch Springs Nursing Home, Balch Springs, TX
Baldwin Care Center, Baldwin, WI
Baldwin House, Duluth, MN
Baldwin Manor Nursing Home Inc, Cleveland, OH
Baldwin Park Convalescent Hospital, Baldwin Park, CA
Baldwin Park Health Care Center, Baldwin Park, CA
Baldwinville Nursing Home, Templeton, MA
Ball Pavilion Inc, Erie, PA
Ballard Convalescent Center, Seattle, WA
Ballard Nursing Center, Ada, OK
Ballard Nursing Center Inc, Des Plaines, IL
Ballinger Manor, Ballinger, TX
Ballinger Nursing Center, Ballinger, TX
Ballou Home for the Aged, Woonsocket, RI
Balmoral Nursing Centre Inc, Chicago, IL
Balmoral Skilled Nursing Home, Trenton, MI
Balowen Convalescent Hospital, Van Nuys, CA
Baltic Country Manor, Baltic, OH
Bamberg County Memorial Nursing Center, Bamberg, SC
Bancroft Convalescent Hospital, San Leandro, CA
Bancroft House Healthcare Nursing Home, Worcester, MA
Bangor City Nursing Facility, Bangor, ME
Bangor Convalescent Center, Bangor, ME
Bangor Mental Health Institute, Bangor, ME
Bangs Nursing Home, Bangs, TX
Banks-Jackson-Commerce Nursing Home, Commerce, GA
Banning Convalescent Hospital, Banning, CA
Bannister Nursing Care Center, Providence, RI
Bannochie Nursing Home, Minneapolis, MN
Bannock County Nursing Home, Pocatello, ID
Baptist Convalescent Center, Newport, KY
Baptist Health Care Center, Lenoir City, TN
The Baptist Home, Ironton, MO
Baptist Home East, Louisville, KY
Baptist Home for Senior Citizens Inc, Cook Springs, AL
Baptist Home Inc, Bismarck, ND
Baptist Home of Brooklyn New York, Rhinebeck, NY
The Baptist Home of Maryland Del Inc, Owings Mills, MD
Baptist Home of Massachusetts, Newton, MA
The Baptist Home of Philadelphia, Philadelphia, PA
Baptist Homes Nursing Center, Pittsburgh, PA
Baptist Manor, Portland, OR
Baptist Medical Center Nursing Home, Brooklyn, NY
Baptist Memorial Geriatric Center, San Angelo, TX
Baptist Memorial Home Elm Crest Apartments, Harlan, IA
Baptist Residence, Minneapolis, MN
Baptist Retirement Center, Scotia, NY

Baptist Retirement Home, Maywood, IL
Baptist Retirement Homes of North Carolina Inc, Winston-Salem, NC
Baptist Village Inc, Waycross, GA
Baraga County Memorial Hospital, Lanse, MI
Dr Gertrude A Barber Center Inc, Erie, PA
Barbour County Good Samaritan Center, Belington, WV
BARC Housing Inc, Davie, FL
Barcley Boarding Home, Seattle, WA
Barcroft Institute, Falls Church, VA
Barfield Health Care Inc, Guntersville, AL
Grace Barker Nursing Home Inc, Warren, RI
Barker Rest Home, Galena, KS
Barley Convalescent Home—North, York, PA
Barley Convalescent Home—South Nursing & Rehabilitation Center, York, PA
Barn Hill Convalescent Center, Newton, NJ
Frances Merry Barnard Home, Boston, MA
Barnard Nursing Home, Calais, ME
Barnard Rest Home, Westfield, MA
Barnegat Nursing Center, Barnegat, NJ
Barnes-Kasson County Hospital Skilled Nursing Facility, Susquehanna, PA
Barnesville Care Center, Barnesville, MN
Barnesville Health Care Center, Barnesville, OH
Barnett Stilhaven Nursing Home, Dayton, OH
Barnsdall Nursing Home, Barnsdall, OK
Barnwell County Nursing Home, Barnwell, SC
Barnwell Nursing Home & Health Facilities Inc, Valatie, NY
Barr House, Canon, CO
Warren N Barr Pavilion, Chicago, IL
Barren County Health Care Center, Glasgow, KY
Barrett Care Center Inc, Barrett, MN
Barrett Convalescent Home Inc, Commerce, GA
Barrett Convalescent Hospital Inc, Hayward, CA
Barrington Terrace Nursing Home, Orlando, FL
Barron Center, Portland, ME
Barron Memorial Medical Center SNF, Barron, WI
Barron Riverside Manor, Barron, WI
Barry Care Center of Carlinville, Carlinville, IL
Barry Care Center of Gillespie, Gillespie, IL
Barry Care Center of Litchfield, Litchfield, IL
Barry Care Center of Pana, Pana, IL
Barry Care Center of Staunton, Staunton, IL
Barry Community Care Center, Barry, IL
M A Barthell Order of Eastern Star Home, Decorah, IA
Bartels Lutheran Home Inc, Waverly, IA
Barth Nursing Home, Anacortes, WA
Bartholomew County Home, Columbus, IN
Bartlett Convalescent Hospital, Hayward, CA
Bartlett Manor Nursing Home, Malden, MA
Bartley Manor Convalescent Center, Jackson, NJ
Bartmann Nursing & Home Sheltered Care Facility, Atlanta, IL
Barton Heights Nursing Home Inc, Austin, TX
A Barton Hepburn Hospital Skilled Nursing Facility, Ogdensburg, NY
The Barton House, Indianapolis, IN
Kathryn Barton Nursing Home, Wayland, MA
Barton Nursing Home Inc, Detroit, MI
Barton W Stone Christian Home, Jacksonville, IL
Bartow Convalescent Center, Bartow, FL
Bashford East Health Care Facility, Louisville, KY
Basile Care Center Inc, Basile, LA
Bassard Convalescent Hospital Inc, Hayward, CA
Bastrop Nursing Center, Bastrop, TX
Batavia Nursing & Convalescent Inn, Batavia, OH
Batavia Nursing Home Inc, Batavia, NY
Batavia Nursing Home Inc, Batavia, OH
Batesville Manor Nursing Home, Batesville, MS
Bath Nursing Home, Bath, ME

Baton Rouge Extensive Care Facility, Baton Rouge, LA
Baton Rouge Heritage House II, Baton Rouge, LA
Battersby Convalescent Home, Erie, PA
Batterson Convalescent Hospital, Santa Cruz, CA
Battle Lake Care Center, Battle Lake, MN
Battlefield Park Convalescent Center, Petersburg, VA
Battles Home, Lowell, MA
Bauer-Home Residential Care, Rocky Ford, CO
Baxley Manor Inc—Intermediate Care Facility, Baxley, GA
Baxter Group Home ICF/MR, Baxter, MN
Baxter Manor Nursing Home, Mountain Home, AR
Bay Convalescent Center, Panama City, FL
Bay Convalescent Hospital, Long Beach, CA
Bay County Medical Care Facility, Essexville, MI
Bay Crest Convalescent Hospital, Torrance, CA
Bay Harbor Rehabilitation Center, Torrance, CA
Bay Health Care—Palo Alto, Palo Alto, CA
Bay Manor Health Care Center, Mobile, AL
Bay Manor Nursing Home Inc, Annapolis, MD
Bay St Joseph Care Center, Port Saint Joe, FL
Bay Shore Sanitarium, Hermosa Beach, CA
Bay State Rehabilitation Care, Billerica, MA
Bay to Bay Nursing Center, Tampa, FL
Bay Tower Nursing Center, Providence, RI
Bay View Nursing Center Inc, Beaufort, SC
Bay View Nursing Home, Winthrop, MA
Bay Villa Nursing Center, Bay City, TX
Bay Village of Sarasota, Sarasota, FL
Bay Vista Convalescent Hospital, Santa Monica, CA
Bayard Care Center, Bayard, IA
Bayberry Convalescent Hospital, Concord, CA
Bayberry Nursing Home, New Rochelle, NY
Bayless Boarding Home, Farmington, MO
Bayou Chateau Nursing Center, Simmesport, LA
Bayou Glen Jones Road, Houston, TX
Bayou Glen Nursing Center, Houston, TX
Bayou Glen-Northwest Nursing Center, Houston, TX
Bayou Heath Care Center, Monroe, LA
Bayou Manor, Houston, TX
Bayou Manor Health Care Center, Saint Petersburg, FL
Bayou Village Nursing Center, Crowley, LA
Bayou Vista Manor Nursing Home, Bunkie, LA
Bayside Nursing Center, Lexington Park, MD
Bayside Nursing Home, Boston, MA
Bayside Terrace, Waukegan, IL
Baytown Nursing Home, Baytown, TX
Baytree Nursing Center, Palm Harbor, FL
Bayview Convalescent Center, Bayville, NJ
Bayview Convalescent Hospital, Burlingame, CA
Bayview Inn, Olympia, WA
Bayview Manor, Seattle, WA
Bayview Nursing Home, Island Park, NY
Bayview Nursing Home Inc, Middletown, RI
Baywood Convalescent Hospital, Pleasant Hill, CA
Baywood Nursing Home, Ludington, MI
Beach Cliff Lodge Nursing Home, Michigan City, IN
Beach Convalescent Nursing Home, Saint Petersburg Beach, FL
Beach Haven Health Care Center, Beachwood, OH
Beach Nursing Home, Monroe, MI
Beach Wood, Kennebunk, ME
Beachview Rest ICF, Keansburg, NJ
Beacon Hill, Lombard, IL
Beacon Hill Nursing Home, Kansas City, MO
Beacon-Donegan Manor, Fort Myers, FL
Beadles Rest Home, Alva, OK
Bear Creek Health Care Center, Bear Creek, PA

Bear Creek House, Rochester, MN
Bear Creek Nursing Center, Morrison, CO
Bear Creek Nursing Center, Hudson, FL
Bear Hill Nursing Center at Wakefield, Stoneham, MA
Bear Lake Memorial Nursing Home, Montpelier, ID
Beatitudes Care Center, Phoenix, AZ
Beatrice Catherine Rest Home, Boston, MA
Beatrice Lawson Nursing Home Inc, Clairton, PA
Beatrice Manor Care Center, Beatrice, NE
Beaulieu Nursing Home, Newnan, GA
Beaumont at the Willows, Westborough, MA
Beaumont Convalescent Hospital, Beaumont, CA
Beaumont Nursing Home, Northbridge, MA
The Beaumont Nursing Home, Denton, TX
Beauregard Nursing Home, DeRidder, LA
Beautiful Savior Home, Belton, MO
Beaven-Kelly Rest Home, Holyoke, MA
Beaver City Manor, Beaver City, NE
Beaver County Nursing Home, Beaver, OK
Beaver Dam Care Center, Beaver Dam, WI
Beaver Dam Health Care Manor, Beaver Dam, KY
Beaver Dam Lakeview Unit, Beaver Dam, WI
Beaver Valley Geriatrics Center, Beaver, PA
Beaver Valley Nursing Center, Beaver Falls, PA
Bechthold Convalescent Hospital, Lodi, CA
Peter Becker Community, Harleysville, PA
The Becker/Shoop Center, Racine, WI
Becky Thatcher Nursing Home, Hannibal, MO
Bedford County Nursing Home, Shelbyville, TN
Bedford County Nursing Home, Bedford, VA
Bedford Group Home, Woodinville, WA
Bedford Manor, Bedford, IA
Bedford Nursing Center, Gardner, KS
Bedford Nursing Home, Bedford, IN
Bedford Nursing Home, Bedford, NH
Bedford Villa Nursing Center, Southfield, MI
Beech Grove Healthcare Center, Beech Grove, IN
Beech Manor Rest Home, Springfield, MA
Beechaven Nursing Home, Worcester, MA
Beechknoll Centers, Cincinnati, OH
Beechwood Home for Incurables Inc, Cincinnati, OH
Beechwood Manor Inc, New London, CT
Beechwood Nursing Home, Elma, WA
Beechwood Rest Home, Kewaskum, WI
Beechwood Sanitarium, Rochester, NY
Beehaven Nursing Home, Jackson, MS
Beemans Sanitarium, Whittier, CA
Beggs Nursing Home, Beggs, OK
Viola Behling Memorial Home Inc, Clintonville, WI
Bel Air Care Center, Beaverton, OR
Bel Air Convalescent Center Inc, Bel Air, MD
Bel Air Health Care Center, Tacoma, WA
Bel Air Health Care Center Inc, Milwaukee, WI
Bel-Air Manor, Newington, CT
Bel Arbor Health Care Facility, Macon, GA
Bel Isle Nursing Home, Phoenix, AZ
Bel Pre Health Care Center, Silver Spring, MD
Bel Tooren Villa Convalescent Hospital, Bellflower, CA
Bel Vista Convalescent Hospital Inc, Long Beach, CA
The Belair Convalesarium, Baltimore, MD
Bel-Air Convalescent Center, Alliance, OH
Bel-Air Health Care Inc, Columbia, TN
Bel-Air Lodge Convalescent Hospital, Turlock, CA
Belair Nursing Center, Lower Burrell, PA
Bel-Air Nursing Home, Grasmere, NH
Belair Nursing Home, North Bellmore, NY
Bel-Aire Quality Care Nursing Home, Newport, VT
Belchertown State School, Belchertown, MA
Belcourt Terrace Nursing Home, Nashville, TN
Belding Christian Home, Belding, MI
Belgrade Nursing Home, Belgrade, MN

Belinda Care Center, Celina, TX
Belknap County Nursing Home, Laconia, NH
Bell Crest Inc, Cool Valley, MO
Bell Gardens Convalescent Center, Bell Gardens, CA
Bell Health Care Inc, Kimbolton, OH
Bell Manor Inc, Normandy, MO
Bell Nursing Home Inc, Belmont, OH
Bella Vista Convalescent Hospital Inc, Ontario, CA
Bella Vita Towers, Denver, CO
Belle Fourche Health Care Center—Long-Term Care Unit, Belle Fourche, SD
Belle Haven Nursing Home Inc, Quakertown, PA
Belle Hoffman Michael Home, Bucyrus, OH
Belle Maison Nursing Home, Hammond, LA
Belle Manor Nursing Home, New Carlisle, OH
Belle Meade Home, Greenville, KY
Belleair East Health Care Center, Clearwater, FL
Bellerose Convalescent Hospital, San Jose, CA
Belleview Valley Nursing Homes Inc, Belleview, MO
Belleville Health Care Center, Belleville, KS
Belleville Nursing Center, Belleville, IL
Bellevue Care Center, Trenton, NJ
Bellevue Care Center Inc, Tacoma, WA
Bellevue Center, Bellevue, WA
Bellevue Nursing Center, Oklahoma City, OK
Bellevue Nursing Home, Bellevue, OH
Bellevue Terrace, Bellevue, WA
Bellevue-Newport Health Center, Newport, RI
Bellflower Convalescent Hospital, Bellflower, CA
Bellflower Golden Age Convalescent Home, Bellflower, CA
Bellflower Nursing Home, Montgomery City, MO
Bellingham Care Center, Bellingham, WA
Bellmead Nursing Home Inc, Waco, TX
Bell-Minor Home Inc, Gainesville, GA
Bellmire Home Inc, Bowie, TX
Bells Lodge, Phoenix, AZ
Belmond Nursing Home, Belmond, IA
Belmont Care Center, Portland, OR
Belmont Convalescent Hospital, Belmont, CA
Belmont County Oakview Nursing Home, Saint Clairsville, OH
Belmont Habilitation Center, Saint Clairsville, OH
Belmont Home, Worcester, MA
Belmont Lodge Inc, Pueblo, CO
Belmont Manor Nursing Home, Belmont, MA
Belmont Nursing Home Inc, Chicago, IL
Belmont Terrace Inc, Bremerton, WA
Beloit Convalescent Center, Beloit, WI
Beltrami Nursing Home, Bemidji, MN
The Belvedere, Chester, PA
Bel-Wood Nursing Home, Peoria, IL
Bement Manor, Bement, IL
Ben Hur Home Inc, Crawfordsville, IN
Benbrook Sweetbriar Nursing Home, Benbrook, TX
Bender Terrace Nursing Home, Lubbock, TX
Benedictine Nursing Center, Mount Angel, OR
Beneva Nursing Pavilion, Sarasota, FL
Benner Convalescent Center, Houston, TX
Bennett County Nursing Home, Martin, SD
Bennington Convalescent Center, Bennington, VT
Bennion Care Center, Salt Lake City, UT
Benson Heights Rehabilitation Center, Kent, WA
Benson's Nursing Home Inc, Nashville, AR
Bent County Memorial Nursing Home, Las Animas, CO
Bent Nursing Home Inc, Reisterstown, MD
Bentley Gardens Health Care Center, West Haven, CT
Bentley Gardens Health Care Center Inc, Commerce City, CO
Benton Care Center, Kansas City, MO
Benton County Care Facility, Vinton, IA
Benton Services Center Nursing Home, Benton, AR
Bentonville Manor Nursing Home, Bentonville, AR

Benzie County Medical Care Facility, Frankfort, MI
Berea Health Care Center, Berea, KY
Berea Hospital—Skilled Nursing Facility, Berea, KY
Berea North Quality Care Nursing Center, Berea, OH
Berea Quality Care Nursing Center, Berea, OH
Berkeley Convalescent Center, Moncks Corner, SC
Berkeley Hall Nursing Home, Berkeley Heights, NJ
Berkeley Heights Convalescent Center, Berkeley Heights, NJ
Berkeley Hills Convalescent Hospital, Berkeley, CA
Berkley East Convalescent Hospital, Santa Monica, CA
Berkley Manor Care Center, Denver, CO
Berkley Retirement Home, Lawrence, MA
Berkley West Convalescent Hospital, Santa Monica, CA
Berks County Home, Reading, PA
Berkshire, A Skilled Nursing Facility, Santa Monica, CA
The Berkshire Health Care Center, Vinton, VA
Berkshire Hills Nursing Home—North, Lee, MA
Berkshire Nursing Center Inc, West Babylon, NY
Berkshire Nursing Home Inc, Pittsfield, MA
Berkshire Place, Pittsfield, MA
Berkshire Residence, Osseo, MN
Berlin Convalescent Center, Barre, VT
Berlin Nursing Home Inc, Berlin, MD
Bernard West Pine Nursing Home, Saint Louis, MO
Berne Nursing Home, Berne, IN
Berrien General Hospital, Berrien Center, MI
Berrien Nursing Center Inc, Nashville, GA
Berry Hill Nursing Home Inc, South Boston, VA
Martha T Berry Medical Care Facility, Mount Clemens, MI
Berryman Health Healdsburg Convalescent Hospital, Healdsburg, CA
Berryman Health West Whittier, Whittier, CA
Berryville Health Care Center, Berryville, AR
Bert Anne Annex, West Chesterfield, NH
Bert Anne Home for the Aged, West Chesterfield, NH
Bertram Nursing Home, Bertram, TX
Bertran Home for Aged Men, Salem, MA
Bertrand Nursing Home, Bertrand, NE
Bertrand Retirement Home Inc, Bertrand, MO
Berwick Retirement Village Nursing Home, Berwick, PA
Bescare Nursing Home, Columbus, OH
Best Care Convalescent Hospital Corp, Torrance, CA
Best Care Nursing Home, Wheelersburg, OH
Beth Abraham Hospital, Bronx, NY
Beth Haven Nursing Home, Hannibal, MO
Beth Israel Hospital & Geriatric Center, Denver, CO
Beth Rifka Nursing Home, Staten Island, NY
Beth Sholom Home of Central Virginia, Richmond, VA
Beth Sholom Home of Eastern Virginia, Virginia Beach, VA
Bethalto Care Center Inc, Bethalto, IL
Bethany Care Center, Lakewood, CO
Bethany Convalescent Hospital, San Jose, CA
Bethany Covenant Home, Minneapolis, MN
Bethany Good Samaritan Center, Brainerd, MN
Bethany Home, Dubuque, IA
Bethany Home, New Orleans, LA
Bethany Home, Litchfield, MN
Bethany Home, Minden, NE
Bethany Home, Waupaca, WI
Bethany Home Association of Lindsborg, Lindsborg, KS
Bethany Home/Bethel Manors, Alexandria, MN
Bethany Home for Ladies, Vidalia, GA

Bethany Home for Men, Millen, GA
Bethany Home for the Aged Inc, Everett, WA
Bethany Home of Rhode Island, Providence, RI
Bethany Home Society San Joaquin County, Ripon, CA
Bethany Homes, Fargo, ND
Bethany Inc, Albion, ME
Bethany Lutheran Home, Sioux Falls, SD
Bethany Lutheran Home Inc, Council Bluffs, IA
Bethany Lutheran Village, Dayton, OH
Bethany Manor Inc, Story City, IA
Bethany Methodist Home, Chicago, IL
Bethany MHS Care Center, Lafayette, LA
Bethany Nursing Home, Canton, OH
Bethany Nursing Home & Health Related Facility Inc, Horseheads, NY
Bethany Nursing Home Inc, Bloomingdale, MI
Bethany Riverside, La Crosse, WI
Bethany St Joseph Care Center, La Crosse, WI
Bethany Samaritan Heights, Rochester, MN
Bethany Terrace Retirement & Nursing Home, Morton Grove, IL
Bethany Village Health Care Center, Bethany, OK
Bethany Village Nursing Home, Indianapolis, IN
Bethany Village Retirement Center, Mechanicsburg, PA
Bethea Baptist Home, Darlington, SC
Bethel Care Center, Saint Paul, MN
Bethel Home, Oshkosh, WI
Bethel Home Inc, Montezuma, KS
Bethel Home & Services Inc, Viroqua, WI
Bethel Living Center, Arpin, WI
Bethel Lutheran Home, Williston, ND
Bethel Lutheran Home, Madison, SD
Bethel Lutheran Home Inc, Selma, CA
Bethel Nursing Home Company Inc, Ossining, NY
Bethel Rest Home, Cuyahoga Falls, OH
Bethel Sanitarium Inc, Evansville, IN
Bethesda Care Center, Canon City, CO
Bethesda Care Center, Colorado Springs, CO
Bethesda Care Center, Delta, CO
Bethesda Care Center, Grand Junction, CO
Bethesda Care Center, Paonia, CO
Bethesda Care Center, Saint Maries, ID
Bethesda Care Center, Clarinda, IA
Bethesda Care Center, Mediapolis, IA
Bethesda Care Center, Muscatine, IA
Bethesda Care Center, Toledo, IA
Bethesda Care Center, Winterset, IA
Bethesda Care Center, Smith Center, KS
Bethesda Care Center, Tarkio, MO
Bethesda Care Center, Ainsworth, NE
Bethesda Care Center, Aurora, NE
Bethesda Care Center, Central City, NE
Bethesda Care Center, Exeter, NE
Bethesda Care Center, Sutherland, NE
Bethesda Care Center, Utica, NE
Bethesda Care Center, Fremont, OH
Bethesda Care Center, San Antonio, TX
Bethesda Care Center of Ashland, Ashland, NE
Bethesda Care Center of Bassett, Bassett, NE
Bethesda Care Center of Blue Hill, Blue Hill, NE
Bethesda Care Center of Edgar, Edgar, NE
Bethesda Care Center of Gretna, Gretna, NE
Bethesda Care Center of Laramie, Laramie, WY
Bethesda Care Center of Seward, Seward, NE
Bethesda Care Center of Worland, Worland, WY
Bethesda Care Centers, Colorado Springs, CO
Bethesda-Dilworth Memorial Home, Saint Louis, MO
Bethesda Health Care Facility, Fayetteville, NC
Bethesda Heritage Center, Willmar, MN
Bethesda Home, Hayward, CA
Bethesda Home, Webster, SD
Bethesda Home for the Aged, Beresford, SD
Bethesda Home of Aberdeen, Aberdeen, SD
Bethesda Home & Retirement Center, Chicago, IL

Bethesda Lutheran Care Center, Saint Paul, MN
Bethesda Manor & Convalescent Center, Los Gatos, CA
Bethesda Montgomery Care Center, Cincinnati, OH
Bethesda Nursing Center, Chanute, KS
Bethesda Nursing Home—Pleasantview, Willmar, MN
Bethesda Retirement Nursing Center, Chevy Chase, MD
Bethesda-Ritter Dierker, Watertown, WI
Bethesda Scarlet Oaks Retirement Community, Cincinnati, OH
Bethesda Skilled Nursing Facility, Saint Louis, MO
Bethlen Home of the Hungarian Reformed Federation of America, Ligonier, PA
Bethpage at Axtell, Axtell, NE
Bethphage at Lincoln, Lincoln, NE
Bethune Plaza Inc, Chicago, IL
Betsy Ross Health Related Facility, Rome, NY
Bettendorf Health Care Center, Bettendorf, IA
Betty Ann Nursing Home, Grove, OK
Betz Nursing Home Inc, Auburn, IN
Beulah Community Nursing Home, Beulah, ND
Beulah Home Inc, Oakland, CA
Beulah Land Christian Home, Flanagan, IL
Beverly Farm Foundation, Godfrey, IL
Beverly Health Care Center, Tarboro, NC
Beverly Health Care Center, Glasgow, WV
Beverly La Cumbre Convalescent Hospital, Santa Barbara, CA
Beverly Manor, Burbank, CA
Beverly Manor, Saint Joseph, MO
Beverly Manor Convalescent Center, Sun City, AZ
Beverly Manor Convalescent Center, Saint Petersburg, FL
Beverly Manor Convalescent Center, Augusta, GA
Beverly Manor Convalescent Center, Decatur, GA
Beverly Manor Convalescent Center, Honolulu, HI
Beverly Manor Convalescent Center, Belle Plaine, IA
Beverly Manor Convalescent Center, Iowa City, IA
Beverly Manor Convalescent Center, Southgate, MI
Beverly Manor Convalescent Center, Rutland, VT
Beverly Manor Convalescent Hospital, Anaheim, CA
Beverly Manor Convalescent Hospital, Bakersfield, CA
Beverly Manor Convalescent Hospital, Burbank, CA
Beverly Manor Convalescent Hospital, Canoga Park, CA
Beverly Manor Convalescent Hospital, Capistrano Beach, CA
Beverly Manor Convalescent Hospital, Chico, CA
Beverly Manor Convalescent Hospital, Costa Mesa, CA
Beverly Manor Convalescent Hospital, Escondido, CA
Beverly Manor Convalescent Hospital, Fresno, CA
Beverly Manor Convalescent Hospital, Glendale, CA
Beverly Manor Convalescent Hospital, La Mesa, CA
Beverly Manor Convalescent Hospital, Laguna Hills, CA
Beverly Manor Convalescent Hospital, Los Altos, CA
Beverly Manor Convalescent Hospital, Los Gatos, CA
Beverly Manor Convalescent Hospital, Los Gatos, CA
Beverly Manor Convalescent Hospital, Monrovia, CA
Beverly Manor Convalescent Hospital, Monterey, CA

Beverly Manor Convalescent Hospital, Panorama City, CA
Beverly Manor Convalescent Hospital, Redding, CA
Beverly Manor Convalescent Hospital, Redlands, CA
Beverly Manor Convalescent Hospital, Riverside, CA
Beverly Manor Convalescent Hospital, San Francisco, CA
Beverly Manor Convalescent Hospital, Santa Barbara, CA
Beverly Manor Convalescent Hospital, Santa Monica, CA
Beverly Manor Convalescent Hospital, Seal Beach, CA
Beverly Manor Convalescent Hospital, Van Nuys, CA
Beverly Manor Convalescent Hospital, West Covina, CA
Beverly Manor Convalescent Hospital, Las Vegas, NV
Beverly Manor of Brighton, Brighton, CO
Beverly Manor of Los Angeles, Los Angeles, CA
Beverly Manor of Petaluma, Petaluma, CA
Beverly Manor of Portsmouth, Portsmouth, VA
Beverly Manor of Yreka, Yreka, CA
Beverly Manor Sanitarium, Riverside, CA
Beverly Manor-Charlotte, Charlotte, NC
Beverly Nursing Center, Pittsburg, KS
Beverly Nursing Home, Chicago, IL
Beverly Nursing Home, Beverly, MA
Beverly Palms Rehabilitation Hospital, Los Angeles, CA
Beverly Terrace Nursing Home, Watertown, WI
Beverwyck Nursing Home, Parsippany, NJ
Bezalel Nursing Home Company, Far Rockaway, NY
Bialystoker Home for the Aged, New York, NY
Bibb Medical Center Hospital & Nursing Home, Centreville, AL
Bible Fellowship Church Home, Nazareth, PA
Bickford Convalescent and Rest Home, Windsor Locks, CT
Bicknell Health Care, Bicknell, IN
Bi-County Clinic & Nursing Home Inc, Bloxom, VA
Big Horn County Memorial Nursing Home, Hardin, MT
Big Meadows Inc, Savanna, IL
Big Spring Manor, Huntsville, AL
Big Springs Nursing Home, Humansville, MO
Big Town Nursing Home, Mesquite, TX
Billdora Rest Home, Tylertown, MS
Billings Fairchild Center, Billings, OK
Biltmore Manor, Asheville, NC
Bingham County Nursing Home, Blackfoot, ID
Birch Hill Health Care Center, Shawano, WI
Birch Manor, Kalamazoo, MI
Birch Manor Nursing Home, Chicopee, MA
Birch Street Manor, Dallas, OR
Birch View Nursing Home, Birch Tree, MO
Birchway Nursing Home, Saint Louis, MO
Birchwood, Casey, IL
Birchwood Care Center, Marne, MI
Birchwood Care Home, Minneapolis, MN
Birchwood Cluter Manor Inc, Waterbury, CT
Birchwood Health Care Center, Forest Lake, MN
Birchwood Health Care Center Inc, Liverpool, NY
Birchwood Manor, Holland, MI
Birchwood Manor, North Bend, NE
Birchwood Manor Nursing Home, Fitchburg, MA
Birchwood Manor Nursing Home, Cooper, TX
Birchwood Nursing Center, Traverse City, MI
Birchwood Nursing Center, Nanticoke, PA
Birchwood Nursing & Convalescent Center, Edison, NJ
Birchwood Nursing Home, Derry, NH
Birchwood Nursing Home, Huntington Station, NY

Birchwood Plaza Inc, Chicago, IL
Birchwood Terrace Healthcare, Burlington, VT
Bird Haven Christian Convalescent Hospital, Norwalk, CA
Bird Haven Christian Convalescent Hospital, Paramount, CA
Bird Island Manor Healthcare Center, Bird Island, MN
Birk's Mountain Home, Hurricane, UT
Bishop Nursing Home Inc, Media, PA
Elizabeth Jane Bivins Home for the Aged, Amarillo, TX
Bivins Memorial Nursing Home, Amarillo, TX
Bixby Knolls Towers Nursing Home, Long Beach, CA
Bixby Manor Nursing Home, Bixby, OK
Black Earth Manor, Black Earth, WI
Black Hawk County Health Care, Waterloo, IA
Black Hills Retirement Center, Rapid City, SD
Black Mountain Center, Black Mountain, NC
Blackfeet Nursing Home, Browning, MT
Black's Nursing Home, Tulsa, OK
Blackstone Nursing Home, Blackstone, MA
Blackwell Nursing Home Inc, Blackwell, OK
Blair House, Augusta, GA
Blair House of Milford, Milford, MA
Blair Nursing Home Inc-Blair Personal Care Homes Inc, Beaver Falls, PA
Blaire House LTCF of New Bedford, New Bedford, MA
Blaire House of Worcester, Worcester, MA
Blakedale Rest Home, Danvers, MA
Blakely Care Center, North Baltimore, OH
Blalock Nursing Home—East, Houston, TX
Blalock Nursing Home—North, Houston, TX
Blalock Nursing Home—Southeast, Pasadena, TX
Blanchester Care Center, Blanchester, OH
Blanco Health Care Center, Blanco, TX
Bland Residential Care Home, Erie, CO
Bledsoe County Nursing Home, Pikeville, TN
Blenwood Nursing Home, Methuen, MA
Blevins Retirement & Care Center, McAlester, OK
Blind Girl's Home, Kirkwood, MO
Bliss Manor, Saint Joseph, MO
Bloomfield Good Samaritan Center, Bloomfield, NE
Bloomfield Health Care Center, Bloomfield, IN
Bloomfield Hills Care Center, Bloomfield Hills, MI
Bloomfield Manor Nursing Home, Dodgeville, WI
Bloomfield Nursing Center, Bloomfield, MO
Bloomfield Nursing Home, Macon, GA
Bloomingdale Pavilion, Bloomingdale, IL
Bloomington Convalescent Center, Bloomington, IN
Bloomington Manor, Bloomington, IL
Bloomington Maple Manor Care Center, Bloomington, MN
Bloomington Nursing Home, Bloomington, IN
Bloomington Nursing Home, Bloomington, MN
Bloomington Nursing & Rehabilitation Center, Bloomington, IL
Bloomsburg Health Care Center, Bloomsburg, PA
Bloomville Nursing Care Center, Bloomville, OH
Blose McGregor Health Care Center Inc, Punxsutawney, PA
Blossom Care Center, Benton Harbor, MI
Blossom Convalescent Hospital, San Jose, CA
Blossom Hill Nursing Home, Huntsburg, OH
Blossom Nursing Center, Alliance, OH
Blossom Nursing Home, Rochester, NY
Blossom View Nursing Home, Sodus, NY
Blough Nursing Home Inc, Bethlehem, PA
Blowing Rock Hospital—SNF/ICF, Blowing Rock, NC
Blue Ash Nursing & Convalescent Home Inc, Blue Ash, OH
Blue Hills Centre, Kansas City, MO

Blue Hills Convalescent Home, Stoughton, MA
Blue Island Nursing Home, Blue Island, IL
Blue Mountain Convalescent Center, College Place, WA
Blue Mountain Nursing Home, Prairie City, OR
Blue Ridge Haven Convalescent Center West, Camp Hill, PA
Blue Ridge Haven East Convalescent Center Inc, Harrisburg, PA
Blue Ridge Highlands Nursing Home, Galax, VA
Blue Ridge Nursing Home Inc, Kansas City, MO
Blue Ridge Nursing Home Inc, Stuart, VA
Blue Springs Care Center, Blue Springs, MO
Blue Spruce Rest Home, Springfield, MA
Blue Valley Lutheran Home Society Inc, Hebron, NE
Blue Valley Nursing Home, Blue Rapids, KS
Blueberry Hill Healthcare Nursing Home, Beverly, MA
Blueberry Hill Rest Home, Kingston, MA
Bluebonnet Nursing Center of Granger, Granger, TX
Bluebonnet Nursing Home, Albany, TX
Bluefield Multi-Care, Bluefield, WV
Bonnie Bluejacket Memorial Nursing Home, Greybull, WY
Bluemound Manor Nursing Home, Milwaukee, WI
Bluff Manor Nursing Home, Poplar Bluff, MO
The Bluffs Care Center, Pensacola, FL
Blu-Fountain Manor, Godfrey, IL
The Bluementhal Jewish Home for the Aged Inc, Clemmons, NC
Rose Blumkin Jewish Home, Omaha, NE
Blythe Convalescent Hospital, Blythe, CA
Blytheville Nursing Center Inc, Blytheville, AR
Board of Social Ministry, Saint Paul, MN
Boardman Community Care Home, Rapid City, SD
Boca Raton Convalescent Center, Boca Raton, FL
Boddy Nursing Center, Woodstock, GA
Bohannon Nursing Home Inc, Lebanon, IL
Bohemian Home for the Aged, Chicago, IL
Boise Group Home 1, Boise, ID
Boise Group Home 2, Boise, ID
Boise Group Home 3, Boise, ID
Boise Samaritan Village, Boise, ID
Elizabeth E Boit Home, Wakefield, MA
Boley Intermediate Care Facility, Boley, OK
Bolivar County Hospital—Long-Term Care Facility, Cleveland, MS
Bolivar Nursing Home Inc, Bolivar, MO
Bolle's Boarding Home Inc, Festus, MO
Bolster Heights Health Care Facility, Auburn, ME
Bolton Convalescent Home, Bratenahl, OH
Bolton Manor Nursing Home, Marlborough, MA
Bon Air Life Care Center, Augusta, GA
Bon Air Nursing Home, Auburn, ME
Bon-Ing Care Center, Gahanna, OH
Bon Secours Extended Care Facility, Ellicott City, MD
Bon Secours Hospital/Villa Maria Nursing Center, North Miami, FL
Bonell Good Samaritan Center, Greeley, CO
Bonetti Health Care Center Inc, Harrisville, PA
Bonham Nursing Center, Stillwater, PA
Bonham Nursing Center, Bonham, TX
Bonifay Nursing Home, Bonifay, FL
Bon-Ing Inc, Columbus, OH
Bonne Terre Rest Home Inc, Bonne Terre, MO
Bonner Health Center, Bonner Springs, KS
Bonnie Brae Manor Convalescent Hospital, Los Angeles, CA
Bonnie Brae's, Tucson, AZ
Bonnie's Nursing Home, Westchester, OH
Bono Nursing Home, Henryetta, OK
Bonterra Nursing Center, East Point, GA
Booker Convalescent Annex, Dayton, WA

Boone Guest Home, Boone, CO
Boone Nursing Home, Millville, PA
Boone Retirement Center Inc, Columbia, MO
Booneville Human Development Center, Booneville, AR
Boonville Convalescent Center Inc, Boonville, IN
Borden Nursing Home Inc, Forrest City, AR
Borderview Manor Inc, Van Buren, ME
Borger Nursing Center, Borger, TX
Bornemann Nursing Home, Green Bay, WI
Bortz Health Care of Petoskey, Petoskey, MI
Bortz Health Care of Traverse City, Traverse City, MI
Bortz Health Care of West Branch, West Branch, MI
Bossier Health Care Center, Bossier City, LA
Boston Home Inc, Boston, MA
Bostonian Nursing Care Center, Boston, MA
Boswell Extended Care Center, Sun City, AZ
Bottineau Good Samaritan Center, Bottineau, ND
Boulder City Care Center, Boulder City, NV
Boulder Good Samaritan Health Care Center, Boulder, CO
Boulder Manor, Boulder, CO
Boulevard Community Residence, Orangeburg, SC
Boulevard Manor Care Center, Richland Hills, TX
Boulevard Manor Nursing Center, Boynton Beach, FL
Boulevard Nursing Home, Philadelphia, PA
Boulevard Temple United Methodist Retirement Home, Detroit, MI
Boulevard Terrace Nursing Home, Murfreesboro, TN
Boundary County Nursing Home, Bonners Ferry, ID
Bountiful Convalescent Center, Bountiful, UT
Bountiful Nursing Home, Bountiful, UT
Bourbon Heights Nursing Home, Paris, KY
Bourbonnais Terrace, Bourbonnais, IL
Bowden Nursing Home, Wilmington, NC
Bowdle Nursing Home, Bowdle, SD
Bowen Health Center, Raytown, MO
Bowerston Health Care Center, Bowerston, OH
Bowie Convalescing Home, Bowie, TX
Bowling Green Manor, Bowling Green, OH
Bowman Nursing Home, Midlothian, IL
Bowman-Harrison Convalescent Hospital, San Francisco, CA
Bowman's Nursing Center, Ormond Beach, FL
Box Elder County Nursing Home, Tremonton, UT
Boyce Manor Inc, Holdenville, OK
Boyd's Kinsman Home, Kinsman, OH
Bozeman Convalescent Center, Bozeman, MT
Bozeman Deaconess Hospital—Extended Care Facility, Bozeman, MT
Bra-Ton Nursing Home Inc, Kansas City, MO
Bracken Center Inc, Augusta, KY
Bradbury Manor, Belfast, ME
Bradenton Convalescent Center, Bradenton, FL
Bradenton Manor, Bradenton, FL
Bradford County Manor, Troy, PA
Bradford Living Care Center, Bradford, OH
Bradford Nursing Pavilion, Bradford, PA
Bradlee Rest Home, Boston, MA
Bradley Convalescent Center, Milwaukee, WI
Bradley County Nursing Home, Cleveland, TN
The Bradley Home Infirmary, Meriden, CT
Bradley Manor Nursing Home, Weymouth, MA
Bradley Nursing Home, Jamaica Plain, MA
Bradley Road Nursing Home, Bay Village, OH
Bradley Royale Inc, Bradley, IL
Bradner Village Health Care Center Inc, Marion, IN
Brady Memorial Home, Mitchell, SD
Brae Burn Inc, Bloomfield Hills, MI
Brae Burn Nursing Home, Whitman, MA
Braeburn Nursing Home, Waban, MA
Braemoor Nursing Home Inc, Brockton, MA

Braewood Convalescent Center, South Pasadena, CA

Bragg Residential Care Home Inc, Denver, CO

Brainerd Good Samaritan Center, Brainerd, MN

Braintree Manor Nursing & Retirement Center, Braintree, MA

Brakebill Nursing Homes Inc, Knoxville, TN

Branch Villa Health Care Center, Seattle, WA

Brandel Care Center, Northbrook, IL

Brandel Manor, Turlock, CA

Joseph D Brandenburg Center, Cumberland, MD

Brandon Woods of Dartmouth, Dartmouth, MA

Brandywine Convalescent Home, Wilmington, DE

Brandywine Hall Care Center, West Chester, PA

Brandywine Manor, Greenfield, IN

Brandywine Nursing Home Inc, Briarcliff Manor, NY

Brandywood Nursing Home, Gallatin, TN

Branford Hills Health Care Center, Branford, CT

Braswell's Ivy Retreat, Mentone, CA

Braswells Yucaipa Valley Convalescent Hospital, Yucaipa, CA

Braun's Nursing Home Inc, Evansville, IN

Braxton Health Care Center, Sutton, WV

Brazos Valley Care Home Inc, Knox City, TX

Brazos Valley Geriatric Center, College Station, TX

Brazosview Healthcare Center, Richmond, TX

Breakers Convalescent Home, West Haven, CT

Breese Nursing Home, Breese, IL

Breightonwood, Reisterstown, MD

Bremerton Convalescent Center, Bremerton, WA

Bremond Nursing Center, Bremond, TX

Brendan House Skilled Nursing Facility, Kalispell, MT

Brenham Rest Home Inc, Brenham, TX

Brenn Field Nursing Center, Orrville, OH

Brent Lox Hall Nursing Center, Chesapeake, VA

Brentwood Care Center, Tacoma, WA

Brentwood Convalescent Hospital, Red Bluff, CA

Brentwood Good Samaritan Center, Lemars, IA

Brentwood Hills Nursing Center, Asheville, NC

Brentwood Manor, Yarmouth, ME

Brentwood Manor Care Center, Lubbock, TX

Brentwood North Nursing & Rehabilitation Center Inc, Riverwoods, IL

Brentwood Nursing Home Inc, Brookline, MA

Brentwood Nursing Home Inc, Warwick, RI

Brentwood Nursing & Rehabilitation Center, Burbank, IL

Brentwood Park/Three Rivers Health Care Co, Rome, GA

Brentwood Place One, Dallas, TX

Brentwood Terrace Health Center, Waynesboro, GA

Brethren Care Inc, Ashland, OH

The Brethren Home, New Oxford, PA

Brethren Village, Lancaster, PA

The Brethren's Home, Greenville, OH

Brethren's Home of Indiana Inc, Flora, IN

Brevin Nursing Home Inc, Havre de Grace, MD

Brewer Conv Center, Brewer, ME

Brewster Manor Nursing & Retirement Home, Brewster, MA

Brewster Parke Convalescent Center, Brewster, OH

Brewster Place—The Congregational Home, Topeka, KS

Brian Center—Asheboro, Asheboro, NC

Brian Center Health & Retirement—Asheville, Asheville, NC

Brian Center Health & Retirement—Brevard, Brevard, NC

Brian Center Nursing Care—Catawba County, Hickory, NC

Brian Center Nursing Care—Gastonia Inc, Gastonia, NC

Brian Center Nursing Care—Lenoir, Lenoir, NC

Brian Center Nursing Care—Lexington Inc, Lexington, NC

Brian Center Nursing Care—Mooresville, Mooresville, NC

Brian Center Nursing Care—Raleigh, Raleigh, NC

Brian Center Nursing Care—Statesville Inc, Statesville, NC

Brian Center of Hickory, Hickory, NC

Brian Center of Nursing Care, Austell, GA

Brian Center of Nursing Care—Columbia, Columbia, SC

Briar Crest Nursing Home, Ossining, NY

Briar Glen Healthcare Centre, Rockford, IL

Briar Hill Nursing Home, Middlefield, OH

Briar Hill Rest Home Inc, Florence, MS

Briar Place Nursing Center, Indian Head Park, IL

Briarcliff Haven, Atlanta, GA

Briarcliff Manor, New London, CT

Briarcliff Manor Inc, Topeka, KS

Briarcliff Nursing Home Inc, Alabaster, AL

Briarcliff Pavilion Special Care, North Huntingdon, PA

Briarcliffe Healthcare Facility, Johnston, RI

Briarfield Inc, Sylvania, OH

Briarleaf Nursing & Convalescent Center, Doylestown, PA

Briarstone Manor, Anson, TX

Briarwood Convalescent Center, Needham, MA

Briarwood Manor, Flint, MI

Briarwood Nursing Center Inc, Tucker, GA

Briarwood Nursing & Convalescent Center, Louisville, KY

Briarwood Terrace Nursing Home, Cincinnati, OH

The Briarwood Way, Lakewood, CO

Bridge View Nursing Home, Whitestone, NY

Bridgeport Terrace, Bridgeport, IL

Bridgeton Nursing Centre, Bridgeton, NJ

Bridgeview Convalescent Center, Bridgeview, IL

Bridgewater Home Inc, Bridgewater, VA

Bridgewater Nursing Home, Bridgewater, MA

Bridgeway Convalescent Center, Bridgewater, NJ

Bridgewood Manor Inc, Plainwell, MI

Brier Oak Terrace Convalescent Center, Los Angeles, CA

Briggs Nursing Home, Manning, SC

Brigham Manor Convalescent Home, Newburyport, MA

Bright Glade Convalescent Center, Memphis, TN

Bright Horizon, Saint Joseph, MO

Brighter Day Residence, Mora, MN

Brightmoor Medical Care Home, Griffin, GA

Brighton Care Center, Brighton, CO

Brighton Hall Nursing Center, New Haven, IN

Brighton Place North, Topeka, KS

Brightonian Nursing Home, Rochester, NY

Brightview Care Center Inc, Chicago, IL

Brightview Nursing & Retirement Center Ltd, Avon, CT

Brightwood Nursing Home, Follansbee, WV

Brint Nursing Home, Bolivar, TN

Briody Nursing Home, Lockport, NY

Bristol Extended Care, Bristol, CT

Bristol Health Care Center, Bristol, VA

Bristol Nursing & Convalescent Home, New Bedford, MA

Bristol Nursing Home, Attleboro, MA

Bristol Nursing Home Inc, Bristol, TN

The British Home, Brookfield, IL

Brittany Convalescent Home, Natick, MA

Brittany Farms Health Center, New Britain, CT

Britthaven of Bowling Green, Bowling Green, KY

Britthaven of Clyde, Clyde, NC

Britthaven of Edenton, Edenton, NC

Britthaven of Jacksonville, Jacksonville, NC

Britthaven of Kinston, Kinston, NC

Britthaven of Madison, Madison, NC

Britthaven of Morganton, Morganton, NC

Britthaven of New Bern, New Bern, NC

Britthaven of Onslow, Jacksonville, NC

Britthaven of Outer Banks, Nags Head, NC

Britthaven of Piedmont, Albemarle, NC

Britthaven of Pineville, Pineville, KY

Britthaven of Prospect, Prospect, KY

Britthaven of Snow Hill, Snow Hill, NC

Britthaven of Somerset, Somerset, KY

Britthaven of South Louisville, Louisville, KY

Britthaven of Washington, Washington, NC

Britthaven of Wilkesboro, Wilkesboro, NC

Broad Acres Nursing Home, Wellsboro, PA

Broad Mountain Nursing Home, Frackville, PA

Broad Ripple Nursing Home, Indianapolis, IN

Broadacres, Utica, NY

Broadfield Manor Nursing & Convalescent Home, Madison, OH

Broadlawn Manor, Purcell, OK

Broadlawn Manor Nursing Home and Health Related Facility, Amityville, NY

Broadlawns West, Des Moines, IA

Broadmead, Cockeysville, MD

Broadmoor Health Care Center Inc, Meridian, MS

Broadstreet Nursing Center, Detroit, MI

Broadview Developmental Center, Broadview Heights, OH

Broadview Nursing Home, Parma, OH

Broadwater County Rest Home, Townsend, MT

Broadway Arms Community Living Center, Lewistown, IL

Broadway Care Home, Albert Lea, MN

Broadway Convalescent Home, Methuen, MA

Broadway Convalescent Hospital, San Gabriel, CA

Broadway Lodge, San Antonio, TX

Broadway Manor, Muskogee, OK

Broadway Manor Convalescent Hospital, Glendale, CA

Broadway Nursing Home, Geneva, OH

Broadway Nursing Home Inc, Joliet, IL

Broderick Convalescent Hospital, San Francisco, CA

Broen Memorial Home, Fergus Falls, MN

Broken Arrow Nursing Home Inc, Broken Arrow, OK

Broken Bow Nursing Home, Broken Bow, OK

Brommer Manor, Santa Cruz, CA

Bronte Nursing Home, Bronte, TX

Brook Haven Rest Home, West Brookfield, MA

Brook Hollow Health Care Center, Wallingford, CT

Brook Manor Nursing Center, Brookhaven, MS

Brook View Nursing Home Inc, Maryland Heights, MO

Brook Wood Convalescent Home, Saddle Brook, NJ

Brookbend Rest Home, Weymouth, MA

Brookcrest Nursing Home, Grandville, MI

Brooke Grove Nursing Home, Olney, MD

Brookfield Manor, Hopkinsville, KY

Brookfield Nursing Center, Brookfield, MO

Brookhaven Beach Health Related Facility, Far Rockaway, NY

Brookhaven Care Facility, Kalamazoo, MI

Brookhaven Convalescent Center, Toledo, OH

Brookhaven Group Home, Woodinville, WA

Brookhaven Medical Care Facility, Muskegon, MI

Brookhaven Nursing Care Center, Brookville, OH

Brookhaven Nursing Center, Farmers Branch, TX

Brookhaven Nursing & Convalescent Center, Fort Worth, TX

Brookhaven Nursing Home, Brooklyn, IA

Brookhollow Manor Nursing Home Inc, Grapevine, TX

Brooking Park Geriatric Center Inc, Sedalia, MO

Brookline Manor Convalescent Home, Mifflintown, PA

Brooklyn Center Outreach Home, Brooklyn Center, MN

Brooklyn Rest Home, Brooklyn, CT

Brooklyn United Methodist Church Home, Brooklyn, NY

Brookmont Health Care Center Inc, Effort, PA

Brooks Center Health Care Facility, Marquette, MI

Brookshire Arms Inc, Brookshire, TX

Brooks-Howell Home, Asheville, NC

Brookside Care Center, Kenosha, WI

Brookside Convalescent Hospital, San Mateo, CA

Brookside Extended Care Center, Mason, OH

Brookside Manor, Overbrook, KS

Brookside Manor Inc, Centralia, IL

Brookside Manor Nursing Home, Madill, OK

Brookside Manor Nursing Home, Bountiful, UT

Brookside Manor Nursing Home & Home for the Aged, Whites Creek, TN

Brookside Nursing Home, White River Junction, VT

Brooksville Nursing Manor, Brooksville, FL

Brookview Health Care Facility, West Hartford, CT

Brookview House Inc, Gaffney, SC

Brookview Manor, Indianapolis, IN

Brookview Manor, Brookings, SD

Brookwood Court Nursing Home, Holyoke, MA

Brookwood Nursing Home, Stafford, VA

Broomall Presbyterian Home, Broomall, PA

Brother James Court, Springfield, IL

Brothers of Mercy Nursing & Rehabilitation Center, Clarence, NY

Broughton Hospital, Morganton, NC

Broward Convalescent Home, Fort Lauderdale, FL

Brown County Community Care Center Inc, Nashville, IN

Brown County Health Care Center, Green Bay, WI

Mary J Brown Good Samaritan Center, Luverne, MN

Brown Memorial Convalescent Center, Royston, GA

Brown Memorial Home Inc, Circleville, OH

Brown Nursing Home, Alexander City, AL

Brown Nursing Home, Evart, MI

Brown Rest Home, Madisonville, KY

Brownfield Nursing Home, Brownfield, TX

The Hannah Browning Home, Mount Vernon, OH

Browning House, Durango, CO

Browning Manor Convalescent Hospital, Delano, CA

Browns Nursing Home, Statesboro, GA

Brown's Nursing Home, Lincoln Heights, OH

Brown's Nursing Home Inc, Fredericksburg, TX

Browns Valley Community Nursing Home, Browns Valley, MN

Brownsboro Hills Nursing Home, Louisville, KY

Brownsville Golden Age, Brownsville, PA

Brownsville Good Samaritan Center, Brownsville, TX

Brownwood Care Center, Brownwood, TX

Brownwood Life Care Center Inc, Fort Smith, AR

Brownwood Manor Inc, Van Buren, AR

Brownwood Nursing Home, Moultrie, GA

Bruce Manor Nursing Home, Clearwater, FL

Bruckner Nursing Home, Bronx, NY

Brugman Home, Watertown, SD

Brunswick Conv Center, Brunswick, ME

Brunswick Hospital Center Inc, Amityville, NY

Brunswick Manor, Brunswick, ME

Brunswick Manor Care Center, New Brunswick, NJ

Bry Fern Care Center, Berrien Center, MI

Bryan County Manor, Durant, OK

Bryan Manor, Salem, IL

Bryan Manor Nursing Home, Dallas, TX

Bryan Nursing Care Center, Bryan, OH

Bryant Avenue Residence, South Saint Paul, MN

Lee Alan Bryant Health Care Facilities Inc, Rockville, IN

Mary Bryant Home for the Visually Impaired, Springfield, IL

Bryant Nursing Center, Cochran, GA

Bryant-Butler-Kitchen Nursing Home, Kansas City, KS

Bryanwood Care Center, Amarillo, TX

Bryden Manor, Columbus, OH

Brykirk Extended Care Hospital, Alhambra, CA

Bryn Mawr Nursing Home, Minneapolis, MN

Bryn Mawr Terrace Convalescent, Bryn Mawr, PA

June Bluchanan Primary Care Center, Hindman, KY

Buchanan Nursing Home, Chisholm, MN

Buchanan Nursing Home Inc, Malden, MA

Buchanan Nursing Home of Okeene Inc, Okeene, OK

Buckeye Community Services—Bidwell Home, Bidwell, OH

Buckeye Community Services—Culver Street Home, Logan, OH

Buckeye Community Services—Grandview Avenue Homes, Waverly, OH

Buckeye Community Services—Hunter Street Home, Logan, OH

Buckeye Community Services—South Street Home, Jackson, OH

Buckeye Community Services—Transitional Facility, Gallipolis, OH

Buckeye Community Services—Walnut Street Home, Logan, OH

Buckeye Community Services-Childrens Transitional Facility, The Plains, OH

Buckeye Nursing Home, Clyde, OH

Buckingham Nursing Home, Greenfield, OH

Buckingham Pavilion, Chicago, IL

Buckingham Valley Nursing Home, Buckingham, PA

Buckingham-Smith Memorial Home, Saint Augustine, FL

Buckley Convalescent Home, Hartford, CT

Buckley Nursing & Retirement Home, Holyoke, MA

Buckner Baptist Haven, Houston, TX

Buckner Baptist Trew Retirement Center, Dallas, TX

Buckner Monte Siesta Home, Austin, TX

Buckner Villa Siesta Home, Austin, TX

Bucks County Association of Retarded Citizens, Doylestown, PA

Bucktail Medical Center, Renovo, PA

Buckwell Rest Home, Monson, MA

Budd Terrace Intermediate Care Home, Atlanta, GA

Buena Ventura Convalescent Hospital, Los Angeles, CA

Buena Vista Convalescent Hospital, Anaheim, CA

Buena Vista Home for the Aged, Sedalia, MO

Buena Vista Inc, Colville, WA

Buena Vista Manor, Duarte, CA

Buena Vista Manor, Storm Lake, IA

Buena Vista Nursing Center Inc, Lexington, NC

Bueno's Group Home, Las Animas, CO

Buffalo Lake Nursing Home Inc, Buffalo Lake, MN

Buffalo Nursing Center, Buffalo, TX

Buffalo Valley Lutheran Village, Lewisburg, PA

Buford Manor Nursing Home, Buford, GA

Buhler Sunshine Home Inc, Buhler, KS

Bullock County Hospital & Nursing Home, Union Springs, AL

Buna Nursing Home, Buna, TX

Bunce Care Center, Provo, UT

The Bungalow, Salt Lake City, UT

Burbank Convalescent Hospital, Burbank, CA

Burcham Hills Retirement Center, East Lansing, MI

Ollie Steele Burden Nursing Home, Baton Rouge, LA

Burdick Convalescent Home Inc, Warwick, RI

Bureau of Habilitation Services-Forest Haven, Laurel, MD

Burford Manor, Davis, OK

Burgess Manor Nursing Center, Graham, TX

Burgess Nursing Home, Birmingham, AL

Burgess Square Health Care Centre, Rockford, IL

Burgess Square Healthcare Centre, Westmont, IL

Joe-Anne Burgin Nursing Home, Cuthbert, GA

Burgin Manor, Olney, IL

Burgoyne Rest Home, Boston, MA

Burien Terrace Nursing Center, Seattle, WA

Burleson Nursing Center, Burleson, TX

Burley Care Center, Burley, ID

Burlington Care Center, Burlington, IA

Burlington Convalescent Center, Burlington, VT

Burlington Convalescent Hospital, Los Angeles, CA

Burlington Medical Center—Klein Unit, Burlington, IA

Burlington Woods Convalescent Center, Burlington, NJ

Bur-Mont Nursing Center, Abilene, TX

Bur-Mont Nursing Center, Henrietta, TX

Bur-Mont Nursing Center, Livingston, TX

Bur-Mont Nursing Center, Silsbee, TX

Bur-Mont Nursing Center, Temple, TX

Burncoat Plains Rest Home, Worcester, MA

Burnett General Hospital—LTC, Grantsburg, WI

Burnham Terrace Care Center, Chicago, IL

Burns Manor Nursing Home, Hutchinson, MN

Burns Nursing Home, Burns, OR

Burns Nursing Home Inc, Russellville, AL

Burnside Convalescent Home Inc, East Hartford, CT

Burnside Nursing Home Inc, Marshall, IL

Burr Oak Manor, Austin, MN

Burroughs Home Inc, Bridgeport, CT

Burt Manor Nursing Home, DeSoto, MO

Burt Manor Nursing Home, Sedalia, MO

Burt Sheltered Care Home, Alton, IL

Burton Convalescent Home Corp, Newton, MA

Burton Family Care Home, Denver, CO

Burton Nursing Home, Burlington, WA

Burzenski Nursing Home, Sarasota, FL

Butler County Home, Hamilton, OH

Butler Health Care Center, Butler, IN

Butler Rest Home Inc, Butler, KY

Butler Valley Manor, Drums, PA

Butte Nursing Home, Butte, NE

Butte Park Royal Convalescent Center Inc, Butte, MT

Buttonwood Hospital of Burlington County, New Lisbon, NJ

Buttonwoods Crest Home, Warwick, RI

Byrd Haven Nursing Home, Searcy, AR

Byrnebrook Nursing Home, Toledo, OH

Byrnes Convalescent Center, Cincinnati, OH

Byron Health Center, Fort Wayne, IN

Bywood East Health Care, Minneapolis, MN

C R Center, Springfield, PA

Cabarrus Nursing Center Inc, Concord, NC

Cabot Manor Nursing Home Inc, Cabot, AR

Cabrillo Extended Care Hospital, San Luis Obispo, CA

Cabs Nursing Home Company Inc, Brooklyn, NY

Cadbury Health Care Center, Cherry Hill, NJ

Caddo Nursing Home, Caddo, OK

Cadillac Nursing Home, Detroit, MI

Caguas Regional Skilled Nursing Facility, Caguas, PR

Cal Haven Convalescent Hospital, Glendale, CA

Allen Calder Skilled Nursing Facility—St Lukes Memorial Hospital Center, Utica, NY

Caldsted Foundation Inc, Chattanooga, TN

Caldwell Care Center, Caldwell, ID

Caldwell Health Center at Judson Park, Des Moines, WA

Caldwell Manor Nursing Home, Kansas City, MO

Calera Manor Nursing Home, Calera, OK
Calhoun Care Center, Hardin, IL
Calhoun County Medical Care Facility, Battle Creek, MI
Calhoun County Nursing Home, Calhoun, MS
Calhoun Nursing Home, Edison, GA
California Care Center, California, MO
California Christian Home, Rosemead, CA
California Convalescent Center 1, Los Angeles, CA
California Convalescent Center 2, Los Angeles, CA
California Convalescent Hospital, Long Beach, CA
California Convalescent Hospital, San Francisco, CA
California Convalescent Hospital of La Mesa, La Mesa, CA
California Gardens Nursing Center, Chicago, IL
California Home for the Aged Inc, Fresno, CA
California Nursing & Rehabilitation Center of Palm Springs, Palm Springs, CA
California PEO Home, Alhambra, CA
California PEO Home—San Jose Unit, San Jose, CA
The California-Ventura Convalescent Hospital, Ventura, CA
The Californian—Pasadena Convalescent Hospital, Pasadena, CA
Calistoga Convalescent Hospital, Calistoga, CA
Callaway Good Samaritan Home, Callaway, NE
Callaway Nursing Home, Sulphur, OK
Calumet Homestead, New Holstein, WI
Calvary Fellowship Home Inc, Lancaster, PA
Calvary Manor Nursing Home, Ottawa, OH
Calvert City Convalescent Center, Calvert City, KY
Calvert County Nursing Center Inc, Prince Frederick, MD
Calvert House Corp, Prince Frederick, MD
Calvert Manor Nursing Home Inc, Rising Sun, MD
Calvert Nursing Center, Calvert, TX
Calvin Manor, Des Moines, IA
Camano Shores Nursing Home, Camano Island, WA
Camargo Manor Nursing Home, Cincinnati, OH
Camarillo Convalescent Hospital, Camarillo, CA
Cambridge Convalescent Center, Tampa, FL
Cambridge Court Manor Inc, Charleston, IL
Cambridge Developmental Center, Cambridge, OH
Cambridge Health Care Center, Cambridge, MN
Cambridge Health Care Center, Cambridge, OH
The Cambridge Homes, Cambridge, MA
Cambridge House, Cambridge, MD
Cambridge Manor, Richmond, VA
Cambridge North Inc, Clawson, MI
Cambridge Nursing Center—East, Madison Heights, MI
Cambridge Nursing Center—South, Birmingham, MI
Cambridge Nursing Home, Cambridge, MA
Cambridge Poplar Creek, Hoffman Estate, IL
Cambridge Regional Human Services Center, Cambridge, MN
Cambridge West Nursing Centre, Redford Township, MI
Camden Care Center, Minneapolis, MN
Camden Convalescent Hospital, Campbell, CA
Camden County Health Service Center, Blackwood, NJ
Camden Health Care Center, Camden, ME
Camden Health Care Center, Rockland, ME
Camden Health Care Center, Monett, MO
Camden Health Center, Harrisonville, MO
Camden Nursing Facility, Camden, AL
Camden Nursing Home, Camden, ME
Camellia Care Center, Aurora, CO
Camellia Garden Nursing Home, Pineville, LA

Camellia Garden of Life Care, Thomasville, GA
Camelot Arms Care Center, Youngstown, OH
Camelot Care Center, Logansport, IN
Camelot Care Center, Forest Grove, OR
Camelot Care Intermediate Care Facility, Gainesville, GA
Camelot Group Home, Seattle, WA
Camelot Hall Convalescent Centre, Livonia, MI
Camelot Hall Nursing Home, Arlington, VA
Camelot Hall Nursing Home, Chesapeake, VA
Camelot Hall Nursing Home, Danville, VA
Camelot Hall Nursing Home, Harrisonburg, VA
Camelot Hall Nursing Home, Lynchburg, VA
Camelot Hall Nursing Home, Richmond, VA
Camelot Hall Nursing Home, Salem, VA
Camelot Hall Nursing Home, Virginia Beach, VA
Camelot Manor, Peoria, AZ
Camelot Manor, Streator, IL
Camelot Nursing Home, New London, CT
Camelot Nursing Home, Farmington, MO
Cameo Convalescent Center, Milwaukee, WI
Cameron Manor Inc, Indiana, PA
Cameron Manor Nursing Home, Cameron, MO
Cameron Nursing Home, Cameron, TX
Cameron Villa Rest Home, Austin, TX
Camilia Rose Convalescent Center, Coon Rapids, MN
Camilia Rose Group Home, Coon Rapids, MN
Camilla Hall, Immaculata, PA
Camilla Street Intermediate Care Home, Atlanta, GA
Camlu Care Center of Oak Hills, San Antonio, TX
Camlu Care Center of Woodlawn Hills, San Antonio, TX
Camlu Care Center-Louis Pasteur, San Antonio, TX
Camp Care Inc, Inman, SC
Camp Hill Care Center, Camp Hill, PA
Mary Campbell Center Inc, Wilmington, DE
Campbell's Ingersoll Rest Home, Springfield, MA
Campen's Nursing Home Inc, Norfolk, VA
Camphaven Nursing Home, Inman, SC
Campion Residence & Renewal Center, Weston, MA
Canby Care Center, Canby, OR
Canby Community Health Services, Canby, MN
Candle Light Lodge Retirement Center, Columbia, MO
Candlewood Valley Care Center, New Milford, CT
Caney Nursing Center, Caney, KS
Canistota Good Samaritan Center, Canistota, SD
Cannon Falls Manor Nursing Home, Cannon Falls, MN
Canoga Care Center Inc, Canoga Park, CA
Canon Lodge, Canon City, CO
Cantabridgia Health Care Inc, Cambridge, MA
Canteburg Villa of Fort Worth, Fort Worth, TX
Canterburry Villa of Cisco, Cisco, TX
The Canterbury, Rancho Palos Verdes, CA
Canterbury Care Center, New Lebanon, OH
Canterbury Court Intermediate Care Unit, Atlanta, GA
Canterbury Health Facility, Phenix City, AL
Canterbury Manor, Rochester, IN
Canterbury Manor Nursing Center Inc, Waterloo, IL
Canterbury Place, Valparaiso, IN
Canterbury Place, Pittsburgh, PA
Canterbury Towers, Tampa, FL
Canterbury Villa of Alliance, Alliance, OH
Canterbury Villa of Baird, Baird, TX
Canterbury Villa of Bloomfield, Bloomfield, CT
Canterbury Villa of Centerburg, Centerburg, OH

Canterbury Villa of Danielson Inc, Danielson, CT
Canterbury Villa of Eagle Pass, Eagle Pass, TX
Canterbury Villa of Gatesville, Gatesville, TX
Canterbury Villa of Gorman, Gorman, TX
Canterbury Villa of Hillsboro, Hillsboro, TX
Canterbury Villa of Milan, Milan, OH
Canterbury Villa of Navasota, Navasota, TX
Canterbury Villa of Savoy, Savoy, TX
Canterbury Villa of Seville, Seville, OH
Canterbury Villa of Stephenville, Stephenville, TX
Canterbury Villa of Waterford Inc, Waterford, CT
Canterbury Villa of Willimantic, Willimantic, CT
Canterbury Woods, Pacific Grove, CA
Cantex Convalescent Center (Westwood), Lufkin, TX
Cantex Healthcare Center—Denison, Denison, TX
Canton Christian Home, Canton, OH
Canton Good Samaritan Center, Canton, SD
Canton Health Care Center, Canton, NC
Canton Health Care Center, Canton, OH
Canton Manor, Canton, MS
Canton Nursing Center, Canton, GA
Canton Nursing Center, Canton, TX
Canton Residential Center, Canton, TX
Canyon Hills Manor, Thermapolis, WY
Canyon Manor, Novato, CA
Cape Cod Nursing & Retirement Home, Buzzards Bay, MA
Cape Coral Nursing Pavilion, Cape Coral, FL
Cape End Manor Nursing Home, Provincetown, MA
Cape Girardeau Care Center, Cape Girardeau, MO
Cape Girardeau Nursing Center, Cape Girardeau, MO
Cape May Care Center, Cape May Court House, NJ
Cape Regency Nursing Home, Barnstable, MA
Capeside Cove Good Samaritan Center, Siren, WI
Capital Care Center, Boise, ID
Capital Care Healthcare Facility, Indianapolis, IN
Capital Hall, Frankfort, KY
Capital Health Care Center, Tallahassee, FL
Capital Region Ford Nursing Home, Cohoes, NY
Capitol City Nursing Home, Austin, TX
Capitol Convalescent Center, Columbia, SC
Capitol Health Care Center Inc, Washington, DC
Capitol Hill Healthcare Center, Montgomery, AL
Capitol Manor, Salem, OR
Capitol Nursing Home, Baton Rouge, LA
Capitol Park Care Center, Tumwater, WA
Capitol View Health Care Center, Salem, OR
Capri Nursing Home, Phoenix, AZ
Caravilla, Beloit, WI
Carbon County Health Care Center, Red Lodge, MT
Carbon County Home, Weatherly, PA
Carbon County Memorial Nursing Home, Red Lodge, MT
Carbon County Nursing Home, Price, UT
Carbon Hill Health Care Inc, Carbon Hill, AL
Carbondale Manor, Carbondale, IL
Carbondale Nursing Home Inc, Carbondale, PA
Carci Hall, Chicago, IL
Cardigan Nursing Home, Scituate, MA
Cardinal Manor, South Bend, IN
Cardinal Shehan Center for the Aging, Towson, MD
The Care Center, Baton Rouge, LA
Care Center at Martins Run, Media, PA
Care Center East, Portland, OR
Care Center East, Fond Du Lac, WI
Care Center of Abingdon, Abingdon, IL
Care Center of Iowa Inc, Creston, IA
Care Center of Phillipsburg, Phillipsburg, NJ
Care House, Medina, OH

C.A.R.E., Inc Nursing Center, Brownwood, TX
Care Inn, Ripley, WV
Care Inn Blountville, Blountville, TN
Care Inn—Bolivar, Bolivar, TN
Care Inn—Clinton, Clinton, MS
Care Inn Collierville, Collierville, TN
Care Inn Convalescent Center of LaSalle, La Salle, IL
Care Inn Convalescent Center of Litchfield, Litchfield, IL
Care Inn—Corinth, Corinth, MS
Care Inn—Greenwood, Greenwood, MS
Care Inn—Grenada, Grenada, MS
Care Inn—Holly Springs, Holly Springs, MS
Care Inn—Huntingdon, Huntingdon, TN
Care Inn—Loudon, Loudon, TN
Care Inn—Maryville, Maryville, TN
Care Inn—Memphis, Memphis, TN
Care Inn of Abilene, Abilene, TX
Care Inn of Commerce, Commerce, TX
Care Inn of Conroe Inc, Conroe, TX
Care Inn of Denison, Denison, TX
Care Inn of Edna, Edna, TX
Care Inn of Ganado, Ganado, TX
Care Inn of Gonzales, Gonzales, TX
Care Inn of La Grange, La Grange, TX
Care Inn of Llano, Llano, TX
Care Inn of Mayfield, Mayfield, KY
Care Inn of Plainview, Plainview, TX
Care Inn of Sanger, Sanger, TX
Care Inn of Seguin, Seguin, TX
Care Inn of Shamrock, Shamrock, TX
Care Inn of Voorhees, Marlton, NJ
Care Inn of Waco, Waco, TX
Care Inn—Ripley, Ripley, TN
Care Inn—Rockingham, Rockingham, NC
Care Inn—Rolling Fork, Rolling Fork, MS
Care Inn—West Point, West Point, MS
Care Inn—Yazoo City, Yazoo City, MS
Care Inn-Indianola, Indianola, MS
Care Manor Nursing Center, Stroud, OK
Care Manor Nursing Center, Burkburnett, TX
Care Manor Nursing Center of Tuttle, Tuttle, OK
Care Manor of Farmington, Farmington, CT
Care Manor—Parkway, Wichita Falls, TX
Care Nursing Home, Miami, OK
Care Nursing Home Inc, Oakdale, LA
Care Pavilion of Walnut Park, Philadelphia, PA
Care Villa Nursing Center, Kingfisher, OK
Care Vista, Portland, OR
Care Well Manor Nursing Home, Malden, MA
CareWest-Kingsburg, Kingsburg, CA
CareWest-Murray, Murray, VT
Careage North Health Care Center, Fairbanks, AK
Carehouse Convalescent Center, Santa Ana, CA
Careousel Care Center, McMinnville, OR
Careview Home Inc, Minneapolis, MN
Carewell B & B Nursing Home, Comanche, OK
Carewell Rest Home, New Haven, CT
CareWest Arizona Nursing Center, Santa Monica, CA
CareWest Bayside Nursing & Rehabilitation Center, Kentfield, CA
CareWest Clearfield Nursing & Rehabilitation Center, Clearfield, UT
CareWest Heber Nursing Center, Heber City, UT
CareWest Huntington Valley Nursing Center, Huntington Beach, CA
CareWest La Mariposa Nursing & Rehabilitation Center, Fairfield, CA
CareWest Mt Ogden, Ogden, UT
CareWest—Northbrook Nursing Center, Willits, CA
CareWest Plaza Inc, Portland, OR
CareWest Redlands Nursing Center, Redlands, CA
CareWest Santa Barbara, Santa Barbara, CA
CareWest Weed Nursing Center, Weed, CA
CareWest-Gateway Nursing Center, Hayward, CA

CareWest-Manteca Nursing & Rehabilitation Center, Manteca, CA
CareWest-Pomona Vista Nursing Center, Pomona, CA
CareWest-Salt Lake Nursing & Rehabilitation Center, Salt Lake City, UT
CareWest-Sierra Nursing Center, Roseville, CA
Carey Nursing Home, Carey, OH
Caribou Memorial Nursing Home, Soda Springs, ID
Caribou Nursing Home, Caribou, ME
Carillon House Nursing Home, Huntington, NY
The Carle Arbours, Savoy, IL
Carleton Nursing Home, Wellsboro, PA
Carleton-Willard Retirement & Nursing Center, Bedford, MA
Carlin Park Healthcare Center, Angola, IN
Carlisle Care Center, Carlisle, IA
Carlisle Manor, Franklin, OH
Carlmont Convalescent Hospital, Belmont, CA
Carlsbad Nursing Home, Dry Ridge, KY
Carlton Group Home, Duvall, WA
Carlton House Nursing Center, Chicago, IL
Carlton Nursing Home, Carlton, MN
Carlton Nursing Home, Brooklyn, NY
The Carlyle, Beloit, WI
Carlyle Health Care Corp, South Bend, IN
Carlyle Healthcare Center Inc, Carlyle, IL
Carmel Convalescent Hospital, Carmel, CA
Carmel Hills, Independence, MO
Carmel Home, Owensboro, KY
Carmel Ltd, Boulder, CO
Carmel Manor, Fort Thomas, KY
Carmel Richmond Nursing Home Inc, Staten Island, NY
Carmel Valley Manor, Carmel, CA
Carmen Home, Carmen, OK
Carmen Manor, Chicago, IL
Carmen Nursing Home Inc, Crawfordsville, IN
Carmichael Convalescent Hospital, Carmichael, CA
Carnegie Care Center, Cleveland, OH
Carnegie Gardens Nursing Center, Melbourne, FL
Carnegie Nursing Home, Carnegie, OK
Carol Woods, Chapel Hill, NC
Carolina Care Center of Cherryville, Cherryville, NC
Carolina Village Inc, Hendersonville, NC
Caroline Nursing Home Inc, Denton, MD
Carolton Chronic & Convalescent Hospital Inc, Fairfield, CT
Caromin House—Dodge, Duluth, MN
Caromin House—Tioga, Duluth, MN
Carpenter Care Center Inc, Tunkhannock, PA
Carriage Health Care Center, Nashville, TN
Carriage Hill—Arlington, Arlington, VA
Carriage Hill—Bethesda Inc, Bethesda, MD
Carriage Hill—Silver Spring, Silver Spring, MD
Carriage Inn Convalescent Center, Coldwater, MI
Carriage Inn of Cadiz Inc, Cadiz, OH
Carriage Square Health Care Center, Saint Joseph, MO
Carriage Square Nursing Home, San Antonio, TX
Carriage-by-the-Lake Nursing Center, Bellbrook, OH
Carrier Mills Nursing Home Inc, Carrier Mills, IL
Carrington Health Care LTC, Carrington, ND
Carrizo Springs Nursing Home Inc, Carrizo Springs, TX
Ann Carroll Nursing Home, Lynn, MA
Carroll Convalescent Center, Carrollton, GA
Carroll County Good Samaritan Center, Mount Carroll, IL
Carroll Health Center, Carroll, IA
Carroll Healthcare Center, Carrollton, OH
Carroll Manor, Carroll, IA
Carroll Manor Inc, Hyattsville, MD
Carroll Nursing Home, Oak Grove, LA
Carroll Nursing Home, Carrollton, OH
Carroll's Intermediate Care, El Cajon, CA

Carroll's Intermediate Care—Anza, El Cajon, CA
Carrollton Manor, Carrollton, KY
Carrollton Manor, Carrollton, TX
Carrollton Nursing Center, Carrollton, MO
Carrollton's Resthaven Inc, Carrollton, MO
Carson Convalescent Center, Carson City, NV
Walter P Carter Center—Intensive Behavior Management Program, Baltimore, MD
Carter Hall Nursing Home, Dryden, VA
Carter Nursing Home, Jonesboro, LA
Carter Nursing Home, Seagoville, TX
Carter's Guest Home Inc, Jackson, MS
Carter's Nursing Home, Oberlin, OH
Carthage Area Hospital Skilled Nursing Facility, Carthage, NY
Carthage Health Care Center Inc, Carthage, MS
Carthage Nursing Home, Carthage, AR
Cartie's Health Center, Central Falls, RI
Cartmell Home for Aged, Palestine, TX
Cartwheel Lodge—Gonzales, Gonzales, TX
Cartwheel Lodge—Lockhart, Lockhart, TX
Cartwheel Lodge Nursing Home, Brookhaven, MS
Cartwheel Lodge of Luling, Luling, TX
Caruthersville Nursing Center, Caruthersville, MO
Casa Angelica, Albuquerque, NM
Casa Bonita Convalescent Hospital, San Dimas, CA
Casa Central Center, Chicago, IL
Casa Coloma Health Care Center, Rancho Cordova, CA
Casa De Modesto, Modesto, CA
Casa De Paz, Sioux City, IA
Casa de San Antonio, San Antonio, TX
Casa De Vida, San Luis Obispo, CA
Casa Delmar, Scottsdale, AZ
Casa Dorinda, Montecito, CA
Casa Grande Intermediate Care Facility, Anaheim, CA
Casa Grande Long-Term Care Facility, Tewksbury, MA
Casa Inc, Scarborough, ME
Casa Loma Convalescent Center, Payette, ID
Casa Maria Convalescent Hospital, Fontana, CA
Casa Maria Health Care Centre, Roswell, NM
Casa Olga Intermediate Health Care Facility, Palo Alto, CA
Casa Pacifica Convalescent Hospital, Anaheim, CA
Casa San Miguel, Concord, CA
Casa Serena, San Jose, CA
Casa Serena de Salinas, Salinas, CA
Casa Verdugo Convalescent Lodge, Glendale, CA
Casabello Estate Intermediate Care Facility, Salmon, ID
Cascade Care Center, Caldwell, ID
Cascade Care Center, Grand Rapids, MI
Cascade County Convalescent Nursing Home, Great Falls, MT
Cascade Manor, Eugene, OR
Cascade Terrace Nursing Center, Portland, OR
Cascade Vista Convalescent Center, Redmond, WA
Casey Manor Health Facility I, Mount Vernon, IL
Casey Nursing Home, Piketon, OH
Cashmere Convalescent Center, Cashmere, WA
Casitas Care Center, Granada Hills, CA
Cass County Medical Care Facility, Cassopolis, MI
Cassia Memorial Hospital & Medical Center, Burley, ID
Cassville Nursing Center, Cassville, MO
Castle Acres Nursing Home Inc, Hillsboro, MO
Castle Gardens Nursing Home, Northglenn, CO
Castle Manor Nursing Home, Garland, TX
Castle Nursing Home, Tewksbury, MA
Castle Park Nursing Home, Worcester, MA

Castle Park Professional Care Center, Normandy, MO
Castle Rest Nursing Home, Syracuse, NY
Castle Ridge Care Center & Manor House, Eden Prairie, MN
Castle Rock Care Center, Castle Rock, CO
Castle Shannon Nursing Home, Rockville, IN
Castlehaven Nursing Center, Belleville, IL
Caswell Annex, Goldsboro, NC
Caswell Center, Kinston, NC
Catalpa Manor, Dayton, OH
Catered Manor, Long Beach, CA
Cathcart Health Center, Devon, PA
Cathedral Health & Rehabilitation Center, Jacksonville, FL
Cathedral Village, Philadelphia, PA
Catherine Ellen Convalescent Home, Geneva, OH
Catherine Manor, Newport, RI
Catherine Rest Home, Worcester, MA
Catherine-Windsor Rest Home, Worcester, MA
Catholic Care Center, Wichita, KS
Catholic Memorial Home Inc, Fall River, MA
Caton Park Nursing Home, Brooklyn, NY
Cattaraugus County Home & Infirmary, Machias, NY
Cattaraugus County Public Nursing Home, Olean, NY
Cavallo Convalescent Hospital, Antioch, CA
Cedar I, Austin, MN
Cedar Apartments, Montesano, WA
Cedar County Care Facility, Tipton, IA
Cedar Crest, Montgomery, AL
Cedar Crest Convalescent Center Inc, Roosevelt, UT
Cedar Crest Health Center, Janesville, WI
Cedar Crest Health Center East, Indianapolis, IN
Cedar Crest Manor, Lawton, OK
Cedar Crest Nursing Centre Inc, Cranston, RI
Cedar Crest Training Center, Medicine Lodge, KS
Cedar Crest Training Center at Haven, Haven, KS
Cedar Falls Health Center, Cedar Falls, IA
Cedar Falls Lutheran Home, Cedar Falls, IA
Cedar Glen Nursing Home, Danvers, MA
Cedar Grove Nursing Home, Hillsboro, MO
Cedar Haven, Lebanon, PA
Cedar Hedge Nursing Home, Rouses Point, NY
Cedar Hill Care Center, Zanesville, OH
Cedar Hill Nursing Center, Cedar Hill, TX
Cedar Hill Nursing Home, Athens, GA
Cedar Hills Nursing Center, Jacksonville, FL
Cedar II, Austin, MN
Cedar III, Austin, MN
Cedar IV, Austin, MN
Cedar Knoll Rest Home Inc, Grass Lake, MI
Cedar Lake Home Campus, West Bend, WI
Cedar Lake Lodge, LaGrange, KY
Cedar Lake Nursing Home, Malakoff, TX
Cedar Lane Rehabilitation & Health Care Center, Waterbury, CT
Cedar Lawn Convalescent Center, Abingdon, VA
Cedar Lodge Nursing Home, Center Moriches, NY
Cedar Lodge Nursing Home Inc, Marvell, AR
Cedar Manor, Tipton, IA
Cedar Manor, Baker, OR
Cedar Manor, Cedar City, UT
Cedar Manor Nursing Home, Ossining, NY
Cedar Manor Nursing Home Inc, Windsor, VT
Cedar Pines Health Care Facility, Minneapolis, MN
Cedar Rapids Care Center, Cedar Rapids, IA
Cedar Ridge Inc, Skowhegan, ME
Cedar Springs Nursing Center, Cedar Springs, MI
Cedar Street Home, Helena, MT
Cedar Street Home Inc, Fitchburg, MA
Cedar Vale Manor, Cedar Vale, KS
Cedar View Nursing Center, Wellington, KS
Cedar Wood Care Center, Lawrence, KS
Cedarbrook, Allentown, PA

Cedarbrook Fountain Hill Annex, Bethlehem, PA
Cedarcrest Inc, Westmoreland, NH
Cedarcrest Manor Inc, Washington, MO
Cedarcroft Nursing Home, Valley Park, MO
Cedardale Health Care Facility, Wray, CO
Cedargate, Poplar Bluff, MO
The Cedars, Charlottesville, VA
Cedars Convalescent Hospital, Red Bluff, CA
Cedars Health Care Center, Lakewood, CO
Cedars Health Center, Tupelo, MS
The Cedars Inc, McPherson, KS
The Cedars Intermediate Care Facility, Columbia, MS
Cedars Manor Inc, Checotah, OK
Cedars Nursing Home, Lebanon, TN
Cedars of Lebanon Rest Home, Lebanon, KY
Cedartown Nursing Home, Cedartown, GA
Cedarview Nursing Home, Owatonna, MN
Cedarwood Care Center, Independence, OR
Cedarwood Health Care Center Inc, Colorado Springs, CO
Celebrity Care Center, Des Moines, IA
Celina Manor, Celina, OH
Centenary Heritage Manor, Shreveport, LA
Centennial Health Care Center, Greeley, CO
Centennial Health Care Center, Portland, OR
The Centennial Homestead, Washington, KS
Centennial Spring Health Care Center, Warminster, PA
Center for Personal Development, Ames, IA
Center for the Retarded—Cullen, Houston, TX
Center Green Rest Home, Fairhaven, MA
Center Haven Health Center Inc, Hamilton, OH
Center of Care, Eau Claire, WI
Center of Family Love, Okarche, OK
Center Ridge Nursing Home, North Ridgeville, OH
Center Skilled Nursing Facility, Sacramento, CA
Centerbury Villa—Beaumont, Beaumont, TX
Centerclair Inc, Lexington, NC
Centerville Care Center Inc, Centerville, IA
Centerville Health Care Center, Centerville, TN
Centerville Nursing Home Corp, Centerville, MA
Centinela Park Convalescent Hospital, Inglewood, CA
Central Baptist Home for the Aged, Norridge, IL
Central Care Center, Minneapolis, MN
Central Convalescent, Yakima, WA
Central Dakota Nursing Home, Jamestown, ND
Central Dutchess Nursing Home Inc, Wappingers Falls, NY
Central Gardens, San Francisco, CA
Central Health Care, Le Center, MN
Central Healthcare Center, Indianapolis, IN
Central Island Nursing Home Inc, Plainview, NY
Central Montana Nursing Home, Lewistown, MT
Central New Jersey Jewish Home for the Aged, Somerset, NJ
Central Nursing, Chicago, IL
Central Oklahoma Christian Home, Oklahoma City, OK
Central Oregon Health Care Center, Bend, OR
Central Park Lodge, Broomall, PA
Central Park Lodge—Chestnut Hill, Philadelphia, PA
Central Park Lodge Nursing Center, Auburndale, FL
Central Park Lodge Nursing Home-Whitemarsh, Philadelphia, PA
Central Park Lodge-Tarpon Springs, Tarpon Springs, FL
Central Park Manor Inc, Dallas, TX
Central Piedmont Nursing Center, Burlington, NC
Central Plaza Residential Home, Chicago, IL
Central Point Care Center, Central Point, OR
Central State Hospital, Milledgeville, GA
Central Texas Care Center, Austin, TX

Central Todd County Care Center, Clarissa, MN
Central Utah Rehabilitation & Convalescent Center, Orem, UT
Central Wisconsin Center for the Developmentally Disabled, Madison, WI
Centralia Care Center, Centralia, IL
Centralia Convalescent Center, Centralia, WA
Centralia Convalescent Center Inc, Long Beach, CA
Centralia Fireside House, Centralia, IL
Centralia Friendship House, Centralia, IL
Centre Crest, Bellefonte, PA
Centreville Health Care Center, Centreville, MS
Centuria Care Center, Centuria, WI
Century Care Center Inc, Whiteville, NC
Century Care of Laurinburg, Laurinburg, NC
Century Home Inc, Baltimore, MD
Cerri Painesville Nursing Home, Painesville, OH
Hattie Ide Chaffee Home, East Providence, RI
Chaffey Nursing Home Inc, Superior, WI
Chalet Healthcare, Yakima, WA
Chamberlain Nursing Home, Brookline, MA
Chambers Nursing Home Inc, Carlisle, AR
Sarah Jane E Chambers Geriatric Center, Delphos, OH
Chamor Nursing Center, Tulsa, OK
Champaign Childrens Home, Champaign, IL
Champaign County Nursing Home, Urbana, IL
Champaign County Residential Services Inc Home No 1, Urbana, OH
Champaign Nursing Home, Urbana, OH
Champion Childrens Home, Duluth, MN
Champlain Valley Physicians Hospital Medical Center—Skilled Nursing Facility, Plattsburgh, NY
Chandler Care Center—Bristol, Santa Ana, CA
Chandler Care Center—El Monte, El Monte, CA
Chandler Care Center—Fairfax, Los Angeles, CA
Chandler Care Center—Ramona, El Monte, CA
Chandler Convalescent Hospital, Glendale, CA
Chandler Convalescent Hospital Inc, North Hollywood, CA
Chandler Hall Health Services, Newtown, PA
Chandler Health Care Center, Chandler, AZ
Chandler Hillcrest Manor Inc, Chandler, OK
Chandler Manor Rest Home, Somerville, MA
Changing Seasons Commuity Care Complex, Vidor, TX
Chanhassen Center, Chanhassen, MN
Channing House, Palo Alto, CA
Chaparral House, Berkeley, CA
Chapel Hill Convalescent Home, Randallstown, MD
Chapel Hill Home, Canal Fulton, OH
Chapel Hill Nursing Home, Holyoke, MA
Chapel Manor Nursing & Convalescent Home, Philadelphia, PA
Chapel of Care Nursing Center, Sherman, TX
Chapel View Inc, Hopkins, MN
Chapin Center, Springfield, MA
Chapin Center Skilled Nursing Facility, Springfield, MA
Chapin Home for the Aging, Jamaica, NY
Chaplinwood Nursing Home, Milledgeville, GA
Chapman Convalescent Home, Hazelhurst, GA
Chapman Convalescent Hospital, Riverside, CA
Chapman Harbor Skilled Nursing Center, Garden Grove, CA
Chapman Nursing Home Inc, Alexander City, AL
Chapman Valley Manor, Chapman, KS
Chapparal Nursing Center, Clovis, NM
Char Mund Nursing Home, Orangeville, PA
Chariot Nursing & Convalescent Home, Wilmington, DE
Charis House, Brainerd, MN
Chariton County Rest Home, Keytesville, MO

Chariton Group Home Development Corporation, Chariton, IA

Chariton Manor, Chariton, IA

Chariton Park Care Center, Salisbury, MO

Charity Nursing Facility, Dennison, OH

Charles Cole Memorial Hospital-ECF, Coudersport, PA

Charles County Nursing Home, La Plata, MD

Charles Harwood Memorial Hospital—Skilled Nursing Unit, Christiansted, VI

Charles House Convalescent Home, Boston, MA

Charles Parrish Memorial Nursing Center, Dunn, NC

Charles the First Medical Center, Saint Louis, MO

Charlesgate Manor Convalescent Home Inc, Watertown, MA

Charlesgate Nursing Center, Providence, RI

The Charless Home, Saint Louis, MO

Charleston Health Care Center, Las Vegas, NV

Charleston Manor, Charleston, IL

Charleston Manor, East Prairie, MO

Charlevoix Professional Nursing Home, Saint Charles, MO

Char-Lotte Nursing Home Inc, Rock Creek, OH

Charlton Manor Rest Home, Charlton, MA

Charlwell House Nursing Home, Norwood, MA

Chase County Nursing Center, Cottonwood Falls, KS

Chase Manor Nursing & Convalescent Center, Logansport, IN

Chase Memorial Nursing Home Co Inc, New Berlin, NY

Chastain's Joplin House Nursing Home, Joplin, MO

Chastain's of Buffalo Inc, Buffalo, MO

Chastains of Highland, Highland, IL

Chastain's of Jefferson City, Jefferson City, MO

Chastain's of Lamar Inc, Lamar, MO

Chastain's of Marceline Nursing Home, Marceline, MO

Chastain's of Thayer Inc, Thayer, MO

Chastain's Tradition House Nursing Home, Joplin, MO

Chateau Convalescent Centre, Muncie, IN

Chateau Convalescent Hospital, Stockton, CA

Chateau de Notre Dame, New Orleans, LA

Chateau Gardens, Flint, MI

Chateau Girardeau, Cape Girardeau, MO

Chateau Healthcare Center, Minneapolis, MN

The Chateau Nursing & Rehabilitation Center, Bryn Mawr, PA

Chatham Acres, Chatham, PA

Hugh Chatham Memorial Hospital—SNF, Elkin, NC

Chatham Nursing Home I, Savannah, GA

Chatham Nursing Home II, Savannah, GA

Chatsworth Health Care Center, Chatsworth, GA

Chatsworth Health & Rehabilitation Center, Chatsworth, CA

Chatsworth Park Convalescent Hospital, Chatsworth, CA

Chautauqua Avenue Guest Home 1, Charles City, IA

Chautauqua County Home, Dunkirk, NY

Chautauqua Guest Home 2, Charles City, IA

Chautauqua Guest Home 3, Charles City, IA

Cheatham County Rest Home, Ashland City, TN

Checotah Manor Inc, Checotah, OK

Chehalem Care Center, Newberg, OR

Chelsea Group Home, Duvall, WA

Chelsea Jewish Nursing Home, Chelsea, MA

Chelsea United Methodist Retirement Home, Chelsea, MI

Cheltenham Nursing & Rehabilitation Center, Philadelphia, PA

Cheltenham-York Road Nursing Rehabilitation Center, Philadelphia, PA

Chemung County Health Center—Nurs Facility, Elmira, NY

Chenango Bridge Nursing Home, Binghamton, NY

Chenango Memorial Hospital Inc—Skilled Nursing Facility, Norwich, NY

Cheney Care Center, Cheney, WA

Cheney Golden Age Home Inc, Cheney, KS

Chenita Nursing Home 1, Mansfield, OH

Chenita Nursing Home 2, Mansfield, OH

Cheraw Nursing Home Inc, Cheraw, SC

Cherish Nursing Center, Richmond, IN

Cherokee County Hospital—Long-Term Care Unit, Gaffney, SC

Cherokee County Nursing Home, Centre, AL

Cherokee Lodge Adult Care, Oskaloosa, KS

Cherokee Manor, Cherokee, OK

Cherokee Nursing Home, Calhoun, GA

Cherokee Villa, Cherokee, IA

Cherrelyn Manor Health Care Center, Littleton, CO

Cherry Care Centre Inc, Springfield, MO

Cherry Creek Nursing Center Inc, Aurora, CO

Cherry Creek Village, Wichita, KS

Cherry Hill Manor, Johnston, RI

Cherry Hill Nursing Home, Toledo, OH

Cherry Hills Nursing Home, Englewood, CO

Cherry Hospital—ICF, Goldsboro, NC

Cherry Nursing Home, Montclair, NJ

Cherry Oaks Nursing Center, Graham, TX

Cherry Park Health Care Facility, Englewood, CO

Cherry Ridge Guest Care Center, Bastrop, LA

Cherry Street Annex, Paris, TX

Cherry Street Manor, Paris, TX

Cherry Village, Great Bend, KS

Cherrylee Lodge Sanitarium, El Monte, CA

Cherryvale Medi-Lodge, Cherryvale, KS

Chesaning Nursing Care Center Inc, Chesaning, MI

Cheshire Convalescent Center, Cheshire, CT

Cheshire County Maplewood Nursing Home, Westmoreland, NH

Cheshire Home, Florham Park, NJ

Chestelm Conv Home, Moodus, CT

Chester Care Center, Chester, PA

Chester Care Center, Chester, PA

Chester County Hospital & Nursing Center Inc, Chester, SC

Chester County Nursing Home, Henderson, TN

Chester Manor Rest Home, Cambridge, MA

Chesterfield Manor Inc, Chesterfield, MO

Chesterfields Chronic & Convalescent Hospital, Chester, CT

Chestnut Corner Sheltered Care, Louisville, IL

Chestnut Hill Convalescent Center, Passaic, NJ

Chestnut Knoll Inc, Springfield, MA

Chestor House, Boulder, CO

Chetopa Nursing Home, Chetopa, KS

Chetwynde Convalescent Home, Newton, MA

Chetwynde Nursing Home, Newton, MA

Cheviot Garden Convalescent Hospital, Los Angeles, CA

Chevy Chase Nursing Center, Chicago, IL

Chevy Chase Retirement & Nursing Center, Silver Spring, MD

Cheyenne Convalescent Home, Cheyenne, OK

Cheyenne Lodge Nursing Home, Jamestown, KS

Cheyenne Manor, Cheyenne Wells, CO

Cheyenne Mountain Nursing Center, Colorado Springs, CO

Cheyenne Village Inc, Manitou Springs, CO

Chez Nous—St Anthony Park, Saint Paul, MN

Chicago Ridge Nursing Center, Chicago Ridge, IL

Chickasha Nursing Center Inc, Chickasha, OK

Chico Convalescent Hospital, Chico, CA

Chicopee Municipal Home, Chicopee, MA

Chicopee Rest Home Inc, Chicopee, MA

Chicora Medical Center Inc, Chicora, PA

Childrens Convalescent Hospital, San Diego, CA

Childrens Developmental Center Inc, Abbottstown, PA

Children's Extended Care Center, Groton, MA

Children's Habilitation Center, Harvey, IL

Childress Nursing Center, Childress, TX

Childs Nursing Home, Albany, NY

Mary Chiles Hospital, Mount Sterling, KY

Chilton Village Skilled Care Center, Chilton, WI

Chimney Rock Villa, Bayard, NE

Chinle Nursing Home, Chinle, AZ

Chipeta Drive, Montrose, CO

Chippendale Nursing Home, Kansas City, MO

Chippenham Manor Inc, Richmond, VA

Chippewa County War Memorial Hospital, Sault Sainte Marie, MI

Chippewa Manor Nursing Home, Chippewa Falls, WI

Choctaw County Nursing Home, Ackerman, MS

Chosen Valley Care Center, Chatfield, MN

Chouteau County District Nursing Home, Fort Benton, MT

Chowan Hospital Inc-Skilled Nursing Facility, Edenton, NC

Chowchilla Convalescent Hospital, Chowchilla, CA

Christ the King Manor, Dubois, PA

Christ Villa Nursing Center, Wichita, KS

Christel Manor Nursing Home, Fairborn, OH

Christensen's Nursing Home, Greenville, MI

Christian Anchorage Retirement Home Inc, Marietta, OH

Christian Buehler Memorial Home, Peoria, IL

Christian Care Center, Mesquite, TX

Christian Care Center North, Dallas, TX

Christian Care Nursing Center, Phoenix, AZ

Christian Care of Cincinnati Inc, Cincinnati, OH

Christian City Convalescent Center, Atlanta, GA

Christian Community Home of Hudson, Hudson, WI

Christian Convalescent Home, Muskegon, MI

Christian Health Care Center, Wyckoff, NJ

Christian Health Center, Louisville, KY

Christian Health Center—Corbin, Corbin, KY

Christian Health Center—Hopkinsville, Hopkinsville, KY

Christian Hill Convalescent Home, Lowell, MA

Christian Hill Rest Home, Barre, MA

Christian Home for the Aged, Columbus, OH

Christian Home Inc, Waupun, WI

Christian Homes Inc, Holdrege, NE

The Christian League for the Handicapped, Walworth, WI

Christian Manor Nursing Home, Tracy, MN

Christian Nursing Center, Grand Rapids, MI

Christian Nursing Center, Willmar, MN

Christian Nursing Home Inc, Lincoln, IL

Christian Old Peoples Home, Ferguson, MO

Christian Opportunity Center, Pella, IA

Christian Rest Home, Lynden, WA

Christian Rest Home Association, Grand Rapids, MI

Christian Sheltcenter, Quincy, IL

Christian Union Home, Minneapolis, MN

Christian Villa, Crowley, LA

Christopher East Living Center, Evansville, IN

Christopher—East Nursing Center, Louisville, KY

Christopher House Nursing Home, Wheat Ridge, CO

Christoval Golden Years Nursing Home Inc, Christoval, TX

Christs Home Retirement Center, Warminster, PA

Christus Group Home, Grand Rapids, MN

Christus Group Home, Little Falls, MN

Chrystal's Country Home Inc, Parker City, IN

Chula Vista Nursing Home, Mesa, AZ

Church Home for the Aged, Perry, GA

Church Lane Convalescent Hospital, San Pablo, CA

Church Lane Health Care Center, Broomall, PA

Church of Christ Care Center, Mount Clemens, MI

Church of Christ Home for Aged, Nashville, TN

Church of God Home, Inc, Carlisle, PA

Church of the Brethren Home, Windber, PA

Church Street Manor, Saint Joseph, MO
Churchman Manor, Indianapolis, IN
Churchman Village, Newark, DE
Churchview Health Center Retirement Home, Haverhill, MA
Cicero Children's Center Inc, Cicero, IN
Sheridan Special Care Center, Sheridan, IN
Cimarron Nursing Home, Boise City, OK
Cinnaminson Manor Nursing Center, Cinnaminson, NJ
Cinnamon Hill Manor Inc, Lanagan, MO
Circle Manor Nursing Home, Kensington, MD
Circle Manor Nursing Home, Boston, MA
Cisne Manor Inc, Cisne, IL
Citadel Health Care & Day Health Care, Pueblo, CO
Citadel Health Care Pavilion, Saint Joseph, MO
Citizens Nursing Home of Frederick County, Frederick, MD
Citizens Nursing Home of Harford County, Havre de Grace, MD
Citronelle Convalescent Center, Citronelle, AL
Citrus Nursing Center, Fontana, CA
City Care Center, Anna, IL
City & Country Convalescent Homes Inc, Inkster, MI
City View Nursing Home, Madison, WI
City View Nursing Home Inc, Brookline, MA
Civic Center Nursing Home, Birmingham, AL
CLA—Southwest Manor, Worthington, MN
Clackamas Terrace Convalescent Center, Gladstone, OR
Cla-Clif Home for the Aged, Brinkley, AR
Claiborne County Nursing Home, Tazewell, TN
Claiborne & Hughes Convalescent Center Inc, Franklin, TN
The Clairemont, Eau Claire, WI
Clanton Health Care Center Inc, Clanton, AL
Clapp's Convalescent Nursing Home Inc, Asheboro, NC
Clapp's Nursing Center Inc, Pleasant Garden, NC
Clara Baldwin Stocker Home for Women, West Covina, CA
Clara Barton Terrace Convalescent Home, Flint, MI
Clara Burke Nursing Home, Plymouth Meeting, PA
Clara City Community Nursing Home, Clara City, MN
Clara Doerr-Lindley Hall, Minneapolis, MN
Clare Nursing Home, Clare, MI
Claremont Care Center, Point Pleasant, NJ
Claremont Convalescent Hospital, Berkeley, CA
Claremont Convalescent Hospital, Claremont, CA
Claremore Nursing Home Inc, Claremore, OK
Clarence Johnson Care Center, Greensboro, NC
Clarence Nursing Home, Clarence, IA
Clarence Nursing Home District, Clarence, MO
Clarendon Hill Nursing Home, Somerville, MA
Clarewood House Infirmary, Houston, TX
Claridge House Nursing & Rehabilitation Center, North Miami, FL
Clarion Care Center, Clarion, IA
Clarion Care Center, Clarion, PA
Clark Care Center, Clark, SD
Clark County Health Care Center, Owen, WI
Clark County Nursing Home, Kahoka, MO
Clark Fort Valley Nursing Home, Plains, MT
Clark Institute of Restorative Tech, Battle Ground, WA
Lida Clark Nursing Home, Clarksburg, WV
Clark-Lindsey Village Inc, Urbana, IL
M J Clark Memorial Home, Grand Rapids, MI
Clark Manor, Chicago, IL
Clark Manor Nursing Home, Worcester, MA
Clark Memorial Home, Springfield, OH
Clark Nursing Home, Vergennes, VT
Clark Residential Care Facility, Sterling, CO

The John Clarke Retirement Center, Middletown, RI
Clarkfield Care Center, Clarkfield, MN
Clark's Mountain Nursing Center, Piedmont, MO
Clarks Summit State Hospital—Long-Term Care Facility, Clarks Summit, PA
Clarkson Mountain View Guest Home, Rapid City, SD
Clarkston Care Center, Clarkston, WA
Clarksville Convalescent Home Inc, Clarksville, AR
Clarksville Healthcare Center, Clarksville, IN
Clarksville Manor Nursing Center, Clarksville, TN
Clarksville Nursing Center, Clarksville, TX
Clarview Rest Home, Sligo, PA
Clarytona Manor, Lewistown, IL
Classic Care South, Sandusky, OH
Classic Center, Sandusky, OH
Clatsop Care & Rehabilitation Center, Astoria, OR
Claxton Nursing Home, Claxton, GA
Clay Center Presbyterian Manor, Clay Center, KS
Clay County Health Center Inc, Brazil, IN
Clay County Hospital & Nursing Home, Ashland, AL
Clay County Manor Inc, Celina, TN
Clay County Residence, Hawley, MN
Clay County Residence II, Moorhead, MN
The Clayberg, Cuba, IL
Claystone Manor, Ennis, TX
Clayton House Healthcare, Ballwin, MO
Clayton House Healthcare, Manchester, MO
Clayton-on-the-Green Nursing Center, Ballwin, MO
Clayton Residential Home, Chicago, IL
Claywest House, Saint Charles, MO
Clear Haven Nursing Center, Clearfield, PA
Clear View Convalescent Center, Gardena, CA
Clear View Nursing Care Center, Thomaston, GA
Clear View Sanitarium, Gardena, CA
Clearview Convalescent Center, Columbus, OH
Clearview Home, Clearfield, IA
Clearview Home, Mount Ayr, IA
Clearview Manor, Prairie City, IA
Clearview Manor Convalescent Center, Tacoma, WA
Clearview Nursing Home, Framingham, MA
Clearview Nursing Home, Whitestone, NY
Clearview Nursing Home, Juneau, WI
Clearview Nursing Home Inc, Hagerstown, MD
Clearwater Convalescent Center, Clearwater, FL
Cleaver Memorial Convalescent Center, Longview, TX
Cleburne County Hospital & Nursing Home, Heflin, AL
Clement Manor, Greenfield, WI
Clemson Health Care Center, Clemson, SC
Clepper Convalescent Home, Sharon, PA
Clermont Nursing & Convalescent Center, Milford, OH
Cleveland County Nursing Home, Rison, AR
Cleveland Golden Age Nursing Home, Cleveland, OH
Cleveland Health Care Center, Cleveland, MS
Cleveland Health Care Center, Kansas City, MO
Cleveland Manor Nursing Home Inc, Cleveland, OK
Clewiston Health Care Center, Clewiston, FL
Cliff Gables Nursing Home, Fall River, MA
Cliff Gardens Nursing Home, Dallas, TX
Cliff Haven Nursing Home, Fall River, MA
Cliff Health Care Facility Inc, Waterbury, CT
Cliff Heights Nursing Home, Fall River, MA
Cliff House, Duluth, MN
Cliff House, Englewood Cliffs, NJ
Cliff House Nursing Home Inc, Winthrop, MA
Cliff Lawn Nursing Home, Fall River, MA
Cliff Manor, Spokane, WA
Cliff Manor Inc, Kansas City, MO

Cliff Manor Nursing Home, Fall River, MA
Cliff Towers Nursing Home, Dallas, TX
Cliffside Health Care Center, Key Point, NJ
Cliffside Nursing Home, Flushing, NY
Clifton Care Center Inc, Cincinnati, OH
Clifton Geriatric Center Long-Term Care Facility, Somerset, MA
Clifton House, Minneapolis, MN
Clifton Lutheran Sunset Home, Clifton, TX
Clifton Springs Hospital & Clinic Extended Care, Clifton Springs, NY
Clifton Villa Inc, Cincinnati, OH
Clifty Falls Convalescent Center, Madison, IN
Clinic Convalescent Center, Madisonville, KY
Clinton Aire Nursing Center, Mount Clemens, MI
Clinton Convalescent Center, Clinton, MD
Clinton Country Manor, Clinton, MS
Clinton County Nursing Home & Health Related Facility, Plattsburgh, NY
Clinton Good Samaritan Center, Clinton, MN
Clinton Health Care Center, Clinton, CT
Clinton-Hickman County Hospital—ICF, Clinton, KY
Clinton Home for Aged People, Clinton, MA
Clinton House Inc, Frankfort, IN
Clinton Manor, New Baden, IL
Clinton Manor Inc, Plattsburg, MO
Clinton Manor Nursing Home, Clinton, MA
Clinton Nursing Home, Clinton, IN
Clinton Retirement Village, Clinton, IA
Clinton Village Convalescent Hospital, Oakland, CA
Clintonview Care, Mount Clemens, MI
Clio Convalescent Center Inc, Clio, MI
Clipper Home, Portsmouth, NH
Cloisters of La Jolla Convalescent Hospital, La Jolla, CA
Cloisters of Mission Hills Convalescent Hospital, San Diego, CA
Clove Lakes Nursing Home & Health Related Facility, Staten Island, NY
Clover Manor Inc, Auburn, ME
Clover Rest Home, Columbia, NJ
Clover Rest Nursing Home, Montclair, NJ
Cloverlodge Care Center, Saint Edward, NE
Clovis Convalescent Hospital, Clovis, CA
Clovis Nursing Home, Clovis, CA
Clyatt Memorial Center, Daytona Beach, FL
Clyde Street Home, Florence, SC
Coachella House Inc, Palm Springs, CA
Coaldale State General Hospital, Coaldale, PA
Coalinga Convalescent Center, Coalinga, CA
Coastal Care Center, Texas City, TX
Coastal Center—Live Oak Village, Ladsom, SC
Coastal Healthcare Center, Port Lavaca, TX
Coastal Manor, Yarmouth, ME
Coastview Convalescent Hospital, Long Beach, CA
Cobalt Lodge Convalescent Home, East Hampton, CT
Cobble Hill Nursing Home Inc, Brooklyn, NY
Cobbs Creek Nursing Inc, Philadelphia, PA
Coberly Green Intermediate Care Facility, Oakland, CA
Coburn Charitable Society, Ipswich, MA
Thomas A Coccomo Memorial, Meriden, CT
Cochituate Nursing Home Inc, Wayland, MA
Cochran Family Care Home, Arvada, CO
Cocke County Baptist Convalescent Center, Newport, TN
Coeur d'Alene Convalescent Center, Coeur d'Alene, ID
Coffee Medical Center Nursing Home, Manchester, TN
Coffman Home for the Aging Inc, Hagerstown, MD
Cogburn Health Center Inc, Mobile, AL
Cohasset Knoll Nursing Home, Cohasset, MA
Cohen's Retreat, Savannah, GA
Coit Street Community Residence, Florence, SC
Cojeunaze Nursing Center, Chicago, IL
Cokato Manor Inc, Cokato, MN
Coker Intermediate Care Home, Canton, GA
Martha Coker Convalescent Home, Yazoo City, MS

Cokesbury Village, Hockessin, DE
Colbert Nursing Home Inc, Gresham, OR
Colbert Place, Cedar Rapids, IA
Colby Manor Nursing Home, Everett, WA
Colchester Conv Home, Colchester, CT
Colchester Nursing Center, Colchester, IL
Coldwater Manor Nursing Home, Stratford, TX
Coldwell Nursing Home, Mexico, MO
Coleman Care Center, Coleman, TX
Coleman's Personal Care Home, Jackson, MS
Coler Memorial Hospital—Skilled Nursing Facility, New York, NY
Coles Rest Haven Nursing Home, Guthrie, OK
Colfax General Hospital—Intermediate Care Facility, Springer, NM
Coliseium Park Nursing Home, Hampton, VA
Coliseum Medical Center, New Orleans, LA
College Hill Skilled Nursing Center, Manhattan, KS
College Park Care Center, Texas City, TX
College Park Convalescent Home, College Park, GA
College Park Convalescent Hospital, Menlo Park, CA
College Street Nursing Center, Beaumont, TX
College Vista Convalescent Hospital, Los Angeles, CA
Collier Manor, Highland, KS
Collier's Nursing Home, Ellsworth, ME
Collingswood Nursing Center, Rockville, MD
Collingwood Manor, Chula Vista, CA
Collins Chapel Health Care Center, Memphis, TN
Collins Nursing Home Inc, Pittsburgh, PA
Collins Rest Home Inc, Ashburnham, MA
Collinsville Care Home Inc, Collinsville, TX
Collinsville Manor, Collinsville, OK
Collinsville Nursing Home Inc, Collinsville, AL
Collville Tribal Convalescent Center, Nespelem, WA
Colonial Acres, Rock Falls, IL
Colonial Acres Health Care Center, Golden Valley, MN
Colonial Acres Nursing Home, Lincoln, ME
Colonial Acres Nursing Home, Humboldt, NE
Colonial Acres Nursing Home, Loveland, OH
Colonial Arms Nursing Home, Salem, OR
Colonial Belle Nursing Home, Bellville, TX
Colonial Care Center, Saint Petersburg, FL
Colonial Care Home, Somerset, KY
Colonial Columns Health Care Center, Colorado Springs, CO
Colonial Convalescent Hospital, Bakersfield, CA
Colonial Convalescent Hospital Inc, San Jacinto, CA
Colonial Convalescent & Nursing Home, Nixon, TX
Colonial Gardens Care Center, Tallmadge, OH
Colonial Gardens Nursing Home, Pico Rivera, CA
Colonial Gardens Retirement Center, Boonville, MO
Colonial Hall Manor, Shelbyville, KY
Colonial Hall Nursing Home, Princeton, IL
Colonial Haven, Beemer, NE
Colonial Haven Nursing Home Inc, Granite City, IL
Colonial Health Care Services Inc, Superior, WI
Colonial Heights Convalescent Center, Colonial Heights, VA
Colonial Hill Health Care Center, Johnson City, TN
Colonial Hills Nursing Center, Maryville, TN
Colonial House, Bardstown, KY
Colonial House Living Center, Colby, WI
Colonial House Manor, Waterville, ME
Colonial House of Shepherdsville, Shepherdsville, KY
Colonial Lodge, Independence, KS
Colonial Lodge Nursing Home, McAlester, OK
Colonial Manor, Anita, IA
Colonial Manor, Corning, IA

Colonial Manor, Kingsley, IA
Colonial Manor, LaPorte City, IA
Colonial Manor, Valley, NE
Colonial Manor, Fremont, NH
Colonial Manor, Armour, SD
Colonial Manor, Madison, WI
Colonial Manor—Columbus Junction, Columbus Junction, IA
Colonial Manor Convalescent Hospital, West Covina, CA
Colonial Manor Convalescent Hospital—Extended Care Facility, Long Beach, CA
Colonial Manor Corporation, Middletown, OH
Colonial Manor Guest House, Rayville, LA
Colonial Manor Health Care Center Inc, Loudonville, OH
Colonial Manor Health Care Center Inc II, Loudonville, OH
Colonial Manor I, Hollis, OK
Colonial Manor II, Hollis, OK
Colonial Manor Inc, Danville, IL
Colonial Manor Living Center, La Grange, IL
Colonial Manor Nursing & Care Center, Wheatland, IA
Colonial Manor Nursing & Care Center, Lansing, KS
Colonial Manor Nursing & Care Center, Wathena, KS
Colonial Manor Nursing Center, Fort Worth, TX
Colonial Manor Nursing & Convalescent Center, Cleburne, TX
Colonial Manor Nursing & Convalescent Center, Nephi, UT
Colonial Manor Nursing Home, Bowling Green, KY
Colonial Manor Nursing Home, Lakefield, MN
Colonial Manor Nursing Home, Appleton City, MO
Colonial Manor Nursing Home, Whitefish, MT
Colonial Manor Nursing Home, Youngstown, OH
Colonial Manor Nursing Home, Midwest City, OK
Colonial Manor Nursing Home, Tulsa, OK
Colonial Manor Nursing Home, York, PA
Colonial Manor Nursing Home, New Braunfels, TX
Colonial Manor Nursing Home of Woodward Inc, Woodward, OK
Colonial Manor of Albany, Albany, MO
Colonial Manor of Amana Inc, Amana, IA
Colonial Manor of Avoca, Avoca, IA
Colonial Manor of Balaton, Balaton, MN
Colonial Manor of Chelsea, Chelsea, OK
Colonial Manor of Clarkson, Clarkson, NE
Colonial Manor of Correctionville, Correctionville, IA
Colonial Manor of Custer, Custer, SD
Colonial Manor of Deer Lodge, Deer Lodge, MT
Colonial Manor of Edinburg, Edinburg, TX
Colonial Manor of Elma Inc, Elma, IA
Colonial Manor of Glasgow, Glasgow, MO
Colonial Manor of Groton, Groton, SD
Colonial Manor of Hudson, Hudson, SD
Colonial Manor of Ipswich, Ipswich, SD
Colonial Manor of Jasper Co Inc, Baxter, IA
Colonial Manor of LaMoure, LaMoure, ND
Colonial Manor of Lawrence, Lawrence, KS
Colonial Manor of McAllen, McAllen, TX
Colonial Manor of Odebolt, Odebolt, IA
Colonial Manor of Randolph Inc, Randolph, NE
Colonial Manor of Salem, Salem, SD
Colonial Manor of Tyler, Tyler, TX
Colonial Manor of Wausau, Wausau, WI
Colonial Manor of Zearing, Zearing, IA
Colonial Manor Retirement & Convalescent Home, Glendale, WI
Colonial Nursing Center, Canton, OH
Colonial Nursing Home, Kansas City, MO
Colonial Nursing Home, Rockford, OH
Colonial Nursing Home, Toledo, OH

Colonial Nursing Home, Pauls Valley, OK
Colonial Nursing Home, Cameron, TX
Colonial Nursing Home, San Angelo, TX
Colonial Nursing Home Inc, Nashville, AR
Colonial Nursing Home Inc, Crown Point, IN
Colonial Nursing Home Inc, Marksville, LA
Colonial Nursing Home Inc, Schulenburg, TX
Colonial Nursing & Rehabilitation Center, Weymouth, MA
Colonial Oaks Health Care Center, Marion, IN
Colonial Oaks Nursing Home, Metairie, LA
Colonial Oaks Nursing Home, Cross Plains, TX
Colonial Palms, Pompano Beach, FL
Colonial Palms East Nursing Home, Pompano Beach, FL
Colonial Park Nursing Home, McAlester, OK
Colonial Park Nursing Home, Marshall, TX
Colonial Pines Health Care Center, Oxford, AL
Colonial Plaza Nursing Home Inc, Cushing, OK
Colonial Rest Home, Owingsville, KY
Colonial Rest Home, Haydenville, MA
Colonial Rest Home, Lowell, MA
Colonial Rest Home, Bay City, MI
Colonial Rest Home, Saint Charles, MO
Colonial Retirement Center Inc, Bismarck, MO
Colonial Terrace, Independence, KS
Colonial Terrace Care Center Inc, Pryor, OK
Colonial Terrace Nursing Home, Sebree, KY
Colonial Villa Good Samaritan Center, Alma, NE
Colonial Villa Nursing Home, Silver Spring, MD
Colonial Village, Grandfield, OK
Colonial Vista Convalescent Center, Wenatchee, WA
The Colonnades, Granite City, IL
Colony House Healthcare Nursing Home, Abington, MA
Colony Oaks Care Center, Appleton, WI
Colony Park Care Center, Modesto, CA
Colorado Lutheran Health Care Center, Arvada, CO
Colorado State Veterans Center—Homelake, Homelake, CO
Colorado State Veterans Nursing Home, Florence, CO
Colorow Care Center, Olathe, CO
Colter Village, Glendale, AZ
Colton Villa Nursing Center, Hagerstown, MD
Columbia Basin Nursing Home, The Dalles, OR
Columbia Care Center, Lima, OH
Columbia City Community Care Center, Columbia City, IN
Columbia City Nursing Home, Columbia City, IN
Columbia Convalescent Home, Long Beach, CA
Columbia County Home, Wyocena, WI
Columbia Health Care Center, Columbia, TN
Columbia Health Care Facility, Evansville, IN
Columbia Heights Nursing Home Inc, Columbia, LA
Columbia House Healthcare, Columbia, MO
Columbia Lutheran Home, Seattle, WA
Columbia Manor Care Center, Columbia, MO
Columbia Manor Convalescent Center, Portland, OR
Columbia Regional Nursing Home, Andalusia, AL
Columbia State School, Columbia, LA
Columbia View Nursing Home, Cathlamet, WA
Columbine Care Center, Fort Collins, CO
Columbine Manor, Salida, CO
Columbine Manor Inc, Wheat Ridge, CO
Columbus Care Center, Columbus, WI
Columbus Colony for the Elderly Care Inc, Westerville, OH
Columbus Convalescent Center, Columbus, IN
Columbus Convalescent Center, Columbus, TX

Columbus Developmental Center, Columbus, OH
Columbus Intermediate Care Home, Columbus, GA
Columbus Manor, Columbus, NE
Columbus Manor Residential Care Home, Chicago, IL
Columbus Nursing Home, Columbus, IN
Columbus Nursing Home, Boston, MA
Columbus Nursing Homes Inc, Columbus, OH
Colvin Nursing Home, Newton Falls, OH
Colwich Health Center, Colwich, KS
Comanche View Nursing Home, Fort Stockton, TX
Combined Rehabilitation Services Inc, Philadelphia, PA
Comer Health Care Inc, Comer, GA
J W Comer Nursing Home, Carlisle, AR
Comforcare Care Center, Austin, MN
Comfort Harbor Home, Milan, IL
Comfort Retirement & Nursing Home Inc, Lafayette, IN
Commander Nursing Home, Florence, SC
Commodore Inn Inc, Chicago, IL
Commonwealth Care Center, Des Moines, IA
Commonwealth Health Care, Martinsville, VA
Commonwealth Healthcare Center, Saint Paul, MN
CommuniCare, Boise, ID
Community Care Center, Duarte, CA
Community Care Center, Hondo, TX
Community Care Center Inc, Chicago, IL
Community Care Center Inc, Stuart, IA
Community Care Center of Cuba, Cuba, MO
Community Care Center of Dale, Dale, IN
Community Care Center of Festus, Festus, MO
Community Care Center of Lemay, Saint Louis, MO
Community Care Center of North Vernon, North Vernon, IN
Community Center, De Kalb, IL
Community Comfort Cottage, Rayville, LA
Community Convalescent Center, Riverside, CA
Community Convalescent Center, Gainesville, FL
Community Convalescent Center, Plant City, FL
Community Convalescent Center of Sunland Tujunga, Tujunga, CA
Community Convalescent Center of Yucaipa/ Calimesa, Yucaipa, CA
Community Convalescent Hospital, Lynwood, CA
Community Convalescent Hospital of Glendora, Glendora, CA
Community Convalescent Hospital of La Mesa, La Mesa, CA
Community Convalescent Hospital of San Gabriel, San Gabriel, CA
Community Foundation for Human Development, Sellersville, PA
Community General Hospital of Sullivan County, Harris, NY
Community Health Center, Wakita, OK
Community Healthcare of Danville, Danville, IN
Community Healthcare of Indianapolis, Indianapolis, IN
Community Hospital & Health Care Center, Saint Peter, MN
Community Hospital & Health Center, Sioux Center, IA
Community Hospital & Nursing Home, Poplar, MT
Community Hospital Skilled Nursing Facility, Stamford, NY
Community Intermediate Care Facility, Sumter, SC
Community Living, Coon Rapids, MN
Community Living, Victoria, MN
Community Memorial Home, Osakis, MN
Community Memorial Hospital, Hartley, IA
Community Memorial Hospital, Winona, MN
Community Memorial Hospital-Extended Care Facility, Cheboygan, MI

Community Memorial Hospital—W S Hundley Annex, South Hill, VA
Community Memorial Hospital Inc—Nurs Home Unit, Hamilton, NY
Community Memorial Hospital Long-Term Care Unit, Postville, IA
Community Memorial Nursing Home, Lisbon, ND
Community Multicare Center, Fairfield, OH
Community Nursing Center, Marion, OH
Community Nursing Home, Jackson, MS
Community Nursing Home, El Dorado Springs, MO
Community Nursing Home, Bowling Green, OH
Community Nursing Home, Wilburton, OK
Community Nursing Home, Stephenville, TX
Community Nursing Home Inc, Clarksville, IA
Community Nursing Home of Anaconda, Anaconda, MT
Community Nursing & Rehabilitation Facility, Missoula, MT
Community Services Inc, Leola, PA
Community Services Inc-Main, Landisville, PA
Community Services Inc-Stanley, Landisville, PA
Community Skilled Nursing Centre, Warren, OH
Compere's Nursing Home Inc, Jackson, MS
Comprehensive Systems Inc, Charles City, IA
Compton Convalescent Hospital, Compton, CA
Compton's Oak Grove Lodge, Mountain View, AR
Comstock Nursing Home, Milwaukee, WI
Con Lea Nursing Home, Geneva, OH
Concerned Services Inc, Stanberry, MO
Concho Nursing Center, Eden, TX
Concord Care Manor, Garner, IA
Concord Extended Care, Oak Lawn, IL
Concord Manor Nursing Home, Cleveland, OH
Concord Nursing Center, Concord, NC
Concord Nursing Home Inc, Brooklyn, NY
Concord Villa Convalescent, Concordville, PA
Concordia Care Center, Bella Vista, AR
Concordia Manor, Saint Petersburg, FL
Concordia Nursing Center, Concordia, KS
Concordia Parish Rest Home, Ferriday, LA
Concourse Nursing Home, Bronx, NY
Condon Nursing Home, Condon, OR
Conestoga View, Lancaster, PA
Conesus Lake Nursing Home, Livonia, NY
Congregational Home Inc, Brookfield, WI
Congress Care Center, Chicago, IL
Congress Convalescent Hospital, Pasadena, CA
Conner Nursing Home, Glenwood, GA
Conner-Williams, Ridley Park, PA
Connersville Nursing Home, Connersville, IN
Conser House, Overland Park, KS
Consolata Home, New Iberia, LA
Consolation Nursing Home Inc, West Islip, NY
Contemporary Care Inc, Bluefield, WV
Continana Convalescent Hospital, National City, CA
Continana Convalescent Hospital, Santa Maria, CA
Continental Care Center Inc, Chicago, IL
Continental Convalescent Center, Indianapolis, IN
Continental Manor, Abbotsford, WI
Continental Manor Nursing Center, Randolph, WI
Continental Manor Nursing Home, Wisconsin Dells, WI
Continental Manor Nursing & Rehabilitation Center, Blanchester, OH
Continental Manor of Dwight, Dwight, IL
Continental Manor of Newman, Newman, IL
Conv Care of Enfield Inc, Enfield, NC
Conv Center of Sanford Inc, Sanford, NC
Conva-Rest North Gate—Warren Hall, Hattiesburg, MS
Conva-Rest of Newton Inc, Newton, MS

Conv-A-Center, Neptune, NJ
Convalescent Care, Canton, OH
Convalescent Care Center, Los Angeles, CA
Convalescent Care Center, Saint Petersburg, FL
Convalescent Care Center of Mattoon, Mattoon, IL
Convalescent Care, Inc, Richmond, VA
The Convalescent Center, Dallas, TX
Convalescent Center 2, East Liverpool, OH
Convalescent Center Inc, Tulsa, OK
Convalescent Center Mission Street Inc, San Francisco, CA
Convalescent Center of Honolulu, Honolulu, HI
Convalescent Center of Lee County Inc, Sanford, NC
Convalescent Center of Norwich Inc, Norwich, CT
The Convalescent Center of Oklahoma City, Oklahoma City, OK
Convalescent Center of Reseda, Reseda, CA
Convalescent Center of Shuttuck, Shattuck, OK
Convalescent Center of the Palm Beaches, West Palm Beach, FL
Convalescent Home for Children, Johnston City, IA
Convalescent Hospital Casa Descanso, Los Angeles, CA
Convalescent Hospital University Branch, Menlo Park, CA
Conva-Rest of Hattiesburg, Hattiesburg, MS
Conva-Rest of Petal, Petal, MS
Convention Street Nursing Center, Baton Rouge, LA
Convoy Care Center, Convoy, OH
Conway Convalescent Center, Conway, AR
Conway Human Development Center, Conway, AR
Conway Nursing Center Inc, Conway, SC
Cook Community Hospital, Cook, MN
Cook County Northshore Hospital—Care & Nursing Center, Grand Marais, MN
Cookeville Health Care Center Inc, Cookeville, TN
Cookeville Manor Nursing Home, Cookeville, TN
Cook-Willow Conv Hospital Inc, Plymouth, CT
G B Cooley Hospital for Retarded Citizens, West Monroe, LA
The Coolidge Center, Palmer, NE
Coolidge Street Rest Home, Brookline, MA
Coon Memorial Home, Dalhart, TX
Cooney Convalescent Home, Helena, MT
Cooper Community Care Center, Bluffton, IN
Cooper County Rest Haven Nursing Home, Boonville, MO
Cooper Hall Nursing Center, Mount Pleasant, SC
Cooper Nursing Home Inc, Tallmadge, OH
Cooper River Convalescent Center, Pennsauken, NJ
Coos Bay Care Center, Coos Bay, OR
Coos County Nursing Home, Berlin, NH
Coos County Nursing Hospital, West Stewartstown, NH
Coosa Valley Healthcare Inc, Glencoe, AL
Coplin Manor Convalescent Home, Detroit, MI
Rosa Coplon Jewish Home & Infirmary, Buffalo, NY
Copper Queen Community Hospital, Bisbee, AZ
Coquille Care Center, Coquille, OR
Coral Gables Convalescent Home, Miami, FL
Corbin Convalescent Hospital, Reseda, CA
Cordell Christian Home, Cordell, OK
Cordelleras Center, Redwood City, CA
Cordova Community Hospital, Cordova, AK
Cordova Health Care Center, Cordova, AL
Cordova Residential Care, Pueblo, CO
Corey Hill Nursing Home, Boston, MA
Cori Manor Nursing Home, Fenton, MO
The Corinthian Nursing Facility, Kenton, OH
Cormon Health Care, Canton, OH

Cornelia Nixon Davis Health Care Center, Wilmington, NC
Cornell Area Care Center Inc, Cornell, WI
Cornell Hall Convalescent Center, Union, NJ
Corner House Nursing Inc, Meriden, CT
Cornerstone Services Inc CLF, Joliet, IL
Corning Hospital—Founders Pavilion, Corning, NY
Corning Nursing Home, Corning, AR
Cornwall Manor of the United Methodist Church, Cornwall, PA
Corona Gables Retirement Home & Convalescent Hospital, Corona, CA
Coronado Nursing Center, Pampa, TX
Coronado Nursing Center Inc, El Paso, TX
Coronado Sanitarium, Los Angeles, CA
Corpus Christi Nursing Center, Corpus Christi, TX
Lucy Corr Nursing Home, Chesterfield, VA
Corry Manor Nursing Home, Corry, PA
Corsicana Nursing Home, Corsicana, TX
Cortland Nursing Home, Cortland, NY
Cortland Quality Care Nursing Center, Cortland, OH
Cortlandt Nursing Care Center Inc, Peekskill, NY
Corvallis Care Center, Corvallis, OR
Corvallis Manor, Corvallis, OR
Corydon Care Center, Corydon, IA
Corydon Nursing Home, Corydon, IN
Cosada Villa Nursing Center, Mesa, AZ
Coshocton County Home, Coshocton, OH
Coshocton County Memorial Hospital, Coshocton, OH
Coshocton Health Care Center, Coshocton, OH
Cosmos Healthcare Center, Cosmos, MN
Costigan Family Care Home, Denver, CO
Cotillion Ridge Nursing Center, Robinson, IL
Cottage-Belmont Nursing Center Inc, Harper Woods, MI
Cottage Grove Hospital Skilled Nursing Facility, Cottage Grove, OR
Cottage Grove Nursing Home, Jackson, MS
Cottage Hill Nursing Home, Pleasant Grove, AL
Cottage Manor Nursing Home, Chelsea, MA
Cottage Park Place, Sacramento, CA
The Cottage Rest Home, New Bedford, MA
Cottesmore Nursing Home Inc, Gig Harbor, WA
Cottingham Retirement Community, Sharonville, OH
Cottle County Nursing Home, Paducah, TX
Cotton's Nursing Home, Lawton, OK
Cottonwood Care Center, Gardnerville, NV
Cottonwood Care Center, Wichita Falls, TX
Cottonwood Manor Nursing Home, Yukon, OK
Coulee Community Hospital Nursing Home, Grand Coulee, WA
Council Bluffs Care Center, Council Bluffs, IA
Country Care Convalescent Hospital, Atascadero, CA
Country Care Manor Inc, Effingham, IL
Country Club Center, Dover, OH
Country Club Center II, Mount Vernon, OH
Country Club Convalescent Hospital Inc, Santa Ana, CA
Country Club Home, Council Grove, KS
Country Club Manor, Amarillo, TX
Country Club Retirement Center, Ashtabula, OH
Country Court, Mount Vernon, OH
Country Estate, Westlake, OH
Country Gardens Nursing Home, Swansea, MA
Country Haven Adult Care Center, Paola, KS
Country Haven Corp, Corning, IA
Country Haven Nursing Home, Norton, MA
Country Health Inc, Gifford, IL
Country House, Pomona, CA
The Country House, Independence, MO
Country Inn Care Center, Van, TX
Country Inn Nursing Center Inc, Benton, AR
Country Lawn Nursing Home, Navarre, OH
Country Living Residential Care, Webb City, MO

Country Manor, Louisville, IL
Country Manor Convalescent Home, Newburyport, MA
Country Manor Convalescent Hospital, San Fernando, CA
Country Manor Health Care Center, Prospect, CT
Country Manor Nursing Home, Coopers Mills, ME
Country Manor Nursing Home, Sartell, MN
Country Manor Nursing Home, Toms River, NJ
Country Manor of Kenton Inc, Kenton, OH
Country Manor of Todd County, Elkton, KY
Country Meadows, Ogden, UT
Country Meadows Rest Haven, Providence, KY
Country Rest Home, Greenwood, DE
Country Rest Home, Dartmouth, MA
Country Side Estates, Cherokee, IA
Country Side Manor, Vandalia, MO
Country Trace Healthcare Center, Indianapolis, IN
Country Valley Home, Saint James, MO
Country View Care Center, Longmont, CO
Country View Care Center, Weld County, CO
Country View Convalescent Hospital, Fresno, CA
Country View Estates, Seneca, KS
Country View Manor Inc, Sibley, IA
Country View Nursing Home, Billerica, MA
Country Villa South Convalescent Center, Los Angeles, CA
Country Villa Westwood, Los Angeles, CA
Country Villa Wilshire, Los Angeles, CA
Country Village Health Care Center, Lancaster, NH
Country Way Retirement Care Center, Keene, NH
Countryside Continuing Care Center, Fremont, OH
Countryside Convalescent Home, Mercer, PA
Countryside Estates, Iola, KS
Countryside Estates Inc, Warner, OK
Countryside Health Center, Buchanan, GA
Countryside Health Center, Topeka, KS
Countryside Healthcare Center, Aurora, IL
Countryside Healthcare Center, Lebanon, IN
Countryside Home, Madison, NE
Countryside Home, Jefferson, WI
Countryside Intermediate Care Facility, Woodland, CA
Countryside Manor, Bristol, CT
Countryside Manor, Elgin, IL
Countryside Manor, Stokesdale, NC
Countryside Nursing Home, South Haven, MI
Countryside Nursing Home Inc, Framingham, MA
Countryside Place of Knox, Knox, IN
Countryside Place of LaPorte, LaPorte, IN
Countryside Place of Mishawaka, Mishawaka, IN
Countryside Plaza, Dolton, IL
Countryside Rehabilitation, Kirksville, MO
Countryside Retirement Home, Sioux City, IA
County Manor Nursing Home, Tenafly, NJ
Courage Residence, Golden Valley, MN
Court House Manor, Washington Court House, OH
Court Manor, Ashland, WI
Courthouse Convalescent Center, Cape May Court House, NJ
Courtland Gardens Health Care, Stamford, CT
Courtland Manor Nursing & Conv Home, Dover, DE
Courtyard Convalescent Center, Houston, TX
The Courville at Nashua, Nashua, NH
Cove Manor Conv Center Inc, New Haven, CT
Covenant Health Care Center Inc, Batavia, IL
Covenant Home, Chicago, IL
Covenant Home, New Orleans, LA
Covenant House—Jewish Home for Aged, Dayton, OH
Covenant Village, Gastonia, NC
Coventry Hall Nursing Home, Spencer, MA
Coventry Health Center, Coventry, RI

Coventry Manor Nursing Home Inc, Pottstown, PA
Coventry Village, Indianapolis, IN
Covina Convalescent Center, Covina, CA
Covington Community Care Center, Covington, OH
Covington County Nursing Center, Collins, MS
Covington Heights Health Care Center, Sioux Falls, SD
Covington Ladies Home, Covington, KY
Covington Manor Health Care Center, Covington, IN
Covington Manor Inc, Opp, AL
Covington Manor Inc, Covington, TN
Covington Manor Intermediate Care Home, Covington, GA
Covington Manor Nursing Center, Fort Wayne, IN
Covingtons Convalescent Center Inc, Hopkinsville, KY
Coweta Manor, Coweta, OK
Cowlitz Convalescent Center, Longview, WA
Cox Convalescent Center, Jacksboro, TX
Cozy Corner Nursing Home Inc, Sunderland, MA
Cozy Inn Nursing Home, Rumford, ME
Craft Care Center, Panora, IA
Craighead Nursing Center, Jonesboro, AR
Craigmont Care Center, Des Moines, IA
Cra-Mar Nursing Home Inc, Cranston, RI
Cranbrook Nursing Home, Detroit, MI
Crandall Medical Center, Sebring, OH
Crandon Health Care Center Inc, Crandon, WI
Crane Retirement Home Inc, Cordele, GA
Cranford Hall Nursing Home, Cranford, NJ
Cranford Health & Extended Care Center, Cranford, NJ
Crawford Convalescent Center Inc, Dayton, OH
Crawford County Conv Center, Robinson, IL
Crawford County Home, Smith Institute, Saegertown, PA
Crawford House Convalescent Home, Fall River, MA
Kathy Crawford Nursing Center, Atlanta, GA
Crawford Nursing Home Inc, Jackson, MS
Crawford Retreat Inc, Baltimore, MD
Crawford's Boarding Home, Ironton, MO
Crawford's Convalescent Home, Haleiwa, HI
Creal Springs Nursing Home, Creal Springs, IL
Creekside Convalescent Hospital, Santa Rosa, CA
Creekside Terrace Intermediate Care Facility Inc, Hayward, CA
Creighton Care Centre, Creighton, NE
Crenshaw Nursing Home, Los Angeles, CA
Crescent Bay Convalescent Hospital, Santa Monica, CA
Crescent Care Center, Crescent, OK
Crescent City Convalescent Hospital, Crescent City, CA
Crescent Convalescent Center, Yakima, WA
Crescent Farm Nursing & Conv Home, Dover, DE
Crescent Hill Nursing Center, Springfield, MA
Crescent Manor Nursing Home, Greenfield, IN
Crescent Manor Nursing Home, Bennington, VT
Crescent Manor Rest Home, Grafton, MA
Cresco Care Center Inc, Cresco, IA
Crest Group Home, Des Moines, IA
Crest Group Home, Ottumwa, IA
Crest Hall Health Related Facility, Middle Island, NY
Crest Haven Nursing Home, Cape May Court House, NJ
Crest Haven Rest Home, Plainfield, CT
Crest Home of Albert Lea, Albert Lea, MN
Crest Knoll Convalescent Hospital, Long Beach, CA
Crest Manor Nursing Center, Lake Worth, FL
Crest Manor Nursing Home, Fairport, NY
Crest Nursing Home Inc, Butte, MT

Crest View Lutheran Home, Columbia Heights, MN
Crest View Manor, Chadron, NE
Crest View Manor Inc, Houlton, ME
Cresta Loma Convalescent & Guest Home, Lemon Grove, CA
Crestfield Convalescent Home, Manchester, CT
Cresthaven Childrens Center, Austin, TX
Cresthaven Childrens Center, San Antonio, TX
Cresthaven Inc, Santa Cruz, CA
Cresthaven Nursing Center, Austin, TX
Cresthaven Nursing Home, Kansas City, MO
Cresthaven Nursing Residence, Groves, TX
Crestline Nursing Home, Crestline, OH
Crestmont Medical Care Facility, Fenton, MI
Crestmont Nursing Home North Inc, Lakewood, OH
Creston Manor Nursing Home, Creston, IA
Crestpark Inn of Forrest City, Forrest City, AR
Crestpark Inn of Helena—Intermediate Care Facility, Helena, AR
Crestpark Inn of Helena Skilled Nursing Facility, Helena, AR
Crestpark Inn of Marianna, Marianna, AR
Crestpark Inn of Stuttgart Inc, Stuttgart, AR
Crestpark of Wynne, Skilled, Wynne, AR
Crestridge Inc, Maquoketa, IA
Crestview Acres, Marion, IA
Crestview Care Center, West Branch, IA
Crestview Care Center, Milford, NE
Crestview Care Center, Astoria, OR
Crestview Convalescent, Portland, OR
Crestview Convalescent Care Center, Provo, UT
Crestview Convalescent Center, Vincennes, IN
Crestview Convalescent Center, Moses Lake, WA
Crestview Convalescent Hospital, Petaluma, CA
Crestview Convalescent Hospital, Rialto, CA
Crestview Convalescent Lodge, Phoenix, AZ
Crestview Health Care Center, Shelbyville, KY
Crestview Health Care Facility, Indianapolis, IN
Crestview Healthcare, Ava, MO
Crestview Home, Thief River Falls, MN
Crestview Home Inc, Bethany, MO
Crestview Lodge, Arma, KS
Crestview Manor, Haleyville, AL
Crestview Manor, Seneca, KS
Crestview Manor Convalescent Center & Apartments, Webster City, IA
Crestview Manor Inc, Evansville, MN
Crestview Manor Nursing Center, Belton, TX
Crestview Manor Nursing Home, Lynn, MA
Crestview Manor Nursing Home I, Lancaster, OH
Crestview Manor Nursing Home II, Lancaster, OH
Crestview Manor Retirement & Convalescent Center, Waco, TX
Crestview Methodist Retirement Community, Bryan, TX
Crestview North Nursing & Rehabilitation Center, Langhorne, PA
Crestview Nursing Center, Clinton, IL
Crestview Nursing & Convalescent Home, Crestview, FL
Crestview Nursing Home, Atlanta, GA
Crestview Nursing Home, Ottawa, KS
Crestview Nursing Home, Quincy, MA
Crestview Nursing Home, Medina, OH
Crestview Nursing Home, Brownsville, TN
Crestview Nursing Home Inc, Nashville, TN
Crestview Nursing Home II, Dayton, OH
Crestview Parke Nursing Home, Cincinnati, OH
Crestview Personal Care Home, Richmond, KY
Crestview Personal Care Home, Somerset, KY
Crestview Personal Care Home, Somerset, KY
Crestwood Care Center, Shelby, OH
Crestwood Care Center, Ogden, UT
Crestwood Care Center Inc, Fairfield, OH

Crestwood Care Center—Mansfield, Mansfield, OH
Crestwood Convalescent Center, Port Angeles, WA
Crestwood Convalescent Home, Fall River, MA
Crestwood Convalescent Hospital, Chico, CA
Crestwood Convalescent Hospital, Pasadena, CA
Crestwood Convalescent Hospital, Redding, CA
Crestwood Convalescent Hospital, Stockton, CA
Crestwood Convalescent Hospital—Sylmar, Sylmar, CA
Crestwood Health Care Center—Milford, Milford, NH
Crestwood Manor, Bakersfield, CA
Crestwood Manor, Eureka, CA
Crestwood Manor, Modesto, CA
Crestwood Manor, Sacramento, CA
Crestwood Manor, San Jose, CA
Crestwood Manor, Stockton, CA
Crestwood Manor, Vallejo, CA
Crestwood Manor—Carmichael, Carmichael, CA
Crestwood Nursing & Convalescent Home Inc, Warren, RI
Crestwood Nursing Home, Valdosta, GA
Crestwood Nursing Home, Whippany, NJ
Crestwood Nursing Home, Manchester, TN
Crestwood Rehabilitation & Convalescent Hospital, Fremont, CA
Crestwood Terrace, Midlothian, IL
Crestwood Terrace Intermediate Care Nursing Home, Crestwood, IL
Creswell Care Center, Creswell, OR
Creswell Convalescent Center, Rome, GA
Crete Manor, Crete, NE
Cridersville Nursing Home, Cridersville, OH
Crisp County Medical Nursing Center, Cordele, GA
Crista Senior Community, Seattle, WA
Crites Nursing Home, Lancaster, OH
Crittenden County Convalescence Center, Marion, KY
Crocker Family Care Home, Commerce City, CO
Crockett County Care Center, Ozona, TX
Crockett County Nursing Home, Alamo, TN
Crofton Convalescent Center, Crofton, MD
Croixdale Residence, Bayport, MN
Cromwell Crest Convalescent Home Inc, Cromwell, CT
Crook County Nursing Home, Prineville, OR
Crookston Group Home 1, Crookston, MN
Crookston Group Home 2, Crookston, MN
Crookston Group Home 3, Crookston, MN
Crosby Good Samaritan Center, Crosby, ND
Crosbyton Care Center, Crosbyton, TX
Cross Country Care Center, Brownwood, TX
Cross Roads Intermediate Care Facility, Cleveland, GA
Crossgate Manor Inc, Brandon, MS
Crossroads Development Center, Fort Worth, TX
Crossville Nursing Home Inc, Crossville, AL
Crotinger Nursing Home, Union City, OH
Crowell Memorial Home, Blair, NE
Crowell Nursing Center, Crowell, TX
Crowley County Nursing Center, Ordway, CO
Crowley Town & Country Nursing Center Inc, Crowley, LA
Crown Manor Living Center, Zion, IL
Crown Nursing Home, Saint Petersburg Beach, FL
Crown Nursing Home, Brooklyn, NY
Crystal Care Center, Napa, CA
Crystal Care Center, Crystal, MN
Crystal City Nursing Center, Arlington, VA
Crystal Hill Nursing Home Inc, Dallas, TX
Crystal Lake Health Care Center, Robbinsdale, MN
Crystal Manor, Crystal Falls, MI
Crystal Pines Health Care Center, Crystal Lake, IL
Crystal River Geriatric Center, Crystal River, FL

Crystal Valley Care Center, Goshen, IN
Cuba Memorial Hospital Inc—Skilled Nursing Facility, Cuba, NY
Cullen Avenue Rest Home, Austin, TX
Victor Cullen Center, Sabillasville, MD
Cullman Health Care Center, Cullman, AL
Culver West Convalescent Hospital, Los Angeles, CA
Cumberland County Home, Carlisle, PA
Cumberland Manor, Bridgeton, NJ
Cumberland Manor Rest Home, Parker's Lake, KY
Cumberland Memorial Hospital—Extended Care Unit, Cumberland, WI
Cumberland Nursing Center, Greenup, IL
Cumberland Valley Manor Inc, Burkesville, KY
Cumberland Villa Nursing Center, Cumberland, MD
Cumming Convalescent Home, Cumming, GA
Cummings Health Care Facility Inc, Howland, ME
Cupola Nursing Home, Brockport, NY
Cuppett & Weeks Nursing Home Inc, Oakland, MD
Currey Nursing Home Inc, Mount Pleasant, TX
Curry Good Samaritan Center, Brookings, OR
Curry Memorial Home, Waynesburg, PA
Carl T Curtis Health Education Center, Macy, NE
The Curtis Home—St Elizabeth Center, Meriden, CT
Curtis Manor Retirement Home, Dalton, MA
Cushing Care Center Inc, Cushing, TX
Cushing Manor Rest Home, Boston, MA
Custer County Rest Home, Miles City, MT
Cuyahoga County Hospital—Sunny Acres Skilled Nursing Facility, Warrensville, OH
Cuyahoga County Nursing Home, Cleveland, OH
Cuyahoga Falls Country Place, Cuyahoga Falls, OH
Cuy-La Home, Euclid, OH
Cypress Acres Convalescent Hospital, Paradise, CA
Cypress Acres Intermediate Care Facility, Paradise, CA
Cypress Care Center of Santa Cruz, Santa Cruz, CA
Cypress Convalescent Center, Burbank, CA
Cypress Cove Care Center, Crystal River, FL
Cypress Gardens Convalescent Hospital, Riverside, CA
Cypress Manor, Fort Myers, FL
Cypress Manor, Hancock, MI
Cypress Nurs Facility Inc, Sumter, SC
Cyril Nursing Home, Cyril, OK
Czech Catholic Home for the Aged, El Campo, TX
Dacotah Alpha, Mandan, ND
Dade City Geriatric Center, Dade City, FL
Dade County Nursing Home, Greenfield, MO
Dadeville Convalescent Home, Dadeville, AL
D'Adrian Convalescent Center, Godfrey, IL
Daggett Crandall Newcomb Home, Norton, MA
Dahl Memorial Nursing Home, Ekalaka, MT
Dakotas Childrens Home, West Saint Paul, MN
Daleview Nursing Home & Manor, Farmingdale, NY
Dallas County Nursing Home, Fordyce, AR
Dallas Health & Rehabilitation Center, Dallas, WI
Dallas Home for Jewish Aged, Dallas, TX
Dallas Lamb Foundation Home, Payne, OH
Dallas Nursing Home, Dallas, OR
Dalton Health Center, Ironton, OH
Dalton Nursing Home Inc, Dalton, MA
Dalton Rest Home, Worcester, MA
Dalworth Care Center, Arlington, TX
Daly Parke Nursing Home, Cincinnati, OH
Dammert Geriatric Center, Belleville, IL
D'Amore Rest Haven Inc, East Windsor, CT
Dana Home of Lexington, Lexington, MA
Danbury Pavilion Healthcare, Danbury, CT

Dane County Home—West Building, Verona, WI
Danforth Nursing Home, Danforth, ME
Dania Nursing Home, Dania, FL
Kathleen Daniel Health Care Center, Framingham, MA
Daniel Nursing Home, Fulton, MS
Daniels Memorial Nursing Home, Scobey, MT
Daniel's Nursing Home Inc, Reading, MA
Danish Convalescent Home, Atascadero, CA
Danridge Nursing Home, Youngstown, OH
Dan's Boarding Care Home, Saint Cloud, MN
Danvers Twin Oaks Nursing Home, Danvers, MA
Danville Care Center, Danville, IL
Danville Care Center, Danville, IA
Danville Manor, Danville, IL
Danville State Hospital Long-Term Care Facility, Danville, PA
Dar-Way Nursing Home Inc, Forksville, PA
Darcy Hall Nursing Home, West Palm Beach, FL
Dardanelle Nursing Center Inc, Dardanelle, AR
Betty Dare Good Samaritan Center, Alamogordo, NM
Darien Convalescent Center, Darien, CT
Darlington Care Center, Pawtucket, RI
Darlington Convalescent Center, Darlington, SC
Darlington House, Toledo, OH
Dartmouth Manor Rest Home, Dartmouth, MA
Dassel Lakeside Community Home, Dassel, MN
Daughters of Israel Pleasant Valley Home, West Orange, NJ
Daughters of Jacob Geriatric Center, Bronx, NY
Daughters of Sarah Nursing Home Company Inc, Albany, NY
Dauphin Manor, Harrisburg, PA
Davco Rest Home, Owensboro, KY
Davenport Good Samaritan, Davenport, IA
Davenport Lutheran Home, Davenport, IA
Davenport Memorial Home, Malden, MA
Davenport Nursing Home, Davenport, IA
David Nursing Home, Detroit, MI
Davidson Nursing Center, Thomasville, NC
Bishop Davies Center Inc, Hurst, TX
Daviess County Nursing Home Corp, Gallatin, MO
Davis Gardens Health Center, Terre Haute, IN
George Davis Manor, West Lafayette, IN
Davis Home for the Aged, Oak Hill, OH
Davis Nursing Home, Tahlequah, OK
Davis Nursing Home, Denver, CO
Davis Nursing Home Inc, Mountaintop, PA
Davis Skilled Nursing Facility, Pine Bluff, AR
Davison Rest Home Inc, Laurel, MS
Dawn View Manor, Fort Ashby, WV
Dawson Manor, Dawson, GA
Dawson Place Inc, Hill City, KS
Dawson Springs Health Care Center, Dawson Springs, KY
William L Dawson Nursing Home, Chicago, IL
Daystar Home, Needham, MA
Daystar Inc, Fort Lauderdale, FL
Dayton Boarding Care Home, Saint Paul, MN
Dayton Residential Care Facility, Kenosha, WI
Daytona Beach Geriatric Center, Daytona Beach, FL
Daytona Beach Olds Hall Good Samaritan Nursing Center, Daytona Beach, FL
Daytona Manor Nursing Home, South Daytona, FL
Dayview Care Center, New Carlisle, OH
DC Village, Washington, DC
DCI Dakota Adults, Mendota Heights, MN
De Kalb County Nursing Home, De Kalb, IL
De Leon Nursing Home, De Leon, TX
De Paul Belleview Extended Care, Milwaukee, WI
DePaul Health Center St Anne's Division, Bridgeton, MO

Deacon Home Ltd, Rockford, IL
Deaconess Manor, Saint Louis, MO
Deaconess Skilled Nursing Center, Great Falls, MT
Deal Nursing Home Inc, Jackson, MO
Deanview Nursing Home Inc, Washington Court House, OH
Dearborn Heights Convalescent Center, Dearborn Heights, MI
John L Deaton Medical Center Inc, Baltimore, MD
Deauville Healthcare Center, Chicago, IL
DeBary Manor, DeBary, FL
DeBoer Nursing Home, Muskegon, MI
Deborah House, Chicago, IL
Decatur Community Care Center, Decatur, IN
Decatur Convalescent Center, Decatur, TX
Decatur County Good Samaritan Center, Oberlin, KS
Decatur County Manor Nursing Center, Parsons, TN
Decatur Retirement Park, Indianapolis, IN
Dee-Maret Nursing Home, Akron, OH
Deep River Conv Home Inc, Deep River, CT
Deer Parke Nursing Home, Cincinnati, OH
Deerbrook Nursing Centre, Joliet, IL
Deerfield Episcopal Retirement Community Inc, Asheville, NC
Deering Nursing Home Inc, Hingham, MA
Deerings Nursing Home, Odessa, TX
Deerings West Nursing Home, Odessa, TX
Deers Head Center Comprehensive Care Facility, Salisbury, MD
Defiance Health Care Center, Defiance, OH
Degraff Memorial Hospital—Skilled Nursing Facility, North Tonawanda, NY
Deiber Nursing Home Inc, Sabina, OH
DeKalb General Skilled Nursing Unit, Decatur, GA
Del Capri Terrace Convalescent Hospital, San Diego, CA
Del Manor Nursing Home, Rockland, MA
Del Mar Convalescent Hospital, Rosemead, CA
Del Mar Health Care Center, Corpus Christi, TX
Del Mar Nursing Home, Indianapolis, IN
Del Rio Convalescent Center, Bell Gardens, CA
Del Rio Nursing Home Inc, Del Rio, TX
Del Rio Sanitarium, Bell Gardens, CA
Del Rosa Convalescent Hospital, San Bernardino, CA
Delamarter Care Center, Pendleton, OR
Deland Convalescent Center, Deland, FL
Delano Healthcare Center, Delano, MN
Delaware Care Center, Milford, DE
Delaware County Health Center, Muncie, IN
Delaware County Home & Infirmary, Delhi, NY
Delaware County Memorial Hospital, Manchester, IA
Delaware Health Care Facility, Indianapolis, IN
Delaware Hospital for the Chronically Ill, Smyrna, DE
Delaware Park Care Center, Delaware, OH
Delhaven Nursing Center, Saint Louis, MO
Delhi Guest Home, Delhi, LA
Thomas Dell Nursing Home Inc, Farmington, MO
Dellridge Nursing Home, Paramus, NJ
The Dells Place Inc, Delano, MN
Delmar Gardens East Inc, University City, MO
Delmar Gardens of Chesterfield, Chesterfield, MO
Delmar Gardens of Lenexa, Lenexa, KS
Delmar Gardens West, Chesterfield, MO
Delmar House, Aurora, CO
Delphi, Shakopee, MN
Delphi Nursing Home, Delphi, IN
Delphos Memorial Home, Delphos, OH
Delphos Rest Home Inc, Delphos, KS
Del's Care Center Inc, Portland, OR
Delta Care Center, Delta, CO
Delta Convalescent Hospital, Lodi, CA
Delta Convalescent Hospital, Visalia, CA

Delta Haven Nursing Home, Tallulah, LA
Delta Manor Nursing Center, Clarksdale, MS
Delta Nursing Home, Cooper, TX
Delta Rehabilitation Center, Snohomish, WA
Delta Valley Convalescent Hospital, Stockton, CA
Deltona Health Care Center, Deltona, FL
Deluxe Care Inn, South Pasadena, FL
Delwood Nursing Center Inc, Austin, TX
Demars Childrens Home, Coon Rapids, MN
Demes Rehabilitation Center, Green Bay, WI
Dempsey Nursing Home Inc, Chattanooga, TN
Den-Mar Nursing Home, Rockport, MA
Denison Care Center, Denison, IA
Denison Manor Inc, Denison, TX
Dennett Road Manor Inc, Oakland, MD
Denny House Nursing Home Inc, Norwood, MA
Denton Development Center, Denton, TX
Denton Good Samaritan Village, Denton, TX
Denton Nursing Center, Denton, TX
Denver Nursing Home, Stevens, PA
Denver Sunset Home, Denver, IA
Deport Nursing Home, Deport, TX
Mary Lee Depugh Nursing Home, Winter Park, FL
DeQueen Nursing Home, DeQueen, AR
Derby Nursing Center, Derby, CT
Derrer Road ICF/MR, Columbus, OH
Des Arc Convalescent Center, Des Arc, AR
Des Peres Health Care, Des Peres, MO
Desert Haven Nursing Center, Phoenix, AZ
Desert Knolls Convalescent Hospital, Victorville, CA
Desert Life Health Care, Tucson, AZ
Desert Palms Convalescent Hospital, Indio, CA
Desert Terrace Nursing Facility, Phoenix, AZ
Desha's Rest Home, San Antonio, TX
Desilets Nursing Home Inc, Warren, RI
Desloge Health Care Center, Desloge, MO
DeSoto Manor Nursing Home, Arcadia, FL
DeSoto Nursing Home, DeSoto, TX
Desserich House, Lakewood, CO
Detroiter Residence, Detroit, MI
Detwiler Manor, Wauseon, OH
Deuel County Good Samaritan Center, Clear Lake, SD
Deutsches Altenheim Inc, West Roxbury, MA
Deveaux Manor Nursing Home, Niagara Falls, NY
Dever Nursing Home, Houston, TX
Paul A Dever State School, Taunton, MA
Devereux House Nursing Home Inc, Marblehead, MA
Devine Haven Convalescent Home, Elkton, MD
Joseph B Devlin Public Medical Institute, Lynn, MA
Devon Gables Health Center, Tucson, AZ
Devon Manor Retirement Center, Devon, PA
Devonshire Acres Ltd, Sterling, CO
Devonshire Manor, Portland, ME
Devonshire Oaks, Redwood City, CA
DeWitt City Nursing Home, DeWitt, AR
Dewitt County Nursing Home, Clinton, IL
Dewitt Nursing Home, New York, NY
Dexter House Nursing Facility, Malden, MA
Dexter Nursing Center, Dexter, MO
Dexter Nursing Home, Dexter, ME
Diablo Convalescent Hospital, Danville, CA
Diamond Care Center, Bridgewater, SD
Diamond Hill Nursing Center Inc, Cumberland, RI
Diamondhead Extended Care Center, North Lima, OH
Diamondhead Extended Care Center 1, North Lima, OH
Diana Lynn Lodge, Sunland, CA
Dickey Nursing Home Inc, Elwood, IN
Todd Dickey Medical Center, Leavenworth, IN
Dickinson County Care Facility, Spirit Lake, IA
Dickinson Nursing Center, Dickinson, ND
Jane Dickman House, Woodbury, MN
Dickson County Nursing Home, Dickson, TN

Dighton Nursing & Convalescent Home, Dighton, MA
Dillsboro Manor, Dillsboro, IN
Grover C Dils Medical Center, Caliente, NV
Dinan Memorial Center, Bridgeport, CT
Dinuba Convalescent Hospital, Dinuba, CA
Dirksen House Healthcare, Springfield, IL
Dishman Personal Care Home, Monticello, KY
District Home, Waynesboro, VA
District Nursing Home, Warrenton, VA
Divine Providence Community Home, Sleepy Eye, MN
Divine Providence—Extended Care Facility, Williamsport, PA
Divine Providence Hospital & Home, Ivanhoe, MN
Divine Savior Hospital & Nursing Home, Portage, WI
Divine Saviour Nursing Home, York, SC
Dixfield Health Care Center, Dixfield, ME
Dixie Manor Sheltered Care, Harvey, IL
Dixie White House Nursing Home Inc, Pass Christian, MS
Dixon Health Care Center, Dixon, IL
Dixon Home Care Center, Martinsville, IN
Dixon Village Inn, Dixon, IL
DLA Senn Park Nursing Center, Chicago, IL
Doanes Nursing Home, Campbell Hall, NY
Dobbins Nursing Home Inc, New Richmond, OH
Dobson Plaza Nursing Home, Evanston, IL
Dock Terrace, Lansdale, PA
The Doctors' Convalescent Center Inc, Selinsgrove, PA
Doctor's Convalescent Hospital, Whittier, CA
Doctor's Nursing Center Foundation Inc, Dallas, TX
Doctors Nursing Center Inc, Little Rock, AR
Doctors Nursing Home, Salem, IL
Dodge County Community Health Center, Juneau, WI
Dodge Park Rest Home, Worcester, MA
Dogwood Acres ICF, Durham, CT
Dolly Mt Nursing Home, Clifton, NJ
Dolton Healthcare Center, Dolton, IL
Don Orione Nursing Home, Boston, MA
Donahoe Manor, Bedford, PA
Donalson Care Center, Fayetteville, TN
Donely House ICFMR, Quincy, PA
Doniphan Retirement Home Inc, Doniphan, MO
Donna Kay Rest Home Inc, Worcester, MA
Donnellson Manor Care Center, Donnellson, IA
Doolittle Home Inc, Foxboro, MA
Door County Memorial Hospital—Skilled Nursing Facility, Sturgeon Bay, WI
Doral Country Manor, Carlinville, IL
Dorchester Nursing Center, Sturgeon Bay, WI
Dorothe Lane Home, Sauk Centre, MN
David M Dorsett Health Care Facility, Spearfish, SD
Dorvin Convalescent & Nursing Center, Livonia, MI
Double Springs Health Care Center, Double Springs, AL
Douglas Living Center, Mattoon, IL
Douglas Manor Nursing Complex, Tuscola, IL
Douglas Memorial Nursing Home, Jefferson, TX
Douglas Nursing Home Inc, Milan, TN
Dove Nursing Facility, Uhrichsville, OH
The Dove Tree, Fort Wayne, IN
Dover House Healthcare, Dover, NH
Dover Manor Inc, Georgetown, KY
Dover Nursing Home, Brooklyn, NY
Dover Nursing Home, Westlake, OH
Dowagiac Nursing Home, Dowagiac, MI
Dowden Nursing Home, Newtown Square, PA
Dowling Convalescent Hospital, Oakland, CA
Downey Care Center, Downey, CA
Downey Community Health Center, Downey, CA
Downs Nursing Center, Downs, KS
Downtown Nursing Home Inc, Buffalo, NY
Dow-Rummel Village, Sioux Falls, SD
Dows Care Center, Dows, IA

Doxie-Hatch Medical Center, Salt Lake City, UT
Doylestown Manor, Doylestown, PA
Daniel Drake Memorial Hospital, Cincinnati, OH
Drake Nursing Home, Zanesville, OH
Drake Residential Care Facility, Carthage, MO
Draper Plaza, Joliet, IL
Dreiers Sanitarium, Glendale, CA
Dresher Hill Nursing Center, Fort Washington, PA
Dresser Memorial Presbyterian Home, Bradford, PA
Drew Village Nursing Center, Clearwater, FL
Mary J Drexel Home, Bala Cynwyd, PA
Dreyerhaus, Batesville, IN
Driftwood Care Center, Yuba City, CA
Driftwood Convalescent Center, Torrance, CA
Driftwood Convalescent Hospital, Davis, CA
Driftwood Convalescent Hospital, Fremont, CA
Driftwood Convalescent Hospital, Gilroy, CA
Driftwood Convalescent Hospital, Modesto, CA
Driftwood Convalescent Hospital, Monterey, CA
Driftwood Convalescent Hospital, Salinas, CA
Driftwood Convalescent Hospital, San Jose, CA
Driftwood Convalescent Hospital, Santa Cruz, CA
Driftwood Health Care Center, Charleston, SC
Driftwood Health Care Center—Long-Term Care Facility, Charleston, SC
Driftwood Manor, Hayward, CA
Driftwood Nursing Center, Gulfport, MS
Druid Hills Nursing Home, Clearwater, FL
Bishop Drumm Care Center, Johnston City, IA
Drumright Nursing Home, Drumright, OK
Dry Harbor Nursing Home, Middle Village, NY
Dry Ridge Personal Care Home, Dry Ridge, KY
Du Page Convalescent Center, Wheaton, IL
Dublin Nursing Center, Dublin, TX
Dublinaire Nursing Home, Dublin, GA
Dubois Nursing Home, Dubois, PA
Dubuque Health Care Center, Dubuque, IA
Duff Memorial Nursing Home, Nebraska City, NE
Dugan Memorial Home, West Point, MS
Duke Convalescent Residence, Lancaster, PA
Dukeland Nursing Home & Convalescent Center, Baltimore, MD
Dulaney Towson Nursing & Convalescent Center, Towson, MD
Duluth Regional Care Center II, Duluth, MN
Duluth Regional Care Center III, Duluth, MN
Duluth Regional Care Center IV, Duluth, MN
Dumas Memorial Home, Dumas, TX
Dumas Nursing Center, Dumas, AR
Dumont Nursing & Convalescent Center, Morrisville, VT
Dumont Nursing Home, Dumont, IA
W F & Mada Dunaway Manor Inc, Guymon, OK
Dunbar Nursing Home, Cleveland, OH
Duncan Care Center, Duncan, OK
Dundee Nursing Home, Bennettsville, SC
Dunedin Care Center, Dunedin, FL
Dungarvin I, Saint Paul, MN
Dungarvin III—Balbriggen, Saint Paul, MN
Dungarvin II Camara, Roseville, MN
Dungarvin V—Tyrothy, Crystal, MN
Dungarvin VI—Moores Haven, Shoreview, MN
Dungarvin X Alice Haney Annex, Lester Prairie, MN
Dunlap Care Center, Dunlap, IA
Dunlap Sanitarium, Los Angeles, CA
Dunn County Health Care Center, Menomonie, WI
Dunn Rest Home, Selma, AL
Dunroven Nursing Home, Cresskill, NJ
Dunseith Community Nursing Home, Dunseith, ND

Dunsworth Estates, Harrisonville, MO
Dunsworth Manor, Harrisonville, MO
Dunwoody Home Medical Center, Newtown Square, PA
Duplex Nursing Home Inc, Boston, MA
Dupoint House, Janesville, WI
Durand Convalescent Center, Durand, MI
Durham Retirement Center, Memphis, TN
Durham-Hensley Nursing Homes Inc, Chuckey, TN
Dutchess County Health Care Facility, Millbrook, NY
Duvall Home for Retarded Children, Glenwood, FL
Duxbury House Nursing Home, Duxbury, MA
D'Ville House, Donaldsonville, LA
D'Youville Manor, Lowell, MA
d'Youville Pavilion Nursing Home, Lewiston, ME
E & M Rainbow Home Inc, McPherson, KS
Eagle Creek Nursing Center, West Union, OH
Eagle Lake Nursing Home, Eagle Lake, ME
Eagle Nursing Home, Bloomington, MN
Eagle River Healthcare Center Inc, Eagle River, WI
Eagle Valley Children's Home, Carson City, NV
Eagle Valley Healthcare Center, Indianapolis, IN
Eagleton Nursing Home, Bloomer, WI
Earl Park Nursing Home, Earl Park, IN
Earle Street Personal Care Home, Jackson, MS
Earlham Manor Care Center, Earlham, IA
Earlwood Convalescent Hospital, Torrance, CA
Early Memorial Nursing Home, Blakley, GA
Eason Nursing Home, Lake Worth, FL
East Broad Manor, Columbus, OH
East Carroll Nursing Home Inc, Kensington, OH
East End Conv Home Inc, Waterbury, CT
East Galbraith Health Care Center, Cincinnati, OH
East Galbraith Nursing Home, Cincinnati, OH
East Grand Forks Group Home I, Crookston, MN
East Grand Forks II, East Grand Forks, MN
East Grand Nursing Home, Detroit, MI
East Haven Health Related Facility, Bronx, NY
East Haven Rest Home, East Haven, CT
East Lake Health Care, Birmingham, AL
East Lawn Manor, Marion, OH
East Liverpool Convalescent Center, East Liverpool, OH
East Liverpool Extended Care Center, East Liverpool, OH
East Longmeadow Nursing Center/Longmeadow House, East Longmeadow, MA
East Los Angeles Convalescent Hospital, Los Angeles, CA
East Manor Medical Care Center, Sarasota, FL
East Manor Nusing Center, El Dorado, AR
East Mesa Care Center, Mesa, AZ
East Mississippi State Nursing Home, Meridian, MS
East Moline Care Center, East Moline, IL
East Moline Garden Plaza, East Moline, IL
East Ohio Regional Hospital Long-Term Care Unit, Martins Ferry, OH
East Orange Nursing Home, East Orange, NJ
East Park Manor, Fort Worth, TX
East Ridge Retirement Village Health Center, Miami, FL
East Rockaway Nursing Home, Lynbrook, NY
East Side Manor, East Providence, RI
East Side Nursing Home, Warsaw, NY
East Tennessee Health Care Center, Madisonville, TN
East Texas Convalescent Home, San Augustine, TX
East-Towne Care Center, Independence, IA
East Village Nursing Home, Lexington, MA
Eastbrooke Health Care Center, Brooksville, FL
Eastchester Park Nursing Home, Bronx, NY
Eastern Maine Medical Center, Bangor, ME

Eastern Oklahoma Medical Center Skilled Nursing Facility, Poteau, OK
Eastern Oregon Hospital & Training Center, Pendleton, OR
Eastern Pennsylvania Eastern Star Home, Warminster, PA
Eastern Star Home, Los Angeles, CA
Eastern Star Home, Macon, IL
Eastern Star Home, Orange, MA
Eastern Star Home, Arlington, TX
Eastern Star Home in Kentucky, Louisville, KY
Eastern Star Home Inc, Redfield, SD
Eastern Star Home & Infirmary, Oriskany, NY
Eastern Star Home of Cuyahoga County, East Cleveland, OH
Eastern Star Masonic Home, Boone, IA
Eastern Star Nursing Home, Bothell, WA
Easter's Home of Ruth Inc, Farmington, MO
Easterwood Nursing Home, Dadeville, AL
Eastgate Healthcare Associates Inc, Pocatello, ID
Eastgate Manor, Springfield, IL
Eastgate Manor Nursing & Residential Center Inc, Washington, IN
Eastland Care Center, Columbus, OH
Eastland Manor, Eastland, TX
Eastmont Human Services Center, Glendive, MT
Eastmont Tower, Lincoln, NE
The Easton Home for Aged Women, Easton, PA
Easton Manor, Easton, KS
Easton-Lincoln Nursing Home, Easton, MA
Eastport Memorial Nursing Home, Eastport, ME
Eastside Healthcare Center, Indianapolis, IN
Eastview Manor, Antigo, WI
Eastview Manor Care Center, Trenton, MO
Eastview Manor Inc, Prospect, CT
Eastview Nursing Home, Macon, GA
Eastview Nursing Home, Tyler, TX
Eastwood at Dedham Convalescent Center, Dedham, MA
Eastwood Convalescent Home Inc, Easton, PA
Eastwood Convalescent Hospital, Long Beach, CA
Eastwood Manor Nursing & Rehabilitation Center, Commerce, OK
Eastwood Nursing Center, Detroit, MI
Eastwood Pines Nursing Home, Gardner, MA
Eastwood Rest Home Inc, Amesbury, MA
Eastwood Village Nursing & Retirement Center, Fort Worth, TX
Eaton Care Nursing Center, Los Angeles, CA
Eaton County Medical Care Facility, Charlotte, MI
Eatontown Convalescent Center, Eatontown, NJ
Eben Ezer Lutheran Care Center, Brush, CO
Ebenezer Covenant Home, Buffalo, MN
Ebenezer Hall, Minneapolis, MN
Ebenezer Ridges Geriatric Care Center, Lakeville, MN
Ebenezer Society Luther & Field, Minneapolis, MN
Ebensburg Center, Ebensburg, PA
Echo Manor Extended Care Center, Pickerington, OH
Echo Park Skilled Nursing Facility Hospital Inc, Los Angeles, CA
Echo Specialized Group Home, Spokane, WA
Echoing Hills Residential Center, Warsaw, OH
Echoing Meadows Residential Center, Athens, OH
Echoing Ridge Residential Center, Canal Fulton, OH
Echoing Valley Residential Center, Dayton, OH
Echoing Woods Residential Center, Dayton, OH
Eckfield Rest Home, Medina, OH
Eddington Group Home, Brewer, ME
James A Eddy Memorial Geriatric Center, Troy, NY
Eden Gardens Nursing Center, Shreveport, LA
Eden Home Inc, New Braunfels, TX

Eden House Convalescent Center, Yakima, WA
Eden Manor Nursing Home, Sabina, OH
Eden Park Health Services Inc, Cobleskill, NY
Eden Park Health Services Inc, Troy, NY
Eden Park Nursing Home, Albany, NY
Eden Park Nursing Home, Hudson, NY
Eden Park Nursing Home, Poughkeepsie, NY
Eden Park Nursing Home & Health Related Facility, Catskill, NY
Eden Park Nursing Home & Health Related Facility, Glens Falls, NY
Eden Park Nursing Home & HRF, Utica, NY
Eden Park Nursing Home of Brattleboro, Brattleboro, VT
Eden Park Nursing Home of Rutland, Rutland, VT
Eden Retirement Center Inc, Edwardsville, IL
Eden Valley Nursing Home, Loveland, CO
Eden West Rehabilitation Hospital, Hayward, CA
Edenwald, Towson, MD
Edgebrook Rest Center Inc, Edgerton, MN
Edgecombe Nursing & Convalescent Home, Lenox, MA
Edgecombe Nursing Home, Lenox, MA
Edgefield Health Care Center, Edgefield, SC
Edgefield Manor Nursing Home, Troutdale, OR
Edgehill Nursing & Rehabilitation Center, Glenside, PA
Edgell Rest Home, Framingham, MA
Edgemont Manor Nursing Home, Cynthiana, KY
Edgemoor Geriatric Hospital, Santee, CA
Edgerton Manor—ICF/MR, West Lafayette, OH
Edgewater Care Center, Kerrville, TX
Edgewater Convalescent Hospital, Long Beach, CA
Edgewater Haven Nursing Home, Port Edwards, WI
Edgewater Home Inc, Saint Louis, MO
Edgewater Methodist Retirement Community, Galveston, TX
Edgewater Nursing & Geriatric Center, Chicago, IL
Edgewater Quality Care Nursing Center, Lake Milton, OH
The Edgewood Centre, Portsmouth, NH
Edgewood Convalescent Home, Edgewood, IA
Edgewood Convalescent Home, Dorchester, MA
Edgewood Healthcare, Oxford, IN
Edgewood Manor, Farmington, ME
Edgewood Manor, Greenfield, OH
Edgewood Manor, Montesano, WA
Edgewood Manor Nursing Center, Port Clinton, OH
Edgewood Manor Nursing Home, Texarkana, TX
Edgewood Manor of Fostoria Inc, Fostoria, OH
Edgewood Manor of Mason, Mason, OH
Edgewood Manor of Westerville, Westerville, OH
Edgewood Nursing Center, Hopkins, MN
Edgewood Nursing Center, Cottage Grove, OR
Edgewood Nursing Center Inc, Youngstown, PA
Edgewood Nursing Home, Toledo, OH
Edgewood Nursing Home Inc, Grafton, MA
Edgewood Rest Home, Pittsfield, MA
Edina Care Center, Edina, MN
Edison Estates Inc, Edison, NJ
Edison Manor, Centralia, WA
Edisto Convalescent Center, Orangeburg, SC
Edmond Nursing Center, Edmond, OK
Edmond Oaks Center, Lewisville, TX
Edmonds Care Center, Edmonds, WA
Edson Convalescent Hospital, Modesto, CA
Edward Abraham Memorial Home, Canadian, TX
Edwardsville Care Center, Edwardsville, IL
Edwardsville Convalescent Center, Edwardsville, KS
Edwardsville Manor, Edwardsville, KS

Edwin Morgan Center Scotland Memorial Hospital—SNF, Laurinburg, NC
Effingham County Hospital—E C F, Springfield, GA
Eger Nursing Home Inc, Staten Island, NY
Egle Nursing Home, Lonaconing, MD
Eisenhower Nursing & Convalescent Hospital, Pasadena, CA
El Cajon Valley Convalescent Center, El Cajon, CA
El Camino Convalescent Hospital, Carmichael, CA
El Castillo Retirement Residence, Santa Fe, NM
El Centro Villa Nursing Center Inc, Albuquerque, NM
El Dorado Convalescent Hospital, Placerville, CA
El Dorado Manor Nursing Home, Trenton, NE
El Dorado Nursing Center, El Dorado, KS
El Jen Convalescent Hospital, Las Vegas, NV
El Monte Convalescent Hospital, El Monte, CA
El Monte Golden Age Convalescent Home, El Monte, CA
El Paso Convalescent Center, El Paso, TX
El Paso Hawthorne Lodge, El Paso, IL
El Ponce De Leon Convalescent Center, Miami, FL
El Rancho Rest Home, Payson, UT
El Rancho Vista Convalescent Center, Pico Rivera, CA
El Reno Nursing Center, El Reno, OK
El Reposo Sanitarium, Florence, AL
Elaine Boyd Creche Childrens Home, Bloomingdale, IL
Elba General Hospital & Nursing Home, Elba, AL
Elberta Convalescent Home, Warner Robins, GA
Elcor Health Services, Horseheads, NY
Elcor's Marriott Manor, Horseheads, NY
Elder Crest Nursing Home, Munhall, PA
Elder House, Fenton, MI
Eldercare Convalescent Hospital, Capitola, CA
Eldercare Convalescent Hospital, Morgan Hill, CA
Eldercare Gardens, Charlottesville, VA
Eldercare of Alton, Alton, IL
Eldercare of Farmville, Farmville, VA
Eldercare of Franklin County, Rocky Mount, VA
Elderlodge of Fayetteville, Fayetteville, NC
Elders Home Inc, New York Mills, MN
Eldora Manor, Eldora, IA
Eldorado Nursing Home Inc, Eldorado, IL
Electra Nursing Center, Iowa Park, TX
El-Encanto Convalescent Hospital, City of Industry, CA
Eleven Seven, New Ulm, MN
Elgin Community Living Facility, Elgin, IL
Elgin Golden Years Retirement Nursing Home, Elgin, TX
Elim Home, Milaca, MN
Elim Home, Princeton, MN
Elim Home, Watertown, MN
Elim Home, Fargo, ND
The Elim Park Baptist Home Inc, Cheshire, CT
Elite Rest & Nursing Home, Cincinnati, OH
Eliza Bryant Center, Cleveland, OH
Eliza Memorial Hospital Mitchell Hollingsworth Annex, Florence, AL
Elizabeth Adam Crump Manor, Glen Allen, VA
Elizabeth Carleton House, Boston, MA
Elizabeth Church Manor, Binghamton, NY
The Jane Elizabeth House Nursing Home, Cambridge, MA
Elizabeth Manor, Los Angeles, CA
Elizabeth Manor Convalescent Hospital, Sacramento, CA
Elizabeth Nursing Home, Elizabeth, NJ
Elizabeth Nursing Home Inc, Elizabeth, IL
Elizabethan Nursing Home, Elizabethtown, KY

Elizabethtown Nursing Center, Elizabethtown, NC

Elk Grove Convalescent Hospital, Elk Grove, CA

Elk Haven Nursing Home, Saint Marys, PA

Elk Manor Home, Moline, KS

Elk River Nursing Home, Elk River, MN

Elkader Care Center, Elkader, IA

Elkhart Healthcare Center, Elkhart, IN

Elkhart Nursing Home Inc, Elkhart, TX

Elkhorn Manor, Elkhorn, NE

Elkton Rest Home, Elkton, SD

Ellen Memorial Convalescent Home, Scranton, PA

Ellen Memorial Health Care Center, Honesdale, PA

Ellen S Memorial Convalescent Hospital, Richmond, CA

Ellenburg Nursing Center Inc, Anderson, SC

Ellendale Nursing Center, Ellendale, ND

Ellens Convalescent Health Center Inc, Fort Dodge, IA

Ellet Manor, Akron, OH

Elliot Avenue Boarding Care Home, Minneapolis, MN

Elliot Manor Nursing Home, Newton, MA

Ellis Good Samaritan Center, Ellis, KS

The Ellis Nursing Center, Norwood, MA

Ellisville State School-Clover Circle ICF/MR, Ellisville, MS

Ellisville State School-Hillside SNF/ICF, Ellisville, MS

Ellisville State School-Peacan Grove, Ellisville, MS

Ellsworth Care Centers Inc, Ellsworth, WI

Ellsworth Conv Center, Ellsworth, ME

Ellsworth Good Samaritan Center—Villa Grace, Ellsworth, KS

Ellsworth Good Samaritan Center—Villa Hope, Ellsworth, KS

Elm Brook Home Inc, Smithfield, RI

Elm Creek Nursing Center, West Carrollton, OH

Elm Crest Manor, New Salem, ND

Elm Heights Parkcrest Center, Shenandoah, IA

Elm Hill Nursing Center, Rocky Hill, CT

Elm Hill Nursing Home, Boston, MA

Elm Hurst Nursing Home Inc, Springfield, TN

Elm Manor Nursing Home, Canandaigua, NY

Elm Terrace Gardens, Lansdale, PA

Elm View Care Center, Burlington, IA

Elmachri Convalescent Home, Norwich, CT

Elmbrook Home, Ardmore, OK

Elmcrest Convalescent Hospital, El Monte, CA

ElmHaven, Parsons, KS

Elmhaven Convalescent Hospital Inc, Stockton, CA

Ray Graham Elmhurst Conv Living Facility, Elgin, IL

Elmhurst Extended Care Center Inc, Elmhurst, IL

Elmhurst Nursing Home, Webb City, MO

Elmhurst Nursing Home, Canby, OR

Elmhurst Nursing & Retirement Home, Melrose, MA

Elmira Jeffries Memorial Home, Philadelphia, PA

Elmore Memorial Nursing Home, Mountain Home, ID

The Elms, Cranbury, NJ

Elms Convalescent Home & Rehabilitation Center, Wellington, OH

Elms Convalescent Hospital, Glendale, CA

Elms Health Care Center Inc, Ponca, NE

Elms Manor Nursing Home, Chicopee, MA

Elms Nursing Home, Macomb, IL

The Elms Residence Nursing Home, Old Orchard Beach, ME

Elmwood Convalescent Hospital, Berkeley, CA

Elmwood Geriatric Village, Detroit, MI

Elmwood Health Center Inc, Providence, RI

Elmwood Living Center, Aurora, IL

Elmwood Manor Inc, Beardstown, IL

Elmwood Manor Inc, Wewoka, OK

Elmwood Manor Nursing Home, Worcester, MA

Elmwood Manor Nursing Home Inc, Nanuet, NY

Elmwood Nursing Center, Marlin, TX

Elmwood Nursing Home, Green Springs, OH

Elmwood Nursing Home, Omaha, TX

Elmwood Village, Ashland, KY

Elmwood Village, Portsmouth, OH

Elness Convalescent Hospital, Turlock, CA

Elsberry Health Care Center, Elsberry, MO

Elsie Dryer Nursing Home, Brookville, IN

Elsie May's Rest Home Inc, Pawtucket, RI

Elston Nursing Center, Chicago, IL

Elwood Care Center, Elwood, NE

Elwood Nursing Home, Salem, MO

Ely Bloomenson Community Hospital & Nursing Home, Ely, MN

The Elyria United Methodist Home, Elyria, OH

Elzora Manor, Milton-Freewater, OR

Emanuel County Nursing Home, Swainsboro, GA

Embassy House Healthcare Nursing Home, Brockton, MA

Embassy Manor Care Center, Newton, IA

Embreeville Center, Coatesville, PA

Emerald Care Center, Boise, ID

Emerald Circle Convalescent Center, Wapato, WA

Emerald Nursing Center, Eugene, OR

Emerald Terrace Nursing Center, Vancouver, WA

Emerson Boarding Care Home, Minneapolis, MN

Emerson Convalescent Center, Emerson, NJ

Emerson Convalescent Home Inc, Watertown, MA

Emerson Nursing Home, Indianapolis, IN

Emerson Place North, Minneapolis, MN

Emery County Nursing Home, Ferron, UT

Emery Manor Nursing Home, Matawan, NJ

Emery Retirement & Convalescent Home, Medford, MA

Emery Street Community Residence, Portland, ME

Emmanuel Home, Litchfield, MN

Emmanuel Nursing Home, Detroit Lakes, MN

Emmet County Medical Care Facility, Harbor Springs, MI

Emmetsburg Care Center, Emmetsburg, IA

Emmett Care Center, Emmett, ID

Emory Convalescent Home, Atlanta, GA

Empire Nursing Home, Joplin, MO

Emporia Presbyterian Manor, Emporia, KS

Empress Convalescent Center, Long Beach, CA

Empress Convalescent Home—1, Cincinnati, OH

Empress Convalescent Home—2, Cincinnati, OH

Empress Convalescent Hospital, San Jose, CA

Enderlin Hillcrest Manor Ltd, Enderlin, ND

Enfield Nursing Center, Enfield, CT

England Manor Nursing Home Inc, England, AR

England Nursing Center, England, AR

Englewood House, Englewood, CO

Englewood Manor Nursing Home, Englewood, OH

Englewood Nursing Home, Boston, MA

English Nursing Home, Lebanon, IN

English Oaks Convalescent Hospital, Modesto, CA

English Valley Nursing Care Center, North English, IA

English Village Manor Inc, Altus, OK

Englishton Park, Lexington, IN

Enid Living Center, Enid, OK

Ennoble Center of Long Beach, Long Beach, CA

Ennoble Manor Care Center, Dubuque, IA

Enterprise Estates Nursing Center, Enterprise, KS

Enterprise Hospital & Nursing Home, Enterprise, AL

Ephrata Nursing Home Inc, Ephrata, PA

Episcopal Church Home, Hockessin, DE

Episcopal Church Home, Louisville, KY

Episcopal Church Home, Rochester, NY

Episcopal Church Home of Minnesota, Saint Paul, MN

Epsom Manor, Epsom, NH

Epworth Manor, Tyrone, PA

Erick Nursing Home, Erick, OK

Erie County Care Facility, Huron, OH

Erie County Geriatric Annex, Erie, PA

Erie County Geriatric Center, Girard, PA

Erie County Home & Infirmary, Alden, NY

Erinkay-Aneskarn II, Robbinsdale, MN

Escambia County Nursing Home, Pensacola, FL

Escondido Convalescent Center, Escondido, CA

Eshelman Nursing Home Inc, Clyde, OH

Eskaton Glenwood Manor, Sacramento, CA

Eskaton Manzanita Manor, Carmichael, CA

Esma A Wright Pavilion, Robbins, IL

Essex Convalescent Home, Lynn, MA

Essex County Geriatrics Center, Belleville, NJ

Estelle's Nursing Home, Clifton, KS

Estelline Nursing & Care Center, Estelline, SD

Estes Health Care Center—East, Birmingham, AL

Estes Health Care Center—Fairhope, Fairhope, AL

Estes Health Care Center—Glen Haven, Northport, AL

Estes Health Care Center—Oakridge, Eight Mile, AL

Estes Health Care Center—Park Manor, Northport, AL

Estes Health Care Center—Riverchase, Birmingham, AL

Estes Health Care—North, Northport, AL

Estes Oak Knoll Nursing Facility, Birmingham, AL

Esther Marie Nursing Center, Geneva, OH

Etna Valley Health Center, Lebanon, NH

Etowah Health Care Center, Etowah, TN

Euclid Convalescent Center, San Diego, CA

Euclid Manor Nursing Home, Cleveland, OH

Eudora Nursing Center, Eudora, KS

Eufaula Geriatric Center, Eufaula, AL

Eufaula Manor Inc, Eufaula, OK

Eugene Good Samaritan Center, Eugene, OR

Euless Nursing Center, Euless, TX

Eupora Health Care Center Inc, Eupora, MS

Eureka Apostolic Christian Home, Eureka, IL

Eureka Springs Convalescent Center, Eureka Springs, AR

Eustis Manor Inc, Eustis, FL

Eva Dawn Care Center, Salt Lake City, UT

Evamor Manor, Worcester, MA

Evangelical Baptist Home, Ashford, CT

Evangelical Congregational Church Retirement Village, Myerstown, PA

Evangelical Free Church Home, Boone, IA

Evangelical Home, Saline, MI

Evangelical Home—Detroit, Detroit, MI

Evangelical Home Port Huron, Port Huron, MI

Evangelical Manor, Philadelphia, PA

Evans Health Care, Evans, GA

Helen Evans Home for Retarded Children, Hacienda Heights, CA

Evans Manor Nursing Home, Worcester, MA

Mary Evans Extended Care Facility, Ellwood City, PA

Evans Memorial Home for the Aged Inc, Cresco, IA

Evansville Manor, Evansville, WI

Evansville Protestant Home Inc, Evansville, IN

Eveleth Fitzgerald Community Hospital C & NC, Eveleth, MN

Evenglow Lodge, Pontiac, IL

Evening Star Nursing Home, Bethany, OK

Eventide Care Center, Chickasha, OK

Eventide Convalescent Center Inc, Topeka, KS

Eventide Home, Mountain Lake, MN

Eventide Home, Roseau, MN

Eventide Home Inc, Exeter, NH

Eventide Lutheran Home, Moorhead, MN

Eventide Lutheran Home for the Aged, Denison, IA

Eventide Nursing Home, Massillon, OH

Eventide Nursing Home Inc, San Saba, TX

Eventide of Sheridan, Sheridan, WY

Everett Court Community, Lakewood, CO
Evergreen Care Center, Safford, AZ
Evergreen Care Center, Montrose, CO
Evergreen Care Center, Lincoln City, OR
Evergreen Care Center, Memphis, TN
Evergreen Care Center, Burkburnett, TX
Evergreen Convalescent Center Inc, Temple City, CA
Evergreen Convalescent Home, Harmony, PA
Evergreen Convalescent Hospital Inc, Modesto, CA
Evergreen Health Care Center Inc, Shawano, WI
Evergreen Hills Nursing Center, Ypsilanti, MI
Evergreen House Health Center, East Providence, RI
Evergreen Manor, Minden, LA
Evergreen Manor, Saco, ME
Evergreen Manor, Delaware, OH
Evergreen Manor Inc, Phillipsburg, KS
Evergreen Manor Nursing Home, Evergreen Park, IL
Evergreen Manor Nursing Home, Montpelier, OH
Evergreen Manor Retirement Community, Oshkosh, WI
Evergreen North Nursing Home, Alvordton, OH
Evergreen Nursing Home, Alamosa, CO
Evergreen Nursing Home, Del City, OK
Evergreen Nursing Home, Provo, UT
Evergreen Nursing Home Inc, Evergreen, AL
Evergreen Nursing Home & Rehabilitation Center Inc, Creve Coeur, MO
Evergreen Place, Texarkana, AR
Evergreen Place A Rest Home, Springfield, MA
Evergreen Terrace Nursing Center, Mount Vernon, WA
Evergreen Vista Convalescent Center, Kirkland, WA
Evergreen Woods, Spring Hill, FL
The Evergreens, La Rose, IL
The Evergreens—High Point, High Point, NC
The Evergreens Inc—Greensboro, Greensboro, NC
Evergreens Nursing Home Inc, Woonsocket, RI
Ewing Nursing Home, Terre Haute, IN
Ewing Parkway Nursing Home, Trenton, NJ
Excelsior Nursing Home, Excelsior, MN
Excelsior Springs Care Center, Excelsior Springs, MO
Excepticon—Lexington Campus, Lexington, KY
Exceptional Care & Training Center, Sterling, IL
Exeter Healthcare Inc, Exeter, NH
Exeter House, Seattle, WA
Exira Care Center, Exira, IA
The Extended Care Center of Toledo, Toledo, OH
Extended Care Hospital of Anaheim, Anaheim, CA
Extended Care Hospital of Long Beach, Long Beach, CA
Extended Care Hospital of Los Angeles, Los Angeles, CA
Extended Care Hospital of Riverside, Riverside, CA
Extended Care Hospital of Santa Barbara, Santa Barbara, CA
Extendicare Health Center, Dothan, AL
Faber Nursing Home Inc, Cortland, OH
Faheney-Keedy Memorial Home Inc, Boonsboro, MD
Fair Acres, Carthage, MO
Fair Acres Geriatric Center, Lima, PA
Fair Acres Nursing Home, Armada, MI
Fair Acres Nursing Home Inc, Du Quoin, IL
Fair Haven Convalescent Home Inc, Douglas, GA
Fair Haven Shelby County Home, Sidney, OH
Fair Havens Center, Miami, FL
Fair Havens Christian Home, Decatur, IL
Fair Havens Rest Home Inc, Middleboro, MA
Fair Holme Convalescent Center, Seaford, DE

Fair Lawn Manor Nursing Home, Fair Lawn, NJ
Fair Lodge Health Care Center Inc, Louisville, KY
Fair Meadow Nursing Home, Fertile, MN
Fair Oaks Nursing Health Care Center, South Beloit, IL
Fair Oaks Nursing Home, Crystal Lake, IL
Fair Oaks Nursing Home, Hineston, LA
Fair Oaks Personal Care Home, Jamestown, KY
Fair Park Health Care Center, Dallas, TX
Fair Park Nursing Center, Huntsville, TX
Fair View Home, Mauston, WI
Fair View Nursing Home, Sedalia, MO
Fair Villa Nursing Home, King of Prussia, PA
Fair Winds Inc, Sarver, PA
Fairacres Manor Inc, Greeley, CO
Fairburn Health Care Center, Fairburn, GA
Fairchild Manor Nursing Home, Lewiston, NY
Fairchild Nursing Home, Fairchild, WI
Fairfax Community Home Inc, Fairfax, MN
Fairfax Health Care Center, Berwyn, IL
Fairfax Nursing Center, Fairfax, VA
Fairfax Nursing Home, Fairfax, OK
Fairfax Rest Home, Boston, MA
Fairfield Convalescent, Fairfield, CA
Fairfield Good Samaritan Center, Fairfield, WA
Fairfield Health Care Center, Fairfield, AL
Fairfield Homes, Ridgeway, SC
Fairfield Manor Health Care Center Inc, Norwalk, CT
Fairhaven Christian Home, Rockford, IL
Fairhaven Corporation, Whitewater, WI
Fairhaven Nursing Home, Sykesville, MD
Fairhaven Nursing Home, Westminster, MD
Fairhaven Nursing Home, Lowell, MA
Fairhaven Rest Home, Huntington, WV
Fairhaven Retirement & Health Care Community, Upper Sandusky, OH
Fairland Nursing Home, Silver Spring, MD
Fairland Nursing Home, Fairland, OK
Fairlane Nursing Center, Detroit, MI
Fairlawn Care Center, Gresham, OR
Fairlawn Chateau, Fairlawn, OH
Fairlawn Convalescent Home, Norwich, CT
Fairlawn Haven, Archbold, OH
Fairlawn Heights Nursing Center, Topeka, KS
Fairlawn Nursing Home Inc, Leominster, MA
Fairlawn Nursing Home Inc, Lexington, MA
Fairmont Community Hospital & Lutz Wing Nursing Home, Fairmont, MN
Fairmont Rehabilitation Hospital, Lodi, CA
Fairmont Rest Home, Ephrata, PA
Fairmount Geriatric Center, Philadelphia, PA
Fairmount Health Center, Willoughby, OH
Fairmount Rest Home, Leominster, MA
Fairmount Rest Home Inc, Boston, MA
Fairport Baptist Home, Fairport, NY
Fairview, Groton, CT
Fairview Baptist Home, Downers Grove, IL
Fairview Care Center, Colorado Springs, CO
Fairview Care Center of Bethlehem Pike, Philadelphia, PA
Fairview Care Center of Papermill Rd, Philadelphia, PA
Fairview Castle Nursing Home, Millersburg, OH
Fairview Convalescent Center, Salt Lake City, UT
Fairview Fellowship Home Inc, Fairview, OK
Fairview Gardens, Saint Louis, MO
Fairview Haven Inc, Fairbury, IL
Fairview Health Care Center, La Grange Park, IL
Fairview House Nursing Home, Rosiclare, IL
Fairview Manor, Belvidere, IL
Fairview Manor, Fairmont, NE
Fairview Manor, Fairview, PA
Fairview Manor, Fairfield, TX
Fairview Manor Nursing Center, Toledo, OH
Fairview Manor Nursing Center, Oklahoma City, OK
Fairview Manor Nursing Home Inc, Beverly, OH

Fairview Medical Care Facility, Centreville, MI
Fairview Nursing Care Center, Decatur, IL
Fairview Nursing Center, Du Quoin, IL
Fairview Nursing & Convalescent Home, Birmingham, AL
Fairview Nursing Home, Dodge Center, MN
Fairview Nursing Home, Hudson, NH
Fairview Nursing Home, Forest Hills, NY
Fairview Nursing Home, Cincinnati, OH
Fairview Nursing Home, Bonham, TX
Fairview Nursing Home, Salt Lake City, UT
Fairview Rest Home, Brockton, MA
Fairview Training Center, Salem, OR
Fairway Convalescent Center, Fullerton, CA
Fairway Group Home, Waterloo, IA
Fairways Caring Center, Maryland Heights, MO
Faith Countryside Homes Nursing Center, Highland, IL
Faith Haven Care Center, Jackson, MI
Faith Health Care Facility Inc, Florence, SC
Faith Lutheran Home, Wolf Point, MT
Faith Medical Care Center, Saint Clair, MI
Faith Memorial Nursing Home, Pasadena, TX
Faith Nursing Home, Edinburg, IN
Faith Village, Shawnee Mission, KS
Falkville Nursing Home Inc, Falkville, AL
Fall Creek Valley Nursing Home, Fall Creek, WI
Fall River Jewish Home for the Aged, Fall River, MA
Fall River Nursing Home Inc, Fall River, MA
Fallbrook Convalescent Hospital, Fallbrook, CA
Fallon Convalescent Center, Fallon, NV
Fallon Memorial Nursing Home, Baker, MT
Falls Care Center, International Falls, MN
Falls Nursing Home, South Hadley, MA
Falls Nursing Home—East, Oconto Falls, WI
Falls Nursing Home—West, Oconto Falls, WI
Falmouth Convalescent Center, Falmouth, ME
Falmouth Nursing Home, Falmouth, MA
Falmouth Rest Home, Falmouth, KY
Family Health West, Fruita, CO
Family Heritage Nursing Home, Black River Falls, WI
Family Heritage Nursing Home, Wisconsin Rapids, WI
Family House, Mankato, MN
Family Life Enrichment, High Shoals, GA
Family Nursing Home & Rehabilitation Center, Milwaukee, WI
Family Rest Home, Lynn, MA
Family Tree Care Center, Oregon, OH
Familystyle Home, Saint Paul, MN
Fannin County Nursing Home, Blue Ridge, GA
Far Rockaway Nursing Home, Far Rockaway, NY
Fargo Nursing Home, Fargo, ND
Faribault Manor Nursing Home, Faribault, MN
Faribault Regional Center, Faribault, MN
Farmdale Convalescent Hospital, Buena Park, CA
Farmington Convalescent Home, Farmington, CT
Farmington Nursing Home, Farmington, IL
Farmington Nursing Home, Farmington Hills, MI
Farnsworth Nursing Home, Peabody, MA
Farwell Convalescent Center, Farwell, TX
Father Murray Nursing Center, Centerline, MI
Father Purcell Memorial Exceptional Children's Center, Montgomery, AL
Father Walter Memorial Child Care Center, Montgomery, AL
Fauskee Nursing Home Inc, Worthington, MN
Fay Case Nursing Home, Salt Lake City, UT
Fayette Continuous Care Center, Fayetteville, WV
Fayette County Nursing Home, Fayette, AL
Fayette Health Care Center, Uniontown, PA
Fayetteville City Hospital Geriatrics Center, Fayetteville, AR
Federal Hill Manor Nurs/Conv Center, Bardstown, KY

Federal Way Convalescent Center, Federal Way, WA
Feghtly Lutheran Home, Tipp City, OH
Fejervary Health Care Center, Davenport, IA
Fellowship Club, Saint Paul, MN
Fellowship Deaconry Inc, Bernardsville, NJ
Fellowship Home, Danville, KY
Fellowship Nursing Home, Warrenton, MO
Felton Convalescent Home, Felton, DE
Fennimore Good Samaritan Center, Fennimore, WI
Fenton Extended Care Center, Fenton, MI
Fenton Park Health Related Facility, Greenhurst, NY
Fenton Park Nursing Home, Jamestown, NY
Fentress County Nursing Home, Jamestown, TN
Fenwood Manor Inc, Manchester, CT
Fergus Falls Regional Treatment Center, Fergus Falls, MN
Ferguson Convalescent Home, Lapeer, MI
Ferguson Nursing Center, Dallas, TX
Ferguson Rest Home, Clinton, MA
Fern Terrace Lodge, Mayfield, KY
Fern Terrace Lodge, Murray, KY
Fern Terrace Lodge of Bowling Green, Bowling Green, KY
Fern Terrace Lodge of Owensboro, Owensboro, KY
Ferncliff Nursing Home Co Inc, Rhinebeck, NY
Fernview Convalescent Hospital, San Gabriel, CA
Fernwood House Retirement & Nursing Center, Bethesda, MD
Ferrier Harris Home for Aged, Saint Louis, MO
Ferris Nursing Care Center, Ferris, TX
J Ferry Nursing Home, Elyria, OH
Ferry Nursing Home, Elyra, OH
Ferry Point—SNCF, Old Saybrook, CT
Festus Nursing Center, Festus, MO
Festus Rest Home, Festus, MO
Fiddlers Green Manor Nursing Home, Springville, NY
Field Crest Nursing Home, Hayfield, MN
Field House, Canon City, CO
Fieldcrest Manor Inc, Waldoboro, ME
Fieldston Lodge Nursing Home, Bronx, NY
Fieldview Manor Healthcare, Superior, WI
Fieser Nursing Home, Fenton, MO
Fifth Avenue Convalescent Hospital Inc, San Rafael, CA
Fifth Avenue Health Care Center, Rome, GA
Fifth Avenue Home, Texas City, TX
58th Avenue, Arvada, CO
Filling Memorial Home of Mercy Inc, Napoleon, OH
Fillmore Convalescent Center, Fillmore, CA
Fillmore County Long-Term Care, Geneva, NE
Fillmore Place, Preston, MN
Filosa Convalescent Home Inc, Danbury, CT
Hazel I Findlay Country Manor, Saint Johns, MI
Finnie Good Shepherd Nursing Home Inc, Galatia, IL
Fir Lane Terrace Convalescent Center, Shelton, WA
Fircrest Convalescent Hospital, Sebastopol, CA
Fircrest School, Seattle, WA
Firelands Nursing Center, New London, OH
Firemans Home of the State of New York Volunteer Firemens Assoc, Hudson, NY
Fireside Convalescent Hospital, Santa Monica, CA
Fireside Foster Inn, Mora, MN
Fireside Lodge, Cleburne, TX
Fireside Lodge Retirement Center Inc, Fort Worth, TX
Firesteel Heights Nursing Home, Mitchell, SD
Firestone Community Residence, Charleston, SC
First Christian Church Residence, Minneapolis, MN
First Community Village Healthcare Center, Columbus, OH

First Hill Care Center, Seattle, WA
First Midlands ICMRF, Columbia, SC
Fisher Convalescent Home, Mayville, MI
Fisher County Nursing Home, Rotan, TX
Fishkill Health Related Center Inc, Beacon, NY
The Fitch Home Inc, Melrose, MA
Fitzgerald Nursing Home, Fitzgerald, GA
Thomas Fitzgerald Veterans Home, Omaha, NE
Five Counties Nursing Home, Lemmon, SD
Five Oaks Nursing Center, Concord, NC
Flagship Convalescent Center, Newport Beach, CA
Flambeau-Aneskarn 1, Minneapolis, MN
Flannery's Health Care Center, Portsmouth, OH
Flat Rock Care Center, Flat Rock, OH
Flatbush Manor Care Center, Brooklyn, NY
Flathead County Nursing Home, Kalispell, MT
Fleetcrest Manor Inc, Waterbury, CT
Fleetwood Nursing Home, Athol, MA
Mary Fletcher Health Care Center 1, Salem, OH
Mary Fletcher Health Care Center 2, Wellsville, OH
Fleur de Lis, Farmington, MO
Flinn Memorial Home Inc, Marion, IN
Flint City Nursing Home Inc, Decatur, AL
Flint Hills Manor, Emporia, KS
Floadrian Manor, Columbia, MS
Flora Care Center Inc, Flora, IL
Flora Manor, Flora, IL
Flora Nursing Center, Flora, IL
Flora Terrace Convalescent Hospital Inc, Los Angeles, CA
Flora Terrace West Convalescent & Rehabilitation Hospital, Los Angeles, CA
Florence Convalescent Center, Florence, SC
Florence Hand Home—Skilled Nursing Facility, LaGrange, GA
Florence Height Village Nursing Center Inc, Omaha, NE
Florence Home, Omaha, NE
Florence Nightingale Nursing Home, New York, NY
Florence Nursing Home, Marengo, IL
Florence Nursing Home, Florence, NJ
Florence Rest Home, Northampton, MA
Florence Villa, Florence, WI
Floresville Nursing Home, Floresville, TX
Florida Baptist Retirement Center, Vero Beach, FL
Florida Christian Health Center, Jacksonville, FL
Florida Living Nursing Center, Forest City, FL
Florida Manor Nursing Home, Orlando, FL
Floridean Nursing Home Inc, Miami, FL
Florin Convalescent Hospital, Sacramento, CA
Florissant Nursing Center, Florissant, MO
Flower Square Health Care Center, Tucson, AZ
Floy Dyer Manor, Houston, MS
J H Floyd Sunshine Manor, Sarasota, FL
Floydada Nursing Home, Floydada, TX
Flushing Manor Nursing Home & Flushing Manor Care Center, Flushing, NY
Foley Nursing Center, Foley, MN
Foley Nursing Home, Foley, AL
Folk Convalescent Home, Florence, SC
Folsom Convalescent Hospital, Folsom, CA
Folts Home, Herkimer, NY
Fond Du Lac County Health Care Center, Fond Du Lac, WI
Fond Du Lac Lutheran Home, Fond Du Lac, WI
Fonda Care Center, Fonda, IA
Fondulac Nursing Home, East Peoria, IL
Fontaine Woods Nursing Home, Saint Louis, MO
Fontanbleu Nursing Center, Bloomington, IN
Fontanelle Good Samaritan Center, Fontanelle, IA
Foothill Acres Inc, Neshanic, NJ
Foothill Convalescent Hospital, Pomona, CA

Foothill Health & Rehabilitation Center, Sylmar, CA
Foothills Care Center Inc, Longmont, CO
Foothills ICF/MR Group Home, Morganton, NC
Forbes Center for Gerontology, Pittsburgh, PA
Ford County Nursing Home, Paxton, IL
The Charles Ford Memorial Home, New Harmony, IN
Ford-Hull-Mar Nursing Home, Yorkville, OH
Forest Cove Nursing Center, Jackson, TN
Forest Del Convalescent Home Inc, Princeton, IN
Forest Farm Health Care Centre Inc, Middletown, RI
Forest Haven Nursing Home, Catonsville, MD
Forest Hill Convalescent Center, Richmond, VA
Forest Hill Manor Inc, Fort Kent, ME
Forest Hill Nursing Center Inc, Fort Worth, TX
Forest Hills Nursing Center, Columbia, SC
Forest Hills Nursing Home, Forest Hills, NY
Forest Hills Nursing Home Inc, Cleveland, OH
Forest Manor Health Care Center, Hope, NJ
Forest Manor Health Related Facility, Glen Cove, NY
Forest Manor Inc, Northport, AL
Forest Manor Long-Term Care Facility, Middleboro, MA
Forest Manor Nursing Home, Covington, LA
Forest Oaks Nursing Home, Hamilton, TX
Forest Park Health Center, Carlisle, PA
Forest Park Healthcare Center, Kokomo, IN
Forest Park Nursing Center, Plant City, FL
Forest Ridge Convalescent Center, Bremerton, WA
Forest View Care Center, Forest Grove, OR
Forest View Nursing Home, Forest Hills, NY
Forest Villa Nursing Center, Niles, IL
Forestdale Health Care Center, Birmingham, AL
Forestdale Nusing Home, Malden, MA
Forester Haven, San Fernando, CA
Forester Nursing Home Inc, Wintersville, OH
Forestview Hemingway, Cottage Grove, MN
Forestview James, Minneapolis, MN
Forestview Kentucky, Crystal, MN
Forestview Lexington, Lexington, MN
Forestview Minnetonka, Minnetonka, MN
Forestview Nursing Home, Cincinnati, OH
Forestview Sunlen, Bloomington, MN
Forestview Vincent, Richfield, MN
Forestville Nursing Center, Forestville, CT
Forge Pond Nursing Home, East Bridgewater, MA
Forks Community Hospital, Forks, WA
For-Rest Convalescent Home, Hattiesburg, MS
Forrest Lake Manor Inc, Martinez, GA
Forrest Manor Nursing Home, Dewey, OK
Forsyth Nursing Home, Forsyth, GA
Fort Atkinson Health Care Center, Fort Atkinson, WI
Fort Bayard Medical Center—Nurs Home Unit, Fort Bayard, NM
Fort Bend Nursing Home, Rosenberg, TX
Fort Collins Good Samaritan Retirement Village, Fort Collins, CO
Fort Collins Health Care Center, Fort Collins, CO
Fort Dodge Group Home, Fort Dodge, IA
Fort Dodge Villa Care Center, Fort Dodge, IA
Fort Gaines Nursing Home, Fort Gaines, GA
Fort Gibson Nursing Home, Fort Gibson, OK
Fort Hudson Nursing Home Inc, Fort Edward, NY
Fort Logan Hospital—ECF, Stanford, KY
Fort Madison Nursing Care Center, Fort Madison, IA
Fort Myers Care Center, Fort Myers, FL
Fort Oglethorpe Nursing Center, Fort Oglethorpe, GA
Fort Pierce Care Center, Fort Pierce, FL
Fort Sanders—Sevier Medical Center Nursing Home, Sevierville, TN
Fort Scott Manor, Fort Scott, KS

Fort Stanton Hospital & Training School, Fort Stanton, NM
Fort Tryon Nursing Home, New York, NY
Fort Valley Health Care Center, Fort Valley, GA
Fort Vancouver Convalescent Center, Vancouver, WA
Fort Walton Developmental Center, Fort Walton Beach, FL
Fort Washington Estates, Fort Washington, PA
Fort Washington Rehabilitation Center, Fort Washington, MD
Fort Wayne Nursing Home, Fort Wayne, IN
Fort Worth Western Hills Nursing Home Inc, Fort Worth, TX
Forum Convalescent Center, Trenton, TN
Foss Home, Seattle, WA
Fosston Group Home, Fosston, MN
Fosston Municipal Nursing Home, Fosston, MN
Wendell Foster Center, Owensboro, KY
Fostrian Manor, Flushing, MI
Foulk Manor—North, Wilmington, DE
Foulk Manor South, Wilmington, DE
Foulkeways at Gwynedd Inc, Gwynedd, PA
Fountain Care Center, Orange, CA
Fountain Care Center, Springfield, OH
Fountain Gardens Convalescent Hospital, Los Angeles, CA
Fountain Inn Convalescent Home, Fountain Inn, SC
Fountain Lodge Nursing Home, Baton Rouge, LA
Fountain Manor, Hicksville, OH
Fountain Nursing Home, Reform, AL
Fountain Park Nursing Home, Woodstock, OH
Fountain Terrace, Rockford, IL
Fountain View Convalescent Hospital, Los Angeles, CA
Fountain View Inc, Eldorado, IL
Fountain View Manor, Henryetta, OK
Fountain View Nursing Home, Springhill, LA
Fountain View Villa, Ashland, KS
Fountain Villa Care Center, Sabetha, KS
Fountain West Health Center, West Des Moines, IA
Fountainbleau Nursing Centre, Anaheim, CA
Fountainbleau Nursing Home, Little Rock, AR
Fountainhead Nursing & Convalescent Home, North Miami, FL
Fountainhead Nursing Home, Franklin Furnace, OH
Fountains Convalescent Center, Yakima, WA
Fountains Nursing Home, Boca Raton, FL
Fountains Nursing Home, Marion, IL
Fountainview Convalescent Center, Atlanta, GA
Fountainview Place, Elkhart, IN
Fountainview Place, Goshen, IN
Fountainview Place of Indianapolis, Indianapolis, IN
Fountainview Place of Mishawaka, Mishawaka, IN
Fountainview Place of Muncie, Muncie, IN
Fountainview Place of Portage, Portage, IN
Fountainview Terrace, LaPorte, IN
Four Chaplains Convalescent Home, Westland, MI
Four Corners Good Samaritan, Aztec, NM
Four Corners Health Care Center, Durango, CO
Four Corners Regional Care Center, Blanding, UT
Four Courts Inc, Louisville, KY
Four Fountains Convalescent Center, Belleville, IL
Four Oaks Health Care Center, Jonesborough, TN
Four Oaks Rest Home Inc, Imperial, MO
Four Pines Retirement Home Inc, Independence, MO
Four Seasons Care Center—Central, Saint Paul, MN
Four Seasons Care Center—Metro, Minneapolis, MN

Four Seasons Health Care Center, Fort Collins, CO
Four Seasons Nursing Care of Northwest Oklahoma City, Oklahoma City, OK
Four Seasons Nursing Center, Durant, OK
Four Seasons Nursing Center, Austin, TX
Four Seasons Nursing Center, Ennis, TX
Four Seasons Nursing Center, Odessa, TX
Four Seasons Nursing Center, Temple, TX
Four Seasons Nursing Center—Babcock, San Antonio, TX
Four Seasons Nursing Center—Camino Vista, Albuquerque, NM
Four Seasons Nursing Center — Dallas, Dallas, TX
Four Seasons Nursing Center—North, San Antonio, TX
Four Seasons Nursing Center—North Richland Hills, Fort Worth, TX
Four Seasons Nursing Center—Northeast Heights, Albuquerque, NM
Four Seasons Nursing Center—Northwest, Fort Worth, TX
Four Seasons Nursing Center—Northwest, San Antonio, TX
Four Seasons Nursing Center of El Paso, El Paso, TX
Four Seasons Nursing Center of Midwest City, Midwest City, OK
Four Seasons Nursing Center of Norman, Norman, OK
Four Seasons Nursing Center of Southwest Oklahoma City, Oklahoma City, OK
Four Seasons Nursing Center of Tulsa, Tulsa, OK
Four Seasons Nursing Center of Warr Acres, Oklahoma City, OK
Four Seasons Nursing Center of Windsor Hills, Oklahoma City, OK
Four Seasons Nursing Center—Pecan Valley, San Antonio, TX
Four Seasons Nursing Center—Ridgecrest, Albuquerque, NM
Four Seasons Nursing Center—Santa Fe, Santa Fe, NM
Four Seasons Nursing Center—South, San Antonio, TX
Four Seasons Nursing Center—Windcrest, San Antonio, TX
Four Seasons Nursing Home, Moscow Mills, MO
Four Seasons Rest Home, Millis, MA
Four Seasons Retirement & Health Care Center, Columbus, IN
Four States Nursing Home, Texarkana, TX
Four Winds Manor, Verona, WI
Fowler Convalescent Hospital, Fowler, CA
Fowler Health Care Center, Fowler, CO
Juliette Fowler Homes, Dallas, TX
Fowler Nursing Center Inc, Guilford, CT
Fowler Nursing Home, Fowler, KS
Aurelia Osborn Fox Memorial Hospital Nursing Home, Oneonta, NY
Fox Nursing and Rehabilitation Center, Warrington, PA
Fox Nursing Home Inc, Chester, WV
Fox Run Manor, Findlay, OH
Fox Valley Nursing Center Inc, South Elgin, IL
Fox View Acres, Berlin, WI
Foxcrest Manor, West Chicago, IL
Foxwood Springs Living Center, Raymore, MO
Frame House Manor, Indianapolis, IN
Frame Nursing Home Inc, Indianapolis, IN
Framingham Nursing Home, Framingham, MA
Jan Frances Care Center, Ada, OK
Frances Mahon Deaconess Hospital—Extended Care Facility, Glasgow, MT
Frances Residence I, Saint Paul, MN
Sarah Frances/Tally-Ho Manor, Boonton, NJ
Francis Convalescent Center, Fort Worth, TX
Jane Francis Nursing Home, Ravenna, OH
Francis Marion Manor, Marion, VA
Francis N Sanders Nursing Home Inc, Gloucester, VA

Francis T Crimmins Rest Home, Stoughton, MA
Franciscan Convalescent Hospital, Merced, CA
Franciscan Nursing Home, Joliet, IL
Franciscan Terrace at St Clare Center, Cincinnati, OH
Franciscan Villa, Broken Arrow, OK
Franciscan Villa of South Milwaukee, South Milwaukee, WI
Franida House Nursing Home, Boston, MA
Frankenmuth Convalescent Center, Frankenmuth, MI
Frankfort Community Care Home Inc, Frankfort, KS
Frankfort Heights Manor, West Frankfort, IL
Frankfort Nursing Home, Frankfort, IN
Frankfort Terrace, Frankfort, IL
Franklin Care Center, Gladstone, OR
Franklin Convalescent Center, Franklin Park, NJ
Franklin County Health Care Center, Winchester, TN
Franklin County Nursing Home, Preston, ID
Franklin County Nursing Home, Malone, NY
Franklin County Nursing Home, Chambersburg, PA
Franklin General Hospital, Hampton, IA
Franklin Grove Health Care Center, Franklin Grove, IL
Franklin Guest Home, Winnsboro, LA
Franklin Health Care Center, Franklin, GA
Franklin Health Care Center, Franklin, TN
Franklin Healthcare Center, Franklin, IN
Franklin Healthcare Center, Franklin, MN
Franklin House Health Care, Franklin, MA
Franklin Manor, Frankfort, KY
Franklin Manor Convalescent Center, Southfield, MI
Franklin Manor II Inc, Farmington, ME
Franklin Medco Center, Franklin, KY
Franklin Nursing Center, Franklin, NE
Franklin Nursing Center of Sidney, Sidney, OH
Franklin Nursing Center of Vandalia, Vandalia, OH
Franklin Nursing Home, Franklin, IN
Franklin Nursing Home, Hampton, IA
Franklin Nursing Home, Franklin, LA
Franklin Nursing Home, Braintree, MA
Franklin Nursing Home, Flushing, NY
Franklin Nursing Home of Dayton, Dayton, OH
Franklin Nursing Home of Franklin, Franklin, OH
Franklin Nursing & Rehabilitation Center, Greenfield, MA
Franklin Park Nursing Home, Franklin Square, NY
Franklin Personal Care, Franklin, KY
Franklin Place East, Minneapolis, MN
Franklin Plaza, Cleveland, OH
The Franklin United Methodist Home, Franklin, IN
Martha Franks Baptist Retirement Center, Laurens, SC
Frankston Nursing Center, Frankston, TX
Franvale Nursing Home, Braintree, MA
Fraser Intermediate Care Facility, San Diego, CA
Fraser Rest Home of Falmouth, Falmouth, MA
Fraser Rest Home of Hyannis, Barnstable, MA
Fraser Rest Home of Sandwich, Sandwich, MA
Frasier Meadows Manor Health Care Center, Boulder, CO
Frazee Retirement Center, Frazee, MN
Frazier Nursing Home, Saint Louis, MO
Frederic Municipal Nursing Home Inc, Frederic, WI
Frederick Mennonite Home, Frederick, PA
Frederick Villa Nursing Center, Catonsville, MD
Fredericka Manor Convalescent Hospital, Chula Vista, CA
Fredericksburg Nursing Home, Fredericksburg, TX

Fredericksburg Nursing Home, Fredericksburg, VA
Free State Crestwood Inc, Wills Point, TX
Freeburg Care Center Inc, Freeburg, IL
Freelandville Community Home Inc, Freelandville, IN
Freeman Community Nursing Home, Freeman, SD
Freeman Convalescent Home, Iron Mountain, MI
Freeman Nursing Home, Pepperell, MA
Freeport Convalescent Center, Freeport, ME
Freeport Manor Nursing Center, Freeport, IL
The Freeport Nursing Home Inc, Freeport, ME
Freeport Towne Square I, Freeport, ME
Freeport Towne Square II, Freeport, ME
Freezers Home for the Aged, South Williamsport, PA
Fremont Care Center, Fremont, NE
Fremont Convalescent Hospital, Fremont, CA
French Prairie Care Center, Woodburn, OR
Sarah Roberts French Home, San Antonio, TX
Frenchtown Convalescent Center, Monroe, MI
Frene Valley Geriatric & Rehabilitation Center, Hermann, MO
Frene Valley Health Center, Hermann, MO
Fresno Care & Guidance Center, Fresno, CA
Fresno Convalescent Hospital, Fresno, CA
Fresno Westview Convalescent Hospital, Fresno, CA
Frey Village, Middletown, PA
Frickell Family Care Home, Denver, CO
Fridley Convalescent Home, Fridley, MN
Friedler's Guest House, Baltimore, MD
Friedwald House, New City, NY
Friel Nursing Home Inc, Wallaston, MA
Friend Manor, Friend, NE
Friendly Acres Inc, Newton, KS
The Friendly Home Inc, Woonsocket, RI
Friendly Manor Nursing Home, Eufaula, OK
Friendly Nursing Home, Millmont, PA
Friendly Nursing Home, Pitman, PA
Friendly Nursing Home Inc, Miamisburg, OH
The Friendly Village, Rhinelander, WI
Friends Care Center, Yellow Springs, OH
Friends Fellowship Community Inc, Richmond, IN
Friends Hall at Fox Chase, Philadelphia, PA
Friends Hall at West Chester, West Chester, PA
Friends Home at Woodstown, Woodstown, NJ
Friends Home Inc, Greensboro, NC
Friends Nursing Home Inc, Sandy Spring, MD
Friendship Care Center, Marion, IL
Friendship Care Center—Herrin, Herrin, IL
Friendship Community, Lititz, PA
Friendship Haven, Chattanooga, TN
Friendship Haven I, Sherburn, MN
Friendship Haven II, Sherburn, MN
Friendship Haven Inc, Fort Dodge, IA
Friendship Health Center, Portland, OR
Friendship Home, Carlinville, IL
Friendship Home, Audubon, IA
Friendship Home, Deadwood, SD
Friendship Homes, National City, CA
Friendship House, Danville, KY
Friendship House, Willmar, MN
Friendship Manor, Rock Island, IL
Friendship Manor, Scottsville, KY
Friendship Manor, McVille, ND
Friendship Manor, Anadarko, OK
Friendship Manor Convalescent Center, National City, CA
Friendship Manor Convalescent Center, Roanoke, VA
Friendship Manor Inc, Nashville, IL
Friendship Manor Inc, Grinnell, IA
Friendship Manor Lakeside, Lakeside, CA
Friendship Manor Nursing Home, Pewee Valley, KY
Friendship Manor Nursing Home, Detroit, MI
Friendship Villa Care Center, Miles City, MT
Friendship Villa of Spalding, Spalding, NE
Friendship Village, Kalamazoo, MI
Friendship Village, Bloomington, MN
Friendship Village, Saint Louis, MO

Friendship Village, Dayton, OH
Friendship Village Health Care Center, Schaumburg, IL
Friendship Village of Columbus Health Care Center, Columbus, OH
Friendship Village of Dublin Health Center, Dublin, OH
Friendship Village of Greater Milwaukee Inc, Milwaukee, WI
Friendship Village of Tempe Health Center, Tempe, AZ
Friendship Village Retirement Center, Waterloo, IA
Friendship Village West County, Chesterfield, MO
Friendsview Manor Healthcenter, Newburg, OR
Friendswood Arms Convalescent Center, Friendswood, TX
Frigon Nursing Home Inc, Central Falls, RI
Frio County Nursing Center, Pearsall, TX
Frontier Extended Care Facility, Longview, WA
Frontier Manor, Gainesville, TX
Frost Street Convalescent Hospital, San Diego, CA
Frostburg Village Nursing Home of Allegany County, Frostburg, MD
Fruitvale Care Convalescent Hospital, Oakland, CA
Fryeburg Health Care Center, Fryeburg, ME
Fueller Nursing Home, Saint Louis, MO
Fullerton Care Convalescent Hospital, Fullerton, CA
Fullerton Manor, Fullerton, NE
Fulton County Infirmary, Gloversville, NY
Fulton County Medical Center, McConnellsburg, PA
Fulton County Nursing Center, Salem, AR
Fulton Manor Care Center, Fulton, MO
Fulton Presbyterian Manor, Fulton, MO
Furgala Nursing Home, Lancaster, NY
G A F Lake Cook Terrace, Northbrook, IL
A G Gaston Home for Senior Citizens, Birmingham, AL
A G Rhodes Home Inc, Atlanta, GA
The Gables Inc, Hartford, CT
Gables Nursing Home, Madison, OH
Gade ICF/MR, Union City, OH
Gade Nursing Home Inc, Greenville, OH
Gade Nursing Home Inc 1, Greenville, OH
Gadsden Health Care Center Inc, Gadsden, AL
Gadsden Nursing Home, Quincy, FL
Gafney Home for the Aged, Rochester, NH
Gainesville Convalescent Center, Gainesville, TX
Gainesville Health Care Center, Gainesville, GA
Gainesville Manor, Hopkinsville, KY
Gainesville Nursing Center, Gainesville, FL
Galaxy Manor Nursing Home, Cleveland, TX
Gale Home, Manchester, NH
Galen State Hospital, Deer Lodge, MT
Galena Manor, Galena, KS
Galena Park Home, Peoria, IL
Galena Stauss Hospital & Nursing Care Facility, Galena, IL
Galesburg Nursing & Rehabilitation Center, Galesburg, IL
Caroline K Galland Home, Seattle, WA
Gallant Rest Home, Gardner, MA
Gallatin County Nursing Home, Bozeman, MT
Gallatin Health Care Associates, Gallatin, TN
Gallipolis State Institute, Gallipolis, OH
Mary Galloway Home for the Aged Women, Memphis, TN
Gallup Care Center, Gallup, NM
Gamma Road Lodge, Wellsville, MO
Garber Nursing Home, Garber, OK
Garber's University Nursing Center, Eugene, OR
Garden County Lewellen Nursing Home, Lewellen, NE
Garden Court Convalescent Hospital, Sacramento, CA

Garden Crest Convalescent Hospital Inc, Los Angeles, CA
Garden Gate Manor, Cheektowaga, NY
Garden Grove Convalescent Hospital, Garden Grove, CA
Garden Grove Nursing Home, Kansas City, MO
Garden Manor Extended Care Center Inc, Middletown, OH
Garden Manor Nursing Home Inc, Lakewood, CO
Garden Nursing Home & Convalescent Hospital, Santa Cruz, CA
Garden of the Gods Care Center, Colorado Springs, CO
Garden Plaza Convalescent Hospital, Los Angeles, CA
Garden State Health Care Center, East Orange, NJ
Garden State Manor Nursing Home, Holmdel, NJ
Garden Terrace Manor, Spokane, WA
Garden Terrace Nursing Center, Douglasville, GA
Garden Terrace Nursing Center, Graham, TX
Garden Valley Retirement Village, Garden City, KS
Garden View Care Center, Shenandoah, IA
Garden View Home Inc, Chicago, IL
Garden Villa Nursing Home, El Campo, TX
Gardena Convalescent Center, Gardena, CA
Gardendale Nursing Home, Jacksonville, TX
Gardendale Nursing Home Inc, Gardendale, AL
Gardens Skilled Nursing Facility, Sacramento, CA
The Gardens, Laguna Beach, CA
Gardenview Care Center, Hillsboro, OR
Gardenview Nursing Home, Cincinnati, OH
Gardiner Group Home, Gardiner, ME
Gardiner Nursing Home, Houlton, ME
Gardner Heights Convalescent Center Inc, Shelton, CT
Gardner House Rest Home, Boston, MA
Gardner Manor Nursing Home, Gardner, MA
Gardner Nursing Home of Star City Inc, Star City, AR
Gardner Pierce Nursing & Rest Home, Boston, MA
Gardner's Grove Nursing Home, Swansea, MA
Garfield Care Convalescent Hospital, Huntington Beach, CA
Garfield County Health Center Inc, Jordan, MT
Garfield Geropsychiatric Hospital, Oakland, CA
Garfield Memorial Hospital, Panguitch, UT
Garfield Park Health Facility Inc, Indianapolis, IN
Garland Convalescent Center, Hot Springs, AR
Garland Convalescent Center, Garland, TX
Garland Manors Nursing Home Inc, Garland, TX
Garland Rest Home, Newton, MA
Garlock Memorial Convalescent Home Inc, Hagerstown, MD
Garnets Chateau, Jerseyville, IL
Garrard Convalescent Home, Covington, KY
Garrard County Home for Senior Citizens, Lancaster, KY
Garrard County Memorial Hospital—SNF, Lancaster, KY
Garrett Park Manor, Dallas, TX
Garrison Memorial Hospital—ICF, Garrison, ND
Garrison Nursing Home Inc, Baltimore, MD
Garrison Nursing Home Inc, Garrison, ND
Garrison Nursing Home Inc, Garrison, TX
Garrison Valley Center Inc, Garrison, MD
Garvey Manor, Hollidaysburg, PA
Marcus Garvey Nursing Company Inc, Brooklyn, NY
The Garwood Home, Champaign, IL
Gasconade Manor Nursing Home, Owensville, MO

Gaslite Villa Convalescent Center Inc, Canal Fulton, OH
Gaspard's Nursing Care Center Inc, Port Arthur, TX
Gatesway Foundation Inc, Broken Arrow, OK
Gateway Care Center, Portland, OR
Gateway Intermediate Care, Clinton, IA
Gateway Manor Inc, Lincoln, NE
Gateways to Better Living 1, Youngstown, OH
Gateways to Better Living 3, Youngstown, OH
Gateways to Better Living Inc—No 9, Youngstown, OH
Gateways to Better Living 16, Youngstown, OH
Gaulden Manor, Baltimore, OH
Virginia Gay Hospital, Vinton, IA
Gaye Haven Intermediate Care Facility Inc, Las Vegas, NV
Gayhart's Nursing Home, Piketon, OH
Gayle Street Residential Center, Fort Morgan, CO
Gaylord Lakeview Home, Gaylord, MN
Gaymont Nursing Center, Norwalk, OH
Geary Community Nursing Home Inc, Geary, OK
Geer Memorial Health Center, Canaan, CT
Gem Care Center, Miami Beach, FL
Gem Convalescent Hospital, Los Gatos, CA
Gem State Homes Inc 1, Nampa, ID
Gem State Homes Inc 2, Meridian, ID
Gem State Homes Inc 4, Boise, ID
General Baptist Nursing Home, Mount Carmel, IL
General Baptist Nursing Home, Independence, MO
General Baptist Nursing Home Inc, Campbell, MO
General Care Convalescent Center, Clarksville, TN
Genesee Care Center, Flint, MI
Genesee County Nursing Home, Batavia, NY
Genesee Hospital—Extended Care Facility, Rochester, NY
Genesee Nursing Home, Utica, NY
Geneseo Good Samaritan, Geneseo, IL
Genesis, Columbus, OH
Genesis House, Genoa, IL
Geneva General Hospital Nursing Home Co Inc, Geneva, NY
Geneva Health Care, Geneva, OH
Geneva Lake Manor, Lake Geneva, WI
Geneva Retirement Center, Geneva, IL
Genoa Care Center, Genoa, OH
George Community Good Samaritan Center, George, IA
Georgetown Manor, Aledo, IL
Georgetown Manor Health Care Services, Louisville, KY
Georgetown Nursing Home Inc, Georgetown, OH
Georgetown Sweetbriar Nursing Home Inc, Georgetown, TX
Georgia Grace Memorial Home Inc, Statesboro, GA
Georgia Manor Nursing Home, Amarillo, TX
Georgia Regional Development Learning Center, Decatur, GA
Georgia Retardation Center, Atlanta, GA
Georgia Retardation Center—Athens, Athens, GA
Georgia War Veterans Nursing Home, Augusta, GA
Georgian—Bloomfield, Bloomfield Hills, MI
Georgian Court Nursing Home of Buffalo Inc, Buffalo, NY
Georgian Court Nursing Home of Tulsa, Tulsa, OK
Georgian Court Nursing & Rehabilitation Center, San Diego, CA
Georgian East, Grosse Pointe Woods, MI
The Georgian Home, Evanston, IL
Georgian House Health Care Center, Tacoma, WA
Georgian Manor Nursing Home, Brackenridge, PA
Georgiana Nursing Facility, Georgiana, AL
Gerarda House, Bloomington, MN
Geras Nursing Home, Mount Pleasant, TX

Geri-Care Inc, Cleveland, OH
Geriatric Authority of Milford, Milford, MA
Geriatric Center of Grandview, Grandview, MO
Geriatric Center of Stockbridge Inc, Stockbridge, MI
Geriatric Center-Mansfield Memorial Homes, Mansfield, OH
Geriatrics Nursing Center, Jonesboro, AR
Geriatrics Nursing Center Inc—Forrest City, Forrest City, AR
Geriatrics Nursing Center Inc—Heber Springs, Heber Springs, AR
Geriatrics Nursing Center Inc—West Memphis, West Memphis, AR
German Masonic Home Corp, New Rochelle, NY
German Old Folks Home Inc, Lawrence, MA
Germantown Home, Philadelphia, PA
Gerrit Smith Memorial Infirmary, Eaton, NY
Gerry Nursing Home Co Inc, Gerry, NY
Gertha's Nursing Center Inc, Evansville, IN
Gethsemane Group Home, Virginia, MN
Gettysburg Lutheran Retirement Village, Gettysburg, PA
Ghana Village Home Inc, Oklahoma City, OK
Ghent Arms Nursing Home, Norfolk, VA
Gibbs Boarding Home, Wilmington, DE
Gibbs Care Center, Steelville, MO
Gibbs & McRaven Sheltered Care Home, Jonesboro, IL
Gibson Community Hospital Annex, Gibson City, IL
Gibson Manor, Gibson City, IL
Gibson Nursing Center, Aspermont, TX
Gibson Rest & Convalescent Home, Gibson, GA
Giddings Convalescent Center, Giddings, TX
Carrie Elligson Gietner Home Inc, Saint Louis, MO
Gig Harbor Group Home, Gig Harbor, WA
Gil Mor Manor, Morgan, MN
Gila County General Hospital, Globe, AZ
Gilbert Nursing Home, Leonard, TX
Gilbert Old People's Home, Ypsilanti, MI
Giles Family Care Home, Commerce City, CO
Gill Odd Fellows Home of Vermont Inc, Ludlow, VT
Gillett Nursing Home Inc, Gillett, WI
Gillette Nursing Home, Warren, OH
Gillette's The Country Place, Warren, OH
Gilman Nursing Center, Gilman, IL
Gilman Nursing Home, Gilman, WI
Gilmer Convalescent & Nursing Center, Gilmer, TX
Gilmer Nursing Home, Saint Augustine, FL
Gilmer Nursing Home, Ellijay, GA
Gilmore Lane Convalescent Hospital, Oroville, CA
Gilmores White Cliff Nursing Home, Greenville, PA
Gina's Granny Home, Sedalia, MO
Girdler House, Beverly, MA
Girouard St Jude Nursing Home Inc, South Barre, VT
Glacier County Medical Center, Cut Bank, MT
Glacier Hills Nursing Center, Ann Arbor, MI
Glad Day Nursing Center, Beaumont, TX
Glades Health Care Center, Pahokee, FL
Gladstone Convalescent Care, Gladstone, OR
Gladstone Nursing Home, Kansas City, MO
Gladwin Nursing Home, Gladwin, MI
Glasgow Nursing Home Inc, Cambridge, MD
Glasgow Rest Home, Glasgow, KY
Glasgow State—ICF, Glasgow, KY
Glen Ayr Health Center, Lakewood, CO
Glen Convalescent Hospital, Stockton, CA
Glen Ellen Convalescent Hospital, Hayward, CA
Glen Field Health Care Center, Milwaukee, WI
Glen Halla Intermediate Care Facility, Henderson, NV
Glen Haven Home, Glenwood, IA
Glen Haven Personal Care Home, Lexington, KY
Glen Hill Conv Center, Danbury, CT

Glen Manor Home for Jewish Aged, Cincinnati, OH
Glen Oaks Care Center, New London, MN
Glen Oaks Convalescent Center, Shelbyville, TN
Glen Oaks Nursing Home, Auburn, IN
Glen Oaks Nursing Home, Lucedale, MS
Glen Oaks Nursing Home Inc, Northbrook, IL
Glen Oaks Retirement Home, Shreveport, LA
Glen Parke Nursing Home, Cincinnati, OH
The Glen Retirement Village, Shreveport, LA
Glen Ridge Manor, Glendale, AZ
Glen Terrace Convalescent Center, Norwalk, CA
Glen Terrace Nursing Center, Seattle, WA
Glen Valley Nursing Home, Glenwood Springs, CO
Glenaire Care Center, Portland, OR
Glenburn Rest Haven Home Inc, Linton, IN
Glenburney Nursing Home, Natchez, MS
Glencoe Area Health Center, Glencoe, MN
Glencrest Nursing Rehabilitation Center Ltd, Chicago, IL
GlenCroft Care Center, Glendale, AZ
Glendale Care Center, Glendale, AZ
Glendale Health Care Center Inc, Naugatuck, CT
The Glendale Home, Mansfield, OH
Glendale Manor, Topeka, KS
Glendale Nursing Home, Glendale, AZ
Glendale Nursing Home, Woburn, MA
Glendale Nursing Home, Scotia, NY
Glendale Nursing Home Inc, Wadley, GA
Glendeen Nursing Home, Billings, MT
Glendive Coummunity Nursing Home, Glendive, MT
Glendora Nursing Home, Wooster, OH
The Glengariff Health Care Center, Glen Cove, NY
Glenhaven, Glenwood City, WI
Glenkirk Circle, Mundelein, IL
Glenlora Nursing Home, Chester, NJ
Glenn Haven Nursing Home, Dayton, OH
Glenn View Manor, Mineral Ridge, OH
Glenn-Mor Home, Thomasville, GA
Glennon Place, Kansas City, MO
Glenoaks Convalescent Hospital, Glendale, CA
Glenpool Health Care Center, Glenpool, OK
Glenridge Center, Glendale, CA
Glenside Nursing Center, New Providence, NJ
Glenview Manor, Glasgow, KY
Glenview of Tyler Nursing Home Inc, Tyler, TX
Glenview Terrace Nursing Center, Glenview, IL
Glenvue Nursing Home, Glenville, GA
Glenward Health Care Center, Hamilton, OH
Glenwood Care, Salt Lake City, UT
Glenwood Care Center, Defiance, OH
Glenwood Christian Nursing Home, Lamont, MI
Glenwood Convalescent Center, Florence, AL
Glenwood Convalescent Hospital, Oxnard, CA
Glenwood Estate, Independence, KS
Glenwood Hills Intermediate Care Facility, Raleigh, NC
Glenwood Manor, Decatur, GA
Glenwood Manor Convalescent Home, Lowell, MA
Glenwood Nursing Home Inc, Glenwood, AR
Glenwood Park United Methodist Home, Princeton, WV
Glenwood Retirement Home Inc, Glenwood, MN
Glenwood Terrace Nursing Center, Glenwood, IL
Glisan Care Center Inc, Portland, OR
Gloria Dei Village Health Care Center, Holland, PA
Gloversville Extended Care & Nursing Home Co Inc, Gloversville, NY
Glynn Memorial Nursing Home, Haverhill, MA
Gnaden Huetten Nursing & Convalescent Home, Lehighton, PA
Go Ye Village Medical Center, Tahlequah, OK

Goble Nursing Home, Anderson, IN
Goddard Homestead Inc A Community for Elders, Worcester, MA
Godfrey's Foothill Retreat, Brigham City, UT
Gogebic County Medical Care Facility, Wakefield, MI
Gold City Convalescent Center, Dahlonega, GA
Gold Crest Nursing Home, Cincinnati, OH
Gold Crest Retirement Center, Adams, NE
Gold Leaf Care Center, Ellensburg, WA
Gold Star Nursing Home, Danville, PA
Gold Star Nursing Home, Milton, PA
Gold Star Nursing Home, Goldthwaite, TX
Golden Acres, Onaga, KS
Golden Acres Health Care Center, Bethany, OK
Golden Acres Intermediate Care Facility, Iva, SC
Golden Acres Manor, Carrington, ND
Golden Acres Nursing Home, Leoti, KS
Golden Age Care Center, Oregon City, OR
Golden Age Care Center, Amarillo, TX
Golden Age Convalescent Hospital, Capitola, CA
Golden Age Guest Home, Albert Lea, MN
Golden Age Guest Home Inc, Sykesville, MD
Golden Age Health Care, Daytona Beach, FL
Golden Age Health Care Center, Roseville, MN
Golden Age Home, Lockhart, TX
Golden Age Inc, Lexington, NC
Golden Age Lodge of Burlington, Burlington, KS
Golden Age Manor, Houston, TX
Golden Age Manor, Amery, WI
Golden Age Manor—Bellfort, Houston, TX
Golden Age Manor—Holmes, Houston, TX
Golden Age Manor Inc, Centerville, IA
Golden Age Manor—Long Point, Houston, TX
Golden Age Manor—North Loop, Houston, TX
Golden Age Manor Nursing Center, Dublin, TX
Golden Age Nursing Center, Jena, LA
Golden Age Nursing Center, Clovis, NM
Golden Age Nursing Home, Marion, IN
Golden Age Nursing Home, Denham Springs, LA
Golden Age Nursing Home, Greenwood, MS
Golden Age Nursing Home, Lubbock, TX
Golden Age Nursing Home, Tomahawk, WI
Golden Age Nursing Home District, Braymer, MO
Golden Age Nursing Home District 1, Stover, MO
Golden Age Nursing Home Inc, Cleburne, TX
Golden Age Nursing Home of Guthrie Inc, Guthrie, OK
Golden Age Project—Boarding Home, Blue Springs, MO
Golden Age Retirement Home, Cincinnati, OH
Golden Charm Nursing Home, Liberty, TX
Golden Crest, Hibbing, MN
Golden Crest Nursing Center Inc, North Providence, RI
Golden Crest Nursing Home, Atlantic City, NJ
Golden Empire Convalescent Hospital, Grass Valley, CA
Golden Gate Health Care Center, Staten Island, NY
Golden Good Shepherd Home Inc, Golden, IL
Golden Haven Home, Roby, TX
Golden Haven Nursing Home, Toledo, OH
Golden Heights Health Care Center Inc, Bridgeport, CT
Golden Heights Living Center, Garnett, KS
Golden Heritage Care Center, Temple, TX
Golden Heritage Nursing Home 2, Valley Mills, TX
Golden Hill Health Care Center, Milford, CT
Golden Hill Healthcare Center, San Diego, CA
Golden Hill Nursing Home Inc, New Castle, PA
Golden Keys Nursing Home, Neodesha, KS

Golden Manor Health Care Center, Ladoga, IN
Golden Manor Inc, Steele, ND
Golden Manor Jewish Home for the Aged, San Antonio, TX
Golden Manor Nursing Home, Crane, TX
Golden Manor of Salt Lake, Salt Lake City, UT
Golden Mesa Nursing Home, Mesa, AZ
Golden Oaks Nursing Home, South Saint Paul, MN
Golden Plains Care Center, Canyon, TX
Golden Plains Inc, Hutchinson, KS
Golden Rule Home Inc, Shawnee, OK
Golden Rule Nursing Center, Richmond, IN
Golden Springs Nursing Facility Inc, Anniston, AL
Golden State Colonial Convalescent Hospital, North Hollywood, CA
Golden State Habilitation Convalescent Center, Baldwin Park, CA
Golden State West Valley Convalescent Hospital, Canoga Park, CA
Golden Sunset Guest Home, Meridian, MS
Golden Triangle Convalescent Center, Port Arthur, TX
Golden Valley Nursing Home, Clinton, MO
Golden View Health Care Center, Meredith, NH
Golden Villa Nursing Home, Angleton, TX
Golden West Convalescent Hospital, Hawthorne, CA
Golden West Nursing Home Inc, Fort Collins, CO
Golden West Skills Center, Goodland, KS
Golden Years Boarding Facility, Poplar Bluff, MO
Golden Years Convalescent Center, Portsmouth, OH
Golden Years Haven, Decatur, TX
Golden Years Healthcare, Hamilton, OH
The Golden Years Home, Walworth, WI
Golden Years Homestead Inc, Fort Wayne, IN
Golden Years Lodge, Mount Pleasant, TX
Golden Years Manor, Lonoke, AR
Golden Years Manor, Felton, DE
Golden Years Nursing Home, Falcon, NC
Golden Years Rest Home, Lackey, KY
Golden Years Rest Home, Marlin, TX
Golden Years Retirement Center, Oxford, MS
Golden Years Retreat, Bridgeport, TX
Goldenrod Manor Care Center, Clarinda, IA
George J Goldman Memorial Home for the Aged, Niles, IL
Goldwater Memorial Hospital—Extended Care Facility, New York, NY
Golf Mill Plaza I, Niles, IL
Golfcrest Nursing Home, Hollywood, FL
Golfview Developmental Center Inc, Des Plaines, IL
Golfview Manor Nursing Home, Aliquippa, PA
Golfview Nursing Home, Saint Petersburg, FL
Goliad Manor Inc, Goliad, TX
Gonzales Health Care Center, Gonzales, LA
Good Hope Convalescent Hospital, Los Angeles, CA
Good Neighbor Home, Manchester, IA
Good Neighbor Home—Fairmount, Saint Paul, MN
Good Neighbors Inc, Bridgton, ME
Good Samaritan Cedar Lodge, Hot Springs Village, AR
Good Samaritan Center, Idaho Falls, ID
Good Samaritan Center, Estherville, IA
Good Samaritan Center, Forest City, IA
Good Samaritan Center, Ottumwa, IA
Good Samaritan Center, Postville, IA
Good Samaritan Center, Atwood, KS
Good Samaritan Center, Dodge City, KS
Good Samaritan Center, Winfield, KS
Good Samaritan Center, Clearbrook, MN
Good Samaritan Center, Jackson, MN
Good Samaritan Center, Warren, MN
Good Samaritan Center, Gibbon, NE
Good Samaritan Center, Nelson, NE
Good Samaritan Center, Superior, NE
Good Samaritan Center, Syracuse, NE

Good Samaritan Center, Devils Lake, ND
Good Samaritan Center, Hobart, OK
Good Samaritan Center, Centerville, SD
Good Samaritan Center, De Smet, SD
Good Samaritan Center, Herreid, SD
Good Samaritan Center, Lennox, SD
Good Samaritan Center, Parkston, SD
Good Samaritan Center, Selby, SD
Good Samaritan Center, Sioux Falls, SD
Good Samaritan Center, Tripp, SD
Good Samaritan Health Care Center, Yakima, WA
Good Samaritan Healthcare Center, East Peoria, IL
Good Samaritan Home, Colby, KS
Good Samaritan Home, Menominee, MI
Good Samaritan Home, Saint Louis, MO
Good Samaritan Home, Liverpool, PA
Good Samaritan Home & Center, Beatrice, NE
The Good Samaritan Home Inc, Evansville, IN
Good Samaritan Home Inc, Oakland City, IN
Good Samaritan Home of Flanagan, Flanagan, IL
Good Samaritan Home of Quincy, Quincy, IL
Good Samaritan—LTC, Rugby, ND
Good Samaritan Luther Manor, Sioux Falls, SD
Good Samaritan Medical Center, Zanesville, OH
Good Samaritan Nursing Center, East Grand Forks, MN
Good Samaritan Nursing Center, Parkston, SD
Good Samaritan Nursing Home, Saint Petersburg, FL
Good Samaritan Nursing Home, Knoxville, IL
Good Samaritan Nursing Home, Cole Camp, MO
Good Samaritan Nursing Home, Delmar, NY
Good Samaritan Nursing Home, Sayville, NY
Good Samaritan Nursing Home, Avon, OH
Good Samaritan Village, Moscow, ID
Good Samaritan Village, Saint Francis, KS
Good Samaritan Village, Mountain Lake, MN
Good Samaritan Village, Pipestone, MN
Good Samaritan Village, Alliance, NE
Good Samaritan Village—Perkins Pavilion, Hastings, NE
Good Shepard Lutheran Home of the West, Littleton, CO
The Good Shepherd Village, Springfield, OH
The Good Shepherd Home Long-Term Care Facility Inc, Allentown, PA
Good Shephard Villa, Mesa, AZ
Good Shepherd Convalescent Center, Lakeview Terrace, CA
Good Shepherd Convalescent Hospital, Santa Monica, CA
Good Shepherd Geriatric Center, Mason City, IA
Good Shepherd Health Care Facility, Lewiston, ME
The Good Shepherd Home, Watford City, ND
Good Shepherd Home, Fostoria, OH
Good Shepherd Home for the Aged, Ashland, OH
Good Shepherd Lutheran Home, Rushford, MN
Good Shepherd Lutheran Home, Sauk Rapids, MN
Good Shepherd Lutheran Home, Blair, NE
Good Shepherd Lutheran Home for Mentally Retarded, Cornelius, OR
Good Shepherd Manor, Momence, IL
Good Shepherd Nursing Home, Lockwood, MO
Good Shepherd Nursing Home, Versailles, MO
Good Shepherd Nursing Home, Wheeling, WV
Good Shepherd Nursing Home Inc, Los Angeles, CA
Good Shepherd Nursing Home Ltd, Seymour, WI
Good Shepherd Retirement Center, Peoria, AZ
Good Shepherd Villa Inc, Biddeford, ME

Good Shepherd-Fairview Home Inc, Binghamton, NY

Goodin's Rest Home, Columbia, KY

Goodman Gardens Nursing Home Co Inc, Rochester, NY

Goodwater Nursing Home, Goodwater, AL

Goodwill Intermediate Care Home, Brunswick, GA

Goodwill Mennonite Home Inc, Grantsville, MD

Goodwill Nursing Home, Macon, GA

Goodwin House—Nurs Care Unit, Alexandria, VA

Goodwin's of Exeter, Exeter, NH

Gordon Good Samaritan Center, Gordon, NE

Gordon Health Care Inc, Calhoun, GA

Gordon Lane Convalescent Hospital, Fullerton, CA

Gordon Memorial Health Care Facility, Spencer, WV

Gorham Manor, Gorham, ME

Goshen County Memorial Nursing Wing, Torrington, WY

Gospel Light Nursing Home, Kingston, OH

Gosport Nursing Home, Gosport, IN

Mary Goss Nursing Home, Monroe, LA

David Gottesfeld House, Denver, CO

Governor Bacon Health Center, Delaware City, DE

Governor Harris Homestead, Eaton, OH

Governor Winthop Nursing Home, Winthrop, MA

Governor's House Nursing Home, Westfield, MA

Governors Park of Barrington, Barrington, IL

Gowanda Nursing Home, Gowanda, NY

Gower Convalescent Center Inc, Gower, MO

Gowrie Care Center, Gowrie, IA

Grace Brethren Village, Englewood, OH

Grace Convalescent Center, Detroit, MI

Grace Home, Graceville, MN

Grace Manor Care Center, Burlington, CO

Grace Manor Nursing Home, Cincinnati, OH

Grace Nursing Home, Livingston, CA

Grace Nursing Home, Clinton, LA

Grace Plaza of Great Neck Inc, Great Neck, NY

Grace Village Health Care Facility, Winona Lake, IN

Graceland Manor, Lawson, MO

Gracelands Inc, Oxford, MS

Gracelands of Pontotoc, Pontotoc, MS

Gracell Terrace Inc, Chicago, IL

Gracewood Developmental Center, Gracewood, GA

Gracewood Nursing Home, Gracewood, GA

Gracewood State School & Hospital, Gracewood, GA

Grady H Hipp Nursing Center, Greenville, SC

Grafton County Nursing Home, Woodsville, NH

Grahams Nursing Home Inc, Valencia, PA

Theron Grainger Nursing Home, Hughes Springs, TX

Gramercy Park Nursing Center, Miami, FL

Grampian Nursing Home, Dorchester, MA

Granada Convalescent Hospital, Eureka, CA

Granada de Santa Fe, Santa Fe, NM

Granada Hills Convalescent Hospital, Granada Hills, CA

Granada Nursing Center, Baltimore, MD

Granbury Care Center, Granbury, TX

Grancare Nursing Center, Fond Du Lac, WI

Grancare Nursing Center, Green Bay, WI

Grand Avenue Convalescent Hospital, Long Beach, CA

Grand Avenue Rest Home, Minneapolis, MN

Grand Bay Convalescent Home, Grand Bay, AL

Grand Blanc Convalescent Center Inc, Grand Blanc, MI

Grand Care Convalescent Hospital, Anaheim, CA

Grand Chariton Manor Inc, Brunswick, MO

Grand Haven Nursing Home, Cynthiana, KY

Grand Island Manor Nursing Home, Grand Island, NY

Grand Islander Health Care Center Inc, Middletown, RI

Grand Junction Care Center, Grand Junction, CO

Grand Junction Regional Center, Grand Junction, CO

Grand Lake Manor, Grove, OK

Grand Manor, Saint Louis, MO

Grand Manor Health Related Facility, Bronx, NY

Grand Oaks Healthcare, Boise, ID

Grand Park Convalescent Hospital, Los Angeles, CA

Grand Place, Lakewood, CO

Grand Saline Manor, Grand Saline, TX

Grand Terrace Convalescent Hospital, Colton, CA

Grand Traverse County Medical Care Facility, Traverse City, MI

Grand Valley Care Center Inc, Pryor, OK

Grand Valley Nursing Center, Grand Rapids, MI

Grand View Care Center Inc, Blair, WI

Grand View Hospital SNF/Senior Care Center, Sellersville, PA

Grand View Rest Home, Fitchburg, MA

Grandview Care Center, Dayton, IA

Grandview Care Center, Saint Peter, MN

Grandview Care Center, Roseburg, OR

Grandview Care Center, Inc, Athens, GA

Grandview Christian Home, Cambridge, MN

Grandview Convalescent Center, Martinsville, IN

Grandview Health Care Center, Jasper, GA

Grandview Health Care Center, Grenada, MS

Grandview Health Care Inc—Oil City, Oil City, PA

Grandview Health Homes Inc, Danville, PA

Grandview Heights, Marshalltown, IA

Grandview Manor, Berthoud, CO

Grandview Manor, Camp Point, IL

Grandview Manor Care Center, Grandview, MO

Grandview Manor Care Center, Junction City, OR

Grandview Manor Nursing Home, Campbell, NE

Grandview Manor Nursing Home Inc, Dayton, OH

Grandview Nursing Center, Oelwein, IA

Grandview Nursing Home, Grandview, TX

Grandview Nursing Home Inc, Cumberland, RI

Grandview Quality Care Center, Dayton, OH

Grandvue Medical Care Facility, East Jordan, MI

The Grange Nursing Home, Mascoutah, IL

Granger Manor Care Center, Granger, IA

Grangers Nursing Home, Northborough, MA

Grangeville Convalescent & Shelter Care Center, Inc, Grangeville, ID

Granite Care Home, Sauk Rapids, MN

Granite County Memorial Nursing Home, Philipsburg, MT

Granite Falls Municipal Hospital & Manor, Granite Falls, MN

Grant County Nursing Home, Sheridan, AR

Grant County Nursing Home, Petersburg, WV

Grant Cuesta Convalescent Hospital, Mountain View, CA

Grant Manor Nursing Home, Colfax, LA

Grant Park Care Center, Washington, DC

Grants Good Samaritan Center, Grants, NM

Grants Lake I C Home, Butler, KY

Granview Health Care Inc—Franklin, Franklin, PA

Granville County Group Home, Oxford, NC

Grapeland Nursing Home, Grapeland, TX

Grapevine Nursing Home, Grapevine, TX

Grasmere Resident Home Inc, Chicago, IL

Grass Valley Convalescent Hospital, Grass Valley, CA

Gravenstein Convalescent Hospital, Sebastopol, CA

Gravette Manor Nursing Home, Gravette, AR

Gravois Rest Haven Inc, Saint Louis, MO

Gray Nursing Home, Gray, GA

Graymere Nursing Center Inc, Columbia, TN

Grays Harbor Convalescent Center, Aberdeen, WA

Grays Harbor Resthaven, Hoquiam, WA

Grays Nursing Home Inc, Platteville, WI

Grayson Manor, Leitchfield, KY

Grayson Square Health Care Center Inc, San Antonio, TX

Graystone Home Inc, Franklin, TN

Graystone Manor Convalescent Center, Portland, OR

Graystone Manor Nursing Home 2, Houston, TX

Graysville Nursing Home, Graysville, TN

Great Barrington Healthcare Nursing Home, Great Barrington, MA

Great Bend Manor, Great Bend, KS

Great Hall-Riverbend Center, Tuscumbia, AL

Great Lakes Convalescent Center, Detroit, MI

Great Oaks Center, Silver Spring, MD

Great Oaks Inc, Kansas City, MO

Great Oaks Nursing Home, Roswell, GA

Great River Care Center, McGregor, IA

Great River Homes Inc, Lake City, MN

Great Southwest Convalescent Center, Grand Prairie, TX

Great Trail Care Center Inc, Minerva, OH

Greater Harlem Nursing Home Co Inc, New York, NY

Greater Laurel Nursing Home, Laurel, MD

Greater Pennsylvania Ave Nursing Center Inc, Baltimore, MD

Greeley Care Home, Greeley, NE

Greeley Healthcare Center, Stillwater, MN

Green Acres, Saint Joseph, MO

Green Acres Adams County Home, Gettysburg, PA

Green Acres Care Center, Gooding, ID

Green Acres Convalescent Center, Baytown, TX

Green Acres Convalescent Center, Center, TX

Green Acres Convalescent Center, Huntsville, TX

Green Acres Convalescent Center, Vidor, TX

Green Acres Convalescent Center, Ansted, WV

Green Acres Convalescent Center—Humble, Humble, TX

Green Acres Convalescent Center—Parkdale, Beaumont, TX

Green Acres Convalescent & Development Center, Bridge City, TX

Green Acres Home for Convalescence Inc, Wyndmoor, PA

Green Acres Intermediate Care Facility, Milledgeville, GA

Green Acres Lodge, Rosemead, CA

Green Acres Nursing Home, North Branch, MN

Green Acres Nursing Home, South Sioux City, NE

Green Acres Nursing Home, Washington Court House, OH

Green Acres Nursing Home Inc, Kenton, OH

Green Acres Personal Care Inc, Mayfield, KY

Green Briar Nursing Center, Miami, FL

Green Cove Springs Geriatric Center, Green Cove Springs, FL

Green Forest Convalescent Home, Hattiesburg, MS

Green Hill Manor, Greensburg, KY

Green Hills Center, West Liberty, OH

The Green Home Inc, Wellsboro, PA

Green Lea Manor Nursing Home, Mabel, MN

Green Meadows Health Care Center, Linn, MO

Green Meadows Nursing Center, Haysville, KS

Green Meadows Nursing Home, Cheboygan, MI

Green Mountain Nursing Home, Winooski, VT

Green Oak Nursing Home, Brockton, MA

Green Pine Acres Nursing Home, Menahga, MN

Green Ridge Nursing Center, Scranton, PA

Green River Rest Home, Liberty, KY

Green River Terrace Nursing Home, Auburn, WA

Green Valley Care Center Inc, Eugene, OR
Green Valley Convalescent Center, New Albany, IN
Green Valley Group, Island Falls, ME
Green Valley Health Care Center, Carrollton, KY
Green Valley Health Care Center Inc, Dickson, TN
Green Valley Patten Group House, Patten, ME
Green View Nursing & Convalescent Center, Schuylkill Haven, PA
Greenbelt Nursing Center, Greenbelt, MD
Greenbough Nursing Center, Clarksdale, MS
Greenbrae Convalescent Hospital Inc, Greenbrae, CA
Greenbriar Care Center, Howell, MI
Greenbriar Convalescent Center, Wheelersburg, OH
The Greenbriar Home, Fayette, MO
Greenbriar Manor, Cairo, IL
Greenbriar Manor, Indianapolis, IN
Greenbriar Nursing Center, Bradenton, FL
Greenbriar Nursing & Convalescent Center, Woodbury, NJ
Greenbriar Nursing & Convalescent Home, Slidell, LA
Greenbriar Nursing Home, Sterling, MI
Greenbriar Nursing Home, Carthage, NY
Greenbriar Terrace Healthcare, Nashua, NH
Greenbriar-East Nursing Center, Deptford, NJ
Greenbrier Home Inc, Saint Paul, MN
Greenbrier Lodge, Piper City, IL
Greenbrier Manor, Lewisburg, WV
The Greenbrier Nursing Center Inc, Champaign, IL
Greenbrier Nursing Home, Enid, OK
Greenbrook Nursing Center, Saint Petersburg, FL
Greenbrook Nursing Home, Greenbrook, NJ
Greencastle Nursing Home, Greencastle, IN
Greencrest Manor Inc, Greenville, TX
Greencroft Nursing Center, Goshen, IN
Greendale Health Center, Sheboygan, WI
Greene Acres Manor Inc, Greene, ME
Greene Acres Nursing Home Inc, Paragould, AR
Greene County Hospital—Extended Care Facility, Leakesville, MS
Greene County Hospital & Nursing Home, Eutaw, AL
Greene County Medical Center, Jefferson, IA
Greene Haven, Springfield, MO
Greene Point Health Care, Union Point, GA
Greenery Rehabilitation Center, Dallas, TX
Greenery Rehabilitation Center, Durham, NC
Greenery Rehabilitation Center, Seattle, WA
Greenery Rehabilitation & Skilled Nursing Center, Boston, MA
Greenewood Manor, Xenia, OH
Greenfield Convalescent Center, Bridgewater Township, NJ
Greenfield Home, Princeton, IL
Greenfield Manor Inc, Greenfield, IA
Greenfields Nursing Home, Sainte Genevieve, MO
Greenhill Farm, Kezar Falls, ME
Green-Hill Manor Inc, Fowler, IN
Greenhill Residence, Biddeford, ME
Greenhills Nursing Home, DeQuincy, LA
Greenhurst Nursing Home, Charleston, AR
Greenlawn Health Care Center, Mentor, OH
Greenlawn Nursing Home, Middleboro, MA
Greenleaf Extension, Moorestown, NJ
Greenleaf House Nursing Home, Salisbury, PA
Greenleaf Nursing & Convalescent Center Inc, Doylestown, PA
Greenpark Care Center, Brooklyn, NY
Greenridge Heights Convalescent Hospital, Richmond, CA
Greenridge Nursing Center, Big Rapids, MI
Greens Geriatric Health Center Inc, Gary, IN
Green's Nursing Center, Kenedy, TX
Greensboro Health Care Center, Greensboro, NC
Greensboro Health Care Inc, Greensboro, AL
Greensboro Nursing Home, Greensboro, VT

Greensburg Home, Greensburg, PA
Greensburg Nursing & Convalescent Center Inc, Greensburg, PA
Greensburg Nursing Home, Greensburg, IN
Greensview Nursing Home, Bagley, MN
Greentree Health Care Center, Clintonville, WI
Greentree Manor Convalescent Home, Waterford, CT
Greentree Nursing Center, Oak Lawn, IL
Greenvale Convalescent Hospital, San Pablo, CA
Greenview Manor, Waco, TX
Greenview Manor Nursing Home, Wakefield, MA
Greenview Nursing Home, Grand Rapids, MI
Greenview Pavilion, Chicago, IL
Greenville Convalescent Home Inc, Greenville, MS
Greenville Nursing Home, Greenville, AL
Greenville Nursing Home Inc, Greenville, TX
Greenville Villa, Greenville, NC
Greenway Manor, Spring Green, WI
Greenwich Bay Manor, East Greenwich, RI
Greenwich Laurelton Nursing & Convalescent Home, Greenwich, CT
Greenwood Acres Nursing Home, Baltimore, MD
Greenwood Community Residence, Greenwood, SC
Greenwood Convalescent Center, Greenwood, IN
Greenwood Health Center, Hartford, CT
Greenwood House Nursing Home Inc, Warwick, RI
Greenwood Manor Nursing Home, Jerseyville, IL
Greenwood Nursing Care Center Inc, East Lebanon, ME
Greenwood Nursing Home, Wakefield, MA
Greenwood Nursing Home Inc, Greenwood, SC
Greenwood Oaks Rest Home, Warwick, RI
Greenwood Park Care Center, Seattle, WA
Greenwood Quality Care Center, Hamilton, OH
Greenwood Residence East, Saint Paul, MN
Greenwood Residence West, Saint Louis Park, MN
Greenwood Village Manor, Greenwood, IN
Greenwood Village South, Greenwood, IN
Greer Health Care Inc, Greer, SC
Gregg Home for the Aged Inc, Kilgore, TX
Arnold Gregory Memorial Hospital—Skilled Nursing Facility, Albion, NY
Gregory House, Topsham, ME
Gregston Nursing Home, Marlow, OK
Grcycliff at Cape Ann Nursing Home, Gloucester, MA
Greynolds Park Manor Rehabilitation Center, North Miami Beach, FL
Greystone on the Greene Inc, Philadelphia, PA
Griffeth Nursing Home, Ashland, OH
Griffeth Nursing Home, Lexington, OH
Griffin Nursing Center, Knoxville, IA
Griggs County Nursing Home, Cooperstown, ND
Griswold Care Center Inc, Griswold, IA
Gronna Good Samaritan Center, Lakota, ND
Gross Convalescent Hospital, Lodi, CA
Grosse Nursing Home Inc, Kansas City, MO
Grosvenor Health Care Center Inc, Bethesda, MD
Grotgen Nursing Home, Wilmington, NC
Groton Regency Retirement & Nursing Center, Groton, CT
Groton Residential Care Facility, Groton, NY
Theresa Grotta Center for Rehabilitation, West Orange, NJ
Group Home I, Ellsworth, WI
Grouse Valley Manor, Dexter, KS
Grove Center Rest Home, Morganfield, KY
The Grove Health Care Center, Neptune, NJ
Grove Manor, Grove City, PA
Grove Manor Nursing Home Inc, Waterbury, CT

Grove Manor Nursing Home Inc, Honey Grove, TX
Grove School Comm Liv Center, Lake Forest, IL
Grovecrest Convalescent Center, Pontiac, MI
Grovemont Nursing & Rehabilitation Center, Winter Haven, FL
Groveton Hospital & Nursing Home, Groveton, TX
Grundy Care Center, Grundy Center, IA
Grundy County Home, Morris, IL
Grundy County Memorial Hospital—Nurs Home, Grundy Center, IA
Guardian Angel Health Care Center, Green Bay, WI
Guardian Angel Nursing Home Inc, Kansas City, MO
Guardian Care, Elizabeth City, NC
Guardian Care, Roanoke Rapids, NC
Guardian Care Convalescent Center, Orlando, FL
Guardian Care Nursing Home, Ahoskie, NC
Guardian Care of Burgaw, Burgaw, NC
Guardian Care of Elkin, Elkin, NC
Guardian Care of Farmville, Farmville, NC
Guardian Care of Gastonia, Gastonia, NC
Guardian Care of Goldsboro, Goldsboro, NC
Guardian Care of Henderson, Henderson, NC
Guardian Care of Kenansville, Kenansville, NC
Guardian Care of Kinston, Kinston, NC
Guardian Care of Monroe, Monroe, NC
Guardian Care of New Bern, New Bern, NC
Guardian Care of Rocky Mount, Rocky Mount, NC
Guardian Care of Scotland Neck, Scotland Neck, NC
Guardian Care of Walnut Cove, Walnut Cove, NC
Guardian Care of Zebulon, Zebulon, NC
Guardian Nursing Home, Londonderry, NH
Guardian Rehabilitation Hospital, Los Angeles, CA
The Guest House, Shreveport, LA
Guest House of Baton Rouge, Baton Rouge, LA
Guest House of Nashville, Nashville, AR
Guest House of Slidell Nursing Home, Slidell, LA
Guest House/Rochester Treatment Center, Rochester, MN
Guggenheimer Nursing Home, Division of Centra Health Inc, Lynchburg, VA
Guidance Center Sanitarium, Anaheim, CA
Guilderland Center Nursing Home Inc, Guilderland Center, NY
Guilford Convalesarium, Fayetteville, PA
Guilliams Family Home, West Lafayette, OH
Guinn Nursing Home 1, Jay, OK
Guinn Nursing Home 2, Jay, OK
Gulf Coast Center/Sunland, Fort Myers, FL
Gulf Coast Convalescent Center, Panama City, FL
Gulf Coast Nursing Home of Moss Point Inc, Pascagoula, MS
Gulf Convalescent Center, Fort Walton Beach, FL
Gulfport Convalescent Center, Gulfport, FL
Gulfport Convalescent Center, Gulfport, MS
Gunderson's Retirement Home, Evergreen Park, IL
Gunnison Health Care Center, Gunnison, CO
Gunnison Valley Hospital, Gunnison, UT
The Rosaline & Joseph Gurwin Jewish Geriatric Center of Long Island, Commack, NY
Guthrie Nursing Center, Guthrie, OK
Guy & Mary Felt Manor Inc, Emporium, PA
Gwynedd Square for Nursing Convalescent Care, Lansdale, PA
H & S Care Center, Tamms, IL
Harold S Haaland Home, Rugby, ND
Habersham Home, Demorest, GA
Hacienda Convalescent Hospital, Concord, CA
Hacienda Convalescent Hospital, Long Beach, CA
Hacienda Convalescent Hospital, Porterville, CA

Hacienda Convalescent Hospital, Roseville, CA
Hacienda Convalescent Hospital, Ukiah, CA
Hacienda Convalescent Hospital—South, Pasadena, CA
Hacienda Convalescent Hospitals Inc, Livermore, CA
Hacienda de la Mesa Convalescent Hospital, La Mesa, CA
Hacienda de Salud, Raton, NM
Haddonfield Presbyterian Home of Southern New Jersey, Haddonfield, NJ
Hadley Manor, Detroit, MI
Hage House, Bloomington, IL
Henry Hagen Residence, Hastings, MN
Hahn Rest Home, Springfield, MA
Haida Manor, Hastings, PA
Halcyon House, Washington, IA
Halcyon House Rest Home, Methuen, MA
Hale Aloha Convalescent Hospital, Ceres, CA
Hale Convalescent & Nursing Home Inc, Groton, MA
Hale Ho Aloha ICF, Honolulu, HI
Hale Makua, Wailuku, HI
Hale Makua Home Health Care Agency, Wailuku, Maui, HI
Hale Malamalama, Honolulu, HI
Hale Nani Health Center, Honolulu, HI
Hale-Barnard Home, Boston, MA
Hales Rest Home, Spanish Fork, UT
Anthony Hall Nursing Home, Indianapolis, IN
Mattie C Hall Health Care Center, Aiken, SC
William T Hall Memorial Convalescent Home, Portsmouth, VA
Hallandale Rehabilitation Center, Hallandale, FL
Hallmar Mercy Hospital, Cedar Rapids, IA
Hallmark-Anderson Health Care Center, Houston, TX
Hallmark Care Center, Mount Vernon, IA
Hallmark Care Center, Omaha, NE
Hallmark House Nursing Home, Pekin, IL
Hallmark Manor Nursing Home, Indianapolis, IN
Hallmark Nursing Centre, Glens Falls, NY
Hallmark Nursing Centre, Troy, NY
Hallmark Nursing Centre Inc, Minoa, NY
Hallmark Nursing Centre Inc, Schenectady, NY
Hallmark Nursing Home, Warner Robins, GA
Hallmark Nursing Home of New Bedford, New Bedford, MA
Hallworth House, Providence, RI
Halstad Lutheran Memorial Home, Halstad, MN
Halsted Manor, Harvey, IL
Halsted Terrace Nursing Center, Chicago, IL
Haltom Convalescent Center, Fort Worth, TX
Hamburg Center, Hamburg, PA
Hamburg Center Annex, Wernersville, PA
Hamburg Health Care Center Inc, Hamburg, NY
Hamden Health Care Facility, Hamden, CT
Hamilton Arms of Pennsylvania, Lancaster, PA
Hamilton County Eastern Star Home Inc, Cincinnati, OH
Hamilton County Nursing Home, Chattanooga, TN
Hamilton County Rest Home, Syracuse, KS
Hamilton Grove, New Carlisle, IN
Hamilton Heights Health Center, Arcadia, IN
Hamilton Hill Crest Manor, Hamilton, MO
Hamilton House, Columbus, GA
Hamilton House Nursing Home, Needham, MA
Hamilton Manor, Aurora, NE
Hamilton Manor Nursing Home, Rochester, NY
Hamilton Memorial Home, Two Rivers, WI
Hamilton Nursing Home, Detroit, MI
Hamilton Nursing Home, Hamilton, TX
Hamilton Nursing Home Inc, Beaumont, TX
Hamilton Pavilion Healthcare, Norwich, CT
Hamilton Plaza Nursing Center, Passaic, NJ
Hamilton's Personal Care Home, Ashland, KY
Hamlet Manor, Chagrin Falls, OH

Hamlin Terrace Health Care Center, Buffalo, NY
Hammer Residence—Gleason Lake Residence, Wayzata, MN
Hammond Holiday Home, Larned, KS
Hammond House Convalescent Home, Worcester, MA
Hammond Nursing Home, Hammond, IN
Hammond Nursing Home, Hammond, LA
Hammond Rest Home, Fenton, MI
Hammond State School, Hammond, LA
Hammond-Whiting Convalescent Center, Whiting, IN
Hampden House Retirement Home, Springfield, MA
Hampshire Charitable Hospital, North Hampton, MA
Hampshire Manor Nursing Home, Easthampton, MA
Hampstead Nursing Home, Hampstead, TX
Hampton Convalescent Center, Hampton, VA
Hampton Court, West Jefferson, OH
Hampton Drive Home, Colorado Springs, CO
Hampton House, Wilkes-Barre, PA
Hampton Manor, Bay City, MI
Hampton Nursing Care Inc, Alhambra, IL
Hampton Nursing Center Inc, Sumter, SC
Hampton Nursing Home, Hampton, AR
Hampton Nursing Home, Hampton, IA
Hanceville Nursing Home, Hanceville, AL
Hancock County Nursing Home, Carthage, IL
Hancock County Rest Haven Inc, Lewisport, KY
Hancock County Shelter Care, Augusta, IL
Hancock Park Convalescent Hospital & Rehabilitation Center, Los Angeles, CA
Handmaker Jewish Geriatric Center, Tucson, AZ
Hanford Convalescent Hospital, Hanford, CA
Hannah Duston Long-Term Health Care Facility, Haverhill, MA
Hannum Memorial Rest Home Inc, Bradford, PA
Hanover Hall, Hanover, PA
Hanover Hill Healthcare Center, Manchester, NH
Hanover House, Birmingham, AL
Hanover House Inc, Massillon, OH
Hanover House Retirement Facility, Fall River, MA
Hanover Nursing Center, Hanover, IN
Hanover Terrace Healthcare, Hanover, NH
Knud Hansen Memorial Hospital, Saint Thomas, VI
Hansford Manor, Spearman, TX
Hanson Court Convalescent Center, Springfield, VT
Hanson Nursing Home, Natick, MA
Happiness House Rest Home, South Easton, MA
Happy Acres Home, Ronan, MT
Happy Harbor Methodist Home, La Porte, TX
Happy Haven Nursing Center, Abilene, TX
Happy Siesta Nursing, Remsen, IA
Har-Lyn Care Center, Portland, OR
Haralson County Nursing Home, Bremen, GA
Harbert Hills Academy Nursing Home, Savannah, TN
Harbor Beach Community Hospital, Harbor Beach, MI
Harbor Beach Convalescent Home, Fort Lauderdale, FL
Harbor Convalescent Hospital, Torrance, CA
Harbor Crest Home Inc, Fulton, IL
Harbor Health Care, Aberdeen, WA
Harbor Hills, Santa Cruz, CA
Harbor Home, York Harbor, ME
Harbor Inn Nursing Home Inc, South Boston, MA
Harbor View House, San Pedro, CA
Harbor View Manor, West Haven, CT
Harborview Development Center, Valdez, AK
Harborview Manor Nursing Home, South Dartmouth, MA
Harborview Nursing Home, Morehead City, NC
Hardee Manor Nursing Home, Wachula, FL
Hardin County Home, Kenton, OH

Hardin County Nursing Home, Savannah, TN
Hardin Home Nursing Home, Savannah, TN
Mary Harding Home Inc, Owensboro, KY
Harding Nursing Home, Waterville, NY
Harford Gardens Nursing Center, Baltimore, MD
William L Hargrave Health Center, Davenport, FL
Harlan Appalachian Regional Hospital—ECF, Harlan, KY
Harlan Morris Home, Trenton, TN
Harlan Nursing Home Inc, Harlan, KY
Harlee Manor, Springfield, PA
Harlem Rest Home, Harlem, MT
Harlingen Good Samaritan Center, Harlingen, TX
Harmony Community Hospital, Harmony, MN
Harmony House, Brewster, WA
Harmony House Health Care Center, Waterloo, IA
Harmony House Nursing Home, Shreveport, LA
Harmony House Nursing Home, Bend, OR
Harmony Nursing Home, Saint Paul, MN
Harold Group Home, Olathe, CO
Harper Home for the Aged, Edmonton, KY
Stiles M Harper Convalescent Center, Estill, SC
Harpeth Terrace Convalescent Center Inc, Franklin, TN
Harr-Wood Nursing Home, Oswego, NY
Harral's Nursing Home, Buhl, ID
Harris Avenue Rest Home, Boston, MA
Harris Manor, Glen Rose, TX
Harris Nursing Home Inc, East Providence, RI
Harrisburg Manor Inc, Harrisburg, IL
George L Harrison Memorial, Philadelphia, PA
Harrison House, Snow Hill, MD
Harrison House, Christiana, PA
Harrison House Inc, Cincinnati, OH
Harrison House of Georgetown, Georgetown, DE
Harrison Memorial Hospital, Cynthiana, KY
Harrison Nursing Center, Harrison, AR
Harrisonburg Nursing Center, Harrisonburg, LA
Harrison's Booker T Washington Nursing Home, Shreveport, LA
Harrison's Sanitorium, Lexington, KY
Harrod Nursing Home, Centerburg, OH
Harrodsburg Health Care Manor, Harrodsburg, KY
Harry Meyering Center Inc, Mankato, MN
Harston Hall Nursing Home Inc, Chestnut Hill, PA
Hart Care Center, Hartwell, GA
Nancy Hart Intermediate Care Facility, Elberton, GA
John Edward Harter Nursing Center, Fairfax, SC
Hartford Care Center, Hartford, WI
Hartford City Community Care Center, Hartford City, IN
Hartford Manor Training Center, Hartford, KS
Hartington Nursing Center, Hartington, NE
Hartley Hall Nursing Home, Pocomoke, MD
Hartsville Convalescent Center, Hartsville, TN
Hartville Healthcare Center, Hartville, OH
Hartville Meadows, Hartville, OH
Hartwyck at Cedar Brook, Plainfield, NJ
Hartwyck West Nursing Convalescent & Rehabilitation Center, Cedar Grove, NJ
Harty Nursing Home, Knightsville, IN
Harvard Manor Nursing Home, Cambridge, MA
Harvard Nursing Home Inc, Worcester, MA
Harvard Rest Haven, Harvard, NE
Harvest Heights Baptist Home Center, Decatur, GA
Harvest Home Estates, Kansas City, MO
Harvest Manor Nursing Home, Denham Springs, LA
Harveys Love & Care Home Inc, Six Mile, SC
Haskell Nursing Center, Haskell, TX

Haskell Shamrock Care Center, Haskell, OK
Haskins Nursing Home, Secane, PA
Hass Hillcrest Care Center Inc, Hawarden, IA
Haster Convalescent Hospital, Garden Grove, CA
Hastings Regional Center, Hastings, NE
Hatley Health Care Inc, Clanton, AL
Hattie Larlham Foundation, Mantua, OH
Hattiesburg Convalescent Center, Hattiesburg, MS
Hautamaki Westgate Rest Home, Ironwood, MI
Havana Healthcare Center, Havana, IL
Haven Convalescent Home Inc, New Castle, PA
Haven Crest Inc, Monongahela, PA
Haven Hall Nursing Center, Brookhaven, MS
Haven Health Center, Red Wing, MN
Haven Hill Home, Brecksville, OH
Haven Hill Residential Home, Harrington, DE
Haven Home of Kenesaw, Kenesaw, NE
Haven Homes Health Center, Hastings, MN
Haven Homes of Maple Plain, Maple Plain, MN
Haven House, Omaha, NE
Haven House, Wahoo, NE
Haven In The Hills, Bostic, NC
Haven Manor Health Care Center, Far Rockaway, NY
Haven Manor Nursing Home, Kansas City, MO
Haven Manor Nursing Home, Waco, TX
Haven Nursing Home, Baltimore, MD
Haven Nursing Home, Boston, MA
Haven Nursing Home, Mexia, TX
Haven of Our Lady of Peace, Pensacola, FL
Haven Park Nursing Center, Zeeland, MI
Haven Retirement Center, Springfield, IL
Havenwood Care Center Inc, Marysville, WA
Havenwood Rest Home, New Bedford, MA
Havenwood-Heritage Heights Retirement Community, Concord, NH
Haverford Nursing & Rehabilitation Center, Havertown, PA
Haverhill Manor Nursing Home, Haverhill, MA
Hawaii Select Care Inc, Honolulu, HI
Hawkins Care Center, Hawkins, TX
Hazel Hawkins Convalescent Hospital, Hollister, CA
J F Hawkins Nursing Home, Newberry, SC
Haws Memorial Nursing Home, Fulton, KY
The Hawthorne, Reading, PA
Hawthorne Convalescent Center, Hawthorne, CA
Hawthorne House, Bovey, MN
Hawthorne House, Sedalia, MO
Hawthorne Manor Retirement Residence, Spokane, WA
Hawthorne Nursing Center, Charlotte, NC
Haxtun Hospital District, Haxtun, CO
Hayden House, Hallowell, ME
Hayden Manor Care Center, Scottsdale, AZ
Hayden's Personal Care Home, Lexington, KY
Hayes Care Home, Baltimore, MD
Hayes Convalescent Hospital, San Francisco, CA
Hayes Residence, Saint Paul, MN
Haym Salomon Home for the Aged, Brooklyn, NY
Hays Good Samaritan Center, Hays, KS
Hays House Nursing Home, Nowata, OK
Hayward Convalescent Hospital, Hayward, CA
Hayward Hills Convalescent Hospital, Hayward, CA
Hayward Nursing Home, Hayward, WI
Hazard Nursing Home, Hazard, KY
Hazel Dell Care Center, Vancouver, WA
Hazelcrest Manor Nursing Home, Bloomfield, NJ
Hazelden Foundation, Center City, MN
Hazelden Pioneer House, Plymouth, MN
Hazels Rest Home, Watertown, SD
Hazelwood Intermediate Care Facility for the Mentally Retarded, Louisville, KY
Hazen Nursing Home, West Valley City, UT
Hazlet Manor Care Center, Hazlet, NJ
HCF Inc Briarwood Manor, Coldwater, OH

Healdton Nursing Home, Healdton, OK
Health Care Center at Washington, Sewell, NJ
Health Care Institute, Washington, DC
Health Care Manor, New Hampton, IA
Health Center at Abbey Delray, Delray Beach, FL
The Health Center at Friendship Village of South Hills, Pittsburgh, PA
Health Center Inc, Alliance, OH
Health Havens Inc, East Providence, RI
Health Inn Inc, Fayetteville, TN
Health Related Facility & Nursing Home Company of Rome Inc, Rome, NY
Healthaven Nursing Home, Akron, OH
Healthhaven Nursing Center, Greensboro, NC
Healthwin Hospital, South Bend, IN
Heardmont Health Care Center, Elberton, GA
Heart Manor Nursing Home, Navasota, TX
Heart of Georgia Nursing Home, Eastman, GA
Heart of the Valley Center, Corvallis, OR
The Hearth, Corpus Christi, TX
Hearthside Homes, Tower, MN
Hearthside Nursing Home Inc, Chicago, IL
Hearthside Rehabilitation Center, Brown Deer, WI
The Hearthstone, Seattle, WA
The Hearthstone Inc, York, NE
Hearthstone Manor, Medford, OR
Hearthstone Nursing Center, Saint John, KS
Hearthstone Nursing Home, Fort Worth, TX
Hearthstone Nursing Home, Tyler, TX
Hearthstone Nursing Home Inc, Stillwater, OK
Heartland—Beavercreek, Dayton, OH
Heartland Care Center, Johnston City, IL
Heartland Care Center—Belleville, Belleville, KS
Heartland Centre, Saint Joseph, MO
Heartland Home, Park Rapids, MN
Heartland Manor Inc Nursing Center, Casey, IL
Heartland Manor—Wakeeny, Wakeeny, KS
Heartland of Beckley, Beckley, WV
Heartland of Bellefontaine, Bellefontaine, OH
Heartland of Bucyrus HCR Inc, Bucyrus, OH
Heartland of Cedar Springs, New Paris, OH
Heartland of Charleston, Charleston, WV
Heartland of Chillicothe, Chillicothe, OH
Heartland of Clarksburg, Clarksburg, WV
Heartland of Connersville, Connersville, IN
Heartland of Eaton, Eaton, OH
Heartland of Greenville, Greenville, OH
Heartland of Indian Lake, Indian Lake, OH
Heartland of Jackson, Jackson, OH
Heartland of Kettering, Kettering, OH
Heartland of Keyser, Keyser, WV
Heartland of Liberty, Liberty, MO
Heartland of Marietta, Marietta, OH
Heartland of Martinsburg, Martinsburg, WV
Heartland of Marysville, Marysville, OH
Heartland of Milwaukee, Milwaukee, WI
Heartland of Perrysburg, Perrysburg, OH
Heartland of Portsmouth, Portsmouth, OH
Heartland of Preston County, Kingwood, WV
Heartland of St Petersburg, Saint Petersburg, FL
Heartland of Shawano, Shawano, WI
Heartland of Springfield, Springfield, OH
Heartland of Urbana, Urbana, OH
Heartland Rehabilitation Center, Wichita, KS
Heartland Thurber Village, Columbus, OH
Heartland Willow Lane Nursing Center, Butler, MO
Heartland-Lansing, Lansing, OH
Heartwood Avenue Living Center, Vallejo, CA
Heath Nursing & Convalescent Center, Newark, OH
Heather Hill, Willmar, MN
Heather Hill Inc, Chardon, OH
Heather Hill Nursing Home, New Port Richey, FL
Heather Manor, Des Moines, IA
Heather Manor Nursing Center, Hope, AR
Heather Manor Nursing Center, Harvey, IL
Heatherbank, Columbia, PA
Heathergreen II Inc, Jamestown, OH
Heathergreene I, Xenia, OH

Heathside Haven Inc, Laurel, MS
Heathwood Health Care Center Inc, Williamsville, NY
Heathwood Nursing Home, Newton, MA
Heatland-Fairfield, Thornville, OH
Heaton House, Montpelier, VT
Heavener Nursing Home, Heavener, OK
F Edward Hebert Hospital—SNF, New Orleans, LA
Hebert's Nursing Home Inc, Smithfield, RI
Hebrew Home for Aged Disabled, San Francisco, CA
The Hebrew Home for the Aged at Riverdale, New York, NY
Hebrew Home for the Aged/Fairfield Division, Bronx, NY
Hebrew Home for the Aged—North Dade, North Miami Beach, FL
Hebrew Home & Hospital, Hartford, CT
Hebrew Home of Greater Washington, Rockville, MD
Hebrew Hospital for the Chronic Sick, Bronx, NY
Heffner's Ivy Cottage Nursing Home, Waynesville, OH
Hefner Village Nursing Center, Oklahoma City, OK
Hegg Memorial Health Center—Valley Manor Division, Rock Valley, IA
Heights Colonial Manor, Peoria Heights, IL
Heinzerling Developmental Center, Columbus, OH
Helena Nursing Home Co, Helena, MT
Helix View Nursing Home Inc, El Cajon, CA
Hellenic Nursing Home for The Aged, Canton, MA
Helmwood Care Home, Tribune, KS
Helton Health Center Inc, Hamilton, OH
Hemet Convalescent Center, Hemet, CA
Hempstead Park Nursing Home, Hempstead, NY
Henard Sheltered Care Home, Jonesboro, IL
Henderson Convalescent Hospital, Henderson, NV
Henderson Nursing Home Inc, Morgantown, IN
Henderson Rest Home, Henderson, KY
Henderson's Personal Care, Jackson, MS
Hendersonville Nursing Home, Hendersonville, TN
Hendricks County Home, Danville, IN
Hendricks Nursing Home, Hendricks, MN
Hennesey Nursing Home Inc, Giddings, TX
Hennessey Care Center, Hennessey, OK
Henning Nursing Home, Henning, MN
Hennis Care Center, Dover, OH
Henrietta Care Center, Henrietta, TX
Henry County Health Center Long-Term Care Unit, Mount Pleasant, IA
Henry County Hospital & Nursing Home, Abbeville, AL
Henry County Nursing Home, Paris, TN
Hensley Nursing Home, Sayre, OK
The Heritage, San Francisco, CA
The Heritage, Girard, KS
The Heritage, Findlay, OH
Heritage, Tacoma, WA
Heritage 53, Moline, IL
Heritage Acres, Hardin, MT
Heritage Acres Care Center, Cedar Rapids, IA
Heritage Care Center, Iowa Falls, IA
Heritage Care Center, Mason City, IA
Heritage Care Center, Shelby, OH
Heritage Center Inc—Conway, Conway, AR
Heritage Conv Center, Paris, IL
Heritage Convalescent Center, Atlanta, GA
Heritage Convalescent Center, Amarillo, TX
Heritage Convalescent Center of Torrance, Torrance, CA
Heritage Convalescent Hospital, Sacramento, CA
Heritage Gardens, Loma Linda, CA
Heritage Hall Care Center, Lawrenceburg, KY
Heritage Hall Dillwyn, Dillwyn, VA
Heritage Hall East, Agawam, MA
Heritage Hall Health Care II, Big Stone Gap, VA
Heritage Hall Health Care IV, Blackstone, VA

Heritage Hall Health Care I, Blacksburg, VA
Heritage Hall Health Care V, Leesburg, VA
Heritage Hall Health Care VI, Nassawadox, VA
Heritage Hall Health Care VIII, Clintwood, VA
Heritage Hall North, Agawam, MA
Heritage Hall Nursing Center, Centralia, MO
Heritage Hall Nursing Home, Tinton Falls, NJ
Heritage Hall South, Agawam, MA
Heritage Hall III, Tazewell, VA
Heritage Hall West, Agawam, MA
Heritage Hall—Wise, Wise, VA
Heritage Haven Care Center, Schofield, WI
Heritage Health Care Center, Tuscaloosa, AL
Heritage Health Care Center, Chanute, KS
Heritage Health Care Center, Takoma Park, MD
Heritage Health Care Center, Gering, NE
Heritage Healthcare Center, Naples, FL
Heritage Healthcare Center, Naples, FL
Heritage Healthcare Centre, Zeeland, MI
Heritage Healthcare Inc, West Lafayette, IN
Heritage Hills, McAlester, OK
Heritage Hills Nursing Centre, Smithfield, RI
The Heritage Home, Parsons, KS
Heritage Home, Plainview, TX
Heritage Home Care Center, Saint Elmo, IL
Heritage Home of Bancroft, Bancroft, IA
Heritage Home of Florence Inc, Florence, SC
The Heritage House, Kankakee, IL
Heritage House, Orange City, IA
Heritage House, Miami, OK
Heritage House, Wilkes-Barre, PA
Heritage House, Eagle Lake, TX
Heritage House, Rosebud, TX
Heritage House Children's Center, Shelbyville, IN
Heritage House Continuing Care Community, Atlantic, IA
Heritage House Convalescent Center, Martinsville, IN
The Heritage House Convalescent Center, Shelbyville, IN
Heritage House Convalescent Center of Putnam County Inc, Greencastle, IN
Heritage House Nursing Home, Valdosta, GA
Heritage House Nursing Home, Winfield, KS
Heritage House Nursing Home, Danvers, MA
Heritage House Nursing Home, Bartlesville, OK
Heritage House of Champaign, Champaign, IL
Heritage House of Charleston, Charleston, IL
Heritage House of Cherry Hill, Cherry Hill, NJ
Heritage House of Greensburg, Greensburg, IN
Heritage House of New Castle, New Castle, IN
Heritage House of Richmond Inc, Richmond, IN
Heritage House of Vandalia, Vandalia, IL
Heritage House-Columbus Jewish Home for the Aged, Columbus, OH
The Heritage, Bridgeport, WV
Heritage Inn, Saint Simons Island, GA
Heritage Inn—Barnesville, Barnesville, GA
Heritage Inn Nursing Home, Fairborn, OH
Heritage Inn of Hartwell, Hartwell, GA
Heritage Inn of Whigham, Whigham, GA
Heritage Lakewood Health Care Center, Wichita, KS
Heritage Living Center, Saint Paul, NE
Heritage Manor, Bloomington, IL
Heritage Manor, Streator, IL
Heritage Manor, Dubuque, IA
Heritage Manor, Cleveland, MS
Heritage Manor, Youngstown, OH
Heritage Manor, Canton, TX
Heritage Manor, Plano, TX
Heritage Manor, Rice Lake, WI
Heritage Manor Care Center, Newton, IA
Heritage Manor Care Center, Dayton, TX
Heritage Manor Care Center of Hondo Inc, Hondo, TX
Heritage Manor Convalescent Center, Flint, MI
Heritage Manor Estates, Fort Wayne, IN

Heritage Manor Health Care Center, Fort Wayne, IN
Heritage Manor Health Care Center, Chisholm, MN
Heritage Manor Inc, Shelbyville, IN
Heritage Manor Inc, Winthrop, ME
Heritage Manor Inc, Devine, TX
Heritage Manor-North, Fort Wayne, IN
Heritage Manor North Nursing Home, Pineville, LA
Heritage Manor Nursing Center, Minster, OH
Heritage Manor & Nursing Conv Home, Mendota, IL
Heritage Manor Nursing & Conv Home, Springfield, IL
Heritage Manor Nursing & Convalescent Center, Bartlesville, OK
Heritage Manor Nursing Home, Sherman, TX
Heritage Manor Nursing Home, Elroy, WI
Heritage Manor Nursing Home Inc, Chattanooga, TN
Heritage Manor Nursing Home of Bossier City, Bossier City, LA
Heritage Manor Nursing Home of Lafayette, Lafayette, LA
Heritage Manor Nursing Home of Marrero, Marrero, LA
Heritage Manor Nursing Home of Shreveport, Shreveport, LA
Heritage Manor of Alexandria 1, Alexandria, LA
Heritage Manor of Alexandria 2, Alexandria, LA
Heritage Manor of Banner Elk, Banner Elk, NC
Heritage Manor of Crowley, Crowley, LA
Heritage Manor of Elizabethton, Elizabethton, TN
Heritage Manor of Emporia, Emporia, KS
Heritage Manor of Ferriday, Ferriday, LA
Heritage Manor of Franklinton, Franklinton, LA
Heritage Manor of Gonzales, Gonzales, LA
Heritage Manor of Hammond, Hammond, LA
Heritage Manor of Holly Springs, Holly Springs, MS
Heritage Manor of Iowa Park, Iowa Park, TX
Heritage Manor of Kaplan, Kaplan, LA
Heritage Manor of Mansfield, Mansfield, LA
Heritage Manor of Many Number 1, Many, LA
Heritage Manor of Many Number 2, Many, LA
Heritage Manor of Mountain Grove, Mountain Grove, MO
Heritage Manor of New Iberia—North, New Iberia, LA
Heritage Manor of New Iberia—South, New Iberia, LA
Heritage Manor of Normal, Normal, IL
Heritage Manor of Peru, Peru, IL
Heritage Manor of Rogersville, Rogersville, TN
Heritage Manor of Springfield, Springfield, MO
Heritage Manor of Thibodaux, Thibodaux, LA
Heritage Manor Vivian, Vivian, LA
Heritage Nursing Center, Haynesville, LA
Heritage Nursing Center, Sheboygan, WI
Heritage Nursing Center Inc, Muskogee, OK
Heritage Nursing & Convalescent Center, Mobile, AL
Heritage Nursing Home, Quitman, TX
Heritage Nursing Home, Port Washington, WI
Heritage Nursing Home Inc, Athens, PA
Heritage Nursing Home Inc, Goldthwaite, TX
Heritage Nursing Manor, Lamesa, TX
Heritage Nursing & Rehabilitation Center, North Miami Beach, FL
Heritage of Bel Air, Norfolk, NE
Heritage of Bridgeport, Bridgeport, NE
Heritage of Cimarron, Cimarron, KS
Heritage of David City, David City, NE
Heritage of Edina, Edina, MN
Heritage of Elmwood Nursing Home, Elmwood, WI
Heritage of Emerson, Emerson, NE
Heritage of Fairbury, Fairbury, NE

Heritage of Geneva, Geneva, NE
Heritage of St Louis, Saint Louis, MO
Heritage of Wauneta, Wauneta, NE
Heritage of White River, White River, SD
Heritage Park, Plano, TX
Heritage Place, Soldotna, AK
Heritage Place, Mesquite, TX
Heritage Residential Care Center, Devine, TX
Heritage Sheltered Care Home, Hutsonville, IL
Heritage Square Retirement Home, Dixon, IL
Heritage Towers, Doylestown, PA
Heritage Village, Richardson, TX
Heritage Village at Park Place Meadows, Raytown, MO
Heritage Village of Eskridge, Eskridge, KS
Heritage Village of Grand Island—North, Grand Island, NE
Heritage Village of Neligh, Neligh, NE
Heritage Village of Rose Hill, Rose Hill, KS
Heritage Village of Wakefield, Wakefield, KS
David Herman Health Care Center, Minneapolis, MN
The Herman Sanitarium, San Jose, CA
Hermann Park Manor, Houston, TX
Hermina Traeye Memorial Nursing Home, Johns Island, SC
Hermiston Good Samaritan Center, Hermiston, OR
Hermitage in Northern Virginia, Alexandria, VA
Hermitage Manor, Owensboro, KY
Hermitage Nursing Home, Worcester, MA
Hermitage Nursing Home Inc, Elizabethton, TN
Hermitage on the Eastern Shore—Nurs Home Unit, Onancock, VA
Herrick Nursing Home, Tecumseh, MI
K W Hess Ohio Pythian Home, Springfield, OH
Hessmer Nursing Home Inc, Hessmer, LA
Hester Memorial Nursing Home, Dayton, OH
Sarah Ann Hester Memorial Home, Benkelman, NE
Hetzel Care Center Inc, Bloomer, WI
The Flora & Mary Hewitt Memorial Hospital Inc, Shelton, CT
Hewitt House, Vancouver, WA
Hewitt House Retirement Center, Pulaski, TN
Hewitt Manor Inc, Shinglehouse, PA
Heyde Health System Inc, Chippewa Falls, WI
Heywood Valley Nursing Home, Worcester, MA
Hi Acres Manor Nursing Center, Jamestown, ND
Hialeah Convalescent Home, Hialeah, FL
Hiawatha Childrens Home, Rochester, MN
Hiawatha Manor, Pipestone, MN
Hibbard Nursing Home, Dover-Foxcroft, ME
Hickman County Nursing Home, Centerville, TN
Hickory Creek Nursing Home Inc, Dayton, OH
Hickory Creek of Athens, The Plains, OH
Hickory House Nursing Home Inc, Honeybrook, PA
Hickory Manor Nursing Home Inc, Bastrop, LA
Hickory Nursing Pavilion Inc, Hickory Hills, IL
Hicks Golden Years Nursing Home, Monticello, KY
Hicks Nursing Home, Fryeburg, ME
Hidden Acres Manor, Mount Pleasant, TN
Hidden Hollow Rest Home, Orem, UT
Hi-Desert Convalescent Hospital, Yucca Valley, CA
Higgins Learning Center, Morganfield, KY
Higginsville State School & Hospital, Higginsville, MO
High Hope Care Center, Sulphur, LA
High Point Lodge Nursing Home, Clear Lake, MN
High Street Convalescent Hospital, Oakland, CA
High Street Rest Home, Fitchburg, MA
High Valley Lodge, Sunland, CA
High View Nursing Center Inc, Peoria, IL

Highgate Manor of Cortland, Cortland, NY
Highgate Manor of Rensselaer, Troy, NY
Highland Acres Extend-A-Care Center, Winsted, CT
Highland Care, Klamath Falls, OR
Highland Care Center, Jamaica, NY
Highland Care Center, Salt Lake City, UT
Highland Care Home, Abilene, KS
Highland Chateau Health Care Center, Saint Paul, MN
Highland Convalescent Center, Bellingham, WA
Highland Convalescent Hospital, Duarte, CA
Highland Farms Inc, Black Mountain, NC
Highland Guest Care Center, Shreveport, LA
Highland Hall Care Center, New Castle, PA
Highland Hall Manor, Essex, CT
Highland Health Facility-Mental Retardation Unit, Baltimore, MD
Highland House Nursing Home, Grants Pass, OR
Highland House of Fayetteville Inc, Fayetteville, NC
Highland Manor, New Ulm, MN
Highland Manor Nursing Home, Phoenix, AZ
Highland Manor Nursing Home, Portland, TN
Highland Manor Nursing Home, Dublin, VA
Highland Manor Nursing Home Inc, Fall River, MA
Highland Manor Rest Home, Worcester, MA
Highbrook Nursing Center, Ponca City, OK
Highland Nursing Center, Wichita Falls, TX
Highland Nursing Home, Highland, IN
Highland Nursing Home, San Antonio, TX
Highland Nursing Home Inc, Massena, NY
Highland Nursing & Rehabilitation Center, Brackenridge, PA
Highland Park Care Center, Denver, CO
Highland Park Care Center, Houston, TX
Highland Park Health Care Center Inv, Highwood, IL
Highland Park Manor, Clinton, OK
Highland Park Manor, Enid, OK
Highland Park Manor, Okmulgee, OK
Highland Pines, Longview, TX
Highland Pines Nursing Manor, Clearwater, FL
Highland Rest Home, Boston, MA
Highland Rest Home Inc, Genoa City, WI
Highland Terrace Nursing Center, Camas, WA
Highland View Nursing Home, Troy, OH
Highland Villa, Topeka, KS
Highlands Center Hospital, Denver, CO
Highlands Convalescent Center Inc, Renton, WA
Highlands Homes, Princeton, KY
Highline Care Center, Seattle, WA
Highline Convalescent Center, East Wenatchee, WA
Highmore Nursing Home, Highmore, SD
Highview Manor, Madawaska, ME
Highview Retirement Home, Rockford, IL
Hilaire Farm Nursing Home, Huntington, NY
Hildebrand Care Center, Canon City, CO
Hill Country Manor, Llano, TX
Hill Haven Nursing Home, Syracuse, NY
Hill Haven Nursing Home of Rochester Co, Webster, NY
Hill Haven Skilled Nursing Home & Rest Home, Statesville, NC
Keith Hill Nursing Home Inc, Grafton, MA
Hill Nursing Home, Idabel, OK
Hill Road Convalescent Hospital, Novato, CA
Hill Top, Lake Bluff, IL
Hill Top House, Bucklin, KS
Hill Top House Nursing Home Inc, Dayton, OH
Hill Top Nursing Home, Boerne, TX
Hill Top Residential Care Facility, Cape Girardeau, MO
Hill View Health Center, Portsmouth, OH
Hill View Manor, New Castle, PA
William Hill Manor, Easton, MD
Hillandale Nursing Home, Hamilton, OH
Hillbrook Nursing Home, Clancy, MT
Hillcreek Manor Convalescent Center, Louisville, KY
Hillcrest Care Center, Boise, ID

Hillcrest Care Center, Laurel, NE
Hillcrest Care Center, Waterville, OH
Hillcrest Care Center, Sandy, UT
Hillcrest Care Center Inc, Bellevue, NE
Hillcrest Care Center Inc, Hettinger, ND
Hillcrest Central, Knoxville, TN
Hillcrest Convalescent Center, Detroit, MI
Hillcrest Convalescent Center, Pasco, WA
Hillcrest Convalescent Center Inc, Durham, NC
Hillcrest Convalescent Home, Milwaukee, WI
Hillcrest Convalescent Hospital, Fresno, CA
Hillcrest Convalescent Hospital Inc, Long Beach, CA
Hillcrest Estates, Liberty, IN
Hillcrest Haven Convalescent Center, Pocatello, ID
Hillcrest Health Care Center, Mankato, MN
Hillcrest Health Care Center, Rush City, MN
Hillcrest Health Care Center, Wayzata, MN
Hillcrest Health Center Inc, Magee, MS
Hillcrest Health Center Skilled Nursing Facility, Oklahoma City, OK
Hillcrest Healthcare Center, Jeffersonville, IN
Hillcrest Healthcare Center, Owensboro, KY
Hillcrest Home, Geneseo, IL
Hillcrest Home, Scottsville, KY
Hillcrest Home—Harrison, Harrison, AR
Hillcrest Home Inc, Milford, PA
Hillcrest Manor, Fredonia, KS
Hillcrest Manor, Blackwell, OK
Hillcrest Manor, Luling, TX
Hillcrest Manor, Wylie, TX
Hillcrest Manor Inc, Aberdeen, MS
Hillcrest Manor Nursing Home, Charlotte, NC
Hillcrest Manor Nursing Home, Waco, TX
Hillcrest Manor Nursing Home, Winchester, VA
Hillcrest Manor Sanitarium, National City, CA
Hillcrest Manor—Sunnyside, Sunnyside, WA
Hillcrest—North, Knoxville, TN
Hillcrest Nursing Center, Moore, OK
Hillcrest Nursing Center Inc, Fredericktown, OH
Hillcrest Nursing Home, San Bernardino, CA
Hillcrest Nursing Home, Avon Park, FL
Hillcrest Nursing Home, Lafayette, IN
Hillcrest Nursing Home, Corbin, KY
Hillcrest Nursing Home, Fitchburg, MA
Hillcrest Nursing Home, North Muskegon, MI
Hillcrest Nursing Home, Plainview, MN
Hillcrest Nursing Home, Red Lake Falls, MN
Hillcrest Nursing Home, McCook, NE
Hillcrest Nursing Home, Oswego, NY
Hillcrest Nursing Home, Spring Valley, NY
Hillcrest Nursing Home, Peebles, OH
Hillcrest Nursing Home, Tishomingo, OK
Hillcrest Nursing Home, Hamilton, TX
Hillcrest Nursing Home, Grandview, WA
Hillcrest Nursing Home, Twin Lakes, WI
Hillcrest Nursing Home, West Allis, WI
Hillcrest Nursing Home Inc, East Providence, RI
Hillcrest Nursing Home—Prescott, Prescott, AR
Hillcrest of Watonga Inc, Watonga, OK
Hillcrest Rehabilitation & Convalescent Center, San Diego, CA
Hillcrest Rest Home, Gloucester, MA
Hillcrest Rest Home Inc, Sumner, IA
Hillcrest Retirement Community, Bozeman, MT
Hillcrest Retirement Village Ltd, Round Lake Beach, IL
Hillcrest Skilled Care Div, Sanford, ME
Hillcrest—South, Knoxville, TN
Hillcrest—West, Knoxville, TN
Hilldale Convalescent Center, La Mesa, CA
Hillebrand Nursing Center, Cheviot, OH
Hillhaven, Woodland, CA
Hillhaven Alameda, Alameda, CA
Hillhaven Care Center, Pasadena, CA
Hillhaven Care Center, San Luis Obispo, CA
Hillhaven Conv Center, Raleigh, NC
Hillhaven Conv Center of Chapel Hill, Chapel Hill, NC
Hillhaven Convalescent Center, Mobile, AL

Hillhaven Convalescent Center, Hemet, CA
Hillhaven Convalescent Center, San Francisco, CA
Hillhaven Convalescent Center, Sarasota, FL
Hillhaven Convalescent Center, Savannah, GA
Hillhaven Convalescent Center, Des Moines, IA
Hillhaven Convalescent Center, Adrian, MI
Hillhaven Convalescent Center, Las Vegas, NV
Hillhaven Convalescent Center, Akron, OH
Hillhaven Convalescent Center, Camden, TN
Hillhaven Convalescent Center, Madison, TN
Hillhaven Convalescent Center, Memphis, TN
Hillhaven Convalescent Center, Corpus Christi, TX
Hillhaven Convalescent Center, El Paso, TX
Hillhaven Convalescent Center, Salt Lake City, UT
Hillhaven Convalescent Center, Vancouver, WA
Hillhaven Convalescent Center Germantown, Cordova, TN
Hillhaven Convalescent Center & Nursing Home, Birmingham, AL
Hillhaven Convalescent Center Ripley, Ripley, TN
Hillhaven Convalescent Hospital, Anaheim, CA
Hillhaven Convalescent Hospital, Burlingame, CA
Hillhaven Convalescent Hospital, Carmichael, CA
Hillhaven Convalescent Hospital, Castro Valley, CA
Hillhaven Convalescent Hospital, Claremont, CA
Hillhaven Convalescent Hospital, Hanford, CA
Hillhaven Convalescent Hospital, Menlo Park, CA
Hillhaven Convalescent Hospital, Mill Valley, CA
Hillhaven Convalescent Hospital, Modesto, CA
Hillhaven Convalescent Hospital, Oakland, CA
HIllhaven Convalescent Hospital, Orange, CA
Hillhaven Convalescent Hospital, Palo Alto, CA
Hillhaven Convalescent Hospital, Santa Ana, CA
Hillhaven Convalescent Hospital, Yuba City, CA
Hillhaven Extended Care Hospital, Santa Cruz, CA
Hillhaven Health Care, Monterey Park, CA
Hillhaven Health Care Center, Phoenix, AZ
Hillhaven Health Care Center of Raleigh, Memphis, TN
Hillhaven Health Care—Jefferson City, Jefferson City, TN
Hillhaven Healthcare, Yuma, AZ
Hillhaven Healthcare Center, Sanford, FL
Hillhaven Highland House, Highland, CA
Hillhaven LaSalle Nursing Center, Durham, NC
Hillhaven Nursing Home, Adelphi, MD
Hillhaven Nursing Home, Vancouver, WA
Hillhaven of Alamance, Graham, NC
Hillhaven of Little Rock, Little Rock, AR
Hillhaven of Topeka, Topeka, KS
Hillhaven—Omaha, Omaha, NE
Hillhaven Orange Nursing Center, Durham, NC
Hillhaven Rehabilitation & Conv Center, Wilmington, NC
Hillhaven Rehabilitation & Conv Center—Asheville, Asheville, NC
Hillhaven Rehabilitation Convalescent Center, Marietta, GA
Hillhaven Rehabilitation & Convalescent Center, Durham, NC
Hillhaven Rehabilitation & Convalescent Center, Norfolk, VA
Hillhaven Rest Home, Baton Rouge, LA
Hillhaven Rest Home 1, Baton Rouge, LA
Hillhaven Rose Manor, Durham, NC

Hillhaven—Sherwood Convalescent Hospital, Sacramento, CA

Hillhaven Sunnybrook Conv Center, Raleigh, NC

Hillhaven Wichita, Wichita, KS

Hillhaven-Brookvue Convalescent Hospital, San Pablo, CA

Hillhouse Convalescent Home, Bath, ME

Hillsboro Community Nursing Home, Hillsboro, ND

Hillsboro Health Care Center, Hillsboro, IL

Hillsboro House Nursing Home, Hillsborough, NH

Hillsboro Manor Nursing Home, El Dorado, AR

Hillsboro Nursing Home, Hillsboro, IL

Hillsborough County Nursing Home, Goffstown, NH

Hillsdale County Medical Care Facility, Hillsdale, MI

Hillsdale Manor Convalescent Hospital, San Mateo, CA

Hillside Acres, Willard, OH

Hillside Convalescent Inc, Portland, OR

Hillside Haven Nursing Home, Rushville, IN

Hillside Health Care Center, Inc, Milwaukee, WI

Hillside Heights Convalescent Center, Eugene, OR

Hillside House, Wilmington, DE

Hillside House Inc, Santa Barbara, CA

Hillside Lodge Nursing Home, Beeville, TX

Hillside Manor, Washington, IN

Hillside Manor, Glenwood, IA

Hillside Manor, Missoula, MT

Hillside Manor Convalescent Hospital, San Rafael, CA

Hillside Manor Health Care Facility Inc, Cincinnati, OH

Hillside Manor Health Related Facility, Jamaica Estates, NY

Hillside Manor Inc, McMinnville, OR

Hillside Manor Nursing Center, Gatesville, TX

Hillside Manor Nursing Home, Hartford, CT

Hillside Manor Nursing Home Inc, San Antonio, TX

Hillside Manor Retirement Home, Waterbury, CT

Hillside Manor—San Marcos, San Marcos, TX

Hillside Nursing & Convalescent Home, Yorkville, IL

Hillside Nursing Home, Deerfield, MA

Hillside Nursing Home, Marion, OH

Hillside Nursing Home Inc, Asheville, NC

Hillside Rest Home, Amesbury, MA

Hillside Rest Home, Winchendon, MA

Hillside Rest & Nursing Home Inc, South Portland, ME

Hillside Terrace Retirement Home, Ann Arbor, MI

Hillside Terrace Skilled & Intermediate Nursing Facility, Cobden, IL

Hillside Villa Inc, Salt Lake City, UT

Hilltop Care Center, Cherokee, IA

Hilltop Care Center, Spirit Lake, IA

Hilltop Care Center, Watkins, MN

Hilltop Care Center, Pine Brook, NJ

Hilltop Conv Center, Charleston, IL

Hilltop Convalescent Center, Escondido, CA

Hilltop Convalescent Hospital, Bakersfield, CA

Hilltop Haven Home for the Aged, Gunter, TX

Hilltop Health Care Center, Hilltop, WV

Hilltop Home, Lyndon, KS

Hilltop Inn, Seattle, WA

Hilltop Lodge, Owingsville, KY

Hilltop Lodge Inc Nursing Home, Beloit, KS

Hilltop Manor, Brookston, MN

Hilltop Manor Convalescent Hospital 2, Auburn, CA

Hilltop Manor Inc, Cunningham, KS

Hilltop Manor Inc, Union, MS

Hilltop Nursing Center, Harrison, AR

Hilltop Nursing Center No I, Pineville, LA

Hilltop Nursing Home, Cripple Creek, CO

Hilltop Nursing Home, Forsyth, GA

Hilltop Nursing Home, Portsmouth, OH

Hilltop Nursing Home, Parker, SD

Hilltop Nursing Home, Hilltop, WV

Hilltop Nursing Home Inc, Kuttawa, KY

Hilltop Nursing Home No I, Pineville, LA

Hilltop Nursing & Retirement Home Inc, Cincinnati, OH

Hilltop Private Nursing Home, Middletown, NJ

Hilltop Rehabilitation Center, Grand Junction, CO

Hilltop Rest Home, Science Hill, KY

Hilltop Rest Home, Carver, MA

Hilltop Rest Home, Hardwick, MA

Hilltop Rest Home, Springfield, MA

Hilltop Retirement Home, Quinn, SD

Hilltop Village, Kerrville, TX

Hillview Care Center, Altoona, PA

Hillview Care Center, Milwaukee, WI

Hillview Convalescent Hospital, Morgan Hill, CA

Hillview Health Care Center, La Crosse, WI

Hillview Health Care Center Inc, Columbia, TN

Hillview Healthcare Center, Vienna, IL

Hillview House—Hanover General Hospital, Hanover, PA

Hillview Lodge, Arnold, MO

Hillview Manor, Scottsville, KY

Hillview Manor, Goldthwaite, TX

Hillview Nursing & Convalescent Center, Huntington, WV

Hillview Nursing Home, Bastrop, LA

Hillview Nursing Home, Cincinnati, OH

Hillview Nursing Home, Flushing, OH

Hillview Nursing Home, Rapid City, SD

Hillview Nursing Home, Elizabethton, TN

Hillview Nursing Home Corp, Dresden, TN

Hillview Retirement Center, Greenville, IL

Hilo Hospital (DP), Hilo, HI

Hilton Convalescent Home, Ferndale, MI

Hilton Head Center of South Carolina Inc, Hilton Head Island, SC

Hilty Memorial Home, Pandora, OH

Hines Nursing Home, Pineland, TX

Hinton Home Inc, Farmersville, TX

Hi-Plains Nursing Home, Hale Center, TX

Caleb Hitchcock Health Center—Duncaster, Bloomfield, CT

Hitchcock Nursing Home, Hitchcock, TX

Hitz Memorial Home, Alhambra, IL

Hobart Good Samaritan Home, Hobart, OK

Hobbs Health Care Center, Hobbs, NM

Hobe Sound Geriatric Village, Hobe Sound, FL

Hocking Valley Community Hospital, Logan, OH

Hodgdon Rest Home, Boston, MA

Arthur B Hodges Center Inc, Charleston, WV

Hodges Boulevard Cluster Homes, Jacksonville, FL

Bishop Joseph H Hodges Continuous Care Center, Wheeling, WV

Hodges Nursing Home Inc, Elk City, OK

Hodges Rest Home, Springfield, MA

Hoemako Long-Term Care, Casa Grande, AZ

Hoffman Care Center, Hoffman, MN

Charles V Hogan Regional Center & John T Berry Rehabilitation Center, Danvers, MA

Hoikka House Inc, Saint Paul, MN

Hoikka House Inc, Saint Paul, MN

Holbrook Nursing Home, Holbrook, MA

Holbrook on the Hill, Buckhannon, WV

Holden Manor Care Center, Holden, MO

Holden Nursing Home Inc, Holden, MA

Holdenville Nursing Home, Holdenville, OK

Holiday Care Center, Daytona Beach, FL

Holiday Heights Nursing Home, Norman, OK

Holiday Hill Nursing Home, Newfoundland, PA

Holiday Hills Retirement & Nursing Center Inc, Dallas, TX

Holiday Home of Evansville, Evansville, IN

Holiday House, Manchester, CT

Holiday House, Saint Albans, VT

Holiday Lodge, Hamlin, TX

Holiday Lodge Nursing Home, Longview, TX

Holiday Manor, Princeton, IN

Holiday Manor, Scranton, PA

Holiday Manor Nursitarium, Canoga Park, CA

Holiday Nursing Home, Center, TX

Holiday Pines Manor, Woodville, TX

Holiday Retirement Center, Sweetwater, TX

Holiday Retirement Home Inc, Lincoln, RI

Holladay Park Plaza, Portland, OR

Holland Home—Brown Home, Grand Rapids, MI

Holland Home—Crestview Nursing Center, Wyoming, MI

Holland Home for the Aged, South Holland, IL

Holland Home—Fulton Manor, Grand Rapids, MI

Holland Home—Raybrook Manor, Grand Rapids, MI

Holland Nursing Center North, Springdale, AR

Holland Nursing Center West Inc, Springdale, AR

The Hollenbeck Home for Gracious Retirement Living, Los Angeles, CA

Hollidaysburg Veterans Home, Hollidaysburg, PA

Hollingsworth House, Braintree, MA

Hollis Park Manor Nursing Home, Hollis, NY

Hollister Convalescent Hospital, Hollister, CA

Holliston Manor Nursing Home, Holliston, MA

Holliswood Care Center Inc, Hollis, NY

Holly Care Center, Nampa, ID

Holly Center, Salisbury, MD

Holly Glen Care Center Inc, Toledo, OH

Holly Hall, Houston, TX

Holly Heights Nursing Home Inc, Denver, CO

Holly Hill, Anna, IL

Holly Hill, New Castle, IN

Holly Hill Health Care, Simsbury, CT

Holly Hill Health Care Facility, Brazil, IN

Holly Hill House, Sulphur, LA

Holly Hill Intermediate Care Facility, Valdosta, GA

Holly Hill Manor Inc, Towson, MD

Holly Hills Care Center, Emmett, ID

Holly Hills Farms, Newbury, OH

Holly Manor Nursing Home, Mendham, NJ

Holly Manor Nursing Home, Farmville, VA

Holly Nursing Care Center, Holly, CO

Holly Terrace Nursing Home, North Ridgeville, OH

Holly Tree Convalescent Hospital, Hayward, CA

Hollycrest Home Inc, Snohomish, WA

Hollywell Nursing Home, Randolph, MA

Hollywood Hills Nursing Home, Hollywood, FL

Holmdel Nursing Home, Holmdel, NJ

Holmes Convalescent Center Inc, Virginia Beach, VA

Holmes Lake Manor, Lincoln, NE

Holmes Regional Convalescent Home, Melbourne, FL

Holmesdale Convalescent Center, Kansas City, MO

Holstein Good Samaritan Center, Holstein, IA

Holton Manor, Elkhorn, WI

Holy Cross Hospital & Health Center—Geriatric Center, Nogales, AZ

Holy Family Health Center, Des Plaines, IL

Holy Family Home, Parma, OH

Holy Family Home, Philadelphia, PA

Holy Family Home for the Aged, Brooklyn, NY

Holy Family Manor, Bethlehem, PA

Holy Family Residence, Scranton, PA

Holy Family Villa, Lemont, IL

Holy Spirit Retirement Home, Sioux City, IA

Holyoke Geriatric & Convalescent Center, Holyoke, MA

Holyoke Nursing Home, Holyoke, MA

Homage Manor, Jonesville, LA

The Home Association Inc, Tampa, FL

Home Association Jewish Blind, Chicago, IL

Home for Aged People, Stoneham, MA

Home for Aged People, Winchester, MA

Home for Aged People in Fall River, Fall River, MA
Home for Aged Protestant Women, Pittsburgh, PA
Home for Aged Pythians Inc, Greenville, TX
Home for Aged Women, Boston, MA
Home for Aged Women in Salem, Salem, MA
Home for Aged Women—Minquadale, Wilmington, DE
Home for Creative Living, Windom, MN
Home for Jewish Parents, Oakland, CA
Home for the Aged Blind, Yonkers, NY
Home for the Aged—Frederick, Frederick, MD
The Home for the Aged of the Protestant Episcopal Church of the Diocese of Los Angeles, Alhambra, CA
Home for the Jewish Aged, Philadelphia, PA
Home of Angels, Ontario, CA
Home of Hope Inc, Vinita, OK
Home of the Innocents, Louisville, KY
Home of the Sages of Isreal Inc, New York, NY
Homedale Nursing Home Inc, Homedale, ID
Homeland, Harrisburg, PA
Homestead, Kittery, ME
The Homestead Nursing & Rehabilitation Center, Willow Grove, PA
Homestead Hall, Worcester, MA
Homestead Health Center, Stamford, CT
Homestead Health Center Inc, Wichita, KS
Homestead II Nursing Home, Painesville, OH
Homestead Manor Nursing Home, Stamps, AR
Homestead Manor Nursing Home, Homestead, FL
Homestead Nursing Center, Lexington, KY
Homestead Nursing Center of New Castle, New Castle, KY
Homestead Nursing Home, Deer River, MN
Homestead Nursing Home, Lincoln, NE
Homestead Nursing Home, Geneva, OH
Homestead Nursing Home, Tulsa, OK
Homestead Nursing Home 1, Painesville, OH
The Homestead Nursing & Rehabilitation Center, Willow Grove, PA
Homestead Rest Home, Phoenix, AZ
Homestead Rest Home, Leominster, MA
Homestead Rest Home, North Adams, MA
Hometown Nursing Home, Celina, OH
Hometown Nursing Home, Paulding, OH
Homeview Center of Franklin, Franklin, IN
Homeward Bound, New Hope, MN
Homeward Bound—Brooklyn Park, Brooklyn Park, MN
Homewood Convalescent Hospital Inc, San Jose, CA
Homewood Health Care Center, Glasgow, KY
Homewood Retirement Center, Hanover, PA
Homewood Retirement Center, Martinsburg, PA
Homewood Retirement Center—Frederick, Frederick, MD
Homewood Retirement Center—Williamsport, Williamsport, MD
Hominy Nursing Home, Hominy, OK
Homme Home for the Aging Inc, Wittenberg, WI
Honokaa Hospital, Honokaa, HI
Honor Heights Nursing Center, Muskogee, OK
Honorage Nursing Center, Florence, SC
Hood River Care Center, Hood River, OR
Hoodkroft Convalescent Center, Derry, NH
Hooper Care Center, Hooper, NE
Hoopeston Regional Nursing Home, Hoopeston, IL
Hoosick Falls Health Center, Hoosick Falls, NY
Hoosier Christian Village, Brownstown, IN
The Hoosier Village, Indianapolis, IN
Hooverwood, Indianapolis, IN
Hope Hall Convalescent Home Inc, Waterbury, CT
Hope House Manor Inc, Springfield, OH
Hope Intermediate Residences Inc, Williamsport, PA
Hope Manor, Fresno, CA
Hope Manor, Joplin, MO

Hope Nursing Home, Lomira, WI
Hope Park Cottage, Anchorage, AK
Hope Residences Inc, Waterville, MN
Hope Street Group Home, Bremerton, WA
Hopedale Garden Nursing Home, Hopedale, MA
Hopedale House, Hopedale, IL
Hopedale Nursing Home, Hopedale, IL
Hopewell Convalescent Center, Hopewell, VA
Hopewell Healthcare Center, Sumter, SC
Hopkins County Nursing Home, Sulphur Springs, TX
Hopkins Health Center, North Providence, RI
Hopkins House Nursing & Rehabilitation Center, Wyncote, PA
Hopkins Nursing Facility, Woodburn, KY
Hopkins Nursing Home, Waltham, MA
Horace Nye Home, Elizabethtown, NY
Horizon Apartments, West Saint Paul, MN
Horizon House II, Fort Thomas, KY
Horizon House Inc, Seattle, WA
Horizon Manor, Nocona, TX
Horizon South Living Center, Oglesby, IL
Horizon West Health Care Center, Minneapolis, MN
Horizons Health Care & Retirement Community, Cory, CO
Horizons of Tuscarawas & Carroll Counties Inc, New Philadelphia, OH
Horizons Unlimited, Rhinelander, WI
Horn Harbor Nursing Home Inc, New Point, VA
Horn Home for Aged, Lowell, MA
Horn Nursing Home Inc, Wooster, OH
Horne Home, Manzanola, CO
Hornell Nursing Home & HRF, Hornell, NY
Hospice of Southeastern Michigan, Southfield, MI
The Hospital—Skilled Nursing Facility, Sidney, NY
Hospitality Care Center, Jacksonville, FL
Hospitality Care Center, Madison, GA
Hospitality Care Center 1, Sandusky, OH
Hospitality Care Center 2, Sandusky, OH
Hospitality Care Center Inc—Toledo, Toledo, OH
Hospitality Care Center of Charlotte, Charlotte, NC
Hospitality Care Center of Clayton, Riverdale, GA
Hospitality Care Center of Hermitage Inc, Hermitage, PA
Hospitality Care Center of Macon, Macon, GA
Hospitality Care of Thomasville, Thomasville, GA
Hospitality Home East, Xenia, OH
Hospitality Home West, Xenia, OH
Hospitality House, Bedford, IN
Hospitality House, Massillon, OH
Hospitality House Inc, Bloomington, IN
Hospitality House Inc, Alice, TX
Hospitality House Nursing Home, Anderson, CA
Hospitality Manor, Kenosha, WI
Hospitality Nursing Home, Clyde, OH
Hostel House, Edina, MO
Hot Springs Convalescent Inc, Hot Springs, MT
Hot Springs Nursing Home, Hot Springs, AR
Hotel Reed Nursing Center, Bay Saint Louis, MS
Houghton County Medical Care Facility, Hancock, MI
Houghton Nursing Care Center Inc, Houghton, NY
Houlton Regional Hospital, Houlton, ME
Houlton Residential Center, Houlton, ME
House of Care Inc, Portland, OR
House of Loreto, Canton, OH
House of the Holy Comforter, Bronx, NY
Houston County Group Home, Caledonia, MN
Houston County Group Home, LaCrescent, MN
Houston County Nursing Home Inc, Crockett, TX
Houston Health Care Inc, Crawfordsville, IN

Houston Health Care Inc—Clarks Hill, Clarks Hill, IN
Houston Healthcare Inc—Cloverdale, Cloverdale, IN
Houston Village Inc, Indianapolis, IN
Hovenden Memorial Good Samaritan Home, Laurens, IA
Howard Good Samaritan Center, Howard, SD
Howard Lake Care Center, Howard Lake, MN
Howard Twilight Manor, Howard, KS
Howd Nursing Home, Moravia, NY
Howe Avenue Nursing Home Inc, New Rochelle, NY
Howell's Child Care Center, Inc/Bear Creek, LaGrange, NC
Howell's Child Care Center Inc (Riverbend), New Bern, NC
Howell's Child Care Center—Walnut Creek, Goldsboro, NC
Hoyt Cresthome Inc, Scranton, PA
Hoyt Nursing Home, Saginaw, MI
Hubbard Hill Estates Inc, Elkhart, IN
The Huber Restorium, Saint Petersburg, FL
Hudson Elms Inc, Hudson, OH
Hudson House, Aurora, MO
Hudson Memorial Nursing Home, El Dorado, AR
Hudson Valley Nursing Center, Highland, NY
Hudson View Care & Rehabilitation Center, North Bergen, NJ
Hudson View Nursing Home Inc, Yonkers, NY
Hudsonville Christian Nursing Home, Hudsonville, MI
Hudspeth Center Azalea Intermediate Care Facility, Whitfield, MS
Hudspeth Center-Rosewood Skilled Nursing Facility, Whitfield, MS
Lillian M Hudspeth Nursing Home, Sonora, TX
Hueytown Nursing Home Inc, Hueytown, AL
Hughes Convalescent Inc, Hartford, CT
Rose Anna Hughes Presbyterian Home, Louisville, KY
Hughes Springs Convalescent Center, Hughes Springs, TX
Hugo Golden Age Home, Hugo, OK
Hugo Manor Nursing Home, Hugo, OK
Human Development Center, Corpus Christi, TX
Human Resources Health Center, Miami, FL
Humble Skilled Care Facility, Humble, TX
Humboldt Care Center—North, Humboldt, IA
Humboldt Care Center—South, Humboldt, IA
Humboldt General Hospital, Winnemucca, NV
Humiston Haven, Pontiac, IL
Humphreys County Nursing Home, Belzoni, MS
Humphreys County Nursing Home Inc, Waverly, TN
Hunt Community, Nashua, NH
Hunt Nursing & Retirement Home Inc, Danvers, MA
Hunt Street Personal Care Home, Jackson, MS
Hunterdon Hills Nursing Home, Glen Gardner, NJ
Huntersville Oaks Nursing Home, Huntersville, NC
Huntingburg Convalescent Center Inc, Huntingburg, IN
Huntingdon County Nursing Home, Huntingdon, PA
Huntington Beach Convalescent Hospital, Huntington Beach, CA
Huntington Convalescent Center, Newport News, VA
Huntington Convalescent Home Inc, Cleveland, GA
Huntington Drive Convalescent Hospital, Arcadia, CA
Huntington Nursing Home, Huntington, IN
Huntington Park Care Center, Papillion, NE
Huntington Park Convalescent Center, Huntington Park, CA
Huntsville Nursing Home, Huntsville, AL
Hurlbut Nursing Home, Rochester, NY

Huron County Medical Care Facility, Bad Axe, MI
Huron Nursing Home, Huron, SD
Huron Valley Nursing Facility, Ypsilanti, MI
Huron View Lodge, Ann Arbor, MI
Huron Woods Nursing Home, Kawkawlin, MI
Hurstdale Rest Home, Springfield, MA
Hurwitz House, Baltimore, MD
Huston Nursing Home Inc, Hamden, OH
Hutcheson Medical Center Extended Care Unit, Fort Oglethorpe, GA
Hutchinson Good Samaritan Center, Hutchinson, KS
Hutchinson Heights, Hutchinson, KS
Hutton Nursing Center I, Salem, OH
Hutton Nursing Center II Inc, Salem, OH
Hutton Nursing Home, Kingston, NY
Hyattsville Manor, Hyattsville, MD
Alice Hyde Nursing Home, Malone, NY
Hyde Park Convalescent Home, Boston, MA
Hyde Park Convalescent Home Inc, Hamden, CT
Hyde Park Convalescent Hospital, Los Angeles, CA
Hyde Park Nursing Center Inc, Chicago, IL
Hyde Park Nursing Home, Kansas City, MO
Hyde Park Nursing Home, Staatsburg, NY
Hyde Park Villa Inc, Cincinnati, OH
Hydro Manor Inc, Hydro, OK
Hyland Convalescent Home, Iron Mountain, MI
Hy-Lond Convalescent Hospital, Fresno, CA
Hy-Lond Convalescent Hospital, Merced, CA
Hy-Lond Convalescent Hospital, Modesto, CA
Hy-Lond Convalescent Hospital, Napa, CA
Hy-Lond Convalescent Hospital, Sacramento, CA
Hy-Lond Convalescent Hospital, Santa Clara, CA
Hy-Lond Convalescent Hospital, Sunnyvale, CA
Hy-Lond Convalescent Hospital, Westminster, CA
Hy-Lond Home, Garden Grove, CA
Hy-Pana House Convalescent Hospital, Fresno, CA
Hy-Pana House Convalescent Hospital, Stockton, CA
Hy-Vue, Davenport, IA
I Street House, Salida, CO
Iberville Living Center, Plaquemine, LA
Idaho County Nursing Home, Grangeville, ID
Idaho Falls Nursing Home, Idaho Falls, ID
Idaho State School & Hospital—Intermediate Care Facility, Nampa, ID
Idaho State Veterans Home, Boise, ID
Ideal Health Care Center, Americus, GA
Ideal Nursing Home Inc, Norton, OH
Ideal Rest Home Inc, Mobile, AL
Idle Acre Sanitarium & Convalescent Hospital, El Monte, CA
Idlehour Nursing Center Inc, Murfreesboro, AR
Idlewood Nursing Center, Saint Francisville, LA
Idylwood Acres Convalescent Hospital, Sunnyvale, CA
Iliff Care Center, Denver, CO
Iliff Nursing Home, Dunn Loring, VA
Illinois Knights Templar Home, Paxton, IL
Illinois Masonic Home, Sullivan, IL
Illinois Presbyterian Home, Springfield, IL
Immaculate Mary Home, Philadelphia, PA
Immanuel Lutheran Home, Kalispell, MT
Immanuel Nursing Home, Charlotte, MI
Imperial Convalescent Center, La Mirada, CA
Imperial Convalescent Hospital, Studio City, CA
Imperial Health Care Center, Atlanta, GA
Imperial Health Center, Richmond, VA
Imperial Manor, Imperial, NE
Imperial Manor, Toledo, OH
Imperial Manor Convalescent Center, Salem, OR
Imperial Manor Convalescent Center, Madison, TN
Imperial Manor Inc, Imperial, CA
Imperial Nursing Center of Elgin, Elgin, IL

Imperial Nursing Center of Hazel Crest, Hazel Crest, IL
Imperial Nursing Center of Joliet, Joliet, IL
Imperial Skilled Care Center, Warren, OH
Independence Care Center, Independence, IA
Independence Health Care Center, Independence, MO
Independence House, Wheat Ridge, CO
Independence Manor, Meriden, CT
Independence Manor, Shawnee, OK
Independence Manor Care Center, Independence, MO
Independence Regional Health Center—Extended Care, Independence, MO
Independent Living Club, Indianapolis, IN
Indian Creek Convalescent Center, Corydon, IN
Indian Creek Nursing Center, Overland Park, KS
Indian Creek Nursing Center, New Castle, PA
Indian Creek Nursing Center of Missouri, Kansas City, MO
Indian Haven Nursing Home, Indiana, PA
Indian Hills Care Center, Sioux City, IA
Indian Hills Manor, Ogallala, NE
Indian Hills Nursing Center, Council Bluffs, IA
Indian Hills Nursing Center, Cameron, MO
Indian Hills Nursing Home Inc, Chillicothe, MO
Indian Meadows Nursing Center, Overland Park, KS
Indian River Nursing Home & Health Related Facility Inc, Granville, NY
Indian Trail Nursing Home Inc, Carey, OH
Indian Trails Mental Health Living Center, Topeka, KS
Indian Village Health Center Inc, Fort Wayne, IN
Indiana Asbury Towers United Methodist Home Inc, Greencastle, IN
Indiana Christian Retirement Park, Zionsville, IN
Indiana Masonic Home, Franklin, IN
Indiana Presbyterian Homes, Indiana, PA
Indiana Pythian Home, Lafayette, IN
Indiana Veterans Home, West Lafayette, IN
Indianapolis Retirement Home Inc, Indianapolis, IN
Indianola Good Samaritan Center—East, Indianola, IA
Indianola Good Samaritan Center—West, Indianola, IA
Ingham County Medical Care Facility, Okemos, MI
Inglemoor Nursing Home, Englewood, NJ
Inglemoor West Nursing Home, Livingston, NJ
Inglenook Nursing Center, Baltimore, MD
Ingleside, Mount Horeb, WI
Ingleside Convalescent Center, Detroit, MI
Ingleside Nursing Home, Old Tappan, NJ
Inglewood Convalarium, Inglewood, CA
Inglewood Manor Nursing Home, Jackson, MS
Inglis House—The Philadelphia Home for Physically Disabled Persons, Philadelphia, PA
Ingram Manor Inc, Pell City, AL
Ingram's Rest Home, Milford, DE
Inland Christian Home Inc, Ontario, CA
Inman Nursing Home, Inman, SC
Inn-Conneaut Health Center, Conneaut, OH
Inner City Nursing Home Inc, Cleveland, OH
Inns of Evergreen-Central, Baltimore, MD
Inns of Evergreen Northeast, Baltimore, MD
Inns of Evergreen-South, Baltimore, MD
Innsbruck Healthcare Center, New Brighton, MN
Inter-City Christian Manor, Allen Park, MI
Intercommunity Center of Bloomington, Bloomington, CA
Intercommunity Convalescent Hospital, Norwalk, CA
Intercommunity Sanitarium, Long Beach, CA
Interlake School, Medical Lake, WA
Intermed of Batesville, Batesville, AR
Intermediate Care Facility for Mentally Retarded—Facility I, Marianna, FL

International Falls Group Home, International Falls, MN
International Nursing Home, Danville, IL
Inver Grove Care Center, Inver Grove Heights, MN
Inverness Health Care Facility, Inverness, FL
Inyo County Sanitorium, Big Pine, CA
Iola Nursing Home, Iola, WI
Iona Glos Specialized Living Center, Addison, IL
Ionia Manor, Ionia, MI
IOOF Home of Ohio Inc, Springfield, OH
Iosco County Medical Care Facility, Tawas City, MI
Iowa City Care Center, Iowa City, IA
Iowa Jewish Home, Des Moines, IA
Iowa Masonic Nursing Home, Bettendorf, IA
Iowa Odd Fellows Home, Mason City, IA
Iowa Veterans Home, Marshalltown, IA
Iris Haven Nursing Home, Chillicothe, TX
Iron County Medical Care Facility, Crystal Falls, MI
Iron County Nursing Home, Parowan, UT
Iron River Nursing Home Inc, Iron River, MI
The Iroquois Resident Home, Watseka, IL
Irvine Health Care Center, Irvine, KY
Irving Campus of Care, Irving, TX
Irving Care Center, Irving, TX
Isabella County Medical Care Facility, Mount Pleasant, MI
Isabella Home Nursing Home Company Inc, New York, NY
Island Care Center, Freeland, WA
Island Manor Nursing Center, Vashon Island, WA
Island Nursing Home, Honolulu, HI
Island Nursing Home, Deer Isle, ME
Island Nursing Home Inc, Deer Isle, ME
Island Terrace Nursing Home, Lakeville, MA
Island View Manor, Ketchikan, AK
The Islands Convalescent Center Inc, Friday Harbor, WA
Issaquah Villa Care Center, Issaquah, WA
Italy Convalescent Center, Italy, TX
Itasca Nursing Home, Grand Rapids, MN
Itasca Nursing Home, Itasca, TX
Ivanhoe Manor Health Care Center Inc, Jacksonville, IL
Ivanhoe Manor Nursing Center, Jacksonville, IL
Ivorena Care Center, Eugene, OR
Ivy Hall Geriatric Center, Baltimore, MD
Ivy Hall Nursing Home, Elizabethton, TN
Ivy House, Painesville, OH
Ivy Manor Rest Home, Salem, MA
Ivy Manor Rest Home, Springfield, MA
Ivy Nursing Home, Denver, CO
Ivy Nursing Home Inc, Pittsburgh, PA
Ivy Ridge Nursing Home Inc, Philadelphia, PA
J & C Residential Care Facility, Pueblo, CO
J Claude Fort Community Residence, Gaffney, SC
Jacaranda Manor, Saint Petersburg, FL
Jack Cline Nursing Home, Pell City, AL
Jack Rees Nursing & Rehabilitation Center, New Castle, PA
Jackman Region Health Center, Jackman, ME
Jacksboro Nursing Center, Jacksboro, TX
Jackson Center, Milwaukee, WI
Jackson County Convalescent Center, Graceville, FL
Jackson County Hospital & Nursing Home, Scottsboro, AL
Jackson County Medical Care Facility, Jackson, MI
Jackson County Nursing Home, Murphysboro, IL
Jackson County Nursing Home Inc, Holton, KS
Jackson County Personal Care Home, Pascagoula, MS
Jackson County Public Hospital, Maquoketa, IA
Jackson Heights Nursing Home, Miami, FL
Jackson Heights Nursing Home, Farmer City, IL
Jackson Manor, Jackson, TN

Jackson Manor Nursing Home, Jonesboro, LA
Jackson Manor Nursing Home, Jackson, MO
Jackson Manor Nursing Home Inc, Miami, FL
Jackson Municipal Hospital C&CN, Jackson, MN
Jackson Park Christian Home, Nashville, TN
Jackson Park Convalescent Center, Seymour, IN
Jackson Park Convalescent Center Inc, Seymour, IN
Jackson Square East Nursing Center, Fort Worth, TX
Jackson Square Nursing Center of Texas Inc, Fort Worth, TX
Jackson's Senior Citizens Home, Vevay, IN
Jacksonville Conv Center, Jacksonville, IL
Jacksonville Convalescent Center, Jacksonville, FL
Jacksonville Nursing Center, Jacksonville, AR
Jacob's Dwelling, Coshocton, OH
Jacobsen Nursing Home, Seattle, WA
Jacobson Memorial Hospital Care Center, Elgin, ND
Jallo's Nursing Home, Portland, OR
Jamaica Hospital Nursing Home Company Inc, Jamaica, NY
Jamaica Towers Nursing Home, Boston, MA
Ellen James Rest Home, Boston, MA
Larry James Home, Waseca, MN
James Manor Rest Home, Fitchburg, MA
Mary James Nursing Home, Montrose, MI
James River Convalescent Center, Newport News, VA
James Square Nursing Home, Syracuse, NY
James Valley Nursing Home, Redfield, SD
Jamieson Nursing Home, Harrisville, MI
Janesville Health Care Center, Janesville, WI
The Janesville Nursing Home, Janesville, MN
Janney House, Mont Clare, PA
January Care Home, Evant, TX
Janwynella Nursing Home Inc, Lafayette, TN
Japanese Retirement Home-Intermediate Care Facility, Los Angeles, CA
Jaquith Nursing Home—Adams Inn, Whitfield, MS
Jaquith Nursing Home—Washington Inn, Whitfield, MS
W L Jaquith ICF/MR, Sanatorium, MS
Jarvis Heights Nursing Center, Fort Worth, TX
Jasper Convalescent Center Inc, Jasper, TX
Jasper County Care Facility, Newton, IA
Jasper County Nursing Home, Bay Springs, MS
Jasper Memorial Hospital & Nursing Home, Monticello, GA
Jasper Nursing Center Inc, Jasper, IN
Jaylene Manor Nursing Home, Saint Petersburg, FL
Jean Carol's Nursing Home Inc, Canton, OH
Jeanne Jugan Residence, Newark, DE
Jeanne Jugan Residence, Washington, DC
Jeanne Jugan Residence, Somerville, MA
Jeanne Jugan Residence, Bronx, NY
Jeanne Jugan Residence, Pawtucket, RI
Jean's Nursing Home, College Station, AR
Jefferson Christian Nursing Home, Grand Rapids, MI
Jefferson City Manor Care Center, Jefferson City, MO
Jefferson Convalescent Home Inc, Pine Bluff, AR
Jefferson County Home, Birmingham, AL
Jefferson County Nursing Home, Dandridge, TN
Jefferson Davis County—Extended Care Facility, Prentiss, MS
Jefferson Davis Nursing Home, Jennings, LA
Jefferson Health Care Center, Jefferson, LA
Jefferson Hills Manor Inc, Pittsburgh, PA
Jefferson House, Newington, CT
Jefferson House Care Center, Tacoma, WA
Jefferson Manor, Jefferson, IA
Jefferson Manor, Louisville, KY
Jefferson Manor, Brookville, PA
Jefferson Manor, Green Bay, WI
Jefferson Manor Nursing Center, Passaic, NJ

Jefferson Manor Nursing Home, Baton Rouge, LA
Jefferson Meadows Care Center, Baraboo, WI
Jefferson Nursing Center, Monticello, FL
Jefferson Rest Home, Arlington, MA
Jefferson Street Nursing Home, Saint Charles, MO
Jeffersonian Manor, Charles Town, WV
The Jeffersonian, Mount Vernon, IL
Jeffersonville Nursing Home, Jeffersonville, IN
Jeffrey Place Nursing Center, Waco, TX
Jenkins Hall-Reid Memorial Hospital, Richmond, IN
Jenkins Memorial Nursing Home, Baltimore, MD
Jenkins Memorial Nursing Home, Wellston, OH
Jenkins Methodist Home Inc, Watertown, SD
Jenkins Nursing Home Inc, Marion, SC
Jennie Wiley Health Care Center, Paintsville, KY
Jennies Retirement Home, Villard, MN
Jennings Caring Center, Jennings, MO
Eliza Jennings Home, Cleveland, OH
Jennings Guest House, Jennings, LA
Jennings Hall Inc, Garfield Heights, OH
Jennings Healthcare Inc, Augusta, GA
Jennings Terrace, Aurora, IL
Chris Jensen Nursing Home, Duluth, MN
Jerome Home, New Britain, CT
Jerri's Benevolent Manor, Saint Louis, MO
Jerseyville Care Center, Jerseyville, IL
Jesmond Nursing Home, Nahant, MA
Jesup Manor Nursing Center, Jesup, GA
Jesup Rest-A-While Nursing Home, Jesup, GA
Jewish Center for Aged, Chesterfield, MO
Jewish Convalescent & Nursing Home Inc, Baltimore, MD
Jewish Geriatric Center, Cherry Hill, NJ
The Jewish Home & Hospital for Aged-Kingsbridge Center, Bronx, NY
Jewish Home for the Aged, New Haven, CT
The Jewish Home for the Aged, Atlanta, GA
Jewish Home for the Aged, Portland, ME
Jewish Home for the Aged, Worcester, MA
Jewish Home for the Aged, Houston, TX
Jewish Home for the Aged 2, Detroit, MI
Jewish Home for the Aged of Rhode Island, Providence, RI
Jewish Home for the Elderly, Fairfield, CT
Jewish Home & Hospital for the Aged, New York, NY
Jewish Home of Central New York, Syracuse, NY
Jewish Home of Eastern Pennsylvania, Scranton, PA
Jewish Home of Greater Harrisburg, Harrisburg, PA
Jewish Home of Rochester, Rochester, NY
Jewish Institute for Geriatric Care Nursing Home Co Inc, New Hyde Park, NY
Jewish Nursing Home of Western Massachusetts, Longmeadow, MA
Jewish Peoples Convalescent Home, Chicago, IL
Jewish Rehabilitation Center for Aged of the North Shore Inc, Swampscott, MA
JHMCB Center for Nursing & Rehabilitation, Brooklyn, NY
Jo Lene's Nursing Home, Salisbury, NC
Jodoin Home, Chester, NH
Johanna Nursing Home, Salt Lake City, UT
John Paul II Nursing Center, Kenedy, TX
John XXIII Home For Senior Citizens, Hermitage, PA
Amy Johnson Residence, Saint Paul, MN
C W Johnson Intermediate Care Facility, Inman, SC
Calvin D Johnson Nursing Home, Belleville, IL
Dale Johnson Center, Bellwood, IL
Johnson County Health Care, Mountain City, TN
Johnson County Intermediate Care Home, Adrian, GA
Johnson County Nursing Center, Olathe, KS
Johnson Home, Westminster, CO

Johnson House, Boulder, CO
J B Johnson Nursing Center, Washington, DC
Lyndon B Johnson Memorial Nursing Home, Johnson City, TX
Johnson Memorial Hospital Home, Dawson, MN
Johnson Nursing Home, Boston, MA
Johnson Nursing Home, Memphis, TN
Johnson Rehabilitation Nursing Home, Chicago, IL
Johnson Rest Home, Erskine, MN
Johnson Rest Home, Fosston, MN
Johnson-Mathers Health Care Inc, Carlisle, KY
Johnson's Health Care Center Inc, Harriman, TN
Johnsons Long Lake Home, Walker, MN
Johnson's Meadowlake Home Inc, Conway, AR
Johnsons Riverside Boarding Care Home, Thief River Falls, MN
Johnston County Memorial Nursing Center Inc, Smithfield, NC
Johnston Nursing Home, Lancaster, OH
Johnston Nursing Home, Troy, OH
Johnstone Developmental Center, Wheat Ridge, CO
Joliet Terrace, Joliet, IL
Jo-Lin Health Center Inc, Ironton, OH
Jolley Acres Nursing Home Inc, Orangeburg, SC
Jolly Rest Home Inc, Pascoag, RI
Jones County Rest Home, Ellisville, MS
Franke Tobey Jones Home, Tacoma, WA
Jones-Harrison Residence, Minneapolis, MN
Jones Health Center Inc, Orange, TX
Jones Nursing & Convalescent Home, Dayton, OH
Jones Nursing Home, Beech Bottom, WV
Jones Rest Home & Convalescent Hospital, San Leandro, CA
Jones Valley Nursing Home, Bessemer, AL
Jonesboro Human Development Center, Jonesboro, AR
Jonesboro Nursing Home Inc, Jonesborough, TN
Jonesburg Caring Center, Jonesburg, MO
Jonesville Rest Home, Jonesville, KY
Joplin Health Care Center, Joplin, MO
Jordan & Cole Residential Care Facility, Las Animas, CO
J J Jordan Geriatric Center, Louisa, KY
Ranken Jordan Home for Convalescent Crippled Children, Saint Louis, MO
Jordan Residential Services Inc, Pueblo, CO
Jordan's Nursing Home, Bridgman, MI
Maria Joseph Manor, Danville, PA
Josephine Nursing Home, Dayton, OH
Josephine Sunset Home, Stanwood, WA
Joseph's Nursing Home, Lawton, OK
Josephson Nursing Home, Ironwood, MI
Helen Newberry Joy Hospital Annex, Newberry, MI
Joywells, Brownsville, KY
Judson Palmer Home, Findlay, OH
Judson Park, Cleveland Heights, OH
Judson Village, Cincinnati, OH
Julia Convalescent Hospital, Mountain View, CA
Julias Valley Manor, Sioux City, IA
Juliette Manor, Berlin, WI
Junction City Good Samaritan Center, Junction City, KS
Junction City Nursing Home, Junction City, AR
Jupiter Convalescence Pavilion, Jupiter, FL
K F J Manor Inc 2, Saint Louis, MO
Kabul Nursing Home, Cabool, MO
Kachina Point Health Center, Sedona, AZ
Kade Nursing Home, Washington, PA
Kadoka Care Center, Kadoka, SD
Kah Tai Care Center, Port Townsend, WA
Kahl Home for the Aged, Davenport, IA
Kahuku Hospital, Kahuku, HI
Kalkaska Memorial Hospital, Kalkaska, MI
Kanawha Community Home, Kanawha, IA
Kane County Hospital—Skilled Nursing Facility, Kanab, UT

John J Kane Allegheny County Home, Pittsburgh, PA
Kankakee Terrace, Bourbonnais, IL
Kansas Christian Home Inc, Newton, KS
Kansas City Presbyterian Manor, Kansas City, KS
Kansas Masonic Home, Wichita, KS
Kanukuk Nursing Home, Duncan, OK
Kappes Nursing Home, West Allis, WI
Karen Acres Nursing Home, Urbandale, IA
A Sam Karesh LTC Center, Camden, SC
Karlson Rest Home Inc, Lynn, MA
Karlstad Memorial Nursing Center, Karlstad, MN
Karmenta Health Care Center, Madison, WI
Karnes City Care Center, Karnes City, TX
Katahdin Nursing Home, Millinocket, ME
Kateri Residence, New York, NY
Katherine Convalescent Hospital, Salinas, CA
Katie Jane Memorial Home, Warrenton, MO
Katyville Healthcare Center, Katy, TX
Kau Hospital, Pahala, HI
Kauai Veterans Memorial Hospital (DP), Waimea, HI
Andrew Kaul Memorial Hospital—Extended Care Facility, Saint Marys, PA
Kaw Valley Manor, Bonner Springs, KS
Kaweah Manor Convalescent Hospital, Visalia, CA
Sena Kean Manor, Smethport, PA
Kearney Home, Sharon Hill, PA
Kearny Mesa Convalescent & Nursing Home, San Diego, CA
Kearsley/Christ Church Hospital, Philadelphia, PA
Keen Agers Nursing Home, Wichita, KS
Keeneland Nursing Home, Weatherford, TX
Keiro Nursing Home, Los Angeles, CA
Keith Acres Nursing Home, Blytheville, AR
Keizer Retirement & Health Care Center, Salem, OR
Keller Nursing Home, Spokane, WA
Keller Sheltered Care Home 1, Dongola, IL
Kelley Rest Home, Agawam, MA
Kelliher Good Samaritan Center, Kelliher, MN
Kelly Nursing Home, Kansas City, MO
Kelsey Memorial Hospital, Lakeview, MI
Kemp Care Center Inc, Kemp, TX
Kemp Horn Home, Smithsburg, MD
Kemper County Nursing Home, DeKalb, MS
Mary Kendall Ladies Home, Owensboro, KY
Kendallville Nursing Home, Kendallville, IN
Kendallwood Trails Nursing Center, Gladstone, MO
Kenesaw Nursing Home Inc, Baltimore, MD
Ken-Joy Nursing Home, Hope, IN
Kenmare Community Health Care Corporation, Kenmare, ND
Kenmore Mercy Skilled Nursing Facility, Kenmore, NY
Kennebunk Nursing Home, Kennebunk, ME
Kennedale Nursing Home, Kennedale, TX
Kennedy Convalescent Hospital, Los Angeles, CA
Kennedy Memorial Christian Home Inc, Martinsville, IN
Kennett Health Care Center, Kennett, MO
Kenney Presbyterian Home, Seattle, WA
Kenney Retirement Community, Ligonier, IN
Kenniebrew Home, Harvey, IL
Kenoza Hillcrest Nursing Home, Haverhill, MA
Kenoza Manor Convalescent Center, Haverhill, MA
Kenoza Nursing Home, Haverhill, MA
Kensington Gardens Nursing Center, Kensington, MD
Kensington Manor, Dallas, TX
Kensington Manor Inc, Sarasota, FL
Kenson Nursing Home, Baltimore, MD
Kent Community Hospital Complex, Grand Rapids, MI
Kent Convalescent Center, Smyrna, DE
Kent Convalescent Hospital, Pasadena, CA
Kent County Nursing Home, Jayton, TX
Kent Nursing Home, Holmes, NY
Kent Nursing Home Inc, Warwick, RI

Kent Quality Care Nursing Center, Kent, OH
Kentland Nursing Home 2669, Kentland, IN
Kentmere—The Home of Merciful Rest Society Inc, Wilmington, DE
Kenton Manor, Greeley, CO
Kent's Nursing Center, Fort Worth, TX
Kentuckiana Christian Home Inc, Charlestown, IN
Kentucky Rest Haven, Madisonville, KY
Kentwood Manor Nursing Home, Kentwood, LA
Kenwood House, Richmond, KY
Kenwood Manor, Enid, OK
Kenwood Nursing Home, Dallas, TX
Kenwood Terrace, Chicago, IL
Kenwood Terrace Nursing Center Inc, Cincinnati, OH
Kenwood View Nursing Home, Salina, KS
Kenya Village Nursing Home, Duncan, OK
Kenyon Sunset Home, Kenyon, MN
Keokuk Convalescent Center, Keokuk, IA
The Kepler Home Inc, Elizabethville, PA
Kermit Nursing Center, Kermit, TX
Kern Place, Grand Prairie, TX
Lillian E Kerr Nursing Home, Phelps, WI
James E Kerwin Housing for the Elderly & Elderly Disabled, Memphis, TN
Keswick Home for Incurables of Baltimore City, Baltimore, MD
Bertha D Garten Ketcham Memorial Center Inc, Odon, IN
Ketcham's Nursing Home, Crooksville, OH
Ketter Manor Inc, Falls City, NE
Kettering Convalescent Center, Kettering, OH
Kewanee Care Home, Kewanee, IL
Kewanee Convalescent Center, Kewanee, IL
Kewaunee Health Care Center, Kewaunee, WI
Key Circle Hospice Inc, Baltimore, MD
Key Pine Village, Lecanto, FL
Key West Convalescent Center, Key West, FL
Keystone Nursing Care Center, Keystone, IA
Keystone Nursing Home Inc, Leominster, MA
Keysville Convalescent & Nursing Center Inc, Keysville, GA
Kidron Bethel Retirement Services, Newton, KS
Kidwell Rest Home, Romney, WV
Kilbourn Care Center Inc, Milwaukee, WI
Kilgore Nursing Center, Kilgore, TX
Killeen Nursing Home, Killeen, TX
Kimball County Manor, Kimball, NE
Kimberly Convalescent Hospital, Santa Maria, CA
Kimberly Hall Nursing Home—North, Windsor, CT
Kimberly Hall Nursing Home—South, Windsor, CT
Kimberly Manor Nursing & Convalescent Home, Rock Springs, WY
Kimbrough Nursing Home, Springfield, MO
Kimes Convalescent Center, Athens, OH
Kimwell Health Care Center, Fall River, MA
Kin Kora Pythian Home, Duncannon, PA
Kinder Nursing Home, Kinder, LA
Kindlehope, Willmar, MN
King Bruwaert House, Hinsdale, IL
King City Convalescent Center, Tigard, OR
King City Manor, King City, MO
King David Care Center of Atlantic City, Atlantic City, NJ
King David Center at Palm Beach, West Palm Beach, FL
King Family Care Home, Arvada, CO
James C King Home, Evanston, IL
King James Care Center of Chatham, Chatham, NJ
King James Care Center of Mercer, Trenton, NJ
King James Care Center of Middletown, Navesink, NJ
King James Care Center of Somerset, Somerset, NJ
King Manor Nursing Home, Lakewood, NJ
King Nursing Home, Houghton Lake, MI
King Rest Home, Marceline, MO
King Street Nursing Home, Rye Brook, NY
King Tree Center, Dayton, OH

Kingdom Nursing Home Association Inc, Fulton, MO
Kingman Health Care Center, Kingman, AZ
Kings Convalescent Center, Hanford, CA
King's Daughters Home, Mexico, MO
Kings Daughters & Sons Home, Louisville, KY
Kings Daughters & Sons Home, Memphis, TN
King's Daughters & Sons Home for Aged Men & Women, Ashland, KY
Kings Daughters & Sons Home for the Aged in Norfolk County, Wrentham, MA
King's Daughters & Sons Nursing Home, Durant, OK
King's Daughters & Sons Rest Home Inc, Meridian, MS
King's Guest Home, Winnsboro, LA
Kings Harbor Care Center, Bronx, NY
King's Manor Methodist Home, Hereford, TX
Kings Mountain Convalescent Center, Kings Mountain, NC
King's Nursing Home, Kansas City, MO
Kings Terrace Nursing Home HRF, Bronx, NY
Kings Vista Convalescent Hospital, Fowler, CA
Kingsbridge Heights Long-Term Home Health Care, Bronx, NY
Kingsbridge Heights Nursing Home, New York, NY
Kingsbury Memorial Manor, Lake Preston, SD
Kingsdale Manor, Lumberton, NC
Kingsland Hills Care Center, Kingsland, TX
Kingsley Manor Convalescent Hospital, Los Angeles, CA
Kingstree Community Residence, Kingstree, SC
Kingstree Nursing Facility Inc, Kingstree, SC
Kingsway Arms Nursing Center Inc, Schenectady, NY
Kinney Nursing Home, Gouverneur, NY
Kinton Nursing Home, Fuquay-Varina, NC
Kirbyhaven, Spokane, WA
Kirkland Convalescent Center, Kirkland, WA
Kirkland Convalescent Home Inc, Williston, SC
Kirksville Manor Care Center, Kirksville, MO
Kirkwood by the River, Birmingham, AL
Kirkwood Nursing Home, Wakefield, MA
Kissimmee Good Samaritan Nursing Center, Kissimmee, FL
Kissimmee Health Care Center, Kissimmee, FL
Kit Carson Convalescent Hospital, Jackson, CA
Kith Haven, Flint, MI
Kittson County Nursing Home, Hallock, MN
Kittson Memorial Hospital, Hallock, MN
Kiva House, Lexington, KY
Kivel Geriatric Center-Nursing Home-Kivel Care Center, Phoenix, AZ
Kiwanis Manor Inc, East Troy, WI
Klamath County Convalescent Center, Klamath Falls, OR
Klearview Manor, Fairfield, ME
Klingerman Nursing Center, Orangeville, PA
Klondike Manor, Louisville, KY
Knapp Haven Nursing Home, Chetek, WI
Knight's Nursing Home, Littlefield, TX
Knights Templar Clinic, Arlington, TX
Knollview Manor Nursing Home, Muskegon, MI
Knollwood Manor, Millersville, MD
Knollwood Manor Intermediate Care Facility, Raleigh, NC
Knollwood Nursing Home Inc, Worcester, MA
Knopp Nursing Home 2 Inc, Fredericksburg, TX
Knopp Nursing Home Inc 1, Fredericksburg, TX
Knott County Nursing Home, Kindman, KY
Knott Nursing Home, Charles Town, WV
Knottsville Home, Philpot, KY
Joseph B Knowles Home for the Aged, Nashville, TN
Knowlton Manor Nursing Home, West Upton, MA
Knox County Nursing Home, Knoxville, IL

Knox County Nursing Home, Edina, MO
Knox Estates Living Center, Streator, IL
John Knox Manor Inc II, Montgomery, AL
John Knox Village, Lubbock, TX
John Knox Village, Weslaco, TX
John Knox Village Medical Center, Orange City, FL
John Knox Village Medical Center, Pompano Beach, FL
John Knox Village Medical Center, Tampa, FL
Knox Manor, Galesburg, IL
Knoxville Convalescent & Nursing Home Inc, Knoxville, TN
Knoxville Health Care Center Inc, Knoxville, TN
Knoxville Rest Home, Knoxville, IA
Knutson Manor Nursing Center, El Dorado, KS
Robert Koch Hospital, Saint Louis, MO
Kodiak Island Hospital, Kodiak, AK
Koep Group Homes Inc, Fergus Falls, MN
Kohala Hospital (DP), Kapaau, HI
Kokomo Nursing Home-Greentree Manor, Kokomo, IN
Kona Hospital (DP), Kealakekua, HI
Kosary Home, Oak Forest, IL
Kountze Nursing Center, Kountze, TX
Kramm Healthcare Center Inc, Milton, PA
Kramm Nursing Home Inc, Watsontown, PA
Kraus Home Inc, Chicago, IL
Kraus House, Milton, NH
Kraver Institute, North Miami Beach, FL
Kristen Beth Nursing Home Inc, New Bedford, MA
Kristi Lee Manor Inc, Colorado City, TX
Kuakini Geriatric Care Inc, Honolulu, HI
Kula Hospital, Kula, HI
Kurthwood Manor Nursing Home, Leesville, LA
Milton & Hattie Kutz Home Inc, Wilmington, DE
Kutztown Manor Inc, Kutztown, PA
K'Way Kare Nursing Home, Holland, TX
Kyakameena Skilled Nursing Facility, Berkeley, CA
La Belle Manor, LaBelle, MO
La Belle's Rest Home, Shelburne Falls, MA
La Boure Care Center, Dallas, TX
La Colina Healthcare, Tucson, AZ
La Dora Lodge Nursing Home, Bedford, TX
La Habra Convalescent Hospital, La Habra, CA
La Hacienda Nursing Home, Tucson, AZ
La Hacienda Nursing Home Inc, San Diego, TX
La Jolla Convalescent Hospital, La Jolla, CA
La Mesa Care Center, Yuma, AZ
La Mesa Convalescent Hospital, La Mesa, CA
La Moine Christian Nursing Home, Roseville, IL
La Porte Care Center, La Porte, TX
La Posada, Alamosa, CO
La Posada Convalescent Home, Miami, FL
La Residencia, Santa Fe, NM
La Rocca Nursing Home, Tuscaloosa, AL
La Salette Rehabilitation & Convalescent Hospital, Stockton, CA
La Salle County Nursing Home, Ottawa, IL
La Salle Nursing Home Inc, Jena, LA
La Sierra Convalescent Hospital, Merced, CA
La Sierra Convalescent Hospital, Riverside, CA
La Siesta Retirement Center, Hobbs, NM
La Vida Llena Retirement Center, Albuquerque, NM
La Villa Nursing Center, Detroit, MI
Labelle View Nursing Center, Steubenville, OH
Lackawanna County Home, Olyphant, PA
Lackey Convalescent Home, Forest, MS
Lackey Manor Nursing Home, Oklahoma City, OK
LaCoba Homes Inc, Monett, MO
Lacombe Nursing Home, Mandeville, LA
Laconia Nursing Home, Bronx, NY
LaCrescent Healthcare Center, LaCrescent, MN

Kate Macy Ladd Convalescent Home, Far Hills, NJ
Ladies GAR Home, Pittsburgh, PA
Ladysmith Nursing Home, Ladysmith, WI
Lafayette Christian Nursing Home, Grand Rapids, MI
Lafayette Convalescent Home, Marblehead, MA
Lafayette Convalescent Hospital, Lafayette, CA
Lafayette Extended Care, Lafayette, AL
Lafayette Good Samaritan Center, Lafayette, MN
Lafayette Guest House, Lafayette, LA
LaFayette Health Care Inc, LaFayette, GA
Lafayette Health Care Inc, Lafayette, LA
Lafayette Healthcare Center, Lafayette, IN
Lafayette Manor, Uniontown, PA
Lafayette Manor, Darlington, WI
Lafayette Manor Nursing Home, Lexington, MO
LaFayette Nursing Home Inc, Lafayette, AL
Lafayette Nursing Home Inc, North Kingstown, RI
The Lafayette-Philadelphia, Philadelphia, PA
Lafayette Villa Health Care, Norfolk, VA
LaFollette Community Nursing Home, LaFollette, TN
Lafon Nursing Home of the Holy Family, New Orleans, LA
Lafon United Methodist Nursing Home, New Orleans, LA
Lafourche Home for the Aged, Thibodaux, LA
LaGrande Nursing Center, LaGrande, OR
LaGrange Medcraft Nursing Home, LaGrange, GA
LaGrange Nursing Home, LaGrange, IN
Laguna Rainbow Nursing & Elderly Care Center, New Laguna, NM
Morris Lahasky Nursing Home, Erath, LA
Lahey's Nursing Home, Duncan, OK
Lahser Hills Nursing Center, Southfield, MI
Lake Alfred Restorium & ACLF, Lake Alfred, FL
Lake Andes Health Care Center, Lake Andes, SD
Lake Auburn Home for Aged, Excelsior, MN
Lake Bluff Health Care Center, Lake Bluff, IL
Lake City Health Care Center, Morrow, GA
Lake City Health Care Center, Lake City, TN
Lake City Nursing Home, Lake City, MN
Lake Country Manor, Marietta, OK
Lake County Adult Resident Center, Mentor, OH
Lake County Child Development Center, Mentor, OH
Lake County Convalescent Home, Crown Point, IN
Lake County Rehabilitation Center, East Chicago, IN
Lake Crest Villa, Evanston, IL
Lake Crystal Healthcare Center, Lake Crystal, MN
Lake District Hospital, Lakeview, OR
Lake Drive Nursing Home Inc, Baltimore, MD
Lake Drive Nursing Home Inc, Henryetta, OK
Lake Erie Institute of Rehabilitation, Erie, PA
Lake Eustis Care Center, Eustis, FL
Lake Front Healthcare Center Inc, Chicago, IL
Lake Havasu Nursing Center, Lake Havasu City, AZ
Lake Haven Health Care Center, Benton, KY
Lake Haven Health Care Center Inc, Benton, KY
Lake Haven Manor, Duluth, MN
Lake Haven Nursing Home, Worthington, MN
Lake Highlands Nursing Home, Clermont, FL
Lake Holiday Manor Nursing Home, DeMotte, IN
Lake Jackson Nursing Home, Lake Jackson, TX
Lake Lodge Retirement & Nursing Center, Lake Worth, TX
Lake Memorial Nursing Home, Leesburg, FL
Lake Mills Nursing Home Inc, Lake Mills, IA
Lake Norden Care Center, Lake Norden, SD
Lake Owasso Residence, Shoreview, MN

Lake Park Care Center, Lake Park, IA
Lake Park Hospital & Nursing Care Center, Sylvania, OH
Lake Park Retirement Residence, Oakland, CA
Lake Region Hospital & Nursing Home, Fergus Falls, MN
Lake Region Lutheran Home, Devils Lake, ND
Lake Ridge Health Care Center, Roseville, MN
Lake Shore Hospital Inc HRF, Irving, NY
Lake Shore Nursing Centre Inc, Chicago, IL
Lake Taylor City Hospital, Norfolk, VA
Lake Towers Health Center, Sun City Center, FL
Lake View, Arvada, CO
Lake View Care Center, Bigfork, MT
Lake View Community Nursing Home, Lawton, MI
Lake View Home, Monticello, IN
Lake View Rest Home, Wareham, MA
Lake Vue Gardens Convalescent Center, Kirkland, WA
Lake Waccamaw Convalescent Center Inc, Lake Waccamaw, NC
Lake Wales Convalescent Center, Lake Wales, FL
Lake Worth Health Care Center, Lake Worth, FL
Lake Worth Nursing Home, Fort Worth, TX
Lakecrest Development Center, Orem, UT
Lakehaven Nursing Home, Valdosta, GA
Lakeland Convalescent Center, Lakeland, FL
Lakeland Convalescent Center, Detroit, MI
Lakeland Health Care Center, Lakeland, FL
Lakeland Healthcare Center, Effingham, IL
Lakeland Lodge Nursing Home, Heber Springs, AR
Lakeland Loving Care Center Inc, Milford, IN
Lakeland Manor, Chicago, IL
Lakeland Manor, Woodruff, WI
Lakeland Manor Inc, Ardmore, OK
Lakeland Nursing Center, Angola, IN
Lakeland Nursing Center, Jackson, MS
Lakeland Nursing Home, Pineville, LA
Lakeland Nursing Home, Geneva, OH
Lakeland Nursing Home of Walworth County, Elkhorn, WI
Lakeland Villa Convalescent Center, Lakeland, GA
Lakeport Skilled Nursing Center Inc, Lakeport, CA
Lakeridge Village Health Care Center, Lakewood, CO
Lakeshore Convalescent, Oakland, CA
Lakeshore Estates Inc, Nashville, TN
Lakeshore Heights Nursing Care Center, Gainesville, GA
Lakeshore Home for the Aged, Nashville, TN
Lakeshore Inn Nursing Home, Waseca, MN
Lakeshore Lutheran Home, Duluth, MN
Lakeshore Manor Nursing Home, Decatur, IL
Lakeshore Nursing Home, Crescent City, FL
Lakeshore Nursing Home, Rochester, NY
Lakeside Boarding Home, Chicago, IL
Lakeside Health Center, West Palm Beach, FL
Lakeside Health Center Inc, Michigan City, IN
Lakeside Lodge, Wellington, KS
Lakeside Lutheran Home, Emmetsburg, IA
Lakeside Manor Home for the Aged, Winchester, TN
Lakeside Medical Center, Pine City, MN
Lakeside Memorial Home, Lubbock, TX
Lakeside Nursing Center, Lake City, AR
Lakeside Nursing Center, Dallas, PA
Lakeside Nursing Home Inc, Ithaca, NY
Lakeside Place, Highland Heights, KY
Lakeside Plantation, Naples, FL
Lakeside Residential Care Facility, East Hampton, CT
Lakeview Care Center, Glenwood, MN
Lakeview Childrens Home, Sauk Centre, MN
Lakeview Christian Home—Northgate Unit, Carlsbad, NM
Lakeview Christian Home of the Southwest, Carlsbad, NM

Lakeview Convalescent Center, Wayne, NJ
Lakeview Developmental Disability Center, Riverside, CA
Lakeview Health Care Center, Carmel, IN
Lakeview Health Center, Harrisville, RI
Lakeview Health Center, West Salem, WI
Lakeview Manor, New Roads, LA
Lakeview Manor, Chapel Hill, NC
Lakeview Manor, Weyauwega, WI
Lakeview Manor Inc, Opp, AL
Lakeview Manor Inc, Indianapolis, IN
Lakeview Manor Nursing Home, West Palm Beach, FL
Lakeview Manor Nursing Home, Cadillac, MI
Lakeview Methodist Health Care Center, Fairmont, MN
Lakeview Nursing Center, Sanford, FL
Lakeview Nursing Center, Grand Island, NE
Lakeview Nursing Center, Spartanburg, SC
Lakeview Nursing & Geriatric Center Inc, Chicago, IL
Lakeview Nursing Home, Birmingham, AL
Lakeview Nursing Home, Morgantown, KY
Lakeview Nursing Home, Farmerville, LA
Lakeview Nursing Home Inc, Birmingham, AL
Lakeview Nursing Home Inc, Oroville, CA
Lakeview Rest Home, Newton, MA
Lakeview Rest Home, Firth, NE
Lakeview Rest Home Inc, Forsyth, MO
Lakeview Terrace Christian Retirement Community, Altoona, FL
Lakeview Terrace Medical Care Facility, Altoona, FL
Lakeview Terrace Sanitarium, Sunland, CA
Lakeview Village Inc, Lenexa, KS
Lakewood Care Center, Milwaukee, WI
Lakewood Convalescent Home, Hot Springs, AR
Lakewood Living Center, Plainfield, IL
Lakewood Manor, Waterville, ME
Lakewood Manor North, Los Angeles, CA
Lakewood Manor Nursing Center, Hendersonville, NC
Lakewood Nursing Home, Lakewood, CO
Lakewood of Voorhees, Gibbsboro, NJ
Lakewood Park Health Center, Downey, CA
Lakewood Village Med Center, Fort Worth, TX
Lamar Boarding & Rest Home, Lamar, MO
Lamar Convalescent Center Inc, Vernon, AL
Lamar County Hospital & Nursing Home, Vernon, AL
The Lambs Inc, Libertyville, IL
Lambs Nursing Home, High Point, NC
Lamesa Nursing Center, Lamesa, TX
Lamoni Manor, Lamoni, IA
The Lamp, Brook Park, OH
The Lamp Nursing Home, Lisbon, ME
Lampasas Manor, Lampasas, TX
Lanai Community Hospital (DP), Lanai, HI
The Lancashire, Kilmarnock, VA
Lancashire Hall Inc, Lancaster, PA
Lancaster Convalescent Hospital, Lancaster, CA
Lancaster County Care Center, Lancaster, SC
Lancaster Health Care Center, Lancaster, OH
Lancaster Living Center, Lancaster, WI
Lancaster Manor, Lincoln, NE
Lancaster Nursing Home Inc, Lancaster, TX
Lancaster Residential Center, Lancaster, TX
Lancia Convalescent Center, Steubenville, OH
Lancia Villa Royale, Steubenville, OH
Landis Home, Lititz, PA
Landmark Learning Center—Facility I, Opa Locka, FL
Landmark Learning Center—Miami Facility II, Opa Locka, FL
Landmark Medical Center, Pomona, CA
Landry Road Nursing Home, Lafayette, LA
Lane House Inc, Crawfordsville, IN
Lane Memorial Hospital—Geriatric Unit, Zachary, LA
Lane's Convalescent Home Inc, Wichita Falls, TX
Lane's Nursing Home Inc, Wichita Falls, TX
Lane's Nursing Home—Monette, Monette, AR
Lane's Rest Home Inc—Caraway, Caraway, AR

Lanett Geriatric Center Inc, Lanett, AL
Langhorne Gardens Nursing Center, Langhorne, PA
George H Lanier Memorial Nursing Home, Valley, AL
Lanier North Intermediate Care Facility, Gainesville, GA
Lanier Nursing Home, Comming, GA
Lanore's Nursing Home, Draper, UT
Lansdowne Rest Home, East Lansdowne, PA
Lanterman Developmental Center, Pomona, CA
Lantern Park Care Center, Coralville, IA
Lantern Park Manor, Colby, KS
Lapeer County Medical Care Facility, Lapeer, MI
LaPlata Nursing Home District, LaPlata, MO
Larchwood Lodge Nursing Home, Waltham, MA
Largo Manor Care, Largo, MD
Larimore Good Samaritan Center, Larimore, ND
Lark Ellen Towers Skilled Nursing Facility, West Covina, CA
Lark Manor Convalescent Hospital, Los Gatos, CA
Larsen Memorial Home, Peshtigo, WI
Larsen Nursing Home, Lehi, UT
Las Cruces Manor, Las Cruces, NM
Las Flores Convalescent Hospital, Gardena, CA
Las Flores Nursing Center, Mesa, AZ
Las Vegas Convalescent Center, Las Vegas, NV
LaSalle Convalescent Home, Minneapolis, MN
LaSalle Nursing Home, Detroit, MI
Lasata, Cedarburg, WI
Latah Care Center, Moscow, ID
Latah Center Inc, Spokane, WA
Latham Care Center Inc, California, MO
Latham Estates, Lake Forest, IL
Latham Nursing Home, Anderson, SC
Latham Nursing Home, Salt Lake City, UT
Lathrop Health Facility Inc, Lathrop, MO
Lathrop Home for Aged Women, Northampton, MA
Rose Hawthorne Lathrop Home, Fall River, MA
Latimer Nursing Home, Wilburton, OK
Latta Road Nursing Home, Rochester, NY
Latta Road Nursing Home A, Rochester, NY
Laub Pavillion of Cleveland Ohio, Cleveland, OH
Lauderdale Christian Nursing Home, Killen, AL
Lauderdale County Nursing Home, Ripley, TN
Laundsun Homes Inc, Carlsbad, NM
Laurel Avenue Rest Home Inc, Bridgeport, CT
Laurel Care Center, Laurel, MT
Laurel Convalescent Hospital, Fontana, CA
Laurel Creek Health Care Center, Manchester, KY
Laurel Foster Home Inc, Coventry, RI
Laurel Glen Convalescent Hospital, Redwood City, CA
Laurel Health Center, Uniontown, PA
Laurel Heights Convalescent Hospital, San Francisco, CA
Laurel Heights Home for the Elderly, London, KY
Laurel Hill Inc, Dunmore, PA
Laurel Hill Nursing Center, Grants Pass, OR
Laurel Hill Nursing Center Inc, Pickens, SC
Laurel Lane, Clifton, CO
Laurel Living Center, Hamburg, PA
Laurel Living Center Inc, Manchester, CT
Laurel Manor, Stroudsburg, PA
Laurel Manor Care Center, Colorado Springs, CO
Laurel Manor Health Care Facility, New Tazewell, TN
Laurel Park—A Center for Effective Living, Pomona, CA
Laurel Wood Health Care Inc, Jackson, TN
Laurelbrook Sanitarium, Dayton, TN
Laurelhurst Care Center, Portland, OR
The Laurels Inc, Harlan, KY

Laurelton Center, Laurelton, PA
Laurelwood Convalescent Center, North Hollywood, CA
Laurelwood Manor Nursing Home, Gaston, OR
Laurelwood Nursing Center, Elkton, MD
Laurenceburg Health Care Center, Lawrenceburg, TN
Laurens Community Residence, Aiken, SC
Laurens County Convalescent Center, Dublin, GA
Laurens Nursing Center, Laurens, SC
Laurie Nursing Home, Laurie, MO
LaVerna Heights, Savannah, MO
LaVerna Village Nursing Home, Savannah, MO
Lavilla Grande Care CTR, Grand Junction, CO
Law-Den Nursing Home, Detroit, MI
Lawn View Nursing Home, Tishomingo, OK
Lawrence Convalescent Center, Portland, OR
Lawrence County Lions Nursing Home Inc, Lawrenceburg, TN
Lawrence County Medical Center Inc, Monticello, MS
Lawrence County Nursing Home District, Mount Vernon, MO
Lawrence Hall Nursing Home, Walnut Ridge, AR
Lawrence Manor Nursing Home, Indianapolis, IN
Lawrence Manor Nursing Home, Lynn, MA
Lawrence Nursing Home Inc, Arverne, NY
Lawrence Presbyterian Manor, Lawrence, KS
Lawrenceville Nursing Home, Lawrenceville, NJ
Walter J Lawson Memorial Home for Children, Rockford, IL
Lawton Heights Nursing Center, Lawton, OK
Lawton Nursing Home, Fort Wayne, IN
The Layton Home for Aged Person, Wilmington, DE
Le Havre Convalescent Hospital, Menlo Park, CA
Albert Lea Boarding Care Center, Albert Lea, MN
Lea County Good Samaritan Village, Hobbs, NM
Lea Manor Health Care Center, Norwalk, CT
Leader Health Care Center, Norristown, PA
Leader Nursing and Rehabilitation Center, Lebanon, PA
Leader Nursing & Rehabilitation Center—North, Williamsport, PA
Leader Nursing & Rehabilitation Center I, Bethlehem, PA
Leader Nursing & Rehabilitation Center, Cherry Hill, NJ
Leader Nursing & Rehabilitation Center, Camp Hill, PA
Leader Nursing & Rehabilitation Center, Dallastown, PA
Leader Nursing & Rehabilitation Center, East Norristown, PA
Leader Nursing & Rehabilitation Center, Easton, PA
Leader Nursing & Rehabilitation Center, Elizabethtown, PA
Leader Nursing Rehabilitation Center, Harrisburg, PA
Leader Nursing & Rehabilitation Center, Jersey Shore, PA
Leader Nursing & Rehabilitation Center, Laureldale, PA
Leader Nursing Rehabilitation Center, Pottsville, PA
Leader Nursing & Rehabilitation Center, Sinking Spring, PA
Leader Nursing & Rehabilitation Center, Sunbury, PA
Leader Nursing & Rehabilitation Center, West Reading, PA
Leader Nursing & Rehabilitation Center, Yeadon, PA
Leader Nursing & Rehabilitation Center, Madison, WI
Leader Nursing & Rehabilitation Center—Chambersburg, Chambersburg, PA

Leader Nursing & Rehabilitation Center—East, Kingston, PA
Leader Nursing & Rehabilitation Center—Pottstown, Pottstown, PA
Leader Nursing Rehabilitation Center—South, Williamsport, PA
Leader Nursing & Rehabilitation Center—West, Kingston, PA
Leahi Hospital (DP), Honolulu, HI
Leake County Skilled Nursing Facility, Carthage, MS
Leavenworth County Convalescent Infirmary, Leavenworth, KS
Lebanon Care Center, Lebanon, MO
Lebanon County Life Support, Lebanon, PA
Lebanon Health Care Center, Lebanon, OH
Lebanon Nursing Home, Lebanon, IN
Lebanon Nursing Home, Lebanon, MO
Lebanon Nursing Home, Lebanon, OH
Lebanon Valley Brethren Home, Palmyra, PA
Lebanon Valley Home, Annville, PA
Lebraun Convalescent Home, Cincinnati, OH
Ledgecrest Conv Home, Kensington, CT
Ledges Manor Corporation, Boone, IA
Ledgeview Memorial Home, West Paris, ME
Ledgewood Manor, North Windham, ME
Ann Lee Home, Albany, NY
Lee Convalescent Center, Fort Myers, FL
Lee County Nursing Home, Dixon, IL
Lee County Personal Care Home Inc, Beattyville, KY
Linda Lee Rest Home, Worcester, MA
Lee Manor, Des Plaines, IL
Lee Manor Nursing Home, Tupelo, MS
Marjorie P Lee Retirement Community, Cincinnati, OH
Lee Rest Home, Waltham, MA
Robert E Lee Retirement Inn, New Albany, IN
Sara Lee Nursing Home, Doylestown, OH
Lee Street, Arvada, CO
Leelanau Memorial Hospital, Northport, MI
Lee's Rest Home, Newell, SD
Lees Summit Nursing Center, Lees Summit, MO
Leesburg Healthcare Center, Leesburg, FL
Leesburg Nursing Center, Leesburg, FL
Leesville State School, Leesville, LA
Leeward Nursing Home Inc, Waianae, HI
Leewood Manor Nursing Home Inc, Milan, MO
Leewood Nursing Home, Tucson, AZ
Leewood Nursing Home Inc, Annandale, VA
LeFlore Nursing Home, Poteau, OK
Legacy Lodge Nursing Home, Russellville, AR
Lehmans Guest & Nursing Home, Rheems, PA
Leisure Arms Health Related Facility, Troy, NY
Leisure Arms Nursing Home, Houston, TX
Leisure Care, Caldwell, KS
Leisure Chateau Care Center, Lakewood, NJ
Leisure Hills Healthcare Center, Hibbing, MN
Leisure Hills Inc, Grand Rapids, MN
Leisure Homestead Association, Stafford, KS
Leisure Lodge—Anahuac, Anahuac, TX
Leisure Lodge Bryan, Bryan, TX
Leisure Lodge—Caldwell, Caldwell, TX
Leisure Lodge—Carthage, Carthage, TX
Leisure Lodge—Cleburne, Cleburne, TX
Leisure Lodge—Clyde, Clyde, TX
Leisure Lodge—Coleman, Coleman, TX
Leisure Lodge—Corsicana, Corsicana, TX
Leisure Lodge—Crock	, Crockett, TX
Leisure Lodge—Ctrville, Centerville, TX
Leisure Lodge—Gilmer, Gilmer, TX
Leisure Lodge—Hamilton, Hamilton, TX
Leisure Lodge—Hearne, Hearne, TX
Leisure Lodge—Henderson, Henderson, TX
Leisure Lodge Inc, Camden, AR
Leisure Lodge Inc—Camden, Bruce Street, Camden, AR
Leisure Lodge Inc—Crossett, Crossett, AR
Leisure Lodge Inc—DeWitt, DeWitt, AR
Leisure Lodge Inc—Hamburg, Hamburg, AR
Leisure Lodge Inc—Lake Village, Lake Village, AR

Leisure Lodge Inc—Monticello, Monticello, AR
Leisure Lodge Inc—Searcy, Searcy, AR
Leisure Lodge Inc—West Memphis, West Memphis, AR
Leisure Lodge—Junction, Junction, TX
Leisure Lodge—Kaufman, Kaufman, TX
Leisure Lodge—Lampasas, Lampasas, TX
Leisure Lodge Nursing Center, McGehee, AR
Leisure Lodge of Brady, Brady, TX
Leisure Lodge of Nashville, Nashville, AR
Leisure Lodge—Overton, Overton, TX
Leisure Lodge—Palacios, Palacios, TX
Leisure Lodge—Rosenberg, Rosenberg, TX
Leisure Lodge—Rusk, Rusk, TX
Leisure Lodge—Sulphur Springs, Sulphur Springs, TX
Leisure Lodge Texarkana, Texarkana, TX
Leisure Lodge—Tyler, Tyler, TX
Leisure Lodge—Weatherford, Weatherford, TX
Leisure Lodge—Wortham, Wortham, TX
Leisure Manor, Saint Petersburg, FL
Leisure Manor Nursing Home, Okmulgee, OK
Leisure Oaks Convalescent Center, Defiance, OH
Leisure Village Nursing Center, Tulsa, OK
Leisure Years Nursing Home, Owensboro, KY
Leithchfield Health Care Manor, Leitchfield, KY
Lela Wilson's Residential Care Facility, Las Animas, CO
Lelah G Wagner Nursing Home, Panama City, FL
The Leland Home, Waltham, MA
Lemay Nursing Home, Lemay, MO
Lemberg Home & Geriatric Institute Inc, Brooklyn, NY
Lemington Home for the Aged, Pittsburgh, PA
Lemon Grove Convalescent Center, Lemon Grove, CA
Lena Continental Manor Nursing Home Inc, Lena, IL
Lena Crews Family Care Home, Denver, CO
Lenawee Medical Care Facility, Adrian, MI
Lenevar Community Residence, Charleston, SC
Lenoir Health Care Center, Columbia, MO
Lenox Care Center, Lenox, IA
Lenox Hill Nursing & Rehabilitation Care Facility, Lynn, MA
Lenox Nursing Home Inc, Haverhill, MA
Leon Care Center, Leon, IA
Leon Valley Lodge, San Antonio, TX
Leonardville Nursing Home, Leonardville, KS
Leroy Village Green Nursing Home & Health Related Facility Inc, Leroy, NY
Leslie Family Care Home, Denver, CO
Letcher County Golden Years Rest Home Inc, Jenkins, KY
Levelland Development Center, Levelland, TX
Levelland Nursing Home, Levelland, TX
Levindale Hebrew Geriatric Center & Hospital, Baltimore, MD
Elizabeth Levinson Center, Bangor, ME
Lewes Convalescent Center, Lewes, DE
Lewis Bay Convalescent Home, Barnstable, MA
Lewis County General Hospital—Nurs Home Unit, Lowville, NY
Lewis County Manor, Hohenwald, TN
Lewis County Nursing Home Dist, Canton, MO
Mary Lewis Convalescent Center Inc, Birmingham, AL
Lewis Memorial Christian Village, Springfield, IL
Lewis Memorial Methodist Home, Franklin, KY
Lewisburg United Methodist Homes, Lewisburg, PA
Lewiston Care Center, Lewiston, ID
Lewiston Villa Nursing Home, Lewiston, MN
Lewisville Hotel for Senior Citizens, Lewisville, IN
Lewisville Nursing Home, Lewisville, TX
Lexington Clusters, Lexington, SC

Lexington Convalescent Home Inc, New Britain, CT
Lexington Country Place, Lexington, KY
Lexington House Healthcare Center, Lexington, IL
Lexington Manor Health Care Facility, Lexington, KY
Lexington Manor Nursing Center, Lexington, TN
Lexington Nursing Home, Lexington, OK
Lexington West Inc, Columbia, SC
Libby Care Center, Libby, MT
Liberal Good Samaritan Center, Liberal, KS
Liberty County Nursing Home, Chester, MT
Liberty Hall Nursing Center, Colchester, CT
Liberty Hill Healthcare Center, Winfield, IL
Liberty House Nursing Home, Southbridge, MA
Liberty House Nursing Home, Jersey City, NJ
Liberty House Nursing Home, Thomasville, NC
Liberty House Nursing Home, Clifton Forge, VA
Liberty House Nursing Home, Harrisonburg, VA
Liberty House Nursing Home, Roanoke, VA
Liberty House Nursing Home, Waynesboro, VA
Liberty Intermediate Care—Bristol, Bristol, FL
Liberty Manor, Midway, GA
Liberty Manor Care Facility Inc, Centralia, WA
Liberty Nursing Center, Allentown, PA
Liberty Nursing Home, Liberty, TX
Liberty Pavilion Nursing Home, Danvers, MA
Libertyville Manor Extended Care, Libertyville, IL
Lida Home Nursing Home, Minonk, IL
Lieberman Geriatric Health Centre, Skokie, IL
Life Care Center—Athens, Athens, TN
Life Care Center Inc, Fitzgerald, GA
Life Care Center of Altamonte Springs, Altamonte Springs, FL
Life Care Center of Bruceton Hollow Rock, Bruceton, TN
Life Care Center of Church Hill, Church Hill, TN
Life Care Center of Cleveland, Cleveland, TN
Life Care Center of Collegedale, Collegedale, TN
Life Care Center of Coos Bay, Coos Bay, OR
Life Care Center of Crossville, Crossville, TN
Life Care Center of Donelson, Nashville, TN
Life Care Center of East Ridge, East Ridge, TN
Life Care Center of Greeneville, Greeneville, TN
Life Care Center of Hilo, Hilo, HI
Life Care Center of Kennewick, Kennewick, WA
Life Care Center of LaCenter, LaCenter, KY
Life Care Center of Morehead, Morehead, KY
Life Care Center of Morgan County, Wartburg, TN
Life Care Center of Morristown, Morristown, TN
Life Care Center of Overland Park, Overland Park, KS
Life Care Center of Paducah, Paducah, KY
Life Care Center of Richland, Richland, WA
Life Care Center of Ritzville, Ritzville, WA
Life Care Center of Tullahoma, Tullahoma, TN
Life Care of Anthony, Anthony, KS
Life Care of Harper, Harper, KS
Life Care—West Nursing Center, Greeneville, TN
Lifecare Center of Alton, Alton, IL
Lifecare Center of Benton, Benton, IL
Lifecare Center of Eldorado I, Eldorado, IL
Lifecare Center of Enfield, Enfield, IL
Lifecare Center of Jonesboro, Jonesboro, IL
Lifecare Center of McLeansboro Inc, McLeansboro, IL
Lifecare of Greensburg Kansas, Greensburg, KS
Lifecare of Kingman, Kingman, KS
Lifecare of Kiowa, Kiowa, KS

Lifecare of Pratt, Pratt, KS
Lifecare Rehabilitation Center, Haviland, KS
Lighthouse Convalescent Home, Selma, AL
Lila Doyle Nursing Care Facility, Seneca, SC
Lilac City Convalescent Center, Spokane, WA
Lilburn Health Care Center, Lilburn, GA
Lily Pond Nursing Home, New York, NY
Lima Convalescent Home, Lima, OH
Lima Estates, Lima, PA
Lima Manor, Lima, OH
Limestone Health Facility, Athens, AL
Lincoln Avenue & Crawford's Home for the Aged, Cincinnati, OH
Lincoln Care Center, Detroit, MI
Lincoln Care Center, Fayetteville, TN
Lincoln Community Hospital & Nursing Home, Hugo, CO
Lincoln Community Nursing Home, Lincoln, MO
Lincoln Convalescent Center Inc, Baltimore, MD
Lincoln East Nursing Home, Wichita, KS
Lincoln Glen Intermediate Care, San Jose, CA
Lincoln Haven Rest Home, Lincoln, MI
Lincoln Hill Manor Rest Home, Spencer, MA
Lincoln Hill Nursing Center, Quincy, IL
Lincoln Hills Nursing Home, Tell City, IN
Lincoln Hills of New Albany, New Albany, IN
The Lincoln Home, Belleville, IL
Lincoln Hospital Nursing Home, Davenport, WA
Lincoln Land Nursing Home, Lincoln, IL
Lincoln Lutheran Home, Racine, WI
Lincoln Manor North Inc, Decatur, IL
Lincoln Manor Nursing Center, Connersville, IN
Lincoln Memorial Nursing Home, Goulds, FL
Lincoln Nursing Center, Jefferson City, MO
Lincoln Nursing Center Inc, Lincolnton, NC
Lincoln Nursing Home, Worcester, MA
Lincoln Park Intermediate Care Center, Lincoln Park, NJ
Lincoln Park Nursing & Convalescent Home, Lincoln Park, NJ
Lincoln Park Nursing Home, Monroe, LA
Lincoln Park Terrace Inc, Chicago, IL
Lincoln Residential Center, Brookhaven, MS
Lincoln Rest Home, Lincoln, MA
Lincoln Village Convalescent Center, Racine, WI
Linda Mar Convalescent Hospital, Pacifica, CA
Linda Terra Convalescent Hospital, San Rafael, CA
Linda Valley Convalescent Hospital, Loma Linda, CA
Linda Vista Care Center, Ashland, OR
Lindale Nursing Center, Lindale, TX
Lindberg Rest Home, Kerkhoven, MN
Linden Hall Nursing Home, Kennett Square, PA
Linden Health Care Center, Dayton, OH
Linden Healthcare Center, Stillwater, MN
Linden Lodge, Brattleboro, VT
Linden Manor Nursing Home, North Platte, NE
Linden Nursing & Retirement Home, Rockland, MA
LindenGrove—Northview, Waukesha, WI
Lindenwood Nursing Home Inc, Omaha, NE
Lindon Care & Training Center, Lindon, UT
Lindsay Care Center, Lindsay, OK
Lineville Geriatric Center Inc, Lineville, AL
Linn Care Center, Albany, OR
Linn Community Nursing Home Inc, Linn, KS
Linn Manor, Marion, IA
Linn Manor Nursing Home, Linn, MO
Linnea Residential Home, Chisago City, MN
Linton Nursing Home, Linton, IN
Linwood Convalescent Center, Linwood, NJ
Linwood Gardens Convalescent Center, Visalia, CA
Linwood Place, Victoria, TX
Lions Manor Nursing Home, Cumberland, MD
Lisner-Louise Home Inc, Washington, DC
Litchfield Nursing Center, Litchfield, MI

Little Angels Nursing Home Inc, Elgin, IL
Little Bird Nursing Home Inc, Weatherford, OK
Little Brook Nursing & Convalescent Center, Califon, NJ
Little City Foundation, Palatine, IL
Little Company of Mary Health Facility Inc, San Pierre, IN
Little Creek Sanitarium, Knoxville, TN
Little Egypt Manor, Harrisburg, IL
Little Falls Hospital, Little Falls, NY
Little Flower Haven, Earling, IA
Little Flower Manor, Darby, PA
Little Flower Manor, Wilkes-Barre, PA
Little Flower Nursing Home, Saint Louis, MO
Little Flower Nursing Home & HRF, East Islip, NY
Little Forest Medical Center, Akron, OH
Little Forest Medical Center, Youngstown, OH
Little Neck Nursing Home, Little Neck, NY
Little Nursing Home, Montclair, NJ
Little River Nursing Home, Ashdown, AR
Little Rock Nursing Center, Little Rock, AR
Little Sisters of the Poor, San Pedro, CA
Little Sisters of the Poor, Chicago, IL
Little Sisters of the Poor, Evansville, IN
Little Sisters of the Poor, Detroit, MI
Little Sisters of the Poor, Saint Paul, MN
Little Sisters of the Poor, Saint Louis, MO
Little Sisters of the Poor, Cleveland, OH
Little Sisters of the Poor Home for the Aged, Pittsburgh, PA
Little Sisters of the Poor—Sacred Heart Home, Mobile, AL
Little Sisters of the Poor—St Alexis Home, Kansas City, MO
Little Sisters of the Poor—St Joseph Home for Aged, Richmond, VA
Little Sisters of the Poor—St Martin's, Baltimore, MD
Littlefield Hospitality House, Littlefield, TX
Littleton House, Littleton, CO
Littleton House Nursing Home, Littleton, MA
Littleton Manor Nursing Home, Littleton, CO
Live Oak Medical Center, Blanco, TX
Live Oak Multi Faith Retirement Center, Shreveport, LA
Live Oak Skilled Nursing & Manor, Santa Cruz, CA
Livermore Manor Convalescent Hospital, Livermore, CA
Living Center of Griffin, Griffin, GA
Living Skills Center, Saint Paul, KS
Livingston Care Center Inc, Howell, MI
Livingston Convalescent Center, Livingston, MT
Livingston County HRF & Campus SNF, Mount Morris, NY
Livingston County Rest Home, Smithland, KY
Livingston County Skilled Nursing Facility, Geneseo, NY
Livingston Manor, Pontiac, IL
Livingston Manor Care Center, Chillicothe, MO
Livingston Nursing Home Inc, Bessemer, AL
Livngston Convalescent Center, Livingston, TX
Livonia Nursing Center, Livonia, MI
Llanfair House, Wayne, NJ
Llanfair Terrace, Cincinnati, OH
Martha Lloyd School—Camelot ICF/MR, Troy, PA
Loch Haven Lodge, Orlando, FL
Lock Haven Hospital—Extended Care Facility, Lock Haven, PA
Lockerbie Healthcare Center, Indianapolis, IN
Lockney Care Center, Lockney, TX
Lockview Nursing Home, Seattle, WA
Locust Grove Nursing Home, Wills Point, TX
Locust Grove Retirement Village, Mifflin, PA
Locust Ridge Nursing Home Inc, Williamsburg, OH
The Lodge Intermediate Care Facility, Neptune, NJ
Lodge Nursing Home, Navarre, OH
Lodgepole Plaza Nursing Home, Sidney, NE

Lodi Good Samaritan Center, Lodi, WI
Loeb Center-Montefiore, Bronx, NY
Lofton Nursing Home Inc, Franklin, TN
Logan Acres, Bellefontaine, OH
Logan County Home for the Aged, Napoleon, ND
Logan County Nursing Center, Paris, AR
Logan Elm Health Care Center, Circleville, OH
Logan Health Care Center, Logan, OH
Logan Manor Health Care Center, Whiting, NJ
Logan Manor Nursing Home, Logan, KS
Logan Park Care Center, Logan, WV
Logan Square East Care Center, Philadelphia, PA
Logan Valley Manor, Lyons, NE
Lo-Har Lodge Incorporated, El Cajon, CA
Loma Linda Rest Home, Pine Bluff, AR
Ray Graham Lombard Comm Living Center, Lombard, IL
Lomita Golden Age Convalescent Home, Lomita, CA
Lompoc Hospital District Convalescent Care Center, Lompoc, CA
London House Convalescent Hospital, Santa Rosa, CA
London House Convalescent Hospital, Sonoma, CA
Lone Pine Congregate Center, Ironton, MO
Lone Pine Nursing Home Inc, New Bremen, OH
Lone Tree Convalescent Hospital, Antioch, CA
Lone Tree Health Care Center, Lone Tree, IA
Lone Tree Lodge, Meade, KS
Long Beach Grandell Co, Long Beach, NY
Long Beach Memorial Nursing Home Inc, Long Beach, NY
Henry G Long Asylum, Lancaster, PA
Long Island Nursing Home, Flushing, NY
Long Island Tides Nursing Home, Long Beach, NY
Long Lake Manor Inc, Port Orchard, WA
Long Lake Nursing Home, Long Lake, MN
Long Prairie Memorial Hospital, Long Prairie, MN
Long View Nursing Home, Manchester, MD
Long-Blum Retirement Center, Chillicothe, MO
Longhouse Residence, Spencer, IA
Longleaf Nursing Home, Ruston, LA
Longmeadow Care Center, Kent, OH
Longmeadow Nursing Home—Camden, Camden, AR
Longmeadow Nursing Home of Malvern, Malvern, AR
Longmeadow of Taunton A Skilled Facility, Taunton, MA
Long-Term Care at Neponset—Ashmont Manor, Dorchester, MA
Long-Term Care at Neponset—Neponset Hall, Dorchester, MA
Long-Term Care Inc, Glendale, CA
Longview Home Inc, Missouri Valley, IA
Longview Unit 22 Group Home, Cincinnati, OH
Longwood Health Care Center, Longwood, FL
Longwood Manor Sanitarium, Los Angeles, CA
Longwood Villa Geriatric Nursing Center, Boothwyn, PA
Longworth Manor, Felicity, OH
Lonoke Nursing Home Inc, Lonoke, AR
Loomis House Nursing Center, Holyoke, MA
Loop Street NE, Poulsbo, WA
Lorain Manor Nursing Home, Lorain, OH
Loraine Nursing Home, Loraine, TX
Lorantffy Care Center Inc, Akron, OH
Lord Chamberlain, Stratford, CT
Mason F Lord Chronic Hospital & Nursing Facility, Baltimore, MD
Loretta Nursing Home, Shawneetown, IL
Loretto Geriatric Center, Syracuse, NY
Loretto Motherhouse Infirmary, Nerinx, KY
Lorien Nursing & Convalescent Home, Columbia, MD
Loring Hospital, Sac City, IA

Loris Hospital—Extended Care Facility, Loris, SC

Lorraine Manor, Hartford, CT

Los Arcos Health Care Center, Flagstaff, AZ

Los Banos Convalescent Hospital, Los Banos, CA

Los Gatos Convalescent Hospital, Los Gatos, CA

Los Gatos Meadows, Los Gatos, CA

Los Lunas Hospital & Training School, Los Lunas, NM

Los Palos Convalescent Hospital, San Pedro, CA

Lost Creek Care Center, Lima, OH

Lost Rivers District Hospital & Nursing Home, Arco, ID

Josina Lott Foundation Residential Center, Toledo, OH

Lou Del Health Care, Forest Grove, OR

Loudonville Nursing Home, Inc, Loudonville, OH

Loudoun Long-Term Care Center, Leesburg, VA

Anthony Louis Center—Plymouth, Plymouth, MN

Louisburg Nursing Center Inc, Louisburg, NC

Louise C Godwin Nursing Home Inc, Norfolk, VA

Louise Caroline Rehabilitation & Nursing Center, Saugus, MA

Louisiana Living Center, Vallejo, CA

Louisiana Nursing Home, Louisiana, MO

Louisiana Special Education Center, Alexandria, LA

Louisville Care Center, Louisville, NE

Louisville Lutheran Home Inc, Jeffersontown, KY

Louisville Protestant Althenheim, Louisville, KY

Lourdes Inc, Pontiac, MI

Lourdes-Noreen McKeen Residence for Geriatric Care Inc, West Palm Beach, FL

Lovato Residential Care Facility, La Junta, CO

Dorothy Love Retirement Community, Sidney, OH

Loveland Good Samaritan Village, Loveland, CO

Loveland Health Care Center, Loveland, OH

Lovelett Health Care Center, Auburn, ME

Lovely Hill Nursing Home, Pawling, NY

Lovely's Rest Home, North Middletown, KY

Loving Care Med Center, Cynthiana, IN

Lovington Good Samaritan Center, Lovington, NM

Lowell Healthcare Center, Lowell, IN

Lowell Medical Care Center, Lowell, MI

Lower Umpqua Hospital, Reedsport, OR

Lowe's Nursing & Convalescent Home, Thonotosassa, FL

The Lowman Home, White Rock, SC

LPN Geriatric Nursing Center Inc, Newark, OH

LPN Health Care Facility, Newark, OH

Lu Ann Nursing Home, Nappanee, IN

Lubbock Hospitality House Inc, Lubbock, TX

Lubbock Nursing Home Inc, Lubbock, TX

Lucas Boarding Home, Saint Joseph, MO

Lucas County Children Services-Extended Care Unit, Maumee, OH

Lucas Rest Home, Lucas, KS

Lucero Residential Care Facility, Las Animas, CO

Lufkin Nursing Center, Lufkin, TX

Lu-Ken Manor, Ardmore, OK

Luling Care Center, Luling, TX

Luling Nursing Home, Luling, LA

Lumber City Healthcare Center, Lumber City, GA

Luther Acres, Lititz, PA

Luther Crest, Allentown, PA

Luther Haven, Detroit, MI

Luther Haven Nursing Home, Montevideo, MN

Luther Home, Grand Rapids, MI

Luther Home, Marinette, WI

Luther Home of Mercy, Williston, OH

Luther Manor, Dubuque, IA

Luther Manor, Saginaw, MI

Luther Manor, Milwaukee, WI

Luther Manor, Wauwatosa, WI

Luther Manor Retirement & Nursing Center, Hannibal, MO

Martin Luther Holt Home, Holt, MI

Martin Luther Home, Beatrice, NE

Martin Luther Manor, Bloomington, MN

Martin Luther Memorial Home, South Haven, MI

Martin Luther Memorial Home, South Lyon, MI

Martin Luther Saginaw Home, Saginaw, MI

Luther Memorial Home, Madelia, MN

Luther Memorial Home, Mayville, ND

Luther Park Health Center, Des Moines, IA

Luther Woods Convalescent Center, Hatboro, PA

Lutheran Altenheim Society of Missouri, Saint Louis, MO

Lutheran Care Center, Altamont, IL

Lutheran Center for the Aging, Smithtown, NY

Lutheran Community Home Inc, Seymour, IN

Lutheran Good Shepherd Home, Concordia, MO

Lutheran Haven, Oviedo, FL

Lutheran Health Care Association Extended Care Facility, Webster Grove, MO

Lutheran Health Facility, Alhambra, CA

Lutheran Health Facility of Anaheim, Anaheim, CA

Lutheran Health Facility of Carlsbad, Carlsbad, CA

The Lutheran Home, Peoria, IL

The Lutheran Home, Frankenmuth, MI

The Lutheran Home, Cape Girardeau, MO

The Lutheran Home, Omaha, NE

Lutheran Home, Westlake, OH

Lutheran Home, Eureka, SD

Lutheran Home at Kane, Kane, PA

Lutheran Home at Ocean View, Ocean View, NJ

Lutheran Home at Topton, Topton, PA

Lutheran Home for the Aged, Vinton, IA

Lutheran Home for the Aged, Erie, PA

Lutheran Home for the Aging Inc, Wauwatosa, WI

The Lutheran Home & Hope Residence, Belle Plaine, MN

Lutheran Home Inc, Herington, KS

Lutheran Home—Monroe, Monroe, MI

Lutheran Home of Brockton Inc, Brockton, MA

Lutheran Home of Middletown Inc, Middletown, CT

Lutheran Home of New Orleans, New Orleans, LA

Lutheran Home of Northwest Indiana Inc, Crown Point, IN

Lutheran Home of Southbury, Southbury, CT

Lutheran Home of the Good Shepherd, Havre, MT

Lutheran Home of the Good Shepherd Inc, New Rockford, ND

Lutheran Home of West Texas, Lubbock, TX

Lutheran Home of Worcester Inc, Worcester, MA

The Lutheran Home—Permian Basin, Midland, TX

Lutheran Home & Services for Aged, Arlington Heights, IL

Lutheran Home—Telford, Telford, PA

Lutheran Homes Inc, Fort Wayne, IN

Lutheran Homes Inc, Kendallville, IN

Lutheran Homes Society, Muscatine, IA

Lutheran Memorial Home, Sandusky, OH

Lutheran Memorial Nursing Home, Twin Valley, MN

Lutheran Memorial Retirement Center, Twin Valley, MN

Lutheran Nursing Home, Hot Springs, SD

Lutheran Nursing Homes Inc—Albemarle Unit, Albemarle, NC

Lutheran Nursing Homes Inc—Hickory Unit, Hickory, NC

Lutheran Nursing Homes Inc—Salisbury Unit, Salisbury, NC

Lutheran Old Folks Home, Toledo, OH

Lutheran Pioneer Home, Mallala, OR

Lutheran Retirement Home, Jamestown, NY

Lutheran Retirement Home Inc, Northwood, IA

Lutheran Retirement Home of Southern Minnesota, Truman, MN

Lutheran Senior Citizen Home Inc, Little Falls, MN

Lutheran Senior City, Columbus, OH

Lutheran Sunset Home, Grafton, ND

Lutheran Welfare Concordia Home, Cabot, PA

Luverne Geriatric Center Inc, Luverne, AL

Lyden Nursing Home, Astoria, NY

The Lydian Corporation, Orange, CT

Sophia Lyn Convalescent Hospital, Pasadena, CA

Lynchburg Nursing Home, Lynchburg, VA

Lyndon Lane Nursing Center, Louisville, KY

Lyngblomsten Care Center, Saint Paul, MN

Lynhurst Healthcare Center, Indianapolis, IN

Lynhurst Healthcare Center, Saint Paul, MN

Lynmark Nursing Home Inc, Boston, MA

Lynn Haven Nursing Home, Gray, GA

Lynn Home for Elderly Persons, Lynn, MA

Lynn Home & Infirmary, Lynn, MA

Lynn Lodge Nursing Home, Longview, TX

Lynn Shore Rest Home, Lynn, MA

Lynn Shores Manor, Virginia Beach, VA

Lynnhaven Nursing Center Inc, Corpus Christi, TX

Lynnwood Manor Health Care Center, Lynnwood, WA

Lynwood Care Center, Lynwood, CA

Lynwood Healthcare Center, Fridley, MN

Lynwood Nursing Home, Mobile, AL

Lyon Health Center, Yerington, NV

Lyon Manor Care Center, Rock Rapids, IA

Mary Lyon Nursing Home, Hampden, MA

Lyon Nursing Home, Canton, OH

Lyons Good Samaritan Center, Lyons, KS

Lysock View Nursing Home, Montoursville, PA

Lytle Nursing Home Inc, Lytle, TX

Lytton Gardens Care Center, Palo Alto, CA

Mabank Nursing Home, Mabank, TX

Mac House, McPherson, KS

Macanell Nursing Home Inc, Center Point, IN

MacArthur Convalescent Hospital, Oakland, CA

Maccabee Gardens, Saginaw, MI

Macdel Health Care Inc, Birmingham, AL

Mackenzie Nursing Home, Melrose, MA

Mackinac County Medical Care Facility, Saint Ignace, MI

Maclare Residence, South Saint Paul, MN

Macomb Manor, Macomb, IL

Macomb Nursing & Rehabilitation Center, Macomb, IL

Macon County Nursing Home District—Loch Haven, Macon, MO

Macon Health Care Center, Macon, GA

Macon Health Care Center, Macon, MO

MACtown Inc, Miami, FL

Madalawn Nursing Home, Brockton, MA

Madden Kimball Home, Kimball, MN

Madeira Nursing Inc, Madeira, OH

Madeleine Villa Convalescent Center, Marysville, WA

Madera Rehabilitation & Convalescent Center, Madera, CA

Madigan Estates, Houlton, ME

Madison Convalescent Center, El Cajon, CA

Madison Convalescent Center, Madison, WI

Madison County Nursing Home, Edwardsville, IL

Madison County Nursing Home, Canton, MS

Madison County Nursing Home, Sheridan, MT

Madison County Nursing Home-Ennis, Ennis, MT

Madison County Sheltered Care, Edwardsville, IL

Madison Elms Nursing Center, London, OH

Madison Health Care, Madison, OH

Madison Lutheran Home, Madison, MN

Madison Manor, Richmond, KY

Madison Manor Inc, Madison, KS
Madison Manor Nursing Center, Passaic, NJ
Madison Manor Nursing Center, Mars Hill, NC
Madison Manor Nursing Home, Madison, AL
Madison Manor Nursing Home, Hyattsville, MD
Madison Memorial Hospital, Fredericktown, MO
Madison Nursing Center, Madison, FL
Madison Nursing Home, Madison, IN
Madison Nursing Home, Montclair, NJ
Madison Nursing Home, Cincinnati, OH
Madison Parish Baptist Nursing Home, Tallulah, LA
Madison Village Nursing Home, Madison, OH
Madisonville Nursing Home No 1, Madisonville, TX
Madisonville Nursing Home No 2, Madisonville, TX
Madisonville Nursing Home No 3, Madisonville, TX
Madonna Centers, Lincoln, NE
Madonna Hall, Cleveland, OH
Madonna Home of Mercy Hospital of Watertown, Watertown, NY
Madonna Manor, Ludlow, KY
Madonna Manor, North Attleboro, MA
Madonna Nursing Center, Detroit, MI
Madonna Residence Inc, Brooklyn, NY
Madonna Towers Inc, Rochester, MN
Madrid Home for the Aging, Madrid, IA
Maggie Johnson's Nursing Center, Austin, TX
Magic Star Nursing Home, Borger, TX
Magic Valley Manor, Wendell, ID
Magnolia Care Center, Wadsworth, OH
Magnolia Center, El Cajon, CA
Magnolia Convalescent Hospital, Riverside, CA
Magnolia Gardens Convalescent Hospital, Granada Hills, CA
Magnolia Gardens Nursing Home, Lanham, MD
Magnolia Hall Inc, Chestertown, MD
Magnolia Haven Nursing Home, Tuskegee, AL
Magnolia Manor, Magnolia, AR
Magnolia Manor, Eldorado, IL
Magnolia Manor, New Madrid, MO
Magnolia Manor, Jefferson, TX
Magnolia Manor Methodist Nursing Home, Americus, GA
Magnolia Manor North, Rock Hill, SC
Magnolia Manor North, Rock Hill, SC
Magnolia Manor Nursing Center, Montgomery, AL
Magnolia Manor Nursing Home, Columbus, MS
Magnolia Manor Nursing Home, Sistersville, WV
Magnolia Manor Nursing Home Inc, Shreveport, LA
Magnolia Manor—SNF, Metropolis, IL
Magnolia Nursing Home, Jackson, MS
Magnolia Rest Home, Fitchburg, MA
Magnolias Nursing & Convalescent Center, Pensacola, FL
Magnus Farm Nursing Home, Arlington Heights, IL
Magoun Manor Nursing Home, Medford, MA
Mahaska Manor, Oskaloosa, IA
Samuel Mahelona Memorial Hospital (DP), Kapaa, HI
Mahoning Valley Nursing & Rehabilitation Center, Lehighton, PA
Main Line Nursing & Rehabilitation Center, Paoli, PA
Maine Stay Nursing Home, Sanford, ME
Maine Veterans Home, Augusta, ME
Maison de Sante, Ville Platte, LA
Maison Hospiere, New Orleans, LA
Maison Orleans Nursing Home, Arabi, LA
Majestic Convalescent Center, Lynwood, CA
Majestic Pines Convalescent Hospital, Hayward, CA
Majestic Towers, Saint Petersburg, FL
Mala Strana Health Care Center, New Prague, MN
Malden Home for Aged Persons, Malden, MA

Malden Nursing Home, Malden, MA
Malden Nursing Home, Seattle, WA
Malheur Memorial Hospital, Nyssa, OR
Malouff Manor, Rocky Ford, CO
Malta Home for the Aging, Granville, PA
Maluhia (A Long-Term Care Health Center), Honolulu, HI
Malvern Nursing Home, Malvern, AR
Mammoth Nursing Home, Manchester, NH
Manatawny Manor, Pottstown, PA
Manatee Convalescent Center Inc, Bradenton, FL
Manawa Community Nursing Center Inc, Manawa, WI
Manchester House Nursing Home, Media, PA
Manchester Manor Convalescent Hospital, Los Angeles, CA
Manchester Manor Nursing Home, Manchester, CT
Manchester Manor Rest Home, Manchester, CT
Manchester Nursing Home, Ballwin, MO
Manda Ann Convalescent Home Inc, Houston, TX
Mandan Villa, Mandan, ND
Mandarin Manor, Jacksonville, FL
Manden Nursing Home, South Portland, ME
Manderley Health Care Center, Osgood, IN
Mangum Nursing Center, Mangum, OK
Manhattan Convalescent Center, Tampa, FL
Manhattan Health Care Center, Jackson, MS
Manhattan Manor Extended Care Facility, Harvey, LA
Manhattan Manor Guest House, Harvey, LA
Manhattan Manor Nursing Home, Buffalo, NY
Manila Nursing Home, Manila, AR
Manilla Manor, Manilla, IA
Manistee County Medical Care Facility, Manistee, MI
Manistee Heights Care Center, Manistee, MI
Manitowoc Health Care Center, Manitowoc, WI
Mankato House Health Care Center, Mankato, MN
Mankato Lutheran Home, Mankato, MN
Manley's Manor Nursing Home Inc, Findlay, OH
Manly Care Center, Manly, IA
Mann Nursing Home, Westerville, OH
Manning Convalescent Home, Portsmouth, VA
Manning Gardens Convalescent Hospital, Fresno, CA
The Manning Plaza, Manning, IA
Manning's Residential Care Center, Maquoketa, IA
Manor Care, Mayfield Heights, OH
Manor Care Arlington Nursing & Rehabilitation Center, Arlington, VA
Manor Care Belden Village, Canton, OH
Manor Care—Columbia Nursing Center, Columbia, SC
Manor Care, Division of Miller's Merry Manor, Wabash, IN
Manor Care Lakeshore Nursing Center, Cleveland, OH
Manor Care Nursing Center, Boca Raton, FL
Manor Care Nursing Center, Barberton, OH
Manor Care Nursing Center—Rocky River, Cleveland, OH
Manor Care Nursing Home, Cincinnati, OH
Manor Care of Akron Inc, Akron, OH
Manor Care of Barley Kingston Court, York, PA
Manor Care of Charleston Inc, Charleston, SC
Manor Care of North Olmsted Inc, North Olmsted, OH
Manor Care of Pinehurst, Pinehurst, NC
Manor Care—Plantation, Plantation, FL
Manor Care Rehabilitation & Nursing Center, West Columbia, SC
Manor Care—Rossville, Baltimore, MD
Manor Care—Ruxton, Towson, MD
Manor Care—Sharpview Rehabilitation & Nursing Center, Houston, TX
Manor Care Texas City, Texas City, TX
Manor Care—Towson, Towson, MD

Manor Care—Webster, Webster, TX
Manor Care—Westerville Nursing Center, Westerville, OH
Manor Care—Wheaton, Wheaton, MD
Manor Care—Willoughby, Willoughby, OH
Manor Care—Woodside Nursing Facility, Cincinnati, OH
Manor Grove, Kirkwood, MO
Manor Home for the Aged, Erie, PA
Manor Home Management Inc, Geneva, OH
Manor House, Sigourney, IA
Manor House, Inc, Youngstown, OH
The Manor House of Carmel, Carmel, IN
Manor House of Dover, Dover, TN
Manor House Residential Care Inc, Bolivar, MO
Manor Lodge Convalescent Hospital, Bakersfield, CA
Martha Manor Home for Aged Women, Steubenville, OH
Manor Nursing Home, Independence, KS
The Manor Nursing Home, Morrisville, VT
The Manor Nursing Home, Longview, WA
Manor Oak Skilled Nursing Facilities Inc, Cheektowaga, NY
Manor Oak Skilled Nursing Facilities Inc, Jamestown, NY
Manor Oak Skilled Nursing Facilities Inc, Warsaw, NY
Manor Oaks Nursing Home, Rockdale, TX
The Manor of Kansas City, Kansas City, KS
The Manor of Topeka, Topeka, KS
Manor Pines Convalescent Center, Fort Lauderdale, FL
The Manor Retirement & Convalescent Center, Mexia, TX
Manor Square Convalescent Home, San Antonio, TX
Mansfield Nursing Home, Mansfield, MO
Mansfield Nursing Home, Mansfield, TX
Mansion Nursing Home, Central Falls, RI
Mansion House Nursing Home, Spokane, WA
Mansion Nursing & Convalescent Home Inc, Sunbury, PA
Mansion Rest Home, Malden, MA
Manson Good Samaritan Center, Manson, IA
Manzanita Manor Convalescent Hospital, Cloverdale, CA
Manzano del Sol Good Samaritan Village, Albuquerque, NM
Maple Care Center, Maple Heights, OH
Maple Convalescent Hospital, Los Angeles, CA
Maple Crest Manor, Fayette, IA
Maple Crest-Boone County Nursing Home, Belvidere, IL
Maple Farm Nursing Center, Akron, PA
Maple Grove Home, Tecumseh, NE
Maple Grove Intermediate Care Home, Sanger, CA
Maple Grove Lodge Inc, Louisiana, MO
Maple Grove Manor Convalescent Home, Norwood, MA
Maple Hall Nursing Home, Worcester, MA
Maple Heights Inc, Mapleton, IA
Maple Heights Nursing Home Inc, Wellston, OH
Maple Hill Convalescent Center, Maple Shade, NJ
Maple Hill Nursing Home, Dallas, PA
Maple Hill Nursing Home, Selmer, TN
Maple Hill Nursing Home Ltd, Long Grove, IL
Maple Hill Rest Home, Springfield, MA
Maple Knoll Village, Cincinnati, OH
Maple Lane Health Care Facility, Shawano, WI
Maple Lane Inc, Merchantville, NJ
Maple Lane Nursing Home, Barton, VT
Maple Lawn Health Center, Eureka, IL
Maple Lawn Home, Marion, IA
Maple Lawn Lodge, Moberly, MO
Maple Lawn Medical Care Facility, Coldwater, MI
Maple Lawn Nursing Home Inc, Fulda, MN
Maple Lawn Rest Home Inc, Fayette, MO
Maple Leaf Health Care Center, Manchester, NH

Maple Leaf Nursing Home, Manchester, NH
Maple Manor, Osage, IA
Maple Manor Christian Home Inc—Adult Division, Sellersburg, IN
Maple Manor Health Care Center, Greenville, KY
Maple Manor Health Care Center, New Richmond, WI
Maple Manor Nursing Center, Ontonagon, MI
Maple Manor Nursing Home, Aplington, IA
Maple Manor Nursing Home, Rochester, MN
Maple Manor Nursing Home, Langdon, ND
Maple Mountain Manor, Berlin, PA
Maple Nursing Home, Chesterland, OH
Maple Terrace Shelter Care Home, Chicago, IL
Maple Tree Inn Inc, Swanton, OH
Maple Valley Nursing Home, Ashley, MI
Maple Valley Nursing Home, Maple City, MI
Maple View Manor, Bainbridge, OH
Maple View Manor Inc, Rocky Hill, CT
Maple View Nursing Home, Washington, MA
The Maple Wood, Bloomer, WI
Maple Wood Manor Convalescent Center, Philadelphia, PA
Maple-Crest, Omaha, NE
Maplecrest Home, Bucyrus, OH
Maplecrest Manor Inc., Madison, ME
Maplecrest Nursing Home, Sullivan, ME
Maplecrest Nursing Home for the Aged, Struthers, OH
Mapleleaf Health Care Center, Mount Pleasant, IA
Maples Convalescent Home, Wrentham, MA
Mapleside Manor, Amboy, IL
Mapleton Community Home, Mapleton, MN
Mapleton Health Care Facility Inc, Indianapolis, IN
Mapleview Care Center Inc, Louisville, OH
Maplewood Care Center, North Saint Paul, MN
Maplewood Care Center, Lincoln, NE
Maplewood Health Care Center, Jackson, TN
Maplewood Manor, Terre Haute, IN
Maplewood Manor Inc, Keota, IA
Maplewood Manor Nursing Home, Amesbury, MA
Maplewood Maple Manor Care Center, Maplewood, MN
Maplewood Nursing Center, Reidsville, NC
Maplewood Nursing Center Inc, Marion, OH
Maplewood Nursing Home Inc, Webster, NY
Maplewood of Sauk Prairie, Sauk City, WI
Maquoketa Care Center, Maquoketa, IA
Mar Vista Sanitarium, Los Angeles, CA
Maralie Convalescent Hospital, Santa Rosa, CA
Maranatha Baptist Care Center, Brooklyn Center, MN
Maranatha Care Center, Houma, LA
Maranatha Manor, Brookfield, MO
Maranatha Manor, Springfield, MO
Maranatha Rest Home, Westminister, MA
Marble City Nursing Home Inc, Sylacauga, AL
The Marcelle Home, Louisville, OH
Marchalin, Milbridge, ME
Marco Polo Rest Home Inc, Boston, MA
Marcus Manor Convalescent Hospital, San Jose, CA
Samuel Marcus Nursing & Retirement Home, Weymouth, MA
C Howard Marcy State Hospital, Pittsburgh, PA
Marengo Nursing Home, Linden, AL
Margaret Manor, Chicago, IL
Margaret Manor North Branch, Chicago, IL
Margaret-Anthony Nursing Home, Dunkirk, NY
Margaretville Memorial Hospital Nursing Home, Margaretville, NY
Margie Anna Nursing Home, Lebanon, TN
Margies Nursing Home, North Olmsted, OH
Mari de Villa Retirement Center Inc, Manchester, MO
Maria Care Center, Bowling Green, OH
Maria Home, Minneapolis, MN
Maria Linden, Rockford, IL

Maria Manor Health Care, Saint Petersburg, FL
The Maria-Joseph Center, Dayton, OH
Marian Catholic Home, Milwaukee, WI
Marian Franciscan Home, Milwaukee, WI
Marian Home, Fort Dodge, IA
Marian Home, Louisville, KY
Marian Manor, Pittsburgh, PA
Marian Manor Nursing Care Center, Riverview, MI
Marian Manor Nursing Home, South Boston, MA
Marian Manor Nursing Home, Glen Ullin, ND
Marian Manor of Taunton, Taunton, MA
Marian Nursing Home, Sublimity, OR
Marian Nursing Home, Radisson, WI
Marianna Convalescent Center, Marianna, FL
Marianwood Extended Health Care Facility, Issaquah, WA
The Marie Antoinette Pavilion, Marietta, OH
Marie Josephine Rest Home, Johnston, RI
Marietta Convalescent Center, Marietta, OH
Marietta Health Care Center, Marietta, GA
Marietta Manor, Cleveland, OH
Marietta Place, Chillicothe, OH
Marigarde-Sylvania Nursing Home, Toledo, OH
Marigold Health Care Center, Galesburg, IL
Marin Convalescent & Rehabilitation Hospital, Tiburon, CA
Marina Convalescent Center Inc, Alameda, CA
Marina Convalescent Hospital, Culver City, CA
Marina View Manor, Milwaukee, WI
Marine View Convalescent Center, Auburn, WA
Marinuka Manor, Galesville, WI
Mariola Nursing Home, Grants Pass, OR
Marion County Care Facility, Knoxville, IA
Marion County Convalescent Center, Marion, SC
Marion County Healthcare Center, Indianapolis, IN
Marion County Nursing Home, Hamilton, AL
Marion County Nursing Home, Yellville, AR
Marion Manor, Marion, KS
Marion Manor Nursing Home Inc, Marion, OH
Marion Memorial Nursing Home, Buena Vista, GA
Marion Nursing Home, Marion, LA
Marion Sims Nursing Center, Lancaster, SC
Marion Sunset Manor, Guin, AL
Mariposa Manor, Mariposa, CA
Maristhill Nursing Home, Waltham, MA
Mark H Wentworth Home, Portsmouth, NH
Mark Rest Center, McConnelsville, OH
Mark Twain Convalescent Hospital, San Andreas, CA
Marka Nursing Home, Mascoutah, IL
Market Square Health Care Facility, South Paris, ME
Marklund Home, Bloomingdale, IL
Julius Marks Home, Lexington, KY
Marks Sunset Manor, Olney, IL
Marlborough Health Care Center Inc, Marlborough, CT
Mar-Le Nursing Home, Wentzville, MO
Marlesta 1, Findlay, OH
Marlesta 2, Findlay, OH
Marlette Community Hospital, Marlette, MI
Marlin Manor, Jackson, MI
Marlinda Convalescent Hospital, Pasadena, CA
Marlinda-Imperial Convalescent Hospital, Pasadena, CA
Marlinda Nursing Home, Lynwood, CA
Marlinda West Nursing Home, Lynwood, CA
Marlora Manor Convalescent Hospital, Long Beach, CA
Marlow Manor Inc, Marlow, OK
Marmaton Valley Home, Uniontown, KS
Marquardt Memorial Manor Inc, Watertown, WI
Marquette Manor, Indianapolis, IN

Marquette Manor Nursing Home, Saint Louis, MO
The Nicholas Marra Nursing Home, East Providence, RI
Marrs Nursing Home, Mohegan Lake, NY
Mar-Saline Manor Care Center, Marshall, MO
Marshall County Care Facility, Marshalltown, IA
Marshall County Hospital—SNF, Benton, KY
Marshall County Nursing Center, Marysville, KS
Marshall Health Care Facility, Machias, ME
Marshall Home, Watertown, MA
Marshall Lane Manor, Derby, CT
Marshall Manor, Marshall, MI
Marshall Manor, Britton, SD
Marshall Manor Nursing Home Inc, Marshall, TX
Mary Marshall Manor Inc, Marysville, KS
Marshall Nursing Center, Marshall, AR
Marshall State School & Hospital, Marshall, MO
Marshalltown Manor, Marshalltown, IA
Marshalltown Medical Surgical Center Skilled Nursing Facility, Marshalltown, IA
Marshfield Living Center, Marshfield, WI
Marshwood Nursing Care Center, Lewiston, ME
Martha & Mary Nursing Home, Poulsbo, WA
Marthas Vineyard Hospital—Skilled & Intermediate Care Facility, Oak Bluffs, MA
Martin de Porres Multi-Care Center, Lake Charles, LA
Martin Family Care Home, Denver, CO
George A Martin Gerontology Center, Cincinnati, OH
Martin Hills Retirement Village, Essex, MO
Martin House, Burlington, CO
The Martin Luther Nursing Home Inc, Clinton, NY
Martin Nursing Home, Boston, MA
Martin Street Group Home, Silverdale, WA
Martinez Convalescent Hospital, Martinez, CA
Martin's Rest Home Inc, Cynthiana, KY
Martinsville Convalescent Home Inc, Martinsville, VA
Marwood Manor Nursing Home, Port Huron, MI
Marwood Rest Home Inc, Philadelphia, PA
Mary Anna Nursing Home, Wisner, LA
Mary Elizabeth Nursing Center Inc, Mystic, CT
Mary Ellen Convalescent Home Inc, Hellertown, PA
Mary Ellen Nursing Home, Somerville, MA
Mary Health of Sick Convalescent & Nursing Hospital, Newbury Park, CA
Mary-Jude Nursing Home, West Allis, WI
Mary Louise Nursing Home, Cleveland, OH
Mary Margaret Manor, Elgin, IL
Mary, Queen & Mother Center, Saint Louis, MO
Marycrest Manor, Culver City, CA
Marycrest Manor, Livonia, MI
Maryetta's Rest Home, Carthage, MO
Maryfair Manor, Indianapolis, IN
Maryfield Nursing Home, High Point, NC
Mary-Gran Nursing Center, Clinton, NC
Maryhaven Inc, Glenview, IL
Maryhill Manor Inc, Niagara, WI
Maryhouse Inc, Pierre, SD
Mary-Joseph Residence for the Elderly, New Orleans, LA
Maryland Baptist Aged Home, Baltimore, MD
Maryland Gardens, Phoenix, AZ
Maryland Intensive Behavior Management Program, Baltimore, MD
Maryland Manor of Glen Burnie, Glen Burnie, MD
Maryland Masonic Homes, Cockeysville, MD
Mary-Land Rest Home, Medway, MA
Marymount Manor, Eureka, MO
Marysville Care Center, Marysville, CA
Maryville Health Care Center, Maryville, MO
Maryville Nursing Home, Beaverton, OR
Marywood Convalescent Center, Wausau, WI
Mason Care Center, Mason, TX
Mason Health Care Facility Inc, Warsaw, IN

Mason Terrace Rest Home, Brookline, MA

Masonic & Eastern Star Home, Forest Grove, OR

Masonic & Eastern Star Home of North Carolina Inc, Greensboro, NC

Masonic Home, Wilmington, DE

Masonic Home, Charlton, MA

Masonic Home, Manchester, NH

Masonic Home & Health Facility, Utica, NY

Masonic Home & Hospital, Wallingford, CT

Masonic Home of Florida, Saint Petersburg, FL

Masonic Home of New Jersey, Burlington, NJ

Masonic Home of Pennsylvania, Lafayette Hill, PA

Masonic Home of Virginia—Health Care Unit, Richmond, VA

Masonic Home of Washington, Des Moines, WA

Masonic Homes, Elizabethtown, PA

Masonic Widows & Orphans Home & Infirmary Inc, Masonic Home, KY

Mason's Nursing Home, Lake Worth, FL

Massillon State Hospital, Massillon, OH

Mast Boarding Home, Greenwood, DE

Masters Health Care Center, Algood, TN

Matagorda House, Bay City, TX

Mater Dei Nursing Home, Newfield, NJ

Mather Nursing Center, Ishpeming, MI

Mathers Nursing Home, Greene, IA

Matheson Nursing Home, Galesburg, MI

Matney's Colonial Manor, South Sioux City, NE

Matneys Morningside Manor, Sioux City, IA

Matney's Westside Manor, Sioux City, IA

Mattapoisett Nursing Home Inc, Mattapoisett, MA

Mattatuck Health Care Facility Inc, Waterbury, CT

Matthews Care Home, La Junta, CO

Mattingly Health Care Center, Energy, IL

Mattoon Health Care Center Inc, Mattoon, IL

Matulaitis Nursing Home, Putnam, CT

Maunalani Hospital, Honolulu, HI

Maxicare Convalescent Hospital, Vallejo, CA

Max-Ull 1, Springfield, OH

Mayfair Manor, Lexington, KY

Mayfair Nursing Care Center, Columbus, OH

Mayfair Nursing Home, Hempstead, NY

The Mayfair Nursing Home, Tulsa, OK

Mayfield Care Center, Chicago, IL

Mayfield Manor, Mayfield, UT

Mayflower Gardens Convalescent Hospital, Lancaster, CA

Mayflower Home, Grinnell, IA

Mayflower House Nursing Home & Child Care Center, Plymouth, MA

Mayflower Nursing Home, Plymouth, IN

Maynard Rest Home, Pawtucket, RI

Mayo Nursing Center, Philadelphia, PA

Mayo Nursing Home, Northfield, VT

Sadie G Mays Memorial Nursing Home, Atlanta, GA

Maysville Extended Care Facility, Maysville, KY

Mayview Convelescent Center, Raleigh, NC

Mayview State Hospital, Bridgeville, PA

Mayview State Hospital—Long-Term Care Unit, Bridgeville, PA

Maywood Acres Healthcare, Oxnard, CA

Maywood Manor Inc, Kerens, TX

Mazotti Family Care Home, Denver, CO

MBW on Center, New Ulm, MN

The Mc Allister Nursing Home Inc, Tinley Park, IL

McAlester Regional Skilled Nursing Facility, McAlester, OK

McAllen Good Samaritan Center, McAllen, TX

McAllen Nursing Center, McAllen, TX

McAuley Nursing Home, Great Falls, MT

McCalls Chapel School Inc, Ada, OK

McCallum Family Care Center, Denver, CO

Bishop McCarthy Residence, Vineland, NJ

McCarthy Nursing Home, Stoughton, WI

McCaskill Nursing Home Inc, Maysville, OK

McCauley Cluster, Tallahassee, FL

McCaulley Care Center, Mansfield, OH

Mary McClellan Skilled Nursing Facility, Cambridge, NY

McClure Convalescent Hospital, Oakland, CA

McComb Extended Care & Nursing Home, McComb, MS

McConaughey Guest Home, Cameron, WV

McCone County Nursing Home, Circle, MT

McCormack Rest Home, Fairhaven, MA

McCovy Goldon Age Home Inc, Denver, CO

McCrite Plaza Health Center, Topeka, KS

McCurdy Residential Center, Evansville, IN

McCurtain Manor Nursing Center, Broken Bow, OK

McDaniel Nursing Home, El Paso, IL

McDonough Home, Pittsburgh, PA

McDowell Nursing Center, Nebo, NC

McDowell Skilled Nursing Facility, Greensburg, KY

McElrath Rest Home, Paducah, KY

McFadden Memorial Manor, Malden, MA

McFarland House, Barre, VT

McGee Nursing Home, Teague, TX

McGills Nursing Home—South, Dayton, OH

McGirr Nursing Home, Bellows Falls, VT

McGowan Nursing Home, Methuen, MA

McGraw Nursing Home Inc, Adena, OH

A M McGregor Home, East Cleveland, OH

McGuffey Health Care Center Inc, Gadsden, AL

McGuire Memorial Home for Retired Children, New Brighton, PA

McIntosh, McIntosh, MN

McIntosh Nursing Homes Inc, Muskogee, OK

McKay Memorial, Soap Lake, WA

McKay-Dee Transitional Care Center, Ogden, UT

McKendree Village Inc, Hermitage, TN

McKenzie Manor Nursing Home, Springfield, OR

McKerley Harris Hill Nursing Home, Penacook, NH

McKerley Health Care Center, Claremont, NH

McKerley Health Care Center, Laconia, NH

McKerley Health Care Center—Manchester Inc, Manchester, NH

McKerley Nursing Home, Concord, NH

McKinley Court, Decatur, IL

McKinley Life Care Centre, Canton, OH

McKinley Manor, Gallup, NM

McKinney Intensive Care Facility, Pickens, SC

McLarney Manor, Brookfield, MO

McLean County General Hospital—SNU, Calhoun, KY

McLean County Nursing Home, Normal, IL

McLean Home, Simsbury, CT

McMahon Tomlinson Nursing Center, Lawton, OK

McMinn Memorial Nursing Home, Etowah, TN

McMinnville Health Care Center, McMinnville, TN

McMurray Hills Manor Inc, McMurray, PA

McNamara Mercy Hospital & Nursing Home, Fairplay, CO

McRae Manor Inc, McRae, GA

McVane Memorial Nursing Home, Crivitz, WI

McVitty House Inc, Salem, VA

Mead Nursing Home, Meadville, PA

Meadow Brook Manor of North Miami, North Miami, FL

Meadow Brook Medical Care Facility, Bellaire, MI

Meadow Crest Inc, Bethel Park, PA

Meadow Glade Manor, Battle Ground, WA

Meadow Haven Nursing Center, Rock Hill, SC

Meadow Heights Nursing Center Inc, Williamsport, IN

Meadow Lawn Nursing Center, Davenport, IA

Meadow Manor Inc, Taylorville, IL

Meadow Manor Nursing Home, Grand Meadow, MN

Meadow Manor Nursing Home, Saint James, MO

Meadow Park Care Center, Saint Helens, OR

Meadow Park House, Rochester, MN

Meadow Park Nursing Home, Flushing, NY

Meadow Park Nursing Home, Clinton, WI

Meadow View Care Center, Maryville, IL

Meadow View Convalescent Home, North Reading, MA

Meadow View Health Care Center, Salem, IN

Meadow View Manor Nursing Home Inc, Sheboygan, WI

Meadow View Nursing Center, Joplin, MO

Meadow View Nursing Home, Lakeville, MA

Meadow View Park, Garden Grove, CA

Meadow Wood Nursing Home Inc, Georgetown, OH

Meadowbrook Care Center, Holland, MI

Meadowbrook Care Center, Van Alstyne, TX

Meadowbrook Convalescent Hospital Inc, Hemet, CA

Meadowbrook Inc, Shawsville, VA

Meadowbrook Living Center, Montgomery, OH

Meadowbrook Lodge, Magnolia, AR

Meadowbrook Manor, Worcester, MA

Meadowbrook Manor, Clemmons, NC

Meadowbrook Manor, Rapid City, SD

Meadowbrook Manor of Cherryville, Cherryville, NC

Meadowbrook Manor of Gastonia, Gastonia, NC

Meadowbrook Manor of Hartford, Fowler, OH

Meadowbrook Manor of Shelby, Shelby, NC

Meadowbrook Manor of Siler City, Siler City, NC

Meadowbrook Manor Sanitarium, Los Angeles, CA

Meadowbrook Nursing & Convalescent Center, Seattle, WA

Meadowbrook Nursing Home, Lexington, KY

Meadowbrook Nursing Home, Plattsburgh, NY

Meadowbrook Nursing Home, Chouteau, OK

Meadowbrook Nursing Home, Pulaski, TN

Meadowbrook Nursing Home, Fort Worth, TX

Meadowbrook Nursing Home Inc, Tucker, GA

The Meadowgreen, Dallas, TX

Meadowhaven Healthcare Center, Butler, IN

Meadowlands Health Care Center, Canonsburg, PA

Meadowlane Healthcare Center, Benson, MN

Meadowlark Convalescent Hospital, San Diego, CA

Meadowlark Hills, Manhattan, KS

Meadowood, Grayville, IL

Meadowood Nursing Home, Bessemer, AL

Meadows, Rolling Meadows, IL

The Meadows, Cooperstown, NY

Meadows—East, Louisville, KY

Meadows Manor, Manchester, CT

Meadows Manor, Terre Haute, IN

Meadows Manor North Inc, Terre Haute, IN

Meadows Mennonite Home, Chenoa, IL

Meadows Nursing Center, Dallas, PA

Meadows Nursing Home, Fremont, MI

Meadows—South, Louisville, KY

Meadowvale Care Center, Bluffton, IN

Meadowview Care Center, Kerrville, TX

Meadowview Lodge, Huntsville, AR

Meadowview Manor Health Care Center, Bridgeport, WV

Meadowview Nursing & Convalescent Center, Louisville, KY

Meadowview Nursing Home, Minden, LA

Meadowview Retirement Home, Mayfield, KY

Meadville Hillside Home, Meadville, PA

Meadville Nursing Home, Meadville, MS

Mechanicsville Care Center, Mechanicsville, IA

Mecklenburg Autistic Group Homes Inc, Charlotte, NC

Med Arts Health Facility, Columbus, GA

Med Rest Center, Medway, OH

Meda Nipple Convalescent Home, Thompsontown, PA

Medalion Health Center, Colorado Springs, CO

Medallion II Board & Lodge Home, Minneapolis, MN

Medallion Manor Inc, Provo, UT

Medco Center of Bowling Green, Bowling Green, KY

Medco Center of Brandenburg, Brandenburg, KY

Medco Center of Campbellsville, Campbellsville, KY

Medco Center of Clarksville, Clarksville, IN

Medco Center of Danville, Danville, IN

Medco Center of Elizabethtown, Elizabethtown, KY

Medco Center of Elkhart, Elkhart, IN

Medco Center of Evansville—North, Evansville, IN

Medco Center of Fordsville, Fordsville, KY

Medco Center of Fort Wayne, Fort Wayne, IN

Medco Center of French Lick, French Lick, IN

Medco Center of Hardinsburg, Hardinsburg, KY

Medco Center of Henderson, Henderson, KY

Medco Center of Huntingburg, Huntingburg, IN

Medco Center of Loogootee, Loogootee, IN

Medco Center of Morganfield, Morganfield, KY

Medco Center of Mt Vernon, Mount Vernon, IN

Medco Center of Muncie, Muncie, IN

Medco Center of Newburgh, Newburgh, IN

Medco Center of Owensboro, Owensboro, KY

Medco Center of Paducah, Paducah, KY

Medco Center of Pembroke, Pembroke, KY

Medco Center of South Bend, South Bend, IN

Medco Center of Springfield, Springfield, KY

Medco Chandler, Chandler, IN

Medco Springs of French Lick, French Lick, IN

Medford Convalescent & Nursing Center, Medford, NJ

Medford Leas, Medford, NJ

Medford Nursing Home, Medford, OK

Medford Rest Home, Medford, MA

Medi-Home of Arkoma Inc, Arkoma, OK

Medi Park Care Center Inc, Amarillo, TX

Medic Home Health Center, Melbourne, FL

Medical Arts Center—Coastal Georgia, Brunswick, GA

Medical Arts Convalescent Hospital, Perris, CA

Medical Arts Health Facility, Lawrenceville, GA

Medical Arts Nursing Center Inc (Asa Park Manor), Montrose, PA

Medical Care Center, Lynchburg, VA

Medical Care Facility of Memorial Hospital of Iowa Co, Dodgeville, WI

Medical Center Convalescent Hospital, San Bernardino, CA

Medical Center for Aging—Doylestown, Doylestown, PA

Medical Center Nursing Home, Clarendon, TX

Medical Center Nursing Home—DeGoesbriand Unit, Burlington, VT

Medical Park Convalescent Center Inc, Decatur, AL

Medical Park Nursing Center, High Point, NC

Medical Park Nursing Center, Mount Olive, NC

Medical Plaza Nursing Center, Paris, TX

Medicalodge East of Arkansas City, Arkansas City, KS

Medicalodge East of Coffeyville, Coffeyville, KS

Medicalodge East of Kansas City, Kansas City, KS

Medicalodge Inc of Texarkana, Texarkana, AR

Medicalodge North of Arkansas City, Arkansas City, KS

Medicalodge North of Kansas City, Kansas City, KS

Medicalodge North of Pittsburg, Pittsburg, KS

Medicalodge of Atchison, Atchison, KS

Medicalodge of Butler, Butler, MO

Medicalodge of Clay Center, Clay Center, KS

Medicalodge of Columbus, Columbus, KS

Medicalodge of Dewey, Dewey, OK

Medicalodge of Douglass, Douglass, KS

Medicalodge of Eureka, Eureka, KS

Medicalodge of Fort Scott, Fort Scott, KS

Medicalodge of Goddard, Goddard, KS

Medicalodge of Halls Ferry, Saint Louis, MO

Medicalodge of Kinsley, Kinsley, KS

Medicalodge of Leavenworth, Leavenworth, KS

Medicalodge of Neosho, Neosho, MO

Medicalodge of Paola, Paola, KS

Medicalodge of Troy, Troy, MO

Medicalodge of Wichita, Wichita, KS

Medicalodge South of Kansas City, Kansas City, KS

Medicalodge South of Pittsburg, Pittsburg, KS

Medicalodge West of Coffeyville, Coffeyville, KS

Medicana Nursing Center, Lake Worth, FL

Medicare Nursing Homes Inc, Cleveland, OH

Medicare Pavilion Corp, Waterbury, CT

Medic-Ayers Nursing Home, Trenton, FL

Medicenter/Neptune City, Neptune City, NJ

Medicenter of America—Bristol, Bristol, PA

Medicenter of Lakewood, Lakewood, NJ

Medicenter of Tampa, Tampa, FL

Medicenter—Springfield, Springfield, MO

Medicenter—Virginia Beach, Virginia Beach, VA

Medicos Recovery Care Center, Detroit, MI

Medigroup Castle Park Professional Care Center, Normandy, MO

Medigroup Heritage Park, Rolla, MO

Medigroup Oak Park Nursing Home, Saint Louis, MO

Medi-Home Inc—Fort Smith, Fort Smith, AR

Medi-Home of Prairie Grove, Prairie Grove, AR

Medi-Home of Rogers, Rogers, AR

Medilodge of Richmond, Richmond, MI

Medilodge of Romeo, Romeo, MI

Medilodge of Yale, Yale, MI

Medina Memorial Hospital—Skilled Nursing Facility, Medina, NY

Medina Nursing Center, Durand, IL

Mediplex at Lexington—Long-Term Care Facility, Lexington, MA

Mediplex of Beverly: A Long-Term Care Facility, Beverly, MA

Mediplex of Danbury, Danbury, CT

Mediplex of Newington, Newington, CT

Mediplex of Newton—Long-Term Care Facility, Newton, MA

Mediplex of Westport, Westport, CT

Mediplex of Wethersfield, Wethersfield, CT

Medlantic Manor at Lamond—Riggs, Washington, DC

Med-Vale Nursing Home, Medfield, MA

Medway Country Manor Nursing Home, Medway, MA

Meeker County Community Home, Litchfield, MN

Meharry-Hubbard Hospital-Skilled Nursing Facility, Nashville, TN

Meister Road Home, Lorain, OH

Melber Rest Home, Melber, KY

Melchor Nursing Home, Baltimore, MD

Meldonia Residential Care Facility, Kansas, MO

Mel-Haven Convalescent Home, Corsicana, TX

Meline Manor Inc, Jacksonville, IL

Melody Manor Convalescent Center, Leakesville, MS

Mel-Rose Convalescent Home, Tyler, TX

Melrose Manor Health Care Center, Louisville, KY

Melville Rest Home, Boston, MA

Memorial Community Hospital, Bertha, MN

Memorial Community Hospital—Long-Term Care Facility, Edgerton, WI

Memorial Conv Center, Belleville, IL

Memorial Convalescent Center, Adel, GA

Memorial Hall—Bristol Memorial Hospital, Bristol, VA

Memorial Heights Nursing Center, Idabel, OK

Memorial Home for the Aged, Moundridge, KS

Memorial Hospital at Easton Maryland Inc, Easton, MD

Memorial Hospital/Conv Center, Odessa, WA

Memorial Hospital & Home, Perham, MN

Memorial Hospital Inc & Skilled Nursing Unit, Towanda, PA

Memorial Hospital & Nursing Home of Greene County, Catskill, NY

Memorial Hospital—SNF, Manchester, KY

Memorial Intermediate Care Home, Macon, GA

Memorial Manor, Mondovi, WI

Memorial Manor Nursing Home, Bainbridge, GA

Memorial Medical Nursing Center, San Antonio, TX

Memorial Nursing Home, Boscobel, WI

Memorial Nursing Home Long-Term Care Unit, Medford, WI

Memory Manor, Pomeroy, WA

Memphis Convalescent Center, Memphis, TX

Memphis Health Care Center, Memphis, TN

Memphis Sunshine Home for Aged Men, Memphis, TN

Mena Manor, Mena, AR

Menard Conv Center, Petersburg, IL

Menard Manor, Menard, TX

Mendenhall Nursing Home Inc, Mendenhall, MS

Mendon Care Center, Mendon, UT

Mendota Lutheran Home, Mendota, IL

Menlo Park Health Care Center, Portland, OR

Menno-Haven/Menno-Village, Chambersburg, PA

Mennonite Friendship Manor Inc, South Hutchison, KS

Mennonite Home, Albany, OR

Mennonite Home, Lancaster, PA

Mennonite Memorial Home, Bluffton, OH

Mennonite Old People's Home, Maugansville, MD

Menno-Olivet Care Center, Menno, SD

Menomonee Falls Nursing Home, Menomonee Falls, WI

Menonite Bretheren Home for the Aged, Corn, OK

Menorah Home & Hospital for the Aged & Infirm, Brooklyn, NY

Menorah Manor, Saint Petersburg, FL

Menorah Nursing Home Inc, Brooklyn, NY

Menorah Park Center for the Aging, Beachwood, OH

Menorah Village, Reseda, CA

Mentor Way Villa Nursing Home, Mentor, OH

Mequon Care Center Inc, Mequon, WI

Merced Convalescent Hospital, Merced, CA

Merced Manor, Merced, CA

Mercer County Geriatric Center—F W Donnelly Long-Term Care Facility, Trenton, NJ

Mercer County Living Center, Mercer, PA

Mercer County Nursing Home, Aledo, IL

Mercer County Residential Homes Inc, Celina, OH

Mercer Island Villa Care, Mercer Island, WA

Mercerville Nursing & Convalescent Center, Mercerville, NJ

Mercy Care Center, Omaha, NE

Mercy Convalescent Center, Saint Louis, MO

Mercy Douglass Human Service Center, Philadelphia, PA

Mercy Extended Care Facility, Vicksburg, MS

Mercy Health Care Rehabilitation Center, Homewood, IL

Mercy Health Center, Dubuque, IA

Mercy Health & Rehabilitation Center Nursing Home Inc, Auburn, NY

Mercy Healthcare Center, Tupper Lake, NY

Mercy Hospital, Grayling, MI

Mercy Hospital Nursing Care Center, Johnstown, PA

Mercy Hospital—Skilled Nursing Facility, Buffalo, NY

Mercy Manor, Oakland, CA

Mercy Medical, Daphne, AL

Mercy Nursing Home Inc, North Little Rock, AR

Mercy Nursing Home Inc, Houston, TX

Mercy Residential & Rehabilitation Center, Milwaukee, WI
Mercyknoll Inc, West Hartford, CT
Mere Point Nursing Home, Brunswick, ME
Meriden Nursing Home, Meriden, CT
Meridian Convalescent Home, Meridian, MS
Meridian Geriatric Center, Meridian, TX
Meridian Manor, Mounds, IL
Meridian Multi-Medical Nursing Center, Towson, MD
Meridian Nursing Center, Meridian, MS
Meridian Nursing Center—Beeville, Beeville, TX
Meridian Nursing Center—Cardinal, South Bend, IN
Meridian Nursing Center—Caton Manor, Baltimore, MD
Meridian Nursing Center—Catonsville, Catonsville, MD
Meridian Nursing Center—Corsica Hills, Centreville, MD
Meridian Nursing Center—Frederick, Frederick, MD
Meridian Nursing Center—Hamilton, Baltimore, MD
Meridian Nursing Center, Hammonds Lane, Brooklyn Park, MD
Meridian Nursing Center—Heritage, Baltimore, MD
Meridian Nursing Center—Homewood, Baltimore, MD
Meridian Nursing Center—Long Green, Baltimore, MD
Meridian Nursing Center—Plantation, Plantation, FL
Meridian Nursing Center—Randallstown, Randallstown, MD
Meridian Nursing Center—River Park, South Bend, IN
Meridian Nursing Center—Severna Park, Severna Park, MD
Meridian Nursing Center—Shady Oaks, Sherman, TX
Meridian Nursing Center—Suburban, Chicago Heights, IL
Meridian Nursing Center—The Pines, Easton, MD
Meridian Nursing Center—West Side, Gary, IN
Meridian Nursing Center—Westfield, Westfield, NJ
Meridian Nursing Center—Woodview, Michigan City, IN
Meridian Nursing Home, Indianapolis, IN
Meridian Nursing Home, Comanche, OK
Merihil Health Care Center Inc, Lewisburg, TN
Meriwether Memorial Hospital & Nursing Home, Warm Springs, GA
A Merkle-C Knipprath Nursing Home, Clifton, IL
Merlin Health Retreat, Merlin, OR
Merrill Memorial Manor, Gardiner, ME
Merrillville Convalescent Center, Merrillville, IN
Merrimack County Nursing Home, Penacook, NH
Merrimack River Valley House, Lowell, MA
Merrimack Valley Retirement Home, Lowell, MA
Merriman House, North Conway, NH
Merritt Manor Convalescent Hospital, Tulare, CA
Merritt Manor Nursing Home, Merritt Island, FL
Merritt Plaza Nursing Home, Marshall, TX
Merry Haven Health Care Center, Snohomish, WA
Merry Heart Nursing Home, Succasunna, NJ
Merry Manor, Holton, KS
Merrymount Manor Nursing Home, Quincy, MA
Merryville Nursing Center, Merryville, LA
Mesa Christian Home, Mesa, AZ
Mesa Manor Nursing Center, Grand Junction, CO
Mesa Verde Convalescent Hospital, Costa Mesa, CA

Mesabi Home, Buhl, MN
Mesquite Tree Nursing Center, Mesquite, TX
Messenger House Care Center, Bainbridge Island, WA
Messiah Village, Mechanicsburg, PA
Messick Nursing Home Inc, Warrensburg, MO
Metacom Manor Health Center, Bristol, RI
Metairie Healthcare Center, Metairie, LA
Metcalfe County Nursing Home, Edmonton, KY
Methodist Church Home for the Aged, Bronx, NY
Methodist Country House, Wilmington, DE
Methodist Health Center, Madison, WI
The Methodist Home, Chicago, IL
The Methodist Home, Orangeburg, SC
Methodist Home for the Aging, Birmingham, AL
The Methodist Home of Clinton Inc, Clinton, OK
Methodist Home of DC, Washington, DC
Methodist Home of Enid Inc, Enid, OK
Methodist Hospital Extended Care Facility, Saint Louis Park, MN
Methodist Manor, Storm Lake, IA
Methodist Manor House, Seaford, DE
Methodist Memorial Homes Inc, Holdrege, NE
Methodist Nursing Home Inc, Fort Smith, AR
Methodist Nursing Home of Middle Tennessee, Winchester, TN
Methodist Retirement Home—Wesley Pines, Lumberton, NC
Methodist Retirement Homes Inc, Durham, NC
Methuen House Nursing & Convalescent Center, Methuen, MA
Meth-Wick Manor, Cedar Rapids, IA
Metro Care Center, Minneapolis, MN
Metroplex Care Center, Grand Prairie, TX
Metropolis Good Samaritan Home, Metropolis, IL
Metropolitan Developmental Center, Belle Chasse, LA
Metropolitan Jewish Geriatric Center, Brooklyn, NY
Metter Nursing Home, Metter, GA
Metzenbaum Residence, Chesterland, OH
Metzmeier Nursing Home, Campbellsville, KY
Mexia Nursing Home, Mexia, TX
Meyer Care Center, Higginsville, MO
MI Nursing & Restorative Center, Lawrence, MA
Miami Beach Hebrew Home for the Aged, Miami Beach, FL
Miami Christel Manor Inc, Miamisburg, OH
Miami Haven Nursing Home, Cleves, OH
Miami Health Care Center, Troy, OH
Miami Jewish Home for the Aged at Douglas Gardens, Miami, FL
Miami Nursing Center, Miami, OK
Michael Manor, Gettysburg, PA
Michigan Christian Home, Grand Rapids, MI
Michigan Masonic Home, Alma, MI
Michigan Shores, Manitowoc, WI
Michigan Skilled Care, Niles, MI
Michigan Terrace Nursing Center Inc, Chicago, IL
Mickel Nursing Home, Clarksville, AR
Micoll Residence, Hastings, MN
Mid America Nursing Center of Lincoln, Lincoln, KS
Mid State ICFMR Broad, Altoona, PA
Mid State ICFMR Inc, Altoona, PA
Mid State ICFMR Inc, Altoona, PA
Mid-Wilshire Extended Care Facility, Los Angeles, CA
Mid-America Convalescent Centers Inc, Chicago, IL
Mid-City Care Center, Memphis, TN
Mid-Del Manor Nursing Center, Oklahoma City, OK
Middle Georgia Nursing Home, Eastman, GA
Middle River Health Facility, Hawthorne, WI
Middlebelt Nursing Centre, Livonia, MI
Middlebelt-Hope Nursing Center, Westland, MI
Middleboro Rest Home, Middleboro, MA

Middlebury Convalescent Home Inc, Middlebury, CT
Middlebury Manor Nursing & Convalescent Home, Akron, OH
Middlesex Convalescent Center Inc, Middletown, CT
Middlesex Fells Nursing Home, Melrose, MA
Middlesex Manor Nursing Home, Framingham, MA
Middleton Village, Middleton, WI
Middletown Healthcare Center Inc, Middletown, CT
Middletown Nursing Center, Middletown, IN
Middletown Park Manor Health Facility, Middletown, NY
Middletown Quality Care Center, Middletown, OH
Midland Care Center Inc, Midland, TX
Midland Hospital Center—Skilled Care Unit, Midland, MI
Midland Kings Daughters, Midland, MI
Midland Manor, Tacoma, WA
Midland Manor Nursing Home, Nampa, ID
Midland Villa, Falls City, NE
Midlands Center Infant Care Unit, Columbia, SC
Mid-Maine Medical Center—Charles A Dean Div, Greenville, ME
Mid-Nebraska Lutheran Home Inc, Newman Grove, NE
Mid-South Christian Nursing Home, Memphis, TN
Midtown Care Home, Somerset, KY
Midtown Manor Nursing Home, Kansas City, MO
Midway Care Center, Fosston, MN
Midway Care Center Inc, Portland, OR
Midway Manor Convalescent Center, Kent, WA
Midway Manor Health Care Facility, Kenosha, WI
Midway Manor Nursing Home, Shreveport, LA
Midway Nursing Home, Maspeth, NY
Midwest Covenant Home Inc, Stromsburg, NE
Midwest Nursing Center, Baxter Springs, KS
Midwestern Parkway Heritage Manor, Wichita Falls, TX
Mielke's Nursing Home, Swanton, OH
Mifflin Healthcare Centers, Shillington, PA
Milan Care Center Inc, Milan, MO
Milan Health Care Inc, Milan, TN
Milan Healthcare Center, Milan, IN
Milcrest Nursing Center, Marysville, OH
Milder Manor Nursing Home, Lincoln, NE
Milford Health Care Center Inc, Milford, CT
Milford Manor, Milford, DE
Milford Manor Nursing Home, Baltimore, MD
Milford Manor Nursing Home, West Milford, NJ
Milford Manor Rest Home Inc, Milford, MA
Milford Nursing Home, Milford, IA
Milford Nursing Home, Milford, NH
Milford Rest Home Inc, Milford, NE
Milford Valley Convalescent Home Inc, Milford, PA
Milford Valley Memorial—Skilled Nursing Facility, Milford, UT
Mill Haven Care Center, Millstadt, IL
Mill Hill Nursing Home Inc, Worcester, MA
Mill Pond Rest Home, Ashland, MA
Mill Pond Rest Home, Hanover, MA
Mill Street Conv Center, Naperville, IL
Mill Valley Care Center, Bellevue, IA
Millard Fillmore Skilled Nursing Facility, Buffalo, NY
Millard Good Samaritan Center, Omaha, NE
Millbrae Serra Convalescent Hospital, Millbrae, CA
Millcreek Manor, Youngstown, OH
Millcroft, Newark, DE
Mille Lacs Nursing Home, Onamia, MN
Miller Care Center Inc, Louisville, OH
Miller County Nursing Home, Tuscumbia, MO
Miller Memorial Community, Meriden, CT

Miller Memorial Nursing Center, Andover, OH

Miller Memorial Nursing Home, Chappell, NE

Nathan Miller Center for Nursing Care, Inc, White Plains, NY

Miller Nursing Home, Colquitt, GA

Susan B Miller Nursing Homes Inc, Woodstock, VA

Miller's Merry Manor Inc, Garrett, IN

Miller's Merry Manor, Hobart, IN

Miller's Merry Manor, Mooresville, IN

Miller's Merry Manor, Sullivan, IN

Miller's Merry Manor, Tipton, IN

Miller's Merry Manor Community, Indianapolis, IN

Miller's Merry Manor Inc, Columbia City, IN

Miller's Merry Manor Inc, Culver, IN

Miller's Merry Manor Inc, Dunkirk, IN

Miller's Merry Manor Inc, Hartford City, IN

Miller's Merry Manor Inc, Hope, IN

Miller's Merry Manor Inc, Huntington, IN

Miller's Merry Manor Inc, Indianapolis, IN

Miller's Merry Manor Inc, LaGrange, IN

Miller's Merry Manor Inc, New Carlisle, IN

Miller's Merry Manor Inc, Peru, IN

Miller's Merry Manor Inc, Plymouth, IN

Miller's Merry Manor Inc, Rockport, IN

Miller's Merry Manor Inc, Rushville, IN

Miller's Merry Manor Inc, Wabash, IN

Miller's Merry Manor Inc, Walkerton, IN

Miller's Merry Manor Inc, Warsaw, IN

Miller's Merry Manor Middletown, Middletown, IN

Millers Progressive Care, Riverside, CA

Miller's Rest Home Inc, Austin, TX

Millie's Rest Home, Sutherland, IA

Mills Manor, Meriden, CT

Mills Manor, Mayfield, KY

Mills Rest Home, Gary, IN

Millsboro Nursing Home Inc, Millsboro, DE

Millway Nursing Home, Milwaukee, WI

Milner Community Health Care Inc, Rossville, IN

Milton Health Care Facility, Milton, MA

The Milton Home Inc, South Bend, IN

John Milton Nursing Home, Kissimmee, FL

Milton Manor Nursing Home, Lake Milton, OH

Milton View Nursing Home, Boston, MA

Milwaukee Catholic Home, Milwaukee, WI

Milwaukee County Mental Health Complex Rehabilitation Center—Central, Wauwatosa, WI

Milwaukee County Mental Health Complex Rehabilitation Center—West, Wauwatosa, WI

Milwaukee Jewish Convalescent Center, Milwaukee, WI

Milwaukee Jewish Home, Milwaukee, WI

Milwaukee Protestant Bradford Terrace, Milwaukee, WI

Milwaukee Protestant Home Infirmary, Milwaukee, WI

Milwaukie Convalescent Center, Milwaukie, OR

Mimbres Memorial Nursing Home, Deming, NM

Mimosa Manor Care Center, Keller, TX

Minami Keiro Nursing Home, Los Angeles, CA

Mineral County Nursing Home, Superior, MT

Mineral Point Care Center, Mineral Point, WI

Mineral Wells Care Center, Mineral Wells, TX

Miners Colfax Medical Center LTC, Raton, NM

Minerva Convalescent Center Inc, Minerva, OH

Minerva Nursing Home, Minerva, OH

Minerva Park Place, Columbus, OH

Mingo Manor, Williamson, WV

Minidoka Memorial Hospital & Extended Care Unit, Rupert, ID

Minneapolis Good Samaritan Center, Minneapolis, KS

Minneapolis Outreach Home, Minneapolis, MN

Minneola Nursing Home, Minneola, KS

Minneota Manor Health Care Center, Minneota, MN

Minnesota Jewish Group Home 1—Chai House, Saint Louis Park, MN

Minnesota Jewish Group Home II—Tivah, Saint Paul, MN

Minnesota Masonic Care Center, Bloomington, MN

Minnesota Odd Fellows Home, Northfield, MN

Minnesota Veterans Home, Minneapolis, MN

Minnesota Veterans Home—Hastings, Hastings, MN

Minnetonka Health Care Center Inc, Excelsior, MN

Minnewaska Lutheran Home, Starbuck, MN

Mira Costa Convalescent Hospital, Torrance, CA

Miracle Hill Nursing & Convalescent Home, Tallahassee, FL

Mirada Hills Rehabilitation & Convalescent Hospital, La Mirada, CA

Miramar Lodge Nursing Home, Pass Christian, MS

Miranda Manor Ltd, Niles, IL

Mira-Vista Nursing Home, Mount Vernon, WA

Misericordia Convalescent Home, York, PA

Misericordia Home, Chicago, IL

Mission Bay Convalescent Hospital, San Francisco, CA

Mission Convalescent Home, Jackson, TN

Mission Convalescent Hospital, Riverside, CA

Mission Convalescent Hospital, San Diego, CA

Mission Convalescent Hospital, San Gabriel, CA

Mission Convalescent Hospital, Sonoma, CA

Mission Farms Nursing Home, Plymouth, MN

Mission Lodge Sanitarium, San Gabriel, CA

Mission Manor Nursing Home Inc, Mount Vernon, TX

Mission Oaks Convalescent Hospital, Carmichael, CA

Mission Skilled Nursing Facility, Santa Clara, CA

Mission Villa Convalescent Hospital, San Francisco, CA

Mississippi Children's Rehabilitation Center, Jackson, MS

Mississippi County Nursing Home, Blytheville, AR

Mississippi Extended Care of Greenville Inc, Greenville, MS

Mississippi Home, Bemidji, MN

Missouri Slope Lutheran Home Inc, Bismarck, ND

Mitchell Convalescent Center, Camilla, GA

Mitchell Manor, Mitchell, IN

Mitchell Manor Nursing Home, McAlester, OK

Mitchell Retirement Home, Mitchell, SD

Mitchell Village Care Center, Mitchellville, IA

Mitchell's Nursing Home Inc, Danville, AR

Mizpah Nursing Home Inc, Locust Hill, VA

MJG Nursing Home Company Inc, Brooklyn, NY

Mobridge Care Center, Mobridge, SD

Modern Acre Home, Fulton, MO

Modern Care Convalescent & Nursing Home, Jacksonville, IL

Modern Manor Inc, Mount Sterling, IL

Moderncare—West Seattle, Seattle, WA

Modesto Convalescent Hospital, Modesto, CA

Mogck Home for Aged, Mitchell, SD

Mogck Rest Home, Mitchell, SD

Mohawk Manor Rest Home Inc, Shelburne, MA

Mohawk Valley Nursing Home, Ilion, NY

Mohun Hall Infirmary, Columbus, OH

Molalla Manor Care Center, Molalla, OR

Molena Care Home, Molena, GA

Moline Nursing & Rehabilitation Center, Moline, IL

Molokai General Hospital (DP), Kaunakakai, HI

Mom & Dad's Home & Health Care Center, Sioux Falls, SD

Momence Meadows Nursing Center Inc, Momence, IL

Monadnock Christian Nursing Home, Jaffrey, NH

Monadnock Nursing Home, Keene, NH

Monarch Heights, Ortonville, MN

Monclova Care Center, Monclova, OH

Monmouth Convalescent Center, Long Branch, NJ

Monmouth Nursing Home, Monmouth, IL

Monona Drive Rest Home, Madison, WI

Monroe Care Center, Monroe, MI

Monroe City Manor Care Center, Monroe City, MO

Monroe Community Hospital—Extended Care Facility, Rochester, NY

Monroe Convalescent Center, Monroe, MI

Monroe Convalescent Center, Monroe, WA

Monroe County Care Center, Woodsfield, OH

Monroe County Nursing Home, Waterloo, IL

Monroe County Rest Home, Aberdeen, MS

Monroe Health Care Facility, Tompkinsville, KY

Monroe House, Decatur, IL

Monroe Intermediate Care Facility, Monroe, GA

Monroe Manor, Paris, MO

Monroe Manor Nursing Home, Monroeville, AL

Monroe Manor Nursing Home, Monroe, LA

Monroe Manor Nursing Home, Monroe, WI

Monroe Nursing Home Inc, Monroeville, AL

Monroe Pavilion Health Center Inc, Chicago, IL

Monrovia Convalescent Hospital, Duarte, CA

Monsignor Bojnowski Manor Inc, New Britain, CT

Monson State Hospital, Palmer, MA

Montana Center for the Aged, Lewistown, MT

Montana Developmental Center, Boulder, MT

Montana Veterans Home, Columbia Falls, MT

Montcalm Manor, Montclair, NJ

Montclair Health Care Center, Denver, CO

Montclair Manor Convalescent Hospital, Montclair, CA

Montclair Nursing Center, Omaha, NE

Montclair Nursing Home, Montclair, NJ

Montclair Nursing Home, Glen Cove, NY

Monte Cassino Healthcare Center, Toluca, IL

Monte Vista Child Care Center, Montclair, CA

Monte Vista Grove Homes, Pasadena, CA

Monte Vista Lodge, Lemon Grove, CA

Montebello Convalescent Hospital, Montebello, CA

Montebello Nursing Home, Hamilton, IL

Montefiore Home, Cleveland Heights, OH

Montello Care Center, Montello, WI

Montello Manor Nursing Home, Lewiston, ME

Monterey Care Center, Rosemead, CA

Monterey Care Center, San Pablo, CA

Monterey Care Center, Wichita Falls, TX

Monterey Convalescent Hospital, Monterey, CA

Monterey Nursing Center, Scottsdale, AZ

Monterey Nursing Inn, Grove City, OH

Monterey Park Convalescent Hospital, Monterey Park, CA

Monterey Pines Skilled Nursing Facility, Monterey, CA

Montezuma Health Care Center, Montezuma, GA

Montgomery Country Geriatric & Rehabilitation Center, Royersford, PA

Montgomery Country Nursing Home, Mount Ida, AR

Montgomery County Infirmary, Amsterdam, NY

Montgomery County Nursing Home, Ashland City, TN

Montgomery Developmental Center, Huber Heights, OH

John L Montgomery Medical Home, Freehold, NJ

Montgomery Manor, Santa Rosa, CA

Montgomery Manor Inc, Montgomery City, MO

Montgomery Nursing Home, Montgomery, NY
Montgomery Nursing Home, Biscoe, NC
Monticello Big Lake Community Nursing Home, Monticello, MN
Monticello Community Healthcare Center, Monticello, IN
Monticello Convalescent Center, Hinsdale, IL
Monticello Hall, Kelso, WA
Monticello Manor, Fort Lauderdale, FL
Montowese Health Care Center, North Haven, CT
Montrose Bay Health Care Center, Montrose, AL
Montrose Care Center, Houston, TX
Montrose Convalescent Hospital, Montrose, CA
Montrose Health Center, Montrose, IA
Montrose Nursing Home, Montrose, MI
Montvale Health Center, Maryville, TN
MontVue Nursing Home, Luray, VA
Moody Care Center, Moody, TX
E Dene Moore Memorial Home, Rifle, CO
Moore & Pike County Nursing Home, Bowling Green, MO
Sarah Moore Home Inc, Delaware, OH
Moorehaven Care Center, La Center, WA
Mooreland Golden Age Nursing Home, Mooreland, OK
Moore's Nursing Home, Pittsburg, TX
Moorestown Nursing Home, Moorestown, NJ
Moorhead Healthcare Center, Moorhead, MN
Moorings Park Health Center, Naples, FL
Charles P Moorman Home for Women, Louisville, KY
Moose Lake Regional Treatment Center, Moose Lake, MN
Moosehaven Health Center, Orange Park, FL
Carol Lou Mora Care Center, Bradenton, FL
Moran Manor, Moran, KS
Moravian Home Inc, Winston-Salem, NC
Moravian Manor, Lititz, PA
Morehead Nursing Center, Morehead City, NC
The Allen Morgan Nursing Center, Memphis, TN
Morgan County Appalachian Regional Hospital Skilled Nursing Facility, West Liberty, KY
Morgan County Care Center, McConnelsville, OH
Morgan Health Center, Johnston, RI
Morgan Manor Convalescent Center, Morgantown, WV
Morgan Memorial Home, Stockton, IL
Morgantown Health Care Corporation, Morgantown, WV
Morning Star Manor, Fort Washakie, WY
Morning Star Nursing Home, Oklahoma City, OK
Morning Sun Care Center, Morning Sun, IA
Morning View Care Center, Danville, OH
Morning View Care Center, Marion, OH
Morning View Care Center 1, Centerburg, OH
Morning View Care Center III, Sunbury, OH
Morning View Care Center 2, Fulton, OH
Morning View Care Center 2 Annex, Fulton, OH
Morningside Care Center, Ida Grove, IA
Morningside Care Center, Stoughton, WI
Morningside Center, Chillicothe, MO
Morningside Health Center, Sheboygan, WI
Morningside House Nursing Home Company, Bronx, NY
Morningside Inc, Pinellas Park, FL
Morningside Manor, Alcester, SD
Morningside Manor, San Antonio, TX
Morningside Nursing Home, Norman, OK
Moroun Nursing Home, Detroit, MI
Morrell Memorial Convalescent Center Inc, Hartsville, SC
Morrilton Manor Nursing Home, Morrilton, AR
Bishop Morris Care Center, Portland, OR
Morris Hills Multicare Center, Morristown, NJ
Morris Lincoln Nursing Home, Morris, IL

Morris Memorial Nursing & Convalescent Home, Milton, WV
Morris Nursing Home, Bethel, OH
Morris Oak Lawn Nursing Home, Eaton, OH
Morris Park Nursing Home, Bronx, NY
Morris View, Morris Plains, NJ
Morrison Community Hospital, Morrison, IL
Morrison Nursing Home, Whitefield, NH
Morrisons Cove Home, Martinsburg, PA
Morristown Healthcare, Morristown, IN
Morristown Rehabilitation Center, Morristown, NJ
Morro Bay Convalescent Center, Morro Bay, CA
Morrow County Extended Care Facility, Mount Gilead, OH
Morrow Manor Nursing Center, Chesterville, OH
Morrow Memorial Home for the Aged, Sparta, WI
Ora G Morrow Nursing Home, Chicago, IL
Morton F Plant Rehabilitation & Nursing Center, Clearwater, FL
Morton Healthcare Center, Morton, IL
Morton Nursing Home, Morton, WA
Morton Terrace Ltd, Morton, IL
Moses Austin Group Care Home, Potosi, MO
Moses-Ludington Nursing Home Company Inc, Ticonderoga, NY
Moses Taylor Hospital—Skilled Nursing Facility, Scranton, PA
Mosholu Parkway Nursing Home, Bronx, NY
Moss Bluff Manor, Lake Charles, LA
Moss Oaks Health Care, Pooler, GA
Mosser Nursing Home Inc, Trexlertown, PA
Mother Hull Home, Kearney, NE
Mother Joseph Manor, Aberdeen, SD
Mother Margaret Hall, Mount Saint Joseph, OH
Mother of Good Counsel Nursing Home, Saint Louis, MO
Mother of Mercy Nursing Home & Retirement Center, Albany, MN
Mother of Perpetual Help Home, Brownsville, TX
Mother Teresa Home, Cold Spring, MN
Mother Theresa Home Inc, Lemont, IL
Mott Good Samaritan Nursing Center, Mott, ND
Margaret E Moul Home, York, PA
Moulton Health Care Center, Moulton, AL
Moultrie County Community Center, Lovington, IL
Moultrie Rest-A-While Nursing Home, Moultrie, GA
Mound View Health Care Center, Moundsville, WV
Mound View Health Care Inc, Moundsville, WV
Moundridge Manor, Moundridge, KS
Mounds Park Residence, Saint Paul, MN
Moundville Nursing Home Inc, Moundville, AL
Mt Adams Care Center, Goldendale, WA
Mt Alverna Home, Parma, OH
Mt Ascutney Hospital & Health Center, Windsor, VT
Mt Ayr Health Care Center, Mount Ayr, IA
Mt Carmel Care Center, Burlington, WI
Mt Carmel Health Care Center, Milwaukee, WI
Mt Carmel Home—Keens Memorial, Kearney, NE
Mt Carmel Nursing Home, Manchester, NH
Mt Diablo Nursing Center, Martinez, CA
Mt Dora Healthcare Center, Mount Dora, FL
Mt Gilead Shelter Care Home, Carrollton, IL
Mt Healthy Christian Home, Cincinnati, OH
Mt Holly Center, Mount Holly, NJ
Mt Holly Nursing Home, Louisville, KY
Mt Hope Dunkard Brethren Church Home, Manheim, PA
Mt Hope Nursing Center, Mount Hope, KS
Mt Ida Rest Home, Newton, MA
Mt Joseph, Concordia, KS
Mt Laurel Convalescent Center, Mount Laurel, NJ
Mt Lebanon Manor, Pittsburgh, PA

Mt Loretto Nursing Home, Amsterdam, NY
Mt Macrina Manor Nursing Home, Uniontown, PA
Mt Miguel Covenant Village, Spring Valley, CA
Mt Ogden Convalescent Center, Washington Terrace, UT
Mt Olivet Homes Inc, Minneapolis, MN
Mt Olivet Rolling Acres, Excelsior, MN
Mt Olivette Care Center, Carmichael, CA
Mt Olivette Meadows Convalescent Hospital, Sacramento, CA
Mt Orab Nursing Care Center, Mount Orab, OH
Mt Pleasant Convalescent Hospital Inc, San Jose, CA
Mt Pleasant Home, Boston, MA
Mt Pleasant Manor, Matawan, NJ
Mt Pleasant Nursing Home, Cleveland, OH
Mt Pleasant Total Living Center, Mount Pleasant, MI
Mt Pleasant Village, Monroe, OH
Mt Royal Villa, North Royalton, OH
Mt Rubidoux Convalescent Hospital, Rubidoux, CA
Mt St Francis Health Center, Woonsocket, RI
Mt St Joseph, Lake Zurich, IL
Mt St Joseph, Euclid, OH
Mt St Joseph Extended Care Center, Portland, OR
Mt St Joseph Nursing Home, Waterville, ME
Mt St Vincent Nursing Center, Seattle, WA
Mt St Vincent Nursing Home Inc, Holyoke, MA
Mount San Antonio Gardens/Congregational Homes, Pomona, CA
Mt Shelter Care Home, Vienna, IL
Mt Sinai Nursing Home Inc, Baltimore, MD
Mt Tabor Care Center, Portland, OR
Mt Vernon Care Center, Baltimore, MD
Mt Vernon Care Facility Inc, Mount Vernon, IL
Mt Vernon Developmental Center, Mount Vernon, OH
Mt Vernon Manor, Fort Lauderdale, FL
Mt Vernon Nursing Center, Southfield, MI
Mt Vernon Nursing Center, Alexandria, VA
Mt Vernon Nursing Home, Mount Vernon, OH
Mt Vernon Park Care Center, Springfield, MO
Mt Washington Care Center, Cincinnati, OH
Mt Zion Geriatric Center, Indianapolis, IN
Mountain Duplex, Fort Collins, CO
Mountain Home Good Samaritan Village, Mountain Home, AR
Mountain Home Nursing Center, Mountain Home, AR
Mountain Laurel Manor, Corbin, KY
Mountain Manor, Carmichael, CA
Mountain Manor Nursing Home, Pikeville, KY
Mountain Manor Nursing Home Inc, Fort Payne, AL
Mountain Manor of Prestonburg, Prestonsburg, KY
Mountain Meadows, Monte Vista, CO
Mountain Park Convalescent Care Facility, Lake Oswego, OR
Mountain Rest Nursing Home Inc, Scranton, PA
Mountain Shadows—Intermediate Care Facility, Las Cruces, NM
Mountain State Nursing Home, Charleston, WV
Mountain Towers Healthcare, Cheyenne, WY
Mountain Valley Rest Home, Salyersville, KY
Mountain View, Klamath Falls, OR
Mountain View Care Center, Colorado Springs, CO
Mountain View Care Center, Kimberly, ID
Mt View Child Care Center Inc, Loma Linda, CA
Mountain View Convalescent Care Center, Oregon City, OR
Mountain View Convalescent Center, Clayton, GA
Mountain View Convalescent Hospital, Mountain View, CA

Mountain View Health Care Center, Elkhorn City, KY
Mt View Health Facility, Lockport, NY
Mountain View Healthcare, Windsor, CT
Mountain View Hospital, Madras, OR
Mountain View Hospital, Payson, UT
Mountain View House, Aurora, CO
Mountain View Lodge Inc, Big Spring, TX
Mountain View Manor, Hillsdale, PA
Mountain View Manor Nursing Center, Eureka, MT
Mountain View Manor Nursing Center, Bryson City, NC
Mt View Nursing Center, Greensburg, PA
Mountain View Nursing Home, Montgomery, MA
Mountain View Nursing Home, Ossipee, NH
Mountain View Nursing Home, Mountain View, OK
Mountain View Nursing Home, Chattanooga, TN
Mt View Nursing Home, Wausau, WI
Mountain View Nursing Home Inc, Aroda, VA
Mountain View Rest Home, Chattanooga, TN
Mountain View Sanitarium, Sylmar, CA
Mountain Vista Health Park, Denton, NC
Mountain Vista Nursing Home, Wheat Ridge, CO
Mountain Vista Nursing Home, Toppenish, WA
Mountainview Memorial Hospital & Nursing Home, White Sulphur Springs, MT
Mountainview Nursing Home, Spartanburg, SC
Mountrail Bethel Home, Stanley, ND
Moyle Manor, Yucca Valley, CA
Mozark Health Resort, Camdenton, MO
F F Mueller Residential Center, Springfield, OH
C A Mues Memorial Good Samaritan Center, Arapahoe, NE
Muffett Nursing Home, Cornwell Heights, PA
Muhlenberg Community Hospital, Greenville, KY
Mulberry Lutheran Home, Mulberry, IN
Mulberry Manor, Stephenville, TX
Mulberry Manor Inc, Anna, IL
Mulberry Park, Florence, SC
Mul-Care Desert Convalescent Hospital, Indio, CA
Mulder Health Care Facility, West Salem, WI
Muldrow Nursing Home, Muldrow, OK
Muleshoe Nursing Home, Muleshoe, TX
Mullen Home for the Elderly, Denver, CO
Mullican Nursing Home, Savoy, TX
Mullins Nursing Home, Piketon, OH
Mullis Manor II, Folkston, GA
Mullis Manor Inc, Homerville, GA
Muncie Health Care Center Inc, Muncie, IN
Muncy Valley Hospital—Skilled Nursing Facility, Muncy, PA
Munday Nursing Center, Munday, TX
Mundey Manor, Townsend, DE
Munster Med-Inn, Munster, IN
Murdoch Center, Butner, NC
Murfreesboro Health Care Center, Murfreesboro, TN
Mary Murphy Nursing Home, Boston, MA
Murphy Medical Center, Murphy, NC
Murray Manor Convalescent Center, Murraysville, PA
Murray-Calloway County Hospital & Long-Term Care Unit, Murray, KY
Muscatine Care Center, Muscatine, IA
Muscle Shoals Nursing Home, Muscle Shoals, AL
Muscogee Manor, Columbus, GA
Muskego Nursing Home, Muskego, WI
Muskegon Correctional Facility, Muskegon, MI
Muskogee Convalescent Center, Muskogee, OK
Myers Nursing & Convalescent Center Inc, Kansas City, MO
Myers Nursing Home, Beardstown, IL
Myrtle Beach Manor, Myrtle Beach, SC
Myrtle Convalescent Home, Manchester, NH

Myrtle Point Care Center, Myrtle Point, OR
The Myrtles Health Care Facility, Columbia, MS
Mystic Manor Inc, Mystic, CT
Nacogdoches Convalescent Center, Nacogdoches, TX
Naeve Parkview Home, Wells, MN
Nampa Care Center, Nampa, ID
Nancy Ann Convalescent Home, Foster, RI
The Nancy Patch Retirement Home, Leominster, MA
Nansemond Convalescent Center Inc, Suffolk, VA
Naomi Heights Nursing Home, Alexandria, LA
Nashville Health Care Center, Nashville, TN
Nashville Manor Nursing Home, Nashville, TN
Nashville Nursing Home, Nashville, AR
Nassau Nursing Home, Oceanside, NY
Natatana Care Center, De Leon, TX
Natchitoches Manor Nursing Home, Natchitoches, LA
Natchitoches Parish Hospital—Long-Term Care Unit, Natchitoches, LA
The Nathaniel Witherell, Greenwich, CT
National Care Centers of America Inc, Springfield, MO
National Health Care Center, Fort Lauderdale, FL
National Lutheran Home for the Aged, Rockville, MD
Nature Trail Home Inc, Mount Vernon, IL
Naugle Manor Inc, Baden, PA
Navarre Community Health Center, Navarre, OH
Nazareth Hall, El Paso, TX
Nazareth Health Related Facility, Buffalo, NY
Nazareth Home, Louisville, KY
Nazareth House, Fresno, CA
Nazareth House, Los Angeles, CA
Nazareth House, San Diego, CA
Nazareth House, San Rafael, CA
Nazareth House, Stoughton, WI
Nazareth Infirmary, Nazareth, KY
Nazarethville, Des Plaines, IL
NCF Eastridge House, Beloit, WI
Neal Home, Logansport, IN
Nebraska City Manor, Nebraska City, NE
Nebraska Veterans Home, Grand Island, NE
Nebraska Veterans Home Annex, Norfolk, NE
Nederland Nursing Home Inc, Nederland, TX
Needhams Nursing Home, Bellingham, WA
Negley House Nursing Center, Pittsburgh, PA
Negro Old Folks Home Inc, LaGrange, GA
Nehalem Valley Care Center, Wheeler, OR
Neighborhood Convalescent Home Inc, Pawtucket, RI
The Neighbors, Byron, IL
Neighbors of Woodcraft Home, Gresham, OR
Neillsville Memorial Home, Neillsville, WI
Nekton Inc, Saint Paul, MN
Nekton on Frost, Maplewood, MN
Nekton on Goodrich, Saint Paul, MN
Nekton on Greysolon, Duluth, MN
Nekton on Imperial Court, Stillwater, MN
Nekton on London Road, Duluth, MN
Nekton on Minnehaha Park, Minneapolis, MN
Nekton on Queen, Minneapolis, MN
Nekton on Sextant, Little Canada, MN
Nekton on Springvale, Duluth, MN
Nekton on Stillwater Lane, Lake Elmo, MN
Nekton on Wallace, Duluth, MN
Nekton on Wheeler, Saint Paul, MN
Nekton on William, Edina, MN
Nekton on Wyoming, Saint Paul, MN
Nekton-Hodgson Rd, Shoreview, MN
Nella's Inc, Elkins, WV
Nella's Nursing Home Inc, Elkins, WV
Nelson Broadview Nursing Home, Parma, OH
Knute Nelson Memorial Home, Alexandria, MN
Nelson Manor, Newton, IA
Nelson Manor Nursing Home, Boston, MA
Nelson Nursing Home, Fairfield, IA
Nelson's Health Care Center Inc, Waynesboro, TN
Nelson's Rest Home, Sturgis, SD

Nemaha County Good Samaritan Center, Auburn, NE
Nentwick Convalescent Home Inc, East Liverpool, OH
Neodesha Nursing Home, Neodesha, KS
Neosho Senior Center Inc, Neosho, MO
Neponsit Health Care Center, New York, NY
Nesbit Nursing Home, Seguin, TX
Neshaminy Manor, Doylestown, PA
Neshoba County Nursing Home, Philadelphia, MS
Nesika I, Tacoma, WA
Nesika II, Tacoma, WA
Nesika III, Tacoma, WA
Netherland Health Center, Kingsport, TN
George H Nettleton Home, Kansas City, MO
Sarah R Neuman Nursing Home, Mamaroneck, NY
Nevada City Nursing Home, Nevada, MO
Nevada Habilitation Center, Nevada, MO
Nevada Manor Nursing Home, Nevada, MO
Mayor Michael J Neville Manor Nursing Home, Cambridge, MA
Henry C Nevins Home Inc, Methuen, MA
New Albany Nursing Home, New Albany, IN
New Athens Home, New Athens, IL
New Bedford Jewish Convalescent Home, New Bedford, MA
New Boston Nursing Center, New Boston, TX
New Boston Nursing Home Inc, Sandisfield, MA
New Brighton Care Center, New Brighton, MN
New Brighton Manor Care Center, Staten Island, NY
New Brook Hollow Health Care Center Inc, Wallingford, CT
New Bunker Rest Home, Fitchburg, MA
New Castle Community Care Center, New Castle, IN
New Castle Healthcare Center, New Castle, IN
New Community Extended Care Facility, Newark, NJ
New Concord Nursing Center, New Concord, OH
New Dawn Convalescent Center, Furnace, OH
New Dawn Health Care & Retirement Center, Dover, OH
New Dawn Inc, Fulda, MN
New Dawson Springs Nursing Home, Dawson Springs, KY
New Detroit Nursing Center, Detroit, MI
New England Friends Home, Hingham, MA
New England Home for the Deaf, Danvers, MA
New England Rehabilitation Hospital, Woburn, MA
New Fairview Health Care Facility, New Haven, CT
New Florence Nursing & Care Center, New Florence, MO
New Glarus Home Inc, New Glarus, WI
New Glen Oaks Nursing Home, Glen Oaks, NY
New Gouverneur Hospital—Skilled Nursing Facility, New York, NY
New Hampshire Centennial Home for the Aged, Concord, NH
New Hampshire Odd Fellows Home, Concord, NH
New Hampton Care Center Inc, New Hampton, IA
New Haven Convalescent Center, New Haven, CT
New Haven Nursing Home, Anderson, IN
New Haven Nursing Home, Odessa, MO
New Haven O'Rest Inc, Van Buren, AR
The New Homestead, Guthrie Center, IA
New Hope Manor, Brewton, AL
New Hope of Indiana Inc, Indianapolis, IN
New Hope Village Inc, Carroll, IA
New Horizon Nursing Home, Springfield, OH
New Horizon Rehabilitationilitative Center, Ocala, FL
New Horizons, Salt Lake City, UT
New Horizons Care Center, Sioux City, IA
New Horizons Care Center, Lovell, WY
New Horizons Nursing Home, Konawa, OK

New Horizons of Pittsburg, Pittsburg, KS
New Horizons of Valley Center, Valley Center, KS
New Horizons of Winfield, Winfield, KS
New Ivy House, Middletown, NJ
New Jersey Firemen's Home, Boonton, NJ
New Jersey Home for Veterans at Paramus, Paramus, NJ
New Lakeview Convalescent Home, Cheshire, CT
New Life Center, Greeley, CO
New Life Treatment Center, Woodstock, MN
New Light Baptist Church Nursing Home Inc, Detroit, MI
New Lincoln Hospital, Toledo, OR
New London Care Center, New London, IA
New London Convalescent Home, Waterford, CT
New Martinsville Health Care Center, New Martinsville, WV
New Mexico State Hospital Long-Term Care Division, Las Vegas, NM
New Milford Nursing Home, New Milford, CT
New Oaks Care Center Inc, Des Moines, IA
New Orleans Home & Rehabilitation Center, New Orleans, LA
New Paltz Nursing Home, New Paltz, NY
New Perry Nursing Home, Perry, GA
The New Pine Grove Villa Nursing Home, Millbury, MA
New Richland Care Center, New Richland, MN
New Riviera Health Resort, Coral Gables, FL
New Rochelle Nursing Home & Adult Day Care Program, New Rochelle, NY
New Sans Souci Nursing Home, Yonkers, NY
New Seaera Convalescent Home, Long Beach, WA
New Sharon Care Center, New Sharon, IA
New Town Nursing Home, New Town, ND
New Ulm CRF I, New Ulm, MN
New Ulm CRF II, New Ulm, MN
New Underwood Good Samaritan Center, New Underwood, SD
New Vanderbilt Nursing Home, Staten Island, NY
New York Congregational Home for the Aged, Brooklyn, NY
New York State Veterans Home, Oxford, NY
Newark Health & Extended Care Facility, Newark, NJ
Newark Healthcare Centre, Newark, OH
Newark Manor Nursing Home, Newark, DE
Newark Manor Nursing Home, Newark, NY
Newark-Wayne Community Hospital Inc—Skilled Nursing Facility, Newark, NY
Newaygo Medical Care Facility, Fremont, MI
Newberg Care Home, Newberg, OR
Newberry Convalescent Center, Newberry, SC
Newberry Nursing Home, Kansas City, MO
Newburgh Health Care & Residential Center, Newburgh, IN
Newburyport Society Home for Aged Men, Newburyport, MA
Doctor Kate Newcomb Convalescent Center, Woodruff, WI
Newell Good Samaritan Center, Newell, IA
Newfane Health Facility, Newfane, NY
Newfield House Inc, Plymouth, MA
Newhall Nursing Home, Salem, MA
Newkirk Nursing Center, Newkirk, OK
Newmans Lakewood Nursing Home, Lakewood, NJ
Newnan Healthcare Center, Newnan, GA
Newport Convalescent Center, Newport Beach, CA
Newport Convalescent Center Inc, Newport News, VA
Newport Health Care Center, Newport, VT
Newport News Baptist Retirement Community, Newport News, VA
Newton Convalescent Home, West Newton, MA
Newton County Nursing Home, Jasper, AR
Newton Manor Rest Home, Worcester, MA
Newton Nursing Home, Newton, NJ
Newton Presbyterian Manor, Newton, KS

Newton Rest Haven Inc, Newton, IL
Newton & Wellesley Nursing Home, Wellesley, MA
NHE—Greenville Inc, Greenville, SC
NHE—Lansing, Lansing, MI
NHE—Memphis, Memphis, TN
Niagara Falls Memorial Nursing Home Co Inc, Niagara Falls, NY
Niagara Frontier Nursing Home Co Inc, Getzville, NY
Niagara Geriatric Center, Niagara Falls, NY
Niagara Lutheran Home Inc, Buffalo, NY
Niagra Frontier Methodist Home Inc Health Related Facility, Getzville, NY
Nicholas County Health Care Center Inc, Richwood, WV
Nichols Home, Portage, OH
Nichols House Nursing Home, Fairhaven, MA
Nicholson's Nursing Home, Winthrop, ME
The Nicol Home Inc, Glasco, KS
Nicole Manor, Burrillville, RI
Nicollet Health Care Center Inc, Minneapolis, MN
Nightingale Home, Nashua, NH
Nightingale Home Inc, Statesboro, GA
Nightingale North, Sterling Heights, MI
Nightingale Nursing Home, Warren, MI
Nightingale Nursing Home, Waconia, MN
Nightingale West, Westland, MI
Nikkel Family Care Home, Denver, CO
Nile Health Care Center, Minneapolis, MN
Nim Henson Geriatric Center, Jackson, KY
Nims Rest Home, Natick, MA
Ninnescah Manor Inc, Clearwater, KS
Niobrara County Memorial Hospital Nursing Home, Lusk, WY
Nipple Convalescent Home, Liverpool, PA
Nishna Care Center & Nishna Cottage, Malvern, IA
Nisqually Valley Care Center, McKenna, WA
Joseph T Nist Nursing Home, Louisville, OH
Bishop Noa Home for Senior Citizens, Escanaba, MI
Noble Building, Hartford, CT
Edward John Noble Hospital, Alexandria Bay, NY
Noblesville Healthcare Center, Noblesville, IN
Noblesville Nursing Home, Noblesville, IN
Nocona Nursing Home, Nocona, TX
Nodaway Nursing Home Inc, Maryville, MO
Nokomis Golden Manor, Nokomis, IL
Nopeming Nursing Home, Nopeming, MN
Nor-Bell Care Center, Bellingham, WA
Nora Springs Care Center, Nora Springs, IA
Norcliffe Rest Home, Brooklyn, CT
Norfolk Nursing Center, Norfolk, NE
Norfolk Nursing Home, Stoughton, MA
Norhaven, Saint Paul, MN
Norlite Nursing Center, Marquette, MI
Normandy House, Wilmette, IL
Normandy House Nursing Home, Melrose, MA
Normandy Terrace Inc, San Antonio, TX
Normandy Terrace Inc—Northeast, San Antonio, TX
Norridge Nursing Centre Inc, Chicago, IL
Norse Home, Seattle, WA
Norseland Nursing Home, Westby, WI
North Adams Home Inc, Mendon, IL
North Alabama Nursing Home, Russellville, AL
North American Baptist Home, Madison, SD
North American Healthcare Center, White Hall, IL
North Arundel Nursing & Convalescent Center Inc, Glen Burnie, MD
North Aurora Manor, North Aurora, IL
North Bend Nursing Center, North Bend, WA
North Berwick Nursing Home, North Berwick, ME
North Carolina Cancer Institute Inc, Lumberton, NC
North Carolina Special Care Center, Wilson, NC
North Central Good Samaritan Center, Mohall, ND
North Central Health Care Facility, Wausau, WI

North Charleston Convalescent Center, Charleston, SC
North Country Nursing & Rehabilitation Center, Bemidji, MN
North Country Rehabilitation Center, Franconia, NH
North Division Residential Center, Sterling, CO
North Fairfield Geriatric Center Inc, Fairfield, CT
North Grand Care Center, Ames, IA
North Hollywood Extended Care, North Hollywood, CA
North Horizon Health Care Center, Saint Petersburg, FL
North Jersey Nursing Center, Wayne, NJ
North Las Vegas Care Center, North Las Vegas, NV
North Macon Health Care, Macon, GA
North Manor Center, Youngstown, OH
North Ottawa Care Center, Grand Haven, MI
North Panola Regional Hospital & Nursing Center Inc, Sardis, MS
North Pennsylvania Convalescent Residence Inc, Lansdale, PA
North Ridge Care Center, New Hope, MN
North Ridge Care Center, Manitowoc, WI
North River Nursing Home, Hanover, MA
North Rockford Convalescent Home, Rockford, IL
North Sabine Nursing Home, Pleasant Hill, LA
North St Paul Care Center, North Saint Paul, MN
North Shore Convalescent Home, Saugus, MA
North Shore Health Care Center, Milwaukee, WI
North Shore Manor Inc, Loveland, CO
North Shore Nursing Home, Miami, FL
North Shores Health Center, Saint Petersburg, FL
North Side Nursing Home, Youngstown, OH
North Side Nursing Home, Sapulpa, OK
North Star Homes, Bemidji, MN
North Towne Manor, Wichita, KS
North Valley Hospital & Extended Care Center, Whitefish, MT
North Valley Nursing Home, Stevensville, MT
North Vernon Nursing Home, North Vernon, IN
North Village Manor, Moberly, MO
North Willow Center, Indianapolis, IN
Northampton Nursing Home Inc, Northampton, MA
Northaven Nursing Center, Dallas, TX
Northboro Rest Home, Northborough, MA
Northbridge Nursing Home, Northbridge, MA
Northbrook Manor Care Center, Cedar Rapids, IA
Northcrest Care Center, Council Bluffs, IA
Northcrest Health Care Center, Ames, IA
Northcrest Nursing Home, Napoleon, OH
Northeast Care Center, Worcester, MA
Northeast Health Care Center, Wichita, KS
Northeast Healthcare Center of Muncie, Muncie, IN
Northeast House Inc, Minneapolis, MN
Northeast Nursing Center, Oklahoma City, OK
Northeast Ohio Development Center, Cleveland, OH
Northeast Residence Inc, White Bear Lake, MN
Northeast Respite Care, White Bear Lake, MN
Northern Cochise Nursing Home, Willcox, AZ
Northern Dutchess Hospital Skilled Nursing Facility, Rhinebeck, NY
Northern Itasca Health Care Center, Bigfork, MN
Northern Lights Manor Nursing Home, Washburn, WI
Northern Metropolitan Residential Health Care Facility Inc, Monsey, NY
Northern Pines Good Samaritan Center, Blackduck, MN
Northern Wisconsin Center for the Developmentally Disabled, Chippewa Falls, WI

Northfield Manor Health Care Facility, Louisville, KY
Northfield Manor Nursing Home, West Orange, NJ
Northfield Retirement Center, Northfield, MN
Northfield Villa Inc, Gering, NE
Northgate Care Center, Waukon, IA
Northgate Convalescent Hospital, San Rafael, CA
Northgate Manor, North Tonawanda, NY
Northgate Park Nursing Home, Florissant, MO
Northgate Rehabilitation Center, Seattle, WA
Northhampton County Home—Gracedale, Nazareth, PA
Northhaven Health Care Center, Knoxville, TN
Northland Manor, Jackman, ME
Northland Nursing Center, Detroit, MI
Northland Terrace Nursing & Rehabilitation Center, Columbus, OH
Northline Manor, Houston, TX
Northome Nursing Home, Northome, MN
Northridge Residence, Ortonville, MN
Northshore Healthcare Center, Houston, TX
Northshore Manor, Bothell, WA
Northshore Terrace, Waukegan, IL
Northside Convalescent Center, Atlanta, GA
Northside Haven Personal Care Home, Jackson, MS
Northside Manor Living Center, Mount Vernon, OH
Northside Nursing Center, Springfield, MO
Northside Nursing Center, Corsicana, TX
Northumberland County Mountain View Manor, Shamokin, PA
Northview Care Center, Falls City, NE
Northview Community, Pensacola, FL
Northview Development Center, Eastland, TX
Northview Nursing Home, Johnstown, OH
Northway Convalescent Center, Birmingham, AL
Northwest Care Center, Detroit, MI
Northwest Care Center, Wauseon, OH
Northwest Community Continuing Care Center, Arlington Heights, IL
Northwest Continuum Care Center, Longview, WA
Northwest Convalescent Center, Spokane, WA
Northwest Danish Home, Seattle, WA
Northwest Health Center, Milwaukee, WI
Northwest Home for the Aged, Chicago, IL
Northwest Iowa Health Center & Long-Term Care Facility, Sheldon, IA
Northwest Louisiana State School, Bossier City, LA
Northwest Manor Nursing Home, Indianapolis, IN
Northwest Mediplex, Austin, TX
Northwest Nursing Center, Oklahoma City, OK
Northwest Nursing & Convalescent Center, Baltimore, MD
Northwest Ohio Development Center, Toledo, OH
Northwest Progressive Care Center, Seattle, WA
Northwest Regional Intermediate Care Home, Rome, GA
Northwood Care Centre, Tacoma, WA
Northwood Convalescent Center, Lowell, MA
Northwood Deaconess Nursing Home, Northwood, ND
Northwood Good Samaritan Center, Jasper, IN
Northwood Healthcare Center, Marble Falls, TX
Northwood Manor Nursing Home, Carrollton, TX
Northwood Nursing Home, South Bend, IN
Northwood Nursing Home, Manchester, NH
Northwood Nursing Home, Philadelphia, PA
Northwoods Healthcare Center, Belvidere, IL
Northwoods Manor, Escanaba, MI
Northwoods Manor Annex, Escanaba, MI
Norton Sound Regional Hospital, Nome, AK
Nortonian Nursing Home, Rochester, NY
Norwalk Manor Care Center, Norwalk, IA

Norwalk Memorial Home, Norwalk, OH
Norway Nursing Home, Norway, ME
Norwegian Christian Home for the Aged, Brooklyn, NY
Norwegian Old Peoples Home, Boston, MA
Norwell Knoll Nursing Home, Norwell, MA
Norwichtown Convalescent Inc, Norwich, CT
Norwood Health Center, Marshfield, WI
Norwood Nursing Center, Huntington, IN
Norwood Nursing & Retirement Home, Norwood, MA
Norwood Park Home, Chicago, IL
Norworth Convalescent Center, Worthington, OH
Notre Dame Convalescent Home Inc, Norwalk, CT
Notre Dame Hills Living Center, Belleville, IL
Nottingham Manor, Dallas, TX
Nottingham Village, Northumberland, PA
Novi Care Center, Novi, MI
Nowata Nursing Home, Nowata, OK
Nu-Roc Nursing Home, Laona, WI
Nucare Convalescent Center, Laurel, MS
Nucare Convalescent Center, Dyersburg, TN
Nucare Convalescent Center, Humboldt, TN
Nucare Convalescent Center, Lexington, TN
Nucare Convalescent Center Inc, Hot Springs, AR
Nugent Convalescent Home, Inc, Hermitage, PA
Nursecare of Atlanta, Atlanta, GA
Nursecare of Shreveport, Shreveport, LA
Nursing Care Center of Bristol, Bristol, CT
Nursing Center Greenwood Methodist Home, Greenwood, SC
Nursing Center of Canton, Canton, IL
Nursing Home Center, Milledgeville, GA
Nursing Home of Arab Inc, Arab, AL
The Nursing Home of Boaz, Boaz, AL
Nursing Home of Eunice, Eunice, LA
The Nursing Home of Tallassee Inc, Tallassee, AL
Nutmeg Pavilion Healthcare, New London, CT
Nuuanu Hale Hospital, Honolulu, HI
Nyack Manor Nursing Home, Valley Cottage, NY
Nye General Hospital, Tonopah, NV
Nygaard Manor, Stoughton, WI
Oahe Manor, Gettysburg, SD
Oak Bluffs Nursing Center, Clearwater, FL
Oak Brook Nursing Center, Oak Brook, IL
Oak Cove Retirement & Health Center, Clearwater, FL
Oak Crest, DeKalb, IL
Oak Crest Care Center, Salem, OR
Oak Crest Inn, New Braunfels, TX
Oak Crest Manor Inc, Scituate, RI
Oak Crest Nursing Home Inc, Tuscumbia, AL
Oak Crest Residence, Elgin, IL
Oak Dale Manor, Sand Springs, OK
Oak Glen Care Center, McMinnville, OR
Oak Glen Home, Coal Valley, IL
Oak Grove Health Care Center, Oak Grove, MO
Oak Grove Manor, Niles, MI
Oak Grove Manor Inc, Idabel, OK
Oak Grove Nursing Home Inc, Groves, TX
Oak Grove Quality Care Nursing Center, Deshler, OH
Oak Grove Resident Treatment Center, Minneapolis, MN
Oak Grove Retirement Home, Duncan, MS
Oak Haven Nursing Home, Centerpoint, LA
Oak Haven Nursing Home, Boston, MA
Oak Haven Nursing Home, Palestine, TX
Oak Hill Care Center, Farmington, MI
Oak Hill Convalescent Center, Chesapeake, VA
Oak Hill Health Care Inc, Montgomery, AL
Oak Hill Home of Rest & Care, Greensburg, PA
Oak Hill Intermediate Care Home, College Park, GA
Oak Hill Manor Nursing Home, Ithaca, NY
Oak Hill Nursing Home, Middleboro, MA
Oak Hill Nursing Home Annex, Farmington, MI

Oak Hill Nursing Home Inc, Pawtucket, RI
Oak Hill Nursing Home Inc, Staunton, VA
Oak Hill Residence, Littleton, MA
Oak Hills Nursing Home, Lorain, OH
Oak Hills Nursing Home, Jones, OK
Oak Hollow Nursing Center, Middle Island, NY
Oak Island Skilled Nursing Facility, Revere, MA
Oak Knoll Nursing Home, Ferguson, MO
Oak Lawn Convalescent Home, Oak Lawn, IL
Oak Lea Nursing Home, Harrisonburg, VA
Oak Manor Health Care Center, Decatur, IL
Oak Manor Inc, Columbus, GA
Oak Manor Nursing Center, Booneville, AR
Oak Manor Nursing Center, Largo, FL
Oak Manor Nursing Center, Flatonia, TX
Oak Manor Nursing Home, Holyoke, MA
Oak Manor Nursing Home, McKenzie, TN
Oak Manor Nursing Home, Gladewater, TX
Oak Manor Nursing Home, Linden, TX
Oak Manor Nursing Home, Nacogdoches, TX
Oak Manor Nursing Home of Texarkana, Texarkana, TX
Oak Meadow Nursing Center Inc, Alexandria, VA
Oak Park, Oakwood Village, OH
Oak Park Care Center, Nevada, IA
Oak Park Care Center, Lake Charles, LA
Oak Park Convalescent & Geriatric Center, Oak Park, IL
Oak Park Convalescent Hospital, Pleasant Hill, CA
Oak Park Manor, Kansas City, MO
Oak Park Nursing Center Inc, Grass Valley, CA
Oak Park Nursing Home Inc, Pine Bluff, AR
Oak Park Professional Care Center, Saint Louis, MO
Oak Pavilion Nursing Center, Cincinnati, OH
Oak Ridge Acres, Hiawatha, KS
Oak Ridge Care Center, Franksville, WI
Oak Ridge Conv Center, Bloomfield, CT
Oak Ridge Convalescent Center, Richmond, IN
Oak Ridge Health Care Center, Oak Ridge, TN
Oak Ridge Manor, Durant, OK
Oak Ridge Manor Nursing Center, Wayne, NJ
Oak Ridge Manor Nursing Home, Kansas City, MO
Oak Ridge Nursing Home, El Dorado, AR
Oak Springs of Warrenton, Warrenton, VA
Oak Terrace Nursing Home, Minnetonka, MN
Oak Terrace Retirement, Springfield, IL
Oak Tree Convalescent Center Inc, Cincinnati, OH
Oak Tree Convalescent Hospital, Oakland, CA
Oak Tree Lodge, Gainesville, TX
Oak Valley Nursing Home, Macon, GA
Oak View Care Center, Williston, FL
Oak View Home Inc, Waverly Hall, GA
Oak View Manor Inc, Ozark, AL
Oak View Nursing Home, Summerville, GA
Oak Villa Health Care, Hillsboro, OR
Oak Village Care Center, Baldwin, MI
Oak Village Inc, Oaktown, IN
The Oak Woods, Mer Rouge, LA
Oakcliff Convalescent Home Inc, Waterbury, CT
Oakcrest Manor, Austin, TX
Oakdale Convalescent Hospital, Oakdale, CA
Oakdale Nursing Home, Judsonia, AR
Oakdale Nursing Home, West Boylston, MA
Oakes Manor Good Samaritan Center, Oakes, ND
Margaret Clark Oakfield Convalescent Center—Columbus, Columbus, OH
Margaret Clark Oakfield Convalescent Center, Washington Court House, OH
Oakhaven Inc, Darlington, SC
Oakhaven Manor, Warsaw, MO
Oakhaven Nursing Center, Richmond, KS
Oakhaven Nursing Center, Arlington, TX
Oakhurst Convalescent Center, Elma, WA
Oakhurst Manor, Ocala, FL
Oakland Care Center, Royal Oak, MI
Oakland Care Center, Oakland, NJ

Oakland County Medical Care Facility, Pontiac, MI
Oakland Geriatric Village, Pontiac, MI
Oakland Heights, Oakland, NE
Oakland Manor, Milwaukee, WI
Oakland Manor Nursing Homes, Oakland, IA
Oakland Nursing Center, Hillsboro, OH
Oakland Park Nursing Home, Thief River Falls, MN
Oaklawn Health Care Center, Mankato, MN
Oakley Manor, Oakley, KS
Oakmont East Nursing Center, Greenville, SC
Oakmont Manor, Flatwoods, KY
Oakmont North Nursing Center, Travelers Rest, SC
Oakmont Nursing Center, Oakmont, PA
Oakmont Nursing Home, Greenville, SC
Oakmont of Union, Union, SC
Oaknoll Retirement Residence, Iowa City, IA
Oakridge Conv Home Inc, Hillside, IL
Oakridge Convalescent Hospital, Oakland, CA
Oakridge Gardens Nursing Center Inc, Menasha, WI
Oakridge Home, Westlake, OH
Oakridge Home Inc, Wewoka, OK
Oakridge of Plattsburg, Plattsburg, MO
The Oaks, Petaluma, CA
The Oaks, Topeka, KS
The Oaks Care Center Inc, Memphis, TN
Oaks Convalescent Center, Lima, OH
Oaks Lodge Rest Home Inc, Fort Smith, AR
The Oaks Nursing & Rehabilitation Center, Wyncote, PA
The Oaks Nursing Home Inc, Marshallville, GA
Oaks Nursing Home, Burnet, TX
The Oaks Nursing & Rehabilitation Center, Wyncote, PA
Oakton Nursing Home Inc, Oakton, VA
Oakton Pavillion Inc, Des Plaines, IL
Oakview, Lebanon, PA
Oakview Care Center, South Amboy, NJ
Oakview Care Center, Durand, WI
Oakview Convalescent Hospital, Glendora, CA
Oakview Convalescent Hospital, Tujunga, CA
Oakview Home, Conrad, IA
Oakview Manor Health Care Center, Calvert City, KY
Oakview Manor Nursing Home, Hubbard, TX
Oakview Medical Care Facility, Ludington, MI
Oakview Nursing Home, Baldwyn, MS
Oakview Nursing Home, Cincinnati, OH
Oakville Health Care Center, Memphis, TN
Oakwood Convalescent Home, Webster, MA
Oakwood Health Care Center Inc, Walterboro, SC
Oakwood Health Care Center Inc, Lewisburg, TN
Oakwood Intermediate Care Facility, Somerset, KY
Oakwood Knoll Nursing Home, Kernersville, NC
Oakwood Lodge of Natchez, Natchez, MS
Oakwood Lutheran Homes Association Inc, Madison, WI
Oakwood Manor, Bucyrus, OH
Oakwood Manor, Bedford, VA
Oakwood Manor Corporation, Clear Lake, IA
Oakwood Manor Nursing Home, Vidor, TX
Oakwood Nursing Center, Eustis, FL
Oakwood Nursing Home, Manchester, MA
Oakwood Park Su Casa, Tampa, FL
Oakwood Place, Texarkana, AR
Oakwood Residence, Inc, Minnetonka, MN
Oakwood Terrace Inc, Evanston, IL
Oakwood Villa Care Center, Hutchinson, KS
Oakwood Village Nurse Care Center Inc, Lafayette, LA
O'Berry Center, Goldsboro, NC
Obion County Rest Home, Union City, TN
O'Brien Memorial Nursing Home, Masury, OH
O'Brien's Rest Home, Rapid City, SD
Ocala Geriatric Center Inc, Ocala, FL
Ocala Health Care Center, Ocala, FL
Ocean Convalescent Center, Lakewood, NJ

Ocean Grove Nursing Home, Ocean Grove, NJ
Ocean Park Nursing Home, Seaside, OR
Ocean Point Health Care Center, Somers Point, NJ
Ocean Springs Nursing Center, Ocean Springs, MS
Ocean Trail Convalescent Center Inc, Southport, NC
Ocean View Convalescent Center, Long Beach, WA
Oceana County Medical Care Facility, Hart, MI
Oceanside Convalescent & Rehabilitation Center, Atlantic City, NJ
Oceanside Nursing Home, Tybee Island, GA
Oceanside Nursing Home, Quincy, MA
Oceanview Care Center of Care Centers West, Bandon, OR
Ocean-View Nursing Home, New Smyrna Beach, FL
Oceanview Nursing Home, Lubec, ME
Oceanview Nursing Home, Far Rockaway, NY
Ochoco Nursing Home, Prineville, OR
OCI-Thompson Avenue Group Home, West Saint Paul, MN
Oconee Geriatric Center Inc, Seneca, SC
Oconee Health Care Center, Oconee, GA
Octavia Manor Inc, Colfax, IL
Odd Fellow & Rebekah Home, Jackson, MI
Odd Fellow & Rebekah Nursing Home, Ennis, TX
Odd Fellow & Rebekah Nursing Home Inc, Lockport, NY
Odd Fellow-Rebekah Home, Mattoon, IL
Odd Fellows Home, Greensburg, IN
Odd Fellows Home, Liberty, MO
Odd Fellows Home, Dell Rapids, SD
Odd Fellows Home of California, Saratoga, CA
Odd Fellows Home of Massachusetts, Worcester, MA
Odd Fellows Home of Pennsylvania Inc, Middletown, PA
Odd Fellows Rest Home, Checotah, OK
Odell Nursing Center, Concord, NC
Odin Care Center, Odin, IL
Oelwein Care Center, Oelwein, IA
Ogden Care Center North, Ogden, UT
Ogden Manor, Ogden, IA
Ogemaw Valley Medical Facility, Rose City, MI
Ohesson Manor, Lewistown, PA
Ohio District Council Nursing, Zanesville, OH
Ohio Eastern Star Home, Mount Vernon, OH
Ohio Extended Care Center, Lorain, OH
The Ohio Masonic Home, Springfield, OH
Ohio Pythian Sisters Home of Medina, Medina, OH
Ohio Residential Services, Broadview Heights, OH
Ohio Valley Health Care Inc, Parkersburg, WV
Ohio Valley Manor Convalescent Center, Ripley, OH
Oil City Presbyterian Home, Oil City, PA
Ojai Valley Community Hospital—Skilled Nursing Unit, Ojai, CA
Okemah Pioneer Nursing Home Inc, Okemah, OK
Oklahoma Christian Home Inc, Edmond, OK
Oklahoma County Home, Oklahoma City, OK
Oklahoma Methodist Home for the Aged Inc, Tulsa, OK
Okmulgee Terrace Nursing Home Inc, Okmulgee, OK
Olathe Good Samaritan Center, Olathe, KS
Olathe Nursing Home, Olathe, KS
Old Capital Inn Convalescent & Nursing Home, Louisville, GA
Old Colony Road Rest Home, Norton, MA
Old Court Nursing Center, Randallstown, MD
Old Ladies Home, Jackson, MS
Old Masons' Home of Kentucky, Shelbyville, KY
Old Orchard Manor, Skokie, IL
Olds Manor, Grand Rapids, MI
Mary M Olin Clinic, Penny Farms, FL

Olive Vista—A Center for Problems of Living, Pomona, CA
Olivette Nursing Home, Elgin, IL
Olivewood Convalescent Hospital, Colton, CA
Olivia Healthcare Center Inc, Olivia, MN
Olmsted Manor Skilled Nursing Center, North Olmsted, OH
Olney Care Center, Olney, IL
Olney Nursing Center, Olney, TX
Olsen Manor Nursing Home, Amarillo, TX
Julia Olson Rest Home, Belle Fourche, SD
Olympia Convalescent Hospital, Los Angeles, CA
Olympia Manor, Olympia, WA
Olympic Crest Convalescent Center, Seattle, WA
Olympic Health Care Inc, Sequim, WA
Olympus Care Center, Salt Lake City, UT
Omaha Manor Inc, Omaha, NE
Omaha Nursing Home Inc, Omaha, NE
Omni Manor, Youngstown, OH
Omro Care Center, Omro, WI
Onalaska Care Center, Onalaska, WI
Onawa Home for the Aged Inc, Onawa, IA
One-Eighty Court, Keene, NH
One-Fifty-One Court, Keene, NH
Oneida City Hospital—Extended Care Facility, Oneida, NY
Oneida County Nursing Home, Malad, ID
Oneida Nursing Home, Oneida, WI
O'Neill Senior Citizen's Home, O'Neill, NE
Oneonta Manor Nursing Home, Oneonta, AL
Oneonta-Richmond Inc, Oneonta, NY
Ontario County Health Facility, Canandaigua, NY
Ontario Nursing Home Inc, Ontario, CA
Ontonagon Memorial Hospital, Ontonagon, MI
Oosterman Rest Home, Melrose, MA
Oosterman Rest Home, Wakefield, MA
Opelika Nursing Home, Opelika, AL
Opelousas Health Care Inc, Opelousas, LA
Open Arms Nursing Home Inc, Winchendon, MA
Opportunity Foundation of Central Oregon, Redmond, OR
Opportunity Homes Inc, Lisbon, OH
Opportunity House, Champaign, IL
Opportunity House Inc, Sycamore, IL
Opportunity Manor II, Saint Cloud, MN
Orange County Home & Infirmary, Goshen, NY
Orange County Nursing Home and Home for Adults, Orange, VA
Orange Health Care Center, Orange, CT
Orange Home Inc, Hatboro, PA
Orange Park Care Center, Orange Park, FL
Orange Village Care Center Inc, Masury, OH
Orange West Convalescent Hospital, Buena Park, CA
Orangeburg Convalescent Hospital, Modesto, CA
Orangeburg Nursing Home, Orangeburg, SC
Orangegrove Rehabilitation Hospital, Garden Grove, CA
Orangetree Convalescent Hospital, Riverside, CA
Orangevale Convalescent Hospital, Orangevale, CA
Orangeview Convalescent Hospital, Anaheim, CA
Orangewood Health Center, Phoenix, AZ
Orchard Crest Care Center, Sandy, OR
Orchard Gables, Hollywood, CA
Orchard Hill Nursing Home, Omaha, NE
Orchard Lane Nursing Facility, Baldwin City, KS
Orchard Manor Inc, Grove City, PA
Orchard Manor—North, Lancaster, WI
Orchard Manor Nursing Home & Health Related Facility, Medina, NY
Orchard Manor—South, Lancaster, WI
Orchard Park, Tacoma, WA
Orchard Park Health Care Center Inc, Orchard Park, NY
Orchard Village, Skokie, IL
Orchards Villa Nursing Center, Lewiston, ID
Oregon City Nursing Home, Oregon City, OR

Oregon Health Care Center, Oregon, MO
Oregon Manor Ltd, Oregon, WI
Oregon-Washington Pythian Home, Vancouver, WA
Orinda Rehabilitation & Convalescent Hospital, Orinda, CA
Orlando Health Care Center, Orlando, FL
Orlando Lutheran Towers, Orlando, FL
Orlando Memorial Convalescent Center, Orlando, FL
Orleans Convalescent & Retirement Home, Orleans, MA
Orleans County Nursing Home, Albion, NY
Ormond Beach Health Care Center, Ormond Beach, FL
Orofino Care Center Inc, Orofino, ID
Orono Nursing Home, Orono, ME
Oroville Community Convalescent Hospital, Oroville, CA
Orrington Group Home, Orrington, ME
Orsini Boarding Home, Wilmington, DE
Orthodox Jewish Home for the Aged, Cincinnati, OH
Ortonville Nursing Home, Ortonville, MI
Orvilla Inc, Eagan, MN
Osage Beach Health Care Center, Osage Beach, MO
Osage Manor Inc, Osage City, KS
Osage Manor Nursing & Care Center, Eldon, MO
Osage Nursing Home, Nowata, OK
Osawatomie Rest Home, Osawatomie, KS
Osceola Good Samaritan Center, Osceola, NE
Osceola Inn, Clearwater, FL
Osceola Leisure Manor, Osceola, IA
Osceola Nursing Home, Osceola, AR
Osceola Nursing Home, Ocilla, GA
Oshkosh Care Center, Oshkosh, WI
Osnabrock Good Samaritan Center, Osnabrock, ND
Osseo Area Municipal Hospital & Nursing Home, Osseo, WI
Osseo Health Care, Osseo, MN
Ossian Senior Hospice Inc, Ossian, IA
Ossipee House, Center Ossipee, NH
Ostrander Nursing Home, Ostrander, MN
Oswego Guest Home Inc, Oswego, KS
Oswego Hospital Extended Care Facility, Oswego, NY
Othello Convalescent Center, Othello, WA
Otsego County Memorial—Intermediate Care Facility, Gaylord, MI
Ottawa Care Center, Ottawa, IL
Ottawa County Riverview Nursing Home, Oak Harbor, OH
Ottawa Retirement Village, Ottawa, KS
Otter Tail Nursing Home, Battle Lake, MN
Otterbein Home, Lebanon, OH
Otterbein Portage Valley, Pemberville, OH
Ottumwa Manor Nursing Home, Ottumwa, IA
Ouachita Convalescent Center, Camden, AR
Our House of Minnesota I, Saint Paul, MN
Our House/Western Medical Association for Retarded Citizens, Farmington, ME
Our Island Home, Nantucket, MA
Our Lady of Angels Retirement, Joliet, IL
Our Lady of Compassion Care Center, Anchorage, AK
Our Lady of Fatima Villa, Saratoga, CA
Our Lady of Good Counsel Home, Saint Paul, MN
Our Lady of Hope Residence-Little Sisters of the Poor, Latham, NY
Our Lady of Mercy Convalescent Home Inc, Hubbell, MI
Our Lady of Mercy Home, Kansas City, MO
Our Lady of Perpetual Help Home, Atlanta, GA
Our Lady of Victory Nursing Home, Bourbonnais, IL
Our Lady's Haven, Fairhaven, MA
Our Lady's Residence, Pleasantville, NJ
Outagamie County Health Center, Appleton, WI
Outreach-Bloomington, Bloomington, MN
Outreach Group Homes Inc Plymouth West, Plymouth, MN

Outreach Northeast Group Home, Minneapolis, MN
Outwood-ICF/MR, Dawson Springs, KY
Overlook Castle Nursing Home, Millersburg, OH
Overlook House, Cleveland, OH
Overlook Medical Clinic Inc, New Wilmington, PA
Overlook Nursing Home, Bellville, OH
Overlook Nursing Home, Burrillville, RI
Overton County Nursing Home, Livingston, TN
Ovid Convalescent Manor, Ovid, MI
Owatonna Health Care Center, Owatonna, MN
Owen Care Center—Pittsfield, Pittsfield, IL
Owen County Home, Spencer, IN
The Ruth Owen Family Care Home, Commerce City, CO
Owens Home, Montgomery City, MO
Owensville Convalescent Center, Owensville, IN
Owenton Manor Inc, Owenton, KY
Owsley County Health Care Center, Booneville, KY
Oxford Convalescent Home, Oxford, WI
Oxford Manor Nursing Home, Haverhill, MA
Oxford Manor Nursing Home, Dayton, OH
Oxford Manor, The Steward Home & The Woods at Oxford Manor, Oxford, PA
Oxford Nursing Home, Brooklyn, NY
Oxford View Nursing Center, Oxford, OH
Oxnard Manor Convalescent Hospital, Oxnard, CA
Ozanam Hall of Queens Nursing Home Inc, Bayside, NY
Ozark Care Center Inc, Osage Beach, MO
Ozark Nursing & Care Center, Ozark, MO
Ozark Nursing Center, West Plains, MO
Ozark Nursing Home, Fredericktown, MO
Ozark Nursing Home Inc, Ozark, AL
Ozark Nursing Home Inc, Ozark, AR
Ozark Riverview Manor, Ozark, MO
The Ozarks Methodist Manor, Marionville, MO
Pacific Care Convalescent Hospital, Oakland, CA
Pacific Convalescent Hospital, Eureka, CA
Pacific Gardens Health Care Center, Fresno, CA
Pacific Grove Convalescent Hospital, Pacific Grove, CA
Pacific Haven Convalescent Home, Garden Grove, CA
Pacific Park Convalescent Hospital, San Bernardino, CA
Pacific Regency/Taft, Taft, CA
Pacifica Convalescent Hospital, Pacifica, CA
Padgett Nursing Home, Tampa, FL
Padre Pio Health Care Center, Dubuque, IA
Paintsville Health Care Center, Paintsville, KY
Paisley House for Aged Women, Youngstown, OH
Pajaro Convalescent Hospital, Watsonville, CA
Pajaro West Convalescent Hospital, Watsonville, CA
Palatine Nursing Home, Palatine Bridge, NY
Palemon Gaskin Memorial Nursing Home, Ocilla, GA
Palestine Nursing Center, Palestine, TX
Palisade Manor, Garretson, SD
Palisade Nursing Home, Guttenberg, NJ
Palisades Nursing Home, Palisade, CO
Palm Beach County Home & General Care Facility, West Palm Beach, FL
Palm Court Nursing & Rehabilitation Center, Fort Lauderdale, FL
Palm Crest Bellaire Nursing Home, Cleveland, OH
Palm Crest East Nursing Home, Elyria, OH
Palm Crest West Nursing Home Inc, Elyria, OH
Palm Gardens Nursing Home, Brooklyn, NY
Palm Grove Care Center, Garden Grove, CA
Palm Manor Nursing Home Inc, Chelmsford, MA

Palm Shores Retirement Center, Saint Petersburg, FL
Palm Springs Healthcare, Palm Springs, CA
Palm Tree Nursing Home, Brooklyn, NY
Palm Vista Care Center, Baldwin Park, CA
Palmcrest Medallion Convalescent Hospital, Long Beach, CA
Palmcrest North Convalescent Hospital, Long Beach, CA
Palmer Home Inc, Dover, DE
Palmer House Healthcare Nursing Home, Palmer, MA
Palmer Terrace Nursing Center, Chicago, IL
Palmetto Convalescent Center Inc, Simpsonville, SC
Palmetto Extended Care Facility, Miami, FL
Palms Convalescent Home, Miami, FL
Palms Health Care Center, Sebring, FL
Palmyra Intermediate Care Center & New Dawn, Palmyra, TN
Palmyra Nursing Home, Palmyra, PA
Palmyra Nursing Home Inc, Albany, GA
Palo Duro Convalescent Home Inc, Claude, TX
Palo Pinto Nursing Center, Mineral Wells, TX
Palomar Convalescent Hospital, Inglewood, CA
Palomares Center, Pomona, CA
Palouse Nursing Center, Colfax, WA
Pam Group Home IMR, Puyallup, WA
Pampa Nursing Center, Pampa, TX
Pamplico Road Residence, Florence, SC
Pana Health Care Center, Pana, IL
Panama City Developmental Center, Panama City, FL
Panama City Nursing Center, Panama City, FL
Panola Nursing Home, Carthage, TX
Panorama Convalescent & Rehabilitation Center, Lacy, WA
Panorama Residential Care, Bowling Green, KY
Paoli Nursing Home, Paoli, IN
Papillion Manor Inc, Papillion, NE
Paquette Home Inc, Central Falls, RI
Paradise Convalescent Hospital, Los Angeles, CA
Paradise Convalescent Hospital, Paradise, CA
Paradise Hills Convalescent Center, San Diego, CA
Paradise Oaks Quality Care Nursing Center, Cloverdale, OH
Paradise Valley Health Care Center, National City, CA
Paradise Valley Living Center, Belle Plaine, KS
Paradise Villa Convalescent Center, Moscow, ID
Paradise Village, Medina, OH
Paragould Nursing Center, Paragould, AR
Paramount Convalescent Hospital, Paramount, CA
Paramus Health Care Center, Paramus, NJ
Parc Center Apartments, Saint Petersburg, FL
PARC Cottage, Saint Petersburg, FL
PARC Home, Bellwood, IL
Margaret R Pardee Memorial Skilled Nursing Facility, Hendersonville, NC
Parent's Volunteer Association, Cleveland, OH
Louise Parham Health Care Complex, Oxford, NC
Paris Healthcare Center, Paris, IL
Paris Manor Nursing Center, Paris, TN
Paris Retirement Inn Inc, Paris, AR
Park Avenue Baptist Home, Denver, CO
Park Avenue Health Care Center, Bridgeport, CT
Park Avenue Health Care Home, Herrin, IL
Park Avenue Home, Faribault, MN
Park Avenue Nurs, Convalescent & Retirement Home, Arlington, MA
Barbara Park Convalescent Center, Middletown, OH
Park Central Convalescent Hospital, Fremont, CA
Park Dale Rest Home, Boston, MA
Park Forest Care Center, Portland, OR
Park Geriatric Village, Highland Park, MI

Park Haven Care Center, Smithton, IL
Park Haven Nursing Center Inc, Greenville, TX
Park Highlands, Athens, TX
Park Hill Manor Nursing Home, Worcester, MA
Park Home Nursing Home, Rochester, NY
Park Imperial Lodge, Lawndale, CA
Park Lane Manor, Altus, OK
Park Lane Nursing Center, Evergreen Park, IL
Park Lane Nursing Home, Scott City, KS
Park Lawn Center, Worth, IL
Park Lawn Home, Manitowoc, WI
Park Manor, Waterbury, CT
Park Manor, Park Falls, WI
Park Manor Care Center, Muskegon Heights, MI
Park Manor Convalescent Center, Walla Walla, WA
Park Manor Health Care Center, Milwaukee, WI
Park Manor Nursing & Convalescent Home, Rawlins, WY
Park Manor Nursing Home, Liberty, IN
Park Manor Nursing Home, Baltimore, MD
Park Manor Nursing Home, Pepperell, MA
Park Manor Nursing Home, Bloomfield, NJ
Park Manor Nursing Home, Oklahoma City, OK
Park Marino Convalescent Center, Pasadena, CA
Park Marion Nursing Centre, Brookline, MA
Park Merritt Intermediate Care, Oakland, CA
Park Nursing Center, Taylor, MI
Park Nursing & Convalescent Center, Saint Louis Park, MN
Park Nursing Home, Rockaway Park, NY
Park Nursing Home Inc, Chicago, IL
Park Place Convalescent Hospital, Pomona, CA
Park Place Health Care Center, Great Falls, MT
Park Place Nursing Home, Palestine, TX
Park Plaza Nursing Center, Groesbeck, TX
Park Plaza Nursing Center, San Angelo, TX
Park Plaza Nursing Home, Mart, TX
Park Plaza Nursing Home, Whitney, TX
Park Pleasant Inc, Philadelphia, PA
Park Point Manor, Duluth, MN
Park Rehabilitation Center, Euclid, OH
Park Ridge Care Center Inc, Seattle, WA
Park Ridge Healthcare Center, Park Ridge, IL
Park Ridge Manor, Des Moines, IA
Park Ridge Nursing Home, Rochester, NY
Park River Estates Care Center, Coon Rapids, MN
Park River Good Samaritan Center, Park River, ND
Park Rose Care Center, Tacoma, WA
Park Royal Medical Center, Longview, WA
Park Shore, Seattle, WA
Park Strathmoor, Rockford, IL
Park Street Group Home, Houlton, ME
Park Superior Healthcare, Newport Beach, CA
Park Sutter Convalescent Hospital, Sacramento, CA
Park Terrace Convalescent Center, Tulsa, OK
Park Terrace Resident Center, Florissant, MO
Park View Convalescent Center, Paris, TX
Park View Health Care Center, Carney's Point, NJ
Park View Health Center—Pleasant Acres, Winnebago, WI
Park View Health Center—Rehab Pavilion, Winnebago, WI
Park View Healthcare Inc, Parkersburg, WV
Park View Home Inc, Woodville, WI
Park View Manor, Aroma Park, IL
Park View Manor, Sac City, IA
Park View Manor Inc, Massillon, OH
Park View Nursing Center, San Jose, CA
Park View Nursing Center, Edgerton, OH
Park View Nursing Home, Portland, OR
Park View Nursing Home, Providence, RI
Park View Nursing Home, Bountiful, UT
Park View Nursing Home Inc, Massapequa, NY
Park Villa, Clyde, KS

Park Villa Convalescent Center, Tucson, AZ
Park Village Health Care Center, Dover, OH
Park Vista Convalescent Hospital, Los Angeles, CA
Park Vista Retirement Community, Youngstown, OH
Park West Care Center, Seattle, WA
Parkdale Manor Care Center, Maryville, MO
Parke County Nursing Home Inc, Rockville, IN
The Francis E Parker Memorial Home, New Brunswick, NJ
The Francis E Parker Memorial Home, Piscataway, NJ
Sophia Huntington Parker Home, Medina, OH
Parkhill East Nursing Home, Locust Grove, OK
Parkhill North Nursing Home, Salina, OK
Parkhill Skilled Nursing Facility, Chillicothe, IL
Parkhill South Nursing Home, Locust Grove, OK
Parkland Care Center, Tacoma, WA
Parkland Convalescent Hospital Inc, San Leandro, CA
Parkland Health Facility, Wentworth, WI
Parkland Manor, Prague, OK
Parklane Nursing Home Inc, Bloomfield, NJ
Parkmont Care Center, Fremont, CA
Parkrose Nursing Home, Portland, OR
Park's Memorial Home, Auburn, IL
Parkshore Manor Health Care Center, Brooklyn, NY
Parkside Care Center, Little Chute, WI
Parkside Gardens, Burbank, IL
Parkside Health Care Inc, Seattle, WA
Parkside Homes Inc, Hillsboro, KS
Parkside House, Lakewood, CO
Parkside Lutheran Home, Lisbon, ND
Parkside Manor, Stuart, NE
Parkside Manor Convalescent Center, Wenatchee, WA
Parkside Meadows Inc, Saint Charles, MO
Parkside Nursing Care Center, Union Gap, WA
Parkside Rest Home, Peabody, MA
Parkside Special Care Center, El Cajon, CA
Parkside Towers, Saint Louis, MO
Parkview Acres Convalescent Center, Dillon, MT
Parkview Care Center, Fairfield, IA
Parkview Care Center, Fremont, OH
Parkview Care Center, Bryant, SD
Parkview Care Center Inc, Milwaukee, WI
Parkview Colonial Manor, O'Fallon, IL
Parkview Convalescent Center, Paducah, KY
Parkview Convalescent Center Inc, Evansville, IN
Parkview Convalescent Centre, Elwood, IN
Parkview Convalescent Hospital, Anaheim, CA
Parkview Convalescent Hospital, Hayward, CA
Parkview Convalescent Unit, Dyersburg, TN
Parkview East Nursing & Conv Center, Aurora, IL
Parkview Gardens Care Center, Waterloo, IA
Parkview Guest Care Center, Winnfield, LA
Parkview Haven, Coleridge, NE
Parkview Haven, Deshler, NE
Parkview Haven Retirement Home, Francesville, IN
Parkview Home, Frankfort, IN
Parkview Home, Wayland, IA
Parkview Home, Belview, MN
Parkview Home, Volga, SD
Parkview Home Inc, Dodge, NE
Parkview Home of Freeport IL Inc, Freeport, IL
Parkview Julian Convalescent Hospital, Bakersfield, CA
Parkview Manor, Wellman, IA
Parkview Manor, Macksville, KS
Parkview Manor, Walters, OK
Parkview Manor, Weimar, TX
Parkview Manor Care Center, Woodward, IA
Parkview Manor Care Center, Osborne, KS

Parkview Manor Inc, Reinbeck, IA
Parkview Manor Nursing Center, Green Bay, WI
Parkview Manor Nursing Home, Indianapolis, IN
Parkview Manor Nursing Home, Ellsworth, MN
Parkview Manor Nursing Home, Dayton, OH
Parkview Manor Nursing Home—Blytheville, Blytheville, AR
Parkview Manor Nursing Home Inc, Denver, CO
Parkview Medical Recovery Center Inc, New Haven, CT
Parkview Nursing Center, Wilmington, DE
Parkview Nursing Home, West Frankfort, IL
Parkview Nursing Home, Higginsville, MO
Parkview Nursing Home, Bronx, NY
Parkview Nursing Home, Waco, TX
Parkview Nursing Home—Fort Smith, Fort Smith, AR
Parkview Nursing Home Inc, Shawnee, OK
Parkview Nursing Home Inc, Ripon, WI
Parkview of Texarkana, Texarkana, AR
Parkview Real Convalescent Hospital, Bakersfield, CA
Parkview Skilled of Hope, Hope, AR
Parkview Terrace/HCR, Platteville, WI
Parkview Village Ltd, Huntsville, AL
Parkway Care Home, Edwardsville, KS
Parkway Manor, Fulton, KY
Parkway Manor Care Center, Lubbock, TX
Parkway Manor Health Care Center, Saint Paul, MN
Parkway Manor Nursing Home, Everett, MA
Parkway Manor Nursing Home, Lubbock, TX
Parkway Medical Center, Louisville, KY
Parkway North Care Center, Battle Ground, WA
Parkway Nursing Center, Snohomish, WA
Parkway Nursing Home, Pinellas Park, FL
Parkway Nursing Home, Boston, MA
Parkway Parke Nursing Home, Hamilton, OH
Parkway Pavilion Healthcare, Enfield, CT
Parkway Rest Home Inc, Allentown, PA
Parkway Terrace Nursing Home, Wheaton, IL
Parkwell Nursing Home, Boston, MA
Parkwood Development Center, Valdosta, GA
Parkwood Health Care Center, Chattanooga, TN
Parkwood Health Care Inc, Lebanon, IN
Parkwood Health Facility Inc, Phenix City, AL
Parkwood Nursing Home, Columbus, OH
Parma Care Center, Parma, OH
Parmiter Nursing Home, Malta, OH
Margaret S Parmly Residence, Chisago City, MN
Parrott Avenue Home, Portsmouth, NH
Parrott's Home, Lynn, IN
Parr's Rest Home, Louisville, KY
Parsons Good Samaritan Center, Parsons, KS
Parsons Presbyterian Manor, Parsons, KS
Pasadena Care Center, Pasadena, TX
Pasadena Manor, South Pasadena, FL
Pasco Nursing Center, Dade City, FL
Paseo Nursing Home, Kansas City, MO
Paso Robles Convalescent Hospital, Paso Robles, CA
Passaic Care Center, Haskell, NJ
Passavant Retirement & Health Center, Zellenople, PA
Passport, Rhinelander, WI
Patchogue Nursing Center, Patchogue, NY
Patenaude Rest Home, Derby, VT
Patio Lodge Nursing Home, Baton Rouge, LA
Patrician Nursing Center Inc, North Royalton, OH
Patrick Henry Healthcare Center, Newport News, VA
Patterson Health Center, Columbus, OH
A Holly Patterson Home, Uniondale, NY
Patterson Terrace Care Center, Mesa, AZ
Patterson's Pleasant View Personal Care Home, Shepherdsville, KY
Paulding Medical Nursing, Dallas, GA
Pauline Home for the Aged, Columbus, OH
Pauls Run, Philadelphia, PA

Pauls Valley Health Care Facility, Pauls Valley, OK
Pavilion Health Care Center, Louisville, KY
Pavilion Health Care Center of Valparaiso, Valparaiso, IN
Pavilion Health Care of Covington, Covington, KY
Pavilion Healthcare South, Peoria, IL
Pavilion North Healthcare Inc, Peoria, IL
Pavilion Nursing Homne, McKinney, TX
Pavilion Oaks, Peoria, IL
Pavilion West Health Care Center, Peoria, IL
Pawhuska Nursing Home, Pawhuska, OK
Pawnee Care Center, Pawnee, OK
Pawnee Manor Inc, Pawnee City, NE
Pawtucket Institute for Health Services, Pawtucket, RI
Pawtuxet Village Nursing Home, Warwick, RI
Faxton Sunset St Luke's Health Related Facility & Nursing Home Inc, Utica, NY
Payette Lakes Care Center, McCall, ID
Paynesville Community Hospital/Koronis Manor, Paynesville, MN
Paynesville Good Samaritan Center, Paynesville, MN
Payson Care Center, Payson, AZ
Peabody Home, Franklin, NH
Peabody Manor Inc, Appleton, WI
Peabody Memorial Nursing Home Inc, Peabody, KS
Peabody Retirement Community, North Manchester, IN
Peace Memorial Home, Evergreen Park, IL
Peach Belt Nursing Home, Warner Robins, GA
Peach Residential Care Facility, Flat River, MO
Pearl River County Hospital-Nurs Home, Poplarville, MS
Pearlview Extended Care & Nursing Home, Akron, OH
Pearlview Nursing Home, Brunswick, OH
Pearsall Manor, Pearsall, TX
Pecan Grove Training Center, Alexandria, LA
Pecan Lane, Florence, SC
Pecan Manor 1, Milledgeville, GA
Pecan Manor 3, Milledgeville, GA
Peck's Convalescent Home, Honesdale, PA
Pecos Nursing Home, Pecos, TX
Pecos Valley Nursing Home, Fort Sumner, NM
Pedersen Nursing Home Inc, Seattle, WA
Pedone Nursing Center, Maple Heights, OH
Pekin Conv Center, Pekin, IL
Pekrul Manor, Enid, OK
Peleske Group Home, Dent, MN
Pelham House Nursing Home, Newton, MA
Pelham Parkway Nursing Home, Pelham, GA
Pelham Parkway Nursing Home, Bronx, NY
Pelican Lake Health Care Center, Ashby, MN
Pelican Rapids Good Samaritan Center, Pelican Rapids, MN
Pelican Valley Health Center, Pelican Rapids, MN
Pella Community Hospital, Pella, IA
Pellcare, Winston-Salem, NC
Pellcare Nursing Home, Hickory, NC
Pemberton Manor Nursing Home, Greenwood, MS
Pembina County Memorial Nursing Home, Cavalier, ND
Pembina Trail Group Home Inc, Wadena, MN
Pemiscot County Memorial Hospital Long-Term Care Unit, Hayti, MO
Pend Oreille Pines Nursing Home, Newport, WA
Pender Care Centre, Pender, NE
Pendleton Nursing Home, Franklin, WV
Penfield Nursing Home, Penfield, NY
Penick Memorial Home, Southern Pines, NC
Peninsula General Nursing Home, Far Rockaway, NY
Peninsula Rehabilitation Center, Lomita, CA
Penn Yan Manor Nursing Home Inc, Penn Yan, NY
Pennhurst Modular Home Community, Spring City, PA

Pennknoll Village Nursing Home, Everett, PA
Pennsburg Manor, Pennsburg, PA
Pennswood Village, Newtown, PA
Pennsylvania Memorial Home, Brookville, PA
Pennsylvania Soldiers' & Sailors' Home, Erie, PA
Penny Pack Manor Nursing Home, Philadelphia, PA
Pennyrile Home, Hopkinsville, KY
Penobscot Nursing Home, Penobscot, ME
Penobscot Valley Nursing Home, Brewer, ME
Pensacola Health Care Facility, Pensacola, FL
People Inc—Dayton House, Saint Paul, MN
Peoples Child Care Residence, Saint Paul, MN
People's Memorial Hospital Nursing Care Center, Independence, IA
Peotone Bensenville Home, Peotone, IL
Pepin Manor Care Center, Pepin, WI
Perdue Medical Center, Miami, FL
B J Perino Nursing Home Inc, Pekin, IL
Perkins Convalescent Home, Philadelphia, PA
Perring Parkway Nursing Home Inc, Baltimore, MD
Perry Community Hospital & Nursing Home, Marion, AL
Perry County Nursing Center, Perryville, AR
Perry County Nursing Home, Perryville, MO
Perry County Nursing Home, Linden, TN
Perry Green Valley Nursing Center, Perry, OK
Perry Health Facility, Perry, FL
Perry Lutheran Home, Perry, IA
Perry Manor, Pinckneyville, IL
Perry Manor, Perry, IA
Perry Nursing Home, Perry, OK
Perry Ridge Nursing Home Inc, Perry, OH
Perry Village Nursing Home, New Bloomfield, PA
Pershing Convalescent Home Inc, Stickney, IL
Pershing County Hospital & Nursing Home, Lovelock, NV
Pershing Estates, Decatur, IL
Person County Memorial Hospital—SNF, Roxboro, NC
Perth Amboy Nursing Home, Perth Amboy, NJ
Peru Nursing Home, Peru, IN
Petaluma Convalescent Hospital, Petaluma, CA
Petersburg General Hospital, Petersburg, AK
Petersburg Healthcare Center, Petersburg, IN
Petersburg Manor, Petersburg, IL
Peterson Nursing Home Inc, Osage City, KS
P A Peterson Home for the Aging, Rockford, IL
Peterson Park Health Care Center, Chicago, IL
Pettipaug Manor, Essex, CT
Pettit Childrens Home, Sauk Centre, MN
Pfeiffer's Community Home, West Valley City, UT
Pharmcare—Aldine, Houston, TX
Pharr Nursing Home, Pharr, TX
Pheasant Wood Nursing Home, Peterborough, NH
Phelps Community Medical Center, Phelps, KY
Phenix City Nursing Home, Phenix City, AL
Philadelphia Nursing Home, Philadelphia, PA
Philadelphia Nursing Home, Philadelphia, PA
The Philadelphia Protestant Home, Philadelphia, PA
Philip Nursing Home, Philip, SD
Phillips County Good Samaritan Retirement Center, Malta, MT
Phillips County Home, Phillipsburg, KS
The Phillips Home, Fayette, MO
Phillips House Nursing Home, Natick, MA
Phillips Manor Nursing Home, Lynn, MA
Phillips Nursing Home, Provo, UT
Phoebe Home Inc, Allentown, PA
Phoenix Jewish Care Center, Phoenix, AZ
Phoenix Mountain Nursing Center, Phoenix, AZ
Phoenix Nursing & Convalescent Center—East, Phoenix, AZ
Phoenix Nursing & Convalescent Center—West, Phoenix, AZ
Phoenix Residence Inc, Saint Paul, MN

Phoenixville Convalescent Manor Inc, Phoenixville, PA
Physicians Care Center, Gadsden, AL
Physician's Hospital for Extended Care, Reno, NV
Physicians Nursing & Convalescent Center, Mount Pleasant, TX
Piatt County Nursing Home, Monticello, IL
Picayune Convalescent Home, Picayune, MS
Pickard Presbyterian Convalescent, Albuquerque, NM
Pickaway Manor Care Center, Circleville, OH
Pickens General Nursing Center, Jasper, GA
Pickering Manor, Newtown, PA
Pickersgill, Towson, MD
Pickett County Nursing Home, Byrdstown, TN
Pickwick Manor Nursing Home, Iuka, MS
Pico Downey Golden Age Convalescent Home, Downey, CA
Piedmont Center-United Church Retirement Homes Inc, Thomasville, NC
Piedmont Gardens Health Facility, Oakland, CA
Piedmont Hall, Milledgeville, GA
Piedmont Health Care Center, Charlottesville, VA
Piedmont Hospital Extended Care Unit, Atlanta, GA
Piedmont Hospital & Nursing Home, Piedmont, AL
Piedmont Nursing Center Inc, Greenville, SC
Piedmont Residential Developmental Center, Concord, NC
Pierce County Nursing Home, Blackshear, GA
Pierce Manor, Pierce, NE
Pierce Memorial Baptist Home Inc, Brooklyn, CT
Pierce Nursing Home, Alpena, MI
Pierremont Heritage Manor, Shreveport, LA
Piety Corner Nursing Home, Waltham, MA
Piety Place, Ellsworth, WI
Pigeon Falls Nursing Home, Pigeon Falls, WI
Piggott Nursing Center, Piggott, AR
Pike Manor Health Care Center, Troy, AL
Pike Manor Nursing Home, Piketon, OH
Pikes Peak Manor, Colorado Springs, CO
Pikesville Nursing & Convalescent Center, Pikesville, MD
Pilgrim Haven Home, Los Altos, CA
Pilgrim Manor, Cromwell, CT
Pilgrim Manor Inc, Grand Rapids, MI
Pilgrim Manor Nursing Home, Plymouth, MA
Pilgrim Manor Nursing Home of Pineville, Pineville, LA
Pilgrim Manor of Bossier City—North, Bossier City, LA
Pilgrim Manor of Bossier City—South, Bossier City, LA
Pilgrim Manor Rehabilitation & Convalescent Center, Plymouth, IN
Pilgrim Place Health Services Center, Claremont, CA
Pilgrim Rehabilitation & Skilled Nursing Center, Peabody, MA
Pilgrims Convalescent Hospital, Artesia, CA
Pilgrim's Pride Nursing Home, Mashpee, MA
Pillars Nursing Home, Springfield, OH
Pillsbury Board & Care Home, Minneapolis, MN
Pimlico Manor, Baltimore, MD
Pin Oaks Nursing Center, Mexico, MO
Pina Home for the Aged, Sturgis, SD
Pinal County Nursing Center, Florence, AZ
Pinal General Hospital, Florence, AZ
Pine Acres Nursing Home, Madison, NJ
Pine Acres Retirement Center, De Kalb, IL
Pine Bluff Nursing Home, Pine Bluff, AR
Pine Breeze Convalescent Hospital, Angwin, CA
Pine Brook Care Center Inc, Englishtown, NJ
Pine Crest Convalescent Hospital, Maywood, CA
Pine Crest Guest Home, Hazlehurst, MS
Pine Crest Haven, Paola, KS
Pine Crest Manor Nursing Home, Bernice, LA
Pine Crest Nursing Center, Morrow, OH
Pine Crest Nursing Home, Nacogdoches, TX

Pine Crest Nursing Home, Merrill, WI

Pine Grove Rest Home, Marlborough, MA

Pine Haven Care Center, Pine Island, MN

Pine Haven Christian Home, Sheboygan Falls, WI

Pine Haven Conv Center of Henderson Inc, Henderson, NC

Pine Haven Home, Philmont, NY

Pine Haven Nursing Home, Evansville, IN

Pine Haven Nursing Home, Leesville, LA

Pine Haven Nursing Home, Lufkin, TX

Pine Hill Rest Home, Lynn, MA

Pine Hill Senior Citizens Center, Quitman, LA

Pine Hurst Nursing & Convalescent Home, Ligonier, PA

Pine Kirk Nursing Home Inc, Kirkersville, OH

Pine Knoll Convalescent Center Inc, Taylor, MI

Pine Knoll Nursing Home, Carrollton, GA

Pine Knoll Nursing Home, Lexington, MA

Pine Knoll Nursing Home, Lyndonville, VT

Pine Lake ICF/MR—Babcock Center, Columbia, SC

Pine Lake Nursing Home, Greenville, FL

Pine Lane Healthcare, Mountain Home, AR

Pine Lawn Manor Care Center, Sumner, IL

Pine Lodge Health Care, Beckley, WV

Pine Lodge Nursing Home, Warren, AR

Pine Lodge Nursing Home, Atlanta, TX

Pine Manor, Clintonville, WI

Pine Manor Inc, Columbus, GA

Pine Manor Nursing Home, Springfield, MA

Pine Oaks Nursing Center, Allegan, MI

Pine Point Manor, West Scarborough, ME

Pine Rest Nursing Home, Northampton, MA

Pine Rest Nursing Home, Ridgewood, NJ

Pine Ridge Home 1, Cloquet, MN

Pine Ridge Home 2, Cloquet, MN

Pine Ridge Home 3, Cloquet, MN

Pine Ridge Manor, Waupaca, WI

Pine Ridge Residence, Bagley, MN

Pine River Group Home, Pine River, MN

Pine Rock Farm, Warner, NH

Pine Shadow Retreat, Porter, TX

Pine Street Group Home, Bangor, ME

Pine Towers Convalescent Hospital Inc, San Francisco, CA

Pine Tree Lodge Nursing Center, Longview, TX

Pine Tree Nursing Home, Butler, MO

Pine Tree Villa, Louisville, KY

Pine Valley Manor, Richland Center, WI

Pine Valley Nursing Center, Richfield, OH

Pine View, Black River Falls, WI

Pine View Care Center, Saint Charles, IL

Pine View Continuous Care Center, Harrisville, WV

Pine View Good Samaritan Center, Valentine, NE

Pine View Health Care Center, Peshtigo, WI

Pine View Manor Inc, Stanberry, MO

Pinebrook Place Healthcare Center, Venice, FL

Pinecrest Care Center, Humboldt, KS

Pinecrest Care Center, Gallipolis, OH

Pinecrest Convalescent Center, North Miami, FL

Pinecrest Convalescent Home, Daingerfield, TX

Pinecrest Manor, Mount Morris, IL

Pinecrest Manor, Hopkinsville, KY

Pinecrest Manor Convalescent Home, Cle Elum, WA

Pinecrest Medical Care Facility, Powers, MI

Pinecrest Nursing & Convalescent Home, Sewell, NJ

Pinecrest State School, Pineville, LA

Pinedale Nursing Home, Newport, AR

Pinehope Nursing Home, Hope, AR

Pinehurst Convalescent Center Inc, Seattle, WA

Pinehurst Convalescent Facility, Pompano Beach, FL

Pinehurst Nursing Center, Pinehurst, NC

Pinehurst Nursing Home, Centerville, IN

Pinehurst Park Terrace, Seattle, WA

Pineland Center, Pownal, ME

Pineland Nursing Home, Lakewood, NJ

Piners Convalescent Hospital Inc, Napa, CA

Pines Convalescent Center, Williamsburg, VA

Pines Nursing Home, Miami, FL

The Pines Nursing & Convalescent Home, Dillon, SC

Pines Village Care Center, North Fort Myers, FL

Pineview Health Care Center, Pineview, GA

Pineview Home Inc, Gurdon, AR

Pineview Manor, Wexford, PA

Pineview Manor Inc, Beaver, OH

Pineview of Hillman, Hillman, MI

Pineview Residence, Saint Paul, MN

Pinevilla Guest Home, Redmond, WA

Pinewood Acres Inc, Maple Shade, NJ

Pinewood Care Center, Coeur d'Alene, ID

Pinewood Convalescent Center, Spartanburg, SC

Pinewood Manor Inc, Hawkinsville, GA

Pinewood Manor Nursing Home, Jasper, TX

Pinewood Nursing Home, Waldron, AR

Pinewood Terrace Nursing & Retirement Center, Colville, WA

Piney Mountain Home, Fayetteville, PA

Pineywood Acres Nursing Home, Corrigan, TX

Pink Bud Home for the Golden Years, Greenwood, AR

Pinnacle Care Center, Morganton, NC

Pinnacle Nursing Home, Rochester, NY

Pioneer Care Center—Wichita Falls, Wichita Falls, TX

Pioneer Center for the Exceptional's Community Living Facility, Woodstock, IL

Pioneer Estate, Chandler, OK

Pioneer Health Center, Marceline, MO

Pioneer Home, Fort Collins, CO

Pioneer Home Inc, Fergus Falls, MN

Pioneer House, Sacramento, CA

Pioneer Lodge, Coldwater, KS

Pioneer Manor, Hugoton, KS

Pioneer Manor, Hay Springs, NE

Pioneer Manor, Frederick, OK

Pioneer Manor, Gillette, WY

Pioneer Memorial Care Center, Erskine, MN

Pioneer Memorial Hospital & Nursing Home, Heppner, OR

Pioneer Memorial Nursing Home, Viborg, SD

Pioneer Memorial Nursing Home, Brigham City, UT

Pioneer Nursing Home, Baudette, MN

Pioneer Nursing Home, Big Timber, MT

Pioneer Nursing Home, Vale, OR

Pioneer Nursing Home, Prairie Farm, WI

Pioneer Nursing Home Inc, Melbourne, AR

Pioneer Nursing Home of Hughes Inc, Wetumka, OK

Pioneer Place Nursing Home, Irving, TX

Pioneer Place Swedish Retirement Assn, Evanston, IL

Pioneer Ridge Healthcare, Ferndale, WA

Pioneer Trace Nursing Home, Flemingsburg, KY

Pioneer Valley Manor Rest Home, Greenfield, MA

Pioneer Valley Nursing Home, Northampton, MA

Pioneer Village I, Topeka, KS

Pioneer Village II, Topeka, KS

Pioneer Village III, Topeka, KS

Pioneer Village IV, Topeka, KS

Pioneers Memorial Hospital & Nursing Home, Rocky Ford, CO

Piper Group Home, Fergus Falls, MN

Pipestone County Medical Center, Pipestone, MN

Piqua Manor, Piqua, OH

Pisgah Manor Inc, Candler, NC

Pittsburg Manor Convalescent Hospital, Pittsburg, CA

Pittsburg Nursing Center, Pittsburg, TX

Pittsfield Convalescent Center, Pittsfield, ME

Placerville Pines Convalescent Hospital, Placerville, CA

Plains Convalescent Center, Plainview, TX

Plains Nursing Center Inc, Plains, GA

Plainview Manor, Plainview, NE

Plainville Health Care Center Inc, Plainville, CT

Plainville Nursing Home, Plainville, MA

Plano Nursing Home, Plano, TX

Plantation Care Center Inc, Salem, OR

Plantation Convalescent Center, Salt Lake City, UT

Plantation Manor, McCalla, AL

Plantation Manor Inc, Atoka, OK

Plantation Nursing Home, Plantation, FL

Plantation Nursing Home, Brownwood, TX

Plaquemine Nursing Home, Plaquemine, LA

Plateau Valley Hospital District Nursing Home, Collbran, CO

Platte County Memorial Nursing Home, Wheatland, WY

Platte Nursing Home, Platte, SD

Plattsmouth Manor, Plattsmouth, NE

Plaza Care Center Inc, Westminster, CO

Plaza Nursing Center, Pascagoula, MS

Plaza Nursing & Convalescent Center, Elizabeth, NJ

Plaza Nursing Home Company Inc, Syracuse, NY

Pleasant Acres, Everett, WA

Pleasant Acres, New Lisbon, WI

Pleasant Acres Convalescent Hospital, Morgan Hill, CA

Pleasant Acres of Hull, Hull, IA

Pleasant Acres Rest Home, Worcester, MA

Pleasant Care Living Center, Pleasantville, IA

Pleasant Grove Health Care Center, Pleasant Grove, AL

Pleasant Grove Nursing Home, Paris, TX

Pleasant Hill Care Center, Saint Paul, MN

Pleasant Hill Convalescent Center, Piketon, OH

Pleasant Hill Health Facility, Fairfield, ME

Pleasant Hill Nursing Home, Oregon, MO

Pleasant Hill Nursing Home, Wichita Falls, TX

Pleasant Hill Village, Girard, IL

Pleasant Hills Health Center, Jackson, MS

Pleasant Living Convalescent Center, Edgewater, MD

Pleasant Manor Care Center, Mount Pleasant, IA

Pleasant Manor Inc, Mount Pleasant, MI

Pleasant Manor Inc, Faribault, MN

Pleasant Manor Nursing & Convalescent Center, Baltimore, MD

Pleasant Manor Nursing Home, Alexandria, LA

Pleasant Manor Nursing Home, Attleboro, MA

Pleasant Manor Nursing Home, Sapulpa, OK

Pleasant Manor Nursing Home, Rutland, VT

Pleasant Manor Nursing Home Inc, Ashdown, AR

Pleasant Manor Nursing Home—Waxahachie, Waxahachie, TX

Pleasant Meadows Christian Village, Chrisman, IL

Pleasant Park Manor, Oskaloosa, IA

Pleasant Place Home for Care, Louisville, KY

Pleasant Rest Nursing Home, Collinsville, IL

Pleasant Valley Health Care Center, Muskogee, OK

Pleasant Valley Infirmary, Argyle, NY

Pleasant Valley Intermediate Care Facility, Oxnard, CA

Pleasant Valley Manor, Sedan, KS

Pleasant Valley Manor, Stroudsburg, PA

Pleasant Valley Manor Care Center, Liberty, MO

Pleasant Valley Nursing Center, Springdale, AR

Pleasant Valley Rehabilitation & Convalescent Hospital, Oxnard, CA

Pleasant View, Rock Port, MO

Pleasant View Convalescent Home, Northumberland, PA

Pleasant View Convalescent Hospital, Cupertino, CA

Pleasant View Good Samaritan Center, Saint James, MN

Pleasant View Health Care Center, Barberton, OH
Pleasant View Home, Morrison, IL
Pleasant View Home, Albert City, IA
Pleasant View Home, Kalona, IA
Pleasant View Home, Inman, KS
Pleasant View Inc, Whiting, IA
Pleasant View Lodge, Indianapolis, IN
Pleasant View Luther Home, Ottawa, IL
Pleasant View Manor, Reedley, CA
Pleasant View Manor, Watertown, CT
Pleasant View Manor, Huntington, WV
Pleasant View Manor Inc, Pleasanton, KS
Pleasant View Nursing Center, Hiawatha, KS
Pleasant View Nursing Home, Metter, GA
Pleasant View Nursing Home, Mount Airy, MD
Pleasant View Nursing Home, Huntsville, MO
Pleasant View Nursing Home, Kansas City, MO
Pleasant View Nursing Home, Lisbon, OH
Pleasant View Nursing Home, Corsica, SD
Pleasant View Nursing Home, Walla Walla, WA
Pleasant View Nursing Home, Monroe, WI
Pleasant View Nursing Home, Phillips, WI
Pleasant View Rest Home, Winchendon, MA
Pleasant View Rest Home, Harrisonville, MO
Pleasant View Rest Home Inc, Manheim, PA
Pleasantview Care Center, Warrensburg, MO
Pleasantview Nursing Home, Parma, OH
Plott Nursing Home, Ontario, CA
Plum Center Nursing Center, Plum City, WI
Plum Grove Nursing Home, Palatine, IL
Plum Tree Convalescent Hospital, San Jose, CA
Plymouth Court, Plymouth, MI
Plymouth Harbor Inc, Sarasota, FL
Plymouth House Health Care Center, Norristown, PA
Plymouth Manor Care Center, Lemars, IA
Plymouth Manor Nursing, Milwaukee, WI
Plymouth Nursing Home, Plymouth, MA
Plymouth Place Inc, La Grange Park, IL
Plymouth Square, Stockton, CA
Plymouth Tower, Riverside, CA
Plymouth Village Redlands Convalescent Hospital, Redlands, CA
Pocahontas Continuous Care Center Inc, Marlinton, WV
Pocahontas Manor, Pocahontas, IA
Pocopson Home, West Chester, PA
Poet's Seat Nursing Home, Greenfield, MA
Pohai Nani Care Center, Kaneohe, HI
Point Loma Convalescent Hospital, San Diego, CA
Point North Nursing Home, Toledo, OH
Point Pleasant Beach Nursing Home, Point Pleasant, NJ
Pointe Coupee Parish Nursing Home, New Roads, LA
Polk City Manor, Polk City, IA
Polk County Nursing Home, Cedartown, GA
James C Polk Rest Home, Carrollton, GA
Berthold S Pollak Hospital, Jersey City, NJ
Polley's Rest Home Inc, Orange, TX
Polo Continental Manor, Polo, IL
Polyclinic Medical Center Ltc Unit, Harrisburg, PA
Pomeroy Care Center, Pomeroy, IA
Pomeroy Hill Nursing Home, Livermore Falls, ME
Pomeroy-Davis-Heartland Memorial Nursing Home, Rainelle, WV
Pomona Golden Age Convalescent Hospital & Nursing Home, Pomona, CA
Ponca City Nursing Home, Ponca City, OK
Ponce de Leon Care Center, Saint Augustine, FL
Pond Point Health Care Center Inc, Milford, CT
Pondera Pioneer Nursing Home, Conrad, MT
Ponderosa, Aurora, CO
Ponderosa Villa, Crawford, NE
Pontchartrain Guest House, Mandeville, LA
Pontiac Nursing Center, Pontiac, MI
Pontiac Nursing Home, Oswego, NY

Pontotoc Community Hospital—Extended Care Facility, Pontotoc, MS
Pope County Care Center Inc, Golconda, IL
Pope Nursing Home, Weymouth, MA
Poplar Grove Rest Home, Greenville, KY
Poplar Living Center, Casper, WY
Poplar Manor Nursing Home, Baltimore, MD
Port Allen Care Center Inc, Port Allen, LA
Port Angeles Care Center, Port Angeles, WA
Port Charlotte Care Center, Port Charlotte, FL
Port Chester Nursing Home, Port Chester, NY
Port Jefferson Nursing Home & Health Related Facility, Port Jefferson, NY
Port Manor Nursing Home, Newburyport, MA
Port Mesa Convalescent Hospital, Costa Mesa, CA
Port Orchard Care Center, Port Orchard, WA
Port Royal Community Residence, Port Royal, SC
Port St Lucie Convalescent Center, Port Saint Lucie, FL
Portage County Home, Stevens Point, WI
Portage County Nursing Home, Ravenna, OH
Portage Manor, South Bend, IN
Portage View Hospital, Hancock, MI
Helen Porter Nursing Home, Middlebury, VT
Porter Hills Presbyterian Village Inc, Grand Rapids, MI
Porter House Health Care, Nashville, TN
Porters Nursing Home, Saint George, UT
Porthaven Care Center, Portland, OR
Portland Acres Nursing Home, Thomas, WV
Portland Adventist Convalescent Center, Portland, OR
Portland Community Care Center West, Portland, IN
Portland Community Care Center-East, Portland, IN
Portland Convalescent Center Inc, Portland, CT
Portland Health Care Facility, Oklahoma City, OK
Portland Residence Inc, Minneapolis, MN
Posada Del Sol Health Care Facility, Tucson, AZ
Poteau Nursing Home, Poteau, OK
Poteet Nursing Home, Poteet, TX
Potomac Center, Hagerstown, MD
Potomac House of Jane Lew, Jane Lew, WV
Potomac Valley Nursing Center, Rockville, MD
Potsdam Nursing Home, Potsdam, NY
Powder River Nursing Home, Broadus, MT
Powell County Memorial Hospital & LTC Unit, Deer Lodge, MT
Powell Nursing Home, Powell, WY
Powellhurst Nursing Home, Portland, OR
Powell's Convalescent Home, Hamilton, OH
Power County Nursing Home, American Falls, ID
Powhatan Nursing Home Inc, Falls Church, VA
Poydras Home for Elderly Ladies, New Orleans, LA
Poydras Manor, Poydras, LA
Prairie Acres, Friona, TX
Prairie City Nursing Center, Prairie City, IL
Prairie Community Nursing Home, Terry, MT
Prairie Estates, Elk Point, SD
Prairie Good Samaritan Center, Miller, SD
Prairie Haven Nursing Home, Kensington, KS
Prairie Lakes Nursing Home, Watertown, SD
Prairie Living Center, Prairie du Chien, WI
Prairie Manor Inc, Blooming Prairie, MN
Prairie Manor Rest Home, Sharon Springs, KS
Prairie Sunset Home, Pretty Prairie, KS
Prairie View Care Center, Woonsocket, SD
Prairie View Home, Princeton, IL
Prairie View Home, Sanborn, IA
Prairie View Inc, Slauton, MN
Prairie View Nursing Home, Limon, CO
Prairie View Rest Home Inc, Warsaw, IN
Prairie View Rest Home Inc, Lewistown, MO
Prairie Village Living Center, Washington, IN
Prairieview Homes Inc, Underwood, ND
Prairieview Lutheran Home, Danforth, IL
Prarie Vista Care Center, Holyoke, CO

Prather Methodist Memorial Home, Alameda, CA
Praxis Nursing Home, Easton, PA
Prayer Tower Rest Home, New Orleans, LA
Preakness Hospital, Paterson, NJ
Precious Intermediate Care Home, Vidalia, GA
Premont Rest Home Inc, Premont, TX
Prentis Manor Jewish Home for Aged 1, Southfield, MI
The Presbyterian Home, Evanston, IL
Presbyterian Home, Cambridge Springs, PA
Presbyterian Home, Oil City, PA
The Presbyterian Home at Charlotte Inc, Charlotte, NC
The Presbyterian Home at 58th St, Philadelphia, PA
Presbyterian Home for Central New York Inc, New Hartford, NY
The Presbyterian Home Inc, Quitman, GA
Presbyterian Home—Johnstown, Johnstown, PA
Presbyterian Home of Ackley, Ackley, IA
Presbyterian Home of Atlantic City—Madison House, Atlantic City, NJ
Presbyterian Home of DC, Washington, DC
The Presbyterian Home of High Point, High Point, NC
Presbyterian Home of Maryland Inc, Towson, MD
Presbyterian Home of South Carolina—Summerville, Summerville, SC
Presbyterian Homes Johanna Shores, Saint Paul, MN
Presbyterian Homes Langton Place, Saint Paul, MN
Presbyterian Homes of Western New York Inc, Jamestown, NY
Presbyterian Homes-Johanna Shores, Arden Hills, MN
Presbyterian Lodge, Erie, PA
Presbyterian Manor at Farmington, Farmington, MO
Presbyterian Manor at Rolla, Rolla, MO
Presbyterian Manor Inc, Wichita Falls, TX
Presbyterian Manor Inc, Huntington, WV
Presbyterian Medical Center, Denver, CO
Presbyterian Medical Center of Oakmont, Oakmont, PA
Presbyterian Nursing Center—Florida Presbyterian Homes Inc, Lakeland, FL
Presbyterian Nursing Home Inc, Ontario, OR
The Presbyterian Home of Hawfields, Inc, Mebane, NC
Presbyterian Village Health Care Center, Little Rock, AR
Presbyterian Village Inc, Dallas, TX
Presbyterian Village North, Dallas, TX
Presbyterian Village of Homer, Homer, LA
Prescott Country View Nursing Home, Prescott, KS
Prescott House Nursing Home, North Andover, MA
Prescott Nursing Center, Prescott, AR
Prescott Samaritan Village, Prescott, AZ
Presidential Convalescent Home Inc, Quincy, MA
Presidential Woods Health Care Center, Adelphi, MD
Presque Isle Nursing Home Inc, Presque Isle, ME
Preston Care Center, Preston, MN
Price Care Center, Price, UT
Price Hill Nursing Home, Cincinnati, OH
Price Memorial, Eureka, MO
Primghar Care Center, Primghar, IA
Primrose Manor, Danville, IN
Primrose Place Health Care Inc, Springfield, MO
Primus Mason Manor, Springfield, MA
Princeton Care Center Inc, Princeton, MO
Princeton Health Care Center, Princeton, WV
Princeton Health Care Manor Inc, Princeton, KY
Princeton House Rest Home, Lowell, MA
Princeton Nursing Home, Princeton, NJ
Pro Care Development Center, Gaston, IN
Proctor J C Endowment Home, Peoria, IL

Professional Care Home, Hartford, KY
Professional Care Inc, Troy, IL
Professional Care Nursing Center Inc, Dale, IN
Profitts Boarding Home, Centerville, IA
Progress Valley II, Richfield, MN
Progressive Living Center, Lufkin, TX
Project Independence McMillan Home, Worthington, MN
Project Independence Ridgewood, Worthington, MN
Project New Hope 1-5, Alexandria, MN
Project New Hope 6, Alexandria, MN
Project New Hope 7, Alexandria, MN
Project New Hope—Starbuck, Starbuck, MN
Project New Hope-Ada 2, Ada, MN
Project Turnabout, Granite Falls, MN
Promenade Health Care Facility, Auburn, ME
Promenade Nursing Home, Rockaway Park, NY
Prompt Succor Nursing Home, Opelousas, LA
Prophets Riverview Good Samaritan Center, Prophetstown, IL
Prospect Hill Home, Keene, NH
Prospect Hill Manor Nursing Home, Somerville, MA
Prospect Hill Nursing Home, Waltham, MA
Prospect Hill Rehabilitation Center, East Windsor, CT
Prospect Lake Health Care Center, Colorado Springs, CO
Prospect Manor, Cleveland, OH
Prospect Nursing Home, North Bennington, VT
Prospect Park Care Center, Prospect Park, PA
Prospect Park Convalescent Center, Ypsilanti, MI
Prospect Park Living Center, Estes Park, CO
Prospect Park Nursing Home Inc, Brooklyn, NY
Protection Valley Manor, Protection, KS
Providence Children's Nursing Center, Portland, OR
Providence Convalescent Residence Inc, Charlotte, NC
Providence Health Care, Sparta, GA
Providence Health Care, Warrenton, GA
Providence Health Care Center, Beaver Falls, PA
Providence Home, Jasper, IN
Providence House Nursing Home, Worcester, MA
Providence Rest Home, Bronx, NY
Providence Retirement Home, New Albany, IN
Provident Nursing Home, Brighton, MA
Provincial House, Gaylord, MI
Provincial House, Kalamazoo, MI
Provincial House—Adrian, Adrian, MI
Provincial House—Alpena, Alpena, MI
Provincial House—Battle Creek, Battle Creek, MI
Provincial House—Battle Creek, Springfield, MI
Provincial House—Cass City, Cass City, MI
Provincial House—East, East Lansing, MI
Provincial House—Hastings, Hastings, MI
Provincial House—Kalamazoo Total Living Center, Kalamazoo, MI
Provincial House—Marshall, Marshall, MI
Provincial House—Midland, Midland, MI
Provincial House—Portage, Kalamazoo, MI
Provincial House—Sault Ste Marie, Sault Sainte Marie, MI
Provincial House South, Lansing, MI
Provincial House—Traverse City, Traverse City, MI
Provincial House—West, Lansing, MI
Provincial House—Whitehills, East Lansing, MI
Provinical House—Tawas City, Tawas City, MI
Provo Care Center, Provo, UT
Pueblo Manor, Pueblo, CO
Pueblo Norte Nursing Center, Scottsdale, AZ
Pueblo Norte Nursing Center, Show Low, AZ
Pueblo Norte-West Nursing Center, Peoria, AZ

Pulaski Health Care Center, Pulaski, TN
Pulaski Health Care Center, Pulaski, VA
Pulaski Nursing Home, Pulaski, GA
Pulley Care Center, South Point, OH
Pulley Nursing Home, South Point, OH
Pullman Convalescent Center, Pullman, WA
Helen Purcell Home, Zanesville, OH
Purchell Nursing Home, Purcell, OK
Purple Hills Manor Inc, Bandera, TX
Puryear Nursing Home, Puryear, TN
Putnam Acres Care Center, Ottawa, OH
Putnam County Nursing Home, Unionville, MO
Putnam Memorial Nursing Home, Palatka, FL
Puxico Nursing Center, Puxico, MO
QC II Nursing Care Center of Baton Rouge, Baton Rouge, LA
Quaboag Nursing Home, West Brookfield, MA
Quail Ridge Living Center, West Siloam Springs, OK
Quaker Gardens, Stanton, CA
Quaker Heights Nursing Home, Waynesville, OH
Quaker Hill Manor, Baxter Springs, KS
Quaker Villa, Lubbock, TX
Quakertwon Manor Convalescent & Rehabilitation Center, Quakertown, PA
Qualicare Nursing Home, Detroit, MI
Quality Care Health Center, Lebanon, TN
Quality Care Nursing Center, Hot Springs, AR
Quality Care Nursing Facility, Fremont, OH
Quality Care of Waco, Waco, TX
Quality Health Care Center, Winter Garden, FL
Quality Health Care Center, Urbandale, IA
Quapaw Nursing Home, Quapaw, OK
The Quarryville Presbyterian Home, Quarryville, PA
Queen Anne Nursing Home, Hingham, MA
Queen Anne Villa Care Center, Seattle, WA
Queen City Nursing Center, Meridian, MS
Queen City Nursing Home, Cincinnati, OH
Queen Nursing Home, Minneapolis, MN
Queen of Carmel, Morganville, NJ
Queen of Peace Residence, Queens Village, NY
Queen's Convalescent Inc, Middletown, CT
Queens Nassau Nursing Home, Far Rockaway, NY
Quiet Acres Nursing Home Inc, Washington Court House, OH
L F Quigley Memorial Skilled Nursing Facility, Chelsea, MA
Quincy Convalescent Hospital, Quincy, CA
Quincy Nursing Home, Quincy, MA
Quincy United Methodist Home & Quincy Village, Quincy, PA
Quinlan Home, Saint Paul, MN
Quinlan Manor, Sacramento, CA
Quinsippi LTC Facility Inc, Quincy, IL
Quinton Memorial Health Center, Dalton, GA
Quinton Nursing Home Inc, Quinton, OK
Quitman County Nursing Home, Marks, MS
Quitman Nursing Home Inc, Quitman, TX
R N Nursing Home Inc, Bremen, IN
Rach Sovereign Memorial Home, Bay City, MI
Racine Residential Care, Racine, WI
Rae-Ann Geneva, Geneva, OH
Rae-Ann Nursing Center, Cleveland, OH
Rae-Ann Suburban, Westlake, OH
Rafael Convalescent Hospital, San Rafael, CA
Rafferty's Nursing Home, Clinton, OH
Rahway Geriatrics Center Inc, Rahway, NJ
Rainbow House, Manitowoc, WI
Rainbow Nursing Center, Bridgeton, NJ
Rainbow Nursing Home, Peabody, MA
Rainbow Nursing Home, Bristow, OK
Rainbow Springs Care Center, Mineral Point, MO
The Raintree, Mansfield, OH
Raintree Convalescent Hospital, Fresno, CA
Raleigh Care Center, Portland, OR
Ralls Nursing Home, Ralls, TX
Ralston House, Philadelphia, PA
Ramapo Manor Nursing Center, Inc, Suffern, NY

Ramona Manor Convalescent Hospital, Hemet, CA
Ramsbottom Center Inc, Bradford, PA
Ramsey Home, Des Moines, IA
Ramsey Nursing Home, Saint Paul, MN
Ranch Terrace Nursing Home Inc, Sapulpa, OK
Rancho Los Padres Convalescent Hospital, Norwalk, CA
Ranchwood Lodge Home, Wilburton, OK
Randolph County Nursing Home, Pocahontas, AR
Randolph County Nursing Home, Sparta, IL
Randolph Hills Nursing Home, Wheaton, MD
John Randolph Nursing Home Inc, Hopewell, VA
Randolph Manor, Charlotte, NC
Randolph Nursing Home, Andover, MA
Randolph Nursing Home Inc, Winchester, IN
Helen Raney Nursing Home Inc, Broken Arrow, OK
Range Center—Birchwood Home, Eveleth, MN
Range Center Inc, Chisholm, MN
Range Center—Mapleview, Hibbing, MN
Range Center—Oakwood Home, Chisholm, MN
Ranger Park Inn Nursing Home, Santa Anna, TX
Rapid City Care Center, Rapid City, SD
Rapid City Nursing Center, Rapid City, SD
Rapids Nursing Home, Grand Rapids, OH
Rappahannock Westminster-Canterbury, Irvington, VA
Raritan Health & Extended Care Center, Raritan, NJ
Rathfons Convalescent Home, Selinsgrove, PA
Ratliff Nursing Home, Cape Girardeau, MO
Ravenna Good Samaritan Home, Ravenna, NE
Ravenwood Health Care Center, Waterloo, IA
Ravenwood Lutheran Village Nursing Home, Hagerstown, MD
Rawlings Nursing Home, Sandersville, GA
Rawlins House Inc, Pendleton, IN
Rayne Guest House, Rayne, LA
Rayville Guest House Inc, Rayville, LA
Reading Nursing Center, West Reading, PA
Reagan's Resident Care Facility, Somerville, MA
Rebecca Residence for Protestant Ladies, Pittsburgh, PA
Rebekah-Odd Fellow Care Home, Hutchinson, KS
Rebold Manor, Okmulgee, OK
Reconstruction Home Inc, Ithaca, NY
The Recuperative Center, Roslindale, MA
Red Bank Convalescent Center, Red Bank, NJ
Red Bank Medicenter, Red Bank, NJ
Red Bay Nursing Home, Red Bay, AL
Red Bridge Health Care Center, Kansas City, MO
Red Bud Care Center, Red Bud, IL
Red Carpet Health Care Center, Cambridge, OH
Red Haven Nursing Home Inc, Cincinnati, OH
Red Hills Rest Haven, Sumner, IL
Red Oak Good Samaritan Center, Red Oak, IA
Red Oaks Healthcare Center, Michigan City, IN
Red River Haven Nursing Home Inc, Bogata, TX
Red Rock Manor Nursing Home Inc, Hinton, OK
Red Rose Inn, Cassville, MO
Red Wing Group Home, Red Wing, MN
Red Wing Health Center, Red Wing, MN
Redbanks, Henderson, KY
Redbud Retreat, Naples, TX
Redeemer Residence Inc, Minneapolis, MN
Redford Geriatric Village, Detroit, MI
Redman Nursing Home, Omaha, NE
Redmond Health Care Center, Redmond, OR
Redstone Villa, Saint Albans, VT
Redwood Christian Convalescent Hospital, Napa, CA

Redwood Convalescent Hospital, Castro Valley, CA

Redwood Manor, Sesser, IL

Redwood Terrace Lutheran Home, Escondido, CA

The Redwoods, Mill Valley, CA

Reed City Hospital Long-Term Care Facility, Reed City, MI

John M Reed Nursing Home, Limestone, TN

Sarah A Reed Retirement Center, Erie, PA

Walter Reed Convalescent Center, Gloucester, VA

Reeders Memorial Home, Boonsboro, MD

Reedley Convalescent Hospital, Reedley, CA

Reedwood Extended Care Center, Portland, OR

Reelfoot Manor Nursing Home, Tiptonville, TN

Reformed Presbyterian Home, Pittsburgh, PA

Refugio Manor, Refugio, TX

Regency Care Center, Norwalk, IA

Regency Care Center, Walla Walla, WA

Regency Care Center of Spokane, Spokane, WA

Regency Hall Nursing Home Inc, Allison Park, PA

Regency Health Care Center, Lake Worth, FL

Regency Health Care Center, Eatonton, GA

Regency Health Care Center, DeSoto, KS

Regency Health Care Center, Eureka, KS

Regency Health Care Center, Florence, KS

Regency Health Care Center, Halstead, KS

Regency Health Care Center, Hiawatha, KS

Regency Health Care Center, Lawrence, KS

Regency Health Care Center, Olathe, KS

Regency Health Care Center, Osawatomie, KS

Regency Health Care Center, Wichita, KS

Regency Health Care Center, Yates Center, KS

Regency Health Care Center, Monteagle, TN

Regency Health Care Center, Newport, TN

Regency Health Care Center, Red Boiling Springs, TN

Regency Health Care Center—Eaton Street, Lakewood, CO

Regency House Convalescent Center, McAlester, OK

Regency Knollwood Hall, Winston-Salem, NC

Regency Manor, Independence, KY

Regency Manor, Chelan, WA

Regency Manor Inc, Saint Paul, MN

Regency Manor Nursing Center, Temple, TX

Regency Nursing Centre Inc, Niles, IL

Regency Nursing & Rehabilitation Center, Forestville, MD

Regency Oaks, Gainesville, FL

Regency Park Convalescent Center, Detroit, MI

Regency Park Manor Health Care Center, Tulsa, OK

Regency Place, Lafayette, IN

Regency Place Health Care & Rehabilitation Center, Dyer, IN

Regency Place of Castleton, Indianapolis, IN

Regency Place of Greenfield, Greenfield, IN

Regency Place of Greenwood, Greenwood, IN

Regency Rehabilitation Center, Denver, CO

Regency South Care Center, Spokane, WA

Regency Terrace South, Milwaukee, WI

Regent Nursing Home, Brookline, MA

Regent Park Long-Term Care Center, Brockton, MA

Regina Community Nursing Center, Norristown, PA

Regina Community Nursing Center, Philadelphia, PA

The Regina Continuing Care Center, Evansville, IN

Regina Convalescent & Nursing Care Unit, Hastings, MN

Region Park Hall, Faribault, MN

Regional Healthcare Inc, Newport, AR

Regional Memorial Hospital SNF, Brunswick, ME

Regis Multi-Health Center, New Haven, CT

Rego Park Nursing Home, Flushing, NY

Rehabilitation Centers Inc, Magee, MS

Reisch Memorial Nursing Home, Carrollton, IL

REM Bemidji, Bemidji, MN

REM Bloomington, Bloomington, MN

REM Canby A & B, Canby, MN

REM Fairmont A, Fairmont, MN

REM Fairmont Inc B, Fairmont, MN

REM Lyndale Inc, Minneapolis, MN

REM Mankato, Mankato, MN

REM Marshall A, B, & C, Marshall, MN

REM Minnetonka Inc, Minnetonka, MN

REM Montevideo Inc, Montevideo, MN

REM Osakis Inc, Osakis, MN

REM Pillsbury, Minneapolis, MN

REM Pleasant, Minneapolis, MN

REM Redwood Falls, Inc; A & B, Redwood Falls, MN

REM Rochester, Rochester, MN

REM Roseau Inc, Roseau, MN

REM St Cloud, Saint Cloud, MN

REM Southeast Inc, Minneapolis, MN

REM Tyler, Tyler, MN

REM Waite Park Inc, Waite Park, MN

REM-Buffalo, Buffalo, MN

Remington Boarding Home, Chariton, IA

Renaissance House, Chicago, IL

Renaissance Manor Ltd, Oak Park, IL

Rendezvous Medi-Home, McDermott, OH

Renfro Nursing Home, Waxahachie, TX

Rennes Health Center, Peshtigo, WI

Rennie Memorial Nursing Home, Evanston, WY

Reno Convalescent Center, Reno, NV

Reno Convalescent Hospital, Modesto, CA

Renotta Nursing Home, Wray, CO

Rensselaer Care Center, Rensselear, IN

Renton Terrace Nursing Center, Renton, WA

Ren-Villa, Renville, MN

Renville County Community Residence, Bird Island, MN

Resa On Eden Prarie Rd, Minnetonka, MN

Reseda Arms Convalescent Hospital, Reseda, CA

Reservoir Manor, Shelbyville, IL

Reservoir Nursing Home Inc, Waltham, MA

The Residence I, Shoreview, MN

The Residence II, Shoreview, MN

The Residence III, Saint Paul, MN

Resident Homes Inc—Harmony, Faribault, MN

Resident Homes Inc—Haven, Faribault, MN

Residential Alternatives II, Brooklyn Center, MN

Residential Alternatives III, Brooklyn Park, MN

Residential Alternatives IV, Robbinsdale, MN

Residential Alternatives V, Buffalo, MN

Residential Alternatives VI, Cambridge, MN

Residential Alternatives VII, Big Lake, MN

Residential Alternatives VIII, Robbinsdale, MN

Residential Services of Greene County Inc, Xenia, OH

Residential Services of Northeast Minnesota I, Duluth, MN

Residential Services of Northeast Minnesota II, Duluth, MN

Resort Health Related Facility, Arverne, NY

Resort Lodge Inc, Mineral Wells, TX

Resort Nursing Home, Arverne, NY

Rest Awhile Nursing Home, Moultrie, GA

Rest Harbor Nursing Home, Gresham, OR

Rest Haven, Dayton, OH

Rest Haven Central Christian Nursing Home, Palos Heights, IL

Rest Haven Convalescent & Retirement Home, Sedalia, MO

Rest Haven Health Care Center, Verona, WI

Rest Haven Manor Inc, Albion, IL

Rest Haven Manor Nursing Center, Cando, ND

Rest Haven Nursing Home, Bogalusa, LA

Rest Haven Nursing Home, Medford, MA

Rest Haven Nursing Home, Ripley, MS

Rest Haven Nursing Home, Monett, MO

Rest Haven Nursing Home, Fayetteville, NC

Rest Haven Nursing Home, McDermott, OH

Rest Haven Nursing Home, Cushing, OK

Rest Haven Nursing Home, Picher, OK

Rest Haven Nursing Home, Tulsa, OK

Rest Haven Nursing Home, El Paso, TX

Rest Haven Nursing Home, Olympia, WA

Rest Haven Nursing Home Inc, Greenville, OH

Rest Haven Nursing Home Inc, Grafton, WV

Rest Haven Residential Care, Fayette, MO

Rest Haven Rest Home Inc, Adams, MA

Rest Haven South, South Holland, IL

Rest Haven West Christian Nursing Center, Downers Grove, IL

Rest Haven-York, York, PA

Rest Well Rest Home Inc, Burrillville, RI

Restful Acres Nursing Home Inc, Waynesboro, MS

Restful Acres Nursing Home Inc, Kenedy, TX

Resthave Home of Whiteside County, Morrison, IL

Resthaven, Independence, MO

Resthaven Corporation, Boston, MA

Resthaven Geriatric Center, Greenville, SC

Resthaven Intermediate Care Home, Buchanan, GA

Resthaven Nursing Center, Lake Charles, LA

Resthaven Nursing Home, Patten, ME

Resthaven Nursing Home, East Braintree, MA

Resthaven Nursing Home, Hyannis, MA

Resthaven Nursing Home, Memphis, TN

Resthaven Nursing Home, Austin, TX

Resthaven Nursing Home—Bremerton, Bremerton, WA

Resthaven Nursing Home Inc, Jonesport, ME

Restle Home, Portage, OH

Restorative Care Center, Seattle, WA

Restview Nursing Home, Cincinnati, OH

Resurrection Catholic Nursing Home, Marbury, AL

Resurrection Nursing Pavilion, Park Ridge, IL

Resurrection Rest Home, Castleton-on-Hudson, NY

Retama Manor, Kingsville, TX

Retama Manor East—Cuero, Cuero, TX

Retama Manor North, Pleasanton, TX

Retama Manor—North, San Antonio, TX

Retama Manor Nursing Center, Alice, TX

Retama Manor Nursing Center, Brownsville, TX

Retama Manor Nursing Center, Edinburg, TX

Retama Manor Nursing Center, Falfurrias, TX

Retama Manor Nursing Center, McAllen, TX

Retama Manor Nursing Center, Raymondville, TX

Retama Manor Nursing Center, Rio Grande City, TX

Retama Manor Nursing Center—Cuero, Cuero, TX

Retama Manor Nursing Center—Del Rio, Del Rio, TX

Retama Manor Nursing Center—East, Laredo, TX

Retama Manor Nursing Center—Harlingen, Harlingen, TX

Retama Manor Nursing Center Inc, Jourdanton, TX

Retama Manor Nursing Center—North, Corpus Christi, TX

Retama Manor Nursing Center—Robstown, Robstown, TX

Retama Manor Nursing Center—South, Laredo, TX

Retama Manor Nursing Center—South, Pleasanton, TX

Retama Manor Nursing Center—South, San Antonio, TX

Retama Manor Nursing Center—Weslaco, Weslaco, TX

Retama Manor Nursing Center—West, Laredo, TX

Retama Manor Nursing Center—West, San Antonio, TX

Retama Manor Nursing Center—West, Victoria, TX

Retama Manor—South 098, Victoria, TX

Retirement Acres, Altamont, KS

The Retirement Center, Baton Rouge, LA

Retirement Center of Wright County, Buffalo, MN

Retirement & Nursing Center, Austin, TX

Retirement & Nursing Center, Corpus Christi, TX

Retirement Ranch of Clovis, Clovis, NM

Revere Home, Revere, MN

Revmont Nursing Home, West Union, OH

Catherine V Reynolds, Bridgeville, DE

Reynolds Nursing Home Inc, Adena, OH

RFDF Orchard Hill, Madison, WI

RGR Sanitarium, Los Angeles, CA

Rhea County Nursing Home, Dayton, TN

Rheem Valley Convalescent Hospital, Rheem, CA

Rib Lake Health Care Center, Rib Lake, WI

Julia Ribaudo Home, Lake Ariel, PA

Rice Lake Convalescent Center, Rice Lake, WI

Rice Springs Care Home Inc, Haskell, TX

William B Rice Eventide Home, Quincy, MA

Riceville Community Rest Home, Riceville, IA

Rich Mountain Manor, Mena, AR

Richardson Manor Care Center, Richardson, TX

Richardson Nursing Home, Norfolk, VA

Richardson Rest Home Inc, North Adams, MA

Richboro Care Center, Richboro, PA

Richey Manor Nursing Home, New Port Richey, FL

Richfield Care Center, Richfield, UT

Richfield Outreach Group Home, Richfield, MN

Richland Community Residence, Aiken, SC

Richland Convalescent Center, Columbia, SC

Richland Hills Nursing Home, Fort Worth, TX

Richland Homes Inc, Sidney, MT

Richland Manor Nursing Home, Bluffton, OH

Richland Nursing Home, Delhi, LA

Jennie B Richmond Chaffee Nursing Home, Springville, NY

Richmond Nursing Home, Richmond, VA

Richmond's Boarding Home, Jackson, MS

Richton Crossing Convalescent Center, Richton Park, IL

Richview, Richfield, MN

Richwoods Terrace, Peoria, IL

Ridge Convalescent Center, Lake Wales, FL

Ridge Crest Adult Care Center, Warrensburg, MO

Ridge Crest Convalescent Center, Feasterville, PA

Ridge Road Residence, Greenville, SC

Ridge View Manor Nursing Home, Buffalo, NY

Ridgecrest Convalescent Center, Ridgeland, SC

Ridgecrest Manor, Deland, FL

Ridgecrest Manor Nursing Home, Duffield, VA

Ridgecrest Nursing Home, West Monroe, LA

Ridgecrest Village, Davenport, IA

Ridgefield Health Care, Ridgefield, WA

Ridgemont Terrace Inc, Port Orchard, WA

Ridgetop Haven Inc, Ridgetop, TN

Ridgeview Care Center, Oblong, IL

Ridgeview Health Care Center Inc, Jasper, AL

Ridgeview House Inc, Evanston, IL

Ridgeview Lodge Nursing Center, DeQueen, AR

Ridgeview Manor, Kalamazoo, MI

Ridgeview Manor Nursing Home, Malden, MO

Ridgeview Nursing & Convalescent Center, Wichita Falls, TX

Ridgeview Pavilion, Evanston, IL

Ridgeview Rest Home Inc, Cromwell, CT

Ridgeview Terrace Convalescent & Nursing Center, Rutledge, TN

Ridgeway Manor, Owingsville, KY

Ridgeway Manor Nursing Home, Catonsville, MD

Isabelle Ridgway Nursing Center, Columbus, OH

Ridgeway Nursing Home, Sullivan, MO

Ridgewood Care Center, Racine, WI

Ridgewood Care Center Inc, Ottumwa, IA

Ridgewood Central Inc—Health Care Facility, Middletown, CT

Ridgewood Court Nursing Home, Attleboro, MA

Ridgewood Health Care Center, Milan, TN

Ridgewood Health Care Center Inc, Jasper, AL

Ridgewood Health Care Facility Inc, Southington, CT

Ridgewood Home, Ridgewood, NJ

Ridgewood Manor, Dalton, GA

Ridgewood Manor, Washington, NC

Ridgewood Manor, Fort Worth, TX

Ridgewood Nursing Center Inc, Youngstown, OH

Ridgewood Nursing Home, Springfield, OH

Ridgway Manor Inc, Ridgway, IL

Rikard Nursing Home—Rikard Convalescent Bldg, Lexington, SC

Rikard Nursing Homes—Keisler & Holstedt Bldgs, Lexington, SC

Riley Nursing Home, Fresno, CA

Riley's Oak Hill Manor North, North Little Rock, AR

Riley's Oak Hill Manor South, Little Rock, AR

Rinaldi Convalescent Hospital, Granada Hills, CA

Ring Nursing Home—Ridgewood, Springfield, MA

Ring Nursing Home—South, Springfield, MA

Ringling Nursing Home, Ringling, OK

Rio Hondo CareWest Nursing Center, Montebello, CA

Rio Rancho Health Care Center, Rio Rancho, NM

Rio Verde Health Care Center, Cottonwood, AZ

Rio-Sol Nursing Home, Mansura, LA

Ripley Manor Nursing Home, Ripley, MS

Ripley Road Nursing Home Inc, Cohasset, MA

Ripon Area Residential Center, Ripon, WI

Rising Star Nursing Center, Rising Star, TX

Rising Sun Care Center, Rising Sun, IN

Rita's Rest Home, Mystic, CT

Rita's Rest Home, New Bedford, MA

Rittenhouse Care Center, Philadelphia, PA

Ritter Healthcare Center, Indianapolis, IN

River Bluff Convalescent Hospital, Riverbank, CA

River Bluff Nursing Home, Rockford, IL

River Bluffs of Cahokia, Cahokia, IL

River Crest Center/Ken Crest Services, Mont Clare, PA

River Falls Area Hospital Kinnic Home Division, River Falls, WI

River Falls Care Center, River Falls, WI

River Forest Nursing Care Center, Three Rivers, MI

River Garden Hebrew Home for the Aged, Jacksonville, FL

River Glen Continuing Care Center, Southbury, CT

River Heights Nursing Home, Tampa, FL

River Heights Retirement Center Inc, Boonville, MO

River Hills Care Center, Ottumwa, IA

River Hills East Health Care Center, Milwaukee, WI

River Hills Health Care Center—South, Milwaukee, WI

River Hills Health Care Center—West, Pewaukee, WI

River Hills in Keokuk, Keokuk, IA

River Manor HRF, Brooklyn, NY

River Mede Manor, Binghamton, NY

River Oaks Care Center, Fort Worth, TX

River Oaks Health Care Center, Lake City, MN

River Oaks Nursing Home, Steele, MO

River Park Living Center, Eugene, OR

River Pines Living Center, Stevens Point, WI

River Terrace Healthcare Nursing Home, Lancaster, MA

River Valley Living Center, Madison, IN

River Valley Rest Home, Northampton, MA

River View Manor Home, Hannibal, MO

River Walk Manor, Salisbury, MD

Riverbend Convalescent Center, Natick, MA

Riverbend Nursing Home Inc, Grand Blanc, MI

Rivercrest Long-Term Care Facility, Concord, MA

Rivercrest Manor, Pierre, SD

Riverdale Gardens Nursing Home Inc, West Springfield, MA

Riverdale Manor, Markesan, WI

Riverdale Manor, Muscoda, WI

Riverdale Nursing Home, Bronx, NY

Riverfront Manor Inc, Tiffin, OH

Riverfront Terrace Health Care Facility, Paducah, KY

Rivergate Convalescent Center, Riverview, MI

The Rivergate Terrace—Intermediate Care Facility, Riverview, MI

Riverhead Nursing Home/Health Related Facility, Riverhead, NY

Riveridge Manor, Inc, Niles, MI

Riverlands Health Care Center, Lutcher, LA

Rivermont Convalescent & Nursing Center, South Pittsburg, TN

Riverpart Convalescent Center, Spokane, WA

Rivershores Living Center, Marseilles, IL

Riverside Board & Care, McIntosh, MN

Riverside Care Center, Miami, FL

Riverside Center Inc, South Bend, IN

Riverside Convalescent Home, Toledo, OH

Riverside Convalescent Hospital, Chico, CA

Riverside Convalescent Hospital, North Hollywood, CA

Riverside Convalescent Hospital, Sacramento, CA

Riverside Cottage Rest Home, Bakersfield, CA

Riverside Foundation, Mundelein, IL

Riverside Guest Care Center, Natchitoches, LA

Riverside Health Care Center, East Hartford, CT

Riverside Health Care Center, Danville, VA

Riverside Hospital for Skilled Care, Reno, NV

Riverside Manor, Ames, IA

Riverside Manor, Battle Creek, MI

Riverside Manor, San Angelo, TX

Riverside Manor Health Care, Calhoun, KY

Riverside Manor Nursing & Rehabilitation Center, Newcomerstown, OH

Riverside Medical of Covington, Covington, GA

Riverside Medical of Thomaston, Thomaston, GA

Riverside Methodist Hospital's Extended Care Unit, Columbus, OH

Riverside Nursing Center, Milledgeville, GA

Riverside Nursing Center, Oconto, WI

Riverside Nursing & Convalescent Center Inc, Saint Albans, WV

Riverside Nursing Home, Waycross, GA

Riverside Nursing Home, Boston, MA

Riverside Nursing Home, Grand Haven, MI

Riverside Nursing Home, Haverstraw, NY

Riverside Nursing Home, East Providence, RI

Riverside Nursing Home Inc, Monroe, LA

Riverside Nursing Home Inc, Jenks, OK

Riverside of Macon, Macon, GA

Riverside Terrace Nursing Home, Rockford, IL

Riverstreet Manor Nursing & Rehabilitation Center, Wilkes-Barre, PA

Riverton Heights Convalescent Home, Seattle, WA

Riverview Care Center Inc, Guttenberg, IA

Riverview Care Center Residential, Fort Wayne, IN

Riverview Center for Jewish Seniors, Pittsburgh, PA

Riverview Estates Inc, Marquette, KS

Riverview Health Center, Kaukauna, WI

Riverview Heights Nursing Home, Waverly, MO

Riverview Home, Cincinnati, OH

Riverview Homes, Ashland, KY

Riverview Lutheran Memorial Care Center, Spokane, WA

Riverview Manor, Des Moines, IA

Riverview Manor, Flandreau, SD

Riverview Manor, Wisconsin Rapids, WI
Riverview Manor Inc, Oxford, KS
Riverview Manor Inc, Wanamingo, MN
Riverview Manor Nursing Home, Morrilton, AR
Riverview Manor Nursing Home, Marion, IN
Riverview Manor Nursing Home, Pleasant Valley, IA
Riverview Manor Nursing Home, Prestonsburg, KY
Riverview Manor Nursing Home, Sainte Genevieve, MO
Riverview Manor Nursing Home, Owego, NY
Riverview Nursing Center, Mokane, MO
Riverview Nursing Centre, Baltimore, MD
Riverview Nursing Home, Rome, GA
Riverview Nursing Home, Boston, MA
Riverview Nursing Home, Crookston, MN
Riverview Nursing Home, Steubenville, OH
Riverview Nursing Home, Vermillion, OH
Riverview Nursing Home Inc, Coventry, RI
Riverview Nursing Home Inc, Rich Creek, VA
Riverview Rest Home, New Haven, CT
Riverview Terrace, Tomahawk, WI
Riverways Manor Nursing Home, Van Buren, MO
Riverwood Care Center, Puyallup, WA
Riverwood Convalescent Home, Arkadelphia, AR
Riverwood Health Care Center, Biddeford, ME
Riviera Manor Inc, Chicago Heights, IL
Riviera Nursing & Convalescent Home Inc, Pico Rivera, CA
RN Nursing & Convalescent Home Inc, El Paso, TX
Roanoke City Nursing Home, Roanoke, VA
Roanoke Manor Nursing Home, Kansas City, MO
Roanoke United Methodist Home, Roanoke, VA
Roanoke Valley Nursing Home, Rich Square, NC
Robbin House Convalescent Home, Quincy, MA
Roberta Intermediate Care Home, Roberta, GA
Roberts Health Centre Inc, North Kingstown, RI
Roberts Memorial Nursing Home, Morton, TX
Roberts Nursing Home, Napa, CA
Robertson County Health Care Center, Springfield, TN
Robings Manor Nursing Home, Brighton, IL
Robinson Developmental Center, McKees Rocks, PA
Robinson Home, Pasadena, CA
Robinson Nursing Home & Development Center, Robinson, TX
Robinson's Health Care Facility, Gardiner, ME
Robinswood School, Lake Charles, LA
Robinwood Rest Home, Toledo, OH
Robison Jewish Home, Portland, OR
Robison Nursing Home Inc, Dayton, WA
Rochelle Healthcare Center East, Rochelle, IL
Rochelle Nursing & Rehabilitation Center, Rochelle, IL
Rochester Friendly Home, Rochester, NY
Rochester Health Care Center, Rochester, MN
Rochester Manor, Rochester, NH
Rochester Nursing Home, Rochester, IN
Rock County Health Care Center, Janesville, WI
Rock Creek Manor, Washington, DC
Rock Falls Manor, Rock Falls, IL
The Rock Haven Nursing Home, Nacogdoches, TX
Rock Hill Convalescent Center, Rock Hill, SC
Rock Island Conv Center, Rock Island, IL
Rock Island County Health Care Center, Rock Island, IL
Rock Rapids Health Centre, Rock Rapids, IA
Rock View Good Samaritan Center, Parshall, ND
Rockaway Care Center, Edgemere, NY

Rockcastle Hospital & Respiratory Care Center, Mount Vernon, KY
Rockdale Nursing Home, Rockdale, TX
Rockford Manor, Shively, KY
Rockford Manor Inc, Rockford, IL
Rockhaven Sanitarium, Verdugo City, CA
Rockhill Healthcare Center, Kansas City, MO
Rockhill Mennonite Community, Sellersville, PA
Rockingham County Nursing Home, Epping, NH
Rockland Convalescent Center, Rockland, ME
Rockland Nursing Home, Rockland, MA
Rockledge Manor Nursing Home, Nahant, MA
Rockmart Intermediate Care Center, Rockmart, GA
Rockridge at Laurel Park, Northampton, MA
Rockville Memorial Nursing Home, Rockville, CT
Rockville Nursing Center Inc, Rockville Centre, NY
Rockville Nursing Home Inc, Rockville, MD
Rockville Residence Manor, Rockville Centre, NY
Rockwall Nursing Home, Rockwall, TX
Rockwell Community Nursing Home, Rockwell, IA
Rockwood Health Care Center, Rockwood, TN
Rockwood Manor Infirmary, Spokane, WA
Rockwood Manor Nursing Home Inc, Wellston, MO
Rocky Bay Health Care Center, Gig Harbor, WA
Rocky Bay Health Care Facility, Wauna, WA
Rocky Knoll Health Care Facility, Plymouth, WI
Rocky Mountain Health Care Center, Denver, CO
Rockynol Retirement Community, Akron, OH
Rodger Rest Home, Boston, MA
Rodgerson House, Boston, MA
Rofay Nursing Home, Bronx, NY
Roger Huntington Nursing Center, Greer, SC
Rogers City Hospital LTCU, Rogers City, MI
Rogers Nursing Center, Rogers, AR
Rogers Park Manor Nursing Home, Chicago, IL
Rogue Valley Care Center, Medford, OR
Rogue Valley Manor, Medford, OR
The Rohr Home, Bartow, FL
Rohrigs Nursing Home Inc, Uhrichsville, OH
Ro-Ker Nursing Home, Alliance, OH
Roland Park Place, Baltimore, MD
Rol-Ann Rest Home, New Bedford, MA
Rolfe Care Center, Rolfe, IA
Rolla Community Hospital—SNF, Rolla, ND
Rolla Manor Care Center, Rolla, MO
Rolling Acres Care Center, North Lima, OH
Rolling Acres Retirement Center Inc, Raleigh, MS
Rolling Fields Healthcare Community, Conneautville, PA
Rolling Hills, Sparta, WI
Rolling Hills Convalescent Center, Anderson, IN
Rolling Hills Health Care Center, New Albany, IN
Rolling Hills Manor, Zion, IL
Rolling Hills Nursing Center, Starkville, MS
Rolling Hills Nursing Center, Branson, MO
Rolling Meadows, Fond Du Lac, WI
Rollins Nursing Home, Cabot, AR
Roma Memorial Nursing Home, Three Rivers, TX
Roman Eagle Memorial Home Inc, Danville, VA
Rome & Murphy Memorial Hospital, Rome, NY
Rome-Parkway Inc, Rome, NY
Ro-Mel Guest Manor Inc, Helena, OK
Romeo Nursing Center, Romeo, MI
Romie Lane Convalescent Hospital, Salinas, CA
Ron Joy Nursing Home Inc, Boardman, OH
Roncalli Health Center Inc, Bridgeport, CT
Roncalli Woodland Inc, Waterbury, CT

Rondale Nursing & Convalescent Home, Erie, PA
Rooks County Home, Plainville, KS
Roo-Lan Healthcare Center, Lacy, WA
Roosevelt General Hospital—Nurs Home, Portales, NM
Roosevelt Memorial Nursing Home, Culbertson, MT
Roosevelt Square—Murphysboro, Murphysboro, IL
Roosevelt Square Nursing Center, Batavia, IL
Roosevelt Square Nursing Center, Princeton, IL
Roosevelt Square Nursing Home, Springfield, IL
Roosevelt Square—Rockford, Rockford, IL
Roosevelt Square—Sandwich, Sandwich, IL
Roosevelt Square—Silvis, Silvis, IL
Rosalie Nursing Home, Wisner, LA
Rosary Hill Home, Justice, IL
Roscoe Community Nursing Home, Roscoe, NY
Roscoe Nursing Home, Roscoe, TX
Rose Arbor Nursing Home, Sterling, CO
Rose Care Center of Benton I, Benton, AR
Rose Care Center of Benton II, Benton, AR
Rose Care Center of Fort Smith, Fort Smith, AR
Rose Care Center of Jacksonville, Jacksonville, AR
Rose Care Center of Jonesboro, Jonesboro, AR
Rose Care Center of Little Rock, Little Rock, AR
Rose Care Center of Rogers, Rogers, AR
Rose Care Center of Stuttgart, Stuttgart, AR
Rose Care Center of Trumann, Trumann, AR
Rose City Nursing Home, Portland, OR
The Rose Convalescent Hospital, Baldwin Park, CA
Rose Cottage Health Care Center, Central Falls, RI
Rose Crest Nursing Home, Santa Cruz, CA
Rose Garden Nursing Home, Mount Vernon, OH
Rose Haven Health Care Center, Hugo, OK
Rose Haven ICF/MR & Skilled Nursing Facility, Thomasville, GA
Rose Haven Nursing Center, Roseburg, OR
Rose Haven Nursing Home Inc, Marengo, IA
Rose Haven of Kaufman Inc, Kaufman, TX
Rose Haven Retreat Inc, Atlanta, TX
Rose Hill Nursing Home, Berryville, VA
Rose Hill Personal Care Center, Terrell, TX
Rose Lane Health Center, Massillon, OH
Rose Lane Nursing Home, Loup City, NE
Rose Lawn Geriatric Center, Alliance, OH
Rose Lawn ICF/MR, West Lafayette, OH
Rose Manor, Waterbury, CT
Rose Manor Health Care, Birmingham, AL
Rose Manor Rest Home, Lexington, KY
Rose-Mary, The Grasselli Rehabilitation & Education Center, Euclid, OH
Rose Mary's Home, Denver, CO
Rose Nursing Home, Cleveland Heights, OH
Rose of Sharon Manor, Roseville, MN
Rose Park Convalescent & Rehabilitation Center, Cleveland, OH
Rose Skill Care Nursing Center of Jonesboro, Jonesboro, AR
Rose Terrace Lodge Inc, Nicholasville, KY
Rose Villa Inc, Milwaukie, OR
Rose Villa Nursing Center, Roseville, MI
Rose Vista Home Inc, Woodbine, IA
Rose Vista Nursing Center, Vancouver, WA
Rosebud Health Care Center, Forsyth, MT
Rosebud Nursing Home, Gregory, SD
Rosedale Manor, Covington, KY
Rosedale Nursing Home, Silex, MO
Rosedale Rest Home, Owensboro, KY
Rosedale Restorium, Saint Petersburg, FL
Rosegate Care Center, Columbus, OH
Rose-Haven Ltd, Litchfield, CT
Roselawn Manor, Lansing, MI
Roselawn Manor, Spencerville, OH
Roselawn Retirement Home, New Albany, MS
Rosemont Manor, Rosemont, PA
Rosemont Nursing Home, Mansfield, OH

Roseview Nursing Center, Shreveport, LA
Roseville Convalescent Hospital, Roseville, CA
Roseville East, Milwaukee, WI
Roseville Manor, Milwaukee, WI
Roseville Nursing Home, Milwaukee, WI
Roseville of De Pere, De Pere, WI
Rosewood Center, Owings Mills, MD
Rosewood Convalescent Center, Gwynn, VA
Rosewood Convalescent Hospital, Pleasant Hill, CA
Rosewood Gardens Health Related Facility, Rensselaer, NY
Rosewood Health Facility, Bakersfield, CA
Rosewood Manor, Estherville, IA
Rosewood Manor, Galion, OH
Rosewood Manor, Memphis, TN
Rosewood Manor, Veradale, WA
Rosewood Manor Health Care Center, Bowling Green, KY
Rosewood Manor I, Muncie, IN
Rosewood Manor Ltd, Norman, OK
Rosewood Manor Rest Home, Fall River, MA
Rosewood Medical Nursing Center, Byromville, GA
Rosewood Nursing Home, Jacksonville, FL
Rosewood Nursing Home, Lake Charles, LA
Rosewood Nursing Home, West Allis, WI
Rosewood Rest Home Inc, Claymont, DE
Rosewood Terrace, Salt Lake City, UT
Rosewood-Damen Nursing Home Inc, Chicago, IL
Rosholt Nursing Home, Rosholt, SD
Roslyn Nursing & Rehabilitation Center, Roslyn, PA
Ross Manor Nursing Home, Ridley Park, PA
Ross Nursing Home, East Liverpool, OH
Ross Nursing Home 1 Inc, Wagoner, OK
Ross Nursing Home 2 Inc, Wagoner, OK
Ross Nursing Home Inc, Brentwood, NY
Rosscare Convalescent Hospital, Campbell, CA
Rosscare Convalescent Hospital, Milpitas, CA
Rosser Nursing Home, Roanoke, AL
Rossmoor Manor, Walnut Creek, CA
Rossville Convalescent Center Inc, Rossville, GA
Rossville Valley Manor, Rossville, KS
Rotan Nursing Center, Rotan, TX
Rotary Ann Home Inc, Eagle Grove, IA
Roubals Nursing Home, Stephenson, MI
Roundup Memorial Nursing Home, Roundup, MT
Rouse-Warren County Home, Youngsville, PA
Routt Memorial Extended Care Center, Steamboat Springs, CO
Rowan Court, Barre, VT
Rowan Manor Nursing Center, Salisbury, NC
Rowland, Covina, CA
Herman L Rowley Memorial Masonic Home, Perry, IA
Roxboro Nursing Center, Roxboro, NC
Roxbury Home for Aged Women, Roslindale, MA
Royal Care Convalescent Center, Centralia, WA
Royal Care of Erin Inc, Erin, TN
Royal Care of Lawrenceburg, Lawrenceburg, TN
Royal Care Skilled Nursing Facility, Long Beach, CA
Royal Convalescent Hospital Inc, Brawley, CA
Royal Elaine Intermediate Care Facility, LaGrange, GA
Royal Elm Inc, Elmwood Park, IL
Royal Fontana Nursing Center Inc, Urbana, IL
Royal Glades Convalescent Home, North Miami Beach, FL
Royal Grove Convalescent Hospital, Orange, CA
The Royal Home, El Cajon, CA
Royal Manor, Nicholasville, KY
Royal Manor Care Center, Missoula, MT
Royal Manor Health Care Inc, Sacramento, CA
Royal Manor Inc, Warwick, RI

Royal Megansett Nursing Home, Falmouth, MA
Royal Neighbor Home, Davenport, IA
Royal Nursing Center, Highland Park, MI
Royal Nursing Home, Mesa, AZ
Royal Oak Nursing Resort, Dade City, FL
Royal Oaks, Madison, NJ
Royal Oaks Convalescent Hospital, Galt, CA
Royal Palm Convalescent Center, Vero Beach, FL
Royal Pavilion Extended Care Facility, Steubenville, OH
Royal Terrace Inc, McHenry, IL
Royal Vista Care Center, Ellensburg, WA
Royal Willows Nursing Care Center, Wilmington, IL
Royale Convalescent Hospital, Santa Ana, CA
Royale Gardens Health Care Facility, Grants Pass, OR
Royale Oaks Convalescent Hospital, Glendale, CA
Royalwood Convalescent Hospital, Torrance, CA
Royce Manor, Sarcoxie, MO
Rubins Brierwood Terrace, Los Angeles, CA
Ruby Hill Nursing Home Inc, Bessemer, AL
Ruby Mountains Manor, Elko, NV
Rubys Rest Home Inc, Middlesboro, KY
Rucon House, Pocatello, ID
Rudnick Community Residence, Aiken, SC
Ruidoso Care Center, Ruidoso, NM
Ruleville Health Care Center, Ruleville, MS
Rural Health Care Facility, Indianapolis, IN
Rush County Nursing Home, LaCrosse, KS
Rush Nursing Center Butler Inc, Butler, AL
Rusk County Memorial Hospital Nursing Home, Ladysmith, WI
Rusk Nursing Home Inc, Rusk, TX
Abbiejean Russell Care Center, Fort Pierce, FL
Russell Convalescent Home, Russell, KY
Russell Kare Center, Russell, KS
Russell Nursing Home, Winder, GA
Russell Nursing Home, Albany, OH
Russell Park Manor, Lewiston, ME
Russell Retirement RCFI, Charleston, MO
Russellville Health Care Manor, Russellville, KY
Russellville Nursing Center, Russellville, AR
Rust-McGills Nursing Center, Eaton, OH
Ruston State School, Ruston, LA
Ruth Taylor Geriatric & Rehabilitation Institute/Weschester County Medical Center, Hawthorne, NY
Rutherford County Convalescent Center, Rutherfordton, NC
Rutherford County Nursing Home, Murfreesboro, TN
Rutherford Nursing Center, Rutherfordton, NC
Rutland Heights Hospital—Skilled Nursing Facility, Rutland, MA
Rutland Nursing Home Co Inc, Brooklyn, NY
Rutledge Community Residence, Charleston, SC
Hannah M Rutledge Home for the Aged, Chippewa Falls, WI
Rutledge Manor Care Home Inc, Springfield, IL
Ryan Nursing Home, Amherst, VA
Ryan Nursing Home Inc, Ryan, OK
Ryburn Nursing Center, Dallas, TX
Rydal Park of Philadelphia Presbyterian Homes on the Fairway, Rydal, PA
Mary Ryder Home for the Aged, Saint Louis, MO
Mary Ryder Home for the Aged, Saint Louis, MO
Ryder Memorial Skilled Nursing Facility, Humacao, PR
Sabetha Manor, Sabetha, KS
Sabine Oaks Home, Beaumont, TX
Sable Care Center Inc, Aurora, CO
Sacramento Convalescent Hospital, Sacramento, CA
Sacred Heart Culture Hospital, Pasadena, CA
Sacred Heart Free Home, Philadelphia, PA
Sacred Heart Home, Chicago, IL

Sacred Heart Home, Avilla, IN
Sacred Heart Home, Louisville, KY
Sacred Heart Home, Bronx, NY
Sacred Heart Home for Aged—Little Sisters of the Poor, Oregon, OH
Sacred Heart Home Inc, Hyattsville, MD
Sacred Heart Home Inc, Plattsburgh, NY
Sacred Heart Hospice, Austin, MN
Sacred Heart Manor, Philadelphia, PA
Sacred Heart Nursing Home, New Bedford, MA
Saddle Brook Convalescent Home, Saddle Brook, NJ
Ellen Sagar Nursing Home, Union, SC
Sage Healthcare Center, Midland, TX
Sager Nursing Home, Fair Haven, VT
Saginaw Community Hospital, Saginaw, MI
Saginaw Geriatric Home, Saginaw, MI
Sahara House, Princeton, MN
The Sailors' Snug Harbor, Sea Level, NC
St Agnes Health Care Center, Chicago, IL
St Agnes Home, Kirkwood, MO
St Aloisius Skilled Nursing Home, Harvey, ND
St Andre Health Care Facility, Biddeford, ME
St Andrew Home for the Aged, Niles, IL
St Andrew's Hospital & Nursing Home, Bottineau, ND
St Andrews Estates Medical Center, Boca Raton, FL
St Ann Home, Dover, NH
St Ann Skilled Nursing Center, Sandusky, OH
St Anna's Asylum, New Orleans, LA
St Anne Home, Fort Wayne, IN
St Anne Home for the Elderly, Greensburg, PA
St Annes Hospice, Winona, MN
St Annes Convalescent Hospital, Castro Valley, CA
St Annes Convalescent Center, Detroit, MI
St Annes Home, San Francisco, CA
St Anne's Home, Columbia, PA
St Anne's Home for the Elderly, Milwaukee, WI
St Ann's Convalescent Homes, Arabi, LA
St Anns Healthcare Center Inc, Chester, IL
St Ann's Home, Hammond, IN
St Ann's Home, Grand Rapids, MI
St Ann's Home for the Aged Inc—The Heritage, Rochester, NY
St Ann's Nursing Home, Juneau, AK
St Ann's Nursing Home Inc, Oklahoma City, OK
St Ann's Nursing Home, Panhandle, TX
St Anns Residence, Minneapolis, MN
St Ann's Rest Home, Milwaukee, WI
St Ansgar Good Samaritan Center, Saint Ansgar, IA
St Anthony Center, Houston, TX
St Anthony Eldercenter on Main, Minneapolis, MN
St Anthony Health Care Inc, Lafayette, IN
St Anthony Health Center, Saint Anthony Village, MN
St Anthony Home Inc, Crown Point, IN
St Anthony Nursing Center, Warren, MI
St Anthony Nursing Home, Carroll, IA
St Anthonys Continuing Care Center, Rock Island, IL
St Anthony's Medical Center-Rehab Center, Saint Louis, MO
St Anthony's Nursing Home Inc, Metairie, LA
St Antoine Residence, North Smithfield, RI
St Augustine Center for Living, Saint Augustine, FL
St Augustine Geriatric Center, Saint Augustine, FL
St Augustine Home for the Aged, Indianapolis, IN
St Augustine Manor, Cleveland, OH
St Barbara's Memorial Nursing Home Inc, Monongah, WV
St Barnabas Nursing Home, Gibsonia, PA
St Barnabas Nursing Home, Chattanooga, TN
St Benedict Home for Aged, Niles, IL
St Benedict Nursing Home, Detroit, MI
St Benedict Nursing Home, San Antonio, TX
St Benedicts Center, Saint Cloud, MN

St Benedict's Long-Term Care Unit, Jerome, ID

St Brendan Care Center, Spokane, WA

St Cabrini Nursing Home Inc, Dobbs Ferry, NY

St Camillus Health Center Inc, Wauwatosa, WI

St Camillus Residential Health Care Facility, Syracuse, NY

St Casimir Health Care Facility, Lewiston, ME

St Catherine Laboure Manor, Jacksonville, FL

St Catherine's Infirmary Inc, Racine, WI

St Catherine's Residence & Nursing Center, North Bend, OR

St Charles Nursing Home, Newellton, LA

St Charles Care Center & Village, Covington, KY

St Charles Health Care Center, New Orleans, LA

St Charles Health Care Center, Saint Charles, MO

St Christopher Convalescent Hospital, Hayward, CA

St Christopher Convalescent Hospital & Sanitarium, Signal Hill, CA

St Clair County Medical Centre, Goodells, MI

St Clair County Specialized Living Center, Swansea, IL

St Clare Convalescent Center, Detroit, MI

St Claras Manor, Lincoln, IL

St Clare Convent, Colorado Springs, CO

St Clare Home, Newport, RI

St Clare Manor, Lockport, NY

St Cloud Health Care Center, Saint Cloud, FL

St Cloud Manor, Saint Cloud, MN

St Coletta School Alverno Cottage, Jefferson, WI

St Croix Health Center, New Richmond, WI

St Croix Valley Good Samaritan Center, Saint Croix Falls, WI

St Dominic Nursing Home, Houston, TX

St Edna Convalescent Center, Santa Ana, CA

St Edward Home, Akron, OH

St Elizabeth Convalescent Hospital, Anaheim, CA

St Elizabeth Health Care Center, Baker, OR

St Elizabeth Health Center, East Hartford, CT

St Elizabeth Healthcare Center, Delphi, IN

St Elizabeth Home, Saint Cloud, MN

St Elizabeth Home, Providence, RI

St Elizabeth Manor Inc, Saint Elizabeth, MO

St Elizabeth Nursing Home, Wabasha, MN

St Elizabeth Nursing Home, Waco, TX

St Elizabeth Nursing Home, Brookfield, WI

St Elizabeth Toluca Lake Convalescent Hospital, North Hollywood, CA

St Elizabeth's Home, Janesville, WI

St Erne Sanitarium, Inglewood, CA

St Frances Home, Fond Du Lac, WI

St Frances Home for the Aged, Hampshire, NH

St Francis Continuing Care & Nursing Home Center, Burlington, IA

St Francis Convalescent Pavilion Inc, Daly City, CA

St Francis Country Home, Darby, PA

St Francis Extended Care Center, Evanston, IL

St Francis Gardens Inc, Albuquerque, NM

St Francis Heights Convalescent Hospital, Daly City, CA

St Francis Home, Worcester, MA

St Francis Home, Saginaw, MI

St Francis Home, Breckenridge, MN

St Francis Home, Waite Park, MN

St Francis Home, Laconia, NH

St Francis Home for the Aged, Tiffin, OH

St Francis Home Inc, Superior, WI

St Francis Home/La Crosse Inc, La Crosse, WI

St Francis Home of Williamsville, Williamsville, NY

St Francis Hospital (DP), Honolulu, HI

St Francis Hospital Nursing Home, Memphis, TN

St Francis Hopital—SNF/ICF Care Facility, Marceline, MO

St Francis Manor Inc, Grinnell, IA

St Francis Nursing Home, San Antonio, TX

St Francis Rehabilitation Hospital & Nursing Home, Green Springs, OH

St George Care Center, Saint George, UT

St George Health Care Center Inc, Saint George, SC

St George Nursing Home, Eden, NY

St Gerard's Nursing Home, Hankinson, ND

St Ignatius Nursing Home, Philadelphia, PA

St James House of Baytown, Baytown, TX

St James Nursing Center Inc, Greensboro, NC

St James Nursing Home Skilled, Saint James, NY

St Joan Antida Home, West Allis, WI

St John Kronstadt Convalescent Center, Castro Valley, CA

St John Lutheran Care Center, Mars, PA

St John Lutheran Home, Springfield, MN

St John Medical Center, Tulsa, OK

St John Neumann Nursing Home, Philadelphia, PA

St John of God Nursing Hospital & Residence Inc, Los Angeles, CA

St John Rest Home, Brockton, MA

St Johnland Nursing Home Inc, Kings Park, NY

St John's Center, Springfield, OH

St Johns County Senior Citizens Home, Saint Augustine, FL

St Johns Episcopal Homes for the Aged & the Blind, Brooklyn, NY

St Johns Extended Care, New Haven, CT

St John's Home of Milwaukee, Milwaukee, WI

St Johns Hospital Long-Term Care, Jackson, WY

St Johns Lutheran Home, Albert Lea, MN

St Johns Mercy Villa, Springfield, MO

St Johns Nursing & Rehabilitation Hospital/St John's Health Care Center, Lauderdale Lakes, FL

St John's Lutheran Home, Billings, MT

St John's Nursing Home Inc, Rochester, NY

St John's Nursing Home Inc, Lynchburg, VA

St Johns Nursing Home of Lowell Inc, Haverhill, MA

St John's of Hays, Hays, KS

St Johns Rest Home, Victoria, KS

St Johnsbury Convalescent Center, Saint Johnsbury, VT

St Joseph Care Center, Spokane, WA

St Joseph Care Center—Notre Dame, South Bend, IN

St Joseph Convalescent Center, Saint Joseph, MO

St Joseph Convalescent Center, Polson, MT

St Joseph Convalescent Hospital Inc, Castro Valley, CA

St Joseph Gerontology Center, Alliance, NE

St Joseph Home, Brinkley, AR

St Joseph Home, Kansas City, KS

St Joseph Home for the Aged, Freeport, IL

St Joseph Home of Chicago Inc, Chicago, IL

St Joseph Hospice Home for the Aged, Louisville, OH

St Joseph Infant Home, Cincinnati, OH

St Joseph Manor, Florence, CO

St Joseph Manor, Brockton, MA

St Joseph Medical Center Pavilion, Burbank, CA

St Joseph Nursing & Health Care Center, Pittsburgh, PA

St Joseph Nursing Home, Lacon, IL

St Joseph Nursing Home, Upper Frenchville, ME

St Joseph Nursing Home, Hamtramck, MI

St Joseph Nursing Home, Utica, NY

St Joseph Nursing Home, Arcadia, WI

St Joseph of the Pines Hospital—SNF, Southern Pines, NC

St Joseph Residence Inc, New London, WI

St Joseph Villa, Salt Lake City, UT

St Josephs Care Center—Lombardy, South Bend, IN

St Joseph's Care Center—Morningside, South Bend, IN

St Joseph's Care Center—Melrose, Mishawaka, IN

St John's Center, Kearney, NE

St Josephs Convalescent Hospital, Ojai, CA

St Josephs Center, Scranton, PA

St Joseph's Hill Infirmary Inc, Eureka, MO

St Joseph's Home, Monroe, LA

St Joseph's Home, Saint Charles, MO

St Josephs Home, Ogdensburg, NY

St Joseph's Home, Kenosha, WI

St Joseph's Home for the Aged, Jefferson City, MO

St Joseph's Home for the Aged, Holland, PA

St Joseph's Home for the Aged, West Allis, WI

St Joseph's Home for the Elderly, Palatine, IL

St Josephs Home of Peoria, Peoria, IL

St Joseph's Home of Springfield, Springfield, IL

St Josephs Home for the Aged, Detroit, MI

St Joseph's Hospital & Nursing Home of Del Norte Inc, Del Norte, CO

St Josephs Hospital Nursing Home of Yonkers New York Inc, Yonkers, NY

St Josephs Hospital—Skilled Nursing Facility, Elmira, NY

St Joseph's Manor, Trumbull, CT

St Joseph's Manor, Portland, ME

St Joseph's Manor, Boston, MA

St Josephs Manor, Olean, NY

St Josephs Manor, Meadowbrook, PA

St Joseph's Nursing Home, Norfolk, NE

St Joseph's Nursing Home, Catonsville, MD

St Joseph's Nursing Home, Hillsboro, WI

St Joseph's Nursing Home, La Crosse, WI

St Joseph's Residence, Enfield, CT

St Joseph's Residence, Dallas, TX

St Josephs Villa, Flourtown, PA

St Josephs Villa Inc, David City, NE

St Jude Convalescent Center, Livonia, MI

St Jude Convalescent Home, Hudson, MA

St Jude Manor Nursing Home, Jacksonville, FL

St Jude's Health Care Center, Spokane, WA

St Lawrence Diamondale Center, Dimondale, MI

St Louis Altenheim, Saint Louis, MO

St Louis Developmental Disabilities Treatment Center, Saint Louis, MO

St Louis Good Shepherd Homes Inc, Saint Louis, MO

St Louis Park Plaza Healthcare Center, Saint Louis Park, MN

St Lucas Convalescent & Geriatric Center, Faribault, MN

St Luke Lutheran Home, Spencer, IA

St Luke Community Nursing Home, Ronan, MT

St Luke Convalescent Center, Columbus, OH

St Luke-East Convalescent Center, Columbus, OH

St Luke Lutheran Home, Baltimore, MD

St Luke Lutheran Home for the Aging, North Canton, OH

St Luke Manor, Fortuna, CA

St Luke Manor, Hazelton, PA

St Luke Manor of Batavia, Batavia, NY

St Luke Nursing Home Company Inc, Oswego, NY

St Luke Pavilion, Hazelton, PA

St Luke's Extended Care Hospital & Nursing Centre, San Leandro, CA

St Lukes Episcopal Home, Highland Park, MI

St Luke's Good Samaritan Village, Kearney, NE

St Lukes Home, Springfield, MA

St Luke's Home, Dickinson, ND

St Lukes Lutheran Home, Blue Earth, MN

St Luke's Methodist Hospital, Cedar Rapids, IA

St Luke's Nursing Center, Carthage, MO

St Lukes Nursing Home, Birmingham, AL

St Lukes Presbyterian Nursing Center, Buffalo, NY

St Margaret Hall, Cincinnati, OH

St Margaret of Cortona Home, Lexington, KY

St Margaret's Daughters Nursing Home, New Orleans, LA

St Margarets House & Hospital for Babies, Albany, NY

St Mark Village, Palm Harbor, FL

St Marks Lutheran Home, Austin, MN
St Martha Manor, Chicago, IL
St Martin Deporres Nursing Home, Detroit, MI
St Martins-in-the-Pines, Birmingham, AL
St Martinville Nursing Home, Saint Martinville, LA
St Mary's Convalescent Center, Saint Mary's, GA
St Mary's Guest Home, Morgan City, LA
St Mary Home, West Hartford, CT
St Mary Nursing Home, Saint Clair Shores, MI
St Mary Square Living Center Inc, Freeport, IL
St Mary Square Living Center of Chicago, Chicago, IL
St Marys Home, Saint Paul, MN
St Mary's Home for the Aged Inc, Manitowoc, WI
St Marys Home of Erie, Erie, PA
St Marys Hospital & Home, Winsted, MN
St Marys Hospital for Children Inc, Bayside, NY
St Mary's Hospital Long-Term Care, Norton, VA
St Mary's Infant Home Inc, Norfolk, VA
St Marys Manor, Saint Marys, KS
St Marys Nursing Center, Detroit Lakes, MN
St Mary's Manor, Niagara Falls, NY
St Marys Manor, Lansdale, PA
St Mary's Memorial Home, Glendale, OH
St Mary's Nursing Center, Leonardtown, MD
St Marys Nursing Home, Milwaukee, WI
St Mary's Nursing Home, Sparta, WI
St Mary's Residential Training School, Alexandria, LA
St Mary's Square Living Center of Irvington, Irvington, IL
St Mary's Villa Nursing Home, Elmhurst, PA
St Marys Villa Nursing Home, Pierz, MN
St Matthew Lutheran Home, Park Ridge, IL
St Matthews Manor, Louisville, KY
St Michael Convalescent Hospital, Hayward, CA
St Michael's Evangelical Lutheran Home for the Aged, Fountain City, WI
St Michaels Hospital & Nursing Home, Sauk Centre, MN
St Michael's Nursing Home, Tyndall, SD
St Monica's Home, Roxbury, MA
St Olaf Residence, Minneapolis, MN
St Otto's Home, Little Falls, MN
St Patricks Manor Inc, Framingham, MA
St Patricks Home for the Aged & Infirm, Bronx, NY
St Patrick's Residence, Joliet, IL
St Paul Baptist Church Home for the Aged, Indianapolis, IN
St Paul Health Center, Denver, CO
St Paul Hermitage, Beech Grove, IN
St Paul Home, Kaukauna, WI
St Paul Homes, Greenville, PA
St Pauls Church Home, Saint Paul, MN
St Paul's Health Care Center, San Diego, CA
St Pauls Home, Belleville, IL
St Pauls House/Grace Convalescent Home, Chicago, IL
St Paul's Retirement Community Inc, South Bend, IN
St Paul's Towers, Oakland, CA
St Peter Villa Nursing Home, Memphis, TN
St Peters Manor Care Center, Saint Peters, MO
St Petersburg Cluster, Saint Petersburg, FL
St Raphaels Home for the Aged, Columbus, OH
St Regis Nursing Home & Health Related Facility Inc, Massena, NY
St Richard's Villa Inc, Muenster, TX
St Rita's Home for the Aged Inc, Columbus, OH
St Roses Home, New York, NY
St Simeon's Episcopal Home Inc, Tulsa, OK
St Sophia Geriatric Center, Florissant, MO
St Stanislaus Medical Care Center Inc, Nanticoke, PA

St Stephen Group Homes A & B, Bloomington, MN
St Teresa's Manor, Manchester, NH
St Teresas Nursing Home Inc, Middletown, NY
St Theresa Home, Cincinnati, OH
St Theresa Convalescent Hospital, Pico Rivera, CA
St Therese Home, New Hope, MN
St Thomas Convalescent Center, Houston, TX
St Thomas More Progressive Care Center, Canon City, CO
St Vincent Community Living Facility, Freeport, IL
St Vincent de Paul Nursing Home, Berlin, NH
St Vincent's Nursing Home, Montclair, NJ
St Vincent's Nursing Home, Bismarck, ND
St Williams Home for Aged, Milbank, SD
St Williams Nursing Home, Parkers Prairie, MN
Saints Nursing Home, Oklahoma City, OK
Inez Sako Nursing Home II, Houma, LA
Salamanca Nursing Home Inc, Salamanca, NY
Thad E Saleeby Developmental Center, Hartsville, SC
Salem Convalescent Center, Salem, OH
Salem County Nursing Home, Salem, NJ
Salem Hills Health Care Center, Purdys, NY
Salem Lutheran Home Skilled Nursing Facility, Oakland, CA
Salem Lutheran Homes, Elk Horn, IA
Salem Manor, Indianola, IA
Salem Mennonite Home for the Aged, Freeman, SD
Salem Nursing Home, Salem, KY
Salem Parke Nursing Home, Cincinnati, OH
Salem Village, Joliet, IL
Salemhaven, Salem, NH
Salina Nursing Center, Salina, KS
Salina Presbyterian Manor, Salina, KS
Saline Care Center, Harrisburg, IL
Saline County Rest Home Inc, Marshall, MO
Salisbury Nursing Home, Salisbury, MD
Salisbury Nursing Home, Worcester, MA
Salmi Boarding Home, Aurora, MN
Salmon Brook Convalescent Home, Glastonbury, CT
Salsbury Baptist Home, Charles City, IA
Salt Lake DD Center, Salt Lake City, UT
Salt River Nursing Home, Shelbina, MO
Saluda Home, Saluda, VA
Saluda Nursing Center, Saluda, SC
Saluda Nursing & Convalescent Center, Saluda, NC
Salvation Army Adult Day Care Center, Newport, KY
Salyer Nursing Home Inc, Centerburg, OH
Salyersville Health Care Center, Salyersville, KY
Samaritan Bethany Home, Rochester, MN
Samaritan Home, West Bend, WI
Samaritan Home Inc, Topeka, KS
Samaritan-Keep Nursing Home Inc, Watertown, NY
Samarkand Health Center, Santa Barbara, CA
San Andreas Convalescent Hospital, San Andreas, CA
San Angelo Development Center, San Angelo, TX
San Antonio Convalescent Center, San Antonio, TX
San Augustine Nursing & Development Center, San Augustine, TX
San Bruno Convalescent Hospital, San Bruno, CA
San Diego Convalescent Hospital, La Mesa, CA
San Diego Hebrew Home for the Aged, San Diego, CA
San Diego Intermediate Care Center, San Diego, CA
San Dimas Golden Age Convalescent Home, Glendora, CA
San Filippo Rest Home, Malden, MA
San Francisco Community Convalescent Hospital, San Francisco, CA
San Francisco Convalescent Center, San Francisco, CA

San Gabriel Convalescent Center, Rosemead, CA
San Jacinto Heritage Manor, Deer Park, TX
San Joaquin Gardens Health Facility, Fresno, CA
San Jose Care & Guidance Center, San Jose, CA
San Jose Nursing Center, San Antonio, TX
San Juan Gardens, Phoenix, AZ
San Juan Living Center, Montrose, CO
San Juan Manor, Farmington, NM
San Juan Nursing Home, Anacortes, WA
San Juan Nursing Home Inc, San Juan, TX
San Leandro Convalescent Hospital, San Leandro, CA
San Luis Convalescent Hospital, Newman, CA
San Luis Manor, Green Bay, WI
San Marco Convalescent Hospital, Walnut Creek, CA
San Marino Manor, San Gabriel, CA
San Mateo Convalescent Hospital, San Mateo, CA
San Pedro Manor, San Antonio, TX
San Pedro Peninsula Hospital Pavilion, San Pedro, CA
San Saba Nursing Home Inc, San Saba, TX
San Simeon by the Sound —Skilled Nursing Facility, Greenport, NY
San Tomas Convalescent Hospital, San Jose, CA
Sandalwood Convalescent Home, Oxford, MA
Sandalwood Healthcare Centre, Wheaton, IL
Sande Convalescent Home Inc, Big Sandy, MT
Sanders Community Residence, Aiken, SC
Sandhaven Conv Center, Sandwich, IL
Sandhaven Nursing Home, Lamar, CO
Sandhills Manor, Broken Bow, NE
Sandmont Gala Nursing Home, Trenton, GA
Sandpiper Convalescent Center, Mount Pleasant, SC
Sandpoint Manor, Sandpoint, ID
Sands Point Nursing Home, Port Washington, NY
Sandstone Heights, Little River, KS
Sandstrom Home Intermediate Care Facility, Myrtle Beach, SC
Sandusky Nursing Home Inc, Sandusky, OH
Sandy Creek Nursing Center Inc, Wayland, MI
Sandy River Nursing Care Center, Farmington, ME
Sanfield Manor, Hartland, ME
Sanford Health Care Facility, Sanford, ME
Sanford Memorial Nursing Home/Hospital, Farmington, MN
Sanford Nursing Home, Itasca, TX
Sanger Convalescent Hospital, Sanger, CA
Sanibel Convalescent Home, Middletown, CT
Sanilac Medical Care Facility, Sandusky, MI
Sannes, Soldiers Grove, WI
Sansbury Memorial Infirmary, Saint Catherine, KY
Santa Anita Convalescent Hospital & Retirement Center Inc, Temple City, CA
Santa Barbara Convalescent Hospital, Santa Barbara, CA
Santa Clarita Convalescent Hospital, Santa Clarita, CA
Santa Fe Convalescent Hospital, Long Beach, CA
Santa Fe Trail Nursing Center, Burlingame, KS
Santa Marie Nursing Home, Green Bay, WI
Santa Monica Care Convalescent Hospital, Santa Monica, CA
Santa Monica Convalarium, Santa Monica, CA
Santa Monica Lodge, Santa Monica, CA
Santa Paula Healthcare, Santa Paula, CA
Santa Rita Health Care Center, Green Valley, AZ
Santa Rosa Convalescent Center, Tucson, AZ
Santa Rosa Convalescent Center, Milton, FL
Santa Rosa Convalescent Hospital, Santa Rosa, CA
Santa Rosa Extended Care Facility, Guayamas, PR

Santa Ynez Valley Recovery Residence, Solvang, CA
Sapulpa Nursing Center Inc, Sapulpa, OK
Sarasota Nursing Pavilion, Sarasota, FL
Sarasota Welfare Home Inc, Sarasota, FL
Saratoga County Infirmary/Health Related Facility, Ballston Spa, NY
Saratoga Hospital Nursing Home, Saratoga Springs, NY
Saratoga Place Skilled Nursing Facility, Saratoga, CA
Sargent Manor Health Care Center, Forman, ND
Sargent Nursing Home, Sargent, NE
Sartori Hospital Skilled Nursing Facility, Cedar Falls, IA
Sassaquin Nursing Home Inc, New Bedford, MA
Sauer Memorial Home, Winona, MN
Sauk County Health Care Center, Reedsburg, WI
Saunders County Care Center, Wahoo, NE
Saunders House, Philadelphia, PA
Savannah Beach Nursing Home Inc, Tybee Island, GA
Savannah Convalescent Center, Savannah, GA
Savannah Health Care, Savannah, GA
Savoy Care Center Inc, Mamou, LA
Savoy Convalescent Home, New Bedford, MA
Saxony Health Center, Saxonburg, PA
Saxton Nursing Home, Saint Joseph, MO
Saybrook Convalescent Hospital, Old Saybrook, CT
Saylor Lane Convalescent Hospital, Sacramento, CA
Sayre Christian Village Nursing Home, Lexington, KY
Sayre House Inc, Sayre, PA
Scalabrini Villa, North Kingstown, RI
Scallop Shell Nursing Home Inc, South Kingstown, RI
Scandia Village Retirement Center, Sister Bay, WI
Scandinavian Home for the Aged, Cranston, RI
Scenery Hill Manor Inc, Indiana, PA
Scenic Hills Nursing Center, Bidwell, OH
Scenic Manor, Iowa Falls, IA
Scenic View Health Care Center, Baldwin, GA
Scenic View Nursing Home, Millersburg, OH
Olive Schaeffer Home, Sheboygan, WI
Frances Schervier Home & Hospital, Bronx, NY
Scheuber Hospital, Pigeon, MI
Schleicher County Medical Center, Eldorado, TX
A W Schlesinger Geriatric Center, Beaumont, TX
Schmidtke Rest Home, Ceylon, MN
Schmitt Woodland Hills Inc, Richland Center, WI
Schnepps Health Care Center, Saint Louis, MI
Schofield Residence, Kenmore, NY
Schoolcraft Medical Care Facility, Manistique, MI
Schowalter Villa, Hesston, KS
Schroder Manor, Hamilton, OH
The Samuel Schulman Institute for Nursing & Rehabilitation, Brooklyn, NY
Schulze Nursing Home, Dayton, OH
Schussler Rest Home, Worcester, MA
Schuyler County Nursing Home, Queen City, MO
Schuyler Hospital Long-Term Care, Montour Falls, NY
Schuyler Senior Citizen's Home, Schuyler, NE
Schuylkill County Home Rest Haven, Schuylkill Haven, PA
Scituate Ocean Manor, Scituate, MA
Scotland County Nursing Home District, Memphis, MO
Scotland Good Samaritan Center, Scotland, SD
Scott County Nursing Center, Winchester, IL
Scott County Nursing Home, Morton, MS
Scott County Nursing Home, Oneida, TN
Elizabeth Scott Memorial Care Center, Maumee, OH

John Scott House Nursing & Rehabilitation Center, Braintree, MA
Scott Manor Nursing Home Inc, Indianapolis, IN
Mary Scott Nursing Center, Dayton, OH
Scott Nursing Home inc, Smyrna, DE
Scott Villa Living Center, Scottsburg, IN
The Scottish Home, North Riverside, IL
Scottish Rite Park Health Care Center, Des Moines, IA
Scottland Company Community Home, Memphis, MO
Scotts Rest Home, Haverhill, MA
Scottsbluff Villa, Scottsbluff, NE
Scottsboro Nursing Home, Scottsboro, AL
Scottsburg Nursing Home, Scottsburg, IN
Scottsdale Convalescent Plaza, Scottsdale, AZ
Scottsdale Heritage Court, Scottsdale, AZ
Scottsdale Village Square, Scottsdale, AZ
Scribner Good Samaritan Center, Scribner, NE
Scripps Home, Altadena, CA
Scripps Memorial Hospital-Ocean View Convalescent, Encinitas, CA
Sea Crest Health Care Center, Brooklyn, NY
Sea Level Hospital—SNF/ICF, Sea Level, NC
Sea View Convalescent Hospital, Eureka, CA
Sea View Convalescent & Nursing Home, Rowley, MA
Sea View Hospital & Home, Staten Island, NY
Seabreeze Care Center, Texas City, TX
The Seabrook of Hilton Head Annex, Hilton Head Island, SC
Seacoast Health Center, Hampton, NH
Seacrest Convalescent Hospital, San Pedro, CA
Seacrest Nursing & Retire Center, West Haven, CT
Seaford Retirement & Rehabilitation Center, Seaford, DE
Seagirt Health Related Facility, Far Rockaway, NY
Seago Manor, Seagoville, TX
Seal Residential Care Home, Las Animas, CO
Sears Manor, Brunswick, GA
Sears Memorial Methodist Nursing Center, Abilene, TX
Seaside Care Center, Fullerton, CA
Seaside Care Center, Seaside, OR
Seaside Nursing & Retirement Home, Portland, ME
Seatoma Convalescent Center, Kent, WA
Seattle Keiro, Seattle, WA
Seattle Specialized Group Home, Seattle, WA
Seaway Care Center, Muskegon, MI
Sebasticook Valley Health Care Facility, Pittsfield, ME
Sebastopol Convalescent Hospital, Sebastopol, CA
Sebo Heritage Manor Nursing Home, Hobart, IN
Sebring Care Center, Sebring, FL
Second Midlands ICMRF, Columbia, SC
Second Shamrock Care Center, Kingfisher, OK
Sedgwick Convalescent Center, Sedgwick, KS
Sedgwick County Hospital & Nursing Home, Julesburg, CO
Seguin Convalescent Home, Seguin, TX
Sehome Park Care Center, Bellingham, WA
Seidle Memorial Hospital—Extended Care Unit, Mechanicsburg, PA
Seiling Nursing Center, Seiling, OK
Seimon Lakeview Manor Estate, Somerset, PA
Seitz Nursing Home, Dallastown, PA
Selah Convalescent Home Inc, Selah, WA
Self Nursing Home Inc, Hueytown, AL
Selfhelp Home for the Aged, Chicago, IL
Selinsgrove Center, Selinsgrove, PA
Sells Rest Home Inc, Matthews, MO
Selma Convalescent Hospital, Selma, CA
SEM Haven Health Care Center, Milford, OH
Seminary Memorial Home, Red Wing, MN
Seminole Manor, Donalsonville, GA
Seminole Nursing Center Inc, Seminole, TX
Seminole Nursing Pavilion, Seminole, FL

Seminole Pioneer Nursing Home Inc, Seminole, OK
Seminole Villa Care Center, Springfield, OH
Senath Nursing Home, Senath, MO
Senatobia Convalescent Center, Senatobia, MS
Seneca Community Residence, Seneca, SC
Seneca Manor Health Care Facility, West Seneca, NY
Seneca Nursing Home & HRF, Waterloo, NY
Senior Citizens Center, Coushatta, LA
Senior Citizens Home, Hosmer, SD
Senior Citizens Nursing Home, Madisonville, KY
Senior Citizen's Nursing Home, Nevada, MO
Senior Citizens Nursing Home, Broken Arrow, OK
Senior Citizens Nursing Home, Guthrie, OK
Senior Citizens Nursing Home, Winters, TX
Senior Citizens Nursing Home, Spokane, WA
Senior Estates, Kansas City, MO
Senior Health Care Center, Wilmington, OH
Senior Home, Montezuma, IA
Senior Home, Monticello, IA
Senior Manor Nursing Center Inc, Sparta, IL
Senior Village Nursing Home, Opelousas, LA
Senior Village Nursing Home, Blanchard, OK
Senior Village Nursing Home, Perryton, TX
Sentinel Nursing Home, Sentinel, OK
Sephardic Home for the Aged Inc, Brooklyn, NY
Sepulveda Convalescent Hospital Inc, Van Nuys, CA
Sequatchie Health Care Center, Dunlap, TN
Sequim Nursing Center, Sequim, WA
The Sequoias, Portola Valley, CA
Sequoias San Francisco Convalescent Hospital, San Francisco, CA
Sequoyah East Nursing Center, Roland, OK
Sequoyah Manor, Sallisaw, OK
Lefa L Seran Skilled Nursing Facility, Hawthorne, NV
Serene Manor Medical Center, Knoxville, TN
Serenity Haven Nursing Home, Garland, TX
Serenity Hill Nursing Home, Wrentham, MA
Serenity Rest Home, Chelmsford, MA
Serrano Convalescent Hospital, Los Angeles, CA
Serrano Convalescent Hospital—South, Los Angeles, CA
Seth Mann II Home for the Aged, Randolph, MA
Elizabeth Seton Residence, Windsor, MA
Seton Hill Manor, Baltimore, MD
Seven Gables, Youngstown, OH
Seven Hills Health Care Center, Lynchburg, VA
Seven Oaks Convalescent Care Center, Bonham, TX
Seven Oaks Nursing Home, Olney, TX
7th Street, Brighton, CO
Seventh Street House, Faribault, MN
Severin Intermediate Care Facility, Benton, IL
Sevier County Health Care Center Inc, Sevierville, TN
Seville Nursing Home, Salem, MO
Seymour Care Center, Seymour, IA
Shabbona Nursing Home Inc, Shabbona, IL
Shadescrest Health Care Center, Jasper, AL
Shadow Hill Convalescent Hospital, Sunland, CA
Shadow Mountain Health Care Center, Scottsdale, AZ
Shady Acres Convalescent Center, Douglas, GA
Shady Acres Health Care Center, Newton, TX
Shady Acres Inc, Exeter, RI
Shady Creek Health Care Facility, Greencastle, IN
Shady Glade Rest Home, Ayer, MA
Shady Grove Rest Home, Kennesaw, GA
Shady Lake Nursing Home, Lake Providence, LA
Shady Lane Gloucester County Home, Clarksboro, NJ
Shady Lane Home Inc, Manitowoc, WI
Shady Lane Nursing Home, Wadena, MN
Shady Lawn, Savannah, MO
Shady Lawn Home, Cynthiana, KY

Shady Lawn Home Inc, Dalton, OH
Shady Lawn Manor Inc, Emporia, KS
Shady Lawn Nursing Home, Cadiz, KY
Shady Lawn Nursing Home—East, Kenosha, WI
Shady Lawn Nursing Home Inc, Vicksburg, MS
Shady Lawn Rest Home Inc, Hadley, MA
Shady Lawn West Nursing Home, Kenosha, WI
Shady Manor Convalescent Hospital, Bakersfield, CA
Shady Nook Care Center, Lawrenceburg, IN
Shady Oak Nursing Home Inc, Moulton, TX
Shady Oaks, Lake City, IA
Shady Oaks Lodge 1, Abilene, TX
Shady Oaks Lodge 2, Abilene, TX
Shady Oaks Nursing Home, Monroe, LA
Shady Rest Care Center, Cascade, IA
Shady Rest Care Center Inc, Pryor, OK
Shady Rest Home, Plymouth, IN
Shady Rest Nursing Home, Fort Myers, FL
Shady View Nursing Home, Oklahoma City, OK
Shadyside Care Center, Shadyside, OH
Shadyside Nursing Home Inc, Duncanville, TX
Shadyway Group Home, Wayzata, MN
Shaffer Plaza, Steubenville, OH
Shafter Convalescent Hospital, Shafter, CA
Shakamak Good Samaritan Center, Jasonville, IN
Shakopee Friendship Manor, Shakopee, MN
Shalem Rest Nursing Home, Massillon, OH
Shalimar Plaza Nursing Center, Salina, KS
Shalom Geriatric Center, Kansas City, MO
Shalom Nursing Home, Mount Vernon, NY
Shandin Hills Behavior Therapy Center, San Bernardino, CA
Shandin Hills Convalescent Hospital, San Bernardino, CA
Shane Hill Nursing Home, Rockford, OH
Shangri-La, Salem, OR
Shangri-La Health Care Center, LaFontaine, IN
Shangri-La Health Care Center, Medina, OH
Shangri-La Nursing Home, Delmar, DE
Shannondale Retirement Home, Knoxville, TN
Shanoan Springs Residence Inc, Chickasha, OK
Share Medical Center, Alva, OK
Sharmar Nursing Center, Pueblo, CO
Sharon Care Center, Los Angeles, CA
Sharon Care Center, Centralia, WA
Sharon Heights Convalescent Hospital, Menlo Park, CA
Sharon Lane Nursing Home, Shawnee, KS
Sharon Manor Nursing Home, Sharon, MA
Sharon Nursing Home, Olney, MD
Sharon Village, Charlotte, NC
Sharonview Nursing Home, South Vienna, OH
Sharp Knollwood Convalescent Hospital, San Diego, CA
Sharp Nursing Home, Sidney, AR
Sharps Personal Care Home, Falmouth, KY
Shasta Avenue, Columbus, OH
Shasta Convalescent Hospital, Redding, CA
Shaughnessy—Kaplan Rehabilitation Hospital, Salem, MA
Hannah B G Shaw Home for the Aged Inc, Middleboro, MA
Shawn Manor Nursing Home, Ponca City, OK
Shawnee Care Center, Shawnee, OK
Shawnee Christian Nursing Center, Herrin, IL
Shawnee Colonial Estates Nursing Home Inc, Shawnee, OK
Shawnee Manor, Lima, OH
Shawnee Shelter Care, Simpson, IL
Shawnee Springs Nursing Home, Winchester, VA
Shawnee Sunset Estates, Shawnee, OK
Shea Convalescent & California Villa, Upland, CA
Shea Convalescent Hospital, San Bernardino, CA
Shea Convalescent Hospital, Whittier, CA

Shearer-Richardson Memorial Nursing Home, Okolona, MS
Sheboygan Comprehensive Health Center, Sheboygan Falls, WI
Sheboygan Retirement Home & Beach Health Care Center Inc, Sheboygan, WI
Sheepscot Valley Health Center, Coopers Mills, ME
Sheepshead Nursing Home, Brooklyn, NY
Sheffield Care Center Inc, Sheffield, IA
Sheffield Convalescent Hospital, San Francisco, CA
Shelby Convalescent Center, Shelby, NC
Shelby County Health Care Center, Memphis, TN
Shelby Manor, Shelbyville, IL
Shelby Manor, Shelbyville, KY
Shelby Memorial Home, Shelbyville, IL
Shelby Memorial Hospital Nursing Home, Shelbyville, IL
Sheldon Healthcare Inc, Sheldon, IL
Sheldonville Nursing Home, Wrentham, MA
Shell Point Village Nursing Pavilion, Fort Myers, FL
Shell Rock Care Center, Shell Rock, IA
Sheltered Village—Woodstock, Woodstock, IL
Sheltering Arms Nursing Home, Walnut Ridge, AR
Sheltering Oak, Island Lake, IL
Sheltering Pine Convalescent Hospital, Millbrae, CA
Shelton Group Home, Richville, MN
Shelton Lakes Residence & Health Care, Shelton, CT
Shemwell Nursing Home, Providence, KY
Shenandoah County Memorial Hospital—Long-Term Care Unit, Woodstock, VA
Shenandoah Home Inc, Ranson, WV
Shenandoah Manor, Clifton Forge, VA
Shenandoah Manor, Ronceverte, WV
Shenandoah Manor Nursing Center, Shenandoah, PA
Shenango United Presbyterian Home, New Wilmington, PA
Shepherd Hills Health Care, Lafayette, GA
Shepherd of the Valley Nursing Home, Niles, OH
Sheppard Health Care Inc, Ellenboro, WV
Doctor Philip Sher Jewish Home, Omaha, NE
Sheraton Convalescent Center, Sepulveda, CA
Sherbrooke Nursing Home, Grand Rapids, MI
Sheridan Care Center, Sheridan, OR
Sheridan Health Care Center, Zion, IL
Sheridan Health Care Center Inc, Sheridan, IN
Sheridan Manor Nursing Home Inc, Tonawanda, NY
Sheridan Memorial Nursing Home, Plentywood, MT
Sheridan Nursing Home, Kenosha, WI
Sheriff Manor Nursing Home, Boston, MA
Sherman County Good Samaritan Center, Goodland, KS
Sherman Nursing Center, Sherman, TX
Sherman Oaks Care Center, Muskegon, MI
Sherman Oaks Convalescent Hospital, Sherman Oaks, CA
Sherrelwood Residential Care Facility, Denver, CO
Sherrill House Inc, Boston, MA
Sherwin Manor Nursing Center, Chicago, IL
Sherwood Care Center, Williams Bay, WI
Sherwood Convalescent Home, Indianapolis, IN
Sherwood Convalescent Hospital, Van Nuys, CA
Sherwood Health Care Inc, Bryan, TX
Sherwood Healthcare Center of Lubbock, Lubbock, TX
Sherwood Manor Inc, Sequim, WA
Sherwood Manor Nursing Home, Tulsa, OK
Sherwood Oaks & Cranberry Lake Health Center, Mars, PA
Sherwood Park Nursing Home, Salem, OR
Sherwood Terrace Nursing Center, Tacoma, WA
Shetley Nursing Home, Bell City, MO

Sheyenne Care Center—SNF, Valley City, ND
Shiawassee County Medical Care Facility, Corunna, MI
Shields Adult Care Home Inc, Pittsburg, KS
Shields Intermediate Care Facility, El Cerrito, CA
Shields & Terrell Convalescent Hospital, Richmond, CA
Shiloh Manor Nursing Home, Canton, KS
Shipley Manor Health Center, Wilmington, DE
The Shire—Dungarvin IV, Elk River, MN
John P Shirk Memorial Home, Faulkton, SD
Shirkey Leisure Acres, Richmond, MO
Shoals Nursing Home, Tuscumbia, AL
Sholom Home, Saint Paul, MN
John H Shook Home for the Aged, Chambersburg, PA
Shore Acres Nursing & Convalescent Home, Saint Petersburg, FL
Shore Cliff, Gloucester, MA
Shore Drive Convalescent Home Inc, Virginia Beach, VA
Shore Haven Nursing Home, Grand Haven, MI
Shore View Nursing Home, Brooklyn, NY
Shoreham Convalescent Center, Marietta, GA
Shoreham Terrace Inc, Saint Joseph, MI
Shorehaven Health Center, Oconomowoc, WI
Shoreliner Healthcare Center, Taft, TX
Shores Health Center, Bradenton, FL
Shoshone Living Center, Kellogg, ID
Shreveport Manor Guest Care Center, Shreveport, LA
Shrewsbury Lutheran Retirement Village, Shrewsbury, PA
Shrewsbury Manor Nursing Home, Shrewsbury, NJ
Shrewsbury Nursing Home Inc, Shrewsbury, MA
Shuffield Nursing Home Inc 1, Brady, TX
Shuffield Rest Home Inc No 2, Brady, TX
Shuffit Nursing Home 1 Inc, Sikeston, MO
Shuffit Nursing Home 3 Inc, Sikeston, MO
Shuksan Convalescent Center, Bellingham, WA
Shurtleff Manor Residential, Mount Carmel, IL
Sibley Care Center, Sibley, IA
Sidney Health Center, Sidney, IA
Siemers Board & Care, Montgomery, MN
The Siena Home, Dayton, OH
Sierra Convalescent Center, Carson City, NV
Sierra Developmental Center, Sparks, NV
Sierra Health Care Center, Truth or Consequences, NM
Sierra Health Care Convalescent Hospital, Davis, CA
Sierra Health Center, Sparks, NV
Sierra Madre Skilled Nursing Facility, Sierra Madre, CA
Sierra Meadows Convalescent Hospital, Oakhurst, CA
Sierra View Convalescent Hospital, Fresno, CA
Sierra View Homes Inc, Reedley, CA
Sierra Vista, Highland, CA
Sierra Vista Care Center, Sierra Vista, AZ
Sierra Vista Care Center, Oregon City, OR
Sierra Vista Health Care Center, Loveland, CO
Siesta Home of Pratt Inc, Pratt, KS
Siesta Park Manor, Oskaloosa, IA
Sigourney Care Center Ltd, Sigourney, IA
Sikeston Convalescent Center, Sikeston, MO
Sikeston Manor Nursing Home, Sikeston, MO
Silent Night Nursing Home, Lancaster, TX
Silsbee Convalescent Center, Silsbee, TX
Silver Bell Nursing Home, Versailles, IN
Silver Creek Manor, Bristol, RI
Silver Crest Manor Inc, Anadarko, OK
Silver Cross Home, Brookhaven, MS
Silver Gardens Care Home Inc, Silverton, OR
Silver Haven Care Center, Burleson, TX
Silver Haven Nursing Home, Schenectady, NY
Silver Lake Nursing Home, Staten Island, NY
Silver Lake Nursing & Rehabilitation Center, Dover, DE

Silver Leaves Inc, Garland, TX
Silver Ridge Village, Bullhead City, AZ
Silver Spring Convalescent Center, Milwaukee, WI
Silver Star Nursing Home, Ardmore, OK
Silver Threads Nursing Center, Houston, TX
Silver Wood Good Samaritan Center, Silverton, ID
Silverstream Nursing & Rehabilitation Home, Spring House, PA
Silverton Nursing Home, Silverton, OR
L O Simenstad Nursing Care Unit, Hudson, WI
Simla Good Samaritan Center, Simla, CO
Simmons Loving Care Health Facility, Gary, IN
Simmons Nursing Home Inc, Violet, LA
Simmons Nursing Home Inc, Billerica, MA
Simpson House of the United Methodist Church, Philadelphia, PA
Simpson Memorial Home, West Liberty, IA
Simpsons Foster Care, Aguilar, CO
Singing River Hospital System—Extended Care Facility, Pascagoula, MS
Singleton Health Care Center, Cleveland, OH
Sinton Manor Nursing Home, Sinton, TX
Sioux Care Center, Sioux Rapids, IA
Sioux Falls Good Samaritan Village, Sioux Falls, SD
Sister James' Nursing Home, Yankton, SD
Sisters of Charity Hospital—Skilled Nursing Facility, Buffalo, NY
Charles T Sitrin Nursing Home Company Inc, New Hartford, NY
Siuslaw Care Center, Florence, OR
Sixth Street House, Rochester, MN
Skaalen Sunset Home, Stoughton, WI
Skagit Valley Convalescent Center Inc, Sedro Woolley, WA
Skiatook Nursing Home, Skiatook, OK
The Skilled Nursing Facility at North Hill, Needham, MA
Skokie Meadows Nursing Center No I, Skokie, IL
Skokie Meadows Nursing Center No II, Skokie, IL
Sky Ranch Nursing Home, Atlanta, GA
Sky View Haven Nursing Home, Croton-on-Hudson, NY
Sky View Nursing Center, Hurley, WI
Sky Vue Terrace Nursing Center, Pittsburgh, PA
Skyland Care Center Inc, Sylva, NC
Skyline Convalescent Hospital, Los Angeles, CA
Skyline Convalescent Hospital, Salinas, CA
Skyline Convalescent Hospital, San Jose, CA
Skyline Manor Nursing Home, Floyd, VA
Skyline Manor & Skyline Villa, Omaha, NE
Skyline Nursing Home, DeSoto, TX
Skyline Terrace Convalescent Home, Woodstock, VA
Skyline Terrace Nursing Center, Tulsa, OK
Skyview Convalescent Hospital Inc, Wallingford, CT
Skyview—Hazeldel, Twin Falls, ID
Skyview Living Center of Stamford, Stamford, TX
Skyview Living Center—San Antonio, San Antonio, TX
Skyview Nursing Manor, Jacksonville, IL
Skyview Personal Care Home, Mayfield, KY
Slack Nursing Home Inc, Gothenburg, NE
Slate Belt Medical Center Inc, Bangor, PA
Slaton Rest Home, Slaton, TX
Slayton Manor Care Center, Slayton, MN
Sleepy Eye Care Center, Sleepy Eye, MN
Sleepy Hollow Manor Nursing Home, Annandale, VA
Sleigh Bell Residence, Youngstown, OH
Smackover Nursing Home, Smackover, AR
Smith County Manor, Carthage, TN
Eunice C Smith Nursing Home, Alton, IL
Smith Group Home, Frazee, MN
Helen Lewis Smith Pavilion, Fairbury, IL
Smith Home for Aged Women, Ashtabula, OH
Smith House Skilled Nursing Facility, Stamford, CT

Smith Medical Nursing Care Center, Sandersville, GA
Smith Nursing & Convalescent Home of Mountaintop, Mountaintop, PA
Smith Nursing Home, Millbury, MA
Smith Nursing Home, Walla Walla, WA
Smith Nursing Home Inc, Canton, OH
Smith-Barr Manor Nursing Home, Louisiana, MO
Ella Smither Geriatric Center, Huntsville, TX
Smithfield Home, Smithfield, VA
Smith's Nursing Home, Wolfe City, TX
Smiths Rest Home, Worcester, MA
Smithview Manor Nursing Home, Lawson, MO
Smithville Convalescent Center, Smithville, MO
Smithville Western Care Center, Wooster, OH
Smyrna Nursing Center, Smyrna, TN
Snapper Creek Nursing Home Inc, Miami, FL
Snellville Nursing & Rehabilitation Center, Snellville, GA
Snow Valley Nursing Home, Lisle, IL
Snyder Nursing Center, Snyder, TX
Snyder Nursing Home Inc, Salem, VA
Snyder Oaks Care Center, Snyder, TX
Edward Snyder Memorial Home, Reedsburg, WI
Snyder's Vaughn-Haven Inc, Rushville, IL
Social Circle Intermediate Care Facility, Social Circle, GA
Society for the Danish Home, Chicago, IL
Socorro Good Samaritan Village, Socorro, NM
Sodonia's Home, Fulton, MO
Sogge Memorial Good Samaritan Center, Windom, MN
Soldiers & Sailors Memorial Hospital Health Related Facility, Penn Yan, NY
Solheim Lutheran Home for the Aged, Los Angeles, CA
Solomon Valley Manor, Stockton, KS
Solon Nursing Care Center, Solon, IA
Somers Manor Nursing Home Inc, Somers, NY
Somerset Community Hospital, Somerset, PA
Somerset Golden State Convalescent Hospital, West Sacramento, CA
Somerset House, Chicago, IL
Somerset Manor Inc, Bingham, ME
Somerset State Hospital—Mentally Retarded Unit, Somerset, PA
Somerset Valley Nursing Home, Bound Brook, NJ
Somerville Health Care Center, Somerville, TN
Somerville Home for the Aged, Somerville, MA
Sonogee Estates, Bar Harbor, ME
Sonoma Acres, Sonoma, CA
Sonora Convalescent Hospital Inc, Sonora, CA
Sorenson Convalescent Hospital, Whittier, CA
Souderton Mennonite Homes, Souderton, PA
Sound View Nursing Center, West Haven, CT
Souris Valley Care Center, Velva, ND
South Bay Child Care Center, Hawthorne, CA
South Bay Keiro Nursing Home, Gardena, CA
South Broadway Nursing Home Inc, New Philadelphia, OH
South Cape Nursing Home, Cape May Court House, NJ
South Carolina Crippled Children's Convalescent Center, Palmetto, SC
South Carolina Department of Mental Retardation-Coastal Regional Center, Ladson, SC
South Carolina Episcopal Home at Still Hopes, West Columbia, SC
South Carolina Vocational Rehabilitation Comprehensive Center, West Columbia, SC
South Center Manor Inc, Center City, MN
South County Convalescent Center, Arroyo Grande, CA
South County Nursing Centre, North Kingstown, RI
South Dallas Nursing Home, Dallas, TX
South Davis Community Hospital Inc, Bountiful, UT
South Elgin Manor, South Elgin, IL

South 4th Street, Montrose, CO
South Fulton Hospital—Extended Care Facility, East Point, GA
South Gate Care Center, Saint Louis, MO
South Haven Manor Nursing Home, Montgomery, AL
South Haven Nursing Home, Birmingham, AL
South Heritage Health Care Center, Saint Petersburg, FL
South Hills Convalescent Center, Canonsburg, PA
South Hills Manor, Dimmitt, TX
South Lafourche Nursing Center, Cut Off, LA
South Lake Care Center, Merrillville, IN
South Lawn Sheltered Care, Bunker Hill, IL
South Meadows Nursing Home, Diboll, TX
South Mississippi Retardation Center, Long Beach, MS
South Monaco Care Center, Denver, CO
South Mountain Manor, Phoenix, AZ
South Mountain Restoration Center, South Mountain, PA
South Oaks Health Care Inc, McMinnville, TN
South Park Development Center, Brownwood, TX
South Park Group Home, Pocatello, ID
South Park Guest Care Center, Shreveport, LA
South Park Health Care Center, Oklahoma City, OK
South Park Manor, Corpus Christi, TX
The South Pasadena Convalescent Hospital & Sanitarium, South Pasadena, CA
South Peninsula Hospital, Homer, AK
South Plains Memorial Home, Brownfield, TX
South Portland Nursing Home Inc, South Portland, ME
South Roanoke Nursing Home Inc, Roanoke, VA
South Salem Care Center, Salem, OR
South Shore Convalescent Hospital, Alameda, CA
South Shore Health Care Center, South Shore, KY
South Shore Kosher Rest Home Inc, Chicago, IL
South Shore Manor, Saint Francis, WI
South Shore Nursing Facility, Rockland, MA
South Shore Nursing Home Inc, Freeport, NY
South Side Manor, Decatur, IL
South Tower Rest Home, Centralia, WA
South Washington Street Nursing Home, Tiffin, OH
South Windsor Convalescent Home Inc, South Windsor, CT
Southampton Memorial Hospital—East Pavilion, Franklin, VA
Southampton Nursing Home Inc, Southampton, NY
Southcrest Convalescent Center, Spokane, WA
Southdale Health Care Services Inc, Superior, WI
Southeast Arizona Medical Center, Douglas, AZ
Southeast Arkansas Human Development Center, Warren, AR
Southeast Colorado Hospital & LTC, Springfield, CO
Southeast Nursing Center, San Antonio, TX
Southeastern Dakota Nursing Home, Vermillion, SD
Southeastern General Hospital SNC/ICF, Lumberton, NC
Southeastern Nursing Home, Indianapolis, IN
Southern Hills Nursing Center, Tulsa, OK
Southern Hospitality Living Center, Saint George, UT
Southern Inyo County Sanatorium, Lone Pine, CA
Southern Manor Inc, Temple, TX
Southern Medical of Dublin Inc, Dublin, GA
Southern Medical of East Macon, Macon, GA
Southern Medical of Springhill Nursing Home, Mobile, AL
Southern Nursing Home, Fordyce, AR
Southern Oaks Manor Nursing Home, Oklahoma City, OK

Southern Pines Nursing Center, New Port Richey, FL
Southern Wisconsin Center for the Developmentally Disabled, Union Grove, WI
Southfield Care Center, Webster City, IA
Southfield Rehabilitation Hospital, Southfield, MI
Southgate Health Care Center, Metropolis, IL
Southgate Nursing Center, Jefferson City, MO
Southgate Village, Bessemer, AL
Southhampton Estates, Southampton, PA
Southhaven Health Care Center, Southaven, MS
Southland Geriatric Center, Norwalk, CA
Southland Nursing Home, Marion, AL
Southland Villa Nursing Center, Temple, TX
Southpoint Manor, Miami Beach, FL
Southport Manor Convalescent Center, Southport, CT
Southridge Manor, Louisburg, KS
Southside Care Center, Minneapolis, MN
Southside Healthcare Center, Indianapolis, IN
Southside House, Rochester, MN
Southside Nursing Center Inc, Jacksonville, FL
Southview Acres Health Care Center, West Saint Paul, MN
Southview Manor Care Center, Cuzad, NE
Southwest Care Centers Inc, San Antonio, TX
Southwest Convalescent Center, Hawthorne, CA
Southwest Extended Care Center, McComb, MS
Southwest Health Center Nursing Home, Cuba City, WI
Southwest Health Center Nursing Home, Platteville, WI
Southwest Homes, Little Rock, AR
Southwest Louisiana State School, Iota, LA
Southwest Mediplex, Austin, TX
Southwest Senior Care Inc, Las Vegas, NM
Southwestern Convalescent Manor, Oklahoma City, OK
Southwestern Developmental Center, Bainbridge, GA
Southwood Convalescent Center Inc, Henderson, TX
Francis Southwood Nursing Home Inc, Austin, TX
Southwood Nursing Home, Elizabethton, TN
The Sovereign Home, Chicago, IL
Sowder Nursing Home, Brodhead, KY
Spa View Nursing Home Inc, Excelsior Springs, MO
Spalding Convalescent Center, Griffin, GA
Spang Crest Home, Lebanon, PA
Spanish Gardens Nursing Center, Dunedin, FL
Spanish Lake Nursing Center, Florissant, MO
Spanish Oaks Center, Anna, IL
Spanish Peaks Mental Health Center, Pueblo, CO
Sparks Nursing Center, Central City, KY
Sparr Convalescent Home, Hazelton, PA
Sparr Convalescent Hospital, Los Angeles, CA
Sparta Health Care Center Inc, Sparta, TN
Sparta Intermediate Care Center, Sparta, GA
Spartanburg Community Residence 1, Spartanburg, SC
Spartanburg Commununity Residence 2, Spartanburg, SC
Spartanburg Convalescent Center, Spartanburg, SC
Spear Convalescent Home, Marklesburg, PA
Spears & Spears Nursing Home, Piketon, OH
Gladys Spellman Nursing Center, Cheverly, MD
Spencer Health Care Center, Spencer, IN
Spencer's Personal Care Home, Jackson, MS
Spiro Nursing Home, Spiro, OK
Theo Spivey Nursing Home, Gainesboro, TN
SPJST Rest Home 1, Taylor, TX
SPJST Rest Home 2, Needville, TX
Split Rock Nursing Home, Bronx, NY
Spokane Valley Good Samaritan Center, Greenacres, WA

Spooner Hospital & Nursing Home, Spooner, WI
W W Spradling Rest Home, Louisville, KY
Sprague Nursing Home, Red Cloud, NE
Sprain Brook Manor Nursing Home, Scarsdale, NY
Spring Branch Healthcare Center, Houston, TX
Spring Creek Health Care Center, Fort Collins, CO
Spring Grove Care Center, Richmond, IN
Spring Hill Manor, Spring Hill, KS
Spring Hill Manor Convalescent Hospital, Grass Valley, CA
Spring House Estates Medical Care Facility, Spring House, PA
Spring Valley, Arvada, CO
Spring Valley Convalescent Home, Worcester, MA
Spring Valley Convalescent Hospital, Spring Valley, CA
Spring Valley Health Care Center, Elberton, GA
Spring Valley Intermediate Care Facility, Jeffersonville, GA
Spring Valley Municipal Nursing Home, Spring Valley, WI
Spring Valley Nursing Center, Spring Valley, IL
Spring View Manor Inc, Conway Springs, KS
Spring View Nursing Home, Lebanon, KY
Springbrook Manor, Grand Rapids, MI
Springdale Convalescent Center, Atlanta, GA
Springdale Convalescent Center, Cartersville, GA
Springfield Convalescent Center, Springfield, VT
Springfield Health Care Center, Springfield, MO
Springfield Health Care Center, Springfield, TN
Springfield Manor, Springfield, IL
Springfield Municipal Hospital, Springfield, MA
Springfield Rest Home, Springfield, MO
Springhaven Care Center, Tacoma, WA
Springhaven Nursing Care, Georgetown, KY
Springhill Manor, Battle Creek, MI
Springhill Manor Nursing Home, Mobile, AL
Springs Manor, Cambridge Springs, PA
Springs Road Living Center, Vallejo, CA
Springs Senior Citizens Home Inc Weskota Manor, Wessington Springs, SD
Springs Village Recovery Center, Colorado Springs, CO
Springside of Pittsfield Long-Term Care Facility, Pittsfield, MA
Springview Center, Springfield, OH
Springview Manor, Lima, OH
Springview Nursing Home, Freehold, NJ
Springville Nursing Center, Coushatta, LA
Springwood Nursing Center Ltd, Sarasota, FL
Springwood Nursing Home, Rome, GA
Spruce Avenue Residence, South Saint Paul, MN
Spruce Manor Nursing Home, Springfield, MA
Spruce Villa Inc, Salem, OR
Spur Care Center, Spur, TX
Spurgeon Manor, Dallas Center, IA
Square Road ICF/MR Group Home, Saint Albans, ME
Squire's Sheltered Care Home, Chicago, IL
Stacyville Community Nursing Home, Stacyville, IA
Stadium Manor Nursing Home, Boston, MA
Stafholt Good Samaritan Center, Blaine, WA
Standing Stone Health Care Center, Monterey, TN
Standish Community Hospital, Standish, MI
Stanford Convalescent Center—Bedford, Bedford, TX
Stanford Convalescent Center—Eighth Ave, Fort Worth, TX
Stanford Convalescent Center Hemphill, Fort Worth, TX
Stanford Convalescent Center—Jennings, Fort Worth, TX

Stanford Convalescent Center—Pennsylvania, Fort Worth, TX
Stanford House, Stanford, KY
Stanley Convalescent Hospital, Westminster, CA
Stanmarie, Linden, MI
Stanton Care Center, Stanton, IA
Stanton Care Center, Stanton, TX
Stanton Hill Convalescent Hospital Inc, Castro Valley, CA
Stanton Nursing Center, Stanton, KY
Stanton Nursing Home, Stanton, NE
Stanton Pines Inc, Hopkins, SC
Star City Nursing Center, Star City, AR
Star Nursing Home, Bethesda, OH
Star of David Convalescent Home, Boston, MA
Starcrest Home of Conyers, Conyers, GA
Starcrest of Lithonia, Lithonia, GA
Stark County Health Center, Toulon, IL
Molly Stark Hospital, Louisville, OH
Starkville Manor Nursing Home, Starkville, MS
Starmount Villa, Greensboro, NC
Starnes Nursing Home Inc, Harvey, IL
Starr Nursing Home, Merkel, TX
Starzecki Boarding Care Home, Winona, MN
State Center Manor, State Center, IA
State College Manor Ltd, State College, PA
State Convalescent Hospital, South Gate, CA
State Home & Training School—Eleventh St, Pueblo, CO
Statesboro Nursing Home, Statesboro, GA
Staunton Manor Nursing Home Inc, Staunton, VA
Steere House, Providence, RI
Steffen Group Home, Barrett, MN
Stella Manor Nursing Center, Russellville, AR
Stella Maris, Baltimore, MD
Stellar Homes Inc, Saint Louis, MO
Stenton Hall Nursing & Convalescent Center, Philadelphia, PA
Step by Step Inc, Carnegie, PA
Step by Step Inc, Wilkes-Barre, PA
Stephen Caldwell Memorial Convalescent Home Inc, Ipswich, MA
Stephen Smith Home for the Aged, Philadelphia, PA
Stephens House, Alamosa, CO
Stephens Nursing Home, Lexington, KY
Stephenson Nursing Home, Freeport, IL
Stephenville Nursing Inc, Stephenville, TX
Stepping Stones Group Home, Milaca, MN
Stepping Stones Inc, Moscow, ID
Sterling Care Center, Sterling, IL
Sterling County Nursing Home, Sterling City, TX
Sterling Home of Bridgeport, Bridgeport, CT
Sterling Manor, Niles, IL
Sterling Place, Baton Rouge, LA
Sterling Presbyterian Manor, Sterling, KS
Stetson Manor Nursing Home, Norwell, MA
Steuben County Infirmary, Bath, NY
Stevencroft, Saint Paul, MN
Stevens-Bennett Home Inc, Haverhill, MA
Stevens Convalescent Center Inc, Hallettsville, TX
Stevens Hall Long-Term Care Facility, North Andover, MA
Stevens Nursing Home Inc, Yoakum, TX
Stevens Square, Minneapolis, MN
Stewart Health Center, Raleigh, NC
Stewart Lodge, Madison, OH
Stewartville Nursing Home, Stewartville, MN
Stigler Nursing Home, Stigler, OK
Still Waters Nursing Home, Danforth, ME
Stillmeadow Convalescent Center, Malvern, AR
Stillwater Convalescent Center, Columbus, MT
Stillwater Health Care, Bangor, ME
Stillwater Health Center, Dayton, OH
Stillwater Health Center/ICFMR, Dayton, OH
Stillwater Maple Manor Health Care Center Inc, Stillwater, MN
Stillwater Nursing Home Inc, Stillwater, OK
Stillwater Residence, Stillwater, MN

Stillwater Rosewood Nursing Home Inc, Stillwater, OK
Stilwell Nursing Home, Stilwell, OK
Stockdale Nursing Home, Stockdale, TX
Stockton Convalescent Hospital, Stockton, CA
Stockton Nursing Home Inc, Stockton, MO
Stokes-Reynolds Memorial Hospital—SNF, Danbury, NC
Stollwood Convalescent Hospital, Woodland, CA
Stone Acre Rest Home Inc, Springfield, MA
Stone Arch Health Care Center, Pittstown, NJ
Stone Haven, Lewistown, MO
Stone Institution & Newton Home for Aged People, Newton, MA
Stone Manor Convalescent Center, Indianapolis, IN
Stone Road Nursing Center Inc, Kilgore, TX
Stonebrook Nurse Center, Denver City, TX
Stonebrook Nursing Home, Austin, TX
Stonegate Nursing Center, Stonewall, OK
Stonehaven Convalescent Hospital Inc, Hayward, CA
Stonehedge Nursing Home, Boston, MA
Stonehedge Nursing Home, Rome, NY
Stonehedge-Chittenango Nursing Home, Chittenango, NY
Stonehenge Health Care Center Inc, Huntsville, TN
Stonehill Manor Nursing & Retirement Home, North Easton, MA
Stonehouse Hill Nursing Home, Holden, MA
C K Stones Manor Inc, Smethport, PA
Stones River Manor, Murfreesboro, TN
Stonewall Jackson Hospital Extended Care Facility, Lexington, VA
Stoneybrook Healthcare Center, Houston, TX
Storla Sunset Home, Letcher, SD
Story County Hospital & Long-Term Care Facility, Nevada, IA
Stovall Care Center, Denver, CO
Stow Rest Home, Stow, MA
Strafford County Home, Dover, NH
Strand-Kjorsvig Community Rest Home, Roslyn, SD
Strasburg Nursing Home, Strasburg, ND
Stratford Care Center, Stratford, IA
Stratford Hall Nursing Home, Richmond, VA
Stratford Nursing Center, Stratford, OK
Stratford Nursing & Convalescent Center, Stratford, NJ
Stratford Square Ltd, Kankakee, IL
Stratton House Nursing Home, Townshend, VT
Strawberry Point Lutheran Home, Strawberry Point, IA
Strawn Nursing Home Inc, Naches, WA
Stroh Resident Home, Colorado Springs, CO
Strong Memorial Hospital Skilled Nursing Facility, Rochester, NY
Strong Nursing Home, Strong, ME
Stroud Health Care Center, Stroud, OK
Stroud Manor Inc, East Stroudsburg, PA
Stroud Memorial Intermediate Care Facility, Marietta, SC
Strum Nursing Home, Strum, WI
Stuart Convalescent Center, Stuart, FL
Studio City Convalescent Hospital, Studio City, CA
Sturges Convalescent Home, Mansfield, OH
Sturgis Community Health Care Center, Sturgis, SD
Sturgis Community Rest Home, Sturgis, KY
Stuttle Community Living Facility, Peoria, IL
Styrest Nursing Home, Carbondale, IL
Styrons Arrowhead Nursing Center, Jonesboro, GA
Su Casa Personal Care Residence, Tucson, AZ
Sublette County Retirement Center, Pinedale, WY
Suburban Acres Nursing Center, Marshall, TX
Suburban Manor Convalescent & Nursing Home, Acton, MA
Suburban Pavillion Inc, North Randall, OH
Suburban Square Nursing Center, Oklahoma City, OK
Sudbury Pines Nursing Home, Sudbury, MA
Suffolk Infirmary, Yaphank, NY

Sugar Creek Convalescent Center Inc, Greenfield, IN
Sugar Creek Rest Inc, Worthington, PA
Sugar Valley Home Inc, Mound City, KS
Sullivan County Home & Infirmary, Liberty, NY
Sullivan County Nursing Home, Claremont, NH
Sullivan Health Care Center, Sullivan, IL
Sullivan Living Center, Sullivan, IL
Sullivan Nursing Center, Sullivan, MO
Sullivan Park Health Care Center Inc, Endicott, NY
Sulphur Springs Nursing Home, Sulphur Springs, TX
Summer Hill Nursing Home, Old Bridge, NJ
Summer Trace, Carmel, IN
Summerfield Convalescent Hospital, Santa Rosa, CA
Summerfield Manor Nursing Home, Louisville, KY
Summerford Nursing Home Inc, Falkville, AL
Summerlin Lane Nursing Home, Bastrop, LA
Summers County Continuous Care Center, Hinton, WV
Summit Acres Nursing Home, Caldwell, OH
Summit Acres Nursing Home Inc—Home B, Caldwell, OH
Summit Avenue Residence, South Saint Paul, MN
Summit Conv Home Inc, Jewett City, CT
Summit Convalescent Center Inc, Summitville, IN
Summit Convalescent Home, Lakewood, NJ
Summit County Nursing Home, Tallmadge, OH
Summit Health Care Center, Wilkes-Barre, PA
Summit Home, Detroit Lakes, MN
The Summit House, Fort Wayne, IN
Summit House Health Care Center, Bar Harbor, ME
Summit House II, Saint Louis Park, MN
Summit Manor, Columbia, KY
Summit Manor Health Care Center, Saint Paul, MN
Summit Medical Center Inc, Providence, RI
Summit Nursing & Convalescent Home Inc, Cincinnati, OH
Summit Nursing Home Inc, Catonsville, MD
Summit Park Hospital—Rockland County Infirmary, Pomana, NY
Summitview Manor, Yakima, WA
Sumner Home, Akron, OH
Sumner Lodge, Sumner, WA
Sumter Nursing Home, York, AL
Sun Air Convalescent Hospital, Panorama City, CA
Sun City Convalescent Center, Sun City, CA
Sun Dial Manor Inc, Bristol, SD
Sun Mountain Nursing Center, Rome, GA
Sun Prairie Health Care Center, Sun Prairie, WI
Sun Terrace Health Care Center, Sun City Center, FL
Sun Valley Lodge, Sun City, AZ
Sun Valley Manor, Saginaw, MI
Sun Valley Manor Convalescent Hospital, Pleasant Hill, CA
Sun Valley Nursing Home, Alliance, OH
Sunair Home for Asthmatic Children, Van Nuys, CA
Sunbury Community Hospital—Skilled Nursing Unit, Sunbury, PA
Sunbury Nursing Home, Sunbury, OH
Suncoast Manor, Saint Petersburg, FL
SunCoast Manor Nursing Home, Bradenton, FL
Suncoast Nursing Home, Saint Petersburg, FL
Suncrest Nursing Center, Chillicothe, MO
Sundale Nursing Home, Morgantown, WV
Anna Sundermann Home, Seward, NE
Sundial Manors Nursing Home, Pilot Point, TX
Sunharbor Manor, Roslyn Heights, NY
Sunhaven Convalescent & Rehabilitation Hospital, Fullerton, CA
Sunland Center—Gainesville Facility I, Gainesville, FL

Sunland Center—Gainesville Facility II, Gainesville, FL
Sunland Center—Gainesville Facility III, Gainesville, FL
Sunland Center—Miami Facility III, Opa Locka, FL
Sunland—Marianna Facility II, Marianna, FL
Sunlawn Nursing Home, Hightstown, NJ
Sunny Acres, Calhoun, KY
Sunny Acres, Covington, OH
Sunny Acres Care Center, Sidney, OH
Sunny Acres Convalescent Hospital, Fairfield, CA
Sunny Acres Nursing Center Inc, Bad Axe, MI
Sunny Acres Nursing Home, Petersburg, IL
Sunny Acres Nursing Home, Chelmsford, MA
Sunny Acres Nursing Home, Williamsburg, MA
Sunny Acres Nursing Home Inc, Fork, SC
Sunny Acres of Dekalb Inc, Dekalb, TX
Sunny Acres Villa, Denver, CO
Sunny Haven Convalescent Center, Sunnyside, WA
Sunny Hill, Denver, CO
Sunny Hill Care Center, Tama, IA
Sunny Hill Health Care Center, Madison, WI
Sunny Hill Nursing Home, Joliet, IL
Sunny Hills Convalescent Hospital, Fullerton, CA
Sunny Hills Nursing Center, Decatur, TX
Sunny Knoll Care Center Inc, Rockwell City, IA
Sunny Knoll Retirement Home Inc, Franklin, NH
Sunny Point Health Care Center Inc, Smithville, TN
Sunny Ridge, Sheboygan, WI
Sunny Ridge Manor, Nampa, ID
Sunny Shores Villas Health Center, Saint Petersburg, FL
Sunny Side Center, Enid, OK
Sunny Vale Nursing Home, Wausau, WI
Sunny Vee Nursing Home Inc, Delaware, OH
Sunny View Adult Care Home Inc, Coffeyville, KS
Sunny View Care Center, Ankeny, IA
Sunny View Manor, Cupertino, CA
Sunny View Nursing Home, Zanesville, OH
Sunny View Nursing Home, Warwick, RI
Sunny Villa Care Center, Upper Sandusky, OH
Sunny Vista Care Center, Portland, OR
Sunnybreeze Health Care Inc, Hamilton, OH
Sunnycrest Nursing Center, Dysart, IA
Sunnydale Acres, Vandalia, IL
Sunnyfield Nursing Home Inc, Cranbury, NJ
Sunnyland Villa, Springfield, OH
Sunnymere Inc, Aurora, IL
Sunnypines Convalescent Center, Rockledge, FL
Sunnyrest Sanatorium, Colorado Springs, CO
Sunnyside Care Center, Salem, OR
Sunnyside Convalescent Hospital, Fresno, CA
Sunnyside Nursing Center, Torrance, CA
Sunnyside Nursing Home, Sarasota, FL
Sunnyside Nursing Home, Lake Park, MN
Sunnyside Nursing Home, East Syracuse, NY
Sunnyside Nursing Home & Convalescent Home, Manasquan, NJ
Sunnyside Presbyterian Retirement Community, Harrisonburg, VA
Sunnyside Rest Home, Oxbridge, MA
Sunnyside Retirement Center 2, Taylor, TX
Sunnyside Van Ness Convalescent Hospital, San Francisco, CA
Sunnyslope Care Center, Ottumwa, IA
Sunnyslope Nursing Home, Bowerston, OH
Sunnytide Nursing Home, Chickasha, OK
Sunnyvale Convalescent Hospital, Sunnyvale, CA
Sunnyvale Manor, Dallas, TX
Sunnyvale Rest Home, Ashburnham, MA
Sunnyview Home, Butler, PA
Sunnyview Nursing Home & Apartments, Trenton, MO
Sunnyview Village, Princeton, WI
Sunray East Convalescent Hospital, Los Angeles, CA

Sunray North Convalescent Hospital, Los Angeles, CA
Sunrest Health Facilities Inc, Port Jefferson, NY
Sunrise Community-Miami, Goulds, FL
Sunrise Courts, Roselle, IL
Sunrise Group Home 1—Goulds, Goulds, FL
Sunrise Guest Home, Fredericksburg, IA
Sunrise Haven, Puyallup, WA
Sunrise Hill Care Center, Traer, IA
Sunrise Home, Two Harbors, MN
Sunrise Manor, Tyler, MN
Sunrise Manor Care Center, Fayetteville, AR
Sunrise Manor & Convalescent Center Inc, Amelia, OH
Sunrise Manor Nursing Home, Fort Pierce, FL
Sunrise Manor Nursing Home, Hodgenville, KY
Sunrise Manor Nursing Home, Somerset, KY
Sunrise Manor Nursing Home, Bay Shore, NY
Sunrise Manor of Virden Inc, Virden, IL
Sunrise Nursing Home, Somerville, MA
Sunrise Nursing Home for the Blind Inc, Milwaukee, WI
Sunrise Nursing Home of Georgia Inc, Moultrie, GA
Sunrise Retirement Community, Sioux City, IA
Sunrise Terrace, Winfield, IA
Sunrise View Convalescent Center, Everett, WA
Sunset Boulevard Convalescent Hospital, Hayward, CA
Sunset Boulevard Convalescent Hospital 1, Hayward, CA
Sunset Care Center, Jacksonville, TX
Sunset Convalescent Hospital, Eureka, CA
Sunset Estates Inc, Tecumseh, OK
Sunset Estates of El Reno Inc, El Reno, OK
Sunset Estates of Enid Inc, Enid, OK
Sunset Estates of Maud, Maud, OK
Sunset Haven Convalescent Hospital, Cherry Valley, CA
Sunset Haven Nursing Center Ltd, El Paso, TX
Sunset Haven Nursing Home, Curtis, NE
Sunset Healthcare Center, Canton, IL
Sunset Heights Nursing Home, Belle Glade, FL
Sunset Hill Home for Aged & Infirm, Lawrenceburg, KY
Sunset Home Inc, Maysville, MO
Sunset Home Inc, Bowman, ND
Sunset Home of the United Methodist Church, Quincy, IL
Sunset House, Toledo, OH
Sunset Knoll Inc, Aurelia, IA
Sunset Manor, Brush, CO
Sunset Manor, Woodstock, IL
Sunset Manor, Frontenac, KS
Sunset Manor, Waverly, KS
Sunset Manor, Lexington, OK
Sunset Manor, Titusville, PA
Sunset Manor, Irene, SD
Sunset Manor Convalescent Hospital, El Monte, CA
Sunset Manor Nursing Home Inc, Greencastle, IN
Sunset Nursing Center, Concordia, KS
Sunset Nursing Home, Park Rapids, MN
Sunset Nursing Home, Boonville, NY
Sunset Nursing Home, Cleveland, OH
Sunset Nursing Home, Clute, TX
Sunset Nursing Home Inc, Ironton, OH
Sunset Nursing & Retirement, Bowling Green, MO
Sunset Nursing & Retirement Home of Elsberry, Elsberry, MO
Sunset Nursing & Retirement Home of Farmington, Farmington, MO
Sunset Nursing & Retirement Home of Union, Union, MO
Sunset Point Nursing Center, Clearwater, FL
Sunset Terrace Convalescent Center, Coeur d'Alene, ID
Sunset Valley Haven, Chamberlain, SD
Sunset Valley Nursing Home, Cassville, MO
Sunset View, Millersburg, OH

Sunset Villa Care Center, Roswell, NM
Sunset Village of the Ozarks, Waynesville, MO
Sunshine Gardens, Spokane, WA
Sunshine Haven, Lordsburg, NM
Sunshine Health Care Center Inc, Commerce City, CO
Sunshine Manor Nursing Center, Carlinville, IL
Sunshine Manor I, Dexter, MO
Sunshine Manor II, Dexter, MO
Sunshine Meadow Care Center, Lincoln, IL
Sunshine Nursing Home, Yankton, SD
Sunshine Nursing Home Inc, Stoneham, MA
Sunshine Nursing Home Inc, New London, TX
Sunshine Place, Harmony, MN
Sunshine Rest Home, Pontotoc, MS
Sunshine Terrace Convalescent Hospital Inc, Los Angeles, CA
Sunshine Terrace Foundation Inc, Logan, UT
Sunshine Villa, Mora, MN
Sunshine Vista, Seattle, WA
Suntown at Montclair Convalescent Hospital, Montclair, CA
Sunwood Care Center, Redwood Falls, MN
Superior Care Home, Paducah, KY
Superior Shores Nursing Center, Munising, MI
Sur La Rue de Breen, Saint Paul, MN
Sur La Rue de Skillman, Maplewood, MN
Sur La Rue De Wheelock Ridge, Saint Paul, MN
Surburan Manor Nursing Home, Acton, MA
Surf & Sand Health Center, Duluth, MN
Surfside Nursing Home, Far Rockaway, NY
Surry Community Nursing Center, Mount Airy, NC
Susanville Convalescent Hospital, Susanville, CA
Susque View Home Inc, Lock Haven, PA
Susquehanna Center for Nursing & Rehabilitation, Harrisburg, PA
Susquehanna Lutheran Village, Millersburg, PA
Susquehanna Nursing Home & Health Related Facility, Johnson City, NY
Sussex County Homestead, Newton, NJ
Sutton Community Home, Sutton, NE
Suwannee Health Care Center, Live Oak, FL
Suwannee Valley Nursing Center, Jasper, FL
Swaim Health Center, Newville, PA
Swainsboro Nursing Home Inc, Swainsboro, GA
Swampscotta Nursing Home, South Windham, ME
Swan Manor Inc, Lacygne, KS
Swanholm Nursing & Rehabilitation Center, Saint Petersburg, FL
Swansea Rest Home Inc, Swansea, MA
L M Swanson Nursing Home, Gallatin, TN
Swedish Home for the Aged, Newton, MA
Sweeny House, Sweeny, TX
Sweet Brook Nursing Home Inc, Williamstown, MA
Sweet Memorial Nursing Home, Chinook, MT
Sweet Springs Caring Center, Sweet Springs, MO
Sweetbriar Development Center, West Columbia, TX
Sweetbriar Nursing Home, Bellville, TX
Sweetbriar Nursing Home, Brenham, TX
Sweetbriar Nursing Home, Columbus, TX
Sweetbriar Nursing Home, Taylor, TX
Sweetwater Nursing Center, Sweetwater, TX
Sweetwater Valley Convalescent & Nursing Home Inc, Sweetwater, TN
Swift County Home, Benson, MN
Swiss Home Health Related Facility, Mount Kisco, NY
Swiss Villa Living Center, Vevay, IN
Swiss Village Inc, Berne, IN
Swope Ridge Health Care Center, Kansas City, MO
Sycamore Creek Nursing Center, Coraopolis, PA
Sycamore Manor Nursing Home, Montoursville, PA
Sycamore Park Convalescent Hospital, Los Angeles, CA

Sycamore View Healthcare, Clinton, MO
Sycamore Village Health Center, Kokomo, IN
Sydney House, Vicksburg, MS
Sykesville Eldercare Center, Sykesville, MD
Sylacauga Hospital & Nursing Home, Sylacauga, AL
Sylcox Nursing Home & Health Related Facility, Newburgh, NY
Sylvan Manor Health Care Center, Silver Spring, MD
Sylvan Manor Inc, Bridgeport, CT
Sylvester Health Care Inc, Sylvester, GA
Sylvester Nursing Home, Muncie, IN
Syl-View Health Care Center, Sylvania, GA
Syracuse Home Association, Baldwinsville, NY
Syrings Chalet, Blackfoot, ID
M B Syverson Lutheran Home, Eau Claire, WI
Taber Street Nursing Home, New Bedford, MA
Tabitha Home, Lincoln, NE
Table Rock Health Care Center, Kimberling City, MO
Tabor Manor Care Center, Tabor, IA
Tacoma Lutheran Home & Retirement Community, Tacoma, WA
Tacoma Narrows Care Center, Tacoma, WA
Tacoma Terrace Convalescent Center, Tacoma, WA
Taft Hospital District, Taft, TX
Tahlequah Nursing Home, Tahlequah, OK
Tahoka Care Center, Tahoka, TX
Takamah Nursing Center, Tekamah, NE
Talihina Manor Nursing Home, Talihina, OK
Talladega Nursing Home, Talladega, AL
Tallahassee Convalescent Home, Tallahassee, FL
Tallahassee Developmental Center, Tallahassee, FL
Tallahatchie General Hospital—Extended Care Facility, Charleston, MS
Tally Ho Manor, Boonton, NJ
Talmadge Park Health Care, East Haven, CT
Tamalpais, Larkspur, CA
Tamarac Convalescent Center, Tamarac, FL
Tampa Health Care Center, Tampa, FL
Tanglewood Convalescent Center, Lake City, FL
Tanglewood Health Care Center, Ridgeway, SC
Tanner Chapel Manor Nursing Home, Phoenix, AZ
Tappahannock Manor Convalescent Center & Home for Adults, Tappahannock, VA
Tara Gardens Personal Care Home, Iola, KS
Tara Nursing Home, Boston, MA
Tarpon Health Care Center, Tarpon Springs, FL
Tarpon Springs Convalescent Center, Tarpon Springs, FL
Tarrytown Hall Nursing Home, Tarrytown, NY
Tarzana Health Care Center, Tarzana, CA
Tates Creek Health Care Center, Lexington, KY
Tattnall Nursing Care, Reidsville, GA
Taunton Female Charity Association Inc, Taunton, MA
Taunton Nursing Home, Taunton, MA
Tawes/Bland Bryant Nursing Center, Catonsville, MD
Taylor/Brown Memorial Hospital Nursing Home, Waterloo, NY
Fannie E Taylor Home for the Aged, Jacksonville, FL
Taylor Home, Laconia, NH
Taylor Hospital, Bangor, ME
James S Taylor Memorial Home, Louisville, KY
Taylor Manor Nursing Home, Versailles, KY
Taylor Nursing Home, Taylor, AR
Taylor Park Health Care & Rehabilitation Center, Rhinelander, WI
Taylor Total Living Center, Taylor, MI
Taylor's Health Care Inc—Riverview, Lucasville, OH
Taylorville Care Center Inc, Taylorville, IL

Teachers Home Care Center, Minneapolis, MN

Teague Nursing Home, Teague, TX

Teakwood Manor, Stamford, TX

Teaneck Nursing Home, Teaneck, NJ

Teat Personal Care Home, Jackson, MS

Tecumseh Care Center, Tecumseh, NE

Tehema County Health Center, Red Bluff, CA

Tekakwitha Nursing Home, Sisseton, SD

Tekoa Care Center, Tekoa, WA

Tel Hai Retirement Community, Honeybrook, PA

Temenos House Inc, Wheat Ridge, CO

Temple City Convalescent Hospital, Temple City, CA

Julia Temple Center, Englewood, CO

Temple Manor Inc, Temple, OK

Temple Park Convalescent Hospital, Los Angeles, CA

Tender Care Home, Gulfport, MS

Tensas Care Center, Newellton, LA

Teresa Rest Home Inc, East Haven, CT

Teresian House Nursing Home Co Inc, Albany, NY

The Terrace, Waukegan, IL

Terrace Care Convalescent Hospital, Fresno, CA

Terrace Garden Care Center, Garden City, KS

Terrace Gardens Convalescent Center, Paramount, CA

Terrace Gardens Health Care Center, Colorado Springs, CO

Terrace Gardens Nursing Home, Oklahoma City, OK

Terrace Gardens Nursing Home, Midland, TX

Terrace Gardens Retirement Center, Wichita, KS

Terrace Heights Care Center, Boulder, CO

Terrace Manor, Dell Rapids, SD

Terrace Manor Nursing Home Inc, Russellville, AL

Terrace Park Convalescent Hospital, Tulare, CA

Terrace View Castle Nursing Home, Millersburg, OH

Terrace View Convalescent Center Inc, Seattle, WA

Terrace View Extended Care Facility, Lawrenceburg, IN

Terrace Villa, Salt Lake City, UT

Terrace West, Midland, TX

Terraceview Living Center, Shell Lake, WI

Terracina Convalescent Hospital, Redlands, CA

Terre Haute Nursing Home, Terre Haute, IN

Terrell Care Center, Terrell, TX

Terrell Convalescent Center 1, Terrell, TX

Terrell Convalescent Center 2, Terrell, TX

Terry Haven Nursing Home Inc, Mount Vernon, TX

Terwilliger Plaza Inc, Portland, OR

Teton Nursing Home, Choteau, MT

Texarkana Nursing Center, Texarkana, TX

Texas County Missouri Health Care Center Inc, Licking, MO

Texas County Rest Home Inc, Houston, MO

Texas Healthcare Center, Lancaster, TX

Texas Terrace Convalescent Center, Saint Louis Park, MN

Texhoma Christian Care Center, Wichita Falls, TX

Texoma Health Care Center Inc, Kingston, OK

Roland Thatcher Nursing Home, Wareham, MA

Therapeutic Intervention Model Dev Disability, Aurora, CO

Thirty-Nine Summer, Keene, NH

Henry Thodes Oakwood Villa, Altoona, WI

Thomas Care Centers Inc, Houston, TX

Thomas County Care Center, Colby, KS

Thomas House, Washington, DC

Thomas Nursing Center, Thomas, OK

Thomas Nursing Center Inc, McLean, TX

Thomasville Health Care Center, Thomasville, GA

Thomasville Hospital & Nursing Home, Thomasville, AL

Geraldine L Thompson Medical Home, Allenwood, NJ

Thompson House Nursing Home, Brattleboro, VT

Jessie Thompson Convalescent Home Inc, Detroit, MI

Thompson Nursing Home Inc, Canandaigua, NY

Thomson Manor Nursing Home Inc, Thomson, GA

Thornapple Manor, Hastings, MI

Thorne Crest Retirement Center, Albert Lea, MN

Thornton Heights Terrace Ltd, Chicago Heights, IL

Thornton Manor, Lansing, IA

Thornton Nursing Home, Northborough, MA

Thornwald Home, Carlisle, PA

Thorp Care Center, Thorp, WI

Thousand Oaks Healthcare Center, Thousand Oaks, CA

The Three Fountains, Medford, OR

301 Sylvan Way, Bremerton, WA

377 Main Street, Winona, MN

Three Oaks Intermediate Care Home, Macon, GA

Three Rivers Convalescent Center, Fort Wayne, IN

Three Rivers Convalescent Center, Cincinnati, OH

Three Rivers Health Care Center Inc, Painted Post, NY

Three Rivers Manor, Three Rivers, MI

Three Rivers Nursing Center, Marked Tree, AR

Three Sisters Nursing Home Inc, Indianapolis, IN

Three Springs Lodge Nursing Home Inc, Chester, IL

Three Thirty-Five Ridgewood, Minneapolis, MN

Throckmorton Nursing Center, Throckmorton, TX

Thunderbird House, Duluth, MN

Thurston Woods Village-Nursing Center, Sturgis, MI

Tibbits Health Care Facility, White Plains, NY

Tidd Home, Woburn, MA

Tidings of Peace Nursing Center Inc, Broken Arrow, OK

Tierra Pines Convalescent Center, Largo, FL

The Tieszen Memorial Home, Marion, SD

Margaret Tietz Center for Nursing Care, Jamaica, NY

Tiffany Heights, Mound City, MO

Tiffany Rest & Retirement Home, Rockland, MA

Tiffany Square Convalescent Center, Saint Joseph, MO

Tiffany II Rest Home, Rockland, MA

Tiffin Developmental Center, Tiffin, OH

Tift Health Care Inc, Tifton, GA

Tifton Nursing Home, Tifton, GA

Tigard Care Center, Tigard, OR

Tiger Residential Programs (Fairview House), Denver, CO

Tilden Nursing Center, Tilden, NE

Tillamook Care Center, Tillamook, OR

The Tillers Nursing Home Inc, Oswego, IL

Tilton Nursing Home Inc, California, MO

Tilton Terrace, Wilmington, DE

Timbercrest—Church of the Brethren Home Inc, North Manchester, IN

Timberlane Manor Nursing Home, Edmond, OK

Timberlyn Heights, Great Barrington, MA

Timely Mission Nursing Home, Buffalo Center, IA

Timpanogos Psychiatric Unit, Provo, UT

Timpanogos Valley Care Center, Orem, UT

Tindles Personal Care Home, Cloverport, KY

Tioga Community Nursing Home, Tioga, ND

Tioga General Hospital Health Related Facility, Waverly, NY

Tioga Manor Nursing Center, Tioga, LA

Tioga Nursing Home Inc, Waverly, NY

Tippecanoe Villa, West Lafayette, IN

Tipton Manor, Tipton, MO

Tipton Nursing Home, Tipton, IN

Tishomingo County Rest Home, Iuka, MS

Titonka Care Center, Titonka, IA

Titus Memorial Presbyterian Home, Sullivan, IL

Titusville Nursing & Convalescent Center, Titusville, FL

TLC Convalescent Hospital, El Cajon, CA

TLC Home for the Elderly, Ocean Springs, MS

TLC Nursing Center, Harlingen, TX

TLC Nursing Home Inc, Bremen, IN

TMC Hart County Personal Care Home, Munfordville, KY

Toccoa Nursing Center, Toccoa, GA

Tockwotton Home, Providence, RI

Sarah A Todd Memorial Homes, Carlisle, PA

Todholm Care Center, Springville, UT

Toledo Mental Health Center, Toledo, OH

Tolstoy Foundation Nursing Home Company Inc, Valley Cottage, NY

Tomah Care Center, Tomah, WI

Tomorrows Hope Inc, Meridian, ID

Toms River Convalescent Center, Toms River, NJ

Tooele Valley Nursing Home, Tooele, UT

Toole County Nursing Home, Shelby, MT

Toombs Nursing & Intermediate Care Home, Lyons, GA

Topanga Terrace Convalescent Center, Canoga Park, CA

Topeka Convalescent Center, Topeka, KS

Topeka Presbyterian Manor Inc, Topeka, KS

Topham's Tiny Tots Care Center, Orem, UT

Torrance Convalescent Hospital, Torrance, CA

Torrance State Hospital—IMR Unit, Torrance, PA

Torrance State Hospital—Long-Term Care Facility, Torrance, PA

Torrey Pines Care Center, Las Vegas, NV

Torrey Pines Convalescent Hospital, La Jolla, CA

Torrington Extend-A-Care Centre, Torrington, CT

Total Care of Ottawa, Ottawa, OH

Toth's Rest Home, Barberton, OH

Touro Shakespeare Home, Algiers, LA

Tower Hill Nursing Home, Muskogee, OK

Tower Hill Rest Home, Fitchburg, MA

Tower Lodge Nursing Home, Wall Township, NJ

Tower Village Inc, Saint Louis, MO

Towers Nursing Home, Smithville, TX

Town & Country Manor, Milwaukee, WI

Town & Country Manor Health Care Center, Santa Ana, CA

Town & Country Manor Inc, Boerne, TX

Town & Country Nursing Center, Minden, LA

Town & Country Nursing Home, Lowell, MA

Town & Country Nursing Home, Midland, MI

Town Hall Estates, Wauconda, IL

Town Hall Estates, Breckenridge, TX

Town Hall Estates, Hillsboro, TX

Town Hall Estates, Keene, TX

Town Hall Estates, Rusk, TX

Town Hall Estates Nursing Center, Sayre, OK

Town Hall Estates Nursing Home, Windsor, OH

Town Hall Estates Nursing Home, Whitney, TX

Town Hall Estates Retirement Center, Rochester, MN

Town Manor Nursing Home Inc, Lawrence, MA

Town N County Convalescent Center, Tampa, FL

Town of Vici Nursing Home, Vici, OK

Towne Avenue Convalescent Hospital, Pomona, CA

Towne House Health Center, Fort Wayne, IN

Towne Oaks Nursing Center, Ruston, LA

Townhouse Convalescent Hospital, Fresno, CA

Towns County Nursing Home, Hiawassee, GA

Towson Convalescent Home Inc, Towson, MD

Trace Haven Nursing Home, Natchez, MS

Tracy Convalescent Hospital, Tracy, CA

Tracy Nursing Home Inc, Tracy, MN
Tranquility Nursing Home, Randolph, VT
Traverse County Nursing Home, Wheaton, MN
Traylor Nursing Home Inc, Roanoke, AL
The Traymore, Dallas, TX
Treasure Isle Care Center, North Bay Village, FL
Treasure Valley Manor, Boise, ID
Treats Falls, Orono, ME
Treemont Health Care Center, Houston, TX
Treemot Health Care Center, Dallas, TX
Tremont Nursing Center, Tremont, PA
Trempealeau County Health Care Center, Whitehall, WI
Trenton Convalescent Center, Trenton, MI
Tressie's Nursing Home, Oberlin, OH
Treutlen County Nursing Home, Soperton, GA
Trevecca Health Care Center, Nashville, TN
Trevilla of Golden Valley, Golden Valley, MN
Trevilla of New Brighton, New Brighton, MN
Trevilla of Robbinsdale, Robbinsdale, MN
Tri-City Convalescent Center, Oceanside, CA
Tri-County Nursing Home Inc, Louisville, MS
Tri County Nursing Home, Vandalia, MO
Tri-County Retirement & Nursing Home, Hatton, ND
Tri-State Convalescent Center, Clarkston, WA
Tri State Manor Nursing Home, Lansing, IL
Triad Rehabilitation Center, Winston-Salem, NC
Tri-City Nursing Center, Bay City, MI
Tri-County Convalescent Home Inc, Adamsville, TN
Tri-County Extended Care Center, Fairfield, OH
Tri-County Manor Nursing Center, Horton, KS
Tri-County Memorial Hospital—Nurs Home, Whitehall, WI
Tri-County Nursing Home Inc, Richland, MO
Trigg County Manor Personal Care Home, Cadiz, KY
Trimble Nursing Center, Bedford, KY
Trimont Nursing Home, Trimont, MN
Trinidad State Nursing Home, Trinidad, CO
Trinity Court Nursing Home, Little Rock, AR
Trinity Haven, Jeannette, PA
Trinity House, Sacramento, CA
Trinity Lutheran Home, Shiner, TX
Trinity Lutheran Home—Round Rock, Round Rock, TX
Trinity Lutheran Manor, Merriam, KS
Trinity Manor Adult Care Home, Dodge City, KS
Trinity Memorial Hospital, Trinity, TX
Trinity Nursing Unit, Minot, ND
Trinity Retirement Community, Dayton, OH
Trinity Terrace, Fort Worth, TX
Trinity Towers, Midland, TX
Tripoli Nursing Home, Tripoli, IA
Tripp Shelter Care Home, Cobden, IL
Troost Avenue Nursing Home, Kansas City, MO
Tropico Convalescent Hospital, Glendale, CA
Troy Hills Nursing Center, Parsippany, NJ
Troy House Inc, Troy, MO
True Light Nursing Home, Sandusky, OH
Trull Nursing Home, Biddeford, ME
Truman Health Center, Clinton, MO
Truman Lake Manor Inc, Lowry City, MO
Truman Medical Center, Kansas City, MO
Trumbull St Mary's Convalescent Home & Rest Home, Trumbull, CT
Trussville Nursing Home Inc, Trussville, AL
Violet Tschetter Memorial Home, Huron, SD
Tucker House, Philadelphia, PA
C M Tucker Jr Human Resources Center, Columbia, SC
Tucker Nursing Center, Tucker, GA
Tudor House Nursing Home, Jamaica Plain, MA
Tudor Oaks Health Center, Muskego, WI
Tuell Nursing Home Inc, Melrose, MA
Tuff Memorial Home, Hills, MN
Tule Lake Manor, Tacoma, WA
Tulia Care Center, Tulia, TX

Tully Brook Rest Home, Athol, MA
Tulsa Christian Home Inc, Tulsa, OK
Tulsa Nursing Center, Tulsa, OK
Tupelo Manor Nursing Home, Tupelo, MS
Isla Carroll Turner Health Care Center, Houston, TX
Turner Nursing Home, Cincinnati, OH
Turner Nursing Home, Childress, TX
Turtle Creek Health Care Center, Jacksonville, FL
Tuscola County Medical Care Facility, Caro, MI
Tuskegee Health Care Inc, Tuskegee, AL
Tustin Convalescent Hospital, Tustin, CA
Tustin Manor, Tustin, CA
Tutor Nursing Home Inc, Temple, TX
Twain Haven Nursing Home, Perry, MO
Mark Twain Manor, Bridgeton, MO
Tweeten Memorial Hospital—Nurs Home, Spring Grove, MN
24 Rhode Island Street Nursing Home Company Inc, Buffalo, NY
Twilight Acres Inc, Wall Lake, IA
Twilight Acres Nursing Home, Eugene, OR
Twilight Gardens Home Inc, Norwalk, OH
Twilight Haven, Fresno, CA
Twilight Haven Sheltered Care Home, Louisville, IL
Twilight Home, Corsicana, TX
Twilight Nursing Home Inc, Jeffersonville, IN
Twilight Nursing Home Inc, Bangs, TX
Twilight Personal Care Home, Woodburn, KY
Twin Birch Health Care Center, Spring Park, MN
Twin Cedar Nursing Home, Post, TX
Twin City Health Care Center Inc, Uhrichsville, OH
Twin City Linnea Home, Saint Paul, MN
Twin City Nursing Home, Gas City, IN
Twin City Nursing Home, Hartshorne, OK
Twin Lakes Care Center, Burlington, NC
Twin Lakes Care Center, San Augustine, TX
Twin Lakes Nursing Home, Albany, KY
Twin-M Nursing Home, Canton, OH
Twin Maples Home Inc, Durham, CT
Twin Maples Nursing Home, McArthur, OH
Twin Oaks, Mansfield, OH
Twin Oaks Care Center Inc, Sweet Home, OR
Twin Oaks Community Living Facility, Pekin, IL
Twin Oaks Convalescent Center, Alma, GA
Twin Oaks Convalescent Center, Jacksonville, TX
Twin Oaks Convalescent Home Inc, South Boston, VA
Twin Oaks Estate Inc, O'Fallon, MO
Twin Oaks Nursing & Convalescent Home, LaPlace, LA
Twin Oaks Nursing Home, Campbelltown, PA
Twin Oaks Nursing Home Inc, Mobile, AL
Twin Oaks Retirement Center, Waco, TX
Twin Palms Care Center, Artesia, CA
Twin Pines Adult Care Center, Kirksville, MO
Twin Pines Care Center, Salt Lake City, UT
Twin Pines Healthcare, Santa Paula, CA
Twin Pines Nursing Center, Lewisville, TX
Twin Pines Nursing Home, Victoria, TX
Twin Pines Retreat, Cuyahoga Falls, OH
Twin Rivers Care Center, Anoka, MN
Twin Rivers Medical Center, Arkadelphia, AR
Twin Rivers Nursing Care Center, Defiance, OH
Twin Towers, Cincinnati, OH
Twin Town Treatment Center, Saint Paul, MN
Twin View Nursing Home, Twin City, GA
Twin Willow Nursing Center, Salem, IL
Twinbrook Medical Center, Erie, PA
Twinbrook Nursing Home, Louisville, KY
Twinbrooke South—McAllen, McAllen, TX
Twinbrooke South—San Benito, San Benito, TX
Two Fifty Two West Wabasha Street, Winona, MN
2201 East 10th Street Home, Pueblo, CO
Twomey Rest Home, Lynn, MA
Tylertown Extended Care Center, Tylertown, MS

Tyndall Good Samaritan Center, Tyndall, SD
Tyrone Medical Inn, Saint Petersburg, FL
Tyson Manor Health Facility, Montgomery, AL
Uihlein Mercy Center, Lake Placid, NY
Uintah Care Center, Vernal, UT
Ukiah Convalescent Hospital, Ukiah, CA
Ulster County Infirmary Health Related Facility, Kingston, NY
John Umstead Hospital—ICF, Butner, NC
Unicoi County Nursing Home, Erwin, TN
Unicrest, Spokane, WA
Union City Health Care Center, Union City, TN
Union City Manor Nursing Center, Union City, TN
Union County Nursing Home, Blairsville, GA
Union County Skilled Nursing Home, Anna, IL
Union Forge Nursing Home, Annandale, NJ
Union House Nursing Home Inc, Glover, VT
Union Manor, Marysville, OH
Union Memorial Hospital, Monroe, NC
Union Mission Nursing Home Inc, Haverhill, MA
Union Printers Home & Hospital, Colorado Springs, CO
Unitarian Universalist House, Philadelphia, PA
United Cerebral Palsy Association Home of Cuyahoga County, Cleveland, OH
United Cerebral Palsy Intermediate Care Facility, Oklahoma City, OK
United Cerebral Palsy of Columbus & Franklin County Inc Genesis Facility, Columbus, OH
United Cerebral Palsy Residential Center, Seattle, WA
United Cerebral Palsy/Spastic Childrens Foundation, Los Angeles, CA
United Cerebral Palsy/Spastic Children's Foundation, Sylmar, CA
United Christian Church Home, Annville, PA
United Church Colony Homes Inc, Gasport, NY
United Convalescent of Post, Post, TX
United District Hospital & Home, Staples, MN
United Health Care Center, Big Spring, TX
United Helpers Canton Nursing Home Inc, Canton, NY
United Helpers Cedars Nursing Home Inc, Ogdensburg, NY
United Helpers Nursing Home Inc, Ogdensburg, NY
United Home for Aged Hebrews, New Rochelle, NY
United Memorial Hospital, Greenville, MI
United Methodist Conv Home of Connecticut Inc, Shelton, CT
United Methodist Health Care Center, East Providence, RI
United Methodist Home, Topeka, KS
United Methodist Memorial Home, Warren, IN
The United Methodist Village Inc, Lawrenceville, IL
United Nursing Home for the Aged Inc, New Rochelle, NY
United Odd Fellow & Rebekah Home, Bronx, NY
United Pioneer Home, Luck, WI
United Presbyterian Home, Washington, IA
United Presbyterian Home at Syosset Inc, Woodbury, NY
United Presbyterian Home of Hollidaysburg, Hollidaysburg, PA
United Presbyterian Home of Philipsburg, Philipsburg, PA
United Presbyterian Womens Association Home for Aged, Pittsburgh, PA
United Retirement Center, Brookings, SD
United Zion Home Inc, Lititz, PA
Unity House, Worthington, MN
University Center for Continuing Care, Mercerville, NJ
University Convalescent Center East Inc, Deland, FL

University Convalescent Center West, Deland, FL
University Convalescent & Nursing Home, Livonia, MI
University Convalescent & Nursing Home Inc, Wheaton, MD
University Health Care Center, Minneapolis, MN
University Health Care Center Inc, Nashville, TN
University Heights Nursing Home, Albany, NY
University Hills Christian Nursing Home, Denver, CO
University Hospital—Extended Care Facility, Augusta, GA
University Manor, Lubbock, TX
University Nursing Care Center, Gainesville, FL
University Nursing Center, Upland, IN
University Nursing Center, Greenville, NC
University Nursing Center, McKinney, TX
University Nursing Home, New York, NY
University Park, Richmond, VA
University Park Care Center, Muskegon, MI
University Park Convalescent Center, Tampa, FL
University Park Heritage Manor, Wichita Falls, TX
University Park Nursing Center, Fort Wayne, IN
University Terrace Good Samaritan Village, Las Cruces, NM
University Village Inc, Tulsa, OK
Upjohn Community Nursing Home, Kalamazoo, MI
Upland Convalescent Hospital, Upland, CA
Uplands Home for Church Women, Baltimore, MD
Upper Bucks Nursing & Convalescent Center, Quakertown, PA
Upper Valley Rest Home, Spearfish, SD
Upton County Convalescent Center, McCamey, TX
Uptown Home for the Aged, Philadelphia, PA
Uptown Shelter Care Home, Chicago, IL
Urbana Nursing Home, Urbana, IL
Utah State Training School, American Fork, UT
Utica Nursing Home, Utica, OH
Val Morys Haven, Columbus, NE
Valborg Lutheran Home, Des Moines, IA
Valencia Woods Nursing Center, Valencia, PA
Valle Verde Health Facility, Santa Barbara, CA
Valle Vista Care Center, The Dalles, OR
Valle Vista Convalescent Hospital Inc, Escondido, CA
Valle Vista Manor, Lewistown, MT
Vallejo Convalescent Hospital, Vallejo, CA
Valley Brook Park Inc, Wetumpka, AL
Valley Care Center, Porterville, CA
Valley Care Center, Idaho Falls, ID
Valley Care Center A Prestige Facility, Okanogan, WA
Valley Care & Guidance Center, Fresno, CA
Valley Convalescent Hospital, Bakersfield, CA
Valley Convalescent Hospital, El Centro, CA
Valley Convalescent Hospital, Fresno, CA
Valley Convalescent Hospital, San Bernardino, CA
Valley Convalescent Hospital, Watsonville, CA
Valley Crest Nursing Home, Wilkes-Barre, PA
Valley Fair Lodge, Colorado City, TX
Valley Grande Manor, Weslaco, TX
Valley Grande Manor Inc, Brownsville, TX
Valley Group Home 1, Moorhead, MN
Valley Group Home 2, Karlstad, MN
Valley Haven Geriatric Center & Personal Care Home Inc, Wellsburg, WV
Valley Haven Personal Care Home, Sanders, KY
Valley Health Care Center, Chilhowie, VA
Valley Health Care Center, Chilhowie, VA
Valley Health Care Center, Hayward, WI
Valley Health Services Inc, Herkimer, NY
Valley Hi Nursing Home, Woodstock, IL
Valley Hi Nursing Home Inc, Denver, CO

Valley Home, Thief River Falls, MN
Valley Homes, Mount Vernon, WA
Valley Hospital, Palmer, AK
Valley House Health Care, Tucson, AZ
Valley Manor, Denver, CO
Valley Manor Care Center, Montrose, CO
Valley Manor Convalescent Hospital, Concord, CA
Valley Manor Nursing Center, Coopersburg, PA
Valley Manor Nursing Home, New Philadelphia, OH
Valley Manor Nursing Home, Plymouth, WI
Valley Memorial Home—Almonte, Grand Forks, ND
Valley Memorial Home—Medical Park, Grand Forks, ND
Valley Nursing & Convalescent Center Inc, Baltimore, MD
Valley Nursing Home, Billings, MT
Valley Nursing Home, Westwood, NJ
Valley Nursing Home, Saint Marys, OH
Valley Palms Care Center, North Hollywood, CA
Valley Park Conv Center, Barbourville, KY
Valley Park Nursing Home, Valley Park, MO
Valley Rest Home, Eden Valley, MN
Valley Rest Nursing Home, Totowa Boro, NJ
Valley Road Nursing Home, Salem, OH
Valley Skilled Nursing Facility, Sacramento, CA
Valley Star Nursing Home, Alpine, TX
Valley Terrace Nursing Center, Puyallup, WA
Valley View, Beaumont, CA
Valley View Care Center, LaGrande, OR
Valley View Care Center, Anson, TX
Valley View Care Centre, North Platte, NE
Valley View Care Home, Lawrence, KS
Valley View Care Inc, Nebraska City, NE
Valley View Castle Nursing Home, Millersburg, OH
Valley View Estates Nursing Home, Hamilton, MT
Valley View Health Care, Rome, GA
Valley View Health Care Center, Canon City, CO
Valley View Health Care Center, Elkhart, IN
Valley View Health Care Facility, Marksville, LA
Valley View Home, Glasgow, MT
Valley View Home, Wausa, NE
Valley View Home, Altoona, PA
Valley View Home, Granbury, TX
Valley View Lodge, Eastland, TX
Valley View Manor, Craig, CO
Valley View Manor, Lamberton, MN
Valley View Manor, Frankfort, OH
Valley View Manor, Saratoga, WY
Valley View Manor Inc, Frenchtown, NJ
Valley View Manor Nursing Home, Norwich, NY
Valley View Medical Center, Cedar City, UT
Valley View Nursing Center, Eldora, IA
Valley View Nursing Home, Baltimore, MD
Valley View Nursing Home, Lenox, MA
Valley View Nursing Home, Westfield, MA
Valley View Nursing Home, Houston, MN
Valley View Nursing Home, Adena, OH
Valley View Nursing Home, Akron, OH
Valley View Nursing Home, Lancaster, OH
Valley View Nursing Home, Cheswick, PA
Valley View Nursing Home, Berkeley Springs, WV
Valley View Professional Care Center, Junction City, KS
Valley View Residential Care Home, Bayfield, CO
Valley View Retirement Community, Belleville, PA
Valley View Skilled Nursing Center, Ukiah, CA
Valley View Villa Nursing Home, Fort Morgan, CO
Valley View Village, Des Moines, IA
Valley Villa Care Center, Renton, WA
Valley Vista Care Center, Junction City, KS
Valley Vista Good Samaritan Center, Wamego, KS

Valley Vue Nursing Home, Armstrong, IA
Valley West Convalescent Hospital, Williams, CA
Valley West Health Care Center, Eugene, OR
Valleyview Health Care Center, Jordan, MN
Vallhaven Care Center, Neenah, WI
Valliant Care Center Inc, Valliant, OK
Valvista Pavillion, Athens, TX
Van Allen Nursing Home, Little Falls, NY
Van Ark Nursing Home, Tucumcari, NM
Van Ayer Manor Nursing Center, Martin, TN
Van Buren Convalescent Center, Belleville, MI
Van Buren County Nursing Home, Clinton, AR
Van Buren Good Samaritan Center, Keosauqua, IA
Van Buren Hall, Green Bay, WI
Van Buren Nursing Center, Van Buren, AR
Van Dora Nursing Home Inc, Foxboro, MA
Van Doren Nursing Home, Rego Park, NY
Van Duyn Home & Hospital, Syracuse, NY
Van Dyk Manor, Montclair, NJ
Van Dyk Nursing & Convalescent Home, Ridgewood, NJ
Van Dyke Care Center-Effingham, Effingham, IL
Van Hook School of Fla Inc, DeLeon Springs, FL
Van Orden Adult Living Center, Muskogee, OK
Van Rensselaer Manor, Troy, NY
Van Wert Manor, Van Wert, OH
Vanceburg Health Care Center, Vanceburg, KY
Vanco Manor Nursing Home, Goodlettsville, TN
Vancrest Nursing Home, Van Wert, OH
Vanderklish Hall Nursing Home, Newton, MA
Vanguard Extended Care, Plymouth, MN
Vantage Convalescent Center, Phoenix, AZ
Vantage Convalescent Center, Little Rock, AR
Varnum Park Rest Home, Waltham, MA
Vasa Lutheran Home, Red Wing, MN
Vegas Valley Convalescent Hospital, Las Vegas, NV
Venango Manor, Franklin, PA
Venice Nursing Pavilion—North, Venice, FL
Venice Nursing Pavilion—South, Venice, FL
Venoy Continued Care Center, Wayne, MI
Ventura Estates Health Manor, Newbury Park, CA
Ventura Estates Health Manor, Newbury Park, CA
The Venturan Convalescent Center, Ventura, CA
VerDelle Village, Saint Albans, VT
Verdries Nursing Home, Kalamazoo, MI
Verdugo Valley Convalescent Hospital, Montrose, CA
Verdugo Vista Convalescent Hospital, La Crescenta, CA
Verland Foundation Inc, Sewickly, PA
Vermilion Health Care Center, Kaplan, LA
Vermillion Convalescent Center, Clinton, IN
Vermillion Manor Nursing Home, Danville, IL
Vermont Achievement Center—Pediatric Convalescent Unit, Rutland, VT
Vermont Knolls Convalescent Hospital, Los Angeles, CA
Vermont Veterans Home, Bennington, VT
Vernon Care Center, Vernon, TX
Vernon Convalescent Hospital, Los Angeles, CA
Vernon Green Nursing Home, Vernon, VT
Vernon Hall Inc, Cambridge, MA
Vernon House Inc, Framingham, MA
Vernon Manor, Viroqua, WI
Vernon Manor Children's Home, Wabash, IN
Vernon Manor Health Care Facility, Vernon, CT
Vero Beach Care Center Inc, Vero Beach, FL
Verrazano Nursing Home, Staten Island, NY
Versailles Health Care Center, Versailles, OH
Vespers Nursing Home, Wilkesboro, NC
Vestal Nursing Center, Vestal, NY
Via Health Care Center for the Hermitage Methodist Home, Richmond, VA

Vian Nursing Home, Vian, OK
Vicksburg Convalescent Home, Vicksburg, MS
Vicksburg Trace Haven, Vicksburg, MS
Victoria Haven Nursing Facility, Norwood, MA
Victoria Health Care Center, Asheville, NC
Victoria Home for Retired Men & Women, Ossining, NY
Victoria Martin Nursing Home, Saint Petersburg, FL
Victoria Nursing Home, Portland, OR
Victorian Convalescent Hospital Inc, San Francisco, CA
Victorian Manor, Scappoose, OR
Victorian Mansion Retirement Home, Attleboro, MA
Victorian Villa, Canton, ME
Victory Lake Nursing Center, Hyde Park, NY
Victory Memorial Hospital & Nursing Home, Stanley, WI
Victory Park Nursing Home Inc, Norwood, OH
Victory Way House, Craig, CO
Vienna Golden State Convalescent Hospital, Lodi, CA
View Heights Convalescent Hospital, Los Angeles, CA
Viewcrest Convalescent Center, Tacoma, WA
Viewcrest Nursing Home, Duluth, MN
Vigo County Home, Terre Haute, IN
The Viking Intermediate Care Facility, Cape Elizabeth, ME
The Villa Camillus, Columbia Station, OH
Villa Campana Health Center, Tucson, AZ
Villa Capri Manor, Maryland Heights, MO
Villa Care Center, Cleveland, OH
Villa Cascade Nursing Home, Lebanon, OR
Villa Clement, West Allis, WI
Villa Convalescent Center Inc, Troy, OH
Villa Convalescent Hospital, Riverside, CA
Villa del Sol, Marshalltown, IA
Villa Demarillac Nursing Home Inc, Pittsburgh, PA
Villa Elena Convalescent Hospital, Norwalk, CA
Villa Elizabeth Inc, Grand Rapids, MI
Villa Feliciana State Hospital, Jackson, LA
Villa Gardens Health Care Unit, Pasadena, CA
Villa Grace Good Samaritan Village, Hastings, NE
Villa Haven, Breckenridge, TX
Villa Homes West Inc, Monclova, OH
Villa Inn Home, Des Moines, IA
Villa Inn Nursing Center, Palestine, TX
Villa Loretto Nursing Home, Mount Calvary, WI
Villa Manor Care Center Inc, Porterville, CA
Villa Manor Nursing Home, Lakewood, CO
Villa Maria Conv Home Inc, Plainfield, CT
Villa Maria Convalescent Hospital, Santa Maria, CA
Villa Maria Geriatric Center, Tucson, AZ
Villa Maria Healthcare Center, Hurley, WI
Villa Maria Healthcare Ltd, Fargo, ND
Villa Maria Inc, Mulvane, KS
Villa Marie Skilled Nursing Facility, Jefferson City, MO
Villa Mary Immaculate, Albany, NY
Villa North Nursing Home, Toledo, OH
Villa Northwest Convalescent Center, Houston, TX
Villa Nursing Center, Mount Pleasant, TX
Villa Nursing Center Inc, Arlington, TX
Villa Oaks Convalescent Hospital, Pasadena, CA
Villa of Divine Providence, Lansdale, PA
Villa of St Francis Nursing Home, Morris, MN
Villa of the Woods, Fort Wayne, IN
Villa Park Care Center, Fort Dodge, IA
Villa Pines Living Center, Friendship, WI
Villa Pueblo Towers, Pueblo, CO
Villa Rehabilitation Center, Stockton, CA
Villa Rosa Nursing Home, Mitchellville, MD
Villa Royal Health Care Center, Medford, OR
Villa St Cyril, Highland Park, IL
Villa St Vincent, Crookston, MN

Villa Sancta Anna Home for the Aged Inc, Cleveland, OH
Villa Scalabrini, Northlake, IL
Villa Siena, Mountain View, CA
Villa Siesta Nursing Home, Van, TX
Villa Teresa Nursing Home, Harrisburg, PA
Villa Vista Inc, Cromwell, MN
The Village Health Care Center, Cameron, MO
The Village at Vance Jackson, San Antonio, TX
The Village at Westerville Nursing Center, Westerville, OH
Village Care Center, Lee's Summit, MO
Village Care Center, Galion, OH
Village Convalescent Center, Gresham, OR
Village Convalescent Center, McAllen, TX
Village East, Aurora, CO
Village Green, Phoenix, AZ
Village Haven Rest Home, Barnstable, MA
The Village Healthcare Center, Houston, TX
Village House Convalescent Home Inc, Newport, RI
Village Manor Nursing Home, Boston, MA
Village Manor Nursing Home, Lincoln, NE
Village North Inc, Saint Louis, MO
Village Northwest Unlimited, Sheldon, IA
Village Nursing Home, Sullivan, IN
Village Nursing Home, Hico, TX
Village Nursing Home Inc, Skokie, IL
Village Nursing Home Inc, New York, NY
Village Rest Home, Easton, MA
Village Rest Home, Leominster, MA
Village Sheltered Care Home, Cobden, IL
Village Square Nursing Center, Orwell, OH
Village Villa Nursing Home, Nortonville, KS
Village Vista Skilled Nursing Facility, Lancaster, PA
Villas of Shannon Nursing Home, Shannon, IL
Ville de Sante Nursing Home, Omaha, NE
Villisca Good Samaritan Center, Villisca, IA
Vincennes Nursing Home, Vincennes, IN
Vincention Home, Pittsburgh, PA
Vindobona Nursing Home Inc, Braddock Heights, MD
Vinewood Nursing Home, Plainfield, IN
Carl Vinson Skilled Nursing Home, Milledgeville, GA
Vintage Convalescent Hospital, Saint Helena, CA
Vintage Villa Nursing Home, Dexter, MO
VIP Manor, Wood River, IL
Virden Nursing Center, Virden, IL
Virgil Sanitarium & Convalescent Hospital, Los Angeles, CA
Virginia Baptist Home Inc, Culpeper, VA
Virginia Baptist Hospital Skilled Nursing Unit, Lynchburg, VA
Virginia Hall, Shreveport, LA
The Virginia Health Care Center, Waukesha, WI
The Virginia Home, Richmond, VA
Virginia Lee Care Center, Tiffin, OH
Virginia Manor Convalescent Home Inc, Everett, WA
Virginia Regional Medical Center-Conv Center, Virginia, MN
Virginia Synod Lutheran Home at Roanoke, Roanoke, VA
The Virginian, Fairfax, VA
Visalia Convalescent Hospital, Visalia, CA
Vista Continuing Care Center, Pasadena, TX
Vista Del Cerro Convalescent Center, El Cajon, CA
Vista Del Monte, Santa Barbara, CA
Vista Del Rio Medical Center, Kansas City, MO
Vista Del Sol Care Center, Los Angeles, CA
Vista Gardens Nursing Home, Red Oak, IA
Vista Golden Age Convalescent Home, Vista, CA
Vista Grande Nursing Home, Cortez, CO
Vista Grande Villa, Jackson, MI
Vista Hills Health Care Center, El Paso, TX
Vista Laguna Aftercare Facility Inc, Chicago, IL
Vista Nursing Home, Heavener, OK

Vista Pacifica Convalescent Home, Riverside, CA
Vista Pacificia—A Center for Rehabilitation & Growth, Riverside, CA
Vista Ray Convalescent Hospital, Lodi, CA
Vista Ray Convalescent Hospital 2, Lodi, CA
Vistavue Care Center, Kennewick, WA
Vivian's Nursing Home, Amarillo, TX
Vogue Retirement Residence, Fayette, MO
Volmer Nursing Home, North Vassalboro, ME
The Henry & Jane Vonderlieth Living Center Inc, Mount Pulaski, IL
W K Nursing Home Corporation, Bronx, NY
Wabash Christian Retirement Center, Carmi, IL
Wabash Healthcare Center, Wabash, IN
Wabasha Nursing Home, Wabasha, MN
Wabasso Health Care Center, Wabasso, MN
Wachusett Manor, Gardner, MA
Waconia Healthcare Center, Waconia, MN
Waddell Nursing Home, Galax, VA
Waddington Convalescent Home, Fayette City, PA
Wadesboro Nursing Home, Wadesboro, NC
Wadsworth Health Care Center Inc, Wadsworth, OH
Wagner Good Samaritan Center, Wagner, SD
Margaret Wagner House, Cleveland Heights, OH
Wagnon Place Inc, Warren, AR
Wahiawa General Hospital, Wahiawa, HI
Wahpeton Nursing Center, Wahpeton, ND
Waimano Training School & Hospital, Pearl City, HI
Waite Park Nursing Home Inc, Waite Park, MN
Wakefield Health Care Center, Wakefield, NE
Wakonda Heritage Manor, Wakonda, SD
Wakulla Manor, Crawfordville, FL
Walbridge Memorial Conv Wing, Meeker, CO
Walden House Healthcare Nursing Home, Concord, MA
Waldon Healthcare Center, Kenner, LA
Waldron Health Care Home Inc, Waldron, IN
Walhalla Community Hospital Assoc, Walhalla, ND
Walker Care Center, Grand Rapids, MI
Walker Care Center, Centralia, WA
Walker Convalescent Hospital Inc, Richmond, CA
Walker Methodist Health Center Inc, Minneapolis, MN
Walker Nursing Home Inc, Virginia, IL
Walker Post Manor, Oxford, NE
Walker's Veterans Home, Spearfish, SD
The Wallingford, Wallingford, PA
Wallingford Convalescent Home Inc, Wallingford, CT
Wallowa County Nursing Home, Enterprise, OR
Walnut Convalescent Hospital, Long Beach, CA
Walnut Creek Convalescent Hospital Inc, Walnut Creek, CA
Walnut Creek Nursing Home, Oklahoma City, OK
Walnut Grove Nursing Home, Grandview, WA
Walnut Hill Convalescent Center, Petersburg, VA
Walnut Hill Convalescent Home, New Britain, CT
Walnut Hills Convalescent Center, Austin, TX
Walnut Hills Nursing & Retirement Home, Walnut Creek, OH
Walnut Hills Pavillion, Massillon, OH
Walnut Manor, Walnut, IL
Walnut Manor Care Center, Clarksburg, OH
Walnut Mountain Nursing Home, Liberty, NY
Walnut Place, Dallas, TX
Walnut Ridge Convalescent Center, Walnut Ridge, AR
Walnut Valley Manor, Augusta, KS
Walnut Whitney Convalescent Hospital, Carmichael, CA
Walsenburg Care Center Inc, Walsenburg, CO
Mary Manning Walsh Nursing Home Company Inc, New York, NY

Walterboro Community Residence, Walterboro, SC
Waltham Nursing Home Inc, Waltham, MA
Walton Caring Center, Saint Charles, MO
Walton County Convalescent Center, DeFuniak Springs, FL
Walton County Hospital Convalescent Unit, Monroe, GA
Walton Retirement Home, Barnesville, OH
Wapakoneta Manor, Wapakoneta, OH
Wapello Nursing Home, Wapello, IA
Ward County Nursing Home, Monahans, TX
Ward Nursing Home, Tahlequah, OK
Ware Avenue Personal Care Home, East Point, GA
Ware Manor Nursing Home, Waycross, GA
Wareheime Residential Care, Greeley, CO
Warm Beach Health Care Center, Stanwood, WA
Warm Springs State Hospital, Warm Springs, MT
Warner Care Home 1, Cokato, MN
Warner Care Home 2, Cokato, MN
Warner Care Home 3, Cokato, MN
Warnerview Convalescent Hospital, Alturas, CA
Warren Geriatric Village, Warren, MI
Warren Haven—The Warren County Nursing Home, Oxford, NJ
Warren Manor, Warren, PA
Warren Manor Nursing Home, Selma, AL
Warren Medical Services, Warren, PA
Warren Memorial Hospital—Lynn Care Center, Front Royal, VA
Warren Nursing Home Inc, Warren, PA
Warren Park Nursing Home, Indianapolis, IN
Warren State Hospital—Long-Term Care Facility, Warren, PA
Warrensburg Manor Care Center, Warrensburg, MO
Warrensville Center, Warrensville Heights, OH
Warroad Care Center, Warroad, MN
Warsaw Health Care Center, Warsaw, VA
Warsaw Nursing Home, Warsaw, IN
The Wartburg Home of the Evangelical Lutheran Church, Mount Vernon, NY
Wartburg Lutheran Home for the Aging, Brooklyn, NY
Warwick Health Centre, Warwick, RI
Warwick Rest Home Inc, Warwick, RI
Wasatch Care Center, Ogden, UT
Wasatch County Hospital—Skilled Nursing Facility, Heber City, UT
Wasatch Villa, Salt Lake City, UT
Washburn House-Home For Aged Women, Worcester, MA
The Washington, Cincinnati, OH
Washington Care Center, Washington, IA
Washington Center for Aging Services, Washington, DC
Washington Christian Village, Washington, IL
Washington Convalescent Hospital, San Leandro, CA
Washington County Convalescent Center, Chipley, FL
Washington County Extended Care Facility, Sandersville, GA
Washington County Health Center, Washington, PA
Washington County Infirmary, Chatom, AL
Washington County Public Nursing Home, Akron, CO
Washington County Woman's Home, Marietta, OH
Washington Health Care Center—Aldercrest, Edmonds, WA
Washington Health Care Center—Northcrest, Spokane, WA
Washington Health Care Center—Valley Crest, Spokane, WA
Washington Home, Washington, DC
The Washington House—Health Care Unit, Alexandria, VA
Washington & Jane Smith Home, Chicago, IL
Washington Manor, Dayton, OH
Washington Manor, Kenosha, WI

Washington Manor Convalescent Hospital, San Leandro, CA
Washington Manor Nursing & Rehabilitation Center, Hollywood, FL
Washington Nursing Center Annex, Washington, IN
Washington Nursing Center Inc, Washington, IN
Washington Nursing & Convalescent, Los Angeles, CA
Washington Odd Fellows Home, Walla Walla, WA
Washington Senior Care, Washington, PA
Washington Square Nursing Center, Warren, OH
Washoe Care Center, Sparks, NV
Watauga Nursing Care Center, Boone, NC
Watch Hill Manor Ltd, Westerly, RI
Waterbury Convalescent Center Inc, Waterbury, CT
Waterbury Extended Care Facility Inc, Watertown, CT
Waterbury Nursing Center, Waterbury, CT
Waterford Commons, Toledo, OH
The Waterford Health Center, Juno Beach, FL
Waterfront Terrace, Chicago, IL
Waterman Convalescent Hospital, San Bernardino, CA
Waterman Heights Nursing Home Ltd, Smithfield, RI
The Waters Edge, Alameda, CA
Watertown Convalarium, Watertown, CT
Waterview Hills Nursing Center Inc, Purdys, NY
Waterview Nursing Care Center, Flushing, NY
Waterview Nursing Center, Cedar Grove, NJ
Waterview Villa, East Providence, RI
Waterville Care Center, Waterville, MN
Waterville Convalescent Center, Waterville, ME
The Watkins Home, Winona, MN
Manda Ann Watkins, Houston, TX
Watkins Rest Home, Madisonville, KY
Watkins Stephens Skyview Nursing Home, Oklahoma City, OK
Watrous Nursing Center, Madison, CT
Watseka Health Care Center, Watseka, IL
Watseka Manor, Watseka, IL
Layton W Watson Nursing Home, Gallaway, TN
Watson Nursing Home, Fort Worth, TX
Waubay Rest Home, Waubay, SD
Waukegan Pavilion, Waukegan, IL
Waukegan Terrace, Waukegan, IL
Waukon Good Samaritan Center, Waukon, IA
Waunakee Manor Health Care Center, Waunakee, WI
Wausau Manor, Wausau, WI
Wautoma Care Center Inc, Wautoma, WI
Waveny Care Center, New Canaan, CT
Way Fair Restorium, Fairfield, IL
Way Twelve Halfway House, Wayzata, MN
Wayland Health Center, Providence, RI
Anthony Wayne Living Center, Fort Wayne, IN
Wayne Care Center, Wayne, NE
Wayne Convalescent Center, Wayne, MI
Wayne County Memorial Hospital Skilled Nursing Facility, Honesdale, PA
Wayne County Nursing Home, Waynesboro, TN
Wayne County Nursing Home & Health Related Facility, Lyons, NY
Wayne Haven Nursing Home, Wayne, NJ
Wayne Health Related Facility/Skilled Nursing Facility, Bronx, NY
Wayne Manor Nursing Home, Boston, MA
Wayne Nursing & Rehabilitation Center, Wayne, PA
Wayne Rounseville Memorial Convalescent Hospital, Oakland, CA
Wayne Total Living Center, Wayne, MI
Waynesburg Rest Home, Waynesburg, KY
Waynesville Nursing Center, Waynesville, MO
Waynoka Nursing Home, Waynoka, OK
Wayside Farm Inc, Peninsula, OH
Wayside Health Care Center, Andersonville, TN

Wayside Nursing Care Facility, Missoula, MT
Wayside Nursing Home Inc, Worcester, MA
WCTU Home for Women, Los Angeles, CA
We Care Health Facility, Columbus, OH
We Care Home for the Aged, Sturgis, SD
We Care Nursing Facilities Inc, Arcola, IL
We Care Wildwood Healthcare Inc, Wildwood, FL
Weakley County Nursing Home, Dresden, TN
Weatherford Care Center 1, Weatherford, TX
Weatherford Care Center 2, Weatherford, TX
Weatherford Nursing Center, Weatherford, OK
Webber Nursing Center, Fort Worth, TX
Webco Manor, Marshfield, MO
Weber Memorial Care Center, Roy, UT
Webers Nursing Home, Wellington, OH
Webster Manor LTCF, Webster, MA
Webster's Rest Home, Terre Haute, IN
Wedgemere Convalescent Home, Taunton, MA
Wedgewood, Grand Island, NE
Wedgewood Health Care, Saint Petersburg, FL
Wedgewood Health Care Center, Inver Grove Heights, MN
Wedgewood Nursing Home, Great Neck, NY
Wedgewood Nursing Home, Spencerport, NY
Wedgewood Nursing Home, Fort Worth, TX
Wedow Private Home Care, Michigan City, IN
Wee Rest Home, Sioux Falls, SD
Weier Retirement Nursing Home, Belleville, IL
Weirton Geriatric Center, Weirton, WV
Weisbrod Hospital & Nursing Home, Eads, CO
Weiser Care Center, Weiser, ID
Welbourne Hall, Watertown, WI
Susan Welch Rest Home, Middleboro, MA
Welcome Home for the Blind & Aged Inc, San Antonio, TX
Welcome Nursing Home, Franklin, IN
Welcome Nursing Home Inc, Oberlin, OH
Weld County Community Center Group Home, Greeley, CO
Weldwood Health Care Center, Golden Valley, MN
Wellesley Manor Convalescent Hospital, El Monte, CA
Wellesley Manor Nursing Home, Wellesley, MA
Wellington Care Center, Wellington, TX
Wellington Hall Nursing Home, Hackensack, NJ
Wellington Manor, Tampa, FL
Wellington Manor Nursing Home, Arlington, MA
Wellington Manor Nursing Home Inc, Wellington, OH
Wellington Plaza Therapy & Nursing Center, Chicago, IL
Wellman House Rest Home, Brookline, MA
Wells Nursing Home, Johnstown, NY
Wells Nursing Home, Wells, TX
Wells Personal Care Home, Jackson, MS
W Frank Wells Nursing Home, MacClenny, FL
Wellston Nursing Home, Wellston, OH
Wellsville Highland Inc, Wellsville, NY
Wellsville Manor Care Center, Wellsville, KS
Welsh Home for the Aged, Rocky River, OH
Welsh Nursing Facility, Welsh, LA
Wentworth Home for the Aged, Dover, NH
Wentworth Nursing Center, Chicago, IL
Clara Werner Dormitory, Watertown, WI
Werner Home, Portage, OH
Wernersville State Hospital—Long-Term Care Unit, Wernersville, PA
Wesley Acres, Des Moines, IA
Wesley Care Center, Des Moines, WA
Wesley Gardens—The Gardens, Des Moines, WA
Wesley Gardens—The Terrace, Des Moines, WA
Wesley Glen Inc, Columbus, OH
Wesley Hall Inc, Cincinnati, OH
Wesley Health Care Center Inc, Saratoga Springs, NY

Wesley Highland Manor, Memphis, TN
Wesley Home Inc, Baltimore, MD
Wesley Manor Health Care Center Inc, Kittanning, PA
Wesley Manor Inc, Frankfort, IN
Wesley Manor Methodist Home for the Aging, Dothan, AL
Wesley Manor Retirement Community, Louisville, KY
Wesley Manor Retirement Village, Jacksonville, FL
Wesley Towers Inc, Hutchinson, KS
Wesley Village, Pittston, PA
Wesley Village U M C Health Care Center, Macomb, IL
Wesley Wilcourt Willows Health Center, Rockford, IL
Wesley Woods Health Center, Atlanta, GA
Wesleyan Arms Inc, High Point, NC
Wesleyan Health Care Center, Marion, IN
Wesleyan Health Care Center Inc, Denton, MD
Wesleyan Nursing Home, Georgetown, TX
Wesleyan Nursing Home Inc, Seward, AK
Wesleyan Nursing Home Inc, Charlotte, NC
Wesley-on-East Ltd, Rochester, NY
Wessel's Nursing Home Inc, Charlotte, NC
Wessex House of Jacksonville Inc, Jacksonville, AL
West Acres Nursing Home, Brockton, MA
West Bay Manor, Warwick, RI
West Bay Nursing Center, Oldsmar, FL
West Bend Care Center, West Bend, IA
West Bloomfield Geriatric Center, West Bloomfield, MI
West Boarding Home, Warrenton, MO
West Chester Arms of Pennsylvania Inc, West Chester, PA
West Chicago Terrace, West Chicago, IL
West Coke County Hospital District Nursing Home, Robert Lee, TX
West Elm Nursing Home, Brockton, MA
West Hartford Manor, West Hartford, CT
West Haven Health Care, Bluffton, IN
West Haven Nursing Facility, West Haven, CT
West Haven Nursing Home, Apollo, PA
West Hickory Haven, Milford, MI
West Hill Convalescent Home, Rocky Hill, CT
West Hills Convalescent Center, Portland, OR
West Hills Lodge, Owatonna, MN
West Hills Nursing Home Inc, Cincinnati, OH
West Home, Detroit Lakes, MN
West Jordan Care Center, West Jordan, UT
West Kentucky Manor Inc, Clinton, KY
West Lafayette Care Center, West Lafayette, OH
West Lake Lodge Nursing Home, Guilford, CT
West Lake Manor Health Care Center, Augusta, GA
West Linn Care Center Inc, West Linn, OR
West Main Nursing Home, Mascoutah, IL
West Melbourne Health Care Center, West Melbourne, FL
West Michigan Care Center, Allendale, MI
West Millard Care Center, Delta, UT
West Monroe Guest House Inc, West Monroe, LA
West Morgan Health Care Center, Decatur, AL
West Orange Manor, Winter Garden, FL
West Park Long-Term Care Center, Cody, WY
West Park Villa Health Care Center, Cincinnati, OH
West Plains Nursing Home, West Plains, MO
West Point Care Center, West Point, IA
West Point Nursing Home, West Point, NE
West Rest Haven Inc, West, TX
West Ridge Manor, Knoxville, IA
West Rock Health Care, New Haven, CT
West Roxbury Manor Nursing Home, Boston, MA
West Salem Manor, West Salem, IL
West Side Health Care Center, Cincinnati, OH
West Side Nursing Home, Worcester, MA
West Side Rest Home, Ronan, MT

West Springfield Nursing Home, West Springfield, MA
West Suburban Shelter Care Center, Hinsdale, IL
West Texas Nursing Center, Abilene, TX
West Torrance Convalescent Hospital, Torrance, CA
West Trail Nursing Home, Plymouth, MI
West Union Good Samaritan Center, West Union, IA
West View Manor Retirement Center, Wooster, OH
West View Nursing Home, Murray, KY
West View Nursing Home Inc, West Warwick, RI
West Vue Home Inc, West Plains, MO
West Winds Nursing Home, Union Lake, MI
Westbay Manor I, Westlake, OH
Westbay Manor II, Westlake, OH
Westborough Nursing Home, Westborough, MA
Westbrook Acres, Gladbrook, IA
Westbrook Good Samaritan Center, Westbrook, MN
Westbrook Heights Rest Home, West Brookfield, MA
Westbrook Manor, Kalamazoo, MI
Westbrook Manor Nursing Center, Parsons, KS
Westbrook Park Nursing Center, Canton, OH
Westbury Home, McDonough, GA
Westbury Nursing Home, Jenkinsburg, GA
The Westbury Place Nursing & Retirement Center, Houston, TX
Westbury United Methodist Community, Meadville, PA
Westchester Care Center, Tempe, AZ
Westchester House, Chesterfield, MO
Westerly Health Center, Westerly, RI
Westerly Nursing Home Inc, Westerly, RI
Western Avenue Residence, Waterville, ME
Western Care Nursing Home, Helena, MT
Western Carolina Center, Morganton, NC
Western Center, Canonsburg, PA
Western Convalescent Hospital, Los Angeles, CA
Western Eldercare Nursing Center, Albuquerque, NM
Western Hall Good Samaritan Center, Wood River, NE
Western Hills Health Care Center, Lakewood, CO
Western Hills Nursing Center, Abilene, TX
Western Hills Nursing Home, Comanche, TX
Western Home, Cedar Falls, IA
Western Maine Association for Retarded Citizens, Minot, ME
Western Manor, Ranger, TX
Western Manor Nursing Home, Billings, MT
Western Maryland Center, Hagerstown, MD
Western Nebraska Rest Home, Mitchell, NE
Western Nursing Home, Buffalo, OK
Western Oaks Health Care Center, Bethany, OK
Western Pennsylvania Eastern Star Home, Pittsburgh, PA
Western Prairie Care Home, Ulysses, KS
Western Reserve Convalescent Home of Erie, Erie, PA
Western Reserve Convalescent Homes Inc, Kirtland, OH
Western Reserve Extended Care Inc, Kirtland, OH
Western Restoration Center, Pittsburgh, PA
Western Village, Green Bay, WI
Westfall Nursing Home, Bucyrus, OH
Westfield Health Care Center Inc, Westfield, NY
Westfield Manor Health Care Center, Meriden, CT
Westfield Manor Nursing Home, Westfield, MA
Westfield Village, Westfield, IN
Westford Nursing Home Inc, Westford, MA
Westgate Convalescent Center, San Jose, CA
Westgate Manor, Bangor, ME
Westgate Manor Convalescent Hospital, Madera, CA

Westgate Manor Nursing Home, Saint Louis, MI
Westgate Nursing Center, Rocky Mount, NC
Westgate Nursing Home, Rochester, NY
Westgate of Tarboro, Tarboro, NC
Westhaven Home, Jackson, MS
Westhaven Nursing Home Inc, Stillwater, OK
Westhaven Quality Care Center, Hamilton, OH
Westhope Home, Westhope, ND
Westlake Convalescent Hospital, Los Angeles, CA
Westlake Pavillion, Franklin Park, IL
Westland Convalescent Center, Westland, MI
Westland Manor Nursing Center, Lakewood, CO
Westledge Nursing Home, Peekskill, NY
Westmere Convalescent Home, Albany, NY
Westminister Oaks Nursing Home, Tallahassee, FL
Westminster-Canterbury in Virginia Beach, Virginia Beach, VA
Westminster Gardens Health Center, Duarte, CA
Westminster Manor, Dallas, TX
Westminster Terrace, Louisville, KY
Westminster Thurber Community, Columbus, OH
Westminster Towers, Orlando, FL
Westminster Villa Nursing & Convalescent Center, Westminster, MD
Westminster Village, Spanish Fort, AL
Westminster Village, Ponca City, OK
Westminster Village, Allentown, PA
Westminster Village Health Care Center, Clarksville, IN
Westminster Village Inc, Bloomington, IL
Westminster Village North Inc, Indianapolis, IN
Westminster Village West Lafayette, West Lafayette, IN
Westminster-Canterbury House, Richmond, VA
Westminster-Canterbury of Lynchburg Inc, Lynchburg, VA
Westmont Care Center, Logan, IA
Westmont Convalescent Center, Westmont, IL
Westmoreland Health Center, Waukesha, WI
Westmoreland Manor, Greensburg, PA
Westmoreland Place Nursing Home, Chillicothe, OH
Westmount Health Facility, Glens Falls, NY
Weston County Manor, Newcastle, WY
Weston Manor Nursing & Retirement, Weston, MA
Westover Retirement Community, Hamilton, OH
Westport Convalescent Center, Richmond, VA
Westridge Apartments, Canon City, CO
Westridge Health Care Center, Terre Haute, IN
Westridge Health Care Center, Marlborough, MA
Westridge Manor Inc, Nacogdoches, TX
Westshire Retirement & Healthcare Center, Cicero, IL
Westside Boarding Care Home, Owatonna, MN
Westside Christian Retirement Village Inc, Indianapolis, IN
Westside Convalescent Center, Atlantic City, NJ
Westside Development Center, Corsicana, TX
Westside Health Care, Greenville, SC
Westside Home Inc, Lexington, NE
Westview Acres, Leon, IA
Westview Care Center, Seymour, TX
Westview Care Center Inc, Indianola, IA
Westview Conv Center Inc, Dayville, CT
Westview Health Care Center Inc, Racine, WI
Westview Manor, Britt, IA
Westview Manor, Peabody, KS
Westview Manor, McGregor, TX
Westview Manor, Odessa, TX
Westview Manor Health Care Center, Bedford, IN
Westview Manor Inc, Derby, KS

Westview Medical Care Home, Port Wentworth, GA

Westview Nursing Center, Herculaneum, MO

Westview Nursing Center, Guthrie, OK

Westview Nursing Home, Indianapolis, IN

Westview Nursing Home, Milwaukee, WI

Westview Rest Home, East Bridgewater, MA

Westville Nursing Home, Westville, OK

Westward Heights Nursing Home, Lander, WY

Westwinds Geriatric Center, Ellisville, MO

Westwood, Fremont, CA

Westwood Convalescent Home Inc, Troup, TX

Westwood Convalescent & Rest Home, Sioux City, IA

Westwood Hall Hebrew Home, Long Branch, NJ

Westwood Healthcare Center, Keene, NH

Westwood Heritage Manor, Shreveport, LA

Westwood Hills Health Care Center, Poplar Bluff, MO

Westwood Home Inc, Clinton, MO

Westwood Manor, Topeka, KS

Westwood Manor, Corpus Christi, TX

The Westwood Manor Inc, Chicago, IL

Westwood Manor Nursing Home, DeRidder, LA

Westwood Manor Nursing Home, Wilson, NC

Westwood Nursing Center, Detroit, MI

Westwood Nursing Home, Saint Louis Park, MN

Westwood Rehabilitation Medical Center, Boardman, OH

Westwood Retirement Center, Fort Walton Beach, FL

Westy Community Care Home, Westmoreland, KS

Wetumka Nursing Home Inc, Wetumka, OK

Wetzler Convalescent Home Inc, Blue Ball, PA

Wewoka Nursing Home Inc, Wewoka, OK

Wexford House, Wexford, PA

Weyauwega Health Care Center, Weyauwega, WI

Weymouth Manor Nursing Home, Weymouth, MA

May Cravath Wharton Nursing Home, Pleasant Hill, TN

Wharton Manor, Manhattan, KS

Wharton Manor, Wharton, TX

Wheat Ridge Regional Center, Wheat Ridge, CO

Wheat State Manor Inc, Whitewater, KS

Wheatland Lodge, South Haven, KS

Wheatland Memorial Nursing Home, Harlowton, MT

Wheaton Convalescent Center, Wheaton, IL

Wheatridge Manor Nursing Home Inc, Denver, CO

Wheeler Care Center, Wheeler, TX

Wheeling Continuous Care Center, Wheeling, WV

Wheelwright House, Newburyport, MA

Whetstone Convalescent Center, Columbus, OH

Whetstone Valley Nursing Home, Milbank, SD

Whibbey Island Manor Inc, Oak Harbor, WA

Whispering Pines Care Center, Starke, FL

Whispering Pines Good Samaritan Center, Pine River, MN

Whispering Pines Health Care Center, Valparaiso, IN

Whispering Pines Nursing Home, Plain Dealing, LA

Whispering Pines Nursing Home, Jackson, MS

Whispering Pines Nursing Home, Fayetteville, NC

Whispering Pines Nursing Home Inc, Winnsboro, TX

White Acres-Good Samaritan Retirement Village & Nursing Center, El Paso, TX

White Bear Lake Care Center, White Bear Lake, MN

The White Billet, Hatboro, PA

White Birch Nursing Home, Paterson, NJ

White Community Hospital, Aurora, MN

White County Nursing Home, Carmi, IL

White Cross Health Center, Smolan, KS

Eartha M M White Nursing Home, Jacksonville, FL

Elihu White Nursing & Rehabilitation Center, Braintree, MA

White Gables Rest Home of Natick, Natick, MA

Griffin White Home for Aged Men & Aged Couples, Haverhill, MA

White Haven Annex at Clark Summit, Clarks Summit, PA

White Haven Center, White Haven, PA

White Haven Center Annex—Allentown, Allentown, PA

White House Nursing Home, Orange, NJ

Mary E White Developmental Center, Columbia, SC

White Oak Convalescent Home, Canton, OH

White Oak Manor, Mio, MI

White Oak Terrace, Tryon, NC

White Pine Care Center, East Ely, NV

White Pines Manor Inc, Oregon, IL

White Plains Nursing Home, Bronx, NY

White River Convalescent Home Inc, Calico Rock, AR

White Sands of La Jolla, La Jolla, CA

White Settlement Nursing Center, Fort Worth, TX

Whitecliff Manor Nursing Home, Cleveland Heights, OH

Whitehall Convalescent Home, Ann Arbor, MI

Whitehall Convalescent Home 2, Novi, MI

Whitehall Convalescent & Nursing Home Inc, Chicago, IL

Whitehall Health Care Facilities, Hyannis, MA

Whitehall Manor, Whitehall, MI

The Whitehall North, Deerfield, IL

Whitehall Nursing Center Inc, Crockett, TX

Whitehall Nursing & Convalescent Center, Lancaster, PA

Whitehall Nursing Home, Saint Petersburg, FL

Whitehaven Care Center, Memphis, TN

Whitehouse Country Manor, Whitehouse, OH

Whitehouse Health Care Center, Roseville, MN

Whitehouse Health Care Center, Hillsboro, OH

Whitesboro Nursing Home Inc, Whitesboro, TX

Whitesburg Manor Health Center, Huntsville, AL

Whitewater Healthcare Center, Saint Charles, MN

Whitewood Rehabilitation Center, Waterbury, CT

Whitewright Nursing Home Inc, Whitewright, TX

Whitfield Nursing Home Inc, Corinth, MS

Whitmore Lake Convalescent Center, Whitmore Lake, MI

Whitney Center Medical Unit, Hamden, CT

Whitney Homestead Rest Home, Stow, MA

Whitney Manor Convalescent Center Inc, Hamden, CT

Whitridge Nursing Wing, Salisbury, CT

Whittaker Rest Home, Weymouth, MA

Whitten Center, Clinton, SC

Whittier Care Center, Whittier, CA

Whoolery's Residential Care Facility, Colorado Springs, CO

Wibaux County Nursing Home, Wibaux, MT

Wichita Care Center, Wichita, KS

Wichita Falls Convalescent Center, Wichita Falls, TX

Wichita Presbyterian Manor, Wichita, KS

Wickliffe Country Place, Wickliffe, OH

Wicomico Nursing Home, Salisbury, MD

Wide Horizons Care Center, Ogden, UT

Wide Horizons Inc, Wheat Ridge, CO

Wide View Rest Home, Paullina, IA

Widows Home of Dayton, Dayton, OH

Wiener Memorial Medical Center, Marshall, MN

Wiersma's Nursing Home, Allendale, NJ

Wightman Health Center, Pittsburgh, PA

Wil Mar Convalescent Home, Utica, MI

Wilber Nursing Home, Wilber, NE

G N Wilcox Memorial Hospital, Lihue, HI

Wilcox Nursing Home, Alma, MI

Wild Rose Manor, Wild Rose, WI

Wilder Nursing Home, Dadeville, AL

Wilder Residence East, Saint Paul, MN

Wilder Residence West, Saint Paul, MN

Wildwood Health Care Center, Blackville, SC

Wildwood Healthcare Center, Puyallup, WA

Wildwood Intermediate Care Home, Talking Rock, GA

Wildwood Manor Inc, Gary, IN

Wildwood Manor Mt Inc, Gary, IN

Wildwood Nursing Home, Madison, MO

Wileyvale Community Nursing Home, Houston, TX

Wilge Memorial Home, Mitchell, SD

Wilhelms Nursing Home, Sarasota, FL

Wilkes Health Care, Washington, GA

Helen Wilkes Residence, Lake Park, FL

Wilkin County Group Home Inc, Breckenridge, MN

Wilkinsons Residential Care Facility, Grant City, MO

Will-O-Lee Nursing Home No 1 Inc, Oberlin, OH

Willamette Lutheran Homes Inc, Salem, OR

Willamette Methodist Convalescent Center, Milwaukie, OR

Willamette Nursing Home Inc, Portland, OR

Willapa Harbor Care Center, Raymond, WA

Willard F Bond Home, Madison, MS

Willard Quality Care Nursing Center, Willard, OH

William & Mary Nursing Home, Saint Petersburg, FL

William Penn Nursing Center, Lewistown, PA

Williams Care Manor, Omaha, NE

Williams County Hillside Nursing Home, Bryan, OH

Williams Health Care, Augusta, ME

Williams Health Care, Augusta, ME

Williams Health Facility, Mitchell, IN

Williams House IMR-E, Richland, WA

Williams Manor, Scottsburg, IN

Williamsbridge Manor Nursing Home, Bronx, NY

Williamsburg Care Center, Williamsburg, IA

Williamsburg Convalescent Center, Farmington Township, MI

Williamsburg Landing, Williamsburg, VA

Williamsburg Nursing Center, Sumter, SC

Williamsburg Nursing Home, Williamsburg, KY

Williamsburg Retirement Inn, Little Rock, AR

Williamson Appalachian Regional Hospital, South Williamson, KY

Williamsport Home, Williamsport, PA

Williamsport Nursing Home, Williamsport, MD

Williamsville Suburban Nursing Home, Williamsville, NY

Williamsville View Manor, Williamsville, NY

Willimansett East Nursing Home, Chicopee, MA

Willimansett West Nursing Home, Chicopee, MA

Willis Convalescent Center, Willis, TX

Willis Nursing Center, Homestead, PA

Willmar Health Care Center, Willmar, MN

Willmar Regional Treatment Center, Willmar, MN

Will-O-Bell Inc, Bartlett, TX

Will-O-Lee Nursing Home 2, Oberlin, OH

Willoughby Nursing Home, Brooklyn, NY

Willow Brook Care Center, Wheat Ridge, CO

Willow Brook Christian Home, Worthington, OH

Willow Care Center, Hannibal, MO

Willow Care Nursing Home, Willow Springs, MO

Willow Dale Care Center, Battle Creek, IA

Willow Gardens Care Center, Marion, IA

Willow Glen Convalescent Hospital Rest Care Center, San Jose, CA

Willow Haven, Tonkawa, OK

Willow Haven Nursing Home, Zanesville, OH

Willow Lake Convalescent Hospital, Long Beach, CA
Willow Manor Convalescent Center Inc, Vincennes, IN
Willow Manor Nursing Home, Lowell, MA
Willow Park Care Facility, Hudson, WI
Willow Point Nursing Home & Health Related Facility, Vestal, NY
Willow Rest Home, Waterbury, CT
Willow Ridge Living Center, Fort Wayne, IN
Willow Tree Care Center, Gresham, OR
Willow Tree Convalescent Hospital Ltd, Oakland, CA
Willow View Manor, Willow, CA
Willow Wood, Algiers, LA
Willowbrook Care Center, Kernersville, NC
Willowbrook Manor Nursing Home, Longview, TX
Willowbrook Nursing Home, Lake Mills, WI
Willowcrest Bamberger, Philadelphia, PA
Willowcrest Home Inc, Gardiner, ME
Willowcrest Nursing Home, South Milwaukee, WI
Willowdale Nursing Home, New Holstein, WI
Willowfield Nursing Home, Delavan, WI
Willowood Nursing Home Inc, Brunswick, OH
Willowood Nursing Home of Williamstown, Williamstown, MA
Willowood Nursing & Retirement Facility, Great Barrington, MA
Willowood of North Adams, North Adams, MA
The Willows Nursing Home, Alexandria, IN
The Willows, Parkersburg, WV
Willows Convalescent Center Central, Minneapolis, MN
Willows Convalescent Center South, Minneapolis, MN
Willows East Health Care Center, Minneapolis, MN
Willows Nursing Home, West Chester, OH
The Willows Nursing Home, Sun Prairie, WI
Willows Rehabilitation Center, Valparaiso, IN
Wilmington Extended Care Facility, Wilmington, OH
Wilmot Community Home, Wilmot, SD
Wilmot Nursing Home, Wilmot, AR
Wilshire Care Center, Fullerton, CA
Wilshire Manor Nursing Home, Alexandria, LA
Wilshire Nursing Home, Oklahoma City, OK
Wilson Apartments, Saint Paul, MN
Wilson Care Inc, Chicago, IL
Wilson Convalescent Center, Wilson, NC
Herman M Wilson Health Care Center, Gaithersburg, MD
Wilson Hospital Skilled Nursing Facility, Johnson City, NY
Wilson Manor Convalescent Hospital Inc, Spring Valley, CA
Mary E Wilson Home for the Aged, Springfield, MO
Wilson Nursing Center, Wilson, OK
Wilson Nursing Home, Wilson, KS
Wilson's Family Care Services, Brighton, CO
Wilton Memorial Home, Wilton, IA
Winamac Nursing Home, Winamac, IN
Winchester House, Libertyville, IL
Winchester Living Center, San Jose, CA
Winchester Lodge Nursing Home, Alvin, TX
Winchester Manor Health Care Center, Winchester, KY
Winchester Nursing Center, Winchester, MA
Winchester Place, Canal Winchester, OH
Winchester Terrace Inc, Mansfield, OH
Wincrest Nursing Center, Chicago, IL
Wind Crest Nursing Center Inc, Copperas Cove, TX
Windermere, Augusta, GA
Windmill Nursing Pavilion LTD, South Holland, IL
Windom CRF, Windom, MN
Windsong Village Convalescent Center, Pearland, TX
The Windsor, Richmond, VA
Windsor Care Center, Cedar Falls, IA
Windsor Care Center, Mount Sterling, KY

Windsor Estates Convalescent Center, Camdenton, MO
Windsor Estates Nursing Home, Salina, KS
Windsor Estates of Independence, Independence, MO
Windsor Estates of Kokomo, Kokomo, IN
Windsor Hall Retirement Center, Windsor, CT
Windsor Health Care Center, Windsor, CO
Windsor House, Youngstown, OH
Windsor House Convalescent Hospital, Vacaville, CA
Windsor Manor, Glendale, CA
Windsor Manor Nursing Home, Lisbon, OH
Windsor Manor Nursing & Rehabilitation Center, Palos Hills, IL
Windsor Medical Center Inc, North Canton, OH
Windsor Nursing & Retirement Home, South Yarmouth, MA
Windsor Park Nursing Home Inc, Queens Village, NY
Windsor Park Nursing Home Inc, Cincinnati, OH
Windsor's Resthaven Inc, Windsor, MO
Winebrenner Extended Care Facility, Findlay, OH
Winebrenner Haven, Findlay, OH
Winfield Nursing Home Inc, Winfield, AL
Winfield Rest Haven Inc, Winfield, KS
Winkler Nursing Home, L'anse, MI
Winnebago Baptist Home, Winnebago, MN
Winner Nursing Home, Winner, SD
Winneshiek County Health Care Facility, Decorah, IA
Winning Wheels Inc, Prophetstown, IL
Winnsboro Manor Nursing Center, Winnsboro, LA
Winnsboro Nursing Home, Winnsboro, TX
Winnwood Nursing Home Inc, Winnsboro, TX
Winona Manor Nursing Home, Winona, MS
Winslow Convalescent Center, Winslow, AZ
Winslow Convalescent Center, Bainbridge Island, WA
Winslow House, Marion, IA
L & J Winslow Memorial Nursing Home, Tomball, TX
W R Winslow Memorial Home Inc, Elizabeth City, NC
Winston County Nursing Home, Louisville, MS
Winston Manor Conv & Nursing Home, Chicago, IL
Winston-Salem Convalescent Center, Winston-Salem, NC
Winter Gables Nursing Home, Framingham, MA
Winter Gables Rest Home, Framingham, MA
Winter Haven Nursing Home, Houston, TX
Winter Hill Nursing Home, Somerville, MA
Winter Hill Rest Home, Worcester, MA
Winter House, Zanesville, OH
Winter Park Care Center, Winter Park, FL
Winter Park Towers, Winter Park, FL
Winterset Care Center—North, Winterset, IA
Winterset Care Center—South, Winterset, IA
Wintersong Village of Delaware, Delaware, OH
Wintersong Village of Hayesville Inc, Hayesville, OH
Wintersong Village of Laurelvillle, Laurelville, OH
Winthrop Care Center, Winthrop, MN
Winthrop Health Care Center Inc, New Haven, CT
Winthrop House Nursing Home, Medford, MA
Winthrop Road Rest Home, Brookline, MA
Wintonbury Continuing Care Center, Bloomfield, CT
Winyah Extended Care Center Inc, Georgetown, SC
Wiregrass Nursing Home, Geneva, AL
Wisconsin Avenue Nursing Home, Washington, DC
Wisconsin Lutheran Child & Family Service, Milwaukee, WI

Wisconsin Odd Fellow-Rebekah Nursing Home, Green Bay, WI
Wisconsin Veterans Home, King, WI
Wisconsin Veterans Home No 422, King, WI
Wisconsin Veterans Home No 600, King, WI
Wisconsin Veterans Home No 700, King, WI
Wishek Home for the Aged, Wishek, ND
Wish-I-Ah Lodge, Auberry, CA
Wishing Well Health Center, Fairmont, WV
Wishing Well Manor, Inc, Northville, MI
Wisner Manor, Wisner, NE
Witmer House, Long Branch, NJ
Woburn Nursing Center, Woburn, MA
Wofford Personal Care Home, Woodburn, KY
Wolcott Hall Nursing Center, Torrington, CT
Wolcott Rest Home, Wolcott, CT
Wolcott View Manor, Wolcott, CT
Wolf Memorial Good Samaritan Center, Albion, NE
Wolfe Nursing Home Inc, Scottdale, PA
Wollaston Nursing & Retirement Home, Quincy, MA
Women's Aid Home, Manchester, NH
Wood Convalescent Center, Wichita Falls, TX
Wood Convalescent Center 1, Quanah, TX
Wood County Nursing Home, Bowling Green, OH
Wood Dale Health Care Center, Dalton, GA
Wood Dale Home Inc, Redwood Falls, MN
Frank Wood Convalescent Home, Boston, MA
Wood Lake Nursing Home, Clute, TX
Wood Lane—North Mississippi Retardation Center, Oxford, MS
Wood Manor Inc, Claremore, OK
Wood Memorial Nursing Center, Mineola, TX
Wood Mill Convalescent Home, Lawrence, MA
Wood Nursing & Convalescent Center, Waurika, OK
Wood Nursing Convalescent Center, Vernon, TX
Wood Nursing Home, San Antonio, TX
Wood Presbyterian Home Inc, Sweetwater, TN
Wood River Convalescent Center, Shoshone, ID
Wood Village Nursing Manor Inc, Troutdale, OR
Wood-Acre Inc, Berkeley, MO
The Woodbine, Oak Park, IL
Woodbine Nursing & Convalescent Center, Alexandria, VA
Woodbridge Health Care, Evansville, IN
Woodbridge Nursing Center Inc, Woodbridge, VA
Woodburn Convalescent Center, Woodburn, OR
Woodbury Country Care Facility, Sioux City, IA
Woodbury East Skilled Nursing & Health Related Facility, Woodbury, NY
Woodbury Health Care Center, Woodbury, MN
Woodbury Manor Nursing Home, Fitchburg, MA
Woodbury Nursing Center Inc, Woodbury, TN
Woodbury Nursing Home, Woodbury, NY
Woodbury West Health Care Center, West Des Moines, IA
Woodcliff Lake Manor Nursing Home, Woodcliff Lake, NJ
Woodcrest Center, New Milford, NJ
Woodcrest Nursing Home, Flushing, NY
Wooddale Health Centre, Sun City, AZ
Woodfield Manor Inc, Niles, MI
Woodford of Ayer Long-Term Care Facility, Ayer, MA
Woodfords Group Home I, Portland, ME
Woodfords Group Home II, Portland, ME
Woodhaven Care Center, Ellinwood, KS
Woodhaven Manor Nursing Home, Demopolis, AL
Woodhaven Nursing Home, Port Jefferson Station, NY
Woodhaven Nursing Home, Sulphur Springs, TX
Woodhaven Village Inc, Roanoke, VA

Woodland Acres County Home, Logansport, IN
Woodland Acres Health Care Center, Brianerd, MN
Woodland Acres Nursing Home Inc, Saint Clairsville, OH
Althea Woodland Nursing Home, Silver Springs, MD
Woodland Convalescent Center, Woodland, WA
Woodland Convalescent Center Inc, North Smithfield, RI
Woodland Estates, Saint James, MO
Woodland Health Center, Topeka, KS
Woodland Health Center, Brookfield, WI
Woodland Hills Nursing Center, Allen, OK
Woodland Lafayette, Lafayette, CA
Woodland Manor, Columbus, OH
Woodland Manor Inc, Siloam Springs, AR
Woodland Manor Nursing Center, Attica, IN
Woodland Manor Nursing Home, Oxford, OH
Woodland Nursing Center, Mount Zion, IL
Woodland Nursing Home, Muncie, IN
Woodland Nursing Home, New Rochelle, NY
Woodland Park Home, Tulsa, OK
Woodland Retirement Center, Orbisonia, PA
Woodland Skilled Nursing Facility, Woodland, CA
Woodland Springs Nursing Home, Waco, TX
Woodland Terrace, Elizabethtown, KY
Woodland Terrace Residential Training Center, Montesano, WA
Woodland Village Nursing Home Inc, Suring, WI
Wood-Lawn Inc, Batesville, AR
Woodlawn Manor Nursing Home, Everett, MA
Woodlawn Manor Residential Care Facility, Anderson, MO
Woodlawn Nursing Home, Skowhegan, ME
Woodlawn Nursing Home, Newport, NH
Woodlawn Nursing Home, Mansfield, OH
Woodlawn Nursing Home Inc, Wichita, KS
Woodlea Skilled Nursing Home—North Mississippi Retardation Center, Oxford, MS
Woodley Manor Nursing Home Inc, Montgomery, AL
Woodmere Health Care Center, Platteville, CT
Woodmere Health Care Center Inc, Woodmere, NY
Woodmont Nursing Home Inc, Fredericksburg, VA
Woodpecker Hill Foster Home, Coventry, RI
Woodrest Nursing Home, Walker, MN
Woodridge House Nursing Home, Brockton, MA
Woodrow Intermediate Care Facility, Columbia, SC
Woodruff Convalescent Center, Bellflower, CA
Woodruff County Nursing Home, McCrory, AR
Woods Haven Senior Citizens Home, Pollock, LA
Woods Memorial Convalescent Hospital, La Verne, CA
Woodside Convalescent Center, Rochester, MN
Woodside Lutheran Home, Green Bay, WI
Woodside Manor Nursing Home Inc, Rochester, NY
Woodside Nursing Center, Oklahoma City, OK
Woodside Village Care Center Ltd, Mount Gilead, OH
Woodspoint Nursing Home, Florence, KY
The Woodstock Residence, Woodstock, IL
Woodstock-Kenosha Health Center, Kenosha, WI
Woodvak Dodge Center, Dodge Center, MN
Woodvale III, Austin, MN
Woodvale Kasson, Kasson, MN
Woodvale V, Albert Lea, MN
Woodvale VI, Owatonna, MN
Woodvale VII, Albert Lea, MN
The Woodview, South Boston, VA
Woodview Healthcare Inc, Fort Wayne, IN
Woodview Home, Ardmore, OK

Woodville Convalescent Center, Woodville, TX
Woodward Nursing Center, Woodward, OK
Woonsocket Health Centre, Woonsocket, RI
Wooster Nursing Home, Bowling Green, OH
Workmens Circle Home, Media, PA
Workmens Circle Home & Infirmary, Bronx, NY
Worth County Convalescent Center, Grant City, MO
Worthington Manor Inc, Parkersburg, WV
Worthington Nursing & Convalescent Center, Worthington, OH
Worthington Regional Hospital, Worthington, MN
Wrangell General Hospital—LTC Facility, Wrangell, AK
Wright Nursing Center, Lakewood, OH
Wright Nursing Home Inc, San Antonio, TX
Wright Rest Home, Fitchburg, MA
Wrights Nursing Home, Largo, FL
Wrightsville Manor Nursing Home, Wrightsville, GA
Wunderley Nursing Home, Toledo, OH
Wurtland Health Care Center, Wurtland, KY
Wyandot County Nursing Home, Upper Sandusky, OH
Wyandot Manor HCF Inc, Upper Sandusky, OH
Wyatt Manor Nursing Home, Jonesboro, LA
Wymore Good Samaritan Center, Wymore, NE
Wyncote Church Home, Wyncote, PA
Wyndcrest Nursing Home, Clinton, IA
Wynkoop Nursing Home, Leesburg, VA
Wynnewood Nursing Center, Wynnewood, OK
Wyoming County Community Hospital, Skilled Nursing Facility, Warsaw, NY
Wyoming Retirement Center, Basin, WY
Wyomissing Lodge, Reading, PA
Yadkin Nursing Care Center, Yadkinville, NC
Yakima Convalescent, Yakima, WA
Yale Manor Inc, Dayton, OH
Yale Nursing Home, Yale, OK
Yalobusha County Nursing Home, Water Valley, MS
Yankton Care Center, Yankton, SD
Yaquina Care Center Inc, Newport, OR
Ye Olde House, Mont Clare, PA
Yell County Nursing Home Inc, Ola, AR
Yellow House, Denver, CO
Yellowstone Care Center, Idaho Falls, ID
Yellowstone County Nursing Home, Billings, MT
Ygnacio Convalescent Hospital, Walnut Creek, CA
Yingst Nursing Home Inc, Quakertown, PA
Yoakum Memorial Nursing Home, Yoakum, TX
York Convalescent Center, Elmhurst, IL
York County Hospital & Home, York, PA
York Hospital—Henry Strater Skilled Nursing Facility, York, ME
York Lutheran Home, York, PA
York Manor Nursing Home, Muskogee, OK
York Terrace Nursing Center, Pottsville, PA
Yorkshire Health Care Center, Columbus, OH
Yorkshire Manor Health Care Facility, Minneapolis, MN
Yorktown Manor Home, Yorktown, TX
Yorkview Convalescent & Nursing Home, York, PA
Young at Heart Personal Care Center, Okolona, MS
Bertha M Young Rest Home, Pittsfield, MA
C C Young Memorial Home—Young Health Center, Dallas, TX
Youngstown Developmental Center, Mineral Ridge, OH
Yukon Convalescent Center, Yukon, OK
Yuma Life Care Center, Yuma, CO
YWCA Arnett Pritchett Foundation Home, Lexington, KY
Zachary Manor Nursing Home, Zachary, LA
Zartman Nursing Home, Franklin, OH
Zastrow Care Center Inc, Gilman, WI
Zeigler Colonial Manor Inc, Zeigler, IL
The Zendt Home, Richfield, PA

Zenith Apartments, Lakeville, MN
Zephyr Haven Nursing Home, Zephyrhills, FL
Zerbe Sisters Nursing Center Inc, Narvon, PA
Zimmerman Nursing Home, Reedsburg, WI
Zimmerman Nursing Home Inc, Carlisle, AR
Zion Grove Nursing Center, Shelby, MS
Zion Nursing Home Inc, Cincinnati, OH
Zion's Mountain View, Salt Lake City, UT
Zohlman Nursing Home, Richlandtown, PA
Zumbrota Nursing Home, Zumbrota, MN

CORPORATE NURSING HOME HEADQUARTERS

ABCM Corporation
PO Box 402
Hampton, IA 50441
(505) 456-4791

Adventist Health Systems-USA
2301 E Lomar Blvd
Arlington, TX 76006
(817) 649-8700

Advocare Inc
4343 Langley Ave
Pensacola, FL 32504
(904) 478-2049

Alden Management Services
4200 W Peterson Ste 140
Chicago, IL 60646
(312) 286-3883

Alexian Brothers Health Systems
600 Alexian Wy
Elk Grove Village, IL 60007
(312) 640-7550

Altercare Inc
7222 Day Ave SW
Navarre, OH 44662
(216) 767-3458

American Baptist Homes
11985 W Technology Dr
Eden Prairie, MN 55344
(612) 941-3175

American Baptist Homes West
400 Roland Way PO Box 6669
Oakland, CA 94621
(415) 635-7600

American Health Care Centers
661 Weber Dr
Wadsworth, OH 44281
(216) 336-6684

American Health Centers Inc
PO Box 10
Parsons, TN 38368
(901) 847-6343

American Health Systems
600 Cooper Pkwy
Pennsauken, NJ 08109
(609) 663-1101

American Medical Services Inc
1051 E Ogden Ave
Milwaukee, WI 53202
(414) 271-1300

Americare Corporation
438 Wilson Ridge
Worthington, OH 43085
(614) 431-3315

Amity Care
4415 Highline Blvd Ste 100
Oklahoma City, OK 73108
(405) 943-1144

Angell Group
PO Box 1670
Clemons, NC 27012
(919) 721-1200

ARA Living Centers
1545 Katy Freeway Ste 800
Houston, TX 77094
(713) 578-4600

Arbor Health Care
PO Box 840, 1100 Shawnee Rd
Lima, OH 45802
(419) 227-3000

Arvada Management
1390 Stuart St
Denver, CO 80204
(303) 825-8846

Associated Health Care
6759 Mayfield Rd Ste 119
Mayfield Heights, OH 44124
(216) 449-0900

Autumn Corporation
PO Box 7728
Rocky Mount, NC 27804
(919) 443-6265

Baptist Home Associates
4790 Tabor St
Wheatridge, CO 80032
(303) 424-5589

Beth Shalom Homes of Virginia
PO Box 29331
Richmond, VA 23229
(804) 282-9471

Bethesda Care Centers
1465 Kelly Johnson Blvd Ste 200
Colorado Springs, CO 80920
(303) 548-0500

Beverly Enterprises
873 S Fair Oaks Ave
Pasadena, CA 91105
(213) 684-1100

Blackeye Family & Nursing Home
573 Superior Ave
Dayton, OH 45407
(513) 278-7849

Bon Secours Health Systems
Overlook Ctr 5457 Twin Knolls
Columbia, MD 21045
(301) 992-7330

Brian Center Management Corp
PO Drawer 1148 First Plaza
Hickory, NC 28603
(704) 322-3362

Britthaven Inc
4th St
Hookerton, NC 28538
(919) 747-3314

Buckner Baptist Retirement Village
PO Box 271189
Dallas, TX 75227
(214) 328-3141

Cambridge Group Inc
5151 Beltline Rd Ste 501
Dallas, TX 75240
(214) 980-8862

Cantex Healthcare Centers
6060 N Central Expy Ste 440
Dallas, TX 75206
(214) 739-0411

Care Enterprises
2742 Dow Ave
Tustin, CA 92680
(714) 544-4443

Catholic Charities
25 Washington St
Buffalo, NY 14203
(716) 856-4494

Catholic Charities-Arch of NY
1011 First Ave
New York, NY 10022
(212) 371-1000

Cedar Crest Inc
PO Box 428
Medicine Lodge, KS 67104
(316) 886-3469

Chartham Management
850 Promontory Pl SE
Salem, OR 97302
(503) 585-0200

Christian Church Campuses
920 S Fourth St
Louisville, KY 40203
(502) 583-6533

Christian Homes
200 N Postville
Lincoln, IL 62656
(217) 732-9651

Cloverleaf Enterprises
8355 Rockville Rd
Indianapolis, IN 46234
(317) 271-8888

Coastal Care Centers Inc
2885 Harris St
Eureka, CA 95501
(707) 443-1627

Columbia Corporation
3401 West End Ave
Nashville, TN 37203
(615) 297-9090

Community Care Centers
2101 Enterprise Ave
Muncie, IN 47303
(317) 286-6035

Community Lifecare Enterprises
828 S 2nd St
Springfield, IL 62074

Comprehensive Health Care Assn
1266 15th St Ste 8
Sarasota, FL 32436
(813) 365-6194

Continental Medical Systems Inc
Mechanicsburg, PA 17055
(717) 691-9443

Convalescent Services
200 Galleria Pkwy Suite 1800
Atlanta, GA 30339
(404) 956-8999

Country Villa Service Corp
11266 Washington Pl
Culver City, CA 90230
(213) 390-8049

Courville Management
49 Derry Rd
Hudson, NH 03051
(603) 883-4422

Covenant Benevolent Inst
2725 W Foster
Chicago, IL 60625
(312) 878-8200

Crestwood Hospitals
4635 Georgetown Pl
Stockton, CA 95207
(209) 478-5291

Crowne Management
PO Box 187
Greenville, AL 36037
(205) 382-8770

CV American
10530 Santa Monica Blvd
Los Angeles, CA 90025
(213) 450-7595

Diversicare Corp of America
Gonzalez, TX 78629
(512) 672-9565

Ebenezer Society
2523 Portland Ave S
Minneapolis, MN 55404
(612) 879-2200

Eden Park Management
22 Holland Ave
Albany, NY 12209
(518) 436-4731

Episcopal Homes Foundation
PO Box 1027
Lafayette, CA 94549
(415) 283-0680

EV Lutheran/Good Samaritan Society
1000 West Ave N PO Box 503
Sioux Falls, SD 57117
(605) 336-2998

Everhealth Foundation
8000 S Painter
Whittier, CA 90602
(213) 945-2861

First American Care Facility
5100 Eden Ave S Ste 305
Edina, MN 55436
(612) 929-2122

First Humanics Inc
1600 Genessee Ste 760
Kansas City, MO 64106
(816) 472-1440

Florida Living Care Inc
1073 Orienta Ave PO Box 815
Altamonte Springs, FL 32701
(305) 831-2212

Forum Group
8900 Keystone Crossing Ste 1200
Indianapolis, IN 46240
(317) 846-0700

Franciscan Sisters
1220 Main St
Lemont, IL 60439
(312) 257-7776

General Health Management, Inc
333 E River Dr
East Hartford, CT 06108
(203) 243-5800

Genesis Health Ventures
148 W State St Ste 100
Kennett Square, PA 19348
(215) 444-6350

Georgia Baptist Medical Center
300 Parkway Blvd NE
Atlanta, GA 30312
(404) 653-3591

Geriatric and Medical Centers
63rd & Walnut Sts
Philadelphia, PA 19139
(215) 476-2250

Glenmark Associates
1150 Greenbag Exec Plaza Ste A
Morgantown, WV 26505
(304) 291-6348

Good Neighbor Services
2177 Youngman Ave Ste 200
Saint Paul, MN 55116
(612) 698-6544

Good Shepherd Health Facilities
14325 W Center Dr
Lakewood, CO 80228
(303) 989-1858

Golden State Health Centers Inc
13347 Ventura Blvd
Sherman Oaks, CA 91423
(818) 986-1550

GraceCare Inc
140 Germantown Pike Ste 100
Plymouth Meeting, PA 19462
(215) 834-8006

Greenery Rehabilitation Group
215 First St
Cambridge, MA 02142
(617) 938-8430

Guardian Foundation Inc
2855 Telegraph Ave Ste 511
Berkeley, CA 94705
(415) 845-4396

Hannover Healthcare
20251 Century Blvd
Germantown, MD 20874
(301) 540-0440

HBA Management Inc
1330 S Andrews Ave
Fort Lauderdale, FL 33316
(305) 524-5587

HCF Incorporated
2615 Fort Amanda Rd
Lima, OH 45804
(419) 999-2010

Health Care & Retirement Corp
1885 McCullough St, PO Box 1709
Lima, OH 45802
(419) 227-1837

Health Care Associates
22 Waterville Rd
Avon, CT 06001
(203) 678-9755

Health Care Group
1060 Eighth
San Diego, CA 92101
(619) 234-4327

Health Care Management
1010 S Main St
Dayton, OH 45409
(513) 461-2707

Health Concepts Corp
303 Hurstbourne Ln
Louisville, KY 40222
(502) 425-0366

Health East
642 E 7th St
Saint Paul, MN 55109
(612) 772-5560

Health Enterprises of America
1268 N River Rd
Warren, OH 44483
(216) 372-4700

Health Resources Development
2941 Donny Ln
Columbus, OH 43220
(614) 761-2322

Health Systems
PO Box 1450
Corbin, KY 40701
(606) 528-9600

Healthcare Management
PO Box 1155
Columbus, GA 39102
(404) 322-4761

Heritage Enterprises
525 N East St
Bloomington, IL 61701
(309) 828-4361

Hillhaven Corporation
1148 Broadway Plaza
Tacoma, WA 98401
(206) 575-4901

Homewood Retirement Ctrs/UCC
2750 Virginia Ave
Williamsport, MD 21795
(301) 582-1628

Horizon Healthcare Corp
6002 E Indian School Rd NE
Albuquerque, NM 87110
(505) 881-4961

HS Healthcare
118 S Dunlop Rd
Savoy, IL 61874
(217) 398-5966

Integrated Health Care Management
130 S 1st St
Ann Arbor, MI 48104
(313) 663-3130

JE Holland Associates
846 N Cleveland-Masillon Rd
Akron, OH 44313
(216) 666-4161

King Care Centers Inc
Minneapolis, MN
(612) 339-8459

Lemire Enterprises
130 Silver St
Manchester, NH 03103
(603) 669-1810

Life Care Centers of America
PO Box 3480
Cleveland, TN 37311
(615) 476-3254

Life Care Centers of Kansas
Box 428
Medicine Lodge, KS 67104
(316) 886-3469

Life Care Services Corporaiton
800 Second Ave
Des Moines, IA 50309
(515) 245-7650

Lincoln Lutheran of Racine WI
3716 Douglas Ave
Racine, WI 53402
(414) 639-3174

Little Sisters of the Poor
110-39 Springfield Blvd
Queens Village, NY 11429
(718) 464-4920

LTC
1430 Latimer St Ste 300
Denver, CO 80202
(303) 592-1227

Lutheran Hosp and Homes Society
1202 Westrac Dr PO Box 2087
Fargo, ND 58107
(701) 293-9053

Lutheran Social Services
189 S Broad St
Trenton, NJ 08601
(609) 393-3440

Manor Care Inc
10720 Columbia Pike
Silver Spring, MD 20901
(301) 593-9600

Medicalodges Inc
PO Box 509
Coffeyville, KS 67337
(316) 251-6700

Medical Facilities of America
2917 Penn Forest Blvd Ste 300
Roanoke, VA 24018
(703) 989-3618

Medicrest of California
12183 Lockley Ste 102
Auburn, CA 95603
(916) 885-0880

Mediplex Inc
2101 Washington St
Newton, MA 02162
(617) 969-6480

Medstar Management Systems, Inc
8501 Wilshire Blvd Ste 230
Beverly Hills, CA 90211
(213) 855-0452

Mennonite Brethren Homes
856 S Reed Ave
Reedley, CA 93654
(209) 638-8123

Meridan Healthcare
21 West Rd
Towson, MD 21204
(301) 296-1000

Methodist Homes for the Aging
1424 Montclair Rd
Birmingham, AL 35210
(205) 956-4150

Millers Merry Manor
104 E Central Ave
La Grange, IN 46761
(219) 463-7411

Minn Synod/Lutheran Ch Board
559 Capital Blvd
Saint Paul, MN 55103
(612) 221-1764

Missionary Oblates of Mary Imm
267 E 8th St
Saint Paul, MN 55101
(612) 292-8622

Morning View Care Center
236 S Main St PO Box 1064
Mount Vernon, OH 43050
(614) 393-6822

Multicare Management
411 Hackensack Ave
Hackensack, NJ 07601
(201) 488-8818

National Health Corporation
PO Box 1398
Murfresboro, TN 37133
(615) 896-5921

National Healthcare Affiliates Inc
651 Delaware Ave
Buffalo, NY 14202
(716) 881-4425

National Healthcare Inc
PO Box 1649
Dothan, AL 36302
(205) 793-2399

National Heritage
1230 Liberty Bank Ln Ste 230
Louisville, KY 40222
(502) 426-6992

Natl Bnvlnt Assn of Chrstn Hms
11780 Borman Dr Ste 200
Saint Louis, MO 63146
(314) 993-9000

New Medico Associates
150 Lincoln St
Boston, MA 02111
(617) 426-4100

North Carolina Lutheran Homes
PO Box 947
Salisbury, NC 28144
(704) 637-3784

North Central Health Services Inc
930 10th St
Spearfish, SD 57783
(605) 642-4641

Northport Health Services
2707 Hwy 82 Bypass
Northport, AL 35476
(205) 333-0600

Northwestern Service Corp
181 Front St
Berea, OH 44017
(216) 243-4732

Ohio Presbyterian Homes
6800 N High St
Columbia, OH 43085
(614) 888-7800

OMG Corporation
Rt 8 PO Box 300D
Kinston, NC 28501
(919) 522-5207

Omnilife Systems Inc
1207 N High St
Columbus, OH 43201
(614) 299-3100

Pacific Homes
15760 Ventura Blvd Ste A10
Encino, CA 91436
(818) 981-6200

Parke Care Inc
7433 Montgomery Rd
Cincinnati, OH 45236
(513) 793-4780

Pavilion Health Care Centers
432 E Jefferson
Louisville, KY 40202
(502) 636-9200

Peninsula United Methodist Homes
3801 Kennett Pike Bldg D
Wilmington, DE 19807
(302) 656-7864

Philadelphia Presbyterian Homes
PO Box 607
Villanova, PA 19085
(215) 527-6370

Pinnacle Care Corp
101 Westpark Dr Ste 350
Brentwood, TN 37027
(615) 377-9300

Pleasant Valley Health Services
3801 Las Pasas Rd Ste 106
Camarillo, CA 93010
(805) 484-2831

Presbyterian Homes of Western
4455 Transit Rd
Williamsville, NY 14221
(716) 631-0120

Presbyterian Ministries
720 Seneca
Seattle, WA 98101
(206) 622-1300

Prestige Care Inc
6623 NE 82nd Ave
Portland, OR 97220
(503) 253-9650

Quality Health Care Specialists Inc
714 14th Ave N
Fort Dodge, IA 50501
(515) 573-5011

Redwood Empire Enterprises
1349 S Dora
Ukiah, CA 95482
(707) 433-4813

Regency Health Care Centers
500 Northridge Rd Ste 200
Atlanta, GA 30338
(404) 396-8425

Riverside Medical Services
Rt 1 Bowling Green Office Park
Macon, GA 31210
(912) 477-4222

Rose Care Inc
7 Halstead Circle
Rogers, AR 72756
(501) 636-5716

School Sisters of St Francis
1501 S Layton
Milwaukee, WI 53215
(414) 384-4105

Shive Nursing Centers
1330 Medical Park Dr
Fort Wayne, IN 46825
(219) 482-3551

Signature Corporation
2501 W Peterson
Chicago, IL 60659
(312) 784-0800

Soundcare, Inc
1748 Jefferson Ave
Tacoma, WA 98402
(206) 383-5495

So California Presbyterian Homes
315 Arden Ave Ste 24
Glendale, CA 91203
(818) 247-0420

Southern Management Services
1520 Jeffords St
Clearwater, FL 33516
(813) 441-2804

Southmark Heritage Corp
1601 LBJ Freewy Ste 415
Dallas, TX 75234
(214) 243-0088

Southwood Health Care
112 E "H" St
Elizabethton, TN 37643
(615) 543-6494

Stuckey Health Care
PO Box 907
Thomson, GA 30824
(404) 595-8727

Summit Health Ltd
1800 Ave of the Stars Ste 1200
Los Angeles, CA 90667
(213) 201-4000

Sunbelt Healthcare Centers Inc
306 W Due West Ave
Madison, TN 37115
(615) 865-9100

Texas Health Enterprises
829 Greenview
Grand Prairie, TX 75050
(214) 985-3871

Thro Company
PO Box 1236
Mankato, MN 56001
(507) 625-8741

Tiffany Care Centers
Box 208, 507 State St
Mound City, MO 64470
(618)

TJ Rock
299 Hurley Ave
Rockville, MD 20850
(301) 762-8900

Tressler-Lutheran Services Assoc
2331 Market St
Camp Hill, PA 17011
(717) 692-4340

Truco Incorporated
4723 Taft St
Wichita Falls, TX 76308
(817) 692-8977

Tullock Management
PO Box 70
Advance, NC 27006
(919) 582-7503

Unicare
105 W Michigan
Milwaukee, WI 53203
(414) 271-9696

United Church Homes
320 W Maple St
Upper Sandusky, OH 43351
(419) 294-4941

United Presbyterian Homes
16 Lakehunter Dr
Lakeland, FL 33803
(813) 688-5521

US Care Corporation
141 S Adams St
Marion, IN 46952
(317) 668-7535

Van Dyke Health Services
4239 War Memorial Dr
Peoria, IL 61614
(309) 685-0044

Vantage Healthcare
PO Box 16
Evansville, IN 47701
(812) 425-8716

Vari-Care Inc
800 Medical Arts Bldg 277 Alex
Rochester, NY 14607
(716) 325-6940

Vetter Health Services, Inc
Box 37232
Omaha, NE 68173
(402) 895-3932

Vincentian Sisters of Charity
8200 McKnight Rd
Pittsburgh, PA 15237
(412) 364-3000

Volunteers of America Care
7530 Market Place Dr
Eden Prairie, MN 55344
(612) 941-0305

Waverly Group
PO Box 1200
Jackson, MS 39236
(601) 932-2984

Wesley Homes
1817 Clifton Rd NE
Atlanta, GA 30029
(404) 325-2988

Wessex Corporation
PO Box 986
Franklin, TN 37065
(615) 794-3313

White Oak Manor Inc
PO Box 3347
Spartanburg, SC 29304
(803) 582-7503

Wilshire Foundation
9100 Wilshire Blvd
Beverly Hills, CA 90212
(213) 278-5240

Wis-Care Inc
PO Box 67
Walworth, WI 53184
(414) 275-9331